SCOTT

# 2019 STANDARD POSTAGE STAMP CATALOGUE

ONE HUNDRED AND SEVENTY-FIFTH EDITION IN SIX VOLUMES

## VOLUME 2B

Cyp-F



Released May 2018
Includes New Stamp Listings through the March 2018 *Linn's Stamp News Monthly* Catalogue Update



AMOS MEDIA

911 Vandemark Road, Sidney, OH 45365-0828
Publishers of *Linn's Stamp News, Linn's Stamp News Monthly, Coin World* and *Coin World Monthly.*

# Table of Contents



See the following volumes for other country listings:
Volume 1A: United States, United Nations, Abu Dhabi-Australia; Volume 1B: Austria-B
Volume 2A: C-Cur
Volume 3A: G; Volume 3B: H-I
Volume 4A: J-L; Volume 4B: M
Volume 5A: N-Phil; Volume 5B: Pit-Sam
Volume 6A: San-Tete; Volume 6B: Thai-Z

**Scott Catalogue Mission Statement**

The Scott Catalogue Team exists to serve the recreational, educational and commercial hobby needs of stamp collectors and dealers.

We strive to set the industry standard for philatelic information and products by developing and providing goods that help collectors identify, value, organize and present their collections.

Quality customer service is, and will continue to be, our highest priority. We aspire toward achieving total customer satisfaction.

## Copyright Notice



## Trademark Notice



ISBN 978-0-89487-544-1

Library of Congress Card No. 2-3301

# Acknowledgments

Our appreciation and gratitude go to the following individuals who have assisted us in preparing information included in this year's Scott Catalogues. Some helpers prefer anonymity. These individuals have generously shared their stamp knowledge with others through the medium of the Scott Catalogue.

Those who follow provided information that is in addition to the hundreds of dealer price lists and advertisements and scores of auction catalogues and realizations that were used in producing the catalogue values. It is from those noted here that we have been able to obtain information on items not normally seen in published lists and advertisements. Support from these people goes beyond data leading to catalogue values, for they also are key to editorial changes.

A special acknowledgment to Liane and Sergio Sismondo of The Classic Collector for their assistance and knowledge sharing that have aided in the preparation of this year's Standard and Classic Specialized Catalogues.

Roland Austin
Jim Bardo (Bardo Stamps)
William Barclay (South Sudan Philatelic Society)
John Birkinbine II
Roger S. Brody
Tina & John Carlson (JET Stamps)
Henry Chlanda
Bob Coale
David & Julia Crawford
Tony L. Crumbley (Carolina Coin & Stamp, Inc.)
Christopher Dahle
Ubaldo Del Toro
Leon Djerahian
Bob & Rita Dumaine (Sam Houston Duck Co.)
Sister Theresa Durand
Paul G. Eckman
George Epstein (Allkor Stamp Co.)
Robert A. Fisher
Jeffrey M. Forster
Robert S. Freeman
Ernest E. Fricks
Michael Fuchs
Bob Genisol (Sultan Stamp Center)
Stan Goldfarb
Allen Grant (Rushstamps (Retail) Ltd.)
Daniel E. Grau
Robin Harris
Bruce Hecht (Bruce L. Hecht Co.)
Peter Hoffman
John Hotchner
Armen Hovsepian (Armenstamp)
Doug Iams
Eric Jackson
John Jamieson (Saskatoon Stamp and Coin)
Peter Jeannopoulos
William A. Jones
Allan Katz (Ventura Stamp Co.)
Lewis Kaufman (The Philatelic Foundation)
Patricia Kaufmann (Confederate Stamp Alliance)
Jon Kawaguchi (Ryukyu Philatelic Specialist Society)
Roland Kretschmer
William V. Kriebel (Brazil Philatelic Association)
Frederick P. Lawrence
John R. Lewis (The William Henry Stamp Co.)
Ulf Lindahl
Ignacio Llach (Filatelia Llach S.L.)
Marilyn R. Mattke
William K. McDaniel
Mauricio Mejia
Gary Morris (Pacific Midwest Co.)
Peter Mosiondz, Jr.
Bruce M. Moyer (Moyer Stamps & Collectibles)
Richard H. Muller
Scott Murphy (Professional Stamp Experts)
Leonard Nadybal
Dr. Tiong Tak Ngo
Gerald Nylander
Nik & Lisa Oquist
Dr. Everett Parker
Don Peterson (International Philippine Philatelic Society)
Stanley M. Piller (Stanley M. Piller & Associates)
Virgil Pirvulescu
Todor Drumev Popov
Peter W. W. Powell
Bob Prager (Gary Posner, Inc.)
Siddique Mahmudur Rahman
Ghassan D. Riachi
Mehrdad Sadri (Persiphila)
Sabah Jawad Salih
Theodosios Sampson PhD
Michael Schreiber
Alexander Schauss (Schauss Philatelics)
Jacques C. Schiff, Jr.
Jeff Siddiqui
Sergio & Liane Sismondo (The Classic Collector)
Jay Smith
Kenneth Thompson
Peter Thy
Scott R. Trepel (Robert A. Siegel Auction Galleries, Inc.)
Dan Undersander (United Postal Stationery Society)
Herbert R. Volin
Philip T. Wall
Giana Wayman
Don White (Dunedin Stamp Centre)
Ralph Yorio
Val Zabijaka

SCOTT®

# What's new for 2019 Scott Standard Volume 2B?

Greetings, Fellow Scott Catalog User:

This year celebrates another milestone in the 150-year history of the Scott catalogs. The 2019 catalogs are the 175th edition of the Scott *Standard Postage Stamp Catalogue*. Vol. 2B includes listings for countries of the world Cyprus through F. Listings for countries of the world C-Curacao can be found in Vol. 2A.

The almost 600 value changes recorded for **Cyprus** reflect a flat to slightly declining market for unused stamps from the mid-1940s through mid-2001. In contrast, many values for used stamps during this time period went up, an acknowledgment that postally used examples of stamps that exist in abundance in unused condition are tougher to come by used. Healthy increases are seen for stamps issued during the past decade. And be sure to review the postal tax stamp listings, where values also have gone up.

**Czechoslovakia** came under careful scrutiny, which yielded more than 2,800 value changes. Declines are the norm for all periods, although there are a few scattered increases and new values for footnoted items. The 2016 Holy Roman Emperor Charles IV souvenir sheet with the erroneous Latin inscription "Karolus Quatrus," described in a footnote to the normal sheet inscribed "Karolus Quartus" (Scott 3671), is valued for the first time at $90.

Careful attention was paid to the listings for **Dominican Republic**, which generated more than 1,350 value changes. Increases predominate over decreases, and the advances are particularly noticeable for stamps issued from early 2000 through late 2016. The 2014 set of two sheets of 12 honoring the heroes and flags of nations of North America and South America climbs more than 25 percent mint and used, from $55 in 2018 to $70 this year.

Don't overlook the back-of-the-book sections, where values rise for selected semipostal, airmail, airmail semipostal, Official, and postal tax stamps.

Almost 90 value changes were made among the listings of the Persian Gulf sheikdom of **Dubai**, exhibiting a mixture of increases and decreases. The 1970 Charles Dickens set of four stamps (Scott 127-130) jumps in value, from $5.80 mint to $7.05. The used value for the set remains at $1.25.

A blend of increases and decreases also characterizes the almost 750 value changes in **Estonia**. Substantial jumps are seen among the Russian stamps handstamped "Eesti Post" for provisional use in Tallinn in 1919 (Scott 8-26). The 1-kopeck orange rises to $8,000 unused and used, from $5,500 both ways in the 2018 catalog. A footnote points out that the handstamp "has been extensively counterfeited." The values for these stamps are for genuine examples that have been expertized.

For the modern issues, which began in 1991 following independence from the Soviet Union, modest drops in value are seen through 2006. Stamps issued since 2007 show small gains in value. Typical is the 2009 International Polar Year sheet of two, which moves from $5.25 mint and used last year to $5.50 both ways in the 2019 catalog.

Numerous values for the 1920-40 semipostals have been updated; increases for used stamps are scattered throughout. Values also rise for used examples of the German occupation stamps (Scott N1-N5).

The **Falkland Islands** fell under the editors' watchful eyes, resulting in a bit more than 1,000 value changes. Almost without exception, values are down across the board. There are, however, some bright spots among classic-era issues. The yellow-orange and black color variety of the sought-after 1933 5-shilling King Penguin (Scott 74a) advances to $3,250 unused and $3,750 used, from $3,000 and $3,500, respectively, in the 2018 catalog.

Unlike many British Commonwealth countries, values for stamps issued during the past 10 years or so are down somewhat — likely a reflection of low demand against well-stocked dealer inventories. A notable exception is the 2009 Cobb's Wren sheet of 16 (Scott 997a), which soars from $45 mint and used in 2018 to $52.50 both ways this year.

The almost 1,500 value changes in **Fiji** are concentrated in postage issues from 1938 through early 2006. Declines predominate, although there are a few sets that rise in value. The 1992 Expo 92 set (Scott 657-660) moves from $16.85 mint last year to $19.50 in the 2019 catalog. Collectors of the myriad surcharged Bird definitives will be pleased to see upward movement for 30 of these stamps.

More than 450 value changes for **French Southern and Antarctic Territories** reflect a softening of the market, with mostly decreases and just a sprinkling of increases in values. The 2000 The Third Millennium sheet of four (Scott 274) advances from $7.50 mint to $8.50 but decreases from $7.50 used to $5.50.

***Editorial enhancements for Vol. 2B***

Various notes and footnotes have been clarified or expanded throughout the catalog to further explain complicated listings, and other notes have been screened carefully to ensure accuracy.

**Dominican Republic:** New photographs have been added to help collectors identify the two types of the 1915 2-centavo olive green and black stamps. Type I stamps (Scott 202) feature "DOS" in small letters. Type II stamps (203) show "DOS" in larger letters, with a white dot at left and right of the denomination inscription.

**Fiji:** Six new major numbers and 13 new minor numbers were added to the listings of the surcharged Bird definitive stamps of 2007-17. Changes implemented in 2015 by Post Fiji have greatly improved the consistency of the surcharges, resulting in fewer varieties and errors during production. Time will tell if this will result in fewer new listings in future editions of the catalog.

As with the stock market, a softening in the stamp market for some countries can be looked upon as an opportunity to buy stamps to fill spaces in your stamp albums.

As always, we encourage you to pay special attention to the Number Additions, Deletions & Changes found on page 939 in this volume. We also suggest reading the catalog introduction, which includes an abundance of useful information.

Enjoy this wonderful hobby every day!

Donna Houseman

Donna Houseman/Catalogue Editor

# Addresses, Telephone Numbers, Web Sites, E-Mail Addresses of General & Specialized Philatelic Societies

Collectors can contact the following groups for information about the philately of the areas within the scope of these societies, or inquire about membership in these groups. Aside from the general societies, we limit this list to groups that specialize in particular fields of philately, particular areas covered by the Scott Standard Postage Stamp Catalogue, and topical groups. Many more specialized philatelic society exist than those listed below. These addresses are updated yearly, and they are, to the best of our knowledge, correct and current. Groups should inform the editors of address changes whenever they occur. The editors also want to hear from other such specialized groups not listed. Unless otherwise noted all website addresses begin with http://

**American Philatelic Society**
100 Match Factory Place
Bellefonte PA 16823-1367
Ph: (814) 933-3803
www.stamps.org
E-mail: apsinfo@stamps.org

**American Stamp Dealers Association, Inc.**
P.O. Box 692
Leesport PA 19553
Ph: (800) 369-8207
www.americanstampdealer.com
E-mail: asda@americanstampdealer.com

**National Stamp Dealers Association**
Richard Kostka, President
3643 Private Road 18
Pinckneyville IL 62274-3426
Ph: (800) 875-6633 or (618) 357-5497
www.nsdainc.org
E-mail: nsda@nsdainc.org

**International Society of Worldwide Stamp Collectors**
Joanne Berkowitz, MD
P.O. Box 19006
Sacramento CA 95819
www.iswsc.org
E-mail: executivedirector@iswsc.org

**Royal Philatelic Society**
41 Devonshire Place
London, W1G 6JY
UNITED KINGDOM
www.rpsl.org.uk
E-mail: secretary@rpsl.org.uk

**Royal Philatelic Society of Canada**
P.O. Box 69080
St. Clair Post Office
Toronto, ON, M4T 3A1
CANADA
Ph: (888) 285-4143
www.rpsc.org
E-mail: info@rpsc.org

**Young Stamp Collectors of America**
Janet Houser
100 Match Factory Place
Bellefonte PA 16823-1367
Ph: (814) 933-3820
www.stamps.org/ysca/intro.htm
E-mail: ysca@stamps.org

## Philatelic Research Resources

(The Scott editors encourage any additional research organizations to submit data for inclusion in this listing category)

**American Philatelic Research Library**
Scott Tiffney
100 Match Factory Place
Bellefonte PA 16823
Ph: (814) 933-3803
www.stamplibrary.org
E-mail: libraryestamps.org

**Institute for Analytical Philately, Inc.**
P.O. Box 8035
Holland MI 49422-8035
Ph: (616) 399-9299
www.analyticalphilately.org
E-mail: info@analyticalphilately.org

**The Western Philatelic Library**
P.O. Box 2219
1500 Partridge Ave.
Sunnyvale CA 94087
Ph: (408) 733-0336
www.fwpf.org

## Groups focusing on fields or aspects found in worldwide philately (some might cover U.S. area only)

**American Air Mail Society**
Stephen Reinhard
P.O. Box 110
Mineola NY 11501
www.americanairmailsociety.org
E-mail: sreinhard1@optonline.net

**American First Day Cover Society**
Douglas Kelsey
P.O. Box 16277
Tucson AZ 85732-6277
Ph: (520) 321-0880
www.afdcs.org
E-mail: afdcs@afdcs.org

**American Revenue Association**
Eric Jackson
P.O. Box 728
Leesport PA 19533-0728
Ph: (610) 926-6200
www.revenuer.org
E-mail: eric@revenuer.com

**American Topical Association**
Vera Felts
P.O. Box 8
Carterville IL 62918-0008
Ph: (618) 985-5100
www.americantopicalassn.org
E-mail: americantopical@msn.com

**Christmas Seal & Charity Stamp Society**
John Denune
234 E. Broadway
Granville OH 43023
Ph: (740) 587-0276
www.seal-society.org
E-mail: john@christmasseals.net

**Errors, Freaks and Oddities Collectors Club**
Scott Shaulis
P.O. Box 549
Murrysville PA 15668-0549
Ph: (724) 733-4134
www.efocc.org
E-mail: Scott@shaulisstamps.com

**First Issues Collectors Club**
Kurt Streepy, Secretary
3128 E. Mattatha Drive
Bloomington IN 47401
www.firstissues.org
E-mail: secretary@firstissues.org

**International Society of Reply Coupon Collectors**
Peter Robin
P.O. Box 353
Bala Cynwyd PA 19004
E-mail: peterrobin@verizon.net

**The Joint Stamp Issues Society**
Richard Zimmermann
29A Rue Des Eviats
Lalaye F-67220
FRANCE
www.philarz.net
E-mail: richard.zimmermann@club-internet.fr

**National Duck Stamp Collectors Society**
Anthony J. Monico
P.O. Box 43
Harleysville PA 19438-0043
www.ndscs.org
E-mail: ndscs@ndscs.org

**No Value Identified Club**
Albert Sauvanet
Le Clos Royal B, Boulevard des Pas Enchantes
St. Sebastien-sur Loire, 44230
FRANCE
E-mail: alain.vailly@irin.univ nantes.fr

**The Perfins Club**
Ken Masters
111 NW 94th Street Apt. 102
Kansas City MO 64155-2993
Ph: (816) 835-5907
www.perfins.org
E-mail: kmasters@aol.com

**Postage Due Mail Study Group**
John Rawlins
13, Longacre
Chelmsford, CM1 3BJ
UNITED KINGDOM
E-mail: john.rawlins2@ukonline.co.uk.

**Post Mark Collectors Club**
Bob Milligan
7014 Woodland Oaks
Magnolia TX 77354
Ph: (281) 259-2735
www.postmarks.org
E-mail: bob.milligan@gmail.net

**Postal History Society**
Gary Wayne Loew
P.O. Box 468101
Atlanta GA 31146-8101
www.postalhistorysociety.org
E-mail: garywloew@gmail.com

**Precancel Stamp Society**
Dick Kalmbach
2658 Iron Works Drive
Buford GA 30519
Ph: (610) 248-8844
www.precancels.com
E-mail: promo@precancels.com

**United Postal Stationery Society**
Stuart Leven
1659 Branham Lane Suite F-307
San Jose CA 95118-2291
www.upss.org
E-mail: poststat@gmail.com

**United States Possessions Philatelic Society**
Daniel F. Ring
P.O. Box 113
Woodstock IL 60098
www.uspps.net
E-mail: danielfring@hotmail.com

## Groups focusing on U.S. area philately as covered in the Standard Catalogue

**Canal Zone Study Group**
Tom Brougham
737 Neilson St.
Berkeley CA 94707
www.CanalZoneStudyGroup.com
E-mail: czsgsecretary@gmail.com

**Carriers and Locals Society**
Martin Richardson
P.O. Box 74
Grosse Ile MI 48138
www.pennypost.org
E-mail: martinr362@aol.com

**Confederate Stamp Alliance**
Patricia A. Kaufmann
10194 N. Old State Road
Lincoln DE 19960
Ph. (302) 422-2656
www.csalliance.org
E-mail: trishkauf@comcast.net

**Hawaiian Philatelic Society**
Gawwon Sugimura
P.O. Box 10115
Honolulu HI 96816-0115
E-mail: hiphilsoc@gmail.com

**Plate Number Coil Collectors Club**
Gene Trinks
16415 W. Desert Wren Court
Surprise AZ 85374
Ph: (623) 322-4619
www.pnc3.org
E-mail: gctrinks@cox.net

**Ryukyu Philatelic Specialist Society**
Laura Edmonds, Secy.
P.O. Box 240177
Charlotte NC 28224-0177
Ph: (336) 509-3739
www.ryukyustamps.org
E-mail: secretary@ryukyustamps.org

**United Nations Philatelists**
Blanton Clement, Jr.
P.O. Box 146
Morrisville PA 19067-0146
www.unpi.com
E-mail: bclemjunior@gmail.com

**United States Stamp Society**
Executive Secretary
Larry Ballantyne
P.O. Box 6634
Katy TX 77491-6634
www.usstamps.org

**U.S. Cancellation Club**
Roger Curran
20 University Avenue
Lewisburg PA 17837
E-mail: rcurran@dejazzd.com

**U.S. Philatelic Classics Society**
Rob Lund
2913 Fulton St.
Everett WA 98201-3733
www.uspcs.org
E-mail: membershipchairman@uspcs.org

## Groups focusing on philately of foreign countries or regions

**Aden & Somaliland Study Group**
Gary Brown
P.O. Box 106
Briar Hill, Victoria, 3088
AUSTRALIA
E-mail: garyjohn951@optushome.com.au

**American Society of Polar Philatelists (Antarctic areas)**
Alan Warren
P.O. Box 39
Exton PA 19341-0039
www.polarphilatelists.org

**Andorran Philatelic Study Circle**
D. Hope
17 Hawthorn Drive
Stalybridge, Cheshire, SK15 1UE
UNITED KINGDOM
www.andorranpsc.org.uk
E-mail: andorranpsc@btinternet.com

**Australian States Study Circle of The Royal Sydney Philatelic Club**
Ben Palmer
GPO 1751
Sydney, N.S.W., 2001
AUSTRALIA
www.philas.org.au/states

**Austria Philatelic Society**
Ralph Schneider
P.O. Box 23049
Belleville IL 62223
Ph: (618) 277-6152
www.austriaphilatelicsociety.com
E-mail: rschneiderstamps@att.net

**Bechuanalands and Botswana Society**
Neville Midwood
69 Porlock Lane
Furzton, Milton Keynes, MK4 1JY
UNITED KINGDOM
www.nevsoft.com
E-mail: bbsoc@nevsoft.com

**Bermuda Collectors Society**
John Pare
405 Perimeter Road
Mount Horeb WI 53572
www.bermudacollectorssociety.com
E-mail: pare16@mhtc.net

**Brazil Philatelic Association**
William V. Kriebel
1923 Manning St.
Philadelphia PA 19103-5728
www.brazilphilatelic.org
E-mail: info@brazilphilatelic.org

**British Caribbean Philatelic Study Group**
Duane Larson
2 Forest Blvd.
Park Forest IL 60466
www.bcpsg.com
E-mail: dlarson283@aol.com

**The King George VI Collectors Society (British Commonwealth)**
Brian Livingstone
21 York Mansions, Prince of Wales Drive
London, SW11 4DL
UNITED KINGDOM
www.kg6.info
E-mail: livingstone484@btinternet.com

**British North America Philatelic Society (Canada & Provinces)**
Andy Ellwood
10 Doris Avenue
Gloucester, ON, KIT 3W8
CANADA
www.bnaps.org
E-mail: secretary@bnaps.org

**British West Indies Study Circle**
John Seidl
4324 Granby Way
Marietta GA 30062
Ph: (404) 229-6863
www.bwisc.org
E-mail: john.seidl@gmail.com

**Burma Philatelic Study Circle**
Michael Whittaker
1, Ecton Leys, Hillside
Rugby, Warwickshire, CV22 5SL
UNITED KINGDOM
www.burmastamps.homecall.co.uk
E-mail: manningham8@mypostoffice.co.uk

**Cape and Natal Study Circle**
Dr. Guy Dillaway
P.O. Box 181
Weston MA 02493
www.nzsc.demon.co.uk

**Ceylon Study Circle**
R. W. P. Frost
42 Lonsdale Road, Cannington
Bridgwater, Somerset, TA5 2JS
UNITED KINGDOM
www.ceylonsc.org
E-mail: rodney.frost@tiscali.co.uk

**Channel Islands Specialists Society**
Richard Flemming
64, Falconers Green, Burbage
Hinckley, Leicestershire, LE10 2SX
UNITED KINGDOM
www.ciss1950.org.uk
E-mail: secretary@ciss1950.org.uk

**China Stamp Society**
H. James Maxwell
1050 West Blue Ridge Blvd.
Kansas City MO 64145-1216
www.chinastampsociety.org
E-mail: president@chinastampsociety.org

**Colombia/Panama Philatelic Study Group (COPAPHIL)**
Thomas P. Myers
P.O. Box 522
Gordonsville VA 22942
www.copaphil.org
E-mail: tpmphil@hotmail.com

**Association Filatelic de Costa Rica**
Giana Wayman (McCarty)
SJO 4935, P.O. Box 025723
Miami FL 33102-5723
E-mail: scotland@racsa.co.cr

**Society for Costa Rica Collectors**
Dr. Hector R. Mena
P.O. Box 14831
Baton Rouge LA 70808
www.socorico.org
E-mail: hrmena@aol.com

**International Cuban Philatelic Society**
Ernesto Cuesta
P.O. Box 34434
Bethesda MD 20827
www.cubafil.org
E-mail: ecuesta@philat.com

**Cuban Philatelic Society of America ®**
P.O. Box 141656
Coral Gables FL 33114-1656
www.cubapsa.com
E-mail: cpsa.usa@gmail.com

**Cyprus Study Circle**
Colin Dear
10 Marne Close, Wem
Shropshire, SY4 5YE
UNITED KINGDOM
www.cyprusstudycircle.org/index.htm
E-mail: colindear@talktalk.net

**Society for Czechoslovak Philately**
Tom Cossaboom
P.O. Box 4124
Prescott AZ 86302
Ph: (928) 771-9097
www.csphilately.org
E-mail: klfck1@aol.com

**Danish West Indies Study Unit of the Scandinavian Collectors Club**
Arnold Sorensen
7666 Edgedale Drive
Newburgh IN 47630
Ph: (812) 480-6532
www.scc-online.org
E-mail: valbydwi@hotmail.com

**East Africa Study Circle**
Michael Vesey-Fitzgerald
Gambles Cottage, 18 Clarence Road
Lyndhurst, SO43 7AL
UNITED KINGDOM
www.easc.org.uk
E-mail: secretary@easc.org.uk

**Egypt Study Circle**
Mike Murphy
109 Chadwick Road
London, SE15 4PY
UNITED KINGDOM
Trent Ruebush: North American Agent
E-mail: tkruebrush@gmail.com
www.egyptstudycircle.org.uk
E-mail: egyptstudycircle@hotmail.com

**Estonian Philatelic Society**
Juri Kirsimagi
29 Clifford Ave.
Pelham NY 10803
Ph: (914) 738-3713

**Ethiopian Philatelic Society**
Ulf Lindahl
21 Westview Place
Riverside CT 06878
Ph: (203) 722-0769
http://ethiopianphilatelicsociety.weebly.com
E-mail: ulindahl@optonline.net

**Falkland Islands Philatelic Study Group**
Carl J. Faulkner
615 Taconic Trail
Williamstown MA 01267-2745
Ph: (413) 458-4421
www.fipsg.org.uk
E-mail: cfaulkner@taconicwilliamstown.com

**Faroe Islands Study Circle**
Norman Hudson
40 Queen's Road, Vicar's Cross
Chester, CH3 5HB
UNITED KINGDOM
www.faroeislandssc.org
E-mail: jntropics@hotmail.com

**Former French Colonies Specialist Society**
COLFRA
BP 628
75367 Paris, Cedex 08
FRANCE
www.colfra.org
E-mail: secretaire@colfra.org

**France & Colonies Philatelic Society**
Edward Grabowski
111 Prospect St., 4C
Westfield NJ 07090
www.franceandcolps.org
E-mail: edjjg@alum.mit.edu

**Gibraltar Study Circle**
Susan Dare
22, Byways Park, Strode Road,
Clevedon, North Somerset, BS21 6UR
UNITED KINGDOM
www.gibraltarstudycircle.wordpress.com
E-mail: smldare@yahoo.co.uk

**Germany Philatelic Society**
P.O. Box 6547
Chesterfield MO 63006
www.germanyphilatelicusa.org

**Plebiscite-Memel-Saar Study Group of the German Philatelic Society**
Clayton Wallace
100 Lark Court
Alamo CA 94507
E-mail: claytonwallace@comcast.net

**Great Britain Collectors Club**
Steve McGill
10309 Brookhollow Circle
Highlands Ranch CO 80129
www.gbstamps.com/gbcc
E-mail: steve.mcgill@comcast.net

**International Society of Guatemala Collectors**
Jaime Marckwordt
449 St. Francis Blvd.
Daly City CA 94015-2136
www.guatemalastamps.com
E-mail:
membership@guatamalastamps.com

**Haiti Philatelic Society**
Ubaldo Del Toro
5709 Marble Archway
Alexandria VA 22315
www.haitiphilately.org
E-mail: u007ubi@aol.com

**Federacion Filatelica de la Republica de Honduras (Honduran Philatelic Federation, FFRH)**
Mauricio Mejia
Apartado postal 1465
Tegucigalpa
HONDURAS

**Hong Kong Stamp Society**
Ming W. Tsang
P.O. Box 206
Glenside PA 19038
www.hkss.org
E-mail: hkstamps@yahoo.com

**Society for Hungarian Philately**
Alan Bauer
P.O. Box 3024
Andover MA 01810
Ph: (978) 682-0242
www.hungarianphilately.org
E-mail: alan@hungarianstamps.com

**India Study Circle**
John Warren
P.O. Box 7326
Washington DC 20044
Ph: (202) 488-7443
www.indiastudycircle.org
E-mail: jw-kbw@earthlink.net

**Indian Ocean Study Circle**
E. S. Hutton
29 Patermoster Close
Waltham Abby, Essex, EN9 3JU
UNITED KINGDOM
www.indianoceanstudycircle.com
E-mail: secretary@indianoceanstudycircle.com

**Society of Indo-China Philatelists**
Ron Bentley
2600 N. 24th St.
Arlington VA 22207
www.sicp-online.org
E-mail: ron.bentley@verizon.net

**Iran Philatelic Study Circle**
Mehdi Esmaili
P.O. Box 750096
Forest Hills NY 11375
www.iranphilatelic.org
E-mail: m.esmaili@earthlink.net

**Eire Philatelic Association (Ireland)**
David J. Brennan
P.O. Box 704
Bernardsville NJ 07924
www.eirephilatelicassoc.org
E-mail: brennan704@aol.com

**Society of Israel Philatelists**
Jacqueline Baca
100 Match Factory Place
Bellefonte PA 16823-1367
Ph: (814) 933-3803 ext. 212
www.israelstamps.com
E-mail: israelstamps@gmail.com

**Italy and Colonies Study Circle**
Richard Harlow
7 Duncombe House, 8 Manor Road
Teddington, TW11 8BE
UNITED KINGDOM
www.icsc.pwp.blueyonder.co.uk
E-mail: richardharlow@outlook.com

**International Society for Japanese Philately**
William Eisenhauer
P.O. Box 230462
Tigard OR 97281
www.isjp.org
E-mail: secretary@isjp.org

**Korea Stamp Society**
John Talmage
P.O. Box 6889
Oak Ridge TN 37831
www.koreastampsociety.org
E-mail: jtalmage@usit.net

**Latin American Philatelic Society**
Jules K. Beck
30½ St. #209
St. Louis Park MN 55426-3551

**Liberian Philatelic Society**
William Thomas Lockard
P.O. Box 106
Wellston OH 45692
Ph: (740) 384-2020
E-mail: tlockard@zoomnet.net

**Liechtenstudy USA (Liechtenstein)**
Paul Tremaine
410 SW Ninth St.
Dundee OR 97115
Ph: (503) 538-4500
www.liechtenstudy.org
E-mail: editor@liechtenstudy.org

**Lithuania Philatelic Society**
John Variakojis
8472 Carlisle Court
Burr Ridge IL 60527
Ph: (630) 974-6525
www.lithuanianphilately.com/lps
E-mail: variakojis@sbcglobal.net

**Luxembourg Collectors Club**
Gary B. Little
7319 Beau Road
Sechelt, BC, VON 3A8
CANADA
lcc.luxcentral.com
E-mail: gary@luxcentral.com

**Malaya Study Group**
David Tett
4 Amenbury Court
Harpenden Herts,
Wheathampstead Herts AL5 2BU
UNITED KINGDOM
www.m-s-g.org.uk
E-mail: davidtett@aol.com

**Malta Study Circle**
Rodger Evans
Ravensbourne, Hook Heath Road
Woking, Surrey, GU22 0LB
UNITED KINGDOM
www.maltastudycircle.org.uk
E-mail: carge@hotmail.co.uk

**Mexico-Elmhurst Philatelic Society International**
Eric Stovner
P.O. Box 10097
Santa Ana CA 92711-0097
www.mepsi.org
E-mail: treasurer@mepsi.org

**Asociacion Mexicana de Filatelia AMEXFIL**
Alejando Grossman
Jose Maria Rico, 129, Col. Del Valle
Mexico City DF, 03100
MEXICO
www.amexfil.mx
E-mail: amexfil@gmail.com

**Society for Moroccan and Tunisian Philately S.P.L.M.**
206, bld Pereire
Paris 75017
FRANCE
splm-philatelie.org
E-mail: splm206@aol.com

**Nepal & Tibet Philatelic Study Group**
Ken Goss
2643 Wagner Place
EL Dorado Hills CA 95762
Ph: (510) 207-5369
www.fuchs-online.com/ntpsc/
E-mail: kfgoss@comcast.net

**American Society for Netherlands Philately**
Hans Kremer
50 Rockport Court
Danville CA 94526
Ph: (925) 820-5841
www.asnp1975.com
E-mail: hkremer@usa.net

**New Zealand Society of Great Britain**
Michael Wilkinson
121 London Road
Sevenoaks, Kent, TN13 1BH
UNITED KINGDOM
www.nzsgb.org.uk
E-mail: mwilkin799@aol.com

**Nicaragua Study Group**
Erick Rodriguez
11817 SW 11th St.
Miami FL 33184-2501
clubs.yahoo.com/clubs/nicaraguastudygroup
E-mail: nsgsec@yahoo.com

**Society of Australasian Specialists/Oceania**
David McNamee
P.O. Box 37
Alamo CA 94507
www.sasoceania.org
E-mail: treasurer@sasoceania.org

**Orange Free State Study Circle**
J. R. Stroud
24 Hooper Close
Burnham-on-sea, Somerset, TA8 1JQ
UNITED KINGDOM
orangefreestatephilately.org.uk
E-mail: richard@richardstroud.plus.com

**Pacific Islands Study Circle**
John Ray
24 Woodvale Ave.
London, SE25 4AE
UNITED KINGDOM
www.pisc.org.uk
E-mail: secretary@pisc.org.uk

**Pakistan Philatelic Study Circle**
Jeff Siddiqui
P.O. Box 7002
Lynnwood WA 98046
E-mail: jeffsiddiqui@msn.com

**Asociacion Filatelica de Panama (ASOFILPA)**
Edward D. Vianna
Apartado Postal 0819-03400
El Dorado, Panama
PANAMA
www.asociacionfilatelicadepanama.blogspot.com
E-mail: asofilpa@gmail.com

**Papuan Philatelic Society**
Steven Zirinsky
P.O. Box 49, Ansonia Station
New York NY 10023
Ph: (718) 706-0616
www.communigate.co.uk/york/pps
E-mail: szirinsky@cs.com

**International Philippine Philatelic Society**
Donald J. Peterson
P.O. Box 122
Brunswick MD 21716
Ph: (301) 834-6419
www.theipps.info
E-mail: dpeterson4526@gmail.com

**Pitcairn Islands Study Group**
Dr. Everett L. Parker
117 Cedar Breeze South
Glenburn ME 04401-1734
Ph: (207) 573-1686
www.pisg.net
E-mail: eparker@hughes.net

**Polonus Philatelic Society (Poland)**
Daniel Lubelski
P.O. Box 2212
Benicia CA 94510
Ph: (419) 410-9115
www.polonus.org
E-mail: info@polonus.org

**International Society for Portuguese Philately**
Clyde Homen
1491 Bonnie View Road
Hollister CA 95023-5117
www.portugalstamps.com
E-mail: ispp1962@sbcglobal.net

**Rhodesian Study Circle**
William R. Wallace
P.O. Box 16381
San Francisco CA 94116
www.rhodesianstudycircle.org.uk
E-mail: bwall8rscr@earthlink.net

**Rossica Society of Russian Philately**
Alexander Kolchinsky
1506 Country Lake Drive
Champaign IL 6821-6428
www.rossica.org
E-mail: alexander.kolchinsky@rossica.org

**St. Helena, Ascension & Tristan Da Cunha Philatelic Society**
Dr. Everett L. Parker
117 Cedar Breeze South
Glenburn ME 04401-1734
Ph: (207) 573-1686
www.shatps.org
E-mail: eparker@hughes.net

**St. Pierre & Miquelon Philatelic Society**
James R. (Jim) Taylor
2335 Paliswood Road SW
Calgary, AB, T2V 3P6
CANADA
www.stamps.org/spm

**Asociacion Filatelica Salvadorena**
Joseph D. Hahn
301 Rolling Ridge Drive, Apt. 111
State College PA 16801-6149
www.elsalvadorphilately.org
E-mail: joehahn100@hotmail.com

**Fellowship of Samoa Specialists**
Donald Mee
23 Leo St.
Christchurch, 8051
NEW ZEALAND
www.samoaexpress.org
E-mail: donanm@xtra.co.nz

**Sarawak Specialists' Society**
Stephen Schumann
2417 Cabrillo Drive
Hayward CA 94545
Ph: (510) 785-4794
www.britborneostamps.org.uk
E-mail: stephen.schumann@att.net

**Scandinavian Collectors Club**
Steve Lund
P.O. Box 16213
St. Paul MN 55116
www.scc-online.org
E-mail: steve88h@aol.com

**Slovakia Stamp Society**
Jack Benchik
P.O. Box 555
Notre Dame IN 46556

**Philatelic Society for Greater Southern Africa**
Alan Hanks
34 Seaton Drive
Aurora, ON, L4G 2K1
CANADA
www.psgsa.thestampweb.com

**South Sudan Philatelic Society**
William Barclay
1370 Spring Hill Road
South Londonderry VT 05155
E-mail: barclayphilatelics@gmail.com

**Spanish Philatelic Society**
Robert H. Penn
1108 Walnut Drive
Danielsville PA 18038
Ph: (610) 844-8963
E-mail: roberthpenn43@gmail.com

**Sudan Study Group**
David Sher
5 Ellis Park Road
Toronto, ON, M6S2V1
CANADA
www.sudanstamps.org
e-mail: sh3603@hotmail.com

**American Helvetia Philatelic Society (Switzerland, Liechtenstein)**
Richard T. Hall
P.O. Box 15053
Asheville NC 28813-0053
www.swiss-stamps.org
E-mail: secretary2@swiss-stamps.org

**Tannu Tuva Collectors Society**
Ken R. Simon
P.O. Box 385
Lake Worth FL 33460-0385
Ph: (561) 588-5954
www.tuva.tk
E-mail: yurttuva@yahoo.com

**Society for Thai Philately**
H. R. Blakeney
P.O. Box 25644
Oklahoma City OK 73125
E-mail: HRBlakeney@aol.com

**Transvaal Study Circle**
Chris Board
36 Wakefield Gardens
London, SE19 2NR
UNITED KINGDOM
www.transvaalstamps.org.uk
E-mail: c.board@macace.net

**Ottoman and Near East Philatelic Society (Turkey and related areas)**
Bob Stuchell
193 Valley Stream Lane
Wayne PA 19087
www.oneps.org
E-mail: rstuchell@msn.com

**Ukrainian Philatelic & Numismatic Society**
Martin B. Tatuch
5117 8th Road N.
Arlington VA 22205-1201
www.upns.org
E-mail: treasurer@upns.org

**Vatican Philatelic Society**
Sal Quinonez
1 Aldersgate, Apt. 1002
Riverhead NY 11901-1830
Ph: (516) 727-6426
www.vaticanphilately.org

**British Virgin Islands Philatelic Society**
Giorgio Migliavacca
P.O. Box 7007
St. Thomas VI 00801-0007
www.islandsun.com/category/collectables/
E-mail: issun@candwbvi.net

**West Africa Study Circle**
Martin Bratzel
1233 Virginia Ave.
Windsor, ON, N8S 2Z1
CANADA
www.wasc.org.uk
E-mail: marty_bratzel@yahoo.ca

**Western Australia Study Group**
Brian Pope
P.O. Box 423
Claremont, Western Australia, 6910
AUSTRALIA
www.wastudygroup.com
E-mail: black5swan@yahoo.com.au

**Yugoslavia Study Group of the Croatian Philatelic Society**
Michael Lenard
1514 N. Third Ave.
Wausau WI 54401
Ph: (715) 675-2833
E-mail: mjlenard@aol.com

## Topical Groups

**Americana Unit**
Dennis Dengel
17 Peckham Road
Poughkeepsie NY 12603-2018
www.americanaunit.org
E-mail: ddengel@americanaunit.org

**Astronomy Study Unit**
John Budd
728 Sugar Camp Way
Brooksville FL 34604
Ph: (352) 345-4799
www.astronomystudyunit.net
E-mail: jwgbudd@gmail.com

**Bicycle Stamps Club**
Steve Andreasen
2000 Alaskan Way, Unit 157
Seattle WA 98121
E-mail: steven.w.andreasen@gmail.com

**Biology Unit**
Alan Hanks
34 Seaton Drive
Aurora, ON, L4G 2K1
CANADA
Ph: (905) 727-6993

**Bird Stamp Society**
S. A. H. (Tony) Statham
Ashlyns Lodge, Chesham Road,
Berkhamsted, Hertfordshire HP4 2ST
UNITED KINGDOM
www.bird-stamps.org/bss
E-mail: tony.statham@sky.com

**Captain Cook Society**
Jerry Yucht
8427 Leale Ave.
Stockton CA 95212
www.captaincooksociety.com
E-mail: US@captaincooksociety.com

**The CartoPhilatelic Society**
Marybeth Sulkowski
2885 Sanford Ave, SW, #32361
Grandville MI 49418-1342
www.mapsonstamps.org
E-mail: secretary@mapsonstamps.org

**Casey Jones Railroad Unit**
Jeff Lough
2612 Redbud Lane, Apt. C
Lawrence KS 66046
www.uqp.de/cjr/index.htm
E-mail: jeffydplaugh@gmail.com

**Cats on Stamps Study Unit**
Robert D. Jarvis
2731 Teton Lane
Fairfield CA 94533
www.catstamps.info
E-mail: bobmarci@aol.com

**Chemistry & Physics on Stamps Study Unit**
Dr. Roland Hirsch
20458 Water Point Lane
Germantown MD 20874
www.cpossu.org
E-mail: rfhirsch@cpossu.org

**Chess on Stamps Study Unit**
Ray C. Alexis
608 Emery St.
Longmont CO 80501
E-mail: chessstuff911459@aol.com

**Christmas Philatelic Club**
Jim Balog
P.O. Box 744
Geneva OH 44041
www.christmasphilatelicclub.org
E-mail: jpb4stamps@windstream.net

**Cricket Philatelic Society**
A. Melville-Brown, President
11 Weppons, Ravens Road
Shoreham-by-Sea
West Sussex, BN43 5AW
UNITED KINGDOM
www.cricketstamp.net
E-mail: mel.cricket.100@googlemail.com

**Dogs on Stamps Study Unit**
Morris Raskin
202A Newport Road
Monroe Township NJ 08831
Ph: (609) 655-7411
www.dossu.org
E-mail: mraskin@cellurian.com

**Earth's Physical Features Study Group**
Fred Klein
515 Magdalena Ave.
Los Altos CA 94024
epfsu.jeffhayward.com

**Ebony Society of Philatelic Events and Reflections, Inc. (African-American topicals)**
Manuel Gilyard
800 Riverside Drive, Suite 4H
New York NY 10032-7412
www.esperstamps.org
E-mail: gilyardmani@aol.com

**Europa Study Unit**
Tonny E. Van Loij
3002 S. Xanthia St.
Denver CO 80231-4237
Ph: (303) 752-0189
www.europastudyunit.org
E-mail: tvanloij@gmail.com

**Fine & Performing Arts**
Deborah L. Washington
6922 S. Jeffery Blvd., #7 - North
Chicago IL 60649
E-mail: brasslady@comcast.net

**Fire Service in Philately**
John Zaranek
81 Hillpine Road
Cheektowaga NY 14227-2259
Ph: (716) 668-3352
E-mail: jczaranek@roadrunner.com

**Gay & Lesbian History on Stamps Club**
Joe Petronie
P.O. Box 190842
Dallas TX 75219-0842
www.facebook.com/glhsc
E-mail: glhsc@aol.com

**Gems, Minerals & Jewelry Study Unit**
Mrs. Gilberte Proteau
138 Lafontaine
Beloeil QC J3G 2G7
CANADA
Ph: (978) 851-8283
E-mail: gilberte.ferland@sympatico.ca

**Graphics Philately Association**
Mark H. Winnegrad
P.O. Box 380
Bronx NY 10462-0380
www.graphics-stamps.org
E-mail: indybruce1@yahoo.com

**Journalists, Authors & Poets on Stamps**
Clete Delvaux
800 East River Drive
De Pere WI 54115
E-mail: cdelvaux@msn.com

**Lighthouse Stamp Society**
Dalene Thomas
1805 S Balsam St., #106
Lakewood CO 80232
Ph: (303) 986-6620
www.lighthousestampsociety.org
E-mail: dalene@lighthousestampsociety.org

**Lions International Stamp Club**
John Bargus
108-2777 Barry Road RR 2
Mill Bay, BC, V0R 2P2
CANADA
Ph: (250) 743-5782

**Mahatma Gandhi On Stamps Study Circle**
Pramod Shivagunde
Pratik Clinic, Akluj
Solapur, Maharashtra, 413101
INDIA
E-mail: drnanda@bom6.vsnl.net.in

**Masonic Study Unit**
Gene Fricks
25 Murray Way
Blackwood NJ 08012-4400
E-mail: genefricks@comcast.net

**Mathematical Study Unit**
Monty Strauss
4209 88th St.
Lubbock TX 79423-2941
www.mathstamps.org
E-mail: montystrauss@gmail.com

**Medical Subjects Unit**
Dr. Frederick C. Skvara
P.O. Box 6228
Bridgewater NJ 08807
E-mail: fcskvara@optonline.net

**Military Postal History Society**
Ed Dubin
1 S. Wacker Drive, Suite 3500
Chicago IL 60606
www.militaryPHS.org
E-mail: dubine@comcast.net

**Mourning Stamps and Covers Club**
James Camak, Jr.
3801 Acapulco Ct.
Irving TX 75062
www.mscc.ms
E-mail: jamescamak7@gmail.com

**Napoleonic Age Philatelists**
Ken Berry
4117 NW 146th St.
Oklahoma City OK 73134-1746
Ph: (405) 748-8646
www.nap-stamps.org
E-mail: krb4117@att.net

**Old World Archeological Study Unit**
Caroline Scannell
11 Dawn Drive
Smithtown NY 11787-1761
www.owasu.org
E-mail: editor@owasu.org

**Petroleum Philatelic Society International**
Feitze Papa
922 Meander Dr.
Walnut Creek CA 94598-4239
E-mail: oildad@astound.net

**Rotary on Stamps Unit**
Gerald L. Fitzsimmons
105 Calle Ricardo
Victoria TX 77904
rotaryonstamps.org
E-mail: glfitz@suddenlink.net

**Scouts on Stamps Society International**
Woodrow (Woody) Brooks
498 Baldwin Road
Akron OH 44312
Ph: (330) 612-1294
www.sossi.org
E-mail: rfrank@sossi.org

**Ships on Stamps Unit**
Les Smith
302 Conklin Ave.
Penticton, BC, V2A 2T4
CANADA
Ph: (250) 493-7486
www.shipsonstamps.org
E-mail: lessmith440@shaw.ca

**Space Unit**
David Blog
P.O. Box 174
Bergenfield NJ 07621
www.space-unit.com
E-mail: davidblognj@gmail.com

**Sports Philatelists International**
Mark Maestrone
2824 Curie Place
San Diego CA 92122-4110
www.sportstamps.org
Email: president@sportstamps.org

**Stamps on Stamps Collectors Club**
Alf Jordan
156 W. Elm St.
Yarmouth ME 04096
www.stampsonstamps.org
E-mail: ajordan1@maine.rr.com

**Windmill Study Unit**
Walter J. Hollien
607 N. Porter St.
Watkins Glenn NY 14891-1345
Ph: (607) 229-3541
www.windmillworld.com
E-mail: whollien@earthlink.net

**Wine On Stamps Study Unit**
David Wolfersberger
768 Chain Ridge Road
St. Louis MO 63122-3259
Ph: (314) 961-5032
www.wine-on-stamps.org
E-mail: dewolf2@swbell.net

**Women on Stamps Study Unit**
Hugh Gottfried
2232 26th St.
Santa Monica CA 90405-1902
E-mail: hgottfried@adelphia.net

# Expertizing Services

The following organizations will, for a fee, provide expert opinions about stamps submitted to them. Collectors should contact these organizations to find out about their fees and requirements before submiting philatelic material to them. The listing of these groups here is not intended as an endorsement by Amos Media Co.

## General Expertizing Services

**American Philatelic Expertizing Service (a service of the American Philatelic Society)**
100 Match Factory Place
Bellefonte PA 16823-1367
Ph: (814) 237-3803
Fax: (814) 237-6128
www.stamps.org
E-mail: twhorn@stamps.org
Areas of Expertise: Worldwide

**B. P. A. Expertising, Ltd.**
P.O. Box 1141
Guildford, Surrey, GU5 0WR
UNITED KINGDOM
E-mail: sec@bpaexpertising.org
Areas of Expertise: British Commonwealth, Great Britain, Classics of Europe, South America and the Far East

**Philatelic Foundation**
22 E. 35th St., 4th Floor
New York NY 10016
Ph: (212) 221-6555
Fax: (212) 221-6208
www.philatelicfoundation.org
E-mail: philatelicfoundation@verizon.net
Areas of Expertise: U.S. & Worldwide

**Philatelic Stamp Authentication and Grading, Inc.**
P.O. Box 41-0880
Melbourne FL 32941-0880
Customer Service: (305) 345-9864
www.psaginc.com
E-mail: info@psaginc.com
Areas of Expertise: U.S., Canal Zone, Hawaii, Philippines, Canada & Provinces

**Professional Stamp Experts**
P.O. Box 539309
Henderson NV 89053-9309
Ph: (702) 776-6522
www.gradingmatters.com
www.psestamp.com
E-mail: info@gradingmatters.com
Areas of Expertise: Stamps and covers of U.S., U.S. Possessions, British Commonwealth

**Royal Philatelic Society Expert Committee**
41 Devonshire Place
London, W1N 1PE
UNITED KINGDOM
www.rpsl.org.uk/experts.html
E-mail: experts@rpsl.org.uk
Areas of Expertise: Worldwide

## Expertizing Services Covering Specific Fields or Countries

**China Stamp Society Expertizing Service**
1050 W. Blue Ridge Blvd.
Kansas City MO 64145
Ph: (816) 942-6300
E-mail: hjmesq@aol.com
Areas of Expertise: China

**Confederate Stamp Alliance Authentication Service**
Gen. Frank Crown, Jr.
P.O. Box 278
Capshaw AL 35742-0396
Ph: (302) 422-2656
Fax: (302) 424-1990
www.csalliance.org
E-mail: csaas@knology.net
Areas of Expertise: Confederate stamps and postal history

**Errors, Freaks and Oddities Collectors Club Expertizing Service**
138 East Lakemont Drive
Kingsland GA 31548
Ph: (912) 729-1573
Areas of Expertise: U.S. errors, freaks and oddities

**Estonian Philatelic Society Expertizing Service**
39 Clafford Lane
Melville NY 11747
Ph: (516) 421-2078
E-mail: esto4@aol.com
Areas of Expertise: Estonia

**Hawaiian Philatelic Society Expertizing Service**
P.O. Box 10115
Honolulu HI 96816-0115
Areas of Expertise: Hawaii

**Hong Kong Stamp Society Expertizing Service**
P.O. Box 206
Glenside PA 19038
Fax: (215) 576-6850
Areas of Expertise: Hong Kong

**International Association of Philatelic Experts United States Associate members:**

Paul Buchsbayew
119 W. 57th St.
New York NY 10019
Ph: (212) 977-7734
Fax: (212) 977-8653
Areas of Expertise: Russia, Soviet Union

William T. Crowe
P.O. Box 2090
Danbury CT 06813-2090
E-mail: wtcrowe@aol.com
Areas of Expertise: United States

John Lievsay
(see American Philatelic Expertizing Service and Philatelic Foundation)
Areas of Expertise: France

Robert W. Lyman
P.O. Box 348
Irvington on Hudson NY 10533
Ph and Fax: (914) 591-6937
Areas of Expertise: British North America, New Zealand

Robert Odenweller
P.O. Box 401
Bernardsville NJ 07924-0401
Ph and Fax: (908) 766-5460
Areas of Expertise: New Zealand, Samoa to 1900

Sergio Sismondo
The Regency Tower, Suite 1109
770 James Street
Syracuse NY 13203
Ph: (315) 422-2331
Fax: (315) 422-2956
Areas of Expertise: British East Africa, Camerouns, Cape of Good Hope, Canada, British North America

**International Society for Japanese Philately Expertizing Committee**
132 North Pine Terrace
Staten Island NY 10312-4052
Ph: (718) 227-5229
Areas of Expertise: Japan and related areas, except WWII Japanese Occupation issues

**International Society for Portuguese Philately Expertizing Service**
P.O. Box 43146
Philadelphia PA 19129-3146
Ph and Fax: (215) 843-2106
E-mail: s.s.washburne@worldnet.att.net
Areas of Expertise: Portugal and Colonies

**Mexico-Elmhurst Philatelic Society International Expert Committee**
Expert Committee Administrator
Marc E. Gonzales
P.O. Box 29040
Denver CO 80229-0040
www.mepsi.org/expertization
Areas of Expertise: Mexico

**Ukrainian Philatelic & Numismatic Society Expertizing Service**
30552 Dell Lane
Warren MI 48092-1862
Areas of Expertise: Ukraine, Western Ukraine

**V. G. Greene Philatelic Research Foundation**
P.O. Box 204, Station Q
Toronto, ON, M4T 2M1
CANADA
Ph: (416) 921-2073
Fax: (416) 921-1282
www.greenefoundation.ca
E-mail: vggfoundation@on.aibn.com
Areas of Expertise: British North America

# Information on Catalogue Values, Grade and Condition

## Catalogue Value

The Scott Catalogue value is a retail value; that is, an amount you could expect to pay for a stamp in the grade of Very Fine with no faults. Any exceptions to the grade valued will be noted in the text. The general introduction on the following pages and the individual section introductions further explain the type of material that is valued. The value listed for any given stamp is a reference that reflects recent actual dealer selling prices for that item.

Dealer retail price lists, public auction results, published prices in advertising and individual solicitation of retail prices from dealers, collectors and specialty organizations have been used in establishing the values found in this catalogue. Amos Media Co. values stamps, but Amos Media is not a company engaged in the business of buying and selling stamps as a dealer.

Use this catalogue as a guide for buying and selling. The actual price you pay for a stamp may be higher or lower than the catalogue value because of many different factors, including the amount of personal service a dealer offers, or increased or decreased interest in the country or topic represented by a stamp or set. An item may occasionally be offered at a lower price as a "loss leader," or as part of a special sale. You also may obtain an item inexpensively at public auction because of little interest at that time or as part of a large lot.

Stamps that are of a lesser grade than Very Fine, or those with condition problems, generally trade at lower prices than those given in this catalogue. Stamps of exceptional quality in both grade and condition often command higher prices than those listed.

Values for pre-1900 unused issues are for stamps with approximately half or more of their original gum. Stamps with most or all of their original gum may be expected to sell for more, and stamps with less than half of their original gum may be expected to sell for somewhat less than the values listed. On rarer stamps, it may be expected that the original gum will be somewhat more disturbed than it will be on more common issues. Post-1900 unused issues are assumed to have full original gum. From breakpoints in most countries' listings, stamps are valued as never hinged, due to the wide availability of stamps in that condition. These notations are prominently placed in the listings and in the country information preceding the listings. Some countries also feature listings with dual values for hinged and never-hinged stamps.

## Grade

A stamp's grade and condition are crucial to its value. The accompanying illustrations show examples of Very Fine stamps from different time periods, along with examples of stamps in Fine to Very Fine and Extremely Fine grades as points of reference. When a stamp seller offers a stamp in any grade from fine to superb without further qualifying statements, that stamp should not only have the centering grade as defined, but it also should be free of faults or other condition problems.

**FINE** stamps (illustrations not shown) have designs that are quite off center, with the perforations on one or two sides very close to the design but not quite touching it. There is white space between the perforations and the design that is minimal but evident to the unaided eye. Imperforate stamps may have small margins, and earlier issues may show the design just touching one edge of the stamp design. Very early perforated issues normally will have the perforations slightly cutting into the design. Used stamps may have heavier than usual cancellations.

**FINE-VERY FINE** stamps will be somewhat off center on one side, or slightly off center on two sides. Imperforate stamps will have two margins of at least normal size, and the design will not touch any edge. For perforated stamps, the perfs are well clear of the design, but are still noticeably off center. *However, early issues of a country may be printed in such a way that the design naturally is very close to the edges. In these cases, the perforations may cut into the design very slightly.* Used stamps will not have a cancellation that detracts from the design.

**VERY FINE** stamps will be just slightly off center on one or two sides, but the design will be well clear of the edge. The stamp will present a nice, balanced appearance. Imperforate stamps will be well centered within normal-sized margins. *However, early issues of many countries may be printed in such a way that the perforations may touch the design on one or more sides. Where this is the case, a boxed note will be found defining the centering and margins of the stamps being valued.* Used stamps will have light or otherwise neat cancellations. This is the grade used to establish Scott Catalogue values.

**EXTREMELY FINE** stamps are close to being perfectly centered. Imperforate stamps will have even margins that are slightly larger than normal. Even the earliest perforated issues will have perforations clear of the design on all sides.

**Amos Media Co. recognizes that there is no formally enforced grading scheme for postage stamps, and that the final price you pay or obtain for a stamp will be determined by individual agreement at the time of transaction.**

## Condition

*Grade* addresses only centering and (for used stamps) cancellation. *Condition* refers to factors other than grade that affect a stamp's desirability.

Factors that can increase the value of a stamp include exceptionally wide margins, particularly fresh color, the presence of selvage, and plate or die varieties. Unusual cancels on used stamps (particularly those of the 19th century) can greatly enhance their value as well.

Factors other than faults that decrease the value of a stamp include loss of original gum, regumming, a hinge remnant or foreign object adhering to the gum, natural inclusions, straight edges, and markings or notations applied by collectors or dealers.

Faults include missing pieces, tears, pin or other holes, surface scuffs, thin spots, creases, toning, short or pulled perforations, clipped perforations, oxidation or other forms of color changelings, soiling, stains, and such man-made changes as reperforations or the chemical removal or lightening of a cancellation.

## Grading Illustrations

On the following two pages are illustrations of various stamps from countries appearing in this volume. These stamps are arranged by country, and they represent early or important issues that are often found in widely different grades in the marketplace. The editors believe the illustrations will prove useful in showing the margin size and centering that will be seen on the various issues.

In addition to the matters of margin size and centering, collectors are reminded that the very fine stamps valued in the Scott catalogues also will possess fresh color and intact perforations, and they will be free from defects.

Examples shown are computer-manipulated images made from single digitized master illustrations.

## Stamp Illustrations Used in the Catalogue

It is important to note that the stamp images used for identification purposes in this catlaogue may not be indicative of the grade of stamp being valued. Refer to the written discussion of grades on this page and to the grading illustrations on the following two pages for grading information.

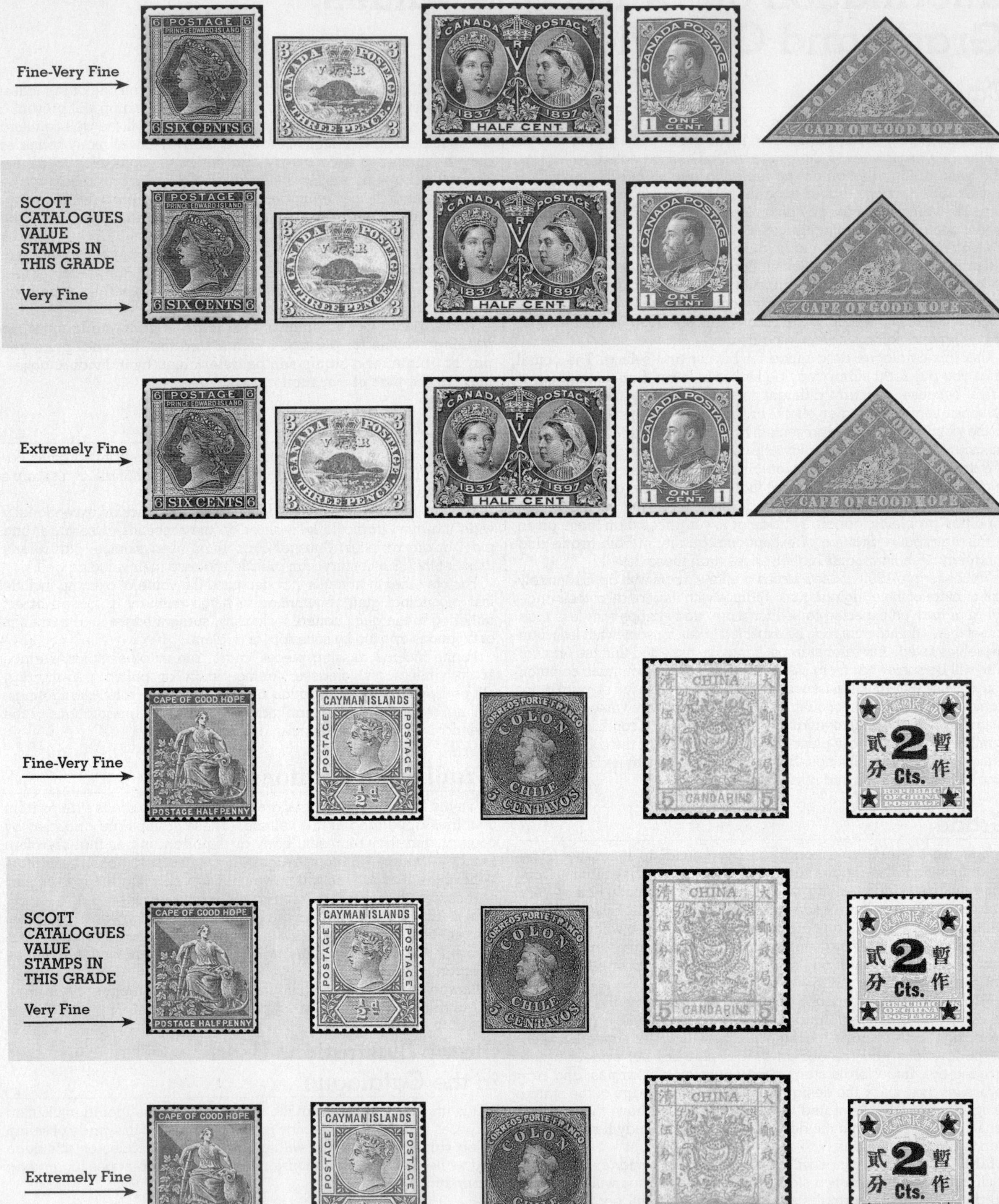

Fine-Very Fine
SCOTT CATALOGUES VALUE STAMPS IN THIS GRADE
Very Fine
Extremely Fine
Fine-Very Fine
SCOTT CATALOGUES VALUE STAMPS IN THIS GRADE
Very Fine
Extremely Fine

Fine-Very Fine

SCOTT CATALOGUES VALUE STAMPS IN THIS GRADE

Very Fine

Extremely Fine

Fine-Very Fine

SCOTT CATALOGUES VALUE STAMPS IN THIS GRADE

Very Fine

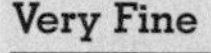

Extremely Fine

For purposes of helping to determine the gum condition and value of an unused stamp, Scott presents the following chart which details different gum conditions and indicates how the conditions correlate with the Scott values for unused stamps. Used together, the Illustrated Grading Chart on the previous pages and this Illustrated Gum Chart should allow catalogue users to better understand the grade and gum condition of stamps valued in the Scott catalogues.

| Gum Categories: | MINT N.H. | ORIGINAL GUM (O.G.) | | | | NO GUM |
|---|---|---|---|---|---|---|
| | **Mint Never Hinged** *Free from any disturbance* | **Lightly Hinged** *Faint impression of a removed hinge over a small area* | **Hinge Mark or Remnant** *Prominent hinged spot with part or all of the hinge remaining* | **Large part o.g.** *Approximately half or more of the gum intact* | **Small part o.g.** *Approximately less than half of the gum intact* | **No gum** *Only if issued with gum* |
| Commonly Used Symbol: | ★★ | ★ | ★ | ★ | ★ | (★) |
| Pre-1900 Issues (Pre-1881 for U.S.) | *Very fine pre-1900 stamps in these categories trade at a premium over Scott value* | | | Scott Value for "Unused" | | Scott "No Gum" listings for selected unused classic stamps |
| From 1900 to breakpoints for listings of never-hinged stamps | Scott "Never Hinged" listings for selected unused stamps | Scott Value for "Unused" (Actual value will be affected by the degree of hinging of the full o.g.) | | | | |
| From breakpoints noted for many countries | Scott Value for "Unused" | | | | | |

**Never Hinged (NH; ★★):** A never-hinged stamp will have full original gum that will have no hinge mark or disturbance. The presence of an expertizer's mark does not disqualify a stamp from this designation.

**Original Gum (OG; ★):** Pre-1900 stamps should have approximately half or more of their original gum. On rarer stamps, it may be expected that the original gum will be somewhat more disturbed than it will be on more common issues. Post-1900 stamps should have full original gum. Original gum will show some disturbance caused by a previous hinge(s) which may be present or entirely removed. The actual value of a post-1900 stamp will be affected by the degree of hinging of the full original gum.

**Disturbed Original Gum:** Gum showing noticeable effects of humidity, climate or hinging over more than half of the gum. The significance of gum disturbance in valuing a stamp in any of the Original Gum categories depends on the degree of disturbance, the rarity and normal gum condition of the issue and other variables affecting quality.

**Regummed (RG; (★)):** A regummed stamp is a stamp without gum that has had some type of gum privately applied at a time after it was issued. This normally is done to deceive collectors and/or dealers into thinking that the stamp has original gum and therefore has a higher value. A regummed stamp is considered the same as a stamp with none of its original gum for purposes of grading.

# Catalogue Listing Policy

It is the intent of Amos Media Co. to list all postage stamps of the world in the *Scott Standard Postage Stamp Catalogue*. The only strict criteria for listing is that stamps be decreed legal for postage by the issuing country and that the issuing country actually have an operating postal system. Whether the primary intent of issuing a given stamp or set was for sale to postal patrons or to stamp collectors is not part of our listing criteria. Scott's role is to provide basic comprehensive postage stamp information. It is up to each stamp collector to choose which items to include in a collection.

It is Scott's objective to seek reasons why a stamp should be listed, rather than why it should not. Nevertheless, there are certain types of items that will not be listed. These include the following:

1. Unissued items that are not officially distributed or released by the issuing postal authority. If such items are officially issued at a later date by the country, they will be listed. Unissued items consist of those that have been printed and then held from sale for reasons such as change in government, errors found on stamps or something deemed objectionable about a stamp subject or design.

2. Stamps "issued" by non-existent postal entities or fantasy countries, such as Nagaland, Occusi-Ambeno, Staffa, Sedang, Torres Straits and others. Also, stamps "issued" in the names of legitimate, stamp-issuing countries that are not authorized by those countries.

3. Semi-official or unofficial items not required for postage. Examples include items issued by private agencies for their own express services. When such items are required for delivery, or are valid as prepayment of postage, they are listed.

4. Local stamps issued for local use only. Postage stamps issued by governments specifically for "domestic" use, such as Haiti Scott 219-228, or the United States non-denominated stamps, are not considered to be locals, since they are valid for postage throughout the country of origin.

5. Items not valid for postal use. For example, a few countries have issued souvenir sheets that are not valid for postage. This area also includes a number of worldwide charity labels (some denominated) that do not pay postage.

6. Egregiously exploitative issues such as stamps sold for far more than face value, stamps purposefully issued in artificially small quantities or only against advance orders, stamps awarded only to a selected audience such as a philatelic bureau's standing order customers, or stamps sold only in conjunction with other products. All of these kinds of items are usually controlled issues and/or are intended for speculation. These items normally will be included in a footnote.

7. Items distributed by the issuing government only to a limited group, club, philatelic exhibition or a single stamp dealer or other private company. These items normally will be included in a footnote.

8. Stamps not available to collectors. These generally are rare items, all of which are held by public institutions such as museums. The existence of such items often will be cited in footnotes.

The fact that a stamp has been used successfully as postage, even on international mail, is not in itself sufficient proof that it was legitimately issued. Numerous examples of so-called stamps from non-existent countries are known to have been used to post letters that have successfully passed through the international mail system.

There are certain items that are subject to interpretation. When a stamp falls outside our specifications, it may be listed along with a cautionary footnote.

A number of factors are considered in our approach to analyzing how a stamp is listed. The following list of factors is presented to share with you, the catalogue user, the complexity of the listing process.

**Additional printings** — "Additional printings" of a previously issued stamp may range from an item that is totally different to cases where it is impossible to differentiate from the original. At least a minor number (a small-letter suffix) is assigned if there is a distinct change in stamp shade, noticeably redrawn design, or a significantly different perforation measurement. A major number (numeral or numeral and capital-letter combination) is assigned if the editors feel the "additional printing" is sufficiently different from the original that it constitutes a different issue.

**Commemoratives** — Where practical, commemoratives with the same theme are placed in a set. For example, the U.S. Civil War Centennial set of 1961-65 and the Constitution Bicentennial series of 1989-90 appear as sets. Countries such as Japan and Korea issue such material on a regular basis, with an announced, or at least predictable, number of stamps known in advance. Occasionally, however, stamp sets that were released over a period of years have been separated. Appropriately placed footnotes will guide you to each set's continuation.

**Definitive sets** — Blocks of numbers generally have been reserved for definitive sets, based on previous experience with any given country. If a few more stamps were issued in a set than originally expected, they often have been inserted into the original set with a capital-letter suffix, such as U.S. Scott 1059A. If it appears that many more stamps than the originally allotted block will be released before the set is completed, a new block of numbers will be reserved, with the original one being closed off. In some cases, such as the U.S. Transportation and Great Americans series, several blocks of numbers exist. Appropriately placed footnotes will guide you to each set's continuation.

**New country** — Membership in the Universal Postal Union is not a consideration for listing status or order of placement within the catalogue. The index will tell you in what volume or page number the listings begin.

**"No release date" items** — The amount of information available for any given stamp issue varies greatly from country to country and even from time to time. Extremely comprehensive information about new stamps is available from some countries well before the stamps are released. By contrast some countries do not provide information about stamps or release dates. Most countries, however, fall between these extremes. A country may provide denominations or subjects of stamps from upcoming issues that are not issued as planned. Sometimes, philatelic agencies, those private firms hired to represent countries, add these later-issued items to sets well after the formal release date. This time period can range from weeks to years. If these items were officially released by the country, they will be added to the appropriate spot in the set. In many cases, the specific release date of a stamp or set of stamps may never be known.

**Overprints** — The color of an overprint is always noted if it is other than black. Where more than one color of ink has been used on overprints of a single set, the color used is noted. Early overprint and surcharge illustrations were altered to prevent their use by forgers.

**Personalized Stamps** — Since 1999, the special service of personalizing stamp vignettes, or labels attached to stamps, has been offered to customers by postal administrations of many countries. Sheets of these stamps are sold, singly or in quantity, only through special orders made by mail, in person, or through a sale on a computer website with the postal administrations or their agents for which an extra fee is charged, though some countries offer to collectors at face value personalized stamps having generic images in the vignettes or on the attached labels. It is impossible for any catalogue to know what images have been chosen by customers. Images can be 1) owned or created by the customer, 2) a generic image, or 3) an image pulled from a library of stock images on the stamp creation website. It is also impossible to know the quantity printed for any stamp having a particular image. So from a valuing standpoint, any image is equivalent to any other image for any personalized stamp having the same catalogue number. Illustrations of personalized stamps in the catalogue are not always those of stamps having generic images.

Personalized items are listed with some exceptions. These include:

1. Stamps or sheets that have attached labels that the customer cannot personalize, but which are nonetheless marketed as "personalized," and are sold for far more than the franking value.
2. Stamps or sheets that can be personalized by the customer, but where a portion of the print run must be ceded to the issuing country for sale to other customers.
3. Stamps or sheets that are created exclusively for a particular commercial client, or clients, including stamps that differ from any similar stamp that has been made available to the public.
4. Stamps or sheets that are deliberately conceived by the issuing authority that have been, or are likely to be, created with an excessive number of different face values, sizes, or other features that are changeable.
5. Stamps or sheets that are created by postal administrations using the same system of stamp personalization that has been put in place for use by the public that are printed in limited quantities and sold above face value.
6. Stamps or sheets that are created by licensees not directly affiliated or controlled by a postal administration.

Excluded items may or may not be footnoted.

**Se-tenants** — Connected stamps of differing features (se-tenants) will be listed in the format most commonly collected. This includes pairs, blocks or larger multiples. Se-tenant units are not always symmetrical. An example is Australia Scott 508, which is a block of seven stamps. If the stamps are primarily collected as a unit, the major number may be assigned to the multiple, with minors going to each component stamp. In cases where continuous-design or other unit se-tenants will receive significant postal use, each stamp is given a major Scott number listing. This includes issues from the United States, Canada, Germany and Great Britain, for example.

# Understanding the Listings

On the opposite page is an enlarged "typical" listing from this catalogue. Below are detailed explanations of each of the highlighted parts of the listing.

**1 Scott number** — Scott catalogue numbers are used to identify specific items when buying, selling or trading stamps. Each listed postage stamp from every country has a unique Scott catalogue number. Therefore, Germany Scott 99, for example, can only refer to a single stamp. Although the Scott catalogue usually lists stamps in chronological order by date of issue, there are exceptions. When a country has issued a set of stamps over a period of time, those stamps within the set are kept together without regard to date of issue. This follows the normal collecting approach of keeping stamps in their natural sets.

When a country issues a set of stamps over a period of time, a group of consecutive catalogue numbers is reserved for the stamps in that set, as issued. If that group of numbers proves to be too few, capital-letter suffixes, such as "A" or "B," may be added to existing numbers to create enough catalogue numbers to cover all items in the set. A capital-letter suffix indicates a major Scott catalogue number listing. Scott generally uses a suffix letter only once. Therefore, a catalogue number listing with a capital-letter suffix will seldom be found with the same letter (lower case) used as a minor-letter listing. If there is a Scott 16A in a set, for example, there will seldom be a Scott 16a. However, a minor-letter "a" listing may be added to a major number containing an "A" suffix (Scott 16Aa, for example).

Suffix letters are cumulative. A minor "b" variety of Scott 16A would be Scott 16Ab, not Scott 16b.

There are times when a reserved block of Scott catalogue numbers is too large for a set, leaving some numbers unused. Such gaps in the numbering sequence also occur when the catalogue editors move an item's listing elsewhere or have removed it entirely from the catalogue. Scott does not attempt to account for every possible number, but rather attempts to assure that each stamp is assigned its own number.

Scott numbers designating regular postage normally are only numerals. Scott numbers for other types of stamps, such as air post, semi-postal, postal tax, postage due, occupation and others have a prefix consisting of one or more capital letters or a combination of numerals and capital letters.

**2 Illustration number** — Illustration or design-type numbers are used to identify each catalogue illustration. For most sets, the lowest face-value stamp is shown. It then serves as an example of the basic design approach for other stamps not illustrated. Where more than one stamp use the same illustration number, but have differences in design, the design paragraph or the description line clearly indicates the design on each stamp not illustrated. Where there are both vertical and horizontal designs in a set, a single illustration may be used, with the exceptions noted in the design paragraph or description line.

When an illustration is followed by a lower-case letter in parentheses, such as "A2(b)," the trailing letter indicates which overprint or surcharge illustration applies.

Illustrations normally are 70 percent of the original size of the stamp. Oversized stamps, blocks and souvenir sheets are reduced even more. Overprints and surcharges are shown at 100 percent of their original size if shown alone, but are 70 percent of original size if shown on stamps. In some cases, the illustration will be placed above the set, between listings or omitted completely. Overprint and surcharge illustrations are not placed in this catalogue for purposes of expertizing stamps.

**3 Paper color** — The color of a stamp's paper is noted in italic type when the paper used is not white.

**4 Listing styles** — There are two principal types of catalogue listings: major and minor.

Major listings are in a larger type style than minor listings. The catalogue number is a numeral that can be found with or without a capital-letter suffix, and with or without a prefix.

Minor listings are in a smaller type style and have a small-letter suffix or (if the listing immediately follows that of the major number) may show only the letter. These listings identify a variety of the major item. Examples include perforation and shade differences, multiples (some souvenir sheets, booklet panes and se-tenant combinations), and singles of multiples.

Examples of major number listings include 16, 28A, B97, C13A, 10N5, and 10N6A. Examples of minor numbers are 16a and C13Ab.

**5 Basic information about a stamp or set** — Introducing each stamp issue is a small section (usually a line listing) of basic information about a stamp or set. This section normally includes the date of issue, method of printing, perforation, watermark and, sometimes, some additional information of note. *Printing method, perforation and watermark apply to the following sets until a change is noted.* Stamps created by overprinting or surcharging previous issues are assumed to have the same perforation, watermark, printing method and other production characteristics as the original. Dates of issue are as precise as Scott is able to confirm and often reflect the dates on first-day covers, rather than the actual date of release.

**6 Denomination** — This normally refers to the face value of the stamp; that is, the cost of the unused stamp at the post office at the time of issue. When a denomination is shown in parentheses, it does not appear on the stamp. This includes the non-denominated stamps of the United States, Brazil and Great Britain, for example.

**7 Color or other description** — This area provides information to solidify identification of a stamp. In many recent cases, a description of the stamp design appears in this space, rather than a listing of colors.

**8 Year of issue** — In stamp sets that have been released in a period that spans more than a year, the number shown in parentheses is the year that stamp first appeared. Stamps without a date appeared during the first year of the issue. Dates are not always given for minor varieties.

**9 Value unused and Value used** — The Scott catalogue values are based on stamps that are in a grade of Very Fine unless stated otherwise. Unused values refer to items that have not seen postal, revenue or any other duty for which they were intended. Pre-1900 unused stamps that were issued with gum must have at least most of their original gum. Later issues are assumed to have full original gum. From breakpoints specified in most countries' listings, stamps are valued as never hinged. Stamps issued without gum are noted. Modern issues with PVA or other synthetic adhesives may appear ungummed. Unused self-adhesive stamps are valued as appearing undisturbed on their original backing paper. Values for used self-adhesive stamps are for examples either on piece or off piece. For a more detailed explanation of these values, please see the "Catalogue Value," "Condition" and "Understanding Valuing Notations" sections elsewhere in this introduction.

In some cases, where used stamps are more valuable than unused stamps, the value is for an example with a contemporaneous cancel, rather than a modern cancel or a smudge or other unclear marking. For those stamps that were released for postal and fiscal purposes, the used value represents a postally used stamp. Stamps with revenue cancels generally sell for less.

Stamps separated from a complete se-tenant multiple usually will be worth less than a pro-rated portion of the se-tenant multiple, and stamps lacking the attached labels that are noted in the listings will be worth less than the values shown.

**10 Changes in basic set information** — Bold type is used to show any changes in the basic data given for a set of stamps. These basic data categories include perforation gauge measurement, paper type, printing method and watermark.

**11 Total value of a set** — The total value of sets of three or more stamps issued after 1900 are shown. The set line also notes the range of Scott numbers and total number of stamps included in the grouping. The actual value of a set consisting predominantly of stamps having the minimum value of 25 cents may be less than the total value shown. Similarly, the actual value or catalogue value of se-tenant pairs or of blocks consisting of stamps having the minimum value of 25 cents may be less than the catalogue values of the component parts.

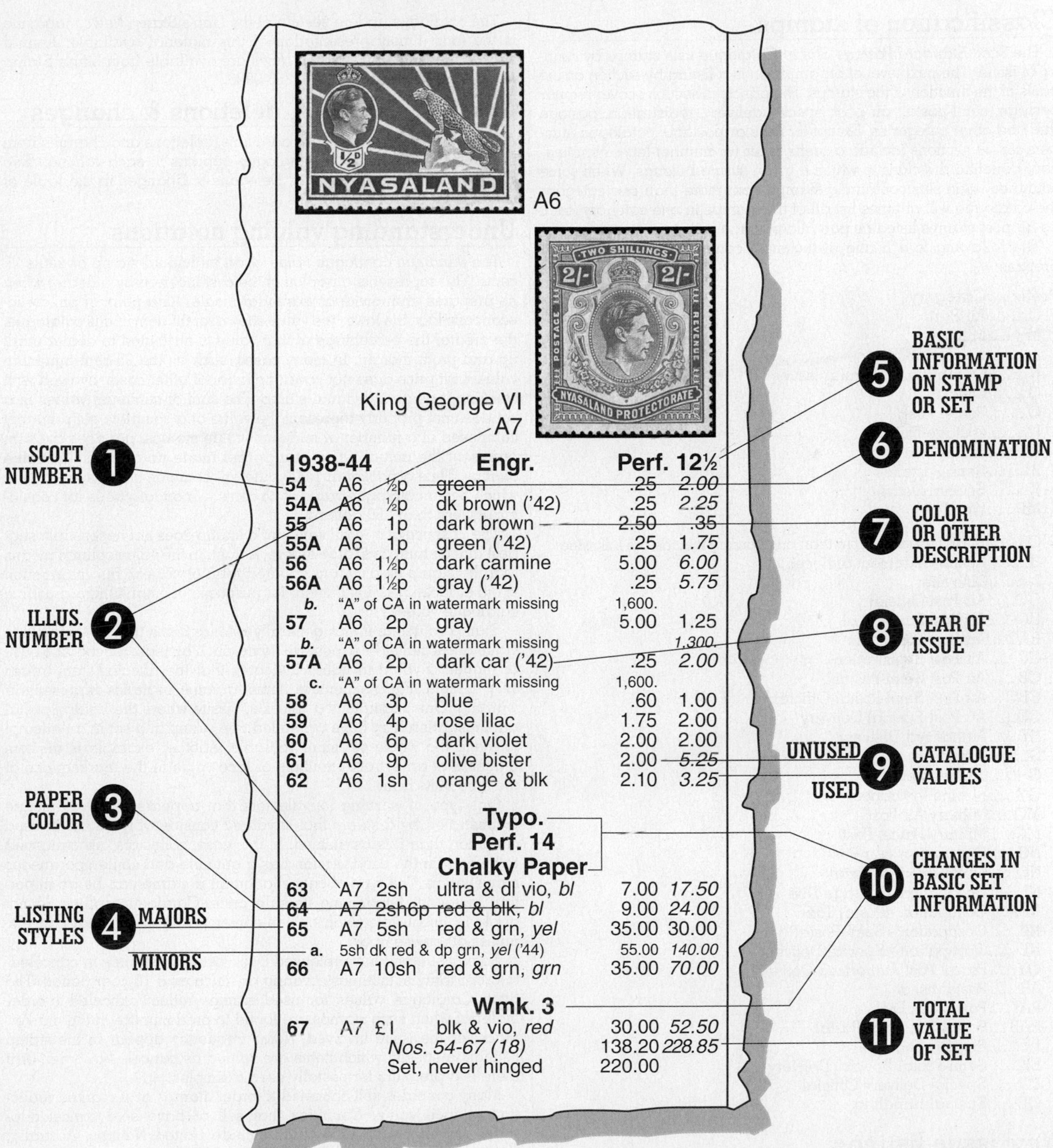


**1938-44 Engr. Perf. 12½**

| | | | | | |
|---|---|---|---|---|---|
| **54** | A6 | ½p | green | .25 | *2.00* |
| **54A** | A6 | ½p | dk brown ('42) | .25 | *2.25* |
| **55** | A6 | 1p | dark brown | 2.50 | .35 |
| **55A** | A6 | 1p | green ('42) | .25 | *1.75* |
| **56** | A6 | 1½p | dark carmine | 5.00 | *6.00* |
| **56A** | A6 | 1½p | gray ('42) | .25 | *5.75* |
| *b.* | | | "A" of CA in watermark missing | 1,600. | |
| **57** | A6 | 2p | gray | 5.00 | 1.25 |
| *b.* | | | "A" of CA in watermark missing | | *1,300.* |
| **57A** | A6 | 2p | dark car ('42) | .25 | *2.00* |
| c. | | | "A" of CA in watermark missing | 1,600. | |
| **58** | A6 | 3p | blue | .60 | 1.00 |
| **59** | A6 | 4p | rose lilac | 1.75 | 2.00 |
| **60** | A6 | 6p | dark violet | 2.00 | 2.00 |
| **61** | A6 | 9p | olive bister | 2.00 | *5.25* |
| **62** | A6 | 1sh | orange & blk | 2.10 | *3.25* |

**Typo.**
**Perf. 14**
**Chalky Paper**

| | | | | | |
|---|---|---|---|---|---|
| **63** | A7 | 2sh | ultra & dl vio, *bl* | 7.00 | *17.50* |
| **64** | A7 | 2sh6p | red & blk, *bl* | 9.00 | *24.00* |
| **65** | A7 | 5sh | red & grn, *yel* | 35.00 | 30.00 |
| a. | | | 5sh dk red & dp grn, *yel* ('44) | 55.00 | *140.00* |
| **66** | A7 | 10sh | red & grn, *grn* | 35.00 | *70.00* |

**Wmk. 3**

| | | | | | |
|---|---|---|---|---|---|
| **67** | A7 | £1 | blk & vio, *red* | 30.00 | *52.50* |
| | | | *Nos. 54-67 (18)* | 138.20 | *228.85* |
| | | | Set, never hinged | 220.00 | |

# Special Notices

## Classification of stamps

The *Scott Standard Postage Stamp Catalogue* lists stamps by country of issue. The next level of organization is a listing by section on the basis of the function of the stamps. The principal sections cover regular postage, semi-postal, air post, special delivery, registration, postage due and other categories. Except for regular postage, catalogue numbers for all sections include a prefix letter (or number-letter combination) denoting the class to which a given stamp belongs. When some countries issue sets containing stamps from more than one category, the catalogue will at times list all of the stamps in one category (such as air post stamps listed as part of a postage set).

The following is a listing of the most commonly used catalogue prefixes.

**Prefix .... Category**
C......... Air Post
M........ Military
P......... Newspaper
N......... Occupation - Regular Issues
O ........ Official
Q ........ Parcel Post
J.......... Postage Due
RA ...... Postal Tax
B ......... Semi-Postal
E......... Special Delivery
MR...... War Tax

Other prefixes used by more than one country include the following:
H......... Acknowledgment of Receipt
I.......... Late Fee
CO...... Air Post Official
CQ...... Air Post Parcel Post
RAC.... Air Post Postal Tax
CF ...... Air Post Registration
CB ...... Air Post Semi-Postal
CBO ... Air Post Semi-Postal Official
CE ...... Air Post Special Delivery
EY....... Authorized Delivery
S ......... Franchise
G ........ Insured Letter
GY...... Marine Insurance
MC ..... Military Air Post
MQ ..... Military Parcel Post
NC...... Occupation - Air Post
NO...... Occupation - Official
NJ........ Occupation - Postage Due
NRA.... Occupation - Postal Tax
NB ...... Occupation - Semi-Postal
NE ...... Occupation - Special Delivery
QY...... Parcel Post Authorized Delivery
AR ...... Postal-fiscal
RAJ ..... Postal Tax Due
RAB .... Postal Tax Semi-Postal
F ......... Registration
EB....... Semi-Postal Special Delivery
EO...... Special Delivery Official
QE...... Special Handling

## New issue listings

Updates to this catalogue appear each month in the *Linn's Stamp News* monthly magazine. Included in this update are additions to the listings of countries found in the *Scott Standard Postage Stamp Catalogue* and the *Specialized Catalogue of United States Stamps and Covers*, as well as corrections and updates to current editions of this catalogue.

From time to time there will be changes in the final listings of stamps from the *Linn's Stamp News* magazine to the next edition of the catalogue. This occurs as more information about certain stamps or sets becomes available.

The catalogue update section of the *Linn's Stamp News* magazine is the most timely presentation of this material available. Annual subscriptions to *Linn's Stamp News* are available from Linn's Stamp News, Box 926, Sidney, OH 45365-0926.

## Number additions, deletions & changes

A listing of catalogue number additions, deletions and changes from the previous edition of the catalogue appears in each volume. See Catalogue Number Additions, Deletions & Changes in the table of contents for the location of this list.

## Understanding valuing notations

The *minimum catalogue value* of an individual stamp or set is 25 cents. This represents a portion of the cost incurred by a dealer when he prepares an individual stamp for resale. As a point of philatelic-economic fact, the lower the value shown for an item in this catalogue, the greater the percentage of that value is attributed to dealer mark up and profit margin. In many cases, such as the 25-cent minimum value, that price does not cover the labor or other costs involved with stocking it as an individual stamp. The sum of minimum values in a set does not properly represent the value of a complete set primarily composed of a number of minimum-value stamps, nor does the sum represent the actual value of a packet made up of minimum-value stamps. Thus a packet of 1,000 different common stamps — each of which has a catalogue value of 25 cents — normally sells for considerably less than 250 dollars!

The *absence of a retail value* for a stamp does not necessarily suggest that a stamp is scarce or rare. A dash in the value column means that the stamp is known in a stated form or variety, but information is either lacking or insufficient for purposes of establishing a usable catalogue value.

Stamp values in *italics* generally refer to items that are difficult to value accurately. For expensive items, such as those priced at $1,000 or higher, a value in italics indicates that the affected item trades very seldom. For inexpensive items, a value in italics represents a warning. One example is a "blocked" issue where the issuing postal administration may have controlled one stamp in a set in an attempt to make the whole set more valuable. Another example is an item that sold at an extreme multiple of face value in the marketplace at the time of its issue.

One type of warning to collectors that appears in the catalogue is illustrated by a stamp that is valued considerably higher in used condition than it is as unused. In this case, collectors are cautioned to be certain the used version has a genuine and contemporaneous cancellation. The type of cancellation on a stamp can be an important factor in determining its sale price. Catalogue values do not apply to fiscal, telegraph or non-contemporaneous postal cancels, unless otherwise noted.

Some countries have released back issues of stamps in canceled-to-order form, sometimes covering as much as a 10-year period. The Scott Catalogue values for used stamps reflect canceled-to-order material when such stamps are found to predominate in the marketplace for the issue involved. Notes frequently appear in the stamp listings to specify which items are valued as canceled-to-order, or if there is a premium for postally used examples.

Many countries sell canceled-to-order stamps at a marked reduction of face value. Countries that sell or have sold canceled-to-order stamps at *full* face value include United Nations, Australia, Netherlands, France and Switzerland. It may be almost impossible to identify such stamps if the gum has been removed, because official government canceling devices are used. Postally used examples of these items on cover, however, are usually worth more than the canceled-to-order stamps with original gum.

## Abbreviations

Scott uses a consistent set of abbreviations throughout this catalogue to conserve space, while still providing necessary information.

## COLOR ABBREVIATIONS

amb. amber
anil.. aniline
ap.... apple
aqua aquamarine
az .... azure
bis ... bister
bl ..... blue
bld... blood
blk ... black
bril... brilliant
brn... brown
brnsh brownish
brnz. bronze
brt.... bright
brnt . burnt
car... carmine
cer ... cerise
chlky chalky
chamchamois
chnt . chestnut
choc chocolate
chr... chrome
cit .... citron
cl...... claret
cob .. cobalt
cop .. copper
crim. crimson
cr ..... cream
dk .... dark
dl ..... dull
dp .... deep
db .... drab
emer emerald
gldn. golden
gryshgrayish
grn... green
grnsh greenish
hel ... heliotrope
hn .... henna
ind ... indigo
int .... intense
lav ... lavender
lem .. lemon
lil ..... lilac
lt ...... light
mag. magenta
man. manila
mar.. maroon
mv ... mauve
multi multicolored
mlky milky
myr .. myrtle
ol ..... olive
olvn . olivine
org... orange
pck .. peacock
pnksh pinkish
Prus. Prussian
pur... purple
redsh reddish
res ... reseda
ros ... rosine
ryl .... royal
sal .... salmon
saph sapphire
scar . scarlet
sep .. sepia
sien . sienna
sil..... silver
sl....... slate
stl ..... steel
turq.. turquoise
ultra ultramarine
Ven .. Venetian
ver ... vermilion
vio ... violet
yel ... yellow
yelsh yellowish

When no color is given for an overprint or surcharge, black is the color used. Abbreviations for colors used for overprints and surcharges include: "(B)" or "(Blk)," black; "(Bl)," blue; "(R)," red; and "(G)," green.

Additional abbreviations in this catalogue are shown below:

Adm. ............Administration
AFL...............American Federation of Labor
Anniv. ...........Anniversary
APS ..............American Philatelic Society
Assoc. ..........Association
ASSR. ..........Autonomous Soviet Socialist Republic
b. ..................Born
BEP...............Bureau of Engraving and Printing
Bicent. ..........Bicentennial
Bklt. .............Booklet
Brit................British
btwn. ............Between
Bur................Bureau
c. or ca.........Circa
Cat. ..............Catalogue
Cent. ............Centennial, century, centenary
CIO ...............Congress of Industrial Organizations
Conf. ............Conference
Cong.............Congress
Cpl. ..............Corporal
CTO ..............Canceled to order
d. ..................Died
Dbl. ..............Double
EDU...............Earliest documented use
Engr. ............Engraved
Exhib............Exhibition
Expo.............Exposition
Fed. ..............Federation
GB .................Great Britain
Gen. ..............General
GPO ...............General post office
Horiz. ............Horizontal
Imperf. ..........Imperforate
Impt...............Imprint
Intl.................International
Invtd.............Inverted
L.....................Left
Lieut., lt.........Lieutenant
Litho..............Lithographed
LL ...................Lower left
LR...................Lower right
mm..................Millimeter
Ms...................Manuscript
Natl.................National
No...................Number
NY ...................New York
NYC .................New York City
Ovpt. ...............Overprint
Ovptd..............Overprinted
P ......................Plate number
Perf...................Perforated, perforation
Phil...................Philatelic
Photo...............Photogravure
PO ....................Post office
Pr......................Pair
P.R....................Puerto Rico
Prec..................Precancel, precanceled
Pres. .................President
PTT ...................Post, Telephone and Telegraph
R .......................Right
Rio....................Rio de Janeiro
Sgt....................Sergeant
Soc. ..................Society
Souv. ................Souvenir
SSR...................Soviet Socialist Republic, see ASSR
St.......................Saint, street
Surch. ...............Surcharge
Typo. ................Typographed
UL.....................Upper left
Unwmkd. ..........Unwatermarked
UPU ..................Universal Postal Union
UR ....................Upper Right
US ....................United States
USPOD .............United States Post Office Department
USSR ................Union of Soviet Socialist Republics
Vert...................Vertical
VP .....................Vice president
Wmk..................Watermark
Wmkd. ..............Watermarked
WWI ..................World War I
WWII .................World War II

## Examination

Amos Media Co. will not comment upon the genuineness, grade or condition of stamps, because of the time and responsibility involved. Rather, there are several expertizing groups that undertake this work for both collectors and dealers. Neither will Amos Media Co. appraise or identify philatelic material. The company cannot take responsibility for unsolicited stamps or covers sent by individuals.

All letters, E-mails, etc. are read attentively, but they are not always answered due to time considerations.

## How to order from your dealer

When ordering stamps from a dealer, it is not necessary to write the full description of a stamp as listed in this catalogue. All you need is the name of the country, the Scott catalogue number and whether the desired item is unused or used. For example, "Japan Scott 422 unused" is sufficient to identify the unused stamp of Japan listed as "422 A206 5y brown."

# Basic Stamp Information

A stamp collector's knowledge of the combined elements that make a given stamp issue unique determines his or her ability to identify stamps. These elements include paper, watermark, method of separation, printing, design and gum. On the following pages each of these important areas is briefly described.

## Paper

Paper is an organic material composed of a compacted weave of cellulose fibers and generally formed into sheets. Paper used to print stamps may be manufactured in sheets, or it may have been part of a large roll (called a web) before being cut to size. The fibers most often used to create paper on which stamps are printed include bark, wood, straw and certain grasses. In many cases, linen or cotton rags have been added for greater strength and durability. Grinding, bleaching, cooking and rinsing these raw fibers reduces them to a slushy pulp, referred to by paper makers as "stuff." Sizing and, sometimes, coloring matter is added to the pulp to make different types of finished paper.

After the stuff is prepared, it is poured onto sieve-like frames that allow the water to run off, while retaining the matted pulp. As fibers fall onto the screen and are held by gravity, they form a natural weave that will later hold the paper together. If the screen has metal bits that are formed into letters or images attached, it leaves slightly thinned areas on the paper. These are called watermarks.

When the stuff is almost dry, it is passed under pressure through smooth or engraved rollers - dandy rolls - or placed between cloth in a press to be flattened and dried.

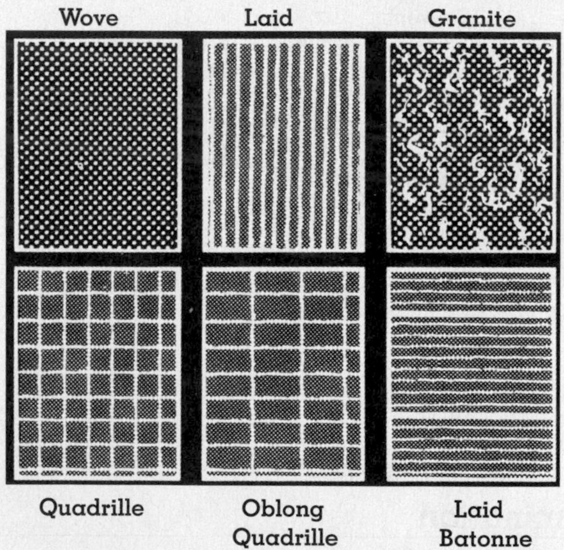


Stamp paper falls broadly into two types: wove and laid. The nature of the surface of the frame onto which the pulp is first deposited causes the differences in appearance between the two. If the surface is smooth and even, the paper will be of fairly uniform texture throughout. This is known as *wove paper*. Early papermaking machines poured the pulp onto a continuously circulating web of felt, but modern machines feed the pulp onto a cloth-like screen made of closely interwoven fine wires. This paper, when held to a light, will show little dots or points very close together. The proper name for this is "wire wove," but the type is still considered wove. Any U.S. or British stamp printed after 1880 will serve as an example of wire wove paper.

Closely spaced parallel wires, with cross wires at wider intervals, make up the frames used for what is known as *laid paper*. A greater thickness of the pulp will settle between the wires. The paper, when held to a light, will show alternate light and dark lines. The spacing and the thickness of the lines may vary, but on any one sheet of paper they are all alike. See Russia Scott 31-38 for examples of laid paper.

*Batonne*, from the French word meaning "a staff," is a term used if the lines in the paper are spaced quite far apart, like the printed ruling on a writing tablet. Batonne paper may be either wove or laid. If laid, fine laid lines can be seen between the batons.

*Quadrille* is the term used when the lines in the paper form little squares. *Oblong quadrille* is the term used when rectangles, rather than squares, are formed. Grid patterns vary from distinct to extremely faint. See Mexico-Guadalajara Scott 35-37 for examples of oblong quadrille paper.

Paper also is classified as thick or thin, hard or soft, and by color. Such colors may include yellowish, greenish, bluish and reddish.

Brief explanations of other types of paper used for printing stamps, as well as examples, follow.

**Colored** — Colored paper is created by the addition of dye in the paper-making process. Such colors may include shades of yellow, green, blue and red. *Surface-colored papers*, most commonly used for British colonial issues in 1913-14, are created when coloring is added only to the surface during the finishing process. Stamps printed on surface-colored paper have white or uncolored backs, while true colored papers are colored through. See Jamaica Scott 71-73.

**Pelure** — Pelure paper is a very thin, hard and often brittle paper that is sometimes bluish or grayish in appearance. See Serbia Scott 169-170.

**Native** — This is a term applied to handmade papers used to produce some of the early stamps of the Indian states. Stamps printed on native paper may be expected to display various natural inclusions that are normal and do not negatively affect value. Japanese paper, originally made of mulberry fibers and rice flour, is part of this group. See Japan Scott 1-18.

**Manila** — This type of paper is often used to make stamped envelopes and wrappers. It is a coarse-textured stock, usually smooth on one side and rough on the other. A variety of colors of manila paper exist, but the most common range is yellowish-brown.

**Silk** — Introduced by the British in 1847 as a safeguard against counterfeiting, silk paper contains bits of colored silk thread scattered throughout. The density of these fibers varies greatly and can include as few as one fiber per stamp or hundreds. U.S. revenue Scott R152 is a good example of an easy-to-identify silk paper stamp.

Silk-thread paper has uninterrupted threads of colored silk arranged so that one or more threads run through the stamp or postal stationery. See Great Britain Scott 5-6 and Switzerland Scott 14-19.

**Granite** — Filled with minute cloth or colored paper fibers of various colors and lengths, granite paper should not be confused with either type of silk paper. Austria Scott 172-175 and a number of Swiss stamps are examples of granite paper.

**Chalky** — A chalk-like substance coats the surface of chalky paper to discourage the cleaning and reuse of canceled stamps, as well as to provide a smoother, more acceptable printing surface. Because the designs of stamps printed on chalky paper are imprinted on what is often a water-soluble coating, any attempt to remove a cancellation will destroy the stamp. *Do not soak these stamps in any fluid.* To remove a stamp printed on chalky paper from an envelope, wet the paper from underneath the stamp until the gum dissolves enough to release the stamp from the paper. See St. Kitts-Nevis Scott 89-90 for examples of stamps printed on this type of chalky paper.

**India** — Another name for this paper, originally introduced from China about 1750, is "China Paper." It is a thin, opaque paper often used for plate and die proofs by many countries.

**Double** — In philately, the term double paper has two distinct meanings. The first is a two-ply paper, usually a combination of a thick and a thin sheet, joined during manufacture. This type was used experimentally as a means to discourage the reuse of stamps.

The design is printed on the thin paper. Any attempt to remove a cancellation would destroy the design. U.S. Scott 158 and other Banknote-era stamps exist on this form of double paper.

The second type of double paper occurs on a rotary press, when the end of one paper roll, or web, is affixed to the next roll to save time feeding the paper through the press. Stamp designs are printed over the joined paper and, if overlooked by inspectors, may get into post office stocks.

**Goldbeater's Skin** — This type of paper was used for the 1866 issue of Prussia, and was a tough, translucent paper. The design was printed in reverse on the back of the stamp, and the gum applied over the printing. It is impossible to remove stamps printed on this type of paper from the paper to which they are affixed without destroying the design.

**Ribbed** — Ribbed paper has an uneven, corrugated surface made by passing the paper through ridged rollers. This type exists on some copies of U.S. Scott 156-165.

Various other substances, or substrates, have been used for stamp manufacture, including wood, aluminum, copper, silver and gold foil, plastic, and silk and cotton fabrics.

## Watermarks

Watermarks are an integral part of some papers. They are formed in the process of paper manufacture. Watermarks consist of small designs, formed of wire or cut from metal and soldered to the surface of the mold or, sometimes, on the dandy roll. The designs may be in the form of crowns, stars, anchors, letters or other characters or symbols. These pieces of metal - known in the paper-making industry as "bits" - impress a design into the paper. The design sometimes may be seen by holding the stamp to the light. Some are more easily seen with a watermark detector. This important tool is a small black tray into which a stamp is placed face down and dampened with a fast-evaporating watermark detection fluid that brings up the watermark image in the form of dark lines against a lighter background. These dark lines are the thinner areas of the paper known as the watermark. Some watermarks are extremely difficult to locate, due to either a faint impression, watermark location or the color of the stamp. There also are electric watermark detectors that come with plastic filter disks of various colors. The disks neutralize the color of the stamp, permitting the watermark to be seen more easily.

**Multiple watermarks of Crown Agents and Burma**

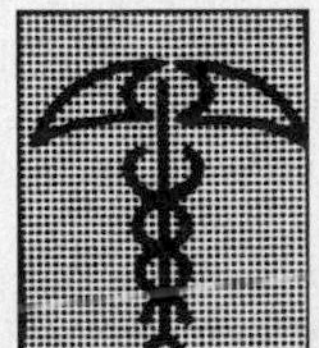

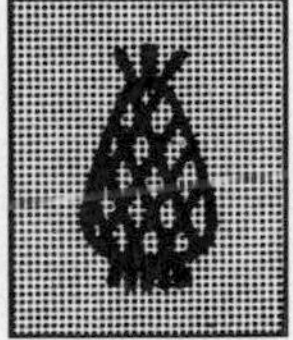

**Watermarks of Uruguay, Vatican City and Jamaica**

**WARNING: Some inks used in the photogravure process dissolve in watermark fluids (Please see the section on Soluble Printing Inks).** Also, see "chalky paper."

Watermarks may be found normal, reversed, inverted, reversed and inverted, sideways or diagonal, as seen from the back of the stamp. The relationship of watermark to stamp design depends on the position of the printing plates or how paper is fed through the press. On machine-made paper, watermarks normally are read from right to left. The design is repeated closely throughout the sheet in a "multiple-watermark design." In a "sheet watermark," the design appears only once on the sheet, but extends over many stamps. Individual stamps may carry only a small fraction or none of the watermark.

"Marginal watermarks" occur in the margins of sheets or panes of stamps. They occur on the outside border of paper (ostensibly outside the area where stamps are to be printed). A large row of letters may spell the name of the country or the manufacturer of the paper, or a border of lines may appear. Careless press feeding may cause parts of these letters and/or lines to show on stamps of the outer row of a pane.

## Soluble Printing Inks

**WARNING:** Most stamp colors are permanent; that is, they are not seriously affected by short-term exposure to light or water. Many colors, especially of modern inks, fade from excessive exposure to light. There are stamps printed with inks that dissolve easily in water or in fluids used to detect watermarks. Use of these inks was intentional to prevent the removal of cancellations. Water affects all aniline inks, those on so-called safety paper and some photogravure printings - all such inks are known as fugitive colors. *Removal from paper of such stamps requires care and alternatives to traditional soaking.*

## Separation

"Separation" is the general term used to describe methods used to separate stamps. The three standard forms currently in use are perforating, rouletting and die-cutting. These methods are done during the stamp production process, after printing. Sometimes these methods are done on-press or sometimes as a separate step. The earliest issues, such as the 1840 Penny Black of Great Britain (Scott 1), did not have any means provided for separation. It was expected the stamps would be cut apart with scissors or folded and torn. These are examples of imperforate stamps. Many stamps were first issued in imperforate formats and were later issued with perforations. Therefore, care must be observed in buying single imperforate stamps to be certain they were issued imperforate and are not perforated copies that have been altered by having the perforations trimmed away. Stamps issued imperforate usually are valued as singles. However, imperforate varieties of normally perforated stamps should be collected in pairs or larger pieces as indisputable evidence of their imperforate character.

### PERFORATION

The chief style of separation of stamps, and the one that is in almost universal use today, is perforating. By this process, paper between the stamps is cut away in a line of holes, usually round, leaving little bridges of paper between the stamps to hold them together. Some types of perforation, such as hyphen-hole perfs, can be confused with roulettes, but a close visual inspection reveals that paper has been removed. The little perforation bridges, which project from the stamp when it is torn from the pane, are called the teeth of the perforation.

As the size of the perforation is sometimes the only way to differentiate between two otherwise identical stamps, it is necessary to be able to accurately measure and describe them. This is done with a perforation gauge, usually a ruler-like device that has dots or graduated lines to show how many perforations may be counted in the space of two centimeters. Two centimeters is the space universally adopted in which to measure perforations.

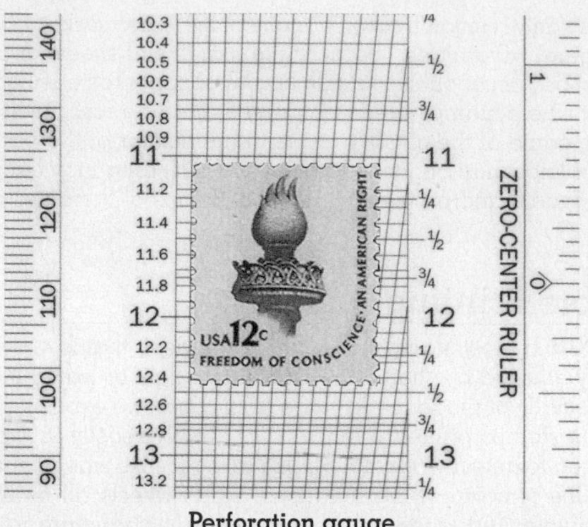

Perforation gauge

To measure a stamp, run it along the gauge until the dots on it fit exactly into the perforations of the stamp. If you are using a graduated-line perforation gauge, simply slide the stamp along the surface until the lines on the gauge perfectly project from the center of the bridges or holes. The number to the side of the line of dots or lines that fit the stamp's perforation is the measurement. For example, an "11" means that 11 perforations fit between two centimeters. The description of the stamp therefore is "perf. 11." If the gauge of the perforations on the top and bottom of a stamp differs from that on the sides, the result is what is known as *compound perforations.* In measuring compound perforations, the gauge at top and bottom is always given first, then the sides. Thus, a stamp that measures 11 at top and bottom and 10½ at the sides is "perf. 11 x 10½." See U.S. Scott 632-642 for examples of compound perforations.

Stamps also are known with perforations different on three or all four sides. Descriptions of such items are clockwise, beginning with the top of the stamp.

A perforation with small holes and teeth close together is a "fine perforation." One with large holes and teeth far apart is a "coarse perforation." Holes that are jagged, rather than clean-cut, are "rough perforations." *Blind perforations* are the slight impressions left by the perforating pins if they fail to puncture the paper. Multiples of stamps showing blind perforations may command a slight premium over normally perforated stamps.

The term *syncopated perfs* describes intentional irregularities in the perforations. The earliest form was used by the Netherlands from 1925-33, where holes were omitted to create distinctive patterns. Beginning in 1992, Great Britain has used an oval perforation to help prevent counterfeiting. Several other countries have started using the oval perfs or other syncopated perf patterns.

A new type of perforation, still primarily used for postal stationery, is known as microperfs. Microperfs are tiny perforations (in some cases hundreds of holes per two centimeters) that allows items to be intentionally separated very easily, while not accidentally breaking apart as easily as standard perforations. These are not currently measured or differentiated by size, as are standard perforations.

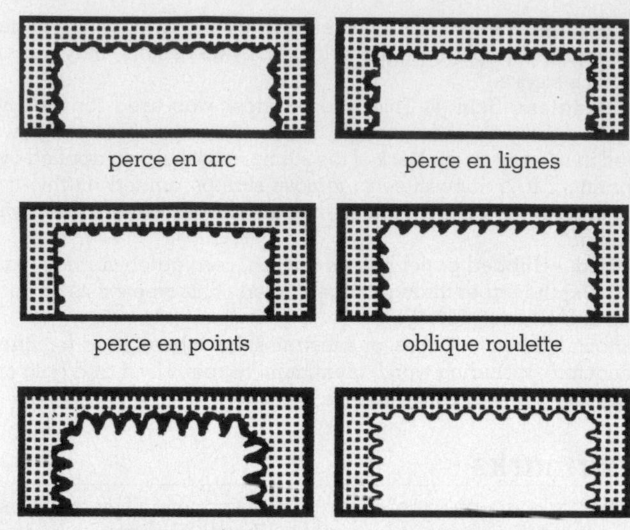


### ROULETTING

In rouletting, the stamp paper is cut partly or wholly through, with no paper removed. In perforating, some paper is removed. Rouletting derives its name from the French roulette, a spur-like wheel. As the wheel is rolled over the paper, each point makes a small cut. The number of cuts made in a two-centimeter space determines the gauge of the roulette, just as the number of perforations in two centimeters determines the gauge of the perforation.

The shape and arrangement of the teeth on the wheels varies. Various roulette types generally carry French names:

*Perce en lignes* - rouletted in lines. The paper receives short, straight cuts in lines. This is the most common type of rouletting. See Mexico Scott 500.

*Perce en points* - pin-rouletted or pin-perfed. This differs from a small perforation because no paper is removed, although round, equidistant holes are pricked through the paper. See Mexico Scott 242-256.

*Perce en arc* and *perce en scie* - pierced in an arc or saw-toothed designs, forming half circles or small triangles. See Hanover (German States) Scott 25-29.

*Perce en serpentin* - serpentine roulettes. The cuts form a serpentine or wavy line. See Brunswick (German States) Scott 13-18.

Once again, no paper is removed by these processes, leaving the stamps easily separated, but closely attached.

### DIE-CUTTING

The third major form of stamp separation is die-cutting. This is a method where a die in the pattern of separation is created that later cuts the stamp paper in a stroke motion. Although some standard stamps bear die-cut perforations, this process is primarily used for self-adhesive postage stamps. Die-cutting can appear in straight lines, such as U.S. Scott 2522, shapes, such as U.S. Scott 1551, or imitating the appearance of perforations, such as New Zealand Scott 935A and 935B.

## Printing Processes

### ENGRAVING (Intaglio, Line-engraving, Etching)

**Master die** — The initial operation in the process of line engraving is making the master die. The die is a small, flat block of softened steel upon which the stamp design is recess engraved in reverse.

Master die

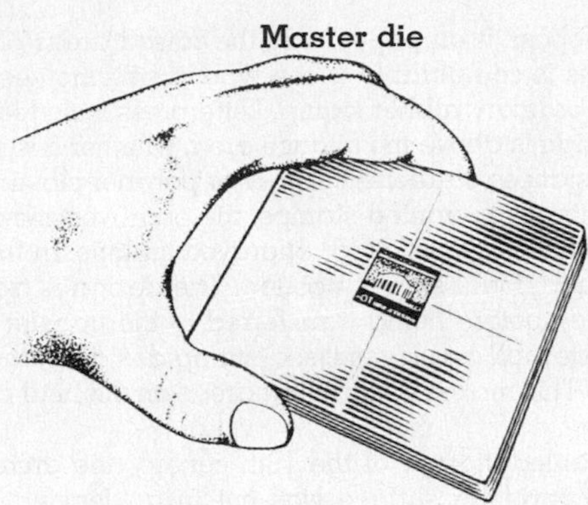

Photographic reduction of the original art is made to the appropriate size. It then serves as a tracing guide for the initial outline of the design. The engraver lightly traces the design on the steel with his graver, then slowly works the design until it is completed. At various points during the engraving process, the engraver hand-inks the die and makes an impression to check his progress. These are known as progressive die proofs. After completion of the engraving, the die is hardened to withstand the stress and pressures of later transfer operations.

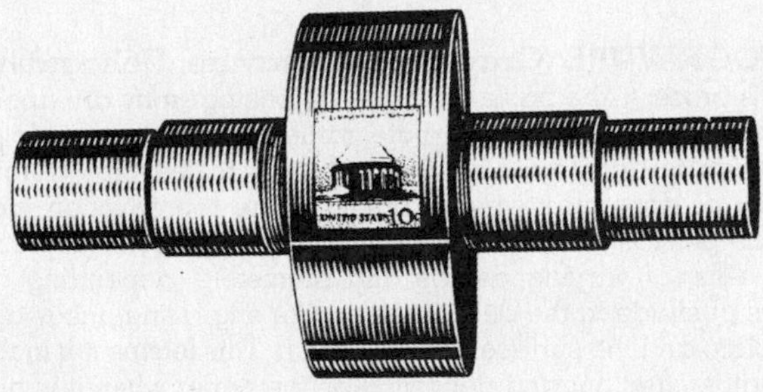

Transfer roll

**Transfer roll** — Next is production of the transfer roll that, as the name implies, is the medium used to transfer the subject from the master die to the printing plate. A blank roll of soft steel, mounted on a mandrel, is placed under the bearers of the transfer press to allow it to roll freely on its axis. The hardened die is placed on the bed of the press and the face of the transfer roll is applied to the die, under pressure. The bed or the roll is then rocked back and forth under increasing pressure, until the soft steel of the roll is forced into every engraved line of the die. The resulting impression on the roll is known as a "relief" or a "relief transfer." The engraved image is now positive in appearance and stands out from the steel. After the required number of reliefs are "rocked in," the soft steel transfer roll is hardened.

Different flaws may occur during the relief process. A defective relief may occur during the rocking in process because of a minute piece of foreign material lodging on the die, or some other cause. Imperfections in the steel of the transfer roll may result in a breaking away of parts of the design. This is known as a relief break, which will show up on finished stamps as small, unprinted areas. If a damaged relief remains in use, it will transfer a repeating defect to the plate. Deliberate alterations of reliefs sometimes occur. "Altered reliefs" designate these changed conditions.

**Plate** — The final step in pre-printing production is the making of the printing plate. A flat piece of soft steel replaces the die on the bed of the transfer press. One of the reliefs on the transfer roll is positioned over this soft steel. Position, or layout, dots determine the correct position on the plate. The dots have been lightly marked on the plate in advance. After the correct position of the relief is determined, the design is rocked in by following the same method used in making the transfer roll. The difference is that this time the image is being transferred from the transfer roll, rather than to it. Once the design is entered on the plate, it appears in reverse and is recessed. There are as many transfers entered on the plate as there are subjects printed on the sheet of stamps. It is during this process that double and shifted transfers occur, as well as re-entries. These are the result of improperly entered images that have not been properly burnished out prior to rocking in a new image.

Modern siderography processes, such as those used by the U.S. Bureau of Engraving and Printing, involve an automated form of rocking designs in on preformed cylindrical printing sleeves. The same process also allows for easier removal and re-entry of worn images right on the sleeve.

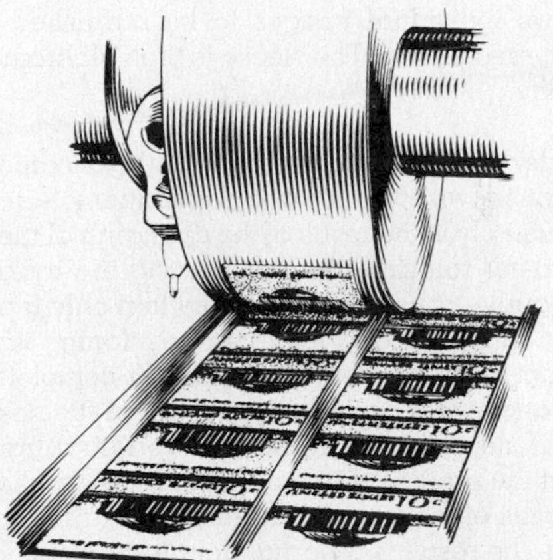

Transferring the design to the plate

Following the entering of the required transfers on the plate, the position dots, layout dots and lines, scratches and other markings generally are burnished out. Added at this time by the siderographer are any required *guide lines, plate numbers* or other *marginal markings*. The plate is then hand-inked and a proof impression is taken. This is known as a plate proof. If the impression is approved, the plate is machined for fitting onto the press, is hardened and sent to the plate vault ready for use.

On press, the plate is inked and the surface is automatically wiped clean, leaving ink only in the recessed lines. Paper is then forced under pressure into the engraved recessed lines, thereby receiving the ink. Thus, the ink lines on engraved stamps are slightly raised, and slight depressions (debossing) occur on the back of the stamp. Prior to the advent of modern high-speed presses and more advanced ink formulations, paper had to be dampened before receiving the ink. This sometimes led to uneven shrinkage by the time the stamps were perforated, resulting in improperly perforated stamps, or misperfs. Newer presses use drier paper, thus both *wet* and *dry printings* exist on some stamps.

**Rotary Press** — Until 1914, only flat plates were used to print engraved stamps. Rotary press printing was introduced in 1914, and slowly spread. Some countries still use flat-plate printing.

After approval of the plate proof, older *rotary press plates* require additional machining. They are curved to fit the press cylinder. "Gripper slots" are cut into the back of each plate to receive the "grippers," which hold the plate securely on the press. The plate is then hardened. Stamps printed from these bent rotary press plates are longer or wider than the same stamps printed from flat-plate presses. The stretching of the plate during the curving process is what causes this distortion.

**Re-entry** — To execute a re-entry on a flat plate, the transfer roll is re-applied to the plate, often at some time after its first use on the press. Worn-out designs can be resharpened by carefully burnishing out the original image and re-entering it from the transfer roll. If the original impression has not been sufficiently removed and the transfer roll is not precisely in line with the remaining impression, the resulting double transfer will make the re-entry obvious. If the registration is true, a re-entry may be difficult or impossible to distinguish. Sometimes a stamp printed from a successful re-entry is identified by having a much sharper and clearer impression than its neighbors. With the advent of rotary presses, post-press re-entries were not possible. After a plate was curved for the rotary press, it was impossible to make a re-entry. This is because the plate had already been bent once (with the design distorted).

However, with the introduction of the previously mentioned modern-style siderography machines, entries are made to the preformed cylindrical printing sleeve. Such sleeves are dechromed and softened. This allows individual images to be burnished out and re-entered on the curved sleeve. The sleeve is then rechromed, resulting in longer press life.

**Double Transfer** — This is a description of the condition of a transfer on a plate that shows evidence of a duplication of all, or a portion of the design. It usually is the result of the changing of the registration between the transfer roll and the plate during the rocking in of the original entry. Double transfers also occur when only a portion of the design has been rocked in and improper positioning is noted. If the worker elected not to burnish out the partial or completed design, a strong double transfer will occur for part or all of the design.

It sometimes is necessary to remove the original transfer from a plate and repeat the process a second time. If the finished re-worked image shows traces of the original impression, attributable to incomplete burnishing, the result is a partial double transfer.

With the modern automatic machines mentioned previously, double transfers are all but impossible to create. Those partially doubled images on stamps printed from such sleeves are more than likely re-entries, rather than true double transfers.

**Re-engraved** — Alterations to a stamp design are sometimes necessary after some stamps have been printed. In some cases, either the original die or the actual printing plate may have its "temper" drawn (softened), and the design will be re-cut. The resulting impressions from such a re-engraved die or plate may differ slightly from the original issue, and are known as "re-engraved." If the alteration was made to the master die, all future printings will be consistently different from the original. If alterations were made to the printing plate, each altered stamp on the plate will be slightly different from each other, allowing specialists to reconstruct a complete printing plate.

**Dropped Transfers** — If an impression from the transfer roll has not been properly placed, a dropped transfer may occur. The final stamp image will appear obviously out of line with its neighbors.

**Short Transfer** — Sometimes a transfer roll is not rocked its entire length when entering a transfer onto a plate. As a result, the finished transfer on the plate fails to show the complete design, and the finished stamp will have an incomplete design printed. This is known as a "short transfer." U.S. Scott No. 8 is a good example of a short transfer.

## TYPOGRAPHY (Letterpress, Surface Printing, Flexography, Dry Offset, High Etch)

Although the word "Typography" is obsolete as a term describing a printing method, it was the accepted term throughout the first century of postage stamps. Therefore, appropriate Scott listings in this catalogue refer to typographed stamps. The current term for this form of printing, however, is "letterpress."

As it relates to the production of postage stamps, letterpress printing is the reverse of engraving. Rather than having recessed areas trap the ink and deposit it on paper, only the raised areas of the design are inked. This is comparable to the type of printing seen by inking and using an ordinary rubber stamp. Letterpress includes all printing where the design is above the surface area, whether it is wood, metal or, in some instances, hardened rubber or polymer plastic.

For most letterpress-printed stamps, the engraved master is made in much the same manner as for engraved stamps. In this instance, however, an additional step is needed. The design is transferred to another surface before being transferred to the transfer roll. In this way, the transfer roll has a recessed stamp design, rather than one done in relief. This makes the printing areas on the final plate raised, or relief areas.

For less-detailed stamps of the 19th century, the area on the die not used as a printing surface was cut away, leaving the surface area raised. The original die was then reproduced by stereotyping or electrotyping. The resulting electrotypes were assembled in the required number and format of the desired sheet of stamps. The plate used in printing the stamps was an electroplate of these assembled electrotypes.

Once the final letterpress plates are created, ink is applied to the raised surface and the pressure of the press transfers the ink impression to the paper. In contrast to engraving, the fine lines of letterpress are impressed on the surface of the stamp, leaving a debossed surface. When viewed from the back (as on a typewritten page), the corresponding line work on the stamp will be raised slightly (embossed) above the surface.

## PHOTOGRAVURE (Gravure, Rotogravure, Heliogravure)

In this process, the basic principles of photography are applied to a chemically sensitized metal plate, rather than photographic paper. The design is transferred photographically to the plate through a halftone, or dot-matrix screen, breaking the reproduction into tiny dots. The plate is treated chemically and the dots form depressions, called cells, of varying depths and diameters, depending on the degrees of shade in the design. Then, like engraving, ink is applied to the plate and the surface is wiped clean. This leaves ink in the tiny cells that is lifted out and deposited on the paper when it is pressed against the plate.

Gravure is most often used for multicolored stamps, generally using the three primary colors (red, yellow and blue) and black. By varying the dot matrix pattern and density of these colors, virtually any color can be reproduced. A typical full-color gravure stamp will be created from four printing cylinders (one for each color). The original multicolored image will have been photographically separated into its component colors.

Modern gravure printing may use computer-generated dot-matrix screens, and modern plates may be of various types including metal-coated plastic. The catalogue designation of Photogravure (or "Photo") covers any of these older and more modern gravure methods of printing.

For examples of the first photogravure stamps printed (1914), see Bavaria Scott 94-114.

## LITHOGRAPHY (Offset Lithography, Stone Lithography, Dilitho, Planography, Collotype)

The principle that oil and water do not mix is the basis for lithography. The stamp design is drawn by hand or transferred from engraving to the surface of a lithographic stone or metal plate in a greasy (oily) substance. This oily substance holds the ink, which will later be transferred to the paper. The stone (or plate) is wet with an acid fluid, causing it to repel the printing ink in all areas not covered by the greasy substance.

Transfer paper is used to transfer the design from the original stone or plate. A series of duplicate transfers are grouped and, in turn, transferred to the final printing plate.

**Photolithography** — The application of photographic processes to lithography. This process allows greater flexibility of design, related to use of halftone screens combined with line work. Unlike photogravure or engraving, this process can allow large, solid areas to be printed.

**Offset** — A refinement of the lithographic process. A rubber-covered blanket cylinder takes the impression from the inked lithographic plate. From the "blanket" the impression is *offset* or transferred to the paper. Greater flexibility and speed are the principal reasons offset printing has largely displaced lithography. The term "lithography" covers both processes, and results are almost identical.

### EMBOSSED (Relief) Printing

Embossing, not considered one of the four main printing types, is a method in which the design first is sunk into the metal of the die. Printing is done against a yielding platen, such as leather or linoleum. The platen is forced into the depression of the die, thus forming the design on the paper in relief. This process is often used for metallic inks.

Embossing may be done without color (see Sardinia Scott 4-6); with color printed around the embossed area (see Great Britain Scott 5 and most U.S. envelopes); and with color in exact registration with the embossed subject (see Canada Scott 656-657).

### HOLOGRAMS

For objects to appear as holograms on stamps, a model exactly the same size as it is to appear on the hologram must be created. Rather than using photographic film to capture the image, holography records an image on a photoresist material. In processing, chemicals eat away at certain exposed areas, leaving a pattern of constructive and destructive interference. When the photoresist is developed, the result is a pattern of uneven ridges that acts as a mold. This mold is then coated with metal, and the resulting form is used to press copies in much the same way phonograph records are produced.

A typical reflective hologram used for stamps consists of a reproduction of the uneven patterns on a plastic film that is applied to a reflective background, usually a silver or gold foil. Light is reflected off the background through the film, making the pattern present on the film visible. Because of the uneven pattern of the film, the viewer will perceive the objects in their proper three-dimensional relationships with appropriate brightness.

The first hologram on a stamp was produced by Austria in 1988 (Scott 1441).

### FOIL APPLICATION

A modern technique of applying color to stamps involves the application of metallic foil to the stamp paper. A pattern of foil is applied to the stamp paper by use of a stamping die. The foil usually is flat, but it may be textured. Canada Scott 1735 has three different foil applications in pearl, bronze and gold. The gold foil was textured using a chemical-etch copper embossing die. The printing of this stamp also involved two-color offset lithography plus embossing.

### THERMOGRAPHY

In the 1990s stamps began to be enhanced with thermographic printing. In this process, a powdered polymer is applied over a sheet that has just been printed. The powder adheres to ink that lacks drying or hardening agents and does not adhere to areas where the ink has these agents. The excess powder is removed and the sheet is briefly heated to melt the powder. The melted powder solidifies after cooling, producing a raised, shiny effect on the stamps. See Scott New Caledonia C239-C240.

### COMBINATION PRINTINGS

Sometimes two or even three printing methods are combined in producing stamps. In these cases, such as Austria Scott 933 or Canada 1735 (described in the preceding paragraph), the multiple-printing technique can be determined by studying the individual characteristics of each printing type. A few stamps, such as Singapore Scott 684-684A, combine as many as three of the four major printing types (lithography, engraving and typography). When this is done it often indicates the incorporation of security devices against counterfeiting.

### INK COLORS

Inks or colored papers used in stamp printing often are of mineral origin, although there are numerous examples of organic-based pigments. As a general rule, organic-based pigments are far more subject to varieties and change than those of mineral-based origin.

The appearance of any given color on a stamp may be affected by many aspects, including printing variations, light, color of paper, aging and chemical alterations.

Numerous printing variations may be observed. Heavier pressure or inking will cause a more intense color, while slight interruptions in the ink feed or lighter impressions will cause a lighter appearance. Stamps printed in the same color by water-based and solvent-based inks can differ significantly in appearance. This affects several stamps in the U.S. Prominent Americans series. Hand-mixed ink formulas (primarily from the 19th century) produced under different conditions (humidity and temperature) account for notable color variations in early printings of the same stamp (see U.S. Scott 248-250, 279B, for example). Different sources of pigment can also result in significant differences in color.

Light exposure and aging are closely related in the way they affect stamp color. Both eventually break down the ink and fade colors, so that a carefully kept stamp may differ significantly in color from an identical copy that has been exposed to light. If stamps are exposed to light either intentionally or accidentally, their colors can be faded or completely changed in some cases.

Papers of different quality and consistency used for the same stamp printing may affect color appearance. Most pelure papers, for example, show a richer color when compared with wove or laid papers. See Russia Scott 181a, for an example of this effect.

The very nature of the printing processes can cause a variety of differences in shades or hues of the same stamp. Some of these shades are scarcer than others, and are of particular interest to the advanced collector.

## Luminescence

All forms of tagged stamps fall under the general category of luminescence. Within this broad category is fluorescence, dealing with forms of tagging visible under longwave ultraviolet light, and phosphorescence, which deals with tagging visible only under shortwave light. Phosphorescence leaves an afterglow and fluorescence does not. These treated stamps show up in a range of different colors when exposed to UV light. The differing wavelengths of the light activates the tagging material, making it glow in various colors that usually serve different mail processing purposes.

Intentional tagging is a post-World War II phenomenon, brought about by the increased literacy rate and rapidly growing mail volume. It was one of several answers to the problem of the need for more automated mail processes. Early tagged stamps served the purpose of triggering machines to separate different types of mail. A natural outgrowth was to also use the signal to trigger machines that faced all envelopes the same way and canceled them.

Tagged stamps come in many different forms. Some tagged stamps have luminescent shapes or images imprinted on them as a form of security device. Others have blocks (United States), stripes, frames (South Africa and Canada), overall coatings (United States), bars (Great Britain and Canada) and many other types. Some types of tagging are even mixed in with the pigmented printing ink (Australia Scott 366, Netherlands Scott 478 and U.S. Scott 1359 and 2443).

The means of applying taggant to stamps differs as much as the intended purposes for the stamps. The most common form of tagging is a coating applied to the surface of the printed stamp. Since the taggant ink is frequently invisible except under UV light, it does not interfere with the appearance of the stamp. Another common application is the use of phosphored papers. In this case the paper itself either has a coating of taggant applied before the stamp is printed, has taggant applied during the papermaking process (incorporating it into the fibers), or has the taggant mixed into the coating of the paper. The latter method, among others, is currently in use in the United States.

Many countries now use tagging in various forms to either expedite mail handling or to serve as a printing security device against counterfeiting. Following the introduction of tagged stamps for public use in 1959 by Great Britain, other countries have steadily joined the parade. Among those are Germany (1961); Canada and Denmark (1962); United States, Australia, France and Switzerland (1963); Belgium and Japan (1966); Sweden and Norway (1967); Italy (1968); and Russia (1969). Since then, many other countries have begun using forms of tagging, including Brazil, China, Czechoslovakia, Hong Kong, Guatemala, Indonesia, Israel, Lithuania, Luxembourg, Netherlands, Penrhyn Islands, Portugal, St. Vincent, Singapore, South Africa, Spain and Sweden to name a few.

In some cases, including United States, Canada, Great Britain and Switzerland, stamps were released both with and without tagging. Many of these were released during each country's experimental period. Tagged and untagged versions are listed for the aforementioned countries and are noted in some other countries' listings. For at least a few stamps, the experimentally tagged version is worth far more than its untagged counterpart, such as the 1963 experimental tagged version of France Scott 1024.

In some cases, luminescent varieties of stamps were inadvertently created. Several Russian stamps, for example, sport highly fluorescent ink that was not intended as a form of tagging. Older stamps, such as early U.S. postage dues, can be positively identified by the use of UV light, since the organic ink used has become slightly fluorescent over time. Other stamps, such as Austria Scott 70a-82a (varnish bars) and Obock Scott 46-64 (printed quadrille lines), have become fluorescent over time.

Various fluorescent substances have been added to paper to make it appear brighter. These optical brightners, as they are known, greatly affect the appearance of the stamp under UV light. The brightest of these is known as Hi-Brite paper. These paper varieties are beyond the scope of the Scott Catalogue.

Shortwave UV light also is used extensively in expertizing, since each form of paper has its own fluorescent characteristics that are impossible to perfectly match. It is therefore a simple matter to detect filled thins, added perforation teeth and other alterations that involve the addition of paper. UV light also is used to examine stamps that have had cancels chemically removed and for other purposes as well.

## Gum

The Illustrated Gum Chart in the first part of this introduction shows and defines various types of gum condition. Because gum condition has an important impact on the value of unused stamps, we recommend studying this chart and the accompanying text carefully.

The gum on the back of a stamp may be shiny, dull, smooth, rough, dark, white, colored or tinted. Most stamp gumming adhesives use gum arabic or dextrine as a base. Certain polymers such as polyvinyl alcohol (PVA) have been used extensively since World War II.

The *Scott Standard Postage Stamp Catalogue* does not list items by types of gum. The *Scott Specialized Catalogue of United States Stamps and Covers* does differentiate among some types of gum for certain issues.

Reprints of stamps may have gum differing from the original issues. In addition, some countries have used different gum formulas for different seasons. These adhesives have different properties that may become more apparent over time.

Many stamps have been issued without gum, and the catalogue will note this fact. See, for example, United States Scott 40-47. Sometimes, gum may have been removed to preserve the stamp. Germany Scott B68, for example, has a highly acidic gum that eventually destroys the stamps. This item is valued in the catalogue with gum removed.

## Reprints and Reissues

These are impressions of stamps (usually obsolete) made from the original plates or stones. If they are valid for postage and reproduce obsolete issues (such as U.S. Scott 102-111), the stamps are *reissues.* If they are from current issues, they are designated as *second, third,* etc., *printing*. If designated for a particular purpose, they are called *special printings.*

When special printings are not valid for postage, but are made from original dies and plates by authorized persons, they are *official reprints. Private reprints* are made from the original plates and dies by private hands. An example of a private reprint is that of the 1871-1932 reprints made from the original die of the 1845 New Haven, Conn., postmaster's provisional. *Official reproductions* or imitations are made from new dies and plates by government authorization. Scott will list those reissues that are valid for postage if they differ significantly from the original printing.

The U.S. government made special printings of its first postage stamps in 1875. Produced were official imitations of the first two stamps (listed as Scott 3-4), reprints of the demonetized pre-1861 issues (Scott 40-47) and reissues of the 1861 stamps, the 1869 stamps and the then-current 1875 denominations. Even though the official imitations and the reprints were not valid for postage, Scott lists all of these U.S. special printings.

Most reprints or reissues differ slightly from the original stamp in some characteristic, such as gum, paper, perforation, color or watermark. Sometimes the details are followed so meticulously that only a student of that specific stamp is able to distinguish the reprint or reissue from the original.

## Remainders and Canceled to Order

Some countries sell their stock of old stamps when a new issue replaces them. To avoid postal use, the *remainders* usually are canceled with a punch hole, a heavy line or bar, or a more-or-less regular-looking cancellation. The most famous merchant of remainders was Nicholas F. Seebeck. In the 1880s and 1890s, he arranged printing contracts between the Hamilton Bank Note Co., of which he was a director, and several Central and South American countries. The contracts provided that the plates and all remainders of the yearly issues became the property of Hamilton. Seebeck saw to it that ample stock remained. The "Seebecks," both remainders and reprints, were standard packet fillers for decades.

Some countries also issue stamps *canceled-to-order (CTO),* either in sheets with original gum or stuck onto pieces of paper or envelopes and canceled. Such CTO items generally are worth less than postally used stamps. In cases where the CTO material is far more prevalent in the marketplace than postally used examples, the catalogue value relates to the CTO examples, with postally used examples noted as premium items. Most CTOs can be detected by the presence of gum. However, as the CTO practice goes back at least to 1885, the gum inevitably has been soaked off some stamps so they could pass as postally used. The normally applied postmarks usually differ slightly from standard postmarks, and specialists are able to tell the difference. When applied individually to envelopes by philatelically minded persons, CTO material is known as *favor canceled* and generally sells at large discounts.

## Cinderellas and Facsimiles

*Cinderella* is a catch-all term used by stamp collectors to describe phantoms, fantasies, bogus items, municipal issues, exhibition seals, local revenues, transportation stamps, labels, poster stamps and many other types of items. Some cinderella collectors include in their collections local postage issues, telegraph stamps, essays and proofs, forgeries and counterfeits.

A *fantasy* is an adhesive created for a nonexistent stamp-issuing authority. Fantasy items range from imaginary countries (Occusi-Ambeno, Kingdom of Sedang, Principality of Trinidad or Torres Straits), to non-existent locals (Winans City Post), or nonexistent transportation lines (McRobish & Co.'s Acapulco-San Francisco Line).

On the other hand, if the entity exists and could have issued stamps (but did not) or was known to have issued other stamps, the items are considered *bogus* stamps. These would include the Mormon postage stamps of Utah, S. Allan Taylor's Guatemala and Paraguay inventions, the propaganda issues for the South Moluccas and the adhesives of the Page & Keyes local post of Boston.

*Phantoms* is another term for both fantasy and bogus issues.

*Facsimiles* are copies or imitations made to represent original stamps, but which do not pretend to be originals. A catalogue illustration is such a facsimile. Illustrations from the Moens catalogue of the last century were occasionally colored and passed off as stamps. Since the beginning of stamp collecting, facsimiles have been made for collectors as space fillers or for reference. They often carry the word "facsimile," "falsch" (German), "sanko" or "mozo" (Japanese), or "faux" (French) overprinted on the face or stamped on the back. Unfortunately, over the years a number of these items have had fake cancels applied over the facsimile notation and have been passed off as genuine.

## Forgeries and Counterfeits

Forgeries and counterfeits have been with philately virtually from the beginning of stamp production. Over time, the terminology for the two has been used interchangeably. Although both forgeries and counterfeits are reproductions of stamps, the purposes behind their creation differ considerably.

Among specialists there is an increasing movement to more specifically define such items. Although there is no universally accepted terminology, we feel the following definitions most closely mirror the items and their purposes as they are currently defined.

*Forgeries* (also often referred to as *Counterfeits*) are reproductions of genuine stamps that have been created to defraud collectors. Such spurious items first appeared on the market around 1860, and most old-time collections contain one or more. Many are crude and easily spotted, but some can deceive experts.

An important supplier of these early philatelic forgeries was the Hamburg printer Gebruder Spiro. Many others with reputations in this craft included S. Allan Taylor, George Hussey, James Chute, George Forune, Benjamin & Sarpy, Julius Goldner, E. Oneglia and L.H. Mercier. Among the noted 20th-century forgers were Francois Fournier, Jean Sperati and the prolific Raoul DeThuin.

Forgeries may be complete replications, or they may be genuine stamps altered to resemble a scarcer (and more valuable) type. Most forgeries, particularly those of rare stamps, are worth only a small fraction of the value of a genuine example, but a few types, created by some of the most notable forgers, such as Sperati, can be worth as much or more than the genuine. Fraudulently produced copies are known of most classic rarities and many medium-priced stamps.

In addition to rare stamps, large numbers of common 19th- and early 20th-century stamps were forged to supply stamps to the early packet trade. Many can still be easily found. Few new philatelic forgeries have appeared in recent decades. Successful imitation of well-engraved work is virtually impossible. It has proven far easier to produce a fake by altering a genuine stamp than to duplicate a stamp completely.

*Counterfeit* (also often referred to as *Postal Counterfeit* or *Postal Forgery*) is the term generally applied to reproductions of stamps that have been created to defraud the government of revenue. Such items usually are created at the time a stamp is current and, in some cases, are hard to detect. Because most counterfeits are seized when the perpetrator is captured, postal counterfeits, particularly used on cover, are usually worth much more than a genuine example to specialists. The first postal counterfeit was of Spain's 4-cuarto carmine of 1854 (the real one is Scott 25). Apparently, the counterfeiters were not satisfied with their first version, which is now very scarce, and they soon created an engraved counterfeit, which is common. Postal counterfeits quickly followed in Austria, Naples, Sardinia and the Roman States. They have since been created in many other countries as well, including the United States.

An infamous counterfeit to defraud the government is the 1-shilling Great Britain "Stock Exchange" forgery of 1872, used on telegraph forms at the exchange that year. The stamp escaped detection until a stamp dealer noticed it in 1898.

## Fakes

*Fakes* are genuine stamps altered in some way to make them more desirable. One student of this part of stamp collecting has estimated that by the 1950s more than 30,000 varieties of fakes were known. That number has grown greatly since then. The widespread existence of fakes makes it important for stamp collectors to study their philatelic holdings and use relevant literature. Likewise, collectors should buy from reputable dealers who guarantee their stamps and make full and prompt refunds should a purchased item be declared faked or altered by some mutually agreed-upon authority. Because fakes always have some genuine characteristics, it is not always possible to obtain unanimous agreement among experts regarding specific items. These students may change their opinions as philatelic knowledge increases. More than 80 percent of all fakes on the philatelic market today are regummed, reperforated (or perforated for the first time), or bear forged overprints, surcharges or cancellations.

Stamps can be chemically treated to alter or eliminate colors. For example, a pale rose stamp can be re-colored to resemble a blue shade of high market value. In other cases, treated stamps can be made to resemble missing color varieties. Designs may be changed by painting, or a stroke or a dot added or bleached out to turn an ordinary variety into a seemingly scarcer stamp. Part of a stamp can be bleached and reprinted in a different version, achieving an inverted center or frame. Margins can be added or repairs done so deceptively that the stamps move from the "repaired" into the "fake" category.

Fakers have not left the backs of the stamps untouched either. They may create false watermarks, add fake grills or press out genuine grills. A thin India paper proof may be glued onto a thicker backing to create the appearance an issued stamp, or a proof printed on cardboard may be shaved down and perforated to resemble a stamp. Silk threads are impressed into paper and stamps have been split so that a rare paper variety is added to an otherwise inexpensive stamp. The most common treatment to the back of a stamp, however, is regumming.

Some in the business of faking stamps have openly advertised fool-proof application of "original gum" to stamps that lack it, although most publications now ban such ads from their pages. It is believed that very few early stamps have survived without being hinged. The large number of never-hinged examples of such earlier material offered for sale thus suggests the widespread extent of regumming activity. Regumming also may be used to hide repairs or thin spots. Dipping the stamp into watermark fluid, or examining it under longwave ultraviolet light often will reveal these flaws.

Fakers also tamper with separations. Ingenious ways to add margins are known. Perforated wide-margin stamps may be falsely represented as imperforate when trimmed. Reperforating is commonly done to create scarce coil or perforation varieties, and to eliminate the naturally occurring straight-edge stamps found in sheet margin positions of many earlier issues. Custom has made straight-edged stamps less desirable. Fakers have obliged by perforating straight-edged stamps so that many are now uncommon, if not rare.

Another fertile field for the faker is that of overprints, surcharges and cancellations. The forging of rare surcharges or overprints began in the 1880s or 1890s. These forgeries are sometimes difficult to detect, but experts have identified almost all. Occasionally, overprints or cancellations are removed to create non-overprinted stamps or seemingly unused items. This is most commonly done by removing a manuscript cancel to make a stamp resemble an unused example. "SPECIMEN" overprints may be removed by scraping and repainting to create non-overprinted varieties. Fakers use inexpensive revenues or pen-canceled stamps to generate unused stamps for further faking by adding other markings. The quartz lamp or UV lamp and a high-powered magnifying glass help to easily detect removed cancellations.

The bigger problem, however, is the addition of overprints, surcharges or cancellations - many with such precision that they are very difficult to ascertain. Plating of the stamps or the overprint can be an important method of detection.

Fake postmarks may range from many spurious fancy cancellations to a host of markings applied to transatlantic covers, to adding normally appearing postmarks to definitives of some countries with stamps that are valued far higher used than unused. With the increased popularity of cover collecting, and the widespread interest in postal history, a fertile new field for fakers has come about. Some have tried to create entire covers. Others specialize in adding stamps, tied by fake cancellations, to genuine stampless covers, or replacing less expensive or damaged stamps with more valuable ones. Detailed study of postal rates in effect at the time a cover in question was mailed, including the analysis of each handstamp used during the period, ink analysis and similar techniques, usually will unmask the fraud.

## Restoration and Repairs

Scott bases its catalogue values on stamps that are free of defects and otherwise meet the standards set forth earlier in this introduction. Most stamp collectors desire to have the finest copy of an item possible. Even within given grading categories there are variances. This leads to a controversial practice that is not defined in any universal manner: stamp *restoration*.

There are broad differences of opinion about what is permissible when it comes to restoration. Carefully applying a soft eraser to a stamp or cover to remove light soiling is one form of restoration, as is washing a stamp in mild soap and water to clean it. These are fairly accepted forms of restoration. More severe forms of restoration include pressing out creases or removing stains caused by tape. To what degree each of these is acceptable is dependent upon the individual situation. Further along the spectrum is the freshening of a stamp's color by removing oxide build-up or the effects of wax paper left next to stamps shipped to the tropics.

At some point in this spectrum the concept of *repair* replaces that of restoration. Repairs include filling thin spots, mending tears by reweaving or adding a missing perforation tooth. Regumming stamps may have been acceptable as a restoration or repair technique many decades ago, but today it is considered a form of fakery.

Restored stamps may or may not sell at a discount, and it is possible that the value of individual restored items may be enhanced over that of their pre-restoration state. Specific situations dictate the resultant value of such an item. Repaired stamps sell at substantial discounts from the value of sound stamps.

# Terminology

**Booklets** — Many countries have issued stamps in small booklets for the convenience of users. This idea continues to become increasingly popular in many countries. Booklets have been issued in many sizes and forms, often with advertising on the covers, the panes of stamps or on the interleaving.

The panes used in booklets may be printed from special plates or made from regular sheets. All panes from booklets issued by the United States and many from those of other countries contain stamps that are straight edged on the sides, but perforated between. Others are distinguished by orientation of watermark or other identifying features. Any stamp-like unit in the pane, either printed or blank, that is not a postage stamp, is considered to be a *label* in the catalogue listings.

Scott lists and values booklet panes. Modern complete booklets also are listed and valued. Individual booklet panes are listed only when they are not fashioned from existing sheet stamps and, therefore, are identifiable from their sheet stamp counterparts.

Panes usually do not have a used value assigned to them because there is little market activity for used booklet panes, even though many exist used and there is some demand for them.

**Cancellations** — The marks or obliterations put on stamps by postal authorities to show that they have performed service and to prevent their reuse are known as cancellations. If the marking is made with a pen, it is considered a "pen cancel." When the location of the post office appears in the marking, it is a "town cancellation." A "postmark" is technically any postal marking, but in practice the term generally is applied to a town cancellation with a date. When calling attention to a cause or celebration, the marking is known as a "slogan cancellation." Many other types and styles of cancellations exist, such as duplex, numerals, targets, fancy and others. See also "precancels," below.

**Coil Stamps** — These are stamps that are issued in rolls for use in dispensers, affixing and vending machines. Those coils of the United States, Canada, Sweden and some other countries are perforated horizontally or vertically only, with the outer edges imperforate. Coil stamps of some countries, such as Great Britain and Germany, are perforated on all four sides and may in some cases be distinguished from their sheet stamp counterparts by watermarks, counting numbers on the reverse or other means.

**Covers** — Entire envelopes, with or without adhesive postage stamps, that have passed through the mail and bear postal or other markings of philatelic interest are known as covers. Before the introduction of envelopes in about 1840, people folded letters and wrote the address on the outside. Some people covered their letters with an extra sheet of paper on the outside for the address, producing the term "cover." Used airletter sheets, stamped envelopes and other items of postal stationery also are considered covers.

**Errors** — Stamps that have some major, consistent, unintentional deviation from the normal are considered errors. Errors include, but are not limited to, missing or wrong colors, wrong paper, wrong watermarks, inverted centers or frames on multicolor printing, inverted or missing surcharges or overprints, double impressions, missing perforations, unintentionally omitted tagging and others. Factually wrong or misspelled information, if it appears on all examples of a stamp, are not considered errors in the true sense of the word. They are errors of design. Inconsistent or randomly appearing items, such as misperfs or color shifts, are classified as freaks.

**Color-Omitted Errors** — This term refers to stamps where a missing color is caused by the complete failure of the printing plate to deliver ink to the stamp paper or any other paper. Generally, this is caused by the printing plate not being engaged on the press or the ink station running dry of ink during printing.

**Color-Missing Errors** — This term refers to stamps where a color or colors were printed somewhere but do not appear on the finished stamp. There are four different classes of color-missing errors, and the catalog indicates with a two-letter code appended to each such listing what caused the color to be missing. These codes are used only for the United States' color-missing error listings.

**FO** = A *foldover* of the stamp sheet during printing may block ink from appearing on a stamp. Instead, the color will appear on the back of the foldover (where it might fall on the back of the selvage or perhaps on the back of the stamp or another stamp). FO also will be used in the case of foldunders, where the paper may fold underneath the other stamp paper and the color will print on the platen.

**EP** = A piece of *extraneous paper* falling across the plate or stamp paper will receive the printed ink. When the extraneous paper is removed, an unprinted portion of stamp paper remains and shows partially or totally missing colors.

**CM** = A misregistration of the printing plates during printing will result in a *color misregistration*, and such a misregistraion may result in a color not appearing on the finished stamp.

**PS** = A *perforation shift* after printing may remove a color from the finished stamp. Normally, this will occur on a row of stamps at the edge of the stamp pane.

**Measurements** - When measurements are given in the Scott catalogues for stamp size, grill size or any other reason, the first measurement given is always for the top and bottom dimension, while the second measurement will be for the sides (just as perforation gauges are measured). Thus, a stamp size of 15mm x 21mm will indicate a vertically oriented stamp 15mm wide at top and bottom, and 21mm tall at the sides. The same principle holds for measuring or counting items such as U.S. grills. A grill count of 22x18 points (B grill) indicates that there are 22 grill points across by 18 grill points down.

**Overprints and Surcharges** — Overprinting involves applying wording or design elements over an already existing stamp. Overprints can be used to alter the place of use (such as "Canal Zone" on U.S. stamps), to adapt them for a special purpose ("Porto" on Denmark's 1913-20 regular issues for use as postage due stamps, Scott J1-J7) or to commemorate a special occasion (United States Scott 647-648).

A *surcharge* is a form of overprint that changes or restates the face value of a stamp or piece of postal stationery.

Surcharges and overprints may be handstamped, typeset or, occasionally, lithographed or engraved. A few hand-written overprints and surcharges are known.

**Personalized Stamps** — In 1999, Australia issued stamps with se-tenant labels that could be personalized with pictures of the customer's choice. Other countries quickly followed suit, with some offering to print the selected picture on the stamp itself within a frame that was used exclusively for personalized issues. As the picture used on these stamps or labels vary, listings for such stamps are for any picture within the common frame (or any picture on a se-tenant label), be it a "generic" image or one produced especially for a customer, almost invariably at a premium price.

**Precancels** — Stamps that are canceled before they are placed in the mail are known as precancels. Precanceling usually is done to expedite the handling of large mailings and generally allow the affected mail pieces to skip certain phases of mail handling.

In the United States, precancellations generally identified the point of origin; that is, the city and state. This information appeared across the face of the stamp, usually centered between parallel lines. More recently, bureau precancels retained the parallel lines, but the city and state designations were dropped. Recent coils have a service inscription that is present on the original printing plate. These show the mail service paid for by the stamp. Since these stamps are not intended to receive further cancellations when used as intended, they are considered precancels. Such items often do not have parallel lines as part of the precancellation.

In France, the abbreviation *Affranchts* in a semicircle together with the word *Postes* is the general form of precancel in use. Belgian precancellations usually appear in a box in which the name of the city appears. Netherlands precancels have the name of the city enclosed between concentric circles, sometimes called a "lifesaver." Precancellations of other countries usually follow these patterns, but may be any arrangement of bars, boxes and city names.

Precancels are listed in the Scott catalogues only if the precancel changes the denomination (Belgium Scott 477-478); if the precanceled stamp is different from the non-precanceled version (such as untagged U.S. precancels); or if the stamp exists only precanceled (France Scott 1096-1099, U.S. Scott 2265).

**Proofs and Essays** — Proofs are impressions taken from an approved die, plate or stone in which the design and color are the same as the stamp issued to the public. Trial color proofs are impressions taken from approved dies, plates or stones in colors that vary from the final version. An essay is the impression of a design that differs in some way from the issued stamp. "Progressive die proofs" generally are considered to be essays.

**Provisionals** — These are stamps that are issued on short notice and intended for temporary use pending the arrival of regular issues. They usually are issued to meet such contingencies as changes in government or currency, shortage of necessary postage values or military occupation.

During the 1840s, postmasters in certain American cities issued stamps that were valid only at specific post offices. In 1861, postmasters of the Confederate States also issued stamps with limited validity. Both of these examples are known as "postmaster's provisionals."

**Se-tenant** — This term refers to an unsevered pair, strip or block of stamps that differ in design, denomination or overprint.

Unless the se-tenant item has a continuous design (see U.S. Scott 1451a, 1694a) the stamps do not have to be in the same order as shown in the catalogue (see U.S. Scott 2158a).

**Specimens** — The Universal Postal Union required member nations to send samples of all stamps they released into service to the International Bureau in Switzerland. Member nations of the UPU received these specimens as samples of what stamps were valid for postage. Many are overprinted, handstamped or initial-perforated "Specimen," "Canceled" or "Muestra." Some are marked with bars across the denominations (China-Taiwan), punched holes (Czechoslovakia) or back inscriptions (Mongolia).

Stamps distributed to government officials or for publicity purposes, and stamps submitted by private security printers for official approval, also may receive such defacements.

The previously described defacement markings prevent postal use, and all such items generally are known as "specimens."

**Tete Beche** — This term describes a pair of stamps in which one is upside down in relation to the other. Some of these are the result of intentional sheet arrangements, such as Morocco Scott B10-B11. Others occurred when one or more electrotypes accidentally were placed upside down on the plate, such as Colombia Scott 57a. Separation of the tete-beche stamps, of course, destroys the tete beche variety.

# Currency Conversion

| Country | Dollar | Pound | S Franc | Yen | HK $ | Euro | Cdn $ | Aus $ |
|---|---|---|---|---|---|---|---|---|
| Australia | 1.2768 | 1.7315 | 1.3148 | 0.0114 | 0.1634 | 1.5404 | 1.0185 | — |
| Canada | 1.2536 | 1.7000 | 1.2909 | 0.0112 | 0.1604 | 1.5124 | — | 0.9818 |
| European Union | 0.8289 | 1.1241 | 0.8536 | 0.0074 | 0.1061 | — | 0.6612 | 0.6492 |
| Hong Kong | 7.8143 | 10.597 | 8.0469 | 0.0697 | — | 9.4273 | 6.2335 | 6.1202 |
| Japan | 112.14 | 152.07 | 115.48 | — | 14.351 | 135.29 | 89.454 | 87.829 |
| Switzerland | 0.9711 | 1.3169 | — | 0.0087 | 0.1243 | 1.1716 | 0.7746 | 0.7606 |
| United Kingdom | 0.7374 | — | 0.7594 | 0.0066 | 0.0944 | 0.8896 | 0.5882 | 0.5775 |
| United States | — | 1.3561 | 1.0298 | 0.0089 | 0.1280 | 1.2064 | 0.7977 | 0.7832 |

| Country | Currency | U.S. $ Equiv. |
|---|---|---|
| Cyprus | euro | 1.2064 |
| Czech Republic | koruna | .0473 |
| Denmark | krone | .1621 |
| Djibouti | franc | .0056 |
| Dominica | East Caribbean dollar | .3704 |
| Dominican Republic | peso | .0207 |
| Ecuador | US dollar | 1.0000 |
| Egypt | pound | .0565 |
| Equatorial Guinea | CFA franc | .0018 |
| Eritrea | nakfa | .0667 |
| Estonia | euro | 1.2064 |
| Ethiopia | birr | .0366 |
| Falkland Islands | pound | 1.3561 |
| Faroe Islands | krone | .1621 |
| Fiji | dollar | .4911 |
| Finland | euro | 1.2064 |
| Aland Islands | euro | 1.2064 |
| France | euro | 1.2064 |
| French Polynesia | Community of French Pacific (CFP) franc | .0101 |
| French So. & Antarctic Terr. | euro | 1.2064 |

*Source:* ***xe.com*** *Jan. 2, 2018. Figures reflect values as of Jan. 2, 2018.*

# COMMON DESIGN TYPES

Pictured in this section are issues where one illustration has been used for a number of countries in the Catalogue. Not included in this section are overprinted stamps or those issues which are illustrated in each country. Because the location of Never Hinged breakpoints varies from country to country, some of the values in the listings below will be for unused stamps that were previously hinged.

## EUROPA

### Europa, 1956

The design symbolizing the cooperation among the six countries comprising the Coal and Steel Community is illustrated in each country.

| | |
|---|---|
| *Belgium* | *496-497* |
| *France* | *805-806* |
| *Germany* | *748-749* |
| *Italy* | *715-716* |
| *Luxembourg* | *318-320* |
| *Netherlands* | *368-369* |

| | | |
|---|---|---|
| *Nos. 496-497 (2)* | 9.00 | .70 |
| *Nos. 805-806 (2)* | 5.25 | 1.00 |
| *Nos. 748-749 (2)* | 7.30 | 1.20 |
| *Nos. 715-716 (2)* | 9.25 | 1.25 |
| *Nos. 318-320 (3)* | 65.50 | 42.00 |
| *Nos. 368-369 (2)* | 72.50 | 1.75 |
| *Set total (13) Stamps* | 168.80 | 47.90 |

### Europa, 1958

"E" and Dove — CD1

European Postal Union at the service of European integration.

**1958, Sept. 13**

| | |
|---|---|
| Belgium | 527-528 |
| France | 889-890 |
| Germany | 790-791 |
| Italy | 750-751 |
| Luxembourg | 341-343 |
| Netherlands | 375-376 |
| Saar | 317-318 |

| | | |
|---|---|---|
| *Nos. 527-528 (2)* | 4.25 | .60 |
| *Nos. 889-890 (2)* | 1.65 | .55 |
| *Nos. 790-791 (2)* | 3.65 | .65 |
| *Nos. 750-751 (2)* | 1.05 | .60 |
| *Nos. 341-343 (3)* | 2.35 | 1.15 |
| *Nos. 375-376 (2)* | 2.50 | .75 |
| *Nos. 317-318 (2)* | 1.05 | 2.30 |
| *Set total (15) Stamps* | 16.50 | 6.60 |

### Europa, 1959

6-Link Enless Chain — CD2

**1959, Sept. 19**

| | |
|---|---|
| Belgium | 536-537 |
| France | 929-930 |
| Germany | 805-806 |
| Italy | 791-792 |
| Luxembourg | 354-355 |
| Netherlands | 379-380 |

| | | |
|---|---|---|
| *Nos. 536-537 (2)* | 1.55 | .60 |
| *Nos. 929-930 (2)* | 1.40 | .80 |
| *Nos. 805-806 (2)* | 1.55 | .65 |
| *Nos. 791-792 (2)* | .80 | .50 |
| *Nos. 354-355 (2)* | 3.50 | 1.40 |
| *Nos. 379-380 (2)* | 9.90 | 1.25 |
| *Set total (12) Stamps* | 18.70 | 5.20 |

### Europa, 1960

19-Spoke Wheel CD3

First anniversary of the establishment of C.E.P.T. (Conference Europeenne des Administrations des Postes et des Telecommunications.) The spokes symbolize the 19 founding members of the Conference.

**1960, Sept.**

| | |
|---|---|
| Belgium | 553-554 |
| Denmark | 379 |
| Finland | 376-377 |
| France | 970-971 |
| Germany | 818-820 |
| Great Britain | 377-378 |
| Greece | 688 |
| Iceland | 327-328 |
| Ireland | 175-176 |
| Italy | 809-810 |
| Luxembourg | 374-375 |
| Netherlands | 385-386 |
| Norway | 387 |
| Portugal | 866-867 |
| Spain | 941-942 |
| Sweden | 562-563 |
| Switzerland | 400-401 |
| Turkey | 1493-1494 |

| | | |
|---|---|---|
| *Nos. 553-554 (2)* | 1.25 | .55 |
| *No. 379 (1)* | .55 | .50 |
| *Nos. 376-377 (2)* | 1.70 | 1.80 |
| *Nos. 970-971 (2)* | .50 | .50 |
| *Nos. 818-820 (3)* | 2.25 | 1.50 |
| *Nos. 377-378 (2)* | 8.00 | 5.00 |
| *No. 688 (1)* | 5.00 | 2.00 |
| *Nos. 327-328 (2)* | 1.30 | 1.85 |
| *Nos. 175-176 (2)* | 47.50 | 27.50 |
| *Nos. 809-810 (2)* | .50 | .50 |
| *Nos. 374-375 (2)* | 1.00 | .80 |
| *Nos. 385-386 (2)* | 3.65 | 1.50 |
| *No. 387 (1)* | 1.25 | 1.25 |
| *Nos. 866-867 (2)* | 2.25 | 1.25 |
| *Nos. 941-942 (2)* | 1.50 | .75 |
| *Nos. 562-563 (2)* | 1.05 | .55 |
| *Nos. 400-401 (2)* | 1.25 | .65 |
| *Nos. 1493-1494 (2)* | 2.10 | 1.35 |
| *Set total (34) Stamps* | 82.60 | 49.80 |

### Europa, 1961

19 Doves Flying as One — CD4

The 19 doves represent the 19 members of the Conference of European Postal and Telecommunications Administrations C.E.P.T.

**1961-62**

| | |
|---|---|
| Belgium | 572-573 |
| Cyprus | 201-203 |
| France | 1005-1006 |
| Germany | 844-845 |
| Great Britain | 382-384 |
| Greece | 718-719 |
| Iceland | 340-341 |
| Italy | 845-846 |
| Luxembourg | 382-383 |
| Netherlands | 387-388 |
| Spain | 1010-1011 |
| Switzerland | 410-411 |
| Turkey | 1518-1520 |

| | | |
|---|---|---|
| *Nos. 572-573 (2)* | .75 | .50 |
| *Nos. 201-203 (3)* | *2.10* | *1.20* |
| *Nos. 1005-1006 (2)* | .50 | .50 |
| *Nos. 844-845 (2)* | .60 | .75 |
| *Nos. 382-384 (3)* | .75 | .75 |
| *Nos. 718-719 (2)* | .80 | .50 |
| *Nos. 340-341 (2)* | 1.10 | 1.60 |
| *Nos. 845-846 (2)* | .50 | .50 |
| *Nos. 382-383 (2)* | .70 | .70 |
| *Nos. 387-388 (2)* | .55 | .50 |
| *Nos. 1010-1011 (2)* | .70 | .55 |
| *Nos. 410-411 (2)* | 1.25 | .60 |
| *Nos. 1518-1520 (3)* | 2.45 | 1.30 |
| *Set total (29) Stamps* | 12.75 | 9.95 |

### Europa, 1962

Young Tree with 19 Leaves CD5

The 19 leaves represent the 19 original members of C.E.P.T.

**1962-63**

| | |
|---|---|
| Belgium | 582-583 |
| Cyprus | 219-221 |
| France | 1045-1046 |
| Germany | 852-853 |
| Greece | 739-740 |
| Iceland | 348-349 |
| Ireland | 184-185 |
| Italy | 860-861 |
| Luxembourg | 386-387 |
| Netherlands | 394-395 |
| Norway | 414-415 |
| Switzerland | 416-417 |
| Turkey | 1553-1555 |

| | | |
|---|---|---|
| *Nos. 582-583 (2)* | .65 | .65 |
| *Nos. 219-221 (3)* | *76.25* | *6.75* |
| *Nos. 1045-1046 (2)* | .60 | .50 |
| *Nos. 852-853 (2)* | .70 | .80 |
| *Nos. 739-740 (2)* | 2.25 | 1.15 |
| *Nos. 348-349 (2)* | .85 | .85 |
| *Nos. 184-185 (2)* | 2.00 | .50 |
| *Nos. 860-861 (2)* | 1.00 | .55 |
| *Nos. 386-387 (2)* | .85 | .70 |
| *Nos. 394-395 (2)* | 1.40 | .75 |
| *Nos. 414-415 (2)* | 2.25 | 2.25 |
| *Nos. 416-417 (2)* | 1.65 | 1.00 |
| *Nos. 1553-1555 (3)* | *3.00* | 1.55 |
| *Set total (28) Stamps* | 93.45 | 18.00 |

### Europa, 1963

Stylized Links, Symbolizing Unity — CD6

**1963, Sept.**

| | |
|---|---|
| Belgium | 598-599 |
| Cyprus | 229-231 |
| Finland | 419 |
| France | 1074-1075 |
| Germany | 867-868 |
| Greece | 768-769 |
| Iceland | 357-358 |
| Ireland | 188-189 |
| Italy | 880-881 |
| Luxembourg | 403-404 |
| Netherlands | 416-417 |
| Norway | 441-442 |
| Switzerland | 429 |
| Turkey | 1602-1603 |

| | | |
|---|---|---|
| *Nos. 598-599 (2)* | 1.60 | .55 |
| *Nos. 229-231 (3)* | *64.00* | *9.40* |
| *No. 419 (1)* | 1.25 | .55 |
| *Nos. 1074-1075 (2)* | .60 | .50 |
| *Nos. 867-868 (2)* | .50 | .55 |
| *Nos. 768-769 (2)* | 5.25 | 1.90 |
| *Nos. 357-358 (2)* | 1.20 | 1.20 |
| *Nos. 188-189 (2)* | 4.75 | 3.25 |
| *Nos. 880-881 (2)* | .50 | .50 |
| *Nos. 403-404 (2)* | 1.00 | .80 |
| *Nos. 416-417 (2)* | 2.25 | 1.00 |
| *Nos. 441-442 (2)* | 4.75 | 3.00 |
| *No. 429 (1)* | .90 | .60 |
| *Nos. 1602-1603 (2)* | 1.40 | .60 |
| *Set total (27) Stamps* | 89.95 | 24.40 |

### Europa, 1964

Symbolic Daisy — CD7

5th anniversary of the establishment of C.E.P.T. The 22 petals of the flower symbolize the 22 members of the Conference.

**1964, Sept.**

| | |
|---|---|
| Austria | 738 |
| Belgium | 614-615 |
| Cyprus | 244-246 |
| France | 1109-1110 |
| Germany | 897-898 |
| Greece | 801-802 |
| Iceland | 367-368 |
| Ireland | 196-197 |
| Italy | 894-895 |
| Luxembourg | 411-412 |
| Monaco | 590-591 |
| Netherlands | 428-429 |
| Norway | 458 |
| Portugal | 931-933 |
| Spain | 1262-1263 |
| Switzerland | 438-439 |
| Turkey | 1628-1629 |

| | | |
|---|---|---|
| *No. 738 (1)* | 1.20 | .80 |
| *Nos. 614-615 (2)* | 1.40 | .60 |
| *Nos. 244-246 (3)* | *32.25* | *5.10* |
| *Nos. 1109-1110 (2)* | .50 | .50 |
| *Nos. 897-898 (2)* | .50 | .50 |
| *Nos. 801-802 (2)* | 5.00 | 1.90 |
| *Nos. 367-368 (2)* | 1.40 | 1.15 |
| *Nos. 196-197 (2)* | 17.00 | 4.25 |
| *Nos. 894-895 (2)* | .50 | .50 |
| *Nos. 411-412 (2)* | .90 | .55 |
| *Nos. 590-591 (2)* | 2.50 | .70 |
| *Nos. 428-429 (2)* | 1.80 | .60 |
| *No. 458 (1)* | 4.50 | 4.50 |
| *Nos. 931-933 (3)* | *10.00* | *2.00* |
| *Nos. 1262-1263 (2)* | 1.30 | .80 |
| *Nos. 438-439 (2)* | 1.60 | .50 |
| *Nos. 1628-1629 (2)* | 2.65 | 1.35 |
| *Set total (34) Stamps* | 85.00 | 26.30 |

### Europa, 1965

Leaves and "Fruit" CD8

**1965**

| | |
|---|---|
| Belgium | 636-637 |
| Cyprus | 262-264 |
| Finland | 437 |
| France | 1131-1132 |
| Germany | 934-935 |
| Greece | 833-834 |
| Iceland | 375-376 |
| Ireland | 204-205 |
| Italy | 915-916 |
| Luxembourg | 432-433 |
| Monaco | 616-617 |
| Netherlands | 438-439 |
| Norway | 475-476 |
| Portugal | 958-960 |
| Switzerland | 469 |
| Turkey | 1665-1666 |

| | | |
|---|---|---|
| *Nos. 636-637 (2)* | .50 | .50 |
| *Nos. 262-264 (3)* | *25.35* | *6.00* |
| *No. 437 (1)* | 1.25 | .55 |
| *Nos. 1131-1132 (2)* | .70 | .55 |
| *Nos. 934-935 (2)* | .50 | .50 |
| *Nos. 833-834 (2)* | 2.25 | 1.15 |
| *Nos. 375-376 (2)* | 2.50 | 1.75 |
| *Nos. 204-205 (2)* | 16.00 | 3.35 |
| *Nos. 915-916 (2)* | .50 | .50 |
| *Nos. 432-433 (2)* | 80 | .00 |
| *Nos. 616-617 (2)* | 3.25 | 1.65 |
| *Nos. 438-439 (2)* | .75 | .55 |
| *Nos. 475-476 (2)* | 4.00 | 3.10 |
| *Nos. 958-960 (3)* | *10.00* | *2.75* |
| *No. 469 (1)* | 1.15 | .25 |
| *Nos. 1665-1666 (2)* | 3.50 | 2.10 |
| *Set total (32) Stamps* | 73.00 | 25.85 |

### Europa, 1966

Symbolic Sailboat — CD9

**1966, Sept.**

| | |
|---|---|
| Andorra, French | 172 |
| Belgium | 675-676 |
| Cyprus | 275-277 |
| France | 1163-1164 |
| Germany | 963-964 |

Greece 862-863
Iceland 384-385
Ireland 216-217
Italy 942-943
Liechtenstein 415
Luxembourg 440-441
Monaco 639-640
Netherlands 441-442
Norway 496-497
Portugal 980-982
Switzerland 477-478
Turkey 1718-1719

| | | |
|---|---|---|
| *No. 172 (1)* | 3.00 | 3.00 |
| *Nos. 675-676 (2)* | .80 | .50 |
| *Nos. 275-277 (3)* | *4.75* | *2.75* |
| *Nos. 1163-1164 (2)* | .55 | .50 |
| *Nos. 963-964 (2)* | .50 | .55 |
| *Nos. 862-863 (2)* | 2.25 | 1.05 |
| *Nos. 384-385 (2)* | 4.50 | 3.50 |
| *Nos. 216-217 (2)* | 6.75 | 2.00 |
| *Nos. 942-943 (2)* | .50 | .50 |
| *No. 415 (1)* | .40 | .35 |
| *Nos. 440-441 (2)* | .80 | .60 |
| *Nos. 639-640 (2)* | 2.00 | .65 |
| *Nos. 441-442 (2)* | 1.50 | .65 |
| *Nos. 496-497 (2)* | 5.00 | 3.00 |
| *Nos. 980-982 (3)* | *9.75* | 2.25 |
| *Nos. 477-478 (2)* | 1.60 | .60 |
| *Nos. 1718-1719 (2)* | 3.35 | 1.75 |
| *Set total (34) Stamps* | 48.00 | 24.20 |

### Europa, 1967

Cogwheels
CD10

### 1967

Andorra, French 174-175
Belgium 688-689
Cyprus 297-299
France 1178-1179
Germany 969-970
Greece 891-892
Iceland 389-390
Ireland 232-233
Italy 951-952
Liechtenstein 420
Luxembourg 449-450
Monaco 669-670
Netherlands 444-447
Norway 504-505
Portugal 994-996
Spain 1465-1466
Switzerland 482
Turkey B120-B121

| | | |
|---|---|---|
| *Nos. 174-175 (2)* | 10.75 | 6.25 |
| *Nos. 688-689 (2)* | 1.05 | .55 |
| *Nos. 297-299 (3)* | *4.25* | *2.50* |
| *Nos. 1178-1179 (2)* | .55 | .50 |
| *Nos. 969-970 (2)* | .55 | .55 |
| *Nos. 891-892 (2)* | 3.75 | 1.00 |
| *Nos. 389-390 (2)* | 3.00 | 2.00 |
| *Nos. 232-233 (2)* | 5.90 | 2.30 |
| *Nos. 951-952 (2)* | .60 | .50 |
| *No. 420 (1)* | .45 | .40 |
| *Nos. 449-450 (2)* | 1.00 | .70 |
| *Nos. 669-670 (2)* | 2.75 | .70 |
| *Nos. 444-447 (4)* | 5.00 | 1.85 |
| *Nos. 504-505 (2)* | 3.25 | 2.75 |
| *Nos. 994-996 (3)* | *9.50* | 1.85 |
| *Nos. 1465-1466 (2)* | .50 | .50 |
| *No. 482 (1)* | .70 | .25 |
| *Nos. B120-B121 (2)* | 3.50 | 2.75 |
| *Set total (38) Stamps* | 57.05 | 27.90 |

### Europa, 1968

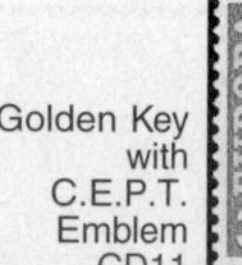

Golden Key with C.E.P.T. Emblem
CD11

### 1968

Andorra, French 182-183
Belgium 705-706
Cyprus 314-316
France 1209-1210
Germany 983-984
Greece 916-917
Iceland 395-396
Ireland 242-243
Italy 979-980
Liechtenstein 442
Luxembourg 466-467
Monaco 689-691
Netherlands 452-453
Portugal 1019-1021
San Marino 687
Spain 1526
Switzerland 488
Turkey 1775-1776

| | | |
|---|---|---|
| *Nos. 182-183 (2)* | 16.50 | 10.00 |
| *Nos. 705-706 (2)* | 1.25 | .50 |
| *Nos. 314-316 (3)* | *2.90* | *2.50* |
| *Nos. 1209-1210 (2)* | .85 | .55 |
| *Nos. 983-984 (2)* | .50 | .55 |
| *Nos. 916-917 (2)* | 3.75 | 1.65 |
| *Nos. 395-396 (2)* | 3.00 | 2.20 |
| *Nos. 242-243 (2)* | 3.30 | 2.25 |
| *Nos. 979-980 (2)* | .50 | .50 |
| *No. 442 (1)* | .45 | .40 |
| *Nos. 466-467 (2)* | .80 | .70 |
| *Nos. 689-691 (3)* | *5.40* | .95 |
| *Nos. 452-453 (2)* | 2.10 | .70 |
| *Nos. 1019-1021 (3)* | *9.75* | 2.10 |
| *No. 687 (1)* | .55 | .35 |
| *No. 1526 (1)* | .25 | .25 |
| *No. 488 (1)* | .45 | .25 |
| *Nos. 1775-1776 (2)* | 5.00 | 2.00 |
| *Set total (35) Stamps* | 57.30 | 28.40 |

### Europa, 1969

"EUROPA" and "CEPT"
CD12

Tenth anniversary of C.E.P.T.

### 1969

Andorra, French 188-189
Austria 837
Belgium 718-719
Cyprus 326-328
Denmark 458
Finland 483
France 1245-1246
Germany 996-997
Great Britain 585
Greece 947-948
Iceland 406-407
Ireland 270-271
Italy 1000-1001
Liechtenstein 453
Luxembourg 475-476
Monaco 722-724
Netherlands 475-476
Norway 533-534
Portugal 1038-1040
San Marino 701-702
Spain 1567
Sweden 814-816
Switzerland 500-501
Turkey 1799-1800
Vatican 470-472
Yugoslavia 1003-1004

| | | |
|---|---|---|
| *Nos. 188-189 (2)* | 18.50 | 12.00 |
| *No. 837 (1)* | .65 | .30 |
| *Nos. 718-719 (2)* | .75 | .50 |
| *Nos. 326-328 (3)* | *3.00* | *2.25* |
| *No. 458 (1)* | .75 | .75 |
| *No. 483 (1)* | 3.50 | .75 |
| *Nos. 1245-1246 (2)* | .55 | .50 |
| *Nos. 996-997 (2)* | .80 | .50 |
| *No. 585 (1)* | .25 | .25 |
| *Nos. 947-948 (2)* | 5.00 | 1.50 |
| *Nos. 406-407 (2)* | 4.20 | 2.40 |
| *Nos. 270-271 (2)* | 3.50 | 2.00 |
| *Nos. 1000-1001 (2)* | .50 | .50 |
| *No. 453 (1)* | .45 | .45 |
| *Nos. 475-476 (2)* | 1.00 | .70 |
| *Nos. 722-724 (3)* | *10.50* | 2.00 |
| *Nos. 475-476 (2)* | 2.60 | 1.15 |
| *Nos. 533-534 (2)* | 3.75 | 2.35 |
| *Nos. 1038-1040 (3)* | 17.75 | 2.40 |
| *Nos. 701-702 (2)* | .90 | .90 |
| *No. 1567 (1)* | .25 | .25 |
| *Nos. 814-816 (3)* | 4.00 | 2.85 |
| *Nos. 500-501 (2)* | 1.85 | .60 |
| *Nos. 1799-1800 (2)* | 3.85 | 2.25 |
| *Nos. 470-472 (3)* | .75 | .75 |
| *Nos. 1003-1004 (2)* | 4.00 | 4.00 |
| *Set total (51) Stamps* | 93.60 | 44.85 |

### Europa, 1970

Interwoven Threads
CD13

### 1970

Andorra, French 196-197
Belgium 741-742
Cyprus 340-342
France 1271-1272
Germany 1018-1019
Greece 985, 987
Iceland 420-421
Ireland 279-281
Italy 1013-1014
Liechtenstein 470
Luxembourg 489-490
Monaco 768-770
Netherlands 483-484
Portugal 1060-1062
San Marino 729-730
Spain 1607
Switzerland 515-516
Turkey 1848-1849
Yugoslavia 1024-1025

| | | |
|---|---|---|
| *Nos. 196-197 (2)* | 20.00 | 8.50 |
| *Nos. 741-742 (2)* | 1.10 | .55 |
| *Nos. 340-342 (3)* | *2.70* | *2.75* |
| *Nos. 1271-1272 (2)* | .65 | .50 |
| *Nos. 1018-1019 (2)* | .60 | .50 |
| *Nos. 985,987 (2)* | 7.75 | 2.00 |
| *Nos. 420-421 (2)* | 6.00 | 4.00 |
| *Nos. 279-281 (3)* | 7.50 | 2.50 |
| *Nos. 1013-1014 (2)* | .50 | .50 |
| *No. 470 (1)* | .45 | .45 |
| *Nos. 489-490 (2)* | .80 | .80 |
| *Nos. 768-770 (3)* | *6.35* | 2.10 |
| *Nos. 483-484 (2)* | 2.50 | 1.15 |
| *Nos. 1060-1062 (3)* | *9.75* | 2.35 |
| *Nos. 729-730 (2)* | .90 | .55 |
| *No. 1607 (1)* | .25 | .25 |
| *Nos. 515-516 (2)* | 1.85 | .60 |
| *Nos. 1848-1849 (2)* | 5.00 | 2.25 |
| *Nos. 1024-1025 (2)* | .80 | .80 |
| *Set total (40) Stamps* | 75.45 | 33.10 |

### Europa, 1971

"Fraternity, Cooperation, Common Effort"
CD14

### 1971

Andorra, French 205-206
Belgium 803-804
Cyprus 365-367
Finland 504
France 1304
Germany 1064-1065
Greece 1029-1030
Iceland 429-430
Ireland 305-306
Italy 1038-1039
Liechtenstein 485
Luxembourg 500-501
Malta 425-427
Monaco 797-799
Netherlands 488-489
Portugal 1094-1096
San Marino 749-750
Spain 1675-1676
Switzerland 531-532
Turkey 1876-1877
Yugoslavia 1052-1053

| | | |
|---|---|---|
| *Nos. 205-206 (2)* | 20.00 | 7.75 |
| *Nos. 803-804 (2)* | 1.30 | .55 |
| *Nos. 365-367 (3)* | *2.60* | *3.25* |
| *No. 504 (1)* | 5.00 | .75 |
| *No. 1304 (1)* | .45 | .40 |
| *Nos. 1064-1065 (2)* | .60 | .50 |
| *Nos. 1029-1030 (2)* | 4.00 | 1.80 |
| *Nos. 429-430 (2)* | 5.00 | 3.75 |
| *Nos. 305-306 (2)* | 4.50 | 1.50 |
| *Nos. 1038-1039 (2)* | .65 | .50 |
| *No. 485 (1)* | .45 | .45 |
| *Nos. 500-501 (2)* | 1.00 | .80 |
| *Nos. 425-427 (3)* | *.80* | *.80* |
| *Nos. 797-799 (3)* | *15.00* | 2.80 |
| *Nos. 488-489 (2)* | 2.50 | 1.15 |
| *Nos. 1094-1096 (3)* | *9.75* | 1.75 |
| *Nos. 749-750 (2)* | .65 | .55 |
| *Nos. 1675-1676 (2)* | .75 | .55 |
| *Nos. 531-532 (2)* | 1.85 | .65 |
| *Nos. 1876-1877 (2)* | 5.60 | 2.50 |
| *Nos. 1052-1053 (2)* | .50 | .50 |
| *Set total (43) Stamps* | 82.95 | 33.25 |

### Europa, 1972

Sparkles, Symbolic of Communications
CD15

### 1972

Andorra, French 210-211
Andorra, Spanish 62
Belgium 825-826
Cyprus 380-382
Finland 512-513
France 1341
Germany 1089-1090
Greece 1049-1050
Iceland 439-440
Ireland 316-317
Italy 1065-1066
Liechtenstein 504
Luxembourg 512-513
Malta 450-453
Monaco 831-832
Netherlands 494-495
Portugal 1141-1143
San Marino 771-772
Spain 1718
Switzerland 544-545
Turkey 1907-1908
Yugoslavia 1100-1101

| | | |
|---|---|---|
| *Nos. 210-211 (2)* | 21.00 | 7.00 |
| *No. 62 (1)* | 45.00 | 45.00 |
| *Nos. 825-826 (2)* | .95 | .55 |
| *Nos. 380-382 (3)* | *5.95* | *4.25* |
| *Nos. 512-513 (2)* | 7.00 | 1.40 |
| *No. 1341 (1)* | .50 | .35 |
| *Nos. 1089-1090 (2)* | 1.30 | .50 |
| *Nos. 1049-1050 (2)* | 2.00 | 1.55 |
| *Nos. 439-440 (2)* | 2.90 | 2.65 |
| *Nos. 316-317 (2)* | 13.00 | 4.50 |
| *Nos. 1065-1066 (2)* | .55 | .50 |
| *No. 504 (1)* | .45 | .45 |
| *Nos. 512-513 (2)* | 1.00 | .80 |
| *Nos. 450-453 (4)* | 1.05 | 1.40 |
| *Nos. 831-832 (2)* | 5.00 | 1.40 |
| *Nos. 494-495 (2)* | 3.25 | 1.15 |
| *Nos. 1141-1143 (3)* | *9.75* | 1.50 |
| *Nos. 771-772 (2)* | .70 | .50 |
| *No. 1718 (1)* | .50 | .40 |
| *Nos. 544-545 (2)* | 1.65 | .60 |
| *Nos. 1907-1908 (2)* | 7.50 | 3.00 |
| *Nos. 1100-1101 (2)* | 1.20 | 1.20 |
| *Set total (44) Stamps* | 132.20 | 80.65 |

### Europa, 1973

Post Horn and Arrows
CD16

### 1973

Andorra, French 219-220
Andorra, Spanish 76
Belgium 839-840
Cyprus 396-398
Finland 526
France 1367
Germany 1114-1115
Greece 1090-1092
Iceland 447-448
Ireland 329-330
Italy 1108-1109
Liechtenstein 528-529
Luxembourg 523-524
Malta 469-471
Monaco 866-867
Netherlands 504-505
Norway 604-605
Portugal 1170-1172
San Marino 802-803
Spain 1753
Switzerland 580-581
Turkey 1935-1936
Yugoslavia 1138-1139

| | | |
|---|---|---|
| *Nos. 219-220 (2)* | 20.00 | 11.00 |
| *No. 76 (1)* | .65 | .55 |
| *Nos. 839-840 (2)* | 1.00 | .65 |
| *Nos. 396-398 (3)* | *4.25* | *3.85* |
| *No. 526 (1)* | 1.25 | .55 |
| *No. 1367 (1)* | 1.25 | .75 |
| *Nos. 1114-1115 (2)* | .90 | .50 |
| *Nos. 1090-1092 (3)* | 2.10 | 1.40 |
| *Nos. 447-448 (2)* | 6.65 | 3.35 |

| | | |
|---|---|---|
| *Nos. 329-330 (2)* | 5.25 | 2.00 |
| *Nos. 1108-1109 (2)* | .50 | .50 |
| *Nos. 528-529 (2)* | .60 | .60 |
| *Nos. 523-524 (2)* | .90 | 1.00 |
| *Nos. 469-471 (3)* | .90 | 1.20 |
| *Nos. 866-867 (2)* | 15.00 | 2.40 |
| *Nos. 504-505 (2)* | 2.85 | 1.10 |
| *Nos. 604-605 (2)* | 6.25 | 2.40 |
| *Nos. 1170-1172 (3)* | 13.00 | 2.15 |
| *Nos. 802-803 (2)* | 1.00 | .60 |
| *No. 1753 (1)* | .35 | .25 |
| *Nos. 580-581 (2)* | 1.55 | .60 |
| *Nos. 1935-1936 (2)* | 10.00 | 4.50 |
| *Nos. 1138-1139 (2)* | 1.15 | 1.10 |
| *Set total (46) Stamps* | 97.35 | 43.00 |

**Europa, 2000**

CD17

**2000**

Albania....................2621-2622
Andorra, French....................522
Andorra, Spanish....................262
Armenia....................610-611
Austria....................1814
Azerbaijan....................698-699
Belarus....................350
Belgium....................1818
Bosnia & Herzegovina (Moslem)....358
Bosnia & Herzegovina (Serb)........111-112
Croatia....................428-429
Cyprus....................959
Czech Republic....................3120
Denmark....................1189
Estonia....................394
Faroe Islands....................376
Finland....................1129
Aland Islands....................166
France....................2771
Georgia....................228-229
Germany....................2086-2087
Gibraltar....................837-840
Great Britain (Jersey)....................935-936
Great Britain (Isle of Man)....................883
Greece....................1959
Greenland....................363
Hungary....................3699-3700
Iceland....................910
Ireland....................1230-1231
Italy....................2349
Latvia....................504
Liechtenstein....................1178
Lithuania....................668
Luxembourg....................1035
Macedonia....................187
Malta....................1011-1012
Moldova....................355
Monaco....................2161-2162
Poland....................3519
Portugal....................2358
Portugal (Azores)....................455
Portugal (Madeira)....................208
Romania....................4370
Russia....................6589
San Marino....................1480
Slovakia....................355
Slovenia....................424
Spain....................3036
Sweden....................2394
Switzerland....................1074
Turkey....................2762
Turkish Rep. of Northern Cyprus....500
Ukraine....................379
Vatican City....................1152

| | | |
|---|---|---|
| *Nos. 2621-2622 (2)* | 11.00 | 11.00 |
| *No. 522 (1)* | 2.00 | 1.00 |
| *No. 262 (1)* | 1.60 | .70 |
| *Nos. 610-611 (2)* | 4.75 | 4.75 |
| *No. 1814 (1)* | 1.40 | 1.40 |
| *Nos. 698-699 (2)* | 6.00 | 6.00 |
| *No. 350 (1)* | 1.75 | 1.75 |
| *No. 1818 (1)* | 1.40 | .60 |
| *No. 358 (1)* | 4.75 | 4.75 |
| *Nos. 111-112 (2)* | 110.00 | 110.00 |
| *Nos. 428-429 (2)* | 6.25 | 6.25 |
| *No. 959 (1)* | 2.10 | 1.40 |
| *No. 3120 (1)* | 1.20 | .40 |
| *No. 1189 (1)* | 3.50 | 2.25 |
| *No. 394 (1)* | 1.25 | 1.25 |
| *No. 376 (1)* | 2.40 | 2.40 |
| *No. 1129 (1)* | 2.00 | .60 |
| *No. 166 (1)* | 2.00 | 1.10 |
| *No. 2771 (1)* | 1.25 | .40 |
| *No. 228-229 (1)* | 9.00 | 9.00 |
| *Nos. 2086-2087 (2)* | 4.15 | 1.90 |
| *Nos. 837-840 (4)* | 5.50 | 5.30 |
| *Nos. 935-936 (2)* | 2.40 | 2.40 |
| *No. 883 (1)* | 1.75 | 1.75 |
| *No. 363 (1)* | 1.90 | 1.90 |
| *Nos. 3699-3700 (2)* | 6.50 | 2.50 |
| *No. 910 (1)* | 1.60 | 1.60 |
| *Nos. 1230-1231 (2)* | 4.35 | 4.35 |
| *No. 2349 (1)* | 1.50 | .40 |
| *No. 504 (1)* | 5.00 | 2.40 |
| *No. 1178 (1)* | 2.25 | 1.75 |
| *No. 668 (1)* | 1.50 | 1.50 |
| *No. 1035 (1)* | 1.40 | 1.00 |
| *No. 187 (1)* | 3.25 | 3.25 |
| *Nos. 1011-1012 (2)* | 4.35 | 4.35 |
| *No. 355 (1)* | 3.50 | 3.50 |
| *Nos. 2161-2162 (2)* | 2.80 | 1.40 |
| *No. 3519 (1)* | 1.10 | .50 |
| *No. 2358 (1)* | 1.25 | .65 |
| *No. 455 (1)* | 1.25 | .50 |
| *No. 208 (1)* | 1.25 | .50 |
| *No. 4370 (1)* | 2.50 | 1.25 |
| *No. 6589 (1)* | 2.00 | .85 |
| *No. 1480 (1)* | 1.00 | 1.00 |
| *No. 355 (1)* | 1.25 | .55 |
| *No. 424 (1)* | 3.25 | 1.60 |
| *No. 3036 (1)* | .75 | .40 |
| *No. 2394 (1)* | 3.00 | 2.25 |
| *No. 1074 (1)* | 2.10 | .75 |
| *No. 2762 (1)* | 2.00 | 2.00 |
| *No. 500 (1)* | 2.50 | 2.50 |
| *No. 379 (1)* | 4.50 | 3.00 |
| *No. 1152 (1)* | 1.25 | 1.25 |
| *Set total (67) Stamps* | 260.25 | 227.80 |

The Gibraltar stamps are similar to the stamp illustrated, but none have the design shown above. All other sets listed above include at least one stamp with the design shown, but some include stamps with entirely different designs. Bulgaria Nos. 4131-4132, Guernsey Nos. 802-803 and Yugoslavia Nos. 2485-2486 are Europa stamps with completely different designs.

**PORTUGAL & COLONIES**
**Vasco da Gama**

Fleet Departing CD20

Fleet Arriving at Calicut — CD21

Embarking at Rastello CD22

Muse of History CD23

San Gabriel, da Gama and Camoens CD24

Archangel Gabriel, the Patron Saint CD25

Flagship San Gabriel — CD26

Vasco da Gama — CD27

Fourth centenary of Vasco da Gama's discovery of the route to India.

**1898**

Azores....................93-100
Macao....................67-74
Madeira....................37-44
Portugal....................147-154
Port. Africa....................1-8
Port. Congo....................75-98
Port. India....................189-196
St. Thomas & Prince Islands...170-193
Timor....................45-52

| | | |
|---|---|---|
| *Nos. 93-100 (8)* | 122.00 | 76.25 |
| *Nos. 67-74 (8)* | 136.00 | 96.75 |
| *Nos. 37-44 (8)* | 44.55 | 34.00 |
| *Nos. 147-154 (8)* | 169.30 | 43.45 |
| *Nos. 1-8 (8)* | 24.75 | 21.70 |
| *Nos. 75-98 (24)* | 50.50 | 34.45 |
| *Nos. 189-196 (8)* | 20.25 | 12.95 |
| *Nos. 170-193 (24)* | 38.75 | 34.30 |
| *Nos. 45-52 (8)* | 19.50 | 8.75 |
| *Set total (104) Stamps* | 625.60 | 362.60 |

**Pombal**
**POSTAL TAX**
**POSTAL TAX DUES**

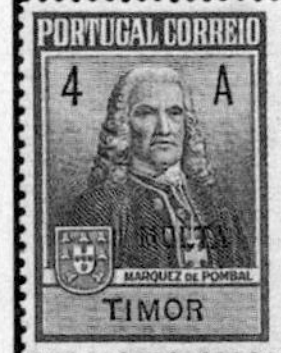


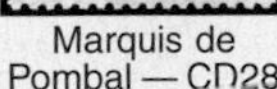

Marquis de Pombal — CD28

Planning Reconstruction of Lisbon, 1755 — CD29

Pombal Monument, Lisbon — CD30

Sebastiao Jose de Carvalho e Mello, Marquis de Pombal (1699-1782), statesman, rebuilt Lisbon after earthquake of 1755. Tax was for the erection of Pombal monument. Obligatory on all mail on certain days throughout the year. Postal Tax Dues are inscribed "Multa."

**1925**

Angola.............RA1-RA3, RAJ1-RAJ3
Azores............RA9-RA11, RAJ2-RAJ4
Cape Verde......RA1-RA3, RAJ1-RAJ3
Macao.............RA1-RA3, RAJ1-RAJ3
Madeira...........RA1-RA3, RAJ1-RAJ3
Mozambique.....RA1-RA3, RAJ1-RAJ3
Nyassa.............RA1-RA3, RAJ1-RAJ3
Portugal........RA11-RA13, RAJ2-RAJ4
Port. Guinea.....RA1-RA3, RAJ1-RAJ3
Port. India.........RA1-RA3, RAJ1-RAJ3
St. Thomas & Prince Islands.............RA1-RA3, RAJ1-RAJ3
Timor..............RA1-RA3, RAJ1-RAJ3

| | | |
|---|---|---|
| *Nos. RA1-RA3,RAJ1-RAJ3 (6)* | 6.60 | 6.60 |
| *Nos. RA9-RA11,RAJ2-RAJ4 (6)* | 6.60 | 9.30 |
| *Nos. RA1-RA3,RAJ1-RAJ3 (6)* | 6.00 | 5.40 |
| *Nos. RA1-RA3,RAJ1-RAJ3 (6)* | 18.50 | 10.50 |
| *Nos. RA1-RA3,RAJ1-RAJ3 (6)* | 4.35 | 12.45 |
| *Nos. RA1-RA3,RAJ1-RAJ3 (6)* | 2.55 | 2.70 |
| *Nos. RA1-RA3,RAJ1-RAJ3 (6)* | 52.50 | 38.25 |
| *Nos. RA11-RA13,RAJ2-RAJ4 (6)* | 5.80 | 5.20 |
| *Nos. RA1-RA3,RAJ1-RAJ3 (6)* | 3.30 | 2.70 |
| *Nos. RA1-RA3,RAJ1-RAJ3 (6)* | 3.45 | 3.45 |
| *Nos. RA1-RA3,RAJ1-RAJ3 (6)* | 3.60 | 3.60 |
| *Nos. RA1-RA3,RAJ1-RAJ3 (6)* | 2.10 | 3.90 |
| *Set total (72) Stamps* | 115.35 | 104.05 |

Vasco da Gama CD34

Mousinho de Albuquerque CD35

Dam CD36

Prince Henry the Navigator CD37

Affonso de Albuquerque CD38

Plane over Globe CD39

**1938-39**

Angola....................274-291, C1-C9
Cape Verde....................234-251, C1-C9
Macao....................289-305, C7-C15
Mozambique....................270-287, C1-C9
Port. Guinea....................233-250, C1-C9
Port. India....................439-453, C1-C8
St. Thomas & Prince Islands... 302-319, 323-340, C1-C18
Timor....................223-239, C1-C9

| | | |
|---|---|---|
| *Nos. 274-291,C1-C9 (27)* | 132.90 | 22.85 |
| *Nos. 234-251,C1-C9 (27)* | 100.00 | 31.20 |
| *Nos. 289-305,C7-C15 (26)* | 701.70 | 135.60 |
| *Nos. 270-287,C1-C9 (27)* | 63.45 | 11.20 |
| *Nos. 233-250,C1-C9 (27)* | 88.05 | 30.70 |
| *Nos. 439-453,C1-C8 (23)* | 74.75 | 25.50 |
| *Nos. 302-319,323-340,C1-C18 (54)* | 319.25 | 190.35 |
| *Nos. 223-239,C1-C9 (26)* | 149.25 | 73.15 |
| *Set total (237) Stamps* | 1,629. | 520.55 |

**Lady of Fatima**

Our Lady of the Rosary, Fatima, Portugal — CD40

**1948-49**

Angola....................315-318
Cape Verde....................266
Macao....................336
Mozambique....................325-328
Port. Guinea....................271
Port. India....................480
St. Thomas & Prince Islands..........351
Timor....................254

| | | |
|---|---|---|
| *Nos. 315-318 (4)* | 68.00 | 17.25 |
| *No. 266 (1)* | 8.50 | 4.50 |
| *No. 336 (1)* | 40.00 | 12.00 |
| *Nos. 325-328 (4)* | 20.00 | 4.50 |
| *No. 271 (1)* | 3.25 | 3.00 |
| *No. 480 (1)* | 2.50 | 2.25 |
| *No. 351 (1)* | 7.25 | 6.50 |
| *No. 254 (1)* | 2.75 | 2.75 |
| *Set total (14) Stamps* | 152.25 | 52.75 |

A souvenir sheet of 9 stamps was issued in 1951 to mark the extension of the 1950 Holy Year. The sheet contains: Angola No. 316, Cape Verde No. 266, Macao No. 336, Mozambique No. 325, Portuguese Guinea No. 271, Portuguese India Nos. 480, 485, St Thomas & Prince Islands No. 351, Timor No. 254. The sheet also contains a portrait of Pope Pius XII and is inscribed "Encerramento do

Ano Santo, Fatima 1951." It was sold for 11 escudos.

### Holy Year

Church Bells and Dove CD41

Angel Holding Candelabra CD42

Holy Year, 1950.

**1950-51**

Angola ....................331-332
Cape Verde ....................268-269
Macao ....................339-340
Mozambique ....................330-331
Port. Guinea ....................273-274
Port. India ..........490-491, 496-503
St. Thomas & Prince Islands ...353-354
Timor ....................258-259

| | | |
|---|---|---|
| *Nos. 331-332 (2)* | 7.60 | 1.35 |
| *Nos. 268-269 (2)* | 4.75 | 2.20 |
| *Nos. 339-340 (2)* | 55.00 | 12.50 |
| *Nos. 330-331 (2)* | 1.75 | .85 |
| *Nos. 273-274 (2)* | 3.50 | 2.60 |
| *Nos. 490-491,496-503 (10)* | 12.80 | 5.40 |
| *Nos. 353-354 (2)* | 7.50 | 4.40 |
| *Nos. 258-259 (2)* | 3.75 | 3.25 |
| *Set total (24) Stamps* | 96.65 | 32.55 |

A souvenir sheet of 8 stamps was issued in 1951 to mark the extension of the Holy Year. The sheet contains: Angola No. 331, Cape Verde No. 269, Macao No. 340, Mozambique No. 331, Portuguese Guinea No. 275, Portuguese India No. 490, St. Thomas & Prince Islands No. 354, Timor No. 258, some with colors changed. The sheet contains doves and is inscribed 'Encerramento do Ano Santo, Fatima 1951.' It was sold for 17 escudos.

### Holy Year Conclusion

Our Lady of Fatima — CD43

Conclusion of Holy Year. Sheets contain alternate vertical rows of stamps and labels bearing quotation from Pope Pius XII, different for each colony.

**1951**

Angola ....................357
Cape Verde ....................270
Macao ....................352
Mozambique ....................356
Port. Guinea ....................275
Port. India ....................506
St. Thomas & Prince Islands ..........355
Timor ....................270

| | | |
|---|---|---|
| *No. 357 (1)* | 5.25 | 1.50 |
| *No. 270 (1)* | 1.50 | 1.25 |
| *No. 352 (1)* | 37.50 | 10.00 |
| *No. 356 (1)* | 2.25 | 1.00 |
| *No. 275 (1)* | 1.00 | .65 |
| *No. 506 (1)* | 1.60 | 1.00 |
| *No. 355 (1)* | 2.50 | 2.00 |
| *No. 270 (1)* | 2.00 | 1.75 |
| *Set total (8) Stamps* | 53.60 | 19.15 |

### Medical Congress

CD44

First National Congress of Tropical Medicine, Lisbon, 1952. Each stamp has a different design.

**1952**

Angola ....................358
Cape Verde ....................287
Macao ....................364
Mozambique ....................359
Port. Guinea ....................276
Port. India ....................516
St. Thomas & Prince Islands ..........356
Timor ....................271

| | | |
|---|---|---|
| *No. 358 (1)* | 1.50 | .50 |
| *No. 287 (1)* | .70 | .50 |
| *No. 364 (1)* | 9.75 | 4.25 |
| *No. 359 (1)* | 1.10 | .55 |
| *No. 276 (1)* | .45 | .35 |
| *No. 516 (1)* | 4.75 | 2.00 |
| *No. 356 (1)* | .30 | .30 |
| *No. 271 (1)* | 1.00 | 1.00 |
| *Set total (8) Stamps* | 19.55 | 9.45 |

### Postage Due Stamps

CD45

**1952**

Angola ....................J37-J42
Cape Verde ....................J31-J36
Macao ....................J53-J58
Mozambique ....................J51-J56
Port. Guinea ....................J40-J45
Port. India ....................J47-J52
St. Thomas & Prince Islands ...J52-J57
Timor ....................J31-J36

| | | |
|---|---|---|
| *Nos. J37-J42 (6)* | 4.05 | 3.15 |
| *Nos. J31-J36 (6)* | 2.80 | 2.30 |
| *Nos. J53-J58 (6)* | 17.45 | 6.85 |
| *Nos. J51-J56 (6)* | 1.80 | 1.55 |
| *Nos. J40-J45 (6)* | 2.55 | 2.55 |
| *Nos. J47-J52 (6)* | 6.10 | 6.10 |
| *Nos. J52-J57 (6)* | 4.15 | 4.15 |
| *Nos. J31-J36 (6)* | 6.20 | 3.50 |
| *Set total (48) Stamps* | 45.10 | 30.15 |

### Sao Paulo

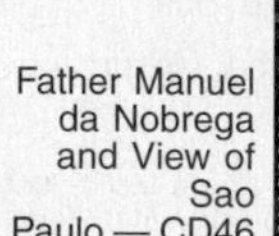

Father Manuel da Nobrega and View of Sao Paulo — CD46

Founding of Sao Paulo, Brazil, 400th anniv.

**1954**

Angola ....................385
Cape Verde ....................297
Macao ....................382
Mozambique ....................395
Port. Guinea ....................291
Port. India ....................530
St. Thomas & Prince Islands ..........369
Timor ....................279

| | | |
|---|---|---|
| *No. 385 (1)* | .80 | .50 |
| *No. 297 (1)* | .70 | .60 |
| *No. 382 (1)* | 14.00 | 3.00 |
| *No. 395 (1)* | .40 | .30 |
| *No. 291 (1)* | .35 | .25 |
| *No. 530 (1)* | .80 | .40 |
| *No. 369 (1)* | .80 | .60 |
| *No. 279 (1)* | .85 | .70 |
| *Set total (8) Stamps* | 18.70 | 6.35 |

### Tropical Medicine Congress

CD47

Sixth International Congress for Tropical Medicine and Malaria, Lisbon, Sept. 1958. Each stamp shows a different plant.

**1958**

Angola ....................409
Cape Verde ....................303
Macao ....................392
Mozambique ....................404
Port. Guinea ....................295
Port. India ....................569
St. Thomas & Prince Islands ..........371
Timor ....................289

| | | |
|---|---|---|
| *No. 409 (1)* | 3.50 | 1.10 |
| *No. 303 (1)* | 5.50 | 2.10 |
| *No. 392 (1)* | 8.00 | 3.00 |
| *No. 404 (1)* | 4.00 | .85 |
| *No. 295 (1)* | 2.75 | 1.10 |
| *No. 569 (1)* | 1.75 | .75 |
| *No. 371 (1)* | 2.75 | 2.25 |
| *No. 289 (1)* | 3.00 | 2.75 |
| *Set total (8) Stamps* | 31.25 | 13.90 |

### Sports

CD48

Each stamp shows a different sport.

**1962**

Angola ....................433-438
Cape Verde ....................320-325
Macao ....................394-399
Mozambique ....................424-429
Port. Guinea ....................299-304
St. Thomas & Prince Islands ...374-379
Timor ....................313-318

| | | |
|---|---|---|
| *Nos. 433-438 (6)* | 5.50 | 3.20 |
| *Nos. 320-325 (6)* | 15.25 | 5.20 |
| *Nos. 394-399 (6)* | 74.00 | 14.60 |
| *Nos. 424-429 (6)* | 5.70 | 2.45 |
| *Nos. 299-304 (6)* | 4.95 | 2.15 |
| *Nos. 374-379 (6)* | 6.75 | 3.20 |
| *Nos. 313-318 (6)* | 6.40 | 3.70 |
| *Set total (42) Stamps* | 118.55 | 34.50 |

### Anti-Malaria

Anopheles Funestus and Malaria Eradication Symbol — CD49

World Health Organization drive to eradicate malaria.

**1962**

Angola ....................439
Cape Verde ....................326
Macao ....................400
Mozambique ....................430
Port. Guinea ....................305
St. Thomas & Prince Islands ..........380
Timor ....................319

| | | |
|---|---|---|
| *No. 439 (1)* | 1.75 | .90 |
| *No. 326 (1)* | 1.40 | .90 |
| *No. 400 (1)* | 6.50 | 2.00 |
| *No. 430 (1)* | 1.40 | .40 |
| *No. 305 (1)* | 1.25 | .45 |
| *No. 380 (1)* | 2.00 | 1.50 |
| *No. 319 (1)* | .75 | .60 |
| *Set total (7) Stamps* | 15.05 | 6.75 |

### Airline Anniversary


Map of Africa, Super Constellation and Jet Liner — CD50

Tenth anniversary of Transportes Aereos Portugueses (TAP).

**1963**

Angola ....................490
Cape Verde ....................327
Mozambique ....................434
Port. Guinea ....................318
St. Thomas & Prince Islands ..........381

| | | |
|---|---|---|
| *No. 490 (1)* | 1.00 | .35 |
| *No. 327 (1)* | 1.10 | .70 |
| *No. 434 (1)* | .40 | .25 |
| *No. 318 (1)* | .65 | .35 |
| *No. 381 (1)* | .70 | .60 |
| *Set total (5) Stamps* | 3.85 | 2.25 |

### National Overseas Bank

Antonio Teixeira de Sousa — CD51

Centenary of the National Overseas Bank of Portugal.

**1964, May 16**

Angola ....................509
Cape Verde ....................328
Port. Guinea ....................319
St. Thomas & Prince Islands ..........382
Timor ....................320

| | | |
|---|---|---|
| *No. 509 (1)* | .90 | .30 |
| *No. 328 (1)* | 1.10 | .75 |
| *No. 319 (1)* | .65 | .40 |
| *No. 382 (1)* | .70 | .50 |
| *No. 320 (1)* | .75 | .60 |
| *Set total (5) Stamps* | 4.10 | 2.55 |

### ITU

ITU Emblem and the Archangel Gabriel — CD52

International Communications Union, Cent.

**1965, May 17**

Angola ....................511
Cape Verde ....................329
Macao ....................402
Mozambique ....................464
Port. Guinea ....................320
St. Thomas & Prince Islands ..........383
Timor ....................321

| | | |
|---|---|---|
| *No. 511 (1)* | 1.25 | .65 |
| *No. 329 (1)* | 2.10 | 1.40 |
| *No. 402 (1)* | 5.00 | 2.00 |
| *No. 464 (1)* | .40 | .25 |
| *No. 320 (1)* | 1.90 | .75 |
| *No. 383 (1)* | 1.50 | 1.00 |
| *No. 321 (1)* | 1.50 | .90 |
| *Set total (7) Stamps* | 13.65 | 6.95 |

### National Revolution

CD53

40th anniv. of the National Revolution. Different buildings on each stamp.

**1966, May 28**

Angola ....................525
Cape Verde ....................338
Macao ....................403
Mozambique ....................465
Port. Guinea ....................329
St. Thomas & Prince Islands ..........392
Timor ....................322

| | | |
|---|---|---|
| *No. 525 (1)* | .50 | .25 |
| *No. 338 (1)* | .60 | .45 |
| *No. 403 (1)* | 5.00 | 2.00 |
| *No. 465 (1)* | .50 | .30 |
| *No. 329 (1)* | .55 | .35 |
| *No. 392 (1)* | .75 | .50 |
| *No. 322 (1)* | 1.50 | .90 |
| *Set total (7) Stamps* | 9.40 | 4.75 |

### Navy Club

CD54

Centenary of Portugal's Navy Club. Each stamp has a different design.

**1967, Jan. 31**

Angola ....527-528
Cape Verde ....339-340
Macao ....412-413
Mozambique ....478-479
Port. Guinea ....330-331
St. Thomas & Prince Islands ...393-394
Timor ....323-324

| | | |
|---|---|---|
| *Nos. 527-528 (2)* | 1.75 | .75 |
| *Nos. 339-340 (2)* | 2.00 | 1.40 |
| *Nos. 412-413 (2)* | 9.50 | 3.75 |
| *Nos. 478-479 (2)* | 1.20 | .65 |
| *Nos. 330-331 (2)* | 1.20 | .90 |
| *Nos. 393-394 (2)* | 3.20 | 1.25 |
| *Nos. 323-324 (2)* | 4.00 | 2.00 |
| *Set total (14) Stamps* | 22.85 | 10.70 |

### Admiral Coutinho

CD55

Centenary of the birth of Admiral Carlos Viegas Gago Coutinho (1869-1959), explorer and aviation pioneer. Each stamp has a different design.

**1969, Feb. 17**

Angola ....547
Cape Verde ....355
Macao ....417
Mozambique ....484
Port. Guinea ....335
St. Thomas & Prince Islands ....397
Timor ....335

| | | |
|---|---|---|
| *No. 547 (1)* | .85 | .35 |
| *No. 355 (1)* | .35 | .25 |
| *No. 417 (1)* | 3.75 | 1.50 |
| *No. 484 (1)* | .25 | .25 |
| *No. 335 (1)* | .35 | .25 |
| *No. 397 (1)* | .50 | .35 |
| *No. 335 (1)* | 1.10 | .85 |
| *Set total (7) Stamps* | 7.15 | 3.80 |

### Administration Reform

Luiz Augusto Rebello da Silva — CD56

Centenary of the administration reforms of the overseas territories.

**1969, Sept. 25**

Angola ....549
Cape Verde ....357
Macao ....419
Mozambique ....491
Port. Guinea ....337
St. Thomas & Prince Islands ....399
Timor ....338

| | | |
|---|---|---|
| *No. 549 (1)* | .35 | .25 |
| *No. 357 (1)* | .35 | .25 |
| *No. 419 (1)* | 5.00 | 1.00 |
| *No. 491 (1)* | .25 | .25 |
| *No. 337 (1)* | .25 | .25 |
| *No. 399 (1)* | .45 | .45 |
| *No. 338 (1)* | .40 | .25 |
| *Set total (7) Stamps* | 7.05 | 2.70 |

### Marshal Carmona

CD57

Birth centenary of Marshal Antonio Oscar Carmona de Fragoso (1869-1951), President of Portugal. Each stamp has a different design.

**1970, Nov. 15**

Angola ....563
Cape Verde ....359
Macao ....422
Mozambique ....493
Port. Guinea ....340
St. Thomas & Prince Islands ....403
Timor ....341

| | | |
|---|---|---|
| *No. 563 (1)* | .45 | .25 |
| *No. 359 (1)* | .55 | .35 |
| *No. 422 (1)* | 2.25 | 1.25 |
| *No. 493 (1)* | .40 | .25 |
| *No. 340 (1)* | .35 | .25 |
| *No. 403 (1)* | .75 | .45 |
| *No. 341 (1)* | .25 | .25 |
| *Set total (7) Stamps* | 5.00 | 3.05 |

### Olympic Games

CD59

20th Olympic Games, Munich, Aug. 26-Sept. 11. Each stamp shows a different sport.

**1972, June 20**

Angola ....569
Cape Verde ....361
Macao ....426
Mozambique ....504
Port. Guinea ....342
St. Thomas & Prince Islands ....408
Timor ....343

| | | |
|---|---|---|
| *No. 569 (1)* | .65 | .25 |
| *No. 361 (1)* | .65 | .30 |
| *No. 426 (1)* | 3.25 | 1.00 |
| *No. 504 (1)* | .30 | .25 |
| *No. 342 (1)* | .45 | .25 |
| *No. 408 (1)* | .35 | .25 |
| *No. 343 (1)* | .50 | .50 |
| *Set total (7) Stamps* | 6.15 | 2.80 |

### Lisbon-Rio de Janeiro Flight

CD60

50th anniversary of the Lisbon to Rio de Janeiro flight by Arturo de Sacadura and Coutinho, March 30-June 5, 1922. Each stamp shows a different stage of the flight.

**1972, Sept. 20**

Angola ....570
Cape Verde ....362
Macao ....427
Mozambique ....505
Port. Guinea ....343
St. Thomas & Prince Islands ....409
Timor ....344

| | | |
|---|---|---|
| *No. 570 (1)* | .35 | .25 |
| *No. 362 (1)* | 1.50 | .30 |
| *No. 427 (1)* | 22.50 | 7.50 |
| *No. 505 (1)* | .25 | .25 |
| *No. 343 (1)* | .25 | .25 |
| *No. 409 (1)* | .35 | .25 |
| *No. 344 (1)* | .25 | .40 |
| *Set total (7) Stamps* | 25.45 | 9.20 |

### WMO Centenary

WMO Emblem — CD61

Centenary of international meterological cooperation.

**1973, Dec. 15**

Angola ....571
Cape Verde ....363
Macao ....429
Mozambique ....509
Port. Guinea ....344
St. Thomas & Prince Islands ....410
Timor ....345

| | | |
|---|---|---|
| *No. 571 (1)* | .45 | .25 |
| *No. 363 (1)* | .65 | .30 |
| *No. 429 (1)* | 6.25 | 1.75 |
| *No. 509 (1)* | .30 | .25 |
| *No. 344 (1)* | .45 | .35 |
| *No. 410 (1)* | .60 | .50 |
| *No. 345 (1)* | 1.75 | 2.00 |
| *Set total (7) Stamps* | 10.45 | 5.40 |

## FRENCH COMMUNITY

**Upper Volta can be found under Burkina Faso in Vol. 1**
**Madagascar can be found under Malagasy in Vol. 3**

### Colonial Exposition

People of French Empire CD70

Women's Heads CD71

France Showing Way to Civilization CD72

"Colonial Commerce" CD73

International Colonial Exposition, Paris.

**1931**

Cameroun ....213-216
Chad ....60-63
Dahomey ....97-100
Fr. Guiana ....152-155
Fr. Guinea ....116-119
Fr. India ....100-103
Fr. Polynesia ....76-79
Fr. Sudan ....102-105
Gabon ....120-123
Guadeloupe ....138-141
Indo-China ....140-142
Ivory Coast ....92-95
Madagascar ....169-172
Martinique ....129-132
Mauritania ....65-68
Middle Congo ....61-64
New Caledonia ....176-179
Niger ....73-76
Reunion ....122-125
St. Pierre & Miquelon ....132-135
Senegal ....138-141
Somali Coast ....135-138
Togo ....254-257
Ubangi-Shari ....82-85
Upper Volta ....66-69
Wallis & Futuna Isls. ....85-88

| | | |
|---|---|---|
| *Nos. 213-216 (4)* | 23.00 | 18.25 |
| *Nos. 60-63 (4)* | 22.00 | 22.00 |
| *Nos. 97-100 (4)* | 26.00 | 26.00 |
| *Nos. 152-155 (4)* | 22.00 | 22.00 |
| *Nos. 116-119 (4)* | 19.75 | 19.75 |
| *Nos. 100-103 (4)* | 18.00 | 18.00 |
| *Nos. 76-79 (4)* | 30.00 | 30.00 |
| *Nos. 102-105 (4)* | 19.00 | 19.00 |
| *Nos. 120-123 (4)* | 17.50 | 17.50 |
| *Nos. 138-141 (4)* | 19.00 | 19.00 |
| *Nos. 140-142 (3)* | 12.00 | 11.50 |
| *Nos. 92-95 (4)* | 22.50 | 22.50 |
| *Nos. 169-172 (4)* | 7.90 | 5.00 |
| *Nos. 129-132 (4)* | 21.00 | 21.00 |
| *Nos. 65-68 (4)* | 22.00 | 22.00 |
| *Nos. 61-64 (4)* | 20.50 | 20.50 |
| *Nos. 176-179 (4)* | 24.00 | 24.00 |
| *Nos. 73-76 (4)* | 21.50 | 21.50 |
| *Nos. 122-125 (4)* | 22.00 | 22.00 |
| *Nos. 132-135 (4)* | 24.00 | 24.00 |
| *Nos. 138-141 (4)* | 20.00 | 20.00 |
| *Nos. 135-138 (4)* | 22.00 | 22.00 |
| *Nos. 254-257 (4)* | 22.00 | 22.00 |
| *Nos. 82-85 (4)* | 21.00 | 21.00 |
| *Nos. 66-69 (4)* | 19.00 | 19.00 |
| *Nos. 85-88 (4)* | 35.00 | 35.00 |
| *Set total (103) Stamps* | 552.65 | 544.50 |

### Paris International Exposition Colonial Arts Exposition

"Colonial Resources"
CD74 CD77

Overseas Commerce CD75

Exposition Building and Women CD76

"France and the Empire" CD78

Cultural Treasures of the Colonies CD79

Souvenir sheets contain one imperf. stamp.

**1937**

Cameroun ....217-222A
Dahomey ....101-107
Fr. Equatorial Africa ....27-32, 73
Fr. Guiana ....162-168
Fr. Guinea ....120-126
Fr. India ....104-110
Fr. Polynesia ....117-123
Fr. Sudan ....106-112
Guadeloupe ....148-154
Indo-China ....193-199
Inini ....41
Ivory Coast ....152-158
Kwangchowan ....132
Madagascar ....191-197
Martinique ....179-185
Mauritania ....69-75
New Caledonia ....208-214
Niger ....77-83
Reunion ....167-173
St. Pierre & Miquelon ....165-171
Senegal ....172-178
Somali Coast ....139-145
Togo ....258-264
Wallis & Futuna Isls. ....89

| | | |
|---|---|---|
| *Nos. 217-222A (7)* | 18.80 | 20.30 |
| *Nos. 101-107 (7)* | 23.60 | 27.60 |
| *Nos. 27-32, 73 (7)* | 28.10 | 32.10 |
| *Nos. 162-168 (7)* | 22.50 | 24.50 |
| *Nos. 120-126 (7)* | 24.00 | 28.00 |
| *Nos. 104-110 (7)* | 21.15 | 36.50 |
| *Nos. 117-123 (7)* | 58.50 | 75.00 |
| *Nos. 106-112 (7)* | 23.60 | 27.60 |
| *Nos. 148-154 (7)* | 19.55 | 21.05 |
| *Nos. 193-199 (7)* | 17.70 | 19.70 |
| *No. 41 (1)* | 21.00 | 27.50 |
| *Nos. 152-158 (7)* | 22.20 | 26.20 |
| *No. 132 (1)* | 9.25 | 11.00 |
| *Nos. 191-197 (7)* | 19.25 | 21.75 |
| *Nos. 179-185 (7)* | 19.95 | 21.70 |
| *Nos. 69-75 (7)* | 20.50 | 24.50 |
| *Nos. 208-214 (7)* | 39.00 | 50.50 |
| *Nos. 73-83 (11)* | 42.70 | 46.70 |
| *Nos. 167-173 (7)* | 21.70 | 23.20 |
| *Nos. 165-171 (7)* | 49.60 | 64.00 |
| *Nos. 172-178 (7)* | 21.00 | 23.80 |
| *Nos. 139-145 (7)* | 25.60 | 32.60 |
| *Nos. 258-264 (7)* | 20.40 | 20.40 |
| *No. 89 (1)* | 28.50 | 37.50 |
| *Set total (154) Stamps* | 618.15 | 743.70 |

### Curie

Pierre and Marie Curie CD80

40th anniversary of the discovery of radium. The surtax was for the benefit of the Intl. Union for the Control of Cancer.

**1938**

Cameroun........................................ B1
Cuba...........................................B1-B2
Dahomey ........................................ B2
France.......................................... B76
Fr. Equatorial Africa ........................ B1
Fr. Guiana ...................................... B3
Fr. Guinea ...................................... B2
Fr. India ........................................ B6
Fr. Polynesia................................... B5
Fr. Sudan........................................ B1
Guadeloupe...................................... B3
Indo-China..................................... B14
Ivory Coast..................................... B2
Madagascar...................................... B2
Martinique....................................... B2
Mauritania...................................... B3
New Caledonia ................................ B4
Niger.............................................. B1
Reunion .......................................... B4
St. Pierre & Miquelon...................... B3
Senegal ........................................... B3
Somali Coast.................................... B2
Togo............................................... B1

| | | |
|---|---|---|
| *No. B1 (1)* | 10.00 | 10.00 |
| *Nos. B1-B2 (2)* | 12.00 | 3.35 |
| *No. B2 (1)* | 9.50 | 9.50 |
| *No. B76 (1)* | 21.00 | 12.50 |
| *No. B1 (1)* | 24.00 | 24.00 |
| *No. B3 (1)* | 13.50 | 13.50 |
| *No. B2 (1)* | 8.75 | 8.75 |
| *No. B6 (1)* | 10.00 | 10.00 |
| *No. B5 (1)* | 20.00 | 20.00 |
| *No. B1 (1)* | 12.50 | 12.50 |
| *No. B3 (1)* | 11.00 | 10.50 |
| *No. B14 (1)* | 12.00 | 12.00 |
| *No. B2 (1)* | 11.00 | 7.50 |
| *No. B2 (1)* | 11.00 | 11.00 |
| *No. B2 (1)* | 13.00 | 13.00 |
| *No. B3 (1)* | 7.75 | 7.75 |
| *No. B4 (1)* | 16.50 | 17.50 |
| *No. B1 (1)* | 15.00 | 15.00 |
| *No. B4 (1)* | 14.00 | 14.00 |
| *No. B3 (1)* | 21.00 | 22.50 |
| *No. B3 (1)* | 10.50 | 10.50 |
| *No. B2 (1)* | 7.75 | 7.75 |
| *No. B1 (1)* | 20.00 | 20.00 |
| *Set total (24) Stamps* | 311.75 | 293.10 |

### Caillie

Rene Caillie and Map of Northwestern Africa — CD81

Death centenary of Rene Caillie (1799-1838), French explorer. All three denominations exist with colony name omitted.

**1939**

Dahomey ................................108-110
Fr. Guinea ..............................161-163
Fr. Sudan................................113-115
Ivory Coast.............................160-162
Mauritania..............................109-111
Niger.........................................84-86
Senegal ..................................188-190
Togo.......................................265-267

| | | |
|---|---|---|
| *Nos. 108-110 (3)* | 1.20 | 3.60 |
| *Nos. 161-163 (3)* | 1.20 | 3.20 |
| *Nos. 113-115 (3)* | 1.20 | 3.20 |
| *Nos. 160-162 (3)* | 1.05 | 2.55 |
| *Nos. 109-111 (3)* | 1.05 | 3.80 |
| *Nos. 84-86 (3)* | 1.05 | 2.35 |
| *Nos. 188-190 (3)* | 1.05 | 2.90 |
| *Nos. 265-267 (3)* | 1.05 | 3.30 |
| *Set total (24) Stamps* | 8.85 | 24.90 |

### New York World's Fair

Natives and New York Skyline CD82

**1939**

Cameroun..................................223-224
Dahomey ...................................111-112
Fr. Equatorial Africa ....................78-79
Fr. Guiana ................................169-170
Fr. Guinea ................................164-165
Fr. India ...................................111-112
Fr. Polynesia.............................124-125
Fr. Sudan..................................116-117
Guadeloupe...............................155-156
Indo-China................................203-204
Inini..............................................42-43
Ivory Coast...............................163-164
Kwangchowan ...........................133-134
Madagascar...............................209-210
Martinique.................................186-187
Mauritania.................................112-113
New Caledonia ..........................215-216
Niger.............................................87-88
Reunion .....................................174-175
St. Pierre & Miquelon................205-206
Senegal .....................................191-192
Somali Coast.............................179-180
Togo..........................................268-269
Wallis & Futuna Isls. ....................90-91

| | | |
|---|---|---|
| *Nos. 223-224 (2)* | 2.80 | 2.40 |
| *Nos. 111-112 (2)* | 1.60 | 3.20 |
| *Nos. 78-79 (2)* | 1.60 | 3.20 |
| *Nos. 169-170 (2)* | 2.60 | 2.60 |
| *Nos. 164-165 (2)* | 1.60 | 3.20 |
| *Nos. 111-112 (2)* | 3.00 | *8.00* |
| *Nos. 124-125 (2)* | 4.80 | 4.80 |
| *Nos. 116-117 (2)* | 1.60 | 3.20 |
| *Nos. 155-156 (2)* | 2.50 | 2.50 |
| *Nos. 203-204 (2)* | 2.05 | 2.05 |
| *Nos. 42-43 (2)* | 7.50 | 9.00 |
| *Nos. 163-164 (2)* | 1.50 | 3.00 |
| *Nos. 133-134 (2)* | 2.50 | 2.50 |
| *Nos. 209-210 (2)* | 1.50 | 2.50 |
| *Nos. 186-187 (2)* | 2.35 | 2.35 |
| *Nos. 112-113 (2)* | 1.40 | 2.80 |
| *Nos. 215-216 (2)* | 3.35 | 3.35 |
| *Nos. 87-88 (2)* | 1.40 | 2.80 |
| *Nos. 174-175 (2)* | 2.80 | 2.80 |
| *Nos. 205-206 (2)* | 4.80 | 6.00 |
| *Nos. 191-192 (2)* | 1.40 | 2.80 |
| *Nos. 179-180 (2)* | 1.40 | 2.80 |
| *Nos. 268-269 (2)* | 1.40 | 2.80 |
| *Nos. 90-91 (2)* | 6.00 | 6.00 |
| *Set total (48) Stamps* | 63.45 | 86.65 |

### French Revolution

Storming of the Bastille CD83

French Revolution, 150th anniv. The surtax was for the defense of the colonies.

**1939**

Cameroun..................................B2-B6
Dahomey ...................................B3-B7
Fr. Equatorial Africa .......... B4-B8, CB1
Fr. Guiana ........................ B4-B8, CB1
Fr. Guinea .................................B3-B7
Fr. India ....................................B7-B11
Fr. Polynesia................... B6-B10, CB1
Fr. Sudan...................................B2-B6
Guadeloupe................................B4-B8
Indo-China................... B15-B19, CB1
Inini............................................B1-B5
Ivory Coast.................................B3-B7
Kwangchowan .............................B1-B5
Madagascar.......................... B3-B7, CB1
Martinique..................................B3-B7
Mauritania..................................B4-B8
New Caledonia ................ B5-B9, CB1
Niger...........................................B2-B6
Reunion ........................... B5-B9, CB1
St. Pierre & Miquelon.................B4-B8
Senegal ........................... B4-B8, CB1
Somali Coast...............................B3-B7
Togo............................................B2-B6
Wallis & Futuna Isls. ...................B1-B5

| | | |
|---|---|---|
| *Nos. B2-B6 (5)* | 60.00 | 60.00 |
| *Nos. B3-B7 (5)* | 47.50 | 47.50 |
| *Nos. B4-B8,CB1 (6)* | 120.00 | 120.00 |
| *Nos. B4-B8,CB1 (6)* | 79.50 | 79.50 |
| *Nos. B3-B7 (5)* | 47.50 | 47.50 |
| *Nos. B7-B11 (5)* | 28.75 | *32.50* |
| *Nos. B6-B10,CB1 (6)* | 122.50 | 122.50 |
| *Nos. B2-B6 (5)* | 50.00 | 50.00 |
| *Nos. B4-B8 (5)* | 50.00 | 50.00 |
| *Nos. B15-B19,CB1 (6)* | 85.00 | 85.00 |
| *Nos. B1-B5 (5)* | 80.00 | 100.00 |
| *Nos. B3-B7 (5)* | 43.75 | 43.75 |
| *Nos. B1-B5 (5)* | 46.25 | 46.25 |
| *Nos. B3-B7,CB1 (6)* | 65.50 | 65.50 |
| *Nos. B3-B7 (5)* | 52.50 | 52.50 |
| *Nos. B4-B8 (5)* | 42.50 | 42.50 |
| *Nos. B5-B9,CB1 (6)* | 101.50 | 101.50 |
| *Nos. B2-B6 (5)* | 60.00 | 60.00 |
| *Nos. B5-B9,CB1 (6)* | 87.50 | 87.50 |
| *Nos. B4-B8 (5)* | 67.50 | 72.50 |
| *Nos. B4-B8,CB1 (6)* | 56.50 | 56.50 |
| *Nos. B3-B7 (5)* | 45.00 | 45.00 |
| *Nos. B2-B6 (5)* | 42.50 | 42.50 |
| *Nos. B1-B5 (5)* | 95.00 | 95.00 |
| *Set total (128) Stamps* | 1,577. | 1,606. |

Plane over Coastal Area CD85

All five denominations exist with colony name omitted.

**1940**

Dahomey ..................................... C1-C5
Fr. Guinea ................................... C1-C5
Fr. Sudan..................................... C1-C5
Ivory Coast.................................. C1-C5
Mauritania................................... C1-C5
Niger............................................ C1-C5
Senegal ..................................... C12-C16
Togo............................................ C1-C5

| | | |
|---|---|---|
| *Nos. C1-C5 (5)* | 4.00 | 4.00 |
| *Nos. C1-C5 (5)* | 4.00 | 4.00 |
| *Nos. C1-C5 (5)* | 4.00 | 4.00 |
| *Nos. C1-C5 (5)* | 3.80 | 3.80 |
| *Nos. C1-C5 (5)* | 3.50 | 3.50 |
| *Nos. C1-C5 (5)* | 3.50 | 3.50 |
| *Nos. C12-C16 (5)* | 3.50 | 3.50 |
| *Nos. C1-C5 (5)* | 3.15 | 3.15 |
| *Set total (40) Stamps* | 29.45 | 29.45 |

### Defense of the Empire

Colonial Infantryman — CD86

**1941**

Cameroun...................................B13B
Dahomey ...................................... B13
Fr. Equatorial Africa .................. B8B
Fr. Guiana ................................... B10
Fr. Guinea ................................... B13
Fr. India ...................................... B13
Fr. Polynesia................................ B12
Fr. Sudan..................................... B12
Guadeloupe.................................. B10
Indo-China..................................B19B
Inini.............................................. B7
Ivory Coast.................................. B13
Kwangchowan .............................. B7
Madagascar................................... B9
Martinique..................................... B9
Mauritania................................... B14
New Caledonia ............................ B11
Niger............................................ B12
Reunion ....................................... B11
St. Pierre & Miquelon.................. B8B
Senegal ....................................... B14
Somali Coast.................................. B9
Togo............................................ B10B
Wallis & Futuna Isls. .................... B7

| | | |
|---|---|---|
| *No. B13B (1)* | 1.60 | |
| *No. B13 (1)* | 1.20 | |
| *No. B8B (1)* | 3.50 | |
| *No. B10 (1)* | 1.40 | |
| *No. B13 (1)* | 1.40 | |
| *No. B13 (1)* | 1.25 | |
| *No. B12 (1)* | 3.50 | |
| *No. B12 (1)* | 1.40 | |
| *No. B10 (1)* | 1.00 | |
| *No. B19B (1)* | 1.60 | |
| *No. B7 (1)* | 1.75 | |
| *No. B13 (1)* | 1.25 | |
| *No. B7 (1)* | .85 | |
| *No. B9 (1)* | 1.50 | |
| *No. B9 (1)* | 1.40 | |
| *No. B14 (1)* | .95 | |
| *No. B12 (1)* | 1.40 | |
| *No. B11 (1)* | 1.60 | |
| *No. B8B (1)* | 4.50 | |
| *No. B14 (1)* | 1.25 | |
| *No. B9 (1)* | 1.60 | |
| *No. B10B (1)* | 1.10 | |
| *No. B7 (1)* | 2.40 | |
| *Set total (23) Stamps* | 39.40 | |

Each of the CD86 stamps listed above is part of a set of three stamps. The designs of the other two stamps in the set vary from country to country. Only the values of the Common Design stamps are listed here.

### Colonial Education Fund

CD86a

**1942**

Cameroun.......................................CB3
Dahomey .......................................CB4
Fr. Equatorial Africa ....................CB5
Fr. Guiana ....................................CB4
Fr. Guinea ....................................CB4
Fr. India ......................................CB3
Fr. Polynesia................................CB4
Fr. Sudan......................................CB4
Guadeloupe...................................CB3
Indo-China...................................CB5
Inini..............................................CB3
Ivory Coast...................................CB4
Kwangchowan ...............................CB4
Malagasy ......................................CB5
Martinique.....................................CB3
Mauritania.....................................CB4
New Caledonia ..............................CB4
Niger..............................................CB4
Reunion .........................................CB4
St. Pierre & Miquelon....................CB3
Senegal ..........................................CB5
Somali Coast...................................CB3
Togo...............................................CB3
Wallis & Futuna .............................CB3

| | | |
|---|---|---|
| *No. CB3 (1)* | 1.10 | |
| *No. CB4 (1)* | .80 | 5.50 |
| *No. CB5 (1)* | .80 | |
| *No. CB4 (1)* | 1.10 | |
| *No. CB4 (1)* | .40 | 5.50 |
| *No. CB3 (1)* | .90 | |
| *No. CB4 (1)* | 2.00 | |
| *No. CB4 (1)* | .40 | 5.50 |
| *No. CB3 (1)* | 1.10 | |
| *No. CB5 (1)* | 1.10 | |
| *No. CB3 (1)* | 1.25 | |
| *No. CB4 (1)* | 1.00 | 5.50 |
| *No. CB4 (1)* | 1.00 | |
| *No. CB5 (1)* | .65 | |
| *No. CB3 (1)* | 1.00 | |
| *No. CB4 (1)* | .80 | |
| *No. CB4 (1)* | 2.25 | |
| *No. CB4 (1)* | .35 | |
| *No. CB4 (1)* | .90 | |
| *No. CB3 (1)* | 7.00 | |
| *No. CB5 (1)* | .80 | 6.50 |
| *No. CB3 (1)* | .70 | |
| *No. CB3 (1)* | .35 | |
| *No. CB3 (1)* | 2.25 | |
| *Set total (24) Stamps* | 30.00 | 28.50 |

Cross of Lorraine & Four-motor Plane CD87

**1941-5**

Cameroun.................................... C1-C7
Fr. Equatorial Africa .............. C17-C23
Fr. Guiana ................................. C9-C10
Fr. India ..................................... C1-C6
Fr. Polynesia.............................. C3-C9
Fr. West Africa .......................... C1-C3
Guadeloupe................................. C1-C2
Madagascar............................. C37-C43

Martinique .................................. C1-C2
New Caledonia ........................ C7-C13
Reunion .................................. C18-C24
St. Pierre & Miquelon ................ C1-C7
Somali Coast ............................ C1-C7

| | | |
|---|---|---|
| *Nos. C1-C7 (7)* | 6.30 | 6.30 |
| *Nos. C17-C23 (7)* | 10.40 | 6.35 |
| *Nos. C9-C10 (2)* | 3.80 | 3.10 |
| *Nos. C1-C6 (6)* | 9.30 | *15.00* |
| *Nos. C3-C9 (7)* | 13.75 | 10.00 |
| *Nos. C1-C3 (3)* | 9.50 | 3.90 |
| *Nos. C1-C2 (2)* | 3.75 | 2.50 |
| *Nos. C37-C43 (7)* | 5.60 | 3.80 |
| *Nos. C1-C2 (2)* | 3.00 | 1.60 |
| *Nos. C7-C13 (7)* | 8.85 | 7.30 |
| *Nos. C18-C24 (7)* | 7.05 | 5.00 |
| *Nos. C1-C7 (7)* | 11.60 | 9.40 |
| *Nos. C1-C7 (7)* | 13.95 | 11.10 |
| *Set total (71) Stamps* | 106.85 | 85.35 |

Somali Coast stamps are inscribed "Djibouti".

Transport Plane CD88

Caravan and Plane CD89

**1942**

Dahomey ................................ C6-C13
Fr. Guinea .............................. C6-C13
Fr. Sudan ................................ C6-C13
Ivory Coast ............................. C6-C13
Mauritania ............................... C6-C13
Niger ...................................... C6-C13
Senegal ................................. C17-C25
Togo ....................................... C6-C13

| | |
|---|---|
| *Nos. C6-C13 (8)* | 7.15 |
| *Nos. C6-C13 (8)* | 5.75 |
| *Nos. C6-C13 (8)* | 8.00 |
| *Nos. C6-C13 (8)* | 11.15 |
| *Nos. C6-C13 (8)* | 9.75 |
| *Nos. C6-C13 (8)* | 6.90 |
| *Nos. C17-C25 (9)* | 9.45 |
| *Nos. C6-C13 (8)* | 6.75 |
| *Set total (65) Stamps* | 64.90 |

### Red Cross

Marianne CD90

The surtax was for the French Red Cross and national relief.

**1944**

Cameroun ..................................... B28
Fr. Equatorial Africa ...................... B38
Fr. Guiana ..................................... B12
Fr. India ........................................ B14
Fr. Polynesia .................................. B13
Fr. West Africa ................................. B1
Guadeloupe .................................... B12
Madagascar .................................... B15
Martinique ...................................... B11
New Caledonia ................................ B13
Reunion ......................................... B15
St. Pierre & Miquelon ...................... B13
Somali Coast .................................. B13
Wallis & Futuna Isls. .......................... B9

| | | |
|---|---|---|
| *No. B28 (1)* | 2.00 | 1.60 |
| *No. B38 (1)* | 1.60 | 1.20 |
| *No. B12 (1)* | 1.75 | 1.25 |
| *No. B14 (1)* | 1.50 | 1.25 |
| *No. B13 (1)* | 2.00 | 1.60 |
| *No. B1 (1)* | 6.50 | 4.75 |
| *No. B12 (1)* | 1.40 | 1.00 |
| *No. B15 (1)* | .90 | .90 |
| *No. B11 (1)* | 1.20 | 1.20 |
| *No. B13 (1)* | 1.50 | 1.50 |
| *No. B15 (1)* | 1.60 | 1.10 |
| *No. B13 (1)* | 2.40 | 2.40 |
| *No. B13 (1)* | 1.75 | 2.00 |
| *No. B9 (1)* | 4.50 | 3.25 |
| *Set total (14) Stamps* | 30.60 | 25.00 |

### Eboue

CD91

Felix Eboue, first French colonial administrator to proclaim resistance to Germany after French surrender in World War II.

**1945**

Cameroun ................................ 296-297
Fr. Equatorial Africa ................ 156-157
Fr. Guiana .............................. 171-172
Fr. India ................................. 210-211
Fr. Polynesia ........................... 150-151
Fr. West Africa ............................ 15-16
Guadeloupe ............................. 187-188
Madagascar ............................. 259-260
Martinique ............................... 196-197
New Caledonia ......................... 274-275
Reunion .................................. 238-239
St. Pierre & Miquelon ............... 322-323
Somali Coast ........................... 238-239

| | | |
|---|---|---|
| *Nos. 296-297 (2)* | 2.40 | 1.95 |
| *Nos. 156-157 (2)* | 2.55 | 2.00 |
| *Nos. 171-172 (2)* | 2.45 | 2.00 |
| *Nos. 210-211 (2)* | 2.20 | 1.95 |
| *Nos. 150-151 (2)* | 3.60 | 2.85 |
| *Nos. 15-16 (2)* | 2.40 | 2.40 |
| *Nos. 187-188 (2)* | 2.05 | 1.60 |
| *Nos. 259-260 (2)* | 2.00 | 1.45 |
| *Nos. 196-197 (2)* | 2.05 | 1.55 |
| *Nos. 274-275 (2)* | 3.40 | 3.00 |
| *Nos. 238-239 (2)* | 2.40 | 2.00 |
| *Nos. 322-323 (2)* | 4.40 | 3.45 |
| *Nos. 238-239 (2)* | 2.45 | 2.10 |
| *Set total (26) Stamps* | 34.35 | 28.30 |

### Victory

Victory — CD92

European victory of the Allied Nations in World War II.

**1946, May 8**

Cameroun ........................................ C8
Fr. Equatorial Africa ...................... C24
Fr. Guiana ...................................... C11
Fr. India .......................................... C7
Fr. Polynesia .................................. C10
Fr. West Africa ................................. C4
Guadeloupe ...................................... C3
Indo-China ...................................... C19
Madagascar ..................................... C44
Martinique ........................................ C3
New Caledonia ................................ C14
Reunion .......................................... C25
St. Pierre & Miquelon ........................ C8
Somali Coast .................................... C8
Wallis & Futuna Isls. .......................... C1

| | | |
|---|---|---|
| *No. C8 (1)* | 1.60 | 1.20 |
| *No. C24 (1)* | 1.60 | 1.25 |
| *No. C11 (1)* | 1.75 | 1.25 |
| *No. C7 (1)* | 1.00 | 4.00 |
| *No. C10 (1)* | 2.75 | 2.00 |
| *No. C4 (1)* | 1.60 | 1.20 |
| *No. C3 (1)* | 1.25 | 1.00 |
| *No. C19 (1)* | 1.00 | .55 |
| *No. C44 (1)* | 1.00 | .35 |
| *No. C3 (1)* | 1.30 | 1.00 |
| *No. C14 (1)* | 1.50 | 1.25 |
| *No. C25 (1)* | 1.10 | .90 |
| *No. C8 (1)* | 2.10 | 2.10 |
| *No. C8 (1)* | 1.75 | 1.40 |
| *No. C1 (1)* | 2.50 | 1.90 |
| *Set total (15) Stamps* | 23.80 | 21.35 |

### Chad to Rhine

Leclerc's Departure from Chad — CD93

Battle at Cufra Oasis — CD94

Tanks in Action, Mareth — CD95

Normandy Invasion — CD96

Entering Paris — CD97

Liberation of Strasbourg — CD98

"Chad to the Rhine" march, 1942-44, by Gen. Jacques Leclerc's column, later French 2nd Armored Division.

**1946, June 6**

Cameroun ............................... C9-C14
Fr. Equatorial Africa .............. C25-C30
Fr. Guiana .............................. C12-C17
Fr. India .................................. C8-C13
Fr. Polynesia .......................... C11-C16
Fr. West Africa ......................... C5-C10
Guadeloupe .............................. C4-C9
Indo-China ............................. C20-C25
Madagascar ............................ C45-C50
Martinique ................................. C4-C9
New Caledonia ....................... C15-C20
Reunion .................................. C26-C31
St. Pierre & Miquelon ................ C9-C14
Somali Coast ............................ C9-C14
Wallis & Futuna Isls. ................. C2-C7

| | | |
|---|---|---|
| *Nos. C9-C14 (6)* | 12.05 | 9.70 |
| *Nos. C25-C30 (6)* | 14.70 | 10.80 |
| *Nos. C12-C17 (6)* | 12.65 | 10.35 |
| *Nos. C8-C13 (6)* | 12.80 | *15.00* |
| *Nos. C11-C16 (6)* | 17.55 | 13.40 |
| *Nos. C5-C10 (6)* | 16.05 | 11.95 |
| *Nos. C4-C9 (6)* | 12.00 | 9.60 |
| *Nos. C20-C25 (6)* | 6.40 | 6.40 |
| *Nos. C45-C50 (6)* | 10.30 | 8.40 |
| *Nos. C4-C9 (6)* | 8.85 | 7.30 |
| *Nos. C15-C20 (6)* | 13.40 | 11.90 |
| *Nos. C26-C31 (6)* | 10.25 | 6.55 |
| *Nos. C9-C14 (6)* | 17.30 | 14.35 |
| *Nos. C9-C14 (6)* | 18.10 | 12.65 |
| *Nos. C2-C7 (6)* | 13.75 | 10.45 |
| *Set total (90) Stamps* | 196.15 | 158.80 |

### UPU

French Colonials, Globe and Plane — CD99

Universal Postal Union, 75th anniv.

**1949, July 4**

Cameroun ......................................... C29
Fr. Equatorial Africa ....................... C34
Fr. India ........................................... C17
Fr. Polynesia .................................... C20
Fr. West Africa ................................. C15
Indo-China ....................................... C26
Madagascar ..................................... C55
New Caledonia ................................. C24
St. Pierre & Miquelon ....................... C18
Somali Coast ................................... C18
Togo ................................................ C18
Wallis & Futuna Isls. ....................... C10

| | | |
|---|---|---|
| *No. C29 (1)* | 8.00 | 4.75 |
| *No. C34 (1)* | 16.00 | 12.00 |
| *No. C17 (1)* | 11.50 | 8.75 |
| *No. C20 (1)* | 20.00 | 15.00 |
| *No. C15 (1)* | 12.00 | 8.75 |
| *No. C26 (1)* | 4.75 | 4.00 |
| *No. C55 (1)* | 4.00 | 2.75 |
| *No. C24 (1)* | 7.50 | 5.00 |
| *No. C18 (1)* | 20.00 | 12.00 |
| *No. C18 (1)* | 14.00 | 10.50 |
| *No. C18 (1)* | 8.50 | 7.00 |
| *No. C10 (1)* | 12.50 | 8.25 |
| *Set total (12) Stamps* | 138.75 | 98.75 |

### Tropical Medicine

Doctor Treating Infant CD100

The surtax was for charitable work.

**1950**

Cameroun ......................................... B29
Fr. Equatorial Africa ....................... B39
Fr. India ........................................... B15
Fr. Polynesia .................................... B14
Fr. West Africa ................................... B3
Madagascar ...................................... B17
New Caledonia ................................. B14
St. Pierre & Miquelon ....................... B14
Somali Coast ................................... B14
Togo ................................................ B11

| | | |
|---|---|---|
| *No. B29 (1)* | 7.25 | 5.50 |
| *No. B39 (1)* | 7.25 | 5.50 |
| *No. B15 (1)* | 6.00 | 4.00 |
| *No. B14 (1)* | 10.50 | 8.00 |
| *No. B3 (1)* | 9.50 | 7.25 |
| *No. B17 (1)* | 5.50 | 5.50 |
| *No. B14 (1)* | 6.75 | 5.25 |
| *No. B14 (1)* | 14.00 | 13.00 |
| *No. B14 (1)* | 7.75 | 6.25 |
| *No. B11 (1)* | 5.00 | 3.50 |
| *Set total (10) Stamps* | 79.50 | 63.75 |

### Military Medal

Medal, Early Marine and Colonial Soldier — CD101

Centenary of the creation of the French Military Medal.

**1952**

Cameroun ......................................... 322
Comoro Isls. ....................................... 39
Fr. Equatorial Africa ......................... 186

Fr. India ....................233
Fr. Polynesia ....................179
Fr. West Africa ....................57
Madagascar ....................286
New Caledonia ....................295
St. Pierre & Miquelon ....................345
Somali Coast ....................267
Togo ....................327
Wallis & Futuna Isls. ....................149

| | | |
|---|---|---|
| *No. 322 (1)* | 7.25 | 3.25 |
| *No. 39 (1)* | 50.00 | 40.00 |
| *No. 186 (1)* | 8.00 | 5.50 |
| *No. 233 (1)* | 5.50 | 7.00 |
| *No. 179 (1)* | 13.50 | 10.00 |
| *No. 57 (1)* | 8.75 | 6.50 |
| *No. 286 (1)* | 3.75 | 2.50 |
| *No. 295 (1)* | 6.50 | 6.00 |
| *No. 345 (1)* | 12.00 | 12.00 |
| *No. 267 (1)* | 9.00 | 8.00 |
| *No. 327 (1)* | 5.50 | 4.75 |
| *No. 149 (1)* | 9.50 | 7.00 |
| *Set total (12) Stamps* | 139.25 | 112.50 |

### Liberation

Allied Landing, Victory Sign and Cross of Lorraine — CD102

Liberation of France, 10th anniv.

**1954, June 6**

Cameroun ....................C32
Comoro Isls. ....................C4
Fr. Equatorial Africa ....................C38
Fr. India ....................C18
Fr. Polynesia ....................C22
Fr. West Africa ....................C17
Madagascar ....................C57
New Caledonia ....................C25
St. Pierre & Miquelon ....................C19
Somali Coast ....................C19
Togo ....................C19
Wallis & Futuna Isls. ....................C11

| | | |
|---|---|---|
| *No. C32 (1)* | 7.25 | 4.75 |
| *No. C4 (1)* | 35.00 | 20.00 |
| *No. C38 (1)* | 12.00 | 8.00 |
| *No. C18 (1)* | 11.00 | 8.00 |
| *No. C22 (1)* | 10.00 | 8.00 |
| *No. C17 (1)* | 12.00 | 5.50 |
| *No. C57 (1)* | 3.25 | 2.00 |
| *No. C25 (1)* | 7.50 | 5.00 |
| *No. C19 (1)* | 20.00 | 12.00 |
| *No. C19 (1)* | 10.50 | 8.50 |
| *No. C19 (1)* | 7.00 | 5.50 |
| *No. C11 (1)* | 12.50 | 8.25 |
| *Set total (12) Stamps* | 148.00 | 95.50 |

### FIDES

Plowmen CD103

Efforts of FIDES, the Economic and Social Development Fund for Overseas Possessions (Fonds d' Investissement pour le Developpement Economique et Social). Each stamp has a different design.

**1956**

Cameroun ....................326-329
Comoro Isls. ....................43
Fr. Equatorial Africa ....................189-192
Fr. Polynesia ....................181
Fr. West Africa ....................65-72
Madagascar ....................292-295
New Caledonia ....................303
St. Pierre & Miquelon ....................350
Somali Coast ....................268-269
Togo ....................331

| | | |
|---|---|---|
| *Nos. 326-329 (4)* | 6.90 | 3.20 |
| *No. 43 (1)* | 2.25 | 1.60 |
| *Nos. 189-192 (4)* | 3.20 | 1.65 |
| *No. 181 (1)* | 4.00 | 2.00 |
| *Nos. 65-72 (8)* | 16.00 | 6.35 |
| *Nos. 292-295 (4)* | 2.25 | 1.20 |
| *No. 303 (1)* | 1.90 | 1.10 |
| *No. 350 (1)* | 5.50 | 3.50 |
| *Nos. 268-269 (2)* | 5.35 | 3.15 |
| *No. 331 (1)* | 4.25 | 2.10 |
| *Set total (27) Stamps* | 51.60 | 25.85 |

### Flower

CD104

Each stamp shows a different flower.

**1958-9**

Cameroun ....................333
Comoro Isls. ....................45
Fr. Equatorial Africa ....................200-201
Fr. Polynesia ....................192
Fr. So. & Antarctic Terr. ....................11
Fr. West Africa ....................79-83
Madagascar ....................301-302
New Caledonia ....................304-305
St. Pierre & Miquelon ....................357
Somali Coast ....................270
Togo ....................348-349
Wallis & Futuna Isls. ....................152

| | | |
|---|---|---|
| *No. 333 (1)* | 1.60 | .80 |
| *No. 45 (1)* | 5.50 | 4.50 |
| *Nos. 200-201 (2)* | 3.60 | 1.60 |
| *No. 192 (1)* | 6.50 | 4.00 |
| *No. 11 (1)* | 8.75 | 7.50 |
| *Nos. 79-83 (5)* | 10.45 | 5.60 |
| *Nos. 301-302 (2)* | 1.60 | .60 |
| *Nos. 304-305 (2)* | 8.00 | 3.00 |
| *No. 357 (1)* | 4.25 | 2.10 |
| *No. 270 (1)* | 4.25 | 1.40 |
| *Nos. 348-349 (2)* | 1.10 | .50 |
| *No. 152 (1)* | 4.50 | 2.50 |
| *Set total (20) Stamps* | 60.10 | 34.10 |

### Human Rights

Sun, Dove and U.N. Emblem CD105

10th anniversary of the signing of the Universal Declaration of Human Rights.

**1958**

Comoro Isls. ....................44
Fr. Equatorial Africa ....................202
Fr. Polynesia ....................191
Fr. West Africa ....................85
Madagascar ....................300
New Caledonia ....................306
St. Pierre & Miquelon ....................356
Somali Coast ....................274
Wallis & Futuna Isls. ....................153

| | | |
|---|---|---|
| *No. 44 (1)* | 11.00 | 11.00 |
| *No. 202 (1)* | 2.40 | 1.25 |
| *No. 191 (1)* | 13.00 | 8.75 |
| *No. 85 (1)* | 2.40 | 2.00 |
| *No. 300 (1)* | .80 | .40 |
| *No. 306 (1)* | 2.00 | 1.50 |
| *No. 356 (1)* | 3.50 | 2.50 |
| *No. 274 (1)* | 3.50 | 2.10 |
| *No. 153 (1)* | 5.75 | 4.00 |
| *Set total (9) Stamps* | 44.35 | 33.50 |

### C.C.T.A.

CD106

Commission for Technical Cooperation in Africa south of the Sahara, 10th anniv.

**1960**

Cameroun ....................339
Cent. Africa ....................3
Chad ....................66
Congo, P.R. ....................90
Dahomey ....................138
Gabon ....................150
Ivory Coast ....................180
Madagascar ....................317
Mali ....................9
Mauritania ....................117
Niger ....................104
Upper Volta ....................89

| | | |
|---|---|---|
| *No. 339 (1)* | 1.60 | .75 |
| *No. 3 (1)* | 1.90 | .65 |
| *No. 66 (1)* | 1.90 | .50 |
| *No. 90 (1)* | 1.00 | 1.00 |
| *No. 138 (1)* | .50 | .25 |
| *No. 150 (1)* | 1.40 | 1.10 |
| *No. 180 (1)* | 1.10 | .50 |
| *No. 317 (1)* | .60 | .30 |
| *No. 9 (1)* | 1.20 | .50 |
| *No. 117 (1)* | .75 | .40 |
| *No. 104 (1)* | .85 | .45 |
| *No. 89 (1)* | .65 | .40 |
| *Set total (12) Stamps* | 13.45 | 6.80 |

### Air Afrique, 1961

Modern and Ancient Africa, Map and Planes — CD107

Founding of Air Afrique (African Airlines).

**1961-62**

Cameroun ....................C37
Cent. Africa ....................C5
Chad ....................C7
Congo, P.R. ....................C5
Dahomey ....................C17
Gabon ....................C5
Ivory Coast ....................C18
Mauritania ....................C17
Niger ....................C22
Senegal ....................C31
Upper Volta ....................C4

| | | |
|---|---|---|
| *No. C37 (1)* | 1.00 | .50 |
| *No. C5 (1)* | 1.00 | .55 |
| *No. C7 (1)* | 1.00 | .25 |
| *No. C5 (1)* | 1.75 | .90 |
| *No. C17 (1)* | .80 | .40 |
| *No. C5 (1)* | 11.00 | 6.00 |
| *No. C18 (1)* | 2.00 | 1.25 |
| *No. C17 (1)* | 2.50 | 1.25 |
| *No. C22 (1)* | 1.75 | .90 |
| *No. C31 (1)* | .80 | .30 |
| *No. C4 (1)* | 3.50 | 1.75 |
| *Set total (11) Stamps* | 27.10 | 14.05 |

### Anti-Malaria

CD108

World Health Organization drive to eradicate malaria.

**1962, Apr. 7**

Cameroun ....................B36
Cent. Africa ....................B1
Chad ....................B1
Comoro Isls. ....................B1
Congo, P.R. ....................B3
Dahomey ....................B15
Gabon ....................B4
Ivory Coast ....................B15
Madagascar ....................B19
Mali ....................B1
Mauritania ....................B16
Niger ....................B14
Senegal ....................B16
Somali Coast ....................B15
Upper Volta ....................B1

| | | |
|---|---|---|
| *No. B36 (1)* | 1.00 | .45 |
| *No. B1 (1)* | 1.40 | 1.40 |
| *No. B1 (1)* | 1.25 | .50 |
| *No. B1 (1)* | 4.00 | 4.00 |
| *No. B3 (1)* | 1.40 | 1.00 |
| *No. B15 (1)* | .75 | .75 |
| *No. B4 (1)* | 1.00 | 1.00 |
| *No. B15 (1)* | 1.25 | 1.25 |
| *No. B19 (1)* | .75 | .50 |
| *No. B1 (1)* | 1.25 | .60 |
| *No. B16 (1)* | .80 | .80 |
| *No. B14 (1)* | .60 | .60 |
| *No. B16 (1)* | 1.10 | .65 |
| *No. B15 (1)* | 7.00 | 7.00 |
| *No. B1 (1)* | .75 | .70 |
| *Set total (15) Stamps* | 24.30 | 21.20 |

### Abidjan Games

CD109

Abidjan Games, Ivory Coast, Dec. 24-31, 1961. Each stamp shows a different sport.

**1962**

Cent. Africa ....................19-20, C6
Chad ....................83-84, C8
Congo, P.R. ....................103-104, C7
Gabon ....................163-164, C6
Niger ....................109-111
Upper Volta ....................103-105

| | | |
|---|---|---|
| *Nos. 19-20,C6 (3)* | 3.90 | 2.60 |
| *Nos. 83-84,C8 (3)* | 6.30 | 1.55 |
| *Nos. 103-104,C7 (3)* | 3.85 | 1.80 |
| *Nos. 163-164,C6 (3)* | 5.00 | 3.00 |
| *Nos. 109-111 (3)* | 2.60 | 1.10 |
| *Nos. 103-105 (3)* | 2.80 | 1.75 |
| *Set total (18) Stamps* | 24.45 | 11.80 |

### African and Malagasy Union

Flag of Union CD110

First anniversary of the Union.

**1962, Sept. 8**

Cameroun ....................373
Cent. Africa ....................21
Chad ....................85
Congo, P.R. ....................105
Dahomey ....................155
Gabon ....................165
Ivory Coast ....................198
Madagascar ....................332
Mauritania ....................170
Niger ....................112
Senegal ....................211
Upper Volta ....................106

| | | |
|---|---|---|
| *No. 373 (1)* | 2.00 | .75 |
| *No. 21 (1)* | 1.25 | .60 |
| *No. 85 (1)* | 1.25 | .25 |
| *No. 105 (1)* | 1.50 | .50 |
| *No. 155 (1)* | 1.25 | .90 |
| *No. 165 (1)* | 1.60 | 1.25 |
| *No. 198 (1)* | 2.10 | .75 |
| *No. 332 (1)* | .80 | .80 |
| *No. 170 (1)* | .75 | .50 |
| *No. 112 (1)* | .80 | .40 |
| *No. 211 (1)* | .80 | .50 |
| *No. 106 (1)* | 1.10 | .75 |
| *Set total (12) Stamps* | 15.20 | 7.95 |

### Telstar

Telstar and Globe Showing Andover and Pleumeur-Bodou — CD111

First television connection of the United States and Europe through the Telstar satellite, July 11-12, 1962.

**1962-63**

Andorra, French ....................154
Comoro Isls. ....................C7
Fr. Polynesia ....................C29
Fr. So. & Antarctic Terr. ....................C5
New Caledonia ....................C33
St. Pierre & Miquelon ....................C26
Somali Coast ....................C31
Wallis & Futuna Isls. ....................C17

| | | |
|---|---|---|
| *No. 154 (1)* | 2.00 | 1.60 |
| *No. C7 (1)* | 5.00 | 3.00 |
| *No. C29 (1)* | 11.50 | 8.00 |

| | | |
|---|---|---|
| *No. C5 (1)* | 29.00 | 21.00 |
| *No. C33 (1)* | 25.00 | 18.50 |
| *No. C26 (1)* | 6.00 | 4.50 |
| *No. C31 (1)* | 1.00 | 1.00 |
| *No. C17 (1)* | 3.50 | 3.50 |
| *Set total (8) Stamps* | 83.00 | 61.10 |

### Freedom From Hunger

World Map and Wheat Emblem CD112

U.N. Food and Agriculture Organization's "Freedom from Hunger" campaign.

**1963, Mar. 21**

Cameroun....................B37-B38
Cent. Africa....................B2
Chad....................B2
Congo, P.R....................B4
Dahomey....................B16
Gabon....................B5
Ivory Coast....................B16
Madagascar....................B21
Mauritania....................B17
Niger....................B15
Senegal....................B17
Upper Volta....................B2

| | | |
|---|---|---|
| *Nos. B37-B38 (2)* | 2.25 | .75 |
| *No. B2 (1)* | 1.25 | 1.25 |
| *No. B2 (1)* | 2.00 | .50 |
| *No. B4 (1)* | 1.40 | 1.00 |
| *No. B16 (1)* | .80 | .80 |
| *No. B5 (1)* | 1.00 | 1.00 |
| *No. B16 (1)* | 1.50 | 1.50 |
| *No. B21 (1)* | .60 | .45 |
| *No. B17 (1)* | .80 | .80 |
| *No. B15 (1)* | .60 | .60 |
| *No. B17 (1)* | .80 | .50 |
| *No. B2 (1)* | .75 | .70 |
| *Set total (13) Stamps* | 13.75 | 9.85 |

### Red Cross Centenary

CD113

Centenary of the International Red Cross.

**1963, Sept. 2**

Comoro Isls....................55
Fr. Polynesia....................205
New Caledonia....................328
St. Pierre & Miquelon....................367
Somali Coast....................297
Wallis & Futuna Isls....................165

| | | |
|---|---|---|
| *No. 55 (1)* | 9.50 | 7.00 |
| *No. 205 (1)* | 15.00 | 12.00 |
| *No. 328 (1)* | 8.00 | 6.75 |
| *No. 367 (1)* | 12.00 | 5.50 |
| *No. 297 (1)* | 6.25 | 6.25 |
| *No. 165 (1)* | 4.00 | 3.50 |
| *Set total (6) Stamps* | 54.75 | 41.00 |

### African Postal Union, 1963

UAMPT Emblem, Radio Masts, Plane and Mail CD114

Establishment of the African and Malagasy Posts and Telecommunications Union.

**1963, Sept. 8**

Cameroun....................C47
Cent. Africa....................C10
Chad....................C9
Congo, P.R....................C13
Dahomey....................C19
Gabon....................C13
Ivory Coast....................C25
Madagascar....................C75
Mauritania....................C22
Niger....................C27
Rwanda....................36
Senegal....................C32
Upper Volta....................C9

| | | |
|---|---|---|
| *No. C47 (1)* | 2.25 | 1.00 |
| *No. C10 (1)* | 1.90 | .85 |
| *No. C9 (1)* | 2.40 | .60 |
| *No. C13 (1)* | 1.40 | .75 |
| *No. C19 (1)* | .75 | .25 |
| *No. C13 (1)* | 1.90 | .80 |
| *No. C25 (1)* | 2.50 | 1.50 |
| *No. C75 (1)* | 1.25 | .80 |
| *No. C22 (1)* | 1.50 | .60 |
| *No. C27 (1)* | 1.25 | .60 |
| *No. 36 (1)* | .90 | .55 |
| *No. C32 (1)* | 1.75 | .50 |
| *No. C9 (1)* | 1.50 | .75 |
| *Set total (13) Stamps* | 21.25 | 9.55 |

### Air Afrique, 1963

Symbols of Flight — CD115

First anniversary of Air Afrique and inauguration of DC-8 service.

**1963, Nov. 19**

Cameroun....................C48
Chad....................C10
Congo, P.R....................C14
Gabon....................C18
Ivory Coast....................C26
Mauritania....................C26
Niger....................C35
Senegal....................C33

| | | |
|---|---|---|
| *No. C48 (1)* | 1.25 | .40 |
| *No. C10 (1)* | 2.40 | .60 |
| *No. C14 (1)* | 1.60 | .60 |
| *No. C18 (1)* | 1.40 | .65 |
| *No. C26 (1)* | 1.00 | .50 |
| *No. C26 (1)* | .70 | .25 |
| *No. C35 (1)* | .90 | .50 |
| *No. C33 (1)* | 2.00 | .65 |
| *Set total (8) Stamps* | 11.25 | 4.15 |

### Europafrica

Europe and Africa Linked — CD116

Signing of an economic agreement between the European Economic Community and the African and Malagasy Union, Yaounde, Cameroun, July 20, 1963.

**1963-64**

Cameroun....................402
Cent. Africa....................C12
Chad....................C11
Congo, P.R....................C16
Gabon....................C19
Ivory Coast....................217
Niger....................C43
Upper Volta....................C11

| | | |
|---|---|---|
| *No. 402 (1)* | 2.25 | .60 |
| *No. C12 (1)* | 2.50 | 1.75 |
| *No. C11 (1)* | 2.00 | .50 |
| *No. C16 (1)* | 1.60 | 1.00 |
| *No. C19 (1)* | 1.40 | .75 |
| *No. 217 (1)* | 1.10 | .35 |
| *No. C43 (1)* | .85 | .50 |
| *No. C11 (1)* | 1.50 | .80 |
| *Set total (8) Stamps* | 13.20 | 6.25 |

### Human Rights

Scales of Justice and Globe CD117

15th anniversary of the Universal Declaration of Human Rights.

**1963, Dec. 10**

Comoro Isls....................56
Fr. Polynesia....................206
New Caledonia....................329
St. Pierre & Miquelon....................368
Somali Coast....................300
Wallis & Futuna Isls....................166

| | | |
|---|---|---|
| *No. 56 (1)* | 9.50 | 7.50 |
| *No. 205 (1)* | 15.00 | 12.00 |
| *No. 329 (1)* | 7.00 | 6.00 |
| *No. 368 (1)* | 7.00 | 3.50 |
| *No. 300 (1)* | 8.50 | 8.50 |
| *No. 166 (1)* | 8.00 | 7.50 |
| *Set total (6) Stamps* | 55.00 | 45.00 |

### PHILATEC

Stamp Album, Champs Elysees Palace and Horses of Marly CD118

Intl. Philatelic and Postal Techniques Exhibition, Paris, June 5-21, 1964.

**1963-64**

Comoro Isls....................60
France....................1078
Fr. Polynesia....................207
New Caledonia....................341
St. Pierre & Miquelon....................369
Somali Coast....................301
Wallis & Futuna Isls....................167

| | | |
|---|---|---|
| *No. 60 (1)* | 4.50 | 4.00 |
| *No. 1078 (1)* | .25 | .25 |
| *No. 206 (1)* | 15.00 | 10.00 |
| *No. 341 (1)* | 6.50 | 6.50 |
| *No. 369 (1)* | 11.00 | 8.00 |
| *No. 301 (1)* | 7.75 | 7.75 |
| *No. 167 (1)* | 3.50 | 3.50 |
| *Set total (7) Stamps* | 48.50 | 40.00 |

### Cooperation

CD119

Cooperation between France and the French-speaking countries of Africa and Madagascar.

**1964**

Cameroun....................409-410
Cent. Africa....................39
Chad....................103
Congo, P.R....................121
Dahomey....................193
France....................1111
Gabon....................175
Ivory Coast....................221
Madagascar....................360
Mauritania....................181
Niger....................143
Senegal....................236
Togo....................495

| | | |
|---|---|---|
| *Nos. 409-410 (2)* | 2.50 | .50 |
| *No. 39 (1)* | 1.00 | .55 |
| *No. 103 (1)* | 1.00 | .25 |
| *No. 121 (1)* | .80 | .35 |
| *No. 193 (1)* | .80 | .35 |
| *No. 1111 (1)* | .25 | .25 |
| *No. 175 (1)* | .90 | .60 |
| *No. 221 (1)* | 1.10 | .35 |
| *No. 360 (1)* | .60 | .25 |
| *No. 181 (1)* | .60 | .35 |
| *No. 143 (1)* | .80 | .40 |
| *No. 236 (1)* | 1.60 | .85 |
| *No. 495 (1)* | .70 | .25 |
| *Set total (14) Stamps* | 12.65 | 5.30 |

### ITU

Telegraph, Syncom Satellite and ITU Emblem CD120

Intl. Telecommunication Union, Cent.

**1965, May 17**

Comoro Isls....................C14
Fr. Polynesia....................C33
Fr. So. & Antarctic Terr....................C8
New Caledonia....................C40
New Hebrides....................124-125
St. Pierre & Miquelon....................C29
Somali Coast....................C36
Wallis & Futuna Isls....................C20

| | | |
|---|---|---|
| *No. C14 (1)* | 20.00 | 10.00 |
| *No. C33 (1)* | 80.00 | 52.50 |
| *No. C8 (1)* | 200.00 | 160.00 |
| *No. C40 (1)* | 10.00 | 8.00 |
| *Nos. 124-125 (2)* | 40.50 | 34.00 |
| *No. C29 (1)* | 20.00 | 10.00 |
| *No. C36 (1)* | 15.00 | 9.00 |
| *No. C20 (1)* | 21.00 | 15.00 |
| *Set total (9) Stamps* | 406.50 | 298.50 |

### French Satellite A-1

Diamant Rocket and Launching Installation — CD121

Launching of France's first satellite, Nov. 26, 1965.

**1965-66**

Comoro Isls....................C16a
France....................1138a
Reunion....................359a
Fr. Polynesia....................C41a
Fr. So. & Antarctic Terr....................C10a
New Caledonia....................C45a
St. Pierre & Miquelon....................C31a
Somali Coast....................C40a
Wallis & Futuna Isls....................C23a

| | | |
|---|---|---|
| *No. C16a (1)* | 11.00 | 11.00 |
| *No. 1138a (1)* | .65 | .65 |
| *No. 359a (1)* | 3.50 | 3.00 |
| *No. C41a (1)* | 14.00 | 14.00 |
| *No. C10a (1)* | 29.00 | 24.00 |
| *No. C45a (1)* | 7.00 | 7.00 |
| *No. C31a (1)* | 12.50 | 12.50 |
| *No. C40a (1)* | 7.00 | 7.00 |
| *No. C23a (1)* | 9.25 | 9.25 |
| *Set total (9) Stamps* | 93.90 | 88.40 |

### French Satellite D-1

D-1 Satellite in Orbit — CD122

Launching of the D-1 satellite at Hammaguir, Algeria, Feb. 17, 1966.

**1966**

Comoro Isls....................C17
France....................1148

Fr. Polynesia.................................C42
Fr. So. & Antarctic Terr. ................C11
New Caledonia..............................C46
St. Pierre & Miquelon.....................C32
Somali Coast..................................C49
Wallis & Futuna Isls. ....................C24

| | | |
|---|---|---|
| *No. C17 (1)* | 4.00 | 4.00 |
| *No. 1148 (1)* | .25 | .25 |
| *No. C42 (1)* | 7.00 | 4.75 |
| *No. C11 (1)* | 57.50 | 40.00 |
| *No. C46 (1)* | 2.25 | 2.00 |
| *No. C32 (1)* | 8.00 | 6.00 |
| *No. C49 (1)* | 4.25 | 2.75 |
| *No. C24 (1)* | 3.50 | 3.50 |
| *Set total (8) Stamps* | 86.75 | 63.25 |

### Air Afrique, 1966

Planes and Air Afrique Emblem — CD123

Introduction of DC-8F planes by Air Afrique.

**1966**

Cameroun......................................C79
Cent. Africa ..................................C35
Chad..............................................C26
Congo, P.R.....................................C42
Dahomey ........................................C42
Gabon.............................................C47
Ivory Coast ....................................C32
Mauritania......................................C57
Niger...............................................C63
Senegal ..........................................C47
Togo...............................................C54
Upper Volta....................................C31

| | | |
|---|---|---|
| *No. C79 (1)* | .80 | .25 |
| *No. C35 (1)* | 1.00 | .40 |
| *No. C26 (1)* | 1.00 | .25 |
| *No. C42 (1)* | 1.00 | .25 |
| *No. C42 (1)* | .75 | .25 |
| *No. C47 (1)* | .90 | .35 |
| *No. C32 (1)* | 1.00 | .60 |
| *No. C57 (1)* | .80 | .30 |
| *No. C63 (1)* | .65 | .35 |
| *No. C47 (1)* | .80 | .30 |
| *No. C54 (1)* | .80 | .25 |
| *No. C31 (1)* | .75 | .50 |
| *Set total (12) Stamps* | 10.25 | 4.05 |

### African Postal Union, 1967

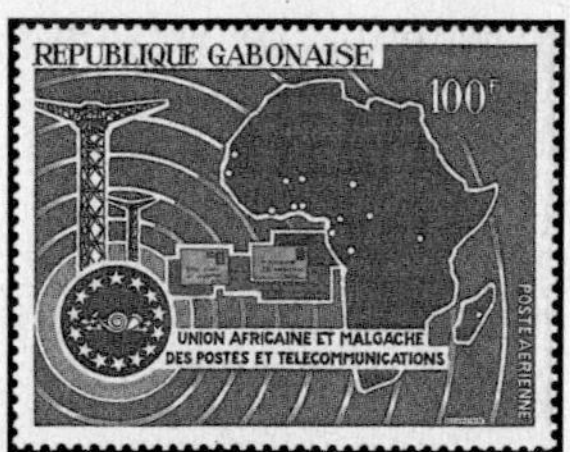


Telecommunications Symbols and Map of Africa — CD124

Fifth anniversary of the establishment of the African and Malagasy Union of Posts and Telecommunications, UAMPT.

**1967**

Cameroun......................................C90
Cent. Africa ..................................C46
Chad..............................................C37
Congo, P.R.....................................C57
Dahomey ........................................C61
Gabon.............................................C58
Ivory Coast ....................................C34
Madagascar....................................C85
Mauritania......................................C65
Niger...............................................C75
Rwanda ......................................C1-C3
Senegal ..........................................C60
Togo...............................................C81
Upper Volta....................................C50

| | | |
|---|---|---|
| *No. C90 (1)* | 2.40 | .65 |
| *No. C46 (1)* | 2.25 | .85 |
| *No. C37 (1)* | 2.00 | .60 |
| *No. C57 (1)* | 1.60 | .60 |
| *No. C61 (1)* | 1.75 | .95 |
| *No. C58 (1)* | 2.25 | .95 |
| *No. C34 (1)* | 3.50 | 1.50 |
| *No. C85 (1)* | 1.25 | .60 |
| *No. C65 (1)* | 1.25 | .60 |
| *No. C75 (1)* | 1.40 | .60 |
| *Nos. C1-C3 (3)* | 2.30 | 1.25 |
| *No. C60 (1)* | 1.75 | .50 |
| *No. C81 (1)* | 1.90 | .30 |
| *No. C50 (1)* | 1.80 | .70 |
| *Set total (16) Stamps* | 27.40 | 10.65 |

### Monetary Union

Gold Token of the Ashantis, 17-18th Centuries — CD125

West African Monetary Union, 5th anniv.

**1967, Nov. 4**

Dahomey .........................................244
Ivory Coast .....................................259
Mauritania.......................................238
Niger...............................................204
Senegal ..........................................294
Togo...............................................623
Upper Volta.....................................181

| | | |
|---|---|---|
| *No. 244 (1)* | .65 | .65 |
| *No. 259 (1)* | .85 | .40 |
| *No. 238 (1)* | .45 | .25 |
| *No. 204 (1)* | .45 | .25 |
| *No. 294 (1)* | .60 | .25 |
| *No. 623 (1)* | .60 | .25 |
| *No. 181 (1)* | .65 | .35 |
| *Set total (7) Stamps* | 4.25 | 2.40 |

### WHO Anniversary

Sun, Flowers and WHO Emblem CD126

World Health Organization, 20th anniv.

**1968, May 4**

Afars & Issas...................................317
Comoro Isls. .....................................73
Fr. Polynesia............................241-242
Fr. So. & Antarctic Terr. ....................31
New Caledonia................................367
St. Pierre & Miquelon.......................377
Wallis & Futuna Isls. .......................169

| | | |
|---|---|---|
| *No. 317 (1)* | 3.00 | 3.00 |
| *No. 73 (1)* | 2.75 | 2.00 |
| *Nos. 241-242 (2)* | 22.00 | 12.75 |
| *No. 31 (1)* | 62.50 | 47.50 |
| *No. 367 (1)* | 4.00 | 2.25 |
| *No. 377 (1)* | 10.00 | 8.00 |
| *No. 169 (1)* | 6.50 | 4.50 |
| *Set total (8) Stamps* | 110.75 | 80.00 |

### Human Rights Year

Human Rights Flame — CD127

**1968, Aug. 10**

Afars & Issas............................322-323
Comoro Isls. .....................................76
Fr. Polynesia............................243-244
Fr. So. & Antarctic Terr. ....................32
New Caledonia................................369
St. Pierre & Miquelon.......................382
Wallis & Futuna Isls. .......................170

| | | |
|---|---|---|
| *Nos. 322-323 (2)* | 6.75 | 4.00 |
| *No. 76 (1)* | 3.50 | 3.50 |
| *Nos. 243-244 (2)* | 24.00 | 14.00 |
| *No. 32 (1)* | 55.00 | 47.50 |
| *No. 369 (1)* | 2.75 | 1.50 |
| *No. 382 (1)* | 8.00 | 5.50 |
| *No. 170 (1)* | 3.75 | 3.75 |
| *Set total (9) Stamps* | 103.75 | 79.75 |

### 2nd PHILEXAFRIQUE

CD128

Opening of PHILEXAFRIQUE, Abidjan, Feb. 14. Each stamp shows a local scene and stamp.

**1969, Feb. 14**

Cameroun......................................C118
Cent. Africa ..................................C65
Chad..............................................C48
Congo, P.R.....................................C77
Dahomey ........................................C94
Gabon.............................................C82
Ivory Coast ...........................C38-C40
Madagascar....................................C92
Mali ................................................C65
Mauritania......................................C80
Niger.............................................C104
Senegal ..........................................C68
Togo.............................................C104
Upper Volta....................................C62

| | | |
|---|---|---|
| *No. C118 (1)* | 3.25 | 1.25 |
| *No. C65 (1)* | 1.90 | 1.90 |
| *No. C48 (1)* | 2.40 | 1.00 |
| *No. C77 (1)* | 2.00 | 1.75 |
| *No. C94 (1)* | 2.25 | 2.25 |
| *No. C82 (1)* | 2.25 | 2.25 |
| *Nos. C38-C40 (3)* | 14.50 | 14.50 |
| *No. C92 (1)* | 1.75 | .85 |
| *No. C65 (1)* | 1.75 | 1.00 |
| *No. C80 (1)* | 1.90 | .75 |
| *No. C104 (1)* | 2.75 | 1.90 |
| *No. C68 (1)* | 2.00 | 1.40 |
| *No. C104 (1)* | 2.25 | .45 |
| *No. C62 (1)* | 4.00 | 3.25 |
| *Set total (16) Stamps* | 44.95 | 34.50 |

### Concorde

Concorde in Flight CD129

First flight of the prototype Concorde supersonic plane at Toulouse, Mar. 1, 1969.

**1969**

Afars & Issas..................................C56
Comoro Isls. ...................................C29
France............................................C42
Fr. Polynesia..................................C50
Fr. So. & Antarctic Terr. ................C18
New Caledonia..............................C63
St. Pierre & Miquelon.....................C40
Wallis & Futuna Isls. .....................C30

| | | |
|---|---|---|
| *No. C56 (1)* | 26.00 | 16.00 |
| *No. C29 (1)* | 24.00 | 16.00 |
| *No. C42 (1)* | .75 | .35 |
| *No. C50 (1)* | 55.00 | 35.00 |
| *No. C18 (1)* | 55.00 | 37.50 |
| *No. C63 (1)* | 27.50 | 20.00 |
| *No. C40 (1)* | 30.00 | 11.00 |
| *No. C30 (1)* | 15.00 | 10.00 |
| *Set total (8) Stamps* | 233.25 | 145.85 |

### Development Bank

Bank Emblem — CD130

African Development Bank, fifth anniv.

**1969**

Cameroun.........................................499
Chad................................................217
Congo, P.R..................................181-182
Ivory Coast .....................................281
Mali .........................................127-128
Mauritania.......................................267
Niger...............................................220
Senegal .....................................317-318
Upper Volta.....................................201

| | | |
|---|---|---|
| *No. 499 (1)* | .80 | .25 |
| *No. 217 (1)* | .70 | .25 |
| *Nos. 181-182 (2)* | .80 | .50 |
| *No. 281 (1)* | .70 | .40 |
| *Nos. 127-128 (2)* | 1.00 | .50 |
| *No. 267 (1)* | .60 | .25 |
| *No. 220 (1)* | .60 | .30 |
| *Nos. 317-318 (2)* | 1.55 | .50 |
| *No. 201 (1)* | .65 | .30 |
| *Set total (12) Stamps* | 7.40 | 3.25 |

### ILO

ILO Headquarters, Geneva, and Emblem — CD131

Intl. Labor Organization, 50th anniv.

**1969-70**

Afars & Issas...................................337
Comoro Isls. .....................................83
Fr. Polynesia............................251-252
Fr. So. & Antarctic Terr. ....................35
New Caledonia................................379
St. Pierre & Miquelon.......................396
Wallis & Futuna Isls. .......................172

| | | |
|---|---|---|
| *No. 337 (1)* | 2.75 | 2.00 |
| *No. 83 (1)* | 1.25 | .75 |
| *Nos. 251-252 (2)* | 24.00 | 12.50 |
| *No. 35 (1)* | 15.00 | 10.00 |
| *No. 379 (1)* | 2.25 | 1.10 |
| *No. 396 (1)* | 8.50 | 5.50 |
| *No. 172 (1)* | 3.00 | 2.90 |
| *Set total (8) Stamps* | 56.75 | 34.75 |

### ASECNA

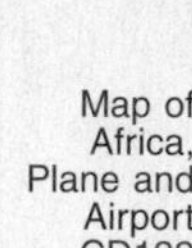

Map of Africa, Plane and Airport CD132

10th anniversary of the Agency for the Security of Aerial Navigation in Africa and Madagascar (ASECNA, Agence pour la Securite de la Navigation Aerienne en Afrique et a Madagascar).

**1969-70**

Cameroun.........................................500
Cent. Africa .....................................119
Chad................................................222
Congo, P.R.......................................197
Dahomey .........................................269
Gabon..............................................260
Ivory Coast .....................................287
Mali .................................................130
Niger...............................................221
Senegal ..........................................321
Upper Volta.....................................204

| | | |
|---|---|---|
| *No. 500 (1)* | 2.00 | .60 |
| *No. 119 (1)* | 2.25 | .80 |
| *No. 222 (1)* | 1.00 | .25 |
| *No. 197 (1)* | 2.00 | .40 |
| *No. 269 (1)* | .90 | .55 |
| *No. 260 (1)* | 1.75 | .75 |
| *No. 287 (1)* | .90 | .40 |
| *No. 130 (1)* | .90 | .40 |
| *No. 221 (1)* | 1.25 | .70 |
| *No. 321 (1)* | 1.60 | .50 |
| *No. 204 (1)* | 1.75 | 1.00 |
| *Set total (11) Stamps* | 16.30 | 6.35 |

### U.P.U. Headquarters

CD133

New Universal Postal Union headquarters, Bern, Switzerland.

### 1970

Afars & Issas ........ 342
Algeria ........ 443
Cameroun ........ 503-504
Cent. Africa ........ 125
Chad ........ 225
Comoro Isls. ........ 84
Congo, P.R. ........ 216
Fr. Polynesia ........ 261-262
Fr. So. & Antarctic Terr. ........ 36
Gabon ........ 258
Ivory Coast ........ 295
Madagascar ........ 444
Mali ........ 134-135
Mauritania ........ 283
New Caledonia ........ 382
Niger ........ 231-232
St. Pierre & Miquelon ........ 397-398
Senegal ........ 328-329
Tunisia ........ 535
Wallis & Futuna Isls. ........ 173

| | | |
|---|---|---|
| *No. 342 (1)* | 2.50 | 1.40 |
| *No. 443 (1)* | 1.10 | .40 |
| *Nos. 503-504 (2)* | 2.60 | .55 |
| *No. 125 (1)* | 1.90 | .70 |
| *No. 225 (1)* | 1.00 | .25 |
| *No. 84 (1)* | 5.50 | 2.00 |
| *No. 216 (1)* | .80 | .25 |
| *Nos. 261-262 (2)* | 20.00 | 10.00 |
| *No. 36 (1)* | 40.00 | 27.50 |
| *No. 258 (1)* | .90 | .55 |
| *No. 295 (1)* | 1.10 | .50 |
| *No. 444 (1)* | .55 | .25 |
| *Nos. 134-135 (2)* | 1.05 | .50 |
| *No. 283 (1)* | .60 | .30 |
| *No. 382 (1)* | 3.00 | 1.50 |
| *Nos. 231-232 (2)* | 1.20 | .60 |
| *Nos. 397-398 (2)* | 28.00 | 17.00 |
| *Nos. 328-329 (2)* | 1.55 | .55 |
| *No. 535 (1)* | .60 | .25 |
| *No. 173 (1)* | 4.00 | 4.00 |
| *Set total (26) Stamps* | 117.95 | 69.05 |

### De Gaulle

CD134

First anniversary of the death of Charles de Gaulle, (1890-1970), President of France.

### 1971-72

Afars & Issas ........ 356-357
Comoro Isls. ........ 104-105
France ........ 1325a
Fr. Polynesia ........ 270-271
Fr. So. & Antarctic Terr. ........ 52-53
New Caledonia ........ 393-394
Reunion ........ 380a
St. Pierre & Miquelon ........ 417-418
Wallis & Futuna Isls. ........ 177-178

| | | |
|---|---|---|
| *Nos. 356-357 (2)* | 12.50 | 7.50 |
| *Nos. 104-105 (2)* | 9.00 | 5.75 |
| *No. 1325a (1)* | 3.00 | 2.50 |
| *Nos. 270-271 (2)* | 51.50 | 29.50 |
| *Nos. 52-53 (2)* | 40.00 | 29.50 |
| *Nos. 393-394 (2)* | 23.00 | 11.75 |
| *No. 380a (1)* | 9.25 | 8.00 |
| *Nos. 417-418 (2)* | 40.00 | 30.00 |
| *Nos. 177-178 (2)* | 24.00 | 16.25 |
| *Set total (16) Stamps* | 212.25 | 140.75 |

### African Postal Union, 1971

UAMPT Building, Brazzaville, Congo — CD135

10th anniversary of the establishment of the African and Malagasy Posts and Telecommunications Union, UAMPT. Each stamp has a different native design.

### 1971, Nov. 13

Cameroun ........ C177
Cent. Africa ........ C89
Chad ........ C94
Congo, P.R. ........ C136
Dahomey ........ C146
Gabon ........ C120
Ivory Coast ........ C47
Mauritania ........ C113
Niger ........ C164
Rwanda ........ C8
Senegal ........ C105
Togo ........ C166
Upper Volta ........ C97

| | | |
|---|---|---|
| *No. C177 (1)* | 2.00 | .50 |
| *No. C89 (1)* | 2.25 | .85 |
| *No. C94 (1)* | 1.50 | .50 |
| *No. C136 (1)* | 1.60 | .75 |
| *No. C146 (1)* | 1.75 | .80 |
| *No. C120 (1)* | 1.75 | .70 |
| *No. C47 (1)* | 2.00 | 1.00 |
| *No. C113 (1)* | 1.20 | .65 |
| *No. C164 (1)* | 1.25 | .60 |
| *No. C8 (1)* | 2.75 | 2.25 |
| *No. C105 (1)* | 1.60 | .50 |
| *No. C166 (1)* | 1.25 | .40 |
| *No. C97 (1)* | 1.50 | .70 |
| *Set total (13) Stamps* | 22.40 | 10.20 |

### West African Monetary Union

African Couple, City, Village and Commemorative Coin — CD136

West African Monetary Union, 10th anniv.

### 1972, Nov. 2

Dahomey ........ 300
Ivory Coast ........ 331
Mauritania ........ 299
Niger ........ 258
Senegal ........ 374
Togo ........ 825
Upper Volta ........ 280

| | | |
|---|---|---|
| *No. 300 (1)* | .65 | .25 |
| *No. 331 (1)* | 1.00 | .50 |
| *No. 299 (1)* | .75 | .25 |
| *No. 258 (1)* | .55 | .30 |
| *No. 374 (1)* | .50 | .30 |
| *No. 825 (1)* | .60 | .25 |
| *No. 280 (1)* | .60 | .25 |
| *Set total (7) Stamps* | 4.65 | 2.10 |

### African Postal Union, 1973

Telecommunications Symbols and Map of Africa — CD137

11th anniversary of the African and Malagasy Posts and Telecommunications Union (UAMPT).

### 1973, Sept. 12

Cameroun ........ 574
Cent. Africa ........ 194
Chad ........ 294
Congo, P.R. ........ 289
Dahomey ........ 311
Gabon ........ 320
Ivory Coast ........ 361
Madagascar ........ 500
Mauritania ........ 304
Niger ........ 287
Rwanda ........ 540
Senegal ........ 393
Togo ........ 849
Upper Volta ........ 297

| | | |
|---|---|---|
| *No. 574 (1)* | 1.75 | .40 |
| *No. 194 (1)* | 1.25 | .75 |
| *No. 294 (1)* | 1.75 | .40 |
| *No. 289 (1)* | 1.60 | .50 |
| *No. 311 (1)* | 1.25 | .55 |
| *No. 320 (1)* | 1.40 | .75 |
| *No. 361 (1)* | 2.50 | 1.00 |
| *No. 500 (1)* | 1.10 | .35 |
| *No. 304 (1)* | 1.10 | .40 |
| *No. 287 (1)* | .90 | .60 |
| *No. 540 (1)* | 3.75 | 2.00 |
| *No. 393 (1)* | 1.60 | .50 |
| *No. 849 (1)* | 1.00 | .35 |
| *No. 297 (1)* | 1.25 | .70 |
| *Set total (14) Stamps* | 22.20 | 9.25 |

### Philexafrique II — Essen

CD138

CD139

Designs: Indigenous fauna, local and German stamps. Types CD138-CD139 printed horizontally and vertically se-tenant in sheets of 10 (2x5). Label between horizontal pairs alternately commemoratives Philexafrique II, Libreville, Gabon, June 1978, and 2nd International Stamp Fair, Essen, Germany, Nov. 1-5.

### 1978-1979

Benin ........ C286a
Central Africa ........ C201a
Chad ........ C239a
Congo Republic ........ C246a
Djibouti ........ C122a
Gabon ........ C216a
Ivory Coast ........ C65a
Mali ........ C357a
Mauritania ........ C186a
Niger ........ C292a
Rwanda ........ C13a
Senegal ........ C147a
Togo ........ C364a

| | | |
|---|---|---|
| *No. C286a (1)* | 9.00 | 8.50 |
| *No. C201a (1)* | 7.50 | 7.50 |
| *No. C239a (1)* | 8.00 | 4.00 |
| *No. C246a (1)* | 7.00 | 7.00 |
| *No. C122a (1)* | 8.50 | 8.50 |
| *No. C216a (1)* | 6.50 | 4.00 |
| *No. C65a (1)* | 9.00 | 9.00 |
| *No. C357a (1)* | 5.00 | 3.00 |
| *No. C186a (1)* | 4.50 | 4.00 |
| *No. C292a (1)* | 6.00 | 5.00 |
| *No. C13a (1)* | 4.00 | 4.00 |
| *No. C147a (1)* | 10.00 | 4.00 |
| *No. C364a (1)* | 3.00 | 1.50 |
| *Set total (13) Stamps* | 88.00 | 70.00 |

---

## BRITISH COMMONWEALTH OF NATIONS

The listings follow established trade practices when these issues are offered as units by dealers. The Peace issue, for example, includes only one stamp from the Indian state of Hyderabad. The U.P.U. issue includes the Egypt set. Pairs are included for those varieties issued with bilingual designs se-tenant.

### Silver Jubilee

Windsor Castle and King George V CD301

Reign of King George V, 25th anniv.

### 1935

Antigua ........ 77-80
Ascension ........ 33-36
Bahamas ........ 92-95
Barbados ........ 186-189
Basutoland ........ 11-14
Bechuanaland Protectorate ........ 117-120
Bermuda ........ 100-103
British Guiana ........ 223-226
British Honduras ........ 108-111
Cayman Islands ........ 81-84
Ceylon ........ 260-263
Cyprus ........ 136-139
Dominica ........ 90-93
Falkland Islands ........ 77-80
Fiji ........ 110-113
Gambia ........ 125-128
Gibraltar ........ 100-103
Gilbert & Ellice Islands ........ 33-36
Gold Coast ........ 108-111
Grenada ........ 124-127
Hong Kong ........ 147-150
Jamaica ........ 109-112
Kenya, Uganda, Tanzania ........ 42-45
Leeward Islands ........ 96-99
Malta ........ 184-187
Mauritius ........ 204-207
Montserrat ........ 85-88
Newfoundland ........ 226-229
Nigeria ........ 34-37
Northern Rhodesia ........ 18-21
Nyasaland Protectorate ........ 47-50
St. Helena ........ 111-114
St. Kitts-Nevis ........ 72-75
St. Lucia ........ 91-94
St. Vincent ........ 134-137
Seychelles ........ 118-121
Sierra Leone ........ 166-169
Solomon Islands ........ 60-63
Somaliland Protectorate ........ 77-80
Straits Settlements ........ 213-216
Swaziland ........ 20-23
Trinidad & Tobago ........ 43-46
Turks & Caicos Islands ........ 71-74
Virgin Islands ........ 69-72

The following have different designs but are included in the omnibus set:

Great Britain ........ 226-229
Offices in Morocco (Sp. Curr.) ........ 67-70
Offices in Morocco (Br. Curr.) ........ 226-229
Offices in Morocco (Fr. Curr.) ........ 422-425
Offices in Morocco (Tangier) ........ 508-510
Australia ........ 152-154
Canada ........ 211-216
Cook Islands ........ 98-100
India ........ 142-148
Nauru ........ 31-34
New Guinea ........ 46-47
New Zealand ........ 199-201
Niue ........ 67-69
Papua ........ 114-117
Samoa ........ 163-165
South Africa ........ 68-71
Southern Rhodesia ........ 33-36
South-West Africa ........ 121-124

| | | |
|---|---|---|
| *Nos. 77-80 (4)* | 20.25 | *23.25* |
| *Nos. 33-36 (4)* | 58.50 | *127.50* |
| *Nos. 92-95 (4)* | 25.00 | *46.00* |
| *Nos. 186-189 (4)* | 30.00 | 46.80 |
| *Nos. 11-14 (4)* | 11.60 | *21.25* |
| *Nos. 117-120 (4)* | 15.75 | *36.00* |
| *Nos. 100-103 (4)* | 16.80 | *58.50* |
| *Nos. 223-226 (4)* | 18.35 | 35.50 |
| *Nos. 108-111 (4)* | 15.25 | *16.35* |
| *Nos. 81-84 (4)* | 21.60 | *24.50* |
| *Nos. 260-263 (4)* | 10.40 | 21.60 |
| *Nos. 136-139 (4)* | 39.75 | *34.40* |
| *Nos. 90-93 (4)* | 18.85 | 19.85 |
| *Nos. 77-80 (4)* | 55.00 | 14.75 |
| *Nos. 110-113 (4)* | 15.25 | 27.90 |
| *Nos. 125-128 (4)* | 12.20 | *25.25* |
| *Nos. 100-103 (4)* | 28.75 | 42.75 |
| *Nos. 33-36 (4)* | 36.80 | *67.00* |
| *Nos. 108-111 (4)* | 25.75 | *78.10* |
| *Nos. 124-127 (4)* | 16.70 | *40.60* |
| *Nos. 147-150 (4)* | 59.00 | 18.75 |
| *Nos. 109-112 (4)* | 17.00 | 39.00 |
| *Nos. 42-45 (4)* | 8.75 | *11.00* |
| *Nos. 96-99 (4)* | 35.75 | 49.60 |
| *Nos. 184-187 (4)* | 22.00 | 33.70 |
| *Nos. 204-207 (4)* | 47.60 | 58.25 |
| *Nos. 85-88 (4)* | 10.25 | *30.25* |
| *Nos. 226-229 (4)* | 17.50 | 12.05 |
| *Nos. 34-37 (4)* | 13.25 | *59.75* |
| *Nos. 18-21 (4)* | 16.75 | 16.25 |
| *Nos. 47-50 (4)* | 39.75 | *80.25* |
| *Nos. 111-114 (4)* | 31.15 | *33.25* |
| *Nos. 72-75 (4)* | 11.55 | *18.50* |
| *Nos. 91-94 (4)* | 16.00 | *20.80* |
| *Nos. 134-137 (4)* | 9.45 | *21.25* |
| *Nos. 118-121 (4)* | 17.50 | *32.50* |
| *Nos. 166-169 (4)* | 24.25 | *56.00* |
| *Nos. 60-63 (4)* | 27.25 | 38.00 |
| *Nos. 77-80 (4)* | 17.00 | *48.25* |
| *Nos. 213-216 (4)* | 15.00 | *25.10* |
| *Nos. 20-23 (4)* | 6.80 | 18.25 |
| *Nos. 43-46 (4)* | 14.05 | 27.75 |
| *Nos. 71-74 (4)* | 8.40 | 14.50 |
| *Nos. 69-72 (4)* | 25.00 | 55.25 |
| *Nos. 226-229 (4)* | 5.15 | *4.40* |

| | | |
|---|---|---|
| *Nos. 67-70 (4)* | 14.35 | *26.10* |
| *Nos. 226-229 (4)* | 8.20 | *28.90* |
| *Nos. 422-425 (4)* | 3.90 | 2.00 |
| *Nos. 508-510 (3)* | 18.80 | *23.85* |
| *Nos. 152-154 (3)* | 45.75 | 60.35 |
| *Nos. 211-216 (6)* | 24.85 | 13.35 |
| *Nos. 98-100 (3)* | 9.65 | *12.00* |
| *Nos. 142-148 (7)* | 28.85 | 14.00 |
| *Nos. 31-34 (4)* | 9.90 | *9.90* |
| *Nos. 46-47 (2)* | 4.35 | 1.70 |
| *Nos. 199-201 (3)* | 21.75 | *31.75* |
| *Nos. 67-69 (3)* | 11.30 | *26.50* |
| *Nos. 114-117 (4)* | 9.20 | *17.00* |
| *Nos. 163-165 (3)* | 4.40 | 5.50 |
| *Nos. 68-71 (4)* | 57.00 | *155.00* |
| *Nos. 33-36 (4)* | 27.75 | *45.25* |
| *Nos. 121-124 (4)* | 13.00 | *36.10* |
| *Set total (245) Stamps* | 1,322. | 2,140. |

## Coronation

Queen Elizabeth and King George VI CD302

### 1937

Aden ..........13-15
Antigua ..........81-83
Ascension ..........37-39
Bahamas ..........97-99
Barbados ..........190-192
Basutoland ..........15-17
Bechuanaland Protectorate ..........121-123
Bermuda ..........115-117
British Guiana ..........227-229
British Honduras ..........112-114
Cayman Islands ..........97-99
Ceylon ..........275-277
Cyprus ..........140-142
Dominica ..........94-96
Falkland Islands ..........81-83
Fiji ..........114-116
Gambia ..........129-131
Gibraltar ..........104-106
Gilbert & Ellice Islands ..........37-39
Gold Coast ..........112-114
Grenada ..........128-130
Hong Kong ..........151-153
Jamaica ..........113-115
Kenya, Uganda, Tanzania ..........60-62
Leeward Islands ..........100-102
Malta ..........188-190
Mauritius ..........208-210
Montserrat ..........89-91
Newfoundland ..........230-232
Nigeria ..........50-52
Northern Rhodesia ..........22-24
Nyasaland Protectorate ..........51-53
St. Helena ..........115-117
St. Kitts-Nevis ..........76-78
St. Lucia ..........107-109
St. Vincent ..........138-140
Seychelles ..........122-124
Sierra Leone ..........170-172
Solomon Islands ..........64-66
Somaliland Protectorate ..........81-83
Straits Settlements ..........235-237
Swaziland ..........24-26
Trinidad & Tobago ..........47-49
Turks & Caicos Islands ..........75-77
Virgin Islands ..........73-75

The following have different designs but are included in the omnibus set:

Great Britain ..........234
Offices in Morocco (Sp. Curr.) ..........82
Offices in Morocco (Fr. Curr.) ..........439
Offices in Morocco (Tangier) ..........514
Canada ..........237
Cook Islands ..........109-111
Nauru ..........35-38
Newfoundland ..........233-243
New Guinea ..........48-51
New Zealand ..........223-225
Niue ..........70-72
Papua ..........118-121
South Africa ..........74-78
Southern Rhodesia ..........38-41
South-West Africa ..........125-132

| | | |
|---|---|---|
| *Nos. 13-15 (3)* | 2.70 | *5.65* |
| *Nos. 81-83 (3)* | 1.85 | *8.00* |
| *Nos. 37-39 (3)* | 2.75 | *2.75* |
| *Nos. 97-99 (3)* | 1.05 | *3.05* |
| *Nos. 190-192 (3)* | 1.10 | 1.95 |
| *Nos. 15-17 (3)* | 1.15 | *3.00* |
| *Nos. 121-123 (3)* | .95 | 3.35 |
| *Nos. 115-117 (3)* | 1.25 | 5.00 |
| *Nos. 227-229 (3)* | 1.45 | 3.05 |
| *Nos. 112-114 (3)* | 1.20 | 2.40 |
| *Nos. 97-99 (3)* | 1.10 | 2.70 |
| *Nos. 275-277 (3)* | 8.25 | 10.35 |
| *Nos. 140-142 (3)* | 3.75 | 6.50 |
| *Nos. 94-96 (3)* | .85 | 2.40 |
| *Nos. 81-83 (3)* | 2.90 | *2.30* |
| *Nos. 114-116 (3)* | 1.50 | *5.75* |
| *Nos. 129-131 (3)* | .95 | 3.95 |
| *Nos. 104-106 (3)* | 2.25 | 6.45 |
| *Nos. 37-39 (3)* | .85 | *2.15* |
| *Nos. 112-114 (3)* | 3.10 | *10.00* |
| *Nos. 128-130 (3)* | 1.00 | .85 |
| *Nos. 151-153 (3)* | 23.00 | 12.50 |
| *Nos. 113-115 (3)* | 1.25 | 1.25 |
| *Nos. 60-62 (3)* | 1.00 | 2.35 |
| *Nos. 100-102 (3)* | 1.55 | 4.00 |
| *Nos. 188-190 (3)* | 1.25 | 1.60 |
| *Nos. 208-210 (3)* | 2.05 | 3.75 |
| *Nos. 89-91 (3)* | 1.00 | 3.35 |
| *Nos. 230-232 (3)* | 7.00 | 2.80 |
| *Nos. 50-52 (3)* | 3.25 | 8.50 |
| *Nos. 22-24 (3)* | .95 | 2.25 |
| *Nos. 51-53 (3)* | 1.05 | 1.30 |
| *Nos. 115-117 (3)* | 1.45 | 2.05 |
| *Nos. 76-78 (3)* | .95 | 2.05 |
| *Nos. 107-109 (3)* | 1.05 | 2.05 |
| *Nos. 138-140 (3)* | .80 | *4.75* |
| *Nos. 122-124 (3)* | 1.20 | *1.90* |
| *Nos. 170-172 (3)* | 1.95 | 5.65 |
| *Nos. 64-66 (3)* | .90 | 2.00 |
| *Nos. 81-83 (3)* | 1.10 | *3.40* |
| *Nos. 235-237 (3)* | 3.25 | 1.60 |
| *Nos. 24-26 (3)* | 1.05 | 1.75 |
| *Nos. 47-49 (3)* | 1.00 | 1.00 |
| *Nos. 75-77 (3)* | 1.30 | 1.15 |
| *Nos. 73-75 (3)* | 2.20 | 6.90 |

| | | |
|---|---|---|
| *No. 234 (1)* | .25 | .25 |
| *No. 82 (1)* | .80 | .80 |
| *No. 439 (1)* | .35 | .25 |
| *No. 514 (1)* | .55 | .55 |
| *No. 237 (1)* | .35 | .25 |
| *Nos. 109-111 (3)* | .85 | .80 |
| *Nos. 35-38 (4)* | 1.10 | *5.50* |
| *Nos. 233-243 (11)* | 41.90 | 30.40 |
| *Nos. 48-51 (4)* | 1.40 | *7.90* |
| *Nos. 223-225 (3)* | 1.40 | *2.75* |
| *Nos. 70-72 (3)* | .80 | *2.05* |
| *Nos. 118-121 (4)* | 1.60 | *5.25* |
| *Nos. 74-78 (5)* | 9.25 | 10.80 |
| *Nos. 38-41 (4)* | 3.55 | 15.50 |
| *Nos. 125-132 (8)* | 5.00 | 8.40 |
| *Set total (189) Stamps* | 172.65 | 262.95 |

## Peace

King George VI and Parliament Buildings, London CD303

Return to peace at the close of World War II.

### 1945-46

Aden ..........28-29
Antigua ..........96-97
Ascension ..........50-51
Bahamas ..........130-131
Barbados ..........207-208
Bermuda ..........131-132
British Guiana ..........242-243
British Honduras ..........127-128
Cayman Islands ..........112-113
Ceylon ..........293-294
Cyprus ..........156-157
Dominica ..........112-113
Falkland Islands ..........97-98
Falkland Islands Dep. ..........1L9-1L10
Fiji ..........137-138
Gambia ..........144-145
Gibraltar ..........119-120
Gilbert & Ellice Islands ..........52-53
Gold Coast ..........128-129
Grenada ..........143-144
Jamaica ..........136-137
Kenya, Uganda, Tanzania ..........90-91
Leeward Islands ..........116-117
Malta ..........206-207
Mauritius ..........223-224
Montserrat ..........104-105
Nigeria ..........71-72
Northern Rhodesia ..........46-47
Nyasaland Protectorate ..........82-83
Pitcairn Islands ..........9-10
St. Helena ..........128-129
St. Kitts-Nevis ..........91-92
St. Lucia ..........127-128
St. Vincent ..........152-153
Seychelles ..........149-150
Sierra Leone ..........186-187
Solomon Islands ..........80-81
Somaliland Protectorate ..........108-109
Trinidad & Tobago ..........62-63
Turks & Caicos Islands ..........90-91
Virgin Islands ..........88-89

The following have different designs but are included in the omnibus set:

Great Britain ..........264-265
Offices in Morocco (Tangier) ..........523-524
Aden
  Kathiri State of Seiyun ..........12-13
  Qu'aiti State of Shihr and Mukalla ..........12-13
Australia ..........200-202
Basutoland ..........29-31
Bechuanaland Protectorate ..........137-139
Burma ..........66-69
Cook Islands ..........127-130
Hong Kong ..........174-175
India ..........195-198
  Hyderabad ..........51-53
New Zealand ..........247-257
Niue ..........90-93
Pakistan-Bahawalpur ..........O16
Samoa ..........191-194
South Africa ..........100-102
Southern Rhodesia ..........67-70
South-West Africa ..........153-155
Swaziland ..........38-40
Zanzibar ..........222-223

| | | |
|---|---|---|
| *Nos. 28-29 (2)* | .95 | 2.50 |
| *Nos. 96-97 (2)* | .50 | *.80* |
| *Nos. 50-51 (2)* | .80 | *2.00* |
| *Nos. 130-131 (2)* | .50 | 1.40 |
| *Nos. 207-208 (2)* | .50 | 1.10 |
| *Nos. 131-132 (2)* | .55 | .55 |
| *Nos. 242-243 (2)* | 1.05 | *1.40* |
| *Nos. 127-128 (2)* | .50 | .50 |
| *Nos. 112-113 (2)* | .80 | .80 |
| *Nos. 293-294 (2)* | .60 | *2.10* |
| *Nos. 156-157 (2)* | .90 | .70 |
| *Nos. 112-113 (2)* | .50 | .50 |
| *Nos. 97-98 (2)* | .90 | 1.35 |
| *Nos. 1L9-1L10 (2)* | 1.30 | 1.00 |
| *Nos. 137-138 (2)* | .50 | *1.75* |
| *Nos. 144-145 (2)* | .50 | .95 |
| *Nos. 119-120 (2)* | .75 | *1.00* |
| *Nos. 52-53 (2)* | .50 | *1.10* |
| *Nos. 128-129 (2)* | 1.85 | *3.75* |
| *Nos. 143-144 (2)* | .50 | *.95* |
| *Nos. 136-137 (2)* | .80 | *12.50* |
| *Nos. 90-91 (2)* | .65 | .65 |
| *Nos. 116-117 (2)* | .50 | 1.50 |
| *Nos. 206-207 (2)* | .65 | 2.00 |
| *Nos. 223-224 (2)* | .50 | 1.05 |
| *Nos. 104-105 (2)* | .50 | .50 |
| *Nos. 71-72 (2)* | .70 | *2.75* |
| *Nos. 46-47 (2)* | 1.25 | *2.00* |
| *Nos. 82-83 (2)* | .50 | .50 |
| *Nos. 9-10 (2)* | 1.40 | 1.40 |
| *Nos. 128-129 (2)* | .65 | .70 |
| *Nos. 91-92 (2)* | .50 | .50 |
| *Nos. 127-128 (2)* | .50 | .60 |
| *Nos. 152-153 (2)* | .50 | .50 |
| *Nos. 149-150 (2)* | .55 | .50 |
| *Nos. 186-187 (2)* | .50 | .50 |
| *Nos. 80-81 (2)* | .50 | 1.50 |
| *Nos. 108-109 (2)* | .70 | .50 |
| *Nos. 62-63 (2)* | .50 | .50 |
| *Nos. 90-91 (2)* | .50 | .50 |
| *Nos. 88-89 (2)* | .50 | .50 |

| | | |
|---|---|---|
| *Nos. 264-265 (2)* | .50 | .50 |
| *Nos. 523-524 (2)* | 1.50 | 3.00 |
| *Nos. 12-13 (2)* | .50 | .90 |
| *Nos. 12-13 (2)* | .50 | *1.25* |
| *Nos. 200-202 (3)* | 1.60 | *3.00* |
| *Nos. 29-31 (3)* | 2.10 | 2.60 |
| *Nos. 137-139 (3)* | 2.05 | *4.75* |
| *Nos. 66-69 (4)* | 1.60 | 1.30 |
| *Nos. 127-130 (4)* | 2.00 | 1.85 |
| *Nos. 174-175 (2)* | 6.75 | 3.15 |
| *Nos. 195-198 (4)* | 5.60 | 5.50 |
| *Nos. 51-53 (3)* | 1.50 | 1.70 |
| *Nos. 247-257 (11)* | 3.95 | 3.90 |
| *Nos. 90-93 (4)* | 1.70 | *2.20* |
| *No. O16 (1)* | 5.50 | *7.00* |
| *Nos. 191-194 (4)* | 2.05 | 1.00 |
| *Nos. 100-102 (3)* | 1.20 | 4.00 |
| *Nos. 67-70 (4)* | 1.40 | 1.75 |
| *Nos. 153-155 (3)* | 1.85 | 3.25 |
| *Nos. 38-40 (3)* | 2.40 | *5.50* |
| *Nos. 222-223 (2)* | .65 | 1.00 |
| *Set total (151) Stamps* | 75.20 | 116.95 |

## Silver Wedding

King George VI and Queen Elizabeth

CD304 CD305

### 1948-49

Aden ..........30-31
  Kathiri State of Seiyun ..........14-15
  Qu'aiti State of Shihr and Mukalla ..........14-15
Antigua ..........98-99
Ascension ..........52-53
Bahamas ..........148-149
Barbados ..........210-211
Basutoland ..........39-40
Bechuanaland Protectorate ..........147-148
Bermuda ..........133-134
British Guiana ..........244-245
British Honduras ..........129-130
Cayman Islands ..........116-117
Cyprus ..........158-159
Dominica ..........114-115
Falkland Islands ..........99-100
Falkland Islands Dep. ..........1L11-1L12
Fiji ..........139-140
Gambia ..........146-147
Gibraltar ..........121-122
Gilbert & Ellice Islands ..........54-55
Gold Coast ..........142-143
Grenada ..........145-146
Hong Kong ..........178-179
Jamaica ..........138-139
Kenya, Uganda, Tanzania ..........92-93
Leeward Islands ..........118-119
Malaya
  Johore ..........128-129
  Kedah ..........55-56
  Kelantan ..........44-45
  Malacca ..........1-2
  Negri Sembilan ..........36-37
  Pahang ..........44-45
  Penang ..........1-2
  Perak ..........99-100
  Perlis ..........1-2
  Selangor ..........74-75
  Trengganu ..........47-48
Malta ..........223-224
Mauritius ..........229-230
Montserrat ..........106-107
Nigeria ..........73-74
North Borneo ..........238-239
Northern Rhodesia ..........48-49
Nyasaland Protectorate ..........85-86
Pitcairn Islands ..........11-12
St. Helena ..........130-131
St. Kitts-Nevis ..........93-94
St. Lucia ..........129-130
St. Vincent ..........154-155
Sarawak ..........174-175
Seychelles ..........151-152
Sierra Leone ..........188-189
Singapore ..........21-22
Solomon Islands ..........82-83
Somaliland Protectorate ..........110-111
Swaziland ..........48-49
Trinidad & Tobago ..........64-65
Turks & Caicos Islands ..........92-93
Virgin Islands ..........90-91
Zanzibar ..........224-225

The following have different designs but are included in the omnibus set:

Great Britain ..........267-268
  Offices in Morocco (Sp. Curr.) ..........93-94
  Offices in Morocco (Tangier) ..........525-526
Bahrain ..........62-63
Kuwait ..........82-83
Oman ..........25-26
South Africa ..........106
South-West Africa ..........159

| | | |
|---|---|---|
| *Nos. 30-31 (2)* | 40.40 | 47.25 |
| *Nos. 14-15 (2)* | 17.85 | *16.00* |
| *Nos. 14-15 (2)* | 18.55 | *12.50* |
| *Nos. 98-99 (2)* | 13.55 | *15.75* |
| *Nos. 52-53 (2)* | 55.55 | 50.45 |
| *Nos. 148-149 (2)* | 45.25 | 40.30 |
| *Nos. 210-211 (2)* | 18.35 | 13.05 |
| *Nos. 39-40 (2)* | 52.80 | *55.25* |
| *Nos. 147-148 (2)* | 42.85 | *47.75* |
| *Nos. 133-134 (2)* | 47.75 | *55.25* |
| *Nos. 244-245 (2)* | 24.25 | *28.45* |
| *Nos. 129-130 (2)* | 25.25 | *53.20* |
| *Nos. 116-117 (2)* | 25.25 | *33.50* |
| *Nos. 158-159 (2)* | 58.50 | *78.05* |
| *Nos. 114-115 (2)* | 25.25 | *32.75* |
| *Nos. 99-100 (2)* | 112.10 | 76.10 |
| *Nos. 1L11-1L12 (2)* | 4.25 | 6.00 |
| *Nos. 139-140 (2)* | 17.00 | 11.50 |
| *Nos. 146-147 (2)* | 21.25 | 21.25 |
| *Nos. 121-122 (2)* | 61.00 | *78.00* |
| *Nos. 54-55 (2)* | 14.25 | *26.25* |
| *Nos. 142-143 (2)* | 35.25 | 48.20 |
| *Nos. 145-146 (2)* | 21.75 | 21.75 |
| *Nos. 178-179 (2)* | 283.50 | 96.50 |
| *Nos. 138-139 (2)* | 27.85 | *60.25* |
| *Nos. 92-93 (2)* | 50.25 | *67.75* |
| *Nos. 118-119 (2)* | 7.00 | 8.25 |
| *Nos. 128-129 (2)* | 29.25 | *53.25* |
| *Nos. 55-56 (2)* | 35.25 | *50.25* |
| *Nos. 44-45 (2)* | 35.75 | *62.75* |
| *Nos. 1-2 (2)* | 35.40 | *49.75* |
| *Nos. 36-37 (2)* | 28.10 | *38.20* |
| *Nos. 44-45 (2)* | 28.00 | *38.05* |
| *Nos. 1-2 (2)* | 40.50 | 37.80 |

| | | |
|---|---|---|
| *Nos. 99-100 (2)* | 27.80 | *37.75* |
| *Nos. 1-2 (2)* | 33.50 | *58.00* |
| *Nos. 74-75 (2)* | 30.25 | 25.30 |
| *Nos. 47-48 (2)* | 35.25 | *62.75* |
| *Nos. 223-224 (2)* | 40.55 | 45.25 |
| *Nos. 229-230 (2)* | 17.75 | *45.25* |
| *Nos. 106-107 (2)* | 9.25 | *18.25* |
| *Nos. 73-74 (2)* | 17.85 | *22.80* |
| *Nos. 238-239 (2)* | 35.30 | *45.75* |
| *Nos. 48-49 (2)* | 92.80 | 90.25 |
| *Nos. 85-86 (2)* | 18.25 | *30.25* |
| *Nos. 11-12 (2)* | 44.75 | 48.50 |
| *Nos. 130-131 (2)* | 32.80 | *42.80* |
| *Nos. 93-94 (2)* | 11.25 | 7.25 |
| *Nos. 129-130 (2)* | 22.25 | *45.25* |
| *Nos. 154-155 (2)* | 27.75 | *30.25* |
| *Nos. 174-175 (2)* | 50.40 | *52.90* |
| *Nos. 151-152 (2)* | 16.25 | *45.75* |
| *Nos. 188-189 (2)* | 24.75 | *26.25* |
| *Nos. 21-22 (2)* | 116.00 | 45.40 |
| *Nos. 82-83 (2)* | 13.40 | 13.40 |
| *Nos. 110-111 (2)* | 8.40 | *8.75* |
| *Nos. 48-49 (2)* | 40.30 | *47.75* |
| *Nos. 64-65 (2)* | 32.75 | *38.25* |
| *Nos. 92-93 (2)* | 11.25 | *16.25* |
| *Nos. 90-91 (2)* | 16.25 | 22.25 |
| *Nos. 224-225 (2)* | 29.60 | 38.00 |
| *Nos. 267-268 (2)* | 30.40 | 25.25 |
| *Nos. 93-94 (2)* | 20.10 | 25.35 |
| *Nos. 525-526 (2)* | 23.10 | 29.25 |
| *Nos. 62-63 (2)* | 38.50 | *57.75* |
| *Nos. 82-83 (2)* | 45.50 | 45.50 |
| *Nos. 25-26 (2)* | 46.00 | *47.50* |
| *No. 106 (1)* | .90 | 1.25 |
| *No. 159 (1)* | 1.10 | .35 |
| *Set total (136) Stamps* | 2,461. | 2,674. |

### U.P.U.

Mercury and Symbols of Communications — CD306

Plane, Ship and Hemispheres — CD307

Mercury Scattering Letters over Globe CD308

U.P.U. Monument, Bern CD309

Universal Postal Union, 75th anniversary.

**1949**

Aden ... 32-35
Kathiri State of Seiyun ... 16-19
Qu'aiti State of Shihr and Mukalla ... 16-19
Antigua ... 100-103
Ascension ... 57-60
Bahamas ... 150-153
Barbados ... 212-215
Basutoland ... 41-44
Bechuanaland Protectorate ... 149-152
Bermuda ... 138-141
British Guiana ... 246-249
British Honduras ... 137-140
Brunei ... 79-82
Cayman Islands ... 118-121
Cyprus ... 160-163
Dominica ... 116-119
Falkland Islands ... 103-106
Falkland Islands Dep. ... 1L14-1L17
Fiji ... 141-144
Gambia ... 148-151
Gibraltar ... 123-126
Gilbert & Ellice Islands ... 56-59
Gold Coast ... 144-147
Grenada ... 147-150
Hong Kong ... 180-183
Jamaica ... 142-145
Kenya, Uganda, Tanzania ... 94-97
Leeward Islands ... 126-129
Malaya
Johore ... 151-154
Kedah ... 57-60
Kelantan ... 46-49
Malacca ... 18-21
Negri Sembilan ... 59-62
Pahang ... 46-49
Penang ... 23-26
Perak ... 101-104
Perlis ... 3-6
Selangor ... 76-79
Trengganu ... 49-52
Malta ... 225-228
Mauritius ... 231-234
Montserrat ... 108-111
New Hebrides, British ... 62-65
New Hebrides, French ... 79-82
Nigeria ... 75-78
North Borneo ... 240-243
Northern Rhodesia ... 50-53
Nyasaland Protectorate ... 87-90
Pitcairn Islands ... 13-16
St. Helena ... 132-135
St. Kitts-Nevis ... 95-98
St. Lucia ... 131-134
St. Vincent ... 170-173
Sarawak ... 176-179
Seychelles ... 153-156
Sierra Leone ... 190-193
Singapore ... 23-26
Solomon Islands ... 84-87
Somaliland Protectorate ... 112-115
Southern Rhodesia ... 71-72
Swaziland ... 50-53
Tonga ... 87-90
Trinidad & Tobago ... 66-69
Turks & Caicos Islands ... 101-104
Virgin Islands ... 92-95
Zanzibar ... 226-229

The following have different designs but are included in the omnibus set:

Great Britain ... 276-279
Offices in Morocco (Tangier) ... 546-549
Australia ... 223
Bahrain ... 68-71
Burma ... 116-121
Ceylon ... 304-306
Egypt ... 281-283
India ... 223-226
Kuwait ... 89-92
Oman ... 31-34
Pakistan-Bahawalpur 26-29, O25-O28
South Africa ... 109-111
South-West Africa ... 160-162

| | | |
|---|---|---|
| *Nos. 32-35 (4)* | 5.85 | *8.45* |
| *Nos. 16-19 (4)* | 2.75 | *5.50* |
| *Nos. 16-19 (4)* | 2.60 | 4.20 |
| *Nos. 100-103 (4)* | 3.60 | *7.70* |
| *Nos. 57-60 (4)* | 11.10 | 9.00 |
| *Nos. 150-153 (4)* | 5.35 | 9.30 |
| *Nos. 212-215 (4)* | 4.40 | 14.15 |
| *Nos. 41-44 (4)* | 4.75 | *10.00* |
| *Nos. 149-152 (4)* | 3.35 | *7.25* |
| *Nos. 138-141 (4)* | 4.75 | 6.15 |
| *Nos. 246-249 (4)* | 2.75 | 4.20 |
| *Nos. 137-140 (4)* | 3.30 | 6.35 |
| *Nos. 79-82 (4)* | 9.50 | 8.45 |
| *Nos. 118-121 (4)* | 3.60 | *7.25* |
| *Nos. 160-163 (4)* | 4.60 | *10.70* |
| *Nos. 116-119 (4)* | 2.30 | 5.65 |
| *Nos. 103-106 (4)* | 14.00 | 17.10 |
| *Nos. 1L14-1L17 (4)* | 14.60 | 14.50 |
| *Nos. 141-144 (4)* | 3.35 | 14.75 |
| *Nos. 148-151 (4)* | 3.10 | 7.10 |
| *Nos. 123-126 (4)* | 5.90 | *8.75* |
| *Nos. 56-59 (4)* | 4.30 | *13.00* |
| *Nos. 144-147 (4)* | 2.55 | *10.35* |
| *Nos. 147-150 (4)* | 2.15 | 3.55 |
| *Nos. 180-183 (4)* | 57.25 | 18.25 |
| *Nos. 142-145 (4)* | 2.25 | 2.45 |
| *Nos. 94-97 (4)* | 2.90 | 3.40 |
| *Nos. 126-129 (4)* | 3.05 | *9.60* |
| *Nos. 151-154 (4)* | 4.70 | 8.90 |
| *Nos. 57-60 (4)* | 4.80 | 12.00 |
| *Nos. 46-49 (4)* | 4.25 | 12.65 |
| *Nos. 18-21 (4)* | 4.25 | *17.30* |
| *Nos. 59-62 (4)* | 3.50 | 10.75 |
| *Nos. 46-49 (4)* | 3.00 | 7.25 |
| *Nos. 23-26 (4)* | 5.10 | 11.75 |
| *Nos. 101-104 (4)* | 3.65 | 10.75 |
| *Nos. 3-6 (4)* | 3.95 | 14.25 |
| *Nos. 76-79 (4)* | 4.90 | 12.30 |
| *Nos. 49-52 (4)* | 4.95 | 9.75 |
| *Nos. 225-228 (4)* | 4.50 | 4.85 |
| *Nos. 231-234 (4)* | 4.35 | 6.70 |
| *Nos. 108-111 (4)* | 3.40 | 3.85 |
| *Nos. 62-65 (4)* | 1.60 | *4.25* |
| *Nos. 79-82 (4)* | 24.25 | 24.25 |
| *Nos. 75-78 (4)* | 2.80 | *9.25* |
| *Nos. 240-243 (4)* | 7.15 | 6.50 |
| *Nos. 50-53 (4)* | 5.00 | *6.50* |
| *Nos. 87-90 (4)* | 4.05 | 4.05 |
| *Nos. 13-16 (4)* | 18.50 | 16.50 |
| *Nos. 132-135 (4)* | 4.85 | 7.10 |
| *Nos. 95-98 (4)* | 3.35 | 4.70 |
| *Nos. 131-134 (4)* | 2.55 | *3.85* |
| *Nos. 170-173 (4)* | 2.20 | *5.05* |
| *Nos. 176-179 (4)* | 8.15 | 10.85 |
| *Nos. 153-156 (4)* | 3.25 | 4.10 |
| *Nos. 190-193 (4)* | 3.00 | 5.10 |
| *Nos. 23-26 (4)* | 18.00 | 13.20 |
| *Nos. 84-87 (4)* | 4.05 | 4.90 |
| *Nos. 112-115 (4)* | 3.95 | 8.70 |
| *Nos. 71-72 (2)* | 1.95 | *2.25* |
| *Nos. 50-53 (4)* | 2.80 | 4.65 |
| *Nos. 87-90 (4)* | 3.00 | *5.25* |
| *Nos. 66-69 (4)* | 3.15 | 3.15 |
| *Nos. 101-104 (4)* | 2.70 | 4.10 |
| *Nos. 92-95 (4)* | 2.60 | 5.90 |
| *Nos. 226-229 (4)* | 5.45 | 13.50 |
| *Nos. 276-279 (4)* | 1.35 | 1.00 |
| *Nos. 546-549 (4)* | 3.20 | *10.15* |
| *No. 223 (1)* | .60 | .55 |
| *Nos. 68-71 (4)* | 4.75 | *16.50* |
| *Nos. 116-121 (6)* | 7.30 | 5.35 |
| *Nos. 304-306 (3)* | 3.35 | 4.25 |
| *Nos. 281-283 (3)* | 5.75 | 2.70 |
| *Nos. 223-226 (4)* | 27.25 | 10.50 |
| *Nos. 89-92 (4)* | 6.10 | 10.25 |
| *Nos. 31-34 (4)* | 5.55 | 15.75 |
| *Nos. 26-29,O25-O28 (8)* | 2.00 | *42.00* |
| *Nos. 109-111 (3)* | 2.20 | 3.00 |
| *Nos. 160-162 (3)* | 3.00 | 5.50 |
| *Set total (313) Stamps* | 460.00 | 695.30 |

### University

Arms of University College CD310

Alice, Princess of Athlone CD311

1948 opening of University College of the West Indies at Jamaica.

**1951**

Antigua ... 104-105
Barbados ... 228-229
British Guiana ... 250-251
British Honduras ... 141-142
Dominica ... 120-121
Grenada ... 164-165
Jamaica ... 146-147
Leeward Islands ... 130-131
Montserrat ... 112-113
St. Kitts-Nevis ... 105-106
St. Lucia ... 149-150
St. Vincent ... 174-175
Trinidad & Tobago ... 70-71
Virgin Islands ... 96-97

| | | |
|---|---|---|
| *Nos. 104-105 (2)* | 1.35 | *3.75* |
| *Nos. 228-229 (2)* | 1.85 | 1.55 |
| *Nos. 250-251 (2)* | 1.10 | *1.25* |
| *Nos. 141-142 (2)* | 1.40 | 2.20 |
| *Nos. 120-121 (2)* | 1.40 | *1.75* |
| *Nos. 164-165 (2)* | 1.20 | *1.60* |
| *Nos. 146-147 (2)* | .90 | .70 |
| *Nos. 130-131 (2)* | 1.35 | 4.00 |
| *Nos. 112-113 (2)* | .85 | *1.50* |
| *Nos. 105-106 (2)* | .90 | 1.50 |
| *Nos. 149-150 (2)* | 1.40 | 1.50 |
| *Nos. 174-175 (2)* | 1.00 | *2.15* |
| *Nos. 70-71 (2)* | .75 | .75 |
| *Nos. 96-97 (2)* | 1.50 | *3.75* |
| *Set total (28) Stamps* | 16.95 | 27.95 |

### Coronation

Queen Elizabeth II — CD312

**1953**

Aden ... 47
Kathiri State of Seiyun ... 28
Qu'aiti State of Shihr and Mukalla ... 28
Antigua ... 106
Ascension ... 61
Bahamas ... 157
Barbados ... 234
Basutoland ... 45
Bechuanaland Protectorate ... 153
Bermuda ... 142
British Guiana ... 252
British Honduras ... 143
Cayman Islands ... 150
Cyprus ... 167
Dominica ... 141
Falkland Islands ... 121
Falkland Islands Dependencies ... 1L18
Fiji ... 145
Gambia ... 152
Gibraltar ... 131
Gilbert & Ellice Islands ... 60
Gold Coast ... 160
Grenada ... 170
Hong Kong ... 184
Jamaica ... 153
Kenya, Uganda, Tanzania ... 101
Leeward Islands ... 132
Malaya
Johore ... 155
Kedah ... 82
Kelantan ... 71
Malacca ... 27
Negri Sembilan ... 63
Pahang ... 71
Penang ... 27
Perak ... 126
Perlis ... 28
Selangor ... 101
Trengganu ... 74
Malta ... 241
Mauritius ... 250
Montserrat ... 127
New Hebrides, British ... 77
Nigeria ... 79
North Borneo ... 260
Northern Rhodesia ... 60
Nyasaland Protectorate ... 96
Pitcairn Islands ... 19
St. Helena ... 139
St. Kitts-Nevis ... 119
St. Lucia ... 156
St. Vincent ... 185
Sarawak ... 196
Seychelles ... 172
Sierra Leone ... 194
Singapore ... 27
Solomon Islands ... 88
Somaliland Protectorate ... 127
Swaziland ... 54
Trinidad & Tobago ... 84
Tristan da Cunha ... 13
Turks & Caicos Islands ... 118
Virgin Islands ... 114

The following have different designs but are included in the omnibus set:

Great Britain ... 313-316
Offices in Morocco (Tangier) ... 579-582
Australia ... 259-261
Bahrain ... 92-95
Canada ... 330
Ceylon ... 317
Cook Islands ... 145-146
Kuwait ... 113-116
New Zealand ... 280-284
Niue ... 104-105
Oman ... 52-55
Samoa ... 214-215
South Africa ... 192
Southern Rhodesia ... 80
South-West Africa ... 244-248
Tokelau Islands ... 4

| | | |
|---|---|---|
| *No. 47 (1)* | 1.25 | 1.25 |
| *No. 28 (1)* | .75 | *1.50* |
| *No. 28 (1)* | 1.10 | .60 |
| *No. 106 (1)* | .40 | *.75* |
| *No. 61 (1)* | 1.25 | 2.75 |
| *No. 157 (1)* | 1.40 | .75 |
| *No. 234 (1)* | 1.00 | .25 |
| *No. 45 (1)* | .50 | *.60* |
| *No. 153 (1)* | .75 | .35 |
| *No. 142 (1)* | .85 | .50 |
| *No. 252 (1)* | .45 | .25 |
| *No. 143 (1)* | .60 | .40 |
| *No. 150 (1)* | .40 | *1.75* |
| *No. 167 (1)* | 1.60 | .75 |
| *No. 141 (1)* | .40 | .40 |
| *No. 121 (1)* | .90 | 1.50 |
| *No. 1L18 (1)* | 1.80 | 1.40 |
| *No. 145 (1)* | 1.00 | .60 |
| *No. 152 (1)* | .50 | .50 |
| *No. 131 (1)* | .50 | .50 |
| *No. 60 (1)* | .65 | *2.25* |
| *No. 160 (1)* | 1.00 | .25 |

| | | |
|---|---|---|
| *No. 170 (1)* | .30 | .25 |
| *No. 184 (1)* | 6.00 | .35 |
| *No. 153 (1)* | .70 | .25 |
| *No. 101 (1)* | .40 | .25 |
| *No. 132 (1)* | 1.00 | *2.25* |
| *No. 155 (1)* | 1.40 | .30 |
| *No. 82 (1)* | 2.25 | .60 |
| *No. 71 (1)* | 1.60 | 1.60 |
| *No. 27 (1)* | 1.10 | *1.50* |
| *No. 63 (1)* | 1.40 | .65 |
| *No. 71 (1)* | 2.25 | .25 |
| *No. 27 (1)* | 1.75 | .30 |
| *No. 126 (1)* | 1.60 | .25 |
| *No. 28 (1)* | 1.75 | *4.00* |
| *No. 101 (1)* | 1.75 | .25 |
| *No. 74 (1)* | 1.50 | 1.00 |
| *No. 241 (1)* | .50 | .25 |
| *No. 250 (1)* | 1.00 | .25 |
| *No. 127 (1)* | .65 | .50 |
| *No. 77 (1)* | .75 | .60 |
| *No. 79 (1)* | .45 | .25 |
| *No. 260 (1)* | 2.00 | 1.00 |
| *No. 60 (1)* | .70 | .25 |
| *No. 96 (1)* | .75 | .75 |
| *No. 19 (1)* | 2.25 | 2.25 |
| *No. 139 (1)* | 1.25 | 1.25 |
| *No. 119 (1)* | .35 | .25 |
| *No. 156 (1)* | .70 | .35 |
| *No. 185 (1)* | .50 | .30 |
| *No. 196 (1)* | 2.00 | *1.75* |
| *No. 172 (1)* | .80 | .80 |
| *No. 194 (1)* | .40 | .40 |
| *No. 27 (1)* | 2.50 | .40 |
| *No. 88 (1)* | 1.00 | 1.00 |
| *No. 127 (1)* | .40 | .25 |
| *No. 54 (1)* | .30 | .25 |
| *No. 84 (1)* | .25 | .25 |
| *No. 13 (1)* | 1.00 | 1.75 |
| *No. 118 (1)* | .40 | *1.10* |
| *No. 114 (1)* | .40 | *1.00* |

| | | |
|---|---|---|
| *Nos. 313-316 (4)* | 16.35 | 5.95 |
| *Nos. 579-582 (4)* | 7.40 | 5.20 |
| *Nos. 259-261 (3)* | 4.60 | 3.25 |
| *Nos. 92-95 (4)* | 15.25 | 12.75 |
| *No. 330 (1)* | .25 | .25 |
| *No. 317 (1)* | 1.50 | .25 |
| *Nos. 145-146 (2)* | 2.65 | 2.65 |
| *Nos. 113-116 (4)* | 16.00 | 8.50 |
| *Nos. 280-284 (5)* | 5.65 | 6.85 |
| *Nos. 104-105 (2)* | 1.60 | 1.60 |
| *Nos. 52-55 (4)* | 15.25 | 6.50 |
| *Nos. 214-215 (2)* | 2.10 | 1.00 |
| *No. 192 (1)* | .30 | .25 |
| *No. 80 (1)* | 7.25 | 7.25 |
| *Nos. 244-248 (5)* | 3.00 | 2.35 |
| *No. 4 (1)* | 2.75 | 2.75 |
| *Set total (106) Stamps* | 169.00 | 118.45 |

Separate designs for each country for the visit of Queen Elizabeth II and the Duke of Edinburgh.

### Royal Visit 1953

**1953**

| | |
|---|---|
| Aden | 62 |
| Australia | 267-269 |
| Bermuda | 163 |
| Ceylon | 318 |
| Fiji | 146 |
| Gibraltar | 146 |
| Jamaica | 154 |
| Kenya, Uganda, Tanzania | 102 |
| Malta | 242 |
| New Zealand | 286-287 |

| | | |
|---|---|---|
| *No. 62 (1)* | .65 | 1.25 |
| *Nos. 267-269 (3)* | 2.35 | 1.90 |
| *No. 163 (1)* | .50 | .25 |
| *No. 318 (1)* | 1.25 | .25 |
| *No. 146 (1)* | .65 | .35 |
| *No. 146 (1)* | .50 | .30 |
| *No. 154 (1)* | .50 | .25 |
| *No. 102 (1)* | .50 | .25 |
| *No. 242 (1)* | .35 | .25 |
| *Nos. 286-287 (2)* | .50 | .50 |
| *Set total (13) Stamps* | 7.75 | 5.55 |

### West Indies Federation

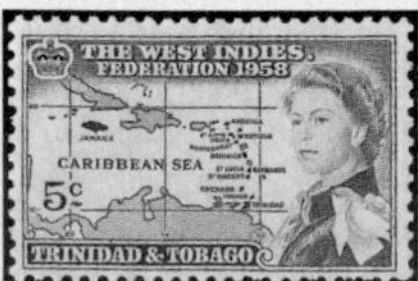


Map of the Caribbean CD313

Federation of the West Indies, April 22, 1958.

**1958**

| | |
|---|---|
| Antigua | 122-124 |
| Barbados | 248-250 |
| Dominica | 161-163 |
| Grenada | 184-186 |
| Jamaica | 175-177 |
| Montserrat | 143-145 |
| St. Kitts-Nevis | 136-138 |
| St. Lucia | 170-172 |
| St. Vincent | 198-200 |
| Trinidad & Tobago | 86-88 |

| | | |
|---|---|---|
| *Nos. 122-124 (3)* | 5.80 | 3.80 |
| *Nos. 248-250 (3)* | 1.60 | *2.90* |
| *Nos. 161-163 (3)* | 1.95 | 1.85 |
| *Nos. 184-186 (3)* | 1.50 | 1.20 |
| *Nos. 175-177 (3)* | 2.65 | 3.45 |
| *Nos. 143-145 (3)* | 2.35 | 1.35 |
| *Nos. 136-138 (3)* | 3.00 | 1.85 |
| *Nos. 170-172 (3)* | 2.05 | 2.80 |
| *Nos. 198-200 (3)* | 1.50 | 1.75 |
| *Nos. 86-88 (3)* | .75 | .90 |
| *Set total (30) Stamps* | 23.15 | 21.85 |

### Freedom from Hunger

Protein Food CD314

U.N. Food and Agricultural Organization's "Freedom from Hunger" campaign.

**1963**

| | |
|---|---|
| Aden | 65 |
| Antigua | 133 |
| Ascension | 89 |
| Bahamas | 180 |
| Basutoland | 83 |
| Bechuanaland Protectorate | 194 |
| Bermuda | 192 |
| British Guiana | 271 |
| British Honduras | 179 |
| Brunei | 100 |
| Cayman Islands | 168 |
| Dominica | 181 |
| Falkland Islands | 146 |
| Fiji | 198 |
| Gambia | 172 |
| Gibraltar | 161 |
| Gilbert & Ellice Islands | 76 |
| Grenada | 190 |
| Hong Kong | 218 |
| Malta | 291 |
| Mauritius | 270 |
| Montserrat | 150 |
| New Hebrides, British | 93 |
| North Borneo | 296 |
| Pitcairn Islands | 35 |
| St. Helena | 173 |
| St. Lucia | 179 |
| St. Vincent | 201 |
| Sarawak | 212 |
| Seychelles | 213 |
| Solomon Islands | 109 |
| Swaziland | 108 |
| Tonga | 127 |
| Tristan da Cunha | 68 |
| Turks & Caicos Islands | 138 |
| Virgin Islands | 140 |
| Zanzibar | 280 |

| | | |
|---|---|---|
| *No. 65 (1)* | 1.50 | 1.75 |
| *No. 133 (1)* | .35 | .35 |
| *No. 89 (1)* | 1.00 | .50 |
| *No. 180 (1)* | .65 | .65 |
| *No. 83 (1)* | .50 | .25 |
| *No. 194 (1)* | .50 | .50 |
| *No. 192 (1)* | 1.00 | .50 |
| *No. 271 (1)* | .45 | .25 |
| *No. 179 (1)* | .60 | .25 |
| *No. 100 (1)* | 3.25 | 2.25 |
| *No. 168 (1)* | .55 | .30 |
| *No. 181 (1)* | .30 | .30 |
| *No. 146 (1)* | 10.50 | 2.50 |
| *No. 198 (1)* | 3.50 | 2.25 |
| *No. 172 (1)* | .50 | .25 |
| *No. 161 (1)* | 4.00 | 2.25 |
| *No. 76 (1)* | 1.40 | .40 |
| *No. 190 (1)* | .30 | .25 |
| *No. 218 (1)* | 47.50 | 7.50 |
| *No. 291 (1)* | 2.00 | 2.00 |
| *No. 270 (1)* | .50 | .50 |
| *No. 150 (1)* | .55 | .45 |
| *No. 93 (1)* | .60 | .25 |
| *No. 296 (1)* | 1.90 | .75 |
| *No. 35 (1)* | 10.00 | 4.50 |
| *No. 173 (1)* | 2.25 | 1.10 |
| *No. 179 (1)* | .40 | .40 |
| *No. 201 (1)* | .90 | .50 |
| *No. 212 (1)* | 1.60 | *1.75* |
| *No. 213 (1)* | .85 | .35 |
| *No. 109 (1)* | 3.00 | .85 |
| *No. 108 (1)* | .50 | .50 |
| *No. 127 (1)* | .60 | .35 |
| *No. 68 (1)* | .75 | .35 |
| *No. 138 (1)* | .50 | .25 |
| *No. 140 (1)* | .50 | .50 |
| *No. 280 (1)* | 1.50 | .80 |
| *Set total (37) Stamps* | 107.25 | 39.40 |

### Red Cross Centenary

Red Cross and Elizabeth II CD315

**1963**

| | |
|---|---|
| Antigua | 134-135 |
| Ascension | 90-91 |
| Bahamas | 183-184 |
| Basutoland | 84-85 |
| Bechuanaland Protectorate | 195-196 |
| Bermuda | 193-194 |
| British Guiana | 272-273 |
| British Honduras | 180-181 |
| Cayman Islands | 169-170 |
| Dominica | 182-183 |
| Falkland Islands | 147-148 |
| Fiji | 203-204 |
| Gambia | 173-174 |
| Gibraltar | 162-163 |
| Gilbert & Ellice Islands | 77-78 |
| Grenada | 191-192 |
| Hong Kong | 219-220 |
| Jamaica | 203-204 |
| Malta | 292-293 |
| Mauritius | 271-272 |
| Montserrat | 151-152 |
| New Hebrides, British | 94-95 |
| Pitcairn Islands | 36-37 |
| St. Helena | 174-175 |
| St. Kitts-Nevis | 143-144 |
| St. Lucia | 180-181 |
| St. Vincent | 202-203 |
| Seychelles | 214-215 |
| Solomon Islands | 110-111 |
| South Arabia | 1-2 |
| Swaziland | 109-110 |
| Tonga | 134-135 |
| Tristan da Cunha | 69-70 |
| Turks & Caicos Islands | 139-140 |
| Virgin Islands | 141-142 |

| | | |
|---|---|---|
| *Nos. 134-135 (2)* | 1.00 | *2.00* |
| *Nos. 90-91 (2)* | 6.75 | 3.35 |
| *Nos. 183-184 (2)* | 2.30 | 2.80 |
| *Nos. 84-85 (2)* | 1.20 | .90 |
| *Nos. 195-196 (2)* | .95 | .85 |
| *Nos. 193-194 (2)* | 3.00 | 2.80 |
| *Nos. 272-273 (2)* | 1.05 | .80 |
| *Nos. 180-181 (2)* | 1.00 | 2.50 |
| *Nos. 169-170 (2)* | 1.10 | *3.00* |
| *Nos. 182-183 (2)* | .70 | *1.05* |
| *Nos. 147-148 (2)* | 18.00 | 5.50 |
| *Nos. 203-204 (2)* | 3.25 | 2.80 |
| *Nos. 173-174 (2)* | .75 | 1.00 |
| *Nos. 162-163 (2)* | 6.25 | 5.40 |
| *Nos. 77-78 (2)* | 2.00 | *3.50* |
| *Nos. 191-192 (2)* | .80 | .50 |
| *Nos. 219-220 (2)* | 35.00 | 7.35 |
| *Nos. 203-204 (2)* | .75 | *1.65* |
| *Nos. 292-293 (2)* | 2.50 | 4.75 |
| *Nos. 271-272 (2)* | .90 | .90 |
| *Nos. 151-152 (2)* | 1.00 | .80 |
| *Nos. 94-95 (2)* | 1.00 | .50 |
| *Nos. 36-37 (2)* | 6.50 | 5.50 |
| *Nos. 174-175 (2)* | 1.70 | 2.30 |
| *Nos. 143-144 (2)* | .90 | .90 |
| *Nos. 180-181 (2)* | 1.25 | 1.25 |
| *Nos. 202-203 (2)* | .90 | .90 |
| *Nos. 214-215 (2)* | 1.10 | .90 |
| *Nos. 110-111 (2)* | 1.25 | 1.15 |
| *Nos. 1-2 (2)* | 1.25 | 1.25 |
| *Nos. 109-110 (2)* | 1.10 | 1.10 |
| *Nos. 134-135 (2)* | 1.00 | 1.25 |
| *Nos. 69-70 (2)* | 1.15 | .80 |
| *Nos. 139-140 (2)* | .85 | .75 |
| *Nos. 141-142 (2)* | .80 | 1.25 |
| *Set total (70) Stamps* | 111.00 | 74.00 |

### Shakespeare

Shakespeare Memorial Theatre, Stratford-on-Avon — CD316

400th anniversary of the birth of William Shakespeare.

**1964**

| | |
|---|---|
| Antigua | 151 |
| Bahamas | 201 |
| Bechuanaland Protectorate | 197 |
| Cayman Islands | 171 |
| Dominica | 184 |
| Falkland Islands | 149 |
| Gambia | 192 |
| Gibraltar | 164 |
| Montserrat | 153 |
| St. Lucia | 196 |
| Turks & Caicos Islands | 141 |
| Virgin Islands | 143 |

| | | |
|---|---|---|
| *No. 151 (1)* | .35 | .25 |
| *No. 201 (1)* | .60 | .35 |
| *No. 197 (1)* | .35 | .35 |
| *No. 171 (1)* | .35 | .30 |
| *No. 184 (1)* | .35 | .35 |
| *No. 149 (1)* | 1.60 | .50 |
| *No. 192 (1)* | .35 | .25 |
| *No. 164 (1)* | .65 | .55 |
| *No. 153 (1)* | .35 | .25 |
| *No. 196 (1)* | .45 | .25 |
| *No. 141 (1)* | .40 | .25 |
| *No. 143 (1)* | .45 | .45 |
| *Set total (12) Stamps* | 6.25 | 4.10 |

### ITU

ITU Emblem CD317

Intl. Telecommunication Union, cent.

**1965**

| | |
|---|---|
| Antigua | 153-154 |
| Ascension | 92-93 |
| Bahamas | 219-220 |
| Barbados | 265-266 |
| Basutoland | 101-102 |
| Bechuanaland Protectorate | 202-203 |
| Bermuda | 196-197 |
| British Guiana | 293-294 |
| British Honduras | 187-188 |
| Brunei | 116-117 |
| Cayman Islands | 172-173 |
| Dominica | 185-186 |
| Falkland Islands | 154-155 |
| Fiji | 211-212 |
| Gibraltar | 167-168 |
| Gilbert & Ellice Islands | 87-88 |
| Grenada | 205-206 |
| Hong Kong | 221-222 |
| Mauritius | 291-292 |
| Montserrat | 157-158 |
| New Hebrides, British | 108-109 |
| Pitcairn Islands | 52-53 |
| St. Helena | 180-181 |
| St. Kitts-Nevis | 163-164 |
| St. Lucia | 197-198 |
| St. Vincent | 224-225 |
| Seychelles | 218-219 |
| Solomon Islands | 126-127 |
| Swaziland | 115-116 |
| Tristan da Cunha | 85-86 |
| Turks & Caicos Islands | 142-143 |
| Virgin Islands | 159-160 |

| | | |
|---|---|---|
| *Nos. 153-154 (2)* | 1.45 | 1.35 |
| *Nos. 92-93 (2)* | 1.90 | 1.30 |
| *Nos. 219-220 (2)* | 1.35 | 1.50 |
| *Nos. 265-266 (2)* | 1.50 | 1.25 |
| *Nos. 101-102 (2)* | .85 | .65 |
| *Nos. 202-203 (2)* | 1.10 | .75 |
| *Nos. 196-197 (2)* | 2.15 | *2.25* |
| *Nos. 293-294 (2)* | .60 | .55 |
| *Nos. 187-188 (2)* | .75 | .75 |
| *Nos. 116-117 (2)* | 1.75 | 1.75 |
| *Nos. 172-173 (2)* | 1.00 | .85 |
| *Nos. 185-186 (2)* | .55 | .55 |
| *Nos. 154-155 (2)* | 6.75 | 3.15 |
| *Nos. 211-212 (2)* | 2.00 | 1.05 |
| *Nos. 167-168 (2)* | 9.00 | 5.95 |
| *Nos. 87-88 (2)* | .85 | .60 |
| *Nos. 205-206 (2)* | .50 | .50 |
| *Nos. 221-222 (2)* | 24.50 | 3.80 |
| *Nos. 291-292 (2)* | 1.20 | .65 |
| *Nos. 157-158 (2)* | 1.25 | 1.15 |
| *Nos. 108-109 (2)* | .65 | .50 |
| *Nos. 52-53 (2)* | 6.25 | 4.30 |
| *Nos. 180-181 (2)* | .80 | .60 |
| *Nos. 163-164 (2)* | .60 | .60 |
| *Nos. 197-198 (2)* | 1.25 | 1.25 |
| *Nos. 224-225 (2)* | .80 | .90 |
| *Nos. 218-219 (2)* | .90 | .60 |
| *Nos. 126-127 (2)* | .70 | .55 |
| *Nos. 115-116 (2)* | .75 | .75 |
| *Nos. 85-86 (2)* | 1.00 | .65 |
| *Nos. 142-143 (2)* | .75 | .50 |
| *Nos. 159-160 (2)* | .85 | .85 |
| *Set total (64) Stamps* | 76.30 | 42.40 |

## Intl. Cooperation Year

ICY Emblem CD318

### 1965

| | |
|---|---|
| Antigua | 155-156 |
| Ascension | 94-95 |
| Bahamas | 222-223 |
| Basutoland | 103-104 |
| Bechuanaland Protectorate | 204-205 |
| Bermuda | 199-200 |
| British Guiana | 295-296 |
| British Honduras | 189-190 |
| Brunei | 118-119 |
| Cayman Islands | 174-175 |
| Dominica | 187-188 |
| Falkland Islands | 156-157 |
| Fiji | 213-214 |
| Gibraltar | 169-170 |
| Gilbert & Ellice Islands | 104-105 |
| Grenada | 207-208 |
| Hong Kong | 223-224 |
| Mauritius | 293-294 |
| Montserrat | 176-177 |
| New Hebrides, British | 110-111 |
| New Hebrides, French | 126-127 |
| Pitcairn Islands | 54-55 |
| St. Helena | 182-183 |
| St. Kitts-Nevis | 165-166 |
| St. Lucia | 199-200 |
| Seychelles | 220-221 |
| Solomon Islands | 143-144 |
| South Arabia | 17-18 |
| Swaziland | 117-118 |
| Tristan da Cunha | 87-88 |
| Turks & Caicos Islands | 144-145 |
| Virgin Islands | 161-162 |

| | | |
|---|---|---|
| *Nos. 155-156 (2)* | .55 | .50 |
| *Nos. 94-95 (2)* | 1.30 | 1.40 |
| *Nos. 222-223 (2)* | .65 | 1.90 |
| *Nos. 103-104 (2)* | .75 | .85 |
| *Nos. 204-205 (2)* | .85 | 1.00 |
| *Nos. 199-200 (2)* | 2.05 | 1.25 |
| *Nos. 295-296 (2)* | .65 | .60 |
| *Nos. 189-190 (2)* | .60 | .55 |
| *Nos. 118-119 (2)* | .85 | .85 |
| *Nos. 174-175 (2)* | 1.00 | .75 |
| *Nos. 187-188 (2)* | .55 | .55 |
| *Nos. 156-157 (2)* | 6.00 | 1.65 |
| *Nos. 213-214 (2)* | 1.95 | 1.25 |
| *Nos. 169-170 (2)* | 1.25 | 2.75 |
| *Nos. 104-105 (2)* | .85 | .60 |
| *Nos. 207-208 (2)* | .50 | .50 |
| *Nos. 223-224 (2)* | 22.00 | 3.10 |
| *Nos. 293-294 (2)* | .70 | .70 |
| *Nos. 176-177 (2)* | .80 | .65 |
| *Nos. 110-111 (2)* | .50 | .50 |
| *Nos. 126-127 (2)* | 12.00 | 12.00 |
| *Nos. 54-55 (2)* | 6.35 | 4.50 |
| *Nos. 182-183 (2)* | .95 | .50 |
| *Nos. 165-166 (2)* | .70 | .60 |
| *Nos. 199-200 (2)* | .55 | .55 |
| *Nos. 220-221 (2)* | .90 | .65 |
| *Nos. 143-144 (2)* | .70 | .60 |
| *Nos. 17-18 (2)* | 1.20 | .50 |
| *Nos. 117-118 (2)* | .75 | .75 |
| *Nos. 87-88 (2)* | 1.05 | .65 |
| *Nos. 144-145 (2)* | .65 | .50 |
| *Nos. 161-162 (2)* | .65 | .50 |
| *Set total (64) Stamps* | 70.80 | 44.20 |

## Churchill Memorial

Winston Churchill and St. Paul's, London, During Air Attack CD319

### 1966

| | |
|---|---|
| Antigua | 157-160 |
| Ascension | 96-99 |
| Bahamas | 224-227 |
| Barbados | 281-284 |
| Basutoland | 105-108 |
| Bechuanaland Protectorate | 206-209 |
| Bermuda | 201-204 |
| British Antarctic Territory | 16-19 |
| British Honduras | 191-194 |
| Brunei | 120-123 |
| Cayman Islands | 176-179 |
| Dominica | 189-192 |
| Falkland Islands | 158-161 |
| Fiji | 215-218 |
| Gibraltar | 171-174 |
| Gilbert & Ellice Islands | 106-109 |
| Grenada | 209-212 |
| Hong Kong | 225-228 |
| Mauritius | 295-298 |
| Montserrat | 178-181 |
| New Hebrides, British | 112-115 |
| New Hebrides, French | 128-131 |
| Pitcairn Islands | 56-59 |
| St. Helena | 184-187 |
| St. Kitts-Nevis | 167-170 |
| St. Lucia | 201-204 |
| St. Vincent | 241-244 |
| Seychelles | 222-225 |
| Solomon Islands | 145-148 |
| South Arabia | 19-22 |
| Swaziland | 119-122 |
| Tristan da Cunha | 89-92 |
| Turks & Caicos Islands | 146-149 |
| Virgin Islands | 163-166 |

| | | |
|---|---|---|
| *Nos. 157-160 (4)* | 3.05 | 3.05 |
| *Nos. 96-99 (4)* | 10.00 | 6.40 |
| *Nos. 224-227 (4)* | 2.30 | 3.20 |
| *Nos. 281-284 (4)* | 3.00 | 4.45 |
| *Nos. 105-108 (4)* | 2.80 | 3.25 |
| *Nos. 206-209 (4)* | 2.50 | 2.50 |
| *Nos. 201-204 (4)* | 4.00 | 4.75 |
| *Nos. 16-19 (4)* | 37.85 | 18.00 |
| *Nos. 191-194 (4)* | 2.45 | 1.30 |
| *Nos. 120-123 (4)* | 7.65 | 6.55 |
| *Nos. 176-179 (4)* | 3.10 | 3.65 |
| *Nos. 189-192 (4)* | 1.15 | 1.15 |
| *Nos. 158-161 (4)* | 12.75 | 9.55 |
| *Nos. 215-218 (4)* | 4.40 | 3.00 |
| *Nos. 171-174 (4)* | 3.05 | 5.30 |
| *Nos. 106-109 (4)* | 1.50 | 1.30 |
| *Nos. 209-212 (4)* | 1.10 | 1.10 |
| *Nos. 225-228 (4)* | 52.50 | 11.40 |
| *Nos. 295-298 (4)* | 4.05 | 4.05 |
| *Nos. 178-181 (4)* | 1.60 | 1.55 |
| *Nos. 112-115 (4)* | 2.30 | 1.00 |
| *Nos. 128-131 (4)* | 10.25 | 10.25 |
| *Nos. 56-59 (4)* | 11.00 | 6.75 |
| *Nos. 184-187 (4)* | 1.85 | 1.95 |
| *Nos. 167-170 (4)* | 1.70 | 1.70 |
| *Nos. 201-204 (4)* | 1.50 | 1.50 |
| *Nos. 241-244 (4)* | 1.50 | 1.75 |
| *Nos. 222-225 (4)* | 3.20 | 3.60 |
| *Nos. 145-148 (4)* | 1.50 | 1.60 |
| *Nos. 19-22 (4)* | 2.95 | 2.20 |
| *Nos. 119-122 (4)* | 1.70 | 2.55 |
| *Nos. 89-92 (4)* | 5.95 | 2.70 |
| *Nos. 146-149 (4)* | 1.60 | 1.75 |
| *Nos. 163-166 (4)* | 1.90 | 1.90 |
| *Set total (136) Stamps* | 209.70 | 136.70 |

## Royal Visit, 1966

Queen Elizabeth II and Prince Philip CD320

Caribbean visit, Feb. 4 - Mar. 6, 1966.

### 1966

| | |
|---|---|
| Antigua | 161-162 |
| Bahamas | 228-229 |
| Barbados | 285-286 |
| British Guiana | 299-300 |
| Cayman Islands | 180-181 |
| Dominica | 193-194 |
| Grenada | 213-214 |
| Montserrat | 182-183 |
| St. Kitts-Nevis | 171-172 |
| St. Lucia | 205-206 |
| St. Vincent | 245-246 |
| Turks & Caicos Islands | 150-151 |
| Virgin Islands | 167-168 |

| | | |
|---|---|---|
| *Nos. 161-162 (2)* | 3.50 | 2.60 |
| *Nos. 228-229 (2)* | 3.05 | 3.05 |
| *Nos. 285-286 (2)* | 3.00 | 2.00 |
| *Nos. 299-300 (2)* | 3.35 | 1.60 |
| *Nos. 180-181 (2)* | 3.45 | 1.80 |
| *Nos. 193-194 (2)* | 3.00 | .60 |
| *Nos. 213-214 (2)* | .80 | .50 |
| *Nos. 182-183 (2)* | 1.70 | 1.00 |
| *Nos. 171-172 (2)* | .80 | .75 |
| *Nos. 205-206 (2)* | 1.50 | 1.35 |
| *Nos. 245-246 (2)* | 2.75 | 1.35 |
| *Nos. 150-151 (2)* | 1.20 | .55 |
| *Nos. 167-168 (2)* | 1.75 | 1.75 |
| *Set total (26) Stamps* | 29.85 | 18.90 |

## World Cup Soccer

Soccer Player and Jules Rimet Cup CD321

World Cup Soccer Championship, Wembley, England, July 11-30.

### 1966

| | |
|---|---|
| Antigua | 163-164 |
| Ascension | 100-101 |
| Bahamas | 245-246 |
| Bermuda | 205-206 |
| Brunei | 124-125 |
| Cayman Islands | 182-183 |
| Dominica | 195-196 |
| Fiji | 219-220 |
| Gibraltar | 175-176 |
| Gilbert & Ellice Islands | 125-126 |
| Grenada | 230-231 |
| New Hebrides, British | 116-117 |
| New Hebrides, French | 132-133 |
| Pitcairn Islands | 60-61 |
| St. Helena | 188-189 |
| St. Kitts-Nevis | 173-174 |
| St. Lucia | 207-208 |
| Seychelles | 226-227 |
| Solomon Islands | 167-168 |
| South Arabia | 23-24 |
| Tristan da Cunha | 93-94 |

| | | |
|---|---|---|
| *Nos. 163-164 (2)* | .80 | .85 |
| *Nos. 100-101 (2)* | 2.50 | 2.00 |
| *Nos. 245-246 (2)* | .65 | .65 |
| *Nos. 205-206 (2)* | 1.75 | 1.75 |
| *Nos. 124-125 (2)* | 1.30 | 1.25 |
| *Nos. 182-183 (2)* | .75 | .65 |
| *Nos. 195-196 (2)* | 1.20 | .75 |
| *Nos. 219-220 (2)* | 1.70 | .60 |
| *Nos. 175-176 (2)* | 1.85 | 1.75 |
| *Nos. 125-126 (2)* | .70 | .60 |
| *Nos. 230-231 (2)* | .65 | .95 |
| *Nos. 116-117 (2)* | 1.00 | 1.00 |
| *Nos. 132-133 (2)* | 7.00 | 7.00 |
| *Nos. 60-61 (2)* | 5.50 | 5.00 |
| *Nos. 188-189 (2)* | 1.25 | .60 |
| *Nos. 173-174 (2)* | .85 | .80 |
| *Nos. 207-208 (2)* | 1.15 | .90 |
| *Nos. 226-227 (2)* | .85 | .85 |
| *Nos. 167-168 (2)* | 1.10 | 1.10 |
| *Nos. 23-24 (2)* | 1.90 | .55 |
| *Nos. 93-94 (2)* | 1.25 | .80 |
| *Set total (42) Stamps* | 35.70 | 30.40 |

## WHO Headquarters

World Health Organization Headquarters, Geneva — CD322

### 1966

| | |
|---|---|
| Antigua | 165-166 |
| Ascension | 102-103 |
| Bahamas | 247-248 |
| Brunei | 126-127 |
| Cayman Islands | 184-185 |
| Dominica | 197-198 |
| Fiji | 224-225 |
| Gibraltar | 180-181 |
| Gilbert & Ellice Islands | 127-128 |
| Grenada | 232-233 |
| Hong Kong | 229-230 |
| Montserrat | 184-185 |
| New Hebrides, British | 118-119 |
| New Hebrides, French | 134-135 |
| Pitcairn Islands | 62-63 |
| St. Helena | 190-191 |
| St. Kitts-Nevis | 177-178 |
| St. Lucia | 209-210 |
| St. Vincent | 247-248 |
| Seychelles | 228-229 |
| Solomon Islands | 169-170 |
| South Arabia | 25-26 |
| Tristan da Cunha | 99-100 |

| | | |
|---|---|---|
| *Nos. 165-166 (2)* | 1.15 | .55 |
| *Nos. 102-103 (2)* | 6.60 | 3.35 |
| *Nos. 247-248 (2)* | .80 | .80 |
| *Nos. 126-127 (2)* | 1.35 | 1.35 |
| *Nos. 184-185 (2)* | 2.25 | 1.20 |
| *Nos. 197-198 (2)* | .75 | .75 |
| *Nos. 224-225 (2)* | 4.70 | 3.30 |
| *Nos. 180-181 (2)* | 6.50 | 4.50 |
| *Nos. 127-128 (2)* | .80 | .70 |
| *Nos. 232-233 (2)* | .80 | .50 |
| *Nos. 229-230 (2)* | 11.25 | 2.30 |
| *Nos. 184-185 (2)* | 1.00 | 1.00 |
| *Nos. 118-119 (2)* | .75 | .50 |
| *Nos. 134-135 (2)* | 8.75 | 8.75 |
| *Nos. 62-63 (2)* | 7.25 | 6.50 |
| *Nos. 190-191 (2)* | 3.50 | 1.50 |
| *Nos. 177-178 (2)* | .65 | .65 |
| *Nos. 209-210 (2)* | .80 | .80 |
| *Nos. 247-248 (2)* | 1.15 | 1.05 |
| *Nos. 228-229 (2)* | 1.25 | .75 |
| *Nos. 169-170 (2)* | .95 | .80 |
| *Nos. 25-26 (2)* | 2.10 | .70 |
| *Nos. 99-100 (2)* | 1.90 | 1.25 |
| *Set total (46) Stamps* | 67.00 | 43.55 |

## UNESCO Anniversary

"Education" — CD323

"Science" (Wheat ears & flask enclosing globe). "Culture" (lyre & columns). 20th anniversary of the UNESCO.

### 1966-67

| | |
|---|---|
| Antigua | 183-185 |
| Ascension | 108-110 |
| Bahamas | 249-251 |
| Barbados | 287-289 |
| Bermuda | 207-209 |
| Brunei | 128-130 |
| Cayman Islands | 186-188 |
| Dominica | 199-201 |
| Gibraltar | 183-185 |
| Gilbert & Ellice Islands | 129-131 |
| Grenada | 234-236 |
| Hong Kong | 231-233 |
| Mauritius | 299-301 |
| Montserrat | 186-188 |
| New Hebrides, British | 120-122 |
| New Hebrides, French | 136-138 |
| Pitcairn Islands | 64-66 |
| St. Helena | 192-194 |
| St. Kitts-Nevis | 179-181 |
| St. Lucia | 211-213 |
| St. Vincent | 249-251 |
| Seychelles | 230-232 |
| Solomon Islands | 171-173 |
| South Arabia | 27-29 |
| Swaziland | 123-125 |
| Tristan da Cunha | 101-103 |
| Turks & Caicos Islands | 155-157 |
| Virgin Islands | 176-178 |

| | | |
|---|---|---|
| *Nos. 183-185 (3)* | 1.90 | 2.50 |
| *Nos. 108-110 (3)* | 11.00 | 5.80 |
| *Nos. 249-251 (3)* | 2.35 | 2.35 |
| *Nos. 287-289 (3)* | 2.50 | 2.15 |
| *Nos. 207-209 (3)* | 3.80 | 3.90 |
| *Nos. 128-130 (3)* | 4.65 | 5.40 |
| *Nos. 186-188 (3)* | 2.50 | 1.50 |
| *Nos. 199-201 (3)* | 1.60 | .75 |
| *Nos. 183-185 (3)* | 6.50 | 3.25 |
| *Nos. 129-131 (3)* | 2.50 | 2.45 |
| *Nos. 234-236 (3)* | 1.10 | 1.20 |
| *Nos. 231-233 (3)* | 69.50 | 17.50 |
| *Nos. 299-301 (3)* | 2.10 | 1.50 |
| *Nos. 186-188 (3)* | 2.40 | 2.40 |
| *Nos. 120-122 (3)* | 1.90 | 1.90 |
| *Nos. 136-138 (3)* | 7.75 | 7.75 |
| *Nos. 64-66 (3)* | 7.10 | 4.75 |
| *Nos. 192-194 (3)* | 5.25 | 3.65 |
| *Nos. 179-181 (3)* | .90 | .90 |
| *Nos. 211-213 (3)* | 1.15 | 1.15 |
| *Nos. 249-251 (3)* | 2.30 | 1.35 |
| *Nos. 230-232 (3)* | 2.40 | 2.40 |
| *Nos. 171-173 (3)* | 2.00 | 1.50 |
| *Nos. 27-29 (3)* | 5.50 | 5.50 |
| *Nos. 123-125 (3)* | 1.45 | 1.45 |
| *Nos. 101-103 (3)* | 2.00 | 1.40 |
| *Nos. 155-157 (3)* | 1.05 | .90 |
| *Nos. 176-178 (3)* | 1.40 | 1.30 |
| *Set total (84) Stamps* | 156.55 | 88.55 |

## Silver Wedding, 1972

Queen Elizabeth II and Prince Philip — CD324

Designs: borders differ for each country.

### 1972

| | |
|---|---|
| Anguilla | 161-162 |
| Antigua | 295-296 |
| Ascension | 164-165 |
| Bahamas | 344-345 |
| Bermuda | 296-297 |
| British Antarctic Territory | 43-44 |
| British Honduras | 306-307 |
| British Indian Ocean Territory | 48-49 |

| | |
|---|---|
| Brunei | 186-187 |
| Cayman Islands | 304-305 |
| Dominica | 352-353 |
| Falkland Islands | 223-224 |
| Fiji | 328-329 |
| Gibraltar | 292-293 |
| Gilbert & Ellice Islands | 206-207 |
| Grenada | 466-467 |
| Hong Kong | 271-272 |
| Montserrat | 286-287 |
| New Hebrides, British | 169-170 |
| New Hebrides, French | 188-189 |
| Pitcairn Islands | 127-128 |
| St. Helena | 271-272 |
| St. Kitts-Nevis | 257-258 |
| St. Lucia | 328-329 |
| St.Vincent | 344-345 |
| Seychelles | 309-310 |
| Solomon Islands | 248-249 |
| South Georgia | 35-36 |
| Tristan da Cunha | 178-179 |
| Turks & Caicos Islands | 257-258 |
| Virgin Islands | 241-242 |

| | | |
|---|---|---|
| *Nos. 161-162 (2)* | 1.30 | 1.50 |
| *Nos. 295-296 (2)* | .50 | .50 |
| *Nos. 164-165 (2)* | .70 | .70 |
| *Nos. 344-345 (2)* | .60 | .60 |
| *Nos. 296-297 (2)* | .50 | .65 |
| *Nos. 43-44 (2)* | 7.75 | 6.10 |
| *Nos. 306-307 (2)* | .80 | .80 |
| *Nos. 48-49 (2)* | 2.00 | 1.00 |
| *Nos. 186-187 (2)* | .70 | .70 |
| *Nos. 304-305 (2)* | .75 | .75 |
| *Nos. 352-353 (2)* | .65 | .65 |
| *Nos. 223-224 (2)* | 1.00 | 1.15 |
| *Nos. 328-329 (2)* | .70 | .70 |
| *Nos. 292-293 (2)* | .50 | .50 |
| *Nos. 206-207 (2)* | .50 | .50 |
| *Nos. 466-467 (2)* | .70 | .70 |
| *Nos. 271-272 (2)* | 1.70 | 1.50 |
| *Nos. 286-287 (2)* | .55 | .55 |
| *Nos. 169-170 (2)* | .50 | .50 |
| *Nos. 188-189 (2)* | 1.05 | 1.05 |
| *Nos. 127-128 (2)* | .90 | .85 |
| *Nos. 271-272 (2)* | .70 | 1.20 |
| *Nos. 257-258 (2)* | .65 | .50 |
| *Nos. 328-329 (2)* | .75 | .75 |
| *Nos. 344-345 (2)* | .55 | .55 |
| *Nos. 309-310 (2)* | .95 | .95 |
| *Nos. 248-249 (2)* | .50 | .50 |
| *Nos. 35-36 (2)* | 1.40 | 1.40 |
| *Nos. 178-179 (2)* | .70 | .70 |
| *Nos. 257-258 (2)* | .50 | .50 |
| *Nos. 241-242 (2)* | .50 | .50 |
| *Set total (62) Stamps* | 31.55 | 29.50 |

### Princess Anne's Wedding

Princess Anne and Mark Phillips — CD325

Wedding of Princess Anne and Mark Phillips, Nov. 14, 1973.

**1973**

| | |
|---|---|
| Anguilla | 179-180 |
| Ascension | 177-178 |
| Belize | 325-326 |
| Bermuda | 302-303 |
| British Antarctic Territory | 60-61 |
| Cayman Islands | 320-321 |
| Falkland Islands | 225-226 |
| Gibraltar | 305-306 |
| Gilbert & Ellice Islands | 216-217 |
| Hong Kong | 289-290 |
| Montserrat | 300-301 |
| Pitcairn Islands | 135-136 |
| St. Helena | 277-278 |
| St. Kitts-Nevis | 274-275 |
| St. Lucia | 349-350 |
| St. Vincent | 358-359 |
| St. Vincent Grenadines | 1-2 |
| Seychelles | 311-312 |
| Solomon Islands | 259-260 |
| South Georgia | 37-38 |
| Tristan da Cunha | 189-190 |
| Turks & Caicos Islands | 286-287 |
| Virgin Islands | 260-261 |

| | | |
|---|---|---|
| *Nos. 179-180 (2)* | .55 | .55 |
| *Nos. 177-178 (2)* | .60 | .60 |
| *Nos. 325-326 (2)* | .50 | .50 |
| *Nos. 302-303 (2)* | .50 | .50 |
| *Nos. 60-61 (2)* | 1.10 | 1.10 |
| *Nos. 320-321 (2)* | .50 | .50 |
| *Nos. 225-226 (2)* | .70 | .60 |
| *Nos. 305-306 (2)* | .55 | .55 |
| *Nos. 216-217 (2)* | .50 | .50 |
| *Nos. 289-290 (2)* | 2.65 | 2.00 |
| *Nos. 300-301 (2)* | .65 | .65 |
| *Nos. 135-136 (2)* | .70 | .60 |
| *Nos. 277-278 (2)* | .50 | .50 |
| *Nos. 274-275 (2)* | .50 | .50 |
| *Nos. 349-350 (2)* | .50 | .50 |
| *Nos. 358-359 (2)* | .50 | .50 |
| *Nos. 1-2 (2)* | .50 | .50 |
| *Nos. 311-312 (2)* | .70 | .70 |
| *Nos. 259-260 (2)* | .70 | .70 |
| *Nos. 37-38 (2)* | .75 | .75 |
| *Nos. 189-190 (2)* | .50 | .50 |
| *Nos. 286-287 (2)* | .50 | .50 |
| *Nos. 260-261 (2)* | .50 | .50 |
| *Set total (46) Stamps* | 15.65 | 14.80 |

### Elizabeth II Coronation Anniv.

CD326

CD327

CD328

Designs: Royal and local beasts in heraldic form and simulated stonework. Portrait of Elizabeth II by Peter Grugeon. 25th anniversary of coronation of Queen Elizabeth II.

**1978**

| | |
|---|---|
| Ascension | 229 |
| Barbados | 474 |
| Belize | 397 |
| British Antarctic Territory | 71 |
| Cayman Islands | 404 |
| Christmas Island | 87 |
| Falkland Islands | 275 |
| Fiji | 384 |
| Gambia | 380 |
| Gilbert Islands | 312 |
| Mauritius | 464 |
| New Hebrides, British | 258 |
| New Hebrides, French | 278 |
| St. Helena | 317 |
| St. Kitts-Nevis | 354 |
| Samoa | 472 |
| Solomon Islands | 368 |
| South Georgia | 51 |
| Swaziland | 302 |
| Tristan da Cunha | 238 |
| Virgin Islands | 337 |

| | | |
|---|---|---|
| *No. 229 (1)* | 2.00 | 2.00 |
| *No. 474 (1)* | 1.35 | 1.35 |
| *No. 397 (1)* | 1.40 | 1.75 |
| *No. 71 (1)* | 6.00 | 6.00 |
| *No. 404 (1)* | 2.00 | 2.00 |
| *No. 87 (1)* | 3.50 | 4.00 |
| *No. 275 (1)* | 4.00 | 5.50 |
| *No. 384 (1)* | 1.75 | 1.75 |
| *No. 380 (1)* | 1.50 | 1.50 |
| *No. 312 (1)* | 1.25 | 1.25 |
| *No. 464 (1)* | 2.75 | 2.75 |
| *No. 258 (1)* | 1.75 | 1.75 |
| *No. 278 (1)* | 3.50 | 3.50 |
| *No. 317 (1)* | 1.75 | 1.75 |
| *No. 354 (1)* | 1.00 | 1.00 |
| *No. 472 (1)* | 2.00 | 2.00 |
| *No. 368 (1)* | 2.50 | 2.50 |
| *No. 51 (1)* | 3.00 | 3.00 |
| *No. 302 (1)* | 1.75 | 1.75 |
| *No. 238 (1)* | 1.50 | 1.50 |
| *No. 337 (1)* | 1.80 | 1.80 |
| *Set total (21) Stamps* | 48.05 | 50.40 |

### Queen Mother Elizabeth's 80th Birthday

CD330

Designs: Photographs of Queen Mother Elizabeth. Falkland Islands issued in sheets of 50; others in sheets of 9.

**1980**

| | |
|---|---|
| Ascension | 261 |
| Bermuda | 401 |
| Cayman Islands | 443 |
| Falkland Islands | 305 |
| Gambia | 412 |
| Gibraltar | 393 |
| Hong Kong | 364 |
| Pitcairn Islands | 193 |
| St. Helena | 341 |
| Samoa | 532 |
| Solomon Islands | 426 |
| Tristan da Cunha | 277 |

| | | |
|---|---|---|
| *No. 261 (1)* | .40 | .40 |
| *No. 401 (1)* | .45 | .75 |
| *No. 443 (1)* | .40 | .40 |
| *No. 305 (1)* | .40 | .40 |
| *No. 412 (1)* | .40 | .50 |
| *No. 393 (1)* | .35 | .35 |
| *No. 364 (1)* | 1.10 | 1.25 |
| *No. 193 (1)* | .60 | .60 |
| *No. 341 (1)* | .50 | .50 |
| *No. 532 (1)* | .55 | .55 |
| *No. 426 (1)* | .50 | .50 |
| *No. 277 (1)* | .45 | .45 |
| *Set total (12) Stamps* | 6.10 | 6.65 |

### Royal Wedding, 1981

Prince Charles and Lady Diana — CD331

CD331a

Wedding of Charles, Prince of Wales, and Lady Diana Spencer, St. Paul's Cathedral, London, July 29, 1981.

**1981**

| | |
|---|---|
| Antigua | 623-627 |
| Ascension | 294-296 |
| Barbados | 547-549 |
| Barbuda | 497-501 |
| Bermuda | 412-414 |
| Brunei | 268-270 |
| Cayman Islands | 471-473 |
| Dominica | 701-705 |
| Falkland Islands | 324-326 |
| Falkland Islands Dep. | 1L59-1L61 |
| Fiji | 442-444 |
| Gambia | 426-428 |
| Ghana | 759-764 |
| Grenada | 1051-1055 |
| Grenada Grenadines | 440-443 |
| Hong Kong | 373-375 |
| Jamaica | 500-503 |
| Lesotho | 335-337 |
| Maldive Islands | 906-909 |
| Mauritius | 520-522 |
| Norfolk Island | 280-282 |
| Pitcairn Islands | 206-208 |
| St. Helena | 353-355 |
| St. Lucia | 543-549 |
| Samoa | 558-560 |
| Sierra Leone | 509-518 |
| Solomon Islands | 450-452 |
| Swaziland | 382-384 |
| Tristan da Cunha | 294-296 |
| Turks & Caicos Islands | 486-489 |
| Caicos Island | 8-11 |
| Uganda | 314-317 |
| Vanuatu | 308-310 |
| Virgin Islands | 406-408 |

| | | |
|---|---|---|
| *Nos. 623-627 (5)* | 6.55 | 2.55 |
| *Nos. 294-296 (3)* | 1.00 | 1.00 |
| *Nos. 547-549 (3)* | .90 | .90 |
| *Nos. 497-501 (5)* | 10.95 | 10.95 |
| *Nos. 412-414 (3)* | 2.00 | 2.00 |
| *Nos. 268-270 (3)* | 2.15 | 4.50 |
| *Nos. 471-473 (3)* | 1.20 | 1.30 |
| *Nos. 701-705 (5)* | 8.35 | 2.35 |
| *Nos. 324-326 (3)* | 1.65 | 1.70 |
| *Nos. 1L59-1L61 (3)* | 1.45 | 1.45 |
| *Nos. 442-444 (3)* | 1.35 | 1.35 |
| *Nos. 426-428 (3)* | .80 | .80 |
| *Nos. 759-764 (9)* | 6.20 | 6.20 |
| *Nos. 1051-1055 (5)* | 9.85 | 1.85 |
| *Nos. 440-443 (4)* | 2.35 | 2.35 |
| *Nos. 373-375 (3)* | 3.05 | 2.85 |
| *Nos. 500-503 (4)* | 1.45 | 1.35 |
| *Nos. 335-337 (3)* | .90 | .90 |
| *Nos. 906-909 (4)* | 1.55 | 1.55 |
| *Nos. 520-522 (3)* | 2.75 | 2.75 |
| *Nos. 280-282 (3)* | 1.35 | 1.35 |
| *Nos. 206-208 (3)* | 1.10 | 1.10 |
| *Nos. 353-355 (3)* | .85 | .85 |
| *Nos. 543-549 (5)* | 8.50 | 8.50 |
| *Nos. 558-560 (3)* | .85 | .85 |
| *Nos. 509-518 (10)* | 15.50 | 15.50 |
| *Nos. 450-452 (3)* | 1.25 | 1.25 |
| *Nos. 382-384 (3)* | 1.30 | 1.25 |
| *Nos. 294-296 (3)* | .90 | .90 |
| *Nos. 486-489 (4)* | 2.20 | 2.20 |
| *Nos. 8-11 (4)* | 5.00 | 5.00 |
| *Nos. 314-317 (4)* | 3.30 | 3.00 |
| *Nos. 308-310 (3)* | 1.15 | 1.15 |
| *Nos. 406-408 (3)* | 1.10 | 1.10 |
| *Set total (131) Stamps* | 110.80 | 94.65 |

### Princess Diana

CD332

CD333

Designs: Photographs and portrait of Princess Diana, wedding or honeymoon photographs, royal residences, arms of issuing country. Portrait photograph by Clive Friend. Souvenir sheet margins show family tree, various people related to the princess. 21st birthday of Princess Diana of Wales, July 1.

**1982**

| | |
|---|---|
| Antigua | 663-666 |
| Ascension | 313-316 |
| Bahamas | 510-513 |
| Barbados | 585-588 |
| Barbuda | 544-547 |
| British Antarctic Territory | 92-95 |
| Cayman Islands | 486-489 |
| Dominica | 773-776 |
| Falkland Islands | 348-351 |
| Falkland Islands Dep. | 1L72-1L75 |
| Fiji | 470-473 |
| Gambia | 447-450 |
| Grenada | 1101A-1105 |
| Grenada Grenadines | 485-491 |
| Lesotho | 372-375 |
| Maldive Islands | 952-955 |
| Mauritius | 548-551 |
| Pitcairn Islands | 213-216 |
| St. Helena | 372-375 |
| St. Lucia | 591-594 |
| Sierra Leone | 531-534 |
| Solomon Islands | 471-474 |
| Swaziland | 406-409 |
| Tristan da Cunha | 310-313 |
| Turks and Caicos Islands | 531-534 |
| Virgin Islands | 430-433 |

| | | |
|---|---|---|
| *Nos. 663-666 (4)* | 8.25 | 7.35 |
| *Nos. 313-316 (4)* | 3.50 | 3.50 |
| *Nos. 510-513 (4)* | 6.00 | 3.85 |
| *Nos. 585-588 (4)* | 3.40 | 3.25 |
| *Nos. 544-547 (4)* | 9.75 | 7.70 |
| *Nos. 92-95 (4)* | 5.30 | 3.45 |
| *Nos. 486-489 (4)* | 4.75 | 2.70 |
| *Nos. 773-776 (4)* | 7.05 | 7.05 |
| *Nos. 348-351 (4)* | 2.95 | 2.95 |
| *Nos. 1L72-1L75 (4)* | 2.50 | 2.60 |
| *Nos. 470-473 (4)* | 3.25 | 2.95 |
| *Nos. 447-450 (4)* | 2.85 | 2.85 |
| *Nos. 1101A-1105 (7)* | 16.05 | 15.55 |

| | | |
|---|---|---|
| *Nos. 485-491 (7)* | 17.65 | 17.65 |
| *Nos. 372-375 (4)* | 4.00 | 4.00 |
| *Nos. 952-955 (4)* | 5.50 | 3.90 |
| *Nos. 548-551 (4)* | 5.50 | 5.50 |
| *Nos. 213-216 (4)* | 2.15 | 2.15 |
| *Nos. 372-375 (4)* | 2.95 | 2.95 |
| *Nos. 591-594 (4)* | 9.90 | 9.90 |
| *Nos. 531-534 (4)* | 7.20 | 7.20 |
| *Nos. 471-474 (4)* | 2.90 | 2.90 |
| *Nos. 406-409 (4)* | 3.85 | 2.25 |
| *Nos. 310-313 (4)* | 3.65 | 1.45 |
| *Nos. 486-489 (4)* | 2.20 | 2.20 |
| *Nos. 430-433 (4)* | 3.00 | 3.00 |
| *Set total (110) Stamps* | 146.05 | 130.80 |

**250th anniv. of first edition of Lloyd's List (shipping news publication) & of Lloyd's marine insurance.**

CD335

Designs: First page of early edition of the list; historical ships, modern transportation or harbor scenes.

**1984**

| | |
|---|---|
| Ascension | 351-354 |
| Bahamas | 555-558 |
| Barbados | 627-630 |
| Cayes of Belize | 10-13 |
| Cayman Islands | 522-526 |
| Falkland Islands | 404-407 |
| Fiji | 509-512 |
| Gambia | 519-522 |
| Mauritius | 587-590 |
| Nauru | 280-283 |
| St. Helena | 412-415 |
| Samoa | 624-627 |
| Seychelles | 538-541 |
| Solomon Islands | 521-524 |
| Vanuatu | 368-371 |
| Virgin Islands | 466-469 |

| | | |
|---|---|---|
| *Nos. 351-354 (4)* | 2.90 | 2.55 |
| *Nos. 555-558 (4)* | 4.15 | 2.95 |
| *Nos. 627-630 (4)* | 6.10 | 5.15 |
| *Nos. 10-13 (4)* | 2.65 | 2.65 |
| *Nos. 522-526 (5)* | 9.30 | 8.45 |
| *Nos. 404-407 (4)* | 3.50 | 3.65 |
| *Nos. 509-512 (4)* | 5.30 | 4.90 |
| *Nos. 519-522 (4)* | 4.20 | 4.30 |
| *Nos. 587-590 (4)* | 8.95 | 8.95 |
| *Nos. 280-283 (4)* | 2.40 | 2.35 |
| *Nos. 412-415 (4)* | 2.40 | 2.40 |
| *Nos. 624-627 (4)* | 2.75 | 2.55 |
| *Nos. 538-541 (4)* | 5.25 | 5.25 |
| *Nos. 521-524 (4)* | 4.65 | 3.95 |
| *Nos. 368-371 (4)* | 2.40 | 2.40 |
| *Nos. 466-469 (4)* | 4.25 | 4.25 |
| *Set total (65) Stamps* | 71.15 | 66.70 |

**Queen Mother 85th Birthday**

CD336

Designs: Photographs tracing the life of the Queen Mother, Elizabeth. The high value in each set pictures the same photograph taken of the Queen Mother holding the infant Prince Henry.

**1985**

| | |
|---|---|
| Ascension | 372-376 |
| Bahamas | 580-584 |
| Barbados | 660-664 |
| Bermuda | 469-473 |
| Falkland Islands | 420-424 |
| Falkland Islands Dep. | 1L92-1L96 |
| Fiji | 531-535 |
| Hong Kong | 447-450 |
| Jamaica | 599-603 |
| Mauritius | 604-608 |
| Norfolk Island | 364-368 |
| Pitcairn Islands | 253-257 |
| St. Helena | 428-432 |
| Samoa | 649-653 |
| Seychelles | 567-571 |
| Zil Elwannyen Sesel | 101-105 |
| Solomon Islands | 543-547 |
| Swaziland | 476-480 |
| Tristan da Cunha | 372-376 |
| Vanuatu | 392-396 |

| | | |
|---|---|---|
| *Nos. 372-376 (5)* | 4.65 | 4.65 |
| *Nos. 580-584 (5)* | 7.70 | 6.45 |
| *Nos. 660-664 (5)* | 8.00 | 6.70 |
| *Nos. 469-473 (5)* | 9.40 | 9.40 |
| *Nos. 420-424 (5)* | 7.35 | 6.65 |
| *Nos. 1L92-1L96 (5)* | 8.00 | 8.00 |
| *Nos. 531-535 (5)* | 6.15 | 6.15 |
| *Nos. 447-450 (4)* | 9.50 | 8.50 |
| *Nos. 599-603 (5)* | 6.15 | 7.00 |
| *Nos. 604-608 (5)* | 11.80 | 11.80 |
| *Nos. 364-368 (5)* | 5.05 | 5.05 |
| *Nos. 253-257 (5)* | 5.25 | 5.95 |
| *Nos. 428-432 (5)* | 5.25 | 5.25 |
| *Nos. 649-653 (5)* | 8.65 | 7.80 |
| *Nos. 567-571 (5)* | 8.70 | 8.70 |
| *Nos. 101-105 (5)* | 7.15 | 7.15 |
| *Nos. 543-547 (5)* | 3.95 | 3.95 |
| *Nos. 476-480 (5)* | 8.00 | 7.50 |
| *Nos. 372-376 (5)* | 5.40 | 5.40 |
| *Nos. 392-396 (5)* | 5.25 | 5.25 |
| *Set total (99) Stamps* | 141.35 | 137.30 |

**Queen Elizabeth II, 60th Birthday**

CD337

**1986, April 21**

| | |
|---|---|
| Ascension | 389-393 |
| Bahamas | 592-596 |
| Barbados | 675-679 |
| Bermuda | 499-503 |
| Cayman Islands | 555-559 |
| Falkland Islands | 441-445 |
| Fiji | 544-548 |
| Hong Kong | 465-469 |
| Jamaica | 620-624 |
| Kiribati | 470-474 |
| Mauritius | 629-633 |
| Papua New Guinea | 640-644 |
| Pitcairn Islands | 270-274 |
| St. Helena | 451-455 |
| Samoa | 670-674 |
| Seychelles | 592-596 |
| Zil Elwannyen Sesel | 114-118 |
| Solomon Islands | 562-566 |
| South Georgia | 101-105 |
| Swaziland | 490-494 |
| Tristan da Cunha | 388-392 |
| Vanuatu | 414-418 |
| Zambia | 343-347 |

| | | |
|---|---|---|
| *Nos. 389-393 (5)* | 2.80 | 3.30 |
| *Nos. 592-596 (5)* | 2.75 | 3.70 |
| *Nos. 675-679 (5)* | 3.35 | 3.20 |
| *Nos. 499-503 (5)* | 4.65 | 5.15 |
| *Nos. 555-559 (5)* | 4.55 | 5.60 |
| *Nos. 441-445 (5)* | 3.95 | 4.95 |
| *Nos. 544-548 (5)* | 3.00 | 3.00 |
| *Nos. 465-469 (5)* | 8.75 | 6.75 |
| *Nos. 620-624 (5)* | 2.75 | 2.70 |
| *Nos. 470-474 (5)* | 2.10 | 2.10 |
| *Nos. 629-633 (5)* | 3.70 | 3.70 |
| *Nos. 640-644 (5)* | 4.50 | 4.50 |
| *Nos. 270-274 (5)* | 2.70 | 2.70 |
| *Nos. 451-455 (5)* | 3.05 | 3.05 |
| *Nos. 670-674 (5)* | 2.90 | 2.90 |
| *Nos. 592-596 (5)* | 2.70 | 2.70 |
| *Nos. 114-118 (5)* | 2.25 | 2.25 |
| *Nos. 562-566 (5)* | 2.90 | 2.90 |
| *Nos. 101-105 (5)* | 3.30 | 3.65 |
| *Nos. 490-494 (5)* | 2.30 | 2.30 |
| *Nos. 388-392 (5)* | 3.00 | 3.00 |
| *Nos. 414-418 (5)* | 3.10 | 3.10 |
| *Nos. 343-347 (5)* | 1.75 | 1.75 |
| *Set total (115) Stamps* | 76.80 | 78.95 |

**Royal Wedding**

Marriage of Prince Andrew and Sarah Ferguson CD338

**1986, July 23**

| | |
|---|---|
| Ascension | 399-400 |
| Bahamas | 602-603 |
| Barbados | 687-688 |
| Cayman Islands | 560-561 |
| Jamaica | 629-630 |
| Pitcairn Islands | 275-276 |
| St. Helena | 460-461 |
| St. Kitts | 181-182 |
| Seychelles | 602-603 |
| Zil Elwannyen Sesel | 119-120 |
| Solomon Islands | 567-568 |
| Tristan da Cunha | 397-398 |
| Zambia | 348-349 |

| | | |
|---|---|---|
| *Nos. 399-400 (2)* | 1.60 | 1.60 |
| *Nos. 602-603 (2)* | 2.75 | 2.75 |
| *Nos. 687-688 (2)* | 2.25 | 1.25 |
| *Nos. 560-561 (2)* | 1.70 | 2.35 |
| *Nos. 629-630 (2)* | 1.35 | 1.35 |
| *Nos. 275-276 (2)* | 2.40 | 2.40 |
| *Nos. 460-461 (2)* | 1.05 | 1.05 |
| *Nos. 181-182 (2)* | 1.50 | 1.50 |
| *Nos. 602-603 (2)* | 2.50 | 2.50 |
| *Nos. 119-120 (2)* | 2.30 | 2.30 |
| *Nos. 567-568 (2)* | 1.00 | 1.00 |
| *Nos. 397-398 (2)* | 1.40 | 1.40 |
| *Nos. 348-349 (2)* | 1.10 | 1.30 |
| *Set total (26) Stamps* | 22.90 | 22.75 |

**Queen Elizabeth II, 60th Birthday**

Queen Elizabeth II & Prince Philip, 1947 Wedding Portrait — CD339

Designs: Photographs tracing the life of Queen Elizabeth II.

**1986**

| | |
|---|---|
| Anguilla | 674-677 |
| Antigua | 925-928 |
| Barbuda | 783-786 |
| Dominica | 950-953 |
| Gambia | 611-614 |
| Grenada | 1371-1374 |
| Grenada Grenadines | 749-752 |
| Lesotho | 531-534 |
| Maldive Islands | 1172-1175 |
| Sierra Leone | 760-763 |
| Uganda | 495-498 |

| | | |
|---|---|---|
| *Nos. 674-677 (4)* | 8.00 | 8.00 |
| *Nos. 925-928 (4)* | 5.50 | 6.20 |
| *Nos. 783-786 (4)* | 23.15 | 23.15 |
| *Nos. 950-953 (4)* | 7.25 | 7.25 |
| *Nos. 611-614 (4)* | 8.25 | 7.90 |
| *Nos. 1371-1374 (4)* | 6.80 | 6.80 |
| *Nos. 749-752 (4)* | 6.75 | 6.75 |
| *Nos. 531-534 (4)* | 5.25 | 5.25 |
| *Nos. 1172-1175 (4)* | 6.25 | 6.25 |
| *Nos. 760-763 (4)* | 6.30 | 6.30 |
| *Nos. 495-498 (4)* | 8.50 | 8.50 |
| *Set total (44) Stamps* | 92.00 | 92.35 |

**Royal Wedding, 1986**

CD340

Designs: Photographs of Prince Andrew and Sarah Ferguson during courtship, engagement and marriage.

**1986**

| | |
|---|---|
| Antigua | 939-942 |
| Barbuda | 809-812 |
| Dominica | 970-973 |
| Gambia | 635-638 |
| Grenada | 1385-1388 |
| Grenada Grenadines | 758-761 |
| Lesotho | 545-548 |
| Maldive Islands | 1181-1184 |
| Sierra Leone | 769-772 |
| Uganda | 510-513 |

| | | |
|---|---|---|
| *Nos. 939-942 (4)* | 7.00 | 8.75 |
| *Nos. 809-812 (4)* | 14.55 | 14.55 |
| *Nos. 970-973 (4)* | 7.25 | 7.25 |
| *Nos. 635-638 (4)* | 8.55 | 8.55 |
| *Nos. 1385-1388 (4)* | 8.30 | 8.30 |
| *Nos. 758-761 (4)* | 9.00 | 9.00 |
| *Nos. 545-548 (4)* | 7.45 | 7.45 |
| *Nos. 1181-1184 (4)* | 8.45 | 8.45 |
| *Nos. 769-772 (4)* | 5.35 | 5.35 |
| *Nos. 510-513 (4)* | 9.25 | 10.00 |
| *Set total (40) Stamps* | 85.15 | 87.65 |

**Lloyds of London, 300th Anniv.**

CD341

Designs: 17th century aspects of Lloyds, representations of each country's individual connections with Lloyds and publicized disasters insured by the organization.

**1986**

| | |
|---|---|
| Ascension | 454-457 |
| Bahamas | 655-658 |
| Barbados | 731-734 |
| Bermuda | 541-544 |
| Falkland Islands | 481-484 |
| Liberia | 1101-1104 |
| Malawi | 534-537 |
| Nevis | 571-574 |
| St. Helena | 501-504 |
| St. Lucia | 923-926 |
| Seychelles | 649-652 |
| Zil Elwannyen Sesel | 146-149 |
| Solomon Islands | 627-630 |
| South Georgia | 131-134 |
| Trinidad & Tobago | 484-487 |
| Tristan da Cunha | 439-442 |
| Vanuatu | 485-488 |

| | | |
|---|---|---|
| *Nos. 454-457 (4)* | 5.00 | 5.00 |
| *Nos. 655-658 (4)* | 8.90 | 4.95 |
| *Nos. 731-734 (4)* | 12.50 | 8.35 |
| *Nos. 541-544 (4)* | 8.00 | 6.60 |
| *Nos. 481-484 (4)* | 5.45 | 3.85 |
| *Nos. 1101-1104 (4)* | 4.25 | 4.25 |
| *Nos. 534-537 (4)* | 11.00 | 7.85 |
| *Nos. 571-574 (4)* | 8.35 | 8.35 |
| *Nos. 501-504 (4)* | 8.70 | 7.15 |
| *Nos. 923-926 (4)* | 9.40 | 9.40 |
| *Nos. 649-652 (4)* | 13.10 | 13.10 |
| *Nos. 146-149 (4)* | 11.25 | 11.25 |
| *Nos. 627-630 (4)* | 7.00 | 4.45 |
| *Nos. 131-134 (4)* | 6.30 | 3.70 |
| *Nos. 484-487 (4)* | 10.25 | 6.35 |
| *Nos. 439-442 (4)* | 7.60 | 7.60 |
| *Nos. 485-488 (4)* | 5.90 | 5.90 |
| *Set total (68) Stamps* | 142.95 | 118.10 |

**Moon Landing, 20th Anniv.**

CD342

Designs: Equipment, crew photographs, spacecraft, official emblems and report profiles created for the Apollo Missions. Two stamps in each set are square in format rather than like the stamp shown; see individual country listings for more information.

**1989**

| | |
|---|---|
| Ascension | 468-472 |
| Bahamas | 674-678 |
| Belize | 916-920 |
| Kiribati | 517-521 |
| Liberia | 1125-1129 |
| Nevis | 586-590 |
| St. Kitts | 248-252 |
| Samoa | 760-764 |
| Seychelles | 676-680 |
| Zil Elwannyen Sesel | 154-158 |
| Solomon Islands | 643-647 |
| Vanuatu | 507-511 |

| | | |
|---|---|---|
| *Nos. 468-472 (5)* | 9.40 | 8.60 |
| *Nos. 674-678 (5)* | 23.00 | 19.70 |
| *Nos. 916-920 (5)* | 22.85 | 18.10 |
| *Nos. 517-521 (5)* | 12.50 | 12.50 |
| *Nos. 1125-1129 (5)* | 8.50 | 8.50 |
| *Nos. 586-590 (5)* | 7.50 | 7.50 |

| | | |
|---|---|---|
| *Nos. 248-252 (5)* | 8.00 | 8.00 |
| *Nos. 760-764 (5)* | 9.60 | 9.05 |
| *Nos. 676-680 (5)* | 16.05 | 16.05 |
| *Nos. 154-158 (5)* | 26.85 | 26.85 |
| *Nos. 643-647 (5)* | 9.00 | 6.75 |
| *Nos. 507-511 (5)* | 9.90 | 9.90 |
| *Set total (60) Stamps* | 163.15 | 151.50 |

### Queen Mother, 90th Birthday

CD343

CD344

Designs: Portraits of Queen Elizabeth, the Queen Mother. See individual country listings for more information.

**1990**

Ascension....491-492
Bahamas....698-699
Barbados....782-783
British Antarctic Territory....170-171
British Indian Ocean Territory....106-107
Cayman Islands....622-623
Falkland Islands....524-525
Kenya....527-528
Kiribati....555-556
Liberia....1145-1146
Pitcairn Islands....336-337
St. Helena....532-533
St. Lucia....969-970
Seychelles....710-711
Zil Elwannyen Sesel....171-172
Solomon Islands....671-672
South Georgia....143-144
Swaziland....565-566
Tristan da Cunha....480-481

| | | |
|---|---|---|
| *Nos. 491-492 (2)* | 4.75 | 4.75 |
| *Nos. 698-699 (2)* | 5.25 | 5.25 |
| *Nos. 782-783 (2)* | 4.00 | 3.70 |
| *Nos. 170-171 (2)* | 6.75 | 6.75 |
| *Nos. 106-107 (2)* | 18.00 | 18.50 |
| *Nos. 622-623 (2)* | 4.00 | *5.50* |
| *Nos. 524-525 (2)* | 4.75 | 4.75 |
| *Nos. 527-528 (2)* | 7.00 | 7.00 |
| *Nos. 555-556 (2)* | 4.75 | 4.75 |
| *Nos. 1145-1146 (2)* | 3.25 | 3.25 |
| *Nos. 336-337 (2)* | 4.25 | 4.25 |
| *Nos. 532-533 (2)* | 5.25 | 5.25 |
| *Nos. 969-970 (2)* | 5.25 | 5.25 |
| *Nos. 710-711 (2)* | 6.60 | 6.60 |
| *Nos. 171-172 (2)* | 8.25 | 8.25 |
| *Nos. 671-672 (2)* | 5.00 | *5.30* |
| *Nos. 143-144 (2)* | 5.50 | 6.50 |
| *Nos. 565-566 (2)* | 4.35 | 4.35 |
| *Nos. 480-481 (2)* | 5.60 | 5.60 |
| *Set total (38) Stamps* | 112.55 | 115.55 |

### Queen Elizabeth II, 65th Birthday, and Prince Philip, 70th Birthday

CD345

CD346

Designs: Portraits of Queen Elizabeth II and Prince Philip differ for each country. Printed in sheets of 10 + 5 labels (3 different) between. Stamps alternate, producing 5 different triptychs.

**1991**

Ascension....506a
Bahamas....731a
Belize....970a
Bermuda....618a
Kiribati....572a
Mauritius....734a
Pitcairn Islands....349a
St. Helena....555a
St. Kitts....319a
Samoa....791a
Seychelles....724a
Zil Elwannyen Sesel....178a
Solomon Islands....689a
South Georgia....150a
Swaziland....587a
Vanuatu....541a

| | | |
|---|---|---|
| *No. 506a (1)* | 3.50 | 3.75 |
| *No. 731a (1)* | 4.00 | 4.00 |
| *No. 970a (1)* | 3.75 | 3.75 |
| *No. 618a (1)* | 3.50 | *4.00* |
| *No. 572a (1)* | 4.00 | 4.00 |
| *No. 734a (1)* | 3.75 | 3.75 |
| *No. 349a (1)* | 3.25 | 3.25 |
| *No. 555a (1)* | 2.75 | 2.75 |
| *No. 319a (1)* | 3.00 | 3.00 |
| *No. 791a (1)* | 4.25 | 4.25 |
| *No. 724a (1)* | 5.00 | 5.00 |
| *No. 178a (1)* | 6.50 | 6.50 |
| *No. 689a (1)* | 3.75 | 3.75 |
| *No. 150a (1)* | 4.75 | 7.00 |
| *No. 587a (1)* | 4.25 | 4.25 |
| *No. 541a (1)* | 2.50 | 2.50 |
| *Set total (16) Stamps* | 62.50 | 65.50 |

### Royal Family Birthday, Anniversary

CD347

Queen Elizabeth II, 65th birthday, Charles and Diana, 10th wedding anniversary: Various photographs of Queen Elizabeth II, Prince Philip, Prince Charles, Princess Diana and their sons William and Henry.

**1991**

Antigua....1446-1455
Barbuda....1229-1238
Dominica....1328-1337
Gambia....1080-1089
Grenada....2006-2015
Grenada Grenadines....1331-1340
Guyana....2440-2451
Lesotho....871-875
Maldive Islands....1533-1542
Nevis....666-675
St. Vincent....1485-1494
St. Vincent Grenadines....769-778
Sierra Leone....1387-1396
Turks & Caicos Islands....913-922
Uganda....918-927

| | | |
|---|---|---|
| *Nos. 1446-1455 (10)* | 21.70 | 20.05 |
| *Nos. 1229-1238 (10)* | 125.00 | 119.50 |
| *Nos. 1328-1337 (10)* | 30.20 | 30.20 |
| *Nos. 1080-1089 (10)* | 24.65 | 24.40 |
| *Nos. 2006-2015 (10)* | 25.45 | 22.10 |
| *Nos. 1331-1340 (10)* | 23.85 | 23.35 |
| *Nos. 2440-2451 (12)* | 21.40 | 21.15 |
| *Nos. 871-875 (5)* | 13.55 | 13.55 |
| *Nos. 1533-1542 (10)* | 28.10 | 28.10 |
| *Nos. 666-675 (10)* | 25.65 | 25.65 |
| *Nos. 1485-1494 (10)* | 26.75 | 25.90 |
| *Nos. 769-778 (10)* | 25.40 | 25.40 |
| *Nos. 1387-1396 (10)* | 26.55 | 26.55 |
| *Nos. 913-922 (10)* | 27.50 | 25.30 |
| *Nos. 918-927 (10)* | 26.60 | 26.60 |
| *Set total (147) Stamps* | 472.35 | 457.80 |

### Queen Elizabeth II's Accession to the Throne, 40th Anniv.

CD348

Various photographs of Queen Elizabeth II with local Scenes.

**1992**

Antigua....1513-1518
Barbuda....1306-1311
Dominica....1414-1419
Gambia....1172-1177
Grenada....2047-2052
Grenada Grenadines....1368-1373
Lesotho....881-885
Maldive Islands....1637-1642
Nevis....702-707
St. Vincent....1582-1587
St. Vincent Grenadines....829-834
Sierra Leone....1482-1487
Turks and Caicos Islands....978-987
Uganda....990-995
Virgin Islands....742-746

| | | |
|---|---|---|
| *Nos. 1513-1518 (6)* | 15.00 | *15.10* |
| *Nos. 1306-1311 (6)* | 125.25 | 83.65 |
| *Nos. 1414-1419 (6)* | 12.50 | 12.50 |
| *Nos. 1172-1177 (6)* | 16.60 | 16.35 |
| *Nos. 2047-2052 (6)* | 15.95 | 15.95 |
| *Nos. 1368-1373 (6)* | 17.00 | 15.35 |
| *Nos. 881-885 (5)* | 11.90 | 11.90 |
| *Nos. 1637-1642 (6)* | 17.55 | 17.55 |
| *Nos. 702-707 (6)* | 13.80 | 13.80 |
| *Nos. 1582-1587 (6)* | 14.40 | 14.40 |
| *Nos. 829-834 (6)* | 19.65 | 19.65 |
| *Nos. 1482-1487 (6)* | 22.50 | 22.50 |
| *Nos. 913-922 (10)* | 27.50 | 25.30 |
| *Nos. 990-995 (6)* | 19.50 | 19.50 |
| *Nos. 742-746 (5)* | 15.50 | 15.50 |
| *Set total (92) Stamps* | 364.60 | 319.00 |

CD349

**1992**

Ascension....531-535
Bahamas....744-748
Bermuda....623-627
British Indian Ocean Territory....119-123
Cayman Islands....648-652
Falkland Islands....549-553
Gibraltar....605-609
Hong Kong....619-623
Kenya....563-567
Kiribati....582-586
Pitcairn Islands....362-366
St. Helena....570-574
St. Kitts....332-336
Samoa....805-809
Seychelles....734-738
Zil Elwannyen Sesel....183-187
Solomon Islands....708-712
South Georgia....157-161
Tristan da Cunha....508-512
Vanuatu....555-559
Zambia....561-565

| | | |
|---|---|---|
| *Nos. 531-535 (5)* | 6.10 | 6.10 |
| *Nos. 744-748 (5)* | 6.90 | 4.70 |
| *Nos. 623-627 (5)* | 7.40 | *7.55* |
| *Nos. 119-123 (5)* | 22.75 | 19.25 |
| *Nos. 648-652 (5)* | 7.60 | 6.60 |
| *Nos. 549-553 (5)* | 5.95 | 5.90 |
| *Nos. 605-609 (5)* | 5.15 | *5.50* |
| *Nos. 619-623 (5)* | 5.10 | 5.25 |
| *Nos. 563-567 (5)* | 9.10 | 9.10 |
| *Nos. 582-586 (5)* | 3.85 | 3.85 |
| *Nos. 362-366 (5)* | 5.35 | 5.35 |
| *Nos. 570-574 (5)* | 5.70 | 5.70 |
| *Nos. 332-336 (5)* | 6.60 | 5.50 |
| *Nos. 805-809 (5)* | 8.10 | 6.15 |
| *Nos. 734-738 (5)* | 10.80 | 10.80 |
| *Nos. 183-187 (5)* | 9.40 | 9.40 |
| *Nos. 708-712 (5)* | 5.00 | 5.30 |
| *Nos. 157-161 (5)* | 5.60 | 5.90 |
| *Nos. 508-512 (5)* | 8.75 | 8.30 |
| *Nos. 555-559 (5)* | 3.65 | 3.65 |
| *Nos. 561-565 (5)* | 5.60 | 5.60 |
| *Set total (105) Stamps* | 154.45 | 145.45 |

### Royal Air Force, 75th Anniversary

CD350

**1993**

Ascension....557-561
Bahamas....771-775
Barbados....842-846
Belize....1003-1008
Bermuda....648-651
British Indian Ocean Territory....136-140
Falkland Is.....573-577
Fiji....687-691
Montserrat....830-834
St. Kitts....351-355

| | | |
|---|---|---|
| *Nos. 557-561 (5)* | 15.60 | 14.60 |
| *Nos. 771-775 (5)* | 24.65 | 21.45 |
| *Nos. 842-846 (5)* | 13.65 | 12.35 |
| *Nos. 1003-1008 (6)* | 16.55 | 16.50 |
| *Nos. 648-651 (4)* | 9.65 | *10.45* |
| *Nos. 136-140 (5)* | 16.10 | 16.10 |
| *Nos. 573-577 (5)* | 10.85 | 10.85 |
| *Nos. 687-691 (5)* | 17.75 | 17.40 |
| *Nos. 830-834 (5)* | 14.35 | 14.35 |
| *Nos. 351-355 (5)* | 24.45 | 23.95 |
| *Set total (50) Stamps* | 163.60 | 158.00 |

### Royal Air Force, 80th Anniv.

Design CD350 Re-inscribed

**1998**

Ascension....697-701
Bahamas....907-911
British Indian Ocean Terr....198-202
Cayman Islands....754-758
Fiji....814-818
Gibraltar....755-759
Samoa....957-961
Turks & Caicos Islands....1258-1265
Tuvalu....763-767
Virgin Islands....879-883

| | | |
|---|---|---|
| *Nos. 697-701 (5)* | 16.10 | 16.10 |
| *Nos. 907-911 (5)* | 13.60 | 12.65 |
| *Nos. 136-140 (5)* | 16.10 | 16.10 |
| *Nos. 754-758 (5)* | 15.25 | 15.25 |
| *Nos. 814-818 (5)* | 14.00 | 12.75 |
| *Nos. 755-759 (5)* | 9.70 | 9.70 |
| *Nos. 957-961 (5)* | 16.70 | 15.90 |
| *Nos. 1258-1265 (2)* | 27.50 | 27.50 |
| *Nos. 763-767 (5)* | 9.75 | 9.75 |
| *Nos. 879-883 (5)* | 15.00 | 15.00 |
| *Set total (47) Stamps* | 153.70 | 150.70 |

### End of World War II, 50th Anniv.

CD351

CD352

**1995**

Ascension....613-617
Bahamas....824-828
Barbados....891-895
Belize....1047-1050
British Indian Ocean Territory....163-167
Cayman Islands....704-708
Falkland Islands....634-638
Fiji....720-724
Kiribati....662-668
Liberia....1175-1179
Mauritius....803-805
St. Helena....646-654
St. Kitts....389-393
St. Lucia....1018-1022
Samoa....890-894
Solomon Islands....799-803
South Georgia....198-200
Tristan da Cunha....562-566

| | | |
|---|---|---|
| *Nos. 613-617 (5)* | 21.50 | 21.50 |

*Nos. 824-828 (5)* 22.00 18.70
*Nos. 891-895 (5)* 14.20 11.90
*Nos. 1047-1050 (4)* 6.05 5.90
*Nos. 163-167 (5)* 16.25 16.25
*Nos. 704-708 (5)* 17.65 13.95
*Nos. 634-638 (5)* 18.65 17.15
*Nos. 720-724 (5)* 17.50 14.50
*Nos. 662-668 (7)* 16.30 16.30
*Nos. 1175-1179 (5)* 15.25 11.15
*Nos. 803-805 (3)* 7.50 7.50
*Nos. 646-654 (9)* 26.10 26.10
*Nos. 389-393 (5)* 13.60 13.60
*Nos. 1018-1022 (5)* 14.25 11.15
*Nos. 890-894 (5)* 14.25 13.50
*Nos. 799-803 (5)* 14.75 14.75
*Nos. 198-200 (3)* 14.50 15.50
*Nos. 562-566 (5)* 20.10 20.10
*Set total (91) Stamps* 290.40 269.50

**UN, 50th Anniv.**

CD353

**1995**

Bahamas ....................839-842
Barbados ....................901-904
Belize ....................1055-1058
Jamaica ....................847-851
Liberia ....................1187-1190
Mauritius ....................813-816
Pitcairn Islands ....................436-439
St. Kitts ....................398-401
St. Lucia ....................1023-1026
Samoa ....................900-903
Tristan da Cunha ....................568-571
Virgin Islands ....................807-810

*Nos. 839-842 (4)* 7.15 6.40
*Nos. 901-904 (4)* 7.00 5.75
*Nos. 1055-1058 (4)* 4.70 4.70
*Nos. 847-851 (5)* 5.40 5.45
*Nos. 1187-1190 (4)* 9.65 9.65
*Nos. 813-816 (4)* 3.90 3.90
*Nos. 436-439 (4)* 8.15 8.15
*Nos. 398-401 (4)* 6.15 6.15
*Nos. 1023-1026 (4)* 7.50 7.25
*Nos. 900-903 (4)* 9.35 8.20
*Nos. 568-571 (4)* 13.50 13.50
*Nos. 807-810 (4)* 7.45 7.45
*Set total (49) Stamps* 89.90 86.55

**Queen Elizabeth, 70th Birthday**

CD354

**1996**

Ascension ....................632-635
British Antarctic Territory ....................240-243
British Indian Ocean Territory ........176-180
Falkland Islands ....................653-657
Pitcairn Islands ....................446-449
St. Helena ....................672-676
Samoa ....................912-916
Tokelau ....................223-227
Tristan da Cunha ....................576-579
Virgin Islands ....................824-828

*Nos. 632-635 (4)* 5.30 5.30
*Nos. 240-243 (4)* 10.50 8.90
*Nos. 176-180 (5)* 11.50 11.50
*Nos. 653-657 (5)* 13.55 11.20
*Nos. 446-449 (4)* 8.60 8.60
*Nos. 672-676 (5)* 12.70 12.70
*Nos. 912-916 (5)* 11.50 11.50
*Nos. 223-227 (5)* 10.50 10.50
*Nos. 576-579 (4)* 8.35 8.35
*Nos. 824-828 (5)* 11.30 11.30
*Set total (46) Stamps* 103.80 99.85

**Diana, Princess of Wales (1961-97)**

CD355

**1998**

Ascension ....................696
Bahamas ....................901A-902
Barbados ....................950
Belize ....................1091
Bermuda ....................753
Botswana ....................659-663
British Antarctic Territory ....................258
British Indian Ocean Terr. ....................197
Cayman Islands ....................752A-753
Falkland Islands ....................694
Fiji ....................819-820
Gibraltar ....................754
Kiribati ....................719A-720
Namibia ....................909
Niue ....................706
Norfolk Island ....................644-645
Papua New Guinea ....................937
Pitcairn Islands ....................487
St. Helena ....................711
St. Kitts ....................437A-438
Samoa ....................955A-956
Seycelles ....................802
Solomon Islands ....................866-867
South Georgia ....................220
Tokelau ....................252B-253
Tonga ....................980
  Niuafo'ou ....................201
Tristan da Cunha ....................618
Tuvalu ....................762
Vanuatu ....................718A-719
Virgin Islands ....................878

*No. 696 (1)* 5.25 5.25
*Nos. 901A-902 (2)* 5.30 5.30
*No. 950 (1)* 5.00 5.00
*No. 1091 (1)* 5.00 5.00
*No. 753 (1)* 5.00 5.00
*Nos. 659-663 (5)* 8.25 8.80
*No. 258 (1)* 6.25 6.25
*No. 197 (1)* 5.50 5.50
*Nos. 752A-753 (3)* 7.40 7.40
*No. 694 (1)* 5.00 5.00
*Nos. 819-820 (2)* 5.25 5.25
*No. 754 (1)* 4.75 4.75
*Nos. 719A-720 (2)* 4.85 4.85
*No. 909 (1)* 1.75 1.75
*No. 706 (1)* 5.50 5.50
*Nos. 644-645 (2)* 5.25 5.25
*No. 937 (1)* 6.50 6.50
*No. 487 (1)* 4.75 4.75
*No. 711 (1)* 4.25 4.25
*Nos. 437A-438 (2)* 5.15 5.15
*Nos. 955A-956 (2)* 7.00 7.00
*No. 802 (1)* 6.25 6.25
*Nos. 866-867 (2)* 5.40 5.40
*No. 220 (1)* 4.50 5.00
*Nos. 252B-253 (2)* 5.50 5.50
*No. 980 (1)* 5.75 5.75
*No. 201 (1)* 6.50 6.50
*No. 618 (1)* 5.00 5.00
*No. 762 (1)* 4.00 4.00
*Nos. 718A-719 (2)* 8.00 8.00
*No. 878 (1)* 4.50 4.50
*Set total (46) Stamps* 168.35 169.40

**Wedding of Prince Edward and Sophie Rhys-Jones**

CD356

**1999**

Ascension ....................729-730
Cayman Islands ....................775-776
Falkland Islands ....................729-730
Pitcairn Islands ....................505-506
St. Helena ....................733-734
Samoa ....................971-972
Tristan da Cunha ....................636-637
Virgin Islands ....................908-909

*Nos. 729-730 (2)* 4.50 4.50
*Nos. 775-776 (2)* 4.95 4.95
*Nos. 729-730 (2)* 14.00 14.00
*Nos. 505-506 (2)* 7.00 7.00
*Nos. 733-734 (2)* 5.00 5.00
*Nos. 971-972 (2)* 5.00 5.00
*Nos. 636-637 (2)* 7.50 7.50
*Nos. 908-909 (2)* 7.50 7.50
*Set total (16) Stamps* 55.45 55.45

**1st Manned Moon Landing, 30th Anniv.**

CD357

**1999**

Ascension ....................731-735
Bahamas ....................942-946
Barbados ....................967-971
Bermuda ....................778
Cayman Islands ....................777-781
Fiji ....................853-857
Jamaica ....................889-893
Kirbati ....................746-750
Nauru ....................465-469
St. Kitts ....................460-464
Samoa ....................973-977
Solomon Islands ....................875-879
Tuvalu ....................800-804
Virgin Islands ....................910-914

*Nos. 731-735 (5)* 12.80 12.80
*Nos. 942-946 (5)* 14.10 14.10
*Nos. 967-971 (5)* 8.65 7.75
*No. 778 (1)* 9.00 9.00
*Nos. 777-781 (5)* 9.25 9.25
*Nos. 853-857 (5)* 9.25 8.45
*Nos. 889-893 (5)* 8.30 7.18
*Nos. 746-750 (5)* 8.85 8.85
*Nos. 465-469 (5)* 8.90 10.15
*Nos. 460-464 (5)* 12.00 12.00
*Nos. 973-977 (5)* 13.45 13.30
*Nos. 875-879 (5)* 7.50 7.50
*Nos. 800-804 (5)* 7.45 7.45
*Nos. 910-914 (5)* 11.75 11.75
*Set total (66) Stamps* 141.25 139.53

**Queen Mother's Century**

CD358

**1999**

Ascension ....................736-740
Bahamas ....................951-955
Cayman Islands ....................782-786
Falkland Islands ....................734-738
Fiji ....................858-862
Norfolk Island ....................688-692
St. Helena ....................740-744
Samoa ....................978-982
Solomon Islands ....................880-884
South Georgia ....................231-235
Tristan da Cunha ....................638-642
Tuvalu ....................805-809

*Nos. 736-740 (5)* 15.50 15.50
*Nos. 951-955 (5)* 13.75 12.65
*Nos. 782-786 (5)* 8.35 8.35
*Nos. 734-738 (5)* 30.00 28.25
*Nos. 858-862 (5)* 12.80 13.25
*Nos. 688-692 (5)* 10.30 10.30
*Nos. 740-744 (5)* 16.15 16.15
*Nos. 978-982 (5)* 12.50 12.10
*Nos. 880-884 (5)* 7.50 7.00
*Nos. 231-235 (5)* 29.75 30.00
*Nos. 638-642 (5)* 18.00 18.00
*Nos. 805-809 (5)* 8.65 8.65
*Set total (60) Stamps* 183.25 180.20

**Prince William, 18th Birthday**

CD359

**2000**

Ascension ....................755-759
Cayman Islands ....................797-801
Falkland Islands ....................762-766
Fiji ....................889-893
South Georgia ....................257-261
Tristan da Cunha ....................664-668
Virgin Islands ....................925-929

*Nos. 755-759 (5)* 15.50 15.50
*Nos. 797-801 (5)* 11.15 10.90
*Nos. 762-766 (5)* 24.60 22.50
*Nos. 889-893 (5)* 12.90 12.90
*Nos. 257-261 (5)* 29.00 28.75
*Nos. 664-668 (5)* 21.50 21.50
*Nos. 925-929 (5)* 14.50 14.50
*Set total (35) Stamps* 129.15 126.55

**Reign of Queen Elizabeth II, 50th Anniv.**

CD360

**2002**

Ascension ....................790-794
Bahamas ....................1033-1037
Barbados ....................1019-1023
Belize ....................1152-1156
Bermuda ....................822-826
British Antarctic Territory ....................307-311
British Indian Ocean Territory ........239-243
Cayman Islands ....................844-848
Falkland Islands ....................804-808
Gibraltar ....................896-900
Jamaica ....................952-956
Nauru ....................491-495
Norfolk Island ....................758-762
Papua New Guinea ....................1019-1023
Pitcairn Islands ....................552
St. Helena ....................788-792
St. Lucia ....................1146-1150
Solomon Islands ....................931-935
South Georgia ....................274-278
Swaziland ....................706-710
Tokelau ....................302-306
Tonga ....................1059
  Niuafo'ou ....................239
Tristan da Cunha ....................706-710
Virgin Islands ....................967-971

*Nos. 790-794 (5)* 14.10 14.10
*Nos. 1033-1037 (5)* 15.25 15.25
*Nos. 1019-1023 (5)* 13.15 13.15
*Nos. 1152-1156 (5)* 12.65 12.25
*Nos. 822-826 (5)* 18.00 18.00
*Nos. 307-311 (5)* 25.00 25.00
*Nos. 239-243 (5)* 19.40 19.40
*Nos. 844-848 (5)* 13.25 13.25
*Nos. 804-808 (5)* 23.00 22.00
*Nos. 896-900 (5)* 6.65 6.65
*Nos. 952-956 (5)* 16.65 16.65
*Nos. 491-495 (5)* 18.75 18.75
*Nos. 758-762 (5)* 19.50 19.50
*Nos. 1019-1023 (5)* 14.50 14.50
*No. 552 (1)* 9.25 9.25
*Nos. 788-792 (5)* 19.75 19.75
*Nos. 1146-1150 (5)* 12.25 12.25
*Nos. 931-935 (5)* 12.40 12.40
*Nos. 274-278 (5)* 28.00 28.50
*Nos. 706-710 (5)* 12.75 12.75
*Nos. 302-306 (5)* 14.50 14.50
*No. 1059 (1)* 8.50 8.50
*No. 239 (1)* 8.75 8.75
*Nos. 706-710 (5)* 18.50 18.50
*Nos. 967-971 (5)* 16.50 16.50
*Set total (113) Stamps* 391.00 390.10

**Queen Mother Elizabeth (1900-2002)**

CD361

**2002**

| | |
|---|---|
| Ascension | 799-801 |
| Bahamas | 1044-1046 |
| Bermuda | 834-836 |
| British Antarctic Territory | 312-314 |
| British Indian Ocean Territory | 245-247 |
| Cayman Islands | 857-861 |
| Falkland Islands | 812-816 |
| Nauru | 499-501 |
| Pitcairn Islands | 561-565 |
| St. Helena | 808-812 |
| St. Lucia | 1155-1159 |
| Seychelles | 830 |
| Solomon Islands | 945-947 |
| South Georgia | 281-285 |
| Tokelau | 312-314 |
| Tristan da Cunha | 715-717 |
| Virgin Islands | 979-983 |

| | | |
|---|---|---|
| *Nos. 799-801 (3)* | 8.85 | 8.85 |
| *Nos. 1044-1046 (3)* | 9.10 | 9.10 |
| *Nos. 834-836 (3)* | 12.25 | 12.25 |
| *Nos. 312-314 (3)* | 19.25 | 19.25 |
| *Nos. 245-247 (3)* | 17.35 | 17.35 |
| *Nos. 857-861 (5)* | 15.00 | 15.00 |
| *Nos. 812-816 (5)* | 28.50 | 28.50 |
| *Nos. 499-501 (3)* | 16.00 | 16.00 |
| *Nos. 561-565 (5)* | 15.25 | 15.25 |
| *Nos. 808-812 (5)* | 12.00 | 12.00 |
| *Nos. 1155-1159 (5)* | 13.00 | 13.00 |
| *No. 830 (1)* | 6.50 | 6.50 |
| *Nos. 945-947 (3)* | 9.25 | 9.25 |
| *Nos. 281-285 (5)* | 19.50 | 19.50 |
| *Nos. 312-314 (3)* | 11.85 | 11.85 |
| *Nos. 715-717 (3)* | 16.25 | 16.25 |
| *Nos. 979-983 (5)* | 23.50 | 23.50 |
| *Set total (63) Stamps* | 253.40 | 253.40 |

**Head of Queen Elizabeth II**

CD362

**2003**

| | |
|---|---|
| Ascension | 822 |
| Bermuda | 865 |
| British Antarctic Territory | 322 |
| British Indian Ocean Territory | 261 |
| Cayman Islands | 878 |
| Falkland Islands | 828 |
| St. Helena | 820 |
| South Georgia | 294 |
| Tristan da Cunha | 731 |
| Virgin Islands | 1003 |

| | | |
|---|---|---|
| *No. 822 (1)* | 12.50 | 12.50 |
| *No. 865 (1)* | 50.00 | 50.00 |
| *No. 322 (1)* | 10.00 | 10.00 |
| *No. 261 (1)* | 11.00 | 11.00 |
| *No. 878 (1)* | 14.00 | 14.00 |
| *No. 828 (1)* | 9.00 | 9.00 |
| *No. 820 (1)* | 9.00 | 9.00 |
| *No. 294 (1)* | 8.50 | 8.50 |
| *No. 731 (1)* | 10.00 | 10.00 |
| *No. 1003 (1)* | 10.00 | 10.00 |
| *Set total (10) Stamps* | 144.00 | 144.00 |

**Coronation of Queen Elizabeth II, 50th Anniv.**

CD363

**2003**

| | |
|---|---|
| Ascension | 823-825 |
| Bahamas | 1073-1075 |
| Bermuda | 866-868 |
| British Antarctic Territory | 323-325 |
| British Indian Ocean Territory | 262-264 |
| Cayman Islands | 879-881 |
| Jamaica | 970-972 |
| Kiribati | 825-827 |
| Pitcairn Islands | 577-581 |
| St. Helena | 821-823 |
| St. Lucia | 1171-1173 |
| Tokelau | 320-322 |
| Tristan da Cunha | 732-734 |
| Virgin Islands | 1004-1006 |

| | | |
|---|---|---|
| *Nos. 823-825 (3)* | 12.50 | 12.50 |
| *Nos. 1073-1075 (3)* | 13.00 | 13.00 |
| *Nos. 866-868 (2)* | 14.25 | 14.25 |
| *Nos. 323-325 (3)* | 26.00 | 26.00 |
| *Nos. 262-264 (3)* | 28.00 | 28.00 |
| *Nos. 879-881 (3)* | 19.25 | 19.25 |
| *Nos. 970-972 (3)* | 10.00 | 10.00 |
| *Nos. 825-827 (3)* | 13.50 | 13.50 |
| *Nos. 577-581 (5)* | 14.40 | 14.40 |
| *Nos. 821-823 (3)* | 7.25 | 7.25 |
| *Nos. 1171-1173 (3)* | 8.75 | 8.75 |
| *Nos. 320-322 (3)* | 17.25 | 17.25 |
| *Nos. 732-734 (3)* | 16.75 | 16.75 |
| *Nos. 1004-1006 (3)* | 25.00 | 25.00 |
| *Set total (43) Stamps* | 225.90 | 225.90 |

**Prince William, 21st Birthday**

CD364

**2003**

| | |
|---|---|
| Ascension | 826 |
| British Indian Ocean Territory | 265 |
| Cayman Islands | 882-884 |
| Falkland Islands | 829 |
| South Georgia | 295 |
| Tokelau | 323 |
| Tristan da Cunha | 735 |
| Virgin Islands | 1007-1009 |

| | | |
|---|---|---|
| *No. 826 (1)* | 7.25 | 7.25 |
| *No. 265 (1)* | 8.00 | 8.00 |
| *Nos. 882-884 (3)* | 6.95 | 6.95 |
| *No. 829 (1)* | 13.50 | 13.50 |
| *No. 295 (1)* | 8.50 | 8.50 |
| *No. 323 (1)* | 7.25 | 7.25 |
| *No. 735 (1)* | 6.00 | 6.00 |
| *Nos. 1007-1009 (3)* | 10.00 | 10.00 |
| *Set total (12) Stamps* | 67.45 | 67.45 |

# British Commonwealth of Nations

## Dominions, Colonies, Territories, Offices and Independent Members

Comprising stamps of the British Commonwealth and associated nations.

A strict observance of technicalities would bar some or all of the stamps listed under Burma, Ireland, Kuwait, Nepal, New Republic, Orange Free State, Samoa, South Africa, South-West Africa, Stellaland, Sudan, Swaziland, the two Transvaal Republics and others but these are included for the convenience of collectors.

## 1. Great Britain

Great Britain: Including England, Scotland, Wales and Northern Ireland.

## 2. The Dominions, Present and Past

### AUSTRALIA

The Commonwealth of Australia was proclaimed on January 1, 1901. It consists of six former colonies as follows:

New South Wales
Queensland
South Australia
Victoria
Tasmania
Western Australia

The following islands and territories are, or have been, administered by Australia: Australian Antarctic Territory, Christmas Island, Cocos (Keeling) Islands, Nauru, New Guinea, Norfolk Island, Papua.

### CANADA

The Dominion of Canada was created by the British North America Act in 1867. The following provinces were former sepa- rate colonies and issued postage stamps:

British Columbia and Vancouver Island
New Brunswick
Newfoundland
Nova Scotia
Prince Edward Island

### FIJI

The colony of Fiji became an independent nation with dominion status on Oct. 10, 1970.

### GHANA

This state came into existence Mar. 6, 1957, with dominion status. It consists of the former colony of the Gold Coast and the Trusteeship Territory of Togoland. Ghana became a republic July 1, 1960.

### INDIA

The Republic of India was inaugurated on January 26, 1950. It succeeded the Dominion of India which was proclaimed August 15, 1947, when the former Empire of India was divided into Pakistan and the Union of India. The Republic is composed of about 40 predominantly Hindu states of three classes: governor's provinces, chief commissioner's provinces and princely states. India also has various territories, such as the Andaman and Nicobar Islands.

The old Empire of India was a federation of British India and the native states. The more important princely states were autonomous. Of the more than 700 Indian states, these 43 are familiar names to philatelists because of their postage stamps.

### CONVENTION STATES

Chamba
Faridkot
Gwalior
Jhind
Nabha
Patiala

### FEUDATORY STATES

Alwar
Bahawalpur
Bamra
Barwani
Bhopal
Bhor
Bijawar
Bundi
Bussahir
Charkhari
Cochin
Dhar
Dungarpur
Duttia
Faridkot (1879-85)
Hyderabad
Idar
Indore
Jaipur
Jammu
Jammu and Kashmir
Jasdan
Jhalawar
Jhind (1875-76)
Kashmir
Kishangarh
Kotah
Las Bela
Morvi
Nandgaon
Nowanuggur
Orchha
Poonch
Rajasthan
Rajpeepla
Sirmur
Soruth
Tonk
Travancore
Wadhwan

### NEW ZEALAND

Became a dominion on September 26, 1907. The following islands and territories are, or have been, administered by New Zealand:

Aitutaki
Cook Islands (Rarotonga)
Niue
Penrhyn
Ross Dependency
Samoa (Western Samoa)
Tokelau Islands

### PAKISTAN

The Republic of Pakistan was proclaimed March 23, 1956. It succeeded the Dominion which was proclaimed August 15, 1947. It is made up of all or part of several Moslem provinces and various districts of the former Empire of India, including Bahawalpur and Las Bela. Pakistan withdrew from the Commonwealth in 1972.

### SOUTH AFRICA

Under the terms of the South African Act (1909) the self-governing colonies of Cape of Good Hope, Natal, Orange River Colony and Transvaal united on May 31, 1910, to form the Union of South Africa. It became an independent republic May 3, 1961.

Under the terms of the Treaty of Versailles, South-West Africa, formerly German South-West Africa, was mandated to the Union of South Africa.

### SRI LANKA (CEYLON)

The Dominion of Ceylon was proclaimed February 4, 1948. The island had been a Crown Colony from 1802 until then. On May 22, 1972, Ceylon became the Republic of Sri Lanka.

## 3. Colonies, Past and Present; Controlled Territory and Independent Members of the Commonwealth

Aden
Aitutaki
Anguilla
Antigua
Ascension
Bahamas
Bahrain
Bangladesh
Barbados
Barbuda
Basutoland
Batum
Bechuanaland
Bechuanaland Prot.
Belize
Bermuda
Botswana
British Antarctic Territory
British Central Africa
British Columbia and Vancouver Island
British East Africa
British Guiana

British Honduras
British Indian Ocean Territory
British New Guinea
British Solomon Islands
British Somaliland
Brunei
Burma
Bushire
Cameroons
Cape of Good Hope
Cayman Islands
Christmas Island
Cocos (Keeling) Islands
Cook Islands
Crete,
British Administration
Cyprus
Dominica
East Africa & Uganda
Protectorates
Egypt
Falkland Islands
Fiji
Gambia
German East Africa
Gibraltar
Gilbert Islands
Gilbert & Ellice Islands
Gold Coast
Grenada
Griqualand West
Guernsey
Guyana
Heligoland
Hong Kong
Indian Native States
(see India)
Ionian Islands
Jamaica
Jersey
Kenya
Kenya, Uganda & Tanzania
Kuwait
Labuan
Lagos
Leeward Islands
Lesotho
Madagascar
Malawi
Malaya
Federated Malay States
Johore
Kedah
Kelantan
Malacca
Negri Sembilan
Pahang
Penang
Perak
Perlis
Selangor
Singapore
Sungei Ujong
Trengganu
Malaysia
Maldive Islands
Malta
Man, Isle of
Mauritius
Mesopotamia
Montserrat
Muscat
Namibia
Natal
Nauru
Nevis
New Britain
New Brunswick
Newfoundland
New Guinea
New Hebrides
New Republic
New South Wales
Niger Coast Protectorate
Nigeria
Niue
Norfolk Island
North Borneo
Northern Nigeria
Northern Rhodesia
North West Pacific Islands
Nova Scotia
Nyasaland Protectorate
Oman
Orange River Colony
Palestine
Papua New Guinea
Penrhyn Island
Pitcairn Islands
Prince Edward Island
Queensland
Rhodesia
Rhodesia & Nyasaland
Ross Dependency
Sabah
St. Christopher
St. Helena
St. Kitts
St. Kitts-Nevis-Anguilla
St. Lucia
St. Vincent
Samoa
Sarawak
Seychelles
Sierra Leone
Solomon Islands
Somaliland Protectorate
South Arabia
South Australia
South Georgia
Southern Nigeria
Southern Rhodesia
South-West Africa
Stellaland
Straits Settlements
Sudan
Swaziland
Tanganyika
Tanzania
Tasmania
Tobago
Togo
Tokelau Islands
Tonga
Transvaal
Trinidad
Trinidad and Tobago
Tristan da Cunha
Trucial States
Turks and Caicos
Turks Islands
Tuvalu
Uganda
United Arab Emirates
Victoria
Virgin Islands
Western Australia
Zambia
Zanzibar
Zululand

**POST OFFICES IN FOREIGN COUNTRIES**

Africa
East Africa Forces
Middle East Forces
Bangkok
China
Morocco
Turkish Empire

# Colonies, Former Colonies, Offices, Territories Controlled by Parent States

## Belgium

Belgian Congo
Ruanda-Urundi

## Denmark

Danish West Indies
Faroe Islands
Greenland
Iceland

## Finland

Aland Islands

## France

### COLONIES PAST AND PRESENT, CONTROLLED TERRITORIES

Afars & Issas, Territory of
Alaouites
Alexandretta
Algeria
Alsace & Lorraine
Anjouan
Annam & Tonkin
Benin
Cambodia (Khmer)
Cameroun
Castellorizo
Chad
Cilicia
Cochin China
Comoro Islands
Dahomey
Diego Suarez
Djibouti (Somali Coast)
Fezzan
French Congo
French Equatorial Africa
French Guiana
French Guinea
French India
French Morocco
French Polynesia (Oceania)
French Southern & Antarctic Territories
French Sudan
French West Africa
Gabon
Germany
Ghadames
Grand Comoro
Guadeloupe
Indo-China
Inini
Ivory Coast
Laos
Latakia
Lebanon
Madagascar
Martinique
Mauritania
Mayotte
Memel
Middle Congo
Moheli
New Caledonia
New Hebrides
Niger Territory
Nossi-Be
Obock
Reunion
Rouad, Ile
Ste.-Marie de Madagascar
St. Pierre & Miquelon
Senegal
Senegambia & Niger
Somali Coast
Syria
Tahiti
Togo
Tunisia
Ubangi-Shari
Upper Senegal & Niger
Upper Volta
Viet Nam
Wallis & Futuna Islands

### POST OFFICES IN FOREIGN COUNTRIES

China
Crete
Egypt
Turkish Empire
Zanzibar

## Germany

### EARLY STATES

Baden
Bavaria
Bergedorf
Bremen
Brunswick
Hamburg
Hanover
Lubeck
Mecklenburg-Schwerin
Mecklenburg-Strelitz
Oldenburg
Prussia
Saxony
Schleswig-Holstein
Wurttemberg

### FORMER COLONIES

Cameroun (Kamerun)
Caroline Islands
German East Africa
German New Guinea
German South-West Africa
Kiauchau
Mariana Islands
Marshall Islands
Samoa
Togo

## Italy

### EARLY STATES

Modena
Parma
Romagna
Roman States
Sardinia
Tuscany
Two Sicilies
  Naples
  Neapolitan Provinces
  Sicily

### FORMER COLONIES, CONTROLLED TERRITORIES, OCCUPATION AREAS

Aegean Islands
  Calimno (Calino)
  Caso
  Cos (Coo)
  Karki (Carchi)
  Leros (Lero)
  Lipso
  Nisiros (Nisiro)
  Patmos (Patmo)
  Piscopi
  Rodi (Rhodes)
  Scarpanto
  Simi
  Stampalia
Castellorizo
Corfu
Cyrenaica
Eritrea
Ethiopia (Abyssinia)
Fiume
Ionian Islands
  Cephalonia
  Ithaca
  Paxos
Italian East Africa
Libya
Oltre Giuba
Saseno
Somalia (Italian Somaliland)
Tripolitania

### POST OFFICES IN FOREIGN COUNTRIES

"ESTERO"*
Austria
China
  Peking
  Tientsin
Crete
Tripoli
Turkish Empire
  Constantinople
  Durazzo
  Janina
Jerusalem
Salonika
Scutari
Smyrna
Valona

*Stamps overprinted "ESTERO" were used in various parts of the world.

## Netherlands

Aruba
Caribbean Netherlands
Curacao
Netherlands Antilles (Curacao)
Netherlands Indies
Netherlands New Guinea
St. Martin
Surinam (Dutch Guiana)

## Portugal

### COLONIES PAST AND PRESENT, CONTROLLED TERRITORIES

Angola
Angra
Azores
Cape Verde
Funchal
Horta
Inhambane
Kionga
Lourenco Marques
Macao
Madeira
Mozambique
Mozambique Co.
Nyassa
Ponta Delgada
Portuguese Africa
Portuguese Congo
Portuguese Guinea
Portuguese India
Quelimane
St. Thomas & Prince Islands
Tete
Timor
Zambezia

## Russia

### ALLIED TERRITORIES AND REPUBLICS, OCCUPATION AREAS

Armenia
Aunus (Olonets)
Azerbaijan
Batum
Estonia
Far Eastern Republic
Georgia
Karelia
Latvia
Lithuania
North Ingermanland
Ostland
Russian Turkestan
Siberia
South Russia
Tannu Tuva
Transcaucasian Fed. Republics
Ukraine
Wenden (Livonia)
Western Ukraine

## Spain

### COLONIES PAST AND PRESENT, CONTROLLED TERRITORIES

Aguera, La
Cape Juby
Cuba
Elobey, Annobon & Corisco
Fernando Po
Ifni
Mariana Islands
Philippines
Puerto Rico
Rio de Oro
Rio Muni
Spanish Guinea
Spanish Morocco
Spanish Sahara
Spanish West Africa

### POST OFFICES IN FOREIGN COUNTRIES

Morocco
Tangier
Tetuan

# Dies of British Colonial Stamps

**DIE A:**

**1.** The lines in the groundwork vary in thickness and are not uniformly straight.

**2.** The seventh and eighth lines from the top, in the groundwork, converge where they meet the head.

**3.** There is a small dash in the upper part of the second jewel in the band of the crown.

**4.** The vertical color line in front of the throat stops at the sixth line of shading on the neck.

**DIE B:**

**1.** The lines in the groundwork are all thin and straight.

**2.** All the lines of the background are parallel.

**3.** There is no dash in the upper part of the second jewel in the band of the crown.

**4.** The vertical color line in front of the throat stops at the eighth line of shading on the neck.

**DIE I:**

**1.** The base of the crown is well below the level of the inner white line around the vignette.

**2.** The labels inscribed "POSTAGE" and "REVENUE" are cut square at the top.

**3.** There is a white "bud" on the outer side of the main stem of the curved ornaments in each lower corner.

**4.** The second (thick) line below the country name has the ends next to the crown cut diagonally.

| DIE Ia. | DIE Ib. |
|---|---|
| 1 as die II. | 1 and 3 as die II. |
| 2 and 3 as die I. | 2 as die I. |

**DIE II:**

**1.** The base of the crown is aligned with the underside of the white line around the vignette.

**2.** The labels curve inward at the top inner corners.

**3.** The "bud" has been removed from the outer curve of the ornaments in each corner.

**4.** The second line below the country name has the ends next to the crown cut vertically.

Wmk. 1
Crown and C C

Wmk. 2
Crown and C A

Wmk. 3
Multiple Crown and C A

Wmk. 4
Multiple Crown and Script C A

Wmk. 4a

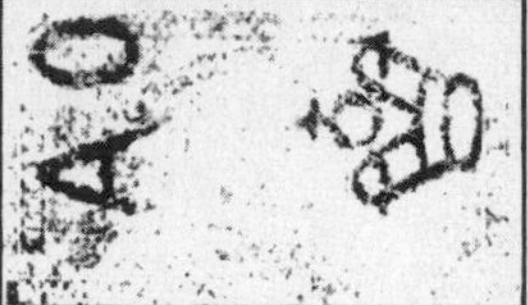
Wmk. 46

Wmk. 314
St. Edward's Crown and C A Multiple

Wmk. 373

Wmk. 384

Wmk. 406

# British Colonial and Crown Agents Watermarks

Watermarks 1 to 4, 314, 373, 384 and 406, common to many British territories, are illustrated here to avoid duplication.

The letters "CC" of Wmk. 1 identify the paper as having been made for the use of the Crown Colonies, while the letters "CA" of the others stand for "Crown Agents." Both Wmks. 1 and 2 were used on stamps printed by De La Rue & Co.

Wmk. 3 was adopted in 1904; Wmk. 4 in 1921; Wmk. 46 in 1879; Wmk. 314 in 1957; Wmk. 373 in 1974; Wmk. 384 in 1985; Wmk 406 in 2008.

In Wmk. 4a, a non-matching crown of the general St. Edwards type (bulging on both sides at top) was substituted for one of the Wmk. 4 crowns which fell off the dandy roll. The non-matching crown occurs in 1950-52 printings in a horizontal row of crowns on certain regular stamps of Johore and Seychelles, and on various postage due stamps of Barbados, Basutoland, British Guiana, Gold Coast, Grenada, Northern Rhodesia, St. Lucia, Swaziland and Trinidad and Tobago. A variation of Wmk. 4a, with the non-matching crown in a horizontal row of crown-CA-crown, occurs on regular stamps of Bahamas, St. Kitts-Nevis and Singapore.

Wmk. 314 was intentionally used sideways, starting in 1966. When a stamp was issued with Wmk. 314 both upright and sideways, the sideways varieties usually are listed also – with minor numbers. In many of the later issues, Wmk. 314 is slightly visible.

Wmk. 373 is usually only faintly visible.

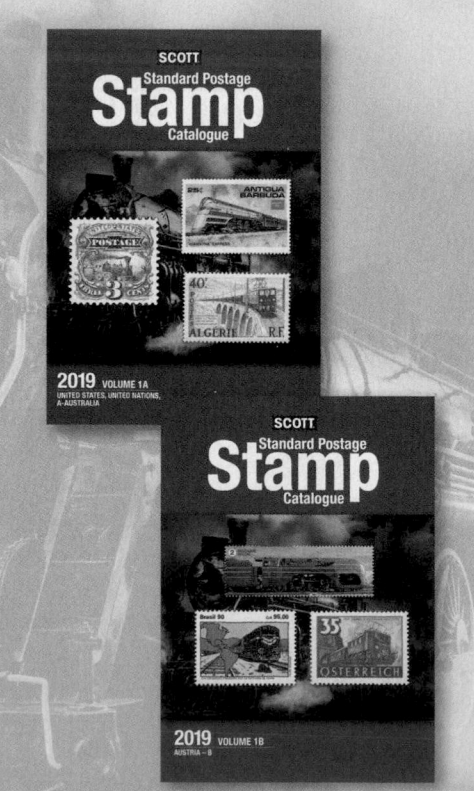

# CYPRUS

ˈsī-prəs

LOCATION — An island in the Mediterranean Sea off the coast of Turkey
GOVT. — Republic
AREA — 3,572 sq. mi.
POP. — 754,064 (1999 est.)
CAPITAL — Nicosia

The British Crown Colony of Cyprus became a republic in 1960.

Turkey invaded Cyprus in 1974 resulting in the the northern 40% of the island becoming the Turkish Republic of Northern Cyprus. No other country recognizes this division of the island.

See Turkey in Volume 6.

12 Pence = 1 Shilling
40 Paras = 1 Piaster
9 Piasters = 1 Shilling
20 Shillings = 1 Pound
1000 Milliemes = 1 Pound (1955)
100 Cents = 1 Cyprus Pound (1983)
100 Cents = 1 Euro (2008)

**Catalogue values for unused stamps in this country are for Never Hinged items, beginning with Scott 156 in the regular postage section and Scott RA1 in the postal tax section.**

Values for unused stamps are for examples with original gum as defined in the catalogue introduction. Very fine examples of Nos. 1, 2 and 7-10 will have perforations touching the design on at least one or more sides due to the narrow spacing of the stamps on the plates and to imperfect perforation methods. Stamps with perfs clear on all four sides are scarce and will command higher prices.

**Watermark**

Wmk. 344 — Map of Cyprus and KC/K Delta

Queen Victoria — A1

A2 A3

A4 A5

A6

A7

**Various Watermarks as in Great Britain (#20, 23, 25, 27 & 29)**

**1880 Typo. *Perf. 14***

| No. | Type | Description | Unused | Used |
|---|---|---|---|---|
| **1** | A1 | ½p rose (P 15) | 125.00 | 115.00 |
| | | Plate 12 | 240.00 | *300.00* |
| | | Plate 19 | 5,750. | 950.00 |
| *b.* | | Double overprint (P 15) | | *45,000.* |
| **2** | A2 | 1p red (P 216) | 22.50 | *55.00* |
| | | Plate 217 | 22.50 | *60.00* |
| | | Plate 174 | 1,500. | 1,500. |
| | | Plate 181 | 525.00 | 210.00 |
| | | Plate 184 | 22,000. | 3,500. |
| | | Plate 193 | 840.00 | |
| | | Plate 196 | 725.00 | |
| | | Plate 201 | 27.50 | *57.50* |
| | | Plate 205 | 90.00 | 57.50 |
| | | Plate 208 | 135.00 | 65.00 |
| | | Plate 215 | 22.50 | *57.50* |
| | | Plate 218 | 32.50 | *65.00* |
| | | Plate 220 | 550.00 | 475.00 |
| *b.* | | Double overprint (P 218) | 5,400. | |
| | | Double overprint (P 208) | *27,500.* | |
| *c.* | | Pair, one without ovpt. (P 208) | *27,500.* | |
| **3** | A3 | 2½p claret (P 14) | 4.50 | *19.00* |
| | | Plate 15 | 8.00 | *50.00* |
| **4** | A4 | 4p lt ol grn (P 16) | 150.00 | *240.00* |
| **5** | A5 | 6p ol gray (P 16) | 575.00 | *750.00* |
| **6** | A6 | 1sh green (P 13) | 900.00 | 525.00 |

**Black Surcharge**

| No. | Type | Description | Unused | Used |
|---|---|---|---|---|
| **7** | A7 | 30 paras on 1p red (P 216) | 150.00 | *95.00* |
| | | Plate 201 | 180.00 | 110.00 |
| | | Plate 217 | 210.00 | 210.00 |
| | | Plate 220 | 175.00 | *190.00* |
| *b.* | | Dbl. surch., one invtd. (P 220) | 2,000. | *1,500.* |
| | | Dbl. surch., one invtd. (P 216) | 7,750. | |

**No. 2 Surcharged**

18mm Long

**1881**

| No. | Type | Description | Unused | Used |
|---|---|---|---|---|
| **8** | A2 | ½p on 1p (205, 216) | 82.50 | *100.00* |
| | | Plate 174 | 225.00 | *400.00* |
| | | Plate 181 | 210.00 | *260.00* |
| | | Plate 201 | 115.00 | *140.00* |
| | | Plate 205 | 85.00 | *100.00* |
| | | Plate 208 | 225.00 | *375.00* |
| | | Plate 215 | 840.00 | *1,000.* |
| | | Plate 217 | 1,000. | 900.00 |
| | | Plate 218 | 550.00 | *675.00* |
| | | Plate 220 | 325.00 | *450.00* |

16mm Long

| No. | Type | Description | Unused | Used |
|---|---|---|---|---|
| **9** | A2 | ½p on 1p (P 201) | 140.00 | *190.00* |
| | | Plate 216 | 400.00 | *460.00* |
| | | Plate 218 | | *17,500.* |
| *a.* | | Double surcharge (P 201, 216) | 3,750. | 3,000. |

13mm Long

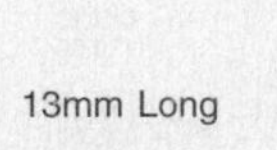

| No. | Type | Description | Unused | Used |
|---|---|---|---|---|
| **10** | A2 | ½p on 1p red (P 215) | 52.50 | *75.00* |
| | | Plate 205 | 425.00 | |
| | | Plate 217 | 175.00 | 105.00 |
| | | Plate 218 | 90.00 | *125.00* |
| *c.* | | Double surcharge (P 215) | 550.00 | *700.00* |
| | | Double surcharge (P 205) | 875.00 | |
| *e.* | | Triple surcharge (P 215) | 875.00 | |
| | | Triple surcharge (P 205) | *4,750.* | |
| | | Triple surcharge (P 217) | — | |
| | | Triple surcharge (P 218) | *4,750.* | |
| *h.* | | Quadruple surch. (P 205, 215) | *7,500.* | |
| *j.* | | "CYPRUS" double (P 218) | *6,000.* | |

A8

**1881, July Typo. Wmk. 1**

| No. | Type | Description | Unused | Used |
|---|---|---|---|---|
| **11** | A8 | ½pi emer grn | 210.00 | 52.50 |
| **12** | A8 | 1pi rose | 425.00 | 37.50 |
| **13** | A8 | 2pi ultramarine | 525.00 | 37.50 |
| **14** | A8 | 4pi olive green | 1,050. | 325.00 |
| **15** | A8 | 6pi olive gray | 1,900. | 500.00 |

Postage and revenue stamps of Cyprus with "J.A.B." (the initials of Postmaster J.A. Bulmer) in manuscript, or with "POSTAL SURCHARGE" (with or without "J. A. B."), were not Postage Due stamps but were employed for accounting purposes between the chief PO at Larnaca and the sub-offices.

See Nos. 19-25, 28-37. For surcharges see Nos. 16-18, 26-27.

**Nos. 1881-1894 Surcharged in Black**

**1882 Wmk. 1**

| No. | Type | Description | Unused | Used |
|---|---|---|---|---|
| **16** | A8 | ½pi on ½pi grn | 750.00 | 92.50 |
| **17** | A8 | 30pa on 1pi rose | 1,750. | 140.00 |
| *a.* | | Double surcharge, one inverted | *1,400.* | *850.00* |

**1884 Wmk. 2**

| No. | Type | Description | Unused | Used |
|---|---|---|---|---|
| **18** | A8 | ½pi on ½pi grn | 190.00 | 10.00 |
| *a.* | | Double surcharge | | *3,200.* |

See Nos. 26, 27.

**1882-94 Die B**

For description of Dies A and B see "Dies of British Colonial Stamps" in Table of Contents.

| No. | Type | Description | Unused | Used |
|---|---|---|---|---|
| **19** | A8 | ½pi green | 16.00 | 2.50 |
| **20** | A8 | 30pa violet | 11.00 | *14.00* |
| **21** | A8 | 1pi rose | 15.50 | 8.50 |
| **22** | A8 | 2pi blue | 17.50 | 2.10 |
| **23** | A8 | 4pi pale ol grn | 20.00 | *40.00* |
| *24a* | A8 | 6pi | 275.00 | *800.00* |
| *25a* | A8 | 12pi | 190.00 | *450.00* |
| | | *Nos. 19-25a (7)* | 545.00 | *1,317.* |

**Die A**

| No. | Type | Description | Unused | Used |
|---|---|---|---|---|
| *19a* | A8 | ½pi | 22.50 | 3.25 |
| *b.* | | ½pi emerald | *6,000.* | 525.00 |
| *20a* | A8 | 30pa lilac | 85.00 | 27.50 |
| *21a* | A8 | 1pi | 110.00 | 4.00 |
| *22a* | A8 | 2pi | 170.00 | 4.00 |
| *23a* | A8 | 4pi | 375.00 | 35.00 |
| **24** | A8 | 6pi olive gray | 75.00 | 21.00 |
| **25** | A8 | 12pi brown org | 225.00 | 45.00 |
| | | *Nos. 19a-25 (7)* | 1,063. | 139.75 |

Nos. 1881-1894 Surcharged in Black

Type I — Figures "½" 8mm apart.
Type II — Figures "½" 6mm apart.
The space between the fraction bars varies from 5½ to 8½mm but is usually 6 or 8mm.

**Black Surcharge Type I**

**1886 Wmk. 2**

| No. | Type | Description | Unused | Used |
|---|---|---|---|---|
| **26** | A8 | ½pi on ½pi grn | 525.00 | 16.00 |
| *a.* | | Type II | 325.00 | 100.00 |
| *b.* | | Double surcharge, type II | | |

**Wmk. 1**

| No. | Type | Description | Unused | Used |
|---|---|---|---|---|
| **27** | A8 | ½pi on ½pi grn | *8,750.* | 500.00 |
| *a.* | | Type II | *24,000.* | |

No. 27a probably is a proof.

**1894-96 Wmk. 2**

| No. | Type | Description | Unused | Used |
|---|---|---|---|---|
| **28** | A8 | ½pi grn & car rose | 5.25 | 1.75 |
| **29** | A8 | 30pa violet & green | 4.75 | *5.00* |
| **30** | A8 | 1pi rose & ultra | 8.50 | 1.75 |
| **31** | A8 | 2pi ultra & mar | 17.50 | 1.75 |
| **32** | A8 | 4pi ol green & vio | 21.00 | 17.50 |
| **33** | A8 | 6pi ol gray & grn | 22.50 | *40.00* |
| **34** | A8 | 9pi brown & rose | 29.00 | *35.00* |
| **35** | A8 | 12pi brn org & blk | 25.00 | *67.50* |
| **36** | A8 | 18pi slate & brown | 60.00 | 62.50 |
| **37** | A8 | 45pi dk vio & ultra | 125.00 | *165.00* |
| | | *Nos. 28-37 (10)* | 318.50 | *397.75* |

King Edward VII — A12

**1903 Typo.**

| No. | Type | Description | Unused | Used |
|---|---|---|---|---|
| **38** | A12 | ½pi grn & car rose | 13.00 | 1.40 |
| **39** | A12 | 30pa violet & green | 26.00 | 5.50 |
| **40** | A12 | 1pi car rose & ultra | 40.00 | 7.50 |
| **41** | A12 | 2pi ultra & mar | 90.00 | 18.00 |
| **42** | A12 | 4pi ol grn & vio | 57.50 | 27.50 |
| **43** | A12 | 6pi ol brn & grn | 52.50 | *145.00* |
| **44** | A12 | 9pi brn & car rose | 125.00 | *275.00* |
| **45** | A12 | 12pi org brn & blk | 37.50 | *87.50* |
| **46** | A12 | 18pi blk & brn | 100.00 | *175.00* |
| **47** | A12 | 45pi dk vio & ultra | 250.00 | *600.00* |
| | | *Nos. 38-47 (10)* | 791.50 | *1,342.* |

**1904-07 Wmk. 3**

| No. | Type | Description | Unused | Used |
|---|---|---|---|---|
| **48** | A12 | 5pa bis & blk ('07) | 1.25 | 2.00 |
| **49** | A12 | 10pa org & grn ('07) | 6.00 | 1.90 |
| **50** | A12 | ½pi grn & car rose | 12.00 | 1.60 |
| **51** | A12 | 30pa redsh vio & grn | 20.00 | 2.75 |
| **52** | A12 | 1pi car rose & ultra | 16.00 | 1.10 |
| **53** | A12 | 2pi ultra & mar | 20.00 | 2.00 |
| **54** | A12 | 4pi ol grn & red vio | 30.00 | 20.00 |
| **55** | A12 | 6pi ol brn & grn | 30.00 | 17.00 |
| **56** | A12 | 9pi brn & car rose | 52.50 | 9.75 |
| **57** | A12 | 12pi org brn & blk | 40.00 | *67.50* |
| **58** | A12 | 18pi blk & brn | 55.00 | 15.00 |
| **59** | A12 | 45pi dk vio & ultra | 120.00 | *175.00* |
| | | *Nos. 48-59 (12)* | 402.75 | *315.60* |

King George V — A13

**1912**

| No. | Type | Description | Unused | Used |
|---|---|---|---|---|
| **61a** | A13 | 10pa org yel & br grn ('15) | 2.75 | 1.60 |
| **62** | A13 | ½pi grn & car rose | 2.90 | .35 |
| **63** | A13 | 30pa vio & grn | 3.25 | 2.40 |
| **64** | A13 | 1pi car & ultra | 5.75 | 1.90 |
| **65** | A13 | 2pi ultra & mar | 8.50 | 2.25 |
| **66** | A13 | 4pi ol grn & red vio | 5.50 | *5.25* |
| **67** | A13 | 6pi ol brn & grn | 6.00 | *11.50* |
| **68** | A13 | 9pi brn & car rose | 42.50 | 28.00 |
| **69** | A13 | 12pi org brn & blk | 25.00 | *57.50* |
| **70** | A13 | 18pi blk & brn | 50.00 | *50.00* |
| **71** | A13 | 45pi dl vio & ultra | 130.00 | *170.00* |
| | | *Nos. 61a-71 (11)* | 282.15 | 330.75 |

**1921-23 Wmk. 4**

| No. | Type | Description | Unused | Used |
|---|---|---|---|---|
| **72** | A13 | 10pa org & grn | 16.00 | 13.50 |
| **73** | A13 | 10pa gray & yel | 16.00 | 9.50 |
| **74** | A13 | 30pa violet & grn | 3.75 | 2.00 |
| **75** | A13 | 30pa green | 9.00 | 1.75 |
| **76** | A13 | 1pi rose & ultra | 26.00 | *45.00* |
| **77** | A13 | 1pi violet & car | 4.00 | 5.00 |
| **78** | A13 | 1½pi org & blk | 12.50 | 7.25 |
| **79** | A13 | 2pi ultra & red vio | 35.00 | 25.00 |
| **80** | A13 | 2pi rose & ultra | 16.00 | *27.50* |
| **81** | A13 | 2¾pi ultra & red vio | 11.00 | *12.00* |
| **82** | A13 | 4pi ol grn & red vio | 19.00 | *26.00* |
| **83** | A13 | 6pi ol brn & grn | 37.50 | *80.00* |
| **84** | A13 | 9pi brn & car | 47.50 | *95.00* |
| **85** | A13 | 18pi black & brn | 90.00 | *175.00* |
| **86** | A13 | 45pi dl vio & ultra | 275.00 | *325.00* |
| | | *Nos. 72-86 (15)* | 618.25 | *849.50* |

**Wmk. 3**

| No. | Type | Description | Unused | Used |
|---|---|---|---|---|
| **87** | A13 | 10sh grn & red, *yel* | 425.00 | *900.00* |
| **88** | A13 | £1 vio & blk, *red* | 1,400. | *3,250.* |

Years of issue: Nos. 73, 75, 77-78, 80-81, 87-88, 1923; others, 1921.

A14

**1924-28 Chalky Paper Wmk. 4**

| No. | Type | Denom. | Description | Unused | Used |
|---|---|---|---|---|---|
| 89 | A14 | ¼pi | gray & brn org | 2.10 | .55 |
| 90 | A14 | ½pi | gray blk & blk | 6.25 | *14.50* |
| 91 | A14 | ½pi | grn & dp grn ('25) | 2.50 | 1.10 |
| 92 | A14 | ¾pi | grn & dp grn | 4.25 | 1.10 |
| 93 | A14 | ¾pi | gray blk & blk ('25) | 4.50 | 1.10 |
| 94 | A14 | 1pi | brn vio & org brn | 2.40 | 2.10 |
| 95 | A14 | 1½pi | org & blk | 3.50 | *14.50* |
| 96 | A14 | 1½pi | car ('25) | 5.25 | 1.60 |
| 97 | A14 | 2pi | car & grn | 4.25 | *21.00* |
| 98 | A14 | 2pi | org & blk ('25) | 15.00 | 4.25 |
| 99 | A14 | 2½pi | ultra ('25) | 9.00 | 1.90 |
| 100 | A14 | 2¾pi | ultra & dl vio | 3.75 | 5.00 |
| 101 | A14 | 4pi | ap grn & vio | 5.25 | 5.25 |
| 102 | A14 | 4½pi | blk & yel, *emer* | 4.00 | 5.25 |
| 103 | A14 | 6pi | grn ol & grn | 5.25 | *9.00* |
| 104 | A14 | 9pi | brn & dk vio | 9.00 | 5.75 |
| 105 | A14 | 12pi | org brn & blk | 14.50 | *65.00* |
| 106 | A14 | 18pi | blk & org | 29.00 | 5.75 |
| | | | Revenue cancel | | 1.00 |
| 107 | A14 | 45pi | gray vio & ultra | 65.00 | 45.00 |
| | | | Revenue cancel | | 1.50 |
| 108 | A14 | 90pi | grn & red, *yel* | 125.00 | *270.00* |
| | | | Revenue cancel | | 3.75 |
| 109 | A14 | £5 | blk, *yel* ('28) | 3,750. | *8,000.* |
| | | | On cover (overfranked) | | 275.00 |
| | | | Revenue cancel | | 275.00 |

**Wmk. 3**

| No. | Type | Denom. | Description | Unused | Used |
|---|---|---|---|---|---|
| 110 | A14 | £1 | vio & blk, *red* | 350.00 | *900.00* |
| | | | Revenue cancel | | 12.50 |
| | | | *Nos. 89-108 (20)* | 319.75 | *479.70* |

Nos. 96 and 99 are on ordinary paper.

Silver Coin of Amathus — A15

Philosopher Zeno — A16

Map of Cyprus — A17

Discovery of Body of St. Barnabas — A18

Cloisters of Bella Paise Monastery — A19

Badge of the Colony — A20

Hospice of Umm Haram at Larnaca — A21

Statue of Richard Coeur de Lion, London — A22

St. Nicholas Cathedral, Famagusta — A23

King George V — A24

***Perf. 12***

**1928, Feb. 1 Engr. Wmk. 4**

| No. | Type | Denom. | Description | Unused | Used |
|---|---|---|---|---|---|
| 114 | A15 | ¾pi | dark violet | 3.75 | 1.60 |
| 115 | A16 | 1pi | Prus bl & blk | 4.00 | 2.00 |
| 116 | A17 | 1½pi | red | 7.50 | 2.25 |
| 117 | A18 | 2½pi | ultramarine | 4.75 | 2.75 |
| 118 | A19 | 4pi | dp red brown | 9.50 | 9.50 |
| 119 | A20 | 6pi | dark blue | 14.00 | *32.50* |
| 120 | A21 | 9pi | violet brown | 11.00 | *17.50* |
| 121 | A22 | 18pi | dk brn & blk | 30.00 | *35.00* |
| 122 | A23 | 45pi | dp blue & vio | 52.50 | *62.50* |
| 123 | A24 | £1 | ol brn & dp blue | 275.00 | *400.00* |
| | | | *Nos. 114-123 (10)* | 412.00 | *565.60* |

50th year of Cyprus as a British colony.

Ruins of Vouni Palace — A25

Columns at Salamis — A26

Peristerona Church — A27

Soli Theater — A28

Kyrenia Castle and Harbor — A29

Kolossi Castle — A30

St. Sophia Cathedral — A31

Bairakdar Mosque — A32

Queen's Window, St. Hilarion Castle — A33

Buyuk Khan, Nicosia — A34

Forest Scene — A35

**1934, Dec. 1 Engr. *Perf. 12½***

| No. | Type | Denom. | Description | Unused | Used |
|---|---|---|---|---|---|
| 125 | A25 | ¼pi | yel brn & ultra | 1.40 | 1.10 |
| | | | Never hinged | 2.10 | |
| *a.* | | | Vert. pair, imperf. between | *52,500.* | *35,000.* |
| 126 | A26 | ½pi | green | 1.90 | 1.25 |
| | | | Never hinged | 2.10 | |
| *a.* | | | Vert. pair, imperf. between | *18,000.* | *20,000.* |
| 127 | A27 | ¾pi | vio & blk | 3.50 | .45 |
| | | | Never hinged | 4.50 | |
| *a.* | | | Vert. pair, imperf. between | *52,500.* | |
| 128 | A28 | 1pi | brn & blk | 3.00 | 2.50 |
| | | | Never hinged | 4.50 | |
| *a.* | | | Vert. pair, imperf. between | *26,000.* | *26,000.* |
| *b.* | | | Horiz. pair, imperf. btwn. | *19,000.* | |
| 129 | A29 | 1½pi | rose red | 4.00 | 2.10 |
| | | | Never hinged | 6.00 | |
| 130 | A30 | 2½pi | dk ultra | 5.25 | 2.40 |
| | | | Never hinged | 7.75 | |
| 131 | A31 | 4½pi | dk car & blk | 5.25 | 5.00 |
| | | | Never hinged | 14.00 | |
| 132 | A32 | 6pi | blue & blk | 12.50 | *20.00* |
| | | | Never hinged | 26.00 | |
| 133 | A33 | 9pi | dl vio & blk brn | 20.00 | 8.50 |
| | | | Never hinged | 32.50 | |
| 134 | A34 | 18pi | ol grn & blk | 55.00 | 50.00 |
| | | | Never hinged | 120.00 | |
| 135 | A35 | 45pi | blk & emer | 120.00 | 85.00 |
| | | | Never hinged | 225.00 | |
| | | | *Nos. 125-135 (11)* | 231.80 | *178.30* |
| | | | Set, never hinged | 405.00 | |

Common Design Types pictured following the introduction.

**Silver Jubilee Issue**

Common Design Type

**1935, May 6 *Perf. 11x12***

| No. | Type | Denom. | Description | Unused | Used |
|---|---|---|---|---|---|
| 136 | CD301 | ¾pi | gray blk & ultra | 4.25 | 1.50 |
| 137 | CD301 | 1½pi | car & dk bl | 6.25 | 3.00 |
| 138 | CD301 | 2½pi | ultra & brn | 5.25 | 1.90 |
| 139 | CD301 | 9pi | brn vio & ind | 24.00 | *28.00* |
| | | | *Nos. 136-139 (4)* | 39.75 | *34.40* |
| | | | Set, never hinged | 60.00 | |

**Coronation Issue**

Common Design Type

**1937, May 12 *Perf. 11x11½***

| No. | Type | Denom. | Description | Unused | Used |
|---|---|---|---|---|---|
| 140 | CD302 | ¾pi | dark gray | 1.00 | 1.00 |
| 141 | CD302 | 1½pi | dark car | 1.25 | *2.50* |
| 142 | CD302 | 2½pi | deep ultra | 1.50 | *3.00* |
| | | | *Nos. 140-142 (3)* | 3.75 | 6.50 |
| | | | Set, never hinged | 7.75 | |

Ruins of Vouni Palace — A36

Columns at Salamis — A37

Peristerona Church — A38

Soli Theater — A39

Kyrenia Castle and Harbor — A40

Kolossi Castle — A41

Map of Cyprus — A42

Bairakdar Mosque — A43

Citadel, Famagusta — A44

Buyuk Khan — A45

Forest Scene A46

King George VI A47

**1938-44 Wmk. 4 *Perf. 12½***

**143** A36 ¼pi yel brn & ultra .60 .60
**144** A37 ½pi green .80 .50
**145** A38 ¾pi violet & blk 7.25 1.75
**146** A39 1pi orange .90 .40
*a.* Perf. 13½x12½ ('44) 375.00 30.00
Never hinged 575.00
**147** A40 1½pi rose car 3.25 2.00
**147A** A40 1½pi lt vio ('43) .90 .75
**147B** A38 2pi car & blk ('42) .90 .45
*c.* Perf. 12½x13½ ('44) 2.00 *12.50*
Never hinged 0.25
**148** A41 2½pi ultramarine 15.00 4.50
**148A** A41 3pi dp ultra ('42) 1.25 .60
**149** A42 4½pi gray .90 .40
**150** A43 6pi blue & blk 1.25 *1.10*
**151** A44 9pi dk vio & blk 1.00 .80
**152** A45 18pi ol grn & blk 5.00 1.75
**153** A46 45pi blk & emer 16.00 5.00
**154** A47 90pi blk & brt vio 21.00 8.00
**155** A47 £1 ind & dl red 45.00 32.50
*Nos. 143-155 (16)* 121.00 61.10
Set, never hinged 275.00

See Nos. 164-166.

**Catalogue values for unused stamps in this section, from this point to the end of the section, are for Never Hinged items.**

### Peace Issue

Common Design Type

**1946, Oct. 21 Engr. *Perf. 13½x14***

**156** CD303 1½pi purple .45 .25
**157** CD303 3pi deep blue .45 .45

### Silver Wedding Issue

Common Design Types

**1948, Dec. 20 Photo. *Perf. 14x14½***

**158** CD304 1½pi purple 1.00 .55

**Engr.; Name Typo.**

***Perf. 11½x11***

**159** CD305 £1 dark blue 57.50 *77.50*

### UPU Issue

Common Design Types

***Perf. 13½, 11x11½***

**1949, Oct. 10 Engr. Wmk. 4**

**160** CD306 1½pi violet .65 *1.60*
**161** CD307 2pi deep carmine 1.75 1.60
**162** CD308 3pi indigo 1.10 *1.50*
**163** CD309 9pi rose violet 1.10 *6.00*
*Nos. 160-163 (4)* 4.60 *10.70*

### Types of 1938-43

**1951, July 2 Engr. *Perf. 12½***

**164** A37 ½pi purple 3.75 .75
**165** A40 1½pi deep green 6.25 1.25
**166** A41 4pi deep ultra 6.75 1.40
*Nos. 164-166 (3)* 16.75 3.40

### Coronation Issue

Common Design Type

**1953, June 2 *Perf. 13½x13***

**167** CD312 1½pi brt grn & black 1.60 .75

Carobs A48

Copper Pyrites Mine A49

St. Hilarion Castle A50

Queen Elizabeth II and Cyprian Coin Devices — A51

Designs: 3m, Grapes. 5m, Oranges. 15m, Troodos forest. 20m, Aphrodite beach. 25m, Coin of Paphos. 30m, Kyrenia. 35m, Harvest in Mesaoria. 40m, Famagusta harbor. 100m, Hala Sultan Tekke. 250m, Kanakaria church. £1, Queen Elizabeth II and devices of Byzantium, Lusignan, Ottoman Empire and Venice.

***Perf. 11½***

**1955, Aug. 1 Engr. Wmk. 4**

**168** A48 2m chocolate .25 *.50*
**169** A48 3m violet blue .25 .25
**170** A48 5m orange 1.00 .25
**171** A49 10m gray grn & chocolate 1.25 .25
**172** A49 15m indigo & olive 3.50 .50
**173** A49 20m ultra & brown 1.25 .25
**174** A49 25m aquamarine 3.25 .70
**175** A49 30m carmine & blk 3.00 .25
**176** A49 35m aqua & orange 1.25 .50
**177** A49 40m choc & dk grn 2.00 .75

***Perf. 13½***

**178** A50 50m red brn & aqua 2.10 .30
**179** A50 100m bl green & mag 13.00 .60
**180** A50 250m vio brn & dk blue gray 16.00 13.00

***Perf. 11x11½***

**181** A51 500m lilac rose & grnsh gray 37.50 15.00
**182** A51 £1 grnsh gray & brn red 30.00 *52.50*
Revenue cancel 1.00
*Nos. 168-182 (15)* 115.60 85.60

### Republic

Nos. 168-182 Overprinted in Dark Blue

**1960, Aug. 16 Ovpt. 10x6½mm**

**183** A48 2m chocolate .25 *.75*
**184** A48 3m violet blue .25 .25
**185** A48 5m orange 2.25 .25

**Overprint 12½x11mm**

**186** A49 10m gray grn & choc 1.00 .25
**187** A49 15m indigo & ol 3.25 .30
**188** A49 20m ultra & brn 1.75 *1.50*
*a.* Double overprint *12,000.*
**189** A49 25m aquamarine 1.75 1.75
**190** A49 30m car & black 1.75 .30
*a.* Double overprint *45,000.*
**191** A49 35m aqua & org 1.75 .70
**192** A49 40m choc & dk grn 2.00 *2.50*

**2-line overprint 2½mm apart**

**193** A50 50m red brown & aqua 2.00 .75
**194** A50 100m bl grn & mag 9.00 2.50
**195** A50 250m vio brn & dk blue gray 30.00 5.50

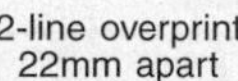

2-line overprint 22mm apart

**196** A51 500m lil rose & grnsh gray 45.00 27.00
**197** A51 £1 grnsh gray & brn red 50.00 *62.50*
*Nos. 183-197 (15)* 152.00 106.80

The overprint, in Greek and Turkish, reads "Republic of Cyprus."

Map of Cyprus — A52

**Wmk. 314**

**1960, Aug. 16 Engr. *Perf. 11½***

**198** A52 10m brown & green .25 .25
**199** A52 30m blue & brown .80 .70
**200** A52 100m purple & black 2.40 2.25
*Nos. 198-200 (3)* 3.45 3.20

Independence of Republic of Cyprus.

### Europa Issue

Nineteen Doves Flying as One CD4

***Perf. 14x13½***

**1962, Mar. 19 Litho. Unwmk.**

**201** CD4 10m lilac *.30 .25*
**202** CD4 40m deep ultra *.90 .35*
**203** CD4 100m emerald *.90 .60*
*Nos. 201-203 (3)* *2.10 1.20*

Admission of Cyprus to Council of Europe.

Malaria Eradication Emblem A54

**1962, May 14 *Perf. 14x13½***

**204** A54 10m gray green & black .25 .25
**205** A54 30m red brown & black .45 .25

WHO drive to eradicate malaria.

Iron Age Jug — A55

St. Barnabas Church, Salamis A56

Designs: 5m, Grapes. 10m, Head of Apollo. 15m, St. Sophia Church, Nicosia. 30m, Temple of Apollo. 35m, Head of Aphrodite. 40m, Skiing on Mt. Troodos. 50m, Ruins of Gymnasium, Salamis. 100m, Hala Sultan Tekke (sheep, Salt Lake Larnaca and tomb). 250m, Bella Paise Monastery. 500m, Cyprus mouflon. £1, St. Hilarion Castle.

***Perf. 13½x14, 14x13½***

**1962, Sept. 17 Wmk. 344**

**206** A55 3m dk brn & sal .25 .30
**207** A55 5m dull green & red lilac .25 .25
**208** A55 10m dk slate grn & yel green .25 .25
**209** A55 15m dk brn & rose vio .40 .25
**210** A56 25m salmon & brn .45 .25
**211** A56 30m lt bl & dk bl .25 .25
**212** A55 35m dk bl & pale grn .45 .25
**213** A56 40m vio bl & dk bl 1.50 *1.75*
**214** A56 50m olive bis & dk grn .60 .25
**215** A55 100m brn & yel brn 4.25 .30
**216** A56 250m tan & black 11.00 2.40
**217** A55 500m brown & olive 21.00 9.00
**218** A56 £1 gray & green 22.50 *30.00*
*Nos. 206-218 (13)* 63.15 45.50

Wmk. 344 is found in two positions: normal or inverted on vertical stamps, and reading up or down on horizontal stamps.

For overprints see Nos. 232-236, 265-268. For surcharge see No. 273.

### Europa Issue, 1962

Common Design Type

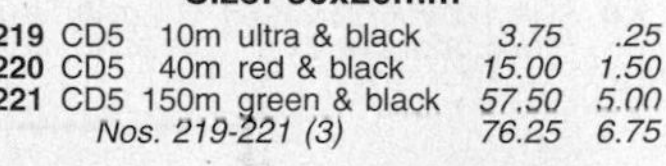

***Perf. 14x13½***

**1963, Jan. 28 Wmk. 344**

**Size: 36x20mm**

**219** CD5 10m ultra & black *3.75 .25*
**220** CD5 40m red & black *15.00 1.50*
**221** CD5 150m green & black *57.50 5.00*
*Nos. 219-221 (3)* *76.25 6.75*

Cypriot Farm Girl — A57

75m, Statue of Demeter, goddess of agriculture.

**1963, Mar. 21 *Perf. 13½x14***

**222** A57 25m blk, ultra & ocher .50 .45
**223** A57 75m dk car, gray & blk 3.25 2.25

FAO "Freedom from Hunger" campaign.

Cub Scout and Tents — A58

20m, Sea Scout. 150m, Boy Scout & mouflon.

**1963, Aug. 21 Wmk. 344**

**224** A58 3m multicolored .25 .25
**225** A58 20m multicolored .40 .25
**226** A58 150m multicolored 2.00 2.50
*a.* Souvenir sheet of 3 120.00 *175.00*
*Nos. 224-226 (3)* 2.65 3.00

Boy Scout movement in Cyprus, 50th anniv. No. 226a contains 3 imperf. stamps similar to Nos. 224-226 with simulated perforations. Sold for 250m.

Red Cross Nurse — A59

Children's Home, Kyrenia A60

*Perf. 13½x14, 14x13½*

**1963, Sept. 9 Litho. Wmk. 344**

**227** A59 10m multicolored .75 .25
**228** A60 100m multicolored 3.50 *4.25*

Intl. Red Cross, cent.

### Europa Issue

Stylized Links, Symbolizing Unity — CD6

**1963, Nov. 4** ***Perf. 14x13½***

**229** CD6 20m multicolored *6.50* .70
**230** CD6 30m multicolored *7.50* .70
**231** CD6 150m multicolored *50.00* *8.00*
*Nos. 229-231 (3)* *64.00* *9.40*

Nos. 208, 211, 213-215 Overprinted in Ultramarine

**1964, May 5** ***Perf. 13½x14, 14x13½***

**232** A55 10m dk sl grn & yel grn .25 .25
**233** A55 30m lt blue & dk blue .25 .25
**234** A55 40m vio bl & dull bl .40 .30
**235** A55 50m ol bis & dk grn .30 .35
**236** A55 100m brn & yel brown .40 *.75*
*Nos. 232-236 (5)* 1.60 1.90

Decision by the UN and its Security Council to help restore the country to normality and to seek a solution of its problems.

Clay Mask and Soli Theater A62

Designs: 35m, Curium theater. 50m, Salamis theater. 100m, Performance of "Othello" in front of Othello Tower.

**1964, June 15** ***Perf. 13½x14***

**237** A62 15m multicolored .45 .25
**238** A62 35m multicolored .45 .25
**239** A62 50m multicolored .45 .25
**240** A62 100m multicolored 1.75 *2.25*
*Nos. 237-240 (4)* 3.10 3.00

400th anniversary of Shakespeare's birth.

Boxers A63

14th century B.C. art: 10m, Runners, vert. 75m, Chariot.

**1964, July 6** ***Perf. 13½x14, 14x13½***

**241** A63 10m brn, bis & blk .25 .25
**242** A63 25m gray bl, bl & brn .30 .25
**243** A63 75m brick red, blk & brn .65 .80
*a.* Souvenir sheet of 3 8.00 *15.00*
*Nos. 241-243 (3)* 1.20 1.30

18th Olympic Games, Tokyo, Oct. 10-25, 1964. No. 243a contains three imperf. stamps similar to Nos. 241-243 with gray marginal inscription. Sheet sold for 250m; the difference between face value and selling price went for the promotion of classical athletics in Cyprus.

### Europa Issue

Symbolic Daisy — CD7

*Perf. 13½x14*

**1964, Sept. 14 Litho. Wmk. 344**

**244** CD7 20m bis brn & red brn *2.25* *.30*
**245** CD7 30m lt blue & dk blue *3.00* *.30*
**246** CD7 150m grn & ol grn *27.00* *4.50*
*Nos. 244-246 (3)* *32.25* *5.10*

CEPT, 5th anniv. The 22 petals of the flower symbolize the 22 members of the organization.

Satyr Drinking Wine, 5th Century B.C. Statuette — A65

Modern Winery A66

Cypriot Wine Industry: 10m, Dionysus and Acme drinking wine, 3rd century mosaic. 50m, Commandaria wine, Knight Templar and Kolossi Castle.

*Perf. 14x13½, 13½x14*

**1964, Oct. 26 Wmk. 344**

**247** A66 10m multicolored .45 .25
**248** A65 40m multicolored .80 *1.00*
**249** A65 50m multicolored .80 .30
**250** A66 100m multicolored 1.75 *2.00*
*Nos. 247-250 (4)* 3.80 3.55

Old Couple — A68

Mother and Children by A. Diamantis — A69

Pres. John F. Kennedy (1917-1963) — A67

*Perf. 14x13½*

**1965, Feb. 15 Litho. Wmk. 344**

**251** A67 10m violet blue .25 .25
**252** A67 40m green .35 .35
**253** A67 100m rose claret .45 .35
*a.* Souvenir sheet of 3 4.00 *7.00*
*Nos. 251-253 (3)* 1.05 .95

No. 253a contains 3 imperf. stamps similar to Nos. 251-253 with simulated perforations. Sold for 250m, 100m going to charitable organizations in Cyprus.

45m, Man with broken leg (accident insurance).

**1965, Apr. 12** ***Perf. 13½x14***

**254** A68 30m dull green & tan .25 .25
**255** A68 45m dk vio bl, bl & gray .40 .30

***Perf. 13½x12½***

**256** A69 75m buff & red brown 1.25 *1.75*
*Nos. 254-256 (3)* 1.90 2.30

Introduction of Social Insurance Law.

ITU Emblem, Old and New Communication Equipment — A70

**1965, May 17 Litho.** ***Perf. 14x13½***

**257** A70 15m brn, yel & blk .65 .25
**258** A70 60m grn, lt grn & blk 7.00 3.25
**259** A70 75m dk & lt bl & blk 8.00 4.75
*Nos. 257-259 (3)* 15.65 8.25

ITU, cent.

ICY Emblem A71

**1965, May 17 Wmk. 344**

**260** A71 50m multicolored .90 .25
**261** A71 100m multicolored 1.60 .75

International Cooperation Year.

### Europa Issue

Leaves and Fruit CD8

*Perf. 14x13½*

**1965, Sept. 27 Litho. Wmk. 344**

**262** CD8 5m org, org brn & black 1.10 *.25*
**263** CD8 45m lt grn, org brn & black *5.25* *1.75*
**264** CD8 150m gray, org brn & black *19.00* *4.00*
*Nos. 262-264 (3)* *25.35* *6.00*

Nos. 206, 208, 211 and 216 Overprinted in Dark Blue

**1966, Jan. 31** ***Perf. 13½x14, 14x13½***

**265** A55 3m dk brn & salmon .35 .40
**266** A55 10m dk sl grn & yel green .40 .25
**267** A56 30m lt bl & dk blue .40 .25
**268** A56 250m tan & black 1.35 *2.25*
*Nos. 265-268 (4)* 2.50 3.15

UN General Assembly's resolution to mediate the dispute between Greeks and Turks on Cyprus, Dec. 18, 1965.

St. Barnabas, Ancient Icon — A73

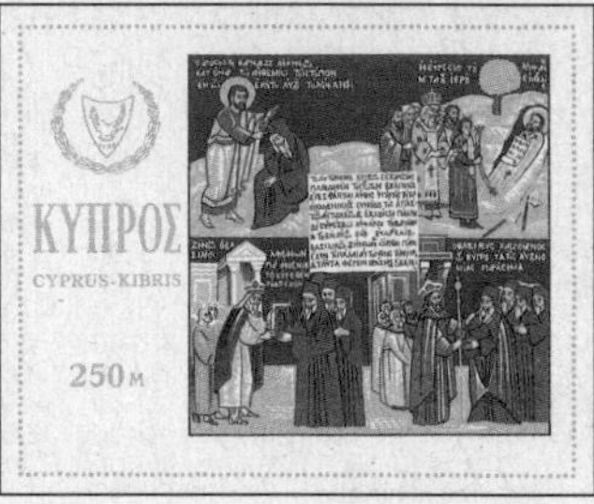


Chapel over Tomb of St. Barnabas A74

Bishop Anthemios of Constantine Dreaming of St. Barnabas, Discovering Tomb, etc. — A75

Design: 15m, Discovery of body of St. Barnabas (scene as in type A18).

***Perf. 13x14, 14x13***

**1966, Apr. 25 Litho. Wmk. 344**

**269** A73 15m multicolored .25 .25
**270** A74 25m multicolored .25 .25
**271** A73 100m multicolored .65 *2.00*

**Size: 110x91mm**

***Imperf***

**272** A75 250m multicolored 5.25 *11.00*
*Nos. 269-272 (4)* 6.40 13.50

1900th anniv. of the death of St. Barnabas.

**No. 206 Surcharged with New Value and Three Bars**

***Perf. 13½x14***

**1966, May 30 Litho. Wmk. 344**

**273** A55 5m on 3m dk brn & sal .45 .25

Gen. K. S. Thimayya A76

**1966, June 6** ***Perf. 14x13½***

**274** A76 50m tan & black .35 .25

In memory of Gen. Kodendera Subayya Thimayya (1906-1965), commander of the UN Peace-keeping Force on Cyprus.

### Europa Issue

EUROPA CEPT ΚΥΠΡΟΣ CYPRUS-KIBRIS 30M

Symbolic Sailboat — CD9

*Perf. 13½x14*

**1966, Sept. 26 Litho. Wmk. 344**

**275** CD9 20m multicolored *.50 .25*
**276** CD9 30m multicolored *.50 .25*
**277** CD9 150m multicolored *3.75 2.25*
*Nos. 275-277 (3) 4.75 2.75*

Stavrovouni Monastery A78

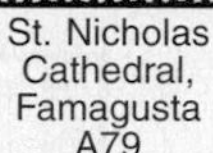


St. Nicholas Cathedral, Famagusta A79

Ingot Bearer, Bronze Age — A80

Designs: 5m, St. James' Church, Tricomo, vert. 10m, Zeno of Citium, marble bust, vert. 15m, Ship from 7th cent. BC vase, horiz. 20m, Silver coin, 4th cent. BC (head of Hercules with lion skin). 25m, Sleeping Eros (1st cent. marble statue; horiz.). 35m, Hawks on 11th cent. gold and enamel scepter from Curium. 40m, Marriage of David (7th cent. silver disc). 50m, Silver coin of Alexander the Great showing Hercules and Zeus, horiz. 100m, Bird catching fish on 7th cent. BC jug. 500m, The Rape of Ganymede (3rd cent. mosaic). £1, Aphrodite (1st cent. marble statue).

*Perf. 12x12½, 12½x12*

**1966, Nov. 21 Litho. Wmk. 344**

**278** A78 3m bl, dl yel, grn & black .40 .25
**279** A78 5m dk bl, ol & blk .25 .25
**280** A78 10m olive & black .25 .25

*Perf. 14x13½, 13½x14*

**281** A79 15m org brn, blk & red brn .25 .25
**282** A79 20m red brn & blk 1.25 1.25
**283** A79 25m red brn, gray & black .40 .25
**284** A79 30m aqua, tan & blk .60 .30
**285** A79 35m dk car, yel & blk .60 .45
**286** A79 40m brt bl, gray & blk .80 .45
**287** A79 50m org brn, gray & blk 1.10 .25
**288** A79 100m gray, buff, blk & red 4.00 .25

*Perf. 13x14*

**289** A80 250m dull yel, grn & blk 1.10 .50
**290** A80 500m multicolored 3.00 .90
**291** A80 £1 gray, lt gray & black 2.50 *6.75*
*Nos. 278-291 (14)* 16.50 12.35

Electric Power Station, Limassol — A81

Arghaka-Maghounda Dam — A82

Designs: 35m, Troodos Highway. 50m, Cyprus Hilton Hotel. 100m, Ships in Famagusta Harbor.

*Perf. 14x13½, 13½x14*

**1967, Apr. 10 Litho. Wmk. 344**

**292** A81 10m lt brn, dark brn & yellow .25 .25
**293** A82 15m lt bl, bl & grn .25 .25
**294** A82 35m dark gray, indigo & dark grn .30 .25
**295** A82 50m gray, olive & blue .30 .25
**296** A82 100m gray, ind & bl .30 *1.00*
*Nos. 292-296 (5)* 1.40 2.00

1st development program, 1962-66, completion.

**Europa Issue, 1967**
Common Design Type

**1967, May 2** ***Perf. 13x14***

**Size: 21x37mm**

**297** CD10 20m yel grn & olive *.50 .25*
**298** CD10 30m rose vio & pur *.50 .25*
**299** CD10 150m pale brn & brn *3.25 2.00*
*Nos. 297-299 (3) 4.25 2.50*

Javelin Thrower, Map of Eastern Mediterranean and "Victory" — A83

Map of Eastern Mediterranean, Victory Statue and: 35m, Runner. 100m, High jumper. 250m, Amphora, map of Eastern Mediterranean and Victory statue.

*Perf. 13½x13*

**1967, Sept. 4 Litho. Wmk. 344**

**300** A83 15m multicolored .25 .25
**301** A83 35m multicolored .25 .30
**302** A83 100m multicolored .60 *1.00*

**Size: 97x77mm**

***Imperf***

**303** A83 250m multicolored 2.50 *6.50*
*Nos. 300-303 (4)* 3.60 8.05

Cyprus-Crete-Salonika Athletic Games.

Marble Forum at Salamis, Church of St. Barnabas and Bellapais Abbey A84

ITY Emblem and: 40m, Famagusta Beach. 50m, Plane and Nicosia International Airport. 100m, Youth Hostel and skiing on Mt. Troodos.

*Perf. 13½x13*

**1967, Oct. 16 Litho. Wmk. 344**

**304** A84 10m multicolored .25 .25
**305** A84 40m multicolored .25 *1.00*
**306** A84 50m multicolored .25 .25
**307** A84 100m multicolored .25 *1.00*
*Nos. 304-307 (4)* 1.00 2.50

Intl. Tourist Year, 1967.

St. Andrew, 6th Century Mosaic — A85

Crucifixion, 15th Century — A86

The Three Kings, 15th Century Fresco — A87

**1967, Nov. 8** ***Perf. 13x13½***

**308** A85 25m multicolored .25 .25
**309** A86 50m multicolored .25 .25
**310** A87 75m multicolored .25 .25
*Nos. 308-310 (3)* .75 .75

St. Andrew's Monastery, cent. (25m); Exhibition of Art of Cyprus, Paris, Nov. 7, 1967-Jan. 3, 1968 (50m); 20th anniv. of UNESCO (75m).

Human Rights Flame and Stars — A88

Designs: 90m, Human Rights flame and UN emblem. 250m, Scroll showing Article One of the Declaration of Human Rights.

*Perf. 13½x14*

**1968, Mar. 18 Litho. Wmk. 344**

**311** A88 50m multicolored .25 .25
**312** A88 90m multicolored .25 *.70*

**Size: 110x90mm**

***Imperf***

**313** A88 250m multicolored 1.25 *4.75*
*Nos. 311-313 (3)* 1.75 *5.70*

Intl. Human Rights Year.

**Europa Issue, 1968**
Common Design Type

**1968, Apr. 29** ***Perf. 14x13½***

**314** CD11 20m multicolored *.40 .25*
**315** CD11 30m dk car rose, gray brn & blk *.50 .25*
**316** CD11 150m multicolored *2.00 2.00*
*Nos. 314-316 (3) 2.90 2.50*

Boy Holding Milk, UNICEF Emblem A89

Aesculapius and WHO Emblem — A90

*Perf. 14x13½, 13½x14*

**1968, Sept. 2 Wmk. 344**

**317** A89 35m dk red, lt brn & blk .25 .25
**318** A90 50m gray ol, blk & grn .25 .25

21st anniv. of UNICEF (No. 317), 20th anniv. of the WHO (No. 318).

Discus Thrower — A91

25m, Runners. 100m, Stadium, Mexico City.

*Perf. 13½x14, 14x13½*

**1968, Oct. 24 Litho.**

**319** A91 10m multicolored .25 .25
**320** A91 25m vio blue & multi .25 .25
**321** A91 100m blue & multi, horiz. .25 *1.25*
*Nos. 319-321 (3)* .75 1.75

19th Olympic Games, Mexico City, 10/12-27.

ILO Emblem — A92

*Perf. 12x13½*

**1969, Mar. 3 Wmk. 344**

**322** A92 50m bl, vio bl & org brn .25 .25
**323** A92 90m gray, blk & org brn .25 *.55*

ILO, 50th anniv.

Ancient Map of Cyprus A93

Design: 50m, Medieval map of Cyprus.

*Perf. 13½x13*

**1969, Apr. 7 Wmk. 344**

**324** A93 35m multicolored .25 .30
**325** A93 50m olive & multi .25 .30

1st Intl. Congress of Cypriot Studies.

**Europa Issue**

"EUROPA" and "CEPT" CD12

**1969, Apr. 28 Litho.** ***Perf. 14x13½***

**326** CD12 20m bl, blk & gray *.55 .25*
**327** CD12 30m cop red, blk & ocher *.55 .25*
**328** CD12 150m grn, blk & yel *1.90 1.75*
*Nos. 326-328 (3) 3.00 2.25*

CEPT, 10th anniv.

European Roller — A95

Birds: 15m, Audouin's gull. 20m, Cyprus warbler. 30m, Eurasian jay, vert. 40m, Hoopoe, vert. 90m, Eleonora's falcon, vert.

*Perf. 13½x12, 12x13½*

**1969, July 7 Wmk. 344**

**329** A95 5m multicolored .45 .25
**330** A95 15m multicolored .60 .25
**331** A95 20m multicolored .60 .25
**332** A95 30m multicolored .65 .25

**333** A95 40m multicolored .75 .30
**334** A95 90m multicolored 1.90 *4.00*
*Nos. 329-334 (6)* 4.95 5.30

Nativity, Mural, 1192 A96

Christmas: 45m, Nativity, mural in Church of Ayios Nicolaos tis Steghis, 14th century. 250m, Virgin and Child between Archangels Michael and Gabriel, mosaic in Church of Panayia Angeloktistos, 6th-7th centuries. Design of 20m is a mural in Church of Panayia tou Arakos, Lagoudhera.

**1969, Nov. 24 Litho.** ***Perf. 13½x13***
**335** A96 20m multicolored .25 .25
**336** A96 45m multicolored .25 .25

**Size: 109x89mm**

***Imperf***

**337** A96 250m dk blue & multi 5.00 *12.00*
*Nos. 335-337 (3)* 5.50 12.50

Mahatma Gandhi A97

**1970, Jan. 26** ***Perf. 14x13½***
**338** A97 25m multicolored .35 .35
**339** A97 75m multicolored 1.40 1.50

Birth cent. of Mohandas K. Gandhi (1869-1948), leader in India's struggle for independence.

**Europa Issue**

Interwoven Threads CD13

**1970, May 4 Litho. Wmk. 344**
**340** CD13 20m brn, yel & org *.40 .25*
**341** CD13 30m brt bl, yel & org *.40 .25*
**342** CD13 150m brt rose lil, yel & orange *1.90 2.25*
*Nos. 340-342 (3) 2.70 2.75*

Landscape with Flowers — A99

Designs: Various landscapes with flowers.

***Perf. 13x14***

**1970, Aug. 3 Litho. Wmk. 344**
**343** A99 10m multicolored .25 .25
**344** A99 50m multicolored .25 .25
**345** A99 90m multicolored .60 *1.25*
*Nos. 343-345 (3)* 1.10 1.75

European Nature Conservation Year.

Education Year Emblem — A100

Grapes and Partridge (Mosaic) A101

UN Emblem, Dove, Globe and Wheat A102

***Perf. 13x14, 14x13***

**1970, Sept. 7 Litho. Wmk. 344**
**346** A100 5m tan, blk & brn .25 .25
**347** A101 15m multicolored .25 .25
**348** A102 75m multicolored .25 *.75*
*Nos. 346-348 (3)* .75 1.25

Intl. Education Year (No. 346); 50th General Assembly of the Intl. Vine and Wine Office (No. 347); 25th anniv. of the UN (No. 348).

Virgin and Child, Mural from Podhithou Church, 16th Century — A103

***Perf. 14x14½***

**1970, Nov. 23 Photo. Unwmk.**
**349** A103 Strip of three .45 *.55*
*a.* 25m Left angel .25 .25
*b.* 25m Virgin and Child .25 .25
*c.* 25m Right angel .25 .25
**350** A103 75m multicolored .35 .35

Christmas.

Design of No. 349 is same as No. 350, but divided by perforation into 3 stamps with 25m denomination each. Size of No. 349: 71x46mm; size of No. 350: 42x31mm.

Cotton Napkin — A104

Festive Costume — A105

Drinking Cup, 7th Cent. B.C. A106

Mouflon from Mosaic Pavement, 3rd Century — A107

Cypriot Art: 5m, St. George, bas-relief on pine board, 19th cent. 20m, kneeling donors, painting, Church of St. Mamas, 1465. 25m, Mosaic head, 5th cent. A.D. 30m, Athena mounting horse-drawn chariot, terracotta figurine, 5th cent. B.C. 40m, Shepherd playing pipe, 14th cent. fresco. 50m, Woman's head, limestone, 3rd cent. B.C. 75m, Angel, mosaic, 6th cent. 90m, Mycenaean silver bowl, 14th cent. B.C. 500m, Woman and tree, decoration from amphora, 7th-6th cent. B.C. £1, God statue (horned helmet), from Enkomi, 12th cent. B.C., vert.

***Perf. 12½x13½ (A104), 13x14 (A105), 14x13 (A106), 13½x13, 13x13½ (A107)***

**1971, Feb. 22 Litho. Wmk. 344**
**351** A104 3m blk, red & brn .35 .50
**352** A104 5m citron, red brn & black .25 .25
**353** A105 10m multicolored .25 .30
**354** A106 15m bister brn, blk & slate .25 .25
**355** A105 20m slate, red brn & black .40 .50
**356** A105 25m multicolored .30 .25
**357** A106 30m multicolored .30 .25
**358** A105 40m gray & multi 1.10 1.10
**359** A105 50m bl, bis & blk .90 .25
**360** A105 75m cit & multi 2.00 1.25
**361** A106 90m multicolored 2.25 2.50
**362** A107 250m lt red brn, brn & black 1.75 .40
**363** A107 500m tan & multi .90 .50
**364** A107 £1 multicolored 1.75 .75
*Nos. 351-364 (14)* 12.75 9.05

For surcharges & overprints see Nos. 403, 424-427, 444, RA1.

**Europa Issue**

"Fraternity, Co-operation, Common Effort" — CD14

**1971, May 3 Litho.** ***Perf. 14x13½***

**Size: 36½x23½mm**

**365** CD14 20m lt bl, vio bl & blk *.30 .25*
**366** CD14 30m brt yel grn, grn & blk *.30 .25*
**367** CD14 150m yel, grn & blk *2.00 2.75*
*Nos. 365-367 (3) 2.60 3.25*

Archbishop Kyprianos, 1821 — A109

Paintings: 30m, Young Greek Taking Oath, horiz. 100m, Bishop Germanòs of Patras Declaring Greek Independence.

***Perf. 13x13½, 13½x13***

**1971, July 9 Wmk. 344**
**368** A109 15m multicolored .25 .25
**369** A109 30m multicolored .25 .25
**370** A109 100m multicolored .25 *.50*
*Nos. 368-370 (3)* .75 1.00

150th anniversary of Greek independence.

Arch and Castle A110

Tourist Publicity: 25m, Decorated gourd and sun over shore, vert. 60m, Mountain road, vert. 100m, Village church.

***Perf. 13½x13, 13x13½***

**1971, Sept. 20**
**371** A110 15m vio bl & multi .25 .25
**372** A110 25m ocher & multi .25 .25
**373** A110 60m green & multi .25 *.60*
**374** A110 100m blue & multi .25 *.65*
*Nos. 371-374 (4)* 1.00 1.75

Virgin and Child — A111

**1971, Nov. 22** ***Perf. 13½x14***
**375** A111 10m shown .25 .35
**376** A111 50m The Three Kings .25 .35
**377** A111 100m Shepherds .25 .35
*a.* Strip of 3, Nos. 375-377 .65 *.95*

Christmas.

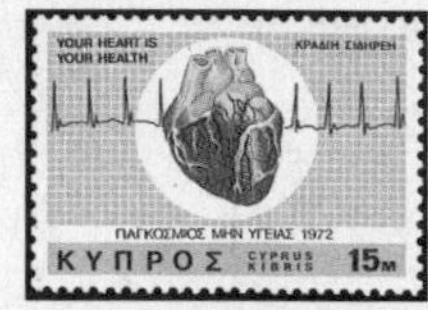


Heart and Electrocardiogram — A112

**1972, Apr. 11** ***Perf. 13½x12½***
**378** A112 15m bister & multi .25 .25
**379** A112 50m brown & multi .25 *.45*

"Your heart is your health," World Health Day.

**Europa Issue**

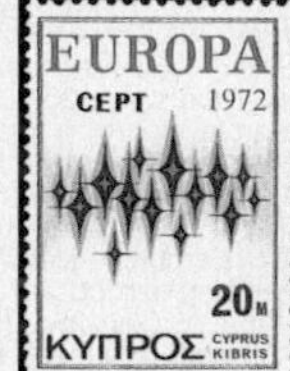


Sparkles, Symbolic of Communications CD15

**1972, May 22** ***Perf. 12½x13½***
**380** CD15 20m brn, org & fawn *.60 .30*
**381** CD15 30m pur, org & lilac *.60 .45*
**382** CD15 150m dk ol, org & brt green *4.75 3.50*
*Nos. 380-382 (3) 5.95 4.25*

Archery, Olympic and Motion Emblems A114

**1972, July 24** ***Perf. 14x13½***
**383** A114 10m shown .25 .25
**384** A114 40m Wrestling .35 .25
**385** A114 100m Soccer .65 *1.75*
*Nos. 383-385 (3)* 1.25 2.25

20th Olympic Games, Munich, 8/26-9/11.

Apollo, Silver Stater, Marion, 5th Century B.C. A115

Silver Staters of Cyprus: 30m, Eagle's head, Paphos, c. 460 B.C. 40m, Pallas Athena, Lapithos, 388-387 B.C. 100m, Sphinx (obverse) and lotus flower (reverse), Idalion, c. 460 B.C.

**1972, Sept. 25 Litho. Wmk. 344**

**Coins in Silver**

**386** A115 20m lt grnsh bl & blk .25 .25
**387** A115 30m pale bl & silver .25 .25
**388** A115 40m ol bister & black .25 .30
**389** A115 100m pale brn & blk .75 *1.00*
*Nos. 386-389 (4)* 1.50 1.80

Bathing the Christ Child — A116

Christmas: 20m, The Three Kings. 100m, Nativity. 250m, The Nativity, 1466, mural in Church of the Holy Cross, Platanistasa. The designs of the 10m, 20m, 100m, show details from mural shown entirely on 250m.

**1972, Nov. 20 Litho. *Perf. 13½x14***

**390** A116 10m multicolored .25 .25
**391** A116 20m multicolored .25 .25
**392** A116 100m multicolored .25 *.40*

**Size: 110x90mm**

***Imperf***

**393** A116 250m multicolored 1.75 *4.25*
*Nos. 390-393 (4)* 2.50 5.15

Landscape, Troodos Mountains A117

100m, FIS Congress emblem and map of Cyprus.

***Perf. 14x13½***

**1973, Mar. 13 Wmk. 344**

**394** A117 20m blue & multi .25 .25
**395** A117 100m blue & multi .25 *.40*

29th Meeting of the Intl. Ski Fed. (FIS), Nicosia, June 1973.

**Europa Issue**

Post Horn of Arrows CD16

**1973, May 7 Size: 37x21mm**

**396** CD16 20m dl bl & multi *.50* .25
**397** CD16 30m multicolored *.50* .35
**398** CD16 150m multicolored *3.25* 3.25
*Nos. 396-398 (3)* 4.25 3.85

Archbishop's Palace, Nicosia — A119

Traditional Architecture: 30m, Konak, Nicosia, 18th century, vert. 50m, House, Gourri, 1850, vert. 100m, House, Rizokarpaso, 1772.

**1973, July 23 *Perf. 14x13, 13x14***

**399** A119 20m multicolored .25 .25
**400** A119 30m multicolored .25 .25
**401** A119 50m multicolored .25 .25
**402** A119 100m multicolored .25 *.85*
*Nos. 399-402 (4)* 1.00 1.60

No. 354 Surcharged

**1973, Sept. 24 *Perf. 14x13***

**403** A106 20m on 15m multi .35 .35

Cyprus Scout Emblem — A120

EEC Emblem A121

Cyprus Airways Emblem — A122

35m, FAO emblem. 100m, INTERPOL emblem.

**1973, Sept. 24 *Perf. 13x14, 14x13***

**404** A120 10m brn ol, ol & buff .30 .30
**405** A121 25m pur, bl & plum .30 .30
**406** A121 35m grn, gray grn & citron .30 .30
**407** A122 50m black & blue .30 .30
**408** A120 100m brown & fawn .40 *.80*
*Nos. 404-408 (5)* 1.60 2.00

60th anniv. of Cyprus Boy Scout Organ.; association of Cyprus with EEC; 10th anniv. of FAO; 25th anniv. of Cyprus Airways; 50th anniv. of Intl. Criminal Police Organization.

Archangel Gabriel — A123

Virgin and Child — A124

Christmas: 100m, Panaya tou Araka Church, horiz. Designs of 10m, 20m are from wall paintings in Arakas Church.

**1973, Nov. 26 Wmk. 344**

**409** A123 10m multicolored .25 .25
**410** A124 20m multicolored .25 .25
**411** A124 100m multicolored .25 *.75*
*Nos. 409-411 (3)* .75 1.25

Grapes — A125

**1974, Mar. 18 Litho. *Perf. 13x14***

**412** A125 25m shown .25 .25
**413** A125 50m Grapefruit .25 *.60*
**414** A125 50m Oranges .25 *.60*
**415** A125 50m Lemons .25 *.60*
*a.* Strip of 3, #413-415 1.00 *2.00*
*Nos. 412-415 (4)* 1.00 *2.05*

**Europa Issue**

Rape of Europa — A126

Design shows a silver stater of Marion, second half of 5th century B.C.

**1974, Apr. 29**

**416** A126 10m org brn & multi *.60* .30
**417** A126 40m multicolored *.60* *.60*
**418** A126 150m dk car & multi *2.75* *2.75*
*Nos. 416-418 (3)* 3.95 3.65

Solon, 3rd Century Mosaic A127

Designs: 10m, Front page of "History of Cyprus," by Archimandrite Kyprianos, 1788, vert. 100m, St. Neophytos, mural, vert. 250m, Maps of Cyprus and Greek Islands, by Abraham Ortelius, 1584.

***Perf. 13x14, 14x13***

**1974, July 22 Litho. Wmk. 344**

**419** A127 10m multicolored .25 .25
**420** A127 25m multicolored .25 .25
**421** A127 100m multicolored .30 .85

**Size: 110x90mm**

***Imperf***

**422** A127 250m multicolored 2.25 *4.75*
*Nos. 419-422 (4)* 3.05 6.10

2nd Intl. Congress of Cypriot Studies, Nicosia, Sept. 15-21. No. 422 has simulated perforations.

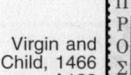

Nos. 353, 358-359, 362 Overprinted

***Perf. 13x14, 13½x13***

**1974, Oct. 14 Litho.**

**424** A105 10m multicolored .25 .25
**425** A105 40m multicolored .35 .50
**426** A105 50m multicolored .35 .35
**427** A107 250m multicolored .70 *2.75*
*Nos. 424-427 (4)* 1.65 3.85

UN Security Council Resolution No. 353 to end hostilities on Cyprus. Overprint is in 3 lines on No. 427.

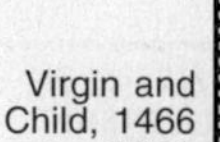

Virgin and Child, 1466 A129

Adoration of the Kings, c. 1500 — A130

Christmas: 100m, Flight into Egypt, mural, Monastery Church of Ayios Neophytos, c. 1500. (50m is from same church). Mural on 10m is in Church of Stavros tou Agiasmati.

***Perf. 14x13, 13x14***

**1974, Dec. 2 Wmk. 344**

**429** A129 10m multicolored .25 .25
**430** A130 50m multicolored .25 .25
**431** A129 100m multicolored .25 *.45*
*Nos. 429-431 (3)* .75 .95

Disabled Persons, Emblem — A131

Council of Europe Flag — A132

**1975, Feb. 17 Unwmk. *Perf. 14½***

**432** A131 30m ocher & ultra .25 .25
**433** A132 100m multicolored .55 *1.25*

8th European Meeting of the Intl. Society for the Rehabilitation of Disabled Persons (30m; design shows society's emblem); 25th anniv. of Council of Europe (100m).

First Mail Coach in Cyprus A133

**1975, Feb. 17**

**434** A133 20m multicolored .25 .25
**435** A133 50m ultra & multi .80 .40

Centenary (in 1974) of UPU.

The Distaff, by Michael Kashalos — A134

Europa (Paintings): 30m, Still Life, by Christoforos Savva. 150m, Virgin and Child of Liopetri, by Georghios P. Georghiou.

***Perf. 13½x14½***

**1975, Apr. 28 Photo.**

**436** A134 20m multicolored *.25* .25
**437** A134 30m multicolored *.30* .25
**438** A134 150m multicolored *.80* .60
*a.* Strip of 3, #436-438 *1.40* *1.60*

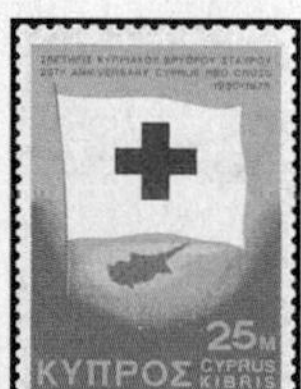

Red Cross Flag over Cyprus — A135

Nurse and Nurses Emblem A136

Steatite Female Figure, c. 3000 B.C. — A137

*Perf. 12½x13½, 13½x12½*

**1975, Aug. 4 Litho. Wmk. 344**

| | | | | |
|---|---|---|---|---|
| **439** | A135 | 25m blue green & red | .25 | .25 |
| **440** | A136 | 30m dp blue & lt grn | .25 | .25 |
| **441** | A137 | 75m multicolored | .25 | *.85* |
| | | *Nos. 439-441 (3)* | .75 | 1.35 |

Cyprus Red Cross, 25th anniv.; Intl. Nurses' Day 1975; IWY.

Submarine Cable — A138

International Telephone A139

*Perf. 12½x13½, 13½x12½*

**1975, Oct. 13 Litho.**

| | | | | |
|---|---|---|---|---|
| **442** | A138 | 50m multicolored | .30 | .25 |
| **443** | A139 | 100m purple & org | .60 | *.85* |

Telecommunications achievements.

No. 351 Surcharged

**1976, Jan. 5** *Perf. 12½x13½*

| | | | | |
|---|---|---|---|---|
| **444** | A104 | 10m on 3m multi | .45 | *.90* |

Vessel in Shape of Woman, 19th Century — A140

Composite Vessel, 2100-2000 B.C. — A141

Europa: 100m, Byzantine goblet, 15th cent.

*Perf. 13x14*

**1976, May 3 Litho. Wmk. 344**

| | | | | |
|---|---|---|---|---|
| **445** | A140 | 20m violet & multi | *.35* | *.25* |
| **446** | A141 | 60m gray & multi | *.80* | *.70* |
| **447** | A140 | 100m brown & multi | *1.60* | *1.60* |
| | | *Nos. 445-447 (3)* | *2.75* | *2.55* |

Self-help Housing A142

Cyprus Airways Jet — A143

Designs: 25m, Women sewing in front of tents. 30m, Aforestation.

**1976, May 3** *Perf. 14x13*

| | | | | |
|---|---|---|---|---|
| **448** | A142 | 10m multicolored | .25 | .25 |
| **449** | A142 | 25m multicolored | .25 | .25 |
| **450** | A142 | 30m multicolored | .25 | .25 |
| **451** | A143 | 60m multicolored | .25 | .55 |
| | | *Nos. 448-451 (4)* | 1.00 | 1.30 |

Re-activation of the economy.

Terracotta Statue, 7th-6th Centuries B.C. — A144

Bronze Plate with Inscription, Idalion, 5th Century B.C. A145

Designs: 10m, Limestone head of bearded man, 5th cent. B.C. 20m, Gold necklace, Lamboussa, 6th cent. A.D. 25m, Terracotta warrior on horseback, 7th cent. B.C. 30m, Limestone figure, priest of Aphrodite, 5th cent. B.C. 50m, Mycenaean crater, 13th cent. B.C. 60m, Limestone sarcophagus, Amathus, 550-500 B.C. 100m, Gold bracelet, Lamboussa, 6th cent. A.D. 250m, Silver dish, Lamboussa, 6th cent. A.D. 500m, Bronze stand, 12th cent. B.C. £1, Marble statue of Artemis, Larnaca, 4th cent. B.C.

*Perf. 12x13½*

**1976, June 7 Wmk. 344**

**Size: 22x33mm**

| | | | | |
|---|---|---|---|---|
| **452** | A144 | 5m brn & multi | .25 | *.75* |
| **453** | A144 | 10m gray & multi | .25 | *.65* |

**Size: 24x37mm, 37x24mm**

*Perf. 13x14, 14x13*

| | | | | |
|---|---|---|---|---|
| **454** | A144 | 20m red & multi | .25 | *.60* |
| **455** | A144 | 25m lt brn & blk | .25 | .25 |
| **456** | A144 | 30m green & multi | .25 | .25 |
| **457** | A145 | 40m bis gray & blk | .25 | *.60* |
| **458** | A145 | 50m brn & multi | .25 | .25 |
| **459** | A145 | 60m dk brn & multi | .25 | .25 |
| **460** | A145 | 100m crim & multi | .40 | *.60* |

**Size: 28x40mm**

*Perf. 13x12½*

| | | | | |
|---|---|---|---|---|
| **461** | A144 | 250m dk bl & multi | .50 | *1.60* |
| **462** | A144 | 500m yel & multi | 1.00 | *1.75* |
| **463** | A144 | £1 slate & multi | 2.10 | *2.50* |
| | | *Nos. 452-463 (12)* | 6.00 | *10.05* |

George Washington A146

**1976, July 5** *Perf. 13x13½*

| | | | | |
|---|---|---|---|---|
| **464** | A146 | 100m multicolored | .50 | .40 |

American Bicentennial.

Montreal Olympic Games Emblem — A147

Various Sports A148

100m, like 60m, with different sports.

**1976, July 5 Unwmk.** *Perf. 14*

| | | | | |
|---|---|---|---|---|
| **465** | A147 | 20m yel, blk & dk car | .25 | .25 |
| **466** | A148 | 60m ultra & multi | .25 | *.30* |
| **467** | A148 | 100m lilac & multi | .35 | *.40* |
| | | *Nos. 465-467 (3)* | .85 | *.95* |

21st Olympic Games, Montreal, Canada, July 17-Aug. 1.

Children in Library — A149

Low-cost Housing Development A150

Hands Shielding Eye — A151

*Perf. 13½x14, 13x13½*

**1976, Sept. 27 Litho. Wmk. 344**

| | | | | |
|---|---|---|---|---|
| **468** | A149 | 40m black & multi | .25 | .25 |
| **469** | A150 | 50m multicolored | .25 | .25 |
| **470** | A151 | 80m ultra & multi | .35 | *.55* |
| | | *Nos. 468-470 (3)* | .85 | 1.05 |

Books for Children (40m); Habitat, UN Conference on Human Settlements, Vancouver, Canada, May 31-June 11 (50m); World Health Day: Foresight prevents blindness (80m).

Archangel Michael — A152

Christmas: 15m, Archangel Gabriel. 150m, Nativity. Icons in Ayios Neophytos Monastery, 16th century.

**1976, Nov. 15 Unwmk.** *Perf. 12½*

| | | | | |
|---|---|---|---|---|
| **471** | A152 | 10m multicolored | .25 | .25 |
| **472** | A152 | 15m multicolored | .25 | .25 |
| **473** | A152 | 150m multicolored | .30 | *.80* |
| | | *Nos. 471-473 (3)* | .80 | 1.30 |

Landscape, by A. Diamantis — A154

Europa (Paintings): 60m, Trees and Meadow, by T. Kanthos. 120m, Harbor, by V. Ioannides.

*Perf. 13½x13*

**1977, May 2 Litho. Unwmk.**

| | | | | |
|---|---|---|---|---|
| **475** | A154 | 20m multicolored | *.30* | *.25* |
| **476** | A154 | 60m multicolored | *.70* | *.40* |
| **477** | A154 | 120m multicolored | *1.25* | *2.00* |
| | | *Nos. 475-477 (3)* | *2.25* | *2.65* |

Cyprus No. 196 — A155

*Perf. 13x13½*

**1977, June 13 Litho. Wmk. 344**

| | | | | |
|---|---|---|---|---|
| **478** | A155 | 120m multicolored | .40 | .40 |

25th anniv. of reign of Queen Elizabeth II.

Silver Tetradrachm of Demetrios Poliorcetes — A156

Ancient Coins of Cyprus: 10m, Bronze coin of Emperor Trajan. 60m, Silver Tetradrachm of Ptolemy VIII. 100m, Gold octadrachm of Arsinoe II.

**1977, June 13 Unwmk.** *Perf. 14*

| | | | | |
|---|---|---|---|---|
| **479** | A156 | 10m multicolored | .25 | .25 |
| **480** | A156 | 40m multicolored | .30 | .25 |
| **481** | A156 | 60m multicolored | .35 | .30 |
| **482** | A156 | 100m multicolored | .50 | *.85* |
| | | *Nos. 479-482 (4)* | 1.40 | 1.65 |

Archbishop Makarios (1913-1977), Pres. of Cyprus — A157

20m, Archbishop in full vestments. 250m, Head.

*Perf. 13x14*

**1977, Sept. 10 Litho. Unwmk.**

| | | | | |
|---|---|---|---|---|
| **483** | A157 | 20m multicolored | .25 | .25 |
| **484** | A157 | 60m multicolored | .25 | .25 |
| **485** | A157 | 250m multicolored | .60 | *1.00* |
| | | *Nos. 483-485 (3)* | 1.10 | 1.50 |

Handicrafts A158

Sputnik over Earth — A159

Designs: 40m, Map of the Mediterranean Sea. 60m, Gold medals and sports emblems.

*Perf. 13½x12*

**1977, Oct. 17 Wmk. 344**

| | | | | |
|---|---|---|---|---|
| **486** | A158 | 20m multicolored | .25 | .25 |
| **487** | A158 | 40m multicolored | .25 | .25 |
| **488** | A158 | 60m multicolored | .25 | .25 |
| **489** | A159 | 80m multicolored | .25 | *.75* |
| | | *Nos. 486-489 (4)* | 1.00 | 1.50 |

Revitalization of handicrafts (20m); Man and the biosphere (40m); Gold medals won by secondary school students in France for long jump and 200 meter race (60m); 60th anniv. of Bolshevik Revolution (80m).

Nativity A160

Christmas (Children's Drawings): 10m, Three Kings following the star. 150m, Flight into Egypt.

*Perf. 14x13½*

**1977, Nov. 21 Litho. Unwmk.**

| | | | | |
|---|---|---|---|---|
| **490** | A160 | 10m multicolored | .25 | .25 |
| **491** | A160 | 40m multicolored | .25 | .25 |
| **492** | A160 | 150m multicolored | .25 | *.70* |
| | | *Nos. 490-492 (3)* | .75 | 1.20 |

Demetrios Lipertis (1866-1937) — A161

150m, Vasilis Michaelides (1849-1917).

**1978, Mar. 6 Wmk. 344 *Perf. 14x13***

| | | | | |
|---|---|---|---|---|
| **493** | A161 | 40m bister & olive | .25 | .25 |
| **494** | A161 | 150m gray, ver & blk | .35 | *.70* |

Cypriot poets.

Chrysorrhogiatissa Monastery — A162

Europa: 75m, Kolossi Castle. 125m, Municipal Library, Paphos.

*Perf. 14½x13*

**1978, Apr. 24 Litho. Unwmk.**

| | | | | |
|---|---|---|---|---|
| **495** | A162 | 25m multicolored | *.30* | *.25* |
| **496** | A162 | 75m multicolored | *.80* | *.40* |
| **497** | A162 | 125m multicolored | *1.40* | *1.40* |
| | | *Nos. 495-497 (3)* | *2.50* | *2.05* |

Makarios as Archbishop 1950-1977 A163

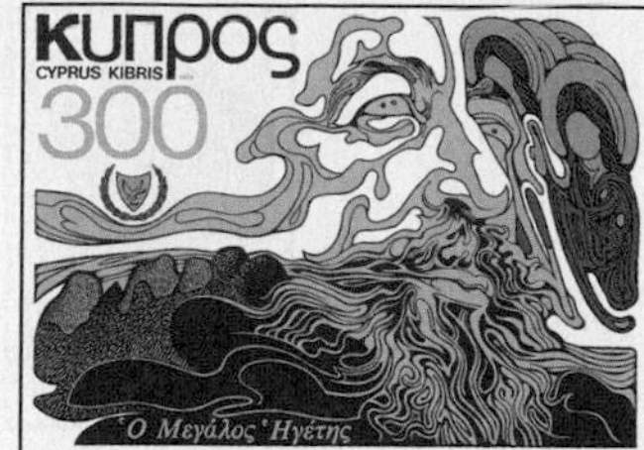
"The Great Leader" — A164

Archbishop Makarios: 25m, Exiled, Seychelles, 1956-1957. 50m, President of Cyprus, 1960-1977. 75m, Soldier of Christ. 100m, Freedom fighter.

*Perf. 14x14½*

**1978, Aug. 3 Litho. Unwmk.**

| | | | | |
|---|---|---|---|---|
| **498** | A163 | 15m multicolored | .25 | .25 |
| **499** | A163 | 25m multicolored | .25 | .25 |
| **500** | A163 | 50m multicolored | .25 | .25 |
| **501** | A163 | 75m multicolored | .25 | .35 |
| **502** | A163 | 100m multicolored | .25 | .35 |
| *a.* | | Strip of 5, #498-502 | 1.25 | *1.50* |

**Size: 110x80mm**

***Imperf***

| | | | | |
|---|---|---|---|---|
| **503** | A164 | 300m multicolored | 2.00 | *2.50* |
| | | *Nos. 498-503 (6)* | 3.25 | 3.95 |

Archbishop Makarios, President of Cyprus.

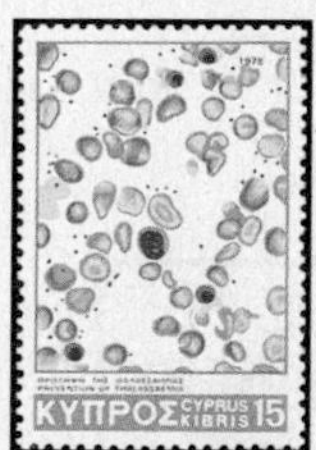
Blood Cells with Low Hemoglobin A165

Bust of Aristotle A166

Heads and Human Rights Emblem A167

Wilbur and Orville Wright, Flyer I A168

*Perf. 13x14, 14x13*

**1978, Oct. 23 Unwmk. Litho.**

| | | | | |
|---|---|---|---|---|
| **504** | A165 | 15m multicolored | .25 | .25 |
| **505** | A166 | 35m multicolored | .25 | .25 |
| **506** | A167 | 75m black | .25 | .35 |
| **507** | A168 | 125m multicolored | .35 | *.70* |
| | | *Nos. 504-507 (4)* | 1.10 | 1.55 |

Anemia prevention (15m); 2300th death anniv. of Aristotle (35m); 30th anniv. of Universal Declaration of Human Rights (75m); 75th anniv. of first powered flight (125m).

Kiti Icon Stand — A169

Christmas: 35m, Athienou icon stand. 150m, Omodhos icon stand.

**1978, Dec. 4 *Perf. 14x14½***

| | | | | |
|---|---|---|---|---|
| **508** | A169 | 15m multicolored | .25 | .25 |
| **509** | A169 | 35m multicolored | .25 | .25 |
| **510** | A169 | 150m multicolored | .40 | *.70* |
| | | *Nos. 508-510 (3)* | .90 | 1.20 |

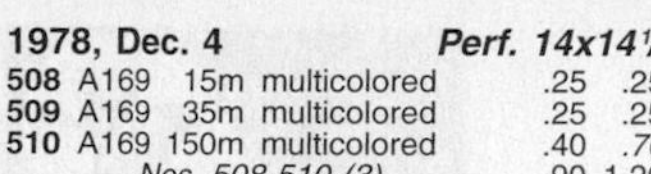

Venus Statue from Soli A170

125m, Birth of Venus, by Botticelli (detail).

**1979, Mar. 12 Litho. *Perf. 14x13½***

| | | | | |
|---|---|---|---|---|
| **511** | A170 | 75m multicolored | .30 | .25 |
| **512** | A170 | 125m multicolored | .50 | .40 |

Mail Coach, Envelope and Truck A171

Europa: 75m, Old telephone, dish antenna and satellite. 125m, Steamship, jet and envelopes.

**1979, Apr. 30 Litho. *Perf. 14x13½***

| | | | | |
|---|---|---|---|---|
| **513** | A171 | 25m multicolored | *.55* | *.25* |
| **514** | A171 | 75m multicolored | *.95* | *.40* |
| **515** | A171 | 125m multicolored | *2.75* | *1.25* |
| | | *Nos. 513-515 (3)* | *4.25* | *1.90* |

Peacock Wrasse A172

Designs: 50m, Black partridge, vert. 75m, Cyprus cedar, vert. 125m, Mule.

*Perf. 13½x12½, 12½x13½*

**1979, June 25 Litho.**

| | | | | |
|---|---|---|---|---|
| **516** | A172 | 25m multicolored | .25 | .25 |
| **517** | A172 | 50m multicolored | .40 | *.55* |
| **518** | A172 | 75m multicolored | .40 | .35 |
| **519** | A172 | 125m multicolored | .60 | *1.10* |
| | | *Nos. 516-519 (4)* | 1.65 | 2.25 |

Children Holding Globe, UNESCO Emblem — A173

Dove, Magnifying Glass, Album A174

Lord Kitchener, Map of Cyprus A175

Smiling Child, IYC Emblem A176

Soccer A177

Rotary Emblem — A178

**1979, Oct. 1 Litho. *Perf. 12½***

| | | | | |
|---|---|---|---|---|
| **520** | A173 | 15m multicolored | .25 | .25 |
| **521** | A174 | 25m multicolored | .25 | .25 |
| **522** | A175 | 50m multicolored | .25 | .25 |
| **523** | A176 | 75m multicolored | .25 | .25 |
| **524** | A177 | 100m multicolored | .25 | *.35* |
| **525** | A178 | 125m multicolored | .25 | *.70* |
| | | *Nos. 520-525 (6)* | 1.50 | 2.05 |

Intl. Bureau of Education, Geneva, 50th anniv.; Cyprus Philatelic Society, 20th anniv.; Horatio Herbert Kitchener's survey of Cyprus, cent.; IYC; European Soccer Assoc., 25th anniv.; Rotary Club of Cyprus, 75th anniv.

Jesus, Icon, 12th Century — A179

Christmas (Icons): 35m, Nativity, 16th cent. 150m, Virgin and Child, 12th cent.

*Perf. 13½x14, 13x14*

**1979, Nov. 5 Litho.**

**Sizes: 24x37mm; 27x40mm (35m)**

| | | | | |
|---|---|---|---|---|
| **526** | A179 | 15m multicolored | .25 | .25 |
| **527** | A179 | 35m multicolored | .25 | .25 |
| **528** | A179 | 150m multicolored | .25 | *.45* |
| | | *Nos. 526-528 (3)* | .75 | .95 |

Cyprus No. 1, Nicosia Cancel A180

Cyprus Stamp Centenary: 125m, #3, Kyrenia cancel. 175m, #6, Larnaca cancel. 500m, #1-6.

**1980, Mar. 17 Litho. *Perf. 14x13***

| | | | | |
|---|---|---|---|---|
| **529** | A180 | 40m multicolored | .25 | .25 |
| **530** | A180 | 125m multicolored | .25 | .25 |
| **531** | A180 | 175m multicolored | .50 | .50 |

**Size: 105x85mm**

***Imperf***

| | | | | |
|---|---|---|---|---|
| **532** | A180 | 500m multicolored | 1.40 | 1.40 |
| | | *Nos. 529-532 (4)* | 2.40 | 2.40 |

Holy Cross, St. Barnabas Church, Agiasmati — A181

Europa: 125m, Zeno of Citium, Ny Carsberg Glyptothek, Copenhagen.

**1980, Apr. 28 *Perf. 12½***

| | | | | |
|---|---|---|---|---|
| **533** | A181 | 40m multicolored | *.25* | .25 |
| **534** | A181 | 125m multicolored | *.45* | *.30* |

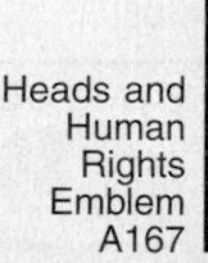

Sailing, Moscow '80 Emblem A182

**1980, June 23 Litho. *Perf. 14x13***

**535** A182 40m shown .25 .25
**536** A182 125m Swimming .25 .25
**537** A182 200m Gymnast .40 .40
*Nos. 535-537 (3)* .90 .90

22nd Summer Olympic Games, Moscow, July 19-Aug. 3.

Gold Necklace — A183

Clay Amphora — A184

Archaeological finds on Cyprus, 12th cent. B.C. to 3rd cent. A.D. 15m, 40m, 150m, 500m, horiz.

***Perf. 13½x14, 14x13½***

**1980, Sept. 15 Litho. Wmk. 344**

**538** A183 10m shown .30 *.90*
**539** A184 15m Bronze cow .30 *.90*
**540** A184 25m shown .30 .30
**541** A184 40m Lion, gold ring .40 *.65*
**542** A184 50m Bronze cauldron .40 .25
**543** A184 75m Stele 1.10 *1.40*
**544** A184 100m Clay jug .80 .25
**545** A184 125m Warrior, terra-cotta bust .80 *.90*
**546** A184 150m Lions attacking bull 1.25 .25
**547** A184 175m Faience and enamel vase .90 *1.25*
**548** A184 200m Warrior god, bronze .90 .40
**549** A184 500m Stone bowl .90 *1.50*
**550** A183 £1 Ivory plaque 1.10 *1.25*
**551** A183 £2 Leda and the swan, mosaic 1.90 *2.25*
*Nos. 538-551 (14)* 11.35 *12.45*

For surcharges see Nos. 584, 600-611.

Cyprus Flag — A185

Archbishop Makarios — A187

Treaty Signing Establishing Republic, 20th Anniversary — A186

**1980, Oct. 1 *Perf. 13½x14, 14x13***

**552** A185 40m multicolored .25 .25
**553** A186 125m multicolored .25 .25
**554** A187 175m multicolored .35 .35
*Nos. 552-554 (3)* .85 .85

Dove and Woman A188

***Perf. 14x13***

**1980, Nov. 29 Litho. Wmk. 344**

**555** A188 40m shown .25 .25
**556** A188 125m Dove and man .40 .40
*a.* Pair, #555-556 .65 .65

Intl. Palestinian Solidarity Day.

Pulpit, Ayios Lazaros Church, Larnaca — A189

Christmas: 25m, Pulpit, Tripiotis Church, Nicosia. 100m, Iconostatis (Holy Door), Panayia Church, Paralimni.

**1980, Nov. 29 *Perf. 13½x14***

**557** A189 25m multicolored .25 .25

**Size: 24x37mm**

**558** A189 100m multicolored .25 .25

**Size: 21x37mm**

**559** A189 125m multicolored .25 .25
*Nos. 557-559 (3)* .75 .75

**Europa Issue**

Folk Dance — A190

**1981, May 4 Photo. *Perf. 14***

**560** A190 40m shown *.30* .25
**561** A190 175m Dance, diff. *.65* .50

Self-portrait, by Leonardo Da Vinci — A191

The Last Supper, by Da Vinci — A192

***Perf. 13½x14, 12½x13½***

**1981, June 15 Wmk. 344 Litho.**

**562** A191 50m shown .35 .30
**563** A192 125m shown .75 .50
**564** A191 175m Lace pattern, Milan Cathedral .90 .70
*Nos. 562-564 (3)* 2.00 1.50

Da Vinci's visit to Cyprus, 500th anniv.

Ophrys Kotschyi — A193

Orchids: 50m, Orchis puntulata. 75m, Ophrys argolica elegantis. 150m, Epipactis veratrifolia.

**1981, July 6 *Perf. 13½x14***

**565** A193 25m shown .30 .30
**566** A193 50m multi .55 .55
**567** A193 75m multi .90 .90
**568** A193 150m multi 1.50 1.50
*a.* Block of 4, #565-568 3.25 3.25
*Nos. 565-568 (4)* 3.25 3.25

Prince Charles and Lady Diana, St. Paul's Cathedral A194

***Perf. 14x13***

**1981, Sept. 28 Wmk. 344**

**569** A194 200m multicolored .70 *.80*

Royal wedding.

Heinrich von Stephan (1831-1897), UPU Founder — A195

World Food Day (Oct. 16) A196

Intl. Year of the Disabled A197

European Campaign for Urban Renaissance — A198

**1981, Sept. 28**

**570** A195 25m multicolored .25 .25
**571** A196 40m multicolored .25 .25
**572** A197 125m multicolored .30 .30
**573** A198 150m multicolored .35 .35
*Nos. 570-573 (4)* 1.15 1.15

Our Lady of the Angels, Transfiguration Church, Palekhori A199

Christmas (Frescoes): 100m, Christ, Madonna of Arakas Church, Lagoudera, vert. 125m, Baptism of Christ, Our Lady of Assinou Church, Nikitari.

**1981, Nov. 16 *Perf. 12½***

**574** A199 25m multicolored .25 .25
**575** A199 100m multicolored .60 .35
**576** A199 125m multicolored .70 .45
*Nos. 574-576 (3)* 1.55 1.05

Bathing Aphrodite, Sculpture, Soloi, 250 B.C. — A200

Design: 175m, Aphrodite Emerging from the Water, by Titian, 16th cent.

***Perf. 13½x14***

**1982, Apr. 12 Litho. Wmk. 344**

**577** A200 125m multicolored .70 .50
**578** A200 175m multicolored .90 .70

**Europa Issue**

Liberation by Emperor Nicephorus II Phocas, 965 A.D. A201

175m, Conversion of Sergius Paulus, 45 A.D.

***Perf. 12½***

**1982, May 3 Photo. Unwmk.**

**579** A201 40m shown *.45* .25
**580** A201 175m multi *.80* *1.75*

Mosaic Chrismon A202

Cultural Heritage: 125m, King of Palaepaphos (High Priest of Aphrodite), sculpture, vert. 225m, Theseus Struggling with the Minotaur, mosaic.

**1982, July 5 Litho. Wmk. 344**

**581** A202 50m multicolored .25 .25
**582** A202 125m multicolored .55 .55
**583** A202 225m multicolored 1.00 1.00
*Nos. 581-583 (3)* 1.80 1.80

**No. 543 Surcharged**

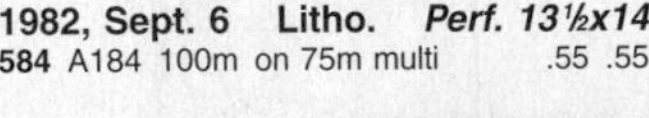

**1982, Sept. 6 Litho. *Perf. 13½x14***

**584** A184 100m on 75m multi .55 .55

Scouting Year — A203

***Perf. 13½x12½, 12½x13½***

**1982, Nov. 8 Wmk. 344**

**585** A203 100m Emblem, horiz. .40 .40
**586** A203 125m Baden-Powell .50 .50
**587** A203 175m Camp site, horiz. .60 *.90*
*Nos. 585-587 (3)* 1.50 1.80

A203a

Christmas — A204

Designs: 25m, 250m, Christ Giving Holy Communion (bread, 25m: wine, 250m) to the Apostles, St. Neophytos Monastery Church, Paphos. 100m, Chalice, Church of St. Savvas, Nicosia.

***Perf. 12½, 13½x14 (100m)***

**1982, Dec. 6**

**588** A203a 25m multicolored .25 .25
**589** A204 100m multicolored .40 .35
**590** A203a 250m multicolored .85 *1.50*
*Nos. 588-590 (3)* 1.50 2.10

A204a

50m, Cyprus Forest Industries, Ltd. 125m, Mosaic, 3rd cent. 150m, Dancers. 175m, Royal Exhibition Building, Melbourne.

**1983, Mar. 14** ***Perf. 14x13½***

**591** A204a 50m multi .25 .25
**592** A204a 125m multi .25 .25
**593** A204a 150m multi .25 .35
**594** A204a 175m multi .25 *.45*
*Nos. 591-594 (4)* 1.00 1.30

Commonwealth Day.

Europa A205

50m, Cyprosyllabic script funerary stele, 6th cent. B.C. 200m, Copper ore, Enkomi ingot, 1400-1250 BC, bronze jug, 2nd cent.

**1983, May 3** **Photo.** ***Perf. 14½x14***

**595** A205 50m multicolored *.25* .25
**596** A205 200m multicolored *.75* *1.75*

Local Butterflies A206

60m, Pararge aegeria. 130m, Aricia medon. 250m, Glaucopsyche paphos.

**Wmk. 344**

**1983, June 28** **Litho.** ***Perf. 12½***

**597** A206 60m multi .35 .30
**598** A206 130m multi .75 .50
**599** A206 250m multi 1.40 *2.00*
*Nos. 597-599 (3)* 2.50 2.80

**Nos. 538-549 Surcharged**

***Perf. 13½x14, 14x13½***

**1983, Oct. 3** **Litho.** **Wmk. 344**

**600** A183 1c on 10m multi .25 *.90*
**601** A184 2c on 15m multi .25 *1.10*
**602** A184 3c on 25m multi .25 *.90*
**603** A184 4c on 40m multi .25 *.90*
**604** A184 5c on 50m multi .40 .40
**605** A184 6c on 75m multi .40 *.90*
**606** A184 10c on 100m multi .55 .50
**607** A184 13c on 125m multi .65 .60
**608** A184 15c on 150m multi .65 .70
**609** A184 20c on 200m multi .70 .80
**610** A184 25c on 175m multi 1.10 *1.25*
**611** A184 50c on 500m multi 1.90 *2.25*
*Nos. 600-611 (12)* 7.35 *11.20*

Electricity Authority of Cyprus, 30th Anniv. — A207

World Communications Year — A208

Intl. Maritime Org., 25th Anniv. — A209

Universal Declaration of Human Rights, 35th Anniv. — A210

Nicos Kazantzakis, 100th Birth Anniv. — A211

Archbishop Makarios III, 70th Birth Anniv. — A212

**1983, Oct. 27** **Litho.** ***Perf. 13½x14***

**612** A207 3c multicolored .25 .25
**613** A208 6c multicolored .25 .25
**614** A209 13c multicolored .25 .25
**615** A210 15c multicolored .25 .25
**616** A211 20c multicolored .30 *.75*
**617** A212 25c multicolored .30 *.80*
*Nos. 612-617 (6)* 1.60 2.55

Christmas — A213

Designs: 4c, Belfry, St. Lazaros Church, Larnaca. 13c, Belfry, St. Varvara Church, Kaimakli, Nicosia. 20c, Belfry, St. Ioannis Church, Larnaca.

**1983, Dec. 12** ***Perf. 12½x14***

**618** A213 4c multicolored .25 .25
**619** A213 13c multicolored .60 .60
**620** A213 20c multicolored .85 *1.40*
*Nos. 618-620 (3)* 1.70 2.25

Waterside Cafe at the Marina, Larnaca — A214

19th Century engravings. Size of 6c: 41x27mm; 75c, 110x85mm.

***Perf. 14½x14 (6c), 14, Imperf. (75c)***

**1984, Mar. 6**

**621** A214 6c shown .25 .25
**622** A214 20c Bazaar, Larnaca .40 *.75*
**623** A214 30c East Gate, Nicosia .65 *1.40*
**624** A214 75c St. Lazarus Church Interior, Larnaca 1.50 *2.10*
*Nos. 621-624 (4)* 2.80 *4.50*

Europa (1959-1984) — A215

**1984, Apr. 30** **Wmk. 344** ***Perf. 12½***

**625** A215 6c multicolored *.40* .25
**626** A215 15c multicolored *.90* *1.75*

1984 Summer Olympics A216

**1984, June 18** **Litho.** ***Perf. 14***

**627** A216 3c Running .25 .25
**628** A216 4c Olympic column .25 .25
**629** A216 13c Swimming .50 *.75*
**630** A216 20c Gymnastics .70 *1.40*
*Nos. 627-630 (4)* 1.70 2.65

Turkish Invasion, 10th Anniv. A217

15c, Prisoners, barbed wire. 20c, Map.

**1984, July 20** **Litho.** ***Perf. 14x13½***

**631** A217 15c multicolored .45 .45
**632** A217 20c multicolored .60 .60

Cyprus Philatelic Society, 25th Anniv. — A218

Cyprus Soccer Assoc., 50th Anniv. A219

George Papanicolaou (1883-1962), Cancer Researcher — A220

Medieval Map A221

**1984, Oct. 15** **Wmk. 344** ***Perf. 12½***

**633** A218 6c multicolored .25 .25
**634** A219 10c multicolored .40 .40
**635** A220 15c multicolored .70 .70
**636** A221 25c multicolored 1.25 *2.00*
*Nos. 633-636 (4)* 2.60 3.35

Intl. Symposium of Cyprus Cartography and First Intl. Symposium on Medieval Paleography (25c).

Christmas — A222

4c, St. Mark. 13c, Gospel page (St. Mark). 20c, St. Luke.

**1984, Nov. 26** **Litho.** ***Perf. 12½***

**637** A222 4c multicolored .30 .30
**638** A222 13c multicolored .90 .90
**639** A222 20c multicolored 1.40 *2.00*
*Nos. 637-639 (3)* 2.60 3.20

Landscapes — A223

1c, Autumn at Platania. 2c, Ayia Napa Monastery. 3c, Phine Village. 4c, Kykko Monastery. 5c, Beach at Makronissos. 6c, Village Street, Omodhos, vert. 10c, Sea view. 13c, Water sports. 15c, Beach at Protaras. 20c, Forestry, vert. 25c, Sunrise at Protaras, vert. 30c, Village houses, Pera Orinis. 50c, Apollo Hylates Sanctuary. £1, Troodos Mountain, vert. £5, Personification of Autumn, Dionyssos House, vert.

***Perf. 15x14, 14x15***

**1985, Mar. 18** **Litho.**

**640** A223 1c multicolored .25 *.65*
**641** A223 2c multicolored .25 *.65*
**642** A223 3c multicolored .25 *.65*
**643** A223 4c multicolored .25 *.35*
**644** A223 5c multicolored .25 .25
**645** A223 6c multicolored .25 .25
**646** A223 10c multicolored .30 .30
**647** A223 13c multicolored .40 .30
**648** A223 15c multicolored .45 .35
**649** A223 20c multicolored .50 .50
**650** A223 25c multicolored .80 *.90*
**651** A223 30c multicolored 1.10 1.10
**652** A223 50c multicolored 2.25 *2.75*
**653** A223 £1 multicolored 5.00 3.00
**654** A223 £5 multicolored 18.00 16.00
*Nos. 640-654 (15)* 30.30 28.00

For surcharges see Nos. 684-685, 712.

Europa A224

6c, Ceramic figures playing the double flute, lyre and tambourine, 7th-6th cent. B.C. 15c, Cypriot violin, lute, flute, the Fourth Women's Dance from the Cyprus Suite.

**1985, May 6** **Litho.** ***Perf. 12½***

**655** A224 6c multicolored *.40* *.40*
**656** A224 15c multicolored *1.10* *2.00*

Republic of Cyprus, 25th Anniv. — A225

UN 40th Anniv. — A229

Natl. Liberation Movement, 30th Anniv. — A226

Intl. Youth Year A227

Solon Michaelides (1905-1979), Conductor, European Music Year — A228

***Perf. 14½ (#657), 14½x14, 15 (#661)***

**1985, Sept. 23** **Litho.**

| | | | | |
|---|---|---|---|---|
| **657** | A225 | 4c multicolored | .25 | .25 |
| **658** | A226 | 6c multicolored | .25 | .25 |
| **659** | A227 | 13c multicolored | .55 | *1.10* |
| **660** | A228 | 15c multicolored | .90 | *1.25* |
| **661** | A229 | 20c multicolored | .50 | *1.75* |
| | | *Nos. 657-661 (5)* | 2.45 | *4.60* |

Christmas — A230

Murals of the St. Ioannis Lampadistis Monastery, Kalopanyiotis: 4c, Virgin Mary's Visit to Elizabeth. 13c, The Nativity. 20c, The Candlemas, Church of Our Lady of Assinous, Nikitari.

**1985, Nov. 18** **Litho.** ***Perf. 12½***

| | | | | |
|---|---|---|---|---|
| **662** | A230 | 4c multicolored | .25 | .25 |
| **663** | A230 | 13c multicolored | .50 | .50 |
| **664** | A230 | 20c multicolored | .85 | *7.50* |
| | | *Nos. 662-664 (3)* | 1.60 | 8.25 |

Hellenistic Platinum Spoon A231

Designs: 20c, Ionian helmet, foot of a sculpture. 25c, Union of Eros and Intellect personified, abstract. 30c, Statue profile.

**1986, Feb. 17** ***Perf. 15x14***

| | | | | |
|---|---|---|---|---|
| **665** | A231 | 15c multicolored | .70 | .70 |
| **666** | A231 | 20c multicolored | .95 | .95 |
| **667** | A231 | 25c multicolored | 1.20 | 1.20 |
| **668** | A231 | 30c multicolored | 1.50 | 1.50 |
| *a.* | | Souv. sheet of 4, #665-668 | 15.00 | *17.00* |
| | | *Nos. 665-668 (4)* | 4.35 | 4.35 |

Construction of the New Archaeological Museum, Nicosia. Department of Antiquities, 50th anniv. No. 668a sold for £1.

**Europa Issue**

Mouflon, Cedar Trees A232

17c, Flamingos, Larnaca Salt Lake.

**1986, Apr. 28** **Litho.** ***Perf. 14x13***

| | | | | |
|---|---|---|---|---|
| **669** | A232 | 7c shown | *.40* | *.35* |
| **670** | A232 | 17c multicolored | *1.50* | *2.50* |

Seashells A233

**1986, July 1** ***Perf. 14x13½***

| | | | | |
|---|---|---|---|---|
| **671** | A233 | 5c Chlamys pesfelis | .35 | .35 |
| **672** | A233 | 7c Charonia variegata | .40 | .40 |
| **673** | A233 | 18c Murex brandaris | 1.00 | 1.00 |
| **674** | A233 | 25c Cypraea spurca | 1.30 | *2.00* |
| | | *Nos. 671-674 (4)* | 3.05 | 3.75 |

Overseas Cypriots Year A234

ΚΥΠΡΟΣ·CYPRUS·KIBRIS 18c

HALLEY'S COMET 1986

Halley's Comet A235

Anniversaries and events: No. 677, Comet tail, Edmond Halley.

***Perf. 13½x13***

**1986, Oct. 13** **Litho.** **Wmk. 344**

| | | | | |
|---|---|---|---|---|
| **675** | A234 | 15c multicolored | 1.10 | .75 |
| **676** | A235 | 18c shown | 1.60 | *2.00* |
| **677** | A235 | 18c multicolored | 1.60 | *2.00* |
| *a.* | | Pair, #676-677 | 3.25 | *4.00* |
| | | *Nos. 675-677 (3)* | 4.30 | *4.75* |

No. 677a has continuous design.

Road Safety A236

5c, Pedestrian crossing. 7c, Helmet, motorcycle controls. 18c, Seatbelt, rearview mirror.

**1986, Nov. 10** ***Perf. 14x13***

| | | | | |
|---|---|---|---|---|
| **678** | A236 | 5c multicolored | .60 | .50 |
| **679** | A236 | 7c multicolored | 1.00 | .50 |
| **680** | A236 | 18c multicolored | 2.40 | *3.00* |
| | | *Nos. 678-680 (3)* | 4.00 | 4.00 |

Intl. Peace Year, Christmas A237

Nativity frescoes (details): 5c, Church of Panayia tou Araka. 15c, Church of Panayia tou Moutoulla. 17c, Church of St. Nicholaos tis Steyis.

**1986, Nov. 24** ***Perf. 13½x14***

| | | | | |
|---|---|---|---|---|
| **681** | A237 | 5c multicolored | .40 | .30 |
| **682** | A237 | 15c multicolored | 1.25 | .60 |
| **683** | A237 | 17c multicolored | 1.60 | *2.00* |
| | | *Nos. 681-683 (3)* | 3.25 | 2.90 |

**Nos. 645 and 647 Surcharged**

***Perf. 14x15, 15x14***

**1986, Oct. 13** **Litho.** **Wmk. 344**

| | | | | |
|---|---|---|---|---|
| **684** | A223 | 7c on 6c multi | .90 | .50 |
| **685** | A223 | 18c on 13c multi | 1.75 | 1.00 |

**Miniature Sheet**

Troodos Churches on UNESCO World Heritage List — A238

Churches and frescoes: a, Assinou, Nikitari. b, Moutoulla, Moutoullas. c, Podithou, Galata. d, Ayios Ioannis Lampadistis, Kalopanayiotis. e, Timios Stavros, Pelentri. f, Stavros Ayiasmati, Platanistasa. g, Archangelos Pedoula, Pedoulas. h, Ayios Nicolaos tis Steyis, Kakopetria. i, Araka, Lagoudera.

***Perf. 12½***

**1987, Apr. 22** **Photo.** **Unwmk.**

| | | | | |
|---|---|---|---|---|
| **686** | A238 | Sheet of 9 | 10.00 | 10.00 |
| *a.-i.* | | 15c any single | 1.00 | 1.00 |

**Europa Issue**

Modern Architecture A239

7c, Central Bank of Cyprus. 18c, Cyprus Communications Authority.

***Perf. 14x13½***

**1987, May 11** **Litho.** **Wmk. 344**

| | | | | |
|---|---|---|---|---|
| **687** | A239 | 7c multicolored | *.50* | *.40* |
| **688** | A239 | 18c multicolored | *1.00* | *1.75* |

Ships Named Kyrenia A240

2c, The Kyrenia, Kyrenia Castle. 3c, Kyrenia II, Perama Shipyard. 5c, Kyrenia II, Paphos. 17c, Kyrenia II, NY Harbor.

**1987, Oct. 3**

| | | | | |
|---|---|---|---|---|
| **689** | A240 | 2c multicolored | .45 | .30 |
| **690** | A240 | 3c multicolored | .60 | .75 |
| **691** | A240 | 5c multicolored | .80 | .50 |
| **692** | A240 | 17c multicolored | 1.75 | 1.25 |
| | | *Nos. 689-692 (4)* | 3.60 | 2.80 |

Blood Donation Coordinating Committee, 10th Anniv. — A241

European Campaign for Countryside — A242

TROODOS '87 — A243

***Perf. 14x13½***

**1987, Nov. 2** **Litho.** **Wmk. 344**

| | | | | |
|---|---|---|---|---|
| **693** | A241 | 7c multicolored | .60 | .55 |
| **694** | A242 | 15c multicolored | 1.40 | 1.25 |
| **695** | A243 | 20c multicolored | 2.00 | *2.75* |
| | | *Nos. 693-695 (3)* | 4.00 | 4.55 |

Christmas A244

**1987, Nov. 30** ***Perf. 14***

| | | | | |
|---|---|---|---|---|
| **696** | A244 | 5c Babe in a manger | .35 | .35 |
| **697** | A244 | 15c Ornament | 1.25 | 1.25 |
| **698** | A244 | 17c Fruit bowl | 1.50 | *2.00* |
| | | *Nos. 696-698 (3)* | 3.10 | 3.60 |

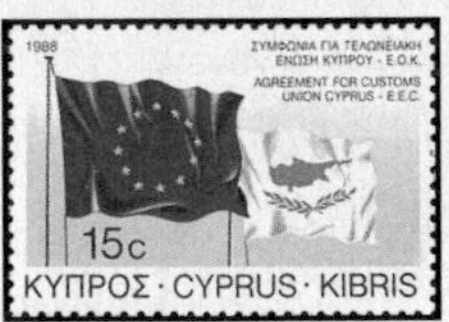


Cyprus Customs Union in Cooperation with the EEC — A245

15c, Natl. and EEC flags. 18c, Maps.

***Perf. 13x13½***

**1988, Jan. 11** **Wmk. 344**

| | | | | |
|---|---|---|---|---|
| **699** | A245 | 15c multicolored | 1.25 | *1.60* |
| **700** | A245 | 18c multicolored | 1.60 | 1.60 |

A246

Europa (Communication and transportation): No. 701, Electronic mail (Intelpost). No. 702, Cellular telephone system. No. 703, Cyprus Airways, technology vs. ecology (jet, 3 flamingos). No. 704, Cyprus Airways (jet, 4 flamingos).

**1988, May 9** ***Perf. 14x14½***

| | | | | |
|---|---|---|---|---|
| **701** | A246 | 7c multicolored | *.65* | *1.00* |
| **702** | A246 | 7c multicolored | *.65* | *1.00* |
| *a.* | | Pair, #701-702 | *1.30* | *2.00* |

**703** A246 18c multicolored 2.25 3.00
**704** A246 18c multicolored 2.25 3.00
*a.* Pair, #703-704 6.50 6.00
*Nos. 701-704 (4)* 5.80 8.00

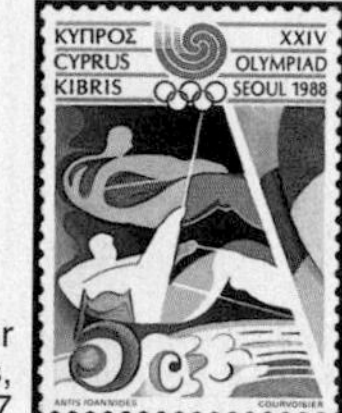


1988 Summer Olympics, Seoul — A247

**Unwmk.**

**1988, June 27 Photo. *Perf. 12***

**Granite Paper**

**705** A247 5c Sailing .40 .30
**706** A247 7c Track .45 .45
**707** A247 10c Marksmanship .50 .70
**708** A247 20c Judo 1.10 1.50
*Nos. 705-708 (4)* 2.45 2.95

Non-Aligned Foreign Minister's Conference — A248

Designs: 10c, Natl. coat of arms. 50c, Jawaharlal Nehru, Tito, Gamal Abdel Nasser and Makarios III (1913-77).

***Perf. 14x13½***

**1988, Sept. 5 Litho. Wmk. 344**

**709** A248 1c shown .25 .25
**710** A248 10c multicolored .65 .65
**711** A248 50c multicolored 3.00 3.00
*Nos. 709-711 (3)* 3.90 3.90

No. 643 Srchd.

**1988, Oct. 3 Litho. *Perf. 15x14***

**712** A223 15c on 4c multi 1.75 1.40

Christmas A249

5c, Candlemas. 15c, Madonna and child. 17c, Adoration of the Magi.

***Perf. 13½x14***

**1988, Nov. 28 Litho. Wmk. 344**

**713** A249 5c multicolored .40 .25
**714** A249 15c multicolored .85 .30
**715** A249 17c multicolored 1.30 *1.75*
*Nos. 713-715 (3)* 2.55 2.30

A250

**1988, Dec. 10**

**716** A250 25c lt ultra & int blue 1.40 1.40

UN Declaration of Human Rights, 40th anniv.

3rd Games of Small European States, Nicosia A251

***Perf. 13½***

**1989, Apr. 10 Litho. Unwmk.**

**717** A251 1c Discus .40 .30
**718** A251 5c Javelin .40 .30
**719** A251 15c Wrestling .90 .50
**720** A251 18c Running 1.10 1.10

**Size: 110x80mm**

***Imperf***

**721** A251 £1 Nike, laurel, bird 7.50 7.50
*Nos. 717-721 (5)* 10.30 9.70

Various Children's Games A252

***Perf. 13x13½***

**1989, May 8 Litho. Unwmk.**

**722** A252 7c multi (5 boys) *.85 .75*
**723** A252 7c multi (6 boys) *.85 .75*
*a.* Pair, #722-723 *1.90 1.90*
**724** A252 18c multi (6 boys) *1.25 1.10*
**725** A252 18c multi (5 boys) *1.25 1.10*
*a.* Pair, #724-725 *2.75 2.75*
*Nos. 722-725 (4)* 4.20 3.70

Europa.

French Revolution, Bicent. — A253

***Perf. 11½***

**1989, July 7 Litho. Unwmk.**

**Granite Paper**

**726** A253 18c multicolored 1.40 1.00

A254

A255

**1989, Sept. 4 *Perf. 13½***

**727** A254 15c multicolored .65 .65
**728** A255 30c multicolored 1.40 1.40

15c for Interparliamentary Union, cent. 30c for 9th Non-Aligned Summit Conf., Belgrade.

Apiculture A256

3c, Honeycomb and bees. 10c, Gathering nectar on pink flower. 15c, Gathering nectar on white flower. 18c, Queen, worker bees.

**1989, Oct. 15 *Perf. 13½x14***

**729** A256 3c multicolored .50 .30
**730** A256 10c multicolored .90 .60
**731** A256 15c multicolored 1.10 .60
**732** A256 18c multicolored 1.25 *1.75*
*Nos. 729-732 (4)* 3.75 3.25

Annivs. & Events — A257

Designs: 3c, Armenian earthquake. 5c, Cyprus Philatelic Society. 7c, European Cancer Year. 17c, World Food Day.

**1989, Nov. 13**

**733** A257 3c multicolored .35 *1.10*
**734** A257 5c multicolored .50 .30
**735** A257 7c multicolored .85 *1.40*
**736** A257 17c multicolored 1.25 *1.40*
*Nos. 733-736 (4)* 2.95 *4.20*

A258

A259

Mosaics, 3rd-5th Cent. A260

Details: 1c, Winter, from *The Four Seasons,* House of Dionysos. 2c, Personification of Crete, from *Theseus Slaying the Minotaur,* Villa of Theseus. 3c, Centaur and Maenad, from *The Dionysiac Procession,* House of Aion, vert. 4c, *Poseidon and Amymone,* House of Dionysos. 5c, Leda, from *Leda and the Swan,* House of Aion. 7c, Apollon, from *Apollo and Marsyas,* House of Aion. 10c, Hermes and Dionysos, from *Hermes Presenting Dionysos to Tropheus,* House of Aion, vert. 15c, Cassiopeia, from *Cassiopeia and the Nereids,* House of Aion. 18c, *Orpheus Playing the Lyre,* House of Orpheus. 20c, Nymphs preparing bath, from *Hermes Presenting Dionysos to Tropheus,* vert. 25c, Amazon holding double ax and reins, House of Orpheus, vert. 40c, Doris, one of 3 Nereids in *Cassiopeia and the Nereids.* 50c, Hercules and the lion, from *The First Labor of Hercules,* House of Orpheus. £1, *Apollon and Daphne,* House of Dionysos. £3, Cupid hunting, Villa of Theseus.

***Perf. 13, 13x13½ (2c, 4c, 18c, 40c), 13½x13 (3c, 10c, 20c, 25c)***

**1989, Dec. 29**

**737** A258 1c multicolored .50 *1.50*
**738** A259 2c multicolored .50 *1.50*
**739** A259 3c multicolored .65 *1.50*
**740** A259 4c multicolored .85 *1.50*
**741** A258 5c multicolored .85 .30
**742** A258 7c multicolored 1.10 .35
**743** A259 10c multicolored 1.30 .40
**744** A258 15c multicolored 2.10 .65
**745** A259 18c multicolored 2.10 .70
**746** A259 20c multicolored 2.50 .90
**747** A259 25c multicolored 2.50 .90
**748** A259 40c multicolored 3.75 2.00

***Perf. 13½x14***

**749** A260 50c multicolored 2.75 2.00
**750** A260 £1 multicolored 6.25 3.75
**751** A260 £3 multicolored 13.00 *14.00*
*Nos. 737-751 (15)* 40.70 31.95

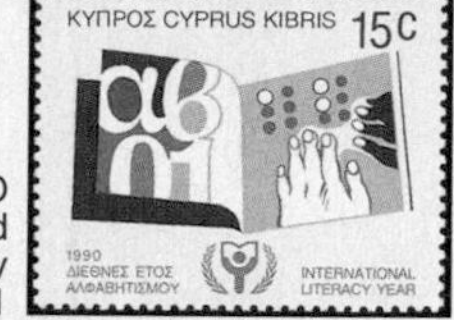


UNESCO World Literacy Year — A261

83rd Interparliamentary Conference, Nicosia — A262

Lions Europa Forum A263

Anniversaries & events.

**1990, Apr. 3 *Perf. 14x13½***

**752** A261 15c multicolored .80 .80
**753** A262 17c multicolored .95 .95
**754** A263 18c multicolored 1.25 1.25
*Nos. 752-754 (3)* 3.00 3.00

Europa A264

Post Offices: 7c, Paphos. 18c, Limassol City Center.

**1990, May 10 Litho. *Perf. 13x13½***

**755** A264 7c multicolored *1.00* *.45*
**756** A264 18c multicolored *1.75* *2.50*

European Year of Tourism — A265

Designs: 5c, Hotel and Catering Institute, 25th anniv. 7c, Holy Church of St. Lazarus, 1100th anniv. 15c, Female silhouette, butterflies. 18c, Male silhouette, birds.

**1990, July 9 *Perf. 14***

**757** A265 5c multicolored .60 .60
**758** A265 7c multicolored .75 .75
**759** A265 15c multicolored 2.10 1.75
**760** A265 18c multicolored 2.40 *3.75*
*Nos. 757-760 (4)* 5.85 6.85

Republic of Cyprus, 30th Anniv. A266

**1990, Sept. 29 Photo. *Perf. 11½***

**761** A266 15c Sun .75 .60
**762** A266 17c shown .95 .70
**763** A266 18c Fish 1.25 .80
**764** A266 40c Birds, flowers 3.00 *5.00*

**Size: 90x90mm**

***Imperf***

**765** A266 £1 Stylized bird 6.50 6.50
*Nos. 761-765 (5)* 12.45 13.60

Flowers — A267

2c, Chionodoxa lochiae. 3c, Pancrayium maritimum. 5c, Paeonia mascula. 7c, Cyclamen cyprium. 15c, Tulipa cypria. 18c, Crocus cyprius.

**1990, Nov. 5 Litho. *Perf. 13½x13***

**766** A267 2c multicolored .40 *1.50*
**767** A267 3c multicolored .60 *1.50*
**768** A267 5c multicolored .85 .65
**769** A267 7c multicolored 1.10 1.00
**770** A267 15c multicolored 2.25 2.25
**771** A267 18c multicolored 2.40 *3.50*
*Nos. 766-771 (6)* 7.60 10.40

Christmas A268

**1990, Dec. 3 *Perf. 13½x14***

**772** A268 5c Nativity .90 .30
**773** A268 15c Virgin and Child 1.90 .45
**774** A268 17c Nativity, diff. 2.25 *3.00*
*Nos. 772-774 (3)* 5.05 3.75

Mosaics From Kanakaria Church — A269

**1991, Mar. 28 Photo. *Perf. 12***

**Granite Paper**

**775** A269 5c Archangel .80 .25
**776** A269 15c Christ Child .85 .75
**777** A269 17c St. James 1.60 *1.75*
**778** A269 18c St. Matthew 1.75 *2.25*
*Nos. 775-778 (4)* 5.00 5.00

Europa A270

**1991, May 6 Litho. *Perf. 13x13½***

**779** A270 7c Spacecraft Ulysses *.75 .40*
**780** A270 18c Spacecraft Giotto *1.60 2.25*

Oenanthe Cypriaca (Cyprus Wheatear) A271

**1991, July 4 Litho. *Perf. 13½***

**781** A271 5c Juvenile bird 1.10 .50
**782** A271 7c Autumn plumage 1.25 .50
**783** A271 15c Male bird 1.50 .75
**784** A271 30c Female bird 2.40 *3.75*
*Nos. 781-784 (4)* 6.25 5.50

UN High Commissioner for Refugees, 40th Anniv. — A272

**1991, Oct. 7 Litho. *Perf. 14x13½***

**785** A272 5c shown .35 .25
**786** A272 15c Legs 1.40 .75
**787** A272 18c Faces 1.75 *2.25*
*Nos. 785-787 (3)* 3.50 3.25

Christmas A273

**1991, Nov. 25 Litho. *Perf. 13½***

**788** A273 5c Nativity scene .35 .25
**789** A273 15c St. Basil .85 .85
**790** A273 17c Baptism of Jesus 1.10 1.50
*a.* Strip of 3, #788-790 2.75 2.75

Strips of 3 are from sheets of 9.

A274

**1992, Apr. 3 Litho. *Perf. 12***

**Granite Paper**

**791** A274 10c Swimming 1.10 .60
**792** A274 20c Long jump 1.50 1.00
**793** A274 30c Running 2.25 2.25
**794** A274 35c Discus 2.50 2.50
*Nos. 791-794 (4)* 7.35 6.35

1992 Summer Olympics, Barcelona.

Expo '92, Seville A275

10th Youth Under 16 European Soccer Tournament — A276

Opening of University of Cyprus A277

**1992, Apr. 20 Litho. *Perf. 14***

**795** A275 20c multicolored 2.00 .95
**796** A276 25c multicolored 2.10 1.25
**797** A277 30c multicolored 2.10 *2.75*
*Nos. 795-797 (3)* 6.20 4.95

Discovery of America, 500th Anniv. A278

No. 798, Map. No. 799, Embarkation at Palos. No. 800, Three ships. No. 801, Columbus.

**1992, May 29 Litho. *Perf. 13x13½***

**798** A278 10c multicolored *1.00 .90*
**799** A278 10c multicolored *1.00 .90*
*a.* Pair, #798-799 *2.25 2.25*
**800** A278 30c multicolored *1.50 1.25*
**801** A278 30c multicolored *1.50 1.25*
*a.* Pair, #800-801 *3.25 3.25*
*Nos. 798-801 (4)* 5.00 4.30

Europa.

Reptiles A279

Designs: 7c, Chamaeleo chamaeleon. 10c, Lacerta laevis troodica. 15c, Mauremys caspica. 20c, Coluber cypriensis.

**1992, Sept. 14 Litho. *Perf. 14x13½***

**802** A279 7c multicolored 1.00 .40
**803** A279 10c multicolored 1.10 .65
**804** A279 15c multicolored 1.60 1.10
**805** A279 20c multicolored 2.10 *2.50*
*Nos. 802-805 (4)* 5.80 4.65

Intl. Maritime and Shipping Conference — A280

**Unwmk.**

**1992, Nov. 9 Litho. *Perf. 14***

**806** A280 50c multicolored 4.00 4.00

Christmas A281

Church wall paintings: 7c, "Virgin Mary Greeting Elizabeth," Church of Timios Stavros, Pelendri. 15c, "The Virgin and Child," Church of Panayia tou Araka. 20c, "Holy Mother Odigitria," Church of Ayios Nicolaos tis Steyis.

**1992, Nov. 9 *Perf. 13½x14***

**807** A281 7c multicolored .65 .35
**808** A281 15c multicolored 1.00 .75
**809** A281 20c multicolored 1.60 *2.25*
*Nos. 807-809 (3)* 3.25 3.35

A282

**1993, Feb. 15 Litho. *Perf. 14***

**810** A282 10c multicolored 1.00 .80

Pancyprian Gymnasium, cent.

A283

Europa: 10c, Bronze sculpture, Motherhood, by N. Dymiotis (1930-1990). 30c, Applique, Motherhood, by Savva (1924-1968), horiz.

**1993, Apr. 3 *Perf. 13½x14, 14x13½***

**811** A283 10c multicolored *.90 .65*
**812** A283 30c multicolored *1.60 2.00*

13th European Cup for Women Athletes A284

Scouting in Cyprus, 80th Anniv. — A285

Water Skiing Moufflon Encouragement Cup — A286

Archbishop Makarios III, 80th Anniv. of Birth — A287

***Perf. 13½x14, 14x13½***

**1993, May 24 Litho.**

**813** A284 7c multicolored .50 .40
**814** A285 10c multicolored .70 .55
**815** A286 20c multicolored 1.25 1.25
*a.* Inscribed "MUFFLON" *13.00*
**816** A287 25c multicolored 1.75 *2.25*
*Nos. 813-816 (4)* 4.20 4.45

Fish — A288

**1993, Sept. 6 Litho. *Perf. 14x13½***

**817** A288 7c Holocentrus ruber .60 .35
**818** A288 15c Scorpaena scrofa .90 .70
**819** A288 20c Serranus scriba 1.00 1.00
**820** A288 30c Balistes capriscus 2.00 *2.40*
*Nos. 817-820 (4)* 4.50 4.45

Maritime Cyprus A289

**1993, Oct. 4 *Perf. 14***

**821** A289 25c multicolored 2.25 2.25

12th Commonwealth Summit Conference — A290

**1993, Oct. 4 *Perf. 14x13½***

**822** A290 35c red brown & tan 2.10 2.10
**823** A290 40c olive brown & tan 2.75 2.75

Christmas A291

7c, Carved wooden cross, Stavrovouni Monastery. 20c, Crucifixion, cross from Lefkara Church. 25c, Nativity, cross from Pedoulas Church.

**1993, Nov. 22 Litho. *Perf. 13½x14***

**824** A291 7c multicolored .40 .30
**825** A291 20c multicolored .95 .95

***Perf. 14x13½***

**826** A291 25c multi, horiz. 1.40 2.00
*Nos. 824-826 (3)* 2.75 3.25

Copper Industry A292

Europa: 10c, Early smelting of copper. 30c, Map, boat, copper ingot.

**1994, Mar. 1 Litho. *Perf. 13x13½***

**827** A292 10c multicolored *.70 .70*
**828** A292 30c multicolored *1.25 1.75*

Persons with Special Needs — A293

Intl. Olympic Committee, Cent. — A294

World Gymnasiade, Nicosia — A295

Intl. Year of the Family — A296

**1994, May 9 Litho. *Perf. 13***

**829** A293 7c multicolored .55 .35
**830** A294 15c multicolored 1.00 .65
**831** A295 20c multicolored 1.25 1.25
**832** A296 25c multicolored 1.50 *2.00*
*Nos. 829-832 (4)* 4.30 4.25

Turkish Invasion and Occupation of Cyprus, 20th Anniv. — A297

**1994, June 27 Litho. *Perf. 14***

**833** A297 10c Human rights .80 .40
**834** A297 50c Cultural heritage 3.25 3.25

Trees — A298

7c, Pinus nigra. 15c, Cedrus libani. 20c, Quercus alnifolia. 30c, Arbutus andrachne.

**1994, Oct. 10 Litho. *Perf. 13½***

**835** A298 7c multicolored .70 .40
**836** A298 15c multicolored 1.10 .80
**837** A298 20c multicolored 1.25 1.25
**838** A298 30c multicolored 1.90 *2.50*
*Nos. 835-838 (4)* 4.95 4.95

ICAO, 50th Anniv. A299

**1994, Nov. 21 Litho. *Perf. 14***

**839** A299 30c multicolored 3.25 3.25

Christmas A300

Designs: 7c, Virgin Mary (Vlahernitissa). 20c, Nativity. 25c, Archangel Michael.

**1994, Nov. 21 *Perf. 13½***

**840** A300 7c multicolored .80 .50
**841** A300 20c multicolored 1.90 1.00
**842** A300 25c multicolored 2.50 *3.00*
*Nos. 840-842 (3)* 5.20 4.50

Traditional Costumes — A301

Costumes: 1c, Female, Phapos. 2c, Bridal, Karpess. 3c, Female, Phapos, diff. 5c, Female, Messaoria. 7c, Bridegroom's. 10c, Shepherd's, Messaoria. 15c, Festive female, Nicosia. 20c, Festive female, Karpass. 25c, Female, Mountain-Pitsillia. 30c, Festive female, Karpass, diff. 35c, Rural male. 40c, Plain festive male, Messaoria. 50c, Urban male. £1, Urban festive female, Sarka.

**1994, Dec. 27 Litho. *Perf. 13½x13***

**843** A301 1c multicolored .40 .40
**844** A301 2c multicolored .60 .60
**845** A301 3c multicolored .65 .65
**846** A301 5c multicolored .80 .80
**847** A301 7c multicolored .85 .85
**848** A301 10c multicolored 1.25 1.25
**849** A301 15c multicolored 2.10 2.10
**850** A301 20c multicolored 2.10 2.10
**851** A301 25c multicolored 2.40 2.40
**852** A301 30c multicolored 2.40 2.40
**853** A301 35c multicolored 2.40 2.40
**854** A301 40c multicolored 2.75 2.75
**855** A301 50c multicolored 3.50 3.50
**856** A301 £1 multicolored 6.00 6.00
*a.* Inscribed "1998" 6.00 6.00
*Nos. 843-856 (14)* 28.20 28.20

Third Intl. Congress of Cypriot Studies — A302

Excavations: 20c, Hearth room, Ashlar building, Paliotaverna. 30c, Hall, Agios Demetrios area, Kalavasos. £1, Old Nicosia Archbishorpic building, 18th cent.

**1995, Feb. 27 Litho. *Perf. 14***

**859** A302 20c multicolored 1.25 1.25
**860** A302 30c multicolored 1.90 1.90

**Size: 107x71mm**

***Imperf***

**861** A302 £1 multicolored 6.25 6.25
*Nos. 859-861 (3)* 9.40 9.40

A303

Liberation Monument, Nicosia: a, People walking left. b, Statue of Liberty, prisoners leaving prison. c, People walking right.

**1995, Mar. 31 Litho. *Perf. 13x14***

**862** Strip of 3 4.25 4.25
*a.-c.* A303 20c any single 1.35 1.35

No. 862 is a continuous design.

Formation of EOKA (Natl. Organization of Cypriot Struggle), 40th anniv.

Europa — A304

10c, Concentration camp prisoners, dove, rainbow, map of Europe. 30c, Prisoner, dove.

**1995, May 8 Litho. *Perf. 13½***

**863** A304 10c multicolored *1.00 .75*
**864** A304 30c multicolored *2.00 3.00*

Liberation of the concentration camps, 50th anniv.

Health A305

7c, Proper nutrition, exercise. 10c, Fight against AIDS. 15c, Fight against illegal drugs. 20c, Stop smoking campaign.

**1995, June 26 Litho. *Perf. 13½***

**865** A305 7c multi, vert. .35 .30
**866** A305 10c multi .75 .75
**867** A305 15c multi .80 .80
**868** A305 20c multi, vert. 1.10 *1.50*
*Nos. 865-868 (4)* 3.00 3.35

European Cultural Month A306

25c, Map of Europe, building.

**1995, Sept. 18 Litho. *Perf. 13x13½***

**869** A306 20c shown .85 .85
**870** A306 25c multicolored 1.10 *1.25*

Souvenir Sheet

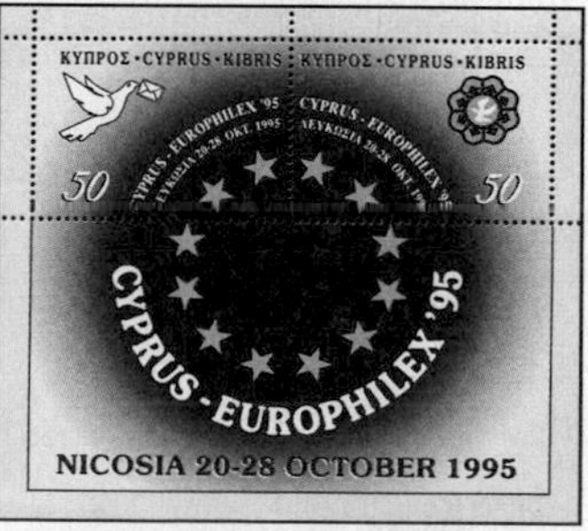


Europhilex '95 — A307

Designs: a, Dove carrying letter, stars. b, Stars, exhibition emblem.

**1995, Sept. 18 Litho. *Perf. 14***

**871** A307 Sheet of 2 8.75 8.75
*a.-b.* 50c any single 4.00 4.00

A limited number were surcharged £5 on each stamp and sold at "Europhilex '95" on Oct. 27 and 28, 1995.

UN, 50th Anniv. A308

Volleyball, Cent. — A309

European Conservation Year — A310

World Clay Target Shooting Championships — A311

***Perf. 13x13½, 13½x13***

**1995, Oct. 24** **Litho.**

**872** A308 10c multicolored .65 .65
**873** A309 15c multicolored 1.00 .75
**874** A310 20c multicolored 1.40 1.10
**875** A311 25c multicolored 1.60 *2.25*
*Nos. 872-875 (4)* 4.65 4.75

Christmas A312

Various reliquaries, Kykko Monastery.

**1995, Nov. 27** **Litho.** ***Perf. 13½x13***

**876** A312 7c multicolored .60 .45
**877** A312 20c multicolored 1.40 1.10
**878** A312 25c multicolored 1.75 *2.25*
*Nos. 876-878 (3)* 3.75 3.80

A313

A314

A315

Anniversaries and Events — A316

**1996, Jan. 4** **Litho.** ***Perf. 13½x13***

**879** A313 10c multicolored .90 .65
**880** A314 20c multicolored 1.50 1.10
**881** A315 35c multicolored 2.25 2.25
**882** A316 40c multicolored 2.25 *2.75*
*Nos. 879-882 (4)* 6.90 6.75

Pancyprian Organization of Large Families, 25th anniv. (No. 879). Motion pictures, cent. (NO. 880). UNICEF, 50th anniv. (No. 881). 13th Conf. of Commonwealth Speakers and Presiding Officers (No. 882).

Portraits of Women
A317 A318

**1996, Apr. 8** **Litho.** ***Perf. 14***

**883** A317 10c multicolored *1.10 .50*
**884** A318 30c multicolored *2.40 2.75*

Europa.

1996 Summer Olympics, Atlanta A319

**1996, June 10** **Litho.** ***Perf. 13***

**885** A319 10c High jump .90 .35
**886** A319 20c Javelin 1.25 .70
**887** A319 25c Wrestling 1.75 1.10
**888** A319 30c Swimming 2.10 *2.50*
*Nos. 885-888 (4)* 6.00 4.65

Mills of Cyprus — A320

**1996, Sept. 23** **Litho.** ***Perf. 13***

**889** A320 10c Watermill .95 .70
**890** A320 15c Olivemill 1.40 1.00
**891** A320 20c Windmill 1.50 1.40
**892** A320 25c Handmill 2.00 2.00
*Nos. 889-892 (4)* 5.85 5.10

Icons, Religious Landmarks A321

Designs: No. 893, Icon of Our Lady of Iberia, Moscow. No. 894, Holy Monastery of Stavrovouni, Cyprus. No. 895, Icon of St. Nicholas, Cyprus. No. 896, Iveron Mother of God Resurrection Gate, Moscow.

**1996, Nov. 13** **Litho.** ***Perf. 11½***

**893** A321 30c multicolored 2.10 2.10
**894** A321 30c multicolored 2.10 2.10
**895** A321 30c multicolored 2.10 2.10
**896** A321 30c multicolored 2.10 2.10
*a.* Block of 4, #893-896 9.00 9.00

See Russia No. 6356.

Christmas A322

Paintings from Church of the Virgin of Asinou: 7c, Detail from Nativity. 20c, Virgin Mary between Archangels Gabriel and Michael. 25c, Christ bestowing blessings, vert.

**1996, Dec. 2** ***Perf. 13x13½, 13½x13***

**897** A322 7c multicolored .90 .50
**898** A322 20c multicolored 2.00 1.25
**899** A322 25c multicolored 2.40 *2.75*
*Nos. 897-899 (3)* 5.30 4.50

Easter A323

**1997, Mar. 24** **Litho.** ***Perf. 13x13½***

**900** A323 15c The Last Supper 1.25 .75
**901** A323 25c The Crucifixion 1.75 1.75

A324

**1997, Mar. 24** ***Perf. 13½x13***

**902** A324 30c multicolored 4.25 3.75

European Men's Clubs Basketball Cup finals.

A325

Europa (Stories and Legends): 30c, Man in red cape fighting Death, eagle above.

**1997, May 5** **Litho.** ***Perf. 13½x13***

**903** A325 15c shown *1.10 .50*
**904** A325 30c multicolored *2.10 2.50*

Insects A326

10c, Oedipoda miniata. 15c, Acherontia atropos. 25c, Daphnis nerii. 35c, Ascalaphus macaronius.

**1997, June 30** **Litho.** ***Perf. 13x13½***

**905** A326 10c multicolored 1.00 .40
**906** A326 15c multicolored 1.50 .60
**907** A326 25c multicolored 2.00 1.25
**908** A326 35c multicolored 2.50 2.50
*Nos. 905-908 (4)* 7.00 4.75

Archbishop Makarios III (1913-77), 1st Pres. of Cyprus Republic A327

**1997, Aug. 1** **Litho.** ***Perf. 13x13½***

**909** A327 15c multicolored 1.50 1.00

Christmas A328

Frescoes from Church of Ayios Ioannis Lambadestis: 10c, Nativity. 25c, Magi on way to Bethlehem. 30c, Flight into Egypt.

**1997, Nov. 17** **Litho.** ***Perf. 13½x13***

**910** A328 10c multicolored .95 .65
**911** A328 25c multicolored 2.40 1.40
**912** A328 30c multicolored 2.75 2.75
*Nos. 910-912 (3)* 6.10 4.80

Minerals A329

**1998, Mar. 9** **Litho.** ***Perf. 13x13½***

**913** A329 10c Green jasper .55 .40
**914** A329 15c Iron pyrite .80 .65
**915** A329 25c Gypsum 1.30 1.30
**916** A329 30c Chalcedony 1.60 1.60
*Nos. 913-916 (4)* 4.25 3.95

1998 World Cup Soccer Championships, France — A330

**1998, May 4** **Litho.** ***Perf. 14***

**917** A330 35c multicolored 2.75 1.75

Europa A331

Festivals, holidays: 15c, "Katakklysmos" Larnaca. 30c, People watching proclamation of independence, 1960.

**1998, May 4**

| | | | | |
|---|---|---|---|---|
| 918 | A331 | 15c multicolored | *1.10* | *.55* |
| 919 | A331 | 30c multicolored | *2.40* | *1.60* |

Ovis Gmelini Ophion A332

World Wildlife Fund: No. 920, Male, female, calf. No. 921, Group running. No. 922, Male up close. No. 923, Male with front legs up on rock, one grazing.

**1998, June 22 Litho. *Perf. 13x13½***

| | | | | |
|---|---|---|---|---|
| 920 | A332 | 25c multicolored | 1.50 | 1.50 |
| 921 | A332 | 25c multicolored | 1.50 | 1.50 |
| 922 | A332 | 25c multicolored | 1.50 | 1.50 |
| 923 | A332 | 25c multicolored | 1.50 | 1.50 |
| a. | | Block of 4, #920-923 | 6.00 | 6.00 |

Issued in sheets of 16.

World Stamp Day A333

**1998, Oct. 9 Litho. *Perf. 14***

| | | | | |
|---|---|---|---|---|
| 924 | A333 | 30c multicolored | 2.75 | 2.75 |
| a. | | Booklet pane of 8 | 22.00 | |
| | | Complete booklet, #924a | 25.00 | |

A334

**1998, Oct. 9**

| | | | | |
|---|---|---|---|---|
| 925 | A334 | 50c multicolored | 2.00 | 2.00 |

Universal Declaration of Human Rights, 50th anniv.

A335

Christmas (Scenes from paintings in the Church of the Virgin of Théosképasti, Kalopanayiotis): 10c, The Annunciation. 25c, The Nativity. 30c, Baptism of Christ.

**1998, Nov. 16 Litho. *Perf. 14***

| | | | | |
|---|---|---|---|---|
| 926 | A335 | 10c multicolored | .35 | .35 |
| 927 | A335 | 25c multicolored | .90 | .90 |
| 928 | A335 | 30c multicolored | 2.75 | 2.75 |
| a. | | Souvenir sheet, #926-928 | 4.00 | 4.00 |
| | | *Nos. 926-928 (3)* | 4.00 | 4.00 |

Mushrooms — A336

10c, Pleurotus eryngii. 15c, Lactarius deliciosus. 25c, Sparassis crispa. 30c, Morchella elata.

**1999, Mar. 4 Litho. *Perf. 13½x13***

| | | | | |
|---|---|---|---|---|
| 929 | A336 | 10c multicolored | .50 | .50 |
| 930 | A336 | 15c multicolored | 1.00 | .60 |
| 931 | A336 | 25c multicolored | 1.50 | 1.50 |
| 932 | A336 | 30c multicolored | 1.60 | *2.50* |
| | | *Nos. 929-932 (4)* | 4.60 | 5.10 |

Natl. Parks and Nature Preserves A337

**1999, May 6 Litho. *Perf. 14***

| | | | | |
|---|---|---|---|---|
| 933 | A337 | 15c Tripylos Reserve | *.90* | *.50* |
| 934 | A337 | 30c Lara Reserve | *1.60* | *2.10* |
| a. | | Booklet pane, 4 each #933-934 | *11.00* | |
| | | Complete booklet, #934a | *12.00* | |

Europa.

Council of Europe, 50th Anniv. A338

**1999, May 6**

| | | | | |
|---|---|---|---|---|
| 935 | A338 | 30c multicolored | 2.10 | 2.10 |

4000 Years of Hellenism — A339

a, Sanctuary of Apollo Hylates, Kourion. b, Mycenaean "Krater of the Warriors," Athens. c, Mycenaean amphoral krater, Cyprus Museum. d, Sanctuary of Apollo Epikourios, Delphi.

**1999, June 28 Litho. *Perf. 13½x13***

| | | | | |
|---|---|---|---|---|
| 936 | A339 | 25c Block of 4, #a.-d. | 6.25 | 6.25 |

See Greece No. 1938.

UPU, 125th Anniv. A340

**1999, Sept. 30 Litho. *Perf. 14***

| | | | | |
|---|---|---|---|---|
| 937 | A340 | 15c shown | 1.00 | .90 |
| 938 | A340 | 35c "125" | 2.50 | 2.00 |

Souvenir Sheet

Maritime Cyprus Shipping Conference — A341

Cyprus flag and: a, Container ship. b, Binoculars, chart, cap. c, Ship with yellow stripe on tower. d, Tanker.

**1999, Sept. 30**

| | | | | |
|---|---|---|---|---|
| 939 | A341 | 25c Sheet of 4, #a.-d. | 5.00 | 5.00 |

Souvenir Sheet

Turkish Invasion of Cyprus, 25th Anniv. — A342

**1999, Nov. 11 Litho. *Imperf.***

| | | | | |
|---|---|---|---|---|
| 940 | A342 | 30c multicolored | 2.50 | 2.50 |

A343

**1999, Nov. 11 *Perf. 14***

| | | | | |
|---|---|---|---|---|
| 941 | A343 | 10c Angel | .70 | .55 |
| 942 | A343 | 25c Magi | 1.40 | 1.25 |
| 943 | A343 | 30c Madonna and child | 1.60 | 1.60 |
| | | *Nos. 941-943 (3)* | 3.70 | 3.40 |

Christmas.

Souvenir Sheet

A344

Miss Universe 2000: a, 15c, Woman, stars. b, 35c, Armless nude statue of woman.

**2000, Mar. 30 Litho. *Perf. 13¼x13***

| | | | | |
|---|---|---|---|---|
| 944 | A344 | Sheet of 2, #a.-b. | 3.00 | 3.00 |

Jewelry — A345

Various pieces of jewelry. Nos. 945-952 vert.

**2000, Mar. 30 Litho. *Perf. 14***

| | | | | |
|---|---|---|---|---|
| 945 | A345 | 10c multi | .45 | .45 |
| 946 | A345 | 15c multi | .60 | .60 |
| 947 | A345 | 20c multi | .80 | .80 |
| 948 | A345 | 25c multi | 1.00 | 1.00 |
| 949 | A345 | 30c multi | 1.25 | 1.25 |
| 950 | A345 | 35c multi | 1.40 | 1.40 |
| 951 | A345 | 40c multi | 1.60 | 1.60 |
| 952 | A345 | 50c multi | 2.25 | 2.25 |
| 953 | A345 | 75c multi | 3.00 | 3.00 |
| 954 | A345 | £1 multi | 4.00 | 4.00 |
| 955 | A345 | £2 multi | 7.50 | 7.50 |
| 956 | A345 | £3 multi | 11.00 | 11.00 |
| | | *Nos. 945-956 (12)* | 34.85 | 34.85 |

Cyprus Red Cross, 50th Anniv. A346

**2000, May 9 Litho. *Perf. 13x13¼***

| | | | | |
|---|---|---|---|---|
| 957 | A346 | 15c multi | 2.25 | 2.25 |

Memorial to Heroes of 1955-59 Independence Struggle — A347

**2000, May 9 *Perf. 13¼x13***

| | | | | |
|---|---|---|---|---|
| 958 | A347 | 15c multi | 2.40 | 2.40 |

**Europa, 2000**

Common Design Type

**2000, May 9 *Perf. 14***

| | | | | |
|---|---|---|---|---|
| 959 | CD17 | 30c multi | *2.10* | *1.40* |

World Meteorological Org., 50th Anniv. — A348

**2000, May 9**

| | | | | |
|---|---|---|---|---|
| 960 | A348 | 30c multi | 2.25 | 2.25 |

European Convention of Human Rights, 50th Anniv. A349

**2000, June 29 Litho. *Perf. 13x13¼***

| | | | | |
|---|---|---|---|---|
| 961 | A349 | 30c multi | 3.00 | 3.00 |

Churches Damaged Under Turkish Occupation A350

Designs: 10c, Monastery of Antifonitis, Kalograia, vert. 15c, Church of St. Themonianos, Lysi, vert. 25c, Church of Panagia Kanakaria, Lytrhagkomi. 30c, Avgasida Monastery Church, Milia.

***Perf. 13¼x13, 13x13¼***

**2000, June 29**

| | | | | |
|---|---|---|---|---|
| 962 | A350 | 10c multi | 1.10 | .60 |
| 963 | A350 | 15c multi | 1.50 | .80 |
| 964 | A350 | 25c multi | 2.00 | 1.60 |
| 965 | A350 | 30c multi | 2.40 | 2.40 |
| | | *Nos. 962-965 (4)* | 7.00 | 5.40 |

2000 Summer Olympics, Sydney A351

Designs: 10c, Archery. 15c, Pommel horse. 25c, Diving. 35c, Trampoline.

**2000, Sept. 14 Litho. *Perf. 13x13½***

| | | | | |
|---|---|---|---|---|
| 966-969 | A351 | Set of 4 | 6.00 | 6.00 |

Christmas — A352

Gospel covers: 10c, Annunciation. 25c, Nativity. 30c, Baptism of Jesus.

**2000, Nov. 2** *Perf. 13½x13*
**970-972** A352 Set of 3 5.00 5.00

Pavlos Liasides (1901-85), Poet — A353

**2001, Mar. 12 Litho.** *Perf. 13¼x13*
**973** A353 13c multi 1.25 .65

Commonwealth Day, 25th Anniv. — A354

**2001, Mar. 12** *Perf. 13x13¼*
**974** A354 30c multi 2.75 2.75

UN High Commissioner for Refugees, 50th Anniv. — A355

**2001, Mar. 12**
**975** A355 30c multi 2.50 2.50

Europa A356

Designs: 20c, Bridge over Diarizos River. 30c, Akaki River.

**2001, May 3**
**976-977** A356 Set of 2 *4.00 2.00*
*977a* Booklet pane, 4 each #976-977 *17.00*
Booklet, #977a *19.00*

Crabs A357

Designs: 13c, Parthenope massena. 20c, Calappa granulata. 25c, Ocypode cursor. 30c, Pagurus bernhardus.

**2001, June 7**
**978-981** A357 Set of 4 9.00 9.00

Loukis Akritas (1909-65), Writer — A358

**2001, Oct. 25 Litho.** *Perf. 13½x13*
**982** A358 20c multi 2.50 1.25

Christmas — A359

Holy Monastery of Macheras, 800th anniv.: 13c, Icon of Madonna. 25c, Monastery building. 30c, Crucifix.

**2001, Oct. 25**
**983-985** A359 Set of 3 5.00 5.00

Cats — A360

No. 986, 20c: a, Red brown panel. b, Green panel.
No. 987, 25c: a, Dark brown panel. b, Orange brown panel.

**2002, Mar. 21 Litho.** *Perf. 13x13½*
**Horiz. Pairs, #a-b**
**986-987** A360 Set of 2 7.00 7.00

Europa — A361

Designs: 20c, Equestrian act. 30c, Tightrope walker.

**2002, May 9** *Perf. 13½x13*
**988-989** A361 Set of 2 *4.00 2.00*
*a.* Booklet pane, 4 each #988-989 *17.00* —
Booklet, #989a *19.00*

Medicinal Plants A362

Designs: 13c, Myrtus communis. 20c, Lavandula stoechas. 25c, Capparis spinosa. 30c, Ocimum basilicum.

**2002, June 13** *Perf. 13x13½*
**990-993** A362 Set of 4 7.00 7.00

Mother Teresa (1910-97) — A363

**2002, Sept. 12 Litho.** *Perf. 13½x13*
**994** A363 40c multi 4.00 4.00

Intl. Teachers' Day — A364

No. 995: a, 13c, Blackboard and teachers. b, 30c, Computer and teachers.

**2002, Sept. 12** *Perf. 13x13½*
**995** A364 Horiz. pair, #a-b 3.75 3.75

Cyprus-Europhilex 02 Philatelic Exhibition — A365

No. 996: a, Seal, 490-470 B.C. (red brown background). b, Silver coin of Timoharis, 5th-4th cent B.C. (blue background) c, Silver coin of Stasioikos, 449 B.C. (yellow background).
No. 997: a, Clay oil lamp, 2nd cent. A.D. (olive green background). b, Clay statue of Europa on a bull, 7th-6th cent. B.C. (yellow background). c, Clay oil lamp, 1st cent. B.C. (lilac background)
No. 998: a, 15th cent. map of eastern Crete and western Cyprus, and statue of Aphrodite, 1st cent. B.C. b, Map of eastern Cyprus, and Abduction of Europe, by Francesco di Giorgio.

**2002, Sept. 22**
**996** Horiz. strip of 3 4.50 4.50
*a.-c.* A365 20c Any single 1.50 1.50
**997** Horiz. strip of 3 6.75 6.75
*a.-c.* A365 30c Any single 2.25 2.25

**Souvenir Sheet**

**998** Sheet of 2, #a-b 9.50 9.50
*a.-b.* A365 50c Any single 3.75 3.75

Christmas A366

Wall painting in Church of Metamorphosis Sotiros, Palechori: 13c, Nativity, detail. 25c, Angels, detail. 30c, Entire painting (37x37mm).

***Perf. 13x13½, 13¾ (30c)***

**2002, Nov. 21**
**999-1001** A366 Set of 3 5.75 5.75

Antique Automobiles A367

No. 1002: a, 20c, 1946 Triumph Roadster 1800. b, 25c, 1917 Ford Model T. c, 30c, 1932 Baby Ford.

**2003, Mar. 20 Litho.** *Perf. 13x13½*
**1002** A367 Vert. strip of 3, #a-c 6.50 6.50

Europa — A368

**2003, May 8** *Perf. 13½x13*
**Color of Triangles**

**1003** A368 20c yellow *1.00 .65*
*a.* Perf. 13½x13¾ on 3 sides *1.75 1.10*
**1004** A368 30c red *1.60 1.00*
*a.* Perf. 13½x13¾ on 3 sides *3.00 1.60*
*b.* Booklet pane, 4 each #1003a-1004a *20.00* —
Complete booklet, #1004b *24.00*

European Ministers of Education, 7th Conference — A369

**2003, June 12 Litho.** *Perf. 13½x13*
**1005** A369 30c multi 2.25 2.25

Worldwide Fund for Nature (WWF) — A370

Mediterranean horseshoe bat: a, In flight. b, Close-up. c, Hanging from rock. d, With open mouth.

**2003, June 12** *Perf. 13x13½*
**1006** A370 25c Block of 4, #a-b 7.00 7.00



Birds of Prey — A371

No. 1007, 20c: a, Eleonora's falcon. b, Eleonora's falcons in flight.
No. 1008, 25c: a, Head of Imperial eagle. b, Imperial eagles in flight.
No. 1009, 30c: a, Owl on branch. b, Owl in flight, eggs.

**2003, Sept. 25 Litho. *Perf. 14***
**Horiz. pairs, #a-b**

**1007-1009** A371 Set of 3 9.50 9.50

Famous Men A372

Designs: No. 1010, 5c, Constantinos Spyridakis (1903-76), Education minister. No. 1011, 5c, Tefkros Anthias (1903-68), poet (23x31mm).

***Perf. 13x13¼, 13¼x13***
**2003, Nov. 13**

**1010-1011** A372 Set of 2 1.25 1.25

Christmas A373

Details of Nativity icon from church in Kourdali: 13c, Angels. 30c, Three Magi on horses. 40c, Entire icon (37x60mm).

***Perf. 13¾x13¼, 13¾x14 (40c)***
**2003, Nov. 13**

**1012-1014** A373 Set of 3 5.50 5.50

FIFA (Fédération Internationale de Football Association), Cent. — A374

***Perf. 13¼x13¾***
**2004, Mar. 11 Litho.**

**1015** A374 30c multi 2.25 2.25

UEFA (European Soccer Union), 50th Anniv. — A375

**2004, Mar. 11 *Perf. 13¼x13***

**1016** A375 30c multi 2.25 2.25

Yiannos Kranidiotis (1947-99), Politician A376

**2004, May 1 *Perf. 13¼x13½***

**1017** A376 20c multi 1.10 1.10

Admission to European Union — A377

**2004, May 1 *Perf. 14¼x14***

**1018** A377 30c multi 2.25 2.25

Europa A378

Cliff and: 20c, Amphitheater, ship. 30c, Family at seashore, sculpture

**2004, May 1 *Perf. 13¾x13¼***

**1019** A378 20c multi 1.25 .60
*a.* Perf. 13¾ on 3 sides 1.50 .70
**1020** A378 30c multi 1.75 .90
*a.* Perf. 13¾ on 3 sides 2.00 1.10
*b.* Booklet pane, 4 each #1019a, 1020a 16.00 —
Complete booklet, #1020b 18.00

2004 Summer Olympics, Athens — A379

Designs: 13c, Equestrian. 20c, Runners. 30c, Swimmers. 40c, Athletes, man in robe.

**2004, June 10 Litho. *Perf. 13¼x13***

**1021-1024** A379 Set of 4 5.75 5.75

Mammals — A380

No. 1025, 20c — Tursiops truncatus: a, Blue background. b, White background.
No. 1026, 30c — Vulpes vulpes indutus: a, Green background. b, White background.
No. 1027, 40c, Lepus europaeus cyprium: a, Orange brown background. b, White background.

**2004, Sept. 9 Litho. *Perf. 13¾x13½***
**Horiz. Pairs, #a-b**

**1025-1027** A380 Set of 3 13.00 13.00

Georgios Philippou Pierides (1904-99), Writer — A381

Emilios Chourmouzios (1904-73), Writer — A382

**2004, Nov. 11 *Perf. 13¼x13***

**1028** A381 5c multi .65 .65
**1029** A382 5c multi .65 .65

Christmas A383

Details from icon depicting the birth of Christ, Monastery of Chrysoroyiatissa: 13c, Angels. 30c, Magi on horseback. 40c, Annunciation, vert. (37x60mm).
£1, Adoration of the Shepherds.

***Perf. 13¾x13¼, 13¾x14 (40c)***
**2004, Nov. 11**

**1030-1032** A383 Set of 3 6.00 6.00

**Souvenir Sheet**
***Perf. 13¾ on 3 Sides***

**1033** A383 £1 multi 6.75 6.75

No. 1033 contains one 37x38mm stamp.

Carolina Pelendritou, Swimming Gold Medalist at 2004 Paralympics A384

**2005, Mar. 3 Litho. *Perf. 13¼x13¾***

**1034** A384 20c multi 1.50 1.50

Rotary International, Cent. — A385

**2005, Mar. 3**

**1035** A385 40c multi 2.50 2.50

Natl. Organization of Cypriot Struggle (EOKA), 50th Anniv. — A386

**2005, Mar. 3**

**1036** A386 50c multi 3.00 3.00

Europa — A387

Table with food and: 20c, Purple grapes, sailboat. 30c, Green grapes, steamship.

**2005, May 5 *Perf. 13½x13***
**White Frame All Around**

**1037** A387 20c multi .90 .90
**1038** A387 30c multi 1.40 1.40

**Booklet Stamps**
**White Frame on 3 Sides**
***Perf. 13½ on 3 Sides***

**1039** A387 20c multi 1.25 .75
**1040** A387 30c multi 1.75 1.25
*a.* Horiz. pair, #1039-1040 3.25 2.25
*b.* Booklet pane, 4 #1040a 13.50 —
Complete booklet, #1040b 15.00
*Nos. 1037-1040 (4)* 5.30 4.30

Dogs — A388

Designs: 13c, German shepherd. 20c, Hungarian vizsla. 30c, Labrador retriever. 40c, Dalmatian.

**2005, June 16 Litho. *Perf. 13¼***

**1041-1044** A388 Set of 4 8.00 8.00
*1044a* Booklet pane, #1041-1044 8.50 —
Complete booklet, #1044a 8.50

Christmas A389

Icons: 13c, Annunciation to the Shepherds. 30c, Adoration of the Magi. 40c, Madonna and Child, vert. (38x60mm).

***Perf. 13¼, 13¾x14 (40c)***
**2005, Nov. 10 Litho.**

**1045-1047** A389 Set of 3 4.25 4.25

**Souvenir Sheet**

Europa Stamps, 50th Anniv. — A390

No. 1048: a, Cyprus #246. b, Cyprus #202. c, Cyprus #220. d, Cyprus #231.

**2006, Feb. 23 Litho. *Perf. 13¾***

**1048** A390 30c Sheet of 4, #a-d 7.00 7.00

Postal Museum, 25th Anniv. A391

**2006, Mar. 30 *Perf. 13¾x13¼***

**1049** A391 25c multi 1.75 1.75

Rembrandt (1606-69), Painter A392

**2006, Mar. 30**

**1050** A392 40c multi 3.00 3.00

2006 World Cup Soccer Championships, Germany A393

**2006, Mar. 30** ***Perf. 13¼x13¾***
**1051** A393 50c multi 3.25 3.25

Souvenir Sheet

Folk Dances — A394

No. 1052 — Folk dancers from: a, Cyprus. b, India.

**2006, Apr. 12** ***Perf. 13x13½***
**1052** A394 40c Sheet of 2, #a-b 5.50 5.50

See India No. 2151.

Europa — A395

**2006, May 4** ***Perf. 13½x13***
**1053** A395 30c grn & multi 1.60 1.60
*a.* Perf. 13½x13¾ on 3 sides 1.60 1.60
**1054** A395 40c red & multi 2.10 2.10
*a.* Perf. 13½x13¾ on 3 sides 2.10 2.10
*b.* Booklet pane, 4 each #1053a-1054a 15.50 —
Complete booklet, #1054b 15.50

Organ Transplantation — A396

**2006, June 15** **Litho.** ***Perf. 13¼***
**1055** A396 13c multi .90 .90

Fruit — A397

Designs: 20c, Elaeagnus angustifolia. 25c, Mespilus germanica, horiz. 60c, Opuntia ficus barbarica.

***Perf. 13¼x13½, 13½x13¼***
**2006, June 15**
**1056-1058** A397 Set of 3 6.75 6.75

Fire Trucks A398

Designs: 13c, Bedford water carrier. 20c, Hino pump water tender. 50c, Bedford ladder truck.

**2006, Sept. 14** ***Perf. 13¾x13¼***
**1059-1061** A398 Set of 3 6.25 6.25

Nicos Nicolaides (1884-1956), Writer — A399

**2006, Nov. 16** **Litho.** ***Perf. 13½x13***
**1062** A399 5c multi .60 .60

Christmas — A400

Items from Agiou Eleftheriou Church: 13c, Carved wood iconostasis. 30c, Cross. 40c, Bas-relief of cross, spear and sponge.

**2006, Nov. 16** ***Perf. 13¼x13¾***
**1063-1065** A400 Set of 3 4.75 4.75

St. Xenon, the Postman — A401

**Litho. & Embossed**
**2007, Feb. 8** ***Imperf.***
**1066** A401 £1 multi 8.00 8.00

Echinoderms — A402

No. 1067: a, Antedon mediterranea. b, Centrostephanus longispinus. c, Astropecten jonstoni. d, Ophioderma longicadum.

**2007, Feb. 8** **Litho.** ***Perf. 13¾x13¼***
**1067** Horiz. strip of 4 6.50 6.50
*a.-d.* A402 25c Any single 1.60 1.60

Motorcycles A403

Designs: 13c, 1972 Triumph Daytona. 20c, 1941 Matchless. 40c, 1940 BSA. 60c, 1939 Ariel Red Hunter.

**2007, Mar. 15**
**1068-1071** A403 Set of 4 7.25 7.25

Treaty of Rome, 50th Anniv. — A404

**2007, May 3** ***Perf. 13¼x13¾***
**1072** A404 30c multi 1.60 1.60

Europa — A405

Scouting emblem in gold, knot in: 30c, Light blue. 40c, Buff.

**Litho. & Embossed With Foil Application**
**2007, May 3**
**1073-1074** A405 Set of 2 3.25 3.25
*1074a* Booklet pane, 4 each #1073-1074, perf. on 3 sides 13.00 —
Complete booklet, #1074a 13.00

Scouting, cent.

Social Insurance, 50th Anniv. — A406

No. 1075: a, Text in Greek. b, Text in English.

**2007, June 14** **Litho.** ***Perf. 13x13¼***
**1075** A406 40c Horiz. pair, #a-b 4.00 4.00

Miniature Sheet

Cyprus Throughout the Ages — A407

No. 1076: a, Skeleton of pygmy hippopotamus, 10,000 B.C. b, Stone vessel, 7000 B.C. c, Choirokoitia Settlement, 7000 B.C. d, Female terracotta figurine, 3000 B.C. e, Terracotta vessel, 2000 B.C. f, Greek inscriptions on bronze skewer, 1000 B.C. g, Bird-shaped vessel, 800 B.C. h, Map of ancient kingdoms of Cyprus.

**2007, Oct. 2** ***Perf. 13¾***
**1076** A407 25c Sheet of 8, #a-h 12.00 12.00

See Nos. 1101, 1116, 1138.

Neoclassical Buildings A408

Designs: 13c, Limassol District Administration Building. 15c, National Bank of Greece Building, Nicosia. 20c, Archaeological Research Unit Building, Nicosia. 30c, National Art Gallery, Nicosia. 40c, Paphos Municipal Library. 50c, A. G. Leventis Foundation Office Building, Nicosia. £1, Limassol Municipal Library. £3, Phaneromeni Gymnasium, Nicosia.

**2007, Oct. 2** ***Perf. 13¾x13½***
**1077** A408 13c multi .65 .65
**1078** A408 15c multi .75 .75
**1079** A408 20c multi 1.00 1.00
**1080** A408 30c multi 1.50 1.50
**1081** A408 40c multi 2.00 2.00
**1082** A408 50c multi 2.40 2.40
**1083** A408 £1 multi 5.00 5.00
**1084** A408 £3 multi 14.50 14.50
*Nos. 1077-1084 (8)* 27.80 27.80

Christmas — A409

Murals from Chapel of St. Themonianus, Lysi: 13c, Virgin Mary. 30c, Archangel Gabriel. 40c, Christ Pantocrator (35x45mm).

***Perf. 14x13¾, 13¾ (40c)***
**2007, Nov. 15**
**1085-1087** A409 Set of 3 4.75 4.75

**100 Cents = 1 Euro**
Souvenir Sheet

Introduction of Euro Currency — A410

No. 1088: a, Statue of Aphrodite, map of Cyprus. b, Sleeping Lady statue.

**2008, Jan. 1** **Litho.** ***Perf. 13¾***
**1088** A410 €1 Sheet of 2, #a-b 5.50 5.50

See Malta No. 1329.

Anemone Flowers — A411

Variously colored Anemone coronaria flowers with background colors of: 26c, Blue. 34c, Red. 51c, Green. 68c, Yellow orange.

**2008, Mar. 6** ***Perf. 13¼x13¾***
**1089-1092** A411 Set of 4 6.25 6.25

Europa — A412

Designs: 51c, Closed and open envelopes. 68c, Envelopes and mail boxes.

**2008, May 2 Litho.** ***Perf. 13¼x13¾***
**1093-1094** A412 Set of 2 3.75 3.75
*1094a* Booklet pane, 4 each #1093-1094, perf. 13¼x13¾ on 3 sides 15.00 —
Complete booklet, #1094a 15.00

Souvenir Sheet

Fourth Intl. Congress of Cypriot Studies, Nicosia — A413

**2008, May 2** ***Perf. 13¾ on 3 Sides***
**1095** A413 85c multi 3.50 3.50

12th Francophone Summit, Quebec — A414

**2008, June 5 Litho.** ***Perf. 13¾***
**1096** A414 85c multi 3.25 3.25

2008 Summer Olympics, Beijing A415

Designs: 22c, Sailboarding. 34c, High jump. 43c, Tennis. 51c, Shooting.

**2008, June 5** ***Perf. 13x13¼***
**1097-1100** A415 Set of 4 4.75 4.75

**Cyprus Throughout the Years Type of 2007**

Miniature Sheet

No. 1101: a, Coin from Archaic period, 750 B.C.-480 B.C. b, Ship from Archaic period. c, Bust of Kimon the Athenian and ship, Classical period, 480 B.C.-310 B.C. d, Tomb of the Kings, Hellenistic period, 310 B.C.-30 B.C. e, Coin from Hellenistic period. f, Painting of St. Paul from Roman period, 30 B.C.-A.D. 324. g, Bust of Septimus Severus from Roman period. h, Granting of church privileges from Early Byzantine period, 324-841.

**2008, Oct. 2 Litho.** ***Perf. 13¾***
**1101** A407 43c Sheet of 8, #a-h 12.00 12.00

Christmas — A416

Icons from church, Pelendri: 22c, Archangel Gabriel. 51c, Archangel Michael. 68c, Madonna and Child.

**2008, Nov. 13** ***Perf. 13¼x13***
**1102-1104** A416 Set of 3 4.75 4.75

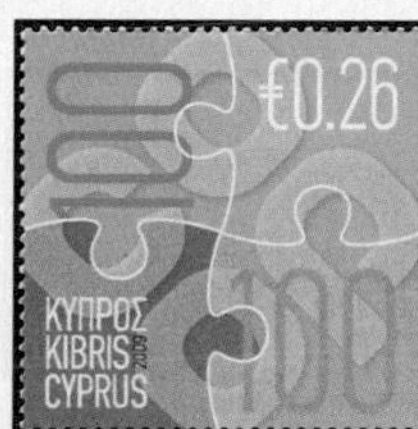
Cooperative Movement, Cent. A417

**2009, Mar. 12 Litho.** ***Perf. 13¾***
**1105** A417 26c multi 1.00 1.00

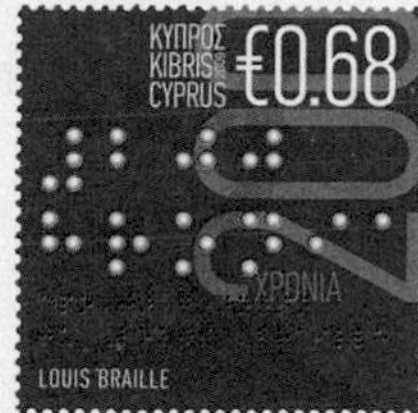
Louis Braille (1809-52), Educator of the Blind A418

**2009, Mar. 12 Litho. & Embossed**
**1106** A418 68c multi 2.50 2.50

Introduction of the Euro, 10th Anniv. A419

Reverse of Cyprus: 51c, Cent coin. 68c, 2-euro coin.

**2009, Mar. 12 Litho.**
**1107-1108** A419 Set of 2 4.75 4.75

Intl. Year of Planet Earth — A420

No. 1109: a, Western Hemisphere. b, Eastern Hemisphere.

**2009, May 4 Litho.** ***Perf. 13x13¼***
**1109** A420 51c Horiz. pair, #a-b 3.75 3.75

Europa — A421

Constellations: 51c, Cassiopeia. 68c, Andromeda.

**2009, May 4** ***Perf. 13¼x13¾***
**1110-1111** A421 Set of 2 3.75 3.75
*1111a* Booklet pane of 8, 4 each #1110-1111, perf. 13¼x13¾ on 3 sides 15.00 —
Complete booklet, #1111a 15.00

Intl. Year of Astronomy.

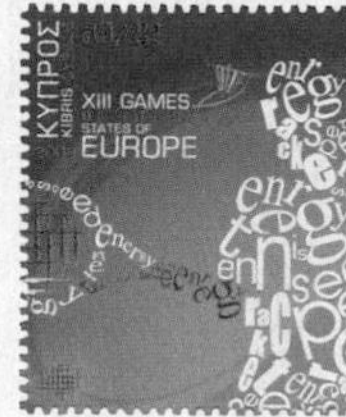
18th Games of the Small States of Europe, Cyprus — A422

Designs: 22c, Tennis. 34c, Sailing. 43c, Cycling.

**2009, June 1 Litho.** ***Perf. 13¼x13¾***
**1112-1114** A422 Set of 3 3.50 3.50

Souvenir Sheet

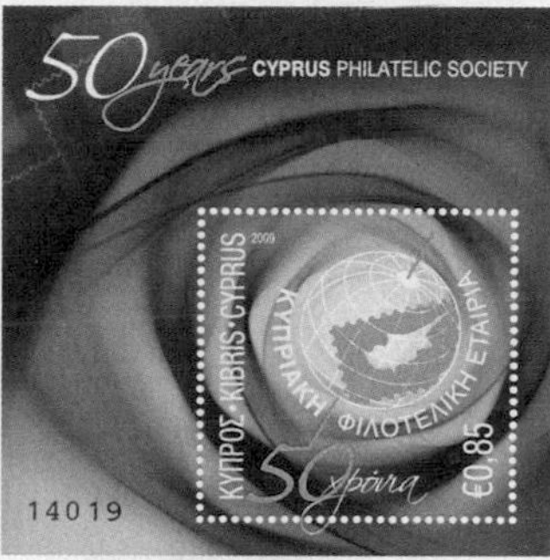
Cyprus Philatelic Society, 50th Anniv. — A423

**Litho. & Embossed With Foil Application**

**2009, June 1** ***Perf. 13¾***
**1115** A423 85c multi 3.25 3.25

**Cyprus Throughout the Years Type of 2007**

Miniature Sheet

No. 1116: a, St. Paraskevi Church, 9th cent. b, Monastery of St. John Chrysostom, 1090-1100. c, Lusignan coat of arms, 1192-1489. d, Chronicle of Leontios Machairas, 15th cent. e, Queen Caterina Cornaro cedes Cyprus to Venice, 1489. f, Venetian Walls, Nicosia, 1567-70. g, Ottoman siege of Nicosia, 1570. h, Larnaca Aqueduct, 18th cent.

**2009, Sept. 10 Litho.** ***Perf. 13¾***
**1116** A407 43c Sheet of 8, #a-h 14.00 14.00

Domesticated Birds — A424

Designs: 22c, Pigeon. 34c, Turkey. 43c, Rooster. 51c, Duck.

**2009, Sept. 10** ***Perf. 13¾x13¼***
**1117-1120** A424 Set of 4 5.75 5.75

European Court of Human Rights, 50th Anniv. A425

**2009, Nov. 12 Litho.** ***Perf. 13x13¼***
**1121** A425 51c multi 2.00 2.00

A426

Christmas A427

***Perf. 13¼x13¾***

**2009, Nov. 12 Litho.**
**1122** A426 22c shown .75 .75

**Litho. & Embossed With Foil Application**

***Perf. 13¾***

**1123** A427 51c shown 1.75 1.75
**1124** A427 68c Solid silver star 2.75 2.75
*Nos. 1122-1124 (3)* 5.25 5.25

Republic of Cyprus, 50th Anniv. A428

Denomination color: 68c, Bister. 85c, Blue.

**Litho. & Embossed With Foil Application**

**2010, Jan. 27** ***Perf. 13¾x13¼***
**1125-1126** A428 Set of 2 5.25 5.25

Expo 2010, Shanghai A429

**2010, Mar. 17 Litho.** ***Perf. 13x13¼***
**1127** A429 51c multi 1.60 1.60

2010 World Cup Soccer Championships, South Africa — A430

**2010, Mar. 17** ***Perf. 13¾***
**1128** A430 €1.71 multi 5.75 5.75

Barnyard Animals A431

Designs: 22c, Pig. 26c, Sheep. 34c, Goat. 43c, Cow. €1.71, Rabbit.

**2010, Mar. 17** ***Perf. 13¾x13¼***
**1129-1133** A431 Set of 5 10.00 10.00

Europa — A432

No. 1134 — Stack of books and: a, Sun, flowers, tree, snails, bees. b, Tree, bees.

**2010, May 5** ***Perf. 13¼x13¾***
**1134** A432 51c Horiz. pair, #a-b 3.25 3.25
*c.* Booklet pane of 8, 4 each #1134a-1134b, perf. 13¼x13¾ on 3 sides 13.00 —
Complete booklet, #1134c 13.00

Visit of Pope Benedict XVI — A433

**2010, June 4** ***Perf. 13¾x14¼***
**1135** A433 51c multi 1.60 1.60

Cyprus Railway — A434

No. 1136 — Locomotive with denomination in: a, Black. b, White.
85c, Train, map of stations.

**2010, June 4** ***Perf. 13¾x13¼***
**1136** A434 43c Pair, #a-b 2.75 2.75

**Souvenir Sheet**

**1137** A434 85c multi 3.00 3.00

**Cyprus Through the Ages Type of 2007**

Miniature Sheet

No. 1138: a, Treaties of Sevres, 1920, and Lausanne, 1923. b, Burnt Government House, 1931. c, Imprisoned graves, 1955-59. d, Statue of Gregoris Afxentiou (1928-57), anti-colonialist leader. e, Presidential Palace, 1960. f, Black Summer 1974, painting by Telemachos Kanthos. g, Pres. Tassos Papadopoulos signing Treaty of Accession to the European Union, 2004. h, Flag of Cyprus.

**2010, Oct. 1** **Litho.** ***Perf. 13¾***
**1138** A407 43c Sheet of 8, #a-h 11.00 11.00

Souvenir Sheet

Viticulture — A435

No. 1139: a, Wine barrels, wine glass. b, Grapes, pitcher.

***Perf. 14 on 3 Sides***

**2010, Nov. 10** **Litho.**
**1139** A435 51c Sheet of 2, #a-b 3.25 3.25

See Romania Nos. 5216-5217.

Nativity — A436

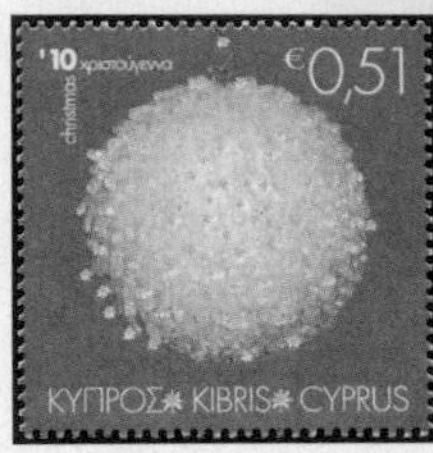
Christmas Ornament A437

***Perf. 13¼x13¾***

**2010, Nov. 10** **Litho.**
**1140** A436 22c shown .65 .65

**Litho. & Embossed With Foil Application**

***Perf. 13¾***

**1141** A437 51c shown 1.50 1.50
**1142** A437 68c Ornament, diff. 2.10 2.10
*Nos. 1140-1142 (3)* 3.90 3.90

Anorthosis Ammochostos Soccer Team, Cent. — A438

**2011, Jan. 28** **Litho.** ***Perf. 13¾***
**1143** A438 34c multi .95 .95

Composers — A439

No. 1144: a, Johann Sebastian Bach (1685-1750). b, Wolfgang Amadeus Mozart (1756-91). c, Ludwig van Beethoven (1770-1827).

**2011, Jan. 28** ***Perf. 13¾x14¼***
**1144** Horiz. strip of 3 4.25 4.25
*a.-c.* A439 51c Any single 1.40 1.40

Lace A440

Lace with: 26c, Floral pattern. 43c, Diamonds and squares pattern.

**2011, Mar. 23** ***Perf. 13¾x14***
**1145-1146** A440 Set of 2 2.00 2.00

Rosa Damascena A441

**2011, Mar. 23** ***Perf. 13¾***
**1147** A441 34c shown 1.00 1.00

**Souvenir Sheet**

**1148** A441 85c Roses, diff. 2.50 2.50

Nos. 1147-1148 are impregnated with a rose scent.

Europa A442

**2011, May 4** ***Perf. 14***
**1149** A442 51c Blue forest 1.50 1.50
*a.* Perf. 13x13½ on 3 sides 1.50
**1150** A442 68c Green forest 2.00 2.00
*a.* Perf. 13x13½ on 3 sides 2.00 2.00
*b.* Booklet pane of 8, 4 each #1149a-1150a 14.00 —
Complete booklet, #1150b 14.00

Intl. Year of Forests.

Lighthouses A443

Map and: 34c, Paphos Lighthouse. 43c, Cape Greco Lighthouse.
€1.71 Cape Kiti Lighthouse.

**2011, May 4** ***Perf. 14***
**1151-1152** A443 Set of 2 3.00 3.00

**Souvenir Sheet**

***Perf. 13½x13¼***

**1153** A443 €1.71 multi 6.00 6.00

**Booklet Stamp Self-Adhesive**

***Die Cut Perf. 13¼x13***

**1153A** A443 43c multi (RA28Ab) 1.50 1.50

No. 1153 contains one 27x35mm stamp.

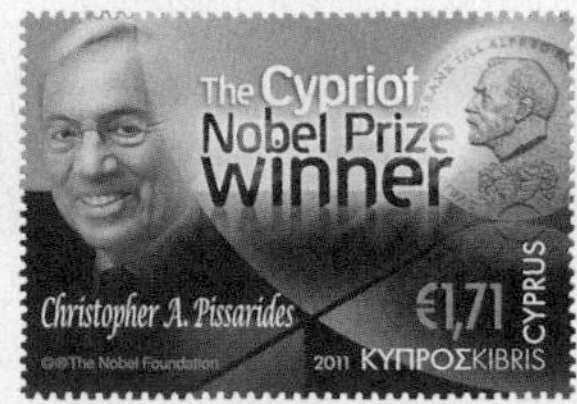
Christopher A. Pissarides, 2010 Nobel Laureate in Economics — A444

**2011, June 8** ***Perf. 14x14¼***
**1154** A444 €1.71 multi 5.00 5.00

Tall Ships A445

Designs: 22c, Galleon. 43c, Caravel. 85c, Brig.

**2011, June 8** ***Perf. 13¾***
**1155-1157** A445 Set of 3 4.25 4.25

The Hare and the Tortoise — A446

No. 1158: a, Hare. b, Tortoise. c, Tortoise passing sleeping hare, horiz. d, Hare running. e, Tortoise crossing finish line.

***Die Cut Perf. 11½x12, 12x11½***

**2011, Oct. 5** **Litho.**

**Self-Adhesive**

**1158** A446 34c Booklet pane of 5, #a-e 4.75 4.75

Nativity — A447

Christmas Ornament A448

***Perf. 13¼x13¾***

**2011, Nov. 11** **Litho.**
**1159** A447 22c shown .60 .60

**Litho. & Embossed With Foil Application**

***Perf. 13¾***

**1160** A448 51c shown 1.40 1.40
**1161** A448 68c Ornament, diff. 1.90 1.90
*Nos. 1159-1161 (3)* 3.90 3.90

Horses A449

Various horses: 26c, 34c, 51c, 85c.

**2012, Jan. 31** **Litho.** ***Perf. 13¾x13¼***
**1162-1165** A449 Set of 4 6.50 6.50

2012 Summer Olympics, London A450

Designs: 22c, Men's gymnastics. 26c, Men's tennis. 34c, Men's high jump. 43c, Shooting.

**Litho. With Foil Application**

**2012, Mar. 21** ***Perf. 14***
**1166-1169** A450 Set of 4 4.00 4.00

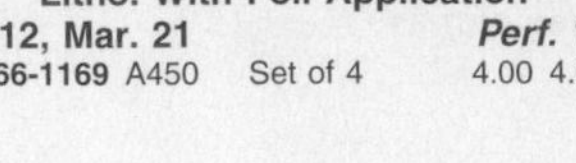

Souvenir Sheet

Soccer — A451

**2012, Mar. 21** **Litho.** ***Perf.***
**1170** A451 €1.71 multi 5.50 5.50

Jasminum Grandiflorum — A452

**2012, May 2** ***Perf. 13¾***
**1171** A452 34c shown 1.10 1.10

**Souvenir Sheet**

**1172** A452 85c Flowers, diff. 2.60 2.60

Nos. 1171-1172 are impregnated with a jaasmine scent.

Europa A453

Various Cyprus tourist attractions and silhouette of: 51c, Family. 68c, Man and woman with bicycles.

**2012, May 2** ***Perf. 13¾x13½***
**1173-1174** A453 Set of 2 3.25 3.25
*1174a* Booklet pane of 8, 4 each #1173-1174, perf. 13¾x13½ on 3 sides 13.00 —
Complete booklet, #1174a 13.00

Cyprus Presidency of European Union Council A454

**Litho. With Foil Application**

**2012, July 1** ***Perf. 13¾***
**1175** A454 51c multi 1.75 1.75

**Souvenir Sheet**

**1176** A454 €10 multi 28.00 28.00

The Cricket and the Ant — A455

No. 1177: a, Cricket with fiddle, sun. b, Ant with seeds. c, Ant carrying seeds. d, Cricket fiddling under tree. e, Cricket outside in winter, ant at door.

**2012, Oct. 3** ***Die Cut Perf. 11¼x12***

**Self-Adhesive**

**1177** A455 34c Booklet pane of 5, #a-e 5.25 5.25

Pavlos Kontides, Silver Medalist in Sailing at 2012 Summer Olympics A456

**Litho. With Foil Application**

**2012, Nov. 14** ***Perf. 14***
**1178** A456 34c multi .90 .90

Christmas — A457

Icons from: 22c, Madonna and Child, Christ Antiphonitis Church. 51c, Madonna and Child, Panayia Church, Lysi. 68c, Madonna and Child Enthroned Between St. George and St. Nicholas, St. George's Church, Vatyli.

***Perf. 13¼x13¾***

**2012, Nov. 12** **Litho.**
**1179** A457 22c multi .60 .60
**1180** A457 51c multi 1.40 1.40

**Size: 65x65mm**

***Imperf***

**1181** A457 68c multi 1.75 1.75

Admission of Cyprus Red Cross to International Red Cross, 1st Anniv. — A458

**2013, Jan. 30** ***Perf. 14¼x13¾***
**1182** A458 22c multi .80 .80

Cyprus Scouts Association, Cent. A459

**2013, Jan. 30** ***Perf. 13¾***
**1183** A459 43c multi 1.40 1.40

Archbishop Makarios (1913-77), President of Cyprus A460

**2013, Jan. 30** ***Perf. 14***
**1184** A460 85c multi 2.60 2.60

Easter — A461

Icons depicting: 26c, Christ's entry into Jerusalem. 34c, Crucifixion. €1.71, Resurrection (27x40mm).

**2013, Apr. 3** ***Perf. 14x14¼***
**1185-1187** A461 Set of 3 6.50 6.50

Origanum Dubium A462

**2013, May 2** ***Perf. 13¾***
**1188** A462 22c shown .75 .75

**Souvenir Sheet**

**1189** A462 85c Flowers, diff. 2.75 2.75

Nos. 1188-1189 are impregnated with an oregano scent.

Europa A463

Mailbox and postal vehicles: 34c, Automobile, van and airplane. 51c, Automobile.

**2013, May 2** ***Perf. 14***
**1190-1191** A463 Set of 2 2.50 2.50
*1191a* Booklet pane of 8, 4 each #1190-1191, perf. 14 on 3 sides 10.00 —
Complete booklet, #1191a 10.00

Marine Life — A464

Designs: 34c, Seahorse. 43c, Sea anemone. €1.71, Sea fan coral.

**2013, June 5** ***Perf. 13¾***
**1192-1194** A464 Set of 3 7.50 7.50

For surcharge, see No. 1225.

Cypriot Folk Tale "Spanos and the Forty Dragons" — A465

No. 1195: a, Spanos in cloud near dragon. b, Boar chasing Spanos up a tree, vert. c, Spanos, river, woman holding flowers. d, Spanos sitting near dragon. e, Spanos pouring water on dragon.

***Die Cut Perf. 13x13½, 13½x13***

**2013, Nov. 13** **Litho.**

**Self-Adhesive**

**1195** A465 34c Booklet pane of 5, #a-e 5.75 5.75

Christmas A466

Winning art in children's stamp design contest: 22c, Santa Claus and Christmas tree. 34c, Snowman, Christmas trees and houses. 85c, Christmas tree and gifts, vert.

***Perf. 14¼x14, 14x14¼***

**2013, Nov. 13** **Litho.**
**1196-1198** A466 Set of 3 4.75 4.75

Olive Production A467

Designs: 34c, Olive tree and grove.
No. 1200: a, Olives. b, Olives, container of olive oil.

**2014, Jan. 30** **Litho.** ***Perf. 14***
**1199** A467 34c multi 1.00 1.00
**1200** A467 51c Horiz. pair, #a-b 3.00 3.00

Four Seasons A468

Designs: 22c, Child under umbrella (winter). 43c, Girl wearing butterfly costume standing in flowers (spring). 85c, Girl with balloons, fish and dolphins (summer). €1.71, Child holding fallen leaf in front of face (autumn).

**2014, Mar. 12** **Litho.** ***Perf. 13¾***
**1201-1204** A468 Set of 4 9.00 9.00

For surcharges, see Nos. 1212-1214.

Europa A469

Musicians with instruments: 34c, Cyprus flute. 51c, Lute.

**2014, May 2** **Litho.** ***Perf. 14***
**1205-1206** A469 Set of 2 2.40 2.40
*1206a* Booklet pane of 8, 4 each #1205-1206, perf. 14 on 3 sides 9.75 —
Complete booklet, #1206a 9.75

Famous Men A470

Designs: 41c, El Greco (1541-1614), painter. 50c, Michelangelo (1475-1564), painter and sculptor. 64c, Galileo Galilei (1564-1642), astronomer. 75c, Henri de Toulouse-Lautrec (1864-1901), painter.

**2014, June 30** **Litho.** ***Perf. 14***
**1207-1210** A470 Set of 4 6.25 6.25

Euromed Postal Emblem and Mediterranean Sea — A471

**2014, July 9** **Litho.** ***Perf. 14***
**1211** A471 60c multi 1.60 1.60

Nos. 1201, 1202 and 1204 Surcharged

**Methods and Perfs. As Before**

**2014, Aug. 1**

| | | | | |
|---|---|---|---|---|
| **1212** | A468 | 4c on 22c #1201 | .25 | .25 |
| **1213** | A468 | €1 on 43c #1202 | 2.75 | 2.75 |
| **1214** | A468 | €1.88 on €1.71 #1204 | 5.00 | 5.00 |
| | | *Nos. 1212-1214 (3)* | 8.00 | 8.00 |

Famous People — A472

No. 1215: a, Theodoulos Kallinikos (1904-2004), cantor and musicologist. b, Stylianos Hourmouzios (1850-1937), cantor and journalist.
No. 1216: a, Sozos Tombolis (1914-2002), cantor and music professor. b, Achilleas Lymbourides (1917-2008), composer.
No. 1217: a, Telemachos Kanthos (1910-93), painter. b, Loukia Nicolaidou (1909-94), painter.
No. 1218: a, George Pol Georgiou (1901-72), painter. b, Michael Kashalos (1885-1974), painter.
No. 1219: a, Kypros Chrysanthis (1915-98), writer. b, Antis Pernaris (1903-80), writer.
No. 1220: a, Glafkos Alithersis (1897-1965), writer. b, Costas Montis (1914-2004), writer.

**2014, Oct. 10 Litho. *Perf. 14***

| | | | | |
|---|---|---|---|---|
| **1215** | A472 | Horiz. pair | .25 | .25 |
| *a.-b.* | | 4c Either single | .25 | .25 |
| **1216** | A472 | Horiz. pair | 1.75 | 1.75 |
| *a.-b.* | | 34c Either single | .85 | .85 |
| **1217** | A472 | Horiz. pair | 2.00 | 2.00 |
| *a.-b.* | | 41c Either single | 1.00 | 1.00 |
| **1218** | A472 | Horiz. pair | 2.50 | 2.50 |
| *a.-b.* | | 50c Either single | 1.25 | 1.25 |
| **1219** | A472 | Horiz. pair | 3.25 | 3.25 |
| *a.-b.* | | 64c Either single | 1.60 | 1.60 |
| **1220** | A472 | Horiz. pair | 4.25 | 4.25 |
| *a.-b.* | | 85c Either single | 2.10 | 2.10 |
| | | *Nos. 1215-1220 (6)* | 14.00 | 14.00 |

See Nos. 1226-1231.

Cypriot Folk Tale "The Prince of Venice" — A473

No. 1221: a, Prince carried by angel. b, Angel carrying sword, vert. c, Woman with veil, vert. d, Angel and woman, vert. e, Ship at sea.

***Die Cut Perf. 13½***

**2014, Nov. 24 Litho.**

**Self-Adhesive**

| | | | | |
|---|---|---|---|---|
| **1221** | A473 | Booklet pane of 5 | 5.00 | |
| *a.-e.* | | 41c Any single | 1.00 | 1.00 |

Christmas — A474

Icons depicting: 41c, Nativity. 64c, Madonna and Child. 75c, Nativity, diff.

**2014, Nov. 24 Litho. *Perf. 14***

| | | | | |
|---|---|---|---|---|
| **1222-1224** | A474 | Set of 3 | 4.50 | 4.50 |

No. 1193 Surcharged

**Method and Perf. As Before**

**2015, Feb. 4**

| | | | | |
|---|---|---|---|---|
| **1225** | A464 | 34c on 43c #1193 | .75 | .75 |

**Famous People Type of 2014**

No. 1226: a, Adamantios Diamantis (1900-94), painter. b, Theodosis Pierides (1908-68), poet.
No. 1227: a, Maria Rousia (1894-1957), writer. b, Melis Nicolaides (1892-1979), writer.
No. 1228: a, Kyriakos Hadjioannou (1909-97), folklorist. b, Polyxeni Loizia (1855-1942), educator.
No. 1229: a, Loizos Philippou (1895-1950), newspaper editor. b, Persefoni Papadopoulou (1888-1948), educator.
No. 1230: a, Georgios Frangoudes (1869-1939), politician. b, Porfyrios Dikaios (1904-71), archaeologist.
No. 1231: a, Nicos Pantelides (1906-84), actor. b, Pavlos Xioutas (1908-91), folklorist.

**2015, Feb. 4 Litho. *Perf. 14***

| | | | | |
|---|---|---|---|---|
| **1226** | A472 | Horiz. pair | .25 | .25 |
| *a.-b.* | | 4c Either single | .25 | .25 |
| **1227** | A472 | Horiz. pair | 2.25 | 2.25 |
| *a.-b.* | | 50c Either single | 1.10 | 1.10 |
| **1228** | A472 | Horiz. pair | 2.80 | 2.80 |
| *a.-b.* | | 60c Either single | 1.40 | 1.40 |
| **1229** | A472 | Horiz. pair | 3.50 | 3.50 |
| *a.-b.* | | 75c Either single | 1.75 | 1.75 |
| **1230** | A472 | Horiz. pair | 4.50 | 4.50 |
| *a.-b.* | | €1 Either single | 2.25 | 2.25 |
| **1231** | A472 | Horiz. pair | 7.00 | 7.00 |
| *a.-b.* | | €1.50 Either single | 3.50 | 3.50 |
| | | *Nos. 1226-1231 (6)* | 20.30 | 20.30 |

Melkonian Orphanage — A475

**2015, Apr. 2 Litho. *Perf. 13¾x14¼***

| | | | | |
|---|---|---|---|---|
| **1232** | A475 | 64c multi | 1.40 | 1.40 |

See Armenia No. 1034.

Preserved Fruit — A476

Designs: 34c, Bitter orange. 41c, Bitter orange, diff. €1.88, Cherry.

**2015, Apr. 2 Litho. *Perf. 13¾***

| | | | | |
|---|---|---|---|---|
| **1233-1235** | A476 | Set of 3 | 5.75 | 5.75 |

Souvenir Sheet

Independence Struggle of National Organization of Cypriot Fighters, 60th Anniv. — A477

**Litho., Sheet Margin Litho. With Foil Application**

**2015, Apr. 2 *Perf. 13¾***

| | | | | |
|---|---|---|---|---|
| **1236** | A477 | €2 multi | 4.50 | 4.50 |

Europa — A478

Children and: 34c, Top. 64c, Marbles.

**2015, May 5 Litho. *Perf. 14***

| | | | | |
|---|---|---|---|---|
| **1237-1238** | A478 | Set of 2 | 2.25 | 2.25 |
| *1238a* | | Booklet pane of 8, 4 each #1237-1238, perf. 14 on 3 sides | 9.00 | — |
| | | Complete booklet, #1238a | 9.00 | |

Map of Mediterranean Sea and Cypriot Boats — A479

**2015, July 9 Litho. *Perf. 14***

| | | | | |
|---|---|---|---|---|
| **1239** | A479 | 75c multi | 1.75 | 1.75 |

Akamas Peninsula A480

Avakas Gorge — A481

**2015, July 9 Litho. *Perf. 14***

| | | | | |
|---|---|---|---|---|
| **1240** | A480 | 34c multi | .75 | .75 |
| **1241** | A481 | 64c multi | 1.40 | 1.40 |

International Telecommunication Union, 150th Anniv. — A482

**2015, Sept. 14 Litho. *Perf. 14***

| | | | | |
|---|---|---|---|---|
| **1242** | A482 | 64c multi | 1.50 | 1.50 |

Castles A483

Designs: 4c, Buffavento Castle. 34c, Kantara Castle. 41c, Agios Ilarionas (St. Hilarion) Castle. 75c, Kyrenia Castle.

***Perf. 13¾x13½***

**2015, Sept. 14 Litho.**

| | | | | |
|---|---|---|---|---|
| **1243-1246** | A483 | Set of 4 | 3.50 | 3.50 |

Handicrafts — A484

No. 1247: a, Carved wooden chair. b, Decorated gourds.
No. 1248: a, Silver merrecha. b, Clay vessels.

**2015, Sept. 14 Litho. *Perf. 14***

| | | | | |
|---|---|---|---|---|
| **1247** | A484 | Pair | 1.50 | 1.50 |
| *a.-b.* | | 34c Either single | .75 | .75 |
| **1248** | A484 | Pair | 3.00 | 3.00 |
| *a.-b.* | | 64c Either single | 1.50 | 1.50 |

A485 A486

Christmas — A487

Designs: 34c, Girl burning olive leaves. 41c, Madonna and Child icon. 64c, Child mailing letter to Santa Claus. €2, Nativity.

**2015, Nov. 19 Litho. *Perf. 14***

| | | | | |
|---|---|---|---|---|
| **1249** | A485 | 34c multi | .75 | .75 |
| **1250** | A486 | 41c multi | .90 | .90 |
| **1251** | A485 | 64c multi | 1.40 | 1.40 |
| | | *Nos. 1249-1251 (3)* | 3.05 | 3.05 |

***Imperf***

| | | | | |
|---|---|---|---|---|
| **1252** | A487 | €2 multi | 4.25 | 4.25 |

Traditional Crafts A488

Designs: 41c, Basket weaving. 64c, Wood carving.

**2016, Mar. 10 Litho. *Perf. 14***
**1253-1254** A488 Set of 2 2.40 2.40

2016 Summer Olympics, Rio de Janeiro — A489

Designs: 34c, Taekwondo. 41c, Tennis. 64c, High jump. 75c, Sprinter.

**2016, Apr. 11 Litho. *Perf. 13¾***
**1255-1258** A489 Set of 4 5.00 5.00

No. 1258 is a square stamp.

A490

Europa A491

**2016, May 9 Litho. *Perf. 14***
**1259** A490 34c multi .80 .80
**1260** A491 64c multi 1.50 1.50
*a.* Booklet pane of 8, 4 each #1259-1260, perf. 14 on 3 sides 9.25 —

Think Green Issue.

No. 1260a was sold with but unattached to a booklet cover.

A492

Winning Art in "Principles and Values of the European Union" Children's Stamp Design Contest
A493 A494

**2016, May 9 Litho. *Perf. 14***
**1261** A492 34c multi .75 .75
**1262** A493 41c multi .95 .95
**1263** A494 64c multi 1.50 1.50
*Nos. 1261-1263 (3)* 3.20 3.20

Montage of Fish of the Mediterranean Sea — A495

**2016, July 8 Litho. *Perf. 14***
**1264** A495 €1.88 multi 4.25 4.25

Fountains A496

Designs: 34c, Children at Panayla Fountain, Paphos. 41c, Woman carrying water jug, Pegeia Fountain, Pegia.

**2016, July 8 Litho. *Perf. 14***
**1265-1266** A496 Set of 2 1.75 1.75

Stelios Joannou (1915-99), Businessman and Philanthropist A497

Georgios Paraskevaides (1916-2007), Businessman and Philanthropist A498

Anastasios Georgios Leventis (1902-78), Businessman and Philanthropist A499

**2016, Oct. 17 Litho. *Perf. 14***
**1267** A497 34c multi .75 .75
**1268** A498 34c multi .75 .75
**1269** A499 34c multi .75 .75
*Nos. 1267-1269 (3)* 2.25 2.25

Cyprus Chairmanship of the Council of Europe — A500

**2016, Nov. 17 Litho. *Perf. 13¾***
**1270** A500 €1 multi 2.25 2.25

A501

Christmas A502

Designs: 34c, String of Christmas lights. 41c, Christmas tree. 64c, Adoration of the Magi icon.

**2016, Nov. 17 Litho. *Perf. 14***
**1271** A501 34c multi .75 .75
**1272** A501 41c multi .90 .90
**1273** A502 64c multi 1.40 1.40
*Nos. 1271-1273 (3)* 3.05 3.05

Flowers — A503

Designs; 34c, Crocus hartmannianus. 41c, Carlina pygmaea. 64c, Centaurea akamantis. €1, Tulipa cypria.

**2017, Feb. 16 Litho. *Perf. 14***
**1274-1277** A503 Set of 4 5.00 5.00

Television Broadcasting in Cyprus, 60th Anniv. — A504

**2017, Mar. 24 Litho. *Perf. 14***
**1278** A504 34c multi .75 .75

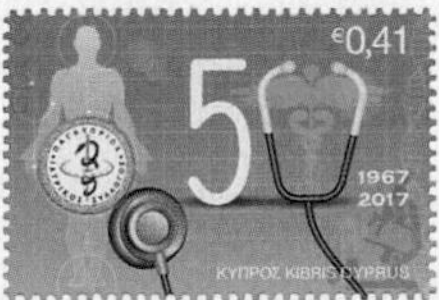

Cyprus Medical Association, 50th Anniv. — A505

**2017, Mar. 24 Litho. *Perf. 14***
**1279** A505 41c multi .90 .90

Lions Clubs International, Cent. — A506

**2017, Mar. 24 Litho. *Perf. 14***
**1280** A506 64c multi 1.40 1.40

Paphos, 2017 European Capital of Culture A507

No. 1281: a, Aphrodite's Rock. b, Emblem. c, Pillars of House of Theseus.

**2017, Mar. 24 Litho. *Perf. 14***
**1281** Horiz. strip of 3 4.25 4.25
*a.-c.* A507 64c Any single 1.40 1.40

International Year of Sustainable Tourism for Development — A508

**2017, May 4 Litho. *Perf. 14***
**1282** A508 64c multi 1.50 1.50

Europa A509

Designs: 41c, Larnaka Castle. 64c, Paphos Castle.

**2017, May 4 Litho. *Perf. 14***
**1283-1284** A509 Set of 2 2.40 2.40
*1284a* Booklet pane of 8, 4 each #1283-1284, perf. 14 on 3 sides 9.75 —
Complete booklet, #1284a 9.75

Stylized Tree — A510

**2017, July 10 Litho. *Perf. 14***
**1285** A510 64c multi 1.50 1.50

Triptych From Church of Our Lady Chryseleousa Strovolos — A511

Children Opening Gift — A512

Boy Writing Letter to Santa Claus — A513

No. 1286: a, St. Minas the Egyptian (carmine panel at left). b, Madonna and Child, ship (carmine panel at bottom). c, St. Spyridon (carmine panel at right).
No. 1287: a, Child in red and white striped shirt, Santa Claus and reindeer. b, Child in green shirt.

**2017, Nov. 24 Litho. *Perf. 14***

**1286** A511 34c Horiz. strip of 3, #a-c 2.50 2.50
**1287** A512 41c Horiz. pair, #a-b 2.00 2.00
**1288** A513 64c multi 1.60 1.60
*Nos. 1286-1288 (3)* 6.10 6.10

Christmas.

## POSTAL TAX STAMPS

**Catalogue values for unused stamps in this section are for Never Hinged items.**

Unless otherwise stated, Cyprus postal tax stamps are for the Refugee Fund.

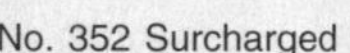

No. 352 Surcharged

***Perf. 12x12½***

**1974, Dec. 2 Wmk. 344**

**RA1** A104 10m on 5m multi .70 .70

Old Woman and Child — PT1

**1974, Oct. 1 *Perf. 12½x13½***

**RA2** PT1 10m gray & black .60 .60

Child and Barbed Wire — PT2

***Perf. 13x12½***

**1977, Jan. 10 Litho. Wmk. 344**

**RA3** PT2 10m black .60 .60

**Inscribed 1984**

**1984, June 18 *Perf. 13x12½***

**RA4** PT2 1c black .60 .60

There are two types of No. RA4.

Inscribed 1988 — PT3

**1988-2007 *Perf. 13x12½***

**Design Size 22x28mm**

**RA5** PT3 1c black & pale gray .60 .60

***Perf. 11½x12***

**RA6** PT3 1c Inscribed 1989 .60 .60
**RA7** PT3 1c Inscribed 1990 .60 .60

**Unwmk.**

***Perf. 13***

**RA8** PT3 1c Inscribed 1991 .60 .60
**RA9** PT3 1c Inscribed 1992 .60 .60
**RA10** PT3 1c Inscribed 1993 .60 .60
**RA11** PT3 1c Inscribed 1994 .60 .60

***Perf. 14½x13¾***

**Design Size 21x24.5mm**

**RA12** PT3 1c Inscribed 1995 .60 .60
**RA13** PT3 1c Inscribed 1996 .60 .60
**RA14** PT3 1c Inscribed 1997 .60 .60
**RA15** PT3 1c Inscribed 1998 .60 .60
**RA16** PT3 1c Inscribed 1999 .60 .60
**RA17** PT3 1c Inscribed 2000 .60 .60
**RA18** PT3 1c Inscribed 2001 .60 .60

**Size: 22x27mm**

***Perf. 12¾***

**RA19** PT3 1c Inscribed 2002 .60 .60
**RA20** PT3 1c Inscribed 2003 .60 .60

***Perf. 12¾x13***

**RA21** PT3 1c Inscribed 2004 .60 .60
**RA22** PT3 1c Inscribed 2005 .60 .60
**RA23** PT3 1c Inscribed 2006 .60 .60

***Perf. 13½x14***

**RA24** PT3 1c Inscribed 2007 .50 .50
*Nos. RA5-RA24 (20)* 11.90 11.90

Issued: No. RA5, 9/12/88; No. RA6, 9/4/89; No. RA7, 9/29/90; No. RA8, 10/7/91; No. RA9, 11/9/92; No. RA10, 1993; No. RA11, 11/21/94; No. RA12, 10/24/95; No. RA13, 6/10/96; No. RA14, 6/30/97; No. RA15, 1998; No. RA16, 1999; No. RA17, 2000; No. RA18, 2001. No. RA19, 2002. No. RA19, 2003. No. RA20, 2003. No. RA21, 11/11/04. No. RA22, 6/16/05. No. RA23, 5/4/06. No. RA24, 3/15/07.

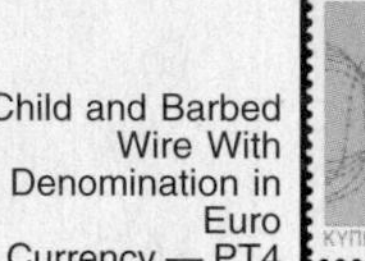

Child and Barbed Wire With Denomination in Euro Currency — PT4

**2008-17 Litho. *Perf. 13½x14***

**RA25** PT4 2c dk gray & gray .50 .50

**Inscribed "2009"**

**RA26** PT4 2c blk & lilac gray .50 .50

**Inscribed "2010"**

**RA27** PT4 2c blk & tan .50 .50

**Inscribed "2011"**

**RA28** PT4 2c blk & lt green .50 .50

**Booklet Stamp**
**Self-Adhesive**

***Die Cut Perf. 13½x14¼***

**RA28A** PT4 2c blk & lt grn .50 .50
*b.* Booklet pane of 12, 6 each #1153A, RA28A 18.00

**Inscribed "2012"**

***Perf. 13½***

**RA29** PT4 2c blk & lt blue .50 .50

**Inscribed "2013"**

**RA30** PT4 2c blk & dull org .50 .50

**Inscribed "2014"**

**RA31** PT4 2c blk & gray .50 .50

**Inscribed "2015"**

**RA32** PT4 2c blk & bl gray .50 .50

**Inscribed "2016"**

**RA33** PT4 2c ol gray & lt brnish gray .50 .50

**Inscribed "2017"**

***Perf. 13½x14***

**RA34** PT4 2c blk & bl gray .50 .50

Issued: Nos. RA28, RA28A, 5/4/11; No. RA29, 1/31/12; No. RA30, 1/30/13; No. RA31, 3/12/14; No. RA32, 4/2/15; No. RA33, 3/10/16. No. RA34, 2/16/17.

# CYRENAICA

ˌsir-ə-ˈnā-ə-kə

LOCATION — In northern Africa bordering on the Mediterranean Sea
GOVT. — Italian colony
AREA — 75,340 sq. mi.
POP. — 225,000 (approx. 1934)
CAPITAL — Bengasi (Benghazi)

Cyrenaica was an Italian Colony. In 1949 Great Britain granted the Amir of Cyrenaica autonomy in internal affairs. Cyrenaica was incorporated into the kingdom of Libya in 1951.

100 Centesimi = 1 Lira
1000 Milliemes = 1 Pound (1950)

**Catalogue values for unused stamps in this country are for Never Hinged items, beginning with Scott 65 in the regular postage section, Scott J1 in the postage due section.**

**Used values in italics are for postally used stamps. CTO's sell for about the same as unused, hinged stamps.**

**Watermark**

Wmk. 140 — Crown

**Propaganda of the Faith Issue**
Italy Nos. 143-146 Overprinted

**1923, Oct. 24 Wmk. 140 *Perf. 14***

**1** A68 20c ol grn & brn org 9.50 *42.50*
**2** A68 30c claret & brn org 9.50 *42.50*
**3** A68 50c violet & brn org 6.00 *47.50*
**4** A68 1 l blue & brn org 6.00 *75.00*
*Nos. 1-4 (4)* 31.00 *207.50*
Set, never hinged 75.00

**Fascisti Issue**

Italy Nos. 159-164 Overprinted in Red or Black

**1923, Oct. 29 Unwmk. *Perf. 14***

**5** A69 10c dk grn (R) 8.50 *15.00*
**6** A69 30c dk vio (R) 8.50 *15.00*
**7** A69 50c brn car 8.50 *21.00*

**Wmk. 140**

**8** A70 1 l blue 8.50 *40.00*
**9** A70 2 l brown 8.50 *47.50*
**10** A71 5 l blk & bl (R) 8.50 *72.50*
*Nos. 5-10 (6)* 51.00 *211.00*
Set, never hinged 120.00

**Manzoni Issue**

Italy Nos. 165-170 Ovptd. in Red

**1924, Apr. 1 *Perf. 14***

**11** A72 10c brn red & blk 9.00 *60.00*
**12** A72 15c bl grn & blk 9.00 *60.00*
**13** A72 30c blk & slate 9.00 *60.00*
**14** A72 50c org brn & blk 9.00 *60.00*
**15** A72 1 l bl & blk 55.00 *350.00*
*a.* Double overprint *1,200.*
Never hinged *1,800.*
**16** A72 5 l vio & blk 350.00 *2,700.*
*Nos. 11-16 (6)* 441.00 *3,290.*
Set, never hinged 1,125.

Vertical overprints on Nos. 11-14 are essays. On Nos. 15-16 the overprint is vertical at the left.

All examples of No. 15a are poorly centered.

**Victor Emmanuel Issue**

Italy Nos. 175-177 Overprinted

**1925-26 Unwmk. *Perf. 11***

**17** A78 60c brn car 1.60 *11.00*
**18** A78 1 l dark blue 1.60 *11.00*
**19** A78 1.25 l dk bl ('26) 4.75 *24.00*
*a.* Perf. 13½ 350.00 *1,000.*
Never hinged 900.00
*Nos. 17-19 (3)* 7.95 *46.00*
Set, never hinged 20.00

Issue dates: Nov. 1925, July 1926.

**Saint Francis of Assisi Issue**

Italian Stamps of 1926 Ovptd.

**1926, Apr. 12 Wmk. 140 *Perf. 14***

**20** A79 20c gray green 1.80 *11.00*
**21** A80 40c dark violet 1.80 *11.00*
**22** A81 60c red brown 1.80 *19.00*

Ovptd. in Red

**Unwmk.**

**23** A82 1.25 l dk bl, perf. 11 1.80 *20.00*
**24** A83 5 l + 2.50 l ol grn 6.00 *55.00*
*Nos. 20-24 (5)* 13.20 *116.00*
Set, never hinged 30.00

**Volta Issue**

Type of Italy 1927, Overprinted

**1927, Oct. 10 Wmk. 140 *Perf. 14***

**25** A84 20c purple 4.75 *30.00*
**26** A84 50c dp org 7.25 *40.00*
**27** A84 1.25 l brt bl 11.00 *47.50*
*Nos. 25-27 (3)* 23.00 *117.50*
Set, never hinged 55.00

**Monte Cassino Issue**

Types of 1929 Issue of Italy, Ovptd. in Red or Blue

**1929, Oct. 14**

**28** A96 20c dk grn (R) 4.75 *17.00*
**29** A96 25c red org (Bl) 4.75 *17.00*
**30** A98 50c + 10c crim (Bl) 4.75 *18.00*
**31** A98 75c + 15c ol brn (R) 4.75 *18.00*
**32** A96 1.25 l + 25c dk vio (R) 11.00 *32.50*
**33** A98 5 l + 1 l saph (R) 11.00 *28.50*

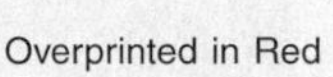

Overprinted in Red

**Unwmk.**

| | | | | |
|---|---|---|---|---|
| **34** | A100 | 10 l + 2 l gray brn | 11.00 | *45.00* |
| | | *Nos. 28-34 (7)* | 52.00 | *176.00* |
| | | Set, never hinged | 123.00 | |

**Royal Wedding Issue**

Type of Italian Stamps of 1930 Overprinted

**1930, Mar. 17 Wmk. 140**

| | | | | |
|---|---|---|---|---|
| **35** | A101 | 20c yel grn | 2.40 | *8.50* |
| **36** | A101 | 50c + 10c dp org | 1.80 | *8.50* |
| **37** | A101 | 1.25 l + 25c rose red | 1.80 | *14.50* |
| | | *Nos. 35-37 (3)* | 6.00 | *31.50* |
| | | Set, never hinged | 16.00 | |

**Ferrucci Issue**

Types of Italian Stamps of 1930, Ovptd. in Red or Blue

**1930, July 26**

| | | | | |
|---|---|---|---|---|
| **38** | A102 | 20c violet (R) | 6.50 | *6.50* |
| **39** | A103 | 25c dk grn (R) | 6.50 | *6.50* |
| **40** | A103 | 50c black (R) | 6.50 | *12.00* |
| **41** | A103 | 1.25 l dp bl (R) | 6.50 | *22.50* |
| **42** | A104 | 5 l + 2 l dp car | 14.50 | *47.50* |
| | | *Nos. 38-42 (5)* | 40.50 | *95.00* |
| | | Set, never hinged | 94.00 | |

**Virgil Issue**

Italian Stamps of 1930 Ovptd. in Red or Blue

**1930, Dec. 4**

| | | | | |
|---|---|---|---|---|
| **43** | A106 | 15c vio blk | .90 | *9.00* |
| **44** | A106 | 20c org brn (Bl) | .90 | *3.50* |
| **45** | A106 | 25c dk grn | .90 | *3.50* |
| **46** | A106 | 30c lt brn (Bl) | .90 | *3.50* |
| **47** | A106 | 50c dl vio | .90 | *3.50* |
| **48** | A106 | 75c rose red (Bl) | .90 | *8.50* |
| **49** | A106 | 1.25 l gray bl | .90 | *9.00* |

**Unwmk.**

| | | | | |
|---|---|---|---|---|
| **50** | A106 | 5 l + 1.50 l dk vio | 3.50 | *35.00* |
| **51** | A106 | 10 l + 2.50 l ol brn (Bl) | 3.50 | *55.00* |
| | | *Nos. 43-51 (9)* | 13.30 | *130.50* |
| | | Set, never hinged | 30.00 | |

**Saint Anthony of Padua Issue**

Italian Stamps of 1931 Ovptd. in Blue or Red

**1931, May 7 Wmk. 140**

| | | | | |
|---|---|---|---|---|
| **52** | A116 | 20c brown (Bl) | 1.25 | *22.50* |
| **53** | A116 | 25c green (R) | 1.25 | *8.00* |
| **54** | A118 | 30c gray brn (Bl) | 1.25 | *8.00* |
| **55** | A118 | 50c dl vio (Bl) | 1.25 | *8.00* |
| **56** | A120 | 1.25 l slate bl (R) | 1.25 | *22.50* |

**Overprinted like Nos. 23-24 in Red or Black**

**Unwmk.**

| | | | | |
|---|---|---|---|---|
| **57** | A121 | 75c black (R) | 1.25 | *22.50* |
| **58** | A122 | 5 l + 2.50 l dk brn | 11.00 | *80.00* |
| | | *Nos. 52-58 (7)* | 18.50 | *171.50* |
| | | Set, never hinged | 36.00 | |

Carabineer A1

**1934, Oct. 16 Photo. Wmk. 140**

| | | | | |
|---|---|---|---|---|
| **59** | A1 | 5c dk ol grn & brn | 4.25 | *17.00* |
| **60** | A1 | 10c brn & blk | 4.25 | *17.00* |
| **61** | A1 | 20c scar & indigo | 4.25 | *15.00* |
| **62** | A1 | 50c pur & brn | 4.25 | *15.00* |
| **63** | A1 | 60c org brn & ind | 4.25 | *21.00* |
| **64** | A1 | 1.25 l dk bl & grn | 4.25 | *35.00* |
| | | *Nos. 59-64 (6)* | 25.50 | *120.00* |
| | | Set, never hinged | 60.00 | |

2nd Colonial Art Exhibition held at Naples. See Nos. C24-C29.

**Catalogue values for unused stamps in this section, from this point to the end of the section, are for Never Hinged items.**

**Autonomous State**

Senussi Warrior
A2 A3

***Perf. 12½***

**1950, Jan. 16 Unwmk. Engr.**

| | | | | |
|---|---|---|---|---|
| **65** | A2 | 1m dark brown | .65 | *2.25* |
| **66** | A2 | 2m rose car | .85 | *2.00* |
| **67** | A2 | 3m orange | .85 | *2.00* |
| **68** | A2 | 4m dark green | 4.25 | *3.25* |
| **69** | A2 | 5m gray | 1.10 | *1.25* |
| **70** | A2 | 8m red orange | 1.25 | *1.50* |
| **71** | A2 | 10m purple | 1.25 | *1.50* |
| **72** | A2 | 12m red | 1.25 | *1.50* |
| **73** | A2 | 20m deep blue | 1.25 | *1.50* |
| **74** | A3 | 50m choc & ultra | 6.75 | *8.50* |
| **75** | A3 | 100m bl blk & car rose | 21.00 | *42.50* |
| **76** | A3 | 200m vio & pur | 25.00 | *67.50* |
| **77** | A3 | 500m dk grn & org | 110.00 | *135.00* |
| | | *Nos. 65-77 (13)* | 175.45 | *270.25* |

## SEMI-POSTAL STAMPS

Many issues of Italy and Italian Colonies include one or more semipostal denominations. To avoid splitting sets, these issues are generally listed as regular postage unless all values carry a surtax.

**Holy Year Issue**

Italian Semi-Postal Stamps of 1924 Overprinted in Black or Red

**1925, June 1 Wmk. 140 *Perf. 12***

| | | | | |
|---|---|---|---|---|
| **B1** | SP4 | 20c + 10c dk grn & brn | 3.00 | *10.00* |
| **B2** | SP4 | 30c + 15c dk brn & brn | 3.00 | *19.00* |
| **B3** | SP4 | 50c + 25c vio & brn | 3.00 | *18.00* |
| **B4** | SP4 | 60c + 30c dp rose & brn | 3.00 | *24.00* |
| **B5** | SP8 | 1 l + 50c dp bl & vio (R) | 3.00 | *30.00* |
| **B6** | SP8 | 5 l + 2.50 l org brn & vio (R) | 3.00 | *45.00* |
| | | *Nos. B1-B6 (6)* | 18.00 | *154.00* |
| | | Set, never hinged | 40.50 | |

**Colonial Institute Issue**

"Peace" Substituting Spade for Sword — SP1

**1926, June 1 Typo. *Perf. 14***

| | | | | |
|---|---|---|---|---|
| **B7** | SP1 | 5c + 5c brown | .90 | *7.25* |
| **B8** | SP1 | 10c + 5c olive grn | .90 | *7.25* |
| **B9** | SP1 | 20c + 5c blue grn | .90 | *7.25* |
| **B10** | SP1 | 40c + 5c brown red | .90 | *7.25* |
| **B11** | SP1 | 60c + 5c orange | .90 | *7.25* |
| **B12** | SP1 | 1 l + 5c blue | .90 | *15.00* |
| | | *Nos. B7-B12 (6)* | 5.40 | *51.25* |
| | | Set, never hinged | 16.00 | |

Surtax for Italian Colonial Institute.

**Types of Italian Semi-Postal Stamps of 1926 Overprinted like Nos. 17-19**

**1927, Apr. 21 Unwmk. *Perf. 11***

| | | | | |
|---|---|---|---|---|
| **B13** | SP10 | 40c + 20c dk brn & blk | 4.00 | *45.00* |
| **B14** | SP10 | 60c + 30c brn red & ol brn | 4.00 | *45.00* |
| **B15** | SP10 | 1.25 l + 60c dp bl & blk | 4.00 | *65.00* |
| *a.* | | Double overprint | 1,750. | |
| | | Never hinged | 2,600. | |
| **B16** | SP10 | 5 l + 2.50 l dk grn & blk | 6.50 | *100.00* |
| | | *Nos. B13-B16 (4)* | 18.50 | *255.00* |
| | | Set, never hinged | 43.00 | |

The surtax on these stamps was for the charitable work of the Voluntary Militia for Italian National Defense.

Allegory of Fascism and Victory — SP2

**1928, Oct. 15 Wmk. 140 *Perf. 14***

| | | | | |
|---|---|---|---|---|
| **B17** | SP2 | 20c + 5c bl grn | 3.25 | *14.50* |
| **B18** | SP2 | 30c + 5c red | 3.25 | *14.50* |
| **B19** | SP2 | 50c + 10c purple | 3.25 | *24.00* |
| **B20** | SP2 | 1.25 l + 20c dk bl | 4.00 | *32.50* |
| | | *Nos. B17-B20 (4)* | 13.75 | *85.50* |
| | | Set, never hinged | 34.00 | |

46th anniv. of the Societa Africana d'Italia. The surtax aided that society.

**Types of Italian Semi-Postal Stamps of 1926 Overprinted in Red or Black like Nos. 52-56**

**1929, Mar. 4 Unwmk. *Perf. 11***

| | | | | |
|---|---|---|---|---|
| **B21** | SP10 | 30c + 10c red & blk | 4.75 | *27.50* |
| **B22** | SP10 | 50c + 20c vio & blk | 4.75 | *30.00* |
| **B23** | SP10 | 1.25 l + 50c brn & bl | 7.25 | *52.50* |
| **B24** | SP10 | 5 l + 2 l ol grn & blk (Bk) | 7.25 | *100.00* |
| | | *Nos. B21-B24 (4)* | 24.00 | *210.00* |
| | | Set, never hinged | 60.00 | |

Surtax for the charitable work of the Voluntary Militia for Italian Natl. Defense.

**Types of Italian Semi-Postal Stamps of 1926 Overprinted in Black or Red like Nos. 52-56**

**1930, Oct. 20 *Perf. 14***

| | | | | |
|---|---|---|---|---|
| **B25** | SP10 | 30c + 10c dk grn & bl grn (Bk) | 35.00 | *65.00* |
| **B26** | SP10 | 50c + 10c dk grn & vio | 35.00 | *100.00* |
| **B27** | SP10 | 1.25 l + 30c ol brn & red brn | 35.00 | *100.00* |
| **B28** | SP10 | 5 l + 1.50 l ind & grn | 120.00 | *275.00* |
| | | *Nos. B25-B28 (4)* | 225.00 | *540.00* |
| | | Set, never hinged | 562.50 | |

Surtax for the charitable work of the Voluntary Militia for Italian Natl. Defense.

Sower — SP3

**1930, Nov. 27 Photo. Wmk. 140**

| | | | | |
|---|---|---|---|---|
| **B29** | SP3 | 50c + 20c ol brn | 3.00 | *21.00* |
| **B30** | SP3 | 1.25 l + 20c dp bl | 3.00 | *21.00* |
| **B31** | SP3 | 1.75 l + 20c green | 3.00 | *24.00* |
| **B32** | SP3 | 2.55 l + 50c purple | 11.00 | *35.00* |
| **B33** | SP3 | 5 l + 1 l dp car | 11.00 | *55.00* |
| | | *Nos. B29-B33 (5)* | 31.00 | *156.00* |
| | | Set, never hinged | 53.00 | |

25th anniv. of the Italian Colonial Agricultural Institute. The surtax was for the aid of that institution.

## AIR POST STAMPS

**Air Post Stamps of Tripolitania, 1931, Overprinted in Blue like Nos. 38-42**

**1932, Jan. 7 Wmk. 140 *Perf. 14***

| | | | | |
|---|---|---|---|---|
| **C1** | AP1 | 50c rose car | 1.25 | *.30* |
| **C2** | AP1 | 60c dp org | 4.75 | *7.25* |
| **C3** | AP1 | 80c dl vio | 4.75 | *17.00* |
| | | *Nos. C1-C3 (3)* | 10.75 | *24.55* |
| | | Set, never hinged | 24.00 | |

Air Post Stamps of Tripolitania, 1931, Overprinted in Blue

**1932, May 12**

| | | | | |
|---|---|---|---|---|
| **C4** | AP1 | 50c rose car | 1.60 | 2.00 |
| **C5** | AP1 | 80c dull violet | 6.50 | *27.50* |
| | | Set, never hinged | 16.50 | |

This overprint was also applied to the 60c, Tripolitania No. C9. The overprinted stamp was never used in Cyrenaica, but was sold at Rome in 1943 by the Postmaster General for the Italian Colonies. Value $10.

Arab on Camel — AP2

Airplane in Flight AP3

**1932, Aug. 8 Photo.**

| | | | | |
|---|---|---|---|---|
| **C6** | AP2 | 50c purple | 12.00 | *.25* |
| **C7** | AP2 | 75c brn rose | 12.00 | *12.00* |
| **C8** | AP2 | 80c deep blue | 12.00 | *23.00* |
| **C9** | AP3 | 1 l black | 4.25 | *.25* |
| **C10** | AP3 | 2 l green | 4.25 | *12.00* |
| **C11** | AP3 | 5 l deep car | 8.50 | *24.00* |
| | | *Nos. C6-C11 (6)* | 53.00 | *71.50* |
| | | Set, never hinged | 160.00 | |

For surcharges and overprint see Nos. C20-C23.

### Graf Zeppelin Issue

Zeppelin and Clouds forming Pegasus AP4

Zeppelin and Ancient Galley AP5

Zeppelin and Giant Bowman AP6

**1933, Apr. 15**

| | | | | |
|---|---|---|---|---|
| **C12** | AP4 | 3 l dk brn | 10.00 | *100.00* |
| **C13** | AP5 | 5 l purple | 10.00 | *100.00* |
| **C14** | AP6 | 10 l dp grn | 10.00 | *180.00* |
| **C15** | AP5 | 12 l deep blue | 10.00 | *200.00* |
| **C16** | AP4 | 15 l carmine | 10.00 | *200.00* |
| **C17** | AP6 | 20 l black | 10.00 | *275.00* |
| | | *Nos. C12-C17 (6)* | 60.00 | *1,055.* |
| | | Set, never hinged | 135.00 | |

### North Atlantic Crossing Issue

Airplane Squadron and Constellations — AP7

**1933, June 1**

| | | | | |
|---|---|---|---|---|
| **C18** | AP7 | 19.75 l grn & dp bl | 16.00 | *500.00* |
| **C19** | AP7 | 44.75 l red & indigo | 16.00 | *500.00* |
| | | Set, never hinged | 105.00 | |

Type of 1932 Ovptd. and Srchd.

**1934, Jan. 20**

| | | | | |
|---|---|---|---|---|
| **C20** | AP3 | 2 l on 5 l org brn | 4.75 | *95.00* |
| **C21** | AP3 | 3 l on 5 l yel grn | 4.75 | *95.00* |
| **C22** | AP3 | 5 l ocher | 4.75 | *110.00* |
| **C23** | AP3 | 10 l on 5 l rose | 6.50 | *110.00* |
| | | *Nos. C20-C23 (4)* | 20.75 | *410.00* |
| | | Set, never hinged | 52.00 | |

For use on mail to be carried on a special flight from Rome to Buenos Aires.

Transport Plane AP8

Venus of Cyrene AP9

**1934, Oct. 9**

| | | | | |
|---|---|---|---|---|
| **C24** | AP8 | 25c sl bl & org red | 4.25 | *17.00* |
| **C25** | AP8 | 50c dk grn & ind | 4.25 | *15.00* |
| **C26** | AP8 | 75c dk brn & org red | 4.25 | *15.00* |
| *a.* | | Imperf. | 3,250. | |
| | | Never hinged | 4,850. | |
| **C27** | AP9 | 80c org brn & ol grn | 4.25 | *17.00* |
| **C28** | AP9 | 1 l scar & ol grn | 4.25 | *21.00* |
| **C29** | AP9 | 2 l dk bl & brn | 4.25 | *35.00* |
| | | *Nos. C24-C29 (6)* | 25.50 | *120.00* |
| | | Set, never hinged | 60.00 | |

2nd Colonial Arts Exhib. held at Naples.

### AIR POST SEMI-POSTAL STAMPS

King Victor Emmanuel III SPAP1

**Wmk. 104**

**1934, Nov. 5 Photo. *Perf. 14***

| | | | | |
|---|---|---|---|---|
| **CB1** | SPAP1 | 25c + 10c gray grn | 9.50 | *27.50* |
| **CB2** | SPAP1 | 50c + 10c brn | 9.50 | *27.50* |
| **CB3** | SPAP1 | 75c + 15c rose red | 9.50 | *27.50* |
| **CB4** | SPAP1 | 80c + 15c brn blk | 9.50 | *27.50* |
| **CB5** | SPAP1 | 1 l + 20c red brn | 9.50 | *27.50* |
| **CB6** | SPAP1 | 2 l + 20c brt bl | 9.50 | *27.50* |
| **CB7** | SPAP1 | 3 l + 25c pur | 27.50 | *130.00* |
| **CB8** | SPAP1 | 5 l + 25c org | 27.50 | *130.00* |
| **CB9** | SPAP1 | 10 l + 30c dp vio | 27.50 | *130.00* |
| **CB10** | SPAP1 | 25 l + 2 l dp grn | 27.50 | *130.00* |
| | | *Nos. CB1-CB10 (10)* | 167.00 | *685.00* |
| | | Set, never hinged | 415.00 | |

65th birthday of King Victor Emmanuel III and the non-stop flight, Rome-Mogadiscio.

### AIR POST SEMI-POSTAL OFFICIAL STAMP

**Type of Air Post Semi-Postal Stamps, 1934, Overprinted Crown and "SERVIZIO DI STATO" in Black**

**1934, Nov. 5 Wmk. 140 *Perf. 14***

| | | | | |
|---|---|---|---|---|
| **CBO1** | SPAP1 | 25 l + 2 l cop red | | *1,900.* |

### POSTAGE DUE STAMPS

**Catalogue values for unused stamps in this section are for Never Hinged items.**

D1

***Perf. 12½***

**1950, July 1 Unwmk. Engr.**

| | | | | |
|---|---|---|---|---|
| **J1** | D1 | 2m dark brown | 77.50 | *110.00* |
| **J2** | D1 | 4m deep green | 77.50 | *110.00* |
| **J3** | D1 | 8m scarlet | 77.50 | *110.00* |
| **J4** | D1 | 10m vermilion | 77.50 | *120.00* |
| **J5** | D1 | 20m orange yel | 77.50 | *120.00* |
| **J6** | D1 | 40m deep blue | 77.50 | *160.00* |
| **J7** | D1 | 100m dark gray | 77.50 | *250.00* |
| | | *Nos. J1-J7 (7)* | 542.50 | *980.00* |

## CZECHOSLOVAKIA

ˌche-kə-slō-ˈvä-kē-ə

LOCATION — Central Europe
GOVT. — Republic
AREA — 49,355 sq. mi.
POP. — 15,395,970 (1983 est.)
CAPITAL — Prague

The Czechoslovakian Republic consists of Bohemia, Moravia and Silesia, Slovakia and Ruthenia (Carpatho-Ukraine). In March 1939, a German protectorate was established over Bohemia and Moravia, as well as over Slovakia which had meanwhile declared its independence. Ruthenia was incorporated in the territory of Hungary. These territories were returned to the Czechoslovak Republic in 1945, except for Ruthenia, which was ceded to Russia. Czechoslovakia became a federal state on Jan. 2, 1969. On Jan. 1, 1993 Czechoslovakia separated into Slovakia and the Czech Republic. See Volume 5 for the stamps of Slovakia.

100 Haleru = 1 Koruna

**Catalogue values for unused stamps in this country are for Never Hinged items, beginning with Scott 142 in the regular postage section, B144 in the semi-postal section, Scott C19 in the air post section, Scott EX1 in the personal delivery section, and Scott J58 in the postage due section, Scott O1 int he officials section, and Scott P14 in the newspaper section.**

### Watermarks

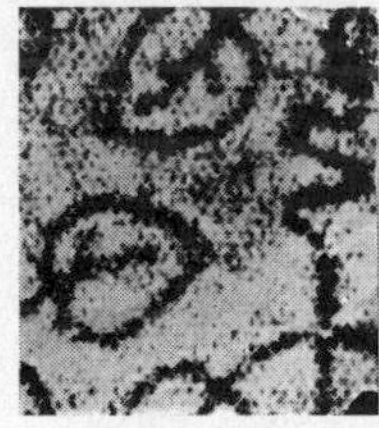
Wmk. 107 — Linden Leaves (Vertical)

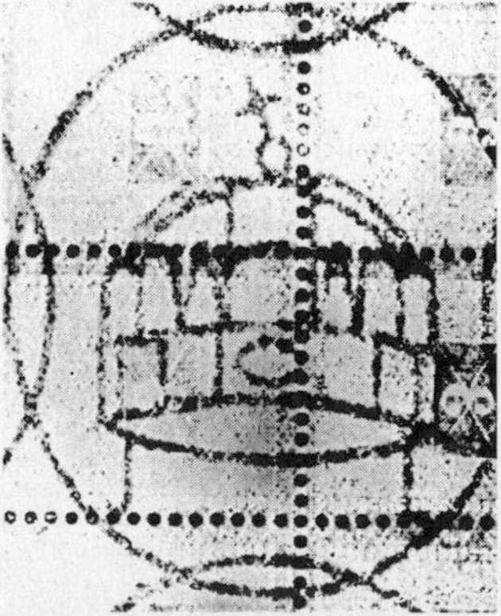
Wmk. 135 — Crown in Oval or Circle, Sideways

Wmk. 136

Wmk. 136a

Wmk. 341 — Striped Ovals

Stamps of Austria overprinted "Ceskoslovenska Republika," lion and "Cesko Slovensky Stat," "Provisorni Ceskoslovenska Vlada" and Arms, and "Ceskoslovenska Statni Posta" and Arms were made privately. A few of them were passed through the post but all have been pronounced unofficial and unauthorized by the Postmaster General.

During the occupation of part of Northern Hungary by the Czechoslovak forces, stamps of Hungary were overprinted "Cesko Slovenska Posta," "Ceskoslovenska Statni Posta" and Arms, and "Slovenska Posta" and Arms. These stamps were never officially issued though examples have passed the post.

Hradcany at Prague — A1

**1918-19 Unwmk. Typo. *Imperf.***

| | | | | |
|---|---|---|---|---|
| **1** | A1 | 3h red violet | .25 | .25 |
| **2** | A1 | 5h yellow green | .25 | .25 |
| **3** | A1 | 10h rose | .25 | .25 |
| **4** | A1 | 20h bluish green | .25 | .25 |
| **5** | A1 | 25h deep blue | .25 | .25 |
| **6** | A1 | 30h bister | .35 | .25 |
| **7** | A1 | 40h red orange | .35 | .25 |
| **8** | A1 | 100h brown | .75 | .25 |
| **9** | A1 | 200h ultra | 1.50 | .25 |
| **10** | A1 | 400h purple | 3.00 | .25 |

On the 3h-40h "Posta Ceskoslovenska" is in white on a colored background; on the higher values the words are in color on a white background.

No. 5c was not valid for postage.

Nos. 1-6 exist as tete-beche gutter pairs.

See Nos. 368, 1554, 1600. For surcharges see Nos. B130, C1, C4, J15, J19-J20, J22-J23, J30.

***Perf. 11½, 13½***

| | | | | |
|---|---|---|---|---|
| **13** | A1 | 5h yellow green | .60 | .25 |
| *a.* | | Perf. 11½x10¾ | 3.00 | .45 |
| **14** | A1 | 10h rose | .35 | .25 |
| **15** | A1 | 20h bluish green | .35 | .25 |
| *a.* | | Perf. 11½ | .35 | .25 |
| **16** | A1 | 25h deep blue | .75 | .35 |
| *a.* | | Perf. 11½ | 1.50 | .35 |
| **20** | A1 | 200h ultra | 6.00 | .25 |
| | | *Nos. 1-10,13-16,20 (15)* | 15.25 | 3.85 |

All values of this issue exist with various private perforations and examples have been used on letters.

The 3h, 30h, 40h, 100h and 400h formerly listed are now known to have been privately perforated.

For overprints see Eastern Silesia Nos. 2, 5, 7-8, 14, 16, 18, 30.

A2

Type II

Type III

Type IV

Type II — Sun behind cathedral. Colorless foliage in foreground.

Type III — Without sun. Shaded foliage in foreground.

Type IV — No foliage in foreground. Positions of buildings changed. Letters redrawn.

**1919** *Imperf.*

| No. | Type | Denomination / Color | Unused | Used |
|---|---|---|---|---|
| **23** | A2 | 1h dark brown (II) | .25 | .25 |
| **25** | A2 | 5h blue green (IV) | .35 | .25 |
| **27** | A2 | 15h red (IV) | .35 | .25 |
| **29** | A2 | 25h dull violet (IV) | .65 | .25 |
| **30** | A2 | 50h dull violet (II) | .40 | .25 |
| **31** | A2 | 50h dark blue (IV) | .35 | .25 |
| **32** | A2 | 60h orange (III) | 1.50 | .25 |
| **33** | A2 | 75h slate (IV) | 1.10 | .25 |
| **34** | A2 | 80h olive grn (III) | .75 | .25 |
| **36** | A2 | 120h gray black (IV) | 2.25 | .25 |
| **38** | A2 | 300h dark green (III) | 7.00 | .35 |
| **39** | A2 | 500h red brown (IV) | 7.00 | .25 |
| **40** | A2 | 1000h violet (III) | 15.00 | 1.10 |
| *a.* | | 1000h bluish violet | 35.00 | 2.25 |
| | | *Nos. 23-40 (13)* | 36.95 | 4.20 |

For overprints see Eastern Silesia Nos. 1, 3-4, 6, 9-13, 15, 17, 20-21.

**1919-20** *Perf. 11½, 13¾, 13¾x11½*

| No. | Type | Denomination / Color | Unused | Used |
|---|---|---|---|---|
| **41** | A2 | 1h dk brown (II) | .25 | .25 |
| **42** | A2 | 5h blue grn (IV), perf. 13½ | .60 | .25 |
| *a.* | | Perf. 11½ | 25.00 | 5.00 |
| **43** | A2 | 10h yellow grn (IV) | .35 | .25 |
| *a.* | | Imperf. | 17.50 | 14.00 |
| *b.* | | Perf. 11¾ | 10.00 | 1.00 |
| **44** | A2 | 15h brick red (IV) | .35 | .25 |
| *a.* | | Perf. 11½x10¾ | 27.50 | 5.00 |
| *b.* | | Perf. 11½x13¾ | 75.00 | 22.50 |
| *c.* | | Perf. 13¾x10¾ | 100.00 | 22.50 |
| **45** | A2 | 20h rose (IV) | .60 | .25 |
| *a.* | | Imperf. | 90.00 | 85.00 |
| **46** | A2 | 25h dull vio (IV), perf. 11½ | .65 | .25 |
| *a.* | | Perf. 11½x10¾ | 4.50 | 1.10 |
| *b.* | | Perf. 13¾x10¾ | 150.00 | 37.50 |
| **47** | A2 | 30h red violet (IV) | .35 | .25 |
| *a.* | | Imperf. | 150.00 | 175.00 |
| *b.* | | Perf. 13¾x13½ | 450.00 | 175.00 |
| *c.* | | 30h deep violet | .60 | .25 |
| *d.* | | As "c," perf. 13¾x13½ | 525.00 | 190.00 |
| *e.* | | As "c," imperf. | 150.00 | 160.00 |
| **50** | A2 | 60h orange (III) | .40 | .25 |
| *a.* | | Perf. 13¾x13½ | 15.00 | 4.50 |
| **53** | A2 | 120h gray black (IV) | 4.00 | 1.00 |
| | | *Nos. 41-53 (9)* | 7.55 | 3.00 |

Nos. 43a, 45a, 47a and 47e were imperforate by accident and not issued in quantities as were Nos. 23 to 40.

Rouletted stamps of the preceding issues are said to have been made by a postmaster in a branch post office at Prague, or by private firms, but without authority from the Post Office Department.

The 50, 75, 80, 300, 500 and 1000h have been privately perforated.

Unlisted color varieties of types A1 and A2 were not officially released, and some are printer's waste.

For surcharges and overprints see Nos. B131, C2-C3, C5-C6, J16-J18, J21, J24-J29, J31, J42-J43, Eastern Silesia 22-29.

Pres. Thomas Garrigue Masaryk — A4

**1920** *Perf. 13½*

| No. | Type | Denomination / Color | Unused | Used |
|---|---|---|---|---|
| **61** | A4 | 125h gray blue | 1.50 | .25 |
| *a.* | | 125h ultramarine | 20.00 | 19.00 |
| **62** | A4 | 500h slate, *grysh* | 2.50 | 1.50 |
| **63** | A4 | 1000h blk brn, *brnsh* | 6.50 | 3.00 |
| | | *Nos. 61-63 (3)* | 10.50 | 4.75 |

Nos. 61, 61a, 63 imperf. were not regularly issued. Values: unused singles, No. 61 $30; No. 61a $150; No. 63 $40.

For surcharge and overprints, see Nos. B131, Eastern Silesia 31-32.

Carrier Pigeon with Letter — A5

Czechoslovakia Breaking Chains to Freedom — A6

Hussite Priest — A7

Agriculture and Science — A8

Type I

Type II

Two types of 40h:
Type I: 9 leaves by woman's hip.
Type II: 10 leaves by woman's hip.

**1920** *Perf. 14*

| No. | Type | Denomination / Color | Unused | Used |
|---|---|---|---|---|
| **65** | A5 | 5h dark blue | .25 | .25 |
| *a.* | | Perf. 13¾ | *275.00* | *150.00* |
| **66** | A5 | 10h blue green | .25 | .25 |
| *a.* | | Perf. 13¾ | *125.00* | 110.00 |
| **67** | A5 | 15h red brown | .25 | .25 |
| **68** | A6 | 20h rose | .25 | .25 |
| **69** | A6 | 25h lilac brown | .25 | .25 |
| **70** | A6 | 30h red violet | .25 | .25 |
| **71** | A6 | 40h red brown (I) | .50 | .25 |
| *a.* | | As "b," tête bêche pair | 2.50 | 1.50 |
| *b.* | | Perf. 13½ | .60 | .25 |
| *c.* | | Type II | .25 | .25 |
| **72** | A6 | 50h carmine | .35 | .25 |
| **73** | A6 | 60h dark blue | .35 | .25 |
| *a.* | | As "b," tête bêche pair | 3.50 | 3.50 |
| *b.* | | Perf. 13½ | .35 | 1.50 |

**Photo.**

| No. | Type | Denomination / Color | Unused | Used |
|---|---|---|---|---|
| **74** | A7 | 80h purple | .25 | .25 |
| **75** | A7 | 90h black brown | .30 | .25 |

**Typo.**

*Perf. 13¾*

| No. | Type | Denomination / Color | Unused | Used |
|---|---|---|---|---|
| **76** | A8 | 100h dark green | .50 | .25 |
| **77** | A8 | 200h violet | .75 | .25 |
| **78** | A8 | 300h vermilion | 1.50 | .25 |
| *a.* | | Perf. 13¾x13½ | 4.50 | .35 |
| **79** | A8 | 400h brown | 3.50 | .45 |
| **80** | A8 | 500h deep green | 3.50 | .45 |
| *a.* | | Perf. 13¾x13½ | 40.00 | 5.50 |
| **81** | A8 | 600h deep violet | 4.50 | .45 |
| *a.* | | Perf. 13¾x13½ | 125.00 | 7.00 |
| | | *Nos. 65-81 (17)* | 17.50 | 4.85 |

No. 69 has background of horizontal lines.

Imperfs. were not regularly issued.

Nos. 71 and 73 exist as tete-beche gutter pairs.

For surcharges and overprint see Nos. C7-C9, J44-J56.

Type I

Type II

Two types of 20h:
Type I: Base of 2 is long, interior of 0 is angular.
Type II: Base of 2 is short, interior of 0 is an oval.

Type I

Type II

Two types of 25h:
Type I: Top of 2 curves up.
Type II: Top of 2 curves down.

**1920-25** *Perf. 14*

| No. | Type | Denomination / Color | Unused | Used |
|---|---|---|---|---|
| **82** | A5 | 5h violet | .25 | .25 |
| *a.* | | As "b," tête bêche pair | 2.00 | 1.00 |
| *b.* | | Perf. 13½ | 1.00 | .35 |
| **83** | A5 | 10h olive bister | .25 | .25 |
| *a.* | | As "b," tête bêche pair | 2.00 | 1.50 |
| *b.* | | Perf. 13½ | .60 | .35 |
| **84** | A5 | 20h deep orange (II) | .25 | .25 |
| *a.* | | As "b," tête bêche pair | 14.00 | 15.00 |
| *b.* | | Perf. 13½ | 3.50 | .60 |
| *c.* | | Type I | — | — |
| **85** | A5 | 25h blue green (I) | .25 | .25 |
| *a.* | | Type II | .25 | .25 |
| **86** | A5 | 30h deep violet ('25) | 3.00 | .25 |
| **87** | A6 | 50h yellow green | .60 | .25 |
| *a.* | | As "b," tête bêche pair | 27.50 | 27.50 |
| *b.* | | Perf. 13½ | 7.50 | 2.00 |
| **88** | A6 | 100h dark brown | 1.00 | .25 |
| *a.* | | Perf. 13½ | 15.00 | .30 |
| **89** | A6 | 150h rose | 2.00 | .50 |
| *a.* | | Perf. 13½ | 35.00 | 2.00 |
| **90** | A6 | 185h orange | 1.50 | .30 |
| **91** | A6 | 250h dark green | 2.25 | .50 |
| | | *Nos. 82-91 (10)* | 11.35 | 3.05 |

Imperfs. were not regularly issued.

Nos. 82-84, 87 exist as tete-beche gutter pairs.

**Type of 1920 Issue Redrawn**

Type I

Type II

Type III

Type I — Rib of leaf below "O" of POSTA is straight and extends to tip. White triangle above book is entirely at left of twig. "P" has a stubby, abnormal appendage.

Type II — Rib is extremely bent; does not reach tip. Triangle extends at right of twig. "P" like Type I.

Type III — Rib of top left leaf is broken in two. Triangle like Type II. "P" has no appendage.

**1923** *Perf. 13¾, 13¾x13½*

| No. | Type | Denomination / Color | Unused | Used |
|---|---|---|---|---|
| **92** | A8 | 100h red, *yellow,* III, perf. 14x13½ | .75 | .50 |
| *a.* | | Type I, perf. 13¾ | 1.00 | .25 |
| *b.* | | Type I, perf. 13¾x13½ | .75 | .25 |
| *c.* | | Type II, perf. 13¾ | 1.25 | .25 |
| *d.* | | Type II, perf. 13¾x13½ | 1.10 | .25 |
| *e.* | | Type III, perf. 13¾ | 7.50 | .25 |
| **93** | A8 | 200h blue, *yellow,* II, perf. 14 | 10.00 | .30 |
| *a.* | | Type II, perf. 13¾x13½ | 10.00 | .30 |
| *b.* | | Type III, perf. 13¾ | 6.50 | .30 |
| *c.* | | Type III, perf. 13¾x13½ | 45.00 | .50 |
| **94** | A8 | 300h violet, *yellow,* I, perf. 13¾ | 4.50 | .25 |
| *a.* | | Type II, perf. 13¾ | 35.00 | .35 |
| *b.* | | Type II, perf. 13¾x13½ | 50.00 | .50 |
| *c.* | | Type III, perf. 13¾x13½ | 6.00 | .25 |
| *d.* | | Type III, perf. 13¾ | 27.50 | .35 |
| | | *Nos. 92-94 (3)* | 15.25 | 1.05 |

President Masaryk
A9 A10

*Perf. 13¾x13½, 13¾*

**1925** **Photo.** **Wmk. 107**

**Size: 19½x23mm**

| No. | Type | Denomination / Color | Unused | Used |
|---|---|---|---|---|
| **95** | A9 | 40h brown orange | .75 | .25 |
| **96** | A9 | 50h olive green | 1.50 | .25 |
| **97** | A9 | 60h red violet | 1.75 | .25 |
| | | *Nos. 95-97 (3)* | 4.00 | .75 |

Distinctive Marks of the Engravings.

I, II, III — Background of horizontal lines in top and bottom tablets. Inscriptions in Roman letters with serifs.

IV — Crossed horizontal and vertical lines in the tablets. Inscriptions in Antique letters without serifs.

I, II, IV — Shading of crossed diagonal lines on the shoulder at the right.

III — Shading of single lines only.

I — "T" of "Posta" over middle of "V" of "Ceskoslovenska." Three short horizontal lines in lower part of "A" of "Ceskoslovenska."

II — "T" over right arm of "V." One short line in "A."

III — "T" as in II. Blank space in lower part of "A."

IV — "T" over left arm of "V."

**Wmk. Horizontally (107)**

**Engr.**

**I. First Engraving**

**Size: 19¾x22½mm**

| No. | Type | Denomination / Color | Unused | Used |
|---|---|---|---|---|
| **98** | A10 | 1k carmine | .85 | .25 |
| **99** | A10 | 2k deep blue | 1.75 | .35 |
| **100** | A10 | 3k brown | 3.75 | .65 |
| **101** | A10 | 5k blue green | 1.25 | .35 |
| | | *Nos. 98-101 (4)* | 7.60 | 1.60 |

**Wmk. Vertically (107)**

**Size: 19¼x23mm**

| No. | Type | Denomination / Color | Unused | Used |
|---|---|---|---|---|
| **101A** | A10 | 1k carmine | 60.00 | 3.50 |
| **101B** | A10 | 2k deep blue | 60.00 | 12.50 |
| **101C** | A10 | 3k brown | 150.00 | 12.50 |
| **101D** | A10 | 5k blue green | 3.50 | .60 |
| | | *Nos. 101A-101D (4)* | 273.50 | 29.10 |

**II. Second Engraving**

**Wmk. Horizontally (107)**

**Size: 19x21½mm**

| No. | Type | Denomination / Color | Unused | Used |
|---|---|---|---|---|
| **102** | A10 | 1k carmine | 35.00 | .60 |
| **103** | A10 | 2k deep blue | 3.50 | .30 |
| **104** | A10 | 3k brown | 4.50 | .35 |
| | | *Nos. 102-104 (3)* | 43.00 | 1.25 |

**III. Third Engraving**

**Size: 19-19½x21½-22mm**

*Perf. 10*

| No. | Type | Denomination / Color | Unused | Used |
|---|---|---|---|---|
| **105** | A10 | 1k carmine rose | .75 | .25 |
| *a.* | | Perf. 14 | 6.00 | .25 |

**IV. Fourth Engraving**

**Size: 19x22mm**

**1926** *Perf. 10*

| No. | Type | Denomination / Color | Unused | Used |
|---|---|---|---|---|
| **106** | A10 | 1k carmine rose | 1.00 | .25 |

*Perf. 14*

| No. | Type | Denomination / Color | Unused | Used |
|---|---|---|---|---|
| **108** | A10 | 3k brown | 4.50 | .25 |

There is a 2nd type of No. 106: with long mustache. Same values. See No. 130, design SP3.

Karlstein Castle — A11

**1926, June 1** **Engr.** *Perf. 10*

| No. | Type | Denomination / Color | Unused | Used |
|---|---|---|---|---|
| **109** | A11 | 1.20k red violet | .50 | .30 |
| **110** | A11 | 1.50k car rose | .35 | .25 |
| **111** | A11 | 2.50k dark blue | 3.25 | .35 |
| | | *Nos. 109-111 (3)* | 4.10 | .90 |

See Nos. 133, 135.

Karlstein Castle — A12

Pernstein Castle — A13

Orava Castle
A14

Masaryk
A15

Strahov
Monastery — A16

Hradcany at
Prague
A17

Great
Tatra — A18

Short Mustache

Long, Wavy
Mustache

**1926-27** **Engr.** **Wmk. 107**

**114** A13 30h gray green 1.25 .25
**115** A14 40h red brown .50 .25
**116** A15 50h deep green .50 .25
**117** A15 60h red vio, *lil* .85 .25
**118** A16 1.20k red violet 4.00 1.50

***Perf. 13½***

**119** A17 2k blue 1.00 .25
*a.* 2k ultramarine 6.00 .75
**120** A17 3k deep red 1.25 .25
**121** A18 4k brn vio ('27) 4.50 .60
**122** A18 5k dk grn ('27) 14.00 3.00
*Nos. 114-122 (9)* 27.85 6.60

No. 116 exists in two types. The one with short, straight mustache at left sells for several times as much as that with longer wavy mustache.

See Nos. 137-140.

**Coil Stamps**

***Perf. 10 Vertically***

**123** A12 20h brick red .50 .40
*a.* Vert. pair, imperf. horiz. 100.00
**124** A13 30h gray green .35 .25
*a.* Vert. pair, imperf. horiz. 100.00
**125** A15 50h deep green .25 .25
*Nos. 123-125 (3)* 1.10 .90

See No. 141.

Short Mustache

Long, Wavy
Mustache

**1927-31** **Unwmk.** ***Perf. 10***

**126** A13 30h gray green .25 .25
**127** A14 40h deep brown .70 .25
**128** A15 50h deep green .25 .25
**129** A15 60h red violet .70 .25
**130** A10 1k carmine rose 1.10 .25
**131** A15 1k deep red .75 .25
**132** A16 1.20k red violet .40 .25
**133** A11 1.50k carmine ('29) .55 .25
**134** A13 2k dp grn ('29) .50 .25
**135** A11 2.50k dark blue 5.50 .30
**136** A14 3k red brown ('31) .60 .25
*Nos. 126-136 (11)* 11.30 2.80

No. 130 exists in two types. The one with longer mustache at right sells for several times as much as that with the short mustache.

**1927-28** ***Perf. 13½***

**137** A17 2k ultra .85 .25
**138** A17 3k deep red ('28) 1.90 .65
**139** A18 4k brown violet ('28) 6.00 1.00
**140** A18 5k dark green ('28) 6.25 .50
*Nos. 137-140 (4)* 15.00 2.40

**Coil Stamp**

**1927** ***Perf. 10 Vertically***

**141** A12 20h brick red .50 .25

**Catalogue values for unused stamps in this section, from this point to the end of the section, are for Never Hinged items.**

Hradec Castle
A19

Brno Cathedral
A25

Masaryk — A27

10th anniv. of Czech. independence: 40h, Town Hall, Levoca. 50h, Telephone exchange, Prague. 60h, Town of Jasina. 1k, Hluboka Castle. 1.20k, Pilgrims' House, Velehrad. 2.50k, Great Tatra. 5k, Old City Square, Prague.

**1928, Oct. 22** ***Perf. 13½***

**142** A19 30h black .25 .25
**143** A19 40h red brown .25 .25
**144** A19 50h dark green .25 .25
**145** A19 60h orange red .25 .25
**146** A19 1k carmine .30 .25
**147** A19 1.20k brown vio 1.00 .45
**148** A25 2k ultra 1.00 .75
**149** A19 2.50k dark blue 3.00 2.50
**150** A27 3k dark brown 1.50 1.25
**151** A25 5k deep violet 3.00 3.00
*Nos. 142-151 (10)* 10.80 9.20

From one to three sheets each of Nos. 142-148, perf 12½, appeared on the market in the early 1950's.

Coat of Arms — A29

**1929-37** ***Perf. 10***

**152** A29 5h dark ultra ('31) .25 .25
**153** A29 10h bister brn ('31) .25 .25
**154** A29 20h red .25 .25
**155** A29 25h green .25 .25
**156** A29 30h red violet .25 .25
**157** A29 40h dk brown ('37) 1.60 .25
*a.* 40h red brown ('29) .25 .25
*Nos. 152-157 (6)* 2.85 1.50

**Coil Stamp**

***Perf. 10 Vertically***

**158** A29 20h red .25 .25

For overprints, see Bohemia and Moravia Nos. 1-5, Slovakia Nos. 2-6.

St. Wenceslas
A30

Founding St.
Vitus' Cathedral
A31

Design: 3k, 5k, St. Wenceslas martyred.

**1929, May 14** ***Perf. 13½***

**159** A30 50h gray green .30 .25
**160** A30 60h slate violet .45 .25
**161** A31 2k dull blue 1.10 .30
**162** A30 3k brown 1.50 .35
**163** A30 5k brown violet 5.50 3.50
*Nos. 159-163 (5)* 8.85 4.65

Millenary of the death of St. Wenceslas.

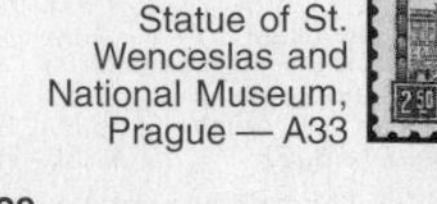

Statue of St.
Wenceslas and
National Museum,
Prague — A33

**1929** ***Perf. 10***

**164** A33 2.50k deep blue 1.00 .25

Brno Cathedral
A34

Tatra Mountain
Scene
A35

Design: 5k, Old City Square, Prague.

**1929, Oct. 15** ***Perf. 13½***

**165** A34 3k red brown 3.00 .25
**166** A35 4k indigo 6.75 .25
**167** A35 5k gray green 9.00 .30
*Nos. 165-167 (3)* 18.75 .80

See No. 183.

A37

Type I

Type II

Two types of 50h:

I — A white space exists across the bottom of the vignette between the coat, shirt and tie and the "HALERU" frame panel.

II — An extra frame line has been added just above the "HALERU" panel which finishes off the coat and tie shading evenly.

**1930, Jan. 2** ***Perf. 10***

**168** A37 50h myrtle green (II) .25 .25
*a.* Type I 1.10 .25
**169** A37 60h brown violet 1.00 .25
**170** A37 1k brown red .40 .25
*Nos. 168-170 (3)* 1.65 .75

See No. 234.

**Coil Stamp**

**1931** ***Perf. 10 Vertically***

**171** A37 1k brown red 1.50 .60

President
Masaryk — A38

**1930, Mar. 1** ***Perf. 13½***

**175** A38 2k gray green 1.50 .35
**176** A38 3k red brown 2.25 .35
**177** A38 5k slate blue 6.00 1.50
**178** A38 10k gray black 16.00 3.50
*Nos. 175-178 (4)* 25.75 5.70

Eightieth birthday of President Masaryk.

Nos. 175-178 were each issued in sheets with ornamental tabs at the bottom. Value, set with tabs $65.50.

St. Nicholas' Church,
Prague — A39

**1931, May 15**

**183** A39 10k black violet 11.00 1.10

Krivoklat
Castle — A40

Krumlov
Castle — A42

Design: 4k, Orlik Castle.

**1932, Jan. 2** ***Perf. 10***

**184** A40 3.50k violet 2.25 1.10
**185** A40 4k deep blue 3.00 .60
**186** A42 5k gray green 4.50 .60
*Nos. 184-186 (3)* 9.75 2.30

A43

A44

**1932, Mar. 16**

**187** A43 50h yellow green .35 .25
**188** A43 1k brown carmine 1.10 .25
**189** A44 2k dark blue 9.00 .35
**190** A44 3k red brown 19.00 .35
*Nos. 187-190 (4)* 29.45 1.20

Miroslav Tyrs — A45

**1933, Feb. 1**

**191** A45 60h dull violet .30 .25

Miroslav Tyrs (1832-84), founder of the Sokol movement; and the 9th Sokol Congress (Nos. 187-190).

First Christian Church at Nitra
A46 A47

**1933, June 20**

**192** A46 50h yellow green .75 .25
**193** A47 1k carmine rose 7.00 .25

Prince Pribina who introduced Christianity into Slovakia and founded there the 1st Christian church in A.D. 833.

All gutter pairs are vertical. Values unused: No. 192 $300; No. 193 $12,000.

Bedrich Smetana,
Czech Composer and
Pianist, 50th Death
Anniv. — A48

**1934, Mar. 26** **Engr.** ***Perf. 10***

**194** A48 50h yellow green .35 .25

Consecration of Legion Colors at Kiev, Sept. 21, 1914 — A49

Ensign Heyduk with Colors A51

Legionnaires A52

1k, Legion receiving battle flag at Bayonne.

**1934, Aug. 15** ***Perf. 10***

**195** A49 50h green .35 .25
**196** A49 1k rose lake .50 .25
**197** A51 2k deep blue 2.75 .25
**198** A52 3k red brown 4.50 .45
*Nos. 195-198 (4)* 8.10 1.20

20th anniv. of the Czechoslovakian Legion which fought in WWI.

Antonin Dvorák, (1841-1904), Composer — A53

**1934, Nov. 22**

**199** A53 50h green .35 .25

Pastoral Scene — A54

**1934, Dec. 17** ***Perf. 10***

**200** A54 1k claret .60 .25
***a.*** Souv. sheet of 15, perf. 13½ 160.00 *250.00*
***b.*** As "a," single stamp 10.00 *12.50*
**201** A54 2k blue 1.75 .45
***a.*** Souv. sheet of 15, perf. 13½ 600.00 *900.00*
***b.*** As "a," single stamp 35.00 27.50

Centenary of the National Anthem.

Nos. 200-201 were each issued in sheets of 100 stamps and 12 blank labels. Value, set with attached labels: mint $21; used $7.

Nos. 200a & 201a have thick paper, darker shades, no gum. Forgeries exist.

A55

President Masaryk — A56

**1935, Mar. 1**

**202** A55 50h green, *buff* .35 .25
**203** A55 1k claret, *buff* .35 .25
**204** A56 2k gray blue, *buff* .50 .60
**205** A56 3k brown, *buff* 3.00 .50
*Nos. 202-205 (4)* 4.20 1.60

85th birthday of President Masaryk.

Nos. 204-205 were each issued in sheets of 100 stamps and 12 blank labels. Value with attached labels: mint $30; used $30.

See No. 235.

Monument to Czech Heroes at Arras, France — A57

**1935, May 4**

**206** A57 1k rose .35 .25
**207** A57 2k dull blue 1.50 .45

20th anniversary of the Battle of Arras.

Nos. 206-207 were each issued in sheets of 100 stamps and 12 blank labels. Value, set with attached labels: mint $8; used $8.

Gen. Milan Stefánik — A58

**1935, May 18**

**208** A58 50h green .25 .25

Sts. Cyril and Methodius — A59

**1935, June 22**

**209** A59 50h green .25 .25
**210** A59 1k claret .45 .25
**211** A59 2k deep blue 1.50 .25
*Nos. 209-211 (3)* 2.20 .75

Millenary of the arrival in Moravia of the Apostles Cyril and Methodius.

Masaryk — A60

**1935, Oct. 20** ***Perf. 12½***

**212** A60 1k rose lake .25 .25

No. 212 exists imperforate. See Bohemia and Moravia No. 1A. For overprints see Bohemia and Moravia Nos. 9-10, Slovakia 12.

Statue of Macha, Prague — A61

**1936, Apr. 30**

**213** A61 50h deep green .25 .25
**214** A61 1k rose lake .40 .25

Karel Hynek Macha (1810-1836), Bohemian poet.

Nos. 213-214 were each issued in sheets of 100 stamps and 12 blank labels. Value, set with attached labels: mint $1; used 75c.

Jan Amos Komensky (Comenius) — A61a

Pres. Eduard Benes A62

Gen. Milan Stefánik A63

**1936**

**215** A61a 40h dark blue .25 .25
**216** A62 50h dull green .25 .25
**217** A63 60h dull violet .25 .25
*Nos. 215-217 (3)* .75 .75

See no. 252, Slovakia 23A. For overprints see Bohemia and Moravia Nos. 6, 8, Slovakia 7, 9-11.

Castle Palanok near Mukacevo A64

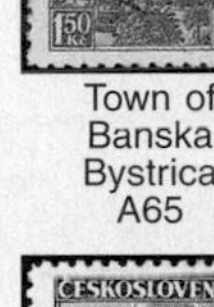

Town of Banska Bystrica A65

Castle at Zvikov — A66

Ruins of Castle at Strecno — A67

Castle at Cesky Raj A68

Palace at Slavkov (Austerlitz) A69

Statue of King George of Podebrad A70

Town Square at Olomouc — A71

Castle Ruins at Bratislava A72

**1936, Aug. 1**

**218** A64 1.20k rose lilac .25 .25
**219** A65 1.50k carmine .25 .25
**220** A66 2k dark blue green .25 .25
**221** A67 2.50k dark blue .25 .25
**222** A68 3k brown .25 .25
**223** A69 3.50k dark violet 1.50 .25
**224** A70 4k dark violet .60 .25
**225** A71 5k green .60 .25
**226** A72 10k blue 1.00 .25
*Nos. 218-226 (9)* 4.95 2.25

Nos. 224-226 were each issued in sheets of 100 stamps and 12 blank labels. Value, with attached labels: mint $6; used $6.

For overprints and surcharge see Nos. 237-238, 254A, Bohemia and Moravia 11-12, 14-19, Slovakia 13-14, 16-23.

President Benes — A73

**1937, Apr. 26 Unwmk.** ***Perf. 12½***

**227** A73 50h deep green .25 .25

For overprints see Nos. 236, Slovakia 8.

Soldiers of the Czech Legion — A74

**1937, June 15**

**228** A74 50h deep green .25 .25
**229** A74 1k rose lake .30 .25

20th anniv. of the Battle of Zborov.

Nos. 228-229 were each issued in sheets of 100 stamps and 12 blank labels. Value, set with attached labels: mint $2; used $1.50.

Cathedral at Prague — A75

**1937, July 1**

**230** A75 2k green .90 .25
**231** A75 2.50k blue 1.40 .30

Founding of the "Little Entente," 16th anniv.

Nos. 230-231 were each issued in sheets with blank labels. Value, set with attached labels: mint $17.50; used $9.

Jan Evangelista Purkyne — A76

**1937, Sept. 2**

**232** A76 50h slate green .25 .25
**233** A76 1k dull rose .30 .25

150th anniv. of the birth of Purkyne, Czech physiologist.

Nos. 232-233 were printed in sheets of 100 with 12 decorated labels. Value, set with labels, $2.50.

**Masaryk Types of 1930-35**

**1937, Sept.** ***Perf. 12½***

**234** A37 50h black .25 .25

**With date "14.IX. 1937" in design**

**235** A56 2k black .30 .25

Death of former President Thomas G. Masaryk on Sept. 14, 1937.

No. 235 was issued in sheets of 100 stamps and 12 inscribed labels. Value, with attached label: mint $3.50; used $3.50.

**International Labor Bureau Issue**

Stamps of 1936-37 Overprinted in Violet or Black

**1937, Oct. 6** ***Perf. 12½***

**236** A73 50h dp green (Bk) .35 .35
**237** A65 1.50k carmine (V) .35 .35
**238** A66 2k dp green (V) .70 .35
*Nos. 236-238 (3)* 1.40 1.05

### Bratislava Philatelic Exhibition Issue
Souvenir Sheet

A77

| 1937, Oct. 24 | | *Perf. 12½* | |
|---|---|---|---|
| **239** A77 | Sheet of 2 | 2.50 | *2.75* |
| *a.* | 50h dark blue | .80 | 1.20 |
| *b.* | 1k brown carmine | .80 | 1.20 |

The stamps show a view of Poprad Lake (50h) and the tomb of General Milan Stefanik (1k).

No. 239 overprinted with the Czechoslovak arms and "Czecho-Slovak Participation New York World's Fair 1939, Czecho-Slovak Pavilion" were privately produced to finance Czechoslovak participation in the exhibition. The overprint exists in black, green, red, blue, gold and silver.

No. 239 overprinted "Liberation de la Tchechoslovaquie, 28-X-1945" etc., was sold at a philatelic exhibition in Brussels, Belgium.

St. Barbara's Church, Kutna Hora — A79

| 1937, Dec. 4 | | | |
|---|---|---|---|
| **240** A79 | 1.60k olive green | .25 | .25 |

For overprints see Bohemia and Moravia Nos. 13, Slovakia 15.

Peregrine Falcon, Sokol Emblem — A80

| 1938, Jan. 21 | | | |
|---|---|---|---|
| **241** A80 | 50h deep green | .25 | .25 |
| **242** A80 | 1k rose lake | .25 | .25 |

10th Intl. Sokol Games.

Nos. 241-242 were each issued in sheets of 100 stamps and 12 inscribed labels. Value, set with attached labels: mint $1.50; used $2.50.

Imperf. examples of No. 242 are essays.

Legionnaires
A81 A82

Legionnaire — A83

| 1938 | | | |
|---|---|---|---|
| **243** A81 | 50h deep green | .25 | .25 |
| **244** A82 | 50h deep green | .25 | .25 |
| **245** A83 | 50h deep green | .25 | .25 |
| | *Nos. 243-245 (3)* | .75 | .75 |

20th anniv. of the Battle of Bachmac, Vouziers and Doss Alto.

Nos. 243-245 were each issued in sheets of 100 stamps and 12 inscribed labels. Value, set with attached labels $2, mint or used.

Jindrich Fügner, Co-Founder of Sokol Movement — A84

| 1938, June 18 | | *Perf. 12½* | |
|---|---|---|---|
| **246** A84 | 50h deep green | .25 | .25 |
| **247** A84 | 1k rose lake | .25 | .25 |
| **248** A84 | 2k slate blue | .40 | .25 |
| | *Nos. 246-248 (3)* | .90 | .75 |

10th Sokol Summer Games.

Nos. 246-248 were each issued in sheets of 100 stamps and 12 inscribed labels. Value, set with attached labels: mint $2.50; used $2.

View of Pilsen — A85

| 1938, June 24 | | | |
|---|---|---|---|
| **249** A85 | 50h deep green | .25 | .25 |

Provincial Economic Council meeting, Pilsen.

No. 249 was issued in sheets of 150 stamps and 10 labels depicting a flower within a cogwheel. Value, with attached label $1, mint or used.

For overprint see Bohemia & Moravia No. 7.

Cathedral of Kosice — A86

| 1938, July 15 | | *Perf. 12½* | |
|---|---|---|---|
| **250** A86 | 50h deep green | .25 | .25 |

Kosice Cultural Exhibition.

No. 250 was issued in sheets of 150 stamps and 10 labels depicting grapes. Value, with attached label $1, $7.50 mint, $4.50 used.

### Prague Philatelic Exhibition Issue
Souvenir Sheet

Vysehrad Castle — Hradcany — A87

| 1938, June 26 | | *Perf. 12½* | |
|---|---|---|---|
| **251** A87 | Sheet of 2 | 5.00 | 5.00 |
| *a.* | 50h dark blue | 1.50 | 1.50 |
| *b.* | 1k deep carmine | 1.50 | 1.50 |

See No. 3036.

### Stefánik Type of 1936

| 1938, Nov. 21 | | | |
|---|---|---|---|
| **252** A63 | 50h deep green | .25 | .25 |

Allegory of the Republic — A89

| 1938, Dec. 19 | | *Unwmk.* | |
|---|---|---|---|
| **253** A89 | 2k lt ultra | .30 | .25 |
| **254** A89 | 3k pale brown | .50 | .40 |

20th anniv. of Independence.

Nos. 253-254 were each issued in sheets of 100 stamps and 12 blank labels. Value, set with attached labels $2, mint or used.

See No. B153.

"Wir sind frei!"

Stamps of Czechoslovakia, 1918-37, overprinted with a swastika in black or red and "Wir sind frei!" were issued locally and unofficially in 1938 as Czech authorities were evacuating and German authorities arriving. They appeared in the towns of Asch, Karlsbad, Reichenberg-Maffersdorf, Rumburg, etc.

The overprint, sometimes including a surcharge or the town name (as in Karlsbad), exists on many values of postage, air post, semi-postal, postage due and newspaper stamps.

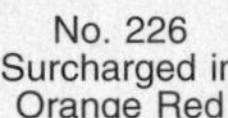

No. 226 Surcharged in Orange Red

| 1939, Jan. 18 | Unwmk. | *Perf. 12½* | |
|---|---|---|---|
| **254A** A72 | 300h on 10k blue | 1.25 | *1.75* |

Opening of the Slovakian Parliament.

No. 254A was issued in sheets of 100 stamps with 12 blank labels. Value with attached labels, mint $4.

View of Jasina — A89a

*Perf. 12½*

| 1939, Mar. 15 | Engr. | *Unwmk.* | |
|---|---|---|---|
| **254B** A89a | 3k ultra | *8.00* | *40.00* |

Inauguration of the Carpatho-Ukraine Diet, Mar. 2, 1939.

Printed for use in the province of Carpatho-Ukraine but issued in Prague at the same time.

No. 254B was issued in sheets of 100 stamps with 12 blank labels. Values with attached labels: mint $12, used $80. Used value is for red commemorative cancel.

The stamps formerly listed as Czechoslovakia Nos. 255, 256 and C18 are now listed with Bohemia and Moravia and Slovakia. No. 255 is now Slovakia 23A. No. 256 and C18 are now listed as Bohemia and Moravia 1A and C1, respectively.

Linden Leaves and Buds — A90

| 1945 | Photo. | *Perf. 14* | |
|---|---|---|---|
| **256A** A90 | 10h black | .25 | .25 |
| **257** A90 | 30h yellow brown | .25 | .25 |
| **258** A90 | 50h dark green | .25 | .25 |
| **258A** A90 | 60h dark blue | .25 | .25 |

**Engr.**
**(Buds Open)**
*Perf. 12½*

| | | | |
|---|---|---|---|
| **259** A90 | 60h blue | .25 | .25 |
| **259A** A90 | 80h orange ver | .25 | .25 |
| **260** A90 | 1.20k rose | .25 | .25 |
| **261** A90 | 3k violet brown | .25 | .25 |
| **262** A90 | 5k green | .25 | .25 |
| | *Nos. 256A-262 (9)* | 2.25 | 2.25 |

Compare with Bohemia-Moravia type A1.

Thomas G. Masaryk — A91

| 1945-46 | Photo. | *Perf. 12* | |
|---|---|---|---|
| **262A** A91 | 5h dull violet ('46) | .25 | .25 |
| **262B** A91 | 10h orange yel ('46) | .25 | .25 |
| **262C** A91 | 20h dk brown ('46) | .25 | .25 |
| **263** A91 | 50h brt green | .25 | .25 |
| **264** A91 | 1k orange red | .25 | .25 |
| **265** A91 | 2k chalky blue | .25 | .25 |
| | *Nos. 262A-265 (6)* | 1.50 | 1.50 |

Coat of Arms — A92

| 1945 | | *Imperf.* | |
|---|---|---|---|
| **266** A92 | 50h olive gray | .25 | .25 |
| **267** A92 | 1k brt red vio | .25 | .25 |
| **268** A92 | 1.50k dk carmine | .25 | .25 |
| **269** A92 | 2k deep blue | .25 | .25 |
| **269A** A92 | 2.40k henna brn | .25 | .25 |
| **270** A92 | 3k brown | .25 | .25 |
| **270A** A92 | 4k dk slate grn | .25 | .25 |
| **271** A92 | 6k violet blue | .25 | .25 |
| **271A** A92 | 10k sepia | .25 | .25 |
| | *Nos. 266-271A (9)* | 2.25 | 2.25 |

Nos. 266, 268, 269, 270 and 271 exist in 2 printings. Stamps of the 1st printing have a coarse impression and are on thin, hard paper in sheets of 100; all values exist in the 2nd printing, with fine impressions on thick, soft wove paper in sheets of 200. Values are the same.

Staff Capt. Ridky (British Army) — A93

Dr. Miroslav Novak (French Army) — A94

Capt. Otakar Jaros (Russian Army) — A95

Staff Capt. Stanislav Zimprich (Foreign Legion) — A96

2nd Lt. Jiri Kral (French Air Force) A97

Josef Gabcik (Parachutist) A98

Staff Capt. Alois Vasatko (Royal Air Force) A99

Private Frantisek Adamek (British Colonial Service) A100

**1945, Aug. 18 Engr. *Perf. 11½x12½***

| | | | | |
|---|---|---|---|---|
| 272 | A93 | 5h intense blue | .25 | .25 |
| 273 | A94 | 10h dark brown | .25 | .25 |
| 274 | A95 | 20h brick red | .25 | .25 |
| 275 | A96 | 25h rose red | .25 | .25 |
| 276 | A97 | 30h purple | .25 | .25 |
| 277 | A98 | 40h sepia | .25 | .25 |
| 278 | A99 | 50h dark olive | .25 | .25 |
| 279 | A100 | 60h violet | .25 | .25 |
| 280 | A93 | 1k carmine | .25 | .25 |
| 281 | A94 | 1.50k lake | .25 | .25 |
| 282 | A95 | 2k ultra | .25 | .25 |
| 283 | A96 | 2.50k deep violet | .25 | .25 |
| 284 | A97 | 3k sepia | .25 | .25 |
| 285 | A98 | 4k rose lilac | .25 | .25 |
| 286 | A99 | 5k myrtle green | .25 | .25 |
| 287 | A100 | 10k brt ultra | .65 | .25 |
| | | *Nos. 272-287 (16)* | 4.40 | 4.00 |

Flags of Russia, Great Britain, US and Czechoslovakia — A101

View of Banská Bystrica A102

Patriot Welcoming Russian Soldier, Turciansky A103

Ruins of Castle at Sklabina A104

Czech Patriot, Strecno A105

**1945, Aug. 29 Photo. *Perf. 10***

| | | | | |
|---|---|---|---|---|
| 288 | A101 | 1.50k brt carmine | .25 | .25 |
| 289 | A102 | 2k brt blue | .25 | .25 |
| 290 | A103 | 4k dark brown | .25 | .25 |
| 291 | A104 | 4.50k purple | .25 | .30 |
| 292 | A105 | 5k deep green | .50 | .50 |
| | | *Nos. 288-292 (5)* | 1.50 | 1.55 |

National uprising against the Germans.

A card contains one each of Nos. 288-292 on thin cardboard, ungummed. Size: 148x210mm. Sold for 50k. Value, $20 unused, $120 used. Forged cancellations exist.

Stefánik A106

Benes A107

Masaryk — A108

**1945-47 Engr. *Perf. 12, 12½***

| | | | | |
|---|---|---|---|---|
| 293 | A106 | 30h rose violet | .25 | .25 |
| 294 | A107 | 60h blue | .25 | .25 |
| 294A | A106 | 1k red org ('47) | .25 | .25 |
| 295 | A108 | 1.20k car rose | .25 | .25 |
| 295A | A108 | 1.20(k) rose lil ('46) | .25 | .25 |
| 296 | A106 | 2.40(k) rose | .25 | .25 |
| 297 | A107 | 3k red violet | .25 | .25 |
| 297A | A108 | 4k dark blue ('46) | .25 | .25 |
| 298 | A108 | 5k Prus green | .25 | .25 |
| 299 | A107 | 7k gray | .25 | .25 |
| 300 | A106 | 10k gray blue | .30 | .25 |
| 300A | A106 | 20k sepia ('46) | .30 | .25 |
| | | *Nos. 293-300A (12)* | 3.10 | 3.00 |

**1945 Photo. *Perf. 14***

| | | | | |
|---|---|---|---|---|
| 301 | A108 | 50h brown | .25 | .25 |
| 302 | A106 | 80h dark green | .25 | .25 |
| 303 | A107 | 1.60(k) olive green | .25 | .25 |
| 304 | A108 | 15k red violet | .30 | .25 |
| | | *Nos. 301-304 (4)* | 1.05 | 1.00 |

Statue of Kozina and Chod Castle, Domazlice — A109

**1945, Nov. 28 Engr. *Perf. 12½***

| | | | | |
|---|---|---|---|---|
| 305 | A109 | 2.40k rose carmine | .25 | .25 |
| 306 | A109 | 4k blue | .25 | .25 |

250th anniv. of the death of Jan Sladky Kozina, peasant leader.

Nos. 305-306 were issued in sheets of 100 stamps with 12 blank labels. Value, set with attached labels, mint $6.

Red Army Soldier — A110

**1945, Mar. 26 Litho. *Imperf.***

| | | | | |
|---|---|---|---|---|
| 307 | A110 | 2k crimson rose | .40 | .40 |
| 308 | A110 | 5k slate black | 1.10 | 1.10 |
| 309 | A110 | 6k ultramarine | 1.10 | 1.10 |
| | | *Nos. 307-309 (3)* | 2.60 | 2.60 |

**Souvenir Sheet**

**1945, July 16 Gray Burelage**

| | | | |
|---|---|---|---|
| 310 | Sheet of 3 | 4.00 | 4.00 |
| *a.* | A110 2k crimson rose | .75 | .75 |
| *b.* | A110 5k slate black | .75 | .75 |
| *c.* | A110 6k ultramarine | .75 | .75 |

Return of Pres. Benes, Apr., 1945.

Clasped Hands — A112

**1945 *Rouletted 12½***

| | | | | |
|---|---|---|---|---|
| 311 | A112 | 1.50k brown red | 1.50 | 1.50 |
| 312 | A112 | 9k red orange | .35 | .35 |
| 313 | A112 | 13k orange brown | .65 | .65 |
| 314 | A112 | 20k blue | 1.50 | 1.50 |
| | | *Nos. 311-314 (4)* | 4.00 | 4.00 |

Karel Havlícek Borovsky — A113

**1946, July 5 Engr. *Perf. 12½***

| | | | | |
|---|---|---|---|---|
| 315 | A113 | 1.20k gray black | .25 | .25 |

Borovsky (1821-56), editor and writer.

Issued in sheets of 100 stamps and 12 inscribed labels. Value with attached label: $1.25.

Old Town Hall, Brno — A114

Hodonin Square — A115

***Perf. 12½x12, 12x12½***

**1946, Aug. 3 Engr. Unwmk.**

| | | | | |
|---|---|---|---|---|
| 316 | A114 | 2.40k deep rose | .25 | .25 |
| 317 | A115 | 7.40k dull violet | .25 | .25 |

See No. B159.

President Eduard Benes — A116

**1946, Oct. 28**

| | | | | |
|---|---|---|---|---|
| 318 | A116 | 60h indigo | .25 | .25 |
| 319 | A116 | 1.60k dull green | .25 | .25 |
| 320 | A116 | 3k red lilac | .25 | .25 |
| 321 | A116 | 8k sepia | .25 | .25 |
| | | *Nos. 318-321 (4)* | 1.00 | 1.00 |

Flag, Symbols — A117

**1947, Jan. 1 *Perf. 12½***

| | | | | |
|---|---|---|---|---|
| 322 | A117 | 1.20k Prus green | .25 | .25 |
| 323 | A117 | 2.40k deep rose | .25 | .25 |
| 324 | A117 | 4k deep blue | .45 | .25 |
| | | *Nos. 322-324 (3)* | .95 | .75 |

Czechoslovakia's two-year reconstruction and rehabilitation program.

Nos. 322-324 each issued in sheets of 100 stamps and 12 inscribed labels. Value, set with attached labels, $3.

Saint Adalbert — A118

**1947, Apr. 23**

| | | | | |
|---|---|---|---|---|
| 326 | A118 | 1.60k gray | .75 | .60 |
| 327 | A118 | 2.40k rose carmine | .90 | .60 |
| 328 | A118 | 5k blue green | 1.10 | .45 |
| | | *Nos. 326-328 (3)* | 2.75 | 1.65 |

950th anniv. of the death of Saint Adalbert, Bishop of Prague.

Nos. 326-328 each issued in sheets of 100 stamps and 12 monogrammed labels. Value, set with attached labels, $35.

Grief — A119

Allegorical Figure — A120

**1947, June 10 Engr.**

| | | | | |
|---|---|---|---|---|
| 329 | A119 | 1.20k black | .40 | .25 |
| 330 | A119 | 1.60k slate black | .45 | .45 |
| 331 | A120 | 2.40k brown violet | .45 | .45 |
| | | *Nos. 329-331 (3)* | 1.30 | 1.15 |

Destruction of Lidice, 5th anniversary.

Nos. 329-331 each issued in sheets of 100 stamps and 12 inscribed labels. Value, set with attached labels, $15.

World Federation of Youth Symbol — A121

**1947, July 20**

| | | | | |
|---|---|---|---|---|
| 332 | A121 | 1.20k violet brown | .50 | .35 |
| 333 | A121 | 4k slate | .50 | .35 |

World Youth Festival held in Prague, July 20-Aug. 17.

Thomas G. Masaryk — A122

**1947, Sept. 14**

| | | | | |
|---|---|---|---|---|
| 334 | A122 | 1.20k gray blk, *buff* | .25 | .25 |
| 335 | A122 | 4k blue blk, *cream* | .30 | .25 |

Death of Masaryk, 10th anniv.

Nos. 334-335 each issued in sheets of 100 stamps and 12 inscribed labels. Value, set with attached labels, $5.

Msgr. Stefan Moyses A123

**1947, Oct. 19**

| | | | | |
|---|---|---|---|---|
| 336 | A123 | 1.20k rose violet | .25 | .25 |
| 337 | A123 | 4k deep blue | .25 | .25 |

150th anniversary of the birth of Stefan Moyses, first Slovakian chairman of the Slavic movement.

Each issued in sheets of 100 stamps and 12 labels with "MOYSES" and floral decoration. Valuc, sct with attached labels, $7.50.

"Freedom from Social Oppression" A124

**1947, Oct. 26 Photo. *Perf. 14***

| | | | | |
|---|---|---|---|---|
| 338 | A124 | 2.40k brt carmine | .40 | .30 |
| 339 | A124 | 4k brt ultra | .50 | .25 |

Russian revolution of Oct., 1917, 30th anniv.

Benes — A125

**1948, Feb. 15 Photo.**

**Size: 17½x21½mm**

| | | | | |
|---|---|---|---|---|
| 340 | A125 | 1.50k brown | .25 | .25 |

**Size: 19x23mm**

| | | | | |
|---|---|---|---|---|
| 341 | A125 | 2k deep plum | .25 | .25 |
| 342 | A125 | 5k brt ultra | .25 | .25 |
| | | *Nos. 340-342 (3)* | .75 | .75 |

"Czechoslovakia" Greeting Sokol Marchers — A126

**1948, Mar. 7 Engr. *Perf. 12½***

**343** A126 1.50k brown .25 .25
**344** A126 3k rose carmine .25 .25
**345** A126 5k blue .50 .25
*Nos. 343-345 (3)* 1.00 .75

The 11th Sokol Congress.

Nos. 343-345 each issued in sheets of 100 stamps and 12 labels depicting dates and bouquet. Values, set with attached labels: mint $4.50; used $3.75.

King Charles IV — A127 St. Wenceslas, King Charles IV — A128

**1948, Apr. 7**

**346** A127 1.50k black brown .25 .25
**347** A128 2k dark brown .25 .25
**348** A128 3k brown red .25 .25
**349** A127 5k dark blue .25 .25
*Nos. 346-349 (4)* 1.00 1.00

600th anniv. of the foundation of Charles University, Prague.

Nos. 346-349 each issued in sheets of 100 stamps and 12 inscribed labels. Value, set with attached labels, $4.50.

Czech Peasants in Revolt — A129

**Unwmk.**

**1948, May 14 Photo. *Perf. 14***

**350** A129 1.50k dk olive brown .25 .25

Centenary of abolition of serfdom.

Jindrich Vanicek — A130

Designs: 1.50k, 2k, Josef Scheiner.

**1948, June 10 Engr. *Perf. 12½***

**351** A130 1k dark green .25 .25
**352** A130 1.50k sepia .25 .25
**353** A130 2k gray blue .25 .25
**354** A130 3k claret .25 .25
*Nos. 351-354 (4)* 1.00 1.00

11th Sokol Congress, Prague, 1948.

Nos. 351-354 each issued in sheets of 100 stamps and 12 labels depicting a sunflower. Values, set with attached labels: $3.75 mint; $3 used.

Frantisek Palacky & F. L. Rieger — A131

**1948, June 20 Unwmk.**

**355** A131 1.50k gray .25 .25
**356** A131 3k brown carmine .25 .25

Constituent Assembly at Kromeriz, cent.

Nos. 355-356 each issued in sheets of 100 stamps and 12 labels depicting a wreath. Value, set with attached labels, $1.50.

Miloslav Josef Hurban — A132

3k, Ludovit Stur. 5k, Michael M. Hodza.

**1948, Aug. 27 *Perf. 12½***

**357** A132 1.50k dark brown .25 .25
**358** A132 3k carmine lake .25 .25
**359** A132 5k indigo .25 .25
*Nos. 357-359 (3)* .75 .75

Cent. of 1848 insurrection against Hungary.

Nos. 357-359 each issued in sheets of 100 stamps and 12 labels depicting signatures. Values, set with attached labels: mint $5; used $3.50.

Eduard Benes — A133

**1948, Sept. 28**

**360** A133 8k black .25 .25

President Eduard Benes, 1884-1948.

Czechoslovak Family — A134

**1948, Oct. 28 *Perf. 12½x12***

**361** A134 1.50k deep blue .25 .25
**362** A134 3k rose carmine .25 .25

Czechoslovakia's Independence, 30th anniv.

Nos. 361-362 each issued in sheets of 100 stamps and 12 labels depicting dates, leaves. Value, set with attached labels, $2.

Pres. Klement Gottwald — A135

**1948-49 *Perf. 12½***

**Size: 18½x23½mm**

**363** A135 1.50k dk brown .25 .25
**364** A135 3k car rose .30 .25
*a.* 3k rose brown 1.00 .25
**365** A135 5k gray blue .25 .25

**Size: 23½x29mm**

**366** A135 20k purple .90 .25
*Nos. 363-366 (4)* 1.70 1.00

No. 366 was issued in sheets of 100 stamps and 12 monogrammed labels. Value, with attached label, $3.50.

See Nos. 373, 564, 600-604.

**Souvenir Sheet**

**1948, Nov. 23 Unwmk. *Imperf.***

**367** A135 30k rose brown 4.25 3.00

52nd birthday of Pres. Klement Gottwald (1896-1953).

**Hradcany Castle Type of 1918**

Souvenir Sheet

**1948, Dec. 18**

**368** A1 10k dk blue violet 3.00 2.40

1st Czech postage stamp, 30th anniv.

Czechoslovak and Russian Workmen Shaking Hands — A138

**1948, Dec. 12 *Perf. 12½***

**369** A138 3k rose carmine .25 .25

5th anniv. of the treaty of alliance between Czechoslovakia and Russia.

No. 369 issued in sheets of 100 stamps and 12 labels depicting Czech and Soviet flags. Value with attached label 60c.

Lenin — A139

**1949, Jan. 21 Engr. *Perf. 12½***

**370** A139 1.50k violet brown .30 .25
**371** A139 5k deep blue .30 .30

25th anniversary of the death of Lenin.

Nos. 370-371 each issued in sheets of 100 stamps and 12 labels depicting torch. Value, set with attached labels: mint $1.75; used $1.50.

**Gottwald Type of 1948 Inscribed: "UNOR 1948" and**

Gottwald Addressing Meeting A140

**1949, Feb. 25 Photo. *Perf. 14***

**372** A140 3k red brown .25 .25

***Perf. 12½***

**Engr.**

**Size: 23½x29mm**

**373** A135 10k deep green .40 .25

1st anniv. of Gottwald's speech announcing the appointment of a new government. No. 372 exists in a souvenir sheet of 1. It was not sold to the public.

No. 373 issued in sheets of 100 stamps and 12 inscribed labels. Values with attached label: mint $2.50; used $1.50.

A141

Writers: 50h, P. O. Hviezdoslav. 80h, V. Vancura. 1k, J. Sverma. 2k, Julius Fucik. 4k, Jiri Wolker. 8k, Alois Jirasek.

**1949 Photo. *Perf. 14***

**374** A141 50h violet brown .25 .25
**375** A141 80h scarlet .25 .25
**376** A141 1k dk olive green .25 .25
**377** A141 2k brt blue .40 .25

***Perf. 12½***

**Engr.**

**378** A141 4k violet brown .40 .25
**379** A141 8k brown black .50 .25
*Nos. 374-379 (6)* 2.05 1.50

A142

3k, Stagecoach and Train. 5k, Postrider and post bus. 13k, Sailing ship and plane.

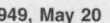

**1949, May 20**

**380** A142 3k brown carmine 1.40 1.40
**381** A142 5k deep blue 1.00 .45
**382** A142 13k deep green 1.40 .85
*Nos. 380-382 (3)* 3.80 2.70

75th anniv. of the UPU.

Reaping A143

Communist Emblem and Workers A144

Workman, Symbol of Industry — A145

***Perf. 12½x12, 12x12½***

**1949, May 24 Unwmk.**

**383** A143 1.50k deep green .50 .45
**384** A144 3k brown carmine .50 .45
**385** A145 5k deep blue .50 .45
*Nos. 383-385 (3)* 1.50 1.35

No. 384 for the 9th meeting of the Communist Party of Czechoslovakia, 5/25/49.

Nos. 383-385 each issued in sheets of 100 stamps and 12 inscribed labels. Value, set with attached labels, $12.

Bedrich Smetana and Natl. Theater, Prague — A146

**1949, June 4 *Perf. 12½x12***

**386** A146 1.50k dull green .25 .25
**387** A146 5k deep blue .75 .25

Birth of Bedrich Smetana, composer, 125th anniv.

Aleksander Pushkin — A147

**1949, June 6 *Perf. 12x12½***

**388** A147 2k olive gray .25 .25

Birth of Aleksander S. Pushkin, 150th anniv.

Frederic Chopin and Conservatory, Warsaw A148

**1949, June 24 *Perf. 12½x12***

**389** A148 3k dark red .40 .25
**390** A148 8k violet brown .75 .50

Cent. of the death of Frederic F. Chopin.

Globe and Ribbon — A149

**1949, Aug. 20** *Perf. 12½x12*

| | | | | | |
|---|---|---|---|---|---|
| **391** | A149 | 1.50k | violet brown | .35 | .35 |
| **392** | A149 | 5k | ultra | .90 | .90 |

50th Prague Sample Fair, Sept. 11-18, 1949.

Starting in October, 1949, some commemorative sets included one "blocked" value, which could be obtained only by purchasing the complete set. These restricted values were printed in smaller quantities than other stamps in the set and were typically sold for more than face value.

Zvolen Castle — A150

**1949, Aug. 28** *Perf. 12½*

| | | | | | |
|---|---|---|---|---|---|
| **393** | A150 | 10k | rose lake | .75 | .25 |

Early Miners — A151

Miner of Today — A152

Design: 5k, Mining Machine.

**1949, Sept. 11** *Perf. 12½*

| | | | | | |
|---|---|---|---|---|---|
| **394** | A151 | 1.50k | sepia | .70 | .50 |
| **395** | A152 | 3k | carmine rose | 5.50 | 2.00 |
| **396** | A151 | 5k | deep blue | 4.00 | 1.50 |
| | | | *Nos. 394-396 (3)* | 10.20 | 4.00 |

700th anniv. of the Czechoslovak mining industry; 150th anniv. of the miner's laws.

Construction Workers — A153

**1949, Dec. 11** *Perf. 12½*

| | | | | | |
|---|---|---|---|---|---|
| **397** | A153 | 1k | shown | 3.00 | 1.40 |
| **398** | A153 | 2k | Machinist | 2.00 | .70 |

2nd Trade Union Congress, Prague, 1949.

Joseph V. Stalin — A154

Design: 3k, Stalin facing left.

**Cream Paper**

**1949, Dec. 21** **Unwmk.**

| | | | | | |
|---|---|---|---|---|---|
| **399** | A154 | 1.50k | greenish gray | .75 | .35 |
| **400** | A154 | 3k | claret | 4.50 | 1.75 |

70th birthday of Joseph V. Stalin.

Skier — A155

Efficiency Badge — A156

**Engr., Photo. (3k)**

**1950, Feb. 15** *Perf. 12½, 13½*

| | | | | | |
|---|---|---|---|---|---|
| **401** | A155 | 1.50k | gray blue | 2.75 | 1.50 |
| **402** | A156 | 3k | vio brn, *cr* | 2.75 | 1.50 |
| **403** | A155 | 5k | ultramarine | 2.00 | 1.10 |
| | | | *Nos. 401-403 (3)* | 7.50 | 4.10 |

51st Ski Championship for the Tatra cup, Feb. 15-26, 1950.

Vladimir V. Mayakovsky, Poet, 20th Death Anniv. — A157

**1950, Apr. 14** **Engr.** *Perf. 12½*

| | | | | | |
|---|---|---|---|---|---|
| **404** | A157 | 1.50k | dark brown | 2.25 | 1.10 |
| **405** | A157 | 3k | brown red | 2.25 | 1.10 |

See Nos. 414-417, 422-423, 432-433, 464-465, 477-478.

Soviet Tank Soldier and Hradcany — A158

2k, Hero of Labor medal. 3k, Two workers (militiamen) and Town Hall, Prague. 5k, Text of government program and heraldic lion.

**1950, May 5**

| | | | | | |
|---|---|---|---|---|---|
| **406** | A158 | 1.50k | gray green | .35 | .25 |
| **407** | A158 | 2k | dark brown | 1.00 | 1.00 |
| **408** | A158 | 3k | brown red | .25 | .25 |
| **409** | A158 | 5k | dark blue | .50 | .25 |
| | | | *Nos. 406-409 (4)* | 2.10 | 1.75 |

5th anniv. of the Czechoslovak People's Democratic Republic.

Factory and Young Couple with Tools — A159

Designs: 2k, Steam shovel. 3k, Farmer and farm scene. 5k, Three workers leaving factory.

**1950, May 9** **Engr.**

| | | | | | |
|---|---|---|---|---|---|
| **410** | A159 | 1.50k | dark green | 1.75 | .85 |
| **411** | A159 | 2k | dark brown | 1.75 | .85 |
| **412** | A159 | 3k | rose red | 1.00 | .35 |
| **413** | A159 | 5k | deep blue | 1.00 | .35 |
| | | | *Nos. 410-413 (4)* | 5.50 | 2.40 |

Canceled to Order

The government philatelic department started about 1950 to sell canceled sets of new issues. Values in the second ("used") column are for these canceled-to-order stamps. Postally used stamps are worth more.

**Portrait Type of 1950**

Design: S. K. Neumann.

**1950, June 5** **Unwmk.** *Perf. 12½*

| | | | | | |
|---|---|---|---|---|---|
| **414** | A157 | 1.50k | deep blue | .35 | .25 |
| **415** | A157 | 3k | violet brown | 1.10 | 1.00 |

Stanislav Kostka Neumann (1875-1947), journalist and poet.

**1950, June 21**

Design: Bozena Nemcova.

| | | | | | |
|---|---|---|---|---|---|
| **416** | A157 | 1.50k | deep blue | 1.25 | .75 |
| **417** | A157 | 7k | dark brown | .30 | .25 |

Bozena Nemcova (1820-1862), writer.

Liberation of Colonies A160

Designs: 2k, Allegory, Fight for Peace. 3k, Group of Students. 5k, Marching Students with flags.

**1950, Aug. 14**

| | | | | | |
|---|---|---|---|---|---|
| **418** | A160 | 1.50k | dark green | .25 | .25 |
| **419** | A160 | 2k | sepia | .25 | .25 |
| **420** | A160 | 3k | rose carmine | .25 | .25 |
| **421** | A160 | 5k | ultra | .60 | .45 |
| | | | *Nos. 418-421 (4)* | 1.35 | 1.20 |

2nd International Students World Congress, Prague, Aug. 12-24, 1950.

**Portrait Type of 1950**

Design: Zdenek Fibich.

**1950, Oct. 15**

| | | | | | |
|---|---|---|---|---|---|
| **422** | A157 | 3k | rose brown | .90 | .55 |
| **423** | A157 | 8k | gray green | .35 | .25 |

Zdenek Fibich, musician, birth centenary.

Miner, Soldier and Farmer A161

Czech and Soviet Soldiers A162

**1950, Oct. 6**

| | | | | | |
|---|---|---|---|---|---|
| **424** | A161 | 1.50k | slate | .35 | .35 |
| **425** | A162 | 3k | carmine rose | .35 | .35 |

Issued to publicize Czech Army Day.

Prague Castle, 16th Century A163

Prague, 1493 A164

3k, Prague, 1606. 5k, Prague, 1794.

**1950, Oct. 21** *Perf. 14*

| | | | | | |
|---|---|---|---|---|---|
| **426** | A163 | 1.50k | black | 4.50 | 2.25 |
| **427** | A164 | 2k | chocolate | 4.50 | 2.25 |
| **428** | A164 | 3k | brown car | 4.50 | 2.25 |
| **429** | A164 | 5k | gray | 4.50 | 2.25 |
| *a.* | | | Block of 4, #426-429 | 25.00 | 15.00 |

See Nos. 434-435.

Communications Symbols — A165

**1950, Oct. 25** *Perf. 12½*

| | | | | | |
|---|---|---|---|---|---|
| **430** | A165 | 1.50k | chocolate | .35 | .25 |
| **431** | A165 | 3k | brown carmine | .75 | .60 |

1st anniv. of the foundation of the Intl. League of P.T.T. Employees.

**Portrait Type of 1950**

Design: J. Gregor Tajovsky.

**1950, Oct. 26**

| | | | | | |
|---|---|---|---|---|---|
| **432** | A157 | 1.50k | brown | 1.00 | .75 |
| **433** | A157 | 5k | deep blue | 1.00 | .75 |

10th anniversary of the death of J. Gregor Tajovsky (1874-1940), Slovakian writer.

**Scenic Type of 1950**

Design: Prague, 1950.

**1950, Oct. 28**

| | | | | | |
|---|---|---|---|---|---|
| **434** | A164 | 1.50k | indigo | .35 | .25 |
| *a.* | | | Souvenir sheet of 4, imperf. | 30.00 | 11.00 |
| **435** | A164 | 3k | brown car | .90 | .50 |

Czech and Soviet Steel Workers A166

**1950, Nov. 4** **Unwmk.**

| | | | | | |
|---|---|---|---|---|---|
| **436** | A166 | 1.50k | chocolate | .45 | .30 |
| **437** | A166 | 5k | deep blue | .90 | .60 |

Issued to publicize the 2nd meeting of the Union of Czechoslovak-Soviet Friendship.

Dove by Picasso A167

**1951, Jan. 20** **Photo.** *Perf. 14*

| | | | | |
|---|---|---|---|---|
| **438** | A167 | 2k deep blue | 6.00 | 4.50 |
| **439** | A167 | 3k rose brown | 4.00 | 1.50 |

1st Czechoslovak Congress of Fighters for Peace, held in Prague.

Julius Fucik — A168

**1951, Feb. 17** **Engr.** *Perf. 12½*

| | | | | | |
|---|---|---|---|---|---|
| **440** | A168 | 1.50k | gray | .75 | .75 |
| **441** | A168 | 5k | gray blue | 1.50 | 1.50 |

No. 441 exists in a sheet of 12. Value, $500.

Drop Hammer — A169

Installing Gear — A170

**1951, Feb. 24**

| | | | | | |
|---|---|---|---|---|---|
| **442** | A169 | 1.50k | gray blk | .25 | .25 |
| **443** | A170 | 3k | violet brn | .25 | .25 |
| **444** | A169 | 4k | gray blue | .60 | .50 |
| | | | *Nos. 442-444 (3)* | 1.10 | 1.00 |

Women Machinists — A171

Designs: 3k, Woman tractor operator. 5k, Women of different races.

**1951, Mar. 8 Photo. *Perf. 14***

| | | | | |
|---|---|---|---|---|
| **445** | A171 | 1.50k olive brown | .40 | .30 |
| **446** | A171 | 3k brown car | 1.40 | 1.00 |
| **447** | A171 | 5k blue | .70 | .40 |
| | | *Nos. 445-447 (3)* | 2.50 | 1.70 |

International Women's Day, Mar. 8.

Apprentice Miners — A172

**1951, Apr. 12 Engr. *Perf. 12½***

| | | | | |
|---|---|---|---|---|
| **448** | A172 | 1.50k gray | .55 | .50 |
| **449** | A172 | 3k red brown | .25 | .25 |

Plowing A173

Collective Cattle Breeding A174

**1951, Apr. 28 Photo. *Perf. 14***

| | | | | |
|---|---|---|---|---|
| **450** | A173 | 1.50k brown | .70 | .70 |
| **451** | A174 | 2k dk green | 1.40 | 1.40 |

Tatra Mountain Recreation Center — A175

Mountain Recreation Centers: 2k, Beskydy (Beskids). 3k, Krkonose (Carpathians).

**1951, May 5 Engr. *Perf. 12½***

| | | | | |
|---|---|---|---|---|
| **452** | A175 | 1.50k deep green | .25 | .25 |
| **453** | A175 | 2k dark brown | 1.00 | .75 |
| **454** | A175 | 3k rose brown | .25 | .25 |
| | | *Nos. 452-454 (3)* | 1.50 | 1.25 |

Issued to publicize the summer opening of trade union recreation centers.

Klement Gottwald and Joseph Stalin A176

Factory Militiaman A177

Red Army Soldier and Partisan A178

Marx, Engels, Lenin and Stalin A179

**1951 Unwmk. *Perf. 12½***

| | | | | |
|---|---|---|---|---|
| **455** | A176 | 1.50k olive gray | .75 | .25 |
| **456** | A177 | 2k red brown | .35 | .25 |
| **457** | A178 | 3k rose brown | .35 | .25 |
| **458** | A176 | 5k deep blue | 1.40 | 1.00 |
| **459** | A179 | 8k gray | .70 | .25 |
| | | *Nos. 455-459 (5)* | 3.55 | 2.00 |

30th anniv. of the founding of the Czechoslovak Communist Party.

A180

Design: 1k, 2k, Antonin Dvorák. 1.50k, 3k, Bedrich Smetana.

**1951, May 30**

| | | | | |
|---|---|---|---|---|
| **460** | A180 | 1k redsh brown | .35 | .25 |
| **461** | A180 | 1.50k olive gray | 1.40 | .70 |
| **462** | A180 | 2k dk redsh brn | 1.40 | .70 |
| **463** | A180 | 3k rose brown | .35 | .25 |
| | | *Nos. 460-463 (4)* | 3.50 | 1.90 |

International Music Festival, Prague.

Nos. 461 and 462 were each issued in sheets of 10 stamps. Value, $700 for 461, $600 for 462.

**Portrait Type of 1950**

Portrait: Bohumir Smeral (facing right).

**1951, June 21**

| | | | | |
|---|---|---|---|---|
| **464** | A157 | 1.50k dark gray | .75 | .50 |
| **465** | A157 | 3k rose brown | .35 | .25 |

10th anniv. of the death of Bohumir Smeral, political leader.

A181

**1951, June 21**

| | | | | |
|---|---|---|---|---|
| **466** | A181 | 1k shown | .75 | .35 |
| **467** | A181 | 1.50k Discus | .75 | .35 |
| **468** | A181 | 3k Soccer | 1.50 | .35 |
| **469** | A181 | 5k Skier | 3.50 | 1.50 |
| | | *Nos. 466-469 (4)* | 6.50 | 2.55 |

Issued to honor the 9th Congress of the Czechoslovak Sokol Federation.

Scene from "Fall of Berlin" A182

Scene from "The Great Citizen" A183

**1951, July 14**

| | | | | |
|---|---|---|---|---|
| **470** | A182 | 80h rose brown | .35 | .35 |
| **471** | A183 | 1.50k dark gray | .35 | .35 |
| **472** | A182 | 4k gray blue | 1.40 | 1.10 |
| | | *Nos. 470-472 (3)* | 2.10 | 1.80 |

Intl. Film Festival, Karlovy Vary, July 14-29.

Alois Jirásek — A184

"Fables and Fate" A185

Design: 4k, Scene from "Reign of Tabor."

**1951, Aug. 23 Engr. *Perf. 12½***

| | | | | |
|---|---|---|---|---|
| **473** | A184 | 1.50k gray | .35 | .25 |
| **474** | A184 | 5k dark blue | 2.10 | .80 |

**Photo.**

***Perf. 14***

| | | | | |
|---|---|---|---|---|
| **475** | A185 | 3k dark red | .50 | .25 |
| **476** | A185 | 4k dark brown | .50 | .25 |
| | | *Nos. 473-476 (4)* | 3.45 | 1.55 |

Cent. of the birth of Alois Jirásek, author.

No. 474 was issued in a sheet of 10 stamps. Value: mint *$900.*

**Portrait Type of 1950**

Design: Josef Hybes (1850-1921), cofounder of Czech Communist Party.

**1951, July 21 Engr.**

| | | | | |
|---|---|---|---|---|
| **477** | A157 | 1.50k chocolate | .35 | .25 |
| **478** | A157 | 2k rose brown | .75 | .40 |

"Ostrava Region" — A186

Mining Iron Ore — A187

**1951, Sept. 9**

| | | | | |
|---|---|---|---|---|
| **479** | A186 | 1.50k dk brown | .25 | .25 |
| **480** | A187 | 3k rose brown | .25 | .25 |
| **481** | A186 | 5k deep blue | 1.00 | .65 |
| | | *Nos. 479-481 (3)* | 1.50 | 1.15 |

Miner's Day, Sept. 9, 1951.

Soldiers on Parade — A188

1k, Gunner and field gun. 1.50k, Klement Gottwald. 3k, Tankman and tank. 5k, Aviators.

**Photo. (80h, 5k), Engr.**

**1951, Oct. 6 *Perf. 14 (80h, 5k), 12½***

**Inscribed: "Den CS Armady 1951"**

| | | | | |
|---|---|---|---|---|
| **482** | A188 | 80h olive brown | .35 | .30 |
| **483** | A188 | 1k dk olive grn | .35 | .30 |
| **484** | A188 | 1.50k sepia | .35 | .30 |
| **485** | A188 | 3k claret | .75 | .35 |
| **486** | A188 | 5k blue | 1.75 | .75 |
| | | *Nos. 482-486 (5)* | 3.55 | 2.00 |

Issued to publicize Army Day, Oct. 6, 1951.

Stalin and Gottwald — A189

Lenin, Stalin and Soldiers — A190

**1951, Nov. 3 Engr. *Perf. 12½***

| | | | | |
|---|---|---|---|---|
| **487** | A189 | 1.50k sepia | .25 | .25 |
| **488** | A190 | 3k red brown | .25 | .25 |
| **489** | A189 | 4k deep blue | 1.00 | .45 |
| | | *Nos. 487-489 (3)* | 1.50 | .95 |

Issued to publicize the month of Czechoslovak-Soviet friendship, 1951.

Peter Jilemnicky — A191

**1951, Dec. 5 Unwmk.**

| | | | | |
|---|---|---|---|---|
| **491** | A191 | 1.50k redsh brown | .25 | .25 |
| **492** | A191 | 2k dull blue | .80 | .30 |

Peter Jilemnicky (1901-1949), writer.

Ladislav Zapotocky — A192

**1952, Jan. 12 *Perf. 11½***

| | | | | |
|---|---|---|---|---|
| **493** | A192 | 1.50k brown red | .25 | .25 |
| **494** | A192 | 4k gray | 1.00 | .45 |

Centenary of the birth of Ladislav Zapotocky, Bohemian socialist pioneer.

Jan Kollar — A193

**1952, Jan. 30 Unwmk. *Perf. 11½***

| | | | | |
|---|---|---|---|---|
| **495** | A193 | 3k dark carmine | .25 | .25 |
| **496** | A193 | 5k violet blue | 1.10 | .60 |

Jan Kollar (1793-1852), poet.

Lenin and Lenin Hall — A194

**1952, Jan. 30 *Perf. 12½***

| | | | | |
|---|---|---|---|---|
| **497** | A194 | 1.50k rose carmine | .30 | .25 |
| **498** | A194 | 5k deep blue | 1.10 | .75 |

6th All-Russian Party Conf., 40th anniv.

Emil Holub and African — A195

**1952, Feb. 21** *Perf. 11½*

**499** A195 3k red brown .35 .25
**500** A195 5k gray 1.50 .90

Death of Emil Holub, explorer, 50th anniv.

Gottwald Metallurgical Plant — A196

Designs: 2k, Foundry. 3k, Chemical plant.

**1952, Feb. 25** **Photo.** *Perf. 14*

**501** A196 1.50k sepia .25 .25
**502** A196 2k red brown 1.50 .60
**503** A196 3k scarlet .25 .25
*Nos. 501-503 (3)* 2.00 1.10

Student, Soldier and Miner — A197

Youths of Three Races — A198

**1952, Mar. 21** **Unwmk.** *Perf. 14*

**504** A197 1.50k blue .25 .25
**505** A198 2k olive black .25 .25
**506** A197 3k lake 1.00 .50
*Nos. 504-506 (3)* 1.50 1.00

International Youth Day, Mar. 25, 1952.

**Similar to Type of 1951**

Portrait: Otakar Sevcik.

**1952, Mar. 22** **Engr.** *Perf. 12½*

**507** A184 2k choc, *cr* .80 .35
**508** A184 3k rose brn, *cr* .25 .25

Otakar Sevcik, violinist, birth cent.

Jan A. Komensky — A199

**1952, Mar. 28**

**509** A199 1.50k dk brown, *cr* 1.50 .65
**510** A199 11k dk blue, *cr* .35 .25

360th anniv. of the birth of Jan Amos Komensky (Comenius), teacher and philosopher.

Industrial and Farm Women — A200

**1952, Mar. 8**

**511** A200 1.50k dp blue, *cr* 1.20 .50

International Women's Day Mar. 8, 1952.

Woman and Children — A201

**1952, Apr. 12**

**512** A201 2k chocolate, *cr* 1.60 1.00
**513** A201 3k dp claret, *cr* .25 .25

Intl. Conf. for the Protection of Children, Vienna, Apr. 12-16, 1952.

Antifascist — A202

**1952, Apr. 11** **Photo.** *Perf. 14*

**514** A202 1.50k red brown .25 .25
**515** A202 2k ultra 1.10 .60

Day of International Solidarity of Fighters against Fascism, Apr. 11, 1952.

Harvester A203

Design: 3k, Tractor and Seeders.

**1952, Apr. 30**

**516** A203 1.50k deep blue 2.10 1.20
**517** A203 2k brown .30 .30
**518** A203 3k brown red .30 .30
*Nos. 516-518 (3)* 2.70 1.80

Youths Carrying Flags — A204

**1952, May 1**

**519** A204 3k brown red .35 .25
**520** A204 4k dk red brown 1.40 1.25

Issued to publicize Labor Day, May 1, 1952.

Crowd Cheering Soviet Soldiers — A205

**1952, May 9**

**521** A205 1.50k dark red .55 .45
**522** A205 5k deep blue 2.25 1.25

Liberation of Czechoslovakia from German occupation, 7th anniversary.

Children A206

Design: 3k, "Pioneer" teaching children.

**1952, May 31** **Engr.** *Perf. 12½*

**523** A206 1.50k dk brn, *cr* .25 .25
**524** A206 2k Prus grn, *cr* 1.50 .60
**525** A206 3k rose brn, *cr* .25 .25
*Nos. 523-525 (3)* 2.00 1.10

International Children's Day May 31, 1952.

J. V. Myslbek — A207

Design: 8k, Allegory, "Music."

**1952, June 2**

**526** A207 1.50k red brown .30 .25
**527** A207 2k dark brown 1.25 .90
**528** A207 8k gray green .25 .25
*Nos. 526-528 (3)* 1.80 1.40

Joseph V. Myslbek (1848-1922), sculptor.

Beethoven — A208

House of Artists — A209

**1952, June 7** **Unwmk.** *Perf. 11½*

**529** A208 1.50k sepia .35 .25
**530** A209 3k red brown .35 .25
**531** A208 5k indigo 1.40 1.10
*Nos. 529-531 (3)* 2.10 1.60

International Music Festival, Prague, 1952.

Lidice, Symbol of a New Life — A210

**1952, June 10** *Perf. 12½*

**532** A210 1.50k dk violet brn .25 .25
**533** A210 5k dark blue 1.00 .60

Destruction of Lidice, 10th anniversary.

Jan Hus — A211

Bethlehem Chapel — A212

**1952, July 5**

**534** A211 1.50k brown .25 .25
**535** A212 3k red brown .25 .25
**536** A211 5k black 1.10 .65
*Nos. 534-536 (3)* 1.60 1.15

550th anniv. of the installation of Jan Hus as pastor of Bethlehem Chapel, Prague.

Doctor Examining Patient — A213

2k, Doctor, Nurse, Mother and child.

**1952, July 31**

**537** A213 1.50k dark brown 1.40 .80
**538** A213 2k blue violet .35 .25
**539** A213 3k rose brown .35 .25
*Nos. 537-539 (3)* 2.10 1.30

Czechoslovakia's Unified Health Service.

A214

United Physical Education Program — A214a

**1952, Aug. 2** *Perf. 11½*

**540** A214 1.50k Relay race .95 .60
**541** A214a 2k Canoeing 2.50 1.10
**542** A214a 3k Cycling .60 .55
**543** A214a 4k Hockey *3.25* *3.00*
*Nos. 540-543 (4)* 7.30 5.25

Issued to publicize Czechoslovakia's Unified Physical Education program.

F. L. Celakovski — A215

**1952, Aug. 5** *Perf. 12½*

**544** A215 1.50k dark brown .25 .25
**545** A215 2k dark green 1.40 .90

Centenary of the death of Frantisek L. Celakovski, poet and writer.

Mikulas Ales — A216

*Perf. 11x11½*

**1952, Aug. 30** **Engr.** **Unwmk.**

**546** A216 1.50k dk gray grn .45 .35
**547** A216 6k red brown 3.00 2.25

Birth centenary of Mikulas Ales, painter.

17th Century Mining Towers — A217

Designs: 1.50k, Coal Excavator. 2k, Peter Bezruc mine. 3k, Automatic coaling crane.

**1952, Sept. 14** *Perf. 12½*

**548** A217 1k sepia 1.25 .45
**549** A217 1.50k dark blue .25 .25
**550** A217 2k olive gray .25 .25
**551** A217 3k violet brown .25 .25
*Nos. 548-551 (4)* 2.00 1.20

Miners' Day, Sept. 14, 1952. No. 550 also for the 85th anniv. of the birth of Peter Bezruc (Vladimir Vasek), poet.

Jan Zizka — A218

Designs: 2k, Fraternization with Russians. 3k, Marching with flag.

**Inscribed: ". . . . Armady 1952,"**

**1952, Oct. 5 Engr. *Perf. 11½***

| | | | | |
|---|---|---|---|---|
| **552** A218 | 1.50k rose lake | .25 | .25 |
| **553** A218 | 2k olive bister | .25 | .25 |
| **554** A218 | 3k dk car rose | .25 | .25 |
| **555** A218 | 4k gray | 1.50 | .45 |
| | *Nos. 552-555 (4)* | 2.25 | 1.20 |

Issued to publicize Army Day, Oct. 5, 1952.

Souvenir Sheet

Statues to Bulgarian Partisans and to Soviet Army — A219

**1952, Oct. 18 Unwmk. *Perf. 12½***

| | | | |
|---|---|---|---|
| **556** A219 Sheet of 2 | 85.00 | 16.00 |
| *a.* 2k deep carmine | 35.00 | 7.50 |
| *b.* 3k ultramarine | 35.00 | 7.50 |

National Philatelic Exhibition, Bratislava, Oct. 18-Nov. 2, 1952.

Danube River, Bratislava A220

**1952, Oct. 18**

| | | | |
|---|---|---|---|
| **557** A220 1.50k dark brown | .25 | .25 |

National Philatelic Exhibition, Bratislava.

Conference with Lenin and Stalin — A221

**1952, Nov. 7**

| | | | |
|---|---|---|---|
| **558** A221 2k brown black | 1.40 | .95 |
| **559** A221 3k carmine | .25 | .25 |

35th anniv. of the Russian Revolution and to publicize Czechoslovak-Soviet friendship.

Worker and Nurse Holding Dove and Olive Branch — A222

**1952, Nov. 15 Photo. *Perf. 14***

| | | | |
|---|---|---|---|
| **560** A222 2k brown | 1.40 | .80 |
| **561** A222 3k red | .25 | .25 |

Issued to publicize the first State Congress of the Czechoslovak Red Cross.

Matej Louda, Hussite Leader, Painted by Mikulas Ales A223

3k, Dragon-killer Trutnov, painted by Ales.

**1952, Nov. 18 Engr. *Perf. 11½***

| | | | |
|---|---|---|---|
| **562** A223 2k red brown | .35 | .25 |
| **563** A223 3k grnsh gray | .75 | .25 |

Mikulas Ales, painter, birth cent.

**Gottwald Type of 1948-49**

**1952, June 2 Unwmk. *Perf. 12½***

**Size: 19x24mm**

| | | | |
|---|---|---|---|
| **564** A135 1k dark green | .60 | .25 |

"Peace" Flags — A224

**1952, Dec. 12 Photo. *Perf. 14***

| | | | |
|---|---|---|---|
| **565** A224 3k red brown | .35 | .25 |
| **566** A224 4k deep blue | .75 | 1.00 |

Issued to publicize the Congress of Nations for Peace, Vienna, Dec. 12-19, 1952.

Dove by Picasso — A225

Design: 4k, Czech Family.

**1953, Jan. 17**

| | | | |
|---|---|---|---|
| **567** A225 1.50k dark brown | .25 | .25 |
| **568** A225 4k slate blue | .65 | .30 |

2nd Czechoslovak Peace Congress.

Smetana Museum — A226

Design: 4k, Jirásek Museum.

**1953, Feb. 10 Engr. *Perf. 11½***

| | | | |
|---|---|---|---|
| **569** A226 1.50k dk violet brn | .25 | .25 |
| **570** A226 4k dark gray | 1.50 | .75 |

Prof. Zdenek Nejedly, 75th birth anniv.

Martin Kukucin — A227

Jaroslav Vrchlicky — A228

Designs: 2k, Karel Jaromir Erben. 3k, Vaclav Matej Kramerius. 5k, Josef Dobrovsky.

**1953, Feb. 28**

| | | | |
|---|---|---|---|
| **571** A227 1k gray | .25 | .25 |
| **572** A228 1.50k olive | .25 | .25 |
| **573** A228 2k rose lake | .25 | .25 |
| **574** A228 3k lt brown | .50 | .25 |
| **575** A228 5k slate blue | 1.50 | .75 |
| *Nos. 571-575 (5)* | 2.75 | 1.75 |

Issued to honor Czech writers and poets: 1k, 25th anniv. of death of Kukucin. 1.50k, birth cent. of Vrchlicky. 2k, cent. of completion of "Kytice" by Erben. 3k, birth bicent. of Kramerius. 5k, birth bicent. of Dobrovsky.

Militia — A229

Gottwald — A230

Design: 8k, Portraits of Stalin and Gottwald and Peoples Assembly.

***Perf. 13½x14***

**1953, Feb. 25 Photo. Unwmk.**

| | | | |
|---|---|---|---|
| **576** A229 1.50k deep blue | .25 | .25 |
| **577** A230 3k red | .25 | .25 |
| **578** A229 8k dark brown | 2.10 | .75 |
| *Nos. 576-578 (3)* | 2.60 | 1.25 |

5th anniv. of the defeat of the attempt to reinstate capitalism.

Book and Torch — A231

Design: 3k, Bedrich Vaclavek.

**1953, Mar. 5 Engr. *Perf. 11½***

| | | | |
|---|---|---|---|
| **579** A231 1k sepia | 1.50 | .60 |
| **580** A231 3k orange brown | .25 | .25 |

Bedrich Vaclavek (1897-1943), socialist writer.

**Stalin Type of 1949**

Inscribed "21 XII 1879-5 III 1953"

**1953, Mar. 12**

| | | | |
|---|---|---|---|
| **581** A154 1.50k black | .35 | .25 |

Death of Joseph Stalin, Mar. 5, 1953.

Mother and Child — A232

Girl Revolutionist A233

**1953, Mar. 8**

| | | | |
|---|---|---|---|
| **582** A232 1.50k ultra | .25 | .25 |
| **583** A233 2k brown red | 1.25 | .60 |

International Women's Day.

Klement Gottwald — A234

**1953, Mar. 19**

| | | | |
|---|---|---|---|
| **584** A234 1.50k black | .25 | .25 |
| **585** A234 3k black | .25 | .25 |

**Souvenir Sheet**

***Imperf***

| | | | |
|---|---|---|---|
| **586** A234 5k black | 5.00 | 4.00 |

Death of Pres. Klement Gottwald, 3/14/53.

Josef Pecka, Ladislav Zapotocky and Josef Hybes — A236

**1953, Apr. 7 Unwmk. *Perf. 11½***

| | | | |
|---|---|---|---|
| **587** A236 2k lt violet brn | .25 | .25 |

75th anniversary of the first congress of the Czech Social Democratic Party.

Cyclists — A237

**1953, Apr. 29**

| | | | |
|---|---|---|---|
| **588** A237 3k deep blue | .75 | .35 |

6th International Peace Bicycle Race, Prague-Berlin-Warsaw.

Medal of "May 1, 1890" A238

Designs: 1.50k, Lenin and Stalin. 3k, May Day Parade. 8k, Marx and Engels.

**Engraved and Photogravure**

**1953, Apr. 30 *Perf. 11½x11, 14***

| | | | |
|---|---|---|---|
| **589** A238 1k chocolate | 1.40 | .35 |
| **590** A238 1.50k dark gray | .25 | .25 |
| **591** A238 3k carmine lake | .25 | .25 |
| **592** A238 8k dk gray green | .30 | .25 |
| *Nos. 589-592 (4)* | 2.20 | 1.10 |

Issued to publicize Labor Day, May 1, 1953.

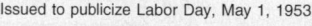

Sowing Grain — A239

**1953, May 8 Photo. *Perf. 14***

| | | | |
|---|---|---|---|
| **593** A239 1.50k shown | .35 | .25 |
| **594** A239 7k Reaper | 1.60 | 1.40 |

Socialization of the village.

Dam — A240

Welder — A241

Design: 3k, Iron works.

**1953, May 8** ***Perf. 11½***

| | | | | |
|---|---|---|---|---|
| **595** | A240 | 1.50k gray | 1.10 | .30 |
| **596** | A241 | 2k blue gray | .25 | .25 |
| **597** | A240 | 3k red brown | .25 | .25 |
| | | *Nos. 595-597 (3)* | 1.60 | .80 |

Josef Slavik — A242 Leos Janacek — A243

**1953, June 19** **Photo.**

| | | | | |
|---|---|---|---|---|
| **598** | A242 | 75h dp gray blue | .75 | .25 |
| **599** | A243 | 1.60k dark brown | 1.00 | .25 |

Issued on the occasion of the International Music Festival, Prague, 1953.

**Gottwald Type of 1948-49**

***Perf. 12½ (15h, 1k), 11½ (20h, 3k)***

**1953**

| | | | | |
|---|---|---|---|---|
| **600** | A135 | 15h yellow green | .35 | .25 |
| **601** | A135 | 20h dk violet brn | .45 | .25 |
| **602** | A135 | 1k purple | 1.10 | .25 |
| **603** | A135 | 3k brown car | .25 | .25 |
| **604** | A135 | 3k gray | .75 | .25 |
| | | *Nos. 600-604 (5)* | 2.90 | 1.25 |

Nos. 600-604 vary slightly in size.

Pres. Antonin Zapotocky — A244

**1953, June 19** ***Perf. 14***

| | | | | |
|---|---|---|---|---|
| **605** | A244 | 30h violet blue | .75 | .25 |
| **606** | A244 | 60h cerise | 1.00 | .25 |

Julius Fucik A245

Book and Carnation A246

**1953, Sept. 8** **Engr.** ***Perf. 12½***

| | | | | |
|---|---|---|---|---|
| **607** | A245 | 40h dk violet brn | .30 | .25 |
| **608** | A246 | 60h pink | .50 | .30 |

10th anniv. of the death of Julius Fucik, Communist leader executed by the Nazis.

Miner and Flag — A247

Design: 60h, Oil field and workers.

**1953, Sept. 10** ***Perf. 11½***

| | | | | |
|---|---|---|---|---|
| **609** | A247 | 30h gray | .30 | .25 |
| **610** | A247 | 60h brown vio | 1.25 | .50 |

Miner's Day, Sept. 10, 1953.

Volleyball Game — A248

Motorcyclist A249

Design: 60h, Woman throwing javelin.

**1953, Sept. 15**

| | | | | |
|---|---|---|---|---|
| **611** | A248 | 30h brown red | 4.50 | 1.50 |
| **612** | A249 | 40h dk violet brn | 2.75 | .85 |
| **613** | A248 | 60h rose violet | 2.50 | .85 |
| | | *Nos. 611-613 (3)* | 9.75 | 3.20 |

Hussite Warrior — A250

Designs: 60h, Soldier presenting arms. 1k, Red army soldiers.

**1953, Oct. 8**

| | | | | |
|---|---|---|---|---|
| **614** | A250 | 30h brown | .30 | .25 |
| **615** | A250 | 60h rose lake | .35 | .25 |
| **616** | A250 | 1k brown red | 1.50 | 1.25 |
| | | *Nos. 614-616 (3)* | 2.15 | 1.75 |

Issued to publicize Army Day, Oct. 3, 1953.

Pres. Antonin Zapotocky — A251

**1953** **Unwmk.** ***Perf. 11½, 12½***

| | | | | |
|---|---|---|---|---|
| **617** | A251 | 30h violet blue | .45 | .25 |
| **618** | A251 | 60h carmine rose | .75 | .25 |

No. 617 is perf. 11½ & measures 19x23mm, No. 618 perf. 12½ & 18½x23½mm.

See No. 780.

Charles Bridge and Prague Castle — A252

**1953, Aug. 15** **Engr.** ***Perf. 11½***

| | | | | |
|---|---|---|---|---|
| **619** | A252 | 5k gray | 3.50 | .25 |

Korean and Czech Girls — A253

**1953, Oct. 11** ***Perf. 11x11½***

| | | | | |
|---|---|---|---|---|
| **620** | A253 | 30h dark brown | 2.25 | 1.50 |

Czechoslovakia's friendship with Korea.

Flags, Hradcany Castle and Kremlin — A254

Designs: 60h, Lomonosov University, Moscow. 1.20k, Lenin Ship Canal.

**1953, Nov. 7**

| | | | | |
|---|---|---|---|---|
| **621** | A254 | 30h dark gray | .75 | .50 |
| **622** | A254 | 60h dark brown | 1.10 | .85 |
| **623** | A254 | 1.20k ultra | 3.00 | 1.90 |
| | | *Nos. 621-623 (3)* | 4.85 | 3.25 |

Czechoslovak-Soviet friendship month.

Emmy Destinn, Opera Singer — A255 National Theater, Prague — A256

Portrait: 2k, Eduard Vojan, actor.

**1953, Nov. 18** ***Perf. 14***

| | | | | |
|---|---|---|---|---|
| **624** | A255 | 30h blue black | 1.10 | .75 |
| **625** | A256 | 60h brown | .35 | .35 |
| **626** | A255 | 2k sepia | 2.75 | 1.10 |
| | | *Nos. 624-626 (3)* | 4.20 | 2.20 |

Natl. Theater founding, 70th anniv.

Nos. 624 and 626 each were issued in sheets of 10. Values: No. 624, $100; No. 626, $75.

Josef Manes — A257

**1953, Nov. 28** ***Perf. 11x11½***

| | | | | |
|---|---|---|---|---|
| **627** | A257 | 60h brown carmine | .35 | .25 |
| **628** | A257 | 1.20k deep blue | 1.50 | .90 |

Issued to honor Josef Manes, painter.

Vaclav Hollar — A258

Portrait: 1.20k, Head framed, facing right.

**1953, Dec. 5**

| | | | | |
|---|---|---|---|---|
| **629** | A258 | 30h brown black | .35 | .25 |
| **630** | A258 | 1.20k dark brown | 1.50 | .65 |

Vaclav Hollar, artist and etcher.

Leo N. Tolstoy — A259

**1953, Dec. 29** **Unwmk.**

| | | | | |
|---|---|---|---|---|
| **631** | A259 | 60h dark green | .35 | .25 |
| **632** | A259 | 1k chocolate | 1.50 | .50 |

Leo N. Tolstoi, 125th birth anniv.

Locomotive — A260

Design: 1k, Plane loading mail.

**Engraved, Center Photogravure**

**1953, Dec. 29** ***Perf. 11½x11***

| | | | | |
|---|---|---|---|---|
| **633** | A260 | 60h brn org & gray vio | 1.50 | .45 |
| **634** | A260 | 1k org brn & brt bl | 3.50 | 1.10 |

Lenin — A261

Lenin Museum, Prague — A262

**1954, Jan. 21** **Engr.** ***Perf. 11½***

| | | | | |
|---|---|---|---|---|
| **635** | A261 | 30h dark brown | .45 | .25 |
| **636** | A262 | 1.40k chocolate | 1.50 | .65 |

30th anniversary of the death of Lenin.

Klement Gottwald — A263

Design: 2.40k, Revolutionist with flag.

**1954, Feb. 18** ***Perf. 11x11½, 14x13½***

| | | | | |
|---|---|---|---|---|
| **637** | A263 | 60h dark brown | .30 | .25 |
| **638** | A263 | 2.40k rose lake | 3.50 | 1.50 |

25th anniversary of the fifth congress of the Communist Party in Czechoslovakia.

No. 638 was issued in a sheet of 10 stamps. Value, $90.

Gottwald Mausoleum, Prague — A264

Gottwald and Stalin A265

1.20k, Lenin & Stalin mausoleum, Moscow.

**1954, Mar. 5** ***Perf. 11½, 14x13½***

| | | | | |
|---|---|---|---|---|
| **639** | A264 | 30h olive brown | .35 | .25 |
| **640** | A265 | 60h deep ultra | .35 | .25 |
| **641** | A264 | 1.20k rose brown | 2.25 | 1.00 |
| | | *Nos. 639-641 (3)* | 2.95 | 1.50 |

1st anniv. of the deaths of Stalin and Gottwald.

No. 641 was issued in a sheet of 10 stamps. Value, $120.

Two Runners — A266

Group of Hikers — A267

Design: 1k, Woman swimmer.

**1954, Apr. 24** *Perf. 11½*
**642** A266 30h dark brown 2.10 1.10
**643** A267 80h dark green 7.00 3.50
**644** A266 1k dk violet blue 1.75 .75
*Nos. 642-644 (3)* 10.85 5.35

No. 643 was issued in a sheet of 10 stamps. Value, $350.

Nurse — A268

Designs: 15h, Construction worker. 40h, Postwoman. 45h, Ironworker. 50h, Soldier. 75h, Lathe operator. 80h, Textile worker. 1k, Farm woman. 1.20k, Scientist and microscope. 1.60k, Miner. 2k, Physician and baby. 2.40k, Engineer. 3k, Chemist.

**1954** *Perf. 12½x12, 11½x11*
**645** A268 15h dark green .30 .25
**646** A268 20h lt violet .35 .25
**647** A268 40h dark brown .45 .25
**648** A268 45h dk gray blue .35 .25
**649** A268 50h dk gray green .45 .25
**650** A268 75h deep blue .45 .25
**651** A268 80h violet brown .45 .25
**652** A268 1k green .75 .25
**653** A268 1.20k dk violet blue .45 .25
**654** A268 1.60k brown blk 1.10 .25
**655** A268 2k orange brown 1.50 .25
**656** A268 2.40k violet blue 1.50 .25
**657** A268 3k carmine 1.50 .25
*Nos. 645-657 (13)* 9.60 3.25

Antonin Dvorák — A269

40h, Leos Janacek. 60h, Bedrich Smetana.

**1954, May 22** *Perf. 11x11½*
**658** A269 30h violet brown 2.25 .25
**659** A269 40h brick red 3.00 .35
**660** A269 60h dark blue .90 .25
*Nos. 658-660 (3)* 6.15 .85

"Year of Czech Music," 1954.

Prokop Divis — A270

**1954, June 15**
**661** A270 30h gray .35 .25
**662** A270 75h violet brown 1.40 .50

200th anniv. of the invention of a lightning conductor by Prokop Divis.

Slovak Insurrectionist A271

Design: 1.20k, Partisan woman.

**1954, Aug. 28** *Perf. 11½*
**663** A271 30h brown orange .25 .25
**664** A271 1.20k dark blue .85 .50

Slovak national uprising, 10th anniv.

Anton P. Chekhov — A272

**1954, Sept. 24**
**665** A272 30h dull gray grn .30 .25
**666** A272 45h dull gray brn 1.10 .50

50th anniv. of the death of Chekhov, writer.

Soviet Representative Giving Agricultural Instruction — A273

Designs: 60h, Soviet industrial instruction. 2k, Dancers (cultural collaboration).

**1954, Nov. 6** *Perf. 11½x11*
**667** A273 30h yellow brown .25 .25
**668** A273 60h dark blue .25 .25
**669** A273 2k vermilion 1.40 .90
*Nos. 667-669 (3)* 1.90 1.40

Czechoslovak-Soviet friendship month.

Jan Neruda — A274

60h, Janko Jesensky. 1.60k, Jiri Wolker.

**1954, Nov. 25** *Perf. 11x11½*
**670** A274 30h dark blue .85 .25
**671** A274 60h dull red 1.40 .50
**672** A274 1.60k sepia .35 .25
*Nos. 670-672 (3)* 2.60 1.00

Issued to honor Czechoslovak poets.

View of Telc A275

Views: 60h, Levoca. 3k, Ceske Budejovice.

**1954, Dec. 10** **Engr. & Photo.**
**673** A275 30h black & bis .50 .25
**674** A275 60h brown & bis .55 .25
**675** A275 3k black & bis 2.10 1.10
*Nos. 673-675 (3)* 3.15 1.60

Pres. Antonin Zapotocky — A276

**1954, Dec. 18** **Engr.** *Perf. 11½*
**676** A276 30h black brown .50 .25
**677** A276 60h dark blue .55 .25

**Souvenir Sheet**

***Imperf***

**678** A276 2k deep claret 15.00 6.00

70th birthday of Pres. Antonin Zapotocky. See Nos. 829-831.

Attacking Soldiers — A278

Design: 2k, Soldier holding child.

**1954, Oct. 3** *Perf. 11½*
**679** A278 60h dark green .30 .25
**680** A278 2k dark brown 1.40 1.25

Army Day, Oct. 6, 1954.

Woman Holding Torch — A279

Design: 45h, Ski jumper.

**1955, Jan. 20** **Engr.**
**681** A279 30h red 2.10 .50

**Engraved and Photogravure**

**682** A279 45h black & blue 3.50 .50

First National Spartacist Games, 1955.

Comenius University Building A280

Design: 75h, Jan A. Komensky medal.

**1955, Jan. 28** **Engr.** *Perf. 11½*
**683** A280 60h deep green .30 .25
**684** A280 75h chocolate 1.40 .65

35th anniversary of the founding of Comenius University, Bratislava.

Czechoslovak Automobile A281

60h, Textile worker. 75h, Lathe operator.

**1955, Mar. 15** **Unwmk.**
**685** A281 45h dull green 1.40 .30
**686** A281 60h dk violet blue .60 .25
**687** A281 75h sepia .90 .25
*Nos. 685-687 (3)* 2.90 .80

Woman Decorating Soviet Soldier — A282

Stalin Memorial, Prague — A283

Designs: 35h, Tankman with flowers. 60h, Children greeting soldier.

**1955, May 5** **Engr.** *Perf. 11½*
**688** A282 30h blue .35 .25
**689** A282 35h dark brown 1.50 .30
**690** A282 60h cerise .35 .25

**Photo.**

**691** A283 60h sepia .35 .25
*Nos. 688-691 (4)* 2.55 1.05

10th anniv. of Czechoslovakia's liberation.

Music and Spring — A284

Design: 1k, Woman with lyre.

**1955, May 12** **Engr. & Photo.**
**692** A284 30h black & pale blue .35 .25
**693** A284 1k black & pale rose 1.40 1.20

International Music Festival, Prague, 1955.

Foundry Worker — A285

Design: 45h, Farm workers.

**1955, May 12** **Engr.**
**694** A285 30h violet .25 .25
**695** A285 45h green 1.20 .60

Issued to publicize the third congress of the Trade Union Revolutionary Movement.

Woman Athlete — A286

60h, Dancing couple. 1.60k, Athlete.

**1955, June 21**
**696** A286 20h violet blue 1.00 .40
**697** A286 60h green .35 .25
**698** A286 1.60k red .75 .25
*Nos. 696-698 (3)* 2.10 .90

Issued to publicize the first National Spartacist Games, Prague, June-July, 1955.

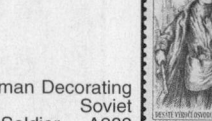

Jakub Arbes — A287

Portraits: 30h, Jan Stursa. 40h, Elena Marothy-Soltesova. 60h, Josef Vaclav Sladek. 75h, Alexander Stepanovic Popov. 1.40k, Jan Holly. 1.60k, Pavel Josef Safarik.

**1955**

| | | | | |
|---|---|---|---|---|
| **699** | A287 | 20h brown | .25 | .25 |
| **700** | A287 | 30h black | .25 | .25 |
| **701** | A287 | 40h gray green | .60 | .25 |
| **702** | A287 | 60h black | .50 | .25 |
| **703** | A287 | 75h claret | 1.75 | .25 |
| **704** | A287 | 1.40k black, *cr* | .50 | .25 |
| **705** | A287 | 1.60k dark blue | .50 | .25 |
| | | *Nos. 699-705 (7)* | 4.35 | 1.75 |

Various anniversaries of prominent Slavs.

Girl and Boy of Two Races — A288

**1955, July 20**

| | | | | |
|---|---|---|---|---|
| **706** | A288 | 60h violet blue | .75 | .25 |

5th World Festival of Youth in Warsaw, July 31-Aug. 14.

Costume of Ocova, Slovakia — A289

Regional Costumes: 75h, Detva man, Slovakia. 1.60k, Chodsko man, Bohemia. 2k, Hana woman, Moravia.

**1955, July 25**

**Frame and Outlines in Brown**

| | | | | |
|---|---|---|---|---|
| **707** | A289 | 60h orange & rose | 10.00 | 7.00 |
| **708** | A289 | 75h orange & lilac | 4.00 | 4.00 |
| **709** | A289 | 1.60k blue & orange | 11.50 | 7.00 |
| **710** | A289 | 2k yellow & rose | 11.50 | 7.00 |
| | | *Nos. 707-710 (4)* | 37.00 | 25.00 |

Nos. 707-710 were each issued in sheets of 10 stamps. Value, $450.

Carp A290

Designs: 30h, Beetle. 35h, Gray Partridge. 1.40k, Butterfly. 1.50k, Hare.

**1955, Aug. 8 Engr. & Photo.**

| | | | | |
|---|---|---|---|---|
| **711** | A290 | 20h sepia & lt bl | 2.25 | .35 |
| **712** | A290 | 30h sepia & pink | 1.50 | .30 |
| **713** | A290 | 35h sepia & buff | 1.50 | .75 |
| **714** | A290 | 1.40k sepia & cream | 7.50 | 4.50 |
| **715** | A290 | 1.50k sepia & lt grn | 2.75 | 1.10 |
| | | *Nos. 711-715 (5)* | 15.50 | 7.00 |

Tabor A291

45h, Prachatice. 60h, Jindrichuv Hradec.

**1955, Aug. 26 Engr.**

| | | | | |
|---|---|---|---|---|
| **716** | A291 | 30h violet brown | .35 | .25 |
| **717** | A291 | 45h rose carmine | 1.50 | .45 |
| **718** | A291 | 60h sage green | .75 | .25 |
| | | *Nos. 716-718 (3)* | 2.60 | .95 |

Issued to publicize the architectural beauty of the towns of Southern Bohemia.

Souvenir Sheet

Various Views of Prague — A292

**1955, Sept. 10 Engr. *Perf. 14x13½***

| | | | | |
|---|---|---|---|---|
| **719** | A292 | Sheet of 5 | 27.50 | 27.50 |
| *a.* | | 30h gray black | 4.75 | 5.25 |
| *b.* | | 45h gray black | 4.75 | 5.25 |
| *c.* | | 60h rose lake | 4.75 | 5.25 |
| *d.* | | 75h rose lake | 4.75 | 5.25 |
| *e.* | | 1.60k gray black | 4.75 | 5.25 |

International Philatelic Exhibition, Prague, Sept. 10-25, 1955. Size: 145x110mm. Exists imperf., value $47.50.

Motorcyclists A293

**1955, Aug. 28**

| | | | | |
|---|---|---|---|---|
| **720** | A293 | 60h violet brown | 3.00 | .75 |

30th International Motorcycle Races at Gottwaldov, Sept. 13-18, 1955.

Workers, Soldier and Pioneer — A294

Army Day: 60h, Tanks and planes.

**1955, Oct. 6 Unwmk. *Perf. 11½***

| | | | | |
|---|---|---|---|---|
| **721** | A294 | 30h violet brown | .35 | .25 |
| **722** | A294 | 60h slate | 1.75 | .75 |

Hans Christian Andersen — A295

Portraits: 40h, Friedrich von Schiller. 60h, Adam Mickiewicz. 75h, Walt Whitman.

**1955, Oct. 27**

| | | | | |
|---|---|---|---|---|
| **723** | A295 | 30h brown red | .35 | .25 |
| **724** | A295 | 40h dark blue | 2.25 | 1.00 |
| **725** | A295 | 60h deep claret | .35 | .25 |
| **726** | A295 | 75h greenish black | .75 | .35 |
| | | *Nos. 723-726 (4)* | 3.70 | 1.85 |

Issued in honor of these four poets and to mark the 100th anniversary of the publication of Walt Whitman's "Leaves of Grass."

Railroad Bridge A296

30h, Train crossing bridge. 60h, Train approaching tunnel. 1.60k, Miners' housing project.

**Inscribed: "Stavba Socialismu"**

**1955, Dec. 15**

| | | | | |
|---|---|---|---|---|
| **727** | A296 | 20h dull green | .75 | .25 |
| **728** | A296 | 30h violet brown | .75 | .25 |
| **729** | A296 | 60h slate | .75 | .25 |
| **730** | A296 | 1.60k carmine rose | .75 | .25 |
| | | *Nos. 727-730 (4)* | 3.00 | 1.00 |

Issued to publicize socialist public works.

Hydroelectric Plant — A297

2nd Five Year Plan: 10h, Miner with drill. 25h, Building construction. 30h, Harvester. 60h, Metallurgical plant.

**Inscribed: "Druhy Petilety Plan 1956-1960."**

**1956, Feb. 20 *Perf. 11½x11***

| | | | | |
|---|---|---|---|---|
| **731** | A297 | 5h violet brown | .30 | .25 |
| **732** | A297 | 10h gray black | .30 | .25 |
| **733** | A297 | 25h dk car rose | .45 | .25 |
| **734** | A297 | 30h green | .30 | .25 |
| **735** | A297 | 60h violet blue | .30 | .25 |
| | | *Nos. 731-735 (5)* | 1.65 | 1.25 |

Jewelry — A298

**1956, Mar. 17 *Perf. 11x11½***

| | | | | |
|---|---|---|---|---|
| **736** | A298 | 30h shown | .45 | .25 |
| **737** | A298 | 45h Glassware | 3.50 | 1.60 |
| **738** | A298 | 60h Ceramics | .45 | .25 |
| **739** | A298 | 75h Textiles | .45 | .30 |
| | | *Nos. 736-739 (4)* | 4.85 | 2.40 |

Products of Czechoslovakian industries.

Karlovy Vary (Karlsbad) — A299

Various Spas: 45h, Marianske Lazne (Marienbad). 75h, Piestany. 1.20k, Tatry Vysne Ruzbachy (Tatra Mountains).

**1956, Mar. 17**

| | | | | |
|---|---|---|---|---|
| **740** | A299 | 30h olive green | 1.50 | .30 |
| **741** | A299 | 45h brown | 1.10 | .30 |
| **742** | A299 | 75h claret | 6.00 | 3.00 |
| **743** | A299 | 1.20k ultra | .75 | .30 |
| | | *Nos. 740-743 (4)* | 9.35 | 3.90 |

Issued to publicize Czechoslovakian spas.

"We Serve our People" — A300

Designs: 60h, Russian War Memorial, Berlin. 1k, Tank crewman with standard.

**1956, Apr. 9 Photo. *Perf. 11x11½***

| | | | | |
|---|---|---|---|---|
| **744** | A300 | 30h olive brown | .75 | .25 |
| **745** | A300 | 60h carmine rose | .75 | .25 |
| **746** | A300 | 1k ultra | 4.50 | 2.75 |
| | | *Nos. 744-746 (3)* | 6.00 | 3.25 |

Exhibition: "The Construction and Defense of our Country," Prague, Apr., 1956.

Cyclists — A301

Girl Basketball Players — A302

Athletes and Olympic Rings — A303

**Engraved and Photogravure**

**1956, Apr. 25 Unwmk. *Perf. 11½***

| | | | | |
|---|---|---|---|---|
| **747** | A301 | 30h green & lt blue | 3.50 | .35 |
| **748** | A302 | 45h dk blue & car | 1.40 | .35 |
| **749** | A303 | 75h brown & lemon | 1.10 | .70 |
| | | *Nos. 747-749 (3)* | 6.00 | 1.40 |

9th Intl. Peace Cycling Race, Warsaw-Berlin-Prague, May 1-15, 1956 (No. 747). 5th European Womens' Basketball Championship (No. 748). Summer Olympics, Melbourne, Nov. 22-Dec. 8, 1956 (No. 749).

See No. 765.

Mozart — A304

45h, Josef Myslivecek. 60h, Jiri Benda. 1k, Bertramka House, Prague. 1.40k, Xaver Dusek (1731-99) and wife Josepha. 1.60k, Nostic Theater, Prague.

**1956, May 12 Engr.**

**Design in Gray Black**

| | | | | |
|---|---|---|---|---|
| **750** | A304 | 30h bister | 1.50 | .35 |
| **751** | A304 | 45h gray green | 8.50 | 6.00 |
| **752** | A304 | 60h pale rose lilac | 1.50 | .35 |
| **753** | A304 | 1k salmon | 1.50 | .35 |
| **754** | A304 | 1.40k lt blue | 4.50 | .75 |
| **755** | A304 | 1.60k lemon | 3.00 | .35 |
| | | *Nos. 750-755 (6)* | 20.50 | 8.15 |

200th anniv. of the birth of Wolfgang Amadeus Mozart and to publicize the International Music Festival in Prague.

Home Guard — A305

**1956, May 25**

| | | | | |
|---|---|---|---|---|
| **756** | A305 | 60h violet blue | .75 | .25 |

Issued to commemorate the first meeting of the Home Guard, Prague, May 25-27, 1956.

Josef Kajetan Tyl — A306

Portraits: 20h, Ludovit Stur. 30h, Frana Sramek. 1.40k, Karel Havlicek Borovsky.

**1956, June 23**

**757** A306 20h dull purple .75 .25
**758** A306 30h blue .45 .25
**759** A306 60h black .45 .25
**760** A306 1.40k claret 3.00 1.75
*Nos. 757-760 (4)* 4.65 2.50

Issued to honor various Czechoslovakian writers. See Nos. 781-784, 873-876.

River Patrol — A307

Design: 60h, Guard and dog.

**1956, July 8** *Perf. 11x11½*

**761** A307 30h ultra .75 .25
**762** A307 60h green .60 .25

Issued to honor men of Frontier Guard.

**Type of 1956 and**

Steeplechase — A308

**1956, Sept. 8 Unwmk. *Perf. 11½***

**763** A308 60h indigo & bister 3.00 .75
**764** A308 80h brown vio & vio 1.50 .35
**765** A303 1.20k slate & orange 3.00 1.50
*Nos. 763-765 (3)* 7.50 2.60

Steeplechase, Pardubice, 1956 (No. 763). Marathon race, Kosice, 1956 (No. 764). Olympic Games, Melbourne, Nov. 22-Dec. 8 (No. 765).

Woman Gathering Grapes — A309

Fishermen — A310

35h, Women gathering hops. 95h, Logging.

**1956, Sept. 20 Engr.**

**766** A309 30h brown lake .35 .25
**767** A309 35h gray green .35 .25
**768** A310 80h dark blue .75 .25
**769** A310 95h chocolate 2.25 1.00
*Nos. 766-769 (4)* 3.70 1.75

Issued to publicize natural resources.

European Timetable Conf., Prague, Nov. 9-13 — A311

A312

Locomotives: 10h, 1846. 30h, 1855. 40h, 1945. 45h, 1952. 60h, 1955. 1k, 1954.

**1956, Nov. 9 Unwmk. *Perf. 11½***

**770** A311 10h brown 2.50 .35
**771** A312 30h gray 2.50 .35
**772** A312 40h green 5.00 .35
**773** A312 45h brown car 8.50 5.00
**774** A312 60h indigo 2.50 .35
**775** A312 1k ultra 6.00 .35
*Nos. 770-775 (6)* 27.00 6.75

Costume of Moravia — A313

Regional Costumes (women): 1.20k, Blata, Bohemia. 1.40k, Cicmany, Slovakia. 1.60k, Novohradsko, Slovakia.

**1956, Dec. 15 *Perf. 13½***

**776** A313 30h brn, ultra & car 1.75 1.75
**777** A313 1.20k brn, car & ultra 2.75 .40
**778** A313 1.40k brn, ocher & ver 10.00 3.25
**779** A313 1.60k brn, car & grn 3.50 .80
*Nos. 776-779 (4)* 18.00 6.20

See Nos. 832-835.
Nos. 776-779 each were issued in sheets of 10 stamps. Value, $160.

**Zapotocky Type of 1953**

**1956, Oct. 7 Unwmk. *Perf. 12½***

**780** A251 30h blue .75 .25

**Portrait Type of 1956**

15h, Ivan Olbracht. 20h, Karel Toman. 30h, F. X. Salda. 1.60k, Terezia Vansova.

**1957, Jan. 18 Engr. *Perf. 11½***

**781** A306 15h dk red brn, *cr* .30 .25
**782** A306 20h dk green, *cr* .30 .25
**783** A306 30h dk brown, *cr* .30 .25
**784** A306 1.60k dk blue, *cr* .60 .25
*Nos. 781-784 (4)* 1.50 1.00

Issued in honor of Czechoslovakian writers.

Kolin Cathedral — A315

Views: No. 786, Banska Stiavnica. No. 787, Uherske Hradiste. No. 788, Karlstein. No. 789, Charles Bridge, Prague. 1.25k, Moravska Trebova.

**1957, Feb. 23**

**785** A315 30h dk blue gray .30 .25
**786** A315 30h rose violet .45 .25
**787** A315 60h deep rose .45 .25
**788** A315 60h gray green .45 .25
**789** A315 60h brown .60 .25
**790** A315 1.25k gray 2.50 1.50
*Nos. 785-790 (6)* 4.75 2.75

Anniversaries of various towns and landmarks.

Komensky Mausoleum, Naarden A316

Jan A. Komensky A317

Old Prints: 40h, Komensky teaching. 1k, Sun, moon, stars and earth.

***Perf. 11½x11, 14 (A317)***

**1957, Mar. 28 Engr. Unwmk.**

**791** A316 30h pale brown .45 .25
**792** A316 40h dark green .45 .25
**793** A317 60h chocolate 3.00 .75
**794** A316 1k carmine rose .60 .25
*Nos. 791-794 (4)* 4.50 1.50

300th anniv. of the publication of "Didactica Opera Omnia" by J. A. Komensky (Comenius). No. 793 issued in sheets of four. Value, $24.

Farm Woman — A318

**1957, Mar. 22 *Perf. 11½***

**795** A318 30h lt blue green .75 .25

3rd Cong. of Agricultural Cooperatives.

Cyclists A319

Woman Archer A320

Boxers — A321

Rescue Team A322

**1957, Apr. 30 *Perf. 11½x11, 11x11½***

**796** A319 30h sepia & ultra .60 .25
**797** A319 60h dull grn & bis *2.25 1.25*
**798** A320 60h gray & emer .45 .25
**799** A321 60h sepia & org .45 .25
**800** A322 60h violet & choc .75 .25
*Nos. 796-800 (5)* 4.50 2.25

10th Intl. Peace Cycling Race, Prague-Berlin-Warsaw (Nos. 796-797). Intl. Archery Championships (No. 798). European Boxing Championships, Prague (No. 799). Mountain Climbing Rescue Service (No. 800).

Jan V. Stamic — A323

Musicians: No. 802, Ferdinand Laub. No. 803, Frantisek Ondricek. No. 804, Josef B. Foerster. No. 805, Vitezslav Novak. No. 806, Josef Suk.

**1957, May 12 *Perf. 11½***

**801** A323 60h purple .35 .25
**802** A323 60h black .35 .25
**803** A323 60h slate blue .35 .25
**804** A323 60h brown .35 .25
**805** A323 60h dull red brn .90 .25
**806** A323 60h blue green .35 .25
*Nos. 801-806 (6)* 2.65 1.50

Spring Music Festival, Prague.

Josef Bozek — A324

School of Engineering A325

60h, F. J. Gerstner. 1k, R. Skuhersky.

**1957, May 25**

**807** A324 30h bluish black .25 .25
**808** A324 60h gray brown .30 .25
**809** A324 1k rose lake .30 .25
**810** A325 1.40k blue violet .65 .25
*Nos. 807-810 (4)* 1.50 1.00

School of Engineering in Prague, 250th anniv.

Pioneer and Philatelic Symbols A326

Design: 60h, Girl and carrier pigeon.

**Engraved and Photogravure**

**1957, June 8 *Perf. 11½***

**811** A326 30h olive grn & org .45 .25

**Engr. *Perf. 13½***

**812** A326 60h brn & vio bl 3.00 2.25

Youth Philatelic Exhibition, Pardubice.
No. 812 was printed in miniature sheets of 4. Value $12.

"Grief" — A327

Design: 60h, Rose, symbol of new life.

**1957, June 10**
**813** A327 30h black .35 .25
**814** A327 60h blk & rose red 1.25 .35

Destruction of Lidice, 15th anniversary.
No. 814 was issued in a sheet of 10 stamps. Value, $28.

Motorcyclists A328

**1957, July 5** ***Perf. 11½***
**815** A328 60h dk gray & blue 1.50 .30

32nd International Motorcycle Race.

Karel Klic — A329

Josef Ressel — A330

**1957, July 5**
**816** A329 30h gray black .60 .25
**817** A330 60h violet blue .60 .25

Klic, inventor of photogravure, and Ressel, inventor of the ship screw.

Chamois — A331

Gentian A332

Designs: 30h, Brown bear. 60h, Edelweiss. 1.25k, Tatra Mountains.

**1957, Aug. 28 Engr.** ***Perf. 11½***
**818** A331 20h emer & brnsh gray 1.00 .25
**819** A331 30h lt blue & brn 1.00 .25
**820** A332 40h gldn brn & vio bl 1.60 .30
**821** A332 60h yellow & grn 1.00 .25

**Size: 48x28½mm**

**822** A332 1.25k ol grn & bis 1.60 .80
*Nos. 818-822 (5)* 6.20 1.85

Tatra Mountains National Park.

"Marycka Magdonova" A333

**Engraved and Photogravure**
**1957, Sept. 15 Unwmk.** ***Perf. 11½***
**823** A333 60h black & dull red .45 .25

90th birthday of Petr Bezruc, poet and author of "Marycka Magdonova."

Man Holding Banner of Trade Union Cong. — A334

**1957, Sept. 28 Engr.**
**824** A334 75h rose red .45 .25

4th Intl. Trade Union Cong., Leipzig, 10/4-15.

Television Transmitter and Antennas — A335

Design: 60h, Family watching television.

**1957, Oct. 19 Engr.** ***Perf. 11½***
**825** A335 40h dk blue & car .30 .25
**826** A335 60h redsh brown & emer .45 .25

Issued to publicize the television industry.

Worker, Globe and Lenin A336

60h, Worker, factory, hammer and sickle.

**1957, Nov. 7** ***Perf. 12x11½***
**827** A336 30h claret .25 .25
**828** A336 60h gray blue .25 .25

Russian Revolution, 40th anniversary.

**Zapotocky Type of 1954 dated: 19 XII 1884-13 XI 1957**

**1957, Nov. 18 Unwmk.** ***Perf. 11½***
**829** A276 30h black .25 .25
**830** A276 60h black .25 .25

**Souvenir Sheet**
***Imperf***

**831** A276 2k black 5.00 1.25

Death of Pres. Antonin Zapotocky.

**Costume Type of 1956**

Regional Costumes: 45h, Pilsen woman, Bohemia. 75h, Slovacko man, Moravia. 1.25k, Hana woman, Moravia. 1.95k, Teshinsko woman, Silesia.

**1957, Dec. 18 Engr.** ***Perf. 13½***
**832** A313 45h brn, bl & dk red 4.25 1.50
**833** A313 75h dk brn, red & grn 3.00 .80
**834** A313 1.25k dk brn, scar & ocher 5.25 1.50
**835** A313 1.95k sepia, bl & ver 6.00 3.75
*Nos. 832-835 (4)* 18.50 7.55

Nos. 832-835 each was issued in sheets of 10 stamps. Value, set $200.

A337

A338

Designs: 30h, Radio telescope and observatory. 45h, Meteorological station in High Tatra. 75h, Sputnik 2 over Earth.

**1957, Dec. 20** ***Perf. 11½***
**836** A337 30h violet brn & yel 1.60 .50
**837** A338 45h sepia & lt bl .65 .30
**838** A337 75h claret & blue 2.00 .85
*Nos. 836-838 (3)* 4.25 1.65

IGY, 1957-58. No. 838 also for the launching of Sputnik 2, Nov. 3, 1957.

Girl Skater — A339

Designs: 40h, Canoeing. 60h, Volleyball. 80h, Parachutist. 1.60k, Soccer.

**1958, Jan. 25 Engr.** ***Perf. 11½x12***
**839** A339 30h rose violet 1.75 .25
**840** A339 40h blue .35 .25
**841** A339 60h redsh brown .35 .25
**842** A339 80h violet blue 1.50 .45
**843** A339 1.60k brt green .65 .25
*Nos. 839-843 (5)* 4.60 1.45

Issued to publicize various sports championship events in 1958.

Litomysl Castle — A340

Design: 60h, Bethlehem Chapel.

**1958, Feb. 10** ***Perf. 11½***
**844** A340 30h green .30 .25
**845** A340 60h redsh brown .30 .25

80th anniversary of the birth of Zdenek Nejedly, restorer of Bethlehem Chapel.

Giant Excavator A341

Peace Dove and: 60h, Soldiers, flame and banner, horiz. 1.60k, Harvester and rainbow, horiz.

**1958, Feb. 25**
**846** A341 30h gray violet & yel .25 .25
**847** A341 60h gray brown & car .25 .25
**848** A341 1.60k green & dull yel .45 .25
*Nos. 846-848 (3)* .95 .75

10th anniv. of the "Victorious February."

Jewelry — A342

Designs: 45h, Dolls. 60h, Textiles. 75h, Kaplan turbine. 1.20k, Glass.

**Engraved and Photogravure**
**1958 Unwmk.** ***Perf. 11½***
**849** A342 30h rose car & blue .40 .25
**850** A342 45h rose red & pale lil .40 .25
**851** A342 60h violet & aqua .60 .25
**852** A342 75h ultra & salmon 1.50 .75
**853** A342 1.20k blue grn & pink .60 .25
*Nos. 849-853 (5)* 3.50 1.75

Issued for the Universal and International Exposition at Brussels.

King George of Podebrad — A343

Design: 60h, View of Prague, 1628.

**1958, May 19 Engr.**
**854** A343 30h carmine rose .50 .25
**855** A343 60h violet blue .30 .25

Issued to publicize the National Archives Exhibition, Prague, May 15-Aug. 15.

"Towards the Stars" — A344

Women of Three Races — A345

Boy, Girl and Globes A346

**1958, May 26**
**856** A344 30h carmine rose .45 .25
**857** A345 45h rose violet .45 .25
**858** A346 60h blue .45 .25
*Nos. 856-858 (3)* 1.35 .75

The Soc. for Dissemination of Political and Cultural Knowledge (No. 856). 4th Cong. of the Intl. Democratic Women's Fed. (No. 857). 1st World Trade Union Conf. of Working Youths, Prague, July 14-20 (No. 858).

Grain, Hammer and Sickle A347

Atomic Reactor A340

45h, Map of Czechoslovakia, hammer & sickle.

**1958, May 26**

| | | | | |
|---|---|---|---|---|
| **859** A347 30h dull red | .25 | .25 |
| **860** A347 45h green | .30 | .25 |
| **861** A348 60h dark blue | .30 | .25 |
| *Nos. 859-861 (3)* | .85 | .75 |

11th Congress of the Czech Communist Party and the 15th anniv. of the Russo-Czechoslovakian Treaty.

Karlovy Vary A349

Various Spas: 40h, Podebrady. 60h, Marianske Lazne. 80h, Luhacovice. 1.20k, Strbske Pleso. 1.60k, Trencianske Teplice.

**1958, June 25**

| | | |
|---|---|---|
| **862** A349 30h rose claret | .45 | .25 |
| **863** A349 40h redsh brown | .45 | .25 |
| **864** A349 60h gray green | .30 | .25 |
| **865** A349 80h sepia | .45 | .25 |
| **866** A349 1.20k violet blue | .60 | .25 |
| **867** A349 1.60k lt violet | 1.20 | .75 |
| *Nos. 862-867 (6)* | 3.45 | 2.00 |

Telephone Operator — A350

Design: 45h, Radio transmitter.

**1958, June 20**

| | | |
|---|---|---|
| **868** A350 30h black & brn org | .40 | .25 |
| **869** A350 45h black & lt grn | .40 | .25 |

Conference of Postal Ministers of Communist Countries, Prague, June 30-July 9.

Pres. Novotny — A351

**1958-59** ***Perf. 12½***

| | | |
|---|---|---|
| **870** A351 30h brt violet blue | .65 | .25 |
| *b.* Perf. 11½ | .50 | .25 |
| **870A** A351 30h violet ('59) | 4.00 | 1.75 |
| **871** A351 60h carmine rose | .45 | .25 |

***Perf. 11½***

**Redrawn**

| | | |
|---|---|---|
| **871A** A351 60h rose red | .50 | .25 |
| *Nos. 870-871A (4)* | 5.60 | 2.50 |

On No. 871 the top of the "6" turns down; on No. 871A it is open.

Czechoslovak Pavilion, Brussels — A352

**1958, July 15** **Engr. & Photo.**

| | | |
|---|---|---|
| **872** A352 1.95k lt blue & bis brn | .90 | .25 |

Czechoslovakia Week at the Universal and International Exhibition at Brussels.

**Portrait Type of 1956**

30h, Julius Fucik. 45h, G. K. Zechenter 60h, Karel Capek. 1.40k, Svatopluk Cech.

**1958, Aug. 20** **Engr.** ***Perf. 11½***

| | | |
|---|---|---|
| **873** A306 30h rose red | .30 | .25 |
| **874** A306 45h violet | 1.50 | .25 |
| **875** A306 60h dk blue gray | .60 | .25 |
| **876** A306 1.40k gray | .60 | .25 |
| *Nos. 873-876 (4)* | 3.00 | 1.00 |

Death anniversaries of four famous Czechs.

The Artist and the Muse — A353

**1958, Aug. 20** ***Perf. 14***

| | | |
|---|---|---|
| **877** A353 1.60k black | 3.50 | 1.10 |

85th birthday of Max Svabinsky, artist and engraver.

No. 877 was printed in miniature sheets of 4. Value $24.

Children's Hospital, Brno — A354

Designs: 60h, New Town Hall, Brno. 1k, St. Thomas Church. 1.60k, View of Brno.

**1958, Sept. 6** **Unwmk.** ***Perf. 11½***

**Size: 40x23mm**

| | | |
|---|---|---|
| **878** A354 30h violet | .25 | .25 |
| **879** A354 60h rose red | .25 | .25 |
| **880** A354 1k brown | .35 | .25 |

***Perf. 14***

**Size: 50x28mm**

| | | |
|---|---|---|
| **881** A354 1.60k dk slate grn | 1.75 | 1.25 |
| *Nos. 878-881 (4)* | 2.60 | 2.00 |

Natl. Phil. Exhib., Brno, Sept. 9.

No. 881 sold for 3.10k, including entrance ticket to exhibition. Issued in sheets of four. Value, $10.

Lepiota Procera — A355

Mushrooms: 40h, Boletus edulis. 60h, Krombholzia rufescens. 1.40k, Amanita muscaria L. 1.60k, Armillariella mellea.

**1958, Oct. 6** ***Perf. 14***

| | | |
|---|---|---|
| **882** A355 30h dk brn, grn & buff | 1.60 | .35 |
| **883** A355 40h vio brn & brn org | 1.60 | .35 |
| **884** A355 60h black, red & buff | 2.40 | .35 |
| **885** A355 1.40k brown, scar & grn | 4.00 | 1.60 |
| **886** A355 1.60k blk, red brn & ol | 8.00 | 4.50 |
| *Nos. 882-886 (5)* | 17.60 | 7.15 |

Nos. 882-886 were each issued in a miniature sheet of 10 stamps. Value, set $275.

Children on Beach — A356

45h, Mother, child and bird. 60h, Skier.

**1958, Oct. 24** **Unwmk.** ***Perf. 14***

| | | |
|---|---|---|
| **887** A356 30h blue, yel & red | .35 | .25 |
| **888** A356 45h ultra & carmine | 1.40 | .60 |
| **889** A356 60h brown, blue & yel | .35 | .25 |
| *Nos. 887-889 (3)* | 2.10 | 1.10 |

UNESCO Headquarters in Paris opening, Nov. 3. Nos. 887-889 each were issued in sheets of 10. Value, set $75.

Bozek's Steam Car of 1815 A357

Designs: 45h, "Präsident" car of 1897. 60h, "Skoda" sports car. 80h, "Tatra" sedan. 1k, "Autocar Skoda" bus. 1.25k, Trucks.

**Engraved and Photogravure**

**1958, Dec. 1** ***Perf. 11½x11***

| | | |
|---|---|---|
| **890** A357 30h vio blk & buff | .70 | .25 |
| **891** A357 45h ol & lt ol grn | .70 | .25 |
| **892** A357 60h ol gray & sal | 1.75 | .25 |
| **893** A357 80h claret & bl grn | 1.10 | .25 |
| **894** A357 1k brn & lt yel grn | 1.40 | .30 |
| **895** A357 1.25k green & buff | 2.10 | .45 |
| *Nos. 890-895 (6)* | 7.75 | 1.75 |

Issued to honor the automobile industry.

Stamp of 1918 and Allegory — A358

**1958, Dec. 18** **Engr.** ***Perf. 11x11½***

| | | |
|---|---|---|
| **896** A358 60h dark blue gray | .85 | .30 |

1st Czechoslovakian postage stamp, 40th anniv.

Ice Hockey A359

30h, Girl throwing javelin. 60h, Ice hockey. 1k, Hurdling. 1.60k, Rowing. 2k, High jump.

**1959, Feb. 14** ***Perf. 11½x11***

| | | |
|---|---|---|
| **897** A359 20h dk brown & gray | .50 | .25 |
| **898** A359 30h red brn & org brn | .40 | .25 |
| **899** A359 60h dk bl & pale grn | .65 | .25 |
| **900** A359 1k maroon & citron | .50 | .25 |
| **901** A359 1.60k dull vio & lt bl | .80 | .25 |
| **902** A359 2k red brn & lt bl | 1.75 | .25 |
| *Nos. 897-902 (6)* | 4.60 | 1.50 |

Congress Emblem — A360

60h, Industrial & agricultural workers, emblem.

**1959, Feb. 27** ***Perf. 11½***

| | | |
|---|---|---|
| **903** A360 30h maroon & lt blue | .45 | .25 |
| **904** A360 60h dk blue & yellow | .45 | .25 |

4th Agricultural Cooperative Cong. in Prague.

"Equality of All Races" — A361

Designs: 1k, "Peace." 2k, Mother and Child: "Freedom for Colonial People."

**1959, Mar. 23**

| | | |
|---|---|---|
| **905** A361 60h gray green | .30 | .25 |
| **906** A361 1k gray | .45 | .25 |
| **907** A361 2k dk gray blue | 1.50 | .50 |
| *Nos. 905-907 (3)* | 2.25 | 1.00 |

10th anniversary of the signing of the Universal Declaration of Human Rights.

Girl Holding Puppet — A362

40h, Pioneer studying map. 60h, Pioneer with radio. 80h, Girl pioneer planting tree.

**1959, Mar. 28** **Engr. & Photo.**

| | | |
|---|---|---|
| **908** A362 30h violet bl & yel | .35 | .25 |
| **909** A362 40h indigo & ultra | .45 | .25 |
| **910** A362 60h black & lilac | .35 | .25 |
| **911** A362 80h brown & lt green | .65 | .25 |
| *Nos. 908-911 (4)* | 1.80 | 1.00 |

10th anniv. of the Pioneer organization.

Frederic Joliot Curie — A363

**1959, Apr. 17** **Engr.**

| | | |
|---|---|---|
| **912** A363 60h sepia | 1.40 | .30 |

Frederic Joliot Curie and the 10th anniversary of the World Peace Movement.

"Reaching for the Moon" — A364

**1959, Apr. 17**

| | | |
|---|---|---|
| **913** A364 30h violet blue | 1.10 | .30 |

2nd Cong. of the Czechoslovak Assoc. for the Propagation of Political and Cultural knowledge.

Town Hall Pilsen — A365

Designs: 60h, Part of steam condenser turbine. 1k, St. Bartholomew's Church, Pilsen. 1.60k, Part of lathe.

**1959, May 2**

| | | | | |
|---|---|---|---|---|
| **914** | A365 | 30h lt brown | .30 | .25 |
| **915** | A365 | 60h violet & lt grn | .30 | .25 |
| **916** | A365 | 1k violet blue | .40 | .25 |
| **917** | A365 | 1.60k black & yellow | 1.10 | .50 |
| | | *Nos. 914-917 (4)* | 2.10 | 1.25 |

2nd Pilsen Stamp Exhib. in connection with the centenary of the Skoda (Lenin) armament works.

Factory and Emblem A366

**Inscribed: "IV Vseodborovy sjezd, 1959"**

**1959, May 13**

| | | | | |
|---|---|---|---|---|
| **918** | A366 | 30h shown | .45 | .25 |
| **919** | A366 | 60h Dam | .30 | .25 |

4th Trade Union Congress.

Zvolen Castle A367

**1959, June 13**

| | | | | |
|---|---|---|---|---|
| **920** | A367 | 60h gray olive & yel | .60 | .25 |

Regional Stamp Exhibition, Zvolen, 1959.

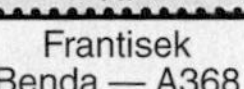

Frantisek Benda — A368

Aurel Stodola — A369

30h, Vaclav Kliment Klicpera. 60h, Karel V. Rais. 80h, Antonin Slavicek. 1k, Peter Bezruc.

**1959, June 22** ***Perf. 11½x11***

| | | | | |
|---|---|---|---|---|
| **921** | A368 | 15h violet blue | .25 | .25 |
| **922** | A368 | 30h orange brown | .25 | .25 |
| **923** | A369 | 40h dull green | .25 | .25 |
| **924** | A369 | 60h dull red brn | .35 | .25 |
| **925** | A369 | 80h dull violet | .55 | .25 |
| **926** | A368 | 1k dark brown | .55 | .25 |
| | | *Nos. 921-926 (6)* | 2.20 | 1.50 |

View of the Fair Grounds A370

Designs: 60h, Fair emblem and world map. 1.60k, Pavilion "Z."

**Inscribed: "Mezinarodni Veletrh Brne 6.-20.IX. 1959"**

**Engraved and Photogravure**

**1959, July 20** **Unwmk.** ***Perf. 11½***

| | | | | |
|---|---|---|---|---|
| **927** | A370 | 30h lilac & yellow | .25 | .25 |
| **928** | A370 | 60h dull blue | .25 | .25 |
| **929** | A370 | 1.60k dk blue & bister | .75 | .25 |
| | | *Nos. 927-929 (3)* | 1.25 | .75 |

International Fair at Brno, Sept. 6-20.

Revolutionist and Flag — A371

Slovakian Fighter — A372

1.60k, Linden leaves, sun and factory.

***Perf. 11½***

**1959, Aug. 29** **Unwmk.** **Engr.**

| | | | | |
|---|---|---|---|---|
| **930** | A371 | 30h black & rose | .25 | .25 |
| **931** | A372 | 60h carmine rose | .25 | .25 |
| **932** | A371 | 1.60k dk blue & yel | .45 | .25 |
| | | *Nos. 930-932 (3)* | .95 | .75 |

Natl. Slovakian revolution, 15th anniv. and Slovakian Soviet Republic, 40th anniv.

Alpine Marmots A373

**1959, Sept. 25** **Engr. & Photo.**

| | | | | |
|---|---|---|---|---|
| **933** | A373 | 30h shown | 1.25 | .25 |
| **934** | A373 | 40h Bison | 1.00 | .40 |
| **935** | A373 | 60h Lynx, vert. | 2.60 | .30 |
| **936** | A373 | 1k Wolf | 2.60 | 1.00 |
| **937** | A373 | 1.60k Red deer | 2.25 | .55 |
| | | *Nos. 933-937 (5)* | 9.70 | 2.50 |

Tatra National Park, 10th anniv.

Lunik 2 Hitting Moon and Russian Flag A374

**1959, Sept. 23** ***Perf. 11½***

| | | | | |
|---|---|---|---|---|
| **938** | A374 | 60h dk red & lt ultra | 1.50 | .30 |

Issued to commemorate the landing of the Soviet rocket on the moon, Sept. 13, 1959.

Stamp Printing Works, Peking A375

**1959, Oct. 1**

| | | | | |
|---|---|---|---|---|
| **939** | A375 | 30h pale green & red | .40 | .25 |

10 years of Czechoslovakian-Chinese friendship.

Haydn — A376

Design: 3k, Charles Darwin.

**1959, Oct. 16** **Engr.** ***Perf. 11½***

| | | | | |
|---|---|---|---|---|
| **940** | A376 | 60h violet black | .50 | .25 |
| **941** | A376 | 3k dark red brown | 1.25 | .65 |

150th death anniv. of Franz Joseph Haydn, Austrian composer, and 150th birth anniv. of Charles Darwin, English naturalist.

Great Spotted Woodpecker A377

Birds: 30h, Blue tits. 40h, Nuthatch. 60th, Golden oriole. 80h, Goldfinch. 1k, Bullfinch. 1.20k, European kingfisher.

**1959, Nov. 16** ***Perf. 14***

| | | | | |
|---|---|---|---|---|
| **942** | A377 | 20h multicolored | 1.50 | .60 |
| **943** | A377 | 30h multicolored | 1.50 | .60 |
| **944** | A377 | 40h multicolored | 4.50 | 1.50 |
| **945** | A377 | 60h multicolored | 1.50 | .60 |
| **946** | A377 | 80h multicolored | 2.25 | .75 |
| **947** | A377 | 1k multicolored | 2.25 | .75 |
| **948** | A377 | 1.20k multicolored | 3.00 | .75 |
| | | *Nos. 942-948 (7)* | 16.50 | 5.55 |

Nos. 942-948 were each issued in miniature sheets of 10. Value, set $275.

Nikola Tesla A378

Designs: 30h, Alexander S. Popov. 35h, Edouard Branly. 60h, Guglielmo Marconi. 1k, Heinrich Hertz. 2k, Edwin Howard Armstrong and research tower, Alpine, N. J.

**Engraved and Photogravure**

**1959, Dec. 7** ***Perf. 11½***

| | | | | |
|---|---|---|---|---|
| **949** | A378 | 25h black & pink | 1.00 | .25 |
| **950** | A378 | 30h black & orange | .25 | .25 |
| **951** | A378 | 35h black & lt vio | .25 | .25 |
| **952** | A378 | 60h black & blue | .25 | .25 |
| **953** | A378 | 1k black & lt grn | .25 | .25 |
| **954** | A378 | 2k black & bister | 1.25 | .25 |
| | | *Nos. 949-954 (6)* | 3.25 | 1.50 |

Issued to honor inventors in the fields of telegraphy and radio.

Gymnast — A379

2nd Winter Spartacist Games: 60h, Skier. 1.60k, Basketball players.

**1960, Jan. 20** ***Perf. 11½***

| | | | | |
|---|---|---|---|---|
| **955** | A379 | 30h salmon pink & brn | 1.00 | .25 |
| **956** | A379 | 60h lt blue & blk | 1.00 | .25 |
| **957** | A379 | 1.60k bister & brn | .85 | .25 |
| | | *Nos. 955-957 (3)* | 2.85 | .75 |

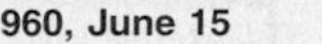

**1960, June 15** **Unwmk.**

Designs: 30h, Two girls in "Red Ball" drill. 60h, Gymnast with stick. 1k, Three girls with hoops.

| | | | | |
|---|---|---|---|---|
| **958** | A379 | 30h lt grn & rose claret | .65 | .25 |
| **959** | A379 | 60h pink & black | .50 | .25 |
| **960** | A379 | 1k ocher & vio bl | .85 | .25 |
| | | *Nos. 958-960 (3)* | 2.00 | .75 |

2nd Summer Spartacist Games, Prague, June 23-July 3.

River Dredge Boat A380

Ships: 60h, River tug. 1k, Tourist steamer. 1.20k, Cargo ship "Lidice."

**1960, Feb. 22** ***Perf. 11½***

| | | | | |
|---|---|---|---|---|
| **961** | A380 | 30h slate grn & sal | 2.75 | .30 |
| **962** | A380 | 60h maroon & pale bl | 1.40 | .30 |
| **963** | A380 | 1k dk violet & yel | 2.50 | .30 |
| **964** | A380 | 1.20k lilac & pale grn | 3.50 | .90 |
| | | *Nos. 961-964 (4)* | 10.15 | 1.80 |

Ice Hockey Players — A381

Design: 1.80k, Figure skaters.

**1960, Feb. 27**

| | | | | |
|---|---|---|---|---|
| **965** | A381 | 60h sepia & lt blue | 2.00 | .40 |
| **966** | A381 | 1.80k black & lt green | 6.00 | 1.75 |

8th Olympic Winter Games, Squaw Valley, Calif., Feb. 18-29, 1960.

**1960, June 15** **Unwmk.**

Designs: 1k, Running. 1.80k, Women's gymnastics. 2k, Rowing.

| | | | | |
|---|---|---|---|---|
| **967** | A381 | 1k black & orange | .85 | .30 |
| **968** | A381 | 1.80k black & sal pink | 1.40 | .40 |
| **969** | A381 | 2k black & blue | 2.50 | .75 |
| | | *Nos. 967-969 (3)* | 4.75 | 1.45 |

17th Olympic Games, Rome, 8/25-9/11.

Trencin Castle — A382

Castles: 10h, Bezdez. 20h, Kost. 30h, Pernstein. 40h, Kremnica. 50h, Krivoklát castle. 60h, Karlstein. 1k, Smolenice. 1.60k, Kokorin.

**1960-63** **Engr.** ***Perf. 11½***

| | | | | |
|---|---|---|---|---|
| **970** | A382 | 5h gray violet | .30 | .25 |
| **971** | A382 | 10h black | .30 | .25 |
| **972** | A382 | 20h brown org | .35 | .25 |
| **973** | A382 | 30h green | .30 | .25 |
| **974** | A382 | 40h brown | .35 | .25 |
| **974A** | A382 | 50h black ('63) | 3.50 | .25 |
| **975** | A382 | 60h rose red | .45 | .25 |
| **976** | A382 | 1k lilac | .45 | .25 |
| **977** | A382 | 1.60k dark blue | .75 | .25 |
| | | *Nos. 970-977 (9)* | 6.75 | 2.25 |

**1961, Oct.** **Wmk. 341**

| | | | | |
|---|---|---|---|---|
| **977A** | A382 | 30h green | 3.00 | .40 |

Lenin — A383

**1960, Apr. 22** **Unwmk.**

| No. | Type | Description | Unused | Used |
|---|---|---|---|---|
| **978** | A383 | 60h gray olive | 1.40 | .25 |

90th anniversary of the birth of Lenin.

Soldier Holding Child — A384

Designs: No. 980, Child eating pie. No. 981, Soldier helping concentration camp victim. No. 982, Welder and factory, horiz. No. 983, Tractor driver and farm, horiz.

**1960, May 5** **Engr. & Photo.**

| No. | Type | Description | Unused | Used |
|---|---|---|---|---|
| **979** | A384 | 30h maroon & lt blue | .35 | .25 |
| **980** | A384 | 30h dull red | .35 | .25 |
| **981** | A384 | 30h green & dull blue | .40 | .25 |
| **982** | A384 | 60h dk blue & buff | .35 | .25 |
| **983** | A384 | 60h redsh brn & yel grn | .40 | .25 |
| | | *Nos. 979-983 (5)* | 1.85 | 1.25 |

15th anniversary of liberation.

Steelworker — A385

Design: 60h, Farm woman and child.

**1960, May 24**

| No. | Type | Description | Unused | Used |
|---|---|---|---|---|
| **984** | A385 | 30h maroon & gray | .30 | .25 |
| **985** | A385 | 60h green & pale blue | .30 | .25 |

1960 parliamentary elections.

Red Cross Nurse Holding Dove A386

Fire Fighters A387

**1960, May 26** **Unwmk.**

| No. | Type | Description | Unused | Used |
|---|---|---|---|---|
| **986** | A386 | 30h brown car & bl | .30 | .25 |
| **987** | A387 | 60h dk blue & pink | .45 | .25 |

3rd Congress of the Czechoslovakian Red Cross (No. 986), and the 2nd Fire Fighters' Congress (No. 987).

Hand of Philatelist with Tongs and Two Stamps — A388

Design: 1k, Globe and 1937 Bratislava stamp (shown in miniature on 60h).

**1960, July 11** ***Perf. 11½***

| No. | Type | Description | Unused | Used |
|---|---|---|---|---|
| **988** | A388 | 60h black & dull yel | .75 | .25 |
| **989** | A388 | 1k black & blue | .90 | .25 |

Issued to publicize the National Stamp Exhibition, Bratislava, Sept. 24-Oct. 9.

See Nos. C49-C50.

Stalin Mine, Ostrava-Hermanovice — A390

Designs: 20h, Power station, Hodonin. 30h, Gottwald iron works, Kuncice. 40h, Harvester. 60h, Oil refinery.

**1960, July 25**

| No. | Type | Description | Unused | Used |
|---|---|---|---|---|
| **992** | A390 | 10h black & pale grn | .30 | .25 |
| **993** | A390 | 20h maroon & lt bl | .30 | .25 |
| **994** | A390 | 30h indigo & pink | .30 | .25 |
| **995** | A390 | 40h green & pale lilac | .30 | .25 |
| **996** | A390 | 60h dk blue & yel | .30 | .25 |
| | | *Nos. 992-996 (5)* | 1.50 | 1.25 |

Issued to publicize the new five-year plan.

Viktorin Cornelius, Lawyer — A391

Portraits: 20h, Karel Matej Capek-Chod, writer. 30h, Hana Kvapilova, actress. 40h, Oskar Nedbal, composer. 60h, Otakar Ostrcil, composer.

**1960, Aug. 23** **Engr.**

| No. | Type | Description | Unused | Used |
|---|---|---|---|---|
| **997** | A391 | 10h black | .30 | .25 |
| **998** | A391 | 20h red brown | .45 | .25 |
| **999** | A391 | 30h rose red | .55 | .25 |
| **1000** | A391 | 40h dull green | 1.40 | .60 |
| **1001** | A391 | 60h gray violet | .45 | .25 |
| | | *Nos. 997-1001 (5)* | 3.15 | 1.60 |

See Nos. 1037-1041.

Skoda Sports Plane Flying Upside Down A392

**1960, Aug. 28** **Engr. & Photo.**

| No. | Type | Description | Unused | Used |
|---|---|---|---|---|
| **1002** | A392 | 60h violet blue & blue | 1.40 | .30 |

1st aerobatic world championships, Bratislava.

Constitution and "Czechoslovakia" — A393

**1960, Sept. 18**

| No. | Type | Description | Unused | Used |
|---|---|---|---|---|
| **1003** | A393 | 30h violet bl & pink | .40 | .25 |

Proclamation of the new socialist constitution.

Workers Reading Newspaper — A394

Man Holding Newspaper — A395

**1960, Sept. 18**

| No. | Type | Description | Unused | Used |
|---|---|---|---|---|
| **1004** | A394 | 30h slate & ver | .25 | .25 |
| **1005** | A395 | 60h black & rose | .25 | .25 |

Day of the Czechoslovak Press, Sept. 21, 1960, and 40th anniv. of the Rudé Právo paper.

Globes and Laurel A396

**1960, Sept. 18** **Engr.**

| No. | Type | Description | Unused | Used |
|---|---|---|---|---|
| **1006** | A396 | 30h dk blue & bister | .40 | .25 |

World Federation of Trade Unions, 15th anniv.

Black-crowned Night Heron — A397

Birds: 30h, Great crested grebe. 40h, Lapwing. 60h, Gray heron. 1k, Graylag goose, horiz. 1.60k, Mallard, horiz.

### Engraved and Photogravure

**1960, Oct. 24** **Unwmk.** ***Perf. 11½***

**Designs in Black**

| No. | Type | Description | Unused | Used |
|---|---|---|---|---|
| **1007** | A397 | 25h pale vio blue | .90 | .25 |
| **1008** | A397 | 30h pale citron | .80 | .25 |
| **1009** | A397 | 40h pale blue | .90 | .30 |
| **1010** | A397 | 60h pink | .60 | .25 |
| **1011** | A397 | 1k pale yellow | 1.75 | .25 |
| **1012** | A397 | 1.60k lt violet | 4.50 | 1.25 |
| | | *Nos. 1007-1012 (6)* | 9.45 | 2.55 |

Doronicum Clusii (Thistle) — A398

Flowers: 30h, Cyclamen. 40h, Primrose. 60h, Hen-and-chickens. 1k, Gentian. 2k, Pasqueflower.

**1960, Nov. 21** **Engr.** ***Perf. 14***

| No. | Type | Description | Unused | Used |
|---|---|---|---|---|
| **1013** | A398 | 20h black, yel & grn | .80 | .40 |
| **1014** | A398 | 30h black, car rose & grn | .80 | .40 |
| **1015** | A398 | 40h black, yel & grn | .80 | .40 |
| **1016** | A398 | 60h black, pink & grn | .80 | .40 |
| **1017** | A398 | 1k black, bl, vio & grn | 2.00 | .40 |
| **1018** | A398 | 2k black, lil, yel & grn | 2.75 | 1.60 |
| | | *Nos. 1013-1018 (6)* | 7.95 | 3.60 |

Nos. 1013-1018 were each issued in sheets of 10. Value, set $100.

Alfons Mucha — A399

**1960, Dec. 18** **Engr.** ***Perf. 11½x12***

| No. | Type | Description | Unused | Used |
|---|---|---|---|---|
| **1019** | A399 | 60h dk blue gray | 3.00 | .25 |

Day of the Czechoslovak Postage Stamp and birth cent. of Alfons Mucha, designer of the 1st Czechoslovakian stamp (Type A1).

Rolling-mill Control Bridge — A400

Designs: 30h, Turbo generator. 60h, Ditch-digging machine.

**1961, Jan. 20** **Unwmk.** ***Perf. 11½***

| No. | Type | Description | Unused | Used |
|---|---|---|---|---|
| **1020** | A400 | 20h blue | .30 | .25 |
| **1021** | A400 | 30h rose | .30 | .25 |
| **1022** | A400 | 60h brt green | .30 | .25 |
| | | *Nos. 1020-1022 (3)* | .90 | .75 |

Third Five-Year Plan.

Athletes with Flags — A401

Designs: No. 1024, Motorcycle race, horiz. 40h, Sculling, horiz. 60h, Ice skater. 1k, Rugby. 1.20k, Soccer. 1.60k, Long-distance runners.

***Perf. 11x11½, 11½x11***

**1961, Feb. 20** **Engr. & Photo.**

| No. | Type | Description | Unused | Used |
|---|---|---|---|---|
| **1023** | A401 | 30h rose red & bl | .30 | .25 |
| **1024** | A401 | 30h dk blue & car | .30 | .25 |
| **1025** | A401 | 40h dk gray & car | .45 | .25 |
| **1026** | A401 | 60h lilac & blue | .45 | .25 |
| **1027** | A401 | 1k ultra & yel | .45 | .25 |
| **1028** | A401 | 1.20k green & buff | 1.10 | .25 |
| **1029** | A401 | 1.60k sepia & salmon | 1.50 | .30 |
| | | *Nos. 1023-1029 (7)* | 4.55 | 1.80 |

Various sports events.

Exhibition Emblem — A402

**1961, Mar. 6** **Engr.** ***Perf. 11½***

| No. | Type | Description | Unused | Used |
|---|---|---|---|---|
| **1030** | A402 | 2k dk blue & red | 2.25 | .25 |

"Praga 1962" International Stamp Exhibition, Prague, Sept. 1962.

Rocket Launching — A403

30h, Sputnik III, horiz. 40h, As 20h, but inscribed "Start Kosmicke Rakety k Venusi — 12.II.1961". 60h, Sputnik I, horiz. 1.60k, Interplanetary station, horiz. 2k, Similar to type A404, without commemorative inscription.

**1961, Mar. 6** **Engr. & Photo.**

| | | | | | |
|---|---|---|---|---|---|
| **1031** | A403 | 20h | violet & pink | .30 | .25 |
| **1032** | A403 | 30h | dk green & buff | .65 | .25 |
| **1033** | A403 | 40h | dk red & yel grn | .65 | .30 |
| **1034** | A403 | 60h | violet & buff | .80 | .25 |
| **1035** | A403 | 1.60k | dk bl & pale grn | .55 | .25 |
| **1036** | A403 | 2k | mar & pale bl | 1.25 | .75 |
| | | | *Nos. 1031-1036 (6)* | 4.20 | 2.05 |

Issued to publicize Soviet space research.

### Portrait Type of 1960

No. 1037, Jindrich Mosna. No. 1038, Pavol Orszagh Hviezdoslav. No. 1039, Alois Mrstik. No. 1040, Joza Uprka. No. 1041, Josef Hora.

**1961, Mar. 27** ***Perf. 11½***

| | | | | | |
|---|---|---|---|---|---|
| **1037** | A391 | 60h | green | .30 | .25 |
| **1038** | A391 | 60h | dark blue | .60 | .25 |
| *a.* | | | "ORSZACH" instead of "ORSZAGH" | *175.00* | *25.00* |
| **1039** | A391 | 60h | dull claret | .75 | .25 |
| **1040** | A391 | 60h | gray | .55 | .25 |
| **1041** | A391 | 60h | sepia | .30 | .25 |
| | | | *Nos. 1037-1041 (5)* | 2.50 | 1.25 |

Man Flying into Space A404

**1961, Apr. 13**

| | | | | | |
|---|---|---|---|---|---|
| **1042** | A404 | 60h | car & pale bl | .65 | .25 |
| **1043** | A404 | 3k | ultra & yel | 2.00 | .60 |

1st man in space, Yuri A. Gagarin, Apr. 12, 1961. See No. 1036.

Flute Player — A405

**1961, Apr. 24** **Engr.**

| | | | | | |
|---|---|---|---|---|---|
| **1044** | A405 | 30h | shown | .45 | .25 |
| **1045** | A405 | 30h | Dancer | .45 | .25 |
| **1046** | A405 | 60h | Lyre player | .65 | .25 |
| | | | *Nos. 1044-1046 (3)* | 1.55 | .75 |

Prague Conservatory of Music, 150th anniv.

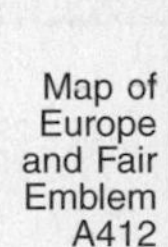

Blast Furnace and Mine, Kladno — A406

**1961, Apr. 24**

| | | | | | |
|---|---|---|---|---|---|
| **1047** | A406 | 3k | dull red | .65 | .25 |

City of Kladno, 400th anniv.

Marching Workers — A407

Woman with Hammer and Sickle — A408

Klement Gottwald Museum A409

Designs: No. 1050, Lenin Museum. No. 1051, Crowd with flags. No. 1053, Man saluting Red Star.

**1961, May 10**

| | | | | | |
|---|---|---|---|---|---|
| **1048** | A407 | 30h | dull violet | .30 | .25 |
| **1049** | A409 | 30h | dark blue | .30 | .25 |
| **1050** | A409 | 30h | redsh brown | .30 | .25 |
| **1051** | A407 | 60h | vermilion | .30 | .25 |
| **1052** | A408 | 60h | dark green | .30 | .25 |
| **1053** | A408 | 60h | carmine | .30 | .25 |
| | | | *Nos. 1048-1053 (6)* | 1.80 | 1.50 |

Czech Communist Party, 40th anniversary.

Puppet — A410

Designs: Various Puppets.

### Engraved and Photogravure

**1961, June 20** **Unwmk.** ***Perf. 11½***

| | | | | | |
|---|---|---|---|---|---|
| **1054** | A410 | 30h | ver & yel | .30 | .25 |
| **1055** | A410 | 40h | sepia & bluish grn | .30 | .25 |
| **1056** | A410 | 60h | vio bl & sal | .30 | .25 |
| **1057** | A410 | 1k | green & lt blue | .30 | .25 |
| **1058** | A410 | 1.60k | mar & pale vio | .95 | .25 |
| | | | *Nos. 1054-1058 (5)* | 2.15 | 1.25 |

Woman, Map of Africa and Flag of Czechoslovakia A411

**1961, June 26**

| | | | | | |
|---|---|---|---|---|---|
| **1059** | A411 | 60h | red & blue | .35 | .25 |

Issued to publicize the friendship between the people of Africa and Czechoslovakia.

Map of Europe and Fair Emblem A412

Fair emblem and: 60h Horizontal boring machine, vert. 1k, Scientists' meeting and nuclear physics emblem.

**1961, Aug. 14** ***Perf. 11½***

| | | | | | |
|---|---|---|---|---|---|
| **1060** | A412 | 30h | dk bl & pale grn | .30 | .25 |
| **1061** | A412 | 60h | green & pink | .30 | .25 |
| **1062** | A412 | 1k | vio brn & lt bl | .60 | .25 |
| | | | *Nos. 1060-1062 (3)* | 1.20 | .75 |

International Trade Fair, Brno, Sept. 10-24.

Sugar Beet, Cup of Coffee and Bags of Sugar — A413

**1961, Sept. 18** **Unwmk.** ***Perf. 11½***

| | | | | | |
|---|---|---|---|---|---|
| **1063** | A413 | 20h | shown | .25 | .25 |
| **1064** | A413 | 30h | Clover | .25 | .25 |
| **1065** | A413 | 40h | Wheat | .25 | .25 |
| **1066** | A413 | 60h | Hops | .25 | .25 |
| **1067** | A413 | 1.40k | Corn | .30 | .25 |
| **1068** | A413 | 2k | Potatoes | 2.00 | .35 |
| | | | *Nos. 1063-1068 (6)* | 3.30 | 1.60 |

Charles Bridge, St. Nicholas Church and Hradcany — A414

**1961, Sept. 25**

| | | | | | |
|---|---|---|---|---|---|
| **1069** | A414 | 60h | violet bl & car | 1.20 | .25 |

26th session of the Governor's Council of the Red Cross Societies League, Prague.

Orlik Dam and Kaplan Turbine A415

Designs: 30h, View of Prague, flags and stamps. 40h, Hluboká Castle, river and fish. 60h, Karlovy Vary and cup. 1k, Pilsen and beer bottle. 1.20k, North Bohemia landscape and vase. 1.60k, Tatra mountains, boots, ice pick and rope. 2k, Ironworks, Ostrava Kuncice and pulley. 3k, Brno and ball bearing. 4k, Bratislava and grapes. 5k, Prague and flags.

**1961** **Unwmk.** ***Perf. 11½***

**Size: 41x23mm**

| | | | | | |
|---|---|---|---|---|---|
| **1070** | A415 | 20h | gray & blue | *1.50* | *.45* |
| **1071** | A415 | 30h | vio blue & red | 1.50 | .75 |
| **1072** | A415 | 40h | dk blue & lt grn | 1.60 | .75 |
| **1073** | A415 | 60h | dk blue & yel | 1.10 | .75 |
| **1074** | A415 | 1k | mar & grn | 1.60 | .75 |
| **1075** | A415 | 1.20k | green & pink | 1.60 | 1.10 |
| **1076** | A415 | 1.60k | brn & vio bl | 1.90 | 1.10 |
| **1077** | A415 | 2k | blk & ocher | 1.90 | .45 |
| **1078** | A415 | 3k | ultra & yel | 2.00 | .55 |
| **1079** | A415 | 4k | purple & sal | 2.40 | 1.10 |

***Perf. 13½***

**Engr.**

**Size: 50x29mm**

| | | | | | |
|---|---|---|---|---|---|
| **1080** | A415 | 5k | multicolored | 20.00 | 20.00 |
| | | | *Nos. 1070-1080 (11)* | 37.10 | 27.75 |

"PRAGA 1962 World Exhib. of Postage Stamps," Aug. 18-Sept. 2, 1962.

No. 1080 was printed in sheet of 4. Value $120.

Globe A416

### Engraved and Photogravure

**1961, Nov. 27** ***Perf. 11½***

| | | | | | |
|---|---|---|---|---|---|
| **1081** | A416 | 60h | red & ultra | .50 | .25 |

Issued to publicize the Fifth World Congress of Trade Unions, Moscow, Dec. 4-16.

Orange Tip Butterfly — A417

Designs (butterflies): 20h, Zerynthia hypsipyle Sch. 30h, Apollo. 40h, Swallowtail. 60h, Peacock. 80h, Mourning cloak (Camberwell beauty). 1k, Underwing (moth). 1.60k, Red admiral. 2k, Brimstone (sulphur).

**1961, Nov. 27** **Engr.**

| | | | | | |
|---|---|---|---|---|---|
| **1082** | A417 | 15h | multicolored | .80 | .30 |
| **1083** | A417 | 20h | multicolored | .80 | .30 |
| **1084** | A417 | 30h | multicolored | .80 | .30 |
| **1085** | A417 | 40h | multicolored | .80 | .30 |
| **1086** | A417 | 60h | multicolored | .80 | .30 |
| **1087** | A417 | 80h | multicolored | 2.40 | .90 |
| **1088** | A417 | 1k | multicolored | 2.40 | .90 |
| **1089** | A417 | 1.60k | multicolored | 2.40 | .90 |
| **1090** | A417 | 2k | multicolored | 6.50 | 3.00 |
| | | | *Nos. 1082-1090 (9)* | 17.70 | 7.20 |

Nos.1082-1090 were each issued in sheets of 10. Value, set $350.

Bicyclists — A418

Sports: 40h, Woman gymnast. 60h, Figure skaters. 1k, Woman bowler. 1.20k, Goalkeeper, soccer. 1.60k, Discus thrower.

### Engraved and Photogravure

**1962, Feb. 5** **Unwmk.** ***Perf. 11½***

| | | | | | |
|---|---|---|---|---|---|
| **1091** | A418 | 30h | black & vio bl | .25 | .25 |
| **1092** | A418 | 40h | black & yel | .25 | .25 |
| **1093** | A418 | 60h | slate & grnsh bl | .35 | .25 |
| **1094** | A418 | 1k | black & pink | .35 | .25 |
| **1095** | A418 | 1.20k | black & green | .35 | .25 |
| **1096** | A418 | 1.60k | blk & dull grn | 1.50 | .45 |
| | | | *Nos. 1091-1096 (6)* | 3.05 | 1.70 |

Various 1962 sports events.

No. 1095 does not have the commemorative inscription.

Karel Kovarovic — A419

Frantisek Zaviska and Karel Petr A420

20h, Frantisek Skroup. 30h, Bozena Nemcova. 60h, View of Prague & staff of Aesculapius. 1.60k, Ladislav Celakovsky. 1.80k, Miloslav Valouch & Juraj Hronec.

**1962, Feb. 26** **Engr.**

| | | | | | |
|---|---|---|---|---|---|
| **1097** | A419 | 10h | red brown | .25 | .25 |
| **1098** | A419 | 20h | violet blue | .25 | .25 |
| **1099** | A419 | 30h | brown | .25 | .25 |
| **1100** | A420 | 40h | claret | .50 | .25 |
| **1101** | A419 | 60h | black | .25 | .25 |
| **1102** | A419 | 1.60k | slate green | .25 | .25 |
| **1103** | A420 | 1.80k | dark blue | .60 | .25 |
| | | | *Nos. 1097-1103 (7)* | 2.35 | 1.75 |

Various cultural personalities and events.

Miner and Flag
A421

**1962, Mar. 19 Engr. & Photo.**

| | | | | |
|---|---|---|---|---|
| **1104** | A421 60h indigo & rose | .25 | .25 |

30th anniv. of the miners' strike at Most.

"Man Conquering Space" — A422

Soviet Spaceship Vostok 2 — A423

40h, Launching of Soviet space rocket. 80h, Multi-stage automatic rocket. 1k, Automatic station on moon. 1.60k, Television satellite.

**1962, Mar. 26**

| | | | | |
|---|---|---|---|---|
| **1105** | A422 | 30h dk red & lt blue | .35 | .25 |
| **1106** | A422 | 40h dk blue & sal | .35 | .25 |
| **1107** | A423 | 60h dk blue & pink | .35 | .25 |
| **1108** | A423 | 80h rose vio & lt grn | .35 | .25 |
| **1109** | A422 | 1k indigo & citron | .35 | .25 |
| **1110** | A423 | 1.60k green & buff | 1.90 | .25 |
| | | *Nos. 1105-1110 (6)* | 3.65 | 1.50 |

Issued to publicize space research.

Polar Bear — A424

Zoo Animals: 30h, Chimpanzee. 60h, Camel. 1k, African and Indian elephants, horiz. 1.40k, Leopard, horiz. 1.60k, Przewalski horse, horiz.

**1962, Apr. 24 Unwmk. *Perf. 11½***
**Design and Inscriptions in Black**

| | | | | |
|---|---|---|---|---|
| **1111** | A424 | 20h grnsh blue | .75 | .25 |
| **1112** | A424 | 30h violet | .75 | .25 |
| **1113** | A424 | 60h orange | .75 | .25 |
| **1114** | A424 | 1k green | .75 | .25 |
| **1115** | A424 | 1.40k carmine rose | .75 | .25 |
| **1116** | A424 | 1.60k lt brown | 1.90 | 1.25 |
| | | *Nos. 1111-1116 (6)* | 5.65 | 2.50 |

Child and Grieving Mother — A425

60h, Flowers growing from ruins of Lezáky.

**1962, June 9 Engr. & Photo.**

| | | | | |
|---|---|---|---|---|
| **1118** | A425 | 30h black & red | .45 | .25 |
| **1119** | A425 | 60h black & dull bl | .75 | .25 |

20th anniversary of the destruction of Lidice and Lezáky by the Nazis.

Klary's Fountain, Teplice — A426

**1962, June 9**

| | | | |
|---|---|---|---|
| **1120** | A426 60h dull grn & yel | .40 | .25 |

1,200th anniversary of the discovery of the medicinal springs of Teplice.

Malaria Eradication Emblem, Cross and Dove — A427

3k, Dove and malaria eradication emblem.

**1962, June 18**

| | | | | |
|---|---|---|---|---|
| **1121** | A427 | 60h black & crimson | .45 | .25 |
| **1122** | A427 | 3k dk blue & yel | 1.10 | .35 |

WHO drive to eradicate malaria.

Soccer Goalkeeper — A428

**1962, June 20 Unwmk. *Perf. 11½***

| | | | |
|---|---|---|---|
| **1123** | A428 1.60k green & yellow | 1.50 | .25 |

Czechoslovakia's participation in the World Cup Soccer Championship, Chile, May 30-June 17. See No. 1095.

Soldier in Swimming Relay Race — A429

Designs: 40h, Soldier hurdling. 60h, Soccer player. 1k, Soldier with rifle in relay race.

**1962, July 20**

| | | | | |
|---|---|---|---|---|
| **1124** | A429 | 30h green & lt ultra | .25 | .25 |
| **1125** | A429 | 40h dk purple & yel | .25 | .25 |
| **1126** | A429 | 60h brown & green | .25 | .25 |
| **1127** | A429 | 1k dk blue & sal pink | .25 | .25 |
| | | *Nos. 1124-1127 (4)* | 1.00 | 1.00 |

2nd Summer Spartacist Games of Friendly Armies, Prague, Sept., 1962.

"Agriculture"
A430

Designs: 60h, Astronaut in capsule. 80h, Boy with flute, horiz. 1k, Workers of three races, horiz. 1.40k, Children dancing around tree. 1.60k, Flying bird, horiz. 5k, View of Prague, horiz.

**1962 Engr. *Perf. 13½***

| | | | | |
|---|---|---|---|---|
| **1128** | A430 | 30h multicolored | 1.20 | .60 |
| **1129** | A430 | 60h multicolored | .60 | .30 |
| *a.* | | Miniature sheet of 8 | *20.00* | *20.00* |
| **1130** | A430 | 80h multicolored | 1.75 | 1.25 |
| **1131** | A430 | 1k multicolored | 1.75 | 1.25 |
| **1132** | A430 | 1.40k multicolored | 1.75 | 1.25 |
| **1133** | A430 | 1.60k multicolored | 3.00 | 2.10 |
| | | *Nos. 1128-1133 (6)* | 10.05 | 6.75 |

**Souvenir Sheet**

| | | | | |
|---|---|---|---|---|
| **1134** | A430 | 5k multicolored | 13.00 | 10.00 |
| *a.* | | Imperf. | 40.00 | 35.00 |

"PRAGA 1962 World Exhib. of Postage Stamps," 8/18-9/2/62. No. 1133 also for FIP Day, Sept. 1. Printed in sheets of 10. Value: Nos. 1128-1133 $150; No. 1134 $80.

No. 1129a contains 4 each of Nos. 1128-1129 and 2 labels arranged in 2 rows of 2 se-tenant pairs of Nos. 1128-1129 with label between. Sold for 5k, only with ticket.

No. 1134 contains one 51x30mm stamp. Sold only with ticket.

Children in Day Nursery and Factory
A431

Sailboat and Trade Union Rest Home, Zinkovy — A432

**Engraved and Photogravure**

**1962, Oct. 29 Unwmk. *Perf. 11½***

| | | | | |
|---|---|---|---|---|
| **1135** | A431 | 30h black & lt blue | .25 | .25 |
| **1136** | A432 | 60h brown & yellow | .25 | .25 |

Cruiser "Aurora"
A433

**1962, Nov. 7**

| | | | | |
|---|---|---|---|---|
| **1137** | A433 | 30h black & gray bl | .25 | .25 |
| **1138** | A433 | 60h black & pink | .25 | .25 |

Russian October revolution, 45th anniv.

Cosmonaut and Worker — A434

Lenin — A435

**1962, Nov. 7**

| | | | | |
|---|---|---|---|---|
| **1139** | A434 | 30h dark red & blue | .25 | .25 |
| **1140** | A435 | 60h black & dp rose | .25 | .25 |

40th anniversary of the USSR.

Symbolic Crane — A436

40h, Agricultural products, vert. 60h, Factories.

**1962, Dec. 4**

| | | | | |
|---|---|---|---|---|
| **1141** | A436 | 30h dk red & yel | .25 | .25 |
| **1142** | A436 | 40h gray blue & yel | .25 | .25 |
| **1143** | A436 | 60h black & dp rose | .30 | .25 |
| | | *Nos. 1141-1143 (3)* | .80 | .75 |

Communist Party of Czechoslovakia, 12th cong.

Ground Beetle — A437

Beetles: 30h, Cardinal beetle. 60h, Stag beetle, vert. 1k, Great water beetle. 1.60k, Alpine longicorn, vert. 2k, Ground beetle, vert.

**1962, Dec. 15 Engr. *Perf. 14***

| | | | | |
|---|---|---|---|---|
| **1144** | A437 | 20h multicolored | .80 | .40 |
| **1145** | A437 | 30h multicolored | .80 | .40 |
| **1146** | A437 | 60h multicolored | .80 | .40 |
| **1147** | A437 | 1k multicolored | 1.60 | .60 |
| **1148** | A437 | 1.60k multicolored | 3.25 | .60 |
| **1149** | A437 | 2k multicolored | 4.50 | 2.00 |
| | | *Nos. 1144-1149 (6)* | 11.75 | 4.40 |

Nos. 1144-1149 were each printed in sheets of 10. Value, set $225.

Table Tennis — A438

Sports: 60h, Bicyclist. 80h, Skier. 1k, Motorcyclist. 1.20k, Weight lifter. 1.60k, Hurdler.

**Engraved and Photogravure**

**1963, Jan. *Perf. 11½***

| | | | | |
|---|---|---|---|---|
| **1150** | A438 | 30h black & dp grn | .25 | .25 |
| **1151** | A438 | 60h black & orange | .25 | .25 |
| **1152** | A438 | 80h black & ultra | .25 | .25 |
| **1153** | A438 | 1k black & violet | .40 | .25 |
| **1154** | A438 | 1.20k blk & pale brn | .40 | .25 |
| **1155** | A438 | 1.60k blk & car | .85 | .25 |
| | | *Nos. 1150-1155 (6)* | 2.40 | 1.50 |

Various 1963 sports events.

Industrial Plant, Laurel and Star — A439

Symbol of Pioneer Summer Camp — A440

Industrial Plant and Symbol of Growth — A441

**1963, Feb. 25 Unwmk. *Perf. 11½***

| | | | | |
|---|---|---|---|---|
| **1156** | A439 | 30h carmine & lt bl | .25 | .25 |
| **1157** | A440 | 60h black & car | .25 | .25 |
| **1158** | A441 | 60h black & red | .25 | .25 |
| | | *Nos. 1156-1158 (3)* | .75 | .75 |

15th anniv. of the "Victorious February" and 5th Trade Union Cong.

Artists' Guild Emblem — A442

Juraj Jánosik — A443

Eduard Urx — A444

National Theater, Prague — A445

No. 1163, Woman reading to children. No. 1164, Juraj Pálkovic. 1.60k, Max Svabinsky.

**Engr. & Photo.; Engr. (A444)**

**1963, Mar. 25 Unwmk. *Perf. 11½***

**1159** A442 20h black & Prus bl .25 .25
**1160** A443 30h car & lt bl .25 .25
**1161** A444 30h carmine .25 .25
**1162** A445 60h dl red brn & lt bl .25 .25
**1163** A444 60h green .25 .25
**1164** A444 60h black .25 .25
**1165** A444 1.60k brown .50 .25
*Nos. 1159-1165 (7)* 2.00 1.75

Various cultural personalities and events.

Boy and Girl with Flag — A446

**Engraved and Photogravure**

**1963, Apr. 18 *Perf. 11½***

**1166** A446 30h slate & rose red .35 .25

The 4th Congress of Czechoslovak Youth.

Television Transmitter — A447

40h, Television camera, mast and set, horiz.

**1963, Apr. 25**

**1167** A447 40h buff & slate .40 .25
**1168** A447 60h dk red & lt blue .40 .25

Czechoslovak television, 10th anniversary.

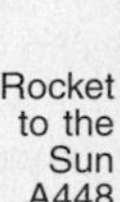

Rocket to the Sun A448

50h, Rockets & Sputniks leaving Earth. 60h, Spacecraft to & from Moon. 1k, 3k, Interplanetary station & Mars 1. 1.60k, Atomic rocket & Jupiter. 2k, Rocket returning from Saturn.

**1963, Apr. 25**

**1169** A448 30h red brn & buff .45 .25
**1170** A448 50h slate & bluish grn .45 .25
**1171** A448 60h dk green & yel .40 .25
**1172** A448 1k dk gray & sal .65 .25
**1173** A448 1.60k gray brn & lt grn .65 .25
**1174** A448 2k dk purple & yel 1.25 .75
*Nos. 1169-1174 (6)* 3.85 2.00

**Souvenir Sheet**

***Imperf***

**1175** A448 3k Prus grn & org red 10.00 5.00

No. 1175 issued for 1st Space Research Exhib., Prague, Apr. 1963.

Studio and Radio A449

1k, Globe inscribed "Peace" & aerial mast, vert.

**1963, May 18 Unwmk. *Perf. 11½***

**1176** A449 30h choc & pale grn .40 .25
**1177** A449 1k bluish grn & lilac .40 .25

40th anniversary of Czechoslovak radio.

Tupolev Tu-104B Turbojet A450

Design: 1.80k, Ilyushin Il-18 Moskva.

**1963, May 25**

**1178** A450 80h violet & lt bl 1.00 .35
**1179** A450 1.80k dk blue & lt grn 1.50 .35

40th anniversary of Czechoslovak airlines.

9th Cent. Ring, Map of Moravian Settlements — A451

1.60k, Falconer, 9th cent. silver disk.

**1963, May 25**

**1180** A451 30h lt green & blk .25 .25
**1181** A451 1.60k dull yel & blk .75 .25

1100th anniversary of Moravian empire.

Woman Singing — A452

**1963, May 25 Engr.**

**1182** A452 30h bright red .55 .25

60th anniversary of the founding of the Moravian Teachers' Singing Club.

Kromeriz Castle and Barley — A453

**Engraved and Photogravure**

**1963, June 20 Unwmk. *Perf. 11½***

**1183** A453 30h slate grn & yel .55 .25

Natl. Agricultural Exhib. and 700th anniv. of Kromeriz.

Centenary Emblem, Nurse and Playing Child — A454

**1963, June 20**

**1184** A454 30h dk gray & car .50 .25

Centenary of the International Red Cross.

Bee, Honeycomb and Emblem A455

**1963, June 20**

**1185** A455 1k brown & yellow .75 .25

19th Intl. Beekeepers Cong., Apimondia, 1963.

Liberec Fair Emblem — A456

**1963, July 13**

**1186** A456 30h black & dp rose .40 .25

Liberec Consumer Goods Fair.

Town Hall, Brno — A457

Design: 60h, Town Hall tower, Brno.

**1963, July 29**

**1187** A457 30h lt blue & maroon .35 .25
**1188** A457 60h pink & dk blue .35 .25

International Trade Fair, Brno.

Cave, Moravian Karst — A458

No. 1190, Trout, Hornad Valley. 60h, Great Hawk Gorge. 80h, Macocha mountains.

**1963, July 29**

**1189** A458 30h brown & lt bl .80 .25
**1190** A458 30h dk bl & dull grn .95 .25
**1191** A458 60h green & blue .80 .25
**1192** A458 80h sepia & pink .80 .25
*Nos. 1189-1192 (4)* 3.35 1.00

Blast Furnace A459

**1963, Aug. 15 Unwmk. *Perf. 11½***

**1193** A459 60h blk & bluish grn .40 .25

30th Intl. Cong. of Iron Founders, Prague.

White Mouse A460

**1963, Aug. 15**

**1194** A460 1k black & carmine .60 .25

2nd Intl. Pharmacological Cong., Prague.

Farm Machinery for Underfed Nations — A461

**1963, Aug. 15 Engr.**

**1195** A461 1.60k black .50 .25

FAO "Freedom from Hunger" campaign.

Wooden Toys — A462

Folk Art (Inscribed "UNESCO"): 80h, Cock and flowers. 1k, Flowers in vase. 1.20k, Janosik, Slovak hero. 1.60k, Stag. 2k, Postilion.

**1963, Sept. 2 Engr. *Perf. 13½***

**1196** A462 60h red & vio bl .65 .30
**1197** A462 80h multi .65 .30
**1198** A462 1k multi .65 .30
**1199** A462 1.20k multi .65 .30
**1200** A462 1.60k multi .65 .30
**1201** A462 2k multi 2.75 1.75
*Nos. 1196-1201 (6)* 6.00 3.25

Nos. 1196-1201 were printed in sheets of 10. Value, set $80.

Canoeing A463

Sports: 40h, Volleyball. 60h, Wrestling. 80h, Basketball. 1k, Boxing. 1.60k, Gymnastics.

**Engraved and Photogravure**

**1963, Oct. 26 *Perf. 11½***

**1202** A463 30h indigo & grn .30 .25
**1203** A463 40h red brn & lt bl .30 .25
**1204** A463 60h brn red & yel .35 .25
**1205** A463 80h dk pur & dp org .45 .25
**1206** A463 1k ultra & dp rose .60 .35
**1207** A463 1.60k vio bl & ultra 2.00 1.00
*Nos. 1202-1207 (6)* 4.00 2.35

1964 Olympic Games, Tokyo.

Tree and Star — A464

Design: 60h, Star, hammer and sickle.

**1963, Dec. 11 Unwmk. *Perf. 11½***

| | | | | |
|---|---|---|---|---|
| **1208** | A464 | 30h bis brn & lt bl | .30 | .25 |
| **1209** | A464 | 60h carmine & gray | .30 | .25 |

Russo-Czechoslovakian Treaty, 20th anniv.

Atom Diagrams Surrounding Head — A465

**1963, Dec. 12 Engr.**

| | | | | |
|---|---|---|---|---|
| **1210** | A465 | 60h dark purple | .40 | .25 |

3rd Congress of the Association for the Propagation of Scientific Knowledge.

Chamois — A466

40h, Alpine ibex. 60h, Mouflon. 1.20k, Roe deer. 1.60k, Fallow deer. 2k, Red deer.

**1963, Dec. 14 *Perf. 14***

| | | | | |
|---|---|---|---|---|
| **1211** | A466 | 30h multi | 1.25 | .35 |
| **1212** | A466 | 40h multi | 1.25 | .35 |
| **1213** | A466 | 60h brn, yel & grn | 1.25 | .35 |
| **1214** | A466 | 1.20k multi | 2.00 | 1.00 |
| **1215** | A466 | 1.60k multi | 2.50 | 1.25 |
| **1216** | A466 | 2k multi | 5.00 | 2.50 |
| | | *Nos. 1211-1216 (6)* | 13.25 | 5.80 |

Nos. 1211-1216 were each issued in sheets of 10 stamps. Value, set $225.

Figure Skating — A467

80h, Skiing, horiz. 1k, Field ball player.

**Engraved and Photogravure**

**1964, Jan. 20 Unwmk. *Perf. 11½***

| | | | | |
|---|---|---|---|---|
| **1217** | A467 | 30h violet bl & yel | .30 | .25 |
| **1218** | A467 | 80h dk blue & org | .45 | .25 |
| **1219** | A467 | 1k brown & lilac | .75 | .25 |
| | | *Nos. 1217-1219 (3)* | 1.50 | .75 |

Intl. University Games (30h, 80h) and the World Field Ball Championships (1k).

Ice Hockey — A468

**1964, Jan. 20**

| | | | | |
|---|---|---|---|---|
| **1220** | A468 | 1k shown | 1.10 | .45 |
| **1221** | A468 | 1.80k Toboggan | 1.20 | .60 |
| **1222** | A468 | 2k Ski jump | 2.25 | 1.00 |
| | | *Nos. 1220-1222 (3)* | 4.55 | 2.05 |

9th Winter Olympic Games, Innsbruck, Jan. 29-Feb. 9, 1964.

Magura Rest Home, High Tatra — A469

Design: 80h, Slovak National Insurrection Rest Home, Low Tatra.

**1964, Feb. 19 Unwmk. *Perf. 11½***

| | | | | |
|---|---|---|---|---|
| **1223** | A469 | 60h green & yellow | .30 | .25 |
| **1224** | A469 | 80h violet bl & pink | .30 | .25 |

Skiers and Ski Lift A470

60h, Automobile camp, Telc. 1k, Fishing, Spis Castle. 1.80k, Lake & boats, Cesky Krumlov.

**1964, Feb. 19 Engr. & Photo.**

| | | | | |
|---|---|---|---|---|
| **1225** | A470 | 30h dk vio brn & bl | .40 | .25 |
| **1226** | A470 | 60h slate & car | .45 | .25 |
| **1227** | A470 | 1k brown & olive | .80 | .25 |
| **1228** | A470 | 1.80k slate grn & org | 1.10 | .35 |
| | | *Nos. 1225-1228 (4)* | 2.75 | 1.10 |

Moses, Day and Night by Michelangelo — A471

Designs: 60h, "A Midsummer Night's Dream," by Shakespeare. 1k, Man, telescope and heaven, vert. 1.60k, King George of Podebrad (1420-71).

**1964, Mar. 20**

| | | | | |
|---|---|---|---|---|
| **1229** | A471 | 40h black & yel grn | .35 | .25 |
| **1230** | A471 | 60h slate & car | .35 | .25 |
| **1231** | A471 | 1k black & lt blue | 1.25 | .25 |
| **1232** | A471 | 1.60k black & yellow | 1.25 | .25 |
| *a.* | | Souvenir sheet of 4, imperf. ('88) | 9.50 | 6.50 |
| | | *Nos. 1229-1232 (4)* | 3.20 | 1.00 |

400th anniv. of the death of Michelangelo (40h); 400th anniv. of the birth of Shakespeare (60h); 400th anniv. of the birth of Galileo (1k); 500th anniv. of the pacifist efforts of King George of Podebrad (1.60k).

No. 1232a for PRAGA '88.

Yuri A. Gagarin — A472

Astronauts: 60h, Gherman Titov. 80h, John H. Glenn, Jr. 1k, Scott M. Carpenter, vert. 1.20k, Pavel R. Popovich and Andrian G. Nikolayev. 1.40k, Walter M. Schirra, vert. 1.60k, Gordon L. Cooper, vert. 2k, Valentina Tereshkova and Valeri Bykovski, vert.

**1964, Apr. 27 Unwmk. *Perf. 11½***
**Yellow Paper**

| | | | | |
|---|---|---|---|---|
| **1233** | A472 | 30h black & vio bl | .50 | .25 |
| **1234** | A472 | 60h dk grn & dk car | .50 | .25 |
| **1235** | A472 | 80h dk car & vio | .55 | .25 |
| **1236** | A472 | 1k ultra & rose vio | .75 | .25 |
| **1237** | A472 | 1.20k ver & ol gray | .60 | .30 |
| **1238** | A472 | 1.40k black & dl grn | 1.00 | .45 |
| **1239** | A472 | 1.60k pale pur & Prus grn | 2.25 | 1.50 |
| **1240** | A472 | 2k dk blue & red | .75 | .40 |
| | | *Nos. 1233-1240 (8)* | 6.90 | 3.65 |

World's first 10 astronauts.

Creeping Bellflower — A473

Flowers: 80h, Musk thistle. 1k, Chicory. 1.20k, Yellow iris. 1.60k, Gentian. 2k, Corn poppy.

**1964, June 15 Engr. *Perf. 14***

| | | | | |
|---|---|---|---|---|
| **1241** | A473 | 60h dk grn, lil & org | .75 | .25 |
| **1242** | A473 | 80h blk, grn & red lil | 1.10 | .25 |
| **1243** | A473 | 1k vio bl, grn & pink | 1.10 | .45 |
| **1244** | A473 | 1.20k black, yel & grn | 1.10 | .30 |
| **1245** | A473 | 1.60k violet & grn | 1.10 | .40 |
| **1246** | A473 | 2k vio, red & grn | 4.50 | 1.50 |
| | | *Nos. 1241-1246 (6)* | 9.65 | 3.15 |

Nos. 1241-1246 were each issued in sheets of 10. Value, set $250.

Film "Flower" and Karlovy Vary Colonnade — A474

**Engraved and Photogravure**

**1964, June 20 Unwmk. *Perf. 13½***

| | | | | |
|---|---|---|---|---|
| **1247** | A474 | 60h black, blue & car | 2.00 | .50 |

14th Intl. Film Festival at Karlovy Vary, July 4-19.

Issued in sheets of 10. Value, $60.

Silesian Coat of Arms — A475

**1964, June 20 *Perf. 11½***

| | | | | |
|---|---|---|---|---|
| **1248** | A475 | 30h black & yel | .30 | .25 |

150th anniv. of the Silesian Museum, Opava.

Young Miner of 1764 — A476

**1964, June 20**

| | | | | |
|---|---|---|---|---|
| **1249** | A476 | 60h sepia & lt grn | .30 | .25 |

Mining School at Banska Stiavnica, bicent.

Skoda Fire Engine A477

**1964, June 20**

| | | | | |
|---|---|---|---|---|
| **1250** | A477 | 60h car rose & lt bl | 1.00 | .25 |

Voluntary fire brigades in Bohemia, cent.

Gulls, Hradcany Castle, Red Cross — A478

**1964, July 10**

| | | | | |
|---|---|---|---|---|
| **1251** | A478 | 60h car & bluish gray | .55 | .25 |

4th Czechoslovak Red Cross Congress at Prague.

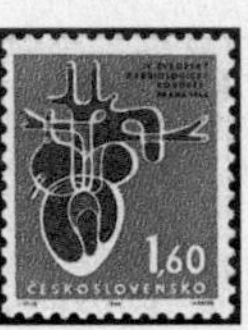
Human Heart — A479

**1964, July 10**

| | | | | |
|---|---|---|---|---|
| **1252** | A479 | 1.60k ultra & car | 1.10 | .25 |

4th European Cardiological Cong. at Prague.

Partisans, Girl and Factories A480

Battle Scene, 1944 — A481

Design: No. 1254, Partisans and flame.

**Engraved and Photogravure**

**1964, Aug. 17 Unwmk. *Perf. 11½***

| | | | | |
|---|---|---|---|---|
| **1253** | A480 | 30h brown & red | .25 | .25 |
| **1254** | A480 | 60h dk blue & red | .25 | .25 |
| **1255** | A481 | 60h black & red | .25 | .25 |
| | | *Nos. 1253-1255 (3)* | .75 | .75 |

20th anniv. of the Slovak Natl. Uprising; No. 1255, 20th anniv. of the Battles of Dukla Pass.

Hradcany at Prague — A482

Design: 5k, Charles Bridge and Hradcany.

**1964, Aug. 30 *Perf. 11½x12***

| | | | | |
|---|---|---|---|---|
| **1256** | A482 | 60h black & red | .65 | .25 |

**Souvenir Sheet**

**Engr. *Imperf.***

| | | | | |
|---|---|---|---|---|
| **1257** | A482 | 5k deep claret | 3.50 | 2.50 |

Millenium of the Hradcany, Prague.
No. 1257 stamp size: 30x50mm.

Discus Thrower and Pole Vaulter — A483

Designs: 60h, Bicycling, horiz. 1k, Soccer. 1.20k, Rowing. 1.60k, Swimming, horiz. 2.80k, Weight lifting, horiz.

**Engraved and Photogravure**

**1964, Sept. 2** *Perf. 13½*

| | | | | | |
|---|---|---|---|---|---|
| **1258** | A483 | 60h | multi | .80 | .30 |
| **1259** | A483 | 80h | multi | .80 | .30 |
| **1260** | A483 | 1k | multi | .80 | .30 |
| **1261** | A483 | 1.20k | multi | .80 | .30 |
| **1262** | A483 | 1.60k | multi | .80 | .30 |
| **1263** | A483 | 2.80k | multi | 4.00 | 2.00 |
| | | | *Nos. 1258-1263 (6)* | 8.00 | 3.50 |

Issued to commemorate the 18th Olympic Games, Tokyo, Oct. 10-25.

Nos. 1258-1263 were issued in sheets of 10. Value, set $125.

Miniature Sheet

Space Ship Voskhod I, Astronauts and Globe — A484

**1964, Nov. 12 Unwmk.** *Perf. 11½*

| | | | | | |
|---|---|---|---|---|---|
| **1264** | A484 | 3k | dk bl & dl lil, *buff* | 5.00 | 3.50 |

Russian 3-man space flight of Vladimir M. Komarov, Boris B. Yegorov and Konstantin Feoktistov, Oct. 12-13.

Steam Engine and Atomic Power Plant — A485

Diesel Engine "CKD Praha" — A486

**1964, Nov. 16** **Engr.**

| | | | | | |
|---|---|---|---|---|---|
| **1265** | A485 | 30h | dull red brown | .25 | .25 |

**Engraved and Photogravure**

| | | | | | |
|---|---|---|---|---|---|
| **1266** | A486 | 60h | green & salmon | .75 | .25 |

Traditions and development of engineering; No. 1265 for 150th anniv. of the First Brno Engineering Works, No. 1266 for the engineering concern CKD Praha.

European Redstart — A487

Birds: 60h, Green woodpecker. 80h, Hawfinch. 1k, Black woodpecker. 1.20k, European robin. 1.60k, European roller.

**1964, Nov. 16 Litho.** *Perf. 10½*

| | | | | | |
|---|---|---|---|---|---|
| **1267** | A487 | 30h | multicolored | 1.10 | .30 |
| **1268** | A487 | 60h | black & multi | 1.10 | .30 |
| **1269** | A487 | 80h | multicolored | 1.40 | .35 |
| **1270** | A487 | 1k | multicolored | 1.75 | .40 |
| **1271** | A487 | 1.20k | lt vio bl & blk | 1.75 | .40 |
| **1272** | A487 | 1.60k | yellow & blk | 3.50 | 1.00 |
| | | | *Nos. 1267-1272 (6)* | 10.60 | 2.75 |

Dancer A488

"In the Sun" Preschool Children A489

Designs: 60h, "Over the Obstacles," teenagers. 1k, "Movement and Beauty," woman flag twirler. 1.60k, Runners at start.

**Engraved and Photogravure**

**1965 Unwmk.** *Perf. 11½*

| | | | | | |
|---|---|---|---|---|---|
| **1273** | A488 | 30h | red & lt blue | .25 | .25 |

*Perf. 11½x12*

| | | | | | |
|---|---|---|---|---|---|
| **1274** | A489 | 30h | vio bl & car | .25 | .25 |
| **1275** | A489 | 60h | brown & ultra | .25 | .25 |
| **1276** | A489 | 1k | black & yellow | .25 | .25 |
| **1277** | A489 | 1.60k | maroon & gray | .60 | .25 |
| | | | *Nos. 1273-1277 (5)* | 1.60 | 1.25 |

3rd Natl. Spartacist Games. Issue dates: No. 1273, Jan. 3; Nos. 1274-1277, May 24.

Mountain Rescue Service — A490

Designs: No. 1279, Woman gymnast. No. 1280, Bicyclists. No. 1281, Women hurdlers.

**1965, Jan. 15 Unwmk.** *Perf. 11½*

| | | | | | |
|---|---|---|---|---|---|
| **1278** | A490 | 60h | violet & blue | .30 | .25 |
| **1279** | A490 | 60h | maroon & ocher | .30 | .25 |
| **1280** | A490 | 60h | black & carmine | .30 | .25 |
| **1281** | A490 | 60h | green & yellow | .30 | .25 |
| | | | *Nos. 1278-1281 (4)* | 1.20 | 1.00 |

Mountain Rescue Service (No. 1278); 1st World Championship in Artistic Gymnastics, Prague, Dec. 1965 (No. 1279); World Championship in Indoor Bicycling, Prague, Oct. 1965 (No. 1280); "Universiada 1965," Brno (No. 1281).

Arms and View, Beroun — A491

Designs: No. 1283, Town Square, Domazlice. No. 1284, Old and new buildings, Frydek-Mystek. No. 1285, Arms and view, Lipnik. No. 1286, Fortified wall, City Hall and Arms, Policka. No. 1287, View and hops, Zatek. No. 1288, Small fortress and rose, Terezin.

**1965, Feb. 15**

| | | | | | |
|---|---|---|---|---|---|
| **1282** | A491 | 30h | vio bl & lt bl | .30 | .25 |
| **1283** | A491 | 30h | dull pur & yel | .30 | .25 |
| **1284** | A491 | 30h | slate & gray | .30 | .25 |
| **1285** | A491 | 30h | green & bis | .30 | .25 |
| **1286** | A491 | 30h | brown & tan | .30 | .25 |
| **1287** | A491 | 30h | dk blue & cit | .30 | .25 |
| **1288** | A491 | 30h | black & rose | .30 | .25 |
| | | | *Nos. 1282-1288 (7)* | 2.10 | 1.75 |

Nos. 1282-1287 for 700th anniv. of the founding of various Bohemian towns; No. 1288 the 20th anniv. of the liberation of the Theresienstadt (Terezin) concentration camp.

Sun's Corona A492

Space Research: 30h, Sun. 60h, Exploration of the Moon. 1k, Twin space craft, vert. 1.40k, Space station. 1.60k, Exploration of Mars, vert. 2k, USSR and US Meteorological collaboration.

**1965, Mar. 15** *Perf. 12x11½, 11½x12*

| | | | | | |
|---|---|---|---|---|---|
| **1289** | A492 | 20h | rose & red lilac | .25 | .25 |
| **1290** | A492 | 30h | rose red & yel | .25 | .25 |
| **1291** | A492 | 60h | bluish blk & yel | .25 | .25 |
| **1292** | A492 | 1k | pur & pale bl | .25 | .25 |
| **1293** | A492 | 1.40k | black & salmon | .35 | .25 |
| **1294** | A492 | 1.60k | black & pink | .50 | .25 |
| **1295** | A492 | 2k | bluish blk & lt bl | *1.50* | *1.00* |
| | | | *Nos. 1289-1295 (7)* | *3.35* | *2.50* |

Space research; Nos. 1289-1290 also for the Intl. Quiet Sun Year, 1964-65.

Frantisek Ventura, Equestrian; Amsterdam, 1928 — A493

Czechoslovakian Olympic Victories: 30h, Discus, Paris, 1900. 60h, Running, Helsinki, 1952. 1k, Weight lifting, Los Angeles, 1932. 1.40k, Gymnastics, Berlin, 1936. 1.60k, Double sculling, Rome, 1960. 2k, Women's gymnastics, Tokyo, 1964.

**1965, Apr. 16** *Perf. 11½x12*

| | | | | | |
|---|---|---|---|---|---|
| **1296** | A493 | 20h | choc & gold | .25 | .25 |
| **1297** | A493 | 30h | indigo & emer | .25 | .25 |
| **1298** | A493 | 60h | ultra & gold | .25 | .25 |
| **1299** | A493 | 1k | red brn & gold | .25 | .25 |
| **1300** | A493 | 1.40k | dk sl grn & gold | 1.10 | .45 |
| **1301** | A493 | 1.60k | black & gold | 1.10 | .45 |
| **1302** | A493 | 2k | maroon & gold | .55 | .30 |
| | | | *Nos. 1296-1302 (7)* | 3.75 | 2.20 |

Astronauts Virgil Grissom and John Young — A494

Designs: No. 1304, Alexei Leonov floating in space. No. 1305, Launching pad at Cape Kennedy. No. 1306, Leonov leaving space ship.

**1965, Apr. 17** *Perf. 11x11½*

| | | | | | |
|---|---|---|---|---|---|
| **1303** | A494 | 60h | slate bl & lil rose | .45 | .25 |
| **1304** | A494 | 60h | vio blk & blue | .45 | .25 |
| **1305** | A494 | 3k | slate bl & lil rose | 1.60 | 1.00 |
| *a.* | | | Pair, #1303, 1305 | 3.50 | 1.50 |
| **1306** | A494 | 3k | vio blk & blue | 1.60 | 1.00 |
| *a.* | | | Pair, #1304, 1306 | 3.50 | 1.50 |
| | | | *Nos. 1303-1306 (4)* | 4.10 | 2.50 |

Issued to honor American and Soviet astronauts. Printed in sheets of 25; one sheet contains 20 No. 1303 and 5 No. 1305, the other sheet contains 20 No. 1304 and 5 No. 1306.

Russian Soldier, View of Prague and Guerrilla Fighters A495

Designs: No. 1308, Blast furnace, workers and tank. 60h, Worker and factory. 1k, Worker and new constructions. 1.60k, Woman farmer, new farm buildings and machinery.

**1965, May 5 Engr.** *Perf. 13½*

| | | | | | |
|---|---|---|---|---|---|
| **1307** | A495 | 30h | dk red, blk & ol | .35 | .25 |
| **1308** | A495 | 30h | multicolored | .35 | .25 |
| **1309** | A495 | 60h | vio bl, red & blk | .35 | .25 |
| **1310** | A495 | 1k | dp org, blk & brn | .50 | .25 |
| **1311** | A495 | 1.60k | yel, red & blk | .55 | .25 |
| | | | *Nos. 1307-1311 (5)* | 2.10 | 1.25 |

20th anniv. of liberation from the Nazis.

Nos. 1307-1311 were each printed in sheets of 10. Value, set $120.

Slovakian Kopov Dog A496

Dogs: 40h, German shepherd. 60h, Czech hunting dog with pheasant. 1k, Poodle. 1.60k, Czech terrier. 2k, Afghan hound.

**1965, June 10** *Perf. 12x11½*

| | | | | | |
|---|---|---|---|---|---|
| **1312** | A496 | 30h | black & red org | .45 | .25 |
| **1313** | A496 | 40h | black & yellow | .45 | .25 |
| **1314** | A496 | 60h | black & ver | .70 | .25 |
| **1315** | A496 | 1k | black & dk car rose | 1.00 | .25 |
| **1316** | A496 | 1.60k | black & orange | 1.25 | .25 |
| **1317** | A496 | 2k | black & orange | 2.00 | 1.25 |
| | | | *Nos. 1312-1317 (6)* | 5.85 | 2.50 |

World Dog Show at Brno and the International Dog Breeders Congress, Prague.

UN Headquarters Building, NY — A497

Emblems: 60h, UN & inscription. 1.60k, ICY.

**1965, June 24** *Perf. 12x11½*

| | | | | | |
|---|---|---|---|---|---|
| **1318** | A497 | 60h | dk red brn & yel | .25 | .25 |
| **1319** | A497 | 1k | ultra & lt blue | .65 | .25 |
| **1320** | A497 | 1.60k | gold & dk red | .55 | .25 |
| | | | *Nos. 1318-1320 (3)* | 1.45 | .75 |

20th anniv. of the UN and the ICY, 1965.

Trade Union Emblem A498

**1965, June 24** **Engr.**

| | | | | | |
|---|---|---|---|---|---|
| **1321** | A498 | 60h | dk red & ultra | .40 | .25 |

Intl. Trade Union Federation, 20th anniv.

Women and Globe — A499

**1965, June 24** *Perf. 11½x12*

| | | | | | |
|---|---|---|---|---|---|
| **1322** | A499 | 60h | violet blue | .40 | .25 |

20th anniv. of the Intl. Women's Federation.

Children's House (Burgraves' Palace), Hradcany A500

Matthias Tower — A501

**1965, June 25** *Perf. 11½*

**1323** A500 30h slate green .30 .25
**1324** A501 60h dark brown .30 .25

Issued to publicize the Hradcany, Prague.

Marx and Lenin — A502

**1965, July 1** **Engr. & Photo.**

**1325** A502 60h car rose & gold .40 .25

6th conf. of Postal Ministers of Communist Countries, Peking, June 21-July 15.

Joseph Navratil — A503

Jan Hus — A504

Gregor Johann Mendel A505

Costume Jewelry A506

Bohuslav Martinu A507

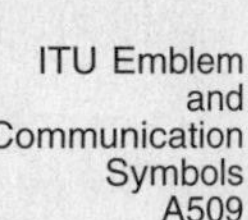


Seated Woman and University of Bratislava A508

ITU Emblem and Communication Symbols A509

Macromolecular Symposium Emblem A510

Design: No. 1327, Ludovit Stur (diff. frame).

**1965** **Unwmk.** *Perf. 11½*

**1326** A503 30h black & fawn .25 .25
**1327** A503 30h black & dull grn .25 .25
**1328** A504 60h black & crimson .25 .25
**1329** A505 60h vio bl & red .25 .25
**1330** A506 60h purple & gold .25 .25
**1331** A507 60h black & orange .25 .25
**1332** A508 60h brn, *yel* .25 .25
**1333** A509 1k orange & blue .35 .25
**1334** A510 1k black & dp org .35 .25
*Nos. 1326-1334 (9)* 2.45 2.25

No. 1326, Navratil (1798-1865), painter; No. 1327, Stur (1815-56), Slovak author and historian; No. 1328, the 550th anniv. of the death of Hus, religious reformer;

No. 1329, cent. of publication of Mendel's laws of inheritance; No. 1330 publicizes the "Jablonec 1965" costume jewelry exhib.; No. 1331, Martinu (1890-1959), composer; No. 1332, 500th anniv. of the founding of the University of Bratislava as Academia Istropolitana; No. 1333, cent. of the ITU; No. 1334, Intl. Symposium on Macromolecular Chemistry, Prague, Sept. 1-8.

Issued: No. 1333, 7/10.

Miniature Sheet

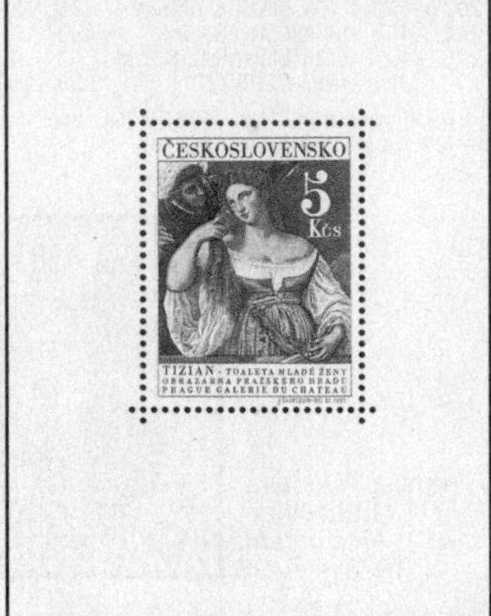


"Young Woman at her Toilette," by Titian — A512

**1965, Aug. 12**

**1336** A512 5k multicolored 6.00 4.00

Hradcany Art Gallery. No. 1336 contains one stamp.

Help for Flood Victims — A513

Rescue of Flood Victims A514

**1965, Sept. 6** **Engr.**

**1337** A513 30h violet blue .25 .25

**Engraved and Photogravure**

**1338** A514 2k dk ol grn & ol .65 .45

Help for Danube flood victims in Slovakia.

Dotterel A515

Mountain Birds: 60h, Wall creeper, vert. 1.20k, Lesser redpoll. 1.40k, Golden eagle, vert. 1.60k, Ring ouzel. 2k, Eurasian nutcracker, vert.

**1965, Sept. 20** **Litho.** *Perf. 11*

**1339** A515 30h multi .80 .25
**1340** A515 60h multi .80 .25
**1341** A515 1.20k multi .80 .25
**1342** A515 1.40k multi 1.50 .25
**1343** A515 1.60k multi 1.00 .45
**1344** A515 2k multi 4.00 1.75
*Nos. 1339-1344 (6)* 8.90 3.20

Levoca — A516

Views of Towns: 10h, Jindrichuv Hradec. 20h, Nitra. 30h, Kosice. 40h, Hradec Králové. 50h, Telc. 60h, Ostrava. 1k, Olomouc. 1.20k, Ceske Budejovice. 1.60k, Cheb. 2k, Brno. 3k, Bratislava. 5k, Prague.

**Engraved and Photogravure**

**1965-66** *Perf. 11½x12*

**Size: 23x19mm**

**1345** A516 5h black & yel .25 .25
**1346** A516 10h ultra & ol bis .65 .25
**1347** A516 20h black & lt bl .25 .25
**1348** A516 30h vio bl & lt grn .25 .25
**1348A** A516 40h dk brn & lt bl ('66) .25 .25
**1348B** A516 50h black & ocher ('66) .50 .25
**1348C** A516 60h red & gray ('66) .65 .25
**1348D** A516 1k pur & pale grn ('66) .65 .25

*Perf. 11½x11*

**Size: 30x23mm**

**1349** A516 1.20k slate & lt bl .50 .25
**1350** A516 1.60k indigo & yel .70 .25
**1351** A516 2k sl grn & pale yel .70 .25
**1352** A516 3k brn & yel .90 .25
**1353** A516 5k black & pink 1.40 .25
*Nos. 1345-1353 (13)* 7.65 3.25

Medicinal Plants — A517

**1965, Dec. 3** **Engr.** *Perf. 14*

**1354** A517 30h Coltsfoot .35 .25
**1355** A517 60h Meadow saffron .35 .25
**1356** A517 80h Corn poppy 1.00 .25
**1357** A517 1k Foxglove 1.00 .40
**1358** A517 1.20k Arnica 1.40 .60
**1359** A517 1.60k Cornflower 1.40 .45
**1360** A517 2k Dog rose 3.50 1.50
*Nos. 1354-1360 (7)* 9.00 3.70

Nos. 1354-1360 were each printed in sheets of 10. Value, set $175.

Strip of "Stamps" — A518

**Engraved and Photogravure**

**1965, Dec. 18** *Perf. 11½*

**1361** A518 1k dark red & gold 3.50 2.00

Issued for Stamp Day, 1965.

Romain Rolland (1866-1944), French Writer — A519

Portraits: No. 1362, Stanislav Sucharda (1866-1916), sculptor. No. 1363, Ignac Josef Pesina (1766-1808), veterinarian. No. 1365, Donatello (1386-1466), Italian sculptor.

**1966, Feb. 14** **Engr.** *Perf. 11½*

**1362** A519 30h deep green .25 .25
**1363** A519 30h violet blue .25 .25
**1364** A519 60h rose lake .25 .25
**1365** A519 60h brown .25 .25
*Nos. 1362-1365 (4)* 1.00 1.00

Symbolic Musical Instruments & Names of Composers — A520

**1966, Jan. 15** **Engr. & Photo.**

**1366** A520 30h black & gold .55 .25

Czech Philharmonic Orchestra, 70th anniv.

Figure Skating Pair A521

No. 1368, Man skater. No. 1369, Volleyball player, spiking, vert. 1k, Volleyball player, saving, vert. 1.60k, Woman skater. 2k, Figure skating pair.

**1966, Feb. 17**

**1367** A521 30h dk car rose .30 .25
**1368** A521 60h green .30 .25
**1369** A521 60h carmine & buff .30 .25
**1370** A521 1k vio & lt bl .40 .25
**1371** A521 1.60k brown & yellow .50 .25
**1372** A521 2k blue & grnsh bl 2.40 .40
*Nos. 1367-1372 (6)* 4.20 1.65

Nos. 1367-1368, 1371-1372 for the European Figure Skating Championships, Bratislava; Nos. 1369-1370 for the World Volleyball Championships.

Souvenir Sheet

Girl Dancing — A522

**1966, Mar. 21** **Engr.** ***Imperf.***

**1373** A522 3k slate bl, red & bl 3.50 1.50

Cent. of the opera "The Bartered Bride" by Bedrich Smetana.

"Ajax" 1841 A523

Locomotives: 30h, "Karlstejn" 1865. 60h, Steam engine, 1946. 1k, Steam engine with tender, 1946. 1.60k, Electric locomotive, 1964. 2k, Diesel locomotive, 1964.

**1966, Mar. 21** *Perf. 11½x11*

**Buff Paper**

**1374** A523 20h sepia 1.10 .25
**1375** A523 30h dull violet 1.60 .25
**1376** A523 60h dull purple 1.10 .25
**1377** A523 1k dark blue 1.25 .50
**1378** A523 1.60k dk blue grn 1.75 .40
**1379** A523 2k dark red 3.25 2.10
*Nos. 1374-1379 (6)* 10.05 3.75

European Perch A524

30h, Brown trout, vert. 1k, Carp. 1.20k, Northern pike. 1.40k, Grayling. 1.60k, Eel.

*Perf. 13x13½, 13½x13*

**1966, Apr. 22 Litho. Unwmk.**

| | | | | |
|---|---|---|---|---|
| **1380** | A524 | 30h multi | .60 | .25 |
| **1381** | A524 | 60h multi | .60 | .25 |
| **1382** | A524 | 1k multi | 1.25 | .25 |
| **1383** | A524 | 1.20k multi | .60 | .25 |
| **1384** | A524 | 1.40k multi | 1.10 | .50 |
| **1385** | A524 | 1.60k multi | 2.50 | 1.00 |
| | | *Nos. 1380-1385 (6)* | 6.65 | 2.50 |

Intl. Fishing Championships, Svit, Sept. 3-5.

WHO Headquarters, Geneva — A525

**Engraved and Photogravure**

**1966, Apr. 25** ***Perf. 12x11½***

**1386** A525 1k dk blue & lt blue .35 .25

Opening of the WHO Headquarters, Geneva.

Symbolic Handshake and UNESCO Emblem A526

**1966, Apr. 25** ***Perf. 11½***

**1387** A526 60h bister & olive gray .45 .25

20th anniv. of UNESCO.

**Prague Castle Issue**

Belvedere Palace and St. Vitus' Cathedral A527

Crown of St. Wenceslas, 1346 — A528

Design: 60h, Madonna, altarpiece from St. George's Church.

**1966, May 9 Engr.** ***Perf. 11½***

**1388** A527 30h dark blue .50 .25

**Engraved and Photogravure**

**1389** A527 60h blk & yel bis .75 .25

**Souvenir Sheet**

**Engr.**

**1390** A528 5k multi 5.00 2.50

See Nos. 1537-1539.

Tiger Swallowtail A529

Butterflies and Moths: 60h, Clouded sulphur. 80h, European purple emperor. 1k, Apollo. 1.20k, Burnet moth. 2k, Tiger moth.

**1966, May 23 Engr.** ***Perf. 14***

| | | | | |
|---|---|---|---|---|
| **1391** | A529 | 30h multi | .90 | .25 |
| **1392** | A529 | 60h multi | .90 | .25 |
| **1393** | A529 | 80h multi | 1.25 | .40 |
| **1394** | A529 | 1k multi | 1.90 | .60 |
| **1395** | A529 | 1.20k multi | 1.90 | .50 |
| **1396** | A529 | 2k multi | 5.50 | 2.00 |
| | | *Nos. 1391-1396 (6)* | 12.35 | 4.00 |

Nos. 1391-1396 were issued in sheets of 10. Value, set $250.

Flags of Russia and Czechoslovakia — A530

Designs: 60h, Rays surrounding hammer and sickle "sun." 1.60k, Girl's head and stars.

**Engraved and Photogravure**

**1966, May 31** ***Perf. 11½***

| | | | | |
|---|---|---|---|---|
| **1397** | A530 | 30h dk bl & crim | .25 | .25 |
| **1398** | A530 | 60h dk bl & red | .25 | .25 |
| **1399** | A530 | 1.60k red & dk bl | .30 | .25 |
| | | *Nos. 1397-1399 (3)* | .80 | .75 |

13th Congress of the Communist Party of Czechoslovakia.

Dakota Chief — A531

Designs: 20h, Indians, canoe and tepee, horiz. 30h, Tomahawk. 40h, Haida totem poles. 60h, Kachina, good spirit of the Hopis. 1k, Indian on horseback hunting buffalo, horiz. 1.20k, Calumet, Dakota peace pipe.

**1966, June 20 Size: 23x40mm**

| | | | | |
|---|---|---|---|---|
| **1400** | A531 | 20h vio bl & dp org | .25 | .25 |
| **1401** | A531 | 30h blk & dl org | .25 | .25 |
| **1402** | A531 | 40h blk & lt bl | .25 | .25 |
| **1403** | A531 | 60h grn & yel | .25 | .25 |
| **1404** | A531 | 1k pur & emer | .40 | .25 |
| **1405** | A531 | 1.20k vio bl & rose lil | .65 | .30 |

***Perf. 14***

**Engr.**

**Size: 23x37mm**

| | | | | |
|---|---|---|---|---|
| **1406** | A531 | 1.40k multi | 1.60 | .90 |
| | | *Nos. 1400-1406 (7)* | 3.65 | 2.45 |

Cent. of the Náprstek Ethnographic Museum, Prague, and "The Indians of North America" exhibition.

No. 1406 was issued in sheets of 10. Value $130.

Model of Molecule — A532

**Engraved and Photogravure**

**1966, July 4 Unwmk.** ***Perf. 11½***

**1407** A532 60h blk & lt bl .50 .25

Czechoslovak Chemical Society, cent.

"Guernica" by Pablo Picasso — A533

**1966, July 5 Size: 75x30mm**

**1408** A533 60h blk & pale bl 2.75 1.40

30th anniversary of International Brigade in Spanish Civil War.

Sheets of 15 stamps and 5 labels inscribed "Picasso-Guernica 1937." Values: with tab attached, $6; sheet $75.

Pantheon, Bratislava — A534

Designs: No. 1410, Devin Castle and Ludovit Stur. No. 1411, View of Nachod. No. 1412, State Science Library, Olomouc.

**1966, July 25 Engr.**

| | | | | |
|---|---|---|---|---|
| **1409** | A534 | 30h dl pur | .30 | .25 |
| **1410** | A534 | 60h dk bl | .35 | .25 |
| **1411** | A534 | 60h green | .35 | .25 |
| **1412** | A534 | 60h sepia | .30 | .25 |
| | | *Nos. 1409-1412 (4)* | 1.30 | 1.00 |

No. 1409, Russian War Memorial, Bratislava; No. 1410, the 9th cent. Devin Castle as symbol of Slovak nationalism; No. 1411, 700th anniv. of the founding of Nachod; No. 1412, the 400th anniv. of the State Science Library, Olomouc.

Atom Symbol and Sun — A535

**Engraved and Photogravure**

**1966, Aug. 29** ***Perf. 11½***

**1413** A535 60h blk & red .40 .25

Issued to publicize Jachymov (Joachimsthal), where pitchblende was first discovered, "cradle of the atomic age."

Brno Fair Emblem — A536

**1966, Aug. 29**

**1414** A536 60h blk & red .40 .25

8th International Trade Fair, Brno.

Olympia Coin and Olympic Rings — A537

Design: 1k, Olympic flame, Czechoslovak flag and Olympic rings.

**1966, Aug. 29**

| | | | | |
|---|---|---|---|---|
| **1415** | A537 | 60h blk & gold | .30 | .25 |
| **1416** | A537 | 1k dk bl & red | 1.10 | .30 |

70th anniv. of the Olympic Committee.

Missile Carrier, Tank and Jet Plane A538

**1966, Aug. 31**

**1417** A538 60h blk & apple grn .40 .25

Issued to commemorate the maneuvers of the armies of the Warsaw Pact countries.

Mercury A539

30h, Moravian silver thaler, 1620, reverse & obverse, vert. 1.60k, Old & new buildings of Brno State Theater. 5k, Intl. Trade Fair Administration Tower & postmark, vert.

**1966, Sept. 10**

| | | | | |
|---|---|---|---|---|
| **1418** | A539 | 30h dk red & blk | .45 | .25 |
| **1419** | A539 | 60h org & blk | .45 | .25 |
| **1420** | A539 | 1.60k blk & brt grn | .75 | .25 |
| | | *Nos. 1418-1420 (3)* | 1.65 | .75 |

**Souvenir Sheet**

**1421** A539 5k multi 3.00 3.00

Brno Philatelic Exhibition, Sept. 11-25. No. 1421 contains one 30x40mm stamp.

First Meeting in Orbit — A540

30h, Photograph of far side of Moon & Russian satellite. 60h, Photograph of Mars & Mariner 4. 80th, Soft landing on Moon. 1k, Satellite, laser beam & binary code. 1.20k, Telstar over Earth & receiving station.

**1966, Sept. 26** ***Perf. 11½***

| | | | | |
|---|---|---|---|---|
| **1422** | A540 | 20h vio & lt grn | .25 | .25 |
| **1423** | A540 | 30h blk & sal pink | .25 | .25 |
| **1424** | A540 | 60h slate & lilac | .35 | .25 |
| **1425** | A540 | 80h dk pur & lt bl | .35 | .25 |
| **1426** | A540 | 1k blk & vio | .40 | .25 |
| **1427** | A540 | 1.20k red & bl | 1.75 | .25 |
| | | *Nos. 1422-1427 (6)* | 3.35 | 1.50 |

Issued to publicize American and Russian achievements in space research.

Badger A541

Game Animals: 40h, Red deer, vert. 60h, Lynx. 80h, Hare. 1k, Red fox. 1.20k, Brown bear, vert. 2k, Wild boar.

**1966, Nov. 28 Litho. *Perf. 13½***

| No. | Type | Description | Mint | Used |
|---|---|---|---|---|
| 1428 | A541 | 30h multi | .60 | .25 |
| 1429 | A541 | 40h multi | .60 | .25 |
| 1430 | A541 | 60h multi | .50 | .25 |
| 1431 | A541 | 80h multi *(europaens)* | 1.25 | .25 |
| *a.* | | 80h multi *(europaeus)* | 6.00 | 3.50 |
| 1432 | A541 | 1k multi | .90 | .30 |
| 1433 | A541 | 1.20k multi | 1.25 | .50 |
| 1434 | A541 | 2k multi | 3.00 | 1.25 |
| | | *Nos. 1428-1434 (7)* | 8.10 | 3.05 |

The sheet of 50 of the 80h contains 40 with misspelling "europaens" and 10 with "europaeus."

"Spring" by Vaclav Hollar, 1607-77 A542

Paintings: No. 1436, Portrait of Mrs. F. Wussin, by Jan Kupecky (1667-1740). No. 1437, Snow Owl by Karel Purkyne (1834-1868). No. 1438, Tulips by Vaclav Spála (1885-1964). No. 1439, Recruit by Ludovít Fulla (1902-1980).

**1966, Dec. 8 Engr. *Perf. 14***

| No. | Type | Description | Mint | Used |
|---|---|---|---|---|
| 1435 | A542 | 1k black | 3.75 | 3.50 |
| 1436 | A542 | 1k multicolored | 5.25 | 1.90 |
| 1437 | A542 | 1k multicolored | 2.40 | 1.90 |
| 1438 | A542 | 1k multicolored | 2.40 | 1.90 |
| 1439 | A542 | 1k multicolored | 19.00 | 16.00 |
| | | *Nos. 1435-1439 (5)* | 32.80 | 25.20 |

Printed in sheets of 4 stamps and 2 labels. The labels in sheet of No. 1435 are inscribed "Vaclav Hollar 1607-1677" in fancy frame. Other labels are blank. Value, set $135.

See No. 1484.

Symbolic Bird — A543

**Engraved and Photogravure**

**1966, Dec. 17 *Perf. 11½***

| No. | Type | Description | Mint | Used |
|---|---|---|---|---|
| 1440 | A543 | 1k dp blue & yel | 1.25 | .80 |

Issued for Stamp Day.

Youth — A544

**1967, Jan. 16 *Perf. 11½***

| No. | Type | Description | Mint | Used |
|---|---|---|---|---|
| 1441 | A544 | 30h ver & lt bl | .30 | .25 |

5th Cong. of the Czechoslovak Youth Org.

Symbolic Flower and Machinery A545

**1967, Jan. 16**

| No. | Type | Description | Mint | Used |
|---|---|---|---|---|
| 1442 | A545 | 30h carmine & yel | .30 | .25 |

6th Trade Union Congress, Prague.

Parents with Dead Child — A545a

**1967, Jan. 16 *Perf. 11½***

| No. | Type | Description | Mint | Used |
|---|---|---|---|---|
| 1442A | A545a | 60h blk & sal | .30 | .25 |

"Peace and Freedom in Viet Nam."

View of Jihlava and Tourist Year Emblem A546

Views and Tourist Year Emblem: 40h, Spielberg Castle and churches, Brno. 1.20k, Danube, castle and churches, Bratislava. 1.60k, Vlatava River bridges, Hradcany and churches, Prague.

**1967, Feb. 13 Engr. *Perf. 11½***

**Size: 40x23mm**

| No. | Type | Description | Mint | Used |
|---|---|---|---|---|
| 1443 | A546 | 30h brown violet | .25 | .25 |
| 1444 | A546 | 40h maroon | .25 | .25 |

**Size: 75x30mm**

| No. | Type | Description | Mint | Used |
|---|---|---|---|---|
| 1445 | A546 | 1.20k violet blue | .60 | .25 |
| 1446 | A546 | 1.60k black | 2.00 | .80 |
| | | *Nos. 1443-1446 (4)* | 3.10 | 1.55 |

International Tourist Year, 1967.

Black-tailed Godwit — A547

Birds: 40h, Shoveler, horiz. 60h, Purple heron. 80h, Penduline tit. 1k, Avocet. 1.40k, Black stork. 1.60k, Tufted duck, horiz.

**1967, Feb. 20 Litho. *Perf. 13½***

| No. | Type | Description | Mint | Used |
|---|---|---|---|---|
| 1447 | A547 | 30h multi | .75 | .30 |
| 1448 | A547 | 40h multi | .75 | .30 |
| 1449 | A547 | 60h multi | .75 | .30 |
| 1450 | A547 | 80h multi | .75 | .30 |
| 1451 | A547 | 1k multi | .75 | .30 |
| 1452 | A547 | 1.40k multi | 1.40 | .60 |
| 1453 | A547 | 1.60k multi | 2.75 | 1.20 |
| | | *Nos. 1447-1453 (7)* | 7.90 | 3.30 |

Solar Research and Satellite — A548

Space Research: 40h, Space craft, rocket and construction of station. 60h, Man on moon and orientation system. 1k, Exploration of solar system and rocket. 1.20k, Lunar satellites and moon photograph. 1.60k, Planned lunar architecture and moon landing.

**Engraved and Photogravure**

**1967, Mar. 24 *Perf. 11½***

| No. | Type | Description | Mint | Used |
|---|---|---|---|---|
| 1454 | A548 | 30h yel & dk red | .30 | .25 |
| 1455 | A548 | 40h vio bl & blk | .45 | .25 |
| 1456 | A548 | 60h lilac & grn | .45 | .25 |
| 1457 | A548 | 1k brt pink & sl | .45 | .25 |
| 1458 | A548 | 1.20k lt violet & blk | .70 | .25 |
| 1459 | A548 | 1.60k brn lake & blk | 2.10 | .60 |
| | | *Nos. 1454-1459 (6)* | 4.45 | 1.85 |

Gothic Painting, by Master Theodoric A549

Designs: 40h, "Burning of Master Hus," from Litomerice Hymnal. 60h, Modern glass sculpture. 80h, "The Shepherdess and the Chimney Sweep," Andersen fairy tale, painting by J. Trnka. 1k, Section of pressure vessel from atomic power station. 1.20k, Three ceramic figurines, by P. Rada. 3k, Montreal skyline and EXPO '67 emblem.

**1967, Apr. 10 Engr. *Perf. 14***

**Size: 37x23mm**

| No. | Type | Description | Mint | Used |
|---|---|---|---|---|
| 1460 | A549 | 30h multi | .25 | .25 |
| 1461 | A549 | 40h multi | .25 | .25 |
| 1462 | A549 | 60h multi | .25 | .25 |
| 1463 | A549 | 80h multi | .25 | .25 |
| 1464 | A549 | 1k multi | 1.00 | .25 |
| 1465 | A549 | 1.20k multi | 1.25 | .60 |
| | | *Nos. 1460-1465 (6)* | 3.25 | 1.85 |

**Souvenir Sheet**

***Perf. 11½***

**Size: 40x30mm**

| No. | Type | Description | Mint | Used |
|---|---|---|---|---|
| 1466 | A549 | 3k multi | 3.00 | 2.50 |

EXPO '67, International Exhibition, Montreal, Apr. 28-Oct. 27, 1967.

Nos. 1460-1465 were each issued in a miniature sheet of 10 stamps. Value, set $50.

Examples of No. 1466 imperf. were not issued.

Canoe Race A550

Women Playing Basketball — A551

No. 1468, Wheels, dove & emblems of Warsaw, Berlin, Prague. 1.60k, Canoe slalom.

***Perf. 12x11½, 11½x12***

**1967, Apr. 17 Engr. & Photo.**

| No. | Type | Description | Mint | Used |
|---|---|---|---|---|
| 1467 | A550 | 60h black & brt bl | .25 | .25 |
| 1468 | A550 | 60h black & salmon | .25 | .25 |
| 1469 | A551 | 60h blk & grnsh bl | .25 | .25 |
| 1470 | A551 | 1.60k black & brt vio | 1.10 | .55 |
| | | *Nos. 1467-1470 (4)* | 1.85 | 1.30 |

No. 1467, 5th Intl. Wild-Water Canoeing Championships; No. 1468, 20th Warsaw-Berlin-Prague Bicycle Race: No. 1469, Women's Basketball Championships; No. 1470, 10th Intl. Water Slalom Championships.

"Golden Street" — A552

Designs: 60h, Interior of Hall of King Wenceslas. 5k, St. Matthew, from illuminated manuscript, 11th century.

**1967, May 9 *Perf. 11½x11***

| No. | Type | Description | Mint | Used |
|---|---|---|---|---|
| 1471 | A552 | 30h rose claret | .25 | .25 |
| 1472 | A552 | 60h bluish black | .50 | .25 |

**Souvenir Sheet**

***Perf. 11½***

| No. | Type | Description | Mint | Used |
|---|---|---|---|---|
| 1473 | A552 | 5k multicolored | 2.60 | 2.40 |

Issued to publicize the Castle of Prague.

Stylized Lyre with Flowers — A553

**1967, May 10 *Perf. 11½***

| No. | Type | Description | Mint | Used |
|---|---|---|---|---|
| 1474 | A553 | 60h dull pur & brt grn | .30 | .25 |

Prague Music Festival.

Old-New Synagogue, Prague — A554

30h, Detail from Torah curtain, 1593. 60h, Prague Printer's emblem, 1530. 1k, Mikulov jug, 1804. 1.40k, Memorial for Concentration Camp Victims 1939-45, Pincas Synagogue (menorah & tablet). 1.60k, Tombstone of David Gans, 1613.

**1967, May 22 *Perf. 11½***

| No. | Type | Description | Mint | Used |
|---|---|---|---|---|
| 1475 | A554 | 30h dull red & lt bl | .30 | .25 |
| 1476 | A554 | 60h blk & lt grn | .25 | .25 |
| 1477 | A554 | 1k dk bl & rose lil | .35 | .25 |
| 1478 | A554 | 1.20k dk brn & mar | .65 | .25 |
| 1479 | A554 | 1.40k black & yellow | .55 | .25 |
| 1480 | A554 | 1.60k green & yel | 4.50 | 2.75 |
| | | *Nos. 1475-1480 (6)* | 6.60 | 4.00 |

Issued to show Jewish relics. The items shown on the 30h, 60h and 1k are from the State Jewish Museum, Prague.

"Lidice" — A555

**1967, June 9 Unwmk. *Perf. 11½***

| No. | Type | Description | Mint | Used |
|---|---|---|---|---|
| 1481 | A555 | 30h black & brt rose | .30 | .25 |

Destruction of Lidice by the Nazis, 25th anniv.

Prague Architecture — A556

**1967, June 10 Engr. & Photo.**

| No. | Type | Description | Mint | Used |
|---|---|---|---|---|
| 1482 | A556 | 1k black & gold | .35 | .25 |

Issued to publicize the 9th Congress of the International Union of Architects, Prague.

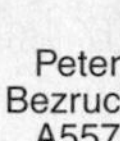

Peter Bezruc A557

**1967, June 21**
**1483** A557 60h dull rose & blk .30 .25

Peter Bezruc, poet & writer, birth cent.

### Painting Type of 1966

2k, Henri Rousseau (1844-1910), self-portrait.

**1967, June 22 Engr. *Perf. 11½***
**1484** A542 2k multicolored 2.00 1.60

Praga 68, World Stamp Exhibition, Prague, June 22-July 7, 1968.
Printed in sheets of 4 stamps (2x2), separated by horizontal gutter with inscription and picture of Natl. Gallery, site of Praga 68. Value, $10.

View of Skalitz — A558

No. 1486, Mining tower & church steeple, Pribram. No. 1487, Hands holding book & view of Presov.

**1967, Aug. 21 Engr. *Perf. 11½***
**1485** A558 30h violet blue .25 .25
**1486** A558 30h slate green .25 .25
**1487** A558 30h claret .25 .25
*Nos. 1485-1487 (3)* .75 .75

Towns of Skalitz, Pribram, Presov, annivs.

Colonnade and Spring, Karlovy Vary and Communications Emblem — A559

**1967, Aug. 21 Engr. & Photo.**
**1488** A559 30h violet bl & gold .30 .25

5th Sports & Cultural Festival of the Employees of the Ministry of Communications, Karlovy Vary.

Ondrejov Observatory and Galaxy — A560

**1967, Aug. 22 Engr.**
**1489** A560 60h vio bl, rose lil & sil 1.50 .25

13th Cong. of the Intl. Astronomical Union.
No. 1489 was issued in a sheet of 10 stamps. Value, set $50.

Orchid — A561

Flowers from the Botanical Gardens: 30h, Cobaea scandens. 40h, Lycaste deppei. 60h, Glottiphyllum davisii. 1k, Anthurium. 1.20k, Rhodocactus. 1.40k, Moth orchid.

**1967, Aug. 30 Litho. *Perf. 12½***
**1490** A561 20h multicolored .30 .25
**1491** A561 30h pink & multi .30 .25
**1492** A561 40h multicolored .45 .25
**1493** A561 60h lt blue & multi .45 .25
**1494** A561 1k multicolored .60 .25
**1495** A561 1.20k lt yellow & multi .65 .30
**1496** A561 1.40k multicolored 1.75 .70
*Nos. 1490-1496 (7)* 4.50 2.25

Red Squirrel A562

Animals from the Tatra National Park: 60h, Wild cat. 1k, Ermine. 1.20k, Dormouse. 1.40k, Hedgehog. 1.60k, Pine marten.

### Engraved and Photogravure

**1967, Sept. 25 *Perf. 11½***
**1497** A562 30h black, yel & org .35 .25
**1498** A562 60h black & buff .35 .25
**1499** A562 1k black & lt blue .40 .25
**1500** A562 1.20k brn, pale grn & yel .50 .25
**1501** A562 1.40k blk, pink & yel .55 .25
**1502** A562 1.60k black, org & yel 2.75 1.25
*Nos. 1497-1502 (6)* 4.90 2.50

Rockets and Weapons — A563

**1967, Oct. 6 Engr. *Perf. 11½***
**1503** A563 30h slate green .30 .25

Day of the Czechoslovak People's Army.

Cruiser "Aurora" Firing at Winter Palace A564

Designs: 60h, Hammer and sickle emblems and Red Star, vert. 1k, Hands reaching for hammer and sickle, vert.

**1967, Nov. 7 Engr. & Photo.**
**1504** A564 30h black & dk car .25 .25
**1505** A564 60h black & dk car .25 .25
**1506** A564 1k black & dk car .25 .25
*Nos. 1504-1506 (3)* .75 .75

Russian October Revolution, 50th anniv.

The Conjurer, by Frantisek Tichy A565

Paintings: 80h, Don Quixote, by Cyprian Majernik. 1k, Promenade in the Park, by Norbert Grund. 1.20k, Self-portrait, by Peter J. Brandl. 1.60k, Saints from Jan of Jeren Epitaph, by Czech Master of 1395.

**1967, Nov. 13 Engr. *Perf. 11½***
**1507** A565 60h multi .35 .25
**1508** A565 80h multi .50 .30
**1509** A565 1k multi .75 .50
**1510** A565 1.20k multi .75 .50
**1511** A565 1.60k multi 3.25 2.75
*Nos. 1507-1511 (5)* 5.60 4.30

Nos. 1507-1511 were issued in sheets of 4. Value, set $24.

See Nos. 1589-1593, 1658-1662, 1711-1715, 1779-1783, 1847-1851, 1908-1913, 2043-2047, 2090-2093, 2147-2151, 2265-2269, 2335-2339, 2386-2390, 2437-2441, 2534-2538, 2586-2590, 2634-2638, 2810-2813, 2843-2847, 2872-2874, 2908-2910, 2936-2938, 2973-2975, 2995, 3001-3002, 3028-3030, 3054-3055, 3075-3076, 3105-3107, 3133-3135, 3160-3162, 3188-3190, 3224-3226, 3233, 3255-3257, 3287-3289, 3323-3325, 3359-3361, 3401-3402, 3435-3436, 3478-3480, 3518-3520, 3552-3553, 3591-3593, 3616, 3618, 3656-3658, 3680, 3690-3692, 3726-3727.

Pres. Antonin Novotny — A566

**1967, Dec. 9 Engr. *Perf. 11½***
**1512** A566 2k blue gray 1.40 .25
**1513** A566 3k brown 1.40 .25

Czechoslovakia Nos. 65, 71 and 81 of 1920 — A567

**1967, Dec. 18**
**1514** A567 1k maroon & silver 1.60 1.10

Issued for Stamp Day.

Symbolic Flag and Dates — A568

**1968, Jan. 15 Engr. *Perf. 11½***
**1515** A568 30h red, dk bl & ultra .75 .25

50th anniversary of Czechoslovakia.
No. 1515 was issued in a sheet of 10. Value, $20.

Figure Skating and Olympic Rings — A569

Olympic Rings and: 1k, Ski course. 1.60k, Toboggan chute. 2k, Ice hockey.

**1968, Jan. 29 Engr. & Photo.**
**1516** A569 60h blk, yel & ocher .30 .25
**1517** A569 1k ol grn, lt bl & lem .55 .25
**1518** A569 1.60k blk, lil & bl grn .70 .25
**1519** A569 2k blk, ap grn & lt bl 1.10 .25
*Nos. 1516-1519 (4)* 2.65 1.00

10th Winter Olympic Games, Grenoble, France, Feb. 6-18.

Factories and Rising Sun — A570

Design: 60h, Workers and banner.

**1968, Feb. 25 *Perf. 11½x12***
**1520** A570 30h car & dk bl .25 .25
**1521** A570 60h car & dk bl .25 .25

20th anniversary of February Revolution.

Map of Battle of Sokolovo A571

Human Rights Flame — A572

**1968, Mar. 8 *Perf. 11½***
**1522** A571 30h blk, brt bl & car .40 .25

**Engr.**

**1523** A572 1k rose carmine 1.10 .40

25th anniv. of the Battle of Sokolovo, Mar. 8, 1943, against the German Army, No. 1522; Intl. Human Rights Year, No. 1523.

Janko Kral and Liptovsky Mikulas — A573

Karl Marx — A574

Girl's Head — A575

Arms and Allegory — A576

Head — A577

**1968, Mar. 25 Engr.**
**1524** A573 30h green .30 .25
**1525** A574 30h claret .25 .25

### Engraved and Photogravure

**1526** A575 30h dk red & gold .25 .25
**1527** A576 30h dk blue & dp org .25 .25
**1528** A577 1k multicolored .50 .25
*Nos. 1524-1528 (5)* 1.55 1.25

The writer Janko Kral and the Slovak town Liptovsky Mikulas (No. 1524); 150th anniv. of the birth of Karl Marx (No. 1525); cent. of the cornerstone laying of the Prague Natl. Theater (No. 1526); 150th anniv. of the Prague Natl. Museum (No. 1527); 20th anniv. of WHO (1k).

Symbolic Radio Waves A578

No. 1530, Symbolic television screens.

**1968, Apr. 29** ***Perf. 11½***

**1529** A578 30h blk, car & vio bl .25 .25
**1530** A578 30h blk, car & vio bl .25 .25

45th anniv. of Czechoslovak broadcasting (No. 1529), 15th anniv. of television (No. 1530).

Olympic Rings, Mexican Sculpture and Diver — A579

Olympic Rings and: 40h, Runner and "The Sanctification of Quetzalcoatl." 60h, Volleyball and Mexican ornaments. 1k, Czechoslovak and Mexican Olympic emblems and carved altar. 1.60k, Soccer and ornaments. 2k, View of Hradcany, weather vane and key.

**1968, Apr. 30**

**1531** A579 30h black, bl & car .25 .25
**1532** A579 40h multi .25 .25
**1533** A579 60h multi .25 .25
**1534** A579 1k multi .35 .25
**1535** A579 1.60k multi .35 .25
**1536** A579 2k black & multi 1.75 .40
*Nos. 1531-1536 (6)* 3.20 1.65

19th Olympic Games, Mexico City, 10/12-27.

### Prague Castle Types of 1966

Designs: 30h, Tombstone of Bretislav I. 60h, Romanesque door knocker, St. Wenceslas Chapel. 5k, Head of St. Peter, mosaic from Golden Gate of St. Vitus Cathedral.

**1968, May 9** ***Perf. 11½***

**1537** A527 30h multicolored .40 .25
**1538** A527 60h black, red & cit .40 .25

### Souvenir Sheet

**Engr.**

**1539** A528 5k multicolored 2.75 2.75

Pres. Ludvik Svoboda — A580

**1968-70** **Engr.** ***Perf. 11½***

**1540** A580 30h ultramarine .25 .25
**1540A** A580 50h green ('70) .25 .25
**1541** A580 60h maroon .25 .25
**1541A** A580 1k rose car ('70) .30 .25
*Nos. 1540-1541A (4)* 1.05 1.00

Shades exist of No. 1541A.

"Business," Sculpture by Otto Gutfreund A581

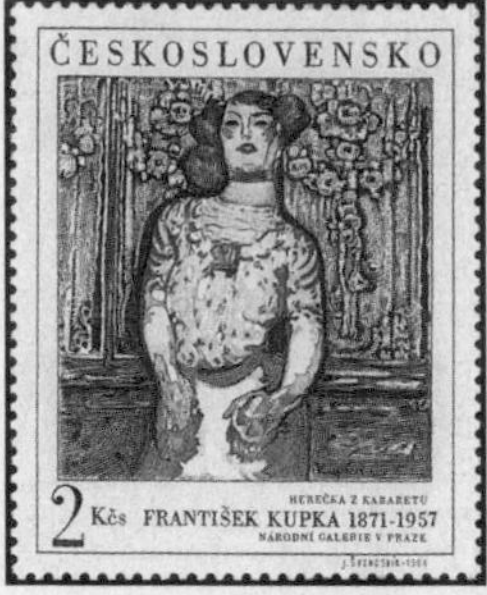


Cabaret Performer, by Frantisek Kupka — A582

Designs (The New Prague): 40h, Broadcasting Corporation Building. 60h, New Parliament. 1.40k, Tapestry by Jan Bauch "Prague 1787." 3k, Presidential standard.

### Engr. & Photo.; Engr. (2k)

**1968, June 5**

**1542** A581 30h black & multi .25 .25
**1543** A581 40h black & multi .25 .25
**1544** A581 60h dk brn & multi .25 .25
**1545** A581 1.40k dk brn & multi .40 .25
**1546** A582 2k indigo & multi .85 .70
**1547** A581 3k black & multi .85 .30
*Nos. 1542-1547 (6)* 2.85 2.00

Designs (The Old Prague): 30h, St. George's Basilica. 60h, Renaissance fountain. 1k, Villa America-Dvorak Museum, 18th cent. building. 1.60k, Emblem from the House of Three Violins, 18th cent. 2k, Josefina, by Josef Manes. 3k, Emblem of Prague, 1475.

**1968, June 21** ***Perf. 11½***

**1548** A581 30h green, gray & yel .25 .25
**1549** A581 60h dk vio, ap grn & gold .25 .25
**1550** A581 1k black, lt bl & pink .30 .25
**1551** A581 1.60k slate grn & multi .55 .25
**1552** A582 2k brown & multi 1.25 .60
**1553** A581 3k blk, yel, bl & pink 1.25 .60
*Nos. 1548-1553 (6)* 3.85 2.20

Nos. 1542-1553 publicized the Praga 68 Philatelic Exhibition. Nos. 1542-1545, 1547-1551, 1553 issued in sheets of 15 + 15 labels with Praga 68 emblem and inscription.

Nos. 1546, 1552 issued in sheets of 4 (2x2) with one horizontal label between top and bottom rows showing Praga 68 emblem. Values for sheets of 4, each $8.

### Souvenir Sheet

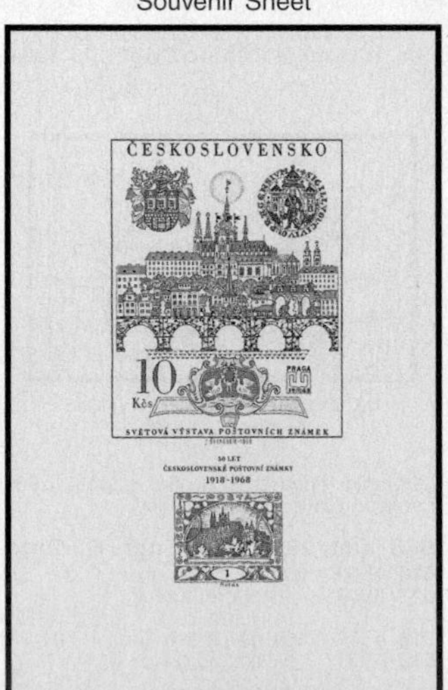


View of Prague and Emblems — A583

### Engraved and Photogravure

**1968, June 22** ***Imperf.***

**1554** A583 10k multicolored 3.25 2.50

Praga 68 and 50th anniv. of Czechoslovak postage stamps. Sold only together with a 5k admission ticket to the Praga 68 philatelic Exhibition. Value $20.

Madonna with the Rose Garlands, by Dürer — A584

**1968, July 6** ***Perf. 11½***

**1555** A584 5k multicolored 3.75 2.75

FIP Day, July 6. Issued in sheets of 4 (2x2) with one horizontal label between, showing Praga 68 emblem. Value, $20.

Stagecoach on Rails — A585

Design: 1k, Steam and electric locomotives.

**1968, Aug. 6**

**1556** A585 60h multicolored .45 .25
**1557** A585 1k multicolored 1.60 .60

No. 1556: 140th anniv. of the horse-drawn railroad Ceské Budejovice to Linz; No. 1557: cent. of the Ceské Budejovice to Plzen railroad.

6th Intl. Slavonic Cong. in Prague — A586

**1968, Aug. 7** ***Perf. 11½***

**1558** A586 30h vio blue & car .40 .25

Ardspach Rocks and Ammonite — A587

60h, Basalt formation & frog skeleton fossil. 80h, Rocks, basalt veins & polished agate. 1k, Pelecypoda (fossil shell) & Belanske Tatra mountains. 1.60k, Trilobite & Barrande rock formation.

**1968, Aug. 8**

**1559** A587 30h black & citron .25 .25
**1560** A587 60h black & rose cl .25 .25
**1561** A587 80h black, lt vio & pink .30 .25
**1562** A587 1k black & lt blue .40 .25
**1563** A587 1.60k black & bister 1.40 .65
*Nos. 1559-1563 (5)* 2.60 1.65

Issued to publicize the 23rd International Geological Congress, Prague, Aug. 8-Sept. 3.

Raising Slovak Flag A588

60h, Slovak partisans, and mountain.

**1968, Sept. 9** **Engr.** ***Perf. 11½***

**1564** A588 30h ultra .25 .25
**1565** A588 60h red .25 .25

No. 1564 for the Slovak Natl. Council, No. 1565 the 120th anniv. of the Slovak national uprising.

Flowerpot, by Jiri Schlessinger (age 10) — A589

Drawings by Children in Terezin Concentration Camp: 30h, Jew and Guard, by Jiri Beutler (age 10). 60h, Butterflies, by Kitty Brunnerova (age 11).

### Engraved and Photogravure

**1968, Sept. 30** ***Perf. 11½***

**Size: 30x23mm**

**1566** A589 30h blk, buff & rose lil .30 .25
**1567** A589 60h black & multi .30 .25

***Perf. 12x11½***

**Size: 41x23mm**

**1568** A589 1k black & multi .80 .25
*Nos. 1566-1568 (3)* 1.40 .75

30th anniversary of Munich Pact.

Arms of Regional Capitals A590

Arms of Prague — A591

**1968, Oct. 21** ***Perf. 11½***

**1569** A590 60h Banská Bystrica .25 .25
**1570** A590 60h Bratislava .25 .25
**1571** A590 60h Brno .25 .25
**1572** A590 60h Ceské Budejovice .25 .25
**1573** A590 60h Hradec Králové .25 .25
**1574** A590 60h Kosice .25 .25
**1575** A590 60h Ostrava (horse) .25 .25
**1576** A590 60h Plzen .25 .25
**1577** A590 60h Usti nad Labem .25 .25

***Perf. 11½x16***

**1578** A591 1k shown .25 .25
*Nos. 1569-1578 (10)* 2.50 2.50

No. 1578 issued in sheets of 10. Value, $30.

See Nos. 1652-1657, 1742-1747, 1886-1888, 2000-2001.

Flag and Linden Leaves A592

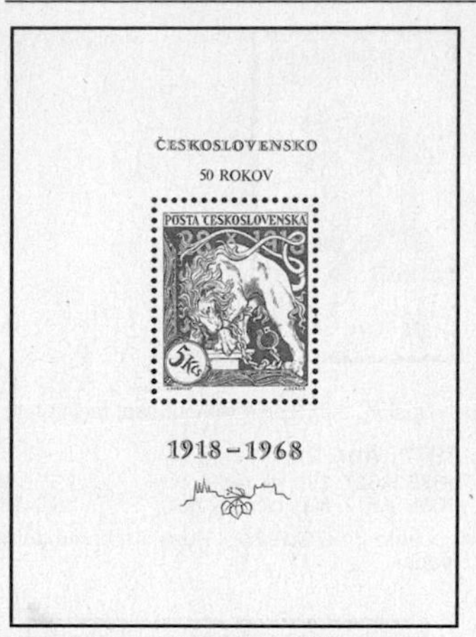


Bohemian Lion Breaking Chains (Type SP1 of 1919) — A593

Design: 60h, Map of Czechoslovakia, linden leaves, Hradcany in Prague and Castle in Bratislava.

**1968, Oct. 28** ***Perf. 12x11½***

**1579** A592 30h dp blue & mag .30 .25
**1580** A592 60h blk, gold, red & ultra .30 .25

**Souvenir Sheet**

**Engr.**

***Perf. 11½x12***

**1581** A593 5k red 3.50 2.75

Founding of Czechoslovakia, 50th anniv.

Ernest Hemingway — A594

Caricatures: 30h, Karel Capek (1890-1938), writer. 40h, George Bernard Shaw. 60h, Maxim Gorki. 1k, Pablo Picasso. 1.20k, Taikan Yokoyama (1868-1958), painter. 1.40k, Charlie Chaplin.

**Engraved and Photogravure**

**1968, Nov. 18** ***Perf. 11½x12***

**1582** A594 20h black, org & red .25 .25
**1583** A594 30h black & multi .30 .25
**1584** A594 40h blk, lic & car .30 .25
**1585** A594 60h black, sky bl & grn .25 .25
**1586** A594 1k black, brn & yel .45 .25
**1587** A594 1.20k black, dp car & vio .45 .25
**1588** A594 1.40k black, brn & dp org 1.75 .40
*Nos. 1582-1588 (7)* 3.75 1.90

Cultural personalities of the 20th cent. and UNESCO. See Nos. 1628-1633.

**Painting Type of 1967**

Czechoslovakian Art: 60h, Cleopatra II, by Jan Zrzavy (1890-1977). 80h, Black Lake (man and horse), by Jan Preisler (1872-1918). 1.20k, Giovanni Francisci as a Volunteer, by Peter Michal Bohun (1822-1879). 1.60k, Princess Hyacinth, by Alfons Mucha (1860-1939). 3k, Madonna and Child, woodcarving, 1518, by Master Paul of Levoca.

**1968, Nov. 29** **Engr.** ***Perf. 11½***

**1589** A565 60h multi .75 .35
**1590** A565 80h multi .75 .35
**1591** A565 1.20k multi .75 .35
**1592** A565 1.60k multi .75 .35
**1593** A565 3k multi 2.50 2.50
*Nos. 1589-1593 (5)* 5.50 3.90

Nos. 1589-1593 were issued in sheets of 4. Value, set $25.

Cinderlad — A595

Slovak Fairy Tales: 60h, The Proud Lady. 80h, The Ruling Knight. 1k, Good Day, Little Bench. 1.20k, The Spellbound Castle. 1.80k, The Miraculous Hunter. The designs are from illustrations by Ludovit Fulla for "Slovak Stories."

**1968, Dec. 18** **Engr. & Photo.**

**1594** A595 30h multi .25 .25
**1595** A595 60h multi .25 .25
**1596** A595 80h multi .40 .25
**1597** A595 1k multi .55 .25
**1598** A595 1.20k multi .55 .25
**1599** A595 1.80k multi 1.50 .65
*Nos. 1594-1599 (6)* 3.50 1.90

Czechoslovakia Nos. 2 and 3 — A596

**1968, Dec. 18**

**1600** A596 1k violet bl & gold .95 .65

50th anniv. of Czechoslovakian postage stamps.

Crescent, Cross and Lion and Sun Emblems — A597

60h, 12 crosses in circles forming large cross.

**1969, Jan. 31** ***Perf. 11½***

**1601** A597 60h black, red & gold .25 .25
**1602** A597 1k black, ultra & red .35 .25

No. 1601: 50th anniv. of the Czechoslovak Red Cross. No. 1602: 50th anniv. of the League of Red Cross Societies.

ILO Emblem — A598

**1969, Jan. 31**

**1603** A598 1k black & gray .30 .25

50th anniv. of the ILO.

Cheb Pistol A599

Historical Firearms: 40h, Italian pistol with Dutch decorations, c. 1600. 60h, Wheellock rifle from Matej Kubik workshop c. 1720. 1k, Flintlock pistol, Devieuxe workshop, Liege, c. 1760. 1.40k, Duelling pistols, from Lebeda workshop, Prague, c. 1835. 1.60k, Derringer pistols, US, c. 1865.

**1969, Feb. 18**

**1604** A599 30h black & multi .25 .25
**1605** A599 40h black & multi .25 .25
**1606** A599 60h black & multi .25 .25
**1607** A599 1k black & multi .25 .25
**1608** A599 1.40k black & multi .35 .25
**1609** A599 1.60k black & multi 1.40 .25
*Nos. 1604-1609 (6)* 2.75 1.50

Bratislava Castle, Muse and Book — A600

No. 1611, Science symbols & emblem (Brno University). No. 1612, Harp, laurel & musicians' names. No. 1613, Theatrical scene. No. 1614, Arms of Slovakia, banner & blossoms. No. 1615, School, outstretched hands & woman with linden leaves.

**1969, Mar. 24** **Engr.** ***Perf. 11½***

**1610** A600 60h violet blue .25 .25

**Engraved and Photogravure**

**1611** A600 60h blk, gold & slate .25 .25
**1612** A600 60h gold, blue, blk & red .25 .25
**1613** A600 60h black & rose red .25 .25
**1614** A600 60h rose red, sil & bl .25 .25
**1615** A600 60h black & gold .25 .25
*Nos. 1610-1615 (6)* 1.50 1.50

50th anniv. of: Komensky University in Bratislava (No. 1610); Brno University (No. 1611); Brno Conservatory of Music (No. 1612); Slovak Natl. Theater (No. 1613); Slovak Soviet Republic (No. 1614); cent. of the Zniev Gymnasium (academic high school) (No. 1615).

Baldachin-top Car and Four-seat Coupé of 1900-1905 — A601

Designs: 1.60k, Laurin & Klement Voiturette, 1907, and L & K touring car with American top, 1907. 1.80k, First Prague bus, 1907, and sectionalized Skoda bus, 1967.

**1969, Mar. 25** **Engr. & Photo.**

**1616** A601 30h blk, lil & lt grn .60 .25
**1617** A601 1.60k blk, org brn & lt bl .75 .25
**1618** A601 1.80k multi 1.40 .60
*Nos. 1616-1618 (3)* 2.75 1.10

Peace, by Ladislav Guderna — A602

**1969, Apr. 21** ***Perf. 11***

**1619** A602 1.60k multi .50 .35

20th anniv. of the Peace Movement. Issued in sheets of 15 stamps and 5 tabs. Stamp with tab $2.50.

Horse and Rider, by Vaclav Hollar — A603

Old Engravings of Horses: 30h, Prancing Stallion, by Hendrik Goltzius, horiz. 80h, Groom Leading Horse, by Matthäus Merian, horiz. 1.80k, Horse and Soldier, by Albrecht Dürer. 2.40k, Groom and Horse, by Johann E. Ridinger.

**1969, Apr. 24** ***Perf. 11x11½, 11½x11***

**Yellowish Paper**

**1620** A603 30h dark brown .25 .25
**1621** A603 80h violet brown .25 .25
**1622** A603 1.60k slate .45 .25
**1623** A603 1.80k sepia .50 .25
**1624** A603 2.40k multi 2.40 .60
*Nos. 1620-1624 (5)* 3.85 1.60

M. R. Stefánik as Astronomy Professor and French General — A604

**1969, May 4** **Engr.** ***Perf. 11½***

**1625** A604 60h rose claret .40 .25

Gen. Milan R. Stefánik, 50th death anniv.

St. Wenceslas Pressing Wine, Mural by the Master of Litomerice — A605

Design: No. 1627, Coronation banner of the Estates, 1723, with St. Wenceslas and coats of arms of Bohemia and Czech Crown lands.

**1969, May 9** **Engr.** ***Perf. 11½***

**1626** A605 3k multicolored 2.00 1.40
**1627** A605 3k multicolored 2.00 1.40

Issued to publicize the art treasures of the Castle of Prague.

Issued in sheets of 4. Value, set $20.

See Nos. 1689-1690.

**Caricature Type of 1968**

Caricatures: 30h, Pavol Orszagh Hviezdoslav (1849-1921), Slovak writer. 40h, Gilbert K. Chesterton (1874-1936), English writer. 60h, Vladimir Mayakovski (1893-1930), Russian poet. 1k, Henri Matisse (1869-1954), French painter. 1.80k, Ales Hrdlicka (1869-1943), Czech-born American anthropologist. 2k, Franz Kafka (1883-1924), Austrian writer.

**Engraved and Photogravure**

**1969, June 17** ***Perf. 11½x12***

**1628** A594 30h blk, red & bl .25 .25
**1629** A594 40h blk, bl & lt vio .25 .25
**1630** A594 60h blk, rose & yel .25 .25
**1631** A594 1k black & multi .25 .25
**1632** A594 1.80k blk, ultra & ocher .25 .25
**1633** A594 2k blk, yel & brt grn 1.50 .50
*Nos. 1628-1633 (6)* 2.75 1.75

Issued to honor cultural personalities of the 20th century and UNESCO.

"Music," by Alfons Mucha — A606

Paintings by Mucha: 60h, "Painting." 1k, "Dance." 2.40k, "Ruby" and "Amethyst."

**1969, July 14** *Perf. 11½x11*

**Size: 30x49mm**

**1634** A606 30h black & multi .80 .25
**1635** A606 60h black & multi .80 .25
**1636** A606 1k black & multi 1.00 .25

**Size: 39x51mm**

**1637** A606 2.40k black & multi 2.00 1.25
*Nos. 1634-1637 (4)* 4.60 2.00

Alfons Mucha (1860-1930), painter and stamp designer (Type A1).

No. 1637 was issued in sheets of 4. Value $12.50.

Pres. Svoboda and Partisans
A607

No. 1639, Slovak fighters and mourners.

**1969, Aug. 29** *Perf. 11*

**1638** A607 30h ol grn & red, *yel* .25 .25
**1639** A607 30h vio bl & red, *yel* .25 .25

25th anniversary of the Slovak uprising and of the Battle of Dukla.

Tatra Mountain Stream and Gentians — A608

Designs: 60h, Various views in Tatra Mountains. No. 1644, Mountain pass and gentians. No. 1645, Houses, Krivan Mountain and autumn crocuses.

**1969, Sept. 8** **Engr.** *Perf. 11*

**Size: 71x33mm**

**1640** A608 60h gray .25 .25
**1641** A608 60h dark blue .25 .25
**1642** A608 60h dull gray vio .25 .25

*Perf. 11½*

**Size: 40x23mm**

**1643** A608 1.60k multi .55 .25
**1644** A608 1.60k multi 1.25 .50
**1645** A608 1.60k multi .55 .25
*Nos. 1640-1645 (6)* 3.10 1.75

20th anniv. of the creation of the Tatra Mountains Natl. Park.

Nos. 1640-1642 are printed in sheets of 15 (3x5) with 5 labels showing mountain plants. Value, set with tabs $2.50.

Nos. 1643-1645 were issued in sheets of 10. Value, $70.

Bronze Belt Ornaments
A609

Archaeological Treasures from Bohemia and Moravia: 30h, Gilt ornament with 6 masks. 1k, Jeweled earrings. 1.80k, Front and back of lead cross with Greek inscription. 2k, Gilt strap ornament with human figure.

**Engraved and Photogravure**

**1969, Sept. 30** *Perf. 11½x11*

**1646** A609 20h gold & multi .25 .25
**1647** A609 30h gold & multi .25 .25
**1648** A609 1k red & multi .25 .25
**1649** A609 1.80k dull org & multi .45 .25
**1650** A609 2k gold & multi 1.75 .25
*Nos. 1646-1650 (5)* 2.95 1.25

"Mail Circling the World"
A610

**1969, Oct. 1** **Engr.** *Perf. 12*

**1651** A610 3.20k multi .95 .60

16th UPU Cong., Tokyo, Oct. 1-Nov. 14. Issued in sheets of 4. Value $9.

**Coat of Arms Type of 1968**

**Engraved and Photogravure**

**1969, Oct. 25** *Perf. 11½*

**1652** A590 50h Bardejov .25 .25
**1653** A590 50h Hranice .25 .25
**1654** A590 50h Kezmarok .25 .25
**1655** A590 50h Krnov .25 .25
**1656** A590 50h Litomerice .25 .25
**1657** A590 50h Manetin .25 .25
*Nos. 1652-1657 (6)* 1.50 1.50

**Painting Type of 1967**

Designs: 60h, Requiem, 1944, by Frantisek Muzika. 1k, Resurrection, 1380, by the Master of the Trebon Altar. 1.60k, Crucifixion, 1950, by Vincent Hloznik. 1.80k, Girl with Doll, 1863, by Julius Bencur. 2.20k, St. Jerome, 1357-67, by Master Theodorik.

**1969, Nov. 25** *Perf. 11½*

**1658** A565 60h multi .75 .25
**1659** A565 1k multi .75 .25
**1660** A565 1.60k multi .75 .40
**1661** A565 1.80k multi .75 .40
**1662** A565 2.20k multi 3.00 2.00
*Nos. 1658-1662 (5)* 6.00 3.30

Nos. 1658-1662 were each issued in sheets of 4. Value, set $30.

Symbolic Sheet of Stamps — A611

**1969, Dec. 18** *Perf. 11½x12*

**1663** A611 1k dk brn, ultra & gold .30 .30

Issued for Stamp Day 1969.

Ski Jump — A612

Designs: 60h, Long distance skier. 1k, Ski jump and slope. 1.60k, Woman skier.

**1970, Jan. 6** *Perf. 11½*

**1664** A612 50h multi .25 .25
**1665** A612 60h multi .25 .25
**1666** A612 1k multi .25 .25
**1667** A612 1.60k multi .60 .30
*Nos. 1664-1667 (4)* 1.35 1.05

Intl. Ski Championships "Tatra 1970."

Ludwig van Beethoven — A613

Portraits: No. 1669, Friedrich Engels (1820-95), German socialist. No. 1670, Maximilian Hell (1720-92), Slovakian Jesuit and astronomer. No. 1671, Lenin, Russian Communist leader. No. 1672, Josef Manes (1820-71), Czech painter. No. 1673, Comenius (1592-1670), theologian and educator.

**1970, Feb. 17** **Engr.** *Perf. 11x11½*

**1668** A613 40h black .25 .25
**1669** A613 40h dull red .25 .25
**1670** A613 40h yellow brn .25 .25
**1671** A613 40h dull red .25 .25
**1672** A613 40h brown .25 .25
**1673** A613 40h black .25 .25
*Nos. 1668-1673 (6)* 1.50 1.50

Anniversaries of birth of Beethoven, Engels, Hell, Lenin and Manes, 300th anniv. of the death of Comenius, and to honor UNESCO.

Bells
A614

80h, Machine tools & lathe. 1k, Folklore masks. 1.60k, Angel & Three Wise Men, 17th cent. icon from Koniec. 2k, View of Orlik Castle, 1787, by F. K. Wolf. 3k, "Passing through Koshu down to Mishima" from Hokusai's 36 Views of Fuji.

**Engraved and Photogravure**

**1970, Mar. 13** *Perf. 11½x11*

**Size: 40x23mm**

**1674** A614 50h multi .25 .25
**1675** A614 80h multi .25 .25
**1676** A614 1k multi .25 .25

**Size: 50x40mm**

*Perf. 11½*

**1677** A614 1.60k multi .35 .30
**1678** A614 2k multi .45 .25
**1679** A614 3k multi 2.10 .70
*Nos. 1674-1679 (6)* 3.65 2.00

EXPO '70 Intl. Exhib., Osaka, Japan, Mar. 15-Sept. 13, 1970.

Nos. 1674-1676 issued in sheets of 50,

Nos. 1677-1679 in sheets of 4. Value, set of 3 sheets, $18.

Kosice Townhall, Laurel and Czechoslovak Arms — A615

**1970, Apr. 5** *Perf. 11*

**1680** A615 60h slate, ver & gold .40 .25

Government's Kosice Program, 25th anniv.

"The Remarkable Horse" by Josef Lada — A616

Paintings by Josef Lada: 60h, Autumn, 1955, horiz. 1.80k, "The Water Sprite." 2.40k, Children in Winter, 1943, horiz.

**1970, Apr. 21** *Perf. 11½*

**1681** A616 60h black & multi .30 .25
**1682** A616 1k black & multi .45 .25
**1683** A616 1.80k black & multi .75 .25
**1684** A616 2.40k black & multi 1.50 .25
*Nos. 1681-1684 (4)* 3.00 1.00

Lenin — A617

Design: 60h, Lenin without cap, facing left.

**1970, Apr. 22**

**1685** A617 30h dk red & gold .25 .25
**1686** A617 60h black & gold .25 .25

Lenin (1870-1924), Russian communist leader.

Fighters on the Barricades — A618

No. 1688, Lilac, Russian tank and castle.

**1970, May 5** *Perf. 11x11½*

**1687** A618 30h dull pur, gold & bl .25 .25
**1688** A618 30h dull grn, gold & red .25 .25

No. 1687: 25th anniv. of the Prague uprising. No. 1688: 25th anniv. of the liberation of Czechoslovakia from the Germans.

**Prague Castle Art Type of 1969**

No. 1689, Bust of St. Vitus, 1486. No. 1690, Hermes and Athena, by Bartholomy Spranger (1546-1611), mural from White Tower.

**1970, May 7** **Engr.** *Perf. 11½*

**1689** A605 3k maroon & multi 1.90 1.25
**1690** A605 3k lt blue & multi 1.75 1.00

Nos. 1689-1690 were issued in sheets of 4. Value, set of 2 sheets, $18.

Compass Rose, UN Headquarters and Famous Buildings of the World — A619

**Engraved and Photogravure**

**1970, June 26** *Perf. 11*

**1691** A619 1k black & multi .40 .25

25th anniv. of the UN. Issued in sheets of 15 (3x5) and 5 labels showing UN emblem. Value of single with tab attached: unused $1; used 75c.

Cannon from 30 Years' War and Baron Munchhausen — A620

Historical Cannons: 60h, Cannon from Hussite war and St. Barbara. 1.20k, Cannon from Prussian-Austrian war, and legendary cannoneer Javurek. 1.80k, Early 20th century cannon and spaceship "La Colombiad" (Jules Verne). 2.40k, World War I cannon and "Good Soldier Schweik."

**1970, Aug. 31** *Perf. 11½*

**1692** A620 30h black & multi .25 .25
**1693** A620 60h black & multi .25 .25
**1694** A620 1.20k black & multi .25 .25
**1695** A620 1.80k black & multi .25 .25
**1696** A620 2.40k black & multi 1.25 .25
*Nos. 1692-1696 (5)* 2.25 1.25

"Rude Pravo" (Red Truth) A621

**1970, Sept. 21** *Perf. 11½x11*
**1697** A621 60h car, gold & blk .25 .25

50th anniv. of the Rude Pravo newspaper.

"Great Sun" House Sign and Old Town Tower Bridge, Prague — A622

60h, "Blue Lion" & Town Hall Tower, Brno. 1k, Gothic corner stone & Town Hall Tower, Bratislava. 1.40k, Coat of Arms & Gothic Tower, Bratislava, & medallion. 1.60k, Moravian Eagle & Gothic Town Hall Tower, Brno. 1.80k, "Black Sun" & "Green Frog" house signs & New Town Hall, Prague.

**1970, Sept. 23** *Perf. 11x11½*
**1698** A622 40h black & multi .25 .25
**1699** A622 60h black & multi .25 .25
**1700** A622 1k black & multi .25 .25
**1701** A622 1.40k black & multi 1.40 .25
**1702** A622 1.60k black & multi .30 .25
**1703** A622 1.80k black & multi .80 .25
*Nos. 1698-1703 (6)* 3.25 1.50

Germany-Uruguay Semifinal Soccer Match — A623

Designs: 20h, Sundisk Games' emblem and flags of participating nations. 60h, England-Czechoslovakia match and coats of arms. 1k, Romania-Czechoslovakia match and coats of arms. 1.20k, Brazil-Italy, final match and emblems. 1.80k, Brazil-Czechoslovakia match and emblems.

**1970, Oct. 29** *Perf. 11½*
**1704** A623 20h blk & multi .25 .25
**1705** A623 40h blk & multi .25 .25
**1706** A623 60h blk & multi .30 .25
**1707** A623 1k blk & multi .45 .25
**1708** A623 1.20k blk & multi .45 .25
**1709** A623 1.80k blk & multi 1.50 .25
*Nos. 1704-1709 (6)* 3.20 1.50

9th World Soccer Championships for the Jules Rimet Cup, Mexico City, 5/30-6/21.

Congress Emblem — A624

**1970, Nov. 9** **Engr. & Photo.**
**1710** A624 30h blk, gold, ultra & red .25 .25

Congress of the Czechoslovak Socialist Youth Federation.

### Painting Type of 1967

Paintings: 1k, Seated Mother, by Mikulas Galanda. 1.20k, Bridesmaid, by Karel Svolinsky. 1.40k, Walk by Night, 1944, by Frantisek Hudecek. 1.80k, Banska Bystrica Market, by Dominik Skutecky. 2.40k, Adoration of the Kings, from the Vysehrad Codex, 1085.

**1970, Nov. 27** **Engr.** *Perf. 11½*
**1711** A565 1k multi .35 .25
**1712** A565 1.20k multi .70 .30
**1713** A565 1.40k multi .35 .30
**1714** A565 1.80k multi .70 .30
**1715** A565 2.40k multi 3.00 2.00
*Nos. 1711-1715 (5)* 5.10 3.15

Nos. 1711-1715 were each issued in sheets of 4. Value, set $20.

Radar A625

Designs: 40h, Interkosmos 3, geophysical satellite. 60h, Kosmos meteorological satellite. 1k, Astronaut and Vostok satellite. No. 1720, Interkosmos 4, solar research satellite. No. 1720A, Space satellite (Sputnik) over city. 1.60k, Two-stage rocket on launching pad.

**1970-71** **Engr. & Photo.** *Perf. 11*
**1716** A625 20h black & multi .25 .25
**1717** A625 40h black & multi .25 .25
**1718** A625 60h black & multi .25 .25
**1719** A625 1k black & multi .25 .25
**1720** A625 1.20k black & multi .25 .25
**1720A** A625 1.20k black & multi ('71) .25 .25
**1721** A625 1.60k black & multi .90 .25
*Nos. 1716-1721 (7)* 2.40 1.75

"Interkosmos," the collaboration of communist countries in various phases of space research.

Issued: No. 1720A, 11/15/71; others, 11/30/70.

Face of Christ on Veronica's Veil — A626

Slovak Ikons, 16th-18th Centuries: 60h, Adam and Eve in the Garden, vert. 2k, St. George and the Dragon. 2.80k, St. Michael, vert.

**1970, Dec. 17** **Engr.** *Perf. 11½*
**Cream Paper**
**1722** A626 60h multi .70 .35
**1723** A626 1k multi 1.00 .35
**1724** A626 2k multi 1.00 .70
**1725** A626 2.80k multi 2.10 1.40
*Nos. 1722-1725 (4)* 4.80 2.80

Nos. 1722-1725 were each issued in sheets of 4. Value, set $22.50.

Carrier Pigeon Type of 1920 — A627

### Engraved and Photogravure

**1970, Dec. 18** *Perf. 11x11½*
**1726** A627 1k red, blk & yel grn .40 .30

Stamp Day.

Song of the Barricades, 1938, by Karel Stika — A628

Czech and Slovak Graphic Art: 50h, Fruit Grower's Barge, 1941, by Cyril Bouda. 60h, Moon (woman) Searching for Lilies of the Valley, 1913, by Jan Zrzavy. 1k, At the Edge of Town (working man and woman), 1931, by Koloman Sokol. 1.60k, Summer, 1641, by Vaclav Hollar. 2k, Gamekeeper and Shepherd of Orava Castle, 1847, by Peter M. Bohun.

**Engr. & Photo.; Engr. (40h, 60h, 1k)**
**1971, Jan. 28** *Perf. 11½*
**1727** A628 40h brown .25 .25
**1728** A628 50h black & multi .25 .25
**1729** A628 60h slate .25 .25
**1730** A628 1k black .30 .25
**1731** A628 1.60k black & buff .30 .25
**1732** A628 2k black & multi 1.25 .25
*Nos. 1727-1732 (6)* 2.60 1.50

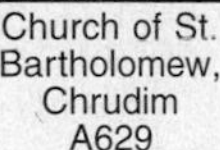

Church of St. Bartholomew, Chrudim A629

Bell Tower, Hronsek A630

Designs: 1k, Roofs and folk art, Horácko. 1.60k, Saris Church. 2.40k, House, Jicin. 3k, House and folk art, Melnik. 5k, Watch Tower, Nachod. 5.40k, Baroque house, Posumavi. 6k, Cottage, Orava. 9k, Cottage, Turnov. 10k, Old houses, Liptov. 14k, House and wayside bell stand. 20k, Houses, Cicmany.

### Engraved and Photogravure

**1971-72** *Perf. 11½x11, 11x11½*
**1733** A630 1k multi .25 .25
**1734** A629 1.60k multi 1.50 .25
**1735** A630 2k multi 2.10 .25
**1736** A629 2.40k multi 1.10 .25
**1736A** A630 3k multi ('72) 2.10 .25
**1737** A629 3.60k multi 1.40 .25
**1737A** A630 5k multi ('72) 2.10 .25
**1738** A629 5.40k multi .75 .25
**1739** A630 6k multi 3.50 .25
**1740** A630 9k multi 1.40 .25
**1740A** A629 10k multi ('72) 2.10 .25
**1741** A629 14k multi 2.25 .25
**1741A** A629 20k multi ('72) 2.10 .30
*Nos. 1733-1741A (13)* 22.65 3.30

Nos. 1736A, 1738, 1740 are horizontal. See No. 2870.

### Coat of Arms Type of 1968

**1971, Mar. 26** *Perf. 11½*
**1742** A590 60h Zilina .25 .25
**1743** A590 60h Levoca .25 .25
**1744** A590 60h Ceska Trebova .25 .25
**1745** A590 60h Uhersky Brod .25 .25
**1746** A590 60h Trutnov .25 .25
**1747** A590 60h Karlovy Vary .25 .25
*Nos. 1742-1747 (6)* 1.50 1.50

"Fight of the Communards and Rise of the International" — A631

Design: No. 1749, World fight against racial discrimination, and "UNESCO."

**1971, Mar. 18** *Perf. 11*
**1748** A631 1k multicolored .30 .25
**1749** A631 1k multicolored .30 .25

No. 1748 for cent. of the Paris Commune. No. 1749 for the Year against Racial Discrimination. Issued in sheets of 15 stamps and 5 labels. Value for single with attached tab, each $1.

A632

Edelweiss, mountaineering map & equipment.

**1971, Apr. 27** *Perf. 11½x11*
**1750** A632 30h multicolored .25 .25

50th anniversary of Slovak Alpine Club.

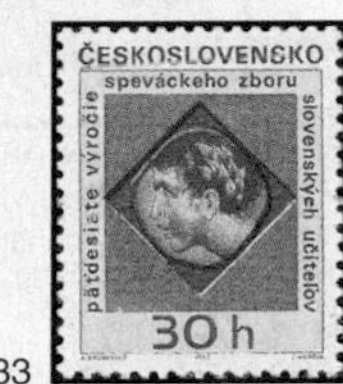

A633

**1971, Apr. 27** *Perf. 11½*
**1751** A633 30h Singer .25 .25

50th anniversary of Slovak Teachers' Choir.

Abbess' Crosier, 16th Century A634

No. 1753, Allegory of Music, 16th cent. mural.

**1971, May 9**
**1752** A634 3k gold & multi 1.90 1.40
**1753** A634 3k blk, dk brn & buff 1.90 1.40

Nos. 1752-1753 were each issued in sheets of 4. Value, set $15.

See Nos. 1817-1818, 1884-1885, 1937-1938, 2040-2041, 2081-2082, 2114-2115, 2176-2177, 2238-2239, 2329-2330, 2384-2385, 2420-2421.

Lenin A635

40h, Hammer & sickle allegory. 60h, Raised fists. 1k, Star, hammer & sickle.

**1971, May 14** *Perf. 11*
**1754** A635 30h blk, red & gold .25 .25
**1755** A635 40h blk, ultra, red & gold .25 .25
**1756** A635 60h blk, ultra, red & gold .25 .25
**1757** A635 1k blk, ultra, red & gold .30 .25
*Nos. 1754-1757 (4)* 1.05 1.00

Czechoslovak Communist Party, 50th anniv.

Star, Hammer-Sickle Emblems — A636

60h, Hammer-sickle emblem, fist & people, vert.

*Perf. 11½x11, 11x11½*

**1971, May 24** **Engr. & Photo.**

| No. | Type | Denomination / Color | Unused | Used |
|---|---|---|---|---|
| **1758** | A636 | 30h blk, red, gold & yel | .25 | .25 |
| **1759** | A636 | 60h blk, red, gold & bl | .25 | .25 |

14th Congress of Communist Party of Czechoslovakia.

Ring-necked Pheasant — A637

Designs: 60h, Rainbow trout. 80h, Mouflon. 1k, Chamois. 2k, Stag. 2.60k, Wild boar.

**1971, Aug. 17** *Perf. 11½x11*

| No. | Type | Denomination / Color | Unused | Used |
|---|---|---|---|---|
| **1760** | A637 | 20h orange & multi | .25 | .25 |
| **1761** | A637 | 60h lt blue & multi | .25 | .25 |
| **1762** | A637 | 80h yellow & multi | .25 | .25 |
| **1763** | A637 | 1k lt green & multi | .30 | .25 |
| **1764** | A637 | 2k lilac & multi | .40 | .25 |
| **1765** | A637 | 2.60k bister & multi | 2.25 | .65 |
| | | *Nos. 1760-1765 (6)* | 3.70 | 1.90 |

World Hunting Exhib., Budapest, Aug. 27-30.

Diesel Locomotive — A638

**1971, Sept. 2** *Perf. 11x11½*

| No. | Type | Denomination / Color | Unused | Used |
|---|---|---|---|---|
| **1766** | A638 | 30h lt bl, blk & red | .40 | .25 |

Cent. of CKD, Prague Machine Foundry.

Gymnasts and Banners — A639

**1971, Sept. 2** *Perf. 11½x11*

| No. | Type | Denomination / Color | Unused | Used |
|---|---|---|---|---|
| **1767** | A639 | 30h red brn, gold & ultra | .25 | .25 |

50th anniversary of Workers' Physical Exercise Federation.

Road Intersections and Bridge — A640

**1971, Sept. 2** **Engr. & Photo.**

| No. | Type | Denomination / Color | Unused | Used |
|---|---|---|---|---|
| **1768** | A640 | 1k blk, gold, red & bl | .30 | .25 |

14th World Highways and Bridges Congress. Sheets of 25 stamps and 25 labels printed se-tenant with continuous design. Value, single with attached tab, unused 60c; used 30c.

Chinese Fairytale, by Eva Bednarova A641

Designs: 1k, Tiger and other animals, by Mirko Hanak. 1.60k, The Miraculous Bamboo Shoot, by Yasuo Segawa, horiz.

*Perf. 11½x11, 11x11½*

**1971, Sept. 10**

| No. | Type | Denomination / Color | Unused | Used |
|---|---|---|---|---|
| **1769** | A641 | 60h multi | .25 | .25 |
| **1770** | A641 | 1k multi | .30 | .25 |
| **1771** | A641 | 1.60k multi | .45 | .25 |
| | | *Nos. 1769-1771 (3)* | 1.00 | .75 |

Bratislava BIB 71 biennial exhibition of illustrations for children's books.

Apothecary Jars and Coltsfoot — A642

Intl. Pharmaceutical Cong.: 60h, Jars and dog rose. 1k, Scales and adonis vernalis. 1.20k, Mortars and valerian. 1.80k, Retorts and chicory. 2.40k, Mill, mortar and henbane.

**1971, Sept. 20** *Perf. 11½x11*

**Yellow Paper**

| No. | Type | Denomination / Color | Unused | Used |
|---|---|---|---|---|
| **1772** | A642 | 30h multi | .25 | .25 |
| **1773** | A642 | 60h multi | .25 | .25 |
| **1774** | A642 | 1k multi | .25 | .25 |
| **1775** | A642 | 1.20k multi | .25 | .25 |
| **1776** | A642 | 1.80k multi | .25 | .25 |
| **1777** | A642 | 2.40k multi | 1.25 | .25 |
| | | *Nos. 1772-1777 (6)* | 2.50 | 1.50 |

**Painting Type of 1967**

Paintings: 1k, "Waiting" (woman's head), 1967, by Imro Weiner-Král. 1.20k, Resurrection, by Master of Vyssi Brod, 14th century. 1.40k, Woman with Pitcher, by Milos Bazovsky. 1.80k, Veruna Cudova (in folk costume), by Josef Mánes. 2.40k, Detail from "Feast of the Rose Garlands," by Albrecht Dürer.

**1971, Nov. 27** *Perf. 11½*

| No. | Type | Denomination / Color | Unused | Used |
|---|---|---|---|---|
| **1779** | A565 | 1k multi | .30 | .30 |
| **1780** | A565 | 1.20k multi | .75 | .45 |
| **1781** | A565 | 1.40k multi | .60 | .30 |
| **1782** | A565 | 1.80k multi | 1.10 | .50 |
| **1783** | A565 | 2.40k multi | 1.75 | .75 |
| | | *Nos. 1779-1783 (5)* | 4.50 | 2.30 |

Nos. 1779-1783 were each issued in sheets of 4. Value, set $25.

Workers Revolt in Krompachy, by Julius Nemcik — A643

**1971, Nov. 28** *Perf. 11x11½*

| No. | Type | Denomination / Color | Unused | Used |
|---|---|---|---|---|
| **1784** | A643 | 60h multi | .30 | .25 |

History of the Czechoslovak Communist Party.

Wooden Dolls and Birds — A644

Folk Art and UNICEF Emblem: 80h, Jug handles, carved. 1k, Horseback rider. 1.60k, Shepherd carrying lamb. 2k, Easter eggs and rattle. 3k, "Zbojnik," folk hero.

**1971, Dec. 11** *Perf. 11½*

| No. | Type | Denomination / Color | Unused | Used |
|---|---|---|---|---|
| **1785** | A644 | 60h multi | .40 | .25 |
| **1786** | A644 | 80h multi | .80 | .25 |
| **1787** | A644 | 1k multi | .40 | .25 |
| **1788** | A644 | 1.60k multi | .40 | .25 |
| **1789** | A644 | 2k multi | .40 | .30 |
| **1790** | A644 | 3k multi | 2.00 | .60 |
| | | *Nos. 1785-1790 (6)* | 4.40 | 1.90 |

25th anniv. of UNICEF.

Nos. 1785-1790 were each issued in sheets of 10. Value, set $45.

Runners, Parthenon, Czechoslovak Olympic Emblem — A645

Designs: 40h, Women's high jump, Olympic emblem and plan for Prague Stadium. 1.60k, Cross-country skiers, Sapporo '72 emblem and ski jump in High Tatras. 2.60k, Discus thrower, Discobolus and St. Vitus Cathedral.

**1971, Dec. 16** **Engr. & Photo.**

| No. | Type | Denomination / Color | Unused | Used |
|---|---|---|---|---|
| **1791** | A645 | 30h multi | .25 | .25 |
| **1792** | A645 | 40h multi | .25 | .25 |
| **1793** | A645 | 1.60k multi | .25 | .25 |
| **1794** | A645 | 2.60k multi | 1.50 | .75 |
| | | *Nos. 1791-1794 (4)* | 2.25 | 1.50 |

75th anniversary of Czechoslovak Olympic Committee (30h, 2.60k); 20th Summer Olympic Games, Munich, Aug. 26-Sept. 10, 1972 (40h); 11th Winter Olympic Games, Sapporo, Japan, Feb. 3-13, 1972 (1.60k).

Post Horns and Lion — A646

**1971, Dec. 17** *Perf. 11x11½*

| No. | Type | Denomination / Color | Unused | Used |
|---|---|---|---|---|
| **1795** | A646 | 1k blk, gold, car & bl | .30 | .25 |

Stamp Day.

Figure Skating — A647

Olympic Emblems and: 50h, Ski jump. 1k, Ice hockey. 1.60k, Sledding, women's.

**1972, Jan. 13** *Perf. 11½*

| No. | Type | Denomination / Color | Unused | Used |
|---|---|---|---|---|
| **1796** | A647 | 40h pur, org & red | .25 | .25 |
| **1797** | A647 | 50h dk bl, org & red | .25 | .25 |
| **1798** | A647 | 1k mag, org & red | .30 | .25 |
| **1799** | A647 | 1.60k bl grn, org & red | 1.25 | .25 |
| | | *Nos. 1796-1799 (4)* | 2.05 | 1.00 |

11th Winter Olympic Games, Sapporo, Japan, Feb. 3-13.

"Lezáky" — A648

No. 1801, Boy's head behind barbed wire, horiz. No. 1802, Hand rising from ruins. No. 1803, Soldier and banner, horiz.

**1972, Feb. 16**

| No. | Type | Denomination / Color | Unused | Used |
|---|---|---|---|---|
| **1800** | A648 | 30h blk, dl org & red | .25 | .25 |
| **1801** | A648 | 30h blk & brn org | .25 | .25 |
| **1802** | A648 | 60h blk, yel & red | .25 | .25 |
| **1803** | A648 | 60h sl grn & multi | .25 | .25 |
| | | *Nos. 1800-1803 (4)* | 1.00 | 1.00 |

30th anniv. of: destruction of Lezáky (No. 1800) and Lidice (No. 1802); Terezin concentration camp (No. 1801); Czechoslovak Army unit in Russia (No. 1803).

Book Year Emblem — A649

**1972, Mar. 17** *Perf. 11½x11*

| No. | Type | Denomination / Color | Unused | Used |
|---|---|---|---|---|
| **1804** | A649 | 1k blk & org brn | .30 | .25 |

International Book Year 1972.

Steam and Diesel Locomotives A650

**1972, Mar. 17** *Perf. 11½x11*

| No. | Type | Denomination / Color | Unused | Used |
|---|---|---|---|---|
| **1805** | A650 | 30h multi | .75 | .25 |

Centenary of the Kosice-Bohumin railroad.

"Pasture," by Vojtech Sedlacek A651

Designs: 50h, Dressage, by Frantisek Tichy. 60h, Otakar Kubin, by Vaclav Fiala. 1k, The Three Kings, by Ernest Zmetak. 1.60k, Woman Dressing, by Ludovit Fulla.

**1972, Mar. 27** *Perf. 11½x11*

| No. | Type | Denomination / Color | Unused | Used |
|---|---|---|---|---|
| **1806** | A651 | 40h multi | .25 | .25 |
| **1807** | A651 | 50h multi | .25 | .25 |
| **1808** | A651 | 60h multi | .25 | .25 |
| **1809** | A651 | 1k multi | .25 | .25 |
| **1810** | A651 | 1.60k multi | 1.25 | .90 |
| | | *Nos. 1806-1810 (5)* | 2.25 | 1.90 |

Czech and Slovak graphic art.

1.60k issued in sheets of 4. Value $9.

See Nos. 1859-1862, 1921-1924.

Ice Hockey A652

Design: 1k, Two players.

**1972, Apr. 7** *Perf. 11*

| No. | Type | Denomination / Color | Unused | Used |
|---|---|---|---|---|
| **1811** | A652 | 60h blk & multi | .25 | .25 |
| **1812** | A652 | 1k blk & multi | .40 | .25 |

World and European Ice Hockey Championships, Prague.

For overprint see Nos. 1845-1846.

Bicycling, Olympic Rings and Emblem A653

**1972, Apr. 7**

**1813** A653 50h shown .25 .25
**1814** A653 1.60k Diving .35 .25
**1815** A653 1.80k Canoeing .55 .25
**1816** A653 2k Gymnast 1.10 .25
*Nos. 1813-1816 (4)* 2.25 1.00

20th Olympic Games, Munich, 8/26-9/11.

**Prague Castle Art Type of 1971**

Designs: No. 1817, Adam and Eve, column capital, St. Vitus Cathedral. No. 1818, Czech coat of arms (lion), c. 1500.

**1972, May 9** ***Perf. 11½***

**1817** A634 3k blk & multi 2.10 1.40
**1818** A634 3k blk, red, sil & gold 1.40 .85

Nos. 1817-1818 were each issued in sheets of 4. Value, set $15.

Andrej Sladkovic (1820-1872), Poet — A654

No. 1820, Janko Kral (1822-1876), poet. No. 1821, Ludmilla Podjavorinska (1872-1951), writer. No. 1822, Antonin Hudecek (1872-1941), painter. No. 1823, Frantisek Bilek (1872-1941), sculptor. No. 1824, Jan Preisler (1872-1918), painter.

**1972, June 14** ***Perf. 11***

**1819** A654 40h pur, ol & bl .25 .25
**1820** A654 40h dk grn, bl & yel .25 .25
**1821** A654 40h blk & multi .25 .25
**1822** A654 40h brn, grn & bl .25 .25
**1823** A654 40h choc, grn & org .25 .25
**1824** A654 40h grn, sl & dp org .25 .25
*Nos. 1819-1824 (6)* 1.50 1.50

Men with Banners — A655

**1972, June 14** ***Perf. 11x11½***

**1825** A655 30h dk vio bl, red & yel .25 .25

8th Trade Union Congress, Prague.

Art Forms of Wire A656

Ornamental Wirework: 60h, Plane and rosette. 80h, Four-headed dragon and ornament. 1k, Locomotive and loops. 2.60k, Tray and owl.

**1972, Aug. 28** ***Perf. 11½x11***

**1826** A656 20h sal & multi .25 .25
**1827** A656 60h multi .25 .25
**1828** A656 80h pink & multi .25 .25
**1829** A656 1k multi .25 .25
**1830** A656 2.60k rose & multi 1.40 .25
*Nos. 1826-1830 (5)* 2.40 1.25

"Jiskra" A657

**Engr. & Photo.**

**1972, Sept. 27** ***Perf. 11½x11***

**Size: 40x22mm**

**Multicolored Design on Blue Paper**

**1831** A657 50h shown .25 .25
**1832** A657 60h "Mir" .25 .25
**1833** A657 80h "Republika" .25 .25

**Size: 48x29mm**

***Perf. 11x11½***

**1834** A657 1k "Kosice" .30 .25
**1835** A657 1.60k "Dukla" .45 .25
**1836** A657 2k "Kladno" 1.40 .55
*Nos. 1831-1836 (6)* 2.90 1.80

Czechoslovak sea-going vessels.

Hussar, 18th Century Tile — A658

60h, Janissary. 80h, St. Martin. 1.60k, St. George. 1.80k, Nobleman's guard. 2.20k, Slovakian horseman.

**1972, Oct. 24** ***Perf. 11½x11***

**1837** A658 30h shown .25 .25
**1838** A658 60h multicolored .25 .25
**1839** A658 80h multicolored .25 .25
**1840** A658 1.60k multicolored .45 .25
**1841** A658 1.80k multicolored .70 .25
**1842** A658 2.20k multicolored 1.25 .25
*Nos. 1837-1842 (6)* 3.15 1.50

Horsemen from 18th-19th century tiles or enamel paintings on glass.

Worker, Flag Hoisted on Bayonet A659

Star, Hammer and Sickle A660

**1972, Nov. 7** ***Perf. 11x11½***

**1843** A659 30h gold & multi .25 .25
**1844** A660 60h rose car & gold .25 .25

55th anniv. of the Russian October Revolution (30h); 50th anniv. of the Soviet Union (60h).

Nos. 1811-1812 Overprinted in Violet Blue or Black

**1972** ***Perf. 11***

**1845** A652 60h multi (VBl) 7.00 6.50
**1846** A652 1k multi (Bk) 7.00 6.50

Czechoslovakia's victorious ice hockey team. The overprint on the 60h (shown) is in Czech and reads CSSR/MISTREM/SVETA; the overprint on the 1k is in Slovak.

**Painting Type of 1967**

Designs: 1k, "Nosegay" (nudes and flowers), by Max Svabinsky. 1.20k, Struggle of St. Ladislas with Kuman nomad, anonymous, 14th century. 1.40k, Lady with Fur Hat, by Vaclav Hollar. 1.80k, Midsummer Night's Dream, 1962, by Josef Liesler. 2.40k, Pablo Picasso, self-portrait.

**1972, Nov. 27** **Engr. & Photo.**

**1847** A565 1k multi .85 .40
**1848** A565 1.20k multi .85 .40
**1849** A565 1.40k blk & cream 1.10 .40
**1850** A565 1.80k multi .85 .50
**1851** A565 2.40k multi 2.10 1.40
*Nos. 1847-1851 (5)* 5.75 3.10

Nos. 1847-1851 were each issued in sheets of 4. Value, set $24.

Goldfinch A661

Songbirds: 60h, Warbler feeding young cuckoo. 80h, Cuckoo. 1k, Black-billed magpie. 1.60k, Bullfinch. 3k, Song thrush.

**1972, Dec. 15** **Size: 30x48½mm**

**1852** A661 60h yel & multi .25 .25
**1853** A661 80h multi .25 .25
**1854** A661 1k lt bl & multi .25 .25

**Engr.**

**Size: 30x23mm**

**1855** A661 1.60k multi 1.50 .70
**1856** A661 2k multi 1.50 .70
**1857** A661 3k multi 1.50 .70
*Nos. 1852-1857 (6)* 5.25 2.85

Nos. 1855-1857 were each issued in a sheet of 10. Value, set $45.

Post Horn and Allegory — A662

**1972, Dec. 18** **Engr. & Photo.**

**1858** A662 1k blk, red lil & gold .30 .30

Stamp Day.

**Art Type of 1972**

Designs: 30h, Flowers in Window, by Jaroslav Grus. 60h, Quest for Happiness, by Josef Balaz. 1.60k, Balloon, by Kamil Lhotak. 1.80k, Woman with Viola, by Richard Wiesner.

**1973, Jan. 25** ***Perf. 11½x11***

**1859** A651 30h multi .25 .25
**1860** A651 60h multi .25 .25
**1861** A651 1.60k multi .30 .25
**1862** A651 1.80k multi .25 .35
*Nos. 1859-1862 (4)* 1.05 1.10

Czech and Slovak graphic art.

Tennis Player — A663

Figure Skater — A664

Torch and Star — A665

**1973, Feb. 22** ***Perf. 11***

**1863** A663 30h vio & multi .25 .25
**1864** A664 60h blk & multi .25 .25
**1865** A665 1k multi .30 .25
*Nos. 1863-1865 (3)* .80 .75

80th anniversary of the tennis organization in Czechoslovakia (30h); World figure skating championships, Bratislava (60h); 3rd summer army Spartakiad of socialist countries (1k).

Star and Factories A666

Workers' Militia, Emblem and Flag — A667

**1973, Feb. 23**

**1866** A666 30h multi .25 .25
**1867** A667 60h multi .25 .25

25th anniversary of the Communist revolution in Czechoslovakia and of the Militia.

Capt. Jan Nalepka, Major Antonin Sochor and Laurel A668

Torch &: 40h, Evzen Rosicky, Mirko Nespor & ivy leaves. 60h, Vlado Clementis, Karol Smidke & linden leaves. 80h, Jan Osoha, Josef Molak & oak leaves. 1k, Marie Kuderikova, Jozka Jaburkova & rose. 1.60k, Vaclav Sinkule, Eduard Urx & palm leaf.

**1973, Mar. 20** ***Perf. 11½x11***

**Yellow Paper**

**1868** A668 30h blk, ver & gold .30 .25
**1869** A668 40h blk, ver & grn .30 .25
**1870** A668 60h blk, ver & gold .30 .25
**1871** A668 80h blk, ver & gold .30 .25
**1872** A668 1k blk, ver & grn .30 .25
**1873** A668 1.60k blk, ver & sil .75 .25
*Nos. 1868-1873 (6)* 2.25 1.50

Fighters against and victims of Fascism and Nazism during German Occupation.

Virgil I. Grissom, Edward H. White, Roger B. Chaffee — A669

Designs: 20h, Soviet planetary station "Venera." 30h, "Intercosmos" station. 40h, Lunokhod on moon. 3.60k, Vladimir M. Komarov, Georgi T. Dobrovolsky, Vladislav N. Volkov, Victor I. Patsayev. 5k, Yuri A. Gagarin.

Two types of 3.60k: type I, Cosmonaut on background of cross-hatched lines; type 2, Cosmonaut on background of parallel diagonal lines.

**1973, Apr. 12** ***Perf. 11½x11***

**Size: 40x22mm**

**1874** A669 20h multi .25 .25
**1875** A669 30h multi .25 .25
**1876** A669 40h multi .25 .25

**Engr.**

***Perf. 11½***

**Size: 49x30mm**

**1877** A669 3k multi 1.00 .50
**1878** A669 3.60k multi, type 1 1.00 .75
*a.* Type 2 20.00 7.50
**1879** A669 5k multi 2.50 2.00
*Nos. 1874-1879 (6)* 5.25 4.00

In memory of American and Russian astronauts.

Nos. 1877-1879 were each issued in sheets of 4. Values: set (with No. 1878) $30; mset (with No. 1878a) $90.

Radio — A670

Telephone and Map of Czechoslovakia A671

Television A672

**1973, May 1** *Perf. 11½x11*

**1880** A670 30h blk & multi .25 .25
**1881** A671 30h lt bl, pink & blk .25 .25
**1882** A672 30h dp bl & multi .25 .25
*Nos. 1880-1882 (3)* .75 .75

Czechoslovak anniversaries: 50 years of broadcasting (No. 1880); 20 years of telephone service to all communities (No. 1881); 20 years of television (No. 1882).

Coat of Arms and Linden Branch — A673

**1973, May 9** *Perf. 11x11½*

**1883** A673 60h red & multi .25 .25

25th anniv. of the Constitution of May 9.

### Prague Castle Art Type of 1971

No. 1884, Royal Legate, 14th century. No. 1885, Seal of King Charles IV, 1351.

**1973, May 9** *Perf. 11½*

**1884** A634 3k blue & multi 1.25 .75
**1885** A634 3k gold, grn & dk brn 1.75 1.50

Nos. 1884-1885 were each issued in sheets of 4. Value, set $13.

### Coat of Arms Type of 1968

**1973, June 20**

**1886** A590 60h Mikulov .25 .25
**1887** A590 60h Zlutice .30 .25
**1888** A590 60h Smolenice .35 .25
*Nos. 1886-1888 (3)* .90 .75

Coats of arms of Czechoslovakian cities.

Heraldic Colors of Olomouc and Moravia — A674

**1973, Aug. 23** **Engr. & Photo.**

**1889** A674 30h multi .25 .25

University of Olomouc, 400th anniv.

Flower Show — A675

60h, Tulips (30x50mm). 1k, Rose (30x50mm). 1.60k, Anthurium (23x39mm). 1.80k, Iris (23x39mm). 2k, Chrysanthemum (30x50mm). 3.60k, Cymbidium ( 23x39mm).

**1973, Aug. 23** *Perf. 11½*

**1890** A675 60h multi .75 .35
**1891** A675 1k multi .75 .35
**1892** A675 1.60k shown .40 .35
**1893** A675 1.80k multi .40 .35
**1894** A675 2k multi 1.90 1.00
**1895** A675 3.60k multi .75 .35
*Nos. 1890-1895 (6)* 4.95 2.75

Olomouc, Aug. 18-Sept. 2. 60h, 1k, 2k issued in sheets of 4, others in sheets of 10. Value, set $50.

Hunting Dogs A676

**1973, Sept. 5**

**1896** A676 20h Irish setter .45 .25
**1897** A676 30h Czech terrier .45 .25
**1898** A676 40h Bavarian hunting dog .55 .25
**1899** A676 60h German pointer .55 .25
**1900** A676 1k Cocker spaniel .85 .25
**1901** A676 1.60k Dachshund 2.10 .50
*Nos. 1896-1901 (6)* 4.95 1.75

Czechoslovak United Hunting Org., 50th anniv.

St. John, the Baptist, by Svabinsky A677

Works by Max Svabinsky: 60h, "August Noon" (woman). 80h, "Marriage of True Minds" (artist and muse). 1k, "Paradise Sonata I" (Adam dreaming of Eve). 2.60k, Last Judgment, stained glass window, St. Vitus Cathedral.

**1973, Sept. 17** **Litho. & Engr.**

**1902** A677 20h blk & pale grn .25 .25
**1903** A677 60h black & buff .25 .25

**Engr.**

**1904** A677 80h black .75 .25
**1905** A677 1k slate green .75 .25
**1906** A677 2.60k multi 1.90 1.25
*Nos. 1902-1906 (5)* 3.90 2.25

Centenary of the birth of Max Svabinsky (1873-1962), artist and stamp designer. 20h and 60h issued in sheets of 25; 80h and 1k se-tenant in sheets of 4 checkerwise (value $4); 2.60k in sheets of 4 (value $10).

Trade Union Emblem A678

**1973, Oct. 15** **Engr. & Photo.**

**1907** A678 1k red, bl & yel .25 .25

8t (valueh Congress of the World Federation of Trade Unions, Varna, Bulgaria.

### Painting Type of 1967

1k, Boy from Martinique, by Antonin Pelc. 1.20k, "Fortitude" (mountaineer), by Martin Benka. 1.80k, Rembrandt, self-portrait. 2k, Pierrot, by Bohumil Kubista. 2.40k, Ilona Kubinyiova, by Peter M. Bohun. 3.60k, Virgin and Child (Veveri Madonna), c. 1350.

**1973, Nov. 27** *Perf. 11½*

**1908** A565 1k multi, vio bl inscriptions 2.50 1.25
*a.* 1k multi, black inscriptions 9.00 9.00
**1909** A565 1.20k multi *2.50 1.25*
**1910** A565 1.80k multi .80 .80
**1911** A565 2k multi .80 .80
**1912** A565 2.40k multi .80 .80
**1913** A565 3.60k multi .80 .80
*Nos. 1908-1913 (6)* 8.20 5.70

Nos. 1908-1909 were each issued in sheets of 4. Nos. 1910-1913 were printed se-tenant with gold and black inscription on gutter. Value, sheet $35. No. 1908a in sheet of 4, value $45.

The central backgroundis light bluish green on No. 1908; grayish blue on No. 1908a.

Postilion — A679

**1973, Dec. 18**

**1914** A679 1k gold & multi .30 .25

Stamp Day 1974 and 55th anniversary of Czechoslovak postage stamps. Printed with 2 labels showing telephone and telegraph. Value of single with two labels, $1.75.

"CSSR" — A680

**1974, Jan. 1**

**1915** A680 30h red, gold & ultra .25 .25

5th anniversary of Federal Government in the Czechoslovak Socialist Republic.

Bedrich Smetana — A681

Pablo Neruda, Chilean Flag — A682

**1974, Jan. 4** *Perf. 11x11½*

**1916** A681 60h shown .25 .25
**1917** A681 60h Josef Suk .25 .25
**1918** A682 60h shown .25 .25
*Nos. 1916-1918 (3)* .75 .75

Smetana (1824-84), composer; Suk (1874-1935), composer, and Pablo Neruda (Neftali Ricardo Reyes, 1904-73), Chilean poet.

Comecon Building, Moscow — A683

**1974, Jan. 23**

**1919** A683 1k gold, red & vio bl .25 .25

25th anniversary of the Council of Mutual Economic Assistance (COMECON).

Symbols of Postal Service — A684

**1974, Feb. 20** *Perf. 11½*

**1920** A684 3.60k multi .85 .45

BRNO '74 National Stamp Exhibition, Brno, June 8-23.

No. 1920 was issue both in normal sheets of 25 stamps and in sheets containing 16 stamps se-tenant with 9 labels depicting Brno. Values: single stamp with attached tab unused $2.50; used $2.50; full sheet of 16 stamps and 9 labels $35.

### Art Type of 1972

Designs: 60h, Tulips 1973, by Josef Broz. 1k, Structures 1961 (poppy and building), by Orest Dubay. 1.60k, Bird and flowers (Golden Sun-Glowing Day), by Adolf Zabransky. 1.80k, Artificial flowers, by Frantisek Gross.

**1974, Feb. 21** *Perf. 11½x11*

**1921** A651 60h multi .25 .25
**1922** A651 1k multi .30 .25
**1923** A651 1.60k multi .40 .25
**1924** A651 1.80k multi 1.10 .30
*Nos. 1921-1924 (4)* 2.05 1.05

Czech and Slovak graphic art.

Oskar Benes and Vaclav Prochazka — A685

40h, Milos Uher, Anton Sedlacek. 60h, Jan Hajecek, Marie Sedlackova. 80h, Jan Sverma, Albin Grznar. 1k, Jaroslav Neliba, Alois Hovorka. 1.60k, Ladislav Exnar, Ludovit Kukorelli.

**1974, Mar. 21** *Perf. 11½x11*

**1925** A685 30h indigo & multi .25 .25
**1926** A685 40h indigo & multi .25 .25
**1927** A685 60h indigo & multi .25 .25
**1928** A685 80h indigo & multi .25 .25
**1929** A685 1k indigo & multi .30 .25
**1930** A685 1.60k indigo & multi .85 .25
*Nos. 1925-1930 (6)* 2.15 1.50

Partisan commanders and fighters.

"Water, the Source of Energy" A686

Symbolic Designs: 1k, Importance of water for agriculture. 1.20k, Study of the oceans. 1.60k, "Hydrological Decade." 2k, Struggle for unpolluted water.

**1974, Apr. 25** **Engr.** *Perf. 11½*

**1931** A686 60h multi .55 .25
**1932** A686 1k multi .55 .25
**1933** A686 1.20k multi 1.10 .45
**1934** A686 1.60k multi 1.10 .45
**1935** A686 2k multi 2.10 1.40
*Nos. 1931-1935 (5)* 5.40 2.80

Hydrological Decade (UNESCO), 1965-1974.

Nos. 1931-1935 were each issued in sheets of 4. Value $25.

Allegory Holding "Molniya," and Ground Station — A687

**1974, Apr. 30 Engr. & Photo.**

**1936** A687 30h vio bl & multi .25 .25

"Intersputnik," first satellite communications ground station in Czechoslovakia.

### Prague Castle Art Type of 1971

No. 1937, Golden Cock, 17th century locket. No. 1938, Glass monstrance, 1840.

**1974, May 9 Engr. *Perf. 11½***

**1937** A634 3k gold & multi 1.50 1.10
**1938** A634 3k blk & multi 2.25 1.50

Nos. 1937-1938 werre each issued in sheets of 4. Value, set $15.

Sousaphone A688

30h, Bagpipe. 40h, Violin, by Martin Benka. 1k, Pyramid piano. 1.60k, Tenor quinton, 1754.

### Engraved and Photogravure

**1974, May 12 *Perf. 11x11½***

**1939** A688 20h shown .25 .25
**1940** A688 30h multi .25 .25
**1941** A688 40h multi .25 .25
**1942** A688 1k multi .25 .25
**1943** A688 1.60k multi .80 .25
*Nos. 1939-1943 (5)* 1.80 1.25

Prague and Bratislava Music Festivals. The 1.60k also commemorates 25th anniversary of Slovak Philharmonic Orchestra.

Child — A689

**1974, June 1 *Perf. 11½***

**1944** A689 60h multi .25 .25

Children's Day. Design is from illustration for children's book by Adolf Zabransky.

Globe, People and Exhibition Emblems — A690

Design: 6k, Rays and emblems symbolizing "Oneness and Mutuality."

**1974, June 1**

**1945** A690 30h multi .25 .25
**1946** A690 6k multi 1.50 .75

BRNO 74 Natl. Stamp Exhib., Brno, June 8-23.

Nos. 2171-2172 were each issued both in sheet of 50 stamps and in sheets of 16 stamps and 14 labels. Values: stamps with attached labels, $1.75; 2 sheets of 16 stamps and 14 labels $35.

Resistance Fighter — A691

**1974, Aug. 29 *Perf. 11½***

**1947** A691 30h multi .25 .25

Slovak National Uprising, 30th anniversary.

Actress Holding Tragedy and Comedy Masks — A692

**1974, Aug. 29**

**1948** A692 30h red, sil & blk .25 .25

Bratislava Academy of Music and Drama, 25th anniversary.

Slovak Girl with Flower — A693

**1974, Aug. 29**

**1949** A693 30h multi .25 .25

SLUK, Slovak folksong and dance ensemble, 25th anniversary.

Hero and Leander A694

Design: 2.40k, Hero watching Leander swim the Hellespont. No. 1952, Leander reaching shore. No. 1953, Hero mourning over Leander's body. No. 1954, Hermione, Leander's sister. No. 1955, Mourning Cupid. Designs are from 17th century English tapestries in Bratislava Council Palace.

**1974-76**

**1950** A694 2k multi 1.25 1.10
**1951** A694 2.40k multi 1.50 1.25
**1952** A694 3k multi 1.00 .45
**1953** A694 3k multi 1.75 1.75
**1954** A694 3.60k multi 2.50 1.10
**1955** A694 3.60k multi .85 .60
*Nos. 1950-1955 (6)* 8.85 6.25

Issued: Nos. 1950-1951, 9/25/74; Nos. 1952, 1954, 8/29/75; Nos. 1953, 1955, 5/9/76.

Nos. 1950-1951 were each issued in sheets of 4, with 2 blank labels; Nos. 1952-1955 were issued in sheets of 4. Value, set $50.

Soldier Standing Guard, Target, 1840 — A695

Painted Folk-art Targets: 60h, Landscape with Pierrot and flags, 1828. 1k, Diana crowning champion marksman, 1832. 1.60k, Still life with guitar, 1839. 2.40k, Salvo and stag in flight, 1834. 3k, Turk and giraffe, 1831.

**1974, Sept. 26 *Perf. 11½***

**Size: 30x50mm**

**1956** A695 30h black & multi .25 .25
**1957** A695 60h black & multi .25 .25
**1958** A695 1k black & multi .30 .25

**Engr.**

***Perf. 12***

**Size: 40x50mm**

**1959** A695 1.60k green & multi .50 .45
**1960** A695 2.40k sepia & multi .90 .75
**1961** A695 3k multi *3.00 3.00*
*Nos. 1956-1961 (6)* *5.20 4.95*

Nos. 1959-1961 were each issued in sheets of 4. Value, set $17.50.

UPU Emblem and Postilion — A696

UPU Cent. (UPU Emblem and): 40h, Mail coach. 60h, Railroad mail coach, 1851. 80h, Early mail truck. 1k, Czechoslovak Airlines mail plane. 1.60k, Radar.

### Engraved and Photogravure

**1974, Oct. 9 *Perf. 11½***

**1962** A696 30h multi .25 .25
**1963** A696 40h multi .25 .25
**1964** A696 60h multi .25 .25
**1965** A696 80h multi .25 .25
**1966** A696 1k multi .40 .25
**1967** A696 1.60k multi 1.25 .25
*Nos. 1962-1967 (6)* 2.65 1.50

Sealed Letter — A697

Post Rider — A698

20h, Post Horn, Old Town Bridge Tower. No. 1971, Carrier pigeon.

**1974, Oct. 31 *Perf. 11½x11***

**1968** A698 20h multi .25 .25
**1969** A697 30h brn, bl & red .25 .25
**1970** A698 40h multi .25 .25
**1971** A697 60h bl, yel & red .25 .25
*Nos. 1968-1971 (4)* 1.00 1.00

Nos. 1968-1971 were reissued in 1979, printed on fluorescent paper. Value, set $15.

See No. 2675.

Stylized Bird — A699

No. 1977, Same design as No. 1976. No. 1979, Map of Czechoslovakia with postal code numbers.

### Coil Stamps

**1975 Photo. *Perf. 14***

**1976** A699 30h brt bl .25 .25
**1977** A699 60h carmine .25 .25

Postal Code Symbol — A699a

**1976 *Perf. 11½***

**1978** A699a 30h emer .25 .25
**1979** A699a 60h scar .25 .25

Nos. 1976-1979 have black control number on back of every fifth stamp.

Ludvik Kuba, Self-portrait, 1941 — A700

Paintings: 1.20k, Violinist Frantisek Ondricek, by Vaclav Brozik. 1.60k, Vase with Flowers, by Otakar Kubin. 1.80k, Woman with Pitcher, by Janko Alexy. 2.40k, Bacchanalia, c. 1635, by Karel Skreta.

**1974, Nov. 27 Engr. *Perf. 11½***

**1980** A700 1k multi .50 .30
**1981** A700 1.20k multi .80 .40
**1982** A700 1.60k multi .80 .60
**1983** A700 1.80k multi 1.00 .40
**1984** A700 2.40k multi 2.50 1.75
*Nos. 1980-1984 (5)* 5.60 3.45

Czech and Slovak art.

Nos. 1980-1984 were each issued in sheets of 4. Value, set $25.

See Nos. 2209-2211, 2678-2682, 2721-2723, 2743, 2766-2768.

Post Horn — A701

### Engraved and Photogravure

**1974, Dec. 18 *Perf. 11x11½***

**1985** A701 1k multicolored .30 .25

Stamp Day.

Still-life with Hare, by Hollar — A702

Designs: 1k, The Lion and the Mouse, by Vaclav Hollar. 1.60k, Deer Hunt, by Philip Galle. 1.80k, Grand Hunt, by Jacques Callot.

**1975, Feb. 26 *Perf. 11½x11***

**1988** A702 60h blk & buff .25 .25
**1989** A702 1k blk & buff .25 .25
**1990** A702 1.60k blk & yel .25 .25
**1991** A702 1.80k blk & buff 1.25 .65
*Nos. 1988-1991 (4)* 2.00 1.40

Hunting scenes from old engravings.

Guns Pointing at Family A703

Designs: 1k, Women and building on fire. 1.20k, People and roses. All designs include names of destroyed villages.

**1975, Feb. 26** *Perf. 11*

| | | | | |
|---|---|---|---|---|
| **1992** | A703 | 60h multi | .25 | .25 |
| **1993** | A703 | 1k multi | .25 | .25 |
| **1994** | A703 | 1.20k multi | .30 | .25 |
| | | *Nos. 1992-1994 (3)* | .80 | .75 |

Destruction of 14 villages by the Nazis, 30th anniversary.

Young Woman and Globe — A704

**1975, Mar. 7** *Perf. 11½x11*

| | | | | |
|---|---|---|---|---|
| **1995** | A704 | 30h red & multi | .25 | .25 |

International Women's Year 1975.

Little Queens, Moravian Folk Custom A705

Folk Customs: 1k, Straw masks (animal heads and blackened faces), Slovak. 1.40k, The Tale of Maid Dorothea (executioner, girl, king and devil). 2k, Drowning of Morena, symbol of death and winter.

**1975, Mar. 26** **Engr.** *Perf. 11½*

| | | | | |
|---|---|---|---|---|
| **1996** | A705 | 60h blk & multi | .45 | .25 |
| **1997** | A705 | 1k blk & multi | .70 | .45 |
| **1998** | A705 | 1.40k blk & multi | .85 | .60 |
| **1999** | A705 | 2k blk & multi | 1.00 | .75 |
| | | *Nos. 1996-1999 (4)* | 3.00 | 2.05 |

Nos. 1996-1999 were each issued in sheets of four. Value $12.50.

### Coat of Arms Type of 1968

### Engraved and Photogravure

**1975, Apr. 17** *Perf. 11½*

| | | | | |
|---|---|---|---|---|
| **2000** | A590 | 60h Nymburk | .25 | .25 |
| **2001** | A590 | 60h Znojmo | .25 | .25 |

Coats of arms of Czechoslovakian cities.

Czech May Uprising — A706

Liberation by Soviet Army — A707

Czechoslovak-Russian Friendship — A708

### Engr. & Photo.; Engr. (A707)

**1975, May 9**

| | | | | |
|---|---|---|---|---|
| **2002** | A706 | 1k multi | .25 | .25 |
| **2003** | A707 | 1k multi | .25 | .25 |
| **2004** | A708 | 1k multi | .25 | .25 |
| | | *Nos. 2002-2004 (3)* | .75 | .75 |

30th anniv. of the May uprising of the Czech people and of liberation by the Soviet Army; 5th anniv. of the Czechoslovak-Soviet Treaty of Friendship, Cooperation and Mutual Aid.

Adolescents' Exercises — A709

Designs: 60th, Children's exercises. 1k, Men's and women's exercises.

### Engraved and Photogravure

**1975, June 15** *Perf. 12x11½*

| | | | | |
|---|---|---|---|---|
| **2005** | A709 | 30h lil & multi | .25 | .25 |
| **2006** | A709 | 60h multi | .25 | .25 |
| **2007** | A709 | 1k vio & multi | .25 | .25 |
| | | *Nos. 2005-2007 (3)* | .75 | .75 |

Spartakiad 1975, Prague, June 26-29. Nos. 2005-2007 each issued in sheets of 30 stamps and 40 labels, showing different Spartakiad emblems. Value, set with tabs, $1.

Datrioides Microlepis and Sea Horse — A710

Tropical Fish (Aquarium): 1k, Beta splendens regan and Pterophyllum scalare. 1.20k, Carassius auratus. 1.60k, Amphiprion percula and Chaetodon sp. 2k, Pomacanthodes semicirculatus, Pomocanthus maculosus and Paracanthorus hepatus.

**1975, June 27** *Perf. 11½*

| | | | | |
|---|---|---|---|---|
| **2008** | A710 | 60h multi | .25 | .25 |
| **2009** | A710 | 1k multi | .35 | .25 |
| **2010** | A710 | 1.20k multi | .40 | .25 |
| **2011** | A710 | 1.60k multi | .55 | .25 |
| **2012** | A710 | 2k multi | 1.75 | .50 |
| | | *Nos. 2008-2012 (5)* | 3.30 | 1.50 |

Pelicans, by Nikita Charushin — A711

Book Illustrations: 30h, The Dreamer, by Lieselotte Schwarz. 40h, Hero on horseback, by Val Munteanau. 60h, Peacock, by Klaus Ensikat. 80h, Woman on horseback, by Robert Dubravec.

**1975, Sept. 5**

| | | | | |
|---|---|---|---|---|
| **2013** | A711 | 20h multi | .25 | .25 |
| **2014** | A711 | 30h multi | .25 | .25 |
| **2015** | A711 | 40h multi | .30 | .25 |
| **2016** | A711 | 60h multi | .30 | .25 |
| **2017** | A711 | 80h multi | .60 | .25 |
| | | *Nos. 2013-2017 (5)* | 1.70 | 1.25 |

Bratislava BIB 75 biennial exhibition of illustrations for children's books.

Nos. 2013-2017 issued in sheets of 25 stamps and 15 labels with designs and inscriptions in various languages. Value, set with attached labels, $2.

Strakonice, 1951 — A712

Designs: Motorcycles.

**1975, Sept. 29** *Perf. 11½*

| | | | | |
|---|---|---|---|---|
| **2018** | A712 | 20h shown | .25 | .25 |
| **2019** | A712 | 40h Jawa 250, 1945 | .25 | .25 |
| **2020** | A712 | 60h Jawa 175, 1935 | .25 | .25 |
| **2021** | A712 | 1k ITAR, 1921 | .25 | .25 |
| **2022** | A712 | 1.20k ORION, 1903 | .25 | .25 |
| **2023** | A712 | 1.80k Laurin & Klement, 1898 | 1.40 | .40 |
| | | *Nos. 2018-2023 (6)* | 2.65 | 1.65 |

Study of Shortwave Solar Radiation — A713

Soyuz-Apollo Link-up in Space — A714

60h, Study of aurora borealis & Oréol satellite. 1k, Study of ionosphere & cosmic radiation. 2k, Copernicus, radio map of the sun & satellite.

**1975, Sept. 30**

| | | | | |
|---|---|---|---|---|
| **2024** | A713 | 30h multi | .25 | .25 |
| **2025** | A713 | 60h yel, rose red & vio | .25 | .25 |
| **2026** | A713 | 1k bl, yel & vio | .25 | .25 |
| **2027** | A713 | 2k red, vio & yel | .35 | .25 |

**Engr.**

| | | | | |
|---|---|---|---|---|
| **2028** | A714 | 5k vio & multi | 2.00 | 1.50 |
| | | *Nos. 2024-2028 (5)* | 3.10 | 2.50 |

International cooperation in space research.

No. 2028 issued in sheets of 4. Value $15.

The design of No. 2026 appears to be inverted.

Slovnaft, Petrochemical Plant — A715

Designs: 60h, Atomic power station. 1k, Construction of Prague subway. 1.20k, Construction of Friendship pipeline. 1.40k, Combine harvesters. 1.60k, Apartment house construction.

### Engraved and Photogravure

**1975, Oct. 28**

| | | | | |
|---|---|---|---|---|
| **2029** | A715 | 30h multi | .25 | .25 |
| **2030** | A715 | 60h multi | .25 | .25 |
| **2031** | A715 | 1k multi | .25 | .25 |
| **2032** | A715 | 1.20k multi | .25 | .25 |
| **2033** | A715 | 1.40k multi | .25 | .25 |
| **2034** | A715 | 1.60k multi | .75 | .30 |
| | | *Nos. 2029-2034 (6)* | 2.00 | 1.55 |

Socialist construction, 30th anniversary. Nos. 2029-2034 printed se-tenant with labels. Value, set with attached labels, $2.50.

Pres. Gustav Husak — A716

**1975, Oct. 28** **Engr.**

| | | | | |
|---|---|---|---|---|
| **2035** | A716 | 30h ultra | .25 | .25 |
| **2036** | A716 | 60h rose red | .25 | .25 |

### Prague Castle Art Type of 1971

3k, Gold earring, 9th cent. 3.60k, Arms of Premysl Dynasty & Bohemia from lid of leather case containing Bohemian crown, 14th cent.

**1975, Oct. 29**

| | | | | |
|---|---|---|---|---|
| **2040** | A634 | 3k blk, grn, pur & gold | .95 | .50 |
| **2041** | A634 | 3.60k red & multi | 2.00 | 1.60 |

Nos. 2040-2041 each issued in sheets of 4. Value, set $12.50.

Miniature Sheet

Ludvik Svoboda, Map of Journey from Buzuluk to Prague, Carnations — A717

**1975, Nov. 25**

| | | | | |
|---|---|---|---|---|
| **2042** | A717 | 10k multi | 9.00 | 7.00 |

Pres. Ludvik Svoboda, 80th birthday.

Exists imperf. Value, $40 unused, $25 used.

### Painting Type of 1967

Paintings: 1k, "May 1975" (Woman and doves for 30th anniv. of peace), by Zdenek Sklenar. 1.40k, Woman in national costume, by Eugen Nevan. 1.80k, "Liberation of Prague," by Alena Cermakova, horiz. 2.40k, "Fire 1938" (woman raising fist), by Josef Capek. 3.40k, Old Prague, 1828, by Vincenc Morstadt.

**1975, Nov. 27** **Engr.** *Perf. 11½*

| | | | | |
|---|---|---|---|---|
| **2043** | A565 | 1k blk, buff & brn | .30 | .25 |
| **2044** | A565 | 1.40k multi | .55 | .25 |
| **2045** | A565 | 1.80k multi | .55 | .30 |
| **2046** | A565 | 2.40k multi | 1.50 | .75 |
| **2047** | A565 | 3.40k multi | 1.50 | 1.25 |
| | | *Nos. 2043-2047 (5)* | 4.40 | 2.80 |

Nos. 2043-2047 were each issued in sheets of 4. Value, set $20.

Carrier Pigeon — A718

### Engraved and Photogravure

**1975, Dec. 18** *Perf. 11½*

| | | | | |
|---|---|---|---|---|
| **2048** | A718 | 1k red & multi | .30 | .25 |

Stamp Day 1975.

Frantisek Halas — A719

Wilhelm Pieck — A720

Frantisek Lexa — A721

Jindrich Jindrich — A722

Ivan Krasko — A723

**1976, Feb. 25** *Perf. 11½*

**2049** A719 60h multi .25 .25
**2050** A720 60h multi .25 .25
**2051** A721 60h multi .25 .25
**2052** A722 60h multi .25 .25
**2053** A723 60h multi .25 .25
*Nos. 2049-2053 (5)* 1.25 1.25

Halas (1901-49), poet; Pieck (1876-1960), pres. of German Democratic Republic; Lexa (1876-1960), professor of Egyptology; Jindrich (1876-1967), composer and writer; Krasko (1876-1958), Slovak poet.

No. 2051 printed in sheets of 10, others in sheets of 50. Value, No. 2051 sheet, $4.

Ski Jump, Olympic Emblem A724

Winter Olympic Games Emblem and: 1.40k, Figure skating, women's. 1.60k, Ice hockey.

**1976, Mar. 22** *Perf. 12x11½*

**2054** A724 1k gold & multi .25 .25
**2055** A724 1.40k gold & multi .25 .25
**2056** A724 1.60k gold & multi 1.00 .30
*Nos. 2054-2056 (3)* 1.50 .80

12th Winter Olympic Games, Innsbruck, Austria, Feb. 4-15.

Javelin and Olympic Rings — A725

**1976, Mar. 22** *Perf. 11½*

**2057** A725 2k shown .30 .25
**2058** A725 3k Relay race .45 .25
**2059** A725 3.60k Shot put 1.40 .90
*Nos. 2057-2059 (3)* 2.15 1.40

21st Olympic Games, Montreal, Canada, July 17-Aug. 1.

Table Tennis — A726

**1976, Mar. 22** *Perf. 11x12*

**2060** A726 1k multi .30 .25

European Table Tennis Championship, Prague, Mar. 26-Apr. 4.

Symbolic of Communist Party — A727

Worker, Derrick, Emblem — A728

**1976, Apr. 12** *Perf. 11x12*

**2061** A727 30h gold & multi .25 .25
**2062** A728 60h gold & multi .25 .25

15th Congress of the Communist Party of Czechoslovakia.

Radio Prague Orchestra A729

Dancer, Violin, Tragic Mask — A730

Actors — A731

Folk Dancers A732

Film Festival — A733

**1976, Apr. 26** *Perf. 11½*

**2063** A729 20h gold & multi .25 .25
**2064** A730 20h pink & multi .25 .25
**2065** A731 20h lt bl & multi .25 .25
**2066** A732 30h blk & multi .25 .25
**2067** A733 30h vio bl, rose & grn .25 .25
*Nos. 2063-2067 (5)* 1.25 1.25

Czechoslovak Radio Symphony Orchestra, Prague, 50th anniv. (No. 2063); Academy of Music and Dramatic Art, Prague, 50th anniv. (No. 2064); Nova Scena Theater Co., Bratislava, 30th anniv. (No. 2065); Intl. Folk Song and Dance Festival, Straznice, 30th anniv. (No. 2066); 20th Intl. Film Festival, Karlovy Vary (No. 2067).

Hammer and Sickle
A734 A735

Design: 6k, Hammer and sickle, horiz.

**1976, May 14**

**2068** A734 30h gold, red & dk bl .25 .25
**2069** A735 60h gold, red & dp car .25 .25

**Souvenir Sheet**

**2070** A735 6k red & multi 2.00 2.00

Czechoslovak Communist Party, 55th anniv. No. 2070 contains a 50x30mm stamp.

Ships in Storm, by Frans Huys (1522-1562) A736

Old Engravings of Ships: 60h, by Václav Hollar (1607-77). 1k, by Regnier Nooms Zeeman (1623-68). 2k, by Francois Chereau (1680-1729).

**Engraved and Photogravure**

**1976, July 21** *Perf. 11x11½*

**2071** A736 40h buff & blk .25 .25
**2072** A736 60h gray, buff & blk .25 .25
**2073** A736 1k lt grn, buff & blk .25 .25
**2074** A736 2k lt bl, buff & blk 1.40 .25
*Nos. 2071-2074 (4)* 2.15 1.00

"UNESCO" A737

**1976, July 30** *Perf. 11½*

**2075** A737 2k gray & multi .35 .30

30th anniversary of UNESCO. Issued in sheets of 10. Value $5.

Souvenir Sheet

Hands Holding Infant, Globe and Dove — A738

**1976, July 30**

**2076** A738 Sheet of 2 4.00 3.50
*a.* 6k multi 2.50 2.00

European Security and Cooperation Conference, Helsinki, Finland, 2nd anniv.

Merino Ram — A739

Designs: 40h, Bern-Hana milk cow. 1.60k, Kladruby stallion Generalissimus XXVII.

**1976, Aug. 28** *Perf. 11½x12*

**2077** A739 30h multi .25 .25
**2078** A739 40h multi .25 .25
**2079** A739 1.60k multi .35 .25
*Nos. 2077-2079 (3)* .85 .75

Bountiful Earth Exhibition, Ceske Budejovice, Aug. 28-Sept. 12.

Couple Smoking, WHO Emblem and Skull — A740

**1976, Sept. 7** *Perf. 12x11½*

**2080** A740 2k multi .60 .30

Fight against smoking, WHO drive against drug addiction.

Printed in sheets of 10 (2x5) with WHO emblems and inscription in margin. Value $10.

**Prague Castle Art Type of 1971**

Designs: 3k, View of Prague Castle, by F. Hoogenberghe, 1572. 3.60k, Faun and Satyr, sculptured panel, 16th century.

**1976, Oct. 22** **Engr.** *Perf. 11½*

**2081** A634 3k multi 2.50 2.10
**2082** A634 3.60k multi .90 .60

Nos. 2081-2082 were each issued in sheets of 4. Value $15.

Guernica 1937, by Imro Weiner-Kral A741

**1976, Oct. 22**

| | | | | |
|---|---|---|---|---|
| 2083 | A741 | 5k multi | .80 | .40 |

40th anniv. of the Intl. Brigade in Spain.

Zebras A742

20h, Elephants. 30h, Cheetah. 40h, Giraffes. 60h, Rhinoceros. 3k, Bongos.

### Engraved and Photogravure

**1976, Nov. 3** *Perf. 11½x11, 11x11½*

| | | | | |
|---|---|---|---|---|
| 2084 | A742 | 10h multi | .25 | .25 |
| 2085 | A742 | 20h multi, vert. | .25 | .25 |
| 2086 | A742 | 30h multi | .30 | .25 |
| 2087 | A742 | 40h multi, vert. | .45 | .25 |
| 2088 | A742 | 60h multi | .45 | .25 |
| 2089 | A742 | 3k multi, vert. | 2.00 | .25 |
| | | *Nos. 2084-2089 (6)* | 3.70 | 1.50 |

African animals in Dvur Kralove Zoo.

### Painting Type of 1967

Paintings of Flowers: 1k, by Peter Matejka. 1.40k, by Cyril Bouda. 2k, by Jan Breughel. 3.60k, J. Rudolf Bys.

**1976, Nov. 27** **Engr.** *Perf. 11½*

| | | | | |
|---|---|---|---|---|
| 2090 | A565 | 1k multi | .75 | .50 |
| 2091 | A565 | 1.40k multi | 1.50 | .90 |
| 2092 | A565 | 2k multi | 1.20 | .90 |
| 2093 | A565 | 3.60k multi | .80 | .40 |
| | | *Nos. 2090-2093 (4)* | 4.25 | 2.70 |

Nos. 2090-2093 were each issued in sheets of 4, with emblem and name of Praga 1978 on horizontal gutter. Value, set $17.50.

Postrider, 17th Century, and Satellites — A743

**1976, Dec. 18** **Engr. & Photo.**

| | | | | |
|---|---|---|---|---|
| 2094 | A743 | 1k multi | .25 | .25 |

Stamp Day 1976.

Ice Hockey — A744

**1977, Feb. 11** *Perf. 11½*

| | | | | |
|---|---|---|---|---|
| 2095 | A744 | 60h shown | .25 | .25 |
| 2096 | A744 | 1k Biathlon | .25 | .25 |
| 2097 | A744 | 1.60k Ski jump | .85 | .25 |
| 2098 | A744 | 2k Downhill skiing | .25 | .25 |
| | | *Nos. 2095-2098 (4)* | 1.60 | 1.00 |

6th Winter Spartakiad of Socialist Countries' Armies.

Arms of Vranov — A745

Coats of Arms of Czechoslovak towns.

**1977, Feb. 20**

| | | | | |
|---|---|---|---|---|
| 2099 | A745 | 60h shown | .25 | .25 |
| 2100 | A745 | 60h Kralupy nad Vltavou | .25 | .25 |
| 2101 | A745 | 60h Jicin | .25 | .25 |
| 2102 | A745 | 60h Valasske Mezirici | .25 | .25 |
| | | *Nos. 2099-2102 (4)* | 1.00 | 1.00 |

See Nos. 2297-2300.

Window, Michna Palace — A746

Prague Renaissance Windows: 30h, Michna Palace. 40h, Thun Palace. 60h, Archbishop's Palace, Hradcany. 5k, St. Nicholas Church.

**1977, Mar. 10**

| | | | | |
|---|---|---|---|---|
| 2103 | A746 | 20h multi | .25 | .25 |
| 2104 | A746 | 30h multi | .25 | .25 |
| 2105 | A746 | 40h multi | .25 | .25 |
| 2106 | A746 | 60h multi | .25 | .25 |
| 2107 | A746 | 5k multi | 1.50 | .25 |
| | | *Nos. 2103-2107 (5)* | 2.50 | 1.25 |

PRAGA 1978 International Philatelic Exhibition, Prague, Sept. 8-17, 1978.

Children, Auxiliary Police A747

**1977, Apr. 21** *Perf. 11½*

| | | | | |
|---|---|---|---|---|
| 2108 | A747 | 60h multi | .25 | .25 |

Auxiliary Police, 25th anniversary.

Warsaw, Polish Flag, Bicyclists A748

Designs: 60h, Berlin, DDR flag, bicyclists. 1k, Prague, Czechoslovakian flag, victorious bicyclist. 1.40k, Bicyclists on highways, modern views of Berlin, Prague and Warsaw.

**1977, May 7**

| | | | | |
|---|---|---|---|---|
| 2109 | A748 | 30h multi | .25 | .25 |
| 2110 | A748 | 60h multi | .25 | .25 |
| 2111 | A748 | 1k multi | .60 | .25 |
| 2112 | A748 | 1.40k multi | .40 | .25 |
| | | *Nos. 2109-2112 (4)* | 1.50 | 1.00 |

30th International Bicycle Peace Race Warsaw-Prague-Berlin.

Congress Emblem — A749

**1977, May 25** *Perf. 11½*

| | | | | |
|---|---|---|---|---|
| 2113 | A749 | 30h car, red & gold | .25 | .25 |

9th Trade Union Congress, Prague 1977.

### Prague Castle Art Type of 1971

Designs: 3k, Onyx footed bowl, 1350. 3.60k, Bronze horse, 1619.

**1977, June 7** **Engr.**

| | | | | |
|---|---|---|---|---|
| 2114 | A634 | 3k multi | 1.25 | 1.10 |
| 2115 | A634 | 3.60k multi | 1.10 | 1.10 |

Nos. 2114-2115 were each issued in sheets of 4. Value, set $11.

French Postrider, 19th Century, PRAGA '78 Emblem — A750

Postal Uniforms: 1k, Austrian, 1838. 2k, Austrian, late 18th century. 3.60k, Germany, early 18th century.

**1977, June 8** **Engr. & Photo.**

| | | | | |
|---|---|---|---|---|
| 2116 | A750 | 60h multi | .25 | .25 |
| 2117 | A750 | 1k multi | .25 | .25 |
| 2118 | A750 | 2k multi | .40 | .25 |
| 2119 | A750 | 3.60k multi | 1.50 | .35 |
| | | *Nos. 2116-2119 (4)* | 2.40 | 1.10 |

PRAGA 1978 International Philatelic Exhibition, Prague, Sept. 8-17, 1978.

Nos. 2116-2119 were each issued both in sheets of 50 and in sheets of 4 stamps with 4 inscribed labels and 2 blank labels. Value, set of sheets of 4, $10.

Coffeepots, Porcelain Mark — A751

Czechoslovak Porcelain and Porcelain Marks: 30h, Urn. 40h, Vase. 60h, Cup and saucer, jugs. 1k, Candlestick and plate. 3k, Cup and saucer, coffeepot.

**1977, June 15**

| | | | | |
|---|---|---|---|---|
| 2120 | A751 | 20h multi | .25 | .25 |
| 2121 | A751 | 30h multi | .25 | .25 |
| 2122 | A751 | 40h multi | .25 | .25 |
| 2123 | A751 | 60h multi | .25 | .25 |
| 2124 | A751 | 1k multi | .25 | .25 |
| 2125 | A751 | 3k multi | 1.10 | .35 |
| | | *Nos. 2120-2125 (6)* | 2.35 | 1.60 |

Mlada Boleslav Costume — A752

PRAGA Emblem and Folk Costumes from: 1.60k, Vazek. 3.60k, Zavadka. 5k, Belkovice.

**1977, Aug. 31** **Engr.** *Perf. 11½*

| | | | | |
|---|---|---|---|---|
| 2126 | A752 | 1k multi | 1.25 | .95 |
| 2127 | A752 | 1.60k multi | 1.25 | .95 |
| 2128 | A752 | 3.60k multi | 1.25 | .95 |
| 2129 | A752 | 5k multi | 1.25 | .95 |
| | | *Nos. 2126-2129 (4)* | 5.00 | 3.80 |

Issued in sheets of 10 and in sheets of 8 plus 2 labels showing PRAGA '78 emblem. Value, set: sheets of 10 $50; sheets of 8 $40.

Old Woman, Devil and Spinner, by Viera Bombova A753

Book Illustrations: 60h, Bear and tiger, by Genadij Pavlisin. 1k, Coach drawn by 4 horses (Hans Christian Andersen), by Ulf Lovgren. 2k, Bear and flamingos (Lewis Carroll), by Nicole Claveloux. 3k, King with keys, and toys, by Jiri Trnka.

**1977, Sept. 9** **Engr. & Photo.**

| | | | | |
|---|---|---|---|---|
| 2130 | A753 | 40h multi | .25 | .25 |
| 2131 | A753 | 60h multi | .25 | .25 |
| 2132 | A753 | 1k multi | .25 | .25 |
| 2133 | A753 | 2k multi | .25 | .25 |
| 2134 | A753 | 3k multi | 1.00 | .35 |
| | | *Nos. 2130-2134 (5)* | 2.00 | 1.35 |

Prize-winning designs, 6th biennial exhibition of illustrations for children's books, Bratislava.

Globe, Violin, Doves, View of Prague — A754

**1977, Sept. 28** *Perf. 11½*

| | | | | |
|---|---|---|---|---|
| 2135 | A754 | 60h multi | .25 | .25 |

Congress of International Music Council of UNESCO, Prague and Bratislava.

### Souvenir Sheets

"For a Europe of Peace" — A755

1.60k, "For a Europe of Cooperation." 2.40k, "For a Europe of Social Progress."

**1977, Oct. 3**

| | | | | |
|---|---|---|---|---|
| 2136 | A755 | Sheet of 2 | .50 | .50 |
| *a.* | | 60h multi | .25 | .25 |
| 2137 | A755 | Sheet of 2 | 1.00 | 1.00 |
| *a.* | | 1.60k multi | .25 | .25 |
| 2138 | A755 | Sheet of 2 | 2.00 | 1.75 |
| *a.* | | 2.40k multi | .50 | .50 |

2nd European Security and Cooperation Conference, Belgrade. Nos. 2136-2138 each contain 2 stamps and 2 blue on buff inscriptions and ornaments.

Nos. 2136-2138 were issued imperforate in sheets of 2. Value, $30.

For overprint of No. 2137, see No. 2334.

S. P. Korolev, Sputnik I Emblem — A756

30h, Yuri A. Gagarin & Vostok I. 40h, Alexei Leonov. 1k, Neil A. Armstrong & footprint on moon. 1.60k, Construction of orbital space station.

**1977, Oct. 4**

2139 A756 20h multi .25 .25
2140 A756 30h multi .25 .25
2141 A756 40h multi .25 .25
2142 A756 1k multi .25 .25
2143 A756 1.60k multi .60 .25
*Nos. 2139-2143 (5)* 1.60 1.25

Space research, 20th anniv. of 1st earth satellite.

Sailors, Cruiser Aurora — A757

**1977, Nov. 7**

2144 A757 30h multi .25 .25

60th anniv. of Russian October Revolution.

"Russia," Arms of USSR, Kremlin — A758

**1977, Nov. 7**

2145 A758 30h multi .25 .25

55th anniversary of the USSR.

"Science" — A759

**1977, Nov. 17**

2146 A759 3k multi .50 .25

Czechoslovak Academy of Science, 25th anniversary.

**Painting Type of 1967**

Paintings: 2k, "Fear" (woman), by Jan Mudroch. 2.40k, Jan Francisci, portrait by Peter M. Bohun. 2.60k, Vaclav Hollar, self-portrait, 1647. 3k, Young Woman, 1528, by Lucas Cranach. 5k, Cleopatra, by Rubens.

**1977, Nov. 27 Engr. *Perf. 11½***

2147 A565 2k multi .75 .45
2148 A565 2.40k multi 1.20 .90
2149 A565 2.60k multi 1.20 .90
2150 A565 3k multi .75 .60
2151 A565 5k multi 1.50 1.50
*Nos. 2147-2151 (5)* 5.40 4.35

Nos. 2147-2151 were each issued in sheets of 4. Value, set $25.

View of Bratislava, by Georg Hoefnagel — A760

Design: 3.60k, Arms of Bratislava, 1436.

**1977, Dec. 6**

2152 A760 3k multi 1.90 1.60
2153 A760 3.60k multi .80 .50

Nos. 2152-21531 were each issued in sheets of 4. Value, set $12.50.

See Nos. 2174-2175, 2270-2271, 2331-2332, 2364-2365, 2422-2423, 2478-2479, 2514-2515, 2570-2571, 2618-2619.

Stamp Pattern and Post Horn — A761

**1977, Dec. 18 Engr. & Photo.**

2154 A761 1k multi .25 .25

Stamp Day.

Zdenek Nejedly — A762 Karl Marx — A763

**1978, Feb. 10 *Perf. 11½***

2155 A762 30h multi .25 .25
2156 A763 40h multi .25 .25

Zdenek Nejedly (1878-1962), musicologist and historian; Karl Marx (1818-1883), political philosopher.

Civilians Greeting Guardsmen — A764

Intellectual, Farm Woman and Steel Worker, Flag — A765

**1978, Feb. 25**

2157 A764 1k gold & multi .25 .25
2158 A765 1k gold & multi .25 .25

30th anniv. of "Victorious February" (No. 2157), and Natl. Front (No. 2158).

An imperforate sheet of four of No. 2157 was sold with an admission ticket to PRAGA 78 international philatelic exhibition. Value, $4.

See note after 2190.

Yuri A. Gagarin, Vostok I — A766

Design: 30h, 3.60k, like No. 2140.

**Engraved; Overprint Photogravure (Blue and carmine on 30h, green and lilac rose on 3.60k)**

**1978, Mar. 2 *Perf. 11½x12***

2159 A766 30h dk red .25 .25
2160 A766 3.60k vio bl 2.40 2.40

Capt. V. Remek, 1st Czechoslovakian cosmonaut on Russian spaceship Soyuz 28, Mar. 2-9.

10k Coin, 1964, and 25k Coin, 1965 — A767

40h, Medal for Culture, 1972. 1.40k, Charles University medal, 1948. 3k, Ferdinand I medal, 1568. 5k, Gold florin, 1335.

**1978, Mar. 14 Engr. & Photo.**

2161 A767 20h sil & multi .25 .25
2162 A767 40h sil & multi .25 .25
2163 A767 1.40k gold & multi 1.00 .25
2164 A767 3k gold & multi .35 .25
2165 A767 5k gold & multi .35 .25
*Nos. 2161-2165 (5)* 2.20 1.25

650th anniversary of Kremnica Mint.

Tire Tracks and Ball — A768

**1978, Mar. 15**

2166 A768 60h multi .25 .25

Road safety.

Congress Emblem — A769

**1978, Apr. 16 *Perf. 11½***

2167 A769 1k multi .25 .25

9th World Trade Union Cong., Prague 1978.

Shot Put and Praha '78 Emblem A770

1k, Pole vault. 3.60k, Women runners.

**1978, Apr. 26**

2168 A770 40h multi .30 .30
2169 A770 1k multi .40 .30
2170 A770 3.60k multi .90 .50
*Nos. 2168-2170 (3)* 1.60 1.10

5th European Athletic Championships, Prague 1978.

Ice Hockey — A771

Designs: 30h, Hockey. 2k, Ice hockey play.

**1978, Apr. 26**

2171 A771 30h multi .25 .25
2172 A771 60h multi .35 .25
2173 A771 2k multi .35 .25
*Nos. 2171-2173 (3)* .95 .75

5th European Ice Hockey Championships and 70th anniversary of Bandy hockey.

**Bratislava Type of 1977**

Designs: 3k, Bratislava, 1955, by Orest Dubay. 3.60k, Fishpound Square, Bratislava, 1955, by Imro Weiner-Kral.

**1978, May 9 Engr. *Perf. 11½***

2174 A760 3k multi .95 .80
2175 A760 3.60k multi 1.25 .80

Nos. 2174-2175 were each issued in sheets of 4. Value, set $10.

**Prague Castle Art Type of 1971**

3k, King Ottokar II, detail from tomb. 3.60k, Charles IV, detail from votive panel by Jan Ocka.

**1978, May 9**

2176 A634 3k multi .75 .60
2177 A634 3.60k multi 3.50 2.40

Nos. 2176-2177 were each issued in sheets of 4. Value, set $18.

Ministry of Post, Prague A772

**Engraved and Photogravure**

**1978, May 29 *Perf. 12x11½***

2178 A772 60h multi .25 .25

14th session of permanent COMECOM Commission (Ministers of Post and Telecommunications of Socialist Countries).

Palacky Bridge A773

Prague Bridges and PRAGA '78 Emblem: 40h, Railroad bridge. 1k, Bridge of May 1. 2k, Manes Bridge. 3k, Svatopluk Cech Bridge. 5.40k, Charles Bridge.

**1978, May 30**

2179 A773 20h blk & multi .25 .25
2180 A773 40h blk & multi .25 .25
2181 A773 1k blk & multi .25 .25
2182 A773 2k blk & multi .25 .25
2183 A773 3k blk & multi .30 .25
2184 A773 5.40k blk & multi 1.40 .25
*Nos. 2179-2184 (6)* 2.70 1.50

PRAGA 1978 International Philatelic Exhibition, Prague, Sept. 8-17.

St. Peter and Apostles, Clock Tower, and Emblem A774

Town Hall Clock, Prague, by Josef Manes, and PRAGA '78 Emblem: 1k, Astronomical clock. 2k, Prague's coat of arms. 3k, Grape harvest (September). 3.60k, Libra. 10k, Arms surrounded by zodiac signs and scenes symbolic of 12 months, horiz. 2k, 3k, 3.60k show details from design of 10k.

**1978, June 20 *Perf. 11½x11***

2185 A774 40h multi .25 .25
2186 A774 1k multi .25 .25
2187 A774 2k multi .25 .25
2188 A774 3k multi 1.50 .35
2189 A774 3.60k multi .55 .25
*Nos. 2185-2189 (5)* 2.80 1.35

### Souvenir Sheet
*Perf. 12x12*

**2190** A774 10k multi 10.00 7.50

PRAGA '78 Intl. Philatelic Exhibition, Prague, Sept. 8-17. No. 2190 contains one 50x40mm stamp. Sheet exists imperf. Value $27.50.

A non-valid souvenir sheet contains 4 imperf. examples of No. 2157. Sold only with PRAGA ticket.

Folk Dancers — A775

**1978, July 7** *Perf. 11½x12*

**2191** A775 30h multi .25 .25

25th Folklore Festival, Vychodna.

Overpass and PRAGA Emblem — A776

1k, 2k, Modern office buildings, diff. 6k, Old & new Prague. 20k, Charles Bridge & Old Town, by Vincent Morstadt, 1828.

**1978** *Perf. 12x11½*

**2192** A776 60h blk & multi .25 .25
**2193** A776 1k blk & multi .25 .25
**2194** A776 2k blk & multi .25 .25
**2195** A776 6k blk & multi 1.50 .75
*Nos. 2192-2195 (4)* 2.25 1.50

### Souvenir Sheet
**Engr.**

**2196** A776 20k multi 9.50 7.50

PRAGA 1978 Intl. Phil. Exhib., Prague, Sept. 8-17. No. 2196 also for 60th anniv. of Czechoslovak postage stamps. No. 2196 contains one 61x45mm stamp.

Issued: Nos. 2192-2195, 9/8; No. 2196, 9/10.

Souvenir Sheet

Titian (1488-1576), Venetian painter — A777

No. 2197a, Apollo's Companion, by Titian. No. 2197b, King Midas. Stamps show details from "Apollo Flaying Marsya" by Titian.

**1978, Sept. 12** *Perf. 11½*

**2197** A777 Sheet of 2 11.00 8.75
*a.* 10k multi 5.00 4.25
*b.* 10k multi 5.00 4.25

No. 2197 with dark blue marginal inscription "FIP" was sold only with entrance ticket to PRAGA Philatelic Exhibition. Value $25.

Exhibition Hall — A778

### Engraved and Photogravure
**1978, Sept. 13** *Perf. 11½x11*

**2198** A778 30h multi .25 .25

22nd International Engineering Fair, Brno.

Postal Newspaper Service — A779

TV Screen, Headquarters and Logo — A780

Newspaper, Microphone A781

**1978, Sept. 21** *Perf. 11½*

**2199** A779 30h multi .25 .25
**2200** A780 30h multi .25 .25
**2201** A781 30h multi .25 .25
*Nos. 2199-2201 (3)* .75 .75

Postal News Service, 25th anniv.; Czechoslovakian television, 25th anniv.; Press, Broadcasting and Television Day.

Sulky Race A782

Pardubice Steeplechase: 10h, Falling horses and jockeys at fence. 30h, Race. 40h, Horses passing post. 1.60k, Hurdling. 4.40k, Winner.

**1978, Oct. 6** *Perf. 12x11½*

**2202** A782 10h multi .25 .25
**2203** A782 20h multi .25 .25
**2204** A782 30h multi .25 .25
**2205** A782 40h multi .25 .25
**2206** A782 1.60k multi .25 .25
**2207** A782 4.40k multi 1.25 .25
*Nos. 2202-2207 (6)* 2.50 1.50

Woman Holding Arms of Czechoslovakia A783

**1978, Oct. 28** *Perf. 11½*

**2208** A783 60h multi .25 .25

60th anniversary of independence.

### Art Type of 1974

2.40k, Flowers, by Jakub Bohdan (1660-1724). 3k, The Dream of Salas, by Ludovit Fulla, horiz. 3.60k, Apostle with Censer, Master of the Spissko Capitals (c. 1480-90).

**1978, Nov. 27** **Engr.**

**2209** A700 2.40k multi .90 .45
**2210** A700 3k multi 1.00 .75
**2211** A700 3.60k multi 2.75 2.25
*Nos. 2209-2211 (3)* 4.65 3.45

Slovak National Gallery, 30th anniversary.

Nos. 2209-2211 were each issued in sheets of 4. Value, set $20.

Musicians, by Jan Könyves — A784

Slovak Ceramics: 30h, Janosik on Horseback, by Jozef Franko. 40h, Woman in Folk Costume by Michal Polasko. 1k, Three Girls Singing, by Ignac Bizmayer. 1.60k, Janosik Dancing, by Ferdis Kostka.

### Engraved and Photogravure
**1978, Dec. 5** *Perf. 11½x12*

**2212** A784 20h multi .25 .25
**2213** A784 30h multi .25 .25
**2214** A784 40k multi .25 .25
**2215** A784 1k multi .25 .25
**2216** A784 1.60k multi .60 .25
*Nos. 2212-2216 (5)* 1.60 1.25

Alfons Mucha and his Design for 1918 Issue — A785

**1978, Dec. 18** *Perf. 11½*

**2217** A785 1k multi .25 .25

60th Stamp Day.

COMECON Building, Moscow — A786

**1979, Jan. 1** *Perf. 11½*

**2218** A786 1k multi .25 .25

Council for Mutual Economic Aid (COMECON), 30th anniversary.

Woman's Head and Grain — A787

Soyuz 28, Rockets and Capsule — A789

Alpine Bellflowers — A790

Stylized Satellite, Dial, Tape — A791

Artist and Model, Dove, Bratislava Castle — A792

Cog Wheels, Transformer and Student — A793

Woman, Workers, Child, Doves — A788

**1979, Jan. 1**

**2219** A787 30h multi .25 .25
**2220** A788 60h multi .25 .25

United Agricultural Production Assoc., 30th anniv. (30h); Czechoslovakian Federation, 10th anniv. (60h).

60h, Astronauts Aleksei Gubarev and Vladimir Remek on launching pad, vert. 1.60k, Soviet astronauts J. Romanenko and G. Grecko, Salyut 6 and recovery ship. 2k, Salyut-Soyuz orbital complex, post office in space and Czechoslovakia No. 2153. 4k, Soyuz 28, crew after landing and trajectory map, vert. 10k, Gubarev and Remek, Intercosmos emblem, arms of Czechoslovakia and USSR.

**1979, Mar. 2**

**2221** A789 30h multi .25 .25
**2222** A789 60h multi .25 .25
**2223** A789 1.60k multi .25 .25
**2224** A789 2k multi 1.40 .25
**2225** A789 4k multi .60 .25
*Nos. 2221-2225 (5)* 2.75 1.25

### Souvenir Sheet

**2226** A789 10k multi 4.50 2.75

1st anniv. of joint Czechoslovak-Soviet space flight. Size of No. 2226: 76x93mm (stamp 39x55mm). No. 2226 has Cyrillic inscription, No. 2455a does not.

No. 2226 exists imperf. Value, $30.

Mountain Flowers: 20h, Crocus. 30h, Pinks. 40h, Alpine hawkweed. 3k, Larkspur.

**1979, Mar. 23** *Perf. 11½*

**2227** A790 10h multi .25 .25
**2228** A790 20h multi .25 .25
**2229** A790 30h multi .25 .25
**2230** A790 40h multi .25 .25

*Perf. 14*

**2231** A790 3k multi 1.10 .25
*Nos. 2227-2231 (5)* 2.10 1.25

Mountain Rescue Service, 25th anniversary.

The 3k exists perf. 11½. Value, $20 unused, $10 used.

The 3k was issued in sheets of 10. Values: perf 14 (No. 2231), $25; perf 11½, $180.

**1979, Apr. 2**

**2232** A791 10h multi .25 .25

Telecommunications research, 30th anniv.

Musical Instruments, Bratislava Castle — A794

Pioneer Scarf, IYC Emblem — A795

Red Star, Man, Child and Doves — A796

**1979, Apr. 2**

**2233** A792 20h multi .25 .25
**2234** A793 20h multi .25 .25
**2235** A794 30h multi .25 .25
**2236** A795 30h multi .25 .25
**2237** A796 60h multi .25 .25
*Nos. 2233-2237 (5)* 1.25 1.25

Fine Arts Academy, Bratislava, 30th anniv.; Slovak Technical University, 40th anniv.; Radio Symphony Orchestra, Bratislava, 30th anniv.; Young Pioneers, 30th anniv. and IYC; Peace Movement, 30th anniversary.

### Prague Castle Art Type of 1971

3k, Burial crown of King Ottokar II. 3.60k, Portrait of Mrs. Reitmayer, by Karel Purkyne.

**1979, May 9** ***Perf. 11½***

**2238** A634 3k multi 1.75 1.10
**2239** A634 3.60k multi 1.75 .80

Nos. 2238-2239 were each issued in sheets of 4. Value, set $13.50.

Arms of Vlachovo Brezi, 1538 — A797

Animals in Heraldry: 60h, Jesenik, 1509 (bear and eagle). 1.20k, Vysoke Myto, 1471 (St. George slaying dragon). 1.80k,Martin, 1854 (St. Martin giving coat to beggar). 2k, Zebrak, 1674 (mythological beast).

**1979, May 25** ***Perf. 11½x12***

**2240** A797 30h multi .25 .25
**2241** A797 60h multi .25 .25
**2242** A797 1.20k multi .25 .25
**2243** A797 1.80k multi *1.00* .25
**2244** A797 2k multi .60 .25
*Nos. 2240-2244 (5)* *2.35* 1.25

Forest, Thriving and Destroyed A798

Designs: 1.80k, Water. 3.60k, City. 4k, Cattle. All designs show good and bad environment, separated by exclamation point; Man and Biosphere emblem.

**1979, June 22** **Engr.** ***Perf. 11½***

**2245** A798 60h multi .25 .25
**2246** A798 1.80k multi .25 .25
**2247** A798 3.60k multi *1.60* *.60*
**2248** A798 4k multi 1.10 .25
*Nos. 2245-2248 (4)* *3.20* *1.35*

Man and Biosphere Program of UNESCO.
Nos. 2245-2248 were each issued in sheets of 10. Value, set $32.50.

Refinery, Smokestacks A799

### Engraved and Photogravure

**1979, Aug. 29** ***Perf. 11x11½***

**2249** A799 30h multi .25 .25

Slovak National Uprising, 35th anniversary.

Frog and Goat A800

Book Illustrations (IYC Emblem and): 40h, Knight on horseback. 60h, Maidens. 1k, Boy with sled following rooster. 3k, King riding flying beast.

**1979, Apr. 2** ***Perf. 11½x11***

**2250** A800 20h multi .25 .25
**2251** A800 40h multi .25 .25
**2252** A800 60h multi .25 .25
**2253** A800 1k multi .25 .25
**2254** A800 3k multi *1.10* *.25*
*Nos. 2250-2254 (5)* *2.10* *1.25*

Prize-winning designs, 7th biennial exhibition of illustrations for children's books, Bratislava; International Year of the Child.
Printed with labels showing story characters. Value, set with attached labels, $2.75.

"Bone Shaker" Bicycles, 1870 A801

Bicycles from: 20h, 1978. 40h, 1910. 60h, 1886. 3.60k, 1820.

**1979, Sept. 14** ***Perf. 12x11½***

**2255** A801 20h multi .25 .25
**2256** A801 40h multi .25 .25
**2257** A801 60h multi .25 .25
**2258** A801 2k multi .25 .25
**2259** A801 3.60k multi 1.50 .30
*Nos. 2255-2259 (5)* 2.50 1.30

Bracket Clock, 18th Century A802

Designs: 18th century clocks.

**1979, Oct. 1** ***Perf. 11½***

**2260** A802 40h multi .25 .25
**2261** A802 60h multi .25 .25
**2262** A802 80h multi 1.25 .25
**2263** A802 1k multi .25 .25
**2264** A802 2k multi .35 .25
*Nos. 2260-2264 (5)* 2.35 1.25

### Painting Type of 1967

Paintings: 1.60k, Sunday by the River, by Alois Moravec. 2k, Self-portrait, by Gustav Mally. 3k, Self-portrait, by Ilia Yefimovic Repin. 3.60k, Horseback Rider, by Jan Bauch. 5k, Dancing Peasants, by Albrecht Dürer.

**1979, Nov. 27** **Engr.** ***Perf. 12***

**2265** A565 1.60k multi .40 .35
**2266** A565 2k multi .60 .50
**2267** A565 3k multi .60 .50
**2268** A565 3.60k multi 2.00 1.75
**2269** A565 5k multi 1.60 1.25
*Nos. 2265-2269 (5)* 5.20 4.35

Nos. 2265-2269 were each issued in sheets of 4. Value, set $20.

### Bratislava Type of 1977

Designs: 3k, Bratislava Castle on the Danube, by L. Janscha, 1787. 3.60k, Bratislava Castle, stone engraving by Wolf, 1815.

**1979, Dec. 5**

**2270** A760 3k multi 1.00 .80
**2271** A760 3.60k multi 1.75 1.50

Nos. 2270-2272 were each issued in sheets of 4. Value, set $12.50.

Stamp Day — A803

### Engraved and Photogravure

**1979, Dec. 18** ***Perf. 11½x12***

**2272** A803 1k multi .25 .25

Electronic Circuits — A804

Designs: 50h, Satellite dish. 2k, Airplane. 3k, Computer punch tape.

**1979-80** **Photo.** ***Perf. 11½x12***

**Coil Stamps**

**2273** A804 50h red .25 .25
**2274** A804 1k brown .25 .25
**2275** A804 2k green ('80) .30 .25
**2276** A804 3k lake ('80) .45 .25
*Nos. 2273-2276 (4)* 1.25 1.00

The 1k comes in two shades.

Runners and Dove A805

### Engraved and Photogravure

**1980, Jan. 29** ***Perf. 12x11½***

**2289** A805 50h multi .25 .25

50th Intl. Peace Marathon, Kosice, Oct. 4.

Downhill Skiing — A806

**1980, Jan. 29** ***Perf. 11½x12***

**2290** A806 1k shown .30 .25
**2291** A806 2k Speed skating .95 .35
**2292** A806 3k Four-man bobsled .80 .35
*Nos. 2290-2292 (3)* 2.05 .95

13th Winter Olympic Games, Lake Placid, NY, Feb. 12-24.

Basketball — A807

**1980, Jan. 29** ***Perf. 11½***

**2293** A807 40h shown .25 .25
**2294** A807 1k Swimming .25 .25
**2295** A807 2k Hurdles 1.50 .35
**2296** A807 3.60k Fencing 1.10 .30
*Nos. 2293-2296 (4)* 3.10 1.15

22nd Olympic Games, Moscow, 7/19-8/3.

### Arms Type of 1977

No. 2297, Bystrice Nad Pernstejnem. No. 2298, Kunstat. No. 2299, Rozmital Pod Tremsinem. No. 2300, Zlata Idka.

**1980, Feb. 20** ***Perf. 11½***

**2297** A745 50h multi .25 .25
**2298** A745 50h multi .25 .25
**2299** A745 50h multi .25 .25
**2300** A745 50h multi .25 .25
*Nos. 2297-2300 (4)* 1.00 1.00

Theatrical Mask — A808

Slovak National Theater, Actors — A809

**1980, Mar. 1**

**2301** A808 50h multi .25 .25
**2302** A809 1k multi .25 .25

50th Jiraskuv Hronov Theatrical Ensemble Review; Slovak National Theater, Bratislava, 60th anniversary.

Mouse in Space, Satellite — A810

Intercosmos: 1k, Weather map, satellite. 1.60k, Intersputnik television transmission. 4k, Camera, satellite. 5k, Czech satellite station, 1978, horiz. 10k, Intercosmos emblem, horiz.

**1980, Apr. 12** ***Perf. 11½x12, 12x11½***

**2303** A810 50h multi .25 .25
**2304** A810 1k multi .25 .25
**2305** A810 1.60k multi 1.40 .25
**2306** A810 4k multi 1.00 .25
**2307** A810 5k multi 1.40 .25
*Nos. 2303-2307 (5)* 4.30 1.25

**Souvenir Sheet**

**2308** A810 10k multi 3.50 2.50

Intercosmos cooperative space program.
No. 2305 was issued in a sheet of 10. Value, $25.
No. 2308 exists imperf. Value, $30.

Police Corps Banner, Emblem — A811

**1980, Apr. 17** ***Perf. 11½***

**2309** A811 50h multi .25 .25

National Police Corps, 35th anniversary.

Lenin's 110th Birth Anniversary — A812

Design: No. 2311, Engels's 160th birth anniv.

**1980, Apr. 22**

| | | | | |
|---|---|---|---|---|
| **2310** | A812 | 1k tan & brn | .25 | .25 |
| **2311** | A812 | 1k lt grn & brn | .25 | .25 |

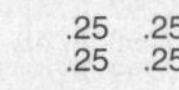

Old and Modern Prague, Czech Flag, Bouquet A813

Boy Writing "Peace" A814

Pact Members' Flags, Dove — A815

Czech and Soviet Arms, Prague and Moscow Views A816

**1980, May 6** ***Perf. 12x11½***

| | | | | |
|---|---|---|---|---|
| **2312** | A813 | 50h multi | .25 | .25 |
| **2313** | A814 | 1k multi | .25 | .25 |
| **2314** | A815 | 1k multi | .25 | .25 |
| **2315** | A816 | 1k multi | .25 | .25 |
| | *Nos. 2312-2315 (4)* | | 1.00 | 1.00 |

Liberation by Soviet army, 35th anniv.; Soviet victory in WWII, 35th anniv.; Signing of Warsaw Pact (Bulgaria, Czechoslovakia, German Democratic Rep., Hungary, Poland, Romania, USSR), 25th anniv.; Czechoslovak-Soviet Treaty of Friendship, Cooperation and Mutual Aid, 10th anniv.

Souvenir Sheet

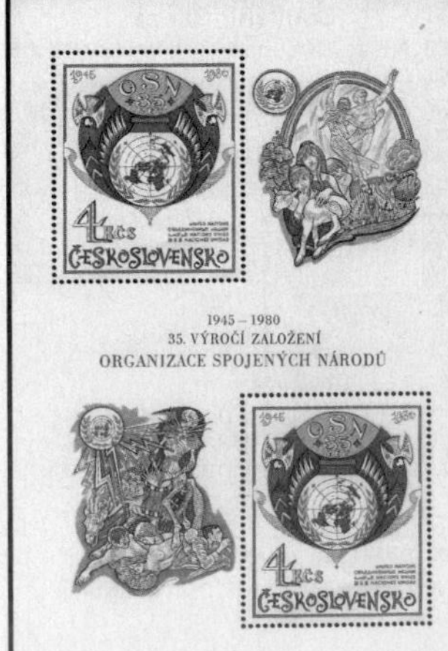


UN, 35th Anniv. — A817

**1980, June 3** **Engr.** ***Perf. 12***

| | | | | |
|---|---|---|---|---|
| **2316** | A817 | Sheet of 2 | 3.25 | 2.50 |
| *a.* | | 4k multicolored | 1.25 | 1.25 |

Athletes Parading Banners in Strahov Stadium, Prague, Spartakiad Emblem — A818

**Engraved and Photogravure**

**1980, June 3** ***Perf. 12x11½***

| | | | | |
|---|---|---|---|---|
| **2317** | A818 | 50h shown | .25 | .25 |
| **2318** | A818 | 1k Gymnast, vert. | .25 | .25 |

Spartakiad 1980, Prague, June 26-29.

Aechmea Fasciata — A819

Flowers: 50ch, Gerbera Jamesonii. 1k, Aechmea fasciata. 2k, Strelitzia reginae. 4k, Paphiopedilum.

**1980, Aug. 13** ***Perf. 12***

| | | | | |
|---|---|---|---|---|
| **2319** | A819 | 50h multicolored | .45 | .25 |
| **2320** | A819 | 1k multicolored | 2.10 | .65 |
| **2321** | A819 | 2k multicolored | .55 | .25 |
| **2322** | A819 | 4k multicolored | 2.25 | .25 |
| | *Nos. 2319-2322 (4)* | | 5.35 | 1.40 |

Olomouc and Bratislava Flower Shows.
Nos. 2319-2322 were each issued in sheets of 10. Values, set: unused, $65; used, $30.

A820

Designs: Folktale character embroideries.

**1980, Sept. 24** ***Perf. 11½x12***

| | | | | |
|---|---|---|---|---|
| **2323** | A820 | 50h Chad girl | .25 | .25 |
| **2324** | A820 | 1k Punch and dog | .25 | .25 |
| **2325** | A820 | 2k Dandy and Posy | .35 | .25 |
| **2326** | A820 | 4k Lion and moon | 1.30 | .75 |
| **2327** | A820 | 5k Wallachian dance | .65 | .25 |
| | *Nos. 2323-2327 (5)* | | 2.80 | 1.75 |

National Census A821

**1980, Sept. 24** ***Perf. 12x11½***

| | | | | |
|---|---|---|---|---|
| **2328** | A821 | 1k multi | .25 | .25 |

**Prague Castle Type of 1971**

Designs: 3k, Old Palace gateway. 4k, Armorial lion, 16th century.

**1980, Oct. 28** ***Perf. 12***

| | | | | |
|---|---|---|---|---|
| **2329** | A634 | 3k multi | 1.60 | 1.25 |
| **2330** | A634 | 4k multi | 1.10 | .65 |

Nos. 2329-2330 were each issued in sheets of 4. Value, set: unused, $12; used, $9.

**Bratislava Type of 1977**

3k, View across the Danube, by J. Eder, 1810. 4k, The Old Royal Bridge, by J.A. Lantz, 1820.

**1980, Oct. 28**

| | | | | |
|---|---|---|---|---|
| **2331** | A760 | 3k multi | 1.60 | 1.40 |
| **2332** | A760 | 4k multi | 1.25 | .80 |

Nos. 2331-2332 were each issued in sheets of 4. Value, set $16.

10th Anniversary of Socialist Youth Federation — A822

**1980, Nov. 9** ***Perf. 12x11½***

| | | | | |
|---|---|---|---|---|
| **2333** | A822 | 50h multi | .25 | .25 |

**No. 2137 Overprinted 3. / MEZINARODNI VELETRH ZNAMEK / ESSEN '80 in Red**

**1980, Nov. 18**

| | | | | |
|---|---|---|---|---|
| **2334** | A755 | 1.60k multi | 18.00 | 10.00 |

Czechoslovak Day/ ESSEN '80, 3rd International Stamp Exhibition, No. 2334 has overprinted red marginal inscription.

**Painting Type of 1967**

Designs: 1k, Pavel Jozef Safarik, by Jozef B. Klemens. 2k, Peasant Revolt mosaic, Anna Podzemna. 3k, St. Lucia, 14th century statue. 4k, Waste Heaps, by Jan Zrzavy, horiz. 5k, Labor, sculpture by Jan Stursa.

**1980, Nov. 27** **Engr.** ***Perf. 12***

| | | | | |
|---|---|---|---|---|
| **2335** | A565 | 1k multi | 1.25 | 1.10 |
| **2336** | A565 | 2k multi | 1.25 | 1.10 |
| **2337** | A565 | 3k multi | .65 | .45 |
| **2338** | A565 | 4k multi | .75 | .55 |
| **2339** | A565 | 5k multi | .75 | .55 |
| | *Nos. 2335-2339 (5)* | | 4.65 | 3.75 |

Nos. 2335-2339 were each issued in sheets of 4. Value, set $27.

Stamp Day — A823

**Engraved and Photogravure**

**1980, Dec. 18** ***Perf. 11½x12***

| | | | | |
|---|---|---|---|---|
| **2340** | A823 | 1k multi | .25 | .25 |

7th Five-year Plan, 1981-1985 A824

**1981, Jan. 1** ***Perf. 11½***

| | | | | |
|---|---|---|---|---|
| **2341** | A824 | 50h multi | .25 | .25 |

International Year of the Disabled A825

**1981, Feb. 24**

| | | | | |
|---|---|---|---|---|
| **2342** | A825 | 1k multi | .25 | .25 |

Landau, 1800 A826

1k, Mail coach, 1830. 3.60k, Mail sled, 1840. 5k, 4-horse mail coach, 1860. 7k, Open carriage, 1840.

**1981, Feb. 25** ***Perf. 12x11½***

| | | | | |
|---|---|---|---|---|
| **2343** | A826 | 50h shown | .25 | .25 |
| **2344** | A826 | 1k multi | .25 | .25 |
| **2345** | A826 | 3.60k multi | 1.00 | .35 |
| **2346** | A826 | 5k multi | .75 | .25 |
| **2347** | A826 | 7k multi | 1.10 | .75 |
| *a.* | | Sheet of 4 | 15.00 | 10.00 |
| | *Nos. 2343-2347 (5)* | | 3.35 | 1.85 |

WIPA '81 Intl. Philatelic Exhibition, Vienna, Austria, May 22-31. No. 2347a issued May 10.

Wolfgang Amadeus Mozart — A827

Famous Men: No. 2348, Josef Hlavka (1831-1908). No. 2349, Juraj Hronec (1881-1959). No. 2350, Jan Sverma (1901-44). No. 2351, Mikulas Schneider-Trnavsky (1881-1958). No. 2352, B. Bolzano (1781-1848). No. 2353, Dimitri Shostakovich, composer. No. 2354, George Bernard Shaw, playwright.

**1981, Mar. 10** ***Perf. 11½***

| | | | | |
|---|---|---|---|---|
| **2348** | A827 | 50h multi | .25 | .25 |
| **2349** | A827 | 50h multi | .25 | .25 |
| **2350** | A827 | 50h multi | .25 | .25 |
| **2351** | A827 | 50h multi | .25 | .25 |
| **2352** | A827 | 1k multi | .45 | .25 |
| **2353** | A827 | 1k multi | .25 | .25 |
| **2354** | A827 | 1k multi | .25 | .25 |
| **2355** | A827 | 1k multi | .25 | .25 |
| | *Nos. 2348-2355 (8)* | | 2.20 | 2.00 |

Souvenir Sheet

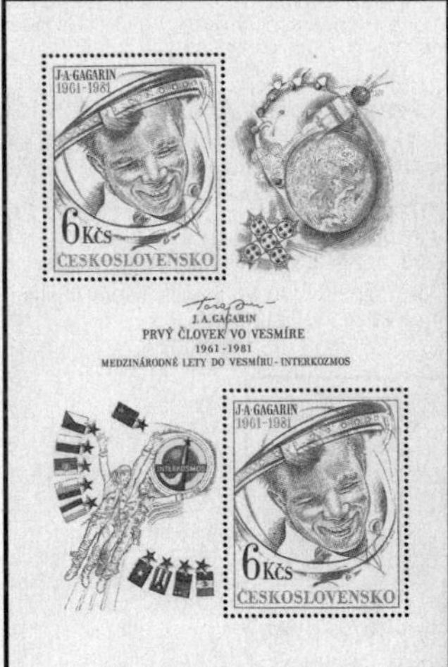


Yuri Gagarin — A828

**1981, Apr. 5** ***Perf. 12***

| | | | | |
|---|---|---|---|---|
| **2356** | A828 | Sheet of 2 | 4.50 | 4.00 |
| *a.* | | 6k multicolored | 2.00 | 1.60 |

20th anniv. of 1st manned space flight.

Workers and Banner A829

1k, Hands holding banner. 4k, Worker holding banner, vert.

**1981, Apr. 6** ***Perf. 12x11½***

| | | | | |
|---|---|---|---|---|
| **2357** | A829 | 50h shown | .25 | .25 |
| **2358** | A829 | 1k multi | .25 | .25 |
| **2359** | A829 | 4k multi | .35 | .25 |
| | *Nos. 2357-2359 (3)* | | .85 | .75 |

Czechoslovakian Communist Party, 60th anniv.

Congress Emblem, View of Prague — A830

**1981, Apr. 6**
2360 A830 50h shown .25 .25
2361 A830 1k Bratislava .25 .25

16th Communist Party Congress.

Agriculture Museum, 90th Anniv. — A831

**1981, May 14** ***Perf. 11½x12***
2362 A831 1k multi .25 .25

Natl. Assembly Elections — A832

**1981, June 1**
2363 A832 50h multi .25 .25

**Bratislava Type of 1977**

Designs: 3k, Bratislava Castle, by G.B. Probst, 1760. 4k, Grassalkovic Palace, by C. Bschor, 1815.

**1981, June 10** ***Perf. 12***
2364 A760 3k multi 1.40 1.25
2365 A760 4k multi 1.00 .75

Nos. 2364-2365 were each issued in sheets of 4. Value, set: unused, $12; used, $9.

Uran and Red October (Health) Resorts A833

Successes of Socialist Achievements Exhibition: 1k, Brno-Bratislava Highway, Jihlava. 2k, Nuclear power station, Jaslovske Bohunice.

**1981, June 10** ***Perf. 12x11½***
2366 A833 80h multi .25 .25
2367 A833 1k multi .25 .25
2368 A833 2k multi .25 .25
*Nos. 2366-2368 (3)* .75 .75

Border Defense Units, 30th Anniv. A834

Civil Defense, 30th Anniv. A835

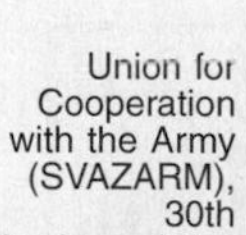

Union for Cooperation with the Army (SVAZARM), 30th Anniv. — A836

Intl.Youth Character Building Contest, Rysy Mtn., 25th Anniv. — A837

**Engraved and Photogravure**

**1981, July 11** ***Perf. 11½***
2369 A834 40h multi .25 .25
2370 A835 50h multi .25 .25
2371 A836 1k multi .25 .25
2372 A837 3.60k multi .75 .30
*Nos. 2369-2372 (4)* 1.50 1.05

30th Natl. Festival of Amateur Puppet Ensembles — A838

**1981, July 2** ***Perf. 11½***
2373 A838 2k Punch and Devil .50 .25

Souvenir Sheet

Guernica, by Pablo Picasso — A839

**1981, July 2 Engr.** ***Perf. 11½x12***
2374 A839 10k multi 3.50 2.50

Picasso's birth centenary; 45th anniv. of Intl. Brigades in Spain.

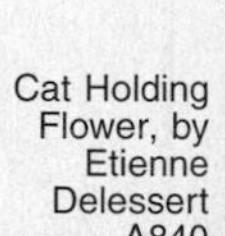

Cat Holding Flower, by Etienne Delessert A840

8th Biennial Exhibition of Children's Book Illustrations (Designs by): 50h, Albin Brunovsky, vert. 1k, Adolf Born. 2k, Vive Tolli. 10k, Suekichi Akaba.

**Engraved and Photogravure**

**1981, Sept. 5** ***Perf. 11½***
2375 A840 50h multi .25 .25
2376 A840 1k multi .25 .25
2377 A840 2k multi .25 .25
2378 A840 4k multi .55 .25
2379 A840 10k multi 1.50 .25
*Nos. 2375-2379 (5)* 2.80 1.25

Prague Zoo, 50th Anniv. — A841

**1981, Sept. 28** ***Perf. 11½x12***
2380 A841 50h Gorillas .45 .25
2381 A841 1k Lions .80 .25
2382 A841 7k Przewalski's horses 2.25 .80
*Nos. 2380-2382 (3)* 3.50 1.30

Anti-smoking Campaign A842

**1981, Oct. 27** ***Perf. 12***
2383 A842 4k multi .85 .45

No. 2383 was issued in sheets of 10, containing 8 stamps and 2 labels. Values: single with label attached, $1.25; sheet, $9.

**Prague Castle Art Type of 1971**

Designs: 3k, Carved dragon, Palais Lobkovitz, 16th cent. 4k, St. Vitus Cathedral, by J. Sember and G. Dobler, 19th cent.

**1981, Oct. 28**
2384 A634 3k multi .75 .45
2385 A634 4k multi 1.75 1.40

Nos. 2384-2385 were each issued in sheets of 4. Value, set $12.

**Painting Type of 1967**

Designs: 1k, View of Prague, by Vaclav Hollar (1607-1677). 2k, Czechoslovak Academy medallion, engraved by Otakar Spaniel (1881-1955). 3k, Jihoceska Vysivka, by Zdenek Sklenar (b. 1910). 4k, Still Life, by A.M. Gerasimov (1881-1963). 5k, Standing Woman, by Pablo Picasso (1881-1973).

**1981, Nov. 27 Engr.** ***Perf. 12***
2386 A565 1k multi 2.10 1.40
2387 A565 2k multi .55 .30
2388 A565 3k multi .70 .45
2389 A565 4k multi .85 .45
2390 A565 5k multi 1.40 1.10
*Nos. 2386-2390 (5)* 5.60 3.70

Nos. 2386-2390 were each issued in sheets of 4. Value, set $27.50.

Sheets of No. 2390 exist with center gutter inscribed with Philexfrance 82 and FIP emblems. Value, $10.

Stamp Day — A843

**Engraved and Photogravure**

**1981, Dec. 18** ***Perf. 11½x12***
2391 A843 1k Engraver Edward Karel .25 .25

Russian Workers' Party, Prague Congress, 70th Anniv. — A844

**1982, Jan. 18** ***Perf. 12***
2392 A844 2k Lenin .50 .25
*a.* Sheet of 4 *4.50 4.00*

No. 2392 issued in sheet of 8. Value $10.

1982 World Cup Soccer A845

Designs: Various soccer players.

**1982, Jan. 29** ***Perf. 12x11½***
2393 A845 1k multi .25 .25
2394 A845 3.60k multi .70 .30
2395 A845 4k multi 1.40 .50
*Nos. 2393-2395 (3)* 2.35 1.05

10th World Trade Union Congress, Havana — A846

**1982, Feb. 10** ***Perf. 11½***
2396 A846 1k multi .25 .25

Arms of Hrob — A847

Arms of various cities: No. 2398, Nove Mesto Nad Metuji. No. 2399, Trencin. No. 2400, Mlada Boleslav.

**1982, Feb. 10** ***Perf. 12x11½***
2397 A847 50h shown .25 .25
2398 A847 50h multicolored .25 .25
2399 A847 50h multicolored .25 .25
2400 A847 50h multicolored .25 .25
*Nos. 2397-2400 (4)* 1.00 1.00

See Nos. 2499-2502, 2542-2544, 2595-2597, 2783-2786.

50th Anniv. of the Great Strike at Most — A848

**1982, Mar. 23** ***Perf. 11½***
2401 A848 1k multi .25 .25

60th Intl. Railway Union Congress — A849

6k, Steam locomotive, 1922, electric, 1982.

**1982, Mar. 23** ***Perf. 12x11½***
2402 A849 6k multicolored 3.25 .95

10th Workers' Congress, Prague — A850

**1982, Apr. 15**
2403 A850 1k multi .25 .25

George Dimitrov — A851

**1982, May 1**
2404 A851 50h multi .25 .25

A852

Engravings: 40h, The Muse Euterpe Playing a Flute, by Crispin de Passe (1565-1637). 50h, The Lute Player, by Jacob de Gheyn (1565-1629). 1k, Woman Flautist, by Adriaen Collaert (1560-1618). 2k, Musicians in a Hostel, by Rembrandt (1606-1669). 3k, Hurdy-gurdy Player, by Jacques Callot (1594-1635).

**1982, May 18** ***Perf. 11½x12***
2405 A852 40h multi .25 .25
2406 A852 50h multi .25 .25
2407 A852 1k multi .25 .25
2408 A852 2k multi .30 .25
2409 A852 3k multi 1.10 .60
*Nos. 2405-2409 (5)* 2.15 1.60

10th Lidice Intl. Children's Drawing Contest — A853

**1982, May 18**
2410 A853 2k multi 1.25 .90

Issued in sheets of 6 with 3 labels. Value $9.

40th Anniv. of Destruction of Lidice and Lezaky — A854

**1982, June 4** ***Perf. 11½***
2411 A854 1k Girl, rose .45 .25
2412 A854 1k Hands, barbed wire .45 .25

Souvenir Sheet

UN Disarmament Conference — A855

**1982, June 4** ***Perf. 12***
2413 A855 Sheet of 2 9.00 7.00
*a.* 6k Woman holding doves 4.00 3.00

Souvenir Sheet

2nd UN Conference on Peaceful Uses of Outer Space, Vienna, Aug. 9-21 — A856

**1982, Aug. 9** **Engr. & Photo.**
2414 A856 Sheet of 2 12.50 9.00
*a.* 5k multi 4.50 3.50

Krivoklat Castle A857

1k, Statues (Krivoklat). 2k, Nitra Castle. 3k, Pottery, lock (Nitra).

**1982, Aug. 31** ***Perf. 12x11½***
2415 A857 50h shown .25 .25
2416 A857 1k multi .25 .25
2417 A857 2k multi .30 .25
2418 A857 3k multi .40 .35
*a.* Souv. sheet of 4, #2415-2418 2.00 1.60
*Nos. 2415-2418 (4)* 1.20 1.10

50th Anniv. of Zizkov Hill Natl. Monument — A858

**1982, Sept. 16**
2419 A858 1k multi .25 .25

## Prague Castle Art Type of 1971

Designs: 3k, St. George and the Dragon, 1373. 4k, Tomb of King Vratislav I, 10th cent.

**1982, Sept. 28** ***Perf. 12***
2420 A634 3k multi 1.60 1.25
2421 A634 4k multi .85 .85

Nos. 2420-2421 were each issued in sheets of 4. Value, set: unused, $11; used, $10.

## Bratislava Type of 1977

Designs: 3k, Paddle steamer, Parnik, 1818. 4k, View from Bridge, 19th cent.

**1982, Sept. 29**
2422 A760 3k multi 1.40 1.00
2423 A760 4k multi 1.40 1.00

Nos. 2422-2423 were each issued in sheets of 4. Value, set $15.

European Danube Commission — A859

3k, Steamer, Bratislava Bridge. 3.60k, Ferry, Budapest.

**1982, Sept. 29** ***Perf. 11½x12***
2424 A859 3k multi .65 .25
*a.* Souvenir sheet of 4 4.00 3.00
2425 A859 3.60k multi .85 .25
*a.* Souvenir sheet of 4 6.00 5.00

16th Communist Party Congress — A860

**1982, Oct. 28** ***Perf. 12x11½***
2426 A860 20h Agriculture .25 .25
2427 A860 1k Industry .25 .25
2428 A860 3k Engineering .25 .25
*Nos. 2426-2428 (3)* .75 .75

30th Anniv. of Academy of Sciences — A861

**1982, Oct. 29** ***Perf. 11½***
2429 A861 6k Emblem .90 .35

65th Anniv. of October Revolution — A862

Design: 1k, 60th anniv. of USSR.

**1982, Nov. 7** ***Perf. 12x11½***
2430 A862 50h multi .25 .25
2431 A862 1k multi .25 .25

Jaroslav Hasek, Writer, Sculpture by Josef Malejovsky — A863

Sculptures: 2k, Jan Zrzavy, painter and graphic artist, by Jan Simota. 4.40k, Leos Janacek, composer, by Milos Axman. 6k, Martin Kukucin, freedom fighter, by Jan Kulich. 7k, Peaceful Work, by Rudolf Pribis.

## Engraved and Photogravure

**1982, Nov. 26** ***Perf. 11½x12***
2432 A863 1k multi .25 .25
2433 A863 2k multi .25 .25
2434 A863 4.40k multi .75 .25
2435 A863 6k multi .80 .25
2436 A863 7k multi 1.20 .50
*Nos. 2432-2436 (5)* 3.25 1.50

Nos. 2432-2436 were each issued in sheets of 4. Value, set $20.

## Painting Type of 1967

1k, Revolution in Spain, by Josef Sima (1891-1971). 2k, Woman Dressing, by Rudolf Kremlicka (1886-1932). 3k, The Girl Bride, by Dezider Milly (1906-1971). 4k, Performers, by Jan Zelibsky (b. 1907). 5k, The Complaint of the Birds, by Emil Filla (1882-1953).

**1982, Nov. 27** ***Perf. 12***
2437 A565 1k multi .70 .45
2438 A565 2k multi 1.40 1.00
2439 A565 3k multi .70 .45
2440 A565 4k multi .70 .45
2441 A565 5k multi 1.40 1.00
*Nos. 2437-2441 (5)* 4.90 3.35

Nos. 2437-2441 were each issued in sheets of 4. Value, set $20.

Stamp Day — A864

1k, Engraver Jaroslav Goldschmied (1890-1977).

**1982, Dec. 8** ***Perf. 11½***
2442 A864 1k multicolored .25 .25

A865

**1983, Jan. 10 Engr.** ***Perf. 12x11½***
2443 A865 50h dark blue .25 .25

Pres. Gustav Husak, 70th birthday. See No. 2686.

A866

Designs: 50h, Jaroslav Hasek (1882-1923), writer. 1k, Julius Fucik (1903-1943), antifascist martyr. 2k, Martin Luther (1483-1546). 5k, Johannes Brahms (1833-1897), composer.

**1983, Feb. 24** **Engr. & Photo.**
2444 A866 50h multi .25 .25
2445 A866 1k multi .25 .25
2446 A866 2k multi .25 .25
*a.* Souvenir sheet of 4 24.00 12.50
2447 A866 5k multi .65 .25
*Nos. 2444-2447 (4)* 1.40 1.00

Nordposta '83 Intl. Stamp Exhibition, Hamburg.
No. 2446a issued Nov. 1.

Workers Marching A867

Family — A868

**1983, Feb. 25** ***Perf. 11½***
2448 A867 50h multi .25 .25
2449 A868 1k multi .25 .25

35th anniv. of "Victorious February" (50h), and Natl. Front (1k).

World Communications Year — A869

***Perf. 11½, 12x11½ (2k)***
**1983, Mar. 16**
2450 A869 40h multi .25 .25
2451 A869 1k multi .25 .25
2452 A869 2k multi .25 .25
2453 A869 3.60k multi .40 .25
*Nos. 2450-2453 (4)* 1.15 1.00

Various wave patterns. 2k, 40x23mm; 3.60k, 49x19mm.

7th World Ski-jumping Championships A870

**1983, Mar. 16** ***Perf. 11½***
2454 A870 1k multi .25 .25

Souvenir Sheet

5th Anniv. of Czechoslovak-USSR Intercosmos Cooperative Space Program — A871

**1983, Apr. 12** ***Perf. 12***
2455 A871 Sheet of 2 11.00 7.50
*a.* 10k multi 3.50 3.50

See No. 2226.

Protected Species — A872

50h, Butterfly, violets. 1k, Water lilies, frog. 2k, Pine cones, crossbill. 3.60k, Herons. 5k, Gentians, lynx. 7k, Stag.

**1983, Apr. 28** ***Perf. 12x11½***
2456 A872 50h multi .30 .25
2457 A872 1k multi .65 .25
2458 A872 2k multi .65 .30
2459 A872 3.60k multi .80 .35

**2460** A872 5k multi 1.10 .45
**2461** A872 7k multi 2.50 1.00
*Nos. 2456-2461 (6)* 6.00 2.60

Soviet Marshals — A873

50h, Ivan S. Konev. 1k, Andrei I. Yeremenko. 2k, Rodion J. Malinovsky.

**1983, May 5** *Perf. 11½*
**2462** A873 50h multi .25 .25
**2463** A873 1k multi .25 .25
**2464** A873 2k multi .25 .25
*Nos. 2462-2464 (3)* .75 .75

30th anniv. of Czechoslovak-Soviet defense treaty.

A874

**1983, July 13** *Perf. 12*
**2465** A874 2k multi .35 .25
*a.* Souvenir sheet of 4 6.50 5.50

World Peace and Life Congress, Prague. No. 2465 issued in sheets of 8. Value $4.50.

Emperor Rudolf II by Adrian De Vries (1560-1626) A875

Art treasures of the Prague Castle: 5k, Kinetic relief, Timepiece, Rudolf Svoboda.

**1983, Aug. 25** *Perf. 11½*
**2466** A875 4k multi .80 .60
**2467** A875 5k multi .80 .60

Nos. 2466-2467 were each issued in sheets of 6. Value, set $12.

See Nos. 2518-2519, 2610-2611, 2654-2655, 2717-2718, 2744-2745, 2792-2793.

9th Biennial of Illustrations for Children and Youth — A876

Illustrators: 50h, Oleg K. Zotov, USSR. 1k, Zbigniew Rychlicki, Poland. 4k, Lisbeth Zwerger, Austria. 7k, Antonio Dominques, Angola.

**1983, Sept. 9** **Engr. & Photo.**
**2468** A876 50h multi .25 .25
**2469** A876 1k multi .25 .25
**2470** A876 4k multi .25 .25
**2471** A876 7k multi .50 .25
*a.* Souv. sheet of 4, #2468-2471 5.00 3.00
*Nos. 2468-2471 (4)* 1.25 1.00

World Communications Year — A877

Emblems and aircraft.

**1983, Sept. 30** *Perf. 11½*
**2472** A877 50h red & black .25 .25
**2473** A877 1k red & black, vert. .25 .25
**2474** A877 4k red & black .75 .25
*Nos. 2472-2474 (3)* 1.25 .75

60th anniv. of the Czechoslovak Airlines.

16th Party Congress Achievements — A878

**1983, Oct. 20** *Perf. 12x11½*
**2475** A878 50h Civil engineering construction .25 .25
**2476** A878 1k Chemical industry .25 .25
**2477** A878 3k Health services .40 .25
*Nos. 2475-2477 (3)* .90 .75

**Bratislava Type of 1977**

Designs: 3k, Two sculptures, Viktor Tilgner (1844-96). 4k, Mirbachov Palace, 1939, by Julius Schubert (1888-1947).

**1983, Oct. 28** *Perf. 12*
**2478** A760 3k multi 1.50 1.25
**2479** A760 4k multi 1.25 1.00

Nos. 2478-2479 were each issued in sheets of 4 stamps. Value, set $12.

Natl. Theater, Prague, Centenary — A879

50h, Natl. Theater building. 2k, State Theater, Natl. Theater.

**1983, Nov. 8** **Engr.** *Perf. 11½*
**2480** A879 50h brown .25 .25
**2481** A879 2k green .30 .25

Messenger of Mourning, by Mikolas Ales — A880

Designs: 2k, Genius, theater curtain by Vojtech Hynais (1854-1925). 3k, Music, Lyric drawings by Frantisek Zenisek (1849-1916). 4k, Symbolic figure of Prague, by Vaclav Brozik (1851-1901). 5k, Hradcany Castle, by Julius Marak (1832-1899).

**1983, Nov. 18** **Engr.**
**2482** A880 1k multi 1.20 .75
**2483** A880 2k multi 1.50 1.10
**2484** A880 3k multi .90 .45
**2485** A880 4k multi 1.40 .45
**2486** A880 5k multi 1.10 .60
*Nos. 2482-2486 (5)* 6.10 3.35

Nos. 2482-2486 were each issued in sheets of 4 stamps. Value, set $30.

Warrior with Sword and Shield, Engraving, 17th Cent. — A881

Engravings of Costumes: 50h, Bodyguard of Rudolf II, by Jacob de Gheyn (1565-1629). 1k, Lady with Lace Collar, by Jacques Callot (1592-1635). 4k, Lady, by Vaclav Hollar (1607-77). 5k, Man, by Antoine Watteau (1684-1721).

**Engraved and Photogravure**

**1983, Dec. 2** *Perf. 11½x12*
**2487** A881 40h multi .25 .25
**2488** A881 50h multi .25 .25
**2489** A881 1k multi .25 .25
**2490** A881 4k multi .55 .25
**2491** A881 5k multi 1.25 .75
*Nos. 2487-2491 (5)* 2.55 1.75

Stamp Day — A882

1k, Karl Seizinger (1889-1978), #114.

**1983, Dec. 18**
**2492** A882 1k multicolored .25 .25

Czechoslovak Federation, 15th Anniv. — A883

50h, Bratislava, Prague Castles.

**1984, Jan. 1** *Perf. 11½*
**2493** A883 50h multicolored .25 .25

35th Anniv. of COMECON A884

1k, Headquarters, Moscow.

**1984, Jan. 23**
**2494** A884 1k dark blue & red brown .25 .25

1984 Winter Olympics A885

**1984, Feb. 7** *Perf. 12x11½*
**2495** A885 2k Cross-country skiing .40 .25
**2496** A885 3k Hockey .50 .25
*a.* Souvenir sheet of 4 5.00 4.00
**2497** A885 5k Biathlon 1.25 .35
*Nos. 2495-2497 (3)* 2.15 .85

Intl. Olympic Committee, 90th Anniv. — A886

**1984, Feb. 7** *Perf. 11½x12*
**2498** A886 7k Rings, runners, torch 1.25 .35

**City Arms Type of 1982**

**1984, Mar. 1** *Perf. 12x11½*
**2499** A847 50h Kutna Hora .25 .25
**2500** A847 50h Turnov .25 .25
**2501** A847 1k Martin .25 .25
**2502** A847 1k Milevsko .25 .25
*Nos. 2499-2502 (4)* 1.00 1.00

Intercosmos Space Program — A887

Various satellites. Nos. 2503-2507 se-tenant with labels showing flags.

**1984, Apr. 12** *Perf. 11½x12*
**2503** A887 50h multi .30 .25
**2504** A887 1k multi .45 .25
**2505** A887 2k multi .45 .25
**2506** A887 4k multi .75 .25
**2507** A887 5k multi .75 .25
*Nos. 2503-2507 (5)* 2.70 1.25

Resistance Heroes — A888

Designs: 50h, Vendelin Opatrny (1908-44). 1k, Ladislav Novomesky (1904-76). 2k, Rudolf Jasiok (1919-44). 4k, Jan Nalepka (1912-43).

**1984, May 9** *Perf. 11x11½*
**2508** A888 50h multi .25 .25
**2509** A888 1k multi .25 .25
**2510** A888 2k multi .25 .25
**2511** A888 4k multi .25 .25
*Nos. 2508-2511 (4)* 1.00 1.00

Music Year — A889

**1984, May 11** *Perf. 11½*
**2512** A889 50h Instruments .25 .25
**2513** A889 1k Organ pipes, vert. .25 .25

**Bratislava Type of 1977**

Designs: 3k, Vintners' Guild arms, 19th cent. 4k, View of Bratislava (painting commemorating shooting competition, 1827).

**1984, June 1** *Perf. 12*
**2514** A760 3k multi 1.10 .85
**2515** A760 4k multi 1.60 1.10

Nos. 2514-2515 were each issued in sheets of 4 stamps. Value, set $12.

Central Telecommunications Building, Bratislava — A890

**1984, June 1** *Perf. 11½*
**2516** A890 2k multi .25 .25

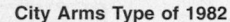

A891

**1984, June 12** *Perf. 12*

**2517** A891 5k UPU emblem, dove, globe 2.50 2.50

1984 UPU Congress. Issued in sheet of 4 with and without Philatelic Salon text. Values, $30 with text, $12 without text.

### Prague Castle Type of 1983

Designs: 3k, Crowing rooster, St. Vitus Cathedral, 19th cent. 4k, King David from the Roundnice, Book of Psalms illuminated manuscript, Bohemia, 15th cent.

**1984, Aug. 9** **Engr. & Photo.**

**2518** A875 3k multi .75 .60
**2519** A875 4k multi 1.00 .75

Nos. 2518-2519 were each issued in sheets of 6 stamps. Value, set $10.

Playing Cards — A893

50h, Jack of Spades, 16th cent. 1k, Queen of spades, 17th cent. 2k, 9 of hearts, 18th cent. 3k, Jack of clubs, 18th cent. 5k, King of hearts, 19th cent.

**1984, Aug. 28** *Perf. 11½x12*

**2520** A893 50h multi .25 .25
**2521** A893 1k multi .25 .25
**2522** A893 2k multi .25 .25
**2523** A893 3k multi .35 .25
**2524** A893 5k multi 1.00 .25
*Nos. 2520-2524 (5)* 2.10 1.25

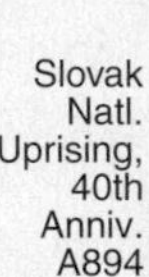

Slovak Natl. Uprising, 40th Anniv. A894

**1984, Aug. 29** *Perf. 12x11½*

**2525** A894 50h Family, factories, flowers .25 .25

Battle of Dukla Pass (Carpathians), 40th Anniv. — A895

**1984, Sept. 8** *Perf. 11½x12*

**2526** A895 2k Soldiers, flag .40 .25

1984 Summer Olympics A896

**1984, Sept. 9** *Perf. 12x11½*

**2527** A896 1k Pole vault .25 .25
**2528** A896 2k Bicycling .40 .25
**2529** A896 3k Rowing .60 .35
**2530** A896 5k Weight lifting 1.00 .45
*a.* Souv. sheet of 4, #2527-2530 4.00 3.25
*Nos. 2527-2530 (4)* 2.25 1.30

16th Party Congress Goals and Projects — A897

**1984, Oct. 28** *Perf. 12x11½*

**2531** A897 1k Communications .25 .25
**2532** A897 2k Transportation .25 .25
**2533** A897 3k Transgas pipeline .35 .25
*a.* Souvenir sheet of 3 2.00 1.60
*Nos. 2531-2533 (3)* .85 .75

### Painting Type of 1967

1k, The Milevsky River, by Karel Stehlik (b. 1912). 2k, Under the Trees, by Viktor Barvitius (1834-1902). 3k, Landscape with Flowers, by Zolo Palugyay (1898-1935). 4k, King in Palace, Visehrad Codex miniature, 1085. 5k, View of Kokorin Castles, by Antonin Manes. Nos. 2534-2537 horiz.; issued in sheets of 4.

**1984, Nov. 16** *Perf. 11½*

**2534** A565 1k multi 1.75 .90
**2535** A565 2k multi 1.75 .90
**2536** A565 3k multi 1.75 .90
**2537** A565 4k multi 2.75 .90
**2538** A565 5k multi 3.25 .90
*Nos. 2534-2538 (5)* 11.25 4.50

Nos. 2534-2538 were each issued in sheets of 4 stamps. Value, set $45.

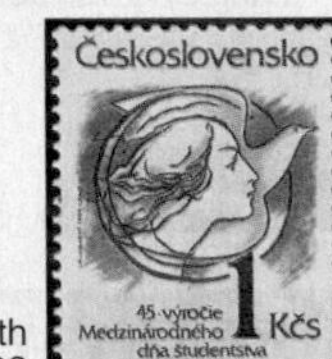


Students' Intl., 45th Anniv. — A898

**1984, Nov. 17**

**2539** A898 1k Head, dove .25 .25

Birth Cent., Antonin Zapotocky — A899

### Engr. & Photo.

**1984, Dec. 18** *Perf. 11½*

**2540** A899 50h multi .25 .25

Stamp Day — A900

1k, Engraver Bohumil Heinz (1894-1940).

**1984, Dec. 18** *Perf. 11½x12*

**2541** A900 1k multi .25 .25

### City Arms Type of 1982

**1985, Feb. 5** *Perf. 12x11½*

**2542** A847 50h Kamyk nad Vltavou .25 .25
**2543** A847 50h Havirov .25 .25
**2544** A847 50h Trnava .25 .25
*Nos. 2542-2544 (3)* .75 .75

University of Applied Arts, Prague, Centenary — A901

**1985, Feb. 6** *Perf. 11½x12*

**2545** A901 3k Art and Pleasure, sculpture .40 .25

Trnava University, 350th Anniv. — A902

**1985, Feb. 6** *Perf. 11½x12*

**2546** A902 2k Town of Trnava .40 .25

Military Museum Exposition — A903

50h, Armor, crossbow, vert. 1k, Medals, vert. 2k, Biplane, spacecraft.

**1985, Feb. 7** *Perf. 11½x12, 12x11½*

**2547** A903 50h multi .25 .25
**2548** A903 1k multi .25 .25
**2549** A903 2k multi .40 .25
*Nos. 2547-2549 (3)* .90 .75

Vladimir I. Lenin (1870-1924), 1st Chairman of Russia — A904

**1985, Mar. 15** **Engr.** *Perf. 12*

**2550** A904 2k multi .80 .40

No. 2550 printed in sheets of 6 stamps. Value $5.

UN 40th Anniv., Peace Year 1986 A905

**1985, Mar. 15**

**2551** A905 6k UN, Peace Year emblems 2.75 2.40

Issued in sheets of 4 stamps. Value $12.

Natl. Arms, Twig, Crowd — A906

### Engraved and Photogravure

**1985, Apr. 5** *Perf. 11½*

**2552** A906 4k multicolored .60 .25

Kosice govt. plan, Apr. 5, 1945.

Natl. Arms, Flag, Soldiers — A907

**1985, Apr. 5**

**2553** A907 50h multicolored .25 .25

Natl. Security Forces, 40th anniv.

Halley's Comet, INTERCOSMOS Project Vega — A908

Design: Emblem, space platform, interstellar map, intercept data.

**1985, Apr. 12** *Perf. 12x11½*

**2554** Sheet of 2 9.00 9.00
*a.* A908 5k multicolored 4.00 3.25

Project Vega, a joint effort of the USSR, France, German Democratic Republic, Austria, Poland, Bulgaria and CSSR, was for the geophysical study of Halley's Comet, Dec. 1984-Mar. 1986.

European Ice Hockey Championships, Prague, Apr. 17-May 3 — A909

**1985, Apr. 13**

**2555** A909 1k Hockey players, emblem .25 .25

### No. 2555 Ovptd. "CSSR MISTREM SVETA" in Violet Blue

**1985, May 31** *Perf. 12x11½*

**2556** A909 1k multi 2.00 2.00

Natl. Chess Org., 80th Anniv. — A910

**1985, Apr. 13** *Perf. 11½*

**2557** A910 6k Emblem, game board, chessmen 1.25 .50

Anniversaries — A911

No. 2558, May Uprising, 1945. No. 2559, Soviet Army in CSSR, 1945. No. 2560, Warsaw Treaty, 1950. No. 2561, Czech-Soviet Treaty, 1970.

**1985, May 5** *Perf. 11½x12*

**2558** A911 1k multicolored .25 .25
**2559** A911 1k multicolored .25 .25
**2560** A911 1k multicolored .25 .25
**2561** A911 1k multicolored .25 .25
*Nos. 2558-2561 (4)* 1.00 1.00

Spartakiad '85, Strahov Stadium, Prague, June 27 — A912

Designs: 50h, Gymnasts warming up with rackets and balls. 1k, Rhythmic gymnastics floor exercise, Prague Castle.

**1985, June 3** *Perf. 11½, 11½x12*

**2562** A912 50h multi .25 .25

**Size: 53x22mm**

**2563** A912 1k multi .25 .25

WWII Anti-Fascist Political Art — A913

Drawings and caricatures: 50h, Fire, and From the Concentration Camp, by Joseph Capek (1887-1945). 2k, The Conference on Disarmament in Geneva, 1927 and The Prophecy of Three Parrots, 1933, by Frantisek Bidlo (1895-1945). 4k, The Unknown Warrior to Order, 1936, and The Almost Peaceful Dove, 1937, by Antonin Pelc (1895-1967).

**1985, June 4** ***Perf. 12x11½***

**2564** A913 50h multi .25 .25
**2565** A913 2k multi .25 .25
**2566** A913 4k multi .90 .25
*Nos. 2564-2566 (3)* 1.40 .75

Helsinki Conference on European Security and Cooperation, 10th Anniv. — A914

**1985, July 1** **Engr. & Photo.**

**2567** A914 7k multi 2.25 1.50
*a.* Souvenir sheet of 4 9.00 7.00

An imperf. souv. sheet similar to No. 2567a was issued June 1, 1988 for FINLANDIA '88 and PRAGA '88. Value $35.

12th World Youth Festival, Moscow A915

**1985, July 2**

**2568** A915 1k Kremlin, youths .25 .25

A916

**1985, Sept. 3** ***Perf. 11½***

**2569** A916 50h multi .25 .25

Federation of World Trade Unions, 40th anniv.

### Bratislava Type of 1977

Designs. 3k, Castle and river, lace embroidery by Elena Holeczyova (1906-1983). 4k, Pottery cups and mugs, 1600-1500 B.C.

**1985, Sept. 4** **Engr.** ***Perf. 12***

**2570** A760 3k multi 1.60 .45
**2571** A760 4k multi 2.10 .60

Nos. 2570-2571 were each issued in sheets of 4 stamps. Value, set $14.

A918

Children's book illustrations: 1k, Rocking Horse, by Kveta Pacovska, USSR. 2k, Fairies, by Gennadij Spirin, USSR. 3k, Butterfly and Girl, by Kaarina Kaila, Finland. 4k, Boy and Animals, by Erick Ingraham, US.

### Engraved and Photogravure

**1985, Sept. 5** ***Perf. 11½***

**2572** A918 1k multi .25 .25
**2573** A918 2k multi .25 .25
**2574** A918 3k multi .70 .25
**2575** A918 4k multi .70 .30
*a.* Souv. sheet of 4, #2572-2575 4.50 3.00
*Nos. 2572-2575 (4)* 1.90 1.05

10th biennial of illustrations.

5-Year Development Plan — A919

50h, Construction machinery. 1k, Prague subway, map. 2k, Modern textile spinning.

**1985, Oct. 28** ***Perf. 12x11½***

**2576** A919 50h multicolored .25 .25
**2577** A919 1k multicolored .25 .25
**2578** A919 2k multicolored .25 .25
*Nos. 2576-2578 (3)* .75 .75

16th Communist Party Congress goals.

Prague Castle — A920

2k, Presidential Palace Gate, 1768. 3k, St. Vitus' Cathedral.

### Engr., Engr. & Photo. (3k)

**1985, Oct. 28** ***Perf. 12***

**2579** A920 2k multicolored .40 .40
**2580** A920 3k multicolored .50 .50

Nos. 2579-2580 were each issued in sheets of 6 stamps. Value, set $9.

A921

Glassware: 50h, Pitcher, Near East, 4th cent. 1k, Venetian pitcher, 16th cent. 2k, Bohemian goblet, c. 1720. 4k, Harrachov Bohemian vase, 18th cent. 6k, Jablonec Bohemian vase, c. 1900.

### Engraved and Photogravure

**1985, Nov. 23** ***Perf. 11½x12***

**2581** A921 50h multi .25 .25
**2582** A921 1k multi .25 .25
**2583** A921 2k multi .30 .25
**2584** A921 4k multi .50 .25
**2585** A921 6k multi 1.00 .35
*Nos. 2581-2585 (5)* 2.30 1.35

Arts and Crafts Museum, Prague, cent.

### Painting Type of 1967

Designs: 1k, Young Woman in a Blue Gown, by Jozef Ginovsky (1800-1857). 2k, Lenin on the Charles Bridge, Prague, 1952, by Martin Sladky (b. 1920). 3k, Avenue of Poplars, 1935, by Vaclav Rabas (1885-1954). 4k, The Martyrom of St. Dorothea, 1516, by Hans Baldung Grien (c. 1484-1545). 5k, Portrait of Jasper Schade van Westrum, 1645, by Frans Hals (c. 1581-1666).

**1985, Nov. 27** **Engr.** ***Perf. 12***

**2586** A565 1k multi 1.60 .80
**2587** A565 2k multi 1.10 .35
**2588** A565 3k multi 1.50 .35
**2589** A565 4k multi .90 .50
**2590** A565 5k multi .90 .50
*Nos. 2586-2590 (5)* 6.00 2.50

Nos. 2586-2590 were each issued in sheets of 4 stamps. Value, set $30.

Bohdan Roule (1921-1960), Engraver — A922

### Engraved and Photogravure

**1985, Dec. 18** ***Perf. 11½x12***

**2591** A922 1k multicolored .25 .25

Stamp Day 1985.

Intl. Peace Year — A923

**1986, Jan. 2**

**2592** A923 1k multi .25 .25

Philharmonic Orchestra, 90th Anniv. — A924

**1986, Jan. 2** ***Perf. 11½***

**2593** A924 1k Victory Statue, Prague .25 .25

EXPO '86, Vancouver A925

Design: Z 50 LS monoplane, Cenyerth Prague-Kladno locomotive, Sahara Desert rock drawing, 5th-6th cent. B.C.

**1986, Jan. 23** ***Perf. 11½***

**2594** A925 4k multicolored .85 .25

### City Arms Type of 1982

**1986, Feb. 10** ***Perf. 12x11½***

**Size: 42x54mm**

**2595** A847 50h Myjava .25 .25
**2596** A847 50h Vodnany .25 .25
**2597** A847 50h Zamberk .25 .25
*Nos. 2595-2597 (3)* .75 .75

17th Natl. Communist Party Congress, Prague, Mar. 24 — A926

**1986, Mar. 20** ***Perf. 11½***

**2598** A926 50h shown .25 .25
**2599** A926 1k Industry .25 .25

Natl. Communist Party, 65th Anniv. — A927

50h, Star, man, woman. 1k, Hammer, sickle, laborers.

**1986, Mar. 20** ***Perf. 12x11½***

**2600** A927 50h multi .25 .25
**2601** A927 1k multi .25 .25

Natl. Front Election Program A928

**1986, Mar. 28**

**2602** A928 50h multi .25 .25

Karlovy Vary Intl. Film Festival, 25th Anniv. — A929

**1986, Apr. 3** ***Perf. 11½***

**2603** A929 1k multi .25 .25

A930

**1986, Apr. 8** **Engr. & Photo.**

**2604** A930 1k multi .25 .25

Spring of Prague Music Festival.

A931

**1986, Apr. 25**

**2605** A931 50h multi .40 .25

Prague-Moscow air service, 50th anniv.

Intl. Olympic Committee, 90th Anniv. — A932

**1986, May 12** ***Perf. 11½x12***

**2606** A932 2k multi .30 .25

1986 World Cup Soccer Championships, Mexico — A933

**1986, May 15** ***Perf. 12x11½***

**2607** A933 4k multi .80 .40

Women's World Volleyball Championships, Prague — A934

**1986, May 19**

| | | | | |
|---|---|---|---|---|
| **2608** | A934 | 1k multi | .25 | .25 |

Souvenir Sheet

Intl. Philatelic Federation, FIP, 60th Anniv. — A935

**1986, June 3** **Engr.** ***Perf. 12***

| | | | | |
|---|---|---|---|---|
| **2609** | A935 | 20k multi | 6.50 | 5.00 |

Exists imperf and with perforations between stamps omitted. Values, $15 and $27.50, respectively.

### Prague Castle Type of 1983

Designs: 2k, Jewelled funerary pendant, 9th cent. 3k, Allegory of Blossoms, sculpture by Jaroslav Horejc (1886-1983), St. Vitus' Cathedral.

**1986, June 6** **Engr.** ***Perf. 12***

| | | | | |
|---|---|---|---|---|
| **2610** | A875 | 2k multi | .40 | .30 |
| **2611** | A875 | 3k multi | .70 | .45 |

Nos. 2610-2611 were each issued in sheets of 6 stamps. Value, set $8.

UN Child Survival Campaign — A937

Toys.

### Engraved and Photogravure

**1986, Sept. 1** ***Perf. 11½***

| | | | | |
|---|---|---|---|---|
| **2612** | A937 | 10h Rooster | .25 | .25 |
| **2613** | A937 | 20h Horse and rider | .25 | .25 |
| **2614** | A937 | 1k Doll | .25 | .25 |
| **2615** | A937 | 2k Doll, diff. | .50 | .25 |
| **2616** | A937 | 3k Tin omnibus, c. 1910 | .65 | .30 |
| | | *Nos. 2612-2616 (5)* | 1.90 | 1.30 |

UNICEF, 40th anniv.

Registration, Cent. — A938

**1986, Sept. 2** ***Perf. 11½x12***

| | | | | |
|---|---|---|---|---|
| **2617** | A938 | 4k Label, mail coach | .45 | .25 |

### Bratislava Type of 1977

**1986, Sept. 11** **Engr.** ***Perf. 12***

| | | | | |
|---|---|---|---|---|
| **2618** | A760 | 3k Sigismund Gate | 1.25 | .80 |
| **2619** | A760 | 4k St. Margaret, bas-relief | 1.25 | .65 |

Nos. 2618-2619 were each issued in sheets of 4 stamps. Value, set $12.

Owls — A939

### Engraved and Photogravure

**1986, Sept. 18** ***Perf. 11½***

| | | | | |
|---|---|---|---|---|
| **2620** | A939 | 50h Bubo bubo | .70 | .25 |
| **2621** | A939 | 2k Asio otus | .85 | .25 |
| **2622** | A939 | 3k Strix aluco | 1.40 | .30 |
| **2623** | A939 | 4k Tyto alba | 1.40 | .45 |
| **2624** | A939 | 5k Asio flammeus | 2.10 | .60 |
| | | *Nos. 2620-2624 (5)* | 6.45 | 1.85 |

Souvenir Sheet

Intl. Brigades in Spain — A940

Theater curtain: Woman Savaged by Horses, 1936, by Vladimir Sychra (1903-1963), Natl Gallery, Prague.

**1986, Oct. 1** **Engr.** ***Perf. 12***

| | | | | |
|---|---|---|---|---|
| **2625** | A940 | Sheet of 2 | 4.50 | 3.50 |
| *a.* | | 5k multi | 2.00 | 1.25 |

Locomotives and Streetcars — A941

### Engraved and Photogravure

**1986, Oct. 6** ***Perf. 12x11½***

| | | | | |
|---|---|---|---|---|
| **2626** | A941 | 50h KT-8 | .25 | .25 |
| **2627** | A941 | 1k E458.1 | .25 | .25 |
| **2628** | A941 | 3k T466.2 | .75 | .30 |
| **2629** | A941 | 5k M152.0 | .80 | .25 |
| | | *Nos. 2626-2629 (4)* | 2.05 | 1.05 |

Paintings in the Prague and Bratislava Natl. Galleries — A942

Designs: 1k, The Circus Rider, 1980, by Jan Bauch (b. 1898). 2k, The Ventriloquist, 1954, by Frantisek Tichy (1896-1961). 3k, In the Circus, 1946, by Vincent Hloznik (b. 1919). 6k, Clown, 1985, by Karel Svolinsky (1896-1986).

**1986, Oct. 13** **Engr.** ***Perf. 12***

| | | | | |
|---|---|---|---|---|
| **2630** | A942 | 1k multi | 1.25 | .65 |
| **2631** | A942 | 2k multi | 1.60 | .85 |
| **2632** | A942 | 3k multi | 1.60 | .85 |
| **2633** | A942 | 6k multi | 1.10 | .95 |
| | | *Nos. 2630-2633 (4)* | 5.55 | 3.30 |

Nos. 2630-2633 were each issued in sheets of 4 stamps. Value, set $25.

### Painting Type of 1967

1k, The Czech Lion, May 1918, by Vratislav H. Brunner (1886-1928). 2k, Boy with Mandolin, 1945, by Jozef Sturdik (b. 1920). 3k, Metra Building, 1984, by Frantisek Gross (1909-1985). 4k, Portrait of Maria Maximiliana at Sternberk, 1665, by Karel Skreta (1610-1674). 5k, Adam & Eve, 1538, by Lucas Cranach (1472-1553).

**1986, Nov. 3** **Engr.** ***Perf. 12***

| | | | | |
|---|---|---|---|---|
| **2634** | A565 | 1k multi | 3.00 | 2.25 |
| **2635** | A565 | 2k multi | 3.00 | 2.25 |
| **2636** | A565 | 3k multi | 3.00 | 2.25 |
| **2637** | A565 | 4k multi | 3.00 | 2.25 |
| **2638** | A565 | 5k multi | 3.00 | 2.25 |
| | | *Nos. 2634-2638 (5)* | 15.00 | 11.25 |

Nos. 2634-2638 were each issued in sheets of 4 stamps. Value, set $75.

Stamp Day — A943

Design: V.H. Brunner (1886-1928), stamp designer, and No. 88.

### Photo. & Engr.

**1986, Dec. 18** ***Perf. 11½x12***

| | | | | |
|---|---|---|---|---|
| **2639** | A943 | 1k multicolored | .25 | .25 |

World Cyclocross Championships, Jan. 24-25, Central Bohemia — A944

**1987, Jan. 22** ***Perf. 11½***

| | | | | |
|---|---|---|---|---|
| **2640** | A944 | 6k multi | .80 | .25 |

Czechoslovakian Bowling Union, 50th Anniv. — A945

**1987, Jan. 22** ***Perf. 11½***

| | | | | |
|---|---|---|---|---|
| **2641** | A945 | 2k multi | .35 | .25 |

State Decorations — A946

Designs: 50h, Gold Stars of Socialist Labor and Czechoslovakia. 2k, Order of Klement Gottwald. 3k, Order of the Republic. 4k, Order of Victorious February. 5k, Order of Labor.

**1987, Feb. 4** ***Perf. 12x11½***

| | | | | |
|---|---|---|---|---|
| **2642** | A946 | 50h multi | .25 | .25 |
| **2643** | A946 | 2k multi | .25 | .25 |
| **2644** | A946 | 3k multi | .30 | .25 |
| **2645** | A946 | 4k multi | .45 | .25 |
| **2646** | A946 | 5k multi | .60 | .40 |
| | | *Nos. 2642-2646 (5)* | 1.85 | 1.40 |

Butterflies — A947

1k, Limenitis populi. 2k, Smerinthus ocellatus. 3k, Pericallia matronula. 4k, Saturnia pyri.

**1987, Mar. 4**

| | | | | |
|---|---|---|---|---|
| **2647** | A947 | 1k multi | .65 | .25 |
| **2648** | A947 | 2k multi | 1.00 | .25 |
| **2649** | A947 | 3k multi | 1.25 | .35 |
| **2650** | A947 | 4k multi | 1.60 | .35 |
| | | *Nos. 2647-2650 (4)* | 4.50 | 1.20 |

Natl. Nuclear Power Industry A948

**1987, Apr. 6**

| | | | | |
|---|---|---|---|---|
| **2651** | A948 | 5k multi | .60 | .25 |

11th Revolutionary Trade Union Movement Congress, Apr. 14-17, Prague — A949

**1987, Apr. 7** ***Perf. 11½***

| | | | | |
|---|---|---|---|---|
| **2652** | A949 | 1k multi | .25 | .25 |

Souvenir Sheet

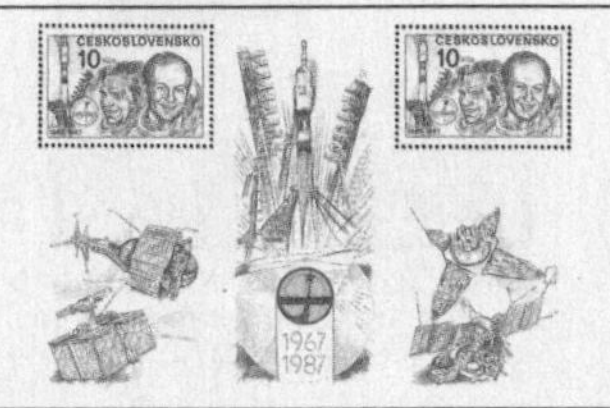

INTERCOSMOS, 20th Anniv. — A950

Cosmonauts Alexei Gubarev of the USSR & Vladimir Remek of Czechoslovakia, rocket & emblem.

**1987, Apr. 12** **Engr.** ***Perf. 12***

| | | | | |
|---|---|---|---|---|
| **2653** | A950 | Sheet of 2 | 6.00 | 5.00 |
| *a.* | | 10k multi | 2.75 | 1.75 |
| *b.* | | Souv. sheet of 4, litho. & engr., imperf. | 9.00 | 7.00 |

No. 2653b issued Nov. 15, 1987, and exists in two formats with either exhibition embelm or "Dni Nametove Filatelie" at top.

### Prague Castle Type of 1983

Designs: 2k, Three Saints, stained-glass window detail, c. 1870, St. Vitus Cathedral, by Frantisek Sequens (1830-1896). 3k, Coat of Arms, New Land Rolls Hall, 1605.

**1987, May 9** ***Perf. 11½***

| | | | | |
|---|---|---|---|---|
| **2654** | A875 | 2k multi | .40 | .30 |
| **2655** | A875 | 3k dk red, slate gray & yel org | .60 | .45 |

Nos. 2634-2638 were each issued in sheets of 6 stamps. Value, set $6.

PRAGA '88 A951

### Photo. & Engr.

**1987, May 12** ***Perf. 12x11½***

| | | | | |
|---|---|---|---|---|
| **2656** | A951 | 3k Telephone, 1894 | .75 | .25 |
| **2657** | A951 | 3k Postal van, 1924 | .75 | .30 |
| **2658** | A951 | 4k Locomotive tender, 1907 | .75 | .30 |
| **2659** | A951 | 4k Tram, 1900 | .75 | .30 |
| **2660** | A951 | 5k Steam roller, 1936 | .75 | .30 |
| | | *Nos. 2656-2660 (5)* | 3.75 | 1.45 |

Printed in sheets of 8 + 2 labels picturing telephone or vehicles. Value $25.

Nos. 2657-2658 were also printed in sheets of 4 + label picturing vehicles. Value, $30 for both sheets.

Destruction of Lidice and Lezaky, 45th Anniv. — A952

Drawings: No. 2661, When the Fighting Ended, 1945, by Pavel Simon. No. 2662, The End of the game, 1945, by Ludmila Jirincova.

**1987, June** *Perf. 11½*

2661 A952 1k blk, cerise & vio .25 .25
2662 A952 1k blk, gold, pale lil & cerise .25 .25

Union of Czechoslovakian Mathematicians and Physicists, 125th Anniv. — A953

Designs: No. 2663, Prague Town Hall mathematical clock, Theory of Functions diagram. No. 2664, J.M. Petzval (1807-1891), C. Strouhal (1850-1922) and V. Jarník (1897-1970). No. 2665, Geographical measurement from A.M. Malletta's book, 1672, earth fold and Brownian motion diagrams.

**1987, July 6** *Perf. 11½x12*

2663 A953 50h multi .25 .25
2664 A953 50h multi .25 .25
2665 A953 50h multi .25 .25
*Nos. 2663-2665 (3)* .75 .75

11th Biennial of Children's Book Illustration — A954

Award-winning illustrations: 50h, Asun Balzola, Spain. 1k, Frederic Clement, France. 2k, Elzbieta Gaudasinska, Poland. 4k, Marija Lucija Stupica, Yugoslavia.

**1987, Sept. 3** *Perf. 11½*

2666 A954 50h multi .25 .25
2667 A954 1k multi .25 .25
2668 A954 2k multi .25 .25
a. Souv. sheet of 2 + label 2.00 1.50
2669 A954 4k multi .55 .35
*Nos. 2666-2669 (4)* 1.30 1.10

Sept. 11-Oct. 30, Bratislava.

Eternal Flame, Flower — A955

**1987, Sept. 23**

2670 A955 50h multicolored .25 .25

Theresienstadt Memorial for the victims from 23 European countries who died in the Small Fortress, Terezin, a Nazi concentration camp.

Socialist Communications Organization, 30th Anniv. — A956

**1987, Sept. 23**

2671 A956 4k Emblem, satellite, dish receiver .40 .25

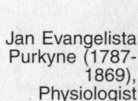

Jan Evangelista Purkyne (1787-1869), Physiologist A957

**1987, Sept. 30**

2672 A957 7k multicolored .80 .25

Views of Bratislava — A958

Designs: 3k, Male and female figures supporting an oriel, Arkier Palace, c. 1552. 4k, View of Bratislava from Ware Conterfactur de Stadt Presburg, from an engraving by Hans Mayer, 1563.

**1987, Oct. 1** **Engr.** *Perf. 12*

2673 A958 3k multicolored .50 .35
2674 A958 4k multicolored .70 .45

Each printed in sheets of 4 with Bratislava Castle (from Mayer's engraving) between. Value, set $5.

See Nos. 2719-2720, 2763-2764, 2800-2801.

**Type of 1974**

**Photo. & Engr.**

**1987, Nov. 1** *Perf. 12x11½*

2675 A699 1k Post rider .25 .25

PRAGA '88, Aug. 26-Sept. 4, 1988. No. 2675 printed se-tenant with label picturing exhibition emblem. Value for single with attached label 40c.

October Revolution, Russia, 70th Anniv. — A959

Establishment of the Union of Soviet Socialist Republics, 65th Anniv. — A960

**1987, Nov. 6** *Perf. 12x11½*

2676 A959 50h multicolored .25 .25
2677 A960 50h multicolored .25 .25

**Art Type of 1974**

Paintings in national galleries: 1k, Enclosure of Dreams, by Kamil Lhotak (b. 1912). 2k, Tulips, by Ester Simerova-Martincekova (b. 1909). 3k, Triptych with Bohemian Landscape, by Josef Lada (1887-1957). 4k, Accordion Player, by Josef Capek (1887-1945). 5k, Self-portrait, by Jiri Trnka (1912-1969).

**1987, Nov. 18** **Engr.** *Perf. 12*

2678 A700 1k multi 3.00 .75
2679 A700 2k multi 3.00 1.60
2680 A700 3k multi 3.00 1.10
2681 A700 4k multi 3.00 .80
2682 A700 5k multi 3.00 1.25
*Nos. 2678-2682 (5)* 15.00 5.50

Czech and Slovak art.

Nos. 2678-2682 were each issued in sheets of 4. Value, set $65.

69th Stamp Day — A961

Portrait of Jacob Obrovsky (1882-1949), stamp designer, Bohemian Lion (Type SP1), sketch of a lion and PRAGA '88 emblem.

**Photo. & Engr.**

**1987, Dec. 18** *Perf. 11½x12*

2683 A961 1k multicolored .25 .25

No. 2683 printed in sheet of four with eight labels se-tenant with stamps, inscribed "100 Years of the National Philatelic Movement in Czechoslovakia" in Czech. The four labels between the "blocks of six" are blank. Value, sheet $3.

Czechoslovak Republic, 70th Anniv. — A962

1k, Woman, natl. arms, linden branch.

**1988, Jan. 1** *Perf. 12x11½*

2684 A962 1k multicolored .25 .25

Natl. Front, 40th Anniv. — A963

**1988, Feb. 25** *Perf. 11½*

2685 A963 50h multicolored .25 .25

**Husak Type of 1983**

**Photo. & Engr.**

**1988, Jan. 10** *Perf. 12x11½*

2686 A865 1k brt rose & dk carmine .25 .25

Olympics — A965

50h, Ski jumping, ice hockey. 1k, Basketball, soccer. 6k, Discus, weight lifting.

**1988, Feb. 1** *Perf. 11½x12*

2687 A965 50h multicolored .25 .25
2688 A965 1k multicolored .25 .25
2689 A965 6k multicolored .70 .25
*Nos. 2687-2689 (3)* 1.20 .75

Exist in souv. sheets of 2, imperf. between and in souv. sheets of 2, imperf. Value, each set, $16.

Victorious February, 40th Anniv. — A966

Statue of Klement Gottwald by Rudolf Svoboda.

**1988, Feb. 25** *Perf. 11½*

2690 A966 50h multicolored .25 .25

No. 2690 exists in a souvenir sheet of two No. 2690 and two postally invalid imperf impressions of No. 637. Value $5.

Sheet exists imperf. Value $9.

Classic Automobiles — A967

50h, 1914 Laurin & Klement. 1k, 1902 Tatra NW Type B. 2k, 1905 Tatra NW Type E. 3k, 1929 Tatra 12 Normandie. 4k, 1899 Meteor.

**1988, Mar. 1** *Perf. 12x11½*

2691 A967 50h multi .25 .25
2692 A967 1k multi .25 .25
2693 A967 2k multi .25 .25
2694 A967 3k multi .45 .25
2695 A967 4k multi .75 .25
a. Bklt. pane, 2 3k, 3 4k + label 4.00
Complete booklet, #2695a 5.00
*Nos. 2691-2695 (5)* 1.95 1.25

Postal Museum, 70th Anniv. A968

Praga '88 emblem and: 50h, Postman, Malostranske Namesti Square p.o., Prague, c. 1742, and Velka Javorina television transmitter, 1979. 1k, Telecommunications Center, Mlada Boleslav, 1986, and Carmelite Street p.o., Prague, c. 1792. 2k, Prague 1 (1873) and Bratislava 56 (1984) post offices. 4k, Communications Center, Prachatice (1982), postman and Maltetske Nameski Square p.o., Prague, c. 1622.

**1988, Mar. 10**

2696 A968 50h multi .25 .25
2697 A968 1k multi .25 .25
2698 A968 2k multi .25 .25
2699 A968 4k multi .30 .25
a. Souv. sheet, 2 ea #2698-2699 2.25 1.25
*Nos. 2696-2699 (4)* 1.05 1.00

In No. 2699a the top pair of Nos. 2698-2699 is imperf. at top and sides.

A969

**1988, Mar. 29** *Perf. 11½*

2700 A969 50h multicolored .25 .25

Matice Slovenska Cultural Assoc., 125th anniv.

A970

PRAGA '88. (Exhibition emblem and aspects of the Museum of Natl. Literature, Prague): 1k, Gate and distant view of museum. 2k, Celestial globe, illuminated manuscript, bookshelves and ornately decorated ceiling. 5k, Illuminated "B" and decorated binder of a medieval Bible. 7k, Celestial globe, illuminated manuscript, Zodiacal signs (Aries and Leo), view of museum.

**1988, May 12** **Photo. & Engr.**

2701 A970 1k multicolored .30 .25
a. Souvenir sheet of 4 1.50 1.25
2702 A970 2k multicolored .55 .25
a. Souvenir sheet of 4 3.25 2.00
2703 A970 5k multicolored .80 .30
a. Souvenir sheet of 4 5.75 4.75
2704 A970 7k multicolored 1.75 .65
a. Souvenir sheet of 4 11.00 9.00
b. Souv. sheet of 4, imperf., #2701-2704 3.75 3.00
*Nos. 2701-2704 (4)* 3.40 1.45

PRAGA '88 — A971

Exhibition emblem and fountains, Prague.

**1988, June 1** *Perf. 11½x12*

2705 A971 1k Waldstein Palace .30 .25
2706 A971 2k Old town square .30 .25
2707 A971 3k Charles University .45 .25
2708 A971 4k Prague Castle .75 .30
a. Souv. sheet of 4, #2705-2708 4.00 2.00
*Nos. 2705-2708 (4)* 1.80 1.05

Souvenir Sheet

Soviet-US Summit Conference on Arms Reduction, Moscow — A972

Design: The Capitol, Washington, and the Kremlin, Moscow.

**1988, June 1** *Perf. 12x11½*
**2709** A972 4k blue blk, dark red & gold 2.50 1.50

Exists imperf. Value $7.

PRAGA '88 A973

Exhibition emblem and modern architecture, Prague: 50h, Trade Unions Central Recreation Center. 1k, Koospol foreign trade company. 2k, Motol Teaching Hospital. 4k, Culture Palace.

**1988, July 1** *Perf. 12x11½*
**2710** A973 50h multicolored .25 .25
**2711** A973 1k blk, lt blue & bister .25 .25
**2712** A973 2k multicolored .25 .25
*a.* Souv. sheet, 2 1k, 2 2k + 4 labels, imperf. 2.00 1.50
**2713** A973 4k multicolored .25 .25
*a.* Souv. sheet, 2 50h, 2 4k + 4 labels, imperf. 2.00 1.50
*Nos. 2710-2713 (4)* 1.00 1.00

Souvenir Sheet

PRAGA '88 — A974

Design: Exhibition emblem and Alfons Mucha (1860-1939), designer of first Czech postage stamp.

**1988, Aug. 18** **Engr.** *Perf. 12*
**2714** A974 Sheet of 2 5.50 3.25
*a.* 5k multicolored 2.40 1.25

Czech postage stamps, 70th anniv.

Souvenir Sheets

PRAGA '88 — A975

5k, *Turin, Monte Superga,* by Josef Navratil (1798-1865), Postal Museum, Prague.
Details of *Bacchus and Ariadne,* by Sebastiano Ricci (1659-1734), Natl. Gallery, Prague: No. 2716a, Ariadne. No. 2716b, Bacchus and creatures.

**1988**
**2715** A975 Sheet of 2 5.00 4.00
*a.* 5k multi 2.50 1.60
**2716** A975 Sheet of 2 9.00 6.00
*a.-b.* 10k any single 4.00 2.40

No. 2716 exists with emblem and inscription "DEN F.I.P. JOURNEE DE LA FEDERATION INTERNATIONALE DE PHILATELIE." Value $12.
Issue dates: 5k, Aug. 19; 10k, Aug. 26.

### Prague Castle Type of 1983

2k, Pottery jug, 17th cent. 3k, *St. Catherine with Angel,* 1580, by Paolo Veronese.

**1988, Sept. 28** **Engr.** *Perf. 12*
**2717** A875 2k shown .40 .40
**2718** A875 3k multi .45 .45

Nos. 2717-2718 were each issued in sheets of 6. Value, set $6.

### Bratislava Views Type of 1987

3k, *Hlavne Square, circa 1840* an etching by R. Alt-Sandman, 1840. 4k, *Ferdinand House, circa 1850,* a pen-and-ink drawing by V. Reim.

**1988, Oct. 19**
**2719** A958 3k multicolored .50 .50
**2720** A958 4k multicolored .65 .65

Nos. 2719-2720 were each issued in sheets of 4. Value, set $4.50.

### Art Type of 1974

Paintings in natl. galleries: 2k, *With Bundles,* 1931, by Martin Benka (1888-1971). 6k, *Blue Bird,* 1903, by Vojtech Preissig (1873-1944). 7k, *A Jaguar Attacking a Rider,* c. 1850, by Eugene Delacroix (1798-1863).

**1988, Nov. 17** **Engr.** *Perf. 12*
**2721** A700 2k multicolored 2.00 1.00
**2722** A700 6k multicolored 3.50 1.50
**2723** A700 7k multicolored 3.50 1.50
*Nos. 2721-2723 (3)* 9.00 4.00

Czech and Slovak art.

Nos. 2721-2723 were each issued in sheets of 4. Value, set $40.

Stamp Day — A978

Design: 1k, Jaroslav Benda (1882-1970), illustrator and stamp designer.

**Photo. & Engr.**

**1988, Dec. 18** *Perf. 11½x12*
**2724** A978 1k multicolored .25 .25

Paris-Dakar Rally — A979

Trucks: 50h, Earth, Motokov Liaz. 1k, Liaz, globe. 2k, Earth, Motokov Tatra. No. 607. 4k, Map of racecourse, turban, Tatra.

**1989, Jan. 2** *Perf. 12x11½*
**2725** A979 50h multicolored .35 .25
**2726** A979 1k multicolored .35 .25
**2727** A979 2k multicolored .45 .25
**2728** A979 4k multicolored .75 .25
*Nos. 2725-2728 (4)* 1.90 1.00

Czechoslovakian Federation, 20th Anniv. — A980

**1989, Jan. 1**
**2729** A980 50h multicolored .25 .25

Jan Botto (1829-1881) A981

Taras Grigorievich Shevchenko (1814-1861) A982

Jean Cocteau (1889-1963) A983

Charlie Chaplin (1889-1977) A984

Jawaharlal Nehru (1889-1964) and "UNESCO" — A985

Famous men: No. 2732, Modest Petrovich Musorgsky (1839-1881).

**Photo. & Engr.**

**1989, Mar. 9** *Perf. 12x11½*
**2730** A981 50h brn blk & lt blue green .25 .25
**2731** A982 50h shown .25 .25
**2732** A982 50h multicolored .25 .25
**2733** A983 50h red brn, grnh blk & org brn .25 .25
**2734** A984 50h blk, int blue & dark red .25 .25
**2735** A985 50h brn blk & lt yel green .25 .25
*Nos. 2730-2735 (6)* 1.50 1.50

Shipping Industry A986

**1989, Mar. 27**
**2736** A986 50h Republika .25 .25
**2737** A986 1k Pionyr, flags .25 .25
**2738** A986 2k Brno, flags .25 .25
**2739** A986 3k Trinec .35 .25
**2740** A986 4k Flags, mast, Orlik .75 .25
**2741** A986 5k Vltava, communication hardware 1.00 .30
*Nos. 2736-2741 (6)* 2.85 1.55

Pioneer Organization, 40th Anniv. — A987

**Photo. & Engr.**

**1989, Apr. 20** *Perf. 11½*
**2742** A987 50h multi .25 .25

### Art Type of 1974

Details of *Feast of Rose Garlands,* 1506, by Albrecht Durer, Natl. Gallery, Prague: a, Virgin and Child. b, Angel playing mandolin.

**1989, Apr. 21** **Engr.** *Perf. 12*

**Miniature Sheet**

**2743** Sheet of 2 7.50 4.00
*a.-b.* A700 10k any single 3.50 2.00

### Prague Castle Art Type of 1983

2k, Bas-relief picturing Kaiser Karl IV, from Kralovske tomb by Alexander Colin (c. 1527-1612). 3k, Self-portrait, by V.V. Reiner (1689-1743).

**1989, May 9** **Photo. & Engr.**
**2744** A875 2k dark red, sepia & buff .35 .30
**2745** A875 3k multi .50 .40

Nos. 2744-2745 were each issued in sheets of 6. Value, set $6.

Souvenir Sheet

PHILEXFRANCE '89, French Revolution Bicent. — A988

**1989, July 14** **Engr.** *Perf. 12*
**2746** A988 5k brt blue, blk & dk red 2.00 1.50

Haliaeetus albicilla — A989

**Photo. & Engr.**

**1989, July 17** *Perf. 12x11½*
**2747** A989 1k multicolored .50 .25

World Wildlife Fund — A990

Toads and newts.

**1989, July 18** *Perf. 11½x12*
**2748** A990 2k Bombina bombina .65 .30
**2749** A990 3k Bombina variegata 1.00 .45
**2750** A990 4k Triturus alpestris 1.40 .60
**2751** A990 5k Triturus montandoni 1.60 .70
*Nos. 2748-2751 (4)* 4.65 2.05

Slovak Folk Art Collective, 40th Anniv. — A991

**1989, Aug. 29** *Perf. 12x11½*
**2752** A991 50h multicolored .25 .25

Slovak Uprising, 45th Anniv. — A992

**Photo. & Engr.**

**1989, Aug. 29** *Perf. 11½x12*
**2753** A992 1k multicolored .25 .25

A993

Award-winning illustrations: 50h, Hannu Taina, Finland. 1k, Aleksander Aleksov, Bulgaria. 2k, Jurgen Spohn, West Berlin. 4k, Robert Brun, Czechoslovakia.

**1989, Sept. 4** *Perf. 11½*
**2754** A993 50h multicolored .25 .25
**2755** A993 1k multicolored .25 .25
**2756** A993 2k multicolored .25 .25
**2757** A993 4k multicolored .60 .25
*a.* Souvenir sheet of 2 2.00 .80
*Nos. 2754-2757 (4)* 1.35 1.00

12th Biennial of Children's Book Illustration, Bratislava.

A994

Poisonous mushrooms: 50h, Nolanea verna. 1k, Amanita phalloides. 2k, Amanita virosa. 3k, Cortinarius orellanus. 5k, Galerina marginata.

**1989, Sept. 5 Engr.** *Perf. 11½x12*
**2758** A994 50h multicolored .30 .25
**2759** A994 1k multicolored .40 .25
**2760** A994 2k multicolored .55 .25
**2761** A994 3k multicolored .90 .25
**2762** A994 5k multicolored 1.00 .25
*Nos. 2758-2762 (5)* 3.15 1.25

Nos. 2758-2762 were each issued in sheets of 10. Value, set $40.

**Bratislava Views Type of 1987**

Views of Devin, a Slavic castle above the Danube, Bratislava.

**1989, Oct. 16 Engr.** *Perf. 12*
**2763** A958 3k Castle, flower .60 .60
**2764** A958 4k Castle, urn .80 .80

Nos. 2763-2764 were each issued in sheets of 4. Value, set $6.

Jan Opletal (1915-39) — A996

**Photo. & Engr.**

**1989, Nov. 17** *Perf. 12x11½*
**2765** A996 1k multicolored .25 .25

Intl. Student's Day. Funeral of Opletal, a Nazi victim, on Nov. 15, 1939, sparked student demonstrations that resulted in the closing of all universities in occupied Bohemia and Moravia.

**Art Type of 1974**

Paintings in Natl. Galleries: 2k, *Nirvana*, c. 1920, by Anton Jasusch (1882-1965). 4k, *Winter Evening in Town*, c. 1907, by Jakub Schikaneder (1855-1924), horiz. 5k, *The Bakers*, 1926, by Pravoslav Kotik (1889-1970), horiz.

**1989, Nov. 27 Engr.** *Perf. 12*
**2766** A700 2k multicolored .80 .60
**2767** A700 4k multicolored 1.40 1.10
**2768** A700 5k multicolored 1.40 1.10
*Nos. 2766-2768 (3)* 3.60 2.80

Nos. 2766-2768 were each issued in sheets of 4. Value, set $15.

Stamp Day — A997

Design: Portrait of Cyril Bouda, stamp designer, art tools and falcon.

**Photo. & Engr.**

**1989, Dec. 18** *Perf. 11½x12*
**2769** A997 1k multicolored .25 .25

A998

**Photo. & Engr.**

**1990, Jan. 8** *Perf. 11½x12*
**2770** A998 1k multicolored .60 .25

UNESCO World Literacy Year. Printed se-tenant with inscribed label picturing UN and UNESCO emblems. Value, single with label attached 75c.

A999

Famous men: No. 2771, Karel Capek, writer. No. 2772, Thomas G. Masaryk. 1k, Lenin. 2k, Emile Zola, French writer. 3k, Jaroslav Heyrovsky (1890-1987), chemical physicist. 10k, Bohuslav Martinu (1890-1959), composer.

**1990, Jan. 9** *Perf. 11½*
**2771** A999 50h multicolored .25 .25
**2772** A999 50h multicolored .25 .25
**2773** A999 1k multicolored .25 .25
**2774** A999 2k multicolored .30 .25
**2775** A999 3k multicolored .50 .30
**2776** A999 10k multicolored 1.60 .90
*Nos. 2771-2776 (6)* 3.15 2.20

Nos. 2771, 2775-2776 inscribed "UNESCO."

Pres. Vaclav Havel — A1000

**1990, Jan. 9** *Perf. 12x11½*
**2777** A1000 50h red, brt vio & bl .30 .25

See Nos. 2879, 2948.

Handball Players — A1001

**1990, Feb. 1** *Perf. 11½*
**2778** A1001 50h multicolored .25 .25

1990 Men's World Handball Championships, Czechoslovakia.

Flora — A1002

Flowers: 50h, Antirrhinum majus. 1k, Zinnia elegans. 3k, Tigridia pavonia. 5k, Lilium candidum.

**Photo. & Engr.**

**1990, Mar. 1** *Perf. 11½*
**2779** A1002 50h multicolored .55 .25
**2780** A1002 1k multicolored .80 .25
**2781** A1002 3k multicolored 1.00 .25

*Perf. 12x12½*

**2782** A1002 5k multicolored 1.40 .60
*Nos. 2779-2782 (4)* 3.75 1.35

No. 2782 was issued in a sheet of 10. Value, $12.50.

**City Arms Type of 1982**

**Photo. & Engr.**

**1990, Mar. 28** *Perf. 12x11½*
**2783** A847 50h Prostejov .25 .25
**2784** A847 50h Bytca .25 .25
**2785** A847 50h Sobeslav .25 .25
**2786** A847 50h Podebrady .25 .25
*Nos. 2783-2786 (4)* 1.00 1.00

A1003

**1990, Apr. 16** *Perf. 11½x12*
**2787** A1003 1k brn vio, rose & buff .60 .25

Visit of Pope John Paul II.

World War II Liberation A1004

**Photo. & Engr.**

**1990, May 5** *Perf. 11½*
**2788** A1004 1k multicolored .25 .25

Souvenir Sheet

150th Anniv. of the Postage Stamp — A1005

**1990, May 6 Engr.** *Perf. 12*
**2789** A1005 7k multicolored 4.00 1.50

Stamp World London 90.

A1006

**Photo. & Engr.**

**1990, May 8** *Perf. 11½*
**2790** A1006 1k multicolored .60 .25

World Cup Soccer Championships, Italy.

Free Elections A1007

**1990, June 1**
**2791** A1007 1k multicolored .60 .25

**Prague Castle Type of 1983**

2k, Gold and jeweled hand. 3k, King Otakar II's Seal.

**1990, June 6, 1990** **Engr.**
**2792** A875 2k multicolored .55 .30
**2793** A875 3k multicolored .80 .40

Art treasures of Prague Castle.

Nos. 2792-2793 were each issued in sheets of 6. Value, set $9.

Helsinki Conference, 15th Anniv. — A1008

**Photo & Engr.**

**1990, June 21** *Perf. 12x11½*
**2794** A1008 7k multicolored .90 .40

Dr. Milada Horakova A1009

**1990, June 25** *Perf. 12x11½*
**2795** A1009 1k multicolored .30 .25

Intercanis Dog Show, Brno — A1010

Designs: 50h, Poodles, 1k, Afghan hound, Irish wolfhound, greyhound. 4k, Czech terrier, bloodhound, Hannoverian hound. 7k, Cavalier King Charles Spaniel, cocker spaniel, American cocker spaniel.

**1990, July 2**

| | | | | |
|---|---|---|---|---|
| **2796** | A1010 | 50h multicolored | .50 | .25 |
| **2797** | A1010 | 1k multicolored | .75 | .25 |
| **2798** | A1010 | 4k multicolored | 1.25 | .30 |
| **2799** | A1010 | 7k multicolored | 1.75 | .65 |
| | | *Nos. 2796-2799 (4)* | 4.25 | 1.45 |

**Bratislava Art Type of 1987**

**1990** **Engr.** ***Perf. 12***

| | | | | |
|---|---|---|---|---|
| **2800** | A958 | 3k Ancient Celtic coin | .65 | .40 |
| **2801** | A958 | 4k Gen. Milan Stefanik | .65 | .45 |

Issue dates: 3k, Sept. 29. 4k, July 21.

Nos. 2800-2801 were each issued in sheets of 4. Value, set $6.

Grand Pardubice Steeplechase, Cent. — A1011

**Photo. & Engr.**

**1990, Sept. 7** ***Perf. 12x11½***

| | | | | |
|---|---|---|---|---|
| **2802** | A1011 | 50h multicolored | .25 | .25 |
| **2803** | A1011 | 4k multi, diff. | .50 | .25 |

Protected Animals — A1012

**Litho. & Engr.**

**1990, Oct. 1** ***Perf. 12x11***

| | | | | |
|---|---|---|---|---|
| **2804** | A1012 | 50h Marmota marmota | 1.00 | .25 |
| **2805** | A1012 | 1k Felis silvestris | 1.00 | .25 |
| **2806** | A1012 | 4k Castor fiber | 1.75 | .30 |
| **2807** | A1012 | 5k Plecotus auritus | 1.75 | .75 |
| | | *Nos. 2804-2807 (4)* | 5.50 | 1.55 |

Conf. of Civic Associations, Helsinki — A1013

**Litho. & Engr.**

**1990, Oct. 15** ***Perf. 12x11½***

| | | | | |
|---|---|---|---|---|
| **2808** | A1013 | 3k blue, gold & yel | .50 | .30 |

Christmas — A1014

**Photo. & Engr.**

**1990, Nov. 15** ***Perf. 11½x12***

| | | | | |
|---|---|---|---|---|
| **2809** | A1014 | 50h multicolored | .25 | .25 |

**Painting Type of 1967**

Works of art: 2k, Krucemburk by Jan Zrzavy (1890-1977), horiz. 3k, St. Agnes of Bohemia from the St. Wenceslas Monument, Prague by Josef V. Myslbek (1848-1922). 4k, The Slavs in their Homeland by Alfons Mucha (1860-1939). 5k, St. John the Baptist by Auguste Rodin (1840-1917).

**1990, Nov. 27** **Engr.** ***Perf. 11½***

| | | | | |
|---|---|---|---|---|
| **2810** | A565 | 2k multicolored | 1.25 | .50 |
| **2811** | A565 | 3k multicolored | 1.25 | .60 |
| **2812** | A565 | 4k multicolored | 2.10 | .60 |
| **2813** | A565 | 5k multicolored | 2.10 | .60 |
| | | *Nos. 2810-2813 (4)* | 6.70 | 2.30 |

Nos. 2810-2813 were each issued in sheets of 4. Value, set $30.

Karel Svolinsky (1896-1986), Vignette from No. 1182 — A1016

**1990, Dec. 18** **Photo. & Engr.**

| | | | | |
|---|---|---|---|---|
| **2814** | A1016 | 1k multicolored | .25 | .25 |

Stamp Day.

A1017

**1991, Jan. 10** ***Perf. 11½***

| | | | | |
|---|---|---|---|---|
| **2815** | A1017 | 1k multicolored | .30 | .25 |

European Judo Championships, Prague.

A1018

Design: A. B. Svojsik (1876-1938), Czech Scouting Founder.

**1991, Jan. 10**

| | | | | |
|---|---|---|---|---|
| **2816** | A1018 | 3k multicolored | .75 | .30 |

Scouting in Czechoslovakia, 80th Anniv.

Bethlehem Chapel, Prague, 600th Anniv. — A1019

**1991, Feb. 4** ***Perf. 12x11½***

| | | | | |
|---|---|---|---|---|
| **2817** | A1019 | 50h multicolored | .25 | .25 |

Wolfgang Amadeus Mozart (1756-1791), Old Theatre — A1020

**1991, Feb. 4**

| | | | | |
|---|---|---|---|---|
| **2818** | A1020 | 1k multicolored | .25 | .25 |

Steamship Bohemia, 150th Anniv. — A1021

**1991, Feb. 4** ***Perf. 11½x12***

| | | | | |
|---|---|---|---|---|
| **2819** | A1021 | 5k multicolored | .85 | .30 |

Famous Men A1022

Designs: No. 2820, Antonin Dvorak (1841-1904), composer. No. 2821, Andrej Kmet (1841-1908), botanist. No. 2822, Jaroslav Seifert (1901-1986), poet, Nobel laureate for Literature. No. 2823, Jan Masaryk (1886-1948), diplomat. No. 2824, Alois Senefelder (1771-1834), lithographer.

**1991, Feb. 18** ***Perf. 12x11½***

| | | | | |
|---|---|---|---|---|
| **2820** | A1022 | 1k multicolored | .25 | .25 |
| **2821** | A1022 | 1k multicolored | .25 | .25 |
| **2822** | A1022 | 1k multicolored | .25 | .25 |
| **2823** | A1022 | 1k multicolored | .25 | .25 |
| **2824** | A1022 | 1k multicolored | .25 | .25 |
| | | *Nos. 2820-2824 (5)* | 1.25 | 1.25 |

Nos. 2820-2824 printed with se-tenant labels.

See No. 2831.

Europa — A1023

**Photo. & Engr.**

**1991, May 6** ***Perf. 11½x12***

| | | | | |
|---|---|---|---|---|
| **2825** | A1023 | 6k blk, bl & red | 2.00 | .60 |

A1024

**Photo. & Engr.**

**1991, May 10** ***Perf. 11½x12***

| | | | | |
|---|---|---|---|---|
| **2826** | A1024 | 1k multicolored | .25 | .25 |

General Exhibition in Prague, cent.

Antarctic Treaty, 30th Anniv. A1025

**1991, May 20** ***Perf. 12x11½***

| | | | | |
|---|---|---|---|---|
| **2827** | A1025 | 8k multicolored | 1.75 | .60 |

Castles — A1026

**1991, June 3** ***Perf. 11½***

| | | | | |
|---|---|---|---|---|
| **2828** | A1026 | 50h Blatna | .25 | .25 |
| **2829** | A1026 | 1k Bouzov | .40 | .25 |
| **2830** | A1026 | 3k Kezmarok | .60 | .25 |
| | | *Nos. 2828-2830 (3)* | 1.25 | .75 |

**Famous Men Type**

Design: Jan Palach (1948-1969), Student.

**Photo. & Engr.**

**1991, Aug. 9** ***Perf. 12x11½***

| | | | | |
|---|---|---|---|---|
| **2831** | A1022 | 4k black | 2.00 | .30 |

Printed se-tenant with label.

Scenic Views — A1027

**Photo. & Engr.**

**1991, Aug. 28** ***Perf. 11½***

| | | | | |
|---|---|---|---|---|
| **2832** | A1027 | 4k Krivan mountains | 1.00 | .60 |
| **2833** | A1027 | 4k Rip mountain | 1.00 | .60 |

A1028

Illustrations by: 1k, Binette Schroeder, Germany. 2k, Stasys Eidrigevicius, Poland.

**Photo. & Engr.**

**1991, Sept. 2** ***Perf. 11½***

| | | | | |
|---|---|---|---|---|
| **2834** | A1028 | 1k multicolored | .25 | .25 |
| **2835** | A1028 | 2k multicolored | .35 | .25 |

13th Biennial Exhibition of Children's Book Illustrators, Bratislava.

A1029

Design: Father Andrej Hlinka (1864-1938), Slovak nationalist.

**1991, Sept. 27** **Engr.** ***Perf. 11½***

| | | | | |
|---|---|---|---|---|
| **2836** | A1029 | 10k blue black | 1.40 | .30 |

Art of Prague and Bratislava A1030

Designs: No. 2837, Holy Infant of Prague. No. 2838, Blue Church of Bratislava.

**1991, Sept. 30**

| | | | | |
|---|---|---|---|---|
| **2837** | A1030 | 3k multicolored | 1.25 | .50 |
| **2838** | A1030 | 3k multicolored | 1.25 | .50 |

Nos. 2837-2838 were each issued in sheets of 8. Value, set $15.

Flowers — A1031

1k, Gagea bohemica. 2k, Aster alpinus. 5k, Fritillaria meleagris. 11k, Daphne cneorum.

**Photo. & Engr.**

**1991, Nov. 3** ***Perf. 12x11½***

| | | | | |
|---|---|---|---|---|
| **2839** | A1031 | 1k multicolored | .60 | .25 |
| **2840** | A1031 | 2k multicolored | .85 | .25 |
| **2841** | A1031 | 5k multicolored | 1.25 | .30 |
| **2842** | A1031 | 11k multicolored | 2.50 | .45 |
| | | *Nos. 2839-2842 (4)* | 5.20 | 1.25 |

**Painting Type of 1967**

Paintings: 2k, Everyday Homelife by Max Ernst. 3k, Lovers by Auguste Renoir. 4k, Head of Christ by El Greco. 5k, Coincidence by Ladislav Guderna. 7k, Two Maidens by Utamaro.

**1991, Nov. 3 Engr. *Perf. 11½***
**2843** A565 2k multicolored 1.25 .60
**2844** A565 3k multicolored 1.25 .60
**2845** A565 4k multicolored 1.25 .75
**2846** A565 5k multicolored 1.75 1.25
**2847** A565 7k multicolored 1.75 1.25
*Nos. 2843-2847 (5)* 7.25 4.45

Nos. 2843-2847 were each issued in sheets of 4. Value, set $30.

Christmas — A1033

**1991, Nov. 19**
**2848** A1033 50h multicolored .30 .25

Stamp Day — A1034

Martin Benka (1888-1971), stamp engraver.

**Photo. & Engr.**
**1991, Dec. 18 *Perf. 11½x12***
**2849** A1034 2k multicolored .45 .25

1992 Winter Olympics, Albertville — A1035

**1992, Jan. 6 *Perf. 11½***
**2850** A1035 1k Biathlon .25 .25

**Photo. & Engr.**
**1992, May 21 *Perf. 11½***
**2851** A1035 2k Tennis .30 .25

1992 Summer Olympics, Barcelona.

Souvenir Sheet

Jan Amos Komensky (Comenius), Educator — A1036

**1992, Mar. 5 Engr.**
**2852** A1036 10k multicolored 4.00 3.50

World Ice Hockey Championships, Prague and Bratislava — A1037

**1992, Mar. 31 Photo. & Engr.**
**2853** A1037 3k multicolored .75 .25

Traffic Safety A1038

**1992, Apr. 2**
**2854** A1038 2k multicolored .50 .25

Expo '92, Seville — A1039

**1992, Apr. 2**
**2855** A1039 4k multicolored .75 .25

Discovery of America, 500th Anniv. — A1040

**1992, May 5 Engr.**
**2856** A1040 22k multicolored 2.00 2.00

Europa. Printed in sheets of 8. Value $18.

Czechoslovak Military Actions in WWII — A1041

Designs: 1k, J. Kubis and J. Gabcik, assassins of Reinhard Heydrich, 1942. 2k, Pilots flying for France and Great Britain. 3k, Defense of Tobruk. 6k, Capture of Dunkirk, 1944-45.

**1992, May 21 Engr. *Perf. 12x11½***
**2857** A1041 1k multicolored .50 .25
**2858** A1041 2k multicolored .60 .25
**2859** A1041 3k multicolored .75 .25
**2860** A1041 6k multicolored 1.60 .35
*Nos. 2857-2860 (4)* 3.45 1.10

A1042

**Photo. & Engr.**
**1992, June 10 *Perf. 11½***
**2861** A1042 2k multicolored .30 .25

Czechoslovakian Red Cross.

A1043

**1992, June 30**
**2862** A1043 1k multicolored .30 .25

Junior European Table Tennis Championships, Topolcany.

Beetles A1044

**1992, July 15**
**2863** A1044 1k Polyphylla fullo .65 .25
**2864** A1044 2k Ergates faber .90 .25
**2865** A1044 3k Meloe violaceus 1.90 .45
**2866** A1044 4k Dytiscus latissimus 1.90 .45
*Nos. 2863-2866 (4)* 5.35 1.40

The 1k exists with denomination omitted.

Troja Castle A1045

**1992, Aug. 28 Engr. *Perf. 11½***
**2867** A1045 6k shown 2.60 1.00
**2868** A1045 7k Statue of St. Martin, vert. 3.00 1.10
**2869** A1045 8k Lednice Castle 3.50 1.25
*Nos. 2867-2869 (3)* 9.10 3.35

Nos. 2867-2869 were each issued in sheets of 8. Value, set $75.

**Chrudim Church Type of 1971**
**Photo. & Engr.**
**1992, Aug. 28 *Perf. 11½x11***
**2870** A629 50h multicolored .75 .25

Postal Bank — A1045a

**Photo. & Engr.**
**1992, Aug. 28 *Perf. 11½x12***
**2870A** A1045a 20k multicolored 2.00 .75

Antonius Bernolak, Georgius Fandly — A1046

**Photo. & Engr.**
**1992, Oct. 6 *Perf. 12x11½***
**2871** A1046 5k multicolored .75 .30

Slovakian Educational Society, bicent.

Cesky Krumlov — A1046a

**Photo. & Engr.**
**1992, Oct. 19 *Perf. 11½x12***
**2871A** A1046a 3k brick red & brn .75 .25

See No. 2890.

**Painting Type of 1967**

6k Old Man on a Raft, by Koloman Sokol. 7k, Still Life of Grapes and Raisins, by Georges Braque, horiz. 8k, Abandoned Corset, by Toyen.

***Perf. 11½x12, 12x11½***
**1992, Nov. 2 Engr.**
**2872** A565 6k multicolored 2.00 .95
**2873** A565 7k multicolored 3.25 1.10
**2874** A565 8k multicolored 3.25 1.25
*Nos. 2872-2874 (3)* 8.50 3.30

Nos. 2872-2874 were each issued in sheets of 4. Value, set $37.50.

Christmas — A1047

**Photo. & Engr.**
**1992, Nov. 9 *Perf. 12x11½***
**2875** A1047 2k multicolored .75 .25

Jindra Schmidt (1897-1984), Graphic Artist and Engraver — A1048

**Photo. & Engr.**
**1992, Dec. 18 *Perf. 11½x12***
**2876** A1048 2k multicolored .75 .25

Stamp Day.

---

On January 1, 1993, Czechoslovakia split into Czech Republic and Slovakia. Czech Republic listings continue here. Slovakia can be found in Volume 5.

---

## CZECH REPUBLIC

AREA — 30,449 sq. mi.
POP. — 10,280,513 (1999 est.)

Natl. Arms A1049

**Photo. & Engr.**
**1993, Jan. 20 *Perf. 11***
**2877** A1049 3k multicolored .40 .25

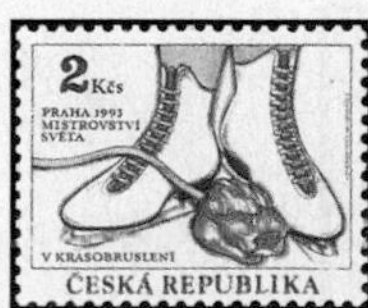

1993 World Figure Skating Championships, Prague A1050

**1993, Feb. 25 *Perf. 11½x11***
**2878** A1050 2k multicolored .30 .25

**Havel Type of 1990 Inscribed "Ceska Republika"**
**Photo. & Engr.**
**1993, Mar. 2 *Perf. 12x11½***
**2879** A1000 2k vio, vio brn & blue .30 .25

St. John Nepomuk, Patron Saint of Czechs, 600th Death Anniv. — A1051

**1993, Mar. 11**
**2880** A1051 8k multicolored 1.00 .35

See Germany No. 1776; Slovakia No. 158.

Holy Hunger, by Mikulas Medek — A1052

**1993, Mar. 11** ***Perf. 11½***
**2881** A1052 14k multicolored *3.75 2.00*

Europa.
Issued in sheets of 4. Value, $16.

Sacred Heart Church, Prague A1053

**1993, Mar. 30** **Engr.** ***Perf. 11½***
**2882** A1053 5k multicolored 1.00 .50

Issued in sheets of 8. Value, $10.

Brevnov Monastery, 1000th Anniv. — A1054

**Litho. & Engr.**

**1993, Apr. 12** ***Perf. 12x11½***
**2883** A1054 4k multicolored .55 .25

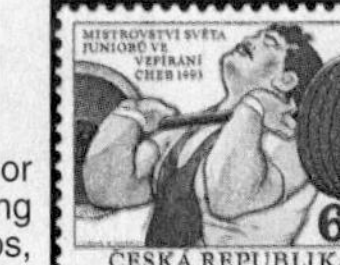

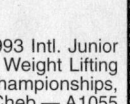

1993 Intl. Junior Weight Lifting Championships, Cheb — A1055

**Photo. & Engr.**

**1993, May 12** ***Perf. 11½***
**2884** A1055 6k multicolored 1.00 .35

Clock Tower and Church, Brno — A1056

**1993, June 16** **Engr.** ***Perf. 12x11½***
**2885** A1056 8k multicolored 1.50 1.50

Brno, 750th anniv.
Issued in sheets of 8. Value, $12.

Arrival of St. Cyril and St. Methodius, 1130th Anniv. — A1057

**1993, June 22** **Photo. & Engr.**
**2886** A1057 8k multicolored 1.00 .50

See Slovakia No. 167.

Souvenir Sheet

State Arms — A1058

**1993, June 22** ***Perf. 11½***
**2887** A1058 8k Sheet of 2 2.60 2.60

**Architecture Type of 1992 Inscribed "Ceska Republika" and**

A1059

Cities: 1k, Ceske Budejovice. 2k, Usti Nad Labem. No. 2890, like #2871A. No. 2891, Brno. 5k, Plzen. 6k, Slany. 7k, Ostrava. 8k, Olomouc. 10k, Hradec Kralove. 20k, Prague. 50k, Opava.

***Perf. 12x11½, 11½x12***

**1993-94** **Photo. & Engr.**

| | | | | |
|---|---|---|---|---|
| **2888** | A1059 | 1k dp cl & org | .25 | .25 |
| **2889** | A1059 | 2k red vio & bl | .25 | .25 |
| **2890** | A1046a | 3k gray bl & red | .25 | .25 |
| | | Complete booklet, 5 #2890 | 4.50 | |
| **2891** | A1059 | 3k dk bl & red | .25 | .25 |
| | | Complete booklet, 5 #2891 | 3.75 | |
| **2892** | A1059 | 5k bluish green & brn | .25 | .25 |
| **2893** | A1059 | 6k grn & org yel | 1.00 | .30 |
| **2894** | A1059 | 7k blk brn & grn | 1.00 | .30 |
| **2895** | A1059 | 8k dp vio & yel | .80 | .30 |
| **2896** | A1059 | 10k olive gray & red | .90 | .40 |
| **2897** | A1059 | 20k red & blue | 2.50 | .75 |
| **2898** | A1059 | 50k brn & grn | 4.75 | 1.75 |
| | | *Nos. 2888-2898 (11)* | 12.20 | 5.05 |

Issued: No. 2891, 3/30/94; 6k, 10/1/94; 7k, 11/23/94; others, 7/1/93.

World Rowing Championships, Racice A1060

**Photo. & Engr.**

**1993, Aug. 18** ***Perf. 11½***
**2901** A1060 3k multicolored .40 .25

A1061

Famous men: 2k, August Sedlacek (1843-1926), historian. 3k, Eduard Cech (1893-1960), mathematician.

**1993, Aug. 26** ***Perf. 12x11½***
**2902** A1061 2k multicolored .40 .25
**2903** A1061 3k multicolored .55 .25

Trees — A1062

**1993, Oct. 26** ***Perf. 11½***

| | | | | |
|---|---|---|---|---|
| **2904** | A1062 | 5k Quercus robur | .60 | .30 |
| **2905** | A1062 | 7k Carpinus betulus | .80 | .40 |
| **2906** | A1062 | 9k Pinus silvestris | 1.25 | .50 |
| | | *Nos. 2904-2906 (3)* | 2.65 | 1.20 |

See Slovakia Nos. 160-162.

Christmas — A1063

**Photo. & Engr.**

**1993, Nov. 8** ***Perf. 11½***
**2907** A1063 2k multicolored .30 .25

**Painting Type of 1967 Inscribed "CESKA REPUBLIKA"**

Paintings: 9k, Strahovska Madonna, by "Bohemian Master" in the year 1350. 11k, Composition, by Miro, horiz. 14k, Field of Green, by Van Gogh, horiz.

**1993** **Engr.** ***Perf. 11½x12***
**2908** A565 9k multicolored 2.00 2.00

***Perf. 12x11½***

| | | | | |
|---|---|---|---|---|
| **2909** | A565 | 11k multicolored | 2.25 | 2.25 |
| **2910** | A565 | 14k multicolored | 3.25 | 3.25 |
| | | *Nos. 2908-2910 (3)* | 7.50 | 7.50 |

Issued: 11k, 14k, Nov. 8; 9k, Dec. 15.
Nos. 2908-2910 were each issued in sheets of 4. Value, set $30.

Intl. Year of the Family — A1064

**Photo. & Engr.**

**1994, Jan. 19** ***Perf. 11½***
**2911** A1064 2k multicolored .30 .25

Jan Kubelik (1880-1940), Composer A1065

**Photo. & Engr.**

**1994, Jan. 19** ***Perf. 11½***
**2912** A1065 3k multicolored .40 .25

UNESCO — A1065a

Designs: 2k, Voltaire (1694-1778), philosopher. 6k, Georgius Agricola (1494-1555), mineralogist, humanist.

**1994, Feb. 2** ***Perf. 12x11½***
**2913** A1065a 2k multicolored .25 .25
**2914** A1065a 6k multicolored .80 .35

1994 Winter Olympics, Lillehammer A1066

**Photo. & Engr.**

**1994, Feb. 2** ***Perf. 11½***
**2915** A1066 5k multicolored .70 .35

A1067

Europa (Marco Polo &): No. 2916, Stylized animals, Chinese woman. No. 2917, Stylized animals.

**Photo. & Engr.**

**1994, May 4** ***Perf. 11½***

| | | | | |
|---|---|---|---|---|
| **2916** | A1067 | 14k multicolored | 1.75 | 1.75 |
| **2917** | A1067 | 14k multicolored | 1.75 | 1.75 |
| *a.* | | Pair, #2916-2917 | 3.50 | 3.50 |

Nos. 2916-2917 were issued in sheets of 2 + 2 labels. Value, $8.

Eduard Benes — A1068

**1994, May 18**
**2918** A1068 5k violet & brt purple .60 .25

Architectural Sights — A1069

UNESCO: 8k, Houses at the square, Telc. 9k, Cubist house designed by Chochol, Prague.

**1994, May 18**
**2919** A1069 8k multicolored 1.25 .75
**2920** A1069 9k multicolored 1.25 .75

Issued in sheets of 8. Value, pair of sheets $20.

Children's Day — A1070

**Photo. & Engr.**

**1994, June 1** ***Perf. 11½***
**2921** A1070 2k multicolored .40 .25

Dinosaurs — A1071

***Perf. 11½x11, 11x11½***

**1994, June 1** **Litho.**

| | | | | |
|---|---|---|---|---|
| **2922** | A1071 | 2k Stegosaurus | .30 | .25 |
| **2923** | A1071 | 3k Apatosaurus | .50 | .25 |
| **2924** | A1071 | 5k Tarbosaurus, vert. | .70 | .35 |
| | | *Nos. 2922-2924 (3)* | 1.50 | .85 |

A1072

**Photo. & Engr.**

**1994, June 1** *Perf. 11½x11*
**2925** A1072 8k multicolored 1.00 .50

1994 World Cup Soccer Championships, US.

A1073

**1994, June 15** *Perf. 11x11½*
**2926** A1073 2k multicolored .35 .25

12th Pan-Sokol Rally, Prague.

Intl. Olympic Committee, Cent. — A1074

**1994, June 15**
**2927** A1074 7k multicolored 1.00 .50

UPU, 120th Anniv. A1075

**1994, Aug. 3** **Engr.** *Perf. 11½*
**2928** A1075 11k multicolored 1.40 1.00

No. 2928 was issued in sheets of 4 + 4 labels. Value, $11.50.

Songbirds — A1076

Designs: 3k, Saxicola torquata. 5k, Carpodacus erythrinus. 14k, Luscinia svecica.

**Photo. & Engr.**

**1994, Aug. 24** *Perf. 11x11½*
**2929** A1076 3k multicolored .40 .25
**2930** A1076 5k multicolored .60 .30
**2931** A1076 14k multicolored 1.50 .80
*Nos. 2929-2931 (3)* 2.50 1.35

Historic Race Cars — A1077

**Photo. & Engr.**

**1994, Oct. 5** *Perf. 11½*
**2932** A1077 2k 1900 NW .25 .25
Complete booklet, 10 #2932 3.00
**2933** A1077 3k 1908 L&K .45 .25
Complete booklet, 5 #2933 2.75
**2934** A1077 9k 1912 Praga 1.10 .50
*Nos. 2932-2934 (3)* 1.80 1.00

Christmas — A1078

**Photo. & Engr.**

**1994, Nov. 9** *Perf. 11½*
**2935** A1078 2k multicolored .45 .25

**Painting Type of 1967 Inscribed "CESKA REPUBLIKA"**

Engraving or paintings: 7k, Stary Posetilec A Zena, by Lucas Van Leyden. 10k, Moulin Rouge, by Henri de Toulouse-Lautrec. 14k, St. Vitus Madonna, St. Vitus Cathedral, Prague.

**1994, Nov. 9** **Engr.** *Perf. 12*
**2936** A565 7k multicolored .95 .95
**2937** A565 10k multicolored 1.40 1.40
**2938** A565 14k multicolored 2.00 2.00
*Nos. 2936-2938 (3)* 4.35 4.35

Nos. 2936-2938 were each printed in sheets of 4. Value, set $17.

World Tourism Organization, 20th Anniv. — A1079

**Photo. & Engr.**

**1995, Jan. 2** *Perf. 11x12*
**2939** A1079 8k green blue & red .95 .50

Czech Stamp Production — A1080

**1995, Jan. 20**
**2940** A1080 3k Design N1 .60 .25

Czech Republic & European Union Association Agreement A1081

**1995, Jan. 20** **Litho.** *Perf. 13½x12½*
**2941** A1081 8k multicolored 1.20 .65

Famous Men A1082

Designs: 2k, Johannes Marcus Marci (1595-1667). 5k, Ferdinand Peroutka (1895-1978). 7k, Premysl Pitter (1895-1976).

**Photo. & Engr.**

**1995, Feb. 1** *Perf. 12x11*
**2942** A1082 2k multicolored .30 .25
**2943** A1082 5k multicolored .30 .25
**2944** A1082 7k multicolored .90 .35
*Nos. 2942-2944 (3)* 1.50 .85

Theater Personalities — A1083

Designs: No. 2945, Jiri Voskovec (1905-81). No. 2946, Jan Werich (1905-80). No. 2947, Jaroslav Jezek (1906-42). 22k, Caricatures of Voskovec, Werich, and Jezek with piano.

**1995** **Photo. & Engr.** *Perf. 12x11*
**2945** A1083 3k multicolored .35 .25
Complete booklet, 3 #2945 6.00
**2946** A1083 3k multicolored .35 .25
Complete booklet, 3 #2946 6.00
**2947** A1083 3k multicolored .35 .25
Complete booklet, 3 #2947 6.00
*a.* Strip of 3, #2945-2947 1.10 1.10
Complete booklet, 2 #2947a 9.00
*Nos. 2945-2947 (3)* 1.05 .75

**Souvenir Sheet**

**Photo.**

*Perf. 12*

**2947B** A1083 22k yellow & black 2.50 2.50

Issued: 3k, 3/15; 22k, 9/20.

**Havel Type of 1990 Inscribed "Ceska Republika"**

**Photo. & Engr.**

**1995, Mar. 22** *Perf. 12x11½*
**2948** A1000 3.60k bl, vio & mag .45 .25
Complete booklet, 5 #2948 4.00

Rural Architecture A1084

**1995, Mar. 22** *Perf. 11½*
**2949** A1084 40h shown .25 .25
**2950** A1084 60h Homes, diff. .25 .25

European Nature Conservation Year — A1085

**1995, Apr. 12**
**2951** A1085 3k Bombus terrestris .55 .30
Complete booklet, 5 #2951 4.00
**2952** A1085 5k Mantis religiosa .70 .30
Complete booklet, 5 #2952 4.50
**2953** A1085 6k Calopteryx splendens .80 .30
Complete booklet, 5 #2953 5.00
*Nos. 2951-2953 (3)* 2.05 .90

Peace & Freedom A1086

**Photo. & Engr.**

**1995, May 3** *Perf. 11½*
**2954** A1086 9k Rose, profiles 1.00 .35
**2955** A1086 14k Butterfly, profiles 1.50 .75

Europa.

Natural Beauties in Czech Republic A1087

Designs: 8k, "Stone Organ" scenic mountain. 9k, Largest sandstone bridge in Europe.

**Photo. & Engr.**

**1995, May 3** *Perf. 11½*
**2956** A1087 8k multicolored .95 .95
**2957** A1087 9k multicolored 1.00 1.00

Nos. 2956-2957 were each issued in sheets of 8. Value, set $16.

Children's Day — A1088

**Photo. & Engr.**

**1995, June 1** *Perf. 11½*
**2958** A1088 3.60k multicolored .60 .25

First Train from Vienna to Prague, 150th Anniv. A1089

3k, Chocen Tunnel. 9.60k, Entering Prague.

**1995, June 21**
**2959** A1089 3k multicolored .35 .25
Complete booklet, 5 #2959 4.00
**2960** A1089 9.60k multicolored 1.15 .50

World Wrestling Championships, Prague A1090

**Photo. & Engr.**

**1995, Sept. 6** *Perf. 11½*
**2961** A1090 3k multicolored .75 .25

Cartoon Characters A1091

Designs: 3k, Man playing violin, woman washing, by Vladimir Rencin. 3.60k, Angel, naked man, by Vladimir Jiranek. 5k, Circus trainer holding ring for champagne cork to pop through, by Jiri Sliva.

**1995, Sept. 6**
**2962** A1091 3k multicolored .35 .25
Complete booklet, 5 #2962 3.50
**2963** A1091 3.60k multicolored .35 .25
Complete booklet, 5 #2963 3.50
**2964** A1091 5k multicolored .35 .30
Complete booklet, 5 #2964 3.50
*Nos. 2962-2964 (3)* 1.05 .80

A1092

**1995, Sept. 20** **Litho.** *Perf. 13½x13*
**2965** A1092 3k multicolored .35 .25

SOS Children's Villages, 25th anniv.

A1093

Designs: 2.40k, Gothic. 3k, Secession. 3.60k, Romance. 4k, Classic portal; 4.60k, Rococo. 9.60k, Renaissance Portal. 12.60k, Cubist. 14k, Baroque.

**Photo. & Engr.**

**1995-97** *Perf. 12x11½*

**2966** A1093 2.40k red & green .30 .25
**2967** A1093 3k grn & bl .35 .25
**2967A** A1093 3.60k pur & grn .45 .25
**2968** A1093 4k blue & red .50 .25
Complete booklet, 5 #2967A 3.00
**2968A** A1093 4.60k multicolored .55 .25
**2969** A1093 9.60k blue & red 1.10 .45
**2969A** A1093 12.60k red brn & bl 1.50 .45
**2970** A1093 14k grn & pur 1.60 .60
*Nos. 2966-2970 (8)* 6.35 2.75

Issued: 9.60k, 9/27; 2.40k, 14k, 10/11; 3k, 3.60k, 10/25; 4k, 6/12/96; 4.60k, 3/26/97; 12.60k, 6/25/97.

UN, 50th Anniv. A1094

**1995, Oct. 11** **Litho.** *Perf. 12x11½*

**2971** A1094 14k multicolored 1.60 .80

Wilhelm Röntgen (1845-1923), Discovery of the X-Ray, Cent. — A1095

**1995, Oct. 11** **Photo. & Engr.**

**2972** A1095 6k blk, buff & bl vio .75 .35

**Painting Type of 1967 Inscribed "CESKA REPUBLIKA"**

Designs: 6k, Parisiene, by Ludek Marold. 9k, Vase of Flowers, by J.K. Hirschely. 14k, Portrait of J. Malinsky, by Antoinín Machek.

**1995, Nov. 8** *Perf. 12*

**2973** A565 6k multicolored .95 .45
**2974** A565 9k multicolored 1.25 .65
**2975** A565 14k multicolored 2.00 1.00
*Nos. 2973-2975 (3)* 4.20 2.10

Nos. 2973-2975 were each printed in sheets of 4. Value, set $13.50.

Christmas — A1096

**1995, Nov. 8** *Perf. 11½*

**2976** A1096 3k multicolored .50 .25
Complete booklet, 3 #2976 2.00

Czech Philharmonic Orchestra, Cent. — A1097

**Photo. & Engr.**

**1996, Jan. 2** *Perf. 12x11½*

**2977** A1097 3.60k multicolored .55 .25

Tradition of Czech Stamp Production — A1098

**Photo. & Engr.**

**1996, Jan. 20** *Perf. 11½x12*

**2978** A1098 3.60k Design A5 of 1920 .55 .25

Vera Mencikova (1906-44), Chess Player — A1099

**Photo. & Engr.**

**1996, Feb. 14** *Perf. 12x11½*

**2979** A1099 6k multicolored .75 .35

Easter — A1100

**1996, Mar. 13** *Perf. 11½x12*

**2980** A1100 3k multicolored .45 .25
Complete booklet, 5 #2980 2.00

Josef Sudek (1896-1976), Photographer A1101

**Photo. & Engr.**

**1996, Mar. 13** *Perf. 11*

**2981** A1101 9.60k multicolored 1.10 .60

Rulers from House of Luxembourg — A1102

Designs: a, John of Luxembourg (1296-1346). b, Charles IV (1316-78). c, Wenceslas IV. (1361-1419). d, Sigismund (1368-1437).

**1996, Mar. 27** **Engr.** *Perf. 11½*

**2982** A1102 14k Sheet of 4, #a.-d. + label 6.00 6.00

Jiri Guth-Jarkovsky, Participant in First Modern Olympic Games, Athens A1103

**Photo. & Engr.**

**1996, Mar. 27** *Perf. 11½*

**2983** A1103 9.60k multicolored 1.25 .60

Modern Olympic Games, cent.

World Wildlife Fund — A1104

Designs: a, 3.60k, Eliomys quercinus. b, 5k, Dryomys nitedula. c, 6k, Spermophilus citellus. d, 8k, Sicista betulina.

**Photo. & Engr.**

**1996, Apr. 24** *Perf. 11½x12*

**2984** A1104 Block of 4, #a.-d. 2.50 2.50

Issued in sheets of 8 stamps. Value $5.

Ema Destinnova (1878-1930), Singer — A1105

**1996, May 2** *Perf. 11½*

**2985** A1105 8k multicolored .85 .35

Europa.

No. 2985 was issued in sheets of 10. Value $8.50.

A1106

**Photo. & Engr.**

**1996, May 15** *Perf. 11x11½*

**2986** A1106 12k multicolored 1.20 .65

Jean Gaspart Deburau (1796-1846), mime.

A1107

**1996, May 29**

**2987** A1107 3k multicolored .35 .25

1996 Summmer Olympic Games, Atlanta.

Intl. Children's Day — A1108

**Photo. & Engr.**

**1996, May 29** *Perf. 11½*

**2988** A1108 3k multicolored .35 .25

Architectural Sites — A1109

UNESCO: 8k, St. Nepomuk Church, Zelena Hora. 9k, Loreta Tower, Prague.

**1996, June 26** **Engr.** *Perf. 11½*

**2989** A1109 8k multicolored 1.00 1.00
**2990** A1109 9k multicolored 1.10 1.10

Nos. 2989-2990 were each issued in sheets of 8. Value, set $16.
See Nos. 3056-3057.

UNICEF, 50th Anniv. A1110

**Photo. & Engr.**

**1996, Sept. 11** *Perf. 12x11*

**2991** A1110 3k multicolored .35 .25

Horses

A1111 A1112

**Photo. & Engr.**

**1996, Sept. 25** *Perf. 11x11½*

**2992** A1111 3k multicolored .50 .25
**2993** A1112 3k multicolored .50 .25
*a.* Pair, #2992-2993 1.00 .75
Complete booklet, 3 #2992, 2 #2993 3.00
Complete booklet, 2 #2992, 3 #2993 3.00

**Souvenir Sheet**

Vaclav Havel, 60th Birthday — A1113

**1996, Oct. 5**

**2994** A1113 Sheet of 2 1.25 1.25
*a.* 6k red & blue .60 .50

**Painting Type of 1967 Inscribed "CESKA REPUBLIKA"**

The Baroque Chair, by Endre Nemes (1909-85).

**1996, Oct. 5 Engr. *Perf. 11½***
**2995** A565 20k multicolored 2.00 2.00

No. 2995 was issued in sheets of 4. Value $8.
See Slovakia No. 255; Sweden No. 2199.

Tycho Brahe (1546-1601), Astronomer — A1114

**Photo. & Engr.**
**1996, Oct. 9 *Perf. 11½x11***
**2996** A1114 5k multicolored .85 .30

Biplanes A1115

**1996, Oct. 9**
**2997** A1115 7k Letov S1 (1920) .70 .40
**2998** A1115 8k Aero A11 (1925) .90 .40
**2999** A1115 10k Avia BH21 (1925) 1.00 .50
*Nos. 2997-2999 (3)* 2.60 1.30

Christmas A1116

**Photo. & Engr.**
**1996, Nov. 13 *Perf. 11½***
**3000** A1116 3k multicolored .45 .25
Complete booklet, 5 #3000 3.50

**Painting Type of 1967 Inscribed "CESKA REPUBLIKA"**

Designs: 9k, Garden of Eden, by Josef Váchal (1884-1969), horiz. 11k, Breakfast, by Georg Flegel (1566-1638).

**1996, Nov. 13 Engr. *Perf. 11½***
**3001** A565 9k multicolored 1.00 1.00
**3002** A565 11k multicolored 1.25 1.25

Nos. 3001-3002 were each issued in sheets of 4. Value, set $10.

Czech Stamp Production — A1117

**Photo. & Engr.**
**1997, Jan. 20 *Perf. 11½x12***
**3003** A1117 3.60k #68, bl & red .75 .25

Easter — A1118

**Photo. & Engr.**
**1997, Mar. 12 *Perf. 11½***
**3004** A1118 3k multicolored .75 .25
Complete booklet, 5 #3004 4.00

Flowers — A1119

3.60k, Erythronium dens-canis. 4k, Calla palustris. 5k, Cypripedium calceolus. 8k, Iris pumila.

**1997, Mar. 12 *Perf. 11x11½***
**3005** A1119 3.60k multicolored .30 .25
Complete booklet, 5 #3005 2.50
**3006** A1119 4k multicolored .30 .25
Complete booklet, 5 #3006 2.50
**3007** A1119 5k multicolored .50 .30
Complete booklet, 5 #3007 3.50
**3008** A1119 8k multicolored .60 .45
Complete booklet, 5 #3008 5.00
*Nos. 3005-3008 (4)* 1.70 1.25

A1120

Jewish Monuments in Prague: 8k, Altneuschul Synagogue. 10k, Tombstone of Rabbi Judah Loew MaHaRal.

**1997, Apr. 30 *Perf. 11½***
**3009** A1120 8k multicolored .75 .45
**3010** A1120 10k multicolored .90 .55
*a.* Sheet, 4 each #3009-3010 7.00 4.00

See Israel Nos. 1302-1303.

Greetings Stamp — A1121

**1997, Mar. 26 Litho. *Perf. 13x13½***
**3011** A1121 4k Girl with cats .50 .25

A1122

**1997, Apr. 23 Engr. *Perf. 11½***
**3012** A1122 7k deep violet .95 .40

St. Adalbert (956-97). See Germany No. 1964, Hungary No. 3569, Poland No. 3337, Vatican City No. 1040.
No. 3012 was issued in sheets of 4 + 4 labels. Value, $7.

A1123

Europa (Stories and Legends): No. 3013, Queen, knight with sword, lion, snakes. No. 3014, Man riding in chariot drawn by chickens, King looking through window.

**Photo. & Engr.**
**1997, Apr. 30 *Perf. 11½x12***
**3013** A1123 8k multicolored 1.00 .60
**3014** A1123 8k multicolored 1.00 .60

Nos. 3013-3014 were each issued in sheets of 8. Value, set $16.

Souvenir Sheet

Collections of Rudolf II (1522-1612), Prague Exhibition — A1124

Designs: a, 6k, Musical instruments, flowers, face of bearded man. b, 8k, Rudolf II wearing laurel wreath, holding rose, Muses. c, 10k, Rudolf II, skull, moth's wings, tree, flowers, leaves, fruit.

**1997, May 14 Engr. *Perf. 12***
**3015** A1124 Sheet of 3, #a.-c. 2.25 2.25

Intl. Children's Day — A1125

**Photo. & Engr.**
**1997, May 28 *Perf. 11½***
**3016** A1125 4.60k multicolored .75 .25

Frantisek Krizik (1847-1941), Electrical Engineer, Inventor of Arc Lamp — A1126

**Photo. & Engr.**
**1997, June 25 *Perf. 12x11½***
**3017** A1126 6k multicolored .85 .25

European Swimming & Diving Championships, Prague — A1127

**Photo. & Engr.**
**1997, Aug. 27 *Perf. 11½***
**3018** A1127 11k multicolored 1.00 .40

"The Good Soldier Schweik," by Jaroslav Hasek, 110th Anniv. — A1128

4k, Mrs. Müller, Schweik in wheelchair. 4.60k, Lt. Lukás, Col. Kraus von Zillergut, dog. 6k, Schweik smoking pipe, winter scene.

**Photo. & Engr.**
**1997, Sept. 10 *Perf. 12x11½***
**3019** A1128 4k multicolored .50 .25
*a.* Booklet pane of 8 + 4 labels 4.50
Complete booklet, #3019a 4.50
**3020** A1128 4.60k multicolored .50 .25
*a.* Booklet pane of 8 + 4 labels 5.00
Complete booklet, #3020a 5.00
**3021** A1128 6k multicolored .50 .30
*a.* Booklet pane of 8 + 4 labels 6.00
Complete booklet, #3021a 6.00
*Nos. 3019-3021 (3)* 1.50 .80

Praga 1998, Intl. Stamp Exhibition — A1129

No. 3022, Lesser Town, Prague Castle. No. 3023, Old Town, bridges over Vltava River.

**Photo. & Engr.**
**1997, Sept. 24 *Perf. 11½***
**3022** A1129 15k multicolored 1.40 .60
**3023** A1129 15k multicolored 1.40 .60
*a.* Souvenir sheet, #3022-3023 + 2 labels 3.75 3.00

Historic Service Vehicles A1130

Designs: 4k, Postal bus, Prague. 4.60k, Sentinel truck, Skoda. 8k, Fire truck, Tatra.

**1997, Oct. 8 *Perf. 12x11½***
**3024** A1130 4k multicolored .30 .25
Complete booklet, 5 #3024 2.50
**3025** A1130 4.60k multicolored .30 .25
Complete booklet, 5 #3025 3.50
**3026** A1130 8k multicolored .60 .40
Complete booklet, 5 #3026 5.00
*Nos. 3024-3026 (3)* 1.20 .90

A1131

**Photo. & Engr.**
**1997, Nov. 12 *Perf. 11½***
**3027** A1131 4k multicolored .50 .25
Complete booklet, 5 #3027 2.75

Christmas.

**Painting Type of 1967 Inscribed "CESKA REPUBLIKA"**

7k, Landscape with Chateau in Chantilly, by Antonín Chittussi (1847-91). 12k, The Prophets Came Out of the Desert, by Frantisek Bílek (1872-1941). 1 6k, Parisian Antiquarians, by T. F. Simon (1877-1942).

**1997, Nov. 12 Engr. *Perf. 12***
**3028** A565 7k multi, horiz. .50 .50
**3029** A565 12k multi 1.00 1.00
**3030** A565 16k multi 1.50 1.50
*Nos. 3028-3030 (3)* 3.00 3.00

Nos. 3028-3030 were each issued in sheets of 4. Value, set $12.

A1132

**1998, Jan. 20 Litho. *Perf. 11½x12***
**3031** A1132 7k multicolored .85 .30

1998 Winter Olympic Games, Nagano.

Tradition of Czech Stamp Production — A1133

**Photo. & Engr.**

**1998, Jan. 20 *Perf. 12x11½***
**3032** A1133 12.60k Type A8 1.25 .55
*a.* Booklet pane of 8 + 4 labels 12.50
Complete booklet, #3032a 12.50

Pres. Václav Havel — A1134

**1998, Jan. 22**
**3033** A1134 4.60k dark grn & red .85 .25

See No. 3114.

Love — A1135

**1998, Feb. 4 *Perf. 11½***
**3034** A1135 4k multicolored .50 .25
Complete booklet, 5 #3034 2.50

Skibob World Championship, Spindleruv Mlyn — A1136

**1998, Feb. 25**
**3035** A1136 8k multicolored .85 .35

**Prague Philatelic Exhibition Type of 1938**

Souvenir Sheet

**1998, Feb. 25 Engr. *Perf. 12x11½***
**3036** A87 Sheet of 2 5.00 5.00
*a.* 30k like #251a 2.50 2.00

Prague '98, Intl. Philatelic Exhibition.

Easter — A1137

**Photo. & Engr.**

**1998, Mar. 25 *Perf. 11x11½***
**3037** A1137 4k multicolored .55 .25
Complete booklet, 5 #3037 2.75

Ondrejov Observatory, Cent. — A1138

**1998, Mar. 25 *Perf. 12x11½***
**3038** A1138 4.60k multicolored .85 .25

Czech Ice Hockey Team, Gold Medalists at Nagano Winter Olympic Games — A1139

**1998, Apr. 1 Litho. *Perf. 11½x12***
**3039** A1139 23k Dominik Hasek 1.50 1.50

No. 3039 was issued in a sheet with two labels. Value, $2.

Charles University and New Town, Prague, 650th Anniv. — A1140

Designs: a, 15k, Hands forming arch, University seal. b, 22k, Charles IV (1316-78), Holy Roman Emperor, King of Bohemia. c, 23k, Groin vault, St. Vitus Cathedral, Prague.

**1998, Apr. 1 Engr. *Perf. 12***
**3040** A1140 Sheet of 3, #a.-c. 5.50 5.50

World Book and Copyright Day — A1141

**1998, Apr. 23 Litho. *Perf. 12x11½***
**3041** A1141 10k multicolored 1.00 .45

Nature Conservation A1142

**1998, Apr. 23 *Perf. 13x13½***
**3042** A1142 4.60k Perdix perdix .45 .25
**3043** A1142 4.60k Lyrurus tetrix .45 .25
*a.* Pair, #3042-3043 1.10 .60
**3044** A1142 8k Cervus elaphus .65 .30
**3045** A1142 8k Alces alces .65 .30
*a.* Pair, #3044-3045 1.50 1.10
*Nos. 3042-3045 (4)* 2.20 1.10

Natl. Festivals and Holidays A1143

Europa: 11k, King's Ride. 15k, Wearing masks for Carnival.

**Litho. & Engr.**

**1998, May 5 *Perf. 11½***
**3046** A1143 11k multicolored .90 .55
**3047** A1143 15k multicolored 1.40 .75

Intl. Children's Day — A1144

Designs: 4k, Two satyr musicians. 4.60k, Character riding on fish.

**Photo. & Engr.**

**1998, May 27 *Perf. 11½***
**3048** A1144 4k multicolored .60 .25
*a.* Booklet of 6 +4 labels 4.00
Complete booklet, #3048a 4.00
**3049** A1144 4.60k multicolored .60 .25
*a.* Booklet of 6 + 4 labels 4.50
Complete booklet, #3049a 4.50

Famous Men — A1145

Designs: 4k, Frantisek Kmoch (1848-1912), bandleader, composer. 4.60k, Frantisek Palacky (1798-1876), historian, politician. 6k, Rafael Kubelík (1914-96), composer, conductor.

**1998, May 27 *Perf. 11½x12***
**3050** A1145 4k multicolored .35 .25
**3051** A1145 4.60k multicolored .45 .25
**3052** A1145 6k multicolored .55 .25
*Nos. 3050-3052 (3)* 1.35 .75

Revolt of 1848, 150th Anniv. A1146

**1998, May 27 *Perf. 12x11½***
**3053** A1146 15k multicolored 1.60 .75

**Painting Type of 1967 Inscribed "CESKA REPUBLIKA"**

Praga 1998 Intl. Stamp Exhibition, works of art: 22k, Amorfa Dvoubarevna Fuga, by Frantisek Kupka (1871-1957), horiz. 23k, Escape, by Paul Gauguin (1848-1903), horiz.

**1998, June 17 Engr. *Perf. 12***
**3054** A565 22k multicolored 1.75 1.75
**3055** A565 23k multicolored 2.25 1.75

Nos. 3054-3055 were each issued in sheets of 4. Value, set $16.

**UNESCO World Heritage Sites Type of 1996**

8k, St. Barbara Cathedral, Kutná Hora, horiz. 11k, The Chateau of Valtice, horiz.

**1998, Oct. 7 Engr. *Perf. 11½x12***
**3056** A1109 8k multicolored .70 .40
**3057** A1109 11k multicolored 1.00 .60

Nos. 3056-3057 were each issued in sheets of 8. Value, set $15.

Czechoslovak Republic, 80th Anniv. — A1147

Designs based on World War I recruitment posters by Vojtech Preissig (1873-1944): 4.60k, Soldiers holding flags, guns. 5k, Three soldiers marching. 12.60k, Flags waving from city buildings.

***Perf. 11½x11¾***

**1998, Oct. 28 Litho. & Engr.**
**3058** A1147 4.60k multicolored .50 .30
**3059** A1147 5k multicolored .70 .30
**3060** A1147 12.60k multicolored 1.25 .90
*Nos. 3058-3060 (3)* 2.45 1.50

No. 3060 was issued in sheets of 6+2 labels. Value $25.

Christmas A1148

Designs: 4k, People following star. 6k, Angel blowing trumpet over town, vert.

**Photo. & Engr.**

**1998, Nov. 18 *Perf. 11½***
**3061** A1148 4k multicolored .45 .25
Complete booklet, 5 #3061 2.50
**3062** A1148 6k multicolored .70 .25
Complete booklet, 5 #3062 4.00

Signs of the Zodiac — A1149

**1998-2000 *Perf. 12x11½***
**3063** A1149 1k Capricorn .25 .25
**3064** A1149 10k Aquarius .75 .25
**3065** A1149 9k Libra .75 .25
**3066** A1149 8k Cancer .65 .25
**3067** A1149 20k Sagittarius 1.60 .45

**Photo. & Engr.**

***Perf. 11¾x11¼***
**3068** A1149 5k Taurus .55 .25
Booklet, 5 #3068 2.75
**3069** A1149 5.40k Scorpio .60 .25
Booklet, 5 #3069 3.00
**3070** A1149 2k Virgo .25 .25
**3071** A1149 40h Pisces .65 .25
**3072** A1149 12k Leo 1.00 .30
**3073** A1149 17k Gemini 1.60 .65
**3074** A1149 26k Aries 2.40 .95
*Nos. 3063-3074 (12)* 11.05 4.35

Issued: 1k, 10k, 11/18; 9k, 5/5/99; 8k, 20k, 9/8/99; 5k, 5.40k, 12/8/99; 2k, 5/9/00. 40h, 1/20/01. 12k, 2/21/01. 17k, 9/1/02. 26k, 2/12/03.

**Painting Type of 1967 Inscribed "CESKA REPUBLIKA"**

15k, Painting from the Greater Cycle, 1902, by Jan Preisler (1872-1918), horiz. 16k, Spinner, by Josef Navrátil (1798-1865).

**1998, Dec. 9 *Perf. 12***
**3075** A565 15k multicolored 1.40 1.00
**3076** A565 16k multicolored 1.40 1.00

Nos. 3075-3076 were each issued in sheets of 4. Value, set $11.

A1150

**Photo. & Engr.**

**1999, Jan. 20 *Perf. 11½x11¾***
**3077** A1150 4.60k #164 .85 .25
*a.* Booklet pane of 8 + 4 labels 5.00
Complete booklet, #3077a 5.50

Tradition of Czech stamp production.

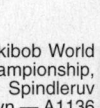

Domestic Cats — A1151

**Photo. & Engr.**

**1999, Feb. 17** ***Perf. 11½***

| | | | | |
|---|---|---|---|---|
| **3078** | A1151 4.60k shown | .55 | .25 |
| | Complete booklet, 5 #3078 | 3.50 | |
| **3079** | A1151 5k Adult, kitten | .55 | .25 |
| | Complete booklet, 5 #3079 | 3.50 | |
| **3080** | A1151 7k Two cats | .80 | .30 |
| | Complete booklet, 5 #3080 | 3.50 | |
| | *Nos. 3078-3080 (3)* | 1.90 | .80 |

Easter — A1152

**Photo. & Engr.**

**1999, Mar. 10** ***Perf. 11¼x11½***

**3081** A1152 3k multicolored .35 .25

Protected Birds — A1153

No. 3082, Merops apiaster. No. 3083, Upupa epops.

Protected butterflies: No. 3084, Catocala electa. No. 3085, Euphydryas maturna.

***Perf. 12¾x13¼***

**1999, Mar. 10** **Litho.**

| | | | |
|---|---|---|---|
| **3082** | A1153 4.60k multicolored | .45 | .25 |
| **3083** | A1153 4.60k multicolored | .45 | .25 |
| *a.* | Pair, #3082-3083 | .95 | .60 |
| | Complete booklet, 3 #3082, 2 #3083 | 5.00 | |
| **3084** | A1153 5k multicolored | .45 | .25 |
| **3085** | A1153 5k multicolored | .45 | .25 |
| *a.* | Pair, #3084-3085 | .95 | .60 |
| | Complete booklet, 3 #3084, 2 #3085 | 5.00 | |

Nature conservation.

Czech Republic's Entry Into NATO — A1154

**Photo. & Engr.**

**1999, Mar. 12** ***Perf. 12x11½***

**3086** A1154 4.60k multicolored .45 .25

Council of Europe, 50th Anniv. A1155

**Photo. & Engr.**

**1999, Apr. 14** ***Perf. 11¾x11¼***

**3087** A1155 7k multicolored 1.20 .40

Natl. Olympic Committee, Cent. — A1156

Design: Josef Rössler-Orovsky (1869-1933), founder of Czech Olympic Committee.

**1999, Apr. 14** ***Perf. 11¼x11¾***

**3088** A1156 9k multicolored 1.20 .35

Europa A1157

Natl. Parks: 11k, Sumava. 17k, Podyji.

**1999, May 5** ***Perf. 11¾x11¼***

| | | | |
|---|---|---|---|
| **3089** | A1157 11k multicolored | .90 | .40 |
| **3090** | A1157 17k multicolored | 1.40 | .65 |

Nos. 3089-3090 were each issued in sheets of 8. Value, set $27.

Ferda the Ant, Pytlik the Beetle and Ladybird A1158

**Photo. & Engr.**

**1999, May 26** ***Perf. 11½x11¼***

| | | | |
|---|---|---|---|
| **3091** | A1158 4.60k multicolored | .75 | .25 |
| | Complete booklet, 8 #3091 | 6.00 | |

Bridges A1159

**1999, May 26** **Engr.** ***Perf. 11¾***

| | | | |
|---|---|---|---|
| **3092** | A1159 8k Stádlec, vert. | .60 | .40 |
| **3093** | A1159 11k Cernvír | 1.00 | .60 |

Nos. 3092-3094 were each issued in sheets of 8. Value, set $13.

Souvenir Sheet

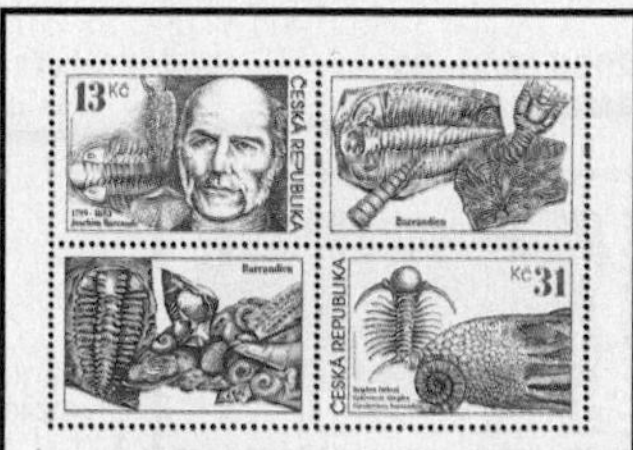

Paleontologist Joachim Barrande (1799-1883) and Trilobite Fossils — A1160

a, 13k, Barrande, fossils. b, 31k, Delphon forbesi, Ophioceras simplex, Carolicrinus barrandei.

**1999, June 23** **Engr.** ***Perf. 11¾***

**3094** A1160 Sheet of 2, #a.-b. + 2 labels 4.00 4.00

Jihlava Mining Rights, 750th Anniv. A1161

**Photo. & Engr.**

**1999, June 23** ***Perf. 11¾x11¼***

| | | | |
|---|---|---|---|
| **3095** | A1161 8k multicolored | .95 | .35 |
| *a.* | Bklt. pane of 8 + 4 labels | 8.00 | |
| | Complete booklet, #3095a | 8.00 | |

UPU, 125th Anniv. — A1162

**Litho. & Engr.**

**1999, June 23** ***Perf. 11¾***

**3096** A1162 9k multicolored 1.00 .40

No. 3096 was issued in sheets of 5 + 10 labels. Value, $6.

Vincenc Preissnitz (1799-1851), Hydrotherapy Advocate A1163

**Photo. & Engr.**

**1999, Sept. 8** ***Perf. 11¼***

**3097** A1163 4.60k multicolored .50 .25

UNESCO.

Carved Beehives — A1164

Designs: 4.60k, Woman. 5k, St. Joseph and Infant Jesus. 7k, Chimney sweep.

**Photo. & Engr.**

**1999, Sept. 29** ***Perf. 11¼x11½***

| | | | |
|---|---|---|---|
| **3098** | A1164 4.60k multi | .55 | .25 |
| | Complete booklet, 5 #3098 | 2.75 | |
| **3099** | A1164 5k multi | .60 | .25 |
| | Complete booklet, 5 #3099 | 3.00 | |
| **3100** | A1164 7k multi | .80 | .30 |
| | Complete booklet, 5 #3100 | 4.00 | |
| | *Nos. 3098-3100 (3)* | 1.95 | .80 |

Cartoons by Miroslav Bartak — A1165

Designs: 4.60k, Doctor in clown mask, infant. 5k, Dog with pipe. 7k, Night seeping through window sill.

**1999, Oct. 20**

| | | | |
|---|---|---|---|
| **3101** | A1165 4.60k multi | .45 | .25 |
| **3102** | A1165 5k multi | .55 | .25 |
| **3103** | A1165 7k multi | .70 | .30 |
| | *Nos. 3101-3103 (3)* | 1.70 | .80 |

Souvenir Sheet

Beuron Art School — A1166

Designs: a, 11k, Mater Dei, 1898. b, 13k, Pantocrator, 1911.

**Litho. & Engr.**

**1999, Oct. 20** ***Perf. 11¾***

**3104** A1166 Sheet of 2, #a.-b. 2.25 2.25

**Painting Type of 1967 Inscribed "CESKA REPUBLIKA"**

Designs: 13k, Red Orchid, by Jindrich Styrsky (1899-1942). 17k, Landscape with Marsh, by Julius Marák (1832-99). 26k, Monument, by Frantisek Hudecek (1909-90).

**1999, Nov. 10** **Engr.** ***Perf. 11¾***

| | | | |
|---|---|---|---|
| **3105** | A565 13k multi | 1.00 | 1.00 |
| **3106** | A565 17k multi | 1.50 | 1.50 |
| **3107** | A565 26k multi | 2.50 | 2.00 |
| | *Nos. 3105-3107 (3)* | 5.00 | 4.50 |

Nos. 3105-3107 were each issued in sheets of 4. Value, set $20.

Christmas — A1167

**Photo. & Engr.**

**1999, Nov. 10** ***Perf. 11¼x11½***

**3108** A1167 3k multi .35 .25

A1168

**Photo. & Engr.**

**2000, Jan. 20** ***Perf. 11¼x11¾***

| | | | |
|---|---|---|---|
| **3109** | A1168 5.40k #B151 | .75 | .25 |
| *a.* | Bklt. pane of 8 + 4 labels | 6.00 | |
| | Booklet, #3109a | 6.00 | |

Tradition of Czech stamp production.

Brno 2000 Philatelic Exhibition — A1169

Designs: 5k, 1593 view of Brno. 50k, St. James's Church, vert.

**2000, Jan. 20** *Perf. 11¾x11¼*
**3110** A1169 5k multi .60 .25

**Souvenir Sheet**
*Perf. 11¼x11¾*
**3111** A1169 50k multi 5.00 4.25

No. 3110 printed in sheets of 35 stamps and 30 labels.

Kutna Hora Royal Mining Law, 700th Anniv. — A1170

**2000, Mar. 1** *Perf. 11¼x11¾*
**3112** A1170 5k multi .60 .25
*a.* Booklet pane of 8 + 4 labels 5.00
Booklet, #3112a 5.00

Souvenir Sheet

Pres. Thomas Garrigue Masaryk (1850-1937) — A1171

**2000, Mar. 1 Engr.** *Perf. 11¾*
**3113** A1171 17k multi 1.75 1.50

**Pres. Havel Type of 1998**
**Photo. & Engr.**
**2000, Mar. 1** *Perf. 11¾x11¼*
**3114** A1134 5.40k Prus bl & org brn .60 .25

Easter — A1172

**Photo. & Engr.**
**2000, Apr. 5** *Perf. 11¼x11½*
**3115** A1172 5k multi .60 .25

Souvenir Sheet

Prague, 2000 European City of Culture — A1173

No. 3116: a, 9k, Statue of man. b, 11k, Statue of harpist. c, 17k, Statue of King Charles IV.

**Litho. & Engr.**
**2000, Apr. 5** *Perf. 11¾*
**3116** A1173 Sheet of 3, #a-c + 3 labels 4.00 4.00

Souvenir Sheet

Trains — A1174

No. 3117: a, 8k, Train from 1900. b, 15k, Train from 2000.

**Litho. & Engr.**
**2000, May 5** *Perf. 11¾*
**3117** A1174 Sheet of 2, #a-b, +3 labels 3.00 3.00

Czech Personalities A1175

5k, Vítezslav Nezval (1900-58), writer. 8k, Gustav Mahler (1860-1911), composer.

**Photo. & Engr.**
**2000, May 5** *Perf. 11¼x11¾*
**3118-3119** A1175 Set of 2 1.40 .50

**Europa, 2000**
Common Design Type
**2000, May 5 Litho.** *Perf. 12¾x13¼*
**3120** CD17 9k multi 1.20 .40

Intl. Children's Year — A1176

**Photo. & Engr.**
**2000, May 31** *Perf. 11½x11¼*
**3121** A1176 5.40k multi .75 .25
*a.* Booklet pane of 8 + 2 labels 6.00
Booklet, #3121a 6.00

1995 Proof of Fermat's Last Theorem by Andrew Wiles A1177

**2000, May 31** *Perf. 11¾x11¼*
**3122** A1177 7k multi .80 .25

Intl. Mathematics Year.

Prague Landmarks — A1178

Designs: 9k, Charles Bridge tower. 11k, St. Nicholas's Church. 13k, Town Hall.

**2000, June 28 Engr.** *Perf. 11¾*
**3123-3125** A1178 Set of 3 3.00 1.10

Issued in sheets of 8. Value, set $24.

Mushrooms — A1179

No. 3126, 5k: a, Geastrum pouzarii. b, Boletus satanoides.
No. 3127, 5.40k: a, Morchella pragensis. b, Verpa bohemica.

**Photo. & Engr.**
**2000, June 28** *Perf. 11¼x11½*
**Pairs, #a-b**
**3126-3127** A1179 Set of 2 2.40 .70
Booklet, 3 #3126a, 2 #3126b 3.50
Booklet, 3 #3127b, 2 #3127a 3.50

Meeting of Intl. Monetary Fund and World Bank Group, Prague — A1180

**2000, Aug. 30** *Perf. 11¾x11¼*
**3128** A1180 7k multi .95 .25

Ancient Olympics A1181

**2000, Aug. 30**
**3129** A1181 9k multi 1.00 .35

2000 Summer Olympics, Sydney — A1182

**2000, Aug. 30**
**3130** A1182 13k multi 1.25 .45

No. 3130 was issued in sheets of 35 + 25 labels. Values: stamp + 1 label, $1.50; stamp + 2 labels, $1.75.

Hunting — A1183

No. 3131: a, 5k, Falconry. b, 5k, Deer at feed trough.
No. 3132: a, 5.40k, Ducks and blind. b, 5.40k, Deer and blind.

**Photo. & Engr.**
**2000, Oct. 4** *Perf. 11¼x11¾*
**Horiz. Pairs, #a-b**
**3131-3132** A1183 Set of 2 2.40 .55
Booklet, 3 #3131a, 2 #3131b 3.50
Booklet, 3 #3132a, 2 #3132b 3.50

**Painting Type of 1967 Inscribed "CESKA REPUBLIKA"**

Designs: 13k, St. Luke the Evangelist, by Master Theodoricus. 17k, Simeon With Infant Jesus, by Petr Jan Brandl. 26k, Brunette, by Alfons Mucha.

**2000, Nov. 15 Engr.** *Perf. 11¾*
**3133-3135** A565 Set of 3 5.00 4.50

Nos. 3133-3135 were each issued in sheets of 4. Value, set $20.

Christmas — A1184

**Photo. & Engr.**
**2000, Nov. 15** *Perf. 11¼x11½*
**3136** A1184 5k multi .60 .25

End of Millennium A1185

**2000, Nov. 22**
**3137** A1185 9k multi 1.20 .35

Advent of New Millennium A1186

**2001, Jan. 2**
**3138** A1186 9k multi 1.20 .35

Tradition of Czech Stamp Production A1187

**2001, Jan. 20** ***Perf. 11¼x11¾***

**3139** A1187 5.40k #474 .75 .25
*a.* Booklet pane of 8 + 4 labels 6.00
Booklet, #3139a 6.00

Jan Amos Komensky (Comenius, 1592-1670), Theologian — A1188

**Photo. & Engr.**

**2001, Mar. 14** ***Perf. 11¼x11½***

**3140** A1188 9k red & black 1.10 .35

**Souvenir Sheet**

Architecture — A1189

No. 3141: a, 13k, Church and decorations, Jakub. b, 17k, Arcade decorations, Bucovice Castle. c, 31k, Dance Hall, Prague.

**2001, Mar. 28 Engr.** ***Perf. 11¾x11½***

**3141** A1189 Sheet of 3, #a-c 6.00 4.50

Easter — A1190

**Photo. & Engr.**

**2001, Mar. 28** ***Perf. 11¼x11½***

**3142** A1190 5.40k multi .75 .25

**Souvenir Sheet**

Allegory of Art, by Vaclav Vavrinec Reiner — A1191

**Litho. & Engr.**

**2001, Apr. 18** ***Perf. 11¾***

**3143** A1191 50k multi 5.00 4.25

Europa A1192

**Photo. & Engr.**

**2001, May 9** ***Perf. 11¾x11¼***

**3144** A1192 9k pur & lilac 1.20 .35

European Men's Volleyball Championships, Ostrova — A1193

**Photo. & Engr.**

**2001, May 9** ***Perf. 11¼x11½***

**3145** A1193 12k multi 1.25 .50

Intl. Children's Day — A1194

**Photo. & Engr.**

**2001, May 30** ***Perf. 11¼x11½***

**3146** A1194 5.40k multi .60 .25
*a.* Booklet pane of 8 + 2 labels 5.00 —
Booklet, #3146a 5.00

Famous Men — A1195

Designs: 5.40k, Frantisek Skroup (1801-62), composer. 16k, Frantisek Halas (1901-49), writer.

**2001, May 30**

**3147-3148** A1195 Set of 2 2.50 .80

Congratulations A1196

**2001, June 20**

**3149** A1196 5.40k multi .75 .25
Booklet, 5 #3149 4.00

Dogs — A1197

No. 3150: a, West Highland terrier. b, Beagle.

No. 3151: a, German shepherd. b, Golden retriever.

**Photo. & Engr.**

**2001, June 20** ***Perf. 11½x11¼***

**3150** Pair 1.25 1.00
*a.-b.* A1197 5.40k Any single .60 .25
Booklet, 3 #3150a, 2 #3150b 3.25
Booklet, 3 #3150b, 2 #3150a 3.25

**3151** Pair 1.25 1.00
*a.-b.* A1197 5.40k Any single .60 .25
Booklet, 3 #3151a, 2 #3151b 3.25

Zoo Animals A1198

No. 3152: a, Pongo pygmaeus. b, Panthera tigris altaica.

No. 3153: a, Ailurus fulgens. b, Fennecus zerda.

**Photo. & Engr.**

**2001, Sept. 5** ***Perf. 11¾x11¼***

**3152** Pair 1.00 1.00
*a.-b.* A1198 5.40k Any single .50 .25
Booklet, 3 #3152b, 2 #3152a 3.25

**3153** Pair 1.00 1.00
*a.-b.* A1198 5.40k Any single .50 .25
Booklet, 3 #3153b, 2 #3153a 3.25

UNESCO World Heritage Sites A1199

Designs: 12k, Kormeríz Castle and Gardens. 14k, Holasovice Historical Village Restoration.

**2001, Oct. 9 Engr.** ***Perf. 11½x11¾***

**3154-3155** A1199 Set of 2 2.00 1.25

See Nos. 3177-3178, 3267-3268.

Year of Dialogue Among Civilizations A1200

**Photo. & Engr.**

**2001, Oct. 9** ***Perf. 11¼x11½***

**3156** A1200 9k multi .85 .35

Mills — A1201

Designs: 9k, Windmill. 14.40k, Water mill.

**2001, Oct. 9**

**3157-3158** A1201 Set of 2 2.25 1.00

Christmas — A1202

**Photo. & Engr.**

**2001, Nov. 14** ***Perf. 11¼x11½***

**3159** A1202 5.40k multi .60 .30

**Painting Type of 1967 Inscribed "CESKA REPUBLIKA"**

Designs: 12k, The Annunciation of the Virgin Mary, by Michael J. Rentz. 17k, The Sans Souci Bar in Nimes, by Cyril Bouda. 26k, The Goose Keeper, by Vaclav Brozík.

**2001, Nov. 14 Engr.** ***Perf. 11¾***

**3160-3162** A565 Set of 3 4.50 4.25

Nos. 3160-3162 were each issued in sheets of 4. Value, set $18.

Tradition of Czech Stamp Production — A1203

**Photo. & Engr.**

**2002, Jan. 20** ***Perf. 11¼x11¾***

**3163** A1203 5.40k Type A89 .75 .25
*a.* Booklet pane of 8 + 4 labels 5.00 —
Booklet, #3163a 5.00

2002 Winter Olympics, Salt Lake City — A1204

**2002, Jan. 30** ***Perf. 11¼***

**3164** A1204 12k multi 1.25 .45

For overprint, see No. 3168.

2002 Winter Paralympics, Salt Lake City — A1205

**2002, Jan. 30** ***Perf. 11¼x11½***

**3165** A1205 5.40k multi .85 .25

Composers Jaromír Vejvoda (1902-88), Josef Poncar (1902-86) and Karel Vacek (1902-82) — A1206

**2002, Mar. 6** ***Perf. 11¾x11¼***

**3166** A1206 9k multi 1.10 .35

Easter — A1207

**2002, Mar. 6** ***Perf. 11¼x11½***

**3167** A1207 5.40k multi .85 .25

No. 3164 Overprinted in Blue

**Photo. & Engr.**

**2002, Mar. 8** ***Perf. 11¼***

**3168** A1204 12k multi 1.25 .65

Divan, by Vlaho Bukovac (1855-1922) — A1208

**Litho. & Engr.**

**2002, Apr. 23** *Perf. 11¾*
**3169** A1208 17k multi 2.00 1.40

Printed in sheets of 4 + 2 labels. Value $8. See Croatia No. 487.

Europa A1209

**Photo. & Engr.**

**2002, May 7** *Perf. 11¾x11¼*
**3170** A1209 9k multi 1.20 .35

Souvenir Sheet

Czech Culture and France — A1210

No. 3171: a, 23k, Klávesy Piana-Jezero, by Frantisek Kupka. b, 31k, Man with Broken Nose, sculpture by Auguste Rodin.

*Perf. 11¾x11½*

**2002, May 7** **Litho. & Engr.**
**3171** A1210 Sheet of 2, #a-b 5.25 4.00

Intl. Children's Day — A1211

**Photo. & Engr.**

**2002, May 29** *Perf. 11¼x11½*
**3172** A1211 5.40k multi .60 .25
*a.* Booklet pane of 8 + 2 labels 5.00 —
Complete booklet, #3172a 5.00

Margaritifera Margaritifera A1212

**2002, June 6**
**3173** A1212 9k multi 1.00 .35

Jan Hus (1372-1415), Religious Leader — A1213

**2002, June 19**
**3174** A1213 9k multi + label 1.00 .35

Souvenir Sheet

Worldwide Fund for Nature (WWF) — A1214

Butterflies: a, 5.40k, Maculinea nausithous. b, 5.40k, Maculinea alcon. c, 9k, Maculinea teleius. d, 9k, Maculinea arion.

**Litho. & Engr.**

**2002, June 19** *Perf. 11¾*
**3175** A1214 Sheet of 4, #a-d + 4 labels 3.50 2.75

Pansy — A1215

**Photo. & Engr.**

**2002, Sept. 1** *Perf. 11¾x11¼*
**3176** A1215 6.40k multi .85 .25

See Nos. 3220-3221, 3262-3263, 3293-3294, 3340, 3345-3347, 3363-3366, 3467-3469, 3500.

**World Heritage Sites Type of 2001**

Designs: 12k, Litomysl Castle. 14k, Holy Trinity Column, Olomouc, vert.

*Perf. 11½x11¾, 11¾x11½*

**2002, Sept. 11** **Engr.**
**3177-3178** A1199 Set of 2 2.75 2.00

Nos. 3177-3178 were each issued in sheets of 8. Value, set $25.

Emil Zátopek (1922-2000), Olympic Long Distance Runner — A1216

**Photo. & Engr.**

**2002, Sept. 11** *Perf. 11¼x11¾*
**3179** A1216 9k multi 1.10 .35

**Pres. Havel Type of 1998**

**Photo. & Engr.**

**2002, Nov. 6** *Perf. 11¾x11¼*
**3180** A1134 6.40k pur & blue .85 .25

St. Nicholas' Day — A1217

**2002, Nov. 6** *Perf. 11¼x11½*
**3181** A1217 6.40k multi .85 .25
*a.* Booklet pane of 8 + 2 labels 6.00 —
Complete booklet, #3181a 6.00

Christmas — A1218

**2002, Nov. 13**
**3182** A1218 6.40k multi .85 .25

NATO Summit, Prague — A1219

**2002, Nov. 14** *Perf. 11¼x11¾*
**3183** A1219 9k multi 1.00 .30

Furniture — A1220

Designs: 6.40k, Armchair, 17th cent. 9k, Sewing table with hemispheric cover, 1820. 12k, Dressing table with mirror, 1860. 17k, Art deco amchair, 1923.

**2002, Dec. 11**
**3184-3187** A1220 Set of 4 4.50 2.25

**Painting Type of 1967 Inscribed "CESKA REPUBLIKA"**

Designs: 12k, The Abandoned, by Jaroslav Panuska, horiz. 20k, St. Wenceslas, by Mikolás Ales. 26k, Portrait of a Young Man with a Lute, by Jan Petr Molitor.

**2002, Dec. 11** **Engr.** *Perf. 11¾*
**3188-3190** A565 Set of 3 5.75 3.75

Nos. 3188-3190 were each issued in sheets of 4. Value, set $23.

Souvenir Sheet

Czech Republic, 10th Anniv. — A1221

**Litho. & Engr.**

**2003, Jan. 1** *Perf. 11¾*
**3191** A1221 25k multi 2.75 1.60

Tradition of Czech Stamp Production — A1222

**Photo. & Engr.**

**2003, Jan. 20** *Perf. 11¼x11¾*
**3192** A1222 6.40k Type A75 .95 .25
*a.* Booklet pane of 8 + 2 labels 7.50 —
Complete booklet, #3192a 7.50

Famous Men — A1223

Designs: 6.40k, Jaroslav Vrchlicky (1853-1912), poet. 8k, Josef Thomayer (1853-1927), physician and writer.

**2003, Feb. 12** *Perf. 11½x11¼*
**3193-3194** A1223 Set of 2 1.75 .50

Easter — A1224

**2003, Mar. 26** *Perf. 11¼x11½*
**3195** A1224 6.40k multi .95 .25

Roses Above Prague — A1225

*Perf. 12¾x13¼*

**2003, Mar. 26** **Litho.**
**3196** A1225 6.40k multi + label .75 .35

Labels could be personalized.
Issued in sheets of 9 stamps and 12 labels. Value $9.
See No. 3517.

Lace
A1226

Designs: 6.40k, Netted lace. 9k, Bobbin lace.

**Photo. & Engr.**

**2003, Mar. 26** *Perf. 11¼*

**3197** A1226 6.40k bl, dk bl & red .75 .25
*a.* Booklet pane of 6 + 4 labels 4.50 —
Complete booklet, #3197a 4.50
**3198** A1226 9k dk bl, bl & red 1.00 .35
*a.* Booklet pane of 6 + 4 labels 6.00 —
Complete booklet, #3197a 6.00

Europa — A1227

**Litho. & Engr.**

**2003, May 7** *Perf. 11¾*

**3199** A1227 9k multi 1.20 .65

Geologic Attractions — A1228

Designs: 12k, Sandstone towers, Hrubá Skála Region. 14k, Punkva Caves, Moravian karst area.

**2003, May 7 Engr.** *Perf. 11½x11¾*

**3200-3201** A1228 Set of 2 3.00 2.00

Nos. 3200-3201 were each issued in sheets of 8. Value, set $25.

Mach and Sebestova, Children's Television Show Characters — A1229

**Photo. & Engr.**

**2003, May 28** *Perf. 11¼x11½*

**3202** A1229 6.40k multi .95 .35
*a.* Booklet pane of 8 + 2 labels 7.50 —
Complete booklet, #3202a 7.50

First Electric Railway, Tábor — Bechyne, Cent. A1230

**2003, May 28** *Perf. 11¾x11¼*

**3203** A1230 10k multi 1.25 .50

A1231

Observation towers: No. 3204, 6.40k, Klet. No. 3205, 6.40k, Slovanka.

**2003, May 28** *Perf. 11¼x11½*

**3204-3205** A1231 Set of 2 1.50 .50

A1232

**2003, June 25** *Perf. 11¾x11¼*

**3206** A1232 9k multi 1.25 .35

European Shooting Championships, Plzen and Brno.

A1233

**2003, June 25** *Perf. 11¼x11½*

**3207** A1233 9k multi 1.20 .35

Josef Dobrovsky (1753-1829), linguist.

Pres. Vaclav Klaus — A1234

**Photo. & Engr.**

**2003** *Perf. 11¾x11¼*

**3208** A1234 6.40k buff, red & vio bl .95 .35
**3209** A1234 6.50k Prus bl & pur .95 .35

Issued: 6.40k, 7/30; 6.50k, 11/5.
See No. 3264.

Souvenir Sheet

Tropical Fish — A1235

No. 3210: a, 12k, Betta splendens (27x44mm). b, 14k, Pterophyllum scalare (27x44mm). c, 16k, Carassius auratus (54x44mm). d, 20k, Symphysodon aequifasciatus (54x44mm).

**Litho. & Engr.**

**2003, Sept. 10** *Perf. 11¾*

**3210** A1235 Sheet of 4, #a-d 6.00 5.00

No. 3210 exists in six different varieties, which may be distinguished by the number of horizontal lines in the stone in the bottom sheet margin below the 14k stamp. Values given are for sheets with 1, 2 or 5 lines in the stone; value for sheet with no lines or 3 lines in the stone, $21; value for sheet with 4 lines in the stone, $72.50.

Oriental Carpets A1236

Designs: 9k, Turkish prayer carpet, 19th cent. 12k, Turkish carpet, 18th cent.

**2003, Oct. 1 Engr.** *Perf. 11¾*

**3211-3212** A1236 Set of 2 2.50 1.75

Nos. 3211-3212 were each issued in sheets of 4. Value, set $10.

Tympanum, Porta Coeli Monastery, Predklásterí — A1237

**Photo. & Engr.**

**2003, Oct. 15** *Perf. 11¾x11¼*

**3213** A1237 6.50k multi .95 .45
*a.* Booklet pane of 8 + 4 labels 7.50 —
Complete booklet, #3213a 7.50

Birds of Prey — A1238

Designs: 6.50k, Milvus milvus. 8k, Falco peregrinus. 9k, Hieraaetus pennatus.

**2003, Oct. 15** *Perf. 11¼x11½*

**3214** A1238 6.50k multi .75 .25
Booklet, 5 #3214 3.75
**3215** A1238 8k multi .90 .30
Booklet, 5 #3215 4.50
**3216** A1238 9k multi 1.00 .30
Booklet, 5 #3216 5.00
*Nos. 3214-3216 (3)* 2.65 .85

Czech Fire Fighters, 140th Anniv. A1239

Fire engines: 6.50k, Wooden fire engine, 1822. 9k, Motorized fire engine, 1933. 12k, CAS 8/Avia Daewoo fire truck, 2002.

**2003, Oct. 15** *Perf. 11¾x11¼*

**3217-3219** A1239 Set of 3 3.00 1.50

**Flower Type of 2002**

Designs: 50h, Cornflower (chrpa). 6.50k, Dahlia (jirina).

**2003, Oct. 22**

**3220** A1215 50h multi .25 .25
**3221** A1215 6.50k multi .75 .25

**Roses Over Prague Type of 2003 and**

Prague Castle Lantern — A1240

**2003, Oct. 22 Litho.** *Perf. 12¾x13¼*

**3222** A1225 6.50k multi + label .75 .25
**3223** A1240 9k multi + label 1.00 .30

Labels could be personalized.
Nos. 3222-3223 were each issued in sheets of 9 stamps and 12 labels. Value, set $17.50.

**Painting Type of 1967 Inscribed "CESKA REPUBLIKA"**

Designs: 17k, Poor Countryside, by Max Svabinsky, horiz. 20k, Autumn in Veltrusy, by Antonín Slavícek. 26k, Eleanora de Toledo, by Agnolo Bronzino.

**2003, Nov. 5 Engr.** *Perf. 11¾*

**3224-3226** A565 Set of 3 6.50 4.00

Nos. 3224-3226 were each issued in sheets of 4. Value, set $26.

Christmas A1241

**Photo. & Engr.**

**2003, Nov. 5** *Perf. 11¼x11½*

**3227** A1241 6.50k multi .75 .35

Tradition of Czech Stamp Production A1242

**Photo. & Engr.**

**2004, Jan. 20** *Perf. 11¼x11¾*

**3228** A1242 6.50k Vignette of #1703 .95 .35
*a.* Booklet pane of 8 + 4 labels 7.50 —
Complete booklet, #3228a 7.50

Church of the Assumption of the Virgin Mary, Brno — A1243

**2004, Feb. 18 Engr.** *Perf. 11¾*

**3229** A1243 17k multi 1.90 1.00

Brno 2005 Philatelic Exhibition.
No. 3229 was issued in sheets of 4. Value $8.

Industrial Building Historical Preservation A1244

Designs: 6.50k, Busek's Water Forging Hammer, Lniste. 17k, Iron Furnace, Stará Hut u Adamova.

**Photo. & Engr.**

**2004, Feb. 18** *Perf. 11½x11¼*

**3230-3231** A1244 Set of 2 2.40 .90

Easter
A1245

**2004, Mar. 17**
**3232** A1245 6.50k multi .95 .25

**Painting Type of 1967 Inscribed "CESKA REPUBLIKA"**

Design: Prometheus, by Antonín Procházka.

**2004, Mar. 17 Engr. *Perf. 11¾***
**3233** A565 26k multi 2.60 1.60

Brno 2005 Philatelic Exhibition. No. 3233 was issued in sheets of 4. Value $11.

World Ice Hockey Championships, Prague and Ostrava — A1246

**Photo. & Engr.**

**2004, Apr. 14 *Perf. 11¼x11¾***
**3234** A1246 12k multi 1.50 .50

Admission to European Union
A1247

**Photo. & Engr.**

**2004, May 1 *Perf. 11¼***
**3235** A1247 9k multi 1.20 .35

Admission to the European Union — A1248

**2004, May 1 Litho. *Perf. 11¾x11¼***
**3236** A1248 9k multi 1.10 .35

No. 3236 was issued in sheets of 10. Value $11.

Europa
A1249

**2004, May 5 *Perf. 11¼***
**3237** A1249 9k multi 1.10 .35

Composers of Czech Operas — A1250

Designs: 6.50k, Dalibor, by Bedrich Smetana (1824-84). 8k, Jakobín, by Antonín Dvorák (1841-1904). 10k, Její Pastorkyna, by Leos Janácek (1854-1928).

**Photo. & Engr.**

**2004, May 5 *Perf. 11¼x11¾***
**3238-3240** A1250 Set of 3 2.60 1.10

For Children
A1251

**Photo. & Engr.**

**2004, May 26 *Perf. 11½x11¼***
**3241** A1251 6.50k multi .85 .25
*a.* Booklet pane of 8 + 2 labels 7.00 —
Complete booklet, #3241a 7.00

Statue of Radegast, by Albín Polásek — A1252

**2004, May 26 *Perf. 11¼x11½***
**3242** A1252 6.50k multi .85 .25

Brno 2005 Philatelic Exhibition.

Tourist Attractions — A1253

Designs: 12k, Holy Mountain, Príbram. 14k, Holy Shrine, Bystrice pod Hostynem.

**2004, May 26 Engr. *Perf. 11½x11¾***
**3243-3244** A1253 Set of 2 2.60 1.50

Nos. 3243-3244 were each issued in sheets of 8. Value, set $24.

A1254

**Photo. & Engr.**

**2004, June 23 *Perf. 11¼x11¾***
**3245** A1254 6.50k multi 1.20 .25

2004 Paralympics, Athens.

A1255

**2004, June 23**
**3246** A1255 9k multi 1.00 .35

2004 Summer Olympics, Athens.

Petrarch (1304-74), Poet — A1256

**2004, June 23 *Perf. 11¾x11¼***
**3247** A1256 14k multi 1.40 .60

Famous Trees — A1257

Designs: 6.50k, Singing lime tree, Telecí. 8k, Jan Zizka oak tree, Podhradí.

**Photo. & Engr.**

**2004, Sept. 8 *Perf. 11¼x11½***
**3248** A1257 6.50k multi .75 .25
Complete booklet, 5 #3248 3.75
**3249** A1257 8k multi .90 .30
Complete booklet, 5 #3249 4.50

Miniature Sheet

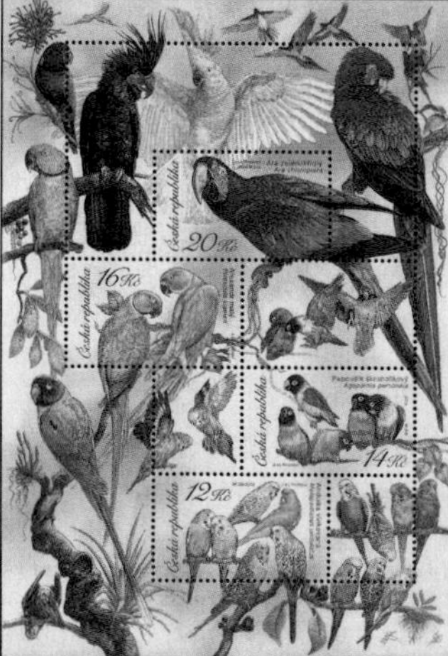

Parrots — A1258

No. 3250: a, 12k, Melopsittacus undulatus. b, 14k, Agapornis personata. c, 16k, Psittacula krameri. d, 20k, Ara chloroptera.

**Litho. & Engr.**

**2004, Sept. 8 *Perf. 11¾***
**3250** A1258 Sheet of 4, #a-d, + 4 labels 6.00 4.50

Compulsory School Attendance, 230th Anniv. — A1259

**Photo. & Engr.**

**2004, Sept. 29 *Perf. 11¼x11½***
**3251** A1259 6.50k multi .85 .25

Baby Carriages — A1260

Carriages made about: 12k, 1880. 14k, 1890. 16k, 1900.

**2004, Oct. 20**
**3252-3254** A1260 Set of 3 4.00 2.00

**Painting Type of 1967 Inscribed "CESKA REPUBLIKA"**

Designs: 20k, On the Outskirts of the Cesky Ráj Region, by Alois Bubák, horiz. 22k, The Long, the Broad and the Sharpsight, by Hanus Schwaiger. 26k, The Spring, by Vojtéch Hynais.

**2004, Nov. 10 Engr. *Perf. 11¾***
**3255-3257** A565 Set of 3 6.50 4.25

Nos. 3255-3257 were each issued in sheets of 4. Value, set $32.

Christmas — A1261

**Photo. & Engr.**

**2004, Nov. 10 *Perf. 11¼x11½***
**3258** A1261 6.50k multi .75 .25

Tradition of Czech Stamp Production
A1262

**2005, Jan. 18 *Perf. 11¼x11¾***
**3259** A1262 6.50k Design of #975 .95 .30
*a.* Booklet pane of 8 + 4 labels 7.50 —
Complete booklet, #3259a 7.50

Peacock and Bugler Portal Decoration — A1263

**2005, Jan. 18 Litho. *Perf. 12¾x13¼***
**3260** A1263 7.50k multi + label .95 .30

Labels could be personalized for an additional fee.

Issued in sheets of 9 stamps and 12 labels. Value $9.

See Nos. 3372, 3516.

Souvenir Sheet

Moonscape, by Petr Ginz — A1264

*Perf. 11¾x11½*

**2005, Jan. 18** **Litho. & Engr.**
3261 A1264 31k multi 3.00 2.00

**Flower Type of 2002**

Designs: 7.50k, Lily (lilie). 19k, Fuchsia (fuchsie).

**Photo. & Engr.**

**2005** *Perf. 11¾x11¼*
3262 A1215 7.50k multi .85 .30
3263 A1215 19k multi 2.25 .85

Issued: 7.50k, 1/20; 19k, 3/2.

**Pres. Vaclav Klaus Type of 2003**

**2005, Feb. 9**
3264 A1234 7.50k claret & red .85 .30

Granny, by Bozena Nemcová, 150th Anniv. of Publication A1265

**2005, Feb. 9** *Perf. 11¼x11¾*
3265 A1265 7.50k multi .85 .30

Easter — A1266

**Photo. & Engr.**

**2005, Mar. 2** *Perf. 11¼x11½*
3266 A1266 7.50k multi .85 .30

**UNESCO World Heritage Sites Type of 2001**

Designs: 14k, St. Prokop's Basilica, Trebíc, vert. 16k, Villa Tugendhat, Brno.

*Perf. 11¾x11½, 11½x11¾*

**2005, Mar. 23** **Engr.**
3267-3268 A1199 Set of 2 3.25 1.90

Nos. 3267-32682 were each issued in sheets of 8. Value, set $26.

Famous Men — A1267

Designs: 7.50k, Bohuslav Brauner (1855-1935), chemist. 12k, Adalbert Stifter (1805-68), writer, painter. 19k, Mikulás Dacicky of Heslov (1555-1626), poet.

**Photo. & Engr.**

**2005, Apr. 13** *Perf. 11¼x11¾*
3269-3271 A1267 Set of 3 3.75 1.60

Europa A1268

**2005, May 4** **Litho.** *Perf. 11¼*
3272 A1268 9k multi 1.20 .35

Issued in sheets of 6. Value, $7.50.

Battle of Austerlitz, Bicent. — A1269

Napoleon Before the Battle of Austerlitz, by Louis-François Lejeune — A1270

**Photo. & Engr.**

**2005, May 4** *Perf. 11¾x11¼*
3273 A1269 19k multi 2.25 .90

**Souvenir Sheet**

**Litho. & Engr.**

*Perf. 11¾*

3274 A1270 30k multi 3.50 2.25

Brno 2005 Stamp Exhibition (No. 3274).
No. 3273 was issued in sheets of 40 + 20 labels. Value, one stamp + label $3.25.
See France No. 3115.

Kremílek and Vochomurka, by Václav Ctvrtek — A1271

**Photo. & Engr.**

**2005, May 25** *Perf. 11¼x11½*
3275 A1271 7.50k multi .85 .30
*a.* Booklet pane of 8 + 2 labels 7.00 —
Complete booklet, #3275a 7.00

Intl. Year of Physics A1272

**2005, May 25** *Perf. 11¼x11¾*
3276 A1272 12k multi 1.40 .75

2005 European Baseball Championships A1273

**2005, June 22**
3277 A1273 9k multi 1.10 .50

Souvenir Sheet

Protected Flora and Fauna of the Krkonose Mountains — A1274

No. 3278: a, 12k, Viola lutea sudetica, Hedysarum hedysaroides (44x28mm). b, 14k, Cinclus cinclus, Leucojum vernum (44x28mm). c, 15k, Sorex alpinus, Salamandra salamandra, Primula minima (44x54mm). d, 22k, Mt. Snezka, Luscinia svecica svecica, Aeschna coerulea, Pneumonanthe asclepiadea (44x54mm).

**Litho. & Engr.**

**2005, June 22** *Perf. 11¾*
3278 A1274 Sheet of 4, #a-d, + 4 labels 7.00 4.25

Church Bells — A1275

Bells from: 7.50k, Benesov, 1322, Havlíckuv Brod, 1335. 9k, Dobrs, 1561, 1596. 12k, Olomouc, 1827.

**Photo. & Engr.**

**2005, Sept. 7** *Perf. 11½x11¾*
3279 A1275 7.50k multi .80 .30
Complete booklet, 5 #3279 4.00
3280 A1275 9k multi .90 .40
Complete booklet, 5 #3280 4.50
3281 A1275 12k multi 1.20 .50
Complete booklet, 5 #3281 6.00
*Nos. 3279-3281 (3)* 2.90 1.20

Tractors A1276

Designs: 7.50k, 1923 John Deere 15/27. 9k, 1921 Lanz Bulldog HL-12, 1596. 18k, 1937 Skoda HT 40.

**2005, Sept. 21** *Perf. 11½x11¼*
3282 A1276 7.50k multi .60 .30
Complete booklet, 5 #3282 3.50
3283 A1276 9k multi .90 .35
Complete booklet, 5 #3283 5.00
3284 A1276 18k multi 1.90 .75
Complete booklet, 5 #3284 9.50
*Nos. 3282-3284 (3)* 3.40 1.40

World Summit on the Information Society, Tunis A1277

**2005, Sept. 21** *Perf. 11¼*
3285 A1277 9k org & violet 1.10 .35

Curling A1278

**Photo. & Engr.**

**2005, Oct. 12** *Perf. 11¾x11¼*
3286 A1278 17k multi 2.00 .70

**Painting Type of 1967 Inscribed "CESKA REPUBLIKA"**

Designs: 22k, Summer Landscape, by Adolf Kosárek. 25k, Deinotherium, by Zdenék Burian. 26k, Osiky Near Velké Nemcice, by Alois Kalvoda.

**2005, Nov. 9** **Engr.** *Perf. 11¾*
3287-3289 A565 Set of 3 8.00 5.25

Nos. 3287-3289 were each issued in sheets of 4. Value, set $32.50.

A1279

Christmas A1280

**Photo. & Engr.**

**2005, Nov. 9** *Perf. 11¼x11½*
3290 A1279 7.50k multi .85 .30

*Perf. 11½x11¼*

3291 A1280 9k multi 1.00 .35

Tradition of Czech Stamp Production A1281

**Photo. & Engr.**

**2006, Jan. 20** *Perf. 11¼x11¾*
**3292** A1281 7.50k Portion of #C59 .95 .30
*a.* Booklet pane of 8 + 2 labels 7.50 —
Complete booklet, #3292a 7.50

**Flower Type of 2002**

Designs: 11k, Marshmallow (ibisek). 24k, Daffodil (narcis).

**2006** *Perf. 11¾x11¼*
**3293** A1215 11k multi 1.25 .45
**3294** A1215 24k multi 2.75 1.00

Issued: 11k, 2/1; 24k, 2/22.

Flowers — A1282

Flowers, Grapes, Glass of Wine — A1283

**2006** **Litho.** *Perf. 12¾x13¼*
**3295** A1282 10k multi + label 1.10 .60
**3296** A1283 12k multi + label 1.40 .75

Issued: 10k, 2/1; 12k, 2/22. Labels could be personalized for an additional fee.

Nos. 3295-3296 were issued in sheets of 9 stamps and 12 labels. Value, set $22.50.

See No. 3373.

Madonna of Zbraslav — A1284

**2006, Feb. 8** **Engr.** *Perf. 11¾*
**3297** A1284 25k multi 2.50 1.75

Printed in sheets of 4. Value $10.

2006 Winter Paralympics, Turin — A1285

**Photo. & Engr.**

**2006, Feb. 8** *Perf. 11¾x11¼*
**3298** A1285 7.50k multi .85 .30

2006 Winter Olympics, Turin — A1286

**2006** *Perf. 11¼x11¾*
**3299** A1286 9k multi 1.00 .40

**With "K. NEUMANNOVA / ZLATA MEDAILE" Overprinted in Red Reading Up**

**3300** A1286 9k multi 1.10 .40

Issued: No. 3299, 2/8; No. 3300, 3/15.

Famous Men — A1287

Designs: 11k, Frantisek Josef Gerstner (1756-1832), mathematician and educator. 12k, Jaroslav Jezek (1906-42), composer. 19k, Sigmund Freud (1856-1939), psychoanalyst.

**2006, Feb. 22** *Perf. 11½x11¼*
**3301-3303** A1287 Set of 3 4.00 1.75

Easter — A1288

**2006, Mar. 22** *Perf. 11¼x11½*
**3304** A1288 7.50k multi 1.20 .30

Osek Monastery — A1289

Kokorinsko Capstones — A1290

**2006, Mar. 22** **Engr.** *Perf. 11½x11¾*
**3305** A1289 12k multi 1.20 .65
**3306** A1290 15k multi 1.40 .85

Nos. 3305-3306 were each issued in sheets of 8. Value, set $22.

Love — A1291

**Photo. & Engr.**

**2006, Apr. 26** *Perf. 11¼x11½*
**3307** A1291 7.50k multi .95 .35
Complete booklet, 5 #3307 4.75

Europa A1292

Silhouette of person and: 10k, Horse. 20k, Dog.

**2006, May 3** *Perf. 11¾x11¼*
**3308-3309** A1292 Set of 2 3.00 1.40

Issued in sheets of 8. Value, set $24.

Rumcajs, Manka and Cipísek, by V. Ctvrtek — A1293

**Photo. & Engr.**

**2006, May 31** *Perf. 11¼x11½*
**3310** A1293 7.50k multi .95 .35
*a.* Booklet pane of 8 + 2 labels 7.50 —
Complete booklet, #3310a 7.50

A1294

**2006, June 14** *Perf. 11¼x11¾*
**3311** A1294 19k multi 2.00 .90

Kamenice Pass, Czech Switzerland National Park.

A1295

Jewelry with garnets: 15k, Silver brooch with pearl, 1904. 18k, Gold pendant, 1930.

**2006, June 14**
**3312-3313** A1295 Set of 2 3.00 1.75

Miniature Sheet

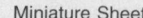

Bohemian Kings of Premyslid Dynasty — A1296

No. 3314: a, 12k, Otakar I Premysl (c. 1155-1230). b, 14k, Václav (Wenceslas) I (1205-53). c, 15k, Otakar II Premysl (1230-78). d, 22k, Václav (Wenceslas) II (1271-1305). e, 28k, Václav (Wenceslas) III (1289-1306).

**2006, June 14** **Engr.** *Perf. 11¾*
**3314** A1296 Sheet of 5, #a-e, + label 8.25 6.00

Souvenir Sheet

Mosaic of Prague Castle, by Giovanni Castrucci — A1297

**Litho. & Engr.**

**2006, Sept. 13** *Perf. 11¾*
**3315** A1297 35k multi 3.50 2.25

Cacti — A1298

No. 3316: a, Gymnocalycium denudatum. b, Obregonia denegrii.

No. 3317: a, Astrophytum asterias. b, Cintia knizei.

*Perf. 11¼x11¾*

**2006, Sept. 13** **Litho.**
**3316** A1298 7.50k Pair, #a-b 1.50 .90
Complete booklet, 2 #3316a, 3 #3316b 3.50
**3317** A1298 10k Pair, #a-b 2.00 1.25
Complete booklet, 2 #3317a, 3 #3317b 5.00

Ecology A1299

**2006, Sept. 27** *Perf. 11¾x11¼*
**3318** A1299 7.50k multi .95 .35

Christmas — A1300

**2006, Oct. 11** *Perf. 12¾x13¼*
**3319** A1300 7.50k multi + label 1.10 .35

Printed in sheets of 9 stamps + 12 labels. Labels could be personalized. Value, $11.

Vrtbovská Garden, Prague — A1301

**Photo. & Engr.**

**2006, Oct. 11** *Perf. 11½x11¾*
**3320** A1301 7.50k multi .95 .35
*a.* Booklet pane of 8 + 4 labels 7.50 —
Complete booklet, #3320a 7.50

Praga 2008 Intl. Philatelic Exhibition, Prague.

Wooden Churches — A1302

Designs: 7.50k, Church of the Virgin Mary, Broumov. 19k, Church of St. Andrew, Hodslavice.

**Photo. & Engr.**

**2006, Oct. 11** *Perf. 11¾x11¼*
**3321-3322** A1302 Set of 2 2.60 1.60

**Painting Type of 1967 Inscribed "CESKA REPUBLIKA"**

Designs: 22k, Still Life with Fruit, by Jan Davidsz de Heem. 25k, Montenegrin Madonna, by Jaroslav Cermak. 28k, Pod Suchym Skalim, by Frantisek Kaván, horiz.

**2006, Nov. 8** **Engr.** *Perf. 11¾*
**3323-3325** A565 Set of 3 7.00 4.50

Christmas — A1303

**Photo. & Engr.**

**2006, Nov. 8** *Perf. 11¾x11½*
**3326** A1303 7.50k multi .95 .35

Emblem of Praga 2008 Intl. Philatelic Exhibition — A1304

**2006, Dec. 1** **Litho.**
**3327** A1304 7.50k multi .95 .35

See Nos. 3341, 3368.

Czech Technical University, Prague, 300th Anniv. — A1305

**Photo. & Engr.**

**2007, Jan. 10** *Perf. 11¾x11½*
**3328** A1305 9k multi 1.10 .50

Famous Men — A1306

Designs: 7.50k, Frána Srámek (1877-1952), writer. 19k, Karel Slavoj Amerling (1807-84), educator.

**2007, Jan. 10** *Perf. 11½x11¼*
**3329-3330** A1306 Set of 2 2.50 1.40

Tradition of Czech Stamp Production A1307

**2007, Jan. 20** *Perf. 11½x11¾*
**3331** A1307 7.50k Type A242 .85 .35
*a.* Booklet pane of 8 + 4 labels 6.75 —
Complete booklet, #3331a 6.75

Cancer Prevention A1308

**Photo. & Engr.**

**2007, Feb. 21** *Perf. 11¼x11½*
**3332** A1308 7.50k multi .85 .35

Snake — A1309

*Perf. 11¼x11¾*

**2007, Feb. 21** **Litho.**
**3333** A1309 12k multi 1.20 .70

Oriental Art A1310

Designs: 12k, Girl with a Puppet, by Kunisawa Utagawa. 24k, Siva, Parvati and Ganesa, 19th cent. Indian glass painting.

**Litho. & Engr.**

**2007, Feb. 21** *Perf. 11¾*
**3334-3335** A1310 Set of 2 3.50 2.10

Easter — A1311

**Photo. & Engr.**

**2007, Mar. 14** *Perf. 11¼x11½*
**3336** A1311 7.50k multi .85 .35

Model of Mala Strana Area of Prague, by Antonín Langweil — A1312

**2007, Mar. 14** *Perf. 11¾x11¼*
**3337** A1312 7.50k multi .85 .35
*a.* Booklet pane of 8 + 4 labels 7.00 —
Complete booklet, #3337a 7.00

Praga 2008 Intl. Philatelic Exhibition, Prague. No. 3337 was issued in sheets of 8 + 4 labels. Value, $10.

Stoclet House, Brussels, Designed by Josef Hoffmann — A1313

Designs: 20k, Building interior. 35k, Building exterior.

**2007, Mar. 26** *Perf. 11¼x11¾*
**3338-3339** A1313 Set of 2 5.00 3.25

See Belgium Nos. 2228-2229.

**Flowers Type of 2006**

*Perf. 12¾x13¼*

**2007, Mar. 26** **Litho.**
**3340** A1282 11k multi + label 1.25 .60

Label could be personalized for an additional fee.

**Praga 2008 Emblem Type of 2006**

**2007, Apr. 4** *Perf. 11¾x11½*
**3341** A1304 11k blue & multi 1.25 .60

Spas A1314

Designs: 12k, Jurkovic House, Luhacovice. 15k, Gocár Pavillion, Lázne Bohdanec.

**2007, Apr. 4** **Engr.** *Perf. 11½x11¾*
**3342-3343** A1314 Set of 2 2.50 1.75

Issued in sheets of 8. Value, $20.

Europa A1315

**Photo. & Engr.**

**2007, May 9** *Perf. 11¼*
**3344** A1315 11k multi 1.25 .60

Scouting, cent.

**Flowers Type of 2002**

Designs: 1k, Cyclamen (bramborik). 15k, Tropaeolum (lichorerisnice). 23k, Geranium (pelargonie).

**Photo. & Engr.**

**2007** *Perf. 11¾x11¼*
**3345** A1215 1k multi .25 .25
**3346** A1215 15k multi 1.60 .90
**3347** A1215 23k multi 2.00 1.25
*Nos. 3345-3347 (3)* 3.85 2.40

Issued: 1k, 23k, 5/9. 15k, 9/5.

Fast Arrows, Comic Strip by Jaroslav Foglar A1316

**Photo. & Engr.**

**2007, May 30** *Perf. 11¾x11¼*
**3348** A1316 7.50k multi .85 .35
*a.* Booklet pane of 8 + 4 labels 7.00 —
Complete booklet, #3348a 7.00

Historic Stoves — A1317

Designs: 7.50k, Gothic era stove, Olomouc, and tile. 12k, Renaissance era stove, Rícany u Prahy and tile.

**Photo. & Engr.**

**2007, June 20** *Perf. 11½x11¾*
**3349** A1317 7.50k multi .70 .35
Complete booklet, 5 #3349 3.50
**3350** A1317 12k multi 1.25 .60
Complete booklet, 5 #3350 6.25

Souvenir Sheet

Vaclav Hollar (1607-77), Engraver — A1318

**Litho. & Engr.**

**2007, June 20** *Perf. 11¾*
**3351** A1318 35k multi + 2 labels 3.00 2.10

Souvenir Sheet

Charles Bridge, Prague, 650th Anniv. — A1319

**2007, June 20**
**3352** A1319 45k multi 4.50 3.00

Praga 2008 World Philatelic Exhibition.

First Movie Theater in Prague, Cent. A1320

**Photo. & Engr.**

**2007, Sept. 5** *Perf. 11¾x11¼*
**3353** A1320 7.50k multi .75 .35

Didactica Opera Omnia, by Comenius, 350th Anniv. — A1321

**2007, Sept. 5**
**3354** A1321 12k multi 1.25 .75

Miniature Sheet

Flora and Fauna of the White Carpathians — A1322

No. 3355: a, 9k, Ophrys holosericea (27x44mm). b, 10k, Colias myrmidone, Anacamptis pyramidalis (27x44mm). c, 11k, Ophrys apifera (27x44mm). d, 12k, Coracias garrulus, Gymnadenia densiflora (54x44mm).

**Litho. & Engr.**

**2007, Sept. 5** *Perf. 11¾*
**3355** A1322 Sheet of 4, #a-d, + 4 labels 4.25 2.75

Emil Holub (1847-1902), Naturalist — A1323

**Photo. & Engr.**

**2007, Oct. 3** *Perf. 11¾x11¼*
**3356** A1323 11k multi 1.25 .65

Water Towers — A1324

Towers in: 7.50k, Karviná. 18k, Plzen.

**2007, Oct. 3** *Perf. 11¼x11¾*
**3357-3358** A1324 Set of 2 2.75 1.50

**Painting Type of 1967 Inscribed "CESKA REPUBLIKA"**

Designs: 22k, Vrbicany Castle, by Amálie Mánesova, horiz. 25k, Way to Bechnye Castle, by Otakar Lebeda. 28k, Montmartre, by Sobeslav Hippolyt Pinkas, horiz.

**2007, Nov. 7** **Engr.** *Perf. 11¾*
**3359-3361** A565 Set of 3 7.25 4.50

Christmas — A1325

**Photo. & Engr.**

**2007, Nov. 7** *Perf. 11¼x11½*
**3362** A1325 7.50k multi .85 .40

**Flower Type of 2002**

Design: 2.50k, Gaillardia (kokarda); 3k, Azalea (azalka); 10k, Rose (ruze); 21k, Gerbera daisy (gerbera).

**Photo. & Engr.**

**2007-08** *Perf. 11¾x11¼*
**3363** A1215 2.50k multi .30 .25
**3364** A1215 3k multi .30 .25
**3365** A1215 10k multi 1.10 .60
**3366** A1215 21k multi 2.00 1.40
*Nos. 3363-3366 (4)* 3.70 2.50

Issued: 2.50k, 12/12/07; 3k, 3/19/08; 10k, 1/30/08; 21k, 3/5/08.

Czech Republic's Entry Into Schengen Border-Free Zone A1326

**2007, Dec. 19** **Litho.** *Perf. 11¼*
**3367** A1326 10k multi 1.10 .55

**Praga 2008 Emblem Type of 2006**

**2007, Dec. 19** *Perf. 11¾x11¼*
**3368** A1304 18k bl grn & blue 2.00 1.00

Tradition of Czech Stamp Production A1327

**Photo. & Engr.**

**2008, Jan. 20** *Perf. 11¼x11¾*
**3369** A1327 10k Type A311 .95 .60
*a.* Booklet pane of 8 + 4 labels 8.00 —
Complete booklet, #3369a 8.00

Famous Men — A1328

Designs: 11k, Karel Klostermann (1848-1923), writer. 14k, Josef Kajetán Tyl (1808-56), playwright.

**2008, Jan. 20** *Perf. 11¼x11½*
**3370-3371** A1328 Set of 2 2.50 1.50

**Peacock and Bugler Type of 2005 and Flowers, Grapes and Glass of Wine Type of 2006 Redrawn**

**2008, Jan. 30** **Litho.** *Perf. 12¾x13¼*
**3372** A1263 10k multi + label 1.00 .60
**3373** A1283 17k multi + label 1.75 1.00

Nos. 3372-3373 were issued in sheets of 9 stamps and 12 labels. Labels could be personalized for an additional fee.

George of Podebrady (1420-71), King of Bohemia — A1329

**Photo. & Engr.**

**2008, Feb. 20** *Perf. 11¼x11¾*
**3374** A1329 12k multi 1.25 .75

No. 3374 was issued in sheets of 8 + 1 label. Values: single stamp + label, $4; complete sheet, $10.

Intl. Year of Planet Earth A1330

**2008, Feb. 20** **Litho.** *Perf. 11¼*
**3375** A1330 18k multi 1.75 1.10

Easter A1331

**Photo. & Engr.**

**2008, Mar. 5** *Perf. 11½x11¼*
**3376** A1331 10k multi 1.25 .60

Bath Servant Zuzana Carrying King Wenceslas IV Over the Vltava River, by J. Navrátil — A1332

**2008, Mar. 5** *Perf. 11¾x11¼*
**3377** A1332 10k multi 1.10 .60
*a.* Booklet pane of 8 + 4 labels 9.00 —
Complete booklet, #3377a 9.00

Praga 2008 Intl. Philatelic Exhibition, Prague.

Publication of Orbis Pictus, Children's Picture Book, by Comenius, 350th Anniv. — A1333

**2008, Mar. 19** *Perf. 11¼x11¾*
**3378** A1333 10k multi 1.25 .60

Mountaintop Hotel With Broadcast Tower, Jested — A1334

Hradec Kralové Buildings and Monuments A1335

**2008, Mar. 19** **Engr.** *Perf. 11½*
**3379** A1334 12k multi 1.10 .75
**3380** A1335 15k multi 1.50 .95

**Pres. Klaus Type of 2003**

**Photo. & Engr.**

**2008, Apr. 2** *Perf. 11¾x11¼*
**3381** A1234 10k multi 1.10 .60

A1336

Items in National Technical Museum: 10k, Reichenbach-Ertel astronomical theodolite, c. 1830. 14k, 1935 Jawa 750 sports car, horiz. 18k, Márky, Bromovsky-Schulz gasoline combustion engine, c. 1889.

*Perf. 11¼x11¾, 11¾x11¼*

**2008, Apr. 16** **Photo. & Engr.**
**3382-3384** A1336 Set of 3 4.25 2.60

National Technical Museum, Prague, cent.

A1337

**2008, Apr. 16** ***Perf. 11¼x11¾***
**3385** A1337 17k multi 1.75 1.10

Czech Hockey Association, cent.

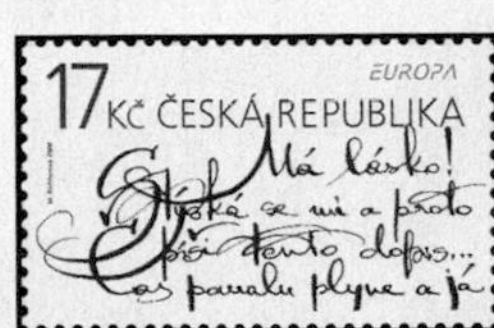

Europa A1338

**2008, May 7** **Litho.** ***Perf. 11¾x11¼***
**3386** A1338 17k multi 1.75 1.10

The Doggy's and Pussy's Tales, Children's Book by Josef Capek A1339

**Photo. & Engr.**

**2008, May 28** ***Perf. 11½x11¼***
**3387** A1339 10k multi 1.00 .70
*a.* Booklet pane of 8 + 2 labels 9.00 —
Complete booklet, #3387a 9.00

Souvenir Sheet

Ledeburk Gardens, Prague — A1340

**Litho. & Engr.**

**2008, May 28** ***Perf. 11¾***
**3388** A1340 51k multi 5.50 3.25

Praga 2008 World Philatelic Exhibition.

Miniature Sheet

Flora and Fauna of Trebon Basin UNESCO Biosphere Reservation — A1341

No. 3389: a, 10k, Alcedo atthis (28x44mm). b, 12k, Lutra lutra and Spiraea salicifolia (54x44mm). c, 14k, Haliaeetus albicilla (54x44mm). d, 18k, Netta rufina and Nymphaea alba (54x44mm).

**2008, May 28**
**3389** A1341 Sheet of 4, #a-d, + 3 labels 6.25 3.50

2008 Paralympics, Beijing — A1342

***Perf. 11¾x11¼***

**2008, June 18** **Litho.**
**3390** A1342 10k multi 1.10 .70

2008 Summer Olympics, Beijing — A1343

**2008, June 18**
**3391** A1343 18k multi 1.75 1.25

Explorers — A1344

Designs: 12k, Ferdinand Stolicka (1838-74), explorer of Himalayas. 21k, Alois Musil (1868-1944), explorer of Jordanian desert.

**2008, June 18** **Photo. & Engr.**
**3392-3393** A1344 Set of 2 3.25 2.25

Children's Book Illustration by Josef Palacek — A1345

**2008, Sept. 3** **Litho.** ***Perf. 12¾x13¼***
**3394** A1345 10k multi + label 1.10 .60

Printed in sheets of 9 stamps + 12 labels. Labels could be personalized. Value, $10.

Emmaus Monastery, Prague — A1346

**Photo. & Engr.**

**2008, Sept. 3** ***Perf. 11¼x11¾***
**3395** A1346 10k multi 1.00 .60
Tete-beche pair 2.00 *2.00*

Praga 2008 World Philatelic Exhibition.

Applied Art Designers' Association, Cent. — A1347

**2008, Sept. 3** ***Perf. 11¾x11¼***
**3396** A1347 26k multi 2.75 1.60

Karel Plicka (1894-1987), Photographer — A1348

**Litho. & Engr.**

**2008, Sept. 12** ***Perf. 11¾***
**3397** A1348 35k multi + 2 labels 4.00 2.10

See Slovakia No. 548.

Souvenir Sheet

Mail Coach — A1349

**2008, Sept. 12**
**3398** A1349 35k multi 4.00 2.10

Praga 2008 Intl. Stamp Exhibition, Prague, and 2008 Vienna Intl. Stamp Exhibition. See Austria No. 2172.

Stoves — A1350

Stove from: 10k, Sternberk Castle. 17k, Archbishop's Palace, Prague.

**Photo. & Engr.**

**2008, Oct. 15** ***Perf. 11¼x11¾***
**3399** A1350 10k multi 1.00 .55
Complete booklet, 5 #3399 5.50
**3400** A1350 17k multi 1.75 .95
Complete booklet, 5 #3400 9.50

**Painting Type of 1967 Inscribed "CESKA REPUBLIKA"**

Designs: 23k, Vltava River at Klecany, by Zdenka Braunerová, horiz. 26k, Autumn Road, by Otakar Nejedly.

**2008, Nov. 5** **Engr.** ***Perf. 11¾***
**3401-3402** A565 Set of 2 5.25 3.00

Issued in sheets of 4. Value, set $21.

Souvenir Sheet

Allegory of Water, by Jan Jakub Hartman — A1351

**2008, Nov. 5** **Litho. & Engr.**
**3403** A1351 30k multi 3.25 1.75

Basket With Apples — A1352

Winter Scene — A1353

Mechanical Christmas Display — A1354

**Photo. & Engr.**

**2008, Nov. 5** ***Perf. 11¼x11½***
**3404** A1352 10k multi .95 .55

**Litho.**

***Perf. 12¾x13¼***

**3405** A1353 10k multi + label .95 .55

**Souvenir Sheet**

**Litho. & Engr.**

***Perf. 11¾***

**3406** A1354 30k multi 3.25 1.75

Christmas.

No. 3405 was printed in sheets of 9 stamps + 12 labels. Value $10. Labels could be personalized.

Czech Republic Presidency of European Union, January to June 2009 — A1355

***Perf. 11¾x11¼***

**2008, Nov. 25** **Litho.**
**3407** A1355 17k multi + label 1.75 .90

No. 3407 was issued in sheets of 30 stamps + 30 labels.

Louis Braille (1809-52), Educator of the Blind — A1356

Charles Darwin (1809-82), Naturalist — A1357

**2009, Jan. 2** **Photo. & Engr.**
**3408** A1356 10k multi .95 .55
**3409** A1357 12k multi 1.10 .60

Tradition of Czech Stamp Production A1358

**2009, Jan. 20** *Perf. 11¼x11¾*

**3410** A1358 10k Design of #980 1.00 .50
*a.* Booklet pane of 8 + 4 labels 8.25 —
Complete booklet, #3410a 8.25

Nordic World Skiing Championships, Liberec — A1359

*Perf. 11¾x11¼*

**2009, Feb. 11** **Litho.**

**3411** A1359 18k multi 1.25 1.25

Souvenir Sheet

Preservation of Polar Regions and Glaciers — A1360

**Litho. & Engr.**

**2009, Feb. 11** *Perf. 11¾*

**3412** A1360 35k multi 3.50 1.90

Easter A1361

**Photo. & Engr.**

**2009, Mar. 18** *Perf. 11½x11¼*

**3413** A1361 10k multi .95 .55

Lu Tung-pin, by Unknown Chinese Artist — A1362

Mythical Beings, by Unknown Balinese Artist — A1363

**Litho. & Engr.**

**2009, Mar. 18** *Perf. 11¾*

**3414** A1362 18k multi 1.75 1.00
**3415** A1363 24k multi 2.25 1.40

Souvenir Sheet

Reliquary of St. Maurus, Becov nad Teplou Castle — A1364

**2009, Apr. 8**

**3416** A1364 51k multi 5.00 3.00

Pardubice to Liberec Rail Line, 150th Anniv. — A1365

**Photo. & Engr.**

**2009, Apr. 22** *Perf. 11¾x11¼*

**3417** A1365 10k multi 1.00 .60

Industry and Trade Ministry Building, 75th Anniv. A1366

**Photo. & Engr.**

**2009, Apr. 22** *Perf. 11¾x11½*

**3418** A1366 10k multi 1.00 .60

Europa A1367

**2009, May 6** **Litho.** *Perf. 11¼*

**3419** A1367 17k multi 1.75 1.00

Intl. Year of Astronomy.

Buildings A1368

Designs: 12k, Cistercian Monastery, Vyssí Brod. 14k, Horsovsky Castle, Tyn.

**2009, May 6** **Engr.** *Perf. 11¾x11½*

**3420-3421** A1368 Set of 2 2.50 1.50

Nos. 3420-3421 also were issued in souvenir sheets of 1. Value, set of two sheets $27.

Marionettes Spejbl and Hurvínek — A1369

**Photo. & Engr.**

**2009, May 27** *Perf. 11¼x11½*

**3422** A1369 10k multi 1.10 .60
*a.* Booklet pane of 8 + 2 labels 9.00 —
Complete booklet, #3422a 9.00

Rabbi Jehuda Löw (c. 1525-1609) A1370

**2009, May 27** **Litho.** *Perf. 11¼x11¾*

**3423** A1370 21k multi 2.00 1.25

Printed in sheets of 5 + 4 labels. Value, $10.

Granting of Religious Freedom by Rudolf II, 400th Anniv. A1371

**Photo. & Engr.**

**2009, June 17** *Perf. 11¼*

**3424** A1371 26k multi 2.50 1.50

Intl. Firefighters' Games, Ostrava — A1372

*Perf. 11¾x11¼*

**2009, June 17** **Litho.**

**3425** A1372 17k multi 1.75 1.00

Miniature Sheet

Krivoklát UNESCO Biosphere Reservation — A1373

No. 3426: a, 10k, Eudia pavonia (44x27mm). b, 12k, Aglia tau, Cervus elaphus (44x54mm). c, 14k, Bubo bubo, Lunaria rediviva, Ciconia nigra (44x54mm). d, 17k, Tyto alba, Krivoklát Castle (44x54mm).

**Litho. & Engr.**

**2009, Sept. 2** *Perf. 11¾*

**3426** A1373 Sheet of 4, #a-d, + 4 labels 5.50 4.50

Souvenir Sheet

Bohemian-Moravian Highlands — A1374

**2009, Sept. 2**

**3427** A1374 43k multi 4.00 2.50

Windmill, Ruprechtov A1375

Water Mill, Hoslovice A1376

**Photo. & Engr.**

**2009, Sept. 23** *Perf. 11¼x11½*
**3428** A1375 10k multi 1.00 .60
Complete booklet, 5 #3428 5.50

*Perf. 11½x11¼*

**3429** A1376 12k multi 1.25 .70
Complete booklet, 5 #3429 7.00

Czech National Anthem, 175th Anniv. — A1377

**2009, Oct. 14** *Perf. 11¼x11¾*
**3430** A1377 10k multi 1.00 .60

Barbora Markéta Eliášová (1874-1957), Travel Writer — A1378

**2009, Oct. 14** *Perf. 11¾x11¼*
**3431** A1378 18k multi 1.75 1.10

Stoves — A1379

Designs: 10k, Empire stove, Litomysl Castle. 14k, Biedermeier stove, Vyskov Castle.

**2009, Oct. 14** *Perf. 11¼x11¾*
**3432** A1379 10k multi 1.00 .60
Complete booklet, 5 #3432 5.50
**3433** A1379 14k multi 1.25 .80
Complete booklet, 5 #3433 7.50

Protest Rallies of Nov. 17, 1939, and Nov. 17, 1989 — A1380

**2009, Nov. 4** **Litho.**
**3434** A1380 14k multi 1.25 .80

**Painting Type of 1967 Inscribed "CESKA REPUBLIKA"**

Designs: 24k, Canal Lock in Moret, by Alfred Sisley, horiz. 26k, Alley, by Alfred Justitz, horiz.

**2009, Nov. 4** **Engr.** *Perf. 11¾*
**3435-3436** A565 Set of 2 5.25 3.00

Souvenir Sheet

Oldrich and Bozena, by Frantisek Zenísek — A1381

**Litho. & Engr.**

**2009, Nov. 4** *Perf. 11¾*
**3437** A1381 34k multi 3.50 2.00

Christmas — A1382

**Photo. & Engr.**

**2009, Nov. 4** *Perf. 11¼x11½*
**3438** A1382 10k multi 1.10 .60

Tradition of Czech Stamp Production A1383

**2010, Jan. 20** *Perf. 11¼x11¾*
**3439** A1383 10k Vignette of #2121 1.10 .55
*a.* Booklet pane of 8 + 4 labels 9.00 —
Complete booklet, #3439a 9.00

Magdalena Dobromila Rettigová (1785-1845), Writer — A1384

**2010, Jan. 20** *Perf. 11¾x11¼*
**3440** A1384 12k multi 1.25 .65

2010 Winter Olympics, Vancouver — A1385

**2010, Feb. 10** *Perf. 11¼x11¾*
**3441** A1385 18k multi 1.25 .95

2010 Winter Paralympics, Vancouver — A1386

**2010, Feb. 10**
**3442** A1386 18k multi 1.25 .95

Souvenir Sheet

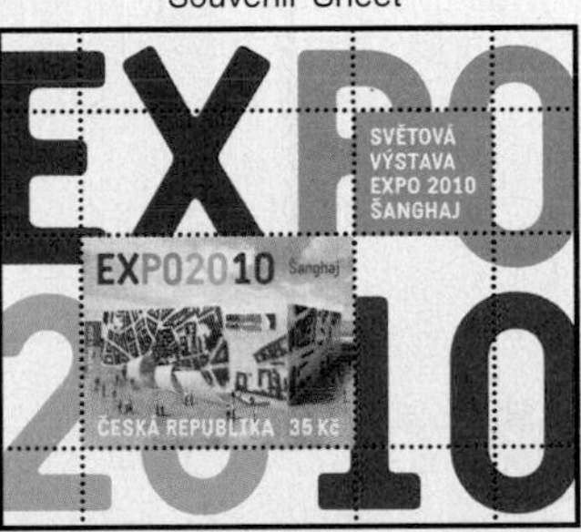

Expo 2010, Shanghai — A1387

**2010, Feb. 10** **Litho.**
**3443** A1387 35k multi + 3 labels 3.00 1.90

Easter A1388

**Photo. & Engr.**

**2010, Mar. 10** *Perf. 11½x11¼*
**3444** A1388 10k multi 1.10 .55

Martina Sáblíková, Gold Medalist at 2010 Winter Olympic Games — A1389

*Perf. 11¼x11¾*

**2010, Mar. 24** **Litho.**
**3445** A1389 10k multi 1.10 .55

Souvenir Sheet

Karel Hynek Macha (1810-36), Writer — A1390

*Perf. 11½x11¾*

**2010, Mar. 10** **Litho. & Engr.**
**3446** A1390 43k multi 4.00 2.40

Enrique Stanko Vráz (1860-1932), Travel Writer — A1391

**Photo. & Engr.**

**2010, Apr. 14** *Perf. 11¾x11¼*
**3447** A1391 24k multi 2.25 1.25

19th Century Transcaucasian Carpets — A1392

Designs: 21k, Kasim Usak carpet. 24k, Celaberd carpet.

**Litho. & Engr.**

**2010, Apr. 14** *Perf. 11¾*
**3448-3449** A1392 Set of 2 4.00 2.40

Ctyrlístek Comic Strip Character Fifinka — A1393

*Serpentine Die Cut 15x16½*

**2010, Apr. 28** **Litho.**

**Booklet Stamp Self-Adhesive**

**3450** A1393 A multi 1.10 .55
*a.* Booklet pane of 10 11.00

No. 3450 sold for 10k on day of issue.

Prague Castle — A1394

**2010, May 5** **Engr.** *Perf. 11¾*
**3451** A1394 17k brown 1.50 .85

Prague Castle in the Art of the Postage Stamp Exhibition, Prague. Printed in sheets of 4 + label. Value, $6.

Dásenka, Children's Book by Karel Capek A1395

**2010, May 5** **Litho.** *Perf. 11¼*
**3452** A1395 17k multi 1.50 .85

Europa.

Children's Book Illustration by Helena Zmatlíková (1923-2005)
A1396

**Photo. & Engr.**

**2010, May 26** ***Perf. 11¼x11½***

**3453** A1396 10k multi 1.10 .50
*a.* Booklet pane of 8 + 2 labels 9.00 —
Complete booklet, #3453a 9.00

Alphonse Mucha (1860-1939), Illustrator — A1397

Designs: E, Gismonda. Z, Zodiac.

***Serpentine Die Cut 14¼x14½***

**2010, May 26** **Litho.**

**Booklet Stamps**

**Self-Adhesive**

**3454** A1397 E multi 1.60 .80
*a.* Booklet pane of 6 9.75

**Size: 43x54mm**

***Serpentine Die Cut 14½***

**3455** A1397 Z multi 1.75 .85
*a.* Booklet pane of 6 10.50

No. 3454 sold for 17k and No. 3455 sold for 18k on day of issue.

Zd'árské Hills Protected Landscape — A1398

**Photo. & Engr.**

**2010, June 16** ***Perf. 11¾x11½***

**3456** A1398 10k multi 1.10 .50

Marriage of John of Luxembourg and Elizabeth of Bohemia, 700th Anniv. — A1399

**Photo. & Engr.**

**2010, June 16** ***Perf. 11¾x11¼***

**3457** A1399 17k multi 1.50 .85

Accession to the throne of Bohemia by the House of Luxembourg. See Luxembourg No. 1292.

No. 3457 was issued in sheets 5 stamps + 4 labels. Values: single stamp + label, $1.75; complete sheet, $9.

Astronomical Clock, Prague, 600th Anniv. — A1400

**2010, June 16** **Litho.**

**3458** A1400 21k multi 2.25 1.10

Towns — A1401

Designs: 12k, Klatovy. 14k, Stramberk.

**2010, June 16** **Engr.**

**3459-3460** A1401 Set of 2 2.40 1.25

Czech Republic, Winners of 2010 World Ice Hockey Championships
A1402

***Perf. 11¼x11¾***

**2010, June 23** **Litho.**

**3461** A1402 10k multi 1.10 .50

Ctyrlístek Comic Strip Characters Fifinka, Pind'a, Bobík and Myspulín — A1403

**2010, Sept. 1** **Litho.** ***Perf. 12¾x13¼***

**3462** A1403 A multi + label 1.10 .55

No. 3462 was printed in sheets of 9 + 12 labels that could be personalized and had a franking value of 10k on day of issue.

Children With Magnifying Glass and Stamp Album — A1404

Boy Examining Stamp — A1405

**2010, Sept. 1**

**3463** A1404 A multi + label 1.10 .55
**3464** A1405 E multi + label 2.10 1.10

Nos. 3463-3464 each were printed in sheets of 9 + 12 labels that could be personalized. On day of issue, No. 3463 had a franking value of 10k and No. 3464 had a franking value of 20k.

2010 Women's World Basketball Championships, Czech Republic — A1406

**2010, Sept. 1** ***Perf. 11¼x11¾***

**3465** A1406 17k multi 1.75 .90

Miniature Sheet

Flora and Fauna of Lower Morava UNESCO Biosphere Reserve — A1407

No. 3466: a, 10k, Tichodroma muraria, Papilio machaon, Aster amellus (45x55mm). b, 12k, Saga pedo, Iris variegata (45x27mm). c, 14k, Lacerta viridis, Pulsatilla grandis (45x27mm). d, 18k, Upupa epops, Arenaria grandiflora (45x55mm).

**Litho. & Engr.**

**2010, Sept. 1** ***Perf. 11¾***

**3466** A1407 Sheet of 4, #a-d, + 3 labels 6.00 3.00

**Flowers Type of 2002**

Designs: 4k, Anemone (sasanka). 25k, Iris (kosatec). 30k, Tulip (tulipán).

**Photo. & Engr.**

**2010** ***Perf. 11¾x11¼***

**3467** A1215 4k multi .45 .25
**3468** A1215 25k multi 2.00 1.50
**3469** A1215 30k multi 2.25 1.75
*Nos. 3467-3469 (3)* 4.70 3.50

Issued: 4k, 9/29; 25k, 30k, 9/15.

Austrian Empire Post Office Sign, Postal Map, Dwarves with Letters, Handstamp and Posthorn
A1408

**2010, Sept. 29** **Litho.** ***Perf. 11¼***

**3470** A1408 A multi 1.10 .55

Postal Musuem, Prague. No. 3470 sold for 10k on day of issue.

Famous Men — A1409

Designs: 10k, Adolf Branald (1910-2008), writer. 12k, Karel Zeman (1910-89), film director and animator.

**Photo. & Engr.**

**2010, Sept. 29** ***Perf. 11¼x11½***

**3471-3472** A1409 Set of 2 2.25 1.25

Ctyrlístek Comic Strip Character Myspulín — A1410

***Serpentine Die Cut 15x16½***

**2010, Oct. 20** **Litho.**

**Booklet Stamp**

**Self-Adhesive**

**3473** A1410 A multi 1.25 .60
*a.* Booklet pane of 10 12.50

No. 3473 sold for 10k on day of issue.

Bridges
A1411

Designs: 10k, Mariánsky Bridge, Ustí nad Labem. 12k, Stone Bridge, Písek.

**Photo. & Engr.**

**2010, Oct. 20** ***Perf. 11¾x11¼***

**3474** A1411 10k multi 1.00 .60
Complete booklet, 5 #3474 5.50
**3475** A1411 12k multi 1.25 .70
Complete booklet, 5 #3475 7.00

Stoves — A1412

Designs: 10k, Art Nouveau stove. 20k, Art Deco stove.

**2010, Oct. 20** ***Perf. 11¼x11¾***

**3476** A1412 10k multi 1.00 .60
Complete booklet, 5 #3476 6.25
**3477** A1412 20k multi 1.75 1.25
Complete booklet, 5 #3477 12.00

**Art Type of 1967 Inscribed "CESKA REPUBLIKA"**

Designs: 24k, Paris and Helen, by Karel Skréta. 26k, Sand Bargemen, by Milos Jiránek. 30k, Spring, by Karel Spillar, horiz.

**Litho. & Engr. (24k), Engr.**

**2010, Nov. 10** ***Perf. 11¾***

**3478-3480** A565 Set of 3 7.50 4.50

Illumination From 1558 Zlutice Hymn Book — A1413

*Perf. 11¼x11¾*

**2010, Nov. 10 Litho.**

**3481** A1413 10k multi 1.10 .55

Christmas.

2011 Census — A1414

**2011, Jan. 5**

**3482** A1414 10k black & green 1.10 .55

Souvenir Sheet

Kaspar Maria von Sternberg (1761-1838), Paleobotanist — A1415

*Perf. 11¾x11½*

**2011, Jan. 5 Litho. & Engr.**

**3483** A1415 43k multi 5.00 2.40

Mail Coach on Charles Bridge, 1966 Envelope Indicia by Josef Hercík — A1416

**Photo. & Engr.**

**2011, Jan. 20** *Perf. 11¾x11¼*

**3484** A1416 10k multi 1.10 .55
*a.* Booklet pane of 8 + 4 labels 9.00 —
Complete booklet, #3484a 9.50

Tradition of Czech stamp production.

St. Agnes of Bohemia (1211-82) — A1417

**2011, Jan. 20** *Perf. 11¼x11¾*

**3485** A1417 12k multi 1.25 .70

Ctyrlístek Comic Strip Character Pind'a — A1418

**Booklet Stamp**

*Serpentine Die Cut 15x16½*

**2011, Feb. 9 Litho. Self-Adhesive**

**3486** A1418 A multi 1.10 .55
*a.* Booklet pane of 10 11.00

No. 3486 sold for 10k on day of issue.

Jirí Melantrich of Aventinum (c. 1511-80), Printer — A1419

**Photo. & Engr.**

**2011, Feb. 9** *Perf. 11¼x11¾*

**3487** A1419 30k multi 3.00 1.75

Cheb, 950th Anniv. — A1420

Black Madonna House, Prague, Cent. — A1421

**2011, Feb. 9 Engr.** *Perf. 11¾x11½*

**3488** A1420 12k multi 1.10 .70

*Perf. 11½x11¾*

**3489** A1421 14k multi 1.40 .80

Visegrád Group, 20th Anniv. — A1422

*Perf. 11¾x11¼*

**2011, Feb. 11 Litho.**

**3490** A1422 20k multi 2.00 1.10

See Hungary No. 4183, Poland No. 4001, and Slovakia No. 611.

No. 3490 was issued in sheets of 8 + 8 labels. Values: single stamp + label, $2.25; complete sheet, $18.

Architecture A1423

Designs: A, House gables from Blatensko region, North Moravia and West Bohemia, gable shutter from North Bohemia. E, House gables from North Bohemia and South Bohemia, Wallachian cottage, Central Bohemian gate. Z, Houses from North Bohemia, West Bohemia and Wallachia, vert.

**Photo. & Engr.**

**2011** *Perf. 11¼x11¾*

**3491** A1423 A blk, lt bl & bl 1.00 .60
**3492** A1423 E blk, beige & brn 2.25 1.25

*Perf. 11¾x11¼*

**3493** A1423 Z blk, gray grn & bl grn 2.25 1.25
*Nos. 3491-3493 (3)* 5.50 3.10

Issued: Nos. 3491-3492, 2/23; No. 3493, 5/27. On day of issue Nos. 3491-3493 sold for 10k, 20k and 21k, respectively.
See No. 3559.

Souvenir Sheet

Petr Vok (1539-1611) and Vilém (1535-92) von Rosenberg, Aristocrats — A1424

**2011, Mar. 9 Engr.** *Perf. 11¾*

**3494** A1424 49k multi 4.50 3.00

Easter — A1425

*Perf. 11¼x11¾*

**2011, Mar. 23 Litho.**

**3495** A1425 A multi 1.10 .60

No. 3495 sold for 10k on day of issue.

Vlasta Burian (1891-1962), Actor — A1426

**Photo. & Engr.**

**2011, Apr. 6** *Perf. 11¾x11¼*

**3496** A1426 10k multi 1.10 .60

Teaching at Prague Conservatory, Bicent. — A1427

**2011, Apr. 6** *Perf. 11¼x11¾*

**3497** A1427 10k multi 1.10 .60

Ctyrlistek Comic Strip Character Bobík — A1428

**Booklet Stamp**

*Serpentine Die Cut 15x16½*

**2011, May 4 Litho. Self-Adhesive**

**3498** A1428 A multi 1.25 .60
*a.* Booklet pane of 10 12.50

No. 3498 sold for 10k on day of issue.

Europa A1429

**2011, May 4 Litho.** *Perf. 11¼*

**3499** A1429 20k multi 2.00 1.25

Intl. Year of Forests.

**Flower Type of 2002**

Design: 2k, Chrysanthemum (chryzantéma).

**Photo. & Engr.**

**2011, May 27** *Perf. 11¾x11¼*

**3500** A1215 2k multi .25 .25

Souvenir Sheet

Johann Gerstner (1851-1939), Violinist — A1430

**Litho. & Engr.**

**2011, May 27** *Perf. 11¾*

**3501** A1430 34k multi 3.50 2.10

See Slovenia No. 891.

The Little Witch and Abraxas, the Raven, Animated Characters by Zdenek Smetana A1431

**Photo. & Engr.**

**2011, June 1** *Perf. 11½x11¼*

**3502** A1431 10k multi 1.25 .60
*a.* Booklet pane of 8 + 2 labels 10.00 —
Complete booklet, #3502a 10.00

First Public Long-Distance Flight of Jan Kaspar (1883-1927), Cent. — A1432

**2011, June 1** *Perf. 11¼x11¾*

**3503** A1432 21k multi 2.25 1.25

Execution of 27 Protestant Leaders in Prague, 390th Anniv. — A1433

**Litho. & Engr.**

**2011, June 1** ***Perf. 11¾***
**3504** A1433 26k rose pink & blk 2.50 1.60

Cricetus Cricetus — A1434

***Perf. 11¼x11¾***

**2011, June 15** **Litho.**
**3505** A1434 10k multi 1.10 .60
Complete booklet, 5 #3505 6.00

Floral Arrangement A1435

**2011, June 15**
**3506** A1435 25k multi 2.50 1.50

Europa Cup, Championships of European Federation of Professional Florist Associations, Havirov.

Men's European Volleyball Championships, Prague and Karlovy Vary — A1436

***Perf. 11¼x11¾***

**2011, Aug. 31** **Litho.**
**3507** A1436 20k multi 2.25 1.10

Wolfgang Amadeus Mozart (1756-91), Composer — A1437

**Booklet Stamp**

***Serpentine Die Cut 11½***

**2011, Aug. 31** **Self-Adhesive**
**3508** A1437 E multi 2.25 1.10
*a.* Booklet pane of 6 13.50

No. 3508 sold for 20k on day of issue.

Miniature Sheet

Flora and Fauna of Sumava UNESCO Biosphere Reserve — A1438

No. 3509: a, 10k,Turdus torquatus, Erebia euryale, Tetrao urogallus (54x44mm). b, 14k, Dactylorhiza traunsteineri, Colias palaeno (27x44mm). c, 18k, Aeshna juncea, Alces alces, Tetrao tetrix (54x44mm). d, 20k, Lynx lynx, Picoides tridactylus (54x44mm).

**Litho. & Engr.**

**2011, Aug. 31** ***Perf. 11¾***
**3509** A1438 Sheet of 4, #a-d, + 4 labels 6.00 3.50

Organ, Church of the Assumption of Our Lady, Plasy — A1439

***Perf. 11¼x11¾***

**2011, Sept. 14** **Litho.**
**3510** A1439 10k multi 1.10 .55

Frantisek Alexander Elstner (1902-74), Travel Writer — A1440

**Photo. & Engr.**

**2011, Sept. 14** ***Perf. 11¾x11¼***
**3511** A1440 14k multi 1.40 .80

Pat and Mat, Characters From Children's Television Show — A1441

**Booklet Stamp**

***Serpentine Die Cut 15x16½***

**2011, Oct. 5** **Litho.** **Self-Adhesive**
**3512** A1441 A multi 1.10 .55
*a.* Booklet pane of 10 11.00

No. 3512 sold for 10k on day of issue.

World Post Day A1442

**2011, Oct. 5** ***Perf. 11¼***
**3513** A1442 21k multi 2.25 1.25

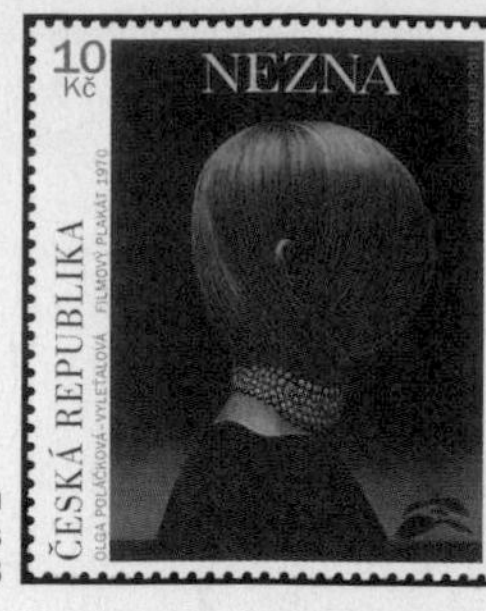


Film Posters A1443

Poster for: No. 3514, 10k, Une Femme Douce, 1970. No. 3515, 10k, Markéta Lazarová, 1966.

**2011, Oct. 5** **Litho.** ***Perf. 11¾x11¼***
**3514-3515** A1443 Set of 2 2.25 1.10

**Peacock & Bugler Type of 2005 and Roses Above Prague Type of 2003**

**2011, Oct. 27** ***Perf. 11¼x11¾***
**3516** A1263 A multi + label 1.10 .55
**3517** A1225 E multi + label 2.25 1.10

On day of issue, No. 3516 sold for 10k and No. 3517 sold for 20k. Nos. 3516-3517 each were issued in sheets of 9 stamps and 12 labels that could be personalized. Value, $30.

**Art Type of 1967 Inscribed "CESKA REPUBLIKA"**

Designs: 24k, Lovers, by Jaroslav Vozniak, horiz. 26k, Woman in Corn Field, by Joza Uprka. 30k, Winter Landscape, by August Bedrich Piepenhagen, horiz.

**2011, Nov. 9** **Engr.** ***Perf. 11¾***
**3518-3520** A565 Set of 3 8.00 4.50

Christmas A1444

**2011, Nov. 9** **Litho.** ***Perf. 11¾x11¼***
**3521** A1444 A multi 1.10 .55

No. 3521 sold for 10k on day of issue.

House, Vidim — A1445

**Photo. & Engr.**

**2012, Jan. 20** ***Perf. 11¼x11¾***
**3522** A1445 6k multi .65 .30

Josef Liesler (1912-2005), Stamp Designer — A1446

**2012, Jan. 20** ***Perf. 11¾x11¼***
**3523** A1446 10k multi 1.10 .55
*a.* Booklet pane of 8 + 4 labels 9.00 —
Complete booklet, #3523a 9.00

Tradition of Czech stamp production.

Jirí Trnka (1912-69), Film Animator and Director — A1447

**2012, Feb. 15**
**3524** A1447 10k multi 1.10 .55

Sokol Movement, 150th Anniv. — A1448

***Perf. 11¼x11¾***

**2012, Feb. 15** **Litho.**
**3525** A1448 14k multi 1.50 .75

Union of Czech Mathematicians and Physicists, 150th Anniv. — A1449

**2012, Mar. 7** ***Perf. 11¾x11¼***
**3526** A1449 10k multi 1.10 .55

Kuks A1450

Designs: 14k, Buildings in Kuks. 18k, Statue by Matthias B. Braun, vert.

***Perf. 11½x11¾, 11¾x11½***

**2012, Mar. 7** **Engr.**
**3527-3528** A1450 Set of 2 3.00 1.75

Hiker at Signpost — A1451

***Perf. 11¼x11¾***

**2012, Mar. 21** **Litho.**
**3529** A1451 A multi + label 1.10 .55

No. 3529 was printed in sheets of 9 + 12 labels that could be personalized and had a franking value of 10k on day of issue.

Gregor Mendel (1822-84), Genetics Pioneer — A1452

**Photo. & Engr.**

**2012, Apr. 4** ***Perf. 11¾x11¼***
**3530** A1452 20k multi 1.90 1.10

First Hebrew Book Printed in Prague, 500th Anniv. A1453

**2012, Apr. 18 Litho. *Perf. 11¼***

**3531** A1453 25k multi 2.40 1.40

Prague Tourist Attractions A1454

**Photo. & Engr.**

**2012, May 2 *Perf. 11¼x11¾***

**3532** A1454 20k multi 2.00 1.10

Europa.

Scouting in Czechoslovakia, Cent. — A1455

**2012, May 2 Litho. *Perf. 11¼***

**3533** A1455 21k multi 2.00 1.10

Boats on Bat'a Canal A1456

**2012, May 16 Engr. *Perf. 11¾x11¼***

**Booklet Stamp**

**3534** A1456 10k dark blue 1.20 .50

*a.* Booklet pane of 8 + 4 labels 9.50 —

Complete booklet, #3534a 9.50

The Whipping of Christ, by Tintoretto — A1457

**2012, May 16 *Perf. 11¾***

**3535** A1457 30k multi 3.50 1.50

Art in Prague Castle. See Nos. 3569, 3605, 3642, 3674, 3705.

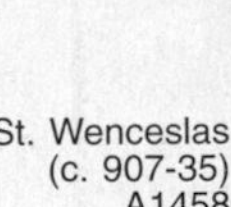

St. Wenceslas (c. 907-35) A1458

***Serpentine Die Cut 11 Syncopated***

**2012, June 6 Litho.**

**Self-Adhesive**

**3536** A1458 A multi 1.00 .50

No. 3536 sold for 10k on day of issue. See No. 3576.

Lezáky Massacre, 70th Anniv. — A1459

**2012, June 6 *Perf. 11¾x11¼***

**3537** A1459 10k multi 1.00 .50

Lidice Massacre, 70th Anniv. — A1460

**2012, June 6 Photo. & Engr.**

**3538** A1460 20k multi 2.00 1.00

Coronation of Statue of Our Lady of Hostyn, Cent. — A1461

**Litho. & Engr.**

**2012, June 20 *Perf. 11¾***

**3539** A1461 21k multi 1.90 1.00

No. 3539 was issued in sheets of 8 stamps + 1 label. Values: single stamp + label, $2.50; complete sheet, $16.

A1462

A1463

Personalized Stamps A1464

***Serpentine Die Cut 11 Syncopated***

**2012, June 20 Litho.**

**Self-Adhesive**

**3540** A1462 A multi .95 .50

**3541** A1463 A multi .95 .50

**3542** A1464 E multi 1.90 .95

*Nos. 3540-3542 (3)* 3.80 1.95

Nos. 3540-3542 each were printed in sheets of 25. Vignette portions of each stamp could be personalized. The generic vignettes of these stamps are shown. On day of issue, the franking value of Nos. 3540-3541 each were 10k, and of No. 3542, 20k.

2012 Summer Olympics, London — A1465

**Litho. & Engr.**

**2012, June 20 *Perf. 11¾***

**3543** A1465 20k multi 1.90 .95

No. 3543 was issued in sheets of 3 stamps + 2 labels. Values: single stamp + label, $2.25; complete sheet, $6.

Alberto Vojtech Fric (1882-1944), Cactus Collector, Botanist and Ethnographer — A1466

**2012, Sept. 5 Litho. *Perf. 11¾x11¼***

**3544** A1466 10k multi 1.10 .55

Illustrations of Antique Automobiles by Václav Zapadlík — A1467

No. 3545: a, 1933 Duesenberg SJ. b, 1931, Wikov 70. c, 1936 Mercedes-Benz 540. d, 1938 Rolls Royce Phantom III. e, 1934 Bugatti Royale 41. f, 1929 Isotta Fraschini Tipo 8A.

***Serpentine Die Cut 11½***

**2012, Sept. 5**

**Self-Adhesive**

**3545** Booklet pane of 6 13.00

*a.-f.* A1467 E Any single 2.10 1.10

On day of issue, Nos. 3545a-3545f each sold for 20k. See Nos. 3580-3581, 3610-3611, 3615-3616.

Miniature Sheet

Orchids — A1468

No. 3546: a, 10k, Dendrobium peguanum (44x27mm). b, 14k, Stanhopea tigrina and Coryanthes feildingii (44x54mm). c, 18k, Cattleya aclandiae and Cattleya maxima (44x54mm). d, 20k, Paphiopedilum charlesworthii, Paphiopedilum insigne, and Paphiopedilum hirsutissimum (44x54mm).

**Litho. & Engr.**

**2012, Sept. 5 *Perf. 11¾***

**3546** A1468 Sheet of 4, #a-d, + 4 labels 6.00 3.25

Souvenir Sheet

Golden Bull of Sicily, 800th Anniv. — A1469

**2012, Sept. 19 Engr. *Perf. 11¾***

**3547** A1469 49k multi 4.75 2.60

Paphiopedilum Venustum — A1470

**2012, Oct. 3 Litho. *Perf. 11¼x11¾***

**3548** A1470 A multi + label 1.10 .55

No. 3548 was printed in sheets of 9 + 12 labels that could be personalized. On day of issue, No. 3548 had a franking value of 10k.

Masaryk Circuit Racers — A1471

Designs: 18k, Frantisek St'astny (1927-2000), motorcycle racer. 25k, Louis Chiron (1899-1979), automobile racer.

**2012, Oct. 3** **Photo. & Engr.**
**3549-3550** A1471 Set of 2 4.50 2.25

1891 Ericsson Desk Telephone A1472

**2012, Oct. 3** **Litho.** ***Perf. 11¼***
**3551** A1472 26k multi 2.75 1.40

World Post Day.

**Art Type of 1967 Inscribed "CESKA REPUBLIKA" and**

Life's Pleasures, by Frantisek Kupka — A1473

Designs: 26k, A Long-haired Girl, by Kamil Lhoták. 32k, Self-portrait with Family, by Jan Kupecky. No. 3554: a, Blonde nude on horse. b, Brunette nude on pony, vert.

**2012, Nov. 7** **Engr.** ***Perf. 11¾***
**3552-3553** A565 Set of 2 5.50 3.00

**Litho. & Engr.**

**Souvenir Sheet**

**3554** A1473 30k Sheet of 2, #a-b 6.00 3.00

Christmas — A1474

**2012, Nov. 7** **Litho.** ***Perf. 11¼x11¾***
**3555** A1474 A multi + label 1.00 .50

No. 3555 sold for 10k on day of issue and was printed in sheets of 9 + 12 labels that could be personalized.

Pinda, Bobik, Myspulin and Fifinka Riding Griffin A1475

Myspulin Taking Picture of Bobik, Fifinka, King Rudolf II, Aurix the Lion and Pinda — A1476

***Serpentine Die Cut 16½x15***

**2012, Nov. 7** **Self-Adhesive**

**Booklet Stamps**

**3556** A1475 A multi 1.00 .50
**3557** A1476 A multi 1.00 .50
*a.* Booklet pane of 10, 5 each #3556-3557 10.00

On day of issue, Nos. 3556-3557 each sold for 10k.

**Architecture Type of 2011 and**

Building, Busanovice, 1847 — A1477

**Photo. & Engr.**

**2012** ***Perf. 11¼x11¾***
**3558** A1477 5k multi .75 .25
**3559** A1423 A black & blue 1.25 .50

Issued: No. 3558, 12/19; No. 3559, 11/8. No. 3559 sold for 10k on day of issue. Compare No. 3559 with No. 3491.

Ivan Strnad (1926-2005), Stamp Designer — A1478

**2013, Jan. 20** ***Perf. 11¾x11¼***
**3560** A1478 10k multi 1.10 .55
*a.* Booklet pane of 8 + 4 labels 9.00 —
Complete booklet, #3560a 9.00

Tradition of Czech stamp production.

Bertha von Suttner (1843-1914), 1905 Nobel Peace Laureate — A1479

***Perf. 11¼x11¾***

**2013, Feb. 13** **Litho.**
**3561** A1479 18k multi 1.90 .95

Cottage, Novy Hrozenkov — A1480

**Photo. & Engr.**

**2013, Mar. 6** ***Perf. 11¾x11¼***
**3562** A1480 14k brn & dk brn 1.50 .75

Transportation — A1481

No. 3563: a, Aero HC2 Heli Baby helicopter. b, Pécko-18 tugboat.

**2013, Mar. 6** **Litho.**
**3563** A1481 25k Vert. pair, #a-b 4.50 2.60

Zlatá Koruna Monastery, 750th Anniv. — A1482

**2013, Apr. 3** **Engr.** ***Perf. 11¾x11½***
**3564** A1482 14k multi 1.40 .70

George Orwell (1903-50), Writer — A1483

**Photo. & Engr.**

**2013, Apr. 3** ***Perf. 11¼x11¾***
**3565** A1483 26k multi 2.60 1.40

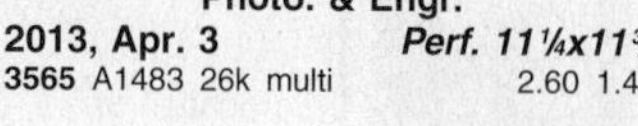

Pres. Milos Zeman — A1484

**2013, Apr. 24** ***Perf. 11¾x11¼***
**3566** A1484 A red & purple 1.00 .50

No. 3566 sold for 10k on day of issue.

Europa A1485

**2013, May 2** **Litho.** ***Perf. 11¼***
**3567** A1485 25k multi 2.25 1.40

Fláje Dam A1486

**2013, May 15** **Engr.** ***Perf. 11¾x11¼***
**3568** A1486 14k green 1.25 .75
*a.* Booklet pane of 8 + 4 labels 10.50 —
Complete booklet, #3568a 10.50

**Art in Prague Castle Type of 2012**

Design: 25k, Portrait of Jacob König, Goldsmith and Bookseller, by Paolo Veronese.

**2013, May 15** **Engr.** ***Perf. 11¾***
**3569** A1457 25k multi 2.25 1.40

Cross of Závis of Falkenstejn A1487

**2013, May 29** ***Perf. 11¾***
**3570** A1487 26k multi 2.40 1.40

Krtek the Mole — A1488

***Serpentine Die Cut 16½x15***

**2013, May 29** **Litho.**

**Booklet Stamp Self-Adhesive**

**3571** A1488 A multi 1.25 .55
*a.* Booklet pane of 10 12.50
*b.* As No. 3571, serpentine die cut 11x11¼ syncopated ('15) 1.50 .55
*c.* Booklet pane of 10 #3571b 15.00

No. 3571 sold for 10k on day of issue. No. 3571b sold for 13k when issued.

Historic Methods of Transportation — A1489

No. 3572: a, Tatra 15/30 automobile. b, Cechie 33 Böhmerland motorcycle.

***Perf. 11¾x11¼***

**2013, June 12** **Litho.**
**3572** A1489 10k Horiz. pair, #a-b 2.40 1.10

**Souvenir Sheet**

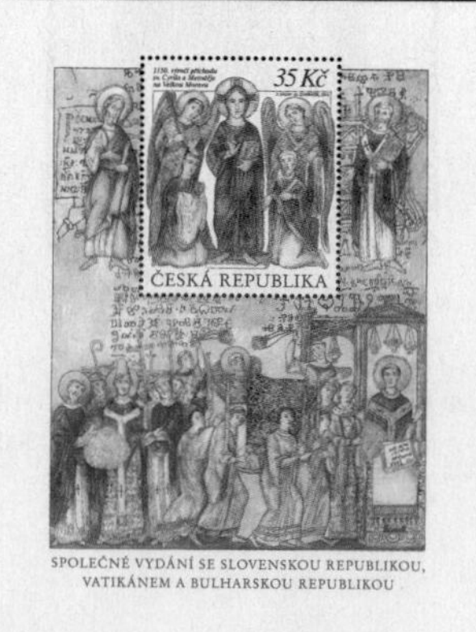


Mission of Sts. Cyril and Methodius to Slavic Lands, 1150th Anniv. — A1490

**Litho. & Engr.**

**2013, June 12** *Perf. 11¾*
**3573** A1490 35k multi 3.75 1.90

See Bulgaria No. 4647, Slovakia No. 666 and Vatican City No. 1536.

Postal Banking Services, 130th Anniv. A1491

*Perf. 11¾x11¼*

**2013, June 26** **Litho.**
**3574** A1491 20k multi 1.75 1.00

Franz Kafka (1883-1924), Writer — A1492

*Serpentine Die Cut 11½*

**2013, June 26** **Litho.**

**Booklet Stamp Self-Adhesive**

**3575** A1492 E multi 2.00 1.00
*a.* Booklet pane of 6 12.00

No. 3575 sold for 20k on day of issue.

**St. Wenceslas Type of 2012**

**2013, July 31 Litho.** *Perf. 11¼x11¾*
**3576** A1458 13k multi 1.40 .70

2013 Canoe Slalom World Championships, Prague — A1493

**Photo. & Engr.**

**2013, Sept. 4** *Perf. 11¾x11¼*
**3577** A1493 10k multi 1.10 .55

Novy Jicín, 700th Anniv. — A1494

**2013, Sept. 4 Engr.** *Perf. 11¾*
**3578** A1494 20k multi 1.75 1.75

Miniature Sheet

Flora and Fauna of the Karlstejn Region — A1495

No. 3579: a, 10k, Dracocephalum austriacum, Chorthippus vagans (27x44mm). b, 14k, Oenanthe oenanthe, Velká Amerika Limestone Quarry (27x44mm). c, 18k, Polyommatus coridon, Pulsatilla pratensis, Colias crocea (54x44mm). d, 20k, Rosa gallica, Karlstejn Castle (54x44mm).

**Litho. & Engr.**

**2013, Sept. 4** *Perf. 11¾*
**3579** A1495 Sheet of 4, #a-d, + 4 labels 6.00 3.25

**Antique Automobiles Type of 2012**

Illustrations by Václav Zapadlík: No. 3580, 1930 Skoda 860. No. 3581, 1932 Skoda 645.

*Serpentine Die Cut 11¼ Syncopated*

**2013, Sept. 4** **Litho.**

**Booklet Stamps Self-Adhesive**

**3580** A1467 A multi 1.25 .70
**3581** A1467 A multi 1.25 .70
*a.* Booklet pane of 8, 4 each #3580-3581 10.00

Nos. 3580-3581 each sold for 13k on day of issue.

A1496

Personalized Stamps — A1497

*Serpentine Die Cut 11¼ Syncopated*

**2013, Sept. 4** **Litho.**

**Booklet Stamps Self-Adhesive**

**3582** A1496 A black 1.50 .70
*a.* Booklet pane of 8 12.00
**3583** A1497 E black 3.00 1.25
*a.* Booklet pane of 8 24.00

On day of issue, No. 3582 sold for 13k, and No. 3583 sold for 25k. Nos. 3582 and 3583 could have the image portions of the stamp personalized for an additional fee. The horizontal generic vignettes of these stamps are shown. Nos. 3582a and 3583a contain four stamps with these horizontal generic vignettes and four stamps with similar generic vignettes but with a vertical orientation. Values for Nos. 3582 and Nos. 3583 are for stamps with images with either a horizontal or vertical orientation.

Josef Bican (1913-2001), Soccer Player — A1498

**Photo. & Engr.**

**2013, Sept. 18** *Perf. 11¼x11¾*
**3584** A1498 13k multi 1.25 .70

Horses From Chlumetz Stud Farm — A1499

Design: 13k, Kinsky horse. 17k, Palomino horse.

*Perf. 11¼x11¾*

**2013, Sept. 18** **Litho.**
**3585-3586** A1499 Set of 2 2.75 1.60

Cottage, Salajna — A1500

**2013, Oct. 2 Engr.** *Perf. 11¼x11¾*
**3587** A1500 29k green 2.60 1.60

Souvenir Sheet

Battle of Leipzig, 200th Anniv. — A1501

**Litho. & Engr.**

**2013, Oct. 2** *Perf. 11¾*
**3588** A1501 53k multi 5.50 3.00

Bible of Kralice, 400th Anniv. A1502

**2013, Oct. 16 Litho.** *Perf. 11¼*
**3589** A1502 17k multi 1.75 .85

Otto Wichterle (1912-98), Inventor of Soft Contact Lenses — A1503

**Photo. & Engr.**

**2013, Oct. 16** *Perf. 11¼x11¾*
**3590** A1503 21k multi 1.90 1.10

**Art Type of 1967 Inscribed "CESKA REPUBLIKA"**

Designs: 25k, A View of Roman Churches, by Giovanni Battista Piranesi, horiz. 30k, Still Life with the Author, by Bohuslav Reynek. 35k, Round Portrait, by Max Svabinsky.

**Engr., Litho & Engr. (30k)**

**2013, Nov. 27** *Perf. 11¾*
**3591-3593** A565 Set of 3 7.50 4.50

Ladislav Jirka (1914-86), Stamp Engraver — A1504

**2014, Jan. 20 Litho.** *Perf. 11¾x11¼*
**3594** A1504 13k multi 1.25 .65
*a.* Booklet pane of 8 + 4 labels 10.00 —
Complete booklet, #3594a 10.00

Tradition of Czech stamp production.

Dog and Four-Leaf Clover — A1505

**2014, Jan. 20 Litho.** *Perf. 11¼x11¾*
**3595** A1505 A multi + label 1.25 .65

No. 3595 was printed in sheets of 9 + 12 labels that could be personalized. On day of issue, No. 3595 had a franking value of 13k.

2014 Winter Olympics, Sochi, Russia — A1506

**2014, Feb. 5 Litho.** *Perf. 11¾x11¼*
**3596** A1506 25k multi 2.50 1.25

2014 Winter Paralympics, Sochi, Russia A1507

**2014, Feb. 5 Litho.** *Perf. 11¾x11¼*
**3597** A1507 13k multi 1.25 .70
*a.* Tête-bêche pair 2.50 1.40

Czech Firefighters, 150th Anniv. — A1508

**2014, Mar. 5 Litho.** *Perf. 11¾x11¼*
**3598** A1508 13k multi 1.25 .70

Transportation — A1509

No. 3599: a, Rapid, 1912 airplane of Eugen Cihák. b, Type R1 Prague Metro train.

**2014, Mar. 5 Litho.** *Perf. 11¾x11¼*
**3599** A1509 13k Pair, #a-b 2.25 1.40

Bohumil Hrabal (1914-97), Writer — A1510

**Photo. & Engr.**

**2014, Mar. 26** *Perf. 11¼x11¾*

**3600** A1510 17k blk & brn 1.75 .85

Cervená Lhota Castle — A1511

**2014, Mar. 26 Engr.** *Perf. 11¾*

**3601** A1511 17k multi 1.50 .85

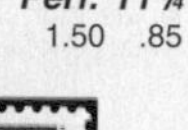

Zdenek Kopal (1914-93), Astronomer — A1512

*Perf. 11¾x11¼*

**2014, Mar. 26** **Litho.**

**3602** A1512 21k multi 2.10 1.10

Silesian Museum, Opava, 200th Anniv. — A1513

**Photo. & Engr.**

**2014, Apr. 30** *Perf. 11¼x11¾*

**3603** A1513 13k multi 1.25 .70

Bagpipes A1514

**Photo. & Engr.**

**2014, Apr. 30** *Perf. 11¼*

**3604** A1514 25k multi 2.10 1.25

Europa.

**Art in Prague Castle Type of 2012**

Design: 37k, Assembly of Olympian Gods, by Peter Paul Rubens.

**Litho. & Engr.**

**2014, May 28** *Perf. 11¾*

**3605** A1457 37k multi 3.75 1.90

No. 3605 was printed in sheets of 2. Value, $7.50.

Paper Mill, Velké Losiny A1515

**Photo. & Engr.**

**2014, May 28** *Perf. 11¾x11¼*

**3606** A1515 13k multi 1.25 .70

Animated Characters Ju and Hele — A1516

***Serpentine Die Cut 11 Syncopated***

**2014, May 28** **Litho.**

**Booklet Stamp Self-Adhesive**

**3607** A1516 A multi 1.25 .70
*a.* Booklet pane of 10 12.50

No. 3607 sold for 13k on day of issue.

Historic Methods of Transportation — A1517

No. 3608: a, Paddle steamer Franz Joseph I. b, 1936 Zbrojovka Brno Z4 automobile.

*Perf. 11¾x11¼*

**2014, June 11** **Litho.**

**3608** A1517 25k Horiz. pair, #a-b 4.50 2.50

Souvenir Sheet

World War I, Cent. — A1518

No. 3609: a, Soldier carrying rifle, mother holding child. b, Soldiers, people falling into pit.

**2014, June 11 Litho.** *Perf. 11¾*

**3609** A1518 29k Sheet of 2, #a-b, + 3 labels 5.00 3.00

**Antique Automobiles Type of 2012**

Designs: No. 3610, 1938 Skoda Popular Monte Carlo. No. 3611, 1941 Skoda Superb 3000.

***Serpentine Die Cut 11¼ Syncopated***

**2014, Sept. 3** **Litho.**

**Booklet Stamps Self-Adhesive**

**3610** A1467 A multi 1.10 .60
**3611** A1467 A multi 1.10 .60
*a.* Booklet pane of 8, 4 each #3610-3611 9.00

Nos. 3610-3611 each sold for 13k on day of issue.

Karel, Elder of Zierotín (1564-1636), Governor of Moravia — A1519

**Photo. & Engr.**

**2014, Sept. 3** *Perf. 11¾x11¼*

**3612** A1519 29k multi 2.50 1.40

Miniature Sheet

Flora and Fauna of the Beskid Mountains — A1520

No. 3613: a, 13k, Meles meles (44x27mm). b, 17k, Felis silvestris (44x27mm). c, 21k, Ursus arctos, Carabus variolosus (44x54mm). d, 25k, Nucifraga caryocatactes, Canis lupus (44x54mm).

**Litho. & Engr.**

**2014, Sept. 3** *Perf. 11¾*

**3613** A1520 Sheet of 4, #a-d, + 3 labels 7.00 3.50

Flower Bouquet in Wine Bottle — A1521

**2014, Oct. 15 Litho.** *Perf. 11¼x11¾*

**3614** A1521 A multi + label 1.25 .60

No. 3614 was printed in sheets of 9 + 12 labels that could be personalized. On day of issue No. 3614 had a franking value of 13k.

Souvenir Sheet

St. Vitus Cathedral, Prague, 670th Anniv. — A1522

**Litho. & Engr.**

**2014, Oct. 15** *Perf. 11¾*

**3615** A1522 58k multi 5.25 2.60

**Art Type of 1967 Inscribed "CESKA REPUBLIKA" and**

Solitude and Spectacles, Photograph by Jaromír Funke — A1523

Designs: 25k, Street in Winter, by Jakub Schikaneder. 37k, Leda Atomica, by Salvador Dalí.

**Engr., Litho. (29k)**

**2014, Nov. 5** *Perf. 11¾*

**3616** A565 25k multi 2.25 1.10
**3617** A1523 29k multi 2.60 1.40
**3618** A565 37k multi 3.50 1.75
*Nos. 3616-3618 (3)* 8.35 4.25

Historical Events of November 17 — A1524

**2014, Nov. 5 Litho.** *Perf. 11¼x11¾*

**3619** A1524 13k multi 1.25 .60

Nazi attack on Czech university students, 75th anniv.; start of Velvet Revolution, 25th anniv.

Andreas Vesalius (1514-64), Anatomist — A1525

**Photo. & Engr.**

**2014, Nov. 5** *Perf. 11¼x11¾*

**3620** A1525 25k multi 2.25 1.10

Bethlehem in Winter, by Josef Lada — A1526

**2014, Nov. 5 Litho.** *Perf. 11¾x11¼*

**3621** A1526 A multi 1.25 .60

Christmas. No. 3621 sold for 13k on day of issue.

A1527

Personalized Stamps A1528

***Serpentine Die Cut Syncopated***

**2014, Nov. 26** **Litho.**

**Self-Adhesive**

**3622** A1527 A multi 1.25 .60
**3623** A1528 Z multi 2.75 1.40

Nos. 3622-3623 were each printed in sheets of 25. Vignette portions of each stamp could be personalized. The generic vignettes of these stamps are shown. On day of issue, the franking value of No. 3622 was 13k; No. 3623, 30k.

Oldrich Kulhánek (1940-2013), Stamp Designer — A1529

**Photo. & Engr.**

**2015, Jan. 20** ***Perf. 11¾x11¼***

**3624** A1529 13k multi 1.20 .55
*a.* Booklet pane of 8 + 4 labels 9.50 —
Complete booklet, #3624a 9.50

Vitezslava Kaprálová (1915-40), Composer — A1530

**2015, Jan. 20** **Litho.** ***Perf. 11¾x11¼***

**3625** A1530 17k multi 1.40 .70

Military Aircraft and Vehicles — A1531

Designs: No. 3626, Supermarine Spitfire LF Mk IXE. No. 3627, T-34/76.2 tank. No. 3628, Harley-Davidson motorcycle. No. 3629, Jeep-Ford GPW.

***Serpentine Die Cut 11¼ Syncopated***

**2015, Jan. 20** **Litho.**

**Booklet Stamps**
**Self-Adhesive**

**3626** A1531 A multi 1.10 .55
**3627** A1531 A multi 1.10 .55
**3628** A1531 A multi 1.10 .55
**3629** A1531 A multi 1.10 .55
*a.* Booklet pane of 8, 2 each #3626-3629 9.00
*Nos. 3626-3629 (4)* 4.40 2.20

On day of issue, Nos. 3626-3629 each sold for 13k.

Cartoon Character Vecernícek, 50th Anniv. A1532

***Serpentine Die Cut 11 Syncopated***

**2015, Feb. 18** **Litho.**

**Self-Adhesive**

**3630** A1532 A multi 1.10 .55

No. 3630 sold for 13k on day of issue.

Plzen, 2015 European Capital of Culture A1533

**Photo. & Engr.**

**2015, Feb. 18** ***Perf. 11¼***

**3631** A1533 25k multi 2.00 1.00

Printed in sheets of 3, with 3 labels. Value, $9.50.

Historic Methods of Transportation — A1534

No. 3632: a, Walter 6B automobile. b, Monoplane of Metodej Vlach.

***Perf. 11¾x11¼***

**2015, Feb. 18** **Litho.**

**3632** A1534 13k Horiz. pair, #a-b 2.10 1.10

Easter — A1535

**2015, Mar. 4** **Litho.** ***Perf. 11¼x11¾***

**3633** A1535 A multi 1.10 .55

No. 3633 sold for 13k on day of issue.

Postmen on Geese Above Charles Bridge — A1536

**2015, Mar. 4** **Litho.** ***Perf. 11¼x11¾***

**3634** A1536 A multi + label 1.10 .55

No. 3633 has a franking value of 13k on day of issue and was printed in sheets of 9 + 12 labels that could be personalized.

Souvenir Sheet

The Last Supper, by Leonardo da Vinci — A1537

***Perf. 11¼x11¾***

**2015, Mar. 18** **Litho.**

**3635** A1537 25k multi 2.25 1.00

Expo 2015, Milan.

Church of St. Ignatius and Spejchar Gallery, Chomutov — A1538

**Photo. & Engr.**

**2015, Apr. 15** ***Perf. 11¼x11¾***

**3636** A1538 25k multi 2.10 2.10
*a.* Booklet pane of 8 + 4 labels 17.00 —
Complete booklet, #3636a 17.00

Sixth Czech and German Philatelic Exhibition, Chomutov.

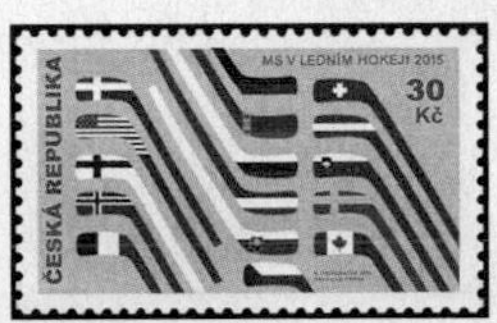


2015 Men's Ice Hockey World Championships, Czech Republic — A1539

**2015, Apr. 15** **Litho.** ***Perf. 11¾x11¼***

**3637** A1539 30k multi 2.50 1.25

Animated Film Characters Bob and Bobek A1540

Bob and Bobek: No. 3638, Playing ice hockey. No. 3639, Rowing raft.

***Serpentine Die Cut 11 Syncopated***

**2015, Apr. 29** **Litho.**

**Booklet Stamps**
**Self-Adhesive**

**3638** A1540 A multi 1.10 .55
**3639** A1540 A multi 1.10 .55
*a.* Booklet pane of 10, 5 each #3638-3639 11.00

Nos. 3638-3639 each sold for 13k on day of issue.

Moldava Railway, 130th Anniv. A1541

**2015, May 6** **Engr.** ***Perf. 11¾x11¼***

**3640** A1541 13k black 1.10 .55
*a.* Booklet pane of 8 + 4 labels 9.00 —
Complete booklet, #3640a 9.00

Europa A1542

**2015, May 6** **Litho.** ***Perf. 11¼***

**3641** A1542 25k multi 2.10 2.10

**Art in Prague Castle Type of 2012**

Design: 34k, Head of a Woman, by Hans von Aachen.

**2015, May 27** **Engr.** ***Perf. 11¾***

**3642** A1457 34k multi 3.00 1.40

Rabí Castle Ruins A1543

**2015, May 27** **Engr.** ***Perf. 11¾***

**3643** A1543 17k multi 1.50 .70

Jan Hus (c. 1370-1415), Church Reformer — A1544

***Perf. 11¼x11¾***

**2015, June 17** **Litho.**

**3644** A1544 13k multi 1.25 .55

**Antique Automobiles Type of 2012**

Illustrations by Václav Zapadlik: No. 3645, 1955 Skoda 1201. No. 3646, 1947 Skoda Rapid 1500.

***Serpentine Die Cut 11¼ Syncopated***

**2015, Sept. 2** **Litho.**

**Booklet Stamps**
**Self-Adhesive**

**3645** A1467 A multi 1.10 .55
**3646** A1467 A multi 1.10 .55
*a.* Booklet pane of 8, 4 each #3645-3646 9.00

Nos. 3645-3646 each sold for 13k on day of issue.

Sir Nicholas Winton (1909-2015), Rescuer of Jewish Children During World War II — A1545

**2015, Sept. 2** **Litho.** ***Perf. 11¾x11¼***

**3647** A1545 13k multi 1.25 .55

Postcrossing A1546

***Serpentine Die Cut 11¼ Syncopated***

**2015, Sept. 2** **Litho.**

**Self-Adhesive**

**3648** A1546 E multi 2.50 1.10

No. 3648 sold for 25k on day of issue.

Miniature Sheet

Owls — A1547

No. 3649: a, 13k, Athene noctua (27x44mm). b, 17k, Aegolius funereus (27x44mm). c, 21k, Nyctea scandiaca (27x44mm). d, 25k, Bubo bubo (44x54mm).

**Litho. & Engr.**

**2015, Sept. 2** *Perf. 11¾*
**3649** A1547 Sheet of 4, #a-d, + 4 labels 6.50 3.25

Historic Methods of Transportation — A1548

No. 3650: a, Tatra T3 tram, 1960s. b, Primátor Dittrich paddle steamer.

*Perf. 11¾x11¼*

**2015, Sept. 23** **Litho.**
**3650** A1548 25k Vert. pair, #a-b 4.25 2.10

Flag of Czech Republic A1549

***Serpentine Die Cut 11¼ on 1 Side Syncopated***

**2015, Oct. 14** **Litho.**

**Self-Adhesive**

**3651** A1549 A multi 1.25 .55

No. 3651 sold for 13k on day of issue.

Organ and Jakub Jan Ryba (1765-1815), Composer — A1550

**Photo. & Engr.**

**2015, Oct. 14** *Perf. 11¼x11¾*
**3652** A1550 13k multi 1.25 .55

Wedding of Oldrich and Bozena, Painting From Dalimil's Chronicle — A1551

**2015, Oct. 14 Litho.** *Perf. 11¾x11¼*
**3653** A1551 21k multi 2.00 .85

Souvenir Sheet

World War I, Cent. — A1552

No. 3654: a, Unveiling of statue of Jan Hus burning at the stake. b, Soldier carrying dying comrade.

**2015, Oct. 14** **Litho.** *Perf. 11¾*
**3654** A1552 27k Sheet of 2, #a-b, + 3 labels 4.50 2.25

Jan Opletal (1915-39), Medical Student Killed in Anti-Nazi Protests — A1553

**Photo. & Engr.**

**2015, Nov. 11** *Perf. 11¼x11¾*
**3655** A1553 13k blue & red 1.25 .55

**Art Type of 1967 Inscribed "CESKA REPUBLIKA"**

Designs: 27k, The Bride, book illustration by Antonín Strnadel. 30k, Sitting, by Bohumír Matal. 34k, Great Dialogue, sculpture by Karel Nepras, horiz.

**Engr., Litho. & Engr. (34k)**

**2015, Dec. 16** *Perf. 11¾*
**3656-3658** A565 Set of 3 8.00 3.75

Postman With Posthorn — A1554

*Perf. 11¼x11¾*

**2015, Dec. 16** **Litho.**
**3659** A1554 Z multi + label 2.60 1.25

No. 3659 was printed in sheets of 9 + 12 labels that could be personalized. On day of issue, No. 3659 had a franking value of 30k.

Karel Svolinsky (1896-1986), Stamp Designer — A1555

**2016, Jan. 20 Litho.** *Perf. 11¾x11¼*
**3660** A1555 13k multi 1.25 .55
*a.* Booklet pane of 8 + 4 labels 10.00 —
Complete booklet, #3660a 10.00

Tradition of Czech stamp production.

Jerome of Prague (c. 1378-1416), Church Reformer — A1556

**2016, Jan. 20 Litho.** *Perf. 11¾x11¼*
**3661** A1556 17k multi 1.60 .70

Czech Spotted Dogs — A1557

**2016, Feb. 3** **Litho.** *Perf. 12*
**3662** A1557 13k multi 1.25 .55

Transportation — A1558

No. 3663: a, Tatra rail coach M290.0. b, Paddle steamer Vysehrad.

*Perf. 11¾x11¼*

**2016, Feb. 17** **Litho.**
**3663** A1558 27k Pair, #a-b 5.00 2.25

Tomás Bat'a (1876-1932), Shoe Manufacturer A1559

**Photo. & Engr.**

**2016, Mar. 16** *Perf. 11¼x11¾*
**3664** A1559 13k black & red 1.25 .55

Petrín Observation Tower and Funicular, 125th Anniv. — A1560

**Photo. & Engr.**

**2016, Mar. 16** *Perf. 11¼x11¾*
**3665** A1560 13k redsh brn & cream 1.25 .55
*a.* Booklet pane of 8 + 4 labels 10.00 —
Complete booklet, #3665a 10.00

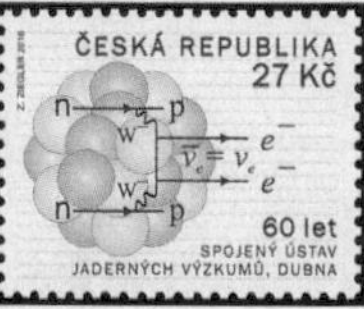

Joint Institute for Nuclear Research, Dubna, Russia, 60th Anniv. A1561

*Perf. 11¾x11¼*

**2016, Mar. 16** **Litho.**
**3666** A1561 27k multi 2.50 1.10

Buchlov Castle A1562

**2016, Apr. 6 Engr.** *Perf. 11½x11¾*
**3667** A1562 17k multi 1.50 .75

Czech and Slovak Philatelic Exhibition, Zd'ár nad Sázavou — A1563

**2016, Apr. 27 Litho.** *Perf. 11¼x11¾*
**3668** A1563 13k multi 1.25 .55
*a.* Booklet pane of 8 + 4 labels 10.00 —
Complete booklet, #3668a 10.00

Common Yellow Swallowtail Butterflies and Thistles A1564

**2016, Apr. 27** **Litho.** *Perf. 12*
**3669** A1564 16k multi 1.50 .70

Europa A1565

**2016, May 4 Litho.** *Perf. 11¾x11¼*
**3670** A1565 27k multi 2.50 1.10

Think Green Issue.
Printed in sheets of 8. Value, $20.

Souvenir Sheet

Holy Roman Emperor Charles IV (1316-78) — A1566

**Litho. & Engr.**

**2016, May 4** ***Perf. 11¾***
**3671** A1566 54k multi + 2 labels 5.00 2.25

No. 3671 was issued on May 4 with the incorrectly-spelled Latin inscription "Karolus Quatrus" in the sheet margin. Value, $90. The sheet was withdrawn from sale on May 5, and replaced soon thereafter with sheets bearing the correct inscription "Karolus Quartus."

Animated Cartoon Character Amálka the Fairy — A1567

***Serpentine Die Cut 11¼ Syncopated***
**2016, May 18** **Litho.**

**Booklet Stamp Self-Adhesive**

**3672** A1567 A multi 1.50 .70
*a.* Booklet pane of 10 15.00

No. 3672 sold for 16k on day of issue.

Premiere of *The Bartered Bride,* by Bedrich Smetana, 150th Anniv. — A1567a

**2016, May 18 Litho. *Perf. 11¼x11¾***
**3673** A1567a 16k multi 1.50 .70

**Art in Prague Castle Type of 2012**

Design: 38k, Prague Altarpiece detail depicting St. Barbara, by Lucas Cranach the Elder.

**2016, May 18 Engr. *Perf. 11¾***
**3674** A1457 38k multi 3.25 1.60

Flower Arrangement A1568

**2016, June 8 Litho. *Perf. 11¾x11¼***
**3675** A1568 A multi + label 1.40 .70

No. 3675 was printed in sheets of 9 + 12 labels that could be personalized. On day of issue, No. 3675 had a franking value of 16k.

International Folklore Festival, Stráznice — A1569

**Photo. & Engr.**

**2016, June 22** ***Perf. 11¼x11¾***
**3676** A1569 20k multi 1.75 .85

Jan Jessenius (1566-1621), Physician and Professor of Anatomy — A1570

**Photo. & Engr.**

**2016, June 22** ***Perf. 11¼x11¾***
**3677** A1570 27k multi + label 2.50 1.10

See Hungary No. 4393, Poland No. 4232, Slovakia No. 743.

2016 Summer Olympics, Rio de Janeiro — A1571

***Perf. 11¾x11¼***

**2016, June 22** **Litho.**
**3678** A1571 32k multi 3.00 1.40

2016 Summer Paralympics, Rio de Janeiro — A1572

***Perf. 11¾x11¼***

**2016, June 22** **Litho.**
**3679** A1572 16k multi 1.50 .70

**Art Type of 1967 Inscribed "CESKA REPUBLIKA"**

Design: Young Woman on a Balcony, by Gerrit Dou.

**2016, Sept. 7 Engr. *Perf. 11¾***
**3680** A565 27k multi 2.50 1.10

See Liechtenstein No. 1691.

Tree Frog — A1573

**2016, Sept. 7 Litho. *Perf. 11¾x11¼***
**3681** A1573 A multi 1.50 .70

No. 3681 sold for 16k on day of issue.

Dr. Antonín Holy (1936-2012), Developer of Antiretroviral Drugs — A1574

**2016, Sept. 7 Litho. *Perf. 11¼x11¾***
**3682** A1574 20k multi 2.00 .85

UNESCO World Heritage Sites in Czech Republic — A1575

Designs: 16k, Lednice-Valtice Cultural Landscape. 27k, Historic Center of Prague.

**2016, Sept. 7 Litho. *Perf. 11¼x11¾***
**3683-3684** A1575 Set of 2 4.00 1.90

See United Nations Nos. 1142, 1144a, 1144e; Offices in Geneva Nos. 626, 627a, 627e; Offices in Vienna Nos. 594a, 594e.

Miniature Sheet

Animals in Czech Republic Zoos — A1576

No. 3685: a, 16k, Panthera uncia, Jihlava Zoo. b, 20k, Oryx gazella gazella, Panthera leo leo, Olomouc Zoo. c, 24k, Diceros bicornis, Lycaon pictus, Dvur Králové Zoo. d, 27k, Equus przewalskii, Prague Zoo.

**Litho. & Engr.**

**2016, Sept. 7** ***Perf. 11¾***
**3685** A1576 Sheet of 4, #a-d, + 3 labels 8.00 3.75

Historic Methods of Transportation — A1577

No. 3686: a, Tatra 87 automobile. b, Aero Ab-11 biplane.

***Perf. 11¾x11¼***

**2016, Sept. 21** **Litho.**
**3686** A1577 16k Horiz. pair, #a-b 3.00 1.40

Zelezné Hory Protected Landscape Area, 25th Anniv. — A1578

**2016, Oct. 12 Litho. *Perf. 11¾x11¼***
**3687** A1578 16k multi 1.50 .70

Bee-eaters — A1579

**2016, Oct. 12 Litho. *Perf. 11¾x11¼***
**3688** A1579 20k multi 2.00 .85

Souvenir Sheet

Fight for Czech Statehood — A1580

No. 3689: a, St. Wenceslas, King Ottokar II of Bohemia, Holy Roman Emperor Charles IV, flags, soldiers. b, Grieving widow and children, Austrian imperial eagle.

**2016, Oct. 12 Litho. *Perf. 11¾***
**3689** A1580 27k Sheet of 2, #a-b, + 3 labels 5.00 2.25

**Art Type of 1967 Inscribed "CESKA REPUBLIKA"**

Designs: 27k, Two Women, by Jaroslav Král, horiz. 30k, Girl with Absinthe, sculpture by Bedrich Stefan. 38k, Clown with Monkey, by Frantisek Tichy.

**2016, Nov. 9 Litho. *Perf. 11¾***
**3690-3692** A565 Set of 3 8.50 3.75

United Nations Educational, Scientific and Cultural Organization, 70th Anniv. — A1581

**2016, Nov. 9 Litho. *Perf. 12***
**3693** A1581 32k multi 2.90 1.40

Oldrich Posmurny (1942-2010), Stamp Designer — A1582

**Photo. & Engr.**

**2017, Jan. 20 *Perf. 11¼x11¾***
**3694** A1582 16k multi 1.50 .70
*a.* Booklet pane of 8 + 4 labels 12.00 —
Complete booklet, #3694a 12.00

Tradition of Czech stamp production.

Czech Crown Jewels — A1583

***Serpentine Die Cut 11½ Syncopated***
**2017, Jan. 20 Litho.**
**Booklet Stamp**
**Self-Adhesive**
**3695** A1583 E multi 2.90 1.40
*a.* Booklet pane of 8 24.00

No. 3695 sold for 32k on day of issue.

Historic Methods of Transportation — A1584

Designs: No. 3696a, Skoda 606DNd postal bus. No. 3696b, Fk-5-1401 railroad mail car. No. 3697, Paddle steamer "Prague." 32k, Aero A-14 biplane.

**2017 Litho. *Perf. 11¾x11¼***
**3696** A1584 16k Horiz. pair, #a-b 3.00 1.25
**3697** A1584 16k multi 1.50 .65
**3698** A1584 32k multi 3.00 1.40
*Nos. 3696-3698 (3)* 7.50 3.30

Issued: No. 3696, 2/15; No. 3697, 3/8; No. 3698, 1/20.

Straka Academy, 120th Anniv. — A1585

**2017, Mar. 8 Litho. *Perf. 11¾x11¼***
**3699** A1585 24k multi 2.25 .95

Porta Bohemica River Valley — A1586

**2017, Apr. 5 Engr. *Perf. 11¾***
**3700** A1586 20k multi 1.75 .85

Prague Airport, 80th Anniv. A1587

**Photo. & Engr.**

**2017, Apr. 5 *Perf. 11¾x11¼***
**3701** A1587 32k multi 2.60 1.40

Vera Cáslavská (1942-2016), Gymnast and President of Czech Olympic Committee A1588

**2017, May 3 Litho. *Perf. 11¼x11¾***
**3702** A1588 16k multi 1.40 .70

Frydlant Castle A1589

**Photo. & Engr.**

**2017, May 3 *Perf. 11¼***
**3703** A1589 32k multi 2.75 1.40

Europa.

Holy Roman Empress Maria Theresa (1717-80) — A1590

**Photo. & Engr.**

**2017, May 3 *Perf. 11¾***
**3704** A1590 32k multi 2.75 1.40

**Art in Prague Castle Type of 2012**

No. 3705 — St. Catherine with Angel, by Paolo Veronese: a, Black image. b, Multicolored image.

**2017, May 17 Engr. *Perf. 11¾***
**3705** A1457 32k Horiz. pair, #a-b 5.50 2.75

Printed in sheets containing two each of Nos. 3705a-3705b + central label.

Souvenir Sheet

Operation Anthropoid (Assassination of Reinhard Heydrich), 75th Anniv. — A1591

**Litho. & Engr.**

**2017, May 17 *Perf. 11¾***
**3706** A1591 46k multi + 7 labels 4.00 2.00

Josef Kainar (1917-71), Writer — A1592

**Photo. & Engr.**

**2017, June 7 *Perf. 11¼x11¾***
**3707** A1592 16k multi 1.40 .70

Heliodor Píka (1897-1949), General Executed by Communists A1593

**Photo. & Engr.**

**2017, June 7 *Perf. 11¼x11¾***
**3708** A1593 37k multi 3.25 1.60

Joze Plecnik (1872-1957), Architect — A1594

***Perf. 11½x11¾***
**2017, June 7 Litho. & Engr.**
**3709** A1594 32k multi 2.75 1.40

No. 3709 was printed in sheets of 2 + central label.

Locomotives — A1595

Designs: No. 3710, Steam locomotive No. 7. No. 3711, Cog locomotive "The Austrian."

***Serpentine Die Cut11½ Syncopated***
**2017, June 7 Litho.**
**Booklet Stamps**
**Self-Adhesive**
**3710** A1595 A multi 1.40 .70
**3711** A1595 A multi 1.40 .70
*a.* Booklet pane of 8, 4 each #3710-3711 11.50

On day of issue, Nos. 3710-3711 each sold for 16k.

Prague Pneumatic Mail System A1596

**2017, June 21 Litho. *Perf. 11¼***
**3712** A1596 A multi 1.40 .70

No. 3712 sold for 16k on day of issue.

Church of the Assumption of Our Lady, Most, 500th Anniv. — A1597

**Photo. & Engr.**

**2017, June 21 *Perf. 11¼x11¾***
**3713** A1597 16k multi 1.40 .70

Moravian Museum, Brno, 200th Anniv. A1598

**Photo. & Engr.**

**2017, June 21 *Perf. 11¾x11¼***
**3714** A1598 20k multi 1.75 .85

Gas Street Lighting in Prague, 170th Anniv. — A1599

**Photo. & Engr.**

**2017, Sept. 6 *Perf. 11¼x11¾***
**3715** A1599 16k multi 1.50 .75
*a.* Booklet pane of 8 + 4 labels 12.00 —
Complete booklet, #3715a 12.00

Josef Balabán (1894-1941), Václav Morávek (1904-42), and Josef Masín (1896-1942), Members of "Three Kings" Anti-Nazi Resistance Group — A1600

**2017, Sept. 6 Litho.** ***Perf. 11¾x11¼***
**3716** A1600 16k multi 1.50 .75

Mauritius No. 2 — A1601

**2017, Sept. 6 Litho.** ***Perf. 12***
**3717** A1601 A multi 1.50 .75

No. 3717 sold for 16k on day of issue.

Worker for Partner Post Office — A1602

**2017, Sept. 6 Litho.** ***Perf. 11¾x11¼***
**3718** A1602 A multi 1.50 .75
Complete booklet, 5 #3718 7.50

No. 3718 sold for 16k on day of issue.

Miniature Sheet

Animals in Czech Republic Zoos — A1603

No. 3719: a, 16k, Bison bonasus, Chomutov Zoo. b, 20k, Pan troglodytes, Panthera leo krugeri, Hodonín Zoo. c, 24k, Ursus maritimus, Brno Zoo. d, 30k, Rhinoceros unicornis, Varanus macraei, Plzen Zoo.

**Litho. & Engr.**

**2017, Sept. 6** ***Perf. 11¾***
**3719** A1603 Sheet of 4, #a-d, + 4 labels 8.25 4.25

Nature Protection.

Václav Hollar Association of Czech Graphic Artists, Cent. — A1604

**Photo. & Engr.**

**2017, Sept. 20** ***Perf. 11¼x11¾***
**3720** A1604 20k multi 1.90 .95

Imperial Austrian Letter Boxes, 200th Anniv. — A1605

**Photo. & Engr.**

**2017, Oct. 4** ***Perf. 11¼x11¾***
**3721** A1605 16k multi 1.50 .75
*a.* Booklet pane of 8 + 4 labels 12.00 —
Complete booklet, #3721a 12.00

Family on Bicycle A1606

**Photo. & Engr.**

**2017, Oct. 4** ***Perf. 11½x11¼***
**3722** A1606 16k blk & red 1.50 .75

Self-Sculpture of Fictional Character Jára Cimrman, 50th Anniv. — A1607

***Serpentine Die Cut 11¼ Syncopated***
**2017, Oct. 4 Litho.**

**Booklet Stamp Self-Adhesive**

**3723** A1607 A multi 1.50 .75
*a.* Booklet pane of 8 12.00

Jára Cimrman, fictional character created for 1967 Czech radio program, selected as "Greatest Czech" in 2005. No. 3723 sold for 16k on day of issue.

Souvenir Sheet

Fight for Czech Statehood — A1608

No. 3724: a, Soldiers, flag, independence leaders Milan R. Stefánik (1880-1919), Tomás G. Masaryk (1850-1937), and Jan Syrovy (1880-1970). b, Writers Alois Jirásek (1851-1930), and Jaroslav Kvapil (1868-1950) and Manifesto of Czech Writers.

**Litho., Sheet Margin Litho. With Foil Application**

**2017, Oct. 4** ***Perf. 11¾***
**3724** A1608 30k Sheet of 2, #a-b, + 3 labels 5.50 2.75

Tatra Automobile at Railroad Crossing A1609

**2017, Oct. 18 Litho.** ***Perf. 11¾x11½***
**3725** A1609 A multi + label 1.50 .75

No. 3725 was printed in sheets of 9 + 12 labels that could be personalized. On day of issue No. 3725 had a franking value of 16k.

**Art Type of 1967 Inscribed "CESKA REPUBLIKA"**

Designs: 32k, Cuddled, photograph by Taras Kuscynskyj. 38k, Tempter, painting by Norbert Grund.

**Litho. (32k), Engr. (38k)**

**2017, Nov. 8** ***Perf. 11¾***
**3726-3727** A565 Set of 2 6.50 3.25

Czech Astronomical Society, Cent. — A1610

**2017, Nov. 8 Litho.** ***Perf. 11¼x11¾***
**3728** A1610 16k multi 1.50 .75

## SEMI-POSTAL STAMPS

Nos. B1-B123 were sold at 1½ times face value at the Philatelists' Window of the Prague P.O. for charity benefit. They were available for ordinary postage.

Almost all stamps between Nos. B1-B123 are known with misplaced or inverted overprints and/or in pairs with one stamp missing the overprint.

The overprints of Nos. B1-B123 have been well forged.

Austrian Stamps of 1916-18 Overprinted in Black or Blue — a

Two sizes of type A40:
Type I: 25x30mm.
Type II: 26x29mm.

**1919** ***Perf. 12½***

| | | | | |
|---|---|---|---|---|
| **B1** | A37 | 3h brt violet | .25 | *.25* |
| **B2** | A37 | 5h lt green | .25 | *.25* |
| **B3** | A37 | 6h dp orange (Bl) | .50 | *.70* |
| **B4** | A37 | 6h dp orange (Bk) | *1,700.* | *1,400.* |
| **B5** | A37 | 10h magenta | 1.00 | *.85* |
| **B6** | A37 | 12h lt blue | .70 | .70 |
| **B7** | A42 | 15h dull red | .35 | *.35* |
| **B8** | A42 | 20h dark green | .35 | *.35* |
| *a.* | | 20h green | 55.00 | 40.00 |
| **B9** | A42 | 25h blue | .30 | .25 |
| **B10** | A42 | 30h dull violet | .30 | .25 |
| **B11** | A39 | 40h olive grn | .35 | .35 |
| **B12** | A39 | 50h dk green | .35 | .35 |
| **B13** | A39 | 60h dp blue | .35 | .35 |
| **B14** | A39 | 80h orange brn | .35 | .35 |
| **B15** | A39 | 90h red violet | .70 | .70 |
| **B16** | A39 | 1k car, *yel* (Bl) | .50 | .50 |
| **B17** | A39 | 1k car, *yel* (Bk) | 52.50 | 52.50 |
| **B18** | A40 | 2k light blue (I) | 3.00 | 3.00 |
| *a.* | | 2k dark blue (II) | *3,000.* | *2,000.* |
| **B19** | A40 | 3k car rose (I) | 32.50 | 32.50 |
| *a.* | | 3k claret (I) | 2,500. | 900.00 |
| **B20** | A40 | 4k yellow grn (I) | 27.50 | 21.00 |
| *a.* | | 4k deep green (I) | 55.00 | 45.00 |
| **B21** | A40 | 10k violet | 300.00 | 160.00 |
| *a.* | | 10k deep violet | 375.00 | 275.00 |
| *b.* | | 10k black violet | 450.00 | 300.00 |

The used value of No. B18a is for a stamp that has only a Czechoslovakian cancellation. Some examples of Austria No. 160, which were officially overprinted with type "a" and sold by the post office, had previously been used and lightly canceled with Austrian cancellations. These canceled-before-overprinting stamps, which were postally valid, sell for about one-fourth as much.

**Granite Paper**

| | | | | |
|---|---|---|---|---|
| **B22** | A40 | 2k light blue | 3.50 | 2.50 |
| **B23** | A40 | 3k carmine rose | 9.00 | 7.00 |

The 4k and 10k on granite paper with this overprint were not regularly issued.

Excellent counterfeits of Nos. B1-B23 exist.

Austrian Newspaper Stamps Overprinted — b

***Imperf***

**On Stamp of 1908**

| | | | | |
|---|---|---|---|---|
| **B26** | N8 | 10h carmine | *3,500.* | 2,000. |

**On Stamps of 1916**

| | | | | |
|---|---|---|---|---|
| **B27** | N9 | 2h brown | .25 | .25 |
| **B28** | N9 | 4h green | .35 | .35 |
| **B29** | N9 | 6h deep blue | .35 | .35 |
| **B30** | N9 | 10h orange | 4.25 | 4.25 |
| **B31** | N9 | 30h claret | 1.40 | 1.40 |
| | | *Nos. B27-B31 (5)* | 6.60 | 6.60 |

Austrian Special Handling Stamps Overprinted in Blue or Black — c

***Perf. 12½***

***Stamps of 1916 Overprinted***

| | | | | |
|---|---|---|---|---|
| **B32** | SH1 | 2h claret, *yel* (Bl) | 25.00 | 25.00 |
| **B33** | SH1 | 5h dp grn, *yel* (Bk) | *800.00* | *700.00* |

Stamps of 1917 Overprinted — d

| | | | | |
|---|---|---|---|---|
| **B34** | SH2 | 2h cl, *yel* (Bl) | .25 | *.35* |
| *a.* | | Vert. pair, imperf. btwn. | *250.00* | |
| **B35** | SH2 | 2h cl, *yel* (Bk) | 35.00 | 32.50 |
| **B36** | SH2 | 5h grn, *yel* (Bk) | .25 | .25 |

**Austrian Air Post Stamps, #C1-C3, Overprinted Type "c" Diagonally**

| | | | | |
|---|---|---|---|---|
| **B37** | A40 | 1.50k on 2k lil | 90.00 | 70.00 |
| **B38** | A40 | 2.50k on 3k ocher | 110.00 | 90.00 |
| **B39** | A40 | 4k gray | *800.00* | *650.00* |

**1919**

**Austrian Postage Due Stamps of 1908-13 Overprinted Type "b"**

| | | | | |
|---|---|---|---|---|
| **B40** | D3 | 2h carmine | *4,500.* | *2,750.* |
| **B41** | D3 | 4h carmine | 17.50 | 17.50 |
| **B42** | D3 | 5h carmine | 10.50 | 9.00 |
| **B43** | D3 | 14h carmine | 35.00 | 32.50 |
| **B44** | D3 | 25h carmine | 30.00 | 30.00 |
| **B45** | D3 | 30h carmine | 325.00 | 250.00 |
| **B46** | D3 | 50h carmine | *650.00* | *650.00* |

**Austria Nos. J49-J56 Overprinted Type "b"**

| | | | | |
|---|---|---|---|---|
| **B47** | D4 | 5h rose red | .25 | *.30* |
| **B48** | D4 | 10h rose red | .25 | *.30* |
| **B49** | D4 | 15h rose red | .25 | *.30* |
| **B50** | D4 | 20h rose red | 1.75 | 1.75 |
| **B51** | D4 | 25h rose red | 1.75 | 1.75 |

| | | | | |
|---|---|---|---|---|
| **B52** | D4 | 30h rose red | .60 | .60 |
| **B53** | D4 | 40h rose red | 1.75 | 1.75 |
| **B54** | D4 | 50h rose red | *300.00* | 250.00 |

### Austria Nos. J57-J59 Overprinted Type "a"

| | | | | |
|---|---|---|---|---|
| **B55** | D5 | 1k ultra | 10.50 | 9.00 |
| **B56** | D5 | 5k ultra | 21.00 | 21.00 |
| **B57** | D5 | 10k ultra | 225.00 | 200.00 |

### Austria Nos. J47-J48, J60-J63 Overprinted Type "c" Diagonally

| | | | | |
|---|---|---|---|---|
| **B58** | A22 | 1h gray | 20.00 | 16.00 |
| **B59** | A23 | 15h on 2h vio | 95.00 | 90.00 |
| **B60** | A38 | 10h on 24h blue | 80.00 | 70.00 |
| **B61** | A38 | 15h on 36h vio | .35 | .35 |
| **B62** | A38 | 20h on 54h org | 70.00 | 65.00 |
| **B63** | A38 | 50h on 42h choc | .75 | .75 |

### Hungarian Stamps Ovptd. Type "b"

**1919 Wmk. 137 *Perf. 15***

**On Stamps of 1913-16**

| | | | | |
|---|---|---|---|---|
| **B64** | A4 | 1f slate | *2,200.* | *1,800.* |
| **B65** | A4 | 2f yellow | 5.25 | 4.50 |
| **B66** | A4 | 3f orange | 32.50 | 25.00 |
| **B67** | A4 | 6f olive green | 5.00 | 5.00 |
| **B68** | A4 | 50f lake, *bl* | .90 | .75 |
| **B69** | A4 | 60f grn, *sal* | 45.00 | 35.00 |
| **B70** | A4 | 70f red brn, *grn* | *2,250.* | *1,750.* |

**On Stamps of 1916**

| | | | | |
|---|---|---|---|---|
| **B71** | A8 | 10f rose | 300.00 | 225.00 |
| **B72** | A8 | 15f violet | 150.00 | 100.00 |

**On Stamps of 1916-18**

| | | | | |
|---|---|---|---|---|
| **B73** | A9 | 2f brown orange | .25 | .25 |
| **B74** | A9 | 3f red lilac | .25 | .25 |
| **B75** | A9 | 5f green | .25 | .25 |
| **B76** | A9 | 6f grnsh blue | .50 | .50 |
| **B77** | A9 | 10f rose red | 1.40 | 1.00 |
| **B78** | A9 | 15f violet | .25 | .25 |
| **B79** | A9 | 20f gray brown | 12.00 | 11.00 |
| **B80** | A9 | 25f dull blue | .90 | .70 |
| **B81** | A9 | 35f brown | 9.00 | 9.00 |
| **B82** | A9 | 40f olive green | 3.00 | 2.25 |

**Overprinted Type "d"**

| | | | | |
|---|---|---|---|---|
| **B83** | A10 | 50f red vio & lil | 1.10 | *1.40* |
| **B84** | A10 | 75f brt bl & pale bl | 1.10 | *1.40* |
| **B85** | A10 | 80f yel grn & pale grn | 1.10 | *1.40* |
| **B86** | A10 | 1k red brn & cl | 2.10 | 2.00 |
| **B87** | A10 | 2k ol brn & bis | 9.00 | 9.00 |
| **B88** | A10 | 3k dk vio & ind | 37.50 | 35.00 |
| **B89** | A10 | 5k dk brn & lt brn | 90.00 | 60.00 |
| **B90** | A10 | 10k vio brn & vio | *1,300.* | 800.00 |

**Overprinted Type "b"**

**On Stamps of 1918**

| | | | | |
|---|---|---|---|---|
| **B91** | A11 | 10f scarlet | .25 | .25 |
| **B92** | A11 | 20f dark brown | .30 | .30 |
| **B93** | A11 | 25f deep blue | 1.10 | .75 |
| **B94** | A12 | 40f olive grn | 3.50 | 2.75 |
| **B95** | A12 | 50f lilac | 30.00 | 22.50 |

**On Stamps of 1919**

| | | | | |
|---|---|---|---|---|
| **B96** | A13 | 10f red | 9.00 | 7.00 |
| **B97** | A13 | 20f dk brn | *6,500.* | *4,500.* |

### Same Overprint On Hungarian Newspaper Stamp of 1914

***Imperf***

| | | | | |
|---|---|---|---|---|
| **B98** | N5 | (2f) orange | .25 | *.25* |

### Same Overprint On Hungarian Special Delivery Stamp

***Perf. 15***

| | | | | |
|---|---|---|---|---|
| **B99** | SD1 | 2f gray grn & red | .25 | *.25* |

### Same Ovpt. On Hungarian Semi-Postal Stamps

| | | | | |
|---|---|---|---|---|
| **B100** | SP3 | 10f + 2f rose red | .70 | .70 |
| **B101** | SP4 | 15f + 2f violet | 1.10 | 1.10 |
| **B102** | SP5 | 40f + 2f brn car | 3.50 | 3.50 |
| | | *Nos. B98-B102 (5)* | 5.80 | 5.80 |

### Hungarian Postage Due Stamps of 1903-18 Overprinted Type "b"

**1919 Wmk. 135 *Perf. 11½, 12***

| | | | | |
|---|---|---|---|---|
| **B103** | D1 | 50f green & black | *350.00* | *300.00* |

### Wmk. Crown (136, 136a)

***Perf. 11½x12, 15***

| | | | | |
|---|---|---|---|---|
| **B104** | D1 | 1f green & black | *1,200.* | *1,000.* |
| **B105** | D1 | 2f green & black | *750.00* | *650.00* |
| **B106** | D1 | 12f green & black | *4,250.* | *3,500.* |
| **B107** | D1 | 50f green & black | 275. | 150. |

### Wmk. Double Cross (137)

***Perf. 15***

**On Stamps of 1914**

| | | | | |
|---|---|---|---|---|
| **B110** | D1 | 1f green & black | 1,250. | 600. |
| **B111** | D1 | 2f green & black | 700. | 550. |
| **B112** | D1 | 5f green & black | 1,325. | 900. |
| **B113** | D1 | 12f green & black | *5,250.* | *4,000.* |
| **B114** | D1 | 50f green & black | 275. | 150. |

**On Stamps of 1915-18**

| | | | | |
|---|---|---|---|---|
| **B115** | D1 | 1f green & red | 125.00 | 100.00 |
| **B116** | D1 | 2f green & red | .75 | .75 |
| **B117** | D1 | 5f green & red | 12.50 | 10.00 |
| **B118** | D1 | 6f green & red | 2.00 | 2.00 |
| **B119** | D1 | 10f green & red | .50 | .50 |
| *a.* | | Pair, one without overprint | | |
| **B120** | D1 | 12f green & red | 2.00 | 2.00 |
| **B121** | D1 | 15f green & red | 5.00 | 4.50 |
| **B122** | D1 | 20f green & red | 1.25 | 1.25 |
| **B123** | D1 | 30f green & red | 40.00 | 35.00 |
| | | *Nos. B115-B123 (9)* | 189.00 | 156.00 |

**Excellent counterfeits of Nos. B1-B123 exist.**

Bohemian Lion Breaking its Chains — SP1

Mother and Child — SP2

***Perf. 11½, 13¾ and Compound***

**1919 Typo. Unwmk.**

**Pinkish Paper**

| | | | | |
|---|---|---|---|---|
| **B124** | SP1 | 15h gray green | .25 | .25 |
| *a.* | | 15h light green | 32.50 | 25.00 |
| **B125** | SP1 | 25h dark brown | .25 | .25 |
| *a.* | | 25h light brown | *5.00* | 4.00 |
| **B126** | SP1 | 50h dark blue | .25 | .25 |

**Photo.**

**Yellowish Paper**

| | | | | |
|---|---|---|---|---|
| **B127** | SP2 | 75h slate | .25 | .25 |
| **B128** | SP2 | 100h brn vio | .25 | .25 |
| **B129** | SP2 | 120h vio, *yel* | .25 | .25 |
| | | *Nos. B124-B129 (6)* | 1.50 | 1.50 |

Values are for perf 13¾. Other perfs are valued higher.

Nos. B124-B126 commemorate the 1st anniv. of Czechoslovak independence. Nos. B127-B129 were sold for the benefit of Legionnaires' orphans. Imperforates exist.

See No. 1581.

### Regular Issues of Czechoslovakia Surcharged in Red

a

b

**1920 *Perf. 13¾***

| | | | | |
|---|---|---|---|---|
| **B130** | A1(a) | 40h + 20h bister | .60 | *.75* |
| **B131** | A2(a) | 60h + 20h green | .60 | *.75* |
| **B132** | A4(b) | 125h + 25h gray bl | 2.75 | *2.25* |
| | | *Nos. B130-B132 (3)* | 3.95 | *3.75* |
| | | Set, never hinged | 8.00 | |

President Masaryk — SP3

### Wmk. Linden Leaves (107)

**1923 Engr. *Perf. 13¾x14¾***

| | | | | |
|---|---|---|---|---|
| **B133** | SP3 | 50h gray green | .60 | .40 |
| **B134** | SP3 | 100h carmine | 1.10 | .75 |
| **B135** | SP3 | 200h blue | 3.25 | 2.50 |
| **B136** | SP3 | 300h dark brown | 3.25 | 3.50 |
| | | *Nos. B133-B136 (4)* | 8.20 | 7.15 |
| | | Set, never hinged | 15.00 | |

5th anniv. of the Republic.

The gum was applied through a screen and shows the monogram "CSP" (Ceskoslovenska Posta). These stamps were sold at double their face values, the excess being given to the Red Cross and other charitable organizations.

### International Olympic Congress Issue

Semi-Postal Stamps of 1923 Overprinted in Blue or Red

**1925**

| | | | | |
|---|---|---|---|---|
| **B137** | SP3 | 50h gray green | 5.50 | 7.50 |
| **B138** | SP3 | 100h carmine | 7.00 | 12.00 |
| **B139** | SP3 | 200h blue (R) | 35.00 | 45.00 |
| | | *Nos. B137-B139 (3)* | 47.50 | 64.50 |
| | | Set, never hinged | 120.00 | |

These stamps were sold at double their face values, the excess being divided between a fund for post office clerks and the Olympic Games Committee.

### Sokol Issue

Semi-Postal Stamps of 1923 Overprinted in Blue or Red

**1926**

| | | | | |
|---|---|---|---|---|
| **B140** | SP3 | 50h gray green | 1.60 | *4.00* |
| **B141** | SP3 | 100h carmine | 3.25 | *4.00* |
| **B142** | SP3 | 200h blue (R) | 10.00 | 11.00 |
| *a.* | | Double overprint | | |
| **B143** | SP3 | 300h dk brn (R) | 20.00 | 15.00 |
| | | *Nos. B140-B143 (4)* | 34.85 | 34.00 |
| | | Set, never hinged | 100.00 | |

These stamps were sold at double their face values, the excess being given to the Congress of Sokols, June, 1926.

**Catalogue values for unused stamps in this section, from this point to the end of the section, are for Never Hinged items.**

Midwife Presenting Newborn Child to its Father; after a Painting by Josef Manes

SP4 SP5

**1936 Unwmk. Engr. *Perf. 12½***

| | | | | |
|---|---|---|---|---|
| **B144** | SP4 | 50h + 50h green | .35 | .35 |
| **B145** | SP5 | 1k + 50h claret | .70 | .50 |
| **B146** | SP4 | 2k + 50h blue | 1.75 | 1.00 |
| | | *Nos. B144-B146 (3)* | 2.80 | 1.85 |

Nos. B144-B146 were each issued in sheets of 100 with 12 labels. Value, set $40.

SP6

"Lullaby" by Stanislav Sucharda SP7

**1937 *Perf. 12½***

| | | | | |
|---|---|---|---|---|
| **B147** | SP6 | 50h + 50h dull green | .35 | .25 |
| **B148** | SP6 | 1k + 50h rose lake | .70 | .50 |
| **B149** | SP7 | 2k + 1k dull blue | 1.75 | 1.00 |
| | | *Nos. B147-B149 (3)* | 2.80 | 1.75 |

Nos. B147-B149 were each issued in sheets of 100 with 12 labels. Value, set of singles with attached labels hinged mint $5; used $5.

President Masaryk and Little Girl in Native Costume — SP8

**1938 *Perf. 12½***

| | | | | |
|---|---|---|---|---|
| **B150** | SP8 | 50h + 50h deep green | .55 | .45 |
| **B151** | SP8 | 1k + 50h rose lake | .70 | .55 |

**Souvenir Sheet**

***Imperf***

| | | | | |
|---|---|---|---|---|
| **B152** | SP8 | 2k + 3k black | 4.25 | 5.00 |

88th anniv. of the birth of Masaryk (1850-1937).

Nos. B150-B151 were each issued in sheets of 100 stamps and 12 blank labels. Value, set of singles with attached labels: mint $4; used $3.

### Allegory of the Republic Type

**Souvenir Sheet**

**1938 *Perf. 12½***

| | | | | |
|---|---|---|---|---|
| **B153** | A89 | 2k (+ 8k) dark blue | 3.00 | 3.50 |

The surtax was devoted to national relief for refugees.

"Republic" and Congress Emblem — SP10

**1945 Engr.**

| | | | | |
|---|---|---|---|---|
| **B154** | SP10 | 1.50k + 1.50k car rose | .25 | .25 |
| **B155** | SP10 | 2.50k + 2.50k blue | .25 | .25 |

Students' World Cong., Prague, 11/17/45.

St. George Slaying the Dragon — SP11

**1946**

| | | | | |
|---|---|---|---|---|
| **B156** | SP11 | 2.40k + 2.60k car rose | .25 | .25 |
| **B157** | SP11 | 4k + 6k blue | .25 | .25 |

**Souvenir Sheet**

***Imperf***

| | | | | |
|---|---|---|---|---|
| **B158** | SP11 | 4k + 6k blue | 1.50 | 1.50 |

1st anniv. of Czechoslovakia's liberation. The surtax aided WW II orphans.

Nos. B156-B157 were each issued in sheets of 100 stamps and 12 inscribed labels. Value for set of singles with attached labels, mint or used $3.50.

### Old Town Hall Type of 1946

**Souvenir Sheet**

**1946, Aug. 3 *Imperf.***

| | | | | |
|---|---|---|---|---|
| **B159** | A114 | 2.40k rose brown | 1.10 | .75 |

Brno Natl. Stamp Exhib., Aug., 1946. The sheet was sold for 10k.

"You Went Away" — SP14

"You Remained Ours" — SP15

"You Came Back" — SP16

**1946, Oct. 28 Photo. *Perf. 14***

| | | | | |
|---|---|---|---|---|
| **B160** | SP14 | 1.60k + 1.40k red brn | .35 | .35 |
| **B161** | SP15 | 2.40k + 2.60k scarlet | .35 | .35 |
| **B162** | SP16 | 4k + 4k deep blue | .70 | .70 |
| | | *Nos. B160-B162 (3)* | 1.40 | 1.40 |

The surtax was for repatriated Slovaks.

Barefoot Boy — SP17

2k+1k, Mother and child. 3k+1k, Little girl.

***Perf. 12½***

**1948, Dec. 18 Unwmk. Engr.**

| | | | | |
|---|---|---|---|---|
| **B163** | SP17 | 1.50k + 1k rose lilac | .35 | .25 |
| **B164** | SP17 | 2k + 1k dp blue | .25 | .25 |
| **B165** | SP17 | 3k + 1k rose car | .35 | .25 |
| | | *Nos. B163-B165 (3)* | .95 | .75 |

The surtax was for child welfare.

Nos. B163-B165 were each issued in sheets of 100 stamps and 12 inscribed labels. Value for set of singles with attached labels: mint $3; used $2.

Woman and Child — SP18

Design: 3k+1k, Man lifting child.

**1949, Dec. 18 *Perf. 12½***

| | | | | |
|---|---|---|---|---|
| **B166** | SP18 | 1.50k + 50h gray | 3.50 | 1.25 |
| **B167** | SP18 | 3k + 1k claret | 5.25 | 2.25 |

The surtax was for child welfare.

SP19

Dove Carrying Olive Branch — SP20

**1949, Dec. 18**

| | | | | |
|---|---|---|---|---|
| **B168** | SP19 | 1.50k + 50h claret | 4.50 | 1.50 |
| **B169** | SP20 | 3k + 1k rose red | 4.50 | 1.50 |

The surtax was for the Red Cross.

## AIR POST STAMPS

Nos. 9, 39-40, 20, and Types of 1919 Srchd. in Red, Blue or Green

**1920 Unwmk. *Imperf.***

| | | | | |
|---|---|---|---|---|
| **C1** | A1 | 14k on 200h (R) | 15.00 | 12.00 |
| a. | | Inverted surcharge | 125.00 | |
| **C2** | A2 | 24k on 500h (Bl) | 40.00 | 25.00 |
| a. | | Inverted surcharge | 225.00 | |
| **C3** | A2 | 28k on 1000h (G) | 25.00 | 20.00 |
| a. | | Inverted surcharge | 150.00 | |
| b. | | Double surcharge | 200.00 | |
| | | *Nos. C1-C3 (3)* | 80.00 | 57.00 |

***Perf. 13¾***

| | | | | |
|---|---|---|---|---|
| **C4** | A1 | 14k on 200h (R) | 22.50 | *22.50* |
| a. | | Perf. 13¾x13½ | 150.00 | 95.00 |
| **C5** | A2 | 24k on 500h (Bl) | 45.00 | *70.00* |
| a. | | Perf. 13¾x13½ | 150.00 | 75.00 |

***Perf. 13¾x13½***

| | | | | |
|---|---|---|---|---|
| **C6** | A2 | 28k on 1000h (G) | 20.00 | 17.50 |
| a. | | Inverted surcharge | 400.00 | — |
| b. | | Perf. 13¾ | 475.00 | 475.00 |
| c. | | As "b," invtd. surcharge | 350.00 | — |
| | | *Nos. C4-C6 (3)* | 87.50 | 110.00 |
| | | *Nos. C1-C6 (6)* | 167.50 | 167.00 |

Excellent counterfeits of the overprint are known.

Stamps of 1920 Srchd. in Black or Violet

**1922, June 15 *Perf. 13¾***

| | | | | |
|---|---|---|---|---|
| **C7** | A8 | 50h on 100h dl grn | 1.75 | 1.50 |
| a. | | Inverted surcharge | 150.00 | |
| b. | | Double surcharge | 160.00 | |
| **C8** | A8 | 100h on 200h vio | 3.50 | 2.25 |
| a. | | Inverted surcharge | 150.00 | |
| **C9** | A8 | 250h on 400h brn (V) | 5.00 | 3.50 |
| a. | | Inverted surcharge | 275.00 | |
| | | *Nos. C7-C9 (3)* | 10.25 | 7.25 |
| | | Set, never hinged | 20.00 | |

Fokker Monoplane AP3

Smolik S 19 AP4

Smolik S 19 — AP5

Fokker over Prague AP6

**1930, Dec. 16 Engr. *Perf. 13½***

| | | | | |
|---|---|---|---|---|
| **C10** | AP3 | 50h deep green | .25 | .25 |
| **C11** | AP3 | 1k deep red | .25 | *.45* |
| **C12** | AP4 | 2k dark green | .40 | *.90* |
| **C13** | AP4 | 3k red violet | .85 | 1.10 |
| **C14** | AP5 | 4k indigo | .75 | 1.10 |
| **C15** | AP5 | 5k red brown | 1.75 | *3.50* |
| **C16** | AP6 | 10k vio blue | 3.00 | 3.50 |
| a. | | 10k ultra | 8.50 | 10.00 |
| **C17** | AP6 | 20k gray violet | 3.00 | 4.50 |
| | | *Nos. C10-C17 (8)* | 10.25 | 15.30 |
| | | Set, never hinged | 17.50 | |

Two types exist of the 50h, 1k and 2k, and three types of the 3k, differing chiefly in the size of the printed area. A "no hill at left" variety of the 3k exists.

Imperf. examples of Nos. C10-C17 are proofs.

See Bohemia and Moravia No. C1.

***Perf. 12***

| | | | | |
|---|---|---|---|---|
| *C10a* | AP3 | 50h deep green | 2.50 | *4.50* |
| *C11a* | AP3 | 1k deep red | 13.00 | *22.50* |
| *C12a* | AP4 | 2k dark green | 13.00 | *22.50* |
| *C14a* | AP5 | 4k indigo | 2.00 | *3.50* |
| *C17a* | AP6 | 20k gray violet | 3.00 | *7.00* |

***Perf. 12x13½, 13½x12***

| | | | | |
|---|---|---|---|---|
| *C11b* | AP3 | 1k deep red | 3.50 | *6.50* |
| *C12b* | AP4 | 2k dark green | 10.00 | *15.00* |

***Perf. 13¾x12¼***

| | | | | |
|---|---|---|---|---|
| *C17b* | AP6 | 20k gray violet | *1,300.* | |

***Perf. 12½***

| | | | | |
|---|---|---|---|---|
| *C15a* | AP5 | 5k red brown | *1,750.* | |

**Catalogue values for unused stamps in this section, from this point to the end of the section, are for Never Hinged items.**

Capt. Frantisek Novak — AP7

Plane over Bratislava Castle — AP8

Plane over Charles Bridge, Prague — AP9

**1946-47 *Perf. 12½***

| | | | | |
|---|---|---|---|---|
| **C19** | AP7 | 1.50k rose red | .25 | .25 |
| **C20** | AP7 | 5.50k dk gray bl | .50 | .25 |
| **C21** | AP7 | 9k sepia ('47) | .85 | .25 |
| **C22** | AP8 | 10k dl grn | .85 | .35 |
| **C23** | AP7 | 16k violet | 1.50 | .60 |
| **C24** | AP8 | 20k light blue | 1.60 | 1.10 |
| **C25** | AP9 | 24k dk bl, *cr* | 1.00 | .65 |
| **C26** | AP9 | 24k rose lake | 1.75 | 1.00 |
| **C27** | AP9 | 50k dk gray bl | 3.25 | 2.60 |
| | | *Nos. C19-C27 (9)* | 11.55 | 7.05 |

No. C25 was issued June 12, 1946, for use on the first Prague-New York flight.

Nos. C22, C24-C27 were each issued in sheets of 100 stamps and 12 labels depicting airplane over globe. Values for singles with attached labels (mint/used): C22, $2/$1.50; C24, $4/$3; C25, $7.50/$4; C26, $5.50/$4.50; C27, $9/$7.50.

**Nos. C19-C24, C26-C27 Surcharged with New Value and Bars in Various Colors**

**1949, Sept. 1 *Perf. 12½***

| | | | | |
|---|---|---|---|---|
| **C28** | AP7 | 1k on 1.50k (Bl) | .25 | .25 |
| **C29** | AP7 | 3k on 5.50k (C) | .35 | .25 |
| **C30** | AP7 | 6k on 9k (Br) | .55 | .25 |
| **C31** | AP7 | 7.50k on 16k (C) | .75 | .25 |
| **C32** | AP8 | 8k on 10k (G) | .75 | .75 |
| **C33** | AP8 | 12.50k on 20k (Bl) | 1.10 | .55 |
| **C34** | AP9 | 15k on 24k rose lake (Bl) | 2.75 | 1.00 |
| **C35** | AP9 | 30k on 50k (Bl) | 2.00 | .90 |
| | | *Nos. C28-C35 (8)* | 8.50 | 4.20 |

Karlovy Vary (Karlsbad) — AP10

**1951, Apr. 2 Engr. *Perf. 13½***

| | | | | |
|---|---|---|---|---|
| **C36** | AP10 | 6k shown | 3.50 | 1.75 |
| **C37** | AP10 | 10k Piestany | 3.50 | 1.75 |
| **C38** | AP10 | 15k Marienbad | 6.00 | 1.75 |
| **C39** | AP10 | 20k Silac | 9.50 | 4.50 |
| | | *Nos. C36-C39 (4)* | 22.50 | 9.75 |

Nos. C36-C39 were each issued in a sheet of 10 stamps. Value, set *$950.*

View of Cesky Krumlov — AP11

Views: 1.55k, Olomouc. 2.35k, Banska Bystrica. 2.75k, Bratislava. 10k, Prague.

**1955 Cream Paper *Perf. 11½***

| | | | | |
|---|---|---|---|---|
| **C40** | AP11 | 80h olive green | 1.00 | .25 |
| **C41** | AP11 | 1.55k violet brn | 1.40 | .45 |
| **C42** | AP11 | 2.35k violet blue | 1.90 | .25 |
| **C43** | AP11 | 2.75k rose brown | 2.75 | .45 |
| **C44** | AP11 | 10k indigo | 5.50 | 2.75 |
| | | *Nos. C40-C44 (5)* | 12.55 | 4.15 |

Issue dates: 10k, Feb. 20. Others, Mar. 28.

Airline: Moscow-Prague-Paris — AP12

2.35k, Airline: Prague-Cairo-Beirut-Damascus.

**Engraved and Photogravure**

**1957, Oct. 15 Unwmk. *Perf. 11½***

| | | | | |
|---|---|---|---|---|
| **C45** | AP12 | 75h ultra & rose | 1.00 | .25 |
| **C46** | AP12 | 2.35k ultra & org yel | 1.00 | .25 |

Planes at First Czech Aviation School, Pardubice — AP13

Design: 1.80k, Jan Kaspar and flight of first Czech plane, 1909.

**1959, Oct. 15**

| | | | | |
|---|---|---|---|---|
| **C47** | AP13 | 1k gray & yel | .25 | .25 |
| **C48** | AP13 | 1.80k blk & pale bl | .75 | .25 |

50th anniv. of Jan Kaspar's 1st flight Aug. 25, 1909, at Pardubice.

Mail Coach, Plane and Arms of Bratislava — AP14

Design: 2.80k, Helicopter over Bratislava.

**1960, Sept. 24 Unwmk. *Perf. 11½***

| | | | | |
|---|---|---|---|---|
| **C49** | AP14 | 1.60k dk bl & gray | 1.50 | .75 |
| **C50** | AP14 | 2.80k grn & buff | 1.75 | 1.10 |

Issued to publicize the National Stamp Exhibition, Bratislava, Sept. 24-Oct. 9.

AP15

Designs: 60h, Prague hails Gagarin. 1.80k, Gagarin, rocket and dove.

**1961, June 22**

| | | | | |
|---|---|---|---|---|
| C51 | AP15 | 60h gray & car | .30 | .25 |
| C52 | AP15 | 1.80k gray & blue | .45 | .25 |

No. C51 commemorates Maj. Gagarin's visit to Prague, Apr. 28-29; No. C52 commemorates the first man in space, Yuri A. Gagarin, Apr. 12, 1961.

AP16

"PRAGA" emblem and: 80h, Dove & Nest of Eggs. 1.40k, Dove. 2.80k, Symbolic flower with five petals. 4.20k, Five leaves.

**1962, May 14 Engr. *Perf. 14***

| | | | | |
|---|---|---|---|---|
| C53 | AP16 | 80h multicolored | .75 | .35 |
| C54 | AP16 | 1.40k blk, dk red & bl | 1.50 | 1.50 |
| C55 | AP16 | 2.80k multicolored | 1.50 | 1.50 |
| C56 | AP16 | 4.20k multicolored | 1.50 | 1.50 |
| | | *Nos. C53-C56 (4)* | 5.25 | 4.85 |

PRAGA 1962 World Exhibition of Postage Stamps, Aug. 18-Sept. 2, 1962.

Nos. C53-C56 were each issued in sheets of 10. Value, set $85.

Vostok 5 and Lt. Col. Valeri Bykovski AP17

2.80k, Vostok VI & Lt. Valentina Tereshkova.

**1963, June 26**

| | | | | |
|---|---|---|---|---|
| C57 | AP17 | 80h slate bl & pink | 1.00 | .35 |
| C58 | AP17 | 2.80k dl red brn & lt bl | 1.75 | .35 |

Space flights of Valeri Bykovski, June 14-19, and Valentina Tereshkova, first woman astronaut, June 16-19, 1963.

PRAGA 1962 Emblem, View of Prague and Plane — AP18

Designs: 60h, Istanbul '63 (Hagia Sophia). 1k, Philatec Paris 1964 (Ile de la Cité). 1.40k, WIPA 1965 (Belvedere Palace, Vienna). 1.60k, SIPEX 1966 (Capitol, Washington). 2k, Amphilex '67 (harbor and old town, Amsterdam). 5k, PRAGA 1968 (View of Prague).

**Engraved and Photogravure**

**1967, Oct. 30 *Perf. 11½***

**Size: 30x50mm**

| | | | | |
|---|---|---|---|---|
| C59 | AP18 | 30h choc, yel & rose | .25 | .25 |
| C60 | AP18 | 60h dk grn, yel & lil | .25 | .25 |
| C61 | AP18 | 1k blk, brick red & lt bl | .35 | .25 |
| C62 | AP18 | 1.40k vio, yel & dp org | .45 | .25 |
| C63 | AP18 | 1.60k ind, tan & lil | .45 | .25 |
| C64 | AP18 | 2k dk grn, org & red | .45 | .25 |

**Size: 40x50mm**

| | | | | |
|---|---|---|---|---|
| C65 | AP18 | 5k multi | 2.50 | 1.60 |
| | | *Nos. C59-C65 (7)* | 4.70 | 3.10 |

PRAGA 1968 World Stamp Exhibition, Prague, June 22-July 7, 1968. No. C59-C64 issued in sheets of 15 stamps and 15 bilingual labels. Values, set of singles with attached labels: mint $6.50; used $4.50. No. C65 issued in sheets of 4 stamps and one center label. Value $15.

Glider L-13 — AP19

Airplanes: 60h, Sports plane L-40. 80h, Aero taxi L-200. 1k, Crop-spraying plane Z-37. 1.60k, Aerobatics trainer Z-526. 2k, Jet trainer L-29.

**1967, Dec. 11**

| | | | | |
|---|---|---|---|---|
| C66 | AP19 | 30h multi | .25 | .25 |
| C67 | AP19 | 60h multi | .25 | .25 |
| C68 | AP19 | 80h multi | .25 | .25 |
| C69 | AP19 | 1k multi | .30 | .25 |
| C70 | AP19 | 1.60k multi | .50 | .25 |
| C71 | AP19 | 2k multi | 1.60 | .90 |
| | | *Nos. C66-C71 (6)* | 3.15 | 2.15 |

Charles Bridge, Prague, and Balloon — AP20

Designs: 1k, Belvedere, fountain and early plane. 2k, Hradcany, Prague, and airship.

**1968, Feb. 5 Unwmk. *Perf. 11½***

| | | | | |
|---|---|---|---|---|
| C72 | AP20 | 60h multicolored | .30 | .25 |
| C73 | AP20 | 1k multicolored | .45 | .30 |
| C74 | AP20 | 2k multicolored | .75 | .30 |
| | | *Nos. C72-C74 (3)* | 1.50 | .85 |

PRAGA 1968 World Stamp Exhibition, Prague, June 22-July 7, 1968.

Nos. C72-C74 were each issued in a sheet of 10 stamps, Value, set $24.

Astronaut, Moon and Manhattan AP21

Design: 3k, Lunar landing module and J. F. Kennedy Airport, New York.

**1969, July 21**

| | | | | |
|---|---|---|---|---|
| C75 | AP21 | 60h blk, vio, yel & sil | .40 | .25 |
| C76 | AP21 | 3k blk, bl, ocher & sil | 1.60 | .25 |

Man's 1st landing on the moon, July 20, 1969, US astronauts Neil A. Armstrong and Col. Edwin E. Aldrin, Jr., with Lieut. Col. Michael Collins piloting Apollo 11.

Nos. C75-C76 printed with label inscribed with names of astronauts and European date of moon landing. Values for pair of singles with attached labels: mint $3; used $1.

TU-104A over Bitov Castle AP22

Designs: 60h, IL-62 over Bezdez Castle. 1.40k, TU-13A over Orava Castle. 1.90k, IL-18 over Veveri Castle. 2.40k, IL-14 over Pernstejn Castle. 3.60k, TU-154 over Trencin Castle.

**1973, Oct. 24 Engr. *Perf. 11½***

| | | | | |
|---|---|---|---|---|
| C77 | AP22 | 30h multi | .25 | .25 |
| C78 | AP22 | 60h multi | .25 | .25 |
| C79 | AP22 | 1.40k multi | .25 | .25 |
| C80 | AP22 | 1.90k multi | .40 | .25 |
| C81 | AP22 | 2.40k multi | 1.50 | .75 |
| C82 | AP22 | 3.60k multi | .70 | .25 |
| | | *Nos. C77-C82 (6)* | 3.35 | 2.00 |

50 years of Czechoslovakian aviation.

Nos. C77-C82 were each printed in sheets of 10. Values, set: mint $50; used $25.

Old Water Tower and Manes Hall — AP23

Designs (Praga 1978 Emblem, Plane Silhouette and): 1.60k, Congress Hall. 2k, Powder Tower, vert. 2.40k, Charles Bridge and Old Bridge Tower. 4k, Old Town Hall on Old Town Square, vert. 6k, Prague Castle and St. Vitus' Cathedral, vert.

**Engraved and Photogravure**

**1976, June 23 *Perf. 11½***

| | | | | |
|---|---|---|---|---|
| C83 | AP23 | 60h ind & multi | .25 | .25 |
| C84 | AP23 | 1.60k ind & multi | .25 | .25 |
| C85 | AP23 | 2k ind & multi | .35 | .25 |
| C86 | AP23 | 2.40k ind & multi | .40 | .25 |
| C87 | AP23 | 4k ind & multi | .80 | .30 |
| C88 | AP23 | 6k ind & multi | 2.00 | .80 |
| | | *Nos. C83-C88 (6)* | 4.05 | 2.10 |

PRAGA 1978 International Philatelic Exhibition, Prague, Sept. 8-17, 1978.

Zeppelin, 1909 and 1928 — AP24

PRAGA '78 Emblem and: 1k, Ader, 1890, L'Eole & Dunn, 1914. 1.60k, Jeffries-Blanchard balloon, 1785. 2k, Otto Lilienthal's glider, 1896. 4.40k, Jan Kaspar's plane, Pardubice, 1911.

**1977, Sept. 15 *Perf. 11½***

| | | | | |
|---|---|---|---|---|
| C89 | AP24 | 60h multi | .25 | .25 |
| C90 | AP24 | 1k multi | .30 | .25 |
| C91 | AP24 | 1.60k multi | .35 | .25 |
| C92 | AP24 | 2k multi | .45 | .25 |
| C93 | AP24 | 4.40k multi | 2.25 | .50 |
| | | *Nos. C89-C93 (5)* | 3.60 | 1.50 |

History of aviation.

Nos. C89-C93 were each issued in sheets of 30 stamps, 15 labels depicting the exhibition emblem, and 5 blank labels. Values for set of singles with attached inscribed labels: mint $5; used $2.50.

## SPECIAL DELIVERY STAMPS

Doves — SD1

**1919-20 Unwmk. Typo. *Imperf.***

| | | | | |
|---|---|---|---|---|
| E1 | SD1 | 2h red vio, *yel* | .25 | .25 |
| E2 | SD1 | 5h yel grn, *yel* | .25 | .25 |
| E3 | SD1 | 10h red brn, *yel* ('20) | .75 | .75 |
| | | *Nos. E1-E3 (3)* | 1.25 | 1.25 |

For overprints and surcharge see Nos. P11-P13, Eastern Silesia E1-E2.

**1921 White Paper**

| | | | | |
|---|---|---|---|---|
| *E1a* | SD1 | 2h red violet | 9.00 | |
| *E2a* | SD1 | 5h yellow green | 6.00 | |
| *E3a* | SD1 | 10h red brown | 140.00 | |
| | | *Nos. E1a-E3a (3)* | 155.00 | |

It is doubted that Nos. E1a-E3a were regularly issued.

## PERSONAL DELIVERY STAMPS

**Catalogue values for unused stamps in this section are for Never Hinged items.**

PD1

Design: No. EX2, "D" in each corner.

**1937 Unwmk. Photo. *Perf. 13½***

| | | | | |
|---|---|---|---|---|
| EX1 | PD1 | 50h blue | .25 | *.25* |
| EX2 | PD1 | 50h carmine | .25 | *.25* |

PD3

**1946 *Perf. 13½***

| | | | | |
|---|---|---|---|---|
| EX3 | PD3 | 2k deep blue | .50 | *.75* |

## POSTAGE DUE STAMPS

D1

**1918-20 Unwmk. Typo. *Imperf.***

| | | | | |
|---|---|---|---|---|
| J1 | D1 | 5h deep bister | .25 | .25 |
| J2 | D1 | 10h deep bister | .25 | .25 |
| J3 | D1 | 15h deep bister | .25 | .25 |
| J4 | D1 | 20h deep bister | .30 | .25 |
| J5 | D1 | 25h deep bister | .45 | .25 |
| J6 | D1 | 30h deep bister | .45 | .25 |
| J7 | D1 | 40h deep bister | .60 | .25 |
| J8 | D1 | 50h deep bister | .75 | .25 |
| J9 | D1 | 100h blk brn | 1.50 | .25 |
| J10 | D1 | 250h orange | 11.00 | 1.40 |
| J11 | D1 | 400h scarlet | 15.00 | 1.40 |
| J12 | D1 | 500h gray grn | 7.50 | .25 |
| J13 | D1 | 1000h purple | 7.50 | .25 |
| J14 | D1 | 2000h dark blue | 22.50 | .60 |
| | | *Nos. J1-J14 (14)* | 68.30 | 6.15 |

For surcharges and overprints see Nos. J32-J41, J57, Eastern Silesia J1-J11.

Nos. 1, 33-34, 10 Surcharged in Blue

**1922**

| | | | | |
|---|---|---|---|---|
| J15 | A1 | 20h on 3h red vio | .30 | .25 |
| J16 | A2 | 50h on 75h slate | 1.50 | .25 |
| J17 | A2 | 60h on 80h olive grn | .80 | .25 |
| J18 | A2 | 100h on 80h olive grn | 3.00 | .25 |
| J19 | A1 | 200h on 400h purple | 4.00 | .25 |
| | | *Nos. J15-J19 (5)* | 9.60 | 1.25 |

**Same Surcharge on Nos. 1, 10, 30-31, 33-34, 36, 40 in Violet**

**1923-26**

| | | | | |
|---|---|---|---|---|
| J20 | A1 | 10h on 3h red vio | .25 | .25 |
| J21 | A1 | 20h on 3h red vio | .30 | .25 |
| J22 | A1 | 30h on 3h red vio | .25 | .25 |
| J23 | A1 | 40h on 3h red vio | .25 | .25 |
| J24 | A2 | 50h on 75h slate | 1.25 | .25 |
| J25 | A2 | 60h on 50h dk vio ('26) | 4.00 | 1.25 |
| J26 | A2 | 60h on 50h dk bl ('26) | 4.00 | 1.50 |

**J27** A2 60h on 75h slate .50 .25
**J28** A2 100h on 80h ol grn 27.50 .25
**J29** A2 100h on 120h gray blk 1.00 .25
**J30** A1 100h on 400h pur ('26) 1.00 .25
**J31** A2 100h on 1000h dp vio ('26) 1.60 .25
*Nos. J20-J31 (12)* 41.90 5.25

Postage Due Stamp of 1918-20 Surcharged in Violet

**1924**

**J32** D1 50h on 400h scar .90 .25
**J33** D1 60h on 400h scar 3.25 .60
**J34** D1 100h on 400h scar 2.00 .25
*Nos. J32-J34 (3)* 6.15 1.10

**Postage Due Stamps of 1918-20 Surcharged with New Values in Violet as in 1924**

**1925**

**J35** D1 10h on 5h bister .25 .25
**J36** D1 20h on 5h bister .25 .25
**J37** D1 30h on 15h bister .25 .25
**J38** D1 40h on 15h bister .25 .25
**J39** D1 50h on 250h org 1.10 .25
**J40** D1 60h on 250h org 1.50 .60
**J41** D1 100h on 250h org 2.25 .25
*Nos. J35-J41 (7)* 5.85 2.10

**Stamps of 1918-19 Surcharged with New Values in Violet as in 1922**

**1926** *Perf. 14, 11½*

**J42** A2 30h on 15h red .50 .30
**J43** A2 40h on 15h red .50 .30

Surcharged in Violet

**1926** *Perf. 14*

**J44** A8 30h on 100h dk grn .25 .25
**J45** A8 40h on 200h violet .25 .25
**J46** A8 40h on 300h ver .95 .25
*a.* Perf. 14x13½ 60.00
**J47** A8 50h on 500h dp grn .50 .25
*a.* Perf. 14x13½ 2.75
**J48** A8 60h on 400h brown 1.00 .25
**J49** A8 100h on 600h dp vio 2.50 .35
*a.* Perf. 14x13½ 30.00 1.25
*Nos. J44-J49 (6)* 5.45 1.60

Surcharged in Violet

**1927**

**J50** A6 100h dark brown .55 .25
*a.* Perf. 13½ 200.00 10.00

Surcharged in Violet

**J51** A6 40h on 185h org .25 .25
**J52** A6 50h on 20h car .25 .25
*a.* 50h on 50h carmine (error) 55,000.
**J53** A6 50h on 150h rose .25 .25
*a.* Perf. 13½ 12.50 2.00
**J54** A6 60h on 25h brown .25 .25
**J55** A6 60h on 185h orange .55 .25
**J56** A6 100h on 25h brown .55 .25
*Nos. J50-J56 (7)* 2.65 1.75

No. J52a is known only used.

No. J12 Surcharged in Deep Violet

**1927** *Imperf.*

**J57** D1 200h on 500h gray grn 8.00 2.50

**Catalogue values for unused stamps in this section, from this point to the end of the section, are for Never Hinged items.**

D5

**1928** *Perf. 14x13½*

**J58** D5 5h dark red .25 .25
**J59** D5 10h dark red .25 .25
**J60** D5 20h dark red .25 .25
**J61** D5 30h dark red .25 .25
**J62** D5 40h dark red .25 .25
**J63** D5 50h dark red .25 .25
**J64** D5 60h dark red .25 .25
**J65** D5 1k ultra .25 .25
**J66** D5 2k ultra .50 .25
**J67** D5 5k ultra .75 .25
**J68** D5 10k ultra 1.90 .25
**J69** D5 20k ultra 3.75 .30
*Nos. J58-J69 (12)* 8.90 3.05

D6

**1946-48** **Photo.** *Perf. 14*

**J70** D6 10h dark blue .25 .25
**J71** D6 20h dark blue .25 .25
**J72** D6 50h dark blue .25 .25
**J73** D6 1k carmine rose .25 .25
**J74** D6 1.20k carmine rose .25 .25
**J75** D6 1.50k carmine rose ('48) .25 .25
**J76** D6 1.60k carmine rose .25 .25
**J77** D6 2k carmine rose ('48) .25 .25
**J78** D6 2.40k carmine rose .25 .25
**J79** D6 3k carmine rose .25 .25
**J80** D6 5k carmine rose .25 .25
**J81** D6 6k carmine rose ('48) .25 .25
*Nos. J70-J81 (12)* 3.00 3.00

D7 D8

**1954-55** **Engr.** *Perf. 12½, 11½*

**J82** D7 5h gray green ('55) .25 .25
**J83** D7 10h gray green ('55) .25 .25
**J84** D7 30h gray green .25 .25
**J85** D7 50h gray green ('55) .25 .25
**J86** D7 60h gray green ('55) .25 .25
**J87** D7 95h gray green .35 .25
**J88** D8 1k violet .35 .25
**J89** D8 1.20k violet ('55) .35 .25
**J90** D8 1.50k violet .70 .25
**J91** D8 1.60k violet ('55) .45 .25
**J92** D8 2k violet .85 .25
**J93** D8 3k violet 1.10 .25
**J94** D8 5k violet ('55) 1.40 .25
*Nos. J82-J94 (13)* 40.50 3.25

Perf. 11½ stamps are from a 1963 printing which lacks the 95h, 1.60k, and 2k.

Stylized Flower — D9

Designs: Various stylized flowers.

**Engraved and Photogravure**

**1971-72** *Perf. 11½*

**J95** D9 10h vio bl & pink .25 .25
**J96** D9 20h vio & lt bl .25 .25
**J97** D9 30h emer & lil rose .25 .25
**J98** D9 60h pur & emer .25 .25
**J99** D9 80h org & vio bl .25 .25
**J100** D9 1k dk red & emer .25 .25
**J101** D9 1.20k grn & org .25 .25
**J102** D9 2k blue & red .25 .25
**J103** D9 3k blk & yel .30 .25
**J104** D9 4k brn & ultra .45 .25
**J105** D9 5.40k red & lilac .60 .25
**J106** D9 6k brick red & org .75 .25
*Nos. J95-J106 (12)* 4.10 3.00

All except 5.40k issued in 1972.

## OFFICIAL STAMPS

**Catalogue values for unused stamps in this section are for Never Hinged items.**

Coat of Arms — O1

**1945** **Unwmk.** **Litho.** *Perf. 10½x10*

**O1** O1 50h dp slate grn .25 .25
**O2** O1 1k dp bl vio .25 .25
**O3** O1 1.20k plum .25 .25
**O4** O1 1.50k crimson rose .25 .25
**O5** O1 2.50k bright ultra .25 .25
**O6** O1 5k dk vio brn .30 .25
**O7** O1 8k rose pink .30 .30
*Nos. O1-O7 (7)* 1.85 1.80

**Redrawn**

**1947** **Photo.** *Perf. 14*

**O8** O1 60h red .25 .25
**O9** O1 80h dk olive grn .25 .25
**O10** O1 1k dk lilac gray .25 .25
**O11** O1 1.20k dp plum .25 .25
**O12** O1 2.40k dk car rose .25 .25
**O13** O1 4k brt ultra .25 .25
**O14** O1 5k dk vio brn .25 .25
**O15** O1 7.40k purple .25 .25
*Nos. O8-O15 (8)* 2.00 2.00

There are many minor changes in design, size of numerals, etc., of the redrawn stamps.

## NEWSPAPER STAMPS

Windhover — N1

**1918-20** **Unwmk.** **Typo.** *Imperf.*

**P1** N1 2h gray green .25 .25
**P2** N1 5h green ('20) .25 .25
*a.* 5h dark green .40 .25
**P3** N1 6h red .30 .25
**P4** N1 10h dull violet .25 .25
**P5** N1 20h blue .25 .25
**P6** N1 30h gray brown .25 .25
**P7** N1 50h orange ('20) .30 .25
**P8** N1 100h red brown ('20) .40 .25
*Nos. P1-P8 (8)* 2.25 2.00

Nos. P1-P8 exist privately perforated.

For surcharges and overprints see Nos. P9-P10, P14-P16, Eastern Silesia P1-P5.

Stamps of 1918-20 Surcharged in Violet

**1925-26**

**P9** N1 5h on 2h gray green .50 .40
**P10** N1 5h on 6h red ('26) .25 .40

Special Delivery Stamps of 1918-20 Overprinted in Violet

**1926**

**P11** SD1 5h apple grn, *yel* .25 .25
*a.* 5h dull green, *yellow* .50 .40
**P12** SD1 10h red brn, *yel* .25 .25

**With Additional Surcharge of New Value**

**P13** SD1 5h on 2h red vio, *yel* .35 .35
*Nos. P11-P13 (3)* .85 .85

**Catalogue values for unused stamps in this section, from this point to the end of the section, are for Never Hinged items.**

Newspaper Stamps of 1918-20 Overprinted in Violet

**1934**

**P14** N1 10h dull violet .25 .25
**P15** N1 20h blue .25 .25
**P16** N1 30h gray brown .25 .25
*Nos. P14-P16 (3)* .75 .75

Overprinted for use by commercial firms only.

Carrier Pigeon — N2

**1937** *Imperf.*

**P17** N2 2h bister brown .25 .25
**P18** N2 5h dull blue .25 .25
**P19** N2 7h red orange .25 .25
**P20** N2 9h emerald .25 .25
**P21** N2 10h henna brown .25 .25
**P22** N2 12h ultra .25 .25
**P23** N2 20h dark green .25 .25
**P24** N2 50h dark brown .25 .25
**P25** N2 1k olive gray .25 .25
*Nos. P17-P25 (9)* 2.25 2.25

For overprint see Slovakia Nos. P1-P9.

**Bratislava Philatelic Exhibition Issue**

Souvenir Sheet

**1937** *Imperf.*

**P26** N2 10h henna brn, sheet of 25 4.00 4.00

Newspaper Delivery Boy — N4

**1945** **Unwmk.** **Typo.** *Imperf.*

**P27** N4 5h dull blue .25 .25
**P28** N4 10h red .25 .25
**P29** N4 15h emerald .25 .25
**P30** N4 20h dark slate green .25 .25
**P31** N4 25h bright red vio .25 .25
**P32** N4 30h ocher .25 .25
**P33** N4 40h red orange .25 .25
**P34** N4 50h brown red .25 .25
**P35** N4 1k slate gray .25 .25
**P36** N4 5k deep vio blue .25 .25
*Nos. P27-P36 (10)* 2.50 2.50

## CZECHOSLOVAK LEGION POST

The Czechoslovak Legion in Siberia issued these stamps for use on its mail and that of local residents. Forgeries exist.

For more detailed listings of Czechoslovak Legion Post issues, see the *Classic Specialized Catalogue of Stamps and Covers.*

Russia No. 79 Overprinted

**1918 Typo. *Perf. 14x14½***

| | | | | |
|---|---|---|---|---|
| **A1** | A15 | 10k dark blue | 2,500. | — |

No. A1 was sold for a few days in Chelyabinsk. It was withdrawn because of a spelling error ("CZESZKJA," instead of "CZESZKAJA").

This overprint was also applied to Russia Nos. 73-78, 80-81, 83-85, 119-121, 123 and 130-131. These were trial printings, never sold to the public, although favor-cancelled covers exist.

Urn and Cathedral at Irkutsk — A1

Armored Railroad Car — A2

Sentinel — A3

**1919-20 Litho. *Imperf.***

| | | | | |
|---|---|---|---|---|
| **1** | A1 25k carmine | | 10.50 | — |
| *a.* | Perf 11½ ('20) | | 15.00 | — |
| **2** | A2 50k yellow green | | 10.50 | — |
| *a.* | Perf 11½ ('20) | | 15.00 | — |
| **3** | A3 1r red brown | | 19.00 | — |
| *a.* | Perf 11½ ('20) | | 22.50 | — |

Originals of Nos. 1-3 and 1a-3a have a crackled yellow gum. Ungummed remainders, which were given a white gum, exist imperforate and perforated 11½ and 13¼. Value per set, $3.

Lion of Bohemia — A4

Two types: 1 — 6 points on star-like mace head at right of goblet; large saber handle; measures 20x25¼mm. 2 — 5 points on mace head; small saber handle; measures 19½x25mm.

***Perce en Arc in Blue***

**1920 Embossed**

| | | | |
|---|---|---|---|
| **4** | A4 (25k) blue & rose | 3.00 | — |

No. 4 Overprinted

**1920**

| | | | |
|---|---|---|---|
| **5** | A4 (25k) bl & rose | 10.00 | — |

Both types of No. 4 received overprint.

No. 5 Surcharged with New Values in Green

| | | | |
|---|---|---|---|
| **6** | A4 | 2k bl & rose | 35.00 |
| **7** | A4 | 3k bl & rose | 35.00 |
| **8** | A4 | 5k bl & rose | 35.00 |
| **9** | A4 | 10k bl & rose | 35.00 |
| **10** | A4 | 15k bl & rose | 35.00 |
| **11** | A4 | 25k bl & rose | 35.00 |
| **12** | A4 | 35k bl & rose | 35.00 |
| **13** | A4 | 50k bl & rose | 35.00 |
| **14** | A4 | 1r bl & rose | 35.00 |
| | | *Nos. 6-14 (9)* | 315.00 |

## BOHEMIA AND MORAVIA

**Catalogue values for unused stamps in this country are for never hinged items, beginning with Scott 20 in the regular postage section, Scott B1 in the semi-postal section, Scott J1 in the postage due section, and Scott P1 in the newspaper section.**

Masaryk Type of Czechoslovakia with hyphen in "Cesko-Slovensko" A60

**1939, Apr. 23**

| | | | |
|---|---|---|---|
| **1A** | A60 1k rose lake | .25 | .25 |

Prepared by Czechoslovakia prior to the German occupation March 15, 1939. Subsequently issued for use in Bohemia and Moravia.

See No. C1.

### German Protectorate

Stamps of Czechoslovakia, 1928-39, Overprinted in Black

***Perf. 10, 12½, 12x12½***

**1939, July 15 Unwmk.**

| | | | | |
|---|---|---|---|---|
| **1** | A29 | 5h dk ultra | .25 | *1.25* |
| **2** | A29 | 10h brown | .25 | *1.25* |
| **3** | A29 | 20h red | .25 | *1.25* |
| **4** | A29 | 25h green | .25 | *1.25* |
| **5** | A29 | 30h red vio | .25 | *1.25* |
| **6** | A61a | 40h dk bl | 2.50 | *5.00* |
| **7** | A85 | 50h dp grn | .25 | *1.25* |
| **8** | A63 | 60h dl vio | 2.50 | *5.00* |
| **9** | A60 | 1k rose lake (#212) | .75 | *1.75* |
| **10** | A60 | 1k rose lake | .30 | *1.25* |
| **11** | A64 | 1.20k rose lilac | 3.00 | *5.00* |
| **12** | A65 | 1.50k carmine | 2.50 | *5.75* |
| **13** | A79 | 1.60k olive grn | 5.00 | *5.75* |
| *a.* | | "Mähnen" | 32.50 | *75.00* |
| **14** | A66 | 2k dk bl grn | 1.10 | *4.00* |
| **15** | A67 | 2.50k dk bl | 3.00 | *5.00* |
| **16** | A68 | 3k brown | 3.00 | *5.75* |
| **17** | A70 | 4k dk vio | 9.50 | *6.50* |
| **18** | A71 | 5k green | 3.50 | *10.00* |
| **19** | A72 | 10k blue | 4.75 | *15.00* |
| | | *Nos. 1-19 (19)* | 34.70 | *264.00* |
| | | Set, never hinged | 60.00 | |

The size of the overprint varies, Nos. 1-10 measure 17½x15½mm, Nos. 11-16 19x18mm, Nos. 17 and 19 28x17½mm and No. 18 23½x23mm.

**Catalogue values for unused stamps in this section, from this point to the end of the section, are for never hinged items.**

Linden Leaves and Closed Buds — A1

**1939-41 Photo. *Perf. 14***

| | | | | |
|---|---|---|---|---|
| **20** | A1 | 5h dark blue | .25 | *.30* |
| **21** | A1 | 10h blk brn | .25 | *.40* |
| **22** | A1 | 20h crimson | .25 | *.30* |
| **23** | A1 | 25h dk bl grn | .25 | *.30* |
| **24** | A1 | 30h dp plum | .25 | *.30* |
| **24A** | A1 | 30h golden brn ('41) | .25 | *.30* |
| **25** | A1 | 40h orange ('40) | .25 | .25 |
| **26** | A1 | 50h slate grn ('40) | .25 | .25 |
| | | *Nos. 20-26 (8)* | 2.00 | 2.40 |

See Nos. 49-51.

Castle at Zvikov — A2

Karlstein Castle — A3

St. Barbara's Church, Kutna Hora — A4

Cathedral at Prague — A5

Brno Cathedral — A6

Town Square, Olomouc — A7

**1939 Engr. *Perf. 12½***

| | | | | |
|---|---|---|---|---|
| **27** | A2 | 40h dark blue | .25 | *.30* |
| **28** | A3 | 50h dk bl grn | .25 | *.30* |
| **29** | A4 | 60h dl vio | .25 | *.30* |
| **30** | A5 | 1k dp rose | .25 | *.30* |
| **31** | A6 | 1.20k rose lilac | .25 | *.50* |
| **32** | A6 | 1.50k rose car | .25 | *.30* |
| **33** | A7 | 2k dk bl grn | .25 | *.45* |
| **34** | A7 | 2.50k dark blue | .25 | *.30* |
| | | *Nos. 27-34 (8)* | 2.00 | *2.75* |

No. 31 measures 23½x29½mm, No. 42 measures 18½x23mm.

See #52-53, 53B. For overprints see #60-61.

Zlin — A8

Iron Works at Moravská Ostrava — A9

Prague — A10

**1939-40**

| | | | | |
|---|---|---|---|---|
| **35** | A8 | 3k dl rose vio | .25 | *.30* |
| **36** | A9 | 4k slate ('40) | .25 | *.40* |
| **37** | A10 | 5k green | .45 | *.65* |
| **38** | A10 | 10k lt ultra | .35 | *.75* |
| **39** | A10 | 20k yel brn | 1.00 | *1.50* |
| | | *Nos. 35-39 (5)* | 2.30 | *3.60* |

### Types of 1939 and

Neuhaus A11

Pernstein Castle A12

Pardubice Castle — A13

Lainsitz Bridge near Bechyne A14

Samson Fountain, Budweis — A15

Kromeriz A16

Wallenstein Palace, Prague — A17

**1940 Engr. *Perf. 12½***

| | | | | |
|---|---|---|---|---|
| **40** | A11 | 50h dk bl grn | .25 | .25 |
| **41** | A12 | 80h dp bl | .25 | *.30* |
| **42** | A6 | 1.20k vio brn | .30 | .25 |
| **43** | A13 | 2k gray grn | .25 | .25 |
| **44** | A14 | 5k dk bl grn | .25 | .25 |
| **45** | A15 | 6k brn vio | .25 | *.50* |
| **46** | A16 | 8k slate grn | .25 | *.30* |
| **47** | A17 | 10k blue | .45 | .30 |
| **48** | A10 | 20k sepia | .75 | *2.00* |
| | | *Nos. 40-48 (9)* | 3.00 | *4.40* |

No. 42 measures 18½x23mm; No. 31, 23½x29½mm.

### Types of 1939-40

**1941**

| | | | | |
|---|---|---|---|---|
| **49** | A1 | 60h violet | .25 | .25 |
| **50** | A1 | 80h red org | .25 | .25 |
| **51** | A1 | 1k brown | .25 | .25 |
| **52** | A5 | 1.20k rose red | .25 | .25 |
| **53** | A4 | 1.50k lil rose | .25 | .25 |
| **53A** | A13 | 2k light blue | .25 | .25 |
| **53B** | A6 | 2.50k ultra | .25 | .25 |
| **53C** | A12 | 3k olive | .25 | .25 |
| | | *Nos. 49-53C (8)* | 2.00 | 2.00 |

Nos. 49-51 show buds open. Nos. 52 and 53B measure 18¾x23½mm and have no inscriptions below design.

For overprints see Nos. 60-61.

Antonin Dvorák — A18

**1941, Aug. 25 Engr. *Perf. 12½***

**54** A18 60h dull lilac .40 *.50*
**55** A18 1.20k sepia .40 *.50*

Antonin Dvorák (1841-1904), composer.
Nos. 54-55 were issued in sheets of 50 stamps and 50 alternating inscribed labels. Value for set of singles with attached labels, unused or used, $1.25.

Farming Scene — A19

Factories — A20

**1941, Sept. 7 Photo. *Perf. 13½***

**56** A19 30h dk red brn .25 *.30*
**57** A19 60h dark green .25 *.30*
**58** A20 1.20k dk plum .25 *.30*
**59** A20 2.50k sapphire .25 *1.50*
*Nos. 56-59 (4)* 1.00 *2.40*

Issued to publicize the Prague Fair.

Nos. 52 and 53B Overprinted in Blue or Red

**1942, Mar. 15 *Perf. 12½***

**60** A5 1.20k rose red (Bl) .70 *1.00*
**61** A6 2.50k ultra (R) .70 *1.00*

3rd anniv. of the Protectorate of Bohemia and Moravia.

Adolf Hitler — A21

**1942 Photo. *Perf. 14***

**Size: 17½x21½mm**

**62** A21 10(h) gray blk .25 *.25*
**63** A21 30(h) bister brn .25 *.25*
**64** A21 40(h) slate blue .25 *.25*
**65** A21 50(h) slate grn .25 *.25*
**66** A21 60(h) purple .25 *.25*
**67** A21 80(h) org ver .25 *.25*

***Perf. 12½***

**Engr.**

**Size: 18x21mm**

**68** A21 1k dl brn .25 *.25*
**69** A21 1.20(k) carmine .25 *.30*
**70** A21 1.50(k) claret .25 *.30*
**71** A21 1.60(k) Prus grn .25 *.30*
**72** A21 2k light blue .25 *.30*
**73** A21 2.40(k) fawn .25 *.30*

**Size: 18½x24mm**

**74** A21 2.50(k) ultra .25 *.30*
**75** A21 3k olive grn .25 *.30*
**76** A21 4k brt red vio .25 *.30*
**77** A21 5k myrtle grn .25 *.30*
**78** A21 6k claret brn .25 *.40*
**79** A21 8k indigo .25 *.40*

**Size: 23½x29¾mm**

**80** A21 10k dk gray grn .25 *.75*
**81** A21 20k gray vio .50 *.90*
**82** A21 30k red .75 *1.50*
**83** A21 50k deep blue 1.50 *2.50*
*Nos. 62-83 (22)* 7.50 *10.90*

17th Century Messenger — A22

**1943, Jan. 10 Photo. *Perf. 13½***

**84** A22 60h dark rose violet .40 .40

Stamp Day.

Scene from "Die Meistersinger" A23

Richard Wagner A24

Scene from "Siegfried" — A25

**1943, May 22**

**85** A23 60h violet .25 .25
**86** A24 1.20k carmine rose .25 .25
**87** A25 2.50k deep ultra .25 .25
*Nos. 85-87 (3)* .75 .75

Richard Wagner (1813-83).

St. Vitus' Cathedral, Prague — A26

**1944, Nov. 21 Engr. *Perf. 12½***

**88** A26 1.50k dull rose brn .25 .25
**89** A26 2.50k dull lilac blue .25 *.35*

Adolf Hitler — A27

**1944**

**90** A27 4.20k green .50 .50

## SEMI-POSTAL STAMPS

**Catalogue values for unused stamps in this section are for never hinged items.**

Nurse and Wounded Soldier — SP1

***Perf. 13½***

**1940, June 29 Photo. Unwmk.**

**B1** SP1 60h + 40h indigo .35 *.75*
**B2** SP1 1.20k + 80h deep plum .35 *.75*

Surtax for German Red Cross.
Nos. B1-B2 were issued in sheets of 50 stamps and 50 alternating inscribed labels. Value for set of singles with attached labels: unused $4.50; used $4.

Red Cross Nurse and Patient — SP2

**1941, Apr. 20**

**B3** SP2 60h + 40h indigo .40 *.75*
**B4** SP2 1.20k + 80h dp plum .40 *.75*

Surtax for German Red Cross.
Nos. B3-B4 were issued in sheets of 50 stamps and 50 alternating inscribed labels. Value for set of singles with attached labels: unused $3.50; used $4.50.

Old Theater, Prague — SP3

Mozart — SP4

**1941, Oct. 26**

**B5** SP3 30h + 30h brown .25 .25
**B6** SP3 60h + 60h Prus grn .25 .25
**B7** SP4 1.20k + 1.20k scar .25 *.25*
**B8** SP4 2.50k + 2.50k dk bl .45 *.45*
*Nos. B5-B8 (4)* 1.20 *1.20*

150th anniversary of Mozart's death.
Labels alternate with stamps in sheets of Nos. B5-B8. The labels with Nos. B5-B6 show two bars of Mozart's opera "Don Giovanni." Those with Nos. B7-B8 show Mozart's piano. Value for set of singles with attached labels: unused $2.50; used $3.50.

Adolf Hitler — SP5

**1942, Apr. 20 Engr. *Perf. 12½***

**B9** SP5 30h + 20h dl brn vio .25 .25
**B10** SP5 60h + 40h dl grn .25 .25
**B11** SP5 1.20k + 80h dp claret .25 .35
**B12** SP5 2.50k + 1.50k dl bl .40 *.75*
*Nos. B9-B12 (4)* 1.15 *1.60*

Hitler's 53rd birthday.
Nos. B9-B12 were issued in sheets of 100 stamps and 12 blank labels. Value for set of singles with attached labels: unused $3; used $2.25.

Nurse and Soldier — SP6

**1942, Sept. 4 *Perf. 13½***

**B13** SP6 60h + 40h deep blue .25 .25
**B14** SP6 1.20(k) + 80(h) dp plum .25 .25

The surtax aided the German Red Cross.

Emperor Charles IV SP7

Peter Parler SP8

John the Blind, King of Bohemia — SP9

**1943, Jan. 29**

**B15** SP7 60h + 40h violet .25 .25
**B16** SP8 1.20k + 80h carmine .25 .25
**B17** SP9 2.50k + 1.50k vio bl .25 .25
*Nos. B15-B17 (3)* .75 *.75*

The surtax was for the benefit of the German wartime winter relief.

Adolf Hitler — SP10

**1943, Apr. 20 Engr. *Perf. 12½***

**B18** SP10 60h + 1.40k dl vio .25 *.45*
**B19** SP10 1.20k + 3.80k carmine .25 *.45*

Hitler's 54th birthday.
Nos. B18-B19 were issued in sheets of 100 stamps and 12 blank labels. Value for set of singles with attached labels: unused $1.10; used $1.

Deathmask of Reinhard Heydrich — SP11

**1943, May 28 Photo. *Perf. 13½***

**B20** SP11 60h + 4.40k black .75 *1.50*

No. B20 exists in a souvenir sheet containing a single stamp. It was given to high Nazi officials attending a ceremony one year after Heydrich's assassination. Value $15,000.

Eagle and Red Cross — SP12

**1943, Sept. 16 *Perf. 13***

**B21** SP12 1.20k + 8.80k blk & car .60 .35

The surtax aided the German Red Cross.

Native Costumes SP13

Nazi Emblem, Arms of Bohemia, Moravia SP14

**1944, Mar. 15 *Perf. 13½***

**B22** SP13 1.20(k) + 3.80(k) rose lake .25 .25
**B23** SP14 4.20(k) + 10.80(k) golden brn .25 .25
**B24** SP13 10k + 20k saph .25 *.25*
*Nos. B22-B24 (3)* .75 *.75*

Fifth anniversary of protectorate.

Adolf Hitler — SP15

**1944, Apr. 20**

| | | | | |
|---|---|---|---|---|
| **B25** | SP15 | 60h + 1.40k olive blk | .30 | .25 |
| **B26** | SP15 | 1.20k + 3.80k slate grn | .30 | .25 |

Bedrich Smetana — SP16

**1944, May 12 Engr. *Perf. 12½***

| | | | | |
|---|---|---|---|---|
| **B27** | SP16 | 60h + 1.40k dk gray grn | .25 | .25 |
| **B28** | SP16 | 1.20k + 3.80k brn car | .25 | .25 |

Bedrich Smetana (1824-84), Czech composer and pianist.

---

### AIR POST STAMP

**Catalogue values for unused stamps in this section are for never hinged items.**

**Type of Czechoslovakia 1930 with hyphen in "Cesko-Slovensko"**

Fokker Monoplane — AP3

**1939, Apr. 22 *Perf. 13½***

| | | | | |
|---|---|---|---|---|
| **C1** | AP3 | 30h rose lilac | 1.60 | .25 |

Prepared by Czechoslovakia prior to the German occupation March 15, 1939. Subsequently issued for use in Bohemia and Moravia. See No. 1A.

---

### PERSONAL DELIVERY STAMPS

PD1

**1939-40 Unwmk. Photo. *Perf. 13½***

| | | | | |
|---|---|---|---|---|
| **EX1** | PD1 | 50h indigo & blue ('40) | 1.00 | *2.50* |
| | | Never hinged | 2.25 | |
| **EX2** | PD1 | 50h carmine & rose | .60 | *3.00* |
| | | Never hinged | 1.60 | |

---

### POSTAGE DUE STAMPS

**Catalogue values for unused stamps in this section are for never hinged items.**

D1

**1939-40 Unwmk. Typo. *Perf. 14***

| | | | | |
|---|---|---|---|---|
| **J1** | D1 | 5h dark carmine | .25 | *.30* |
| **J2** | D1 | 10h dark carmine | .25 | *.30* |
| **J3** | D1 | 20h dark carmine | .25 | *.30* |
| **J4** | D1 | 30h dark carmine | .25 | *.30* |
| **J5** | D1 | 40h dark carmine | .25 | *.30* |
| **J6** | D1 | 50h dark carmine | .25 | *.30* |
| **J7** | D1 | 60h dark carmine | .25 | *.30* |
| **J8** | D1 | 80h dark carmine | .25 | *.30* |
| **J9** | D1 | 1k bright ultra | .25 | *.35* |
| **J10** | D1 | 1.20k brt ultra ('40) | .30 | *.35* |
| **J11** | D1 | 2k bright ultra | .75 | *1.00* |
| **J12** | D1 | 5k bright ultra | .90 | *1.40* |
| **J13** | D1 | 10k bright ultra | 1.40 | *1.75* |
| **J14** | D1 | 20k bright ultra | 2.50 | *2.50* |
| | | *Nos. J1-J14 (14)* | 8.10 | *9.75* |

---

### OFFICIAL STAMPS

**Catalogue values for unused stamps in this section are for never hinged items.**

Numeral — O1

**Unwmk.**

**1941, Jan. 1 Typo. *Perf. 14***

| | | | | |
|---|---|---|---|---|
| **O1** | O1 | 30h ocher | .25 | .25 |
| **O2** | O1 | 40h indigo | .25 | .25 |
| **O3** | O1 | 50h emerald | .25 | .25 |
| **O4** | O1 | 60h slate grn | .25 | .25 |
| **O5** | O1 | 80h org red | .65 | .25 |
| **O6** | O1 | 1k red brn | .35 | .25 |
| **O7** | O1 | 1.20k carmine | .35 | .25 |
| **O8** | O1 | 1.50k dp plum | .50 | .25 |
| **O9** | O1 | 2k brt bl | .50 | .25 |
| **O10** | O1 | 3k olive | .50 | .25 |
| **O11** | O1 | 4k red vio | .70 | .40 |
| **O12** | O1 | 5k org yel | 1.60 | .90 |
| | | *Nos. O1-O12 (12)* | 6.15 | 3.80 |

Eagle — O2

**1943, Feb. 15**

| | | | | |
|---|---|---|---|---|
| **O13** | O2 | 30(h) bister | .25 | *.30* |
| **O14** | O2 | 40(h) indigo | .25 | *.30* |
| **O15** | O2 | 50(h) yel grn | .25 | *.30* |
| **O16** | O2 | 60(h) dp vio | .25 | *.30* |
| **O17** | O2 | 80(h) org red | .25 | *.30* |
| **O18** | O2 | 1k chocolate | .25 | *.30* |
| **O19** | O2 | 1.20(k) carmine | .25 | *.30* |
| **O20** | O2 | 1.50(k) brn red | .25 | *.30* |
| **O21** | O2 | 2k lt bl | .25 | *.30* |
| **O22** | O2 | 3k olive | .25 | *.30* |
| **O23** | O2 | 4k red vio | .25 | *.40* |
| **O24** | O2 | 5k dk grn | .25 | *.40* |
| | | *Nos. O13-O24 (12)* | 3.00 | 3.80 |

---

### NEWSPAPER STAMPS

**Catalogue values for unused stamps in this section are for never hinged items.**

Carrier Pigeon — N1

**1939 Unwmk. Typo. *Imperf.***

| | | | | |
|---|---|---|---|---|
| **P1** | N1 | 2h ocher | .25 | *.30* |
| **P2** | N1 | 5h ultra | .25 | *.30* |
| **P3** | N1 | 7h red orange | .25 | *.30* |
| **P4** | N1 | 9h emerald | .25 | *.30* |
| **P5** | N1 | 10h henna brown | .25 | *.30* |
| **P6** | N1 | 12h dark ultra | .25 | *.30* |
| **P7** | N1 | 20h dark green | .25 | *.30* |
| **P8** | N1 | 50h red brown | .25 | *.35* |
| **P9** | N1 | 1k greenish gray | .25 | *.80* |
| | | *Nos. P1-P9 (9)* | 2.25 | 3.25 |

No. P5 Overprinted in Black

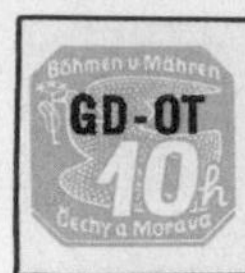


**1940**

| | | | | |
|---|---|---|---|---|
| **P10** | N1 | 10h henna brown | .45 | *.65* |

Overprinted for use by commercial firms.

N2

**1943, Feb. 15**

| | | | | |
|---|---|---|---|---|
| **P11** | N2 | 2(h) ocher | .25 | .25 |
| **P12** | N2 | 5(h) light blue | .25 | .25 |
| **P13** | N2 | 7(h) red orange | .25 | .25 |
| **P14** | N2 | 9(h) emerald | .25 | .25 |
| **P15** | N2 | 10(h) henna brown | .25 | .25 |
| **P16** | N2 | 12(h) dark ultra | .25 | .25 |
| **P17** | N2 | 20(h) dark green | .25 | .25 |
| **P18** | N2 | 50(h) red brown | .25 | .25 |
| **P19** | N2 | 1k slate green | .25 | .25 |
| | | *Nos. P11-P19 (9)* | 2.25 | 2.25 |

# DAHOMEY

də-ˈhō-mē

LOCATION — West coast of Africa
AREA — 43,483 sq. mi.
POP. — 3,030,000 (est. 1974)
CAPITAL — Porto-Novo

Formerly a native kingdom including Benin, Dahomey was annexed by France in 1894. It became part of the colonial administrative unit of French West Africa in 1895. Stamps of French West Africa superseded those of Dahomey in 1945. The Republic of Dahomey was proclaimed Dec. 4, 1958.

The republic changed its name to the People's Republic of Benin on Nov. 30, 1975. See Benin for stamps issued after that date.

100 Centimes = 1 Franc

**Catalog values for unused stamps in this country are for Never Hinged items, beginning with Scott 137 in the regular postage section, Scott B15 in the semi-postal section, Scott C14 in the airpost section, Scott CQ1 in the airpost parcel post section, Scott J29 in the postage due section, and Scott Q1 in the parcel post section.**

See French West Africa No. 71 for stamp inscribed "Dahomey" and "Afrique Occidentale Francaise."

Navigation and Commerce — A1

*Perf. 14x13½*

**1899-1905 Typo. Unwmk.**

**Name of Colony in Blue or Carmine**

| No. | Type | Description | Unused | Used |
|---|---|---|---|---|
| 1 | A1 | 1c black, *lil bl* ('01) | 1.60 | .80 |
| 2 | A1 | 2c brown, *buff* ('04) | 1.60 | .80 |
| 3 | A1 | 4c claret, *lav* ('04) | 2.40 | 2.40 |
| 4 | A1 | 5c yellow grn ('04) | 6.50 | 4.00 |
| 5 | A1 | 10c red ('01) | 8.00 | 4.00 |
| 6 | A1 | 15c gray ('01) | 4.00 | 4.00 |
| 7 | A1 | 20c red, *grn* ('04) | 20.00 | 16.00 |
| 8 | A1 | 25c black, *rose* ('99) | 24.00 | 24.00 |
| 9 | A1 | 25c blue ('01) | 20.00 | 16.00 |
| 10 | A1 | 30c brown, *bis* ('04) | 24.00 | 12.00 |
| 11 | A1 | 40c red, *straw* ('04) | 24.00 | 16.00 |
| 12 | A1 | 50c brn, *az* (name in red) ('01) | 40.00 | 24.00 |
| 12A | A1 | 50c brn, *az* (name in bl) ('05) | 32.50 | 24.00 |
| 13 | A1 | 75c dp vio, *org* ('04) | 85.00 | 55.00 |
| 14 | A1 | 1fr brnz grn, *straw* ('04) | 40.00 | 32.50 |
| 15 | A1 | 2fr violet, *rose* ('04) | 110.00 | 72.50 |
| 16 | A1 | 5fr red lilac, *lav* ('04) | 135.00 | 105.00 |
| | | *Nos. 1-16 (17)* | 578.60 | 413.00 |

Perf. 13½x14 stamps are counterfeits.
For surcharges see Nos. 32-41.

Gen. Louis Faidherbe A2

Oil Palm — A3

Dr. Noel Eugène Ballay A4

**1906-07** *Perf. 13½x14*

**Name of Colony in Red or Blue**

| No. | Type | Description | Unused | Used |
|---|---|---|---|---|
| 17 | A2 | 1c slate | 1.60 | .80 |
| 18 | A2 | 2c chocolate | 2.40 | .80 |
| 19 | A2 | 4c choc, *gray bl* | 4.00 | 3.25 |
| 20 | A2 | 5c green | 8.00 | 3.25 |
| 21 | A2 | 10c carmine (B) | 24.00 | 4.00 |
| 22 | A3 | 20c black & red, *azure* | 16.00 | 12.00 |
| 23 | A3 | 25c blue, *pnksh* | 16.00 | 12.00 |
| 24 | A3 | 30c choc, *pnksh* | 16.00 | 16.00 |
| 25 | A3 | 35c black, *yellow* | 87.50 | 12.00 |
| 26 | A3 | 45c choc, *grnsh* ('07) | 24.00 | 16.00 |
| 27 | A3 | 50c deep violet | 20.00 | 20.00 |
| 28 | A3 | 75c blue, *orange* | 24.00 | 24.00 |
| 29 | A4 | 1fr black, *azure* | 32.00 | 24.00 |
| 30 | A4 | 2fr blue, *pink* | 110.00 | 110.00 |
| 31 | A4 | 5fr car, *straw* (B) | 95.00 | 110.00 |
| | | *Nos. 17-31 (15)* | 480.50 | 368.10 |

**Nos. 2-3, 6-7, 9-13 Surcharged in Black or Carmine**

**Spacing between figures of surcharge 1.5mm (5c), 2mm (10c)**

**1912** *Perf. 14x13½*

| No. | Description | Unused | Used |
|---|---|---|---|
| 32 | 5c on 2c brn, *buff* | 2.00 | *2.40* |
| 33 | 5c on 4c claret, *lav* (C) | 1.60 | *2.00* |
| *a.* | Double surcharge | 275.00 | |
| 34 | 5c on 15c gray (C) | 2.00 | *2.40* |
| 35 | 5c on 20c red, *grn* | 2.00 | *2.40* |
| 36 | 5c on 25c blue (C) | 2.00 | *2.40* |
| *a.* | Inverted surcharge | 240.00 | |
| 37 | 5c on 30c brown, *bis* (C) | 2.00 | *2.40* |
| 38 | 10c on 40c red, *straw* | 2.00 | *2.40* |
| *a.* | Inverted surcharge | 325.00 | |
| 39 | 10c on 50c brn, *az*, name in bl (C) | 2.40 | 2.75 |
| 40 | 10c on 50c brn, *az*, name in red (C) | 1,125. | 1,300. |
| 41 | 10c on 75c violet, *org* | 8.00 | 8.00 |
| *a.* | Double surcharge | *5,500.* | |
| | *Nos. 32-39,41 (9)* | 24.00 | 27.15 |

Two spacings between the surcharged numerals are found on Nos. 32 to 41. For detailed listings, see the *Scott Classic Specialized Catalogue of Stamps and Covers.*

Man Climbing Oil Palm — A5

**1913-39** *Perf. 13½x14*

| No. | Type | Description | Unused | Used |
|---|---|---|---|---|
| 42 | A5 | 1c violet & blk | .40 | .30 |
| 43 | A5 | 2c choc & rose | .40 | .40 |
| 44 | A5 | 4c black & brn | .40 | .40 |
| 45 | A5 | 5c yel grn & bl grn | 1.20 | .55 |
| 46 | A5 | 5c vio brn & vio ('22) | .40 | .80 |
| 47 | A5 | 10c org red & rose | 1.60 | .80 |
| *a.* | | Half used as 5c on wrapper or printed matter | | — |
| 48 | A5 | 10c yel grn & bl grn ('22) | .80 | .80 |
| 49 | A5 | 10c red & ol ('25) | .40 | .40 |
| 50 | A5 | 15c brn org & dk vio ('17) | .80 | .80 |
| 51 | A5 | 20c gray & red brown | .80 | .75 |
| 52 | A5 | 20c bluish grn & grn ('26) | .40 | .40 |
| 53 | A5 | 20c mag & blk ('27) | .40 | .40 |
| 54 | A5 | 25c ultra & dp blue | 2.00 | 1.60 |
| 55 | A5 | 25c vio brn & org ('22) | 1.20 | .80 |
| 56 | A5 | 30c choc & vio | 2.75 | 2.40 |
| 57 | A5 | 30c red org & rose ('22) | 3.25 | 3.25 |
| 58 | A5 | 30c yellow & vio ('25) | .40 | .40 |
| 59 | A5 | 30c dl grn & grn ('27) | .40 | .40 |
| 60 | A5 | 35c brown & blk | .80 | .80 |
| 61 | A5 | 35c bl grn & grn ('38) | .40 | .30 |
| 62 | A5 | 40c black & red org | .80 | .80 |
| 63 | A5 | 45c gray & ultra | .80 | .80 |
| 64 | A5 | 50c chocolate & brn | 6.50 | 6.00 |
| *a.* | | Half used as 25c on cover | | *500.00* |
| 65 | A5 | 50c ultra & bl ('22) | 1.60 | 1.60 |
| 66 | A5 | 50c brn red & bl ('26) | 1.20 | 1.20 |
| 67 | A5 | 55c gray grn & choc ('38) | .80 | .55 |
| 68 | A5 | 60c vio, *pnksh* ('25) | .40 | .40 |
| 69 | A5 | 65c yel brn & ol grn ('26) | 1.20 | 1.20 |
| 70 | A5 | 75c blue & violet | 1.20 | 1.20 |
| 71 | A5 | 80c henna brn & ultra ('38) | .40 | .40 |
| 72 | A5 | 85c dk bl & ver ('26) | 1.60 | 1.60 |
| 73 | A5 | 90c rose & brn red ('30) | .80 | .80 |
| 74 | A5 | 90c yel bis & red org ('39) | 1.20 | .80 |
| 75 | A5 | 1fr blue grn & blk | 1.20 | 1.20 |
| 76 | A5 | 1fr dk bl & ultra ('26) | 1.60 | 1.60 |
| 77 | A5 | 1fr yel brn & lt red ('28) | 1.60 | 1.20 |
| 78 | A5 | 1fr dk red & red org ('38) | 1.05 | .95 |
| 79 | A5 | 1.10fr vio & bis ('28) | 5.50 | *6.00* |
| 80 | A5 | 1.25fr dp bl & dk brn ('33) | 17.50 | 7.25 |
| 81 | A5 | 1.50fr dk bl & lt bl ('30) | 1.60 | .80 |
| 82 | A5 | 1.75fr dk brn & dp buff ('33) | 4.00 | 2.00 |
| 83 | A5 | 1.75fr ind & ultra ('38) | 1.60 | .95 |
| 84 | A5 | 2fr yel org & choc | 1.20 | *1.60* |
| 85 | A5 | 3fr red violet ('30) | 2.40 | 1.75 |
| 86 | A5 | 5fr violet & dp bl | 2.40 | 2.75 |
| | | *Nos. 42-86 (45)* | 79.35 | 62.15 |

The 1c gray and yellow green and 5c dull red and black are Togo Nos. 193a, 196a.

Nos. 47a and 64a were authorized for use in Paouignan during the last part of November 1921. Other values exist as bisects but were not authorized.

For surcharges see Nos. 87-96, B1, B8-B11.

Man Poling a Canoe — A7

Type of 1913 Surcharged

**1922-25**

| No. | Type | Description | Unused | Used |
|---|---|---|---|---|
| 87 | A5 | 60c on 75c vio, *pnksh* | 1.20 | 1.20 |
| *a.* | | Double surcharge | 200.00 | |
| 88 | A5 | 65c on 15c brn org & dk vio ('25) | 2.00 | 2.00 |
| 89 | A5 | 85c on 15c brn org & dk vio ('25) | 2.00 | 2.00 |
| | | *Nos. 87-89 (3)* | 5.20 | 5.20 |

**Stamps and Type of 1913-39 Surcharged with New Value and Bars**

**1924-27**

| No. | Type | Description | Unused | Used |
|---|---|---|---|---|
| 90 | A5 | 25c on 2fr org & choc | 1.20 | 1.20 |
| 91 | A5 | 90c on 75c cer & brn red ('27) | 2.00 | 2.00 |
| 92 | A5 | 1.25fr on 1fr dk bl & ultra (R) ('26) | 1.60 | 1.60 |
| 93 | A5 | 1.50fr on 1fr dk bl & grnsh bl ('27) | 2.75 | 2.75 |
| 94 | A5 | 3fr on 5fr olvn & dp org ('27) | 10.50 | 10.50 |
| 95 | A5 | 10fr on 5fr bl vio & red brn ('27) | 8.00 | 8.00 |
| 96 | A5 | 20fr on 5fr ver & dl grn ('27) | 8.75 | 8.75 |
| | | *Nos. 90-96 (7)* | 34.80 | 34.80 |

Common Design Types pictured following the introduction.

**Colonial Exposition Issue**

Common Design Types

**1931 Engr.** ***Perf. 12½***

**Name of Country in Black**

| No. | Type | Description | Unused | Used |
|---|---|---|---|---|
| 97 | CD70 | 40c deep green | 6.50 | 6.50 |
| 98 | CD71 | 50c violet | 6.50 | 6.50 |
| 99 | CD72 | 90c red orange | 6.50 | 6.50 |
| 100 | CD73 | 1.50fr dull blue | 6.50 | 6.50 |
| | | *Nos. 97-100 (4)* | 26.00 | 26.00 |

**Paris International Exposition Issue**

Common Design Types

**1937 Engr.** ***Perf. 13***

| No. | Type | Description | Unused | Used |
|---|---|---|---|---|
| 101 | CD74 | 20c deep violet | 2.00 | 2.00 |
| 102 | CD75 | 30c dark green | 2.00 | 2.00 |
| 103 | CD76 | 40c car rose | 2.00 | 2.00 |
| 104 | CD77 | 50c dark brown | 1.60 | 1.60 |
| 105 | CD78 | 90c red | 1.60 | 1.60 |
| 106 | CD79 | 1.50fr ultra | 2.40 | 2.40 |
| | | *Nos. 101-106 (6)* | 11.60 | 11.60 |

**Souvenir Sheet**

***Imperf***

| No. | Type | Description | Unused | Used |
|---|---|---|---|---|
| 107 | CD77 | 3fr dp blue & blk | 12.00 | *16.00* |
| *a.* | | Inscription inverted | 1,600. | 1,600. |

**Caillié Issue**

Common Design Type

**1939, Apr. 5 Engr.** ***Perf. 12½x12***

| No. | Type | Description | Unused | Used |
|---|---|---|---|---|
| 108 | CD81 | 90c org brn & org | .40 | 1.20 |
| 109 | CD81 | 2fr brt violet | .40 | 1.20 |
| 110 | CD81 | 2.25fr ultra & dk blue | .40 | 1.20 |
| | | *Nos. 108-110 (3)* | 1.20 | 3.60 |

**New York World's Fair Issue**

Common Design Type

**1939 Engr.**

| No. | Type | Description | Unused | Used |
|---|---|---|---|---|
| 111 | CD82 | 1.25fr car lake | .80 | 1.60 |
| 112 | CD82 | 2.25fr ultra | .80 | 1.60 |

Pile House A8

Sailboat on Lake Nokoué — A9

Dahomey Warrior — A10

**1941** ***Perf. 13***

| No. | Type | Description | Unused | Used |
|---|---|---|---|---|
| 113 | A7 | 2c scarlet | .25 | .25 |
| 114 | A7 | 3c deep blue | .25 | .25 |
| 115 | A7 | 5c brown violet | .70 | .70 |
| 116 | A7 | 10c green | .30 | .30 |
| 117 | A7 | 15c black | .25 | .25 |
| 118 | A8 | 20c violet brown | .30 | .30 |
| 119 | A8 | 30c dk violet | .30 | .30 |
| 120 | A8 | 40c scarlet | .70 | .70 |
| 121 | A8 | 50c slate green | .95 | .95 |
| 122 | A8 | 60c black | .30 | .30 |
| 123 | A8 | 70c brt red violet | 1.20 | 1.20 |
| 124 | A9 | 80c brown black | 1.20 | 1.20 |
| 125 | A9 | 1fr violet | 1.20 | 1.20 |
| 126 | A9 | 1.30fr brown violet | 1.20 | 1.20 |
| 127 | A9 | 1.40fr green | 1.20 | 1.20 |
| 128 | A9 | 1.50fr brt rose | 1.20 | 1.20 |
| 129 | A9 | 2fr brown orange | 1.20 | 1.20 |
| 130 | A10 | 2.50fr dark blue | 1.20 | 1.20 |
| 131 | A10 | 3fr scarlet | 1.20 | 1.20 |
| 132 | A10 | 5fr slate green | 1.20 | 1.20 |
| 133 | A10 | 10fr violet brown | 2.00 | 2.00 |
| 134 | A10 | 20fr black | 2.40 | 2.40 |
| | | *Nos. 113-134 (22)* | 20.70 | 20.70 |

Nos. 121, 122 without "RF," see Nos. 136A-136B.

Pile House and Marshal Pétain
A11

**1941** *Perf. 12½x12*

**135** A11 1fr green .80 —
**136** A11 2.50fr blue .80 —

For surcharges see Nos. B14A-B14B.

### Type of 1941 without "RF"

**1944** *Perf. 13*

**136A** A8 50c slate green 1.20
**136B** A8 60c black 1.20

Nos. 136A-136B were issued by the Vichy government in France, but were not placed on sale in Dahomey.

**Catalogue values for unused stamps in this section, from this point to the end of the section, are for Never Hinged items.**

### Republic

Village Ganvié — A12

**Unwmk.**

**1960, Mar. 1 Engr.** *Perf. 12*

**137** A12 25fr dk blue, brn & red .65 .25

For overprint see No. 152.

Imperforates
Most Dahomey stamps from 1960 onward exist imperforate in issued and trial colors, and also in small presentation sheets in issued colors.

### C.C.T.A. Issue
Common Design Type

**1960, May 16**

**138** CD106 5fr rose lilac & ultra .50 .25

Emblem of the Entente — A13

### Council of the Entente Issue

**1960, May 29 Photo.** *Perf. 13x13½*

**139** A13 25fr multicolored .65 .40

1st anniv. of the Council of the Entente (Dahomey, Ivory Coast, Niger and Upper Volta).

Prime Minister Hubert Maga — A14

**1960, Aug. Engr.** *Perf. 13*

**140** A14 85fr deep claret & blk 1.60 .90

Issued on the occasion of Dahomey's proclamation of independence, Aug. 1, 1960.
For surcharge see No. 149.

Weaver — A15

2fr, 10fr, Wood sculptor. 3fr, 15fr, Fisherman and net, horiz. 4fr, 20fr, Potter, horiz.

**1961, Feb. 17 Engr.** *Perf. 13*

**141** A15 1fr rose, org & red lilac .25 .25
**142** A15 2fr bister brn & choc .25 .25
**143** A15 3fr green & orange .25 .25
**144** A15 4fr olive bis & claret .25 .25
**145** A15 6fr rose, lt vio & ver .40 .25
**146** A15 10fr blue & green .55 .40
**147** A15 15fr red lilac & violet .75 .40
**148** A15 20fr bluish vio & Prus bl .90 .55
*Nos. 141-148 (8)* 3.60 2.60

For surcharges see Nos. 1374, Q1-Q7.

No. 140 Surcharged in Black

**1961, Aug. 1**

**149** A14 100fr on 85fr dp cl & blk 3.25 3.25

First anniversary of Independence.

Doves, UN Building and Emblem — A16

**1961, Sept. 20 Unwmk.** *Perf. 13*

**150** A16 5fr multicolored .35 .25
**151** A16 60fr multicolored 1.20 .90

1st anniv. of Dahomey's admission to the UN. See No. C16 and souvenir sheet No. C16a.

### No. 137 Overprinted in Black

**1961, Dec. 24**

**152** A12 25fr dk blue, brn & red .65 .40

Abidjan Games, Dec 24-31.

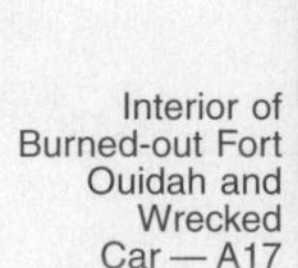

Interior of Burned-out Fort Ouidah and Wrecked Car — A17

**1962, July 31 Photo.** *Perf. 12½*

**153** A17 30fr multicolored .45 .45
**154** A17 60fr multicolored .75 .60

Evacuation of Fort Ouidah by the Portuguese, and its occupation by Dahomey. 1st anniv.

### African and Malgache Union Issue
Common Design Type

**1962, Sept. 8** *Perf. 12½x12*

**155** CD110 30fr red lil, bluish grn, red & gold 1.25 .90

Red Cross Nurses and Map — A18

**1962, Oct. 5 Engr.** *Perf. 13*

**156** A18 5fr blue, choc & red .30 .25
**157** A18 20fr blue, dk grn & red .60 .45
**158** A18 25fr blue, brown & red .65 .45
**159** A18 30fr blue, black & red .85 .70
*Nos. 156-159 (4)* 2.40 1.85

Ganvié Woman in Canoe — A19

Peuhl Herdsman and Cattle A20

Designs: 3fr, 65fr, Bariba chief of Nikki. 15fr, 50fr, Ouidah witch doctor, rock python. 20fr, 30fr, Nessoukoué women carrying vases on heads, Abomey. 25fr, 40fr, Dahomey girl. 60fr, Peuhl herdsman and cattle. 85fr, Ganvié woman in canoe.

**1963, Feb. 18 Unwmk.** *Perf. 13*

**160** A19 2fr grnsh blue & vio .25 .25
**161** A19 3fr blue & black .25 .25
**162** A20 5fr brown, blk & grn .35 .25
**163** A19 15fr brn, bl grn & red brn .35 .25
**164** A19 20fr green, blk & car .30 .25
**165** A20 25fr dk brn, bl & bl grn .40 .25
**166** A19 30fr brn org, choc & mag .60 .40
**167** A20 40fr choc, grn & brt bl 1.00 .40
**168** A19 50fr blk, grn, brn & red brn 1.60 .55
**169** A20 60fr choc, org red & ol 3.50 1.00
**170** A19 65fr orange brn & choc 1.75 .65
**171** A19 85fr brt blue & choc 2.50 1.00
*Nos. 160-171 (12)* 12.85 5.50

For surcharges see Nos. 211, 232, Benin 655A, 690F, 700, 722, 1375, 1417.

Boxers — A21

Designs: 1fr, 20fr, Soccer goalkeeper, horiz. 2fr, 5fr, Runners.

**1963, Apr. 11** **Engr.**

**172** A21 50c green & black .25 .25
**173** A21 1fr olive, blk & brn .25 .25
**174** A21 2fr olive, blue & brn .25 .25
**175** A21 5fr brown, crim & blk .25 .25
**176** A21 15fr dk violet & brn .35 .25
**177** A21 20fr multicolored .55 .55
*Nos. 172-177 (6)* 1.90 1.80

Friendship Games, Dakar, Apr. 11-21.
For surcharges & overprint see Benin Nos. 697, 704, 1372, 1382, 1384.

President's Palace, Cotonou — A22

**1963, Aug. 1 Photo.** *Perf. 12½x12*

**178** A22 25fr multicolored .45 .25

Third anniversary of independence.

Gen. Toussaint L'Ouverture A23

**1963, Nov. 18 Unwmk.** *Perf. 12x13*

**179** A23 25fr multicolored .55 .25
**180** A23 30fr multicolored .70 .25
**181** A23 100fr ultra, brn & red 1.60 .80
*Nos. 179-181 (3)* 2.85 1.30

Pierre Dominique Toussaint L'Ouverture (1743-1803), Haitian gen., statesman and descendant of the kings of Allada (Dahomey). For overprint, see Benin No. 1367. For surcharge, see Benin No. 1466.

UN Emblem, Flame, "15" — A24

**1963, Dec. 10** *Perf. 12*

**182** A24 4fr multicolored .25 .25
**183** A24 6fr multicolored .25 .25
**184** A24 25fr multicolored .45 .25
*Nos. 182-184 (3)* .95 .75

15th anniversary of the Universal Declaration of Human Rights. For surcharge, see Benin No. 1377.

Somba Dance — A25

Regional Dances: 3fr, Nago dance, Pobe-Ketou, horiz. 10fr, Dance of the baton. 15fr, Nago dance, Ouidah, horiz. 25fr, Dance of the Sakpatassi. 30fr, Dance of the Nessouhouessi, horiz.

**1964, Aug. 8 Engr.** *Perf. 13*

**185** A25 2fr red, emerald & blk .25 .25
**186** A25 3fr dull red, blue & grn .25 .25
**187** A25 10fr purple, blk & red .45 .25
**188** A25 15fr magenta, blk & grn .45 .25
**189** A25 25fr Prus blue, brn & org .90 .30
**190** A25 30fr dk red, choc & org 1.15 .40
*Nos. 185-190 (6)* 3.45 1.70

Runner — A26

**1964, Oct. 20 Photo. *Perf. 11***

**191** A26 60fr shown 1.60 1.00
**192** A26 85fr Bicyclist 2.75 1.40

18th Olympic Games, Tokyo, Oct. 10-25.

**Cooperation Issue**
Common Design Type

**1964, Nov. 7 Engr. *Perf. 13***

**193** CD119 25fr org, vio & dk brn .80 .35

UNICEF Emblem, Mother and Child — A27

25fr, Mother holding child in her arms.

**1964, Dec. 11 Unwmk. *Perf. 13***

**194** A27 20fr yel grn, dk red & blk .40 .25
**195** A27 25fr blue, dk red & blk .60 .45

18th anniv. of UNICEF. For overprint, see Benin No. 1368.

IQSY Emblem and Apollo — A28

100fr, IQSY emblem, Nimbus weather satellite.

**1964, Dec. 22 Photo. *Perf. 13x12½***

**196** A28 25fr green & lt yellow .55 .25
**197** A28 100fr deep plum & yellow 2.00 .95

International Quiet Sun Year, 1964-65.

Abomey Tapestry — A29

Designs (Abomey tapestries): 25fr, Warrior and fight scenes. 50fr, Birds and warriors, horiz. 85fr, Animals, ship and plants, horiz.

**1965, Apr. 12 Photo. *Perf. 12½***

**198** A29 20fr multicolored .80 .25
**199** A29 25fr multicolored .95 .40
**200** A29 50fr multicolored 1.50 .80
**201** A29 85fr multicolored 3.25 1.10
*a.* Min. sheet of 4, #198-201 8.00 8.00
*Nos. 198-201 (4)* 6.50 2.55

Issued to publicize the local rug weaving industry.

Baudot Telegraph Distributor and Ader Telephone A30

**1965, May 17 Engr. *Perf. 13***

**202** A30 100fr lilac, org & blk 1.75 1.60

Cent. of the ITU.

Cotonou Harbor — A31

100fr, Cotonou Harbor, denomination at left.

**1965, Aug. 1 Photo. *Perf. 12½***

**203** 25fr multicolored 1.10 .25
**204** 100fr multicolored 2.50 1.10
*a.* A31 Pair, #203-204 4.50 2.10

The opening of Cotonou Harbor. No. 204a has a continuous design.

For surcharges see Nos. 219-220.

Cybium Tritor A32

Fish: 25fr, Dentex filosus. 30fr, Atlantic sailfish. 50fr, Blackish tripletail.

**1965, Sept. 20 Engr. *Perf. 13***

**205** A32 10fr black & brt blue .75 .25
**206** A32 25fr brt blue, org & blk 1.00 .55
**207** A32 30fr violet bl & grnsh bl 1.75 .80
**208** A32 50fr black, gray bl & org 2.75 1.00
*Nos. 205-208 (4)* 6.25 2.60

For surcharge see Benin No. 911.

Independence Monument — A33

**1965, Oct. 28 Photo. *Perf. 12x12½***

**209** A33 25fr gray, black & red .40 .25
**210** A33 30fr lt ultra, black & red .65 .25

October 28 Revolution, 2nd anniv. For surcharge, see Benin No. 1385.

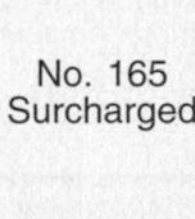

No. 165 Surcharged

**1965, Nov. Engr. *Perf. 13***

**211** A20 1fr on 25fr .30 .25

Porto Novo Cathedral A34

Designs: 50fr, Ouidah Pro-Cathedral, vert. 70fr, Cotonou Cathedral.

**1966, Mar. 21 Engr. *Perf. 13***

**212** A34 30fr Prus bl, vio brn & grn .55 .25
**213** A34 50fr vio brn, Prus bl & brn .70 .50
**214** A34 70fr grn, Prus bl & vio brn 1.25 .75
*Nos. 212-214 (3)* 2.50 1.50

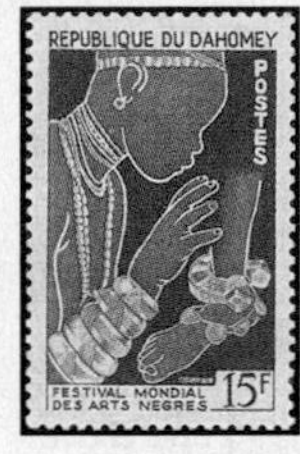


Jewelry — A35

Designs: 30fr, Architecture. 50fr, Musician. 70fr, Crucifixion, sculpture.

**1966, Apr. 4 Engr. *Perf. 13***

**215** A35 15fr dull red brn & blk .45 .25
**216** A35 30fr dk brn, ultra & brn red .70 .45
**217** A35 50fr brt blue & dk brn 1.20 .55
**218** A35 70fr red brown & blk 2.50 .85
*Nos. 215-218 (4)* 4.85 2.10

International Negro Arts Festival, Dakar, Senegal, Apr. 1-24.

**Nos. 203-204 Surcharged**

**1966, Apr. 24 Photo. *Perf. 12½***

**219** A31 15fr on 25fr multi .55 .35
**220** A31 15fr on 100fr multi .55 .35
*a.* Pair, #219-220 1.50 1.10

Fifth anniversary of the Cooperation Agreement between France and Dahomey.

WHO Headquarters from the East — A36

**1966, May 3 *Perf. 12½x13***
**Size: 35x22½mm**

**221** A36 30fr multicolored .75 .25

Inauguration of the WHO Headquarters, Geneva. See No. C32.

Boy Scout Signaling A37

Designs: 10fr, Patrol standard with pennant, vert. 30fr, Campfire and map of Dahomey, vert. 50fr, Scouts building foot bridge.

**1966, Oct. 17 Engr. *Perf. 13***

**222** A37 5fr dk brn, ocher & red .30 .25
**223** A37 10fr black, grn & rose cl .30 .25
**224** A37 30fr org, red brn & pur .70 .35
**225** A37 50fr vio bl, grn & dk brn 1.20 .45
*a.* Min. sheet of 4, #222-225 3.00 3.00
*Nos. 222-225 (4)* 2.50 1.30

Clappertonia Ficifolia — A38

Flowers: 3fr, Hewittia sublobata. 5fr, Butterfly pea. 10fr, Water lily. 15fr, Commelina forskalaei. 30fr, Eremomastax speciosa.

**1967, Feb. 20 Photo. *Perf. 12x12½***

**226** A38 1fr multicolored .25 .25
**227** A38 3fr multicolored .35 .25
**228** A38 5fr multicolored .55 .25
**229** A38 10fr multicolored .90 .35
**230** A38 15fr multicolored 1.10 .55
**231** A38 30fr multicolored 2.10 .90
*Nos. 226-231 (6)* 5.25 2.55

For surcharges see Benin Nos. 707, 715, 1376, 1390, 1402.

Nos. 170-171 Surcharged

**1967, Mar. 1 Engr. *Perf. 13***

**232** A19 30fr on 65fr .85 .60
*a.* Double surcharge 36.00
**233** A19 30fr on 85fr .85 .60
*a.* Double surcharge 60.00
*b.* Inverted surcharge 60.00

Lions Emblem, Dancing Children, Bird — A39

**1967, Mar. 20**

**234** A39 100fr dl vio, dp bl & grn 1.50 1.10

50th anniversary of Lions International.

"Man in the City" Pavilion A40

"The New Africa" Exhibit — A40a

**1967, June 12 Engr. *Perf. 13***

**235** A40 30fr green & choc .70 .25
**236** A40a 70fr green & brn red 1.50 .65

EXPO '67, International Exhibition, Montreal, Apr. 28-Oct. 27, 1967. See No. C57 and miniature sheet No. C57a.

For surcharges see Benin No. 897.

**Europafrica Issue**

Trade (Blood Circulation, Map of Europe and Africa — A41

**1967, July 20 Photo. *Perf. 12x12½***

**237** A41 30fr multicolored .70 .25
**238** A41 45fr multicolored 1.10 .45

For surcharge, see Benin No. 1386.

Scouts Climbing Mountain, Jamboree Emblem A42

70fr, Jamboree emblem, Scouts launching canoe.

**1967, Aug. 7 Engr. Perf. 13**

**239** A42 30fr brt bl, red brn & sl .80 .25
**240** A42 70fr brt bl, sl grn & dk brn 1.60 .65

12th Boy Scout World Jamboree, Farragut State Park, Idaho, Aug. 1-9. For souvenir sheet see No. C59a.

For surcharges see Benin Nos. 902, 912, 1391.

Rhone River and Olympic Emblems A43

Designs (Olympic Emblems and): 45fr, View of Grenoble, vert. 100fr, Rhone Bridge, Grenoble, and Pierre de Coubertin.

**1967, Sept. 2 Engr. Perf. 13**

**241** A43 30fr bis, dp bl & grn .70 .40
**242** A43 45fr ultra, grn & brn .90 .55
**243** A43 100fr choc, grn & brt bl 2.25 1.00
*a.* Min. sheet of 3, #241-243 4.50 4.50
*Nos. 241-243 (3)* 3.85 1.95

10th Winter Olympic Games, Grenoble, Feb. 6-18, 1968.

For surcharges, see Benin No. 903, 1392.

### Monetary Union Issue
Common Design Type

**1967, Nov. 4 Engr. Perf. 13**

**244** CD125 30fr grn, dk car & dk brn .65 .65

Animals from the Pendjari Reservation A45

Designs: 15fr, Cape Buffalo. 30fr, Lion. 45fr, Buffon's kob. 70fr, African slender-snouted crocodile. 100fr, Hippopotamus.

**1968, Mar. 18 Photo. Perf. 12½x13**

**245** A45 15fr multicolored .55 .25
**246** A45 30fr purple & multi .65 .50
**247** A45 45fr blue & multi 1.25 .60
**248** A45 70fr multicolored 2.25 .75
**249** A45 100fr multicolored 4.00 2.25
*Nos. 245-249 (5)* 8.70 4.35

See Nos. 252-256.

For surcharges see No. 310, Benin Nos. 655E, 725, 1415, 1420, 1421.

WHO Emblem A46

**1968, Apr. 22 Engr. Perf. 13**

**250** A46 30fr multicolored .60 .25
**251** A46 70fr multicolored 1.40 .70

20th anniv. of WHO. For surcharges, see Benin Nos. 1387, 1465.

Animals from the Pendjari Reservation A47

Animals: 5fr, Warthog. 30fr, Leopard. 60fr, Spotted hyena. 75fr, Anubius baboon. 90fr, Hartebeest.

**1969, Feb. 10 Photo. Perf. 12½x12**

**252** A47 5fr dark brown & multi .25 .25
**253** A47 30fr deep ultra & multi .70 .50
**254** A47 60fr dark green & multi 1.25 .70
**255** A47 75fr dark blue & multi 3.00 1.00
**256** A47 90fr dark green & multi 4.00 2.25
*Nos. 252-256 (5)* 9.20 4.70

For surcharges, see Benin Nos. 708, 1438.

Heads, Symbols of Agriculture and Science, and Globe A48

**1969, Mar. 10 Engr. Perf. 13**

**257** A48 30fr orange & multi .50 .25
**258** A48 70fr maroon & multi 1.50 .70

50th anniv. of the ILO.

For surcharges see Benin Nos. 904, 913.

Arms of Dahomey — A49

**1969, June 30 Litho. Perf. 13½x13**

**259** A49 5fr yellow & multi .35 .30
**260** A49 30fr orange red & multi 1.50 .45

See No. C101.

### Development Bank Issue

Cornucopia and Bank Emblem — A50

**1969, Sept. 10 Photo. Perf. 13**

**261** A50 30fr black, grn & ocher .75 .55

African Development Bank, 5th anniv.

For surcharge see Benin No. 905.

### Europafrica Issue

Ambary (Kenaf) Industry, Cotonou A51

Design: 45fr, Cotton industry, Parakou.

**1969, Sept. 22 Litho. Perf. 14**

**262** A51 30fr multicolored 1.00 .50
**263** A51 45fr multicolored 1.25 .75

See Nos. C105-C105a.

Sakpata Dance and Tourist Year Emblem — A52

Dances and Tourist Year Emblem: 30fr, Guelede dance. 45fr, Sato dance.

**1969, Dec. 15 Litho. Perf. 14**

**264** A52 10fr multicolored .75 .30
**265** A52 30fr multicolored 1.45 .45
**266** A52 45fr multicolored 2.00 .55
*Nos. 264-266 (3)* 4.20 1.30

See No. C108. For surcharges see Benin Nos. 690J, 1054B, 1388, 1433.

UN Emblem, Garden and Wall — A53

**1970, Apr. 6 Engr. Perf. 13**

**267** A53 30fr ultra, red org & slate .70 .25
**268** A53 40fr ultra, brn & sl grn 1.25 .50

25th anniversary of the United Nations.

For surcharge see No. 294. For overprint see Benin 647B.

### ASECNA Issue
Common Design Type

**1970, June 1 Engr. Perf. 13**

**269** CD132 40fr red & purple .90 .55

For surcharges, see Benin Nos. 906, 1396.

Mt. Fuji, EXPO '70 Emblem, Monorail Train — A54

**1970, June 15 Litho. Perf. 13½x14**

**270** A54 5fr green, red & vio bl .40 .25

EXPO '70 International Exhibition, Osaka, Japan, 3/15-9/13/70. See Nos. C124-C125.

Alkemy, King of Ardres — A55

40fr, Sailing ships "La Justice" & "La Concorde," Ardres, 1670. 50fr, Matheo Lopes, ambassador of the King of Ardres & his coat of arms. 200fr, Louis XIV & fleur-de-lis.

**1970, July 6 Engr. Perf. 13**

**271** A55 40fr brt grn, ultra & brn .75 .25
**272** A55 50fr dk car, choc & emer 1.05 .40
**273** A55 70fr gray, lemon & choc 1.60 .65
**274** A55 200fr Prus bl, dk car & choc 4.00 1.25
*Nos. 271-274 (4)* 7.40 2.55

300th anniv. of the mission from the King of Ardres to the King of France, and of the audience with Louis XIV on Dec. 19, 1670.

For surcharges see Benin Nos. 724, 914.

Star of the Order of Independence — A56

**1970, Aug. 1 Photo. Perf. 12**

**275** A56 30fr multicolored .40 .25
**276** A56 40fr multicolored .60 .25

10th anniversary of independence.

For surcharge see Benin Nos. 720, 1464.

Bariba Warrior — A57

Designs: 2fr, 50fr, Two horsemen. 10fr, 70fr, Horseman facing left.

**1970, Aug. 24 Perf. 12½x13**

**277** A57 1fr yellow & multi .30 .25
**278** A57 2fr gray grn & multi .45 .25
**279** A57 10fr blue & multi .60 .25
**280** A57 40fr yellow grn & multi 1.90 .35
**281** A57 50fr gold & multi 2.40 .50
**282** A57 70fr lilac rose & multi 3.00 .80
*Nos. 277-282 (6)* 8.65 2.40

For surcharges see Benin Nos. 350-351, 613, 703, 1373, 1401.

Globe and Heart A58

Design: 40fr, Hands holding heart, vert.

**1971, June 7 Engr. Perf. 13**

**283** A58 40fr red, green & dk brn 2.00 .50
**284** A58 100fr green, red & blue 4.00 1.25

For surcharges see Benin Nos. 617, 647A, 712, 907, 1429.

Intl. year against racial discrimination.

Ancestral Figures and Lottery Ticket — A59

**1971, June 24 Litho. Perf. 14**

**285** A59 35fr multicolored .80 .25
**286** A59 40fr multicolored 1.25 .35

4th anniv. of the National Lottery.

For overprint and surcharge, see Benin Nos. 710, 1430.

King Behanzin's Emblem (1889-1894) A60

Emblems of the Kings of Abomey: 25fr, Agoliagbo (1894-1900). 35fr, Ganyehoussou (1620-45), bird and cup, horiz. 100fr, Guezo (1818-58), bull, tree and birds. 135fr, Ouegbadja (1645-85), horiz. 140fr, Glèle (1858-89), lion and sword, horiz.

**Photo.; Litho. (25fr, 135fr)**

**1971-72 Perf. 12½**

**287** A60 25fr multicolored .55 .25
**288** A60 35fr green & multi .90 .25
**289** A60 40fr green & multi 1.25 .55
**290** A60 100fr red & multi 2.25 .90
**291** A60 135fr multicolored 3.25 1.40
**292** A60 140fr brown & multi 3.75 1.90
*Nos. 287-292 (6)* 11.95 5.25

Issued: 25fr, 135fr, 7/17/72; others, 8/3/71.

For surcharges and overprint, see Benin Nos. 614, 634B, 791, 1369, 1422, 1431, 1467, 1470.

Kabuki Actor, Long-distance Skiing — A61

**1972, Feb.** **Engr.** ***Perf. 13***
**293** A61 35fr dk car, brn & bl grn 2.50 .75

11th Winter Olympic Games, Sapporo, Japan, Feb. 3-13. See No. C153.

No. 268 Surcharged

**1972**
**294** A53 35fr on 40fr multi .90 .35

Brahms and "Soir d'été" — A62

Design: 65fr, Brahms, woman at piano & music, horiz.

**1972, June 29** **Engr.** ***Perf. 13***
**295** A62 30fr red brn, blk & lilac 4.00 .80
**296** A62 65fr red brn, blk & lilac 6.75 1.50

75th anniversary of the death of Johannes Brahms (1833-1897), German composer.
For surcharges see Benin Nos. 654B, 718, 1389.

The Hare and The Tortoise, by La Fontaine — A63

Fables: 35fr, The Fox and The Stork, vert. 40fr, The Cat, The Weasel and Rabbit.

**1972, Aug. 28** **Engr.** ***Perf. 13***
**297** A63 10fr multicolored 2.25 .75
**298** A63 35fr dark red & multi 4.25 1.25
**299** A63 40fr ultra & multi 5.50 1.75
*Nos. 297-299 (3)* 12.00 3.75

Jean de La Fontaine (1621-1695), French fabulist. For surcharges, see Benin Nos. 1380, 1393, 1397.

**West African Monetary Union Issue**
Common Design Type

**1972, Nov. 2** **Engr.** ***Perf. 13***
**300** CD136 40fr choc, ocher & gray .65 .25

Dr. Armauer Hansen, Microscope, Bacilli — A65

Design: 85fr, Portrait of Dr. Hansen.

**1973, May 14** **Engr.** ***Perf. 13***
**301** A65 35fr ultra, vio brn & brn .50 .35
**302** A65 85fr yel grn, bis & ver 1.25 .75

Centenary of the discovery by Dr. Armauer G. Hansen of the Hansen bacillus, the cause of leprosy.
For surcharges see Benin Nos. 655G, 1084, 1437.

Arms of Dahomey — A66

**1973, June 25** **Photo.** ***Perf. 13***
**303** A66 5fr ultra & multi .25 .25
**304** A66 35fr ocher & multi .40 .25
**305** A66 40fr red orange & multi .60 .25
*Nos. 303-305 (3)* 1.25 .75

For overprint and surcharge see Benin Nos. 690A, 1403.

INTERPOL Emblem and Spiderweb A67

Design: 50fr, INTERPOL emblem and communications symbols, vert.

**1973, July** **Engr.**
**306** A67 35fr ver, grn & brn .60 .30
**307** A67 50fr green, brn & red .85 .45

50th anniversary of International Criminal Police Organization (INTERPOL).
For overprints and surcharges, see Benin Nos. 634A, 810, 1434, 1471.

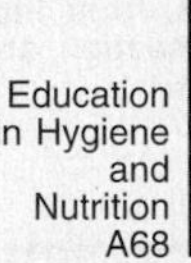

Education in Hygiene and Nutrition A68

WHO, 25th Anniv.: 100fr, Prenatal examination and care, WHO emblem.

**1973, Aug. 2** **Photo.** ***Perf. 12½x13***
**308** A68 35fr multicolored .50 .30
**309** A68 100fr multicolored 1.50 .65

For surcharges, see Benin Nos. 655B, 1439.

No. 248 Srchd. and Ovptd. in Red

**1973, Aug. 16**
**310** A45 100fr on 70fr multi 2.50 1.00

African solidarity in drought emergency.

**African Postal Union Issue**
Common Design Type

**1973, Sept. 12** **Engr.** ***Perf. 13***
**311** CD137 100fr red, purple & blk 1.25 .55

For surcharges, see Benin Nos. 690I, 1440.

Epinephelus Aeneus — A69

Fish: 15fr, Drepane africana. 35fr, Pragus ehrenbergi.

**1973, Sept. 18**
**312** A69 5fr slate blue & indigo 1.00 .30
**313** A69 15fr black & brt blue 1.50 .35
**314** A69 35fr emerald, ocher & sep 4.00 .60
*Nos. 312-314 (3)* 6.50 1.25

For surcharges, see Benin No. 698, 1378, 1383, 1394.

Chameleon A70

40fr, Emblem over map of Dahomey, vert.

**1973, Nov. 30** **Photo.** ***Perf. 13***
**315** A70 35fr olive & multi .55 .30
**316** A70 40fr multicolored 1.25 .35

1st anniv. of the Oct. 26 revolution.

The Chameleon in the Tree — A71

Designs: 5fr, The elephant, the hen and the dog, vert. 10fr, The sparrowhawk and the dog, vert. 25fr, The chameleon in the tree. 40fr, The eagle, the viper and the hen.

**1974, Feb. 14** **Photo.** ***Perf. 13***
**317** A71 5fr emerald & multi .75 .25
**318** A71 10fr slate blue & multi .90 .25
**319** A71 25fr slate blue & multi 1.75 .30
**320** A71 40fr light blue & multi 2.50 .45
*Nos. 317-320 (4)* 5.90 1.25

Folktales of Dahomey.
For surcharges and overprint see Benin Nos. 709, 908, 1363, 1370, 1379, 1381, 1432.

German Shepherd — A72

**1974, Apr. 25** **Photo.** ***Perf. 13***
**321** A72 40fr shown 1.50 .35
**322** A72 50fr Boxer 1.75 .35
**323** A72 100fr Saluki 3.50 .80
*Nos. 321-323 (3)* 6.75 1.50

For surcharges, see Benin No. 1398, 1435, 1441.

**Council Issue**

Map and Flags of Members A73

**1974, May 29** **Photo.** ***Perf. 13x12½***
**324** A73 40fr blue & multi .80 .25

15th anniversary of the Council of Accord.

Locomotive 232, 1911 — A74

Designs: Locomotives.

**1974, Sept. 2** **Photo.** ***Perf. 13x12½***
**325** A74 35fr shown 1.00 .30
**326** A74 40fr Freight, 1877 2.00 .30
**327** A74 100fr Crampton, 1849 3.00 1.00
**328** A74 200fr Stephenson, 1846 6.00 1.60
*Nos. 325-328 (4)* 12.00 3.20

For surcharges see Benin Nos. 654E, 690K, 727, 909, 1395, 1399, 1442, 1444.

Globe, Money, People in Bank A75

**1974, Oct. 31** **Engr.** ***Perf. 13***
**329** A75 35fr multicolored .50 .35

World Savings Day. For surcharge, see Benin No. 1468.

Dompago Dance, Hissi Tribe — A76

Folk Dances: 25fr, Fetish Dance, Vaudou-Tchinan. 40fr, Bamboo Dance, Agbehoun. 100fr, Somba Dance, Sandoua, horiz.

**1975, Aug. 4** **Litho.** ***Perf. 12***
**330** A76 10fr yellow & multi .65 .25
**331** A76 25fr dk green & multi 1.25 .25
**332** A76 40fr red & multi 1.60 .50
**333** A76 100fr multicolored 3.00 .60
*Nos. 330-333 (4)* 6.50 1.60

For surcharges and overprints see Benin Nos. 655D, 713, 1371, 1414, 1443.

Flags of Dahomey and Nigeria over Africa — A77

Design: 100fr, Arrows connecting maps of Dahomey and Nigeria, horiz.

**1975, Aug. 11** **Photo.** ***Perf. 12½x13***
**334** A77 65fr multicolored .75 .25
**335** A77 100fr green & multi 1.00 .45

Year of intensified cooperation between Dahomey and Nigeria.
For surcharges & overprint see Benin Nos. 690H, 701, 899, 901, 1419, 1423.

Map, Pylons, Emblem — A78

Benin Electric Community Emblem and Pylon — A79

**1975, Aug. 18**

| | | | | |
|---|---|---|---|---|
| **336** | A78 | 40fr multicolored | .75 | .35 |
| **337** | A79 | 150fr multicolored | 2.00 | 1.00 |

Benin Electric Community and Ghana-Togo-Dahomey cooperation.

For surcharges see Benin Nos. 601, 900, 910, 1400.

Map of Dahomey, Rising Sun — A80

**1975, Aug. 25 Photo. *Perf. 12½x13***

| | | | | |
|---|---|---|---|---|
| **338** | A80 | 35fr multicolored | .50 | .25 |

Cooperation Year for the creation of a new Dahoman society.

For overprint see Benin No. 690E. For surcharge, see Benin No. 1362.

Albert Schweitzer, Nurse, Patient — A81

**1975, Sept. 22 Engr. *Perf. 13***

| | | | | |
|---|---|---|---|---|
| **339** | A81 | 200fr olive, grn & red brn | 6.25 | 1.50 |

Birth centenary of Albert Schweitzer (1875-1965), medical missionary and musician.

For surcharges, see Benin Nos. 655F, 1445.

Woman Speaking on Telephone, IWY Emblem — A82

150fr, IWY emblem and linked rings.

**1975, Oct. 20 Engr. *Perf. 12½x13***

| | | | | |
|---|---|---|---|---|
| **340** | A82 | 50fr Prus blue & lilac | .75 | .35 |
| **341** | A82 | 150fr emerald, brn & org | 2.00 | .80 |

International Women's Year 1975.

For surcharges, see Benin Nos. 655C, 1436, 1469.

## SEMI-POSTAL STAMPS

Regular Issue of 1913 Surcharged in Red

**1915 Unwmk. *Perf. 14x13½***

| | | | | |
|---|---|---|---|---|
| **B1** | A5 | 10c + 5c orange red & rose | 1.60 | 1.60 |

### Curie Issue
Common Design Type

**1938 *Perf. 13***

| | | | | |
|---|---|---|---|---|
| **B2** | CD80 | 1.75fr + 50c brt ultra | 9.50 | 9.50 |

### French Revolution Issue
Common Design Type

**1939 Photo.**

**Name and Value Typo. in Black**

| | | | | |
|---|---|---|---|---|
| **B3** | CD83 | 45c + 25c green | 9.50 | 9.50 |
| **B4** | CD83 | 70c + 30c brown | 9.50 | 9.50 |
| **B5** | CD83 | 90c + 35c red org | 9.50 | 9.50 |
| **B6** | CD83 | 1.25fr + 1fr rose pink | 9.50 | 9.50 |
| **B7** | CD83 | 2.25fr + 2fr blue | 9.50 | 9.50 |
| | | *Nos. B3-B7 (5)* | 47.50 | 47.50 |

Postage Stamps of 1913-38 Surcharged in Black

**1941 *Perf. 13½x14***

| | | | | |
|---|---|---|---|---|
| **B8** | A5 | 50c + 1fr brn red & bl | 3.25 | 3.25 |
| **B9** | A5 | 80c + 2fr hn brn & ultra | 7.25 | 7.25 |
| **B10** | A5 | 1.50fr + 2fr dk bl & lt bl | 7.25 | 7.25 |
| **B11** | A5 | 2fr + 3fr yel org & choc | 7.25 | 7.25 |
| | | *Nos. B8-B11 (4)* | 25.00 | 25.00 |

### Common Design Type and

Radio Operator — SP1

Senegalese Artillerymen SP2

**1941 Photo. *Perf. 13½***

| | | | |
|---|---|---|---|
| **B12** | SP1 | 1fr + 1fr red | 1.20 |
| **B13** | CD86 | 1.50fr + 3fr claret | 1.20 |
| **B14** | SP2 | 2.50fr + 1fr blue | 1.20 |
| | | *Nos. B12-B14 (3)* | 3.60 |

Surtax for the defense of the colonies.

Nos. B12-B14 were issued by the Vichy government in France, but were not placed on sale in Dahomey.

Nos. 135-136 Srchd. in Black or Red

**1944 Engr. *Perf. 12½x12***

| | | |
|---|---|---|
| **B14A** | 50c + 1.50fr on 2.50fr deep blue (R) | .80 |
| **B14B** | + 2.50fr on 1fr green | .80 |

Colonial Development Fund.

Nos. B14A-B14B were issued by the Vichy government in France, but were not placed on sale in Dahomey.

**Catalogue values for unused stamps in this section, from this point to the end of the section, are for Never Hinged items.**

### Republic
### Anti-Malaria Issue
Common Design Type

**1962, Apr. 7 Engr. *Perf. 12½x12***

| | | | | |
|---|---|---|---|---|
| **B15** | CD108 | 25fr + 5fr orange brn | .75 | .75 |

### Freedom from Hunger Issue
Common Design Type

**1963, Mar. 21 Unwmk. *Perf. 13***

| | | | | |
|---|---|---|---|---|
| **B16** | CD112 | 25fr + 5fr ol, brn red & brn | .80 | .80 |

---

## AIR POST STAMPS

### Common Design Type

**1940 Unwmk. Engr. *Perf. 12½***

| | | | | |
|---|---|---|---|---|
| **C1** | CD85 | 1.90fr ultra | .40 | .40 |
| **C2** | CD85 | 2.90fr dk red | .40 | .40 |
| **C3** | CD85 | 4.50fr dk gray grn | .80 | .80 |
| **C4** | CD85 | 4.90fr yel bister | .80 | .80 |
| **C5** | CD85 | 6.90fr deep org | 1.60 | 1.60 |
| | | *Nos. C1-C5 (5)* | 4.00 | 4.00 |

### Common Design Types

**1942**

| | | | | |
|---|---|---|---|---|
| **C6** | CD88 | 50c car & bl | .30 | |
| **C7** | CD88 | 1fr brn & blk | .30 | |
| **C8** | CD88 | 2fr dk grn & red brn | .50 | |
| **C9** | CD88 | 3fr dk bl & scar | .95 | |
| **C10** | CD88 | 5fr vio & brn red | 1.05 | |

**Frame Engr., Center Typo.**

| | | | | |
|---|---|---|---|---|
| **C11** | CD89 | 10fr ultra, ind & org | 1.05 | |
| **C12** | CD89 | 20fr rose car, mag & gray blk | 1.10 | |
| **C13** | CD89 | 50fr yel grn, dl grn & dp bl | 1.90 | *3.25* |
| *a.* | | 50fr yellow green, dull green & pale blue | 2.75 | *3.75* |
| | | *Nos. C6-C13 (8)* | 7.15 | |

Nos. C6-C12 were issued by the Vichy government in France, but were not placed on sale in Dahomey.

**Catalogue values for unused stamps in this section, from this point to the end of the section, are for Never Hinged items.**

### Republic

Somba House — AP4

Design: 500fr, Royal Court of Abomey.

**Unwmk.**

**1960, Apr. 1 Engr. *Perf. 13***

| | | | | |
|---|---|---|---|---|
| **C14** | AP4 | 100fr multi | 3.25 | .80 |
| **C15** | AP4 | 500fr multi | 13.50 | 4.00 |

For overprint see Benin No. C419. For surcharges, see No. CQ5, Benin Nos. C541, C609.

### Type of Regular Issue, 1961

**1961, Sept. 20**

| | | | | |
|---|---|---|---|---|
| **C16** | A16 | 200fr multi | 3.50 | 2.25 |
| *a.* | | Souv. sheet of 3, #150-151, C16 | 7.00 | 7.00 |

### Air Afrique Issue
Common Design Type

**1962, Feb. 17 *Perf. 13***

| | | | | |
|---|---|---|---|---|
| **C17** | CD107 | 25fr ultra, blk & org brn | .80 | .40 |

Palace of the African and Malgache Union, Cotonou — AP5

**1963, July 27 Photo. *Perf. 13x12***

| | | | | |
|---|---|---|---|---|
| **C18** | AP5 | 250fr multi | 5.00 | 2.75 |

Assembly of chiefs of state of the African and Malgache Union held at Cotonou in July.

### African Postal Union Issue
Common Design Type

**1963, Sept. 8 Unwmk. *Perf. 12½***

| | | | | |
|---|---|---|---|---|
| **C19** | CD114 | 25fr brt bl, ocher & red | .75 | .25 |

See note after Cameroun No. C47.

Boeing 707 — AP6

Boeing 707: 200fr, On the ground. 300fr, Over Cotonou airport. 500fr, In the air.

**1963, Oct. 25 Engr. *Perf. 13***

| | | | | |
|---|---|---|---|---|
| **C20** | AP6 | 100fr multi | 2.00 | .60 |
| **C21** | AP6 | 200fr multi | 3.00 | 2.00 |
| **C22** | AP6 | 300fr multi | 5.00 | 2.00 |
| **C23** | AP6 | 500fr multi | 10.00 | 2.50 |
| | | *Nos. C20-C23 (4)* | 20.00 | 7.10 |

For surcharges see Nos. CQ1-CQ5, Benin No. C610.

Priests Carrying Funerary Boat, Isis Temple, Philae — AP7

**1964, Mar. 9 Unwmk. *Perf. 13***

| | | | | |
|---|---|---|---|---|
| **C24** | AP7 | 25fr vio bl & brn | 2.00 | .95 |

UNESCO world campaign to save historic monuments in Nubia.

Weather Map and Symbols — AP8

**1965, Mar. 23 Photo. *Perf. 12½***

| | | | | |
|---|---|---|---|---|
| **C25** | AP8 | 50fr multi | .80 | .55 |

Fifth World Meteorological Day.

ICY Emblem and Men of Various Races — AP9

**1965, June 26 Engr. *Perf. 13***

| | | | | |
|---|---|---|---|---|
| **C26** | AP9 | 25fr dl pur, mar & grn | .65 | .25 |
| **C27** | AP9 | 85fr dp bl, mar & sl grn | 1.25 | .80 |

International Cooperation Year, 1965

Winston Churchill — AP10

**1965, June 15 Photo. *Perf. 12½***

**C28** AP10 100fr multi 2.25 1.75

For surcharge, see Benin No. C611.

Abraham Lincoln — AP11

**1965, July 15 *Perf. 13***

**C29** AP11 100fr multi 2.00 1.00

Centenary of death of Lincoln
For surcharge see No. C55.

John F. Kennedy and Arms of Dahomey — AP12

**1965, Nov. 22 Photo. *Perf. 12½***

**C30** AP12 100fr dp grn & blk 2.75 1.10

President John F. Kennedy (1917-63).
For surcharge see No. C56.

Dr. Albert Schweitzer and Patients — AP13

**1966, Jan. 17 Photo. *Perf. 12½***

**C31** AP13 100fr multi 3.00 1.25

Dr. Albert Schweitzer (1875-1965), medical missionary, theologian and musician.
For surcharge see Benin No. C435.

**WHO Type of Regular Issue**

Design: WHO Headquarters from the West.

**1966, May 3 Unwmk. *Perf. 13***
**Size: 47x28mm**

**C32** A36 100fr ultra, yel & blk 1.75 1.50

Pygmy Goose — AP14

Broad-billed Rollers — AP15

Birds: 100fr, Fiery-breasted bush-shrike. 250fr, Emerald cuckoos. 500fr, Emerald starling.

**1966-67 *Perf. 12½***

**C33** AP14 50fr multi 2.00 .55
**C34** AP14 100fr multi 3.00 .85
**C35** AP15 200fr multi 10.00 2.25
**C36** AP15 250fr multi 10.00 3.00
**C37** AP14 500fr multi 15.00 6.00
*Nos. C33-C37 (5)* 40.00 12.65

Issued: 50fr, 100fr, 500fr, 6/13/66; others, 1/20/67.
For surcharges see Nos. C107, Benin Nos. 1472, C353-C355, C357, C368, C426, C436, C550, C590.

Industrial Symbols — AP16

**1966, July 21 Photo. *Perf. 12x13***

**C38** AP16 100fr multi 1.75 .80

Agreement between European Economic Community & the African & Malagache Union, 3rd anniv.

Pope Paul VI and St. Peter's, Rome — AP17

Pope Paul VI and UN General Assembly AP18

70fr, Pope Paul VI and view of NYC.

**1966, Aug. 22 Engr. *Perf. 13***

**C39** AP17 50fr multi .75 .45
**C40** AP17 70fr multi .95 .55
**C41** AP18 100fr multi 1.75 1.00
*a.* Min. sheet of 3, #C39-C41 4.50 4.50
*Nos. C39-C41 (3)* 3.45 2.00

Pope Paul's appeal for peace before the UN General Assembly, Oct. 4, 1965.

**Air Afrique Issue, 1966**

Common Design Type

**1966, Aug. 31 Photo. *Perf. 12½***

**C42** CD123 30fr dk vio, blk & gray .75 .25

"Science" — AP20

Designs: 45fr, "Art" (carved female statue), vert. 100fr, "Education" (book and letters).

**1966, Nov. 4 Engr. *Perf. 13***

**C43** AP20 30fr mag, ultra & vio brn .45 .25
**C44** AP20 45fr mar & grn .80 .55
**C45** AP20 100fr blk, mar & brt bl 1.90 1.00
*a.* Min. sheet of 3, #C43-C45 3.25 3.25
*Nos. C43-C45 (3)* 3.15 1.80

20th anniversary of UNESCO.

Madonna by Alessio Baldovinetti AP21

Christmas: 50fr, Nativity after 15th century Beaune tapestry. 100fr, Adoration of the Shepherds, by José Ribera.

**1966, Dec. 25 Photo. *Perf. 12½x12***

**C46** AP21 50fr multi 3.25 2.25
**C47** AP21 100fr multi 4.50 3.25
**C48** AP21 200fr multi 9.00 5.00
*Nos. C46-C48 (3)* 16.75 10.50

See Nos. C95-C96, C109-C115. For surcharge see No. C60. For overprint, see Benin No. C544

**1967, Apr. 10 *Perf. 12½x12***

Paintings by Ingres: No. C49, Self-portrait, 1804. No. C50, Oedipus and the Sphinx.

**C49** AP21 100fr multi 3.25 1.75
**C50** AP21 100fr multi 3.25 1.75

Jean Auguste Dominique Ingres (1780-1867), French painter.

Three-master Suzanne — AP22

Windjammers: 45fr, Three-master Esmeralda, vert. 80fr, Schooner Marie Alice, vert. 100fr, Four-master Antonin.

**1967, May 8 *Perf. 13***

**C51** AP22 30fr multi 1.00 .50
**C52** AP22 45fr multi 1.25 .75
**C53** AP22 80fr multi 2.50 1.25
**C54** AP22 100fr multi 3.25 1.50
*Nos. C51-C54 (4)* 8.00 4.00

For overprint and surcharges see Benin Nos. C369, C420, C606, C612.

**Nos. C29-C30 Surcharged**

**1967, May 29 Photo. *Perf. 13, 12½***

**C55** AP11 125fr on 100fr 2.75 1.25
**C56** AP12 125fr on 100fr 2.75 1.25

50th anniv. of the birth of Pres. John F. Kennedy.

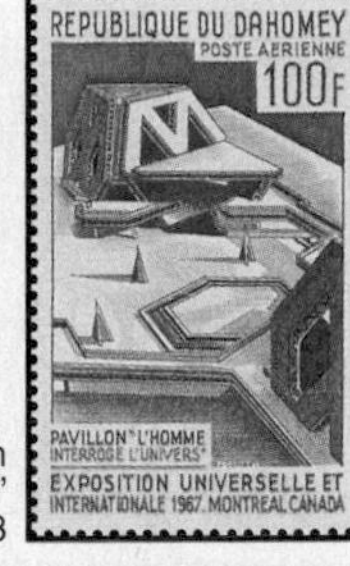


EXPO '67 "Man In Space" Pavilion — AP23

**1967, June 12 Engr. *Perf. 13***

**C57** AP23 100fr dl red & Prus bl 2.00 .75
*a.* Min. sheet of 3, #235-236, C57 4.00 4.00

EXPO '67, International Exhibition, Montreal, Apr. 28-Oct. 27, 1967.

**Europafrica Issue**

Konrad Adenauer, by Oscar Kokoschká AP24

**1967, July 19 Photo. *Perf. 12½x12***

**C58** AP24 70fr multi 2.00 1.25
*a.* Souv. sheet of 4 8.50 8.50

Konrad Adenauer (1876-1967), chancellor of West Germany (1949-1963). For surcharges, see Benin Nos. C572, C602.

Jamboree Emblem, Ropes and World Map — AP25

**1967, Aug. 7 Engr. *Perf. 13***

**C59** AP25 100fr lil, sl grn & dp bl 1.60 .75
*a.* Souv. sheet of 3, #239-240, C59 3.50 3.50

12th Boy Scout World Jamboree, Farragut State Park, Idaho, Aug. 1-9.

No. C48 Srchd. in Red

**1967, Aug. 12 Photo. *Perf. 12½x12***

**C60** AP21 150fr on 200fr 3.50 2.75
*a.* "150F" omitted 300.00 300.00

Riccione, Italy Stamp Exhibition.

### African Postal Union Issue, 1967

Common Design Type

**1967, Sept. 9 Engr. *Perf. 13***

**C61** CD124 100fr red, brt lil & emer 1.75 .95

For surcharge see Benin No. C471.

Charles de Gaulle AP26

**1967, Nov. 21 Photo. *Perf. 12½x13***

**C62** AP26 100fr multi 3.75 2.50
*a.* Souv. sheet of 4 16.00 16.00

Pres. Charles de Gaulle of France on the occasion of Pres. Christophe Soglo's state visit to Paris, Nov. 1967.

Madonna, by Matthias Grunewald AP27

Paintings: 50fr, Holy Family by the Master of St. Sebastian, horiz. 100fr, Adoration of the Magi by Ulrich Apt the Elder. 200fr, Annunciation, by Matthias Grunewald.

**1967, Dec. 11 Photo. *Perf. 12½***

**C63** AP27 30fr multi .55 .45
**C64** AP27 50fr multi 1.10 .60
**C65** AP27 100fr multi 2.00 1.25
**C66** AP27 200fr multi 5.00 2.00
*Nos. C63-C66 (4)* 8.65 4.30

Christmas 1967.

Venus de Milo and Mariner 5 — AP28

#C68, Venus de Milo and Venera 4 rocket.

**1968, Feb. 17 Photo. *Perf. 13***

**C67** AP28 70fr grnsh bl & multi 1.75 .75
**C68** AP28 70fr dp bl & multi 1.75 .75
*a.* Souv. sheet of 2, #C67-C68 4.00 4.00

Explorations of the planet Venus, Oct. 18-19, 1967.

For surcharges see Nos. C103-C104, Benin No. C587.

Gutenberg Monument, Strasbourg Cathedral AP29

Design: 100fr, Gutenberg Monument, Mainz, and Gutenberg press.

**1968, May 20 Litho. *Perf. 14x13½***

**C69** AP29 45fr grn & org 1.00 .40
**C70** AP29 100fr dk & lt bl 2.00 1.00
*a.* Souv. sheet of 2, #C69-C70 3.75 3.75

500th anniv. of the death of Johann Gutenberg, inventor of printing from movable type.

For surcharge see Benin No. C516.

Martin Luther King, Jr. — AP30

Designs: 30fr, "We must meet hate with creative love" in French, English and German. 100fr, Full-face portrait.

***Perf. 12½, 13½x13***

**1968, June 17 Photo.**

**Size: 26x46mm**

**C71** AP30 30fr red brn, yel & blk .60 .35

**Size: 26x37mm**

**C72** AP30 55fr multi 1.00 .45
**C73** AP30 100fr multi 1.50 .90
*a.* Min. sheet of 3, #C71-C73 4.00 4.00
*Nos. C71-C73 (3)* 3.10 1.70

Martin Luther King, Jr. (1929-68), American civil rights leader.

For surcharges, see Benin Nos. C517, C561, C613.

Robert Schuman — AP31

45fr, Alcide de Gasperi. 70fr, Konrad Adenauer.

**1968, July 20 Photo. *Perf. 13***

**C74** AP31 30fr dp yel, blk & grn .40 .40
**C75** AP31 45fr org, dk brn & ol .85 .50
**C76** AP31 70fr multi 1.40 .50
*Nos. C74-C76 (3)* 2.65 1.40

5th anniversary of the economic agreement between the European Economic Community and the African and Malgache Union.

For surcharges, see Benin Nos. C462, C562, C603.

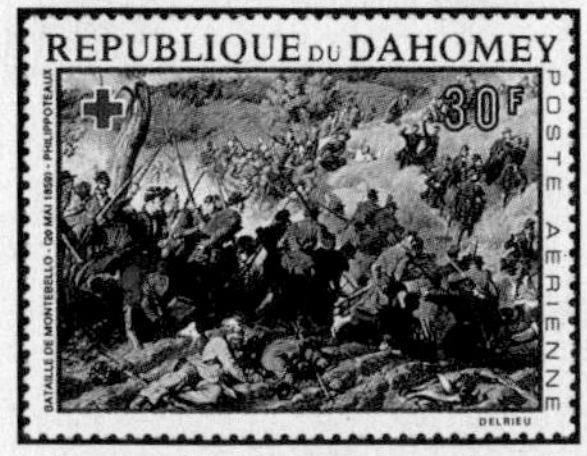


Battle of Montebello, by Henri Philippoteaux — AP32

Paintings: 45fr, 2nd Zouave Regiment at Magenta, by Riballier. 70fr, Battle of Magenta, by Louis Eugène Charpentier. 100fr, Battle of Solferino, by Charpentier.

**1968, Aug. 12 *Perf. 12½x12***

**C77** AP32 30fr multi 1.15 .50
**C78** AP32 45fr multi 1.60 .65
**C79** AP32 70fr multi 3.25 1.25
**C80** AP32 100fr multi 4.00 1.00
*Nos. C77-C80 (4)* 10.00 3.40

Issued for the Red Cross. For surcharges, see Benin Nos. C574, C594, C614.

Mail Truck in Village — AP33

Designs: 45fr, Mail truck stopping at rural post office. 55fr, Mail truck at river bank. 70fr, Mail truck and train.

**1968, Oct. 7 Photo. *Perf. 13x12½***

**C81** AP33 30fr multi .90 .50
**C82** AP33 45fr multi 1.10 .55
**C83** AP33 55fr multi 1.75 .55
**C84** AP33 70fr multi 4.25 1.00
*Nos. C81-C84 (4)* 8.00 2.60

For surcharges see Benin Nos. C352, C357A, C584.

Aztec Stadium, Mexico City — AP34

45fr, Ball player, Mayan sculpture, vert. 70fr, Wrestler, sculpture from Uxpanapan, vert. 150fr, Olympic Stadium, Mexico City.

**1968, Nov. 20 Engr. *Perf. 13***

**C85** AP34 30fr dp cl & sl grn .80 .30
**C86** AP34 45fr ultra & dk rose brn 1.50 .60
**C87** AP34 70fr sl grn & dk brn 2.10 .65
**C88** AP34 150fr dk car & dk brn 3.00 1.25
*a.* Min. sheet of 4, #C85-C88 7.50 7.50
*Nos. C85-C88 (4)* 7.40 2.80

19th Olympic Games, Mexico City, Oct. 12-27. No. C88a is folded down the vertical gutter separating Nos. C85-C86 se-tenant at left and Nos. C87-C88 se-tenant at right.

For overprint and surcharges see Benin Nos. C457, C461, C513.

The Annunciation, by Foujita — AP35

Paintings by Foujita: 30fr, Nativity, horiz. 100fr, The Virgin and Child. 200fr, The Baptism of Christ.

***Perf. 12x12½, 12½x12***

**1968, Nov. 25 Photo.**

**C89** AP35 30fr multi .80 .55
**C90** AP35 70fr multi 1.60 .80
**C91** AP35 100fr multi 1.75 1.25
**C92** AP35 200fr multi 4.00 2.75
*Nos. C89-C92 (4)* 8.15 5.35

Christmas 1968. For surcharges, see Benin Nos. C563, C615, C648.

### PHILEXAFRIQUE Issue

Painting: Diderot, by Louis Michel Vanloo.

**1968, Dec. 16 *Perf. 12½x12***

**C93** AP35 100fr multi 3.75 3.75

PHILEXAFRIQUE, Philatelic Exhibition in Abidjan, Feb. 14-23. Printed with alternating label.

For surcharges, see Benin Nos. C522, C629.

### 2nd PHILEXAFRIQUE Issue

Common Design Type

50fr, Dahomey #119 and aerial view of Cotonou.

**1969, Feb. 14 Engr. *Perf. 13***

**C94** CD128 50fr bl, brn & pur 2.25 2.25

For surcharge see Benin No. C467.

### Christmas Painting Type

Paintings: No. C95, Virgin of the Rocks, by Leonardo da Vinci. No. C96, Virgin with the Scales, by Cesare da Sesto.

**1969, Mar. 17 Photo. *Perf. 12½x12***

**C95** AP21 100fr vio & multi 2.00 1.00
**C96** AP21 100fr grn & multi 2.00 1.00

Leonardo da Vinci (1452-1519).

General Bonaparte, by Jacques Louis David AP36

Paintings: 60fr, Napoleon I in 1809, by Robert J. Lefevre. 75fr, Napoleon on the Battlefield of Eylau, by Antoine Jean Gros, horiz. 200fr, Gen. Bonaparte at Arcole, by Gros.

**1969, Apr. 14 Photo. *Perf. 12½x12***

**C97** AP36 30fr multi 1.50 1.25
**C98** AP36 60fr multi 2.75 1.75
**C99** AP36 75fr multi 3.25 2.50
**C100** AP36 200fr multi 7.50 5.50
*Nos. C97-C100 (4)* 15.00 11.00

Bicentenary of the birth of Napoleon I. For surcharges, see Benin Nos. C599, C605.

### Arms Type of Regular Issue, 1969

**1969, June 30 Litho. *Perf. 13½x13***

**C101** A49 50fr multi .75 .30

For overprint and surcharge see Benin Nos. C417, C596.

Apollo 8 Trip Around the Moon — AP37

### Embossed on Gold Foil

**1969, July *Die-cut Perf. 10½***

**C102** AP37 1000fr gold 20.00 20.00

US Apollo 8 mission, which put the 1st men into orbit around the moon, Dec. 21-27, 1968.

Nos. C67-C68 Surcharged

**1969, Aug. 1 Photo. *Perf. 13***

**C103** AP28 125fr on 70fr, #C67 2.50 1.75
**C104** AP28 125fr on 70fr, #C68 2.50 1.75

Man's 1st landing on the moon, July 20, 1969; US astronauts Neil A. Armstrong, Col. Edwin E. Aldrin, Jr., with Lieut. Col. Michael Collins piloting Apollo 11.

### Europafrica Issue
Type of Regular Issue, 1969

Design: 100fr, Oil palm industry, Cotonou.

**1969, Sept. 22 Litho. *Perf. 14***
**C105** A51 100fr multi 2.25 .35
*a.* Souv. sheet of 3, #262-263, C105 4.25 4.25

For surcharge see Benin No. C523.

Dahomey Rotary Emblem — AP38

**1969, Sept. 25 *Perf. 14x13½***
**C106** AP38 50fr multi 1.00 .75

For surcharge see Benin No. C468.

No. C33 Surcharged

**1969, Nov. 15 Photo. *Perf. 12½***
**C107** AP14 10fr on 50fr multi .45 .25

### Dance Type of Regular Issue

Design: Teke dance and Tourist Year emblem.

**1969, Dec. 15 Litho. *Perf. 14***
**C108** A52 70fr multi 2.50 1.50

For surcharge see Benin No. C398.

### Painting Type of 1966

Christmas: 30fr, Annunciation, by Vrancke van der Stockt. 45fr, Nativity, Swabian School, horiz. 110fr, Madonna and Child, by the Master of the Gold Brocade. 200fr, Adoration of the Kings, Antwerp School.

**1969, Dec. 20 *Perf. 12½x12, 12x12½***
**C109** AP21 30fr multi .50 .40
**C110** AP21 45fr red & multi .85 .65
**C111** AP21 110fr multi 2.10 1.25
**C112** AP21 200fr multi 3.75 2.25
*Nos. C109-C112 (4)* 7.20 4.55

For surcharges see Benin #C425, C463, C475, C532, C595.

**1969, Dec. 27 *Perf. 12½x12***

Paintings: No. C113, The Artist's Studio (detail), by Gustave Courbet. No. C114, Self-portrait with Gold Chain, by Rembrandt. 150fr, Hendrickje Stoffels, by Rembrandt.

**C113** AP21 100fr red & multi 2.25 1.25
**C114** AP21 100fr grn & multi 2.25 1.25
**C115** AP21 150fr multi 3.75 1.75
*Nos. C113-C115 (3)* 8.25 4.25

For overprint and surcharge see Benin Nos. C458, C472.

Franklin D. Roosevelt AP39

**1970, Feb. Photo. *Perf. 12½***
**C116** AP39 100fr ultra, yel grn & blk 1.75 .80

25th anniversary of the death of Pres. Franklin Delano Roosevelt (1882-1945). For surcharge see Benin No. C637.

Astronauts, Rocket, US Flag — AP40

Astronauts: 50fr, Riding rocket through space. 70fr, In landing module approaching moon. 110fr, Planting US flag on moon.

**1970, Mar. 9 Photo. *Perf. 12½***
**C117** AP40 30fr multi .65 .25

### Souvenir Sheet

**C118** Sheet of 4 8.00 8.00
*a.* AP40 50fr violet blue & multi .75 .75
*b.* AP40 70fr violet blue & multi 1.00 1.00
*c.* AP40 110fr violet blue & multi 1.25 1.25

See note after No. C104. No. C118 contains Nos. C117, C118a, C118b and C118c.
For surcharge see No. C120.

Walt Whitman and Dahoman Huts — AP41

**1970, Apr. 30 Engr. *Perf. 13***
**C119** AP41 100fr Prus bl, brn & emer 1.40 .80

Walt Whitman (1818-92), American poet.

No. C117 Surcharged in Silver

**1970, May 15 Photo. *Perf. 12½***
**C120** AP40 40fr on 30fr multi 1.20 .75

The flight of Apollo 13.
For surcharge see Benin No. C464.

Soccer Players and Globe — AP42

Designs: 50fr, Goalkeeper catching ball. 200fr, Players kicking ball.

**1970, May 19**
**C121** AP42 40fr multi .75 .40
**C122** AP42 50fr multi .95 .50
**C123** AP42 200fr multi 3.50 1.25
*Nos. C121-C123 (3)* 5.20 2.15

9th World Soccer Championships for the Jules Rimet Cup, Mexico City, May 30-June 21, 1970.
For surcharge see No. C126.

### EXPO '70 Type of Regular Issue

EXPO '70 Emblems and: 70fr, Dahomey pavilion. 120fr, Mt. Fuji, temple and torii.

**1970, June 15 Litho. *Perf. 13½x14***
**C124** A54 70fr yel, red & dk vio 1.25 .60
**C125** A54 120fr yel, red & grn 2.25 1.00

For surcharges see Benin Nos. C470, C477.

### No. C123 Surcharged and Overprinted

**1970, July 13 Photo. *Perf. 12½***
**C126** AP42 100fr on 200fr multi 2.10 1.00

Brazil's victory in the 9th World Soccer Championships, Mexico City.
For surcharge see Benin No. C515.

Mercury, Map of Africa and Europe — AP43

### Europafrica Issue, 1970

**1970, July 20 Photo. *Perf. 12x13***
**C127** AP43 40fr multi .90 .40
**C128** AP43 70fr multi 1.50 .60

For surcharges see Benin Nos. C429, C488, C566.

Ludwig van Beethoven AP44

**1970, Sept. 21 Litho. *Perf. 14x13½***
**C129** AP44 90fr brt bl & vio blk 1.40 .45
**C130** AP44 110fr yel grn & dk brn 1.75 .65

Bicentenary of the birth of Ludwig van Beethoven (1770-1827), composer.
For surcharges, see Benin Nos. C476, C608.

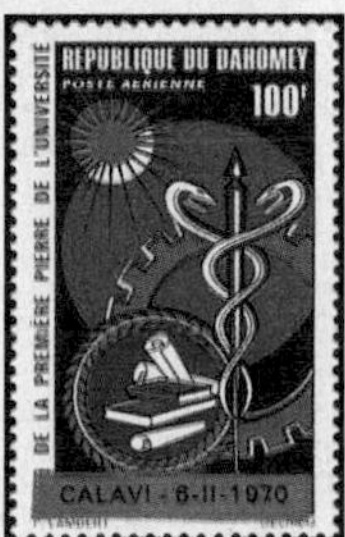


Symbols of Learning — AP45

**1970, Nov. 6 Photo. *Perf. 12½***
**C131** AP45 100fr multi 1.40 .75

Laying of the foundation stone for the University at Calavi.
For overprint and surcharge see Benin Nos. C356, C616.

Annunciation, Rhenish School, c.1340 — AP46

Paintings of Rhenish School, circa 1340: 70fr, Nativity. 110fr, Adoration of the Kings. 200fr, Presentation at the Temple.

**1970, Nov. 9 *Perf. 12½x12***
**C132** AP46 40fr gold & multi .55 .40
**C133** AP46 70fr gold & multi 1.00 .55
**C134** AP46 110fr gold & multi 2.40 1.25
**C135** AP46 200fr gold & multi 4.00 2.00
*Nos. C132-C135 (4)* 7.95 4.20

Christmas 1970.
For surcharge see Benin No. C479.

Charles de Gaulle, Arc de Triomphe and Flag — AP47

Design: 500fr, de Gaulle as old man and Notre Dame Cathedral, Paris.

**1971, Mar. 15 Photo. *Perf. 12½***
**C136** AP47 40fr multi .80 .45
**C137** AP47 500fr multi 6.50 3.25

Gen. Charles de Gaulle (1890-1970), President of France.
For surcharges see Benin Nos. C465, C567.

L'Indifférent, by Watteau — AP48

Painting: No. C139, Woman playing stringed instrument, by Watteau.

**1971, May 3 Photo. *Perf. 13***
**C138** AP48 100fr red brn & multi 3.25 1.75
**C139** AP48 100fr red brn & multi 3.25 1.75

For overprints and surcharge see Nos. C151-C152, Benin Nos. C357D, C456, C526, C617, C638.

**1971, May 29 Photo. *Perf. 13***

Dürer Paintings: 100fr, Self-portrait, 1498. 200fr, Self-portrait, 1500.

**C140** AP48 100fr bl grn & multi 2.25 1.25
**C141** AP48 200fr dk grn & multi 4.50 2.25

Albrecht Dürer (1471-1528), German painter and engraver. See Nos. C151-C152, C174-C175. For surcharges and overprints see Benin Nos. C357B, C381, C545, C618.

Johannes Kepler and Diagram — AP49

200fr, Kepler, trajectories, satellite and rocket.

**1971, July 12 Engr. *Perf. 13***

**C142** AP49 40fr brt rose lil, blk & vio bl .90 .55
**C143** AP49 200fr red, blk & dk bl 3.25 1.75

Kepler (1571-1630), German astronomer.
For overprint and surcharges see Benin Nos. C342, C348, C466, C480, C568.

**Europafrica Issue**

Jet Plane, Maps of Europe and Africa — AP50

100fr, Ocean liner, maps of Europe and Africa.

**1971, July 19 Photo. *Perf. 12½x12***

**C144** AP50 50fr blk, lt bl & org 1.60 .60
**C145** AP50 100fr multi 2.50 1.00

For surcharges see Benin Nos. C374, C404, C421, C585, C630.

**African Postal Union Issue, 1971**

Common Design Type

Design: 100fr, Dahomey coat of arms and UAMPT building, Brazzaville, Congo.

**1971, Nov. 13 *Perf. 13x13½***

**C146** CD135 100fr bl & multi 1.75 .80

For overprint and surcharge see Benin Nos. C357E, C619.

Flight into Egypt, by Van Dyck — AP51

Paintings: 40fr, Adoration of the Shepherds, by the Master of the Hausbuch, c. 1500, vert. 70fr, Adoration of the Kings, by Holbein the Elder, vert. 200fr, The Birth of Christ, by Dürer.

**1971, Nov. 22 *Perf. 13***

**C147** AP51 40fr gold & multi .85 .45
**C148** AP51 70fr gold & multi 1.40 .55
**C149** AP51 100fr gold & multi 2.10 .80
**C150** AP51 200fr gold & multi 5.00 1.75
*Nos. C147-C150 (4)* 9.35 3.55

Christmas 1971

For overprint and surcharges see Benin Nos. C394, C394A, C397, C403, C405, C481, C503, C546, C581, C604, C631.

**Painting Type of 1971 Inscribed: "25e ANNIVERSAIRE DE L'UNICEF"**

Paintings: 40fr, Prince Balthazar, by Velasquez. 100fr, Infanta Margarita Maria, by Velázquez.

**1971, Dec. 11**

**C151** AP48 40fr gold & multi 1.75 .55
**C152** AP48 100fr gold & multi 3.00 .85

25th anniv. of UNICEF.
For surcharges see Benin Nos. C366, C418, C437, C592, C639.

**Olympic Games Type**

Design: 150fr, Sapporo '72 emblem, ski jump and stork flying.

**1972, Feb. Engr. *Perf. 13***

**C153** A61 150fr brn, dp rose lil & bl 3.50 1.25

11th Winter Olympic Games, Sapporo, Japan, Feb. 3-13.
For overprint and surcharge see Benin Nos. C347, C433, C645.

Boy Scout and Scout Flag — AP52

Designs: 40fr, Scout playing marimba. 100fr, Scouts doing farm work.

**1972, Mar. 19 Photo. *Perf. 13***

**Size: 26x35mm**

**C154** AP52 35fr multi .50 .25
**C155** AP52 40fr multi .85 .40

**Size: 26x46mm**

**C156** AP52 100fr yel & multi 1.75 .85
*a.* Souvenir sheet of 3, #C154-C156, perf. 12½ 4.25 4.25
*Nos. C154-C156 (3)* 3.10 1.50

World Boy Scout Seminar, Cotonou, Mar. 1972.
For overprint and surcharges see Benin Nos. C373, C414, C569.

Workers Training Institute and Friedrich Naumann — AP53

Design: 250fr, Workers Training Institute and Pres. Theodor Heuss of Germany.

**1972, Mar. 29 Photo. *Perf. 13x12***

**C157** AP53 100fr brt rose, blk & vio 1.50 .65
**C158** AP53 250fr bl, blk & vio 3.50 1.40

Laying of foundation stone for National Workers Training Institute.
For surcharges see Benin Nos. C380, C473, C640, C649, Q25A.

Mosaic Floor, St. Mark's, Venice — AP54

12th Century Mosaics from St. Mark's Basilica: 40fr, Roosters carrying fox on a pole. 65fr, Noah sending out dove.

**1972, Apr. 10 *Perf. 13***

**C159** AP54 35fr gold & multi 1.35 .75
**C160** AP54 40fr gold & multi 1.50 .90
**C161** AP54 65fr gold & multi 3.00 1.50
*Nos. C159-C161 (3)* 5.85 3.15

UNESCO campaign to save Venice.
For surcharges see Benin Nos. 690G, C600.

Neapolitan and Dahoman Dancers — AP55

**1972, May 3 *Perf. 13½x13***

**C162** AP55 100fr multi 1.50 .65

12th Philatelic Exhibition, Naples.
For surcharges, see Benin Nos. C395, C620.

Running, German Eagle, Olympic Rings — AP56

85fr, High jump and Glyptothek, Munich. 150fr, Shot put and Propylaeum, Munich.

**1972, June 12 Engr. *Perf. 13***

**C163** AP56 20fr ultra, grn & brn .40 .25
**C164** AP56 85fr brn, grn & ultra .95 .60
**C165** AP56 150fr grn, brn & ultra 2.00 1.00
*a.* Min. sheet of 3, #C163-C165 4.00 4.00
*Nos. C163-C165 (3)* 3.35 1.85

20th Olympic Games, Munich, 8/26-9/10.
For overprints and surcharges see Nos. C170-C172, Benin C343, C346, C370, C404A, C559, C651A.

Louis Blériot and his Plane — AP57

**1972, June 26**

**C166** AP57 100fr vio, cl & brt bl 4.00 1.75

Birth centenary of Louis Blériot (1872-1936), French aviation pioneer.
For surcharges see Benin Nos. C386, C621.

Adam, by Lucas Cranach — AP58

Design: 200fr, Eve, by Lucas Cranach.

**1972, Oct. 24 Photo.**

**C167** AP58 150fr multi 2.75 1.25
**C168** AP58 200fr multi 4.50 1.75

Cranach (1472-1553), German painter.
For surcharges see Benin Nos. C402, C537, C643.

Pauline Borghese, by Canova — AP59

**1972, Nov. 8**

**C169** AP59 250fr multi 7.00 1.75

Antonio Canova (1757-1822), Italian sculptor.
For surcharge, see Benin No. 1366.

**Nos. C163-C165 Overprinted**

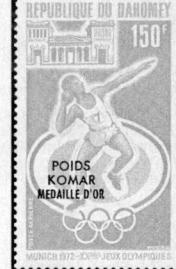

a

b

POIDS
KOMAR
MEDAILLE D'OR

c

**1972, Nov. 13 Engr. *Perf. 13***

**C170** AP56(a) 20fr multi .45 .25
**C171** AP56(b) 85fr multi 1.25 .60
**C172** AP56(c) 150fr multi 2.25 1.25
*a.* Miniature sheet of 3 5.25 5.25
*Nos. C170-C172 (3)* 3.95 2.10

Gold medal winners in 20th Olympic Games: Lasse Viren, Finland, 5,000m. and 10,000m. races (20fr); Ulrike Meyfarth, Germany, women's high jump (85fr); Wladyslaw Komar, Poland, shot put (150fr).
For surcharges, see Benin Nos. C343A, C538, C607.

Louis Pasteur — AP60

**1972, Nov. 30**

**C173** AP60 100fr brt grn, lil & brn 2.50 1.00

Pasteur (1822-95), chemist and bacteriologist.
For surcharges see Benin Nos. C344, C622.

### Painting Type of 1971

Paintings by Georges de La Tour (1593-1652), French painter: 35fr, Vielle player. 150fr, The Newborn, horiz.

**1972, Dec. 11** **Photo.**

**C174** AP48 35fr multi .80 .40
**C175** AP48 150fr multi 2.25 1.25

For surcharges see Benin Nos. C364, C490, C578.

Annunciation, School of Agnolo Gaddi — AP61

Paintings: 125fr, Nativity, by Simone dei Crocifissi. 140fr, Adoration of the Shepherds, by Giovanni di Pietro. 250fr, Adoration of the Kings, by Giotto.

**1972, Dec. 15**

**C176** AP61 35fr gold & multi .75 .25
**C177** AP61 125fr gold & multi 2.00 .65
**C178** AP61 140fr gold & multi 2.75 1.00
**C179** AP61 250fr gold & multi 4.50 1.50
*Nos. C176-C179 (4)* 10.00 3.40

Christmas 1972. See Nos. C195-C198, C234, C251, C253-C254. For overprint and surcharges see Benin Nos. C384, C392, C401, C444, C628, C652.

Statue of St. Teresa, Basilica of Lisieux — AP62

100fr, St. Teresa, roses, and globe, vert.

**1973, May 14** **Photo.** ***Perf. 13***

**C180** AP62 40fr blk, gold & lt ultra .75 .45
**C181** AP62 100fr gold & multi 2.50 1.00

St. Teresa of Lisieux (Therese Martin, 1873-97), Carmelite nun.
For surcharges see Benin Nos. C390, C570, C623.

Scouts, African Scout Emblem — AP63

Designs (African Scout Emblem and): 20fr, Lord Baden-Powell, vert. 40fr, Scouts building bridge.

**1973, July 2** **Engr.** ***Perf. 13***

**C182** AP63 15fr bl, grn & choc .45 .25
**C183** AP63 20fr ol & Prus bl .75 .25
**C184** AP63 40fr grn, Prus bl & brn .90 .35
*a.* Souvenir sheet of 3 3.00 3.00
*Nos. C182-C184 (3)* 2.10 .85

24th Boy Scout World Conference, Nairobi, Kenya, July 16-21. No. C184a contains 3 stamps similar to Nos. C182-C184 in changed colors (15fr in ultramarine, slate green and chocolate; 20fr in chocolate, ultramarine and indigo; 40fr in slate green, indigo and chocolate).
For surcharges see Nos. C217-C218, Benin C365, C409, C558, C560, C571.

Copernicus, Venera and Mariner Satellites — AP64

125fr, Copernicus, sun, earth & moon, vert.

**1973, Aug. 20** **Engr.** ***Perf. 13***

**C185** AP64 65fr blk, dk brn & org 1.50 .55
**C186** AP64 125fr bl, slate grn & pur 2.75 1.00

For surcharges see Benin Nos. C345, C375, C601, C642.

Head and City Hall, Brussels AP64a

**1973, Sept. 17** **Engr.** ***Perf. 13***

**C187** AP64a 100fr blk, Prus bl & dk grn 1.10 .60

African Weeks, Brussels, Sept. 15-30, 1973.
For surcharge see Benin No. C400.

WMO Emblem, World Weather Map — AP65

**1973, Sept. 25**

**C188** AP65 100fr ol grn & lt brn 1.40 .75

Cent. of intl. meteorological cooperation.
For surcharges and overprint see Nos. C199, Benin Nos. C382, C624.

### Europafrica Issue

AP66

Design: 40fr, similar to 35fr.

**1973, Oct. 1** **Engr.** ***Perf. 13***

**C189** AP66 35fr multi .55 .35
**C190** AP66 40fr bl, sepia & ultra .70 .40

For overprint and surcharges, see Benin Nos. C411, C564, C593.

John F. Kennedy — AP67

**1973, Oct. 18**

**C191** AP67 200fr bl grn, vio & sl grn 2.75 2.75
*a.* Souvenir sheet 5.00 5.00

Pres. John F. Kennedy (1917-63). No. C191a contains one stamp in changed colors (bright blue, magenta & brown).
For surcharge and overprint, see Benin Nos. C377, C441, C547.

Soccer — AP68

40fr, 2 soccer players. 100fr, 3 soccer players.

**1973, Nov. 19** **Engr.** ***Perf. 13***

**C192** AP68 35fr multi .55 .25
**C193** AP68 40fr multi .65 .25
**C194** AP68 100fr multi 1.25 .65
*Nos. C192-C194 (3)* 2.45 1.15

World Soccer Cup, Munich 1974.
For surcharges and overprint see Nos. C219-C220, Benin Nos. C396, C591, C644.

### Painting Type of 1972

Christmas: 35fr, Annunciation, by Dirk Bouts. 100fr, Nativity, by Giotto. 150fr, Adoration of the Kings, by Botticelli. 200fr, Adoration of the Shepherds, by Jacopo Bassano, horiz.

**1973, Dec. 20** **Photo.** ***Perf. 13***

**C195** AP61 35fr gold & multi .80 .40
**C196** AP61 100fr gold & multi 1.50 .65
**C197** AP61 150fr gold & multi 3.00 1.10
**C198** AP61 200fr gold & multi 3.25 1.75
*Nos. C195-C198 (4)* 8.55 3.90

For surcharges see Benin Nos. C378, C388, C410, C434, C442, C565, C646.

### No C188 Surcharged in Violet

**1974, Feb. 4** **Engr.** ***Perf. 13***

**C199** AP65 200fr on 100fr multi 2.25 1.25

Skylab US space missions, 1973-74.

Skiers, Snowflake, Olympic Rings — AP69

**1974, Feb. 25** **Engr.** ***Perf. 13***

**C200** AP69 100fr vio bl, brn & brt bl 1.75 1.10

50th anniversary of first Winter Olympic Games, Chamonix, France. For surcharge, see Benin No. C625.

Marie Curie AP70

**1974, June 7** **Engr.** ***Perf. 13***

**C201** AP70 50fr Lenin 1.75 .65
**C202** AP70 125fr shown 2.25 .90
**C203** AP70 150fr Churchill 2.50 1.40
*Nos. C201-C203 (3)* 6.50 2.95

50th anniv. of the death of Lenin; 40th anniv. of the death of Marie Sklodowska Curie; cent. of the birth of Winston Churchill.
For surcharges see Benin Nos. C391A, C489, C597, C632, C634.

Bishop, Persian, 18th Century — AP71

200fr, Queen, Siamese chess piece, 19th cent.

**1974, June 14** **Photo.** ***Perf. 12½x13***

**C204** AP71 50fr org & multi 2.50 1.00
**C205** AP71 200fr brt grn & multi 6.00 2.50

21st Chess Olympiad, Nice, 6/6-30/74.
For surcharges and overprint see Benin Nos. C469, C482, C598, Q11.

Frederic Chopin — AP72

Design: No. C207, Ludwig van Beethoven.

**1974, June 24** **Engr.** ***Perf. 13***

**C206** AP72 150fr blk & copper red 4.50 1.40
**C207** AP72 150fr blk & copper red 4.50 1.40

Famous musicians: Frederic Chopin and Ludwig van Beethoven.
For surcharges see Benin Nos. C376, C452, C459, C539, C579, C647.

Astronaut on Moon, and Earth AP73

**1974, July 10** **Engr.** ***Perf. 13***

**C208** AP73 150fr multi 2.75 1.50

5th anniversary of the first moon walk.
For surcharges and overprint see Benin Nos. C391, C460, C635.

---

Litho. & Embossed 'Gold Foil' Stamps
These stamps generally are of a different design format than the rest of the issue. Since there is a commemorative inscription tying them to the issue a separate illustration is not being shown.

---

There is some question as to the status of 4 sets, Nos. C209-C216, C225-C232, C238-C249.

World Cup Soccer Championships, Munich — AP74

World Cup trophy and players and flags of: 35fr, West Germany, Chile, Australia, DDR. 40fr, Zaire, Scotland, Brazil, Yugoslavia. 100fr, Sweden, Bulgaria, Uruguay, Netherlands. 200fr, Italy, Haiti, Poland, Argentina. 300fr, Stadium. 500fr, Trophy and flags.

*Perf. 14x13, 13x14*

**1974, July 16** **Litho.**

**C209** AP74 35fr multicolored .40 .25
**C210** AP74 40fr multicolored .55 .25
**C211** AP74 100fr multicolored 1.10 .70
**C212** AP74 200fr multicolored 2.50 1.25
**C213** AP74 300fr multi, horiz. 2.50 1.50

**Souvenir Sheet**

**C215** AP74 500fr multi, horiz. 7.25 7.25

It is uncertain if this issue was valid for postage or recognized by the Dahomey government.

**Nos. C182-C183 Srchd. and Ovptd. in Black or Red**

**1974, July 19**

**C217** AP63 100fr on 15fr multi 1.25 .60
**C218** AP63 140fr on 20fr multi (R) 1.75 .90

11th Pan-Arab Jamboree, Batrun, Lebanon, Aug. 1974. Overprint includes 2 bars over old denomination; 2-line overprint on No. C217, 3 lines on No. C218.

**Nos. C193-C194 Overprinted and Surcharged**

**1974, July 26** **Engr.** *Perf. 13*

**C219** AP68 100fr on 40fr 1.10 .65
**C220** AP68 150fr on 100fr 1.60 1.00

World Cup Soccer Championship, 1974, victory of German Federal Republic.

Earth and UPU Emblem — AP75

Designs (UPU Emblem and): 65fr, Concorde in flight. 125fr, French railroad car, c. 1860. 200fr, African drummer and Renault mail truck, pre-1939.

**1974, Aug. 5** **Engr.** *Perf. 13*

**C221** AP75 35fr rose cl & vio .75 .40
**C222** AP75 65fr Prus grn & cl 1.50 .95
**C223** AP75 125fr multi 3.50 1.50
**C224** AP75 200fr multi 3.50 2.00
*Nos. C221-C224 (4)* 9.25 4.85

Centenary of Universal Postal Union.
For surcharges, see Benin Nos. C422, C530, C540, C586, C653, Q17B.

UPU, Cent. — AP76

Communications and transportation: 50fr, Rocket, Indian shooting arrow. 100fr, Airplane, dog sled, vert. 125fr, Rocket launch, balloon. 150fr, Rocket re-entry into Earth's atmosphere, drum. 200fr, Locomotive, Pony Express rider. 500fr, UPU headquarters. No. C230, Train, 1829. No. C232, Astronaut canceling envelope on moon.

**1974** **Litho.** *Perf. 13x14, 14x13*

**C225** AP76 50fr multicolored .50 .30
**C226** AP76 100fr multicolored .75 .60
**C227** AP76 125fr multicolored 1.00 .85
**C228** AP76 150fr multicolored 1.75 1.00
**C229** AP76 200fr multicolored 2.50 1.25

**Litho. & Embossed**

*Perf. 13½*

**Size: 48x60mm**

**C230** AP76 1000fr gold & multi 12.00 12.00

**Souvenir Sheets**

**Litho.**

*Perf. 13x14*

**C231** AP76 500fr multicolored 4.50 4.50

**Litho. & Embossed**

*Perf. 13½*

**C232** AP76 1000fr gold & multi 7.25 7.25

Issued: #C230, C232, Oct. 9; others, Aug. 5.
It is uncertain if this issue was valid for postage or recognized by the Dahomey government.

**Painting Type of 1972 and**

Lion of Belfort by Frederic A. Bartholdi — AP77

Painting: 250fr, Girl with Falcon, by Philippe de Champaigne.

**1974, Aug. 20** **Engr.** *Perf. 13*

**C233** AP77 100fr rose brn 2.50 1.00
**C234** AP61 250fr multi 4.00 2.40

For surcharges see Benin Nos. C363, C387, C445, C626.

Prehistoric Animals — AP78

**1974, Sept. 23** **Photo.**

**C235** AP78 35fr Rhamphorhynchus 1.50 .80
**C236** AP78 150fr Stegosaurus 5.00 2.25
**C237** AP78 200fr Tyrannosaurus 7.00 2.75
*Nos. C235-C237 (3)* 13.50 5.80

For surcharges and overprint, see Benin Nos. C349, C350, C440, C548, C636.

Conquest of Space — AP79

Various spacecraft and: 50fr, Mercury. 100fr, Venus. 150fr, Mars. 200fr, Jupiter. 400fr, Sun.

**1974, Oct. 31** **Litho.** *Perf. 13x14*

**C238** AP79 50fr multicolored .40 .30
**C239** AP79 100fr multicolored 1.00 .50
**C240** AP79 150fr multicolored 1.75 .90
**C241** AP79 200fr multicolored 2.25 1.25
*Nos. C238-C241 (4)* 5.40 2.95

**Souvenir Sheet**

**C242** AP79 400fr multicolored 5.25 5.25

West Germany, World Cup Soccer Champions — AP80

Designs: 100fr, Team. 125fr, Paul Breitner. 150fr, Gerd Muller. 300fr, Presentation of trophy. 500fr, German team positioned on field.

**1974, Nov.** **Litho.** *Perf. 13x14*

**C243** AP80 100fr multicolored .75 .50
**C244** AP80 125fr multicolored 1.00 .75
**C245** AP80 150fr multicolored 1.50 1.00
**C246** AP80 300fr multicolored 3.25 2.00
*Nos. C243-C246 (4)* 6.50 4.25

**Souvenir Sheet**

**C248** AP80 500fr multicolored 5.25 5.25

**Europafrica Issue**

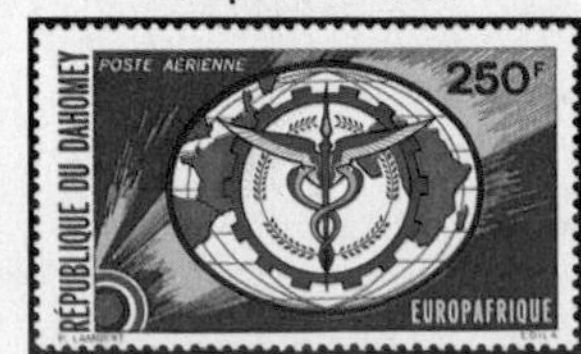


Globe, Cogwheel, Emblem — AP81

**1974, Dec. 20** **Typo.** *Perf. 13*

**C250** AP81 250fr red & multi 3.25 2.75

Printed tête bêche in sheets of 10.
For surcharges see Benin Nos. C430, C509, C650.

**Christmas Type of 1972 and**

Nativity, by Martin Schongauer — AP82

Paintings: 35fr, Annunciation, by Schongauer. 100fr, Virgin in Rose Arbor, by Schongauer. 250fr, Virgin and Child, with St. John the Baptist, by Botticelli.

**1974, Dec. 23** **Photo.** *Perf. 13*

**C251** AP61 35fr gold & multi .60 .30
**C252** AP82 40fr gold & multi .60 .40
**C253** AP61 100fr gold & multi 1.60 .55
**C254** AP61 250fr gold & multi 4.25 1.75
*Nos. C251-C254 (4)* 7.05 3.00

For surcharges, see Benin Nos. C413, C431, C439, C446, C641.

Apollo and Soyuz Spacecraft AP83

200fr, American and Russian flags, rocket take-off. 500fr, Apollo-Soyuz link-up.

**1975, July 16** **Litho.** *Perf. 12½*

**C255** AP83 35fr multi .60 .30
**C256** AP83 200fr vio bl, red & bl 2.40 1.25
**C257** AP83 500fr vio bl, ind & red 5.50 3.00
*Nos. C255-C257 (3)* 8.40 4.55

Apollo Soyuz space test project (Russo-American cooperation); launching July 15; link-up, July 17.
For surcharges and overprints, see Benin Nos. C406, C415-C416, C451, C542-C543, C549, C580.

**Nos. C255-C256 Surcharged**

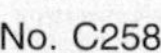
No. C258

No. C259

**1975, July 17** **Litho.** *Perf. 12½*

**C258** AP83 100fr on 35fr (S) 1.25 .60
**C259** AP83 300fr on 200fr 3.25 1.40

Apollo-Soyuz link-up in space, July 17, 1975.

ARPHILA Emblem, "Stamps" and Head of Ceres — AP84

**1975, Aug. 22 Engr. *Perf. 13***

**C260** AP84 100fr blk, bl & lilac 1.50 .75

ARPHILA 75, International Philatelic Exhibition, Paris, June 6-16.

For surcharges see Benin Nos. C383, C474.

### Europafrica Issue

Holy Family, by Micholangclo AP85

**1975, Sept. 29 Litho. *Perf. 12***

**C261** AP85 300fr gold & multi 4.50 1.50

For surcharge and overprint, see Benin Nos. C447, C554.

Infantry and Stars — AP86

American bicentennial (Stars and): 135fr, Drummers and fifer. 300fr, Artillery with cannon. 500fr, Cavalry.

**1975, Nov. 18 Engr. *Perf. 13***

**C262** AP86 75fr grn car & pur 1.00 .45
**C263** AP86 135fr bl, mag & sep 1.75 .90
**C264** AP86 300fr vio bl, ver & choc 3.25 1.75
**C265** AP86 500fr ver, dk grn & brn 5.75 2.50
*Nos. C262-C265 (4)* 11.75 5.60

For overprints and surcharges see Benin Nos. C247-C249, C385, C412, C453, C478, C555, C557, C576, C588.

Diving and Olympic Rings AP87

Design: 250fr, Soccer and Olympic rings.

**1975, Nov. 24**

**C266** AP87 40fr vio, grnsh bl & ol brn .55 .25
**C267** AP87 250fr red, emer & brn 2.40 1.25

Pre-Olympic Year 1975.

For surcharges see Benin Nos. C341, C393, C582.

---

## AIR POST SEMI-POSTAL STAMPS

Maternity Hospital, Dakar — SPAP1

Dispensary, Mopti — SPAP2

Nurse Weighing Baby — SPAP3

***Perf. 13½x12½, 13 (#CB3)***
**Photo, Engr. (#CB3)**

**1942, June 22**

**CB1** SPAP1 1.50fr + 3.50fr green .80 *5.50*
**CB2** SPAP2 2fr + 6fr brown .80 *5.50*
**CB3** SPAP3 3fr + 9fr car red .80 *5.50*
*Nos. CB1-CB3 (3)* 2.40 *16.50*

Native children's welfare fund.

### Colonial Education Fund
Common Design Type
***Perf. 12½x13½***

**1942, June 22 Engr.**

**CB4** CD86a 1.20fr + 1.80fr blue & red .80 *5.50*

---

## AIR POST PARCEL POST STAMPS

**Catalogue values for unused stamps in this section are for Never Hinged items.**

**Nos. C20-C23, C14 Surcharged in Black or Red**

No. CQ2

No. CQ5

**1967-69 Engr. *Perf. 13***

**CQ1** AP6 200fr on 200fr 2.10 2.10
**CQ2** AP6 300fr on 100fr 2.40 2.40
**CQ3** AP6 500fr on 300fr 4.50 4.50
**CQ4** AP6 1000fr on 500fr 9.50 9.50
**CQ5** AP4 5000fr on 100fr (R) ('69) 35.00 35.00
*Nos. CQ1-CQ5 (5)* 53.50 53.50

On No. CQ5, "Colis Postaux" is at top, bar at right.

---

## POSTAGE DUE STAMPS

Dahomey Natives — D1

**1906 Unwmk. Typo. *Perf. 14x13½***

**J1** D1 5c grn, *grnsh* 4.00 4.00
**J2** D1 10c red brn 4.00 4.00
**J3** D1 15c dark blue 8.00 8.00
**J4** D1 20c blk, *yellow* 8.00 8.00
**J5** D1 30c red, *straw* 12.00 12.00
**J6** D1 50c violet 24.00 24.00
**J7** D1 60c blk, *buff* 16.00 16.00
**J8** D1 1fr blk, *pinkish* 52.50 40.00
*Nos. J1-J8 (8)* 128.50 116.00

D2

**1914**

**J9** D2 5c green .25 .25
**J10** D2 10c rose .55 .55
**J11** D2 15c gray .55 .55
**J12** D2 20c brown 1.10 1.10
**J13** D2 30c blue 1.40 1.40
**J14** D2 50c black 1.60 1.60
**J15** D2 60c orange 2.00 2.00
**J16** D2 1fr violet 2.10 2.10
*Nos. J9-J16 (8)* 9.55 9.55

Type of 1914 Issue Surcharged

**1927**

**J17** D2 2fr on 1fr lilac rose 5.50 5.50
**J18** D2 3fr on 1fr org brn 5.50 5.50

Carved Mask — D3

**1941 Engr. *Perf. 14x13***

**J19** D3 5c black .25 .25
**J20** D3 10c lilac rose .25 .25
**J21** D3 15c dark blue .25 .25
**J22** D3 20c bright yel green .30 .30
**J23** D3 30c orange .50 .50
**J24** D3 50c violet brown .70 .70
**J25** D3 60c slate green 1.10 1.10
**J26** D3 1fr rose red 1.40 1.40
**J27** D3 2fr yellow 1.50 1.50
**J28** D3 3fr dark purple 1.90 1.90
*Nos. J19-J28 (10)* 8.15 8.15

### Type D3 without "RF"

**1944**

**J28A** D3 10c lilac rose .50
**J28B** D3 15c dark blue .55
**J28C** D3 20c bright yel green .55
*Nos. J28A-J28C (3)* 1.60

Nos. J28A-J28C were issued by the Vichy government in France, but were not placed on sale in Dahomey.

**Catalogue values for unused stamps in this section, from this point to the end of the section, are for Never Hinged items.**

### Republic

Panther and Man — D4

***Perf. 14x13½***

**1963, July 22 Typo. Unwmk.**

**J29** D4 1fr green & rose .25 .25
**J30** D4 2fr brn & emerald .30 .30
**J31** D4 5fr org & vio bl .30 .30
**J32** D4 10fr magenta & blk .65 .65
**J33** D4 20fr vio bl & org 1.10 1.10
*Nos. J29-J33 (5)* 2.60 2.60

Heliograph — D5

No. J35, Mail boat. No. J36, Morse receiver. No. J37, Mailman on bicycle. No. J38, Early telephone. No. J39, Autorail. No. J40, Mail truck. No. J41, Radio tower. No. J42, DC-8F jet plane. No. J43, Early Bird communications satellite.

**1967, Oct. 24 Engr. *Perf. 11***

**J34** D5 1fr brn, dl pur & bl .25 .25
**J35** D5 1fr dl pur, brn & bl .25 .25
*a.* Pair, #J34-J35 .25
**J36** D5 3fr dk brn, dk grn & org .25 .25
**J37** D5 3fr dk grn, dk brn & org .25 .25
*a.* Pair, #J36-J37 .25
**J38** D5 5fr ol bis, lil & bl .35 .35
**J39** D5 5fr lil, ol bis & bl .35 .35
*a.* Pair, #J38-J39 .75
**J40** D5 10fr brn org, vio & grn .50 .50
**J41** D5 10fr vio, brn org & grn .50 .50
*a.* Pair, #J40-J41 1.10
**J42** D5 30fr Prus bl, mar & vio 1.00 1.00
**J43** D5 30fr vio, Prus bl & mar 1.00 1.00
*a.* Pair, #J42-J43 2.25
*Nos. J34-J43 (10)* 4.70 4.70

Pairs printed tete beche, se-tenant at the base.

---

## PARCEL POST STAMPS

**Catalogue values for unused stamps in this section are for Never Hinged items.**

Nos. 141-146 and 148 Surcharged

**1967, Jan. Unwmk. Engr. *Perf. 13***

**Q1** A15 5fr on 1fr multi .25 .25
**Q2** A15 10fr on 2fr multi .35 .35
**Q3** A15 20fr on 6fr multi .60 .60
**Q4** A15 25fr on 3fr multi .90 .90
**Q5** A15 30fr on 4fr multi 1.00 1.00
**Q6** A15 50fr on 10fr multi 1.40 1.40
*a.* "20" instead of "50" 100.00
**Q7** A15 100fr on 20fr multi 2.50 2.50
*Nos. Q1-Q7 (7)* 7.00 7.00

The surcharge is arranged to fit the shape of the stamp.

No. Q6a occurred once on the sheet.

## DALMATIA

dal-'mă-sh,ē-,ə

LOCATION — A promontory in the northwestern part of the Balkan Peninsula, together with several small islands in the Adriatic Sea.
GOVT. — Part of the former Austro-Hungarian crownland of the same name.
AREA — 113 sq. mi.
POP. — 18,719 (1921)
CAPITAL — Zara.

Stamps were issued during Italian occupation. This territory was subsequently annexed by Italy.

100 Centesimi = 1 Corona = 1 Lira

---

Used values are for postally used stamps.

---

### Issued under Italian Occupation

Italy No. 87 Surcharged

**1919, May 1 Wmk. 140 *Perf. 14***

1 A46 1cor on 1 l brn & grn 3.50 *15.00*
a. Pair, one without surcharge *1,050.* *1,050.*

Italian Stamps of 1906-08 Surcharged — a

**1921-22**

2 A48 5c on 5c green 3.50 *4.75*
3 A48 10c on 10c claret 3.50 *4.75*
a. Pair, one without surcharge 875.00
4 A49 25c on 25c blue ('22) 6.00 *7.25*
5 A49 50c on 50c vio ('22) 6.00 *7.25*
a. Double surcharge *250.00*
b. Pair, one without surcharge *1,050.*

Italian Stamps of 1901-10 Surcharged — b

6 A46 1cor on 1 l brn & grn ('22) 8.00 *24.00*
7 A46 5cor on 5 l bl & rose ('22) 45.00 *120.00*
8 A51 10cor on 10 l gray grn & red ('22) 45.00 *120.00*
*Nos. 2-8 (7)* 117.00 *288.00*

Surcharges similar to these but differing in style or arrangement of type were used in Austria under Italian occupation.

---

### SPECIAL DELIVERY STAMPS

Italian Special Delivery No. E1 Srchd. Type "a"

**1921 Wmk. 140 *Perf. 14***

E1 SD1 25c on 25c rose red 3.50 *15.00*
a. Double surcharge 400.00 *650.00*

### Italian Special Delivery Stamp Surcharged

**1922**

E2 SD2 1.20 l on 1.20 l 240.00

No. E2 was not placed in use.

---

### POSTAGE DUE STAMPS

### Italian Postage Due Stamps and Type Surcharged types "a" or "b"

**1922 Wmk. 140 *Perf. 14***

J1 D3 (a) 50c on 50c buff & mag 4.00 *9.00*
J2 D3 (b) 1cor on 1 l bl & red 9.00 *32.50*
J3 D3 (b) 2cor on 2 l bl & red 55.00 *135.00*
J4 D3 (b) 5cor on 5 l bl & red 55.00 *135.00*
*Nos. J1-J4 (4)* 123.00 *311.50*

---

## DANISH WEST INDIES

'dā-nish 'west 'in-dēs

LOCATION — Group of islands in the West Indies, lying east of Puerto Rico
GOVT. — Danish colony
AREA — 132 sq. mi.
POP. — 27,086 (1911)
CAPITAL — Charlotte Amalie

The US bought these islands in 1917 and they became the US Virgin Islands, using US stamps and currency.



100 Cents = 1 Dollar
100 Bit = 1 Franc (1905)

Wmk. 111 — Small Crown

Wmk. 112 — Crown

Wmk. 113 — Crown

Wmk. 114 — Multiple Crosses

Coat of Arms — A1

### Yellowish Paper
### Yellow Wavy-line Burelage, UL to LR

**1856 Typo. Wmk. 111 *Imperf.***

1 A1 3c dark carmine, brown gum 200. *275.*
a. 3c dark carmine, yellow gum 225. *275.*
b. 3c carmine, white gum *4,250.* —

The brown and yellow gums were applied locally.

*Reprint: 1981, carmine, back-printed across two stamps ("Reprint by Dansk Post og Telegrafmuseum 1978"), value, pair, $10.*

### White Paper

**1866**
**Yellow Wavy-line Burelage UR to LL**

2 A1 3c rose 40. *65.*

*No. 2 reprints, unwatermarked: 1930, carmine, value $100. 1942, rose carmine, back-printed across each row ("Nytryk 1942 G. A. Hagemann Danmark og Dansk Vestindiens Frimaerker Bind 2"), value $50.*

**1872 *Perf. 12½***

3 A1 3c rose 100. *275.*

**1873 Without Burelage**

4 A1 4c dull blue 250. *475.*
a. Imperf., pair 775.
b. Horiz. pair, imperf. vert. 575.

*The 1930 reprint of No. 4 is ultramarine, unwatermarked and imperf., value $100.*

*The 1942 4c reprint is blue, unwatermarked, imperf. and has printing on back (see note below No. 2), value $60.*

A2

Normal Frame

Inverted Frame

The arabesques in the corners have a main stem and a branch. When the frame is in normal position, in the upper left corner the branch leaves the main stem half way between two little leaflets. In the lower right corner the branch starts at the foot of the second leaflet. When the frame is inverted the corner designs are, of course, transposed.

### White Wove Paper
### Varying from Thin to Thick

**1874-79 Wmk. 112 *Perf. 14x13½***

Values for inverted frames, covers and blocks are for the cheapest variety.

5 A2 1c green & brown red 22.50 *30.00*
a. 1c green & rose lilac, thin paper 80.00 *125.00*
b. 1c green & red violet, medium paper 45.00 *65.00*
c. 1c green & claret, thick paper 20.00 *30.00*
e. As "c," inverted frame 25.00 *32.50*
f. As "a," inverted frame *475.00*

No. 5 exists with a surcharge similar to the surcharge on No. 15, with 10 CENTS value and 1895 date. This stamp is an essay.

6 A2 3c blue & carmine 27.50 20.00
a. 3c light blue & rose carmine, thin paper 65.00 50.00
b. 3c deep blue & dark carmine, medium paper 40.00 17.00
c. 3c greenish blue & lake, thick paper 32.50 17.00
d. Imperf., pair 375.00 —
e. Inverted frame, thick paper 30.00 20.00
f. As "a," inverted frame *350.00*
7 A2 4c brown & dull blue 16.00 *19.00*
b. 4c brown & ultramarine, thin paper 225.00 *225.00*
c. Diagonal half used as 2c on cover 140.00
d. As "b," inverted frame *900.00* *1,400.*
8 A2 5c grn & gray ('76) 30.00 20.00
a. 5c yellow green & dark gray, thin paper 55.00 32.50
b. Inverted frame, thick paper 30.00 20.00
9 A2 7c lilac & orange 35.00 *95.00*
a. 7c lilac & yellow 90.00 *100.00*
b. Inverted frame 65.00 *150.00*
10 A2 10c blue & brn ('76) 30.00 25.00
a. 10c dark blue & black brown, thin paper 70.00 40.00
b. Period between "t" & "s" of "cents" 35.00 25.00
c. Inverted frame 27.50 *32.50*
11 A2 12c red lil & yel grn ('77) 42.50 *175.00*
a. 12c lilac & deep green 160.00 *200.00*
12 A2 14c lilac & green 650.00 *1,250.*
a. Inverted frame *2,500.* *3,500.*
13 A2 50c vio, thin paper ('79) 190.00 *300.00*
a. 50c gray violet, thick paper 250.00 *375.00*
*Nos. 5-13 (9)* 1,044. 1,934.

The central element in the fan-shaped scrollwork at the outside of the lower left corner of Nos. 5a and 7b looks like an elongated diamond.

See Nos. 16-20. For surcharges see Nos. 14-15, 23-28, 40.

### No. 9 Surcharged in Black

a

**1887**

14 A2 (a) 1c on 7c lilac & orange 100.00 *200.00*
a. 1c on 7c lilac & yellow 120.00 *225.00*
b. Double surcharge 250.00 *500.00*
c. Inverted frame 110.00 *350.00*

### No. 13 Surcharged in Black

b

**1895**

15 A2 (b) 10c on 50c violet, thin paper 42.50 *67.50*

The "b" surcharge also exists on No. 5, with "10" found in two sizes. These are essays.

### Type of 1874-79

**1896-1901 *Perf. 13***

16 A2 1c grn & red vio, inverted frame ('98) 15.00 *22.50*
a. Normal frame 300.00 *450.00*
17 A2 3c blue & lake, inverted frame ('98) 12.00 *17.50*
a. Normal frame 250.00 *425.00*

18 A2 4c bister & dull blue ('01) 17.50 11.00
a. Diagonal half used as 2c on cover 100.00
b. Inverted frame 60.00 *80.00*
c. As "b," diagonal half used as 2c on cover 350.00
19 A2 5c green & gray, inverted frame 35.00 35.00
a. Normal frame 800.00 *1,200.*
20 A2 10c blue & brn ('01) 80.00 *150.00*
a. Inverted frame 1,000. *2,000.*
b. Period between "t" and "s" of "cents" 170.00 160.00
*Nos. 16-20 (5)* 159.50 *236.00*

Arms — A5

**1900**
21 A5 1c light green 3.00 3.00
22 A5 5c light blue 17.50 *25.00*

See Nos. 29-30. For surcharges see Nos. 41-42.

**Nos. 6, 17, 20 Surcharged**

c

**Surcharge "c" in Black**

**1902** *Perf. 14x13½*
23 A2 2c on 3c blue & carmine, inverted frame 700.00 *900.00*
a. "2" in date with straight tail 750.00 *950.00*
b. Normal frame —

*Perf. 13*

24 A2 2c on 3c blue & lake, inverted frame 10.00 *27.50*
a. "2" in date with straight tail 12.00 *32.50*
b. Dated "1901" 750.00 750.00
c. Normal frame 175.00 *300.00*
d. Dark green surcharge 2,750.
e. As "d" & "a" — —
f. As "d" & "c" —

The overprint on No. 24b exists in two types: with "1901" measuring 2.5 mm or 2.2 mm high.

Only one example of No. 24f can exist.

25 A2 8c on 10c blue & brown 25.00 *42.50*
a. "2" with straight tail 30.00 *45.00*
b. On No. 20b 32.50 *45.00*
c. Inverted frame 250.00 *425.00*

d

**Surcharge "d" in Black**

**1902** *Perf. 13*
27 A2 2c on 3c blue & lake, inverted frame 12.00 *32.50*
a. Normal frame 240.00 *425.00*
28 A2 8c on 10c blue & brown 12.00 12.00
a. On No. 20b 18.50 *25.00*
b. Inverted frame 225.00 *400.00*
*Nos. 23-28 (5)* 759.00 1,015.

**1903** **Wmk. 113**
29 A5 2c carmine 8.00 *22.50*
30 A5 8c brown 27.50 *35.00*

King Christian IX — A8

St. Thomas Harbor — A9

**1905** **Typo.** *Perf. 13*
31 A8 5b green 3.75 3.25
32 A8 10b red 3.75 3.25
33 A8 20b green & blue 8.75 8.75
34 A8 25b ultramarine 8.75 *10.50*
35 A8 40b red & gray 8.25 *9.50*
36 A8 50b yellow & gray 10.00 10.00

*Perf. 12*

**Wmk. Two Crowns (113)**

**Frame Typographed, Center Engraved**

37 A9 1fr green & blue 17.50 *40.00*
38 A9 2fr orange red & brown 30.00 *55.00*
39 A9 5fr yellow & brown 77.50 *275.00*
*Nos. 31-39 (9)* 168.25 *415.25*

Favor cancels exist on Nos. 37-39. Value 25% less.

Nos. 18, 22 and 30 Surcharged in Black

**1905** **Wmk. 112**
40 A2 5b on 4c bister & dull blue 16.00 *50.00*
a. Inverted frame 45.00 *90.00*
41 A5 5b on 5c light blue 10.00 *47.50*

**Wmk. 113**

42 A5 5b on 8c brown 12.50 *50.00*
*Nos. 40-42 (3)* 38.50 147.50

Favor cancels exist on Nos. 40-42. Value 25% less.

Frederik VIII — A10

**Frame Typographed, Center Engraved**

**1908**
43 A10 5b green 1.90 1.90
44 A10 10b red 1.90 1.90
45 A10 15b violet & brown 3.75 *4.50*
46 A10 20b green & blue 30.00 27.50
47 A10 25b blue & dark blue 1.90 *2.50*
48 A10 30b claret & slate 50.00 *52.50*
49 A10 40b vermilion & gray 5.75 *9.50*
50 A10 50b yellow & brown 5.75 *14.00*
*Nos. 43-50 (8)* 100.95 114.30

Christian X — A11

**1915** **Wmk. 114** *Perf. 14x14½*
51 A11 5b yellow green 4.00 *5.50*
52 A11 10b red 4.00 *55.00*
53 A11 15b lilac & red brown 4.00 *55.00*
54 A11 20b green & blue 4.00 *55.00*
55 A11 25b blue & dark blue 4.00 *17.50*
56 A11 30b claret & black 4.00 *100.00*
57 A11 40b orange & black 4.00 *100.00*
58 A11 50b yellow & brown 3.75 *100.00*
*Nos. 51-58 (8)* 31.75 *488.00*

Forged and favor cancellations exist.

**POSTAGE DUE STAMPS**

Royal Cipher, "Christian 9 Rex" D1

**1902** **Litho.** **Unwmk.** *Perf. 11½*
J1 D1 1c dark blue 5.00 *17.50*
J2 D1 4c dark blue 12.50 *22.50*
J3 D1 6c dark blue 22.50 *60.00*
J4 D1 10c dark blue 20.00 *65.00*
*Nos. J1-J4 (4)* 60.00 *165.00*

There are five types of each value. On the 4c they may be distinguished by differences in the figure "4"; on the other values differences are minute.

Used values of Nos. J1-J8 are for canceled stamps. Uncanceled stamps without gum have probably been used. Value 60% of unused.

Excellent counterfeits of Nos. J1-J4 exist.

Numeral of value — D2

**1905-13** *Perf. 13*
J5 D2 5b red & gray 4.50 *6.75*
J6 D2 20b red & gray 7.50 *14.00*
J7 D2 30b red & gray 6.75 *14.00*
J8 D2 50b red & gray 6.00 *30.00*
a. Perf. 14x14½ ('13) 37.50 *140.00*
b. Perf. 11½ 325.00
*Nos. J5-J8 (4)* 24.75 *64.75*

All values of this issue are known imperforate, but were not regularly issued.

Used values of Nos. J5-J8 are for canceled stamps. Uncanceled examples without gum have probably been used. Value 60% of unused.

Counterfeits of Nos. J5-J8 exist.

Danish West Indies stamps were replaced by those of the U.S. in 1917, after the U.S. bought the islands.

## DANZIG

'dan‚t‚-sig

LOCATION — In northern Europe bordering on the Baltic Sea
AREA — 754 sq. mi.
POP. — 407,000 (approx. 1939)
CAPITAL — Danzig

Established as a "Free City and State" under the protection of the League of Nations in 1920, Danzig was seized by Germany in 1939. It became a Polish province in 1945.

100 Pfennig = 1 Gulden (1923)
100 Pfennig = 1 Mark

**Watermarks**

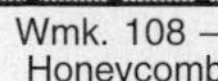

Wmk. 108 — Honeycomb

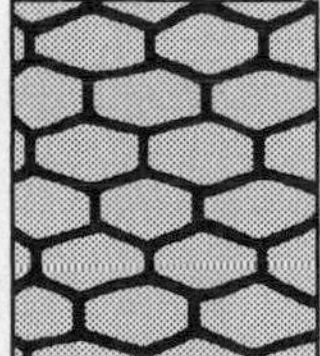

Wmk. 109 — Webbing

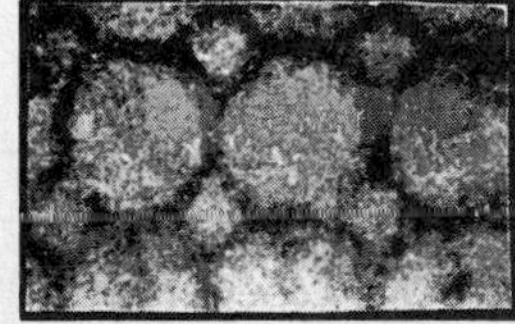

Wmk. 110 — Octagons

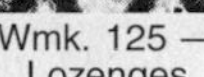

Wmk. 125 — Lozenges

Wmk. 237 — Swastikas

Used Values of 1920-23 are for favor-canceled stamps unless otherwise noted. Postally used examples bring much higher prices.

For additional varieties, see the *Scott Classic Catalogue.*

German Stamps of 1906-20 Overprinted in Black

*Perf. 14, 14½, 15x14½*

**1920** **Wmk. 125**
1 A16 5pf green .30 *.50*
a. Pair, one without overprint 100.00
b. Double overprint —
2 A16 10pf car rose .30 .30
3 A22 15pf violet brown .30 .30
4 A16 20pf blue violet .30 *1.10*
5 A16 30pf org & blk, *buff* .30 .30
a. Pair, one without overprint — —
6 A16 40pf car rose .30 .30
7 A16 50pf pur & blk, *buff* .50 .30
a. Pair, one without overprint 175.00
8 A17 1m red .50 .60
a. Pair, one without overprint 100.00
9 A17 1.25m green .50 .60
10 A17 1.50m yellow brn .90 *1.60*
11 A21 2m blue 3.25 *7.25*
a. Double overprint *375.00*
Never hinged 825.00
12 A21 2.50m lilac rose 3.00 *4.50*
c. Double overprint 1,000.
13 A19 3m black violet 7.50 *10.50*
a. 3m blackish slate-violet 67.50 *135.00*
b. Double overprint
14 A16 4m black & rose 4.75 *6.00*
15 A20 5m slate & car (25x17 holes) 2.50 *3.75*
a. Center & "Danzig" invtd. *15,000.*
Never hinged
b. Inverted overprint *20,000.*
*Nos. 1-15 (15)* 25.20 37.90
Set, never hinged 122.50

The 5pf brown, 10pf orange and 40pf lake and black with this overprint were not regularly issued. Value for trio, $450.

For surcharges see Nos. 19-23, C1-C3.

Issued: 40pf, 9/13; 1.50m, 3m 7/20; 4m, 12/21; others 6/14.

Nos. 5, 4 Surcharged in Various Sizes

**1920**
19 A16 5pf on 30pf (V) .25 .25
20 A16 10pf on 20pf (R) .25 .25
a. Double surcharge 110.00 —
Never hinged 250.00
21 A16 25pf on 30pf (G) .25 .25
a. Inverted surcharge 85.00 *275.00*
Never hinged 250.00
22 A16 60pf on 30pf (Br) .70 *1.00*
a. Double surcharge 85.00 *290.00*
Never hinged 250.00
b. Pair, one without surcharge *75.00*
23 A16 80pf on 30pf (V) .70 *1.00*

Issued: No. 21, 8/10. No. 20, 8/17. Nos. 19, 22-23, 11/1.

**German Stamps Surcharged in Various Styles**

No. 25

No. 27

No. 30

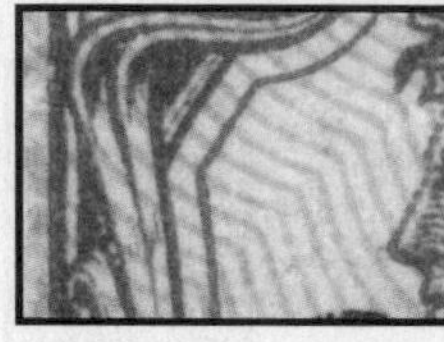
Burelage With Points Up

### Gray Burelage with Points Up

| No. | Type | Description | Unused | Used |
|---|---|---|---|---|
| 25 | A16 | 1m on 30pf org & blk, *buff* (Bk) | .85 | 1.50 |
| a. | | Pair, one without surcharge | | |
| 26 | A16 | 1¼m on 3pf brn (R) | 1.00 | 1.50 |
| 27 | A22 | 2m on 35pf red brn (Bl) | 1.50 | 1.50 |
| d. | | Surcharge omitted | 70.00 | — |
| | | Never hinged | 260.00 | |
| 28 | A22 | 3m on 7½pf org (G) | 1.00 | 1.50 |
| 29 | A22 | 5m on 2pf gray (R) | 1.00 | 2.00 |
| 30 | A22 | 10m on 7½pf org (Bk) | 3.00 | 7.00 |
| | | *Nos. 19-30 (11)* | 10.50 | 17.75 |
| | | Set, never hinged | 64.00 | |

### Gray Burelage with Points Down

| No. | Type | Description | Unused | Used |
|---|---|---|---|---|
| 26a | A16 | 1¼m on 3pf brown | 36.00 | 42.50 |
| 27a | A22 | 2m on 35pf red brn | 400.00 | 325.00 |
| 28a | A22 | 3m on 7½pf orange | 25.00 | 17.00 |
| 29a | A22 | 5m on 2pf gray | 25.00 | 30.00 |
| 30a | A22 | 10m on 7½pf orange | 5.75 | 11.00 |
| | | *Nos. 26a-30a (5)* | 491.75 | 425.50 |
| | | Set, never hinged | 2,100. | |

### Violet Burelage with Points Up

| No. | Type | Description | Unused | Used |
|---|---|---|---|---|
| 25b | A16 | 1m on 30pf org & blk, *buff* | 85.00 | 30.00 |
| 26b | A16 | 1¼m on 3pf brown | 4.50 | 6.50 |
| 27b | A22 | 2m on 35pf red brn | 11.50 | 37.50 |
| 28b | A22 | 3m on 7½pf orange | 2.50 | 2.50 |
| 29b | A22 | 5m on 2pf gray | 1.25 | 2.50 |
| 30b | A22 | 10m on 7½pf orange | 1.25 | 2.50 |
| h. | | Double overprint | 70.00 | |
| | | *Nos. 25b-30b (6)* | 106.00 | 81.50 |
| | | Set, never hinged | 430.00 | |

Burelage with Points Down

### Violet Burelage with Points Down

| No. | Type | Description | Unused | Used |
|---|---|---|---|---|
| 25c | A16 | 1m on 30pf org & blk, *buff* | 1.25 | 2.50 |
| 26c | A16 | 1¼m on 3pf brown | 6.50 | 11.00 |
| e. | | Double overprint | 450.00 | |
| 27c | A22 | 2m on 35pf red brn | 30.00 | 50.00 |
| 28c | A22 | 3m on 7½pf orange | 40.00 | 85.00 |
| 29c | A22 | 5m on 2pf gray | 6.50 | 8.50 |
| 30c | A22 | 10m on 7½pf orange | 13.50 | 29.00 |
| | | *Nos. 25c-30c (6)* | 97.75 | 186.00 |
| | | Set, never hinged | 380.00 | |

Excellent counterfeits of the surcharges are known.

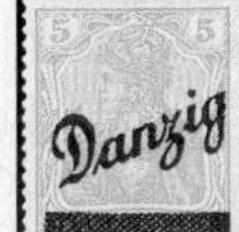

German Stamps of 1906-20 Overprinted in Blue

### 1920

| No. | Type | Description | Unused | Used |
|---|---|---|---|---|
| 31 | A22 | 2pf gray | 110.00 | 200.00 |
| 32 | A22 | 2½pf gray | 150.00 | 300.00 |
| 33 | A16 | 3pf brown | 11.00 | 17.00 |
| a. | | Double overprint | 75.00 | — |
| | | Never hinged | 180.00 | |
| 34 | A16 | 5pf green | .60 | .70 |
| a. | | Double overprint | 85.00 | |
| | | Never hinged | 200.00 | |
| 35 | A22 | 7½pf orange | 40.00 | 57.50 |
| 36 | A16 | 10pf carmine | 3.75 | 7.00 |
| b. | | Double overprint | 75.00 | |
| 37 | A22 | 15pf dk violet | .60 | .70 |
| b. | | Double overprint | 85.00 | |
| | | Never hinged | 200.00 | |
| 38 | A16 | 20pf blue violet | .60 | .70 |

### Overprinted in Carmine or Blue

| No. | Type | Description | Unused | Used |
|---|---|---|---|---|
| 39 | A16 | 25pf org & blk, *yel* | .60 | .70 |
| 40 | A16 | 30pf org & blk, *buff* | 50.00 | 92.50 |
| 42 | A16 | 40pf lake & blk | 2.25 | 2.50 |
| a. | | Inverted overprint | 210.00 | |
| b. | | Double overprint | 425.00 | |
| 43 | A16 | 50pf pur & blk, *buff* | 175.00 | 300.00 |
| 44 | A16 | 60pf mag (Bl) | 1,250. | 2,100. |
| 45 | A16 | 75pf green & blk | .60 | .70 |
| a. | | Double overprint | 450.00 | |
| 46 | A16 | 80pf lake & blk, *rose* | 2.40 | 4.25 |
| 47 | A17 | 1m carmine | 1,200. | 2,100. |
| a. | | Double overprint | 4,250. | |

Overprinted in Carmine

| No. | Type | Description | Unused | Used |
|---|---|---|---|---|
| 48 | A21 | 2m gray blue | 1,200. | 2,100. |

Counterfeit overprints of Nos. 31-48 exist.

Nos. 44, 47 and 48 were issued in small quantities and usually affixed directly to the mail by the postal clerk.

For surcharge see No. 62.

A8

Hanseatic Trading Ship — A9

### Serrate Roulette 13½

**1921, Jan. 31 Typo. Wmk. 108**

| No. | Type | Description | Unused | Used |
|---|---|---|---|---|
| 49 | A8 | 5pf brown & violet | .25 | .25 |
| 50 | A8 | 10pf orange & dk vio | .25 | .25 |
| 51 | A8 | 25pf green & car rose | .50 | .65 |
| 52 | A8 | 40pf carmine rose | 3.75 | 3.25 |
| 53 | A8 | 80pf ultra | .50 | .50 |
| 54 | A9 | 1m car rose & blk | 1.60 | 2.00 |
| 55 | A9 | 2m dk blue & dk grn | 5.00 | 5.00 |
| 56 | A9 | 3m blk & grnsh bl | 2.00 | 2.00 |
| 57 | A9 | 5m indigo & rose red | 2.00 | 2.00 |
| 58 | A9 | 10m dk grn & brn org | 2.50 | 4.50 |
| | | *Nos. 49-58 (10)* | 18.35 | 20.40 |
| | | Set, never hinged | 82.50 | |

Issued in honor of the Constitution.

Nos. 49 and 50 with center in red instead of violet and Nos. 49-51, 54-58 with center inverted are probably proofs. All values of this issue exist imperforate but are not known to have been regularly issued in that condition.

**1921, Mar. 11** *Perf. 14*

| No. | Type | Description | Unused | Used |
|---|---|---|---|---|
| 59 | A8 | 25pf green & car rose | .50 | .85 |
| 60 | A8 | 40pf carmine rose | .50 | .85 |
| 61 | A8 | 80pf ultra | 5.50 | 10.00 |
| | | *Nos. 59-61 (3)* | 6.50 | 11.70 |
| | | Set, never hinged | 34.00 | |

No. 45 Surcharged in Black

**1921, May 6 Wmk. 125**

| No. | Type | Description | Unused | Used |
|---|---|---|---|---|
| 62 | A16 | 60pf on 75pf | .95 | .90 |
| | | Never hinged | 5.50 | |
| a. | | Double surcharge | 100.00 | 110.00 |
| | | Never hinged | 250.00 | |

Surcharge on No. 62 normally appears at top of design.

Arms — A11

Coat of Arms — A12

### Wmk. 108 (Upright or Sideways)

**1921-22** *Perf. 14*

| No. | Type | Description | Unused | Used |
|---|---|---|---|---|
| 63 | A11 | 5(pf) orange | .25 | .25 |
| 64 | A11 | 10(pf) dark brown | .25 | .25 |
| 65 | A11 | 15(pf) green | .25 | .25 |
| 66 | A11 | 20(pf) slate | .25 | .25 |
| 67 | A11 | 25(pf) dark green | .25 | .25 |
| 68 | A11 | 30(pf) blue & car | .25 | .25 |
| | | Never hinged | .85 | |
| a. | | Center inverted | 75.00 | 150.00 |
| | | Never hinged | 225.00 | |
| 69 | A11 | 40pf green & car | .25 | .25 |
| | | Never hinged | .85 | |
| a. | | Center inverted | 75.00 | 150.00 |
| | | Never hinged | 225.00 | |
| 70 | A11 | 50pf dk grn & car | .25 | .25 |
| 71 | A11 | 60pf carmine | .45 | .45 |
| 72 | A11 | 80pf black & car | .35 | .45 |

### Paper With Faint Gray Network

| No. | Type | Description | Unused | Used |
|---|---|---|---|---|
| 73 | A11 | 1m org & car | .50 | .40 |
| a. | | Center inverted | 75.00 | 150.00 |
| | | Never hinged | 225.00 | |
| 74 | A11 | 1.20m blue violet | 1.25 | 1.25 |
| 75 | A11 | 2m gray & car | 3.25 | 4.25 |
| 76 | A11 | 3m violet & car | 9.00 | 10.00 |

### Serrate Roulette 13½

### Wmk. 108 Upright

| No. | Type | Description | Unused | Used |
|---|---|---|---|---|
| 77 | A12 | 5m grn, red & blk | 1.25 | 3.00 |
| 78 | A12 | 9m rose, red & org ('22) | 3.00 | 8.50 |
| 79 | A12 | 10m ultra, red & blk | 1.25 | 3.00 |
| 80 | A12 | 20m red & black | 1.25 | 3.00 |
| | | *Nos. 63-80 (18)* | 23.55 | 36.30 |
| | | Set, never hinged | 85.00 | |

In this and succeeding issues the mark values usually have the face of the paper covered with a gray network. This network is often very faint and occasionally is omitted.

Nos. 64-76 exist imperf. Value, each $16-$50 unused, $50-$150 never hinged.

See Nos. 81-93, 99-105. For surcharges and overprints see Nos. 96-98, O1-O33.

Type of 1921 and

A13

Coat of Arms — A13a

**1922 Wmk. 108 Upright** *Perf. 14*

| No. | Type | Description | Unused | Used |
|---|---|---|---|---|
| 81 | A11 | 75(pf) deep vio | .25 | .25 |
| 82 | A11 | 80(pf) green | .25 | .25 |
| 83 | A11 | 1.25m vio & car | .25 | .25 |
| 84 | A11 | 1.50m slate gray | .25 | .40 |
| 85 | A11 | 2m car rose | .25 | .25 |
| 86 | A11 | 2.40m dk brn & car | 1.15 | 2.00 |
| 87 | A11 | 3m car lake | .25 | .40 |
| 88 | A11 | 4m dark blue | 1.15 | 2.00 |
| 89 | A11 | 5m deep grn | .25 | .35 |
| 90 | A11 | 6m car lake | .25 | .35 |
| a. | | 6m car rose, wmk. 109 sideways | 1,800. | |
| | | Never hinged | 3,900. | |
| 91 | A11 | 8m light blue | .45 | 1.60 |
| 92 | A11 | 10m orange | .25 | .35 |
| 93 | A11 | 20m org brn | .25 | .35 |
| 94 | A13 | 50m gold & car | 2.00 | 6.50 |
| a. | | 50m gold & red | 57.50 | 120.00 |
| | | Never hinged | 220.00 | |
| 95 | A13a | 100m metallic grn & red | 3.25 | 6.00 |
| | | *Nos. 81-95 (15)* | 10.50 | 21.30 |
| | | Set, never hinged | 42.50 | |

No. 95 has buff instead of gray network.

Nos. 81-83, 85-86, 88 exist imperf. Value, each $12.50.

Nos. 94-95 exist imperf. Value, each $50

### Nos. 87, 88 and 91 Surcharged in Black or Carmine

**1922**

| No. | Type | Description | Unused | Used |
|---|---|---|---|---|
| 96 | A11 | 6m on 3m car lake | .35 | .60 |
| a. | | Double surcharge | | |
| 97 | A11 | 8m on 4m dk blue | .35 | .85 |
| a. | | Double surcharge | 70.00 | 145.00 |
| | | Never hinged | 140.00 | |
| b. | | Pair, one without surcharge | 150.00 | |
| 98 | A11 | 20m on 8m lt bl (C) | .35 | .60 |
| | | *Nos. 96-98 (3)* | 1.05 | 2.05 |
| | | Set, never hinged | 4.00 | |

### Wmk. 109 Sideways

**1922-23** *Perf. 14*

| No. | Type | Description | Unused | Used |
|---|---|---|---|---|
| 99 | A11 | 4m dark blue | .25 | .40 |
| 100 | A11 | 5m dark green | .25 | .40 |
| 102 | A11 | 10m orange | .25 | .40 |
| 103 | A11 | 20m orange brn | .25 | .40 |

### Paper Without Network

### Wmk. 109 Upright

| No. | Type | Description | Unused | Used |
|---|---|---|---|---|
| 104 | A11 | 40m pale blue | .25 | .60 |
| 105 | A11 | 80m red | .25 | .60 |
| | | *Nos. 99-105 (6)* | 1.50 | 2.80 |
| | | Set, never hinged | 5.40 | |

Nos. 100, 102 and 103 also exist with watermark vertical. Values slightly higher.

Nos. 104-105 exist imperf. Value, each $12.50 unused, $32.50 never hinged.

A15

A15a

Coat of Arms A16

**1922-23 Wmk. 109 Upright** *Perf. 14*

### Paper With Gray Network

| No. | Type | Description | Unused | Used |
|---|---|---|---|---|
| 106 | A15 | 50m pale bl & red | .25 | .40 |
| 107 | A15a | 100m dk grn & red | .25 | .40 |
| 108 | A15a | 150m violet & red | .25 | .40 |
| 109 | A16 | 250m violet & red | .40 | .40 |
| 110 | A16 | 500m gray blk & red | .40 | .40 |
| 111 | A16 | 1000m brn & red | .40 | .40 |
| 112 | A16 | 5000m silver & red | 1.50 | 6.00 |

### Paper Without Network

| No. | Type | Description | Unused | Used |
|---|---|---|---|---|
| 113 | A15 | 50m pale blue | .40 | .60 |
| 114 | A15a | 100m deep green | .40 | .60 |
| 115 | A15 | 200m orange | .40 | .60 |
| | | *Nos. 106-115 (10)* | 4.65 | 10.20 |
| | | Set, never hinged | 19.00 | |

Nos. 108-112 exist imperf. Value, each $50 unused, $125 never hinged.

Nos. 113-115 exist imperf. Value, each $35 unused, $92.50 never hinged.

See Nos. 123-125. For surcharges and overprints see Nos. 126, 137-140, 143, 156-167, O35-O38.

A17

**1923** *Perf. 14*

**Paper With Gray Network**

**117** A17 250m violet & red .25 *.55*
**118** A17 300m bl grn & red .25 *.55*
**119** A17 500m gray & red .25 *.55*
**120** A17 1000m brown & red .25 *.55*
**121** A17 3000m violet & red .25 *.55*
**123** A16 10,000m orange & red .60 .60
**124** A16 20,000m pale bl & red .60 *1.00*
**125** A16 50,000m green & red .60 *1.00*
*Nos. 117-125 (8)* 3.05 *5.35*
Set, never hinged 12.50

Nos. 117, 119-121 exist imperf. Value, each $19 unused, $45 never hinged; Nos. 123-125 also exist imperf. Values each, $25 unused, $85 never hinged.

See Nos. 127-135. For surcharges & overprints see Nos. 141-142, 144-155, O39-O41.

**No. 124 Surcharged in Red**

**1923, Aug. 14**

**126** A16 100,000m on #124 1.00 *6.00*
Never hinged 4.50

No. 126 exists imperf. Value $50 unused, $125 never hinged.

**1923** *Perf. 14*

**Paper Without Network**

**127** A17 1000m brown .25 *.40*
**129** A17 5000m rose .25 *.40*
**131** A17 20,000m pale blue .25 *.40*
**132** A17 50,000m green .25 *.40*

**Paper With Gray Network**

**133** A17 100,000m deep blue .25 *.40*
*b.* Double impression 80.00
**134** A17 250,000m violet .25 *.40*
**135** A17 500,000m slate .25 *.40*
*Nos. 127-135 (7)* 1.75 2.80
Set, never hinged 5.00

**Abbreviations:**
**th=(tausend) thousand**
**mil=million**

Nos. 115, 114, 132, and Type of 1923 Surcharged

No. 137-139

No. 140

No. 141

No. 142

**1923** *Perf. 14*

**Paper Without Network**

**137** A15 40th m on 200m .85 *2.00*
*a.* Double surcharge 85.00
Never hinged 160.00
**138** A15 100th m on 200m .85 *2.00*
**139** A15 250th m on 200m 6.25 *13.00*
**140** A15a 400th m on 100m .60 .60
**141** A17 500th m on #132 .40 *.60*

**On 10,000m**

**142** A17 1mil m org 3.75 *6.25*

The surcharges on Nos. 140-142 differ in details from those on Nos. 137-139.

**Type of 1923 Surcharged**

**Paper With Gray Network**
**On 1,000,000m**

**143** A16 10mil m org .40 *1.25*
*Nos. 137-143 (7)* 13.10 *25.70*
Set, never hinged 60.00

Nos. 142-143 exist imperf. Values: No. 142 unused $50, never hinged $125; No. 143 unused $25, never hinged $85.

Type of 1923 Surcharged

**Wmk. 109 Upright**
***Perf. 14***
**10,000m rose on paper without Network**

**144** A17 1mil m on 10,000m .25 *.60*
**145** A17 2mil m on 10,000m .25 *.60*
**146** A17 3mil m on 10,000m .25 *.60*
**147** A17 5mil m on 10,000m .35 *.60*
*b.* Double surcharge 85.00
Never hinged 160.00

**10,000m gray lilac on paper without Network**

**148** A17 10mil m on 10,000m .40 *.75*
**149** A17 20mil m on 10,000m .40 *.75*
**150** A17 25mil m on 10,000m .25 *.75*
**151** A17 40mil m on 10,000m .25 *.75*
*a.* Double surcharge 52.50
Never hinged 160.00
**152** A17 50mil m on 10,000m .25 *.75*

Type of 1923 Surcharged in Red

**10,000m gray lilac on paper without Network**

**153** A17 100mil m on 10,000m .25 *.75*
**154** A17 300mil m on 10,000m .25 *.75*
**155** A17 500mil m on 10,000m .25 *.75*
*Nos. 144-155 (12)* 3.40 *8.40*
Set, never hinged 15.00

Nos. 144-147 exist imperf. Value, each $25 unused, $85 never hinged. Nos. 148-155 exist imperf. Value, each $32.50 unused, $85 never hinged.

Types of 1923 Surcharged

**1923, Oct. 31** **Wmk. 110** *Perf. 14*

**156** A15 5pf on 50m .45 .40
**157** A15 10pf on 50m .45 .40
**158** A15a 20pf on 100m .45 .40
**159** A15 25pf on 50m 3.50 *9.00*
**160** A15 30pf on 50m 3.50 2.00
**161** A15a 40pf on 100m 2.25 2.00
**162** A15a 50pf on 100m 2.25 *3.00*
**163** A15a 75pf on 100m 8.00 *16.00*

**Type of 1923 Surcharged**

**1923, Nov. 5**

**164** A16 1g on 1mil m rose 4.50 *6.25*
**165** A16 2g on 1mil m rose 12.00 *17.50*
**166** A16 3g on 1mil m rose 22.00 *62.50*
**167** A16 5g on 1mil m rose 25.00 *67.50*
*Nos. 156-167 (12)* 84.35 *186.95*
Set, never hinged 400.00

Coat of Arms — A19

**1924-37** **Wmk. 109** *Perf. 14*

**168** A19 3pf brn, *yelsh* ('35) 1.25 *1.50*
*a.* 3pf dp brn, *white* ('27) 2.10 1.90
Never hinged 9.50
**170** A19 5pf org, *yelsh* 3.25 .55
*a.* White paper 8.50 2.00
Never hinged 45.00
*c.* Tête bêche pair 375.00
Never hinged 725.00
*d.* Syncopated perf., #170 10.50 9.25
Never hinged 30.00
*e.* Syncopated perf., #170a 25.00 22.50
Never hinged 120.00
**171** A19 7pf yel grn ('33) 1.60 *3.00*
**172** A19 8pf yel grn ('37) 1.60 *6.00*
**173** A19 10pf grn, *yelsh* 5.50 .50
*a.* White paper 11.50 2.50
Never hinged 47.50
*c.* 10pf blue grn, *yellowish* 7.75 1.10
Never hinged 27.50
*d.* Tête bêche pair 325.00
Never hinged 750.00
*e.* Syncopated perf., #173 18.00 11.00
Never hinged 55.00
*f.* Syncopated perf., #173a 27.50 13.00
Never hinged 110.00
*g.* Syncopated perf., #173c 11.00 *14.50*
Never hinged 37.50
**175** A19 15pf gray 3.75 .65
**176** A19 15pf red, *yelsh* ('35) 2.10 1.10
*a.* White paper ('25) 4.50 1.10
Never hinged 25.00
**177** A19 20pf carmine & red 15.00 .65
**178** A19 20pf gray ('35) 2.25 *2.50*
**179** A19 25pf slate & red 27.00 3.75
**180** A19 25pf carmine ('35) 16.00 1.60
**181** A19 30pf green & red 14.00 .85
**182** A19 30pf dk violet ('35) 2.25 *4.25*
**183** A19 35pf ultra 4.50 1.50
**184** A19 40pf dk blue & blue 12.00 1.00
**185** A19 40pf yel brn & red 6.50 *12.50*
**186** A19 40pf dk blue ('35) 2.25 *3.75*
*a.* Imperf. 60.00
Never hinged 170.00
**187** A19 50pf blue & red 16.00 7.50
*a.* Yellowish paper 17.50 *32.50*
Never hinged 57.50
**188** A19 55pf plum & scar 5.00 *14.50*
**189** A19 60pf dk grn & red 6.25 *17.50*
**190** A19 70pf yel grn & red ('35) 2.25 *7.50*
**191** A19 75pf violet & red, *yellowish* 7.50 *29.00*
*a.* White paper 10.00 8.50
Never hinged 47.50
**192** A19 80pf dk org brn & red ('35) 2.25 *7.50*
*Nos. 168-192 (23)* 160.05 *129.15*
Set, never hinged 675.00

The 5pf and 10pf with syncopated perforations (Netherlands type C) are coils.

See Nos. 225-232. For overprints and surcharges see Nos. 200-209, 211-215, 241-252, B9-B11, O42-O52.

Oliva Castle and Cathedral A20

St. Mary's Church A23

Council Chamber on the Langenmarkt A24

2g, Mottlau River & Krantor. 3g, View of Zoppot.

**1924-32** **Engr.** **Wmk. 125**

**193** A20 1g yel grn & blk 21.00 *45.00*
Parcel post cancel 20.00
**194** A20 1g org & gray blk ('32) 17.00 3.75
Parcel post cancel 1.00
*a.* 1g red orange & blk 17.00 11.00
Never hinged 67.50
Parcel post cancel 1.00
**195** A20 2g red vio & blk 45.00 *110.00*
Parcel post cancel 40.00
**196** A20 2g rose & blk 3.75 *8.00*
Parcel post cancel 1.75
**197** A20 3g dk blue & blk 4.75 *5.00*
Parcel post cancel 2.25
**198** A23 5g brn red & blk 4.75 *8.50*
Parcel post cancel 1.90
**199** A24 10g dk brn & blk 21.00 *110.00*
Parcel post cancel 18.00
*Nos. 193-199 (7)* 117.25 *290.25*
Set, never hinged 600.00

See No. 233. For overprints and surcharges see Nos. 210, 253-254, C31-C35.

Stamps of 1924-25 Overprinted in Black, Violet or Red

**1930, Nov. 15** **Typo.** **Wmk. 109**

**200** A19 5pf orange 2.50 *3.50*
**201** A19 10pf yellow grn (V) 3.50 4.25
**202** A19 15pf red 6.00 *10.00*
**203** A19 20pf carmine & red 3.00 *5.50*
**204** A19 25pf slate & red 4.25 *10.00*
**205** A19 30pf green & red 8.50 *22.50*
**206** A19 35pf ultra (R) 32.50 *90.00*
**207** A19 40pf dk bl & bl (R) 11.50 *35.00*
**208** A19 50pf dp blue & red 32.50 *75.00*
**209** A19 75pf violet & red 32.50 *82.50*

**Engr.** **Wmk. (125)**

**210** A20 1g orange & blk (R) 32.50 *75.00*
*Nos. 200-210 (11)* 169.25 *413.25*
Set, never hinged 675.00

10th anniv. of the Free State. Counterfeits exist.

**Nos. 171 and 183 Surcharged in Red, Blue or Green**

Nos. 211-214

No. 215

**1934-36**

**211** A19 6pf on 7pf (R) 1.00 *1.50*
**212** A19 8pf on 7pf (Bl) 2.00 *2.25*
**213** A19 8pf on 7pf (R) 1.15 *2.40*
**214** A19 8pf on 7pf (G) .75 *2.40*
**215** A19 30pf on 35pf (Bl) 11.00 *24.50*
*Nos. 211-215 (5)* 15.90 *33.05*
Set, never hinged 60.00

Bathing Beach, Brösen A25

View of Brösen Beach A26

War Memorial at Brösen — A27

**1936, June 23** **Typo.** **Wmk. 109**

**216** A25 10pf deep green .70 *.70*
**217** A26 25pf rose red 1.25 *2.40*
**218** A27 40pf bright blue 2.25 *4.50*
*Nos. 216-218 (3)* 4.20 *7.60*
Set, never hinged 15.00

Village of Brösen, 125th anniversary.

Exist imperf. Value each, $40 unused, $110 never hinged.

Skyline of Danzig — A28

**1937, Mar. 27**

**219** A28 10pf dark blue .50 *1.40*
**220** A28 15pf violet brown 1.60 *2.00*
Set, never hinged 11.25
Set of 2, #219-220 on one 1st day cover 20.00

Air Defense League.

**Danzig Philatelic Exhibition Issue**
Souvenir Sheet

St. Mary's Church — A29

**1937, June 6 Wmk. 109 *Perf. 14***

**221** A29 50pf dark opal green 4.00 *20.00*
Never hinged 11.00

Danzig Philatelic Exhib., June 6-8, 1937.

Arthur Schopenhauer
A30 A31

Design: 40pf, Full-face portrait, white hair.

**Unwmk.**

**1938, Feb. 22 Photo. *Perf. 14***

**222** A30 15pf dull blue 1.35 *2.40*
**223** A31 25pf sepia 3.25 *8.00*
**224** A31 40pf orange ver 1.35 *3.25*
*Nos. 222-224 (3)* 5.95 *13.65*
Set, never hinged 20.00
Set of 3, #222-224 on one 1st day cover 37.50

150th anniv. of the birth of Schopenhauer.

**Type of 1924-35**

**1938-39 Typo. Wmk. 237 *Perf. 14***

**225** A19 3pf brown .90 *7.25*
**226** A19 5pf orange .90 *2.00*
*b.* Syncopated perf. 1.40 *7.50*
Never hinged 5.50
**227** A19 8pf yellow grn 4.00 *32.50*
**228** A19 10pf blue green .90 *2.00*
*b.* Syncopated perf. 3.00 *10.00*
Never hinged 14.00
**229** A19 15pf scarlet 1.60 *10.00*
**230** A19 25pf carmine 2.10 *7.50*
**231** A19 40pf dark blue 2.10 *27.50*
**232** A19 50pf brt bl & red 2.10 *130.00*

**Engr.**

**233** A20 1g red org & blk 6.75 *110.00*
*Nos. 225-233 (9)* 21.35 *328.75*
Set, never hinged 90.00

Sizes: No. 233, 32½x21¼mm; No. 194, 31x21mm.

Nos. 226b and 228b are coils with Netherlands type C perforation.

Knights in Tournament, 1500 — A33

French Leaving Danzig, 1814 — A35

Stamp Day: 10pf, Signing of Danzig-Sweden neutrality treaty, 1630. 25pf, Battle of Weichselmünde, 1577.

**Unwmk.**

**1939, Jan. 7 Photo. *Perf. 14***

**234** A33 5pf dark green .40 *2.00*
**235** A33 10pf copper brown .85 *2.25*
**236** A35 15pf slate black 1.25 *2.75*
**237** A35 25pf brown violet 1.60 *3.75*
*Nos. 234-237 (4)* 4.10 *10.75*
Set, never hinged 14.00
Set of 4, #234-237 on one 1st day cover 30.00

Gregor Mendel — A37

15pf, Dr. Robert Koch. 25pf, Wilhelm Roentgen.

**1939, Apr. 29 Photo. *Perf. 13x14***

**238** A37 10pf copper brown .65 *.85*
**239** A37 15pf indigo .65 *2.00*
**240** A37 25pf dark olive green 1.25 *2.75*
*Nos. 238-240 (3)* 2.55 *5.60*
Set, never hinged 7.25

Issued in honor of the achievements of Mendel, Koch and Roentgen.

**Issued under German Administration**

Stamps of Danzig, 1925-39, Surcharged in Black

a

b

c

**1939 Wmk. 109 *Perf. 14***

**241** A19(b) 4rpf on 35pf ultra .75 *2.25*
**242** A19(b) 12rpf on 7pf yel grn 1.50 *2.25*
**243** A19(a) 20rpf gray 3.00 *8.50*

**Wmk. 237**

**244** A19(a) 3rpf brown .75 *2.40*
**245** A19(a) 5rpf orange .65 *3.00*
**246** A19(a) 8rpf yellow grn 1.10 *4.25*
**247** A19(a) 10rpf blue grn 2.25 *4.25*
**248** A19(a) 15rpf scarlet 6.00 *11.00*
**249** A19(a) 25rpf carmine 4.50 *10.00*
**250** A19(a) 30rpf dk violet 2.00 *4.50*
**251** A19(a) 40rpf dk blue 2.75 *6.00*
**252** A19(a) 50rpf brt bl & red 4.00 *7.00*

**Thick Paper**

**253** A20(c) 1rm on 1g red org & blk 14.00 *57.50*

**Wmk. 125**

**Thin White Paper**

**254** A20(c) 2rm on 2g rose & blk 20.00 *62.50*
*Nos. 241-254 (14)* 63.25 *185.40*
Set, never hinged 190.00

Nos. 241-254 were valid throughout Germany.

---

## SEMI-POSTAL STAMPS

St. George and Dragon — SP1

**Wmk. 108**

**1921, Oct. 16 Typo. *Perf. 14***

**Size: 19x22mm**

**B1** SP1 30pf + 30pf grn & org .45 .95
**B2** SP1 60pf + 60pf rose & org 1.25 *1.60*

**Size: 25x30mm**

***Serrate Roulette 13½***

**B3** SP1 1.20m + 1.20m dk bl & org 2.00 *2.25*
*Nos. B1-B3 (3)* 3.70 4.80
Set, never hinged 16.00

Nos. B1-B3 exist imperf. Value each, $45 unused, $125 never hinged.

Aged Pensioner SP2

**1923, Mar. Wmk. 109 *Perf. 14***

**Paper With Gray Network**

**B4** SP2 50m + 20m lake .25 *.60*
**B5** SP2 100m + 30m red vio .25 *.60*
Set, never hinged 2.50

Nos. B4-B5 exist imperf. Value each, $50 unused, $30 used, $210 never hinged.

**Philatelic Exhibition Issue**

Neptune Fountain — SP3

Various Frames.

**1929, July 7 Engr. Unwmk.**

**B6** SP3 10pf yel grn & gray 2.40 1.60
**B7** SP3 15pf car & gray 2.40 1.60
**B8** SP3 25pf ultra & gray 8.50 *13.00*
*a.* 25pf violet blue & black 25.00 *80.00*
Never hinged 92.50
*Nos. B6-B8 (3)* 13.30 16.20
Set, never hinged 45.00
Set of 3, #B6-B8 on one 1st day cover 200.00

These stamps were sold exclusively at the Danzig Philatelic Exhibition, June 7-14, 1929, at double their face values, the excess being for the aid of the exhibition.

Regular Issue of 1924-25 Surcharged in Black

**1934, Jan. 15 Wmk. 109**

**B9** A19 5pf + 5pf orange 9.50 *19.00*
**B10** A19 10pf + 5pf yel grn 22.50 *45.00*
**B11** A19 15pf + 5pf carmine 13.50 *35.00*
*Nos. B9-B11 (3)* 45.50 *99.00*
Set, never hinged 220.00

Surtax for winter welfare. Counterfeits exist.

Stock Tower — SP4

George Hall — SP6

City Gate, 16th Century SP5

**1935, Dec. 16 Typo. *Perf. 14***

**B12** SP4 5pf + 5pf orange .65 *1.50*
**B13** SP5 10pf + 5pf green 1.10 *2.25*
**B14** SP6 15pf + 10pf scarlet 2.75 *3.50*
*Nos. B12-B14 (3)* 4.50 *7.25*
Set, never hinged 16.00
Set of 3, #B12-B14 on one 1st day cover 40.00

Surtax for winter welfare.

Milk Can Tower SP7

Frauentor SP8

Krantor — SP9

Langgarter Gate — SP10

High Gate SP11

**1936, Nov. 25**

**B15** SP7 10pf + 5pf dk bl 1.60 *4.50*
*a.* Imperf. 75.00
Never hinged 180.00
**B16** SP8 15pf + 5pf dull grn 1.60 *5.75*
**B17** SP9 25pf + 10pf red brn 2.25 *9.00*
**B18** SP10 40pf + 20pf brn & red brn 3.00 *10.00*
**B19** SP11 50pf + 20pf bl & dk bl 5.25 *15.00*
*Nos. B15-B19 (5)* 13.70 *44.25*
Set, never hinged 80.00

Surtax for winter welfare.

SP12

SP13

**1937, Oct. 30 Wmk. 109 Sideways**
**B20** SP12 25pf + 25pf dk car 2.75 *5.25*

**Wmk. 109 Upright**

**B21** SP13 40pf + 40pf blue & red 2.75 *5.25*
*a.* Souvenir sheet of 2, #B20a-B21 60.00 *110.00*
Never hinged 110.00
Set, never hinged 27.50

Founding of Danzig community at Magdeburg. No. B21a exists imperf. Value, $1,600 unused, $3,250 never hinged.

Madonna SP14

Mercury SP15

Weather Vane, Town Hall SP16

Neptune Fountain SP17

St. George and Dragon — SP18

**1937, Dec. 13**
**B23** SP14 5pf + 5pf brt violet 2.50 *7.50*
**B24** SP15 10pf + 10pf dk brn 2.50 *5.75*
**B25** SP16 15pf + 5pf bl & yel brn 2.50 *8.25*
**B26** SP17 25pf + 10pf bl grn & grn 3.25 *11.00*
**B27** SP18 40pf + 25pf brt car & bl 5.75 *15.00*
*Nos. B23-B27 (5)* 16.50 *47.50*
Set, never hinged 65.00
Set of 5, #B23-B27 on one 1st day cover 100.00

Surtax for winter welfare. Designs are from frieze of the Artushof.

"Peter von Danzig" Yacht Race — SP19

Ships: 10pf+5pf, Dredger Fu Shing. 15pf+10pf, S. S. Columbus. 25pf+10pf, S. S. City of Danzig. 40pf+15pf, Peter von Danzig, 1472.

**1938, Nov. 28 Photo. Unwmk.**
**B28** SP19 5pf + 5pf dk bl grn 1.40 *1.50*
**B29** SP19 10pf + 5pf gldn brn 1.40 *3.00*
**B30** SP19 15pf + 10pf ol grn 1.60 *3.00*
**B31** SP19 25pf + 10pf indigo 2.50 *4.00*
**B32** SP19 40pf + 15pf vio brn 3.00 *6.75*
*Nos. B28-B32 (5)* 9.90 *18.25*
Set, never hinged 50.00
Set of 5, #B28-B32 on one 1st day cover 60.00

Surtax for winter welfare.

## AIR POST STAMPS

**No. 6 Surcharged in Blue or Carmine**

**1920, Sept. 29 Wmk. 125 *Perf. 14***
**C1** A16 40pf on 40pf 1.25 *2.60*
*a.* Double surcharge 160.00 *250.00*
Never hinged 450.00
**C2** A16 60pf on 40pf (C) 1.25 *2.60*
*a.* Double surcharge 125.00 *250.00*
Never hinged 350.00
**C3** A16 1m on 40pf 1.25 *2.60*
*a.* Double surcharge 125.00 250.00
Never hinged 350.00
*Nos. C1-C3 (3)* 3.75 *7.80*
Set, never hinged 13.50

Plane faces left on No. C2.

AP3

Plane over Danzig AP4

**Wmk. (108) Upright**

**1921-22 Typo. *Perf. 14***
**C4** AP3 40(pf) blue green .25 *.45*
**C5** AP3 60(pf) dk violet .25 *.45*
**C6** AP3 1m carmine .25 *.45*
**C7** AP3 2m org brn .25 *.45*

***Serrate Roulette 13½***

**Size: 34½x23mm**

**C8** AP4 5m violet blue 1.25 *2.25*
**C9** AP4 10m dp grn 2.00 *4.25*
*Nos. C4-C9 (6)* 4.25 *8.30*
Set, never hinged 18.00

Nos. C4-C9 exist imperf. Value, each $32.50 unused, $125 never hinged.

**1923 Wmk. (109) Upright *Perf. 14***
**C10** AP3 40(pf) blue green .55 *1.90*
**C11** AP3 60(pf) dk violet .55 *1.90*
*a.* Double impression —
**C12** AP3 1m carmine .55 *1.90*
**C13** AP3 2m org brown .55 *1.90*
**C14** AP3 25m pale blue .40 *.70*

***Serrate Roulette 13½***

**Size: 34½x23mm**

**C15** AP4 5m violet blue .55 *1.00*
**C16** AP4 10m deep green .55 *1.00*

**Paper With Gray Network**

**C17** AP4 20m org brn .55 *1.00*

**Size: 40x23mm**

**C18** AP4 50m orange .40 *.70*
**C19** AP4 100m red .40 *.70*
**C20** AP4 250m dark brown .60 *.70*
**C21** AP4 500m car rose .60 *.70*
*Nos. C10-C21 (12)* 6.25 *14.10*
Set, never hinged 30.00

Nos. C11, C12, C14-C21 exist imperf. Value, Nos. C11, C12, C15-C17, each $8.50 unused, $32.50 never hinged. Value, No. C14, C18-C21, each $40 unused, $125 never hinged.

Nos. C18, C19 and C21 exist with wmk. sideways, both perf and imperf. Value each, $60 unused, $160 never hinged.

Post Horn and Airplanes — AP5

**1923, Oct. 18 *Perf. 14***

**Paper Without Network**

**C22** AP5 250,000m scarlet .35 *1.25*
**C23** AP5 500,000m scarlet .35 *1.25*
Set, never hinged 2.50

Exist imperf. Value, each: $50 unused; $125 never hinged.

Surcharged

**On 100,000m**

**C24** AP5 2mil m scarlet .35 *1.25*

**On 50,000m**

**C25** AP5 5mil m scarlet .35 *1.25*
*b.* Cliché of 10,000m in sheet of 50,000m 32.50 *160.00*
Never hinged 130.00

Exist imperf. Value, each $125 unused, $290 never hinged.

Nos. C24 and C25 were not regularly issued without surcharge, although examples have been passed through the post. Values: C24 unused $8.50, never hinged $32.50; C25 unused $12, never hinged $21.

AP6

Plane over Danzig — AP7

**1924**
**C26** AP6 10(pf) vermilion 21.00 3.50
**C27** AP6 20(pf) carmine rose 2.10 1.50
**C28** AP6 40(pf) olive brown 3.00 1.75
**C29** AP6 1g deep green 3.00 3.00
**C30** AP7 2½g violet brown 17.50 *32.50*
*Nos. C26-C30 (5)* 46.60 *42.25*
Set, never hinged 175.00

Exist imperf. Value Nos. C26, C30, $85 unused, $200 never hinged; others, each $40 unused, $110 never hinged.

Nos. 193, 195, 197-199 Srchd. in Various Colors

**1932 Wmk. 125**
**C31** A20 10pf on 1g (G) 9.00 *21.00*
**C32** A20 15pf on 2g (V) 9.00 *21.00*
**C33** A20 20pf on 3g (Bl) 9.00 *21.00*
**C34** A23 25pf on 5g (R) 9.00 *21.00*
**C35** A24 30pf on 10g (Br) 9.00 *21.00*
*Nos. C31-C35 (5)* 45.00 *105.00*
Set, never hinged 200.00

Intl. Air Post Exhib. of 1932. The surcharges were variously arranged to suit the shapes and designs of the stamps. The stamps were sold at double their surcharged values, the excess being donated to the exhibition funds.

No. C31 exists with inverted surcharge and with double surcharge. Value each, $85 unused, $210 never hinged.

Airplane
AP8 AP9

**1935, Oct. 24 Wmk. 109**
**C36** AP8 10pf scarlet 1.75 .85
**C37** AP8 15pf yellow 1.75 1.25
**C38** AP8 25pf dark green 1.75 1.50
**C39** AP8 50pf gray blue 9.00 *9.25*
**C40** AP9 1g magenta 3.50 *13.00*
*Nos. C36-C40 (5)* 17.75 *25.85*
Set, never hinged 65.00

Nos. C36 and C40 exist imperf. Values: C36 unused $20, never hinged $62.50; C40 unused $29, never hinged $85.

See Nos. C42-C45.

Souvenir Sheet

St. Mary's Church — AP10

**1937, June 6 *Perf. 14***
**C41** AP10 50pf dark grayish blue 3.75 *16.00*
Never hinged 10.50

Danzig Phil. Exhib., June 6-8, 1937.

**Type of 1935**

**1938-39 Wmk. 237**
**C42** AP8 10pf scarlet 1.25 *3.75*
**C43** AP8 15pf yellow ('39) 2.00 *12.00*
**C44** AP8 25pf dark green 1.60 *6.50*
**C45** AP8 50pf gray blue ('39) 4.00 *57.50*
*Nos. C42-C45 (4)* 8.85 *79.75*
Set, never hinged 42.50

## POSTAGE DUE STAMPS

Danzig Coat of Arms — D1

**1921-22 Typo. Wmk. (108) *Perf. 14***

**Paper Without Network**

**J1** D1 10(pf) deep violet .35 *.45*
**J2** D1 20(pf) deep violet .35 *.45*
**J3** D1 40(pf) deep violet .35 *.45*
**J4** D1 60(pf) deep violet .35 *.45*
**J5** D1 75(pf) dp violet ('22) .35 *.45*
**J6** D1 80(pf) deep violet .35 *.45*
**J7** D1 120(pf) deep violet .35 *.45*
**J8** D1 200(pf) dp violet ('22) .95 *1.00*
**J9** D1 240(pf) deep violet .35 *1.00*
**J10** D1 300(pf) dp violet ('22) .95 *1.00*
**J11** D1 400(pf) deep violet .95 *1.00*
**J12** D1 500(pf) deep violet .95 *1.00*
**J13** D1 800(pf) deep violet ('22) .95 *1.00*
**J14** D1 20m dp violet ('22) .95 *1.00*
*Nos. J1-J14 (14)* 8.50 *10.15*
Set, never hinged 27.50

Nos. J1-J14 exist imperf. Value, each $30 unused, $75 never hinged.

**1923 Wmk. 109 Sideways**
**J15** D1 100(pf) deep violet .60 *.75*
**J16** D1 200(pf) deep violet 2.50 *3.75*
**J17** D1 300(pf) deep violet .60 *.75*
**J18** D1 400(pf) deep violet .60 *.75*
**J19** D1 500(pf) deep violet .60 *.75*
**J20** D1 800(pf) deep violet 1.25 *3.75*
**J21** D1 10m deep violet .60 *1.00*
**J22** D1 20m deep violet .60 *.75*
**J23** D1 50m deep violet .60 *.75*

### Paper With Gray Network

| No. | Type | Description | Unused | Used |
|---|---|---|---|---|
| **J24** | D1 | 100m deep violet | .60 | *1.00* |
| **J25** | D1 | 500m deep violet | .60 | *1.00* |
| | | *Nos. J15-J25 (11)* | 9.15 | 15.00 |
| | | Set, never hinged | 25.00 | |

Nos. J15, J17, J22-J25 exist imperf. Value each, $12.50 unused, $40 never hinged.

Nos. J22-J23 and Type of 1923 Surcharged

**1923, Oct. 1**

### Paper without Network

| No. | Type | Description | Unused | Used |
|---|---|---|---|---|
| **J26** | D1 | 5000m on 50m | .40 | *.75* |
| **J27** | D1 | 10,000m on 20m | .40 | *.75* |
| **J28** | D1 | 50,000m on 500m | .40 | *.75* |
| **J29** | D1 | 100,000m on 20m | .85 | *1.25* |
| | | *Nos. J26-J29 (4)* | 2.05 | *3.50* |
| | | Set, never hinged | 8.00 | |

On No. J26 the numerals of the surcharge are all of the larger size.

A 1000(m) on 100m deep violet was prepared but not issued. Value, $145, never hinged $350.

Nos. J26-J28 exist imperf. Value each, $18 unused, $45 never hinged.

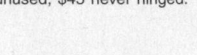

Danzig Coat of Arms — D2

**1923-28** **Wmk. 110**

| No. | Type | Description | Unused | Used |
|---|---|---|---|---|
| **J30** | D2 | 5(pf) blue & blk | .85 | .75 |
| **J31** | D2 | 10(pf) blue & blk | .40 | *.75* |
| **J32** | D2 | 15(pf) blue & blk | 1.25 | 1.10 |
| **J33** | D2 | 20(pf) blue & blk | 1.25 | *2.00* |
| **J34** | D2 | 30(pf) blue & blk | 9.00 | 2.00 |
| **J35** | D2 | 40(pf) blue & blk | 2.10 | *3.00* |
| **J36** | D2 | 50(pf) blue & blk | 2.10 | *2.25* |
| **J37** | D2 | 60(pf) blue & blk | 13.00 | *18.00* |
| **J38** | D2 | 100(pf) blue & blk | 17.50 | 9.75 |
| **J39** | D2 | 3g blue & car | 10.00 | *40.00* |
| *a.* | | "Guldeu" instead of "Gulden" | 325.00 | *1,050.* |
| | | Never hinged | 1,050. | |
| | | *Nos. J30-J39 (10)* | 57.45 | *79.60* |
| | | Set, never hinged | 225.00 | |

Used values of Nos. J30-J39 are for postally used stamps.

See Nos. J43-J47.

Postage Due Stamps of 1923 Issue Surcharged in Red

**1932, Dec. 20**

| No. | Type | Description | Unused | Used |
|---|---|---|---|---|
| **J40** | D2 | 5pf on 40(pf) | 4.25 | *7.50* |
| **J41** | D2 | 10pf on 60(pf) | 32.50 | 9.00 |
| **J42** | D2 | 20pf on 100(pf) | 2.75 | *7.50* |
| | | *Nos. J40-J42 (3)* | 39.50 | *24.00* |
| | | Set, never hinged | 160.00 | |

### Type of 1923

**1938-39** **Wmk. 237** ***Perf. 14***

| No. | Type | Description | Unused | Used |
|---|---|---|---|---|
| **J43** | D2 | 10(pf) bl & blk ('39) | 1.25 | *62.50* |
| **J44** | D2 | 30(pf) bl & blk | 2.25 | *50.00* |
| **J45** | D2 | 40(pf) bl & blk ('39) | 6.75 | *100.00* |
| **J46** | D2 | 60(pf) bl & blk ('39) | 6.75 | *100.00* |
| **J47** | D2 | 100(pf) bl & blk | 11.00 | *72.50* |
| | | *Nos. J43-J47 (5)* | 28.00 | *385.00* |
| | | Set, never hinged | 125.00 | |

## OFFICIAL STAMPS

Regular Issues of 1921-22 Overprinted — a

**1921-22** **Wmk. 108** ***Perf. 14x14½***

| No. | Type | Description | Unused | Used |
|---|---|---|---|---|
| **O1** | A11 | 5(pf) orange | .25 | .25 |
| **O2** | A11 | 10(pf) dark brown | .25 | .25 |
| *a.* | | Inverted overprint | 60.00 | |
| | | Never hinged | 170.00 | |
| **O3** | A11 | 15(pf) green | .25 | .25 |
| **O4** | A11 | 20(pf) slate | .25 | .25 |
| **O5** | A11 | 25(pf) dark green | .25 | .25 |
| *a.* | | Pair, one without overprint | 170.00 | |
| **O6** | A11 | 30(pf) blue & car | .60 | .60 |
| **O7** | A11 | 40(pf) grn & car | .25 | .25 |
| **O8** | A11 | 50(pf) dk grn & car | .25 | .25 |
| **O9** | A11 | 60(pf) carmine | .25 | .25 |
| **O10** | A11 | 75(pf) dp vio | .25 | *.40* |
| **O11** | A11 | 80(pf) black & car | .85 | .85 |
| **O12** | A11 | 80(pf) green | .25 | *2.40* |

### Paper With Faint Gray Network

| No. | Type | Description | Unused | Used |
|---|---|---|---|---|
| **O14** | A11 | 1m org & car | .25 | .25 |
| **O15** | A11 | 1.20m blue violet | 1.25 | 1.25 |
| **O16** | A11 | 1.25m vio & car | .25 | *.40* |
| **O17** | A11 | 1.50m slate gray | .25 | *.40* |
| **O18** | A11 | 2m gray & car | 16.00 | 12.00 |
| *a.* | | Inverted overprint | 110.00 | |
| | | Never hinged | 250.00 | |
| **O19** | A11 | 2m car rose | .25 | *.40* |
| **O20** | A11 | 2.40m dk brn & car | 1.25 | *2.40* |
| **O21** | A11 | 3m violet & car | 8.50 | *10.00* |
| **O22** | A11 | 3m car lake | .25 | *.40* |
| **O23** | A11 | 4m dk blue | 1.25 | .85 |
| **O24** | A11 | 5m dp grn | .25 | *.40* |
| **O25** | A11 | 6m car lake | .25 | *.40* |
| **O26** | A11 | 10m orange | .25 | *.40* |
| **O27** | A11 | 20m org brn | .25 | *.40* |
| | | *Nos. O1-O27 (26)* | 34.45 | *36.20* |
| | | Set, never hinged | 175.00 | |

Double overprints exist on Nos. O1-O2, O5-O7, O10 and O12.

### Same Overprint on No. 96

| No. | Type | Description | Unused | Used |
|---|---|---|---|---|
| **O28** | A11 | 6m on 3m | .35 | *.75* |
| | | Never hinged | 1.00 | |
| *a.* | | Inverted overprint | 30.00 | |
| | | Never hinged | 85.00 | |

No. 77 Overprinted

***Serrate Roulette 13½***

**1922** **Wmk. 108 Sideways**

| No. | Type | Description | Unused | Used |
|---|---|---|---|---|
| **O29** | A12 | 5m grn, red & blk | 3.75 | *6.00* |
| | | Never hinged | 18.00 | |

### Nos. 99-103, 106-107 Overprinted Type "a"

**1922-23** **Wmk. 109** ***Perf. 14***

| No. | Type | Description | Unused | Used |
|---|---|---|---|---|
| **O30** | A11 | 4m dark blue | .25 | *.60* |
| **O31** | A11 | 5m dark green | .25 | *.60* |
| **O32** | A11 | 10m orange | .25 | *.60* |
| **O33** | A11 | 20m orange brn | .25 | *.60* |
| **O34** | A15 | 50m pale blue & red | .25 | *.60* |
| **O35** | A15a | 100m dk grn & red | .25 | *.60* |

### Nos. 113-115, 118-120 Overprinted Type "a"

| No. | Type | Description | Unused | Used |
|---|---|---|---|---|
| **O36** | A15 | 50m pale blue | .25 | *.75* |
| *a.* | | Inverted overprint | 25.00 | |
| | | Never hinged | 62.50 | |
| **O37** | A15a | 100m dark green | .25 | *.75* |
| **O38** | A15 | 200m orange | .25 | *.75* |
| *a.* | | Inverted overprint | 25.00 | |
| | | Never hinged | 62.50 | |

### Paper With Gray Network

| No. | Type | Description | Unused | Used |
|---|---|---|---|---|
| **O39** | A17 | 300m bl grn & red | .25 | *.60* |
| **O40** | A17 | 500m gray & red | .25 | *.75* |
| **O41** | A17 | 1000m brn & red | .25 | *.75* |
| | | *Nos. O30-O41 (12)* | 3.00 | *7.95* |
| | | Set, never hinged | 16.80 | |

Regular Issue of 1924-25 Overprinted

**1924-25** ***Perf. 14x14½***

| No. | Type | Description | Unused | Used |
|---|---|---|---|---|
| **O42** | A19 | 5pf red orange | 2.10 | *3.25* |
| **O43** | A19 | 10pf green | 2.10 | *9.00* |
| **O44** | A19 | 15pf gray | 2.10 | 3.25 |
| **O45** | A19 | 15pf red | 19.00 | 10.00 |
| **O46** | A19 | 20pf car & red | 2.10 | 2.10 |
| **O47** | A19 | 25pf slate & red | 19.00 | 27.50 |
| **O48** | A19 | 30pf green & red | 3.00 | *3.75* |
| **O49** | A19 | 35pf ultra | 60.00 | 50.00 |
| **O50** | A19 | 40pf dk bl & dull bl | 7.00 | *8.50* |
| **O51** | A19 | 50pf dp blue & red | 21.00 | *42.50* |
| **O52** | A19 | 75pf violet & red | 42.50 | *120.00* |
| | | *Nos. O42-O52 (11)* | 179.90 | *279.85* |
| | | Set, never hinged | 640.00 | |

Double overprints exist on Nos. O42-O44, O47, O50-O52.

## DENMARK

'den-ˌmärk

LOCATION — Northern part of a peninsula which separates the North and Baltic Seas, and includes the surrounding islands
GOVT. — Kingdom
AREA — 16,631 sq. mi.
POP. — 5,294,860 (1/1/1999)
CAPITAL — Copenhagen

96 Skilling = 1 Rigsbank Daler
100 Ore = 1 Krone (1875)

**Catalogue values for unused stamps in this country are for Never Hinged items, beginning with Scott 297 in the regular postage section, Scott B15 in the semi-postal section, and Scott Q28 in the parcel post section.**

Values for unused stamps are for examples with original gum as defined in the catalogue introduction. Very fine examples of Nos. 9-37 and O1-O9 will have perforations clear of the framelines but with the design noticeably off center. Well centered stamps are quite scarce and will command substantial premiums.

### Watermarks

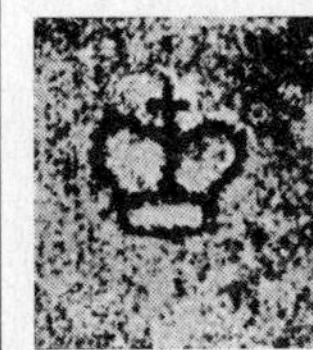
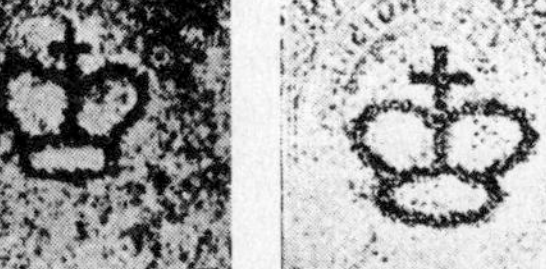

Wmk. 111 — Small Crown

Wmk. 112 — Crown

Wmk. 113 — Crown

Wmk. 114 — Multiple Crosses

A1

Royal Emblems — A2

**1851** **Typo.** **Wmk. 111** ***Imperf.***

**With Yellow Brown Burelage**

| No. | Type | Description | Unused | Used |
|---|---|---|---|---|
| **1** | A1 | 2rs blue | *3,500.* | 1,000. |
| *a.* | | First printing | *8,250.* | *2,400.* |
| **2** | A2 | 4rs brown | 600.00 | 40.00 |
| *a.* | | First printing | 600.00 | 40.00 |
| *b.* | | 4rs yellow brown | 875.00 | 55.00 |

The first printing of Nos. 1 and 2 had the burelage printed from a copper plate, giving a clear impression with the lines in slight relief. The subsequent impressions had the burelage typographed, with the lines fainter and not rising above the surface of the paper.

*Nos. 1-2 were reprinted in 1885 and 1901 on heavy yellowish paper, unwatermarked and imperforate, with a brown burelage. No. 1 was also reprinted without burelage, on both yellowish and white paper. Value for least costly reprint of No. 1, $50.*

*No. 2 was reprinted in 1951 in 10 shades with "Colour Specimen 1951" printed on the back. It was also reprinted in 1961 in 2 shades without burelage and with "Farve Nytryk 1961" printed on the back. Value for least costly reprint of No. 2, $8.50.*

Dotting in Spandrels — A3

**1854-57**

| No. | Type | Description | Unused | Used |
|---|---|---|---|---|
| **3** | A3 | 2s blue ('55) | 75.00 | 60.00 |
| **4** | A3 | 4s brown | 325.00 | 15.00 |
| *a.* | | 4s yellow brown | 350.00 | 15.00 |
| **5** | A3 | 8s green ('57) | 300.00 | 67.50 |
| *a.* | | 8s yellow green | 300.00 | 80.00 |
| **6** | A3 | 16s gray lilac ('57) | 525.00 | 190.00 |
| | | *Nos. 3-6 (4)* | 1,225. | 332.50 |

See No. 10. For denominations in cents see Danish West Indies Nos. 1-4.

Wavy Lines in Spandrels — A4

**1858-62**

| No. | Type | Description | Unused | Used |
|---|---|---|---|---|
| **7** | A4 | 4s yellow brown | 65.00 | 8.50 |
| *a.* | | 4s brown | 67.50 | 8.00 |
| *b.* | | Wmk. 112 ('62) | 62.50 | 9.00 |
| **8** | A4 | 8s green | 800.00 | 82.50 |

Nos. 2 to 8 inclusive are known with unofficial perforation 12 or 13, and Nos. 4, 5, 7 and 8 with unofficial roulette 9½.

*Nos. 3, 6-8 were reprinted in 1885 on heavy yellowish paper, unwatermarked, imperforate and without burelage. Nos. 4-5 were reprinted in 1924 on white paper, unwatermarked, imperforate, gummed and without burelage. Value for No. 3, $15; Nos. 4-5, each $110; No. 6, $20; Nos. 7-8, each $15.*

**1863** **Wmk. 112** ***Rouletted 11***

| No. | Type | Description | Unused | Used |
|---|---|---|---|---|
| **9** | A4 | 4s brown | 100.00 | 15.00 |
| *a.* | | 4s deep brown | 100.00 | 15.00 |
| **10** | A3 | 16s violet | 1,400. | 650.00 |

Royal Emblems — A5

**1864-68** ***Perf. 13***

| No. | Type | Description | Unused | Used |
|---|---|---|---|---|
| **11** | A5 | 2s blue ('65) | 65.00 | 35.00 |
| **12** | A5 | 3s red vio ('65) | 80.00 | 75.00 |
| **13** | A5 | 4s red | 40.00 | 8.00 |
| **14** | A5 | 8s bister ('68) | 275.00 | 95.00 |
| **15** | A5 | 16s olive green | 475.00 | 175.00 |
| | | *Nos. 11-15 (5)* | 935.00 | 388.00 |

*Nos. 11-15 were reprinted in 1886 on heavy yellowish paper, unwatermarked, imperforate and without gum. The reprints of all values except the 4s were printed in two vertical rows of six, inverted with respect to each other, so that horizontal pairs are always tête bêche. Value $12 each.*

*Nos. 13 and 15 were reprinted in 1942 with printing on the back across each horizontal row: "Nytryk 1942. G. A. Hagemann: Danmarks og Vestindiens Frimaerker, Bind 2." Value, $70 each.*

### Imperf, single

*11a* A5 2s blue 95.00 95.00
*12a* A5 3s red violet 140.00
*13a* A5 4s red 77.50 90.00
*14a* A5 8s bister 375.00
*15a* A5 16s olive green 450.00

**1870** ***Perf. 12½***

**11b** A5 2s blue 275.00 350.00
**12b** A5 3s red violet 475.00 650.00
**14b** A5 8s bister 475.00 475.00
**15b** A5 16s olive green 725.00 *1,450.*
*Nos. 11b-15b (4)* 1,950. 2,925.

A6

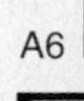

Normal Frame

Inverted Frame

The arabesques in the corners have a main stem and a branch. When the frame is in normal position, in the upper left corner the branch leaves the main stem half way between two little leaflets. In the lower right corner the branch starts at the foot of the second leaflet. When the frame is inverted the corner designs are, of course, transposed.

**1870-71 Wmk. 112 *Perf. 14x13½***

### Paper Varying from Thin to Thick

**16** A6 2s gray & ultra ('71) 70.00 27.50
*a.* 2s gray & blue 70.00 27.50
**17** A6 3s gray & brt lil ('71) 100.00 110.00
**18** A6 4s gray & car 40.00 10.00
**19** A6 8s gray & brn ('71) 200.00 75.00
**20** A6 16s gray & grn ('71) 275.00 175.00

***Perf. 12½***

**21** A6 2s gray & bl ('71) 2,000. *3,250.*
**22** A6 4s gray & car 150.00 125.00
**24** A6 48s brn & lilac 450.00 275.00

*Nos. 16-20, 24 were reprinted in 1886 on thin white paper, unwatermarked, imperforate and without gum. These were printed in sheets of 10 in which 1 stamp has the normal frame (value $32.50 each) and 9 the inverted (value $11 each).*

### Imperf, single

*16b* A6 2s *250.*
*17a* A6 3s *240.*
*18a* A6 4s *200.*
*19a* A6 8s *250.*
*20a* A6 16s *400.*
*24a* A6 48s *425.* —

### Inverted Frame

*16c* A6 2s 1,000. 775.
*17b* A6 3s 2,500. 2,000.
*18b* A6 4s 775. 87.50
*19b* A6 8s 1,750. 900.
*20b* A6 16s 2,000. 1,750.
*24b* A6 48s 2,750. 1,900.

**1875-79** ***Perf. 14x13½***

**25** A6 3o gray blue & gray 18.00 15.00
*a.* 1st "A" of "DANMARK" missing 60.00 150.00
*b.* Imperf *750.00*
*c.* Inverted frame 18.00 16.00
**26** A6 4o slate & blue 25.00 .50
*a.* 4o gray & blue 25.00 1.10
*b.* 4o slate & ultra 90.00 17.00
*c.* 4o gray & ultra 75.00 16.00
*d.* Imperf 75.00 —
*e.* As #26, inverted frame 25.00 .50
**27** A6 5o rose & blue ('79) 30.00 72.50
*a.* Ball of lower curve of large "5" missing 125.00 300.00
*b.* Inverted frame 1,000. *2,250.*
**28** A6 8o slate & car 22.50 .50
*a.* 8o gray & carmine 75.00 5.00
*b.* Imperf 150.00 —
*c.* Inverted frame 22.50 .50
**29** A6 12o sl & dull lake 10.00 4.00
*a.* 12o gray & bright lilac 65.00 8.00
*b.* 12o gray & dull magenta 72.50 10.00
*c.* Inverted frame 14.00 4.00
**30** A6 16o slate & brn 77.50 6.50
*a.* 16o light gray & brown 77.50 17.00
*b.* Inverted frame 52.50 4.50
**31** A6 20o rose & gray 90.00 32.50
*a.* 20o carmine & gray 90.00 32.50
*b.* Inverted frame 90.00 32.50
**32** A6 25o gray & green 65.00 40.00
*a.* Inverted frame 77.50 62.50
**33** A6 50o brown & vio 70.00 37.50
*a.* 50o brown & blue violet 400.00 175.00
*b.* Inverted frame 70.00 32.50
**34** A6 100o gray & org ('77) 110.00 60.00
*a.* Imperf, single 375.00
*b.* Inverted frame 150.00 60.00
*Nos. 25-34 (10)* 518.00 269.00
Set, never hinged 1,625.

The stamps of this issue on thin semi-transparent paper are far scarcer than those on thicker paper.

See Nos. 41-42, 44, 46-47, 50-52. For surcharges see Nos. 55, 79-80, 136.

Arms — A7

Two types of numerals in corners

Small Numerals

Large Numerals

**1882**

### Small Corner Numerals

**35** A7 5o green 240.00 100.00
Never hinged 725.00
**37** A7 20o blue 190.00 70.00
Never hinged 650.00

**1884-88**

### Larger Corner Numerals

**38** A7 5o green 15.00 3.50
*a.* Imperf —
**39** A7 10o carmine ('85) 16.00 2.50
*a.* Small numerals in corners ('88) 550.00 *725.00*
*b.* Imperf, single 175.00
*c.* Pair, Nos. 39, 39a 600.00 *875.00*
**40** A7 20o blue 30.00 5.00
*a.* Pair, Nos. 37, 40 400.00 *875.00*
*b.* Imperf —
*Nos. 38-40 (3)* 61.00 11.00
Set, never hinged 285.00

Stamps with large corner numerals have white line around crown and lower oval touches frame.

The plate for No. 39, was damaged and 3 clichés in the bottom row were replaced by clichés for post cards, which had small numerals in the corners.

Two clichés with small numerals were inserted in the plate of No. 40.

See Nos. 43, 45, 48-49, 53-54. For surcharge see No. 56.

**1895-1901 Wmk. 112 *Perf. 13***

**41** A6 3o blue & gray 10.00 7.25
**42** A6 4o slate & bl ('96) 4.50 .40
**43** A7 5o green 12.00 .75
**44** A6 8o slate & car 4.50 .45
**45** A7 10o rose car 24.00 .65
**46** A6 12o sl & dull lake 7.00 4.00
**47** A6 16o slate & brown 19.00 4.50
**48** A7 20o blue 30.00 2.40
**49** A7 24o brown ('01) 7.00 6.00
**50** A6 25o gray & grn ('98) 110.00 19.50
**51** A6 50o brown & vio ('97) 60.00 24.00
**52** A6 100o slate & org 90.00 35.00
*Nos. 41-52 (12)* 378.00 104.90
Set, never hinged 875.00

### Inverted Frame

*41b* A6 3o 12.00 7.00
*42a* A6 4o 4.50 .45
*44a* A6 8o 4.50 .50
*46a* A6 12o 14.00 4.50
*47a* A6 16o 30.00 5.00
*50a* A6 25o 60.00 27.50
*51a* A6 50o 95.00 32.50
*52a* A6 100o 90.00 57.50
*Nos. 41b-52a (8)* 310.00 134.95
Set, never hinged 635.00

**1902-04 Wmk. 113**

*41c* A6 3o blue & gray 2.75 3.00
*42b* A6 4o slate & blue 17.00 20.00
*43a* A7 5o green 2.00 .25
*44d* A6 8o slate & carmine 525.00 425.00
*45a* A7 10o rose carmine 3.00 .25
*48a* A7 20o blue 20.00 4.75
*50b* A6 25o gray & green 10.50 4.50
*51b* A6 50o brown & violet 27.50 20.00
*52b* A6 100o slate & orange 30.00 15.00
*Nos. 41c-52b (9)* 637.75 492.75
Set, never hinged 1,325.

### Inverted Frame

*41d* A6 3o 75.00 130.00
*42c* A6 4o 140.00 130.00
*50c* A6 25o 210.00 60.00
*51c* A6 50o 260.00 240.00
*52c* A6 100o 225.00 240.00
*Nos. 41d-52c (5)* 910.00 800.00
Set, never hinged 2,500.

**1902 Wmk. 113**

**53** A7 1o orange .75 .65
*a.* Imperf — —
**54** A7 15o lilac 11.00 .75
*a.* Imperf, single *4,250.*

### Nos. 44d, 44, 49 Surcharged

a

b

**1904-12 Wmk. 113**

**55** A6(a) 4o on 8o sl & car 3.50 4.00
*a.* Wmk. 112 ('12) 21.00 *60.00*
Never hinged 42.50
*b.* As "a," inverted frame — *6,000.*

**Wmk. 112**

**56** A7(b) 15o on 24o brown 5.75 17.50
*a.* Short "15" at right 27.50 *105.00*
Never hinged 60.00
Set, never hinged 16.00

A10

**1905-17 Wmk. 113 *Perf. 13***

**57** A10 1o orange ('06) 2.25 .75
**58** A10 2o carmine 4.75 .40
*a.* Perf. 14x14½ ('17) 3.75 *19.00*
**59** A10 3o gray 9.75 .65
**60** A10 4o dull blue 7.00 .60
*a.* Perf. 14x14½ ('17) 11.00 *37.50*
**61** A10 5o dp green ('12) 5.25 .35
**62** A10 10o dp rose ('12) 6.75 .35
**63** A10 15o lilac 25.00 2.25
**64** A10 20o dk blue ('12) 35.00 .90
*Nos. 57-64 (8)* 95.75 6.25
Set, never hinged 310.00

The three wavy lines in design A10 are symbolical of the three waters which separate the principal Danish islands.

See Nos. 85-96, 1338-1342A, 1468-1473. For surcharges and overprints see Nos. 163, 181, J1, J38, Q1-Q2.

King Christian IX — A11

**1904-05 Engr.**

**65** A11 10o scarlet 4.00 .65
**66** A11 20o blue 22.50 3.00
**67** A11 25o brown ('05) 27.50 8.00
**68** A11 50o dull vio ('05) 110.00 *120.00*
**69** A11 100o ocher ('05) 13.00 *60.00*
*Nos. 65-69 (5)* 177.00 *191.65*
Set, never hinged 565.00

**1905-06 Re-engraved**

**70** A11 5o green 4.50 .35
**71** A11 10o scarlet ('06) 21.00 .60
Set, never hinged 56.00

The re-engraved stamps are much clearer than the originals, and the decoration on the king's left breast has been removed.

King Frederik VIII — A12

**1907-12**

**72** A12 5o green 1.75 .40
*a.* Imperf. —
**73** A12 10o red 4.25 .40
*a.* Imperf. —
**74** A12 20o indigo 19.00 .65
*a.* 20o bright blue ('11) 40.00 2.75
**75** A12 25o olive brn 35.00 1.25
**76** A12 35o dp org ('12) 6.00 *10.00*
**77** A12 50o claret 35.00 7.00
**78** A12 100o bister brn 100.00 5.00
*Nos. 72-78 (7)* 201.00 24.70
Set, never hinged 525.00

### Nos. 47, 31 and O9 Surcharged

c

d

### Dark Blue Surcharge

**1912 Wmk. 112 *Perf. 13***

**79** A6(c) 35o on 16o 17.00 *50.00*
*a.* Inverted frame 325.00 *625.00*

***Perf. 14x13½***

**80** A6(c) 35o on 20o 30.00 *85.00*
*a.* Inverted frame 130.00 *325.00*

### Black Surcharge

**81** O1(d) 35o on 32o 42.50 *120.00*
*Nos. 79-81 (3)* 89.50 *255.00*
Set, never hinged 185.00

General Post Office, Copenhagen — A15

**1912 Engr. Wmk. 113 *Perf. 13***

**82** A15 5k dark red 500.00 200.00
Never hinged 1,500.

See Nos. 135, 843.

*Perf. 14x14½*

**1913-30 Typo. Wmk. 114**

**85** A10 1o dp orange ('14) .40 .45
a. Bklt. pane, 2 ea #85, 91 + 2 labels 20.00
**86** A10 2o car ('13) 3.75 .35
a. Imperf 150.00 *300.00*
b. Booklet pane, 4 + 2 labels 27.50
**87** A10 3o gray ('13) 6.75 .40
**88** A10 4o blue ('13) 8.00 .45
a. Half used as 2o on cover 1,250.
**89** A10 5o dk brown ('21) .75 .35
a. Imperf 190.00
b. Booklet pane, 4 + 2 labels 14.00
**90** A10 5o lt green ('30) 1.50 .40
a. Booklet pane, 4 + 2 labels 16.00
b. Booklet pane of 50
**91** A10 7o apple grn ('26) 5.75 *7.25*
a. Booklet pane, 4 + 2 labels 20.00
**92** A10 7o dk violet ('30) 16.00 6.50
**93** A10 8o gray ('21) 7.00 3.25
**94** A10 10o green ('21) .85 .35
a. Imperf 225.00
b. Booklet pane, 4 + 2 labels 37.50
**95** A10 10o bister brn ('30) 2.25 .35
a. Booklet pane, 4 + 2 labels 16.00
b. Booklet pane of 50
**96** A10 12o violet ('26) 25.00 9.75
*Nos. 85-96 (12)* 78.00 29.85
Set, never hinged 200.00

No. 88a was used with No. 97 in Faroe Islands, Jan. 3-23, 1919.

See surcharge and overprint note following No. 64.

King Christian X — A16

**1913-28 Typo. *Perf. 14x14½***

**97** A16 5o green 1.40 .35
a. Bklt. pane of 4, with P# *400.00*
**98** A16 7o orange ('18) 2.25 *2.75*
**99** A16 8o dk gray ('20) 14.00 6.50
**100** A16 10o red 2.40 .40
a. Imperf 300.00
b. Bklt. pane of 4, with P# *500.00*
**101** A16 12o gray grn ('18) 7.50 *10.00*
**102** A16 15o violet 3.25 .40
**103** A16 20o dp blue 13.00 .35
**104** A16 20o brown ('21) 1.25 .40
**105** A16 20o red ('26) 1.50 .40
**106** A16 25o dk brown 13.50 .50
**107** A16 25o brn & blk ('20) 85.00 8.75
**108** A16 25o red ('22) 4.25 .95
**109** A16 25o yel grn ('25) 3.00 .50
**110** A16 27o ver & blk ('18) 30.00 *50.00*
**111** A16 30o green & blk ('18) 35.00 3.25
**112** A16 30o orange ('21) 3.00 2.00
**113** A16 30o dk blue ('25) 1.75 1.00
**114** A16 35o orange 29.00 7.50
**115** A16 35o yel & blk ('19) 9.00 6.50
**116** A16 40o vio & blk ('18) 18.00 4.00
**117** A16 40o gray bl & blk ('20) 37.50 7.50
**118** A16 40o dk blue ('22) 6.00 1.60
**119** A16 40o orange ('25) 1.50 *1.50*
**120** A16 50o claret 37.50 5.75
**121** A16 50o claret & blk ('19) 75.00 2.50
**122** A16 50o lt gray ('22) 9.25 .40
a. 50o olive gray ('21) 75.00 8.00
Never hinged 210.00
**123** A16 60o brn & bl ('19) 60.00 3.75
a. 60o brown & ultra ('19) 225.00 12.50
Never hinged 750.00
**124** A16 60o grn bl ('21) 9.00 .75
**125** A16 70o brn & grn ('20) 26.00 2.25
**126** A16 80o bl grn ('15) 50.00 22.50
**127** A16 90o brn & red ('20) 18.00 3.25
**128** A16 1k brn & bl ('22) 75.00 3.00
**129** A16 2k gray & cl ('25) 67.50 15.00
**130** A16 5k vio & brn ('27) 7.00 *5.75*
**131** A16 10k ver & yel grn ('28) 325.00 65.00
*Nos. 97-131 (35)* 1,082. 247.00
Set, never hinged 3,085.

No. 97 surcharged "2 ORE" is Faroe Islands No. 1. Two of the 14 printings of No. 97a have no P# in the selvage. These sell for more.

Nos. 87 and 98, 89 and 94, 89 and 104, 90 and 95, 97 and 103, 100 and 102 exist se-tenant in coils for use in vending machines.

For surcharges and overprints see Nos. 161-162, 176-177, 182-184, J2-J8, M1-M2, Q3-Q10.

King Christian X — A17

**1913-20 Engr.**

**132** A17 1k yellow brown 95.00 1.25
**133** A17 2k gray 150.00 7.00
**134** A17 5k purple ('20) 15.00 10.00
*Nos. 132-134 (3)* 260.00 18.25
Set, never hinged 940.00

For overprint see No. Q11.

**G.P.O. Type of 1912**

*Perf. 14x14½*

**1915 Wmk. 114 Engr.**

**135** A15 5k dark red ('15) 500.00 175.00
Never hinged 1,500.

**Nos. 46 and O10 Surcharged in Black type "c" and**

e

**1915 Wmk. 112 Typo. *Perf. 13***

**136** A6 (c) 80o on 12o 40.00 *100.00*
a. Inverted frame 600.00 *1,100.*
Never hinged 825.00
**137** O1 (e) 80o on 8o 47.50 *140.00*
a. "POSTERIM" 95.00 *325.00*
Never hinged 140.00
Set, never hinged 155.00

Newspaper Stamps Surcharged

**On Issue of 1907**

**1918 Wmk. 113 *Perf. 13***

**138** N1 27o on 1o olive 105.00 *325.00*
**139** N1 27o on 5o blue 105.00 *325.00*
**140** N1 27o on 7o car 105.00 *325.00*
**141** N1 27o on 10o dp lil 105.00 *325.00*
**142** N1 27o on 68o yel brn 7.50 *37.50*
**143** N1 27o on 5k rose & yel grn 6.75 *26.00*
**144** N1 27o on 10k bis & bl 7.50 *35.00*
*Nos. 138-144 (7)* 441.75 *1,399.*
Set, never hinged 940.00

**On Issue of 1914-15**

**Wmk. Multiple Crosses (114)**

*Perf. 14x14½*

**145** N1 27o on 1o ol gray 5.00 *15.50*
**146** N1 27o on 5o blue 7.50 *30.00*
**147** N1 27o on 7o rose 5.00 *12.50*
**148** N1 27o on 8o green 7.50 *16.00*
**149** N1 27o on 10o dp lil 3.25 *17.00*
**150** N1 27o on 20o green 8.00 *16.50*
**151** N1 27o on 29o org yel 3.25 *14.50*
**152** N1 27o on 38o orange 32.50 *110.00*
**153** N1 27o on 41o yel brn 7.50 *45.00*
**154** N1 27o on 1k bl grn & mar 5.00 *14.50*
*Nos. 145-154 (10)* 84.50 *291.50*
Set, never hinged 150.00

Kronborg Castle — A20

Sonderborg Castle — A21

Roskilde Cathedral — A22

***Perf. 14½x14, 14x14½***

**1920, Oct. 5 Typo.**

**156** A20 10o red 7.00 .50
**157** A21 20o slate 5.00 .50
**158** A22 40o dark brown 17.00 4.50
*Nos. 156-158 (3)* 29.00 5.50
Set, never hinged 52.00

Reunion of Northern Schleswig with Denmark.

See Nos. 159-160. For surcharges see Nos. B1-B2.

**1921**

**159** A20 10o green 9.00 .55
**160** A22 40o dark blue 67.50 11.50
Set, never hinged 174.00

Stamps of 1918 Surcharged in Blue

**1921-22**

**161** A16 8o on 7o org ('22) 2.25 *5.00*
**162** A16 8o on 12o gray grn 2.25 *15.00*
Set, never hinged 15.75

No. 87 Surcharged

**1921**

**163** A10 8o on 3o gray 3.75 *5.25*
Never hinged 8.25

Christian X
A23

Christian IV
A24

A25

A26

**1924, Dec. 1 *Perf. 14x14½***

**164** A23 10o green 7.50 *7.00*
**165** A24 10o green 7.50 *7.00*
**166** A25 10o green 7.50 *7.00*
**167** A26 10o green 7.50 *7.00*
a. Block of 4, #164-167 37.50 *50.00*
**168** A23 15o violet 7.50 *7.00*
**169** A24 15o violet 7.50 *7.00*
**170** A25 15o violet 7.50 *7.00*
**171** A26 15o violet 7.50 *7.00*
a. Block of 4, #168-171 37.50 *50.00*
**172** A23 20o dark brown 7.50 *7.00*
**173** A24 20o dark brown 7.50 *7.00*
**174** A25 20o dark brown 7.50 *7.00*
**175** A26 20o dark brown 7.50 *7.00*
a. Block of 4, #172-175 37.50 *50.00*
*Nos. 164-175 (12)* 90.00 84.00
Set, never hinged 180.00
#167a, 171a, 175a, never hinged 225.00

300th anniv. of the Danish postal service.

**Stamps of 1921-22 Surcharged**

k

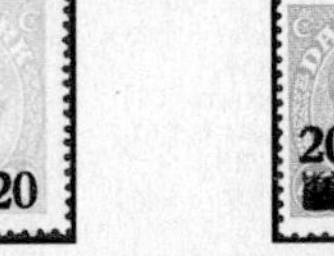


l

**1926**

**176** A16 (k) 20o on 30o org 6.75 *15.00*
**177** A16 (l) 20o on 40o dk bl 9.00 *18.00*
Set, never hinged 31.00

A27

A28

**1926, Mar. 11 *Perf. 14x14½***

**178** A27 10o dull green 1.50 .45
**179** A28 20o dark red 2.00 .45
**180** A28 30o dark blue 8.50 1.50
*Nos. 178-180 (3)* 12.00 2.40
Set, never hinged 24.50

75th anniv. of the introduction of postage stamps in Denmark.

**Stamps of 1913-26 Surcharged in Blue or Black**

No. 181

Nos. 182-184

**1926-27 *Perf. 14x14½***

**181** A10 7o on 8o gray (Bl) 1.50 *4.75*
**182** A16 7o on 27o ver & blk 4.50 *17.00*
**183** A16 7o on 20o red ('27) .75 *2.50*
**184** A16 12o on 15o violet 2.25 *6.00*

**Surcharged on Official Stamps of 1914-23**

**185** O1 (e) 7o on 1o org 4.00 *16.00*
**186** O1 (e) 7o on 3o gray 7.50 *32.50*
**187** O1 (e) 7o on 4o blue 3.75 *7.75*
**188** O1 (e) 7o on 5o grn 52.50 *150.00*
**189** O1 (e) 7o on 10o grn 4.50 *15.50*
**190** O1 (e) 7o on 15o vio 4.50 *15.50*
**191** O1 (e) 7o on 20o ind 19.00 *77.50*
a. Double surcharge *750.00* *975.00*
*Nos. 181-191 (11)* 104.75 *345.00*
Set, never hinged 155.00

Caravel — A30

**1927 Typo. *Perf. 14x14½***

**192** A30 15o red 6.00 .40
**193** A30 20o gray 11.00 2.40
**194** A30 25o light blue 1.25 .40
**195** A30 30o ocher 1.25 .40
**196** A30 35o red brown 25.00 1.50
**197** A30 40o yel green 25.00 .40
*Nos. 192-197 (6)* 69.50 5.50
Set, never hinged 200.00

See Nos. 232-238J. For surcharges & overprints see Nos. 244-245, 269-272, Q12-Q14, Q19-Q25.

Christian X — A31

**1930, Sept. 26**

**210** A31 5o apple grn 2.50 .35
a. Booklet pane, 4 + 2 labels 18.00
**211** A31 7o violet 6.75 3.00
**212** A31 8o dk gray 22.50 32.50
**213** A31 10o yel brn 5.00 .35
a. Booklet pane, 4 + 2 labels 29.00
**214** A31 15o red 10.00 .35
**215** A31 20o lt gray 25.00 9.75
**216** A31 25o lt blue 8.50 1.25
**217** A31 30o yel buff 9.00 1.75
**218** A31 35o red brown 12.00 4.50
**219** A31 40o dp green 10.00 1.25
*Nos. 210-219 (10)* 111.25 55.05
Set, never hinged 295.00

60th birthday of King Christian X.

Wavy Lines and Numeral of Value — A32

**Type A10 Redrawn**

**1933-40 Unwmk. Engr. *Perf. 13***

**220** A32 1o gray blk .45 .30
**221** A32 2o scarlet .35 .30
**222** A32 4o blue .40 .35
**223** A32 5o yel grn 1.00 .35
a. 5o gray green 37.50 *60.00*
b. Tête bêche gutter pair 8.00 *15.50*
c. Booklet pane of 4 11.00
d. Bklt. pane, 1 #223a, 3 #B6 37.50 70.00
Never hinged 60.00
e. As "b," without gutter 17.50 *27.50*
**224** A32 5o rose lake ('38) .30 .30
a. Booklet pane of 4 1.20
b. Booklet pane of 10 12.00
**224C** A32 6o orange ('40) .30 .30
**225** A32 7o violet 2.00 .35
**226** A32 7o yel grn ('38) 1.10 .45
**226A** A32 7o lt brown ('40) .35 .35
**227** A32 8o gray .45 .50
**227A** A32 8o yellow grn ('40) .30 .35

228 A32 10o yellow org 12.50 .35
 a. Tête bêche gutter pair 50.00 55.00
 b. Booklet pane of 4 110.00
 c. As "a," without gutter 60.00 *70.00*
 Never hinged 100.00
229 A32 10o lt brown ('37) 9.50 .35
 a. Booklet pane of 4 100.00
 b. Booklet pane of 4, 1 #229, 3 #B7 32.50 45.00
230 A32 10o violet ('38) .75 .35
 a. Booklet pane of 4 2.75
 b. Bklt. pane, 2 #230, 2 #B10 2.50 7.00
 Never hinged 6.00
 *Nos. 220-230 (14)* 29.75 4.95
 Set, never hinged 75.00

Design A10 was typographed. They had a solid background with groups of small hearts below the heraldic lions in the upper corners and below "DA" and "RK" of "DANMARK." The numerals of value were enclosed in single-lined ovals.

Design A32 is line-engraved and has a background of crossed lines. The hearts have been removed and the numerals of value are now in double-lined ovals. Two types exist of some values.

The 1ö, No. 220, was issued on fluorescent paper in 1969.

No. 230 with wide margins is from booklet pane No. 230b.

Surcharges of 20, 50 & 60öre on #220, 224 and 224C are listed as Faroe Islands #2-3, 5-6.

See Nos. 318, 333, 382, 416, 437-437A, 493-498, 629, 631, 688-695, 793-795, 883-886, 1111-1113, 1116. For overprints and surcharges see Nos. 257, 263, 267-268, 355-356, Q15-Q17, Q31, Q43.

Certain tête-bêche pairs of 1938-55 issues which reached the market in 1971, and were not regularly issued, are not listed. This group comprises 24 different major-number vertical pairs of types A32, A47, A61 and SP3 (13 with gutters, 11 without), and pairs of some minor numbers and shades. They were removed from booklet pane sheets.

### Type of 1927 Issue
### Type I

Type I — Two columns of squares between sail and left frame line.

**1933-34 Engr. *Perf. 13***

232 A30 20o gray 15.00 .35
233 A30 25o blue 85.00 30.00
234 A30 25o brown ('34) 30.00 .35
235 A30 30o orange yel 1.50 1.40
236 A30 30o blue ('34) 1.50 .40
237 A30 35o violet .60 .35
238 A30 40o yellow grn 6.25 .35
 *Nos. 232-238 (7)* 139.85 33.20
 Set, never hinged 325.00

### Type II

Type II — One column of squares between sail and left frame line.

**1933-40**

238A A30 15o deep red 3.00 .35
 k. Booklet pane of 4 26.00
 l. Bklt. pane, 1 #238A, 3 #B8 45.00
 Never hinged 115.00
238B A30 15o yel grn ('40) 9.00 .40
238C A30 20o gray blk ('39) 4.50 .70
238D A30 20o red ('40) .90 .35
238E A30 25o dp brown ('39) .90 .35
238F A30 30o blue ('39) 2.25 .70
238G A30 30o orange ('40) .75 .35
238H A30 35o violet ('40) 1.00 .35
238I A30 40o yel grn ('39) 15.00 .35
238J A30 40o blue ('40) 1.40 .35
 *Nos. 238A-238J (10)* 38.70 4.25
 Set, never hinged 95.00

Nos. 232-238J, engraved, have crosshatched background. Nos. 192-197, typographed, have solid background.

For No. 238A surcharged 20 ore see Denmark No. 271, Faroe Islands No. 4.

See note on surcharges and overprints following No. 197.

King Christian X — A33

**1934-41 *Perf. 13***

239 A33 50o gray 1.20 .30
240 A33 60o blue grn 2.40 .35
240A A33 75o dk blue ('41) .45 .35
241 A33 1k lt brown 3.75 .35

242 A33 2k dull red 6.00 1.00
243 A33 5k violet 9.00 3.50
 *Nos. 239-243 (6)* 22.80 5.85
 Set, never hinged 75.00

For overprints see Nos. Q26-Q27.

Nos. 233, 235 Surcharged in Black

**1934, June 9**

244 A30 4o on 25o blue .50 .50
245 A30 10o on 30o org yel 2.40 *3.25*
 Set, never hinged 7.50

"The Ugly Duckling" A34

Andersen A35

"The Little Mermaid" — A36

**1935, Oct. 1 *Perf. 13***

246 A34 5o lt green 3.00 .30
 a. Tête bêche gutter pair 15.00 *22.50*
 b. Booklet pane of 4 40.00
 c. As "a," without gutter 17.00 *21.00*
 Never hinged 45.00
247 A35 7o dull vio 2.50 *2.50*
248 A36 10o orange 4.50 .30
 a. Tête bêche gutter pair 18.00 *32.50*
 b. Booklet pane of 4 65.00
 c. As "a," without gutter 20.00 *40.00*
 Never hinged 65.00
249 A35 15o red 11.00 .30
 a. Tête bêche gutter pair 45.00 *52.50*
 b. Booklet pane of 4 160.00
 c. As "a," without gutter 42.50 *75.00*
 Never hinged 110.00
250 A35 20o gray 9.50 1.25
251 A35 30o dl bl 3.00 .35
 *Nos. 246-251 (6)* 33.50 *5.00*
 Set, never hinged 87.50

Centenary of the publication of the earliest installment of Hans Christian Andersen's "Fairy Tales."

Nikolai Church A37

Hans Tausen A38

Ribe Cathedral — A39

**1936 *Perf. 13***

252 A37 5o green 1.40 .40
 a. Booklet pane of 4 21.00
253 A37 7o violet 2.00 *4.50*
254 A38 10o lt brown 2.00 .40
 a. Booklet pane of 4 25.00
255 A38 15o dull rose 3.00 .30
256 A39 30o blue 16.00 1.40
 *Nos. 252-256 (5)* 24.40 7.00
 Set, never hinged 62.50

Church Reformation in Denmark, 400th anniv.

No. 229 Overprinted in Blue

**1937, Sept. 17**

257 A32 10o lt brown 1.50 *1.60*
 Never hinged 2.00

Jubilee Exhib. held by the Copenhagen Phil. Club on their 50th anniv. The stamps were on sale at the Exhib. only, each holder of a ticket of admission (1k) being entitled to purchase 20 stamps at face value; of a season ticket (5k), 100 stamps.

Yacht and Summer Palace, Marselisborg A40

Christian X in Streets of Copenhagen A41

Equestrian Statue of Frederik V and Amalienborg Palace — A42

**1937, May 15 *Perf. 13***

258 A40 5o green 1.40 .30
 a. Booklet pane of 4 15.00
259 A41 10o brown 1.40 .30
 a. Booklet pane of 4 15.00
260 A42 15o scarlet 1.40 .30
 a. Booklet pane of 4 17.00
261 A41 30o blue 15.00 2.40
 *Nos. 258-261 (4)* 19.20 3.30
 Set, never hinged 42.50

25th anniv. of the accession to the throne of King Christian X.

Emancipation Column, Copenhagen — A43

**1938, June 20 *Perf. 13***

262 A43 15o scarlet .60 .30
 Never hinged 1.40

Abolition of serfdom in Denmark, 150th anniv.

**No. 223 Overprinted in Red on Alternate Stamps**

**1938, Sept. 2**

263 A32 5o yellow grn, pair 3.25 *7.00*
 Never hinged 4.50

10th Danish Philatelic Exhibition.

Bertel Thorvaldsen A44

Statue of Jason A45

**1938, Nov. 17 Engr. *Perf. 13***

264 A44 5o rose lake .45 .30
265 A45 10o purple .45 .30
266 A44 30o dark blue 1.50 .60
 *Nos. 264-266 (3)* 2.40 1.20
 Set, never hinged 5.25

The return to Denmark in 1838 of Bertel Thorvaldsen, Danish sculptor.

**Stamps of 1933-39 Surcharged with New Values in Black**

a

b

c

**1940**

267 A32 (a) 6o on 7o yel grn .30 *.35*
268 A32 (a) 6o on 8o gray .45 *.35*
269 A30 (b) 15o on 40o #238 .90 *6.00*
270 A30 (b) 15o on 40o #238I .75 *.95*
271 A30 (c) 20o on 15o dp red 1.10 .30
272 A30 (b) 40o on 30o #238F 1.00 .35
 *Nos. 267-272 (6)* 4.50 *8.30*
 Set, never hinged 9.25

Stamps previously listed as Denmark No. 273-276 are listed as Faroe Islands Nos. 2-6 .

Bering's Ship — A46

**1941, Nov. 27 Engr. *Perf. 13***
**277** A46 10o dk violet .35 .30
**278** A46 20o red brown .60 .30
**279** A46 40o dk blue .40 .35
*Nos. 277-279 (3)* 1.35 .95
Set, never hinged 3.00

Death of Vitus Bering, explorer, 200th anniv.

King Christian X — A47

**1942-46 Unwmk. *Perf. 13***
**280** A47 10o violet .30 .35
**281** A47 15o yel grn .35 .35
**282** A47 20o red .40 .35
**283** A47 25o brown ('43) .50 .45
**284** A47 30o orange ('43) .45 .35
**285** A47 35o brt red vio ('44) .40 .35
**286** A47 40o blue ('43) .40 .35
**286A** A47 45o ol brn ('46) .35 .35
**286B** A47 50o gray ('45) .60 .35
**287** A47 60o bluish grn ('44) .55 .35
**287A** A47 75o dk blue ('46) .55 .35
*Nos. 280-287A (11)* 4.85 3.95
Set, never hinged 8.00

For overprints see Nos. Q28-Q30.

Round Tower — A48

**1942, Nov. 27**
**288** A48 10o violet .35 .30
Never hinged .75

300th anniv. of the Round Tower, Copenhagen.
For surcharge see No. B14.

Condor Plane — A49

**1943, Oct. 29**
**289** A49 20o red .25 .25
Never hinged .35

25th anniv. of the Danish Aviation Company (Det Danske Luftfartsselskab).

Ejby Church — A50

15ö, Oesterlars Church. 20ö, Hvidbjerg Church.

**1944 Engr. *Perf. 13***
**290** A50 10o violet .30 .25
**291** A50 15o yellow grn .30 .25
**292** A50 20o red .30 .25
*Nos. 290-292 (3)* .90 .75
Set, never hinged 1.75

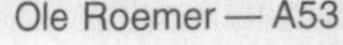
Ole Roemer — A53

**1944, Sept. 25**
**293** A53 20o henna brown .35 .30
Never hinged .65

Birth of Ole Roemer, astronomer, 300th anniv.

Christian X — A54

**1945, Sept. 26**
**294** A54 10o lilac .25 .25
**295** A54 20o red .25 .25
**296** A54 40o deep blue .25 .25
*Nos. 294-296 (3)* .75 .75
Set, never hinged 1.75

75th birthday of King Christian X.

**Catalogue values for unused stamps in this section, from this point to the end of the section, are for Never Hinged items.**

Small State Seal — A55

**1946-47 Unwmk. *Perf. 13***
**297** A55 1k brown 1.00 .25
**298** A55 2k red ('47) 2.40 .25
**299** A55 5k dull blue 6.00 .25
*Nos. 297-299 (3)* 9.40 .75

Nos. 297-299 issued on ordinary and fluorescent paper. Values for ordinary paper are much higher.
See Nos. 395-400, 441A-444D, 499-506, 643-650, 716-720A, 804-815, 909, 1134-1138, 1304-1313, 1474-1478, 1508. For overprints see Nos. Q35, Q40, Q46-Q48.

Tycho Brahe — A56

**1946, Dec. 14 Engr.**
**300** A56 20o dark red .30 .25

Birth of Tycho Brahe, astronomer, 400th anniv.

First Danish Locomotive A57

Modern Steam Locomotive A58

Diesel Locomotive A59

**1947, June 27**
**301** A57 15o steel blue .60 .35
**302** A58 20o red 1.10 .35
**303** A59 40o deep blue 3.50 2.25
*Nos. 301-303 (3)* 5.20 2.95

Inauguration of the Danish State Railways, cent.

Jacobsen — A60

**1947, Nov. 10 *Perf. 13***
**304** A60 20o dark red .30 .25

60th anniv. of the death of Jacob Christian Jacobsen, founder of the Glyptothek Art Museum, Copenhagen.

Frederik IX — A61

Three types among 15ö, 20ö, 30ö:
I — Background of horizontal lines. No outline at left for cheek and ear. King's uniform textured in strong lines.
II — Background of vertical and horizontal lines. Contour of cheek and ear at left. Uniform same.
III — Background and facial contour lines as in II. Uniform lines double and thinner.

**1948-50 Unwmk. *Perf. 13***
**306** A61 15(o) green (II) 2.50 .30
*a.* Type III ('49) 1.60 .50
**307** A61 20(o) dk red (I) 1.10 .25
*a.* Type III ('49) 1.40 .30
**308** A61 25(o) lt brown 1.40 .25
**309** A61 30(o) org (II) 13.00 .50
*a.* Type III ('50) 21.00 .50
**310** A61 40(o) dl blue ('49) 4.75 1.00
**311** A61 45(o) olive ('50) 2.10 .35
**312** A61 50(o) gray ('49) 1.75 .30
**313** A61 60(o) grnsh bl ('50) 2.50 .30
**314** A61 75(o) lil rose ('50) 2.00 .30
*Nos. 306-314 (9)* 31.10 3.55

See Nos. 319-326, 334-341, 354, For surcharges see Nos. 357-358, 370, B20, B24-B25, Q32-Q34, Q36-Q39.

Legislative Assembly, 1849 — A62

**1949, June 5**
**315** A62 20o red brown .35 .25

Adoption of the Danish constitution, cent.

Symbol of UPU — A63

**1949, Oct. 9**
**316** A63 40o dull blue .65 .35

75th anniv. of the UPU.

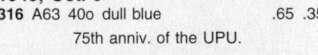

Kalundborg Radio Station and Masts — A64

**1950, Apr. 1 Engr. *Perf. 13***
**317** A64 20o brown red .50 .25

Radio broadcasting in Denmark, 25th anniv.

**Types of 1933-50**

**1950-51 Unwmk. *Perf. 13***
**318** A32 10o green .30 .25
**319** A61 15(o) lilac 1.00 .30
*b.* 15(o) gray lilac 4.00 .25
**320** A61 20(o) lt brown 1.10 .30
**321** A61 25(o) dark red 3.50 .25
**322** A61 35(o) gray grn ('51) .95 .25
**323** A61 40(o) gray .95 .25
**324** A61 50(o) dark blue 3.25 .25
**325** A61 55(o) brown ('51) 32.50 2.75
**326** A61 70(o) deep green 3.00 .30
*Nos. 318-326 (9)* 46.55 4.90

Warship of 1701 — A65

**1951, Feb. 26 Engr. *Perf. 13***
**327** A65 25o dark red .50 .30
**328** A65 50o deep blue 4.00 .80

250th anniv. of the foundation of the Naval Officers' College.

Oersted — A66

**1951, Mar. 9 Unwmk.**
**329** A66 50o blue 1.40 .60

Cent. of the death of Hans Christian Oersted, physicist.

Post Chaise ("Ball Post") — A67

**1951, Apr. 1 *Perf. 13***
**330** A67 15o purple .65 .25
**331** A67 25o henna brown .65 .25

Cent. of Denmark's 1st postage stamp.

Marine Rescue — A68

**1952, Mar. 26**
**332** A68 25o red brown .45 .35

Cent. of the foundation of the Danish Lifesaving Service.

**Types of 1933-50**

**1952-53 *Perf. 13***
**333** A32 12o lt yel grn .30 .25
**334** A61 25(o) lt blue 1.10 .30
**335** A61 30(o) brown red 1.00 .35
**336** A61 50(o) aqua ('53) 1.00 .30
**337** A61 60(o) dp blue ('53) 1.10 .35
**338** A61 65(o) gray ('53) 1.10 .35
**339** A61 80(o) orange ('53) 1.10 .35
**340** A61 90(o) olive ('53) 3.00 .30
**341** A61 95(o) red org ('53) 1.10 .25
*Nos. 333-341 (9)* 10.80 2.80

Jelling Runic Stone — A69

Designs: 15o, Vikings' camp, Trelleborg. 20o, Church of Kalundborg. 30o, Nyborg castle. 60o, Goose tower, Vordinborg.

**1953-56 *Perf. 13***
**342** A69 10o dp green .30 .25
**343** A69 15o lt rose vio .30 .25
**344** A69 20o brown .30 .25
**345** A69 30o red ('54) .30 .25
**346** A69 60o dp blue ('54) .35 .25

Designs: 10o, Manor house, Spottrup. 15o, Hammershus castle ruins. 20o, Copenhagen stock exchange. 30o, Statue of Frederik V, Amalienborg. 60o, Soldier statue at Fredericia.

**347** A69 10o green ('54) .30 .25
**348** A69 15o lilac ('55) .30 .25
**349** A69 20o brown ('55) .30 .25
**350** A69 30o red ('55) .30 .25
**351** A69 60o deep blue ('56) .60 .25
*Nos. 342-351 (10)* 3.35 2.50

1000th anniv. of the Kingdom of Denmark. Each stamp represents a different century.

Telegraph Equipment of 1854 — A70

**1954, Feb. 2** ***Perf. 13***
**352** A70 30o red brown .40 .25

Cent. of the telegraph in Denmark.

Frederik V — A71

**1954, Mar. 31**
**353** A71 30o dark red .55 .35

200th anniv. of the founding of the Royal Academy of Fine Arts.

**Type of 1948-50**

**1955, Apr. 27**
**354** A61 25o lilac 1.00 .30

**Nos. 224C and 226A Surcharged with New Value in Black. Nos. 307 and 321 Surcharged with New Value and 4 Bars**

**1955-56**
**355** A32 5o on 6o org .30 .25
**356** A32 5o on 7o lt brn .30 .25
**357** A61 30(o) on 20(o) dk red (I) .80 .30
*a.* Type III 1.40 .35
*b.* Double surcharge 1,150. 1,150.
*c.* Inverted surcharge 650.00
**358** A61 30(o) on 25(o) dk red ('56) .60 .25
*a.* Double surcharge —
*Nos. 355-358 (4)* 2.00 1.05

A72

**1955, Nov. 11** **Unwmk.**
**359** A72 30o dark red .50 .25

100th anniv. of the death of Sören Kierkegaard, philosopher and theologian.

A73

**1956, Sept. 12** **Engr.**
**360** A73 30o Ellehammer's plane .50 .25

50th anniv. of the 1st flight made by Jacob Christian Hansen Ellehammer in a heavier-than-air craft.

**Northern Countries Issue**

Whooper Swans — A74

**1956, Oct. 30** ***Perf. 13***
**361** A74 30o rose red 1.75 .25
**362** A74 60o ultramarine 1.60 .80

Issued to emphasize the close bonds among the northern countries: Denmark, Finland, Iceland, Norway and Sweden.

Prince's Palace — A75

Design: 60ö, Sun God's Chariot.

**1957, May 15** **Unwmk.**
**363** A75 30o dull red .90 .25
**364** A75 60o dark blue .90 .75

150th anniv. of the National Museum.

Harvester — A76

**1958, Sept. 4** **Engr.** ***Perf. 13***
**365** A76 30o fawn .30 .25

Centenary of the Royal Veterinary and Agricultural College.

Frederik IX — A77

**1959, Mar. 11**
**366** A77 30o rose red .40 .25
**367** A77 35o rose lilac .50 .25
**368** A77 60o ultra .50 .25
*Nos. 366-368 (3)* 1.40 .75

King Frederik's 60th birthday.

Ballet Dancer — A78

**1959, May 16**
**369** A78 35o rose lilac .30 .25

Danish Ballet and Music Festival, May 17-31. See Nos. 401, 422.

No. 319 Surcharged

**1960, Apr. 7**
**370** A61 30o on 15o lilac .30 .25

World Refugee Year, 7/1/59-6/30/60.

Seeder and Farm A79

30ö, Harvester combine. 60ö, Plow.

**1960, Apr. 28** **Engr.** ***Perf. 13***
**371** A79 12o green .25 .25
**372** A79 30o dull red .30 .25
**373** A79 60o dk blue .65 .50
*Nos. 371-373 (3)* 1.20 1.00

King Frederik IX and Queen Ingrid — A80

**1960, May 24** **Unwmk.**
**374** A80 30o dull red .45 .25
**375** A80 60o blue .65 .60

25th anniversary of the marriage of King Frederik IX and Queen Ingrid.

Bascule Light — A81

**1960, June 8** **Engr.**
**376** A81 30o dull red .30 .25

400th anniv. of the Lighthouse Service.

Finsen — A82

**1960, Aug. 1** ***Perf. 13***
**377** A82 30o dark red .30 .25

Centenary of the birth of Dr. Niels R. Finsen, physician and scientist.

Nursing Mother — A83

**1960, Aug. 16** **Unwmk.**
**378** A83 60o ultra .55 .50

10th meeting of the regional committee for Europe of WHO, Copenhagen, Aug. 16-20.

**Europa Issue, 1960**
Common Design Type

**1960, Sept. 19** ***Perf. 13***
**Size: 28x21mm**
**379** CD3 60o ultra .55 .50

DC-8 Airliner — A84

**1961, Feb. 24**
**380** A84 60o ultra .75 .50

10th anniv. of the Scandinavian Airlines System, SAS.

Landscape A85

**1961, Apr. 21** ***Perf. 13***
**381** A85 30o copper brown .30 .25

Denmark's Soc. of Nature Lovers, 50th anniv.

Fluorescent Paper
as well as ordinary paper, was used in printing many definitive and commemorative stamps, starting in 1962. These include No. 220, 224; the 15, 20, 25, 30, 35 (Nos. 386 and 387), 50 and 60ö, 1.50k and 25k definitives of following set, and Nos. 297-299, 318, 333, 380, 401-427, 429-435, 438-439, 493, 543, 548, B30.
Only fluorescent paper was used for Nos. 436-437, 437A and 440 onward; in semipostals from B31 onward.

Frederik IX — A86

**1961-63** **Engr.** ***Perf. 13***
**382** A32 15o green ('63) .50 .35
**383** A86 20o brown .45 .35
**384** A86 25o brown ('63) .30 .35
**385** A86 30o rose red .65 .35
**386** A86 35o olive grn .85 .75
**387** A86 35o rose red ('63) .30 .35
**388** A86 40o gray 1.20 .35
**389** A86 50o aqua .55 .30
**390** A86 60o ultra 1.10 .35
**391** A86 70o green 1.60 .35
**392** A86 80o red orange 1.60 .35
**393** A86 90o olive bister 4.25 .35
**394** A86 95o claret ('63) 1.00 .90
*Nos. 382-394 (13)* 14.35 5.45

See Nos. 417-419, 438-441. For overprints see Nos. Q41-Q42, Q44-Q45.

**State Seal Type of 1946-47**

**1962-65**
**395** A55 1.10k lilac ('65) 5.25 2.00
**396** A55 1.20k gray 3.00 .35
**397** A55 1.25k orange 3.00 .35
**398** A55 1.30k green ('65) 5.50 1.75
**399** A55 1.50k red lilac 2.75 .35
**400** A55 25k yellow grn 8.00 .35
*Nos. 395-400 (6)* 27.50 5.15

**Dancer Type of 1959 Inscribed "15-31 MAJ"**

**1962, Apr. 26**
**401** A78 60o ultra .30 .25

Issued to publicize the Danish Ballet and Music Festival, May 15-31.

Old Mill — A87

**1962, May 10** **Unwmk.** ***Perf. 13***
**402** A87 10o red brown .30 .25

Cent. of the abolition of mill monopolies.

M.S. Selandia — A88

**1962, June 14** **Engr.**
**403** A88 60o dark blue 1.60 1.50

M.S. Selandia, the 1st Diesel ship, 50th anniv.

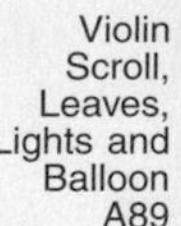

Violin Scroll, Leaves, Lights and Balloon A89

**1962, Aug. 31**
**404** A89 35o rose violet .35 .25

150th anniv. of the birth of Georg Carstensen, founder of Tivoli amusement park, Copenhagen.

Cliffs on Moen Island — A90

**1962, Nov. 22**

**405** A90 20o pale brown .30 .25

Issued to publicize preservation of natural treasures and landmarks.

Germinating Wheat — A91

**1963, Mar. 21 Engr.**

**406** A91 35o fawn .35 .25

FAO "Freedom from Hunger" campaign.

Railroad Wheel, Tire Tracks, Waves and Swallow — A92

**1963, May 14 Unwmk. *Perf. 13***

**407** A92 15o green .60 .40

Inauguration of the "Bird Flight Line" railroad link between Denmark and Germany.

Sailing Vessel, Coach, Postilions and Globe — A93

**1963, May 27**

**408** A93 60o dark blue .40 .40

Cent. of the 1st Intl. Postal Conf., Paris, 1863.

Niels Bohr and Atom Diagram — A94

**1963, Nov. 21 Engr.**

**409** A94 35o red brown .40 .35
**410** A94 60o dark blue .65 .25

50th anniv. of Prof. Niels Bohr's (1885-1962) atom theory.

Early Public School Drawn on Slate — A95

**1964, June 19 Unwmk. *Perf. 13***

**411** A95 35o red brown .60 .25

150th anniversary of the royal decrees for the public school system.

Fish and Chart — A96

**1964, Sept. 7 Engr.**

**412** A96 60o violet blue .35 .40

Conference of the International Council for the Exploration of the Sea, Copenhagen.

Danish Watermarks and Perforations A97

**1964, Oct. 10 *Perf. 13***

**413** A97 35o pink .30 .25

25th anniv. of Stamp Day and to publicize the Odense Stamp Exhibition, Oct. 10-11.

Landscape A98

**1964, Nov. 12 Engr.**

**414** A98 25o brown .30 .25

Issued to publicize preservation of natural treasures and landmarks.

Calculator, Ledger and Inkwell — A99

**1965, Mar. 8 Unwmk.**

**415** A99 15o light olive green .30 .25

First Business School in Denmark, cent.

**Types of 1933 and 1961**

**1965, May 15 Engr. *Perf. 13***

**416** A32 25o apple green .55 .50
**417** A86 40o brown .45 .35
**418** A86 50o rose red .75 .35
**419** A86 80o ultra .75 .65
*Nos. 416-419 (4)* 2.50 1.85

For overprints see Nos. Q41-Q42.

ITU Emblem, Telegraph Key, Teletype Paper — A100

**1965, May 17**

**420** A100 80o dark blue .35 .25

Cent. of the ITU.

Carl Nielsen (1865-1931), Composer — A101

**1965, June 9 Engr.**

**421** A101 50o brown red .40 .25

**Dancer Type of 1959 Inscribed "15-31 MAJ"**

**1965, Sept. 23**

**422** A78 50o rose red .30 .25

Issued to publicize the Danish Ballet and Music Festival, May 15-31.

Bogo Windmill — A102

**1965, Nov. 10 Engr. *Perf. 13***

**423** A102 40o brown .30 .25

Issued to publicize the preservation of natural treasures and landmarks.

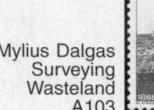

Mylius Dalgas Surveying Wasteland A103

**1966, Feb. 24**

**424** A103 25o olive green .50 .30

Cent. of the Danish Heath Soc. (reclamation of wastelands), founded by Enrico Mylius Dalgas.

Christen Kold (1816-70), Educator — A104

**1966, Mar. 29 *Perf. 13***

**425** A104 50o dull red .50 .50

Poorhouse, Copenhagen A105

Holte Allée, Bregentved A106

Dolmen (Grave) in Jutland — A107

**1966 Unwmk.**

**426** A105 50o dull red .55 .50
**427** A106 80o dk blue 1.00 .40
**428** A107 1.50k dk slate grn 1.40 .25
*Nos. 426-428 (3)* 2.95 1.15

Publicizing preservation of national treasures and ancient monuments. Issued: 50o, May 12; 80o, June 16; 1.50k, Nov. 24.

George Jensen by Ejnar Nielsen — A108

**1966, Aug. 31 Engr. *Perf. 13***

**429** A108 80o dark blue 1.00 .40

George Jensen, silversmith, birth cent.

Music Bar and Instruments A109

**1967, Jan. 9**

**430** A109 50o dark red .70 .25

Royal Danish Academy of Music, cent.

Cogwheels, and Broken Customs Duty Ribbon — A110

**1967, Mar. 2**

**431** A110 80o dark blue .70 .25

European Free Trade Association. Industrial tariffs were abolished Dec. 31, 1966, among EFTA members: Austria, Denmark, Finland, Great Britain, Norway, Portugal, Sweden and Switzerland.

Windmill and Medieval Fortress — A111

Designs: 40ö, Ship's rigging and baroque house front. 50ö, Old Town Hall. 80ö, New building construction.

**1967 Engr. *Perf. 13***

**432** A111 25o green .60 .25
**433** A111 40o sepia .35 .25
**434** A111 50o red brown .35 .40
**435** A111 80o dk blue .85 .80
*Nos. 432-435 (4)* 2.15 1.70

The 800th anniversary of Copenhagen.

Issued: Nos. 432-433, 4/6; Nos. 434-435, 5/11.

Princess Margrethe and Prince Henri — A112

**1967, June 10**

**436** A112 50o red .30 .25

Marriage of Crown Princess Margrethe and Prince Henri de Monpezat.

**Types of 1933-1961**

**1967-71 Engr. *Perf. 13***

**437** A32 30o dk green .70 .35
**437A** A32 40o orange ('71) .80 .35
**438** A86 50o brown 1.25 .35
Complete booklet, 4 #318, 2 each #437, 438 20.00
**439** A86 60o rose red 1.25 .35
**440** A86 80o green .85 .35
**441** A86 90o ultra .90 .35
**441A** A55 1.20k Prus grn ('71) 2.00 .45
**442** A55 2.20k orange 3.50 .35
**443** A55 2.80k gray 3.00 .35
**444** A55 2.90k rose vio 5.25 .35
**444A** A55 3k dk sl grn ('69) 1.00 .35
**444B** A55 3.10k plum ('70) 8.50 .35
**444C** A55 4k gray ('69) 1.40 .35
**444D** A55 4.10k olive ('70) 8.50 .35
*Nos. 437-444D (14)* 38.90 5.00

Issued: Nos. 437-441, 6/30/67; Nos. 442-443, 7/8/67; No. 444, 4/29/68; Nos. 444A, 444C, 8/28/69; Nos. 444B, 444D, 8/27/70; Nos. 437A, 441A, 6/24/71.

For overprints see Nos. Q44-Q45.

Sonne — A113

**1967, Sept. 21**

**445** A113 60o red .30 .25

150th anniv. of the birth of Hans Christian Sonne, pioneer of the cooperative movement in Denmark.

Cross-anchor and Porpoise — A114

**1967, Nov. 9 Engr. *Perf. 13***

**446** A114 90o dk blue .35 .25

Centenary of the Danish Seamen's Church in Foreign Ports.

Esbjerg Harbor — A115

**1968, Apr. 24**

**447** A115 30o dk yellow grn .30 .25

Centenary of Esbjerg Harbor.

Koldinghus A116

**1968, June 13**

**448** A116 60o copper red .65 .25

700th anniversary of Koldinghus Castle.

Shipbuilding Industry — A117

Designs: 50o, Chemical industry. 60o, Electric power. 90o, Engineering.

**1968, Oct. 24 Engr. *Perf. 13***

**449** A117 30o green .25 .25
**450** A117 50o brown .25 .25
**451** A117 60o red brown .25 .25
**452** A117 90o dark blue 1.00 1.00
*Nos. 449-452 (4)* 1.75 1.75

Issued to publicize Danish industries.

Sower — A118

**1969, Jan. 29**

**453** A118 30o gray green .30 .25

Royal Agricultural Soc. of Denmark, 200th anniv.

Five Ancient Ships — A119

**Nordic Cooperation Issue**

**1969, Feb. 28 Engr. *Perf. 13***

**454** A119 60o brown red .80 .25
**455** A119 90o blue 1.60 1.60

50th anniv. of the Nordic Soc. and cent. of postal cooperation among the northern countries. The design is taken from a coin found at the site of Birka, an ancient Swedish town. See also Finland No. 481, Iceland Nos. 404-405, Norway Nos. 523-524 and Sweden Nos. 808-810.

Frederik IX — A120

**1969, Mar. 11**

**456** A120 50o sepia .30 .25
**457** A120 60o dull red .30 .25

70th birthday of King Frederik IX.

---

Common Design Types pictured following the introduction.

---

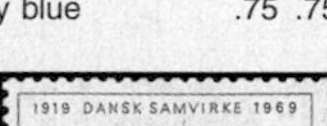

**Europa Issue, 1969**
Common Design Type

**1969, Apr. 28**

**Size: 28x20mm**

**458** CD12 90o chalky blue .75 .75

Kronborg Castle — A121

**1969, May 22 Engr. *Perf. 13***

**459** A121 50o brown .30 .25

Association of Danes living abroad, 50th anniv.

Danish Flag — A122

**1969, June 12**

**460** A122 60o bluish blk, red & gray .30 .25

750th anniversary of the fall of the Dannebrog (Danish flag) from heaven.

Nexo — A123

**1969, Aug. 28**

**461** A123 80o deep green .30 .25

Centenary of the birth of Martin Andersen Nexo (1869-1954), novelist.

Stensen — A124

**1969, Sept. 25**

**462** A124 1k deep brown .35 .25

300th anniv. of the publication of Niels Stensen's geological work "On Solid Bodies."

Abstract Design — A125

**1969, Nov. 10 Engr. *Perf. 13***

**463** A125 60o rose, red & ultra .30 .25

Symbolic Design — A126

**1969, Nov. 20**

**464** A126 30o olive green .30 .25

Valdemar Poulsen (1869-1942), electrical engineer and inventor.

Post Office Bank — A127

**1970, Jan. 15 Engr. *Perf. 13***

**465** A127 60o dk red & org .30 .25

50th anniv. of post office banking service.

School Safety Patrol — A128

**1970, Feb. 19**

**466** A128 50o brown .30 .25

Issued to publicize road safety.

Candle in Window — A129

**1970, May 4 Engr. *Perf. 13***

**467** A129 50o slate, dull bl & yel .30 .25

25th anniv. of liberation from the Germans.

Deer — A130

**1970, May 28**

**468** A130 60o yel grn, red & brn .30 .25

Tercentenary of Jaegersborg Deer Park.

Elephant Figurehead, 1741 — A131

**1970, June 15 *Perf. 11½***

**469** A131 30o multicolored .30 .25

Royal Naval Museum, tercentenary.

"The Homecoming" by Povl Christensen — A132

**1970, June 15 *Perf. 13***

**470** A132 60o org, dl vio & ol grn .30 .25

Union of North Schleswig and Denmark, 50th anniv.

Electromagnet A133

**1970, Aug. 13 Engr.**

**471** A133 80o gray green .30 .25

150th anniversary of Hans Christian Oersted's discovery of electromagnetism.

Bronze Age Ship A134

Ships: 50o, Viking shipbuilding, from Bayeux tapestry. 60o, Thuroe schooner with topgallant. 90o, Tanker.

**1970, Sept. 24**

**472** A134 30o ocher & brown .25 .25
**473** A134 50o brn red & rose brn .25 .25
**474** A134 60o gray ol & red brn .35 .25
**475** A134 90o blue grn & ultra 1.25 1.25
*Nos. 472-475 (4)* 2.10 2.00

UN Emblem A135

**1970, Oct. 22 Engr. *Perf. 13***

**476** A135 90o blue, grn & red 1.00 1.00

25th anniversary of the United Nations.

Bertel Thorvaldsen — A136

**1970, Nov. 19**

**477** A136 2k slate blue .60 .50

Bicentenary of the birth of Bertel Thorvaldsen (1768-1844), sculptor.

Mathide Fibiger — A137

**1971, Feb. 25**

**478** A137 80o olive green .30 .25

Danish Women's Association centenary.

Refugees — A138

**1971, Mar. 26 Engr. *Perf. 13***

**479** A138 50o brown .25 .25
**480** A138 60o brown red .35 .25

Joint northern campaign for the benefit of refugees.

Hans Egede — A139

**1971, May 27**

**481** A139 1k brown .35 .25

250th anniversary of arrival of Hans Egede in Greenland and beginning of its colonization.

A140

**1971, Oct. 14**

**482** A140 30o Swimming .25 .25
**483** A140 50o Gymnastics .50 .25
**484** A140 60o Soccer .75 .25
**485** A140 90o Sailing .75 .75
*Nos. 482-485 (4)* 2.25 1.50

A141

**1971, Nov. 11 Engr. *Perf. 13***

**486** A141 90o dark blue .35 .35

Centenary of first lectures given by Georg Brandes (1842-1927), writer and literary critic.

A142

**1972, Jan. 27**

**487** A142 80o slate green .35 .25

Centenary of Danish sugar production.

A143

**1972, Mar. 11 Engr. *Perf. 13***

**488** A143 60o red brown .30 .25

Frederik IX (1899-1972).

Abstract Design A144

**1972, Mar. 11**

**489** A144 1.20k brt rose lil, bl gray & brn .65 .65

Danish Meteorological Institute, cent.

Nikolai F. S. Grundtvig — A145

**1972, May 4 Engr. *Perf. 13***

**490** A145 1k sepia .50 .50

Nikolai Frederik Severin Grundtvig (1783-1872), theologian and poet.

Locomotive, 1847, Ferry, Travelers A146

**1972, June 26**

**491** A146 70o rose red .30 .25

125th anniversary of Danish State Railways.

Rebild Hills — A147

**1972, June 26**

**492** A147 1k bl, sl grn & mar .35 .25

### Types of 1933-46

**1972-78 Engr. *Perf. 13***

| | | | | | |
|---|---|---|---|---|---|
| **493** | A32 | 20o slate bl ('74) | .35 | .35 |
| **494** | A32 | 50o sepia ('74) | .30 | .30 |
| *a.* | | Bklt. pane of 12 (4 #318, 4 #493, 4 #494) ('85) | 15.00 | |
| **495** | A32 | 60o apple grn ('76) | 1.75 | .90 |
| **496** | A32 | 60o gray ('78) | .70 | .70 |
| **497** | A32 | 70o red | 1.00 | .35 |
| **498** | A32 | 70o apple grn ('77) | 1.10 | .35 |
| **499** | A55 | 2.50k orange | 1.75 | .35 |
| **500** | A55 | 2.80k olive ('75) | 1.25 | .65 |
| **501** | A55 | 3.50k lilac | 2.00 | .35 |
| **502** | A55 | 4.5k olive | 5.50 | .35 |
| **503** | A55 | 6k vio blk ('76) | 2.00 | .35 |
| **504** | A55 | 7k red lilac ('78) | 2.10 | .35 |
| **505** | A55 | 9k brown ol ('77) | 3.00 | .35 |

### With Vertical and Horizontal Engraving Lines

**506** A55 10k lemon ('76) 3.00 .35
*Nos. 493-506 (14)* 25.80 6.05

See footnote after No. 1313.

"Tinker Turned Politician" — A148

**1972, Sept. 14**

**507** A148 70o dark red .30 .25

250th anniv. of the comedies of Ludvig Holberg (1684-1754) on the Danish stage.

WHO Building, Copenhagen — A149

**1972, Sept. 14**

**508** A149 2k bl, blk & lt red brn .60 .60

Opening of WHO Building, Copenhagen.

Bridge Across Little Belt — A150

Highway engineering (Diagrams): 60o, Hanstholm Harbor. 70o, Lim Fjord Tunnel. 90o, Knudshoved Harbor.

**1972, Oct. 19 Engr. *Perf. 13***

**509** A150 40o dk green .25 .25
**510** A150 60o dk brown .35 .25
**511** A150 70o dk red .35 .25
**512** A150 90o dk blue grn 1.40 .50
*Nos. 509-512 (4)* 2.35 1.25

Aeroskobing House c. 1740 — A151

Danish Architecture: 60o, East Bornholm farmhouse, 17th century, horiz. 70o, House, Christianshavn, c. 1710. 1.20k, Hvide Sande Farmhouse, c. 1810, horiz.

**1972, Nov. 23**

**Size: 20x28mm, 27x20mm**

**513** A151 40o red, brn & blk .35 .25
**514** A151 60o blk, vio bl & grn .35 .25

**Size: 18x37mm, 36x20mm**

**515** A151 70o red, dk red & blk .45 .30
**516** A151 1.20k dk brn, red & grn 1.40 1.00
*Nos. 513-516 (4)* 2.55 1.80

Jensen — A152

**1973, Feb. 22 Engr. *Perf. 13***

**517** A152 90o green .35 .25

Centenary of the birth of Johannes Vilhelm Jensen (1873-1950), lyric poet and novelist.

Guard Rails, Cogwheels — A153

**1973, Mar. 22**

**518** A153 50o sepia .55 .25

Centenary of first Danish Factory Act for labor protection.

Abildgaard — A154

**1973, Mar. 22**

**519** A154 1k dull blue .70 .35

Bicentenary of Royal Veterinary College, Christianshaven, founded by Prof. P. C. Abildgaard.

Rhododendron A155

Design: 70o, Dronningen of Denmark rose.

**1973, Apr. 26**

**520** A155 60o brn, grn & vio .50 .25
**521** A155 70o dk red, rose & grn .50 .25

Centenary of the founding of the Horticultural Society of Denmark.

### Nordic Cooperation Issue

Nordic House, Reykjavik A156

**1973, June 26 Engr. *Perf. 13***

**522** A156 70o multicolored .50 .25
**523** A156 1k multicolored 1.50 1.25

A century of postal cooperation among Denmark, Finland, Iceland, Norway and Sweden, and in connection with the Nordic Postal Conference, Reykjavik.

Sextant, Stella Nova, Cassiopeia — A157

**1973, Oct. 18 Engr. *Perf. 13***

**524** A157 2k dark blue 1.75 .30

400th anniversary of the publication of "De Nova Stella," by Tycho Brahe.

St. Mark, from 11th Cent. Book of Dalby — A158

**1973, Oct. 18 Photo. *Perf. 14x14½***

| | | | | |
|---|---|---|---|---|
| **525** | A158 | 120o buff & multi | 1.10 | .65 |

300th anniversary of Royal Library.

Devil and Gossips, Fanefjord Church, 1480 — A159

Frescoes: No. 527, Queen Esther and King Ahasuerus, Tirsted Church, c.1400. No. 528, Miraculous Harvest, Jetsmark Church, c.1474. No. 529, Jesus carrying cross, and wearing crown of thorns, Biersted Church, c.1400. No. 530, Creation of Eve, Fanefjord Church, c.1480.

**1973, Nov. 28 Engr. *Perf. 13***

**Cream Paper**

| | | | | |
|---|---|---|---|---|
| **526** | A159 | 70o dk red, yel & grn | 1.40 | .30 |
| **527** | A159 | 70o dk red, yel & grn | 1.40 | .30 |
| **528** | A159 | 70o dk red, yel & grn | 1.40 | .30 |
| **529** | A159 | 70o dk red, yel & grn | 1.40 | .30 |
| **530** | A159 | 70o dk red, yel & grn | 1.40 | .30 |
| *a.* | | Bklt. pane, 2 each #526-530 | 35.00 | |
| *b.* | | Strip of 5, #526-530 | 6.75 | |

Blood Donors — A160

**1974, Jan. 24**

| | | | | |
|---|---|---|---|---|
| **531** | A160 | 90o purple & red | 1.10 | .25 |

"Blood Saves Lives."

Queen Margrethe — A161

**1974-81 Engr. *Perf. 13***

| | | | | |
|---|---|---|---|---|
| **532** | A161 | 60o brown | 1.00 | .50 |
| **533** | A161 | 60o orange | .60 | .45 |
| **534** | A161 | 70o red | 1.00 | .25 |
| **535** | A161 | 70o dk brown | .80 | .25 |
| **536** | A161 | 80o green | .80 | .25 |
| **537** | A161 | 80o dp brn ('76) | 1.10 | .25 |
| **538** | A161 | 90o red lilac | 1.10 | .25 |
| **539** | A161 | 90o dull red | 1.40 | .30 |
| **540** | A161 | 90o slate grn ('76) | 1.10 | .30 |
| **541** | A161 | 100o dp ultra | 1.10 | .25 |
| **542** | A161 | 100o gray ('75) | 1.10 | .25 |
| **543** | A161 | 100o red ('76) | 1.10 | .35 |
| **544** | A161 | 100o brown ('77) | 1.00 | .25 |
| *a.* | | Bklt. pane of 5 (#544, #494, 2 #493, #318) | 2.50 | |
| | | Complete booklet, #544a | 2.50 | |
| **545** | A161 | 110o orange ('78) | 1.20 | .25 |
| **546** | A161 | 120o slate | 1.00 | .50 |
| **547** | A161 | 120o red ('77) | 1.40 | .25 |
| | | Complete booklet, 4 each #318, 493, 544, 547 | 13.50 | |
| **548** | A161 | 130o ultra ('75) | 1.60 | 1.40 |
| **549** | A161 | 150o vio bl ('78) | 1.40 | .85 |
| **550** | A161 | 180o slate grn ('77) | 1.40 | .40 |
| **551** | A161 | 200o blue ('81) | 1.40 | 1.00 |
| | | *Nos. 532-551 (20)* | 22.60 | 8.55 |

See Nos. 630, 632-642. For overprint see No. Q49.

Pantomime Theater — A162

**1974, May 16**

| | | | | |
|---|---|---|---|---|
| **552** | A162 | 100o indigo | .40 | .30 |

Cent. of the Pantomime Theater, Tivoli.

Hverringe A163

Views: 60o, Norre Lyndelse, Carl Nielsen's childhood home. 70o, Odense, Hans Chr. Andersen's childhood home. 90o, Hesselagergaard, vert. 120o, Hindsholm.

**1974, June 20 Engr. *Perf. 13***

| | | | | |
|---|---|---|---|---|
| **553** | A163 | 50o brown & multi | .50 | .50 |
| **554** | A163 | 60o sl grn & multi | .65 | .65 |
| **555** | A163 | 70o red brn & multi | .50 | .50 |
| **556** | A163 | 90o dk green & mar | .55 | .25 |
| **557** | A163 | 120o red org & dk grn | .70 | .50 |
| | | *Nos. 553-557 (5)* | 2.90 | 2.40 |

Emblem, Runner with Map — A164

**1974, Aug. 22 Engr. *Perf. 13***

| | | | | |
|---|---|---|---|---|
| **558** | A164 | 70o shown | .70 | .70 |
| **559** | A164 | 80o Compass | .25 | .25 |

World Orienteering Championships 1974.

Iris — A165

**1974, Sept. 19**

| | | | | |
|---|---|---|---|---|
| **560** | A165 | 90o shown | .50 | .25 |
| **561** | A165 | 120o Purple orchid | .75 | .75 |

Copenhagen Botanical Garden centenary.

Mailman, 1624, and Postilion, 1780 — A166

Carrier Pigeon — A167

Design: 90o, Balloon and sailing ships.

**1974, Oct. 9 Engr. *Perf. 13***

| | | | | |
|---|---|---|---|---|
| **562** | A166 | 70o lemon & dk brn | .40 | .25 |
| **563** | A166 | 90o dull grn & sepia | .40 | .25 |
| **564** | A167 | 120o dark blue | .65 | .65 |
| | | *Nos. 562-564 (3)* | 1.45 | 1.15 |

350th anniv. of Danish PO (70o, 90o) and cent. of UPU (120o).

Souvenir Sheet

Ferslew's Essays, 1849 and 1852 — A168

**Engraved and Photogravure**

**1975, Feb. 27 *Perf. 13***

| | | | | |
|---|---|---|---|---|
| **565** | A168 | Sheet of 4 | 7.50 | *8.50* |
| *a.* | | 70o Coat of arms | 1.75 | *2.00* |
| *b.* | | 80o King Frederik VII | 1.75 | *2.00* |
| *c.* | | 90o King Frederik VII | 1.75 | *2.00* |
| *d.* | | 100o Mercury | 1.75 | *2.00* |

HAFNIA 76 Intl. Stamp Exhib., Copenhagen, Aug. 20-29, 1976. Sold for 5k.
See No. 585.

Early Radio Equipment — A169

**1975, Mar. 20 Engr. *Perf. 13***

| | | | | |
|---|---|---|---|---|
| **566** | A169 | 90o dull red | .35 | .30 |

Danish broadcasting, 50th anniversary.

Flora Danica Plate — A170

Danish China: 90o, Flora Danica tureen. 130o, Vase and tea caddy, blue fluted china.

**1975, May 22**

| | | | | |
|---|---|---|---|---|
| **567** | A170 | 50o slate grn | .30 | .25 |
| **568** | A170 | 90o brown red | .65 | .65 |
| **569** | A170 | 130o violet bl | 1.10 | 1.10 |
| | | *Nos. 567-569 (3)* | 2.05 | 2.00 |

Church of Moravian Brethren, Christiansfeld A171

120o, Kongsgaard farmhouse, Lejre. 150o, Anna Queenstraede, Helsingor, vert.

**1975, June 19**

| | | | | |
|---|---|---|---|---|
| **570** | A171 | 70o sepia | .65 | .65 |
| **571** | A171 | 120o olive green | .80 | .80 |
| **572** | A171 | 150o violet black | .65 | .25 |
| | | *Nos. 570-572 (3)* | 2.10 | 1.70 |

European Architectural Heritage Year 1975.

Andersen — A172

Designs: 70o, Numbskull Jack, drawing by Vilh. Pedersen. 130o, The Marshking's Daughter, drawing by L. Frohlich.

**1975, Aug. 28 Engr. *Perf. 13***

| | | | | |
|---|---|---|---|---|
| **573** | A172 | 70o brown & blk | .60 | .60 |
| **574** | A172 | 90o brn red & dk brn | .75 | .30 |
| **575** | A172 | 130o blue blk & sepia | 1.75 | 1.75 |
| | | *Nos. 573-575 (3)* | 3.10 | 2.65 |

Hans Christian Andersen (1805-75), writer.

Watchman's Square, Abenra — A173

Designs: 90o, Haderslev Cathedral, vert. 100o, Mögeltönder Polder. 120o, Mouth of Vidaaen at Höjer Floodgates.

**1975, Sept. 25**

| | | | | |
|---|---|---|---|---|
| **576** | A173 | 70o multicolored | .45 | .45 |
| **577** | A173 | 90o multicolored | .40 | .25 |
| **578** | A173 | 100o multicolored | .50 | .25 |
| **579** | A173 | 120o multicolored | .55 | .50 |
| | | *Nos. 576-579 (4)* | 1.90 | 1.45 |

European Kingfisher A174

**1975, Oct. 23 Engr. *Perf. 13***

| | | | | |
|---|---|---|---|---|
| **580** | A174 | 50o shown | .45 | .45 |
| **581** | A174 | 70o Hedgehog | .45 | .45 |
| **582** | A174 | 90o Cats | .45 | .45 |
| **583** | A174 | 130o Avocets | 1.25 | 1.25 |
| **584** | A174 | 200o Otter | .65 | .25 |
| | | *Nos. 580-584 (5)* | 3.25 | 2.85 |

Protected animals, and for the centenary of the Danish Society for the Prevention of Cruelty to Animals (90o).

**HAFNIA Type of 1974**

Souvenir Sheet

**1975, Nov. 20 Engr. & Photo.**

| | | | | |
|---|---|---|---|---|
| **585** | A168 | Sheet of 4 | 4.50 | *6.75* |
| *a.* | | 50o buff & brown, No. 2 | 1.10 | *1.60* |
| *b.* | | 70o buff, brown & blue, No. 1 | 1.10 | *1.60* |
| *c.* | | 90o buff, blue & brown, No. 11 | 1.10 | *1.60* |
| *d.* | | 130o olive, brown & buff, No. 19 | 1.10 | *1.60* |

HAFNIA 76 Intl. Stamp Exhib., Copenhagen, Aug. 20-29, 1976. Sold for 5k.

Copenhagen, Center — A175

View from Round Tower — A176

Copenhagen, Views: 100o, Central Station, interior. 130o, Harbor.

**1976, Mar. 25 Engr. *Perf. 12½***

| | | | | |
|---|---|---|---|---|
| **586** | A175 | 60o multicolored | .45 | .45 |
| **587** | A176 | 80o multicolored | .45 | .45 |
| **588** | A176 | 100o multicolored | .45 | .25 |
| **589** | A175 | 130o multicolored | 1.50 | 1.50 |
| | | *Nos. 586-589 (4)* | 2.85 | 2.65 |

Postilion, by Otto Bache — A177

**1976, June 17 Engr. *Perf. 12½***

| | | | | |
|---|---|---|---|---|
| **590** | A177 | 130o multicolored | 1.00 | 1.25 |

**Souvenir Sheet**

| | | | | |
|---|---|---|---|---|
| **591** | A177 | 130o multicolored | 10.00 | *16.00* |

HAFNIA 76 Intl. Stamp Exhib., Copenhagen, Aug. 20-29. No. 591 contains one stamp

similar to No. 590 with design continuous into sheet margin. Sheet shows painting "A String of Horses Outside an Inn" of which No. 590 shows a detail. Sheet sold for 15k including exhibition ticket.

Emil Chr. Hansen, Physiologist, in Laboratory — A178

**1976, Sept. 23 Engr. *Perf. 13***

| | | | | |
|---|---|---|---|---|
| **592** | A178 | 100o orange red | .40 | .30 |

Carlsberg Foundation (art and science), centenary.

Glass Blower Molding Glass — A179

Danish Glass Production: 80o, Finished glass removed from pipe. 130o, Glass cut off from foot. 150o, Glass blown up in mold.

**1976, Nov. 18 Engr. *Perf. 13***

| | | | | |
|---|---|---|---|---|
| **593** | A179 | 60o slate | .50 | .50 |
| **594** | A179 | 80o dk brown | .50 | .25 |
| **595** | A179 | 130o dk blue | 1.00 | 1.00 |
| **596** | A179 | 150o red brown | .60 | .25 |
| | | *Nos. 593-596 (4)* | 2.60 | 2.00 |

Five Water Lilies — A180

**Photogravure and Engraved**

**1977, Feb. 2 *Perf. 12½***

| | | | | |
|---|---|---|---|---|
| **597** | A180 | 100o brt green & multi | .50 | .35 |
| **598** | A180 | 130o ultra & multi | 2.00 | 2.00 |

Nordic countries cooperation for protection of the environment and 25th Session of Nordic Council, Helsinki, Feb. 19.

Road Accident — A181

**1977, Mar. 24 Engr. *Perf. 12½***

| | | | | |
|---|---|---|---|---|
| **599** | A181 | 100o brown red | .40 | .30 |

Road Safety Traffic Act, May 1, 1977.

Europa — A182

**1977, May 2 Engr. *Perf. 12½***

| | | | | |
|---|---|---|---|---|
| **600** | A182 | 1k Allinge | *.60* | *.30* |
| **601** | A182 | 1.30k View, Ringsted | *3.00* | *3.00* |

Kongeaen A183

Landscapes, Southern Jutland: 90o, Skallingen. 150o, Torskind. 200o, Jelling.

**1977, June 30 Engr. *Perf. 12½***

| | | | | |
|---|---|---|---|---|
| **602** | A183 | 60o multicolored | 1.25 | 1.25 |
| **603** | A183 | 90o multicolored | .65 | .65 |
| **604** | A183 | 150o multicolored | .60 | .50 |
| **605** | A183 | 200o multicolored | .75 | .50 |
| | | *Nos. 602-605 (4)* | 3.25 | 2.90 |

See Nos. 616-619, 655-658, 666-669.

Hammers and Horseshoes A184

Designs: 1k, Chisel, square and plane. 1.30k, Trowel, ceiling brush and folding ruler.

**1977, Sept. 22 Engr. *Perf. 12½***

| | | | | |
|---|---|---|---|---|
| **606** | A184 | 80o dk brown | .30 | .25 |
| **607** | A184 | 1k red | .40 | .25 |
| **608** | A184 | 1.30k violet bl | .75 | .60 |
| | | *Nos. 606-608 (3)* | 1.45 | 1.10 |

Danish crafts.

Globe Flower — A185

Endangered Flora: 1.50k, Cnidium dubium.

**1977, Nov. 17 Engr. *Perf. 12½***

| | | | | |
|---|---|---|---|---|
| **609** | A185 | 1k multicolored | .40 | .25 |
| **610** | A185 | 1.50k multicolored | 1.25 | 1.25 |

Handball — A186

**1978, Jan. 19 *Perf. 12½***

| | | | | |
|---|---|---|---|---|
| **611** | A186 | 1.20k red | .40 | .30 |

Men's World Handball Championships.

Christian IV, Frederiksborg Castle A187

Frederiksborg Museum A188

**1978, Mar. 16**

| | | | | |
|---|---|---|---|---|
| **612** | A187 | 1.20k brown red | .50 | .50 |
| **613** | A188 | 1.80k black | .60 | .30 |

Frederiksborg Museum, centenary.

**Europa Issue**

Jens Bang's House, Aalborg A189

Frederiksborg Castle, Ground Plan and Elevation A190

**1978, May 11 Engr. *Perf. 12½***

| | | | | |
|---|---|---|---|---|
| **614** | A189 | 1.20k red | *.30* | .25 |
| **615** | A190 | 1.50k dk bl & vio bl | *1.25* | *1.25* |

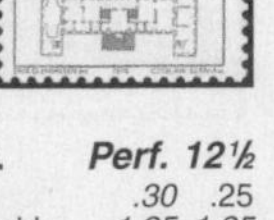

**Landscape Type of 1977**

Landscapes, Central Jutland: 70o, Kongenshus Memorial Park. 120o, Post Office, Old Town in Aarhus. 150o, Lignite fields, Soby. 180o, Church wall, Stadil Church.

**1978, June 15 Engr. *Perf. 12½***

| | | | | |
|---|---|---|---|---|
| **616** | A183 | 70o multicolored | .50 | .50 |
| **617** | A183 | 120o multicolored | .55 | .25 |
| | | Complete booklet, 10 #617 | 9.00 | |
| **618** | A183 | 150o multicolored | .80 | .80 |
| **619** | A183 | 180o multicolored | .60 | .60 |
| | | *Nos. 616-619 (4)* | 2.45 | 2.15 |

Boats in Harbor — A191

Danish fishing industry: 1k, Eel traps. 1.80k, Boats in berth. 2.50k, Drying nets.

**1978, Sept. 7 Engr. *Perf. 12½***

| | | | | |
|---|---|---|---|---|
| **620** | A191 | 70o olive gray | .50 | .50 |
| **621** | A191 | 1k redsh brown | .50 | .25 |
| **622** | A191 | 1.80k slate | .60 | .50 |
| **623** | A191 | 2.50k sepia | .85 | .60 |
| | | *Nos. 620-623 (4)* | 2.45 | 1.85 |

Edible Morel — A192

Design: 1.20k, Satan's mushroom.

**1978, Nov. 16 Engr. *Perf. 12½***

| | | | | |
|---|---|---|---|---|
| **624** | A192 | 1k sepia | .65 | .55 |
| **625** | A192 | 1.20k dull red | .65 | .55 |

Telephones — A193

**1979, Jan. 25 Engr. *Perf. 12½***

| | | | | |
|---|---|---|---|---|
| **626** | A193 | 1.20k dull red | .40 | .30 |

Centenary of Danish telephone.

University Seal A194

Pentagram: University Faculties A195

**1979, Apr. 5 Engr. *Perf. 12½***

| | | | | |
|---|---|---|---|---|
| **627** | A194 | 1.30k vermilion | .40 | .25 |
| **628** | A195 | 1.60k dk vio blue | .55 | .55 |

University of Copenhagen, 500th anniv.

**Types of 1933-1974**

**1979-82 Engr. *Perf. 13***

| | | | | |
|---|---|---|---|---|
| **629** | A32 | 80o green | .35 | .40 |
| **630** | A161 | 90o slate | 3.00 | 3.25 |
| **631** | A32 | 100o dp green ('81) | .50 | .40 |
| **632** | A161 | 110o brown | .65 | .40 |
| *a.* | | Bklt. pane, #493-494, 632, 2 #318 ('79) | 1.50 | |
| | | complete booklet, #632a | 1.50 | |
| **633** | A161 | 130o red | .65 | .40 |
| *a.* | | Bklt. pane, 2 ea #494, 629, 632, 4 #633 ('79) | 7.50 | |
| | | Complete booklet, #633a | 8.00 | |
| **634** | A161 | 130o brown ('81) | .65 | .60 |
| **635** | A161 | 140o red org ('80) | 2.00 | 2.50 |
| **636** | A161 | 150o red org ('81) | .65 | .80 |
| **637** | A161 | 160o ultra | 1.25 | 1.25 |
| **638** | A161 | 160o red ('81) | .65 | .40 |
| *a.* | | Bklt. pane, 2 ea #318, 634, 638, 8 #494) | 12.00 | |
| | | Complete booklet, #638a | 12.00 | |
| **639** | A161 | 180o ultra ('80) | 1.40 | 1.40 |
| **640** | A161 | 210o gray ('80) | 2.00 | 2.50 |
| **641** | A161 | 230o ol grn ('81) | 1.00 | .65 |
| **642** | A161 | 250o blue grn ('81) | 1.40 | 1.00 |
| **643** | A55 | 2.80k dull grn | 1.40 | 1.10 |
| **644** | A55 | 3.30k brn red ('81) | 1.40 | .80 |
| **645** | A55 | 3.50k grnsh bl ('82) | 2.50 | 3.00 |
| **646** | A55 | 4.30k brn red ('80) | 4.00 | 5.25 |
| **647** | A55 | 4.70k rose lil ('81) | 3.50 | 5.25 |
| **648** | A55 | 8k orange | 2.75 | .40 |
| **649** | A55 | 12k red brn ('81) | 5.00 | .65 |
| **650** | A55 | 14k dk red brn ('82) | 5.75 | .80 |
| | | *Nos. 629-650 (22)* | 42.45 | 33.20 |

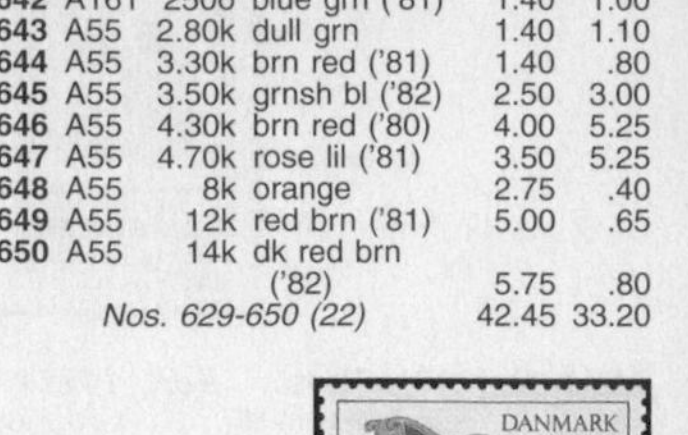

A196

Europa: 1.30k, Mail cart, 1785. 1.60k, Morse key and amplifier.

**1979, May 10 *Perf. 12½***

| | | | | |
|---|---|---|---|---|
| **651** | A196 | 1.30k red | *1.00* | .25 |
| **652** | A196 | 1.60k dark blue | *3.00* | 1.10 |

A197

Viking Art: 1.10k, Gripping beast pendant. 2k, Key with gripping beast design.

**1979, June 14 Engr. *Perf. 13***

| | | | | |
|---|---|---|---|---|
| **653** | A197 | 1.10k sepia | .40 | .40 |
| **654** | A197 | 2k grnsh gray | .50 | .40 |

**Landscape Type of 1977**

Landscapes, Northern Jutland: 80o, Mols Bjerge. 90o, Orslev Kloster. 200o, Trans. 280o, Bovbjerg.

**1979, Sept. 6 Engr. *Perf. 12½***

| | | | | |
|---|---|---|---|---|
| **655** | A183 | 80o multicolored | .50 | .50 |
| **656** | A183 | 90o multicolored | 1.60 | 1.60 |
| **657** | A183 | 200o multicolored | .90 | .35 |
| **658** | A183 | 280o multicolored | 1.10 | 1.10 |
| | | *Nos. 655-658 (4)* | 4.10 | 3.55 |

Adam Oehlenschläger (1799-1850), Poet and Dramatist A198

**1979, Oct, 4 Engr. *Perf. 13***

| | | | | |
|---|---|---|---|---|
| **659** | A198 | 1.30k dk carmine | .40 | .30 |

Score, Violin, Dancing Couple — A199

Ballerina — A200

**1979, Nov. 8 Engr. *Perf. 13x12½***

| | | | | |
|---|---|---|---|---|
| **660** | A199 | 1.10k brown | .40 | .30 |
| **661** | A200 | 1.60k ultra | .60 | .65 |

Jacob Gade (1879-63), composer; August Bournonville (1805-79), ballet master.

Royal Mail Guards' Office, Copenhagen, 1779 — A201

**1980, Feb. 14 Engr. *Perf. 13***
**662** A201 1.30k brown red .50 .35

National Postal Service, 200th anniversary.

Symbols of Occupation, Health and Education A202

**1980, May 5 Engr. *Perf. 13***
**663** A202 1.60k dark blue .65 .50

World Conference of the UN Decade for Women, Copenhagen, July 14-30.

Karen Blixen (1885-1962), Writer (Pen Name Isak Dinesen) — A203

Europa: 1.60k, August Krogh (1874-1949), physiologist.

**1980, May 5**
**664** A203 1.30k red *.65* .25
**665** A203 1.60k blue *1.40 1.40*

**Landscape Type of 1977**

Northern Jutland: 80o, Viking ship burial grounds, Lindholm Hoje. 110o, Lighthouse, Skagen, vert. 200o, Boreglum Monastery. 280o, Fishing boats, Vorupor Beach.

**1980, June 19 Engr. *Perf. 13***
**666** A183 80o multicolored .50 .50
**667** A183 110o multicolored .50 .50
**668** A183 200o multicolored .70 .30
**669** A183 280o multicolored 2.00 2.00
*Nos. 666-669 (4)* 3.70 3.30

**Nordic Cooperation Issue**

Silver Tankard, by Borchardt Rollufse, 1641 — A204

1.80K, Bishop's bowl, Copenhagen faience, 18th cent.

**1980, Sept. 9 Engr. *Perf. 13***
**670** A204 1.30k shown .50 .35
**671** A204 1.80k multicolored 1.40 1.40

Frisian Sceat Facsimile, Obverse and Reverse, 9th Century A205

Coins: 1.40k Silver coin of Valdemar the Great and Absalom, 1157-1182, 1.80k, Gold 12-mark coin of Christian VII, 1781.

**1980, Oct. 9 Engr. *Perf. 13***
**672** A205 1.30k red & redsh brn .50 .45
**673** A205 1.40k ol gray & sl grn 1.60 1.40
**674** A205 1.80k dk bl & sl bl 1.25 1.25
*Nos. 672-674 (3)* 3.35 3.10

Tonder Lace Pattern, North Schleswig — A206

Designs: Tonder lace patterns.

**1980, Nov. 13 Engr. *Perf. 13***
**675** A206 1.10k brown .65 .65
**676** A206 1.30k brown red .50 .30
**677** A206 2k olive gray .70 .30
*Nos. 675-677 (3)* 1.85 1.25

Nyboder Development, Copenhagen, 350th Anniversary A207

Design: 1.30k, View of Nyboder, diff.

**1981, Mar. 19**
**678** A207 1.30k dp org & ocher .90 .90
**679** A207 1.60k dp org & ocher .55 .30

Tilting at a Barrel on Shrovetide A208

Design: 2k, Midsummer's Eve bonfire.

**1981, May 4 Engr. *Perf. 13***
**680** A208 1.60k brown red *.40* .25
Complete booklet, 10 #680 *4.00*
**681** A208 2k dk blue *1.25 .75*

Soro Lake and Academy, Zealand — A209

Designs: Views of Zealand: 150o, Poet N.F.S. Grundtvig's home, Udby. 160o, Kaj Munk's home, Opager. 200o, Gronsund. 230o, Bornholm Island.

**1981, June 18 Engr. *Perf. 13***
**682** A209 100o shown .50 .50
**683** A209 150o multicolored .65 .65
**684** A209 160o multicolored .65 .30
**685** A209 200o multicolored .80 .80
**686** A209 230o multicolored 1.10 .85
*Nos. 682-686 (5)* 3.70 3.10

European Urban Renaissance Year — A210

**1981, Sept. 10 Engr. *Perf. 12½x13***
**687** A210 1.60k dull red .65 .35

**Type of 1933**

**1981-85 Engr. *Perf. 13***
**688** A32 30o orange .60 .40
*a.* Bklt. pane 10 (2 #318, 2 #688, 6 #494)('84) 30.00
Complete booklet, #688a, 6 #708 30.00
**689** A32 40o purple .50 .40
*a.* Bklt. pane of 10 (4 #318, 2 #689, 4 #494) ('89) 4.50
**690** A32 80o ol bis ('85) 1.00 .80
**691** A32 100o blue ('83) .85 .40
*b.* Bklt. pane of 8 (2 #494, 4 #691, 2 #706) ('83) 21.00
Complete booklet, #691b 21.00
**692** A32 150o dk green ('82) .85 .40
**693** A32 200o green ('83) 1.00 .90
**694** A32 230o brt yel grn ('84) 1.50 .60
**695** A32 250o brt yel grn ('85) 1.50 .60
*Nos. 688-695 (8)* 7.80 4.50

Ellehammer's 18-horsepower Biplane, 1906 — A211

1.30k, R-1 Fokker CV reconnaissance plane, 1926. 1.60k, Bellanca J-300, 1931. 2.30k, DC-7C, 1957.

**1981, Oct. 8 Engr. *Perf. 13***
**696** A211 1k black & bluish green .65 .65
**697** A211 1.30k brown & lt brown 1.10 1.10
**698** A211 1.60k red & orange .65 .30
**699** A211 2.30k dark blue & pale blue .90 .70
*Nos. 696-699 (4)* 3.30 2.75

**Arms Type of 1946 and**

Queen Margrethe II, 10th Anniv. of Accession — A212

**1982-85 Engr. *Perf. 13***
**700** A212 1.60k dull red .65 .40
**701** A212 1.60k dk ol grn 2.50 3.00
**702** A212 1.80k sepia .85 .70
**703** A212 2k dull red .90 .30
*b.* Bklt. pane, 4 #494, 2 ea #493, 702, 703 20.00
**704** A212 2.20k ol grn ('83) 1.50 2.75
**705** A212 2.30k violet 1.00 1.20
**706** A212 2.50k org red ('83) .85 .30
**707** A212 2.70k dk blue 1.20 .80
**708** A212 2.70k cop red ('84) 1.25 .40
*c.* Booklet pane, 3 #688, 2 #494, 3 #708 ('84) 13.00
**709** A212 2.80k cop red ('85) 1.00 .50
Complete booklet, #494a, 6 #709 13.50
*b.* Booklet pane, 3 #493, 2 #494, 3 #709 ('85) 6.75
Complete booklet, #709b 7.00
**710** A212 3k violet ('83) 1.20 .50
**711** A212 3.30k bluish blk ('84) 1.75 1.00
**712** A212 3.50k blue ('83) 1.50 .65
**713** A212 3.50k dk vio ('85) 1.50 .80
**714** A212 3.70k dp blue ('84) 1.75 .80
**715** A212 3.80k dk blue ('85) 1.40 .60
**716** A55 4.30k dk ol grn ('84) 4.50 4.75
**717** A55 5.50k dk bl grn ('84) 2.75 1.25
**718** A55 16k cop red ('83) 6.00 .90
**719** A55 17k cop red ('84) 7.75 1.25
**720** A55 18k brn vio ('85) 8.50 1.25
**720A** A55 50k dk red ('85) 17.00 3.25
*Nos. 700-720A (22)* 67.30 27.35

See Nos. 796-803, 887, 889, 896, 899.

World Figure Skating Championships A213

**1982, Feb. 25**
**721** A213 2k dark blue .80 .50

Revenue Schooner Argus — A214

**1982, Feb. 25 Engr. *Perf. 12½***
**722** A214 1.60k carmine red .65 .35

Customs Service centenary

Europa — A215

2k, Abolition of adscription, 1788. 2.70k, Women's voting right, 1915.

**1982, May 3 Engr. *Perf. 12½***
**723** A215 2k brown lake *.75* .25
Complete booklet, 10 #723 7.50
**724** A215 2.70k deep blue *1.75 1.00*

Butter Churn, Barn, Hjedding — A216

**1982, June 10 Engr. *Perf. 13***
**725** A216 1.80k brown .80 .65

Cooperative dairy farming centenary.

Records Office, 400th Anniv. — A217

**1982, June 10**
**726** A217 2.70k green 1.20 .50

Steen Steensen Blicher (1782-1848), Poet, by J.V. Gertner — A218

**1982, Aug. 26 Engr. *Perf. 13***
**727** A218 2k brown red .35 .30

Robert Storm Petersen (1882-1949), Cartoonist — A219

Characters: 1.50k, Three little men and the number man. 2k, Peter and Ping the penguin, horiz.

**1982, Sept. 23 Engr. *Perf. 12½***
**728** A219 1.50k dk bl & red .70 .50
**729** A219 2k red & ol grn 1.10 .40

Printing in Denmark, 500th Anniv. — A220

**1982, Sept. 23**
**730** A220 1.80k Press, text, ink balls .80 .85

A221

**1982, Nov. 4**
**731** A221 2.70k Library seal 1.20 .50

500th anniv. of University Library.

World Communications Year — A222

**1983, Jan. 27 Engr. *Perf. 13***
**732** A222 2k multicolored .80 .35

Amusement Park, 400th Anniv. — A223

**1983, Feb. 24**
**733** A223 2k multicolored .80 .35

Badminton Championship
A224

**1983, Feb. 24**
**734** A224 2.70k multicolored 1.20 .50

Nordic Cooperation Issue — A225

**1983, Mar. 24**
**735** A225 2.50k Egeskov Castle .90 .40
**736** A225 3.50k Troll Church, North Jutland 1.40 .75

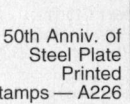

50th Anniv. of Steel Plate Printed Stamps — A226

**1983, Mar. 24 Engr. *Perf. 13***
**737** A226 2.50k car rose 1.00 .35

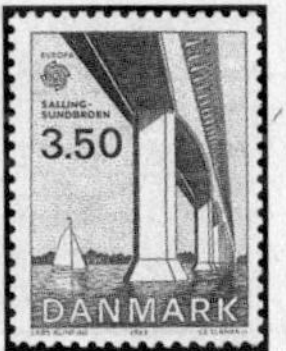


Europa 1983 — A227

2.50k, Kildekovshallen Recreation Center, Copenhagen. 3.50k, Salling Sound Bridge.

**1983, May 5 Engr. *Perf. 13***
**738** A227 2.50k multicolored *1.10* .25
**739** A227 3.50k multicolored *2.00 1.00*

Weights and Measures Ordinance, 300th Anniv. — A228

**1983, June 16**
**740** A228 2.50k red 1.00 .35

Christian V Danish Law, 300th Anniv. — A229

**1983, Sept. 8 Engr.**
**741** A229 5k Codex titlepage 2.00 1.00

A230

1k, Car crash, police. 2.50k, Fire, ambulance service. 3.50k, Sea rescue.

**1983, Oct. 6 Engr. *Perf. 13***
**742** A230 1k brown .50 .50
**743** A230 2.50k red 1.00 .35
**744** A230 3.50k blue 1.25 .85
*Nos. 742-744 (3)* 2.75 1.70

Life saving and salvage services.

Elderly in Society — A231

**1983, Oct. 6**
**745** A231 2k Stages of life .80 .80
**746** A231 2.50k Train passengers 1.00 .30

N.F.S. Grundtvig (1783-1872), Poet — A232

Street Scene, by C.W. Eckersberg (1783-1853) A233

**1983, Nov. 3 Engr.**
**747** A232 2.50k brown red 1.20 .50
**748** A233 2.50k brown red 1.00 .35

Tree Planting Campaign — A234

**1984, Jan. 26 Litho. & Engr.**
**749** A234 2.70k Shovel, sapling 1.20 .35

A235

**1984, Jan. 26 Engr.**
**750** A235 3.70k Game 1.75 .50

1984 Billiards World Championships, Copenhagen, May 10-13.

Hydrographic Dept. Bicentenary A236

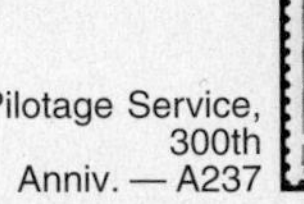


Pilotage Service, 300th Anniv. — A237

**1984, Mar. 22 Engr. *Perf. 13***
**751** A236 2.30k Compass 1.25 .90
**752** A237 2.70k Boat 1.25 .50

2nd European Parliament Elections A238

Scouts Around Campfire, Emblems A239

**Litho. & Engr.**
**1984, Apr. 12 *Perf. 13***
**753** A238 2.70k org & dk bl 1.75 .35
**754** A239 2.70k multi 1.20 .35

Europa (1959-84) A240

**1984, May 3 Engr. *Perf. 12½***
**755** A240 2.70k red *1.75* .25
**756** A240 3.70k blue *2.25 1.60*

Prince Henrik, 50th Birthday A241

D Day, 40th Anniv. A242

**1984, June 6 Engr.**
**757** A241 2.70k brown red 1.20 .35
**758** A242 2.70k War Memorial, Copenhagen 1.20 .35

See Greenland No. 160.

17th Cent. Inn — A243

**1984, June 6**
**759** A243 3k multicolored 1.50 1.40

Fishing and Shipping A244

**1984, Sept. 6 Engr.**
**760** A244 2.30k Research (Herring) 1.60 1.75
**761** A244 2.70k Sea transport 1.10 .60
**762** A244 3.30k Deep-sea fishing 1.60 1.75
**763** A244 3.70k Deep-sea, diff. 1.60 1.75
*Nos. 760-763 (4)* 5.90 5.85

A245

**1984, Oct. 5 Litho. & Engr.**
**764** A245 1k Post bird .35 .35

A246

Holberg Meets with an Officer, by Wilhelm Marstrand (1810-73).

**1984, Oct. 5**
**765** A246 2.70k multicolored 1.20 .35

Ludvig Holberg (1684-1754), writer.

Jewish Community in Copenhagen, 300th Anniv. — A247

3.70k, Woman blessing Sabbath candles.

**1984, Oct. 5**
**766** A247 3.70k multicolored 1.75 1.40

Carnival in Rome, by Christoffer W. Eckersberg (1783-1853) — A248

Paintings: 10k, Ymer and Odhumble (Nordic mythology figures), by Nicolai A. Abildgaard (1743-1809), vert.

***Perf. 12½x13, 13x12½***
**1984, Nov. 22 Litho. & Engr.**
**767** A248 5k multicolored 3.25 3.25
**768** A248 10k multicolored 5.75 5.75

German and French Reform Church, 300th Anniv. — A249

**1985, Jan. 24 Engr. *Perf. 13***
**769** A249 2.80k magenta 1.75 .35

Bonn-Copenhagen Declaration, 30th Anniv. — A250

**1985, Feb. 21 Litho. *Perf. 14***
**770** A250 2.80k Map, flags 1.90 .65

Intl. Youth Year — A251

**1985, Mar. 14 *Perf. 13***
**771** A251 3.80k multicolored 1.75 .90

**Souvenir Sheet**

HAFNIA '87 Philatelic Exhibition — A252

Early Postal Ordinances — 1k, Christian IV's Ordinance on Postmen, 1624. 2.50k, Plague Mandate, 1711. 2.80k, Ordinance on Prohibition of Mail by Means other than the Post, 1775. 3.80k, Act on Postal Articles, 1831.

**1985, Mar. 14 Litho. & Engr.**
**772** Sheet of 4 5.50 *6.50*
*a.* A252 1k multi 1.25 *1.60*
*b.* A252 2.50k multi 1.25 *1.60*
*c.* A252 2.80k multi 1.25 *1.60*
*d.* A252 3.80k multi 1.25 *1.60*

Sold for 15k.

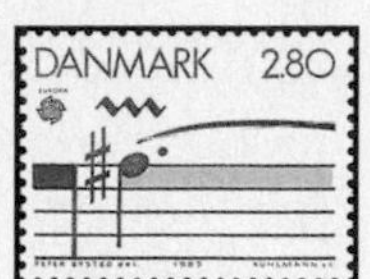


Europa 1985 — A253

**1985, May 2**

**773** A253 2.80k Musical staff *1.50* *.50*
**774** A253 3.80k Musical staff, diff. *1.90* *1.25*

Arrival of Queen Ingrid in Denmark, 50th Anniv. — A254

2.80k, Queen Mother, chrysanthemums.

**1985, May 21**

**775** A254 2.80k multicolored 1.20 .35

See Greenland No. 163.

Opening of the Faro Bridges — A255

**1985, May 21 Litho. *Perf. 13***

**776** A255 2.80k Faro-Falster Bridge 1.20 .35

St. Cnut's Land Grant to Lund Cathedral, 900th Anniv. — A256

Seal of King Cnut and: 2.80k, Lund Cathedral. 3k, City of Helsingdorg, Sweden.

**1985, May 21 Engr.**

**777** A256 2.80k multi 1.10 .45
**778** A256 3k multi 2.00 2.00

See Sweden Nos. 1538-1539.

UN Decade for Women — A257

**1985, June 27 Litho. & Engr.**

**779** A257 3.80k Cyclist 1.75 1.00

Sports — A258

**1985, June 27**

**780** A258 2.80k Women's floor exercise 1.25 .30
**781** A258 3.80k Canoe & kayak 1.75 .95
**782** A258 6k Cycling 2.90 1.75
*Nos. 780-782 (3)* 5.90 3.00

Kronborg Castle, Elsinore, 400th Anniv. — A259

**1985, Sept. 5**

**783** A259 2.80k multi 1.75 .35

UN 40th Anniv. — A260

**1985, Sept. 5**

**784** A260 3.80k Dove, emblem 1.75 1.20

Niels Bohr (1885-1962), Physicist — A261

**1985, Oct. 3 *Perf. 13x12½***

**785** A261 2.80k With wife Margrethe 1.75 1.40

Winner of 1922 Nobel Prize in Physics for theory of atomic structure.

Hand Signing "D" — A262

**1985, Nov. 7 Engr. *Perf. 13***

**786** A262 2.80k multicolored 1.40 .35

Danish Assoc. for the Deaf, 50th anniv.

Boat, by Helge Refn — A263

**1985, Nov. 7 Litho.**

**787** A263 2.80k multicolored 1.40 .35

Abstract Iron Sculpture by Robert Jacobsen A264

**Lithographed and Engraved**

**1985, Nov. 7 *Perf. 13x12½***

**788** A264 3.80k multicolored 3.50 3.75

Painting by Bjorn Wiinblad A265

**1986, Jan. 23 Litho. *Perf. 13x12½***

**789** A265 2.80k multicolored 1.75 1.40

Amnesty Intl., 25th Anniv. A266

**Lithographed and Engraved**

**1986, Jan. 23 *Perf. 13***

**790** A266 2.80k multicolored 1.20 .35

Miniature Sheet

HAFNIA '87 — A267

**1986, Feb. 20**

**791** A267 Sheet of 4 7.50 11.00
*a.* 100o Holstein carriage, c. 1840 1.75 2.50
*b.* 250o Iceboat, c. 1880 1.75 2.50
*c.* 280o 1st mail van, 1908 1.75 2.50
*d.* 380o Airmail service 1919 1.75 2.50

Sold for 15k.

Changing of the Guard — A268

**1986, Mar. 20 *Perf. 13***

**792** A268 2.80k multicolored 1.20 .35

Royal Danish Life Guards barracks and Rosenborg Drilling Ground, bicent.

**Types of 1933-85**

**1986-90 Engr. *Perf. 13***

**793** A32 5o brn org ('89) .35 .40
**794** A32 270o brt yel grn 1.90 1.75
*b.* Bklt. pane, 6 #318, 2 #691, 2 #794 18.00
**795** A32 300o brt yel grn 1.75 .40
Complete booklet, #794b, 4 #795 22.50
**796** A212 3k cop red 1.20 .60
Complete booklet, #691, #794, 3 #318, 2 #796 6.00
**797** A212 3.20k deep vio 1.00 .80
**798** A212 3.20k carmine 1.25 .40
*c.* Bklt. pane, 2 #693, 4 #798 9.00
Complete booklet, #689a, #798c 15.00
Complete booklet, #693, 2 #798, 2 #318, #689, 2 #494 15.50
**799** A212 3.40k dk grn 2.25 3.00
**800** A212 3.80k dark vio 1.20 2.90
**801** A212 4.10k dark blue 1.40 .60
**802** A212 4.20k dk pur 3.50 3.00
**803** A212 4.40k dp bl 2.50 .60
**804** A55 4.60k gray 5.00 5.50
**805** A55 6.50k dp grn 2.50 1.00
**806** A55 6.60k green 5.00 5.50
**807** A55 7.10k brn vio 3.50 3.50
**808** A55 7.30k green 4.75 5.50
**809** A55 7.70k dk brn vio 4.50 2.10
**810** A55 11k brown 5.50 5.25
**811** A55 20k dp ultra 6.75 .80
**812** A55 22k henna brn 7.25 2.25
**813** A55 23k dark olive grn 10.50 2.25
**814** A55 24k dark olive grn 10.50 2.00
**815** A55 26k dark olive grn 12.50 2.25
*Nos. 793-815 (23)* 96.55 52.35

Issued: 6.50k, 20k, 1/9/86; 22k, 1/3/87; 270o, 3k, No. 797, 3.80k, 4.10k, 4.60k, 6.60k, 7.10k, 24k, 1/7/88; No. 794b, 1/28/88; 300o, No. 798, 3.40k, 4.20k, 4.40k, 7.30k, 7.70k, 11k, 26k, 1/26/89; 5o, 1989; 23k, 1/11/90.

No. 793 issued for use in lieu of currency of the same face value.

Soro Academy, 400th Anniv. — A269

**1986, Apr. 28 Litho. & Engr.**

**816** A269 2.80k multi 1.40 .50

Intl. Peace Year — A270

**1986, Apr. 28**

**817** A270 3.80k multi 1.60 1.10

A271

**1986, May 26 Litho.**

**818** A271 2.80k multi 1.75 .50

Crown Prince Frederik, 18th birthday.

Nordic Cooperation Issue 1986 — A272

Sister towns.

**1986, May 27 Engr.**

**819** A272 2.80k Aalborg Harbor 1.40 .35
**820** A272 3.80k Thisted Church and Town Hall 1.60 1.25

Hoje Tastrup Train Station Opening, May 31 — A273

**1986, May 27 Litho.**

**821** A273 2.80k multi 1.20 .35

Mailbox, Telegraph Lines, Telephone — A274

**1986, June 19 Litho. *Perf. 13***

**822** A274 2.80k multi 1.00 .35

19th European Intl. PTT Congress, Copenhagen, Aug. 12-16.

Natl. Bird Candidates — A275

Finalists: a, Corvus corax. b, Sturnus vulgaris. c, Cygnus olor (winner). d, Vanellus vanellus. e, Alauda arvensis.

**1986, June 19** **Litho. & Engr.**

**823** Strip of 5 10.50 24.00
***a.-e.*** A275 2.80k any single 2.00 1.00
Complete booklet, 2 #823 21.00

A276

**1986, June 19**

**824** A276 2.80k multi 1.20 .35

Danish Rifle, Gymnastics and Sports Club, 125th anniv.

Souvenir Sheet

HAFNIA '87 — A277

**1986, Sept. 4**

**825** Sheet of 4 10.00 12.50
***a.*** A277 100o Mailcoach, c. 1841 2.25 3.00
***b.*** A277 250o Postmaster, c. 1840 2.25 3.00
***c.*** A277 280o Postman, c. 1851 2.25 3.00
***d.*** A277 380o Rural postman, c. 1893 2.25 3.00

Sold for 15k.

Europa 1986 — A278

**1986, Sept. 4** **Engr.**

**826** A278 2.80k Street sweeper *2.50* .25
**827** A278 3.80k Garbage truck *3.50 1.50*

Cupid — A279

**1986, Oct. 9** **Litho.**

**828** A279 3.80k multi 1.50 1.00

Premiere of The Whims of Cupid and the Ballet Master, by Vincenzo Galeotti, bicent.

Refugee — A280

**1986, Oct. 9** **Litho. & Engr.**

**829** A280 2.80k multi 1.20 .35

Danish Refugee Council Relief Campaign.

A281

Protestant Reformation in Denmark, 450th Anniv.: Sermon, altarpiece detail, 1561, Thorslunde Church, Copenhagen.

**1986, Oct. 9** **Litho.** ***Perf. 13***

**830** A281 6.50k multi 2.50 1.75

A282

**1986, Nov. 6** **Litho. & Engr.**

**831** A282 3.80k multi 3.00 3.00

Organization for Economic Cooperation and Development, 25th anniv.

Abstract by Lin Utzon — A283

**1987, Jan. 22** **Litho.** ***Perf. 13***

**832** A283 2.80k multi 1.00 .35
Complete booklet, 10 #832 11.00

Art appreciation.

A284

**1987, Feb. 26** **Engr.** ***Perf. 13***

**833** A284 2.80k lake & black 1.00 .35

Danish Consumer Council, 40th anniv.

A285

Religious art (details) from Ribe Cathedral.

**1987, Apr. 9** **Litho.** ***Perf. 13***

**834** A285 3k Fresco 1.40 .60
**835** A285 3.80k Stained-glass window 2.10 2.10
Complete booklet, 10 #835 21.00
**836** A285 6.50k Mosaic 3.50 3.50
*Nos. 834-836 (3)* 7.00 6.20

Ribe Cathedral redecoration, 1982-1987, by Carl-Henning Pedersen.

A286

Europa (Modern architecture): 2.80k, Central Library, Gentofte, 1985. 3.80k, Hoje Tastrup High School, 1985, horiz.

**1987, May 4** **Engr.** ***Perf. 13***

**837** A286 2.80k rose claret *2.50 .35*
**838** A286 3.80k bright ultra *3.50 2.25*

A287

**1987, May 4**

**839** A287 2.50k dk red & bl blk 2.00 2.00

Danish Academy of Technical Sciences (ATV), 50th anniv.

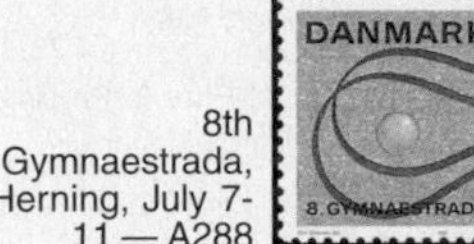

8th Gymnaestrada, Herning, July 7-11 — A288

**1987, June 18** **Litho. & Engr.**

**840** A288 2.80k multi 1.00 .35
Complete booklet, 10 #840 10.00

A289

**1987, June 18**

**841** A289 3.80k multi 1.60 1.40

Danish Cooperative Bacon Factories, cent.

A290

**1987, Aug. 27** **Litho.**

**842** A290 3.80k Single-sculler 1.60 1.20

World Rowing Championships, Aug. 23-30.

HAFNIA '87, Bella Center, Copenhagen, Oct. 16-25 — A291

No. 843, Type A15, mail train c. 1912.

**Litho. & Engr.**

**1987, Aug. 27** ***Perf. 13x12½***

**843** A291 280o multi 1.90 1.50

**Souvenir Sheet**

**843A** A291 280o like No. 843 20.00 26.00

Purchase of No. 843A included admission to the exhibition. Sold for 45k.

Due to a color shift, some examples of No. 843A have a green lawn and locomotive.

Abstact by Ejler Bille — A292

**1987, Sept. 24** **Litho.** ***Perf. 13***

**844** A292 2.80k multi 1.00 .35
Complete booklet, 10 #844 10.00

Rasmus Rask (1787-1832), Linguist — A293

**1987, Oct. 15** **Engr.** ***Perf. 13x12½***

**845** A293 2.80k dk hen brn 1.00 .45

A294

Emblem: Miraculous Catch (Luke 5:4-7), New Testament.

**1987, Oct. 15** ***Perf. 13***

**846** A294 3k carmine lake 1.25 .50

Clerical Assoc. for the Home Mission in Denmark, 125th anniv.

A295

Designs: 3k, Two lions from the gate of Rosenburg Castle around the monogram of Christian IV. 4.10k, Portrait of the monarch painted by P. Isaacsz, vert.

**Photo. & Engr., Litho. (4.10k)**

**1988, Feb. 18** ***Perf. 13***

**847** A295 3k blue gray & gold 1.25 .30
Complete booklet, 10 #847 12.50
**848** A295 4.10k multi 1.60 .75

Accession of Christian IV (1577-1648), King of Denmark and Norway (1588-1648), 400th anniv.

Ole Worm (1588-1654), Archaeologist, and Runic Artifacts — A296

**1988, Feb. 18** **Engr.**

**849** A296 7.10k chocolate 2.75 2.75

Odense, 1000th Anniv. — A297

Design: St. Cnut's Church and statue of Hans Christian Andersen, Odense.

**1988, Mar. 10** **Engr.**

**850** A297 3k multi 1.00 .35
Complete booklet, 10 #850 10.00

A298

**1988, Apr. 7** **Litho.**
**851** A298 2.70k multi 1.25 1.25

Danish Civil Defense and Emergency Planning Agency, 50th Anniv.

WHO, 40th Anniv. — A299

**1988, Apr. 7** **Litho. & Engr.**
**852** A299 4.10k multi 1.75 1.00

Abolition of *Stavnsbaand,* 200th Anniv. — A300

Painting: King Christian VII riding past the Liberty Memorial, Copenhagen, by C.W. Eckersberg (1783-1853).

**1988, May 5** **Litho.**
**853** A300 3.20k multi 1.40 1.00

*Stavnsbaand* (adscription) provided that all Danish farmers' sons from age 4 to 40 would be bound as villeins to the estates on which they were born, thus providing landowners with free labor.

A301

Europa: Transport and communication — 3k, Postwoman on bicycle. 4.10k, Mobile telephone.

**1988, May 5**
**854** A301 3k multicolored *1.75* .25
**855** A301 4.10k multicolored *2.50 1.00*

A302

**1988, June 16** **Litho.**
**856** A302 4.10k multi 1.60 .75

1988 Individual Speedway World Motorcycle Championships, Denmark, Sept. 3.

Federation of Danish Industries, 150th Anniv. — A303

Painting (detail): *The Industrialists,* by P.S. Kroyer.

**1988, June 16** ***Perf. 13½x13***
**857** A303 3k multi 1.00 .50

Danish Metalworkers' Union, Cent. — A304

3k, Glass mosaic by Niels Winkel.

**1988, Aug. 18** **Litho.** ***Perf. 13***
**858** A304 3k multicolored 1.00 .50

Tonder Teachers' Training College, 200th Anniv. — A305

**1988, Aug. 18** **Engr.** ***Perf. 13x12½***
**859** A305 3k lake 1.00 .50

*Homage to Leon Degand,* Sculpture by Robert Jacobsen A306

**1988, Sept. 22** ***Perf. 11½x13***
**860** A306 4.10k blk, lake & gray 3.75 *5.00*

Danish-French cultural exchange program, 10th anniv. See France No. 2130.

Preservation of Historic Sites — A307

3k, Lumby Windmill, 1818. 7.10k, Vejstrup Water Mill, 1837.

**1988, Oct. 13** **Engr.** ***Perf. 13x12½***
**861** A307 3k red & org 1.60 .50
Complete booklet, 10 #861 16.00
**862** A307 7.10k dp blue & bluish grn 4.00 2.75

Paintings in the State Museum of Art, Copenhagen — A308

4.10k, *Bathing Boys,* 1902, by Peter Hansen (1868-1928). 10k, *The Hill at Overkaerby,* 1917, by Fritz Syberg (1862-1939).

**Litho. & Engr.**

**1988, Nov. 3** ***Perf. 13***
**863** A308 4.10k multi 3.25 *4.50*
**864** A308 10k multi 6.50 *8.00*

See Nos. 881-882, 951-952, 972-973, 1018-1019.

*The Little Mermaid,* Sculpture by Edvard Eriksen — A309

**1989, Feb. 16** **Engr.**
**865** A309 3.20k dark green 1.75 .50
Complete booklet, 10 #865 17.50

Tourism industry, cent.

Danish Soccer Assoc., Cent. — A310

**1989, Mar. 16** **Litho.**
**866** A310 3.20k multi 1.60 .50
Complete booklet, 10 #866 16.00

NATO Membership, 40th Anniv. — A311

**1989, Mar. 16**
**867** A311 4.40k dk blue, gold & lt blue 2.00 1.25

Nordic Cooperation Issue — A312

Folk costumes.

**1989, Apr. 20** **Litho. & Engr.**
**868** A312 3.20k Woman from Valby 1.40 .40
**869** A312 4.40k Pork butcher 2.10 1.60

European Parliament 3rd Elections A313

**1989, May 11** **Litho.**
**870** A313 3k blue & yellow 1.60 1.50

Europa 1989 — A314

Children's toys.

**1989, May 11** **Litho. & Engr.**
**871** A314 3.20k Lego blocks *1.90* .25
**872** A314 4.40k Wooden soldiers, by Kay Bojesen *3.00 .90*

Agricultural Museum, Cent. A315

**1989, June 15** **Engr.** ***Perf. 13***
**873** A315 3.20k Tractor, 1889 1.25 .50

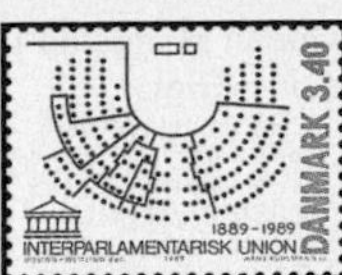

Interparliamentary Union, Cent. — A316

**1989, June 15** **Litho. & Engr.**
**874** A316 3.40k Folketing Chamber layout 3.50 4.00

Danish Fishery and Marine Research Institute, Cent. A317

**1989, Aug. 24** **Litho. & Engr.**
**875** A317 3.20k multi 1.25 .50

Bernhard Severin Ingemann (1789-1862), Poet and Novelist — A318

**1989, Aug. 24** **Engr.**
**876** A318 7.70k dark green 3.00 1.90

A319

Danish Film Office, 50th Anniv.: 3k, Scene from the short feature film *They Reached the Ferry,* 1948. 3.20k, Bodil Ipsen (d. 1964), actress. 4.40k, Carl Th. Dreyer (1889-1968), screenwriter and director.

**1989, Sept. 28** **Litho.**
**877** A319 3k multi 1.40 1.40
**878** A319 3.20k multi 1.25 .50
**879** A319 4.40k multi 1.75 1.00
*Nos. 877-879 (3)* 4.40 2.90

Stamp Day, 50th Anniv. — A320

**1989, Nov. 10** **Litho. & Engr.**
**880** A320 3.20k multi 1.25 .50

**Art Type of 1988**

Paintings: 4.40k, *Part of the Northern Gate of the Citadel Bridge,* c. 1837, by Christen Kobke (1810-1848). 10k, *A Little Girl, Elise Kobke, With a Cup in Front of Her,* c. 1850, by Constantin Hansen (1804-1880).

**1989, Nov. 10** ***Perf. 12½x13***
**881** A308 4.40k multi 3.00 4.00
**882** A308 10k multi 6.25 8.50

**Types of 1933-82 and**

A321

A321a

### Queen Margrethe II

**1990-98 Engr. *Perf. 12¾***

**883** A32 25o bluish black .55 .40
*a.* Bklt. pane, 4 #691, 2 #883 4.75
**884** A32 125o carmine lake .95 .40
**885** A32 325o lt yel grn 2.10 1.75
**886** A32 350o yellow green 2.00 .95
**887** A212 3.50k dark red 1.25 .40
*a.* Bklt. pane, 2 each #691, 885, 887 8.00
Complete booklet, #883, #885, #887, 3 #691 16.00
Complete booklet, #883a, #887a 13.50
**888** A321 3.50k henna brown 1.40 .40
*b.* Bklt. pane, 4 each #883, #884, #888 ('91) 20.00
Complete booklet, #888b 20.00
Complete booklet, 2 each #883, #884, #888 16.00
**889** A212 3.75k dark green 2.25 2.40
**890** A321 3.75k green 4.00 3.75
**891** A321 3.75k red 3.00 .40
*a.* Bklt. pane, 4 each #884, #891 17.50
Complete booklet, #891a 17.50
*b.* Booklet pane, 2 each #691, 883, 891 8.75
Complete booklet, #891b 8.75
**892** A321a 3.75k red 2.25 .50
*a.* Booklet pane, 2 each #691, 883, 892 14.50
Complete booklet, #892a 14.50
*b.* Booklet pane, 2 #883, 4 #494, 2 #892 12.00
Complete booklet, #892b 12.00
**893** A321 4k brown 2.50 1.20
**894** A321a 4k deep bl grn 2.25 .80
**895** A321a 4.25k olive brown 2.90 1.90
**896** A212 4.50k brown violet 2.75 3.25
**897** A321 4.50k violet 2.50 2.40
**898** A321a 4.50k deep bl blk 2.60 2.40
**899** A212 4.75k dark blue 1.90 .40
**900** A321 4.75k blue 2.50 .40
**901** A321 4.75k violet 3.50 2.00
**902** A321a 4.75k brown *3.50* 2.10
**903** A321a 5k violet 2.50 1.75
**904** A321 5k blue 3.50 .40
**905** A321 5.25k black 3.50 1.75
**906** A321a 5.25k deep blue 3.25 .80
**907** A321 5.50k green 3.25 3.75
**908** A321a 5.50k henna brown 3.50 2.75
**909** A55 7.50k dark bl grn 3.00 2.75
*Nos. 883-909 (27)* 69.15 42.15

Queen Margrethe II's 50th birthday (No. 888).

Issued: No. 888, 4/5; Nos. 890, 897, 900, 1990; No. 888a, 2/14/91; Nos. 886, 891, 891a, 901, 904, 6/10/92; 5.50k, 1/13/94; 4k, 5.25k, 6/27/96; Nos. 892, 892a, 1/14/97; Nos. 894, 902, 903, 906, 8/28/97; Nos. 895, 898, 908, 909, 3/26/98; others, 1/11/90.

See Nos. 1114, 1125, 1130.

Museum of Decorative Art, Cent. — A322

Design: Silver coffee pot designed by Axel Johannes Kroyer, Copenhagen, 1726.

**1990, Feb. 15 Engr. *Perf. 13***

**911** A322 3.50k dark blue & blk 1.20 .80
Complete booklet, 10 #911 12.00

A323

Steam engine, 200th anniv.: Steam engine built by Andrew Mitchell, 1790.

**1990, Feb. 15**

**912** A323 8.25k dull red brown 2.75 1.75

Nyholm, 300th Anniv. A324

**1990, Apr. 5 Engr.**

**913** A324 4.75k black 1.75 .90

Europa 1990 — A325

3.50k, Royal Monogram, Haderslev P.O. 4.75k, Odense P.O.

**1990, Apr. 5 Litho.**

**914** A325 3.50k multi *1.10* .25
**915** A325 4.75k multi *1.75* *.60*

A326

Pieces from the Flora Danica Banquet Service produced for King Christian VII: No. 916, Bell-shaped lid, dish. No. 917, Gravy boat, dish. No. 918, Ice pot, casserole, lid. No. 919, Serving dish.

**1990, May 3 Litho.**

**916** A326 3.50k multicolored 1.25 1.90
**917** A326 3.50k multicolored 1.25 1.90
**918** A326 3.50k multicolored 1.25 1.90
**919** A326 3.50k multicolored 1.25 1.90
*a.* Strip of 4, #916-919 5.00 8.50

Flora Danica porcelain, 200th anniv.

A327

Endangered plant species.

**1990, June 14**

**920** A327 3.25k Marshmallow 1.25 1.25
**921** A327 3.50k Red helleborine 2.25 .35
Complete booklet, 10 #921 30.00
**922** A327 3.75k Purple orchis 1.50 1.50
**923** A327 4.75k Lady's slipper 1.90 .65
*Nos. 920-923 (4)* 6.90 3.75

Village Churches, Jutland — A328

***Perf. 13x12½, 12½x13***

**1990, Aug. 30 Engr.**

**924** A328 3.50k Gjellerup 1.20 .35
Complete booklet, 10 #924 12.00
**925** A328 4.75k Veng 1.60 .75
**926** A328 8.25k Bredsten, vert. 3.00 2.00
*Nos. 924-926 (3)* 5.80 3.10

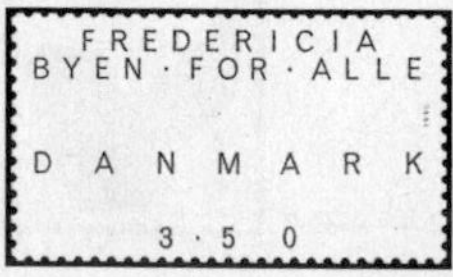


Fredericia, "The Town for Everybody" A329

**Engr. & Embossed**

**1990, Oct. 5 *Perf. 13***

**927** A329 3.50k black & red 1.20 .90

Tordenskiold (Peter Wessel, 1690-1720), Admiral — A330

**1990, Oct. 5 Litho. *Perf. 13½x13***

**928** A330 3.50k multicolored 1.20 .60
Complete booklet, 10 #928 12.00

Prevent Bicycle Thefts — A331

Design: 3.50k, Stop drunk driving.

**1990, Nov. 8 Litho. *Perf. 13x12½***

**930** A331 3.25k shown 1.10 1.10
**931** A331 3.50k Automobile, wine glass 1.10 .30

Locomotives — A332

**1991, Mar. 14 Engr. *Perf. 13***

**932** A332 3.25k IC3 1990 1.40 1.50
**933** A332 3.50k Class A 1882 1.10 .35
Complete booklet, 10 #933 11.00
**934** A332 3.75k Class MY 1954 1.25 1.75
**935** A332 4.75k Class P 1907 1.50 1.50
*Nos. 932-935 (4)* 5.25 5.10

Europa — A333

Satellite photographs showing temperatures of Danish: 3.50k, Waters. 4.75k, Land.

**1991, May 2 Litho. *Perf. 13***

**936** A333 3.50k multicolored *1.75* *.25*
**937** A333 4.75k multicolored *2.10* *1.00*

Jutland Law, 750th Anniv. — A334

**1991, May 2**

**938** A334 8.25k multicolored 3.00 2.75

Danish Islands — A335

**1991, June 6**

**939** A335 3.50k Fano 1.40 .30
Complete booklet, 10 #939 18.00
**940** A335 4.75k Christianso 1.60 .90

Decorative Art — A336

Designs: 3.25k, Earthenware bowl and jars by Christian Poulsen. 3.50k, Chair by Hans Wegner, vert. 4.75k, Silver cutlery by Kay Bojesen, vert. 8k, Lamp by Poul Henningsen.

**1991, Aug. 22 Litho. *Perf. 13***

**941** A336 3.25k multicolored 1.10 1.50
**942** A336 3.50k multicolored 1.00 .35
Complete booklet, 10 #942 10.00
**943** A336 4.75k multicolored 1.25 1.75
**944** A336 8.25k multicolored 3.00 4.50
*Nos. 941-944 (4)* 6.35 8.10

Keep Denmark Clean — A337

Designs: 3.50k, Cleaning up after dog. 4.75k, Picking up litter.

**1991, Sept. 19 Engr. *Perf. 13***

**945** A337 3.50k red 2.00 .30
Complete booklet, 10 #945 20.00
**946** A337 4.75k blue 2.00 1.00

Posters from Danish Museum of Decorative Arts — A338

Posters for: 3.50k, Nordic Advertising Congress, by Arne Ungermann (1902-1981). 4.50k, Poster Exhibition at Copenhagen Zoo (baboon), by Valdemar Andersen (1875-1928). 4.75k, Danish Air Lines, by Ib Andersen (1907-1969). 12k, The Sinner, by Sven Brasch (1886-1970).

**1991, Sept. 19 Litho.**

**947** A338 3.50k multicolored 1.00 .30
**948** A338 4.50k multicolored 1.75 2.50
**949** A338 4.75k multicolored 1.25 1.50
**950** A338 12k multicolored 4.00 3.50
*Nos. 947-950 (4)* 8.00 7.80

### Art Type of 1988

Designs: 4.75k, Lady at her Toilet by Harald Giersing (1881-1927), vert. 14k, Road through a Wood by Edvard Weie (1879-1943), vert.

**Litho. & Engr.**

**1991, Nov. 7 *Perf. 13x12½***

**951** A308 4.75k multicolored 1.75 1.75
**952** A308 14k multicolored 4.50 4.00

A339

Treasures of Natl. Museum: 3.50k, Earthenware bowl, Skarpsalling. 4.50k, Bronze dancer, Grevensvaenge. 4.75k, Bottom plate of silver cauldron, Gundestrup. 8.25k, Flint knife, Hindsgavl.

**1992, Feb. 13 Engr. *Perf. 13***

**953** A339 3.50k dk vio & brown 1.10 .30
Complete booklet, 10 #953 11.00
**954** A339 4.50k dk bl & dk ol green 2.40 2.40
**955** A339 4.75k brown & black 1.25 1.10
**956** A339 8.25k dk ol grn & vio brown 2.75 2.75
*Nos. 953-956 (4)* 7.50 6.55

A340

**1992, Mar. 12 *Perf. 13½x13***

**957** A340 3.50k rose carmine 1.25 .65

Danish Society of Chemical, Civil, Electrical, and Mechanical Engineers, cent.

Souvenir Sheet

Queen Margaret I (1353-1412) — A341

**Litho. & Engr.**

**1992, Mar. 12** ***Perf. 12½***

**958** A341 Sheet of 2 6.25 7.25
*a.* 3.50k Fresco 3.00 3.50
*b.* 4.75k Alabaster bust 3.00 3.50

Nordia '94, Scandinavian Philatelic Exhibition. No. 958 sold for 12k to benefit the exhibition.

Discovery of America, 500th Anniv. — A342

**1992, May 7** **Engr.** ***Perf. 12½***

**959** A342 3.50k Potato plant *2.25 .40*
Complete booklet, 10 #959 *22.50*
**960** A342 4.75k Ear of corn *4.25 1.75*

Europa.

Protect the Environment — A343

3.75k, Hare beside road. 5k, Fish, water pollution. 8.75k, Cut trees, vert.

**Litho. & Engr.**

**1992, June 10** ***Perf. 13***

**961** A343 3.75k multi 1.25 .30
Complete booklet, 10 #961 12.50
**962** A343 5k multi 1.75 .70
**963** A343 8.75k multi 3.50 2.00
*Nos. 961-963 (3)* 6.50 3.00

Queen Margrethe II and Prince Henrik, 25th Wedding Anniv. — A344

**1992, June 10** **Litho.** ***Perf. 12½x13***

**964** A344 3.75k multicolored .90 1.60

See Greenland No. 253.

A345

**1992, July 16** ***Perf. 13***

**965** A345 3.75k multicolored 1.75 .75

Denmark, European soccer champions.

Danish Pavilion, Expo '92, Seville — A346

**1992, Aug. 27** **Engr.** ***Perf. 13***

**966** A346 3.75k blue 1.50 .75

Single European Market — A347

**1992, Oct. 8** **Litho. & Engr.** ***Perf. 13***

**967** A347 3.75k blue & org 1.50 .75

A348

Cartoon characters: 3.50k, A Hug, by Ivar Gjorup. 3.75k, Love Letter, by Phillip Stein Jonsson. 4.75k, Domestic Triangle, by Nikoline Wordelin. 5k, Poet and His Little Wife, by Jorgen Mogensen.

**Litho. & Engr.**

**1992, Oct. 8** ***Perf. 12½***

**968** A348 3.50k multicolored 1.75 1.00

**Engr.**

**969** A348 3.75k red & purple 1.40 .30
**970** A348 4.75k blk & red brn 2.50 2.50
**971** A348 5k blue & red brn 1.75 .70
*Nos. 968-971 (4)* 7.40 4.50

**Art Type of 1988**

5k, Landscape from Vejby, 1843, by John Thomas Lundbye. 10k, Motif from Halleby Brook, 1847, by Peter Christian Skovgaard.

**Litho. & Engr.**

**1992, Nov. 12** ***Perf. 12½x13***

**972** A308 5k multicolored 2.10 2.00
**973** A308 10k multicolored 4.00 3.25

Publication of New Danish Bible — A349

3.75k, Jacob's fight with angel.

**1992, Nov. 12** ***Perf. 13***

**974** A349 3.75k multi 1.75 1.20

A350

Archaeological Treasures. Anthropomorphic gold foil figures found in: 3.75k, Lundeborg, horiz. 5k, Bornholm.

**Litho. & Engr.**

**1993, Feb. 4** ***Perf. 13***

**975** A350 3.75k multicolored 1.40 .30
**976** A350 5k multicolored 1.90 .70

Butterflies — A351

3.75k, Small tortoiseshell. 5k, Large blue. 8.75k, Marsh fritillary. 12k, Red admiral.

**1993, Mar. 11** **Litho.**

**977** A351 3.75k multi 1.75 .40
Complete booklet, 10 #977 17.50
**978** A351 5k multi 2.50 .80
**979** A351 8.75k multi 5.25 3.50
**980** A351 12k multi 5.25 3.50
*Nos. 977-980 (4)* 14.75 8.20

Tivoli Gardens, 150th Anniv. — A352

Posters: 3.75k, Pierrot, by Thor Bogelund, 1947, horiz. 5k, Balloons, by Wilhelm Freddie, 1987.

**1993, May 6** **Litho.** ***Perf. 12½***

**981** A352 3.75k multicolored 1.75 1.00
Complete booklet, 10 #981 17.50
**982** A352 5k multicolored 1.75 .90

A353

Europa (Contemporary paintings by): 3.75k, Troels Worsel, horiz. 5k, Stig Brogger.

**1993, May 6** ***Perf. 13***

**983** A353 3.75k multicolored *1.40 1.10*
**984** A353 5k multicolored *1.90 .90*

A354

**1993, June 17** **Engr.** ***Perf. 13***

**985** A354 5k dark blue green 4.00 1.00

Danish-Russian relations, 500th anniv. See Russia No. 6154.

Training Ships

A355 A356

***Perf. 13, 13½x13 (#987)***

**1993, June 17** **Litho. & Engr.**

**986** A355 3.75k Danmark 2.00 .30
**987** A356 4.75k Jens Krogh 4.00 4.50
**988** A355 5k Georg Stage, horiz. 3.00 1.75

**Size: 39x28mm**

***Perf. 13x13½***

**989** A356 9.50k Marilyn Anne, horiz. 5.50 5.25
*Nos. 986-989 (4)* 14.50 11.80

Child's Drawing of Viking Ships — A357

Letter Writing Campaign — A358

**1993, Aug. 19** **Litho.** ***Perf. 13***

**990** A357 3.75k multicolored 2.25 .65
**991** A358 5k lt & dk bl & blk 2.50 1.40

Ethnic Jewelry — A359

**1993, Sept. 16** **Litho.** ***Perf. 13***

**992** A359 3.50k Falster 1.75 1.25
**993** A359 3.75k Amager 1.75 .30
Complete booklet, 10 #993 17.50
**994** A359 5k Laeso 2.00 .90
**995** A359 8.75k Romo 4.50 3.00
*Nos. 992-995 (4)* 10.00 5.45

Cubist Paintings A360

5k, Assemblage, by Vilhelm Lundstrom, 1929. 15k, Composition, by Franciska Clausen, 1929.

**Litho. & Engr.**

**1993, Nov. 11** ***Perf. 12½***

**996** A360 5k multicolored 2.75 2.25
**997** A360 15k multicolored 6.75 5.00

See Nos. 1033-1034, 1080-1081.

Conservation — A361

**1994, Jan. 27** **Litho.** ***Perf. 13***

**998** A361 3.75k Save water *3.50 .30*
**999** A361 5k CO2 *4.50 1.10*

Castles A362

Castles: 3.50k, Marselisborg, Aarhus. 3.75k, Amalienborg, Copenhagen. 5k, Fredensborg, North Zealand. 8.75k, Graasten, South Jutland.

**Litho. & Engr.**

**1994, Mar. 17** *Perf. 13x12½*

**1000** A362 3.50k multicolored 1.50 .70
**1001** A362 3.75k multicolored 1.75 .30
Complete booklet, 10 #1001 17.50
**1002** A362 5k multicolored 2.25 .30
**1003** A362 8.75k multicolored 3.75 3.50
*a.* Bklt. pane, #1000-1003 30.00 30.00

No. 1003a printed with 2 different labels. One shows a marching band, the other shows a ship.

Danmark Expedition, 1906-08 — A363

Europa: 3.75k, Expedition ship, Danmark, Alfred Wegener's weather balloon. 5k, Theodolite, Johan Peter Koch, cartographer.

**1994, May 5** **Engr.** *Perf. 13*

**1004** A363 3.75k deep brn vio *1.90* .25
**1005** A363 5k dp slate grn *2.60 1.25*
Complete booklet, 10 #1005 *35.00*

Trams — A364

Designs: 3.75k, Copenhagen tram (Engelhardt). 4.75k, Aarhus car. 5k, Odense tram, vert. 12k, Horse-drawn tram.

**Litho. & Engr.**

**1994, June 9** *Perf. 13*

**1006** A364 3.75k multicolored 1.25 .30
**1007** A364 4.75k multicolored 2.25 2.75
**1008** A364 5k multicolored 1.75 1.40

**Size: 38x21mm**

**1009** A364 12k multicolored 5.25 5.25
*Nos. 1006-1009 (4)* 10.50 9.70

Children's Stamp Competition — A365

**1994, Aug. 25** **Litho.** *Perf. 12½*

**1010** A365 3.75k multicolored 1.50 .70

ILO, 75th Anniv. — A366

**1994, Aug. 25** *Perf. 13*

**1011** A366 5k multicolored 2.00 1.00

Wild Animals — A367

**Litho. & Engr.**

**1994, Oct. 20** *Perf. 12½*

**1012** A367 3.75k House sparrows 2.00 .35
**1013** A367 4.75k Badger 3.00 2.25
**1014** A367 5k Squirrel, vert. 2.60 1.00
**1015** A367 9.50k Black grouse 5.00 4.50

**Size: 36x26mm**

*Perf. 13*

**1016** A367 12k Grass snake 6.00 5.25
*Nos. 1012-1016 (5)* 18.60 13.35

A368

**1994, Nov. 10** **Litho.** *Perf. 13*

**1017** A368 3.75k multicolored 1.75 .70

Folk High Schools, 150th anniv.

**Painting Type of 1988**

Designs: 5k, Study of Italian Woman and Sleeping Child, by Wilhelm Marstrand. 15k, Interior from Amaliegade with the Artist's Brothers, by Wilhelm Bendz.

**Litho. & Engr.**

**1994, Nov. 10** *Perf. 12½x13*

**1018** A308 5k multicolored 2.00 1.40
**1019** A308 15k multicolored 6.00 3.25

Aarhus Cathedral School, 800th Anniv. — A369

**Litho. & Engr.**

**1995, Jan. 26** *Perf. 13*

**1020** A369 3.75k multicolored 1.75 .70

UN, 50th Anniv. — A370

**Litho. & Engr.**

**1995, Jan. 26** *Perf. 13*

**1021** A370 5k multicolored 2.50 1.20
Complete booklet, 10 #1021 35.00

Danish Islands A371

**1995, Mar. 16** **Engr.** *Perf. 13*

**1022** A371 3.75k Avernako 2.25 .30
Complete booklet, 10 #1022 22.50
**1023** A371 4.75k Fejo 2.75 2.50
**1024** A371 5k Fur 3.50 .90
**1025** A371 9.50k Endelave 4.50 4.50
*a.* Booklet pane, #1022-1025 + 2 labels 15.00
Complete booklet, 2 #1025a 32.50
*Nos. 1022-1025 (4)* 13.00 8.20

No. 1025a printed with four different large labels. Labels with one pane are MF Faaborg II and MF Endelave. The other pane has MF Bukken-bruse and MF Fursund.

Liberation of Denmark, 50th Anniv. A372

Designs: 3.75k, Gen. Montgomery, Town Hall Square, vert. 5k, White busses returning from concentration camps. 8.75k, Airplane dropping supplies to resistance. 12k, Jews escape across the Sound to Sweden.

**1995, May 4** **Litho.** *Perf. 13*

**1026** A372 3.75k multicolored 2.10 .30
Complete booklet, 10 #1026 21.00
**1027** A372 5k multicolored 2.75 1.00
**1028** A372 8.75k multicolored 4.25 4.00
**1029** A372 12k multicolored 6.00 6.00
*Nos. 1026-1029 (4)* 15.10 11.30

Europa (Nos. 1026-1027).

A373

**1995, June 8** **Litho.** *Perf. 13*

**1030** A373 3.50k multicolored 1.50 .70

Danish Rhymed Chronicle, 500th anniv.

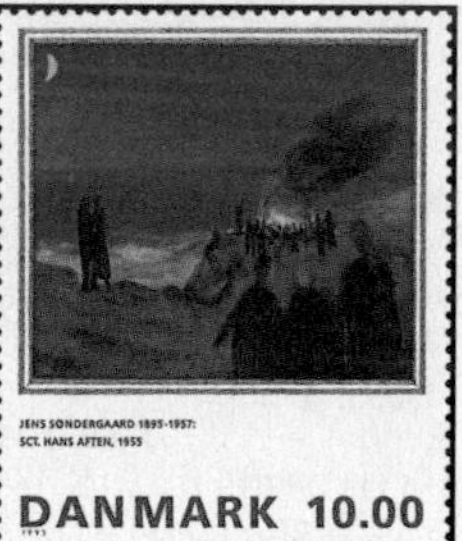


A374

3.75k, Roskilde Festival. 5k, Tonder Festival.

**1995, June 8**

**1031** A374 3.75k multi, horiz. 1.60 .30
Complete booklet, 10 #1031 16.00
**1032** A374 5k multi 2.25 1.00

No. 1031 is 28x21mm.

Paintings A375

Designs: 10k, "Sct. Hans Aften, 1955," by Jens Sondergaard. 15k, "Landskab-Gudhjem, 1939," by Niels Lergaard.

**Litho. & Engr.**

**1995, Aug. 24** *Perf. 13x12½*

**1033** A375 10k multicolored 5.00 5.75
**1034** A375 15k multicolored 7.50 7.50



Tycho Brahe (1546-1601), Astronomer A376

3.75k, Uranienborg Observatory. 5.50k, Sextant.

**Litho. & Engr.**

**1995, Oct. 27** *Perf. 13*

**1035** A376 3.75k multicolored 2.00 .65
**1036** A376 5.50k multicolored 2.75 2.75

See Sweden Nos. 2149-2150.

Toys A377

Designs: 3.75k, Tekno cars. 5k, Dolls, teddy bear. 8.75k, Model trains. 12k, Glud & Marstrand tin horse-drawn carriage & fire pumper.

**1995, Nov. 9** *Perf. 13x12½*

**1037** A377 3.75k multicolored 1.60 .30
Complete booklet, 10 #1037 16.00
**1038** A377 5k multicolored 2.10 1.00
**1039** A377 8.75k multicolored 3.25 3.25
**1040** A377 12k multicolored 4.25 4.25
*Nos. 1037-1040 (4)* 11.20 8.80

A378

Cartoonlike views of Copenhagen: 3.75k, Round Tower as music box. 5k, Christiansborg Castle. 8.75k, Marble Church as top of balloon. 12k, The Little Mermaid statue on stage.

**1996, Jan. 25** **Litho.** *Perf. 13*

**1041** A378 3.75k multicolored 1.25 .30
Complete booklet, 10 #1041 13.00
**1042** A378 5k multicolored 1.75 .70
**1043** A378 8.75k multicolored 3.00 3.00
**1044** A378 12k multicolored 4.00 4.50
*Nos. 1041-1044 (4)* 10.00 8.50

Copenhagen, 1996 cultural capital of Europe.

A379

**1996, Mar. 21** **Litho.** *Perf. 13*

**1045** A379 3.75k Sports for disabled 1.25 .30
Complete booklet, 10 #1045 13.00
**1046** A379 4.75k Swimming 1.60 1.60
**1047** A379 5k Sailing 1.75 .50
**1048** A379 9.50k Cycling 3.25 3.25
*a.* Bklt. pane of 4, #1045-1048 + 2 labels 14.00
Complete booklet, 2 #1048a 28.00

No. 1048a printed with two different large labels. One shows hands and soccer ball, second shows tennis racket and tennis balls.

Danish Federation for Sports for the Disabled (No. 1045). Modern Olympic Games, cent., Sports Confederation of Denmark, cent., 1996 Summer Olympics, Atlanta (Nos. 1046-1048).

A380

**1996, May 9** **Litho.** *Perf. 13*

**1049** A380 3.75k multicolored 1.50 1.00

Danish Employers' Confederation, cent.

A381

Famous Danish Women (Europa): 3.75k, Karen Blixen (1885-1962), writer. 5k, Asta Nielsen (1881-1972), silent screen actress.

**1996, May 9**

**1050** A381 3.75k lt brn & dk brn *1.50* *.50*
**1051** A381 5k gray & dk blue *2.00* *.75*
Complete booklet, 10 #1051 *20.00*

A382

Wooden Dinghies: 3.50k, Roskilde Fjord sail boat. 3.75k, Limfjorden skiff. 12.25k, Two-masted smack, South Funen Archipelago.

***Perf. 13, 12½ (#1053)***

**1996, June 13** **Engr.**

**1052** A382 3.50k multicolored 1.25 1.00
**1053** A382 3.75k multicolored 1.50 .50
Complete booklet, 10 #1053 16.00
**1054** A382 12.25k multicolored 4.50 5.25
*Nos. 1052-1054 (3)* 7.25 6.75

No. 1053 is 20x39mm.

Lighthouses — A383

**Litho. & Engr.**

**1996, Sept. 12** ***Perf. 13x12½***

**1055** A383 3.75k Fornaes 1.50 .30
Complete booklet, 10 #1055 16.00
**1056** A383 5k Blavandshuk 1.75 .50
*a.* Bklt. pane, 8 #1055, 2 #1056 22.00
Complete booklet, #1056a 22.00
**1057** A383 5.25k Bovbjerg 2.00 2.00
**1058** A383 8.75k Mon 3.00 3.00
*Nos. 1055-1058 (4)* 8.25 5.80

Art Works of Thorvald Bindesboll (1846-1908) — A384

**Litho. & Engr.**

**1996, Oct. 10** ***Perf. 13***

**1059** A384 3.75k Pitcher 1.50 .30
Complete booklet, 10 #1059 16.00

**Litho.**

**1060** A384 4k Portfolio cover 1.60 1.10

Paintings A385

Designs: 10k, "At Lunch," by P.S. Kroyer, 1893. 15k, "The Girl with Sunflowers," by Michael Ancher, 1889.

**Litho. & Engr.**

**1996, Nov. 7** ***Perf. 13x12½***

**1061** A385 10k multicolored 4.00 4.00
**1062** A385 15k multicolored 5.25 5.25

A386

Queen Margrethe II: 3.50k, With Prince Henrik. 3.75k, With Crown Prince Frederik. 4k, Delivering New Year speech. 5.25k, Waving to crowd.

**1997, Jan. 14** **Litho.** ***Perf. 13***

**1063** A386 3.50k multicolored 1.25 1.25
**1064** A386 3.75k multicolored 1.50 .30
Complete booklet, 10 #1064 16.00
**1065** A386 4k multicolored 1.40 .70
**1066** A386 5.25k multicolored 2.00 1.50
*a.* Sheet of 4, #1063-1066 + 2 labels 6.50 6.50
*Nos. 1063-1066 (4)* 6.15 3.75

Queen Margrethe II, 25th anniv. of coronation.

A387

Open Air Museum, Copenhagen, Cent.: 3.50k, Kalstrup post mill. 3.75k, Ellested water mill. 5k, Fjellerup manor barn. 8.75k, Romo farm.

**1997, Mar. 13** **Engr.** ***Perf. 13***

**1067** A387 3.50k multicolored 1.25 1.00
**1068** A387 3.75k multicolored 1.25 .30
Complete booklet, 10 #1068 12.50
**1069** A387 5k multicolored 1.75 .75
Complete booklet, 10 #1069 17.50
**1070** A387 8.75k multicolored 3.00 2.50
*a.* Booklet pane, #1067-1070 + label 14.00
Complete booklet, 2 #1070a 28.00
*Nos. 1067-1070 (4)* 7.25 4.55

No. 1070a printed with two different large labels. One shows a view of Ellested water mill, the other shows a farm in Ejersted.

Great Belt Railway Link — A388

**1997, May 15** **Litho.** ***Perf. 13***

**1071** A388 3.75k East Tunnel 1.50 .50
Complete booklet, 10 #1071 15.00
**1072** A388 4.75k West Bridge 1.75 1.75

A389

Kalmar Union, 600th Anniv.: No. 1073, Margrete I and Eric of Pomerania. No. 1074, The Three Graces symbolizing Denmark, Norway and Sweden.

**1997, June 12** **Litho.** ***Perf. 13***

**1073** 4k multicolored 2.60 2.75
**1074** 4k multicolored 2.60 2.75
*a.* A389 Pair, #1073-1074 5.25 6.50

No. 1074a is a continuous design.

Copenhagen-Roskilde Railway, 150th Anniv. — A390

Designs: 3.75k, Two modern trains under Carlsberg Bridge. 8.75k, Early steam train going under Carlsberg Bridge.

**Litho. & Engr.**

**1997, June 12** ***Perf. 13***

**1075** A390 3.75k multicolored 2.75 .30
Complete booklet, 10 #1075 27.50
**1076** A390 8.75k multicolored 5.00 2.50

End of Railway Mail Service A391

**1997, June 12** **Litho.**

**1077** A391 5k multicolored 1.75 .70

Stories and Legends A392

Europa: 3.75k, Large cat on top of treasure chest, from "The Tinder Box." 5.25k, Butterfly, pond, frog, from "Thumbelina."

**1997, Aug. 28** **Engr.** ***Perf. 13***

**1078** A392 3.75k multicolored *1.40* *.40*
**1079** A392 5.25k multicolored *1.75* *1.50*

**Painting Type of 1993**

Designs: 9.75k, "Dust Dancing in the Sun," by Vilhelm Hammershoi (1864-1916). 13k, "Woman Mountaineer," by J.F. Willumsen (1863-1958).

**Litho. & Engr.**

**1997, Sept. 18** ***Perf. 13x12½***

**1080** A360 9.75k multicolored 4.75 5.50
**1081** A360 13k multicolored 6.25 7.00

A393

Danish Design: 3.75k, Faaborg chair, vert. 4k, Margrethe bowl, vert. 5k, The Ant (chair). 12.25k, Georg Jensen silver bowl, vert.

**1997, Nov. 6** **Litho.** ***Perf. 13***

**1082** A393 3.75k multicolored 1.25 .30
Complete booklet, 10 #1082 12.50
**1083** A393 4k multicolored 1.25 .75
**1084** A393 5k multicolored 2.00 .45
**1085** A393 12.25k multicolored 4.50 5.25
*Nos. 1082-1085 (4)* 9.00 6.75

Danish Confederation of Trade Unions, Cent. — A394

3.50k, General Workers Union in Denmark (SiD). 3.75k, Danish Confederation of Trade Unions (LO). 4.75k, Danish Nurse's Organization. 5k, Union of Commercial and Clerical Employees in Denmark (HK).

**1998, Jan. 22** **Litho.** ***Perf. 13***

**1086** A394 3.50k multicolored 1.10 .90
**1087** A394 3.75k multicolored 1.25 .30
Complete booklet, 10 #1087 12.50
**1088** A394 4.75k multicolored 1.90 2.50
**1089** A394 5k multicolored 2.00 .65
Complete booklet, 10 #1089 20.00
*Nos. 1086-1089 (4)* 6.25 4.35

City of Roskilde, 1000th Anniv. — A395

**Litho. & Engr.**

**1998, Mar. 26** ***Perf. 13***

**1090** A395 3.75k multicolored 1.50 .90
Complete booklet, 10 #1090 15.00

A396

**1998, Mar. 26** **Litho.** ***Perf. 13***

**1091** A396 5k Ladybug 1.75 .50

Reduce poison.

A397

New Post & Tele Museum, Copenhagen: 3.75k, Postman, 1922. 4.50k, Morse code operator, c. 1910. 5.50k, Telephone operator, 1910. 8.75k, Modern postman.

**1998, May 28** **Litho.** ***Perf. 13***

**1092** A397 3.75k multicolored 1.25 .30
Complete booklet, 10 #1092 12.50
*a.* Booklet pane, 2 each #1087, 1089, 3 ea. 1090, 1092 30.00
Complete booklet, #1092a 30.00
**1093** A397 4.50k multicolored 1.50 1.50
**1094** A397 5.50k multicolored 2.00 2.00
**1095** A397 8.75k multicolored 2.75 2.75
*a.* Booklet pane, #1092-1095 14.00
Complete booklet, 2 #1095a 28.00
*Nos. 1092-1095 (4)* 7.50 6.55

No. 1095a is printed with two backgrounds. One shows part of King Christian IV's "Order Concerning Postmen," 1624. The other shows part of Copenhagen c. 1923. Complete booklets contain panes with each background.

Bridges over Great Belt A398

No. 1096, West Bridge. No. 1097, East Bridge (suspension).

**1998, May 28** **Engr.** ***Perf. 13***

**1096** A398 5k shown 2.75 .75
**1097** A398 5k multi 2.75 .75
*a.* Pair, #1096-1097 + label 6.00 1.50

Nordic Stamps — A399

Shipping: No. 1098, Signal flags, harbor master with binoculars. No. 1099, Radar image of entrance to Copenhagen harbor, sextant.

**1998, May 28 Litho. *Perf. 13***

**1098** A399 6.50k multicolored 3.50 3.50
**1099** A399 6.50k multicolored 3.50 3.50
*a.* Pair, #1098-1099 7.25 7.25
*b.* Souvenir sheet, #1099a 8.00 10.00

National Festivals — A400

Europa: 3.75k, Horse at Danish agricultural show. 4.50k, Theater, tents at Arhus Festival Week, Arhus.

**Litho. & Engr.**

**1998, Sept. 3 *Perf. 13***

**1100** A400 3.75k multicolored *1.50* *.60*
Complete booklet, 10 #1100 *15.00*
**1101** A400 4.50k multicolored *1.75* *1.00*

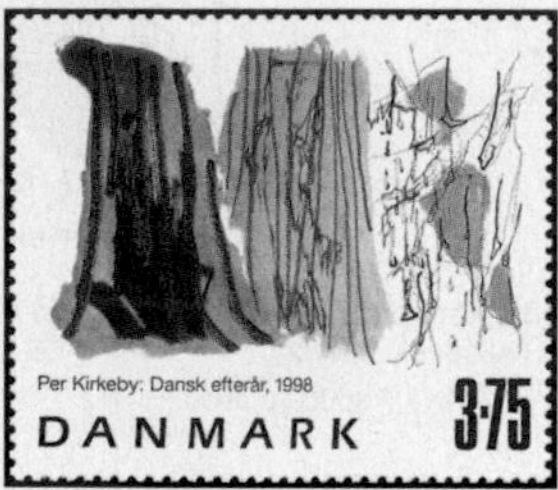

Contemporary Art — A401

Paintings: 3.75k, Danish Autumn, by Per Kirkeby. 5k, Alpha, by Mogens Andersen, vert. 8.75k, Imagery, by Ejler Bille, vert. 19k, Celestial Horse, by Carl-Henning Pedersen.

***Perf. 12½x13, 13x12½***

**1998, Oct. 15 Litho. & Engr.**

**1102** A401 3.75k multicolored 1.25 1.25

**Litho.**

**1103** A401 5k multicolored 2.00 1.50
**1104** A401 8.75k multicolored 3.25 3.25
**1105** A401 19k multicolored 6.50 7.75
*Nos. 1102-1105 (4)* 13.00 13.75

See Nos. 1160-1161, 1190-1191, 1204-1205, 1235-1236, 1255-1256, 1282-1283, 1333-1336.

A402

Fossil, name of Danish geologist: 3.75k, Ammonite, Ole Worm (1588-1654). 4.50k, Shark's teeth, Niels Stensen (1638-86). 5.50k, Sea Urchin, Soren Abildgaard (1718-91). 15k, Slit-shell snail, Erich Pontoppidan (1698-1764).

**1998, Nov. 5 Engr. *Perf. 13***

**1106** A402 3.75k multicolored 1.25 .30
Complete booklet, 10 #1106 12.50
**1107** A402 4.50k multicolored 1.75 1.75
**1108** A402 5.50k multicolored 1.75 1.75
**1109** A402 15k multicolored 5.00 4.50
*a.* Souvenir sheet, #1106-1109 12.00 12.50

**Wavy Lines and Queen Types of 1933, 1997 and**

Queen Margrethe II — A402a

**1999-2004 Engr. *Perf. 12¾***

**1111** A32 150o purple *.60* .25
**1112** A32 375o green 2.60 .70
**1113** A32 400o green 1.75 .65
**1114** A321a 4k red 2.60 .50
*a.* Booklet pane, 4 #883, 2 #494, 2 #1114 6.75
Complete booklet, #1114a 7.00
**1115** A402a 4k red 1.75 .50
*b.* Booklet pane, 4 #883, 2 #494, 2 #1115 5.00
Booklet, #1115b 5.00
*c.* Sheet of 8 + label 16.00
**1116** A32 425o green 2.75 .65
**1117** A402a 4.25k blue 2.60 1.00
**1118** A402a 4.25k red 1.75 .70
*b.* Booklet pane, 6 #883, 2 #1118 5.00
*c.* Sheet of 8 + central label 36.00 —
**1119** A402a 4.50k orange 2.00 1.50
*a.* Vert. strip of 10 + 10 etiquettes 24.00
**1120** A402a 4.50k red 2.90 1.10
*a.* Booklet pane, 2 #494, 2 #1120 6.00 —
Complete booklet, #1120a 6.00
*b.* Sheet of 8 + central label 26.00 —
**1121** A402a 4.75k sepia 3.25 1.75
**1122** A402a 5k dk green 2.00 1.00
*a.* Sheet of 8 + 8 etiquettes *65.00* —
**1123** A402a 5.25k ultra 2.10 1.00
**1124** A402a 5.50k violet 2.50 .90
*a.* Sheet of 8 + label 24.00
*b.* Sheet of 8 + 8 etiquettes 30.00
**1125** A321a 5.75k blue 2.25 1.25
**1126** A402a 5.75k emerald 2.50 1.25
**1127** A402a 6k bister 2.50 .75
*a.* Sheet of 10 + 10 etiquettes 45.00 —
**1128** A402a 6.25k green 4.00 2.00
**1129** A402a 6.50k slate grn *2.50* .90
*a.* Sheet of 8 + 8 etiquettes 32.00
*b.* Sheet of 8 + central label 42.00 —
**1130** A321a 6.75k slate green 4.25 2.75
**1131** A402a 6.75k henna brn 3.25 2.50
**1132** A402a 7k rose lilac 3.00 2.50
**1133** A402a 8.50k bright blue *3.00* 3.00
**1134** A55 10.50k dk bl gray *4.00* 2.50
**1135** A55 11.50k dk bl gray 5.75 4.00
**1136** A55 12.50k gray 6.00 4.50
**1137** A55 13k orange 5.50 4.50
**1138** A55 15k blue 6.50 5.25
*Nos. 1111-1138 (28)* 86.15 49.85

Issued: 375o, Nos. 1114, 1118, 1130, 1/13/99; No. 1125, 1/3/00; Nos. 1115, 1119, 1119a, 4.25k, 4.50k, 5k, 5.25k, 5.50k, Nos. 1126, 1131, 4/12/00; No. 1119b, 6k, 7k, 5/9/01; Nos. 1119c, 1121a, 1124a, 4/17/01; 150o, 4.75k, 6.50k, 10.50k, 1/2/02. 400o, No. 1120, 6.25k, 8.50k, 11.50k, 1/2/03. No. 1120b, 3/12. Nos. 1124b, 1129a, 3/12/03. Nos. 1128b, 1/2/03; No. 1122a, 4/2/02; 425o, No. 1120, 12.50k, 13k, 15k, 1/2/04. Nos. 1120b, 1127a, 1/2/04.

See Nos. 1295, 1296-1303.

A403

**1999, Jan. 13 Litho. *Perf. 13***

**1143** A403 4k Oersted Satellite 1.40 .90

Deciduous Trees A404

4k, Fagus sylvatica. 5k, Fraxinus excelsior, vert. 5.25k, Tilia cordata, vert. 9.25k, Quercus robur.

**1999, Jan. 13 Litho. & Engr.**

**1144** A404 4k multicolored 1.25 .30
Complete booklet, 10 #1144 12.50
**1145** A404 5k multicolored 1.75 1.00
**1146** A404 5.25k multicolored 1.75 .65
**1147** A404 9.25k multicolored 3.00 3.00
*Nos. 1144-1147 (4)* 7.75 4.95

50th Anniversaries — A405

**Litho. & Engr.**

**1999, Feb. 24 *Perf. 13***

**1148** A405 3.75k Home Guard 1.40 .90
**1149** A405 4.25k NATO 2.00 1.00

Harbingers of Spring — A406

**1999, Feb. 24 Litho.**

**1150** A406 4k Lapwing in flight 1.60 .30
Complete booklet, 10 #1150 16.00
**1151** A406 5.25k Geese 1.75 .90
*a.* Souvenir sheet, #1150-1151 6.50 5.00

Nature Reserves — A407

**Litho. & Engr.**

**1999, Apr. 28 *Perf. 13***

**1152** A407 4.50k Vejlerne *1.75* *1.00*
**1153** A407 5.50k Langli *2.00* *1.25*

Europa.

Council of Europe, 50th Anniv. A408

**1999, Apr. 28 Engr.**

**1154** A408 9.75k blue 3.00 3.00

Danish Constitution, 150th Anniv. — A409

**1999, June 2 Litho. *Perf. 13***

**1155** A409 4k red & black 1.40 .70

Danish Revue, 150th Anniv. A410

Performers: 4k, Kjeld Petersen and Dirch Passer, comedians. 4.50k, Osvald Helmuth, singer. 5.25k, Preben Kaas and Jorgen Ryg, comedians, singers. 6.75k, Liva Weel, singer.

**1999, June 2 Engr. *Perf. 13***

**1156** A410 4k deep red 1.60 .50
Complete booklet, 10 #1156 16.00
**1157** A410 4.50k slate 1.75 1.40
**1158** A410 5.25k deep blue 1.75 .85
Complete booklet, 10 #1158 17.50
**1159** A410 6.75k deep claret 2.25 1.60
*a.* Bklt. pane, #1156-1159 + 2 labels 14.00 15.00
Complete booklet, 2 #1159a 28.00
*Nos. 1156-1159 (4)* 7.35 4.35

No. 1159a printed with two different pairs of labels. One version has showgirl label at left, the second version has showgirl label at right. Complete booklets contain one of each pane.

**Contemporary Paintings Type**

9.25k, Fire Farver, by Thomas Kluge. 16k, Dreng, by Lise Malinovsky.

**1999, Aug. 25 Litho. *Perf. 12¾***

**1160** A401 9.25k multi, vert. 3.25 4.00
**1161** A401 16k multi, vert. 5.25 5.25

Opening of New Extension of the Royal Library, "The Black Diamond" A411

**1999, Aug. 25 Engr. *Perf. 13¾***

**1162** A411 8.75k black 4.00 3.00

Migratory Birds — A412

**Litho. & Engr.**

**1999, Sept. 29 *Perf. 12¾***

**1163** A412 4k Swallows 1.60 .30
Complete booklet, 10 #1163 16.00
**1164** A412 5.25k Gray-lag geese 1.75 1.00
*a.* Souvenir sheet, #1163-1164 5.25 6.50
**1165** A412 5.50k Common eider 1.75 .90
**1166** A412 12.25k Arctic tern 4.50 5.25
*a.* Souvenir sheet, #1165-1166 9.00 10.00
*Nos. 1163-1166 (4)* 9.60 7.45

Stamps from Nos. 1164a and 1166a lack white border found on Nos. 1163-1166.

New Year 2000 — A413

**1999, Nov. 10 Litho. *Perf. 13¼***

**1167** A413 4k Hearts 1.40 .50
**1168** A413 4k Wavy lines 1.40 .50
*a.* Bklt. pane, 5 ea #1167-1168 35.00
Complete booklet, #1168a 35.00

The 20th Century — A414

4k, Prof. J.H. Deuntzer on front page of newspaper, 1901. 4.50k, Newspaper illustration, 1903. 5.25k, Asta Nielsen and Poul Reumert in the film "The Abyss," 1910. 5.75k, Advertising sticker showing woman on telephone, 1914.

See sheet of 16, #1184a.

**2000, Jan. 12 Litho. & Engr.**

**1169** A414 4k buff & blk 1.40 .50
Complete booklet, 10 #1169 14.00
**1170** A414 4.50k multicolored 1.75 1.00
**1171** A414 5.25k multicolored 1.75 1.00
Complete booklet, 10 #1171 17.50
**1172** A414 5.75k multicolored 1.75 1.25
*Nos. 1169-1172 (4)* 6.65 3.75

**2000, May 9**

4k, Allegory of women suffrage on front page of newspaper, 1915. 5k, Newspaper caricature of the Kanslergade Agreement, 1933. 5.50k, Film "Long and Short," 1927. 6.75k, Front page of Radio Weekly Review, 1925.

**1173** A414 4k multi 1.40 .55
Booklet, 10 #1173 14.00
**1174** A414 5k multi 1.75 1.00
**1175** A414 5.50k multi 2.00 1.60
**1176** A414 6.75k multi 2.25 2.50
*Nos. 1173-1176 (4)* 7.40 5.65

**2000, Aug. 23**

4k, Liberation of Denmark on front page of newspaper, 1945. 5.75k, Newspaper caricature of new constitution, 1953. 6.75k, Poster for film "Café Paradise," 1950. 12.25k, Advertisement for Arena television, 1957.

**1177** A414 4k multi 1.40 .90
Booklet, 10 #1177 14.00
**1178** A414 5.75k multi 2.00 1.60
**1179** A414 6.75k multi 2.25 2.50
**1180** A414 12.25k multi 4.00 4.25
*Nos. 1177-1180 (4)* 9.65 9.25

**2000, Nov. 8**

4k, Entry of Denmark into European Community on front page of newspaper, 1972. 4.50k, Newspaper caricature of youth revolt, 1969. 5.25k, Poster for film "The Olsen Gang," 1968. 5.50k, Denmark Post website on Internet, 1999.

**1181** A414 4k multi 1.40 .90
Booklet, 10 #1181 14.00
**1182** A414 4.50k multi 1.60 1.60
**1183** A414 5.25k multi 1.75 1.00
Booklet, 10 #1183 17.50
*a.* Booklet pane, #1171, 1175, 1179, 1183 + label 8.00
Booklet, 2 #1183a 16.00
**1184** A414 5.50k multi 2.00 1.25
*a.* Sheet of 16, #1169-1184 47.50 42.50
*Nos. 1181-1184 (4)* 6.75 4.75

No. 1183a comes with two different labels. Booklet contains one of each.

60th Birthday of Queen Margrethe II — A415

**2000, Apr. 12 Litho. *Perf. 12¾***
**1185** A415 4k gray & car 1.60 .60
Complete booklet, 10 #1185 16.00
**1186** A415 5.25k gray & blue 1.75 .90
*a.* Souvenir sheet, #1185-1186 4.00 4.25

Oresund Bridge, Sweden-Denmark — A416

**Litho. & Engr.**

**2000, May 9 *Perf. 12¾***
**1187** A416 4.50k shown 2.00 1.90

**Litho.**

**1188** A416 4.50k Map 2.00 1.90
*a.* Pair, #1187-1188 4.25 3.75

See Sweden Nos. 2391-2393.

**Europa, 2000**
Common Design Type

**2000, May 9 Litho. *Perf. 13***
**1189** CD17 9.75k multi *3.50 2.25*

**Contemporary Art Type of 1998**

Designs: 4k, Pegasus, by Kurt Trampedach. 5.25k, Landscape, by Nina Sten-Knudsen.

**2000, Sept. 27 *Perf. 12¾***
**1190** A401 4k multi 1.50 1.50
**1191** A401 5.25k multi 1.50 1.50

Royal Danish Air Force, 50th Anniv. A417

**2000, Sept. 27 Engr.**
**1192** A417 9.75k black & red 3.00 2.50
*a.* Souvenir sheet of 1 3.00 3.50

Botanical Gardens, Copenhagen — A418

**Litho. & Engr.**

**2001, Jan. 24 *Perf. 12¾***
**1193** A418 4k Palm House 1.40 .60
Booklet, 10 #1193 14.00

**Size: 28x21mm**

**1194** A418 6k Lake 2.00 .85
**1195** A418 12.25k Water lilies 4.00 4.50
*Nos. 1193-1195 (3)* 7.40 5.95

"Use the Language" A419

**2001, Mar. 28 Litho. *Perf. 13***
**1196** A419 4k "A," text 1.40 .55
Booklet, 10 #1196 14.00
**1197** A419 7k "Z," text 2.75 .90

Danish Postage Stamps, 150th Anniv. — A420

Portion of #2 and: 4k, Engraver Martinus Willam Ferslew. 5.50k, Printer Andreas Thiele. 6k, Head Copenhagen postmaster Frantz Christopher von Jessen. 10.25k, Postmaster General Magrius Otto Spohus Count Danneskjold-Samsoe.

**Litho. & Engr.**

**2001, Apr. 1 *Perf. 13¼x13***
**1198** A420 4k multi 1.50 1.00
**1199** A420 5.50k multi 1.90 1.25
Booklet, 10 #1199 19.00
**1200** A420 6k multi 2.00 1.25
**1201** A420 10.25k multi 4.00 2.50
*a.* Booklet pane, #1198-1201 + label 20.00 21.00
Booklet, 2 #1201a 40.00
*Nos. 1198-1201 (4)* 9.40 6.00

No. 1201a printed with two different labels. One version has proof of stamp design, sketch of proposed design and Ferslew's letter to Danneskjold-Samsoe, and other shows two essays and letter from M. T. C. Bartholdy.

Europa — A421

Designs: 4.50k, Hands in water. 9.75k, Woman's head, water.

**2001, May 9 Litho. *Perf. 13¼x13***
**1202** A421 4.50k multi 1.25 .90
*a.* Booklet pane of 5 + 5 etiquettes 7.50
Booklet, 2 #1202a 15.00
**1203** A421 9.75k multi 3.00 3.50

**Contemporary Paintings Type of 1998**

Designs: 18k, Missus, by Jorn Larsen, horiz. 22k, Postbillede, by Henning Damgaard-Sorensen.

***Perf. 13x12½, 12½x13***

**2001, Aug. 22 Litho.**
**1204** A401 18k multi 6.00 6.50
**1205** A401 22k multi 7.25 7.75

Youth Culture A422

Designs: 4k, Skateboarding. 5.50k, Kissing. 6k, Creating music. 10.25k, Tongue piercing.

**2001, Aug. 22 *Perf. 13***
**1206** A422 4k multi 1.60 .60
Booklet, 10 #1206 16.00
**1207** A422 5.50k multi 1.75 1.10
Booklet, 10 #1207 17.50
**1208** A422 6k multi 1.90 1.90
**1209** A422 10.25k multi 4.00 4.00
*a.* Souvenir sheet, #1206-1209 9.00 9.75
*Nos. 1206-1209 (4)* 9.25 7.60

Hafnia 01 Philatelic Exhibition, Copenhagen A423

Monarch and stamps: 4k, Queen Margrethe II, #757, 1000. 4.50k, King Frederik IX, #775, 1003. 5.50k, King Christian X, #1001, B10. 7k, King Christian IX, #1002, 66.

**Litho. & Engr.**

**2001, Oct. 16 *Perf. 13x13¼***
**1210** A423 4k multi 1.60 .75
**1211** A423 4.50k multi 1.75 1.75
**1212** A423 5.50k multi 1.75 1.75
**1213** A423 7k multi 2.50 2.75
*a.* Souvenir sheet, #1210-1213 6.50 7.50
*b.* Strip, #1210-1213 + central label 10.00 11.50
*Nos. 1210-1213 (4)* 7.60 7.00

Island Ferries A424

Designs: 3.75k, Bukken-Bruse. 4k, Ouro. 4.25k, Hjarno. 6k, Barsofaergen.

**2001, Nov. 7 *Perf. 12¾***
**1214** A424 3.75k multi 1.25 1.60
**1215** A424 4k multi 1.60 .60
Booklet, 10 #1215 16.00
**1216** A424 4.25k multi 1.60 1.60
**1217** A424 6k multi 2.00 2.25
*Nos. 1214-1217 (4)* 6.45 6.05

Comics and Cartoons — A425

Designs: 4k, Rasmus Klump, by Vilhelm Hansen. 5.50k, Valhalla, by Peter Madsen. 6.50k, Jungledyret Hugo, by Flemming Quist Moller. 10.50k, Cirkeline, by Hanne Hastrup.

**2002, Jan. 16 Litho. *Perf. 13¼x13***
**1218** A425 4k multi 1.50 .55
Booklet, 10 #1218 15.00
*a.* Sheet of 8 + label 50.00
**1219** A425 5.50k multi 1.75 1.00
Booklet, 10 #1219 17.50
*a.* Sheet of 8 + label 27.50
**1220** A425 6.50k multi 2.10 1.75
**1221** A425 10.50k multi 4.00 4.50
*a.* Souvenir sheet, #1218-1221 8.00 9.00
*Nos. 1218-1221 (4)* 9.35 7.80

The Girls in the Airport, Sculpture by Hanne Varming — A426

Designs: 4k, Rear view. 5k, Front view.

**Photo. & Engr.**

**2002, Mar. 13 *Perf. 12¾***
**1222** A426 4k multi, *cream* 1.60 .55
Booklet, 10 #1222 16.00
**1223** A426 5k multi, *cream* 1.75 1.60

Europa — A427

Winning drawings in children's stamp design contest: 4k, Clown, by Luna Ostergard. 5k, Clown, by Camille Wagner Larsen.

**2002, May 15 Litho. *Perf. 13***
**1224** A427 4k multi *1.50 .90*
Booklet, 10 #1224 *15.00*
**1225** A427 5k multi *1.75 1.75*
*a.* Booklet pane of 5 + 5 etiquettes *8.75* —
Booklet, 2 #1225a *17.50*

Landscapes A428

**2002, May 15 Engr.**
**1226** A428 4k Bornholm 1.60 .90
**1227** A428 6k West Jutland 1.90 1.90
**1228** A428 6.50k Langeland 1.75 2.25
**1229** A428 12.50k Thy 4.50 4.50
*Nos. 1226-1229 (4)* 9.75 9.55

Historic Postal Vehicles A429

Designs: 4k, 1953 Nimbus motorcycle. 5.50k, 1962 Bedford van. 10k, 1984 Renault 4 van. 19k, 1998 Volvo FH12 tractor trailer.

**Litho. & Engr.**

**2002, Aug. 21 *Perf. 13x13¼***
**1230** A429 4k multi 1.60 .65
Booklet, 10 #1230 16.00
*a.* Sheet of 8 + central label 36.00 —
**1231** A429 5.50k multi 1.90 1.50
Booklet, 10 #1231 19.00
**1232** A429 10k multi 4.00 4.00
**1233** A429 19k multi 7.00 7.00
*a.* Booklet pane of 4, #1230-1233 20.00
Booklet, 2 #1233a 40.00
*Nos. 1230-1233 (4)* 14.50 13.15

No. 1233a is printed with two different labels. One shows a 1908 Berlíet van and the other a 2002 Peugeot Partner. Both are included in the booklet.

Opening of Copenhagen Metro — A430

**2002, Sept. 25 Engr. *Perf. 12¾***
**1234** A430 5.50k multi, *tan* 1.50 1.40

**Contemporary Paintngs Type of 1998**

Designs: 5k, Children's Corner, by Jens Birkemose, vert. 6.50k, Maleren og Modellen, by Frans Kannik, vert.

**2002, Sept. 25 *Perf. 13x12½***
**1235** A401 5k red & blue 1.75 1.75
**1236** A401 6.50k multi 2.25 2.25

Intl. Council for the Exploration of the Sea, Cent. — A431

Atlantic cod and: 4k, Exploration ship Dana. 10.50k, Hirtshals lighthouse.

**Litho. & Engr.**

**2002, Sept. 25** *Perf. 13¼x13*

**1237** A431 4k multi 1.60 .65
**1238** A431 10.50k multi 4.00 4.00
*a.* Souvenir sheet, #1237-1238 4.50 5.00

See Faroe Islands No. 426, Greenland Nos. 401-402.

Danish House Architecture A432

Designs: 4k, Dianas Have, Horsholm, by Vandkusten Design Studio, 1992. 4.25k, Blangstedgard, Odense, by Poul Ingemann, 1988. 5.50k, Dansk Folkeferie, Karrebaeksminde, by Stephan Kappel, 1979. 6.50k, Fredensborg Terraces, Fredensborg, by Jorn Utzon, 1963. 9k, Soholm, Klampenborg, by Arne Jacobsen, 1950.

**Litho. & Engr.**

**2002, Nov. 8** *Perf. 12¾*

**1239** A432 4k multi 1.60 1.00
Booklet, 10 #1239 16.00
**1240** A432 4.25k multi 1.60 .70
**1241** A432 5.50k multi 1.90 1.50
**1242** A432 6.50k multi 2.25 1.75
**1243** A432 9k multi 3.00 3.00
*Nos. 1239-1243 (5)* 10.35 7.95

See Nos. 1257-1261, 1267-1271, 1317-1321.

Youth Sports — A433

**2003, Jan. 15** **Litho.** *Perf. 12¾*

**1244** A433 4.25k Soccer 1.50 .70
Booklet, 10 #1244 16.00
*a.* Sheet of 8 + central label *13.00 13.00*
**1245** A433 5.50k Swimming 1.75 1.50
Booklet, 10 #1245 17.50
**1246** A433 8.50k Gymnastics 3.25 3.25
**1247** A433 11.50k Handball 4.00 4.25
*Nos. 1244-1247 (4)* 10.50 9.70

Danish Literary Greenland Expedition, Cent. — A434

Designs: 4.25k, Expedition members Harald Moltke, Knud Rasmussen, Jorgen Bronlund, Ludvig Mylius-Erichsen and Gabriel Olsen. 7k, Campsite.

**2003, Mar. 12** **Engr.** *Perf. 12¾*

**1248** A434 4.25k blue gray 1.25 .70

**Size: 61x22mm**

**1249** A434 7k multi 2.25 2.25
*a.* Souvenir sheet, #1248-1249 + label *5.00 5.00*

See Greenland Nos. 407-408.

Europa — A435

Poster art: 4.25k, Poster for Copenhagen International Theater Festival, by Ole Fick, 1985. 5.50k, Poster for Bertel Thorvaldsen Museum, by Ole Woldbye, 1970.

**2003, May 14** **Litho.** *Perf. 12¾*

**1250** A435 4.25k multi *1.50 .60*
Booklet, 10 #1250 *15.00*

**Engr.**

**1251** A435 5.50k black *1.75 1.40*
Booklet, 10 #1251 *17.50*
*a.* Sheet of 8 + central label *40.00*

Insects — A436

Designs: 4.25k, Ephemera danica. 6.50k, Dytiscus latissimus. 12k, Cordulegaster boltoni, vert.

**2003, May 14** **Litho. & Engr.**

**1252** A436 4.25k multi 1.50 .50
*a.* Sheet of 8 + central label 25.00 —
**1253** A436 6.50k multi 2.00 2.00
*a.* Sheet of 8 + central label 50.00 —

**Size: 21x39mm**

**1254** A436 12k multi 3.75 3.75
*a.* Souvenir sheet, #1252-1254 7.00 7.50
*Nos. 1252-1254 (3)* 7.25 6.25

**Contemporary Art Type of 1998**

Designs: 5.50k, Baering, by Sys Hindsbo. 19k, Det Forjaettede Land, by Poul Anker Bech.

**Litho. & Engr.**

**2003, Aug. 27** *Perf. 12½x13*

**1255** A401 5.50k multi 1.75 1.75

**Litho.**

**1256** A401 19k multi 6.50 6.50

**Danish House Architecture Type of 2002**

Designs: 4k, Bellahoj Apartment Complex, Copenhagen, by Tage Nielsen and Mogens Irming, 1944-58. 4.25k, Anchersvej, Klampenborg, by Mogens Lassen, 1935. 5.25k, Gerthasminde, Odense, by Anton Rosen, 1912-35. 9k, Solvang, Vallekilde College, by Andreas Bentsen and Martin Nyrop, 1889. 15k, Stenbrogard, Brorup, by Peter Holdensen, 1868.

**Litho. & Engr.**

**2003, Aug. 27** *Perf. 12¾*

**1257** A432 4k multi 1.60 1.60
**1258** A432 4.25k multi 1.60 .90
Complete booklet, 10 #1258 16.00
**1259** A432 5.25k multi 1.75 1.75
**1260** A432 9k multi 3.25 3.25
**1261** A432 15k multi 4.50 4.50
*Nos. 1257-1261 (5)* 12.70 12.00

A437

**2003, Nov. 7** **Engr.** *Perf. 12¾*

**1262** A437 6.50k gray blue 2.00 1.75

Awarding of first Nobel Prize to a Dane (Niels Finsen for Physiology and Medicine), cent.

A438

Artifacts from Royal Jelling World Heritage Site: 4.25k, Queen Thyra's stone. 5.50k, King Gorm's cup. 8.50k, King Harald's stone. 11.50k, Wall paintings, Jelling Church.

**2003, Nov. 7** **Litho. & Engr.**

**1263** A438 4.25k multi 1.50 1.25
Booklet, 10 #1263 17.50
**1264** A438 5.50k multi 1.75 1.50
Booklet, 10 #1264 22.50
**1265** A438 8.50k multi 2.75 2.75
**1266** A438 11.50k multi 3.75 3.75
*Nos. 1263-1266 (4)* 9.75 9.25

A spiral-bound booklet, enclosed in a slipcase, with four booklet panes containing single stamps of Nos. 1263-1266, and a booklet pane containing a strip of Nos. 1263-1266, sold for 99k. Value, $35.

**Danish House Architecture Type of 2002**

Designs: 4.50k, Spurveskjul, Virum, by Nicolai Abildgaard, 1805. 6k, Liselund, Mon, by Andreas Kirkerup, 1792. 7k, Kampmann's Yard, Varde, by Hans Wolff Ollgaard, Hack Kampmann and Mikkel Stobberup, 1781. 12.50k, Harsdorff's House, Copenhagen, by Caspar Frederik Harsdorff, 1780. 15k, Nyso Manor, Praesto, by Jens Lauridsen.

**Litho. & Engr.**

**2004, Jan.14** *Perf. 12¾*

**1267** A432 4.50k multi 1.60 1.00
Booklet, 10 #1267 16.00
**1268** A432 6k multi 2.40 1.60
**1269** A432 7k multi 2.50 2.50
**1270** A432 12.50k multi 4.00 4.00
**1271** A432 15k multi 5.25 5.25
*Nos. 1267-1271 (5)* 15.75 14.35

Academy of Fine Arts, Copenhagen, 250th Anniv. — A439

**Litho. & Engr.**

**2004, Mar. 26** *Perf. 13¼x13*

**1272** A439 5.50k multi 2.10 1.25
Booklet, 10 #1272 21.00

Norse Gods — A440

Designs: 4.50k, Heimdal guarding Bifrost bridge. 6k, Gefion plowing Sjaelland out of Sweden.

**2004, Mar. 26**

**1273** A440 4.50k multi 1.75 .85
*a.* Sheet of 8 + central label 35.00 35.00
**1274** A440 6k multi 2.40 1.10
*a.* Souvenir sheet, #1273-1274 8.00 8.00
*b.* Sheet of 8 + central label 55.00 55.00

Wedding of Crown Prince Frederik and Mary Donaldson — A441

No. 1275: a, Couple facing right. b, Couple facing left.

**Litho. & Photo.**

**2004, May 14** *Perf. 13x13¼*

**1275** A441 Horiz. pair 3.50 3.50
Booklet, 5 #1275 20.00
*a.-b.* 4.50k Either single, denomination 8½ mm wide 1.75 1.25
*c.-d.* 4.50k Either single, denomination 7½ mm wide 1.75 1.25
*e.* Souvenir sheet, #1275c-1275d + central label *4.00 4.00*

Frederiksberg Palace, 300th Anniv. — A442

Designs: 4.25k, Doorway overlooking Sondermarken Park. 4.50k, Gatehouse archway, castle yard. 6.50k, Aerial view.

**Litho. & Engr.**

**2004, May 14** *Perf. 13*

**1276** A442 4.25k multi 1.60 1.60
**1277** A442 4.50k multi 1.75 1.00

**Size: 55x32mm**

**1278** A442 6.50k multi 2.50 2.00
*a.* Souvenir sheet, #1276-1278 6.00 7.00
*Nos. 1276-1278 (3)* 5.85 4.60

Prince Henrik, 70th Birthday — A443

**2004, June 9** **Litho.** *Perf. 12¾*

**1279** A443 4.50k multi 1.60 1.00

Europa A444

**2004, June 9** *Perf. 13*

**1280** A444 6k Cyclists 2.50 1.60
**1281** A444 9k Sailboats 3.50 3.00

**Contemporary Paintings Type of 1998**

Designs: 13k, Senses the Body Landscape, by Lars Ravn, vert. 21k, The Dog Bites, by Lars Norgard, vert.

**Litho. & Engr.**

**2004, Aug. 25** *Perf. 13x12½*

**1282** A401 13k multi 5.00 5.00

**Litho.**

**1283** A401 21k multi 7.50 7.50

Viking Ship Museum, Roskilde A445

Designs: 4.50k, Skuldelev 1 on Roskilde Fjord. 5.50k, Reconstruction of Skuldelev 2. 6.50k, Cross-section of ship. 12.50k, Excavation of archaeological site where ships were found.

**Litho. & Engr.**

**2004, Aug. 25** *Perf. 13x13¼*

**1284** A445 4.50k multi 1.60 1.00
Complete booklet, 10 #1284 16.00
**1285** A445 5.50k multi 2.00 1.60
Complete booklet, 10 #1285 20.00

**1286** A445 6.50k multi 2.40 2.00
**1287** A445 12.50k multi 4.50 4.50
*Nos. 1284-1287 (4)* 10.50 9.10

A spiral-bound booklet, enclosed in a slipcase, with four booklet panes containing single stamps of Nos. 1284-1287 and a booklet pane containing a strip of Nos. 1284-1287, sold for 99k. Value, $40.

Birds of Prey A446

Designs: 4.50k, Falco tinnunculus. 5.50k, Accipiter nisus. 6k, Buteo buteo. 7k, Circus aeruginosus.

### Litho. & Engr.

**2004, Nov. 5** *Perf. 13*

**1288** A446 4.50k multi 1.75 .90
Complete booklet, 10 #1288 17.50
*a.* Sheet of 8 + central label 17.50 17.50
**1289** A446 5.50k multi 2.10 1.00
*a.* Sheet of 8 + central label 22.50 22.50
**1290** A446 6k multi 2.40 2.00
**1291** A446 7k multi 2.75 2.25
*Nos. 1288-1291 (4)* 9.00 6.15

### Queen and Small State Seal Types of 1946-2000

**2005-09** **Engr.** *Perf. 12¾*

**1295** A402a 4.75k red 1.90 1.00
*a.* Sheet of 8 + central label 17.00 —
**1296** A402a 5.50k red 2.25 .50
*b.* Sheet of 8 #1296 + central label 20.00 —
**1296A** A402a 6.50k blue 2.75 .50
**1297** A402a 7.25k blk vio 3.00 2.50
**1298** A402a 7.50k blue 3.25 2.50
**1299** A402a 7.75k vio blk 3.50 .90
**1300** A402a 8k indigo 4.00 2.50
**1301** A402a 8.25k Prus blue *2.50* 2.50
**1302** A402a 8.75k Prus blue 3.75 1.00
**1303** A402a 9k blue 3.25 3.25

### With Diagonal Engraving Lines

**1304** A55 10k lemon 3.50 1.25
**1304A** A55 10.50k car rose 4.00 3.25
**1305** A55 13.50k green 5.00 4.25
**1308** A55 16k Prus grn 7.25 1.25
**1309** A55 16.50k red brn 6.00 5.25
**1310** A55 17k sl grn 6.25 5.25
**1311** A55 17.50k purple 6.25 5.25
**1312** A55 20k blue 8.25 1.75
**1312A** A55 20.50k purple 9.25 1.75
**1313** A55 22k brn vio 8.25 6.00
*Nos. 1295-1313 (20)* 94.15 52.40

Issued: 7.50k, 16.50k, 22k, 1/3. 4.75k, 8k, 11/11. 4.75k, 10k, 17k, 1/2/06. 7.25k, 8.25k, 11/10/06. 13.50k, 17.50k, 1/2/07. 20k, 11/8/07. 5.50k, 6.50k, 7.75k, 8.75k, 1/2/08. Nos. 1296b, 1308, 1312, 3/27/08. Nos. 1303, 1304A, 1/2/09. Type A55 stamps with diagonal engraving lines have engraver's name of Mörck at lower right. Earlier stamps of type A55 have vertical and horizontal engraving lines. The lettering was also changed slightly in the Mörck engraving.

### Danish House Architecture Type of 2002

Designs: 4.25k, Hjarup Manse, Vamdrup, c. 1665. 4.50k, Ejdersted Farm, Southwest Schleswig, 1653. 7.50k, Provstegade, Randers, c. 1650. 9.50k, Smith's Yard, Koge, c. 1550. 16.50k, Carmelite Monastery, Elsinore, c. 1500.

### Litho. & Engr.

**2005, Jan. 12** *Perf. 12¾*

**1317** A432 4.25k multi 1.75 1.75
**1318** A432 4.50k multi 1.75 .65
Complete booklet, 10 #1318 17.50
*a.* Booklet pane, 4 #691, 8 #1318 17.00 —
Complete booklet, #1318a 17.00
**1319** A432 7.50k multi 2.90 2.90
**1320** A432 9.50k multi 3.50 3.50
**1321** A432 16.50k multi 7.25 7.25
*Nos. 1317-1321 (5)* 17.15 16.05

Bonn-Copenhagen Declaration, 50th Anniv. — A447

**2005, Mar. 2** **Litho.**

**1322** A447 6.50k multi 2.50 2.00

See Germany No. 2330.

Hans Christian Andersen (1805-75), Author — A448

Paper Cutting by Andersen, Scissors — A449

Designs: 6.50k, Pen, inkwell, illustration of duckling, manuscript handwritten by Andersen. 7.50k, Andersen's drawing of Casino dell'Orlogio, Rome, and boots.

**2005, Mar. 2** **Engr.**

**1323** A448 4.50k black 1.60 1.60
*a.* Sheet of 8 + central label 20.00 20.00

### Litho. & Engr.

**1324** A449 5.50k multi 2.00 2.00
Complete booklet, 10 #1324 20.00
*a.* Sheet of 8 + central label 25.00 25.00
**1325** A449 6.50k multi 2.25 2.00
**1326** A449 7.50k multi 3.00 2.50
*Nos. 1323-1326 (4)* 8.85 8.10

A spiral-bound booklet, enclosed in a slipcase, with four booklet panes containing single stamps of Nos. 1323-1326, and a booklet pane containing a strip of Nos. 1323-1326, sold for 99k. Value, $40.

See Malta Nos. 1196-1199.

August Bournonville (1805-79), Choreographer A450

Bournonville and: 4.50k, Dancer. 5.50k, Dancers.

### Litho. & Engr.

**2005, May 4** *Perf. 13¼x13*

**1327** A450 4.50k multi 1.75 1.75
Complete booklet, 10 #1327 17.50
*a.* Sheet of 8 + central label 19.00 —
**1328** A450 5.50k multi 2.00 2.00
*a.* Sheet of 8 + central label 17.50 —
*b.* Souvenir sheet, #1327-1328 4.00 4.00

Sailors in World War II — A451

Designs: 4.50k, Ship convoy. 7.50k, Unloading of ship's cargo.

**2005, May 4** **Litho.** *Perf. 13*

**1329** A451 4.50k multi 1.60 1.60
**1330** A451 7.50k multi 2.75 2.75

Europa — A452

**2005, May 4** *Perf. 12¾*

**1331** A452 6.50k Hot dog *3.00 1.90*
**1332** A452 9.50k Fish *4.50 3.75*

### Contemporary Art Type of 1998

Designs: 5.50k, Telepathy, by Anna Fro Vodder, vert. 6.50k, Home Again, by Kaspar Bonnén, vert. 7.50k, Unrest, by John Korner, vert. 12.50k, Palace in the Morning, by Tal Rosenzweig.

*Perf. 13x12½, 12½x13*

**2005, Aug. 24** **Litho.**

**1333** A401 5.50k multi 2.40 2.40
**1334** A401 6.50k multi 2.75 2.75
**1335** A401 7.50k multi 3.00 3.00
**1336** A401 12.50k multi 6.00 6.00
*Nos. 1333-1336 (4)* 14.15 14.15

INDEX:2005 Intl. Design Exhibition, Copenhagen A453

**2005, Aug. 24** **Engr.** *Perf. 13¼*

**1337** A453 4.50k black 1.75 1.25
Complete booklet, 10 #1337 17.50

### Wavy Lines Type of 1905-17

**2005-08** **Engr.** *Perf. 12¾*

**1338** A10 25ø indigo .25 .25
*a.* Booklet pane, 2 each #1295, 1338 ('06) 4.00 —
Complete booklet, #1338a 4.00
**1339** A10 50ø brown .25 .25
**1340** A10 100ø bright blue .35 .25
**1341** A10 200ø dark green .70 .25
**1342** A10 450ø green 1.60 .65
**1342A** A10 500ø brt yel grn 2.25 .65
*Nos. 1338-1342A (6)* 5.40 2.30

Wavy Line stamps, cent.

Issued: Nos. 1338-1342, 10/28/05. No. 1338a, 1/2/06. No. 1342A, 3/27/08.

Seals A454

Designs: 4.50k, Phoca vitulina. 5.50k, Halichoerus grypus.

**2005, Nov. 11** **Engr.** *Perf. 13x13¼*

**1343** A454 4.50k multi 1.75 1.25
Complete booklet, 10 #1343 17.50
**1344** A454 5.50k indigo 2.00 1.50
*a.* Souvenir sheet, #1343-1344 4.00 4.00

Flowers — A455

Designs: 4.75k, Calanthus nivalis. 5.50k, Eranthis hyemalis. 7k, Crocus vernus hybrid. 8k, Anemone nemorosa.

**2006, Jan. 11** **Engr.** *Perf. 12¾*

**1345** A455 4.75k multi 1.60 .90
Complete booklet, 10 #1345 16.00
*a.* Sheet of 8 + central label 15.00 —
**1346** A455 5.50k multi 1.75 1.75
Complete booklet, 10 #1346 17.50
*a.* Sheet of 8 + central label 17.00 —
**1347** A455 7k multi 2.25 2.25
**1348** A455 8k multi 2.50 2.50
*Nos. 1345-1348 (4)* 8.10 7.40

Creatures in Norse Mythology — A456

Designs: 4.75k, Elf king and elf girls. 7k, Incubi, werewolves, hel-horse, gnome and troll.

### Litho. & Engr.

**2006, Mar. 29** *Perf. 13¼x13*

**1349** A456 4.75k multi 1.60 1.60
**1350** A456 7k multi 2.40 2.40
*a.* Souvenir sheet, #1349-1350 4.50 7.00

Rosenborg Castle, 400th Anniv. — A457

Designs: 4.75k, Castle exterior. 5.50k, Silver lion, thrones of king and queen. 13k, Royal coat of arms ceiling decoration.

**2006, Mar. 29**

**1351** A457 4.75k multi 1.60 1.60
Complete booklet, 10 #1351 16.00
**1352** A457 5.50k multi 2.00 2.00
**1353** A457 13k multi 4.50 4.50
*Nos. 1351-1353 (3)* 8.10 8.10

A spiral-bound booklet, enclosed in a slipcase, with four booklet panes containing single stamps of Nos. 1351-1353 and a booklet pane containing a strip of Nos. 1351-1353, sold for 99k. Value, $35.

New Carlsberg Glyptotek, Cent. — A458

Designs: 4.75k, Marble relief from Athenian graveyard. 5.50k, Conservatory dome. 8k, Dancer Looking at the Sole of Her Right Foot, sculpture by Edgar Degas.

**2006, June 7**

**1354** A458 4.75k multi 1.60 1.60
Complete booklet, 10 #1354 16.00
**1355** A458 5.50k multi 2.00 2.00
**1356** A458 8k multi 2.75 2.75
*a.* Souvenir sheet, #1354-1356 6.50 6.50
*Nos. 1354-1356 (3)* 6.35 6.35

Race Cars A459

Designs: 4.75k, 1958 Alfa Dana Midget, Swebe Jap. 5.50k, 1965 Austin Mini Cooper S, 1965 Ford Cortina GT, 1965 Alfa Romeo 1600 GTA. 10k, 1963 Jaguar E Type, 1967 Volvo P 1800. 17k, 1965 Lotus Elan, Renault Alpine A 110.

**2006, June 7** *Perf. 13x13¼*

1357 A459 4.75k multi 1.75 1.75
Complete booklet, 10 #1357 17.50
1358 A459 5.50k multi 2.00 2.00
Complete booklet, 10 #1358 20.00
1359 A459 10k multi 3.75 3.75
1360 A459 17k multi 6.00 6.00
*Nos. 1357-1360 (4)* 13.50 13.50

Europa — A460

Winning designs in children's stamp design contest: 4.75k, Smiling children, by Rikke Veber Rasmussen. 7k, Two smiling children, by Anette Bertram Nielsen.

**2006, Aug. 23 Litho.** *Perf. 13¼x13*

1361 A460 4.75k multi 1.90 .90
Booklet, 10 #1361 19.00
1362 A460 7k blk & dull grn 2.75 1.25

Airplanes A461

Designs: 4.50k, J. C. H. Ellehammer's 1906 biplane. 4.75k, KZ II, 1946. 5.50k, KZ IV, 1944. 13k, KZ VII, 1947.

**Litho. & Engr.**

**2006, Aug. 23** *Perf. 12¾*

1363 A461 4.50k multi 1.75 1.75
1364 A461 4.75k multi 1.75 1.75
*a.* Miniature sheet of 8 + central label 14.00 14.00
1365 A461 5.50k multi 2.00 2.00
*a.* Miniature sheet of 8 + central label 16.00 16.00
1366 A461 13k multi 4.50 4.50
*Nos. 1363-1366 (4)* 10.00 10.00

Paintings by COBRA Group Artists A462

Designs: 4.75k, Untitled, by Asger Jorn. 5.50k, Landscape of the Night, by Else Alfelt, vert. 7k, New Skin, by Pierre Alechinsky. 8k, The Olive Eater, by Egill Jacobsen, vert.

***Perf. 13x13¼, 13¼x13***

**2006, Nov. 10** **Litho.**

1367 A462 4.75k multi 1.75 1.75
Booklet, 10 #1367 17.50
1368 A462 5.50k multi 2.00 2.00
1369 A462 7k multi 2.75 2.75
1370 A462 8k multi 3.00 3.00
*Nos. 1367-1370 (4)* 9.50 9.50

See Belgium Nos. 2168-2169.

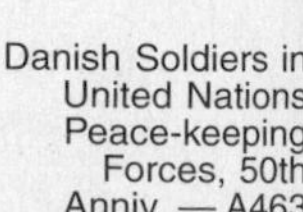

Danish Soldiers in United Nations Peace-keeping Forces, 50th Anniv. — A463

**Litho. & Engr.**

**2007, Jan. 10** *Perf. 13*

1371 A463 4.75k multi 1.75 1.75

Intl. Polar Year A464

Designs: 7.25k, Wooden and walrus tusk carvings of Norse, Late Dorset and Thule cultures of Greenland. 13.50k, Research airplane used for measuring thickness of polar ice.

**2007, Jan. 10** *Perf. 13¼*

1372 A464 7.25k multi 2.50 2.50
1373 A464 13.50k multi 4.75 4.75
*a.* Souvenir sheet, #1372-1373 5.00 5.00

Windmills — A465

Designs: 4.50k, Askov Mill, 1891. 4.75k, Gedser Mil, 1957. 6k, Bogo Mill, 1989. 8.25k, Middelgrunden, 2000.

**2007, Jan. 10** **Engr.**

1374 A465 4.50k brown 1.75 1.75
1375 A465 4.75k red 1.75 1.75
Complete booklet, 10 #1375 17.50
*a.* Sheet of 8 + central label 15.00 15.00
1376 A465 6k green 2.00 2.00
Complete booklet, 10 #1376 20.00
*a.* Sheet of 8 + central label 19.00 19.00
1377 A465 8.25k blue 3.00 3.00
*Nos. 1374-1377 (4)* 8.50 8.50

Galathea 3 Scientific Expedition — A466

Satellite, ship and: 4.75k, Marine life. 7.25k, Globe showing route of expedition.

**Litho. & Engr.**

**2007, Mar. 28** *Perf. 12¾*

1378 A466 4.75k multi 1.75 1.75
1379 A466 7.25k multi 2.50 2.50
*a.* Souvenir sheet, #1378-1379 4.50 4.50

National Museum, Bicent. — A467

Designs: 4.75k, Ceremonial axes. 6k, Funen aquaemanale. 8.25k, Armillary sphere. 10.25k, Wooden mask, Borneo.

**2007, Mar. 28** *Perf. 13¼*

1380 A467 4.75k Prus bl & blk 1.75 1.75
Complete booklet, 10 #1380 17.50
1381 A467 6k brn lake & blk 2.00 2.00
1382 A467 8.25k orange & blk 3.00 3.00
1383 A467 10.25k bl gray, blk & org 3.75 3.75
*Nos. 1380-1383 (4)* 10.50 10.50

A spiral-bound booklet, enclosed in a slipcase, with four booklet panes containing single stamps of Nos. 1380-1383 and a booklet pane containing a strip of Nos. 1380-1383, sold for 109k. Value, $40.

Europa A468

Scouts: 4.75k, On hike. 7.25k, Around campfire.

**2007, June 6** *Perf. 13x13¼*

1384 A468 4.75k multi 1.75 1.75
Complete booklet, 10 #1384 17.50
1385 A468 7.25k multi 2.75 2.75

Scouting, cent.

Modern Art A469

Designs: 4.75k, The Traveler, by Arne Haugen Sorensen. 8.25k, Trionfale, by Seppo Mattinen.

**2007, June 6 Litho.** *Perf. 13x12½*

1386 A469 4.75k multi 1.75 1.60
*a.* Miniature sheet of 8 + central label 15.00 15.00
1387 A469 8.25k multi 3.00 2.50

Mandatory Use of Metric System in Denmark, Cent. A470

**Litho. & Engr.**

**2007, Aug. 22** *Perf. 12¾*

1388 A470 4.75k black & red 1.90 .85

Nature of Denmark A471

Flora and fauna of Rabjerg Dune: 4.75k, Niobe fritillary butterfly (klitperlemorsommerfugl). 6k, Northern dune tiger beetle (sandspringer). 7.25k, Sand lizard (markfirben). 13.50k, Seaside pansy (klitstedmoderblomst).

**2007, Aug. 22**

1389 A471 4.75k multi 1.75 .70
Complete booklet, 10 #1389 17.50
1390 A471 6k multi 2.25 .90
Complete booklet, 10 #1390 22.50
1391 A471 7.25k multi 2.75 1.00
1392 A471 13.50k multi 5.00 1.75
*a.* Souvenir sheet, #1389-1392 12.50 12.50
*Nos. 1389-1392 (4)* 11.75 4.35

Famous Men — A472

Designs: 4.75k, Poul Henningsen (1894-1967), designer, and Artichoke lamp. 6k, Victor Borge (1909-2000), comedian, and piano keys. 7.25k, Arne Jacobsen (1902-71), architect, and Egg chair. 8.25k, Piet Hein (1905-96), inventor, and superellipse.

**2007, Nov. 8 Engr.** *Perf. 12¾*

1393 A472 4.75k multi 1.75 .85
Complete booklet, 10 #1393 17.50
1394 A472 6k blk & blue 2.00 1.00
1395 A472 7.25k multi 2.75 1.25
1396 A472 8.25k blk & purple 3.00 1.60
*Nos. 1393-1396 (4)* 9.50 4.70

See Nos. 1412-1415, 1502-1505.

Danish National Theater A473

Designs: 5.50k, Old Stage. 6.50k, Playhouse. 7.75k, Copenhagen Opera House.

**Litho. & Engr.**

**2008, Jan. 9** *Perf. 13x13¼*

1397 A473 5.50k multi 2.25 1.10
Complete booklet, 10 #1397 22.50
*a.* Sheet of 8 + central label 19.00 —
1398 A473 6.50k multi 2.60 1.25
Complete booklet, 10 #1398 26.00
1399 A473 7.75k multi 3.25 1.60
*Nos. 1397-1399 (3)* 8.10 3.95

Royal Life Guards, 350th Anniv. — A474

Guards in: 5.50k, Red dress uniforms. 10k, Camouflage uniforms.

**Litho. & Engr.**

**2008, Mar. 27** *Perf. 13¼x13*

1400 A474 5.50k multi 2.50 1.25
Complete booklet, 10 #1400 25.00
1401 A474 10k multi 4.50 2.10
*a.* Souvenir sheet, #1400-1401 7.00 7.00

Nordic Mythology A475

Places associated with mythology: 5.50k, Lindholm Hoje burial grounds. 7.75k, Feggeklit.

**2008, Mar. 27** **Litho.**

1402 A475 5.50k black 2.40 1.25
1403 A475 7.75k black 3.25 1.60
*a.* Souvenir sheet, #1402-1403 6.00 6.00

Europa — A476

Designs: 5.50k, Boy writing letter. 7.75k, Girl reading letter.

**2008, June 4 Litho.** *Perf. 13*

1404 A476 5.50k multi 2.40 1.25
Complete booklet, 10 #1404 24.00
1405 A476 7.75k multi 3.25 1.60

Allotment Gardens A477

Designs: 5.50k, Man tending Hjelm Allotment Association garden. 6.50k, Men sitting in Vennelyst Allotment Association garden.

**Litho. & Engr.**

**2008, June 4** *Perf. 13x13¼*

1406 A477 5.50k multi 2.40 1.25
Complete booklet, 10 #1406 24.00
*a.* Miniature sheet of 8 + central label 20.00
1407 A477 6.50k multi 2.75 1.40
*a.* Miniature sheet of 8 + central label 23.00

Louisiana Museum of Art, Humlebaek, 50th Anniv. — A478

Designs: 5.50k, Original Museum building, Figures in Landscape, by Roy Lichtenstein, I Am in You, by Doug Aitken. 7.75k, I Am in You, glass corridor, A Closer Grand Canyon, by David Hockney. 8.75k, Reclining Figure No. 5, by Henry Moore, Walking Man, by Albert Giacometti, Big Head, by Giacometti, Slender Ribs, by Alexander Calder. 16k, Slender Ribs, people in concert hall, Untitled, by Sam Francis, seat designed by Poul Kjaerholm.

**2008, June 4**

**1408** A478 5.50k multi 2.40 1.25
**1409** A478 7.75k multi 3.25 1.60
*a.* Booklet pane, #1408-1409 8.00 —
**1410** A478 8.75k multi 3.75 1.90
**1411** A478 16k multi 6.75 3.50
*a.* Booklet pane, #1410-1411 14.50 —
*b.* Booklet pane, #1408-1411 22.00 —
*c.* Horiz. strip of 4, #1408-1411 19.00 19.00
Complete booklet, #1409a, 1411a, 1411b 50.00
*Nos. 1408-1411 (4)* 16.15 8.25

Complete booklet sold for 102.40k.

**Famous Men Type of 2007**

Designs: 5k, Halfdan Rasmussen (1915-2002), poet, and line from poem. 5.50k, Erik Balling (1924-2005), film and television director, and actors in movie. 6.50k, Bodil Kjer (1917-2003), actress. 10k, Niels-Henning Orsted Pedersen (1946-2005), jazz musician, and bass.

**2008, Aug. 27 Engr. *Perf. 12¾***

**1412** A472 5k blk & claret 2.40 .90
**1413** A472 5.50k multi 2.75 1.10
Complete booklet, 10 #1413 27.50
**1414** A472 6.50k multi 3.25 1.10
Complete booklet, 10 #1414 32.50
**1415** A472 10k multi 4.50 1.75
*Nos. 1412-1415 (4)* 12.90 4.85

Art Photography — A479

Designs: 5.50k, Trappe, by Viggo Rivad. 7.75k, Berlin, by Krass Clement, horiz.

**2008, Aug. 27 Litho. *Perf. 13x12¾***

**1416** A479 5.50k black 2.50 2.00

***Perf. 12¾x13***

**1417** A479 7.75k black 3.25 2.50

Winter Berries and Flowers — A480

Designs: 5.50k, Ilex aquifolium berries. 6.50k, Helleborus niger flower. 7.75k, Taxus baccata berries. 8.75k, Symphoricarpos rivularis berries.

**Litho. & Engr.**

**2008, Nov. 7 *Perf. 13***

**1418** A480 5.50k multi 1.90 .95
Complete booklet, 10 #1418 19.00
*a.* Booklet pane of 4 7.75 —
**1419** A480 6.50k multi 2.25 1.10
**1420** A480 7.75k multi 2.75 1.40
**1421** A480 8.75k multi 3.00 1.50
*a.* Souvenir sheet, #1418-1421 10.00 5.00
*b.* Booklet pane of 4, #1418-1421 10.00 —
Complete booklet, #1418a, 1421b 18.00
*Nos. 1418-1421 (4)* 9.90 4.95

No. 1421b is No. 1421a sewn into the booklet.

COP15 Climate Change Conference, Copenhagen — A481

Designs: 5.50k, Bioenergy. 9k, Low-energy building.

**2009, Jan. 7 Engr. *Perf. 13x13¼***

**1422** A481 5.50k blue 2.00 1.00
**1423** A481 9k blue 3.25 1.75

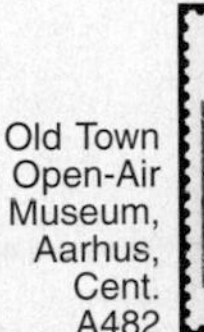

Old Town Open-Air Museum, Aarhus, Cent. A482

Designs. 5.50k, Mintmaster's Mansion, drummer. 6.50k, Mayor's House, woman in period costume. 8k, Museum of Clocks and Watches and Danish Poster Museum, painter. 10.50k, Steps to Kerteminde School, farm hand.

**Litho. & Engr.**

**2009, Jan. 7 *Perf. 13x13¼***

**1424** A482 5.50k multi 2.00 1.00
Complete booklet, 10 #1424 20.00
**1425** A482 6.50k multi 2.40 1.25
Complete booklet, 10 #1425 24.00
**1426** A482 8k multi 3.00 1.50
**1427** A482 10.50k multi 3.75 1.90
*a.* Souvenir sheet, #1424-1427 11.00 11.00
*Nos. 1424-1427 (4)* 11.15 5.65

Europa — A483

Designs: 5.50k, Round Tower, Copenhagen. 8k, Tycho Brahe Planetarium.

**2009, Mar. 25 Litho. *Perf. 13¼***

**1428** A483 5.50k multi 2.00 .95
Complete booklet, 10 #1428 20.00
**1429** A483 8k multi 3.25 1.40

Flora and Fauna — A484

Designs: 5k, Anacamptus pyramidalis. 5.50k, Falco peregrinus. 8k, Zygaena purpuralis. 17k, Tooth of Mosasaurus lemonnieri.

**2009, Mar. 25 Litho. *Perf. 12¾***

**1430** A484 5k multi 1.90 .85
**1431** A484 5.50k multi 2.40 .95
Complete booklet, 10 #1431 24.00
*a.* Miniature sheet of 8 + central label 17.00 17.00
**1432** A484 8k multi 3.00 1.40
**1433** A484 17k multi 6.75 3.00
*a.* Souvenir sheet, #1430-1433 13.50 13.50
*Nos. 1430-1433 (4)* 14.05 6.20

Copenhagen Zoo, 150th Anniv. — A485

Designs: 5.50k, Zoo Tower, rhinoceros. 6.50k, Elephants. 8k, Red-eyed tree frog, flamingos. 9k, Tiger python, golden lion tamarin.

**2009, June 10 Litho. *Perf. 13¼x13***

**1434** A485 5.50k multi 2.10 1.10
Complete booklet, 10 #1434 21.00
*a.* Miniature sheet of 8 + central label 17.00 17.00
**1435** A485 6.50k multi 2.50 1.25
*a.* Miniature sheet of 8 + central label 20.00 20.00
*b.* Booklet pane of 2, #1434-1435 8.00 —
**1436** A485 8k multi 3.00 1.50
**1437** A485 9k multi 3.50 1.75
*a.* Booklet pane of 2, #1436-1437 12.00 —
*b.* Booklet pane of 4, #1434-1437 20.00 —
Complete booklet, #1435b, 1437a, 1437b 40.00
*Nos. 1434-1437 (4)* 11.10 5.60

Complete booklet containing Nos. 1435b, 1437a, 1437b sold for 109k.

Historic Maps A486

Maps of Denmark by: 5.50k, Royal Danish Academy of Sciences and Letters, 1841. 6.50k, Johannes Mejer, 1650. 12k, Marcus Jordan, 1585. 18k, Abraham Ortelius, 1570.

**2009, July 15 Litho. *Perf. 12½***

**1438** A486 5.50k multi 2.10 1.10

**Size: 41x24mm**

***Perf. 12¾***

**1439** A486 6.50k multi 2.50 1.25
**1440** A486 12k multi 4.75 2.40
**1441** A486 18k multi 7.00 3.50
*Nos. 1438-1441 (4)* 16.35 8.25

Intl. Conference on the History of Cartography, Copenhagen.

Metropolitanskolen, 800th Anniv. — A487

Designs: 5.50k, Author Hans Scherfig as boy and Metropolitanskolen building, Copenhagen. 6.50k, Two students and current school building, Norrebro.

**2009, Sept. 9 Engr. *Perf. 13x13¼***

**1442** A487 5.50k red & black 2.25 1.10
**1443** A487 6.50k black & grn 2.60 1.40

COP15, United Nations Climate Conference, Copenhagen — A488

Designs: 5.50k, Fuel cell technology. 8k, Wind turbine.

**2009, Sept. 9**

**1444** A488 5.50k blue 2.25 1.10
Complete booklet, 10 #1444 22.50
**1445** A488 8k gray 3.25 1.60

Modern Art — A489

Designs: 5.50k, Houses in Motion, by Jes Fomsgaard. 12k, Garlic, by Karin Birgitte Lund, vert.

**2009 Litho. *Perf. 12¾x13***

**1446** A489 5.50k multi 2.25 1.10
*a.* Sheet of 8 + central label 18.00 18.00

***Perf. 12½x12¾***

**1447** A489 12k multi 5.00 2.40

Issued: 5.50k, 9/9; 12k, 10/27.

Children Playing in Snow — A490

Designs: 5.50k, Child rolling snow into large ball, snowman. 6.50k, Child in snow, child sledding. 8k, Child throwing snowball at two children. 9k, Two children making snow angels.

**2009, Oct. 27 Litho. *Perf. 12½x12¾***

**1448** A490 Sheet of 4 12.50 12.50
*a.* 5.50k multi 2.25 1.10
*b.* 6.50k multi 2.60 1.40
*c.* 8k multi 3.25 1.60
*d.* 9k multi 3.75 1.90

**Self-Adhesive**

***Die Cut Perf. 13x13½***

**1449** A490 5.50k multi 2.40 1.10
*a.* Booklet pane of 12 29.00
**1450** A490 6.50k multi 2.75 1.40
*a.* Booklet pane of 12 33.00
**1451** A490 8k multi 3.25 1.60
**1452** A490 9k multi 3.75 1.90
*a.* Sheet of 8, 2 each #1449-1452 25.00
*Nos. 1449-1452 (4)* 12.15 6.00

Nos. 1449a and 1450a each exist with six different booklet covers.

Flora and Fauna — A491

Designs: 8.50k, Bufo calamita. 9.50k, Lycaena phlaeas. 12.50k, Alauda arvensis. 18.50k, Astragalus danicus.

**2010, Jan. 2 Litho. *Perf. 12¼***

**1453** Souvenir sheet of 4 19.00 19.00
*a.* A491 8.50k multi 3.25 1.60
*b.* A491 9.50k multi 3.50 1.75
*c.* A491 12.50k multi 4.75 2.40
*d.* A491 18.50k multi 7.00 3.50

**Self-Adhesive**

***Die Cut Perf. 13x13½***

**1454** A491 8.50k multi 3.25 1.60
**1455** A491 9.50k multi 3.50 1.75
**1456** A491 12.50k multi 5.00 2.40
**1457** A491 18.50k multi 7.00 3.50
*Nos. 1454-1457 (4)* 18.75 9.25

Queen Margrethe II — A492

***Die Cut Perf. 13***

**2010, Feb. 10 Litho. & Engr.**

**Self-Adhesive**

**Panel Color**

**1458** A492 5.50k red 2.25 1.00
**1459** A492 6.50k Prus blue 2.60 1.25
*a.* Booklet pane of 10 26.00
**1460** A492 8.50k yel green 3.25 1.60
**1461** A492 9.50k dark blue 3.75 1.75
*a.* Miniature sheet of 8, 2 each #1458-1461 25.00
*Nos. 1458-1461 (4)* 11.85 5.60

No. 1458 was issued in coils as well as sheets. Every fifth coil stamp has a control number printed on the backing paper.

No. 1461a sold for 99k. See Nos. 1516-1519, 1574-1575, 1619-1620, 1635, 1665-1666, 1697-1700.

Issued: No. 1459a, 1/2/14.

Queen Margrethe II and Family A493

***Die Cut Perf. 13¼***

**2010, Mar. 24 Litho. & Engr.**

**Self-Adhesive**

**1462** A493 5.50k multi 2.25 2.00
*a.* Booklet pane of 12 27.00

Queen Margrethe II, 70th birthday.

Ribe, 1300th Anniv. — A494

Designs: 5.50k, Ribe Cathedral. 6.50k, Statue of Queen Dagmar.

**2010, Mar. 24 Engr.**

**Self-Adhesive**

**1463** A494 5.50k black 2.25 1.00
**1464** A494 6.50k black 2.40 1.25
*a.* Booklet pane of 12 29.00
*b.* Miniature sheet of 6, 3 each #1463-1464 16.00

Nordic Coastlines A495

Designs: 5.50k, Ship at Lindo Shipyard. 8.50k, Crane, Port of Aarhus.

***Perf. 12¼x12½***

**2010, Mar. 24 Litho.**

**1465** Sheet of 2 5.50 6.00
*a.* A495 5.50k multi 2.00 1.00
*b.* A495 8.50k multi 3.25 1.60

**Self-Adhesive**

***Die Cut Perf. 13¼***

**1466** A495 5.50k multi 2.00 1.00
**1467** A495 8.50k multi 3.25 1.60

**Wavy Lines Type of 1905 and Small State Seal Type of 1946**

**2010 Engr. *Die Cut Perf. 13***

**Self-Adhesive**

**1468** A10 50o brown .25 .25
**1469** A10 100o blue .40 .25
**1470** A10 200o dark green .75 .25
**1471** A10 300o orange 1.20 .25
**1472** A10 400o purple 1.60 .35
**1473** A10 500o green 1.90 .45
**1474** A55 10k lemon 3.75 .80
**1475** A55 15k blue 5.50 1.25
**1476** A55 20k dark blue 7.50 1.60
**1477** A55 30k red brown 11.50 2.75
**1478** A55 50k red 18.00 4.00
*Nos. 1468-1478 (11)* 52.35 12.20

Issued: 50o, 100o, 200o, 500o, 4/28; 300o, 400o, 30k, 3/24; 10k, 15k, 20k, 50k, 6/1.

Album Cover for Gasolin' 3, by Gasolin' A496

***Die Cut Perf. 13½x13¼***

**2010, Apr. 28 Litho.**

**Self-Adhesive**

**1479** A496 5.50k multi 2.25 1.50
*a.* Booklet pane of 12 27.00
*b.* Sheet of 4 19.00 15.00

Klampenborg Racetrack, Cent. — A497

Designs: 5.50k, Horses at finish line. 24k, Spectators watching race.

**2010, June 1 Self-Adhesive**

**1480** A497 5.50k multi 2.25 1.10
**1481** A497 24k multi 9.25 4.50

Europa — A498

Children's book characters: 5.50k, Sporge-Jorgen. 8.50k, Orla Fro-Snapper, horiz.

***Die Cut Perf. 13¼x13½***

**2010, June 1**

**Self-Adhesive**

**1482** A498 5.50k multi 2.10 1.00
*a.* Sheet of 8 18.00

***Die Cut Perf. 13½x13¼***

**1483** A498 8.50k multi 3.25 2.00

**Booklet Stamp**

***Serpentine Die Cut 13½***

**1484** A498 5.50k multi 8.00 3.50
*a.* Booklet pane of 12 96.00
*b.* Serpentine Die Cut 10 8.00 3.50
*c.* Booklet pane of 12 #1484b 96.00

Royal Danish Navy, 500th Anniv. A499

Designs: 5.50k, Frigate Iver Huitfeldt. 6.50k, Artillery ship Niels Iuel. 8.50k, Ironclad warship Todenskjold. 9.50k, Screw frigate Jylland. 16k, Caravel Maria.

***Die Cut Perf. 13¼x13***

**2010, June 1 Litho. & Engr.**

**Self-Adhesive (#1485-1489, 1491-1495)**

**1485** A499 5.50k red & black 2.00 .90
**1486** A499 6.50k red & black 2.50 1.10
*a.* Booklet pane of 12 25.00
**1487** A499 8.50k red & black 3.25 1.40
**1488** A499 9.50k red & black 4.00 1.60
**1489** A499 16k red & black 6.25 2.60
*Nos. 1485-1489 (5)* 18.00 7.60

**Booklet Stamps**

***Perf. 12¼x12½***

**1490** Booklet pane of 5 30.00 —
*a.* A499 5.50k red & black 3.00 2.60
*b.* A499 6.50k red & black 3.75 3.00
*c.* A499 8.50k red & black 5.25 4.25
*d.* A499 9.50k red & black 5.75 4.75
*e.* A499 16k red & black 9.50 7.75

**Booklet Panes of 1**

***Serpentine Die Cut 13¼x13½***

**1491** A499 5.50k red & black 3.25 2.75
**1492** A499 6.50k red & black 4.00 3.50
**1493** A499 8.50k red & black 5.50 4.50
**1494** A499 9.50k red & black 6.25 5.00
**1495** A499 16k red & black 10.00 8.00
Complete booklet, #1490-1495 60.00
*Nos. 1491-1495 (5)* 29.00 23.75

Complete booklet sold for 139k.

Greetings — A500

***Die Cut Perf. 13x13¼***

**2010, June 1 Litho.**

**Self-Adhesive**

**1496** A500 5.50k Heart 2.25 .90
**1497** A500 5.50k Danish Flag 2.25 .90
**1498** A500 5.50k "Tillykke" 2.25 .90
**1499** A500 5.50k Gift 2.25 .90
**1500** A500 5.50k Flower 2.25 .90
*a.* Sheet of 10, 2 each #1496-1500 22.50
*Nos. 1496-1500 (5)* 11.25 4.50

The right third of Nos. 1496-1500 has straight-edged die cutting. See Nos. 1552-1556.

A501

A502

A503

A504

A505

A506

A507

A508

A509

Post Danmark Rundt Bicycle Race — A510

**2010, Aug. 4 *Die Cut Perf. 13x13¼***

**1501** Sheet of 10 *65.00*
*a.* A501 5.50k multi *6.50 3.25*
*b.* A502 5.50k multi *6.50 3.25*
*c.* A503 5.50k multi *6.50 3.25*
*d.* A504 5.50k multi *6.50 3.25*
*e.* A505 5.50k multi *6.50 3.25*
*f.* A506 5.50k multi *6.50 3.25*
*g.* A507 5.50k multi *6.50 3.25*
*h.* A508 5.50k multi *6.50 3.25*
*i.* A509 5.50k multi *6.50 3.25*
*j.* A510 5.50k multi *6.50 3.25*

The right third of Nos. 1501a-1501j has straight-edged die cutting.

**Famous Men Type of 2007**

Designs: 5.50k, Dan Turèll (1946-93), writer, and lines from poem. 6.50k, Tove Ditlevsen (1917-76), poet, and her childhood home. 9.50k, Henry Heerup (1907-93), and "Love in the Coffee Pot." 12.50k, Dea Trier Morch (1941-2001), writer and artist, and illustration from her novel, *Winter's Child.*

***Die Cut Perf. 13½x12¾***

**2010, Aug. 25 Litho. & Engr.**

**Self-Adhesive**

**1502** A472 5.50k multi 2.25 .80
*a.* Souvenir sheet of 8 17.50
*b.* Booklet pane of 12 27.50
**1503** A472 6.50k multi 2.50 1.10
**1504** A472 9.50k multi 3.50 1.60
**1505** A472 12.50k multi 5.00 3.25
*Nos. 1502-1505 (4)* 13.25 6.75

Art — A511

Designs: 5.50k, Two Roses, by Inge Ellegaard. 18.50k, Night Flower, by Kirstine Roepstorff, vert.

***Die Cut Perf. 13¼x13½***

**2010, Aug. 25 Litho.**

**Self-Adhesive**

**1506** A511 5.50k multi 2.25 1.50

***Die Cut Perf. 13½x13¼***

**1507** A511 18.50k multi 7.25 5.00

**Small State Seal Type of 1946**

***Die Cut Perf. 13***

**2010, Oct. 26 Engr.**

**1508** A55 25k green 9.50 4.75

"Winter Tales" — A512

Designs: 5.50k, Woman on park bench, ducks. 6.50k, Woman on park bench hugging snowman. 8.50k, Woman kissing snowman. 12.50k, Snowman coming to life, dog.

**2010, Oct. 26 Litho. *Perf. 12¼x13***

**1509** Sheet of 4 13.00 6.50
*a.* A512 5.50k multi 2.10 1.10
*b.* A512 6.50k multi 2.50 1.25
*c.* A512 8.50k multi 3.25 1.60
*d.* A512 12.50k multi 4.75 2.40

**Self-Adhesive**

***Die Cut Perf. 13¼***

**1510** A512 5.50k multi 2.10 1.10
**1511** A512 6.50k multi 2.50 1.25
**1512** A512 8.50k multi 3.25 1.60
**1513** A512 12.50k multi 4.75 2.40
*a,* Sheet of 8, #1511-1513, 5 #1510 21.00
*Nos. 1510-1513 (4)* 12.60 6.35

**Booklet Stamps**

***Serpentine Die Cut 13½***

**1514** A512 5.50k multi 5.00 5.00
*a.* Booklet pane of 12 60.00
**1515** A512 6.50k multi 5.00 5.00
*a.* Booklet pane of 12 60.00

**Queen Margrethe II Type of 2010**

***Die Cut Perf. 13***

**2011, Mar. 9 Litho. & Engr.**

**Self-Adhesive**

**Panel Color**

**1516** A492 6k Prus blue 2.50 1.10
**1517** A492 8k red 3.25 1.50
**1518** A492 9k yel green 3.75 1.75
**1519** A492 11k dark blue 4.50 2.10
*Nos. 1516-1519 (4)* 14.00 6.45

Nos. 1516 and 1517 were issued in coils as well as sheets. Every fifth coil stamp has a control number printed on the backing paper.

Art A513

Designs: 8k, Untitled (for Karl Pichert), by Claus Carstensen. 13k, Det Her Sted (This Place), by Lise Harlev.

***Die Cut Perf. 13½x13¼***

**2011, Mar. 23 Litho. & Engr.**

**Self-Adhesive**

**1520** A513 8k sil & black 3.25 1.60

**Litho.**

**1521** A513 13k multi 5.00 2.50

Supreme Court, 350th Anniv. — A514

Designs: 6k, Supreme Court decree of King Frederik III, 1661. 8k, Court and judges.

**Litho. & Engr.**

**2011, Mar. 23 *Perf. 13x12½***

**1522** Sheet of 2 5.75 6.25
*a.* A514 6k multi 2.40 2.40
*b.* A514 8k multi 3.25 1.60

**Self-Adhesive**

***Die Cut Perf. 13x13½***

**1523** A514 6k multi 2.40 1.25
**1524** A514 8k multi 3.25 1.60

Camping — A515

Designs: 6k, Man wearing t-shirt and shorts in front of trailer. 8k, Garden gnome in front of trailer.

***Die Cut Perf. 13x13¼***

**2011, Mar. 23 Litho.**

**Self-Adhesive**

**1525** A515 6k multi 2.50 1.25
**1526** A515 8k multi 3.25 1.60

***Serpentine Die Cut 13½***

**1527** A515 6k multi 2.50 1.25
*a.* Booklet pane of 12 30.00
**1528** A515 8k multi 3.25 1.60
*a.* Booklet pane of 12 39.00
*b.* Pair, #1527-1528 5.75
*Nos. 1525-1528 (4)* 11.50 5.70

Nos. 1527-1528 were printed in sheets of 8 containing four of each stamp. Sheet sold for 56k.

Europa — A516

Designs: 8k, Caterpillar on branch in spring. 11k, Squirrel, tree in autumn.

**2011, May 4 *Die Cut Perf. 13x13¼***

**Self-Adhesive**

**1529** A516 8k multi 3.25 1.60
**1530** A516 11k multi 4.25 2.10

**Booklet Stamp**

***Serpentine Die Cut 13½***

**1531** A516 8k multi 3.25 3.00
*a.* Booklet pane of 12 39.00

Intl. Year of Forests.

Manor Houses A517

Designs: No. 1532, Norre Vosborg, near Holstebro. No. 1533, Voergaard Castle, Vendsyssel. No. 1534, Englesholm Castle, near Vejle. No. 1535, Gammel Estrup, near Randers.

***Die Cut Perf. 13¼x13***

**2011, May 4 Litho. & Engr.**

**Self-Adhesive**

**1532** A517 6k multi 2.40 1.25
**1533** A517 6k multi 2.40 1.25
**1534** A517 8k multi 3.25 1.60
**1535** A517 8k multi 3.25 1.60
*Nos. 1532-1535 (4)* 11.30 5.70

Arabian Expedition of Carsten Niebuhr, 250th Anniv. — A518

Compass rose and: 8k, Niebuhr (1733-1815), explorer. 13k, Horse-drawn grain mill from Egypt.

**2011, May 4 *Die Cut Perf. 13x13¼***

**Self-Adhesive**

**1536** A518 8k multi 3.50 1.60
**1537** A518 13k multi 5.25 2.50
*a.* Souvenir sheet of 2, #1536-1537, + label 8.75

**Booklet Stamp**

***Serpentine Die Cut 13½***

**1538** A518 8k multi 3.25 1.60
*a.* Booklet pane of 12 39.00

Paddle Steamer SS Hjejlen, 150th Anniv. A519

**2011, June 8 *Die Cut Perf. 13***

**Self-Adhesive**

**1539** A519 8k multi 3.50 1.60
*a.* Miniature sheet of 6 21.00

Children's Television Characters A520

Designs: 6k, Bruno the Bear and French fries. 8k, Bamse the Bear and balloons.

***Die Cut Perf. 13¼x13***

**2011, June 8 Litho.**

**Self-Adhesive**

**1540** A520 6k multi 2.50 1.25
*a.* Miniature sheet of 6 15.00
**1541** A520 8k multi 3.50 1.60
*a.* Miniature sheet of 6 21.00

**Booklet Stamps**

***Serpentine Die Cut 13½***

**1542** A520 6k multi 2.50 2.00
*a.* Booklet pane of 10 + 10 etiquettes 25.00
**1543** A520 8k multi 3.50 3.00
*a.* Booklet pane of 12 35.00

Summer Flowers — A521

Designs: 2k, Papaver rhoeas. 6k, Geranium. 8k, Astrantia major. 10k, Papaver nudicaule.

**2011, June 8 *Perf. 12x12¾***

**1544** Miniature sheet of 4 11.00 11.00
*a.* A521 2k multi .80 .40
*b.* A521 6k multi 2.40 1.25
*c.* A521 8k multi 3.25 1.60
*d.* A521 10k multi 4.00 2.00

**Self-Adhesive**

***Die Cut Perf. 13x13¼***

**1545** A521 2k multi .80 .40
**1546** A521 6k multi 2.40 1.25
**1547** A521 8k multi 3.25 1.60
**1548** A521 10k multi 4.00 2.00
*Nos. 1545-1548 (4)* 10.45 5.25

**Booklet Stamp**

***Serpentine Die Cut 13½***

**1549** A521 6k multi 2.50 2.25
*a.* Booklet pane of 10 + 10 etiquettes 25.00

Sketch of Woman's Clothing Designed by Malene Birger — A522

Fashion Accessories Designed by Silas Adler — A523

***Die Cut Perf. 13x13¼***

**2011, Aug. 4 Litho. & Engr.**

**Self-Adhesive**

**1550** A522 6k black 2.40 1.25
**1551** A523 8k multi 3.25 1.60
*a.* Souvenir sheet of 2, #1550-1551 5.75

**Greetings Type of 2010**

***Die Cut Perf. 13x13¼***

**2011, Aug. 4 Litho.**

**Self-Adhesive**

**1552** A500 8k Heart 3.25 1.60
**1553** A500 8k Danish Flag 3.25 1.60
**1554** A500 8k "Tillykke" 3.25 1.60
**1555** A500 8k Open envelope 3.25 1.60
**1556** A500 8k Flower 3.25 1.60
*a.* Sheet of 10, 2 each #1552-1556 32.50
*Nos. 1552-1556 (5)* 16.25 8.00

The right third of Nos. 1552-1556 has straight-edged die cutting.

International Cycling Union Road World Championships, Denmark — A524

**2011, Aug. 4 *Die Cut Perf. 13x13¼***

**Self-Adhesive**

**1557** A524 8k multi 3.25 1.60
*a.* Souvenir sheet of 6 19.50

Copenhagen Central Railway Station, Cent. — A525

People and: 6k, Station's front. 8k, Clock. 9k, Arches. 16k, Train at platform.

**Litho. & Engr.**

**2011, Sept. 10 *Perf. 13x12¼***

**Booklet Stamps (#1558-1561, 1566)**

**1558** A525 6k multi 6.00 6.00
**1559** A525 8k multi 6.00 6.00
*a.* Booklet pane of 2, #1558-1559 12.00 —
**1560** A525 9k multi 9.00 9.00
**1561** A525 16k multi 9.00 9.00
*a.* Booklet pane of 4, #1558-1561 30.00 —
*b.* Booklet pane of 2, #1560-1561 18.00 —
Complete booklet, #1559a, 1561a, 1561b 60.00
*Nos. 1558-1561 (4)* 30.00 30.00

**Self-Adhesive**

***Die Cut Perf. 13¼x13***

**1562** A525 6k multi 2.25 1.25
**1563** A525 8k multi 3.00 1.75
**1564** A525 9k multi 3.50 2.00
**1565** A525 16k multi 6.00 3.00
*Nos. 1562-1565 (4)* 14.75 8.00

***Serpentine Die Cut 13½***

**1566** A525 8k multi 3.25 3.00
*a.* Booklet pane of 12 39.00

The complete booklet sold for 139k.

People in Winter — A526

Designs: 6k, Bathing Viking. 8k, Woman feeding duck. 11k, Man walking dog. 13k, Ice fisherman.

**2011, Oct. 25 Litho. *Perf. 12¼***

**1567** Sheet of 4 15.00 7.50
*a.* A526 6k multi 2.40 1.25
*b.* A526 8k multi 3.00 1.75
*c.* A526 11k multi 4.25 2.90
*d.* A526 13k multi 5.00 3.25

**Self-Adhesive**

***Die Cut Perf. 13x13¼***

**1568** A526 6k multi 2.40 1.25
**1569** A526 8k multi 3.00 1.75
**1570** A526 11k multi 4.25 2.90
**1571** A526 13k multi 5.00 3.25
*Nos. 1568-1571 (4)* 14.65 9.15

**Booklet Stamps**

***Serpentine Die Cut 13½***

**1572** A526 6k multi 2.50 2.25
*a.* Booklet pane of 10 + 10 etiquettes 25.00
**1573** A526 8k multi 3.50 3.25
*a.* Booklet pane of 12 42.50

**Queen Margrethe II Type of 2010**

***Die Cut Perf. 13***

**2012, Jan. 2 Litho. & Engr.**

**Self-Adhesive**

**Panel Color**

**1574** A492 12k purple 4.50 3.75
**1575** A492 14k black 5.25 2.90

Armillary Spheres A527

Designs: No. 1576, Equatorial armillary sphere built by Tycho Brahe, 1595. No. 1577, Simplified armillary sphere built by Guo Shoujing, 1276.

***Die Cut Perf. 13¾***

**2012, Jan. 4 Litho. & Engr.**

**Self-Adhesive**

**1576** A527 6k multi 2.50 1.50
**1577** A527 6k multi 2.50 1.50

See People's Republic of China Nos. 3980-3981.

Reign of Queen Margrethe II, 40th Anniv. — A528

**2012, Jan. 4 *Perf. 13½***

**Souvenir Sheet**

**1578** A528 8k multi 3.00 3.00

**Self-Adhesive**

***Die Cut Perf. 13¼x13½***

**1579** A528 8k multi 3.00 3.00

Bridges A529

Designs: 6k, Queen Alexandrine Bridge. 8k, Faro Bridge.

**2012, Jan. 4 Litho. *Perf. 13¼***

**Souvenir Sheet**

**1580** Sheet of 2 8.25 8.25
*a.* A529 6k multi 3.00 2.00
*b.* A529 8k multi 5.00 3.00

**Self-Adhesive**

***Die Cut Perf. 13¼***

**1581** A529 6k multi 2.10 1.40
**1582** A529 8k multi 3.25 2.00

**Booklet Stamps**

***Serpentine Die Cut 13½***

**1583** A529 6k multi 2.10 1.40
*a.* Booklet pane of 10 + 10 etiquettes 21.00
**1584** A529 8k multi 3.25 2.00
*a.* Booklet pane of 10 + 10 etiquettes 32.50

Nordia 2012 Stamp Exhibition, Roskilde.

Europa — A530

**2012, Mar. 21 *Perf. 14***

**Souvenir Sheet**

**1585** A530 12k multi 4.50 4.50

**Self-Adhesive**

***Die Cut Perf. 14***

**1586** A530 12k multi 4.50 2.75

No. 1586 was printed in sheets of 30.

Sea Rescue — A531

Designs: 6k, Helicopter and rescue boat. 11k, Helicopter over Copenhagen University Hospital helipad.

**2012, Mar. 21 *Perf. 13½x13¼***

**Souvenir Sheet**

**1587** A531 Sheet of 2 6.50 6.50
*a.* 6k multi 2.40 1.60
*b.* 11k multi 4.00 2.40

**Self-Adhesive**

***Die Cut Perf. 13½x13¼***

**1588** A531 6k multi 2.40 1.60
**1589** A531 11k multi 4.00 2.40

Scenes From Tales by Hans Christian Andersen A532

Designs: 2k, The Shepherdess and the Chimney Sweep. 3k, The Nightingale. 6k, The Wild Swans. 8k, What the Old Man Does Is Always Right.

***Die Cut Perf. 13½x13¼***

**2012, June 1 Litho. & Engr.**

**Self-Adhesive**

**1590** A532 2k multi 1.10 .70
**1591** A532 3k multi 1.00 1.00
**1592** A532 6k multi 2.10 1.40
**1593** A532 8k multi 2.75 1.75
*Nos. 1590-1593 (4)* 6.95 4.85

**Booklet Stamps**

***Serpentine Die Cut 13½x13¼***

**1594** A532 6k multi 2.25 1.50
*a.* Booklet pane of 10 + 10 etiquettes 22.50
**1595** A532 8k multi 3.00 1.75
*a.* Booklet pane of 10 + sticker 30.00

Sandwiches

A533 A534

Designs: Nos. 1596, 1600, 1604, Egg and shrimp sandwich. Nos. 1597, 1601, 1605, Rolled sausage sandwich. 8k, Potato sandwich. 16k, Roast beef sandwich.

**2012, June 1 Litho. *Perf. 13x13¼***

**Booklet Stamps**

**1596** A533 6k multi 4.00 4.00
*a.* Booklet pane of 1 4.00 —
**1597** A534 6k multi 4.00 4.00
*a.* Booklet pane of 1 4.00 —
**1598** A534 8k multi 5.25 5.25
*a.* Booklet pane of 1 5.25 —
**1599** A534 16k multi 10.50 10.50
*a.* Booklet pane of 1 10.50 —
*b.* Booklet pane of 4, #1596-1599 24.00 —
Complete booklet, #1596a, 1597a, 1598a, 1599a, 1599b 48.00
*Nos. 1596-1599 (4)* 23.75 23.75

**Self-Adhesive**

***Die Cut Perf. 13x13¼***

**1600** A533 6k multi 2.00 1.00
**1601** A534 6k multi 2.00 1.00
**1602** A534 8k multi 2.75 1.40
**1603** A534 16k multi 5.50 2.75
*Nos. 1600-1603 (4)* 12.25 6.15

***Serpentine Die Cut 13½***

**1604** A533 6k multi 2.10 1.10
**1605** A534 6k multi 2.10 1.10
*a.* Booklet pane of 10, 5 each #1604-1605 + 10 etiquettes 20.00
**1606** A534 8k multi 2.90 1.75
*a.* Booklet pane of 10 27.50
*Nos. 1604-1606 (3)* 7.10 3.95

Complete booklet sold for 139k. Nos. 1604-1606 weree printed in a sheet of 8 containing 3 each nos. 1604-1605 and 2 No. 1606.

Portrait of Johanne Luise Heiberg, by Emilius Baerentzen — A535

***Die Cut Perf. 14x13¾***

**2012, Sept. 5 Litho. & Engr.**

**Self-Adhesive**

**1607** A535 8k multi 3.00 1.75

Heiberg (1812-90), theater actress and director.

Flowers — A536

Designs: 8k, Saponaria officinalis. 12k, Centaurea scabiosa. 14k, Leontodon autumnalis.

***Die Cut Perf. 13x13½***

**2012, Sept. 5 Litho.**

**Self-Adhesive**

**1608** A536 8k multi 3.00 1.75
**1609** A536 12k multi 4.50 2.40
**1610** A536 14k multi 5.25 3.75
*Nos. 1608-1610 (3)* 12.75 7.90

**Booklet Stamp**

***Serpentine Die Cut 13½***

**1611** A536 8k multi 3.00 2.50
*a.* Booklet pane of 10 30.00

Copenhagen Central Post Office, Cent. — A537

**2012, Sept. 12 Engr. *Perf. 13x13¼***

**1612** A537 8k dark red 3.00 3.00

Post Scriptum, by Christian Vind — A538

***Die Cut Perf. 14x13¾***

**2012, Nov. 2 Litho. & Engr.**

**Self-Adhesive**

**1613** A538 16k blk & yel org 5.75 4.00

Tree in Winter — A539

Tree and: 6k, Bird and musical notes. 8k, Birdhouse, bird. 12k, Moon, bird on branch of bush.

***Die Cut Perf. 13x13¼***

**2012, Nov. 2 Litho. Self-Adhesive**

**1614** A539 6k blue 2.10 1.10
**1615** A539 8k dull blue 2.90 1.75
**1616** A539 12k blue 4.25 3.50
*Nos. 1614-1616 (3)* 9.25 6.35

**Booklet Stamps**

***Serpentine Die Cut 13½***

**1617** A539 6k blue 2.10 1.10
*a.* Booklet pane of 10 + 10 etiquettes 21.00
**1618** A539 8k dull blue 2.90 1.75
*a.* Booklet pane of 10 29.00

**Queen Margrethe II Type of 2010**
**Self-Adhesive**
***Die Cut Perf. 13***
**Litho. & Engr.**

**2013, Jan. 2** **Panel Color**
**1619** A492 12.50k purple 4.75 2.75
**1620** A492 14.50k dark gray 5.25 2.75

Kaj and Andrea A540

Mr. Beard — A541

***Die Cut Perf. 13½x13¼***
**2013, Jan. 7** **Self-Adhesive** **Litho.**
**1621** A540 8k multi 3.00 2.50
*a.* Sheet of 6 18.00 15.00

***Die Cut Perf. 13¼x13½***
**1622** A541 8k multi 3.00 2.50

**Booklet Stamps**
***Serpentine Die Cut 13½***
**1623** A540 8k multi 3.00 2.50
**1624** A541 8k multi 3.00 2.50
*a.* Booklet pane of 10, 5 each #1623-1624 30.00

Characters on children's television programs.

Fish — A542

Designs: 6k, Clupea harengus. 8k, Gadus morhua. 12.50k, Platichthys flesus. 14.50k, Anguilla anguilla.

**Booklet Stamps (#1625-1628, 1633-1634)**

**2013, Jan. 7** **Litho.** ***Perf. 13***
**1625** A542 6k multi 3.50 3.50
*a.* Booklet pane of 1 3.50 —
**1626** A542 8k multi 5.00 5.00
*a.* Booklet pane of 1 5.00 —
**1627** A542 12.50k multi 7.50 7.50
*a.* Booklet pane of 1 7.50 —
**1628** A542 14.50k multi 9.00 9.00
*a.* Booklet pane of 1 9.00 —
*b.* Booklet pane of 4, #1625-1628 25.00 —
Complete booklet, #1625a, 1626a, 1627a, 1628a, 1628b 50.00
*Nos. 1625-1628 (4)* 25.00 25.00

**Self-Adhesive**
***Die Cut Perf. 13***
**1629** A542 6k multi 2.25 1.20
**1630** A542 8k multi 3.00 1.75
**1631** A542 12.50k multi 4.50 3.75
**1632** A542 14.50k multi 5.25 3.75
*Nos. 1629-1632 (4)* 15.00 10.45

***Serpentine Die Cut 13½***
**1633** A542 6k multi 2.25 1.20
*a.* Booklet pane of 10 + 10 etiquettes 22.50
**1634** A542 8k multi 3.00 1.75
*a.* Booklet pane of 10 30.00

Complete booklet sold for 139k.

**Queen Margrethe II Type of 2010**
***Die Cut Perf. 13***
**2013, Mar. 4** **Litho. & Engr.**
**Self-Adhesive**
**Panel Color**
**1635** A492 16k orange 6.00 5.00

Soren Kierkegaard (1813-55), Philosopher A543

**2013, Mar. 4** ***Die Cut Perf. 13¼x13***
**1636** A543 8k multi 3.00 2.50

Electric Postal Bicycle, Europa A544

**2013, Mar. 4** ***Perf. 13½x13***
**Souvenir Sheet**
**1637** A544 12.50k multi 4.75 3.00

**Self-Adhesive**
***Die Cut Perf. 13¼x13***
**1638** A544 12.50k multi 4.75 2.25

Manor Houses A545

Designs: Nos. 1639, 1641, Egeskov Castle. Nos. 1640, 1642, Valdemar's Castle.

**2013, Mar. 4** ***Die Cut Perf. 13¼x13***
**Self-Adhesive**
**1639** A545 8k multi 3.00 2.50
**1640** A545 8k multi 3.00 2.50

**Booklet Stamps**
***Serpentine Die Cut 13½***
**1641** A545 8k multi 3.00 2.50
**1642** A545 8k multi 3.00 2.50
*a.* Booklet pane of 10, 5 each #1641-1642 30.00

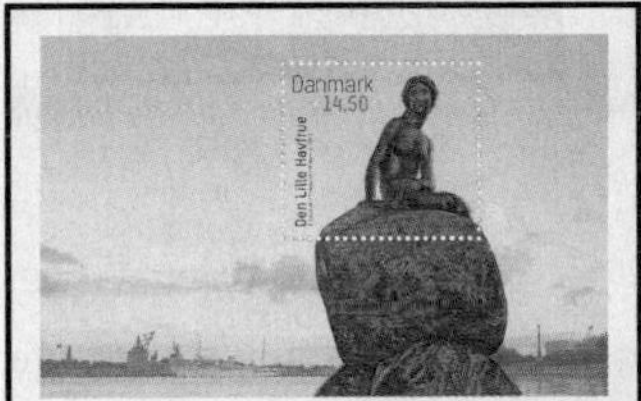
The Little Mermaid Statue, Copenhagen, Cent. — A546

**Litho. & Engr.**
**2013, May 27** ***Perf. 13½x13***
**Souvenir Sheet**
**1643** A546 14.50k multi *5.25* 5.25

**Self-Adhesive**
***Die Cut Perf. 13¼x13***
**1644** A546 14.50k multi 5.25 4.50

Danish Rock Music A547

Designs: Nos. 1645, 1647, Crowd at rock concert. Nos. 1646, 1648, Electric guitar of Kasper Eistrup.

***Die Cut Perf. 13¼x13***
**2013, May 27** **Litho.**
**Self-Adhesive**
**1645** A547 8k multi 3.00 1.75
**1646** A547 8k multi 3.00 1.75

***Serpentine Die Cut 13½***
**1647** A547 8k multi 3.00 1.75
**1648** A547 8k multi 3.00 1.75
*a.* Booklet pane of 10, 5 each #1647-1648 30.00
*Nos. 1645-1648 (4)* 12.00 7.00

Nos. 1647-1648 were printed in sheets containing 3 of each stamp.

Culture Yard, Elsinore — A548

Designs: 8k, Wing of building and reflecting pond. 12.50k, Building entrance and reflecting pond.

**2013, Aug. 29** **Litho.** ***Perf. 13x13¼***
**Souvenir Sheet**
**1649** A548 Sheet of 2 7.50 4.50
*a.* 8k multi 3.00 1.75
*b.* 12.50k multi 4.50 2.75

**Self-Adhesive**
***Die Cut Perf. 13x13¼***
**1650** A548 8k multi 3.00 1.75
**1651** A548 12.50k multi 4.50 2.75

Fifth INDEX: Intl. Design award ceremonies, Elsinore.

Best Wishes, by Jytte Hoy A549

***Die Cut Perf. 13¼x13½***
**2013, Sept. 2** **Litho. & Engr.**
**Self-Adhesive**
**1652** A549 8k multi 3.00 1.75

Scenes from Stories by Hans Christian Andersen A550

Scenes from: 6k, The Tinderbox. 8k, The Flying Trunk. 12.50k, The Sweethearts (The Top and the Ball). 14.50k, The Little Match Girl.

***Die Cut Perf. 13¼x13***
**2013, Sept. 2** **Litho. & Engr.**
**Self-Adhesive**
**1653** A550 6k multi 2.25 1.50
*a.* Booklet pane of 10 + 10 etiquettes 22.50
**1654** A550 8k multi 3.00 1.75
*a.* Booklet pane of 10 30.00
**1655** A550 12.50k multi 4.50 3.00
**1656** A550 14.50k multi 5.25 3.75
*Nos. 1653-1656 (4)* 15.00 10.00

Christmas — A551

Designs: 6k, Christmas rose. 8k, Skating girl. 12.50k, Robins.

**2013, Oct. 29** **Litho.** ***Perf. 13x12¾***
**Souvenir Sheet**
**1657** Sheet of 3 9.75 9.75
*a.* A551 6k multi 2.25 1.20
*b.* A551 8k multi 3.00 1.75
*c.* A551 12.50k multi 4.50 3.75

**Self-Adhesive**
***Die Cut Perf. 13x13¼***
**1658** A551 6k multi 2.25 1.20
**1659** A551 8k multi 3.00 1.75
**1660** A551 12.50k multi 4.50 3.00
*Nos. 1658-1660 (3)* 9.75 5.95

**Booklet Stamps**
***Serpentine Die Cut 13½***
**1661** A551 6k multi 2.25 1.20
*a.* Booklet pane of 10 + 10 etiquettes 22.50
**1662** A551 8k multi 3.00 1.75
*a.* Booklet pane of 10 30.00

Trade Treaty Between Denmark and France, 350th Anniv. A552

Map and compass rose with ship at: 8k, Right. 12.50k, Left.

***Die Cut Perf. 13½x13¼***
**2013, Nov. 7** **Litho. & Engr.**
**Self-Adhesive**
**1663** A552 8k rose & blue 3.00 1.75
**1664** A552 12.50k blue & rose 4.50 2.75

See France Nos. 4526-4527.

**Queen Margrethe II Type of 2010**
***Die Cut Perf. 13***
**2014, Jan. 2** **Litho. & Engr.**
**Self-Adhesive**
**Panel Color**
**1665** A492 9k red 3.75 2.50
*a.* Booklet pane of 10 37.50
**1666** A492 18k blue 7.50 4.50
*a.* Booklet pane of 10 75.00

Nordic Cuisine — A553

Aebleflaesk: 6.50k, Raw ingredients (Pig and apples). 14k, Finished dish.

***Die Cut Perf. 13½x13***
**2014, Jan. 2** **Litho.**
**Self-Adhesive**
**1667** A553 6.50k multi 2.50 1.50
*a.* Booklet pane of 10 25.00
**1668** A553 14k multi 5.25 2.00

Flowers — A554

Designs: No. 1669, Fritillaria meleagris. No. 1670, Muscari botryoides.

***Die Cut Perf. 13¾***
**2014, Jan. 2** **Litho.**
**Self-Adhesive**
**1669** A554 9k multi 3.50 1.75
**1670** A554 9k multi 3.50 1.75
*a.* Horiz. pair, #1669-1670 on backing paper without printing 7.00
*b.* Booklet pane of 10, 5 each #1669-1670 35.00

Nos. 1669 and 1670 were printed in sheets of 6 containing 3 of each stamp.

PH Grand Piano — A555

*Die Cut Perf. 13½x13*

**2014, Mar. 15 Litho. & Engr.**

**Self-Adhesive**

1671 A555 14k multi 5.25 3.75

Europa.

General Peter du Plat (1809-64) — A556

Prussian Soldiers at Battle of Dybbol — A557

**Litho. & Engr.**

**2014, Mar. 15** ***Perf. 13x12¾***

**Souvenir Sheet**

1672 Sheet of 2 + label 10.50 10.50
- *a.* A556 9k multi 3.50 1.75
- *b.* A557 18k multi 6.75 3.50

**Self-Adhesive**

*Die Cut Perf. 13½*

1673 A556 9k multi 3.50 1.75
- *a.* Booklet pane of 10 35.00

*Die Cut Perf. 13x13½*

1674 A557 18k multi 6.75 3.50

Battle of Dybbol, 150th anniv,

Chairs — A558

Designs: 6.50k, Three-legged shell chair, designed by Hans J. Wegner (1914-2007). 16k, Spanish chair, designed by Borge Mogensen (1914-72).

*Die Cut Perf. 13½x13*

**2014, Mar. 15 Litho. & Engr.**

**Self-Adhesive**

1675 A558 6.50k org & gray 2.40 1.50
- *a.* Booklet pane of 10 24.00

1676 A558 16k brn & lt brn 6.00 3.00
- *a.* Booklet pane of 5 30.00

A booklet containing perf. 13½x13 stamps with water-activated gum having designs identical to Nos. 1675 and 1676 sold for 139k. The booklet contained a pane containing one example of the 6.50k, another containing one example of the 16k, and another containing one example each of the 6.50k and 16k.

Sailboats A559

Designs: 6.50k, Laser Radial dinghy. 14k, Hanse 430e yacht.

*Perf. 12½x12¾*

**2014, Mar. 17 Litho.**

**Souvenir Sheet**

1677 Sheet of 2 7.75 7.75
- *a.* A559 6.50k multi 2.40 1.50
- *b.* A559 14k multi 5.25 2.75

**Self-Adhesive**

*Die Cut Perf. 13x13½*

1678 A559 6.50k multi 2.40 1.50
- *a.* Booklet pane of 10 24.00

1679 A559 14k multi 5.25 2.60

Princess Benedikte and Scouts A560

*Die Cut Perf. 13x13½*

**2014, Apr. 29 Litho.**

**Self-Adhesive**

1680 A560 9k multi + label 3.50 3.50
- *a.* Booklet pane of 5 + 5 labels 17.50

Princess Benedikte, 70th birthday.

Danish School System, 200th Anniv. — A561

*Die Cut Perf. 13½*

**2014, June 11 Litho.**

**Self-Adhesive**

1681 A561 6.50k multi 2.40 1.50
- *a.* Booklet pane of 10 24.00

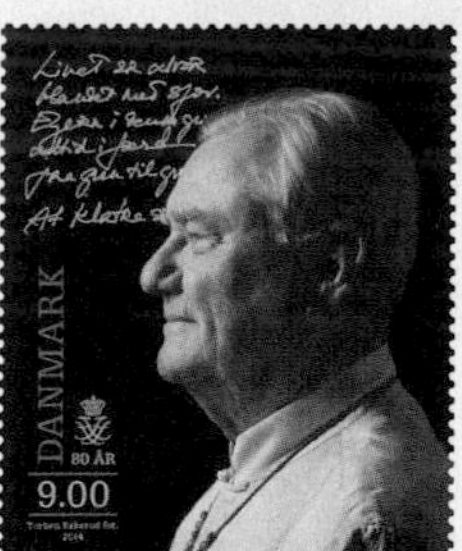

Prince Henrik, 80th Birthday A562

*Die Cut Perf. 13½*

**2014, June 11 Litho.**

**Self-Adhesive**

1682 A562 9k multi 3.50 1.75
- *a.* Booklet pane of 4 14.00

Den Frie Center of Contemporary Art, Cent. — A563

*Die Cut Perf. 13½*

**2014, June 11 Litho. & Engr.**

**Self-Adhesive**

1683 A563 9k multi 3.50 1.75
- *a.* Booklet pane of 2 7.00

Manor Houses A564

Designs: 6.50k, Knuthenborg. 9k, Ledreborg Palace.

*Die Cut Perf. 13x13½*

**2014, June 11 Litho. & Engr.**

**Self-Adhesive**

1684 A564 6.50k multi 2.40 1.25
- *a.* Booklet pane of 10 24.00

1685 A564 9k multi 3.50 1.75
- *a.* Booklet pane of 10 35.00

Guard Hussar Regiment, 400th Anniv. — A565

*Die Cut Perf. 13½*

**2014, Aug. 30 Litho. & Engr.**

**Self-Adhesive**

1686 A565 6.50k multi 2.40 1.25
- *a.* Booklet pane of 10 24.00

Blank Space for Greetings, by Olafur Eliasson — A566

*Serpentine Die Cut 10¼*

**2014, Aug. 30 Litho. & Engr.**

**Self-Adhesive**

1687 A566 9k blk & olive 3.25 1.60
- *a.* Booklet pane of 4 13.00

The central portion of the stamp is die cut.

Characters from Stories by Hans Christian Andersen — A567

Designs: 6.50k, Klods-Hans (Clumsy Hans) and dead crow. 9k, Tommelise (Thumbelina) and toad.

*Perf. 12¾x13¼*

**2014, Aug. 30 Litho. & Engr.**

**Souvenir Sheet**

1688 Sheet of 2 5.75 3.00
- *a.* A567 6.50k multi 2.40 1.25
- *b.* A567 9k multi 3.25 1.60

**Self-Adhesive**

*Die Cut Perf. 13½x13*

1689 A567 6.50k multi 2.40 1.25
- *a.* Booklet pane of 10 24.00

1690 A567 9k multi 3.25 1.60
- *a.* Booklet pane of 10 32.50

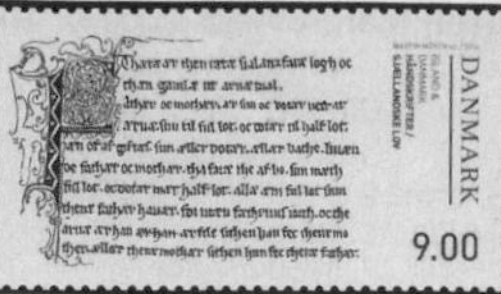

Manuscripts — A568

Designs: 9k, Valdemar's Law of Zealand, 13th cent. 14k, Njáls Saga, c. 1350.

**Litho. & Engr.**

**2014, Aug. 30** ***Perf. 13x12¾***

**Souvenir Sheet**

1691 Sheet of 2 8.25 4.25
- *a.* A568 9k multi 3.25 1.60
- *b.* A568 14k multi 5.00 2.50

**Self-Adhesive**

*Die Cut Perf. 13½*

1692 A568 9k multi 3.25 1.60
- *a.* Booklet pane of 10 32.50

1693 A568 14k multi 5.00 2.50
- *a.* Booklet pane of 5 25.00

See Iceland Nos. 1350-1352.

Berries — A569

Designs: 6.50k, Snowberries. 9k, Lingonberries. 14k, Firethorn.

*Die Cut Perf. 13½x13¼*

**2014, Oct. 18 Litho.**

**Self-Adhesive**

1694 A569 6.50k multi 2.25 1.10
- *a.* Booklet pane of 10 22.50

1695 A569 9k multi 3.00 1.50
- *a.* Booklet pane of 10 30.00

1696 A569 14k multi 4.75 2.40
- *a.* Booklet pane of 5 24.00

*Nos. 1694-1696 (3)* 10.00 5.00

**Queen Margrethe II Type of 2010**

*Die Cut Perf. 13*

**2014, Nov. 17 Litho. & Engr.**

**Self-Adhesive**

**Panel Color**

1697 A492 7k Prus blue 2.40 1.25
- *a.* Booklet pane of 10 24.00

1698 A492 10k red 3.50 1.75
- *a.* Booklet pane of 10 35.00

1699 A492 16.50k orange 5.50 2.75
- *a.* Booklet pane of 10 55.00

1700 A492 19k blue 6.50 3.25
- *a.* Booklet pane of 10 65.00

*Nos. 1697-1700 (4)* 17.90 9.00

Children's Poems by Halfdan Rasmussen (1915-2002) — A570

Poems from *Halfdans ABC*: No. 1701, Bennys Bukser Braendte (Benn's Trouser's Burned). No. 1702, Kanonkongen Knold (Cannon King Knold).

*Die Cut Perf. 13¾x13½*

**2015, Jan. 2 Litho. & Engr.**

**Self-Adhesive**

1701 A570 7k blue & multi 2.25 1.10

1702 A570 7k dl grn & multi 2.25 1.10
- *a.* Booklet pane of 10, 6 #1701, 4 #1702 22.50

Lego Blocks — A571

Blocks of various colors and: 10k, Boy. 14.50k, Girl.

*Die Cut Perf. 13½x13*

**2015, Jan. 2 Self-Adhesive Litho.**

**1703** A571 10k multi 3.25 1.60
*a.* Booklet pane of 10 32.50
*b.* Sheet of 6 + 20 stickers 22.50
**1704** A571 14.50k multi 4.75 2.40
*a.* Booklet pane of 10 4.75 2.40

No. 1703b sold for 70k.

Animals in Wadden Sea National Park — A572

Designs: Nos. 1705a, 1706, Texel sheep. Nos. 1705b, 1707, Black-tailed godwit, vert. Nos. 1705c, 1708, Harbor seals.

**Litho. & Engr.**

**2015, Jan. 2** *Perf. 13*

**1705** Souvenir sheet of 3 9.75 5.00
*a.-c.* A572 10k Any single 3.25 1.60

**Self-Adhesive**

*Die Cut Perf. 13¼x13½, 13½x13¼*

**1706** A572 10k multi 3.25 1.60
**1707** A572 10k multi 3.25 1.60
**1708** A572 10k multi 3.25 1.60
*a.* Booklet pane of 10, 4 #1706, 6 #1708 32.50
*Nos. 1706-1708 (3)* 9.75 4.80

Herlufsholm, 450th Anniv. — A573

*Die Cut Perf. 13½x13*

**2015, Mar. 14 Litho.**

**Self-Adhesive**

**1709** A573 10k multi 3.00 1.50
*a.* Booklet pane of 10 30.00 —

Inventions — A574

Inventions: Nos. 1710a, 1711, Dry cell battery, by Wilhelm Hellesen, 1887. Nos. 1710b, 1712, Ready-mix concrete truck, by Kristian Hindhede, 1929, horiz. Nos. 1710c, 1713, Long John delivery bicycle, by Morten Rasmussen Mortensen, 1929, horiz. Nos. 1710d, 1714, Writing ball, by Rasmus Mallin-Hansen, 1867.

**2015, Mar. 14 Litho.** *Perf. 13*

**Souvenir Sheet**

**1710** Sheet of 4 12.00 6.00
*a.-d.* A574 10k Any single 3.00 1.50

**Booklet Stamps**
**Self-Adhesive**
**Litho. & Engr.**

*Die Cut Perf. 13½x13; 13x13½*

**1711** A574 10k multi 3.00 1.50
**1712** A574 10k multi 3.00 1.50
**1713** A574 10k multi 3.00 1.50
*a.* Booklet pane of 10, 6 #1713, 4 #1712 30.00
**1714** A574 10k multi 3.00 1.50
*a.* Booklet pane of 10, 6 #1711, 4 #1714 30.00
*Nos. 1711-1714 (4)* 12.00 6.00

Medal of Merit — A575

Order of the Elephant — A576

Order of Dannebrog — A577

*Die Cut Perf. 13½x13*

**2015, Mar. 14 Litho. & Engr.**

**Self-Adhesive**

**1715** A575 7k multi 2.10 1.10

**Booklet Stamps**

**1716** A576 7k multi 2.10 1.10
**1717** A577 7k multi 2.10 1.10
*a.* Booklet pane of 10, 6 #1716, 4 #1717 21.00
*Nos. 1715-1717 (3)* 6.30 3.30

A booklet containing perforated examples of Nos. 1715-1717 (three booklet panes containing one of each stamp and one booklet pane containing all three stamps) sold for 199k.

Woman Suffrage, Cent. A578

*Die Cut Perf. 13¼*

**2015, June 13 Litho.**

**Self-Adhesive**

**1718** A578 10k multi 3.00 1.50

Samosvej 8, 2300 Kobenhaven S, Danmark, by Jesper Christiansen — A579

*Die Cut Perf. 13¼*

**2015, June 13 Litho. & Engr.**

**Self-Adhesive**

**1719** A579 10k multi 3.00 1.50

Copenhagen Carpenters' Guild, 500th Anniv. — A580

*Die Cut Perf. 13½x13*

**2015, June 13 Litho. & Engr.**

**Self-Adhesive**

**1720** A580 10k multi 3.00 1.50
*a.* Booklet pane of 10 30.00

Ships — A581

Designs: Nos. 1721a, 1723, Georg Stage. Nos. 1721b, 1722, Danmark. Nos. 1721c, 1724, Kobenhavn. Nos. 1721d, 1725, Fulton.

**2015, June 13 Litho.** *Perf. 13x12¾*

**1721** A581 Sheet of 4 8.50 8.50
*a.-d.* 7k Any single 2.10 1.10

**Self-Adhesive**

*Die Cut Perf. 13x13½*

**1722** A581 7k multi 2.10 1.10
**1723** A581 7k multi 2.10 1.10
*a.* Vert. pair, #1722-1723, on backing paper without printing 4.25
**1724** A581 7k multi 2.10 1.10
**1725** A581 7k multi 2.10 1.10
*a.* Vert. pair, #1724-1725, on backing paper without printing 4.25
*b.* Booklet pane of 10, 2 each #1723-1725, 4 #1722 21.00
*Nos. 1722-1725 (4)* 8.40 4.40

Miniature Sheet

25th Post Danmark Rundt Bicycle Race — A582

No. 1726: a, Moreno Argentin. b, Jakob Fuglsang. c, Cyclists in Randers. d, Matti Breschel. e, Cyclists on Kiddesvej climb, Velje. f, Fabian Cancellara. g, Cyclists on Storebaelts Bridge. h, Cyclist on Frederiksberg Allé, Copenhagen. i, Mark Cavendish. j, Michael Valgren.

*Die Cut Perf. 13x13¼ on 3 Sides*

**2015, June 27 Litho.**

**Self-Adhesive**

**1726** A582 Sheet of 10 25.50
*a.-e.* 7k Any single 2.10 1.10
*f.-j.* 10k Any single 3.00 1.50

Christmas — A583

Honey cakes shaped as: Nos. 1727a, 1728, Man. Nos. 1727b, 1729, Woman. Nos. 1727c, 1730, Heart.

**2015, Oct. 17 Litho.** *Perf. 12¾x13¼*

**Souvenir Sheet**

**1727** Sheet of 3 7.25 3.75
*a.-b.* A583 7k Either single 2.10 1.10
*c.* A583 10k multi 3.00 1.50

**Self-Adhesive**

*Die Cut Perf. 13½x13*

**1728** A583 7k multi 2.10 1.10
**1729** A583 7k multi 2.10 1.10
*a.* Booklet pane of 10, 6 #1728, 4 #1729 21.00

**Size:22x32mm**

*Die Cut Perf. 12¼x13 Syncopated*

**1730** A583 10k multi 3.00 1.50
*Nos. 1728-1730 (3)* 7.20 3.70

Maribo Cathedral, 600th Anniv. — A584

**Litho. & Engr.**

**2016, Jan. 4** *Perf. 13½x13*

**Self-Adhesive**

**1731** A584 19k multi 5.50 2.75
*a.* Booklet pane of 10 55.00

Nordic Food Culture
A585 A586

**2016, Jan. 4 Litho.** *Perf. 13*

**Souvenir Sheet**

**1732** Sheet of 2 4.80 2.50
*a.* A585 8k multi 2.40 1.25
*b.* A586 8k multi 2.40 1.25

**Self-Adhesive**

*Die Cut Perf. 13 Syncopated*

**1733** A585 8k multi 2.40 1.25
*a.* Booklet pane of 5 12.00
**1734** A586 8k multi 2.40 1.25
*a.* Booklet pane of 5 12.00

Souvenir Sheet

Europa — A587

No. 1735: a, Hands holding Earth wrapped in leaves. b, Bicylcist, wind generators, paint roller.

**2016, Mar. 31 Litho.** *Perf. 13*

**1735** A587 Sheet of 2 15.50 15.50
*a.-b.* 25k Either single 7.75 3.75

Think Green Issue.

Sports — A588

Designs: No. 1736, Runner in Lillebaelt Half Marathon. No. 1737, Cyclists in Fyen Rundt Bicycle Race. No. 1738, Cyclist in Haervejslobet Mountain Bike Race. No. 1739, Swimmer in Christiansborg Rundt Swimming Race. No. 1740, Bicycle helmet, running shoes, swimming goggles.

*Die Cut Perf. 13¼ Syncopated*

**2016, Mar. 31 Litho.**

**Booklet Stamps**
**Self-Adhesive**

**1736** A588 8k multi 2.50 1.25
**1737** A588 8k multi 2.50 1.25
**1738** A588 8k multi 2.50 1.25
**1739** A588 8k multi 2.50 1.25
**1740** A588 8k multi 2.50 1.25
*a.* Booklet pane of 10, 2 each #1736-1740 25.00
*Nos. 1736-1740 (5)* 12.50 6.25

Prize-Winning Animals at Agricultural Shows — A589

Designs: No. 1741, Wyandotte cockerel. No. 1742, Danish Red Holstein cow. No. 1743, Oldenburg stallion. No. 1744, Shropshire ram. No. 1745, Satin rabbit.

*Die Cut Perf. 13¼ Syncopated*

**2016, Mar. 31 Litho.**

**Booklet Stamps Self-Adhesive**

| | | | | |
|---|---|---|---|---|
| **1741** | A589 8k multi | | 2.50 | 1.25 |
| **1742** | A589 8k multi | | 2.50 | 1.25 |
| **1743** | A589 8k multi | | 2.50 | 1.25 |
| **1744** | A589 8k multi | | 2.50 | 1.25 |
| **1745** | A589 8k multi | | 2.50 | 1.25 |
| *a.* | Booklet pane of 10, 2 each #1741-1745 | 25.00 | | |
| | *Nos. 1741-1745 (5)* | | 12.50 | 6.25 |

Famous Men — A590

Designs: No. 1746, Maersk Mc-Kinney Moller (1913-2012), shipping magnate, and M/S Emma Maersk. No. 1747, Jorn Utzon (1918-2008), architect, and Sydney Opera House.

*Die Cut Perf. 13¼ Syncopated*

**2016, Mar. 31 Litho. & Engr.**

**Booklet Stamps Self-Adhesive**

| | | | | |
|---|---|---|---|---|
| **1746** | A590 19k multi | | 6.00 | 3.00 |
| **1747** | A590 19k multi | | 6.00 | 3.00 |
| *a.* | Booklet pane of 10, 6 #1746, 4 #1747 | 60.00 | | |

Souvenir Sheet

Art by Trine Sondergaard — A591

No. 1748: a, Interior #12. b, Guldnakke #16.

**2016, June 23 Litho. *Perf. 12½***

| | | | |
|---|---|---|---|
| **1748** | A591 Sheet of 2 | 15.00 | 15.00 |
| *a.-b.* | 25k Either single | 7.50 | 3.75 |

Children's Songs — A592

Illustrations by Bitte Böcher from children's songbook *De Sma Synger*. Nos. 1749a, 1751, Den Lille Ole Med Paraplyen. Nos. 1749b, 1750, Der Sad to Katte pa et Bord. Nos. 1749c, 1753, Bro, Bro, Brille. Nos. 1749d, 1752, Mors Lille Ole.

**2016, June 23 Litho. *Perf. 12¾x13***

| | | | |
|---|---|---|---|
| **1749** | Sheet of 4 | 9.75 | 9.75 |
| *a.-d.* | A592 8k Any single | 2.40 | 1.25 |

**Booklet Stamps Self-Adhesive**

**Litho. & Engr.**

*Die Cut Perf. 13¼ Syncopated*

| | | | | |
|---|---|---|---|---|
| **1750** | A592 8k blk & brt grn | | 2.40 | 1.25 |
| **1751** | A592 8k blk & brt org | | 2.40 | 1.25 |
| **1752** | A592 8k blk & brt grn | | 2.40 | 1.25 |
| **1753** | A592 8k blk & brt org | | 2.40 | 1.25 |
| *a.* | Booklet pane of 10, 2 each #1751-1753, 4 #1750 | 24.00 | | |
| | *Nos. 1750-1753 (4)* | | 9.60 | 5.00 |

Danish Porcelain Designs — A593

Designs: No. 1754, Magestellet (Seagull), 1892. No. 1755, Flora Danica, 1790. No. 1756, Bla Blomst Svejfet (Blue Flower Curved), 1779. No. 1757, Sort Mega Riflet (Black Fluted Mega), 2006. No. 1758, Musselmalet Halvblonde (Blue Fluted Half Lace), 1888.

*Die Cut Perf. 13¼ Syncopated*

**2016, June 23 Litho.**

**Booklet Stamps Self-Adhesive**

| | | | | |
|---|---|---|---|---|
| **1754** | A593 8k multi | | 2.40 | 1.25 |
| **1755** | A593 8k multi | | 2.40 | 1.25 |
| **1756** | A593 8k multi | | 2.40 | 1.25 |
| **1757** | A593 8k multi | | 2.40 | 1.25 |
| **1758** | A593 8k multi | | 2.40 | 1.25 |
| *a.* | Booklet pane of 10, 2 each #1754-1758 | 24.00 | | |
| | *Nos. 1754-1758 (5)* | | 12.00 | 6.25 |

A booklet containing 11 perf. 12¾x13¼ stamps with the designs of Nos. 1754-1758 and four perforated progressive proofs of the Flora Danica design sold for 199k.

Illustrations of Pixies by Peter Moller (1838-1910) A594

Designs: No. 1759, Pixie carrying baskets of toys and balloon. No. 1760, Pixie dancing with cat. No. 1761, Dog biting pixie's cap. No. 1762, Pixies dancing and playing concertina. No. 1763, Five pixie musicians.

*Die Cut Perf. 13¼ Syncopated*

**2016, Sept. 29 Litho.**

**Booklet Stamps Self-Adhesive**

| | | | | |
|---|---|---|---|---|
| **1759** | A594 8k multi | | 2.40 | 1.25 |
| **1760** | A594 8k multi | | 2.40 | 1.25 |
| **1761** | A594 8k multi | | 2.40 | 1.25 |
| **1762** | A594 8k multi | | 2.40 | 1.25 |
| **1763** | A594 8k multi | | 2.40 | 1.25 |
| *a.* | Booklet pane of 5, #1759-1763 | 12.00 | | |
| | *Nos. 1759-1763 (5)* | | 12.00 | 6.25 |

Christmas.

Souvenir Sheet

Frederksborg Castle, Hillerod — A595

No. 1764 — Aerial views of: a, Baroque Gardens. b, Castle.

**2017, Jan. 2 Litho. *Perf. 13***

| | | | |
|---|---|---|---|
| **1764** | A595 Sheet of 2 | 14.00 | 7.00 |
| *a.-b.* | 25k Either single | 7.00 | 3.50 |

Shellfish — A596

Designs: No. 1765, Taskekrabbe (crab). No. 1766, Jomfruhummer (lobster). No. 1767, Nordsoreje (shrimp). No. 1768, Blamusling (mussel). No. 1769, Limfjordsosters (oyster).

*Die Cut Perf. 13¾ Syncopated*

**2017, Jan. 2 Litho.**

**Booklet Stamps Self-Adhesive**

| | | | | |
|---|---|---|---|---|
| **1765** | A596 8k multi | | 2.25 | 1.10 |
| **1766** | A596 8k multi | | 2.25 | 1.10 |
| **1767** | A596 8k multi | | 2.25 | 1.10 |
| **1768** | A596 8k multi | | 2.25 | 1.10 |
| **1769** | A596 8k multi | | 2.25 | 1.10 |
| *a.* | Booklet pane of 10, 2 each #1765-1769 | 22.50 | | |
| | *Nos. 1765-1769 (5)* | | 11.25 | 5.50 |

Heart With Gay Pride Flag Stripes — A597

Heart at: No. 1770, Top. No. 1771, Bottom.

*Die Cut Perf. 13¼ Syncopated*

**2017, Mar. 30 Litho.**

**Booklet Stamps Self-Adhesive**

| | | | | |
|---|---|---|---|---|
| **1770** | A597 8k multi | | 2.40 | 2.40 |
| **1771** | A597 8k multi | | 2.40 | 2.40 |
| *a.* | Booklet pane of 10, 6 #1770, 4 #1771 | 24.00 | | |

Aarhus, 2017 European Capital of Culture A598

Buildings in Aarhus: No. 1772, ARoS Art Museum. No. 1773, Moesgaard Museum. No. 1774, DOKK1 Culture Center. No. 1775, The Iceberg Apartment Complex. No. 1776, City Hall.

*Die Cut Perf. 13¼ Syncopated*

**2017, Mar. 30 Litho.**

**Booklet Stamps Self-Adhesive**

| | | | | |
|---|---|---|---|---|
| **1772** | A598 25k multi | | 7.25 | 7.25 |
| **1773** | A598 25k multi | | 7.25 | 7.25 |
| **1774** | A598 25k multi | | 7.25 | 7.25 |
| **1775** | A598 25k multi | | 7.25 | 7.25 |
| **1776** | A598 25k multi | | 7.25 | 7.25 |
| *a.* | Booklet pane of 10, 2 each #1772-1776 | 72.50 | | |
| | *Nos. 1772-1776 (5)* | | 36.25 | 36.25 |

Souvenir Sheet

Queen Margrethe II and Prince Henrik, 50th Wedding Anniversary — A599

**2017, May 15 Litho. *Perf. 13½***

| | | | |
|---|---|---|---|
| **1777** | A599 50k gold & multi | 15.00 | 15.00 |

See Faroe Islands No. 686, Greenland No. 754.

A600

A601

A602

A603

Summer Houses A604

*Die Cut Perf. 13¼ Syncopated*

**2017, June 15 Litho.**

**Booklet Stamps Self-Adhesive**

| | | | | |
|---|---|---|---|---|
| **1778** | A600 8k multi | | 2.50 | 2.50 |
| **1779** | A601 8k multi | | 2.50 | 2.50 |
| **1780** | A602 8k multi | | 2.50 | 2.50 |
| **1781** | A603 8k multi | | 2.50 | 2.50 |
| **1782** | A604 8k multi | | 2.50 | 2.50 |
| *a.* | Booklet pane of 10, 2 each #1778-1782 | 25.00 | | |
| | *Nos. 1778-1782 (5)* | | 12.50 | 12.50 |

Automobiles — A605

No. 1783: a, 1960 BMW Isetta 300. b, 1959 Volkswagen 1200 De Luxe. c, 1973 Citroen DS21 Pallas.

**2017, June 15 Litho. *Perf. 13x13¼***

| | | | |
|---|---|---|---|
| **1783** | A605 Sheet of 3 | 23.50 | 23.50 |
| *a.-c.* | 25k Any single | 7.75 | 7.75 |
| *d.* | Booklet pane of 1 #1783a | 15.00 | — |
| *e.* | Booklet pane of 1 #1783b | 15.00 | — |
| *f.* | Booklet pane of 1 #1783c | 15.00 | — |
| *g.* | Booklet pane of 1 #1783c + 4 invalid for postage progressive proofs of #1783 | 15.00 | — |
| | Complete booklet, #1783d, 1783e, 1783f, 1783g | 60.00 | |
| *h.* | As #1783, with Nordia 2017 emblem and text in sheet margin | 23.50 | 23.50 |

Complete booklet sold for 199k.

Issued: No. 1783h, 10/27.

A606

A607

A608

A609

Flowers — A610

***Die Cut Perf. 13¼ Syncopated***

**2017, Sept. 28** **Litho.**

**Booklet Stamps**

**Self-Adhesive**

| | | | | |
|---|---|---|---|---|
| **1784** | A606 8k multi | | 2.60 | 2.60 |
| **1785** | A607 8k multi | | 2.60 | 2.60 |
| **1786** | A608 8k multi | | 2.60 | 2.60 |
| **1787** | A609 8k multi | | 2.60 | 2.60 |
| **1788** | A610 8k multi | | 2.60 | 2.60 |
| *a.* | Booklet pane of 10, 2 each #1784-1788 | | 26.00 | |
| | *Nos. 1784-1788 (5)* | | 13.00 | 13.00 |

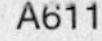

A611

A612

A613

A614

Art by Bjorn Wiinblad (1918-2006) A615

***Die Cut Perf. 13¼ Syncopated***

**2018, Jan. 2** **Litho.**

**Booklet Stamps**

**Self-Adhesive**

| | | | |
|---|---|---|---|
| **1789** | A611 9k multi | 3.00 | 3.00 |
| **1790** | A612 9k multi | 3.00 | 3.00 |
| **1791** | A613 9k multi | 3.00 | 3.00 |
| **1792** | A614 9k multi | 3.00 | 3.00 |
| **1793** | A615 9k multi | 3.00 | 3.00 |
| *a.* | Booklet pane of 10, 2 each #1789-1793 | 30.00 | |
| | *Nos. 1789-1793 (5)* | 15.00 | 15.00 |

Rose Varieties — A616

Designs: No. 1794, Jubilee Celebration. No. 1795, Rhapsody in Blue. No. 1796, Sekel. No. 1797, Ingrid Bergman. No. 1798, Crocus Rose.

***Die Cut Perf. 13¾ Syncopated***

**2018, Jan. 2** **Litho.**

**Booklet Stamps**

**Self-Adhesive**

| | | | |
|---|---|---|---|
| **1794** | A616 27k multi | 8.75 | 8.75 |
| **1795** | A616 27k multi | 8.75 | 8.75 |
| **1796** | A616 27k multi | 8.75 | 8.75 |
| **1797** | A616 27k multi | 8.75 | 8.75 |
| **1798** | A616 27k multi | 8.75 | 8.75 |
| *a.* | Booklet pane of 10, 2 each #1794-1798 | 87.50 | |
| | *Nos. 1794-1798 (5)* | 43.75 | 43.75 |

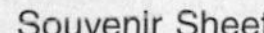

Souvenir Sheet

A617

No. 1799 — Stamps designed by Yoko Ono: a, Moon and "Dream." b, Sun and "Smile."

**2018, Jan. 2** **Litho.** ***Perf. 13¼x13¾***

| | | | |
|---|---|---|---|
| **1799** | A617 Sheet of 2 | 17.50 | 17.50 |
| *a.-b.* | 27k Either single | 8.75 | 8.75 |

## SEMI-POSTAL STAMPS

Nos. 159, 157 Surcharged in Red

**Wmk. Multiple Crosses (114)**

**1921, June 17** ***Perf. 14½x14***

| | | | |
|---|---|---|---|
| **B1** | A20 10o + 5o green | 27.50 | *60.00* |
| **B2** | A21 20o + 10o slate | 30.00 | *77.50* |
| | Set, never hinged | 167.50 | |

Crown and Staff of Aesculapius — SP1

**1929, Aug. 1** **Engr.**

| | | | |
|---|---|---|---|
| **B3** | SP1 10o yellow green | 4.50 | *7.00* |
| *a.* | Booklet pane of 2 | 27.50 | |
| **B4** | SP1 15o brick red | 9.00 | *12.00* |
| *a.* | Booklet pane of 2 | 32.50 | |
| **B5** | SP1 25o deep blue | 25.00 | *40.00* |
| *a.* | Booklet pane of 2 | 135.00 | |
| | *Nos. B3-B5 (3)* | 38.50 | *59.00* |
| | Set, never hinged | 100.00 | |

These stamps were sold at a premium of 5 öre each for benefit of the Danish Cancer Committee.

Dybbol Mill — SP2

**1937, Jan. 20** **Unwmk.** ***Perf. 13***

| | | | |
|---|---|---|---|
| **B6** | SP2 5o + 5o green | .60 | *1.40* |
| **B7** | SP2 10o + 5o lt brown | 2.25 | *9.00* |
| **B8** | SP2 15o + 5o carmine | 3.25 | *9.00* |
| | *Nos. B6-B8 (3)* | 6.10 | *19.40* |
| | Set, never hinged | 13.00 | |

The surtax was for a fund in memory of H. P. Hanssen, statesman.

Nos. 223a and B6, Nos. 229 and B7, Nos. 238A and B8 are found se-tenant in booklets. For booklet panes, see Nos. 223d, 229b and 238Al.

Queen Alexandrine — SP3

**1939-40** ***Perf. 13***

| | | | |
|---|---|---|---|
| **B9** | SP3 5o + 3o rose lake & red ('40) | .25 | .35 |
| *a.* | Booklet pane of 4 | 2.00 | 2.00 |
| **B10** | SP3 10o + 5o dk violet & red | .35 | .25 |
| **B11** | SP3 15o + 5o scarlet & red | .30 | *.50* |
| | *Nos. B9-B11 (3)* | .90 | 1.10 |
| | Set, never hinged | 1.35 | |

The surtax was for the Danish Red Cross.

Nos. 230 and B10 have been issued se-tenant in booklets. See No. 230b. In this pane No. 230 measures 23½x31mm from perf. to perf.

Crown Princess Ingrid and Princess Margrethe — SP4

**1941-43**

| | | | |
|---|---|---|---|
| **B12** | SP4 10o + 5o dk violet | .25 | .25 |
| *a.* | Booklet pane of 10 | 32.50 | |
| **B13** | SP4 20o + 5o red ('43) | .25 | .25 |
| | Set, never hinged | .60 | |

Surtax for the Children's Charity Fund.

No. 288 Surcharged in Red

**1944, May 11**

| | | | |
|---|---|---|---|
| **B14** | A48 10o + 5o violet | .25 | .25 |
| | Never hinged | .30 | |
| *a.* | Booklet pane of 10 | 27.50 | |

The surtax was for the Danish Red Cross.

**Catalogue values for unused stamps in this section, from this point to the end of the section, are for Never Hinged items.**

Symbols of Freedom SP5

Explosions at Rail Junction SP6

Danish Flag — SP7

**1947, May 4** **Engr.** ***Perf. 13***

| | | | |
|---|---|---|---|
| **B15** | SP5 15o + 5o green | .35 | .35 |
| **B16** | SP6 20o + 5o dark red | .35 | .35 |
| **B17** | SP7 40o + 5o deep blue | .85 | .85 |
| | *Nos. B15-B17 (3)* | 1.55 | 1.55 |

Issued in memory of the Danish struggle for liberty and the liberation of Denmark. The surtax was for the Liberty Fund.

For surcharges see Nos. B22-B23.

Princess Anne-Marie — SP8

**1950, Oct. 19** **Unwmk.**

| | | | |
|---|---|---|---|
| **B18** | SP8 25o + 5o rose brown | .55 | .50 |

The surtax was for the National Children's Welfare Association.

S. S. Jutlandia — SP9

**1951, Sept. 13** ***Perf. 13***

| | | | |
|---|---|---|---|
| **B19** | SP9 25o + 5o red | .65 | .60 |

The surtax was for the Red Cross.

No. 335 Surcharged in Black

**1953, Feb. 13**

| | | | |
|---|---|---|---|
| **B20** | A61 30o + 10o brown red | 1.50 | 1.50 |

The surtax was for flood relief in the Netherlands.

Stone Memorial — SP10

**1953, Mar. 26** ***Perf. 13***

| | | | |
|---|---|---|---|
| **B21** | SP10 30o + 5o dark red | 1.40 | 1.25 |

The surtax was for cultural work of the Danish Border Union.

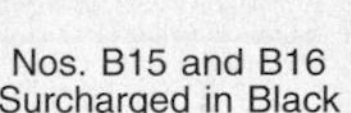

Nos. B15 and B16 Surcharged in Black

**1955, Feb. 17**

| | | | |
|---|---|---|---|
| **B22** | SP5 20o + 5o on No. B15 | 1.00 | .85 |
| **B23** | SP6 30o + 5o on No. B16 | 1.00 | .85 |

The surtax was for the Liberty Fund.

No. 341 Surcharged

**1957, Mar. 25**

| | | | |
|---|---|---|---|
| **B24** | A61 30o + 5o on 95o red org | .65 | .65 |

The surtax went to the Danish Red Cross for aid to Hungary.

No. 335 Surcharged in Black

**1959, Feb. 23**

| | | | |
|---|---|---|---|
| **B25** | A61 30o + 10o brown red | .80 | .90 |

The surtax was for the Greenland Fund.

Globe Encircled by Red Cross Flags — SP11

**1959, June 24 Engr.** ***Perf. 13***

**B26** SP11 30o + 5o rose red .50 .50
**B27** SP11 60o + 5o lt ultra & car .75 .75

Centenary of the Intl. Red Cross idea. The surtax was for the Red Cross. Crosses photogravure on No. B27.

Queen Ingrid — SP12

**1960, Oct. 25** **Unwmk.**

**B28** SP12 30o + 10o dark red 1.00 1.00

Queen Ingrid's 25th anniv. as a Girl Scout. The surtax was for the Scouts' fund for needy and sick children.

African Mother, Child — SP13

**1962, May 24**

**B29** SP13 30o + 10o dark red .75 1.00

Issued to aid underdeveloped countries.

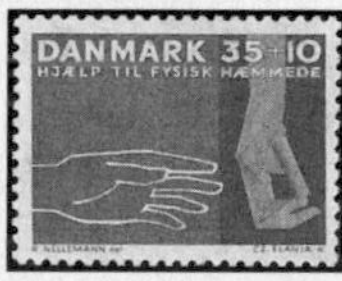


Healthy and Crippled Hands — SP14

**1963, June 24** ***Perf. 13***

**B30** SP14 35o + 10o dark red 1.10 1.10

The surtax was for the benefit of the Cripples' Foundation.

Old Bridge at Danish-German Border — SP15

**1964, May 28** **Engr.**

**B31** SP15 35o + 10o henna brn .85 .90

Surtax for the Danish Border Union.

Princesses Margrethe, Benedikte, Anne-Marie SP16

**1964, Aug. 24**

**B32** SP16 35o + 10o dull red .85 .75
**B33** SP16 60o + 10o dk bl & red 1.10 .95

The surtax was for the Red Cross.

Happy Child — SP17

**1965, Oct. 21 Engr.** ***Perf. 13***

**B34** SP17 50o + 10o brick red .65 .65

The surtax was for the National Children's Welfare Association.

"Red Cross" in 32 Languages and Red Cross, Red Lion and Sun, and Red Crescent Emblems SP18

**1966, Jan. 20 Engr.** ***Perf. 13***

**B35** SP18 50o + 10o red .65 .65

**Engraved and Photogravure**

**B36** SP18 80o + 10o dk bl & red .80 .80

The surtax was for the Red Cross.

"Refugees 66" — SP19

**1966, Oct. 24 Engr.** ***Perf. 13***

**B37** SP19 40o + 10o sepia .80 .80
**B38** SP19 50o + 10o rose red .80 .80
**B39** SP19 80o + 10o blue 1.60 1.60
*Nos. B37-B39 (3)* 3.20 3.20

The surtax was for aid to refugees.

Symbolic Rose — SP20

**1967, Oct. 12**

**B40** SP20 60o + 10o brown red .50 .55

The surcharge was for the Salvation Army.

Two Greenland Boys in Round Tower — SP21

**1968, Sept. 12 Engr.** ***Perf. 13***

**B41** SP21 60o + 10o dark red .65 .65

The surtax was for child welfare work in Greenland.

Princess Margrethe and Prince Henrik with Prince Frederik — SP22

**1969, Dec. 11**

**B42** SP22 50o + 10o brn & red .65 .65
**B43** SP22 60o + 10o brn red & red .65 .65

The surtax was for the Danish Red Cross.

Child Seeking Help — SP23

**1970, Mar. 13**

**B44** SP23 60o + 10o brown red .65 .65

Surtax for "Save the Children Fund."

Child — SP24

**1971, Apr. 29 Engr.** ***Perf. 13***

**B45** SP24 60o + 10o copper red .65 .65

Surtax was for the National Children's Welfare Association.

Marsh Marigold — SP25

**1972, Aug. 17**

**B46** SP25 70o + 10o green & yel .50 .55

Soc. and Home for the Disabled, cent.

Heimaey Town and Volcano — SP26

**1973, Oct. 17 Engr.** ***Perf. 13***

**B47** SP26 70o + 20o vio blue & red 1.00 1.00

The surtax was for the victims of the eruption of Heimaey Volcano, Jan. 23, 1973.

Queen Margrethe, IWY Emblem — SP27

**1975, Mar. 20 Engr.** ***Perf. 13***

**B48** SP27 90o + 20o red & cream .95 .80

International Women's Year 1975. Surtax was for a foundation to benefit women primarily in Greenland and Faroe Islands.

Skuldelev I SP28

Ships: 90o+20o, Thingvalla, emigrant steamer. 100o+20o, Liner Frederick VIII, c. 1930. 130o+20o, Three-master Danmark.

**1976, Jan. 22 Engr.** ***Perf. 13***

**B49** SP28 70 + 20o olive brown .75 .85
**B50** SP28 90 + 20o brick red .75 .85
**B51** SP28 100 + 20o olive green .85 1.10
**B52** SP28 130 + 20o violet blue .90 1.60
*Nos. B49-B52 (4)* 3.25 4.40

American Declaration of Independence, 200th anniv.

People and Red Cross — SP29

**1976, Feb. 26 Engr.** ***Perf. 13***

**B53** SP29 100o + 20o red & black .65 .65
**B54** SP29 130o + 20o bl, red & blk .80 .80

Centenary of Danish Red Cross.

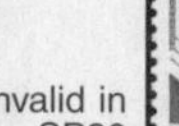

Invalid in Wheelchair — SP30

**1976, May 6 Engr.** ***Perf. 13***

**B55** SP30 100o + 20o ver & blk .65 .65

The surtax was for the Foundation to Aid the Disabled.

Mother and Child — SP31

**1977, Mar. 24 Engr.** ***Perf. 12½***

**B56** SP31 1k + 20o multicolored .80 .80

Danish Society for the Mentally Handicapped, 25th anniv. Surtax was for the Society.

Anti-Cancer Campaign SP32

**1978, Oct. 12 Engr.** ***Perf. 13***

**B57** SP32 120o + 20o red .65 .65

Danish Anti-Cancer Campaign, 50th anniversary. Surtax was for campaign.

Child and IYC Emblem — SP33

**1979, Jan. 25 Engr.** ***Perf. 12½***

**B58** SP33 1.20k + 20o red & brown .65 .65

International Year of the Child.

Foundation for the Disabled, 25th Anniversary SP34

**1980, Apr. 10 Engr.** ***Perf. 13***

**B59** SP34 130o + 20o brown red .65 .70

Children Playing Ball — SP35

**1981, Feb. 5 Engr.** ***Perf. 12½x13***

**B60** SP35 1.60k + 20o brown red .70 .90

Surtax was for child welfare.

Intl. Year of the Disabled — SP36

**1981, Sept. 10 Engr.** ***Perf. 12½x13***

**B61** SP36 2k + 20o dark blue 1.00 1.10

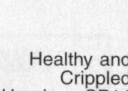

Stem and Broken Line — SP37

**1982, May 3 Engr. *Perf. 13***
**B62** SP37 2k + 40o dull red 1.10 1.20

Surtax was for Danish Multiple Sclerosis Society.

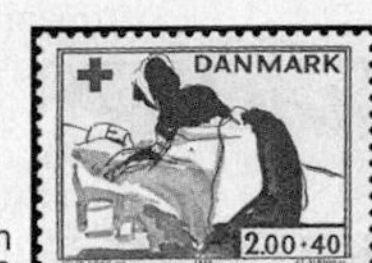

Nurse with Patient — SP38

**1983, Jan. 27 Engr.**
**B63** SP38 2k + 40o multicolored 1.40 1.40

1984 Olympic Games — SP39

**1984, Feb. 23 Litho. & Engr.**
**B64** SP39 2.70k + 40o multi 1.75 1.40

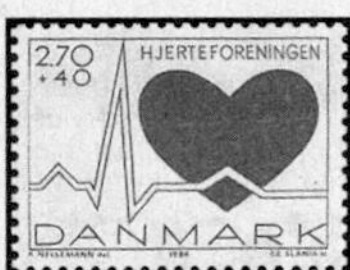

Electrocardiogram Reading, Heart — SP40

**1984, Sept. 6 Engr. *Perf. 12½***
**B65** SP40 2.70k + 40o red 1.75 2.00

Surtax was for Heart Foundation.

SP41

**1985, May 2 Litho. *Perf. 13***
**B66** SP41 2.80k + 50o multi 1.40 2.25

Liberation from German Occupation, 40th Anniv. Surtax for benefit of World War II veterans.

SP42

Design: Tapestry detail, by Caroline Ebbeson (1852-1936), former patient, St. Hans Hospital, Roskilade.

**1985, Oct. 3 Litho. & Engr.**
**B67** SP42 2.80k + 40o multi 1.40 1.90

Natl. Soc. for the Welfare of the Mentally Ill, 25th Anniv. Surtax benefited the mentally ill.

Danish Arthritis Assoc., 50th Anniv. — SP43

**1986, Mar. 20 Litho. *Perf. 13***
**B68** SP43 2.80k + 50o multi 2.25 2.25

Surtax for the Arthritis Assoc.

Poul Reichhart (1913-1985), as Papageno in The Magic Flute — SP44

**1986, Feb. 6 Litho. *Perf. 13***
**B69** SP44 2.80k + 50o multi 2.25 2.25

Surtax for the physically handicapped.

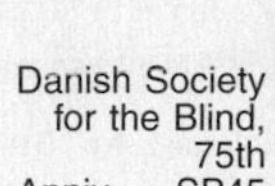

Danish Society for the Blind, 75th Anniv. — SP45

**Litho. & Engr.**

**1986, Feb. 20 *Perf. 13***
**B70** SP45 2.80k +50o blk, vio brn & dk red 2.25 2.75

Danish Assoc. of Epileptics, 25th Anniv. SP46

**1987, Sept. 24 Engr. *Perf. 13***
**B71** SP46 2.80k +50o dk red, brt ultra & dk grn 2.40 3.00

Folkekirkens Nodhjaelp Relief Organization — SP47

**1988, Mar. 10 Engr.**
**B72** SP47 3k +50o multicolored 2.25 2.75

Surtax for the relief organization.

Natl. Council for Unwed Mothers, 5th Anniv. — SP48

**1988, Sept. 22 Photo.**
**B73** SP48 3k +50o dk rose brn 2.50 3.25

Salvation Army — SP49

**1989, Feb. 16 Litho.**
**B74** SP49 3.20k +50o multi 2.50 3.00

Insulin Crystal — SP50

**1990, Aug. 30 Litho. *Perf. 13***
**B75** SP50 3.50k +50o multi 3.25 4.50

Danish Diabetes Assoc., 50th anniv.

Children's Telephone SP51

**1991, June 6 Engr. *Perf. 13***
**B76** SP51 3.50k +50o dark blue 2.40 2.75

Surtax benefits Borns Vilkar, children's welfare organization.

Danish Dyslexia Assoc., 50th Anniv. SP52

**Litho. & Engr.**

**1992, Aug. 27 *Perf. 13***
**B77** SP52 3.75k +50o multi 3.75 5.00

YMCA Social Work, 75th Anniv. — SP53

**1993, Aug. 19 Litho. *Perf. 13***
**B78** SP53 3.75k +50o multi 2.75 3.25

Prince Henrik, 60th Birthday — SP54

**Litho. & Engr.**

**1994, June 9 *Perf. 13***
**B79** SP54 3.75k +50o multi 2.10 3.00

Surtax for Danish Red Cross.

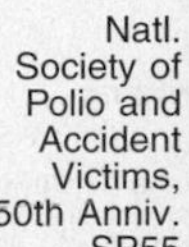

Natl. Society of Polio and Accident Victims, 50th Anniv. SP55

**1995, June 8 Litho. *Perf. 13***
**B80** SP55 3.75k +50o red 1.90 2.75

The AIDS Foundation — SP56

**1996, Oct. 10 Litho. *Perf. 13***
**B81** SP56 3.75k +50o red & black 3.50 2.25

Asthma-Allergy Assoc. — SP57

**1997, May 15 Litho. *Perf. 13***
**B82** SP57 3.75k +50o multi 2.50 2.75

Danish Cancer Society SP58

**1998, Sept. 3 Litho. *Perf. 13***
**B83** SP58 3.75k +50o multi 2.25 2.50

SP59

**1999, Aug. 25 Litho. *Perf. 13***
**B84** SP59 4k +50o blue & red 2.00 2.25

For the Alzheimer's Association.

SP60

**2000, Sept. 27 Engr. *Perf. 13***
**B85** SP60 4k +50o red & blue 1.60 2.00

For the Cerebral Palsy Association.

Amnesty International — SP61

**2001, Jan. 24 Engr. *Perf. 12¾***
**B86** SP61 4k +50o blk & red 2.25 2.25

LEV National Association SP62

**2002, Mar. 13 Engr. *Perf. 12¾***
**B87** SP62 4k + 50o multi, *greenish* 2.25 2.25

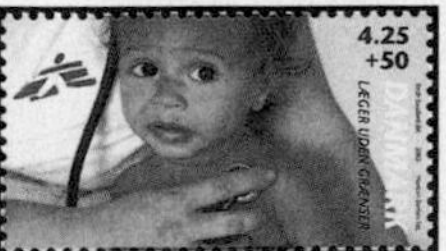

Doctors Without Borders SP63

**2003, Mar. 12 Litho. *Perf. 12¾***
**B88** SP63 4.25k +50o multi 1.60 1.25
Booklet, 10 #B88 16.00

Children's Aid Day — SP64

**2004, Jan. 14 Litho. *Perf. 12¾***

**B89** SP64 4.50k +50o multi 1.75 2.10
Booklet, 10 #B89 17.50

SOS Children's Villages SP65

**2005, Jan. 12 Litho. *Perf. 12¾***

**B90** SP65 4.50k +50o multi 2.40 2.75
Complete booklet, 10 #B90 24.00

Surtax was originally intended for an SOS Children's Village in Burundi, but surtax went to the relief fund for Dec. 26, 2004 tsunami victims. A sticker noting this change was to be applied to the front covers of the booklets.

Danish Refugee Council, 50th Anniv. SP66

**2006, Jan. 11 Engr. *Perf. 12¾***

**B91** SP66 4.75k +50o blk & red, *tan* 2.75 2.75
Complete booklet, 10 #B91 27.50

Crown Prince Frederik, Crown Princess Mary, and Prince Christian SP67

**2007, Jan. 10 Engr. *Perf. 13x13¼***

**B92** SP67 4.75k +50o multi 2.75 2.40
Complete booklet, 10 #B92 27.50

Surtax for Crown Prince Frederik and Crown Princess Mary's Fund for Charitable and Humanitarian Purposes.

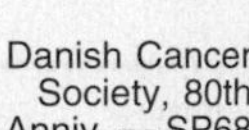

Danish Cancer Society, 80th Anniv. — SP68

**2008, Jan. 9 Engr. *Perf. 12¾***

**B93** SP68 5.50k +50o blk & red 2.50 2.40
Complete booklet, 10 #B93 25.00

Prince Henrik, Farm Field, Viet Nam, Emblem of Worldwide Fund for Nature (WWF) SP69

**2009, Jan. 7 Litho. *Perf. 13x13¼***

**B94** SP69 5.50k + 50o multi 2.75 3.25
Complete booklet, 10 #B94 27.50

Surtax for Worldwide Fund for Nature.

Danish Children's Cancer Foundation SP70

***Die Cut Perf. 13¼x13½***

**2010, Jan. 6 Litho.**

**Self-Adhesive**

**B95** SP70 5.50k +50o multi 2.40 2.50
*a.* Souvenir sheet of 4 9.75

**Booklet Stamp**

***Serpentine Die Cut 10***

**B96** SP70 5.50k +50o multi 2.40 2.50
*a.* Booklet pane of 12 29.00

Issued: No. B95a, 8/4.

Eight People SP71

**2011 Litho. *Die Cut Perf. 13½x13***

**Self-Adhesive**

**B97** SP71 5.50k+50o blk & red 2.50 2.50
**B98** SP71 8k+50o blk & red 3.50 3.50

**Booklet Stamps**

***Serpentine Die Cut 13½***

**B99** SP71 5.50k+50o blk & red 2.50 2.50
*a.* Booklet pane of 10 25.00
**B100** SP71 8k+50o blk & red 3.50 3.50
*a.* Booklet pane of 10 35.00
*b.* Sheet of 6 + 7 labels 21.00 21.00

Surtax for Danish Rheumatism Association. Issued: Nos. B97, B99, 1/6; Nos. B98, B100, 3/9. No. B100b, 8/4.

Crown Princess Mary — SP72

**2012, June 10 *Die Cut Perf. 13x13½***

**Self-Adhesive**

**B101** SP72 8k+50o multi 3.00 3.00

**Booklet Stamp**

***Serpentine Die Cut 13½***

**B102** SP72 8k+50o multi 3.00 3.00
*a.* Booklet pane of 10 + sticker 30.00

Surtax for Danish Heart Foundation.

**Crown Princess Mary Type of 2012**

***Serpentine Die Cut 13½***

**2012, June 10**

**Self-Adhesive**

**Stochastic Litho. Printing**

**B103** SP72 8k+50o multi 3.50 3.50

The black dots that make up the design on No. B102 are arranged in lines, but are randomly placed on No. B103. No. B103 was printed in sheets of 6.

Girl's Head — SP73

***Die Cut Perf. 13x13¼***

**2013-14 Litho.**

**B104** SP73 8k+1k multi 3.25 3.25

**Booklet Stamp**

***Serpentine Die Cut 13½***

**B105** SP73 8k+1k multi 3.25 3.25
*a.* Booklet pane of 10 32.50

**Self-Adhesive**

***Die Cut Perf. 13½x13***

**B106** SP73 9k+1k multi 3.75 3.75
*a.* Booklet pane of 10 37.50

Surtax for Save the Children charity. Issued: Nos. B104-B105, 5/27; No. B106, 1/2/14.

No. B106 was printed in sheets of 6. Surtax was for Save the Children charity.

Red Cross, 150th Anniv. — SP74

**2014-15 Litho. *Die Cut Perf. 13½***

**Self-Adhesive**

**B107** SP74 9k+1k gray & red 3.75 3.75
*a.* Booklet pane of 10 37.50
**B108** SP74 10k+1k gray & red 3.50 3.50
*a.* Booklet pane of 10 35.00

Surtax for Red Cross. Issued: No. B107, 6/3; No. B108, 1/2/15.

Worldwide Fund for Nature (WWF) — SP75

Sun, bird and: No. B109, Deer. No. B110, Farmhouse and wind generator.

***Die Cut Perf. 13¼ Syncopated***

**2015, May 7 Litho.**

**Self-Adhesive**

**B109** SP75 10k+1k multi 3.25 3.25
**B110** SP75 10k+1k multi 3.25 3.25
*a.* Booklet pane of 10, 6 #B109, 4 #B110 32.50

Surtax for Worldwide Fund for Nature. See Sweden No. B63.

**WWF Type of 2015**

Designs: No. B111, Like #B109. No. B112, Like #B110.

***Die Cut Perf. 13½ Syncopated***

**2016, Jan. 4 Litho.**

**Self-Adhesive**

**B111** SP75 8k+1k multi 2.60 2.60
**B112** SP75 8k+1k multi 2.60 2.60
*a.* Booklet pane of 5, 3 #B111, 2 #B112 13.00

## AIR POST STAMPS

Airplane and Plowman — AP1

**Wmk. Multiple Crosses (114)**

**1925-29 Typo. *Perf. 12x12½***

**C1** AP1 10o yellow green 27.50 *50.00*
**C2** AP1 15o violet ('26) 70.00 *110.00*
**C3** AP1 25o scarlet 45.00 *72.50*
**C4** AP1 50o lt gray ('29) 130.00 *315.00*
**C5** AP1 1k choc ('29) 105.00 *300.00*
*Nos. C1-C5 (5)* 377.50 *847.50*
Set, never hinged 975.00

Towers of Copenhagen — AP2

**Unwmk.**

**1934, June 9 Engr. *Perf. 13***

**C6** AP2 10o orange .75 *1.10*
**C7** AP2 15o red 2.60 *5.50*
**C8** AP2 20o Prus blue 2.60 *5.50*
**C9** AP2 50o olive black 2.60 *5.50*
**C10** AP2 1k brown 10.50 *19.00*
*Nos. C6-C10 (5)* 19.05 *36.60*
Set, never hinged 40.00

## LATE FEE STAMPS

LF1

***Perf. 14x14½***

**1923 Typo. Wmk. 114**

**I1** LF1 10o green 17.00 5.25
Never hinged 50.00
*a.* Double overprint *3,000.*

No. I1 was, at first, not a postage stamp but represented a tax for the services of the post office clerks in filling out postal forms and writing addresses. In 1923 it was put into use as a Late Fee stamp.

Coat of Arms — LF2

**1926-31**

**I2** LF2 10o green 13.50 1.00
**I3** LF2 10o brown ('31) 9.00 .70
Set, never hinged 60.00

**1934 Unwmk. Engr. *Perf. 13***

**I4** LF2 5o green .35 .30
**I5** LF2 10o orange .35 .30
Set, never hinged 1.30

## POSTAGE DUE STAMPS

Regular Issues of 1913-20 Overprinted

***Perf. 14x14½***

**1921, May 1 Wmk. 114**

**J1** A10 1o deep orange 2.50 7.00
**J2** A16 5o green 7.00 7.00
**J3** A16 7o orange 4.50 8.50
**J4** A16 10o red 30.00 17.00
**J5** A16 20o deep blue 22.50 14.00
**J6** A16 25o brown & blk 30.00 10.00
**J7** A16 50o claret & blk 13.50 8.50
*Nos. J1-J7 (7)* 110.00 72.00
Set, never hinged 300.00

**Same Overprint in Dark Blue On Military Stamp of 1917**

**1921, Nov. 23**

**J8** A16 10o red 15.00 20.00
Never hinged 37.50
*a.* "S" inverted 175.00 240.00
Never hinged 350.00

Numeral of Value — D1

**Typographed (Solid Panel)**

| **1921-30** | | *Perf. 14x14½* | | |
|---|---|---|---|---|
| **J9** | D1 | 1o orange ('22) | 2.00 | 2.50 |
| **J10** | D1 | 4o blue ('25) | 3.75 | 3.25 |
| **J11** | D1 | 5o brown ('22) | 3.25 | 2.50 |
| **J12** | D1 | 5o lt green ('30) | 3.75 | 2.50 |
| **J13** | D1 | 7o apple grn ('27) | 18.00 | 24.00 |
| **J14** | D1 | 7o dk violet ('30) | 50.00 | 40.00 |
| **J15** | D1 | 10o yellow grn ('22) | 4.50 | 2.25 |
| **J16** | D1 | 10o lt brown ('30) | 4.50 | 2.25 |
| **J17** | D1 | 20o grnsh blue ('21) | 3.50 | 3.25 |
| *a.* | | Double impression | 2,700. | |
| **J18** | D1 | 20o gray ('30) | 4.75 | 5.00 |
| **J19** | D1 | 25o scarlet ('23) | 4.50 | 6.00 |
| **J20** | D1 | 25o violet ('26) | 3.75 | 7.75 |
| **J21** | D1 | 25o lt blue ('30) | 7.25 | 10.75 |
| **J22** | D1 | 1k dk blue ('21) | 90.00 | 20.00 |
| **J23** | D1 | 1k brn & dk bl ('25) | 10.00 | 18.00 |
| **J24** | D1 | 5k purple ('25) | 22.50 | 18.00 |
| | | *Nos. J9-J24 (16)* | 236.00 | 168.00 |
| | | Set, never hinged | 615.00 | |

**Engraved (Lined Panel)**

| **1934-55** | | **Unwmk.** *Perf. 13* | | |
|---|---|---|---|---|
| **J25** | D1 | 1o slate | .30 | .30 |
| **J26** | D1 | 2o carmine | .35 | .30 |
| **J27** | D1 | 5o yellow green | .45 | .30 |
| **J28** | D1 | 6o dk olive ('41) | .45 | .30 |
| **J29** | D1 | 8o magenta ('50) | 2.00 | 4.00 |
| **J30** | D1 | 10o orange | .35 | .30 |
| **J31** | D1 | 12o dp ultra ('55) | .55 | 1.50 |
| **J32** | D1 | 15o lt violet ('54) | .85 | .30 |
| **J33** | D1 | 20o gray | .65 | .30 |
| **J34** | D1 | 25o blue | .75 | .30 |
| **J35** | D1 | 30o green ('53) | .50 | .30 |
| **J36** | D1 | 40o claret ('49) | .60 | .25 |
| **J37** | D1 | 1k brown | .80 | .30 |
| | | *Nos. J25-J37 (13)* | 8.60 | 8.75 |
| | | Set, never hinged | 14.50 | |

No. 96 Surcharged in Black

| **1934** | | **Wmk. 114** *Perf. 14x14½* | | |
|---|---|---|---|---|
| **J38** | A10 | 15o on 12o violet | 6.00 | 4.50 |
| | | Never hinged | 18.00 | |

## MILITARY STAMPS

Nos. 97 and 100 Overprinted in Blue

| **1917** | | **Wmk. 114** *Perf. 14x14½* | | |
|---|---|---|---|---|
| **M1** | A16 | 5o green | 19.00 | 40.00 |
| *a.* | | "S" inverted | 300.00 | 375.00 |
| **M2** | A16 | 10o red | 16.00 | 27.00 |
| *a.* | | "S" inverted | 225.00 | 375.00 |
| | | Set, never hinged | 70.00 | |
| | | #M1a, M2a, never hinged | 975.00 | |

The letters "S F" are the initials of "Soldater Frimaerke" (Soldier's Stamp).

For overprint see No. J8.

## OFFICIAL STAMPS

Small State Seal — O1

**Wmk. Crown (112)**

| **1871** | | **Typo.** *Perf. 14x13½* | | |
|---|---|---|---|---|
| **O1** | O1 | 2s blue | 275.00 | 200.00 |
| *a.* | | 2s ultra | 275.00 | 200.00 |
| *b.* | | Imperf | 450.00 | |
| **O2** | O1 | 4s carmine | 77.50 | 40.00 |
| *a.* | | Imperf | 450.00 | |
| **O3** | O1 | 16s green | 450.00 | 350.00 |
| *a.* | | Imperf | 450.00 | |

*Perf. 12½*

| | | | | |
|---|---|---|---|---|
| **O4** | O1 | 4s carmine | 6,500. | 650.00 |
| **O5** | O1 | 16s green | 450.00 | 600.00 |
| | | #O1-O3, O5, never hinged | 3,575. | |

Nos. O4-O5 values are for stamps with defective perfs.

*Nos. O1-O3 were reprinted in 1886 upon white wove paper, unwatermarked and imperforate. Value $10 each.*

| **1875** | | *Perf. 14x13½* | | |
|---|---|---|---|---|
| **O6** | O1 | 3o violet | 15.00 | 55.00 |
| **O7** | O1 | 4o grnsh blue | 18.00 | 6.25 |
| **O8** | O1 | 8o carmine | 15.00 | 2.00 |
| *a.* | | Imperf | — | |
| **O9** | O1 | 32o green | 32.50 | 30.00 |
| | | *Nos. O6-O9 (4)* | 80.50 | 93.25 |
| | | Set, never hinged | 245.00 | |

For surcharge see No. 81.

| **1899-02** | | *Perf. 13* | | |
|---|---|---|---|---|
| **O9A** | O1 | 3o red lilac ('02) | 4.50 | 15.00 |
| *c.* | | Imperf | 400.00 | |
| | | As "c," pair | 1,100. | |
| **O9B** | O1 | 4o blue | 3.75 | 4.50 |
| **O10** | O1 | 8o carmine | 20.00 | 26.00 |
| | | *Nos. O9A-O10 (3)* | 28.25 | 45.50 |
| | | Set, never hinged | 85.00 | |

For surcharge see No. 137.

| **1902-06** | | **Wmk. 113** | | |
|---|---|---|---|---|
| **O11** | O1 | 1o orange | 2.25 | 3.25 |
| **O12** | O1 | 3o red lilac ('06) | 1.50 | 1.00 |
| **O13** | O1 | 4o blue ('03) | 3.00 | 4.50 |
| **O14** | O1 | 5o green | 3.00 | .85 |
| **O15** | O1 | 10o carmine | 4.50 | 3.50 |
| | | *Nos. O11-O15 (5)* | 14.25 | 14.00 |
| | | Set, never hinged | 36.00 | |

| **1914-23** | | **Wmk. 114** *Perf. 14x14½* | | |
|---|---|---|---|---|
| **O16** | O1 | 1o orange | 1.25 | 2.75 |
| **O17** | O1 | 3o gray ('18) | 4.50 | 17.00 |
| **O18** | O1 | 4o blue ('16) | 30.00 | 60.00 |
| **O19** | O1 | 5o green ('15) | 3.00 | 2.25 |
| **O20** | O1 | 5o choc ('23) | 7.50 | 30.00 |
| **O21** | O1 | 10o red ('17) | 15.00 | 8.00 |
| **O22** | O1 | 10o green ('21) | 5.25 | 6.00 |
| **O23** | O1 | 15o violet ('19) | 20.00 | 37.50 |
| **O24** | O1 | 20o indigo ('20) | 22.50 | 20.00 |
| | | *Nos. O16-O24 (9)* | 109.00 | 183.50 |
| | | Set, never hinged | 250.00 | |

For surcharges see Nos. 185-191.

No. O20 is valued CTO.

Official stamps were discontinued Apr. 1, 1924.

## NEWSPAPER STAMPS

Numeral of Value — N1

| **1907** | | **Typo. Wmk. 113** *Perf. 13* | | |
|---|---|---|---|---|
| **P1** | N1 | 1o olive | 20.00 | 3.00 |
| **P2** | N1 | 5o blue | 30.00 | 15.00 |
| **P3** | N1 | 7o carmine | 18.00 | 1.25 |
| **P4** | N1 | 10o deep lilac | 57.50 | 5.00 |
| **P5** | N1 | 20o green | 45.00 | 1.50 |
| **P6** | N1 | 38o orange | 62.50 | 2.50 |
| **P7** | N1 | 68o yellow brown | 150.00 | 27.50 |
| **P8** | N1 | 1k bl grn & claret | 37.50 | 6.00 |
| **P9** | N1 | 5k rose & yel grn | 225.00 | 45.00 |
| **P10** | N1 | 10k bister & blue | 225.00 | 45.00 |
| | | *Nos. P1-P10 (10)* | 870.50 | 151.75 |
| | | Set, never hinged | 3,050. | |

For surcharges see Nos. 138-144.

| **1914-15** | | **Wmk. 114** *Perf. 14x14½* | | |
|---|---|---|---|---|
| **P11** | N1 | 1o olive gray | 18.00 | 2.00 |
| **P12** | N1 | 5o blue | 45.00 | 12.50 |
| **P13** | N1 | 7o rose | 45.00 | 3.00 |
| **P14** | N1 | 8o green ('15) | 45.00 | 7.00 |
| **P15** | N1 | 10o deep lilac | 75.00 | 3.00 |
| **P16** | N1 | 20o green | 300.00 | 3.25 |
| *a.* | | Imperf., pair | 1,200. | |
| **P17** | N1 | 29o orange yel ('15) | 75.00 | 8.00 |
| **P18** | N1 | 38o orange | 2,000. | 190.00 |
| **P19** | N1 | 41o yellow brn ('15) | 95.00 | 5.75 |
| **P20** | N1 | 1k blue grn & mar | 125.00 | 3.25 |
| | | *Nos. P11-P17,P19-P20 (9)* | 823.00 | 47.75 |
| | | Set, never hinged | 3,200. | |

For surcharges see Nos. 145-154.

## PARCEL POST STAMPS

These stamps were for use on postal packets sent by the Esbjerg-Fano Ferry Service.

Regular Issues of 1913-30 Overprinted

| **1919-41** | | **Wmk. 114** *Perf. 14x14½* | | |
|---|---|---|---|---|
| **Q1** | A10 | 10o green ('22) | 20.00 | 20.00 |
| **Q2** | A10 | 10o bister brn ('30) | 15.00 | 8.50 |
| **Q3** | A16 | 10o red | 45.00 | 90.00 |
| *a.* | | "POSFFAERGE" | 200.00 | 500.00 |
| **Q4** | A16 | 15o violet | 20.00 | 35.00 |
| *a.* | | "POSFFAERGE" | 250.00 | 525.00 |
| **Q5** | A16 | 30o orange ('22) | 22.50 | 47.50 |
| **Q6** | A16 | 30o dk blue ('26) | 4.50 | 8.00 |
| **Q7** | A16 | 50o cl & blk ('20) | 300.00 | 350.00 |
| **Q8** | A16 | 50o lt gray ('22) | 30.00 | 30.00 |
| *a.* | | 50o olive gray ('22) | 225.00 | 450.00 |
| **Q9** | A16 | 1k brn & bl ('24) | 60.00 | 30.00 |
| **Q9A** | A16 | 5k vio & brn ('41) | 3.75 | 3.25 |
| **Q10** | A16 | 10k ver & grn ('30) | 80.00 | 150.00 |
| | | **Engr.** | | |
| **Q11** | A17 | 1k yellow brn | 120.00 | 225.00 |
| *a.* | | "POSFFAERGE" | 1,500. | 2,600. |
| | | *Nos. Q1-Q11 (12)* | 720.75 | 997.25 |
| | | Set, never hinged | 1,750. | |

| **1927-30** | | | | |
|---|---|---|---|---|
| **Q12** | A30 | 15o red ('27) | 27.00 | 15.00 |
| **Q13** | A30 | 30o ocher ('27) | 18.00 | 20.00 |
| **Q14** | A30 | 40o yel grn ('30) | 27.00 | 17.00 |
| | | *Nos. Q12-Q14 (3)* | 72.00 | 52.00 |
| | | Set, never hinged | 180.00 | |

**Overprinted on Regular Issues of 1933-40**

| **1936-42** | | **Unwmk.** *Perf. 13* | | |
|---|---|---|---|---|
| **Q15** | A32 | 5o rose lake ('42) | .35 | .35 |
| **Q16** | A32 | 10o yellow org | 35.00 | 35.00 |
| **Q17** | A32 | 10o lt brown ('38) | 1.50 | 2.75 |
| **Q18** | A32 | 10o purple ('39) | .35 | .35 |
| **Q19** | A30 | 15o deep red | 1.50 | 2.00 |
| **Q20** | A30 | 30o blue, I | 4.50 | 7.50 |
| **Q21** | A30 | 30o blue, II ('40) | 15.00 | 32.50 |
| **Q22** | A30 | 30o org, II ('42) | .60 | 1.25 |
| **Q23** | A30 | 40o yel grn, I | 4.50 | 7.00 |
| **Q24** | A30 | 40o yel grn, II ('40) | 15.00 | 32.50 |
| **Q25** | A30 | 40o blue, II ('42) | .60 | 1.10 |
| **Q26** | A33 | 50o gray | 1.20 | 2.40 |
| **Q27** | A33 | 1k lt brown | 1.40 | 1.40 |
| | | *Nos. Q15-Q27 (13)* | 81.50 | 126.10 |
| | | Set, never hinged | 160.00 | |

**Catalogue values for unused stamps in this section, from this point to the end of the section, are for Never Hinged items.**

**Overprinted on Nos. 284, 286, 286B**

| **1945** | | | | |
|---|---|---|---|---|
| **Q28** | A47 | 30o orange | 4.00 | 2.40 |
| **Q29** | A47 | 40o blue | 1.90 | 1.90 |
| **Q30** | A47 | 50o gray | 2.00 | 2.00 |
| | | *Nos. Q28-Q30 (3)* | 7.90 | 6.30 |

**Ovptd. on #318, 309, 310, 312, 297**

| **1949-53** | | | | |
|---|---|---|---|---|
| **Q31** | A32 | 10o green ('53) | .65 | .50 |
| **Q32** | A61 | 30o orange | 5.50 | 2.25 |
| **Q33** | A61 | 40o dull blue | 4.50 | 2.25 |
| **Q34** | A61 | 50o gray ('50) | 24.00 | 1.25 |
| **Q35** | A55 | 1k brown ('50) | 2.40 | 1.50 |
| | | *Nos. Q31-Q35 (5)* | 37.05 | 7.75 |

Ovptd. on #335, 323, 336, 326, 397

| **1955-65** | | | | |
|---|---|---|---|---|
| **Q36** | A61 | 30o brown red | 2.25 | 2.25 |
| **Q37** | A61 | 40o gray | 2.25 | 2.25 |
| **Q38** | A61 | 50o aqua | 2.25 | 2.25 |
| **Q39** | A61 | 70o deep green | 2.25 | 2.25 |
| **Q40** | A55 | 1.25k orange ('65) | 10.00 | 12.00 |
| | | *Nos. Q36-Q40 (5)* | 19.00 | 21.00 |

Overprinted on Nos. 417 and 419

| **1967** | | **Engr.** *Perf. 13* | | |
|---|---|---|---|---|
| **Q41** | A86 | 40o brown | .65 | 1.25 |
| **Q42** | A86 | 80o ultra | .65 | 1.25 |

Nos. 224, 438, 441, 297-299 Overprinted

| **1967-74** | | **Engr.** *Perf. 13* | | |
|---|---|---|---|---|
| **Q43** | A32 | 5o rose lake | .60 | .50 |
| **Q44** | A86 | 50o brown ('74) | .65 | .90 |
| **Q45** | A86 | 90o ultra ('70) | 1.10 | 1.60 |
| **Q46** | A55 | 1k brown | 2.50 | 2.75 |
| **Q47** | A55 | 2k red ('72) | 2.90 | 4.25 |
| **Q48** | A55 | 5k dull bl ('72) | 3.50 | 4.50 |
| | | *Nos. Q43-Q48 (6)* | 11.25 | 14.50 |

Nos. Q44-Q45, Q47-Q48 are on fluorescent paper.

Overprinted on No. 541

| **1975, Feb. 27** | | | | |
|---|---|---|---|---|
| **Q49** | A161 | 100o deep ultra | 1.60 | 2.40 |

## DIEGO-SUAREZ

dē-ˌā-gō ˈswär-əs

LOCATION — A town at the northern end of Madagascar
GOVT. — French colony
POP. — 12,237

From 1885 to 1896 Diego-Suarez, (Antsirane), a French naval base, was a separate colony and issued its own stamps. These were succeeded by stamps of Madagascar.

100 Centimes = 1 Franc

Values for unused stamps are for examples with original gum as defined in the catalogue introduction except for Nos. 6-10 and J1-J2 which are valued without gum.

Stamps of French Colonies Handstamp Surcharged in Violet

**1890 Unwmk. *Perf. 14x13½***

| | | | | |
|---|---|---|---|---|
| **1** | A9 | 15c on 1c blk, *bl* | 300.00 | 100.00 |
| **2** | A9 | 15c on 5c grn, *grnsh* | 650.00 | 100.00 |
| **3** | A9 | 15c on 10c blk, *lav* | 300.00 | 92.50 |
| **4** | A9 | 15c on 20c red, *grn* | 650.00 | 80.00 |
| **5** | A9 | 15c on 25c blk, *rose* | 130.00 | 52.50 |

This surcharge is found inverted, double, etc. See the *Scott Classic Catalogue.* Counterfeits exist.

Ship Flying French Flag — A2

France — A5

Symbolical of Union of France and Madagascar
A3 A4

**1890 Litho. *Imperf.***

| | | | | |
|---|---|---|---|---|
| **6** | A2 | 1c black | 1,150. | 240.00 |
| **7** | A3 | 5c black | 1,100. | 200.00 |
| **8** | A4 | 15c black | 210.00 | 95.00 |
| **9** | A5 | 25c black | 225.00 | 110.00 |

Counterfeits exist of Nos. 6-9.

A6

**1891**

| | | | | |
|---|---|---|---|---|
| **10** | A6 | 5c black | 350.00 | 100.00 |

Excellent counterfeits exist of No. 10.

### Stamps of French Colonies Surcharged in Red or Black

No. 11

No. 12

**1892 *Perf. 14x13½***

| | | | | |
|---|---|---|---|---|
| **11** | A9 | 5c on 10c blk, *lav* (R) | 210.00 | 105.00 |
| *a.* | | Inverted surcharge | 475.00 | 400.00 |
| **12** | A9 | 5c on 20c red, *grn* | 190.00 | 72.50 |
| *a.* | | Inverted surcharge | 450.00 | 400.00 |

Stamps of French Colonies Overprinted in Black or Red

**1892**

| | | | | |
|---|---|---|---|---|
| **13** | A9 | 1c blk, *lilac blue* (R) | 32.50 | 20.00 |
| **14** | A9 | 2c brown, *buff* | 32.50 | 20.00 |
| **15** | A9 | 4c claret, *lav* | 55.00 | 45.00 |
| **16** | A9 | 5c green, *grnsh* | 120.00 | 80.00 |
| **17** | A9 | 10c black, *lavender* | 40.00 | 32.50 |
| *b.* | | Double overprint | 240.00 | 180.00 |
| **18** | A9 | 15c blue, *pale blue* | 32.50 | 20.00 |
| **19** | A9 | 20c red, *grn* | 40.00 | 32.50 |
| **20** | A9 | 25c black, *rose* | 36.00 | 20.00 |
| **21** | A9 | 30c brown, *bis* (R) | 1,300. | 925.00 |
| **22** | A9 | 35c black, *yellow* | 1,300. | 925.00 |
| **23** | A9 | 75c carmine, *rose* | 72.50 | 52.50 |
| *a.* | | Double overprint | | 400.00 |
| **24** | A9 | 1fr brnz grn, *straw* (R) | 80.00 | 52.50 |
| *a.* | | Double overprint | 240.00 | 210.00 |

**Inverted Overprint**

| | | | | |
|---|---|---|---|---|
| *13a* | A9 | 1c | 225.00 | 190.00 |
| *14a* | A9 | 2c | 225.00 | 190.00 |
| *15a* | A9 | 4c | | 325.00 |
| *16a* | A9 | 5c | 240.00 | 200.00 |
| *17a* | A9 | 10c | 240.00 | 200.00 |
| *20a* | A9 | 25c | 240.00 | 200.00 |
| *21a* | A9 | 30c | | 1,700. |
| *22a* | A9 | 35c | | 1,700. |

Navigation and Commerce
A10 A11

**1892 Typo. *Perf. 14x13½***
**Name of Colony in Blue or Carmine**

| | | | | |
|---|---|---|---|---|
| **25** | A10 | 1c black, *blue* | 2.00 | 2.00 |
| **26** | A10 | 2c brown, *buff* | 2.75 | 2.75 |
| **27** | A10 | 4c claret, *lav* | 3.25 | 3.25 |
| **28** | A10 | 5c green, *grnsh* | 6.50 | 6.50 |
| **29** | A10 | 10c black, *lavender* | 8.75 | 7.25 |
| **30** | A10 | 15c bl, quadrille paper | 16.50 | 11.00 |
| **31** | A10 | 20c red, *green* | 22.50 | 16.00 |
| **32** | A10 | 25c black, *rose* | 17.50 | 14.50 |
| **33** | A10 | 30c brown, *bister* | 22.50 | 16.00 |
| **34** | A10 | 40c red, *straw* | 27.50 | 21.00 |
| **35** | A10 | 50c carmine, *rose* | 45.00 | 35.00 |
| **36** | A10 | 75c violet, *org* | 52.50 | 45.00 |
| **37** | A10 | 1fr brnz grn, *straw* | 75.00 | 60.00 |
| | | *Nos. 25-37 (13)* | 302.25 | 240.25 |

Perf. 13½x14 stamps are counterfeits.

**1894 *Perf. 14x13½***

| | | | | |
|---|---|---|---|---|
| **38** | A11 | 1c black, *blue* | 2.00 | 2.00 |
| **39** | A11 | 2c brown, *buff* | 2.75 | 2.40 |
| **40** | A11 | 4c claret, *lav* | 3.25 | 2.75 |
| **41** | A11 | 5c green, *grnsh* | 5.50 | 4.75 |
| **42** | A11 | 10c black, *lavender* | 7.25 | 7.25 |
| **43** | A11 | 15c blue, quadrille paper | 12.00 | 6.50 |
| **44** | A11 | 20c red, *grn* | 20.00 | 13.50 |
| **45** | A11 | 25c black, *rose* | 12.00 | 9.50 |
| **46** | A11 | 30c brown, *bister* | 13.50 | 6.50 |
| **47** | A11 | 40c red, *straw* | 13.50 | 6.50 |
| **48** | A11 | 50c carmine, *rose* | 20.00 | 13.50 |
| **49** | A11 | 75c violet, *org* | 12.00 | 8.75 |
| **50** | A11 | 1fr brnz grn, *straw* | 27.50 | 24.00 |
| | | *Nos. 38-50 (13)* | 151.25 | 107.90 |

Bisected stamps of type A11 are mentioned in note after Madagascar No. 62.

For surcharges see Madagascar Nos. 56-57, 61-62.

Perf. 13½x14 stamps are counterfeits.

### POSTAGE DUE STAMPS

D1

D2

**1891 Unwmk. Litho. *Imperf.***

| | | | | |
|---|---|---|---|---|
| **J1** | D1 | 5c violet | 240.00 | 120.00 |
| **J2** | D2 | 50c black | 260.00 | 140.00 |

Excellent counterfeits exist of Nos. J1-J2.

Postage Due Stamps of French Colonies Ovptd. Like Nos. 13-24

**1892**

| | | | | |
|---|---|---|---|---|
| **J3** | D1 | 1c black | 130.00 | 72.50 |
| **J4** | D1 | 2c black | 130.00 | 65.00 |
| *a.* | | Inverted overprint | 450.00 | 300.00 |
| **J5** | D1 | 3c black | 130.00 | 65.00 |
| **J6** | D1 | 4c black | 130.00 | 60.00 |
| **J7** | D1 | 5c black | 130.00 | 72.50 |
| **J8** | D1 | 10c black | 40.00 | 32.50 |
| *a.* | | Inverted overprint | 460.00 | 450.00 |
| **J9** | D1 | 15c black | 36.00 | 32.50 |
| *a.* | | Double overprint | 575.00 | 500.00 |
| **J10** | D1 | 20c black | 200.00 | 135.00 |
| *a.* | | Double overprint | 600.00 | 500.00 |
| **J11** | D1 | 30c black | 120.00 | 60.00 |
| *a.* | | Inverted overprint | 450.00 | 300.00 |
| **J12** | D1 | 60c black | 1,200. | 775.00 |
| **J13** | D1 | 1fr brown | 2,800. | 1,500. |

## DJIBOUTI

jə-ˈbü-tē

LOCATION — East Africa
GOVT. — Republic
AREA — 8,958 sq. mi.
POP. — 447,439 (1999 est.)
CAPITAL — Djibouti

The French territory of Afars and Issas became the Republic of Djibouti June 27, 1977. For 1894-1902 issues with "Djibouti" or "DJ," see Somali Coast.

**Catalogue values for all unused stamps in this country are for Never Hinged items.**

**Afars and Issas Issues of 1972-1977 Ovptd. and Srchd. in Black, Dark Green, Blue or Brown**

No. 439

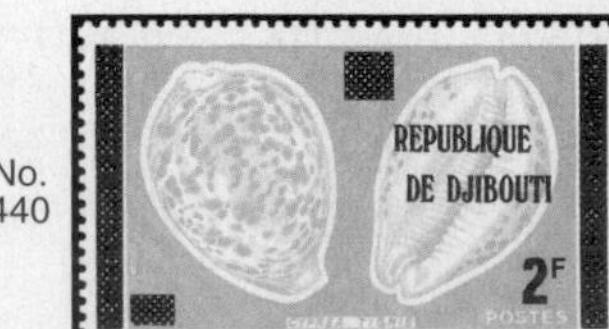

No. 440

No. 441

Nos. 442, 447

Nos. 443, 445

Nos. 444, 451

No. 446

Nos. 448, 453

No. 449

No. 450

No. 452

No. 454

No. 455

No. 456

**Printing and Perforations as Before**

**1977**

| | | | | |
|---|---|---|---|---|
| **439** | A63 | 1fr on 4fr (#358;B) | 3.00 | .25 |
| **440** | A81 | 2fr on 5fr (#433;B) | 3.00 | .25 |
| **441** | A75 | 5fr on 20fr (#421;B) | .40 | .25 |
| **442** | A70 | 8fr (#380;B) | .40 | .25 |
| **443** | A71 | 20fr (#387;DG) | 3.75 | 1.00 |
| **444** | A81 | 30fr (#434;B) | 5.00 | .80 |
| **445** | A71 | 40fr (#388;DG) | 4.50 | 1.25 |
| **446** | A71 | 45fr (#389;Bl) | 5.00 | 1.50 |
| **447** | A78 | 45fr (#428;B) | 8.00 | 1.50 |
| **448** | A72 | 50fr (#394;B) | 9.00 | 1.75 |
| **449** | A71 | 60fr (#391;Br) | 7.50 | 1.75 |
| **450** | A79 | 70fr (#430;B) | 8.00 | 2.50 |
| **451** | A81 | 70fr (#435;B) | 6.50 | 2.25 |
| **452** | A74 | 100fr (#418;B) | 12.00 | 3.50 |
| **453** | A72 | 150fr (#399;B) | 12.00 | 3.50 |
| **454** | A76 | 200fr (#422;B) | 7.00 | 4.50 |
| **455** | A80 | 200fr (#432;B) | 8.00 | 5.00 |
| **456** | A74 | 300fr (#419;B) | 10.00 | 6.50 |
| | | *Nos. 439-456,C106-C108 (21)* | 141.80 | 57.55 |

Map and Flag of Djibouti — A83

Design: 65fr, Map and flag of Djibouti, map of Africa, horiz.

**1977, June 27 Litho. *Perf. 12½***

| | | | | |
|---|---|---|---|---|
| **457** | A83 | 45fr multicolored | 1.50 | .70 |
| **458** | A83 | 65fr multicolored | 2.25 | .80 |

Independence, June 27.

A84

**1977, July 4**

| | | | | |
|---|---|---|---|---|
| **459** | A84 | 10fr Headrest, horiz. | .35 | .25 |
| **460** | A84 | 20fr Water Pipe | .70 | .25 |
| **461** | A84 | 25fr Pitcher | 1.00 | .45 |
| | | *Nos. 459-461 (3)* | 2.05 | .95 |

Ostrich — A85

**1977, Aug. 11 Litho. *Perf. 12½***

| | | | | |
|---|---|---|---|---|
| **462** | A85 | 90fr shown | 3.75 | .80 |
| **463** | A85 | 100fr Weaver | 4.75 | 1.25 |

Snail A86

Designs: 15fr, Fiddler crab. 50fr, Klipspringers. 70fr, Green turtle. 80fr, Priacanthus hamrur (fish). 150fr, Dolphinfish.

**1977 Litho. *Perf. 12½***

| | | | | |
|---|---|---|---|---|
| **464** | A86 | 15fr multicolored | .85 | .25 |
| **465** | A86 | 45fr multicolored | 1.60 | .40 |
| **466** | A86 | 50fr multicolored | 2.00 | .50 |
| **467** | A86 | 70fr multicolored | 2.25 | .60 |
| **468** | A86 | 80fr multicolored | 2.75 | .75 |
| **469** | A86 | 150fr multicolored | 4.50 | 2.00 |
| | | *Nos. 464-469 (6)* | 13.95 | 4.50 |

Issued: 45fr, 70fr, 80fr, 9/14; others, 12/5.

Pres. Hassan Gouled Aptidon and Djibouti Flag — A87

**1978, Feb. 12 Litho. *Perf. 13***

| | | | | |
|---|---|---|---|---|
| **470** | A87 | 65fr multicolored | 2.00 | .50 |

Charaxes Hansali — A88

Butterflies: 20fr, Colias electo. 25fr, Acraea chilo. 150fr, Junonia hierta.

**1978, Mar. 13 Litho. *Perf. 12½x13***

| | | | | |
|---|---|---|---|---|
| **471** | A88 | 5fr multicolored | .50 | .25 |
| **472** | A88 | 20fr multicolored | 1.25 | .25 |
| **473** | A88 | 25fr multicolored | 1.75 | .50 |
| **474** | A88 | 150fr multicolored | 7.00 | 1.75 |
| | | *Nos. 471-474 (4)* | 10.50 | 2.75 |

Necklace — A89

Design: 55fr, Necklace, diff.

**1978, May 29 Litho. *Perf. 12½x13***

| | | | | |
|---|---|---|---|---|
| **475** | A89 | 45fr pink & multi | 1.25 | .35 |
| **476** | A89 | 55fr blue & multi | 1.60 | .45 |

Bougainvillea A90

Flowers: 35fr, Hibiscus schizopetalus. 250fr, Caesalpinia pulcherrima.

**1978, July 10 Photo. *Perf. 12½x13***

| | | | | |
|---|---|---|---|---|
| **477** | A90 | 15fr multicolored | .55 | .25 |
| **478** | A90 | 35fr multicolored | 1.10 | .25 |
| **479** | A90 | 250fr multicolored | 6.50 | .90 |
| | | *Nos. 477-479 (3)* | 8.15 | 1.40 |

Charonia Nodifera — A91

Sea Shell: 80fr, Charonia variegata.

**1978, Oct. 9 Litho. *Perf. 13***

| | | | | |
|---|---|---|---|---|
| **480** | A91 | 10fr multicolored | 1.25 | .35 |
| **481** | A91 | 80fr multicolored | 4.00 | .95 |

Chaetodon A92

30fr, Yellow surgeonfish. 40fr, Harlequinfish.

**1978, Nov. 20 Litho. *Perf. 13x12½***

| | | | | |
|---|---|---|---|---|
| **482** | A92 | 8fr multicolored | .75 | .25 |
| **483** | A92 | 30fr multicolored | 1.40 | .35 |
| **484** | A92 | 40fr multicolored | 2.75 | .65 |
| | | *Nos. 482-484 (3)* | 4.90 | 1.25 |

Alsthom BB 1201 at Dock — A93

55fr, Steam locomotive 231. 60fr, Steam locomotive 130 and map of route. 75fr, Diesel.

**1979, Jan. 29 Litho. *Perf. 13***

| | | | | |
|---|---|---|---|---|
| **485** | A93 | 40fr multicolored | 1.25 | .25 |
| **486** | A93 | 55fr multicolored | 1.40 | .30 |
| **487** | A93 | 60fr multicolored | 1.75 | .30 |
| **488** | A93 | 75fr multicolored | 2.25 | .40 |
| | | *Nos. 485-488 (4)* | 6.65 | 1.25 |

Djibouti-Addis Ababa railroad.

Children and IYC Emblem — A94

Design: 200fr, Mother, child, IYC emblem.

**1979, Feb. 26 Litho. *Perf. 13***

| | | | | |
|---|---|---|---|---|
| **489** | A94 | 20fr multicolored | .50 | .25 |
| **490** | A94 | 200fr multicolored | 4.00 | 1.10 |

International Year of the Child.

Plane over Ardoukoba Volcano — A95

30fr, Helicopter over Ardoukoba Volcano.

**1979, Mar. 19**

| | | | | |
|---|---|---|---|---|
| **491** | A95 | 30fr multi, vert. | 1.00 | .35 |
| **492** | A95 | 90fr multi | 3.00 | .65 |

Rowland Hill, Postal Clerks, No. C109 — A96

100fr, Somali Coast #22, Djibouti #457, letters, Rowland Hill. 150fr, Letters hoisted onto ship, smoke signals, Rowland Hill.

**1979, Apr. 17 Litho. *Perf. 13x12½***

| | | | | |
|---|---|---|---|---|
| **493** | A96 | 25fr multicolored | .40 | .25 |
| **494** | A96 | 100fr multicolored | 2.00 | .45 |
| **495** | A96 | 150fr multicolored | 3.00 | .70 |
| | | *Nos. 493-495 (3)* | 5.40 | 1.40 |

Sir Rowland Hill (1795-1879), originator of penny postage.

View of Djibouti, Bird and Local Woman — A97

Design: 80fr, Map and flag of Djibouti, UPU emblem, Boeing 747, train and mail runner.

**1979, June 8 Litho. *Perf. 13x12½***

| | | | | |
|---|---|---|---|---|
| **496** | A97 | 55fr multicolored | 4.00 | .85 |
| **497** | A97 | 80fr multicolored | 4.75 | 1.10 |

Philexafrique II, Libreville, Gabon, June 8-17. Nos. 496, 497 each printed in sheets of 10 with 5 labels showing exhibition emblem.

Solanacea A98

Flowers: 2fr, Opuntia, vert. 15fr, Trichodesma. 45fr, Acacia etbaica. 50fr, Thunbergia alata, vert.

*Perf. 13x13½, 13½x13*

**1979, June 18**

**498** A98 2fr multicolored .25 .25
**499** A98 8fr multicolored .25 .25
**500** A98 15fr multicolored .50 .25
**501** A98 45fr multicolored 1.00 .25
**502** A98 50fr multicolored 1.25 .25
*Nos. 498-502 (5)* 3.25 1.25

Running — A99

Olympic Emblem and: 70fr, Basketball, vert. 200fr, Soccer.

*Perf. 12½x13, 13x12½*

**1979, Oct. 22 Litho.**

**503** A99 70fr multicolored 1.50 .25
**504** A99 120fr multicolored 2.25 .50
**505** A99 200fr multicolored 3.75 .75
*Nos. 503-505 (3)* 7.50 1.50

Pre-Olympic Year.

Cypraecassis Rufa — A100

Shells: 40fr, Lambis chiragra arthritica. 300fr, Harpa connaidalis.

**1979, Dec. 22 Litho. *Perf. 13***

**506** A100 10fr multicolored .25 .25
**507** A100 40fr multicolored 1.00 .25
**508** A100 300fr multicolored 6.50 1.50
*Nos. 506-508 (3)* 7.75 2.00

Rotary International, 75th Anniversary — A101

**1980, Feb. 19 Litho. *Perf. 13x12½***

**509** A101 90fr multicolored 2.25 .75
*a.* Souvenir sheet of 1 #509 15.00 15.00

Lions Club of Djibouti — A102

**1980, Feb. 19**

**510** A102 100fr multicolored 2.25 .75

Colotis Danae — A103

**1980, Mar. 17 *Perf. 13x13½***

**511** A103 5fr shown .75 .50
**512** A103 55fr Danaus chrysippus 3.50 1.50

Chess Players, Knight — A104

Chess Federation Creation: 75fr, Chess Game, Florence, 1493.

**1980, June 9 Litho. *Perf. 13***

**513** A104 20fr multicolored 1.25 .25
**514** A104 75fr multicolored 3.25 .35

Cribraria A105

**1980, Aug. 12 Litho. *Perf. 13***

**515** A105 15fr shown .75 .25
**516** A105 85fr Nautilius pompilius 2.75 .50

Alexander Fleming, Discoverer of Penicillin — A106

Design: 130fr, Jules Verne, French science fiction writer; earth, moon and spacecraft.

**1980, Sept. 1**

**517** A106 20fr multicolored 1.10 .35
**518** A106 130fr multicolored 3.25 .60

Capt. Cook and Endeavor — A107

Capt. James Cook Death Bicentenary: 90fr, Ships and Maps of voyages.

**1980, Nov. 20 Litho. *Perf. 13***

**519** A107 55fr multicolored 1.40 .65
**520** A107 90fr multicolored 2.25 .90

Souvenir sheets of 1 exist, perf. 12½x12. Value, each $10.

Angel Fish A108

**1981, Apr. 13 Litho. *Perf. 12½***

**521** A108 25fr shown 1.75 .25
**522** A108 55fr Moorish idol 3.25 .50
**523** A108 70fr Scad 3.75 1.50
*Nos. 521-523 (3)* 8.75 2.25

13th World Telecommunications Day — A109

**1981, May 17 Litho. *Perf. 13***

**524** A109 140fr multicolored 2.75 .70

Type 231 Steam Locomotive, Germany, 1958 and Amtrak, US, 1980 — A110

Locomotives: 55fr, Stephenson and his Rocket, Djibouti Railways 230 engine. 65fr, Type TGV, France, Type 962, Japan.

**1981, June 9 Litho. *Perf. 13***

**525** A110 40fr multicolored 1.50 .30
**526** A110 55fr multicolored 2.00 .35
**527** A110 65fr multicolored 2.50 .40
*Nos. 525-527 (3)* 6.00 1.05

Radio Amateurs Club — A111

**1981, June 25**

**528** A111 250fr multicolored 5.00 1.00

Prince Charles and Lady Diana — A112

**1981, June 29**

**529** A112 180fr shown 2.50 .75
**530** A112 200fr Couple, diff. 3.00 1.00

Royal Wedding.

Lord Nelson and Victory — A113

**1981, July 6 Litho. *Perf. 13x12½***

**531** A113 100fr multicolored 1.90 .45
**532** A113 175fr multicolored 3.25 .90

Lord Horatio Nelson (1758-1805).

Scout Tending Campfire — A114

**1981, July 16 Litho. *Perf. 13***

**533** A114 60fr shown 3.00 .70
**534** A114 105fr Scout giving sign 3.75 .80

28th World Scouting Conference, Dakar, Aug. (60fr); 4th Pan-African Scouting Conference, Abidjan, Aug. (105fr).

Pawn and Queen, Swedish Bone Chess Pieces, 13th Cent. — A115

130fr, Pawn, knight, Chinese, 19th cent., vert.

**1981, Oct. 15 Litho. *Perf. 13***

**535** A115 50fr shown 1.50 .35
**536** A115 130fr multicolored 3.00 .85

For overprints see Nos. 542-543.

Sheraton Hotel Opening — A116

**1981, Nov. 15 Litho. *Perf. 13x12½***

**537** A116 75fr multicolored 1.50 .45

For surcharge see No. 623.

Acacia Mellifera A117

**1981, Dec. 21 *Perf. 13***

**538** A117 10fr Clitoria ternatea, vert. .40 .25
**539** A117 30fr shown .80 .25
**540** A117 35fr Punica granatum 1.15 .25
**541** A117 45fr Malvaceous plant, vert. 1.40 .30
*Nos. 538-541 (4)* 3.75 1.05

See Nos. 558-560.

**Nos. 535-536 Overprinted**

**1981, Dec. Litho. *Perf. 13***

**542** A115 50fr multicolored 2.00 .50
**543** A115 130fr multicolored 4.00 1.00

World Chess Championship.

TB Bacillus Centenary A117a

**1982, Mar. 24 Litho. *Perf. 13***
**544** A117a 305fr Koch, slide, microscope 7.00 1.50

A117b

**1982, Apr. 8 Litho. *Perf. 13***
**545** A117b 125fr Ivory bishop 3.50 .75
**546** A117b 175fr Queen, pawn, 19th cent 4.25 1.25

1982 World Chess Championship.

A118

**1982, May 17**
**547** A118 150fr multicolored 3.00 .85

14th World Telecommunications Day.
For surcharge see No. 647.

Bus and Jeep — A119

**1982, July 27 Litho. *Perf. 13***
**548** A119 20fr shown .55 .25
**549** A119 25fr Dhow, ferry .70 .25
**550** A119 55fr Train, jet 1.50 .45
*Nos. 548-550 (3)* 2.75 .95

Shells from the Red Sea A120

10fr, Cypraea erythraeensis. 15fr, Conus sumatrensis. 25fr, Cypraea pulchra. 30fr, Conus inscriptus. 70fr, Casmaria ponderosa. 150fr, Cypraea exusta.

**1982, Nov. 20 Litho. *Perf. 12½***
**551** A120 10fr multicolored .45 .25
**552** A120 15fr multicolored .75 .30
**553** A120 25fr multicolored .90 .35
**554** A120 30fr multicolored 1.10 .40
**555** A120 70fr multicolored 2.25 .50
**556** A120 150fr multicolored 4.50 1.50
*a.* Strip of 6, #551-556 9.95 3.30
*Nos. 551-556 (6)* 9.95 3.30

See Nos. 563-567.

Intl. Palestinian Solidarity Day — A121

**1982, Nov. 29 Litho. *Perf. 13***
**557** A121 40fr multicolored 1.00 .25

**Local Flowers type of 1981**

Various flowers. 5fr, 55fr, vert.

**1983, Apr. 14 Litho. *Perf. 13***
**558** A117 5fr multicolored .25 .25
**559** A117 50fr multicolored 1.25 .40
**560** A117 55fr multicolored 1.40 .40
*Nos. 558-560 (3)* 2.90 1.05

World Communications Year — A123

**1983, June 20 Litho. *Perf. 13***
**561** A123 500fr multicolored 9.00 2.25

Conference of Donors, Nov. 21-23 — A124

**1983, Nov. 21 Litho. *Perf. 13x12½***
**562** A124 75fr multicolored 1.50 .40

**Shell Type of 1982**

15fr, Marginella obtusa. 30fr, Conus jickelli. 55fr, Cypraea macandrewi. 80fr, Conus cuvieri. 100fr, Turbo petholatus.

**1983, Dec. 20 Litho. *Perf. 12½***
**563** A120 15fr multicolored .50 .25
**564** A120 30fr multicolored 1.00 .25
**565** A120 55fr multicolored 1.60 .40
**566** A120 80fr multicolored 2.25 .50
**567** A120 100fr multicolored 2.50 .65
*Nos. 563-567 (5)* 7.85 2.05

Local Butterflies A125

5fr, Colotis chrysonome. 20fr, Colias erate. 30fr, Junonia orithyia. 75fr, Acraea doubledayi. 110fr, Byblia ilithya.

**1984, Jan. 24 Litho. *Perf. 13½x13***
**568** A125 5fr multicolored .50 .25
**569** A125 20fr multicolored 1.00 .25
**570** A125 30fr multicolored 1.50 .35
**571** A125 75fr multicolored 4.25 1.00
**572** A125 110fr multicolored 5.50 1.50
*Nos. 568-572 (5)* 12.75 3.35

Landscapes and Animals — A126

2fr, Randa Klipspringer. 8fr, Ali Sabieh, gazelles. 10fr, Lake Assal, oryx. 15fr, Tadjoura, gazelle. 40fr, Alaila Dada, jackal, vert. 45fr, Lake Abbe, warthog. 55fr, Obock, seagull. 125fr, Presidential Palace, bird.

**1984, Apr. 29 Litho. *Perf. 13***
**573** A126 2fr multicolored .25 .25
**574** A126 8fr multicolored .25 .25
**575** A126 10fr multicolored .25 .25
**576** A126 15fr multicolored .25 .25
**577** A126 40fr multicolored .75 .25
**578** A126 45fr multicolored .75 .30
**579** A126 55fr multicolored 1.90 .75
**580** A126 125fr multicolored 3.75 1.25
*Nos. 573-580 (8)* 8.15 3.55

For surcharges see Nos. 646, 657-658, 660.

Fire Prevention — A127

**1984, Sept. 9 Litho. *Perf. 13***
**581** A127 25fr Fire truck 1.00 .25
**582** A127 95fr Hook & ladder 3.25 .50
**583** A127 100fr Fire plane 3.25 1.00
*Nos. 581-583 (3)* 7.50 1.75

International Olympic Committee Membership A128

**1984, July 22 Litho. *Perf. 13***
**584** A128 45fr Runners .90 .35

Motor Carriage, 1886 A128a

**1984, Nov. 11 Litho. *Perf. 12½***
**585** A128a 35fr shown .80 .30
**586** A128a 65fr Cabriolet, 1896 1.60 .65
**587** A128a 90fr Phoenix, 1900 2.25 .95
*Nos. 585-587 (3)* 4.65 1.90

Gottlieb Daimler (1834-1900), pioneer automobile manufacturer.

Marie and Pierre Curie — A129

**1984, Dec. 3 Litho. *Perf. 12½***
**588** A129 150fr Pierre Curie 3.25 1.10
**589** A129 150fr Marie Curie 3.25 1.10

A130

Audubon Bicentenary — A130a

5fr, Merops albicollis. 15fr, Pterocles exustus. 20fr, Trachyphonus margaritatus somalicus. 25fr, Coracias garrulus.
200fr, Pandion haliaetus, vert.

**1985, Jan. 27 Litho. *Perf. 13***
**590** A130 5fr multi .75 .35
**591** A130 15fr multi 3.25 .85
**592** A130 20fr multi 3.75 1.00
**593** A130 25fr multi 4.50 1.10
*Nos. 590-593 (4)* 12.25 3.30

**Souvenir Sheet**
**Self-Adhesive**
***Perf. 12½***

**593A** A130a 200fr multi 26.00 26.00

No. 593A is airmail and printed on wood.

Intl. Youth Year — A131

**1985, Mar. 26 Litho. *Perf. 13***
**594** A131 10fr multicolored .30 .25
**595** A131 30fr multicolored .65 .30
**596** A131 40fr multicolored .90 .40
*Nos. 594-596 (3)* 1.85 .95

German Railways, 150th Anniv. — A132

Designs: 55fr, Engine No. 29, Addis Ababa-Djibouti Railways. 75fr, Adler, museum facsimile of the first German locomotive.

**1985, Apr. 22 Litho. *Perf. 13***
**597** A132 55fr multicolored 2.00 .65
**598** A132 75fr multicolored 3.00 .90

Scouting — A133

35fr, Planting saplings. 65fr, Hygiene, family health care.

**1985, May 23**

**599** A133 35fr multicolored 1.00 .45
**600** A133 65fr multicolored 1.75 .75

A134

80fr, Victor Hugo (1802-1885), Novelist. 100fr, Arthur Rimbaud (1854-1891), poet.

**1985, June 24** **Litho.**

**601** A134 80fr brt blue & slate 1.60 .80
**602** A134 100fr multicolored 2.00 1.00

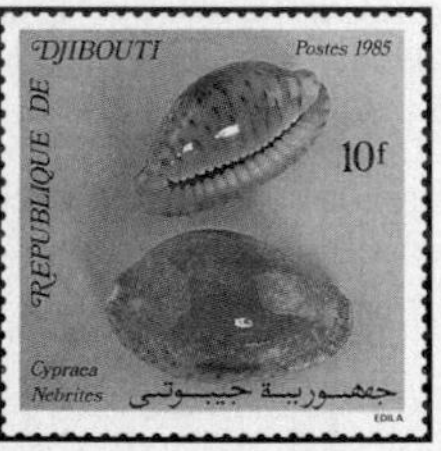


Sea Shells A135

**1985, July 15** **Litho.** ***Perf. 12½***

**603** A135 10fr Cypraea nebrites .40 .25
**604** A135 15fr Cypraea turdus .60 .25
**605** A135 30fr Conus acuminatus 1.50 .30
**606** A135 40fr Cypraea camelopardalis 1.75 .55
**607** A135 55fr Conus terebra 2.75 .70
*Nos. 603-607 (5)* 7.00 2.05

1st World Cup Marathon '85, Hiroshima A136

**1985, Sept. 2** ***Perf. 12½x13***

**608** A136 75fr Winners 1.25 .75
**609** A136 100fr Approaching finish 2.00 1.00

Halley's Comet — A137

Designs: 85fr, Bayeux Tapestry, Comet and Halley. 90fr, Vega I, Giotto space probes, map of planets, comet trajectory.

**1986, Jan. 27** **Litho.** ***Perf. 13***

**610** A137 85fr multicolored 1.50 .50
**611** A137 90fr multicolored 1.75 .85

ISERST Solar Energy Installation — A138

Designs: 50fr, Runners on beach. 150fr, Windmill, headquarters, power control station.

**1986, Mar. 20**

**612** A138 50fr multicolored .95 .40
**613** A138 150fr multicolored 2.75 1.25

Ships from Columbus's Fleet, 1492 — A139

**1986, Apr. 14**

**614** A139 60fr Santa Maria 1.75 .55
**615** A139 90fr Nina, Pinta 3.00 .95

Fish, Red Sea — A140

**1986, June 16** **Litho.** ***Perf. 13½x13***

**616** A140 20fr Elagatis bipinnulatus .65 .30
**617** A140 25fr Valamugil seheli .75 .45
**618** A140 55fr Lutjanus rivulatus 2.00 .75
*Nos. 616-618 (3)* 3.40 1.50

Public Buildings — A141

105fr, People's Palace. 115fr, Ministry of the Interior, Posts & Telecommunications.

**1986, July 21** **Litho.** ***Perf. 13***

**619** A141 105fr multicolored 1.75 .90
**620** A141 115fr multicolored 2.10 1.00

Sea-Me-We Building, Keyboard — A142

**1986, Sept. 8** **Litho.** ***Perf. 13***

**621** A142 100fr multicolored 2.00 .70

**Souvenir Sheet**

***Perf. 12½***

**622** A142 250fr multicolored 13.50 13.50

Southeast Asia, Middle East, Western Europe Submarine Cable System inauguration.

**No. 537 Surcharged**

**1986, Nov. 15** ***Perf. 13x12½***

**623** A116 55fr on 75fr multi 1.40 .50

Pasteur Institute, Cent. — A143

**1987, Feb. 19** **Litho.** ***Perf. 13***

**624** A143 220fr multicolored 5.00 1.60

Natl. Vaccination Campaign.

Edible Mushrooms A144

35fr, Macrolepiota imbricata. 50fr, Lentinus squarrosulus. 95fr, Terfezia boudieri.

**1987, Apr. 16** **Litho.** ***Perf. 13x12½***

**625** A144 35fr multicolored 1.50 .65
**626** A144 50fr multicolored 2.25 .85
**627** A144 95fr multicolored 3.00 1.50
*Nos. 625-627 (3)* 6.75 3.00

Wildlife A145

**1987, May 14** ***Perf. 12½x13***

**628** A145 5fr Hare .50 .25
**629** A145 30fr Dromedary 1.25 .30
**630** A145 140fr Cheetah 5.00 1.00
*Nos. 628-630 (3)* 6.75 1.55

1988 Olympics, Seoul and Calgary — A146

85fr, Pierre de Coubertin (1863-1937), founder of the modern Olympics, & lighting of the flame. 135fr, Ski jumping. 140fr, Running.

**1987, July 16** ***Perf. 13***

**631** A146 85fr multicolored 1.50 .55
**632** A146 135fr multicolored 2.50 .95
**633** A146 140fr multicolored 2.75 1.00
*Nos. 631-633 (3)* 6.75 2.50

Traditional Art — A147

**1988, Jan. 20** **Litho.** ***Perf. 13***

**634** A147 30fr Nomad's comb .60 .30
**635** A147 70fr Wash jug 1.25 .60

UN Universal Immunization by 1990 Campaign A148

**1988, Apr. 10** ***Perf. 12½***

**636** A148 125fr multicolored 2.50 1.00

16th Africa Cup Soccer Championships, Morocco — A149

**1988, Mar. 13** ***Perf. 13***

**637** A149 55fr Athletes, view of Rabat 1.20 .50

1988 Winter Olympics, Calgary — A150

**1988, May 7** **Litho.** ***Perf. 13***

**638** A150 45fr Ski jump 1.00 .40

Campaign Against Thirst A151

**1988, Sept. 10** **Litho.** ***Perf. 12½x13***

**639** A151 50fr multicolored 1.25 .45

Intl. Fund for Agricultural Development, 10th Anniv. — A152

**1988, Nov. 14** *Perf. 13*

**640** A152 135fr multicolored 2.50 1.00

Michel Lafoux Air Club, 40th Anniv. — A153

**1988, Dec. 6**

**641** A153 145fr 1948 Tiger Moth, 1988 Tobago-10 2.75 1.00

Marine Life A154

**1989, Jan. 20 Litho.** *Perf. 12½*

**642** A154 90fr Lobophyllia costata 2.25 .30
**643** A154 160fr Lambis truncata 4.25 1.40

Colotis protomedia A155

**1989, Feb. 15**

**644** A155 70fr multicolored 5.00 2.10

**Nos. 573 and 547 Surcharged**

**1989** *Perf. 13*

**646** A126 70fr on 2fr No. 573 2.25 .50
**647** A118 70fr on 150fr No. 547 2.25 .50

Issued: 646, 12/20; 647, 12/29.

Folk Dances — A157

**1989, Mar. 20**

**648** A157 30fr shown .50 .25
**649** A157 70fr multicolored, diff. 1.40 .50

Francolin of Djibouti — A159

**1989, Apr. 10 Litho.** *Perf. 12½*

**651** A159 35fr multicolored 2.50 .75

Rare Flora A160

**1989, June 12**

**652** A160 25fr Calotropis procera .90 .25

A161

**1989, Aug. 10 Litho.** *Perf. 13*

**653** A161 70fr multicolored 1.60 .75

Interparliamentary Union, cent.

A162

**1989, Oct. 1**

**654** A162 145fr multicolored 2.75 1.10

Intl. Literacy Year.

Petroglyph — A163

**1989, Nov. 18 Litho.** *Perf. 13*

**655** A163 5fr multicolored 1.00 .40

Girl — A164

**1989, Dec. 6**

**656** A164 55fr multicolored 1.60 .65

**Nos. 574, 576-577 Surcharged**

**1989-1990 Litho.** *Perf. 13*

**657** A126 30fr on 8fr multi .50 .30
**658** A126 50fr on 40fr multi 2.00 .55
**660** A126 120fr on 15fr multi 2.25 1.00
*Nos. 657-660 (3)* 4.75 1.85

Issue dates: 30fr, 12/20/89; 50fr, 7/3/90; 120fr, 3/17/90.

Water Conservation — A165

**1990, May 5 Litho.** *Perf. 11½*

**665** A165 120fr multicolored 2.25 .90

Traditional Jewelry A166

**1990, Mar. 10**

**666** A166 70fr multicolored 1.75 .45

Commiphora — A167

**1990, Feb. 20** *Perf. 12*

**667** A167 30fr multicolored .60 .35

Baskets — A168

**1990, July 3**

**668** A168 30fr multicolored .70 .40

A169

**1990, June 12** *Perf. 11½*

**669** A169 100fr multicolored 2.00 .80

World Cup Soccer Championships, Italy.

A170

**1990, Apr. 16** *Perf. 11½*

**670** A170 55fr shown 1.50 .45

20 kilometer race of Djibouti.

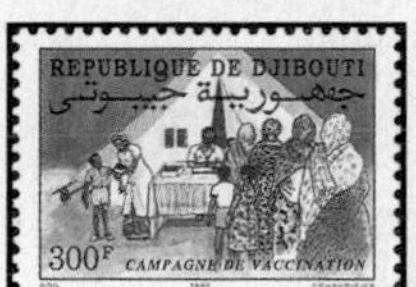


Vaccination Campaign A171

**1990, Aug. 22 Litho.** *Perf. 11½*

**Granite Paper**

**671** A171 300fr multicolored 4.75 2.00

Charles de Gaulle — A172

**1990, Sept. 16** **Granite Paper**

**672** A172 200fr multicolored 4.00 1.25

African Tourism Year — A173

**1991, Jan. 23 Litho.** *Perf. 13*

**673** A173 115fr multicolored 2.25 .80

Corals — A174

**1991, Jan. 28** *Perf. 12½*

**674** A174 40fr Acropora .90 .50
**675** A174 45fr Seriatopora hytrise 1.25 .50

Aquatic Birds — A175

10fr, Pelecanus rufescens. 15fr, Egretta gularis. 20fr, Ardea goliath, horiz. 25fr, Platalea leucorodia, horiz.

**1991, Feb. 12**

**676** A175 10fr multicolored .60 .25
**677** A175 15fr multicolored 1.25 .25
**678** A175 20fr multicolored 1.45 .30
**679** A175 25fr multicolored 1.60 .35
*Nos. 676-679 (4)* 4.90 1.15

UNO Development Conference — A176

**1990, Oct. 9 Litho.** *Perf. 11½x12*
**Granite Paper**

**680** A176 45fr multicolored 1.10 .45

Fossils — A177

**1990, Nov. 1 Granite Paper**

**681** A177 90fr pur, org & blk 5.25 1.75

Papio Hamadryas — A178

**1990, Dec. 6 Granite Paper**

**682** A178 50fr multicolored 1.75 .55

Pandion Haliaetus A179

**1991, Mar. 20 Litho.** *Perf. 12x11½*

**683** A179 200fr multicolored 5.00 1.60

Traditional Game A180

**1991, Apr. 4**

**684** A180 250fr multicolored 5.25 3.25

See No. 696.

Djibouti-Ethiopia Railroad — A181

**1991, May 25 Litho.** *Perf. 11½*

**685** A181 85fr multicolored 4.00 2.25

World Environment Day — A182

**1991, June 10**

**686** A182 110fr multicolored 2.75 .65

Philexafrique — A183

**1991, Jul. 16 Litho.** *Perf. 11½*

**687** A183 120fr Islands 3.25 1.75

Pre-Olympic Year — A184

**1991, Sept. 25**

**688** A184 175fr Handball 4.50 3.00

World Food Day — A185

**1991, Oct. 16 Litho.** *Perf. 11½x12*

**689** A185 105fr multicolored 2.50 1.10

Underwater Cable Network — A186

**1991, Nov. 28** *Perf. 12x11½*

**690** A186 130fr multicolored 3.00 1.00

Discovery of America, 500th Anniv. A187

**1991, Dec. 19 Litho.** *Perf. 11½*

**691** A187 145fr multicolored 3.25 1.60

Arthur Rimbaud (1854-1891) Poet and Merchant — A188

**1991-92** *Perf. 11½*

**692** A188 90fr Young man, ship 2.75 .90
**693** A188 150fr Old man, camels 3.00 .90

Issued: 90fr, 2/5/92; 150fr, 12/23/91.

Djibouti-Ethiopia Railroad — A189

Design: 250fr, Locomotive, map.

**1992 Litho.** *Perf. 12x11½*

**694** A189 70fr multicolored 2.75 1.10

**Souvenir Sheet**
***Perf. 13x12½***

**695** A189 250fr multicolored 5.25 5.25

Issue dates: 70fr, Feb. 2; 250fr, Jan. 30.

**Traditional Game Type of 1991**

**1992, Feb. 10** *Perf. 11½*

**696** A180 100fr Boys playing Go 2.10 .85

A190

**1992, June 9 Litho.** *Perf. 14*

**697** A190 80fr multicolored 2.10 1.25

1992 Summer Olympics, Barcelona.

A191

Traditional food preparation.

**1992 Litho.** *Perf. 14x13½*

**698** A191 30fr Pounding grain 1.25 .50
**698A** A191 45fr Preparing mofo 90.00 —
**699** A191 70fr Winnowing grain 1.25 .65
**699A** A191 75fr Cooking mofo 90.00 —

Issued: Nos. 698, 699, 4/20; No. 698A, 12/6.

Discovery of America, 500th Anniv. A192

**1992, May 16 Litho.** *Perf. 11½*

**700** A192 125fr multicolored 3.25 .95

African Soccer Championships A193

**1992, July 22** *Perf. 14*

**701** A193 15fr multicolored .75 .25

Intl. Space Year — A194

***Perf. 14x13½, 13½x14***

**1992, Sept. 28**

**702** A194 120fr Rocket, satellite 2.75 .85
**703** A194 135fr Astronaut, satellite, horiz. 2.75 .95

Wildlife—A195

**1992, Nov. 11** *Perf. 14*

**704** A195 5fr Dik-dik 1.25 .25
**705** A195 200fr Caretta caretta 5.00 1.60

Taeniura Lymma — A195a

*Perf. 11½x11¾*

**1990, Mar. 24** **Litho.**

**Panel Color**

| | | | | | |
|---|---|---|---|---|---|
| **705A** | A195a | 30fr | pink | — | — |
| **705B** | A195a | 70fr | yellow | — | — |
| **705C** | A195a | 100fr | green | — | — |
| **705D** | A195a | 120fr | lilac | — | — |

Nomad Girls in Traditional Costumes A196

**1993, Jan. 26** **Litho.** ***Perf. 13***

| | | | | | |
|---|---|---|---|---|---|
| **706** | A196 | 70fr | Girl beside hut | 1.75 | .45 |
| **707** | A196 | 120fr | shown | 2.75 | .75 |

White-eyed Seagull A197

**1993, Feb. 28** **Litho.** ***Perf. 12½***

| | | | | | |
|---|---|---|---|---|---|
| **708** | A197 | 300fr | multicolored | 5.25 | 1.75 |

Amin Salman Mosque — A198

**1993, Feb. 17** **Litho.** ***Perf. 13¾x14***

| | | | | | |
|---|---|---|---|---|---|
| **709** | A198 | 500fr | multicolored | *52.50* | *5.50* |

Handcrafts — A199

**1993, Apr. 23** **Litho.** ***Perf. 13¾x14***

| | | | | | |
|---|---|---|---|---|---|
| **710** | A199 | 100fr | Neck rest | 100.00 | 15.00 |
| **711** | A199 | 125fr | Sword | 100.00 | 15.00 |

Cercopithecus Aethiops — A200

**1993, May 29** **Litho.** ***Perf. 14¼x13½***

| | | | | | |
|---|---|---|---|---|---|
| **712** | A200 | 150fr | multi | 80.00 | 5.00 |

Organization of African Unity, 30th Anniv. — A201

*Perf. 14¼x13½*

**1993, June 20** **Litho.**

| | | | | | |
|---|---|---|---|---|---|
| **713** | A201 | 200fr | multi | 100.00 | 2.25 |

Water Carriers — A202

**1993, July 6** **Litho.** ***Perf. 14x13¾***

| | | | | | |
|---|---|---|---|---|---|
| **714** | A202 | 30fr | Woman | 100.00 | — |
| **715** | A202 | 50fr | Man | 100.00 | — |

Conquest of Space — A203

**1993, Sept. 30** **Litho.** ***Perf. 14x13¾***

| | | | | | |
|---|---|---|---|---|---|
| **716** | A203 | 90fr | multicolored | — | — |

A204

Traditional utensils.

**1993, Sept. 30** **Litho.** ***Perf. 13½***

| | | | | | |
|---|---|---|---|---|---|
| **717** | A204 | 15fr | Weyso | .45 | .25 |
| **718** | A204 | 20fr | Hangol | .90 | .25 |
| **719** | A204 | 25fr | Saqaf | 1.00 | .25 |
| **720** | A204 | 30fr | Subrar | 1.40 | .45 |
| | | | *Nos. 717-720 (4)* | 3.75 | 1.20 |

A205

Traditional musical instruments.

**1993, Nov. 10** **Litho.** ***Perf. 14***

| | | | | | |
|---|---|---|---|---|---|
| **721** | A205 | 5fr | Flute | 1.00 | 1.00 |
| **722** | A205 | 10fr | Drum | 1.00 | 1.00 |

Souvenir Sheet

Wedding of Japan's Crown Prince Naruhito and Masako Owada — A206

**1994, Jan. 10** **Litho.** ***Perf. 13x12½***

**Self-Adhesive**

| | | | | | |
|---|---|---|---|---|---|
| **723** | A206 | 500fr | multicolored | 22.50 | 22.50 |

No. 723 printed on wood.

20 Kilometer Race of Djibouti — A207

**1994** **Litho.** ***Perf. 11½***

| | | | | | |
|---|---|---|---|---|---|
| **724** | A207 | 50fr | multicolored | 2.50 | 1.00 |

Promotion of Breastfeeding A208

**1994**

| | | | | | |
|---|---|---|---|---|---|
| **725** | A208 | 40fr | shown | 1.90 | .40 |
| **726** | A208 | 45fr | Mother, infant | 2.10 | .40 |

Hassan Gouled Aptidon Stadium A209

**1994**

| | | | | | |
|---|---|---|---|---|---|
| **727** | A209 | 70fr | multicolored | 2.50 | 1.10 |

Stenella Longlrostris — A210

**1994, May 1** **Litho.** ***Perf. 11¾x11½***

| | | | | | |
|---|---|---|---|---|---|
| **728** | A210 | 120fr | multicolored | — | — |

World Housing Day — A211

**1994, May 9** **Litho.** ***Perf. 11½x11¾***

| | | | | | |
|---|---|---|---|---|---|
| **729** | A211 | 30fr | multi | *100.00* | — |

Eupodotis Senegalensis — A212

*Perf. 11¾x11½*

**1994, June 16** **Litho.**

| | | | | | |
|---|---|---|---|---|---|
| **730** | A212 | 10fr | multicolored | 180.00 | — |

1994 World Cup Soccer Tournament — A213

**1994, Sept. 7**

| | | | | | |
|---|---|---|---|---|---|
| **731** | A213 | 200fr | multicolored | *150.00* | — |

Dress of a Village Leader — A214

Design: 100fr, Traditional nomad costume.

*Perf. 11½x11¾*

**1994, Sept. 18** **Litho.**

| | | | | | |
|---|---|---|---|---|---|
| **732** | A214 | 100fr | multicolored | *100.00* | — |

*Perf. 11¾*

| | | | | | |
|---|---|---|---|---|---|
| **733** | A214 | 150fr | multicolored | *10.00* | — |

Canis Aureus A215

*Perf. 11¾x11½*

**1994, Sept. 28** **Litho.**

| | | | | | |
|---|---|---|---|---|---|
| **734** | A215 | 400fr | multi | *135.00* | — |

World Walking Day A216

**1994, Oct. 19** **Litho.** ***Perf. 11¾x11½***

| | | | | | |
|---|---|---|---|---|---|
| **735** | A216 | 75fr | multicolored | *150.00* | — |

A217

**1994, Nov. 26** **Litho.** ***Perf. 11¾***
**736** A217 55fr Book stand 150.00 —

A218

**1994, Dec. 6** **Litho.** ***Perf. 11½x11¾***
**737** A218 35fr Traditional dance 60.00 12.00

Souvenir Sheet

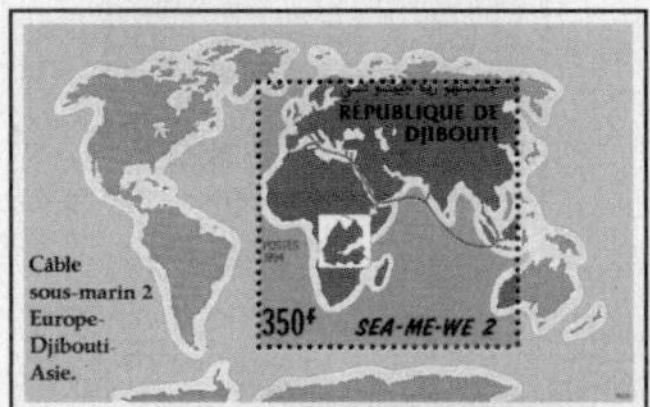


Sea-Me-We 2 Submarine Cable — A218a

**1994** ***Perf. 12½***
**737A** A218a 350fr multi *175.00* —

Volleyball, Cent. — A219

**1995, Feb. 25** **Litho.** ***Perf. 11¾***
**738** A219 70fr multicolored — —

United Nations, 50th Anniv. — A220

**1995, Feb. 25**
**739** A220 120fr multicolored — —

Fight Against Thirst A221

***Perf. 11¾x11½***
**1995, Mar. 29** **Litho.**
**740** A221 100fr multicolored — —

Threskiornis Aethiopica — A222

**1995, Apr. 5** **Litho.** ***Perf. 11¾***
**742** A222 50fr multicolored — —

A number has been reserved for a 30fr stamp in this set. The editors would like to examine it.

World Telecommunications Day — A223

***Perf. 11¾x11½***
**1995, June 10** **Litho.**
**743** A223 125fr multicolored *70.00* 1.25

Crocuta Crocuta A224

**1995, June 12** **Litho.** ***Perf. 11¾***
**744** A224 200fr multi *105.00* —

People Meeting Under Tree A225

**1995, July 3** **Litho.** ***Perf. 11¾x11½***
**745** A225 150fr multi *65.00* —

Nomads Around Fire — A226

**1995, Aug. 9** ***Perf. 11¾***
**746** A226 45fr multi *60.00* 12.00

FAO, 50th Anniv. — A227

**1995, Sept. 27** ***Perf. 11½x11¾***
**747** A227 250fr multi *70.00* 12.00

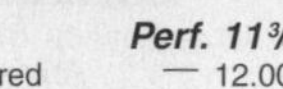

Traditional Costume — A228

**1995, Dec. 6** ***Perf. 11¾***
**748** A228 90fr multicolored — 12.00

African Development Bank, 30th Anniv. — A229

**1995. Dec. 18** ***Perf. 11¾x11½***
**749** A229 300fr multi *60.00* 12.00

African Soccer Cup — A230

**1996, Feb. 28**
**750** A230 70fr multicolored *180.00* —

Ostrich — A231

**1996, Apr. 23**
**751** A231 120fr multi *100.00* —

Leopard A232

**1996, May 6**
**752** A232 70fr multi 105.00 —

Amber Necklace — A233

**1996, June 13** **Litho.**
**753** A233 30fr multi 100.00 —

1996 Summer Olympic Games, Atlanta — A234

***Perf. 11½x11¾***
**1996, Sept. 21** **Litho.**
**754** A234 105fr multicolored *125.00* 12.00

Commicarpus Grandiflorus A236

**1996, Oct. 6** **Litho.** ***Perf. 11½x11¾***
**756** A236 350fr multi *60.00* 12.00

Djibouti Folklore — A237

**1996, Nov. 28** **Litho.** ***Perf. 11¾***
**757** A237 95fr multi *60.00* —

Legend of the Lion and Three Bulls A238

**1996, Nov. 28** **Litho.** ***Perf. 11¾***
**758** A238 95fr multi *70.00* 12.00

Children's Day A239

**1996, Dec. 17** ***Perf. 11¾x11½***
**759** A239 130fr multi *60.00* 12.00

A240

Legend of the Tortoise and the Fox: No. 760, Tortoise and fox at starting line. No. 761, Fox leaves tortoise behind. No. 762, Tortoise passes sleeping fox.

**1997, Jan. 17** ***Perf. 11¾***
**760** A240 60fr multi — —
**761** A240 60fr multi — —
**762** A240 60fr multi — —
*a.* Horiz. strip, #760-762 *135.00*

UNICEF, 50th Anniv. — A241

**1997, Feb. 9 Litho. *Perf. 11¾***
**763** A241 80fr Mother, child *50.00* 10.00
**764** A241 90fr Hands around globe *100.00* 12.00

Dancers — A242

**1997, May 14 Litho. *Perf. 11¾***
**765** A242 70fr multi *70.00* 12.00

Fortune Teller A243

Designs: 200fr, Fortune teller and woman. 300fr, Fortune teller, camel.

**1997, May 29 Litho. *Perf. 11¾***
**766** A243 200fr multi 70.00 12.00
**767** A243 300fr multi 70.00 12.00

Woman's Day — A244

**1997, May 30 Litho. *Perf. 11¾***
**768** A244 250fr multi *175.00 12.00*

Traditional Objects A245

Design: 30fr, Writing board, horiz. 400fr, Bowl and spoon.

**1997, June 5 Litho. *Perf. 11¾***
**769** A245 30fr multi 57.50 10.00
**770** A245 400fr multi 57.50 10.00

Telecommunications A246

Designs: 30fr, Arta post office. 100fr, Map, building with antenna and satellite dishes. 120fr, Ships, map showing submarine cable route, horiz.

**1997, June 27 Litho. *Perf. 11¾***
**771** A246 30fr multi — 12.00
**772** A246 100fr multi — 12.00
**773** A246 120fr multi — 12.00

Goats in Tree A247

**1997, July 26 Litho. *Perf. 11¾***
**774** A247 120fr multi 50.00 15.00

A248

Portrait of Diana: a, 125fr. b, 130fr. c, 150fr.

**1998, Mar. 25 Litho. *Perf. 13½***
**775** A248 Strip of 3, #a.-c. 7.00 7.00

Diana, Princess of Wales (1961-97).
No. 775 was isssued in sheets of 6 stamps.

Mother Teresa (1910-97) — A249

**1998 Litho. *Perf. 13½***
**776** A249 130fr multicolored 2.75 1.40

No. 776 was issued in sheets of 4.

Intl. Year of the Ocean A250

a, Tangara chilensis. b, Agalychnis callidryas. c, Delphinus delphis, megaptera novaeangliae. d, Cercopithecus aethiops (h). e, Laticaudia colubrina (i), sphyrna mokarran. f, Lactoria cornuta, delphinus delphis (g). g, Delphinus delphis (k). h, Aspidontus taeniatus, lo vulpinus. i, Sepioteuthis lessoniana. j, Prionace glauca (i), chaetodon ornatissimus. k, Eupagurus bernherdus. l, Octopus vulgaris (k).

**1998, Apr. 20 Litho. *Perf. 13½***
**777** A250 75fr Sheet of 12, #a.-l. 16.00 16.00

Mahatma Gandhi (1869-1948) A251

**1998, Apr. 20 Litho. *Perf. 11¾***
**778** A251 250fr multi *80.00 12.00*

Traditional Art — A252

**1998, Apr. 25 Litho. *Perf. 11½x11¾***
**779** A252 30fr multicolored *120.00* 12.00

Women's Rights and International Peace — A253

**1998, May 3 *Perf. 11¾x11½***
**780** A253 70fr multicolored *60.00* 12.00

World Water Day A254

**1998, May 10 Litho. *Perf. 11¾***
**781** A254 45fr multi *60.00* 12.00

1998 World Cup Soccer Championships, France — A255

**1998, June 10 Litho. *Perf. 11¾***
**782** A255 200fr multi 160.00 —

Marine Life — A256

***Perf. 11½x11¾, 11¾x11½***
**1998, July 2 Litho.**
**783** A256 20fr Octopus *135.00* —
**784** A256 25fr Shark, horiz. *135.00* —

Cats and Bush — A257

**1998, Aug. 30 *Perf. 11½x11¾***
**785** A257 120fr multi *135.00* —

World Telecommunications Day — A258

**1996, Sept. 27 Litho. *Perf. 11¾***
**786** A258 150fr multi 100.00 —

National Bank — A259

**1998, Sept. 30 Litho. *Perf. 11¾***
**787** A259 100fr multi 135.00 12.00

Flags and IGAD Emblem — A260

***Perf. 11½x11¾***
**1998, Sept. 30 Litho.**
**788** A260 85fr multi *60.00* —

Traditional Game Goos A261

**1998, Oct. 1 *Perf. 11¾x11½***
**789** A261 110fr multi *60.00* —

Fishing Port A262

**1998**
**790** A262 100fr multi *115.00* —

Maskali Island A263

**1998**
**791** A263 500fr multi *140.00* —

Fish A264

**1999** **Litho.** ***Perf. 13¼x13½***
**792** A264 70fr multi *115.00* —

Antelope — A264a

***Perf. 13¼x13½***
**1999, Mar. 16** **Litho.**
**792A** A264a 120fr multi 105.00 —

Djibouti Franc, 50th Anniv. A265

**1999**
**793** A265 100fr multi *60.00* —

World Telecommunications Day — A266

**1999**
**794** A266 125fr multi *55.00* —

Worldwide Fund for Nature (WWF) — A267

Phacochoerus africanus aeliani: a, Adult and young. b, Adult standing. c, Head. d, Adult walking.

**2000, Apr. 13** **Litho.** ***Perf. 14***
**795** A267 100fr Block of 4, #a-d 9.00 9.00

Wild Animals — A268

No. 796: a, Flamingo. b, Ostrich. c, Sifaka. d, Yellow-billed stork. e, Scarlet macaw. f, Dwarf puff adder. g, Toucan. h, Whooping crane.

**2000, Apr. 13**
**796** A268 100fr Sheet of 8, #a-h 20.00 20.00

Butterflies — A269

No. 797: a, Doxocopa cherubina. b, Heliconius charitonius. c, Cantonephele numili. d, Danaus gilippus. e, Morpho peleides. f, Heliconius doris.

No. 798, 250fr, Agraulis vanillae. No. 799, 250fr, Strymon melinus.

**2000, Apr. 13**
**797** A269 100fr Sheet of 6, #a-f 12.00 12.00

**Souvenir Sheets**

**798-799** A269 Set of 2 11.00 11.00

No. 797 contains six 28x42mm stamps.

Water Resources — A270

**2000, Apr. 13**
**800** A270 500fr multi 8.00 8.00

Trains and Landmarks — A271

No. 801: a, 5fr, Class OJ 2-10-2, China. b, 25fr, Eurostar, France-England. c, 15fr, Glacier Express, Switzerland. d, 40fr, Unidentified train. e, 35fr, Class WP 4-6-2, India.

No. 802, 110fr: a, Nord Chapelon Pacific, France. b, Class 23 2-6-2, Germany. c, Class GS-4 4-8-4, US. d, Class A4 4-6-2, Great Britain. e, Pacific 4-6-2, South Africa. f, Class HP, India.

No. 803, 120fr: a, VT601, Germany. b, ICIII Bo-Bo EMU, Netherlands. c, TGV, France. d, ETR 450, Italy. e, AVE, Spain. f, Bullet Train, Japan.

No. 804, 250fr, GM War Bonnet, US. No. 805, 250fr, Class 8 Pacific, Great Britain.

**2000, Apr. 28**
**801** A271 Horiz. strip of 5, #a-e 2.40 2.40

**Sheets of 6, #a-f**

**802-803** A271 Set of 2 20.00 20.00

**Souvenir Sheets**

**804-805** A271 Set of 2 9.50 9.50

Dancers A272

**2000, Apr. 28**
**806** A272 75fr multi *5.50 1.50*

Blacksmith — A273

**2000, May 14**
**807** A273 100fr multi 6.00 2.50

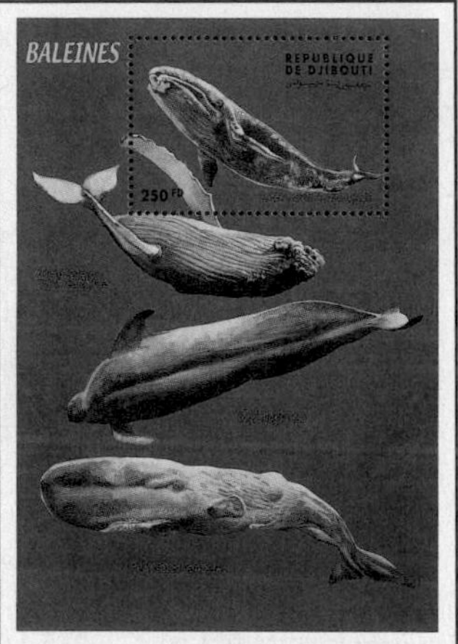


Marine Life — A274

No. 808, vert.: a, Dendrochirus biocellatus. b, Hippocampus. c, Amphiprion ocellaris, Amphiprion percula. d, Periclimenes imperator. e, Pomacnetridae. f, Octopus vulgaris.

No. 809, 50fr: a, Cephalopholis miniata. b, Ptereleotris hanae. c, Sphyraena genie. d, Tripterygion segmentatum. e, Odontaspididae. f, Cirrhitidae. g, Amphiprion. h, Capros aper. i, Balistidae. j, Trygonorhina fasciata. k, Cephalopholis. l, Corythoichthys ocellatus.

No. 810, 60fr: a, Lutjanus kasmira. b, Chaetodon fasciatus. c, Epinephelinae. d, Hypoplectrus gutavarius. e, Loligo opalescens. f, Diodontinae. g, Coelenterata. h, Sargocentron xantherythrum. i, Thalassoma lunare. j, Hemichromis bimaculatus. k, Dasyatis. l, Fromia monilis.

No. 811, 250fr, Eschrichtis robustus. No. 812, 250fr, Cheloniidae.

**2000, May 14**
**808** A274 55fr Sheet of 6, #a-f 10.00 10.00

**Sheets of 12, #a-l**

**809-810** A274 Set of 2 24.00 24.00

**Souvenir Sheets**

**811-812** A274 Set of 2 8.00 8.00

Camels and Tender A275

**2000, June 26**
**813** A275 35fr multi *5.25 .90*

Ships A276

Designs: 10fr, Thomas W. Lawson, 1902. 15fr, BT Global Challenge, 2000. 20fr, Reliance and Shamrock III, 1903. 25fr, Archibald Russell, 1905. 50fr, Greek merchantman, 8th cent. B.C.

No. 819, 130fr: a, Norman warship, 1066. b, Hanseatic cog, c. 1300. c, Santa Maria, 1492. d, Mary Rose, 1510. e, Golden Hind, 1577. f, Sovereign of the Seas, 1637.

No. 820:, 135fr: a, HMS Endeavour, 1768. b, USS Constitution, 1797. c, Chasse-Maree, 1800. d, Baltimore clipper, 1812. e, Lightning, 1853. f, Bluenose, 1921.

No. 821, 250fr, HM Yacht Britannia, 1893. No. 822, 250fr, Herzogin Cecilie, 1902.

**2000, June 26**
**814-818** A276 Set of 5 2.00 2.00

**Sheets of 6, #a-f**

**819-820** A276 Set of 2 25.00 25.00

**Souvenir Sheets**

**821-822** A276 Set of 2 8.00 8.00

Millennium A277

**2000, July 18**
**823** A277 125fr multi 2.75 2.75

Birds A278

**2000, Aug. 23**
**824** Horiz. strip of 5 2.75 2.75
*a.* A278 5fr Lanius excubitor .35 .35
*b.* A278 10fr Phoenicopterus minor .35 .35
*c.* A278 15fr Eupodatis senegalensis .35 .35
*d.* A278 40fr Noephron perchopterus .60 .60
*e.* A278 50fr Pterocles lichtensteinii .75 .75

Space Exploration — A279

No. 825, 100fr, vert.: a, John Glenn and Mercury capsule, 1962. b, Soyuz capsule, Apollo-Soyuz mission, 1975. c, Hubble Telescope, 1990. d, Apollo capsule, Apollo-Soyuz mission. e, Glenn at speaker's stand, 1974. f, Space Shuttle Columbia, 1981.

No. 826, 100fr, vert.: a, Apollo 11 service module, 1969. b, Telstar, 1962. c, Ariane 4, 1988. d, Apollo 11 lunar module. e, Neil Armstrong, 1969. f, Splashdown of Apollo 11, 1969.

No. 827, 200fr, Astronaut on moon saluting. No. 828, 250fr, Astronauts conducting experiments on moon. No. 829, 250fr, Space Shuttle Challenger.

**2000, Aug. 23** **Sheets of 6, #a-f**
**825-826** A279 Set of 2 20.00 20.00

**Souvenir Sheets**

**827-829** A279 Set of 3 12.00 12.00

2000 Summer Olympics, Sydney A280

Olympic flame, flag and: 80fr, Runner. 90fr, Tennis player.

**2000** ***Perf. 14***
**830-831** A280 Set of 2 4.00 4.00

Unknown Soldier Monument—A280a

**2004, Apr. 18** **Litho.** ***Perf. 13x12¾***

| | | | | |
|---|---|---|---|---|
| **832** | A280a | 175fr multi | 40.00 | 20.00 |

Independencc, 27th Anniv. — A281

**2004, June 27** **Litho.** ***Perf. 13***

| | | | | |
|---|---|---|---|---|
| **833** | A281 | 45fr multi | — | — |

Dragon Tree A282

Pregnant Woman at Hospital — A283

Camel Caravan A284

Natl. Union of Djibouti Women — A285

National Arms A286

***Perf. 12¾x13, 13x12¾***

**2004, Dec. 18** **Litho.**

| | | | | |
|---|---|---|---|---|
| **834** | A282 | 15fr multi | 30.00 | 20.00 |
| **835** | A283 | 25fr multi | 30.00 | 20.00 |
| **836** | A284 | 45fr multi | 30.00 | 20.00 |
| **837** | A285 | 70fr multi | 30.00 | 20.00 |
| **838** | A286 | 100fr multi | 20.00 | 20.00 |
| | *Nos. 834-838 (5)* | | 140.00 | 100.00 |

Friendship Between Djibouti and People's Republic of China, 25th Anniv.

Designs: 5fr, Djibouti Electricity Building. 10fr, Hassan Gouled Stadium. 15fr, Djibouti Central Bank. 30fr, People's Palace. 45fr, Ministry of Foreign Affairs Building.

**2004, Dec. 27** ***Perf. 12***

| | | | | |
|---|---|---|---|---|
| **839-843** | A286a | Set of 5 | 100.00 | 100.00 |

Items commemorating the death of Pope John Paul II were declared as "fraudulent" by Djibouti Post.

2006 World Cup Soccer Championships, Germany — A287

**2005, June 8** **Litho.** ***Perf. 13***

| | | | | |
|---|---|---|---|---|
| **844** | A287 | 100fr multi | *80.00* | — |

Tanker in Port of Doraleh — A288

**2006, Nov. 6** **Litho.** ***Perf. 13***

| | | | | |
|---|---|---|---|---|
| **845** | A288 | 120fr multi | *25.00* | — |

Printed in sheets of 4.

Common Market for Eastern and Southern Africa Summit, Djibouti — A289

**2006, Nov. 6** **Litho.** ***Perf. 13¼x13***

| | | | | |
|---|---|---|---|---|
| **846** | A289 | 150fr multi | 25.00 | — |

Djibouti Chamber of Commerce, Cent. — A290

**2007** **Litho.** ***Perf. 12¾***

| | | | | |
|---|---|---|---|---|
| **847** | A290 | 50fr multi | — | — |
| *a.* | | Souvenir sheet of 2 | — | — |

Independence, 30th Anniv. — A291

**2007, June 27** **Litho.** ***Perf. 13***

| | | | | |
|---|---|---|---|---|
| **848** | A291 | 75fr multi | 25.00 | — |
| *a.* | | Souvenir sheet of 2 | 50.00 | — |

Mahamoud Harbi (1921-60), Politician — A292

**2007, Aug. 17** **Litho.** ***Perf. 13x12¾***

| | | | | |
|---|---|---|---|---|
| **849** | A292 | 165fr multi | 30.00 | 5.00 |

Indo-Suez Red Sea Bank — A293

**2008, Oct. 19** **Litho.** ***Perf. 13x13½***

| | | | |
|---|---|---|---|
| **850** | A293 | 220fr multi | — |

2010 World Cup Soccer Championships, South Africa — A295

**2010, May** **Litho.** ***Perf. 13***

| | | | | |
|---|---|---|---|---|
| **852** | A295 | 105fr multi | 25.00 | — |

Djibouti postal authorities have declared "illegal" the following items:

Sheets of 8 stamps of various values: Mushrooms

Sheets of 6 stamps of various values: Fire trucks and Scouts (3 different)

Sheets of 6 700f stamps: Butterflies and Orchids, Butterflies and Scouts, Trains

Sheets of 6 300f stamps: Birds

Sheets of 4 800f stamps: Bonsai

Sheets of 4 700f stamps: Dogs (4 different), Cats (4 different), Babe Ruth and Tiger Woods, Dinosaurs

Sheets of 2 stamps of various values: Fire trucks (2 different).

2014 Africa Internet Summit, Djibouti — A296

**2014** **Litho.** ***Perf. 13***

| | | | | |
|---|---|---|---|---|
| **853** | A296 | 170fr multi | — | — |

A297

A298

A299

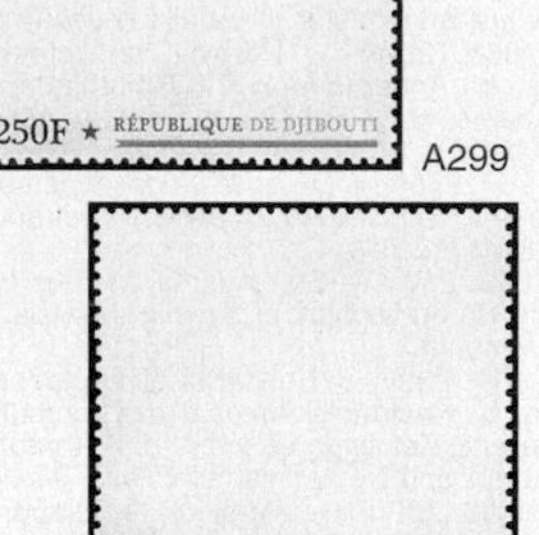

Personalized Stamps — A300

**2016, Jan. 25** **Litho.** ***Perf. 13¼x13***

| | | | | |
|---|---|---|---|---|
| **854** | A297 | 250fr multi | 3.00 | 3.00 |
| **855** | A298 | 250fr multi | 3.00 | 3.00 |
| **856** | A299 | 250fr multi | 3.00 | 3.00 |
| **857** | A300 | 250fr multi | 3.00 | 3.00 |
| | *Nos. 854-857 (4)* | | 12.00 | 12.00 |

Nos. 854-857 were each printed in sheets of 16 that could be personalized. A generic image showing Santa Claus with the inscription "Bonne Année 2016!" was made available. Values are for stamps with or without any printed vignette.

Fauna — A301

A302

No. 858, 260fr — Primates: a, Lemur catta. b, Leontopithecus rosalia. c, Macaca fuscata. d, Mandrillus sphinx.

No. 859, 260fr — Bats: a, Plecotus auritus. b, Erophylla sezekorni. c, Sturnira lilium. d, Desmodus rotundus.

No. 860, 260fr — Wild cats: a, Panthera tigris. b, Panthera pardus melas. c, Panthera onca. d, Panthera leo.

No. 861, 260fr — Lions: a, Panthera leo nubica. b, Panthera leo bleyenberghi. c, Panthera leo leo. d, Panthera leo azandica.

No. 862, 260fr — Dugong dugon: a, One dugong surfacing, fish at LR. b, Two dugongs, and calf. c, Dugong swimming, surrounded by fish. d, One dugong on sea floor, two fish at UL.

No. 863, 260fr — Dolphins: a, Delphinus capensis. b, Lagenorhynchus obscurus. c, Stenella frontalis. d, Delphinus delphis.

No. 864, 260fr — Whales: a, Delphinapterus leucas. b, Megaptera novaeangliae. c, Eubalaena australis. d, Physeter macrocephalus.

No. 865, 260fr — Eagles: a, Lophaetus occipitalis. b, Geranoaetus melanoleucus. c, Haliaeetus leucogaster. d, Aquila heliaca.

No. 866, 260fr — Parrots: a, Eclectus roratus. b, Anodorhynchus hyacinthinus. c, Conuropsis carolinensis. d, Trichoglossus moluccanus.

No. 867, 260fr — Owls: a, Megascops asio. b, Pulsatrix perspicillata. c, Bubo sumatranus. d, Ptilopsis leucotis.

No. 868, 260fr — Starlings: a, Sturnus vulgaris. b, Spreo fischeri. c, Sturnia sinensis. d, Mino dumontii.

No. 869, 260fr — Sunbirds: a, Leptocoma minima. b, Nectarinia famosa. c, Leptocoma sperata and Aetopyga siparaja. d, Anthreptes malacensis and Nectarinia tacazze.

No. 870, 260fr — Warblers: a, Lioparus chrysotis. b, Psittiparus gularis. c, Sylvia rueppelli. d, Parophasma galinieri.

No. 871, 260fr — Butterflies: a, Limenitis archippus. b, Apatura iris. c, Teinopalpus imperialis. d, Iphiclides podalirius.

No. 872, 260fr — Turtles: a, Terrapene carolina bauri. b, Chelonoidis nigra. c, Testudo graeca. d, Stigmochelys pardalis.

No. 873, 260fr — Snakes: a, Bitis arietans. b, Dispholidus typus. c, Echis pyramidum. d, Atractaspis fallax.

No. 874, 260fr — Crocodiles: a, Crocodylus siamensis. b, Crocodylus porosus. c, Crocodylus rhombifer. d, Crocodylus acutus.

No. 875, 260fr — Chameleons: a, Chamaeleo calyptratus. b, Chameleon hoehnelii. c, Chamaeleo chamaeleon. d, Furcifer pardalis.

No. 876, 260fr — Scorpions: a, Centruroides margaritatus. b, Parabuthus liosoma. c, Androctonus crassicauda, Blaptica dubia. d, Babycurus jacksoni.

No. 877, 960fr, Cebus capucinus. No. 878, 960fr, Acerodon jubatus. No. 879, 960fr, Puma concolor. No. 880, 960fr, Panthera leo senegalensis. No. 881, 960fr, Two dugong dugon. No. 882, 960fr, Stenella coeruleoalba. No. 883, 960fr, Physeter macrocephalus, diff. No. 884, 960fr, Aquila rapax. No. 885, 960fr, Psittacus erithacus. No. 886, 960fr, Strix nebulosa. No. 887, 960fr, Lamprotornis hildebrandti. No. 888, 960fr, Cinnyris chalybeus. No. 889, 960fr, Myzornis pyrrhoura. No. 890, 960fr, Lasiommata megera. No. 891, 960fr, Aldabrachelys gigantea. No. 892, 960fr, Naja pallida. No. 893, 960fr, Crocodylus acutus, diff. No. 894, 960fr, Kinyongia fischeri. No. 895, 960fr, Hottentotta tamulus.

**2016, Jan. 25 Litho. *Perf. 13¼***

**Sheets of 4, #a-d**

**858-876** A301 Set of 19 225.00 225.00

**Souvenir Sheets**

**877-895** A301 Set of 19 205.00 205.00

No. 896, 260fr — Nelson Mandela (1918-2013), President of South Africa, and: a, Three doves. b, Prison cell. c, Amethyst crystal. d, Dove and flag of South Africa.

No. 897, 270fr — Mahatma Gandhi (1869-1948), Indian nationalist leader: a, Sitting at small table. b, With spinning wheel, automobile. c, Seated, pulling thread. d, Seated in chair.

No. 898, 270fr — St. John Paul II (1920-2005): a, With two doves. b, With Nelson Mandela. c, With Mother Teresa. d, Holding crucifix.

No. 899, 270fr — Queen Elizabeth II, longest-reigning British monarch, wearing: a, Crown and blue sash. b, Pink hat. c, Green hat. d, Tiara and orange sash.

No. 900, 270fr — Princess Diana (1961-97), with: a, Princes William and Harry. b, Mother Teresa. c, Child and Red Cross flag. d, Princes Charles and William.

No. 901, 270fr — Lord Robert Baden-Powell (1857-1941), founder of Scouting movement, Scouting emblem: a, Wearing military uniform. b, Wearing Indian headdress. c, Holding animal horn, British flag in background. d, With Scout bugler.

No. 902, 270fr — Nobel laureates: a, Ei-ichi Negishi, 2010 Chemistry laureate. b, Malala Yousafzai, 2014 Peace laureate. c, James D. Watson, 1962 Physiology or Medicine laureate. d, Doris Lessing, 2007 Literature laureate.

No. 903, 270fr — Soccer players and stadiums for 2016 European Soccer Championships, France: a, Stade Pierre Mauroy, Lille. b, Stade Vélodrome, Marseille. c, Stade de Lyon, Lyon. d, Stade de Bordeaux, Bordeaux.

No. 904, 270fr — Sports of the 2016 Summer Olympics, Rio de Janeiro: a, Artistic gymnastics. b, Kayak slalom. c, Women's beach volleyball. d, Rugby.

No. 905, 270fr — Attack on Pearl Harbor, 75th anniv.: a, USS Arizona. b, U.S. P-40B airplane. c, Japanese Mitsubishi A6M Zero airplane. d, USS Missouri.

No. 906, 270fr — Walt Disney (1901-66), animated filmmaker, and: a, Bavarian Castle. b, Awards. c, Film camera. d, Drawing board and sketches.

No. 907, 270fr — Marilyn Monroe (1926-62), actress, wearing: a, Necklace. b, Black bathing suit. c, Blue bathing suit. d, White dress and gloves.

No. 908, 270fr — Elvis Presley (1935-77): a, Playing guitar. b, Holding microphone. c, Wearing striped shirt. d, With Hollywood Walk of Fame star.

No. 909, 270fr — Wolfgang Amadeus Mozart (1756-91), composer, and: a, His father, Johann Georg Leopold Mozart (1719-87). b, His mother, Anna Maria Pertl Mozart (1720-78). c, His wife, Maria Constanze Mozart (1762-1842). d, Young Mozart blindfolded behind piano.

No. 910, 270fr — Georg Alfred Schumann (1866-1952), composer: a, Violin, score, hands of conductor. b, Wearing black suit. c, At piano. d, Conducting musicians.

No. 911, 270fr — Paintings by Vincent van Gogh (1853-90): a, Self-portrait, 1889. b, Vase with Twelve Sunflowers, 1889. c, Portrait of Doctor Gachet, 1890. d, Starry Night Over the Rhône, 1888.

No. 912, 270fr — Paintings by Claude Monet (1840-1926): a, Flowering Garden in Saint-Adresse, 1866. b, Les Meules à Giverny, 1884. c, The Bridge at Argenteuil, 1874. d, The Bridge Over the Water Lily Pond, 1905.

No. 913, 270fr — Paintings by Pablo Picasso (1881-1973): a, Self-portrait, 1907. b, Boy with a Pipe, 1905. c, The Old Guitarist, 1903. d, Portrait of Daniel-Henry Kahnweiler, 1910.

No. 914, 270fr — Christmas: a, Ded Moroz and Snegurochka. b, Santa Claus and reindeer. c, Saint Nicholas on horse. d, Joulupukki.

No. 915, 270fr — New Year 2016 (Year of the Monkey): a, Monkey on branch. b, Monkey with open mouth. c, Head of monkey. d, Adult and juvenile monkey.

No. 916, 960fr, Mandela, diff. No. 917, 960fr, Gandhi and tiger. No. 918, 960fr, St. John Paul II and 14th Dalai Lama. No. 919, 960fr, Queen Elizabeth II and Prince Philip. No. 920, 960fr, Princess Diana and Queen Elizabeth II. No. 921, 960fr, Baden-Powell, Boy Scout and Scouting emblem. No. 922, 960fr, 14th Dalai Lama receiving 1989 Nobel Peace Prize. No. 923, 960fr, Soccer player, Stade de France, Saint-Denis. No. 924, 960fr, Women's 100-meter sprint, boxers. No. 925, 960fr, Explosion on USS Shaw, Herbert C. Jones, Medal of Honor. No. 926, 960fr, Disney, diff. No. 927, 960fr, Monroe, diff. No. 928, 960fr, Presley playing guitar, diff. No. 929, 960fr, Mozart, Masonic compass and square. No. 930, 960fr, Schumann conducting musicians, diff. No. 931, 960fr, Self-portrait with Bandaged Ear and Pipe, by van Gogh, 1889. No. 932, 960fr, Woman with a Parasol, by Monet, 1875. No. 933, 960fr, Seated Woman, by Picasso, 1937. No. 934, 960fr, Saint Nicholas waving. No. 935, 960fr, Adult and juvenile monkeys, diff.

**2016, Mar. 15 Litho. *Perf. 13¼***

**Sheets of 4, #a-d**

**896-915** A302 Set of 20 245.00 245.00

**Souvenir Sheets**

**916-935** A302 Set of 20 220.00 220.00

Inscriptions on Nos. 911b and 932 are incorrect.

A303

No. 936, 280fr — Campaign against malaria: a, Two adults watching sleeping child. b, Mosquito, person tending to patient. c, Mother watching sleeping child. d, Child behind mosquito netting.

No. 937, 280fr — Rugby players: a, Player kicking ball. b, Two players with red shirts attempting tackle. c, Player running with ball and opponent. d, Player with black shirt tackling ball carrier.

No. 938, 280fr — Table tennis players: a, Fan Zhendong. b, Liu Shiwen. c, Kasumi Ishikawa. d, Xu Xin.

No. 939, 280fr — Chess players: a, Magnus Carlsen. b, Sergey Karjakin. c, Viswanathan Anand. d, Judit Polgár.

No. 940, 280fr — Pilgrimage to Mecca: a, Pilgrims circling Ka'aba. b, Stoning of the devil. c, Great Mosque of Mecca, Koran. d, Shaving of heads.

No. 941, 280fr — Lighthouses: a, Les Eclaireurs Lighthouse, Argentina. b, Jeddah Lighthouse, Saudi Arabia. c, Lindau Lighthouse, Germany. d, New London Ledge Lighthouse, U.S.

No. 942, 280fr — Ships: a, Kruzenshtern. b, Flying Dutchman and Phocéa. c, Götheborg. d, Europa.

No. 943, 280fr — Steam locomotives: a, Class C38, Australia. b, Class 19D, South Africa. c, DRB Class 52, Germany. d, Class P36, Russia.

No. 944, 280fr — High-speed trains: a, CRH380A, People's Republic of China. b, Shinkansen Series E6, E621-1, Japan. c, Shinkansen Series N700A, Japan. d, Shinkansen Series H5, H523-1, Japan.

No. 945, 280fr — Race cars: a, Aston Martin DBRS 9. b, Ferrari F150 Italia. c, Ford Fiesta RS WRC. d, Maserati MC12 GT1.

No. 946, 280fr — Fire trucks: a, 1964 Bedford. b, 1962 Chevrolet Apache. c, 1959 Ford Galaxie. d, 1937 Chevrolet.

No. 947, 280fr — First commercial flight of the Concorde, 40th anniv.: a, Concorde in flight, passenger cabin. b, Concorde in flight, nose of Concorde. c, Concorde taking off. d, Under wing view of Concorde.

No. 948, 280fr — Scenes from Apollo space missions: a, Apollo 11. b, Apollo 16. c, Apollo 15. d, Apollo 17.

No. 949, 280fr — Sled dogs: a, Samoyeds. b, Siberian huskies and Alaskan malamutes. c, Alaskan malamutes. d, Man carrying Siberian husky.

No. 950, 280fr — Raptors: a, Melierax poliopterus. b, Torgos tracheliotus. c, Glaucidium passerinum. d, Terathopius ecaudatus.

No. 951, 280fr — Butterflies: a, Boloria aquilonaris. b, Pontia protodice. c, Strymon melinus. d, Aricia agestis.

No. 952, 280fr — Dinosaurs: a, Tyrannosaurus rex. b, Microraptor zhaoianus. c, Dakotaraptor steini. d, Chasmosaurus.

No. 953, 280fr — Orchids: a, Caucaea mimetica. b, Diuris magnifica. c, Thelymitra pulcherrima. d, Thelymitra campanulata.

No. 954, 280fr — Mushrooms: a, Craterellus tubaeformis. b, Tricholoma matsutake. c, Cantharellus cibarius. d, Stropharia rugoso.

No. 955, 280fr — Minerals: a, Sulfur. b, Chalcanthite. c, Colemanite. d, Legrandite.

No. 956, 960fr, Malaria-carrying mosquito, horiz. No. 957, 960fr, Rugby players, horiz. No. 958, 960fr, Ma Long playing table tennis, horiz. No. 959, 960fr, Chess players Anatoly Karpov and Garry Kasparov, horiz. No. 960, 960fr, Pilgrims on Mount Arafat, horiz. No. 961, 960fr, Cape Hatteras Lighthouse, U.S., Onychoprion fuscatus, horiz. No. 962, 960fr, El Galeón, horiz. No. 963, 960fr, Erie Berkshire locomotive, horiz. No. 964, 960fr, Frecciarossa 1000 train, Italy, horiz. No. 965, 960fr, Aston Martin DBR9, horiz. No. 966, 960fr, 1927 Ahrens-Fox fire truck, horiz. No. 967, 960fr, Concorde in flight and cockpit, horiz. No. 968, 960fr, Apollo 16 astronaut John Young on Moon, horiz. No. 969, 960fr, Dogs pulling sled, horiz. No. 970, 960fr, Aquila pomarina, horiz. No. 971, 960fr, Colotis danae, horiz. No. 972, 960fr, Deinocheirus mirificus, horiz. No. 973, 960fr, Cattleya schroederae, horiz. No. 974, 960fr, Boletus edulis, horiz. No. 975, 960fr, Galèna and fluorite, horiz.

**2016, May 5 Litho. *Perf. 13¼***

**Sheets of 4, #a-d**

**936-955** A303 Set of 20 255.00 255.00

**Souvenir Sheets**

**956-975** A303 Set of 20 220.00 220.00

No. 940a inscription is missing "c" of circumambulation. Nos. 956-975 each contain one 66x42mm stamp.

Investiture of Pres. Ismail Omar Guelleh — A304

**2016, May 8 Litho. *Perf. 13¼***

**976** A304 1000fr bister & multi 11.50 11.50

**Litho. With Foil Application**

**Souvenir Sheet**

**977** A304 5000fr gold & multi 57.50 57.50

No. 976 was printed in sheets of 4. No. 977 contains one 51x51mm stamp.

A305

Independence, 39th Anniv. — A306

**2016, June 27 Litho. *Perf. 13½x13***

978 A305 250fr multi 3.00 3.00

**Souvenir Sheet**

***Perf. 13¼***

979 A306 500fr multi 5.75 5.75

Souvenir Sheet

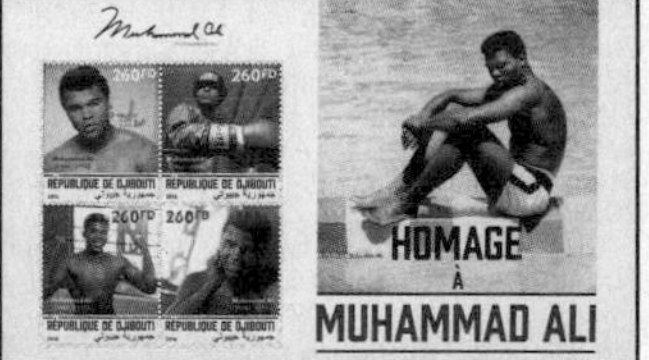

Hassan Gouled Aptidon (1916-2006), First President of Djibouti — A307

**2016, June 27 Litho. *Perf. 13¼***

980 A307 500fr multi 5.75 5.75

Muhammad Ali (1942-2016), Boxer — A308

No. 981 — Ali: a, With sign taped to wall. b, Wearing boxing gloves and headgear. c, In boxing ring. d, With hand touching face.

960fr, Ali running.

**2016, July 28 Litho. *Perf. 13¼***

981 A308 260fr Sheet of 4, #a-d 12.00 12.00

**Souvenir Sheet**

982 A308 960fr multi 11.00 11.00

No. 982 contains one 38x54mm stamp.

A309

No. 983, 260fr — Steve Jobs (1955-2011), co-founder and chief executive officer of Apple Inc., and: a, Steve Wozniak, co-founder of Apple. b, Three computers. c, Apple 1 computer. d, Computer and apple.

No. 984, 260fr — Pope Francis: a, With Patriarch Cyril of Moscow. b, With child and dove. c, With statue and rosary beads. d, Washing feet of refugees.

No. 985, 260fr — Paintings by Pierre-Auguste Renoir (1841-1919): a, Young Woman Sewing, 1879. b, Luncheon of the Boating Party, 1880-81. c, Two Girls at the Piano, 1892. d, The Bridge at Chatou, 1875.

No. 986, 260fr — Paintings by Francisco de Goya (1746-1828): a, The Umbrella, 1777. b, Clothed Maja, 1800. c, Saturn Devouring His Son, 1819-23. d, Charles IV of Spain and His Family, 1800.

No. 987, 260fr — Paintings by Berthe Morisot (1841-95): a, The Garden at Bougival, 1884. b, Hide-and-Seek, 1873. c, Lucie Leon at the Piano, 1892. d, Dahlias, 1876.

No. 988, 260fr — Paintings by Paul Cézanne (1839-1906): a, Kitchen Table, 1888-90. b, The Bridge at Maincy, 1879. c, Still Life with Apples and Oranges, 1895. d, Mont Sainte-Victoire with Large Pine, 1887.

No. 989, 260fr — Museum visitors looking at paintings in the Musée d'Orsay: a, Yellow Haystacks, by Paul Gauguin, 1889. b, Luncheon on the Grass, by Edouard Manet, 1862-63. c, The Floor Scrapers, by Gustave Caillebotte, 1875. d, Self-portrait, by Vincent van Gogh, 1889.

No. 990, 260fr — Items from ancient Egypt: a, Bust of Nefertiti. b, Gayer-Anderson Cat. c, Horus and Temple of Amun, Luxor. d, Funerary mask of Tutankhamun and Giza Pyramids.

No. 991, 260fr — Royal Mail, 500th anniv.: a, Postman emptying pillar box, Morris J Type mail van. b, Horse-drawn mail wagon. c, Postal worker rowing to SS Mona's Queen. d, Postmen on bicycles.

No. 992, 260fr — Battle of Moscow, 75th anniv.: a, German soldier and battlefield map. b, T-34 tank. c, Telegrapher and telegraph key. d, German General Erich Hoepner (1886-1944) and Sturmgeschütz III.

No. 993, 260fr — First flight of LZ-129 (Hindenburg), 80th anniv.: a, Pianist and singer on Hindenburg. b, Workers under docked Hindenburg. c, Hindenburg and hangar. d, Hindenburg, tables and chairs.

No. 994, 260fr — Yuri Gagarin (1934-68), 55th anniv. of first spaceflight, and: a, Launch of rocket. b, Vostok 1 in space. c, Gagarin seated in spacesuit. d, Monument to Gagarin, Moscow.

No. 995, 260fr — Intl. Year of Pulses: a, Woman, child and legumes. b, Hands holding seedling. c, Farm machinery, sprout. d, Poicephalus senegalus, legume.

No. 996, 260fr — Gold medalists at 2014 Winter Olympics, Sochi, Russia: a, Alexander Tretyakov, skeleton. b, Matthias Mayer, downhill skiing. c, Darya Domracheva, mass start, pursuit and individual biathlon. d, Michel Mulder, speed skating.

No. 997, 260fr — Host cities for 2018 World Cup soccer championships, Russia: a, Yekaterinburg. b, St. Petersburg. c, Kazan. d, Volgograd.

No. 998, 260fr — Cat breeds: a, Ragdoll, standing. b, Siamese. c, Ragdoll, prone. d, Australian Mist.

No. 999, 260fr — Dolphins: a, Stenella longirostris. b, Tursiops truncatus with open mouth, beak of Stenella longirostris. c, Stenella coeruleoalba. d, Two Tursiops truncatus.

No. 1000, 260fr — Owls: a, Asio stygius. b, Strix leptogrammica. c, Surnia ulula. d, Tyto alba.

No. 1001, 260fr — Turtles: a, Cuora flavomarginata, Terrapene carolina carolina. b, Terrapene carolina carolina, Geochelone elegans. c, Trachemys scripta elegans. d, Terrapene ornata ornata, Stigmochelys pardalis.

No. 1002, 960fr, Jobs, computer and iPhone. No. 1003, 960fr, Pope Francis and dove. No. 1004, 960fr, Portrait of Marie-Thérèse Durand Ruel, by Renoir, 1882. No. 1005, 960fr, Witches' Sabbath, by Goya, 1789. No. 1006, 960fr, On the Balcony of Eugene Manet's room at Bougival, by Morisot, 1881. No. 1007, 960fr, A Modern Olympia, by Cézanne, 1870. No. 1008, 960fr, Visitor looking at Portrait of Doctor Paul Gachet , 1890 at Musée d'Orsay. No. 1009, 960fr, Painting from Tomb of Userhat. No. 1010, 960fr, British postman, pillar box, Titan Airways Boeing 737. No. 1011, 960fr, Soviet General Georgy Zhukov (1896-1974), anti-aircraft fire of Battle of Moscow. No. 1012, 960fr, Mooring of the Hindenburg at Lakehurst, New Jersey. No. 1013, 960fr, Gagarin, Vostok 1, flag of Soviet Union. No. 1014, 960fr, Hands holding legumes. No. 1015, 960fr, Sage Kotsenburg, 2014 Winter Olympics snowboarding gold medalist. No. 1016, 960fr, Moscow, host city for 2018 World Cup. No. 1017, 960fr, Burmese cat. No. 1018, 960fr, Inia geoffrensis. No. 1019, 960fr, Bubo scandiacus. No. 1020, 960fr, Centrochelys sulcata.

**2016, July 28 Litho. *Perf. 13¼***

**Sheets of 4, #a-d**

983-1001 A309 Set of 19 225.00 225.00

**Souvenir Sheets**

1002-1020 A309 Set of 19 205.00 205.00

A310

No. 1021, 260fr — Ursus maritimus: a, Head of bear with open mouth. b, Looking at water. c, Two adults and cub. d, Bear walking.

No. 1022, 260fr — Hippopotamus amphibius: a, One animal with head near ground. b, One animal with open mouth, Latin name on two lines. c, Adult and juvenile. d, One adult with open mouth, Latin name on one line.

No. 1023, 260fr — Pandas: a, Ailuropoda melanoleuca eating. b, Ailurus fulgens, feet on mound. c, Ailurus fulgens, prone. d, Adult and juvenile Ailuropoda melanoleuca.

No. 1024, 260fr — Tigers: a, Head of Panthera tigris altaica. b, Panthera tigris tigris with open mouth. c, Panthera tigris tigris with closed mouth. d, Panthera tigris altaica walking.

No. 1025, 260fr — Dog breeds: a, Brussels griffon. b, Neapolitan mastiff. c, Canary Island hound. d, Kerry Blue terrier.

No. 1026, 260fr — Elephants: a, Loxodonta africana and tree. b, Two Loxodonta africana. c, Loxodonta africana and man. d, Loxodonta cyclotis.

No. 1027, 260fr — Water birds: a, Morus bassanus. b, Tadorna ferruginea. c, Dendrocygna bicolor. d, Cygnus atratus.

No. 1028, 260fr — Kingfishers: a, Corythornis cristatus, Halcyon smyrnensis. b, Alcedo atthis. c, Corythornis cristatus. d, Ceyx erithaca, Halcyon smyrnensis.

No. 1029, 260fr — Pigeons: a, Columba palumbus. b, Gymnophaps albertisii. c, Columba livia. d, Patagioenas leucocephala.

No. 1030, 260fr — Falcons: a, Falco vespertinus. b, Falco fasciinucha. c, Falco amurensis. d, Falco sparverius.

No. 1031, 260fr — Bees: a, Xylocopa micans. b, Euglossa dilemma. c, Anthidium manicatum. d, Augochlorella aurata.

No. 1032, 260fr — Butterflies: a, Cupidopsis cissus. b, Graphium porthaon. c, Myrina silenus. d, Tarucus sybaris.

No. 1033, 260fr — Fish: a, Acanthurus leucosternon, Acanthurus triostegus. b, Pterois volitans. c, Pygoplites diacanthus. d, Manta alfredi.

No. 1034, 260fr — Shells: a, Cypraecassis rufa. b, Charonia tritonis. c, Trochus nodulosus. d, Conus mustelinus.

No. 1035, 260fr — Extinct animals: a, Mammuthus columbi. b, Moropus elatus. c, Elasmotherium sibiricum. d, Smilodon populator.

No. 1036, 260fr — Prehistoric aquatic animals: a, Enchodus. b, Mosasaurus hoffmannii. c, Ammonoidea. d, Helicoprion bessonovi.

No. 1037, 260fr — Mushrooms: a, Rhodotus palmatus. b, Phallus indusiatus. c, Lactarius deliciosus. d, Leccinum scabrum.

No. 1038, 260fr — Minerals: a, Chalcanthite. b, Legrandite. c, Gadolinite. d, Fluorite.

No. 1039, 260fr — Cartoon characters on stamps: a, U.S. Nos. 4399-4402 (Characters from *The Simpsons*). b, U.S. No. 4470, Switzerland Nos. 1536-1537 (Characters from *Garfield*). c, U.S. Zazzle personalized stamps depicting *SpongeBob SquarePants*. d, Switzerland No. 1497, Belgium Nos. 2320-2321 (Characters from *The Smurfs*).

No. 1040, 960fr, Ursus maritimus adult and cub. No. 1041, 960fr, Hippopotamus amphibius adult and juvenile, diff. No. 1042, 960fr, Two Ailuropoda melanoleuca. No. 1043, 960fr, Two Panthera tigris altaica. No. 1044, 960fr, Akita. No. 1045, 960fr, Elephas maximus. No. 1046, 960fr, Gavia immer. No. 1047, 960fr, Alcedo atthis, diff. No. 1048, 960fr, Goura scheepmakeri. No. 1049, 960fr, Falco peregrinus. No. 1050, 960fr, Andrena cineraria. No. 1051, 960fr, Myrina silenus ficedula. No. 1052, 960fr, Plectorhinchus vittatus, Heniochus pleurotaenia. No. 1053, 960fr, Lambis lambis. No. 1054, 960fr, Glyptodon clavipes. No. 1055, 960fr, Dinichthys terrelli. No. 1056, 960fr, Morchella esculenta. No. 1057, 960fr, Cassiterite. No. 1058, 960fr, Netherlands No.1080a, U.S. Zazzle srtamps depicting *Tom and Jerry.*

**2016, Sept. 26 Litho. *Perf. 13¼***

**Sheets of 4, #a-d**

1021-1039 A310 Set of 19 225.00 225.00

**Souvenir Sheets**

1040-1058 A310 Set of 19 210.00 210.00

Worldwide Fund for Nature (WWF) — A311

No. 1059 — Torgos tracheliotos: a, Bird on branch. b, Two birds. c, Two birds and carrion. d, Bird and animal bones.

960fr, Torgos tracheliotos in flight.

**2016, Sept. 26 Litho. *Perf. 13¼***

1059 A311 260fr Sheet of 4, #a-d 12.00 12.00

**Souvenir Sheet**

1060 A311 960fr multi 11.00 11.00

No. 1060 lacks the WWF emblem on the stamp and sheet margin.

Miniature Sheet

First Batallion of Somali Snipers, Cent. — A312

No. 1061: a, Medal, Battle of Douaumont. b, Tank and Malmaison, 1917. c, Monument. d, Airplane over Pointe de Grave and Cordouan Lighthouse, France, 1945.

**2016, Oct. 24 Litho. *Perf. 13¼***

1061 A312 500fr Sheet of 4, #a-d 22.50 22.50

A313

No. 1062, 280fr — Rotary International in Djibouti: a, Boy holding stick and water bottle. b, Woman and children at well. c, Woman holding child to receive vaccination. d, Children.

No. 1063, 280fr — Red Cross-Red Crescent in Djibouti: a, Red Crescent, map of Africa, Red Crescent workers carrying litter. b, Red

Crescent worker assisting woman. c, Red Crescent worker looking at notebook. d, Red Crescent worker holding water bucket.

No. 1064, 280fr — Canonization of Mother Teresa (1910-97): a, Mother Teresa and building. b, Mother Teresa, dove, Pres. Ronald Reagan and wife, Nancy. c, Mother Teresa holding child. d, Mother Teresa and flag of India.

No. 1065, 280fr — Extraordinary Jubilee of Mercy: a, Pope Francis in Kenya. b, Pope Francis opening holy doors. c, Pope Benedict XVI. d, Dove and Popes Francis, Benedict XVI.

No. 1066, 280fr — British royal family: a, Queen Elizabeth II. b, Duke and Duchess of Cambridge. c, Prince George and Princess Charlotte. d, Duke and Duchess of Cambridge, Prince George and Princess Charlotte.

No. 1067, 280fr — Publication of Albert Einstein's Theory of General Relativity, cent.: a, Einstein, globes, equation, model of atom. b, Einstein and equation. c, Hand holding orb depicting Einstein. d, Einstein and light bulb.

No. 1068, 280fr — Battle of the Somme, cent.: a, Mark I tank. b, British Gen. Ivor Maxse (1862-1958) and soldiers. c, French soldiers at munitions wagon. d, German soldier on horse.

No. 1069, 280fr — Navy ships: a, San Marco, Italy. b, Zubr Class hovercraft, Russia, and tank. c, USS Coronado, United States. d, BSF Azov 151, BF Minsk 127, Russia.

No. 1070, 280fr — Submarines.: a, Type 035, People's Republic of China. b, Typhoon Class Project 941, Russia. c, A26 submarine. d, HMS Triumph, Great Britain.

No. 1071, 280fr — High-speed trains.: a, ETR 500 Frecciarossa, Italy. b, SNCF TGV Duplex, France. c, AVE Class 103, Spain. d, Eurostar e320, Great Britain.

No. 1072, 280fr — Motorcycles: a, BMW K1600GTL. b, Suzuki TU250X. c, MV Agusta F3 800. d, Yamaha Star VMAX.

No. 1073, 280fr — Russian military aircraft: a, Sukhoi Su-35. b, Mil Mi-28 helicopter. c, Kamov KA-50 helicopter. d, Mikoyan MiG-41.

No. 1074, 280fr — Space exploration: a, Mars Rover Spirit, 2004. b, Neil Armstrong (1930-2012) on ladder of Lunar Module, 1969. c, Yuri Gagarin (1934-68), and Vostok 1, 1961. d, Final mission of Space Shuttle Atlantis, 2011.

No. 1075, 280fr — 2016 Ice Hockey World Championships, Russia: a, Players fighting for puck near goaltender. b, U.S. player and Russian goaltender. c, Canadian and Russian players. d, Finnish player and Canadian goaltender.

No. 1076, 280fr — Chess players: a, Magnus Carlsen. b, Anatoly Karpov. c, Bobby Fischer. d, Mariya Muzychuk.

No. 1077, 280fr — Islamic art: a, Battle scene from the Shahnameh. b, Interior of Cathedral-Mosque of Córdoba, Spain. c, Jameh Mosque, Isfahan, Iran. d, Pyxis of al-Mughira.

No. 1078, 280fr — Lighthouses: a, Petit Minou Lighthouse, France. b, Hornby Lighthouse, Australia. c, Store Faerder Lighthouse, Norway. d, Point Betsie Lighthouse, Michigan.

No. 1079, 280fr — Orchids: a, Cattleya labiata. b, Cypripedium kentuckiense. c, Vanda denisoniana. d, Orchis purpurea.

No. 1080, 280fr — New Year 2017 (Year of the Rooster): a, Rooster with leg raised and wings extended. b, Rooster facing right, pagoda in background. c, Rooster facing right, torii in background. d, Rooster in air, flapping wings.

No. 1081, 960fr, Child and containers, Rotary International emblem. No. 1082, 960fr, Red Crescent worker with water bottle tending to injured person. No. 1083, 960fr, Mother Teresa and child, diff. No. 1084, 960fr, Pope Francis kissing creche figure of infant Jesus. No. 1085, 960fr, Queen Elizabeth II, diff. No. 1086, 960fr, Einstein at blackboard. No. 1087, 960fr, German soldier at Battle of the Somme. No. 1088, 960fr, USS Essex and CH-53E helicopters. No. 1089, 960fr, USS Scorpion. No. 1090, 960fr, IC3 3 train, Germany. No. 1091, 960fr, Beta 450 RR motorcycle. No. 1092, 960fr, Mikoyan MiG-35. No. 1093, 960fr, Sputnik 1, 1957. No. 1094, 960fr, Russian ice hockey player sprawled on ice. No. 1095, 960fr, Sergey Karjakin, chess pieces. No. 1096, 960fr, Qutub Minar and Alai Darwaza, India. No. 1097, 960fr, La Vieille Lighthouse, France. No. 1098, 960fr, Vanda coerulea. No. 1099, 960fr, Rooster and Great Wall of China.

**2016, Nov. 25 Litho. *Perf. 13¼***

**Sheets of 4, #a-d**

**1062-1080** A313 Set of 19 240.00 240.00

**Souvenir Sheets**

**1081-1099** A313 Set of 19 205.00 205.00

Election of Donald Trump as U.S. President — A314

No. 1100: a, Trump and stars. b, Trump and Republican Party emblem. c, Trump with wife, Melania, and son, Barron. d, Trump and running mate, Mike Pence.

960fr, Trump, diff.

**2016, Nov. 25 Litho. *Perf. 13¼***

**1100** A314 280fr Sheet of 4, #a-d 12.50 12.50

**Souvenir Sheet**

**1101** A314 960fr multi 11.00 11.00

No. 1101 contains one 51x90mm stamp.

A315

No. 1102, 280fr — St. John Paul II (1920-2005), with: a, Boy and girl. b, Crowd worshiping. c, Candles. d, Religious sculpture.

No. 1103, 280fr — Michèle Morgan (1920-2016), actress, with: a, Unidentified actor. b, Hand on head. c, Clapboard and film reel. d, Gérard Philipe (1922-59), actor.

No. 1104, 280fr — John Glenn, Jr. (1921-2016), astronaut: a, U.S. flag, Mercury capsule, launch of Atlas 8 rocket. b, Glenn and Space Shuttle Discovery. c, Glenn, military airplane and Pres. John F. Kennedy (1917-63). d, Glenn, U.S. flag and rocket launch.

No. 1105, 280fr — Rotary International emblem and: a, Paul P. Harris (1868-1947), founder of Rotary International, holding book. b, Rotary volunteer giving vaccine to child. c, Children reading. d, Harris with reversed Paul Harris Fellow pin.

No. 1106, 280fr — Scouting, 110th anniv.: a, Scouts in canoe, Nettapus auritus. b, Scout with binoculars, Circaetus cinereus. c, Scouts with Scouting flag. d, Scout and Lentinus squarrosulus.

No. 1107, 280fr — Paintings by Ivan Aivazovsky (1817-1900): a, Portrait of Loris-Melikov, 1888. b, Battle of Cesme at Night, 1848. c, Boat Ride by Kumpaki in Constantinople, 1846. d, Odessa, 1840.

No. 1108, 280fr — Paintings by Edgar Degas (1834-1917): a, In a Café, 1875-76. b, Emma Dobigny, 1869. c, A Cotton Office in New Orleans, 1873. d, Ballet Rehearsal on Stage, 1874.

No. 1109, 280fr — Paintings by Frida Kahlo (1907-54): a, Tree of Hope, Keep Firm, 1946. b, Still Life with Parrot, 1951. c, The Wounded Deer, 1946. d, Portrait of Lucha Maria, a Girl from Tehuacan, 1942.

No. 1110, 280fr — Sculptures by Auguste Rodin (1840-1917): a, The Thinker, 1903. b, Lady Sackville-West, 1913. c, Young Woman with Flowered Hat, 1870-75. d, The Clenched Hand, 1885, The Gates of Hell, 1880-90.

No. 1111, 280fr — Primates: a, Pongo pygmaeus. b, Indri indri. c, Loris tardigradus. d, Papio hamadryas.

No. 1112, 280fr — Wild cats: a, Panthera tigris altaica. b, Panthera neofelis nebulosa. c, Puma concolor. d, Panthera pardus kotiya.

No. 1113, 280fr — Dolphins: a, Stenella longirostris. b, Grampus griseus. c, Lagenorhynchus obscurus. d, Tursiops truncatus.

No. 1114, 280fr — Whales: a, Balaena mysticetus. b, Delphinapterus leucas. c, Physeter macrocephalus. d, Balaenoptera musculus.

No. 1115, 280fr — Owls: a, Aegolius harrisii, Aegolius acadicus. b, Athene noctua. c, Bubo virginianus. d, Glaucidium passerinum.

No. 1116, 280fr — Birds of prey: a, Caracara plancus. b, Aegolicus acadicus. c, Coragyps atratus. d, Gymnogyps californianus.

No. 1117, 280fr — Water birds: a, Rynchops niger. b, Eudocimus ruber. c, Gavia immer. d, Mycteria leucocephala.

No. 1118, 280fr — Butterflies: a, Perrhybris pamela. b, Junonia lemonias lemonias. c, Ixias pyrene. d, Colotis euippe.

No. 1119, 280fr — Fish: a, Acanthurus leucosternon. b, Ostracion cubicus. c, Antennarius coccineus. d, Scarus coelestinus.

No. 1120, 280fr — Turtles: a, Batagur trivittata. b, Chelus fimbriatus. c, Lepidochelys kempii. d, Lepidochelys olivacea.

No. 1121, 280fr — Snakes: a, Pituophis catenifer. b, Diadophis punctatus. c, Oxyrhopus trigeminus. d, Natrix natrix.

No. 1122, 280fr — Dinosaurs: a, Iguanodon. b, Spinops sternbergorum. c, Cryolophosaurus. d, Spinosaurus.

No. 1123, 280fr — Endangered animals: a, Campephilus principalis. b, Panthera pardus orientalis. c, Helarctos malayanus. d, Lepilemur septentrionalis.

No. 1124, 280fr — Mushrooms: a, Cantharellus cibarius. b, Gyromitra esculenta. c, Ramaria formosa. d, Tylopilus felleus.

No. 1125, 280fr — Orchids: a, Vanda coerulea. b, Cattleya. c, White Phalaenopsis. d, Zygopetalum.

No. 1126, 280fr — Minerals: a, Amazonite. b, Wulfenite. c, Rhodochrosite. d, Aquamarine.

No. 1127, 960fr, St. John Paul II and crosses. No. 1128, 960fr, Morgan with strings of pearls. No. 1129, 960fr, Glenn receiving Presidential Medal of Freedom from Pres. Barack Obama. No. 1130, 960fr, Rotary International emblem and bust of Harris. No. 1131, 960fr, Scout blowing horn, Colotis danae. No. 1132, 960fr, The Roads at Kronstadt, by Aivazovsky, 1840. No. 1133, 960fr, The Dance Class, by Degas, 1874. No. 1134, 960fr, Portrait of My Father, by Kahlo, 1951. No. 1135, 960fr, The Burghers of Calais, by Rodin, 1884-89. No. 1136, 960fr, Leontopithecus rosalia. No. 1137, 960fr, Lynx pardinus. No. 1138, 960fr, Cephalorhynchus heavisidii. No. 1139, 960fr, Megaptera novaeangliae. No. 1140, 960fr, Asio capensis. No. 1141, 960fr, Buteo lagopus. No. 1142, 960fr, Anas rhynchotis. No. 1143, 960fr, Delias eucharis. No. 1144, 960fr, Sparisoma cretense. No. 1145, 960fr, Geochelone elephantopus. No. 1146, 960fr, Naja sumatrana. No. 1147, 960fr, Parasaurolophus. No. 1148, 960fr, Gyps indicus. No. 1149, 960fr, Clitocybe phyllophila. No. 1150, 960fr, Black Phalaenopsis orchid. No. 1151, 960fr, Pyromorphite.

**2017, Jan. 20 Litho. *Perf. 13¼***

**Sheets of 4, #a-d**

**1102-1126** A315 Set of 25 310.00 310.00

**Souvenir Sheets**

**1127-1151** A315 Set of 25 265.00 265.00

Varanus Komodoensis — A316

No. 1152 — Komodo dragon: a, With head down, tongue out. b, With head raised, tongue not visible. c, Climbing rock. d, With head raised, tongue out.

950fr, Komodo dragon, tongue touching ground.

**2017, Mar. 15 Litho. *Perf. 13¼***

**1152** A316 240fr Sheet of 4, #a-d 11.00 11.00

**Souvenir Sheet**

**1153** A316 950fr multi 10.50 10.50

Bandung 2017 World Stamp Exhibition. No. 1153 contains one 48x48mm stamp.

A317

No. 1154, 240fr — Wilbur Wright (1867-1912), aviation pioneer: a, Wright, with brother, Orville (1871-1948) and Wright Flyer. b, Wind testing of Wright Flyer, 1901. c, Wilbur and Wright Flyer in flight. d, Wilbur at controls of airplane.

No. 1155, 240fr — Concorde: a, British Airways Concorde over Paris. b, British Airways Concorde over Nice, France. c, Air France Concorde over London. d, British Airways Concorde over Mecca, Saudi Arabia.

No. 1156, 240fr — Military aircraft: a, Mikoyan-Gurevich MiG-29. b, A-10 Thunderbolt II. c, Junkers Ju 52. d, Boeing-Bell V-22 Osprey.

No. 1157, 240fr — Disappearance of Amelia Earhart (1897-1937), pilot: a, Earhart and her airplane. b, Earhart, airplane and hangar. c, Earhart and husband, George P. Putnam (1887-1950). d, Electra 10E in flight.

No. 1158, 240fr — Ferdinand von Zeppelin (1838-1917), airship manufacturer: a, Zeppelin, passengers boarding Graf Zeppelin. b, Zeppelin LZ-1. c, Zeppelin LZ-4. d, Zeppelin and schematic drawings of airship.

No. 1159, 240fr — 80th birthday of Valentina Tereshkova, first woman in space: a, In car with Russia Premier Nikita Khrushchev (1894-1971). b, With Yuri Gagarin (1934-68), first man in space. c, With obverse and reverse of 1983 1-ruble Russian coin depicting her. d, With Vostok 6.

No. 1160, 240fr — Steam trains: a, Pennsylvania Railroad 1223. b, London and North Eastern Railway Class A4 Mallard 4468. c, Great Western Railway 4-4-0 City of Truro 3717. d, Deutsche Reichsbahn 18 201.

No. 1161, 240fr — High-speed trains: a, Talgo 350. b, NTV Alstom AGV 575. c, Shinkansen Series 500. d, Renfe Series S-103.

No. 1162, 240fr — Sinking of the Titanic, 105th anniv.: a, Titanic and map of voyage. b, Titanic sinking and overturned lifeboat. c, Titanic and iceberg. d, Titanic and Thomas Andrews (1873-1912), designer of Titanic.

No. 1163, 240fr — Submarines: a, HMAS Collins, Australia. b, SSK Kilo Class Type 636 and Icebreaker Ivan Kruzenshtern, Russia. c, HMS Ambush, Great Britain. d, Terrible, France.

No. 1164, 240fr — Donald Campbell (1921-67), land and water speed record holder: a, Wearing helmet. b, In Bluebird K7, waving. c, Sitting. d, With wife, Tonia Bern-Campbell.

No. 1165, 240fr — Special transportation: a, Telescope transporter. b, Victoria, Australia police vehicle. c, Euclid dump truck. d, Snowcat.

No. 1166, 240fr — Fire-fighting vehicles: a, Caterpillar CT660 fire truck, United States. b, Foremost Nodwell 240, Canada. c, Delta 2 wheeled carrier, Canada. d, Hopedale, Massachusets Tanker 1, United States.

No. 1167, 240fr — 1947 Ferrari 125 S, 70th anniv., with background design of: a, Trees. b, Ferrari emblem. c, Steering wheel and dashboard. d, Clouds.

No. 1168, 240fr — Motorcycles: a, 1912 Henderson 4-cylinder. b, 1923 BMW R32. c, 1962-63 BSA Rocket Gold Star A10. d, 1974 Hercules-Wankel 2000.

No. 1169, 240fr — Transportation for Pres. Donald Trump: a, Sikorsky S-76 helicopter. b, 2015 Mercedes-Benz Class S600. c, 1997 Lamborghini Diablo. d, Boeing 757.

No. 1170, 240fr — Sled dogs: a, Five sled dogs and two drivers. b, Two Seppala Siberian sled dogs. c, Husky and Malamutes. d, Sled dogs resting with driver.

No. 1171, 240fr — Jacques Cousteau (1910-97), conservationist and filmmaker: a, Calypso and hot air balloon in Antarctica. b, Cousteau and SP-350 Denise. c, Cousteau holding cup. d, Cousteau and Calypso.

No. 1172, 240fr — Charles Darwin (1809-82), naturalist: a, Portrait of Darwin and his wife, Emma, by George Richmond. b, HMS Beagle and map of its voyage, Conolophus subcristatus. c, Darwin, primate and skulls of Homo neanderthalensis and Homo sapiens. d, Darwin and specimens of Pseudoscarus lepidus, Eleginops maclovinus, and Ceroglossus darwinii.

No. 1173, 240fr — Russian October Revolution, cent.: a, Barricades at St. Isaac Cathedral, St. Petersburg. b, Soldiers at Hermitage and Winter Palace, St. Petersburg. c, Deomonstrators in St. Petersburg. d, Lenin (1870-1924), and Cruiser Aurora.

No. 1174, 240fr — Battle of Stalingrad, 75th anniv.: a, Aug. 23, 1942 air raid. b, Soviet Gen. Georgi Zhukov (1896-1974). c, German Gen. Friedrich Paulus (1890-1957). d, Soviet troops, Feb. 1943.

No. 1175, 240fr — Lighthouses: a, Punta Palascia Lighthouse, Italy. b, Lindesnes Lighthouse, Norway. c, Pointe aux Barques Lighthouse, Michigan. d, North Head Lighthouse, Washington.

No. 1176, 240fr — Windmills and tulips: a, Kinderddijk, Netherlands windmills, red and white tulips. b, Kuremaa, Estonia windmill, yellow tulips. c, Sonderho, Denmark windmill, orange tulips. d, Halanker, Great Britain windmill, red tulips.

No. 1177, 240fr — Endangered animals: a, Anolis gorgonae. b, Anolis proboscis. c, Neurergus kaiseri. d, Tokay gecko.

No. 1178, 950fr, Orville Wright on bicycle, Wright Flyer in flight. No. 1179, 950fr, British Airways Concorde over New York City. No. 1180, 950fr, F-16 Fighting Falcon. No. 1181, 950fr, Earhart holding propeller. No. 1182, 950fr, Zeppelin and his signature. No. 1183, 950fr, Tereshkova and stylized rocket. No. 1184, 950fr, St. Louis-San Francisco train. No. 1185, 950fr, Shinkansen Series E6. No. 1186, 950fr, Titanic and its captain, Edward Smith (1850-1912). No. 1187, 950fr, Victoria Class submarine, Canada. No. 1188, 950fr, Campbell in Bluebird K7. No. 1189, 950fr, Lockheed Martin hybrid dirigibles. No. 1190, 950fr, San José, California fire truck. No. 1191, 950fr, Enzo Ferrari (1898-1988), automobile manufacturer in 1947 Ferrari 125 S. No. 1192, 950fr, 2006 Royal Enfield Bullet motorcycle. No. 1193, 950fr, Gold Trump motorcyle. No. 1194, 950fr, Siberian husky sled dogs. No. 1195, 950fr, Cousteau holding walkie-talkie. No. 1196, 950fr, Darwin, Geospiza fortis, heads of Galapagos finches. No. 1197, 950fr, Lenin and Cruiser Aurora, diff. No. 1198, 950fr, Vasily Zaytsev (1915-91), Soviet sniper at Battle of Stalingrad. No. 1199, 950fr, Petit Minou Lighthouse, France. No. 1200, 950fr, Mostert, South Africa windmill, red and yellow tulips. No. 1201, 950fr, Neurergus kaiseri, diff.

**2017, Mar. 15 Litho. *Perf. 13¼***

**Sheet of 4, #a-d**

**1154-1177** A317 Set of 24 260.00 260.00

**Souvenir Sheets**

**1178-1201** A317 Set of 24 255.00 255.00

Miniature Sheets

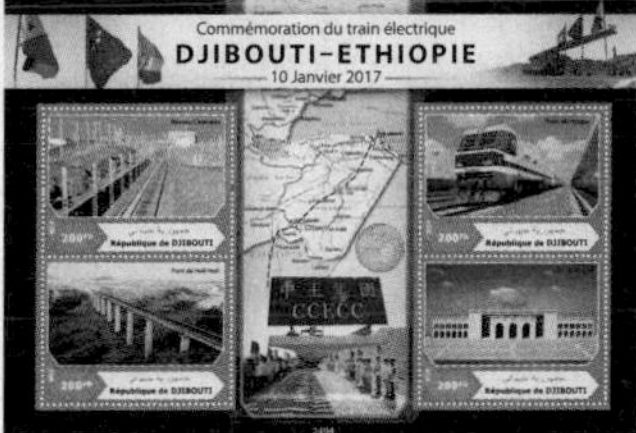


Opening of Djibouti-Ethiopia Electric Rail Line — A318

Nos. 1202 and 1203: a, Tracks and catenary network. b, Electric train. c, Holl Holl Bridge. d, Nagad Station.

**2017, Apr. 25 Litho. *Perf. 12¾x13¼***

**1202** A318 200fr Sheet of 4, #a-d 9.00 9.00
**1203** A318 250fr Sheet of 4, #a-d 11.00 11.00

A319

No. 1204, 240fr — Ailuropoda melanoleuca (Giant panda): a, On branch. b, Adult and cub. c, On back. d, Facing left.

No. 1205, 240fr — Dogs: a, Papillons. b, French bulldog. c, English cocker spaniel. d, Basset hounds.

No. 1206, 240fr — Dolphins: a, Lagenorhynchus obscurus. b, Tursiops truncatus. c, Cephalorhynchus commersonii. d, Stenella frontalis.

No. 1207, 240fr — Owls: a, Tyto alba. b, Bubo cinerascens. c, Bubo lacteus. d, Glaucidium perlatum.

No. 1208, 240fr — Bees and orchids: a, Euglossa imperialis, Cattleya aclandiae. b, Exaerete frontalis, Cymbidium madidum. c, Euglossa tridentata, Maxillaria tenufolia. d, Euglossa dilemma, Cattleya lueddemanniana.

No. 1209, 240fr — Butterflies: a, Batesia hypochlora. b, Papilio demoleus. c, Melitaea didyma. d, Phengaris arion.

No. 1210, 240fr — Turtles: a, Graptemys pseudogeographica kohni. b, Rhinoclemmys pulcherrima. c, Trachemys scripta scripta. d, Trachemys scripta elegans.

No. 1211, 240fr — Extinct animals: a, Mammuthus meridionalis. b, Raphus cucullatus. c, Megacerops coloradensis. d, Thalassocnus antiquus.

No. 1212, 240fr — Mahatma Gandhi (1869-1948), Indian nationalist: a, With spinning wheel. b, Walking, holding walking stick. c, With building. d, With decorated cow.

No. 1213, 240fr — Princess Diana (1961-97): a, With Prince Charles and coat of arms. b, Wearing white blouse. c, Wearing white blouse, with sunglasses in hair. d, Holding Prince Harry.

No. 1214, 950fr, Ailuropoda melanoleuca adult and cub, diff. No. 1215, 950fr, Rottweilers. No. 1216, 950fr, Sotalia fluviatilis. No. 1217, 950fr, Otus senegalensis. No. 1218, 950fr, Euglossa imperialis, Laelia anceps. No. 1219, 950fr, Colotis ione. No. 1220, 950fr, Apalone mutica. No. 1221, 950fr, Glyptodon clavipes. No. 1222, 950fr, Gandhi and Taj Mahal. No. 1223, 950fr, Princess Diana, Duke and Duchess of Cambrige, Prince Harry.

**2017, July 5 Litho. *Perf. 13¼***

**Sheets of 4, #a-d**

**1204-1213** A319 Set of 10 110.00 110.00

**Souvenir Sheets**

**1214-1223** A319 Set of 10 105.00 105.00

A320

No. 1224, 240fr — Formula I race cars: a, Blue and yellow cars. b, Orange car. c, Bright red car. d, Red and orange cars.

No. 1225, 240fr — Ice hockey: a, Norwegian player in dark blue jersey, player in white and blue jersey. b, Henrik Lundqvist, goaltender for New York Rangers. c, Referee and Washington Capitals player with stick raised. d, Boston Bruins player in black and yellow jersey, player in red and white jersey.

No. 1226, 240fr — Cricket players: a, Batsman swinging and falling fielder. b, Shikhar Dhawan. c, Josh Hazlewood. d, Batsman holding bat behind back, celebrating player.

No. 1227, 240fr — Tennis players: a, Rafael Nadal. b, Stan Wawrinka. c, Angelique Kerber. d, Serena Williams.

No. 1228, 240fr — Table tennis players: a, Zhang Jike. b, Liu Shiwen. c, Ding Ning. d, Liu Guoliang.

No. 1229, 240fr — Golfers: a, Dustin Johnson. b, So-yeon Ryu. c, Lydia Ko. d, Rory McIlroy.

No. 1230, 240fr — Pierre de Coubertin (1863-1937), President of International Olympic Committee: a, Coubertin, wrestlers in background. b, Statue of Coubertin, Beijing. c, Coubertin facing right. d, Coubertin, ancient Greek soldiers in background.

No. 1231, 240fr — Chess pieces: a, Black knight, queen in silhouette. b, White queen, hand moving black piece. c, White queen and king, black king. d, Carved piece depicting elephant carrying howdah, queen in background.

No. 1232, 240fr — Metropolitan Museum of Art, 145th anniv.: a, Fragment of bust of Roman Emperor Caracalla. b, Charles Engelhard Court. c, Bust of Young Girl Identified as Anne Audéoud of Geneva, by Jean Antoine Houdon. d, Silver Buffalo Figure from Benin, 19th cent.

No. 1233, 240fr — Red Cross-Red Crescent Campaign Against Malaria: a, Man spraying insecticide in village. b, Woman and mosquito netting. c, Medical worker examining child. d, Medical worker taking blood sample from child.

No. 1234, 240fr — Pres. John F. Kennedy (1917-63), and: a, U.S. flag. b, Wife, Jacqueline. c, Daughter, Caroline. d, Wife, daughter, and son, John, Jr.

No. 1235, 240fr — 35th birthday of Prince William of Cambridge: a, In helicopter. b, With wife and children. c, As child, with parents and brother. d, Playing polo with brother, Prince Harry.

No. 1236, 240fr — Tall ships: a, Royal Clipper, Sweden. b, Belem, France. c, Palinuro, Italy. d, Juan Sebastián de Elcano, Spain.

No. 1237, 240fr — Naval vessels: a, Gloire, France, 1859. b, USS Texas, 1912. c, Yamato, Japan, 1940. d, La Fayette, France, 1996.

No. 1238, 240fr — European high-speed trains: a, TGV Thalys PBKA, France. b, TGV Lyria, France and Switzerland. c, ICE 3, Germany. d, TCDD HT80000, Turkey.

No. 1239, 240fr — Fire trucks: a, Citroen 46 CDU. b, Rosenbauer Panther. c, MAZ7310 Airfield Crash Tender. d, Ladder truck with tank treads.

No. 1240, 240fr — Opel automobiles: a, Opel Ascona A. b, Opel Kapitän. c, Opel Mokka. d, Opel Tigra.

No. 1241, 240fr — Supersonic aircraft: a, Aerion SBJ. b, North American XB-70 Valkyrie. c, Tupolev Tu-22M. d, Lockheed SR-71 Blackbird.

No. 1242, 240fr — Sergei Korolev (1907-66), spacecraft designer: a, Luna 3, Sputnik 1. b, Korolev and Luna 8K72. c, Korolev and R-7 Semyorka missile. d, Yuri Gagarin (1934-68), cosmonaut, and Vostok 1.

No. 1243, 240fr — Birds of Djibouti: a, Dendropicos namaquus. b, Phoeniculus somaliensis. c, Caprimulgus stellatus. d, Trachyphonus darnaudii.

No. 1244, 950fr, Nico Rosberg, 2016 Formula 1 racing champion and car. No. 1245, 950fr, Ice hockey player taking shot. No. 1246, 950fr, Cricket batsman and wicket-keeper. No. 1247, 950fr, Tennis player Andy Murray. No. 1248, 950fr, Table tennis player Ma Long. No. 1249, 950fr, Golfer Jason Day. No. 1250, 950fr, Coubertin and hurdlers. No. 1251, 950fr, King and queen chess pieces. No. 1252, 950fr, Statue of William Shakespeare, by John Quincy Adams Ward. No. 1253, 950fr, Woman carrying child, Anopheles maculipennis. No. 1254, 950fr, Pres. Kennedy and U.S. flag, diff. No. 1255, 950fr, Wedding of Prince William of Cambridge and Catherine Middleton. No. 1256, 950fr, Tovarishch, Russia. No. 1257, 950fr, Gloire, France, 1935. No. 1258, Renfe Series S-114, Spain. No. 1259, 950fr, Bulldog 4x4 fire truck. No. 1260, 950fr, Opel Astra J. No. 1261, 950fr, Panavia Tornado IDS. No. 1262, 950fr, Korolev and Vostok 1. No. 1263, 950fr, Tricholaema melanocephala.

**2017, July 28 Litho. *Perf. 13¼***

**Sheets of 4, #a-d**

**1224-1243** A320 Set of 20 215.00 215.00

**Souvenir Sheets**

**1244-1263** A320 Set of 20 215.00 215.00

Birdpex 8 Philatelic Exhibition, Mondorf-les-Bains, Luxembourg (Nos. 1243, 1263).

A321

No. 1264, 240fr — Marilyn Monroe (1926-62), actress: a, Wearing white fur coat. b, With signature. c, With star from Hollywood Walk of Fame. d, Wearing black sweater.

No. 1265, 240fr — Paul McCartney, rock musician, and: a, Emblem of the Beatles. b, Wife, Linda. c, Beatle bandmates, John Lennon, Ringo Starr and George Harrison. d, Musical score and curved piano keyboard.

No. 1266, 240fr — Charlie Chaplin (1889-1977), film actor, and: a, Actor Ben Turpin. b, Signature. c, Woman holding flower. d, Child actor.

No. 1267, 240fr — Marie Curie (1867-1934), chemist and physicist, and: a, Pitchblende, husband, Pierre (1859-1906). b, Nobel medals and Daughter, Irène Joliot-Curie (1897-1956). c, Curie Pavilion of Institut du Radium. d, World War I mobile radiological unit.

No. 1268, 240fr — Nelson Mandela (1918-2013), President of South Africa: a, With F. W. de Klerk, Pres. of South Africa, and Nobel medals and diplomas. b, With fist raised. c, Holding dove. d, With trophy and South African rugby player.

No. 1269, 240fr — Pres. Franklin D. Roosevelt (1882-1945): a, Signing declaration of war against Germany. b, Wearing top hat. c, With wife, Eleanor (1884-1962). d, Signing Social Security legislation.

No. 1270, 240fr — Battle of Dunkirk: a, British Admiral Bertram Home Ramsay (1883-1945). b, Airplane flying over battle. c, Battle aftermath. d, Troops in water.

No. 1271, 240fr — Pompidou Center, Paris, 40th anniv.: a, La Roue Rouge, by Fernand Léger. b, Quatre Passagers Roses de Face, by Jean Dubuffet. c, Blue in Violet, by Wassily Kandinsky. d, Vieilles Maisons, Saint-Ilpize en Haute Loire.

No. 1272, 240fr — Alexander Pushkin (1799-1837), poet: a, Portrait. b, Dueling pistols. c, Pushkin sitting on railing, signature. d, Sculpture and drawing of Pushkin.

No. 1273, 240fr — Tigers: a, Panthera tigris altaica. b, Panthera tigris tigris cub. c, Two Panthera tigris tigris. d, Panthera tigris tigris with white fur.

No. 1274, 240fr — Shells: a, Lunella smaragdus. b, Nautilus macromphalus. c, Cymbiola innexa. d, Bolinus brandaris.

No. 1275, 240fr — Mushrooms: a, Suillus luteus. b, Macrolepiota rhacodes. c, Boletus edulis. d, Tricholoma portentosum.

No. 1276, 240fr — Windmills and birds: a, Oud-Zuilen, Netherlands windmill and Alopochen aegyptiaca. b, East Hampton, New York windmill and Tyrannus tyrannus. c, Ramsey, United Kingdom windmill and Carduelis carduelis. d, Lautrec, France windmill and Cyanistes caeruleus.

No. 1277, 240fr — Lighthouses: a, Lorain Lighthouse, Ohio. b, Big Sable Point Lighthouse, Michigan. c, Cape Lookout Lighthouse, North Carolina. d, Block Island Southeast Lighthouse, Rhode Island.

No. 1278, 240fr — Japanese high-speed trains: a, Shinkansen Series E3. b, Shinkansen Series E4. c, Shinkansen Series 800. d, Shinkansen Series E5.

No. 1279, 240fr — Louis Renault (1877-1944), automobile manufacturer, and: a, Renault Dauphinoise Juvaquatre fire vehicle. b, Renault FT-17 tank. c, Renault Type B. d, Renault Reinastella, Arc de Triomphe.

No. 1280, 240fr — Louis Blériot (1872-1936), aviation pioneer: a, Blériot XI airplane on ground. b, Blériot and Eiffel Tower. c, Blériot and mountains. d, Blériot XI in flight.

No. 1281, 240fr — Outer Space Treaty, 50th anniv.: a, World Map. b, Moon, planets, balance. c, Earth, satellites in orbit, gavel. d, Satellite and nuclear missile.

No. 1282, 240fr — Christmas: a, Children placing ornaments on Christmas tree. b, Carolers and violinist near Christmas tree. c, Santa Claus and child. d, Child pulling sled carrying Christmas tree.

No. 1283, 240fr — New Year 2018 (Year of the Dog): a, Pekingese dog facing right. b, Pekingese dog facing forward, Chinese characters at top left. c, Pekingese dog facing forward, Chinese characters at top right. d, Pekingese dog facing left.

No. 1284, 950fr, Monroe in automobile. No. 1285, 950fr, McCartney playing guitar. No. 1286, 950fr, Chaplin dancing. No. 1287, 950fr, Marie Curie and model of atom. No. 1288, 950fr, Mandela with fist raised, diff. No. 1289, 950fr, Roosevelt at desk. No. 1290, 950fr, Map of Battle of Dunkirk, troops boarding ship. No. 1291, 950fr, Rythmes, by Robert Delaunay. No. 1292, 950fr, Pushkin holding quill pen. No. 1293, 950fr, Two Panthera tigris altaica. No. 1294, 950fr, Ceratosoma amoenum, Cypraea aurantia. No. 1295, 950fr, Lycoperdon perlatum. No. 1296, 950fr, Kuremaa, Estonia windmill and Ciconia ciconia. No. 1297, 950fr, Greens Ledge Lighthouse, Connecticut. No. 1298, 950fr, Shinkansen Series 500 Type EVA. No. 1299, 950fr, Renault and Renault 4CV. No. 1300, 950fr, Blériot and Eiffel Tower, diff. No. 1301, 950fr, Sputnik 1. No. 1302, 950fr, Santa Claus and reindeer. No. 1303, 950fr, Pekingese dog, diff.

**2017, Sept. 29 Litho. *Perf. 13¼***

**Sheets of 4, #a-d**

**1264-1283** A321 Set of 20 215.00 215.00

**Souvenir Sheets**

**1284-1303** A321 Set of 20 215.00 215.00

A322

A323

A324

Polar Bear — A325

Design: 950fr, Polar bear, diff.

***Perf. 12¾x13¼***

**2017, Dec. 11 Litho.**

| | | | | |
|---|---|---|---|---|
| **1304** | A322 240fr multi | | 2.75 | 2.75 |
| **1305** | A323 240fr multi | | 2.75 | 2.75 |
| **1306** | A324 240fr multi | | 2.75 | 2.75 |
| **1307** | A325 240fr multi | | 2.75 | 2.75 |
| | *Nos. 1304-1307 (4)* | | 11.00 | 11.00 |

**Souvenir Sheet**

***Perf. 13¼***

**1308** A325 950fr multi 11.00 11.00

Nos. 1304-1307 were each printed in sheets of 16 + 4 labels. No. 1308 contains one 45x38mm stamp.

A326

No. 1309, 240fr — Ursus maritimus: a, One polar bear, tree at left. b, Polar bear with head at right. c, Adult and two cubs. d, Polar bear with head at left, mouth open.

No. 1310, 240fr — Cat breeds: a, Korat. b, Toyger. c, Selkirk Rex. d, Chantilly.

No. 1311, 240fr — Wild dogs: a, Cuon alpinus. b, One Canis lupus dingo. c, Lycaon pictus. d, Two Canis lupus dingo.

No. 1312, 240fr — Loxodonta africana: a, One elephant facing right. b, One elephant facing left. c, Two elephants with trunks touching. d, Two elephants walking.

No. 1313, 240fr — Dolphins: a, Inia geoffrensis. b, Stenella coeruleoalba. c, Cephalorhynchus commersonii. d, Grampus griseus.

No. 1314, 240fr — Parrots: a, One Ara ararauna in flight. b, Psittacula krameri. c, Two Ara ararauna. d, Eolophus roseicapilla.

No. 1315, 240fr — Pigeon breeds: a, African Owl. b, Bouclier de Saxe (Saxon Shield). c, American Domestic Show Flight. d, Barbe Anglais (English Barb).

No. 1316, 240fr — Bee-eaters: a, Merops apiaster. b, Merops variegatus. c, Merops malimbicus. d, Merops breweri.

No. 1317, 240fr — Owls: a, Bubo scandiacus. b, Bubo lacteus. c, Bubo bubo. d, Strix seloputo.

No. 1318, 240fr — Butterflies: a, Apatura iris. b, Papilio glaucus. c, Battus philenor. d, Callophrys rubi.

No. 1319, 240fr — Turtles: a, Aldabrachelys gigantea. b, Malaclemys terrapin. c, Trachemys scripta elegans. d, Chelonia mydas.

No. 1320, 240fr — Dinosaurs: a, Lambeosaurus lambei. b, Oviraptor philoceratops. c, Archaeopteryx siemensii. d, Stegosaurus ungulatus.

No. 1321, 240fr — Prehistoric marine animals: a, Pteraspis stensioei, Prognathodon solvayi. b, Dearcmhara shawcrossi. c, Parapuzosia seppenradensis. d, Shastasaurus pacificus.

No. 1322, 240fr — Global warming: a, Giraffa camelopardalis tippelskirchi and text. b, Ursus maritimus and text. c, Cervus elaphus and text. d, Turbinaria reniformis and text.

No. 1323, 240fr — Orchids: a, Odontoglossum crispum. b, Cattleya "Blc. Greenwich." c, Vanda coerulea. d, Miltonia regnellii.

No. 1324, 240fr — Minerals: a, Brookite, quartz. b, Uvarovite. c, Andradite. d, Willemite.

No. 1325, 240fr — Fire trucks: a, 2010 Oshkosh Striker 3000. b, 2012 Iveco Trakker. c, 2011 DAF LF. d, 2011 Scania P.

No. 1326, 240fr — Protestant Reformation, 500th anniv.: a, Martin Luther (1483-1546). b, Martin Bucer (1491-1551). c, Ulrich Zwingli (1484-1531). d, John Calvin (1509-64).

No. 1327, 240fr — 2017 Nobel Laureates: a, Michael Rosbach (Physiology or Medicine). b, Joachim Frank (Chemistry). c, Beatrice Fihn, director of International Campaign to Abolish Nuclear Weapons (Peace). d, Kazuo Ishiguro (Literature).

No. 1328, 950fr, Ursus maritiumus, diff. No. 1329, 950fr, Abyssinian cat. No. 1330, 950fr, Cuon alpinus, diff. No. 1331, 950fr, Loxodonta africana, diff. No. 1332, 950fr, Lagenorhynchus acutus. No. 1333, 950fr, Guaruba guarouba. No. 1334, 950fr, Belgian Ringbeater pigeon. No. 1335, 950fr, Merops nubicoides. No. 1336, 950fr, Megascops kennicottii. No. 1337, 950fr, Papilio troilus. No. 1338, 950fr, Graptemys geographica. No. 1339, 950fr, Pterodactylus antiquus. No. 1340, 950fr, Dunkleosteus terrelli. No. 1341, 950fr, Aptenodytes forsteri. No. 1342, 950fr, Beallara marfitch "Howard's Dream." No. 1343, 950fr, Brazilianite. No. 1344, 950fr, 1984 Oshkosh P19 fire truck. No. 1345, 950fr, Luther, diff. No. 1346, 950fr, Richard H. Thaler, 2017 Nobel Laureate in Economics, Nobel medal, Robert Fludd (1574-1637), mathematician.

**2017, Dec. 11 Litho. *Perf. 13¼***

**Sheets of 4, #a-d**

**1309-1327** A326 Set of 19 200.00 200.00

**Souvenir Sheets**

**1328-1346** A326 Set of 19 200.00 200.00

## AIR POST STAMPS

**Afars and Issas Nos. C104-C105, C103 Overprinted in Brown or Black**

Nos. C106, C107

No. C108

**1977 Engr. *Perf. 13***

| | | | |
|---|---|---|---|
| **C106** | AP37 55fr multi (Br) | 2.75 | 1.75 |
| **C107** | AP37 75fr multi | 11.00 | 4.00 |

**Litho. *Perf. 12***

| | | | |
|---|---|---|---|
| **C108** | AP36 500fr multi | 15.00 | 13.50 |
| | *Nos. C106-C108 (3)* | 22.25 | 18.25 |

Map of Djibouti, Dove, UN Emblem — AP38

**1977, Oct. 19 Photo. *Perf. 13***

**C109** AP38 300fr multi 6.50 4.25

Djibouti's admission to the United Nations.

Marcel Brochet MB 101, 1955 — AP39

Djibouti Aero Club: 85fr, Tiger Moth, 1960. 200fr, Rallye-Commodore, 1973.

**1978, Feb. 27 Litho. *Perf. 13***

| | | | |
|---|---|---|---|
| **C110** | AP39 60fr multi | 1.25 | .40 |
| **C111** | AP39 85fr multi | 1.75 | .65 |
| **C112** | AP39 200fr multi | 4.00 | 1.10 |
| | *Nos. C110-C112 (3)* | 7.00 | 2.15 |

Old Man, by Rubens AP40

500fr, Hippopotamus Hunt, by Rubens.

**1978, Apr. 24 Photo. *Perf. 13***

| | | | |
|---|---|---|---|
| **C113** | AP40 50fr multi | 1.50 | .35 |
| **C114** | AP40 500fr multi, horiz. | 11.00 | 3.25 |

Peter Paul Rubens (1577-1640).

Player Holding Soccer Cup — AP41

Design: 300fr, Soccer player, map of South America with Argentina, Cup and emblem.

**1978, June 20 Litho. *Perf. 13***

| | | | |
|---|---|---|---|
| **C115** | AP41 100fr multi | 2.00 | .50 |
| **C116** | AP41 300fr multi | 6.00 | 1.75 |

11th World Cup Soccer Championship, Argentina, June 1-25.

For overprints see Nos. C117-C118.

**Nos. C115-C116 Overprinted**

a

b

**1978, Aug. 20 Litho. *Perf. 13***

| | | | |
|---|---|---|---|
| **C117** | AP41 (a) 100fr multi | 3.00 | .40 |
| **C118** | AP41 (b) 300fr multi | 7.25 | 1.25 |

Argentina's victory in 1978 Soccer Championship.

Tahitian Women, by Gauguin — AP42

Young Hare, by Dürer AP43

*Perf. 13x12½, 12½x13*

**1978, Sept. 25** **Litho.**

| | | | | |
|---|---|---|---|---|
| **C119** | AP42 | 100fr multi | 3.00 | .40 |
| **C120** | AP43 | 250fr multi | 6.50 | 1.50 |

Paul Gauguin (1848-1903) and Albrecht Dürer (1471-1528), painters.

Common Design Types pictured following the introduction.

**Philexafrique II-Essen Issue**

Common Design Types

Designs: No. C121, Lynx and Djibouti No. 456. No. C122, Jay and Brunswick No. 3.

**1978, Dec. 13** **Litho.** ***Perf. 13x12½***

| | | | | |
|---|---|---|---|---|
| **C121** | CD138 | 90fr multi | 4.00 | 1.75 |
| **C122** | CD139 | 90fr multi | 4.00 | 1.75 |
| *a.* | | Pair, Nos. C121-C122 + label | 8.50 | 8.50 |

UPU Emblem, Map of Djibouti, Dove — AP44

**1978, Dec. 18** **Engr.** ***Perf. 13***

| | | | | |
|---|---|---|---|---|
| **C123** | AP44 | 200fr multi | 3.75 | 1.10 |

Centenary of Congress of Paris.

Junkers JU-52 and Dewoitine D-338 — AP45

Powered Flight, 75th Anniversary: 250fr, Potez P63-11, 1941 and Supermarine Spitfire HF-VII, 1942. 500fr, Concorde, 1969 and Sikorsky S-40 "American Clipper," 1931.

**1979, May 21** **Litho.** ***Perf. 13x12½***

| | | | | |
|---|---|---|---|---|
| **C124** | AP45 | 140fr multi | 3.00 | .60 |
| **C125** | AP45 | 250fr multi | 4.50 | 1.00 |
| **C126** | AP45 | 500fr multi | 9.00 | 1.75 |
| | | *Nos. C124-C126 (3)* | 16.50 | 3.35 |

The Laundress, by Honore Daumier AP46

**1979, July 10** **Litho.** ***Perf. 12½x13***

| | | | | |
|---|---|---|---|---|
| **C127** | AP46 | 500fr multi | 12.00 | 3.00 |

Olympic Emblem, Skis, Sleds — AP47

**1980, Jan. 21** **Litho.** ***Perf. 13***

| | | | | |
|---|---|---|---|---|
| **C128** | AP47 | 150fr multi | 3.00 | .60 |

13th Winter Olympic Games, Lake Placid, N.Y., Feb. 12-24.

For surcharges see Nos. C133-C134.

Cathedral of the Archangel, Basketball, Moscow '80 Emblem — AP48

120fr, Lomonossov Univ., Moscow, soccer. 250fr, Cathedral of the Annunciation, running.

**1980, Apr. 10** **Litho.** ***Perf. 13***

| | | | | |
|---|---|---|---|---|
| **C129** | AP48 | 60fr multi | 1.05 | .25 |
| **C130** | AP48 | 120fr multi | 2.10 | .40 |
| **C131** | AP48 | 250fr multi | 4.25 | 1.00 |
| | | *Nos. C129-C131 (3)* | 7.40 | 1.65 |

22nd Summer Olympic Games, Moscow, July 18-Aug. 3.

Air Djibouti, 1st Anniversary — AP49

**1980, Mar. 29** **Litho.** ***Perf. 13x12½***

| | | | | |
|---|---|---|---|---|
| **C132** | AP49 | 400fr multi | 9.00 | 2.50 |

**No. C128 Surcharged in Black and Blue or Purple**

**1980, Apr. 5** **Litho.** ***Perf. 13***

| | | | | |
|---|---|---|---|---|
| **C133** | AP47 | 80fr on 150fr | 1.75 | .50 |
| **C134** | AP47 | 200fr on 150fr (P) | 4.00 | 1.50 |

Apollo 11 Moon Landing, 10th Anniversary — AP50

Space Conquests: 300fr, Apollo-Soyuz space project, 5th anniversary.

**1980, May 8**

| | | | | |
|---|---|---|---|---|
| **C135** | AP50 | 200fr multi | 4.00 | .75 |
| **C136** | AP50 | 300fr multi | 6.50 | 1.25 |

Satellite Earth Station Inauguration — AP51

**1980, July 3** **Litho.** ***Perf. 13***

| | | | | |
|---|---|---|---|---|
| **C137** | AP51 | 500fr multi | 9.50 | 1.75 |

Graf Zeppelin — AP52

**1980, Oct. 2** **Litho.** ***Perf. 13***

| | | | | |
|---|---|---|---|---|
| **C138** | AP52 | 100fr shown | 2.25 | .40 |
| **C139** | AP52 | 150fr Ferdinand von Zeppelin, blimp | 3.25 | .60 |

Zeppelin flight, 80th anniversary.

Voyager Passing Saturn — AP53

**1980, Dec. 21** **Litho.** ***Perf. 13***

| | | | | |
|---|---|---|---|---|
| **C140** | AP53 | 250fr multi | 5.50 | 1.00 |

AP54

World Cup Soccer Preliminary Games: 200fr, Players, diff.

**1981, Jan. 14**

| | | | | |
|---|---|---|---|---|
| **C141** | AP54 | 80fr multi | 1.75 | .30 |
| **C142** | AP54 | 200fr multi | 4.25 | .65 |

AP55

**1981, Feb. 10** **Litho.** ***Perf. 13***

| | | | | |
|---|---|---|---|---|
| **C143** | AP55 | 100fr multi | 3.00 | .50 |

European-African Economic Convention.

5th Anniversary of Viking I Take-off to Mars — AP56

20th Anniversary of Various Space Flights: 75fr, Vostok I, Yuri Gagarin, vert. 150fr, Freedom 7, Alan B. Shepard, vert.

**1981, Mar. 9** **Litho.** ***Perf. 13***

| | | | | |
|---|---|---|---|---|
| **C144** | AP56 | 75fr multi | 1.75 | .35 |
| **C145** | AP56 | 120fr multi | 2.25 | .45 |
| **C146** | AP56 | 150fr multi | 3.00 | .65 |
| | | *Nos. C144-C146 (3)* | 7.00 | 1.45 |

Football Players, by Picasso (1881-1973) — AP57

Design: 400fr Man Wearing a Turban, by Rembrandt (1606-1669), vert.

*Perf. 13x12½, 12½x13*

**1981, Aug. 3** **Litho.**

| | | | | |
|---|---|---|---|---|
| **C147** | AP57 | 300fr multi | 7.00 | 1.40 |
| **C148** | AP57 | 400fr multi | 7.50 | 1.75 |

Columbia Space Shuttle — AP58

90fr, Shuttle launching.

**1981, Sept. 24** **Litho.** ***Perf. 13***

| | | | | |
|---|---|---|---|---|
| **C149** | AP58 | 90fr multicolored | 1.75 | .40 |
| **C150** | AP58 | 120fr shown | 2.50 | .60 |

**Nos. C149-C150 Overprinted in Brown**

No. C151

No. C152

**1981, Nov. 12** **Litho.** ***Perf. 13***

| | | | | |
|---|---|---|---|---|
| **C151** | AP58 | 90fr multi | 1.75 | .50 |
| **C152** | AP58 | 120fr multi | 2.50 | .75 |

1982 World Cup Soccer — AP59

Designs: Various soccer players.

**1982, Jan. 20**
**C153** AP59 110fr multi 2.10 .60
**C154** AP59 220fr multi 4.75 1.25

For overprints see Nos. C166-C167.

Space Anniversaries — AP60

Designs: 40fr, Luna 9 moon landing, 15th, vert. 60fr, John Glenn's flight, 20th, vert. 180fr, Viking I Mars landing, 5th.

**1982, Feb. 15**
**C155** AP60 40fr multi .70 .25
**C156** AP60 60fr multi 1.10 .30
**C157** AP60 180fr multi 3.00 1.00
*Nos. C155-C157 (3)* 4.80 1.55

21st Birthday of Princess Diana of Wales AP61

**1982, Apr. 29 Litho. *Perf. 12½x13***
**C158** AP61 120fr Portrait 2.25 .75
**C159** AP61 180fr Portrait, diff. 3.50 1.00

For overprints see Nos. C168-C169.

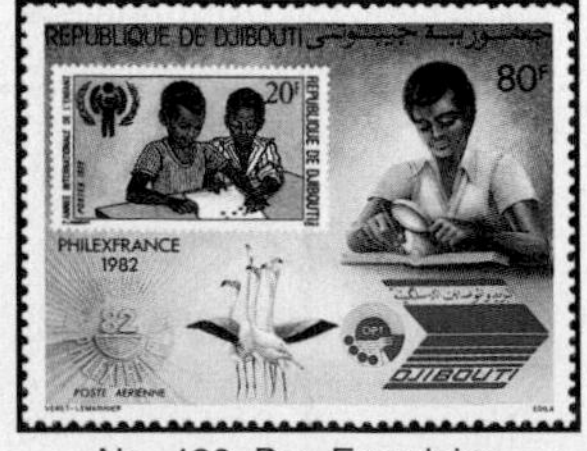


No. 489, Boy Examining Collection — AP62

**1982, May 10 *Perf. 13x12½***
**C160** AP62 80fr shown 2.50 .75
**C161** AP62 140fr No. 495 3.75 1.00
*a.* Pair, Nos. C160-C161 + label 6.50 6.50

PHILEXFRANCE '82 Stamp Exhibition, Paris, June 11-21.

1350th Anniv. of Mohammed's Death at Medina — AP63

**1982, June 8 Litho. *Perf. 13***
**C162** AP63 500fr Medina Mosque 9.00 2.00

Scouting Year — AP64

**1982, June 28**
**C163** AP64 95fr Baden-Powell 1.75 .50
**C164** AP64 200fr Camp, scouts 4.00 1.25

2nd UN Conference on Peaceful Uses of Outer Space, Vienna, Aug. 9-21 — AP65

**1982, Aug. 19**
**C165** AP65 350fr multi 6.75 3.00

**Nos. C153-C154 Overprinted**

**1982, July 21 Litho. *Perf. 13***
**C166** AP59 110fr multi 2.00 .60
**C167** AP59 220fr multi 4.00 1.10

Italy's victory in 1982 World Cup.

**Nos. C158-C159 Overprinted in Blue or Red**

No. C168

No. C169

**1982, Aug. 9 *Perf. 12½x13***
**C168** AP61 120fr multi 2.50 .75
**C169** AP61 180fr multi (R) 3.50 1.00

Birth of Prince William of Wales, June 21.

Franklin D. Roosevelt (1882-1945) AP66

**1982, Oct. 7 Litho. *Perf. 13***
**C170** AP66 115fr shown 2.00 .50
**C171** AP66 250fr George Washington 5.25 1.00

Manned Flight Bicentenary AP67

35fr, Montgolfiere, 1783. 45fr, Giffard, Paris Exposition, 1878. 120fr, Double Eagle II, 1978.

**1983, Jan. 20 Litho.**
**C172** AP67 35fr multi .80 .25
**C173** AP67 45fr multi 1.35 .30
**C174** AP67 120fr multi 3.50 .80
*Nos. C172-C174 (3)* 5.65 1.35

Pre-olympic Year — AP68

**1983, Feb. 15**
**C175** AP68 75fr Volleyball 1.50 .55
**C176** AP68 125fr Wind surfing 2.75 .85

50th Anniv. of Air France — AP69

**1983, Mar. 20 Litho. *Perf. 13***
**C177** AP69 25fr Bloch 220 .50 .25
**C178** AP69 100fr DC-4 1.75 .70
**C179** AP69 175fr Boeing 747 3.50 1.10
*Nos. C177-C179 (3)* 5.75 2.05

AP70

180fr, Martin Luther King, Jr. (1929-68), civil rights leader. 250fr, Alfred Nobel (1833-96)

**1983, May 18 Litho. *Perf. 13***
**C180** AP70 180fr multi 3.50 1.25
**C181** AP70 250fr multi 4.50 2.00

AP71

Service Clubs: 90fr, Rotary Club Intl., Sailing Show, Toronto, June 5-9. 150fr, Lions Club Intl., Honolulu Meeting, June 22-24, Djibouti lighthouse.

**1983, July 18 Litho. *Perf. 13***
**C182** AP71 90fr multi 3.00 1.50
**C183** AP71 150fr multi 3.00 1.00
*a.* Pair, Nos. C182-C183 + label 5.50 5.50

Vintage Motor Cars — AP72

**1983, Sep. 20 Litho. *Perf. 13x12½***
**C184** AP72 60fr Renault, 1904 1.90 .50
**C185** AP72 80fr Mercedes, 1910, vert. 2.50 .65
**C186** AP72 110fr Lorraine-Dietrich, 1912 3.00 .85
*Nos. C184-C186 (3)* 7.40 2.00

Souvenir Sheet

Air France, 50th Anniv. — AP73

**1983, Oct. 7 Litho. *Perf. 12½***
**Self-Adhesive**
**C187** AP73 250fr multicolored 25.00 25.00

Printed on wood.

Vostok VI AP74

**1983, Oct. 20 Litho. *Perf. 12***
**C188** AP74 120fr shown 2.25 .80
**C189** AP74 200fr Explorer I 3.75 1.10

1984 Winter Olympics — AP75

**1984, Feb. 14 Litho. *Perf. 13***

| | | | | |
|---|---|---|---|---|
| **C190** | AP75 | 70fr Speed skating | 1.50 | .55 |
| **C191** | AP75 | 130fr Figure skating | 2.50 | 1.10 |

For overprints see Nos. C196-C197.

Souvenir Sheet

Ship — AP76

**1984, Feb. 14 Litho. *Perf. 12½***

| | | | | |
|---|---|---|---|---|
| **C192** | AP76 | 250fr multi | 11.00 | 11.00 |

Sea-Me-We (South-east Asia-Middle East-Western Europe) submarine cable construction agreement.

Motorized Hang Gliders — AP77

Various hang gliders.

**1984, Mar. 12 *Perf. 13x12½***

| | | | | |
|---|---|---|---|---|
| **C193** | AP77 | 65fr multi | 1.25 | .50 |
| **C194** | AP77 | 85fr multi | 1.60 | .60 |
| **C195** | AP77 | 100fr multi | 2.10 | .75 |
| | | *Nos. C193-C195 (3)* | 4.95 | 1.85 |

**Nos. C190-C191 Overprinted with Winners' Names and Country**

**1984, Mar. 28 *Perf. 13***

| | | | | |
|---|---|---|---|---|
| **C196** | AP75 | 70fr multi | 1.50 | .50 |
| **C197** | AP75 | 130fr multi | 2.75 | 1.00 |

Portrait of Marguerite Matisse, 1910, by Henri Matisse AP78

Design: 200fr, Portrait of Mario Varvogli, by Amedeo Modigliani.

**1984, Apr. 15 Litho. *Perf. 12½x13***

| | | | | |
|---|---|---|---|---|
| **C198** | AP78 | 150fr multi | 3.75 | 1.00 |
| **C199** | AP78 | 200fr multi | 4.75 | 1.40 |

1984 Summer Olympics — AP79

**1984, May 24 *Perf. 13***

| | | | | |
|---|---|---|---|---|
| **C200** | AP79 | 50fr Running | 1.00 | .40 |
| **C201** | AP79 | 60fr High jump | 1.25 | .40 |
| **C202** | AP79 | 80fr Swimming | 1.50 | .60 |
| | | *Nos. C200-C202 (3)* | 3.75 | 1.40 |

Battle Scene — AP80

**1984, June 16 Litho. *Perf. 13x12½***

| | | | | |
|---|---|---|---|---|
| **C203** | AP80 | 300fr multi | 6.00 | 2.75 |

125th anniv. of Battle of Solferino and 120th anniv. of Red Cross.

Bleriot's Flight over English Channel, 75th Anniv. — AP81

**1984, July 8**

| | | | | |
|---|---|---|---|---|
| **C204** | AP81 | 40fr 14-Bis plans | .90 | .40 |
| **C205** | AP81 | 75fr Britten-Norman Islander | 1.40 | .75 |
| **C206** | AP81 | 90fr Air Djibouti jet | 1.50 | 1.00 |
| | | *Nos. C204-C206 (3)* | 3.80 | 2.15 |

375th Anniv., Galileo's Telescope AP82

120fr, Telescopes, spacecraft. 180fr, Galileo, telescopes.

**1984, Oct. 7 Litho. *Perf. 13***

| | | | | |
|---|---|---|---|---|
| **C207** | AP82 | 120fr multicolored | 2.50 | .80 |
| **C208** | AP82 | 180fr multicolored | 3.50 | 1.10 |

1984 Soccer Events — AP83

**1984, Oct. 20 Litho. *Perf. 13***

| | | | | |
|---|---|---|---|---|
| **C209** | AP83 | 80fr Euro Cup | 2.50 | .60 |
| **C210** | AP83 | 80fr Los Angeles Olympics | 2.50 | .60 |
| *a.* | | Pair, Nos. C209-C210 + label | 4.50 | 4.00 |

Service Clubs — AP84

50fr, Lions, World Leprosy Day. 60fr, Rotary, chess board, pieces.

**1985, Feb. 23 Litho. *Perf. 13***

| | | | | |
|---|---|---|---|---|
| **C211** | AP84 | 50fr multicolored | 1.40 | .50 |
| **C212** | AP84 | 60fr multicolored | 1.60 | .55 |

Nos. C211-C212 exist in souvenir sheets of 1.

Telecommunications Technology — AP85

No. C213, Technician, researchist, operator. No. C214, Offshore oil rig, transmission tower, government building.

**1985, July 2 *Perf. 13x12½***

| | | | | |
|---|---|---|---|---|
| **C213** | AP85 | 80fr multi | 2.50 | .55 |
| **C214** | AP85 | 80fr multi | 2.50 | .55 |
| *a.* | | Pair, Nos. C213-C214 + label | 6.25 | 1.25 |

PHILEXAFRICA '85, Lome.

Telecommunications Development — AP86

50fr, Intl. transmission center. 90fr, Ariane rocket, vert. 120fr, ARABSAT satellite.

**1985, Oct. 2 *Perf. 13***

| | | | | |
|---|---|---|---|---|
| **C215** | AP86 | 50fr multi | .90 | .35 |
| **C216** | AP86 | 90fr multi | 1.60 | .65 |
| **C217** | AP86 | 120fr multi | 2.00 | .90 |
| | | *Nos. C215-C217 (3)* | 4.50 | 1.90 |

Youths Windsurfing, Playing Tennis — AP87

No. C219, Tadjoura Highway construction.

**1985, Nov. 13 *Perf. 13x12½***

| | | | | |
|---|---|---|---|---|
| **C218** | AP87 | 100fr multi | 2.50 | 1.00 |
| **C219** | AP87 | 100fr multi | 2.50 | 1.00 |
| *a.* | | Pair, Nos. C218-C219 + label | 6.00 | 5.00 |

PHILEXAFRICA '85, Lome, Togo, 11/16-24.

1986 World Cup Soccer Championships, Mexico — AP88

**1986, Feb. 24 Litho. *Perf. 13***

| | | | | |
|---|---|---|---|---|
| **C220** | AP88 | 75fr shown | 1.50 | .50 |
| **C221** | AP88 | 100fr Players, stadium | 2.00 | .70 |

For overprints see Nos. C223-C224.

Statue of Liberty, Cent. — AP89

**1986, May 21**

| | | | | |
|---|---|---|---|---|
| **C222** | AP89 | 250fr multi | 4.50 | 1.75 |

**Nos. C220-C221 Ovptd. with Winners**

**1986, Sept. 15 Litho. *Perf. 13***

| | | | | |
|---|---|---|---|---|
| **C223** | | 75fr "FRANCE - BELGIQUE / 4-2" | 1.25 | .65 |
| **C224** | | 100fr "3-2 ARGENTINE-RFA" | 1.75 | .80 |

1986 World Chess Championships, May 1-19 — AP89a

Malayan animal chess pieces: 80fr, Knight, bishops. 120fr, Rook, king, pawn.

**1986, Oct. 13 Litho. *Perf. 13***

| | | | | |
|---|---|---|---|---|
| **C225** | AP89a | 80fr multi | 2.00 | .60 |
| **C226** | AP89a | 120fr multi | 3.25 | .90 |

Yuri Gagarin, Sputnik Spacecraft — AP90

**1986, Nov. 27 Litho. *Perf. 13***

| | | | | |
|---|---|---|---|---|
| **C227** | AP90 | 150fr shown | 3.00 | 1.10 |
| **C228** | AP90 | 200fr Space rendezvous, 1966 | 4.25 | 1.25 |

First man in space, 25th anniv.; Gemini 8-Agena link-up, 20th anniv.

Historic Flights — AP91

**1987, Jan. 22 Litho. *Perf. 13***

**C229** AP91 55fr Amiot 370 1.25 .40
**C230** AP91 80fr Spirit of St. Louis 1.75 .55
**C231** AP91 120fr Voyager 2.50 .90
*Nos. C229-C231 (3)* 5.50 1.85

First flight from Istria to Djibouti, 1942; Lindbergh's Transatlantic flight, 1927; nonstop world circumnavigation without refueling.

For surcharge see No. C240.

Souvenir Sheet

Fight Against Leprosy — AP91a

Design: Raoul Follereau (b. 1903), care giver to lepers, Gerhard Hansen (1841-1912), discoverer of bacillus of leprosy.

**1987, Mar. 23 Litho. *Perf. 13x12½***
**Self-Adhesive**

**C231A** AP91a 500fr multi 20.00 15.00

No. C231A printed on wood.

Pres. Aptidon, Natl. Crest and Flag AP92

**1987, June 27 Litho. *Perf. 12½x13***

**C232** AP92 250fr multi 4.50 1.50

Natl. independence, 10th anniv.

Telstar, 25th Anniv. — AP93

**1987, Oct. 1 *Perf. 13***

**C233** AP93 190fr shown 3.50 1.25
*a.* Souvenir sheet, 1 #C233 14.00 —
**C234** AP93 250fr Samuel Morse, telegraph key 4.50 1.50
*a.* Souvenir sheet, 1 #C234 14.00 —

Invention of the telegraph, 150th anniv. (250fr).

Nos. C233a and C234a also exist imperf. Value, set of 2, $40.

City of Djibouti, Cent. — AP94

100fr, Djibouti Creek & quay, 1887. 150fr, Aerial view of city, 1987. 250fr, Somali Coast #6, 20, postmarks of 1898 & 1903.

**1987, Nov. 15 Litho. *Perf. 13x12½***

**C235** AP94 100fr blk & buff 2.00 1.10
**C236** AP94 150fr multi 3.00 1.60
*a.* Pair, Nos. C235-C236 + label 6.00 2.75

**Souvenir Sheet**

**237** AP94 250fr multi 5.50 5.50

No. C237 has decorative margin like design of 100fr.

Intl. Red Cross and Red Crescent Organizations, 125th Anniv. — AP95

**1988, Feb. 17 Litho. *Perf. 13***

**C238** AP95 300fr multi 6.00 3.25

1988 Summer Olympics, Seoul — AP96

**1988, June 15 Litho. *Perf. 13***

**C239** AP96 105fr multi 3.00 1.00

For overprint see No. C242.

**No. C229 Surcharged in Black**

**1988, June 28**

**C240** AP91 70fr on 55fr multi 3.00 1.50

Air race in memory of the Paris-Djibouti-St. Denis flight of French aviator Roland Garros (1888-1913).

World Post Day — AP97

**1988, Oct. 9 Litho. *Perf. 13***

**C241** AP97 1000fr multi 18.00 10.00

**No. C239 Overprinted**

**1988, Dec. 15 Litho. *Perf. 13***

**C242** AP96 105fr multi 2.25 1.50

World Telecommunications Day — AP98

**1989, May 17 Litho. *Perf. 12½***

**C243** AP98 150fr multi 2.75 1.50

PHILEXFRANCE '89, Declaration of Human Rights and Citizenship Bicent. — AP99

**1989, July 14 Litho. *Perf. 12½x13***

**C244** AP99 120fr multi 2.75 1.25

Salt, Lake Assal — AP100

**1989, Sept. 15 Litho. *Perf. 13***

**C245** AP100 300fr multicolored 6.75 3.50

### POSTAGE DUE STAMP

Urn for Milking Camel — D1

**1988, Jan. 20 Litho. *Perf. 13***

**J1** D1 60fr multi 1.20 .65

## DOMINICA

ˌdä-mə-ˈnē-kə

LOCATION — The largest island of the Windward group in the West Indies. Southeast of Puerto Rico.
GOVT. — Republic in British Commonwealth
AREA — 290 sq. mi.
POP. — 64,881 (1999 est.)
CAPITAL — Roseau

Formerly a Presidency of the Leeward Islands, Dominica became a separate colony under the governor of the Windward Islands on January 1, 1940. Dominica joined the West Indies federation April 22, 1958. In 1968, Dominica became an associate state of Britain; in 1978, an independent nation.

12 Pence = 1 Shilling
20 Shillings = 1 Pound
100 Cents = 1 Dollar (1949)

**Catalogue values for unused stamps in this country are for Never Hinged items, beginning with Scott 112.**

**Watermark**

Wmk. 334 — Rectangles

Queen Victoria — A1

***Perf. 12½***

**1874, May 4 Typo. Wmk. 1**

1 A1 1p violet 170.00 55.00
*a.* Vertical half used as ½p on cover *9,000.*
2 A1 6p green 625.00 115.00
3 A1 1sh deep lilac rose 375.00 80.00
*Nos. 1-3 (3)* 1,170. 250.00

During 1875-87 some issues were manuscript dated with village names. These are considered postally used. Stamps with entire village names sell for much more, starting at $100.

**1877-79 *Perf. 14***

4 A1 ½p bister ('79) 19.00 *62.50*
5 A1 1p violet 20.00 3.75
*a.* Diagonal or vertical half used as ½p on cover 2,600.
6 A1 2½p red brown ('79) 275.00 45.00
7 A1 4p blue ('79) 130.00 4.00
8 A1 6p green 170.00 22.50
9 A1 1sh dp lilac rose 140.00 57.50
*Nos. 4-9 (6)* 754.00 195.25

For surcharges see Nos. 10-15.

**No. 5 Bisected and Surcharged in Black or Red**

a b c

**1882**

10 A1(a) ½p on half of 1p 240.00 57.50
*a.* Inverted surcharge 1,150. 900.00
*b.* Surcharge tete beche pair *2,600.* *2,000.*
11 A1(b) ½p on half of 1p 72.50 42.50
*a.* Surch. reading downward 72.50 42.50
*b.* Double surcharge 900.00
12 A1(c) ½p on half of 1p (R) 35.00 20.00
*a.* Inverted surcharge 1,150. 550.00
*b.* Double surcharge 1,850. 750.00
*Nos. 10-12 (3)* 347.50 120.00

The existence of genuine examples of No. 10b has been questioned.

Nos. 8 and 9 Surcharged in Black

**1886**

| | | | | |
|---|---|---|---|---|
| 13 | A1 | ½p on 6p green | 12.00 | 13.00 |
| 14 | A1 | 1p on 6p green | *45,000.* | *12,500.* |
| 15 | A1 | 1p on 1sh | 24.00 | *22.00* |
| *a.* | | Double surcharge | 11,500. | 4,250. |

All examples of No. 14 may have small pin marks which may have been part of the surcharging process.

**1883-89** **Wmk. 2**

| | | | | |
|---|---|---|---|---|
| 16 | A1 | ½p bister ('83) | 7.00 | *11.50* |
| 17 | A1 | ½p green ('86) | 5.75 | *6.25* |
| 18 | A1 | 1p violet ('86) | 60.00 | 16.00 |
| *a.* | | Half used as ½p on cover | | 2,350. |
| 19 | A1 | 1p dp carmine ('89) | 4.25 | *14.00* |
| *a.* | | 1p rose ('87) | 19.00 | *26.00* |
| *b.* | | Vert. half used as ½p on cover | | 2,100. |
| 20 | A1 | 2½p red brn ('84) | 160.00 | 4.00 |
| 21 | A1 | 2½p ultra ('88) | 4.25 | *8.50* |
| 22 | A1 | 4p gray ('86) | 8.25 | *7.75* |
| 23 | A1 | 6p orange ('88) | 23.00 | *92.50* |
| 24 | A1 | 1sh dp lil rose ('88) | 200.00 | *500.00* |
| | | *Nos. 16-24 (9)* | 472.50 | *660.50* |

Roseau, Capital of Dominica — A6

King Edward VII — A7

**1903** **Wmk. 1** ***Perf. 14***

**Ordinary Paper**

| | | | | |
|---|---|---|---|---|
| 25 | A6 | ½p gray green | 5.25 | 4.75 |
| 26 | A6 | 1p car & black | 17.50 | .80 |
| 27 | A6 | 2p brn & gray grn | 6.00 | *8.00* |
| 28 | A6 | 2½p ultra & blk | 13.00 | 5.25 |
| 29 | A6 | 3p black & vio | 11.50 | 4.50 |
| 30 | A6 | 6p org brn & blk | 15.00 | *22.50* |
| 31 | A6 | 1sh gray grn & red vio | 42.50 | *52.50* |
| 32 | A6 | 2sh red vio & blk | 40.00 | *35.00* |
| 33 | A6 | 2sh6p ocher & gray grn | 23.00 | *92.50* |
| 34 | A7 | 5sh brown & blk | 125.00 | *175.00* |
| | | *Nos. 25-34 (10)* | 298.75 | *400.80* |

Nos. 25 to 29 and 31 are on both ordinary and chalky paper. For detailed listings, see the *Scott Classic Specialized Catalogue of Stamps & Covers.*

**1907-20** **Chalky Paper** **Wmk. 3**

| | | | | |
|---|---|---|---|---|
| 35 | A6 | ½p gray green | 15.00 | 11.00 |
| 36 | A6 | 1p car & black | 2.50 | .55 |
| 37 | A6 | 2p brn & gray grn | 16.00 | *24.00* |
| 38 | A6 | 2½p ultra & black | 5.50 | 27.50 |
| 39 | A6 | 3p black & vio | 5.00 | *20.00* |
| 40 | A6 | 3p vio, *yel,* chalky paper ('09) | 3.75 | *5.25* |
| 41 | A6 | 6p org brn & blk ('08) | 65.00 | *100.00* |
| 42 | A6 | 6p vio & dl vio, chalky paper ('09) | 12.50 | *19.00* |
| 43 | A6 | 1sh gray grn & red vio | 4.75 | *67.50* |
| 44 | A6 | 1sh blk, *green,* chalky paper ('10) | 3.75 | 5.00 |
| 45 | A6 | 2sh red vio & blk ('08) | 30.00 | *40.00* |
| 46 | A6 | 2sh ultra & vio, *bl* ('19) | 32.50 | *110.00* |
| 47 | A6 | 2sh6p ocher & gray grn ('08) | 27.50 | *75.00* |
| 48 | A6 | 2sh6p red & blk, *bl* ('20) | 32.50 | *125.00* |
| 49 | A7 | 5sh brn & blk ('08) | 75.00 | 75.00 |
| | | *Nos. 35-49 (15)* | 331.25 | *704.80* |

Nos. 40, 42 and 44 are on both ordinary and chalky paper. For detailed listings, see the *Scott Classic Specialized Catalogue of Stamps & Covers.*

For type surcharged see No. 55.

**1908-09** **Ordinary Paper**

| | | | | |
|---|---|---|---|---|
| 50 | A6 | ½p green | 9.50 | 6.25 |
| 51 | A6 | 1p scarlet | 2.00 | .75 |
| *a.* | | 1p carmine | 4.50 | .45 |
| 52 | A6 | 2p gray ('09) | 5.00 | *17.50* |
| 53 | A6 | 2½p ultramarine | 9.50 | *9.75* |
| *a.* | | 2½p bright blue ('18) | 5.75 | *10.50* |
| | | *Nos. 50-53 (4)* | 26.00 | *34.25* |

King George V — A8

**1914** **Chalky Paper** ***Perf. 14***

| | | | | |
|---|---|---|---|---|
| 54 | A8 | 5sh grn & scar, *yel* | 70.00 | *100.00* |

Type of 1903 Surcharged

**1920**

| | | | | |
|---|---|---|---|---|
| 55 | A6 | 1½p on 2½p orange | 7.50 | 4.75 |

**1921** **Ordinary Paper** **Wmk. 4**

| | | | | |
|---|---|---|---|---|
| 56 | A6 | ½p green | 3.50 | *25.00* |
| 57 | A6 | 1p rose red | 3.00 | *4.00* |
| 58 | A6 | 1½p orange | 4.75 | *18.00* |
| 59 | A6 | 2p gray | 4.25 | *4.00* |
| 60 | A6 | 2½p ultra | 3.25 | *17.50* |
| 61 | A6 | 6p vio & dl vio | 5.00 | *50.00* |
| 62 | A6 | 2sh ultra & vio, *bl* | 50.00 | *145.00* |
| 63 | A6 | 2sh6p red & blk, *bl* | 45.00 | *165.00* |
| | | *Nos. 56-63 (8)* | 118.75 | *428.50* |

No. 61 is on chalky paper.

Seal of Colony and George V — A9

**1923-33** **Chalky Paper** **Wmk. 4**

| | | | | |
|---|---|---|---|---|
| 65 | A9 | ½p green & blk | 2.50 | .85 |
| 66 | A9 | 1p violet & blk | 7.50 | 2.25 |
| 67 | A9 | 1p scar & black | 18.00 | 1.40 |
| 68 | A9 | 1½p car & black | 6.75 | .90 |
| 69 | A9 | 1½p dp brn & blk | 15.50 | .95 |
| 70 | A9 | 2p gray & black | 4.50 | .65 |
| 71 | A9 | 2½p org & black | 4.50 | *10.00* |
| 72 | A9 | 2½p ultra & black | 7.75 | 2.25 |
| 73 | A9 | 3p ultra & black | 4.50 | *19.00* |
| 74 | A9 | 3p red & blk, *yel* | 4.50 | 1.40 |
| 75 | A9 | 4p brown & blk | 5.25 | *7.25* |
| 76 | A9 | 6p red vio & blk | 5.50 | *9.00* |
| 77 | A9 | 1sh blk, *emerald* | 3.50 | *4.25* |
| 78 | A9 | 2sh ultra & blk, *bl* | 26.00 | *40.00* |
| 79 | A9 | 2sh6p red & blk, *bl* | 27.50 | *40.00* |
| 80 | A9 | 3sh vio & blk, *yel* | 4.50 | *15.00* |
| 81 | A9 | 4sh red & blk, *emer* | 22.00 | *40.00* |
| 82 | A9 | 5sh grn & blk, *yel* | 40.00 | *62.50* |
| | | *Nos. 65-82 (18)* | 210.25 | *257.65* |

Issue years: Nos. 80, 82, 1927; Nos. 72, 74, 1928; Nos. 67, 69, 1933; others, 1923.

Many values of this set are known with a forged G.P.O. cancellation dated "MY 19 27".

**1923** **Wmk. 3**

| | | | | |
|---|---|---|---|---|
| 83 | A9 | 3sh vio & blk, *yel* | 5.75 | *72.50* |
| 84 | A9 | 5sh grn & blk, *yel* | 10.00 | *65.00* |
| 85 | A9 | £1 vio & blk, *red* | 240.00 | *375.00* |
| | | *Nos. 83-85 (3)* | 255.75 | *512.50* |

Common Design Types pictured following the introduction.

**Silver Jubilee Issue**

Common Design Type

***Perf. 13½x14***

**1935, May 6** **Wmk. 4** **Engr.**

| | | | | |
|---|---|---|---|---|
| 90 | CD301 | 1p car & blue | 1.60 | .35 |
| 91 | CD301 | 1½p gray blk & ultra | 5.75 | 3.25 |
| 92 | CD301 | 2½p blue & brn | 5.75 | *4.75* |
| 93 | CD301 | 1sh brt vio & ind | 5.75 | *11.50* |
| | | *Nos. 90-93 (4)* | 18.85 | 19.85 |
| | | Set, never hinged | 27.50 | |

**Coronation Issue**

Common Design Type

**1937, May 12** ***Perf. 11x11½***

| | | | | |
|---|---|---|---|---|
| 94 | CD302 | 1p dark carmine | .25 | .25 |
| 95 | CD302 | 1½p brown | .25 | .25 |
| 96 | CD302 | 2½p deep ultra | .35 | *1.90* |
| | | *Nos. 94-96 (3)* | .85 | 2.40 |
| | | Set, never hinged | 1.50 | |

Fresh-Water Lake — A10

Layou River — A11

Picking Limes — A12

Boiling Lake — A13

**1938-47** **Wmk. 4** ***Perf. 12½***

| | | | | |
|---|---|---|---|---|
| 97 | A10 | ½p grn & red brn | .25 | .25 |
| 98 | A11 | 1p car & gray | .25 | .25 |
| 99 | A12 | 1½p rose vio & grn | .25 | *.75* |
| 100 | A13 | 2p brn blk & dp rose | .35 | *2.25* |
| 101 | A12 | 2½p ultra & rose vio | .25 | *2.25* |
| *a.* | | 2½p bl & rose vio | 2.75 | 1.90 |
| 102 | A11 | 3p red brn & ol | .25 | *.60* |
| 103 | A12 | 3½p red vio & brt ultra | 1.00 | *2.10* |
| 104 | A10 | 6p vio & yel grn | .50 | *1.60* |
| 105 | A10 | 7p org brn & grn | 1.00 | *1.60* |
| 106 | A13 | 1sh olive & vio | 2.50 | 1.60 |
| 107 | A11 | 2sh red vio & blk | 4.50 | *12.50* |
| 108 | A10 | 2sh6p scar ver & blk | 10.00 | 5.75 |
| 109 | A11 | 5sh dk brn & bl | 8.00 | *12.00* |
| 110 | A13 | 10sh dl org & blk | 10.00 | *22.50* |
| | | *Nos. 97-110 (14)* | 39.10 | *66.00* |
| | | Set, never hinged | 80.00 | |

Issued: No. 101, 8/42; 3½p, 7p, 2sh, 10sh, 10/15/47; others, 8/15/38.

King George VI — A14

**1940, Apr. 15** **Photo.** ***Perf. 14½x14***

| | | | | |
|---|---|---|---|---|
| 111 | A14 | ¼p brown violet | 1.00 | *.25* |
| *a.* | | Ordinary paper ('42) | .25 | *1.50* |

No. 111 is on chalky paper.

**Catalogue values for unused stamps in this section, from this point to the end of the section, are for Never Hinged items.**

**Peace Issue**

Common Design Type

**1946, Oct. 14** **Engr.** ***Perf. 13½x14***

| | | | | |
|---|---|---|---|---|
| 112 | CD303 | 1p carmine | .25 | .25 |
| 113 | CD303 | 3½p deep blue | .25 | .25 |

**Silver Wedding Issue**

Common Design Types

**1948, Dec. 1** **Photo.** ***Perf. 14x14½***

| | | | | |
|---|---|---|---|---|
| 114 | CD304 | 1p scarlet | .25 | .25 |

**Engraved; Name Typographed**

***Perf. 11½x11***

| | | | | |
|---|---|---|---|---|
| 115 | CD305 | 10sh orange brn | 25.00 | *32.50* |

**UPU Issue**

Common Design Types

**Engr.: Name Typo. on 6c and 12c**

**1949, Oct. 10** ***Perf. 13½, 11x11½***

| | | | | |
|---|---|---|---|---|
| 116 | CD306 | 5c blue | .25 | .25 |
| 117 | CD307 | 6c chocolate | 1.25 | *3.00* |
| 118 | CD308 | 12c rose violet | .50 | *2.10* |
| 119 | CD309 | 24c olive | .30 | .30 |
| | | *Nos. 116-119 (4)* | 2.30 | 5.65 |

**University Issue**

Common Design Types

**1951, Feb. 16** **Engr.** ***Perf. 14x14½***

| | | | | |
|---|---|---|---|---|
| 120 | CD310 | 3c purple & green | .60 | *1.25* |
| 121 | CD311 | 12c dp car & dk bl grn | .80 | .50 |

George VI A15

Drying Cocoa A16

Picking Oranges — A17

Designs: 2c and 60c, Carib Baskets. 3c and 48c, Lime Plantation. 4c, Picking Oranges. 5c, Bananas. 6c, Botanical Gardens. 8c, Drying Vanilla Beans. 12c and $1.20, Fresh Water Lake. 14c, Layou River. 24c, Boiling Lake.

***Perf. 14½x14***

**1951, July 1** **Photo.** **Wmk. 4**

| | | | | |
|---|---|---|---|---|
| 122 | A15 | ½c brown | .25 | .25 |

***Perf. 13x13½***

**Engr.**

| | | | | |
|---|---|---|---|---|
| 123 | A16 | 1c red org & blk | .25 | .30 |
| 124 | A16 | 2c dp grn & red brn | .25 | .25 |
| 125 | A16 | 3c red vio & bl grn | .25 | *3.50* |
| 126 | A16 | 4c dk brn & brn org | .75 | *3.75* |
| 127 | A16 | 5c rose red & blk | .85 | .30 |
| 128 | A16 | 6c org brn & ol grn | 1.00 | .30 |
| 129 | A16 | 8c dp bl & dp grn | 3.00 | 1.75 |
| 130 | A16 | 12c emer & gray | .75 | *1.25* |
| 131 | A16 | 14c pur & blue | 1.25 | *3.50* |
| 132 | A16 | 24c rose car & red vio | 1.00 | .40 |
| 133 | A16 | 48c red org & bl grn | 5.00 | *13.50* |
| 134 | A16 | 60c gray & car | 4.00 | *9.25* |
| 135 | A16 | $1.20 gray & emer | 8.25 | *7.25* |

***Perf. 13½x13***

| | | | | |
|---|---|---|---|---|
| 136 | A17 | $2.40 gray & org | 30.00 | *52.50* |
| | | *Nos. 122-136 (15)* | 56.85 | *98.05* |

Nos. 125, 127, 129 and 131 Overprinted in Black or Carmine

**1951, Oct. 15** ***Perf. 13x13½***

| | | | | |
|---|---|---|---|---|
| 137 | A16 | 3c red vio & bl green | .25 | *.60* |
| 138 | A16 | 5c rose red & black | .25 | *1.75* |
| 139 | A16 | 8c dp blue & dp grn (C) | .30 | .25 |
| 140 | A16 | 14c purple & blue (C) | 1.75 | .30 |
| | | *Nos. 137-140 (4)* | 2.55 | 2.90 |

Adoption of a new constitution for the Windward Islands, 1951.

**Coronation Issue**

Common Design Type

**1953, June 2** **Engr.** ***Perf. 13½x13***

| | | | | |
|---|---|---|---|---|
| 141 | CD312 | 2c dk green & black | .40 | .40 |

**Types of 1951 with Portrait of Queen Elizabeth II**

**1954, Oct. 1** **Photo.** ***Perf. 14½x14***

| | | | | |
|---|---|---|---|---|
| 142 | A15 | ½c brown | .25 | 1.25 |

*Perf. 13x13½*

**Engr.**

**143** A16 1c red org & blk .25 .30
**144** A16 2c dp grn & red brn 1.10 *2.00*
**145** A16 3c red vio & bl grn 1.50 .40
**146** A16 4c dk brn & brn org .25 .30
**147** A16 5c rose red & blk 2.75 1.00
**148** A16 6c org brn & ol grn .55 .30
**149** A16 8c dp bl & dp grn 1.50 .30
**150** A16 12c emer & gray .60 .25
**151** A16 14c pur & bl .45 .25
**152** A16 24c rose car & red vio .55 .30
**153** A16 48c red org & bl grn 2.75 *11.00*
**154** A16 60c gray & car 3.50 1.50
**155** A16 $1.20 gray & emer 22.50 7.00

*Perf. 13½x13*

**156** A17 $2.40 gray & org 22.50 14.00
*Nos. 142-156 (15)* 61.00 40.15

Mat Making — A18

5c, Canoe making. 10c, Bananas.

**1957, Oct. 15 Wmk. 4 *Perf. 13x13½***

**157** A18 3c car rose & black 4.00 2.50
**158** A18 5c brown & blue 12.00 1.10
**159** A18 10c redsh brn & brt grn 6.00 3.25
**160** A18 48c violet & brown 3.25 2.75
*Nos. 157-160 (4)* 25.25 9.60

**West Indies Federation**

Common Design Type

*Perf. 11½x11*

**1958, Apr. 22 Wmk. 314**

**161** CD313 3c green .50 .35
**162** CD313 6c blue .60 *1.10*
**163** CD313 12c car rose .85 .40
*Nos. 161-163 (3)* 1.95 1.85

Sailing Canoe — A19

Traditional Costume — A20

Designs: 1c, Seashore, Rosalie. 2c, 5c, Queen Elizabeth II by Annigoni. 4c, Sulphur Springs. 6c, Road making. 8c, Dugout canoe. 10c, Frog (mountain chicken). 12c, Boats and Scotts Head. 15c, Bananas. 24c, Imperial parrot. 48c, View of Goodwill. 60c, Cacao tree. $1.20, Coat of Arms. $2.40, Trafalgar Falls. $4.80, Coconut palm.

Two types of 14c:

I — Mountain light violet. Girl's eyes look straight out.

II — Mountain blue. Eyes look sideways.

*Perf. 14½x14, 14x14½*

**1963, May 16 Photo. Wmk. 314**

**164** A19 1c bl, brn & grn .25 *.90*
**165** A20 2c ultramarine .30 .25
**166** A19 3c lt ultra & blk 1.50 1.10
**167** A19 4c sl, grn & brn .25 .25
**168** A20 5c magenta .30 .25
**169** A19 6c lt grn, vio & buff .25 .50
**170** A19 8c tan, blk & lt grn .30 .25
**171** A19 10c pink & brn .25 .25
**172** A19 12c bl, blk, grn & brn .90 .25
**173** A20 14c multi (II) 2.50 2.50
*a.* Type I .90 .30
**174** A19 15c grn, yel & brn 1.25 .25
**175** A20 24c multicolored 8.50 .25
**176** A19 48c bl, blk & grn .90 .90
**177** A19 60c blk, grn, org & brn 1.00 .75
**178** A19 $1.20 multicolored 6.25 1.60
**179** A20 $2.40 grn, bl, brn & blk 4.75 4.00
**180** A20 $4.80 bl, brn & grn 20.00 *30.00*
*Nos. 164-180 (17)* 49.45 44.25

For overprints see Nos. 211-232.

**1966-67 Wmk. 314 Sideways**

*167a* A19 4c ('67) 1.25 .90
*169a* A19 6c .25 .80
*170a* A19 8c .45 .90
*171a* A19 10c ('67) .70 .95
*174a* A19 15c ('67) .85 1.50
*Nos. 167a-174a (5)* 3.50 5.05

**Freedom from Hunger Issue**

Common Design Type

**1963, June 4 *Perf. 14x14½***

**181** CD314 15c lilac .30 .30

**Red Cross Centenary Issue**

Common Design Type

**Wmk. 314**

**1963, Sept. 2 Litho. *Perf. 13***

**182** CD315 5c black & red .25 .25
**183** CD315 15c ultra & red .45 *.80*

**Shakespeare Issue**

Common Design Type

**1964, Apr. 23 Photo. *Perf. 14x14½***

**184** CD316 15c lilac rose .35 .35

**ITU Issue**

Common Design Type

**1965, May 17 Litho. *Perf. 11x11½***

**185** CD317 2c emerald & blue .25 .25
**186** CD317 48c grnsh blue & slate .30 .30

**Intl. Cooperation Year Issue**

Common Design Type

**1965, Oct. 25 *Perf. 14½***

**187** CD318 1c blue grn & claret .25 .25
**188** CD318 15c lt violet & grn .30 .30

**Churchill Memorial Issue**

Common Design Type

**1966, Jan. 24 Photo. *Perf. 14***

**Design in Black, Gold and Carmine Rose**

**189** CD319 1c bright blue .25 .25
*a.* Gold omitted *2,000.*
**190** CD319 5c green .25 .25
**191** CD319 15c brown .30 .30
**192** CD319 24c violet .35 .35
*Nos. 189-192 (4)* 1.15 1.15

**Royal Visit Issue**

Common Design Type

**1966, Feb. 4 Litho. *Perf. 11x12***

**193** CD320 5c violet blue .75 .25
**194** CD320 15c dk car rose 2.25 .35

**World Cup Soccer Issue**

Common Design Type

**1966, July 1 Litho. *Perf. 14***

**195** CD321 5c multicolored .35 .25
**196** CD321 24c multicolored .85 .50

**WHO Headquarters Issue**

Common Design Type

**1966, Sept. 20 Litho. *Perf. 14***

**197** CD322 5c multicolored .25 .25
**198** CD322 24c multicolored .50 .50

**UNESCO Anniversary Issue**

Common Design Type

**1966, Dec. 1 Litho. *Perf. 14***

**199** CD323 5c "Education" .35 .25
**200** CD323 15c "Science" .45 .25
**201** CD323 24c "Culture" .80 .25
*Nos. 199-201 (3)* 1.60 .75

Carib, Negro and Caucasian Children — A21

10c, Columbus' ship Santa Maria & banderol. 15c, Hands with banderol. 24c, Belaire dancers.

*Perf. 14½x14*

**1967, Nov. 3 Photo. Wmk. 314**

**202** A21 5c multicolored .25 .25
**203** A21 10c multicolored .25 .25
**204** A21 15c multicolored .25 .25
**205** A21 24c multicolored .25 .25
*Nos. 202-205 (4)* 1.00 1.00

Issued for National Day, Nov. 3.

John F. Kennedy and Human Rights Flame — A22

Human Rights Flame and: 10c, Cecil E. A. Rawle (1891-1938), Dominican crusader for human rights. 12c, Pope John XXIII. 48c, Florence Nightingale. 60c, Dr. Albert Schweitzer.

**Wmk. 314 Sideways**

**1968, Apr. 20 Litho. *Perf. 14***

**206** A22 1c multicolored .25 .25
**207** A22 10c multicolored .25 .25
**208** A22 12c multicolored .25 .25
**209** A22 48c multicolored .25 .25
**210** A22 60c multicolored .25 .25
*Nos. 206-210 (5)* 1.25 1.25

International Human Rights Year.

**Stamps and Types of 1963-67 Overprinted in Silver or Black: "ASSOCIATED / STATEHOOD"**

*Perf. 14½x14, 14x14½*

**1968, July 8 Photo. Wmk. 314**

**211** A19 1c multi .25 .25
**212** A20 2c ultra .25 .25
**213** A19 3c lt ultra & blk .25 .25
**214** A19 4c multi .25 .25
**215** A20 5c magenta .25 .25
**216** A19 6c multi (B) .25 .25
**217** A19 8c multi (B) .25 .25
**218** A19 10c pink & brn .55 .25
**219** A19 12c multi .25 *.50*
*a.* Watermark upright .25 .25
**220** A20 14c multi (II) .25 .25
**221** A19 15c multi .25 .25
**222** A20 24c multi 4.00 .25
**223** A19 48c multi .55 *2.25*
*a.* Watermark upright .50 *1.00*
**224** A19 60c multi (B) .90 .75
**225** A19 $1.20 multi (B) 1.00 *3.00*
**226** A20 $2.40 multi 1.00 *2.25*
**227** A20 $4.80 multi 1.25 8.00
*Nos. 211-227 (17)* 11.75 19.50

In this set, overprint was applied to 2c, 3c, 12c, 14c, 24c, 48c, 60c, $1.20, $2.40 and $4.80 with watermark upright. A reprinting of the 1c, 4c, 6c, 8c, 10c, 12c, No. 219, 15c and 48c, No. 223 on paper with watermark sideways was made. Same value.

**Nos. 164-166, 173 and 178 Overprinted: "NATIONAL DAY / 3 NOVEMBER 1968"**

*Perf. 14½x14, 14x14½*

**1968, Nov. 3 Photo. Wmk. 314**

**228** A19 1c blue, brn & grn .25 .25
**229** A20 2c ultra .25 .25
**230** A19 3c lt ultra & blk .25 .25
**231** A20 14c multi (I) .25 .25
**232** A19 $1.20 multicolored .55 .55
*Nos. 228-232 (5)* 1.55 1.55

A23

No. 233: a, 3 soccer players; b, Soccer player, goalie. No. 234: a, Swimmers at start; b, Divers. No. 235: a, Javelin thrower, hurdlers; b, Hurdlers. No. 236: a, Basketball; b, 3 basketball players.

*Perf. 11½*

**1968, Nov. 23 Unwmk. Litho.**

**233** A23 1c Pair, #a-b .25 .25
**234** A23 5c Pair, #a-b .25 .25
**235** A23 48c Pair, #a-b .50 .50
**236** A23 60c Pair, #a-b 1.40 1.40
*Nos. 233-236 (4)* 2.40 2.40

19th Olympic Games, Mexico City, 10/12-27.

The Small Cowper Madonna, by Raphael A24

*Perf. 12½x12*

**1968, Dec. 23 Photo. Unwmk.**

**241** A24 5c multicolored .30 .30

Christmas. No. 241 printed in sheets of 20. Sheets of 6 (3x2) exist containing two each of 12c, 24c, and $1.20 stamps, each picturing a different madonna painting. Value $6.

Venus and Adonis, by Rubens — A25

Paintings: 15c, The Death of Socrates, by Louis Jacques David. 24c, Christ at Emmaus, by Velazquez. 50c, Pilate Washing his Hands, by Rembrandt.

*Perf. 14½x15*

**1969, Jan. 30 Litho. Wmk. 314**

**242** A25 5c lilac & multi .25 .25
**243** A25 15c emerald & multi .25 .25
**244** A25 24c lt blue & multi .25 .25
**245** A25 50c crimson & multi .45 .45
*Nos. 242-245 (4)* 1.20 1.20

20th anniv. (in 1968) of the WHO.

Citrus Fruit Picker — A26

No. 247, Woman and child. No. 248, Hotel. No. 249, Red-necked parrots. No. 250, Calypso band. No. 251, Women dancers. No. 252, Tropical fish and coelenterates. No. 253, Diver and turtle.

**1969, Mar. 10 *Perf. 14½***

**246** A26 10c multicolored .25 .25
**247** A26 10c multicolored .25 .25
*a.* Pair, #246-247 .25 .25
**248** A26 12c multicolored .25 .25
**249** A26 12c multicolored .25 .25
*a.* Pair, #248-249 .25 .25
**250** A26 24c multicolored .25 .25
**251** A26 24c multicolored .25 .25
*a.* Pair, #250-251 .50 .50
**252** A26 48c multicolored .65 .65
**253** A26 48c multicolored .65 .65
*a.* Pair, #252-253 1.30 1.30
*Nos. 246-253 (8)* 2.80 2.80

Tourist publicity.

Spinning, by Millet, Flags and ILO Emblem — A27

50th anniv. of the ILO (Etchings by Jean F. Millet, Flags and ILO Emblem): 30c, Threshing. 30c, Flax pulling.

**1969, July Unwmk. *Perf. 13½***

**254** A27 15c multicolored .25 .25
**255** A27 30c multicolored .30 .30
**256** A27 38c multicolored .30 .30
*Nos. 254-256 (3)* .85 .85

"Strength in Unity," Bananas and Cacao A28

"Strength in Unity" Emblem and: 8c, Map of Dominica and Hawker Siddeley 748. 12c, Map of Caribbean. 24c, Ships in harbor.

**1969, July Litho.**

**257** A28 5c orange & multi .30 .30
**258** A28 8c gray & multi .30 .30
**259** A28 12c lilac & multi .30 .30
**260** A28 24c lt blue & multi .30 .30
*Nos. 257-260 (4)* 1.20 1.20

Caribbean Free Trade Area (CARIFTA).

Gandhi at Spinning Wheel and Big Ben, London A29

38c, Gandhi, Nehru and Fatehpur Sikri Mausoleum. $1.20, Gandhi & Taj Mahal.

**1969, Oct. Litho. *Perf. 14½***

**261** A29 6c multicolored .55 .25
**262** A29 38c multicolored .75 .25
**263** A29 $1.20 multicolored .85 .85
*Nos. 261-263 (3)* 2.15 1.35

Mohandas K. Gandhi (1869-1948), leader in India's fight for independence. "Gandhi" is misspelled "Ghandi" on Nos. 261-263.

St. Joseph — A30

Stained Glass Windows, from 17th Century French Churches: 8c, St. John. 12c, St. Peter. 60c, St. Paul.

**1969, Nov. 10 Litho. *Perf. 14***

**264** A30 6c black & multi .25 .25
**265** A30 8c black & multi .25 .25
**266** A30 12c black & multi .25 .25
**267** A30 60c black & multi .40 .40
*Nos. 264-267 (4)* 1.15 1.15

National Day, Nov. 3. Issued in sheets of 16 (4x4) with control numbers and 4 tabs with a patriotic poem by W. O. M. Pond.

Queen Elizabeth II — A31

Purplethroated Carib (Hummingbird) — A32

2c, Poinsettia. 3c, Red-necked pigeon. 4c, Imperial parrot. 5c, Swallowtail butterfly. 6c, Brown Julia butterfly. 8c, Banana shipment. 10c, Portsmouth Harbor. 12c, Copra processing plant. 15c, Women with straw work. 25c, Timber plant. 30c, Mining pumice. 38c, Cricket, Grammar School. 50c, Roman Catholic Cathedral. 60c, Government headquarters. $1.20, Melville Hall Airport. $2.40, Coat of Arms. $4.80, Queen Elizabeth II.

***Perf. 13½***

**1969, Nov. 26 Unwmk. Photo.**

**Chalky Paper**

**268** A31 ½c silver & multi .25 *1.50*
**269** A32 1c yellow & multi .75 *2.00*
**270** A32 2c yellow & multi .25 .25
**271** A32 3c yellow & multi 2.50 2.50
**272** A32 4c yellow & multi 2.50 2.50
**273** A32 5c yellow & multi 2.50 2.50
**274** A32 6c brown & multi 2.00 *3.50*
**275** A32 8c brown & multi .25 .25
**276** A32 10c yellow & multi .25 .25
**277** A32 12c citron & multi .25 .25
**278** A32 15c blue & multi .25 .25
**279** A32 25c pink & multi .40 .25
**280** A32 30c olive & multi 1.50 .25
**281** A32 38c multicolored 8.50 1.75
**282** A32 50c brown & multi .65 .65

**Wmk. Rectangles (334)**

***Perf. 14***

**Size: 38x26mm, 26x38mm**

**283** A32 60c yel & multi 1.00 *1.50*
**284** A32 $1.20 yel & multi 2.00 2.00
**285** A32 $2.40 gold & multi 1.50 *4.00*
**286** A31 $4.80 gold & multi 3.00 *7.50*
*Nos. 268-286 (19)* 30.30 *33.65*

**1972 On glazed Paper**

*268a* A31 ½c silver & multi .30 *2.00*
*269a* A32 1c yellow & multi 1.40 *1.50*
*270a* A32 2c yellow & multi .50 .50
*271a* A32 3c yellow & multi 3.00 1.50
*272a* A32 4c yellow & multi 3.00 1.50
*273a* A32 5c yellow & multi 2.75 1.25
*274a* A32 6c brown & multi 2.75 2.75
*275a* A32 8c brown & multi .45 *.60*
*276a* A32 10c yellow & multi .35 .25
*277a* A32 12c citron & multi .35 .25
*278a* A32 15c blue & multi .35 .30
*279a* A32 25c pink & multi .30 .25
*280a* A32 30c olive & multi 1.50 .65
*281a* A32 38c multicolored 8.00 *14.00*
*282a* A32 50c brown & multi .85 *1.25*
*Nos. 268a-282a (15)* 25.85 *28.55*

Madonna and Child, by Filippino Lippi — A33

Paintings: 10c, Holy Family with Lamb, by Raphael. 15c, Virgin and Child, by Perugino. $1.20, Madonna of the Rose Hedge, by Botticelli.

***Perf. 14½***

**1969, Dec. Unwmk. Litho.**

**287** A33 6c lt blue & multi .25 .25
**288** A33 10c multicolored .25 .25
**289** A33 15c lilac & multi .25 .25
**290** A33 $1.20 lt grn & multi .25 .25
*a.* Souvenir sheet of 2 1.25 1.25
*Nos. 287-290 (4)* 1.00 1.00

Christmas. No. 290a contains 2 imperf. stamps with simulated perforations similar to Nos. 289-290.

Neil A. Armstrong, First Man on the Moon — A34

Designs: 5c, American flag and astronauts on moon. 8c, Astronauts collecting moon rocks. 30c, Landing module, moon and earth. 50c, Memorial tablet left on moon. 60c, Astronauts Armstrong, Aldrin and Collins.

**1970, Feb. 2 Litho. *Perf. 12½***

**291** A34 ½c lilac & multi .25 .25
**292** A34 5c lt blue & multi .25 .25
**293** A34 8c orange & multi .25 .25
**294** A34 30c blue & multi .25 .25
**295** A34 50c red brn & multi .40 .30
**296** A34 60c rose & multi .50 .45
*a.* Souvenir sheet of 4 2.60 2.60
*Nos. 291-296 (6)* 1.90 1.75

See note after US No. C76. No. 296a contains 4 stamps similar to Nos. 293-296, but imperf. with simulated perforations.

Giant Green Turtle — A35

Designs: 24c, Flying fish. 38c, Anthurium lily. 60c, Imperial and red-necked parrots.

**1970, Sept. 6 Litho. *Perf. 13½x13***

**297** A35 6c lt green & multi .50 .50
**298** A35 24c multicolored .65 .65
**299** A35 38c green & multi .75 .75
**300** A35 60c yellow & multi 3.50 3.50
*a.* Souvenir sheet of 4, #297-300 8.50 8.50
*Nos. 297-300 (4)* 5.40 5.40

Women in 18th Century Dress A36

Natl. Day: 8c, Carib mace & wife leader, 18th cent. $1, Map & flag of Dominica.

**1970, Nov. 3 Litho. *Perf. 14***

**301** A36 5c yellow & multi .25 .25
**302** A36 8c green & multi .25 .25
**303** A36 $1 lt blue & multi .40 .40
*a.* Souv. sheet of 3, #301-303 + 3 labels 1.25 *1.50*
*Nos. 301-303 (3)* .90 .90

Marley's Ghost — A37

Designs (from A Christmas Carol, by Dickens): 15c, Fezziwig's Ball. 24c, Scrooge and his Nephew's Christmas Party. $1.20, The Ghost of Christmas Present.

**1970, Nov. 23 Litho. *Perf. 14x14½***

**304** A37 2c blue & multi .25 .25
**305** A37 15c multicolored .25 .25
**306** A37 24c red & multi .25 .25
**307** A37 $1.20 multicolored .75 .75
*a.* Souvenir sheet of 4, #304-307 2.75 2.75
*Nos. 304-307 (4)* 1.50 1.50

Christmas; Charles Dickens (1812-1870).

Hands and Red Cross A38

Designs: 8c, The Doctor, by Sir Luke Fildes. 15c, Dominica flag and Red Cross. 50c, The Sick Child, by Edvard Munch.

**1970, Dec. 28 *Perf. 14½x14***

**308** A38 8c multicolored .25 .25
**309** A38 10c multicolored .25 .25
**310** A38 15c multicolored .25 .25
**311** A38 50c multicolored .50 .50
*a.* Souvenir sheet of 4, #308-311 2.00 2.00
*Nos. 308-311 (4)* 1.25 1.25

Centenary of the British Red Cross Society.

Marigot Primary School — A39

Education Year Emblem and: 8c, Goodwill Junior High School. 14c, University of the West Indies. $1, Trinity College, Cambridge, England.

**1971, Mar. 1 Litho. *Perf. 13½***

**312** A39 5c multicolored .25 .25
**313** A39 8c multicolored .25 .25
**314** A39 14c multicolored .25 .25
**315** A39 $1 multicolored .45 .45
*a.* Souvenir sheet of 2, #314-315 1.50 1.50
*Nos. 312-315 (4)* 1.20 1.20

International Education Year.

Waterfall and Bird-of-Paradise Flower — A40

Tourist Publicity: 10c, Boat building. 30c, Sailboat along North Coast. 50c, Speed boat and steamer.

**1971, Mar. 22 *Perf. 13½x14***

**316** A40 5c multicolored .25 .25
**317** A40 10c multicolored .25 .25
**318** A40 30c multicolored .25 .25
**319** A40 50c multicolored .35 .35
*a.* Souvenir sheet of 4, #316-319 1.10 1.10
*Nos. 316-319 (4)* 1.10 1.10

UNICEF Emblem, Letter "D" A41

**1971, June 14 Litho. *Perf. 14***

**320** A41 5c multicolored .25 .25
**321** A41 10c multicolored .25 .25
**322** A41 38c multicolored .25 .25
**323** A41 $1.20 multicolored .25 .25
*a.* Souvenir sheet of 2, #321, 323 .85 .85
*Nos. 320-323 (4)* 1.00 1.00

25th anniv. of UNICEF.

Boy Scout, Jamboree Emblem, Torii, Camp and Mt. Fuji — A42

24c, British Scout, flag. 30c, Japanese Scout, flag. $1, Dominican Scout, flag.

**1971, Oct. 18 Unwmk. *Perf. 11***

**324** A42 20c bister & multi .25 .25
**325** A42 24c green & multi .30 .30
**326** A42 30c red lilac & multi .40 .40
**327** A42 $1 blue & multi .80 .80
*a.* Souvenir sheet of 2, #326-327 1.75 1.75
*Nos. 324-327 (4)* 1.75 1.75

13th Boy Scout World Jamboree, Asagiri Plain, Japan, Aug. 2-10.

Boats at Portsmouth — A43

15c, Carnival street scene. 20c, $1.20, Anthea Mondesire, Carifta Queen. 50c, Rock of Atkinson.

***Perf. 13½x14, 14x13½***

**1971, Nov. 15** **Litho.**

**328** A43 8c multi .25 .25
**329** A43 15c multi .25 .25
**330** A43 20c multi, vert. .25 .25
**331** A43 50c multi, vert. .25 .25
*Nos. 328-331 (4)* 1.00 1.00

**Souvenir Sheet**

***Perf. 15***

**332** A43 $1.20 multi, vert. .85 .85

National Day.

First Dominica Coin, 8 Reals, 1761 — A44

Early Dominica Coins: 30c, Eleven and 3-bit pieces, 1798. 35c, Two-real coin, 1770, vert. 50c, Three "mocos" and piece of 8, 1798.

**1972, Feb. 7** **Litho.** ***Perf. 14***

**333** A44 10c violet, silver & blk .25 .25
**334** A44 30c green, silver & blk .25 .25
**335** A44 35c ultra, silver & blk .25 .25
**336** A44 50c red, silver & blk .25 .25
*a.* Souvenir sheet of 2, #335-336 1.00 1.00
*Nos. 333-336 (4)* 1.00 1.00

Margin of No. 336a inscribed "Christmas 1971."

Common Opossum, Environment Emblem — A45

Environment Emblem and: 35c, Agouti. 60c, Oncidium papillo (orchid). $1.20, Hibiscus.

**1972, June 5**

**337** A45 ½c yel grn & multi .25 .25
**338** A45 35c org brn & multi .30 .30
**339** A45 60c lt blue & multi 2.25 2.25
**340** A45 $1.20 yellow & multi 1.75 1.75
*a.* Souvenir sheet of 4, #337-340 6.75 6.75
*Nos. 337-340 (4)* 4.55 4.55

UN Conf. on Human Environment, Stockholm, June 5-16.

100-meter Sprint, Olympic Rings — A46

Olympic Rings and: 35m, 400-meter hurdles. 58c, Hammer throw, vert. 72c, Broad jump, vert.

**1972, Oct. 9** **Litho.** ***Perf. 14***

**341** A46 30c dp org & multi .25 .25
**342** A46 35c blue & multi .25 .25
**343** A46 58c lilac rose & multi .30 .30
**344** A46 72c yel green & multi .40 .40
*a.* Souv. sheet, #343-344, perf. 15 1.25 1.25
*Nos. 341-344 (4)* 1.20 1.20

20th Olympic Games, Munich, Aug. 26-Sept. 11.

General Post Office — A47

**1972, Nov. 1** ***Perf. 13½***

**345** A47 10c shown .25 .25
**346** A47 20c Morne Diablotin Mountain .25 .25
**347** A47 30c Rodney's Rock .25 .25
*a.* Souv. sheet, #346-347, perf. 15 .60 .60
*Nos. 345-347 (3)* .75 .75

National Day.

Adoration of the Shepherds, by Caravaggio A48

Paintings: 14c, Madonna and Child, by Rubens. 30c, Madonna and Child, with St. Anne by Orazio Gentileschi. $1, Adoration of the Kings, by Jan Mostaert. (On 8c, painting is mistakenly attributed to Boccaccino, according to Fine Arts Philatelist.)

**1972, Dec. 4.**

**348** A48 8c gold & multi .25 .25
**349** A48 14c gold & multi .25 .25
**350** A48 30c gold & multi .25 .25
**351** A48 $1 gold & multi .35 .35
*a.* Souvenir sheet of 2 1.10 1.10
*Nos. 348-351 (4)* 1.10 1.10

Christmas. No. 351a contains one each of Nos. 350-351 with simulated perforations.

**Silver Wedding Issue, 1972**

Common Design Type

Design: Queen Elizabeth II, Prince Philip, bananas, sisseron parrot.

***Perf. 14x14½***

**1972, Nov. 13** **Photo.** **Wmk. 314**

**352** CD324 5c olive & multi .25 .25
**353** CD324 $1 multicolored .40 .40

See note after Antigua No. 296.

Launching of Tiros Weather Satellite — A49

1c, Nimbus satellite. 2c, Radiosonde balloon & equipment. 30c, Radarscope. 35c, General circulation of atmosphere. 50c, Picture of hurricane transmitted by satellite. $1, Computer weather map. 30c, 35c, 50c, $1, horiz.

***Perf. 14½***

**1973, July 16** **Unwmk.** **Litho.**

**354** A49 ½c black & multi .25 .25
**355** A49 1c black & multi .25 .25
**356** A49 2c black & multi .25 .25
**357** A49 30c black & multi .25 .25
**358** A49 35c black & multi .25 .25
**359** A49 50c black & multi .30 .30
**360** A49 $1 black & multi .55 .55
*a.* Souvenir sheet of 2, #359-360 1.40 1.40
*Nos. 354-360 (7)* 2.10 2.10

Intl. meteorological cooperation, cent.

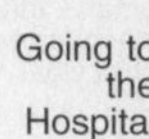

Going to the Hospital A50

WHO Emblem and: 1c, Maternity and infant care. 2c, Inoculation against smallpox. 30c, Emergency service. 35c, Waiting patients. 50c, Examination. $1, Traveling physician.

**1973, Aug. 20** **Unwmk.** ***Perf. 14½***

**361** A50 ½c lt blue & multi .25 .25
**362** A50 1c gray grn & multi .25 .25
**363** A50 2c yellow & multi .25 .25
**364** A50 30c lt vio & multi .25 .25
**365** A50 35c yel grn & multi .30 .30
**366** A50 50c multicolored .30 .30
**367** A50 $1 bister & multi .45 .45
*a.* Souvenir sheet of 2, #366-367, perf. 14x14½ 1.25 1.25
*Nos. 361-367 (7)* 2.05 2.05

WHO, 25th anniv. No. 367a exists perf. 14½.

Cyrique Crab — A51

**1973, Oct.**

**368** A51 ½c shown .25 .25
**369** A51 22c Blue land crab .35 .35
**370** A51 25c Breadfruit .45 .45
**371** A51 $1.20 Sunflower 1.00 1.00
*a.* Souvenir sheet of 4, #368-371 2.75 2.75
*Nos. 368-371 (4)* 2.05 2.05

Princess Anne and Mark Phillips — A52

**1973, Nov. 14** ***Perf. 13½***

**372** A52 25c salmon & multi .25 .25
**373** A52 $2 blue & multi .60 .60
*a.* Souv. sheet of 2 (75c, $1.20) .60 .60

Wedding of Princess Anne and Capt. Mark Phillips.

Nos. 372-373 were issued in sheets of 5 + label. No. 373a contains 2 stamps of type A52: 75c in colors of the 25c, and $1.20 in colors of the $2.

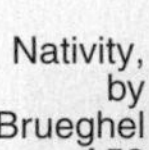

Nativity, by Brueghel A53

Paintings of the Nativity by: 1c, Botticelli. 2c, Dürer. 12c, Botticelli. 22c, Rubens. 35c, Dürer. $1, Giorgione (inscribed "Giorgeone").

**1973** **Unwmk.** ***Perf. 14½x15***

**374** A53 ½c gray & multi .25 .25
**375** A53 1c gray & multi .25 .25
**376** A53 2c gray & multi .25 .25
**377** A53 12c gray & multi .25 .25
**378** A53 22c gray & multi .25 .25
**379** A53 35c gray & multi .25 .25
**380** A53 $1 gray & multi .60 .60
*a.* Souvenir sheet of 2 1.30 1.30
*Nos. 374-380 (7)* 2.10 2.10

Christmas. No. 380a contains one each of Nos. 379-380 in changed colors.

Carib Basket Weaving — A54

Designs: 10c, Staircase of the Snake. 50c, Miss Caribbean Queen, Kathleen Telemacque, vert. 60c, Miss Carifta Queen, Esther Fadelle, vert. $1, La Jeune Etoile Dancers.

**1973, Dec. 17** ***Perf. 13½x14, 14x13½***

**381** A54 5c buff & multi .25 .25
**382** A54 10c multicolored .25 .25
**383** A54 50c multicolored .25 .25
**384** A54 60c multicolored .25 .25
**385** A54 $1 multicolored .25 .25
*a.* Souv. sheet of 3, #381-382, 385 .75 .75
*Nos. 381-385 (5)* 1.25 1.25

National Day.

U.W.I. Center, Dominica — A55

30c, Graduation. $1, University coat of arms.

**1974, Jan. 21** **Litho.** ***Perf. 13½x14***

**386** A55 12c dp orange & multi .25 .25
**387** A55 30c violet & multi .25 .25
**388** A55 $1 multicolored .35 .35
*a.* Souvenir sheet of 3, #386-388 .50 .50
*Nos. 386-388 (3)* .85 .85

University of the West Indies, 25th anniv.

Dominica No. 1 and Map of Island A56

Designs: 1c, 50c, No. 8 and post horn. 2c, $1.20, No. 9 and coat of arms. 10c, Like ½c.

**1974, May 4** **Litho.** ***Perf. 14½***

**389** A56 ½c brt pur & multi .25 .25
**390** A56 1c salmon & multi .25 .25
**391** A56 2c ultra & multi .25 .25
**392** A56 10c violet & multi .25 .25
**393** A56 50c yel grn & multi .40 .40
**394** A56 $1.20 rose & multi .65 .65
*a.* Souv. sheet, #392-394, perf. 15 1.60 1.60
*Nos. 389-394 (6)* 2.05 2.05

Centenary of Dominican postage stamps.

Soccer Player and Cup, Brazilian Flag — A57

Soccer cup, various players and flags: 1c, Germany, Fed. Rep. 2c, Italy. 30c, Scotland. 40c, Sweden. 50c, Netherlands. $1, Yugoslavia.

**1974, July** **Litho.** ***Perf. 14½***

**395** A57 ½c shown .25 .25
**396** A57 1c multicolored .25 .25
**397** A57 2c multicolored .25 .25
**398** A57 30c multicolored .25 .25
**399** A57 40c multicolored .30 .30
**400** A57 50c multicolored .75 .75
**401** A57 $1 multicolored 1.10 1.10
*a.* Souvenir sheet of 2, #400-401, perf. 13½ 1.25 1.25
*Nos. 395-401 (7)* 3.15 3.15

World Cup Soccer Championship, Munich, June 13-July 7.

Indian Hole A58

40c, Teachers' Training College. $1, Petite Savane Co-operative Bay Oil Distillery.

**1974, Nov. 1 Litho. *Perf. 13½x14***

**402** A58 10c multicolored .25 .25
**403** A58 40c multicolored .25 .25
**404** A58 $1 multicolored .50 .50
*a.* Souvenir sheet of 3, #402-404 .80 .80
*Nos. 402-404 (3)* 1.00 1.00

Churchill at Race Track A59

Sir Winston Churchill (1874-1965): 1c, with Gen. Eisenhower. 2c, with Franklin D. Roosevelt. 20c, as First Lord of the Admiralty. 45c, painting outdoors. $2, giving "V" sign.

**1974, Nov. 25 Litho. *Perf. 14½***

**405** A59 ½c multicolored .25 .25
**406** A59 1c multicolored .25 .25
**407** A59 2c multicolored .25 .25
**408** A59 20c multicolored .25 .25
**409** A59 45c multicolored .25 .25
**410** A59 $2 multicolored .50 .50
*a.* Souvenir sheet of 2, #409-410, perf. 13½ 1.25 1.25
*Nos. 405-410 (6)* 1.75 1.75

Virgin and Child, by Oronzo Tiso — A60

Paintings (Virgin and Child): 1c, by Lorenzo Costa. 2c, by unknown Master. 10c, by G. F. Romanelli. 25c, Holy Family, by G. S. da Sermoneta. 45c, Adoration of the Shepherds, by Guido Reni. $1, Adoration of the Kings, by Cristoforo Caselli.

**1974, Dec. 16 Litho. *Perf. 14***

**411** A60 ½c multicolored .25 .25
**412** A60 1c multicolored .25 .25
**413** A60 2c multicolored .25 .25
**414** A60 10c multicolored .25 .25
**415** A60 25c multicolored .25 .25
**416** A60 45c multicolored .35 .25
**417** A60 $1 multicolored .65 .50
*a.* Souvenir sheet of 2, #416-417 1.10 1.10
*Nos. 411-417 (7)* 2.25 2.00

Christmas.

Seamail, "Orinoco," 1851, and "Geesthaven," 1966 — A61

Cent. of UPU: $2, $2.40, Airmail, De Havilland 4, 1918, and Boeing 747, 1974.

**1974, Dec. 4 Litho. *Perf. 13½***

**418** A61 10c multicolored .25 .25
**419** A61 $2 multicolored 1.25 1.25

**Souvenir Sheet**

**419A** Sheet of 2 1.50 1.50
*b.* A61 $1.20 multicolored .45 .45
*c.* A61 $2.40 multicolored .90 .90

Nos. 418-419 were each printed in sheets of 50 and 5 + label.

Oldwife A62

1c, Ocyurus chrysurus. 2c, Blue marlin. 3c, Swordfish. 20c, Great barracuda. $2, Grouper.

**1975, June 2 Litho. *Perf. 14½***

**421** A62 ½c shown .25 .25
**422** A62 1c multicolored .25 .25
**423** A62 2c multicolored .25 .25
**424** A62 3c multicolored .25 .25
**425** A62 20c multicolored .90 .90
**426** A62 $2 multicolored 2.75 2.75
*a.* Souvenir sheet, perf. 13½ 4.00 4.00
*Nos. 421-426 (6)* 4.65 4.65

Myscelia Antholia A63

Butterflies: 1c, Lycorea ceres. 2c, Siderone nemesis. 6c, Battus polydamas. 30c, Anartia lytrea. 40c, Morpho peleides. $2, Dryas Julia.

**1975, July 28 Litho. *Perf. 14½***

**427** A63 ½c shown .25 .25
**428** A63 1c multicolored .25 .25
**429** A63 2c multicolored .25 .25
**430** A63 6c multicolored .75 .75
**431** A63 30c multicolored 1.50 1.00
**432** A63 40c multicolored 1.50 1.00
**433** A63 $2 multicolored 2.25 *6.75*
*a.* Souvenir sheet, perf. 13½ 4.00 4.00
*Nos. 427-433 (7)* 6.75 10.25

Royal Mail Ship Yare A64

Ships Tied in with Dominican History: 1c, Royal mail ship Thames. 2c, Canadian National S.S. Lady Nelson. 20c, C.N. S.S. Lady Rodney. 45c, Harrison Line M.V. Statesman. 50c, Geest Line M.V. Geestcape. $2, Geest Line M.V. Geeststar.

**1975, Sept. 1 *Perf. 14***

**434** A64 ½c black & multi .40 .35
**435** A64 1c black & multi .40 .35
**436** A64 2c black & multi .45 .40
**437** A64 20c black & multi 1.25 .60
**438** A64 45c black & multi 1.50 .80
**439** A64 50c black & multi 1.50 1.00
**440** A64 $2 black & multi 2.50 *4.50*
*a.* Souvenir sheet of 2, #439-440 4.00 4.00
*Nos. 434-440 (7)* 8.00 8.00

IWY Emblem, Farm Women A65

$2, IWY emblem, dressmaker & saleswoman.

**1975, Oct. 30 Litho. *Perf. 14***

**441** A65 10c pink & multi .25 .25
**442** A65 $2 yellow & multi .65 .65

International Women's Year.

Public Library — A66

5c, Miss Caribbean Queen 1975. 30c, Citrus factory. $1, National Day Cup.

**1975, Nov. 6**

**443** A66 5c multi, vert. .25 .25
**444** A66 10c multi .25 .25
**445** A66 30c multi .25 .25
**446** A66 $1 multi, vert. .40 .40
*a.* Souvenir sheet of 3 .90 .90
*Nos. 443-446 (4)* 1.15 1.15

National Day. No. 446a contains 3 stamps similar to Nos. 444-446 with simulated perforations.

Virgin and Child, by Mantegna — A67

Christmas: Paintings of the Virgin and Child.

**1975, Nov. 24**

**447** A67 ½c shown .25 .25
**448** A67 1c Fra Filippo Lippi .25 .25
**449** A67 2c Bellini .25 .25
**450** A67 10c Botticelli .25 .25
**451** A67 25c Bellini .25 .25
**452** A67 45c Correggio .25 .25
**453** A67 $1 Durer .50 .50
*a.* Souvenir sheet of 2, #452-453 1.25 1.25
*Nos. 447-453 (7)* 2.00 2.00

Hibiscus A68

Queen Elizabeth II — A69

Designs: 1c, African tulip. 2c, Castor oil tree. 3c, White cedar flower. 4c, Eggplant. 5c, Garfish. 6c, Okra. 8c, Zenaida doves. 10c, Screw pine. 20c, Mangoes. 25c, Crayfish. 30c, Manicou. 40c, Bay leaf groves. 50c, Tomatoes. $1, Lime factory. $2, Rum distillery. $5, Bay oil distillery.

**1975, Dec. 8 Litho. *Perf. 14½***

**454** A68 ½c ultra & multi .25 *.80*
**455** A68 1c lilac & multi .25 *.80*
**456** A68 2c orange & multi .25 *.80*
**457** A68 3c multicolored .25 *.80*
**458** A68 4c pink & multi .25 *.80*
**459** A68 5c multicolored .25 *.80*
**460** A68 6c gray & multi .25 *1.00*
**461** A68 8c multicolored 3.25 1.10
**462** A68 10c violet & multi .25 .25
*a.* Perf. 13½ 30.00 —
**463** A68 20c yellow & multi .35 .25
**464** A68 25c lemon & multi .40 .25
**465** A68 30c salmon & multi .85 .80
**466** A68 40c multicolored .85 .80
**467** A68 50c red & multi .50 .50
**468** A68 $1 citron & multi .75 .65
**469** A68 $2 multicolored 1.30 *3.25*
**470** A68 $5 multicolored 1.60 *5.00*

***Perf. 14***

**471** A69 $10 blue & multi 2.25 *14.50*
*Nos. 454-471 (18)* 14.10 *33.15*

Nos. 454-465 measure 38½mm x 25mm; nos. 466-470 measure 44½mm x 28mm.

For overprints see Nos. 584-601, 640-643.

All except 3c and 25c exist imperf.

American Infantry — A70

Designs: 1c, English three-decker, 1782. 2c, George Washington. 45c, English sailors. 75c, English ensign with regimental flag. $2, Admiral Hood. All designs have old maps in background.

**1976, Apr. 12 Litho. *Perf. 14½***

**472** A70 ½c green & multi .25 .25
**473** A70 1c purple & multi .25 .25
**474** A70 2c orange & multi .25 .25
**475** A70 45c brown & multi .45 .25
**476** A70 75c ultra & multi .75 .75
**477** A70 $2 red & multi .90 *1.50*
*a.* Souvenir sheet of 2 2.75 *2.75*
*Nos. 472-477 (6)* 2.85 3.25

American Bicentennial. No. 477a contains 2 stamps similar to Nos. 476-477, perf. 13.

Rowing — A71

1c, Shot put. 2c, Swimming. 40c, Relay race. 45c, Gymnastics. 60c, Sailing. $2, Archery.

**1976, May 24 Litho. *Perf. 14½***

**478** A71 ½c ocher & multi .25 .25
**479** A71 1c ocher & multi .25 .25
**480** A71 2c ocher & multi .25 .25
**481** A71 40c ocher & multi .25 .25
**482** A71 45c ocher & multi .25 .25
**483** A71 60c ocher & multi .25 .25
**484** A71 $2 ocher & multi .65 .65
*a.* Souv. sheet, #483-484, perf 13 1.75 1.75
*Nos. 478-484 (7)* 2.15 2.15

21st Olympic Games, Montreal, Canada, July 17-Aug. 1.

Ringed Kingfisher A72

Birds: 1c, Mourning dove. 2c, Green heron. 15c, Broad-winged hawk. 30c, Blue-headed hummingbird. 45c, Banana-quit. $2, Imperial parrot. 15c, 30c, 45c, $2, vert.

**1976, June 28**

**485** A72 ½c multicolored .25 .25
**486** A72 1c multicolored .25 .25
**487** A72 2c multicolored .25 .25
**488** A72 15c multicolored .90 .90
**489** A72 30c multicolored 1.25 1.25
**490** A72 45c multicolored 1.50 1.50
**491** A72 $2 multicolored 3.00 3.00
*a.* Souv. sheet of 3, #489-491, perf. 13 7.00 7.00
*Nos. 485-491 (7)* 7.40 7.40

Map of West Indies, Bats, Wicket and Ball A72a

Prudential Cup — A72b

**1976, July 26 Litho. *Perf. 14***

| | | | | | |
|---|---|---|---|---|---|
| 492 | A72a | 15c | lt blue & multi | .45 | .45 |
| 493 | A72b | 25c | lilac rose & black | .85 | .85 |

World Cricket Cup, won by West Indies Team, 1975.

Viking Spacecraft — A73

1c, Titan launch center, horiz. 2c, Titan 3-D & Centaur D-IT. 3c, Orbiter & landing capsule. 45c, Capsule with closed parachute. 75c, Capsule with open parachute. $1, Landing capsule descending on Mars, horiz. $2, Viking on Mars, horiz.

**1976, Sept. 20 Litho. *Perf. 15***

| | | | | | |
|---|---|---|---|---|---|
| 494 | A73 | ½c | multicolored | .25 | .25 |
| 495 | A73 | 1c | multicolored | .25 | .25 |
| 496 | A73 | 2c | multicolored | .25 | .25 |
| 497 | A73 | 3c | multicolored | .25 | .25 |
| 498 | A73 | 45c | multicolored | .25 | .25 |
| 499 | A73 | 75c | multicolored | .30 | .30 |
| 500 | A73 | $1 | multicolored | .35 | .35 |
| 501 | A73 | $2 | multicolored | .60 | .60 |
| *a.* | | | Souvenir sheet of 2, #500, 501, perf. 13½ | 1.75 | 1.75 |
| | | | *Nos. 494-501 (8)* | 2.50 | 2.50 |

Viking mission to Mars.

Virgin and Child, by Giorgione — A74

Virgin and Child by: 1c, Bellini. 2c, Mantegna. 6c, Mantegna. 25c, Memling. 45c, 50c, Correggio. $1, $3, Raphael.

**1976, Nov. 1 Litho. *Perf. 14***

| | | | | | |
|---|---|---|---|---|---|
| 502 | A74 | ½c | multicolored | .25 | .25 |
| 503 | A74 | 1c | multicolored | .25 | .25 |
| 504 | A74 | 2c | multicolored | .25 | .25 |
| 505 | A74 | 6c | multicolored | .25 | .25 |
| 506 | A74 | 25c | multicolored | .25 | .25 |
| 507 | A74 | 45c | multicolored | .25 | .25 |
| 508 | A74 | $3 | multicolored | .60 | .60 |
| | | | *Nos. 502-508 (7)* | 2.10 | 2.10 |

**Souvenir Sheet**

| | | | | | |
|---|---|---|---|---|---|
| 509 | | | Sheet of 2 | 1.10 | 1.10 |
| *a.* | A74 | 50c | multicolored | .35 | .35 |
| *b.* | A74 | $1 | multicolored | .75 | .75 |

Christmas.

Island Craft Co-operative — A75

National Day: 50c, Banana harvest, Castle Bruce Co-operative. $1, Banana shipping plant, Bourne Farmers' Co-operative.

**1976, Nov. 22 Litho. *Perf. 13½x14***

| | | | | | |
|---|---|---|---|---|---|
| 510 | A75 | 10c | multicolored | .25 | .25 |
| 511 | A75 | 50c | multicolored | .25 | .25 |
| 512 | A75 | $1 | multicolored | .30 | .30 |
| *a.* | | | Souvenir sheet of 3, #510-512 | .75 | .75 |
| | | | *Nos. 510-512 (3)* | .80 | .80 |

Common Sundial — A76

Sea Shells: 1c, Flame helmet. 2c, Mouse cone. 20c, Caribbean vase. 40c, West Indian fighting conch. 50c, Short coral shell. $2, Long-spined star shell. $3, Apple murex.

**1976, Dec. 20 Litho. *Perf. 14***

| | | | | | |
|---|---|---|---|---|---|
| 513 | A76 | ½c | black & multi | .25 | .25 |
| 514 | A76 | 1c | black & multi | .25 | .25 |
| 515 | A76 | 2c | black & multi | .25 | .25 |
| 516 | A76 | 20c | black & multi | .30 | .25 |
| 517 | A76 | 40c | black & multi | .55 | .45 |
| 518 | A76 | 50c | black & multi | .60 | .50 |
| 519 | A76 | $3 | black & multi | 2.25 | 2.25 |
| | | | *Nos. 513-519 (7)* | 4.45 | 4.20 |

**Souvenir Sheet**

| | | | | | |
|---|---|---|---|---|---|
| 520 | A76 | $2 | black & multi | 2.00 | 2.00 |

Queen Enthroned — A77

Designs: 1c, Imperial crown. 45c, Elizabeth II and Princess Anne. $2, Coronation ring. $2.50, Ampulla and spoon. $5, Royal visit to Dominica.

**1977, Feb. 7 *Perf. 14***

| | | | | | |
|---|---|---|---|---|---|
| 521 | A77 | ½c | multicolored | .25 | .25 |
| 522 | A77 | 1c | multicolored | .25 | .25 |
| 523 | A77 | 45c | multicolored | .25 | .25 |
| 524 | A77 | $2 | multicolored | .35 | .35 |
| 525 | A77 | $2.50 | multicolored | .50 | .50 |
| | | | *Nos. 521-525 (5)* | 1.60 | 1.60 |

**Souvenir Sheet**

| | | | | | |
|---|---|---|---|---|---|
| 526 | A77 | $5 | multicolored | 1.40 | 1.40 |

25th anniv. of the reign of Elizabeth II.

Nos. 521-525 were printed in sheets of 40 (4x10), perf. 14, and sheets of 5 plus label, perf. 12, in changed colors.

For overprints see Nos. 549-554.

Joseph Haydn — A78

Designs: 1c, Fidelio, act I, scene IV. 2c, Dancer Maria Casentini. 15c, Beethoven working on Pastoral Symphony. 30c, "Wellington's Victory." 40c, Soprano Henriette Sontag. $2, Young Beethoven.

**1977, Apr. 25 Litho. *Perf. 14***

| | | | | | |
|---|---|---|---|---|---|
| 527 | A78 | ½c | multicolored | .25 | .25 |
| 528 | A78 | 1c | multicolored | .25 | .25 |
| 529 | A78 | 2c | multicolored | .25 | .25 |
| 530 | A78 | 15c | multicolored | .50 | .50 |
| 531 | A78 | 30c | multicolored | .50 | .50 |
| 532 | A78 | 40c | multicolored | .50 | .50 |
| 533 | A78 | $2 | multicolored | 1.60 | 1.60 |
| *a.* | | | Souvenir sheet of 3, #531-533 | 2.60 | 2.60 |
| | | | *Nos. 527-533 (7)* | 3.85 | 3.85 |

Ludwig van Beethoven (1770-1827), composer.

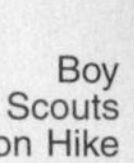

Boy Scouts on Hike A79

Saluting Boy Scout and: 1c, First aid. 2c, Scouts setting up camp. 45c, Rock climbing. 50c, Kayaking. 75c, Map reading. $2, Campfire. $3, Sailing.

**1977, Aug. 8 Litho. *Perf. 14***

| | | | | | |
|---|---|---|---|---|---|
| 534 | A79 | ½c | multicolored | .25 | .25 |
| 535 | A79 | 1c | multicolored | .25 | .25 |
| 536 | A79 | 2c | multicolored | .25 | .25 |
| 537 | A79 | 45c | multicolored | .35 | .35 |
| 538 | A79 | 50c | multicolored | .50 | .50 |
| 539 | A79 | $3 | multicolored | 2.00 | 2.00 |
| | | | *Nos. 534-539 (6)* | 3.60 | 3.60 |

**Souvenir Sheet**

| | | | | | |
|---|---|---|---|---|---|
| 540 | | | Sheet of 2 | 1.90 | 1.90 |
| *a.* | A79 | 75c | multicolored | .55 | .55 |
| *b.* | A79 | $2 | multicolored | 1.35 | 1.35 |

6th Caribbean Jamboree, Kingston, Jamaica, Aug. 5-14.

Nativity A80

Christmas: 1c, Annunciation to the Shepherds. 2c, 45c, Presentation at the Temple (different). 6c, $2, $3, Flight into Egypt (different). 15c, Adoration of the Kings. 50c, Virgin and Child with Angels. ½c to 45c are illustrations from De Lisle Psalter, 14th century. 50c, $2, $3 are from other Psalters.

**1977, Nov. 14 Litho. *Perf. 14***

| | | | | | |
|---|---|---|---|---|---|
| 541 | A80 | ½c | multicolored | .25 | .25 |
| 542 | A80 | 1c | multicolored | .25 | .25 |
| 543 | A80 | 2c | multicolored | .25 | .25 |
| 544 | A80 | 6c | multicolored | .25 | .25 |
| 545 | A80 | 15c | multicolored | .25 | .25 |
| 546 | A80 | 45c | multicolored | .35 | .35 |
| 547 | A80 | $3 | multicolored | .85 | .85 |
| | | | *Nos. 541-547 (7)* | 2.45 | 2.45 |

**Souvenir Sheet**

| | | | | | |
|---|---|---|---|---|---|
| 548 | | | Sheet of 2 | 1.35 | 1.35 |
| *a.* | A80 | 50c | multicolored | .25 | .25 |
| *b.* | A80 | $2 | multicolored | 1.10 | 1.10 |

**Nos. 521-526 Overprinted**

**1977, Nov. 24 Litho. *Perf. 12, 14***

| | | | | | |
|---|---|---|---|---|---|
| 549 | A77 | ½c | multicolored | .25 | .25 |
| 550 | A77 | 1c | multicolored | .25 | .25 |
| 551 | A77 | 45c | multicolored | .25 | .25 |
| 552 | A77 | $2 | multicolored | .40 | .40 |
| 553 | A77 | $2.50 | multicolored | .45 | .45 |
| | | | *Nos. 549-553 (5)* | 1.60 | 1.60 |

**Souvenir Sheet**

***Perf. 14***

| | | | | | |
|---|---|---|---|---|---|
| 554 | A77 | $5 | multicolored | 1.10 | 1.10 |

Caribbean visit of Queen Elizabeth II. Nos. 549-550 are perf. 12, others perf. 12 and 14.

Two types of No. 554: I. Overprinted only on stamp. II. Overprinted "W.I. 1977" on stamp and "Royal Visit W.I. 1977" on margin.

Masqueraders — A81

Designs: 1c, Sensay costume. 2c, Street musicians. 45c, Douiette band. 50c, Pappy Show wedding. $2, $2.50, Masquerade band.

**1978, Jan. 9 *Perf. 14***

| | | | | | |
|---|---|---|---|---|---|
| 555 | A81 | ½c | multicolored | .25 | .25 |
| 556 | A81 | 1c | multicolored | .25 | .25 |
| 557 | A81 | 2c | multicolored | .25 | .25 |
| 558 | A81 | 45c | multicolored | .25 | .25 |
| 559 | A81 | 50c | multicolored | .30 | .30 |
| 560 | A81 | $2 | multicolored | .50 | .50 |
| | | | *Nos. 555-560 (6)* | 1.80 | 1.80 |

**Souvenir Sheet**

| | | | | | |
|---|---|---|---|---|---|
| 561 | A81 | $2.50 | multicolored | 1.50 | 1.50 |

History of Carnival.

Lindbergh and Spirit of St. Louis A82

Designs: 10c, Spirit of St. Louis take-off, Long Island, May 20, 1927. 15c, Lindbergh and map of route New York to Paris. 20c, Lindbergh and plane in Paris. 40c, 1st Zeppelin, trial over Lake Constance. 50c, Spirit of St. Louis. 60c, Count Zeppelin and Zeppelin LZ-2, 1906. $2, Graf Zeppelin, 1928. $3, LZ-127, 1928.

**1978, Mar. 13 Litho. *Perf. 14½***

| | | | | | |
|---|---|---|---|---|---|
| 562 | A82 | 6c | multicolored | .25 | .25 |
| 563 | A82 | 10c | multicolored | .25 | .25 |
| 564 | A82 | 15c | multicolored | .30 | .30 |
| 565 | A82 | 20c | multicolored | .40 | .40 |
| 566 | A82 | 40c | multicolored | .60 | .60 |
| 567 | A82 | 60c | multicolored | .85 | .85 |
| 568 | A82 | $3 | multicolored | 2.25 | 2.25 |
| | | | *Nos. 562-568 (7)* | 4.90 | 4.90 |

**Souvenir Sheet**

| | | | | | |
|---|---|---|---|---|---|
| 569 | | | Sheet of 2 | 2.00 | 2.00 |
| *a.* | A82 | 50c | multicolored | .40 | .40 |
| *b.* | A82 | $2 | multicolored | 1.60 | 1.60 |

Charles A. Lindbergh's solo transatlantic flight from New York to Paris, 50th anniv., and flights of Graf Zeppelin.

Royal Family on Balcony — A83

Designs: 45c, Coronation. $2.50, Elizabeth II and Prince Philip. $5, Elizabeth II.

**1978, June 2 Litho. *Perf. 14***

| | | | | | |
|---|---|---|---|---|---|
| 570 | A83 | 45c | multicolored | .25 | .25 |
| 571 | A83 | $2 | multicolored | .45 | .45 |
| 572 | A83 | $2.50 | multicolored | .55 | .55 |
| | | | *Nos. 570-572 (3)* | 1.25 | 1.25 |

**Souvenir Sheet**

| | | | | | |
|---|---|---|---|---|---|
| 573 | A83 | $5 | multicolored | 1.00 | 1.00 |

Coronation of Queen Elizabeth II, 25th anniv. Nos. 570-572 were issued in sheets of 50, and in sheets of 3 stamps and label, in changed colors, perf. 12.

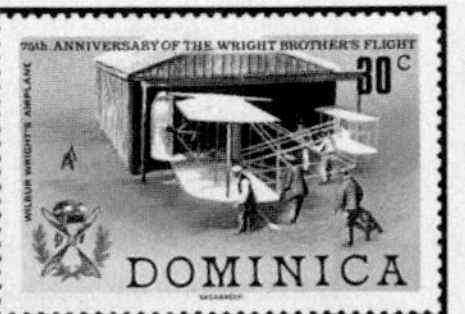

Wright Plane Coming out of Hangar A84

Designs: 40c, 1908 plane. 60c, Flyer I gliding. $2, Flyer I taking off. $3, Wilbur and Orville Wright and Flyer I.

**1978, July 10 Litho. *Perf. 14½***

| | | | | | |
|---|---|---|---|---|---|
| 574 | A84 | 30c | multicolored | .25 | .25 |
| 575 | A84 | 40c | multicolored | .25 | .25 |
| 576 | A84 | 60c | multicolored | .30 | .30 |
| 577 | A84 | $2 | multicolored | 1.25 | 1.25 |
| | | | *Nos. 574-577 (4)* | 2.05 | 2.05 |

**Souvenir Sheet**

| | | | | | |
|---|---|---|---|---|---|
| 578 | A84 | $3 | multicolored | 1.75 | 1.75 |

75th anniv. of first powered flight.

A set of 30 stamps embossed on gold foil exists. Value, $400.

Two Apostles, by Rubens — A85

Rubens Paintings: 45c, Descent from the Cross. 50c, St. Ildefonso Receiving Chasuble. $2, Holy Family. $3, Assumption of the Virgin.

**1978, Oct. 16 Litho. *Perf. 14***

| | | | | |
|---|---|---|---|---|
| **579** | A85 | 20c multicolored | .25 | .25 |
| **580** | A85 | 45c multicolored | .25 | .25 |
| **581** | A85 | 50c multicolored | .25 | .25 |
| **582** | A85 | $3 multicolored | .90 | .90 |
| | | *Nos. 579-582 (4)* | 1.65 | 1.65 |

**Souvenir Sheet**

| | | | | |
|---|---|---|---|---|
| **583** | A85 | $2 multicolored | 1.00 | 1.00 |

Christmas.

**Nos. 454-471 Overprinted**

**1978 Nov. 1 Litho. *Perf. 14½***

| | | | | |
|---|---|---|---|---|
| **584** | A68 | ½c ultra & multi | .25 | .25 |
| **585** | A68 | 1c lilac & multi | .25 | .25 |
| **586** | A68 | 2c orange & multi | .30 | .25 |
| **587** | A68 | 3c multicolored | .30 | .25 |
| **588** | A68 | 4c pink & multi | .30 | .25 |
| **589** | A68 | 5c multicolored | .30 | .25 |
| **590** | A68 | 6c gray & multi | .35 | .25 |
| **591** | A68 | 8c multicolored | 3.00 | .25 |
| **592** | A68 | 10c violet & multi | 1.00 | .25 |
| *a.* | | Perf. 13½ ('79) | .50 | .25 |
| **593** | A68 | 20c yellow & multi | .60 | .25 |
| **594** | A68 | 25c lemon & multi | .65 | .25 |
| **595** | A68 | 30c salmon & multi | .70 | .30 |
| **596** | A68 | 40c multicolored | .70 | .55 |
| **597** | A68 | 50c red & multi | .75 | .75 |
| **598** | A68 | $1 citron & multi | .80 | 1.40 |
| **599** | A68 | $2 multicolored | 1.50 | 2.75 |
| **600** | A68 | $5 multicolored | 2.00 | 5.50 |

***Perf. 14***

| | | | | |
|---|---|---|---|---|
| **601** | A69 | $10 blue & multi | 3.00 | 12.50 |
| | | *Nos. 584-601 (18)* | 16.75 | 26.50 |

Map of Dominica with Parishes — A86

25c, Sabinea carinalis, natl. flower, & map. 45c, New flag & map. 50c, Coat of arms & map. $2, Prime Minister Patrick John.

**1978, Nov. 1 *Perf. 14***

| | | | | |
|---|---|---|---|---|
| **602** | A86 | 10c multicolored | .75 | .40 |
| **603** | A86 | 25c multicolored | .55 | .25 |
| **604** | A86 | 45c multicolored | 1.50 | .35 |
| **605** | A86 | 50c multicolored | .65 | .35 |
| **606** | A86 | $2 multicolored | 1.50 | *2.75* |
| | | *Nos. 602-606 (5)* | 4.95 | 4.10 |

**Souvenir Sheet**

| | | | | |
|---|---|---|---|---|
| **607** | A86 | $2.50 multicolored | 2.60 | 2.60 |

Dominican independence.

Rowland Hill — A87

45c, Great Britain #2. 50c, Dominica #1. $2, Maltese Cross handstamps. $5, Penny Black.

**1979, Mar. 19**

| | | | | |
|---|---|---|---|---|
| **608** | A87 | 25c multicolored | .25 | .25 |
| **609** | A87 | 45c multicolored | .25 | .25 |
| **610** | A87 | 50c multicolored | .25 | .25 |
| **611** | A87 | $2 multicolored | .35 | .35 |
| | | *Nos. 608-611 (4)* | 1.10 | 1.10 |

**Souvenir Sheet**

| | | | | |
|---|---|---|---|---|
| **612** | A87 | $5 multicolored | 1.40 | 1.40 |

Sir Rowland Hill (1795-1879), originator of penny postage.

Nos. 608-611 printed in sheets of 5 plus label, perf. 12x12½, in changed colors.

For overprints see Nos. 663A-663D.

Boys and Dugout Canoe A88

IYC Emblem and: 40c, Children carrying bananas. 50c, Boys playing cricket. $3, Child feeding rabbits. $5, Boy showing catch of fish.

**1979, Apr. 23 Litho. *Perf. 14***

| | | | | |
|---|---|---|---|---|
| **613** | A88 | 30c multicolored | .30 | .30 |
| **614** | A88 | 40c multicolored | .45 | .45 |
| **615** | A88 | 50c multicolored | .50 | .50 |
| **616** | A88 | $3 multicolored | 2.00 | 2.00 |
| | | *Nos. 613-616 (4)* | 3.25 | 3.25 |

**Souvenir Sheet**

| | | | | |
|---|---|---|---|---|
| **617** | A88 | $5 multicolored | 2.00 | 2.00 |

Grouper A89

30c, Striped dolphin. 50c, White-tailed tropic birds. 60c, Brown pelicans. $1, Pilot whale. $2, Brown booby. $3, Elkhorn coral.

**1979, May 21 Litho. *Perf. 14***

| | | | | |
|---|---|---|---|---|
| **618** | A89 | 10c multicolored | .50 | .25 |
| **619** | A89 | 30c multicolored | 1.00 | .50 |
| **620** | A89 | 50c multicolored | 1.75 | .75 |
| **621** | A89 | 60c multicolored | 2.00 | 2.00 |
| **622** | A89 | $1 multicolored | 2.50 | 2.50 |
| **623** | A89 | $2 multicolored | 4.25 | 4.25 |
| | | *Nos. 618-623 (6)* | 12.00 | 10.25 |

**Souvenir Sheet**

| | | | | |
|---|---|---|---|---|
| **624** | A89 | $3 multicolored | 2.75 | 2.75 |

Wildlife protection.

Capt. Cook, Bark Endeavour — A90

Capt. Cook and: 50c, Resolution, map of 2nd voyage. 60c, Discovery, map of 3rd voyage. $2, Cook's map of New Zealand, 1770. $5, Portrait.

**1979, July 16 Litho. *Perf. 14***

| | | | | |
|---|---|---|---|---|
| **625** | A90 | 10c multicolored | .60 | .40 |
| **626** | A90 | 50c multicolored | 1.00 | 1.00 |
| **627** | A90 | 60c multicolored | 1.25 | 1.25 |
| **628** | A90 | $2 multicolored | 1.50 | *2.50* |
| | | *Nos. 625-628 (4)* | 4.35 | 5.15 |

**Souvenir Sheet**

| | | | | |
|---|---|---|---|---|
| **629** | A90 | $5 multicolored | 2.00 | 2.00 |

200th death anniv. of Capt. James Cook (1728-1779).

Girl Guides Cooking A91

Girl Guides: 20c, Setting up emergency rain tent. 50c, Raising flag of independent Dominica. $2.50, Playing accordion and singing. $3, Leader and Guides of different ages.

**1979, July 30**

| | | | | |
|---|---|---|---|---|
| **630** | A91 | 10c multicolored | .25 | .25 |
| **631** | A91 | 20c multicolored | .25 | .25 |
| **632** | A91 | 50c multicolored | .30 | .30 |
| **633** | A91 | $2.50 multicolored | 1.25 | 1.25 |
| | | *Nos. 630-633 (4)* | 2.05 | 2.05 |

**Souvenir Sheet**

| | | | | |
|---|---|---|---|---|
| **634** | A91 | $3 multicolored | 1.50 | 1.50 |

50th anniv. of Dominican Girl Guides.

Colvillea — A92

Flowering Trees: 40c, Lignum vitae. 60c, Dwarf poinciana. $2, Fern tree. $3, Perfume tree.

**1979, Sept. 3 Litho. *Perf. 14***

| | | | | |
|---|---|---|---|---|
| **635** | A92 | 20c multicolored | .25 | .25 |
| **636** | A92 | 40c multicolored | .25 | .25 |
| **637** | A92 | 60c multicolored | .35 | .35 |
| **638** | A92 | $2 multicolored | .90 | .90 |
| | | *Nos. 635-638 (4)* | 1.75 | 1.75 |

**Souvenir Sheet**

| | | | | |
|---|---|---|---|---|
| **639** | A92 | $3 multicolored | 1.75 | 1.75 |

**Nos. 459, 466, 470-471 Overprinted**

No. 640

No. 643

***Perf. 14½, 13½, 13½x14, 14***

**1979, Oct. 29 Litho.**

| | | | | |
|---|---|---|---|---|
| **640** | A68 | 5c multicolored | .25 | .25 |
| **641** | A68 | 40c multicolored | .30 | .30 |
| **642** | A68 | $5 multicolored | 2.00 | 2.00 |
| **643** | A69 | $10 multicolored | 3.50 | 3.50 |
| | | *Nos. 640-643 (4)* | 6.05 | 6.05 |

Hurricane devastation, Aug. 29. Vertical overprint on No. 643, others horizontal.

Music Scenes A92a

½c, Mickey Mouse. 1c, Goofy playing guitar. 2c, Mickey Mouse and Goofy. 3c, Donald Duck. 4c, Minnie Mouse. 5c, Goofy playing accordion. 10c, Horace Horsecollar and Dale. $2, Huey, Dewey, Louie. $2.50, Donald and Huey.

$3, Mickey Mouse playing piano.

**1979, Nov. 2 Litho. *Perf. 11***

| | | | | |
|---|---|---|---|---|
| **644** | A92a | ½c multicolored | .25 | .25 |
| **645** | A92a | 1c multicolored | .25 | .25 |
| **646** | A92a | 2c multicolored | .25 | .25 |
| **647** | A92a | 3c multicolored | .25 | .25 |
| **648** | A92a | 4c multicolored | .25 | .25 |
| **649** | A92a | 5c multicolored | .25 | .25 |
| **650** | A92a | 10c multicolored | .25 | .25 |
| **651** | A92a | $2 multicolored | 1.50 | 1.50 |
| **652** | A92a | $2.50 multicolored | 1.50 | 1.50 |
| | | *Nos. 644-652 (9)* | 4.75 | 4.75 |

**Souvenir Sheet**

***Perf. 13***

| | | | | |
|---|---|---|---|---|
| **653** | A92a | $3 multicolored | 3.25 | 3.25 |

Cathedral of the Assumption — A93

Cathedrals: 40c, St. Patrick's, New York. 45c, St. Paul's, London, vert. 60c, St. Peter's, Rome. $2, Cologne Cathedral. $3, Notre Dame, Paris, vert.

**1979, Nov. 26 Litho. *Perf. 14***

| | | | | |
|---|---|---|---|---|
| **654** | A93 | 6c multicolored | .25 | .25 |
| **655** | A93 | 45c multicolored | .25 | .25 |
| **656** | A93 | 60c multicolored | .25 | .25 |
| **657** | A93 | $3 multicolored | .90 | .90 |
| | | *Nos. 654-657 (4)* | 1.65 | 1.65 |

**Souvenir Sheet**

| | | | | |
|---|---|---|---|---|
| **658** | | Sheet of 2 | .80 | .80 |
| *a.* | | A93 40c multicolored | .25 | .25 |
| *b.* | | A93 $2 multicolored | .55 | .55 |

Christmas.

Nurse and Patients, Rotary Emblem A94

20c, Electrocardiogram machine. 40c, Mental hospital. $2.50, Paul Harris, founder. $3, Map of Africa and Europe.

**1980, Mar. 31 Litho. *Perf. 14***

| | | | | |
|---|---|---|---|---|
| **659** | A94 | 10c shown | .25 | .25 |
| **660** | A94 | 20c multicolored | .25 | .25 |
| **661** | A94 | 40c multicolored | .25 | .25 |
| **662** | A94 | $2.50 multicolored | .75 | .75 |
| | | *Nos. 659-662 (4)* | 1.50 | 1.50 |

**Souvenir Sheet**

| | | | | |
|---|---|---|---|---|
| **663** | A94 | $3 multicolored | 1.25 | 1.25 |

Rotary International, 75th anniv. Nos. 659-662 each contain quadrant of Rotary emblem.

Nos. 608-611 Overprinted in Black

**1980, May 6 Litho. *Perf. 12***

| | | | | |
|---|---|---|---|---|
| **663A** | A87 | 25c multicolored | .35 | .35 |
| **663B** | A87 | 45c multicolored | .55 | .55 |
| **663C** | A87 | 50c multicolored | .60 | .60 |
| **663D** | A87 | $2 multicolored | 1.50 | 1.50 |
| | | *Nos. 663A-663D (4)* | 3.00 | 3.00 |

London 80 Intl. Stamp Exhib., May 6-14.

Shot Put, Moscow '80 Emblem A95

**1980, May 27** **Litho.** ***Perf. 14***

**664** A95 30c shown .25 .25
**665** A95 40c Basketball .60 .30
**666** A95 60c Swimming .40 .40
**667** A95 $2 Gymnast .70 .70
*Nos. 664-667 (4)* 1.95 1.65

**Souvenir Sheet**

**668** A95 $3 Running 1.25 1.25

22nd Summer Olympic Games, Moscow, July 19-Aug. 3.

Embarkation for Cythera, by Watteau — A96

Paintings: 20c, Supper at Emmaus, by Caravaggio. 25c, Charles I Hunting, by Van Dyck, vert. 30c, The Maids of Honor, by Velazquez, vert. 45c, Rape of the Sabine Women, by Poussin. $1, Embarkation for Cythera, by Watteau. $3, Holy Family, by Rembrandt. $5, Girl before a Mirror, by Picasso, vert.

***Perf. 14x13½, 13½x14***

**1980, July 22** **Litho.**

**669** A96 20c multicolored .25 .25
**670** A96 25c multicolored .25 .25
**671** A96 30c multicolored .25 .25
**672** A96 45c multicolored .25 .25
**673** A96 $1 multicolored .40 .40
**674** A96 $5 multicolored 1.50 1.50
*Nos. 669-674 (6)* 2.90 2.90

**Souvenir Sheet**

**675** A96 $3 multicolored 1.10 1.10

Queen Mother Elizabeth, 80th Birthday A97

**1980, Aug. 4** ***Perf. 12, 14***

**676** A97 40c multicolored .25 .25
**677** A97 $2.50 multicolored .50 .50

**Souvenir Sheet**

**678** A97 $3 multicolored .75 .75

Tinkerbell — A98

Designs: Scenes from Disney's Peter Pan.

**1980, Oct. 1** **Litho.** ***Perf. 11***

**679** A98 ½c multicolored .25 .25
**680** A98 1c multicolored .25 .25
**681** A98 2c multicolored .25 .25
**682** A98 3c multicolored .25 .25
**683** A98 4c multicolored .25 .25
**684** A98 5c multicolored .25 .25
**685** A98 10c multicolored .25 .25
**686** A98 $2 multicolored 2.25 1.60
**687** A98 $2.50 multicolored 2.25 1.75
*Nos. 679-687 (9)* 6.25 5.10

**Souvenir Sheet**

**688** A98 $4 multicolored 5.00 5.00

Christmas.

Douglas Bay A99

30c, Valley of Desolation. 40c, Emerald Pool, vert. $3, Indian River, vert. $4, Trafalgar Falls.

**1981, Feb. 12** **Litho.** ***Perf. 14***

**689** A99 20c shown .25 .25
**690** A99 30c multicolored .25 .25
**691** A99 40c multicolored .25 .25
**692** A99 $3 multicolored .70 .70
*Nos. 689-692 (4)* 1.45 1.45

**Souvenir Sheet**

**693** A99 $4 multicolored 1.40 1.40

Pluto and Fifi — A100

$4, Pluto in Blue Note (1947 cartoon).

**1981, Apr. 30** **Litho.** ***Perf. 13½x14***

**694** A100 $2 multicolored 1.75 1.75

**Souvenir Sheet**

**695** A100 $4 multicolored 2.75 2.75

50th anniversary of Walt Disney's Pluto.

Forest Thrush A101

30c, Stolid flycatcher. 40c, Blue-hooded euphonia. $5, Lesser antillean peewee. $3, Sisserou parrot.

**1981, Apr. 30** ***Perf. 14***

**696** A101 20c shown .60 .25
**697** A101 30c multicolored .70 .35
**698** A101 40c multicolored .80 .45
**699** A101 $5 multicolored 4.75 4.75
*Nos. 696-699 (4)* 6.85 5.80

**Souvenir Sheet**

**700** A101 $3 multicolored 3.75 3.75

**Royal Wedding Issue**

Common Design Type

45c, Couple. 60c, Windsor Castle. $4, Charles. $5, Helicopter.

**1981, June 16** **Litho.** ***Perf. 14***

**701** CD331a 45c multi .25 .25
**702** CD331a 60c multi .25 .25
**703** CD331a $4 multi .60 .60
*Nos. 701-703 (3)* 1.10 1.10

**Souvenir Sheet**

**704** CD331 $5 multi 1.25 1.25

**Booklet**

**705** CD331 multi 6.00
*a.* Pane of 6 (3x25c, Lady Diana, 3x$2, Charles) 2.25 *4.50*
*b.* Pane of 1, $5, Couple 3.00 *3.50*

No. 705 contains imperf., self-adhesive stamps.

Nos. 701-703 also printed in sheets of 5 plus label, perf. 12, in changed colors. Value, set of three sheets $10.

Elves Repairing Santa's Sleigh — A102

Christmas: Scenes from Walt Disney's Santa's Workshop.

**1981, Nov. 2** **Litho.** ***Perf. 14***

**706** A102 ½c multicolored .25 .25
**707** A102 1c multicolored .25 .25
**708** A102 2c multicolored .25 .25
**709** A102 3c multicolored .25 .25
**710** A102 4c multicolored .25 .25
**711** A102 5c multicolored .25 .25
**712** A102 10c multicolored .25 .25
**713** A102 45c multicolored 2.00 .40
**714** A102 $5 multicolored 4.00 *5.50*
*Nos. 706-714 (9)* 7.75 7.65

**Souvenir Sheet**

**715** A102 $4 multicolored 5.75 5.75

Ixora A103

2c, Flamboyant. 4c, Poinsettia. 5c, Sabinea carinalis. 8c, Annatto roucou. 10c, Passion fruit. 15c, Breadfruit. 20c, Allamanda buttercup. 25c, Cashew. 35c, Soursop. 40c, Bougainvillea. 45c, Anthurium. 60c, Cacao. 90c, Pawpaw tree. $1, Coconut palm. $2, Coffee tree. $5, Lobster claw. $10, Banana fig.

**1981, Dec. 1** **Litho.** ***Perf. 14***

**716** A103 1c shown .25 .90
**717** A103 2c multicolored .25 .90
**718** A103 4c multicolored .25 .90
**719** A103 5c multicolored .25 .60
**720** A103 8c multicolored .25 .90
**721** A103 10c multicolored .30 .25
**722** A103 15c multicolored .50 .50
**723** A103 20c multicolored .35 .25
**724** A103 25c multicolored .40 .25
**725** A103 35c multicolored .45 .40
**726** A103 40c multicolored .45 .65
**727** A103 45c multicolored .50 .70
**728** A103 60c multicolored 1.00 .95
**729** A103 90c multicolored .75 1.40
**730** A103 $1 multicolored 2.00 1.50
**731** A103 $2 multicolored 1.50 3.00
**732** A103 $5 multicolored 2.00 *7.00*
*c.* Perf. 12½x12 ('85) 3.25 *5.00*
**733** A103 $10 multicolored 3.50 *13.00*
*Nos. 716-733 (18)* 14.95 34.05

For overprints see Nos. 852-853.

**1984** **Inscribed "1984"** ***Perf. 12***

*721a* A103 10c 1.75 .40
*730a* A103 $1 2.50 *3.00*
*732a* A103 $5 3.25 *5.00*
*733a* A103 $10 5.25 *10.00*
*Nos. 721a-733a (4)* 12.75 *18.40*

**1985** **Inscribed "1985"** ***Perf. 14***

*721b* A103 10c 1.00 .65
*722b* A103 15c Breadfruit 4.00 2.00
*728b* A103 60c Cacao 5.00 3.50
*732b* A103 $5 Lobster claw 3.25 *5.00*
*Nos. 721b-732b (4)* 13.25 11.15

Intl. Year of the Disabled — A104

45c, Ramp curb. 60c, Bus steps. 75c, Hand-operated car. $4, Bus lift. $5, Elevator buttons.

**1981, Dec. 22** **Litho.** ***Perf. 14***

**734** A104 45c multicolored .45 .30
**735** A104 60c multicolored .55 .40
**736** A104 75c multicolored .65 .50
**737** A104 $4 multicolored 2.00 *2.40*
*Nos. 734-737 (4)* 3.65 3.60

**Souvenir Sheet**

**738** A104 $5 multicolored 5.00 5.00

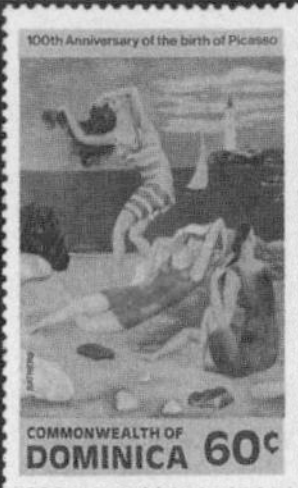

Bathers, by Picasso — A105

45c, Olga in Armchair. 75c, Woman in Spanish Costume. $4, Dog and Cock. $5, Sleeping Peasants.

**1981, Dec. 30** ***Perf. 14½***

**739** A105 45c multicolored .30 .30
**740** A105 60c shown .40 .40
**741** A105 75c multicolored .50 .50
**742** A105 $4 multicolored 2.25 2.25
*Nos. 739-742 (4)* 3.45 3.45

**Souvenir Sheet**

**743** A105 $5 multicolored 4.00 4.00

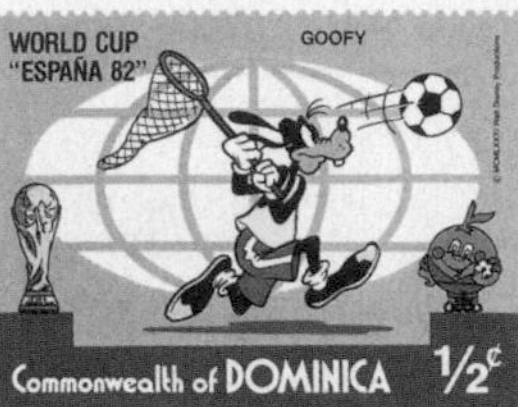

1982 World Cup Soccer — A106

Various Disney characters playing soccer.

**1982, Jan. 29** ***Perf. 14***

**744** A106 ½c multicolored .25 .25
**745** A106 1c multicolored .25 .25
**746** A106 2c multicolored .25 .25
**747** A106 3c multicolored .25 .25
**748** A106 4c multicolored .25 .25
**749** A106 5c multicolored .25 .25
**750** A106 10c multicolored .25 .25
**751** A106 60c multicolored 1.25 1.25
**752** A106 $5 multicolored 6.25 6.25
*Nos. 744-752 (9)* 9.25 9.25

**Souvenir Sheet**

**753** A106 $4 multicolored 5.75 5.75

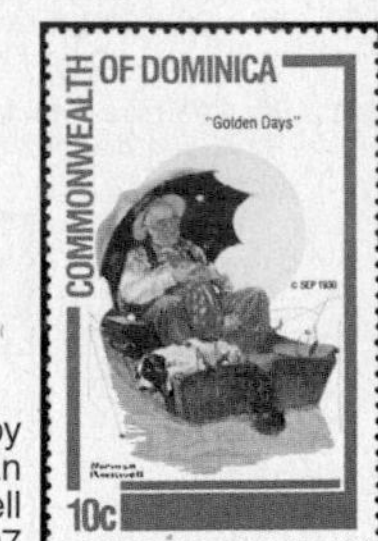

Golden Days, by Norman Rockwell A107

25c, The Morning News. 45c, The Marbles Champ. $1, Speeding Along.

**1982, Mar. 10** **Litho.** ***Perf. 14x13½***

**754** A107 10c shown .25 .25
**755** A107 25c multicolored .25 .25
**756** A107 45c multicolored .30 .30
**757** A107 $1 multicolored .55 .55
*Nos. 754-757 (4)* 1.35 1.35

Intl. Decade for Women (1975-85) A108

Famous Women: 10c, Elma Napier (1890-1973), first woman elected to Legislative Council in British West Indies, 1940. 45c, Margaret Mead (1901-1978), anthropologist. $1, Mabel Caudiron (1909-1968), musician and folk historian. $3, Florence Nightingale, founder of modern nursing. $4, Eleanor Roosevelt.

**1982, Apr. 15 Litho. *Perf. 14***
**758** A108 10c multicolored .25 .25
**759** A108 45c multicolored .35 .35
**760** A108 $1 multicolored .60 .60
**761** A108 $4 multicolored 2.50 2.50
*Nos. 758-761 (4)* 3.70 3.70

**Souvenir Sheet**

**762** A108 $3 multicolored 3.00 3.00

George Washington and Independence Hall, Philadelphia — A109

Washington or Roosevelt and: 60c, Capitol Building. 90c, The Surrender of Cornwallis, by John Trumbull. $2, Dam construction during New Deal (mural by William Gropper). $5, Washington, Roosevelt.

**1982, May 1 *Perf. 14½***
**763** A109 45c multicolored .35 .35
**764** A109 60c multicolored .40 .40
**765** A109 90c multicolored .55 .55
**766** A109 $2 multicolored 1.00 1.00
*Nos. 763-766 (4)* 2.30 2.30

**Souvenir Sheet**

**767** A109 $5 multicolored 3.00 3.00

George Washington's 250th birth anniv. and Franklin D. Roosevelt's birth cent.

Godman's Leaf Butterfly — A110

45c, Zebra. 60c, Mimic. $3, Red rim.
$5, Southern dagger tail.

**1982, June 1 Litho. *Perf. 14***
**768** A110 15c shown 1.75 1.75
**769** A110 45c multicolored 2.75 2.75
**770** A110 60c multicolored 3.00 3.00
**771** A110 $3 multicolored 6.25 6.25
*Nos. 768-771 (4)* 13.75 13.75

**Souvenir Sheet**

**772** A110 $5 multicolored 7.00 7.00

**Princess Diana Issue**
Common Design Type

45c, Buckingham Palace. $2, Engagement portrait. $4, Diana in wedding dress.
$5, Diana sitting in chair in white dress.

**1982, July 1 Litho. *Perf. 14½x14***
**773** CD332 45c multicolored .30 .30
**774** CD332 $2 multicolored 1.00 1.00
**775** CD332 $4 multicolored 2.25 2.25
*Nos. 773-775 (3)* 3.55 3.55

**Souvenir Sheet**

**776** CD332 $5 multicolored 3.50 3.50

Also issued in sheet of 5 plus label.
For overprints see Nos. 782-785.

Scouting Year A111

45c, Cooking. 60c, Meteorological study. 75c, Sisserou parrot, cub scouts. $3, Canoeing, Indian River.
$5, Flagbearer.

**1982, July 1 Litho. *Perf. 14***
**777** A111 45c multicolored 1.25 1.25
**778** A111 60c multicolored 1.75 1.75
**779** A111 75c multicolored 2.25 2.25
**780** A111 $3 multicolored 5.25 5.25
*Nos. 777-780 (4)* 10.50 10.50

**Souvenir Sheet**

**781** A111 $5 multicolored 3.50 3.50

Nos. 773-776 Overprinted

**1982, Sept. 1 Litho. *Perf. 14½x14***
**782** CD332 45c multicolored .30 .30
**783** CD332 $2 multicolored 1.00 1.00
**784** CD332 $4 multicolored 2.25 2.25
*Nos. 782-784 (3)* 3.55 3.55

**Souvenir Sheet**

**785** CD332 $5 multicolored 3.50 3.50

Birth of Prince William of Wales, June 21.
Also issued in sheet of 5 plus label.

Christmas — A112

Holy Family Paintings by Raphael.

**1982, Oct. 18 Litho. *Perf. 14***
**786** A112 25c multicolored .25 .25
**787** A112 30c multicolored .25 .25
**788** A112 90c multicolored .40 .40
**789** A112 $4 multicolored 1.75 1.75
*Nos. 786-789 (4)* 2.65 2.65

**Souvenir Sheet**

**790** A112 $5 multicolored 3.50 3.50

Goosebeak Whale Eating Squid — A113

60c, Humpback whale. 75c, Great right whale. $3, Melonhead whale.
$5, Pygmy sperm whale.

**1983, Feb. 15 Litho. *Perf. 14***
**791** A113 45c shown 1.75 1.75
**792** A113 60c multicolored 2.00 2.00
**793** A113 75c multicolored 2.25 2.25
**794** A113 $3 multicolored 7.50 7.50
*Nos. 791-794 (4)* 13.50 13.50

**Souvenir Sheet**

**795** A113 $5 multicolored 6.25 6.25

Commonwealth Day — A113a

25c, Banana industry. 30c, Road construction. 90c, Community nursing. $3, Basket weavers.

**1983, Mar. 14**
**796** A113a 25c multicolored .25 .25
**797** A113a 30c multicolored .25 .25
**798** A113a 90c multicolored .40 .40
**799** A113a $3 multicolored 1.25 1.25
*Nos. 796-799 (4)* 2.15 2.15

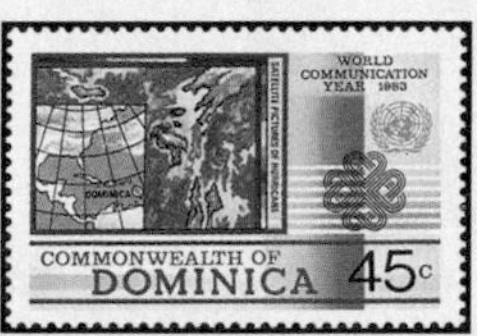


World Communications Year — A114

45c, Hurricane pattern, map. 60c, Air-to-ship communication. 90c, Columbia shuttle, dish antenna. $2, Walkie-talkie.
$5, Satellite.

**1983, Apr. 18 Litho. *Perf. 14***
**800** A114 45c multicolored .30 .30
**801** A114 60c multicolored .35 .35
**802** A114 90c multicolored .50 .50
**803** A114 $2 multicolored 1.00 1.00
*Nos. 800-803 (4)* 2.15 2.15

**Souvenir Sheet**

**804** A114 $5 multicolored 2.50 2.50

Manned Flight Bicentenary — A115

45c, Mayo Composite. 60c, Macchi M-39. 90c, Fairey Swordfish. $4, Zeppelin LZ-3.
$5, Double Eagle II, vert.

**1983, July 19 Litho. *Perf. 15***
**805** A115 45c multicolored .50 .50
**806** A115 60c multicolored .60 .60
**807** A115 90c multicolored .85 .85
**808** A115 $4 multicolored 3.00 3.00
*Nos. 805-808 (4)* 4.95 4.95

**Souvenir Sheet**

**809** A115 $5 multicolored 3.00 3.00

Duesenberg SJ, 1935 — A116

45c, Studebaker Avanti, 1962. 60c, Cord 812, 1936. 75c, MG-TC, 1945. 90c, Camaro 350-SS, 1967. $3, Porsche 356, 1948.
$5, Ferrari 312-T, 1975.

**1983, Sept. 1 Litho. *Perf. 14***
**810** A116 10c shown .35 .35
**811** A116 45c multicolored .45 .45
**812** A116 60c multicolored .50 .50
**813** A116 75c multicolored .55 .55
**814** A116 90c multicolored .60 .60
**815** A116 $3 multicolored 1.75 1.75
*Nos. 810-815 (6)* 4.20 4.20

**Souvenir Sheet**

**816** A116 $5 multicolored 3.00 3.00

Christmas — A117

Raphael Paintings.

**1983, Oct. 4 Litho. *Perf. 13½***
**817** A117 45c multicolored .30 .30
**818** A117 60c multicolored .35 .35
**819** A117 90c multicolored .50 .50
**820** A117 $4 multicolored 2.00 2.00
*Nos. 817-820 (4)* 3.15 3.15

**Souvenir Sheet**

**821** A117 $5 multicolored 3.00 3.00

23rd Olympic Games, Los Angeles, July 28-Aug. 12 — A118

30c, Gymnastics. 45c, Javelin. 60c, Diving. $4, Fencing.
$5, Equestrian.

**1984, Mar. Litho. *Perf. 14***
**822** A118 30c multicolored .25 .25
**823** A118 45c multicolored .35 .35
**824** A118 60c multicolored .45 .45
**825** A118 $4 multicolored 2.50 2.50
*Nos. 822-825 (4)* 3.55 3.55

**Souvenir Sheet**

**826** A118 $5 multicolored 3.75 3.75

Local Birds A119

5c, Plumbeous warbler. 45c, Imperial parrot. 60c, Blue-headed hummingbird. 90c, Red-necked parrot.
$5, Roseate flamingoes.

**1984, May Litho.**
**827** A119 5c multicolored 3.00 3.00
**828** A119 45c multicolored 7.00 7.00
**829** A119 60c multicolored 8.50 8.50
**830** A119 90c multicolored 11.00 11.00
*Nos. 827-830 (4)* 29.50 29.50

**Souvenir Sheet**

**831** A119 $5 multicolored 9.00 9.00

Easter A120

Various Disney characters and Easter bunnies.

**1984, Apr. 15 Litho. *Perf. 11***
**832** A120 ½c multicolored .25 .25
**833** A120 1c multicolored .25 .25
**834** A120 2c multicolored .25 .25
**835** A120 3c multicolored .25 .25
**836** A120 4c multicolored .25 .25
**837** A120 5c multicolored .25 .25
**838** A120 10c multicolored .25 .25
**839** A120 $2 multicolored 3.00 3.00
**840** A120 $4 multicolored 6.25 6.25
*Nos. 832-840 (9)* 11.00 11.00

**Souvenir Sheet**
***Perf. 14***

**841** A120 $5 multicolored 5.75 5.75

Ships A121

45c, Atlantic Star. 60c, Atlantic. 90c, Carib fishing pirogue. $4, Norway.
$5, Santa Maria.

**1984, June 14 Litho. *Perf. 14***

**842** A121 45c multicolored 1.75 1.75
**843** A121 60c multicolored 2.00 2.00
**844** A121 90c multicolored 2.50 2.50
**845** A121 $4 multicolored 6.75 6.75
*Nos. 842-845 (4)* 13.00 13.00

**Souvenir Sheet**

**846** A121 $5 multicolored 5.00 5.00

Local Plants — A122

45c, Guzmania lingulata. 60c, Pitcairnia angustifolia. 75c, Tillandsia fasciculata. $3, Aechmea smithiorum.
$5, Tillandsia utriculata.

**1984, Aug. 13**

**847** A122 45c multicolored .40 .40
**848** A122 60c multicolored .50 .50
**849** A122 75c multicolored .60 .60
**850** A122 $3 multicolored 2.40 2.40
*Nos. 847-850 (4)* 3.90 3.90

**Souvenir Sheet**

**851** A122 $5 multicolored 3.75 3.75

Ausipex Intl. Stamp Exhibition.

**Nos. 721, 732 Overprinted**

**1984 Litho. *Perf. 14***

**852** A103 10c multicolored .25 .25
**853** A103 $5 multicolored 4.00 4.00

Correggio & Degas — A122a

Correggio: 25c, Virgin and Child with Young St. John. 60c, Christ Bids Farewell to the Virgin Mary. 90c, Do Not Touch Me. $4, The Mystical Marriage of St. Catherine. No. 862, Adoration of the Magi,
Degas, horiz.: 30c, Before the Start. 45c, On the Racecourse. $1, Jockeys at the Flagpole. $3, Racehorses at Longchamp. No. 863, Self-portrait.

**1984, Nov. Litho. *Perf. 15***

**854** A122a 25c multicolored .35 .35
**855** A122a 30c multicolored .40 .40
**856** A122a 45c multicolored .45 .45
**857** A122a 60c multicolored .50 .50
**858** A122a 90c multicolored .65 .65
**859** A122a $1 multicolored .75 .75
**860** A122a $3 multicolored 1.75 1.75
**861** A122a $4 multicolored 1.90 1.90
*Nos. 854-861 (8)* 6.75 6.75

**Souvenir Sheets**

**862** A122a $5 multicolored 3.00 3.00
**863** A122a $5 multicolored 3.00 3.00

A123

**1984, Dec. *Perf. 14***

**864** A123 30c Avro 748 1.25 1.25
**865** A123 60c Twin Otter 2.25 2.25
**866** A123 $1 Islander 2.50 2.50
**867** A123 $3 Casa 4.75 4.75
*Nos. 864-867 (4)* 10.75 10.75

**Souvenir Sheet**

**868** A123 $5 Boeing 747 5.50 5.50

Intl. Civil Aviation Org., 40th anniv.

A124

Scenes from various Donald Duck movies.

**1984, Nov. Litho.**

**869** A124 45c multicolored 1.25 1.25
**870** A124 60c multicolored 1.50 1.50
**871** A124 90c multicolored 2.00 2.00
**872** A124 $2 multicolored, perf. 12x12½ 3.50 3.50
**873** A124 $4 multicolored 5.75 5.75
*Nos. 869-873 (5)* 14.00 14.00

**Souvenir Sheet**

***Perf. 13½x14***

**874** A124 $5 multicolored 5.50 5.50

Christmas and 50th anniv. of Donald Duck.

Cats A125

10c, Tabby. 15c, Calico shorthair. 20c, Siamese. 25c, Manx. 45c, Abyssinian. 60c, Tortoise shell longhair. $1, Rex. $2, Persian. $3, Himalayan. No. 884, $5, Burmese.
No. 885, $5, Gray Burmese, Persian, American shorthair.

**1984, Nov. 12 Litho. *Perf. 15***

**875** A125 10c multicolored .25 .25
**876** A125 15c multicolored .25 .25
**877** A125 20c multicolored .25 .25
**878** A125 25c multicolored .25 .25
**879** A125 45c multicolored .40 .40
**880** A125 60c multicolored .50 .50
**881** A125 $1 multicolored .75 .75
**882** A125 $2 multicolored 1.00 1.00
**883** A125 $3 multicolored 2.00 2.00
**884** A125 $5 multicolored 3.50 3.50
*Nos. 875-884 (10)* 9.15 9.15

**Souvenir Sheet**

**885** A125 $5 multicolored 5.50 5.50

Girl Guides, 75th Anniv. A126

35c, Lady Baden-Powell. 45c, Inspecting Dominican troop. 60c, With Dominican troop leaders. $3, Lord and Lady Baden-Powell, vert.
$5, Flag ceremony.

**1985, Feb. 18 *Perf. 14***

**886** A126 35c multicolored .60 .60
**887** A126 45c multicolored .70 .70
**888** A126 60c multicolored .90 .90
**889** A126 $3 multicolored 3.50 3.50
*Nos. 886-889 (4)* 5.70 5.70

**Souvenir Sheet**

**890** A126 $5 multicolored 5.50 5.50

John James Audubon A127

45c, King rails. $1, Black & white warbler, vert. $2, Broad-winged hawks, vert. $3, Ring-necked ducks.
$5, Reddish egrets, vert.

**1985, Apr. 4**

**891** A127 45c multicolored 1.25 1.25
**892** A127 $1 multicolored 2.00 2.00
**893** A127 $2 multicolored 3.25 3.25
**894** A127 $3 multicolored 4.25 4.25
*Nos. 891-894 (4)* 10.75 10.75

**Souvenir Sheet**

**895** A127 $5 multicolored 5.50 5.50

Nos. 891-894 exist vertically se-tenant with labels showing additional bird species.
See Nos. 965-969.

Duke of Edinburgh Awards, 1984 — A128

45c, Woman at computer terminal. 60c, Medical staff, patient. 90c, Runners. $4, Family jogging.
$5, Duke of Edinburgh.

**1985, Apr. 30**

**896** A128 45c multicolored .50 .50
**897** A128 60c multicolored 1.60 1.60
**898** A128 90c multicolored 2.00 2.00
**899** A128 $4 multicolored 3.25 3.25
*Nos. 896-899 (4)* 7.35 7.35

**Souvenir Sheet**

**900** A128 $5 multicolored 4.00 4.00

Intl. Youth Year A129

45c, Cricket match. 60c, Environmental study, parrot. $1, Stamp collecting. $3, Boating, leisure.
$5, Youths join hands.

**1985, July 8 Litho. *Perf. 14***

**901** A129 45c multicolored 3.00 2.00
**902** A129 60c multicolored 3.75 2.50
**903** A129 $1 multicolored 4.00 3.50
**904** A129 $3 multicolored 5.25 *7.50*
*Nos. 901-904 (4)* 16.00 15.50

**Souvenir Sheet**

**905** A129 $5 multicolored 4.00 4.00

Queen Mother, 85th Birthday — A130

60c, Visiting Sadlers Wells. $1, Fishing. $3, At Clarence House, 1984.
$5, Attending Windsor Castle Garter Ceremony.

**1985, July 15**

**906** A130 60c multicolored 1.00 .75
**907** A130 $1 multicolored 1.50 .75
**908** A130 $3 multicolored 2.00 2.00
*Nos. 906-908 (3)* 4.50 3.50

**Souvenir Sheet**

**909** A130 $5 multicolored 3.75 3.75

Johann Sebastian Bach — A131

Portrait, signature, music from Explication and: 45c, Cornett 60c, Coiled trumpet. $1, Piccolo. $3, Violoncello piccolo.

**1985, Sept. 2**

**910** A131 45c multicolored 1.00 1.00
**911** A131 60c multicolored 1.50 1.50
**912** A131 $1 multicolored 2.00 2.00
**913** A131 $3 multicolored 4.25 4.25
*Nos. 910-913 (4)* 8.75 8.75

**Souvenir Sheet**

**914** A131 $5 Portrait 4.00 4.00

State Visit of Elizabeth II, Oct. 25 — A132

60c, Flags of UK, Dominica. $1, Elizabeth II, vert. $4, HMS Britannia.
$5, Map.

**1985, Oct. 25 *Perf. 14½***

**915** A132 60c multicolored .75 .75
**916** A132 $1 multicolored .75 .75
**917** A132 $4 multicolored 3.50 3.50
*Nos. 915-917 (3)* 5.00 5.00

**Souvenir Sheet**

**918** A132 $5 multicolored 3.75 3.75

Mark Twain — A133

Disney characters in Tom Sawyer.

**1985, Nov. 11 Litho. *Perf. 14***

**919** A133 20c multicolored .75 .35
**920** A133 60c multicolored 1.50 .35
**921** A133 $1 multicolored 2.00 2.00
**922** A133 $1.50 multicolored 2.50 2.50
**923** A133 $2 multicolored 3.00 3.00
*Nos. 919-923 (5)* 9.75 8.20

**Souvenir Sheet**

**924** A133 $5 multicolored 6.50 6.50

Christmas.

10¢ Commonwealth of DOMINICA
LITTLE RED CAP • THE BROTHERS GRIMM

The Brothers Grimm — A134

Disney characters in Little Red Cap (Little Red Riding Hood).

**1985, Nov. 11**
**925** A134 10c multicolored .40 .40
**926** A134 45c multicolored 1.00 .50
**927** A134 90c multicolored 2.00 2.00
**928** A134 $1 multicolored 2.25 2.25
**929** A134 $3 multicolored 4.25 4.25
*Nos. 925-929 (5)* 9.90 9.40

**Souvenir Sheet**

**930** A134 $5 multicolored 7.75 7.75

Christmas.

UN, 40th Anniv. A135

Stamps of UN, famous men and events: 45c, No. 442 and Lord Baden-Powell. $2, No. 157 and Maimonides (1135-1204) Judaic scholar. $3, No. 278 and Sir Rowland Hill. $5, Apollo-Soyuz Mission, 10th anniv.

**1985, Nov. 22** *Perf. 14½*
**931** A135 45c multicolored .90 .90
**932** A135 $2 multicolored 2.00 2.00
**933** A135 $3 multicolored 2.00 2.00
*Nos. 931-933 (3)* 4.90 4.90

**Souvenir Sheet**

**934** A135 $5 multicolored 3.75 3.75

1986 World Cup Soccer Championships, Mexico — A136

Various soccer plays.

**1986, Mar. 26** *Perf. 14*
**935** A136 45c multicolored 1.25 1.25
**936** A136 60c multicolored 1.75 1.75
**937** A136 $1 multicolored 2.25 2.25
**938** A136 $3 multicolored 5.50 5.50
*Nos. 935-938 (4)* 10.75 10.75

**Souvenir Sheet**

**939** A136 $5 multicolored 8.50 8.50

For overprints see Nos. 974-978.

Statue of Liberty, Cent. A137

Statue and: 15c, New York police pursuing river pirates, c. 1890. 25c, Police patrol boat. 45c, Hoboken Ferry Terminal, c. 1890. $4, Holland Tunnel.
$5, Statue, vert.

**1986, Mar. 26**
**940** A137 15c multicolored 1.50 .75
**941** A137 25c multicolored 1.50 1.00
**942** A137 45c multicolored 2.50 1.00
**943** A137 $4 multicolored 5.00 5.00
*Nos. 940-943 (4)* 10.50 7.75

**Souvenir Sheet**

**944** A137 $5 multicolored 5.50 5.50

Halley's Comet A138

5c, Jantal Mantar Observatory, Delhi, India, Nasir al Din al Tusi (1201-1274), astronomer. 10c, US Bell X-1 rocket plane breaking sound barrier. 45c, Astronomicum Caesareum, 1540, manuscript diagram of comet's trajectory, 1531. $4, Mark Twain, comet appeared at birth and death. $5, Comet.

**1986, Apr. 17**
**945** A138 5c multicolored .60 .60
**946** A138 10c multicolored .60 .60
**947** A138 45c multicolored 1.25 1.25
**948** A138 $4 multicolored 3.25 3.25
*Nos. 945-948 (4)* 5.70 5.70

**Souvenir Sheet**

**949** A138 $5 multicolored 3.75 3.75

For overprints see Nos. 984-988.

**Queen Elizabeth II, 60th Birthday**
Common Design Type

2c, Wedding, 1947. $1, With Pope John Paul II, 1982. $4, Royal visit, 1971.
$5, Age 10.

**1986, Apr. 21** **Litho.** *Perf. 14*
**950** CD339 2c multicolored .25 .25
**951** CD339 $1 multicolored .75 .75
**952** CD339 $4 multicolored 2.50 2.50
*Nos. 950-952 (3)* 3.50 3.50

**Souvenir Sheet**

**953** CD339 $5 multicolored 3.75 3.75

AMERIPEX '86 — A139

Walt Disney characters involved in stamp collecting: 25c, Mickey Mouse and Pluto. 45c, Donald Duck. 60c, Chip-n-Dale. $4, Donald, nephews.
$5, Uncle Scrooge.

**1986, May 22** *Perf. 11*
**954** A139 25c multicolored .75 .75
**955** A139 45c multicolored .95 .95
**956** A139 60c multicolored 1.25 1.25
**957** A139 $4 multicolored 4.00 4.00
*Nos. 954-957 (4)* 6.95 6.95

**Souvenir Sheet**
*Perf. 14*

**958** A139 $5 multicolored 6.00 6.00

British Monarchs — A140

**1986, June 9** *Perf. 14*
**959** A140 10c William I .40 .40
**960** A140 40c Richard II .75 .75
**961** A140 50c Henry VIII .90 .90
**962** A140 $1 Charles II 1.00 1.00
**963** A140 $2 Queen Anne 1.50 1.50
**964** A140 $4 Queen Victoria 3.00 3.00
*Nos. 959-964 (6)* 7.55 7.55

**Audubon Type of 1985**

25c, Black-throated diver. 60c, Great blue heron. 90c, Yellow-crowned night heron. $4, Shoveler duck.
$5, Goose.

*Perf. 12½x12, 12x12½*
**1986, June 18**
**965** A127 25c multicolored 1.25 .50
**966** A127 60c multicolored 1.75 1.75
**967** A127 90c multicolored 2.25 2.25
**968** A127 $4 multicolored 4.50 4.50
*Nos. 965-968 (4)* 9.75 9.00

**Souvenir Sheet**
*Perf. 14*

**969** A127 $5 multicolored 10.00 10.00

Nos. 966-967 vert.

**Royal Wedding Issue, 1986**
Common Design Type

**1986, July 23** *Perf. 14*
**970** CD340 45c Couple .40 .40
**971** CD340 60c Prince Andrew .60 .60
**972** CD340 $4 Prince, aircraft 2.50 2.50
*Nos. 970-972 (3)* 3.50 3.50

**Souvenir Sheet**

**973** CD340 $5 Couple, diff. 3.75 3.75
*Nos. 970-973 (4)* 7.25 7.25

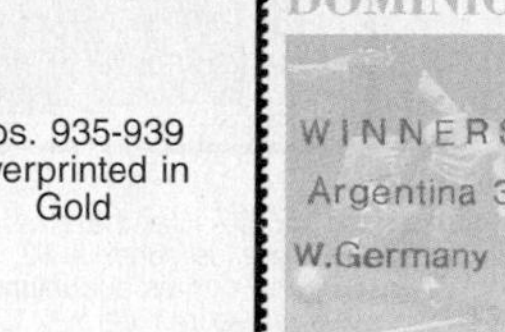


Nos. 935-939 Overprinted in Gold

**1986, Sept. 15** **Litho.** *Perf. 14*
**974** A136 45c multicolored 1.25 .50
**975** A136 60c multicolored 1.50 1.50
**976** A136 $1 multicolored 2.00 2.00
**977** A136 $3 multicolored 4.75 4.75
*Nos. 974-977 (4)* 9.50 8.75

**Souvenir Sheet**

**978** A136 $5 multicolored 8.75 8.75

Paintings by Albrecht Durer — A141

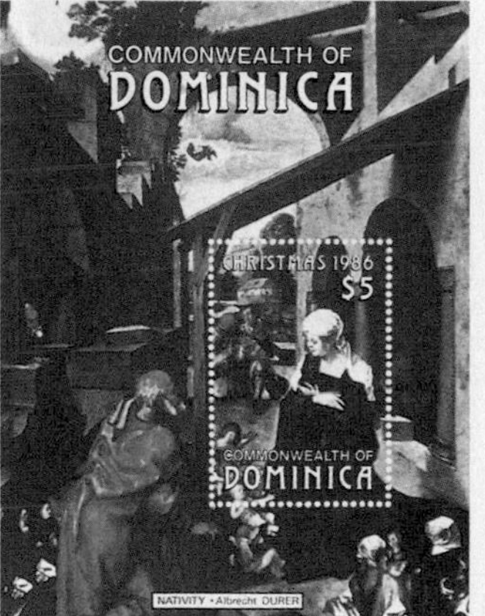


A142

45c, Virgin in Prayer. 60c, Madonna and Child. $1, Madonna and Child, diff. $3, Madonna and Child with St. Anne.
$5, Nativity.

**1986, Dec. 2** **Litho.** *Perf. 14*
**979** A141 45c multicolored .85 .35
**980** A141 60c multicolored 1.40 1.40
**981** A141 $1 multicolored 2.00 2.00
**982** A141 $3 multicolored 5.50 5.50
*Nos. 979-982 (4)* 9.75 9.25

**Souvenir Sheet**

**983** A142 $5 multicolored 8.75 8.75

**Nos. 945-949 Printed with Halley's Comet Logo in Black or Silver**

**1986, Dec. 16**
**984** A138 5c multicolored .25 .25
**985** A138 10c multicolored .25 .25
**986** A138 45c multicolored .50 .50
**987** A138 $4 multicolored 3.75 3.75
*Nos. 984-987 (4)* 4.75 4.75

**Souvenir Sheet**

**988** A138 $5 multi (S) 4.50 4.50

Birds — A143

1c, Broad-winged hawk. 2c, Ruddy quail dove. 5c, Red-necked pigeon. 10c, Green heron. 15c, Common gallinule. 20c, Ringed kingfisher. 25c, Brown pelican. 35c, White-tailed tropicbird. 45c, Red-legged thrush. 60c, Purple throated carib. 90c, Magnificent frigatebird. $1, Trembler. $2, Black-capped petrel. $5, Barn owl. $10, Imperial parrot.

**1987, Jan. 20** **Litho.** *Perf. 15*
**989** A143 1c multicolored .25 *.75*
**990** A143 2c multicolored .25 *.75*
**991** A143 5c multicolored .30 *.75*
**992** A143 10c multicolored .30 .25
**993** A143 15c multicolored .40 .30
**994** A143 20c multicolored .40 .30
**995** A143 25c multicolored .40 .25
**996** A143 35c multicolored .40 .30
**997** A143 45c multicolored .50 .40
**998** A143 60c multicolored .60 .55
**999** A143 90c multicolored .70 .70
**1000** A143 $1 multicolored .80 .80
**1001** A143 $2 multicolored 1.50 1.50
**1002** A143 $5 multicolored 3.75 3.75
**1003** A143 $10 multicolored 6.25 6.25
*Nos. 989-1003 (15)* 16.80 17.60

**Inscribed "1989" and "Questa"**

**1989, Aug. 31** **Litho.** *Perf. 14*
*990a* A143 2c .35 *.90*
*991a* A143 5c .35 *.80*
*992a* A143 10c .40 .25
*993a* A143 15c .55 .30
*994a* A143 20c .65 .35
*995a* A143 25c .65 .35
*996a* A143 35c .85 .30
*997a* A143 45c 1.00 .30
*998a* A143 60c 1.50 .50
*1000a* A143 $1 1.75 1.00
*1001a* A143 $2 3.00 3.00
*1002a* A143 $5 6.00 6.00
*1003a* A143 $10 8.00 8.00
*Nos. 990a-1003a (13)* 25.05 22.05

**Inscribed "1990" and "Questa"**

**1990** **Litho.** *Perf. 12*
*990b* A143 2c .40 *.95*
*991b* A143 5c .40 *.85*
*992b* A143 10c .45 .35
*993b* A143 15c .45 .35
*994b* A143 20c .70 .40
*995b* A143 25c .70 .40
*996b* A143 35c .85 .35
*997b* A143 45c 1.00 .35
*998b* A143 60c 1.50 1.60
*1000b* A143 $1 1.75 1.00
*1001b* A143 $2 3.00 3.00
*1002b* A143 $5 6.25 6.25
*1003b* A143 $10 8.25 8.25
*Nos. 990b-1003b (13)* 25.70 24.10

**Inscribed "1991" and "Questa"**

**1991** **Litho.** *Perf. 13x11½*
*990c* A143 2c .50 *1.10*
*991c* A143 5c .50 *.95*
*992c* A143 10c .55 .40
*993c* A143 15c .55 .35
*994c* A143 20c .75 .35
*995c* A143 25c .75 .40
*996c* A143 35c .85 .40
*997c* A143 45c 1.40 1.25
*998c* A143 60c 2.00 1.40
*1000c* A143 $1 2.00 1.50
*1001c* A143 $2 3.50 3.50
*1002c* A143 $5 7.00 7.00
*1003c* A143 $10 10.00 10.00
*Nos. 990c-1003c (13)* 30.35 28.60

Paintings by Marc Chagall (1887-1985) A144

Designs: 25c, Artist and His Model. 35c, Midsummer Night's Dream. 45c, Joseph the Shepherd. 60c, the Cellist. 90c, Woman with Pigs. $1, the Blue Circus. $3, For Vava. $4, the Rider. No. 1012, Purim. No. 1013, Firebird design for the curtain of the Stravinsky Ballet production.

**1987, Mar. 2** *Perf. 14*

| No. | Type | Description | Unused | Used |
|---|---|---|---|---|
| **1004** | A144 | 25c multicolored | .50 | .25 |
| **1005** | A144 | 35c multicolored | .65 | .30 |
| **1006** | A144 | 45c multicolored | .85 | .35 |
| **1007** | A144 | 60c multicolored | 1.00 | .50 |
| **1008** | A144 | 90c multicolored | 1.10 | .70 |
| **1009** | A144 | $1 multicolored | 1.25 | 1.25 |
| **1010** | A144 | $3 multicolored | 2.50 | 2.50 |
| **1011** | A144 | $4 multicolored | 3.50 | 3.50 |

**Size: 110x95mm**

***Imperf***

| No. | Type | Description | Unused | Used |
|---|---|---|---|---|
| **1012** | A144 | $5 multicolored | 4.00 | 4.00 |
| **1013** | A144 | $5 multicolored | 4.00 | 4.00 |
| | | *Nos. 1004-1013 (10)* | 19.35 | 17.35 |

A145

America's Cup — A146

45c, Reliance, 1903. 60c, Freedom, 1980. $1, Mischief, 1881. $3, Australia, 1977.
$5, Courageous, Australia, 1977.

**1987, Feb. 5** *Perf. 15*

| No. | Type | Description | Unused | Used |
|---|---|---|---|---|
| **1014** | A145 | 45c multicolored | .60 | .45 |
| **1015** | A145 | 60c multicolored | .70 | .50 |
| **1016** | A145 | $1 multicolored | .90 | 1.00 |
| **1017** | A145 | $3 multicolored | 2.75 | 2.00 |
| | | *Nos. 1014-1017 (4)* | 4.95 | 3.95 |

**Souvenir Sheet**

| No. | Type | Description | Unused | Used |
|---|---|---|---|---|
| **1018** | A146 | $5 multicolored | 3.75 | 3.75 |

Conch Shells — A147

Designs: 35c, Morch Poulsen's triton. 45c, Swainson globe purple sea snail. 60c, Banded tulip. No. 1022, Lamarck deltoid rock shell. No. 1023, Junoia volute.

**1987, Apr. 13** **Litho.**

| No. | Type | Description | Unused | Used |
|---|---|---|---|---|
| **1019** | A147 | 35c multicolored | .35 | .35 |
| **1020** | A147 | 45c multicolored | .45 | .45 |
| **1021** | A147 | 60c multicolored | .55 | .55 |
| **1022** | A147 | $5 multicolored | 3.50 | 3.50 |
| | | *Nos. 1019-1022 (4)* | 4.85 | 4.85 |

**Souvenir Sheet**

| No. | Type | Description | Unused | Used |
|---|---|---|---|---|
| **1023** | A147 | $5 multicolored | 4.50 | 4.50 |

CAPEX '87 A148

Mushrooms: 45c, Cantharellus cinnabarinus. 60c, Boletellus cubensis. $2, Eccilia cystiophorus. $3, Xerocomus guadelupae.
$5, Gymnopilus chrysopellus.

**1987, June 15** **Litho.** *Perf. 14*

| No. | Type | Description | Unused | Used |
|---|---|---|---|---|
| **1024** | A148 | 45c multicolored | 1.50 | .75 |
| **1025** | A148 | 60c multicolored | 2.00 | 2.00 |
| **1026** | A148 | $2 multicolored | 3.75 | 3.75 |
| **1027** | A148 | $3 multicolored | 4.50 | 4.50 |
| | | *Nos. 1024-1027 (4)* | 11.75 | 11.00 |

**Souvenir Sheet**

| No. | Type | Description | Unused | Used |
|---|---|---|---|---|
| **1028** | A148 | $5 multicolored | 10.00 | 10.00 |

A149

Discovery of America, 500th Anniv. (in 1992) — A150

Explorations of Christopher Columbus: 10c, Discovery of Dominica. 15c, Ships greeted by Carib Indians. 45c, Claiming New World for Spain. 60c, Wrecking of the Santa Maria. 90c, Fleet setting sail. $1, Sighting land. $3, Trading with the Indians. No. 1036, First settlement. No. 1037, Arrival of Second Fleet at Dominica, Nov. 3, 1493. No. 1038, Map of exploration of the Leeward Islands.

**1987, July 27** *Perf. 15*

| No. | Type | Description | Unused | Used |
|---|---|---|---|---|
| **1029** | A149 | 10c multicolored | .40 | .40 |
| **1030** | A149 | 15c multicolored | .50 | .50 |
| **1031** | A149 | 45c multicolored | .75 | .75 |
| **1032** | A149 | 60c multicolored | .95 | .95 |
| **1033** | A149 | 90c multicolored | 1.20 | 1.20 |
| **1034** | A149 | $1 multicolored | 1.25 | 1.25 |
| **1035** | A149 | $3 multicolored | 2.50 | 2.50 |
| **1036** | A149 | $5 multicolored | 3.25 | 3.25 |
| | | *Nos. 1029-1036 (8)* | 10.80 | 10.80 |

**Souvenir Sheets**

| No. | Type | Description | Unused | Used |
|---|---|---|---|---|
| **1037** | A150 | $5 multicolored | 4.75 | 4.75 |
| **1038** | A150 | $5 multicolored | 4.75 | 4.75 |

For overprints see Nos. 1083-1084.

Transportation — A151

10c, Warrior, 1st iron-clad warship. 15c, Maglev-MLU 001, fastest passenger train. 25c, Clipper Flying Cloud, fastest NYC-San Francisco voyage, 1852. 35c, 1st elevated railway, NYC. 45c, Tom Thumb, 1st US passenger train locomotive. 60c, Joshua Slocum, 1st solo circumnavigation of the world in a sloop. 90c, Se-Land Commerce, fastest Pacific crossing. $1, 1st cable car, San Francisco. $3, Orient Express. $4, The North River Steamboat of Clermont, invented by Robert Fulton, 1st successful commercial steamboat.

**1987** **Litho.** *Perf. 14*

| No. | Type | Description | Unused | Used |
|---|---|---|---|---|
| **1039** | A151 | 10c multicolored | .50 | .50 |
| **1040** | A151 | 15c multicolored | .75 | .75 |
| **1041** | A151 | 25c multi, vert. | .80 | .80 |
| **1042** | A151 | 35c multi, vert. | 1.00 | 1.00 |
| **1043** | A151 | 45c multicolored | 1.10 | 1.10 |
| **1044** | A151 | 60c multi, vert. | 1.25 | 1.25 |
| **1045** | A151 | 90c multi, vert. | 1.40 | 1.40 |
| **1046** | A151 | $1 multicolored | 1.50 | 1.50 |
| **1047** | A151 | $3 multicolored | 3.75 | 3.75 |
| **1048** | A151 | $4 multicolored | 4.00 | 4.00 |
| | | *Nos. 1039-1048 (10)* | 16.05 | 16.05 |

Issued: 10c, 15c, 45c, 60c, $4, 9/28; others 8/1.

For overprints see Nos. 1081-1082.

Christmas — A152

Paintings (details): 20c, Virgin and Child with St. Anne, by Durer. 25c, The Virgin and Child, by Murillo. $2, Madonna and Child, by Vincenzo Foppa (c. 1427-1516). $4, Madonna and Child, by Paolo Veronese (1528-1588). $5, Angel of the Annunciation, anonymous.

**1987, Nov. 16**

| No. | Type | Description | Unused | Used |
|---|---|---|---|---|
| **1049** | A152 | 20c multicolored | .30 | .30 |
| **1050** | A152 | 25c multicolored | .30 | .30 |
| **1051** | A152 | $2 multicolored | 2.00 | 2.00 |
| **1052** | A152 | $4 multicolored | 4.25 | 4.25 |
| | | *Nos. 1049-1052 (4)* | 6.85 | 6.85 |

**Souvenir Sheet**

| No. | Type | Description | Unused | Used |
|---|---|---|---|---|
| **1053** | A152 | $5 multicolored | 3.75 | 3.75 |

Mickey Mouse, 60th Anniv. A153

Disney theme parks and trains: 20c, People Mover, Disney World. 25c, Horse-drawn Trolley, Disneyland. 45c, Roger E. Broggie, Disney World. 60c, Big Thunder Mountain, Disneyland. 90c, Walter E. Disney, Disneyland. $1, Monorail, Disney World. $3, Casey Jr. from Dumbo. $4, Lilly Belle, Disney World. No. 1062, Rainbow Caverns Mine Train, Disneyland, horiz. No. 1063, Toy train from movie Out of Scale, horiz.

**1987, Dec. 7** **Litho.** *Perf. 14*

| No. | Type | Description | Unused | Used |
|---|---|---|---|---|
| **1054** | A153 | 20c multicolored | .55 | .55 |
| **1055** | A153 | 25c multicolored | .55 | .55 |
| **1056** | A153 | 45c multicolored | .90 | .90 |
| **1057** | A153 | 60c multicolored | 1.00 | 1.00 |
| **1058** | A153 | 90c multicolored | 1.60 | 1.60 |
| **1059** | A153 | $1 multicolored | 1.75 | 1.75 |
| **1060** | A153 | $3 multicolored | 4.00 | 4.00 |
| **1061** | A153 | $4 multicolored | 5.25 | 5.25 |
| | | *Nos. 1054-1061 (8)* | 15.60 | 15.60 |

**Souvenir Sheets**

| No. | Type | Description | Unused | Used |
|---|---|---|---|---|
| **1062** | A153 | $5 multicolored | 4.00 | 4.00 |
| **1063** | A153 | $5 multicolored | 4.00 | 4.00 |

40th Wedding Anniv. of Queen Elizabeth II and Prince Philip — A154

45c, Couple, wedding party, 1947. 60c, Elizabeth, Charles, c. 1952. $1, Royal Family, c. 1952. $3, Queen with tiara, c. 1960.
$5, Elizabeth, 1947.

**1988, Feb. 15** **Litho.** *Perf. 14*

| No. | Type | Description | Unused | Used |
|---|---|---|---|---|
| **1064** | A154 | 45c multicolored | .75 | .75 |
| **1065** | A154 | 60c multicolored | .80 | .80 |
| **1066** | A154 | $1 multicolored | 1.00 | 1.00 |
| **1067** | A154 | $3 multicolored | 2.40 | 2.40 |
| | | *Nos. 1064-1067 (4)* | 4.95 | 4.95 |

**Souvenir Sheet**

| No. | Type | Description | Unused | Used |
|---|---|---|---|---|
| **1068** | A154 | $5 multicolored | 3.50 | 3.50 |

1988 Summer Olympics, Seoul — A155

**1988, Mar. 15**

| No. | Type | Description | Unused | Used |
|---|---|---|---|---|
| **1069** | A155 | 45c Kayaking | .85 | .85 |
| **1070** | A155 | 60c Tae kwon-do | 1.25 | 1.25 |
| **1071** | A155 | $1 Diving | 1.40 | 1.40 |
| **1072** | A155 | $3 Parallel bars | 2.50 | 2.50 |
| | | *Nos. 1069-1072 (4)* | 6.00 | 6.00 |

**Souvenir Sheet**

| No. | Type | Description | Unused | Used |
|---|---|---|---|---|
| **1073** | A155 | $5 Soccer | 3.25 | 3.25 |

For overprints see Nos. 1151-1155.

Reunion '88 Tourism Campaign A156

10c, Carib Indian, vert. 25c, Mountainous interior. 35c, Indian River, vert. 60c, Belaire dancer, vert. 90c, The Boiling Lake, vert. $3, Coral reef.
$5, Belaire dancer, diff., vert.

**1988, Apr. 13** **Litho.** *Perf. 15*

| No. | Type | Description | Unused | Used |
|---|---|---|---|---|
| **1074** | A156 | 10c multicolored | .25 | .25 |
| **1075** | A156 | 25c multicolored | .25 | .25 |
| **1076** | A156 | 35c multicolored | .25 | .25 |
| **1077** | A156 | 60c multicolored | .25 | .25 |
| **1078** | A156 | 90c multicolored | .30 | .30 |
| **1079** | A156 | $3 multicolored | .90 | .90 |
| | | *Nos. 1074-1079 (6)* | 2.20 | 2.20 |

**Souvenir Sheet**

| No. | Type | Description | Unused | Used |
|---|---|---|---|---|
| **1080** | A156 | $5 multicolored | 3.00 | 3.00 |

Independence, 10th anniv.

**Nos. 1046-1047, 1037-1038 Ovptd. for Philatelic Exhibitions in Black**

a

b

c

d

**1988, June 1 Litho. *Perf. 14***
**1081** A151(a) $1 multi 1.00 1.00
**1082** A151(b) $3 multi 3.75 3.75

### Souvenir Sheets

***Perf. 15***
**1083** A150(c) $5 multi 4.00 4.00
**1084** A150(d) $5 multi 4.00 4.00

Miniature Sheet

Rain Forest Flora and Fauna — A157

Designs: a, White-tailed tropicbirds. b, Blue-throated euphonia. c, Smooth-billed ani. d, Scaly-breasted thrasher. e, Purple-throated carib. f, Southern daggertail and Clench's hairstreak. g, Trembler. h, Imperial parrot. i, Mangrove cuckoo. j, Hercules beetle. k, Orion. l, Red-necked parrot. m, Tillandsia. n, Polystacha luteola and bananaquit. o, False chameleon. p, Iguana. q, Hypolimnas. r, Green-throated carib. s, Heliconia. t, Agouti.

**1988, July 25 *Perf. 14½***
**1085** A157 Sheet of 20 14.00 14.00
*a.-t.* 45c any single .60 .60

Intl. Fund for Agricultural Development (IFAD), 10th Anniv. — A158

**1988, Sept. 5 Litho. *Perf. 14***
**1086** A158 45c Hen house .65 .65
**1087** A158 60c Pig farm .90 .90
**1088** A158 90c Cattle 1.25 1.25
**1089** A158 $3 Black-belly sheep 3.50 3.50
*Nos. 1086-1089 (4)* 6.30 6.30

### Souvenir Sheet

**1090** A158 $5 Mixed crops, vert. 3.75 3.75

Entertainers A159

10c, Gary Cooper. 35c, Josephine Baker. 45c, Maurice Chevalier. 60c, James Cagney. $1, Clark Gable. $2, Louis Armstrong. $3, Liberace. $4, Spencer Tracy.
No. 1099, Elvis Presley. No. 1100, Humphrey Bogart.

**1988, Sept. 8**
**1091** A159 10c multicolored .40 .25
**1092** A159 35c multicolored .50 .25
**1093** A159 45c multicolored .55 .30
**1094** A159 60c multicolored .75 .30
**1095** A159 $1 multicolored 1.00 .30
**1096** A159 $2 multicolored 1.75 1.75
**1097** A159 $3 multicolored 2.00 2.00
**1098** A159 $4 multicolored 2.50 2.50
*Nos. 1091-1098 (8)* 9.45 7.65

### Souvenir Sheets

**1099** A159 $5 multicolored 4.25 4.25
**1100** A159 $5 multicolored 4.25 4.25

Flowering Trees and Shrubs A160

**1988, Sept. 29 Litho. *Perf. 14***
**1101** A160 15c Sapodilla .25 .25
**1102** A160 20c Tangerine .25 .25
**1103** A160 25c Avocado pear .25 .25
**1104** A160 45c Amherstia .30 .30
**1105** A160 90c Lipstick tree .55 .55
**1106** A160 $1 Cannonball tree .60 .60
**1107** A160 $3 Saman 1.50 1.50
**1108** A160 $4 Pineapple 2.00 2.00
*Nos. 1101-1108 (8)* 5.70 5.70

### Souvenir Sheets

**1109** A160 $5 Lignum vitae 3.75 3.75
**1110** A160 $5 Sea grape 3.75 3.75

Paintings by Titian A161

Designs: 25c, Jacopo Strada, c. 1567. 35c, Titian's Daughter Lavinia, c. 1565. 45c, Andrea Navagero, c. 1515. 60c, Judith with Head of Holoferenes, c. 1570. $1, Emilia di Spilimbergo, c. 1560. $2, Martyrdom of St. Lawrence, c. 1548. $3, Salome With the Head of St. John the Baptist, 1560. $4, St. John the Baptist, c. 1540. No. 1119, Self-portrait, c. 1555. No. 1120, Sisyphus, 1549.

**1988, Oct. 10 Litho. *Perf. 13½x14***
**1111** A161 25c multicolored .25 .25
**1112** A161 35c multicolored .25 .25
**1113** A161 45c multicolored .35 .35
**1114** A161 60c multicolored .45 .45
**1115** A161 $1 multicolored .90 .90
**1116** A161 $2 multicolored 1.25 1.25
**1117** A161 $3 multicolored 2.00 2.00
**1118** A161 $4 multicolored 2.50 2.50
*Nos. 1111-1118 (8)* 7.95 7.95

### Souvenir Sheets

**1119** A161 $5 multicolored 3.50 3.50
**1120** A161 $5 multicolored 3.50 3.50

Independence, 10th Anniv. — A162

20c, Imperial parrot. 45c, No. 1, landscape. $2, No. 602, waterfall. $3, Carib wood.
$5, Natl. band performing

**1988, Oct. 31 Litho. *Perf. 14***
**1121** A162 20c multicolored 1.75 .50
**1122** A162 45c multicolored 1.00 .40
**1123** A162 $2 multicolored 1.75 1.75
**1124** A162 $3 multicolored 2.00 *3.00*
*Nos. 1121-1124 (4)* 6.50 5.65

### Souvenir Sheet

**1125** A162 $5 multicolored 3.75 3.75

Nos. 1122-1123 horiz.

John F. Kennedy — A163

20c, With Jackie. 25c, Sailing Vicuna. $2, Walking in Hyannis Port. $4, Berlin Wall speech.
$5, Portrait.

**1988, Nov. 22**
**1126** A163 20c multicolored .25 .25
**1127** A163 25c multicolored .25 .25
**1128** A163 $2 multicolored .95 .95
**1129** A163 $4 multicolored 2.25 2.25
*Nos. 1126-1129 (4)* 3.70 3.70

### Souvenir Sheet

**1130** A163 $5 multicolored 3.50 3.50

Nos. 1126-1128 horiz.

Miniature Sheet

Christmas, Mickey Mouse 60th Anniv. — A164

No. 1131: a, Huey, Dewey, Louie. b, Daisy Duck. c, Winnie-the-Pooh. d, Goofy. e, Donald Duck. f, Mickey Mouse. g, Minnie Mouse. h, Chip-n-Dale.
No. 1132, Mickey, Morty and Ferdy. No. 1133, Characters visiting shopping mall Santa.

**1988, Dec. 1 *Perf. 13½x14***
**1131** A164 Sheet of 8 6.75 6.75
*a.-h.* 60c any single .80 .80

### Souvenir Sheets

**1132** A164 $6 multi 5.00 5.00
**1133** A164 $6 multi, horiz. 5.00 5.00

UN Declaration of Human Rights, 40th Anniv. — A165

Designs: $3, Flag of Sweden and Raoul Wallenberg, who helped save 100,000 Jews in Budapest from deportation to Nazi concentration camps.
$5, Human Rights Flame.

**1988, Dec. 12 *Perf. 14***
**1134** A165 $3 multicolored 3.00 3.00

### Souvenir Sheet

**1135** A165 $5 multi, vert. 4.00 4.00

Coastal Game Fish A166

10c, Greater amberjack. 15c, Blue marlin. 35c, Cobia. 45c, Dolphin. 60c, Cero. 90c, Mahogany snapper. $3, Yellowfin tuna. $4, Rainbow parrotfish.
No. 1144, Manta ray. No. 1145, Tarpon.

**1988, Dec. 22 Litho. *Perf. 14***
**1136** A166 10c multicolored .25 .25
**1137** A166 15c multicolored .25 .25
**1138** A166 35c multicolored .40 .40
**1139** A166 45c multicolored .50 .50
**1140** A166 60c multicolored .75 .75
**1141** A166 90c multicolored 1.00 1.00
**1142** A166 $3 multicolored 2.50 2.50
**1143** A166 $4 multicolored 3.50 3.50
*Nos. 1136-1143 (8)* 9.15 9.15

### Souvenir Sheets

**1144** A166 $5 multicolored 5.00 5.00
**1145** A166 $5 multicolored 5.00 5.00

Caribbean Insects and Reptiles A167

10c, Leatherback turtle. 25c, Monarch butterfly. 60c, Green anole. $3, Praying mantis.
$5, Hercules beetle.

**1988, Dec. 29**
**1146** A167 10c multicolored .60 .60
**1147** A167 25c multicolored 1.75 1.75
**1148** A167 60c multicolored 2.00 2.00
**1149** A167 $3 multicolored 5.50 5.50
*Nos. 1146-1149 (4)* 9.85 9.85

### Souvenir Sheet

**1150** A167 $5 multicolored 5.00 5.00

### Nos. 1069-1073 Overprinted

a

b

c

d

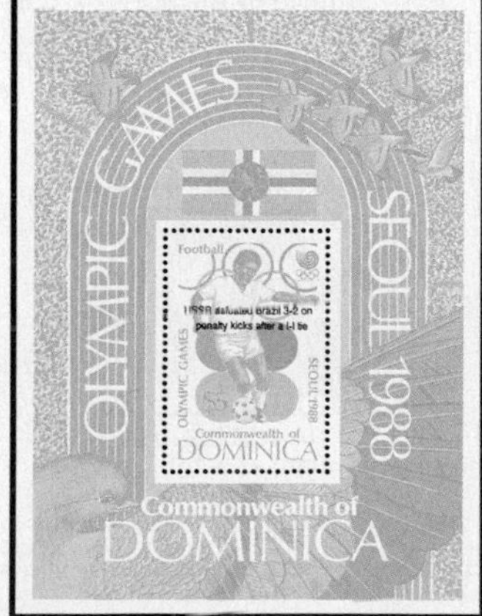

e

**1989, Mar. 20 Litho. *Perf. 14***
**1151** A155(a) 45c multi .30 .30
**1152** A155(b) 60c multi .40 .40
**1153** A155(c) $1 multi .75 .75
**1154** A155(d) $3 multi 1.90 1.90
*Nos. 1151-1154 (4)* 3.35 3.35

### Souvenir Sheet

**1155** A155(e) $5 multi 3.75 3.75

Pre-Columbian Societies and Their Customs — A168

UPAE and discovery of America anniv. emblems and: 20c, Carib Indians canoeing. 35c, Bow hunting. $1, Canoe making. $3, Shield wrestling. $6, Dancing.

**1989, May 8 Litho. *Perf. 14***

| | | | | |
|---|---|---|---|---|
| **1156** | A168 | 20c multicolored | .25 | .25 |
| **1157** | A168 | 35c multicolored | .35 | .35 |
| **1158** | A168 | $1 multicolored | 1.00 | 1.00 |
| **1159** | A168 | $3 multicolored | 2.75 | 2.75 |
| | | *Nos. 1156-1159 (4)* | 4.35 | 4.35 |

**Souvenir Sheet**

| | | | | |
|---|---|---|---|---|
| **1160** | A168 | $6 multicolored | 4.25 | 4.25 |

Discovery of America 500th anniv. (in 1992).

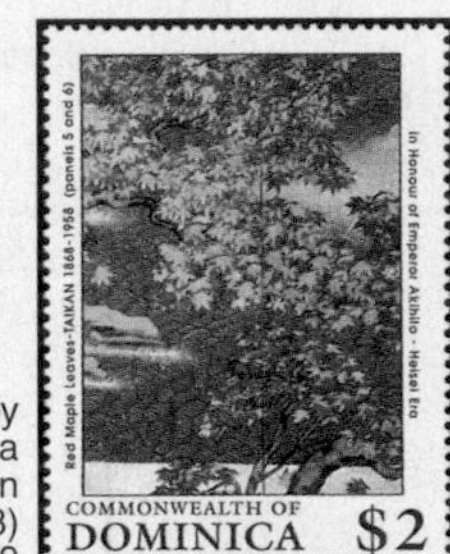


Paintings by Yokoyama Taikan (1868-1958) A169

Designs: 10c, Lao-tzu. 20c, Red Maple Leaves (panels 1-2). 45c, King Wen Learns a Lesson from His Cook. 60c, Red Maple Leaves (panels 3-4). $1, Wild Flowers. $2, Red Maple Leaves (panels 5-6). $3, Red Maple Leaves (panels 7-8). $4, The Indian Ceremony of Floating Lamps on the River. No. 1169, Innocence. No. 1170, Red Maple Leaves (4 panels).

**1989, Aug. 8 Litho. *Perf. 13½x14***

| | | | | |
|---|---|---|---|---|
| **1161** | A169 | 10c multicolored | .25 | .25 |
| **1162** | A169 | 20c multicolored | .25 | .25 |
| **1163** | A169 | 45c multicolored | .30 | .30 |
| **1164** | A169 | 60c multicolored | .40 | .40 |
| **1165** | A169 | $1 multicolored | .65 | .65 |
| **1166** | A169 | $2 multicolored | 1.25 | 1.25 |
| **1167** | A169 | $3 multicolored | 1.75 | 1.75 |
| **1168** | A169 | $4 multicolored | 2.25 | 2.25 |
| | | *Nos. 1161-1168 (8)* | 7.10 | 7.10 |

**Souvenir Sheets**

| | | | | |
|---|---|---|---|---|
| **1169** | A169 | $5 multicolored | 3.75 | 3.75 |
| **1170** | A169 | $5 multicolored | 3.75 | 3.75 |

Hirohito (1901-89) and enthronement of Akihito as emperor of Japan.

PHILEXFRANCE '89, July 7-17, Paris — A170

Designs: 10c, Map of Dominica with French place names, 1766. 35c, French coin, 1688. $1, French ship, 1720. $4, Introduction of coffee to Dominica by the French, 1772. $5, Text.

**1989, July 17 Litho. *Perf. 14***

| | | | | |
|---|---|---|---|---|
| **1171** | A170 | 10c multi, vert. | 1.00 | 1.00 |
| **1172** | A170 | 35c shown | 1.00 | 1.00 |
| **1173** | A170 | $1 multicolored | 1.50 | 1.50 |
| **1174** | A170 | $4 multicolored | 3.00 | 3.00 |
| | | *Nos. 1171-1174 (4)* | 6.50 | 6.50 |

**Souvenir Sheet**

| | | | | |
|---|---|---|---|---|
| **1175** | A170 | $5 multicolored | 5.25 | 5.25 |

Butterflies A171

Designs: 10c, Homerus swallowtail. 15c, *Morpho peleides*. 25c, Julia. 35c, Gundlach's swallowtail. 60c, Monarch. $1, Gulf fritillary. $3, Red-splashed sulphur. $5, *Papilio andraemon*. No. 1184, *Heliconius doris, Adelpha cytherea, Calliona argenissa, Eurema proterpia*. No. 1185, *Adelpha iphicla, Dismorphia spio, Lucinia sida.*

**1989, Sept. 11 Litho. *Perf. 14***

| | | | | |
|---|---|---|---|---|
| **1176** | A171 | 10c multicolored | .40 | .40 |
| **1177** | A171 | 15c multicolored | .40 | .40 |
| **1178** | A171 | 25c multicolored | .70 | .70 |
| **1179** | A171 | 35c multicolored | .80 | .80 |
| **1180** | A171 | 60c multicolored | 1.10 | 1.10 |
| **1181** | A171 | $1 multicolored | 1.50 | 1.50 |
| **1182** | A171 | $3 multicolored | 3.50 | 3.50 |
| **1183** | A171 | $5 multicolored | 6.00 | 6.00 |
| | | *Nos. 1176-1183 (8)* | 14.40 | 14.40 |

**Souvenir Sheets**

| | | | | |
|---|---|---|---|---|
| **1184** | A171 | $6 multicolored | 6.50 | 6.50 |
| **1185** | A171 | $6 multicolored | 6.50 | 6.50 |

Misspellings: No. 1181, "Frittillary"; No. 1182, "Sulper."

Orchids — A172

10c, Oncidium pusillum. 35c, Epidendrum cochleata. 45c, Epidendrum ciliare. 60c, Cyrtopodium andersonii. $1, Habenaria pauciflora. $2, Maxillaria alba. $3, Selenipedium palmifolium. $4, Brassavola cucullata.

No. 1194, Oncidium lanceanum. No. 1195, Comparettia falcata.

**1989, Sept. 28**

| | | | | |
|---|---|---|---|---|
| **1186** | A172 | 10c multicolored | .40 | .40 |
| **1187** | A172 | 35c multicolored | .75 | .75 |
| **1188** | A172 | 45c multicolored | .85 | .85 |
| **1189** | A172 | 60c multicolored | 1.10 | 1.10 |
| **1190** | A172 | $1 multicolored | 1.50 | 1.50 |
| **1191** | A172 | $2 multicolored | 2.50 | 2.50 |
| **1192** | A172 | $3 multicolored | 3.00 | 3.00 |
| **1193** | A172 | $4 multicolored | 4.75 | 4.75 |
| | | *Nos. 1186-1193 (8)* | 14.85 | 14.85 |

**Souvenir Sheets**

| | | | | |
|---|---|---|---|---|
| **1194** | A172 | $5 multicolored | 6.50 | 6.50 |
| **1195** | A172 | $5 multicolored | 6.50 | 6.50 |

1st Moon Landing, 20th Anniv. A173

10c, Columbia in lunar orbit. 60c, Aldrin descending ladder. $2, Aldrin, Sea of Tranquility. $3, Flag raising.

$6, Liftoff.

**1989, Oct. 31 Litho. *Perf. 14***

| | | | | |
|---|---|---|---|---|
| **1196** | A173 | 10c multicolored | .35 | .35 |
| **1197** | A173 | 60c multicolored | .80 | .80 |
| **1198** | A173 | $2 multicolored | 2.25 | 2.25 |
| **1199** | A173 | $3 multicolored | 3.25 | 3.25 |
| | | *Nos. 1196-1199 (4)* | 6.65 | 6.65 |

**Souvenir Sheet**

| | | | | |
|---|---|---|---|---|
| **1200** | A173 | $6 multicolored | 7.00 | 7.00 |

Souvenir Sheets

A174

1990 World Cup Soccer Championships, Italy — A175

Past championship match scenes, flags and soccer ball: a, Brazil vs. Italy, Mexico, 1970. b, England vs. West Germany, England, 1966. c, West Germany vs. Netherlands, West Germany, 1974. d, Italy vs. West Germany, Spain, 1982.

**1989, Nov. 7 *Perf. 14***

| | | | | |
|---|---|---|---|---|
| **1201** | A174 | Sheet of 4 | 8.75 | 8.75 |
| *a.-d.* | | $1 any single | 2.00 | 2.00 |

***Perf. 14***

| | | | | |
|---|---|---|---|---|
| **1202** | A175 | $6 shown | 6.00 | 6.00 |

Souvenir Sheet

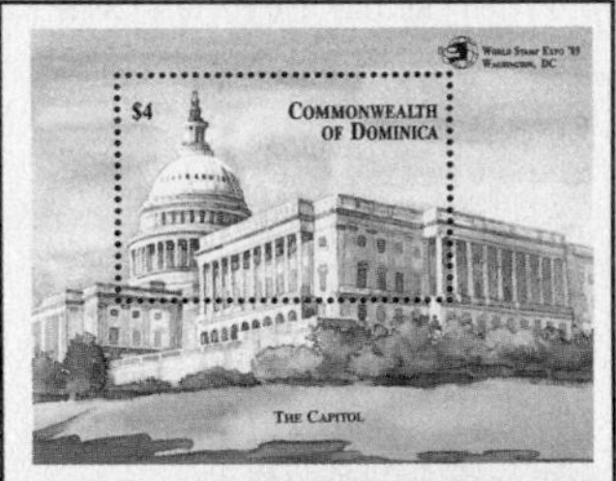


The Capitol, Washington, DC — A176

**1989, Nov. 17 Litho. *Perf. 14***

| | | | | |
|---|---|---|---|---|
| **1203** | A176 | $4 multicolored | 3.75 | 3.75 |

World Stamp Expo '89.

Miniature Sheets

American Presidency, 200th Anniv. — A177

US presidents, historic events and monuments.

No. 1204: a, Washington, 1st inauguration. b, John Adams, presidential mansion, 1800. c, Jefferson, Graff House in Philadelphia, excerpt from the 1st draft of the Declaration of Independence. d, Madison, USS *Constitution* at the defeat of HMS *Guerriere*, 1812. e, Monroe, freed slaves settle Liberia, 1822. f, John Quincy Adams, opening of the Erie Canal, 1825.

No. 1205: a, Fillmore, Commodore Perry laying groundwork for US trade agreement with Japan. b, Pierce, Jefferson Davis and San Xavier del Bac mission, Tucson, AZ, Gadsden Purchase, 1853. c, Buchanan, Pony Express stamp, Buffalo Bill Cody as express rider. d, Lincoln, UPU emblem, Intl. Postal Congress, Paris, 1863. e, Andrew Johnson, polar bear, purchase of Alaska from Russia, 1867. f, Grant, 1st transcontinental railway link, Promontory Point, Utah, 1869.

No. 1206: a, Theodore Roosevelt, construction of the Panama Canal, 1904. b, Taft, Adm. Peary becomes 1st man to reach the North Pole, 1909. c, Wilson, US #C3, cancel commemorating 1st scheduled airmail service, 1918. d, Harding, airship USS *Shenandoah* at Lakehurst, NJ. e, Coolidge, Lindbergh's solo transatlantic flight, 1927. f, Mt. Rushmore, by Gutzon Borglum, 1927.

No. 1207: a, Lyndon B. Johnson, space exploration. b, Nixon visiting PRChina, 1971. c, Ford, tall ship in NY Harbor for Operation Sail, 1976, US bicentennial celebrations. d, Carter, Sadat of Egypt and Begin of Israel during the Camp David Accords, 1979. e, Reagan, European Space Agency emblem, flags and *Columbia* space shuttle. f, Bush, Grumman Avenger bomber he piloted during WWII.

**1989, Nov. 17 *Perf. 14***

| | | | | |
|---|---|---|---|---|
| **1204** | A177 | Sheet of 6 | 6.50 | 6.50 |
| *a.-f.* | | 60c any single | 1.00 | 1.00 |
| **1205** | A177 | Sheet of 6 | 6.50 | 6.50 |
| *a.-f.* | | 60c any single | 1.00 | 1.00 |
| **1206** | A177 | Sheet of 6 | 6.50 | 6.50 |
| *a.-f.* | | 60c any single | 1.00 | 1.00 |
| **1207** | A177 | Sheet of 6 | 6.50 | 6.50 |
| *a.-f.* | | 60c any single | 1.00 | 1.00 |

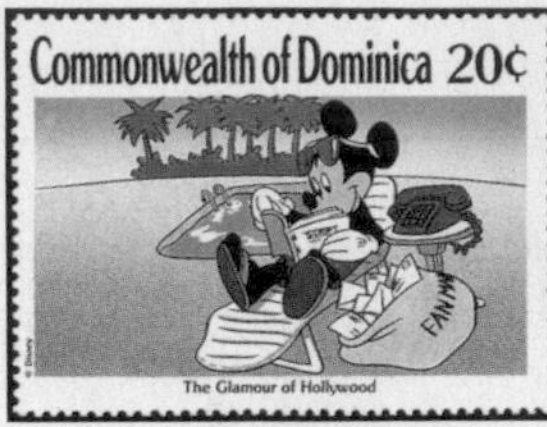


Mickey Mouse as a Hollywood Star — A178

Walt Disney characters: 20c, Reading script. 35c, Television interview. 45c, Named a star in tabloid headline. 60c, Signing autographs. $1, In dressing room, holding fans at bay. $2, Riding in limousine. $3, With Minnie in the limelight. $4, Accepting award. No. 1216, Giving interview during celebrity tennis tournament. No. 1217, Footprint impression in cement outside theater.

**1989, Nov. 30 Litho. *Perf. 14x13½***

| | | | | |
|---|---|---|---|---|
| **1208** | A178 | 20c multicolored | .50 | .50 |
| **1209** | A178 | 35c multicolored | .70 | .70 |
| **1210** | A178 | 45c multicolored | .80 | .80 |
| **1211** | A178 | 60c multicolored | .90 | .90 |
| **1212** | A178 | $1 multicolored | 1.25 | 1.25 |
| **1213** | A178 | $2 multicolored | 2.25 | 2.25 |
| **1214** | A178 | $3 multicolored | 3.00 | 3.00 |
| **1215** | A178 | $4 multicolored | 4.00 | 4.00 |
| | | *Nos. 1208-1215 (8)* | 13.40 | 13.40 |

**Souvenir Sheets**

| | | | | |
|---|---|---|---|---|
| **1216** | A178 | $5 multicolored | 5.50 | 5.50 |
| **1217** | A178 | $5 multicolored | 5.50 | 5.50 |

Christmas — A179

Religious paintings by Botticelli: 20c, *Madonna in Glory with Seraphim*. 25c, *The Annunciation*. 35c, *Madonna of the Pomegranate*. 45c, *Madonna of the Rose Garden*. 60c, *Madonna of the Book*. $1, *Madonna and Child Under a Baldachin with Three Angels*. $4, *Madonna and Child with Angels*. No. 1225, *Bardi Madonna*. No. 1226, *The Mystic Nativity*. No. 1227, *The Adoration of the Magi*.

**1989, Dec. 4 *Perf. 14***

| | | | | |
|---|---|---|---|---|
| **1218** | A179 | 20c multicolored | .45 | .45 |
| **1219** | A179 | 25c multicolored | .45 | .45 |
| **1220** | A179 | 35c multicolored | .60 | .60 |
| **1221** | A179 | 45c multicolored | .75 | .75 |
| **1222** | A179 | 60c multicolored | .90 | .90 |
| **1223** | A179 | $1 multicolored | 1.10 | 1.10 |
| **1224** | A179 | $4 multicolored | 3.00 | 3.00 |
| **1225** | A179 | $5 multicolored | 4.75 | 4.75 |
| | | *Nos. 1218-1225 (8)* | 12.00 | 12.00 |

**Souvenir Sheets**

| | | | | |
|---|---|---|---|---|
| **1226** | A179 | $5 multicolored | 5.00 | 5.00 |
| **1227** | A179 | $5 multicolored | 5.00 | 5.00 |

Nehru — A180

$5, Parliament House, New Delhi, horiz.

**1989, Dec. 27 Litho. *Perf. 14***

**1228** A180 60c shown 2.00 2.00

**Souvenir Sheet**

**1229** A180 $5 multicolored 6.00 6.00

Jawaharlal Nehru (1889-1964), 1st prime minister of independent India.

Girl Guides — A181

Guide movement in Dominica, 60th anniv.: 60c, Lady Baden-Powell and Agatha Robinson, former Guide leader on Dominica. $5, Dorris Stockmann, chairman of the world committee of the World Assoc. of Girl Guides and Girl Scouts, and Judith Pestaina, chief commissioner of the Dominica Girl Guides Assoc., horiz.

**1989, Dec. 29**

**1230** A181 60c multicolored 1.25 1.25

**Souvenir Sheet**

**1231** A181 $5 multi, horiz. 5.25 5.25

Miniature Sheet

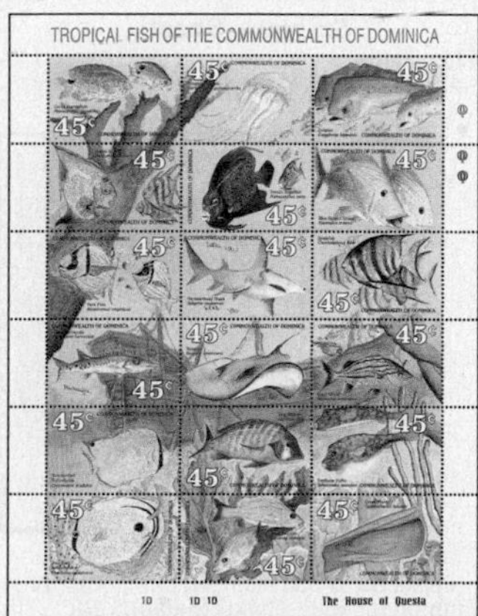


Marine Life — A182

Designs: a, Cocoa damselfish. b, Stinging jellyfish. c, Dolphin. d, Queen angelfish. e, French angelfish. f, Blue striped grunt. g, Pork fish. h, Hammerhead shark. i, Spadefish. j, Great barracuda. k, Stingray. l, Black grunt. m, Two-spotted butterflyfish. n, Dog snapper. o, Southern puffer. p, Four-eyed butterflyfish. q, Lane snapper. r, Green moray.

**1990 Litho. *Perf. 14***

**1232** A182 Sheet of 18 11.00 11.00
*a.-r.* 45c any single .55 .55

Penny Black, 150th Anniv. A183

Stamp World London '90: 50c, Post Office accelerator, 1830. 60c, $4, No. 1239, London skyline, St. Paul's Cathedral. 90c, Railway post car, 1838. $3, Center cycle, 1883. No. 1240, Mail truck, 1899.

**1990, May 3 Litho. *Perf. 13½***

**1233** A183 45c green & black .60 .60
**1234** A183 50c blk & slate blue .80 .80
**1235** A183 60c dk blue & blk .85 .85
**1236** A183 90c black & green 1.50 1.50
**1237** A183 $3 blk & dk bl vio 2.75 2.75
**1238** A183 $4 dk bl vio & blk 3.75 3.75
*Nos. 1233-1238 (6)* 10.25 10.25

**Souvenir Sheet**

**1239** A183 $5 beige & black 4.50 4.50
**1240** A183 $5 gray & red brn 4.50 4.50

A184

Birds: 10c, Blue-headed hummingbird. 20c, Black-capped petrel. 45c, Red-necked parrot. 60c, Black swift. $1, Troupial. $2, Brown noddy. $4, Lesser Antillean pewee. $5. Little blue heron. No. 1249, House wren. No. 1250, Imperial parrot.

**1990, July 16 Litho. *Perf. 14***

**1241** A184 10c multicolored .40 .40
**1242** A184 20c multicolored .55 .55
**1243** A184 45c multicolored .75 .75
**1244** A184 60c multicolored .95 .95
**1245** A184 $1 multicolored 1.60 1.60
**1246** A184 $2 multicolored 2.25 2.25
**1247** A184 $4 multicolored 3.75 3.75
**1248** A184 $5 multicolored 4.25 4.25
*Nos. 1241-1248 (8)* 14.50 14.50

**Souvenir Sheets**

**1249** A184 $6 multicolored 5.00 5.00
**1250** A184 $6 multicolored 5.00 5.00

A185

Shells: 10c, Reticulated cowrie-helmet. 20c, West Indian chank. 35c, West Indian fighting conch. 60c, True tulip. $1, Sunrise tellin. $2, Crown cone. $3, Common dove shell. $4, Atlantic fig shell. No. 1259, Giant tun. No. 1260, King helmet.

**1990, July 19**

**1251** A185 10c multicolored .40 .40
**1252** A185 20c multicolored .55 .55
**1253** A185 35c multicolored .70 .70
**1254** A185 60c multicolored 1.00 1.00
**1255** A185 $1 multicolored 1.40 1.40
**1256** A185 $2 multicolored 2.25 2.25
**1257** A185 $3 multicolored 3.00 3.00
**1258** A185 $4 multicolored 3.75 3.75
*Nos. 1251-1258 (8)* 13.05 13.05

**Souvenir Sheets**

**1259** A185 $5 multicolored 5.00 5.00
**1260** A185 $5 multicolored 5.00 5.00

A186

Queen Mother, 90th Birthday: various photos.

**1990, Sept. 10**

**1261** A186 20c multicolored .25 .25
**1262** A186 45c multicolored .40 .40
**1263** A186 60c multicolored .60 .60
**1264** A186 $3 multicolored 2.50 2.50
*Nos. 1261-1264 (4)* 3.75 3.75

**Souvenir Sheet**

**1265** A186 $5 multicolored 3.50 3.50

A187

45c, Men's singles, tennis. 60c, Men's foil fencing. $2, 100m freestyle swimming. $3, Star class yachting.
$5, Coxless pairs, rowing.

**1990, Nov. 5 Litho. *Perf. 14***

**1266** A187 45c multicolored 1.25 1.25
**1267** A187 60c multicolored 1.40 1.40
**1268** A187 $2 multicolored 2.25 2.25
**1269** A187 $3 multicolored 3.25 3.25
*Nos. 1266-1269 (4)* 8.15 8.15

**Souvenir Sheet**

**1270** A187 $5 multicolored 6.75 6.75

1992 Summer Olympics, Barcelona.

Christmas A188

Walt Disney characters on carousel animals: 10c, Mickey, frog. 15c, Huey, Dewey & Louie, white elephant. 25c, Donald, polar bear. 45c, Goofy, goat. $1, Donald, giraffe. $2, Daisy, stork. $4, Goofy, lion. $5, Daisy, horse. No. 1279, Mickey, swan chariot, horiz. No. 1280, Mickey, Minnie & Goofy, griffin chariot.

**1990, Dec. 13 *Perf. 13½x14***

**1271** A188 10c multicolored .40 .40
**1272** A188 15c multicolored .50 .50
**1273** A188 25c multicolored .60 .60
**1274** A188 45c multicolored .90 .90
**1275** A188 $1 multicolored 1.25 1.25
**1276** A188 $2 multicolored 2.00 2.00
**1277** A188 $4 multicolored 4.00 4.00
**1278** A188 $5 multicolored 5.00 5.00
*Nos. 1271-1278 (8)* 14.65 14.65

**Souvenir Sheets**
***Perf. 14x13½***

**1279** A188 $6 multicolored 7.00 7.00
**1280** A188 $6 multicolored 7.00 7.00

World Cup Soccer Championships, Italy — A189

Players and coaches from participating countries.

**1990, Dec. 28 Litho. *Perf. 14***

**1281** A189 15c England .45 .45
**1282** A189 45c Brazil .75 .75
**1283** A189 60c West Germany 1.00 1.00
**1284** A189 $4 Austria 4.25 4.25
*Nos. 1281-1284 (4)* 6.45 6.45

**Souvenir Sheets**

**1285** A189 $6 Ireland, vert. 5.00 5.00
**1286** A189 $6 USSR, vert. 5.00 5.00

Cog Trains of Switzerland — A190

Designs: 10c, Glion-Roches de Naye, 1890. 35c, Electric cog rail car ascending Mt. Pilatus. 45c, Cog railway to Schynige Platte, view of Eiger, Monch and Jungfrau Mountains. 60c, Furka-Oberalp train on Bugnli Viaduct, vert. $1, 1910 Jungfraubahn Cog Railway, Jungfrau Mountain, 1910. $2, Testing Swiss rail cars built for Pike's Peak on Arth-Rigibahn, 1963. $4, Brienz-Rothorn Bahn, 1991. $5, Private 1870 Rigi-Scheideck Hotel post stamp, 1890 Arth-Rigi Railway Engine. No. 1295, Sherlock Holmes watching Brunigline train descending from Brunig Pass. No. 1296, Switzerland #738 and first passenger train to ascend Mt. Rigi, 1871.

**1991, Mar. 26 Litho. *Perf. 14***

**1287** A190 10c multicolored .60 .60
**1288** A190 35c multicolored 1.00 1.00
**1289** A190 45c multicolored 1.10 1.10
**1290** A190 60c multicolored 1.25 1.25
**1291** A190 $1 multicolored 1.40 1.40
**1292** A190 $2 multicolored 2.00 2.00
**1293** A190 $4 multicolored 3.00 3.00
**1294** A190 $5 multicolored 3.50 3.50
*Nos. 1287-1294 (8)* 13.85 13.85

**Souvenir Sheets**
***Perf. 13½***

**1295** A190 $6 multicolored 6.00 6.00
**1296** A190 $6 multicolored 6.00 6.00

Nos. 1295-1296 each contain one 50x37mm stamp.

Voyages of Discovery A191

Explorer's ships: 10c, Gil Eannes, 1433-1434. 25c, Alfonso Gonclaves Baldaya, 1436. 45c, Bartolomeu Dias, 1487. 60c, Vasco da Gama, 1497-1499. $1, Vallarte the Dane. $2, Aloisio Cadamosto, 1456-1458. $4, Diogo Gomes, 1457. $5, Diogo Cao, 1482-1485.

No. 1305, Blue and yellow macaw. No. 1306, Red and yellow macaw.

**1991, Apr. 8 Litho. *Perf. 14***

**1297** A191 10c multicolored .45 .45
**1298** A191 25c multicolored .55 .55
**1299** A191 45c multicolored .65 .65
**1300** A191 60c multicolored .75 .75
**1301** A191 $1 multicolored 1.10 1.10
**1302** A191 $2 multicolored 1.60 1.60
**1303** A191 $4 multicolored 2.75 2.75
**1304** A191 $5 multicolored 3.25 3.25
*Nos. 1297-1304 (8)* 11.10 11.10

**Souvenir Sheets**

**1305** A191 $6 multicolored 4.75 4.75
**1306** A191 $6 multicolored 4.75 4.75

Discovery of America, 500th anniv. (in 1992).

Japanese Costumes — A192

Walt Disney characters wearing Japanese costumes: 10c, Donald as soldier. 15c, Mickey as Kabuki actor. 25c, Mickey, Minnie in traditional wedding clothes. 45c, Daisy as Geisha girl, vert. $1, Mickey in sokutai dress of high government official, vert. $2, Goofy as mino farmer, vert. $4, Pete as shogun, vert. $5, Donald as warlord. No. 1315, Mickey, as Noh player, vert. No. 1316, Goofy as Kabubei-Jishi street performer, vert.

**1991, May 22 Litho. *Perf. 14***

**1307** A192 10c multicolored .65 .65
**1308** A192 15c multicolored .75 .75
**1309** A192 25c multicolored .90 .90
**1310** A192 45c multicolored 1.10 1.10
**1311** A192 $1 multicolored 2.00 2.00
**1312** A192 $2 multicolored 2.75 2.75
**1313** A192 $4 multicolored 3.50 3.50
**1314** A192 $5 multicolored 4.25 4.25
*Nos. 1307-1314 (8)* 15.90 15.90

**Souvenir Sheets**

**1315** A192 $6 multicolored 7.50 7.50
**1316** A192 $6 multicolored 7.50 7.50

Phila Nippon '91.

Mushrooms
A193

10c, Horn of plenty. 15c, Shaggy mane. 45c, Yellow morel. 60c, Chanterelle. $1, Blewit. $2, Slippery jack. $4, Emetic russula. $5, Honey mushroom.

No. 1326, Beefsteak polypore. No. 1327, Voluminous-latex milky.

**1991, June 3 Litho. *Perf. 14***

| | | | | |
|---|---|---|---|---|
| **1318** | A193 | 10c multicolored | .25 | .25 |
| **1319** | A193 | 15c multicolored | .45 | .45 |
| **1320** | A193 | 45c multicolored | .55 | .55 |
| **1321** | A193 | 60c multicolored | .65 | .65 |
| **1322** | A193 | $1 multicolored | 1.00 | 1.00 |
| **1323** | A193 | $2 multicolored | 1.75 | 1.75 |
| **1324** | A193 | $4 multicolored | 3.00 | 3.00 |
| **1325** | A193 | $5 multicolored | 4.00 | 4.00 |
| | | *Nos. 1318-1325 (8)* | 11.65 | 11.65 |

**Souvenir Sheets**

| | | | | |
|---|---|---|---|---|
| **1326** | A193 | $6 multicolored | 5.00 | 5.00 |
| **1327** | A193 | $6 multicolored | 5.00 | 5.00 |

**Royal Family Birthday, Anniversary**

Common Design Type

**1991, June 17 Litho. *Perf. 14***

| | | | | |
|---|---|---|---|---|
| **1328** | CD347 | 10c multicolored | .45 | .45 |
| **1329** | CD347 | 15c multicolored | .90 | .90 |
| **1330** | CD347 | 40c multicolored | 1.00 | 1.00 |
| **1331** | CD347 | 60c multicolored | 1.10 | 1.10 |
| **1332** | CD347 | $1 multicolored | 2.00 | 2.00 |
| **1333** | CD347 | $2 multicolored | 2.75 | 2.75 |
| **1334** | CD347 | $4 multicolored | 4.00 | 4.00 |
| **1335** | CD347 | $5 multicolored | 4.50 | 4.50 |
| | | *Nos. 1328-1335 (8)* | 16.70 | 16.70 |

**Souvenir Sheets**

| | | | | |
|---|---|---|---|---|
| **1336** | CD347 | $5 Elizabeth, Philip | 5.00 | 5.00 |
| **1337** | CD347 | $5 Charles, Diana, sons | 8.50 | 8.50 |

10c, 60c, $2, $4, No. 1336, Queen Elizabeth II, 65th birthday. Others, Charles and Diana, 10th wedding anniversary.

Vincent Van Gogh (1853-1890), Painter — A194

Paintings: 10c, Thatched Cottages. 25c, The House of Pere Eloi. 45c, The Midday Siesta. 60c, Portrait of a Young Peasant, vert. $1, Still Life: Vase with Irises Against a Yellow Background, vert. $2, Still Life Vase with Irises. $4, Blossoming Almond Tree. $5, Irises. No. 1346, A Meadow in the Mountains: Le Mas De Saint-Paul. No. 1347, Doctor Gachet's Garden in Auvers, vert.

**1991, July 8 Litho. *Perf. 13½***

| | | | | |
|---|---|---|---|---|
| **1338** | A194 | 10c multicolored | .65 | .65 |
| **1339** | A194 | 25c multicolored | .90 | .90 |
| **1340** | A194 | 45c multicolored | 1.10 | 1.10 |
| **1341** | A194 | 60c multicolored | 1.40 | 1.40 |
| **1342** | A194 | $1 multicolored | 2.00 | 2.00 |
| **1343** | A194 | $2 multicolored | 2.50 | 2.50 |
| **1344** | A194 | $4 multicolored | 3.75 | 3.75 |
| **1345** | A194 | $5 multicolored | 4.00 | 4.00 |
| | | *Nos. 1338-1345 (8)* | 16.30 | 16.30 |

**Size: 101x75mm**

***Imperf***

| | | | | |
|---|---|---|---|---|
| **1346** | A194 | $6 multicolored | 6.50 | 6.50 |
| **1347** | A194 | $6 multicolored | 6.50 | 6.50 |

Intl. Literacy Year — A195

Scenes from Walt Disney's "The Little Mermaid": 10c, Ariel with Flounder and Sebastian. 25c, King Triton. 45c, Sebastian drums in "Kiss De Girl" concert. 60c, Flotsam and Jetsam taunt Ariel. $1, Scuttle, Flounder and Ariel. $2, Ariel and Flounder discover a book. $4, Prince Eric, dog Max, manservant Grimsby, and crew. $5, Ursula the sea witch. No. 1356, Ariel transformed into human being. No. 1357, Ariel and Prince Eric dancing in town, vert.

**1991, Aug. 6 *Perf. 14***

| | | | | |
|---|---|---|---|---|
| **1348** | A195 | 10c multicolored | .35 | .35 |
| **1349** | A195 | 25c multicolored | .45 | .45 |
| **1350** | A195 | 45c multicolored | .65 | .65 |
| **1351** | A195 | 60c multicolored | .90 | .90 |
| **1352** | A195 | $1 multicolored | 1.50 | 1.50 |
| **1353** | A195 | $2 multicolored | 2.75 | 2.75 |
| **1354** | A195 | $4 multicolored | 4.50 | 4.50 |
| **1355** | A195 | $5 multicolored | 5.50 | 5.50 |
| | | *Nos. 1348-1355 (8)* | 16.60 | 16.60 |

**Souvenir Sheets**

| | | | | |
|---|---|---|---|---|
| **1356** | A195 | $6 multicolored | 6.50 | 6.50 |
| **1357** | A195 | $6 multicolored | 6.50 | 6.50 |

World Landmarks — A196

Designs: 10c, Empire State Building, US, vert. 25c, Kremlin, USSR. 45c, Buckingham Palace, United Kingdom. 60c, Eiffel Tower, France, vert. $1, Taj Mahal, India. $2, Sydney Opera House, Australia. $4, Colosseum, Italy. $5, Pyramids, Egypt. No. 1366, Galileo demonstrating laws of physics from Tower of Pisa, Italy. No. 1367, Great Wall of China and Emperor Shi Huang Ti.

**1991, Aug. 12 Litho. *Perf. 14***

| | | | | |
|---|---|---|---|---|
| **1358** | A196 | 10c multicolored | .45 | .45 |
| **1359** | A196 | 25c multicolored | .55 | .55 |
| **1360** | A196 | 45c multicolored | .90 | .90 |
| **1361** | A196 | 60c multicolored | 1.10 | 1.10 |
| **1362** | A196 | $1 multicolored | 2.00 | 2.00 |
| **1363** | A196 | $2 multicolored | 3.00 | 3.00 |
| **1364** | A196 | $4 multicolored | 4.75 | 4.75 |
| **1365** | A196 | $5 multicolored | 5.50 | 5.50 |
| | | *Nos. 1358-1365 (8)* | 18.25 | 18.25 |

**Souvenir Sheets**

| | | | | |
|---|---|---|---|---|
| **1366** | A196 | $6 multicolored | 8.00 | 8.00 |
| **1367** | A196 | $6 multicolored | 8.00 | 8.00 |

Japanese Attack on Pearl Harbor, 50th Anniv. A197

Designs: 10c, 6:00am, First wave of Japanese planes leave carrier Akagi. 15c, 6:40am, Destroyer Ward and PBY attack midget submarine. 45c, 7:00am, Second wave of Japanese planes leave carriers. 60c, 7:48am, Japanese Zeros attack on Kaneohe Air Station. $1, 8:30am, Destroyers Breeze, Medusa and Curtiss sink midget submarine. $2, 8:45am, Damaged battleship Nevada sorties. $4, 8:10am, Battleship Arizona explodes, killing 1,177 men. $5, 9:45am, Japanese attack ends. No. 1376, 8:00am, Japanese fighters and bombers attack Hickam Air Base. No. 1377, 7:55am, Pearl Harbor attack begins.

**1991, Sept. 2**

| | | | | |
|---|---|---|---|---|
| **1368** | A197 | 10c multicolored | .60 | .60 |
| **1369** | A197 | 15c multicolored | .70 | .70 |
| **1370** | A197 | 45c multicolored | 1.10 | 1.10 |
| **1371** | A197 | 60c multicolored | 1.25 | 1.25 |
| **1372** | A197 | $1 multicolored | 1.50 | 1.50 |
| **1373** | A197 | $2 multicolored | 2.00 | 2.00 |
| **1374** | A197 | $4 multicolored | 2.75 | 2.75 |
| **1375** | A197 | $5 multicolored | 3.00 | 3.00 |
| | | *Nos. 1368-1375 (8)* | 12.90 | 12.90 |

**Souvenir Sheets**

| | | | | |
|---|---|---|---|---|
| **1376** | A197 | $6 multicolored | 5.25 | 5.25 |
| **1377** | A197 | $6 multicolored | 5.25 | 5.25 |

Butterflies — A198

1c, Little yellow. 2c, Gulf fritillary. 5c, Monarch. 10c, Red rim. 15c, Flambeau. 20c, Large orange sulphur. 25c, Caribbean buckeye. 35c, Polydamas swallowtail. 45c, Cassius blue. 55c, Great southern white. 60c, Godman's leaf. 65c, Hanno blue. 90c, Mimic. $1, Long-tailed skipper. $1.20, Orion. $2, Cloudless sulphur. $5, Painted lady. $10, Southern daggertail. $20, White peacock.

***Perf. 13½x13, 13½x14 (2c, 10c, 15c, 25c, 45c, 90c, $1, $20)***

**1991-93**

| | | | | |
|---|---|---|---|---|
| **1378** | A198 | 1c multi | .35 | *.90* |
| **1379** | A198 | 2c multi | .35 | *.90* |
| **1380** | A198 | 5c multi | .65 | *.90* |
| **1381** | A198 | 10c multi | .65 | .25 |
| **1382** | A198 | 15c multi | .75 | .25 |
| **1383** | A198 | 20c multi | .75 | .25 |
| **1384** | A198 | 25c multi | .75 | .25 |
| **1385** | A198 | 35c multi | .85 | .35 |
| **1386** | A198 | 45c multi | .85 | .35 |
| **1386A** | A198 | 55c multi | 1.25 | .60 |
| **1387** | A198 | 60c multi | 1.00 | .40 |
| **1387A** | A198 | 65c multi | 1.25 | .60 |
| **1388** | A198 | 90c multi | 1.40 | .60 |
| **1389** | A198 | $1 multi | 1.40 | .75 |
| **1389A** | A198 | $1.20 multi | 1.50 | 1.50 |
| **1390** | A198 | $2 multi | 2.25 | 2.25 |
| **1391** | A198 | $5 multi | 3.75 | *5.50* |
| **1391A** | A198 | $10 multi | 9.00 | *11.00* |
| **1391B** | A198 | $20 multi | 14.00 | *16.00* |
| | | *Nos. 1378-1391B (19)* | 42.75 | 43.60 |

Issued: 55c, 65c, $1.20, 1/11/93; others, 10/14/91.

Charles de Gaulle, Birth Cent. — A199

**1991, Nov. 1**

| | | | | |
|---|---|---|---|---|
| **1392** | A199 | 45c shown | 2.25 | 2.25 |

**Souvenir Sheet**

| | | | | |
|---|---|---|---|---|
| **1393** | A199 | $5 blk & bl, horiz. | 6.00 | 6.00 |

Creole Week — A200

45c, Man in 18th cent. costume. 60c, Accordion player. $1, Dancers. $5, Stick fight c. 1785.

**1991, Nov. 1 *Perf. 14***

| | | | | |
|---|---|---|---|---|
| **1394** | A200 | 45c multicolored | .60 | .60 |
| **1395** | A200 | 60c multicolored | .90 | .90 |
| **1396** | A200 | $1 multicolored | 1.50 | 1.50 |
| | | *Nos. 1394-1396 (3)* | 3.00 | 3.00 |

**Souvenir Sheet**

| | | | | |
|---|---|---|---|---|
| **1397** | A200 | $5 multicolored | 6.50 | 6.50 |

Credit Union, 40th Anniv. — A201

60c, Emblem, founder, horiz.

**1991, Nov. 1**

| | | | | |
|---|---|---|---|---|
| **1398** | A201 | 10c black | .55 | .55 |
| **1399** | A201 | 60c blk, red, org, yel | 1.50 | 1.50 |

Year of the Environment and Shelter — A202

15c, Keep the beaches clean. 60c, No. 1402, Amazona imperalis. No. 1403, Lagoon outlet.

**1991, Nov. 18**

| | | | | |
|---|---|---|---|---|
| **1400** | A202 | 15c multicolored | .50 | .50 |
| **1401** | A202 | 60c multicolored | 2.75 | 2.75 |

**Souvenir Sheets**

| | | | | |
|---|---|---|---|---|
| **1402** | A202 | $5 multicolored | 7.75 | 7.75 |
| **1403** | A202 | $5 multicolored | 7.75 | 7.75 |

Christmas
A203

Paintings by Jan van Eyck: 10c, The Virgin Enthroned with Child (detail). 20c, The Madonna at the Fountain. 35c, The Virgin in a Church. 45c, The Madonna with Canon van der Paele. 60c, The Madonna with Canon van der Paele (detail). $1, The Madonna in an Interior. $3, The Annunciation. $5, The Annunciation, diff. No. 1412, The Madonna with Chancellor Rolin. No. 1413, Virgin and Child with Saints and Donor.

**1991, Dec. 2 *Perf. 12***

| | | | | |
|---|---|---|---|---|
| **1404** | A203 | 10c multicolored | .55 | .55 |
| **1405** | A203 | 20c multicolored | .75 | .75 |
| **1406** | A203 | 35c multicolored | .90 | .90 |
| **1407** | A203 | 45c multicolored | 1.00 | 1.00 |
| **1408** | A203 | 60c multicolored | 1.50 | 1.50 |
| **1409** | A203 | $1 multicolored | 1.75 | 1.75 |
| **1410** | A203 | $3 multicolored | 2.75 | 2.75 |
| **1411** | A203 | $5 multicolored | 4.00 | 4.00 |
| | | *Nos. 1404-1411 (8)* | 13.20 | 13.20 |

**Souvenir Sheets**

***Perf. 14x14½***

| | | | | |
|---|---|---|---|---|
| **1412** | A203 | $6 multicolored | 6.50 | 6.50 |
| **1413** | A203 | $6 multicolored | 6.50 | 6.50 |

**Queen Elizabeth II's Accession to the Throne, 40th Anniv.**

Common Design Type

**1992, Feb. 6 Litho. *Perf. 14***

| | | | | |
|---|---|---|---|---|
| **1414** | CD348 | 10c multicolored | .25 | .25 |
| **1415** | CD348 | 15c multicolored | .25 | .25 |
| **1416** | CD348 | $1 multicolored | .75 | .75 |
| **1417** | CD348 | $5 multicolored | 3.75 | 3.75 |
| | | *Nos. 1414-1417 (4)* | 5.00 | 5.00 |

**Souvenir Sheets**

| | | | | |
|---|---|---|---|---|
| **1418** | CD348 | $6 River scene | 3.75 | 3.75 |
| **1419** | CD348 | $6 Seaside village | 3.75 | 3.75 |

Botanical Gardens, Cent. — A204

Designs: 10c, Cricket match. 15c, Scenic entrance. 45c, Traveller's tree. 60c, Bamboo house. $1, Old pavilion. $2, Ficus benjamina. $4, Cricket ground. $5, Thirty-five steps. No. 1428, Fountain. No. 1429, Cricket masters.

**1992, Mar. 30 Litho. *Perf. 14***

**1420** A204 10c multicolored .40 .40
**1421** A204 15c multicolored .40 .40
**1422** A204 45c multicolored .40 .40
**1423** A204 60c multicolored .60 .60
**1424** A204 $1 multicolored 1.00 1.00
**1425** A204 $2 multicolored 1.75 1.75
**1426** A204 $4 multicolored 4.25 4.25
**1427** A204 $5 multicolored 4.50 4.50
*Nos. 1420-1427 (8)* 13.30 13.30

**Souvenir Sheets**

**1428** A204 $6 multicolored 5.00 5.00
**1429** A204 $6 multicolored 5.00 5.00

Spanish Art — A205

Paintings or details from paintings by Velazquez: 10c, Pope Innocent X. 15c, 45c The Forge of Vulcan (different details). 60c, Queen Mariana of Austria. $1, Pablo de Valladolid. $2, Sebastian de Morra. $3, Felipe IV (detail). $4, Felipe IV. No. 1438, Surrender of Breda. No. 1439, The Drunkards.

**1992, May 4 *Perf. 13***

**1430** A205 10c multicolored .25 .25
**1431** A205 15c multicolored .25 .25
**1432** A205 45c multicolored .45 .45
**1433** A205 60c multicolored .55 .55
**1434** A205 $1 multicolored .80 .80
**1435** A205 $2 multicolored 1.50 1.50
**1436** A205 $3 multicolored 2.25 2.25
**1437** A205 $4 multicolored 2.75 2.75

**Size: 120x95mm**

***Imperf***

**1438** A205 $6 multicolored 4.75 4.75
**1439** A205 $6 multicolored 4.75 4.75
*Nos. 1430-1439 (10)* 18.30 18.30

Granada '92.

Easter — A206

Paintings: 10c, The Supper at Emmaus, studio of Gerrit Van Honthorst. 15c, Christ before Caiaphas, by Van Honthorst, vert. 45c, The Taking of Christ, by Valentin de Boulogne. 60c, Pilate Washing his Hands, by Mattia Preti, vert. $1, The Last Supper (detail), by Master of the Reredos of The Chapel of the Church of S. Francisco D'Evora. $2, The Three Marys at the Tomb (detail), by Adolphe William Bouguereau, vert. $3, Denial of St. Peter, by Hendrik Terbrugghen. $5, Doubting Thomas, by Bernardo Strozzi, vert. No. 1448, The Crucifixion (detail), by Mathias Grunewald, vert. No. 1449, The Resurrection (detail), by Caravaggio, vert.

**1992 *Perf. 14***

**1440** A206 10c multicolored .25 .25
**1441** A206 15c multicolored .25 .25
**1442** A206 45c multicolored .50 .50
**1443** A206 60c multicolored .75 .75
**1444** A206 $1 multicolored .90 .90
**1445** A206 $2 multicolored 1.50 1.50
**1446** A206 $3 multicolored 2.25 2.25
**1447** A206 $5 multicolored 3.75 3.75
*Nos. 1440-1447 (8)* 10.15 10.15

**Souvenir Sheets**

**1448** A206 $6 multicolored 5.00 5.00
**1449** A206 $6 multicolored 5.00 5.00

Columbus and New World Flora and Fauna — A207

10c, Hercules beetle. 25c, Crapaud frog. 75c, Parrot. $2, Anole. $4, Royal gramma. $5, Hibiscus.

No. 1456, Giant katydid. No. 1457, Columbus' fleet.

**1992, May 18**

**1450** A207 10c multi .50 .50
**1451** A207 25c multi 1.00 1.00
**1452** A207 75c multi 1.75 1.75
**1453** A207 $2 multi 2.00 2.00
**1454** A207 $4 multi 2.75 2.75
**1455** A207 $5 multi 3.50 3.50
*Nos. 1450-1455 (6)* 11.50 11.50

**Souvenir Sheets**

**1456** A207 $6 multi 5.00 5.00
**1457** A207 $6 multi 5.00 5.00

Nos. 1456-1457 are horiz.

Hummingbirds — A208

10c, Purple throated carib. 15c, Rufous breasted hermit. 45c, Puerto Rican emerald. 60c, Antillean mango. $1, Green throated carib. $2, Blue headed. $4, Eastern streamertail. $5, Antillean crested. No. 1466, Green mango. No. 1467, Vervain hummingbird.

**1992, May 28**

**1458** A208 10c multicolored .50 .50
**1459** A208 15c multicolored .50 .50
**1460** A208 45c multicolored .75 .75
**1461** A208 60c multicolored .90 .90
**1462** A208 $1 multicolored 1.25 1.25
**1463** A208 $2 multicolored 2.25 2.25
**1464** A208 $4 multicolored 3.75 3.75
**1465** A208 $5 multicolored 4.50 4.50
*Nos. 1458-1465 (8)* 14.40 14.40

**Souvenir Sheets**

**1466** A208 $6 multicolored 6.75 6.75
**1467** A208 $6 multicolored 6.75 6.75

Genoa '92.

Dinosaurs A209

10c, Camptosaurus. 15c, Edmontosaurus. 25c, Corythosaurus. 60c, Stegosaurus. $1, Torosaurus. $3, Euoplocephalus. $4, Tyrannosaurus. $5, Parasaurolophus.

**1992, June 23 Litho. *Perf. 14***

**1468** A209 10c multi .50 .50
**1469** A209 15c multi .60 .60
**1470** A209 25c multi .75 .75
**1471** A209 60c multi .85 .85
**1472** A209 $1 multi 1.00 1.00
**1473** A209 $3 multi 1.90 1.90
**1474** A209 $4 multi 3.00 3.00
**1475** A209 $5 multi 3.50 3.50
*Nos. 1468-1475 (8)* 12.10 12.10

**Souvenir Sheets**

**1476** A209 $6 like #1472 4.75 4.75
**1477** A209 $6 like #1470 4.75 4.75

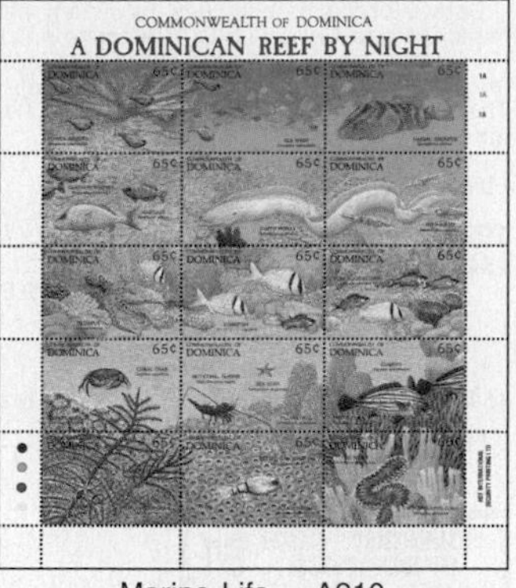

Marine Life — A210

No. 1478: a, Copper sweeper (b). b, Sea wasp (c). c, Nassau grouper. d, Glasseye snapper, margate. e, Green moray (f). f, Reef squid. g, Octopus. h, Porkfish (g, i). i, Reef squirrelfish (h). j, Coral crab, flower coral. k, Red coral shrimp, sea star, pillar coral (l, n). l, Cubbyu, brain coral (o). m, Basket starfish, thick finger coral. n, Belted cardinal fish, boulder coral (k, m). o, Fire worm, crenelated fire coral.

No. 1479: a, Trumpetfish, blue chromis. b, Queen triggerfish. c, Hawksbill turtle. d, Sergeant major, rock beauty. e, Sharksucker. f, Lemon shark. g, Spotted trunkfish, bluehead. h, Blue tang, yellowtail damselfish. i, Queen angelfish, banded butterflyfish. j, Spotted seahorse, flower coral. k, Stoplight parrotfish, pillar coral. l, Smallmouth grunt, brain coral. m, Flamingo tongue, thick finger coral. n, Arrow crab, boulder coral. o, Sharknose goby, crenelated fire coral.

No. 1480, Harlequin bass. No. 1481, Flamefish.

**1992, July 20 Litho. *Perf. 14***

**1478** A210 65c Sheet of 15, #a.-o. 7.75 7.75
**1479** A210 65c Sheet of 15, #a.-o. 7.75 7.75

**Souvenir Sheets**

**1480** A210 $6 multicolored 6.50 6.50
**1481** A210 $6 multicolored 6.50 6.50

A211

10c, Archery. 15c, Two-man canoeing. 25c, 110-meter hurdles. 60c, Men's high jump. $1, Greco-Roman wrestling. $2, Men's rings. $4, Men's parallel bars. $5, Equestrian.

No. 1490, Field hockey. No. 1491, Women's platform diving.

**1992, Aug. 10 Litho. *Perf. 14***

**1482** A211 10c multi .30 .30
**1483** A211 15c multi .35 .35
**1484** A211 25c multi .40 .40
**1485** A211 60c multi .65 .65
**1486** A211 $1 multi .90 .90
**1487** A211 $2 multi 1.50 1.50
**1488** A211 $4 multi 2.75 2.75
**1489** A211 $5 multi 3.25 3.25
*Nos. 1482-1489 (8)* 10.10 10.10

**Souvenir Sheets**

**1490** A211 $6 multi 5.50 5.50
**1491** A211 $6 multi 5.50 5.50

1992 Summer Olympics, Barcelona.

A212

**1992 Litho. *Perf. 14½***

**1492** A212 $1 Coming ashore 1.00 1.00
**1493** A212 $2 Natives, ships 1.75 2.00

Discovery of America, 500th anniv. Organization of East Caribbean States.

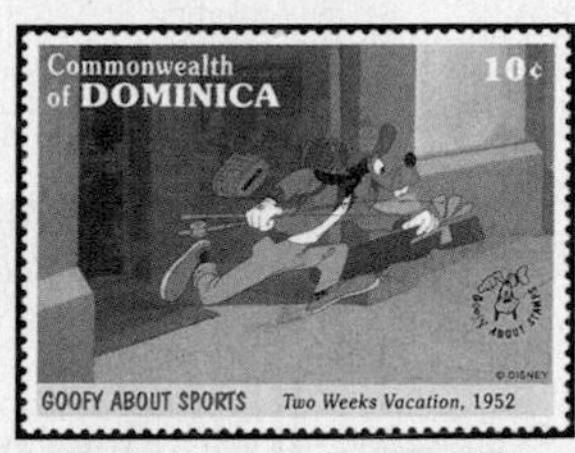

Walt Disney's Goofy, 60th Anniv. — A213

Scenes from Disney cartoon films: 10c, Two Weeks Vacation, 1952. 15c, Aquamania, 1961. 25c, Goofy Gymnastics, 1949. 45c, How to Ride a Horse, 1941. $1, Foul Hunting, 1947. $2, For Whom the Bulls Toil, 1953. $4, Tennis Racquet, 1949. $5, Double Dribble, 1946. No. 1502, Aquamania, 1961, vert. No. 1503, The Goofy Sports Story, 1956, vert.

**1992, Nov. 11 Litho. *Perf. 14x13½***

**1494** A213 10c multicolored .45 .45
**1495** A213 15c multicolored .55 .55
**1496** A213 25c multicolored .80 .80
**1497** A213 45c multicolored .90 .90
**1498** A213 $1 multicolored 1.50 1.50
**1499** A213 $2 multicolored 2.75 2.75
**1500** A213 $4 multicolored 4.75 4.75
**1501** A213 $5 multicolored 5.25 5.25
*Nos. 1494-1501 (8)* 16.95 16.95

**Souvenir Sheets**

***Perf. 13½x14***

**1502** A213 $6 multicolored 7.75 7.75
**1503** A213 $6 multicolored 7.75 7.75

Model Trains A214

15c, Brass Reno 4-4-0, HO scale, c. 1963. 25c, Union Pacific Golden Classic, G gauge, 1992. 55c, LMS 3rd class brake coach, OO scale, 1970s. 65c, Brass Wabash 2-6-0, HO scale, c. 1958. 75c, Pennsylvania RR T-1 duplex, O gauge, 1991. $1, Streamline engine 2-6-0, O gauge, post World War II. $3, Japanese Natl. Railways class C62, HO scale, c. 1960. $5, Tinplate friction-drive floor trains, 1960s. No. 1512, 1st "toy" train in Japan, 1854. No. 1513, Stephenson's Rocket, 1:26 scale, c. 1972, vert.

**1992, Nov. 11 *Perf. 14***

**1504** A214 15c multicolored .45 .45
**1505** A214 25c multicolored .50 .55
**1506** A214 55c multicolored .75 .75
**1507** A214 65c multicolored .90 .90
**1508** A214 75c multicolored 1.00 1.00
**1509** A214 $1 multicolored 1.25 1.25
**1510** A214 $3 multicolored 2.75 2.75
**1511** A214 $5 multicolored 4.50 4.50
*Nos. 1504-1511 (8)* 12.10 12.15

**Souvenir Sheets**

***Perf. 13***

**1512** A214 $6 multicolored 5.50 5.50
**1513** A214 $6 multicolored 5.50 5.50

No. 1512 contains one 52x40mm stamp, No. 1513 one 39x51mm stamp.

Hummel Figurines — A215

Angel: 20c, Playing violin. 25c, Playing horn. 55c, Playing mandolin. 65c, Seated, playing trumpet. 90c, On cloud with lantern. $1, Holding candle. $1.20, Flying. $6, On cloud with candle.

**1992, Nov. 2** *Perf. 14*

**1514** A215 20c multicolored .35 .35
**1515** A215 25c multicolored .35 .35
**1516** A215 55c multicolored .55 .55
**1517** A215 65c multicolored .70 .70
*a.* Sheet of 4, #1514-1517 2.25 2.25
**1518** A215 90c multicolored 1.00 1.00
**1519** A215 $1 multicolored 1.25 1.25
**1520** A215 $1.20 multicolored 1.50 1.50
**1521** A215 $6 multicolored 3.25 3.25
*a.* Sheet of 4, #1518-1521 8.00 8.00
*Nos. 1514-1521 (8)* 8.95 8.95

Anniversaries and Events
A216 A217

Designs: 25c, Graf Zeppelin, 1929. No. 1523, Elderly man, plant. No. 1524, Elderly man on bicycle. No. 1525, Elderly man helping boy bait hook. No. 1526, Konrad Adenauer. No. 1527, Space shuttle. No. 1528, Wolfgang Amadeus Mozart. No. 1529, Snowy egret. No. 1530, Sir Thomas Lipton, Shamrock V, 1930. $2, Men pulling fishing net toward beach. $3, Helen Keller. No. 1533, Earth Resources Satellite. No. 1534, Map of Germany, 1949. No. 1535, Eland. $5, Count Ferdinand von Zeppelin. No. 1537, Cologne Cathedral, Germany. No. 1538, Scene from the Magic Flute. No. 1539, Mir Space Station. No. 1540, Engine of Graf Zeppelin. No. 1541, Rhinoceros hornbill.

**1992** **Litho.** *Perf. 14*

**1522** A216 25c multicolored .60 .60
**1523** A216 45c multicolored .80 .80
**1524** A216 45c multicolored .80 .80
**1525** A216 45c multicolored .80 .80
**1526** A216 90c multicolored .90 .90
**1527** A216 90c multicolored .90 .90
**1528** A217 $1.20 multicolored 2.00 2.00
**1529** A216 $1.20 multicolored 1.50 1.50
**1530** A216 $1.20 multicolored 1.75 1.75
**1531** A216 $2 multicolored 1.75 1.75
**1532** A216 $3 multicolored 3.00 3.00
**1533** A216 $4 multicolored 3.00 3.00
**1534** A216 $4 multicolored 4.25 4.25
**1535** A216 $4 multicolored 4.25 4.25
**1536** A216 $5 multicolored 5.00 5.00
*Nos. 1522-1536 (15)* 31.30 31.30

**Souvenir Sheets**

**1537** A216 $6 multicolored 6.25 6.25
**1538** A217 $6 multicolored 6.75 6.75
**1539** A216 $6 multicolored 6.25 6.25
**1540** A216 $6 multicolored 6.25 6.25
**1541** A216 $6 multicolored 5.75 5.75

Konrad Adenauer, 25th anniv. of death (Nos. 1526, 1534, 1537). Intl. Space Year (Nos. 1527, 1533, 1539). Mozart, 200th anniv. of death (in 1991) (Nos. 1528, 1538). Count Zeppelin, 75th anniv. of death (Nos. 1522, 1536, 1540). Intl. Day of the Elderly (Nos. 1523-1525). UN Earth Summit, Rio (Nos. 1529, 1535, 1541). America's Cup yacht race (No. 1530). WHO Intl. Conference on Nutrition, Rome (No. 1531). Lions Intl., 75th anniv. (No. 1532).

Issued: Nos. 1528, 1539, Oct.; Nos. 1523-1527, 1533-1534, 1537-1538, Nov.; Nos. 1522, 1529, 1535-1536, 1540-1541, Dec.

Miniature Sheet

Louvre Museum, Bicent. — A218

Details or entire paintings by Titian: a-b, Madonna and Child with St. Catherine and a Rabbit (diff. details). c, A Woman at Her Toilet. d-e, The Supper at Emmaus (diff. details). f, The Pastoral Concert. g-h, An Allegory, Perhaps of Marriage (diff. details).

Painting by Hieronymus Bosch: $6, The Ship of Fools.

**1993, Mar. 24** **Litho.** *Perf. 12*

**1542** A218 $1 Sheet of 8, #a.-h. + label 9.50 9.50

**Souvenir Sheet**

*Perf. 14½*

**1543** A218 $6 multicolored 5.75 5.75

No. 1543 contains one 55x88mm stamp.

Elvis Presley, 15th Anniv. of Death (in 1992)
A219

a, Portrait. b, With guitar. c, Holding microphone.

**1993, Feb.** *Perf. 14*

**1544** A219 $1 Strip of 3, #a.-c. 3.75 3.75

Miniature Sheet

Birds of Dominica — A220

a, Plumbeous warbler. b, Black swift. c, Blue-hooded euphonia. d, Rufous-throated solitaire. e, Ringed kingfisher. f, Blue-headed hummingbird. g, Bananaquit. h, Trembler. i, Forest thrush. j, Purple-throated carib. k, Ruddy quail dove. l, Least bittern.

No. 1546, Imperial parrot. No. 1547, Rednecked parrot (Amazona arausiaca).

**1993, Apr. 30**

**1545** A220 90c Sheet of 12, #a.-l. 18.00 18.00

**Souvenir Sheets**

**1546** A220 $6 multicolored 6.50 6.50
**1547** A220 $6 multicolored 6.50 6.50

Turtles
A221

25c, Leatherback laying eggs. 55c, Hawksbill. 65c, Atlantic Ridley. 90c, Green turtle laying eggs. $1, Green turtle at sea. $2, Hawksbill, diff. $4, Loggerhead. $5, Leatherback at sea. No. 1556, Green turtle hatchling. No. 1557, Head of hawksbill.

**1993, May 26** **Litho.** *Perf. 14*

**1548** A221 25c multicolored .45 .45
**1549** A221 55c multicolored .55 .55
**1550** A221 65c multicolored .75 .75
**1551** A221 90c multicolored .95 .95
**1552** A221 $1 multicolored 1.10 1.10
**1553** A221 $2 multicolored 1.75 1.75
**1554** A221 $4 multicolored 3.25 3.25
**1555** A221 $5 multicolored 4.25 4.25
*Nos. 1548-1555 (8)* 13.05 13.05

**Souvenir Sheets**

**1556** A221 $6 multicolored 5.75 5.75
**1557** A221 $6 multicolored 5.75 5.75

For overprints see Nos. 2103-2107.

Automobiles — A222

Designs: 90c, 1928 Model A Ford. $1.20, Mercedes-Benz winning Swiss Grand Prix, 1936. $4, Mercedes-Benz winning German Grand Prix, 1935. $5, 1915 Model T Ford.

No. 1562: a, 1993 Mercedes-Benz coupe/roadster. b, 1893 Benz Viktoria.

No. 1563, Ford GT-40.

**1993, May** **Litho.** *Perf. 14*

**1558** A222 90c multicolored .80 .80
**1559** A222 $1.20 multicolored 1.10 1.10
**1560** A222 $4 multicolored 2.75 2.75
**1561** A222 $5 multicolored 3.75 3.75
*Nos. 1558-1561 (4)* 8.40 8.40

**Souvenir Sheets**

**1562** A222 $3 Sheet of 2, #a.-b. 5.00 5.00
**1563** A222 $6 multicolored 5.00 5.00

No. 1563 contains one 57x42mm stamp.

First Ford gasoline engine, cent. (Nos. 1558, 1561, 1563). Benz's first four-wheeled vehicle, cent. (Nos. 1559-1560, 1562).

Dominica Grammar School, Cent.
A223

Designs: 25c, School crest. 30c, V. A. A. Archer, first West Indian headmaster. 65c, Hubert A. Charles, first Dominican headmaster. 90c, Present school building.

**1993, May**

**1564** A223 25c multicolored .25 .25
**1565** A223 30c multicolored .30 .30
**1566** A223 65c multicolored .60 .60
**1567** A223 90c multicolored .85 .85
*Nos. 1564-1567 (4)* 2.00 2.00

Aviation Anniversaries — A224

Designs: 25c, New York ticker tape parade, 1928. 55c, BAC Lightning F2. 65c, Graf Zeppelin over Sphinx, pyramids, 1929. $1, Boeing 314 flying boat. $2, Astronaut stepping onto moon. $4, Viktoria Louise over Kiel harbor, 1912. $5, Supermarine Spitfire, vert. No. 1575, Royal Air Force Crest, vert. No. 1576, Hugo Eckener in airship cockpit, vert. No. 1577, Jean-Pierre Blanchard's hot air balloon, 1793, vert.

**1993, May 28** **Litho.** *Perf. 14*

**1568** A224 25c multicolored .90 .90
**1569** A224 55c multicolored 1.10 1.10
**1570** A224 65c multicolored 1.50 1.50
**1571** A224 $1 multicolored 1.75 1.75
**1572** A224 $2 multicolored 3.00 3.00
**1573** A224 $4 multicolored 4.00 4.00
**1574** A224 $5 multicolored 4.25 4.25
*Nos. 1568-1574 (7)* 16.50 16.50

**Souvenir Sheets**

**1575** A224 $6 multicolored 6.25 6.25
**1576** A224 $6 multicolored 6.25 6.25
**1577** A224 $6 multicolored 5.75 5.75

Zeppelin Capt. Hugo Eckener, 125th anniv. of birth (Nos. 1568, 1570, 1573, 1576). Royal Air Force, 75th anniv. (Nos. 1569, 1574-1575).

Nos. 1575-1576 each contain one 42x57mm stamp.

Miniature Sheet

Coronation of Queen Elizabeth II, 40th Anniv. — A225

Designs: No. 1578a, 20c, Official coronation photograph. b, 25c, Ceremony. c, 65c, Gold State Coach. d, $5, Queen Elizabeth II, Queen Mother.

$6, Portrait, by Norman Hutchinson, 1969.

**1993, June 2** **Litho.** *Perf. 13½x14*

**1578** A225 Sheet, 2 each #a.-d. 13.00 13.00

**Souvenir Sheet**

*Perf. 14*

**1579** A225 $6 multicolored 6.75 6.75

No. 1579 contains one 28x42mm stamp.

For overprints see Nos. 1688-1689.

Wedding of Japan's Crown Prince Naruhito and Masako Owada
A226

Cameo photos of couple and: 90c, Crown Prince holding flowers. $5, Princess wearing full-length coat.

$6, Princess riding in limousine.

**1993, June 14** **Litho.** *Perf. 14*

**1580** A226 90c multicolored .75 .75
**1581** A226 $5 multicolored 5.00 5.00

**Souvenir Sheet**

**1582** A226 $6 multicolored 6.00 6.00

Inauguration of Pres. William J. Clinton — A227

$5, Bill, Hillary Clinton. $6, Bill Clinton, vert.

**1993, July 30** **Litho.** *Perf. 14*

**1583** A227 $5 multicolored 4.25 4.25

**Souvenir Sheet**

**1584** A227 $6 multicolored 6.00 6.00

Willy Brandt (1913-92), German Chancellor — A228

Brandt and: 65c, Pres. Eisenhower, 1959. $5, N.K. Winston, 1964. $6, Portrait.

**1993, July 30**

**1585** A228 65c black & brown .90 .90
**1586** A228 $5 black & brown 4.75 4.75

**Souvenir Sheet**

**1587** A228 $6 black & brown 6.00 6.00

Picasso (1881-1973) A229

Paintings: 25c, Bather with Beach Ball, 1929. 90c, Portrait of Leo Stein, 1906. $5, Portrait of Wilhelm Unde, 1910. $6, Man with a Pipe, 1915.

**1993, July 30**

**1588** A229 25c multicolored .40 .40
**1589** A229 90c multicolored .85 .85
**1590** A229 $5 multicolored 4.75 4.75
*Nos. 1588-1590 (3)* 6.00 6.00

**Souvenir Sheet**

**1591** A229 $6 multicolored 6.00 6.00

Polska '93 — A230

Paintings: 90c, Self-portrait, by Marian Szczyrbula, 1921. $3, Portrait of Bruno Jasienski, by Tytus Czyzewski, 1921. $6, Miser, by Tadeusz Makowski, 1973.

**1993, July 30**

**1592** A230 90c multicolored 1.50 1.50
**1593** A230 $3 multicolored 3.50 3.50

**Souvenir Sheet**

**1594** A230 $6 multicolored 6.00 6.00

A231

90c, Monika Holzner, speedskating, 1984. $4, US hockey players, Ray Leblanc, Tim Sweeney, 1992. $6, Men's ski jump.

**1993, July 30**

**1595** A231 90c multicolored 1.50 1.50
**1596** A231 $4 multicolored 4.00 4.00

**Souvenir Sheet**

**1597** A231 $6 multicolored 5.75 5.75

1994 Winter Olympics, Lillehammer, Norway.

Copernicus (1473-1543) A232

Designs: $1.20, Astronomer using quadrant. $3, Observatory. $5, Copernicus.

**1993, July 30**

**1598** A232 $1.20 multicolored 1.50 1.50
**1599** A232 $3 multicolored 3.75 3.75

**Souvenir Sheet**

**1600** A232 $5 multicolored 6.00 6.00

Opening of New General Post Office A233

New General Post Office and: 25c, Prince Philip. 90c, Queen Elizabeth II.

**1993, July 30**

**1601** A233 25c multicolored .25 .25
**1602** A233 90c multicolored 1.00 1.00

1994 World Cup Soccer Championships, US — A234

25c, Maradona, Buchwald. 55c, Gullit. 65c, Chavarria, Bliss. No. 1606, 90c, Maradona. No. 1607, 90c, Alvares. $1, Altobelli, Yonghwang. $2, Referee, Stopyra. $5, Renquin, Yaremtchuk.
No. 1611, Brehme. No. 1612, Fabbri.

**1993, Sept. 8 Litho. *Perf. 14***

**1603** A234 25c multicolored .65 .65
**1604** A234 55c multicolored .75 .75
**1605** A234 65c multicolored .85 .85
**1606** A234 90c multicolored 1.00 1.00
**1607** A234 90c multicolored 1.00 1.00
**1608** A234 $1 multicolored 1.25 1.25
**1609** A234 $2 multicolored 2.00 2.00
**1610** A234 $5 multicolored 3.00 3.00
*Nos. 1603-1610 (8)* 10.50 10.50

**Souvenir Sheets**

**1611** A234 $6 multicolored 4.50 4.50
**1612** A234 $6 multicolored 4.50 4.50

Taipei '93 — A235

25c, Tiger Balm Gardens. 65c, Building, Kenting Park. 90c, Tzu-en Tower. $5, Villa, Lan Tao Island.
No. 1617 — Chinese kites: a, Chang E Rising up to the Moon. b, Red Phoenix and Rising Sun. c, Heavenly Judge. d, Monkey King. e, Goddess of the Luo River. f, Heavenly Maiden Scatters Flowers.
$6, Jade Girl, Liao Dynasty.

**1993, Oct. 4 Litho. *Perf. 13½x14***

**1613** A235 25c multi .30 .30
**1614** A235 65c multi .55 .55
**1615** A235 90c multi 1.00 1.00
**1616** A235 $5 multi 4.25 4.25
*Nos. 1613-1616 (4)* 6.10 6.10

**Miniature Sheet**

**1617** A235 $1.65 Sheet of 6, #a.-f. 10.00 10.00

**Souvenir Sheet**

**1618** A235 $6 multi 5.25 5.25

**With Bangkok '93 Emblem**

25c, Tugu Monument, Java. 55c, Candi Cangkuang, West Java. 90c, Pura Taman Ayun, Mengwi. $5, Stone mosaics, Ceto.
No. 1623 — Puppets: a, Thai, Rama and Sita. b, Burmese, Tha Khi Lek. c, Burmese, diff. d, Thai, Demons, Wat Phra Kaew. e, Thai, Hun Lek performing Khun Chang, Khun Phaen. f, Thai, Hun Lek performing Ramakien.
$6, Stone carving, Thailand.

**1993**

**1619** A235 25c multi .30 .30
**1620** A235 55c multi .55 .55
**1621** A235 90c multi 1.00 1.00
**1622** A235 $5 multi 4.00 4.00
*Nos. 1619-1622 (4)* 5.85 5.85

**Miniature Sheet**

**1623** A235 $1.65 Sheet of 6, #a.-f. 10.00 10.00

**Souvenir Sheet**

**1624** A235 $6 multi 5.25 5.25

**With Indopex '93 Emblem**

Designs: 25c, Ornate Chedi, Wat Phra Boromathat Chaiya. 55c, Preserved temple ruins, Sukhothai Historical Park. 90c, Prasat Hin Phimai, Thailand. $5, Main sanctuary, Prasat Phanom Rung, Thailand.
Indonesian puppets — No. 1629: a, Arjuna & Prabu Gilling Wesi. b, Loro Blonyo. c, Yogyanese puppets, Menak cycle. d, Wayang gedog, Ng Setro. e, Wayang golek, Kencana Wungu. f, Wayang gedog, Raden Damar Wulan.
$6, Sculpture of Majapahit noble, Pura Sada, Kapel.

**1993, Oct. 4 Litho. *Perf. 13½x14***

**1625** A235 25c multicolored .40 .40
**1626** A235 55c multicolored .60 .60
**1627** A235 90c multicolored 1.25 1.25
**1628** A235 $5 multicolored 4.00 4.00
*Nos. 1625-1628 (4)* 6.25 6.25

**Miniature Sheet**

**1629** A235 $1.65 Sheet of 6, #a.-f. 10.00 10.00

**Souvenir Sheet**

**1630** A235 $6 multicolored 5.25 5.25

Miniature Sheet

Willie the Operatic Whale — A236

Nos. 1631-1633, Characters and scenes from Disney's animated film Willie the Operatic Whale.

**1993, Nov. 1 Litho. *Perf. 14x13½***

**1631** A236 $1 Sheet of 9, #a.-i. 14.00 14.00

**Souvenir Sheets**

**1632** A236 $6 multicolored 5.00 5.00

***Perf. 13½x14***

**1633** A236 $6 multi, vert. 5.00 5.00

Christmas A237

25c, 55c, 65c, 90c (No. 1637), Details or entire woodcut, The Adoration of the Magi, by Durer.
90c (No. 1638), $1, $3, $5, Details or entire painting, The Foligni Madonna, by Raphael.
Souvenir Sheets: No. 1642, $6, The Adoration of the Magi, by Durer. No. 1643, $6, The Foligni Madonna, by Raphael.

**1993, Nov. 8 Litho. *Perf. 13***

**1634-1643** A237 Set of 10 20.00 20.00

A238

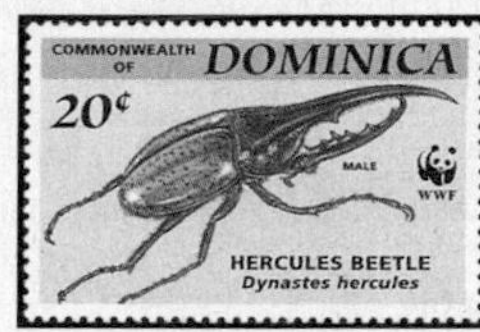


Hong Kong '94 — A239

Stamps, scene from Peak Tram: No. 1644, Hong Kong #527, city buildings, trees. No. 1645, Trees, tram, #1292.
Chinese jade: No. 1646a, Horse. b, Cup with handle. c, Vase with birthday peaches. d, Vase. e, Fu dog and puppy. f, Drinking vessel.

**1994, Feb. 18 Litho. *Perf. 14***

**1644** A238 65c multicolored .50 .50
**1645** A238 65c multicolored .50 .50
*a.* Pair, #1644-1645 1.10 1.10

**Miniature Sheet**

**1646** A239 65c Sheet of 6, #a.-f. 5.75 5.75

Nos. 1644-1645 issued in sheets of 5 pairs. No. 1645a is a continuous design.
New Year 1994 (Year of the Dog) (No. 1646e).

Insects, Butterflies, & Birds — A240

Various Hercules beetles: 20c, 25c, 65c, Male. 90c, Female.
$1, Imperial parrot. $2, Southern dagger tail. $3, The mimic. $5, Purple-throated carib.
Each $6: No. 1655, Snout butterfly. No. 1656, Blue-headed hummingbird.

**1994, Mar. 15 Litho. *Perf. 14***

**1647-1654** A240 Set of 8 11.00 11.00
*1650a* Min. sheet, 3 each #1647-1650 10.00 10.00

**Souvenir Sheets**

**1655-1656** A240 Set of 2 12.00 12.00

World Wildlife Fund (Nos. 1647-1650).

COMMONWEALTH OF DOMINICA
20¢
Russula matoubenis

Mushrooms A241

Designs: 20c, Russula matoubenis. 25c, Leptonia caeruleocapita. 65c, Inocybe littoralis. 90c, Russula hygrophytica. $1, Pyrrhoglossum lilaceipes. $2, Hygrocybe konradii. $3, Inopilus magnificus. $5, Boletellus cubensis.
No. 1665, Gerronema citrinum. No. 1666, Lentinus strigosus.

**1994, Apr. 18**

**1657** A241 20c multicolored .45 .45
**1658** A241 25c multicolored .50 .50
**1659** A241 65c multicolored .65 .65
**1660** A241 90c multicolored .80 .80
**1661** A241 $1 multicolored .95 .95
**1662** A241 $2 multicolored 1.50 1.50
**1663** A241 $3 multicolored 2.00 2.00
**1664** A241 $5 multicolored 3.00 3.00
*Nos. 1657-1664 (8)* 9.85 9.85

**Souvenir Sheets**

**1665** A241 $6 multicolored 4.75 4.75
**1666** A241 $6 multicolored 4.75 4.75

Orchids — A242

Designs: 20c, Laeliocattleya. 25c, Sophrolaeliocattleya. 65c, Odontocidium. 90c, Laeliocattleya, diff. $1, Cattleya. $2, Odontocidium, diff. $3, Epiphronitis. $4, Oncidium.

Each $6: No. 1675, Schombocattleya. No. 1676, Cattleya, diff.

**1994, May 3**

**1667-1674** A242 Set of 8 10.00 10.00

**Souvenir Sheets**

**1675-1676** A242 Set of 2 10.00 10.00

New Year 1994 (Year of the Dog) — A243

Designs: 20c, Dachshund. 25c, Beagle. 55c, Greyhound. 90c, Jack Russell terrier. $1, Pekingese. $2, White fox terrier. $4, English toy spaniel. $5, Irish setter.

No. 1686, Welsh corgi. No. 1687, Labrador retriever.

**1994, May 17**

**1678** A243 20c multicolored .30 .30
**1679** A243 25c multicolored .35 .35
**1680** A243 55c multicolored .50 .50
**1681** A243 90c multicolored .80 .80
**1682** A243 $1 multicolored 1.00 1.00
**1683** A243 $2 multicolored 1.50 1.50
**1684** A243 $4 multicolored 2.50 2.50
**1685** A243 $5 multicolored 3.00 3.00
*Nos. 1678-1685 (8)* 9.95 9.95

**Souvenir Sheets**

**1686** A243 $6 multicolored 5.00 5.00
**1687** A243 $6 multicolored 5.00 5.00

**Nos. 1578-1579 Ovptd. in Black or Silver**

**1994, June 27 Litho.** ***Perf. 13½x14***

**1688** A225 Sheet, 2 ea #a-d 15.00 15.00

**Souvenir Sheet**

**1689** A225 $6 multicolored (S) 7.25 7.25

Overprint on No. 1689 appears in sheet margin.

Miniature Sheet

1994 World Cup Soccer Championships, US — A244

No. 1690: a, Dos Armstrong, US. b, Dennis Bergkamp, Netherlands. c, Roberto Baggio, Italy. d, Rai, Brazil. e, Cafu, Brazil. f, Marco Van Baston, Netherlands.

Each $6: No. 1691, Roberto Mancini, Italy. No. 1692, Stanford Stadium, Palo Alto.

**1994, July 5** ***Perf. 14***

**1690** A244 $1 Sheet of 6, #a.-f. 6.00 6.00

**Souvenir Sheets**

**1691-1692** A244 Set of 2 10.00 10.00

Butterflies A245

20c, Florida white. 25c, Red rim. 55c, Barred sulphur. 65c, Mimic. $1, Large orange sulphur. $2, Southern dagger tail. $3, Dominican snout butterfly. $5, Caribbean buckeye.

No. 1700, Clench's hairstreak. No. 1701, Painted lady.

**1994, May 3 Litho.** ***Perf. 14***

**1693** A245 20c multi .40 .40
**1694** A245 25c multi .40 .40
**1695** A245 55c multi .75 .75
**1696** A245 65c multi .80 .80
**1697** A245 $1 multi 1.00 1.00
**1698** A245 $2 multi 1.50 1.50
**1698A** A245 $3 multi 2.00 2.00
**1699** A245 $5 multi 3.50 3.50
*Nos. 1693-1699 (8)* 10.35 10.35

**Souvenir Sheets**

**1700** A245 $6 multi 5.50 5.50
**1701** A245 $6 multi 5.50 5.50

10th Caribbean Scout Jamboree A246

Designs: 20c, Backpacking. 25c, Cooking over campfire. 55c, Making camp. 65c, Camping. $1, Scout drum unit. $2, Planting trees. $4, Sailing. $5, Scout salute.

Each $6: No. 1710, Early Scout troop. No. 1711, Pres. C.A. Sorhaindo, vert.

**1994, July 18 Litho.** ***Perf. 14***

**1702-1709** A246 Set of 8 11.50 11.50

**Souvenir Sheets**

**1710-1711** A246 Set of 2 11.50 11.50

For overprints see Nos. 1762-1766.

D-Day, 50th Anniv. A247

Designs: 65c, US Waco glider brings reinforcements. $2, British Horsa gliders land more troops. $3, Glider troops take Pegasus Bridge.

$6, Hadrian glider.

**1994, July 26**

**1712-1714** A247 Set of 3 5.00 5.00

**Souvenir Sheet**

**1715** A247 $6 multicolored 4.75 4.75

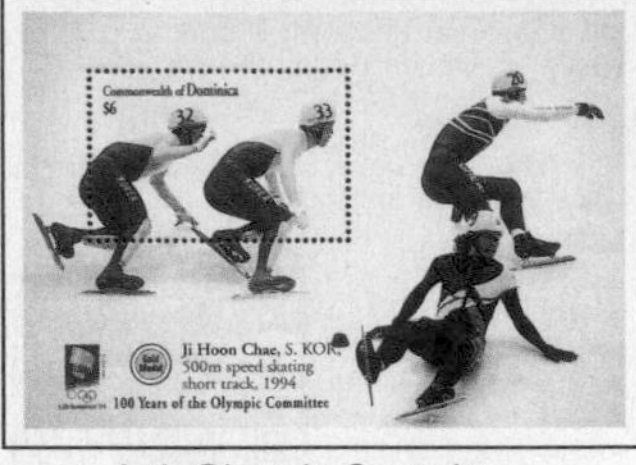


A248

Intl. Olympic Committee, Cent. — A249

Designs: 55c, Ulrike Meyfarth, Germany, high jump, 1984. $1.45, Dieter Baumann, Germany, 5000-meter run, 1992.

$6, Ji Hoon Chae, South Korea, 500-meter short track speed skating, 1994.

**1994, July 26**

**1716** A248 55c multicolored .90 .90
**1717** A248 $1.45 multicolored 2.00 2.00

**Souvenir Sheet**

**1718** A249 $6 multicolored 5.75 5.75

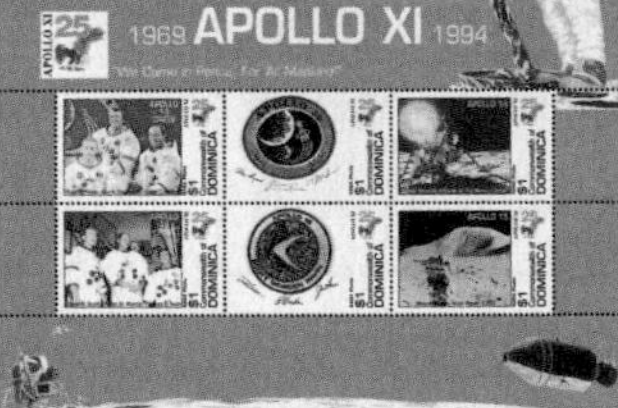


English Touring Cricket, Cent. A250

Designs: 55c, D.I. Goweer Leics, England, vert. 90c, E.C.L. Ambrose, Leeward Islands. $1, G.A. Gooch, England, vert.

$3, First English team, 1895.

**1994, July 26**

**1719-1721** A250 Set of 3 4.00 4.00

**Souvenir Sheet**

**1722** A250 $3 multicolored 5.75 5.75

Miniature Sheet of 6

First Manned Moon Landing, 25th Anniv. — A251

No. 1723: a, Apollo 14 crew. b, Apollo 14 patch. c, Apollo 14 lunar module Antares at Fra Mauro Crater. d, Apollo 15 crew. e, Apollo 15 patch. f, Apollo 15 mission, Mount Hadley from rover.

$6, 25th anniv. emblem, lunar surface.

**1994, July 26**

**1723** A251 $1 #a.-f. 7.75 7.75

**Souvenir Sheet**

**1724** A251 $6 multicolored 6.50 6.50

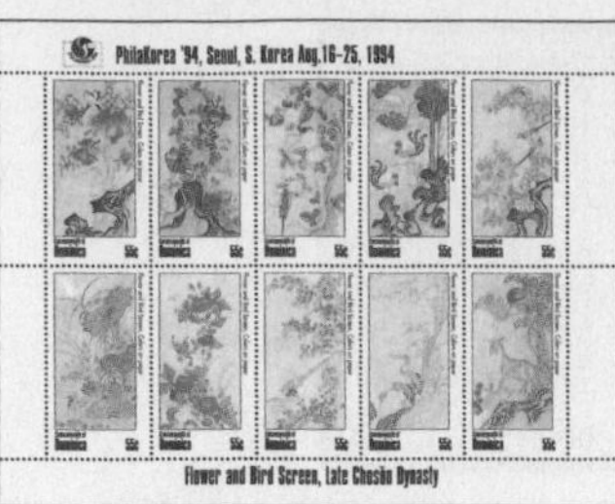


A252

PHILAKOREA '94 — A253

Designs: 65c, P'alsang-jon Hall, Korea. 90c, Popchu-sa Temple. $2, Uhwajong Pavillion, Korea.

Screen, Late Choson Dynasty showing flowers and: No. 1728a, c, e, Birds. b, g, Butterfly. d, Roosters. f, Duck. h, Pheasant. i, Cranes. j, Deer.

$4, Stylized "spirit post" guardian.

**1994, July 26** ***Perf. 14, 13 (#1728)***

**1725-1727** A252 Set of 3 3.50 3.50

**Miniature Sheet of 10**

**1728** A253 55c #a.-j. 6.00 6.00

**Souvenir Sheet**

**1729** A252 $4 multicolored 3.00 3.00

Mickey Mouse, 65th Birthday A254

Disney characters: 20c, Dippy dawg. 25c, Clarabelle Cow. 55c, Horace Horsecollar. 65c, Mortimer Mouse. $1, Joe Piper. $3, Mr. Casey. $4, Chief O'Hara. $5, Mickey and the Blot.

Each $6: No. 1738, Minnie, Tanglefoot. No. 1739, Pluto, Minnie, horiz.

***Perf. 13½x14, 14x13½ (#1739)***

**1994, Oct. 3**

**1730-1737** A254 Set of 8 14.00 14.00

**Souvenir Sheets**

**1738-1739** A254 Set of 2 13.00 13.00



A255

Local Entertainers: 20c, Sonia Llyod, folk singer. 25c, Ophelia Marie, singer. 55c, Edney Francis, accordionist. 65c, Norman Letang, saxophonist. 90c, Edie Andre, steel drummer.

**1994, Dec. 1 Litho.** ***Perf. 14***

**1740-1744** A255 Set of 5 3.25 3.25

Miniature Sheet

A256

Marilyn Monroe (1926-62), Actress: Nos. 1745a-1745i, Various portraits. No. 1746, $6, Hands above head. No. 1747, $6, Holding hat.

**1994, Dec. 1**
**1745** A256 90c #a.-i. 11.50 11.50

**Souvenir Sheets**

**1746-1747** A256 Set of 2 10.00 10.00

Christmas A257

Details or entire Spanish paintings: 20c, Madonna and child, by Luis de Morales. 25c, Madonna and Child with Yarn Winder, by Morales. 55c, Our Lady of the Rosary, by Zurbaran. 65c, Dream of the Patrician, by Bartolome Murillo. 90c, Madonna of Charity, by El Greco. $1, The Annunciation, by Zurbaran. $2, Mystical Marriage of St. Catherine, by Jusepe de Ribera. $3, The Holy Family with St. Bruno and Other Saints, by Ribera.
Each $6: No. 1756, Vision of the Virgin to St. Bernard, by Murillo. No. 1757, Adoration of the Shepherds, by Murillo.

**1994, Dec. 2** ***Perf. 13½x14***
**1748-1755** A257 Set of 8 7.00 7.00

**Souvenir Sheets**

**1756-1757** A257 Set of 2 10.00 10.00

Order of the Caribbean Community — A258

First award recipients: 25c, Sir Shridath Ramphal, statesman, Guyana. 65c, William Gilbert Demas, economist, Trinidad & Tobago. 90c, Derek Walcott, writer, St. Lucia.

**1994, Dec. 16** ***Perf. 14***
**1758-1760** A258 Set of 3 2.00 2.00

Jeffrey Edmund, 1994 World Cup Soccer Player A259

**1994, Dec. 28**
**1761** A259 25c multicolored .35 .35

**Nos. 1705, 1708-1711 Ovptd.**

**1995, Mar. 21** **Litho.** ***Perf. 14***
**1762-1764** A246 Set of 3 7.00 7.00

**Souvenir Sheets**

**1765-1766** A246 Set of 2 10.00 10.00

Location of overprint varies.

New Year 1995 (Year of the Boar) — A260

Stylized boars: a, 25c, Facing right. b, 65c, Facing forward. c, $1, Facing left.
$2, Two facing each other, horiz.

**1995, Apr. 15** **Litho.** ***Perf. 14½***
**1767** A260 Strip of 3, #a.-c. 1.60 1.60
*d.* Souv. sheet of 3, #1767a-1767c 1.60 1.60

**Souvenir Sheet**

**1768** A260 $2 multicolored 1.50 1.50

No. 1767 was issued in sheets of 4 strips.

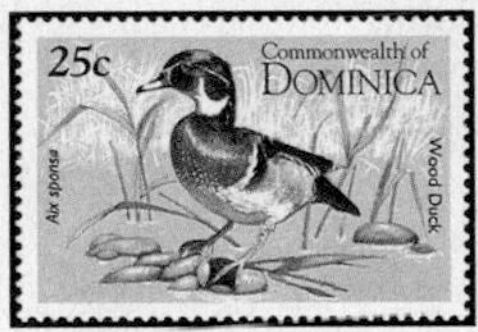


Birds A261

Designs: 25c, Wood duck. 55c, Mallard. 65c, Blue-winged teal. $5, Blood eared parakeet.
No. 1773, vert.: a, Cattle egret. b, Snow goose (a, c). c, Peregrine falcon. d, Barn owl. e, Black-crowned night heron. f, Common grackle. g, Brown pelican. h, Great egret. i, Ruby-throated hummingbird. j, Laughing gull. k, Greater flamingo. l, Common moorhen.
No. 1774, Trumpeter swan, vert. No. 1775, White-eyed vireo.

**1995, Apr. 15** **Litho.** ***Perf. 14***
**1769-1772** A261 Set of 4 5.00 5.00

**Miniature Sheet of 12**

**1773** A261 65c #a.-l. 16.00 16.00

**Souvenir Sheets**

**1774** A261 $5 multicolored 5.00 5.00
**1775** A261 $6 multicolored 6.00 6.00

Miniature Sheets

End of World War II, 50th Anniv. — A262

No. 1776: a, Mitsubishi A6M2 Zero. b, Aichi D3A1 Type 99 "Val." c, Nakajima 97-B5N "Kate." d, Zuikaku. e, Akagi. f, Ryuho.
No. 1777: a, German Panther tank, Ardennes. b, Allied fighter bomber. c, Patton's army crosses the Rhine. d, Rocket-powered ME 163. e, V-2 rocket on launcher. f, German U-boat surrenders in North Atlantic. g, Round the clock bombardment of Berlin. h, Soviet soldiers reach center of Berlin.
Each $6: No. 1778, Statue atop Dresden's town hall after Allied bombing. No. 1779, Japanese attack plane.

**1995** **Litho.** ***Perf. 14***
**1776** A262 $2 #a.-f. + label 9.00 9.00
**1777** A262 $2 #a.-h. + label 13.00 13.00

**Souvenir Sheets**

**1778-1779** A262 Set of 2 14.00 14.00

Issued: Nos. 1777-1778, 5/18; others, 7/21.

1996 Summer Olympics, Atlanta A263

Designs: 15c, Mark Breland, boxing. 20c, Lou Banach, Joseph Atiyeh, freestyle wrestling. 25c, Judo. 55c, Fencing. 65c, Matt Biondi, swimming. $1, Gushiken on rings, vert. $2, Cycling, vert. $5, Volleyball.
Each $6: No. 1788, Joe Fargis on Touch of Class, equestrian. No. 1789, Soccer, vert.

**1995, July 21**
**1780-1787** A263 Set of 8 9.50 9.50

**Souvenir Sheets**

**1788-1789** A263 Set of 2 10.50 10.50

UN, 50th Anniv. — A264

No. 1790: a, 65c, Signatures on UN charter, attendee. b, $1, Attendee. $2, Attendees.
$6, Winston Churchill.

**1995, Aug. 16** **Litho.** ***Perf. 14***
**1790** A264 Strip of 3, #a.-c. 2.75 2.75

**Souvenir Sheet**

**1791** A264 $6 multicolored 5.00 5.00

No. 1790 is a continuous design.

Souvenir Sheets

FAO, 50th Anniv. — A265

Street market scene: a, 90c, Woman in red dress. b, $1, Woman seated. c, $2, Vendors, women.
$6, Woman in field, woman holding water cans, vert.

**1995, Aug. 16**
**1792** A265 Sheet of 3, #a.-c. 2.50 2.50
**1793** A265 $6 multicolored 4.50 4.50

No. 1792 is a continuous design.

Queen Mother, 95th Birthday A266

No. 1794: a, Drawing. b, Wearing crown, green dress. c, Formal portrait. d, Blue dress.
$6, Portrait as younger woman.

**1995, Aug. 16** ***Perf. 13½x14***
**1794** A266 $1.65 Strip or block of 4, #a.-d. 5.50 5.50

**Souvenir Sheet**

**1795** A266 $6 multicolored 5.50 5.50

No. 1794 was issued in sheets of 8 stamps.
Sheet margins of Nos. 1794-1795 exist with black frame and text "In Memoriam — 1900-2002" overprinted in sheet margins.

Rotary, 90th Anniv. A267

**1995** ***Perf. 14***
**1796** A267 $1 Paul Harris, emblem 1.00 1.00

**Souvenir Sheet**

**1797** A267 $6 Rotary emblems 4.75 4.75

Dinosaurs A268

20c, Monoclonius. 25c, Euoplocephalus. 55c, Coelophysis. 65c, Compsognathus.
No. 1802: a, Dimorphodon. b, Ramphorynchus. c, Giant alligator. d, Pentaceratops.
No. 1803, vert: a, Ceratosaurus. b, Comptosaurus (a). c, Stegosaur. d, Camarasaurus. e, Baronyx. f, Dilophosaurus. g, Dromaeosaurids (f). h, Deinonychus. i, Dinicthys. j, Carcharodon (k). k, Nautiloid. l, Trilobite.
$5, Sauropelta. $6, Triceratops, vert.

**1995, Sept. 8**
**1798-1801** A268 Set of 4 1.75 1.75
**1802** A268 90c Strip of 4, #a.-d. 3.00 3.00

**Miniature Sheet of 12**

**1803** A268 $1 #a.-l 10.00 10.00

**Souvenir Sheets**

**1804** A268 $5 multicolored 5.00 5.00
**1805** A268 $6 multicolored 5.00 5.00

Singapore '95 (Nos. 1798-1801, 1803-1805).

Miniature Sheets of 6

Nobel Prize Fund Established, Cent. — A269

Recipients, each $2: No. 1806a, Oscar A. Sanchez, peace, 1987. b, Ernst B. Chain, medicine, 1945. c, Aage Bohr, physics, 1975. d, Jaroslav Seifert, literature, 1984. e, Joseph E. Murray, medicine, 1990. f, Jaroslav Heyrovsky, chemistry, 1959.

No. 1807, each $2: a, Adolf von Baeyer, chemistry, 1905. b, Edward Buchner, chemistry, 1907. c, Carl Bosch, chemistry, 1931. d, Otto Hahn, chemistry, 1944. e, Otto Paul Herman Diels, chemistry, 1950. f, Kurt Alder, chemistry, 1950.

No. 1808, Emil A. von Behring, medicine, 1901.

**1995, Oct. 24 Litho. *Perf. 14***

**1806-1807** A269 Set of 2 19.00 19.00

**Souvenir Sheet**

**1808** A269 $2 multicolored 1.75 1.75

Christmas A270

Details or entire paintings: 20c, Madonna and Child, by Pontormo. 25c, The Immaculate Conception, by Murillo. 55c, The Adoration of the Magi, by Filippino Lippi. 65c, Rest on the Flight into Egypt, by Van Dyck. 90c, Sacred Family, by Van Dyck. $5, The Annunciation, by Van Eyck.

No. 1815, The Virgin and the Infant, by Van Eyck. No. 1816, The Holy Family, by Ribera.

**1995, Nov. 30 Litho. *Perf. 13½x14***

**1809-1814** A270 Set of 6 6.00 6.00

**Souvenir Sheets**

**1815** A270 $5 multicolored 3.75 3.75

**1816** A270 $6 multicolored 4.75 4.75

Miniature Sheets

Sierra Club, Cent. — A271

Designs: No. 1817, each $1: a, Florida panther with mouth open. b, Florida panther looking right. c, Manatee. d, Two manatees. e, Three sockeye salmon. f, Group of sockeye salmon. g, Two southern sea otters. h, Southern sea otter. i, Southern sea otter showing both front paws.

No. 1818, vert, each $1: a, Florida panther. b, Manatee. c, Sockeye salmon. d, Key deer facing left. e, Key deer. f, Key deer with antlers, up close. g, Wallaby with young in pouch. h, Wallaby. i, Wallaby with young.

**1995, Dec. 10 *Perf. 14***

**1817-1818** A271 Set of 2 13.00 13.00

Chinese Paintings, A City of Cathay A272

No. 1819, brown lettering, each 90c: a, Boats docked, people on shore. b, River, bridge. c, Two boats on river. d, River, pavilion along shore. e, Open sea, people in courtyard.

No. 1820, black lettering, each 90c: a, City scene. b, City scene, wall. c, Outside wall, river. d, Large boat on river. e, People crossing over bridge.

No. 1821, $2: a, Boat on river, city above. b, People walking across bridge.

No. 1822, $2: a, Lifting ramp to another boat, vert. b, Holding lines in water, tree, vert.

**1995, Dec. 27 Litho. *Perf. 14½***

**Strips of 5**

**1819-1820** A272 Set of 2 7.50 7.50

**Souvenir Sheets of 2**

**1821-1822** A272 Set of 2 6.00 6.00

Nos. 1819-1822 are each continuous designs.

Classic Western Art — A273

Paintings by Raphael: No. 1823, Agony in the Garden. No. 1824, Pope Leo X with Two Cardinals. No. 1825, Bindo Altoviti.

$6, Triumphant entry of Constantine into Rome, by Rubens.

**1995, Dec. 27 *Perf. 14***

**1823-1825** A273 $2 Set of 3 5.25 5.25

**Souvenir Sheet**

**1826** A273 $6 multicolored 5.25 5.25

New Year 1996 (Year of the Rat) — A274

Stylized rats, Chinese inscriptions: No. 1827a, 25c, purple & brown. b, 65c, orange & green. c, $1, red lilac & blue.

$2, Two rats, horiz.

**1996, Jan. 16 *Perf. 14½***

**1827** A274 Strip of 3, #a.-c. 1.90 1.90

**Miniature Sheet**

**1828** A274 Sheet of 1 #1827 1.60 1.60

**Souvenir Sheet**

**1829** A274 $2 multicolored 1.75 1.75

No. 1827 was issued in sheets of 12 stamps.

Miniature Sheet

Disney Lunar New Year — A275

Disney characters representing year of the: No. 1830a, Rat. b, Ox. c, Tiger. d, Hare. e, Dragon. f, Snake. g, Horse. h, Sheep. i, Monkey. j, Rooster. k, Dog. l, Pig.

$3, Rat character. $6, Pig, rat, ox characters on lunar calendar wheel.

**1996, Jan. 16 *Perf. 14x13½***

**1830** A275 55c Sheet of 12, #a.-l. 11.00 11.00

**Souvenir Sheets**

**1831** A275 $3 multicolored 4.00 4.00

**1832** A275 $6 multicolored 8.00 8.00

Methods of Transportation — A276

Designs: 65c, Donkey cart, 1965. 90c, 1910 Car. $2, 1950 Taxi. $3, 1955 Bus.

**1996, Jan. 29 Litho. *Perf. 14***

**1833-1836** A276 Set of 4 8.00 8.00

Miniature Sheets

Locomotives — A277

No. 1837, each $2: a, "Dragon," Hawaii. b, "Regina," Italy. c, Calazo to Padua, Italy. d, "Mogul," Philippines. e, Nuremberg, Germany. f, "Stanislas," French Natl. Railway. g, "Black Five," Scotland. h, SNCF diesel electric, France. i, "Sir Nigel Gresley," England.

No. 1838, each $2: a, Hohi Line 9600 class, Japan. b, Peloponnese Express, Greece. c, Porter 2-4-0S, Hawaii. d, Norway-Swedish Jodemans Railway. e, 220 Diesel, Federal German Railway. f, 2-8-4T Indian Railways. g, East African Railways. h, Electrical trains, USSR. i, 0-8-0, Austria.

$5, "Duchess of Hamilton," England. $6, Diesel engine, China.

**1996, Jan. 29**

**1837-1838** A277 Set of 2 28.00 28.00

**Souvenir Sheets**

**1839** A277 $5 multicolored 4.75 4.75

**1840** A277 $6 multicolored 5.25 5.25

No. 1837h has a face value of $1.

Giant Panda A278

Designs: a, With right leg up on rock. b, Front legs up on rock. c, Seated. d, Holding head down.

**1996, May 15 Litho. *Perf. 13½x14***

**1841** A278 55c Block of 4, #a.-d. 4.50 4.50

**Souvenir Sheet**

***Perf. 14x13½***

**1842** A278 $3 Panda, horiz. 3.75 3.75

CHINA '96, 9th Asian Intl. Philatelic Exhibition. No. 1841 was issued in sheets of 8 stamps.

See No. 1911.

Queen Elizabeth II, 70th Birthday A279

No. 1843: a, Portrait. b, Wearing regalia of Order of the Garter. c, Wearing bright blue dress, pearls.

$6, In uniform.

**1996, May 16 Litho. *Perf. 13½x14***

**1843** A279 $2 Strip of 3, #a.-c. 4.25 4.25

**Souvenir Sheet**

**1844** A279 $6 multicolored 4.25 4.25

No. 1843 was issued in sheets of 9 stamps.

Legendary Film Detectives A280

Designs: a, Humphrey Bogart as Sam Spade. b, Sean Connery as James Bond. c, Warren Beatty as Dick Tracy. d, Basil Rathbone as Sherlock Holmes. e, William Powell as the Thin Man. f, Sidney Toler as Charlie Chan, g, Peter Sellers as Inspector Clouseau. h, Robert Mitchum as Philip Marlowe. i, Peter Ustinov as Inspector Poirot.

$6, Margaret Rutherford as Miss Marple.

**1996, July**

**1845** A280 $1 Sheet of 9, #a.-i. 13.00 13.00

**Souvenir Sheet**

**1846** A280 $6 multicolored 6.00 6.00

1996 Summer Olympics, Atlanta A281

Designs: 20c, Olympic Stadium, Moscow, 1980. 25c, Hermine Joseph, vert. 55c, Women's field hockey, Zimbabwe, 1980. 90c,

Jerome Romain, vert. $1, Polo, discontinued sport, vert. $2, Greg Louganis, diving.

**1996** ***Perf. 14***
**1847-1852** A281 Set of 6 4.25 4.25

See Nos. 1897-1900.

Local Entertainers A282

Designs: 25c, Irene Peltier, national dress of Dominica. 55c, Rupert Bartley, street band player. 65c, Rosemary Cools-Lartigue, pianist. 90c, Celestine "Orion" Theophile, belle queen, Grand Bay. $1, Cecil Bellot, former government band master.

**1996, July 31** **Litho.** ***Perf. 14***
**1853-1857** A282 Set of 5 2.75 2.75

Jerusalem, 3000th Anniv. — A283

Designs: a, 90c, Shrine of the Book, Israel Museum. b, $1, Church of All Nations. c, $2, The Great Synagogue.
$5, Hebrew University, Mount Scopus.

**1996, July 31**
**1858** A283 Sheet of 3, #a.-c. 3.00 3.00

**Souvenir Sheet**

**1859** A283 $5 multicolored 4.50 4.50

Radio, Cent. A284

Entertainers: 90c, Artie Shaw. $1, Benny Goodman. $2, Duke Ellington. $4, Harry James.
$6, Tommy Dorsey, Jimmy Dorsey, horiz.

**1996, July 31**
**1860-1863** A284 Set of 4 6.25 6.25

**Souvenir Sheet**

**1864** A284 $6 multicolored 5.00 5.00

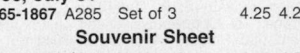

UNICEF, 50th Anniv. A285

20c, Girl looking at globe. 55c, Boy with stethoscope, syringe. $5, Doctor examining child.
No. 1868, Girl, vert.

**1996, July 31**
**1865-1867** A285 Set of 3 4.25 4.25

**Souvenir Sheet**

**1868** A285 $5 multicolored 4.50 4.50

World Post Day — A286

Scenes of 18th cent. life in Dominica: 10c, Captain of ship taking letters by hand. 25c, Anthony Trollope vists Dominica to organize postal service. 55c, Steam vessel "Yare" carries mail around island. 65c, Post offices and agencies. 90c, Country postman carrying mail around mountain tracks. $1, West Indies Federation stamp, first airmail sent on German "goose" seaplane. $2, #602, General Post Office, old and new.
$5, Captain of ship.

**1996, Oct. 1** **Litho.** ***Perf. 14***
**1869-1875** A286 Set of 7 6.25 6.25

**Souvenir Sheet**

**1876** A286 $5 multicolored 5.50 5.50

Fish — A287

Designs: 1c, Scrawled filefish. 2c, Lion fish. 5c, Porcupine fish. 10c, Powder blue surgeonfish. 15c, Red hind. 20c, Golden butterfly fish. 25c, Long-nosed butterfly fish. 35c, Pennant butterfly fish. 45c, Spotted drum. 55c, Blue-girdled angelfish. 60c, Scorpion fish. 65c, Harlequin sweetlips. 90c, Flame angelfish. $1, Queen trigger. $1.20, Stoplight parrot. $1.45, Black durgon. $2, Glasseye snapper. $5, Balloon fish. $10, Creole wrasse. $20, Seabass.

**1996, Oct. 1** **Litho.** ***Perf. 14***

| | | | | | |
|---|---|---|---|---|---|
| **1877** | A287 | 1c | multicolored | .30 | .50 |
| **1878** | A287 | 2c | multicolored | .30 | .50 |
| **1879** | A287 | 5c | multicolored | .35 | .50 |
| **1880** | A287 | 10c | multicolored | .45 | .45 |
| **1881** | A287 | 15c | multicolored | .50 | .50 |
| **1882** | A287 | 20c | multicolored | .55 | .55 |
| **1883** | A287 | 25c | multicolored | .55 | .55 |
| **1884** | A287 | 35c | multicolored | .70 | .70 |
| **1885** | A287 | 45c | multicolored | .90 | .90 |
| **1886** | A287 | 55c | multicolored | 1.00 | 1.00 |
| **1887** | A287 | 60c | multicolored | 1.00 | 1.00 |
| **1888** | A287 | 65c | multicolored | 1.00 | 1.00 |
| **1889** | A287 | 90c | multicolored | 1.25 | 1.00 |
| **1890** | A287 | $1 | multicolored | 1.50 | 1.00 |
| **1891** | A287 | $1.20 | multicolored | 1.60 | 1.00 |
| **1892** | A287 | $1.45 | multicolored | 1.75 | 1.25 |
| **1893** | A287 | $2 | multicolored | 2.00 | 2.00 |
| **1894** | A287 | $5 | multicolored | 5.00 | 5.00 |
| **1895** | A287 | $10 | multicolored | 10.00 | 10.00 |
| **1896** | A287 | $20 | multicolored | 19.00 | 19.00 |
| | *Nos. 1877-1896 (20)* | | | 49.70 | 48.40 |

See Nos. 2024-2039B for size 20x18mm stamps.

**1996 Summer Olympic Games Type**

Past Olympic medalists, vert, each 90c: No. 1897a, Ulrike Meyfarth, high jump. b, Pat McCormick, diving. c, Takeichi Nishi, equestrian. d, Peter Farkas, Greco-Roman wrestling. e, Carl Lewis, track & field. f, Agnes Keleti, gymnastics. g, Yasuhiro Yamashita, judo. h, John Kelly, single sculls. i, Naim Suleymanoglu, weight lifting.

No. 1898, vert, each 90c: a, Sammy Lee, diving. b, Bruce Jenner, decathlon. c, Olga Korbut, gymnastics. d, Steffi Graf, tennis. e, Florence Griffith-Joyner, track and field. f, Mark Spitz, swimming. g, Li Ning, gymnastics. h, Erika Salumae, cycling. i, Abebe Bikila, marathon.

#1899, $5, Joan Benoit, 1st women's marathon, vert.
#1900, $5, Milt Campbell, discus.

**1996, June 7** **Litho.** ***Perf. 14***

**Sheets of 9**

**1897-1898** A281 Set of 2 15.00 15.00

**Souvenir Sheets**

**1899-1900** A281 Set of 2 8.25 8.25

A288

Christmas (Details or entire paintings): 25c, Enthroned Madonna and Child, by Stefano Veneziano. 55c, Noli Me Tangere, by Beato Angelico. 65c, Madonna and Child, by Angelico. 90c, Madonna of Corneta Tarquinia, by Filippo Lippi. $2, Annunciation, by Angelico. $5, Madonna with Child, by Angelico, diff.

Each $6: No. 1907, Coronation of the Virgin, by Beato Angelico. No. 1908, Holy Family with St. Barbara, by Veronese, horiz.

**1996, Nov. 25**
**1901-1906** A288 Set of 6 8.50 8.50

**Souvenir Sheets**

**1907-1908** A288 Set of 2 10.00 10.00

A289

Paintings of "Herdboy and Buffalo," by Li Keran (1907-89): No. 1909: a, f, Herdboy Plays the Flute. b, g, Playing Cricket in the Autumn. c, h, Listen to the Summer Cicada. d, i, Grazing in the Spring.
$2, Return in Wind and Rain.

**1997** **Litho.** ***Perf. 14***
**1909** A289 90c Strip of 4, #a.-d. 3.25 3.25

**Souvenir Sheets**

**1909E** A289 55c Sheet of 4, #f.-i. 2.00 2.00

***Perf. 15x14½***

**1910** A289 $2 multicolored 2.00 2.00

New Year 1997 (Year of the Ox).
No. 1909 was printed in sheets of 8 stamps.
No. 1910 contains one 34x52mm stamp.

Souvenir Sheet

Huangshan Mountain, China — A290

**1996, May 15** **Litho.** ***Perf. 12***
**1911** A290 $2 multicolored 2.25 2.25

China '96. No. 1911 was not available until March 1997.

A291

Lee Lai-Shan, 1996 Olympic Gold Medalist in Wind Surfing — A291a

**1997** **Litho.** ***Perf. 15x14***
**1912** A291 $2 multicolored 1.75 1.75

**Souvenir Sheet**

***Perf. 14***

**1913** A291 $5 multicolored 4.25 4.25

No. 1912 was issued in sheets of 3.
No. 1913 contains one 38x51mm stamp.

**Litho. & Embossed**

***Perf. 9***

**Without Gum**

**1913A** A291a $35 gold & multi, like #1913

Butterflies A292

No. 1914: a, Meticalla metis. b, Coeliades forestan. c, Papilio dardanus. d, Mylothris chloris. e, Poecilmitis thyshe. f, Myrina silenus. g, Bematistes aganice. h, Euphaedra neophron. i, Precis hierta.

No. 1915, vert: a, Striped policeman. b, Mountain sandman. c, Brown-veined white. d, Bowker's widow. e, Foxy charaxes. f, Pirate. g, African clouded yellow. h, Garden inspector.

Each $6: No. 1916, Acraea natalica. No. 1917, Eurytela dryope.

**1997, Apr. 1** **Litho.** ***Perf. 14***
**1914** A292 55c Sheet of 9, #a.-i. 4.75 4.75
**1915** A292 90c Sheet of 8, #a.-h. 6.75 6.75

**Souvenir Sheets**

**1916-1917** A292 Set of 2 12.00 12.00

UNESCO, 50th Anniv. A293

55c, View from temple, China. 65c, Palace of Diocletian, Croatia. 90c, St. Mary's Cathedral, Hildesheim, Germany. $1, Monastery of Rossanou, Mount Athos, Greece. $2, Scandola Nature Reserve, France. $4, Church of San Antao, Portugal.

No. 1924: a, Ruins of Copan, Honduras. b, Cuzco Cathedral, Peru. c, Olinda, Brazil, d, Canaima Natl. Park, Venezuela. e, Galapagos Islands Natl. Park, Ecuador. f, Ruins of Church, Jesuit missions of Santisima, Paraguay. g, Fortress, San Lorenzo, Panama. h, Natl. Park, Fortress, Haiti.

Each $6: No. 1925, Chengde Lakes, China. No. 1926, Kyoto, Japan.

**1997, Apr. 7** ***Perf. 13½x14***
**1918-1923** A293 Set of 6 8.75 8.75
**1924** A293 $1 Sheet of 8, #a.-h. + label 7.75 7.75

**Souvenir Sheets**

**1925-1926** A293 Set of 2 10.50 10.50

Disney Scenes "Sealed with a Kiss" A294

Cartoon film, year released: 25c, Mickey's Horse, Tanglefoot, 1933. 35c, Shanghaied, 1935. 55c, Pluto's Judgment Day, 1935. 65c, Race for Riches, 1935. 90c, Elmer Elephant, 1936. $1, Brave Little Tailor, 1938. $2, Donald's Crime, 1945. $4, In Dutch, 1946.

Each $6: No. 1935, Nifty Nineties, 1941. No. 1936, Mickey's Surprise Party, 1939.

**1997, Apr. 15** *Perf. 13½x14*

**1927-1934** A294 Set of 8 11.00 11.00

**Souvenir Sheets**

**1935-1936** A294 Set of 2 10.00 10.00

Cats — A295

25c, Cream Burmese. $1, Snowshoe. $2, Sorrell Abyssinian. $5, Torbie Persian.

No. 1941: a, British bicolor shorthair (d, e). b, Maine coon kitten, Somali kitten (c). c, Maine coon kitten, diff. d, Lynx point Siamese (e). e, Blue Burmese kitten, white Persian (odd-eyed) (f). f, Persian kitten.

No. 1942, Silver tabby.

**1997, Apr. 24** *Perf. 14*

**1937-1940** A295 Set of 4 7.00 7.00

**1941** A295 $2 Sheet of 6, #a.-f. 10.50 10.50

**Souvenir Sheet**

**1942** A295 $6 multicolored 5.50 5.50

Dogs — A296

Designs: 20c, Afghan hound. 55c, Cocker spaniel. 65c, Smooth fox terrier. 90c, West Highland white terrier.

No. 1947a, St. Bernard. b, Boy with grand basset. c, Rough collie. d, Golden retriever. e, Golden retriever, Tibetan spaniel, smooth fox terrier. f, Smooth fox terrier, diff.

$6, Shetland sheepdog.

**1997, Apr. 24**

**1943-1946** A296 Set of 4 2.00 2.00

**1947** A296 90c Sheet of 6, #a.-f. 5.25 5.25

**Souvenir Sheet**

**1948** A296 $6 multicolored 5.50 5.50

Queen Elizabeth II and Prince Philip, 50th Wedding Anniv. A297

No. 1949: a, Queen Elizabeth II. b, Royal Arms. c, Prince, Queen walking among crowd. d, Queen, Prince in military attire. e, Buckingham Palace. f, Prince Philip.

$6, Portrait of Queen and Prince on balcony.

**1997, May 29** **Litho.** *Perf. 14*

**1949** A297 $1 Sheet of 6, #a.-f. 5.50 5.50

**Souvenir Sheet**

**1950** A297 $6 multicolored 5.00 5.00

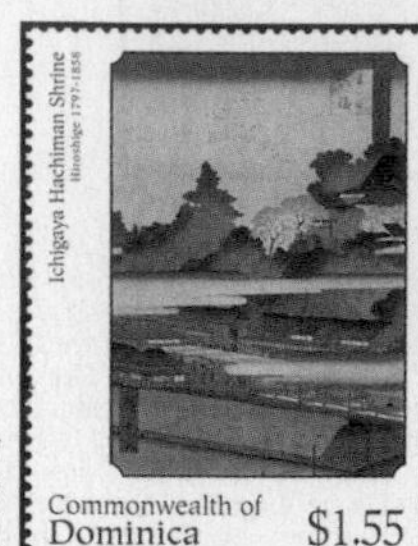


Paintings by Hiroshige (1797-1858) A298

No. 1951: a, Ichigaya Hachiman Shrine. b, Blossoms on the Tama River Embankment. c, Kumano Junisha Shrine, Tsunohazu ("Juniso"). d, Benkei Moat from Soto-Sakurada to Kojimachi. e, Kinokuni Hill & View of Akasak Tameike. f, Naito Shinjuku, Yotsuya.

Each $6: No. 1952, Kasumigaseki. No. 1952A, Sanno Festival Procession at Kojimachi I-chome.

**1997, May 29**

**1951** A298 $1.55 Sheet of 6, #a.-f. 10.50 10.50

**Souvenir Sheets**

**1952-1952A** A298 Set of 2 12.50 12.50

Orchids A299

Designs, vert: 20c, Oncidium altissimum. 25c, Oncidium papilio. 55c, Epidendrum fragrans. 65c, Oncidium lanceanum. 90c, Campylocentrum micranthum. $4, Pogonia rosea.

No. 1959: a, Brassavola cucculata. b, Epidendrum ibaguense. c, Ionopsis utriculariodes. d, Rodriguezia lanceolata. e, Oncidium cebolleta. f, Epidendrum ciliare.

Each $5: No. 1960, Stanhopea grandiflora. No. 1961, Oncidium ampliatum.

**1997, May 10** **Litho.** *Perf. 14*

**1953-1958** A299 Set of 6 8.00 8.00

**1959** A299 $1 Sheet of 6, #a.-f. 7.00 7.00

**Souvenir Sheets**

**1960-1961** A299 Set of 2 11.00 11.00

Paul P. Harris (1868-1947), Founder of Rotary, Intl. — A300

Portrait of Harris and: $2, Rotary Village Corps, irrigation project, Honduras. $6, Emblems, world community service.

**1997, May 29**

**1962** A300 $2 multicolored 1.60 1.60

**Souvenir Sheet**

**1963** A300 $6 multicolored 6.00 6.00

Heinrich von Stephan (1831-97) A301

Portraits of Von Stephan and: No. 1964 a, Kaiser Wilhelm II. b, UPU emblem. c, Postal messenger, ancient Japan.

$6, Von Stephan, Russian dog team carrying post, 1859.

**1997, May 29**

**1964** A301 $2 Sheet of 3, #a.-c. 4.25 4.25

**Souvenir Sheet**

**1965** A301 $6 multicolored 4.50 4.50

PACIFIC 97.

Chernobyl Disaster, 10th Anniv. A302

Designs: No. 1966, Chabad's Children of Chernobyl. No. 1967, UNESCO.

**1997, May 29** *Perf. 13½x14*

**1966** A302 $2 multicolored 2.25 2.25

**1967** A302 $2 multicolored 2.25 2.25

Grimm's Fairy Tales A303

Mother Goose Rhymes — A304

The Goose Girl: No. 1968: a, Girl with horse. b, Geese, pond, castle. c, Girl. No. 1969, Girl, horiz.

No. 1970: Mary, Mary, Quite Contrary.

**1997, May 29** *Perf. 13½x14*

**1968** A303 $2 Sheet of 3, #a.-c. 6.00 6.00

**Souvenir Sheets**

*Perf. 14x13½*

**1969** A303 $6 multicolored 6.00 6.00

*Perf. 14*

**1970** A304 $6 multicolored 5.00 5.00

Return of Hong Kong to China — A305

Designs: $1, View of Hong Kong at night. $1.45, View of Hong Kong in daytime. $2, View of Hong Kong at night, diff.

Hong Kong skyline at dusk: No. 1974: a, 65c. b, 90c. c, $1. d, $3.

**1997, July 1** *Perf. 14*

**1971-1973** A305 Set of 3 3.75 3.75

**1974** A305 Sheet of 4, #a.-d. 5.00 5.00

Nos. 1971-1973 were issued in sheets of 4.

1998 Winter Olympics, Nagano — A306

Medal winners: 20c, Yukio Kasaya, 1972 ski jump. 25c, Jens Weissflog, 1994 ski jump. No. 1977, 55c, Anton Maier, 1968 men's speed skating. No. 1978, 55c, Ljubov Egorova, 1994 women's cross-country skiing. 65c, 1994 Ice hockey, Sweden. 90c, Bernhard Glass, 1980 men's luge. $4, Frank-Peter Roetsch, 1988 men's biathlon.

No. 1982: a, like #1975. b, like #1976. c, like #1977. d, Christa Rothenburger, 1988 women's speed skating.

Each $5: No. 1983, Jacob Tullin Thams, 1924 ski jumping. No. 1984, Charles Jewtraw, 1924 men's speed skating.

**1997, July 15**

**1975-1981** A306 Set of 7 8.75 8.75

**1982** A306 $1 Strip or block of 4, #a.-d. 5.00 5.00

**Souvenir Sheets**

**1983-1984** A306 Set of 2 9.00 9.00

No. 1982 issued in sheets of 8 stamps.

1998 World Cup Soccer Championships, France — A307

Players, vert: 20c, Klinsmann, Germany. 55c, Bergkamp, Holland. 65c, Ravanelli, Italy. 90c, Kinkladze, Georgia. $2, Shearer, England. $4, Dani, Portugal.

Stadiums: No. 1991, each 65c: a, Wembley, England. b, Bernabeu, Spain. c, Maracana, Brazil. d, Torino, Italy. e, Centenary, Uruguay. f, Olympic, Germany. g, Rose Bowl, US. h, Azteca, Mexico.

Team Captains: No. 1992, each 65c: a, Meazza, Italy, 1934. b, Matthaus, Germany, 1990. c, Walter, W. Germany, 1954. d, Maradona, Argentina, 1986. e, Beckenbauer, Germany, 1974. f, Moore, England, 1966. g, Dunga, Brazil, 1994. h, Zoff, Italy, 1982.

$5, Mario Kempes, Argentina, vert. $6, Ally McCoist, Scotland, vert.

**1997, July 21** **Litho.** *Perf. 14*

**1985-1990** A307 Set of 6 8.00 8.00

**Sheets of 8 + Label**

**1991-1992** A307 Set of 2 9.00 9.00

**Souvenir Sheets**

**1993** A307 $5 multicolored 4.50 4.50

**1994** A307 $6 multicolored 5.50 5.50

Dominica Credit Union — A308

25c, Joffre Robinson, former Credit Union president. 55c, Sister Alicia, founder credit union movement in Dominica. 65c, Lorrel Bruce, 1st Cooperative Credit Union president. 90c, Roseau Credit Union Building.

$5, Bruce, Robinson, Sister Alicia.

**1997, Aug. 15 Litho. *Perf. 14x13½***

**1995-1998** A308 Set of 4 2.25 2.25

**Souvenir Sheet**

***Perf. 14***

**1999** A308 $5 multicolored 4.50 4.50

No. 1999 contains one 28x60mm stamp.

A309

Medical Pioneers: 20c, Louis Pasteur, father of bacteriology. 25c, Christiaan Barnard, performed first heart transplant. 55c, Sir Alexander Fleming, developer of penicillin. 65c, Camillo Golgi, neurologist. 90c, Jonas Salk, developer of polio vaccine. $1, Har Ghobind Khorana, geneticist. $2, Elizabeth Blackwell, first woman physician. $3, Sir Frank Macfarlane Burnet, immunologist.

$5, Fleming, diff. $6, Pasteur, diff.

**1997, Sept. 1 Litho. *Perf. 14***

**2000-2007** A309 Set of 8 10.00 10.00

**Souvenir Sheets**

**2008** A309 $5 multicolored 5.25 5.25
**2009** A309 $6 multicolored 6.25 6.25

A310

Diana, Princess of Wales (1961-97): Various portraits.

**1997, Oct. 20 Litho. *Perf. 14***

**2010** A310 $2 Sheet of 4, #a.-d. 6.50 6.50

**Souvenir Sheet**

**2011** A310 $5 multicolored 4.75 4.75

Christmas — A311

Entire paintings or details: 20c, Echo and Narcissus, by Poussin. 55c, Angel Departing from the Family of Tobias, by Rembrandt. 65c, Seated Nymphs with Flute, by Francois Boucher. 90c, Angel, by Rembrandt. $2, Dispute of the Holy Sacrament, by Raphael. $4, Garden of Love, by Rubens.

Each $6: No. 2018, Annunciation, by Botticelli. No. 2019, Christ on the Mount of Olives, by El Greco.

**1997, Nov. 10 Litho. *Perf. 14***

**2012-2017** A311 Set of 6 7.00 7.00

**Souvenir Sheets**

**2018-2019** A311 Set of 2 11.00 11.00

The $4 is incorrectly inscribed Holy Trinity, by Raphael. No. 2018 is incorrectly inscribed Study of a Muse, by Raphael.

A312

Paintings of tigers, by Ling-Nan School: No. 2020: a, 55c, Gao Qifeng. b, 65c, Zhao Shao'ang. c, 90c, Gao Jianfu. d, $1.20, Gao Jianfu, diff.

$3, Tiger running down mountain, by Gao Jianfu.

**1998, Jan. 5 Litho. *Perf. 14½***

**2020** A312 Sheet of 4, #a.-d. 3.00 3.00

**Souvenir Sheet**

***Perf. 14x14½***

**2021** A312 $3 multicolored 2.25 2.25

New Year 1998 (Year of the Tiger). No. 2021 contains one 44x36mm stamp.

**Fish Type of 1996**

5c, Porcupine fish. 10c, Powder-blue surgeonfish. 15c, Red hind. 20c, Golden butterflyfish. 25c, Long-nosed butterflyfish. 35c, Pennant butterflyfish. 45c, Spotted drum. 55c, Blue-girdled angelfish. 60c, Scorpion fish. 65c, Harlequin sweetlips. 90c, Flame angelfish. $1, Queen trigger. $1.20, Stoplight parrot. $1.45, Black durgon. $2, Glasseye snapper. $5, Balloon fish. $10, Creole wrasse. $20, Seabass.

**1998 *Perf. 13x13½***

**Size: 20x18mm**

| | | | | | |
|---|---|---|---|---|---|
| **2024** | A287 | 5c | multi | .30 | .50 |
| **2025** | A287 | 10c | multi | .30 | .50 |
| **2026** | A287 | 15c | multi | .40 | .50 |
| **2027** | A287 | 20c | multi | .40 | .40 |
| **2028** | A287 | 25c | multi | .45 | .45 |
| **2029** | A287 | 35c | multi | .50 | .50 |
| **2030** | A287 | 45c | multi | .70 | .70 |
| **2031** | A287 | 55c | multi | .80 | .80 |
| **2032** | A287 | 60c | multi | .90 | .90 |
| **2033** | A287 | 65c | multi | .90 | .90 |
| **2034** | A287 | 90c | multi | 1.00 | .90 |
| **2035** | A287 | $1 | multi | 1.25 | 1.25 |
| **2036** | A287 | $1.20 | multi | 1.50 | 1.40 |
| **2037** | A287 | $1.45 | multi | 1.75 | 1.75 |
| **2038** | A287 | $2 | multi | 2.25 | 2.25 |
| **2039** | A287 | $5 | multi | 5.00 | 5.00 |
| **2039A** | A287 | $10 | multi | 9.50 | 9.50 |
| **2039B** | A287 | $20 | multi | 20.00 | 20.00 |
| | *Nos. 2024-2039B (18)* | | | 47.90 | 48.20 |

A313

Famous 20th cent. athletes — No. 2040: a, Jesse Owens. b, Owens jumping in 1936 Summer Olympic Games, Berlin. c, Isaac Berger lifting weights. d, Berger. e, Boris Becker. f, Becker playing tennis. g, Arthur Ashe playing tennis, holding Wimbledon trophy. h, Ashe.

No. 2041, Franz Beckenbauer, soccer player, horiz.

**1998, Feb. 9 Litho. *Perf. 14***

**Sheet of 8**

**2040** A313 $1 #a.-h. 7.50 7.50

**Souvenir Sheet**

**2041** A313 $6 multi 6.25 6.25

Nos. 2040b-2040c, 2040f-2040g are each 53x38mm.

A314

Japanese Cinema Stars — No. 2042: a, Akira Kurosawa. b, Kurosawa's 1950 film, "Rashomon." c, Toshiro Mifune in 1954 film, "Seven Samurai." d, Mifune. e, Yasujiro Ozu. f, Ozu's 1949 film, "Late Spring." g, Sessue Hayakawa in 1957 film, "Bridge on the River Kwai." h, Hayakawa.

No. 2043, Akira Kurosawa, director.

**1998, Feb. 9 Litho. *Perf. 14***

**Sheet of 8**

**2042** A314 $1 #a.-h. 7.50 7.50

**Souvenir Sheet**

**2043** A314 $6 multi 6.25 6.25

Nos. 2042b-2042c, 2042f-2042g are each 53x38mm.

A315

Mushrooms: 10c, Omphalotus illudens. 15c, Inocybe fastigiata. 20c, Marasmius plicatulus. 50c, Mycena lilacifolia. 55c, Armillaria straminea. 90c, Tricholomopsis rutilans.

No. 2050, each $1: a, Lepiota naucina. b, Cortinarius violaceus. c, Boletus aereus. d, Tricholoma aurantium. e, Lepiota procera. f, Clitocybe geotropa. g, Lepiota acutesquamosa. h, Tricholoma saponaceum. i, Lycoperdon gemmatum.

No. 2051, each $1: a, Boletus ornatipes. b, Russula xerampelina. c, Cortinarius collinitus. d, Agaricus meleagris. e, Coprinus comatus. f, Amanita caesarea. g, Amanita brunnescens. h, Amanita muscaria. i, Morchella esculenta.

$6, Cortinarius violaceus.

**1998, Mar. 2 Litho. *Perf. 14***

**2044-2049** A315 Set of 6 3.00 3.00

**Sheets of 9**

**2050-2051** A315 Set of 2 17.50 17.50

**Souvenir Sheet**

**2052** A315 $6 multicolored 5.25 5.25

Sailing Ships A316

Designs: 65c, Greek bireme. 90c, Egyptian felucca. $1, Viking longboat. $2, Chinese junk.

No. 2057: a, Two-masted topsail schooner. b, The Golden Hinde. c, Roman merchant ship. d, Gazela Primeiro. e, Moshulu. f, Bluenose.

Each $5: No. 2058, Pinta. No. 2059, Chesapeake Bay skipjack.

**1998, Mar. 16 Litho. *Perf. 14***

**2053-2056** A316 Set of 4 4.50 4.50
**2057** A316 55c Block of 6, #a.-f. 3.25 3.25

**Souvenir Sheets**

**2058-2059** A316 Set of 2 10.00 10.00

No. 2053 incorrectly inscribed "Egyptian felucca."

No. 2057 was issued in sheets of 12 stamps.

Mickey & Minnie Mouse's 70th Anniv. — A317

25c, Steamboat Willie, 1928. 55c, The Brave Little Tailor, 1938. 65c, Nifty Nineties, 1941. 90c, Mickey Mouse Club, 1955. $1, Mickey, Minnie at the opening of Walt Disney World, 1971. $1.45, Mousercise Mickey & Minnie, 1980.

Each $5: No. 2061, Walt Disney, Mickey, Minnie. No. 2062, Surprise Party for Mickey & Minnie.

**1998, June 16 Litho. *Perf. 14x13½***

| | | | | | |
|---|---|---|---|---|---|
| **2060A** | A317 | 25c | black | .30 | .30 |
| **2060B** | A317 | 55c | multi | .60 | .60 |
| **2060C** | A317 | 65c | multi | .75 | .75 |
| **2060D** | A317 | 90c | multi | 1.00 | 1.00 |
| **2060E** | A317 | $1 | multi | 1.10 | 1.10 |
| **2060F** | A317 | $1.45 | multi | 1.60 | 1.60 |
| | *Nos. 2060A-2060F (6)* | | | 5.35 | 5.35 |

**Souvenir Sheet of 7**

**2060G** #2060A-2060F, 2060h 11.50 11.50
*h.* $5 Runaway brain, perf 13½ at left 3.50 3.50

**Size: 130x104mm**

***Imperf***

**2061-2062** A317 Set of 2 10.00 10.00

Souvenir Sheet

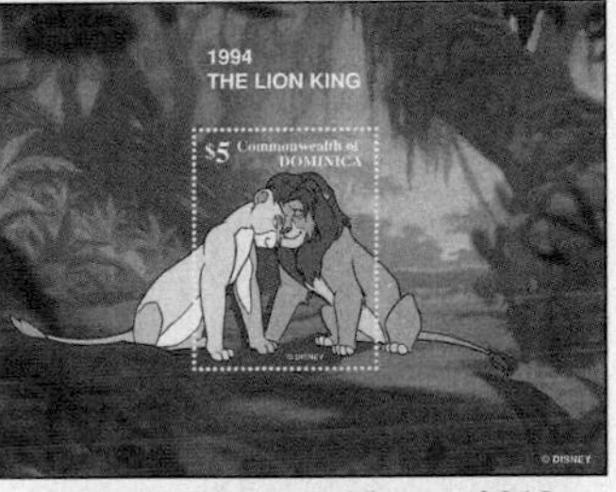


Disney's The Lion King — A318

**1998, June 16 Litho. *Perf. 13½x14***

**2063** A318 $5 multicolored 7.00 7.00

Sea Birds A319

25c, Erect crested penguin. 65c, Humboldt penguin. 90c, Red knot. $1, Audubon's shearwater.

No. 2068: a, Crested tern. b, Franklin's gull. c, Australian pelican. d, Fairy prion. e, Andean gull. f, Imperial shag. g, Red phalarope. h, Hooded grebe. i, Least auklet. j, Little grebe. k, Cape petrel. l, Horned grebe.

Each $5: No. 2069, Sula nebouxii. No. 2070, Fulmarus glacialis.

**1998, Aug. 4 *Perf. 14***

**2064-2067** A319 Set of 4 2.50 2.50
**2068** A319 90c Sheet of 12, #a.-l. 10.00 10.00

**Souvenir Sheets**

**2069-2070** A319 Set of 2 10.50 10.50

Airplanes A320

20c, Jetstar II. 25c, AN 225. 55c, Dash-8. 65c, Beech-99. 90c, American Eagle. $2, HFB 320 Itansa Jet.

No. 2077, each $1: a, SR 71 "Blackbird." b, Stealth bomber. c, Northrop YF23. d, F-14 A "Tomcat." e, F-15 "Eagle S." f, MiG 29 "Fulcrum." g, Europa X5. h, Camion.

No. 2078, each $1: a, E400. b, CL-215 C-GKDN Amphibian. c, Piper jet. d, Beech Hawker. e, Lockheed YF22. f, Piper Seneca V. g, CL-215 Amphibian. h, Vantase.
Each $6: No. 2079, F-1 Fighter. No. 2080, Sea Hopper.

**1998, Aug. 17**
**2071-2076** A320 Set of 6 4.50 4.50

**Sheets of 8**
**2077-2078** A320 Set of 2 17.00 17.00

**Souvenir Sheets**
**2079-2080** A320 Set of 2 11.00 11.00

Intl. Year of the Ocean A321

Marine life: 25c, Fridman fish. 55c, Hydrocoral. 65c, Feather star. 90c, Royal angelfish.
No. 2085, each $1: a, Monk seal. b, Galapagos penguin. c, Manta ray. d, Hawksbill turtle. e, Moorish idol. f, Nautilus. g, Giant clam. h, Tubeworms. i, Nudibranch.
No. 2086, each $1: a, Spotted dolphin. b, Atlantic sailfish. c, Sailfin flying fish. d, Fairy basslet. e, Atlantic spadefish. f, Leatherback turtle. g, Blue tang. h, Coral banded shrimp. i, Rock beauty.
No. 2087, Humpback whale. No. 2088, Leafy sea dragon.

**1998, Sept. 7 Litho. *Perf. 14***
**2081-2084** A321 Set of 4 2.50 2.50

**Sheets of 9**
**2085-2086** A321 Set of 2 19.00 19.00

**Souvenir Sheets**
**2087** A321 $5 multicolored 4.75 4.75
**2088** A321 $6 multicolored 5.50 5.50

Organization of American States, 50th Anniv. A322

**1998, Sept. 1 Litho. *Perf. 14***
**2089** A322 $1 multicolored 1.25 1.25

Ferrari Sports Cars A323

55c, 365 GT 2+2. 90c, Boano/Ellena 250 GT. $1, 375 MM coupe. $5, 212.

**1998, Sept. 1**
**2090-2092** A323 Set of 3 3.75 3.75

**Souvenir Sheet**
**2093** A323 $5 multicolored 5.50 5.50

No. 2093 contains one 91x35mm stamp.

Gandhi — A324

**1998, Sept. 1**
**2094** A324 90c shown 1.50 1.50

**Souvenir Sheet**
**2095** A324 $6 Seated 5.25 5.25

No. 2094 was issued in sheets of 4.

Pablo Picasso A325

Paintings: 90c, The Painter and His Model, 1926. $1, The Crucifixion, 1930. $2, Nude with Raised Arms, 1908, vert.
$6, Cafe at Royan, 1940.

**1998, Sept. 1 *Perf. 14½***
**2096-2098** A325 Set of 3 4.50 4.50

**Souvenir Sheet**
**2099** A325 $6 multicolored 5.75 5.75

Royal Air Force, 80th Anniv. A326

No. 2100: a, Nimrod MR2P. b, C-130 Hercules Mk3. c, Panavia Tornado GR1. d, C-130 Hercules landing.
$5, Biplane, hawk. $6, Hawker Hart, jet.

**1998, Sept. 1 *Perf. 14***
**2100** A326 $2 Sheet of 4, #a.-d. 7.00 7.00

**Souvenir Sheets**
**2101** A326 $5 multicolored 4.75 4.75
**2102** A326 $6 multicolored 5.25 5.25

No. 2100d incorrectly inscribed Panavia Tornado GR1.

**Nos. 1548-1549, 1551-1552, 1554 Ovptd.**

**1998, Sept. 14**
**2103-2107** A221 Set of 5 6.00 6.00

A327

1998 World Scouting Jamboree, Chile: 65c, Scout sign. $1, Scout handshake. $2, World Scout flag.
$5, Lord Baden-Powell.

**1998**
**2108-2110** A327 Set of 3 3.25 3.25

**Souvenir Sheet**
**2111** A327 $5 multicolored 5.25 5.25

A328

Birds: 25c, Northern cardinal. 55c, Eastern bluebird. 65c, Carolina wren. 90c, Blue jay. $1, Evening grosbeak. $2, Bohemian waxwing.
$5, Northern parula. $6, Painted bunting.

**1998, Dec. 1 Litho. *Perf. 14***
**2112-2117** A328 Set of 6 5.50 5.50

**Souvenir Sheets**
**2118** A328 $5 multicolored 5.25 5.25
**2119** A328 $6 multicolored 6.25 6.25

Christmas.

New Year 1999 (Year of the Rabbit) A329

**1999, Jan. 4 Litho. *Perf. 14***
**2120** A329 $1.50 multicolored 2.00 2.00

No. 2120 was issued in sheets of 4.

Orchids — A330

55c, Broughtonia sanguinea. 65c, Cattleyonia Keith Roth "Roma." 90c, Comparettia falcata. $2, Cochleanthes discolor.
No. 2125, each $1: a, Dracula erythiochaete. b, Lycasle aromatica. c, Masdevallia marguerile. d, Encyclia marfae. e, Laelia gouldiana. f, Huntleya meleagris. g, Galeandria baueri. h, Lycale deppei.
No. 2126, each $1: a, Anguloa clowesii. b, Lemboglossum cervantesii. c, Oncidium cebolleta. d, Millonia. e, Pescatorea lehmannll. f, Sophronitis coccinea. g, Pescatorea cerina. h, Encyclia vitellina.
Each $5: No. 2127, Lepanthes ovalis. No. 2128, Encyclia cochleata.

**1999, Apr. 26 Litho. *Perf. 14***
**2121-2124** A330 Set of 4 4.50 4.50

**Sheets of 8**
**2125-2126** A330 Set of 2 17.50 17.50

**Souvenir Sheets**
**2127-2128** A330 Set of 2 10.00 10.00

Trains A331

No. 2129, each $1: a, Class 103.1 Co-Co, Germany. b, Class .24, "Trans Pennine," UK. c, GG1 2-Co-Co-2, US. d, LRC Bo-Bo, Canada. e, Class EW, New Zealand. f, Class SS1 "Shao-Shani," China. g, Gulf, Mobile Ohio, US. h, Class 9100 2-Do-2, France.
No. 2130, each $1: a, County Donegal Petrol Rail Car No. 10, Ireland. b, RDC Single Rail Car, US. c, WDM Class Co-Co, India. d, Bi-Polar No. E-2, US. e, Class X Co-Co, Australia. f, Beijing Bo-Bo, China. g, Class E428 2-Bo-Bo-2, Italy. h, Class 581 Twelve-Car Train, Japan.
$5, X-2000 Tilting Express Train, Sweden, vert. $6, Class 87 Bo-Bo, Great Britain, vert.

**1999, May 10 Litho. *Perf. 14***

**Sheets of 8**
**2129-2130** A331 Set of 2 13.00 13.00

**Souvenir Sheets**
**2131** A331 $5 multicolored 4.00 4.00
**2132** A331 $6 multicolored 5.00 5.00

Australia '99, World Stamp Expo.

Prehistoric Animals — A332

25c, Tyrannosaurus, vert. 65c, Hypacrosaurus. 90c, Sauropelta. $2, Zalambdalestes.
No. 2137, each $1: a, Barosaurus. b, Rhamphorhynchus. c, Apatosaurus. d, Archaeopteryx. e, Diplodocus. f, Ceratosaurus. g, Stegosaurus. h, Elaphrosaurus. i, Vulcanodon.
No. 2138, each $1: a, Psittacosaurus. b, Pteranodon. c, Ichthyornis. d, Spinosaurus. e, Parasaurolophus. f, Ornithomimus. g, Anatosaurus. h, Triceratops. i, Baronyx.
$5, Yangchuanosaurus. $6, Brachiosaurus.

**1999, June 1 Litho. *Perf. 14***
**2133-2136** A332 Set of 4 3.50 3.50

**Sheets of 9**
**2137-2138** A332 Set of 2 18.00 18.00

**Souvenir Sheets**
**2139** A332 $5 multicolored 4.50 4.50
**2140** A332 $6 multicolored 5.50 5.50

Wedding of Prince Edward and Sophie Rhys-Jones A333

No. 2141: a, Sophie. b, Sophie, Edward. c, Edward.
$6, like No. 2141b.

**1999, June 19 Litho. *Perf. 13½***
**2141** A333 $3 Sheet of 3, #a.-c. 7.25 7.25

**Souvenir Sheet**
**2142** A333 $6 multicolored 5.00 5.00

IBRA '99, World Philatelic Exhibition, Nuremberg — A334

Exhibition emblem, sailing ship Eendraght and: 65c, Cameroun #58, #56. 90c, Cameroun #11, #9.
Emblem, early German train and: $1, Cameroun #19. $2, Cameroun #6.
$6, Cover with Cameroun #19.

**1999, June 22 *Perf. 14***
**2143-2146** A334 Set of 4 4.00 4.00

**Souvenir Sheet**
**2147** A334 $6 multicolored 6.25 6.25

Souvenir Sheets

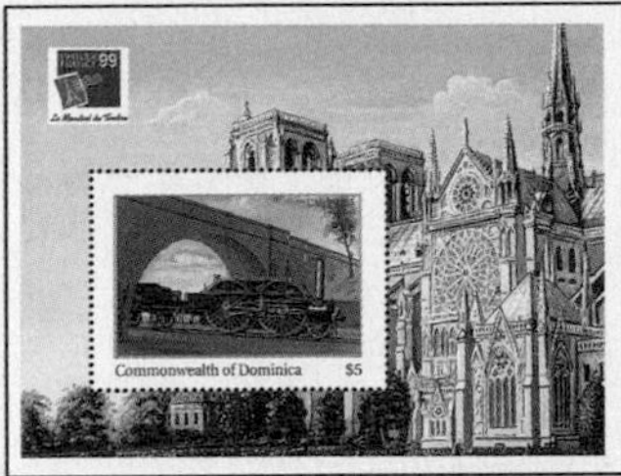

PhilexFrance '99 — A335

Trains: $5, L'Aigle, 1855. $6, Mainline diesel locomotive, 1963.

**1999, June 22** *Perf. 13¾*

**2148** A335 $5 multicolored 4.50 4.50
**2149** A335 $6 multicolored 5.50 5.50

Apollo 11 Moon Landing, 30th Anniv. A336

No. 2150: a, Command Module separation b, Service Module separation. c, 3rd Stage Booster separation. d, Landing, Command Modules go to the moon. e, Apollo Ground Tracker. f, Goldstone Radio Telescope.
$6, Apollo 11 after splashdown.

**1999, June 22** *Perf. 14*

**2150** A336 $1.45 Sheet of 6, #a.-f. 9.00 9.00

**Souvenir Sheet**

**2151** A336 $6 multicolored 6.00 6.00

Paintings by Hokusai (1760-1849) A337

Details or entire paintings — No. 2152:, each $2 a, Pilgrims at Kirifuri Waterfall. b, Kakura-Sato (rats looking at book, pulling on rope). c, Travelers on the Bridge by Ono Waterfall. d, Fast Cargo Boat Battling the Waves. e, Kakura-Sato (rats working with bales). f, Buufinfinh and Weeping cherry.
No. 2153, each $2: a, Cuckoo and Azalea. b, Soldiers (spear in left hand). c, Lover in the snow. d, Ghost of Koheiji. e, Soldiers (spear in right hand). f, Chinese Poet in Snow.
$5, Empress Jitó. $6, One Hundred Poems by One Hundred Poets.

*Perf. 13½x13¾*

**1999, June 22** **Litho.**

**Sheets of 6**

**2152-2153** A337 Set of 2 19.00 19.00

**Souvenir Sheets**

**2154** A337 $5 multicolored 4.50 4.50
**2155** A337 $6 multicolored 5.50 5.50

Johann Wolfgang von Goethe (1749-1832), Poet — A338

No. 2156: a, Faust perceives an astrological sign. b, Portrait of Goethe and Friedrich von Schiller (1759-1805). c, Faust tempted by Mephistopheles.
$6, Profile portrait of Goethe.

**1999, June 22** *Perf. 14*

**2156** A338 $2 Sheet of 3, #a.-c. 5.00 5.00

**Souvenir Sheet**

**2157** A338 $6 multicolored 5.00 5.00

Rights of the Child — A339

No. 2158: a, Woman, child. b, Child in blue sweater. c, Two children.
$6, Dove, horiz.

**1999, June 22** **Litho.** *Perf. 14*

**2158** A339 $3 Sheet of 3, #a.-c. 7.50 7.50

**Souvenir Sheet**

**2159** A339 $6 multicolored 5.00 5.00

Queen Mother (b. 1900) — A340

A340a

**Gold Frames**

No. 2160: a, In 1939. b, In Australia, 1958. c, At Badminton, 1982. d, Hatless, in 1982.
$6, In 1953.

**1999, Aug. 4** *Perf. 14*

**2160** A340 $2 Sheet of 4, #a.-d. + label 7.50 7.50

**Souvenir Sheet**

*Perf. 13¾*

**2161** A340 $6 multicolored 5.00 5.00

No. 2161 contains one 38x51mm stamp.
Compare with Nos. 2345-2346. Backdrop of photo is more pink on No. 2161 than on No. 2346. No. 2161 has embossed arms in margin, while No. 2346 does not.

**Litho. & Embossed**

***Die Cut Perf. 8¾***

**Without Gum**

**2161A** A340a $20 gold & multi 20.00 20.00

See Nos. 2345-2346.

Flora & Fauna A341

Designs: 25c, Heliconia lobster claw. 65c, Broad winged hawk. $1, Anthurium. $1.55, Blue-headed hummingbird. $2, Bananaquit. $4 Agouti.
No. 2168: a, White-throated sparrow. b, Blue-winged teal. c, Raccoon. d, Alfalf butterfly. e, Bridge. f, Whitetail deer. g, Gray squirrel. h, Banded purple butterfly. i, Snowdrop. j, Bullfrog. k, Mushrooms. l, Large-blotched ensatina.
$5, Eastern chipmunk. $6, Black-footed ferret.

**1999**

**2162-2167** A341 Set of 6 9.00 9.00

**Sheet of 12**

**2168** A341 90c #a.-l. 10.00 10.00

**Souvenir Sheets**

**2169** A341 $5 multicolored 5.00 5.00
**2170** A341 $6 multicolored 6.00 6.00

A342

Dominica Festival Commission: 25c, Domfesta. 55c, $5, Dominica's 21st anniv. as a republic. 65c, Carnival development committee. 90c, World Creole Music Festival.

**1999** *Perf. 12½*

**2171-2174** A342 Set of 4 2.00 2.00

**Souvenir Sheet**

*Perf. 13¼*

**2175** A342 $5 multicolored 4.50 4.50

No. 2175 contains one 38x51mm stamp.

A343

Intl. Year of the Elderly: 25c, Family. 65c, Four people. 90c, Four people, one in chair.

**1999, Aug. 4** *Perf. 14*

**2176** A343 Sheet of 3, #a.-c. 1.50 1.50

A345

Christmas: 25c, Yellow-crowned parrot. 55c, Red bishop. 65c, Troupial. 90c, Puerto Rican woodpecker. $2, Mangrove cuckoo. $3, American robin.
$6, Mary with Child Beside the Wall, by Albrecht Dürer.

**1999, Dec. 7** **Litho.** *Perf. 14*

**2178-2183** A345 Set of 6 6.75 6.75

**Souvenir Sheet**

**2184** A345 $6 multi 5.25 5.25

Inscription on No. 2181 is misspelled.

A346

Millennium (Highlights of the early 13th Cent.) — No. 2185: a, Leonardo Fibonacci publishes "Liber Abaci," 1202. b, St. Francis of Assisi. c, Mongols conquer China. d, Children's Crusade begins, 1212. e, Magna Carta signed, 1215. f, Founding of Salamanca University, 1218. g, Snorri Sturluson writes "Prose Edda". h, Chinese painter Ma Yuan dies, 1225. i, Genghis Khan dies, 1227. j, Zen Buddhism in Japan. k, Sixth Crusade. l, Lubeck-Hamburg League. m, Inquisitions begin, 1231. n, Cordoba conquered by Castilians, 1236. o, Democracy in San Marino. p, Maimonides (60x40mm). q, Notre Dame Cathedral, Paris.
Highlights of the 1940s — No. 2186: a, Japan bombs Pearl Harbor. b, Churchill becomes Prime Minister of Great Britain. c, Regular television broadcasting begins in the US. d, Anne Frank hid in Amsterdam. e, D-Day Invasion. f, Yalta Conference. g, Establishment of the UN. h, Germany surrenders, concentration camps exposed. i, Russians hoist flag over gutted Reichstag building. j, Eniac computer. k, Independence for India. l, Bell Laboratories produce 1st transistor. m, Gandhi assassinated. n, Israel achieves statehood. o, Blockade of West Berlin, Berlin Airlift. p, Atomic bomb tested in New Mexico (60x40mm). q, Establishment of People's Republic of China.

*Perf. 12¾x12½*

**1999, Dec. 31** **Sheets of 17** **Litho.**

**2185** A346 55c #a.-q. + label 8.50 8.50
**2186** A346 55c #a.-q. + label 8.50 8.50

See Nos. 2249-2252.

New Year 2000 (Year of the Dragon) A347

**2000, Feb. 5** *Perf. 13¾*

**2187** A347 $1.50 shown 1.25 1.25

**Souvenir Sheet**

**2188** A347 $4 Dragon, horiz. 3.75 3.75

No. 2187 printed in sheets of 4.

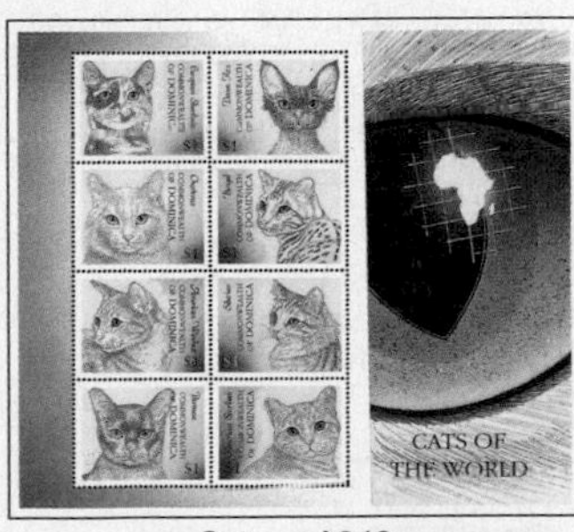


Cats — A348

No. 2189, each $1: a, European Shorthair. b, Devon Rex. c, Chartreux. d, Bengal. e, American Wirehair. f, Siberian. g, Burmese. h, American Shorthair.
No. 2190, each $1: a, Asian Longhair. b, Burmilla. c, Snowshoe. d, Pekeface Persian. e, Himalayan Persian. f, Japanese Bobtail. g, Seychelles Longhair. h, Exotic Shorthair.
Each $6: No. 2191, Awake cat. No. 2192, Sleeping cat.

**2000, Feb. 21** ***Perf. 14¼***

**Sheets of 8, #a.-h.**

**2189-2190** A348 Set of 2 16.00 16.00

**Souvenir Sheets**

**2191-2192** A348 Set of 2 12.00 12.00

Puppies — A349

No. 2193: a, Jack Russell Terrier. b, Shar Peis. c, Basset Hound. d, Boxers. e, Wire-haired Terrier. f, Golden Retrievers.

No. 2194, Beagle.

**2000, Feb. 21** ***Perf. 14½x14¼***

**2193** A349 $1 Sheet of 6, #a.-f. 6.00 6.00

**Souvenir Sheet**

**2194** A349 $6 multi 6.00 6.00

Flowers A350

Various flowers making up a photomosaic of Princess Diana.

**2000, Apr. 3** ***Perf. 13¾***

**2195** A350 $1 Sheet of 8, #a.-h. 7.50 7.50

See No. 2225.

Butterflies A351

No. 2196, each $1.50: a, Giant swallowtail. b, Tiger pierid. c, Orange theope. d, White peacock. e, Blue tharops. f, Mosaic.

No. 2197, each $1.50: a, Banded king shoemaker. b, Figure-of-eight. c, Grecian shoemaker. d, Blue night. e, Monarch. f, Common morpho.

No. 2198, each $1.50: a, Orange-barred sulphur. b, Clorinde. c, Small flambeau. d, Small lace-wing. e, Polydamas swallowtail. f, Atala.

Each $6: No. 2199, Polydamas swallowtail, vert. No. 2200, Sloane's urania, vert. No. 2201, Blue-green reflector, vert.

**2000, Apr. 10** ***Perf. 14***

**Sheets of 6, #a.-f.**

**2196-2198** A351 Set of 3 24.00 24.00

**Souvenir Sheets**

**2199-2201** A351 Set of 3 17.50 17.50

Flowers — A352

Designs: 65c, Passion flower. 90c, Spray orchid. $1, Peach angel's trumpet. $4, Allamanda.

No. 2206, each $1.65: a, Bird of paradise. b, Lobster claw heliconia. c, Candle bush. d, Flor de San Miguel. e, Hibiscus. f, Oleander.

No. 2207, each $1.65: a, Anthurium. b, Fire ginger. c, Shrimp plant. d, Sky vine thunbergia. e, Ceriman. f, Morning glory.

Each $6: No. 2208, Bird of paradise, diff. No. 2109, Hibiscus, diff.

**2000, Apr. 25** **Litho.** ***Perf. 14***

**2202-2205** A352 Set of 4 6.00 6.00

**Sheets of 6, #a-f**

***Perf. 13¾***

**2206-2207** A352 Set of 2 17.00 17.00

**Souvenir Sheets**

***Perf. 13½x 13¾***

**2208-2209** A352 Set of 2 12.00 12.00

Size of stamps: Nos. 2106-2107, 32x48mm; Nos. 2108-2109, 38x51mm.

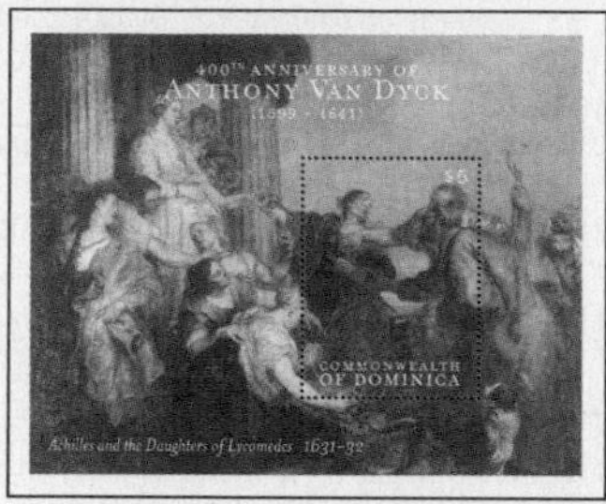


Paintings of Anthony Van Dyck — A353

No. 2210, each $1.65: a, Lady Jane Goodwin. b, Philip Herbert, 4th Earl of Pembroke. c, Philip, Lord Wharton. d, Sir Thomas Hammer. e, Olivia Porter, Wife of Enymion Porter. f, Sir Thomas Chaloner.

No. 2211, horiz, each $1.65: a, Ladies in Waiting. b, Thomas Wentworth, Earl of Strafford, with Sir Philip Mainwaring. c, Dorothy Rivers Savage, Viscountess Andover and Her Sister Lady Elizabeth Thimbleby. d, Mountjoy Blount, Earl of Newport, and Lord George Goring with a Page. e, Thomas Killigrew and an Unidentified Man. f, Elizabeth Villiers, Lady Dalkeith, and Cecilia Killigrew.

No. 2212, horiz, each $1.65: a, The Ages of Man. b, Portrait of a Girl as Erminia Accompanied by Cupid. c, Cupid and Psyche. d, Vertumnus and Pomona. e, The Continence of Scipio. f, Diana and Endymion Surprised by a Satyr.

No. 2213, $5, Achilles and the Daughters of Lycomedes. No. 2214, $5, Amaryllis and Mirtillo. No. 2215, $6, Thomas Howard, 2nd Earl of Arundel, with Alathea, Countess of Arundel.

**2000, May 29** ***Perf. 13¾***

**Sheets of 6, #a-f**

**2210-2212** A353 Set of 3 27.00 27.00

**Souvenir Sheets**

**2213-2214** A353 Set of 2 9.00 9.00

**2215** A353 $6 multi 5.50 5.50

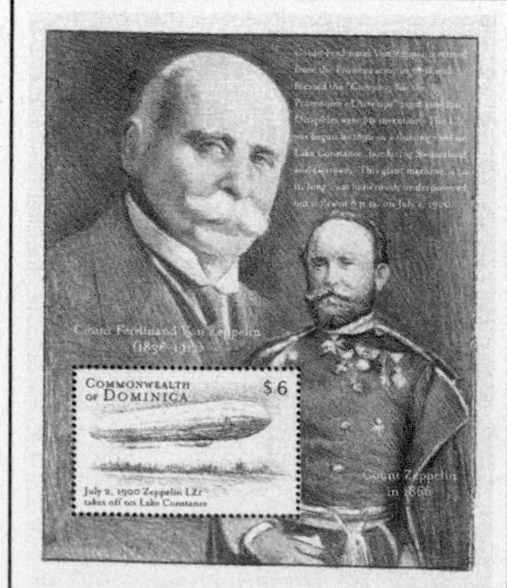


First Zeppelin Flight, Cent. — A354

No. 2216: a, Count Ferdinand von Zeppelin (1838-1917). b, First takeoff of LZ-1. c, LZ-10 over field. d, LZ-6 and Deutschland in hangar. e, Arrival of Z-4 at Luneville. f, Victoria Luise.

No. 2217, LZ-1, diff.

**2000, June 21** **Litho.** ***Perf. 14***

**2216** A354 $1.65 Sheet of 6, #a-f 9.00 9.00

**Souvenir Sheet**

**2217** A354 $6 multi 5.50 5.50

Berlin Film Festival, 50th Anniv. — A355

No. 2218: a, Director Satyajit Ray. b, Mahangar. c, Fanfan La Tulipe. d, Le Salaire de la Peur. e, Les Cousins. f, Hon Dansade en Sommar.

No. 2219, Buffalo Bill and the Indians.

**2000, June 21**

**2218** A355 $1.65 Sheet of 6, #a-f 9.00 9.00

**Souvenir Sheet**

**2219** A355 $6 multi 5.50 5.50

100th Test Match at Lord's Ground — A356

**2000, June 21**

**2220** A356 $4 Norbert Phillip 3.50 3.50

**Souvenir Sheet**

**2221** A356 $6 Lord's Ground 5.50 5.50

Souvenir Sheets

2000 Summer Olympics, Sydney — A357

a, Jesse Owens. b, Pole vault. c, Lenin Stadium Moscow, Soviet Union flag. d, Ancient Greek discus thrower.

**2000, June 21**

**2222** A357 $2 Sheet of 4, #a-d 8.00 8.00

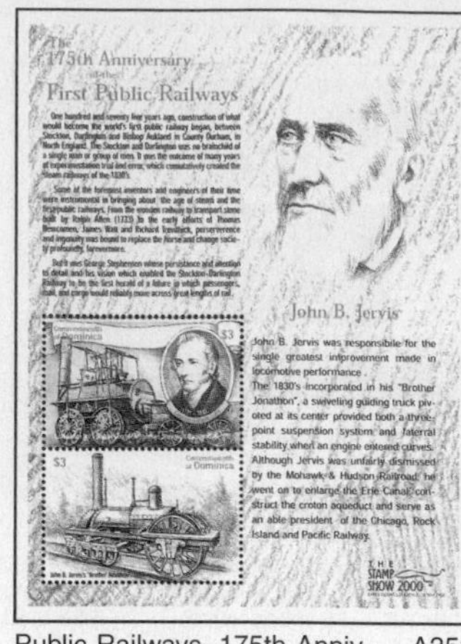


Public Railways, 175th Anniv. — A358

No. 2223: a, Locomotion No. 1, George Stephenson. b, Brother Jonathon.

**2000, June 21**

**2223** A358 $3 Sheet of 2, #a-b 6.25 6.25

The Stamp Show 2000, London.

Johann Sebastian Bach — A359

**2000, June 21**

**2224** A359 $6 multi 5.50 5.50

**Flower Type of 2000**

Various pictures of religious sites making up a photomosaic of Pope John Paul II.

**2000, June 21** **Litho.** ***Perf. 13¾***

**2225** A350 $1 Sheet of 8, #a-h 8.00 8.00

Apollo-Soyuz Mission, 25th Anniv. — A360

No. 2226, vert.: a, Saturn IB launch vehicle. b, Apollo 18. c, Donald K. Slayton.

$6, Apollo and Soyuz docking.

**2000, June 21** ***Perf. 14***

**2226** A360 $3 Sheet of 3, #a-c 9.50 9.50

**Souvenir Sheet**

**2227** A360 $6 multi 6.00 6.00

Souvenir Sheet

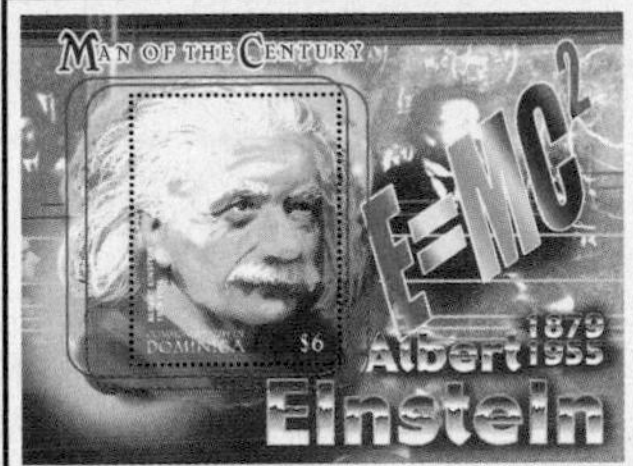


Albert Einstein (1879-1955) — A361

**2000, June 21** *Perf. 14¼*
**2228** A361 $6 multi 5.50 5.50

Prince William, 18th Birthday — A362

No. 2229: a, In ski gear. b, In jacket and red sweater. c, In suit and tie. d, In plaid shirt.
$6, With Prince Harry.

**2000, June 22** *Perf. 14*
**2229** A362 $1.65 Sheet of 4, #a-d 6.25 6.25

**Souvenir Sheet**

*Perf. 13¾*

**2230** A362 $6 multi 5.50 5.50

No. 2229 contains four 28x42mm stamps.

Bob Hope — A363

No. 2231: a, Microphone at right. b, Entertaining troops. c, Wearing bowler. d, Standing in cake. e, Microphone at left. f, With moon.

**2000, Aug. 7** *Perf. 14*

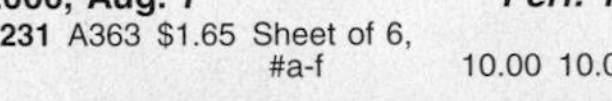

**2231** A363 $1.65 Sheet of 6, #a-f 10.00 10.00

Monty Python and the Holy Grail, 25th Anniv. — A364

No. 2232: a, Close-up of Eric Idle. b, Terry Jones, Graham Chapman and John Cleese as three-headed giant, horiz. c, Knights facing castle wall. d, Chapman as King Arthur, with helmeted knight. e, Beheaded knight. f, Armless and legless Black Knight and King Arthur.

**2000, Aug. 7** *Perf. 13¾*
**2232** A364 90c Sheet of 6, #a-f 5.25 5.25

Popes — A365

No. 2233: a, Clement X, 1670-76. b, Innocent X, 1644-55. c, Nicholas V, 1447-55. d, Martin V, 1417-31. e, Julius III, 1550-55. f, Innocent XII, 1691-1700.
$6, Clement XIV, 1769-74.

**2000, Sept. 5**
**2233** A365 $1.65 Sheet of 6, #a-f 10.00 10.00

**Souvenir Sheet**

**2234** A365 $6 multi 5.50 5.50

Monarchs — A366

No. 2235: a, Edward IV of England, 1461-83. b, Peter the Great of Russia, 1682-1725. c, Henry VI of England, 1422-61. d, Henry III of England, 1216-72. e, Richard III of England, 1483-85. f, Edward I of England, 1272-1307.
$6, Henry VIII of England, 1509-47.

**2000, Sept. 5**
**2235** A366 $1.65 Sheet of 6, #a-f 10.00 10.00

**Souvenir Sheet**

**2236** A366 $6 multi 5.50 5.50

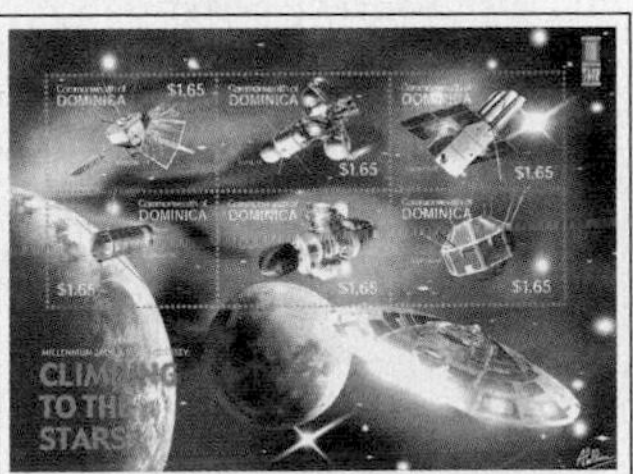


World Stamp Expo 2000, Anaheim — A367

Spacecraft — No. 2237, $1.65: a, Explorer 14. b, Luna 16. c, Copernicus. d, Explorer 16. e, Luna 10. f, Arybhattan.
No. 2238, $1.65: a, ESSA 8. b, Echo 1. c, Topex Poseidon. d, Diademe. e, Early Bird. f, Molniya.
No. 2239, $6, Hipparcos. No. 2240, $6, Eole.

**2000, June 21 Litho.** *Perf. 14¼x14*

**Sheets of 6, #a-f**

**2237-2238** A367 Set of 2 20.00 20.00

**Souvenir Sheets**

**2239-2240** A367 Set of 2 11.00 11.00

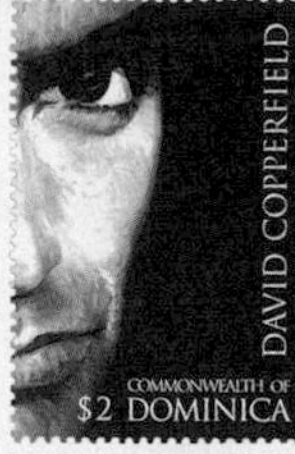


David Copperfield, Magician — A368

**2000, Aug. 8** *Perf. 14*
**2241** A368 $2 multi 1.75 1.75

Printed in sheets of 4.

Souvenir Sheet

Female Recording Groups of the 1960s — A369

No. 2242 — The Crystals, yellow spotlight covering: a, UR, LL and LR corners. b, UL and LL corners. c, UR and LR corners. d, UL, LL and LR corners.

**2000, Aug. 8**
**2242** A369 90c Sheet of 4, #a-d 3.50 3.50

Christmas — A370

Angel: 25c, No. 2247a, Looking right, purple and yellow green background. 65c, No. 2247b, At left, looking left, purple background. 90c, No. 2247c, At right, purple and orange background. $5, No. 2247d, At center, blue and purple background.

**2000, Dec. 4**
**2243-2246** A370 Set of 4 6.25 6.25

**Sheet of 4**

**2247** A370 $1.90 #a-d 7.00 7.00

**Souvenir Sheet**

**2248** A370 $6 Angel 5.50 5.50

**Millennium Type of 1999**

Chinese Art — No. 2249, 55c: a, Eight Prize Steeds, by Giuseppe Castiglione. b, Oleanders, by Wu Hsi Tsai. c, Mynah and Autumn Flowers, by Chang Hsiung. d, Hen and Chicks Beneath Chrysanthemums, by Chu Ch'ao. e, Long Living Pine and Crane, by Xugu. f, Flowers and Fruits, by Chu Lien. g, Lotus and Willow, by Pu Hua. h, Kuan-Yin, by Ch'ien Hui-An. i, Human Figures, by Jen hsun. j, Han-Shan and Shih Te, by Ren Yi. k, Landscape and Human Figure, by Jen Yu. l, Poetic Thoughts While Walking With a Staff, by Wangchen. m, Peony, by Chen Heng-Ko. n, Plum and Orchids, by Wu Chang-Shih. o, Monkey, by Kao Chi-Feng. p, Grapes and Locust, by Ch'i Pai-Shih and Galloping Horse, by Xu Beihong (60x40mm). q, The Beauty, by Lin Fengmian.

History of Change — No. 2250, 55c: a, Star charts. b, Precision tools. c, Science of the stars. d, Investigation into healing a human being. e, Sharing of medical information. f, Church. g, Water alarm clock. h, Weighted clock. i, Spring-loaded miniature clock. j, New technology of glass blowing. k, First screws. l, Wood lathe. m, New systems for assembly blocks for ships. n, Interchangeable parts for rifles. o, Study of movement. p, Efficiency and the Industrial Revolution (60x40mm). q, Concept of efficiency.

Highlights of the 1960s — No. 2251, 55c: a, First birth control pill developed. b, Yuri Gagarin becomes first man in space. c, The first hit for the Beatles in Britain. d, Assassination of John F. Kennedy. e, Dr. Martin Luther King's "I Have a Dream" speech. f, Betty Friedan writes "The Feminine Mystique." g, Kenya gains independence. h, U.S. Surgeon General warns about smoking-related health hazards. i, U.S. Congress passes Civil Rights Act. j, U.S. increases military presence in South Viet Nam. k, Ernesto "Che" Guevara. l, First heart transplant. m, Israel wins Six-day War. n, Ho Chi Minh dies. o, First man on the Moon. p, Communists build wall to divide East and West Berlin (60x40mm). q, Woodstock rock concert.

Highlights of the late 14th Century — No. 2252: a, Minnesingers. b, Acampitzin, King of the Aztecs. c, Black Death eases. d, Giotto's campanile built. e, First French franc. f, Ming Dynasty in China. g, Tamerlane begins conquest of Asia. h, Triumph of Death painted by Francesco Traini. i, Robin Hood. j, Geoffrey Chaucer writes "The Canterbury Tales." k, Succession dispute in Japan. l, Jewish exodus from France. m, Temple of the Golden Pavilion built . n, Strasbourg Cathedral built. o, Alhambra Palace (60x40mm). p, Ife bronzes in Nigeria.

**2000, Dec. 31** *Perf. 12¾x12½*

**Sheets of 17, #a-q**

**2249-2251** A346 Set of 3 26.00 26.00
**2252** A347 65c Sheet of 17, #a-h, j-p, 2 #i 10.00 10.00

Hummingbirds — A371

No. 2253, $1.25: a, Green-throated carib. b, Bee, on branch. c, Bee, in flight. d, Bahama woodstar. e, Antillean mango. f, Blue-headed.
No. 2254, $1.65: a, Eastern streamertail. b, Purple-throated carib. c, Vervain. d, Bahama woodstar. e, Puerto Rican emerald. f, Antillean crested.
No. 2255, $5, Feeders. No. 2256, $6, Hispaniolan.

**2000, Dec. 18 Litho.** *Perf. 14*

**Sheets of 6, #a-f**

**2253-2254** A371 Set of 2 16.00 16.00

**Souvenir Sheets**

**2255-2256** A371 Set of 2 10.00 10.00

Misspellings abound on Nos. 2253-2254.

New Year 2001 (Year of the Snake) A372

**2001, Jan. 2** *Perf. 12x12¼*
**2257** A372 $1.20 multi 1.00 1.00

Printed in sheets of 4.

Fauna A373

Designs: 15c, Puerto Rican crested toad. 20c, Axolotl. $1.90, Panamanian golden frog. $2.20, Manatee.
No. 2262, $1.45: a, St. Vincent parrot. b, Indigo macaw. c, Cock of the rock. d, Cuban solenodon. e, Cuban hutia. f, Chinchilla.
No. 2263, $1.45: a, South American flamingo. b, Golden conure. c, Ocelot. d, Giant armadillo. e, Margay. f, Maned wolf.
No. 2264, $6, Anteater. No. 2265, $6, Hawksbill turtle.

**2000, Dec. 18 Litho. Perf. 14**

2258-2261 A373 Set of 4 4.75 4.75

**Sheets of 6, #a-f**

2262-2263 A373 Set of 2 17.00 17.00

**Souvenir Sheets**

2264-2265 A373 Set of 2 12.00 12.00

Pokémon — A374

No. 2266, horiz.: a, Butterfree. b, Bulbasaur. c, Caterpie. d, Charmander. e, Squirtle. f, Pidgeotto.

**2001, Feb. Perf. 13¾**

2266 A374 $1.65 Sheet of 6, #a-f 7.00 7.00

**Souvenir Sheet**

2267 A374 $6 Nidoking 4.25 4.25

A375

Marine Life A376

Designs: No. 2268, 15c, Banded sea snake. 25c, Soldier fish. 55c, Banner fish. No. 2271, 90c, Crown of thorns starfish.

No. 2272, 15c, Fish. 65c, Ray. No. 2274, 90c, Octopus. $3, Fish, diff.

No. 2276, $1.65: a, White-tip reef shark, lionfish, sergeant major. b, Blue-striped snappers. c, Great hammerhead shark, stovepipe sponge, pink vase sponge. d, Hawaiian monk seal, blue tube coral. e, Seahorse, common clownfish, red feather star coral. f, Bat starfish, brown octopus.

No. 2277, $1.65: a, Red sponge, shoal of Anthias. b, Orange-striped triggerfish. c, Coral grouper, soft tree coral. d, Peacock fan worms, gorgonian sea fan. e, Sweetlips, sea fan. f, Giant clam, golden cup coral.

No. 2278: a, Shark. b, Starfish. c, Seahorse. d, Fish. e, Crab. f, Eel.

No. 2279, $5, Royal angelfish. No. 2280, $5, Pink anemone fish. No. 2281, Turtle.

**2001, Feb. 27 Perf. 14**

2268-2271 A375 Set of 4 2.00 2.00
2272-2275 A376 Set of 4 5.00 5.00

**Sheets of 6, #a-f**

2276-2277 A375 Set of 2 19.00 19.00
2278 A376 $2 Sheet of 6, #a-f 11.00 11.00

**Souvenir Sheets**

2279-2280 A375 Set of 2 10.00 10.00
2281 A376 $5 multi 5.00 5.00

Phila Nippon '01, Japan — A377

Art: 25c, Gathering of Chinese Women, by Tsuji Kako. 55c, Village by Bamboo Grove, by Takeuchi Seiho. 65c, Mountain Village in Spring, by Suzuki Hyakunen. 90c, Gentleman Amusing Himself, by Domoto Insho. $1, Calmness of Spring Light, by Seiho. $2, Su's Embankment on a Spring Morning, by Tomioka Tessai.

No. 2288, $1.65: a, Thatched Cottages in the Willows, by Kako. b, Joy in the Garden, by Kako. c, Azalea and butterfly, by Kikuchi Hobun. d, Pine Grove, by Kako. e, Woodcutters Talking in Autumn Valley, by Kubota Beisen.

No. 2289, $1.65: a, Waterfowl in Snow, by Kako. b, Heron and Willow, by Kako. c, Crow and Cherry Blossoms, by Hobun. d, Chrysanthemum Immortal, by Yamamoto Shunkyo. e, Cranes of Immortality, by Kako.

No. 2290, $6, Kamo Riverbank in the Misty Rain, by Kako. No. 2291, $6, Diamond Gate, by Kako. No. 2292, $6, Woman, by Suzuki Harunobu.

**2001, May 15 Litho. Perf. 14**

2282-2287 A377 Set of 6 5.25 5.25

**Sheets of 5, #a-e**

2288-2289 A377 Set of 2 15.00 15.00

**Souvenir Sheets**

**Perf. 13¾**

2290-2292 A377 Set of 3 12.00 12.00

Nos. 2290-2292 each contain one 38x51mm stamp.

Queen Victoria (1819-1901) — A378

No. 2293: a, Prince Albert in uniform. b, Victoria with silver crown. c, Victoria with gold crown. d, Albert in suit.

$6, Victoria as old woman.

**2001, May 15 Perf. 14**

2293 A378 $2 Sheet of 4, #a-d 7.25 7.25

**Souvenir Sheet**

**Perf. 13¾**

2294 A378 $6 multi 5.50 5.50

No. 2294 contains one 38x51mm stamp.

Queen Elizabeth II, 75th Birthday — A379

No. 2295: a, With crown. b, With white dress. c, Formal portrait by Pietro Annigoni. d, With orange coat. e, With child. f, With green dress.

$6, In uniform.

**2001, May 15 Perf. 14**

2295 A379 $1.20 Sheet of 6, #a-f 6.25 6.25

**Souvenir Sheet**

2296 A379 $6 multi 5.50 5.50

Toulouse-Lautrec Paintings — A380

No. 2297: a, Two Women Waltzing. b, The Medical Inspection. c, The Two Girlfriends. d, Woman Pulling Up Her Stocking.

**2001, May 15 Litho. Perf. 13¾**

2297 A380 $2 Sheet of 4, #a-d 7.25 7.25

**Souvenir Sheet**

2298 A380 $6 Self-portrait 5.50 5.50

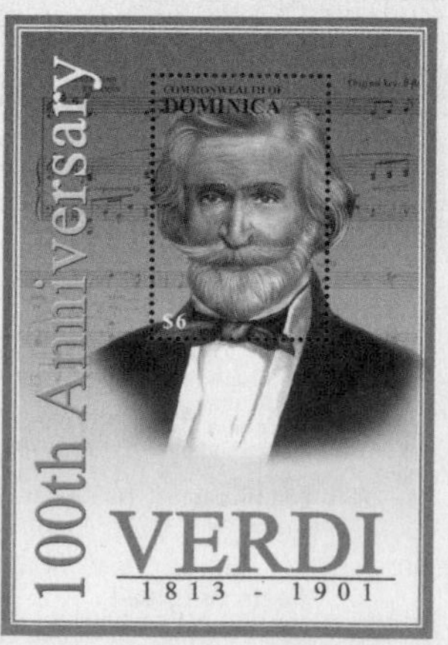

Giuseppe Verdi (1813-1901), Opera Composer — A381

No. 2299: a, Verdi. b, Lady Macbeth. c, Orchestra. d, Score.

**2001, May 15 Perf. 14**

2299 A381 $2 Sheet of 4, #a-d 7.25 7.25

**Souvenir Sheet**

2300 A381 $6 Verdi, score 5.50 5.50

Mushrooms A382

Designs: 15c, Cantharellus cibarius. 25c, Hygrocybe pratensis. 55c, Leccinum aurantiacum. $3, Mycena haematopus.

No. 2305, 90c, horiz.: a, Caesar's amanita. b, Agaricus augustus. c, Clitocybe nuda. d, Hygrocybe plavescens. e, Stropharia kaufmanii. f, Hygrophorus speciosus.

No. 2306, $2: a, Marasmiellus candidus. b, Calostoma cinnabarina. c, Cantharellus infundibuliformis. d, Hygrocybe punicea. e, Basket stinkhorn. f, Agrocybe praecox.

No. 2307, $5, Fly agaric, horiz. No. 2308, $5, Gymnopilus spectabilis, horiz.

**2001, June 18**

2301-2304 A382 Set of 4 4.50 4.50

**Sheets of 6, #a-f**

2305-2306 A382 Set of 2 18.00 18.00

**Souvenir Sheets**

2307-2308 A382 Set of 2 10.00 10.00

Mao Zedong (1893-1976) — A383

No. 2309 — Picture from: a, 1945. b, 1926. c, 1949.

$3, 1930.

**2001, May 15 Litho. Perf. 14**

2309 A383 $2 Sheet of 3, #a-c 5.25 5.25

**Souvenir Sheet**

2310 A383 $3 multi 2.75 2.75

Monet Paintings — A384

No. 2311, horiz.: a, The Basin of Argenteuil. b, The Bridge at Argenteuil. c, The Railway Bridge, Argenteuil. d, The Seine Bridge at Argenteuil.

$6, Woman with a Parasol — Madame Monet and Her Son.

**2001, May 15 Perf. 13¾**

2311 A384 $2 Sheet of 4, #a-d 7.25 7.25

**Souvenir Sheet**

2312 A384 $6 multi 5.25 5.25

Fauna — A385

No. 2313: a, St. Vincent parrot. b, Painted bunting. c, Jamaican giant anole. d, White-fronted capuchin. e, Strand racerunner. f, Agouti.

No. 2314: a, Cook's tree boa. b, Tamandua. c, Common iguana. d, Solenodon.

No. 2315, $5, Purple gallinule. No. 2316, $5, Rufous-tailed jacamar. No. 2317, $5, Ruby-throated hummingbird, horiz. No. 2318, $5, Bottlenose dolphins, horiz.

**2001, Sept. 3** *Perf. 14*

**2313** A385 $1.45 Sheet of 6, #a-f 8.75 8.75
**2314** A385 $2 Sheet of 4, #a-d 8.25 8.25

**Souvenir Sheets**

**2315-2318** A385 Set of 4 19.00 19.00

Birds — A386

Designs: 5c, Yellow warbler. 10c, Palmchat. 15c, Snowy cotinga. 20c, Blue-gray gnat-catcher. 25c, Belted kingfisher. 55c, Red-legged thrush. 65c, Bananaquit. 90c, Yellow-bellied sapsucker. $1, White-tailed tropicbird. $1.45, Ruby-throated hummingbird. $1.90, Painted bunting. $2, Great frigatebird. $5, Brown trembler. $10, Red-footed booby. $20, Sooty tern.

**2001, Sept. 3 Litho.** *Perf. 14¾x14*

| No. | Type | Value | | Unused | Used |
|---|---|---|---|---|---|
| **2319** | A386 | 5c | multi | .30 | .80 |
| **2320** | A386 | 10c | multi | .30 | .80 |
| **2321** | A386 | 15c | multi | .35 | .35 |
| **2322** | A386 | 20c | multi | .35 | .35 |
| **2323** | A386 | 25c | multi | .35 | .35 |
| **2324** | A386 | 55c | multi | .65 | .65 |
| **2325** | A386 | 65c | multi | .75 | .75 |
| **2326** | A386 | 90c | multi | 1.00 | .80 |
| **2327** | A386 | $1 | multi | 1.25 | 1.25 |
| **2328** | A386 | $1.45 | multi | 1.60 | 1.60 |
| **2329** | A386 | $1.90 | multi | 2.00 | 2.00 |
| **2330** | A386 | $2 | multi | 2.50 | 2.50 |
| **2331** | A386 | $5 | multi | 5.00 | 5.00 |
| **2332** | A386 | $10 | multi | 8.50 | 8.50 |
| **2333** | A386 | $20 | multi | 17.50 | 17.50 |
| | *Nos. 2319-2333 (15)* | | | 42.40 | 43.20 |

No. 2323 exists dated "2005."

See No. 2513.

Photomosaic of Queen Elizabeth II — A387

**2001, Nov. 15** *Perf. 14*

**2334** A387 $1 multi 1.00 1.00

Issued in sheets of 8.

Christmas — A388

Paintings by Giovanni Bellini: 25c, Madonna and Child. 65c, Madonna and Child, diff. 90c, Baptism of Christ. $1.20, Madonna and Child, diff. $4, Madonna and Child, diff.

$6, Madonna and Child with Sts. Catherine and Mary Magdalene.

**2001, Dec. 3**

**2335-2339** A388 Set of 5 6.75 6.75

**Souvenir Sheet**

**2340** A388 $6 multi 5.50 5.50

2002 World Cup Soccer Championships, Japan and Korea — A389

No. 2341, $2: a, US team, 1950. b, Poster, 1954. c, Poster, 1958. d, Zozimo, 1962. e, Gordon Banks, 1966. f, Pelé, 1970.

No. 2342, $2: a, Daniel Passarella, 1978. b, Paolo Rossi, 1982. c, Diego Maradona, 1986. d, Poster, 1990. e, Seo Jungulon, 1994. f, Jürgen Klinsmann, 1998.

No. 2343, $5, Face on World Cup, 1930. No. 2344, $5, Face and globe on Jules Rimet Trophy, 2002.

**2001, Dec. 13** *Perf. 13¾x14¼*

**Sheets of 6, #a-f**

**2341-2342** A389 Set of 2 21.00 21.00

**Souvenir Sheets**

*Perf. 14¼*

**2343-2344** A389 Set of 2 10.00 10.00

**Queen Mother Type of 1999 Redrawn**

No. 2345: a, In 1939. b, In Australia, 1958. c, At Badminton, 1982. d, Hatless, in 1982.

$6, In 1953.

**2001, Dec.** *Perf. 14*

**Yellow Orange Frames**

**2345** A340 $2 Sheet of 4, #a-d, + label 7.00 7.00

**Souvenir Sheet**

*Perf. 13¾*

**2346** A340 $6 multi 5.25 5.25

Queen Mother's 101st birthday. No. 2346 contains one 38x51mm stamp with a bluer backdrop than that found on No. 2161. Sheet margins of Nos. 2345-2346 lack embossing and gold arms and frames found on Nos. 2160-2161.

Souvenir Sheets

Betty Boop — A390

Betty Boop: No. 2347, $5, In chair, pink rose background. No. 2348, $5, Wearing blue blouse, in jungle. No. 2349, $5, With heart and stars, cat with film reel. No. 2350, $5, Wearing nurse's cap.

**2001, Oct. 1 Litho.** *Perf. 13¾*

**2347-2350** A390 Set of 4 18.00 18.00

The Three Stooges — A391

No. 2351: a, Man, Larry, Moe with sledge-hammer, Joe Besser. b, Larry, woman, Joe Besser, Moe. c, Joe Besser, Larry and Moe on hands and knees. d, Larry grabbing throat of woman holding Joe Besser and Moe. e, Joe Besser drinking from baby bottle, pony, Moe and Larry. f, Military policeman, Joe Besser, Larry, woman. g, Larry. h, Joe Besser. i, Moe.

No. 2352, $5, Moe and Larry, "On the air" sign. No. 2353, $5, Larry and pony.

**2001, Oct. 1 Litho.** *Perf. 13¾*

**2351** A391 $1 Sheet of 9, #a-i 8.00 8.00

**Souvenir Sheets**

**2352-2353** A391 Set of 2 9.00 9.00

Souvenir Sheet

New Year 2002 (Year of the Horse) — A392

No. 2354: a, Man with pole, horse. b, Horses grazing. c, Man currying horse. d, Horses with heads up.

**2001, Dec. 17** *Perf. 14*

**2354** A392 $1.65 Sheet of 4, #a-d 6.00 6.00

Reign of Queen Elizabeth II, 50th Anniv. — A393

No. 2355: a, Wearing blue coat. b, With Prince Philip. c, Wearing tiara. d, Wearing flowered hat.

$6, With Prince Philip, diff.

**2002, Feb. 6** *Perf. 14¼*

**2355** A393 $2 Sheet of 4, #a-d 7.00 7.00

**Souvenir Sheet**

**2356** A393 $6 multi 5.00 5.00

United We Stand — A394

**2002, Feb.** *Perf. 13½x13¼*

**2357** A394 $2 multi 1.50 1.50

Printed in sheets of 4.

Shirley Temple in "Just Around the Corner" — A395

No. 2358, horiz.: a, Temple, woman with dogs. b, Temple, man and woman. c, Temple and man. d, Boy eating turkey leg, Temple carving turkey. e, Temple with old man. f, Temple with group of boys.

No. 2359: a, Boy, Temple with purse. b, Man and Temple using fingers as guns. c, Temple and man. d, Temple cutting boy's hair.

$6, Temple with black man on toadstool.

**2002, Apr. 8** *Perf. 12¼*

**2358** A395 $1.90 Sheet of 6, #a-f 10.00 10.00
**2359** A395 $2 Sheet of 4, #a-d 7.25 7.25

**Souvenir Sheet**

**2360** A395 $6 multi 5.25 5.25

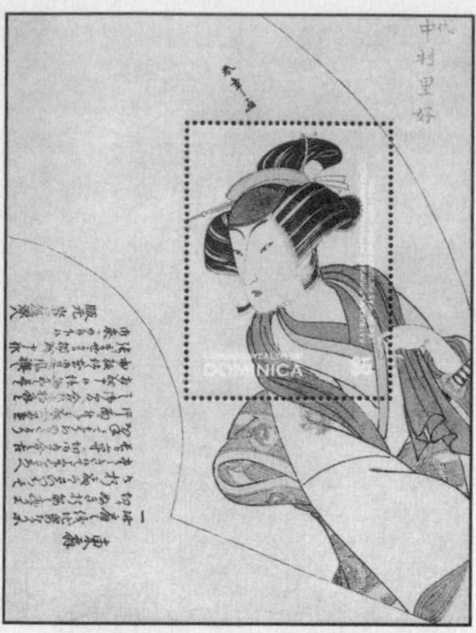

Japanese Art — A396

No. 2361, $1.20: a, The Courtesan Tsukioka of the Teahouse Hyogo-Ya, by Eisui Ichirakutei. b, Woman and Servant in the Snow, by Choki Eishosai. c, The Courtesan Shiratsuyu of the Teahouse Wakana-Ya, by Eisho Chokosai. d, Ohisa of the Takashima-Ya, by Toyokuni Utagawa. e, Woman and a Cat, by Kunimasa Utagawa. f, One of "Genre Scenes of Beauties," by Eisen Keisai.

No. 2362, $1.65: a, Women Inside and Outside a Mosquito Net, by Harushige Suzuki. b, Komachi at Shimizu, by Harushige Suzuki. c, Women Viewing Plum Blossoms, by Harunobu Suzuki. d, Women Cooling Themselves at Shijogawara in Kyoto, by Toyohiro Utagawa. e, Woman Reading a Letter, by Utamaro Kitagawa. f, Women Dressed for the Kashima Dance at the Niwaka Festival, by Utamaro Kitagawa.

No. 2363, $1.90: a, Actor Kiyotaro Iwai, by Kunimasa Utagawa. b, Actors Hiriji Otani III and Ryuzo Arashi, by Sharaku Toshusai. c, Actor Komazo Ichikawa II, by Shunko Katsukawa. d, Actors Yaozo Ichikawa and Hangoro Sakata III, by Sharaku Toshusai. e, Actor Torazo Tanimura, by Sharaku Toshusai. f, Actor Kiyotaro Iwai as Oishi, by Toyokuni Utagawa.

No. 2464, $5, Actor Riko Nakamura, by Shunsho Katsukawa. No. 2365, $5, Actors Hanshiro Iwai IV and Sojuro Sawamura III, by Kiyonaga Torii, horiz. No. 2366, $6, Ofuji, Daughter of the Motoyanagi-Ya, by Harunobu Suzuki.

**2002, June 17** ***Perf. 14¼***

**Sheets of 6, #a-f**

**2361-2363** A396 Set of 3 24.00 24.00

**Souvenir Sheets**

**2364-2366** A396 Set of 3 12.00 12.00

Souvenir Sheet

Intl. Year of Mountains — A397

No. 2367: a, Mt. Everest. b, Mt. Kilimanjaro. c, Mt. McKinley.

**2002, July 15** ***Perf. 14***

**2367** A397 $2 Sheet of 3, #a-c 5.00 5.00

2002 Winter Olympics, Salt Lake City A398

Designs: No. 2368, $2, Skiing. No. 2369, $2, Bobsled.

**2002, July 15** ***Perf. 13½***

**2368-2369** A398 Set of 2 3.50 3.50

*a.* Souvenir sheet, #2368-2369 3.50 3.50

First Solo Trans-Atlantic Flight, 75th Anniv. — A399

No. 2370: a, Charles Lindbergh and Spirit of St. Louis. b, Charles and Anne Morrow Lindbergh.

$6, Charles Lindbergh and Spirit of St. Louis, diff.

**2002, July 15** ***Perf. 14***

**2370** A399 $3 Sheet of 2, #a-b 5.00 5.00

**Souvenir Sheet**

**2371** A399 $6 multi 5.00 5.00

Popeye in New York — A400

No. 2372, $1: a, Olive Oyl. b, Brutus. c, Sweet Pea. d, Wimpy. e, Jeep. f, Popeye.

No. 2373, $1.90: a, Popeye and Olive Oyl, giraffe at Bronx Zoo. b, Popeye and Olive Oyl, Statue of Liberty. c, Popeye, Olive Oyl, Empire State Building. d, Popeye skating at Rockefeller Center. e, Popeye at Yankee Stadium. f, Popeye helping firefighters.

No. 2374, $6, Popeye, Atlas Statue, Rockefeller Center. No. 2375, $6, Popeye, Olive Oyl and Radio City Music Hall Rockettes, horiz.

**2002, July 22**

**Sheets of 6, #a-f**

**2372-2373** A400 Set of 2 15.00 15.00

**Souvenir Sheets**

**2374-2375** A400 Set of 2 10.50 10.50

20th World Scout Jamboree, Thailand — A401

No. 2376: a, Lord Robert Baden-Powell (facing forward). b, Lady Olave Baden-Powell. c, Maceo Johnson.

$6, Lord Baden-Powell (profile).

**2002, July 15 Litho.** ***Perf. 14¼x14***

**2376** A401 $3 Sheet of 3, #a-c 8.00 8.00

**Souvenir Sheet**

**2377** A401 $6 multi 5.25 5.25

Birds, Insects, Moths and Whales — A402

No. 2378, $1.50, vert. — Birds: a, Brown trembler. b, Snowy ctinga. c, Bananaquit. d, Painted bunting. e, Belted kingfisher. f, Ruby-throated hummingbird.

No. 2379, $1.50, vert. — Insects: a, Field cricket. b, Migratory grasshopper. c, Honey bee. d, Hercules beetle. e, Black ant. f, Cicada.

No. 2380, $1.50, vert. — Moths: a, Carolina sphinx. b, White-lined sphinx. c, Orizaba silkmoth. d, Hieroglyphic moth. e, Hickory tussock moth. f, Diva moth.

No. 2381, $1.50, vert. — Whales: a, Sei. b, Killer. c, Blue. d, White. e, Pygmy. f, Sperm.

No. 2382, $6, Yellow-bellied sapsucker. No. 2383, $6, Bumble bee. No. 2384, $6, Ornate moth. No. 2385, $6, Gray whale.

**2002, July 29** ***Perf. 14***

**Sheets of 6, #a-f**

**2378-2381** A402 Set of 4 28.00 28.00

**Souvenir Sheets**

**2382-2385** A402 Set of 4 22.00 22.00

A403

A404

Amphilex 2002 Intl. Stamp Exhibition, Amsterdam — A405

No. 2386 — Dutch Nobel Prize winners: a, Willem Einthoven, Medicine, 1924. b, Nobel Economics medal. c, Peter J. W. Debye, Chemistry, 1936. d, Frits Zernike, Physics, 1953. e, Jan Tinbergen, Economics, 1969. f, Simon van der Meer, Physics, 1984.

No. 2387 — Dutch lighthouses: a, Marken. b, Harlingen. c, Den Oever. d, De Ven. e, Urk. f, Oosterleek.

No. 2388 — Traditional women's costumes: a, South Holland woman with small white head covering (facing forward). b, Zeeland woman with large white head covering (facing backwards). c, Limburg woman with black scarf.

**2002, Aug. 30** ***Perf. 13½x13¼***

**2386** A403 $1.50 Sheet of 6, #a-f 8.00 8.00

**2387** A404 $1.50 Sheet of 6, #a-f 8.00 8.00

***Perf. 13½***

**2388** A405 $3 Sheet of 3, #a-c 8.00 8.00

Intl. Year of Ecotourism A406

Island scenes and cartoon characters: 45c, Detective H2O. 50c, Factman. 55c, B.B. 60c, Stanley the Starfish. 90c, Toxi. $1.20, Adopt. $6, Litterbit.

**2002, Oct. 16** ***Perf. 14¼***

**2389-2394** A406 Set of 6 3.25 3.25

**Souvenir Sheet**

**2395** A406 $6 multi 5.00 5.00

Elvis Presley (1935-77) A407

**2002, Oct. 28** ***Perf. 13¾***

**2396** A407 $1.50 multi 1.10 1.10

Printed in sheets of 6 stamps with slightly differing frames.

Amerigo Vespucci (1454-1512), Explorer — A408

No. 2397: a, Compass rose. b, Vespucci with map. c, Map scroll.

$5, Two men.

**2002, Nov. 28** ***Perf. 13¾***

**2397** A408 $3 Sheet of 3, #a-c 8.00 8.00

**Souvenir Sheet**

***Perf. 14***

**2398** A408 $5 multi 4.50 4.50

No. 2397 contains three 50x38mm stamps.

Pres. John F. Kennedy (1917-63) — A409

No. 2399, $1.90: a, Wearing military uniform. b, With red denomination at UL. c, With blue denomination at UR. d, Wearing tan suit.

No. 2400, $1.90 (denominations at UL in blue): a, Wearing red tie. b, Wearing blue tie (profile). c, Wearing black tie. d, With hand on chin.

**2002, Dec. 16** ***Perf. 14***

**Sheets of 4, #a-d**

**2399-2400** A409 Set of 2 13.50 13.50

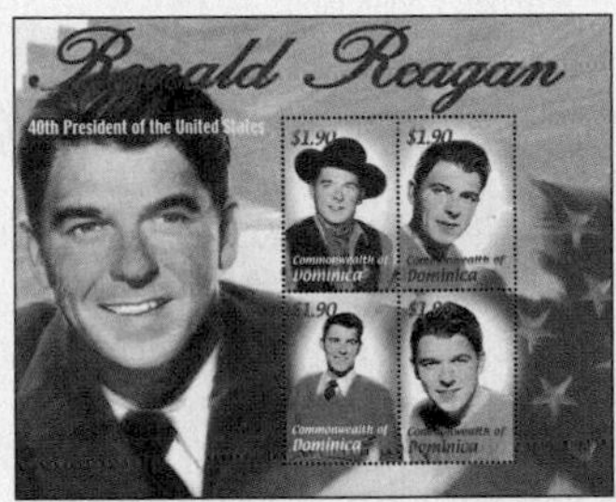


Pres. Ronald Reagan — A410

No. 2401, $1.90: a, Wearing cowboy hat. b, Wearing blue green sweater. c, Wearing red sweater. d, Wearing blue sweater.

No. 2402, $1.90, horiz.: a, Wearing blue shirt, and with wife, Nancy. b, Nancy and US flag. c, Ronald. d, Wearing pink shirt, and with wife.

**2002, Dec. 16** **Litho.** ***Perf. 14***

**Sheets of 4, #a-d**

**2401-2402** A410 Set of 2 13.50 13.50

Princess Diana (1961-97) — A411

No. 2403 — Various depictions of Princess Diana with background colors of: a, Tan. b, Pink. c, Light blue. d, Light green.

**2002, Dec. 16**

**2403** A411 $1.90 Sheet of 4, #a-d 7.00 7.00

**Souvenir Sheet**

**2404** A411 $5 multi 4.50 4.50

Elizabeth "Ma Pampo" Israel, 128th Birthday — A412

**2003, Jan. 27** ***Perf. 13½x13¼***

**2405** A412 90c multi .70 .70

New Year 2003 (Year of the Ram) — A413

**2003, Feb. 10** ***Perf. 13¾***

**2406** A413 $1.65 multi 1.25 1.25

Printed in sheets of 4.

**Souvenir Sheets**

Science Fiction — A414

Designs: No. 2407, $6, Mayan calendar. No. 2408, $6, Atlas. No. 2409, $6, Confucius. No. 2410, $6, Nazca Lines. No. 2411, $6, Pres. Franklin D. Roosevelt and Pres. John F. Kennedy. No. 2412, $6, Zoroaster.

**2003, Feb. 10** ***Perf. 13¼***

**2407-2412** A414 Set of 6 27.50 27.50

A415

Coronation of Queen Elizabeth II, 50th Anniv. — A416

No. 2413: a, Wearing white dress, no crown. b, Wearing black robe. c, Wearing crown.

$6, Wearing crown, diff. $20, Wearing red robe.

**2003** **Litho.** ***Perf. 14***

**2413** A415 $3 Sheet of 3, #a-c 6.25 6.25

**Souvenir Sheet**

**2414** A415 $6 multi 4.25 4.25

**Miniature Sheet**

**Litho. & Embossed**

***Perf. 13¼x13***

**2415** A416 $20 gold & multi 14.00 14.00

Issued: Nos. 2413-2414, 5/13; No. 2415, 2/24.

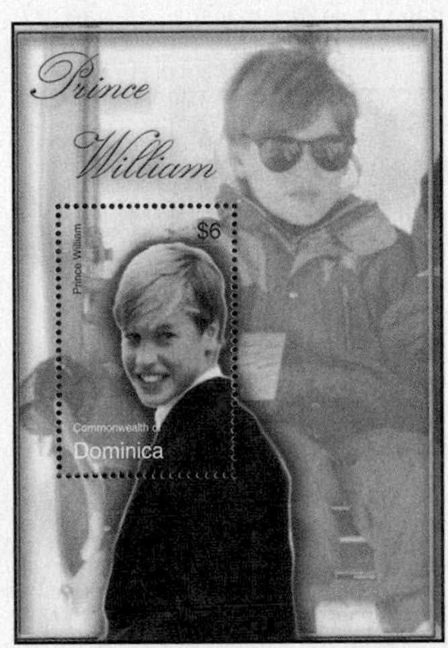


Prince William, 21st Birthday — A417

No. 2416: a, Wearing dark blue shirt. b, Wearing blue suit, holding flowers. c, In polo uniform.

$6, Wearing black suit.

**2003, June 21** **Litho.** ***Perf. 14***

**2416** A417 $3 Sheet of 3, #a-c 6.50 6.50

**Souvenir Sheet**

**2417** A417 $6 multi 4.50 4.50

Intl. Year of Fresh Water — A418

No. 2418: a, Trafalgar Falls. b, YS Falls. c, Dunn's River.

$6, Annandale Falls.

**2003, June 21** ***Perf. 13½***

**2418** A418 $3 Sheet of 3, #a-c 6.75 6.75

**Souvenir Sheet**

**2419** A418 $6 multi 4.50 4.50

Teddy Bears, Cent. — A419

No. 2420 — Bear with: a, Purple shirt. b, Pink shirt and party favor. c, Green shirt and party favor. d, Black hat. e, Purple hat. f, Pink shirt and birthday cake.

No. 2421 — Bear with: a, Reindeer sweater, text at top. b, Santa Claus costume, text at top. c, Santa Claus costume, text at bottom. d, Reindeer sweater, text at bottom.

**2003, June 21** ***Perf. 13½***

**2420** A419 $1.65 Sheet of 6, #a-f 7.50 7.50

**2421** A419 $2 Sheet of 4, #a-d 6.00 6.00

No. 2421 contains four 37x51mm stamps.

General Motors Automobiles — A420

No. 2422, $2 — Cadillacs: a, 1903 Model A Runabout. b, 1912 Model 30. c, 1918 Type 57 Victoria Coupe. d, 1927 Lasalle Convertible Coupe.

No. 2423, $2 — Corvettes: a, 1953. b, 1956. c, 1957. d, 1962.

No. 2424, $5, 1933 Cadillac 355-C V8 sedan. No. 2425, $5, 1959 Corvette.

**2003, June 21** ***Perf. 13¼***

**Sheets of 4, #a-d**

**2422-2423** A420 Set of 2 12.00 12.00

**Souvenir Sheets**

**2424-2425** A420 Set of 2 7.50 7.50

Tour de France Bicycle Race, Cent. — A421

No. 2426 — Champions: a, Firmin Lambot, 1919. b, Phillippe Thys, 1920. c, Léon Scieur, 1921. d, Lambot, 1922.

$5, François Faber.

**2003, June 21**

**2426** A421 $2 Sheet of 4, #a-d 6.00 6.00

**Souvenir Sheet**

**2427** A421 $5 multi 3.75 3.75

History of Aviation — A422

No. 2428: a, Sputnik, first orbiting satellite, 1957. b, Yuri Gagarin, first man in space, 1961. c, Neil Armstrong, first man on the Moon, 1969. d, Skylab 1, 1973.

$6, Flight over Mt. Everest, 1933.

**2003, June 21** ***Perf. 14***

**2428** A422 $2 Sheet of 4, #a-d 6.50 6.50

**Souvenir Sheet**

**2429** A422 $6 multi 5.00 5.00

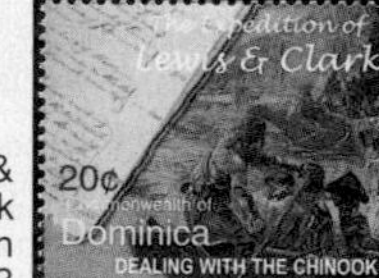


Lewis & Clark Expedition A423

Designs: 20c, Dealing with the Chinook Indians. 50c, Compass used in expedition. 55c, Rocky Mountains. 65c, Medals presented to the Indians, vert. 90c, First encounter with grizzly bear. $1, Befriending Shoshone Indians. $2, Lewis after the expedition, vert. $4, Lewis & Clark, vert.

No. 2438, $5, Meriwether Lewis, vert. No. 2439, $5, William Clark, vert.

**2003, June 21**

**2430-2437** A423 Set of 8 7.50 7.50

**Souvenir Sheets**

**2438-2439** A423 Set of 2 7.00 7.00

2002 World Cup Soccer Championships, Japan and Korea — A424

No. 2440, $1.45: a, Danny Mills. b, Paul Scholes. c, Darius Vassell. d, Michael Owen. e, Emile Heskey. f, Rio Ferdinand.

No. 2441, $1.45: a, Bobby Moore. b, Roger Hunt. c, Gordon Banks. d, Bobby Charlton. e, Alan Ball. f, Geoff Hurst.

No. 2442, $3: a, Ashley Cole. b, David Seaman.

No. 2443, $3: a, Sven-Goran Eriksson. b, Nikki Butt.

No. 2444, $3: a, Robbie Fowler. b, Sol Campbell.

No. 2445, $3: a, Charlton, Ball and Hunt. b, Nobby Stiles.

No. 2446, $3: a, Franz Beckenbauer. b, Oliver Kahn.

**2003, June 21** ***Perf. 13¼***

**Sheets of 6, #a-f**

**2440-2441** A424 Set of 2 11.00 11.00

**Souvenir Sheets of 2, #a-b**

**2442-2446** A424 Set of 5 20.00 20.00

CARICOM, 30th Anniv. — A425

**2003, July 25** ***Perf. 13½***

**2447** A425 $1 multi .75 .75

Christmas A426

Painting details: 50c, Madonna and Child with the Young St. John, by Correggio. 90c, Madonna in Glory with the Christ Child and Sts. Frances and Alvise with the Donor, by Titian. $1.45, Madonna and Child with Angels Playing Musical Instruments, by Correggio. $3, Madonna of the Cherries, by Titian.

$6, Holy Family with John the Baptist, by Andrea del Sarto.

**2003, Nov. 17** **Litho.** ***Perf. 14¼***

**2448-2451** A426 Set of 4 4.50 4.50

**Souvenir Sheet**

**2452** A426 $6 multi 4.50 4.50

New Year 2004 (Year of the Monkey) — A427

No. 2453: a, Orange monkey, hindquarters of brown monkey. b, Monkey with brown face. c, Brown monkey drinking water. d, Monkey with blue face.

**2004, Jan. 5** **Litho.** ***Perf. 14***

**2453** A427 $1.50 Sheet of 4, #a.-d. 4.50 4.50

Paintings of Pablo Picasso — A428

No. 2454, vert.: a, Portrait of Manuel Pallarés. b, Woman with Vase of Flowers. c, Woman with a Fan (Fernande). d, Portrait of Clovis Sagot.

$5, Brick Factory at Torosa (The Factory).

**2004, Mar. 8** ***Perf. 14¼***

**2454** A428 $1 Sheet of 4, #a.-d. 3.00 3.00

***Imperf***

**2455** A428 $5 multi 3.75 3.75

No. 2454 contains four 38x50mm stamps.

Paintings of Paul Gauguin — A429

No. 2456: a, Village Tahitien avec la Femme en Marche. b, La Barriere. c, Bonjour, Monsieur Gauguin. d, Vegetation Tropicale.

$5, Petites Bretonnes Devant la Mer.

**2004, Mar. 8** ***Perf. 14¼***

**2456** A429 $2 Sheet of 4, #a.-d. 6.00 6.00

***Imperf***

**2457** A429 $5 multi 3.75 3.75

No. 2456 contains four 38x50mm stamps.

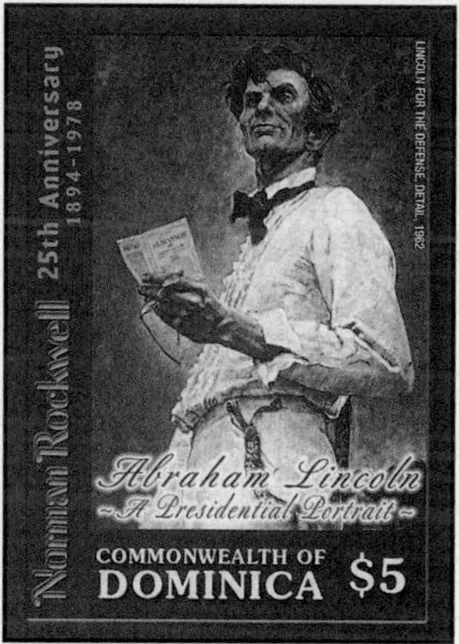


Paintings of Presidents by Norman Rockwell — A430

No. 2458: a, Dwight D. Eisenhower. b, John F. Kennedy. c, Lyndon B. Johnson. d, Richard M. Nixon.

$5, Abraham Lincoln.

**2004, Mar. 8** ***Perf. 14¼***

**2458** A430 $2 Sheet of 4, #a.-d. 6.00 6.00

***Imperf***

**2459** A430 $5 multi 3.75 3.75

No. 2458 contains four 38x50mm stamps.

Paintings of James McNeill Whistler — A431

Designs: 50c, Symphony in White No. 3. $1, The Artist's Studio, vert. $1.65, The Thames in Ice, vert. No. 2463, $2, Arrangement in Black: Portrait of F. R. Leyland, vert.

No. 2464, $2, vert.: a, Arrangement in Brown & Black: Portrait of Miss Rosa Corder. b, Harmony in Red: Lamplight. c, Symphony in Flesh Color & Pink: Portrait of Mrs. Frances Leyland. d, Arrangement in Yellow & Gray: Effie Deans.

$5, Harmony in Gray and Green: Miss Cicely Alexander, vert.

**2004, Mar. 8** ***Perf. 14¼***

**2460-2463** A431 Set of 4 4.00 4.00

***Perf. 13½***

**2464** A431 $2 Sheet of 4, #a-d 6.00 6.00

***Imperf***

**Size: 71x103mm**

**2465** A431 $5 multi 3.75 3.75

No. 2464 contains four 35x70mm stamps.

Fish A432

Designs: 20c, Banded butterflyfish. 25c, Queen angelfish. 55c, Porkfish. No. 2469, $5, Redband parrotfish.

No. 2470: a, Beaugregory. b, Porkfish, diff. c, Bicolor cherubfish. d, Rock beauty. e, Blackfin snapper. f, Blue tang.

No. 2471, $5, Indigo hamlet.

**2004, Mar. 8** ***Perf. 14¼x14¾***

**2466-2469** A432 Set of 4 4.50 4.50

***Perf. 14***

**2470** A432 $2 Sheet of 6, #a-f 9.00 9.00

**Souvenir Sheet**

**2471** A432 $5 multi 3.75 3.75

Nos. 2470-2471 each contain 42x28mm stamps.

Shells A433

Designs: 20c, Siratus perelegans. 90c, Polystira albida. $1.45, Cypraea cervus. $2, Strombus gallus.

No. 2476: a, Strombus pugilis. b, Cittarium pica. c, Distorsio clathrata. d, Melongena morio. e, Prunum labiata. f, Chione paphia.

$5, Strombus alatus, vert.

**2004, Mar. 8** ***Perf. 14¼x14¾***

**2472-2475** A433 Set of 4 3.50 3.50

***Perf. 14***

**2476** A433 $1.90 Sheet of 6, #a-f 8.50 8.50

**Souvenir Sheet**

**2477** A433 $5 multi 3.75 3.75

No. 2476 contain six 42x28mm stamps; No. 2477 contains one 28x42mm stamp.

Orchids — A434

Designs: 25c, Epidendrum pseudepidendrum. 55c, Aspasia epidendroides. $1.50, Cochleanthes discolor. $4, Brassavola nodosa.

No. 2482: a, Laelia anceps. b, Caularthron bicornutum. c, Cattleya velutina. d, Cattleya warneri. e, Oncidium splendidum. f, Psychlis atropurpurea.

$5, Maxillaria cuculata, vert.

**2004, Mar. 8** ***Perf. 14¼x14¾***

**2478-2481** A434 Set of 4 4.75 4.75

***Perf. 14***

**2482** A434 $1.90 Sheet of 6, #a-f 8.50 8.50

**Souvenir Sheet**

**2483** A434 $5 multi 3.75 3.75

No. 2482 contains six 42x28mm stamps; No. 2483 contains one 28x42mm stamp.

Butterflies — A435

Designs: 50c, Small flambeau. 90c, Tiger pierid. $1, White peacock. No. 2469, $2, Cramer's mesene.

No. 2488, $2: a, Figure-of-eight. b, Orange theope. c, Clorinde. d, Grecian shoemaker. e, Orange-barred sulphur. f, Common morpho.

$5, Giant swallowtail, vert.

**2004, Mar. 8** *Perf. 14¼x14¾*

**2484-2487** A435 Set of 4 3.00 3.00

*Perf. 14*

**2488** A435 $2 Sheet of 6, #a-f 8.00 8.00

**Souvenir Sheets**

**2489** A435 $5 multi 3.75 3.75

No. 2488 contains six 42x28mm stamps; No. 2489 contains one 28x42mm stamp.

Olympic Gold Medalists A436

Designs: 20c, Elizabeth Robinson, Amsterdam, 1928. 25c, Károly Takács, London, 1948. 55c, Bob Beamon, Mexico City, 1968. 65c, Mildred Didrikson, Los Angeles, 1932. $1, Ville Ritola, Paris, 1924. $1.65, Alfred Hajós (Guttman), Athens, 1896. $2, Paavo Nurmi, Antwerp, 1920. $4, Nedo Nadi, Antwerp, 1920.

**2004, Apr. 12** *Perf. 13¼*

**2490-2497** A436 Set of 8 7.75 7.75

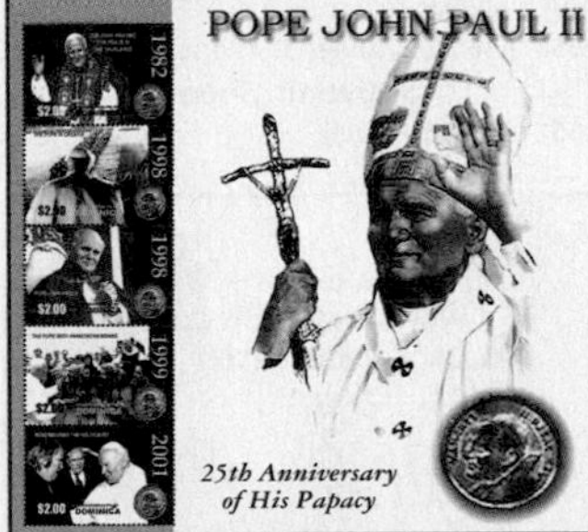

Election of Pope John Paul II, 25th Anniv. (in 2003) — A437

No. 2498: a, Praying for peace in Falkland Islands, 1982. b, In Croatia, 1998. c, Seated, 1998. d, With Franciscan monks, 1999. e, Remembering the Holocaust, 2001.

**2004, June 21** **Litho.** *Perf. 14*

**2498** A437 $2 Sheet of 5, #a-e 7.50 7.50

European Soccer Championships, Portugal — A438

No. 2499, vert.: a, Jose Luis Villalonga. b, Lev Yashin. c, Marcelino Martinez. d, Santiago Bernabeu Stadium.

$6, 1964 Spain team.

**2004, June 21** *Perf. 14*

**2499** A438 $2 Sheet of 4, #a-d 6.00 6.00

**Souvenir Sheet**

*Perf. 14¼*

**2500** A438 $6 multi 4.50 4.50

No. 2499 contains four 28x42mm stamps.

Trains — A439

No. 2501, $1: a, Engine #22, V7 T4-4-0, V7T4-6-0. b, Don J12. c, Baldwin 2-D-D. d, Southern Engine #20. e, 143-890 2DB class electric locomotive. f, Engine #1.

No. 2502, $1: a, Canadian Pacific freight train. b, Queensland Rail IM U railroad. c, Green and white Shinkansen locomotive. d, Amtrak locomotive. e, Shinkansen locomotive in station. f, YPDMU rail cars.

No. 2503, $1: a, Santa Fe Railroad locomotive. b, Via Rail train, Canada. c, Two Conrail road switchers. d, Strasburg Railroad #90. e, Deltic diesel-electric engine. f, Brighton Belle.

No. 2504, $6, Golsdorf two cylinder compound locomotive 4-4-0. No. 2505, $6, Southern Pacific 4449 4-8-4. No. 2506, $6, White, yellow and blue Shinkansen.

**2004, July 12** *Perf. 13¼x13½*

**Sheets of 6, #a-f**

**2501-2503** A439 Set of 3 13.50 13.50

**Souvenir Sheets**

**2504-2506** A439 Set of 3 13.50 13.50

D-Day, 60th Anniv. A440

Designs: $1, Eddie Hannath. $4, Pres. Franklin D. Roosevelt.

No. 2509: a, Rangers make their way towards the cliffs of Pointe du Hoc. b, Rangers begin scaling the cliffs of Pointe du Hoc. c, British troops advance on Sword Beach. d, An AVRE Petard heads inland off Sword Beach.

$6, British troops landing on Sword Beach.

**2004, July 22** *Perf. 14*

**Stamp + Label (#2507-2508)**

**2507-2508** A440 Set of 2 3.75 3.75

**2509** A440 $2 Sheet of 4, #a-d 6.00 6.00

**Souvenir Sheet**

**2510** A440 $6 multi 4.50 4.50

George Herman "Babe" Ruth (1895-1948), Baseball Player — A441

No. 2511: a, Swinging bat. b, Swinging bat, looking up. c, Holding three bats. d, Hand on knee.

**2004, Aug. 18** *Perf. 13½x13¼*

**2511** A441 $2 Sheet of 4, #a-d 6.00 6.00

Marilyn Monroe (1926-62), Actress — A442

No. 2512: a, Wearing earrings and necklace. b, Wearing earrings. c, Wearing no earrings or necklace. d, Wearing necklace.

**2004, Aug. 18**

**2512** A442 $2 Sheet of 4, #a-d 6.00 6.00

**Bird Type of 2001**

**2004, Sept. 3** *Perf. 14¾x14*

**2513** A386 50c Baltimore oriole .45 .45

Exists dated "2005."

Queen Juliana of the Netherlands (1909-2004) A443

**2004, Sept. 21** *Perf. 13¼*

**2514** A443 $2 multi 1.50 1.50

Printed in sheets of 6.

Intl. Year of Peace — A444

No. 2515: a, Mother Teresa, UN emblem. b, Mother Teresa feeding poor. c, Dove.

**2004, Sept. 21** *Perf. 14*

**2515** A444 $2 Sheet of 3, #a-c 4.50 4.50

**Souvenir Sheet**

Deng Xiaoping (1904-97) and Mao Zedong (1893-1976), Chinese Leaders — A445

**2004, Sept. 21** *Perf. 14*

**2516** A445 $6 multi 4.50 4.50

National Soccer Team — A446

**2004, Nov. 8** **Litho.** *Perf. 12*

**2517** A446 90c multi .70 .70

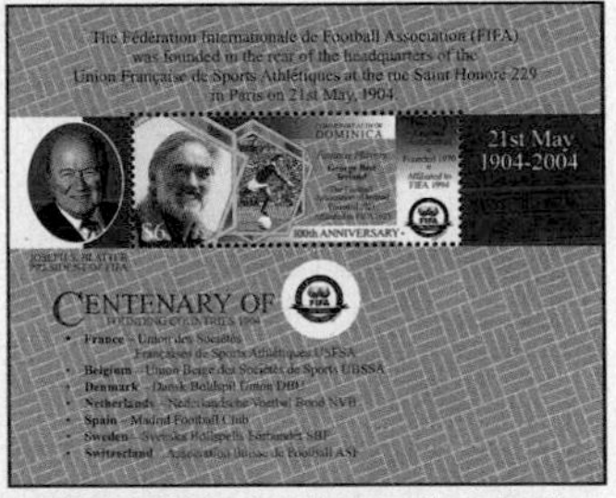

FIFA (Fédération Internationale de Football Association), Cent. — A447

No. 2518: a, Ferenc Puskas. b, Rivaldo. c, Carsten Jancker. d, Johan Cruyff.

$6, George Best.

**2004, Nov. 8** *Perf. 12¾x12½*

**2518** A447 $2 Sheet of 4, #a-d 6.00 6.00

**Souvenir Sheet**

**2519** A447 $6 multi 4.50 4.50

Worldwide Fund for Nature (WWF) — A448

No. 2520: a, Green-throated Carib (denomination in blue). b, Purple-throated Carib (denomination in white). c, Green-throated Carib (denomination in white). d, Purple-throated Carib (denomination in red).

**2005, Jan. 10** *Perf. 14*

**2520** A448 $2 Block of 4, #a-d 5.50 5.50

*e.* Miniature sheet, 2 each #2520a-2520d 11.00 11.00

Prehistoric Animals — A449

No. 2521, $2: a, Tyrannosaurus rex. b, Velociraptor. c, Stegosaurus. d, Psittacosaurus.

No. 2522, $2: a, Mammuthus columbi. b, Spinosaurus. c, Ankylosaurus. d, Mammuthus primigenius.

No. 2523, $2: a, Pterodactylus. b, Pteranodon. c, Sordes. d, Caudiptheryx zoui.

$3, Compsognathus. $5, Archaeopteryx. $6, Mammuthus primigenius, diff.

**2005, Jan. 10** *Perf. 12¾*

**Sheets of 4, #a-d**

**2521-2523** A449 Set of 3 18.00 18.00

**Souvenir Sheets**

**2524-2526** A449 Set of 3 10.50 10.50

Birds A450

Designs: 25c, Brown booby. 90c, Brown pelican. $1, Red-billed tropicbird. $4, Northern gannet.

No. 2531: a, Great egret. b, Black-necked grebe. c, Turkey vulture. d, Snail kite.

$6, Red knot.

**2005, Jan. 10** *Perf. 14*

**2527-2530** A450 Set of 4 4.50 4.50

**2531** A450 $2 Sheet of 4, #a-d 5.75 5.75

**Souvenir Sheet**

**2532** A450 $6 multi 4.00 4.00

Mushrooms — A451

No. 2533: a, Cortinarius mucosus. b, Cortinarius splendens. c, Cortinarius rufo-olivaceus. d, Inocybe erubescens.

$6, Split fibercap.

**2005, Jan. 10**

**2533** A451 $2 Sheet of 4, #a-d 6.00 6.00

**Souvenir Sheet**

**2534** A451 $6 multi 4.50 4.50

Miniature Sheet

Flowers — A452

No. 2535: a, Sweetshrub. b, Pink turtleheads. c, Flowering quince. d, Water lily.

$6, Glory of the snow, vert.

**2005, Jan. 10** **Litho.** *Perf. 14*

**2535** A452 $2 Sheet of 4, #a-d 6.00 6.00

**Souvenir Sheet**

**2535E** A452 $6 multi 4.50 4.50

New Year 2005 (Year of the Rooster) — A453

**2005, Jan. 24** *Perf. 12¾x12½*

**2536** A453 $1 shown .75 .75

**Souvenir Sheet**

*Perf. 12*

**2537** A453 $4 Roosters 3.00 3.00

No. 2537 contains one 56x36mm stamp.

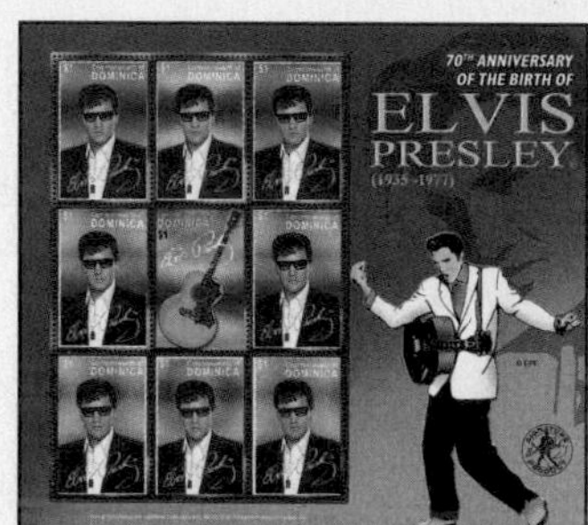

A454

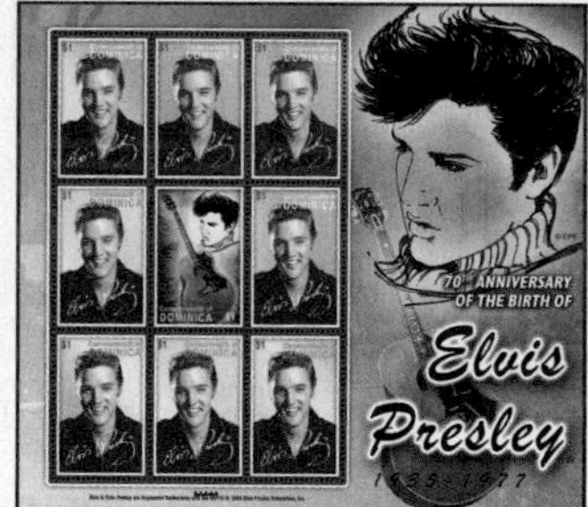

Elvis Presley (1935-77) — A455

Elvis Presley (1935-77) — A455a

No. 2538: a, Green background under country name and near shirt collar. b, Guitar. c, Large red violet areas at side of head. d, Dark green background under country name, blue background near shirt collar. e, Purple background near shirt collar. f, Small red violet areas at side of head.

No. 2539: a, Country name in white, blue background at UR. b, Country name in white, pink background at UR. c, Country name in white, orange background at UR. d, Country name in blue, green background at UR. e, Presley and guitar. f, Country name in blue, yellow background at UR. g, Country name in blue, blue background at UR.

No. 2539H illustration reduced.

**2005, Apr. 5** *Perf. 13½*

**2538** A454 $1 Sheet of 9, #a-c, 2 each #d-f 6.75 6.75

**2539** A455 $1 Sheet of 9, #a, c, e-g, 2 each #b, d 6.75 6.75

**Litho. & Embossed**

***Variable Serpentine Die Cut***

**Without Gum**

**2539H** A455a $20 gold & multi 14.00 14.00

No. 2539H was not available in the market-place until 2006.

Miniature Sheet

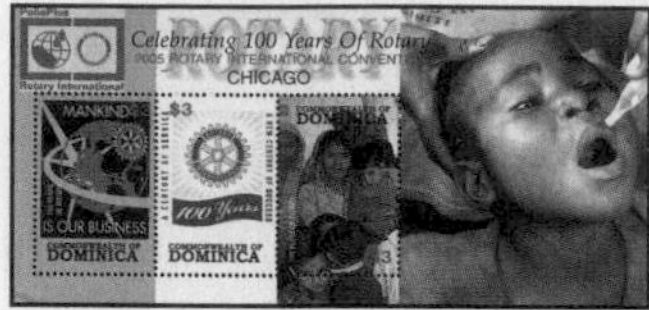

Rotary International, Cent. — A456

No. 2540: a, Globe and Rotary emblem. b, Rotary emblem. c, Women and children.

**2005, Sept. 7** *Perf. 12½x12¾*

**2540** A456 $3 Sheet of 3, #a-c 6.75 6.75

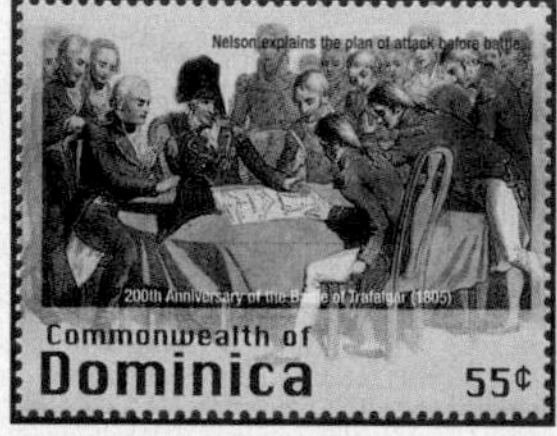

Battle of Trafalgar, Bicent. — A457

Designs: 55c, Admiral Horatio Nelson explaining plan of attack before battle. 65c, Orient explodes during the Battle of the Nile, vert. $1, Nelson and his men board San Nicolas during the Battle of Cape St. Vincent, vert. $2, Ships Agamemnon and Ca Ira in battle.

$6, HMS Victory.

**2005, Sept. 7** *Perf. 13¼*

**2541-2544** A457 Set of 4 3.25 3.25

**Souvenir Sheet**

*Perf. 12*

**2545** A457 $6 multi 4.50 4.50

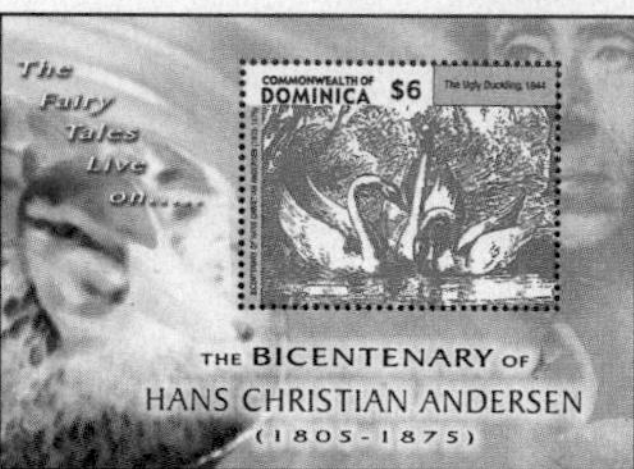

Hans Christian Andersen (1805-75), Author — A458

No. 2546: a, The Swineherd. b, The Nightingale. c, The Fir Tree.

$6, The Ugly Duckling.

**2005, Sept. 7** *Perf. 12¾*

**2546** A458 $2 Sheet of 3, #a-c 4.50 4.50

**Souvenir Sheet**

*Perf. 12*

**2547** A458 $6 multi 4.50 4.50

No. 2546 contains three 42x28mm stamps.

Friedrich von Schiller (1759-1805), Writer — A459

No. 2548, vert. — Schiller and German Democratic Republic stamps: a, #241. b, #242. c, #243.

$6, Statue of Schiller.

**2005, Sept. 7** *Perf. 12¾*

**2548** A459 $3 Sheet of 3, #a-c 6.75 6.75

**Souvenir Sheet**

**2549** A459 $6 multi 4.50 4.50

Jules Verne (1828-1905), Writer — A460

No. 2550: a, Men, dog and rooster in space. b, Astronauts. c, Men looking at undersea creature. d, Submarine.

$6, Portrait of Verne.

**2005, Sept. 7**

**2550** A460 $2 Sheet of 4, #a-d 6.00 6.00

**Souvenir Sheet**

**2551** A460 $6 multi 4.50 4.50

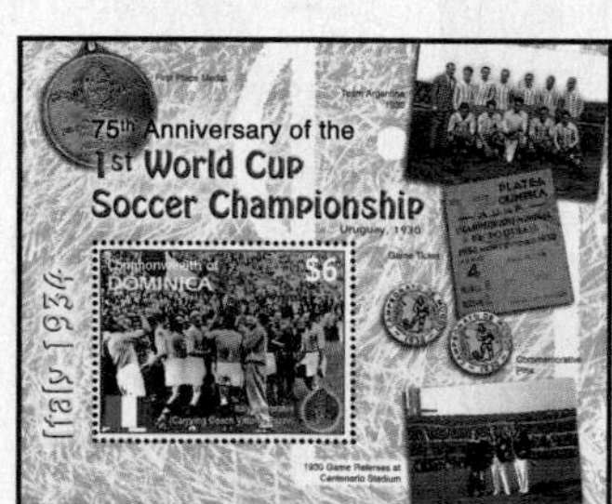

World Cup Soccer Championships, 75th Anniv. — A461

No. 2552: a, 1934 Italy team. b, Scene from 1934 Italy victory over Czechoslovakia. c, Flaminio Stadium. d, Angelos Schiavo.

$6, Italian team celebrating.

**2005, Sept. 7** *Perf. 12*

**2552** A461 $2 Sheet of 4, #a-d 6.00 6.00

**Souvenir Sheet**

**2553** A461 $6 multi 4.50 4.50

Christmas — A462

Painting details: 25c, Madonna and Child with Two Angels, by Sandro Botticelli. 50c, Madonna and Child with Angels, by Botticelli. 65c, Madonna and Child, by Pietro Lorenzetti. 90c, Madonna del Roseto, by Botticelli. $1.20, Adoration of the Magi, by Lorenzetti. $3, Madonna in Glory with the Seraphim, by Botticelli.

$5, Madonna of Frari, by Titian, horiz.

**2005, Nov. 15** ***Perf. 12¾***

**2554-2559** A462 Set of 6 5.00 5.00

**Souvenir Sheet**

**2560** A462 $5 multi 3.75 3.75

Pope John Paul II (1920-2005) and Princess Diana (1961-97) — A463

**2005** ***Perf. 13½x13¼***

**2561** A463 $3 multi 2.25 2.25

Pope Benedict XVI — A464

**2005** **Litho.** ***Perf. 13½x13¼***

**2562** A464 $2 multi 1.50 1.50

Printed in sheets of 4.

Souvenir Sheet

New Year 2006 (Year of the Dog) — A465

No. 2563 — Dog figurines with background colors of: a, Pale green and green. b, Orange and pink. c, Rose pink and yellow.

**2006, Jan. 3** ***Perf. 13¼x13½***

**2563** A465 $1 Sheet of 3, #a-c 2.25 2.25

Miniature Sheets

National Basketball Association Players and Team Emblems — A466

No. 2564, 90c: a, Orlando Magic emblem. b, Hedo Turkoglu.

No. 2565, 90c: a, Denver Nuggets emblem. b, Kenyon Martin.

No. 2566, 90c: a, Miami Heat emblem. b, Antoine Walker.

No. 2567, 90c: a, Golden State Warriors emblem. b, Jason Richardson.

No. 2568, 90c: a, Phoenix Suns emblem. b, Amaré Stoudemire.

No. 2569, 90c: a, Los Angeles Clippers emblem. b, Elton Brand.

**2006, Feb. 14** ***Perf. 14***

**Sheets of 12, 2 each #a, 10 each #b**

**2564-2569** A466 Set of 6 47.50 47.50

Léopold Sédar Senghor (1906-2001), First President of Senegal — A467

**2006, Mar. 20** ***Perf. 13¼***

**2570** A467 $2 multi 1.50 1.50

2006 Winter Olympics, Turin — A468

Designs: 75c, Yugoslavia #1670. 90c, 1984 Sarajevo Winter Olympics poster, vert. $2, Japan #2607g, vert. $3, 1998 Nagano Winter Olympics poster, vert.

**2006, Mar. 29**

**2571-2574** A468 Set of 4 5.00 5.00

Each stamp printed in sheets of 4.

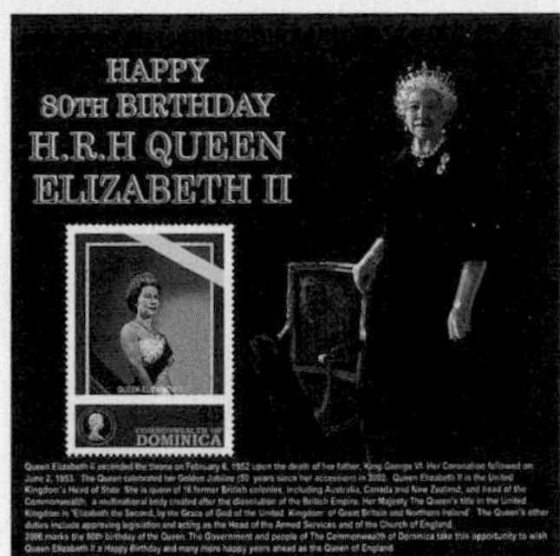


Queen Elizabeth II, 80th Birthday — A469

No. 2575: a, As infant, with mother. b, As young child. c, As baby, wearing bonnet. d, As young girl, wearing jacket.

$5, Wearing tiara and sash.

**2006, Mar. 29**

**2575** A469 $2 Sheet of 4, #a-d 6.00 6.00

**Souvenir Sheet**

**2576** A469 $5 multi 3.75 3.75

Marilyn Monroe (1926-62), Actress — A470

**2006, Apr. 7**

**2577** A470 $3 multi 2.25 2.25

Printed in sheets of 4.

Space Achievements — A471

No. 2578 — Viking I: a, Trenches dug by Viking I. b, Sunset at Viking I landing site. c, Chryse Planitia looking northwest over Viking I. d, First panoramic image of Chryse Planitia, country name and denomination in white. e, As "d," country name in black, denomination in white. f, As "d", country name and denomination in black.

No. 2579, $3, vert. — Luna 9: a, Flight apparatus. b, Modified SS-6 Sapwood rocket. c, Luna 9 Soft Lander. d, Tyuratam.

No. 2580, $3, vert. — Giotto Comet Probe: a, Launch of Giotto. b, Giotto during solar simulation test. c, Halley's Comet develops seven tails. d, Giotto and Comet Grigg-Skjellerup approach trajectories.

No. 2581, $6, Intl. Space Station. No. 2582, $6, Mars Reconnaissance Orbiter. No. 2583, $6, Venus Express Orbiter.

**2006, June 6** **Litho.** ***Perf. 14***

**2578** A471 $2 Sheet of 6, #a-f 9.00 9.00

**Sheets of 4, #a-d**

**2579-2580** A471 Set of 2 18.00 18.00

**Souvenir Sheets**

**2581-2583** A471 Set of 3 13.50 13.50

Miniature Sheet

Wolfgang Amadeus Mozart (1756-91), Composer — A472

No. 2584: a, Oval portrait. b, Playing harpsichord. c, Wearing red coat. d, Head of Mozart.

**2006, Sept. 1** ***Perf. 13¼***

**2584** A472 $3 Sheet of 4, #a-d 9.00 9.00

Miniature Sheet

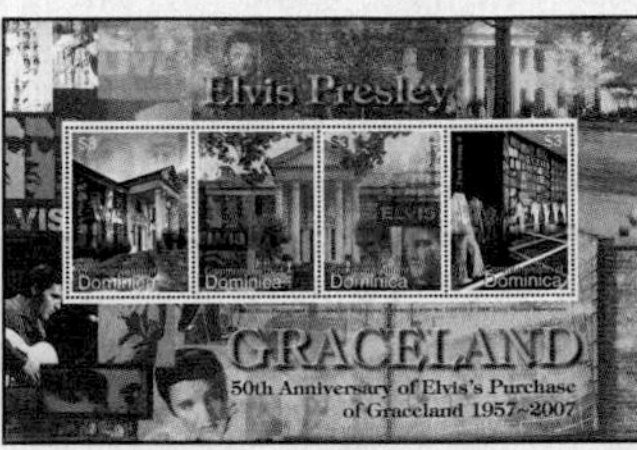


Purchase of Graceland by Elvis Presley, 50th Anniv. — A473

No. 2585: a, View of path leading to front door. b, Graceland, columns at right. c, Graceland, columns at left. d, Room with Presley's costumes.

**2006, Sept. 1** ***Perf. 13¼***

**2585** A473 $3 Sheet of 4, #a-d 9.00 9.00

Miniature Sheets

Pres. John F. Kennedy (1917-63) — A474

No. 2586, $3: a, Supporters holding campaign sign. b, Kennedy campaigning. c, Kennedy waiting for concession. d, Kennedy addressing the nation.

No. 2587, $3: a, Kennedy on crutches from war injuries. b, Kennedy on stretcher. c, Dust jacket of *Profiles in Courage.* d, Kennedy as senator.

**2006, Oct. 1** ***Perf. 13¼***

**Sheets of 4, #a-d**

**2586-2587** A474 Set of 2 18.00 18.00

Shells — A475

Designs: 5c, Turbinella angulata. 10c, Vasum muricatum. 15c, Fusinus closter. 20c, Crasispira gibbosa. 25c, Terebra strigata. 50c, Prunum carneum. 65c, Purpura patula. 90c, C. chrysostoma. $1, M. nodulosa. $2, Conus regius. $3.50, Conus hieroglyphus. $5, Anodontia alba, vert. $10, C. cassidiformis. $20, Strigilla carnaria, vert.

**2006, Oct. 1** ***Perf. 14x15, 15x14***

**2588** A475 5c multi .30 *.50*
**2589** A475 10c multi .30 *.50*
**2590** A475 15c multi .40 *.80*
**2591** A475 20c multi .40 .30
**2592** A475 25c multi .40 .30

| | | | | | |
|---|---|---|---|---|---|
| **2593** | A475 | 50c | multi | .55 | .35 |
| **2594** | A475 | 65c | multi | .75 | .50 |
| **2595** | A475 | 90c | multi | 1.00 | .75 |
| **2596** | A475 | $1 | multi | 1.25 | 1.25 |
| **2597** | A475 | $2 | multi | 2.00 | 2.00 |
| **2598** | A475 | $3.50 | multi | 3.25 | 3.25 |
| **2599** | A475 | $5 | multi | 4.00 | 4.00 |
| **2600** | A475 | $10 | multi | 7.00 | 7.00 |
| **2601** | A475 | $20 | multi | 14.00 | 14.00 |
| | *Nos. 2588-2601 (14)* | | | 35.60 | 35.50 |

Souvenir Sheet

Ludwig Durr (1878-1956), Engineer — A476

**2006, Nov. 15 Litho. *Perf. 12¾***

**2602** A476 $5 multi 3.75 3.75

Betty Boop — A477

No. 2603, vert.: a, Betty Boop with black background and leg raised. b, Lips. c, Betty Boop with black background. d, Dog on leash, star. e, Betty Boop, white background. f, Dog, two stars.

No. 2604 — Betty Boop with: a, Light blue panel at top. b, Light yellow panel at top.

**2006, Nov. 15**

**2603** A477 $2 Sheet of 6, #a-f 9.00 9.00

**Souvenir Sheet**

**2604** A477 $3.50 Sheet of 2, #a-b 5.25 5.25

Christmas A478

Christmas stocking showing: No. 2605, 25c, No. 2609a, $2, Christmas tree. No. 2606, 50c, No. 2609b, $2, Bell. No. 2607, 90c, No. 2609c, $2, Candy canes. No. 2608, $1, No. 2609d, $2, Stars.

**2006, Dec. 1 *Perf. 14¼***

**2605-2608** A478 Set of 4 2.00 2.00

**Souvenir Sheet**

**2609** A478 $2 Sheet of 4, #a-d 5.00 3.00

Souvenir Sheet

Christopher Columbus (1451-1506), Explorer — A479

**2007, Jan. 10 *Perf. 12***

**2610** A479 $5 brn & black 3.75 3.75

Scouting, Cent. — A480

**2007, Jan. 10**

**2611** A480 $3.50 blue & multi 2.60 2.60

**Souvenir Sheet**

**2612** A480 $5 org & multi 3.75 3.75

No. 2611 was printed in sheets of 3.

Concorde Prototype 001 F-WTSS — A481

No. 2613: a, $1, Airplane in hangar. b, $2, Airplane out of hangar.

**2007, Jan. 23 *Perf. 13¼***

**2613** A481 Pair, #a-b 2.25 2.25

Printed in sheets containing 3 of each stamp.

Rembrandt (1606-69), Painter — A482

No. 2614, vert. — Details from Christ Driving the Money Changers from the Temple: a, Christ. b, Man with moustache looking up. c, Man with striped headdress. d, Man protecting face with hands.

$5, Jesus and His Disciples.

**2007, Jan. 23 *Perf. 13¼***

**2614** A482 $2 Sheet of 4, #a-d 6.00 6.00

***Imperf***

**2615** A482 $5 shown 3.75 3.75

No. 2614 contains four 38x50mm stamps.

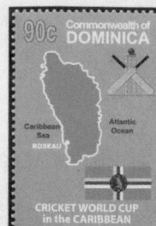


Cricket World Cup — A483

Designs: 90c, Cricket bats, ball and wicket, map and flag of Dominica. $1, Umpire Billy Doctrove.

$5, Cricket bats, ball and wicket.

**2007, Apr. 11 *Perf. 14***

**2616-2617** A483 Set of 2 2.50 2.50

**Souvenir Sheet**

**2618** A483 $5 multi 4.00 4.00

Birds A484

Designs: 10c, Great frigatebird. 25c, Peruvian booby. 90c, Black stork, vert. No. 2622, $5, Lipkin, vert.

No. 2623: a, Antillean crested hummingbird. b, Rufous-breasted hermit. c, Cuban hummingbird. d, Blue-headed hummingbird.

No. 2624, $5, Red-capped manakin, vert.

**2007, Apr. 11 *Perf. 12¾***

**2619-2622** A484 Set of 4 5.25 5.25

**2623** A484 $2 Sheet of 4, #a-d 7.50 7.50

**Souvenir Sheet**

**2624** A484 $5 multi 5.25 5.25

Flowers — A485

Designs: 10c, Red jasmine. 25c, Bougainvillea. 90c, Portia tree. No. 2628, $5, Rose bay.

No. 2629 — Orchids: a, $1, Tolumnia urophylla. b, $1, Brassavola cucullata. c, $2, Isochilus linearis. d, Spathoglottis plicata.

No. 2630, horiz.: a, Red ginger. b, Baobab. c, Purple wreath. d, Thunbergia.

No. 2631, $5, Flamboyant. No. 2632, $5, Oncidium altissimum.

**2007, Apr. 11 Litho. *Perf. 12¾***

**2625-2628** A485 Set of 4 4.75 4.75

**2629** A485 Sheet of 4, #a-d 4.50 4.50

**2630** A485 $2 Sheet of 4, #a-d 6.00 6.00

**Souvenir Sheets**

**2631-2632** A485 Set of 2 7.50 7.50

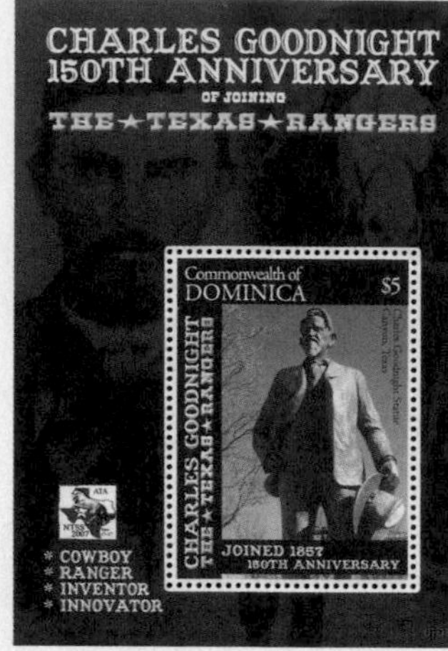


Princess Diana (1961-97) — A486

No. 2633: a, Holding flowers, wearing purple hat. b, Without hat. c, Not holding flowers, wearing purple hat. d, Close-up of #2633a, lines on face. e, Close-up of #2633b, lines on face. f, Close-up of #2633c, lines on face.

$5, Wearing purple sweater.

**2007, June 11 *Perf. 13½***

**2633** A486 $1 Sheet of 6, #a-f 4.50 4.50

**Souvenir Sheet**

**2634** A486 $5 multi 3.75 3.75

No. 2633 contains six 28x42mm stamps.

Texas Rangers — A487

No. 2635, horiz.: a, Two Rangers on horses. b, Seven Rangers in front of building with pillars. c, Ten rangers showing rifles. d, Rangers on horses. e, Rangers around still. f, Three Rangers at Justice of the Peace office. g, Rangers and tents. h, Rangers and locomotive. i, Five Rangers on horses near house.

$5, Statue of Charles Goodnight.

**2007, June 15 *Perf. 13½***

**2635** A487 $1 Sheet of 9, #a-i 6.75 6.75

**Souvenir Sheet**

**2636** A487 $5 multi 3.75 3.75

American Topical Association National Topical Stamp Show, Irving, TX.

Miniature Sheet

New Year 2007 (Year of the Pig) — A488

No. 2637 — Text in: a, Red. b, Green. c, Blue green. d, Purple.

**2007, July 2**

**2637** A488 $2 Sheet of 4, #a-d 6.00 6.00

A489

MERRY
50¢
COMMONWEALTH OF DOMINICA

A490

A491

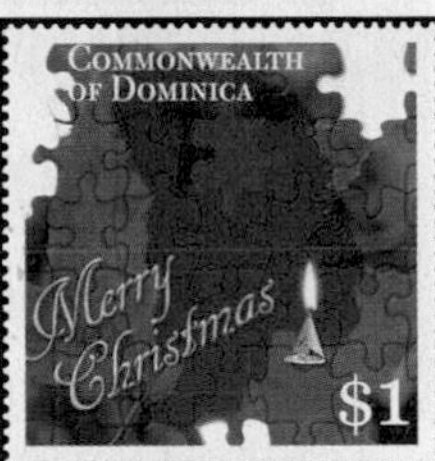


Christmas
A492

**2007, Nov. 19 Litho. *Perf. 14¾x14***

**2638** A489 25c multi .25 .25
**2639** A490 50c multi .40 .40
**2640** A491 90c multi .70 .70
**2641** A492 $1 multi .75 .75
*Nos. 2638-2641 (4)* 2.10 2.10

New Year 2008 (Year of the Rat) — A493

**2008, Feb. 28 *Perf. 12***

**2642** A493 $1 multi .75 .75

Printed in sheets of 4.

University of the West Indies, 60th Anniv. A494

University crest, Dr. Bernard A. Sorhaindo and denomination in: 50c, Red brown. 65c, Green. 90c, Brown.

No. 2646, $5, Crest, Sorhaindo, denomination in black. No. 2647, $5, Crest, Sorhaindo, denomination in blue. No. 2648, $5, Crest, diploma, 60th anniversary emblem.

**2008, Apr. 8 *Perf. 13¼***

**2643-2645** A494 Set of 3 1.60 1.60

**Souvenir Sheets**

**2646-2648** A494 Set of 3 11.50 11.50

Miniature Sheet

2008 Summer Olympics, Beijing — A495

No. 2649: a, Archery. b, Men's gymnastics. c, Badminton. d, Boxing.

**2008, Apr. 8 *Perf. 13¼x13***

**2649** A495 $1.40 Sheet of 4, #a-d 4.25 4.25

Miniature Sheet

Visit of Pope Benedict XVI to New York — A496

No. 2650 — Pope and part of St. Patrick's Cathedral in background: a, Small circular window under spire. b, Large central circular window. c, Archway below spire. d, Archway above main door.

**2008, June 16 Litho. *Perf. 13½***

**2650** A496 $1.40 Sheet of 4, #a-d 4.25 4.25

Miniature Sheet

Wedding of Queen Elizabeth II and Prince Philip, 60th Anniv. — A497

No. 2651: a, Couple, denomination in white. b, Queen, denomination in red violet. c, Couple, denomination in black. d, Queen, denomination in white. e, Couple, denomination in red violet. f, Queen, denomination in black.

**2008, June 16**

**2651** A497 $1 Sheet of 6, #a-f 4.50 4.50

Miniature Sheet

Elvis Presley (1935-77) — A498

No. 2652 — Presley and: a, Black and red background, Prussian blue denomination. b, Gray and black background, purple denomination. c, Blue and black background, Prussian blue denomination. d, Purple and black background, purple denomination. e, Gray and black background, Prussian blue denomination. f, Brown and black background, purple denomination.

**2008, June 16**

**2652** A498 $1.50 Sheet of 6 #a-f 6.75 6.75

A499

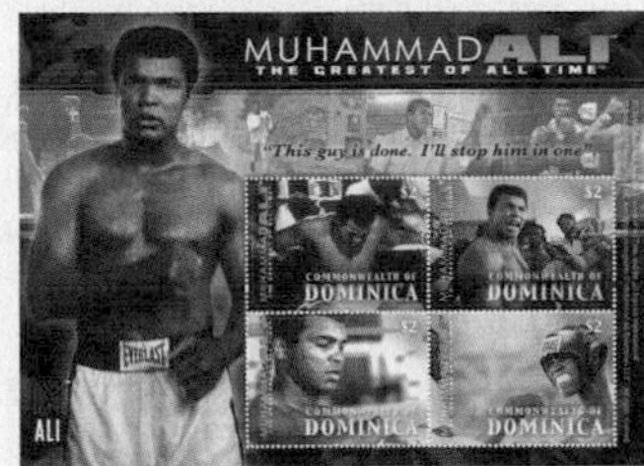


Muhammad Ali, Boxer — A500

No. 2653 — Ali: a, Sweating, denomination in white. b, Smiling, denomination in black. c, Wearing headgear. d, With arms raised.

No. 2654 — Ali: a, Seated in corner of boxing ring. b, Speaking to the press. c, Punching bag. d, Wearing headgear and mouth guard.

**2008, July 7**

**2653** A499 $2 Sheet of 4, #a-d 6.25 6.25
**2654** A500 $2 Sheet of 4, #a-d 6.25 6.25

Convent High School, 150th Anniv. A501

Panel color: 50c, Red violet. 65c, Yellow orange. 90c, Blue. $1, Red.

$5, Denomination in LR corner.

**2008, Oct. 1 *Perf. 12½***

**2655-2658** A501 Set of 4 2.40 2.40

**Souvenir Sheet**

**2659** A501 $5 multi 4.00 4.00

Dogs — A502

Designs: 25c, Dandie Dinmont terrier. 50c, Alaskan malamute. 90c, Welsh Springer spaniel. $1, Pug. $2, Norfolk terrier. $5, Vizsla.

No. 2666: a, Akita. b, Australian cattle dog. c, Border collie. d, Staffordshire bull terrier cross.

***Perf. 14¼x14¾***

**2008, Dec. 11 Litho.**

**2660-2665** A502 Set of 6 8.50 8.50
**2666** A502 $2.50 Sheet of 4, #a-d 9.00 9.00

Miniature Sheet

Marilyn Monroe (1926-62), Actress — A503

No. 2667 — Monroe wearing: a, Purple sweater, hand on arm. b, Orange sweater, looking in mirror. c, Purple sweater, holding post. d, Orange sweater, holding wine glass.

**2008, Dec. 11 *Perf. 14***

**2667** A503 $2 Sheet of 4, #a-d 6.00 6.00

Christmas A504

Designs: 25c, Santa Claus. 50c, Palm tree with Christmas ornaments. 90c, Christmas stocking. $1, Poinsettias.

**2008, Dec. 15 *Perf. 12***

**2668-2671** A504 Set of 4 2.00 2.00

New Year 2009 (Year of the Ox) A505

**2009, Jan. 5 *Perf. 14¾x14¼***

**2672** A505 $2 multi 1.50 1.50

Printed in sheets of 4.

Inauguration of Barack Obama as US President A506

Pres. Obama: 65c, With raised hand. 90c, Hand not showing.

No. 2675: a, $2.25, Like 65c. b, $2.25, Looking over shoulder. c, $2.25, Like 90c. d, $2.50, Like 90c. e, $2.50, Looking over shoulder. f, $2.50, Like 65c.

**2009, Jan. 20 *Perf. 11½***

**2673-2674** A506 Set of 2 1.25 1.25
**2675** A506 Sheet of 6, #a-f 11.00 11.00



Diplomatic Relations Between Dominica and People's Republic of China, 5th Anniv. A507

Denominations: 50c, 65c, 90c, $1.

**2009, Mar. 23** ***Perf. 14¾x14¼***
**2676-2679** A507 Set of 4 2.40 2.40

**Souvenir Sheet**

**2680** A507 $5 multi 3.75 3.75

Peony A508

**2009, Apr. 10** ***Perf. 13¼***
**2681** A508 75c shown .55 .55

**Souvenir Sheet**

**2682** A508 $5 Peonies 3.75 3.75

No. 2682 contains one 44x44mm stamp.

Miniature Sheet

Elvis Presley (1935-77) — A509

No. 2683 — Various photos of Presley with background colors of: a, Yellow orange. b, Gray and blue. c, Blue. d, Gray.

**2009, May 23** ***Perf. 13¼***
**2683** A509 $2.50 Sheet of 4, #a-d 7.75 7.75

Miniature Sheet

Joseph Haydn (1732-1809), Composer — A510

No. 2684: a, Haydn. b, Haydn's birthplace, Rohrau, Austria. c, Wolfgang Amadeus Mozart. d, St. Stephen's Cathedral, Vienna. e, Nikolaus Esterházy, sponsor of Haydn. f, Esterházy Palace, Fertod, Hungary.

**2009, June 10** ***Perf. 11½***
**2684** A510 $2.25 Sheet of 6, #a-f 10.00 10.00

Mushrooms A511

Designs: 50c, Leucopaxillus gracillimus. 65c, Calvatia cyathiformis. 90c, Hygrocybe viridiphylla. $1, Boletellus coccineus.

No. 2689, $2: a, Hygrocybe acutoconica. b, Lepiota sulphureocyanescens. c, Lactarius rubrilacteus. d, Lactarius ferrugineus. e, Asterophora lycoperdoides. f, Amanita polypyramis.

**2009, Sept. 8** **Litho.** ***Perf. 14x14¾***
**2685-2688** A511 Set of 4 2.25 2.25
**2689** A511 $2 Sheet of 6, #a-f 9.00 9.00

A512

Corals and Marine Life — A513

Designs: 50c, Lobed star coral and shark. 65c, Orange cup coral and fish. 90c, Grooved brain coral and turtle. $1, Elkhorn coral and fish.

No. 2694, $2: a, Rough star coral and fish. b, Branched finger coral and fish. c, Wire coral and ray. d, Great star coral and fish. e, Pillar coral and fish. f, Rose lace coral and fish.

**2009, Sept. 8** ***Perf. 14¾x14***
**2690-2693** A512 Set of 4 2.25 2.25
**2694** A513 $2 Sheet of 6, #a-f 9.00 9.00

Butterflies A514

Designs: 90c, Banded orange heliconian. $1, Gulf fritillary. $2, Julia longwing. $5, Zebra longwing.

No. 2699: a, Cuban cattleheart. b, White peacock. c, Bahamian swallowtail. d, Tropical buckeye.

No. 2700, $6, Purple emperor. No. 2701, $6, Atala black.

**2009, Sept. 8** ***Perf. 14¾x14***
**2695-2698** A514 Set of 4 6.75 6.75
**2699** A514 $2.50 Sheet of 4, #a-d 7.50 7.50

**Souvenir Sheets**
***Perf. 14¼***

**2700-2701** A514 Set of 2 9.00 9.00

Nos. 2700-2701 each contain one 50x38mm stamp.

Dolphins and Whales A515

Designs: 50c, Irawaddy dolphin. 65c, Pantropical spotted dolphin. 90c, Atlantic humpback dolphin. $1, Indian humpback dolphin.

No. 2706: a, Melon-headed whale. b, Striped dolphin. c, Atlantic spotted dolphin. d, Clymene dolphin. e, Pantropical spotted dolphin (Stenella attenuata graffmani). f, Pantropical spotted dolphin (Stenella attenuata).

**2009, Sept. 8** **Litho.** ***Perf. 14¾x14***
**2702-2705** A515 Set of 4 2.25 2.25
**2706** A515 $2 Sheet of 6, #a-f 9.00 9.00

See No. 2732.

Shells A516

Designs: 50c, Oliva reticularis. 65c, Vasum muricatum. 90c, Olivella nivea. $1, Olivella mutica.

No. 2711: a, Hyalina avena. b, Persicula fluctuata. c, Agatrix agassizi. d, Trigonostoma rugosum. e, Olivella floralia. f, Marginella eburneola.

**2009, Sept. 8**
**2707-2710** A516 Set of 4 2.25 2.25
**2711** A516 $2 Sheet of 6, #a-f 9.00 9.00

Miniature Sheet

Expo 2010, Shanghai — A517

No. 2712: a, Bund. b, Shanghai Museum. c, Yangpu Bridge. d, Shanghai Theater.

**2009, Oct. 16** ***Perf. 13x12¾***
**2712** A517 $1.50 Sheet of 4, #a-d 4.50 4.50

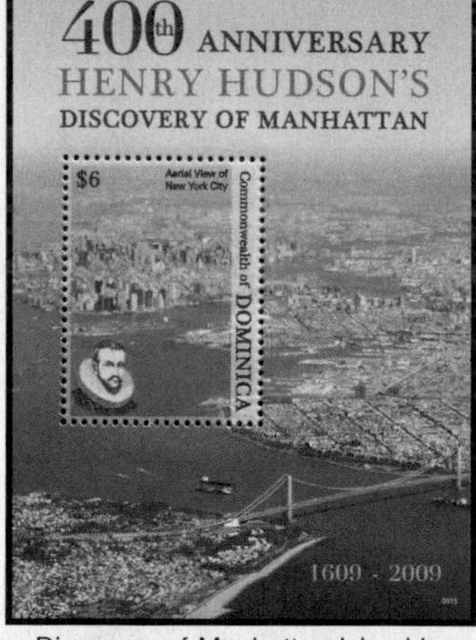

Discovery of Manhattan Island by Henry Hudson, 400th Anniv. — A518

No. 2713, horiz.: a, Panoramic view of New York City, 1913. b, Hudson, the Dreamer, by Jean L.G. Ferris. c, Henry Hudson. d, Hudson's ship, Half Moon. e, Map of Hudson River, c. 1600. f, Henry Hudson Memorial Column, Bronx, NY.

$6, Hudson, aerial view of New York City.

**2009, Oct. 16** ***Perf. 13x12¾***
**2713** A518 $2.25 Sheet of 6, #a-f 10.00 10.00

**Souvenir Sheet**
***Perf. 12¾x13***

**2714** A518 $6 multi 4.50 4.50

Miniature Sheet

Pres. John F. Kennedy (1917-63) — A519

No. 2715 — Pres. Kennedy: a, On telephone. b, With family. c, With Vice-president Lyndon B. Johnson. d, Pointing.

**2009, Oct. 30** ***Perf. 11½x12***
**2715** A519 $2.50 Sheet of 4, #a-d 7.50 7.50

Miniature Sheet

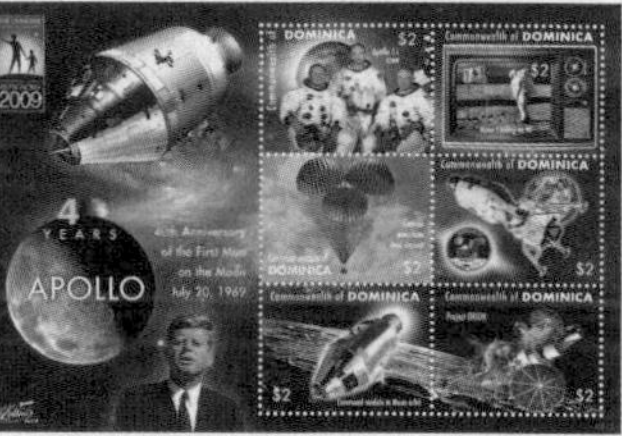

First Man on the Moon, 40th Anniv. — A520

No. 2716: a, Apollo 11 crew. b, Moon landing on television. c, Apollo 11 capsule with parachutes. d, Earth, Apollo 11 modules and patch. e, Command Module in Moon orbit. f, Project Orion.

**2009, Nov. 2** ***Perf. 11½***
**2716** A520 $2 Sheet of 6, #a-f 9.00 9.00

Chinese Aviation, Cent. — A521

No. 2717: a, H-5. b, H-6. c, H-6H. d, H-6L. $6, H-6U.

**2009, Nov. 12** ***Perf. 14***
**2717** A521 $2 Sheet of 4, #a-d 6.50 6.50

**Souvenir Sheet**
***Perf. 14¼***

**2718** A521 $6 multi 4.75 4.75

Aeropex 2009 Intl. Philatelic Exhibition, Beijing. No. 2717 contains four 42x28mm stamps.

Christmas A522

Designs: 50c, Bell-shaped Christmas tree ornament. 65c, Candles and poinsettia. 90c, Gingerbread man. $1.10, Decorated palm tree. $2.25, Christmas tree ornaments. $2.75, Women dancers.

**2009, Nov. 16** ***Perf. 11½***
**2719-2724** A522 Set of 6 6.25 6.25

Personalized Stamp — A523

**2009, Dec. 18** ***Perf. 14x14¾***
**2725** A523 $3 gray 2.25 2.25

The vignette on the stamp shown is a generic image. Stamps without a vignette were also made available. Printed in sheets of 12.

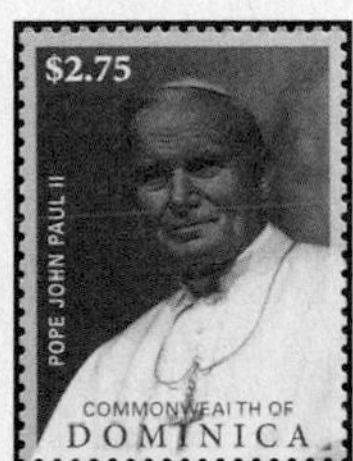


Pope John Paul II (1920-2005) A524

**2010, Jan. 4** ***Perf. 12x11½***
**2726** A524 $2.75 multi 2.10 2.10

Printed in sheets of 4.

Miniature Sheet

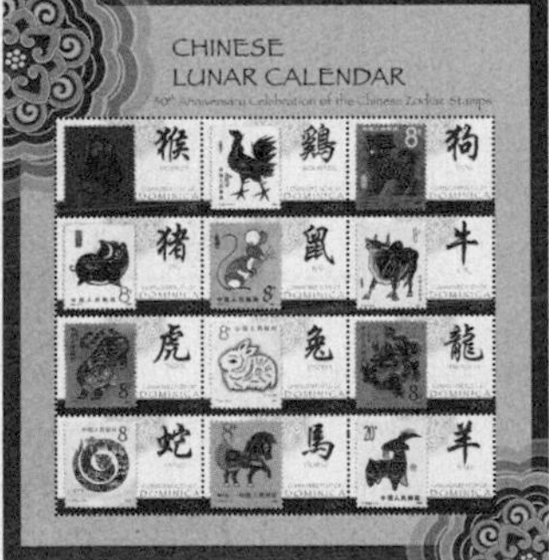


Chinese Zodiac Animals — A524a

No. 2726A — Various stamps of People's Republic of China depicting Zodiac animals: b, Monkey. c, Rooster. d, Dog. e, Pig. f, Rat. g, Ox. h, Tiger. i, Rabbit. j, Dragon. k, Snake. l, Horse. m, Ram.

**2010, Jan. 4** **Litho.** ***Perf. 12¾***
**2726A** A524a 60c Sheet of 12, #b-m 6.00 6.00

Souvenir Sheet

New Year 2010 (Year of the Tiger) — A525

**2010, Jan. 4** ***Perf. 12¾***
**2727** A525 $5 multi 4.00 4.00

Miniature Sheet

Elvis Presley (1935-77) — A526

Various drawings of Presley.

**2010, Jan. 8** ***Perf. 11½***
**2728** A526 $2.50 Sheet of 4, #a-d 7.75 7.75

Miniature Sheet

NASCAR Drivers and Their Cars — A527

No. 2729: a, Denny Hamlin. b, Kyle Busch. c, Joey Logano. d, Hamlin's car (#11). e, Busch's car (#18). f, Logano's car (#20).

**2010, Jan. 19** **Litho.**
**2729** A527 $3.25 Sheet of 6, #a-f 15.00 15.00

Miniature Sheets

Dogs — A528

No. 2730, $2.50 — Dalmatian and: a, Books. b, Stone wall. c, Swimming pool. d, Stack of logs.

No. 2731, $2.50 — Boxer and: a, Brick wall. b, Bush. c, Window. d, Fence.

**2010, Jan. 19** ***Perf. 11½x11¾***
**Sheets of 4, #a-d**
**2730-2731** A528 Set of 2 15.50 15.50

**No. 2706 With "Haiti Earthquake Relief Fund" and Map of Haiti Added to Stamps and Sheet Margin**

Miniature Sheet

Designs as before.

**2010, Feb. 4** ***Perf. 14¾x14***
**2732** A515 $2 Sheet of 6, #a-f 9.25 9.25

Position of added text varies on each stamp.

Ferraris and Their Parts A529

No. 2733, $1.25: a, Engine of 1982 208 GTB Turbo. b, 1982 208 GTB Turbo.

No. 2734, $1.25: a, Engine of 1983 126 C3. b, 1983 126 C3.

No. 2735, $1.25: a, Side panel and rear wheel of 1984 Testarossa. b, 1984 Testarossa.

No. 2736, $1.25: a, Suspension of 1987 408 4RM. b, 1987 408 4RM.

**2010, Feb. 17** ***Perf. 12***
**Vert. Pairs, #a-b**
**2733-2736** A529 Set of 4 8.00 8.00

Nos. 2733-2736 each were printed in sheets containing four pairs.

Miniature Sheet

Mother Teresa (1910-97), Humanitarian — A530

No. 2737 — Mother Teresa: a, Denomination in black. b, Holding rosary. c, Wearing white habit. d, Kissing hand of Pope John Paul II.

**2010, Feb. 24** ***Perf. 11¼x11½***
**2737** A530 $2.50 Sheet of 4, #a-d 8.00 8.00

Boy Scouts of America, Cent. — A531

No. 2738, $2.50: a, Outdoor skills. b, Campfire inspirations.

No. 2739, $2.50: a, Emergency one-man carry. b, Swimming fun with safety.

**2010, Feb. 24** ***Perf. 13¼***
**Pairs, #a-b**
**2738-2739** A531 Set of 2 8.00 8.00

Nos. 2738-2739 each were printed in sheets containing two pairs.

Miniature Sheet

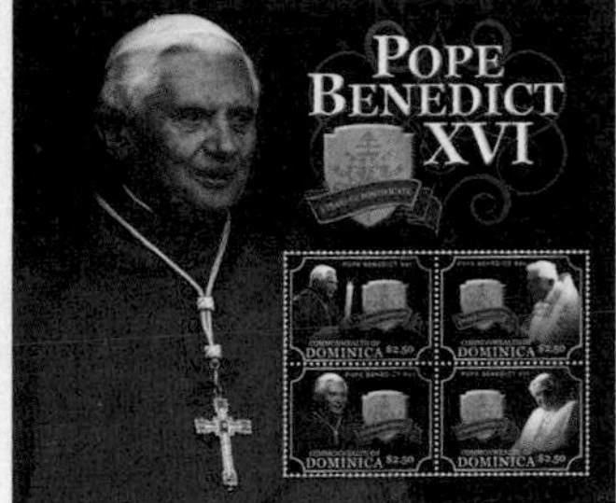


Pope Benedict XVI — A532

No. 2740 — Pope Benedict XVI: a, Wearing red, holding candle. b, Wearing white, hands clasped. c, Wearing red, not holding candle. d, Wearing white, hands not clasped.

**2010, Mar. 23** ***Perf. 11½x12***
**2740** A532 $2.50 Sheet of 4, #a-d 7.50 7.50

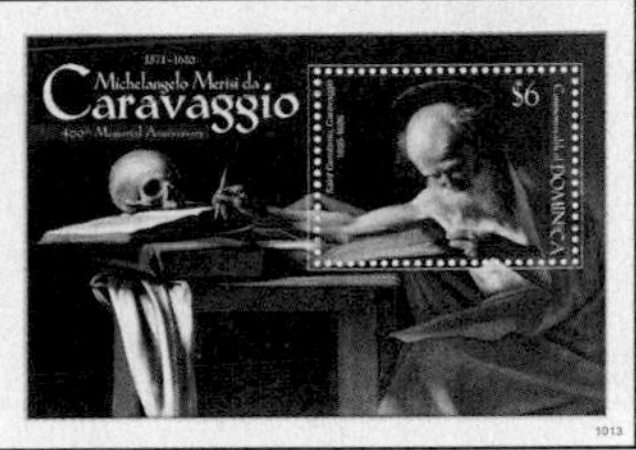


Caravaggio Paintings — A533

No. 2741, vert.: a, Mary Magdalene. b, Sick Bacchus. c, Bacchus. d, The Inspiration of Saint Matthew.

$6, Saint Gerolamo.

**2010, Mar. 23** ***Perf. 12x11½***
**2741** A533 $2.50 Sheet of 4, #a-d 7.50 7.50

**Souvenir Sheet**
***Perf. 11½***
**2742** A533 $6 multi 4.50 4.50

Miniature Sheet

Girl Guides, Cent. — A534

No. 2743: a, Rainbows. b, Brownies. c, Guides. d, Senior Section. $6, Girl Guide, vert.

**2010, Apr. 19** ***Perf. 11½x12***
**2743** A534 $2.75 Sheet of 4, #a-d 8.25 8.25

**Souvenir Sheet**
***Perf. 11¼x11½***
**2743E** A534 $6 multi 4.50 4.50

Souvenir Sheets

A535

A536

A537

Elvis Presley (1935-77) — A538

**2010, May 12** ***Perf. 13½***

| | | | | | |
|---|---|---|---|---|---|
| **2744** | A535 | $6 | multi | 4.50 | 4.50 |
| **2745** | A536 | $6 | multi | 4.50 | 4.50 |
| **2746** | A537 | $6 | multi | 4.50 | 4.50 |
| **2747** | A538 | $6 | multi | 4.50 | 4.50 |
| | | *Nos. 2744-2747 (4)* | | 18.00 | 18.00 |

Miniature Sheets

Pres. Abraham Lincoln (1809-65) — A539

No. 2748, $2.50 — Photographs of Lincoln: a, Without beard. b, Without beard, arms crossed. c, Reading to son, Tad. d, With beard.

No. 2749, $2.50: a, Statue of Lincoln, Bascom Hill, University of Wisconsin. b, Aerial view of Lincoln Memorial. c, Statue of Lincoln in Lincoln Memorial. d, Sculpture of Lincoln, Mount Rushmore.

**2010, June 22** **Litho.** ***Perf. 11½***
**Sheets of 4, #a-d**

| | | | | |
|---|---|---|---|---|
| **2748-2749** | A539 | Set of 2 | 15.00 | 15.00 |

Whales — A540

No. 2750: a, Sowerby's beaked whale. b, Blainville's beaked whale. c, Short-finned pilot whale. d, True's beaked whale. e, False killer whale. f, Dwarf sperm whale.
$6, Sperm whale.

**2010, June 22** **Litho.** ***Perf. 13x13½***

| | | | | | |
|---|---|---|---|---|---|
| **2750** | A540 | $2 | Sheet of 6, #a-f | 9.00 | 9.00 |

**Souvenir Sheet**

| | | | | | |
|---|---|---|---|---|---|
| **2751** | A540 | $6 | multi | 4.50 | 4.50 |

Miniature Sheets

A541

Princess Diana (1961-97) — A542

No. 2752 — Princess Diana wearing: a, Plaid jacket. b, Wedding gown. c, Black jacket. d, Red and white dress.
No. 2753 — Princess Diana with: a, Prince Charles. b, Princes Charles, William and Harry. c, Crowd, holding flowers. d, Small child.

**2010, May 12** **Litho.** ***Perf. 13x13¼***

| | | | | | |
|---|---|---|---|---|---|
| **2752** | A541 | $2.75 | Sheet of 4, #a-d | 8.25 | 8.25 |
| **2753** | A542 | $2.75 | Sheet of 4, #a-d | 8.25 | 8.25 |

Christmas — A543

Painting details: 90c, Geburt Christi (Birth of Christ), by Hans Baldung. $1.45, Thomas Altar, by Meister Francke. $2, Nativity, by Baldung.

**2010, Dec. 1** ***Perf. 13x13½***

| | | | | |
|---|---|---|---|---|
| **2754-2756** | A543 | Set of 3 | 3.25 | 3.25 |

Nos. 2754-2756 each were printed in sheets of 6.

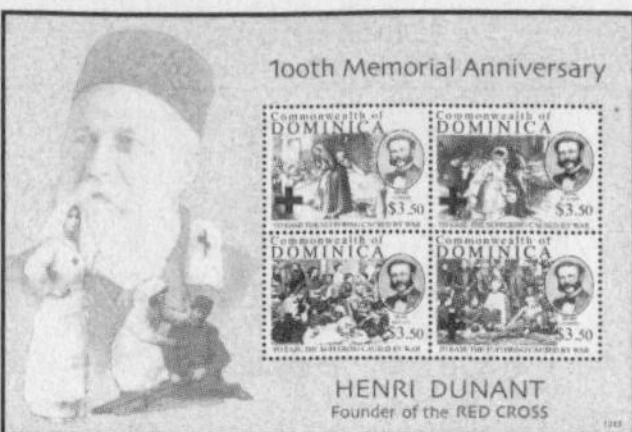

Henri Dunant (1828-1910), Founder of Red Cross — A544

No. 2757 — Red Cross, nurses aiding wounded and portrait of Dunant in: a, Green. b, Brown. c, Purple. d, Blue.
$5, Red Cross, nurses, Dunant in purplish gray.

**2010, Dec. 15** ***Perf. 12½x12***

| | | | | | |
|---|---|---|---|---|---|
| **2757** | A544 | $3.50 | Sheet of 4, #a-d | 10.50 | 10.50 |

**Souvenir Sheet**

| | | | | | |
|---|---|---|---|---|---|
| **2758** | A544 | $5 | multi | 3.75 | 3.75 |

Tenth Cricket World Cup, India, Sri Lanka and Bangladesh A545

Designs: 90c, Chris Gayle. $2, Windsor Park Sports Stadium, Roseau, horiz.
$5, Cricket World Cup.

**2011, June 1** **Litho.** ***Perf. 12½***

| | | | | |
|---|---|---|---|---|
| **2759-2760** | A545 | Set of 2 | 2.25 | 2.25 |

**Souvenir Sheet**
***Perf. 12***

| | | | | | |
|---|---|---|---|---|---|
| **2761** | A545 | $5 | multi | 3.75 | 3.75 |

No. 2761 contains one 30x40mm stamp.

National HIV and AIDS Response Program — A545a

**2011, June 1** **Litho.** ***Perf. 13½***

| | | | | | |
|---|---|---|---|---|---|
| **2761A** | A545a | 90c | multi | — | — |

Lizards — A546

Designs: 5c, Golden skink. 10c, Dominican ground lizard. 15c, Crested anole. 20c, Dominican tree lizard. 25c, Pygmy skink. 50c, House gecko. 65c, Fantastic gecko. 90c, Iguana. $1, Vincent's least gecko. $2, Turnip-tailed gecko. $5, House gecko, diff. $10, Fantastic gecko, diff. $20, Vincent's least gecko, diff.

**2011, Oct. 1** ***Perf. 14***

| | | | | | |
|---|---|---|---|---|---|
| **2762** | A546 | 5c | multi | .25 | .25 |
| **2763** | A546 | 10c | multi | .25 | .25 |
| **2764** | A546 | 15c | multi | .25 | .25 |
| **2765** | A546 | 20c | multi | .25 | .25 |
| **2766** | A546 | 25c | multi | .25 | .25 |
| **2767** | A546 | 50c | multi | .40 | .40 |
| **2768** | A546 | 65c | multi | .50 | .50 |
| **2769** | A546 | 90c | multi | .70 | .70 |
| **2770** | A546 | $1 | multi | .75 | .75 |
| **2771** | A546 | $2 | multi | 1.50 | 1.50 |
| **2772** | A546 | $5 | multi | 3.75 | 3.75 |
| **2773** | A546 | $10 | multi | 7.50 | 7.50 |
| **2774** | A546 | $20 | multi | 15.00 | 15.00 |
| | | *Nos. 2762-2774 (13)* | | 31.35 | 31.35 |

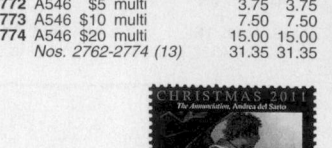

Christmas A547

Paintings: 90c, The Annunciation, by Andrea del Sarto. $1.45, Madonna with Child, by Jacopo Bellini. $2, The Virgin, by Carlo Dolci.

**2011, Nov. 1**

| | | | | |
|---|---|---|---|---|
| **2775-2777** | A547 | Set of 3 | 3.25 | 3.25 |

Christmas A548

Paintings: 50c, Virgin in Adoration Before the Christ Child, by Peter Paul Rubens. 90c, Altarpiece of the Rose Garlands, by Albrecht Dürer. $3.50, Crowning of St. Catherine, by Rubens. $5, Adoration of the Magi, by Dürer.

**2012, Nov. 19** ***Perf. 13¾***

| | | | | |
|---|---|---|---|---|
| **2778-2781** | A548 | Set of 4 | 7.50 | 7.50 |

New Year 2011 (Year of the Rabbit) A549

**2013, Aug. 29** **Litho.** ***Perf. 12***

| | | | | | |
|---|---|---|---|---|---|
| **2782** | A549 | $4 | multi | 3.00 | 3.00 |

No. 2782 was printed in sheets of 2.

Cats — A550

No. 2783: a, Cat with brown-tipped tail, eyes not visible. b, Cat with black tail and four white paws. c, Head of cat and two front paws. d, Cat with black tail, paw touching "A" in "Cats." e, Cat with white tail, with one black paw visible. f, Cat with one black and three white paws.
$5, Cat, diff.

**2013, Sept. 2** **Litho.** ***Perf. 14***

| | | | | | |
|---|---|---|---|---|---|
| **2783** | A550 | $1 | Sheet of 6, #a-f | 4.50 | 4.50 |

**Souvenir Sheet**
***Perf. 12***

| | | | | | |
|---|---|---|---|---|---|
| **2784** | A550 | $5 | multi | 3.75 | 3.75 |

Dogs — A551

No. 2785, $1.45: a, Airedale terrier. b, Bernese mountain dog. c, Pekingese. d, Samoyed.
No. 2786, $1.45, horiz.: a, Labrador retriever. b, Border collie. c, Cocker spaniel. d, Dalmatian.
No. 2787, $5, Rottweiler. No. 2788, $5, Great Dane.

**2013, Sept. 2 Litho. *Perf. 12***
**Sheets of 4, #a-d**

2785-2786 A551 Set of 2 8.75 8.75

**Souvenir Sheets**

2787-2788 A551 Set of 2 7.50 7.50

Bees and Wasps — A552

No. 2789: a, Carpenter bee. b, Golden digger wasp. c, Bumblebee. d, Yellowjacket.
$5, Golden paper wasp.

**2013, Sept. 2 Litho. *Perf. 13¾***

2789 A552 $2 Sheet of 4, #a-d 6.00 6.00

**Souvenir Sheet**

2790 A552 $5 multi 3.75 3.75

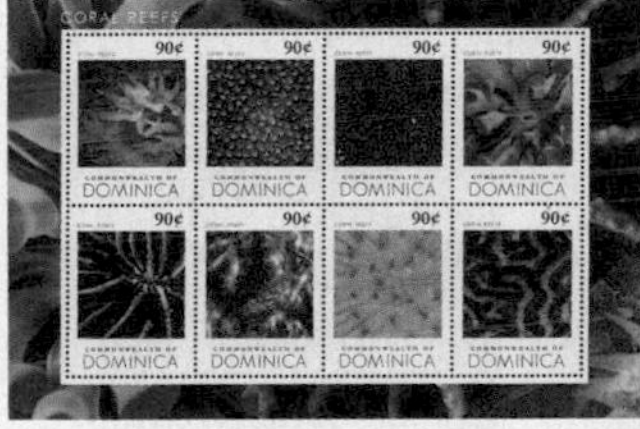

Corals — A553

No. 2791 — Various unnamed corals with colors of; a, Pink (with anemone-like tips). b, Purple and pink (small bead-like appearance). c, Dark red. d, Blue (tubes). e, Purple and pink (with lines). f, Pink (with branches). g, Yellow green. h, Blue (with black curved lines).
$5, Nephthyigorgia sp.

**2013, Sept. 2 Litho. *Perf. 14***

2791 A553 90c Sheet of 8, #a-h 5.50 5.50

**Souvenir Sheet**
***Perf. 12¾x12½***

2792 A553 $5 multi 3.75 3.75

No. 2792 contains one 38x51mm stamp.

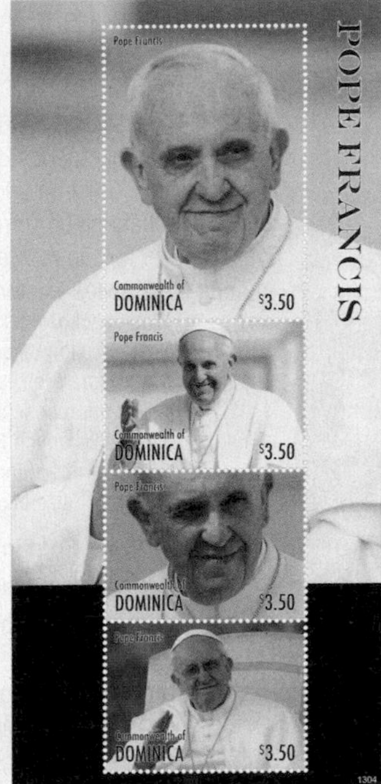


Election of Pope Francis — A554

No. 2793 — Pope Francis: a, With top of head visible (40x60mm). b, Waving, without eyeglasses, horiz. (40x30mm). c, With top of head not visible, horiz. (40x30mm). d, Waving, wearing eyeglasses, horiz. (40x30mm).
$5, Pope Francis, horiz.

**2013, Sept. 2 Litho. *Perf. 14***

2793 A554 $3.50 Sheet of 4, #a-d 10.50 10.50

**Souvenir Sheet**
***Perf. 12¾x12½***

2794 A554 $5 multi 3.75 3.75

No. 2794 contains one 51x38mm stamp.

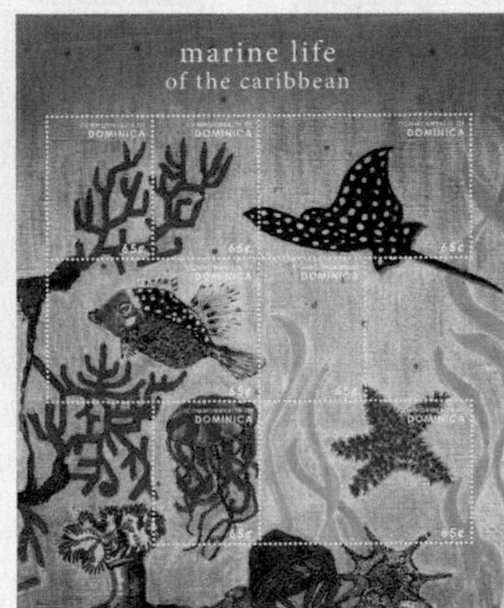


Painting of Marine Life — A555

Painting of Parrot — A556

No. 2795: a, Coral, denomination on coral (30x40mm). b, Coral, denomination on blue background (30x40mm). c, Ray (60x40mm). d, Fish and coral (60x40mm). e, Sea grass (30x40mm). f, Jellyfish (30x40mm). g, Sea grass and starfish (60x40mm).

**2013, Sept. 2 Litho. *Perf. 14***

2795 A555 65c Sheet of 7, #a-g 3.50 3.50

**Souvenir Sheet**
***Perf. 12***

2796 A556 $5 multi 3.75 3.75

Butterflies A557

No. 2797, $2: a, Malachite. b, Silver-banded hairstreak.
No. 2798, $2: a, Gold rim swallowtail. b, Mangrove buckeye.

**2013, Sept. 2 Litho. *Perf. 13¾***
**Pairs, #a-b**

2797-2798 A557 Set of 2 6.00 6.00

Nos. 2797 and 2798 each were printed in sheets containing two pairs.

Birth of Prince George of Cambridge — A558

No. 2799: a, Duke and Duchess of Cambridge, Prince George. b, Duke of Cambridge holding Prince George. c, Duchess of Cambridge holding Prince George. d, Close-up of Prince George.
$6, Duke and Duchess of Cambridge, Prince George, diff.

**2013 Litho. *Perf. 14***

2799 A558 $2 Sheet of 4, #a-d 6.00 6.00

**Souvenir Sheet**

2800 A558 $6 multi 4.50 4.50

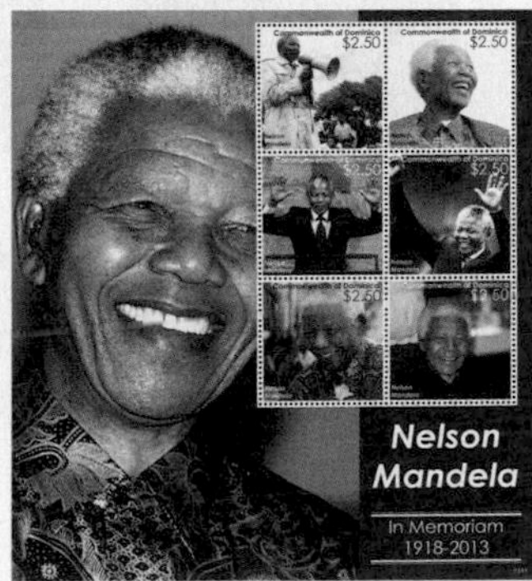


A559

Nelson Mandela (1918-2013), President of South Africa — A560

No. 2801 — Mandela: a, Holding loudspeaker. b, Wearing green and black shirt and jacket. c, With arms raised, color photograph. d, With arms raised, black-and-white photograph. e, Wearing black and gray shirt. f, Wearing black shirt.
$5, Mandela wearing gray shirt. $20, Mandela wearing shirt with leaf design.

**2014, Jan. 6 Litho. *Perf. 13¾***

2801 A559 $2.50 Sheet of 6, #a-f 11.00 11.00

**Souvenir Sheets**

2802 A559 $5 multi 3.75 3.75

**Litho., Margin Embossed With Foil Application**
***Imperf***

2803 A560 $20 multi 15.00 15.00

New Year 2014 (Year of the Horse) — A561

No. 2804 — Various Chinese characters for "horse" and: a, Horse in red at left, red chop at right, orange background. b, Horse in yellow at left, yellow chop at left, red orange background. c, Horse in red at left, red chop at left, yellow orange background. d, Horse in yellow at right, red chop at left, brown background. e, Horse in red at right, red chop at left, yellow orange background. f, Horse in yellow at right, red chop at left, dull orange background.
No. 2805 — Chinese characters for "horse" and: a, Horse in red at right. b, Horse in yellow brown at right.

**2014, Jan. 8 Litho. *Perf. 14***

2804 A561 $2.50 Sheet of 6, #a-f 11.00 11.00

**Souvenir Sheet**

2805 A561 $5 Sheet of 2, #a-b 7.50 7.50

Sea Turtles — A562

No. 2806: a, Leatherback turtle. b, Green sea turtle. c, Hawksbill turtle.
$5, Green sea turtle, diff.

**2014, May 1 Litho. *Perf. 11½x12***

2806 A562 $3.50 Sheet of 3, #a-c 7.75 7.75

**Souvenir Sheet**

2807 A562 $5 multi 3.75 3.75

Morne Trois Pitons National Park UNESCO World Heritage Site, 70th Anniv. — A563

No. 2808: a, Fumarole, mountain in background. b, Fumarole, rocks in foreground. c, Lesser Antillean iguana. d, Smoke-enshrouded landscape. e, Smoke above waterfall. g. Waterfall.
$10, Waterfall, diff.

**2015, Dec. 1** **Litho.** ***Perf. 12***

**2808** A563 $3.50 Sheet of 6, #a-f 15.50 15.50

**Souvenir Sheet**

**2809** A563 $10 multi 7.50 7.50

**WAR TAX STAMPS**

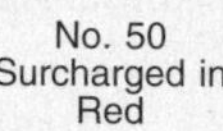
No. 50 Surcharged in Red

**1916** **Wmk. 3** ***Perf. 14***

**MR1** A6 ½p on ½p green 3.50 .85

No. 50 Overprinted in Black

**1918**

**MR2** A6 ½p green 7.50 *6.25*

Nos. 50, 40 in Black or Red

**1918**

**MR3** A6 ½p green .25 *.30*

**MR4** A6 3p violet, *yel* (R) 5.50 *4.50*

Type of 1908-09 Surcharged in Red

**1919**

**MR5** A6 1½p on 2½p orange .25 *.60*

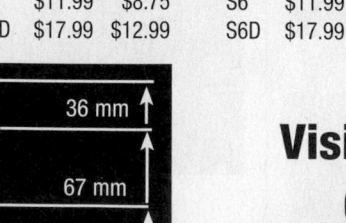

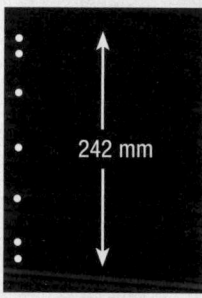

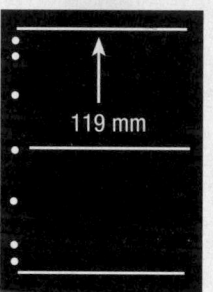

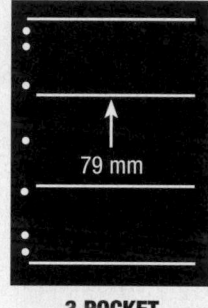

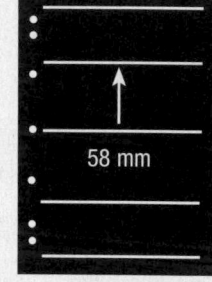

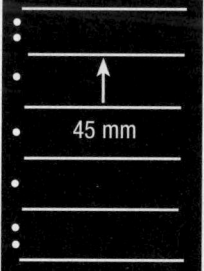

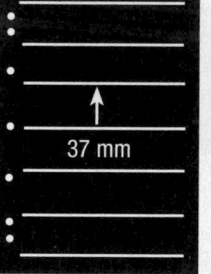

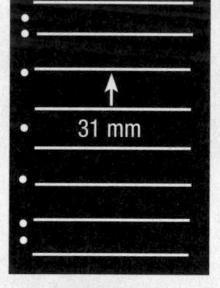

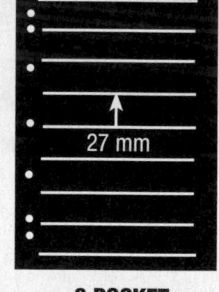

# DOMINICAN REPUBLIC

də-'mi-ni-kən ri-'pə-blik

LOCATION — Comprises about two-thirds of the island of Hispaniola in the West Indies
GOVT. — Republic
AREA — 18,700 sq. mi.
POP. — 8,129,734 (1999 est.)
CAPITAL — Santo Domingo

8 Reales = 1 Peso
100 Centavos = 1 Peso (1880)
100 Centimos = 1 Franco (1883)
100 Centavos = 1 Peso (1885)

**Catalogue values for unused stamps in this country are for Never Hinged items, beginning with Scott 437 in the regular postage section, Scott B1 in the semi-postal section, Scott C75 in the airpost section, Scott CB1 in the airpost semi-postal section, Scott E7 in the special delivery section, Scott G13 in the insured letter section, Scott J14 in the postage due section, Scott O26 in the officials section, and Scott RA20 in the postal tax section.**

### Watermarks

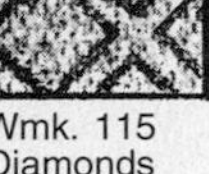

Wmk. 115 Diamonds

Wmk. 116 Crosses and Circles

Coat of Arms
A1 A2

**1865 Unwmk. Typo. *Imperf.***

**Wove Paper**

| No. | Type | Description | Unused | Used |
|---|---|---|---|---|
| 1 | A1 | ½r black, *rose* | 700. | 650. |
| 2 | A1 | 1r black, *dp green* | 1,100. | 1,000. |

Twelve varieties of each.

**Laid Paper**

| No. | Type | Description | Unused | Used |
|---|---|---|---|---|
| 3 | A2 | ½r black, *pale green* | 550. | 475. |
| 4 | A2 | 1r black, *straw* | 1,800. | 1,200. |

Twelve varieties of the ½r, ten of the 1r.

A3

A4

**1866 Laid Paper Unwmk.**

| No. | Type | Description | Unused | Used |
|---|---|---|---|---|
| 5 | A3 | ½r black, *straw* | 200.00 | 160.00 |
| 6 | A3 | 1r black, *pale green* | 2,500. | 2,000. |
| 7 | A4 | 1r black, *pale green* | 175.00 | 125.00 |

Nos. 5-8 have 21 varieties (sheets of 21).

**Wmk. 115**

| No. | Type | Description | Unused | Used |
|---|---|---|---|---|
| 8 | A3 | 1r blk, *pale grn* | 13,000. | 13,000. |
| *a.* | | "CORREOS" and "Un Real" doubled | 21,000. | |

The unique example of No. 8a is centered in the grade of fine, has a shallow thin spot and pinhole.

**1866-67 Wove Paper Unwmk.**

| No. | Type | Description | Unused | Used |
|---|---|---|---|---|
| 9 | A3 | ½r blk, *rose* ('67) | 60.00 | 60.00 |
| 10 | A3 | 1r blk, *pale green* | 85.00 | 75.00 |
| *a.* | | Inscription dbl., top & bottom | *400.00* | *400.00* |
| 11 | A3 | 1r black, *blue* ('67) | 60.00 | 37.50 |
| *a.* | | 1r black, *light blue* ('67) | 50.00 | 30.00 |
| *b.* | | No space btwn. "Un" and "real" | *600.00* | 500.00 |
| *c.* | | Without inscription at top & bottom | *1,500.* | 1,000. |
| *d.* | | Inscription invtd., top & bottom | | — |
| | | *Nos. 9-11 (3)* | 205.00 | 172.50 |

**1867-71 Pelure Paper**

| No. | Type | Description | Unused | Used |
|---|---|---|---|---|
| 13 | A3 | ½r black, *rose* | 150.00 | 75.00 |
| 15 | A3 | ½r black, *lav* ('68) | 250.00 | 210.00 |
| *a.* | | Without inscription at top and bottom | | 525.00 |
| *b.* | | Dbl. inscriptions, one invtd. | | *425.00* |
| 16 | A3 | ½r black, *grnsh gray* ('68) | 260.00 | 225.00 |
| 17 | A3 | ½r black, *yel* ('68) | 12,000. | |
| 18 | A3 | ½r blk, *ol* ('69) | 3,000. | 5,500. |
| 22 | A3 | 1r black, *blue* | 4,000. | |
| 23 | A3 | 1r black, *lav* | 225.00 | 200.00 |
| 24 | A4 | 1r blk, *rose* ('68) | 225.00 | 225.00 |
| 25 | A4 | 1r blk, *mag* ('69) | 2,250. | 1,300. |
| 26 | A4 | 1r blk, *sal* ('71) | 300.00 | 225.00 |

Value for No. 17 is for an example with very fine centering and small faults. Value for No. 22 is for a faulty example with very fine centering and appearance.

**1870-73 Ordinary Paper**

| No. | Type | Description | Unused | Used |
|---|---|---|---|---|
| 27 | A3 | ½r blk, *mag* | 2,500. | 4,750. |
| 28 | A3 | ½r blue, *rose* (blk inscription) ('71) | 50.00 | 42.50 |
| *a.* | | Blue inscription | 500.00 | 500.00 |
| *b.* | | Without inscription at top and bottom | | |
| 29 | A3 | ½r blk, *yel* ('73) | 30.00 | 21.00 |
| *a.* | | Without inscription at top and bottom | 700.00 | 700.00 |
| 30 | A4 | 1r blk, *vio* ('73) | 30.00 | 21.00 |
| *a.* | | Without inscription at top and bottom | 700.00 | 700.00 |
| 31 | A4 | 1r black, *dk grn* | 60.00 | 50.00 |

Nos. 9-31 have 21 varieties (sheets of 21). Nos. 29 and 30 are known pin-perforated, unofficially.

Bisects are known of several of the early 1r stamps.

A5

**1879 *Perf. 12½x13***

| No. | Type | Description | Unused | Used |
|---|---|---|---|---|
| 32 | A5 | ½r violet | 3.00 | 2.10 |
| *a.* | | Imperf., pair | 9.00 | 9.00 |
| *b.* | | Horiz. pair, imperf. vert. | 17.00 | |
| 33 | A5 | ½r violet, *bluish* | 2.50 | 1.80 |
| *a.* | | Imperf., pair | 9.00 | 7.50 |
| 34 | A5 | 1r carmine | 4.50 | 2.10 |
| *a.* | | Imperf., pair | 11.50 | 9.00 |
| *b.* | | Perf. 13 | 11.50 | 7.50 |
| *c.* | | Perf. 13x12½ | 11.50 | 7.50 |
| 35 | A5 | 1r carmine, *sal* | 2.50 | 1.50 |
| *a.* | | Imperf., pair | 8.25 | 8.25 |
| | | *Nos. 32-35 (4)* | 12.50 | 7.50 |

In 1891 15 stamps of 1879-83 were surcharged "U P U," new values and crossed diagonal lines.

A6

**1880 Typo. *Rouletted in Color***

| No. | Type | Description | Unused | Used |
|---|---|---|---|---|
| 36 | A6 | 1c green | 1.40 | .90 |
| *b.* | | Laid paper | 50.00 | 50.00 |
| 37 | A6 | 2c red | 1.00 | .75 |
| *a.* | | Pelure paper | 40.00 | 40.00 |
| *b.* | | Laid paper | 40.00 | 40.00 |
| 38 | A6 | 5c blue | 1.50 | .70 |
| 39 | A6 | 10c rose | 3.25 | .90 |
| 40 | A6 | 20c brown | 2.00 | .75 |
| 41 | A6 | 25c violet | 2.25 | 1.25 |
| 42 | A6 | 50c orange | 3.00 | 1.75 |
| 43 | A6 | 75c ultra | 5.75 | 3.00 |
| *a.* | | Laid paper | 40.00 | 40.00 |
| 44 | A6 | 1p gold | 7.50 | 4.50 |
| *a.* | | Laid paper | 50.00 | 50.00 |
| *b.* | | Double impression | 42.50 | 42.50 |
| | | *Nos. 36-44 (9)* | 27.65 | 14.50 |

**1881 Network Covering Stamp**

| No. | Type | Description | Unused | Used |
|---|---|---|---|---|
| 45 | A6 | 1c green | .90 | .50 |
| 46 | A6 | 2c red | .90 | .50 |
| 47 | A6 | 5c blue | 1.25 | .50 |
| 48 | A6 | 10c rose | 1.50 | .65 |
| 49 | A6 | 20c brown | 1.50 | .90 |
| 50 | A6 | 25c violet | 1.75 | 1.00 |
| 51 | A6 | 50c orange | 2.00 | 1.40 |
| 52 | A6 | 75c ultra | 6.00 | 4.50 |
| 53 | A6 | 1p gold | 8.00 | 7.00 |
| | | *Nos. 45-53 (9)* | 23.80 | 16.95 |

**Preceding Issues (Type A6) Srch. with Value in New Currency**

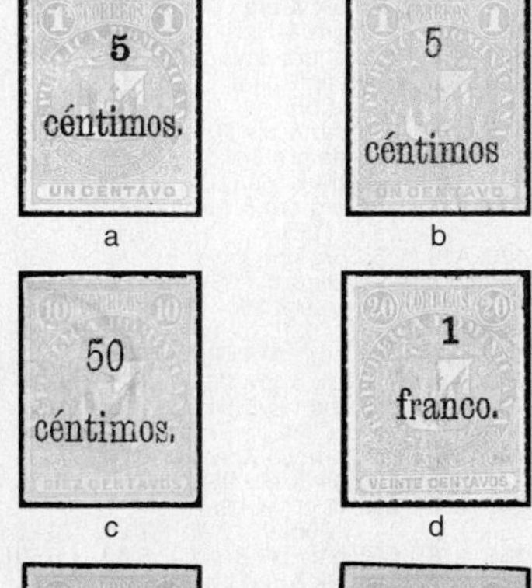


a b c d

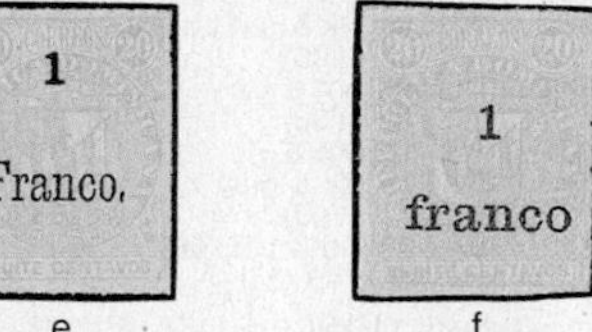


e f

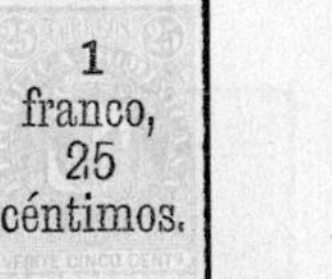


g

h



i

**1883 Without Network**

| No. | Type | Description | Unused | Used |
|---|---|---|---|---|
| 54 | (a) | 5c on 1c green | 1.50 | 1.60 |
| *b.* | | Inverted surcharge | 21.00 | 21.00 |
| *c.* | | Surcharged "25 céntimos" | 50.00 | 50.00 |
| *d.* | | Surcharged "10 céntimos" | 27.50 | 27.50 |
| 55 | (b) | 5c on 1c green | 25.00 | 9.00 |
| *b.* | | Double surcharge | 100.00 | |
| *c.* | | Inverted surcharge | 65.00 | 65.00 |
| 56 | (c) | 5c on 1c green | 17.00 | 9.50 |
| *b.* | | Surcharged "10 céntimos" | 35.00 | 35.00 |
| *c.* | | Surcharged "25 céntimos" | 37.50 | 37.50 |
| 57 | (a) | 10c on 2c red | 5.00 | 3.00 |
| *a.* | | Inverted surcharge | 27.50 | 27.50 |
| *d.* | | Surcharged "5 céntimos" | 52.50 | 52.50 |
| *e.* | | Surcharged "25 céntimos" | 75.00 | 75.00 |
| 58 | (c) | 10c on 2c red | 4.50 | 3.50 |
| *a.* | | "Céntimso" | | |
| *b.* | | Inverted surcharge | 37.50 | 37.50 |
| *c.* | | Surcharged "25 céntimos" | 60.00 | 60.00 |
| *d.* | | "10" omitted | 60.00 | |
| 59 | (a) | 25c on 5c blue | 7.00 | 4.50 |
| *a.* | | Surcharged "5 céntimos" | 52.50 | |
| *b.* | | Surcharged "10 céntimos" | 52.50 | 52.50 |
| *c.* | | Surcharged "50 céntimos" | 75.00 | 75.00 |
| *d.* | | Inverted surcharge | 50.00 | 50.00 |
| 60 | (c) | 25c on 5c blue | 7.50 | 3.50 |
| *a.* | | Inverted surcharge | 45.00 | 37.50 |
| *b.* | | Surcharged "10 céntimos" | 45.00 | 37.50 |
| *e.* | | "25" omitted | 75.00 | |
| *f.* | | Surcharged on back | | 75.00 |
| 61 | (a) | 50c on 10c rose | 27.50 | 12.50 |
| *a.* | | Inverted surcharge | 70.00 | 60.00 |
| 62 | (c) | 50c on 10c rose | 35.00 | 17.50 |
| *a.* | | Inverted surcharge | 52.50 | 52.50 |
| 63 | (d) | 1fr on 20c brn | 15.00 | 10.00 |
| 64 | (e) | 1fr on 20c brn | 17.50 | 10.00 |
| *a.* | | Comma after "Franco," | 27.50 | 27.50 |
| 65 | (f) | 1fr on 20c brn | 25.00 | 20.00 |
| *a.* | | Inverted surcharge | | 75.00 |
| 66 | (g) | 1fr25c on 25c violet | 21.00 | 15.00 |
| *a.* | | Inverted surcharge | 65.00 | 65.00 |
| 67 | (g) | 2fr50c on 50c org | 16.00 | 12.00 |
| *a.* | | Inverted surcharge | 35.00 | 27.50 |
| 68 | (g) | 3fr75c on 75c ultra | 30.00 | 25.00 |
| *b.* | | Inverted surcharge | 60.00 | 60.00 |
| *c.* | | Laid paper | 75.00 | 75.00 |
| 70 | (i) | 5fr on 1p gold | 550.00 | 500.00 |
| *a.* | | "s" of "francos" inverted | 700.00 | 700.00 |

**With Network**

| No. | Type | Description | Unused | Used |
|---|---|---|---|---|
| 71 | (a) | 5c on 1c green | 3.00 | 2.50 |
| *b.* | | Inverted surcharge | 22.50 | 22.50 |
| *c.* | | Double surcharge | 22.50 | 22.50 |
| *d.* | | Surcharged "25 céntimos" | 42.50 | 42.50 |
| *e.* | | "5" omitted | 75.00 | 75.00 |
| 72 | (b) | 5c on 1c green | 21.00 | 9.00 |
| *b.* | | Inverted surcharge | 60.00 | 60.00 |
| 73 | (c) | 5c on 1c green | 27.50 | 11.50 |
| *b.* | | Surcharged "10 céntimos" | 50.00 | 42.50 |
| *c.* | | Surcharged "25 céntimos" | 60.00 | |
| 74 | (a) | 10c on 2c red | 3.75 | 2.25 |
| *a.* | | Surcharged "5 céntimos" | 52.50 | 45.00 |
| *b.* | | Surcharged "25 céntimos" | 67.50 | 67.50 |
| *c.* | | "10" omitted | 57.50 | |
| 75 | (c) | 10c on 2c red | 3.00 | 2.00 |
| *a.* | | Inverted surcharge | 30.00 | 20.00 |
| 76 | (a) | 25c on 5c blue | 7.50 | 3.50 |
| *a.* | | Surcharged "10 céntimos" | 75.00 | |
| *b.* | | Surcharged "5 céntimos" | 60.00 | |
| *c.* | | Surcharged "50 céntimos" | 67.50 | |
| 77 | (c) | 25c on 5c blue | 60.00 | 30.00 |
| *a.* | | Inverted surcharge | | |
| *b.* | | Surcharged on back | | |
| 78 | (a) | 50c on 10c rose | 25.00 | 7.50 |
| *a.* | | Inverted surcharge | 50.00 | 30.00 |
| *b.* | | Surcharged "25 céntimos" | 60.00 | |
| 79 | (c) | 50c on 10c rose | 30.00 | 9.50 |
| *a.* | | Inverted surcharge | 60.00 | |
| 80 | (d) | 1fr on 20c brn | 12.00 | 10.00 |
| 81 | (e) | 1fr on 20c brn | 14.50 | 12.50 |
| *a.* | | Comma after "Franco" | 35.00 | 35.00 |
| *b.* | | Inverted surcharge | 75.00 | |
| 82 | (f) | 1fr on 20c brown | 25.00 | 20.00 |
| 83 | (g) | 1fr25c on 25c violet | 45.00 | 30.00 |
| *a.* | | Inverted surcharge | 75.00 | |
| 84 | (g) | 2fr50c on 50c org | 19.00 | 12.50 |
| *a.* | | Inverted surcharge | 35.00 | 27.50 |
| 85 | (g) | 3fr75c on 75c ultra | 45.00 | 42.50 |
| 86 | (h) | 5fr on 1p gold | 140.00 | 140.00 |
| *a.* | | Inverted surcharge | | |
| 87 | (i) | 5fr on 1p gold | 190.00 | 190.00 |

Many minor varieties exist in Nos. 54-87: accent on "i" of "centimos"; "5" with straight top; "1" with straight serif.

A7

A7a

**1885-91 Engr. *Perf. 12***

| No. | Type | Description | Unused | Used |
|---|---|---|---|---|
| 88 | A7 | 1c green | 1.00 | .50 |
| 89 | A7 | 2c vermilion | 1.00 | .50 |
| 90 | A7 | 5c blue | 1.40 | .50 |
| 91 | A7a | 10c orange | 2.25 | .65 |
| 92 | A7a | 20c dark brown | 2.25 | .80 |
| 93 | A7a | 50c violet ('91) | 7.50 | 7.50 |
| 94 | A7 | 1p carmine ('91) | 20.00 | 20.00 |
| 95 | A7 | 2p red brown ('91) | 25.00 | 25.00 |
| | | *Nos. 88-95 (8)* | 60.40 | 55.45 |

Nos. 93, 94, 95 were issued without gum.
Imperf. varieties are proofs.
For surcharges see Nos. 166-168.

Coat of Arms — A8

**1895 *Perf. 12½x14***

| No. | Type | Description | Unused | Used |
|---|---|---|---|---|
| 96 | A8 | 1c green | 1.25 | .50 |
| 97 | A8 | 2c orange red | 1.25 | .50 |
| 98 | A8 | 5c blue | 1.40 | .50 |
| 99 | A8 | 10c orange | 3.25 | 1.60 |
| | | *Nos. 96-99 (4)* | 7.15 | 3.10 |

Exist imperforate but were not issued.

**1897 *Perf. 14***

| No. | Type | Description | Unused | Used |
|---|---|---|---|---|
| *96a* | A8 | 1c green | 1.40 | .50 |
| *97a* | A8 | 2c orange red | 8.00 | .75 |
| *98a* | A8 | 5c blue | 1.40 | .75 |
| *99a* | A8 | 10c orange | 2.75 | 1.50 |
| | | *Nos. 96a-99a (4)* | 13.55 | 3.50 |

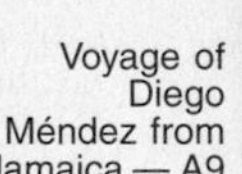

Voyage of Diego Méndez from Jamaica — A9

Enriquillo's Revolt — A10

Sarcophagus of Columbus A11

"Española" Guarding Remains of Columbus A12

Toscanelli Replying to Columbus A13

Bartolomé de las Casas Defending Indians — A14

Columbus at Salamanca A15

Columbus' Mausoleum A16

**1899, Feb. 27 Litho. *Perf. 11½***

**100** A9 1c brown violet 7.25 5.25
**102** A10 2c rose red 1.75 .70
**103** A11 5c blue 2.00 .70
**104** A12 10c orange 5.00 1.60
*a.* Tête bêche pair 42.50 42.50
**105** A13 20c brown 10.00 8.25
**106** A14 50c yellow green 11.50 9.75
*a.* Tête bêche pair 60.00 60.00
**107** A15 1p black, *gray bl* 27.00 22.00
**108** A16 2p bister brown 45.00 47.50

**1900, Jan.**

**109** A11 ¼c black .75 *1.60*
**110** A15 ½c black .75 *1.60*
**110A** A9 1c gray green .75 .65
*Nos. 100-110A (11)* 111.75 99.60

Nos. 100-110A were issued to raise funds for a Columbus mausoleum.

**Imperf., Pairs**

*100a* A9 1c brown violet 16.50 16.50
*102a* A10 2c rose red 5.00
*103a* A11 5c blue 5.75
*104b* A12 10c orange 8.75
*105a* A13 20c brown 15.00
*106b* A14 50c yellow green 17.50
*c.* As "b," tête bêche pair 125.00
*107a* A15 1p black, *gray blue* 42.50
*108a* A16 2p bister brown 70.00
*109a* A11 ¼c black 3.75 *4.25*
*110b* A15 ½c black 3.75 *4.25*
*110c* A9 1c gray green 3.50

Map of Hispaniola A17

**1900, Oct. 21 Unwmk. *Perf. 14***

**111** A17 ¼c dark blue .75 .40
**112** A17 ½c rose .75 .40
**113** A17 1c olive green .75 .40
**114** A17 2c deep green .75 .40
**115** A17 5c red brown .75 .40
*a.* Vertical pair, imperf. between 17.50

***Perf. 12***

**116** A17 10c orange .75 .40
**117** A17 20c lilac 3.00 2.50
*a.* 20c rose (error) 25.00 25.00
**118** A17 50c black 2.75 2.50
**119** A17 1p brown 3.00 2.50
*Nos. 111-119 (9)* 13.25 9.90

Several varieties in design are known in this issue. They were deliberately made. Counterfeits of Nos. 111-119 abound.

A18

**1901-06 Typo. *Perf. 14***

**120** A18 ½c carmine & vio .70 .40
**121** A18 ½c blk & org ('05) 1.80 .95
**122** A18 ½c grn & blk ('06) .85 .30
**123** A18 1c ol grn & vio .70 .30
**124** A18 1c blk & ultra ('05) 1.80 .85
**125** A18 1c car & blk ('06) 1.00 .45
**126** A18 2c dp grn & vio .80 .30
**127** A18 2c blk & vio ('05) 2.25 .70
**128** A18 2c org brn & blk ('06) 1.40 .30
**129** A18 5c org brn & vio .80 .30
**130** A18 5c blk & cl ('05) 2.50 1.25
**131** A18 5c blue & blk ('06) 1.25 .30
**132** A18 10c orange & vio 1.40 .45
**133** A18 10c blk & grn ('05) 4.25 2.25
**134** A18 10c red vio & blk ('06) 1.40 .40
**135** A18 20c brn vio & vio 2.50 .95
**136** A18 20c blk & ol ('05) 13.50 8.75
**137** A18 20c ol grn & blk ('06) 7.25 3.25
**138** A18 50c gray blk & vio 8.00 5.50
**139** A18 50c blk & red brn ('05) 47.50 34.00
**140** A18 50c brn & blk ('06) 8.75 7.75
**141** A18 1p brn & vio 18.00 10.00
**142** A18 1p blk & gray ('05) 200.00 *225.00*
**143** A18 1p vio & blk ('06) 21.00 13.50
*Nos. 120-143 (24)* 349.40 318.20

Issued: 11/15/01; 5/11/05; 8/17/06.

See Nos. 172-176. For surcharges see Nos.151-156.

Francisco Sánchez — A19

Juan Pablo Duarte — A20

Ramón Mella — A21

Ft. Santo Domingo — A22

**1902, Feb. 25 Engr. *Perf. 12***

**144** A19 1c dk grn & blk .35 .35
**145** A20 2c scarlet & blk .35 .35
**146** A20 5c blue & blk .35 .35
**147** A19 10c orange & blk .35 .35
**148** A21 12c purple & blk .35 .35
**149** A21 20c rose & blk .60 .60
**150** A22 50c brown & blk .90 .90
*Nos. 144-150 (7)* 3.25 3.25

**Center Inverted**

*144a* A19 1c 17.50 *17.50*
*145a* A20 2c 17.50 *17.50*
*146a* A20 5c 17.50 *17.50*
*148a* A21 12c 17.50 *17.50*
*149a* A21 20c 17.50 *17.50*
*150a* A22 50c 17.50 *17.50*
*Nos. 144a-150a (6)* 105.00 *105.00*

400th anniversary of Santo Domingo.

Imperforate varieties of Nos. 144 to 150 were never sold to the public.

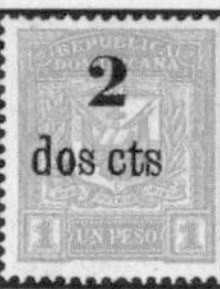
Nos. 138, 141 Surcharged in Black

**1904, Aug.**

**151** A18 2c on 50c 9.25 7.25
**152** A18 2c on 1p 13.50 9.25
*b.* "2" omitted 50.00 50.00
**153** A18 5c on 50c 4.25 2.25
**154** A18 5c on 1p 5.25 4.00
**155** A18 10c on 50c 8.25 6.75
**156** A18 10c on 1p 8.75 6.75
*Nos. 151-156 (6)* 49.25 36.25

**Inverted Surcharge**

*151a* A18 2c on 50c 15.00 15.00
*152a* A18 2c on 1p 15.00 15.00
*c.* As "a," "2" omitted 85.00 85.00
*153a* A18 5c on 50c 5.50 5.50
*154a* A18 5c on 1p 7.00 6.50
*155a* A18 10c on 50c 14.00 14.00
*156a* A18 10c on 1p 10.00 10.00
*Nos. 151a-156a (6)* 66.50 66.00

Official Stamps of 1902 Overprinted

**1904, Aug. 16 Red Overprint**

**157** O1 5c dk blue & blk 5.75 3.00
*a.* Inverted overprint 7.25 5.75

**Black Overprint**

**158** O1 2c scarlet & blk 17.00 5.25
*a.* Inverted overprint 20.00 6.50
**159** O1 5c dk blue & blk 3,500. 3,500.
**160** O1 10c yellow grn & blk 10.50 10.50
*a.* Inverted overprint 15.00 15.00

Official Stamps of 1902 Surcharged

**161** O1 1c on 20c yellow & blk 4.75 3.00
*a.* Inverted surcharge 7.25 7.25

Nos. J1-J2 Surcharged or Overprinted in Black

**1904-05 Surcharged "CENTAVOS"**

**162** D1 1c on 2c olive gray 250.00 200.00
*a.* "entavos" —
*b.* "Dominican" 350.00 300.00
*c.* "Centavo" 350.00 300.00

**Carmine Surcharge or Overprint**

**163** D1 1c on 2c olive gray 3.50 1.10
*a.* Inverted surcharge 4.75 4.75
*b.* "Domihicana" 15.00 15.00
*c.* As "b," inverted 40.00 40.00
*d.* "Dominican" 10.50 10.50
*e.* "Centavos" omitted 30.00 30.00
*g.* "entavos" 30.00
**163F** D1 1c on 4c olive gray 35.00 7.00
**164** D1 2c olive gray .95 .60
*a.* "Domihicana" 11.00 11.00
*b.* Inverted overprint 2.00 2.00
*c.* As "a," inverted 25.00 25.00
*d.* "Dominican" 25.00 25.00
*e.* "Centavo" omitted 12.50 10.00
*f.* "entavos" 12.50 12.50
*g.* As "f," inverted 40.00 40.00
*h.* As "d," inverted 40.00 40.00

**Surcharged "CENTAVO"**

**165** D1 1c on 4c olive gray .95 .70
*a.* "Domihicana" 10.00 10.00
*c.* Inverted surcharge 1.75 1.75
*d.* "1" omitted 3.50 3.50
*e.* As "a," inverted 32.50 32.50
*f.* As "d," inverted 40.00 40.00
*g.* Double surcharge 30.00 30.00

No. 92 Surcharged in Red

**1905, Apr. 4**

**166** A7a 2c on 20c dk brown 8.75 7.25
*a.* Inverted surcharge 15.00 15.00
**167** A7a 5c on 20c dk brown 4.75 2.50
*a.* Inverted surcharge 16.00 16.00
*b.* Double surcharge 25.00 25.00
**168** A7a 10c on 20c dk brown 8.75 7.25
*Nos. 166-168 (3)* 22.25 17.00

Nos. 166-168 exist with inverted "A" for "V" in "CENTAVOS" in surcharge.

No. J2 Surcharged in Red

**1906, Jan. 16 *Perf. 14***

**169** D1 1c on 4c olive gray .95 .50
*a.* Inverted surcharge 10.50 10.50
*b.* Double surcharge 25.00

**Nos. J4, J3 Surcharged in Black**

**1906, May 1**

**170** D1 1c on 10c olive gray 1.10 .40
*a.* Inverted surcharge 10.50 10.50
*b.* Double surcharge 14.00 14.00
*c.* "OMINICANA" 20.00 20.00
*d.* As "c," inverted 150.00
**171** D1 2c on 5c olive gray 1.10 .40
*a.* Inverted surcharge 10.50 10.50
*b.* Double surcharge 35.00

The varieties small "C" or small "A" in "REPUBLICA" are found on Nos.169, 170, 171.

**Arms Type of 1901-06**

**1907-10 Wmk. 116**

**172** A18 ½c grn & blk ('08) .85 .25
**173** A18 1c carmine & blk .85 .25
**174** A18 2c orange brn & blk .85 .25
**175** A18 5c blue & blk .85 .25
**176** A18 10c red vio & blk ('10) 8.00 1.00
*Nos. 172-176 (5)* 11.40 2.00

No. O6 Overprinted in Red

**1911, July 11 *Perf. 13½x14, 13½x13***

**177** O2 2c scarlet & black 1.60 .60
*a.* "HABILITAOO" 8.75 6.00
*b.* Inverted overprint 21.00
*c.* Double overprint 21.00

A23

**1911-13 Center in Black *Perf. 14***

**178** A23 ½c orange ('13) .25 .25
**179** A23 1c green .25 .25
**180** A23 2c carmine .25 .25
**181** A23 5c gray blue ('13) .80 .25
**182** A23 10c red violet 1.60 .45
**183** A23 20c olive green 11.50 11.50
**184** A23 50c yellow brn ('12) 3.75 3.75
**185** A23 1p violet ('12) 5.75 4.25
*Nos. 178-185 (8)* 24.15 20.95

See Nos. 230-232.

Juan Pablo Duarte — A24

**1914, Apr. 13** *Perf. 13x14*

**Background Red, White and Blue**

| | | | | |
|---|---|---|---|---|
| **186** | A24 | ½c orange & blk | .60 | .30 |
| **187** | A24 | 1c green & blk | .60 | .30 |
| **188** | A24 | 2c rose & blk | .60 | .30 |
| **189** | A24 | 5c slate & blk | .60 | .40 |
| **190** | A24 | 10c magenta & blk | 1.40 | .70 |
| **191** | A24 | 20c olive grn & blk | 2.50 | 1.90 |
| **192** | A24 | 50c brown & blk | 3.50 | 2.75 |
| **193** | A24 | 1p dull lilac & blk | 5.50 | 4.00 |
| | | *Nos. 186-193 (8)* | 15.30 | 10.65 |

Cent. of the birth of Juan Pablo Duarte (1813-1876), patriot and revolutionary.

**Official Stamps of 1909-12 Surcharged in Violet or Overprinted in Red**

a

b

**1915, Feb.** *Perf. 13½x13, 13½x14*

| | | | | |
|---|---|---|---|---|
| **194** | O2 (a) | ½c on 20c org & blk | .50 | .35 |
| *a.* | | Inverted surcharge | 6.00 | 6.00 |
| *b.* | | Double surcharge | 8.75 | 8.75 |
| *c.* | | "Habilitado" omitted | 5.25 | 5.25 |
| **195** | O2 (b) | 1c blue grn & blk | .80 | .25 |
| *a.* | | Inverted overprint | 6.00 | 6.00 |
| *b.* | | Double overprint | 7.00 | |
| *c.* | | Overprinted "1915" only | 12.50 | |
| **196** | O2 (b) | 2c scarlet & blk | 1.25 | .25 |
| *a.* | | Inverted overprint | 5.25 | 5.25 |
| *b.* | | Double overprint | 7.75 | 7.75 |
| *c.* | | Overprinted "1915" only | 8.75 | |
| *d.* | | "1915" double | | |
| **197** | O2 (b) | 5c dk blue & blk | 1.00 | .25 |
| *a.* | | Inverted overprint | 7.00 | 7.00 |
| *b.* | | Double overprint | 8.75 | 8.75 |
| *c.* | | Double ovpt., one invtd. | 27.50 | |
| *d.* | | Overprinted "1915" only | 8.50 | |
| **198** | O2 (b) | 10c yel grn & blk | 2.75 | 2.50 |
| *a.* | | Inverted overprint | 15.00 | |
| **199** | O2 (b) | 20c orange & blk | 9.25 | 7.25 |
| *a.* | | "Habilitado" omitted | | |
| | | *Nos. 194-199 (6)* | 15.55 | 10.85 |

Nos. 194, 196-198 are known with both perforations. Nos. 195, 199 are only perf. 13½x13.

The variety capital "I" for "1" in "Habilitado" occurs once in each sheet in all denominations.

**Type of 1911-13 Redrawn**

A25

SMALL LETTERS

LARGE LETTERS

TWO CENTAVOS:
Type I — "DOS" in small letters.
Type II — "DOS" in larger letters with white dot at each end of the word.

**Overprinted "1915" in Red**

**1915 Unwmk. Litho.** *Perf. 11½*

| | | | | |
|---|---|---|---|---|
| **200** | A25 | ½c violet & blk | .85 | .25 |
| *a.* | | Imperf., pair | 5.75 | |
| **201** | A25 | 1c yel brn & blk | .85 | .25 |
| *a.* | | Imperf., pair | 6.50 | |
| *b.* | | Vert. pair, imperf. horiz. | 10.50 | |
| *c.* | | Horiz. pair, imperf. vert. | 10.50 | |
| **202** | A25 | 2c ol grn & blk (I) | 3.75 | .25 |
| *a.* | | Imperf., pair | 10.00 | |
| **203** | A25 | 2c ol grn & blk (II) | 6.00 | .25 |
| *a.* | | Center omitted | 87.50 | |
| *b.* | | Frame omitted | 87.50 | |
| *c.* | | Imperf., pair | 15.00 | |
| *d.* | | Horiz. pair, imperf. vert. | 15.00 | |
| **204** | A25 | 5c magenta & blk | 3.75 | .25 |
| *a.* | | Pair, one without overprint | 65.00 | |
| *b.* | | Imperf., pair | 6.50 | |
| **205** | A25 | 10c gray blue & blk | 3.75 | .50 |
| *a.* | | Imperf., pair | 10.00 | |
| *b.* | | Horiz. pair, imperf. vert. | 35.00 | |
| **206** | A25 | 20c rose red & blk | 8.25 | 1.40 |
| *a.* | | Imperf., pair | 12.50 | |
| **207** | A25 | 50c green & blk | 10.50 | 4.00 |
| *a.* | | Imperf., pair | 25.00 | |
| **208** | A25 | 1p orange & blk | 21.00 | 7.00 |
| *a.* | | Imperf., pair | 52.50 | |
| | | *Nos. 200-208 (9)* | 58.70 | 14.15 |

Type of 1915 Overprinted "1916" in Red

**1916**

| | | | | |
|---|---|---|---|---|
| **209** | A25 | ½c violet & blk | 2.25 | .25 |
| *a.* | | Imperf., pair | 21.00 | |
| **210** | A25 | 1c green & blk | 3.25 | .25 |
| *a.* | | Imperf., pair | 21.00 | |

Type of 1915 Overprinted "1917" in Red

**1917-19**

| | | | | |
|---|---|---|---|---|
| **213** | A25 | ½c red lilac & blk | 3.50 | .30 |
| *a.* | | Horiz. pair, imperf. btwn. | 47.50 | 47.50 |
| **214** | A25 | 1c yellow grn & blk | 1.60 | .25 |
| *a.* | | Vert. pair, imperf. btwn. | 50.00 | |
| **215** | A25 | 2c olive grn & blk | 2.25 | .25 |
| *a.* | | Imperf., pair | 35.00 | |
| **216** | A25 | 5c magenta & blk | 23.00 | .85 |
| | | *Nos. 213-216 (4)* | 30.35 | 1.65 |

Type of 1915 Overprinted "1919" in Red

**1919**

| | | | | |
|---|---|---|---|---|
| **219** | A25 | 2c olive grn & blk | 17.00 | .25 |

Type of 1915 Overprinted "1920" in Red

**1920-27**

| | | | | |
|---|---|---|---|---|
| **220** | A25 | ½c lilac rose & blk | .60 | .25 |
| *a.* | | Horiz. pair, imperf. btwn. | 25.00 | 25.00 |
| *b.* | | Inverted overprint | | |
| *c.* | | Double overprint | | |
| *d.* | | Double overprint, one invtd. | | |
| **221** | A25 | 1c yellow grn & blk | .75 | .25 |
| *a.* | | Overprint omitted | 70.00 | |
| *b.* | | Horiz. pair, imperf. btwn. | 40.00 | |
| **222** | A25 | 2c olive grn & blk | .75 | .25 |
| *a.* | | Vertical pair, imperf. between | 27.50 | |
| **223** | A25 | 5c dp rose & blk | 9.00 | .50 |
| **224** | A25 | 10c blue & black | 5.75 | .25 |
| **225** | A25 | 20c rose red & blk ('27) | 7.75 | .50 |
| **226** | A25 | 50c green & blk ('27) | 65.00 | 21.00 |
| | | *Nos. 220-226 (7)* | 89.60 | 23.00 |

Type of 1915 Overprinted "1921" in Red

**1921**

| | | | | |
|---|---|---|---|---|
| **227** | A25 | 1c yellow grn & blk | 5.25 | .30 |
| *a.* | | Horiz. pair, imperf. btwn. | 45.00 | 45.00 |
| *b.* | | Imperf., pair | 45.00 | 45.00 |
| **228** | A25 | 2c olive grn & blk | 5.75 | .40 |
| *a.* | | Vert. pair, imperf. btwn. | 45.00 | |

Redrawn Design of 1915 without Overprint

**1922**

| | | | | |
|---|---|---|---|---|
| **230** | A25 | 1c green | 3.75 | .30 |
| **231** | A25 | 2c carmine (II) | 3.75 | .30 |
| **232** | A25 | 5c blue | 5.75 | .30 |
| | | *Nos. 230-232 (3)* | 13.25 | .90 |

Nos. 230-232 exist imperf.

A26

**Type I**

**Type II**

TEN CENTAVOS:
Type I — Numerals 2mm high. "DIEZ" in thick letters with large white dot at each end.
Type II — Numerals 3mm high. "DIEZ" in thin letters with white dot with colored center at each end.

**1924-27** **Second Redrawing**

| | | | | |
|---|---|---|---|---|
| **233** | A26 | 1c green | 1.60 | .25 |
| *a.* | | Vert. pair, imperf. btwn. | 35.00 | 35.00 |
| **234** | A26 | 2c red | .85 | .25 |
| **235** | A26 | 5c blue | 2.25 | .25 |
| **236** | A26 | 10c pale bl & blk (I) ('26) | 12.00 | 3.00 |
| **236A** | A26 | 10c pale bl & blk (II) | 22.50 | 1.10 |
| **236B** | A26 | 50c gray grn & blk ('26) | 60.00 | 33.00 |
| **237** | A26 | 1p org & blk ('27) | 19.00 | 12.50 |
| | | *Nos. 233-237 (7)* | 118.20 | 50.35 |

In the second redrawing the shield has a flat top and the design differs in many details from the stamps of 1911-13 and 1915-22.

A27

**1927**

| | | | | |
|---|---|---|---|---|
| **238** | A27 | ½c lilac rose & blk | .30 | .25 |

Exhibition Pavilion — A28

**1927 Unwmk.** *Perf. 12*

| | | | | |
|---|---|---|---|---|
| **239** | A28 | 2c carmine | 1.10 | .50 |
| **240** | A28 | 5c ultra | 2.10 | .50 |

Natl. and West Indian Exhib. at Santiago de los Caballeros.

Ruins of Columbus' Fortress A29

**1928**

| | | | | |
|---|---|---|---|---|
| **241** | A29 | ½c lilac rose | .95 | .35 |
| **242** | A29 | 1c deep green | .70 | .25 |
| *a.* | | Horiz. pair, imperf. btwn. | 25.00 | |
| **243** | A29 | 2c red | .95 | .25 |
| **244** | A29 | 5c dark blue | 2.75 | .35 |
| **245** | A29 | 10c light blue | 2.75 | .30 |
| **246** | A29 | 20c rose | 4.75 | .40 |
| **247** | A29 | 50c yellow green | 13.50 | 8.25 |
| **248** | A29 | 1p orange yellow | 35.00 | 27.00 |
| | | *Nos. 241-248 (8)* | 61.35 | 37.15 |

*Reprints exist of 1c, 2c and 10c.*
Issued: 1c, 2c, 10c, Oct. 1; others, Dec.

Horacio Vasquez — A30

**1929, May-June**

| | | | | |
|---|---|---|---|---|
| **249** | A30 | ½c dull rose | .60 | .30 |
| **250** | A30 | 1c gray green | .60 | .25 |
| **251** | A30 | 2c red | .70 | .25 |
| **252** | A30 | 5c dark ultra | 1.40 | .35 |
| **253** | A30 | 10c pale blue | 2.10 | .50 |
| | | *Nos. 249-253 (5)* | 5.40 | 1.65 |

Signing of the "Frontier" treaty with Haiti.
Issue dates: 2c, May; others, June.

**Imperf., Pairs**

| | | | |
|---|---|---|---|
| *249a* | A30 | ½c | 12.50 |
| *250a* | A30 | 1c | 12.50 |
| *251a* | A30 | 2c | 12.50 |
| *252a* | A30 | 5c | 14.00 |

Convent of San Ignacio de Loyola — A31

**1930, May 1** *Perf. 11½*

| | | | | |
|---|---|---|---|---|
| **254** | A31 | ½c red brown | .70 | .45 |
| *a.* | | Imperf., pair | 55.00 | 55.00 |
| **255** | A31 | 1c deep green | .65 | .25 |
| **256** | A31 | 2c vermilion | .65 | .25 |
| *a.* | | Imperf., pair | 60.00 | |
| **257** | A31 | 5c deep blue | 2.10 | .35 |
| **258** | A31 | 10c light blue | 4.25 | 1.25 |
| | | *Nos. 254-258 (5)* | 8.35 | 2.55 |

Cathedral of Santo Domingo, First Church in America A32

**1931** *Perf. 12*

| | | | | |
|---|---|---|---|---|
| **260** | A32 | 1c deep green | .85 | .25 |
| *a.* | | Imperf., pair | 50.00 | |
| **261** | A32 | 2c scarlet | .60 | .25 |
| *a.* | | Imperf., pair | 50.00 | |
| **262** | A32 | 3c violet | .85 | .25 |
| **263** | A32 | 7c dark blue | 2.50 | .25 |
| **264** | A32 | 8c bister | 3.00 | .85 |
| **265** | A32 | 10c light blue | 5.75 | 1.25 |
| *a.* | | Imperf., pair | 35.00 | |
| | | *Nos. 260-265 (6)* | 13.55 | 3.10 |

Issued: 3c-7c, Aug. 1; others, July 11.
For overprint see No. RAC8.

A33

**Overprinted or Surcharged in Black**

**1932, Dec. 20** *Perf. 12*

**Cross in Red**

| | | | | |
|---|---|---|---|---|
| **265B** | A33 | 1c yellow green | .55 | .50 |
| **265C** | A33 | 3c on 2c violet | .80 | .60 |
| **265D** | A33 | 5c blue | 4.50 | 4.75 |
| **265E** | A33 | 7c on 10c turq bl | 6.00 | 6.25 |
| | | *Nos. 265B-265E (4)* | 11.85 | 12.10 |

Proceeds of sale given to Red Cross. Valid Dec. 20 to Jan. 5, 1933.

Inverted and pairs, one without surcharge or overprint, exist on Nos. 265B-265D, as well as missing letters.

Fernando Arturo de Merino (1833-1906) as President — A35

Cathedral of Santo Domingo A36

Designs: ½c, 5c, 8c, Tomb of Merino. 1c, 3c, 10c, as Archbishop.

**1933, Feb. 27** **Engr.** *Perf. 14*

| | | | | |
|---|---|---|---|---|
| **266** | A35 | ½c lt violet | .45 | .35 |
| **267** | A35 | 1c yellow green | .60 | .25 |
| **268** | A35 | 2c lt red | 1.00 | .75 |
| **269** | A35 | 3c deep violet | .70 | .30 |
| **270** | A35 | 5c dark blue | .80 | .35 |
| **271** | A35 | 7c ultra | 1.40 | .50 |
| **272** | A35 | 8c dark green | 1.75 | 1.00 |
| **273** | A35 | 10c orange yel | 1.50 | .60 |
| **274** | A35 | 20c carmine rose | 3.00 | 1.75 |
| **275** | A36 | 50c lemon | 11.25 | 7.75 |
| **276** | A36 | 1p dark brown | 26.00 | 19.00 |
| | | *Nos. 266-276 (11)* | 48.45 | 32.60 |

For surcharges see Nos. G1-G7.

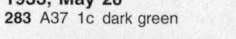

Tower of Homage, Ozama Fortress — A37

**1932** **Litho.** *Perf. 12*

| | | | | |
|---|---|---|---|---|
| **278** | A37 | 1c green | 1.75 | .25 |
| **279** | A37 | 3c violet | 1.10 | .25 |

Issue dates: 1c, July 2; 3c, June 22.

**"CORREOS" added at left**

**1933, May 28**

| | | | | |
|---|---|---|---|---|
| **283** | A37 | 1c dark green | .50 | .25 |

President Rafael L. Trujillo
A38 A39

**1933, Aug. 16** **Engr.** *Perf. 14*

| | | | | |
|---|---|---|---|---|
| **286** | A38 | 1c yellow grn & blk | 1.75 | .35 |
| **287** | A39 | 3c dp violet & blk | 2.50 | .35 |
| **288** | A38 | 7c ultra & blk | 5.75 | .75 |
| | | *Nos. 286-288 (3)* | 10.00 | 1.45 |

42nd birthday of President Rafael Leonidas Trujillo Molina.

San Rafael Bridge — A40

**1934** **Litho.** *Perf. 12*

| | | | | |
|---|---|---|---|---|
| **289** | A40 | ½c dull violet | .70 | .40 |
| **290** | A40 | 1c dark green | 1.00 | .25 |
| **291** | A40 | 3c violet | 1.75 | .25 |
| | | *Nos. 289-291 (3)* | 3.45 | .90 |

Opening of San Rafael Bridge.

Issue dates: ½c, 3c, Mar. 3; 1c, Feb. 17.

Trujillo Bridge A41

**1934**

| | | | | |
|---|---|---|---|---|
| **292** | A41 | ½c red brown | .70 | .25 |
| **293** | A41 | 1c green | 1.00 | .25 |
| **294** | A41 | 3c purple | 1.40 | .25 |
| | | *Nos. 292-294 (3)* | 3.10 | .75 |

Opening of the General Trujillo Bridge near Ciudad Trujillo.

Issue dates: 1c, Aug. 24. Others, Sept. 7.

Ramfis Bridge A42

**1935, Apr. 6**

| | | | | |
|---|---|---|---|---|
| **295** | A42 | 1c green | .70 | .25 |
| **296** | A42 | 3c yellow brown | .70 | .25 |
| **297** | A42 | 5c brown violet | 2.10 | 1.00 |
| **298** | A42 | 10c rose | 4.25 | 1.40 |
| | | *Nos. 295-298 (4)* | 7.75 | 2.90 |

Opening of the Ramfis Bridge over the Higuamo River.

President Trujillo — A43

A44

A45

**1935** *Perf. 11*

| | | | | |
|---|---|---|---|---|
| **299** | A43 | 3c yellow & brown | .30 | .25 |
| **300** | A44 | 5c org red, bl, red & bis | .40 | .25 |
| **301** | A45 | 7c ultra, bl, red & brn | .60 | .25 |
| **302** | A44 | 10c red vio, bl, red & bis | 1.00 | .25 |
| | | *Nos. 299-302 (4)* | 2.30 | 1.00 |

Ratification of a treaty setting the frontier between Dominican Republic and Haiti.

Issued: 3c, 10/29; 5c, 10c, 11/25; 7c, 11/8.

National Palace A46

**1935, Apr. 1** *Perf. 11½*

| | | | | |
|---|---|---|---|---|
| **303** | A46 | 25c yellow orange | 3.75 | .30 |

Obligatory for all mail addressed to the president and cabinet ministers.

Post Office, Santiago A47

**1936**

| | | | | |
|---|---|---|---|---|
| **304** | A47 | ½c bright violet | .30 | .35 |
| **305** | A47 | 1c green | .30 | .25 |

Issue dates: ½c, Jan. 14; 1c, Jan. 4.

George Washington Ave., Ciudad Trujillo — A48

**1936, Feb. 22**

| | | | | |
|---|---|---|---|---|
| **306** | A48 | ½c brn & vio brn | .40 | .45 |
| *a.* | | Imperf., pair | 52.50 | |
| **307** | A48 | 2c carmine & brn | .40 | .30 |
| **308** | A48 | 3c yel org & red brn | .70 | .25 |
| **309** | A48 | 7c ultra, blue & brn | 1.60 | 1.25 |
| *a.* | | Imperf., pair | 52.50 | |
| | | *Nos. 306-309 (4)* | 3.10 | 2.25 |

Dedication of George Washington Avenue, Ciudad Trujillo.

José Nuñez de Cáceres — A49 Felix M. del Monte — A55

Proposed National Library — A56

1c, Gen. Gregorio Luperon. 2c, Emiliano Tejera. 3c, Pres. Trujillo. 5c, Jose Reyes. 7c, Gen. Antonio Duverge. 25c, Francisco J. Peynado. 30c, Salome Urena. 50c, Gen. Jose M. Cabral. 1p, Manuel de Jesus Galvan. 2p, Gaston F. Deligne.

**1936** **Unwmk.** **Engr.** *Perf. 13½, 14*

| | | | | |
|---|---|---|---|---|
| **310** | A49 | ½c dull violet | .40 | .25 |
| **311** | A49 | 1c dark green | .30 | .25 |
| **312** | A49 | 2c carmine | .30 | .25 |
| **313** | A49 | 3c violet | .40 | .25 |
| **314** | A49 | 5c deep ultra | .70 | .30 |
| **315** | A49 | 7c slate blue | 1.25 | .60 |
| **316** | A55 | 10c orange | 1.25 | .30 |
| **317** | A56 | 20c olive green | 5.75 | 3.00 |
| **318** | A55 | 25c gray violet | 6.75 | 8.75 |
| **319** | A55 | 30c scarlet | 8.25 | 11.50 |
| **320** | A55 | 50c black brown | 9.75 | 6.25 |
| **321** | A55 | 1p black | 27.50 | 35.00 |
| **322** | A55 | 2p yellow brown | 80.00 | 90.00 |
| | | *Nos. 310-322 (13)* | 142.60 | 156.70 |

The funds derived from the sale of these stamps were returned to the National Treasury Fund for the erection of a building for the National Library and Archives.

Issued: 3c, 7c, Mar. 18; others, May 22.

President Trujillo and Obelisk — A62

**1937, Jan. 11** **Litho.** *Perf. 11½*

| | | | | |
|---|---|---|---|---|
| **323** | A62 | 1c green | .30 | .25 |
| **324** | A62 | 3c violet | .40 | .25 |
| **325** | A62 | 7c blue & turq blue | 1.10 | 1.10 |
| | | *Nos. 323-325 (3)* | 1.80 | 1.60 |

1st anniv. of naming Ciudad Trujillo.

Discus Thrower and Flag — A63

**Flag in Red and Blue**

**1937, Aug. 14**

| | | | | |
|---|---|---|---|---|
| **326** | A63 | 1c dark green | 6.00 | .75 |
| **327** | A63 | 3c violet | 9.00 | .75 |
| **328** | A63 | 7c dark blue | 15.00 | 3.50 |
| | | *Nos. 326-328 (3)* | 30.00 | 5.00 |

1st Natl. Olympic Games, Aug. 16, 1937.

Symbolical of Peace, Labor and Progress — A64

**1937, Sept. 18** *Perf. 12*

| | | | | |
|---|---|---|---|---|
| **329** | A64 | 3c purple | .50 | .25 |

"8th Year of the Benefactor."

Monument to Father Francisco Xavier Billini (1837-90) — A65

**1937, Dec. 29**

| | | | | |
|---|---|---|---|---|
| **330** | A65 | ½c deep orange | .25 | .25 |
| **331** | A65 | 5c purple | .60 | .25 |

Globe and Torch of Liberty — A66

**1938, Feb. 22** *Perf. 11½*

| | | | | |
|---|---|---|---|---|
| **332** | A66 | 1c green | .50 | .25 |
| **333** | A66 | 3c purple | .70 | .25 |
| **334** | A66 | 10c orange | 1.40 | .25 |
| | | *Nos. 332-334 (3)* | 2.60 | .75 |

150th anniv. of the Constitution of the US.

Pledge of Trinitarians, City Gate and National Flag — A67

**1938, July 16** *Perf. 12*

| | | | | |
|---|---|---|---|---|
| **335** | A67 | 1c green, red & dk bl | .50 | .25 |
| **336** | A67 | 3c purple, red & bl | .60 | .25 |
| **337** | A67 | 10c orange, red & bl | 1.25 | .40 |
| | | *Nos. 335-337 (3)* | 2.35 | .90 |

Trinitarians and patriots, Francisco Del Rosario Sanchez, Matías Ramón Mella and Juan Pablo Duarte, who helped free their country from foreign domination.

Seal of the University of Santo Domingo — A68

**1938, Oct. 28**

| | | | | |
|---|---|---|---|---|
| **338** A68 | ½c orange | .40 | .25 |
| **339** A68 | 1c dp green & lt green | .40 | .25 |
| **340** A68 | 3c purple & pale vio | .50 | .25 |
| **341** A68 | 7c dp blue & lt blue | 1.00 | .50 |
| | *Nos. 338-341 (4)* | 2.30 | 1.25 |

Founding of the University of Santo Domingo, on Oct. 28, 1538.

Trylon and Perisphere, Flag and Proposed Columbus Lighthouse — A69

**Flag in Blue and Red**

**1939, Apr. 30 Litho. *Perf. 12***

| | | | |
|---|---|---|---|
| **342** A69 | ½c red org & org | .35 | .25 |
| **343** A69 | 1c green & lt green | .40 | .25 |
| **344** A69 | 3c purple & pale vio | .40 | .25 |
| **345** A69 | 10c orange & yellow | 1.40 | .65 |
| | *Nos. 342-345,C33 (5)* | 4.55 | 2.25 |

New York World's Fair.

A70

**1939, Sept. Typo.**

| | | | |
|---|---|---|---|
| **346** A70 | ½c black & pale gray | .40 | .25 |
| **347** A70 | 1c black & yel grn | .50 | .25 |
| **348** A70 | 3c black & yel brn | .50 | .25 |
| **349** A70 | 7c black & dp ultra | 1.10 | .90 |
| **350** A70 | 10c black & brt red vio | 2.10 | .40 |
| | *Nos. 346-350 (5)* | 4.60 | 2.05 |

José Trujillo Valdez (1863-1935), father of President Trujillo Molina.

A71

Map of the Americas and flags of 21 American republics.

**Flags in National Colors**

**1940, Apr. 14 Litho. *Perf. 11½***

| | | | |
|---|---|---|---|
| **351** A71 | 1c deep green | .35 | .25 |
| **352** A71 | 2c carmine | .45 | .25 |
| **353** A71 | 3c red violet | .60 | .25 |
| **354** A71 | 10c orange | 1.25 | .25 |
| **355** A71 | 1p chestnut | 18.00 | 13.50 |
| | *Nos. 351-355 (5)* | 20.65 | 14.50 |

Pan American Union, 50th anniv.

Sir Rowland Hill — A72

**1940, May 6 *Perf. 12***

| | | | |
|---|---|---|---|
| **356** A72 | 3c brt red vio & rose lil | 3.25 | .40 |
| **357** A72 | 7c dk blue & lt blue | 6.75 | 1.75 |

Centenary of first postage stamp.

Julia Molina Trujillo A73

**1940, May 26**

| | | | |
|---|---|---|---|
| **358** A73 | 1c grn, lt grn & dk grn | .40 | .25 |
| **359** A73 | 2c brt red, buff & dp rose | .40 | .25 |
| **360** A73 | 3c org, dl org & brn org | .55 | .25 |
| **361** A73 | 7c bl, pale bl & dk bl | 1.10 | .35 |
| | *Nos. 358-361 (4)* | 2.45 | 1.10 |

Issued in commemoration of Mother's Day.

Map of Caribbean A74

**1940, June 6 *Perf. 11½***

| | | | |
|---|---|---|---|
| **362** A74 | 3c brt car & pale rose | .50 | .25 |
| **363** A74 | 7c dk blue & lt blue | 1.00 | .25 |
| **364** A74 | 1p yel grn & pale grn | 10.00 | 9.00 |
| | *Nos. 362-364 (3)* | 11.50 | 9.50 |

2nd Inter-American Caribbean Conf. held at Ciudad Trujillo, May 31 to June 6.

Marion Military Hospital — A75

**1940, Dec. 24**

| | | | |
|---|---|---|---|
| **365** A75 | ½c chestnut & fawn | .25 | .25 |

Fortress, Ciudad Trujillo A76

Statue of Columbus, Ciudad Trujillo — A77

**1941**

| | | | |
|---|---|---|---|
| **366** A76 | 1c dk green & lt green | .25 | .25 |
| **367** A77 | 2c brt red & rose | .25 | .25 |
| **368** A77 | 10c orange brn & buff | .70 | .25 |
| | *Nos. 366-368 (3)* | 1.20 | .75 |

Issue dates: 1c, Mar. 27; others, Apr. 7.

Sánchez, Duarte, Mella and Trujillo — A78

**1941, May 16**

| | | | |
|---|---|---|---|
| **369** A78 | 3c brt red lil & red vio | .30 | .25 |
| **370** A78 | 4c brt red, crim & pale rose | .40 | .25 |
| **371** A78 | 13c dk blue & lt blue | .85 | .35 |
| **372** A78 | 15c orange brn & buff | 2.75 | 2.10 |
| **373** A78 | 17c lt bl, bl & pale bl | 2.75 | 2.10 |
| **374** A78 | 1p org, yel brn & pale org | 11.50 | 10.50 |
| **375** A78 | 2p lt gray & pale gray | 25.00 | 10.50 |
| | *Nos. 369-375 (7)* | 43.55 | 26.05 |

Trujillo-Hull Treaty signed Sept. 24, 1940 and effective Apr. 1, 1941.

Bastion of February 27 — A79

**1941, Oct. 20**

| | | | |
|---|---|---|---|
| **376** A79 | 5c brt blue & lt blue | .50 | .25 |

School, Torch of Knowledge, Pres. Trujillo — A80

**1941**

| | | | |
|---|---|---|---|
| **377** A80 | ½c chestnut & fawn | .25 | .25 |
| **378** A80 | 1c dk green & lt green | .25 | .25 |

Education campaign.
Issue dates: ½c, Dec. 12, 1c, Dec. 2.

Reserve Bank of Dominican Republic A81

**1942 Unwmk.**

| | | | |
|---|---|---|---|
| **379** A81 | 5c lt brown & buff | .50 | .25 |
| **380** A81 | 17c dp blue & lt blue | 1.00 | .45 |

Founding of the Reserve Bank, 10/24/41.

Representation of Transportation A82

**1942, Aug. 15**

| | | | |
|---|---|---|---|
| **381** A82 | 3c dk brn, grn yel & lt bl | 4.25 | .50 |
| **382** A82 | 15c pur, grn, yel & lt bl | 11.00 | 5.50 |

Day of Posts and Telegraph, 8th anniv.

Virgin of Altagracia — A83

**1942, Aug. 15**

| | | | |
|---|---|---|---|
| **383** A83 | ½c gray & pale gray | 1.00 | .25 |
| **384** A83 | 1c dp grn & lt grn | 2.10 | .25 |
| **385** A83 | 3c brt red lil & lil | 13.50 | .25 |
| **386** A83 | 5c dk vio brn & vio brn | 2.75 | .25 |
| **387** A83 | 10c rose pink & pink | 4.75 | .25 |
| **388** A83 | 15c dp blue & lt blue | 10.50 | .30 |
| | *Nos. 383-388 (6)* | 34.60 | 1.55 |

20th anniv. of the coronation of Our Lady of Altagracia.

Bananas — A84

Cows — A85

**1942-43**

| | | | |
|---|---|---|---|
| **389** A84 | 3c dk brn & grn ('43) | .60 | .25 |
| **390** A84 | 4c vermilion & blk ('43) | .60 | .40 |
| **391** A85 | 5c dp blue & cop brn | .60 | .25 |
| **392** A85 | 15c dk pur & blue grn | 1.00 | .50 |
| | *Nos. 389-392 (4)* | 2.80 | 1.40 |

Issue date: 5c, 15c, Aug. 18.

Emblems of Dominican and Trujillista Parties A86

**1943, Jan. 15**

| | | | |
|---|---|---|---|
| **393** A86 | 3c orange | .50 | .25 |
| **394** A86 | 4c dark red | .60 | .25 |
| **395** A86 | 13c brt red lilac | 1.40 | .25 |
| **396** A86 | 1p lt blue | 6.75 | 1.60 |
| | *Nos. 393-396 (4)* | 9.25 | 2.35 |

Re-election of President Rafael Trujillo Molina, May 16, 1942.

Model Market, Ciudad Trujillo A87

**1944**

| | | | |
|---|---|---|---|
| **397** A87 | 2c dk brown & buff | .25 | .25 |

Bastion of Feb. 27 and National Flag — A88

**1944, Feb. 27 Unwmk.**

**Flag in Dark Blue and Carmine**

| | | | |
|---|---|---|---|
| **398** A88 | ½c ocher | .25 | .25 |
| **399** A88 | 1c yellow green | .25 | .25 |
| **400** A88 | 2c scarlet | .25 | .25 |
| **401** A88 | 3c brt red vio | .25 | .25 |
| **402** A88 | 5c yellow orange | .25 | .25 |
| **403** A88 | 7c brt blue | .25 | .25 |
| **404** A88 | 10c orange brown | .40 | .30 |
| **405** A88 | 20c olive green | .65 | .60 |
| **406** A88 | 50c lt blue | 1.90 | 1.75 |
| | *Nos. 398-406,C46-C48 (12)* | 7.25 | 6.15 |

**Souvenir Sheet**

***Imperf***

407 A88 Sheet of 12 110.00 110.00
*a.-l.* Single stamp 3.00 3.00

Centenary of Independence.
No. 407 contains 1 each of Nos. 398-406 and C46-C48 with simulated perforations. Size: 141x205mm.

Battlefield and Nurse with Child A90

**1944, Aug. 1**

408 A90 1c dk bl grn, buff & car .25 .25
*a.* Vertical pair, imperf. btwn. 15.00
*b.* Horiz. pair, imperf. vert. 15.00
409 A90 2c dk brn, buff & car .40 .25
410 A90 3c brt bl, buff & car .40 .25
411 A90 10c rose car, buff & car .80 .25
*Nos. 408-411 (4)* 1.85 1.00

80th anniv. of the Intl. Red Cross.

Municipal Building, San Cristóbal — A91

**Unwmk.**

**1945, Jan. 10 Litho. *Perf. 12***

412 A91 ½c blue & lt blue .25 .25
413 A91 1c dk green & green .25 .25
414 A91 2c red org & org .25 .25
415 A91 3c dk brown & brown .25 .25
416 A91 10c ultra & gray blue 1.25 .25
*Nos. 412-416 (5)* 2.25 1.25

Centenary of the constitution.

Emblem of Communications A92

**1945, Sept. 1**

**Center in Dark Blue and Carmine**

417 A92 3c orange .25 .25
418 A92 20c yellow green .85 .25
419 A92 50c light blue 1.75 .70
*Nos. 417-419,C53-C56 (7)* 5.00 2.20

Palace of Justice, Ciudad Trujillo A93

**1946 *Perf. 11½***

420 A93 3c dk red brown & buff .25 .25

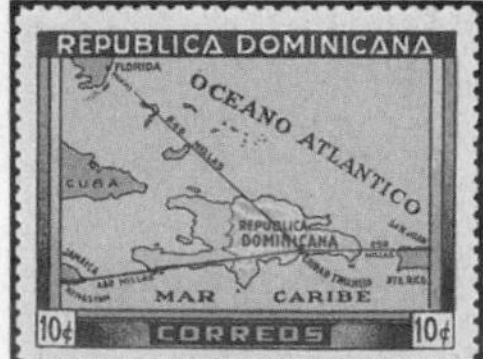


Map of Hispaniola — A94

**1946, Aug. 4 *Perf. 12***

421 A94 10c multicolored .75 .25
*Nos. 421,C62-C63 (3)* 2.85 .75

450th anniv. of the founding of Santo Domingo.

Waterfall of Jimenoa — A95

**1946-47 Center Multicolored**

422 A95 1c yellow grn ('47) .25 .25
423 A95 2c carmine ('47) .25 .25
424 A95 3c deep blue .25 .25
425 A95 13c red violet ('47) .45 .35
426 A95 20c chocolate ('47) .80 .35
427 A95 50c orange ('47) 1.75 1.25
*Nos. 422-427,C64-C67 (10)* 11.45 5.50

Nos. 422-423, 425-427 issued Mar. 18.
For surcharge see No. 540.

Executive Palace A96

**1948, Feb. 27**

428 A96 1c yellow green .25 .25
429 A96 3c deep blue .25 .25
*Nos. 428-429,C68-C69 (4)* 8.35 3.60

Church of San Francisco Ruins — A97

**1949, Apr. 13 *Perf. 11½***

430 A97 1c dk grn & pale grn .25 .25
431 A97 3c dp bl & pale bl .25 .25
*Nos. 430-431,C70-C73 (6)* 4.30 1.90

Gen. Pedro Santana — A98

**1949, Aug. 10**

432 A98 3c deep blue & blue .25 .25

Battle of Las Carreras, cent. See No. C74.

Pigeon and Globe — A99

**Center and Inscriptions in Brown**

**1950, Mar. 23**

433 A99 1c green & pale green .25 .25
434 A99 2c yel grn & yel .25 .25
435 A99 5c blue & pale blue .25 .25
436 A99 7c dk vio bl & pale bl .40 .25
*Nos. 433-436 (4)* 1.15 1.00

75th anniv. of the UPU.

**Catalogue values for unused stamps in this section, from this point to the end of the section, are for Never Hinged items.**

Hotel Jimani A100

Hotels: 1c, 2c, Hamaca. 5c, Montana. 15c, San Cristobal. 20c, Maguana.

**1950-52**

437 A100 ½c org brn & buff .25 .25
438 A100 1c dp grn & grn ('51) .25 .25
439 A100 2c red org & sal ('52) .25 .25
440 A100 5c blue & lt blue .50 .25
441 A100 15c dp orange & yel .75 .25
442 A100 20c lilac & rose lilac 1.40 .25
443 A100 1p chocolate & yel 5.75 1.90
*Nos. 437-443,C75-C76 (9)* 12.90 6.15

Issue dates: 1c, Dec. 1, 1951; 2c, Jan. 11, 1952; others, Sept. 8, 1950.
The ½c, 15c and 20c exist imperf.

Ruins of Church and Hospital of San Nicolas de Bari A101

School of Medicine — A102

**1950, Oct. 2**

444 A101 2c dk green & rose brn .55 .25
445 A102 5c vio blue & org brn .70 .25
*Nos. 444-445,C77 (3)* 2.25 .75

13th Pan-American Health Conference. Nos. 444-445 and C77 exist imperf.

Queen Isabella I — A103

**1951, Oct. 12**

446 A103 5c dk blue & red brn .95 .25

500th anniversary of the birth of Queen Isabella I of Spain. Exists imperf.

Dr. Salvador B. Gautier Hospital A104

**1952, Aug.**

447 A104 1c dark green .35 .25
448 A104 2c red .35 .25
449 A104 5c violet blue .55 .25
*Nos. 447-449,C78-C79 (5)* 5.70 4.20

Columbus Lighthouse and Flags of 21 Republics A105

**1953, Jan. 6 Engr. *Perf. 13***

450 A105 2c dark green .30 .25
451 A105 5c deep blue .40 .25
452 A105 10c deep carmine .70 .25
*Nos. 450-452,C80-C86 (10)* 6.75 4.80

Treasury Building, Ciudad Trujillo A106

Sugar Industry, "Central Rio Haina" A107

**1953 Litho. *Perf. 11½***

453 A106 ½c brown .45 .25
454 A106 2c dark blue .45 .25
455 A107 5c blue & vio brn .45 .25
456 A106 15c orange 1.40 .25
*Nos. 453-456 (4)* 2.75 1.00

For surcharge see No. 539.

José Marti — A108

**1954 *Perf. 12½***

457 A108 10c dp blue & dk brown .85 .25

Centenary of the birth of Jose Marti (1853-1895), Cuban patriot.

Monument to the Peace of Trujillo — A109

**1954, May 25**

458 A109 2c green .50 .25
459 A109 7c blue .50 .25
460 A109 20c orange 1.75 .25
*Nos. 458-460 (3)* 2.75 .75

See No. 493.

Rotary Emblem A110

**1955, Feb. 23 *Perf. 12***

461 A110 7c deep blue 1.00 .25

50th anniv., Rotary Intl. See No. C90.

Gen. Rafael L. Trujillo — A111

4c, Trujillo in civilian clothes. 7c, Trujillo statue. 10c, Symbols of culture & prosperity.

**1955, May 16 Engr. *Perf. 13½x13***

**462** A111 2c red .50 .25
**463** A111 4c lt olive green .50 .25
**464** A111 7c indigo .65 .25
**465** A111 10c brown 1.25 .25
*Nos. 462-465,C91-C93 (7)* 7.10 2.05

25th anniversary of the Trujillo era.

General Rafael L. Trujillo — A112

**1955, Dec. 20 Unwmk. *Perf. 13***

**466** A112 7c deep claret .60 .25
**467** A112 10c dark blue .80 .25
*Nos. 466-467,C94 (3)* 2.00 .75

Angelita Trujillo — A113

**1955, Dec. 20 Litho. *Perf. 12½***

**468** A113 10c blue & ultra .75 .25

Nos. 466-468 were issued to publicize the International Fair of Peace and Brotherhood in Ciudad Trujillo, Dec. 1955.

Airport A114

**1956, Apr. 6 *Perf. 12½***

**469** A114 1c brown .25 .25
**470** A114 2c red orange .25 .25
*Nos. 469-470,C95 (3)* 1.75 .75

3rd Caribbean conf. of the ICAO.

Cedar — A115

**1956, Dec. 8 *Perf. 11½x12***

**471** A115 5c car rose & grn *1.75* .25
**472** A115 6c red vio & grn *2.00* .25
*Nos. 471-472,C96 (3)* 6.00 .75

Reforestation program.

Fair Emblem — A116

**1957, Jan. 10 *Perf. 12½***

**473** A116 7c blue, lt brn & ver .40 .25

2nd International Livestock Show, Ciudad Trujillo, Jan. 10-20, 1957. Exists imperf.

Fanny Blankers-Koen, Netherlands A117

Olympic Winners and Flags: 2c, Jesse Owens, US. 3c, Kee Chung Sohn, Japan. 5c, Lord Burghley, England. 7c, Bob Mathias, US.

**Flags in National Colors**

**Engraved & Lithographed**

**1957, Jan. 24 *Perf. 11½, Imperf.***

**474** A117 1c brn, lt bl, vio & mar .30 .25
**475** A117 2c dk brn, lt bl & vio .30 .25
**476** A117 3c red lilac & red .30 .25
**477** A117 5c red org & vio .40 .25
**478** A117 7c green & violet .50 .25
*Nos. 474-478,C97-C99 (8)* 2.75 2.00

16th Olympic Games, Melbourne, Nov. 22-Dec. 8, 1956.

Miniature sheets of 5 exist, perf. and imperf., containing Nos. 474-478. Value, 2 sheets, perf. and imperf., $16.

For surcharges see Nos. B1-B5, B26-B30, CB1-CB3, CB16-CB18.

Lars Hall, Sweden, Pentathlon — A118

Olympic Winners and Flags: 2c, Betty Cuthbert, Australia, 100 & 200 meter dash. 3c, Egil Danielsen, Norway, javelin. 5c, Alain Mimoun, France, marathon. 7c, Norman Read, New Zealand, 50 km. walk.

***Perf. 13½, Imperf.***

**1957, July 18 Photo. Unwmk.**

**Flags in National Colors**

**479** A118 1c brn & brt bl .50 .25
**480** A118 2c org ver & dk bl .50 .25
**481** A118 3c dark blue .50 .25
**482** A118 5c ol & dk bl .50 .25
**483** A118 7c rose brn & dk bl .50 .30
*Nos. 479-483,C100-C102 (8)* 3.45 2.05

1956 Olympic winners.

Miniature sheets of 8 exist, perf. and imperf., containing Nos. 479-483 and C100-C102. The center label in these sheets is printed in two forms: Olympic gold medal or Olympic flag. Sheets measure 140x140mm. Value, 4 sheets, perf. and imperf., medal and flag, $20.

A third set of similar miniature sheets (perf. and imperf.) with center label showing an incorrect version of the Dominican Republic flag (colors transposed) was printed. These sheets are said to have been briefly sold on the first day, then withdrawn as the misprint was discovered. Value, 2 sheets, perf. & imperf., $150.

For surcharges see Nos. B6-B10, CB4-CB6.

Gerald Ouellette, Canada, Small Bore Rifle, Prone — A119

Ron Delaney, Ireland, 1,500 Meter Run — A120

Olympic Winners and Flags: 3c, Tenley Albright, US, figure skating. 5c, Joaquin Capilla, Mexico, platform diving. 7c, Ercole Baldini, Italy, individual road race (cycling).

**Engraved and Lithographed**

**1957, Nov. 12 *Perf. 13½, Imperf.***

**Flags in National Colors**

**484** A119 1c red brown .30 .25
**485** A120 2c gray brown .30 .25
**486** A119 3c violet .30 .25
**487** A120 5c red orange .30 .25
**488** A119 7c Prus green .30 .25
*Nos. 484-488,C103-C105 (8)* 2.55 2.00

1956 Olympic winners.

Miniature sheets of 5 exist, perf. and imperf., containing Nos. 484-488. Value, 2 sheets, perf. and imperf., $5.50.

For surcharges see Nos. B11-B20, CB7-CB12.

Mahogany Flower — A121

**1957-58 Litho. *Perf. 12½***

**489** A121 2c green & maroon .30 .25

***Perf. 12***

**490** A121 4c lilac & rose ('58) .30 .25
**491** A121 7c ultra & gray grn .40 .25
**492** A121 25c brown & org ('58) 1.20 .35
*Nos. 489-492 (4)* 2.20 1.10

Sizes: No. 489, 25x29¼mm; Nos. 490-492, 24x28¾mm. In 1959, the 2c was reissued in size 24¼x28½mm with slightly different tones of green and maroon.

Issued: 2c, 10/24; 7c, 11/6; 4c, 25c, 4/7/58.

For surcharges see Nos. 537-538.

**Type of 1954, Redrawn**

***Perf. 12x11½***

**1957, June 12 Unwmk.**

**493** A109 7c bright blue .75 .25

On No. 493 the cent symbol is smaller, the shading of the sky and steps stronger and the letters in "Correos" shorter and bolder.

Cervantes, Globe, Book — A122

**1958, Apr. 23 Litho. *Perf. 12½***

**494** A122 4c yellow green .45 .25
**495** A122 7c red lilac .45 .25
**496** A122 10c lt olive brown .75 .25
*Nos. 494-496 (3)* 1.65 .75

4th Book Fair, Apr. 23-28. Exist imperf.

Gen. Rafael L. Trujillo — A123

**1958, Aug. 16 *Perf. 12***

**497** A123 2c red lilac & yel .35 .25
**498** A123 4c green & yel .35 .25
**499** A123 7c brown & yel .35 .25
*a.* Souv. sheet of 3, #497-499, imperf. 1.25 .80
*Nos. 497-499 (3)* 1.05 .75

25th anniv. of Gen. Trujillo's designation as "Benefactor of his country."

S. S. Rhadames A124

**1958, Oct. 27 *Perf. 12½***

**500** A124 7c bright blue 1.50 .30

Day of the Dominican Merchant Marine. Exists imperf.

Shozo Sasahara, Japan, Featherweight Wrestling — A125

Olympic Winners and Flags: 1c, Gillian Sheen, England, fencing, vert. 2c, Milton Campbell, US, decathlon, vert. 5c, Madeleine Berthod, Switzerland, downhill skiing. 7c, Murray Rose, Australia, 400 & 1,500 meter freestyle.

***Perf. 13½, Imperf.***

**1958, Oct. 30 Photo.**

**Flags in National Colors**

**501** A125 1c rose, ind & ultra .40 .25
**502** A125 2c brown & blue .40 .25
**503** A125 3c gray, vio, blk & buff .40 .25
**504** A125 5c rose, dk bl, brn & red .40 .25
**505** A125 7c lt brn, dk bl & red .40 .25
*Nos. 501-505,C106-C108 (8)* 3.10 2.00

1956 Olympic winners.

Miniature sheets of 5 exist, perf. and imperf. containing Nos. 501-505. Value, 2 sheets, perf. and imperf., $5.

For surcharges see Nos. B21-B25, CB13-CB15.

Globe and Symbolic Fire — A126

**1958, Nov. 3 Litho. *Perf. 11½***

**506** A126 7c blue & dp carmine .50 .25

UNESCO Headquarters in Paris opening, Nov. 3.

Dominican Republic Pavilion, Brussels Fair — A127

**1958, Dec. 9 Unwmk. *Perf. 12½***

**507** A127 7c blue green .30 .25
*Nos. 507,C109-C110 (3)* 1.45 .90

Universal & Intl. Exposition at Brussels.

Gen. Trujillo Placing Wreath on Altar of the Nation — A128

**1959, July 10** *Perf. 12*

**508** A128 9c brn, grn, red & gold .45 .25
*a.* Souv. sheet of 1, imperf. 1.25 .75

29th anniversary of the Trujillo regime.

Lt. Leonidas Rhadames Trujillo, Team Captain — A129

Jamaican Polo Team A130

Design: 10c, Lt. Trujillo on polo pony.

**1959, May 15**

**509** A129 2c violet .25 .25
**510** A130 7c yellow brown .50 .25
**511** A130 10c green .60 .25
*Nos. 509-511,C111 (4)* 1.75 1.05

Jamaica-Dominican Republic polo match at Ciudad Trujillo.

Symbolical of Census A131

**1959, Aug. 15** **Litho.** *Perf. 12½*
**Flag in Ultramarine and Red**

**512** A131 1c blue & black .30 .25
**513** A131 9c green & black .50 .25
**514** A131 13c orange & black .60 .30
*Nos. 512-514 (3)* 1.40 .80

Issued to publicize the 1960 census.

Trujillo Stadium — A132

**1959, Aug. 27**

**515** A132 9c green & gray .60 .25

Issued to publicize the 3rd Pan American Games, Chicago, Aug. 27-Sept. 7.

Charles V A133

**1959, Oct. 12** **Unwmk.** *Perf. 12*

**516** A133 5c bright pink .40 .25
**517** A133 9c violet blue .60 .25

400th anniv. of the death of Charles V (1500-1558), Holy Roman Emperor.

Rhadames Bridge — A134

1c and No. 520, Different view of bridge.

**1959-60** **Litho.** *Perf. 12*

**518** A134 1c green & gray ('60) .40 .25
**519** A134 2c ultra & gray .40 .25
**520** A134 2c red & gray ('60) .40 .25
**521** A134 5c brn & dull red brn .40 .25
*Nos. 518-521 (4)* 1.60 1.00

Issued: No. 519, 10/22; 5c, 11/30; 1c, No. 520, 2/6.
For surcharge see No. 536.

Sosua Refugee Settlement and WRY Emblem — A135

**1960, Apr. 7** *Perf. 12½*
**Center in Gray**

**522** A135 5c red brn & yel grn .25 .25
**523** A135 9c carmine & lt blue .25 .25
**524** A135 13c orange & green .50 .25
*Nos. 522-524,C113-C114 (5)* 2.55 1.35

World Refugee Year, 7/1/59-6/30/60.
For surcharges see Nos. B31-B33.

Sholam Takhti, Iran, Lightweight Wrestling — A136

Olympic Winners: 2c, Masaru Furukawa, Japan, 200 meter breast stroke. 3c, Mildred McDaniel, US, high jump. 5c, Terence Spinks, England, featherweight boxing. 7c, Carlo Pavesi, Italy, fencing.

*Perf. 13½, Imperf.*
**1960, Sept. 14** **Photo.**
**Flags in National Colors**

**525** A136 1c red, yel grn & blk .35 .25
**526** A136 2c org, grnsh bl & brn .35 .25
**527** A136 3c henna brn & bl .35 .25
**528** A136 5c brown & ultra .35 .25
**529** A136 7c grn, bl & rose brn .35 .25
*Nos. 525-529,C115-C117 (8)* 2.80 2.20

17th Olympic Games, Rome, 8/25-9/11.
Miniature sheets of 5 exist, perf. and imperf., containing Nos. 525-529. Value, 2 sheets, perf. & imperf., $5.
For surcharges see Nos. B34-B38, CB21-CB23.

Post Office, Ciudad Trujillo A137

**1960, Aug. 26** **Litho.** *Perf. 11½x12*

**530** A137 2c ultra & gray .30 .25

Exists imperf.

Cattle A138

**1960, Aug. 30**

**531** A138 9c carmine & gray .30 .25

Issued to publicize the Agricultural and Industrial Fair, San Juan de la Maguana.

Nos. 518, 490-491, 453, 427 Surcharged in Red, Black or Blue

**1960-61** *Perf. 12*

**536** A134 2c on 1c grn & gray (R) .30 .25
**537** A121 9c on 4c lilac & rose .60 .25
*a.* Inverted surcharge 21.00
**538** A121 9c on 7c ultra & gray grn (R) .60 .25
**539** A106 36c on ½c brown 1.90 1.75
*a.* Inverted surcharge 18.00
**540** A95 1p on 50c multi (Bl) 4.25 3.25
*Nos. 536-540 (5)* 7.65 5.75

Issue dates: No. 536, Dec. 30, 1960; No. 537, Dec. 20, 1960; others, Feb. 4, 1961.

Trujillo Memorial — A139

**1961** **Unwmk.** *Perf. 11½*

**548** A139 1c brown .30 .25
**549** A139 2c green .30 .25
**550** A139 4c rose lilac .50 .30
**551** A139 5c light blue .60 .25
**552** A139 9c red orange .50 .25
*Nos. 548-552 (5)* 2.20 1.30

Gen. Rafael L. Trujillo (1891-1961).
Issued: 2c, 8/7; 4c, 10/24; others 8/30.

Coffee, Cacao — A140

**1961, Dec. 30** **Litho.** *Perf. 12½*

**553** A140 1c blue green .35 .25
**554** A140 2c orange brown .35 .25
**555** A140 4c violet .35 .25
**556** A140 5c blue .35 .25
**557** A140 9c gray .45 .25
*Nos. 553-557,C118-C119 (7)* 3.00 2.25

Nos. 553-557 exist imperf.

Dagger Pointing at Mosquito — A141

**1962, Apr. 29** **Photo.** *Perf. 12*

**558** A141 10c brt pink & red lilac .30 .25
**559** A141 20c pale brn & brn .60 .30
**560** A141 25c pale grn & yel grn .85 .40
*Nos. 558-560,B39-B40,C120-C121 (9)* 6.05 3.75

WHO drive to eradicate malaria.

Broken Fetters and Laurel A142

"Justice," Map of Dominican Republic — A143

Design: 20c, Flag, torch and inscription.

**1962, May 30** **Litho.** *Perf. 12½*

**561** A142 1c grn, yel, ultra & red .25 .25
**562** A143 9c bister ultra & red .40 .25
**563** A142 20c lt blue, ultra & red .85 .25
*a.* Souvenir sheet of 3, #561-563 1.90 1.90
**564** A143 1p lilac, ultra & red 4.50 2.50
*Nos. 561-564,C122-C123 (6)* 7.80 4.55

1st anniv. of end of Trujillo era. Nos. 561-564 exist imperf.

Farm, Factory and Flag — A144

**1962, May 22**

**565** A144 1c ultra, red & green .30 .25
**566** A144 2c ultra & red .30 .25
**567** A144 3c ultra, red & brown .30 .25
**568** A144 5c ultra, red & blue .30 .25
**569** A144 15c ultra, red & orange .40 .30
*Nos. 565-569 (5)* 1.60 1.30

Map and Laurel A145

**1962, June 14** **Litho.**

**570** A145 1c black .45 .25

Honoring the martyrs of June 1959 revolution.

Western Hemisphere and Carrier Pigeon — A146

**1962, Oct. 23 Unwmk. *Perf. 12½***

**571** A146 2c rose red .30 .25
**572** A146 9c orange .30 .25
**573** A146 14c blue green .60 .25
*Nos. 571-573,C124-C125 (5)* 2.25 1.50

50th anniv. of the founding of the Postal Union of the Americas and Spain, UPAE.

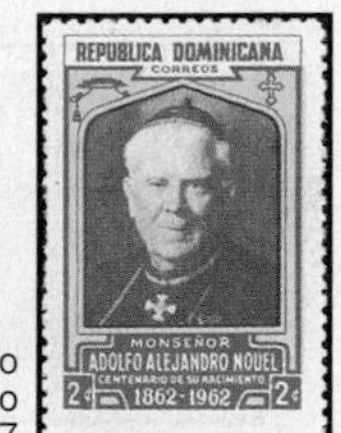


Archbishop Adolfo Alejandro Nouel — A147

**1962, Dec. 18**

**574** A147 2c bl grn & dull bl .30 .25
**575** A147 9c orange & red brn .35 .25
**576** A147 13c maroon & vio brn .45 .25
*Nos. 574-576,C126-C127 (5)* 2.30 1.50

Cent. of the birth of Archbishop Adolfo Alejandro Nouel, President of Dominican Republic in 1911.

Globe, Banner and Emblems A148

**1963, Apr. 15 Unwmk. *Perf. 11½***
**Banner in Dark Blue & Red**

**577** A148 2c green .30 .25
**578** A148 5c brt rose lilac .30 .25
**579** A148 9c orange .60 .25
*Nos. 577-579,B41-B43 (6)* 2.25 1.50

FAO "Freedom from Hunger" campaign.

Juan Pablo Duarte — A149

**1963, July 7 Litho. *Perf. 12x11½***

**580** A149 2c shown .30 .25
**581** A149 7c Francisco Sanchez .35 .25
**582** A149 9c Ramon Mella .45 .25
*Nos. 580-582 (3)* 1.10 .75

120th anniv. of separation from Haiti. See No. C128.

Ulises F. Espaillat, Benigno F. de Rojas and Pedro F. Bono — A150

Designs: 4c, Generals Santiago Rodriguez, Jose Cabrera and Benito Moncion. 5c, Capotillo monument. 9c, Generals Gaspar Polanco, Gregorio Luperon and Jose A. Salcedo.

**1963, Aug. 16 Unwmk. *Perf. 11½***

**583** A150 2c green .30 .25
**584** A150 4c red orange .30 .25
**585** A150 5c brown .75 .25
**586** A150 9c bright blue .35 .25
*a.* Souvenir sheet of 4 1.20 1.00
*Nos. 583-586 (4)* 1.70 1.00

Cent. of the Restoration. No. 586a contains 4 imperf. stamps similar to Nos. 583-586.

Patient and Nurse — A151

**1963, Oct. 25 Unwmk. *Perf. 12½***

**587** A151 3c gray & carmine .35 .25
**588** A151 6c emerald & red .35 .25
*Nos. 587-588,C129 (3)* 1.15 .75

Centenary of International Red Cross. Nos. 587-588 exist imperf. Value, set of pairs $18. See No. C129.

Scales, Globe, UNESCO Emblem A152

**1963, Dec. 10 Litho.**

**589** A152 6c pink & deep pink .30 .25
**590** A152 50c lt green & green .85 .85
*Nos. 589-590,C130-C131 (4)* 1.75 1.60

Universal Declaration of Human Rights, 15th anniv. Nos. 589-590 exist imperf.

Ramses II Battling the Hittites (from Abu Simbel) — A153

Design: 6c, Two heads of Ramses II.

**1964, Mar. 8 Unwmk. *Perf. 12½***

**591** A153 3c pale pink & ver .30 .25
**592** A153 6c pale blue & ultra .30 .25
**593** A153 9c pale rose & red brn .30 .25
*Nos. 591-593,C132-C133 (5)* 1.50 1.25

UNESCO world campaign to save historic monuments in Nubia.
For surcharges see Nos. B44-B46.

Maximo Gomez — A154

**1964, Apr. 30 Litho.**

**594** A154 2c lt blue & blue .30 .25
**595** A154 6c dull pink & dull claret .30 .25

Bicent. of the founding of the town of Bani.

Palm Chat — A155

Design: 6c, Hispaniolan parrot.

**Size: 27x37½mm**

**1964, June 8 Unwmk. *Perf. 12½***

**596** A155 3c ultra, brn & yel 2.50 .25
**597** A155 6c gray & multi 3.25 .25
*Nos. 596-597,C134 (3)* 11.50 .75

See Nos. 602-604.

Rocket Leaving Earth A156

Designs: 1c, Launching of rocket, vert. 3c, Space capsule orbiting earth. 6c, As 2c.

**1964, July 28 Litho.**

**598** A156 1c sky blue .30 .25
**599** A156 2c emerald .30 .25
**600** A156 3c blue .30 .25
**601** A156 6c sky blue .40 .25
*Nos. 598-601,C135-C136 (6)* 2.00 1.55

Conquest of space.

**Bird Type of 1964**

Designs: 1c, Narrow-billed tody. 2c, Hispaniolan emerald hummingbird. 6c, Hispaniolan trogon.

**1964, Nov. 7 *Perf. 11½***
**Size: 26x37mm**
**Birds in Natural Colors**

**602** A155 1c bright pink 2.50 .25
**603** A155 2c dark brown 2.50 .25
**604** A155 6c blue 4.25 .25
*Nos. 602-604 (3)* 9.25 .75

Universal Postal Union and United Nations Emblems A157

**1964, Dec. 5 Litho. *Perf. 12½***

**605** A157 1c red .35 .25
**606** A157 4c green .35 .25
**607** A157 5c orange .35 .25
*Nos. 605-607,C138 (4)* 1.40 1.00

15th UPU Cong., Vienna, May-June 1964.

International Cooperation Year Emblem A158

**1965, Feb. 16 Unwmk. *Perf. 12½***

**608** A158 2c lt blue & ultra .35 .25
**609** A158 3c emerald & dk grn .35 .25
**610** A158 6c salmon pink & red .35 .25
*Nos. 608-610,C139 (4)* 1.50 1.05

UN Intl. Cooperation Year.

Virgin of Altagracia A159

Design: 2c, Hands holding lily.

**1965, Mar. 18 Unwmk. *Perf. 12½***

**611** A159 2c grn, emer & dp rose .35 .25
**612** A159 6c multicolored .45 .25
*Nos. 611-612,C140 (3)* 1.30 .75

4th Mariological Cong. and 11th Intl. Marian Cong. No. 612 exists imperf.

Flags of 21 American Nations — A160

**1965, Apr. 14 Litho. *Perf. 11½***

**613** A160 2c brown, yel & multi .30 .25
**614** A160 6c red lilac & multi .50 .25

Organization of American States.

Stamp of 1865 (No. 1) — A161

**1965, Dec. 28 Litho. *Perf. 12½***

**615** A161 1c pink, buff & blk .35 .25
**616** A161 2c blue, buff & blk .35 .25
**617** A161 6c emerald, buff & blk .35 .25
*a.* Souvenir sheet of 2 1.20 1.10
*Nos. 615-617,C142-C143 (5)* 1.85 1.30

Cent. of 1st Dominican postage stamps. No. 617a shows replicas of Nos. 1-2. Sold for 50c.

WHO Headquarters, Geneva — A162

**1966, May 21 Litho. *Perf. 12½***

**618** A162 6c blue .30 .25
**619** A162 10c red lilac .50 .25

New WHO Headquarters, Geneva.

Man Holding Map of Republic — A163

**1966, May 23**

**620** A163 2c black & brt green .30 .25
**621** A163 6c black & dp orange .50 .25

General elections, June 1, 1966.

Ascia Monuste A164

**1966 Litho. *Perf. 12½***
**Various Butterflies in Natural Colors**
**Size: 31x21mm**

**622** A164 1c blue & vio bl 1.50 .25
**623** A164 2c lt grn & brt grn 1.50 .25
**624** A164 3c lt gray & gray 2.00 .25
**625** A164 6c pink & magenta 2.25 1.00
**626** A164 8c buff & brown 4.00 1.40
*Nos. 622-626,C146-C148 (8)* 41.50 7.90

Issued: 1c, 9/7; 3c, 9/11; others, 11/8.
For surcharges see Nos. B47-B51, CB28-CB30.

Natl. Altar — A165

**1967, Jan. 18 Litho. *Perf. 11½***

**627** A165 1c bright blue .30 .25
**628** A165 2c carmine rose .30 .25
**629** A165 3c emerald .30 .25
**630** A165 4c gray .30 .25
**631** A165 5c orange yellow .30 .25
**632** A165 6c orange .30 .25
*Nos. 627-632,C149-C151 (9)* 2.95 2.30

Map of Republic and Emblem A166

**1967, Mar. 30 Litho. *Perf. 12½***

**633** A166 2c yellow, blue & blk .30 .25
**634** A166 6c orange, blue & blk .30 .25
**635** A166 10c emerald, blue & blk .85 .45
*Nos. 633-635 (3)* 1.45 .95

Development Year, 1967.

Rook and Knight A167

**1967, June 23 Litho. *Perf. 12½***

**636** A167 25c multicolored 3.00 .50

5th Central American Chess Championships, Santo Domingo. See Nos. C152-C152a.

Alliance for Progress — A168

**1967, Sept. 16 Litho. *Perf. 12½***

**637** A168 1c bright green .35 .25
*Nos. 637,C153-C154 (3)* 1.45 .85

6th anniv. of the Alliance for Progress.

Institute Emblem — A169

**1967, Oct. 7**

**638** A169 3c bright green .35 .25
**639** A169 6c salmon pink .35 .25
*Nos. 638-639,C155 (3)* 1.45 .80

25th anniversary of the Inter-American Agriculture Institute.

Globe and Satellite A170

**1968, June 15 Typo. *Perf. 12***

**640** A170 6c black & multi .35 .25
*Nos. 640,C156-C157 (3)* 1.20 .80

World Meteorological Day, Mar. 23.

Boxers A171

**1968, June 29**

**641** A171 6c rose red & dp claret .35 .25
*Nos. 641,C158-C159 (3)* 1.70 .75

Fight between Carlos Ortiz, Puerto Rico, and Teo Cruz, Dominican Republic, for the World Lightweight Boxing Championship.

Lions Emblem — A172

**1968, Aug. 9 Litho. *Perf. 11½***

**642** A172 6c brown & multi .30 .25

Lions Intl., 50th anniv. (in 1967). See No. C160.

Wrestling and Olympic Emblem A173

**1968, Nov. 12 Litho. *Perf. 11½***

**643** A173 1c shown .30 .25
**644** A173 6c Running .35 .25
**645** A173 25c Boxing 1.25 .40
*Nos. 643-645,C161-C162 (5)* 3.50 1.90

19th Olympic Games, Mexico City, 10/12-27.

Map of Americas and House — A174

**1969, Jan. 25 Litho. *Perf. 12½***

**646** A174 6c brt bl, lt bl & grn .35 .25

7th Inter-American Conference for Savings and Loans, Santo Domingo, Jan. 25-31. See No. C163.

Stool in Human Form A175

Taino Art: 2c, Wood carved mother figure, vert. 3c, Face carved on 3-cornered stone. 4c, Stone hatchet, vert. 5c, Clay pot.

**1969, Jan. 31 Litho. *Perf. 12½***

**647** A175 1c yellow, org & blk .40 .25
**648** A175 2c lt grn, grn & blk .40 .25
**649** A175 3c citron, ol & brt grn .40 .25
**650** A175 4c lt lil, lil & brt grn .40 .25
**651** A175 5c yellow, org & brn .40 .25
*Nos. 647-651,C164-C166 (8)* 3.50 2.05

Taino art flourished in the West Indies at the time of Columbus.

Community Day Emblem — A176

**1969, Mar. 25 Litho. *Perf. 12½***

**652** A176 6c dull green & gold .30 .25

Community Development Day, Mar. 22.

COTAL Emblem — A177

Headquarters Building and COTAL Emblem — A178

Design: 2c, Boy and COTAL emblem.

**1969, May 25 Litho. *Perf. 12½***

**653** A177 1c lt & dk blue & red .40 .25
**654** A177 2c emerald & dk grn .40 .25
**655** A178 6c vermilion & pink .40 .25
*Nos. 653-655,C167 (4)* 1.60 1.00

12th Congress of the Confederation of Latin American Tourist Organizations (COTAL), Santo Domingo, May 25-29.

ILO Emblem — A179

**1969, June 27 Litho. *Perf. 12½***

**656** A179 6c lt grnsh bl, grnsh bl & blk .40 .25

50th anniv. of the ILO. See No. C168.

Sliding into Base — A180

Designs: 1c, Catching a fly ball. 2c, View of Cibao Stadium, horiz.

**Size: 21x31mm (1c, 3c); 43x30mm (2c)**

**1969, Aug. 15 Litho. *Perf. 12½***

**657** A180 1c green & gray .35 .25
**658** A180 2c green & lt green .35 .25
**659** A180 3c purple & red brown .35 .25
*Nos. 657-659,C169-C171 (6)* 7.30 4.85

17th World Amateur Baseball Championships, Santo Domingo.

Las Damas Dam A181

Tavera Dam — A182

Designs: 2c, Las Damas hydroelectric station, vert. 6c, Arroyo Hondo substation.

**1969 Litho. *Perf. 12***

**660** A181 2c green & multi .35 .25
**661** A181 3c dk blue & multi .35 .25
**662** A181 6c brt rose lilac .35 .25
**663** A182 6c multicolored .60 .25
*Nos. 660-663,C172-C173 (6)* 2.70 1.50

National electrification plan.

Issued: Nos. 660-662, Sept. 15; No. 663, Oct. 15.

Juan Pablo Duarte — A183

**1970, Jan. 26 Litho. *Perf. 12***

**664** A183 1c emerald & dk grn .35 .25
**665** A183 2c sal pink & dp car .35 .25
**666** A183 3c brt pink & plum .35 .25
**667** A183 6c blue & violet blue .35 .25
*Nos. 664-667,C174 (5)* 2.15 1.25

Issued for Duarte Day in memory of Juan Pablo Duarte (1813-1876), liberator.

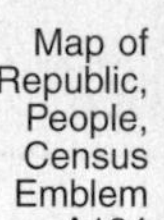

Map of Republic, People, Census Emblem A184

Design: 6c, Census emblem and inscription.

**1970, Feb. 6 *Perf. 11***

**668** A184 5c emerald & blk .35 .25
**669** A184 6c ultra & blue .35 .25
*Nos. 668-669,C175 (3)* 1.45 .75

Census of 1970.

Abelardo Rodriguez Urdaneta — A185

"One of Many" A186

**1970, Feb. 20 Litho. *Perf. 12½***

**670** A185 3c ultramarine .35 .25
**671** A186 6c green & yel grn .35 .25
*Nos. 670-671,C176 (3)* 1.25 .75

Issued to honor Abelardo Rodriguez Urdaneta, sculptor.

Masonic Symbols — A187

**1970, Mar. 2**
**672** A187 6c green .30 .25

8th Inter-American Masonic Conference, Santo Domingo, Mar. 1-7. See No. C177.

Communications Satellite — A188

**1970, May 25 Litho.** ***Perf. 12½***
**673** A188 20c olive & gray .80 .30

World Telecommunications Day. See No. C178.

UPU Headquarters, Bern — A189

**1970, June 5** ***Perf. 11***
**674** A189 6c gray & brown .40 .25

Inauguration of the new UPU headquarters in Bern. See No. C179.

Education Year Emblem — A190

**1970, June 26 Litho.** ***Perf. 12½***
**675** A190 4c rose lilac .40 .25

Issued for International Education Year, 1970. See No. C180.

Pedro Alejandrino Pina — A191

**1970, Aug. 24 Litho.** ***Perf. 12½***
**676** A191 6c lt red brn & blk .40 .25

Pedro Alejandrino Pina (1820-70), author.

Children Reading A192

**1970, Oct. 12 Litho.** ***Perf. 12½***
**677** A192 5c dull green .40 .25
*Nos. 677,C181-C182 (3)* 1.25 .75

1st World Exhibition of Books and Culture Festival, Santo Domingo, Oct. 11-Dec. 11.

Virgin of Altagracia A193

**1971, Jan. 20 Litho.** ***Perf. 12½***
**678** A193 3c multicolored .45 .25

Inauguration of the Basilica of Our Lady of Altagracia. See No. C184.

Rodriguez Objio — A194

**1971, June 18 Litho.** ***Perf. 11***
**679** A194 6c light blue .45 .25

Manuel Rodriguez Objio (1838-1871), poet.

Boxing and Canoeing — A195

**1971, Sept. 10**
**680** A195 2c shown .30 .25
**681** A195 5c Basketball .30 .25
*Nos. 680-681,C186 (3)* 1.00 .75

2nd National Games.

Goat and Fruit A196

Designs: 2c, Cow and goose. 3c, Cacao and horse. 6c, Bananas, coffee and pig.

**1971, Sept. 29** ***Perf. 12½***
**682** A196 1c brown & multi .40 .25
**683** A196 2c plum & multi .40 .25
**684** A196 3c green & multi .40 .25
**685** A196 6c blue & multi .40 .25
*Nos. 682-685,C187 (5)* 3.60 1.35

6th Natl. agriculture and livestock census.

José Nuñez de Cáceres — A197

**1971, Dec. 1** ***Perf. 11***
**686** A197 6c lt bl, lil & dk bl .45 .25

Sesquicentennial of first national independence. See No. C188.

Shepherds and Star — A198

**1971, Dec. 10** ***Perf. 12½***
**687** A198 6c blue, brown & yel .45 .25

Christmas 1971. See No. C189.

UNICEF Emblem, Child on Beach — A199

**1971, Dec. 14 Litho.** ***Perf. 11***
**688** A199 6c gray blue & multi .30 .25

UNICEF, 25th anniv. See No. C190.

Book Year Emblem A200

**1972, Jan. 25** ***Perf. 12½***
**689** A200 1c green, ultra & red .30 .25
**690** A200 2c brown, ultra & red .30 .25
*Nos. 689-690,C191 (3)* 1.35 .80

Intl. Book Year 1972.

Taino Mask — A201

4c, Ladle and amulet. 6c, Human figure.

**1972, May 10 Litho.** ***Perf. 11***
**691** A201 2c pink & multi .50 .25
**692** A201 4c black, bl & ocher .50 .25
**693** A201 6c gray & multi .50 .25
*Nos. 691-693,C194-C196 (6)* 4.20 1.70

Taino art. See note after No. 651.

Globe A202

**1972, May 17** ***Perf. 12½***
**694** A202 6c blue & multi .35 .25

4th World Telecommunications Day. See No. C197.

"1972," Stamps and Map of Dominican Republic A203

**1972, June 3**
**695** A203 2c green & multi .30 .25

First National Philatelic Exhibition, Santo Domingo, June 3-17. See No. C198.

Basketball — A204

**1972, Aug. 25 Litho.** ***Perf. 12½***
**696** A204 2c blue & multi .30 .25

20th Olympic Games, Munich, Aug. 26-Sept. 11. See No. C199.

Club Emblem A205

**1972, Sept. 29 Litho.** ***Perf. 10½***
**697** A205 1c lt green & multi .30 .25

50th anniversary of the Club Activo 20-30 International. See No. C200.

Emilio A. Morel A206

**1972, Oct. 20** ***Perf. 12½***
**698** A206 6c brt pink & multi .30 .25

Emilio A. Morel (1884-1958), poet and journalist. See No. C201.

Central Bank Building A207

**1972, Oct. 23**
**699** A207 1c shown .30 .25
**700** A207 5c 1-peso note .30 .25
*Nos. 699-700,C202 (3)* 1.85 1.05

25th anniv. of Central Bank.

Holy Family — A208

Poinsettia A209

**1972, Nov. 21**

**701** A208 2c rose lil, pur & gold .30 .25
**702** A209 6c red & multi .30 .25
*Nos. 701-702,C203 (3)* 1.55 .75

Christmas 1972.

Mail Box and Student A210

**1972, Dec. 15**

**703** A210 2c rose red .30 .25
**704** A210 6c blue .30 .25
**705** A210 10c emerald .50 .25
*Nos. 703-705 (3)* 1.10 .75

Publicity for correspondence schools.

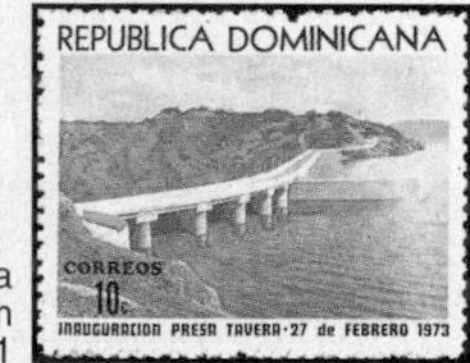

Tavera Dam A211

**1973, Feb. 26 Litho. *Perf. 12½***

**706** A211 10c multicolored .45 .25

Inauguration of the Tavera Dam.

Various Sports — A212

Designs: a, UL. b, UR. c, LL. d, LR.

**1973, Mar. 30 *Perf. 13½x13***

**707** A212 Block of 4 1.00 1.00
***a.-d.*** 2c, any single .30 .25
**708** A212 Block of 4 5.50 5.50
***a.-d.*** 25c, any single 1.00 .35
*Nos. 707-708,C204-C205 (4)* 11.00 11.00

12th Central American and Caribbean Games, Santo Domingo, Summer 1974.

Christ Carrying the Cross A213

6c, Belfry of Church of Our Lady of Carmen.

**1973, Apr. 18 Litho. *Perf. 10½***

**709** A213 2c multicolored .30 .25
**710** A213 6c multicolored, vert. .30 .25
*Nos. 709-710,C206 (3)* 1.35 .75

Holy Week, 1973.

WMO Emblem, Weather Satellite, "Weather" A214

**1973, Aug. 10 Litho. *Perf. 13½x13***

**711** A214 6c magenta & multi .35 .25

Centenary of international meteorological cooperation. See No. C208.

Mask, Cibao — A215

**1973, Oct. 12 Litho. *Perf. 10½***

**712** A215 1c Maguey drum, horiz .40 .25
**713** A215 2c Carved amber, horiz .40 .25
**714** A215 4c shown .40 .25
**715** A215 6c Pottery .40 .25
*Nos. 712-715,C210-C211 (6)* 3.35 1.50

Opening of Museum of Mankind in Santo Domingo.

Nativity A216

Christmas: 6c, Stained glass window, vert.

***Perf. 13½x13, 13x13½***

**1973, Nov. 26**

**716** A216 2c black, bl & yel .35 .25
**717** A216 6c rose & multi .35 .25
*Nos. 716-717,C212 (3)* 1.20 .75

No. 717 exists imperf.

Dominican Scout Emblem A217

Design: 5c, Scouts and flag.

**1973, Dec. 7 Litho. *Perf. 12***

**Size: 35x35mm**

**718** A217 1c ultra & multi .35 .25

**Size: 26x36mm**

**719** A217 5c black & multi .35 .25
*Nos. 718-719,C213 (3)* 1.95 1.25

Dominican Republic Boy Scouts, 50th anniv.

Sports Palace, Basketball Players A218

Design: 6c, Bicyclist and race track.

**1974, Feb. 25 Litho. *Perf. 13½***

**720** A218 2c red brown & multi .30 .25
**721** A218 6c yellow & multi .30 .25
*Nos. 720-721,C214-C215 (4)* 2.00 1.00

12th Central American and Caribbean Games, Santo Domingo, 1974.

Bell Tower, Cathedral of Santo Domingo — A219

Mater Dolorosa — A220

**1974, June 27 Litho. *Perf. 13½***

**722** A219 2c multicolored .30 .25
**723** A220 6c multicolored .40 .25
*Nos. 722-723,C216 (3)* 1.35 .75

Holy Week 1974.

Francisco del Rosario Sanchez Bridge — A221

**1974, July 12 *Perf. 12***

**724** A221 6c multicolored .45 .25

See No. C217.

Map, Emblem and Patient — A222

Design: 5c, Map of Dominican Republic, diabetics' emblem and pancreas.

**1974, Aug. 22 Litho. *Perf. 13***

**725** A222 4c blue & multi .30 .25
**726** A222 5c yellow grn & multi .30 .25
*Nos. 725-726,C218-C219 (4)* 3.05 1.50

Fight against diabetes.

Train and UPU Emblem A223

Design: 6c, Mail coach and UPU emblem.

**1974, Oct. 9 Litho. *Perf. 13½***

**727** A223 2c blue & multi .60 .60
**728** A223 6c brown & multi .45 .25
*Nos. 727-728,C220-C221 (4)* 5.55 1.95

Cent. of UPU.

Golfers — A224

Design: 2c, Championship emblem and badge of Dominican Golf Association, horiz.

**1974, Oct. 24 *Perf. 13x13½, 13½x13***

**729** A224 2c yellow & blk *1.00* .25
**730** A224 6c blue & multi *1.25* .25
*Nos. 729-730,C222-C223 (4)* 3.55 1.15

World Amateur Golf Championships.

Christmas Decorations A225

Virgin and Child — A226

**1974, Dec. 3 Litho. *Perf. 12***

**731** A225 2c multicolored .30 .25
**732** A226 6c multicolored .40 .25
*Nos. 731-732,C224 (3)* 1.20 .75

Christmas 1974.

Tomatoes, FAO Emblem — A227

**1974, Dec. 5**

**733** A227 2c shown 1.00 .25
**734** A227 3c Avocados 1.00 .25
**735** A227 5c Coconuts 1.00 .25
*Nos. 733-735,C225 (4)* 4.75 1.00

World Food Program, 10th anniv.

Dr. Fernando A. Defillo (1874-1949), Physician — A228

**1975, Feb. 14 Litho. *Perf. 13½x13***

**736** A228 1c dull brown .40 .25
**737** A228 6c dull green .40 .25

Tower, Our Lady of the Rosary Convent — A229

Design: 2c, Jesus saying "I am the Resurrection and the Life."

**1975, Mar. 26 Litho. *Perf. 13½***

**738** A229 2c brown & multi .30 .25
**739** A229 6c multicolored .30 .25
*Nos. 738-739,C226 (3)* 1.25 .75

Holy Week 1975.

Hands (Steel Beams) with Symbols of Agriculture, Industry A230

**1975, May 19 Litho. *Perf. 10½x10***

**740** A230 6c dull blue & multi .35 .25

16th Assembly of the Governors of the International Development Bank, Santo Domingo, May 1975. See No. C228.

Satellite Tracking Station — A231

**1975, June 21 Litho. *Perf. 13½***

**741** A231 5c multicolored .30 .25

Opening of first earth satellite tracking station in Dominican Republic. See No. C229.

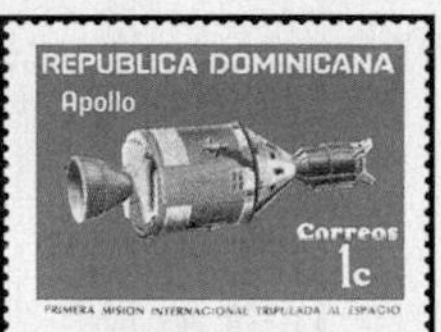


Apollo A232

**1975, July 24 Size: 35x25mm**

**742** A232 1c shown .30 .25
**743** A232 4c Soyuz .30 .25
*Nos. 742-743,C230 (3)* 6.60 4.50

Apollo Soyuz space test project (Russo-American cooperation), launching July 15; link-up, July 17.

Father Rafael C. Castellanos A233

**1975, Aug. 6 Litho. *Perf. 12***

**744** A233 6c brown & buff .45 .25

Castellanos (1875-1934), 1st Apostolic Administrator in Dominican Republic.

Women and Men Around IWY Emblem — A234

**1975, Aug. 6 *Perf. 13***

**745** A234 3c orange & multi .45 .25

International Women's Year 1975.

Guacanagarix A235

Indian Chiefs: 2c, Guarionex. 3c, Caonabo. 4c, Bohechio. 5c, Cayacoa. 6c, Anacona (woman). 9c, Hatuey.

**1975, Sept. 27 Litho. *Perf. 12***

**746** A235 1c yellow & multi .60 .25
**747** A235 2c salmon & multi .60 .25
**748** A235 3c violet bl & multi .60 .25
**749** A235 4c green & multi .60 .25
**750** A235 5c blue & multi .60 .25
**751** A235 6c violet & multi .60 .25
**752** A235 9c rose & multi 1.00 .25
*Nos. 746-752,C231-C233 (10)* 7.10 2.60

Basketball A236

Design: 6c, Baseball and Games' emblem.

**1975, Oct. 24 Litho. *Perf. 12***

**753** A236 2c pink & multi .50 .25
**754** A236 6c orange & multi .50 .25
*Nos. 753-754,C234-C235 (4)* 3.00 1.05

7th Pan-American Games, Mexico City, Oct. 13-26.

Carolers — A237

6c, Dominican nativity with farmers & shepherds.

**1975, Dec. 12 Litho. *Perf. 13x13½***

**755** A237 2c yellow & multi .40 .25
**756** A237 6c blue & multi .40 .25
*Nos. 755-756,C236 (3)* 1.40 .75

Christmas 1975.

Abudefdul Marginatus — A238

**1976, Jan. 23 Litho. *Perf. 13***

**757** A238 10c shown .75 .25
**758** A238 10c Doncella .75 .25
**759** A238 10c Carajuelo .75 .25
**760** A238 10c Reina de los Angeles .75 .25
**761** A238 10c Pargo Colorado .75 .25
*a.* Strip of 5, #757-761 7.00 7.00

Ascension, by J. Priego — A239

2c, Mary Magdalene, by Enrique Godoy.

**1976, Apr. 14 Litho. *Perf. 13½***

**762** A239 2c blue & multi .40 .25
**763** A239 6c yellow & multi .40 .25
*Nos. 762-763,C238 (3)* 1.55 .80

Holy Week 1976.

"Separacion Dominicana" and Adm. Cambiaso A240

**1976, Apr. 15 *Perf. 13½x13***

**764** A240 20c multicolored 1.25 .45

Naval Battle off Tortuga, Apr. 15, 1844.

Maps of US and Dominican Republic — A241

Design: 9c, Maps within cogwheels.

**1976, May 29 Litho. *Perf. 13½***

**765** A241 6c violet bl & multi .40 .25
**766** A241 9c violet bl & multi .40 .25
*Nos. 765-766,C239-C240 (4)* 3.15 2.00

American Bicentennial.

Flags of Dominican Republic and Spain A242

**1976, May 31**

**767** A242 6c multicolored .65 .25

Visit of King Juan Carlos I and Queen Sofia of Spain. See No. C241.

Various Telephones A243

**1976, July 15 *Perf. 12x12½***

**768** A243 6c multicolored .40 .25

Cent. of 1st telephone call by Alexander Graham Bell, Mar. 10, 1876. See No. C242.

Vision of Duarte, by Luis Desangles — A244

Juan Pablo Duarte, by Rhadames Mejia — A245

**1976, July 20 Litho. *Perf. 13x13½***

**769** A244 2c multicolored .30 .25

***Perf. 13½***

**770** A245 6c multicolored .30 .25
*Nos. 769-770,C243-C244 (4)* 3.25 1.85

Juan Pablo Duarte, liberation hero, death centenary.

Fire Hydrant — A246

Design: 6c, Firemen's emblem.

**1976, Sept. 13 Litho. *Perf. 12***

**771** A246 4c multicolored .50 .25
**772** A246 6c multicolored .50 .25
*Nos. 771-772,C245 (3)* 4.50 .80

Honoring firemen. Nos. 771-772 inscribed "Corrreos."

Radio and Atom Symbols A247

**1976, Oct. 8 Litho. *Perf. 13½***

**773** A247 6c red & black .40 .25

Dominican Radio Club, 50th anniv. See No. C246.

Spain, Central and South America, Galleon
A248

**1976, Oct. 22 Litho.** ***Perf. 13½***

**774** A248 6c multicolored .40 .25

Spanish heritage. See No. C247.

Boxing and Montreal Emblem
A249

Design: 3c, Weight lifting.

**1976, Oct. 22** ***Perf. 12***

**775** A249 2c blue & multi .40 .25
**776** A249 3c multicolored .40 .25
*Nos. 775-776,C248-C249 (4)* 2.90 1.50

21st Olympic Games, Montreal, Canada, July 17-Aug. 1.

Virgin and Child — A250

Three Kings — A251

**1976, Dec. 8 Litho.** ***Perf. 13½***

**777** A250 2c multicolored .40 .25
**778** A251 6c multicolored .40 .25
*Nos. 777-778,C250 (3)* 1.55 .80

Christmas 1976.

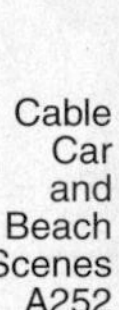

Cable Car and Beach Scenes
A252

**1977, Jan. 7**

**779** A252 6c multicolored .40 .25
*Nos. 779,C251-C253 (4)* 2.35 1.20

Tourist publicity.

Championship Emblem — A253

**1977, Mar. 4 Litho.** ***Perf. 13½***

**780** A253 3c rose & multi .40 .25
**781** A253 5c yellow & multi .40 .25
*Nos. 780-781,C254-C255 (4)* 2.90 1.50

10th Central American and Caribbean Children's and Young People's Swimming Championships, Santo Domingo.

Christ Carrying Cross — A254

Design: 6c, Head with crown of thorns.

**1977, Apr. 18 Litho.** ***Perf. 13½x13***

**782** A254 2c multicolored .40 .25
**783** A254 6c black & rose .40 .25
*Nos. 782-783,C256 (3)* 1.55 .75

Holy Week 1977.

Doves, Lions Emblem
A255

**1977, May 6** ***Perf. 13½x13***

**784** A255 2c lt blue & multi .40 .25
**785** A255 6c salmon & multi .40 .25
*Nos. 784-785,C257 (3)* 1.40 .75

12th annual Dominican Republic Lions Convention.

Battle Scene
A256

**1977, June 15 Litho.** ***Perf. 13x13½***

**786** A256 20c multicolored 1.20 .35

Dominican Navy.

Water Lily — A257

National Botanical Garden: 4c, "Flor de Mayo" (orchid). 6c, Sebesten.

**1977, Aug. 19 Litho.** ***Perf. 12***

**787** A257 2c multicolored .50 .25
**788** A257 4c multicolored .50 .25
**789** A257 6c multicolored .60 .25
*Nos. 787-789,C259-C260 (5)* 5.10 2.10

Chart and Computers — A258

**1977, Nov. 30 Litho.** ***Perf. 13***

**790** A258 6c multicolored .40 .25

7th Interamerican Statistics Conf. See No. C261.

Solenodon Paradoxus — A259

Design: 20c, Iguana and Congress emblem.

**1977, Dec. 29 Litho.** ***Perf. 13***

**791** A259 6c multicolored 2.50 .25
**792** A259 20c multicolored 4.25 .30
*Nos. 791-792,C262-C263 (4)* 14.75 1.35

8th Pan-American Veterinary and Zoo-technical Congress.

Main Gate, Casa del Cordon, 1503 — A260

**1978, Jan. 19** ***Perf. 13x13½***

**Size: 26x36mm**

**793** A260 6c multicolored .40 .25

Spanish heritage. See No. C264.

Crown of Thorns, Tools at the Cross — A261

6c, Head of Jesus with crown of thorns.

**Size: 22x33mm**

**1978, Mar. 21 Litho.** ***Perf. 12***

**794** A261 2c multicolored .40 .25
**795** A261 6c slate .40 .25
*Nos. 794-795,C265-C266 (4)* 2.30 1.05

Holy Week 1978.

Cardinal Octavio A. Beras Rojas — A262

**1978, May 5 Litho.** ***Perf. 13***

**796** A262 6c multicolored .40 .25

First Cardinal from Dominican Republic, consecrated May 24, 1976. See No. C268.

Pres. Manuel de Troncoso — A263

**1978, June 12 Litho.** ***Perf. 13½***

**797** A263 2c black, rose & brn .40 .25
**798** A263 6c black, gray & brn .60 .25

Manuel de Jesus Troncoso de la Concha (1878-1955), pres. of Dominican Republic, 1940-42.

Father Juan N. Zegri y Moreno — A264

**1978, July 11 Litho.** ***Perf. 13x13½***

**799** A264 6c multicolored .40 .25

Congregation of the Merciful Sisters of Charity, centenary. See No. C273.

Boxing and Games' Emblem
A265

**1978, July 21** ***Perf. 12***

**800** A265 2c shown .50 .25
**801** A265 6c Weight lifting .75 .25
*Nos. 800-801,C274-C275 (4)* 3.75 1.00

13th Central American & Caribbean Games, Medellin, Colombia.

Sun over Landscape
A266

Design: 6c, Sun over beach and boat.

**1978, Sept. 12 Litho.** ***Perf. 12***

**802** A266 2c multicolored .40 .25
**803** A266 6c multicolored .40 .25
*Nos. 802-803,C280-C281 (4)* 2.35 1.00

Tourist publicity.

Ships of Columbus, Map of Dominican Republic — A267

**1978, Oct. 12 Litho.** ***Perf. 13½***

**804** A267 2c multicolored .40 .25

Spanish heritage. See No. C282.

Dove, Lamp, Poinsettia
A268

Design: 6c, Dominican family and star, vert.

**1978, Dec. 5 Litho.** ***Perf. 12***

**805** A268 2c multicolored .40 .25
**806** A268 6c multicolored .50 .25
*Nos. 805-806,C284 (3)* 1.65 .80

Christmas 1978.

Starving Child, IYC Emblem — A269

**1979, Feb. 26 Litho. *Perf. 12***
**807** A269 2c orange & black .40 .25
*Nos. 807,C287-C289 (4)* 3.15 1.85

Intl. Year of the Child.

Crucifixion A270

Design: 3c, Jesus carrying cross, horiz.

**1979, Apr. 9 Litho. *Perf. 13½***
**808** A270 2c multicolored .40 .25
**809** A270 3c multicolored .60 .25
*Nos. 808-809,C290 (3)* 5.00 1.75

Holy Week.

Stigmaphyllon Periplocifolium — A271

**1979, May 17 Litho. *Perf. 12***
**810** A271 50c multicolored 2.00 .50
*Nos. 810,C293-C295 (4)* 7.00 1.80

Dr. Rafael M. Moscoso National Botanical Garden.

Heart, Diseased Blood Vessel A272

Design: 1p, Cardiology Institute and heart.

**1979, June 2 Litho. *Perf. 13½***
**811** A272 3c multicolored .40 .25
**812** A272 1p multicolored 2.75 .75
*Nos. 811-812,C296 (3)* 3.90 1.40

Dominican Cardiology Institute.

Baseball, Games' Emblem A273

3c, Bicycling and Games' emblem, vert.

**1979, June 20**
**813** A273 2c multicolored .40 .25
**814** A273 3c multicolored .40 .25
*Nos. 813-814,C297 (3)* 2.30 .80

8th Pan American Games, Puerto Rico, June 30-July 15.

Soccer — A274

Design: 25c, Swimming, horiz.

**1979, Aug. 9 Litho. *Perf. 12***
**815** A274 2c multicolored .40 .25
**816** A274 25c multicolored .50 .25
*Nos. 815-816,C298 (3)* 1.55 .80

Third National Games.

Thomas A. Edison — A275

**1979, Aug. 27 *Perf. 13½***
**817** A275 25c multicolored 1.00 .45

Cent. of invention of electric light. See No. C300.

Hand Holding Electric Plug A276

Design: 6c, Filling automobile gas tank.

**1979, Aug. 30**
**818** A276 2c multicolored .40 .25
**819** A276 6c multicolored .50 .25

Energy conservation.

Parrot A277

Birds: 6c, Temnotrogon roseigaster.

**1979, Sept. 12 Litho. *Perf. 12***
**820** A277 2c multicolored 2.10 .25
**821** A277 6c multicolored 2.10 .25
*Nos. 820-821,C301-C303 (5)* 20.20 2.10

A278

Lions Emblem, Map of Dominican Republic.

**1979, Nov. 13 Litho. *Perf. 12***
**822** A278 20c multicolored .75 .40

Lions International Club of Dominican Republic, 15th anniversary. See No. C304.

Christmas A279

**1979, Dec. 18 Litho. *Perf. 12***
**823** A279 2c Holy Family .40 .25

See No. C305.

Holy Week — A280

Design: Jesus Carrying Cross.

**1980, Mar. 27 Litho. *Perf. 12***
**824** A280 3c multicolored .40 .25
*Nos. 824,C306-C307 (3)* 1.55 .80

A281

**1980, May 15 Litho. *Perf. 13½***
**825** A281 1c shown .60 .25
**826** A281 2c Coffee .60 .25
**827** A281 3c Plantain .60 .25
**828** A281 4c Sugar cane .60 .25
**829** A281 5c Corn .60 .25
*Nos. 825-829 (5)* 3.00 1.25

Cacao Harvest (Agriculture Year)

Cotuf Gold Mine, Pueblo Viejo, Flag of Dominican Republic A282

**1980, July 8 Litho. *Perf. 13½***
**830** A282 6c multicolored .40 .25
*Nos. 830,C310-C311 (3)* 2.40 1.15

Nationalization of gold mining.

Blind Man's Buff A283

**1980, July 21 *Perf. 12***
**831** A283 3c shown .40 .25
**832** A283 4c Marbles .40 .25
**833** A283 5c Drawing in sand .50 .25
**834** A283 6c Hopscotch .50 .25
*Nos. 831-834 (4)* 1.80 1.00

Iguana A284

**1980, Aug. 30 Litho. *Perf. 12***
**835** A284 20c multicolored 2.75 .45
*Nos. 835,C314-C317 (5)* 16.15 2.80

Dance, by Jaime Colson A285

50c, *Woman, by Gilberto Hernandez Ortega*, vert.

***Perf. 13x13½, 13½x13***
**1980, Sept. 23 Litho.**
**836** A285 3c shown .40 .25
**837** A285 50c multicolored 1.50 .90
*Nos. 836-837,C318-C319 (4)* 3.40 2.00

Three Kings — A286

**1980, Dec. 5 Litho. *Perf. 13½***
**838** A286 3c shown .40 .25
**839** A286 6c Carolers .40 .25
*Nos. 838-839,C327 (3)* 1.45 .80

Christmas 1980.

Salcedo Province Cent. — A287

**1981, Jan. 14 Litho. *Perf. 13½***
**840** A287 6c multicolored .40 .25

See No. C328.

Juan Pablo Duarte, Liberation Hero, 105th Anniv. of Death — A288

**1981, Feb. 6 Litho. *Perf. 12***
**841** A288 2c sepia & deep bister .60 .25

Gymnast — A289

**1981, Mar. 31 Litho. *Perf. 13½***
**842** A289 1c shown .50 .25
**843** A289 2c Running .50 .25
**844** A289 3c Pole vault .50 .25
**845** A289 6c Boxing 1.00 .25
*Nos. 842-845,C331 (5)* 5.00 1.35

5th National Games.

Mother Mazzarello A290

**1981, Apr. 14** *Perf. 12*
**846** A290 6c multicolored .45 .25

Mother Maria Mazzarello (1837-1881), founder of Daughters of Mary.

A291

**1981, May 18** **Litho.** *Perf. 13½*
**847** A291 6c gray vio & lt gray .45 .25

Pedro Henriquez Urena, Historian (1884-1946)

Forest Conservation A292

**1981, June 30** **Litho.** *Perf. 12*
**848** A292 2c shown .45 .25
**849** A292 6c River, forest .45 .25

Family in House, Census Emblem A293

**1981, Aug. 14** **Litho.** *Perf. 12*
**850** A293 3c shown .45 .25
**851** A293 6c Farmer .45 .25

1981 natl. population and housing census.

Christmas A294

**1981, Dec. 23** **Litho.** *Perf. 13½*
**852** A294 2c Bells .45 .25
**853** A294 3c Poinsettia .45 .25
*Nos. 852-853,C353 (3)* 1.80 .95

A295

**1982, Jan. 29** **Litho.** *Perf. 13½*
**854** A295 2c Juan Pablo Duarte .80 .25

National Elections A296

Designs: Voters casting votes. 3c, 6c vert.

**1982, Mar. 30** **Litho.** *Perf. 13½*
**855** A296 2c multicolored .40 .25
**856** A296 3c multicolored .40 .25
**857** A296 6c multicolored .50 .25
*Nos. 855-857 (3)* 1.30 .75

A297

Energy Conservation: Various forms of energy.

**1982, May 10** **Litho.** *Perf. 12*
**858** A297 1c multicolored .40 .25
**859** A297 2c multicolored .40 .25
**860** A297 3c multicolored .40 .25
**861** A297 4c multicolored .50 .25
**862** A297 5c multicolored .50 .25
**863** A297 6c multicolored .50 .25
*Nos. 858-863 (6)* 2.70 1.50

A298

**1982, Aug. 2** *Perf. 12x12½*
**864** A298 6c multicolored .40 .25

Emilio Prud'Homme (1856-1932), composer.

Pres. Antonio Guzman Fernandez (1911-1982) A299

**1982, Aug. 4** *Perf. 13x13½*
**865** A299 6c multicolored .40 .25

14th Central American and Caribbean Games A300

**1982, Aug. 13** *Perf. 12, Imperf.*
**866** A300 3c Baseball 1.00 .25

See Nos. C368-C370.

San Pedro de Macoris Province Centenary — A301

**1982, Aug. 26** *Perf. 13*
**867** A301 1c Wagon .40 .25
**868** A301 2c Stained-glass window .40 .25
**869** A301 5c Views .50 .25
*Nos. 867-869,C375 (4)* 2.05 1.05

Size of 2c, 25x35mm.

St. Teresa of Jesus of Avila (1515-1582) A302

**1982, Nov. 17** **Litho.** *Perf. 13½*
**870** A302 6c multicolored .60 .25

Christmas 1982 — A303

Various Christmas balls.

**1982, Dec. 8**
**871** A303 6c multicolored 1.10 .25

See No. C380.

Environmental Protection A304

**1982, Dec. 15** *Perf. 12*
**872** A304 2c Bird .40 .25
**873** A304 3c Water .40 .25
**874** A304 6c Forest .40 .25
**875** A304 20c Fish 1.25 .35
*Nos. 872-875 (4)* 2.45 1.10

Natl. Literacy Campaign A305

**1983, Mar. 9** **Litho.** *Perf. 13½*
**876** A305 2c Vowels on blackboard .40 .25
**877** A305 3c Writing, reading .40 .25
**878** A305 6c Children, pencil .50 .25
*Nos. 876-878 (3)* 1.30 .75

A306

5c, similar arms, incorporating stylized centenary monument.

**1983, Apr. 4** *Perf. 12*
**879** A306 1c multicolored .40 .25
**880** A306 5c multicolored .50 .25

Mao City centenary.

A307

Dominican Historians: 2c, Antonio del Monte y Tejada (1780-1861). 3c, Manuel Ubaldo Gomez (1857-1941). 5c, Emiliano Tejera (1841-1923). 6c, Bernardo Pichardo (1877-1924). 7c, Americo Lugo (1870-1952). 10c, José Gabriel Garcia (1834-1910). 7c, 10c airmail.

**1983, Apr. 25** **Litho.** *Perf. 12*
**881** A307 2c multicolored .40 .25
**882** A307 3c multicolored .40 .25
**883** A307 5c multicolored .40 .25
**884** A307 6c multicolored .40 .25
**885** A307 7c multicolored .50 .25
**886** A307 10c multicolored .75 .30
*Nos. 881-886 (6)* 2.85 1.55

National Anthem, 100th Anniv. A308

Emilio Prud'Homme, & Jose Reyes, composer.

**1983, Sept. 13** **Litho.** *Perf. 13½*
**887** A308 6c copper red & blk .45 .25

Free Masons, 125th Anniv. — A309

**1983, Oct. 24** **Litho.** ***Perf. 12***

| | | | |
|---|---|---|---|
| **888** | A309 4c Emblem | .45 | .25 |

Church of Our Lady of Regla, 300th Anniv. — A310

**1983, Nov. 5** ***Perf. 13½***

| | | | |
|---|---|---|---|
| **889** | A310 3c Church | .40 | .25 |
| **890** | A310 6c Statue | .50 | .25 |

450th Anniv. of Monte Cristi Province — A311

Designs: 1c, Tower. 2c, Arms. 5c, Cuban independence site, horiz. 7c, Workers, horiz.

**1983, Nov. 25** ***Perf. 12***

| | | | |
|---|---|---|---|
| **891** | A311 1c dark grn & blk | .45 | .25 |
| **892** | A311 2c multicolored | .45 | .25 |
| **893** | A311 5c gray | .45 | .25 |
| **894** | A311 7c gray & blue | .45 | .25 |
| | *Nos. 891-894 (4)* | 1.80 | 1.00 |

6th Natl. Games — A312

6c, Bicycling, boxing, baseball. 10c, Runner, weight lifting, swimming.

**1983, Dec. 9**

| | | | |
|---|---|---|---|
| **895** | A312 6c multicolored | .40 | .25 |
| **896** | A312 10c multicolored | .65 | .25 |

10c airmail.

Restoration of the Republic, 120th Anniv. — A313

Design: 1c, Capotillo Heroes Monument.

**1983, Dec. 30** **Litho.** ***Perf. 13½***

| | | | |
|---|---|---|---|
| **897** | A313 1c multicolored | .45 | .25 |

140th Anniv. of Independence — A314

Designs: 6c, Matia Ramon Mella (Patriot), flag. 25c, Mella's Blunderbuss rifle, Gate of Deliverance (independence declaration site).

**1984, Feb. 24** **Litho.** ***Perf. 13½***

| | | | |
|---|---|---|---|
| **898** | A314 6c multicolored | .40 | .25 |
| **899** | A314 25c multicolored | 1.00 | .35 |

Heriberto Pieter (1884-1972), Physician, First Negro Graduate — A315

**1984, Mar. 16**

| | | | |
|---|---|---|---|
| **900** | A315 3c multicolored | .45 | .25 |

Battle of Barranquita, 67th Anniv. — A316

**1983, Dec. 30** ***Perf. 12***

| | | | |
|---|---|---|---|
| **901** | A316 5c multicolored | .45 | .25 |

Battle of Santiago, 140th Anniv. A317

**1984, Mar. 29** ***Perf. 13½***

| | | | |
|---|---|---|---|
| **902** | A317 7c multicolored | .45 | .25 |

Coast Guard Ship DC-1, 1934 A318

**1984, Apr. 13** **Litho.**

| | | | |
|---|---|---|---|
| **903** | A318 10c multicolored | .65 | .25 |

Navy Day and 140th anniv. of Battle of Tortuguero.

Birth Centenary of Pedro Henriquez Urena — A319

**1984, June 29** **Litho.** ***Perf. 12***

| | | | |
|---|---|---|---|
| **904** | A319 7c Salome Urena | .45 | .25 |
| **905** | A319 10c Text | .65 | .25 |
| **906** | A319 22c Urena | .60 | .25 |
| | *Nos. 904-906 (3)* | 1.70 | .75 |

Monument to Heroes of June 1959 A320

**1984, June 20** ***Perf. 13½***

| | | | |
|---|---|---|---|
| **907** | A320 6c silver & blue | .60 | .25 |

Costal towns of Constanza, Maimon and Estero Hondo - sites of attempted overthrow of Rafael Trujillo, 25th anniv.

1984 Summer Olympics A321

**1984, Aug. 1**

| | | | |
|---|---|---|---|
| **908** | A321 1p Hurdles | 2.50 | 1.90 |
| **909** | A321 1p Weightlifting | 2.50 | 1.90 |
| **910** | A321 1p Boxing | 2.50 | 1.90 |
| **911** | A321 1p Baseball | 2.50 | 1.90 |
| ***a.*** | Block of 4, #908-911 | 18.00 | 18.00 |
| | *Nos. 908-911 (4)* | 10.00 | 7.60 |

Protection of Fauna — A322

**1984, Oct. 3** **Litho.** ***Perf. 12***

| | | | |
|---|---|---|---|
| **912** | A322 10c Owl | 3.50 | .25 |
| **913** | A322 15c Flamingo | 4.00 | .35 |
| **914** | A322 25c Wild Pig | 6.00 | .50 |
| **915** | A322 35c Solenodon | 7.00 | .70 |
| | *Nos. 912-915 (4)* | 20.50 | 1.80 |

500th Anniv. of Discovery of America A323

10c, Landing on Hispaniola. 35c, Destruction of Ft. Navidad. 65c, First Mass in America. 1p, Battle of Santo Cerro.

**1984, Oct. 10** **Litho.** ***Perf. 13½x13***

| | | | |
|---|---|---|---|
| **916** | A323 10c multicolored | .45 | .25 |
| **917** | A323 35c multicolored | .80 | .35 |
| **918** | A323 65c multicolored | 1.50 | .80 |
| **919** | A323 1p multicolored | 2.50 | 1.10 |
| | *Nos. 916-919 (4)* | 5.25 | 2.50 |

Visit of Pope John Paul II — A324

**1984, Oct. 11** **Litho.** ***Perf. 13x13½***

| | | | |
|---|---|---|---|
| **920** | Block of 4 | 9.00 | 9.00 |
| ***a.*** | A324 75c shown | 1.90 | 1.90 |
| ***b.*** | A324 75c Pope, map of Caribbean | 1.90 | 1.90 |
| ***c.*** | A324 75c Pope, globe | 1.90 | 1.90 |
| ***d.*** | A324 75c Bishop's crozier | 1.90 | 1.90 |

150th Anniv. of Birth of Maximo Gomez (1986) A325

10c, Gomez on horseback. 20c, Maximo Gomez.

**1984, Dec. 6** **Litho.** ***Perf. 13½***

| | | | |
|---|---|---|---|
| **921** | A325 10c multicolored | .45 | .25 |
| **922** | A325 20c multicolored | .55 | .25 |

Christmas 1984 A326

***Perf. 13½x13, 13x13½***

**1984, Dec. 14** **Litho.**

| | | | |
|---|---|---|---|
| **923** | A326 5c multicolored | .40 | .25 |
| **924** | A326 10c multicolored, vert. | .50 | .25 |

Sacrifice of the Goat, by Eligio Pichardo A327

Paintings and sculpture: 10c, The Pumpkin Sellers, by Gaspar Mario Cruz; 25c, The Market, by Celeste Woss y Gil; 50c, Horses in the Rain, by Dario Suro.

**1984, Dec. 19** **Litho.** ***Perf. 13½***

| | | | |
|---|---|---|---|
| **925** | A327 5c multi | .50 | .25 |
| **926** | A327 10c multi, vert. | .50 | .25 |
| **927** | A327 25c multi | .85 | .45 |
| **928** | A327 50c multi | 1.50 | .65 |
| | *Nos. 925-928 (4)* | 3.35 | 1.60 |

Day of Our Lady of Altagracia A328

5c, Old church at Higuey, 1572. 10c, Our Lady of Altagracia 1514, vert. 25c, Basilica of the Protector, Higuey 1971, vert.

**1985, Jan. 21**

| | | | |
|---|---|---|---|
| **929** | A328 5c multicolored | .40 | .25 |
| **930** | A328 10c multicolored | .60 | .25 |
| **931** | A328 25c multicolored | .75 | .35 |
| | *Nos. 929-931 (3)* | 1.65 | .85 |

Independence, 141st Anniv. — A329

Painting: The Fathers of Our Country (Duarte, Sanchez and Mella).

**1985, Mar. 8** ***Perf. 12½***

| | | | |
|---|---|---|---|
| **932** | A329 5c multicolored | .40 | .25 |
| **933** | A329 10c multicolored | .45 | .25 |
| **934** | A329 25c multicolored | .70 | .25 |
| | *Nos. 932-934 (3)* | 1.55 | .75 |

Battle of Azua, 141st Anniv. A330

10c, Gen. Antonio Duverge, Statue.

**1985, Apr. 8 Litho. *Perf. 13½***
**935** A330 10c multicolored .55 .25

Santo Domingo Lighthouse, 1853 — A331

**1985, Apr. 15 Litho.**
**936** A331 25c multicolored .85 .25

Battle of Tortuguero, 141st anniv.

A332

**1985, Apr. 15 Litho. *Perf. 12***
**937** A332 35c multicolored 1.10 .45

American Airforces Cooperation System, 25th anniv.

Espaillat Province Cent. — A333

10c, Don Carlos M. Rojas, 1st governor.

**1985, May 24 Litho. *Perf. 13½***
**938** A333 10c multicolored .55 .30

A334

**1985, July 5 Litho. *Perf. 12***
**939** A334 5c Table tennis .40 .25
**940** A334 10c Walking race .50 .30

MOCA '85, 7th Natl. Games.



Intl. Youth Year A335

**1985, July 29 *Perf. 13½***
**941** A335 5c Youth .35 .25
**942** A335 25c The Haitises 1.10 .45
**943** A335 35c Mt. Duarte summit 1.25 .50
**944** A335 2p Mt. Duarte 7.25 2.75
*Nos. 941-944 (4)* 9.95 3.95

Interamerican Development Bank, 25th Anniv. — A336

10c, Haina Harbor. 25c, Map of development sites. 1p, Tavera-Bao-Lopez Hydroelectric Complex.

**1985, Aug. 23**
**945** A336 10c multicolored .40 .25
**946** A336 25c multicolored .85 .40
**947** A336 1p multicolored 2.75 1.75
*Nos. 945-947 (3)* 4.00 2.40

Intl. Decade for Women — A337

Design: Evangelina Rodriguez (1879-1947), first Dominican woman doctor.

**1985, Sept. 26**
**948** A337 10c multicolored .55 .25

15th Central American and Caribbean Games, Santiago — A338

**1985, Oct. 9 *Perf. 12***
**949** A338 5c multicolored .50 .25
**950** A338 25c multicolored 1.40 .45

4th Adm. Christopher Columbus Regatta, Casa de Espana A339

Designs: 50c, Founding of Santo Domingo, 1496. 65c, Chapel of Our Lady of the Rosary, 1496, Santo Domingo. 1p, Columbus, American Indian and old Spanish coat of arms.

**1985, Oct. 10 *Perf. 13½***
**951** A339 35c multicolored 1.40 .85
**952** A339 50c multicolored 1.80 1.20
**953** A339 65c multicolored 2.50 1.50
**954** A339 1p multicolored 4.50 2.40
*Nos. 951-954 (4)* 10.20 5.95

Discovery of America, 500th anniv. (in 1992).

Cacique Enriquillo — A340

Designs: 5c, Enriquillo in the Bahuroco Mountains, mural detail.

**1985, Oct. 31**
**955** A340 5c multicolored .50 .25
**956** A340 10c multicolored .75 .25

Enriquillo (d. 1536), leader of revolution against Spain. Size of No. 955: 47x33mm.

Archbishop Fernando Arturo de Merino — A341

**1985, Dec. 3 *Perf. 12***
**957** A341 25c multicolored .75 .40

Cent. of holy orders granted to Merino (1833-1906), pres. of the republic 1880-82.

Mirabal Sisters, Political Martyrs 1960 A342

**1985, Dec. 18 *Perf. 13½***
**958** A342 10c multicolored .50 .25

Christmas A343

**1985, Dec. 18**
**959** A343 10c multicolored .40 .25
**960** A343 25c multicolored .90 .35

Day of Independence, Feb. 27 — A344

Design: Mausoleum of founding fathers Duarte, Sanchez and Mella.

**1986, Feb. 26 Litho. *Perf. 13½***
**961** A344 5c multicolored .40 .25
**962** A344 10c multicolored .50 .25



Holy Week A345

Colonial churches.

**1986, Apr. 10**
**963** A345 5c San Miguel .60 .25
**964** A345 5c San Andres .60 .25
**965** A345 10c Santa Barbara .65 .25
**966** A345 10c San Lazaro .65 .25
**967** A345 10c San Carlos .65 .25
*Nos. 963-967 (5)* 3.15 1.25



Navy Day A346

Design: Juan Bautista Cambiaso, Juan Bautista Maggiolo and Juan Alejandro Acosta, 1844 independence battle heroes.

**1986, Apr. 15**
**968** A346 10c multicolored .60 .25

Natl. Elections — A347

**1986, Apr. 29**
**969** A347 5c Voters, map .45 .25
**970** A347 10c Ballot box .55 .25

Natl. Postal Institute Inauguration A348

**1986, June 10**
**971** A348 10c gold, blue & red .40 .25
**972** A348 25c silver, blue & red 1.00 .30
**973** A348 50c black, blue & red 1.75 .65
*Nos. 971-973 (3)* 3.15 1.20

Central America and Caribbean Games, Santiago — A349

**1986, July 17 Litho. *Perf. 13½***
**974** A349 10c Weight lifting .40 .25
**975** A349 25c Gymnastics .85 .30
**976** A349 35c Diving 1.25 .45
**977** A349 50c Equestrian 1.50 .70
*Nos. 974-977 (4)* 4.00 1.70

Historians A350

Designs: 5c, Ercilia Pepin (b. 1886), vert. 10c, Ramon Emilio Jimenez (b. 1886) and Victor Garrido (1886-1972).

**1986, Aug. 1 Litho. *Perf. 13½***
**978** A350 5c silver & dull brn .40 .25
**979** A350 10c silver & dull brn .55 .25

A351

A352

Discovery of America, 500th Anniv. (in 1992) — A353

Designs: 25c, Yachts racing, 5th Adm. Christopher Columbus Regatta, Casa de Espana. 50c, Columbus founding La Isabela City. 65c, Exploration of the hidalgos. 1p, Columbus returning to the Court of Ferdinand and Isabella. 1.50p, Emblems.

**1986, Oct. 10 Litho. *Perf. 13½***

| | | | | |
|---|---|---|---|---|
| **980** | A351 | 25c multicolored | .75 | .35 |
| **981** | A352 | 50c multicolored | 1.50 | .55 |
| **982** | A352 | 65c multicolored | 2.00 | .95 |
| **983** | A352 | 1p multicolored | 3.50 | 1.30 |

**Textured Paper**

**Size: 86x58mm**

***Imperf***

| | | | | |
|---|---|---|---|---|
| **984** | A353 | 1.50p multicolored | 6.25 | 6.00 |
| | | *Nos. 980-984 (5)* | 14.00 | 9.15 |

1986 World Cup Soccer Championships, Mexico — A354

Various soccer plays.

**1986, Oct. 21 *Perf. 13½***

| | | | | |
|---|---|---|---|---|
| **985** | A354 | 50c multicolored | 1.40 | .65 |
| **986** | A354 | 75c multicolored | 3.00 | 1.10 |

Medicinal Plants — A355

5c, Zea mays. 10c, Bixa orellana. 25c, Momordica charantia. 50c, Annona muricata.

**1986, Dec. 5**

| | | | | |
|---|---|---|---|---|
| **987** | A355 | 5c multicolored | .40 | .25 |
| **988** | A355 | 10c multicolored | .45 | .25 |
| **989** | A355 | 25c multicolored | .75 | .25 |
| **990** | A355 | 50c multicolored | 1.60 | .55 |
| | | *Nos. 987-990 (4)* | 3.20 | 1.30 |

Second Caribbean Pharmacopeia Seminar.

Christmas A356

**1986, Dec. 19**

| | | | | |
|---|---|---|---|---|
| **991** | A356 | 5c Urban scene | .50 | .25 |
| **992** | A356 | 25c Rural scene | 1.50 | .35 |

A357

**1986, Dec. 31 Litho. *Perf. 13½***

| | | | | |
|---|---|---|---|---|
| **993** | A357 | 10c shown | .40 | .25 |
| **994** | A357 | 25c Portrait, c. 1900 | 1.00 | .40 |

Maximo Gomez (1836-1905), revolutionary, statesman.

A358

**1987, Mar. 30 Litho. *Perf. 13½***

| | | | | |
|---|---|---|---|---|
| **995** | A358 | 50c brt blue, blk & red | 1.40 | .65 |

16th Pan American Ophthalmological Conf., Apr. 5-10.

A359

Stained-glass window, San Juan Bosco church, Santo Domingo: Ascension of Christ to Heaven.

**1987, May 28**

| | | | | |
|---|---|---|---|---|
| **996** | A359 | 35c multicolored | 1.50 | .50 |

Edible Plants — A360

5c, Sorghum bicolor. 25c, Martanta arundinacea. 65c, Calathaea allouia. 1p, Voandzeia subterranea.

**1987, Aug. 21**

| | | | | |
|---|---|---|---|---|
| **997** | A360 | 5c multicolored | .25 | .25 |
| **998** | A360 | 25c multicolored | .60 | .30 |
| **999** | A360 | 65c multicolored | 1.90 | .95 |
| **1000** | A360 | 1p multicolored | 3.00 | 1.40 |
| | | *Nos. 997-1000 (4)* | 5.75 | 2.90 |

Activo 20-30 Intl., 25th Anniv. A361

**1987, Aug. 26**

| | | | | |
|---|---|---|---|---|
| **1001** | A361 | 35c multicolored | 1.75 | .50 |

Adm. Christopher Columbus Regatta A362

A363

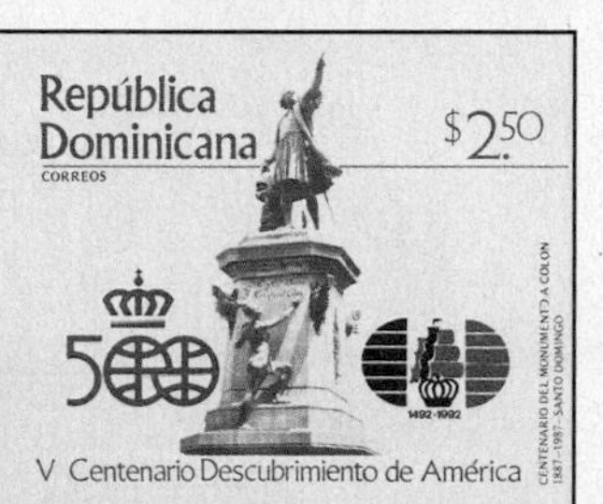


Columbus Memorial, Santo Domingo — A364

1p, Building Ft. Santiago. 1.50p, Columbus imprisoned by Bombadilla.

**1987, Oct. 14**

| | | | | |
|---|---|---|---|---|
| **1002** | A362 | 50c shown | 1.50 | .70 |
| **1003** | A363 | 75c shown | 2.25 | 1.00 |
| **1004** | A363 | 1p multicolored | 3.00 | 1.30 |
| **1005** | A363 | 1.50p multicolored | 4.50 | 2.00 |

**Size: 82x70mm**

***Imperf***

| | | | | |
|---|---|---|---|---|
| **1006** | A364 | 2.50p shown | 10.00 | 6.50 |
| | | *Nos. 1002-1006 (5)* | 21.25 | 11.50 |

Discovery of America, 500th anniv. in 1992.

A365

**1987, Sept. 28**

| | | | | |
|---|---|---|---|---|
| **1007** | A365 | 40c multicolored | 1.20 | .50 |

Junior Olympics, La Vega, 50th anniv.

A366

Historians and authors: 10c, Jose Antonio Hungria. 25c, Joaquin Sergio Inchaustegui.

**1987, Nov. 10 Litho. *Perf. 13½***

| | | | | |
|---|---|---|---|---|
| **1008** | A366 | 10c buff & brown | .35 | .25 |
| **1009** | A366 | 25c pale grn & grn | .90 | .25 |

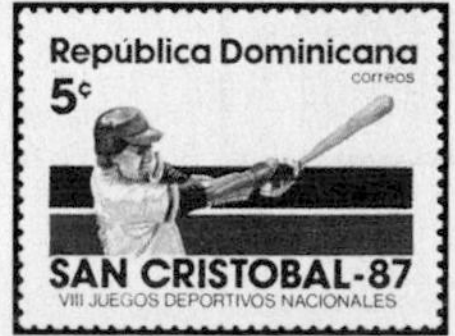


SAN CRISTOBAL '87, 8th Natl. Games — A367

**1987, Nov. 19**

| | | | | |
|---|---|---|---|---|
| **1010** | A367 | 5c Baseball | .90 | .25 |
| **1011** | A367 | 10c Boxing | 1.00 | .25 |
| **1012** | A367 | 50c Judo | 3.00 | .70 |
| | | *Nos. 1010-1012 (3)* | 4.90 | 1.20 |

Christmas 1987 A368

**1987, Dec. 9 Litho. *Perf. 13½***

| | | | | |
|---|---|---|---|---|
| **1013** | A368 | 10c Roasting pig | .55 | .25 |
| **1014** | A368 | 50c Arriving at airport | 1.75 | .60 |

Fr. Xavier Billini (b. 1837) — A369

10c, Statue. 25c, Portrait. 75c, Ana Hernandez de Billini, his mother.

**1987, Dec. 18 Litho. *Perf. 13½***

| | | | | |
|---|---|---|---|---|
| **1015** | A369 | 10c blue gray & dark blue | .35 | .25 |
| **1016** | A369 | 25c cream & dark grn | .75 | .35 |
| **1017** | A369 | 75c pink & blkish pur | 2.25 | 1.10 |
| | | *Nos. 1015-1017 (3)* | 3.35 | 1.70 |

Frank Feliz, Sr., and Aircraft A370

**1987, Dec. 22**

| | | | | |
|---|---|---|---|---|
| **1018** | A370 | 25c shown | .80 | .25 |

**Size: 86x106mm**

***Imperf***

| | | | | |
|---|---|---|---|---|
| **1019** | A370 | 2p No. C30, map | 12.50 | 6.50 |

Pan-American goodwill flight to South American countries by the planes Colon, Pinta, Nina and Santa Maria, 50th anniv.

Flora A371

No. 1020, Bromelia pinguin. No. 1021, Tillandsia fasciculata. No. 1022, Tillandsia hotteana, vert. No. 1023, Tillandsia compacta, vert.

**1988, Feb. 3 Litho. *Perf. 13½***

| | | | | |
|---|---|---|---|---|
| **1020** | A371 | 50c multi | 2.10 | .70 |
| **1021** | A371 | 50c multi | 2.10 | .70 |
| **1022** | A371 | 50c multi | 2.10 | .70 |
| **1023** | A371 | 50c multi | 2.10 | .70 |
| | | *Nos. 1020-1023 (4)* | 8.40 | 2.80 |

St. John Bosco (1815-1888) A372

**1988, Feb. 23 Litho. *Perf. 13½***

| | | | | |
|---|---|---|---|---|
| **1024** | A372 | 10c shown | .45 | .25 |
| **1025** | A372 | 70c Stained-glass window | 2.70 | .95 |

Dominican Rehabilitation Assoc., 25th Anniv. — A373

**1988, Mar. 1**

**1026** A373 20c multicolored .75 .30

A374

**1988, Apr. 6 Litho. *Perf. 13½***

**1027** A374 20c dk red brn & lt fawn .75 .30

Dr. Manuel Emilio Perdomo (b.1886).

A375

**1988, Apr. 29 Litho. *Perf. 13½***

**1028** A375 20c multicolored .75 .30

Dominican College of Engineers, Architects and Surveyors (CODIA), 25th Anniv.

Independence Day, Mexico — A376

Flags and: No. 1029, Fr. Miguel Hidalgo y Costilla (1753-1811), Mexican revolutionary. No. 1030, Juan Pablo Duarte (1813-1876), father of Dominican independence.

**1988, Sept. 12 Litho. *Perf. 13½***

**1029** A376 50c multicolored 1.40 .65
**1030** A376 50c multicolored 1.40 .65

1988 Summer Olympics, Seoul A377

50c, Running, vert. 70c, Table tennis, vert. 1p, Judo, vert. 1.50p, Mural by Tete Marella.

**1988, Sept. 21 Litho. *Perf. 13½***

| | | | | | |
|---|---|---|---|---|---|
| **1031** | A377 | 50c | multicolored | 1.10 | .50 |
| **1032** | A377 | 70c | multicolored | 1.60 | .75 |
| **1033** | A377 | 1p | multicolored | 2.50 | .95 |
| **1034** | A377 | 1.50p | multicolored | 3.75 | 1.50 |
| | *Nos. 1031-1034 (4)* | | | 8.95 | 3.70 |

A378

Discovery of America, 500th Anniv. (in 1992) — A379

Designs: 50c, 7th Adm. Christopher Columbus Regatta, Casa de Espana, 1988. 70c, La Concepcion Fortress, La Vega Real, 1494. 1.50p, Ft. Bonao. 2p, Nicolas de Ovando (c. 1451-1511), governor of Spanish possessions in America from 1502 to 1509. 3p, Mausoleum of Christopher Columbus, Santo Domingo Cathedral.

**1988, Oct. 14 *Perf. 13½***

| | | | | | |
|---|---|---|---|---|---|
| **1035** | A378 | 50c | multicolored | 1.10 | .65 |
| **1036** | A378 | 70c | multicolored | 1.75 | .95 |
| **1037** | A378 | 1.50p | multicolored | 3.50 | 1.90 |
| **1038** | A378 | 2p | multicolored | 5.00 | 2.40 |

**Size: 78x109mm**

***Imperf***

| | | | | | |
|---|---|---|---|---|---|
| **1039** | A379 | 3p | multicolored | 6.25 | 5.50 |
| | *Nos. 1035-1039 (5)* | | | 17.60 | 11.40 |

Discovery of America, 500th anniv. (in 1992). No. 1038 inscribed "1501-1509."

Duverge Parish, Cent. — A380

**1988, July 13 Litho. *Perf. 13½***

**1040** A380 50c multicolored 1.25 .40

A381

Trinitarians, 150th Anniv. — A382

**1988, Nov. 11**

| | | | | | |
|---|---|---|---|---|---|
| **1041** | A381 | 10c | shown | .45 | .25 |
| **1042** | A382 | 1p | Trinitarian Plaza | 2.00 | .45 |
| **1043** | A382 | 5p | Independence Plaza | 13.00 | 4.75 |
| | *Nos. 1041-1043 (3)* | | | 15.45 | 5.45 |

See footnote after No. 337.

Pharmacology and Biochemistry A383

**1988, Nov. 28 Litho. *Perf. 13½***

**1044** A383 1p multicolored 2.00 1.40

13th Pan American and 16th Central American Congresses.

*The Holy Family, 1504, by Miguel Angel* — A384

**1988, Dec. 12**

**1045** A384 10c shown .45 .25
**1046** A384 20c Stained-glass window .75 .30

Christmas.

Municipal Technical Advisory Organization (LIGA), 50th Anniv. — A385

**1988, Dec. 23**

**1047** A385 20c multicolored .75 .35

Ana Teresa Paradas (1890-1960), 1st Female Lawyer of the Republic, 1913 — A386

**1988, Dec. 26**

**1048** A386 20c deep claret .75 .35

French Revolution Bicent. A387

**1989, Mar. 10 Litho. *Perf. 13½***

**1049** A387 3p red & violet blue 3.25 2.75

Battle of Tortuga, Apr. 15, 1844 A388

**1989, Apr. 14 Litho. *Perf. 13½***

**1050** A388 40c multicolored 1.10 .50

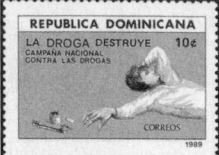

Natl. Anti-drug Campaign A389

**1989, May 15**

| | | | | | |
|---|---|---|---|---|---|
| **1051** | A389 | 10c | multicolored | .30 | .25 |
| **1052** | A389 | 20c | multicolored | .35 | .25 |
| **1053** | A389 | 50c | multicolored | .65 | .25 |
| **1054** | A389 | 70c | multicolored | .90 | .30 |
| **1055** | A389 | 1p | multicolored | 1.40 | .45 |
| **1056** | A389 | 1.50p | multicolored | 1.90 | .50 |
| **1057** | A389 | 2p | multicolored | 2.60 | .70 |
| **1058** | A389 | 5p | multicolored | 6.50 | 1.50 |
| **1059** | A389 | 10p | multicolored | 12.50 | 3.75 |
| | *Nos. 1051-1059 (9)* | | | 27.10 | 7.95 |

Mother's Day A390

**1989, May 30 Litho. *Perf. 13½***

**1060** A390 20c multicolored .70 .25

Eugenio Maria de Hostos (b. 1839) — A391

**1989, Aug. 22 Litho. *Perf. 13½***

**1061** A391 20c multicolored .70 .25

Gen. Gregorio Luperon (b. 1839) — A392

**1989, Aug. 28**

**1062** A392 20c multicolored .70 .25

Little League Baseball, 50th Anniv. A393

**1989, Sept. 29**

**1063** A393 1p multicolored 1.75 1.00

Diabetes '89, 7th Latin American Congress A394

**1989, Oct. 9 Litho. *Perf. 13½***

| | | | | |
|---|---|---|---|---|
| **1064** | A394 1p multicolored | | 1.75 | .60 |

America Issue A395

UPAE emblem, pre-Columbian artifacts and customs: 20c, Cohoba silver statue and ritual dance. 1p, Taina mortar, pestle and family preparing cazabe.

**1989, Oct. 12**

| | | | |
|---|---|---|---|
| **1065** | A395 20c multicolored | .75 | .25 |
| **1066** | A395 1p multicolored | 3.75 | 2.10 |

8th Adm. Christopher Columbus Regatta, Casa de Espana — A396

European Colonization of the Americas — A397

Designs: 70c, Fr. Pedro de Cordoba converting the Indians to Catholicism. 1p, Christopher Columbus trading with the Indians. 3p, Sermon of Pedro de Cordoba.

**1989, Oct. 13**

| | | | |
|---|---|---|---|
| **1067** | A396 50c shown | .65 | .30 |
| **1068** | A397 70c shown | .85 | .55 |
| **1069** | A397 1p multicolored | 1.75 | .75 |
| **1070** | A397 3p multicolored | 3.25 | 2.10 |
| | *Nos. 1067-1070 (4)* | 6.50 | 3.70 |

Discovery of America, 500th anniv. (in 1992).

Natl. Afforestation A398

**1989, Oct. 30 Litho. *Perf. 13½***

| | | | |
|---|---|---|---|
| **1071** | A398 10c shown | .30 | .25 |
| **1072** | A398 20c Tree | .35 | .25 |
| **1073** | A398 50c Forest | 1.10 | .55 |
| **1074** | A398 1p Sapling, mature trees | 2.25 | 1.20 |
| | *Nos. 1071-1074 (4)* | 4.00 | 2.25 |

9th Natl. Games, La Vega — A399

**1990, Mar. 20 Litho. *Perf. 13½***

| | | | |
|---|---|---|---|
| **1075** | A399 10c Cycling | .30 | .25 |
| **1076** | A399 20c Running | .45 | .30 |
| **1077** | A399 50c Basketball | 1.40 | .75 |
| | *Nos. 1075-1077 (3)* | 2.15 | 1.30 |

Holy Week (Easter) — A400

**1990, Apr. 5**

| | | | |
|---|---|---|---|
| **1078** | A400 20c shown | .50 | .30 |
| **1079** | A400 50c Jesus carrying cross | 1.25 | .75 |

Labor Day, Cent. A401

**1990, Apr. 30 Litho. *Perf. 13½***

| | | | |
|---|---|---|---|
| **1080** | A401 1p multicolored | 1.60 | .65 |

Urban Renewal A402

**1990, May 10**

| | | | |
|---|---|---|---|
| **1081** | A402 10c shown | .30 | .25 |
| **1082** | A402 20c Highway underpass | .40 | .25 |
| **1083** | A402 50c Library | .85 | .25 |
| **1084** | A402 1p City street | 2.00 | .80 |
| | *Nos. 1081-1084 (4)* | 3.55 | 1.55 |

No. 1084 inscribed $100 instead of $1.00.

Penny Black, 150th Anniv. — A403

**1990, May 29**

| | | | |
|---|---|---|---|
| **1085** | A403 1p multicolored | 2.25 | 1.60 |

**Size: 62x80mm**

***Imperf***

| | | | |
|---|---|---|---|
| **1086** | A403 3p Sir Rowland Hill, Penny Black | 6.25 | 6.25 |

Organization of American States, Cent. — A404

**1990, Oct. 5 Litho. *Perf. 13½***

| | | | |
|---|---|---|---|
| **1087** | A404 2p Flags | 4.00 | 2.40 |

Children's Drawings A405

No. 1088, House of Tostado. No. 1089, Ruins of St. Nicolas of Bari.

**1990, Aug. 7**

| | | | |
|---|---|---|---|
| **1088** | A405 50c multicolored | 1.25 | .75 |
| **1089** | A405 50c multicolored | 1.25 | .75 |

Discovery of America, 500th Anniv. (in 1992) A406

Designs: 1p, Fight at the Gulf of Arrows. 2p, Columbus talking with Guacanagari Indians. 5p, Columbus and Caonabo Indian prisoner.

**1990, Oct. 12**

| | | | |
|---|---|---|---|
| **1090** | A406 1p multicolored | 2.25 | 1.40 |
| **1091** | A406 2p multicolored | 4.50 | 3.00 |
| **1092** | A406 5p multicolored | 11.00 | 7.50 |
| | *Nos. 1090-1092 (3)* | 17.75 | 11.90 |

9th Adm. Christopher Columbus Regatta — A407

**1990, Oct. 12**

| | | | |
|---|---|---|---|
| **1093** | A407 50c multicolored | 1.50 | .70 |

America Issue A408

UPAE emblem and: 50c, Men in canoe. 3p, Man on hammock.

**1990, Nov. 7 Litho. *Perf. 13½***

| | | | |
|---|---|---|---|
| **1094** | A408 50c multicolored | 1.90 | .70 |
| **1095** | A408 3p multicolored | 8.00 | 4.75 |

A409

Discovery of Hispaniola: 50c, 1st official mass in Americas. 1p, Arms of 1st religious order in Americas. 3p, Map of island, horiz. 4p, Christopher Columbus, 1st viceroy and governor in Americas.

**1991, July 17 Litho. *Perf. 13½***

| | | | |
|---|---|---|---|
| **1096** | A409 50c multicolored | .90 | .55 |
| **1097** | A409 1p multicolored | 1.75 | 1.20 |
| **1098** | A409 3p multicolored | 4.75 | 2.75 |
| **1099** | A409 4p multicolored | 8.25 | 5.00 |
| | *Nos. 1096-1099 (4)* | 15.65 | 9.50 |

A410

**1991**

| | | | |
|---|---|---|---|
| **1100** | A410 30c Boxing | .40 | .25 |
| **1101** | A410 50c Cycling | 1.25 | .50 |
| **1102** | A410 1p Bowling | 2.50 | 1.00 |
| | *Nos. 1100-1102 (3)* | 4.15 | 1.75 |

11th Pan American Games, Havana.

Dr. Tomas Eudoro Perez Rancier, Birth Cent. — A411

**1991, July 3**

| | | | |
|---|---|---|---|
| **1103** | A411 2p yellow & black | 7.50 | 1.90 |

10th Columbus Regatta, Casa de Espana — A412

Discovery of America, 500th Anniv. (in 1992) A413

Designs: 50c, Encounter of three cultures. 3p, Columbus and Dr. Alvarez Chanca caring for sick. 4p, Rebellion of Enriquillo.

**1991, Oct. 15 Litho. *Perf. 13½***

| | | | |
|---|---|---|---|
| **1104** | A412 30c multicolored | .65 | .25 |
| **1105** | A413 50c multicolored | .90 | .50 |
| **1106** | A413 3p multicolored | 5.50 | 3.00 |
| **1107** | A413 4p multicolored | 7.50 | 4.00 |
| | *Nos. 1104-1107 (4)* | 14.55 | 7.75 |

See No. 1116.

A414

**1991, Nov. 18**

| | | | |
|---|---|---|---|
| **1108** | A414 3p black & red | 4.75 | 2.10 |

Cornea Bank.

America Issue — A415

**1991** **Litho.** ***Perf. 13½***
**1109** A415 1p Santa Maria 3.00 .85
**1110** A415 3p Christopher Columbus 7.00 3.50

33rd Meeting of Inter-American Development Bank Governors, Santo Domingo — A416

**1992** **Litho.** ***Perf. 13½***
**1111** A416 1p multicolored 1.75 .85

A417

**1992** **Litho.** ***Perf. 13½***
**1112** A417 3p multicolored 5.25 2.75

Espanola '92 Philatelic Exposition.

A418

Valentin Salinero, Order of the Apostles founder.

**1992** **Litho.** ***Perf. 13½***
**1113** A418 1p blue & brown 1.75 .90

Order of the Apostles, cent.

Ruins of Monastery of San Francisco A419

Designs: 3p, Ruins of San Nicolas hospital, first in the Americas.

**1992, July 28**
**1114** A419 50c multicolored .75 .50
**1115** A419 3p multicolored 5.50 3.25

**Type of 1991 and**

A420

Designs: 50c, Racing yacht. 1p, Native women, Columbus. 2p, Natives offering Columbus tobacco. 3p, Native woman, Columbus, corn.

**1992, Oct. 6** **Litho.** ***Perf. 13½***
**1116** A412 50c multicolored .70 .35
**1117** A420 1p multicolored 1.60 .75
**1118** A420 2p multicolored 4.50 2.75
**1119** A420 3p multicolored 6.50 3.25
*Nos. 1116-1119 (4)* 13.30 7.10

11th Columbus Regatta (No. 1116), Discovery of America, 500th anniv. (Nos. 1117-1119).

23rd Convention of the Alliance of Panamerican Round Tables, Santo Domingo — A421

**1992, Oct. 14**
**1120** A421 1p multicolored 1.75 .85

Visit by Pope John Paul II A422

Cathedrals: 50c, Vega. 3p, Santo Domingo.

**1992, Oct. 1** **Photo.**
**1121** A422 50c multicolored 1.40 .60
**1122** A422 3p multicolored 4.75 2.25

Columbus Lighthouse A423

**1992, Oct. 12** **Litho.**
**1123** A423 30c multicolored 1.00 .45
**1124** A423 1p multicolored 2.00 .70

**Size: 70x133mm**

***Imperf***

**1125** A423 3p Lighthouse at night 10.00 10.00

America Issue A424

Designs: 50c, First royal residence in America, Santo Domingo. 3p, First viceregal residence in America, Royal Palace, Colon.

**1992, Nov. 13** **Litho.** ***Perf. 13½***
**1126** A424 50c multicolored .75 .40
**1127** A424 3p multicolored 4.00 2.50

A425

**1992, Dec. 2** **Litho.** ***Perf. 13½***
**1128** A425 30c Torch bearer .45 .25
**1129** A425 1p Emblems 1.50 .80
**1130** A425 4p Judo 7.00 3.50
*Nos. 1128-1130 (3)* 8.95 4.55

1992 Natl. Sports Games, San Juan. Secretary of Sports, Education, Exercise and Recreation (No. 1129).

Natl. Census — A426

**1992-93** **Litho.** ***Perf. 13½***
**1131** A426 50c black, buff & blue .70 .25
**1132** A426 1p blk, brn & blue 1.40 .75
**1133** A426 3p blk, gray & bl 4.75 2.50
**1134** A426 4p blk, yel grn & bl 6.00 3.00
*Nos. 1131-1134 (4)* 12.85 6.50

Issued: 50c, 1p, 5/12/92; 3p, 4p, 9/9/93.

A427

**1993, May 30**
**1135** A427 30c multicolored .50 .25
**1136** A427 50c multicolored .90 .30
**1137** A427 1p multicolored 1.90 .80
*Nos. 1135-1137 (3)* 3.30 1.35

Ema Balaguer, humanitarian.

A428

**1993, Oct. 7** **Litho.** ***Perf. 13½***
**1138** A428 30c shown 1.00 .45
**1139** A428 1p Emblem, flags 2.75 1.00

Rotary Club of Santo Domingo, 50th anniv.

17th Central American & Caribbean Games, Ponce A429

**1993, Dec. 21** **Litho.** ***Perf. 13½***
**1140** A429 50c Tennis .65 .25
**1141** A429 4p Swimming 7.00 2.00

Natl. Education Plan — A430

**1993, Dec. 8**
**1142** A430 1.50p multicolored 2.40 .90

Spanish America — A431

**1993, Dec. 28**
**1143** A431 50c First university lecturn .75 .25
**1144** A431 3p First city coat of arms 5.25 1.50

America Issue A432

**1993, Dec. 30**
**1145** A432 1p Aratinga chloroptera 1.25 .50
**1146** A432 3p Cyclura cornuta 5.25 2.75

Opening of New Natl. Post Office A433

**1993, Nov. 12**

**Color of Inscription**

**1147** A433 1p olive 1.00 .55
**1148** A433 3p red 3.00 1.60
**1149** A433 4p blue 3.75 1.90
**1150** A433 5p green 4.75 2.25
**1151** A433 10p black 9.50 4.50

**Size: 105x96mm**

***Imperf***

**1152** A433 5p black 12.50 12.50
*Nos. 1147-1152 (6)* 34.50 23.30

First Mass in America, 500th Anniv. — A434

**1994, Feb. 3** **Litho.** ***Perf. 13½***
**1153** A434 2p multicolored 3.00 1.25

5th Natl. Philatelic Exhibition A435

**1994, Feb. 25**
**1154** A435 3p multicolored 4.50 1.60

Natl. Independence, 150th Anniv. — A436

No. 1155: a, Men with document, left side of table. b, Document on right side of table, men. c, Flag. d, Couple at window. e, Child holding material, mother making flag.

No. 1156: a, Men looking upward, shooting muskets. b, Men with guns, swords looking backwards. c, Natl. coat of arms. d, Men with guns, swords, one pointing upward. e, Men with weapons, one with flag.

10p, Three men, angel carrying musket, flag.

**1994, Feb. 26** **Strips of 5**

**1155** A436 2p #a.-e. 8.25 4.00
**1156** A436 3p #a.-e. 12.50 6.00

**Size: 161x104mm**

***Imperf***

**1157** A436 10p multicolored 11.50 11.50
*Nos. 1155-1157 (3)* 32.25 21.50

Nos. 1155a-1155b, 1155d-1155e, 1156a-1156b, 1156d-1156e have a continuous design.

Solenodon Paradoxus — A437

Designs: a, Crawling on rock. b, Walking in leaves. c, Looking up. d, With food in mouth.

**1994, Mar. 15** **Litho.** ***Perf. 13½***

**1158** A437 1p Block of 4, #a.-d. 9.00 5.25

World Wildlife Fund.

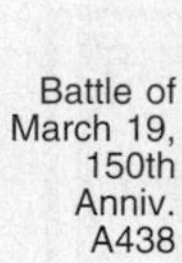

Battle of March 19, 150th Anniv. A438

No. 1160, Soldiers advancing uphill toward fort.

**1994**

**1159** A438 2p multicolored 3.00 1.50
**1160** A438 2p multicolored 3.00 1.50

Issued: No. 1159, Mar. 18; No. 1160, Mar. 29.

Virgin of Amparo — A439

**1994, Apr. 15** **Litho.** ***Perf. 13½***

**1161** A439 3p multicolored 4.50 1.75

Battle of Puerto Tortuguero, 150th anniv.

Natl. Elections, May 16 — A440

**1994, Apr. 4**

**1162** A440 2p multicolored 3.00 1.50

1994 World Cup Soccer Championships, US — A441

**1994, June 24** **Litho.** ***Perf. 13½***

**1163** A441 4p multicolored 5.00 2.25
**1164** A441 6p multicolored 7.00 3.25

Ema Balaguer City of Children A442

**1994, July 20** **Litho.** ***Perf. 13½***

**1165** A442 1p magenta & brown 2.75 .60

Stamp Day A443

**1994, Oct. 18** **Litho.** ***Perf. 13½***

**1166** A443 5p Type A3 7.75 3.00

America Issue — A444

**1994, Oct. 28**

**1167** A444 2p Pony Express 3.00 1.50
**1168** A444 6p Sailing ship 10.00 4.00

Province of LaVega, 500th Anniv. A445

3p, Ruins of San Francisco Monastery.

**1994, Nov. 24** **Litho.** ***Perf. 13½***

**1169** A445 3p multicolored 7.25 1.60

First Church the New World, 500th Anniv. — A446

a, "La Isabela," cradle of evangelization. b, "Temple of the Americas," first mission.

**1994, Dec. 5** ***Perf. 11½***

**1170** A446 3p Pair, #a.-b. 10.00 3.00

Constitution, 150th Anniv. — A447

**1994, Nov. 6** ***Perf. 13½***

**1171** A447 3p multicolored 5.00 1.60

Christmas A448

2p, Holy family's flight into Egypt. 3p, Modern family of three standing at river's edge.

**1994, Nov. 18**

**1172** A448 2p multicolored 3.50 1.25
**1173** A448 3p multicolored 4.75 1.60

Intl. Year of the Family.

Firsts in America — A449

**1994, Dec. 21** **Litho.** ***Perf. 13½***

**1174** A449 2p Circulating coins 3.50 .75
**1175** A449 5p Sermon for Justice 7.75 2.00

Snakes A450

No. 1176, Hypsirhynchus ferox. No. 1177, Antillophis parvifrons. No. 1178, Uromacer catesbyi. No. 1179, Epicrates striatus.

**1994, Dec. 26**

**1176** A450 2p multicolored 3.00 1.00
**1177** A450 2p multicolored 3.00 1.00
*a.* Pair, #1176-1177 6.00 5.50
**1178** A450 2p multicolored 3.00 1.00
**1179** A450 2p multicolored 3.00 1.00
*a.* Pair, #1178-1179 6.00 5.50

Nos. 1177a, 1179a are continuous designs.

Pan American Games, Mar Del Plata, Argentina A451

**1995, Apr. 20** ***Perf. 13½***

**1180** A451 4p Tae kwon do 4.75 1.75
**1181** A451 13p Tennis 14.50 5.00

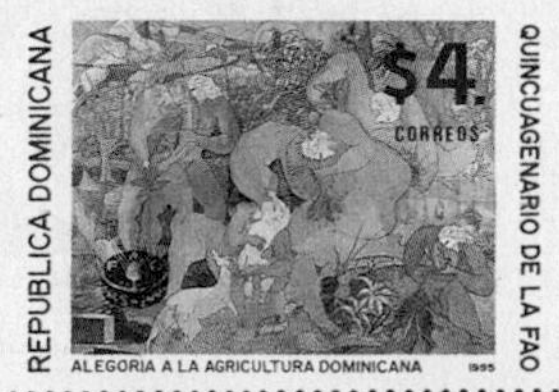


FAO, 50th Anniv. — A452

**1995, Apr. 21** **Litho.** ***Perf. 11½***

**1182** A452 4p multicolored 4.50 2.25

A453

Designs: 2p, Jose Marti, Maximo Gomez. 3p, Marti. 4p, Marti seated at desk, Gomez.

**1995, May 19** **Litho.** ***Perf. 13½***

**1183** A453 2p multicolored 1.90 .75
**1184** A453 3p multicolored 2.50 1.40
**1185** A453 4p multicolored 3.75 2.00
*Nos. 1183-1185 (3)* 8.15 4.15

Jose Marti (1853-95), Montecristi Manifesto, cent.

Basketball, Cent. — A454

**1995, May 22**

**1186** A454 3p multicolored 3.00 .45

Medicinal Plants — A455

**1995, May 26**

**1187** A455 2p Pimenta ozua 2.00 1.00
**1188** A455 2p Melocactus communis 2.00 1.00
**1189** A455 3p Smilax 3.00 1.50
**1190** A455 3p Zamia 3.00 1.50
*Nos. 1187-1190 (4)* 10.00 5.00

Tourism A456

4p, San Souci Port. 5p, Barahona Airport. 6p, G. Luperon Airport. 13p, Airport of the Americas.

**1995, June 21**

**1191** A456 4p multicolored 3.00 .50
**1192** A456 5p multicolored 3.75 .75
**1193** A456 6p multicolored 4.75 .85
**1194** A456 13p multicolored 10.00 1.75
*Nos. 1191-1194 (4)* 21.50 3.85

Santiago de Los Caballeros, 500th Anniv. A457

**1995, July 29** **Litho.** ***Perf. 13½***

**1195** A457 3p Jacagua ruins 4.75 .90

Whales
A458

Designs: No. 1196, Physeter macrocephalus. No. 1197, Balaenoptera borealis. No. 1198, Ziphius cavirostris. No. 1199, Megaptera novaeangliae.

**1995, Aug. 14**

| | | | |
|---|---|---|---|
| **1196** | A458 3p multicolored | 3.00 | .50 |
| **1197** | A458 3p multicolored | 3.00 | .50 |
| **1198** | A458 3p multicolored | 3.00 | .50 |
| **1199** | A458 3p multicolored | 3.00 | .50 |
| | *Nos. 1196-1199 (4)* | 12.00 | 2.00 |

Stamp Day
A459

**1995, Oct. 18 Litho. *Perf. 13½***

| | | | |
|---|---|---|---|
| **1200** | A459 4p No. 37 | 3.25 | .50 |

Popular Singers — A460

**1995, Oct. 8**

| | | | |
|---|---|---|---|
| **1201** | A460 2p Rafael Colon | 1.75 | .75 |
| **1202** | A460 3p Casandra Damiron | 2.25 | 1.10 |

Cathedral of Santiago, Cent.
A461

**1995, Dec. 28 Litho. *Perf. 13½***

| | | | |
|---|---|---|---|
| **1203** | A461 3p multicolored | 2.50 | 1.10 |

4th World Conference of Women, Beijing — A462

**1995, Nov. 23**

| | | | |
|---|---|---|---|
| **1204** | A462 2p multicolored | 5.25 | 1.10 |

Volleyball, Cent. — A463

Norceca '95 — A464

**1995, Oct. 19 *Imperf.***

| | | | |
|---|---|---|---|
| **1205** | A463 5p multicolored | 4.75 | 1.90 |

***Perf. 13½***

| | | | |
|---|---|---|---|
| **1206** | A464 6p multicolored | 5.00 | 4.25 |

Singers — A465

**1995, Dec. 27 *Perf. 13½***

| | | | |
|---|---|---|---|
| **1207** | A465 2p Antonio Mesa | 1.75 | .80 |
| **1208** | A465 2p Julieta Otero | 1.75 | .80 |
| **1209** | A465 2p Susano Polanco | 1.75 | .80 |
| | *Nos. 1207-1209 (3)* | 5.25 | 2.40 |

Columbus Lighthouse
A466

**1995, Dec. 5**

| | | | |
|---|---|---|---|
| **1210** | A466 10p dk bl, bl & gray | 11.00 | 3.50 |

See Nos. 1241, 1265, 1299, 1337, 1371, 1375, 1382.

A467

UN, 50th Anniv.
A468

**1995, Oct. 24**

| | | | |
|---|---|---|---|
| **1211** | A467 2p multicolored | 1.75 | .75 |

***Perf. 11½***

| | | | |
|---|---|---|---|
| **1212** | A468 6p multicolored | 5.00 | 1.00 |

Environmental Protection — A469

America issue: 2p, Flamingos, sea gull. 6p, Manglar.

**1995, Dec. 19 Litho. *Perf. 13½***

| | | | |
|---|---|---|---|
| **1213** | A469 2p multicolored | 1.75 | .65 |
| **1214** | A469 6p multicolored | 5.00 | 1.00 |

Dominican Republic Air Force, 50th Anniv. — A470

Aircraft: a, O2U-35D Corsair. b, PT-17 Stearman. c, AT-6 Texan. d, PBY-5A Catalina. e, TF-10 Beaufighter. f, FB-6 Mosquito. g, P-38 Lightning. h, P-51D Mustang. i, B-17G Flying Fortress. j, P-47D Thunderbolt. k, FB-5 Vampire. l, C-46 Commander. m, B-26 Invader. n, C-47 Skytrain. o, T-28D Trojan. p, T-33A Silverstar. q, Cessna T-41D. r, T-34 Mentor. s, Cessna O-2A. t, A-37B Dragonfly.

**1995, Dec. 30**

| | | | |
|---|---|---|---|
| **1215** | A470 2p Sheet of 20, #a-t | 30.00 | 17.00 |

See No. 1228.

UNICEF, 50th Anniv. — A471

**1996, Feb. 23**

| | | | |
|---|---|---|---|
| **1216** | A471 2p shown | 1.50 | .45 |
| **1217** | A471 4p Mirror image of #1216 | 3.00 | 1.40 |

Intl. Sailing Competition
A472

**1996, Mar. 8**

| | | | |
|---|---|---|---|
| **1218** | A472 5p multicolored | 3.25 | 1.60 |

Eduardo Brito, Singer, 50th Death Anniv. — A473

**1996, Jan. 15**

| | | | |
|---|---|---|---|
| **1219** | A473 1p shown | .65 | .30 |
| **1220** | A473 2p With maracas | 1.40 | .75 |
| **1221** | A473 3p Portrait | 2.10 | 1.10 |
| | *Nos. 1219-1221 (3)* | 4.15 | 2.15 |

No. 1220 is 54x35mm.

Natl. Journalist Day — A474

Design: Arturo J. Pellerano Alfau, Dr. Freddy Gaton Arce, Rafael Herrera Cabral.

**1996, Apr. 17 Litho. *Perf. 13½***

| | | | |
|---|---|---|---|
| **1222** | A474 5p multicolored | 3.75 | 1.75 |

ESPAMER '96, Seville — A475

**1996, June 7 Litho. *Perf. 13½***

| | | | |
|---|---|---|---|
| **1223** | A475 15p multicolored | 9.50 | 4.75 |

1996 Summer Olympic Games, Atlanta — A476

**1996, July 5**

| | | | |
|---|---|---|---|
| **1224** | A476 5p Judo | 3.75 | 1.40 |
| **1225** | A476 15p Torch | 9.75 | 4.25 |

Modern Olympic Games, Cent. — A477

**1996, July 5**

1226 A477 6p Greece No. 118 3.75 1.90
1227 A477 15p No. 328 9.00 4.25

**Dominican Republic Air Force, 50th Anniv. Type of 1995**

Helicoptors: a, Sikorsky S-55. b, Alouette II. c, Alouette III. d, OH-6A Cayuse. e, Bell 205 A-1. f, Dauphin II SA.365C.

**1996, July 31 Litho. *Perf. 13½***

1228 A470 3p Sheet of 6, #a.-f. 8.00 8.00

World Day Against Illegal Drugs — A478

**1996, Sept. 23 Litho. *Perf. 13½***

1229 A478 15p multicolored 9.75 4.25

Mail Delivery A479

No. 1230, World delivery, putting mail in letter box, mailman receiving mail on motorcycle. No. 1231, Woman giving mail to man on horseback, vert. No. 1232, Child holding letter beside mailbox.

**1996, July 17 Litho. *Perf. 13½***

1230 A479 3p multicolored 2.50 1.25
1231 A479 3p multicolored 2.50 1.25
1232 A479 3p multicolored 2.50 1.25
*Nos. 1230-1232 (3)* 7.50 3.75

America Issue — A480

**1996, Oct. 15 Litho. *Perf. 13½***

1233 A480 2p Men's costume 1.40 .65
1234 A480 6p Women's costume 3.75 1.75

Stamp Day A481

**1996, Oct. 18**

1235 A481 5p No. 142 3.25 1.40

26th Intl. Sunfish Championships — A482

6p, Sun, natl. flag, sailboat, vert. 10p, Man sailing boat.

**1996, Oct. 16**

1236 A482 6p multicolored 3.75 1.75
1237 A482 10p multicolored 6.25 3.25

A483

**1996, Nov. 25 Litho. *Perf. 13½***

1238 A483 5p green & multi 3.25 1.60
1239 A483 10p pink & multi 6.25 3.25

Intl. Day to End Violence Against Women.

Birds — A484

a, Buteo ridgwayi. b, Aratinga chloroptera. c, Amazona ventralis. d, Hyetornis rufigularis. e, Saurothera longirostris. f, Siphonorhis brewsteri. g, Chlorostilbon swainsonii. h, Todus angustirostris. i, Todus subulatus. j, Temnotrogon roseigaster. k, Nesoctites micromegas. l, Melanerpes striatus. m, Turdus swalesi. n, Carduelis dominicensis. o, Dulus dominicus. p, Microligea palustris. q, Vireo nanus. r, Xenoligea montanta. s, Turdus swalesi dodae. t, Calyptophilus frugivorus tertius. u, Corvus leucognaphalus. v, Calyptophilus frugivorus neibae.

**1996, Nov. 11**

1240 A484 2p Sheet of 22, #a-v 45.00 30.00

**Lighthouse Type of 1995**

**1996, Dec. 27 Litho. *Perf. 13½***

1241 A466 10p grn, sil & gray 7.00 3.50

Turtles — A485

a, Dermochelys coriacea. b, Caretta caretta. c, Chelonia mydas. d, Eretmochelys imbricata.

**1996, Dec. 30**

1242 A485 5p Block of 4, #a.-d. 12.00 10.00

Natl. Youth Day — A486

**1997, Jan. 31**

1243 A486 3p multicolored 2.00 1.00

National Anthem — A487

Designs: 2p, Lyrics, by Emilio Prudhome. 3p, Music, by Jose Reyes.

**1997, Feb. 26**

1244 A487 2p multicolored 1.50 .65
1245 A487 3p multicolored 2.00 .95

Salomé Urena (1850-97), Poet — A488

**1997, Mar. 6 *Perf. 13½***

1246 A488 3p multicolored 1.90 .95

Comet Hale-Bopp A489

**1997, Apr. 1**

1247 A489 5p multicolored 4.25 1.60

**Size: 72x47mm**

***Imperf***

1248 A489 10p multicolored 11.00 11.00

A490

11th Natl. Sports Games, Mao '97 — A491

2p, Mascot running with torch. 3p, Mascot in batting stance, vert. 5p, Runner breaking finish line.

**1997, Apr. 3**

1249 A490 2p multicolored 1.75 .65
1250 A491 3p multicolored 2.75 1.00
1251 A491 5p multicolored 4.25 1.60
*Nos. 1249-1251 (3)* 8.75 3.25

A492

Design: 10p, 5p, Heinrich von Stephan (1831-97), founder of UPU.

**1997, Apr. 8 Litho. *Perf. 13½***

1252 A492 10p multicolored 6.25 3.25

**Souvenir Sheet**

***Imperf***

1253 A492 5p like #1252 3.25 2.75

No. 1253 has simulated perforations.

A493

**1997, Apr. 29 *Perf. 13½***

1254 A493 10p multicolored 9.50 3.25

25th Intl. Congress of CLAHT (Caracas and Latin American Group of Hemostasis and Thrombosis).

Gregorio Luperón (1839-1897), Politician — A494

**1997, May 21**

1255 A494 3p multicolored 2.00 1.00

House of Spain, 80th Anniv. — A495

**1997, July 4**

1256 A495 5p multicolored 3.25 1.60

First Peso Coin, Cent. A496

**1997, Aug. 6 Litho. *Perf. 13½***

1257 A496 2p multicolored 1.50 .65

A497

Coronation of the Image of Our Lady of Alta Gracia, 75th Anniv. — A498

**1997, Aug. 12**

**1258** A497 3p multicolored 1.90 .85
**1259** A498 5p multicolored 3.25 1.60

America Issue A499

Life of a postman: 2p, Dog grabbing pants leg of postman on motorcycle. 6p, Dog tearing pants leg of postman with letter.

**1997, Oct. 9 Litho. *Perf. 13½***

**1260** A499 2p multicolored 1.25 .65

**Size: 35½x35½mm**

**1261** A499 6p multicolored 3.25 1.60

Mother Teresa (1910-97) A500

**1997, Oct. 17**

**1262** A500 5p multicolored 3.00 1.60

Stamp Day — A501

**1997, Oct. 18**

**1263** A501 5p Nos. 108, 322 2.75 1.60

Central Bank of the Dominican Republic, 50th Anniv. — A502

**1997, Oct. 30 *Perf. 11½***

**1264** A502 10p multicolored 5.50 3.25

**Lighthouse Type of 1995**

**1997, Dec. 15 Litho. *Perf. 13½***

**1265** A466 10p bright rose & gray 7.50 3.25

Bats A503

a, Erophylius bombifrons. b, Brachyphylla nana. c, Molossus molossus. d, Lasiurus borealis.

**1997, Nov. 11**

**1266** A503 5p Block of 4, #a.-d. 11.00 11.00

Dominican Air Force, 50th Anniv. A504

Insignias: a, Air Force, red, white, and blue target. b, Northern Air Command, "shark plane." c, Air Command, eagle's wings over target. d, Rescue Force, eagle. e, Maintenance Command. f, Combat Force, dragon, target.

**1997, Dec. 19**

**1267** A504 3p Sheet of 6, #a.-f. 11.00 11.00

Construction of the National Palace, 50th Anniv. — A505

**1997, Dec. 30 Litho. *Perf. 13½***

**1268** A505 10p multicolored 6.25 3.50

First Regional Symposium on Pre-Columbian Culture and Caribbean Contemporary Art — A506

**1998, Jan. 28**

**1269** A506 6p multicolored 3.75 1.60

A507

**1998, Apr. 2 Litho. *Perf. 13½***

**1270** A507 10p multicolored 6.25 3.25

American Chamber of Commerce of the Dominican Republic, 75th anniv.

A508

Book Fair: 3p, Natl. Book Fair, 25th anniv. 5p, Intl. Book Fair, Santo Domingo '98.

**1998, Apr. 26**

**1271** A508 3p black, blue & red 1.90 .85

**Size: 35x33mm**

**1272** A508 5p black, blue & red 3.25 1.60

Organization of American States, 50th Anniv. — A509

**1998, Apr. 30**

**1273** A509 5p blue & multi 3.25 1.60
**1274** A509 5p pink & multi 3.25 1.60

Establishment of the State of Israel, 50th Anniv. — A510

**1998, Apr. 30**

**1275** A510 10p multicolored 9.00 4.50

Dominican Air Force, 50th Anniv. — A511

a, Gen. Frank Felix Miranda, portrait at left. b, Early aircraft. c, Col. Ernesto Tejeda, portrait at right. d, As "c," portrait at left. e, As "a," portrait at right.

**1998, June 26 Sheet of 6**

**1276** A511 3p Block of 5, #a, c-e, 2 #b 11.00 11.00

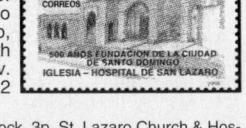

City of Santo Domingo, 500th Anniv. A512

2p, Sun clock. 3p, St. Lazaro Church & Hospital. 4p, First Cathedral in America. 5p, Royal Palace. 6p, Tower of Honor. 10p, St. Nicolas of Bari Church & Hospital.

**1998, Aug. 6 Litho. *Perf. 13½***

**1277** A512 2p multi, vert. 1.25 .65
**1278** A512 3p multi 1.90 .90
**1279** A512 4p multi 2.50 1.25
**1280** A512 5p multi 3.25 1.60
**1281** A512 6p multi 3.75 1.90
**1282** A512 10p multi, vert. 6.25 3.25
*Nos. 1277-1282 (6)* 18.90 9.55

National Theater, 25th Anniv. — A513

**1998, Aug. 14 *Perf. 13x13½***

**1283** A513 10p multicolored 6.25 3.00

Latin Union, 44th Anniv. A514

**1998, Aug. 26 *Perf. 13½***

**1284** A514 10p multicolored 6.25 3.00

ICCO (Intl. Cocoa Organization of America & Europe), 25th Anniv. — A515

**1998, Sept. 3**

**1285** A515 10p multicolored 7.75 3.50

Nino Ferrua (1909-79), Stamp Designer A516

**1998, Oct. 18 Litho. *Perf. 13½x13***

**1286** A516 5p multicolored 3.25 1.50

Stamp Day.

Pontificate of John Paul II, 20th Anniv. A517

**1998, Oct. 22 *Perf. 13½***

**1287** A517 5p shown 3.25 1.50
**1288** A517 10p Portrait, diff. 6.75 2.10

Medicinal Plants — A518

a, Pimenta racemosa. b, Pimenta haitiensis. c, Cymbopogon citratus. d, Citrus aurantium.

**1998, Nov. 2**

**1289** A518 3p Block of 4, #a.-d. 7.00 3.25

Famous Women
A519

America Issue: 2p, Juana Saltitopa standing with cannon. 6p, Anacaona, Indian maiden, group of Indians.

**1998, Nov. 5**

**1290** A519 2p multicolored 2.00 .65
**1291** A519 6p multicolored 4.50 2.00

Intl. Year of the Ocean — A520

**1998, Nov. 20**

**1292** A520 5p multicolored 4.00 1.50

A521

**1998, Nov. 23**

**1293** A521 5p multicolored 2.75 1.50

Expofila '98, Santo Domingo. Santo Domingo, 500th anniv.

National Military Heroes — A522

Designs: a, Fernando Valerio. b, Benito Moncion. c, Jose Maria Cabral. d, Antonio Duverge. e, Gregorio Luperon. f, Jose A. Salcedo. g, Fco. A. Salcedo. h, Gaspar Polanco. i, Santiago Rodriguez. j, Juan Bta. Cambiaso. k, Jose J. Puello. l, Jose Ma. Imbert. m, Juan A. Acosta. n, Marcos Adon. o, Matias R. Mella. p, Francisco R. Sanchez. q, Juan Pablo Duarte. r, Olegario Tenares. s, Pedro Santana. t, Juan Sanchez Ramirez.

**1998, Nov. 29**

**1294** A522 3p Sheet of 20, #a.-t. 27.50 24.50

1st Natl. Paper Money, 150th Anniv. — A523

**1998, Nov. 30** *Perf. 11½*

**1295** A523 10p multicolored 4.75 2.10

Christmas
A524

**1998, Dec. 7** *Perf. 13½*

**1296** A524 2p Roasting hog .90 .45
**1297** A524 5p Magi 2.25 1.10

Universal Declaration of Human Rights, 50th Anniv.
A525

**1998, Dec. 10**

**1298** A525 10p multicolored 4.50 2.10

**Columbus Lighthouse Type of 1995**

**1998, Dec. 11**

**1299** A466 10p orange & black 6.00 3.00

Shells
A526

Designs: a, Lyria vegai. b, Strombus gigas. c, Cittarium pica. d, Nerita peloronta.

**1998, Dec. 16**

**1300** A526 5p Block of 4, #a.-d. 11.00 5.25

Gaspar Hernández (1798-1858), Priest — A527

**1998, Dec. 18**

**1301** A527 3p multicolored 1.40 .70

Dominican Society of Endocrinology and Nutrition, 25th Anniv. — A528

**1999, Feb. 24** **Litho.** *Perf. 13¼*

**1302** A528 10p multicolored 4.00 2.00

Office of Comptroller General — A529

**1999, May 4** **Litho.** *Perf. 13¼*

**1303** A529 2p multicolored 1.00 .45

Export Industries
A530

*Perf. 13½x13¼, 13¼x13½*

**1999, Apr. 30** **Litho.**

**1304** A530 6p Tobacco 2.25 1.10
**1305** A530 10p Textiles, vert. 3.75 1.60

Pan American Games, Winnipeg
A530a

**1999, July 29** **Litho.** *Perf. 13¼x13½*

**1306** A530a 5p Baseball 2.75 1.25
**1307** A530a 6p Weight lifting 3.25 1.50

Native Plants — A531

Designs: a, Pseudophoenix ekmanii. b, Murtigia calabura. c, Pouteria dominguensis. d, Rubus dominguensis focke.

**1999, July 13**

**1308** A531 5p Block of 4, #a.-d. 9.50 9.50

Presidents of the Dominican Republic
A532

Designs: a, Tomas Bobadilla y Briones. b, Pedro Santana. c, Manuel Jimenez. d, Buenaventura Baez. e, Manuel de Regla Mota. f, José Desiderio Valverde. g, José A. Salcedo. h, Gaspar Polanco.

**1999, Aug. 31** *Perf. 13½x13¼*

**1309** A532 3p Sheet of 8, #a.-h. + label 10.00 10.00

A533

Sovereign Military Order of Malta
A534

*Perf. 13¼x13½*

**1999, Sept. 20** **Litho.**

**1310** A533 2p multicolored .85 .45

*Perf. 13½*

**1311** A534 10p multicolored 4.50 2.75

Paintings by José Vela Zanetti (1913-99) — A535

Various paintings.

*Perf. 13½x13¼, 13¼x 13½*

**1999, Sept. 8**

**1312** A535 2p multi, vert. .70 .45
**1313** A535 3p multi, vert. 1.25 .80
**1314** A535 5p multi 1.90 1.10
**1315** A535 6p multi, vert. 2.40 1.40
**1316** A535 10p multi, vert. 3.75 2.10
*Nos. 1312-1316 (5)* 10.00 5.85

Insects — A536

Designs: a, Strataegus quadrifoveatus. b, Anetia jaegeri. c, Polyancistroydes tettigonidae. d, Aploppus phasmidae.

**1999, Sept. 10** *Perf. 13½x13¼*

**1317** A536 5p Block of 4, #a.-d. 8.00 8.00

SOS Children's Villages, 50th Anniv. — A537

**1999, Sept. 29** *Perf. 13¼x13½*

**1318** A537 10p multicolored 4.00 2.10

Intl. Year of the Elderly — A538

**1999, Oct. 1**

**1319** A538 2p Man .75 .25
**1320** A538 5p Woman 2.00 1.00

World Education Day — A539

**1999, Oct. 5**

**1321** A539 5p multicolored 2.00 .90

A540

Designs: 2p, Skull and crossbones, land mines, shattered gun. 6p, Mushroom cloud.

**1999, Oct. 18**

**1322** A540 2p multicolored .80 .50
**1323** A540 6p multicolored 2.60 1.25

America Issue, a new millennium without arms.

Stamp Day — A541

**1999, Oct. 22**

**1324** A541 5p Luis F. Thomen 2.00 .90

Account of Gen. Juan Pablo Duarte A542

**1999, July 16** *Perf. 13½*

**1325** A542 3p multicolored 1.25 .25

A543

Contemporary Writers — A544

*Perf. 13¼x13½, 13½x13¼*

**1999, June 23**

**1326** A543 2p multicolored .75 .25
**1327** A544 10p multicolored 4.75 2.25

Dermatological Society, 50th Anniv. — A545

**1999, Sept. 15** **Litho.** *Perf. 13¼*

**1328** A545 3p multi 1.75 .80

Millennium — A546

3p, Earth, trees. 5p, Scientific achievements.

*Perf. 13¼x13½*

**1999, Nov. 10** **Litho.**

**1329** A546 3p multi 1.25 .75
**1330** A546 5p multi 2.25 1.10

2nd Summit of African, Caribbean and Pacific Heads of State — A547

Emblem and: 5p, Map of Caribbean area, whale. 6p, Map of Pacific area, Easter Island statues. 10p, Map of Africa, lion.

**1999, Nov. 23**

**1331** A547 5p multi 2.00 1.00
**1332** A547 6p multi 2.50 1.10
**1333** A547 10p multi 4.00 2.00
*Nos. 1331-1333 (3)* 8.50 4.10

UPU, 125th Anniv. A548

6p, Globe, envelope, computer, electronic circuits. 10p, Envelope, electronic circuits.

**1999, Nov. 29**

**1334** A548 6p multi 2.25 1.00

**Size: 50x75mm**

***Imperf***

**1335** A548 10p multi 4.50 2.10

Union of Latin American Universities, 50th Anniv. — A549

**1999, Dec. 3** *Perf. 13½x13¼*

**1336** A549 6p multi 2.25 1.00

**Lighthouse Type of 1995**

**1999, Dec. 14** *Perf. 13¼x13½*

**1337** A466 10p brown & silver 4.50 2.10

Classical Musicians A550

No. 1338, José de Jésus Ravelo (1876-1951), clarinet. No. 1339, Juan Francisco Garcia (1892-1974), cornet. No. 1340, Manuel Simo (1916-88), saxophone.

**1999, Dec. 17**

**1338** A550 5p multi 2.00 1.00
**1339** A550 5p multi 2.00 1.00
**1340** A550 5p multi 2.00 1.00
*Nos. 1338-1340 (3)* 6.00 3.00

Municipal Notes, Cent. — A551

Notes and background colors — No. 1341: a, Santo Domingo, San Pedro de Macorís, deep purple. b, Puerto Plata, Moca, purple.

No. 1342, vert.: a, Santiago, Cotui, blue green. b, San Francisco de Macorís, La Vega, golden brown. c, San Cristobal, Samana, peacock blue.

No. 1343: a, As No. 1342a, green background. b, As No. 1342b, brown background. c, As No. 1342c, Prussian blue background.

**1999, Dec. 30** *Perf. 13¼*

**1341** A551 2p Pair, #a.-b. 2.00 1.00
**1342** A551 2p Strip of 3, #a.-c. 2.50 1.10

**Souvenir Sheet**

***Imperf***

**1343** A551 2p Sheet of 5, Nos. 1341a-1341b, 1343a-1343c 4.50 2.25

Chamber of Spanish Commerce and Industry, 75th Anniv. — A552

**1999, Dec. 30** *Perf. 13¼x13½*

**1344** A552 10p multi 4.50 2.40

Fight Against Drugs A553

**2000, Feb. 17** **Litho.** *Perf. 13½*

**1345** A553 5p multi 2.25 1.10

Hogar Crea Dominicana Inc., 25th anniv.

Duarte Institute — A554

**2000, Feb. 25** *Perf. 13¼*

**1346** A554 2p multi 1.00 .50

Prevention of Child Abuse — A555

**2000, Mar. 31**

**1347** A555 2p multi 1.00 .45

National Police A556

**2000, Apr. 6** *Perf. 13½*

**1348** A556 2p shown 1.50 .45

**Size: 37x28mm**

*Perf. 13½x13¼*

**1349** A556 5p Crest 3.00 1.10

Dominican Institute of Industrial Technology, 25th Anniv. A557

**2000, Apr. 11** *Perf. 13½*

**1350** A557 2p multi 1.00 .45

Independencia Province, 50th Anniv. — A558

**2000, Apr. 15**

**1351** A558 3p multi 1.25 .65

A559

12th Natl. Games, La Romana A560

**2000, Apr. 27** *Perf. 13½x13¼*

**1352** A559 2p Baseball 1.00 .45
**1353** A559 3p Boxing 2.00 .80

*Perf. 13½*

**1354** A560 5p Emblem 3.00 1.00
*Nos. 1352-1354 (3)* 6.00 2.25

Paintings A561

Designs: 5p, The Violinist, by Darío Suro. 10p, Self-portrait, by Théodore Chassériau.

**2000, May 5** *Perf. 13¼*
**1355** A561 5p multi 3.25 1.10
**1356** A561 10p multi 5.50 2.50

Presidential Elections A562

**2000, May 12**
**1357** A562 2p multi 1.40 .45

Classical Musicians A563

No. 1358, Julio Alberto Hernandez Camejo (1900-99), pianist. No. 1359, Ramon Diaz (1901-76), bassoonist. No. 1360, Enrique de Marchena Dujarric (1908-88), pianist.

**2000, May 31** *Perf. 13½*
**1358** A563 5p multi 3.25 1.10
**1359** A563 5p multi 3.25 1.10
**1360** A563 5p multi 3.25 1.10
*Nos. 1358-1360 (3)* 9.75 3.30

Expo 2000, Hanover A564

**2000, June 1**
**1361** A564 5p shown 2.25 1.10
**1362** A564 10p Emblem, diff. 4.50 2.10

Art by Jaime Colson — A565

Designs: 2p, Woman on horseback. 3p, Abstract. 5p, Musicians and dancers, horiz. 6p, Nudes. 10p, Colson.

**2000** **Litho.** *Perf. 13¼*
**1363-1367** A565 Set of 5 19.00 6.75

Holy Year 2000 A566

Churches: 2p, Santo Cristo de los Milagros de Bayaguana Sanctuary. 5p, Santa Maria la Menor Cathedral, first in the Americas, vert. 10p, Nuestra Señora de la Altagracia Basilica, vert.

**2000** *Perf. 13½x13¼, 13¼x13½*
**1368-1370** A566 Set of 3 10.00 4.00

**Lighthouse Type of 1995**

**2000** *Perf. 13¼x13½*
**1371** A466 10p buff, brn & sil 7.25 3.50

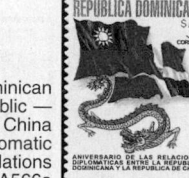

Dominican Republic — Republic of China Diplomatic Relations A566a

Flags of Dominican Republic and Republic of China and: 5p, Illustration of dragon. 10p, Carved dragon.

***Serpentine Die Cut 11¼***
**2000, Dec. 15** **Litho.**
**Self-Adhesive**
**1371A-1371B** A566a Set of 2 12.00 3.50

America Issue — Campaign Against AIDS — A566b

Designs: 2p, Child. 6p, AIDS patient (38x38mm).

**2000, Dec. 21** **Self-Adhesive**
**1371C-1371D** A566b Set of 2 4.00 2.00

UN High Commissioner for Refugees, 50th Anniv. — A566c

**2000, Dec. 29** **Self-Adhesive**
**1371E** A566c 10p multi 4.50 2.25

Environmental Protection — A567

Designs: 2p, Lizard on leaf, vert. $3, House. $5, River rapids, vert.

***Serpentine Die Cut 11¼***
**2000** **Litho.**
**Self-Adhesive**
**1372-1374** A567 Set of 3 6.50 2.50

**Lighthouse Type of 1995**

**2001** **Litho.** *Perf. 13¼x13½*
**1375** A466 15p lt bl, dk bl & sil 9.00 3.50

Concepcion Bona, Seamstress of First Dominican Republic Flag, Cent. of Death — A568

**2001** *Perf. 13½x13¼*
**1376** A568 10p multi 5.50 2.75

Stamp Day — A569

**2001**
**1377** A569 5p multi 3.00 1.10

Year of Dialogue Among Civilizations A570

**2001** *Perf. 13¼x13½*
**1378** A570 12p multi 5.50 2.50

America Issue — UNESCO World Heritage A571

Designs: 4p, San Felipe Fort. 15p, Ruins of San Nicolas de Bari Hospital (27x37mm).

**2001** *Perf. 13½, 13¼x13½ (15p)*
**1379-1380** A571 Set of 2 10.00 4.25

**Lighthouse Type of 1995**

**2002, Oct. 17** **Litho.** *Perf. 13½x13¾*
**1382** A466 15p yel & multi 5.00 2.00

Mushrooms — A572

No. 1383: a, Pycnoporus sanguineus. b, Morchella elata. c, Mycena epipterygia. d, Coriolopsis polyzona.

*Perf. 13¼x13½*
**2001, Sept. 13** **Litho.**
**1383** A572 6p Block of 4, #a-d 13.00 6.50

National Botanical Gardens, 25th Anniv. — A573

No. 1384: a, Isidorea pungens. b, Pereskia quisqueyana. c, Goetzea ekmanii. d, Cubanola domingensis.

*Perf. 13¼x13½*
**2001, Sept. 20** **Litho.**
**1384** A573 4p Block of 4, #a-d *9.50 9.50*

Presidents of the Dominican Republic — A574

No. 1385: a, Gen. José María Cabral. b, Gen. Gregório Luperón. c, Gen. Ignacio María González. d, Ulises Espaillat. e, Pedro A. Pimentel. f, Federico de Jesús García. g, Frenando Arturo de Mariño. h, Gen. Ulises Heureaux.

**2001, Sept. 27** **Litho.** *Perf. 13¼*
**1385** A574 6p Sheet of 8, #a-h, + label 27.50 15.00

Blessed Josemaría Escrivá de Balaguer (1902-75), Founder of Opus Dei — A575

**2002, Aug. 29** *Perf. 13½x13¼*
**1386** A575 10p multi 6.50 1.90

Loyola Polytechnic Institute, 50th Anniv. — A576

**2002, Oct. 24** *Perf. 13¼x13½*
**1387** A576 6p multi 2.25 1.40

12th Iberoamerican Heads of State Summit — A577

Designs: 12p, Flags below map. 15p, Flags above map.

*Perf. 13¾x13½*
**2002, Nov. 14** **Litho.**
**1388-1389** A577 Set of 2 12.00 4.75

Compare with Type A637a.

America Issue — Youth Education and Literacy — A578

Designs: 4p, Teacher helping child write. 15p, Child writing on blackboard.

**2002, Dec. 20** *Perf. 13¼x13½*
**1390-1391** A578 Set of 2 8.50 3.00

Coccothrinax Spissa — A579

*Perf. 13¼x13½*
**2002, Dec. 20** **Litho.**
**1392** A579 10p multi 4.00 1.50

2003 Pan American Games, Santo Domingo — A580

Color of "2003" in design: 4p, Light green blue. 6p, Blue. 12p, Red.

**2003, Feb. 25**
**1393-1395** A580 Set of 3 6.50 3.00

Medicinal Plants — A581

No. 1396: a, Hymenaea courbaril. b, Spondias mombin. c, Genipa americana. d, Guazuma ulmifonia.

**2003, June 17**
**1396** A581 5p Block of 4, #a-d 6.00 2.75

Dr. José Francisco Peña Gomez (1937-98), Politician A582

**Litho. & Engr.**
**2003, Dec. 17** *Perf. 11½*
**1397** A582 10p multi 4.00 1.40

José Marti (1853-95), Cuban Patriot — A583

**2003, Nov. 5** **Litho.** *Perf. 13x13¼*
**1398** A583 15p multi 4.50 2.25

Pan American Health Organization, Cent. (in 2002) — A583a

*Perf. 13½x13¼*
**2006, July. 12** **Litho.**
**1398A** A583a 20p multi 5.00 2.00

America Issue — Flora and Fauna — A584

Designs: 5p, Aristelliger lar. 15p, Corpernicia berteroana, vert.

*Perf. 13½x13¼, 13¼x13½*
**2004, Jan. 19**
**1399-1400** A584 Set of 2 8.50 3.00

Nos. 1399-1400 are dated "2003."

Election of Pope John Paul II, 25th Anniv. — A585

Pope John Paul II: 10p, With hand touching face. 15p, Blessing crowd, horiz.
25p, Vignettes of 10p and 15p stamps.

*Perf. 13¼x13½, 13½x13¼*
**2005, Nov. 26**
**1401-1402** A585 Set of 2 11.00 3.25

**Size: 57x85mm**
***Imperf***
**1403** A585 25p multi 12.00 3.50

National Council for Children A586

**2004, Mar. 10** *Perf. 13½x13¼*
**1404** A586 7p multi 2.75 1.10

Exfilna National Philatelic Exhibition A587

**2004, Dec. 8** **Litho.** *Perf. 13½x13¼*
**1405** A587 7p multi 3.00 1.10

America Issue — Fight Against Poverty A588

Design: 10p, Shack. 20p, Poor woman.

**2004, Dec. 23**
**1406-1407** A588 Set of 2 12.00 5.75

Dominican Republic - Canada Diplomatic Relations, 50th Anniv. A589

**2004, Dec. 31**
**1408** A589 20p multi 8.50 3.75

Interexpo '05 Intl. Philatelic Exhibition A590

Designs: 7p, Dove and stamp. 20p, Map highlighting Dominican Republic, vert.

*Perf. 13½x13¼, 13¼x13½*
**2005** **Litho.**
**1409-1410** A590 Set of 2 11.00 4.75

**Souvenir Sheet**

Design: 10p, Similar to 7p.

**1410A** A590 10p multi *15.00* 2.00

Dominican Republic Philatelic Society, 50th anniv.
Issued: 20p, 10/16; 7p, 10/17; 10p, 2005.

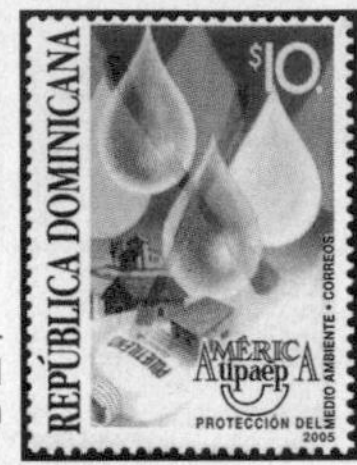

America Issue — Environmental Protection A591

Prevention of: 10p, Water pollution. 20p, Air pollution.

**2005** *Perf. 13¼x13½*
**1411-1412** A591 Set of 2 11.00 4.75

Monte Plata Maternity Clinic A592

*Perf. 13½x13¼*
**2005, Nov. 14** **Litho.**
**1413** A592 15p multi 6.25 2.50

Proclamation of Sister City Status of Santo Domingo and La Guardia, Spain — A593

**2005, Nov. 11**
**1414** A593 10p multi 3.50 1.50

Stamp Day A594

**2005** **Litho.** *Perf. 13½x13¼*
**1415** A594 10p multi 3.50 1.50

Palace of Fine Arts, 50th Anniv. A595

**2006, Oct. 10** **Litho.** *Perf. 13¾x13¼*
**1416** A595 7p multi 3.00 1.10

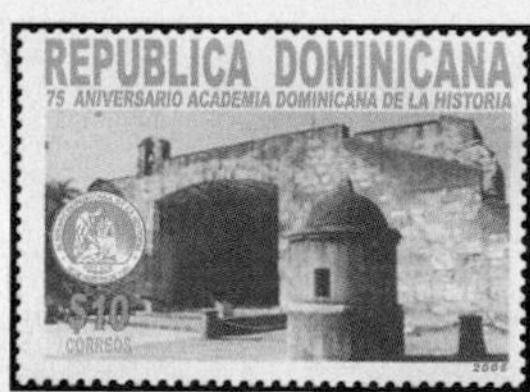


Dominican History Academy, 75th Anniv. — A596

**2006, Oct. 30** ***Perf. 13¼***
**1417** A596 10p multi 3.75 1.50

16th Intl. Boxing Congress, Santo Domingo — A597

**2006, Nov. 2** ***Perf. 13¼x13½***
**1418** A597 20p multi 6.50 2.50

Pope John Paul II (1920-2005) A598

Pope and: 10p, Crucifix. 20p, Dove, horiz.

**2006, Nov. 4** ***Perf. 13½***
**1419-1420** A598 Set of 2 11.50 4.50

Blessing of Natl. Sacred Heart of Jesus Sanctuary, 50th Anniv. — A599

**2006, Nov. 24** ***Perf. 13½x13¼***
**1421** A599 10p multi 4.50 1.50

Ninth Latin American Botanical Congress A600

**2007, Feb/ 26** ***Perf. 13¼x13½***
**1422** A600 20p multi 7.00 3.00

America Issue, Energy Conservation — A601

Designs: 10p, Light bulb in hands. 20p, Transmission lines and tower.

**2007, June 11** ***Perf. 13x13¼***
**1423-1424** A601 Set of 2 9.00 4.50

Pres. Joaquin Balaguer (1906-2002) A602

Balaguer: 7p, Wearing bow tie. 10p, Holding book.

**2006, Sept. 1** ***Perf. 13¼x13½***
**1425-1426** A602 Set of 2 7.00 2.75

Office of the First Lady A603

Emblem and: 10p, Tree. 25p, Computer and keyboard.

**2007, Mar. 1** ***Perf. 13½x13¼***
**1427-1428** A603 Set of 2 11.00 4.75

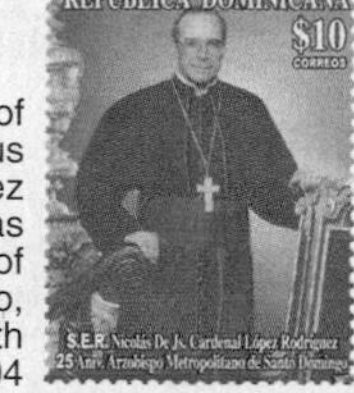


Selection of Nicolás de Jesus Cardinal López Rodríguez as Archbishop of Santo Domingo, 25th Anniv. — A604

López Rodríguez: 10p, Standing next to chair. 15p, With Pope John Paul II. 25p, Holding crucifix.

**2007, May 25** ***Perf. 13¼x13½***
**1429-1431** A604 Set of 3 15.00 6.00

2007 Pan American Games, Rio de Janeiro — A605

Designs: 15p, High jump. 20p, Weight lifting.

**2007, July 6** **Litho.**
**1432-1433** A605 Set of 2 11.00 4.50

Podilymbus Podiceps A606

**2007, Sept. 7** **Litho.** ***Perf. 13½x13¼***
**1434** A606 20p multi 7.00 3.00

Dated 2006.

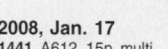

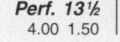

Stamp Day — A607

**2007, Oct. 4** ***Perf. 13¼x13½***
**1435** A607 15p multi 5.00 2.00

America Issue, Education For All — A608

Top panel in: 10p, Red. 20p, Blue.

**2007, Dec. 26**
**1436-1437** A608 Set of 2 11.00 4.50

Treaty of Friendship With the Netherlands, 150th Anniv. — A609

**2007, Nov. 9** ***Perf. 13½x13¼***
**1438** A609 25p multi 7.00 3.00

Palace of Columbus A610

**2008, Apr. 18**
**1439** A610 10p multi 3.50 1.50

Barahona Province, Cent. — A611

**2007, Nov. 23** ***Perf. 13¼x13***
**1440** A611 10p multi 2.50 1.00

Salvaléon de Higuey, 500th Anniv. A612

**2008, Jan. 17** ***Perf. 13½***
**1441** A612 15p multi 4.00 1.50

Friendship and Cooperation Between Dominican Republic and Republic of China — A613

Designs: 10p, Prunus mume, Swietenia mahagonni. 15p, Urocissa caeruela, Dulus dominicus. 35p, Buildings from China and Dominican Republic.

**2008, Feb. 6**
**1442-1444** A613 Set of 3 13.00 5.50

Children's Book Illustrations by Dr. Sophie Jakowska A614

Initials of Dr. Jakowska and: No. 1445, 7p, Trichechus manatus manatus. No. 1446, 7p, Eretmochelys imbricata, horiz. No. 1447, 10p, Photograph of Jakowska. No. 1448, 10p, Amazona ventralis. 15p, Crocodylus acutus, horiz.

**2007, Dec. 7** ***Perf. 13¼x13, 13x13¼***
**1445-1449** A614 Set of 5 12.50 5.00

Scouting, Cent. — A615

Designs: 10p, Dominican Republic Scouting emblem. 15p, Scouts, knotted rope.

**2008, Jun. 5** **Litho.** ***Perf. 13½***
**1450-1451** A615 Set of 2 6.50 2.50

Dominican Diaspora — A616

**2008, Apr. 5** ***Perf. 13¼x13***
**1452** A616 15p multi 3.50 1.50

Freemasonry in Dominican Republic, 150th Anniv. — A617

**2008, Oct. 25** ***Perf. 13¼x13½***
**1453** A617 25p multi 6.50 2.50

Stamp Day
A618

**2008, Oct. 2** *Perf. 13¼*
**1454** A618 20p brown 5.25 2.00

2008 Summer Olympics, Beijing — A619

No. 1455: a, Taekwondo. b, Boxing. c, Table tennis. d, Judo.

**2008, Aug. 15** *Perf. 13x13¼*
**1455** A619 10p Block of 4, #a-d 10.00 4.00

Women Involved in Fight for Independence
A620

No. 1456: a, Juana de la Merced Trinidad (d. 1860). b, Joaquina Filomena Gomez de la Cova (1800-93). c, Maria Baltasara de los Reyes (1789-1867). d, Rosa Protomartir Duarte y Diaz (1820-88). e, Manuela Diaz y Jimenez (1786-1858). f, Petronila Abreu y Delgado (1815-1904). g, Micaela de Rivera de Santana (1785-1854). h, Froilana Febles de Santana (1814-88). i, Rosa Montas de Duvergé (1813-95). j, Josefa Antonia Perez de la Paz (1788-1855). k, Ana Valverde (1798-1864). l, Maria de la Concepción Bona y Hernandez (1824-1901). m, Maria de Jesus Pina y Benitez (1825-58). n, Maria Trinidad Sanchez y Ramona (1794-1845).

**2008, Mar. 10** *Perf. 13¼x13½*
**1456** Sheet of 14 + 31 labels 32.50 16.00
*a.-n.* A620 10p Any single 1.75 .90

Arms of Santiago, 500th Anniv.
A621

**2008, Dec. 7** **Litho.** *Perf. 13x13¼*
**1457** A621 10p multi 1.50 .50

Discovery of Quisqueya (Hispaniola) by Christopher Columbus, 1492 — A622

**2008, Dec. 17**
**1458** A622 10p multi 1.50 .50

General Timoteo Ogando Encarnación (1818-1908)
A623

**2008** *Perf. 13¼x13*
**1459** A623 10p multi 1.50 .50

Campaign Against Commercial Sexual Exploitation
A624

**2008, Nov. 14**
**1460** A624 10p multi 1.50 .50

Intl. Swimming Federation, Cent. — A625

**2009, Feb. 23** *Perf. 13½*
**1461** A625 15p multi 1.50 .50

America Issue, National Festivals — A626

No. 1462: a, 15p, Shot of Independence. b, 25p, Sword of the Restoration.

**2008** *Perf. 13¼x13*
**1462** A626 Horiz. pair, #a-b 6.50 2.50

Duarte y Díez Family Tree — A627

No. 1463: a, Juan J. Duarte (1768-1843) and wife, Manuela Díez (1786-1858). b, Juan J. Duarte's sons, Juan Pablo (1813-76), Dominican independence leader, and Vicente (1802-65). c, Juan J. Duarte's son, Manuel (1826-90), and daughter, Rosa (1820-88). d, Juan J. Duarte's daughters, Francisca (1831-99), and Filomena (1818-65).

**2009, Feb. 26** *Perf. 13½x13¼*
**1463** A627 10p Block of 4, #a-d 6.50 2.50

Chinatown, Santo Domingo
A628

Designs: 15p, Confucius Plaza. 20p, Gateway.

**2009, Apr. 17**
**1464-1465** A628 Set of 2 7.50 3.00

De La Salle Schools in Dominican Republic, 75th Anniv.
A629

St. Jean Baptiste de la Salle (1651-1719)
A630

**2009, May 14** *Perf. 13½x13¼*
**1466** A629 7p multi 1.50 .60

*Perf. 13¼x13½*

**1467** A630 10p multi 2.50 1.10

Invasion of Constanza, Maimón and Estero Hondo by Dominican Exiles, 50th Anniv.
A631

**2009, June 17** *Perf. 13½*
**1468** A631 10p multi 2.75 1.10

Pres. Juan Bosch (1909-2001)
A632

**2009, Jun. 19** *Perf. 13¼x13*
**1469** A632 20p multi 4.25 1.90

Crabs — A633

No. 1470: a, Epilobocera haytensis. b, Gecarcinus ruricola. c, Coenobita clypeatus. d, Callinectes sapidus.

*Perf. 13½x13¼*

**2009, Sept. 17** **Litho.**
**1470** A633 10p Block of 4, #a-d 4.50 2.25

Winning Designs in Children's Christmas Stamp Design Contest — A634

No. 1471: a, Dancers and musicians in front of house. b, Parade. c, Family and livestock. d, Villagers, manger and Christmas tree.

**2009, Oct. 5** **Litho.** *Perf. 13x13¼*
**1471** A634 10p Block of 4, #a-d 6.00 2.25

Plazas
A635

Designs: 15p, Galicia Plaza, Santo Domingo. 25p, Santo Domingo Plaza, La Guardia, Spain.

**2009, Oct. 15** *Perf. 13¼*
**1472-1473** A635 Set of 2 5.00 2.25

15th American Genealogical Reunion — A636

**2009, Nov. 3** *Perf. 13x13¼*
**1474** A636 75p multi 10.00 4.25

REPUBLICA DOMINICANA
$7
ESCUELA NACIONAL DE LA JUDICATURA
CORREOS 2009

Natl. School of Judicature
A637

**2009, Nov. 4** *Perf. 13½*
**1475** A637 7p multi .85 .40

12th Iberoamerican Heads of State Summit — A637a

Designs: 12p, Ribbon of flags below map. 15p, Flags above and to sides of map.

**2009 Litho. *Perf. 13¾x13½***
**1475A-1475B** A637a Set of 2 7.00 —

Dated 2002. Compare with type A577.

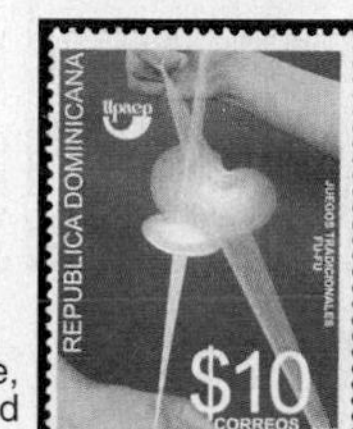

America Issue, Toys and Games — A638

Designs: 10p, Fu-fu. 15p, Hopscotch, horiz. 20p, Pañuelo, horiz.

**2009, Dec. 15 *Perf. 13x13, 13x13¼***
**1476-1477** A638 Set of 2 5.00 1.75

***Imperf***

**Size: 76x50mm**

**1478** A638 20p multi 4.50 1.75

Miniature Sheet

Dominican Republic Presidents — A639

No. 1479: a, Benigno Filomeno De Rojas. b, Jacinto B. De Castro. c, Maetos Cabral. d, Gen. Cesáreo Guillermo. e, Francisco G. Billini. f, Alejandro Woss y Gil. g, Carlos Felipe Morales Languasco. h, Ramón Cáceres.

**2009 *Perf. 13¼***
**1479** A639 7p Sheet of 8, #a-h, + central label 7.50 3.25

See Nos. 1531, 1585.

National Coat of Arms — A640

**2010, Feb. 10 *Perf. 13¼x13½***
**1480** A640 50p multi 5.00 2.75

14th Ibero-American Notaries Meeting — A641

**2010, June 3 Litho. *Perf. 13¼x13***
**1481** A641 26p multi 3.25 1.40

Preservation of Polar Regions — A642

**2010, July 7 *Perf. 13½x13¼***
**1482** A642 20p multi 2.25 1.10

Solenodon Paradoxus A643

**2010, July 28**
**1483** A643 25p multi 3.00 1.40

Biodiversity protection.

National Philatelic and Numismatic Museum, 25th Anniv. — A644

**2010, Aug. 10 *Perf. 13¼x13***
**1484** A644 33p ocher & black 4.00 1.90

Juan Pablo Duarte (1813-76), Independence Leader, and Birthplace, Santo Domingo — A645

**2010, Aug. 30 *Perf. 11½x13¼***
**1485** A645 25p multi 3.25 1.40

Delivery of the Flag A646

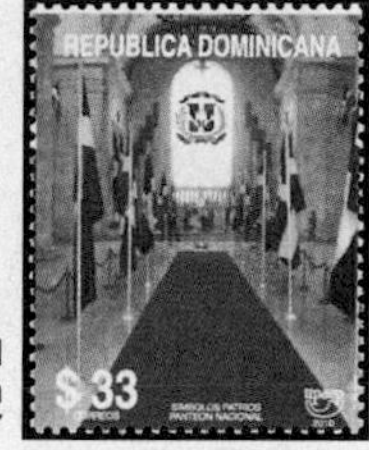

National Pantheon A647

**2010, Oct. 12 Litho. *Perf. 13½***
**1486** A646 26p multi 3.25 1.40

***Perf. 13¼x13***

**1487** A647 33p multi 4.25 1.75

America Issue.

Stamp Day A648

**2010, Oct. 18 *Perf. 13x13¼***
**1488** A648 15p multi 1.75 .80

Miniature Sheet

Tourism — A649

No. 1489 — Tourist attractions: a, Los Tres Ojos. b, Juan Dolio Beach. c, Altos de Chavón. d, Bayahibe Beach. e, Bávaro Beach. f, Cayo Levantado. g, Las Terrenas Beach. h, Cabarete Beach. i, River rafters, Jarabacoa. j, Lake Enriquillo.

**2010, Nov. 4**
**1489** A649 10p Sheet of 10, #a-j, + 2 labels 10.00 10.00

Veritas Odd Fellows Lodge, Santo Domingo A650

**2010, Nov. 26 *Perf. 13½x13¼***
**1490** A650 60p multi 6.50 3.25

World AIDS Day — A651

Designs: 15p, Hands with AIDS ribbons on thumbs. 46p, Flower with AIDS ribbon petals.

**2010, Dec. 1 *Perf. 13¼x13***
**1491-1492** A651 Set of 2 6.50 3.25

Dominican Order in the Americas, 500th Anniv. A652

Designs: 15p, Monastery. 26p, Dominican monk and native boy, vert.

**2010, Dec. 7 *Perf. 13x13¼, 13¼x13***
**1493-1494** A652 Set of 2 4.50 2.25

National Archives, 75th Anniv. A653

**2010, Dec. 14 *Perf. 13½x13¼***
**1495** A653 20p multi 2.50 1.10

Santo Domingo, 2010 American Capital of Culture — A654

**2010, Dec. 16 *Imperf.***
**1496** A654 26p multi 3.00 3.00

Santo Domingo Gates — A655

No. 1497: a, Puerta de la Misericordia, "Republica" at bottom. b, Puerta del Conde, "Republica" at left. c, Puerta del Conde, "Republica" at top. d, Puerta de la Misericordia, "Republica" at left.

20p, Puerta de la Misericordia, Puerta del Conde, arms of Domincan Republic.

**2011, Feb. 21 *Perf. 13x13¼***
**1497** A655 10p Block of 4, #a-d 4.50 4.50

**Size: 90x70mm**

***Imperf***

**1498** A655 20p multi 2.25 2.25

Sur Futuro Foundation A656

Designs: 15p, Tree and rainbow. 20p, Lake.

**2011, Mar. 3 *Perf. 13¼x13½***
**1499-1500** A656 Set of 2 4.00 1.90

Caves — A657

No. 1501: a, Pomier Caves, San Cristobal. b, Fun Fun Cave, Hato Mayor del Rey. c, Guácara de Hernando Alonzo, La Mata, Sánchez Ramírez. d, Golondrinas Cave, Río San Juan.

**2011, Mar. 15** *Perf. 13½x13¼*
**1501** A657 10p Block of 4, #a-d 4.50 4.50

Dated 2010.

Postal Union of the Americas, Spain and Portugal (UPAEP), Cent. A658

Designs: 20p, "100" with map of Americas and Iberian peninsula in zeroes. 26p, Map of Americas and Iberian peninsula, doves with letters.

**2011, Mar. 18** **Litho.**
**1502-1503** A658 Set of 2 4.50 2.50

Flowers — A659

No. 1504: a, Pereskia quisqueyana. b, Cereus hexagonus. c, Catalpa longissima. d, Tolumnia variegata.

**2011, Mar. 31** *Perf. 13¼x13*
**1504** A659 10p Block of 4, #a-d 4.50 4.50

Dated 2010.

Colonel Rafael T. Fernandez Dominguez (1934-65) A660

**2011, May 19 Litho.** *Perf. 13¼x13*
**1505** A660 15p multi 1.75 .80

Liberty Day, 50th Anniv. — A661

**2011, June 2** *Imperf.*
**1506** A661 33p multi 4.00 4.00

Assassination of Pres. Rafael Trujillo, 50th anniv.

Aviation A662

No. 1507: a, 20p, Airplane of Zoilo H. Garcia. b, 25p, Garcia (1849-1922), first Dominican pilot.

**2011, June 16** *Perf. 13x13¼*
**1507** A662 Vert. pair, #a-b 5.00 5.00

Places Associated With Independence Leader Juan Pablo Duarte — A663

Designs: 15p, Santa Barbara Church, Santo Domingo. 20p, Baptismal font.

**2011, Aug. 30**
**1508-1509** A663 Set of 2 4.25 1.90

Worldwide Fund for Nature (WWF) — A664

No. 1510 — Hypsiboas heilprini: a, Blue denomination at LR. b, Red denomination at LL. c, Red denomination at LR. d, Blue denomination at LL.

**2011, Sept. 7**
**1510** A664 10p Block of 4, #a-d 5.00 5.00

Father of the Fatherland, by Martin de San Juan — A665

**2011, Nov. 9** **Litho.** *Imperf.*
**1511** A665 20p multi 2.50 2.50

Execution of Francisco del Rosario Sánchez, 150th anniv.

Pastoral and Social Work in Dominican Rpeublic of Bishop Francisco José Arnáiz, 50th Anniv. — A666

**2011, Dec. 21**
**1512** A666 33p multi 3.00 1.75

Juan Pablo Duarte and Camara de Cuentas (Governmental Accounting Office) Document — A667

**2011**
**1513** A667 20p multi 2.50 1.10

Sermon Denouncing Mistreatment of Indians of Friar Antonio de Montesinos, 500th Anniv. (in 2011) — A668

**2012, Jan. 5** *Perf. 11½*
**1514** A668 60p multi 7.50 3.25

Dated 2011.

National Police, 75th Anniv. (in 2011) A669

**2012, Jan. 12** *Perf. 13x13¼*
**1515** A669 20p multi 2.50 1.10

Dated 2011.

Order of the Pilgrims of the Way of St. James — A670

**2012, Feb. 8** *Perf. 13¼x13½*
**1516** A670 33p multi 3.50 1.75

Miniature Sheets

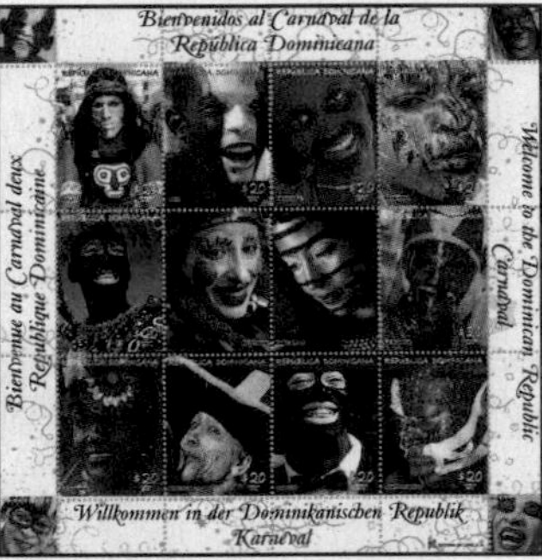

A671

A672

A673

A674

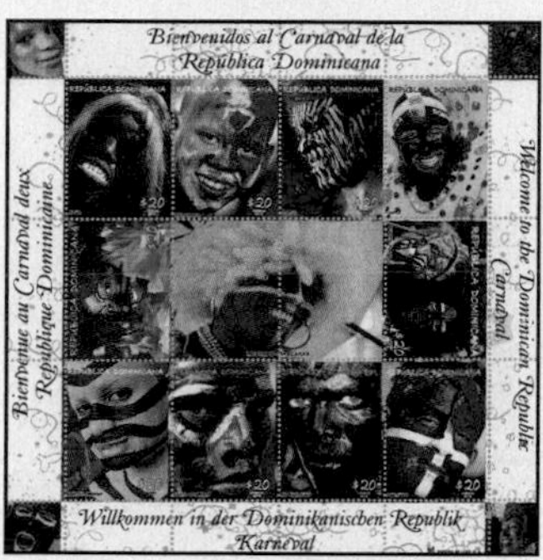
Carnival Masks and Painted Faces — A675

No. 1517: a, Azua (white face with headband). b, Bani. c, Barahona (red and black face). d, Barahona (green, yellow and red face). e, Cotuí (black and red face). f, La Romana (red, white and blue face with hat). g, La Romana (red and blue face with flower). h, Montecristi (yellow face with black and yellow hat). i, San Luis. j, Santo Domingo (red and yellow face with blue spots).

No. 1518: a, Cotuí (pink and red woman's face mask with blue eye lashes), horiz. b, Navarrette. c, Puerto Plata (white and brown mask). d, La Vega (mask with large pointed teeth), horiz. e, Rio San Juan (fish-head mask with large teeth), horiz. f, Samaná. g, San Juan de la Maguana. h, San Pedro de Macoris. i, Santo Domingo (green mask with horns). j, Villa Rivas.

No. 1519: a, Bonao (blue, green and red dragon's head mask). b, Cotuí (hat in flag colors with slits for eyes and mouth). c, La Vega (green and red dragon's head mask). d, Montecristi (red, gold, white, black and green mask). e, La Joya, Guerra, horiz. f, La Romana (yellow and blue bull's head mask with open mouth), horiz. g, Rio San Juan (blue, yellow, green and red demon-head mask with projections). h, Salcedo. i, Santiago (red, white and blue mask with spiked horns). j, Santo Domingo (mask with yellow beard).

No. 1520: a, Barahona (red, white and blue bull's head mask with horns), horiz. b, Bonao (mask with beard, moustache and gold hat). c, Constanza. d, Cabral, horiz. e, Elías Piña. f, La Vega (black, green and red cat's head mask). g, Valverde-Mao, horiz. h, Santiago (white, red and orange mask with spiked horns). i, Santo Domingo (red and yellow mask with horns). j, Puerto Plata (green, white and black pottery head mask), horiz.

No. 1521: a, Azua (red face with green hair). b, Barahona (blue, red, white and black face). c, Cotuí (black and white striped face with green hat). d, Cotuí (black face with flag hat). e, Cotuí (yellow, green, red and black face), horiz. f, Puerto Plata (brown and red mask, black, red and white face), horiz. g, Santo Domingo (yellow and black striped face). h, Santo Domingo (red, blue, white, green and black face). i, Rio San Juan (black face). j, Santiago (red, white and blue face).

***Perf. 13¼x13 (vert. stamps), 13x13¼ (horiz. stamps)***

**2012, Feb. 27**

**1517** A671 20p Sheet of 10, #a-j, + 2 central labels 20.00 20.00
**1518** A672 20p Sheet of 10, #a-j, + 2 central labels 20.00 20.00
**1519** A673 20p Sheet of 10, #a-j, + 2 central labels 20.00 20.00
**1520** A674 20p Sheet of 10, #a-j, + 2 central labels 20.00 20.00
**1521** A675 20p Sheet of 10, #a-j, + 2 central labels 20.00 20.00
*Nos. 1517-1521 (5)* 100.00 100.00

Diplomatic Relations Between Dominican Republic and Ecuador, 125th Anniv. A676

**2012, Mar. 1** ***Perf. 13½x13¼***
**1522** A676 20p multi 2.50 1.10

Dated 2011.

Pontifical Catholic University, Santo Domingo, 50th Anniv. — A677

**2012, Apr. 17** ***Perf. 13¼x13***
**1523** A677 25p multi 4.50 1.40

Mailboxes A678

Designs: 20p, Mailbox with legs. 25p, Mailbox without legs.

**2012, May 8** ***Perf. 13¼x13½***
**1524-1525** A678 Set of 2 5.00 2.40

America Issue. Dated 2011.

Maria Montez (1912-51), Actress — A679

**2012, June 2** ***Perf. 13¼x13***
**1526** A679 100p multi 10.00 5.25

Juan Pablo Duarte (1813-76), Patriot — A680

No. 1527: a, 15p, Photograph of Duarte in Hamburg. b, 25p, Oath of the Trinitaria.

**2012, July 24** ***Perf. 13½x13¼***
**1527** A680 Pair, #a-b 4.50 2.10

Expo Cibao, 25th Anniv. — A681

**2012, Sept. 5** ***Perf. 13¼x13***
**1528** A681 20p multi 2.00 1.10
*a.* Tete-beche pair 4.50 4.50

Miniature Sheet

Birds — A682

No. 1529: a, Caprimulgus eckmani. b, Contopus hispaniolensis. c, Phaenicophilus palmarum. d, Icterus dominicensis. e, Loxia megaplaga. f, Calyptophilus frugivorus. g, Geotrygon leucometopia. h, Spindalis dominicensis. i, Corvus palmarum. j, Tyto glaucops.

**2012, Sept. 19**
**1529** A682 20p Sheet of 10, #a-j, + 2 central labels 25.00 25.00

No. 1529d in the sheet of 10 was inscribed "CIGUA AMARILLA" in the first part of the print run. The error was discovered and corrected to "CIGUA CANARIA" on the remainder of the printing.

Orchids — A683

No. 1530: a, Sudamerylcaste peguerol. b, Tolumnia calochila. c, Quisqueya ekmanii. d, Tolumnia henekenii.

**2012, Oct. 18**
**1530** A683 15p Block of 4, #a-d 6.50 6.50

**Presidents Type of 2009**

Miniature Sheet

No. 1531: a, Pedro Guillermo. b, Wenceslao Figuereo. c, Horacio Vásquez. d, Juan Isidro Jiménez. e, Eladio Victoria. f, Adolfo Alejandro Nouel. g, José Bordas Valdéz. h, Ramón Báez Machado.

**2012** ***Perf. 13¼***
**1531** A639 15p Sheet of 8, #a-h, + central label 12.00 12.00

America Issue — A684

No. 1532 — Legend of: a, El Caracaracol. b, La Ciguapa.

**2012, Dec. 18** ***Perf. 13¼x13***
**1532** A684 20p Horiz. pair, #a-b 15.00 15.00

Miniature Sheet

Tourism — A685

No. 1533: a, Beach, Saona Island. b, Beach, Bahia de las Aguilas. c, San Rafael Beach. d, Gri-Gri Lagoon. e, Dominican Republic flag. f, Playa Dorada. g, El Morro Beach. h, Puerto Plata. i, Monument to the Heroes of the Restoration, Santiago. j, Historic center of Santiago. k, Jordobadas Whale Sanctuary. l, Beach, Punta Cana.

**2013, May 23** ***Perf. 13½x13¼***
**1533** A685 10p Sheet of 12, #a-l 15.00 15.00

Arachnids — A686

No. 1534: a, Phrynus longipes. b, Mastigoproctus proscorpio. c, Phormictopus cancerides. d, Rhopalurus princeps.

**2013, May 20**
**1534** A686 20p Block of 4, #a-d 10.00 10.00

Pedro Mir (1913-2000), Poet — A687

**2013, June 24** ***Perf. 13¼x13***
**1535** A687 50p multi 3.00 2.40

La Trinitaria Secret Society, 175th Anniv. — A688

**2013, July 15** *Imperf.*
**1536** A688 60p multi 3.75 3.75

María Ugarte (1914-2011), Investigative Reporter — A689

**2013, July 31 Litho.** *Perf. 13¼x13*
**1537** A689 33p multi 2.25 1.60

A690

General Gregoio Luperón (1839-97) — A691

*Perf. 13½x13¼*

**2013, Aug. 12 Litho.**
**1538** A690 15p multi 1.10 .70

*Imperf*

**1539** A691 33p multi 2.10 2.10

Dominican War of the Restoration, 150th anniv.

Dominican Rehabilitation Association, Inc., 50th Anniv. — A692

**2013, Oct. 23 Litho.** *Perf. 13½x13*
**1540** A692 15p red & blue 1.10 .70

Dominican Postal Institute (Inposdom), 50th Anniv. — A693

Designs: 15p, Emblem for InposPak service. 20p, Inposdom emblem, vert. 25p, Exhibit frames at stamp exhibition. 80p, Inposdom Headquarters.

**2013, Nov. 28 Litho.** *Perf. 13¼*
**1541** A693 15p multi .70 .70

**Size: 30x40mm**
*Perf. 13¼x13½*

**1542** A693 20p multi .95 .95

**Size: 40x30mm**
*Perf. 13½x13¼*

**1543** A693 25p multi 1.25 1.25
*Nos. 1541-1543 (3)* 2.90 2.90

**Size: 80x50mm**
*Imperf*

**1544** A693 80p multi 5.50 5.50

Juan Pablo Duarte (1813-76), Leader of Independence Movement — A694

No. 1545: a, Atarazana School where Duarte taught fencing. b, House of Josefa Pérez de la Paz, birthplace of La Trinitaria Secret Society. c, Duarte directing "La Dramatica." d, 1844 return of Duarte from exile. e, Duarte and Dominican Republic Constitution and flag.

**2013, Dec. 9 Litho.** *Perf. 13*
**1545** Horiz. strip of 5 5.00 5.00
***a.-e.*** A694 15p Any single 1.00 1.00

An additional stamp was issued in this set. The editors would like to examine any example of it.

Campaign Against Discrimination — A696

Designs: 15p, Five children. 20p, Map of Dominican Republic, hands.

**2014, Jan. 30 Litho.** *Perf. 13x13¼*
**1547-1548** A696 Set of 2 2.75 1.75

America issue. Dated 2013.

Founding of St. Thomas Aquinas University, Santo Domingo, 475th Anniv. (in 2013) A697

Designs: 20p, Building. 25p, Buildings and university crest.

**2014, Feb. 14 Litho.** *Perf. 13x13¼*
**1549** A697 20p multi 1.40 .95

**Size: 89x60mm**
*Imperf*

**1550** A697 25p multi 1.75 1.75

Reopening of university as Autonomous University of Santo Domingo, cent. Dated 2013.

Julia de Burgos (1914-53), Poet — A698

**2014, Mar. 28 Litho.** *Perf. 13¼x13*
**1551** A698 100p multi 6.75 4.75

Souvenir Sheets

Centro León Museum — A699

National Botanical Gardens — A700

Bellapart Museum — A701

Numismatic and Philatelic Museum — A702

National Museum of Natural History — A703

Museum of Modern Art — A704

No. 1552: a, Entrance to Jimenes Cultural Center. b, Caribeño Patio of Eduardo León Jimenes Cultural Center.

No. 1553: a, Bridge in Japanese Garden. b, Path in Japanese Garden.

No. 1554: a, Permanent Gallery. b, Merengue, painting by Jaime Colson.

No. 1555: a, Exhibit of money with metal ingot. b, Display case in Numismatics Gallery.

No. 1556: a, Museum entrance. b, Skeleton of humpback whale.

No. 1557: a, Sculptures. b, Sculptures and paintings in Permanent Gallery.

**2014, May 21 Litho.** *Perf. 13½*
**1552** A699 50p Sheet of 2, #a-b, + 2 labels 6.50 6.50
**1553** A700 50p Sheet of 2, #a-b, + 2 labels 6.50 6.50
**1554** A701 50p Sheet of 2, #a-b, + 2 labels 6.50 6.50
**1555** A702 50p Sheet of 2, #a-b, + 2 labels 6.50 6.50
**1556** A703 50p Sheet of 2, #a-b, + 2 labels 6.50 6.50
**1557** A704 50p Sheet of 2, #a-b, + 2 labels 6.50 6.50
*Nos. 1552-1557 (6)* 39.00 39.00

World Museum Day.

Duarte Institute, 50th Anniv. A705

**2014, June 24 Litho.** *Perf. 13½*
**1558** A705 50p multi 3.50 2.40

Flowers — A706

No. 1559: a, Salcedoa mirabaliarum. b, Ekmanianthe longiflora, vert. c, Coccothrinax jienezii, vert. d, Rhytidophyllum daisyanum.

**2014, Aug. 27 Litho.** *Perf. 13x13¼*
**1559** A706 20p Block of 4, #a-d 5.75 5.75

Dated 2013.

National Literacy Plan A707

**2014, Sept. 8 Litho.** *Perf. 13½*
**1560** A707 15p multi 1.10 .70

Dated 2013.

Miniature Sheets

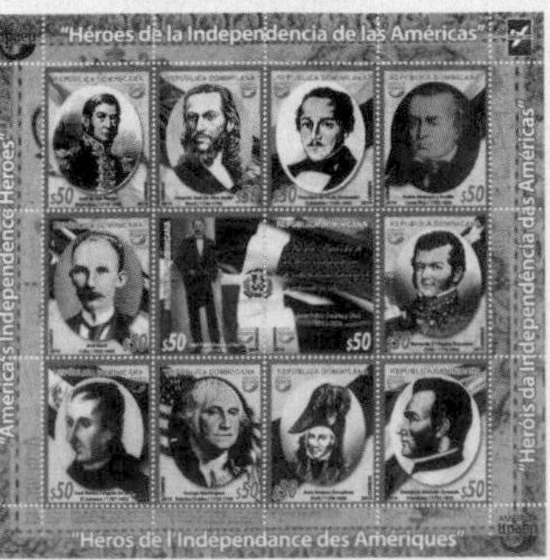

Heroes and Flags of Nations of North and South America — A708

No. 1561, 50p: a, José de San Martín, flag of Argentina. b, Joaquim José Da Silva Xavier (Tiradentes), flag of Brazil. c, Francisco de Paula Santander, flag of Colombia. d, Pedro

Alvarado y Bonilla, flag of Costa Rica. e, José Martí, flag of Cuba. f, Juan Pablo Duarte (standing), flag of Dominican Republic. g, Quote by Duarte, flag of Dominican Republic. h, Bernardo O'Higgins Riquelme, flag of Chile. i, José Matías Delgado de León, flag of El Salvador. j, George Washington, flag of United States. k, Jean Jacques Dessalines, flag of Haiti. l, Francisco Morazán Quezada, flag of Honduras.

No. 1562, 50p: a, Simón Bolívar, flag of Bolivia. b, Georges-Etienne Cartier, flag of Canada. c, Máximo Gómez y Báez, flag of Cuba. d, Manuela Sáenz y Aizpuru, flag of Ecuador. e, Pedro Molina Mazariegos, flag of Guatemala. f, Miguel Hidalgo y Costilla, flag of Mexico. g, Head of Duarte, flag of Dominican Republic. h, Augusto César Sandino, flag of Nicaragua. i, Gaspar Rodríguez de Francia, flag of Paraguay. j, José Gabriel Condorcanqui (Túpac Amaru II), flag of Peru. k, José Gervado Artigas Arnal, flag of Uruguay. l, Bolívar, flag of Venezuela.

**2014, Sept. 30 Litho. *Perf. 13¼x13***
**Sheets of 12, #a-l**

**1561-1562** A708 Set of 2 70.00 70.00

America issue.

World Food Day — A709

No. 1563: a, Boy holding apple. b, Boy eating broccoli, vert. c, Fruit picker on ladder. d, Girl eating cob of corn, vert.

**2014, Oct. 15 Litho. *Perf. 13½***

**1563** A709 25p Block of 4, #a-d 7.00 7.00

Miniature Sheet

Wildlife — A710

No. 1564, 25p — Fish: a, Pomacanthus paru. b, Holacanthus ciliaris. c, Serranus tigrinus. d, Nandopsis haitensis. e, Haemulon flavolineatum. f, Anisotremus virginicus. g, Cantherhines macrocerus. h, Agonostomus monticola. i, Epinephelus striatus. j, Gymnothorax funebris. k, Aulostomus maculatus. l, Dasyatis americana.

No. 1565, 25p — Butterflies: a, Anaea troglodyta. b, Anartia lytrea. c, Burca stillmani. d, Burca hispaniolae. e, Myscelia aracynthia. f, Archimestra teleboas. g, Atlante cryptadia. h, Greta diaphanus quisqueya. i, Heraclides machaonides. j, Choranthus haitensis. k, Memphis verticordia. l, Pyrisitia pyro.

***Perf. 13½x13¼***
**2014, Nov. 20 Litho.**
**Sheets of 12, #a-l**

**1564-1565** A710 Set of 2 35.00 35.00

Miniature Sheet

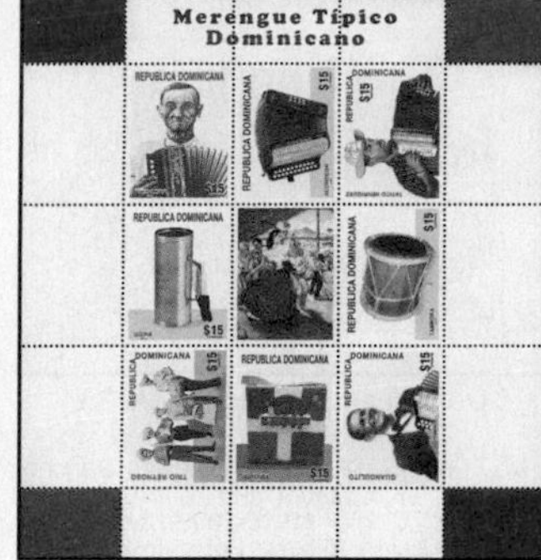

Merengue Musicians and Instruments — A711

No. 1566: a, Nico Lora playing accordion. b, Accordion, horiz. c, Tatico Henriquez playing accordion, horiz. d, Güira. e, Tambora. f, Trio Reynosa performing, horiz. g, Marimba. g, Guandulito playing accordion, horiz.

***Perf. 13¼x13½, 13½x13¼***
**2014, Nov. 26 Litho.**

**1566** A711 15p Sheet of 8, #a-h, + central label 7.50 7.50

Scouting in the Dominican Republic, Cent. A712

**2014, Dec. 3 Litho. *Perf. 13½x13¼***

**1567** A712 20p multi 1.25 .90

ISA University, 50th Anniv. (in 2014) A713

**2015, May 5 Litho. *Perf. 13½***

**1568** A713 200p multi 10.00 9.00

Bani, 250th Anniv. (in 2014) A714

**2015, Mar. 6 Litho. *Perf. 13¼***

**1569** A714 100p multi 5.50 4.50

Dated 2014.

Gustavo A. Moré González (1925-2002), President of Dominican Philatelic Society — A715

**2015, Apr. 9 Litho. *Perf. 13½***

**1570** A715 75p multi 4.00 3.50

Stamp Day. Dated 2014.

Programs Run Through Office of the First Lady — A716

No. 1571: a, Newborn Screening Program. b, Comprehensive Care Center for Disability.

**2015, Apr. 28 Litho. *Perf. 13¼x13***

**1571** A716 250p Horiz. pair, #a-b 25.00 25.00

Miniature Sheets

National Parks — A717

No. 1572, 20p: a, Pyramids, Valle Nuevo National Park. b, Rio Grande Waterfall, Francisco Alberto Caamaño Deñó National Park. c, Coral reef and fish, Monte Cristi Underwater National Park. d, Hatillo Dam Reservoir with small islands at left, Aniana Vargas National Park. e, Hoyo de Pelempito, Sierra de Bahoruco National Park. f, Aerial view of El Morro Beach, El Morro National Park. g, Coastal hills, Los Haitises National Park. h, Sierra de Neiba, Sierra de Neiba National Park. i, Salado de Neiba, La Gran Sabana National Park. j, Haemulon spp., La Caleta Underwater National Park. k, Quita Coraza, Anacona National Park. l, La Isabela ruins, La Hispaniola National Park.

No. 1573, 20p: a, Baiguate Waterfall, Baiguate National Park. b, Punta Aguila Cliffs, Jaragua National Park. c, Waterfall, Saltos de la Jalda National Park, vert. d, Cliffs, Sierra Martin García National Park. e, Cyclura ricordii, Lago Enriquillo e Isla Cabritos National Park. f, Offshore rocks, Los Haitises National Park. g, Rock art, Aniana Vargas National Park, vert. h, Whales, Cabo Cabrón National Park. i, Plagiodontia aedium, Sierra de Bahoruco National Park. j, Mountains, Nalga de Maco National Park. k, Sea level view of cliffs and El Morro Beach, El Morro National Park. l, Palm trees, Sierra Martin García National Park.

No. 1574, 20p: a, Tetero Valley, José del Carmen Ramírez National Park. b, Isla Saona, Este National Park. c, Fregata magnificens, Este National Park. d, Mountains, Armando Bermúdez National Park. e, Sun over water, Lago Enriquillo e Isla Cabritos National Park. f, Cabo Cabrón, Cabo Cabrón National Park. g, Epilobocera wetherbeei, Valle Nuevo National Park. h, Punta Espada, Punta Espada National Park. i, Río Amina, Manolo Tavárez Justo National Park. j, La Humeadora, La Humeadora National Park. k, Rivers, Humedales del Ozama National Park. l, Río Mana, Máximo Gómez National Park, vert.

No. 1575, 20p: a, Balsa Estuary, Mangiares de Estero Balsa National Park. b, Río Mao, Piky Lora National Park. c, Lakes, Humedales del Ozama National Park. d, Shoreline, Mangiares del Bajo Yuna National Park. e, Foggy landscape, Valle Nuevo National Park. f, Bahia de las Aguilas, Jaragua National Park. g, Siproeta stelenes, Máximo Gómez National Park, vert. h, Hatillo Dam Reservoir with rocks at LR, Aniana Vargas National Park. i, Phaenicophilus palmarum, Luis Quin National Park. j, Loma La Tachuela, Luis Quin National Park. k, Shoreline, Este National Park. l, Mountains, Manolo Tavárez Justo National Park.

**2015, May 22 Litho. *Perf. 13½***
**Sheets of 12, #a-l**

**1572-1575** A717 Set of 4 55.00 55.00

Dominican Chapter of Lions International, 50th Anniv. — A718

**2015, May 24 Litho. *Perf. 13¼***

**1576** A718 50p multi 2.75 2.25

Matías Ramón Mella Castillo (1816-64), Vice-President — A719

**2015, June 10 Litho. *Imperf.***

**1577** A719 300p multi 16.00 16.00

Dated 2014.

Cooperation Between Brazilian and Dominican Republic Universities, 50th Anniv. — A720

**2015, June 22 Litho. *Perf. 13½***

**1578** A720 50p multi 2.50 2.25

Santiago Chamber of Commerce, Cent. — A721

**2015, July 9 Litho. *Perf. 13¼***

**1579** A721 50p multi 2.50 2.25

Oscar de la Renta (1932-2014), Fashion Designer — A722

**2015, Oct. 13 Litho. *Perf. 13¼x13***

**1580** A722 250p multi 12.50 11.00

St. Teresa of Avila (1515-82) — A723

**2015, Oct. 16 Litho. *Perf. 13¼x13½***

**1581** A723 45p multi 2.25 2.00

Rights for Disabled People — A724

**2015, Nov. 16 Litho. *Perf. 13¼***
**1582** A724 100p multi 5.00 4.50

Campaign to End Violence Against Women — A725

***Perf. 13¼x13½***
**2015, Nov. 25 Litho.**
**1583** A725 35p multi 1.75 1.60

See Ecuador No. 2173, Guatemala No. 717, El Salvador No. 1747, and Venezuela No. 1731.

Religious Objects — A726

No. 1584: a, Pax, 17th cent. (portapaz). b, Processional cross, 18th cent. (cruz procesional). c, Monstrance, 19th cent. (custodia). d, Eucharistic ark, 16th cent. (arca eucaristica). e, Chalice, 16th cent. (cáliz).

**2015, Dec. 1 Litho. *Perf. 13¼x13½***
**1584** Strip of 5 12.00 12.00
***a.-e.*** A726 45p Any single 2.00 2.00

**Presidents Type of 2009**
Miniature Sheet

No. 1585: a, Francisco Henríquez y Carvajal. b, Juan Bautista Vicini Burgos. c, Rafael Estrella Ureña. d, Inscriptions "1930-1938" and "1942-1952" (rule of Rafael Trujillo). e, Inscription "1952-1960" (rule of Hector Trujillo). f, Jacinto Bienvenido Peynado. g, Manuel de Jesús Troncoso de la Concha. h, Joaquín Balaguer Ricardo.

**2015, Dec. 18 Litho. *Perf. 13¼***
**1585** A639 20p Sheet of 8, #a-h, + central label 9.00 9.00

Dated 2014.

Campaign Against Human Trafficking A727

No. 1586: a, People in suitcase. b, Chained hands holding Earth.

**2015, Dec. 18 Litho. *Perf. 13x13½***
**1586** A727 50p Pair, #a-b 5.25 5.25

America Issue.

Dominican Republic Postage Stamps, 150th Anniv. A728

Designs: 30p, Dominican Republic #1. 35p, Dominican Republic #2. 45p, Dominican Republic #3. 50p, Dominican Republic #4.
150p, Dominican Republic #1-4, cover bearing #1, printing press.

**2015, Dec. 18 Litho. *Perf. 13x13½***
**1587-1590** A728 Set of 4 8.50 7.00

**Size: 140x100mm**

***Imperf***

**1591** A728 150p multi 7.50 7.50

Luis María "Billo" Frómeta (1915-88), Orchestra Conductor A729

**2016, Mar. 30 Litho. *Perf. 13½***
**1592** A729 150p multi 8.50 6.75

Pedro Henriquez Ureña National University, 50th Anniv. A730

**2016, Apr. 20 Litho. *Perf. 13½***
**1593** A730 50p multi 2.50 2.25

Marine Mammals — A731

No. 1594: a, Tursiops truncatus. b, Trichechus manatus manatus. c, Megaptera novaeangliae. d, Globicephala.

***Perf. 13½x13¼***
**2016, June 15 Litho.**
**1594** A731 50p Block of 4, #a-d 11.00 11.00

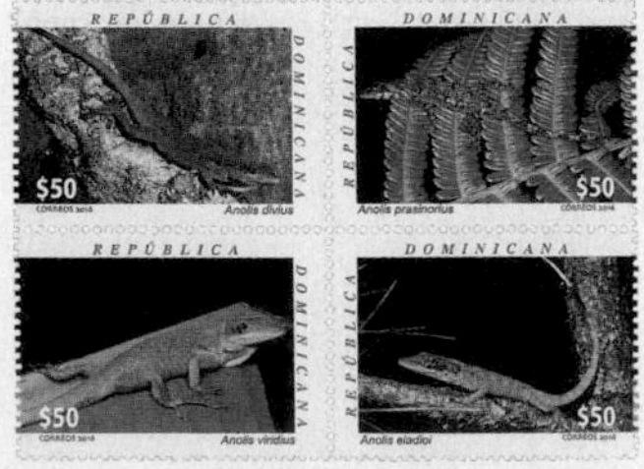
Anoles — A732

No. 1595: a, Anolis divius. b, Anolis prasinorius. c, Anolis viridius. d, Anolis eladioi.

***Perf. 13½x13¼***
**2016, June 15 Litho.**
**1595** A732 50p Block of 4, #a-d 11.00 11.00

Miniature Sheet

Dominican Scientists — A733

No. 1596: a, Dr. Pedro Troncoso Sánchez (1904-89), ambassador and historian. b, Dr. Henri Alain Liogier (1916-2009), botanist. c, Dr. Pablo Rafael Iñiguez Pérez (1925-2007), gastroenterologist. d, Dr. José Luís Alemán Dupuy (1928-2007), economist. e, Dr. Juan Manuel Taveras Rodríguez (1919-2002), neuroradiologist. f, Dr. José Altagracia Silié Gatón (1919-2014), judge. g, Dr. Hugo R. Mendoza Tapia (1930-2009), pediatrician. h, Dr. Francisco R. Guarocuya Batista del Villar (1934-2013), cardiologist.

**2016, Aug. 10 Litho. *Perf. 13½***
**1596** A733 20p Sheet of 8, #a-h 11.00 11.00

Matías Ramón Mella Castillo (1816-64), National Hero — A734

**2016, Sept. 29 Litho. *Imperf.***
**1597** A734 150p multi 9.50 9.50

Florence Terry Griswold (1875-1941), Founder of Pan America Round Tables, and Hotel Menger, San Antonio, Texas — A735

**2016, Oct. 12 Litho. *Perf. 13x13¼***
**1598** A735 35p multi 2.75 1.50

First Pan American Round Table, cent.

2016 Summer Olympics, Rio de Janeiro — A736

No. 1599: a, Track and field. b, Boxing. c, Weight lifting. d, Taekwondo.

**2016, Oct. 18 Litho. *Perf. 13½x13¼***
**1599** A736 15p Block of 4, #a-d 4.75 4.75

America Issue.

Miniature Sheet

National Botanical Garden — A737

No. 1600: a, Peltophorum berteroanum. b, Phyllostylon rhamnoides. c, Guarea guidonia. d, Haematoxylon campechianum. e, Magnolia pallescens. f, Capparis cynophollophora. g, Guaiacum officinale. h, Coccoloba pubescens. i, Calophyllum calaba. j, Krugiodendron ferreum. k, Ekmanianthe longiflora. l, Juniperus gracilior.

**2016, Oct. 27 Litho. *Perf. 13x13¼***
**1600** A737 10p Sheet of 12, #a-l 9.50 9.50

No. 1600h "pubescens" is spelled wrong on stamp.

Dr. Román Bautista Brache (1905-65), Physician and Politician — A738

**2016, Nov. 4 Litho. *Perf. 13¼x13½***
**1601** A738 20p multi 1.25 .90

Mountains — A739

No. 1602: a, Matterhorn, Switzerland. b, Loma Isabel de Torres, Dominican Republic.

***Perf. 13½x13¼***
**2016, Nov. 17 Litho.**
**1602** A739 60p Pair, #a-b 8.00 8.00

80th anniv. of relations between Dominican Republic and Switzerland.
See Switzerland Nos. 1617.

Specification of Dominican Republic National Anthem in National Constitution, 50th Anniv, — A740

**2016, Nov. 28 Litho. *Imperf.***
**1603** A740 50p multi 3.50 3.50

Miguel de Cervantes (1547-1616), Writer — A741

**2017, Jan. 31 Litho. *Perf. 13¼x13½***
**1604** A741 100p multi + label 4.50 4.50

BanReservas (Reserve Bank), 75th Anniv. — A742

**2017, Mar. 2 Litho. *Perf. 13¼x13½***
**1605** A742 75p multi 3.25 3.25

Popes — A743

No. 1606: a, Pope Emeritus Benedict XVI, denomination at LL. b, Pope Francis, denomination at LR. c, Pope Francis, denomination at LL. d, Pope Emeritus Benedict XVI, denomination at LR.

**2017, Mar. 14 Litho. *Perf. 13½***
**1606** A743 60p Block of 4, #a-d 10.50 10.50

Francisco del Rosario Sánchez (1817-61), Leader in Dominican War of Independence — A744

**2017, Mar. 29 Litho. *Imperf.***
**1607** A744 150p multi 6.50 6.50

Bridges — A745

No. 1608: a, Mauricio Báez Bridge. b, Matías Ramón Mella Bridge. c, Rio Chavón Bridge. d, Hermanos Patiño Bridge.

**2017, Apr. 24 Litho. *Perf. 13½x13¼***
**1608** A745 50p Block of 4, #a-d 8.50 8.50

Painters and Their Paintings — A746

No. 1609: a, Silvano Lora (1931-2003). b, Domingo Líz (1931-2013), horiz. c, Gordas en Bicicletas, by Líz, horiz. d, Serie Concieno Ecologico, by Lora.

***Perf. 13¼x13½, 13½x13¼ (horiz. stamps)***

**2017, Apr. 24 Litho.**
**1609** A746 25p Block of 4, #a-d 4.25 4.25

YMCA in Dominican Republic, 50th Anniv. — A747

**2017, Apr. 28 Litho. *Perf. 13¼x13½***
**1610** A747 50p multi 2.10 2.10

Miniature Sheet

Buildings Designed by José Antonio Caro Alvarez (1910-78) — A748

No. 1611: a, University of Santo Domingo Faculty of Medical Science Building, 1944. b, Menendez Building, 1941. c, Faculty of Engineering and Architecture Building, 1959. d, Rodriguez Building, 1949. e, Central Bank Building, 1956. f, National Library, 1971.

**2017, May 9 Litho. *Perf. 13½x13¼***
**1611** A748 15p Sheet of 6, #a-f, + 6 labels 4.00 4.00

Fe y Alegría Organization in Dominican Republic, 25th Anniv. — A749

**2017, May 17 Litho. *Perf. 13¼x13½***
**1612** A749 25p multi 1.10 1.10

Lions Clubs International, Cent. (in 2016) — A750

**2017, May 21 Litho. *Perf. 13½x13¼***
**1613** A750 100p multi 4.25 4.25

Casa de España Organization, Cent. — A751

**2017, June 14 Litho. *Perf. 13½***
**1614** A751 12p multi .50 .50

Miniature Sheet

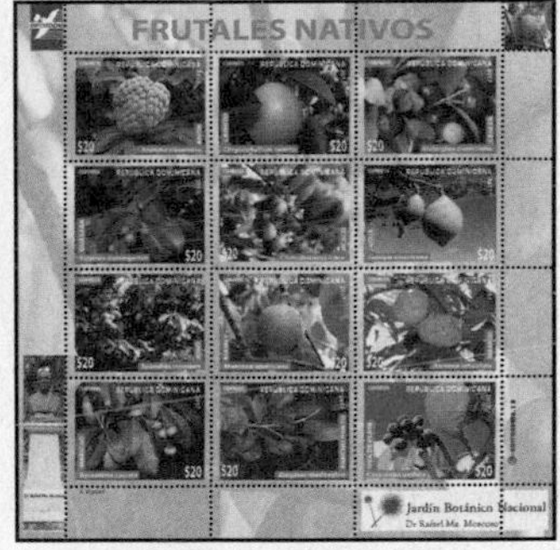


Fruit — A752

No. 1615: a, Annona squamosa. b, Chrysophyllum cainito. c, Malpighia punicifolia. d, Eugenia domingensis. e, Chrisobalanus icaco. f, Genipa americana. g, Spondias mombin. h, Mammea americana. i, Annona reticulata. j, Byrsonima spicata. k, Ziziphus rhodoxylon. l, Coccoloba uvifera.

***Perf. 13½x13¼***

**2017, Sept. 12 Litho.**
**1615** A752 20p Sheet of 12, #a-l 10.50 10.50

Miniature Sheets

Historic Maps of Hispaniola — A753

No. 1616, 10p — Map by: a, Christopher Columbus, 1493. b, Bologna, 1516. c, Benedetto Bordone, 1528. d, Giovanni B. Ramusio, 1534. e, Giacomo Gastaldi, 1548. f, Giacomo Ruscelli, 1561. g, Paolo Forlani, 1564. h, Ramusio, 1565. i, Bertelli Lafreri, 1566. j, Tomasso Porcacchi, 1572. k, Girolamo Ruscelli, 1580. l, Cornelius Wytfliet, 1597.

No. 1617, 10p — Map by: a, Laugenes, 1598. b, Metellus, 1598. c, Petrus Bertius, 1616. d, Arent Roggeveen, 1675. e, P. Coronelli, 1696. f, Guillaume de l'Isle, 1722-23. g, Emanuel Bowen, 1747. h, M. Bellin, 1754. i, M. Bonne, 1788. j, William Foden, 1795. k, I. Sonis, 1796. l, Tardieu, 1802.

**2017, Sept. 26 Litho. *Perf. 13x13¼***
**Sheets of 12, #a-l**
**1616-1617** A753 Set of 2 10.50 10.50

Martin Luther (1483-1546), Religious Reformer — A754

**2017, Oct. 9 Litho. *Perf. 13½x13¼***
**1618** A754 100p multi 4.25 4.25

Protestant Reformation, 500th anniv.

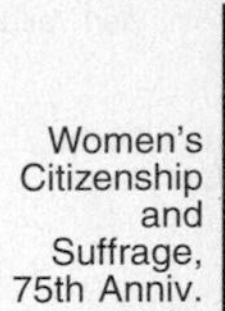

Women's Citizenship and Suffrage, 75th Anniv. A755

**2017, Nov. 7 Litho. *Perf. 13½x13¼***
**1619** A755 75p multi 3.25 3.25

---

## SEMI-POSTAL STAMPS

**Catalogue values for unused stamps in this section are for Never Hinged items.**

Nos. 474-478 Surcharged in Red

**Engraved and Lithographed**
**1957, Feb. 8 Unwmk. *Perf. 11½***
**Flags in National Colors**

**B1** A117 1c + 2c brn, lt bl, vio & mar .40 .40
**B2** A117 2c + 2c dk brn, lt bl & vio .40 .40
**B3** A117 3c + 2c red lilac & red .40 .40
**B4** A117 5c + 2c red orange & vio .40 .40
**B5** A117 7c + 2c green & violet .50 .50
*Nos. B1-B5,CB1-CB3 (8)* 3.90 3.90

The surtax was to aid Hungarian refugees. A similar 25c surcharge was applied to the miniature sheets described in the footnote following No. 478. Value, 2 sheets, perf. and imperf., $45

**Nos. 479-483 Surcharged in Red Orange**

**1957, Sept. 9 Photo. *Perf. 13½***
**Flags in National Colors**

**B6** A118 1c + 2c brown & brt bl .30 .30
**B7** A118 2c + 2c org ver & dk bl .35 .35
**B8** A118 3c + 2c dark blue .40 .40
**B9** A118 5c + 2c olive & dk bl .55 .55
**B10** A118 7c + 2c rose brn & dk bl .60 .60
*Nos. B6-B10,CB4-CB6 (8)* 4.75 4.15

Cent. of the birth of Lord Baden Powell and the 50th anniv. of the Scout Movement. The surtax was for the Dominican Republic Boy Scouts.

A similar 5c surcharge was applied to the miniature sheets described in the footnote following No. 483. Value 4 sheets, perf. and imperf., medal and flag, $62.50

**Types of Olympic Regular Issue, 1957, Surcharged in Carmine**

a

b

**1958, May 26 Engr. & Litho.**
**Flags in National Colors**
**Pink Paper**

**B11** A119(a) 1c + 2c red brown .30 .30
**B12** A119(b) 1c + 2c red brown .30 .30
**B13** A120(a) 2c + 2c gray brown .40 .40
**B14** A120(b) 2c + 2c gray brown .40 .40
**B15** A119(a) 3c + 2c violet .40 .40
**B16** A119(b) 3c + 2c violet .40 .40
**B17** A120(a) 5c + 2c red orange .55 .55
**B18** A120(b) 5c + 2c red orange .55 .55
**B19** A119(a) 7c + 2c Prus green .65 .65
**B20** A119(b) 7c + 2c Prus green .65 .65
*Nos. B11-B20,CB7-CB12 (16)* 7.80 7.80

Surtax for the UN Relief and Works Agency for Palestine Refugees.

A similar 5c surcharge, plus marginal United Nations emblem and "UNRWA," was applied to the miniature sheets described in the footnote following No. 488. Value, 4 sheets, perf. and imperf., $20.

Nos. 501-505 Surcharged

***Perf. 13½***
**1959, Apr. 13 Photo. Unwmk.**
**Flags in National Colors**

**B21** A125 1c + 2c rose, indigo & ultra .45 .45
**B22** A125 1c + 2c brown & blue .45 .45
**B23** A125 3c + 2c gray, vio, blk & buff .55 .55
**B24** A125 5c + 2c rose, dk bl, brn & red .70 .70
**B25** A125 7c + 2c lt brn, dk bl & red .80 .80
*Nos. B21-B25,CB13-CB15 (8)* 6.45 6.45

International Geophysical Year, 1957-58.

A similar 5c surcharge was applied to the miniature sheets described in the footnote following No. 505. Value, 2 sheets, perf. and imperf., $40.

Type of 1957 Surcharged in Red

**Engraved and Lithographed**
**1959, Sept. 10 Unwmk. *Imperf.***
**Flags in National Colors**

**B26** A117 1c + 2c brn, lt bl, vio & mar .40 .40
**B27** A117 2c + 2c dk brn, lt bl & vio .40 .40
**B28** A117 3c + 2c red lilac & red .45 .45
**B29** A117 5c + 2c red org & vio .45 .45
**B30** A117 7c + 2c green & violet .55 .55
*Nos. B26-B30,CB16-CB18 (8)* 4.85 4.85

3rd Pan American Games, Chicago, Aug. 27-Sept. 7, 1959.

**Nos. 522-524 Surcharged in Red**

**1960, Apr. 7 Litho. *Perf. 12½***
**Center in Gray**

**B31** A135 5c + 5c red brn & yel grn .35 .35
**B32** A135 9c + 5c car & lt bl .35 .35
**B33** A135 13c + 5c org & grn .80 .80
*Nos. B31-B33,CB19-CB20 (5)* 2.40 2.40

World Refugee Year, July 1, 1959-June 30, 1960. The surtax was for aid to refugees.

Souvenir sheets exist perf. and imperf., containing one each of Nos. B31-B33 and CB19-CB20. Value, 2 sheets, perf. and imperf., $12.50

**Nos. 525-529 Surcharged**

**1962, Jan. 8 Photo. *Perf. 13½***
**Flags in National Colors**

**B34** A136 1c + 2c red, yel grn & blk .35 .35
**B35** A136 2c + 2c org, grnsh bl & brn .35 .35
**B36** A136 3c + 2c henna brn & bl .35 .35
**B37** A136 5c + 2c brown & ultra .35 .35
**B38** A136 7c + 2c grn, bl & rose brn .35 .35
*Nos. B34-B38,CB21-CB23 (8)* 3.10 3.10

15th anniv. (in 1961) of UNESCO.

A similar 5c surcharge was applied to the miniature sheets described in the footnote following No. 529. Value, 2 sheets, perf. and imperf., $20.

**Anti-Malaria Type of 1962**

**1962, Apr. 29 Litho. *Perf. 12***

**B39** A141 10c + 2c brt pink & red lil .50 .40
**B40** A141 20c + 2c pale brn & brn .75 .55

**Freedom from Hunger Type of 1963**

**1963, Apr. 15 Unwmk. *Perf. 11½***
**Banner in Dark Blue & Red**

**B41** A148 2c + 1c green .35 .25
**B42** A148 5c + 2c brt rose lil .35 .25
**B43** A148 9c + 2c orange .35 .25
*Nos. B41-B43 (3)* 1.05 .75

A souvenir sheet contains three imperf. stamps similar to Nos. B41-B43. Value, $1.50.

**Nos. 591-593 Surcharged**

**1964, Mar. 8 *Perf. 12½***

**B44** A153 3c + 2c pale pink & ver .35 .35
**B45** A153 6c + 2c pale bl & ultra .35 .35
**B46** A153 9c + 2c pale rose & red brn .35 .35
*Nos. B44-B46,CB26-CB27 (5)* 1.80 1.80

UNESCO world campaign to save historic monuments in Nubia.

Nos. 622-626 Surcharged

**1966, Dec. 9 Litho. *Perf. 12½***
**Size: 31x21mm**

**B47** A164 1c + 2c multi *8.50* *1.25*
**B48** A164 2c + 2c multi *8.50* *1.25*
**B49** A164 3c + 2c multi *8.50* *1.25*
**B50** A164 6c + 4c multi *8.50* *1.25*
**B51** A164 8c + 4c multi *8.50* *1.25*
*Nos. B47-B51,CB28-CB30 (8)* 56.00 14.00

Surtax for victims of Hurricane Inez.

---

## AIR POST STAMPS

Map of Hispaniola — AP1

***Perf. 11½***
**1928, May 31 Litho. Unwmk.**

**C1** AP1 10c deep ultra 5.25 2.50

**1930**

**C2** AP1 10c ocher 3.50 3.00
*a.* Vert. pair, imperf. btwn. *600.00*
**C3** AP1 15c scarlet 6.75 4.00
**C4** AP1 20c dull green 3.25 .85
**C5** AP1 30c violet 6.75 4.50
*Nos. C2-C5 (4)* 20.25 12.35

Nos. C2-C5 have only "CENTAVOS" in lower panel. Issued: 10c, 20c, 1/24; 15c, 30c, 2/14.

**1930**

**C6** AP1 10c light blue 1.75 .60
**C7** AP1 15c blue green 3.25 1.00
**C8** AP1 20c yellow brown 3.50 .85
*a.* Horiz. pair, imperf. vert. 450.00 450.00
**C9** AP1 30c chocolate 6.25 1.75
*Nos. C6-C9 (4)* 14.75 4.20

Issue dates: 10c, 15c, 20c, Sept.; 30c, Oct.

Batwing Sundial Erected in 1753 — AP2

**1931-33 *Perf. 12***

**C10** AP2 10c carmine 3.50 .50
**C11** AP2 10c light blue 1.75 .50
**C12** AP2 10c dark green 6.25 2.75
**C13** AP2 15c rose lilac 2.75 .50
**C14** AP2 20c dark blue 6.25 2.25
*a.* Numerals reading up at left and down at right 5.75 2.75
*b.* Imperf., pair 250.00
**C15** AP2 30c green 2.50 .25
**C16** AP2 50c red brown 6.25 .50
**C17** AP2 1p deep orange 10.00 2.75
*Nos. C10-C17 (8)* 39.25 10.00

Issued: No. C11, 7/2/32; No. C12, 5/28/33; others 8/16.

Airplane and Ozama Fortress AP3

**1933, Nov. 20**

**C18** AP3 10c dark blue 3.50 .60

Airplane and Trujillo Bridge AP4

**1934, Sept. 20**

**C19** AP4 10c dark blue 3.00 .50

Symbolic of Flight AP5

**1935, Apr. 29**

**C20** AP5 10c lt blue & dk blue 1.60 .50

AP6

**1936, Feb. 11 *Perf. 11½***

**C21** AP6 10c dk bl & turq bl 2.50 .50

Allegory of Flight AP7

**1936, Oct. 17**

**C22** AP7 10c dk bl, bl & turq bl 2.25 .40

Macoris Airport AP8

**1937, Oct. 22**
**C23** AP8 10c green 1.00 .25

Fleet of Columbus AP9

Air Fleet AP10

Proposed Columbus Lighthouse — AP11

**1937, Nov. 9** ***Perf. 12***
**C24** AP9 10c rose red 1.75 1.40
**C25** AP10 15c purple 1.40 .95
**C26** AP11 20c dk bl & lt bl 1.40 1.25
**C27** AP10 25c red violet 2.00 1.25
**C28** AP11 30c yellow green 1.75 1.25
**C29** AP10 50c brown 3.50 1.75
**C30** AP11 75c dk olive grn 10.50 10.50
**C31** AP9 1p orange 6.25 2.50
*Nos. C24-C31 (8)* 28.55 20.85

Goodwill flight to all American countries by the planes "Colon," "Pinta," "Nina" and "Santa Maria."

No. C30 was reproduced imperf. on No. 1019.

Pan American Clipper AP12

**1938, July 30**
**C32** AP12 10c green 1.25 .25

Trylon and Perisphere, Plane and Proposed Columbus Lighthouse — AP13

**1939, Apr. 30**
**C33** AP13 10c green & lt green 2.00 .85

New York World's Fair.

Airplane AP14

**1939, Oct. 18**
**C34** AP14 10c green & dp green 1.60 .25
*a.* Pair, imperf. btwn. 450.00

Proposed Columbus Lighthouse, Plane and Caravels — AP15

Christopher Columbus and Proposed Lighthouse — AP16

Proposed Lighthouse — AP17

Christopher Columbus — AP18

Caravel — AP19

**1940, Oct. 12**
**C35** AP15 10c sapphire & lt bl 1.10 .60
**C36** AP16 15c org brn & brn 1.60 1.00
**C37** AP17 20c rose red & red 1.60 1.00
**C38** AP18 25c brt red lil & red vio 1.60 .50
**C39** AP19 50c green & lt green 3.00 1.75
*Nos. C35-C39 (5)* 8.90 4.85

Discovery of America by Columbus and proposed Columbus memorial lighthouse in Dominican Republic.

Posts and Telegraph Building, San Cristobal AP20

**1941, Feb. 21**
**C40** AP20 10c brt red lil & pale lil rose .50 .25

Globe, Wing and Letter AP21

**1942, Feb. 13**
**C41** AP21 10c dark violet brn .60 .30
**C42** AP21 75c deep orange 3.25 2.00

Plane AP22

**1943, Sept. 1**
**C43** AP22 10c brt red lilac .40 .25
**C44** AP22 20c dp blue & blue .40 .25
**C45** AP22 25c yellow olive 5.75 3.25
*Nos. C43-C45 (3)* 6.55 3.75

Plane, Flag, Coat of Arms and Torch of Liberty — AP23

**1944, Feb. 27** ***Perf. 11½***
**Flag in Gray, Dark Blue, Carmine**
**C46** AP23 10c multicolored .35 .25
**C47** AP23 20c multicolored .45 .25
**C48** AP23 1p multicolored 2.00 1.50
*Nos. C46-C48 (3)* 2.80 2.00

Centenary of Independence. See No. 407 for souvenir sheet listing.

Communications Building, Ciudad Trujillo — AP24

**1944, Nov. 12** **Litho.** ***Perf. 12***
**C49** AP24 9c yel grn & blue .25 .25
**C50** AP24 13c dull brn & rose car .25 .25
**C51** AP24 25c org & dull red .35 .25
*b.* Vert. pair, imperf. btwn. 45.00
**C52** AP24 30c black & ultra .75 .65
*Nos. C49-C52 (4)* 1.60 1.40

Twenty booklets of 100 (25 panes of 4) of the 25c were issued. All booklets are still intact.

**Communications Type**

**1945, Sept. 1**
**Center in Dark Blue and Carmine**
**C53** A92 7c deep yellow green .35 .25
**C54** A92 12c red orange .40 .25
**C55** A92 13c deep blue .50 .25
**C56** A92 25c orange brown .90 .25
*Nos. C53-C56 (4)* 2.15 1.00

AP26

Flags and National Anthem AP27

**Unwmk.**
**1946, Feb. 27** **Litho.** ***Perf. 12***
**Center in Dark Blue, Deep Carmine and Black**
**C57** AP26 10c carmine .95 .40
**C58** AP26 15c blue 2.10 .85
**C59** AP26 20c chocolate 2.50 .85
**C60** AP26 35c orange 3.00 .95
**C61** AP27 1p grn, yel grn & cit 25.00 10.00
*Nos. C57-C61 (5)* 33.55 13.05

Nos. C57-C61 exist imperf.

**Map Type of Regular Issue**

**1946, Aug. 4**
**C62** A94 10c multicolored .75 .25
**C63** A94 13c multicolored 1.35 .25

**Waterfall Type of Regular Issue**

**1947, Mar. 18** **Litho.**
**Center Multicolored**
**C64** A95 18c light blue 1.00 .50
**C65** A95 23c carmine 1.60 .60
**C66** A95 50c red violet 2.10 .60
**C67** A95 75c chocolate 3.00 1.10
*Nos. C64-C67 (4)* 7.70 2.80

**Palace Type of Regular Issue**

**1948, Feb. 27**
**C68** A96 37c orange brown 2.10 1.00
**C69** A96 1p orange yellow 5.75 2.10

**Ruins Type of Regular Issue**

**1949** **Unwmk.** ***Perf. 11½***
**C70** A97 7c ol grn & pale ol grn .40 .25
**C71** A97 10c orange brn & buff .40 .25
**C72** A97 15c brt rose & pale pink 1.25 .30
**C73** A97 20c green & pale green 1.75 .60
*Nos. C70-C73 (4)* 3.80 1.40

Issue dates: 10c, Apr. 4; others, Apr. 13.

Las Carreras Monument — AP32

**1949, Aug. 10**
**C74** AP32 10c red & pink .75 .25

Cent. of the Battle of Las Carreras.

**Catalogue values for unused stamps in this section, from this point to the end of the section, are for Never Hinged items.**

**Hotel Type of Regular Issue**

Hotels: 12c, Montana. 37c, San Cristobal.

**1950, Sept. 8**
**C75** A100 12c dk blue & blue .50 .25
**C76** A100 37c carmine & pink 3.25 2.50

Map, Plane and Caduceus AP34

**1950, Oct. 2**
**C77** AP34 12c orange brn & yel 1.00 .25

13th Pan-American Health Conf. Exists imperf.

**Hospital Type of Regular Issue**

**1952, Aug.**
**C78** A104 23c deep blue 1.20 1.20
**C79** A104 29c carmine 3.25 2.25

Columbus Lighthouse and Plane — AP36

**1953, Jan. 6** **Engr.** ***Perf. 13***
**C80** AP36 12c ocher .30 .25
**C81** AP36 14c dark blue .30 .25
**C82** AP36 20c black brown .70 .60
**C83** AP36 23c deep plum .40 .40
**C84** AP36 25c dark blue .95 .70
**C85** AP36 29c deep green .70 .60
**C86** AP36 1p red brown 2.00 1.25
*a.* Miniature sheet of 10 21.00 21.00
*Nos. C80-C86 (7)* 5.35 4.05

No. C86a is lithographed and contains Nos. 450-452 and C80-C86, in slightly different shades. Sheet measures 190x130mm and is imperf. with simulated perforations.

A miniature sheet similar to No. C86a, but measuring 200x163mm and in folder, exists. Value $100.

Ano Mariano Initials in Monogram — AP37

**1954, Aug. 5 Litho. *Perf. 11½***

**C87** AP37 8c claret .30 .25
**C88** AP37 11c blue .35 .25
**C89** AP37 33c brown orange 1.20 .60
*Nos. C87-C89 (3)* 1.85 1.10

Marian Year. Nos. C87-C89 exist imperf.

### Rotary Type of Regular Issue

**1955, Feb. 23 *Perf. 12***

**C90** A110 11c rose red .50 .25

Flags — AP39

Portraits of General Hector B. Trujillo: 25c, In civilian clothes. 33c, In uniform.

**1955, May 16 Engr. *Perf. 13½x13***

**C91** AP39 11c blue, yel & car .80 .25
**C92** AP39 25c rose violet 1.40 .30
**C93** AP39 33c orange brown 2.00 .50
*Nos. C91-C93 (3)* 4.20 1.05

The center of No. C91 is litho. 25th anniv. of the inauguration of the Trujillo era.

### Fair Type of Regular Issue

**1955, Dec. 20 Unwmk. *Perf. 13***

**C94** A112 11c vermilion .60 .25

### ICAO Type of Regular Issue

**1956, Apr. 6 Litho. *Perf. 12½***

**C95** A114 11c ultra 1.25 .25

### Tree Type of Regular Issue

Design: 13c, Mahogany tree.

**1956, Dec. 8 Litho. *Perf. 11½x12***

**C96** A115 13c orange & green 2.25 .25

### Type of Regular Issue, 1957

Olympic Winners and Flags: 11c, Paavo Nurmi, Finland. 16c, Ugo Frigerio, Italy. 17c, Mildred Didrikson ("Didrickson" on stamp), US.

### Engraved and Lithographed
***Perf. 11½, Imperf.***

**1957, Jan. 24 Unwmk.**

**Flags in National Colors**

**C97** A117 11c ultra & red org .25 .25
**C98** A117 16c carmine & lt grn .30 .25
**C99** A117 17c black, vio & red .40 .25
*Nos. C97-C99 (3)* .95 .75

16th Olympic Games, Melbourne, Nov. 22-Dec. 8, 1956.

Souvenir sheets of 3 exist, perf. and imperf., containing Nos. C97-C99. Value, 2 sheets, perf. & imperf., $15.

For surcharges see Nos. CB1-CB3, CB16-CB18.

### Type of Regular Issue

Olympic Winners and Flags: 11c, Robert Morrow, US, 100 & 200 meter dash. 16c, Chris Brasher, England, steeplechase. 17c, A. Ferreira Da Silva, Brazil, hop, step and jump.

***Perf. 13½, Imperf.***

**1957, July 18 Photo.**

**Flags in National Colors**

**C100** A118 11c yellow grn & dk bl .25 .25
**C101** A118 16c lilac & dk blue .30 .25
**C102** A118 17c brown & blue grn .40 .25
*Nos. C100-C102 (3)* .95 .75

1956 Olympic winners.

See note on miniature sheets following No. 483.

For surcharges see Nos. CB4-CB6.

### Types of Regular Issue

Olympic Winners and Flags: 11c, Hans Winkler, Germany, individual jumping. 16c, Alfred Oerter, US, discus throw. 17c, Shirley Strickland, Australia, 800 meter hurdles.

### Engraved and Lithographed
***Perf. 13½, Imperf.***

**1957, Nov. 12 Unwmk.**

**Flags in National Colors**

**C103** A119 11c ultra .25 .25
**C104** A120 16c rose carmine .40 .25
**C105** A119 17c claret .40 .25
*Nos. C103-C105 (3)* 1.05 .75

1956 Olympic winners.

Miniature sheets of 3 exist, perf. and imperf., containing Nos. C103-C105. Value, 2 sheets, perf. and imperf., $5.50.

For surcharges see Nos. CB7-CB12.

### Type of Regular Issue

Olympic Winners and Flags: 11c, Charles Jenkins, 400 & 800 meter run, and Thomas Courtney, 1,600 meter relay, US. 16c, Field hockey team, India. 17c, Yachting team, Sweden.

***Perf. 13½, Imperf.***

**1958, Oct. 30 Unwmk. Photo.**

**Flags in National Colors**

**C106** A125 11c blue, olive & brn .30 .25
**C107** A125 16c lt grn, org & dk bl .40 .25
**C108** A125 17c ver, blue & yel .40 .25
*Nos. C106-C108 (3)* 1.10 .75

1956 Olympic winners.

Miniature sheets of 3 exist, perf. and imperf., containing Nos. C106-C108. Value, 2 sheets, perf. and imperf., $3.

For surcharges see Nos. CB13-CB15.

### Fair Type of Regular Issue

**1958, Dec. 9 Litho. *Perf. 12½***

**C109** A127 9c gray .30 .25
**C110** A127 25c lt violet .85 .40
*a.* Souv. sheet of 3, #C109-C110, 507, imperf. 2.25 2.25

### Polo Type of Regular Issue

**1959, May 15 *Perf. 12***

**C111** A130 11c Dominican polo team .40 .30

"San Cristobal" Plane — AP42

***Perf. 11½***

**1960, Feb. 25 Unwmk. Litho.**

**C112** AP42 13c org, bl, grn & gray .50 .25

Dominican Civil Aviation.

Children and WRY Emblem AP43

**1960, Apr. 7 *Perf. 12½***

**C113** AP43 10c plum, gray & grn .65 .30
**C114** AP43 13c gray & green .90 .30

World Refugee Year, 7/1/59-6/30/60.

For surcharges see Nos. CB19-CB20.

### Olympic Type of Regular Issue

Olympic Winners: 11c, Pat McCormick, US, diving. 16c, Mithat Bayrack, Turkey, welterweight wrestling. 17c, Ursula Happe, Germany, 200 meter breast stroke.

***Perf. 13½, Imperf.***

**1960, Sept. 14 Photo.**

**Flags in National Colors**

**C115** A136 11c blue, gray & brn .35 .25
**C116** A136 16c red, brown & ol .35 .30
**C117** A136 17c black, blue & ocher .35 .40
*Nos. C115-C117 (3)* 1.05 .95

17th Olympic Games, Rome, 8/25-9/11.

Miniature sheets of 3 exist, perf. and imperf., containing Nos. C115-C117. Value, 2 sheets, perf. and imperf., $3.75.

For surcharges see Nos. CB21-CB23.

### Coffee-Cacao Type of Regular Issue

**1961, Dec. 30 Litho. *Perf. 12½***

**C118** A140 13c orange ver .35 .30
**C119** A140 33c brt yellow .80 .70

Nos. C118-C119 exist imperf.

### Anti-Malaria Type of Regular Issue

**1962, Apr. 29 Unwmk. *Perf. 12***

**C120** A141 13c pink & red .50 .25
**C121** A141 33c org & dp org .95 .50

See Nos. CB24-CB25.

### Type of Regular Issue

Designs: 13c, Broken fetters and laurel. 50c, Flag, torch and inscription.

**1962, May 30 *Perf. 12½***

**C122** A142 13c brn, yel, ol, ultra & red .40 .30
**C123** A142 50c rose lilac, ultra & red 1.40 1.00

No. C122 exists imperf.

### UPAE Type of Regular Issue

**1962, Oct. 23 *Perf. 12½***

**C124** A146 13c bright blue .45 .25
**C125** A146 22c dull red brown .60 .50

Nos. C124-C125 exist imperf.

### Nouel Type of Regular Issue

Design: Frame altered with rosary and cross surrounding portrait.

**1962, Dec. 18**

**C126** A147 13c blue & pale blue .45 .25
**C127** A147 25c vio & pale vio .75 .50
*a.* Souv. sheet, #C126-C127, imperf 1.25 1.25

Nos. C126-C127 exist imperf.

Sanchez, Duarte, Mella AP44

**1963, July 7 Litho. *Perf. 11½x12***

**C128** AP44 15c orange .50 .25

120th anniv. of separation from Haiti.

World Map AP45

**1963, Oct. 25 Unwmk. *Perf. 12½***

**C129** AP45 10c gray & carmine .45 .25

Cent. of Intl. Red Cross. Exists imperf.

### Human Rights Type

**1963, Dec. 10 Litho.**

**C130** A152 7c fawn & red brn .30 .25
**C131** A152 10c lt blue & blue .30 .25

Nos. C130-C131 exist imperf.

Ramses II Battling the Hittites (from Abu Simbel) — AP46

**1964, Mar. 8 *Perf. 12½***

**C132** AP46 10c brt violet .30 .25
**C133** AP46 13c yellow .30 .25

UNESCO world campaign to save historic monuments in Nubia.

Nos. C132-C133 exist imperf.

For surcharges see Nos. CB26-CB27.

Striated Woodpecker — AP47

**1964, June 8 Litho.**

**C134** AP47 10c multicolored 5.75 .25

### Type of Space Issue

Designs: 7c, Rocket leaving earth. 10c, Space capsule orbiting earth.

**1964, July 28 Unwmk. *Perf. 12½***

**C135** A156 7c brt green .30 .25
**C136** A156 10c violet blue .40 .30
*a.* Souvenir sheet 4.25 3.50

No. C136a contains 7c and 10c stamps similar to Nos. C135-C136 with simulated perforations.

Pres. John F. Kennedy — AP48

**1964, Nov. 22 *Perf. 11½***

**C137** AP48 10c buff & dk brown .60 .25

President John F. Kennedy (1917-63). Sheets of 10 (5x2) and sheets of 50.

### UPU Type of Regular Issue

**1964, Dec. 5 Litho. *Perf. 12½***

**C138** A157 7c blue .35 .25

### ICY Type of Regular Issue

**1965, Feb. 16 Unwmk. *Perf. 12½***

**C139** A158 10c lilac & violet .45 .30

Basilica of Our Lady of Altagracia — AP49

**1965, Mar. 18 Unwmk. *Perf. 12½***

**C140** AP49 10c multicolored .50 .25

Fourth Mariological Congress and the Eleventh International Marian Congress.

Abraham Lincoln — AP50

**1965, Apr. 15 Litho. *Perf. 12½***
**C141** AP50 17c bright blue .65 .40

Cent. of the death of Abraham Lincoln.

### Stamp Centenary Type of 1965

Design: Stamp of 1865, (No. 2).

**1965, Dec. 28 Litho. *Perf. 12½***
**C142** A161 7c violet, lt grn & blk .40 .25
**C143** A161 10c yellow, lt grn & blk .40 .30

ITU Emblem, Old and New Communication Equipment — AP51

**1966, Apr. 6 Litho. *Perf. 12½***
**C144** AP51 28c pink & carmine .85 .85
**C145** AP51 45c brt grn & grn 1.50 1.50

Cent. (in 1965) of the ITU.

### Butterfly Type of Regular Issue

**1966, Nov. 8 Litho. *Perf. 12½***
**Various Butterflies in Natural Colors**
**Size: 35x24mm**
**C146** A164 10c lt violet & violet 7.75 .75
**C147** A164 50c org & dp org 10.00 1.50
**C148** A164 75c pink & rose red 12.50 2.50
*Nos. C146-C148 (3)* 30.25 4.75

For surcharges see Nos. CB28-CB30.

### Altar Type of Regular Issue

**1967, Jan. 18 Litho. *Perf. 11½***
**C149** A165 7c lt olive green .35 .25
**C150** A165 10c lilac .35 .25
**C151** A165 20c yellow brown .45 .30
*Nos. C149-C151 (3)* 1.15 .80

### Chess Type of Regular Issue

Design: 10c, Pawn and Bishop.

**1967, June 23 Litho. *Perf. 12½***
**C152** A167 10c ol, lt ol & blk 1.25 .30
*a.* Souvenir sheet 10.00 1.90

No. C152a contains 2 imperf. stamps similar to Nos. 636 and C152.

### Alliance for Progress Type

**1967, Sept. 16 Litho. *Perf. 12½***
**C153** A168 8c gray .50 .30
**C154** A168 10c blue .60 .30

Cornucopia and Emblem — AP52

**1967, Oct. 7**
**C155** AP52 12c multicolored .75 .30

25th anniversary of the Inter-American Agriculture Institute.

### Satellite Type of Regular Issue

**1968, June 15 Typo. *Perf. 12***
**C156** A170 10c dp blue & multi .35 .25
**C157** A170 15c purple & multi .50 .30

### Boxing Type of Regular Issue

Designs: Two views of boxing match.

**1968, June 29**
**C158** A171 7c orange yel & grn .60 .25
**C159** A171 10c gray & blue .75 .25

See note after No. 641.

### Lions Type of Regular Issue

**1968, Aug. 9 Litho. *Perf. 11½***
**C160** A172 10c ultra & multi .30 .25

### Olympic Type of Regular Issue

Designs (Olympic Emblem and): 10c, Weight lifting. 33c, Pistol shooting.

**1968, Nov. 12 Litho. *Perf. 11½***
**C161** A173 10c buff & multi .35 .25
**C162** A173 33c pink & multi 1.25 .75

Latin American Flags — AP53

**1969, Jan. 25 Litho. *Perf. 12½***
**C163** AP53 10c pink & multi .45 .25

7th Inter-American Savings and Loan Conference, Santo Domingo, Jan. 25-31.

### Taino Art Type of Regular Issue

7c, Various vomiting spoons with human heads, vert. 10c, Female torso forming drinking vessel. 20c, Vase with human head, vert.

**1969, Jan. 31 Litho. *Perf. 12½***
**C164** A175 7c lt bl, bl & lem .40 .25
**C165** A175 10c pink, ver & brn .50 .25
**C166** A175 20c yellow, org & brn .60 .30
*Nos. C164-C166 (3)* 1.50 .80

### COTAL Type of Regular Issue

10c, Airport of the Americas and COTAL emblem.

**1969, May 25 Litho. *Perf. 12½***
**C167** A178 10c brown & pale fawn .40 .25

### ILO Type of Regular Issue

**1969, June 27 Litho. *Perf. 12½***
**C168** A179 10c rose, red & black .40 .25

### Baseball Type of Regular Issue

Designs: 7c, Bleachers, Tetelo Vargas Stadium, horiz. 10c, Batter, catcher and umpire. 1p, Quisqueya Stadium, horiz.

**1969, Aug. 15 Litho. *Perf. 12½***
**Size: 43x30mm (7c, 1p); 21x31mm (10c)**
**C169** A180 7c magenta & org .55 .30
**C170** A180 10c mar & rose red .70 .30
**C171** A180 1p violet blue & brn 5.00 3.50
*Nos. C169-C171 (3)* 6.25 4.10

### Electrification Types of Regular Issue

Design: No. C172, Rio Haina steam plant. No. C173, Valdesa Dam.

**1969 Litho. *Perf. 12***
**C172** A181 10c orange ver .50 .25
**C173** A182 10c multicolored .55 .25

Issued: No. C172, Sept. 15; No. C173, Oct. 15.

### Duarte Type of Regular Issue

**1970, Jan. 26 Litho. *Perf. 12***
**C174** A183 10c brown & dk brown .75 .25

### Census Type of Regular Issue

Design: 10c, Buildings and census emblem.

**1970, Feb. 6 *Perf. 11***
**C175** A184 10c lt blue & multi .75 .25

### Sculpture Type of Regular Issue

Design: 10c, The Prisoner, by Abelardo Rodriguez Urdaneta, vert.

**1970, Feb. 20 Litho. *Perf. 12½***
**C176** A186 10c bluish gray .55 .25

### Masonic Type of Regular Issue

**1970, Mar. 2**
**C177** A187 10c brown .30 .25

### Satellite Type of Regular Issue

**1970, May 25 Litho. *Perf. 12½***
**C178** A188 7c blue & gray .40 .25

### UPU Type of Regular Issue

**1970, June 5 *Perf. 11***
**C179** A189 10c yellow & brown .40 .25

### Education Year Type of Regular Issue

**1970, June 26 Litho. *Perf. 12½***
**C180** A190 15c bright pink .60 .25

Dancers AP54

Design: 10c, UN emblem and wheel.

**1970, Oct. 12 Litho. *Perf. 12½***
**C181** AP54 7c blue & multi .35 .25
**C182** AP54 10c pink & multi .50 .25

1st World Exhib. of Books and Culture Festival, Santo Domingo, Oct. 11-Dec. 11.

Album, Globe and Emblem — AP55

**1970, Oct. 26 Litho. *Perf. 11***
**C183** AP55 10c multicolored .65 .25

EXFILCA 70, 2nd Interamerican Philatelic Exhibition, Caracas, Venezuela, 11/27-12/6.

Basilica of Our Lady of Altagracia — AP56

**1971, Jan. 20 Litho. *Perf. 12½***
**C184** AP56 17c multicolored 1.00 .45

Inauguration of the Basilica of Our Lady of Altagracia.

Map of Dominican Republic, CARE Package AP57

**1971, May 28 Litho. *Perf. 12½***
**C185** AP57 10c blue & green .45 .25

25th anniversary of CARE, a US-Canadian Cooperative for American Relief Everywhere.

### Sports Type of Regular Issue

**1971, Sept. 10 *Perf. 11***
**C186** A195 7c Volleyball .40 .25

### Animal Type of Regular Issue

Design: 25c, Cock and grain.

**1971, Sept. 29 *Perf. 12½***
**C187** A196 25c black & multi 2.00 .35

### Independence Type

10c, Dominican-Colombian flag of 1821.

**1971, Dec. 1 *Perf. 11***
**C188** A197 10c vio bl, yel & red .75 .30

### Christmas Type of Regular Issue

**1971, Dec. 10 *Perf. 12½***
**C189** A198 10c Bell, 1493 .45 .25

### UNICEF Type of Regular Issue

Design: UNICEF emblem & child on beach.

**1971, Dec. 14 *Perf. 11***
**C190** A199 15c multicolored .80 .45

### Book Year Type of Regular Issue

**1972, Jan. 25 Litho. *Perf. 12½***
**C191** A200 12c lilac, dk bl & red .75 .30

Magnifying Glass over Peru on Map of Americas — AP58

**1972, Mar. 7 Litho. *Perf. 12***
**C192** AP58 10c blue & multi .60 .30

EXFILIMA '71, 3rd Inter-American Philatelic Exposition, Lima, Peru, Nov. 6-14, 1971.

"Your Heart is your Health" — AP59

**1972, Apr. 27 Litho. *Perf. 11***
**C193** AP59 7c red & multi .50 .25

World Health Day.

### Taino Art Type of 1972

Taino Art: 8c, Ritual vessel showing human figures. 10c, Trumpet (shell). 25c, Carved vomiting spoons. All horiz.

**1972, May 10 Litho. *Perf. 11***
**C194** A201 8c multicolored .50 .25
**C195** A201 10c lt blue & multi .70 .25
**C196** A201 25c multicolored 1.50 .45
*Nos. C194-C196 (3)* 2.70 .95

### Telecommunications Type of Regular Issue

**1972, May 17 *Perf. 12½***
**C197** A202 21c yellow & multi 1.00 .45

### Exhibition Type of Regular Issue

**1972, June 3**
**C198** A203 33c orange & multi 1.00 .55

### Olympic Type of Regular Issue

**1972, Aug. 25 Litho. *Perf. 12½***
**C199** A204 33c Running 1.25 .75

### Club Type of Regular Issue

**1972, Sept. 29 Litho. *Perf. 10½***
**C200** A205 20c blue & multi .75 .25

### Morel Type of Regular Issue

**1972, Oct. 20 Litho. *Perf. 12½***
**C201** A206 10c multicolored .50 .25

### Bank Type of Regular Issue

25c, 1947 silver coin, entrance to the Mint.

**1972, Oct. 23**
**C202** A207 25c ocher & multi 1.25 .55

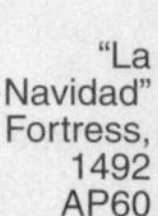

"La Navidad" Fortress, 1492
AP60

**1972, Nov. 21 Litho. *Perf. 12½***

| | | | | |
|---|---|---|---|---|
| **C203** | AP60 | 10c multicolored | .95 | .25 |

Christmas 1972.

### Sports Type of Regular Issue

Various sports; a, UL. b, UR. c, LL. d, LR.

**1973, Mar. 30 Litho. *Perf. 13½x13***

| | | | | |
|---|---|---|---|---|
| **C204** | A212 | Block of 4 | 1.75 | 1.75 |
| *a.-d.* | | 8c, any single | .30 | .25 |
| **C205** | A212 | Block of 4 | 2.75 | 2.75 |
| *a.-d.* | | 10c, any single | .50 | .30 |

### Easter Type 1973

10c, Belfry of Church of Our Lady of Help.

**1973, Apr. 18 Litho. *Perf. 10½***

| | | | | |
|---|---|---|---|---|
| **C206** | A213 | 10c multicolored, vert. | .75 | .25 |

North and South America on Globe — AP61

**1973, May 29 Litho. *Perf. 12***

| | | | | |
|---|---|---|---|---|
| **C207** | AP61 | 7c multicolored | .45 | .25 |

Pan-American Health Organization, 70th anniversary (in 1972).

### WMO Type of Regular Issue

**1973, Aug. 10 Litho. *Perf. 13½x13***

| | | | | |
|---|---|---|---|---|
| **C208** | A214 | 7c green & multi | .50 | .25 |

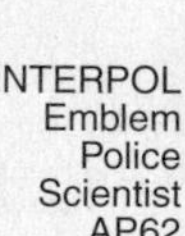

INTERPOL Emblem Police Scientist
AP62

**1973, Sept. 28 Litho. *Perf. 10½***

| | | | | |
|---|---|---|---|---|
| **C209** | AP62 | 10c vio bl, bl & emer | .60 | .25 |

50th anniversary of International Criminal Police Organization.

### Handicraft Type of Regular Issue

**1973, Oct. 12**

| | | | | |
|---|---|---|---|---|
| **C210** | A215 | 7c Sailing ship, mosaic | .75 | .25 |
| **C211** | A215 | 10c Maracas rattles, horiz. | 1.00 | .25 |

### Christmas Type of Regular Issue

Design: 10c, Angels adoring Christ Child.

**1973, Nov. 26 Litho. *Perf. 13½x13***

| | | | | |
|---|---|---|---|---|
| **C212** | A216 | 10c multicolored | .50 | .25 |

### Scout Type of Regular Issue

21c, Scouts cooking, Lord Baden-Powell.

**1973, Dec. 7 Litho. *Perf. 12***

| | | | | |
|---|---|---|---|---|
| **C213** | A217 | 21c red & multi | 1.25 | .75 |

### Sport Type of Regular Issue

10c, Olympic swimming pool and diver. 25c, Olympic Stadium, soccer and discus.

**1974, Feb. 25 Litho. *Perf. 13½***

| | | | | |
|---|---|---|---|---|
| **C214** | A218 | 10c blue & multi | .40 | .25 |
| **C215** | A218 | 25c multicolored | 1.00 | .25 |

The Last Supper
AP63

**1974, June 27 Litho. *Perf. 13½***

| | | | | |
|---|---|---|---|---|
| **C216** | AP63 | 10c multicolored | .65 | .25 |

Holy Week 1974.

### Bridge Type

Design: 10c, Higuamo Bridge.

**1974, July 12 *Perf. 12***

| | | | | |
|---|---|---|---|---|
| **C217** | A221 | 10c multicolored | .65 | .25 |

### Diabetes Type

Map of Dominican Republic, Diabetics' Emblem and: 7c, Kidney. 33c, Eye & heart.

**1974, Aug. 22 Litho. *Perf. 13***

| | | | | |
|---|---|---|---|---|
| **C218** | A222 | 7c yellow & multi | .45 | .25 |
| **C219** | A222 | 33c lt blue & multi | 2.00 | .75 |

### UPU Type

**1974, Oct. 9 Litho. *Perf. 13½***

| | | | | |
|---|---|---|---|---|
| **C220** | A223 | 7c Ships | 1.75 | .35 |
| **C221** | A223 | 33c Jet | 2.75 | .75 |
| *a.* | | Souvenir sheet of 4 | 7.50 | 7.50 |

No. C221a contains Nos. 727-728, C220-C221 forming continuous design.

Golfers and Championship Emblem — AP64

20c, Golfer and Golf Association emblem.

**1974, Oct. 24 Litho. *Perf. 13x13½***

| | | | | |
|---|---|---|---|---|
| **C222** | AP64 | 10c green & multi | *.50* | .25 |
| **C223** | AP64 | 20c green & multi | *.80* | .40 |

World Amateur Golf Championships.

Hand Holding Dove
AP65

**1974, Dec. 3 Litho. *Perf. 12***

| | | | | |
|---|---|---|---|---|
| **C224** | AP65 | 10c multicolored | .50 | .25 |

Christmas 1974.

### FAO Type

10c, Bee, beehive and barrel of honey.

**1974, Dec. 5**

| | | | | |
|---|---|---|---|---|
| **C225** | A227 | 10c multicolored | 1.75 | .25 |

Chrismon, Lamb, Candle and Palm — AP66

**1975, Mar. 26 Litho. *Perf. 13½***

| | | | | |
|---|---|---|---|---|
| **C226** | AP66 | 10c gold & multi | .65 | .25 |

Holy Week 1975.

Spain No. 1, España 75 Emblem — AP67

**1975, Apr. 10**

| | | | | |
|---|---|---|---|---|
| **C227** | AP67 | 12c red, yel & blk | .65 | .30 |

Espana 75, International Philatelic Exhibition, Madrid, Apr. 4-13.

### Development Bank Type

**1975, May 19 Litho. *Perf. 10½x10***

| | | | | |
|---|---|---|---|---|
| **C228** | A230 | 10c rose car & multi | .60 | .25 |

Three Satellites and Globe
AP68

**1975, June 21 Litho. *Perf. 13½***

| | | | | |
|---|---|---|---|---|
| **C229** | AP68 | 15c multicolored | .60 | .35 |

Opening of first earth satellite tracking station in Dominican Republic.

### Apollo Type

Design: 2p, Apollo-Soyuz link-up over earth.

**1975, July 24 *Perf. 13***

**Size: 42x28mm**

| | | | | |
|---|---|---|---|---|
| **C230** | A232 | 2p multicolored | 6.00 | 4.00 |

### Indian Chief Type

7c, Mayobanex. 8c, Cotubanama & Juan de Esquivel. 10c, Enriquillo & Mencia.

**1975, Sept. 27 Litho. *Perf. 12***

| | | | | |
|---|---|---|---|---|
| **C231** | A235 | 7c lt green & multi | .60 | .25 |
| **C232** | A235 | 8c orange & multi | .90 | .30 |
| **C233** | A235 | 10c gray & multi | 1.00 | .30 |
| | | *Nos. C231-C233 (3)* | 2.50 | .85 |

Volleyball
AP69

10c, Weight lifting and Games' emblem.

**1975, Oct. 24 Litho. *Perf. 12***

| | | | | |
|---|---|---|---|---|
| **C234** | AP69 | 7c blue & multi | .75 | .25 |
| **C235** | AP69 | 10c multicolored | 1.25 | .30 |

7th Pan-American Games, Mexico City, Oct. 13-26.

### Christmas Type

Design: 10c, Dove and peace message.

**1975, Dec. 12 Litho. *Perf. 13x13½***

| | | | | |
|---|---|---|---|---|
| **C236** | A237 | 10c yellow & multi | .60 | .25 |

Valdesia Dam — AP70

**1976, Jan. 26 Litho. *Perf. 13***

| | | | | |
|---|---|---|---|---|
| **C237** | AP70 | 10c multicolored | .50 | .25 |

### Holy Week Type 1976

Design: 10c, Crucifixion, by Eliezer Castillo.

**1976, Apr. 14 Litho. *Perf. 13½***

| | | | | |
|---|---|---|---|---|
| **C238** | A239 | 10c multicolored | .75 | .30 |

### Bicentennial Type and

George Washington, Independence Hall — AP71

Design: 10c, Hands holding maps of US and Dominican Republic.

**1976, May 29 Litho. *Perf. 13½***

| | | | | |
|---|---|---|---|---|
| **C239** | A241 | 10c vio bl, grn & blk | .60 | .25 |
| **C240** | AP71 | 75c black & orange | 1.75 | 1.25 |

American Bicentennial; No. C240 also for Interphil 76 International Philatelic Exhibition, Philadelphia, Pa., May 29-June 6.

King Juan Carlos I and Queen Sofia — AP72

**1976, May 31**

| | | | | |
|---|---|---|---|---|
| **C241** | AP72 | 21c multicolored | 1.25 | .85 |

Visit of King Juan Carlos I and Queen Sofia of Spain.

### Telephone Type

Design: 10c, Alexander Graham Bell and telephones, 1876 and 1976.

**1976, July 15**

| | | | | |
|---|---|---|---|---|
| **C242** | A243 | 10c multicolored | .65 | .25 |

### Duarte Types

10c, Scroll with Duarte letter and Dominican flag. 33c, Duarte return from Exile, by E. Godoy.

**1976, July 20 Litho. *Perf. 13½***

| | | | | |
|---|---|---|---|---|
| **C243** | A245 | 10c blue & multi | .65 | .25 |

***Perf. 13x13½***

| | | | | |
|---|---|---|---|---|
| **C244** | A244 | 33c brown & multi | 2.00 | 1.10 |

Fire Engine
AP73

**1976, Sept. 13 Litho. *Perf. 12***

| | | | | |
|---|---|---|---|---|
| **C245** | AP73 | 10c multicolored | 3.50 | .30 |

Honoring firemen.

### Radio Club Type

**1976, Oct. 8 Litho. *Perf. 13½***

| | | | | |
|---|---|---|---|---|
| **C246** | A247 | 10c blue & black | .60 | .25 |

Various People — AP74

**1976, Oct. 22 Litho. *Perf. 13½***

| | | | | |
|---|---|---|---|---|
| **C247** | AP74 | 21c multicolored | .90 | .55 |

Spanish heritage.

### Olympic Games Type

**1976, Oct. 22** *Perf. 12*
**C248** A249 10c Running .60 .25
**C249** A249 25c Basketball 1.50 .75

### Christmas Type

Design: 10c, Angel with bells.

**1976, Dec. 8 Litho.** *Perf. 13½*
**C250** A251 10c multicolored .75 .30

Tourist Activities AP75

Tourist publicity: 12c, Angling and hotel. 25c, Horseback riding and waterfall, vert.

**1977, Jan. 7 Size: 36x36mm**
**C251** AP75 10c multicolored .45 .25
**Size: 34x25½mm, 25½x34mm**
**C252** AP75 12c multicolored .50 .25
**C253** AP75 25c multicolored 1.00 .45
*Nos. C251-C253 (3)* 1.95 .95

### Championship Type

**1977, Mar. 4 Litho.** *Perf. 13½*
**C254** A253 10c yel grn & multi .60 .25
**C255** A253 25c lt brown & multi 1.50 .75

### Holy Week Type 1977

Design: 10c, Belfry and open book.

**1977, Apr. 18 Litho.** *Perf. 13½x13*
**C256** A254 10c multicolored .75 .25

### Lions Type

**1977, May 6** *Perf. 13½x13*
**C257** A255 7c lt green & multi .60 .25

Caravel under Sail — AP76

**1977, July 16 Litho.** *Perf. 13*
**C258** AP76 10c multicolored .60 .30

Miss Universe Contest, held in Dominican Republic.

Melon Cactus — AP77

Design: 33c, Coccothrinax (tree).

**1977, Aug. 19 Litho.** *Perf. 12*
**C259** AP77 7c multicolored 1.00 .25
**C260** AP77 33c multicolored 2.50 1.10

National Botanical Garden.

Chart and Factories — AP78

**1977, Nov. 30 Litho.** *Perf. 13x13½*
**C261** AP78 28c multicolored 1.00 .65

7th Interamerican Statistics Conference.

### Animal Type

Congress Emblem and: 10c, "Dorado," red Roman stud bull. 25c, Flamingo, vert.

**1977, Dec. 29 Litho.** *Perf. 13*
**C262** A259 10c multicolored 3.00 .30
**C263** A259 25c multicolored 5.00 .50

### Spanish Heritage Type

21c, Window, Casa del Tostado, 16th cent.

**1978, Jan. 19** *Perf. 13x13½*
**Size: 28x41mm**
**C264** A260 21c multicolored .85 .55

### Holy Week Type, 1978

7c, Facade, Santo Domingo Cathedral. 10c, Facade of Dominican Convent.

**1978, Mar. 21 Litho.** *Perf. 12*
**Size: 27x36mm**
**C265** A261 7c multicolored .50 .25
**C266** A261 10c multicolored 1.00 .30

Schooner Duarte AP79

**1978, Apr. 15 Litho.** *Perf. 13½*
**C267** AP79 7c multicolored .70 .25

Dominican naval forces training ship.

### Cardinal Type

**1978, May 5 Litho.** *Perf. 13*
**C268** A262 10c multicolored .60 .25

Antenna AP80

**1978, May 17 Litho.** *Perf. 13½*
**C269** AP80 25c silver & multi 1.00 .55

10th World Telecommunications Day.

No. C1 and Map AP81

**1978, June 6**
**C270** AP81 10c multicolored .60 .25

1st Dominican Rep. airmail stamp, 50th anniv.

Globe, Soccer Ball, Emblem — AP82

33c, Soccer field, Argentina '78 emblem, globe.

**1978, June 29**
**C271** AP82 12c multicolored .65 .35
**C272** AP82 33c multicolored 1.40 1.00

11th World Cup Soccer Championship, Argentina, June 1-25.

Crown, Cross and Rosary Emblem — AP83

**1978, July 11** *Perf. 13x13½*
**C273** AP83 21c multicolored .85 .65

Congregation of the Merciful Sisters of Charity, centenary.

### Sports Type

**1978, July 21 Litho.** *Perf. 13½*
**C274** A265 7c Baseball, vert. 1.00 .25
**C275** A265 10c Basketball, vert. 1.50 .25

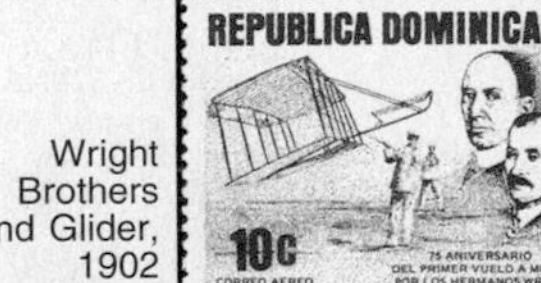

Wright Brothers and Glider, 1902 AP84

Designs: 7c, Diagrams of Flyer I and jet, vert. 13c, Diagram of air flow over wing. 45c, Flyer I over world map.

**1978, Aug. 8** *Perf. 12*
**C276** AP84 7c multicolored .25 .25
**C277** AP84 10c multicolored .60 .25
**C278** AP84 13c multicolored .85 .30
**C279** AP84 45c multicolored 2.25 1.40
*Nos. C276-C279 (4)* 3.95 2.20

75th anniversary of first powered flight.

### Tourist Type

Designs: 7c, Sun and musical instruments. 10c, Sun and plane over Santo Domingo.

**1978, Sept. 12 Litho.** *Perf. 12*
**C280** A266 7c multicolored .65 .25
**C281** A266 10c multicolored .90 .25

People and Globe AP85

**1978, Oct. 12 Litho.** *Perf. 13½*
**C282** AP85 21c multicolored .90 .70

Spanish heritage.

Dominican Republic and UN Flags AP86

**1978, Oct. 23** *Perf. 12*
**C283** AP86 33c multicolored 1.25 .75

33rd anniversary of the United Nations.

Statue of the Virgin — AP87

**1978, Dec. 5 Litho.** *Perf. 12*
**C284** AP87 10c multicolored .75 .30

Christmas 1978.

Pope John Paul II — AP88

**1979, Jan. 25 Litho.** *Perf. 13½*
**C285** AP88 10c multicolored 3.75 3.25

Visit of Pope John Paul II to the Dominican Republic, Jan. 25-26.

Map of Beata Island AP89

**1979, Jan. 25** *Perf. 12*
**C286** AP89 10c multicolored 1.50 .30

1st expedition of radio amateurs to Beata Is.

### Year of the Child Type, 1979

Designs (ICY Emblem and): 7c, Children reading book. 10c, Symbolic head and protective hands. 33c, Hands and jars.

**1979, Feb. 26**
**C287** A269 7c multicolored .40 .25
**C288** A269 10c multicolored .60 .25
**C289** A269 33c multicolored 1.75 1.10
*Nos. C287-C289 (3)* 2.75 1.60

Pope John Paul II Giving Benediction AP90

**1979, Apr. 9 Litho.** *Perf. 13½*
**C290** AP90 10c multicolored 4.00 1.25

Holy Week.

Adm. Juan Bautista Cambiaso AP91

**1979, Apr. 14** ***Perf. 12***
**C291** AP91 10c multicolored .60 .25

135th anniv. of the Battle of Tortuguero.

Map of Dominican Rep., Album, Magnifier AP92

**1979, Apr. 18**
**C292** AP92 33c multicolored 1.10 .75

EXFILNA, 3rd National Philatelic Exhibition, Apr. 18-22.

### Flower Type

Designs: 7c, Passionflower. 10c, Isidorea pungens. 13c, Calotropis procera.

**1979, May 17** **Litho.** ***Perf. 12***
**C293** A271 7c multicolored 1.00 .30
**C294** A271 10c multicolored 1.50 .35
**C295** A271 13c multicolored 2.50 .65
*Nos. C293-C295 (3)* 5.00 1.30

### Cardiology Type, 1979

10c, Figure of man showing blood circulation.

**1979, June 2** **Litho.** ***Perf. 13½***
**C296** A272 10c multicolored, vert. .75 .40

### Sports Type

7c, Runner and Games' emblem, vert.

**1979, June 20**
**C297** A273 7c multicolored 1.50 .30

### Soccer Type

**1979, Aug. 9** **Litho.** ***Perf. 12***
**C298** A273 10c Tennis, vert. .65 .30

Rowland Hill, Dominican Republic No. 1 — AP93

**1979, Aug. 21** ***Perf. 13½***
**C299** AP93 2p multicolored 4.75 3.25

Sir Rowland Hill (1795-1879), originator of penny postage.

### Electric Light Type

Design: 10c, "100" and light bulb, horiz.

**1979, Aug. 27** ***Perf. 13½***
**C300** A275 10c multicolored .50 .30

### Bird Type

Birds: 7c, Phaenicophilus palmarum. 10c, Calyptophilus frugivorus tertius. 45c, Icterus dominicensis.

**1979, Sept. 12** **Litho.** ***Perf. 12***
**C301** A277 7c multicolored 2.75 .30
**C302** A277 10c multicolored 3.75 .30
**C303** A277 45c multicolored 9.50 1.00
*Nos. C301-C303 (3)* 16.00 1.60

### Lions Type

10c, Melvin Jones, organization founder.

**1979, Nov. 13** **Litho.** ***Perf. 12***
**C304** A278 10c multicolored .60 .30

### Christmas Type

Christmas: 10c, Three Kings riding camels.

**1979, Dec. 18** **Litho.** ***Perf. 12***
**C305** A279 10c multicolored .50 .25

### Holy Week Type

**1980, Mar. 27** **Litho.** ***Perf. 12***
**C306** A280 7c Crucifixion .40 .25
**C307** A280 10c Resurrection .75 .30

Navy Day — AP94

**1980, Apr. 15** **Litho.** ***Perf. 13½***
**C308** AP94 21c multicolored .75 .55

Dominican Philatelic Society, 25th Anniversary AP95

**1980, Apr. 18**
**C309** AP95 10c multicolored .55 .30

### Gold Type

**1980, July 8** **Litho.** ***Perf. 13½***
**C310** A282 10c Drag line mining .75 .35
**C311** A282 33c Mine 1.25 .55

Tourism Secretariat Emblem — AP96

**1980, Aug. 26** **Litho.** ***Perf. 13½***
**C312** AP96 10c shown .45 .30
**C313** AP96 33c Conf. emblem 1.60 1.10

World Tourism Conf., Manila, Sept. 27.

### Iguana Type

**1980, Aug. 30** ***Perf. 12***
**C314** A284 7c American crocodile 2.00 .35
**C315** A284 10c Cuban rat 2.40 .40
**C316** A284 25c Manatee 3.75 .65
**C317** A284 45c Turtle 5.25 .95
*Nos. C314-C317 (4)* 13.40 2.35

### Painting Type

**1980, Sept. 23** **Litho.** ***Perf. 13½x13***
**C318** A285 10c Abstract, by Paul Guidicelli, vert. .60 .30
**C319** A285 17c Farmer, by Yoryi Morel, vert. .90 .55

Visit of Radio Amateurs to Catalina Island AP97

**1980, Oct. 3**
**C320** AP97 7c multicolored .60 .50

Rotary International, 75th Anniversary — AP98

**1980, Oct. 23** **Litho.** ***Perf. 12***
**C321** AP98 10c Globe, emblem, vert. .60 .45
**C322** AP98 33c shown 1.25 .85

Carrier Pigeons, UPU Emblem AP99

**1980, Oct. 31** ***Perf. 13½***
**C323** AP99 33c shown .75 .50
**C324** AP99 45c Pigeons, diff. 1.00 .65
**C325** AP99 50c Pigeon, stamp 1.40 .75
*Nos. C323-C325 (3)* 3.15 1.90

### Souvenir Sheet

#### *Imperf*

**C326** AP99 1.10p UPU emblem 2.00 2.00

UPU cent. No. C326 contains one 48½x31mm stamp.

### Christmas Type

**1980, Dec. 5** **Litho.** ***Perf. 13½***
**C327** A286 10c Holy Family .65 .30

Christmas 1980.

### Salcedo Type

Design: Map and arms of Salcedo.

**1981, Jan. 14** **Litho.** ***Perf. 13½***
**C328** A287 10c multicolored .50 .25

AP100

Industrial Symbols, Seminar Emblem.

**1981, Feb. 18** **Litho.** ***Perf. 13½***
**C329** AP100 10c shown .55 .30
**C330** AP100 33c Seminar emblem .90 .55

CODIA Chemical Engineering Seminar.

### National Games Type

**1981, Mar. 31** **Litho.** ***Perf. 13½***
**C331** A289 10c Baseball 2.50 .35

AP101

Design: Admiral Juan Alejandro Acosta.

**1981, Apr. 15**
**C332** AP101 10c multicolored .40 .25

Battle of Tortuguero anniversary.

13th World Telecommunications Day — AP102

**1981, May 16** **Litho.** ***Perf. 12***
**C333** AP102 10c multicolored .65 .25

Heinrich von Stephan AP103

**1981, July 15** **Litho.** ***Perf. 13½***
**C334** AP103 33c tan & lt red brn 1.10 .75

Birth sesquicentennial of UPU founder.

Worker in Wheelchair AP104

**1981, July 24**
**C335** AP104 7c Stylized people .50 .30
**C336** AP104 33c shown 1.25 .75

Intl. Year of the Disabled.

EXPURIDOM '81 Intl. Stamp Show, Santo Domingo, July 31-Aug. 2 — AP105

**1981, July 31**
**C337** AP105 7c multicolored .75 .35

Bullet Holes in Target, Competition Emblem AP106

**1981, Aug. 12**
**C338** AP106 10c shown .35 .25
**C339** AP106 15c Riflemen .55 .30
**C340** AP106 25c Pistol shooting 1.00 .65
*Nos. C338-C340 (3)* 1.90 1.20

2nd World Sharpshooting Championship.

Exports — AP107

**1981, Oct. 16 Litho. *Perf. 12***

**C341** AP107 7c Jewelry .55 .25
**C342** AP107 10c Handicrafts .65 .30
**C343** AP107 11c Fruit .80 .30
**C344** AP107 17c Vegetables 1.00 .35
*Nos. C341-C344 (4)* 3.00 1.20

World Food Day — AP108

**1981, Oct. 16 Litho. *Perf. 13½***

**C345** AP108 10c Fruits .75 .30
**C346** AP108 50c Vegetables 1.75 1.40

5th Natl. Games AP109

**1981, Dec. 5 Litho. *Perf. 13½***

**C347** AP109 10c Javelin, vert. .45 .35
**C348** AP109 50c Cycling 2.10 1.75

Orchids AP110

7c, Encyclia cochleata. 10c, Broughtonia domingensis. 25c, Encyclia truncata. 75c, Elleanthus capitatus.

**1981, Dec. 14**

**C349** AP110 7c multicolored .85 .25
**C350** AP110 10c multicolored 1.00 .30
**C351** AP110 25c multicolored 1.60 .75
**C352** AP110 75c multicolored 4.00 2.25
*Nos. C349-C352 (4)* 7.45 3.55

**Christmas Type**

**1981, Dec. 23**

**C353** A294 10c Dove, sun .90 .45

Battle of Tortuguero Anniv. AP111

**1982, Apr. 15 Litho. *Perf. 13½***

**C354** AP111 10c Naval Academy, cadets .60 .30

1982 World Cup Soccer — AP112

Designs: Various soccer players.

**1982, Apr. 19**

**C355** AP112 10c multicolored .60 .35
**C356** AP112 21c multicolored .75 .45
**C357** AP112 33c multicolored 1.40 .90
*Nos. C355-C357 (3)* 2.75 1.70

American Air Forces Cooperation System — AP113

**1982, Apr. 12 *Perf. 12***

**C358** AP113 10c multicolored .70 .30

Scouting Year AP114

10c, Baden-Powell, vert. 15c, Globe. 25c, Baden-Powell, scout, vert.

**1982, Apr. 30 Litho. *Perf. 13½***

**C359** AP114 10c multi .45 .25
**C360** AP114 15c multi .65 .30
**C361** AP114 25c multi .95 .45
*Nos. C359-C361 (3)* 2.05 1.00

Dancers — AP115

7c, Emblem. 10c, Cathedral, Casa del Tostado, Santo Domingo.

**1982, June 1 Litho. *Perf. 13½***

**C362** AP115 7c multi .30 .25
**C363** AP115 10c multi .35 .25
**C364** AP115 33c shown 1.75 .85
*Nos. C362-C364 (3)* 2.40 1.35

Tourist Org. of the Americas, 25th Congress (COTAL '82), Santo Domingo.

Espamer '82 Emblem — AP116

Espamer '82 Intl. Stamp Exhibition, San Juan, Oct. 12-17: Symbolic stamps.

**1982, July 5**

**C365** AP116 7c multi .30 .25
**C366** AP116 13c multi, horiz. .50 .30
**C367** AP116 50c multi 2.10 1.60
*Nos. C365-C367 (3)* 2.90 2.15

**Sports Type**

**1982, Aug. 13 *Perf. 12, Imperf.***

**C368** A300 10c Basketball 1.00 .25
**C369** A300 13c Boxing 1.50 .30
**C370** A300 25c Gymnast 2.00 .45
*Nos. C368-C370 (3)* 4.50 1.00

Harbor, by Alejandro Bonilla — AP117

Paintings: 10c, Portrait of a Woman, by Leopoldo Navarro. 45c, Amelia Francasci, by Luis Desangles. 2p, Portrait, by Abelardo Rodriguez Urdaneta. 10c, 45c, 2p vert.

**1982, Aug. 20 *Perf. 13, Imperf.***

**C371** AP117 7c multicolored .30 .25
**C372** AP117 10c multicolored .45 .30
**C373** AP117 45c multicolored 2.10 1.40
**C374** AP117 2p multicolored 9.00 6.00
*Nos. C371-C374 (4)* 11.85 7.95

**San Pedro de Macoris Type**

**1982, Aug. 26**

**Size: 42x29mm**

**C375** A301 7c Lake .75 .30

35th Anniv. of Central Bank AP118

**1982, Oct. 22 Litho. *Perf. 13½x13***

**C376** AP118 10c multicolored .60 .35

490th Anniv. of Discovery of America AP119

**1982, Oct. 7 Litho. *Perf. 13½***

**C377** AP119 7c Map 1.25 .95
**C378** AP119 10c Santa Maria, vert. 1.60 1.10
**C379** AP119 21c Columbus, vert. 2.10 1.10
*Nos. C377-C379 (3)* 4.95 3.15

**Christmas Type**

**1982, Dec. 8**

**C380** A303 10c multicolored .55 .35

French Alliance Centenary AP120

**1983, Mar. 31 LIitho. *Perf. 13½***

**C381** AP120 33c multicolored .85 .55

Battle of Tortuguero Anniv. AP121

**1983, Apr. 15 Litho. *Perf. 13½***

**C382** AP121 15c Frigate Mella-451 .95 .35

World Communications Year — AP122

**1983, May 6 Litho. *Perf. 13½***

**C383** AP122 10c dk blue & blue .60 .30

AP123

**1983, July 5 Litho. *Perf. 13½***

**C384** AP123 9c multicolored .60 .35

Simon Bolivar (1783-1830).

AP124

7c, Gymnast, basketball. 10c, Highjump, boxing. 15c, Baseball, weight lifting, bicycling.

**1983, Aug. 22 Litho. *Perf. 12***

**C385** AP124 7c multi .70 .25
**C386** AP124 10c multi .80 .25
**C387** AP124 15c multi 1.00 .30
*Nos. C385-C387 (3)* 2.50 .80

9th Pan American Games, Caracas, Aug. 13-28.

491st Anniv. of Discovery of America AP125

10c, Columbus' ships, map. 21c, Santa Maria (trophy). 33c, Yacht Sotavento, vert. 50c, Ship models.

**1983, Oct. 11 Litho. *Perf. 13½***

**C388** AP125 10c multi 1.25 .45
**C389** AP125 21c multi 1.90 .75
**C390** AP125 33c multi 2.10 .85
*Nos. C388-C390 (3)* 5.25 2.05

**Size: 103x103mm**

***Imperf***

**C391** AP125 50c multi 15.00 15.00

10th Anniv. of Latin American Civil Aviation Commission AP126

**1983, Dec. 7**

**C392** AP126 10c dark blue .60 .35

Funeral Procession, by Juan Bautista Gomez — AP127

Designs: 15c, Meeting of Maximo Gomez and Jose Marti in Guayubin, by Enrique Garcia Godoy. 21c, St. Francis, by Angel Perdomo, vert. 33c, Portrait of a Girl, by Adriana Billini, vert.

**1983, Dec. 26 *Perf. 13½***

**C393** AP127 10c multicolored .40 .25
**C394** AP127 15c multicolored .40 .25
**C395** AP127 21c multicolored .50 .25
**C396** AP127 33c multicolored .75 .25
*Nos. C393-C396 (4)* 2.05 1.00

Christmas 1983 — AP128

**1983, Dec. 13 Litho. *Perf. 13½***
C397 AP128 10c Bells, ornaments .60 .25

## AIR POST SEMI-POSTAL STAMPS

**Catalogue values for unused stamps in this section are for Never Hinged items.**

### Nos. C97-C99 Surcharged in Red like Nos. B1-B5

**Engraved and Lithographed**

**1957, Feb. 8 Unwmk. *Perf. 11½***

**Flags in National Colors**

CB1 A117 11c + 2c ultra & red org .40 .40
CB2 A117 16c + 2c car & lt grn .70 .70
CB3 A117 17c + 2c blk, vio & red .70 .70
*Nos. CB1-CB3 (3)* 1.80 1.80

The surtax was to aid Hungarian refugees.
A similar 25c surcharge was applied to the souvenir sheets described in the footnote following No. C99. Value, 2 sheets, perf. and imperf., $17.50.

### Nos. C100-C102 Surcharged in Red Orange like Nos. B6-B10

**1957, Sept. 9 Photo. *Perf. 13½***

**Flags in National Colors**

CB4 A118 11c + 2c yel grn & dk bl .70 .50
CB5 A118 16c + 2c lilac & dk bl .85 .70
CB6 A118 17c + 2c brn & bl grn 1.00 .75
*Nos. CB4-CB6 (3)* 2.55 1.95

See note after No. B10.
A similar 5c surcharge was applied to the miniature sheets described in the footnote following No. 483. Value, 4 sheets, perf. & imperf., medal and flag, $40.

### Types of Olympic Air Post Stamps, 1957, Surcharged in Carmine like Nos. B11-B20

**1958, May 26 Engr. & Litho.**

**Flags in National Colors**

**Pink Paper**

CB7 A119(a) 11c + 2c ultra .40 .40
CB8 A119(b) 11c + 2c ultra .40 .40
CB9 A120(a) 16c + 2c rose car .55 .55
CB10 A120(b) 16c + 2c rose car .55 .55
CB11 A119(a) 17c + 2c claret .65 .65
CB12 A119(b) 17c + 2c claret .65 .65
*Nos. CB7-CB12 (6)* 3.20 3.20

A similar 5c surcharge, plus marginal UN emblem and "UNRWA," was applied to the miniature sheets described in the footnote following No. C105. Value, 4 sheets, perf. and imperf., $20.

### Nos. C106-C108 Surcharged like Nos. B21-B25

**1959, Apr. 13 Photo. *Perf. 13½***

**Flags in National Colors**

CB13 A125 11c + 2c blue, ol & brn .80 .80
CB14 A125 16c + 2c lt grn, org & dk bl 1.10 1.10
CB15 A125 17c + 2c ver bl & yel 1.60 1.60
*Nos. CB13-CB15 (3)* 3.50 3.50

A similar 5c surcharge was applied to the miniature sheets described in the footnote following No. C108. Value, 2 sheets, perf. and imperf., $25.

### Type of Regular Issue 1957 Surcharged in Red like Nos. B26-B30

**Engraved and Lithographed**

**1959, Sept. 10 *Imperf.***

**Flags in National Colors**

CB16 A117 11c + 2c ultra & red org .80 .80
CB17 A117 16c + 2c carmine & lt grn .90 .90
CB18 A117 17c + 2c black, vio & red .90 .90
*Nos. CB16-CB18 (3)* 2.60 2.60

### Nos. C113-C114 Surcharged in Red like Nos. B31-B33

**1960, Apr. 7 Litho. *Perf. 12½***
CB19 AP43 10c + 5c plum, gray & grn .35 .35
CB20 AP43 13c + 5c gray & green .55 .55

World Refugee Year.
For souvenir sheets see note after No. B33.

### Nos. C115-C117 Surcharged

***Perf. 13½***

**1962, Jan. 8 Unwmk. Photo.**

**Flags in National Colors**

CB21 A136 11c + 2c blue, gray & brn .35 .35
CB22 A136 16c + 2c red, brn & ol .50 .50
CB23 A136 17c + 2c blk, bl & ocher .50 .50
*Nos. CB21-CB23 (3)* 1.35 1.35

See note after No. B38.
A similar 5c surcharge was applied to the miniature sheets described in the footnote following No. C117. Value, 2 sheets, perf. and imperf., $9.

### Anti-Malaria Type of 1962

**1962, Apr. 29 Litho. *Perf. 12***
CB24 A141 13c + 2c pink & red .50 .35
CB25 A141 33c + 2c org & dp org 1.10 .75

Souvenir sheets exist, perf. and imperf. containing one each of Nos. B39-B40, CB24-CB25 and a 25c+2c pale grn and yel grn. Value, 2 sheets, perf. and imperf., $7.50.

### Nos. C132-C133 Surcharged like Nos. B44-B46

**1964, Mar. 8**
CB26 AP46 10c + 2c brt violet .35 .35
CB27 AP46 13c + 2c yellow .40 .40

### Nos. C146-C148 Surcharged like Nos. B47-B51

**1966, Dec. 9 Litho. *Perf. 12½***

**Size: 35x24mm**

CB28 A164 10c + 5c multi *3.00 1.00*
CB29 A164 50c + 10c multi *4.50 3.00*
CB30 A164 75c + 10c multi *6.00 3.75*
*Nos. CB28-CB30 (3)* *13.50 7.75*

## AIR POST OFFICIAL STAMPS

Nos. O13-O14 Overprinted in Blue

**Unwmk.**

**1930, Dec. 3 Typo. *Perf. 12***
CO1 O3 10c light blue 17.50 *17.50*
a. Pair, one without ovpt. *1,100.*
CO2 O3 20c orange 17.50 *17.50*

## SPECIAL DELIVERY STAMPS

Biplane SD1

***Perf. 11½***

**1920, Apr. Unwmk. Litho.**
E1 SD1 10c deep ultra 6.75 1.40
a. Imperf., pair

Special Delivery Messenger — SD2

**1925**
E2 SD2 10c dark blue 21.00 5.75

SD3

**1927**
E3 SD3 10c red brown 6.75 1.40
a. "E EXPRESO" at top 55.00 55.00

### Type of 1927

**1941 Redrawn**
E4 SD3 10c yellow green 3.00 3.25
E5 SD3 10c dark blue green 2.75 .60

The redrawn design differs slightly from SD3.
Issue dates: No. E4, Mar. 27; No. E5, Aug. 7.

Emblem of Communications — SD4

**1945, Sept. 1 *Perf. 12***
E6 SD4 10c rose car, car & dk bl 1.25 .25

**Catalogue values for unused stamps in this section, from this point to the end of the section, are for Never Hinged items.**

SD5

**1950 Litho. Unwmk.**
E7 SD5 10c multicolored .70 .25

Exists imperf.

Modern Communications System — SD6

**1956, Aug. 18 *Perf. 11½***
E8 SD6 25c green 1.25 .30

Carrier Pigeon SD7

**1967 Litho. *Perf. 11½***
E9 SD7 25c light blue .80 .30

Carrier Pigeon, Globe — SD8

**1978, Aug. 2 Litho. *Perf. 13½***
E10 SD8 25c multicolored 1.10 .45

Messenger, Plane — SD9

**1979, Nov. 30 *Perf. 13½***
E11 SD9 25c multicolored .75 .45

Motorcycling — SD10

**1989, May Litho. *Perf. 13½***
E12 SD10 1p multicolored 2.50 1.10

Postman SD11

**1999 Litho. *Perf. 13½x13¼***
E13 SD11 8p multicolored 3.25 2.75

## INSURED LETTER STAMPS

Merino Issue of 1933 Surcharged in Red or Black

**1935, Feb. 1 Unwmk. *Perf. 14***

G1 A35 8c on 7c ultra .60 .25
a. Inverted surcharge 18.00
G2 A35 15c on 10c org yel .65 .25
a. Inverted surcharge 18.00
G3 A35 30c on 8c dk green 2.25 .90
G4 A35 45c on 20c car rose (Bk) 3.25 1.10
G5 A36 70c on 50c lemon 7.75 1.75
*Nos. G1-G5 (5)* 14.50 4.25

Merino Issue of 1933 Surcharged in Red

**1940**

G6 A35 8c on ½c lt vio 2.75 2.75
G7 A35 8c on 7c ultra 3.25 3.25

Coat of Arms — IL1

**1940-45 Litho. *Perf. 11½***
**Arms in Black**

G8 IL1 8c brown red .85 .25
a. 8c dk red, no shading on inner frame 1.10 .25
G9 IL1 15c dp orange ('45) 1.75 .25
G10 IL1 30c dk green ('41) 2.00 .25
a. 30c yellow green 2.00 .25
G11 IL1 45c ultra ('44) 2.25 .30
G12 IL1 70c olive brn ('44) 2.10 .30
*Nos. G8-G12 (5)* 8.95 1.35

See Nos. G13-G16, G24-G27.

**Catalogue values for unused stamps in this section, from this point to the end of the section, are for Never Hinged items.**

**Redrawn Type of 1940-45**

**1952-53 Arms in Black**

G13 IL1 8c car lake ('53) 4.00 .50
G14 IL1 15c red orange ('53) 2.50 .75
G15 IL1 70c dp brown car 9.50 1.75
*Nos. G13-G15 (3)* 16.00 3.00

Larger and bolder numerals on 8c and 15c. Smaller and bolder "70." There are many other minor differences in the design.

**Type of 1940-45**

**1954 Arms in Black, 15x16mm**

G16 IL1 10c carmine .85 .25

Coat of Arms — IL2

**1955-69 Unwmk. Litho. *Perf. 11½***
**Arms in Black, 13½x11½mm**

G17 IL2 10c carmine rose .40 .25
G18 IL2 15c red orange ('56) 5.25 2.25
G19 IL2 20c red orange ('58) 1.25 .30
a. 20c orange ('69) 1.25 .30
b. 20c orange, retouched ('69) 3.50 1.25
G20 IL2 30c dark green ('55) 2.00 .40
G21 IL2 40c dark green ('58) 2.10 .90
a. 40c lt yellow grn ('62) 2.10 .45
G22 IL2 45c ultra ('56) 4.00 3.75
G23 IL2 70c dp brn car ('56) 6.75 2.25
*Nos. G17-G23 (7)* 21.75 10.10

On No. G19b the horizontal shading lines of shield are omitted.
See Nos. G28-G37.

**Type of 1940-45**
**Second Redrawing**

**1963 *Perf. 12½***
**Arms in Black, 17x16mm**

G24 IL1 10c red orange 1.25 .30
G25 IL1 20c orange 1.90 1.25

**Third Redrawing**

**1966 Litho. *Perf. 12½***
**Arms in Black, 14x14mm**

G26 IL1 10c violet .40 .25
G27 IL1 40c orange 1.50 1.00

**Type of 1955-62**

**1968 Litho. *Perf. 11½***
**Arms in Black, 13½x11½mm**

G28 IL2 20c red 2.50 1.00
G29 IL2 60c yellow 2.10 2.10

**1973-76 Litho. *Perf. 12½***
**Arms in Black, 11x11mm**

G30 IL2 10c car rose ('76) .50 .35
G31 IL2 20c yellow 1.40 .90
G32 IL2 20c orange ('76) 1.75 .50
G33 IL2 40c yel grn 1.60 1.00
a. 40c green ('76) 3.00 3.00
G34 IL2 70c blue 1.90 1.90
*Nos. G30-G34 (5)* 7.15 4.65

**1973 *Perf. 11½***
**Arms in Black, 13½x11½mm**

G35 IL2 10c dark violet .90 .30

**1978, Aug. 9 *Perf. 10½***
**Arms in Black, 11x11mm**

G36 IL2 10c rose magenta .45 .25
G37 IL2 40c bright green 1.75 1.50

IL3

**1982-83 Litho. *Perf. 10½***
**Arms in Black**

G38 IL3 10c deep magenta .30 .25
G39 IL3 20c deep orange .45 .30
G40 IL3 40c bluish green 1.00 .50
*Nos. G38-G40 (3)* 1.75 1.05

IL4

**1986 Litho. *Perf. 10½***
**Arms in Black**

G41 IL4 20c brt rose lilac .35 .25
G42 IL4 60c orange 1.20 .85
G43 IL4 1p light blue 2.10 1.40
G44 IL4 1.25p pink 2.75 1.75
G45 IL4 1.50p vermilion 3.25 2.50
G46 IL4 3p light green 6.25 4.25
G47 IL4 3.50p olive bister 7.00 4.50
G48 IL4 4p yellow 8.75 5.50
G49 IL4 4.50p lt blue grn 9.75 6.25
G50 IL4 5p brown olive 10.50 7.00
G51 IL4 6p gray 12.50 8.50
G52 IL4 6.50p lt ultra 14.50 9.50
*Nos. G41-G52 (12)* 78.90 52.25

Issue dates: Nos. G42-G43, G45, July 16. Nos. G46-G52, Sept. 2. Nos. G41, G44, Nov. 6.

Coat of Arms — IL5

**1989-90 Litho. *Perf. 13½***
**Arms in Black**

G53 IL5 20c brt lilac rose .35 .25
G54 IL5 60c orange ('90) 1.00 .45
G55 IL5 1p sky blue 1.60 .75
G56 IL5 1.25p lt salmon pink 1.90 .90
G57 IL5 1.50p dark red 2.40 1.40
*Nos. G53-G57 (5)* 7.25 3.75

"RD$" in lower left square on Nos. G55-G57.

IL6

**1994, Oct. Litho. *Perf. 13½***
**Arms in Black**

G58 IL6 50c lilac rose .35 .25
G59 IL6 1p sky blue .50 .25
G60 IL6 1.50p red .65 .30
G61 IL6 2p pink .85 .50
G62 IL6 3p violet blue 1.40 .60
G63 IL6 5p yellow 1.90 .90
G64 IL6 6p apple green 2.50 1.25
G65 IL6 8p green 3.00 1.50
G66 IL6 10p silver gray 4.25 2.00
*Nos. G58-G66 (9)* 15.40 7.55

## POSTAGE DUE STAMPS

D1

**1901 Unwmk. Typo. *Perf. 14***

J1 D1 2c olive gray .90 .25
J2 D1 4c olive gray 1.10 .25
J3 D1 5c olive gray 1.90 .30
J4 D1 10c olive gray 3.25 .95
*Nos. J1-J4 (4)* 7.15 1.75

For surcharges and overprint see Nos. 162-165, 169-171.

**1909 Wmk. 116**

J5 D1 2c olive gray 1.50 .50
J6 D1 4c olive gray 1.50 .50
J7 D1 6c olive gray 2.00 .75
J8 D1 10c olive gray 4.00 2.50
*Nos. J5-J8 (4)* 9.00 4.25

**1913**

J9 D1 2c olive green .60 .30
J10 D1 4c olive green .70 .40
J11 D1 6c olive green 1.10 .50
J12 D1 10c olive green 1.25 .60
*Nos. J9-J12 (4)* 3.65 1.80

**1922 Unwmk. Litho. *Perf. 11½***

J13 D1 1c olive green .70 .70

**Catalogue values for unused stamps in this section, from this point to the end of the section, are for Never Hinged items.**

D2

**1942**

J14 D2 1c dk red & pale pink .40 .25
J15 D2 2c dk bl & pale bl .40 .25
J16 D2 4c dk grn & pale grn .40 .25
J17 D2 6c green & buff .50 .25
J18 D2 8c yel org & pale yel .50 .30
J19 D2 10c mag & pale pink .75 .50
*Nos. J14-J19 (6)* 2.95 1.80

**1955 Size: 20½x25mm**

J20 D2 2c dark blue 1.40 1.00

D3

**1959 Litho. *Perf. 11½***
**Size: 21x25½mm**

J21 D3 1c dark car rose 1.25 1.25
J22 D3 2c dark blue 1.25 1.25
J23 D3 4c green 3.00 3.00
*Nos. J21-J23 (3)* 5.50 5.50

## OFFICIAL STAMPS

Bastion of February 27
O1

**Unwmk.**

**1902, Feb. 25 Litho. *Perf. 12***

O1 O1 2c scarlet & blk .65 .30
O2 O1 5c dk blue & blk .85 .25
O3 O1 10c yel grn & blk 1.00 .55
O4 O1 20c yellow & blk 1.25 .55
a. Imperf., pair 11.00
*Nos. O1-O4 (4)* 3.75 1.65

For overprints and surcharge see Nos. 157-161.

Bastion of Feb. 27 — O2

***Perf. 13½x13, 13½x14***

**1909-12 Wmk. 116 Typo.**

O5 O2 1c blue grn & blk .40 .25
O6 O2 2c scarlet & blk .50 .30
O7 O2 5c dk blue & blk 1.00 .40
O8 O2 10c yel grn & blk ('12) 1.60 .95
O9 O2 20c orange & blk ('12) 2.75 2.25
*Nos. O5-O9 (5)* 6.25 4.15

The 2c, 5c are found in both perforations; 1c, 20c perf. 13½x13; 10c perf. 13½x14.
For overprints and surcharge see Nos. 177, 194-199.

Columbus Lighthouse — O3

**1928 Unwmk. *Perf. 12***

O10 O3 1c green .30 .30
O11 O3 2c red .30 .30
O12 O3 5c ultramarine .35 .35
O13 O3 10c light blue .40 .40
O14 O3 20c orange .60 .60
*Nos. O10-O14 (5)* 1.95 1.95

For overprints see Nos. CO1-CO2.

Proposed Columbus Lighthouse
O4

**1937 Litho. *Perf. 11½***

O15 O4 3c dark purple 1.60 .50
O16 O4 7c indigo & blue 1.90 .60
O17 O4 10c orange yellow 2.25 .85
*Nos. O15-O17 (3)* 5.75 1.95

Proposed Columbus Lighthouse
O5

**1939-41**

O18 O5 1c dp grn & lt grn .90 .40
O19 O5 2c crim & pale pink .90 .40
O20 O5 3c purple & lt vio .90 .40
O21 O5 5c dk bl & lt bl ('40) 1.20 .60
O21A O5 5c lt blue ('41) 2.40 1.25
O22 O5 7c brt bl & lt bl ('41) 2.10 .40
O23 O5 10c yel org & pale org ('41) 2.10 .60
O24 O5 20c brn org & buff ('41) 7.00 1.00

**O25** O5 50c brt red lil & pale lil ('41) 8.50 3.00
*Nos. O18-O25 (9)* 26.00 8.05

**Catalogue values for unused stamps in this section, from this point to the end of the section, are for Never Hinged items.**

### Type of 1939

**1950** **Redrawn**
**O26** O5 50c dp car & rose 10.00 2.00

The numerals "50" measure 3mm, and are close to left and right frames; numerals measure 4mm on No. O25. There are other minor differences.

### Denominations in "Centavos Oro"

**1950**
**O27** O5 5c light blue 1.00 .40
**O28** O5 10c yel & pale yel 1.25 .60
**O29** O5 20c dl org brn & buff 2.50 2.25
*Nos. O27-O29 (3)* 4.75 3.25

Letters of top inscription are 1½mm high.

### Second Redrawing

Type of 1939-41 Denominations in "Centavos Oro"

**1956** **Unwmk.** ***Perf. 11½***
**O30** O5 7c blue & lt blue 1.00 1.00
**O31** O5 20c yellow brn & buff 2.50 2.50
**O32** O5 50c red lil & brt pink 6.00 6.00
*Nos. O30-O32 (3)* 9.50 9.50

The letters of top inscription are 2mm high, the trees at base of monument have been redrawn, etc. On No. O32 the numerals are similar to No. O26.

---

## POSTAL TAX STAMPS

Santo Domingo after Hurricane PT1

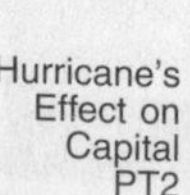

Hurricane's Effect on Capital PT2

**1930, Dec.** **Unwmk.** **Litho.** ***Perf. 12***
**RA1** PT1 1c green & rose .25 .25
**RA2** PT1 2c red rose .25 .25
**RA3** PT2 5c ultra & rose .30 .25
**RA4** PT2 10c yellow & rose .40 .30

***Imperf***

**RA5** PT1 1c green & rose .40 .30
**RA6** PT1 2c red & rose .50 .30
**RA7** PT2 5c ultra & rose .60 .50
**RA8** PT2 10c yellow & rose .90 .75
*Nos. RA1-RA8 (8)* 3.60 2.90

For surcharges see Nos. RAC1-RAC7.

### Tête bêche Pairs

| | | | | | |
|---|---|---|---|---|---|
| *RA1a* | PT1 | 1c | green & rose | 1.75 | 1.75 |
| *RA2a* | PT1 | 2c | red rose | 1.75 | 1.50 |
| *RA3a* | PT1 | 5c | ultra & rose | 1.75 | 2.10 |
| *RA4a* | PT1 | 10c | yellow & rose | 2.10 | 2.10 |
| *RA5a* | PT1 | 1c | green & rose | 1.75 | 1.75 |
| *RA6a* | PT1 | 2c | red & rose | 1.75 | 1.75 |
| *RA7a* | PT1 | 5c | ultra & rose | 2.10 | 2.10 |
| *RA8a* | PT1 | 10c | yellow & rose | 2.10 | 2.10 |
| | *Nos. RA1a-RA8a (8)* | | | 15.05 | 15.15 |

Dr. Martos Sanatorium PT3

**1944, Apr. 1** **Litho.** ***Perf. 11½***
**RA9** PT3 1c dp bl, sl bl & red .40 .30

Nurse and Child — PT4

**1947, Apr. 1** **Unwmk.**
**RA10** PT4 1c dp bl, pale bl & car .50 .30

Sanatorium of the Holy Help — PT5

**1949, Apr. 1**
**RA11** PT5 1c dp bl, pale bl & car .35 .25

Youth Holding Banner — PT6

**1950, Apr. 1** ***Perf. 11½***
**RA12** PT6 1c dp bl, pale bl & car .30 .25

"Suffer Little Children to Come Unto Me" — PT7

**1950, Dec. 1** ***Perf. 12***
**Size: 22½x32mm**
**RA13** PT7 1c lt bl & pale bl 1.25 .30
*b.* Perf. 12½ ('52) 4.50 .25

Vertical line centering side borders merges into dots toward the bottom. See Nos. RA13A, RA17, RA19, RA26, RA32, RA35.
The tax was for child welfare.

**1951, Dec. 1** **Redrawn**
**RA13A** PT7 1c lt blue & pale blue 6.25 .30

In the redrawn stamp, the standing child, a blonde in No. RA13, is changed to a brunette; more foliage has been added above child's head and to branches showing in upper right corner. Vertical dashes in side borders.

Tuberculosis Sanatorium, Santiago — PT8

**1952, Apr. 1** **Litho.** ***Perf. 11½***
**RA14** PT8 1c lt blue & car .30 .25

Sword, Serpent and Crab — PT9

**1953, Feb. 1** **Unwmk.** ***Perf. 12.***
**RA15** PT9 1c carmine .50 .30

The tax was for the Dominican League Against Cancer. See Nos. RA18, RA21, RA43, RA46, RA51, RA56, RA61, RA67, RA72, RA76, RA82, RA88, RA93, RA96.

Tuberculosis Dispensary for Children — PT10

**1953, Apr. 1** **Litho.** ***Perf. 12½***
**RA16** PT10 1c dp bl, pale bl & red .40 .30

See No. RA22.

### Jesus Type of 1950

Second Redrawing

**1953, Dec. 1** ***Perf. 11½***
**Size: 22x31mm**
**RA17** PT7 1c blue .35 .25

Solid shading in sky reduced to a few scattered dots. Girl's left arm indicated. Rough white dots in side borders.

### Cancer Type of 1952

**1954, Oct. 1** **Redrawn** ***Perf. 12½***
**RA18** PT9 1c rose carmine .30 .25
*a.* 1c red orange ('58) .40 .25
*b.* 1c carmine ('70) 1.25 .25

Upper right serif of numeral "1" eliminated; diagonal line added through "C" and period removed; sword extended, placing top on a line with top of "1." Dots of background screen arranged diagonally. Many other differences.
The tax was for the Dominican League Against Cancer. No. RA18a exists imperf.
On No. RA18b background screen eliminates white outline of crab.

### Jesus Type of 1950

**1954, Dec. 1** **Third Redrawing**
**Size: 23x32¾mm**
**RA19** PT7 1c bright blue .40 .30
*a.* 1c pale blue ('59) .40 .30

Center completely screened. Tiny white horizontal rectangles in side borders.

**Catalogue values for unused stamps in this section, from this point to the end of the section, are for Never Hinged items.**

Lorraine Cross as Bell Clapper — PT11

**1955, Apr. 1** **Litho.** ***Perf. 11½x12***
**RA20** PT11 1c black, yel & red .50 .30

### Cancer Type of 1952

Second Redrawing

**1956, Oct. 1** ***Perf. 12½***
**RA21** PT9 1c carmine .70 .30
*a.* 1c red orange ('64) 1.25 .50

Similar to No. RA18, but dots of background screen arranged in vertical and horizontal rows. Outlines of central device, lettering and frame clearly delineated. "C" of cent-sign smaller. Upper claw in solid color.

### TB Dispensary Type of 1953

Redrawn

**1954, Apr. 1**
**RA22** PT10 1c blue & red .90 .25
*a.* Red (cross) omitted 55.00

No. RA22 has third color omitted; clouds added; bolder letters and numerals.

Angelita Trujillo — PT12

**1955, Dec. 1** **Unwmk.** ***Perf. 12½***
**RA23** PT12 1c violet .95 .30

The tax was for child welfare.

Lorraine Cross — PT13

**1956, Apr. 1** **Litho.** ***Perf. 11½***
**RA24** PT13 1c blk, grn, lem & red .50 .30

The tax was for the Anti-Tuberculosis League. Inscribed: B.C.G. (Bacillus Calmette-Guerin).

PT14

**1957, Apr. 1**
**RA25** PT14 1c red, blk, yel, grn & bl .50 .30

### Jesus Type of 1950

Fourth Redrawing

**1956, Dec. 1** **Unwmk.** ***Perf. 12***
**Size: 21¾x31¼mm**
**RA26** PT7 1c blue .40 .25

Thin white lines around numeral boxes. Girl's bouquet touches Jesus' sleeve. Tiny white squares or rectangles in side borders. Foliage at either side of "Era de Trujillo" panel.

PT15

**1958, Apr. 1** **Litho.** ***Perf. 12½***
**RA27** PT15 1c brown car & red .45 .25

**1959, Apr. 1** **Inscribed "1959"**
**RA28** PT15 1c brown car & red .45 .25

PT16

**1960, Apr. 1 Litho. *Perf. 12***
**RA29** PT16 1c bl, pale yel & red .55 .30

PT17

**1961, Apr. 1 Unwmk. *Perf. 11½***
**RA30** PT17 1c blue & red .40 .25

Nos. RA29-RA30: tax was for the Anti-Tuberculosis League.
See No. RA33.

Maria de los Angeles M. de Trujillo and Housing Project
PT18

**1961, Aug. 1 Litho. *Perf. 12***
**RA31** PT18 1c carmine rose .40 .25

The tax was for aid to the needy.
Nos. RA31-RA33 exist imperf.

**Jesus Type of 1950**
Fifth Redrawing

**1961, Dec. 1 Unwmk. *Perf. 12½***
**RA32** PT7 1c blue .40 .25

No. RA32 is similar to No. RA19, but "Era de Trujillo" has been replaced by a solid color panel.

**Type of 1961 Dated "1962"**

**1962, Apr. 2 *Perf. 12½***
**RA33** PT17 1c blue & red .95 .30

Tax for the Anti-Tuberculosis League.

Man's Chest — PT19

**1963, Apr. 1 *Perf. 12x11½***
**RA34** PT19 1c ultra & red .50 .30

**Jesus Type of 1950**
Sixth Redrawing

**1963, Dec. 1 *Perf. 11½***
**Size: 21¾x32mm**
**RA35** PT7 1c blue .40 .25
*a.* 1c deep blue ('64) .40 .25

No. RA35 is similar to No. RA26, but "Era de Trujillo" panel has been omitted.

Hibiscus — PT20

**1966, Apr. 1 Litho. *Perf. 11½***
**RA36** PT20 1c emerald & car .40 .25

Tax for the Anti-Tuberculosis League.

Domingoa Nodosa — PT21

**1967, Apr. 1 Litho. *Perf. 12½***
**RA37** PT21 1c lilac & red 1.00 .30

Tax for the Anti-Tuberculosis League.

Civil Defense Emblem — PT22

**1967, July 1 Litho. *Rouletted 13***
**RA38** PT22 1c multicolored .40 .25

Tax for the Civil Defense Organization.

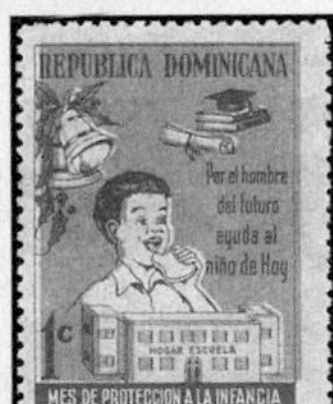

Boy, School and Yule Bells — PT23

**1967, Dec. 1 Litho. *Perf. 12½***
**RA39** PT23 1c rose red & pink .50 .30

**1968 *Perf. 11***
**RA40** PT23 1c vermilion .45 .25

No. RA40 has screened background; No. RA39, smooth background.
The tax was for child welfare.
See Nos. RA49A, RA52, RA57, RA62, RA68, RA73, RA77, RA81.

Hand Holding Invalid — PT24

**1968, Mar. 19 Litho. *Perf. 12½***
**RA41** PT24 1c green & yellow .40 .25
*a.* 1c olive green & deep yellow, perf. 11½x12 ('69) .40 .25

The tax was for the rehabilitation of the handicapped. See Nos. RA47, RA50, RA54.

Dogbane — PT25

**1968, Apr. 25 Litho. *Perf. 12½***
**RA42** PT25 1c emerald, yel & red .40 .25

The tax was for the Anti-Tuberculosis League. See Nos. RA45, RA49.

**Redrawn Cancer Type of 1955**

**1968, Oct. 1 Litho. *Perf. 12***
**RA43** PT9 1c emerald .40 .25

The tax was for the Dominican League against Cancer.

Schoolyard, Torch — PT26

**1969, Feb. 1 Litho. *Perf. 12½***
**RA44** PT26 1c light blue .40 .25

Issued for Education Year 1969.

**Flower Type of 1968**

Design: No. RA45, Violets.

**1969, Apr. 25 Litho. *Perf. 12½***
**RA45** PT25 1c emerald, lil & red .70 .30

Tax for the Anti-Tuberculosis League.

**Redrawn Cancer Type of 1955**

**1969, Oct. 1 Litho. *Perf. 11***
**RA46** PT9 1c brt rose lilac .40 .25

Tax for Dominican League against Cancer.

**Invalid Type of 1968**

**1970, Mar. 2 *Perf. 12½***
**RA47** PT24 1c blue .40 .25

The tax was for the rehabilitation of the handicapped.

Book, Sun and Education Year Emblem — PT27

**1970, Feb. 6 *Perf. 11***
**RA48** PT27 1c bright pink .40 .25

International Education Year.

**Flower Type of 1968**

Design: 1c, Elleanthus capitatus; cross in upper left corner, denomination in lower right.

**1970, Apr. 30 *Perf. 11***
**RA49** PT25 1c emerald, red & yel 1.10 .30

Tax for Anti-Tuberculosis League.

**Boy Type of 1967**

**1970, Dec. 1 *Perf. 12½***
**RA49A** PT23 1c orange .45 .30

Communications Emblem — PT28

**1971, Jan. 2 Litho. *Perf. 11***
**Size: 17½x20½mm**
**RA49B** PT28 1c vio bl & red (white frame) .55 .30

Tax was for Postal and Telegraph Communications School.
See Nos. RA53, RA58, RA63, RA69, RA78, RA91.

**Invalid Type of 1968**

**1971, Mar. 1 Litho. *Perf. 11***
**RA50** PT24 1c brt rose lilac .40 .25

Tax for rehabilitation of the handicapped.

**Cancer Type of 1952**
Third Redrawing

**1971, Oct. 1 *Perf. 11½***
**RA51** PT9 1c dp yellow green .40 .25

Background of No. RA51 appears white and design stands out. No. RA43 has greenish background and design appears faint. Numeral "1" on No. RA51 is 3½mm high, on No. RA43 it is 3mm.

**Boy Type of 1967**

**1971, Dec. 1 Litho. *Perf. 11***
**RA52** PT23 1c green .45 .25

**Communications Type of 1971**

**1972, Jan. 3 Litho. *Perf. 12½***
**Size: 19x22mm**
**RA53** PT28 1c dk bl & red (bl frame) .40 .25

Tax was for the Postal and Telegraph Communications School.

**Invalid Type of 1968**

**1972, Mar. 1 Litho. *Perf. 11½***
**RA54** PT24 1c brown .75 .25

Orchid — PT29

**1972, Apr. 2 *Perf. 11***
**RA55** PT29 1c lt grn, red & yel 1.60 .45

Tax was for the Anti-Tuberculosis League.

**Redrawn Cancer Type of 1954-58**

**1972, Oct. 2 *Perf. 12½***
**RA56** PT9 1c orange .45 .25

Tax for Dominican League against Cancer.

**Boy Type of 1967**

**1972, Dec. 1 *Perf. 12***
**RA57** PT23 1c violet .40 .25

Tax was for child welfare.

**Communications Type of 1971**

**1973, Jan. 2 *Perf. 10½***
**Size: 19x22mm**
**RA58** PT28 1c dk bl & red (red frame) .40 .25

Tax was for Postal and Telegraph Communications School.

Invalid — PT30

**1973, Mar. 1 Litho. *Perf. 12½***
**Size: 21x25mm**
**RA59** PT30 1c olive .40 .25

Tax was for the Dominican Rehabilitation Association. See Nos. RA66, RA70, RA74, RA79, RA86.

Hibiscus — PT31

**1973, Apr. 17 Litho. *Perf. 10½***
**RA60** PT31 1c multicolored 1.20 .30

Tax was for Anti-Tuberculosis League. Exists imperf.

**Cancer Type of 1952 Redrawn and "1973" Added**

**1973, Oct. 1 *Perf. 13½***
**RA61** PT9 1c olive green .55 .30

Tax was for Dominican League Against Cancer.

**Boy Type of 1967**

**1973, Dec. 1 Litho. *Perf. 13x13½***
**RA62** PT23 1c blue .70 .25

**Communications Type of 1971**

**1973, Nov. 3** *Perf. 10½*
**Size: 19x22mm**

**RA63** PT28 1c bl & red (lt grn frame) .40 .25

Tax was for Postal and Telegraph Communications School. Exists imperf.

**Invalid Type of 1973**

**1974, Mar. 1 Litho.** *Perf. 10½*
**Size: 22x27½mm**

**RA66** PT30 1c light ultra .55 .30

See note after No. RA59.

**Cancer Type of 1952 Redrawn and "1974" Added**

**1974, Oct. 1** *Perf. 12*

**RA67** PT9 1c orange .55 .30

Tax for Dominican League Against Cancer.

**Boy Type of 1967**

**1974, Dec. 2 Litho.** *Perf. 11½*

**RA68** PT23 1c dk brown & buff .40 .25

**Communications Type of 1971**

**1974, Nov. 13** *Perf. 10½*

**RA69** PT28 1c blue & red (yel frame) .40 .25

**Invalid Type of 1973 Dated "1975"**

**1975, Mar. 1** *Perf. 13½x13*
**Size: 21x32mm**

**RA70** PT30 1c olive brown .55 .30

See note after No. RA59.

Catteeyopsis Rosea — PT32

**1975, Apr. 1** *Perf. 12*

**RA71** PT32 1c blue & multi 1.40 .95

Tax was for Anti-Tuberculosis League.

**Cancer Type of 1952 Redrawn and "1975" Added**

**1975, Oct. 1 Litho.** *Perf. 12*

**RA72** PT9 1c violet blue .55 .30

Tax was for Dominican League Against Cancer. Exists imperf.

**Boy Type of 1967**

**1975, Dec. 1 Litho.** *Perf. 12*

**RA73** PT23 1c red orange .40 .25

Tax was for child welfare.

**Invalid Type of 1973 Dated "1976"**

**1976, Mar. 1 Litho.** *Perf. 12*
**Size: 21x31mm**

**RA74** PT30 1c ultra .55 .30

See note after No. RA59.

Oncidium Colochilum — PT33

**1976, Apr. 6** *Perf. 13x13½*

**RA75** PT33 1c green & multi 1.00 .30

Tax was for Anti-Tuberculosis League. See Nos. RA80, RA84.

**Cancer Type of 1952 Redrawn and "1976" Added**

**1976, Oct. 1 Litho.** *Perf. 13½*

**RA76** PT9 1c green .55 .30

Tax was for Dominican League Against Cancer.

**Boy Type of 1967**

**1976, Dec. 1 Litho.** *Perf. 13½*

**RA77** PT23 1c purple .55 .30

Tax was for child welfare.

**Communications Type of 1971**

**1977, Jan. 7 Litho.** *Perf. 10½*
**Size: 19x22mm**

**RA78** PT28 1c blue & red (lil frame) .40 .25

Tax was for Postal and Telegraph Communications School.

**Invalid Type of 1973 Dated "1977"**

**1977, Mar. 11** *Perf. 12*
**Size: 21x31mm**

**RA79** PT30 1c ultra .55 .30

See note after No. RA59.

**Orchid Type of 1976 Dated "1977"**

Orchid: Oncidium variegatum.

**1977, Apr. 22 Litho.** *Perf. 13½*

**RA80** PT33 1c multicolored 1.25 .30

Tax was for Anti-Tuberculosis League.

**Boy Type of 1967**

**1977, Dec. 27 Litho.** *Perf. 12*

**RA81** PT23 1c emerald .40 .25

Tax was for child welfare.

**Cancer Type of 1952 Redrawn and "1977" Added**

**1978, Oct. 2 Litho.** *Perf. 13½*

**RA82** PT9 1c lilac rose .55 .30

Tax for Dominican League Against Cancer.

Mother, Child, Holly — PT34

**1978, Dec. 1 Litho.** *Perf. 13½*

**RA83** PT34 1c green .40 .25

Tax was for child welfare. See Nos. RA89, RA92, RA97.

**Orchid Type of 1973 Dated "1978"**

Flower: Yellow alder.

**1979, Apr. Litho.** *Perf. 13½*

**RA84** PT33 1c lt blue & multi 1.10 .30

Tax was for Anti-Tuberculosis League.

University Seal — PT35

**1979, Feb. 10 Litho.** *Perf. 13½*

**RA85** PT35 2c ultra & gray .40 .25

450th anniv. of University of Santo Domingo.

**Invalid Type of 1973 Dated "1978"**

**1979, Mar. 1 Litho.** *Perf. 12*

**RA86** PT30 1c emerald .95 .30

See note after No. RA59.

Invalid — PT36

**1980, Mar. 28 Litho.** *Perf. 13½*

**RA87** PT36 1c olive & citron .95 .30

**Cancer Type of 1952 Redrawn and "1980" Added**

**1980, Oct. 1**

**RA88** PT9 1c violet & dk pur .40 .25

**Mother and Child Type of 1978**

**1980, Dec. 1 Litho.** *Perf. 13½*

**RA89** PT34 1c bright blue .40 .25

Turnera Ulmifolia (Marilope) — PT37

**1981, Apr. 27 Litho.** *Perf. 12*

**RA90** PT37 1c multicolored .60 .25

Tax was for Anti-Tuberculosis League. See Nos. RA98-RA99.

**Communications Type of 1971**

**1981, Feb. Litho.** *Perf. 10½*

**RA91** PT28 1c blue & red (lt bl frame) .75 .25

**Mother and Child Type of 1978**

**1982, Dec. 1 Litho.** *Perf. 12x12½*

**RA92** PT34 1c lt bluish green .40 .25

Inscribed 1981.

**Cancer Type of 1952 Redrawn and "1981" Added**

**1982 Litho.** *Perf. 13½*

**RA93** PT9 1c blue & dp blue .95 .30

PT38

**1983, Apr. 29 Litho.** *Perf. 12*

**RA94** PT38 1c multicolored .40 .25

Tax was for Red Cross.

Disabled — PT39

**1984 Litho.** *Perf. 13½*

**RA95** PT39 1c sky blue .60 .25

**Cancer Type of 1952 Redrawn and "1983" Added**

**1983, Oct. 1 Litho.** *Perf. 13½*

**RA96** PT9 1c lt bluish grn & dk grn 1.00 .25

**Mother and Child Type of 1978**

**1983, Dec. 1 Litho.** *Perf. 12*

**RA97** PT34 1c light green 1.00 .25

Inscribed 1983.

**Flower Type of 1981 Dated "1983" or "1984"**

**1983-85 Litho.** *Perf. 12x12½*

**RA98** PT37 1c 1983 2.25 .25
**RA99** PT37 1c 1984 2.25 .25

Issued: #RA98, 4/19/83; #RA99, 4/1/85.

## POSTAL TAX AIR POST STAMPS

Postal Tax Stamps Surcharged in Red or Gold

**1930, Dec. 3 Unwmk.** *Perf. 12*

**RAC1** PT2 5c + 5c blk & rose (R) 27.00 31.00
*a.* Tête bêche pair 125.00
*b.* "Habilitado Para" missing 52.50
**RAC2** PT2 10c + 10c blk & rose (R) 27.00 31.00
*a.* Tête bêche pair 125.00
*b.* "Habilitado Para" missing 52.50
*c.* Gold surcharge 95.00 95.00
*d.* As "c," tête bêche pair 450.00
*e.* As "c" and "b" 250.00

Nos. RAC1-RAC2 were on sale one day.

**RAC4** PT2 5c + 5c ultra & rose (R) 6.75 6.75
*a.* Tête bêche pair 45.00
*b.* Inverted surcharge 42.50
*c.* Tête bêche pair, inverted surcharge 600.00
*d.* Pair, one without surcharge 190.00
*e.* "Habilitado Para" missing 15.00
**RAC5** PT2 10c + 10c yel & rose (G) 5.25 5.25
*a.* Tête bêche pair 42.50
*b.* "Habilitado Para" missing 18.00

***Imperf***

**RAC6** PT2 5c + 5c ultra & rose (R) 6.75 6.75
*a.* Tête bêche pair 52.50
*b.* "Habilitado Para" missing 18.00
**RAC7** PT2 10c + 10c yel & rose (G) 6.75 6.75
*a.* Tête bêche pair 52.50
*b.* "Habilitado Para" missing 18.00
*Nos. RAC1-RAC7 (6)* *79.50* *87.50*

It was obligatory to use Nos. RA1-RA8 and RAC1-RAC7 on all postal matter, in amounts equal to the ordinary postage.

This surtax was for the aid of sufferers from the hurricane of Sept. 3, 1930.

No. 261 Overprinted in Green

**1933, Oct. 11**

**RAC8** A32 2c scarlet .50 .40
*a.* Double overprint 9.00
*b.* Pair, one without overprint 375.00

By official decree this stamp, in addition to the regular postage, had to be used on every letter, etc., sent by the internal air post service.

## DUBAI

dü-'bī

LOCATION — Oman Peninsula, Arabia, on Persian Gulf
GOVT. — Sheikdom under British protection
AREA — 1,500 sq. mi.
POP. — 60,000
CAPITAL — Dubai

Dubai is one of six Persian Gulf sheikdoms to join the United Arab Emirates which proclaimed its independence Dec. 2, 1971. See United Arab Emirates.

100 Naye Paise = 1 Rupee
100 Dirhams = 1 Riyal (1966)

Imperforate

Many issues were accompanied by smaller quantities of imperforate stamps.

**Catalogue values for all unused stamps in this country are for Never Hinged items.**

Hermit Crab — A1

Sheik Rashid bin Said al Maktum — A2

2np, 20np, Cuttlefish. 3np, 25np, Snail. 4np, 30np, Crab. 5np, 35np, Sea urchin. 10np, 50np, Sea shell. 1r, Fortress wall. 2r, View of Dubai. 3r, Fortress wall. 5r, View of Dubai.

*Perf. 12x11½*

**1963, June 15 Litho. Unwmk.**

| No. | Type | Description | Unused | Used |
|---|---|---|---|---|
| 1 | A1 | 1np dl bl & car rose | .30 | .25 |
| 2 | A1 | 2np lt bl & bis brn | .35 | .25 |
| 3 | A1 | 3np green & sepia | .35 | .25 |
| 4 | A1 | 4np pink & orange | .35 | .25 |
| 5 | A1 | 5np violet & blk | .35 | .25 |
| 6 | A1 | 10np brn org & blk | .35 | .25 |
| 7 | A1 | 15np gray ol & dp car | .70 | .25 |
| 8 | A1 | 20np rose red & org brn | .75 | .40 |
| 9 | A1 | 25np ap grn & red brn | .90 | .40 |
| 10 | A1 | 30np gray & red | 1.50 | .40 |
| 11 | A1 | 35np dl lil & dl vio | 1.50 | .40 |
| 12 | A1 | 50np org & sepia | 2.25 | .75 |
| 13 | A1 | 1r brt bl & red org | 6.00 | 1.50 |
| 14 | A1 | 2r dull yel & brn | 9.50 | 3.50 |
| 15 | A1 | 3r rose car & blk | 16.00 | 5.50 |
| 16 | A1 | 5r grn & dl red brn | 27.50 | 9.50 |

*Perf. 12*

| No. | Type | Description | Unused | Used |
|---|---|---|---|---|
| 17 | A2 | 10r rose lake, grnsh bl & blk | 60.00 | 19.00 |
| | | *Nos. 1-17 (17)* | 128.65 | 43.10 |

Nos. 13-17 exist perf 10½. Values are much higher.

Dhows A3

Designs: 2np, First-aid tent. 3np, Camel caravan. 4np, Butterfly.

**1963, Sept. 1 Unwmk. *Perf. 12***

| No. | Type | Description | Unused | Used |
|---|---|---|---|---|
| 18 | A3 | 1np ultra, yel & red | .80 | .35 |
| 19 | A3 | 2np brn, yel & red | .80 | .35 |
| 20 | A3 | 3np red brn, org & red | .80 | .35 |
| 21 | A3 | 4np brn, brt grn & red | .80 | .35 |
| | | *Nos. 18-21,C9-C12 (8)* | 11.00 | 4.10 |

Intl. Red Cross, cent. Exist perf. 10½. Values, each $1.75.

Four imperf. souvenir sheets exist in the denominations and designs of Nos. C9-C12, with "Air-Mail" omitted and colors changed. Size: 119x99mm. Value $50.

For overprints see Nos. C52-C54.

A4

Anopheles Mosquito: 2np, Mosquito and entwined snakes. 3np, Mosquitoes over swamp.

**1963, Dec. 20 Unwmk. *Perf. 12***

| No. | Type | Description | Unused | Used |
|---|---|---|---|---|
| 22 | A4 | 1np emer & red brn | .35 | .25 |
| 23 | A4 | 1np red & dark brn | .35 | .25 |
| 24 | A4 | 1np blue & carmine | .35 | .25 |
| 25 | A4 | 2np brn & orange | .35 | .25 |
| 26 | A4 | 2np carmine & blue | .35 | .25 |
| 27 | A4 | 3np org brn & blue | .35 | .25 |
| | | *Nos. 22-27,C13-C15 (9)* | 4.55 | 2.35 |

WHO drive to eradicate malaria.

A5

Designs: 1np, Scouts forming pyramid. 2np, Bugler. 3np, Cub Scouts. 4np, Scouts and bugler. 5np, Scouts presenting flag.

**1964 Unwmk.**

| No. | Type | Description | Unused | Used |
|---|---|---|---|---|
| 28 | A5 | 1np dk brn & ocher | .25 | .25 |
| 29 | A5 | 2np car rose & sep | .25 | .25 |
| 30 | A5 | 3np blue & red org | .25 | .25 |
| 31 | A5 | 4np carmine & blue | .25 | .25 |
| 32 | A5 | 5np ind & bluish grn | .35 | .25 |
| | | *Nos. 28-32,C20-C24 (10)* | 6.35 | 3.20 |

11th Boy Scout Jamboree, Marathon, Greece, Aug., 1963.

For overprints see Nos. C47-C51.

Unisphere, New York Skyline and Dubai Harbor — A6

2np, 4np, 10np, Views of NYC and Dubai.

**1964, Apr. 22 Litho. *Perf. 12***

| No. | Type | Description | Unused | Used |
|---|---|---|---|---|
| 33 | A6 | 1np dk bl & rose red | .25 | .25 |
| 34 | A6 | 2np dl red, lil rose & bl | .25 | .25 |
| 35 | A6 | 3np brown & green | .25 | .25 |
| 36 | A6 | 4np emer, brt grn & red | .25 | .25 |
| 37 | A6 | 5np ol, sl grn & lil | .25 | .25 |
| 38 | A6 | 10np brn org, red org & blk | .70 | .50 |
| | | *Nos. 33-38,C36-C38 (9)* | 6.15 | 4.05 |

New York World's Fair, 1964-65.

Gymnast — A8

Designs: 2np, 5np, 20np, 40np, Various exercises on bar. 3np, 30np, Various exercises on vaulting horse. 4np, 10np, 1r, Various exercises on rings.

**1964 Photo. *Perf. 14***

| No. | Type | Description | Unused | Used |
|---|---|---|---|---|
| 43 | A8 | 1np org brn & yel grn | .25 | .25 |
| 44 | A8 | 2np dk brn & grnsh bl | .25 | .25 |
| 45 | A8 | 3np ultra & org brn | .25 | .25 |
| 46 | A8 | 4np dk pur & yel | .25 | .25 |
| 47 | A8 | 5np ocher & dk bl | .25 | .25 |
| 48 | A8 | 10np brt bl & ocher | .40 | .25 |
| 49 | A8 | 20np ol & lil rose | .50 | .25 |
| 50 | A8 | 30np dk bl & yel | 1.00 | .25 |
| 51 | A8 | 40np Prus grn & dl org | 1.75 | .50 |
| 52 | A8 | 1r rose vio & grnsh bl | 3.75 | 1.25 |
| | | *Nos. 43-52 (10)* | 8.65 | 3.75 |

18th Olympic Games, Tokyo, Oct. 10-25, 1964. An imperf. miniature sheet contains a 67x67mm stamp similar to No. 52. Value $11.

Palace — A9

Sheik Rashid bin Said — A10

Designs: 20np, 25np, View of new Dubai. 35np, 40np, Bridge and dhow. 60np, 1r, Bridge. 1.25r, Minaret. 1.50r, 3r, Old Dubai.

**1966, May 30 Photo. *Perf. 14x14½***

**Size: 23x18mm**

| No. | Type | Description | Unused | Used |
|---|---|---|---|---|
| 53 | A9 | 5np brown & indigo | .25 | .25 |
| 54 | A9 | 10np black & orange | .30 | .25 |
| 55 | A9 | 15np ultra & brown | .40 | .25 |

*Perf. 13*

**Size: 27½x20½mm**

| No. | Type | Description | Unused | Used |
|---|---|---|---|---|
| 56 | A9 | 20np blue & red brn | .50 | .30 |
| 57 | A9 | 25np org ver & ultra | .55 | .40 |
| 58 | A9 | 35np violet & emer | .75 | .50 |
| 59 | A9 | 40np grnsh bl & bl | 1.10 | .50 |

*Perf. 14½*

**Size: 31½x24mm**

| No. | Type | Description | Unused | Used |
|---|---|---|---|---|
| 60 | A9 | 60np yel grn & org ver | 1.75 | 1.00 |
| 61 | A9 | 1r ultra & blue | 2.75 | 1.50 |
| 62 | A9 | 1.25r brn org & blk | 3.00 | 2.00 |
| 63 | A9 | 1.50r rose lil & yel grn | 5.50 | 2.10 |
| 64 | A9 | 3r dk ol bis & vio | 10.00 | 4.00 |

**Engr.**

*Perf. 14*

| No. | Type | Description | Unused | Used |
|---|---|---|---|---|
| 65 | A10 | 5r rose carmine | 18.00 | 7.50 |
| 66 | A10 | 10r dark blue | 37.50 | 16.00 |
| | | *Nos. 53-66 (14)* | 82.35 | 36.55 |

**Nos. 53-62, 64-66 Overprinted with New Currency Names and Bars**

**1967**

| No. | Type | Description | Unused | Used |
|---|---|---|---|---|
| 67 | A9 | 5d on 5np | .30 | .25 |
| 68 | A9 | 10d on 10np | .35 | .25 |
| 69 | A9 | 15d on 15np | .50 | .25 |
| 70 | A9 | 20d on 20np | 1.00 | .25 |
| 71 | A9 | 25d on 25np | 1.25 | .25 |
| 72 | A9 | 35d on 35np | 1.50 | .25 |
| 73 | A9 | 40d on 40np | 1.75 | .30 |
| 74 | A9 | 60d on 60np | 3.00 | .40 |
| 75 | A9 | 1r on 1r | 4.00 | .95 |
| 76 | A9 | 1.25r on 1.25r | 7.25 | 1.30 |
| 77 | A9 | 3r on 3r | 15.00 | 3.75 |
| 78 | A10 | 5r on 5r | 27.50 | 7.50 |
| 79 | A10 | 10r on 10r | 40.00 | 14.00 |
| | | *Nos. 67-79 (13)* | 103.40 | 29.70 |

Sheik and Falcon — A11

Dhow — A12

**Litho. & Engr.**

**1967, Aug. 21 *Perf. 13½***

| No. | Type | Description | Unused | Used |
|---|---|---|---|---|
| 80 | A11 | 5d dp car & org | 1.10 | .30 |
| 81 | A11 | 10d sepia & green | 1.25 | .25 |
| 82 | A11 | 20d dp cl & bl gray | 1.40 | .30 |
| 83 | A11 | 35d slate & car | 1.75 | .30 |
| 84 | A11 | 60d vio bl & emer | 3.25 | .50 |
| 85 | A11 | 1r green & lilac | 4.50 | .50 |
| 86 | A12 | 1.25r lt bl & claret | 5.50 | .65 |
| 87 | A12 | 3r dull vio & claret | 11.00 | 1.75 |
| 88 | A12 | 5r brt grn & vio | 22.50 | 3.75 |
| 89 | A12 | 10r lil rose & grn | 30.00 | 6.75 |
| | | *Nos. 80-89 (10)* | 82.25 | 15.05 |

S. S. Bamora, 1914 — A13

35d, De Havilland 66 plane, 1930. 60d, S. S. Sirdhana, 1947. 1r, Armstrong Whitworth 15 "Atlanta," 1938. 1.25r, S. S. Chandpara, 1949. 3r, BOAC Sunderland amphibian plane, 1943. No. 96, Freighter Bombala, 1961, and BOAC Super VC10, 1967.

**1969, Feb. 12 Litho. *Perf. 14x13½***

| No. | Type | Description | Unused | Used |
|---|---|---|---|---|
| 90 | A13 | 25d lt grn, bl & blk | .25 | *.25* |
| 91 | A13 | 35d multicolored | .25 | *.25* |
| 92 | A13 | 60d multicolored | .70 | *.25* |
| 93 | A13 | 1r lil, blk & dl yel | 1.15 | *.25* |
| 94 | A13 | 1.25r gray, blk & dp org | 1.60 | *.25* |
| 95 | A13 | 3r pink, blk & bl grn | 2.50 | *.35* |
| | | *Nos. 90-95 (6)* | 6.45 | *1.60* |

**Miniature Sheet**

***Imperf***

| No. | Type | Description | Unused | Used |
|---|---|---|---|---|
| 96 | A13 | 1.25r pink, blk & bl grn | 16.00 | 16.00 |

60 years of postal service.

Mother and Children, by Rubens A14

Arab Mother's Day: 60d, Madonna and Child, by Murillo. 1r, Mother and Child, by Francesco Mazzuoli. 3r, Madonna and Child, by Correggio.

**1969, Mar. 21 Litho. *Perf. 13½***

| No. | Type | Description | Unused | Used |
|---|---|---|---|---|
| 97 | A14 | 60d silver & multi | .75 | *.25* |
| 98 | A14 | 1r silver & multi | 1.50 | *.25* |
| 99 | A14 | 1.25r silver & multi | 1.75 | *.25* |
| 100 | A14 | 3r silver & multi | 3.50 | *.45* |
| | | *Nos. 97-100 (4)* | 7.50 | *1.20* |

Porkfish — A15

**1969, May 26 Litho. *Perf. 11***

**101** A15 60d shown 2.00 *.35*
**102** A15 60d Spotted grouper 2.00 *.35*
**103** A15 60d Moonfish 2.00 *.35*
**104** A15 60d Sweetlips 2.00 *.35*
**105** A15 60d Blue angel 2.00 *.35*
**106** A15 60d Texas skate 2.00 *.35*
**107** A15 60d Striped butterflyfish 2.00 *.35*
**108** A15 60d Imperial angelfish 2.00 *.35*
*a.* Block of 8, #101-108 35.00
*Nos. 101-108 (8)* 16.00 *2.80*

Nos. 101-108 printed in se-tenant blocks of 8, each sheet containing two such blocks.

Explorers and Map of Arabia — A16

**1969, July 21 Litho. *Perf. 13½x13***

**109** A16 35d brown & green 1.50 *.35*
**110** A16 60d vio & sepia 2.00 *.45*
**111** A16 1r green & dl bl 5.50 *.55*
**112** A16 1.25r gray & rose car 7.00 *.65*
*Nos. 109-112 (4)* 16.00 *2.00*

European explorers of Arabia: Sir Richard Francis Burton (1821-1890), Charles Montagu Doughty (1843-1926), Johann Ludwig Burckhardt (1784-1817) and Wilfred Patrick Thesiger (1910- ).

Construction of World's First Underwater Oil Storage Tank — A17

Designs: 20d, Launching of oil storage tank. 35d, Oil storage tank in place on ocean ground. 60d, Sheik Rashid bin Said, offshore drilling platform and monument commemorating first oil export. 1r, Offshore production platform and helicopter port.

**1969, Oct. 13 Litho. *Perf. 11***

**113** A17 5d blue & multi .30 *.25*
**114** A17 20d blue & multi 1.00 *.25*
**115** A17 35d blue & multi 1.90 *.25*
**116** A17 60d blue & multi 2.75 *.25*
**117** A17 1r blue & multi 4.00 *.25*
*Nos. 113-117 (5)* 9.95 *1.25*

Astronauts Collecting Moon Rocks — A18

Designs: 1r, Astronaut at foot of ladder. 1.25r, Astronauts planting American flag.

**1969, Dec. 15 Litho. *Perf. 14½***

**118** Strip of 3 3.75 *1.00*
*a.* A18 60d multicolored .40 *.25*
*b.* A18 1r multicolored .80 *.25*
*c.* A18 1.25r multicolored (airmail) 1.50 *.25*

The 1.25r is inscribed "AIRMAIL."

Sizes: 60d and 1r, 28½x41mm; 1.25r, 60½x41mm.

See note after US No. C76.

Ocean Weather Ship Launching Radio Sonde, and Hastings Plane — A19

WMO Emblem and: 1r, Kew-type radio sonde, weather balloon and radar antenna. 1.25r, Tiros satellite and weather sounding rocket. 3r, Ariel satellite and rocket launching.

**1970, Mar. 23 Litho. *Perf. 11***

**121** A19 60d dl grn, brn & blk .40 *.25*
**122** A19 1r brown & multi .75 *.25*
**123** A19 1.25r dk blue & multi .90 *.25*
**124** A19 3r multicolored 2.00 *.30*
*Nos. 121-124 (4)* 4.05 *1.05*

10th World Meteorological Day.

UPU Headquarters and Monument, Bern — A20

60d, UPU monument, Bern, telecommunications satellite and London PO tower.

**1970, May 20 Litho. *Perf. 13½x14***

**125** A20 5d lt green & multi .75 *.25*
**126** A20 60d dp blue & multi 1.90 *.25*

UPU Headquarters opening, May 20.

Charles Dickens, London Skyline — A21

60d, Dickens' portrait, vert. 1.25r, Dickens & "Old Curiosity Shop." 3r, Bound volumes.

**1970, July 23 Litho. *Perf. 13½***

**127** A21 60d olive & multi .85 *.25*
**128** A21 1r multicolored 1.00 *.25*
**129** A21 1.25r buff & multi 1.20 *.25*
**130** A21 3r multicolored 4.00 *.50*
*Nos. 127-130 (4)* 7.05 *1.25*

Dickens (1812-70), English novelist.

The Graham Children, by William Hogarth — A22

Paintings: 60d, Caroline Murat and her Children, by François Pascal Gerard, vert. 1r, Napoleon with the Children on the Terrace in St. Cloud, by Louis Ducis.

**1970, Oct. 1 Litho. *Perf. 13½***

**131** A22 35d multicolored .75 .25
**132** A22 60d multicolored 1.25 .25
**133** A22 1r multicolored 2.00 .25
*Nos. 131-133 (3)* 4.00 .75

Issued for Children's Day.

Sheik Rashid bin Said — A23

Television Station — A25

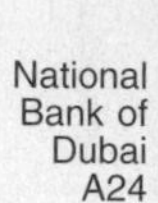


National Bank of Dubai A24

Designs: 10d, Boat building. 20d, Al Maktum Bascule Bridge. 35d, Great Mosque, Dubai, vert. 1r, Dubai International Airport, horiz. 1.25r, Port Rashid harbor project, horiz. 3r, Rashid Hospital, horiz. 5r, Dubai Trade School, horiz.

***Perf. 14x14½, 14½x14***

**1970-71 Litho.**

**134** A23 5d multi ('71) .30 .25
**135** A24 10d multi ('71) .30 .25
**136** A24 20d multi ('71) .40 .25
**137** A24 35d multi ('71) .55 .25
**138** A24 60d multicolored .80 .25

***Perf. 14***

**139** A25 1r multicolored 1.20 .25
**140** A25 1.25r multicolored 1.20 .25
**141** A25 3r multicolored 3.75 .25
**142** A25 5r multicolored 6.00 .40
**143** A25 10r multi ('71) 14.00 .85
*Nos. 134-143 (10)* 28.50 3.25

Dubai Airport A26

Designs: 1.25r, Airport entrance.

**1971, May 15 Litho. *Perf. 13½x14***

**144** A26 1r multicolored 3.25 .25
**145** A26 1.25r multicolored 4.00 .25

Opening of Dubai International Airport.

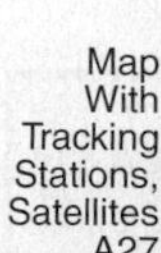

Map With Tracking Stations, Satellites A27

**1971, June 21 Litho. *Perf. 14½***

**146** A27 60d multicolored .60 .30

Outer Space Telecommunications Cong., Paris, Mar. 29-Apr. 2. See Nos. C55-C56.

Fan, Scout Emblem, Map of Japan — A28

Designs: 1r, Boy Scouts in kayaks. 1.25r, Mountaineering. 3r, Campfire, horiz.

***Perf. 14x13½, 13½x14***

**1971, Aug. 30 Litho.**

**147** A28 60d multicolored .45 *.25*
**148** A28 1r multicolored .90 *.25*
**149** A28 1.25r multicolored 1.15 *.25*
**150** A28 3r multicolored 2.50 *.30*
*Nos. 147-150 (4)* 5.00 *1.05*

13th Boy Scout World Jamboree, Asagiri Plain, Japan, Aug. 2-10.

Albrecht Dürer, Self-portrait A29

**1971, Oct. 18 *Perf. 14x13½***

**151** A29 60d gold & multi .80 *.25*

See Nos. C57-C59.

Boy in Meadow A30

5r, Boys playing and UNICEF emblem.

**1971, Dec. 11 *Perf. 13½***

**152** A30 60d multi .45 *.25*
**153** A30 5r multi, horiz. 3.50 *.50*

25th anniv. of UNICEF. See No. C60.

Ludwig van Beethoven A31

Portrait: 10d, Leonardo da Vinci.

**1972, Feb. 7**

**154** A31 10d lt tan & multi .30 *.25*
**155** A31 35d lt tan & multi .45 *.25*

See Nos. C61-C62.

Olympic Emblems, Gymnast on Rings — A32

**1972, July 31 Litho. *Perf. 13½***

**156** A32 35d shown .55 *.25*
**157** A32 40d Fencing .65 *.25*
**158** A32 65d Hockey .80 *.25*
*Nos. 156-158,C65-C67 (6)* 7.50 1.50

20th Olympic Games, Munich, 8/26-9/11.

Stamps of Dubai were replaced in 1972 by those of United Arab Emirates.

## AIR POST STAMPS

### Type of Regular Issue and

Peregrine Falcon — AP1

Design: A1, Falcon over bridge.

*Perf. 12x11½, 11½x12*

**1963, June 15 Litho. Unwmk.**

**C1** A1 20np dk red brn & lt blue 2.50 .35
**C2** AP1 25np ol & blk brn 2.75 .45
**C3** A1 30np red org & blk 3.25 .55
**C4** AP1 40np grayish brn & dk violet 3.50 .65
**C5** A1 50np emer & rose cl 4.25 .75
**C6** AP1 60np brn org & blk 5.25 .85
**C7** A1 75np vio & dp grn 6.50 1.00
**C8** AP1 1r org & red brn 9.00 1.25
*Nos. C1-C8 (8)* 37.00 5.85

### Red Cross Type

Designs: 20np, Dhows. 30np, First-aid tent. 40np, Camel caravan. 50np, Butterfly.

**1963, Sept. 1 Unwmk. *Perf. 12***

**C9** A3 20np brown, yel & red 1.40 .50
**C10** A3 30np dk bl, buff & red 1.40 .50
**C11** A3 40np black, yel & red 1.75 .60
**C12** A3 50np vio, lt bl & red 3.25 1.10
*Nos. C9-C12 (4)* 7.80 2.70

### Malaria Type

Designs: 30np, Anopheles mosquito. 40np, Mosquito and coiled arrows. 70np, Mosquitoes over swamp.

**1963, Dec. 20 Unwmk. *Perf. 12***

**C13** A4 30np purple & emer .65 .25
**C14** A4 40np red & dull grn .75 .25
**C15** A4 70np slate & citron 1.05 .35
*Nos. C13-C15 (3)* 2.45 .85

Three imperf. souv. sheets exist containing 4 stamps each in changed colors similar to Nos. C13-C15. Value $30.

Wheat — AP2

40np, Wheat and palm tree. 70np, Hands holding wheat. 1r, Woman carrying basket.

**1963, Dec. 30 Litho.**

**C16** AP2 30np vio bl & ocher .50 .30
**C17** AP2 40np red & olive .75 .45
**C18** AP2 70np green & orange 1.15 .65
**C19** AP2 1r org brn & Prus bl 1.75 1.00
*Nos. C16-C19 (4)* 4.15 2.40

### Boy Scout Type

Designs: 20np, Human pyramid. 30np, Bugler. 40np, Cub Scouts. 70np, Scouts and bugler. 1r, Scouts presenting flag.

**1964, Jan. 20**

**C20** A5 20np green & dk brn .30 .25
**C21** A5 30np lilac & ocher .60 .25
**C22** A5 40np vio bl & yel grn .80 .30
**C23** A5 70np dk grn & gray 1.40 .45
**C24** A5 1r vio bl & red org 1.90 .70
*Nos. C20-C24 (5)* 5.00 1.95

Five imperf. souv. sheets exist containing 4 stamps each in changed colors similar to Nos. C20-C24. Value $60.

For overprints see Nos. C47-C51.

John F. Kennedy and US Seal AP3

**1964, Jan. 15 Litho.**

**C25** AP3 75np grn & blk, *lt grn* .90 .55
**C26** AP3 1r ocher & blk, *tan* 1.25 .60
**C27** AP3 1.25r mag & blk, *gray* 1.60 .85
*Nos. C25-C27 (3)* 3.75 2.00

Pres. John F. Kennedy (1917-1963).

Nos. C25-C27 exist imperf. Value, set $9.50.

A souvenir sheet contains one imperf. 1.25r in buff and black with simulated perforations. Value $5.

For overprints see Nos. C52-C54.

Spacecraft — AP4

Designs: 1np, 5np, Ascending rocket, vert. 2np, 1r, Mercury capsule, vert. 4np, 2r, Twin spacecraft.

**1964, Jan. 25 Unwmk. *Perf. 12***

**C28** AP4 1np emerald & org .25 .25
**C29** AP4 2np multicolored .30 .25
**C30** AP4 3np multicolored .35 .25
**C31** AP4 4np multicolored .40 .25
**C32** AP4 5np blue & orange .45 .25
**C33** AP4 1r vio bl, dp car & buff 1.25 .70
**C34** AP4 1.50r vio bl, dp car & buff 2.00 1.25
**C35** AP4 2r blue, yel & red 2.75 1.50
*Nos. C28-C35 (8)* 7.75 4.70

Issued to honor the astronauts.

Nos. C28-C35 exist imperf. Value, set $10.

An imperf. souvenir sheet contains one stamp similar to No. C35. Value $7.

### New York World's Fair Type

Statue of Liberty and ships in Dubai harbor.

**1964, Apr. 22 Litho.**

**C36** A6 75np gray bl, ultra & blk .80 .40
**C37** A6 2r gray grn, dk brn & bis 1.40 .80
**C38** A6 3r dl grn, gray ol & dp org 2.00 1.10
*Nos. C36-C38 (3)* 4.20 2.30

An imperf. souvenir sheet contains 2 stamps in Statue of Liberty design: 2r dark brown and rose carmine, and 3r ultramarine and gold. Value $10.

Scales and Flame AP5

**1964, Apr. 30 Litho. *Perf. 12***

**C39** AP5 35np bl, brn & scar .60 .30
**C40** AP5 50np lt bl, dk grn & scar .75 .35
**C41** AP5 1r grnsh bl, blk & scar 1.40 .60
**C42** AP5 3r lt ultra, ultra, & scar 4.00 2.00
*Nos. C39-C42 (4)* 6.75 3.25

15th anniv. of the Universal Declaration of Human Rights. An imperf. souvenir sheet contains one 3r light green, ultramarine and scarlet stamp. Value $7.50.

Nos. C20-C24 Overprinted in Red and Black (Shield in Red)

**1964, June 20**

**C47** A5 20np green & dk brn 1.15 .40
**C48** A5 30np lilac & ocher 1.35 .50
**C49** A5 40np vio bl & yel grn 2.00 .75
**C50** A5 70np dk grn & gray 3.25 1.50
**C51** A5 1r vio bl & red org 4.50 2.00
*Nos. C47-C51 (5)* 12.25 5.15

9th Winter Olympic Games, Innsbruck, Austria, Jan. 29-Feb. 9, 1964.

A similar but unauthorized overprint, with shield in black, exists on Nos. 28-32, C20-C24, and the five souvenir sheets mentioned below No. C24. The Dubai G.P.O. calls this black-shield overprint "bogus."

Nos. C25-C27 Overprinted in Brown or Green

**1964, Sept. 15**

**C52** AP3 75np (Br) 2.00 2.00
**C53** AP3 1r (G) 2.40 2.40
**C54** AP3 1.25r (G) 3.00 3.00
*Nos. C52-C54 (3)* 7.40 7.40

Pres. John F. Kennedy 48th birth anniv. The same overprint in black was applied to the souv. sheet noted after No. C27.

### Communications Type

Designs: 1r, Intelsat 4, tracking station on globe and rocket. 5r, Eiffel Tower, Syncom 3 and Goonhilly radar station.

**1971, June 21 Litho. *Perf. 14½***

**C55** A27 1r lt brown & multi .60 *.25*
**C56** A27 5r multicolored 3.00 *.45*

### Portrait Type

1r, Newton. 1.25r, Avicenna. 3r, Voltaire.

**1971, Oct. 18 Litho. *Perf. 14x13½***

**C57** A29 1r gold & multi 1.10 *.25*
**C58** A29 1.25r gold & multi 1.40 *.25*
**C59** A29 3r gold & multi 4.00 *.50*
*Nos. C57-C59 (3)* 6.50 *1.00*

### UNICEF Type

1r, Mother, children, UNICEF emblem.

**1971, Dec. 11 *Perf. 13½***

**C60** A30 1r gold & multi 1.00 *.25*

### Portrait Type

75d, Khalil Gibran. 5r, Charles de Gaulle.

**1972, Feb. 7 Litho. *Perf. 13½***

**C61** A31 75d lt tan & multi .75 *.25*
**C62** A31 5r lt tan & multi 5.25 *.35*

Infant Health Care AP6

Design: 75d, Nurse supervising children at meal, and WHO emblem, vert.

**1972, Apr. 7 Litho. *Perf. 14x13½***

**C63** AP6 75d multicolored 1.60 *.25*
**C64** AP6 1.25r multicolored 2.40 *.25*

World Health Day.

### Olympic Type

**1972, July 31 Litho. *Perf. 13½***

**C65** A32 75d Water polo 1.50 *.25*
**C66** A32 1r Steeplechase 1.75 *.25*
**C67** A32 1.25r Running 2.25 *.25*
*Nos. C65-C67 (3)* 5.50 *.60*

## POSTAGE DUE STAMPS

### Type of Regular Issue

Designs: 1np, 4np, 15np, Clam. 2np, 5np, 25np, Mussel. 3np, 10np, 35np, Oyster.

*Perf. 12x11½*

**1963, June 15 Litho. Unwmk.**

**J1** A1 1np gray grn & ver 1.00 .35
**J2** A1 2np lemon & brt bl 1.50 .45
**J3** A1 3np dl rose & green 1.75 .75
**J4** A1 4np light grn & mag 2.50 1.00
**J5** A1 5np vermilion & blk 3.00 1.25
**J6** A1 10np citron & violet 3.50 1.50
**J7** A1 15np brt ultra & ver 4.50 1.90
**J8** A1 25np buff & olive grn 6.00 2.00
**J9** A1 35np turq bl & dp org 6.50 2.75
*Nos. J1-J9 (9)* 30.25 11.95

Sheik Rashid bin Said — D1

**1972, May 22 Litho. *Perf. 14x14½***

**J10** D1 5d blk & gray grn 2.00 .75
**J11** D1 10d vio bl, blk & bis 2.50 .85
**J12** D1 20d sl grn, blk & brick red 4.25 1.50
**J13** D1 30d grnsh gray, blk & lil 7.00 2.25
**J14** D1 50d lilac, brn & bis 11.00 4.50
*Nos. J10-J14 (5)* 26.75 9.85

# EAST AFRICA & UGANDA PROTECTORATES

ˈēst ˈa-fri-kə and ü-ˈgan-də
prə-ˈtek-tˌə-ˌrəts

LOCATION — Central East Africa, bordering on the Indian Ocean
GOVT. — British Protectorate
AREA — 350,000 sq. mi. (approx.)
POP. — 6,503,507 (approx.)
CAPITAL — Mombasa

This territory, formerly administered by the British East Africa Colony, was divided between Kenya Colony and the Uganda Protectorate. See Kenya, Uganda and Tanzania.

16 Annas = 1 Rupee
100 Cents = 1 Rupee (1907)

**Altered high value stamps of East Africa and Uganda are plentiful.**
**Expertization by competent authorities is recommended.**

A1

A2

King Edward VII

**1903 Typo. Wmk. 2 *Perf. 14***

| | | | | |
|---|---|---|---|---|
| **1** | A1 | ½a gray green | 6.50 | *22.50* |
| **2** | A1 | 1a car & black | 2.25 | 2.00 |
| **3** | A1 | 2a vio & dull vio | 10.50 | 3.00 |
| **4** | A1 | 2½a ultramarine | 14.50 | *60.00* |
| **5** | A1 | 3a gray grn & brn | 30.00 | *70.00* |
| **6** | A1 | 4a blk & gray grn | 13.50 | *27.50* |
| **7** | A1 | 5a org brn & blk | 22.50 | *60.00* |
| **8** | A1 | 8a pale blue & blk | 28.00 | *50.00* |

**Wmk. 1**

| | | | | |
|---|---|---|---|---|
| **9** | A2 | 1r gray green | 27.50 | *65.00* |
| **10** | A2 | 2r vio & dull vio | 92.50 | *100.00* |
| **11** | A2 | 3r blk & gray grn | 175.00 | *325.00* |
| **12** | A2 | 4r lt green & blk | 175.00 | *350.00* |
| **13** | A2 | 5r car & black | 175.00 | *350.00* |
| **14** | A2 | 10r ultra & black | 475.00 | *675.00* |
| **15** | A2 | 20r ol gray & blk | 825.00 | *1,950.* |
| **16** | A2 | 50r org brn & blk | 2,600. | *4,750.* |
| | | *Nos. 1-14 (14)* | 1,248. | *2,160.* |

Nos. 9 and 14 are on both ordinary and chalky paper. Values are for examples on ordinary paper. Values are for the least expensive varieties. See *Scott Classic Specialized Catalogue of Stamps & Covers* for detailed listings.

**1904-07 Wmk. 3 Chalky Paper**

| | | | | |
|---|---|---|---|---|
| **17** | A1 | ½a gray green | 16.00 | 3.75 |
| **18a** | A1 | 1a car & black | 11.00 | 1.00 |
| **19** | A1 | 2a vio & dull vio | 3.50 | 3.25 |
| **20** | A1 | 2½a blue | 10.00 | 37.50 |
| *a.* | | 2½a blue & ultramarine | 9.50 | *35.00* |
| **21** | A1 | 3a gray grn & brn | 4.75 | *45.00* |
| **22** | A1 | 4a blk & gray grn | 9.25 | *22.50* |
| **23** | A1 | 5a org brn & blk | 8.00 | *32.50* |
| **24a** | A1 | 8a pale blue & blk | 8.75 | 10.50 |
| **25** | A2 | 1r gray green | 35.00 | *75.00* |
| **26** | A2 | 2r vio & dl vio | 50.00 | *77.50* |
| **27** | A2 | 3r blk & gray grn | 100.00 | *160.00* |
| **28** | A2 | 4r lt green & blk | 140.00 | *200.00* |
| **29** | A2 | 5r car & black | 175.00 | *700.00* |
| **29A** | A2 | 10r ultra & black | 400.00 | *450.00* |
| **30** | A2 | 20r ol gray & blk | 875.00 | *1,600.* |
| **30A** | A2 | 50r org brn & blk | 2,750. | *4,500.* |
| | | *Nos. 17-29 (10)* | 541.50 | *1,320.* |

Nos. 17-19, 21-24 are on both ordinary and chalky paper. No. 20 is on ordinary paper. Values are for the least expensive varieties. See *Scott Classic Specialized Catalogue of Stamps & Covers* for detailed listings.

**1907-08**

| | | | | |
|---|---|---|---|---|
| **31** | A1 | 1c brown ('08) | 3.00 | .25 |
| **32** | A1 | 3c gray green | 22.50 | .80 |
| **33** | A1 | 6c carmine | 3.25 | .25 |
| **34** | A1 | 10c citron & violet | 12.00 | 10.00 |
| **35** | A1 | 12c red vio & dl vio | 12.00 | 3.50 |
| **36** | A1 | 15c ultramarine | 34.00 | 11.00 |
| **37** | A1 | 25c blk & blue green | 22.50 | *8.50* |
| **38** | A1 | 50c org brn & green | 17.50 | 16.00 |
| **39** | A1 | 75c pale bl & gray blk ('08) | 5.50 | *40.00* |
| | | *Nos. 31-39 (9)* | 132.25 | *90.30* |

Nos. 31-33, 36 are on ordinary paper.
There are two dies of the 6c differing very slightly in many details.

King George V
A3 A4

**1912-18 Ordinary Paper Wmk. 3**

| | | | | |
|---|---|---|---|---|
| **40** | A3 | 1c black | .40 | *2.10* |
| **41** | A3 | 3c green | 2.50 | .75 |
| *a.* | | Booklet pane of 6 | | |
| **42** | A3 | 6c carmine | 1.50 | .70 |
| *a.* | | Booklet pane of 6 | | |
| **43** | A3 | 10c yel orange | 2.50 | .65 |
| **44** | A3 | 12c gray | 3.25 | .65 |
| **45** | A3 | 15c ultramarine | 3.25 | 1.00 |

**Chalky Paper**

| | | | | |
|---|---|---|---|---|
| **46** | A3 | 25c scar & blk, *yel* | .65 | *1.60* |
| **47** | A3 | 50c violet & black | 1.90 | 1.60 |
| **48** | A3 | 75c black, *green* | 1.90 | *21.00* |
| *a.* | | 75c black, *emerald* | 13.50 | *65.00* |
| *b.* | | 75c blk, *bl grn, olive back* | 9.25 | 9.25 |
| *c.* | | 75c blk, *emer, olive back* | 50.00 | *175.00* |
| **49** | A4 | 1r black, *green* | 2.25 | *5.25* |
| *a.* | | 1r black, *emerald* | 6.00 | *60.00* |
| **50** | A4 | 2r blk & red, *bl* | 26.00 | *45.00* |
| **51** | A4 | 3r gray grn & vio | 32.50 | *130.00* |
| **52** | A4 | 4r grn & red, *yel* | 65.00 | *130.00* |
| **53** | A4 | 5r dl vio & ultra | 65.00 | *160.00* |
| **54** | A4 | 10r grn & red, *grn* | 260.00 | *375.00* |
| **55** | A4 | 20r vio & blk, *red* | 500.00 | 475.00 |
| **56** | A4 | 20r bl & violet, *blue* ('18) | 575.00 | *875.00* |
| **57** | A4 | 50r gray grn & rose red | 925.00 | *975.00* |
| **58** | A4 | 100r blk & vio, *red* | *9,750.* | *4,000.* |
| **59** | A4 | 500r red & grn, *grn* | *40,000.* | |
| | | *Nos. 40-54 (15)* | 468.60 | *875.30* |

**1914 Surface-colored Paper**

| | | | | |
|---|---|---|---|---|
| **60** | A3 | 25c scarlet & blk, *yel* | .65 | *5.50* |
| **61** | A3 | 75c black, *green* | 1.25 | *19.50* |

Stamps of types A3 and A4 with watermark 4 are listed under Kenya, Uganda and Tanzania.
The 1r through 50r with revenue cancellations sell for minimal prices. The 100r and 500r were available for postage but were nearly always used fiscally.
For surcharge see No. 62.

No. 42 Surcharged

**1919**

| | | | | |
|---|---|---|---|---|
| **62** | A3 | 4c on 6c carmine | 1.50 | .25 |
| *a.* | | Double surcharge | 150.00 | *240.00* |
| *b.* | | Without squares over old value | 50.00 | *85.00* |
| *c.* | | Pair, one without surcharge | 2,000. | *2,250.* |
| *d.* | | Inverted surcharge | 350.00 | *475.00* |

For later issues see Kenya, Uganda and Tanzania.
For stamps of East Africa and Uganda overprinted "G. E. A." see German East Africa.

# EASTERN RUMELIA

ˈē-stərn rü-ˈmēl-yə

## (South Bulgaria)

LOCATION — In southern Bulgaria
GOVT. — An autonomous unit of the Turkish Empire.
CAPITAL — Philippopolis (Plovdiv)

In 1885 the province of Eastern Rumelia revolted against Turkish rule and united with Bulgaria, adopting the new name of South Bulgaria. This union was assured by the Treaty of Bucharest in 1886, following the war between Serbia and Bulgaria.

40 Paras = 1 Piaster

Counterfeits of all overprints are plentiful.

**Stamps of Turkey, 1876-84, Overprinted in Blue**

No. 1

A2

A3

**1880 Unwmk. *Perf. 13½***

| | | | | |
|---|---|---|---|---|
| **1** | A5 | ½pi on 20pa yel grn | 67.50 | 57.50 |
| *a.* | | Horiz. pair, one without overprint | | *400.00* |
| **3** | A2 | 10pa blk & rose | *55.00* | |
| **4** | A2 | 20pa vio & grn | 87.50 | 67.50 |
| **6** | A2 | 2pi blk & buff | 115.00 | 100.00 |
| **7** | A2 | 5pi red & bl | 450.00 | *500.00* |
| **8** | A3 | 10pa blk & red lil | 57.50 | |

Nos. 3 & 8 were not placed in use.
Inverted and double overprints of all values exist.

**Same, with Extra Overprint "R. O."**

| | | | | |
|---|---|---|---|---|
| **9** | A3 | 10pa blk & red lil | 97.50 | 95.00 |

Crescent and Turkish Inscriptions of Value — A4

**1881 Typo. *Perf. 13½***

| | | | | |
|---|---|---|---|---|
| **10** | A4 | 5pa blk & olive | 17.00 | 1.35 |
| **11** | A4 | 10pa blk & green | 65.00 | 1.35 |
| **12** | A4 | 20pa blk & rose | 1.75 | 1.25 |
| **13** | A4 | 1pi blk & blue | 5.75 | 4.50 |
| **14** | A4 | 5pi rose & blue | 57.50 | *82.50* |

Tête bêche pairs, imperforates and all perf. 11½ examples of Nos. 10-14 were not placed in use, and were found only in the remainder stock. This is true also of a 10pa cliché in the 20pa plate, and of a cliché of Turkey No. 63 in the 1pi plate. See the *Scott Classic Catalogue.*

**1884 *Perf. 11½***

| | | | | |
|---|---|---|---|---|
| **15** | A4 | 5pa lil & pale lil | .75 | .45 |
| **16** | A4 | 10pa grn & pale grn | .25 | .45 |
| **17** | A4 | 20pa car & pale rose | .55 | |
| **18** | A4 | 1pi bl & pale bl | 1.15 | |
| **19** | A4 | 5pi brn & pale brn | *400.00* | |

Nos. 17-19 were not placed in use, and were found only in the remainder stock.
Nos. 15-19 imperf. are from remainders.
See the *Scott Classic Catalogue for perf 13½ listings.*
For overprints see Turkey Nos. 542-545.

**South Bulgaria**

Counterfeits of all overprints are plentiful.

**Nos. 10-14 Overprinted in Two Types**

a

b

Type a — Four toes on each foot.
Type b — Three toes on each foot.

**Blue Overprint**

**1885 Unwmk. *Perf. 13½***

| | | | | |
|---|---|---|---|---|
| **20** | A4 (a) | 5pa blk & olive | *325.00* | *375.00* |
| **21** | A4 (a) | 10pa blk & grn | *875.00* | *825.00* |
| **22** | A4 (a) | 20pa blk & rose | 325.00 | — |
| **23** | A4 (a) | 1pi blk & blue | 37.50 | *72.50* |
| **24** | A4 (b) | 5pi rose & blue | *1,100.* | — |

See the *Scott Classic Catalogue* for Nos. 22-23, type b, No. 24, type a, and No. 22, perf 11½, types a and b.

**Black Overprint**

| | | | | |
|---|---|---|---|---|
| **24B** | A4 (a) | 20pa blk & rose | 275.00 | — |
| **25** | A4 (a) | 1pi blk & bl | 55.00 | *115.00* |
| **26** | A4 (b) | 5pi rose & bl | *675.00* | — |

See the *Scott Classic Catalogue* for No. 25 type b.

**Same Overprint on Nos. 15-17**

**Blue Overprint**

***Perf. 11½***

| | | | | |
|---|---|---|---|---|
| **27** | A4 (b) | 5pa lil & pale lil, type "b" | 22.50 | *57.50* |
| **28** | A4 (b) | 10pa grn & pale grn | 40.00 | *75.00* |
| **29** | A4 (b) | 20pa car & pale rose | 275.00 | *375.00* |

**Black Overprint**

***Perf. 13½***

| | | | | |
|---|---|---|---|---|
| **30** | A4 (b) | 5pa lil & pale lil | 40.00 | *67.50* |

***Perf. 11½***

| | | | | |
|---|---|---|---|---|
| **31** | A4 (a) | 10pa grn & pale grn | 42.50 | *85.00* |
| **32** | A4 (b) | 20pa car & pale rose | 55.00 | *65.00* |

See the *Scott Classic Catalogue* for detailed listings of Nos. 27-32.

**Nos. 10-17 Handstamped in Black in Two Types**

a

b

Type a — First letter at top circular.
Type b — First letter at top oval.

**1885 *Perf. 13½***

| | | | | |
|---|---|---|---|---|
| **33** | A4 (b) | 5pa blk & olive | *300.00* | 250.00 |
| **34** | A4 (b) | 10pa blk & grn | *225.00* | 250.00 |
| **35** | A4 (b) | 20pa blk & rose | 72.50 | *85.00* |
| **36** | A4 (a) | 1pi blk & bl | 87.50 | *115.00* |
| **37** | A4 (a) | 5pi rose & blue, type "a" | *2,500.* | — |

***Perf. 13½***

| | | | | |
|---|---|---|---|---|
| **38** | A4 (a) | 5pa lil & pale lil | 26.00 | *44.00* |

***Perf. 11½***

| | | | | |
|---|---|---|---|---|
| **39** | A4 (a) | 10pa grn & pale grn | 29.00 | *35.00* |
| **40** | A4 (a) | 20pa car & pale rose | 29.00 | *50.00* |

See the *Scott Classic Catalogue* for Nos. 38-40, type b, and No. 38, perf 11½, types a and b.
Nos. 20-40 exist with inverted and double handstamps. Overprints in unlisted colors are proofs.
The stamps of South Bulgaria were superseded in 1886 by those of Bulgaria.

## EASTERN SILESIA

'ē-stərn sī-'lē-zh̦ē-̧ə

LOCATION — In central Europe
GOVT. — Austrian crownland
AREA — 1,987 sq. mi.
POP. — 680,422 (estimated 1920)
CAPITAL — Troppau

After World War I, this territory was occupied by Czechoslovakia and eventually was divided between Poland and Czechoslovakia, the dividing line running through Teschen.

100 Heller = 1 Krone
100 Fennigi = 1 Marka

### Plebiscite Issues

Stamps of Czechoslovakia 1918-20, Overprinted in Black, Blue, Violet or Red

| 1920 | | Unwmk. | *Imperf.* | |
|---|---|---|---|---|
| **1** | A2 | 1h dark brown | .25 | .30 |
| **2** | A1 | 3h red violet | .25 | .25 |
| **3** | A2 | 5h blue green | 23.50 | 22.50 |
| **4** | A2 | 15h red | 11.50 | 11.00 |
| **5** | A1 | 20h blue green | .25 | .25 |
| **6** | A2 | 25h dull violet | .75 | .75 |
| **7** | A1 | 30h bister (R) | .25 | .25 |
| **8** | A1 | 40h red orange | .30 | .30 |
| **9** | A2 | 50h dull violet | .60 | .45 |
| **10** | A2 | 50h dark blue | 2.60 | 1.50 |
| **11** | A2 | 60h orange (Bl) | .75 | .75 |
| **12** | A2 | 75h slate (R) | .50 | .75 |
| **13** | A2 | 80h olive grn (R) | .50 | .75 |
| **14** | A1 | 100h brown | 1.10 | 1.10 |
| **15** | A2 | 120h gray blk (R) | 1.60 | *2.25* |
| **16** | A1 | 200h ultra (R) | 1.60 | *2.00* |
| **17** | A2 | 300h green (R) | 6.25 | *7.50* |
| **18** | A1 | 400h purple (R) | 2.60 | *3.00* |
| **20** | A2 | 500h red brn (Bl) | 5.25 | *6.00* |
| *a.* | | Black overprint | 6.25 | *9.00* |
| **21** | A2 | 1000h violet (Bl) | 13.00 | *13.50* |
| *a.* | | Black overprint | 62.50 | *75.00* |
| | | *Nos. 1-21 (20)* | 73.40 | 75.15 |
| | | ***Perf. 11½, 13¾*** | | |
| **22** | A2 | 1h dark brown | .25 | .25 |
| **23** | A2 | 5h blue green | .30 | .25 |
| **24** | A2 | 10h yellow green | .30 | .25 |
| *a.* | | Imperf. | *260.00* | *210.00* |
| **25** | A2 | 15h red | .50 | .25 |
| **26** | A2 | 20h rose | .50 | .35 |
| *a.* | | Imperf. | *300.00* | *250.00* |
| **27** | A2 | 25h dull violet | .50 | .35 |
| **28** | A2 | 30h red violet (Bl) | .35 | .35 |
| **29** | A2 | 60h orange (Bl) | .50 | .50 |
| **30** | A1 | 200h ultra (R) | 3.00 | 3.00 |
| | | *Nos. 22-30 (9)* | 6.20 | 5.55 |

The letters "S. O." are the initials of "Silésie Orientale."

Forged cancellations are found on Nos. 1-30.

Overprinted in Carmine or Violet

| | | | |
|---|---|---|---|
| **31** | A4 | 500h sl, *grysh* (C) | 40.00 |
| **32** | A4 | 1000h blk brn, *brnsh* | 40.00 |

Excellent counterfeits of this overprint exist.

Stamps of Poland, 1919, Overprinted

| 1920 | | | *Perf. 11½* | |
|---|---|---|---|---|
| **41** | A10 | 5f green | .25 | .25 |
| **42** | A10 | 10f red brown | .25 | .25 |
| **43** | A10 | 15f light red | .25 | .25 |
| **44** | A11 | 25f olive green | .25 | .25 |
| **45** | A11 | 50f blue green | .25 | .25 |

Overprinted

| | | | | |
|---|---|---|---|---|
| **46** | A12 | 1k deep green | .25 | .25 |
| **47** | A12 | 1.50k brown | .25 | .25 |
| **48** | A12 | 2k dark blue | .25 | .25 |
| **49** | A13 | 2.50k dull violet | .30 | .25 |
| **50** | A14 | 5k slate blue | .50 | .25 |
| | | *Nos. 41-50 (10)* | 2.80 | 2.50 |

### SPECIAL DELIVERY STAMPS

Czechoslovakia Special Delivery Stamps Ovptd. in Blue

| 1920 | | Unwmk. | *Imperf.* | |
|---|---|---|---|---|
| **E1** | SD1 | 2h red violet, *yel* | .25 | .25 |
| *a.* | | Black overprint | 4.75 | .80 |
| **E2** | SD1 | 5h yellow green, *yel* | .25 | .25 |
| *a.* | | Black overprint | 8.00 | 5.00 |

Nos. E1-E2a exist on white paper.

### POSTAGE DUE STAMPS

Czechoslovakia Postage Due Stamps Overprinted In Blue or Red

| 1920 | | Unwmk. | *Imperf.* | |
|---|---|---|---|---|
| **J1** | D1 | 5h deep bis (Bl) | .25 | .25 |
| *a.* | | Black overprint | 72.50 | 62.50 |
| **J2** | D1 | 10h deep bister | .25 | .25 |
| **J3** | D1 | 15h deep bister | .25 | .25 |
| **J4** | D1 | 20h deep bister | .25 | .25 |
| **J5** | D1 | 25h deep bister | .25 | .25 |
| **J6** | D1 | 30h deep bister | .25 | .25 |
| **J7** | D1 | 40h deep bister | .50 | .25 |
| **J8** | D1 | 50h deep bister | 2.60 | 3.00 |
| **J9** | D1 | 100h blk brn (R) | 2.60 | 3.00 |
| **J10** | D1 | 500h gray grn (R) | 5.75 | 4.50 |
| **J11** | D1 | 1000h purple (R) | 8.50 | 11.50 |
| | | *Nos. J1-J11 (11)* | 21.45 | 23.75 |

Forged cancellations exist.

### NEWSPAPER STAMPS

**Czechoslovakia Newspaper Stamps Overprinted in Black like Nos. 1-30**

| 1920 | | Unwmk. | *Imperf.* | |
|---|---|---|---|---|
| **P1** | N1 | 2h gray green | .30 | .30 |
| **P2** | N1 | 6h red | .25 | .25 |
| **P3** | N1 | 10h dull violet | .40 | .25 |
| **P4** | N1 | 20h blue | .65 | .25 |
| **P5** | N1 | 30h gray brown | .65 | .25 |
| | | *Nos. P1-P5 (5)* | 2.25 | 1.30 |

# ECUADOR

ˈe-kwə-ˌdor

LOCATION — Northwest coast of South America, bordering on the Pacific Ocean
GOVT. — Republic
AREA — 116,270 (?) sq. mi.
POP. — 12,562,496 (1999 est.)
CAPITAL — Quito

The Republic of Ecuador was so constituted on May 11, 1830, after the Civil War that separated the original members of the Republic of Colombia, founded by Simon Bolivar by uniting the Presidency of Quito with the Viceroyalty of New Grenada and the Captaincy of Venezuela. The Presidency of Quito became the Republic of Ecuador.

8 Reales = 1 Peso
100 Centavos = 1 Sucre (1881)
100 Cents = 1 Dollar (2000)

**Catalogue values for unused stamps in this country are for Never Hinged items, beginning with Scott 453 in the regular postage section, Scott C147 in the airpost section, Scott CO19 in the airpost officials section, Scott O201 in the officials section, Scott RA60 in the postal tax section, and all entries in the Galapagos section.**

## Watermarks

Wmk. 117 — Liberty Cap

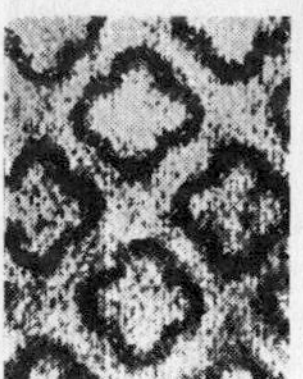
Wmk. 127 Quatrefoils

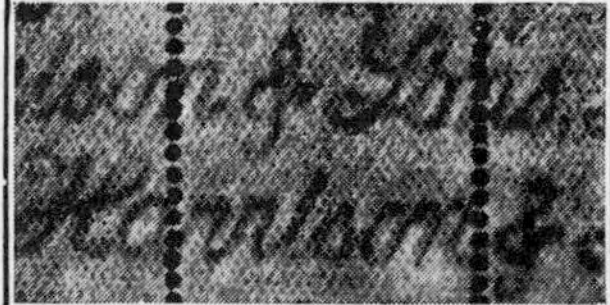
Wmk. 233 — "Harrison & Sons, London" in Script Letters

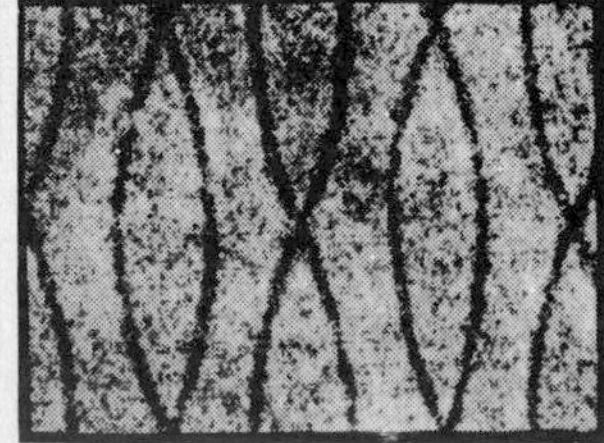
Wmk. 340 — Alternating Interlaced Wavy Lines

Wmk. 367 — Liberty Cap, Emblem, Inscription

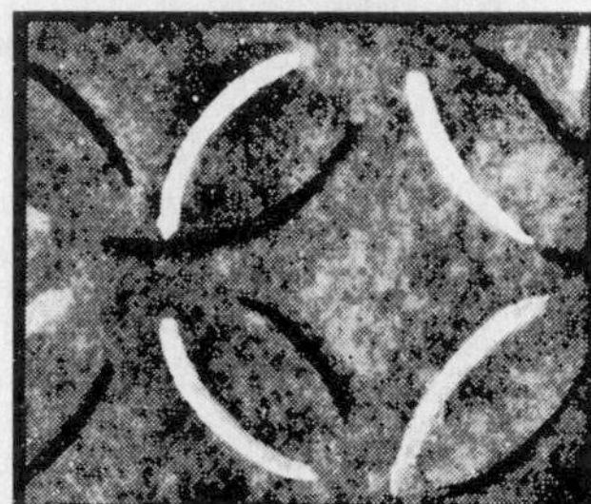
Wmk. 377 — Interlocking Circles

Wmk. 395 — Emblem, Inscription

Coat of Arms
A1 A2

**1865-72 Unwmk. Typo. *Imperf.***

**Quadrille Paper**

| | | | | |
|---|---|---|---|---|
| 1 | A1 | 1r yellow ('72) | 60.00 | 55.00 |

**Wove Paper**

| | | | | |
|---|---|---|---|---|
| 2 | A1 | ½r ultra | 40.00 | 20.00 |
| a. | | ½r gray blue ('67) | 40.00 | 15.00 |
| b. | | Batonne paper ('70) | 50.00 | 25.00 |
| c. | | Blue paper ('72) | 250.00 | 100.00 |
| 3 | A1 | 1r buff | 25.00 | 18.00 |
| a. | | 1r orange buff | 30.00 | 20.00 |
| 4 | A1 | 1r yellow | 25.00 | 15.00 |
| a. | | 1r olive yellow ('66) | 32.50 | 22.50 |
| b. | | Laid paper | 175.00 | 110.00 |
| c. | | Half used as ½r on cover | | 900.00 |
| d. | | Batonne paper | 40.00 | 30.00 |
| 5 | A1 | 1r green | 300.00 | 55.00 |
| a. | | Half used as ½r on cover | | *900.00* |
| 6 | A2 | 4r red ('66) | 500.00 | 200.00 |
| a. | | 4r red brown ('66) | 700.00 | 200.00 |
| b. | | Arms in circle | 500.00 | 250.00 |
| c. | | Printed on both sides | 550.00 | — |
| d. | | Half used as 2r on cover | | 1,600. |
| | | *Nos. 1-6 (6)* | 950.00 | 363.00 |

Letter paper embossed with arms of Ecuador was used in printing a number of sheets of Nos. 2, 4-6.

On the 4r the oval holding the coat of arms is usually 13½-14mm wide, but on about one-fifth of the stamps in the sheet it is 15-15½mm wide, almost a circle.

The 2r, 8r and 12r, type A1, are bogus.

Proofs of the ½r, type A1, are known in black and green.

An essay of type A2 shows the condor's head facing right.

**1871-72 Blue-surface Paper**

| | | | | |
|---|---|---|---|---|
| 7 | A1 | ½r ultra | 50.00 | 25.00 |
| 8 | A1 | 1r yellow | 300.00 | 100.00 |

*Unofficial reprints of types A1-A2 differ in color, have a different sheet makeup and lack gum. Type A1 reprints usually have a double frameline at left. All stamps on blue paper with horiz. blue lines are reprints.*

A3

A4

**1872 White Paper Litho. *Perf. 11***

| | | | | |
|---|---|---|---|---|
| 9 | A3 | ½r blue | 30.00 | 5.00 |
| 10 | A4 | 1r orange | 40.00 | 7.00 |
| 11 | A3 | 1p rose | 5.00 | *25.00* |
| | | *Nos. 9-11 (3)* | 75.00 | *37.00* |

The 1r surcharged 4c is fraudulent.

A5

A6

A7

A8

A9

A10

**1881, Nov. 1 Engr. *Perf. 12***

| | | | | |
|---|---|---|---|---|
| 12 | A5 | 1c yellow brn | .40 | .25 |
| 13 | A6 | 2c lake | .40 | .25 |
| 14 | A7 | 5c blue | 10.00 | .50 |
| 15 | A8 | 10c orange | .40 | .25 |
| 16 | A9 | 20c gray violet | .40 | .25 |
| 17 | A10 | 50c blue green | 2.00 | *3.00* |
| | | *Nos. 12-17 (6)* | 13.60 | *4.50* |

The 1c surcharged 3c, and 20c surcharged 5c are fraudulent.

For overprints see Nos. O1-O6.

No. 17 Surcharged in Black

**1883, Apr.**

| | | | | |
|---|---|---|---|---|
| 18 | A10 | 10c on 50c blue grn | 50.00 | 30.00 |
| a. | | Double surcharge | | |

Dangerous forgeries exist.

A12

A13

A14

A15

**1887**

| | | | | |
|---|---|---|---|---|
| 19 | A12 | 1c blue green | .50 | .40 |
| 20 | A13 | 2c vermilion | 1.00 | .40 |
| 21 | A14 | 5c blue | 3.00 | .50 |
| 22 | A15 | 80c olive green | 6.00 | *15.00* |
| | | *Nos. 19-22 (4)* | 10.50 | *16.30* |

For overprints see Nos. O7-O10.

President Juan Flores — A16

**1892**

| | | | | |
|---|---|---|---|---|
| 23 | A16 | 1c orange | .30 | 1.00 |
| 24 | A16 | 2c dk brown | .30 | 1.00 |
| 25 | A16 | 5c vermilion | .30 | 1.00 |
| 26 | A16 | 10c green | .30 | 1.00 |
| 27 | A16 | 20c red brown | .30 | 1.00 |
| 28 | A16 | 50c maroon | .30 | *2.00* |
| 29 | A16 | 1s blue | .30 | *4.00* |
| 30 | A16 | 5s purple | 1.00 | *8.00* |
| | | *Nos. 23-30 (8)* | 3.10 | *19.00* |

The issues of 1892, 1894, 1895 and 1896 were printed by the Hamilton Bank Note Co., New York, to the order of N. F. Seebeck, who held a contract for stamps with the government of Ecuador.

No. 30 in green is said to be an essay or color trial.

For surcharges and overprints see Nos. 31-37, O11-O17.

Nos. 29 and 30 Surcharged in Black

**1893**

**Surcharge Measures 25½x2½mm**

| | | | | |
|---|---|---|---|---|
| 31 | A16 | 5c on 1s blue | 6.00 | 6.00 |
| 32 | A16 | 5c on 5s purple | 10.00 | 9.00 |
| a. | | Double surcharge | | |

**Surcharge Measures 24x2¼mm**

| | | | | |
|---|---|---|---|---|
| 33 | A16 | 5c on 1s blue | 3.00 | 3.00 |
| a. | | Double surcharge, one inverted | | |
| 34 | A16 | 5c on 5s purple | 12.00 | 10.00 |
| a. | | Double surcharge, one invtd. | | |

Nos. 28-30 Surcharged in Black

| | | | | |
|---|---|---|---|---|
| 35 | A16 | 5c on 50c maroon | 2.00 | 2.00 |
| a. | | Inverted surcharge | 5.00 | |
| 36 | A16 | 5c on 1s blue | 2.50 | 2.00 |
| 37 | A16 | 5c on 5s purple | 10.00 | 10.00 |
| | | *Nos. 31-37 (7)* | 45.50 | 42.00 |

Pres. Juan Flores — A19

| | | | | |
|---|---|---|---|---|
| 38 | A19 | 5c on 5s lake | 4.00 | 4.00 |

It is stated that No. 38 was used exclusively as a postage stamp and not for telegrams.

Pres. Vicente Rocafuerte — A20

**Dated "1894"**

**1894 Various Frames *Perf. 12***

| | | | | |
|---|---|---|---|---|
| 39 | A20 | 1c blue | .40 | .40 |
| 40 | A20 | 2c yellow brn | .40 | .40 |
| 41 | A20 | 5c green | .40 | .40 |
| b. | | Perf. 14 | 6.00 | 2.00 |
| 42 | A20 | 10c vermilion | .70 | .60 |
| 43 | A20 | 20c black | 1.10 | .70 |
| 44 | A20 | 50c orange | 6.00 | 2.00 |
| 45 | A20 | 1s carmine | 9.50 | 4.00 |
| 46 | A20 | 5s dark blue | 12.00 | 6.00 |
| | | *Nos. 39-46 (8)* | 30.50 | 14.50 |

**1895 Same, Dated "1895"**

| No. | Type | Value | Color | Unused | Used |
|---|---|---|---|---|---|
| **47** | A20 | 1c | blue | .90 | .70 |
| **48** | A20 | 2c | yellow brn | .90 | .70 |
| **49** | A20 | 5c | green | .70 | .50 |
| **50** | A20 | 10c | vermilion | .70 | .40 |
| **51** | A20 | 20c | black | 1.00 | 1.00 |
| **52** | A20 | 50c | orange | 3.50 | 2.25 |
| **53** | A20 | 1s | carmine | 21.00 | 8.00 |
| **54** | A20 | 5s | dark blue | 8.50 | 4.00 |
| | | | *Nos. 47-54 (8)* | 37.20 | 17.55 |

*Reprints of the 2c, 10c, 50c, 1s and 5s of the 1894-95 issues are generally on thick paper. Original issues are on thin to medium thick paper. To distinguish reprints from originals, a comparison of paper thickness, paper color, gum, printing clarity and direction of paper weave is necessary. Value 20 cents each.*

For overprints see Nos. 77-112, O20-O33, O50-O91.

A21

A22

A23

A24

A25

A26

A27

A28

**1896 Wmk. 117**

| No. | Type | Value | Color | Unused | Used |
|---|---|---|---|---|---|
| **55** | A21 | 1c | dk green | .70 | .60 |
| **56** | A22 | 2c | red | .70 | .40 |
| **57** | A23 | 5c | blue | .70 | .40 |
| **58** | A24 | 10c | bister brn | .60 | *.90* |
| **59** | A25 | 20c | orange | 1.40 | *2.00* |
| **60** | A26 | 50c | dark blue | 5.00 | 3.00 |
| **61** | A27 | 1s | yellow brn | 4.00 | *4.00* |
| **62** | A28 | 5s | violet | 14.00 | 5.50 |
| | | | *Nos. 55-62 (8)* | 27.10 | *16.80* |

**Unwmk.**

| No. | Type | Value | Color | Unused | Used |
|---|---|---|---|---|---|
| **62A** | A21 | 1c | dk green | 1.00 | .40 |
| **62B** | A22 | 2c | red | 1.10 | .40 |
| **62C** | A23 | 5c | blue | 1.10 | .70 |
| **62D** | A24 | 10c | bister brn | .70 | *1.40* |
| **62E** | A25 | 20c | orange | 6.00 | 5.50 |
| **62F** | A26 | 50c | dark blue | 2.00 | *2.75* |
| **62G** | A27 | 1s | yellow brn | 6.00 | *8.00* |
| **62H** | A28 | 5s | violet | 15.00 | 6.00 |
| | | | *Nos. 62A-62H (8)* | *32.90* | *25.15* |

*Reprints of Nos. 55-62H are on very thick paper, with paper weave direction vertical. Value 20 cents each.*

For surcharges and overprints see Nos. 74, 76, 113-114, O34-O49.

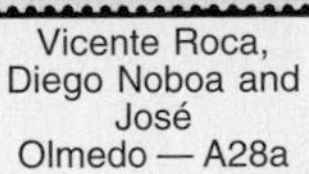

Vicente Roca, Diego Noboa and José Olmedo — A28a

General Juan Francisco Elizalde — A28b

***Perf. 11½***

**1896, Oct. 9 Unwmk. Litho.**

| No. | Type | Value | Color | Unused | Used |
|---|---|---|---|---|---|
| **63** | A28a | 1c | rose | .55 | .55 |
| **64** | A28b | 2c | blue | .55 | .55 |
| **65** | A28a | 5c | green | .75 | .75 |
| **66** | A28b | 10c | ocher | .75 | .75 |
| **67** | A28a | 20c | red | 1.10 | *3.25* |
| **68** | A28b | 50c | violet | 1.75 | *4.75* |
| **69** | A28a | 1s | orange | 3.25 | *8.00* |
| | | | *Nos. 63-69 (7)* | 8.70 | *18.60* |

Success of the Liberal Party in 1845 & 1895.
For overprints see Nos. 115-125.

A29

**Black Surcharge**

**1896, Nov.** ***Perf. 12***

| No. | Type | Description | Unused | Used |
|---|---|---|---|---|
| **70** | A29 | 1c on 1c ver, "1893-1894" | 1.00 | .60 |
| *a.* | | Inverted surcharge | 2.50 | 2.00 |
| *b.* | | Double surcharge | 8.00 | 7.00 |
| **71** | A29 | 2c on 2c bl, "1893-1894" | 2.00 | 1.75 |
| *a.* | | Inverted surcharge | 4.00 | 3.50 |
| **72** | A20 | 5c on 10c org, "1887-1888" | 2.00 | .60 |
| *a.* | | Inverted surcharge | 4.00 | 1.75 |
| *b.* | | Double surcharge | 7.00 | 4.00 |
| *c.* | | Surcharged "2cts" | 1.00 | .80 |
| *d.* | | "1893-1894" | 6.00 | 5.00 |
| **73** | A29 | 10c on 4c brn, "1887-1888" | 2.00 | 1.10 |
| *a.* | | Inverted surcharge | 4.00 | 1.75 |
| *b.* | | Double surcharge | 6.00 | 3.50 |
| *c.* | | Double surcharge, one inverted | | |
| *d.* | | Surcharged "1 cto" | 2.00 | *2.75* |
| *e.* | | "1891-1892" | 17.00 | 13.50 |
| | | *Nos. 70-73 (4)* | 7.00 | 4.05 |

Similar surcharges of type A29 include: Dated "1887-1888" — 1c on 1c blue green, 1c on 2c red, 1c on 4c brown, 1c on 10c yellow; 2c on 2c red, 2c on 10c yellow; 10c on 1c green.

Dated "1891-1892" — 1c on 1c blue green, 1c on 4c brown.

Dated "1893-1894" — 2c on 10c yellow; 10c on 1c vermilion, 10c on 10s black.

For overprints see Nos. O18-O19.

Nos. 59-60 Surcharged in Black or Red

**1896, Oct. Wmk. 117**

| No. | Type | Description | Unused | Used |
|---|---|---|---|---|
| **74** | A25 | 5c on 20c orange | 40.00 | 40.00 |
| **76** | A26 | 10c on 50c dk bl (R) | 50.00 | 50.00 |
| *a.* | | Double surcharge | | |

The surcharge is diag., horiz. or vert.

Nos. 39-54 Overprinted

**On Issue of 1894**

**1897 Unwmk.**

| No. | Type | Value | Color | Unused | Used |
|---|---|---|---|---|---|
| **77** | A20 | 1c | blue | 2.25 | 2.25 |
| **78** | A20 | 2c | yellow brn | 1.90 | 1.30 |
| **79** | A20 | 5c | green | .90 | .90 |
| **80** | A20 | 10c | vermilion | 2.75 | 2.25 |
| **81** | A20 | 20c | black | 3.00 | 2.75 |
| **82** | A20 | 50c | orange | 6.50 | 3.25 |
| **83** | A20 | 1s | carmine | 19.00 | 6.50 |
| **84** | A20 | 5s | dark blue | 110.00 | 90.00 |
| | | | *Nos. 77-84 (8)* | 146.30 | 109.20 |

**On Issue of 1895**

| No. | Type | Value | Color | Unused | Used |
|---|---|---|---|---|---|
| **85** | A20 | 1c | blue | 6.00 | 5.50 |
| **86** | A20 | 2c | yellow brn | 2.25 | 2.25 |
| **87** | A20 | 5c | green | 1.90 | 1.60 |
| **88** | A20 | 10c | vermilion | 7.00 | 6.00 |
| **89** | A20 | 20c | black | 1.90 | 1.75 |
| **90** | A20 | 50c | orange | 32.50 | 13.00 |
| **91** | A20 | 1s | carmine | 14.50 | 7.50 |
| **92** | A20 | 5s | dark blue | 14.50 | 14.50 |
| | | | *Nos. 85-92 (8)* | 80.55 | 52.10 |

Nos. 39-54 Overprinted

**On Issue of 1894**

| No. | Type | Value | Color | Unused | Used |
|---|---|---|---|---|---|
| **93** | A20 | 1c | blue | 1.40 | .90 |
| **94** | A20 | 2c | yellow brn | 1.20 | .75 |
| **95** | A20 | 5c | green | .60 | .50 |
| **96** | A20 | 10c | vermilion | 3.50 | 1.75 |
| **97** | A20 | 20c | black | 3.75 | 2.50 |
| **98** | A20 | 50c | orange | 7.00 | 2.75 |
| **99** | A20 | 1s | carmine | 13.00 | 8.50 |
| **100** | A20 | 5s | dark blue | 115.00 | 85.00 |
| | | | *Nos. 93-100 (8)* | 145.45 | 102.65 |

**On Issue of 1895**

| No. | Type | Value | Color | Unused | Used |
|---|---|---|---|---|---|
| **101** | A20 | 1c | blue | 3.25 | 1.60 |
| **102** | A20 | 2c | yellow brn | 1.60 | 1.60 |
| **103** | A20 | 5c | green | 1.75 | 1.00 |
| **104** | A20 | 10c | vermilion | 5.50 | 4.50 |
| **105** | A20 | 20c | black | 5.00 | 1.20 |
| **106** | A20 | 50c | orange | 1.75 | 1.75 |
| **107** | A20 | 1s | carmine | 8.00 | 7.00 |
| **108** | A20 | 5s | dark blue | 9.50 | 9.50 |
| | | | *Nos. 101-108 (8)* | 36.35 | 28.15 |

Overprints on Nos. 77-108 are to be found reading upward from left to right and downward from left to right, as well as inverted.

Overprinted

**1897 On Issue of 1894**

| No. | Type | Value | Color | Unused | Used |
|---|---|---|---|---|---|
| **109** | A20 | 10c | vermilion | — | — |

**On Issue of 1895**

| No. | Type | Value | Color | Unused | Used |
|---|---|---|---|---|---|
| **110** | A20 | 2c | yellow brn | — | — |
| **111** | A20 | 1s | carmine | — | — |
| **112** | A20 | 5s | dark blue | — | — |

**Nos. 56, 59 Overprinted like Nos. 93-108**

**1897, June Wmk. 117**

| No. | Type | Value | Color | Unused | Used |
|---|---|---|---|---|---|
| **113** | A22 | 2c | red | — | — |
| **114** | A25 | 20c | orange | — | — |

Many forged overprints on Nos. 77-114 exist, made on original stamps and reprints.

Stamps or Types of 1896 Overprinted in Black

**1897 Unwmk.** ***Perf. 11½***

| No. | Type | Value | Color | Unused | Used |
|---|---|---|---|---|---|
| **115** | A28a | 1c | rose | 3.75 | 3.75 |
| **116** | A28b | 2c | blue | 3.00 | 3.00 |
| **117** | A28b | 10c | ocher | 3.00 | 3.00 |
| **118** | A28a | 1s | yellow | 15.00 | 15.00 |
| | | | *Nos. 115-118 (4)* | 24.75 | 24.75 |

No. 63 Overprinted in Black

**1897**

| No. | Type | Value | Color | Unused | Used |
|---|---|---|---|---|---|
| **119** | A28a | 1c | rose | .60 | .50 |

Nos. 63-66 Overprinted in Black

**1897**

| No. | Type | Value | Color | Unused | Used |
|---|---|---|---|---|---|
| **122** | A28a | 1c | rose | 4.50 | 4.00 |
| **123** | A28b | 2c | blue | 4.50 | 4.00 |
| **124** | A28a | 5c | green | 4.50 | 4.00 |
| **125** | A28b | 10c | ocher | 4.50 | 4.00 |
| *a.* | | | Double overprint | 10.50 | 9.50 |
| | | | *Nos. 122-125 (4)* | 18.00 | 16.00 |

*The 20c, 50c and 1s with this overprint in black and all values of the issue overprinted in blue are reprints.*

**Overprint Inverted**

| No. | Type | Value | Unused | Used |
|---|---|---|---|---|
| *122a* | A28a | 1c | 6.00 | 5.50 |
| *123a* | A28b | 2c | 6.00 | 5.50 |
| *124a* | A28a | 5c | 6.00 | 5.50 |
| *125b* | A28b | 10c | 6.00 | 5.50 |

Coat of Arms — A33

**1897, June 23 Engr.** ***Perf. 14-16***

| No. | Type | Value | Color | Unused | Used |
|---|---|---|---|---|---|
| **127** | A33 | 1c | dk yellow grn | .35 | .25 |
| **128** | A33 | 2c | orange red | .35 | .25 |
| **129** | A33 | 5c | lake | .35 | .25 |
| **130** | A33 | 10c | dk brown | .35 | .25 |
| **131** | A33 | 20c | yellow | .45 | .40 |
| **132** | A33 | 50c | dull blue | .45 | *.65* |
| **133** | A33 | 1s | gray | .90 | *1.25* |
| **134** | A33 | 5s | dark lilac | 4.00 | *5.00* |
| | | | *Nos. 127-134 (8)* | 7.20 | *8.30* |

No. 135

No. 136

**1899, May**

| No. | Type | Description | Unused | Used |
|---|---|---|---|---|
| **135** | A33 | 1c on 2c orange red | 3.00 | 1.50 |
| **136** | A33 | 5c on 10c brown | 2.50 | 1.00 |
| *a.* | | Double surcharge | | |

Luis Vargas Torres A36

Abdón Calderón A37

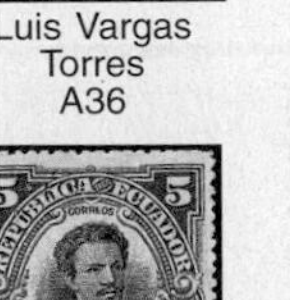

Juan Montalvo A38

José Mejia A39

Santa Cruz y Espejo — A40

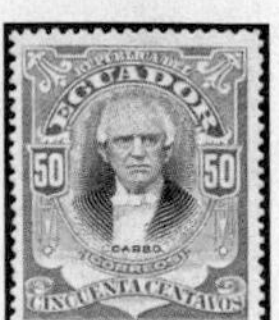

Pedro Carbo — A41

José Joaquin Olmedo
A42

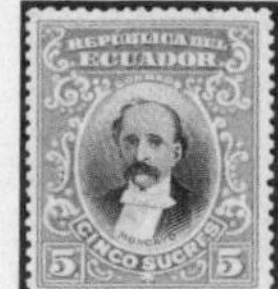

Pedro Moncayo
A43

**1899** *Perf. 12½-16*

| No. | Type | Denomination | Color | Unused | Used |
|---|---|---|---|---|---|
| 137 | A36 | 1c | gray blue & blk | .40 | .25 |
| *a.* | | Horiz. pair, imperf. vert. | | | |
| 138 | A37 | 2c | brown lil & blk | .40 | .25 |
| 139 | A38 | 5c | lake & blk | .70 | .25 |
| 140 | A39 | 10c | violet & blk | .70 | .25 |
| 141 | A40 | 20c | green & blk | .70 | .25 |
| 142 | A41 | 50c | lil rose & blk | 1.75 | .55 |
| 143 | A42 | 1s | ocher & blk | 8.00 | 2.75 |
| 144 | A43 | 5s | lilac & blk | 14.50 | 7.50 |
| | | *Nos. 137-144 (8)* | | 27.15 | 12.05 |

**1901**

| No. | Type | Denomination | Color | Unused | Used |
|---|---|---|---|---|---|
| 145 | A36 | 1c | scarlet & blk | .45 | .25 |
| 146 | A37 | 2c | green & blk | .45 | .25 |
| 147 | A38 | 5c | gray lil & blk | .45 | .25 |
| 148 | A39 | 10c | dp blue & blk | .50 | .25 |
| 149 | A40 | 20c | gray & blk | .50 | .25 |
| 150 | A41 | 50c | lt blue & blk | 1.75 | .95 |
| 151 | A42 | 1s | brown & blk | 6.00 | 2.75 |
| 152 | A43 | 5s | gray blk & blk | 9.00 | 5.75 |
| | | *Nos. 145-152 (8)* | | 19.10 | 10.70 |

In July, 1902, following the theft of a quantity of stamps during a fire at Guayaquil, the Government authorized the governors of the provinces to handstamp their stocks. Many varieties of these handstamps exist.

Other control marks were used in 1907.

For overprints see Nos. O103-O106, O167.

A44

**Surcharged on Revenue Stamp Dated 1901-1902**

**1903-06** *Perf. 14, 15*

| No. | Type | Description | Unused | Used |
|---|---|---|---|---|
| 153 | A44 | 1c on 5c gray lil ('06) | .75 | .40 |
| 154 | A44 | 1c on 20c gray ('06) | 10.00 | 4.50 |
| 155 | A44 | 1c on 25c yellow | 1.50 | .40 |
| *a.* | | Double surcharge | | |
| 156 | A44 | 1c on 1s bl ('06) | 77.50 | 50.00 |
| 157 | A44 | 3c on 5c gray lil ('06) | 10.00 | 4.00 |
| 158 | A44 | 3c on 20c gray ('06) | 25.00 | 15.00 |
| 159 | A44 | 3c on 25c yel ('06) | 24.00 | 15.00 |
| 159A | A44 | 3c on 1s blue ('06) | 3.75 | 2.25 |
| | | *Nos. 153-159A (8)* | 152.50 | 91.55 |

Counterfeits are plentiful.

See Nos. 191-197.

Capt. Abdón Calderón
A45 A46

**1904, July 31** *Perf. 12*

| No. | Type | Denomination | Color | Unused | Used |
|---|---|---|---|---|---|
| 160 | A45 | 1c | red & blk | .45 | .30 |
| 161 | A45 | 2c | blue & blk | .50 | .35 |
| 162 | A46 | 5c | yellow & blk | 1.90 | 1.00 |
| 163 | A45 | 10c | red & blk | 6.00 | 2.00 |
| 164 | A45 | 20c | blue & blk | 10.00 | 8.00 |
| 165 | A46 | 50c | yellow & blk | 85.00 | *120.00* |
| | | *Nos. 160-165 (6)* | | 103.85 | 131.65 |

Centenary of the birth of Calderón.

**Presidents**

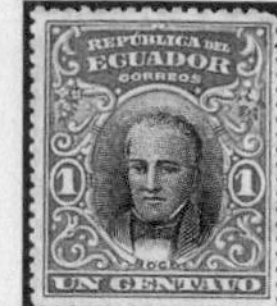

Vicente Roca — A47

Diego Noboa — A48

Francisco Robles — A49

José M. Urvina — A50

García Moreno — A51

Jerónimo Carrión — A52

Javier Espinoza
A53

Antonio Borrero
A54

**1907, July** *Perf. 14, 15*

| No. | Type | Denomination | Color | Unused | Used |
|---|---|---|---|---|---|
| 166 | A47 | 1c | red & blk | 1.00 | .25 |
| 167 | A48 | 2c | pale blue & blk | 2.00 | .25 |
| 168 | A49 | 3c | orange & blk | 3.00 | .25 |
| 169 | A50 | 5c | lilac rose & blk | 3.75 | .25 |
| 170 | A51 | 10c | dp blue & blk | 7.50 | .25 |
| 171 | A52 | 20c | yellow grn & blk | 10.00 | .35 |
| 172 | A53 | 50c | violet & blk | 22.50 | .70 |
| 173 | A54 | 1s | green & blk | 30.00 | 2.00 |
| | | *Nos. 166-173 (8)* | | 79.75 | 4.30 |

The stamps of the 1907 issue frequently have control marks similar to those found on the 1899 and 1901 issues. These marks were applied to distinguish the stamps issued in the various provinces and to serve as a check on local officials.

Locomotive — A55

García Moreno — A56

Gen. Eloy Alfaro — A57

Abelardo Moncayo — A58

Archer Harman — A59

James Sivewright — A60

Mt. Chimborazo
A61

**1908, June 25**

| No. | Type | Denomination | Color | Unused | Used |
|---|---|---|---|---|---|
| 174 | A55 | 1c | red brown | 1.10 | *2.10* |
| 175 | A56 | 2c | blue & blk | 1.30 | *2.25* |
| 176 | A57 | 5c | claret & blk | 2.75 | *5.25* |
| 177 | A58 | 10c | ocher & blk | 1.75 | *2.75* |
| 178 | A59 | 20c | green & blk | 1.75 | *3.75* |
| 179 | A60 | 50c | gray & blk | 1.75 | *3.75* |
| 180 | A61 | 1s | black | 3.50 | *8.00* |
| | | *Nos. 174-180 (7)* | | 13.90 | *27.85* |

Opening of the Guayaquil-Quito Railway.

José Mejía Vallejo — A62

Principal Exposition Building — A70

Designs: 2c, Francisco J. E. Santa Cruz y Espejo. 3c, Francisco Ascásubi. 5c, Juan Salinas. 10c, Juan Pio de Montúfar, el Marques de Selva Alegre. 20c, Carlos de Montúfar. 50c, Juan de Dios Morales. 1s, Manuel R. de Quiroga.

**1909, Aug. 10** *Perf. 12*

| No. | Type | Denomination | Color | Unused | Used |
|---|---|---|---|---|---|
| 181 | A62 | 1c | green | .35 | *.65* |
| 182 | A62 | 2c | blue | .35 | *.65* |
| 183 | A62 | 3c | orange | .35 | *.75* |
| 184 | A62 | 5c | claret | .35 | *.75* |
| 185 | A62 | 10c | yellow brn | .45 | *.75* |
| 186 | A62 | 20c | gray | .45 | *1.10* |
| 187 | A62 | 50c | vermilion | .45 | *1.10* |
| 188 | A62 | 1s | olive grn | .45 | *1.40* |
| 189 | A70 | 5s | violet | 1.25 | *2.75* |
| | | *Nos. 181-189 (9)* | | 4.45 | *9.90* |

National Exposition of 1909.

No. 187 Surcharged

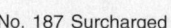

**1909**

| No. | Type | Description | Unused | Used |
|---|---|---|---|---|
| 190 | A62 | 5c on 50c vermilion | .90 | .75 |

**Revenue Stamps Surcharged as in 1903**

**1910** *Perf. 14, 15*

**Stamps Dated 1905-1906**

| No. | Type | Description | Unused | Used |
|---|---|---|---|---|
| 191 | A44 | 1c on 5c green | 2.25 | 1.75 |
| 192 | A44 | 5c on 20c blue | 9.50 | 2.00 |
| 193 | A44 | 5c on 25c violet | 18.00 | 3.50 |

**Stamps Dated 1907-1908**

| No. | Type | Description | Unused | Used |
|---|---|---|---|---|
| 194 | A44 | 1c on 5c green | .40 | .40 |
| 195 | A44 | 5c on 20c blue | 14.00 | 9.50 |
| 196 | A44 | 5c on 25c violet | 1.20 | .40 |

**Stamp Dated 1909-1910**

| No. | Type | Description | Unused | Used |
|---|---|---|---|---|
| 197 | A44 | 5c on 20c blue | *80.00* | *60.00* |
| | | *Nos. 191-197 (7)* | *125.35* | *77.55* |

**Presidents**

Roca — A71

Noboa — A72

Robles — A73

Urvina — A74

Moreno — A75

Borrero — A76

**1911-28** *Perf. 12*

| No. | Type | Denomination | Color | Unused | Used |
|---|---|---|---|---|---|
| 198 | A71 | 1c | scarlet & blk | .80 | .25 |
| 199 | A71 | 1c | orange ('16) | .80 | .25 |
| 200 | A71 | 1c | lt blue ('25) | .40 | .25 |
| 201 | A72 | 2c | blue & blk | 1.10 | .25 |
| 202 | A72 | 2c | green ('16) | 1.10 | .25 |
| 203 | A72 | 2c | dk violet ('25) | 1.10 | .25 |
| 204 | A73 | 3c | orange & blk ('13) | 2.25 | .30 |
| 205 | A73 | 3c | black ('15) | 1.50 | .25 |
| 206 | A74 | 5c | scarlet & blk | 1.90 | .25 |
| 207 | A74 | 5c | violet ('15) | 1.90 | .25 |
| 208 | A74 | 5c | rose ('25) | .70 | .25 |
| 209 | A74 | 5c | dk brown ('28) | .70 | .25 |
| 210 | A75 | 10c | dp blue & blk | 2.25 | .25 |
| 211 | A75 | 10c | dp blue ('15) | 2.25 | .25 |
| 212 | A75 | 10c | yellow grn ('25) | .70 | .25 |
| 213 | A75 | 10c | black ('28) | 1.60 | .25 |
| 214 | A76 | 1s | green & blk | 12.00 | 1.50 |
| 215 | A76 | 1s | orange & blk ('27) | 8.00 | .25 |
| | | *Nos. 198-215 (18)* | | 41.05 | 5.80 |

For overprints see Nos. 260-262, 264-265, O107-O122, O124-O134, O156-O157, O160-O162, O164-O166, O168-O173, O175-O178, O183-O184, O189, RA1.

A77

**1912** *Perf. 14, 15*

| No. | Type | Description | Unused | Used |
|---|---|---|---|---|
| 216 | A77 | 1c on 1s green | 1.00 | 1.00 |
| 217 | A77 | 2c on 2s carmine | 2.50 | 1.50 |
| 218 | A77 | 2c on 5s dull blue | 1.50 | 1.50 |
| 219 | A77 | 2c on 10s yellow | 5.00 | 5.00 |
| *a.* | | Inverted surcharge | 16.00 | 12.00 |
| | | *Nos. 216-219 (4)* | 10.00 | 9.00 |

No. 216 exists with narrow "V" and small "U" in "UN" and Nos. 217, 218 and 219 with "D" with serifs or small "O" in "DOS."

Enrique Váldez — A78

Jerónimo Carrión — A79

Javier Espinoza — A80

**1915-17** ***Perf. 12***

| | | | | |
|---|---|---|---|---|
| **220** | A78 | 4c red & blk | .40 | .25 |
| **221** | A79 | 20c green & blk ('17) | 3.50 | .25 |
| **222** | A80 | 50c dp violet & blk | 6.00 | .45 |
| | | *Nos. 220-222 (3)* | 9.90 | .95 |

For overprints see Nos. O123, O135, O163, O174.

Olmedo — A86

Monument to "Fathers of the Country" — A95

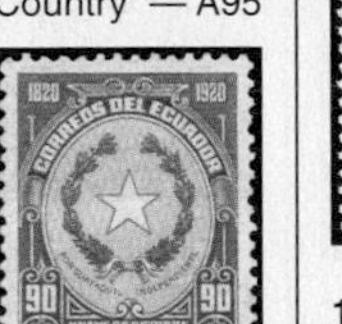


Laurel Wreath and Star — A104

Designs: 2c, Rafael Ximena. 3c, Roca. 4c, Luis F. Vivero. 5c, Luis Febres Cordero. 6c, Francisco Lavayen. 7c, Jorge Antonio de Elizalde. 8c, Baltazar Garcia. 9c, Jose de Antepara. 15c, Luis Urdaneta. 20c, Jose M. Villamil. 30c, Miguel Letamendi. 40c, Gregorio Escobedo. 50c, Gen. Antonio Jose de Sucre. 60c, Juan Illingworth. 70c, Roca. 80c, Rocafuerte. 1s, Simon Bolivar.

**1920**

| | | | | |
|---|---|---|---|---|
| **223** | A86 | 1c yellow grn | .35 | .25 |
| **224** | A86 | 2c carmine | .35 | .25 |
| **225** | A86 | 3c yellow brn | .35 | .25 |
| **226** | A86 | 4c myrtle green | .55 | .25 |
| **227** | A86 | 5c pale blue | .55 | .25 |
| **228** | A86 | 6c red orange | .90 | .30 |
| **229** | A86 | 7c brown | 2.25 | .75 |
| **230** | A86 | 8c apple green | 1.25 | .35 |
| **231** | A86 | 9c lake | 4.25 | 1.50 |
| **232** | A95 | 10c lt blue | 1.50 | .25 |
| **233** | A86 | 15c dk gray | 2.25 | .35 |
| **234** | A86 | 20c dk violet | 2.25 | .25 |
| **235** | A86 | 30c brt violet | 4.25 | 1.40 |
| **236** | A86 | 40c dk brown | 7.50 | 2.10 |
| **237** | A86 | 50c dk green | 5.25 | .55 |
| **238** | A86 | 60c dk blue | 9.50 | 2.10 |
| **239** | A86 | 70c gray | 16.00 | 4.75 |
| **240** | A86 | 80c orange yel | 16.50 | 4.75 |
| **241** | A104 | 90c green | 17.00 | 4.75 |
| **242** | A86 | 1s pale blue | 24.00 | 8.50 |
| | | *Nos. 223-242 (20)* | 116.80 | 33.90 |

Cent. of the independence of Guayaquil.

For overprints and surcharges see Nos. 263, 274-292, O136-O155, O179-O182, O185-O188.

Postal Tax Stamp of 1924 Overprinted

**1925**

| | | | | |
|---|---|---|---|---|
| **259** | PT6 | 20c bister brown | 4.00 | 1.50 |

Stamps of 1915-25 Overprinted in Black or Red Upright (1c, 3c, 5c) or Inverted (2c, 4c, 10c)

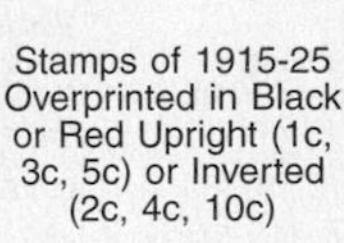

**1926**

| | | | | |
|---|---|---|---|---|
| **260** | A71 | 1c lt blue | 12.50 | 10.50 |
| **261** | A72 | 2c dk violet | 12.50 | 10.50 |
| **262** | A73 | 3c black (R) | 12.50 | 10.50 |
| **263** | A86 | 4c myrtle green | 12.50 | 10.50 |
| **264** | A74 | 5c rose | 17.50 | 10.50 |
| **265** | A75 | 10c yellow grn | 17.50 | 10.50 |
| | | *Nos. 260-265 (6)* | 85.00 | 63.00 |

Quito-Esmeraldas railway opening.

Upright overprints on 2c, 4c, 10c and inverted overprints on 1c, 3c, 5c sell for more.

Postal Tax Stamps of 1920-24 Overprinted

**1927**

| | | | | |
|---|---|---|---|---|
| **266** | PT6 | 1c olive green | .50 | .25 |
| *a.* | | "POSTAI" | 1.40 | .85 |
| *b.* | | Double overprint | 2.00 | .85 |
| *c.* | | Inverted overprint | 2.00 | .85 |
| **267** | PT6 | 2c deep green | .50 | .25 |
| *a.* | | "POSTAI" | 1.40 | .85 |
| *b.* | | Double overprint | 2.00 | .85 |
| **268** | PT6 | 20c bister brown | 1.00 | .25 |
| *a.* | | "POSTAI" | 8.50 | 5.00 |
| | | *Nos. 266-268 (3)* | 2.00 | .75 |

Quito Post Office — A109

**1927, June**

| | | | | |
|---|---|---|---|---|
| **269** | A109 | 5c orange | .50 | .25 |
| **270** | A109 | 10c dark green | .70 | .25 |
| **271** | A109 | 20c violet | .80 | .25 |
| | | *Nos. 269-271 (3)* | 2.00 | .75 |

Opening of new Quito P.O.

For overprint see No. O190.

Postal Tax Stamp of 1924 Overprinted in Dark Blue

**1928**

| | | | | |
|---|---|---|---|---|
| **273** | PT6 | 20c bister brown | .50 | .25 |
| *a.* | | Double overprint, one inverted | 2.00 | .70 |

See No. 339 for 10c with same overprint.

Nos. 235, 239-240 Ovptd. in Red Brown and Srchd. in Dark Blue

**1928, July 8**

| | | | | |
|---|---|---|---|---|
| **274** | A86 | 10c on 30c violet | 16.00 | 16.00 |
| **275** | A86 | 50c on 70c gray | 20.00 | 20.00 |
| **276** | A86 | 1s on 80c org yel | 22.50 | 22.50 |
| | | *Nos. 274-276 (3)* | 58.50 | 58.50 |

Quito-Cayambe railway opening.

Stamps of 1920 Surcharged

**1928, Oct. 9**

| | | | | |
|---|---|---|---|---|
| **277** | A86 | 1c on 1c yel grn | 15.00 | 15.00 |
| **278** | A86 | 1c on 2c car | .30 | .30 |
| **279** | A86 | 2c on 3c yel brn | 2.25 | 2.25 |
| *a.* | | Dbl. surch., one reading up | 30.00 | 30.00 |
| **280** | A86 | 2c on 4c myr grn | 1.50 | 1.50 |
| **281** | A86 | 2c on 5c lt blue | .60 | .45 |
| *a.* | | Dbl. surch., one reading up | 30.00 | 30.00 |
| **282** | A86 | 2c on 7c brown | 75.00 | 75.00 |
| **283** | A86 | 5c on 6c red org | .40 | .30 |
| *a.* | | "5 ctvos." omitted | 37.50 | 37.50 |
| **284** | A86 | 10c on 7c brown | 1.25 | 1.25 |
| **285** | A86 | 20c on 8c apple grn | .35 | .30 |
| *a.* | | Double surcharge | | |
| **286** | A95 | 40c on 10c blue | 4.25 | 4.25 |
| **287** | A86 | 40c on 15c dk gray | 1.25 | 1.25 |
| **288** | A86 | 50c on 20c dk vio | 13.25 | 13.25 |
| **289** | A86 | 1s on 40c dk brown | 4.50 | 4.50 |
| **290** | A86 | 5s on 50c dk green | 5.25 | 5.25 |
| **291** | A86 | 10s on 60c dk blue | 19.50 | 19.50 |

With Additional Surcharge in Red

| | | | | |
|---|---|---|---|---|
| **292** | A86 | 10c on 2c on 7c brn | .55 | .55 |
| *a.* | | Red surcharge double | 30.00 | 30.00 |
| | | *Nos. 277-292 (16)* | 145.20 | 144.90 |

National Assembly of 1928.

Counterfeit overprints exist of Nos. 277-291.

A111

**Surcharged in Various Colors**

**1928, Oct. 31** ***Perf. 14***

| | | | | |
|---|---|---|---|---|
| **293** | A111 | 5c on 20c gray lil (Bk) | 3.00 | 1.75 |
| **294** | A111 | 10c on 20c gray lil (R) | 3.00 | 1.75 |
| **295** | A111 | 20c on 1s grn (O) | 3.00 | 1.75 |
| **296** | A111 | 50c on 1s grn (Bl) | 3.75 | 1.40 |
| **297** | A111 | 1s on 1s grn (V) | 4.75 | 1.75 |
| **298** | A111 | 5s on 2s red (G) | 15.00 | 9.00 |
| **299** | A111 | 10s on 2s red (Br) | 18.00 | 12.00 |
| *a.* | | Black surcharge | 15.00 | 10.00 |
| | | *Nos. 293-299 (7)* | 50.50 | 29.40 |

Quito-Otavalo railway opening.

See Nos. 586-587.

Postal Tax Stamp of 1924 Overprinted in Red

**1929** ***Perf. 12***

| | | | | |
|---|---|---|---|---|
| **302** | PT6 | 2c deep green | .50 | .25 |

There are two types of overprint on No. 302 differing slightly.

A112

**1929** **Red Overprint**

| | | | | |
|---|---|---|---|---|
| **303** | A112 | 1c dark blue | .50 | .25 |
| *a.* | | Overprint reading down | .75 | .60 |

See Nos. 586-587.

Plowing — A113

Cultivating Cacao — A114

Cacao Pod — A115

Growing Tobacco — A116

Exportation of Fruits — A117

Landscape — A118

Loading Sugar Cane — A119

Scene in Quito A120

Scene in Quito A121

Olmedo — A122

Monument to Simón Bolívar — A125

Designs: 2s, Sucre. 5s, Bolivar.

**1930, Aug. 1** *Perf. 12½*

| No. | Type | Description | Unused | Used |
|---|---|---|---|---|
| 304 | A113 | 1c yellow & car | .30 | .25 |
| 305 | A114 | 2c yellow & grn | .30 | .25 |
| 306 | A115 | 5c dp grn & vio brn | .35 | .25 |
| 307 | A116 | 6c yellow & red | .45 | .25 |
| 308 | A117 | 10c orange & ol grn | .45 | .25 |
| 309 | A118 | 16c red & yel grn | .55 | .25 |
| 310 | A119 | 20c ultra & yel | .90 | .25 |
| 311 | A120 | 40c orange & sepia | 1.10 | .35 |
| 312 | A121 | 50c orange & sepia | 1.10 | .40 |
| 313 | A122 | 1s dp green & blk | 4.25 | .45 |
| 314 | A122 | 2s dk blue & blk | 6.50 | 2.00 |
| 315 | A122 | 5s dk violet & blk | 11.50 | 3.00 |
| 316 | A125 | 10s car rose & blk | 40.00 | 6.50 |
| | | *Nos. 304-316 (13)* | 67.75 | 14.45 |

Centenary of founding of republic.

For surcharges and overprints see Nos. 319-320, 331-338, RA25, RA33, RA43.

A126

A127

**1933** **Red Overprint** *Perf. 15*

| No. | Type | Description | Unused | Used |
|---|---|---|---|---|
| 317 | A126 | 10c olive brown | 1.15 | .25 |

**Blue Overprint**

| No. | Type | Description | Unused | Used |
|---|---|---|---|---|
| 318 | A127 | 10c olive brown | .70 | .25 |
| a. | | Inverted overprint | 5.00 | 5.00 |

For overprint see No. 339.

**Nos. 307, 309 Surcharged in Black**

**1933** *Perf. 12½*

| No. | Type | Description | Unused | Used |
|---|---|---|---|---|
| 319 | A116 | 5c on 6c yellow & red | 1.00 | .25 |
| 320 | A118 | 10c on 16c red & yel grn | 2.00 | .25 |
| a. | | Inverted overprint | 4.00 | 4.00 |

Landscape A128

Mt. Chimborazo A129

**1934-45** *Perf. 12*

| No. | Type | Description | Unused | Used |
|---|---|---|---|---|
| 321 | A128 | 5c violet | 1.40 | .55 |
| 322 | A128 | 5c blue | 1.40 | .55 |
| 323 | A128 | 5c dark brown | 1.40 | .55 |
| 323A | A128 | 5c slate blk ('45) | 1.40 | .55 |
| 324 | A128 | 10c rose | 1.40 | .55 |
| 325 | A128 | 10c dark green | 1.40 | .55 |
| 326 | A128 | 10c brown | 1.40 | .55 |
| 327 | A128 | 10c orange | 1.40 | .55 |
| 328 | A128 | 10c olive green | 1.40 | .55 |
| 329 | A128 | 10c gray blk ('35) | 1.40 | .55 |
| 329A | A128 | 10c red lilac ('44) | 1.40 | .55 |

*Perf. 14*

| No. | Type | Description | Unused | Used |
|---|---|---|---|---|
| 330 | A129 | 1s carmine rose | 1.60 | .55 |
| | | *Nos. 321-330 (12)* | 17.00 | 6.60 |

Stamps of 1930 Srchd. or Ovptd. in various colors

**1935** *Perf. 12½*

| No. | Type | Description | Unused | Used |
|---|---|---|---|---|
| 331 | A116 | 5c on 6c (Bl) | .90 | .35 |
| 332 | A116 | 10c on 6c (G) | 1.25 | .35 |
| 333 | A119 | 20c (R) | 1.75 | .35 |
| 334 | A120 | 40c (G) | 2.50 | .35 |
| 335 | A121 | 50c (G) | 3.00 | .45 |
| 336 | A122 | 1s on 5s (Gold) | 7.00 | 1.25 |
| 337 | A122 | 2s on 5s (Gold) | 9.50 | 1.75 |
| 338 | A125 | 5s on 10s (Bl) | 12.00 | 5.00 |
| | | *Nos. 331-338,C35-C38 (12)* | 87.90 | 29.85 |

Unveiling of a monument to Bolivar at Quito, July 24, 1935.

A129a

**1935, Oct. 13** **Photo.** *Perf. 11½x11*

| No. | Type | Description | Unused | Used |
|---|---|---|---|---|
| 338A | A129a | 5c ultra & black | .25 | .25 |
| 338B | A129a | 10c orange & blue | .25 | .25 |
| 338C | A129a | 40c dk carmine & red | .25 | *.30* |
| 338D | A129a | 1S blue green & red | .30 | *.70* |
| 338E | A129a | 2S violet & red | .55 | *1.20* |
| | | *Nos. 338A-338E,C38A-C38E (10)* | 4.35 | *7.60* |

Columbus Day. Nos. 338A-338E and C38A-C38E were prepared by the Sociedad Colombista Panamericana and were sold by the Ecuadorian post office through Oct. 30.

**Telegraph Stamp Overprinted Diagonally in Red like No. 273**

**1935** *Perf. 14½*

| No. | Type | Description | Unused | Used |
|---|---|---|---|---|
| 339 | A126 | 10c olive brown | .75 | .25 |

Map of Galápagos Islands A130

Galapagos Land Iguana A131

Galápagos Tortoise — A132

Charles R. Darwin — A133

Columbus A134

Island Scene A135

**1936** *Perf. 14*

| No. | Type | Description | Unused | Used |
|---|---|---|---|---|
| 340 | A130 | 2c black | 1.00 | .25 |
| 341 | A131 | 5c olive grn | 1.25 | .25 |
| 342 | A132 | 10c brown | 2.40 | .30 |
| 343 | A133 | 20c dk violet | 2.75 | .45 |
| 344 | A134 | 1s dk carmine | 5.00 | .85 |
| 345 | A135 | 2s dark blue | 7.75 | 1.40 |
| | | *Nos. 340-345 (6)* | 20.15 | 3.50 |

Cent. of the visit of Charles Darwin to the Galápagos Islands, Sept. 17, 1835.

For overprints see Nos. O191-O195.

**Tobacco Stamp Overprinted in Black**

**1936** *Rouletted 7*

| No. | Type | Description | Unused | Used |
|---|---|---|---|---|
| 346 | PT7 | 1c rose red | .50 | .25 |
| a. | | Horiz. pair, imperf. vert. | | |
| b. | | Double surcharge | | |

No. 346 is similar to type PT7 but does not include "CASA CORREOS."

Louis Godin, Charles M. de la Condamine and Pierre Bouguer A136

Portraits: 5c, 20c, Antonio Ulloa, La Condamine and Jorge Juan.

**1936** **Engr.** *Perf. 12½*

| No. | Type | Description | Unused | Used |
|---|---|---|---|---|
| 347 | A136 | 2c deep blue | .50 | .30 |
| 348 | A136 | 5c dark green | .50 | .30 |
| 349 | A136 | 10c deep orange | .50 | .30 |
| 350 | A136 | 20c violet | .80 | .30 |
| 351 | A136 | 50c dark red | 1.25 | .30 |
| | | *Nos. 347-351,C39-C42 (9)* | 6.60 | 2.60 |

Bicentenary of Geodesical Mission to Quito.

Independence Monument — A137

**1936** *Perf. 13½x14*

| No. | Type | Description | Unused | Used |
|---|---|---|---|---|
| 352 | A137 | 2c green | 2.25 | 1.25 |
| 353 | A137 | 5c dark violet | 2.25 | 1.25 |
| 354 | A137 | 10c carmine rose | 2.25 | 1.25 |
| 355 | A137 | 20c black | 2.25 | 1.25 |
| 356 | A137 | 50c blue | 3.25 | 2.10 |
| 357 | A137 | 1s dark red | 3.75 | 3.25 |
| | | *Nos. 352-357,C43-C50 (14)* | 50.50 | 41.35 |

1st Intl. Philatelic Exhibition at Quito.

Coat of Arms — A138

**Overprint in Black or Red**

**1937** *Perf. 12½*

| No. | Type | Description | Unused | Used |
|---|---|---|---|---|
| 359 | A138 | 5c olive green | 2.00 | .30 |
| 360 | A138 | 10c dark blue (R) | 2.00 | .25 |

For overprint see No. 562.

Andean Landscape A139

Atahualpa, the Last Inca A140

Hat Weavers — A141

Coast Landscape A142

Gold Washing A143

**1937, Aug. 19** *Perf. 11½*

| No. | Type | Description | Unused | Used |
|---|---|---|---|---|
| 361 | A139 | 2c green | .50 | .25 |
| 362 | A140 | 5c deep rose | .50 | .25 |
| 363 | A141 | 10c blue | .50 | .25 |
| 364 | A142 | 20c deep rose | 1.50 | .30 |
| 365 | A143 | 1s olive green | 2.00 | .35 |
| | | *Nos. 361-365 (5)* | 5.00 | 1.40 |

For overprints see Nos. O196-O200.

"Liberty" Carrying Flag of Ecuador — A144

**Engraved and Lithographed**

**1938, Feb. 22** *Perf. 12*

**Center Multicolored**

| No. | Type | Description | Unused | Used |
|---|---|---|---|---|
| 366 | A144 | 2c blue | .25 | .25 |
| 367 | A144 | 5c violet | .35 | .25 |
| 368 | A144 | 10c black | .55 | .25 |
| 369 | A144 | 20c brown | .65 | .25 |
| 370 | A144 | 50c black | 1.10 | .25 |
| 371 | A144 | 1s olive blk | 1.75 | .30 |
| 372 | A144 | 2s dk brn | 3.25 | .55 |
| | | *Nos. 366-372,C57-C63 (14)* | 22.40 | 4.50 |

US Constitution, 150th anniversary.

For overprints and surcharges see Nos. 413-415, 444-446, RA46, RA52.

A145

A146

A147

A148

Designs: 10c, Winged figure holding globe. 50c, Cactus, winged wheel. 1s, "Communications." 2s, "Construction."

*Perf. 13, 13x13½*

**1938, Oct. 30** **Engr.**

| No. | Type | Description | Unused | Used |
|---|---|---|---|---|
| 373 | A145 | 10c bright ultra | .40 | .25 |
| 374 | A146 | 50c deep red violet | .40 | .25 |
| 375 | A147 | 1s copper red | .70 | .25 |
| 376 | A148 | 2s dark green | 1.10 | .25 |
| | | *Nos. 373-376 (4)* | 2.60 | 1.00 |

Progress of Ecuador Exhibition.

For overprints see Nos. C105-C113.

Parade of Athletes — A149

Runner — A150

Basketball — A151

Wrestlers A152

Diver A153

**1939, Mar.** ***Perf. 12***

| | | | | |
|---|---|---|---|---|
| **377** | A149 | 5c carmine rose | 3.00 | .55 |
| **378** | A150 | 10c deep blue | 3.50 | .65 |
| **379** | A151 | 50c gray olive | 5.75 | .85 |
| **380** | A152 | 1s dull violet | 7.75 | .85 |
| **381** | A153 | 2s dull olive green | 12.50 | .95 |
| | | *Nos. 377-381,C65-C69 (10)* | 78.35 | 6.15 |

First Bolivarian Games (1938), Bogota.

Dolores Mission — A154

**1939, June 16** ***Perf. 12½x13***

| | | | | |
|---|---|---|---|---|
| **382** | A154 | 2c blue green | .50 | .25 |
| **383** | A154 | 5c rose red | .50 | .25 |
| **384** | A154 | 10c ultra | .50 | .25 |
| **385** | A154 | 50c yellow brown | 1.20 | .25 |
| **386** | A154 | 1s black | 1.90 | .25 |
| **387** | A154 | 2s purple | 1.25 | .40 |
| | | *Nos. 382-387,C73-C79 (13)* | 11.25 | 3.40 |

Golden Gate International Exposition.
For surcharges see Nos. 429, 436.

Trylon and Perisphere — A155

**1939, June 30**

| | | | | |
|---|---|---|---|---|
| **388** | A155 | 2c lt olive green | .80 | .35 |
| **389** | A155 | 5c red orange | .80 | .35 |
| **390** | A155 | 10c ultra | .80 | .35 |
| **391** | A155 | 50c slate gray | 1.10 | .35 |
| **392** | A155 | 1s rose carmine | 1.90 | .35 |
| **393** | A155 | 2s black brown | 2.25 | .40 |
| | | *Nos. 388-393,C80-C86 (13)* | 16.55 | 4.20 |

New York World's Fair.
For surcharge see No. 437.

Flags of the 21 American Republics — A156

**1940** ***Perf. 12***

| | | | | |
|---|---|---|---|---|
| **394** | A156 | 5c dp rose & blk | 1.00 | .25 |
| **395** | A156 | 10c dk blue & blk | .40 | .25 |
| **396** | A156 | 50c Prus green & blk | .60 | .25 |
| **397** | A156 | 1s dp violet & blk | 1.00 | .30 |
| | | *Nos. 394-397,C87-C90 (8)* | 8.30 | 2.75 |

Pan American Union, 50th anniversary.

Francisco J. E. Santa Cruz y Espejo — A157

**1941, Dec. 15**

| | | | | |
|---|---|---|---|---|
| **398** | A157 | 30c blue | 1.25 | .25 |
| **399** | A157 | 1s red orange | 2.50 | .35 |
| | | *Nos. 398-399,C91-C92 (4)* | 21.50 | 1.30 |

Exposition of Journalism held under the auspices of the Natl. Newspaper Men's Union.

Francisco de Orellana A158

Gonzalo Pizarro A159

View of Guayaquil A160

View of Quito — A161

**1942, Jan. 30**

| | | | | |
|---|---|---|---|---|
| **400** | A158 | 10c sepia | .90 | .35 |
| **401** | A159 | 40c deep rose | 2.50 | .35 |
| **402** | A160 | 1s violet | 3.50 | .35 |
| **403** | A161 | 2s dark blue | 4.50 | .45 |
| | | *Nos. 400-403,C93-C96 (8)* | 23.45 | 3.35 |

400th anniv. of the discovery and exploration of the Amazon River by Orellana.

Remigio Crespo Toral — A162

**1942** ***Perf. 13½***

| | | | | |
|---|---|---|---|---|
| **404** | A162 | 10c green | .60 | .25 |
| **405** | A162 | 50c brown | 1.00 | .25 |
| | | *Nos. 404-405,C97 (3)* | 2.85 | 1.00 |

Alfredo Baquerizo Moreno — A163

**1942**

| | | | | |
|---|---|---|---|---|
| **406** | A163 | 10c green | .25 | .25 |

Mt. Chimborazo A164

**1942-47** ***Perf. 12***

| | | | | |
|---|---|---|---|---|
| **407** | A164 | 30c red brown | .60 | .30 |
| **407A** | A164 | 30c lt blue ('43) | .60 | .30 |
| **407B** | A164 | 30c red orange ('44) | .60 | .30 |
| **407C** | A164 | 30c green ('47) | .60 | .30 |
| | | *Nos. 407-407C (4)* | 2.40 | 1.20 |

View of Guayaquil A165

**1942-44**

| | | | | |
|---|---|---|---|---|
| **408** | A165 | 20c red | .55 | .25 |
| **408A** | A165 | 20c deep blue ('44) | .55 | .25 |

Gen. Eloy Alfaro — A166

Devil's Nose — A167

President Alfaro (1842-1912): 30c, Military College. 1s, Montecristi, Alfaro's birthplace.

**1942**

| | | | | |
|---|---|---|---|---|
| **409** | A166 | 10c dk rose & blk | .60 | .25 |
| **410** | A167 | 20c ol blk & red brn | .60 | .25 |
| **411** | A167 | 30c ol gray & grn | .75 | .25 |
| **412** | A167 | 1s slate & salmon | 1.80 | .25 |
| | | *Nos. 409-412,C98-C101 (8)* | 20.15 | 4.40 |

**Nos. 370-372 Overprinted in Red Brown**

**1943, Apr. 15** ***Perf. 11½***

| | | | | |
|---|---|---|---|---|
| **413** | A144 | 50c multicolored | .65 | .65 |
| **414** | A144 | 1s multicolored | 1.25 | 1.25 |
| **415** | A144 | 2s multicolored | 2.75 | 2.75 |
| | | *Nos. 413-415,C102-C104 (6)* | 14.65 | 10.25 |

Visit of US Vice-Pres. Henry A. Wallace.

"30 Centavos" — A170

**1943** **Black Surcharge** ***Perf. 12½***

| | | | | |
|---|---|---|---|---|
| **416** | A170 | 30c on 50c red brn | 1.00 | .25 |
| *a.* | | Without bars | 1.00 | .25 |

Map Showing US and Ecuador — A171

**1943, Oct. 9** ***Perf. 12***

| | | | | |
|---|---|---|---|---|
| **417** | A171 | 10c dull violet | .75 | .50 |
| **418** | A171 | 20c red brown | .75 | .50 |
| **419** | A171 | 30c orange | .75 | .50 |
| **420** | A171 | 50c olive green | .90 | .60 |
| **421** | A171 | 1s deep violet | 1.00 | .65 |
| **422** | A171 | 10s olive bister | 8.25 | 5.25 |
| | | *Nos. 417-422,C114-C118 (11)* | 32.70 | 15.10 |

Good will tour of Pres. Arroyo del Rio in 1942.

**1944, Feb. 7**

| | | | | |
|---|---|---|---|---|
| **423** | A171 | 10c yellow green | .65 | .45 |
| **424** | A171 | 20c rose pink | .65 | .45 |
| **425** | A171 | 30c dark gray brown | .65 | .45 |
| **426** | A171 | 50c deep red lilac | .65 | .45 |
| **427** | A171 | 1s olive gray | 1.00 | .65 |
| **428** | A171 | 10s red orange | 10.50 | 6.00 |
| | | *Nos. 423-428,C119-C123 (11)* | 24.90 | 13.40 |

For surcharges see Nos. B1-B6.

No. 385 Surcharged in Black

**1944** **Unwmk.** ***Perf. 12½x13***

| | | | | |
|---|---|---|---|---|
| **429** | A154 | 30c on 50c yel brn | 2.00 | .25 |

Archbishop Federico González Suárez, Birth Cent. — A172

**1944** ***Perf. 12***

| | | | | |
|---|---|---|---|---|
| **430** | A172 | 10c deep blue | .40 | .25 |
| **431** | A172 | 20c green | .40 | .25 |
| **432** | A172 | 30c dk violet brn | .50 | .25 |
| **433** | A172 | 1s dull violet | .90 | .25 |
| | | *Nos. 430-433,C124-C127 (8)* | 15.50 | 4.30 |

Air Post Stamps Nos. C76 and C83 Surcharged in Black

**1944** ***Perf. 12½x13***

| | | | | |
|---|---|---|---|---|
| **434** | AP15 | 30c on 50c rose vio | .40 | .25 |
| **435** | AP16 | 30c on 50c sl grn | .40 | .25 |

Nos. 382 and 388 Surcharged in Black

**1944-45**

| | | | | |
|---|---|---|---|---|
| **436** | A154 | 5c on 2c bl grn | .50 | .25 |
| *a.* | | Double surcharge | 4.00 | |
| **437** | A155 | 5c on 2c lt ol grn ('45) | .50 | .25 |

Government Palace, Quito — A173

**1944** **Engr.** ***Perf. 11***

| | | | | |
|---|---|---|---|---|
| **438** | A173 | 10c dark green | .50 | .25 |
| **439** | A173 | 30c blue | .50 | .25 |

See Nos. C128-C130, C221. For surcharges see Nos. 452, RAC1-RAC2.

Symbol of the Red Cross A174

**1945, Apr. 25** *Perf. 12*

**Cross in Rose**

| | | | | |
|---|---|---|---|---|
| **440** | A174 | 30c bister brown | 1.90 | .35 |
| **441** | A174 | 1s red brown | 2.75 | .45 |
| **442** | A174 | 5s turq green | 4.75 | 1.10 |
| **443** | A174 | 10s scarlet | 13.00 | 3.00 |
| | | *Nos. 440-443,C131-C134 (8)* | 58.40 | 14.75 |

International Red Cross, 80th anniversary.

**Nos. 370 to 372 Overprinted in Dark Blue and Gold**

**1945, Oct. 2** *Perf. 11½*

**Center Multicolored**

| | | | | |
|---|---|---|---|---|
| **444** | A144 | 50c black | .80 | .70 |
| *a.* | | Double overprint | *22.50* | |
| **445** | A144 | 1s olive black | 1.40 | 1.40 |
| **446** | A144 | 2s dark brown | 2.75 | 2.50 |
| *a.* | | Double overprint | *22.50* | |
| | | *Nos. 444-446,C139-C141 (6)* | 10.45 | 8.25 |

Visit of Pres. Juan Antonio Rios of Chile.

General Antonio José de Sucre, 150th Birth Anniv. — A175

**1945, Nov. 14** **Engr.** *Perf. 12*

| | | | | |
|---|---|---|---|---|
| **447** | A175 | 10c olive | .55 | .25 |
| **448** | A175 | 20c red brown | .55 | .25 |
| **449** | A175 | 40c olive gray | .55 | .25 |
| **450** | A175 | 1s dark green | 1.10 | .25 |
| **451** | A175 | 2s sepia | 2.25 | .75 |
| | | *Nos. 447-451,C142-C146 (10)* | 13.20 | 6.10 |

No. 438 Surcharged in Blue

**1945** *Perf. 11*

| | | | | |
|---|---|---|---|---|
| **452** | A173 | 20c on 10c dark green | .50 | .25 |
| *a.* | | Fancy bar omitted | | |

**Catalogue values for unused stamps in this section, from this point to the end of the section, are for Never Hinged items.**

Map of Pan-American Highway and Arms of Loja — A176

**1946, Apr. 22** **Engr.** *Perf. 12*

| | | | | |
|---|---|---|---|---|
| **453** | A176 | 20c red brown | .60 | .40 |
| **454** | A176 | 30c bright green | .60 | .45 |
| **455** | A176 | 1s bright ultra | .60 | .45 |
| **456** | A176 | 5s deep red lilac | 1.90 | 1.50 |
| **457** | A176 | 10s scarlet | 3.50 | 2.00 |
| | | *Nos. 453-457,C147-C151 (10)* | 14.55 | 7.95 |

Torch of Democracy — A177

Popular Suffrage A178

Flag of Ecuador — A179

Pres. José M. Velasco Ibarra — A180

**1946, Aug. 9** **Unwmk.** *Perf. 12½*

| | | | | |
|---|---|---|---|---|
| **458** | A177 | 5c dark blue | .25 | .25 |
| **459** | A178 | 10c Prus green | .25 | .25 |
| **460** | A179 | 20c carmine | .30 | .25 |
| **461** | A180 | 30c chocolate | .45 | .25 |
| | | *Nos. 458-461,C152-C155 (8)* | 3.45 | 2.20 |

Revolution of May 28, 1944, 2nd anniv.

"30 Ctvs." — A181

**1946** **Black Surcharge**

| | | | | |
|---|---|---|---|---|
| **462** | A181 | 30c on 50c red brown | .50 | .25 |

For overprint see No. 484.

Nos. CO13-CO14 With Additional Ovpt. in Black

**1946** *Perf. 11½*

| | | | | |
|---|---|---|---|---|
| **463** | AP7 | 10c chestnut | .50 | .25 |
| **464** | AP7 | 20c olive black | .50 | .25 |

Instructor and Student — A182

**1946, Sept. 16** *Perf. 12½*

| | | | | |
|---|---|---|---|---|
| **465** | A182 | 10c deep blue | .40 | .30 |
| **466** | A182 | 20c chocolate | .40 | .30 |
| **467** | A182 | 30c dark green | .40 | .30 |
| **468** | A182 | 50c bluish blk | .55 | .45 |
| **469** | A182 | 1s dark red | 1.10 | .75 |
| **470** | A182 | 10s dark violet | 6.50 | 1.40 |
| | | *Nos. 465-470,C156-C160 (11)* | 21.00 | 6.85 |

Campaign for adult education.

Mariana de Jesus Paredes y Flores — A183

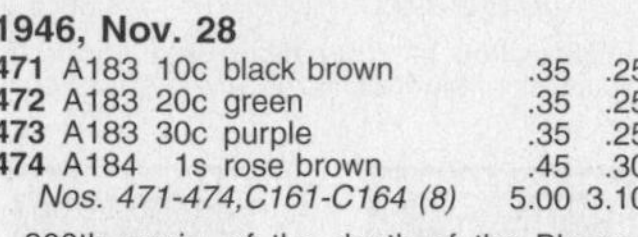

Urn — A184

**1946, Nov. 28**

| | | | | |
|---|---|---|---|---|
| **471** | A183 | 10c black brown | .35 | .25 |
| **472** | A183 | 20c green | .35 | .25 |
| **473** | A183 | 30c purple | .35 | .25 |
| **474** | A184 | 1s rose brown | .45 | .30 |
| | | *Nos. 471-474,C161-C164 (8)* | 5.00 | 3.10 |

300th anniv. of the death of the Blessed Mariana de Jesus Paredes y Flores.

Pres. Vicente Rocafuerte A185

Jesuits' Church Quito A186

45c, 50c, 80c, F.J.E. de Santa Cruz y Espejo.

**1947, Nov. 27** *Perf. 12*

| | | | | |
|---|---|---|---|---|
| **475** | A185 | 5c redsh brown | .25 | .25 |
| **476** | A185 | 10c sepia | .25 | .25 |
| **477** | A185 | 15c gray black | .25 | .25 |
| **478** | A186 | 20c redsh brown | .30 | .25 |
| **479** | A186 | 30c red violet | .50 | .25 |
| **480** | A186 | 40c brt ultra | .65 | .25 |
| **481** | A185 | 45c dk slate grn | .80 | .30 |
| **482** | A185 | 50c olive black | .85 | .30 |
| **483** | A185 | 80c orange red | 1.20 | .35 |
| | | *Nos. 475-483,C165-C171 (16)* | 8.60 | 4.20 |

For overprints and surcharges see Nos. 489, 496, 525-527.

**Type of 1946, Overprinted "POSTAL" in Black but Without Additional Surcharge**

**1948** **Engr.**

| | | | | |
|---|---|---|---|---|
| **484** | A181 | 10c orange | .50 | .25 |

Andrés Bello — A188

**1948, Apr. 21** *Perf. 13*

| | | | | |
|---|---|---|---|---|
| **485** | A188 | 20c lt blue | .30 | .25 |
| **486** | A188 | 30c rose carmine | .30 | .25 |
| **487** | A188 | 40c blue green | .30 | .25 |
| **488** | A188 | 1s black brown | .60 | .25 |
| | | *Nos. 485-488,C172-C174 (7)* | 3.20 | 1.75 |

83rd anniversary of the death of Andrés Bello (1781-1865), educator.

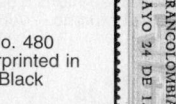

No. 480 Overprinted in Black

**1948, May 24** *Perf. 12*

| | | | | |
|---|---|---|---|---|
| **489** | A186 | 40c bright ultra | .60 | .35 |

See No. C175.

Flagship of Columbus — A189

**1948** *Perf. 14*

| | | | | |
|---|---|---|---|---|
| **490** | A189 | 10c dark blue green | .50 | .25 |
| **491** | A189 | 20c brown | .50 | .25 |
| **492** | A189 | 30c dark purple | 1.20 | .25 |
| **493** | A189 | 50c deep claret | 1.60 | .25 |
| **494** | A189 | 1s ultra | 2.40 | .40 |
| **495** | A189 | 5s carmine | 6.50 | .80 |
| | | *Nos. 490-495,C176-C180 (11)* | 25.65 | 7.55 |

Issued to publicize the proposed Columbus Memorial Lighthouse near Ciudad Trujillo, Dominican Republic.

No. 483 Overprinted in Blue, "MANANA" Reading Down

**1948** *Perf. 12*

| | | | | |
|---|---|---|---|---|
| **496** | A185 | 80c orange red | .25 | .25 |

Issued to publicize the National Fair of Today and Tomorrow, 1948. See No. C181.

Telegrafo I in Flight — A190

**1948** **Engr.** *Perf. 12½*

| | | | | |
|---|---|---|---|---|
| **497** | A190 | 30c red orange | .65 | .25 |
| **498** | A190 | 40c rose lilac | .65 | .25 |
| **499** | A190 | 60c violet blue | .65 | .25 |
| **500** | A190 | 1s brown red | .65 | .25 |
| **501** | A190 | 3s brown | 2.00 | .35 |
| **502** | A190 | 5s gray black | 2.40 | .35 |
| | | *Nos. 497-502,C182-C187 (12)* | 13.80 | 3.50 |

25th anniversary (in 1945) of the first postal flight in Ecuador.

Book and Pen — A191

**1948, Oct. 12** **Unwmk.** *Perf. 14*

| | | | | |
|---|---|---|---|---|
| **503** | A191 | 10c deep claret | .60 | .25 |
| **504** | A191 | 20c brown | .60 | .25 |
| **505** | A191 | 30c dark green | 1.25 | .25 |
| **506** | A191 | 50c red | 2.00 | .25 |
| **507** | A191 | 1s purple | 3.00 | .30 |
| **508** | A191 | 10s dull blue | 8.00 | 1.00 |
| | | *Nos. 503-508,C188-C192 (11)* | 32.45 | 7.80 |

Campaign for adult education.

A192

Franklin D. Roosevelt and Two of "Four Freedoms" — A193

**1948, Oct. 24** *Perf. 12½*

**509** A192 10c rose brn & gray .40 .30
**510** A192 20c brn ol & bl .50 .40
**511** A193 30c ol bis & car rose .50 .40
**512** A193 40c red vio & sep .65 .40
**513** A193 1s org brn & car .70 .50
*Nos. 509-513,C193-C197 (10)* 7.05 3.70

Maldonado and Map — A194

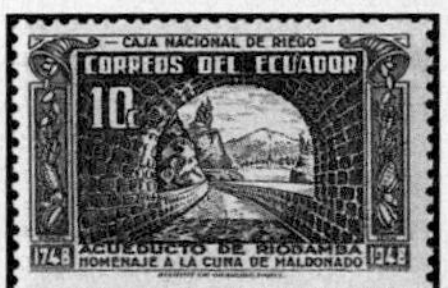

Riobamba Aqueduct A195

Maldonado on Bank of Riobamba A196

Pedro V. Maldonado A197

**1948, Nov. 17** **Engr.** **Unwmk.**

**514** A194 5c gray blk & ver .40 .25
**515** A195 10c car & gray blk .50 .25
**516** A196 30c bis brn & ultra .60 .25
**517** A195 40c sage grn & vio .75 .25
**518** A194 50c grn & car 1.00 .30
**519** A197 1s brn & slate bl 1.25 .35
*Nos. 514-519,C198-C201 (10)* 8.10 2.65

Bicentenary of the death of Pedro Vicente Maldonado, geographer.

For overprints and surcharges see Nos. 537-540.

A198

Miguel de Cervantes Saavedra A199

**1949, May 2** *Perf. 12½x12*

**520** A198 30c dk car rose & dp ultra .75 .25
**521** A199 60c bis & brn vio 1.25 .30
**522** A198 1s grn & rose car 1.75 .25
**523** A199 2s gray blk & red brn 3.25 .30
**524** A198 5s choc & aqua 6.50 1.25
*Nos. 520-524,C202-C206 (10)* 25.75 5.95

400th anniv. of the birth of Miguel de Cervantes Saavedra, novelist, playwright and poet.

No. 480 Surcharged in Carmine

**1949, June 15** *Perf. 12*

**525** A186 10c on 40c brt ultra .40 .25
**526** A186 20c on 40c brt ultra .55 .25
*a.* Double surcharge
**527** A186 30c on 40c brt ultra .55 .25
*Nos. 525-527,C207-C209 (6)* 3.05 1.50

2nd Natl. Eucharistic Cong., Quito, 6/49. No. 526 exists se-tenant with No. 527.

Monument on Equator — A200

**1949, June** **Engr.** *Perf. 12½x12*

**528** A200 10c deep plum .40 .25

For overprint see No. 536.

No. 542 Surcharged in Black and Carmine

**1949** *Perf. 12x12½*

**529** A203 10c on 50c green .55 .25
**530** A203 20c on 50c green .55 .25
**531** A203 30c on 50c green .65 .25
*Nos. 529-531,C210-C213 (7)* 6.05 2.25

Universal Postal Union, 75th anniversary.

**Consular Service Stamps Surcharged in Black**

Arms of Ecuador — R1

**1949** *Perf. 12*

**532** R1 20c on 25c red brown .75 .25
**533** R1 30c on 50c gray .75 .25

For other overprints and surcharges on type R1 see Nos. 544-549, 566-570, C214, C245, C249-C252, RA60-RA62, RA72.

Nos. RA49A and RA55 Overprinted in Black — a

**1950** **Unwmk.** *Perf. 12*

**534** PT18 5c green .30 .25
**535** PT21 5c blue .30 .25

Overprint 15mm on No. 534.

Nos. 528 and 517 to 519 Ovptd. or Srchd. in Black or Carmine

**1950, Feb. 10** *Perf. 12½x12*

**536** A200 10c dp plum .50 .50

*Perf. 12½*

**537** A195 20c on 40c sage grn & vio 1.00 1.00
**538** A195 30c on 40c sage grn & vio 1.25 1.25
**539** A194 50c grn & car 2.00 2.00
**540** A197 1s brn & slate bl (C) 2.50 2.50

No. C220 Overprinted in Carmine

**Overprint 15mm long**

*Perf. 11*

**541** A173 10s violet 6.00 3.00
*Nos. 536-541,C216-C220 (11)* 33.00 22.25

Nos. 536-541 publicize adult education.

San Pablo Lake — A203

*Perf. 12x12½*

**1950, May** **Engr.** **Unwmk.**

**542** A203 50c green .50 .25

For surcharges see Nos. 529-531.

Consular Service Stamp Surcharged Vertically in Black

**1950** *Perf. 12*

**544** R1 30c on 50c gray .50 .25

**Consular Service Stamps Overprinted or Surcharged in Black**

b

c

d

e

f

g

**1951** **Unwmk.** *Perf. 12*

**545** R1 (b) 5c on 10c car rose .50 .25
**546** R1 (c) 10c car rose .50 .25
**547** R1 (d) 10c car rose .50 .25
**548** R1 (e) 20c on 25c red brn .50 .25
**549** R1 (e) 30c on 50c gray .50 .25
**550** R2 (f) 40c on 25c blue .50 .25
**551** R2 (g) 50c on 25c blue .50 .25
*Nos. 545-551 (7)* 3.50 1.75

See Nos. 552-554, C233-C234, C246-C248, RA67.

Consular Service Stamps Surcharged in Black

**1951**

**552** R2 20c on 25c blue .50 .25
**553** R2 30c on 25c blue .50 .25

Adult education. See Nos. C225-C226.

Consular Service Stamp Surcharged in Black

**1951**

**554** R2 $0.30 on 50c car rose .50 .25

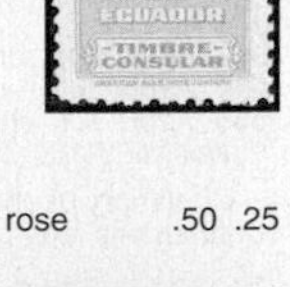

Reliquary of St. Mariana and Vatican — A204

*Perf. 12½x12*

**1952, Feb.** **Engr.** **Unwmk.**

**555** A204 10c emer & red brn .90 .70
**556** A204 20c dp bl & pur .90 .70
**557** A204 30c car & bl grn .90 .70
*Nos. 555-557,C227-C230 (7)* 6.00 3.30

Issued to publicize the canonization of Mariana de Jesus Paredes y Flores.

Presidents Galo Plaza and Harry Truman — A205

2s, Pres. Plaza addressing US Congress.

**1952, Mar. 26** *Perf. 12*

**558** A205 1s rose car & gray blk .70 .60
**559** A205 2s dl bl & sepia 1.75 .90
*Nos. 558-559,C231-C232 (4)* 5.15 3.70

1951 visit of Pres. Galo Plaza y Lasso to the US.

R3

Fiscal Stamps Srchd. or Ovptd. Horiz. in Carmine or Black

Type of 1937 Overprinted Diagonally

**1952 Unwmk. Engr. *Perf. 12***

| | | | | |
|---|---|---|---|---|
| **560** | R3 | 20c on 30c dp bl (C) | .75 | .25 |
| **561** | R3 | 30c deep blue | .75 | .25 |
| **562** | A138 | 50c purple | .75 | .25 |
| | | *Nos. 560-562 (3)* | 2.25 | .75 |

For overprints and surcharge see Nos. RA68-RA69, RA71.

Pres. José M. Urvina, Slave and "Liberty" A206

***Hyphen-hole Perf. 7x6½***

**1952 Litho.**

| | | | | |
|---|---|---|---|---|
| **563** | A206 | 20c red & green | .65 | .45 |
| **564** | A206 | 30c red & vio bl | .80 | .45 |
| **565** | A206 | 50c blue & car | 1.40 | .45 |
| | | *Nos. 563-565,C236-C239 (7)* | 16.85 | 3.15 |

Centenary of abolition of slavery in Ecuador. Counterfeits exist.

Consular Service Stamps Surcharged in Black — h

**1952-53 Unwmk. *Perf. 12***

| | | | | |
|---|---|---|---|---|
| **566** | R1 | 10c on 20s blue ('53) | .75 | .25 |
| **567** | R1 | 20c on 10s gray ('53) | .75 | .25 |
| **568** | R1 | 20c on 20s blue | .75 | .25 |
| **569** | R1 | 30c on 10s gray ('53) | .75 | .25 |
| **570** | R1 | 30c on 20s blue | .75 | .25 |
| | | *Nos. 566-570 (5)* | 3.75 | 1.25 |

Similar surcharges of 60c and 90c on the 20s blue are said to be bogus.

Teacher and Students — A207

New Citizens Voting — A208

Designs: 10c, Instructor with student. 30c, Teaching the alphabet.

**1953, Apr. 13 Engr.**

| | | | | |
|---|---|---|---|---|
| **571** | A207 | 5c lt bl | .30 | .25 |
| **572** | A207 | 10c dk car rose | .45 | .25 |
| **573** | A208 | 20c brt brn org | .50 | .25 |
| **574** | A208 | 30c dp red lil | .75 | .25 |
| | | *Nos. 571-574,C240-C241 (6)* | 4.70 | 1.50 |

1952 adult education campaign.

A209

**1953 Black Surcharge**

| | | | | |
|---|---|---|---|---|
| **575** | A209 | 40c on 50c purple | 1.00 | .25 |

Cuicocha Lagoon — A210

Designs: 10c, Equatorial Line monument. 20c, Quininde countryside. 30c, Tomebamba river. 40c, La Chilintosa rock. 50c, Iliniza Mountains.

**Frames in Black**

**1953 Engr. *Perf. 13x12½***

| | | | | |
|---|---|---|---|---|
| **576** | A210 | 5c brt bl | .50 | .50 |
| **577** | A210 | 10c brt grn | .50 | .50 |
| **578** | A210 | 20c purple | .50 | .50 |
| **579** | A210 | 30c brown | .50 | .50 |
| **580** | A210 | 40c orange | .50 | .50 |
| **581** | A210 | 50c dp car | .90 | .50 |
| | | *Nos. 576-581 (6)* | 3.40 | 3.00 |

A211

Carlos Maria Cardinal de la Torre and arches.

**1954, Jan. Photo. *Perf. 8½***

| | | | | |
|---|---|---|---|---|
| **582** | A211 | 30c blk & ver | .65 | .65 |
| **583** | A211 | 50c blk & rose lil | .65 | .65 |
| | | *Nos. 582-583,C253-C255 (5)* | 3.80 | 2.35 |

1st anniv. of the elevation of Archbishop de la Torre to Cardinal.

A212

**1954, Apr. 22**

| | | | | |
|---|---|---|---|---|
| **584** | A212 | 30c blk & gray | 1.40 | 1.40 |
| **585** | A212 | 50c blk brn & yel | 1.40 | 1.40 |
| | | *Nos. 584-585,C256-C260 (7)* | 6.75 | 4.80 |

Queen Isabella I (1451-1504) of Spain, 500th birth anniv.

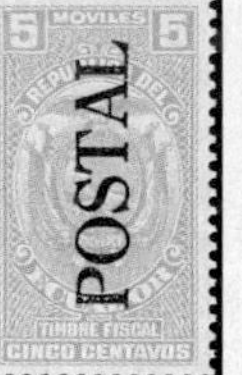


Type of 1929 Overprint Larger, No Letterspacing

**1954-55 Unwmk. *Perf. 12***

| | | | | |
|---|---|---|---|---|
| **586** | A112 | 5c ol grn ('55) | .75 | .25 |
| **587** | A112 | 10c orange | .75 | .25 |

The normal overprint on Nos. 586-587 reads up. It also exists reading down.

Indian Messenger — A213

**1954, Aug. 2 Litho. *Perf. 11***

| | | | | |
|---|---|---|---|---|
| **588** | A213 | 30c dk brn | 1.00 | .25 |

Day of the Postal Employee. See No. C263.

Products of Ecuador — A214

**1954, Sept. 24 Photo.**

| | | | | |
|---|---|---|---|---|
| **589** | A214 | 10c orange | .40 | .25 |
| **590** | A214 | 20c vermilion | .40 | .25 |
| **591** | A214 | 30c rose pink | .40 | .25 |
| **592** | A214 | 40c dk gray grn | .60 | .25 |
| **593** | A214 | 50c yel brn | .80 | .25 |
| | | *Nos. 589-593 (5)* | 2.60 | 1.25 |

José Abel Castillo — A215

***Perf. 11½x11***

**1955, Oct. 19 Engr. Unwmk.**

| | | | | |
|---|---|---|---|---|
| **594** | A215 | 30c olive bister | .60 | .25 |
| **595** | A215 | 50c dk gray | .60 | .25 |
| | | *Nos. 594-595,C282-C286 (7)* | 10.20 | 2.10 |

30th anniv. of the 1st flight of the "Telegrafo I" and to honor Castillo, aviation pioneer.

Babahoyo River Los Rios — A216

Designs: 5c, Palms, Esmeraldas. 10c, Fishermen, Manabi. 30c, Guayaquil, Guayas. 50c, Pital River, El Oro. 70c, Cactus, Galapagos Isls. 80c, Orchids, Napo-Pastaza. 1s, Aguacate Mission, Zamora-Chinchipe. 2s, Jibaro Indian, Morona-Santiago.

**1955-56 Photo. *Perf. 13***

| | | | | |
|---|---|---|---|---|
| **596** | A216 | 5c yel grn ('56) | 1.50 | .30 |
| **597** | A216 | 10c blue ('56) | 1.50 | .30 |
| **598** | A216 | 20c brown | 1.50 | .30 |
| **599** | A216 | 30c dk gray | 1.50 | .30 |
| **600** | A216 | 50c bl grn | 1.50 | .30 |
| **601** | A216 | 70c ol ('56) | 1.50 | .30 |
| **602** | A216 | 80c dp vio ('56) | 3.75 | .30 |
| **603** | A216 | 1s org ('56) | 2.00 | .30 |
| **604** | A216 | 2s rose red ('56) | 3.75 | .30 |
| | | *Nos. 596-604 (9)* | 18.50 | 2.70 |

See Nos. 620-630, 670, C288-C297, C310-C311.

Brother Juan Adam Schwarz, S. J. — A217

**1956, Aug. 27 Engr. *Perf. 13½***

| | | | | |
|---|---|---|---|---|
| **605** | A217 | 5c yel grn | .45 | .25 |
| **606** | A217 | 10c org red | .45 | .25 |
| **607** | A217 | 20c lt vio | .45 | .25 |
| **608** | A217 | 30c dk grn | .45 | .25 |
| **609** | A217 | 40c blue | .45 | .25 |
| **610** | A217 | 50c dp ultra | .45 | .25 |
| **611** | A217 | 70c orange | .45 | .25 |
| | | *Nos. 605-611,C302-C305 (11)* | 5.55 | 2.75 |

Bicentennial of printing in Ecuador and honoring Brother Juan Adam Schwarz, S.J.

Andres Hurtado de Mendoza — A218

Gil Ramirez Davalos A219

Designs: 20c, Brother Vincent Solano.

**1957, Apr. 7 Unwmk. *Perf. 12***

| | | | | |
|---|---|---|---|---|
| **612** | A218 | 5c dk bl, *pink* | .65 | .25 |
| **613** | A219 | 10c grn, *grnsh* | .65 | .25 |
| **614** | A218 | 20c choc, *buff* | .65 | .25 |
| *a.* | | Souvenir sheet of 4, imperf. | 3.50 | 3.50 |
| | | *Nos. 612-614,C312-C314 (6)* | 2.85 | 1.50 |

4th cent. of the founding of Cuenca.

No. 614a contains 2 5c gray & 2 20c brown red stamps in designs similar to #612, 614. It was printed on white ungummed paper.

A220

Design: 40c, 50c, 2s, Francisco Marcos, Gen. Pedro Alcantara Herran and Santos Michelena.

**1957, Sept. 5 Engr. *Perf. 14½x14***

| | | | | |
|---|---|---|---|---|
| **615** | A220 | 40c yellow | .40 | .25 |
| **616** | A220 | 50c ultra | .40 | .25 |
| **617** | A220 | 2s dk red | 1.00 | .25 |
| | | *Nos. 615-617 (3)* | 1.80 | .75 |

7th Postal Congress of the Americas and Spain (in 1955).

**Souvenir Sheets**

Various Railroad Scenes — A221

**1957 Litho. *Perf. 10½x11***

| | | | | |
|---|---|---|---|---|
| **618** | A221 | 20c Sheet of 5 | 9.25 | 4.25 |
| **619** | A221 | 30c Sheet of 5 | 9.25 | 4.25 |

Issued to commemorate the opening of the Quito-Ibarra-San Lorenzo railroad.

Nos. 618-619 contain 2 orange yellow, 1 ultramarine and 2 carmine stamps, each in a different design.

**Scenic Type of 1955-56.**

Designs as before, except: 40c, as 70c. 90c, as 80c. No. 629, San Pablo, Imbabura.

**1957-58 Photo. *Perf. 13***

| | | | | |
|---|---|---|---|---|
| **620** | A216 | 5c light blue | 1.75 | .25 |
| **621** | A216 | 10c brown | 1.75 | .25 |
| **622** | A216 | 20c crimson rose | 1.75 | .25 |
| **623** | A216 | 20c yel green | 1.75 | .25 |
| **624** | A216 | 30c rose red | 2.50 | .25 |
| **625** | A216 | 40c chalky blue | 1.75 | .25 |
| **626** | A216 | 50c lt vio | 2.50 | .25 |
| **627** | A216 | 90c brt ultra | 1.75 | .25 |
| **628** | A216 | 1s dark brown | 1.75 | .25 |
| **629** | A216 | 1s gray blk ('58) | 1.75 | .25 |
| **630** | A216 | 2s brown | 2.75 | .25 |
| | | *Nos. 620-630 (11)* | 21.75 | 2.75 |

Blue and Yellow Macaw — A222

Birds: 20c, Red-breasted toucan. 30c, Condor. 40c, Black-tailed and sword-tailed hummingbirds.

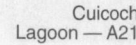

*Perf. 13½x13*

**1958, Jan. 7 Litho. Unwmk.**

**Birds in Natural Colors**

| | | | | |
|---|---|---|---|---|
| **634** | A222 | 10c red brn | 1.40 | .25 |
| **635** | A222 | 20c dk gray | 1.40 | .25 |
| **636** | A222 | 30c brt yel grn | 3.50 | .25 |
| **637** | A222 | 40c red org | 3.50 | .25 |
| | | *Nos. 634-637 (4)* | 9.80 | 1.00 |

Carlos Sanz de Santamaria A223

Richard M. Nixon and Flags — A224

No. 640, Dr. Ramon Villeda Morales, flags. 2.20s, José Carlos de Macedo Soares, horizontal flags.

**1958** *Perf. 12*

**Flags in Red, Blue, Yellow & Green**

| | | | | |
|---|---|---|---|---|
| **638** | A223 | 1.80s dl vio | .65 | .25 |
| **639** | A224 | 2s dk grn | .65 | .25 |
| **640** | A224 | 2s dk brn | .65 | .25 |
| **641** | A223 | 2.20s blk brn | .65 | .25 |
| | | *Nos. 638-641 (4)* | 2.60 | 1.00 |

Visits: Colombia's Foreign Minister Dr. Carlos Sanz de Santamaria; US Vice Pres. Nixon, May 9-10; Pres. Ramon Villeda Morales of Honduras; Brazil's Foreign Minister José Carlos de Macedo Soares. See Nos. C419-C421. For overprints and surcharges see Nos. 775-775C, C419-C421, C460.

Locomotive of 1908 A225

Garcia Moreno, Jose Caamano, L. Plaza and Eloy Alfaro — A226

Design: 50c, Diesel locomotive.

*Perf. 13½x14, 14*

**1958, Aug. 9 Photo. Unwmk.**

| | | | | |
|---|---|---|---|---|
| **642** | A225 | 30c brn blk | .25 | .25 |
| **643** | A225 | 50c dk car | .35 | .25 |
| **644** | A226 | 5s dk brn | 1.75 | .70 |
| | | *Nos. 642-644 (3)* | 2.35 | 1.20 |

Guayaquil-Quito railroad, 50th anniv.

Cardinal — A227

Birds: 30c, Andean cock-of-the-rock. 50c, Glossy cowbird. 60c, Red-fronted Amazon.

**1958 Litho.** *Perf. 13½x13*

**Birds in Natural Colors**

| | | | | |
|---|---|---|---|---|
| **645** | A227 | 20c bluish grn, blk & red | 1.40 | .25 |
| **646** | A227 | 30c buff, blk & brt bl | 1.65 | .25 |
| **647** | A227 | 50c org, blk & grn | 1.90 | .55 |
| **648** | A227 | 60c pale rose, blk & bluish grn | 3.75 | .55 |
| | | *Nos. 645-648 (4)* | 8.70 | 1.60 |

UNESCO Building and Eiffel Tower, Paris — A228

**1958, Nov. 3 Engr.** *Perf. 12½*

| | | | | |
|---|---|---|---|---|
| **649** | A228 | 80c brown | .50 | .25 |

UNESCO Headquarters in Paris opening, Nov. 3.

Globe and Satellites — A229

**1958, Dec. 20 Photo.** *Perf. 14x13½*

| | | | | |
|---|---|---|---|---|
| **650** | A229 | 1.80s dark blue | 1.00 | .45 |

International Geophysical Year, 1957-58. For overprints see Nos. 718, C422.

Virgin of Quito — A230

**1959, Sept. 8 Unwmk.** *Perf. 13*

| | | | | |
|---|---|---|---|---|
| **651** | A230 | 5c ol grn | .25 | .25 |
| **652** | A230 | 10c yel brn | .25 | .25 |
| **653** | A230 | 20c purple | .25 | .25 |
| **654** | A230 | 30c ultra | .25 | .25 |
| **655** | A230 | 80c dk car rose | .25 | .25 |
| | | *Nos. 651-655 (5)* | 1.25 | 1.25 |

See No. C290. For surcharges and overprint see Nos. 695-699.

Uprooted Oak Emblem — A231

**1960, Apr. 7 Litho.** *Perf. 14x13*

| | | | | |
|---|---|---|---|---|
| **656** | A231 | 80c rose car & grn | .25 | .25 |

World Refugee Year, 7/1/59-6/30/60. For overprints see Nos. 709, 719, O205.

Great Anteater and Arms — A232

Animals: 40c, Tapir and map. 80c, Spectacled bear and arms. 1s, Puma and map.

**1960, May 14 Photo.** *Perf. 13*

| | | | | |
|---|---|---|---|---|
| **657** | A232 | 20c org, grn & blk | .60 | .25 |
| **658** | A232 | 40c yel grn, bl grn & brn | .90 | .25 |
| **659** | A232 | 80c bl, blk & red brn | 1.50 | .25 |
| **660** | A232 | 1s Prus bl, plum & ocher | 2.75 | .60 |
| | | *Nos. 657-660 (4)* | 5.75 | 1.35 |

Founding of the city of Baeza, 4th cent. See Nos. 676-679.

Hotel Quito A233

No. 662, Dormitory, Catholic University. No. 663, Dormitory, Central University. No. 664, Airport, Quito. No. 665, Overpass on Highway to Quito. No. 666, Security Bank. No. 667, Ministry of Foreign Affairs. No. 668, Government Palace. No. 669, Legislative Palace.

*Perf. 11x11½*

**1960, Aug. 8 Engr. Unwmk.**

| | | | | |
|---|---|---|---|---|
| **661** | A233 | 1s dk pur & redsh brn | .45 | .25 |
| **662** | A233 | 1s dk bl & brn | .45 | .25 |
| **663** | A233 | 1s blk & red | .45 | .25 |
| **664** | A233 | 1s dk bl & ultra | .45 | .25 |
| **665** | A233 | 1s dk pur & dk car rose | .45 | .25 |
| **666** | A233 | 1s blk & ol bis | .45 | .25 |
| **667** | A233 | 1s dk pur & turq | .45 | .25 |
| **668** | A233 | 1s dk bl & grn | .45 | .25 |
| **669** | A233 | 1s blk & vio | .45 | .25 |
| | | *Nos. 661-669 (9)* | 4.05 | 2.25 |

11th Inter-American Conference, Quito. For surcharges see Nos. 700-708.

**Type of Regular Issue, 1955-56**

Souvenir Sheet

Design: Orchids, Napo-Pastaza.

**1960 Photo.** *Perf. 13*

**Yellow Paper**

| | | | | |
|---|---|---|---|---|
| **670** | | Sheet of 2 | 5.00 | 5.00 |
| *a.* | | A216 80c deep violet | .85 | .45 |
| *b.* | | A216 90c deep green | .85 | .45 |

25th anniv. of Asociacion Filatelica Ecuatoriana. Marginal inscription in silver. Exists with silver inscription omitted.

"Freedom of Expression" — A234

Manabi Bridge A235

10c, "Freedom to vote." 20c, "Freedom to work." 30c, Coins, "Monetary stability."

**1960, Aug. 29 Litho.** *Perf. 13*

| | | | | |
|---|---|---|---|---|
| **671** | A234 | 5c dk bl | .75 | .25 |
| **672** | A234 | 10c lt vio | .75 | .25 |
| **673** | A234 | 20c orange | .75 | .25 |
| **674** | A234 | 30c bluish grn | .75 | .25 |
| **675** | A235 | 40c brn & bluish grn | .75 | .25 |
| | | *Nos. 671-675 (5)* | 3.75 | 1.25 |

Achievements of President Camilo Ponce Enriquez. See Nos. C370-C374.

**Animal Type of 1960**

Animals: 10c, Collared peccary. 20c, Kinkajou. 80c, Jaguar. 1s, Mountain coati.

**Unwmk.**

**1961, July 13 Photo.** *Perf. 13*

| | | | | |
|---|---|---|---|---|
| **676** | A232 | 10c grn, rose red & blk | .55 | .25 |
| **677** | A232 | 20c vio, grnsh bl & brn | 1.00 | .25 |
| **678** | A232 | 80c red org, dl yel & blk | 1.60 | .55 |
| **679** | A232 | 1s brn, brt grn & org | 2.10 | .65 |
| | | *Nos. 676-679 (4)* | 5.25 | 1.70 |

Founding of the city of Tena, 400th anniv.

Graphium Pausianus A236

Butterflies: 30c, Papilio torquatus leptalea. 50c, Graphium molops molops. 80c, Battus lycidas.

**1961, July 13 Litho.** *Perf. 13½*

| | | | | |
|---|---|---|---|---|
| **680** | A236 | 20c pink & multi | .65 | .25 |
| **681** | A236 | 30c lt ultra & multi | 1.10 | .25 |
| **682** | A236 | 50c org & multi | 1.25 | .25 |
| **683** | A236 | 80c bl grn & multi | 2.25 | .25 |
| | | *Nos. 680-683 (4)* | 5.25 | 1.00 |

See Nos. 711-713.

Galapagos Islands Nos. L1-L3 Overprinted in Black or Red

**1961, Oct. 31 Photo.** *Perf. 12*

| | | | | |
|---|---|---|---|---|
| **684** | A1 | 20c dk brn | 1.00 | .25 |
| **685** | A2 | 50c violet | 1.00 | .25 |
| **686** | A1 | 1s dk ol grn (R) | 2.40 | 1.50 |
| | | *Nos. 684-686,C389-C391 (6)* | 12.05 | 3.25 |

Establishment of maritime biological stations on Galapagos Islands by UNESCO. Overprint arranged differently on 20c, 1s. See Nos. C389-C391.

Daniel Enrique Proano School A237

Designs: 60c, Loja-Zamora highway, vert. 80c, Aguirre Abad College, Guayaquil. 1s, Army quarters, Quito.

*Perf. 11x11½, 11½x11*

**1962, Jan. 10 Engr. Unwmk.**

| | | | | |
|---|---|---|---|---|
| **687** | A237 | 50c dl bl & blk | .45 | .25 |
| **688** | A237 | 60c ol grn & blk | .45 | .25 |
| **689** | A237 | 80c org red & blk | .45 | .25 |
| **690** | A237 | 1s rose lake & blk | .45 | .25 |
| | | *Nos. 687-690 (4)* | 1.80 | 1.00 |

Pres. Arosemena, Flags of Ecuador, US — A238

Designs (Arosemena and): 10c, Flags of Ecuador. 20c, Flags of Ecuador and Panama.

**1963, July 1 Litho.** *Perf. 14*

| | | | | |
|---|---|---|---|---|
| **691** | A238 | 10c buff & multi | .25 | .25 |
| **692** | A238 | 20c multi | .25 | .25 |
| **693** | A238 | 60c multi | .25 | .25 |
| | | *Nos. 691-693,C409-C411 (6)* | 2.60 | 1.60 |

Issued to commemorate Pres. Carlos J. Arosemena's friendship trip, July 1962. Imperfs exist. Value $9.

Protection for The Family — A239

**1963, July 9 Unwmk.** *Perf. 14*

| | | | | |
|---|---|---|---|---|
| **694** | A239 | 10c ultra, red, gray & blk | .25 | .25 |

Social Insurance, 25th anniv. See No. C413.

No. 655 Ovptd. or Srchd. in Black or Blue

**1963 Photo. *Perf. 13***

**695** A230 10c on 80c dk car rose .25 .25
**696** A230 20c on 80c dk car rose .25 .25
**697** A230 50c on 80c dk car rose .25 .25
**698** A230 60c on 80c dk car rose (Bl) .25 .25
**699** A230 80c dk car rose .30 .25
*Nos. 695-699 (5)* 1.30 1.25

Nos. 661-669 Surcharged

**1964, Apr. 20 Engr. *Perf. 11x11½***

**700** A233 10c on 1s dk pur & redsh brn .40 .25
**701** A233 10c on 1s dk pur & turq .40 .25
**702** A233 20c on 1s dk bl & brn .40 .25
**703** A233 20c on 1s dk bl & grn .40 .25
**704** A233 30c on 1s dk pur & dk car rose .40 .25
**705** A233 40c on 1s blk & ol bis .40 .25
**706** A233 60c on 1s blk & red .40 .25
**707** A233 80c on 1s dk bl & ultra .40 .25
**708** A233 80c on 1s blk & vio .40 .25
*Nos. 700-708 (9)* 3.60 2.25

No. 656 Overprinted in Black or Light Ultramarine

**1964 Litho. *Perf. 14x13***

**709** A231 80c rose car & grn 4.50 1.25

**Butterfly Type of 1961**

Butterflies: Same as on Nos. 680, 682-683.

**1964, June Litho. *Perf. 13½***

**711** A236 20c brt grn & multi .75 .25
**712** A236 50c sal pink & multi 1.50 .25
**713** A236 80c lt red brn & multi 3.00 .25
*Nos. 711-713 (3)* 5.25 .75

Alliance for Progress Emblem, Agriculture and Industry A240

Designs: 50c, Emblem, gear wheels, mountain and seashore. 80c, Emblem, banana worker, fish, factory and ship.

**1964, Aug. 26 Unwmk. *Perf. 12***

**715** A240 40c bis brn & vio .25 .25
**716** A240 50c red org & blk .25 .25
**717** A240 80c bl & dk brn .40 .25
*Nos. 715-717 (3)* .90 .75

Issued to publicize the Alliance for Progress which aims to stimulate economic growth and raise living standards in Latin America.

No. 650 Overprinted in Red

**1964 Photo. *Perf. 14x13½***

**718** A229 1.80s dark blue 2.75 2.25

**No. 656 Overprinted**

**1964, July Litho. *Perf. 14x13***

**719** A231 80c block of 4 4.00 4.00

Organization of American States.

World Map and Banana Tree — A241

**1964, Oct. 26 *Perf. 12½x12***

**720** A241 50c dk brn, gray & gray ol .30 .25
**721** A241 80c blk, org & gray ol .30 .25

Issued to publicize the Banana Conference, Oct.-Nov. 1964. See Nos. C427-C428a.

King Philip II of Spain and Map of Upper Amazon River A242

Designs (Map and): 20c, Juan de Salinas de Loyola. 30c, Hernando de Santillan.

**1964, Dec. 6 Litho. *Perf. 13½***

**722** A242 10c rose, blk & buff .30 .25
**723** A242 20c bl grn, blk & buff .30 .25
**724** A242 30c bl, blk & buff .30 .25
*Nos. 722-724 (3)* .90 .75

4th centenary of the establishment of the Royal High Court in Quito.

Pole Vaulting A243

**1964, Dec. 16 *Perf. 14x13½***

**725** A243 80c vio bl, yel grn & brn .35 .25

18th Olympic Games, Tokyo, Oct. 10-25. See Nos. C432-C434.

Peter Fleming and Two-toed Sloth — A244

Designs: 20c, James Elliot and armadillo. 30c, T. Edward McCully, Jr., and squirrel. 40c, Roger Youderian and deer. 60c, Nathaniel (Nate) Saint and plane over Napo River.

**1965 Unwmk. *Perf. 13½***

**726** A244 20c emerald & multi 1.00 .25
**727** A244 30c yellow & multi 1.00 .25
**728** A244 40c lilac & multi 1.00 .25
**729** A244 60c multi 1.00 .25
**730** A244 80c multi 1.00 .25
*Nos. 726-730 (5)* 5.00 1.25

Issued in memory of five American Protestant missionaries, killed by the Auca Indians, 1/8/56.

Issue dates: 80c, May 11; others, July 8.

Juan B. Vázquez and Benigno Malo College — A245

**1965, June 6 Litho. *Perf. 14***

**731** A245 20c blk, yel & vio bl .25 .25
**732** A245 60c blk, red, yel & vio bl .25 .25
**733** A245 80c blk, emer, yel & vio bl .25 .25
*Nos. 731-733 (3)* .75 .75

Centenary (in 1964) of the founding of Benigno Malo National College.

National Anthem, Juan Leon Mera and Antonio Neumane A246

**1965, Aug. 10 Litho. *Perf. 13½***

**734** A246 50c pink & blk .25 .25
**735** A246 80c lt grn & blk .35 .25
**736** A246 5s bis & blk .80 .35
**737** A246 10s lt ultra & blk 1.40 .90
*Nos. 734-737 (4)* 2.80 1.75

Cent. of the national anthem. The name of the poet Juan Leon Mera is misspelled on the stamps.

For surcharges see Nos. 766C, 766H.

Torch and Athletes (Shot Put, Discus, Javelin and Hammer Throw) — A247

50c, 1s, Runners. 60c, 1.50s, Soccer.

**1965, Nov. 20 *Perf. 12x12½***

**738** A247 40c org, gold, & blk .25 .25
**739** A247 50c org ver, gold & blk .25 .25
**740** A247 60c bl, gold & blk .25 .25
**741** A247 80c brt yel grn, gold & blk .45 .25
**742** A247 1s lt vio, gold & blk .45 .25
**743** A247 1.50s brt pink, gold & blk .75 .50
*Nos. 738-743,C435-C440 (12)* 6.25 3.75

Issued to publicize the 5th Bolivarian Games, held at Guayaquil and Quito.

For surcharges see Nos. 766B, 766D, C449.

Stamps of 1865 A248

**1965, Dec. 30 Litho. *Perf. 13½***

**Stamps of 1865 in Yellow, Ultramarine & Green**

**744** A248 80c rose red .35 .25
**745** A248 1.30s rose lilac .40 .25
**746** A248 2s chocolate .55 .25
**747** A248 4s black .80 .25
*a.* Souv. sheet, #744-747, imperf. 4.00 4.00
*Nos. 744-747 (4)* 2.10 1.00

Cent. of Ecuadorian postage stamps.

The postal validity of some of the following sets has been questioned.

ITU Centenary — A248a

**1966, Jan. 27 Litho. *Perf. 12x12½***

**748** A248a 10c Telstar .25 .25
**748A** A248a 10c Syncom .25 .25
**748B** A248a 80c Relay .25 .25
**748C** A248a 1.50s Luna 3 .40 .35
**748D** A248a 3s Echo II 2.00 1.25
*f.* Souv. sheet of 3, #748, 748B, 748D, perf. 14x12½ 15.00
**748E** A248a 4s E. Branly, Marconi, Bell, E. Belin 2.00 1.50
*g.* Souv. sheet of 3, #748A, 748C, 748E, perf. 14x12½ 15.00
*Nos. 748-748E (6)* 5.15 3.85

1.50s, 3s, 4s are airmail.

Nos. 748Df, 748Eg are printed on surface colored paper. Exist imperf. Value, each $18.

Space Exploration — A248b

10c, Edward White's space walk, June 8, 1965. 1s, Gemini 5, Aug. 21, 1965. 1.30s, Solar system. 2s, Charles Conrad, L. Gordon Cooper, Gemini 5, Aug. 21-29, 1965. 2.50s, Gemini 6. 3.50s, Alexei L. Leonov's space walk, Mar. 18, 1965.

**1966, Jan. 27 *Perf. 12x12½***

**749** A248b 10c multi .25 .25
**749A** A248b 1s multi .35 .25
**749B** A248b 1.30s multi .35 .25
**749C** A248b 2s multi 1.20 .65
**749D** A248b 2.50s multi 1.20 .65
**749E** A248b 3.50s multi 2.75 2.50
*f.* Souv. sheet of 3, #749, 749B, 749E, perf. 14x12½ 15.00 10.00
*Nos. 749-749E (6)* 6.10 4.55

1.30s, 2s, 2.50s, 3.50s are airmail.

No. 749Ef is printed on surface colored paper. Exists imperf. Value $15.

Dante's Dream by Rossetti — A248c

Designs: 80c, Dante and Beatrix by Holliday. 2s, Galileo Galilei, 400th birth cent., vert. 3s, Dante, 700th birth cent., vert.

**1966, June *Perf. 13½x14, 14x13½***

**750** A248c 10c multicolored .25 .25
**750A** A248c 80c multicolored .25 .25
**750B** A248c 2s multicolored 2.40 1.50

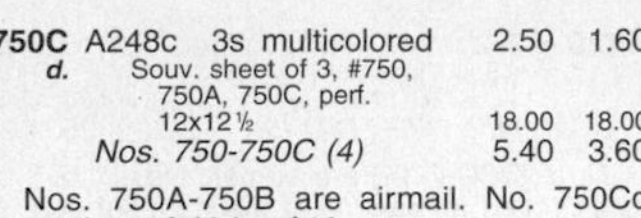

750C A248c 3s multicolored 2.50 1.60
*d.* Souv. sheet of 3, #750, 750A, 750C, perf. 12x12½ 18.00 18.00
*Nos. 750-750C (4)* 5.40 3.60

Nos. 750A-750B are airmail. No. 750Cd exists imperf. Value $18.

Pavonine Quetzal — A249

Birds: 50c, Blue-crowned motmot. 60c, Paradise tanager. 80c, Wire-tailed manakin.

**1966, June 17 Litho. *Perf. 13½***

**Birds in Natural Colors**

| | | | | |
|---|---|---|---|---|
| **751** | A249 40c dl rose & blk | 1.60 | .25 |
| **751A** | A249 50c sal & blk | 1.60 | .25 |
| **751B** | A249 60c lt ocher & blk | 1.60 | .25 |
| **751C** | A249 80c lt bl & blk | 1.60 | .25 |
| | *Nos. 751-751C,C441-C448 (12)* | 31.70 | 6.25 |

For surcharges see Nos. 766E-766F, C450, C455-C457.

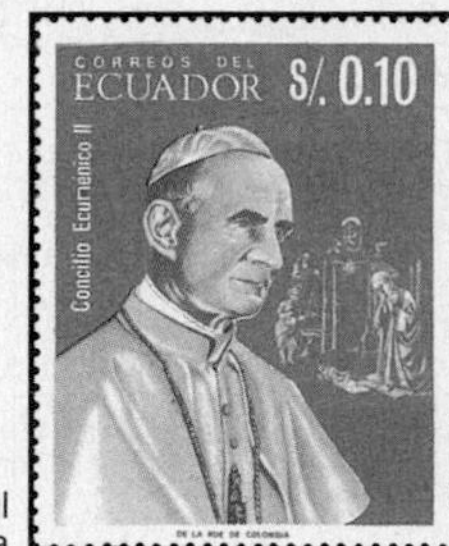


Pope Paul VI — A249a

Pope Paul VI and: 1.30s, Nativity. 3.50s, Virgin of Merced.

**1966, June 24 *Perf. 12½x12***

| | | | |
|---|---|---|---|
| **752** | A249a 10c multicolored | .25 | .25 |
| **752A** | A249a 1.30s multicolored | .75 | .35 |
| **752B** | A249a 3.50s multicolored | 2.25 | .75 |
| *c.* | Souv. sheet of 3, #752, perf. 14x13½, 752A-752B, perf. 12½x12 | 15.00 | 15.00 |
| | *Nos. 752-752B (3)* | 3.25 | 1.35 |

Nos. 752A-752B are airmail.

No. 752Bc is printed on surface colored paper. Exists imperf. Value $18.

Sir Winston Churchill, (1874-1965) — A249b

Famous Men: 10c, Dag Hammarskjold, vert. 1.50s, Albert Schweitzer, vert. 2.50s, John F. Kennedy, vert. 4s, Churchill, Kennedy.

***Perf. 14x13½, 13½x14***

**1966, June 24**

| | | | |
|---|---|---|---|
| **753** | A249b 10c vio bl, brn & blk | .25 | .25 |
| **753A** | A249b 1s ver, bl & blk | .35 | .25 |
| **753B** | A249b 1.50s brn, lil rose & blk | .80 | .30 |
| **753C** | A249b 2.50s ver, bl & blk | 2.00 | 1.00 |
| **753D** | A249b 4s bl, blk & brn | 2.25 | 1.50 |
| *e.* | Souv. sheet of 3, #753, 753B, 753D | 27.50 | 27.50 |
| | *Nos. 753-753D (5)* | 5.65 | 3.30 |

Nos. 753C-753D are airmail.

No. 753De is printed on surface colored paper. 10c stamp is perf. 14x13½, 1.50s is perf. 14x13½x14x12, 4s is perf. 12x12½x13x12½. Exists imperf. Value $27.50.

History of Summer Olympics — A249c

**1966, June 27 *Perf. 12x12½***

| | | | |
|---|---|---|---|
| **754** | A249c 10c Long jump | .25 | .25 |
| **754A** | A249c 10c Wrestling | .25 | .25 |
| **754B** | A249c 80c Discus, javelin | .50 | .25 |
| **754C** | A249c 1.30s Chariot racing | 1.25 | .45 |
| **754D** | A249c 3s High jump | 2.00 | .90 |
| *f.* | Souv. sheet of 3, #754, 754B, 754D | 12.00 | 5.00 |
| **754E** | A249c 3.50s Discus | 3.25 | 1.10 |
| *g.* | Souv. sheet of 3, #754A, 754C, 754E | 12.50 | 5.00 |
| | *Nos. 754-754E (6)* | 7.50 | 3.20 |

Nos. 754C-754D are airmail.

Nos. 754Df, 754Eg are printed on surface colored paper.

Nos. 754Df and 754Eg exist imperf. Value $13.50.

1968 Winter Olympics, Grenoble — A249d

**1966, June 27 *Perf. 14***

| | | | |
|---|---|---|---|
| **755** | A249d 10c Speedskating | .25 | .25 |
| **755A** | A249d 1s Ice hockey | .40 | .25 |
| **755B** | A249d 1.50s Ski jumping | .60 | .30 |
| **755C** | A249d 2s Cross country skiing | 1.20 | .45 |
| **755D** | A249d 2.50s Downhill skiing | 1.60 | 1.25 |
| **755E** | A249d 4s Figure skating | 2.00 | 1.50 |
| *f.* | Souv. sheet of 3, #755, 755B, 755E, perf. 14x13½ | 8.00 | 6.00 |
| | *Nos. 755-755E (6)* | 6.05 | 4.00 |

Nos. 755B-755E are airmail.

No. 755Ef is printed on surface colored paper. Exists imperf. Value same as perf.

French-American Cooperation in Space — A249e

Designs: 1.50s, French satellite D-1, Mt. Gros observatory, vert. 4s, John F. Kennedy, satellites.

**1966 *Perf. 13½x14, 14x13½***

| | | | |
|---|---|---|---|
| **756** | A249e 10c multicolored | .25 | .25 |
| **756A** | A249e 1.50s multicolored | 1.60 | 1.10 |
| **756B** | A249e 4s multicolored | 3.75 | 2.25 |
| *c.* | Sheet of 3, #756-756B | 15.00 | 12.00 |
| | *Nos. 756-756B (3)* | 5.60 | 3.60 |

Nos. 756A-756B are airmail.

No. 756Bc exists imperf. Value same as perf.

Italian Space Program — A249n

Designs: 10c, San Marco satellite. 1.30s, San Marco satellite, diff. 3.50s, Leonardo da Vinci, Moon, and Johannes Kepler.

**1966 Litho. Unwmk. *Perf. 14***

| | | | |
|---|---|---|---|
| **757** | A249n 10c multi | .25 | .25 |
| **757A** | A249n 1.30s multi | .75 | .45 |
| **757B** | A249n 3.50s multi | 2.00 | 1.10 |
| *c.* | Souvenir sheet of 3, #757, 757A, 757B | 12.00 | 8.00 |
| | *Nos. 757- (3)* | 3.00 | 1.80 |

Nos. 757A and 757B are airmail. No. 757Bc is printed on paper with a gray pattern, and exists imperforate on paper printed with a green pattern.

Moon Exploration A249f

**1966 *Perf. 14***

| | | | |
|---|---|---|---|
| **758** | A249f 10c Surveyor | .25 | .25 |
| **758A** | A249f 80c Luna 10 | .25 | .25 |
| **758B** | A249f 1s Luna 9 | .25 | .25 |
| **758C** | A249f 2s Astronaut flight trainer | .80 | .45 |
| **758D** | A249f 2.50s Ranger 7 | 1.00 | .75 |
| **758E** | A249f 3s Lunar Orbiter 1 | 1.20 | .90 |
| *f.* | Sheet of 3, #758, 758A, 758E | 12.00 | 6.00 |
| | *Nos. 758-758E (6)* | 3.75 | 2.85 |

Nos. 758C-758E are airmail. Stamps in No. 758Ef have colored pattern in border.

No. 758Ef exists imperf. Value same as perf.

1968 Summer Olympics, Mexico City — A249g

Paintings by Mexican artists: 10c, Wanderer by Diego Rivera. 1s, Workers by Jose Orozco. 1.30s, Pres. Juarez by Orozco. 2s, Mother and Child by David Siqueiros. 2.50s, Two Women by Rivera. 3.50s, New Democracy by Siqueiros.

**1967, Mar. 13 *Perf. 14***

| | | | |
|---|---|---|---|
| **759** | A249g 10c multicolored | .25 | .25 |
| **759A** | A249g 1s multicolored | .55 | .25 |
| **759B** | A249g 1.30s multicolored | .80 | .30 |
| **759C** | A249g 2s multicolored | 1.00 | .50 |
| **759D** | A249g 2.50s multicolored | 1.20 | .90 |
| **759E** | A249g 3.50s multicolored | 2.25 | 1.75 |
| *f.* | Sheet of 3, #759, 759B, 759E | 15.00 | |
| | *Nos. 759-759E (6)* | 6.05 | 3.95 |

Nos. 759B-759E are airmail.

No. 759f is printed on surface colored paper that differs slightly from Nos. 759-759E. Exists imperf. Value same as perf.

1968 Summer Olympics, Mexico City — A249h

**1967, Mar. 13**

| | | | |
|---|---|---|---|
| **760** | A249h 10c Soccer | .25 | .25 |
| **760A** | A249h 10c Hurdles | .25 | .25 |
| **760B** | A249h 80c Track | .25 | .25 |
| **760C** | A249h 1.50s Fencing | .75 | .30 |
| **760D** | A249h 3s High jump | 1.50 | 1.00 |
| *f.* | Souv. sheet of 3, #760A, 760B, 760D | 15.00 | 7.50 |
| **760E** | A249h 4s Swimming | 3.25 | 1.50 |
| *g.* | Souv. sheet of 3, #760, 760C, 760E | 12.00 | 7.00 |
| | *Nos. 760-760E (6)* | 6.25 | 3.55 |

Nos. 760C-760E are airmail.

Nos. 760f-760g are printed on surface colored paper. Exist imperf. Value same as perf.

4th Natl. Eucharistic Congress A249i

Paintings: 10c, Madonna and Child by unknown artist. 60c, Holy Family by Rodriguez. 80c, Madonna and Child by Samaniego. 1s, Good Shepherd by Samaniego. 1.50s, Assumption of the Virgin by Vargas. 2s, Man in Prayer by Santiago.

10s, Chalice, eucharist, church, wheat.

**1967, May 10**

| | | | |
|---|---|---|---|
| **761** | A249i 10c multicolored | .25 | .25 |
| **761A** | A249i 60c multicolored | .55 | .30 |
| **761B** | A249i 80c multicolored | .80 | .30 |
| **761C** | A249i 1s multicolored | .80 | .50 |
| **761D** | A249i 1.50s multicolored | 1.50 | .75 |
| **761E** | A249i 2s multicolored | 2.50 | .75 |
| | *Nos. 761-761E (6)* | 6.40 | 2.85 |

**Souvenir Sheet**

| | | | |
|---|---|---|---|
| **761F** | A249i 10s multi | 6.50 | 6.50 |

Nos. 761D-761E are airmail. Frames and inscriptions vary greatly.

No. 761F exists imperf. with an orange margin color. Value, same.

Madonna and Child Enthroned by Guido Reni A249j

Paintings of the Madonna and Child by: 40c, van Hemesen. 50c, Memling. 1.30s, Durer. 2.50s, Raphael. 3s, Murillo.

**1967, May 25 *Perf. 14x13½***

| | | | |
|---|---|---|---|
| **762** | A249j 10c multicolored | .25 | .25 |
| **762A** | A249j 40c multicolored | .25 | .25 |
| **762B** | A249j 50c multicolored | .25 | .25 |
| **762C** | A249j 1.30s multicolored | .70 | .30 |
| **762D** | A249j 2.50s multicolored | 1.75 | .95 |
| **762E** | A249j 3s multicolored | 2.75 | 1.20 |
| | *Nos. 762-762E (6)* | 5.95 | 3.20 |

Nos. 762C-762E are airmail.

Portrait of a Young Woman by Rogier van der Weyden
A249k

Designs: 1s, Helene Fourment by Rubens. 1.50s, Venetian Woman by Durer. 2s, Lady Sheffield by Gainsborough. 2.50s, Suzon by Manet. 4s, Lady with a Unicorn by Raphael.

**1967, Sept. 9** *Perf. 14x13½*

**763** A249k 10c multicolored .25 .25
**763A** A249k 1s multicolored .55 .30
**763B** A249k 1.50s multicolored 1.20 .50
**763C** A249k 2s multicolored 1.60 .65
**763D** A249k 2.50s multicolored 2.40 .80
**763E** A249k 4s multicolored 2.75 1.25
*f.* Sheet of 3, #763, 763B, 763E, perf. 14 12.00 8.00
*Nos. 763-763E (6)* 8.75 3.75

Nos. 763B-763E are airmail.
Stamps in No. 763f have colored pattern in border. Exists imperf. Value same as perf.

John F. Kennedy, 50th Birth Anniv.
A249l

JFK and: No. 764A, Dag Hammarskjold. 80c, Pope Paul VI. 1.30s, Konrad Adenauer. 3s, Charles de Gaulle. 3.50s, Winston Churchill.

*Perf. 14x13½, 13½x14*

**1967, Sept. 11**

**764** A249l 10c lil, brn & bl .25 .25
**764A** A249l 10c yel, brn & sky bl .25 .25
**764B** A249l 80c yel, brn & sal .25 .25
**764C** A249l 1.30s yel, brn & pink 2.00 .75
**764D** A249l 3s yel, brn & yel grn 2.90 1.25
**764E** A249l 3.50s yel, brn & bl 4.00 1.75
*Nos. 764-764E (6)* 9.65 4.50

**Souvenir Sheets**

**764F** Sheet of 3 16.00 8.00
*h.* like #764, 35x27mm
*i.* like #764B, 35x27mm
*j.* like #764D, 35x27mm
**764G** Sheet of 3 16.00 8.00
*k.* like #764A, 35x27mm
*l.* like #764C, 35x27mm
*m.* like #764E, 35x27mm

Nos. 764C-764E are airmail. Nos. 764A-764E horiz. Stamps in Nos. 764F-764G have colored pattern in border.
Nos. 764F and 764G exist imperf. Values same as perf.

Christmas — A249m

Designs: No. 765A, Children's procession. 40c, Candlelight procession. 50c, Children singing. 60c, Processional. 2.50s, Christmas celebration.

**1967, Dec. 29** *Perf. 13x14*

**765** A249m 10c multi .40 .25
**765A** A249m 10c multi .40 .25
**765B** A249m 40c multi .40 .25
**765C** A249m 50c multi .40 .25
**765D** A249m 60c multi .40 .25
**765E** A249m 2.50s multi 11.00 9.75
*Nos. 765-765E (6)* 13.00 11.00

No. 765E is airmail. See Nos. 768-768F.

**Various Surcharges on Issues of 1956-66**

**1967-68**

**766** AP72 30c on 1.10s (C337) .35 .25
**766A** AP66 40c on 1.70s (C292) .35 .25
**766B** A247 40c on 3.50s (C438) .35 .25
**766C** A246 50c on 5s (736) ('68) .35 .25
**766D** A247 80c on 1.50s (743) .40 .25
**766E** A249 80c on 2.50s (C445) .40 .25
**766F** A249 1s on 4s (C447) .50 .25
**766G** AP66 1.30s on 1.90s (C293) .65 .55
**766H** A246 2s on 10s (737) ('68) .80 .25
*Nos. 766-766H,C449-C450 (11)* 4.95 3.15

The surcharge on Nos. 766B-766C, 766E and 766G-766H includes "Resello." The obliteration of old denomination and arrangement of surcharges differ on each stamp.

Bust of Peñaherrera, Central University, Quito — A250

50c, Law books. 80c, Open book, laurel, horiz.

*Perf. 12x12½, 12½x12*

**1967, Dec. 29** **Litho.**

**767** A250 50c brt grn & blk .25 .25
**767A** A250 60c rose & blk .25 .25
**767B** A250 80c rose lil & blk .25 .25
*Nos. 767-767B,C451-C452 (5)* 1.35 1.25

Cent. (in 1964) of the birth of Dr. Victor Manuel Peñaherrera (1864-1932), author of the civil and criminal codes of Ecuador.

**Christmas Type of 1967**

Native Christian Art: 10c, Mourning of the Death of Christ, by Manuel Chili. 80c, Ascension of the Holy Virgin, vert. 1s, The Holy Virgin. 1.30s, Coronation of the Holy Virgin, by Bernardo Rodriguez, vert. 1.50s, Madonna and Child with the Heavenly Host, vert. 2s, Madonna and Child, by Manuel Samaniego, vert. 3s, Immaculate Conception, by Bernardo de Legranda, vert. 3.50s, Passion of Christ, by Chili, vert. 4s, The Holy Virgin of Quito, by de Legranda, vert.

**1968 Jan. 19** *Perf. 13½x14, 14x13½*

**768** A249m 10c multi .25 .25
**768A** A249m 80c multi .25 .25
**768B** A249m 1s multi .25 .25
**768C** A249m 1.30s multi .25 .25
**768D** A249m 1.50s multi .50 .30
**768E** A249m 2s multi .80 .75
*Nos. 768-768E (6)* 2.30 2.05

**Souvenir Sheet**

*Perf. 14*

**768F** Sheet of 3 16.00 8.00
*g.* A249m 3s multicolored
*h.* A249m 3.50s multicolored
*i.* A249m 4s multicolored

Nos. 768C-768F are airmail. No. 768F exists imperf. Value same.

Tourism Year — A250a

20c, Woman from Otavalo. 30c, Colorado Indian. 40c, Petroglyph of a cat. 50c, Petroglyph of a mythological predator. 60c, Woman in a bazaar. 80c, 1s, 1.30s, Petroglyphs, diff. 1.50s, Colonial street, Quito. 2s, Amulet.

**1968, Apr. 1** *Perf. 13½x14*

**769** A250a 20c multicolored .25 .25
**769A** A250a 30c multicolored .25 .25
**769B** A250a 40c multicolored .25 .25
**769C** A250a 50c multicolored .25 .25
**769D** A250a 60c multicolored .25 .25
**769E** A250a 80c multicolored .25 .25
**769F** A250a 1s multicolored .30 .25
**769G** A250a 1.30s multicolored .25 .25
**769H** A250a 1.50s multicolored .30 .25
**769I** A250a 2s multicolored .35 .25
*Nos. 769-769I (10)* 2.70 2.50

Eleventh Congress of the Confederation of Latin American Tourist Organizations (COTAL). Nos. 769G-769I are airmail.

Otto Arosemena Gomez — A251

Design: 1s, Page from the Constitution.

**1968, May 9** **Litho.** *Perf. 13½x14*

**770** A251 80c lil & multi .25 .25
**770A** A251 1s multi .25 .25
*Nos. 770-770A,C453-C454 (4)* 1.05 1.00

First anniversary of the administration of Pres. Otto Arosemena Gomez.

Lions Emblem — A252

**1968, May 24** **Litho.** *Perf. 13½x14*

**771** A252 80c multi .25 .25
**771A** A252 1.30s multi .25 .25
**771B** A252 2s pink & multi .30 .25
*c.* Souvenir sheet of 1 4.75 4.75
*Nos. 771-771B (3)* .80 .75

50th anniv. (in 1967) of Lions Intl.
No. 771c contains one 5s 39x49mm stamp. Exists imperf. Value same as perf.

Pope Paul VI, Visit to Latin America — A252a

39th Intl. Eucharistic Congress, Bogota, Colombia
A252b

60c, Pope Paul VI, vert. 1s, Madonna by Botticelli. 1.30s, Pope Paul VI with flags of South American nations. 2s, Madonna and Child by Durer.

**1969** *Perf. 13½x14, 14x13½*

**772** A252a 40c multicolored .25 .25
**772A** A252a 60c multicolored .35 .25
**772B** A252b 1s multicolored 1.10 .30
**772C** A252a 1.30s multicolored .80 .40
*e.* Souv. sheet of 3, #772, 772A, 772C, imperf. 4.00 2.50
**772D** A252b 2s multicolored 1.75 .75
*f.* Souv. sheet of 2, #772B, 772D, imperf. 4.75 2.50
*Nos. 772-772D (5)* 4.25 1.95

Nos. 772C-772D are airmail. Nos. 772-772f overprinted in silver with the national coat of arms.

Madonna with the Angel by Rogier van der Weyden
A252c

Paintings by various artists showing the life of the Virgin Mary: 40c, Annunciation of the Lord, by van der Weyden. 60c, Presentation of the Lord, by van der Weyden. 1s, Holy Family, by Raphael. 1.30s, Adoration of the Shepherds, by Bonifazio Veronese. 2s, Adoration of the Magi, by van der Weyden

**1969** *Perf. 14x13½, 13½x14*

**773** A252c 40c shown .25 .25
**773A** A252c 60c multi .25 .25
**773B** A252c 1s multi .35 .25
**773C** A252c 1.30s multi 1.25 .65
*e.* Souv. sheet of 2, #773B-773C, imperf. 5.75 2.50
**773D** A252c 2s multi 2.00 .80
*f.* Souv. sheet of 3, #773-773A, 773D, imperf. 5.75 2.50
*Nos. 773-773D (5)* 4.10 2.20

Nos. 773-773Df overprinted in silver with the national coat of arms. Sizing of No. 773Df stamps, side stamps are 25mm x 50mm; center stamp is 54.5mm x 50mm. Nos. 773C-773D are airmail.

**Nos. C331 and C326 Surcharged in Violet and Dark Blue**

a

b

**1969, Jan. 10** *Perf. 11½, 14x13½*

**774** AP79 (a) 40c on 1.30s (V) .55 .25
**774A** AP76 (b) 50c on 1.30s (DBl) .55 .25

**Types of 1958**

No. 775 & 775B Srchd. and Ovptd. in Plum and Black

No. 775A Srchd. and Ovptd. in Plum and Black

No. 775C Overprinted in Red & Black

Design: Ignacio Luis Arcaya, Foreign Minister of Venezuela.

**1969, Mar. Litho. *Perf. 12***

**Flags in Red, Blue and Yellow**

775 A223 50c on 2s sepia .30 .25
775A A223 80c on 2s sepia .30 .25
775B A223 1s on 2s sepia .30 .25
775C A223 2s sepia .30 .25
*Nos. 775-775C,C455-C457 (7)* 2.70 1.75

Nos. 775-775C were not issued without overprint. The obliteration of old denomination on No. 775A is a small square around a star. Overprint is plum, except for the black small coat of arms on right flag.

Map of Ecuador and Oriental Region — A253

**Surcharge typographed in Dark Blue, Red Brown, Black or Lilac**

**1969 Litho. *Perf. 14***

776 A253 20c on 30c (DBl) .35 .25
776A A253 40c on 30c (RBr) .35 .25
777 A253 50c on 30c (DBl) .35 .25
778 A253 60c on 30c (DBl) .35 .25
778A A253 60c on 30c (Bk) .40 .40
778B A253 80c on 30c (DBl) — 20.00
779 A253 80c on 30c (Bk) .35 .25
780 A253 1s on 30c (L) .35 .25
780A A253 1s on 30c (DBl) 1.20 .80
781 A253 1.30s on 30c (Bk) .50 .25
782 A253 1.50s on 30c (Bk) .50 .25
783 A253 2s on 30c (DBl) .65 .25
784 A253 3s on 30c (DBl) .75 .25
784A A253 4s on 30c (DBl) 2.00 2.00
785 A253 4s on 30c (Bk) .80 .25
786 A253 5s on 30c (Bk) 1.00 .35
*Nos. 776-786 (16)* 9.90 26.30

Not issued without surcharge.

M. L. King, John and Robert Kennedy — A254

**1969-70 Typo. *Perf. 12½***

787 A254 4s blk, bl, grn & buff .50 .25

***Perf. 13½***

788 A254 4s blk, lt bl & grn ('70) .50 .25

In memory of John F. Kennedy, Robert F. Kennedy and Martin Luther King, Jr.

Thecla Coronata — A255

Butterflies: 20c, Papilio zabreus. 30c, Heliconius chestertoni. 40c, Papilio pausanias. 50c, Pereute leucodrosime. 60c, Metamorpha dido. 80c, Morpho cypris. 1s, Catagramma astarte.

**1970 Litho. *Perf. 12½***

789 A255 10c buff & multi 3.25 .45
790 A255 20c lt grn & multi 3.25 .45
791 A255 30c pink & multi 3.25 .45
792 A255 40c lt bl & multi 3.25 .25
793 A255 50c gold & multi 3.25 .25
794 A255 60c salmon & multi 3.25 .25
795 A255 80c silver & multi 3.25 .25
796 A255 1s lt grn & multi 3.25 .25

**Same, White Background**

***Perf. 13½***

797 A255 10c multi 3.25 .45
798 A255 20c multi 3.25 .45
799 A255 30c multi 3.25 .45
800 A255 40c multi 3.25 .25
801 A255 50c multi 3.25 .25
802 A255 60c multi 3.25 .25
803 A255 80c multi 3.25 .25
804 A255 1s multi 3.25 .25
*Nos. 789-804,C461-C464 (20)* 66.00 6.20

Surcharged Revenue Stamps — A256

**1970, June 16 Litho. *Perf. 14***

**Red Surcharge**

805 A256 1s on 1s light blue .25 .25
806 A256 1.30s on 1s light blue .25 .25
807 A256 1.50s on 1s light blue .30 .30
808 A256 2s on 1s light blue .35 .25
809 A256 5s on 1s light blue .75 .30
810 A256 10s on 1s light blue 1.50 .55
*Nos. 805-810 (6)* 3.40 1.90

Surcharged Revenue Stamps — A257

**1970 Typo. *Perf. 12***

**Black Surcharge**

811 A257 60c on 1s violet .30 .25
812 A257 80c on 1s violet .30 .25
813 A257 1s on 1s violet .30 .25
814 A257 1.10s on 1s violet .30 .25
815 A257 1.30s on 1s violet .30 .25
816 A257 1.50s on 1s violet .35 .25
817 A257 2s on 1s violet .35 .25
818 A257 2.20s on 1s violet .40 .25
819 A257 3s on 1s violet .50 .25
*Nos. 811-819 (9)* 3.10 2.25

**1970**

820 A257 1.10s on 2s green .30 .25
821 A257 1.30s on 2s green .30 .25
822 A257 1.50s on 2s green .35 .25
823 A257 2s on 2s green .35 .25
824 A257 3.40s on 2s green .50 .25
825 A257 5s on 2s green .75 .25
826 A257 10s on 2s green 1.25 .25
827 A257 20s on 2s green 2.10 .70
828 A257 50s on 2s green 5.00 2.25
*Nos. 820-828 (9)* 10.90 4.70

**1970**

829 A257 3s on 5s blue .50 .25
830 A257 5s on 5s blue .65 .35
831 A257 10s on 40s orange 1.25 .65
*Nos. 829-831 (3)* 2.40 1.25

In the surcharge applied to Nos. 811-831, the word "POSTAL" is not locked into horizontal and vertical position relative to the "1970". On some stamps the "P" is directly below the numeral "1", on others the "O" is below the "1". The top of "POSTAL" can vary from 1mm-8mm from the bottom of the date.

Arms of Zamora Chinchipe — A258

Design: 1s, Arms and flag of Esmeraldas.

**1971 Litho. *Perf. 10½***

832 A258 50c pale yel & multi .25 .25
833 A258 1s sal & multi .25 .25
*Nos. 832-833,C465-C469 (7)* 3.50 2.00

Flags of Ecuador and Chile — A259

**1971, Sept. *Perf. 12½***

840 A259 1.30s blk & multi .25 .25
*Nos. 840,C481-C482 (3)* .75 .75

Visit of Pres. Salvador Allende of Chile, Aug. 24.

Ismael Pérez Pazmiño — A260

**1971, Sept. 16 *Perf. 12x11½***

841 A260 1s grn & multi .25 .25
*Nos. 841,C485-C486 (3)* .85 .75

"El Universo," newspaper founded by Ismael Pérez Pazmiño, 50th anniv.

CARE Package — A261

**1971-72 *Perf. 12½***

842 A261 30c lilac ('72) .25 .25
843 A261 40c emerald ('72) .25 .25
844 A261 50c blue .25 .25
845 A261 60c carmine .25 .25
846 A261 80c lt brn ('72) .25 .25
*Nos. 842-846 (5)* 1.25 1.25

25th anniversary of CARE, a US-Canadian Cooperative for American Relief Everywhere.

Flags of Ecuador and Argentina — A262

**1972 *Perf. 11½***

847 A262 1s blk & multi .25 .25
*Nos. 847,C491-C492 (3)* 1.00 .80

Visit of Lt. Gen. Alejandro Agustin Lanusse, president of Argentina, Jan. 25.

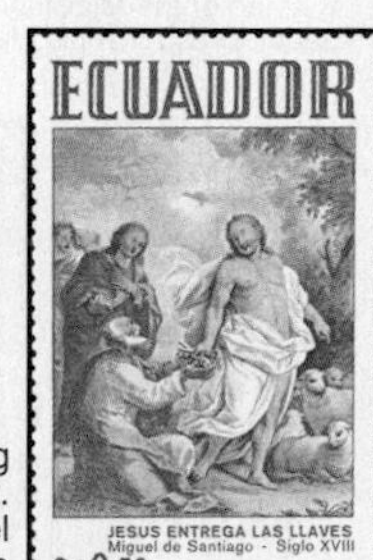


Jesus Giving Keys to St. Peter, by Miguel de Santiago A263

Ecuadorian Paintings: 1.10s, Virgin of Mercy, Quito School. 2s, Virgin Mary, by Manuel Samaniego.

**1972, Apr. 24 Litho. *Perf. 14x13½***

848 A263 50c black & multi .25 .25
849 A263 1.10s black & multi .35 .30
850 A263 2s black & multi .55 .50
a. Souvenir sheet of 3 2.50 2.50
*Nos. 848-850,C494-C495 (5)* 2.60 1.95

No. 850a contains 3 imperf. stamps similar to Nos. 848-850.

**1972, May 4**

Ecuadorian Statues: 50c, Our Lady of Sorrow, by Caspicara. 1.10s, Nativity, Quito School, horiz. 2s, Virgin of Quito, anonymous.

851 A263 50c blk & multi .25 .25
852 A263 1.10s blk & multi .35 .35
853 A263 2s blk & multi .50 .50
a. Souv. sheet of 3 2.90 2.40
*Nos. 851-853,C496-C497 (5)* 2.45 2.00

Letters of "Ecuador" 3mm high on Nos. 851-853, 7mm high on Nos. 848-850. No. 853a contains 3 imperf. stamps similar to Nos. 851-853.

A264

Designs: 30c, Gen. Juan Ignacio Pareja. 40c, Juan José Flores. 50c, Leon de Febres Cordero. 60c, Ignacio Torres. 70c, Francisco de Paula Santander. 1s, José M. Cordova.

**1972, May 24 *Perf. 12½***

854 A264 30c blue & multi .25 .25
855 A264 40c blue & multi .25 .25
856 A264 50c blue & multi .25 .25
857 A264 60c blue & multi .25 .25
858 A264 70c blue & multi .25 .25
859 A264 1s blue & multi .25 .25
*Nos. 854-859,C498-C503 (12)* 5.90 4.10

Sesquicentennial of the Battle of Pichincha and the liberation of Quito.

A265

Designs: 2s, Woman Wearing Poncho. 3s, Striped poncho. 5s, Embroidered poncho. 10s, Metal vase.

**1972, July Photo. *Perf. 13***

860 A265 2s multicolored .25 .25
861 A265 3s multicolored .50 .25
862 A265 5s multicolored .65 .40
863 A265 10s dp blue & multi 1.40 .90
a. Souvenir sheet of 4 4.00 4.00
*Nos. 860-863,C504-C507 (8)* 5.75 3.60

Handicraft of Ecuador. No. 863a contains 4 imperf. stamps similar to Nos. 860-863.

Sucre Statue, Santo Domingo — A266

1.80s, San Agustin Convent. 2.30s, Plaza de la Independencia. 2.50s, Bolivar statue, La Alameda. 4.75s, Chapel door.

**1972, Dec. 6 Litho. *Perf. 11½***

864 A266 1.20s yel & multi .25 .25
865 A266 1.80s yel & multi .25 .25
866 A266 2.30s yel & multi .30 .25
867 A266 2.50s yel & multi .45 .25
868 A266 4.75s yel & multi .60 .30
*Nos. 864-868,C518-C524 (12)* 6.00 3.95

Sesquicentennial of the Battle of Pichincha.

Radar Station — A267

**1973, Apr. 5** **Wmk. 367**

**869** A267 1s multicolored .35 .25

Inauguration of earth telecommunications station, Oct. 19, 1972.

Blue-footed Boobies A268

**Wmk. 367, Unwmkd. (#872)**

**1973** **Litho.** ***Perf. 11½x12***

**870** A268 30c shown .55 .25
**871** A268 40c Blue-faced booby .55 .25
**872** A268 50c Oyster-catcher .55 .25
**873** A268 60c California sea lions 1.10 .25
**874** A268 70c Galapagos giant tortoise 1.25 .25
**875** A268 1s California sea lion 1.75 .25
*Nos. 870-875,C527-C528 (8)* 9.95 2.00

Elevation of Galapagos Islands to a province of Ecuador.

Issue dates: 50c, Oct. 3; others Aug. 16.

Black-chinned Mountain Tanager — A269

Birds of Ecuador: 2s, Moriche oriole. 3s, Toucan barbet, vert. 5s, Masked crimson tanager, vert. 10s, Blue-necked tanager, vert.

***Perf. 11x11½, 11½x11***

**1973, Dec. 6** **Litho.** **Unwmk.**

**876** A269 1s brick red & multi .65 .25
**877** A269 2s lt blue & multi 1.10 .25
**878** A269 3s lt green & multi 1.10 .25
**879** A269 5s pale lilac & multi 2.40 .65
**880** A269 10s pale yel grn & multi 4.75 1.40
*Nos. 876-880 (5)* 10.00 2.80

Two souvenir sheets exist: one contains 2 imperf. stamps similar to Nos. 876-877 with yellow margin and black inscription; the other 3 stamps similar to Nos. 878-880; gray margin and black inscription including "Aereo." Both sheets dated "1972." Size: 143x84mm. Value, each $9.

Marco T. Varea, Botanist — A270

Portraits: 60c, Pio Jaramillo Alvarado, writer. 70c, Prof. Luciano Andrade M. No. 883, Marco T. Varea, botanist. No. 884, Dr. Juan Modesto Carbo Noboa, medical researcher. No. 885, Alfredo J. Valenzuela. No. 886, Capt. Edmundo Chiriboga G. 1.20s, Francisco Campos R., scientist. 1.80s, Luis Vernaza Lazarte, philanthropist.

**1974** **Unwmk.** ***Perf. 12x11½***

**881** A270 60c crimson rose .35 .25
**882** A270 70c lilac .35 .25
**883** A270 1s ultra .25 .25
**884** A270 1s orange .25 .25
**885** A270 1s emerald .25 .25
**886** A270 1s brown .25 .25
**887** A270 1.20s apple green .35 .25
**889** A270 1.80s lt blue .40 .25
*Nos. 881-889 (8)* 2.45 2.00

Arcade A271

Designs: 30c, Monastery, entrance. 40c, Church. 50c, View of Church through gate, vert. 60c, Chapel, vert. 70c, Church and cemetery, vert.

***Perf. 11½x12, 12x11½***

**1975, Feb. 4** **Litho.**

**896** A271 20c yellow & multi .30 .25
**897** A271 30c yellow & multi .30 .25
**898** A271 40c yellow & multi .30 .25
**899** A271 50c yellow & multi .30 .25
**900** A271 60c yellow & multi .30 .25
**901** A271 70c yellow & multi .30 .25
*Nos. 896-901 (6)* 1.80 1.50

Colonial Monastery, Tilipulo, Cotopaxi Province.

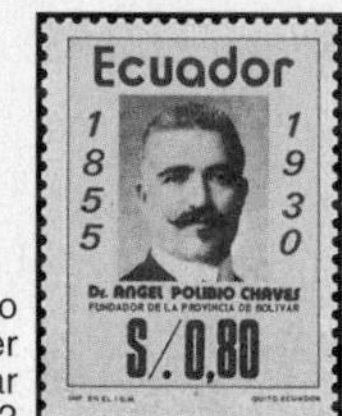


Angel Polibio Chaves, Founder of Bolivar Province — A272

Portrait: No. 903, Emilio Estrada Ycaza (1916-1961), archeologist.

**1975** **Litho.** ***Perf. 12x11½***

**902** A272 80c violet bl & lt bl .25 .25
**903** A272 80c vermilion & pink .25 .25

Issue dates: No. 902, 2/21; No. 903, 3/25.

R. Rodriguez Palacios and A. Duran Quintero — A273

**1975, Apr. 1** **Litho.** ***Perf. 12x11½***

**910** A273 1s multicolored .25 .25
*Nos. 910,C547-C548 (3)* .85 .75

Meeting of the Ministers for Public Works of Ecuador and Colombia, July 27, 1973.

"Woman of Action" — A274

Design: No. 912, "Woman of Peace."

**1975, June**

**911** A274 1s yellow & multi .35 .25
**912** A274 1s blue & multi .45 .25

International Women's Year 1975.

Planes, Soldier and Ship — A275

**1975, July 9** ***Perf. 11½x12***

**913** A275 2s multicolored .40 .25

3 years of Natl. Revolutionary Government.

Hurdling — A276

Designs: Modern sports drawn Inca style.

**1975, Sept. 11** **Litho.** ***Perf. 11½***

**914** A276 20c shown .50 .35
**915** A276 20c Chess .50 .35
**916** A276 30c Basketball .50 .35
**917** A276 30c Boxing .50 .35
**918** A276 40c Bicycling .50 .35
**919** A276 40c Steeplechase .50 .35
**920** A276 50c Soccer .50 .35
**921** A276 50c Fencing .50 .35
**922** A276 60c Golf .50 .35
**923** A276 60c Vaulting .50 .35
**924** A276 70c Judo (standing) .50 .35
**925** A276 70c Wrestling .50 .35
**926** A276 80c Swimming .50 .35
**927** A276 80c Weight lifting .50 .35
**928** A276 1s Table Tennis .50 .35
**929** A276 1s Paddle ball .50 .35
*Nos. 914-929,C554-C558 (21)* 11.35 6.85

3rd Ecuadorian Games.

Genciana A277

Designs: Ecuadorian plants.

***Perf. 12x11½, 11½x12***

**1975, Nov. 18** **Litho.**

**930** A277 20c Orchid, vert .25 .25
**931** A277 30c shown .25 .25
**932** A277 40c Bromeliaceae cactaceae, vert .35 .25
**933** A277 50c Orchid .35 .25
**934** A277 60c Orchid .45 .25
**935** A277 80c Flowering cactus .45 .25
**936** A277 1s Orchid .75 .25
*Nos. 930-936,C559-C563 (12)* 7.20 3.95

Venus, Chorrera Culture — A278

Female Mask, Tolita Culture — A279

Designs: 30c, Venus, Valdivia Culture. 40c, Seated man, Chorrera Culture. 50c, Man with poncho, Panzaleo Culture (late). 60c, Mythical head, Cashaloma Culture. 80c, Musician, Tolita Culture. No. 943, Chief Priest, Mantefia Culture. No. 945, Ornament, Tolita Culture. No. 946, Angry mask, Tolita Culture.

**1976, Feb. 12** **Litho.** ***Perf. 11½***

**937** A278 20c multicolored .40 .25
**938** A278 30c multicolored .40 .25
**939** A278 40c multicolored .40 .25
**940** A278 50c multicolored .40 .25
**941** A278 60c multicolored .40 .25
**942** A278 80c multicolored .40 .25
**943** A278 1s multicolored .40 .25
**944** A279 1s multicolored .40 .25
**945** A279 1s multicolored .40 .25
**946** A279 1s multicolored .40 .25
*Nos. 937-946,C568-C572 (15)* 7.65 4.35

Archaeological artifacts.

Strawberries A280

**1976, Mar. 30**

**947** A280 1s blue & multi .35 .25
*Nos. 947,C573-C574 (3)* 1.55 .90

25th Flower and Fruit Festival, Ambato.

Carlos Amable Ortiz (1859-1937) A281

No. 949, Sixto Maria Duran (1875-1947). No. 950, Segundo Cueva Celi (1901-1969). No. 951, Cristobal Ojeda Davila (1910-1952). No. 952, Luis Alberto Valencia (1918-1970).

**1976, Mar. 15** **Litho.** ***Perf. 11½***

**948** A281 1s ver & multi .35 .25
**949** A281 1s orange & multi .35 .25
**950** A281 1s lt green & multi .35 .25
**951** A281 1s blue & multi .35 .25
**952** A281 1s lt brn & multi .35 .25
*Nos. 948-952 (5)* 1.75 1.25

Ecuadorian composers and musicians.

Institute Emblem A282

**1977, Aug. 15** **Litho.** ***Perf. 11½x12***

**953** A282 2s multicolored .35 .25

11th General Assembly of Pan-American Institute of Geography and History, Quito, Aug. 15-30. See Nos. C597-C597a.

Hands Holding Rotary Emblem A283

**1977, Aug. 31** **Litho.** ***Perf. 12***

**954** A283 1s multicolored .25 .25
**955** A283 2s multicolored .45 .25

**Souvenir Sheets**

***Imperf***

**956** A283 5s multicolored 1.25 1.25
**957** A283 10s multicolored 1.50 1.50

Rotary Club of Guayaquil, 50th anniv.

José Peralta — A284

Design: 2.40s, Peralta statue.

**1977 Litho. *Perf. 11½***
**958** A284 1.80s multi .25 .25
**959** A284 2.40s multi .25 .25
*Nos. 958-959,C609 (3)* .90 .75

José Peralta (1855-1937), writer.

Blue-faced Booby A285

Galapagos Birds: 1.80s, Red-footed booby. 2.40s, Blue-footed boobies. 3.40s, Gull. 4.40s, Galapagos hawk. 5.40s, Map of Galapagos Islands and boobies, vert.

***Perf. 11½x12, 12x11½***
**1977, Nov. 29 Litho.**
**960** A285 1.20s multi .45 .25
**961** A285 1.80s multi .60 .25
**962** A285 2.40s multi 1.00 .25
**963** A285 3.40s multi 1.40 .25
**964** A285 4.40s multi 2.10 .30
**965** A285 5.40s multi 2.75 .30
*Nos. 960-965 (6)* 8.30 1.60

Dr. Corral Moscoso Hospital, Cuenca A286

**1978, Apr. 12 Litho. *Perf. 11½x12***
**966** A286 3s multicolored .30 .25
*Nos. 966,C613-C614 (3)* 1.95 1.00

Inauguration (in 1977) of Dr. Vicente Corral Moscoso Regional Hospital, Cuenca.

Surveyor Plane over Ecuador — A287

**1978, Apr. 12 Litho. *Perf. 11½***
**967** A287 6s multicolored .75 .35
*Nos. 967,C619-C620 (3)* 3.60 2.65

Military Geographical Institute, 50th anniv.

Latin-American Lions Emblem — A288

**1978, May 24**
**968** A288 3s multi .60 .25
**969** A288 4.20s multi .90 .25
*Nos. 968-969,C621-C623 (5)* 5.65 2.40

7th meeting of Latin American Lions, Jan. 25-29.

70th Anniversary Emblem — A289

**1978, Sept. Litho. *Perf. 11½***
**970** A289 4.20s gray & multi .55 .30

70th anniversary of Filanbanco (Philanthropic Bank). See No. C626.

Goalmouth and Net — A290

Designs: 1.80s, "Gauchito" and Games emblem, vert. 4.40s, "Gauchito," vert.

**1978, Nov. 1 Litho. *Perf. 12***
**971** A290 1.20s multi .25 .25
**972** A290 1.80s multi .25 .25
**973** A290 4.40s multi .65 .25
*Nos. 971-973,C627-C629 (6)* 3.35 2.05

11th World Cup Soccer Championship, Argentina, June 1-25.

Symbols for Male and Female — A291

**1979, Feb. 15 Litho. *Perf. 12x11½***
**974** A291 3.40s multi .55 .30

Inter-American Women's Commission, 50th anniversary.

Emblem A292

**1979, June 21 Litho. *Perf. 11½x12***
**975** A292 4.40s multi .45 .30
**976** A292 5.40s multi .55 .30

Ecuadorian Mortgage Bank, 16th anniv.

Street Scene, Quito — A293

***Perf. 12x11½***
**1979, Aug. 3 Litho. Unwmk.**
**977** A293 3.40s multi .35 .25
*Nos. 977,C651-C653 (4)* 8.00 3.70

Natl. heritage: Quito & Galapagos Islands.

Jose Joaquin de Olmedo (1780-1847), Physician — A294

**1980, Apr. 29 Litho. *Perf. 12x11½***
**978** A294 3s multi .35 .25
**979** A294 5s multi .55 .40
*Nos. 978-979,C662 (3)* 2.15 1.30

First Pres. of Free State of Guayaquil, 1820.

Chief Enriquillo, Dominican Republic — A295

Indo-American Tribal Chiefs: 3.40s, Guaycaypuro, Venezuela. No. 982, Abayuba, Uruguay. No. 983, Atlacatl, Salvador.

**Wmk. 367, Unwmkd. (#981-983)**
**1980, May 12**
**980** A295 3s multi .60 .25
**981** A295 3.40s multi .75 .30
**982** A295 5s multi 1.50 .45
**983** A295 5s multi 1.50 .45
*Nos. 980-983,C663-C678 (20)* 39.85 9.70

King Juan Carlos and Queen Sofia, Visit to Ecuador A296

***Perf. 11½x12***
**1980, May 18 Unwmk.**
**984** A296 3.40s multi .55 .30

See No. C679.

Cofan Indian, Napo Province — A297

3.40s, Zuleta man, Imbabura. 5s, Chota woman, Imbabura.

**1980, June 10 Litho. *Perf. 12x11½***
**985** A297 3s shown .45 .25
**986** A297 3.40s multicolored .45 .25
**987** A297 5s multicolored .70 .30
*Nos. 985-987,C681-C684 (7)* 7.10 4.55

Basilica, Our Lady of Mercy Church, Quito A298

**1980, July 7 Litho. *Perf. 11½***
**988** A298 3.40s shown .45 .25
**989** A298 3.40s Balcony .45 .25
**989A** A298 3.40s Dome and cupolas .45 .25

**Sizes: 91x116mm, 116x91mm**
***Imperf***
**990** A298 5s multi 1.75 1.60
**990A** A298 5s multi, horiz. 1.75 1.60
**990B** A298 5s multi 1.75 1.60
*Nos. 988-990B,C685-C691 (13)* 15.60 10.05

Virgin of Mercy, patron saint of Ecuadorian armed forces. No. 990 contains designs of Nos. C686, C685, 989. No. 990A contains designs of Nos. C688, C691, C690. No. 990B contains designs of Nos. C689, C687, 989A, 988.

Olympic Torch and Rings — A299

***Perf. 12x11½***
**1980, July 19 Wmk. 395**
**991** A299 5s multi .70 .25
**992** A299 7.60s multi .80 .30
*Nos. 991-992,C695-C696 (4)* 3.65 2.05

**Souvenir Sheet**
***Imperf***
**993** A299 30s multi 6.75 6.75

22nd Summer Olympic Games, Moscow, July 19-Aug. 3.

No. 993 contains vignettes in designs of Nos. 991 and C695.

Coronation of Virgin of Cisne, 50th Anniv. — A300

**1980 Litho. *Perf. 11½***
**994** A300 1.20s shown .25 .25
**995** A300 3.40s Different statue .50 .30

J.J. Olmedo, Father de Velasco, Flags of Ecuador and Riobamba, Constitution A301

**1980, Sept. 20 Litho. *Perf. 11½***
**996** A301 3.40s multi .25 .25
**997** A301 5s multi .70 .40
*Nos. 996-997,C700-C701 (4)* 2.60 1.35

**Souvenir Sheet**
***Imperf***
**998** A301 30s multi 3.00 3.00

Constitutional Assembly of Riobamba sesquicentennial. No. 998 contains vignettes in designs of #996-997.

Young Indian Girl — A302

***Perf. 12x11½***
**1980, Oct. 9 Litho. Wmk. 395**
**999** A302 1.20s multi .25 .25
**1000** A302 3.40s multi .50 .25
*Nos. 999-1000,C703-C704 (4)* 2.85 1.45

Democratic government, 1st anniversary.

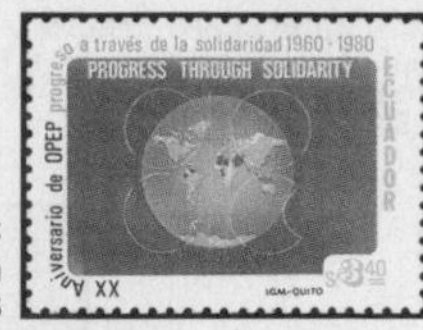

OPEC Emblem A303

**1980, Nov. 8** ***Perf. 11½x12***
**1001** A303 3.40s multi .50 .25

20th anniversary of OPEC. See No. C706.

Decorative Hedges, Capitol Gardens, Carchi A304

**1980, Nov. 21** ***Perf. 13***
**1002** A304 3s multi .45 .25
*Nos. 1002,C707-C708 (3)* 3.60 1.55

Carchi province centennial.

Cattleya Maxima A305

Orchids: 3s, Comparattia speciosa. 3.40s, Cattleya iricolor.

**1980, Nov. 22** ***Perf. 11½x12***
**1003** A305 1.20s shown .75 .25
**1004** A305 3s multicolored 1.00 .30
**1005** A305 3.40s multicolored 1.10 .35
*Nos. 1003-1005,C709-C712 (7)* 21.60 5.20

**Souvenir Sheet**
***Imperf***

**1006** A305 20s multi 14.00 10.00

No. 1006 contains vignettes in designs of Nos. 1003-1005.

Pope John Paul II and Children — A306

**1980, Dec. 27** ***Perf. 12***
**1007** A306 3.40s multi .60 .30
*Nos. 1007,C715-C716 (3)* 2.85 1.40

Christmas and visit of Pope John Paul II.

Carlos and Jorge Mantilla Ortega, Editors of El Comercio — A307

El Comercio Newspaper, 75th Anniv.: 3.40s, Editors Cesar & Carlos Mantilla Jacome.

**1981, Jan. 6**
**1008** A307 2s multi .30 .25
**1009** A307 3.40s multi .50 .25

Soldier on Map of Ecuador A308

**1981, Mar. 10** **Litho.** ***Perf. 13***
**1010** A308 3.40s shown .30 .25
**1011** A308 3.40s Pres. Roldos .30 .25
*a.* Pair, #1010-1011 1.40 .90

National defense.

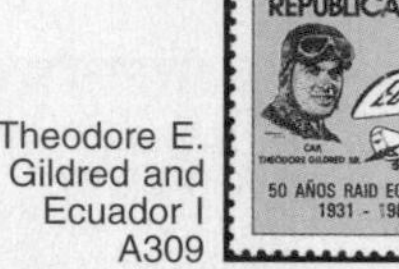

Theodore E. Gildred and Ecuador I A309

**1981, Mar. 31** **Litho.** ***Perf. 13***
**1012** A309 2s lt bl & blk .35 .25

Ecuador-US flight, 50th anniv.

A310

**1981, Apr. 10**
**1013** A310 2s multi .45 .25

Octavio Cordero Palacios (1870-1930), humanist.

Radio Station HCJB, 50th Anniv. — A311

**1981** **Litho.** ***Perf. 13***
**1014** A311 2s multi .30 .30
*Nos. 1014,C721-C722 (3)* 3.30 1.85

Virgin of Dolorosa A312

**1981, Apr. 30** **Litho.** ***Perf. 12***
**1015** A312 2s shown .30 .25
**1016** A312 2s San Gabriel College Church .30 .25

Miracle of the painting of the Virgin of Dolorosa at San Gabriel College, 75th anniv.

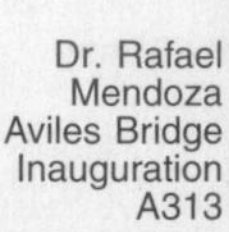

Dr. Rafael Mendoza Aviles Bridge Inauguration A313

**1981, July 25** ***Perf. 13***
**1017** A313 2s multi .45 .25

Pablo Picasso (1881-1973), Painter — A313a

**1981, Oct. 26** **Litho.** ***Imperf.***
**1017A** A313a 20s multi 2.75 2.75
*Nos. 1017A,C728-C731 (5)* 9.30 7.50

No. 1017A contains design of No. C728, additional portrait.

World Food Day — A314

**1981, Dec. 31** **Litho.** ***Perf. 13½x13***
**1018** A314 5s multi .60 .25

See No. C732

Transnave Shipping Co. 10th Anniv. — A315

**1982, Jan. 21** **Litho.** ***Perf. 13***
**1019** A315 3.50s Freighter Isla Salango .60 .25

Intl. Year of the Disabled — A316

**1982, Feb. 25**
**1020** A316 3.40s Man in wheel-chair .35 .25
*Nos. 1020,C733-C734 (3)* 1.95 1.10

Arch — A317

**1982, May** **Litho.** ***Perf. 13***
**1021** A317 2s shown .30 .25
**1022** A317 3s Houses .45 .25

**Miniature Sheet**
***Perf. 12½ on 2 Sides***

**1023** Sheet of 4, 18th cent. map of Quito 4.50 3.50
*a.-d.* A317 6s multi .90 .50

QUITEX '82, 4th Natl. Stamp Exhib., Quito, Apr. 16-22. No. 1023 contains 4 48x31mm stamps.

Juan Montalvo Birth Sesqui. — A318

**1982** ***Perf. 13***
**1024** A318 2s Portrait .35 .25
**1025** A318 3s Mausoleum .35 .25
*Nos. 1024-1025,C735 (3)* 1.95 1.15

American Air Forces Cooperation System — A319

**1982**
**1026** A319 5s Emblem .55 .35

4th World Swimming Champ., Guayaquil A320

**1982, July 30**
**1027** A320 1.80s Stadium .30 .25
**1028** A320 3.40s Water polo .35 .25
*Nos. 1027-1028,C736-C737 (4)* 2.85 1.55

A321

**1982, Dec.** **Litho.** ***Perf. 13***
**1029** A321 5.40s shown .35 .25
**1030** A321 6s Statue .45 .25

Juan L. Mera (1832-?), Writer, by Victor Mideros.

A322

**1983, Mar. 28** **Litho.** ***Perf. 13***
**1031** A322 2s multi .45 .25

St. Teresa of Jesus of Avila (1515-82).

Sea Lions A323

Flamingoes A324

**1983, June 17 Litho. *Perf. 13***

**1032** A323 3s multi 1.40 .25
**1033** A324 5s multi 2.25 .25

Ecuadorian rule over Galapagos Islds., sesqui. (3s); Charles Darwin (1809-1882).

Pres. Rocafuerte A325

Simon Bolivar A326

***Perf. 13x13½***

**1983, Aug. 26 Litho. Wmk. 395**

**1034** A325 5s Statue .25 .25
**1035** A325 20s Portrait .85 .35
**1036** A326 20s Portrait .85 .35
*Nos. 1034-1036 (3)* 1.95 .95

Vicente Rocafuerte Bejarano, president, 1833-39 (Nos. 1034-1035).

A327

**1983, Sept. 3**

**1037** A327 5s River .70 .25
**1038** A327 10s Dam 1.10 .85

**Size: 110x89mm**

***Imperf***

**1039** A327 20s Dam, river 3.50 2.50
*Nos. 1037-1039 (3)* 5.30 3.60

Paute hydroelectric plant opening. No. 1039 is airmail.

World Communication Year — A328

**Wmk. 395**

**1983, Oct. 11 Litho. *Perf. 13***

**1040** A328 2s multi .45 .30

World Communication Year.

A329

**1983, Sept. Litho. *Perf. 13***

**1041** A329 3s multi .45 .30

Cent. of Bolivar and El Oro Provinces (1984).

A330

**1984, Mar. Litho. *Perf. 13***

**1042** A330 15s Engraving .55 .45

Atahualpa (1497-1529), last Incan ruler.

A331

Christmas 1983 — A331a

Creche figures.

***Perf. 13½x13, 13x13½***

**1984, July 7 Litho.**

**1043** A331 5s Jesus & the teachers .30 .25
**1044** A331 5s Three kings .30 .25
**1045** A331 5s Holy Family .30 .25
**1046** A331a 6s Priest .30 .25
*Nos. 1043-1046 (4)* 1.20 1.00

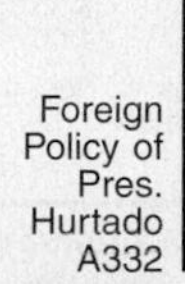

Foreign Policy of Pres. Hurtado A332

State visits.

**1984, July 10 *Perf. 13½x13***

**1047** A332 8s Brazil .35 .25
**1048** A332 9s PRC .40 .25
**1049** A332 24s UN 1.10 .75
**1050** A332 28s US 1.40 .80
**1051** A332 29s Venezuela 1.40 .80
**1052** A332 37s Latin American Economic Conf., Quito 1.75 1.25
*Nos. 1047-1052 (6)* 6.40 4.10

Miguel Diaz Cueva (1884-1942), Lawyer A333

**1984, Aug. 8 Litho. *Perf. 13½x13***

**1053** A333 10s multicolored .75 .30

1984 Winter Olympics — A334

***Perf. 13x13½, 12x11½ (6s)***

**1984, Aug. 15**

**1054** A334 2s Emblem .35 .25
**1055** A334 4s Ice skating .35 .25
**1056** A334 6s Skating, diff. .35 .25
**1057** A334 10s Skiing .65 .25
*Nos. 1054-1057 (4)* 1.70 1.00

**Size: 90x100mm**

**1057A** A334 20s Figure skating 40.00 17.50

Manned Flight Bicentenary A335

3s, Montgolfier. 6s, Charlier's balloon, Paris, 1789.
20s, Graf Zeppelin, Montgolfier.

**1984, Aug. 15 *Perf. 13x13½***

**1058** A335 3s multicolored .25 .25
**1059** A335 6s multicolored .50 .25

**Souvenir Sheet**

**1060** A335 20s multicolored 2.50 1.50

No. 1060 is airmail and contains one imperf. stamp (50x37mm).

SAN MATEO '83, Esmeraldas A336

8s, La Marimba folk dance. 15s, La Marimba, 8 dancers in white.

**1984 Litho. *Perf. 13***

**1061** A336 8s multi 1.75 .25

**Size: 89x110mm**

***Imperf***

**1061A** A336 15s multi 2.50 1.50

No. 1061A is airmail.

Jose Maria de Jesus Yerovi (b. 1824), 4th Archbishop of Quito — A337

**1984**

**1062** A337 5s multi .45 .30

Canonization of Brother Miguel A338

**1984 Litho. *Perf. 13***

**1063** A338 9s Academy of Languages .35 .25
**1064** A338 24s Vatican City, vert. 1.00 .60

***Imperf***

**Size: 110x90mm**

**1065** A338 28s Home of Brother Miguel 3.50 1.50
*Nos. 1063-1065 (3)* 4.85 2.35

No. 1065, airmail, has black control number.

State Visit of Pope John Paul II — A339

**1985, Jan. 23 Litho. *Perf. 13x13½***

**1066** A339 1.60s Papal arms .85 .25
**1067** A339 5s Blessing crowd .85 .25
**1068** A339 9s World map, itinerary .85 .25
**1069** A339 28s Pope waving 2.25 .40
**1070** A339 29s Portrait 2.50 .40

**Size: 90x109mm**

***Imperf***

**1071** A339 30s Pope holding crosier 8.00 6.00
*Nos. 1066-1071 (6)* 15.30 7.55

Beatification of Mercedes de Jesus Molina — A340

Paintings, sculpture.

**1985, Jan. 23**

**1072** A340 1.60s Portrait .30 .25
**1073** A340 5s Czestochowa Madonna .30 .25
**1074** A340 9s Alborada Madonna .50 .25

**Size: 90x110mm**

***Imperf***

**1075** A340 20s Mercedes de Jesus, children 3.00 3.00
*Nos. 1072-1075 (4)* 4.10 3.75

Visit of Pope John Paul II, birth bimillennium of the Virgin Mary.

Samuel Valarezo Delgado, Naturalist, Politician — A341

**1985, Feb.**

**1076** A341 2s Bird .25 .25
**1077** A341 3s Swordfish, tuna .25 .25
**1078** A341 6s Portrait .40 .25
*Nos. 1076-1078 (3)* .90 .75

ESPANA '84, Madrid A342

**1985, Apr. 25 *Perf. 13½x13***

**1079** A342 6s Emblem .30 .25
**1080** A342 10s Spanish royal family .50 .25

**Size: 110x90mm**

***Imperf***

**1081** A342 15s Retiro Park, exhibition site 1.50 1.50

Dr. Pio Jaramillo Alvarado (1884-1968), Historian A343

**1985, May 17**

1082 A343 6s multi .35 .25

Ingenio Valdez Sugar Refinery — A344

Designs: 50s, Sugar cane, emblem. 100s, Rafael Valdez Cervantes, founder.

**1985, June Litho. *Perf. 13***

1082A A344 50s multi 1.10 .50
1082B A344 100s multi 2.40 1.00

**Size: 110x90mm**

***Imperf***

1083 A344 30s multi 1.50 1.50
*Nos. 1082A-1083 (3)* 5.00 3.00

Chamber of Commerce, 10th Anniv. A345

50s, Natl. and American Statues of Liberty.

**1985, Aug. 15 *Perf. 13½x13***

1084 A345 24s multicolored .80 .30
1085 A345 28s multicolored .90 .45

**Size: 110x90mm**

***Imperf***

1086 A345 50s multicolored 2.25 2.25
*Nos. 1084-1086 (3)* 3.95 3.00

Natl. Philatelic Assoc., AFE, 50th Anniv. — A346

**1985, Aug. 25 *Perf. 12***

1087 A346 25s AFE emblem .75 .45
1088 A346 30s No. 357, horiz. 1.10 .50

Guayaquil Fire Dept., 150th Anniv. A347

**1985, Oct. 10 *Perf. 13½x13***

1089 A347 6s Steam fire pump, 1882 .45 .25
1090 A347 10s Fire Wagon, 1899 .75 .25
1091 A347 20s Anniv. emblem, natl. flag 1.50 .75
*Nos. 1089-1091 (3)* 2.70 1.25

Natl. Infant Survival Campaign — A348

**1985, Oct. *Perf. 13x13½***

1092 A348 10s Boy, girl, tree .55 .30

1st Natl. Phil. Cong., Quito, Nov. 25-28 — A349

20th cent. illustrations, natl. cultural collection: 5s, Supreme Court, Quito, by J. M. Roura. 10s, Riobamba Cathedral, by O. Munaz. 15s, House of 100 Windows, by J. M. Roura, horiz. 20s, Rural cottage near Cuenca, by J. M. Roura.

No. 1097: a, Stampless cover, 1779, Riobamba. b, Hand press, 1864, Quito. c, Postrider, 1880, Cuenca. d, Monoplane, 1st airmail flight, 1919, Guayaquil.

**1985, Nov. *Perf. 13x13½, 13½x13***

1093 A349 5s multi .25 .25
1094 A349 10s multi .55 .25
1095 A349 15s multi .65 .40
1096 A349 20s multi .95 .50
*Nos. 1093-1096 (4)* 2.40 1.40

**Souvenir Sheet**

1097 Sheet of 4 1.25 1.25
*a.-d.* A349 5s, any single .25 .25

AFE, 50th anniv. No. 1097 contains 53x42mm stamps, perf. 13x12½ on 2 sides.

10th Bolivarian Games, Cuenca A350

**1985, Nov. *Perf. 13½x13***

1098 A350 10s Boxing .45 .25
1099 A350 25s Women's gymnastics .75 .30
1100 A350 30s Discus .90 .45
*Nos. 1098-1100 (3)* 2.10 1.00

BAE Calderon, Navy Cent. — A351

Military anniv.: No. 1102, Fighter plane, Air Force 65th anniv. No. 1103, Army & paratroops emblems, Special Forces 30th anniv.

**1985, Dec. *Perf. 13x13½***

1101 A351 10s multi .50 .30
1102 A351 10s multi .50 .30
1103 A351 10s multi .50 .30
*Nos. 1101-1103 (3)* 1.50 .90

UN, 40th Anniv. A352

**1985, Oct. Litho. *Perf. 13***

1104 A352 10s UN flag .50 .30
1105 A352 20s Natl. flag .50 .30

**Size: 110x90mm**

***Imperf***

1106 A352 50s UN Building 1.50 1.50
*Nos. 1104-1106 (3)* 2.50 2.10

Christmas — A353

**1985, Nov.**

1107 A353 5s Child riding donkey .25 .25
1108 A353 10s Baked goods .50 .30
1109 A353 15s Riding donkey, diff. .70 .50

**Size: 90x110mm**

***Imperf***

1110 A353 30s like 5s 1.75 1.50
*Nos. 1107-1110 (4)* 3.20 2.55

Indigenous Flowers — A354

**1986, Feb.**

1111 A354 24s Embotrium grandiforum 1.00 .30
1112 A354 28s Topobea sp. 1.50 .30
1113 A354 29s Befaria resinosa mutis 2.00 .40

**Size: 110x90mm**

***Imperf***

1114 A354 15s multi 6.50 3.50
*Nos. 1111-1114 (4)* 11.00 4.50

No. 1114 contains designs of Nos. 1111, 1113, 1112; black control number.

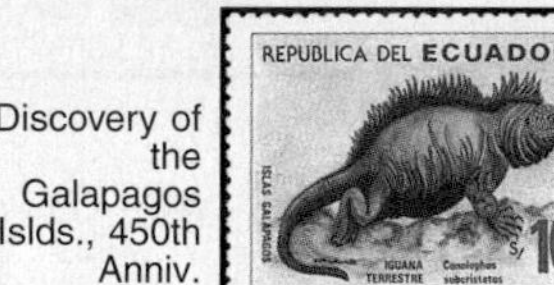

Discovery of the Galapagos Islds., 450th Anniv. A355

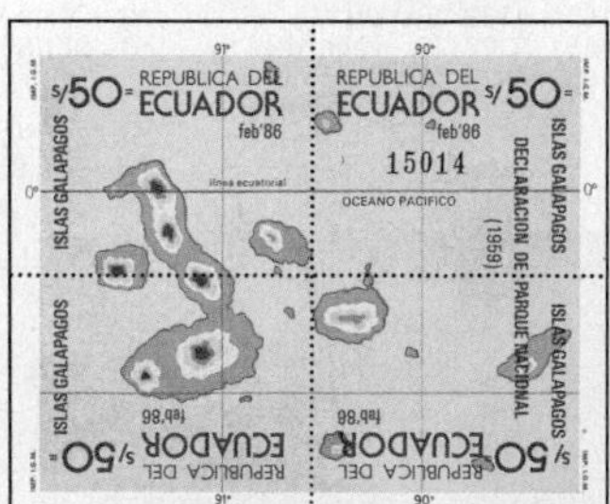

Map of the Islands — A356

**1986, Feb. 12**

1115 A355 10s Land iguana .55 .30
1116 A355 20s Sea lion 1.10 .65
1117 A355 30s Frigate birds 1.75 1.10
1118 A355 40s Penguins 2.25 1.50
1119 A355 50s Giant tortoise 2.75 1.75
1120 A355 100s Charles Darwin 5.50 3.75
1121 A355 200s Bishop Tomas de Berlenga, discoverer 11.00 7.00

***Perf. 12½ on 2 Sides***

1122 A356 Sheet of 4 13.00 13.00
*a.-d.* 50s, any single 1.75 1.75
*Nos. 1115-1122 (8)* 37.90 29.05

No. 1122 contains 53x42mm stamps.

Inter-American Development Bank, 25th Anniv. — A357

5s, Antonio Ortiz Mena, pres. 1971-88. 10s, Felipe Herrera, pres. 1960-71. 50s, Emblem.

**1986, Mar. 6**

1123 A357 5s multi .45 .25
1124 A357 10s multi .65 .25
1125 A357 50s multi 1.25 .80
*Nos. 1123-1125 (3)* 2.35 1.30

Guayaquil Tennis Club, 75th Anniv. A358

**1986, Mar. 7**

1126 A358 10s Emblem .55 .30
1127 A358 10s Francisco Segura Cano, vert. .55 .30
1128 A358 10s Andres Gomez Santos, vert. .55 .30
*Nos. 1126-1128 (3)* 1.65 .90

1986 World Cup Soccer Championships, Mexico — A359

**1986, May 5**

1129 A359 5s Shot .35 .25
1130 A359 10s Block .80 .25

An imperf. stamp exists picturing flags, player and emblem. Value $8.50.

Meeting of Presidents Cordero and Betancourt of Colombia, Feb. 1985 A360

**1986 Litho. *Perf. 13½x13***

1131 A360 20s Presidents .55 .30
1132 A360 20s Embracing .55 .30

Exports A361

35s, No. 1137c, Shrimp. 40s, No. 1137b, Tuna. 45s, No. 1137a, Sardines. No. 1137d, MICIP emblem.

**1986, Apr. 12**

1133 A361 35s ultra & ver 1.10 .40
1134 A361 40s red & yel grn 1.10 .40
1135 A361 45s car & dk yel 1.25 .60

***Perf. 12½ on 2 Sides***

1137 Sheet of 4 2.50 2.50
*a.-d.* A361 10s, any single .40 .40
*Nos. 1133-1137 (4)* 5.95 3.90

No. 1137 contains 4 53x42mm stamps.

A362

La Condamine's First Geodesic Mission, 250th Anniv. — A363

No. 1141a, Triangulation map for determining equatorial meridian, 1736. No. 1141b, Partial map of the Maranon & Amazon Rivers, by Samuel Fritz, 1743-1744. No. 1141c, Base of measurement, Yaruqui plains. No. 1141d, Caraburo & Dyambaru Pyramids near Quito. No. 1141 has a continuous design.

**1986, July 10 Litho. *Perf. 13½x13***

| | | | | | |
|---|---|---|---|---|---|
| **1138** | A362 | 10s | La Condamine | .45 | .25 |
| **1139** | A362 | 15s | Maldonado | .55 | .30 |
| **1140** | A362 | 20s | Middle of the World, Quito | .65 | .30 |
| | | | *Nos. 1138-1140 (3)* | 1.65 | .85 |

**Souvenir Sheet**

***Perf. 12½ on 2 Sides***

| | | | | |
|---|---|---|---|---|
| **1141** | A363 | Sheet of 4 | 3.25 | 3.25 |
| *a.-d.* | | 10s any single | .45 | .45 |

Chambers of Commerce A364

**1986 Litho. *Perf. 13½x13***

| | | | | | |
|---|---|---|---|---|---|
| **1142** | A364 | 10s | Pichincha | .35 | .25 |
| **1143** | A364 | 10s | Cuenca | .35 | .25 |
| **1144** | A364 | 10s | Guayaquil | .35 | .25 |
| | | | *Nos. 1142-1144 (3)* | 1.05 | .75 |

Civil Service and Communications Ministry, 57th Anniv. — A365

Organization emblems.

**1986, Dec. Litho. *Perf. 13x13½***

| | | | | | |
|---|---|---|---|---|---|
| **1145** | A365 | 5s | State railway | .25 | .25 |
| **1146** | A365 | 10s | Post office | .35 | .25 |
| **1147** | A365 | 15s | Communications | .65 | .25 |
| **1148** | A365 | 20s | Ministry of Public Works | .75 | .55 |
| | | | *Nos. 1145-1148 (4)* | 2.00 | 1.30 |

A366

**1987, Feb. 16 Litho. *Perf. 13x13½***

| | | | | | |
|---|---|---|---|---|---|
| **1149** | A366 | 5s | multi | .45 | .25 |

Chamber of Agriculture of the 1st Zone, 50th anniv.

Col. Luis Vargas Torres (d. 1887) — A367

Combat unit, c. 1885 — A367a

A367b

No. 1152a, Torres & his mother, Delfina. No. 1152b, Letter to Delfina written by Torres during imprisonment, 1882. No. 1152c, Arms of Ecuador & combat unit.

**Litho. & Typo.**

**1988, Jan. 6 *Perf. 13***

| | | | | | |
|---|---|---|---|---|---|
| **1150** | A367 | 50s | yel grn, blk & gold | 1.25 | .80 |
| **1151** | A367a | 100s | ver, gold & ultra | 2.75 | 1.40 |

**Size: 95x140mm**

***Perf. 12 on One or Two Sides***

| | | | | |
|---|---|---|---|---|
| **1152** | A367b | Block of 3 | 8.25 | 8.25 |
| *a.-c.* | | 100s any single | 1.50 | 1.50 |
| | | *Nos. 1150-1152 (3)* | 12.25 | 10.45 |

Sizes: Nos. 1152a, 1152c, 95x28mm, No. 1152b, 95x83mm.

Founding of Guayaquil, 450th Anniv. A368

15s, Street in Las Penas. 30s, Rafael Mendoza Aviles Bridge. 40s, Francisco de Orellana (c. 1490-1546), Spanish explorer, founder, & reenactment of landing, 1538.

**1988, Feb. 19 Litho. *Perf. 13***

| | | | | | |
|---|---|---|---|---|---|
| **1153** | A368 | 15s | multi, vert. | .30 | .25 |
| **1154** | A368 | 30s | multi | .55 | .25 |
| **1155** | A368 | 40s | multi | .65 | .25 |
| | | | *Nos. 1153-1155 (3)* | 1.50 | .75 |

Social Security Foundation (IESS), 60th Anniv. A369

**1988, Mar. 11**

| | | | | | |
|---|---|---|---|---|---|
| **1156** | A369 | 50s | shown | .90 | .55 |
| **1157** | A369 | 100s | multi, diff. | 1.90 | 1.10 |

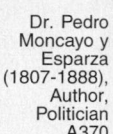

Dr. Pedro Moncayo y Esparza (1807-1888), Author, Politician A370

**1988, Apr. 28 Litho. *Perf. 14x13½***

| | | | | | |
|---|---|---|---|---|---|
| **1158** | A370 | 10s | Yaguarcocha Lake | .25 | .25 |
| **1159** | A370 | 15s | shown | .35 | .25 |
| **1160** | A370 | 20s | Residence | .35 | .25 |

**Size: 89x110mm**

***Imperf***

| | | | | | |
|---|---|---|---|---|---|
| **1161** | A370 | 100s | Full-length portrait | 1.50 | 1.50 |
| | | | *Nos. 1158-1161 (4)* | 2.45 | 2.25 |

A371

Avianca Airlines, 60th Anniv. — A372

10s, Junkers F-13. 20s, Dornier Wal seaplane. 30s, Ford 5AT trimotor. 40s, Boeing 247-D. 50s, Boeing 720-059B. 100s, Douglas DC-3. 200s, Boeing 727-200. 300s, Sikorsky S-38.

**1988, May 12 Litho. *Perf. 14x13½***

| | | | | | |
|---|---|---|---|---|---|
| **1162** | A371 | 10s | shown | .35 | .25 |
| **1163** | A371 | 20s | multi | .35 | .25 |
| **1164** | A371 | 30s | multi | .45 | .25 |
| **1165** | A371 | 40s | multi | .55 | .25 |
| **1166** | A371 | 50s | multi | .65 | .45 |
| **1167** | A371 | 100s | multi | 1.50 | .60 |
| **1168** | A371 | 200s | multi | 2.75 | 1.50 |
| **1169** | A371 | 300s | multi | 4.75 | 2.00 |

***Perf. 13½x14***

| | | | | | |
|---|---|---|---|---|---|
| **1170** | A372 | 500s | shown | 7.25 | 3.75 |
| | | | *Nos. 1162-1170 (9)* | 18.60 | 9.30 |

San Gabriel College, 125th Anniv. A373

15s, Contemporary facility. 35s, College entrance, 19th cent.

**1988, July 25 Litho. *Perf. 14x13½***

| | | | | | |
|---|---|---|---|---|---|
| **1171** | A373 | 15s | multicolored | .25 | .25 |
| **1172** | A373 | 35s | multicolored | .75 | .30 |

A374

Military Geographical Institute, 60th Anniv. A375

25s, Planetarium. 50s, Zeiss projector. 60s, Anniv. emblem. 500s, Creation, mural by E. Kingman.

**1988, July 25 *Perf. 12½ on 2 Sides***

**Size of No. 1173: 110x90mm**

| | | | | | |
|---|---|---|---|---|---|
| **1173** | A374 | | Block of 4 | 2.25 | 2.25 |
| *a.-d.* | | | 5s any single | .30 | .30 |

***Perf. 13½***

| | | | | | |
|---|---|---|---|---|---|
| **1174** | A375 | 25s | multi | .55 | .30 |
| **1175** | A375 | 50s | multi | 1.00 | .30 |
| **1176** | A375 | 60s | multi | 1.25 | .40 |
| **1177** | A375 | 500s | multi | 7.75 | 3.75 |
| | | | *Nos. 1173-1177 (5)* | 12.80 | 7.00 |

In 1996 Nos. 1174, 1183, 1265 were surcharged 800s, 2600s 400s respectively. Only a few sets were sold to the public. The balance were sold by postal employees at greatly inflated prices.

Salesian Brothers in Ecuador, Cent. A376

Designs: 10s, St. John Bosco (1815-88), vert. 50s, 1st Salesian Cong. in Ecuador. 100s, Bosco, Salesian Brothers monument and Andes Mountains.

**1988, July 29 Litho. *Perf. 13½***

| | | | | | |
|---|---|---|---|---|---|
| **1178** | A376 | 10s | multi | .25 | .25 |
| **1179** | A376 | 50s | multi | 1.00 | .40 |

**Size: 89x110mm**

***Imperf***

| | | | | | |
|---|---|---|---|---|---|
| **1180** | A376 | 100s | multi | 2.75 | 1.60 |
| | | | *Nos. 1178-1180 (3)* | 4.00 | 2.25 |

Francisco Coello, Founder — A377

Social Services Council, Guayaquil, Cent. — A378

Flag: a, Emblem (upper left portion). b, Emblem (upper right portion). c, Emblem (lower left portion) and "100 ANOS." d, Emblem (lower right portion) and "DE TRADICION DE FE, AMPARO Y ESPERANZA."

**1988, Nov. 24 Litho. *Perf. 13½x14***

| | | | | | |
|---|---|---|---|---|---|
| **1181** | A377 | 15s | shown | .25 | .25 |
| **1182** | A377 | 20s | Eduardo Arosemena, 1st Director | .30 | .25 |
| **1183** | A377 | 45s | Emblem | .65 | .25 |

**Size: 110x90mm**

***Perf. 12½ on 2 Sides***

| | | | | |
|---|---|---|---|---|
| **1184** | A378 | Block of 4 | 1.75 | 1.75 |
| *a.-d.* | | 10s any single | .25 | .25 |
| | | *Nos. 1181-1184 (4)* | 2.95 | 2.50 |

For surcharge see note following No. 1177.

A379

FUNDACION
Se fundó el 15 de enero de 1913 ante el escribano público de Cuenca, señor Abelardo E. Arízaga, con un capital de S/. 400.000 inscrito en el Registro Mercantil el 10 de febrero de 1913 por resolución del Poder Ejecutivo.
El día 7 de noviembre de 1913 ante el escribano público se procede a declarar abierto el servicio de ventanillas al público.
Nº 02633
correos del ECUADOR S/. 500


Azuay Bank, 75th Anniv. — A380

***Perf. 14x13½, 13½x14***

**1989, Mar. 1** **Litho.**
**1185** A379 20s shown .30 .25
**1186** A379 40s multi, vert. .40 .25

**Size: 90x110mm**

***Imperf***

**1187** A380 500s shown 11.00 2.75
*Nos. 1185-1187 (3)* 11.70 3.25

1988 Summer Olympics, Seoul — A381

Character trademark demonstrating sports.

**1989, Mar. 20** ***Perf. 13½x14***
**1188** A381 10s Running .30 .25
**1189** A381 20s Boxing .30 .25
**1190** A381 30s Cycling .50 .25
**1191** A381 40s Shooting .50 .25
**1192** A381 100s Diving 1.25 .65
**1193** A381 200s Weight lifting 2.25 1.40
**1194** A381 300s Tae kwon do 3.50 2.10

**Size: 90x110mm**

***Imperf***

**1195** A381 200s Emblems 3.50 3.25
*Nos. 1188-1195 (8)* 12.10 8.40

RUMINAHUI '88 — A382

Designs: 50s, *Bird,* by Joaquin Tinta, vert. 70s, Matriz Church, Sangolqui. 300s, Monument to Ruminahui in Sangolqui, Pichincha.

***Perf. 14x13½, 13½x14***

**1989, May 2** **Litho.** **Wmk. 395**
**1196** A382 50s multi .90 .30
**1197** A382 70s multi 1.25 .45

**Size: 90x111mm**

***Imperf***

**1198** A382 300s multi 7.25 2.10
*Nos. 1196-1198 (3)* 9.40 2.85

Cantonization, 50th anniv.

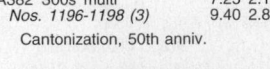

Benjamin Carrion Mora, Educator A383

***Perf. 13½x14, 14x13½***

**1989, May 10** **Litho.**
**1199** A383 50s Portrait, vert. .45 .25
**1200** A383 70s Loja landscape .65 .25
**1201** A383 1000s University 10.50 5.25

**Size: 110x90mm**

***Imperf***

**1202** A383 200s Portrait, diff. 2.00 2.00
*Nos. 1199-1202 (4)* 13.60 7.75

2nd Intl. Art Biennial A384

Prize-winning art: 40s, *The Gilded Frame,* by Myrna Baez. 70s, *Paraguay III,* by Carlos Colorabino, vert. 100s, Ordinance establishing the art exhibition. 180s, *Modulation 892,* by Julio Le Parc, vert.

***Perf. 14x13½, 13½x14, Imperf. (100s)***

**1989, June 2** **Litho.**

**Size of No. 1205: 110x90mm**

**1203** A384 40s multi .55 .25
**1204** A384 70s multi 1.10 .25
**1205** A384 100s multi 2.25 .75
**1206** A384 180s multi 1.75 .95
*Nos. 1203-1206 (4)* 5.65 2.20

Guayaquil Chamber of Commerce, Cent. A385

***Perf. 13½x14, 14x13½, Imperf. (No. 1208)***

**1989, June 20** **Litho.**

**Size of No. 1208: 110x91mm**

**1207** A385 50s Founder Ignacio Molestina, vert. .85 .35
**1208** A385 200s Flags 3.50 2.00
**1209** A385 300s Headquarters 2.50 2.25
**1210** A385 500s Flags, diff. 1.75 1.50
*Nos. 1207-1210 (4)* 8.60 6.10

French Revolution, Bicent. A386

20s, French natl. colors, anniv. emblem. 50s, Cathedral fresco. 100s, Rooster. 200s, Symbols of the revolution. 600s, Story board showing events of the revolution.

**1989, July 11** ***Perf. 13½x14, 14x13½***
**1211** A386 20s multi, vert. .25 .25
**1212** A386 50s multi .55 .25
**1213** A386 100s multi, vert. .90 .45

**Size: 90x110mm**

***Imperf***

**1214** A386 200s multi, vert. 1.75 1.75
**1215** A386 600s multi, vert. 6.75 6.75
*Nos. 1211-1215 (5)* 10.20 9.45

A387

Ministry of Public Works and Communications A388

No. 1216a, MOP emblem, 2-lane roadway. No. 1216b, State railway emblem, train. No. 1216c, Postal service emblem, airmail cover. No. 1216d, Telecommunications (IETEL) emblem, wall telephone. No. 1217, MOP, IETEL, postal service & state railway emblems. 100s, IETEL emblem. 200s, MOP emblem.

**1989, July 7** ***Perf. 12½ on 2 Sides***
**1216** A387 Block of 4 2.00 2.00
*a.-d.* 50s any single .40 .40

***Perf. 13½x14***

**1217** A388 50s shown .45 .25
**1218** A388 100s multi .90 .55
**1219** A388 200s multi 1.90 1.10
*Nos. 1216-1219 (4)* 5.25 3.90

MOP, 60th anniv.; national communications, 105th anniv. (No. 1216d, 100s).

Natl. Red Cross, Intl. Red Cross and Red Crescent Societies, 125th Annivs. A389

**1989, Sept. 14** **Litho.** ***Perf. 13½***
**1220** A389 10s Medical volunteer, vert. .25 .25
**1221** A389 30s shown .25 .25
**1222** A389 200s Two volunteers 2.00 .85
*Nos. 1220-1222 (3)* 2.50 1.35

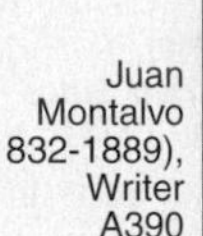

Juan Montalvo (1832-1889), Writer A390

**1989, Nov. 11** **Litho.** ***Perf. 14x13½***
**1223** A390 50s Mausoleum, Ambato .45 .25
**1224** A390 100s Portrait (detail) 1.25 .65
**1225** A390 200s Monument, Ambato 2.10 1.40

**Size: 90x110mm**

***Imperf***

**1226** A390 200s Portrait 1.75 1.75
*Nos. 1223-1226 (4)* 5.55 4.05

America Issue A391

UPAE emblem and pre-Columbian pottery.

**1990, Mar. 6** **Litho.** ***Perf. 13½***
**1227** A391 200s La Tolita incensory, vert. 2.10 1.25
**1228** A391 300s Warrior (plate) 3.25 2.00

Dated 1989.

Dr. Luis Carlos Jaramillo Leon, Founder A392

No. 1233a, Dr. Leon. Nos. 1230, 1233b, Federico Malo Andrade, honorary president. 130s, No. 1233c, Roberto Crespo Toral, 1st president. 200s, Alfonso Jaramillo Leon, founder.

**1990, Jan. 17** **Litho.** ***Perf. 13½***
**1229** A392 100s shown .90 .60
**1230** A392 100s multicolored .90 .60
**1231** A392 130s multicolored 1.25 .75
**1232** A392 200s multicolored 1.75 1.25

**Size: 91x38mm**

***Perf. 12½ Horiz. on 1 or 2 sides***

**1233** Block of 3 3.00 3.00
*a.-c.* A392 100s any single .50 .50
*Nos. 1229-1233 (5)* 7.80 6.20

Chamber of Commerce, 70th anniversary.

World Cup Soccer, Italy — A393

**1990, July 12** **Litho.** ***Perf. 13½***
**1234** A393 100s shown .60 .25
**1235** A393 200s Soccer player 1.25 .60
**1236** A393 300s Map of Italy, trophy 1.90 .90

***Imperf***

**Size: 110x90mm**

**1237** A393 200s Player, flags 1.75 1.75

**Size: 60x90mm**

**1238** A393 300s World Cup Trophy 2.50 2.50
*Nos. 1234-1238 (5)* 8.00 6.00

Nos. 1235-1236, 1238 vert.

A394

**1990, June 12** ***Perf. 13½***
**1239** A394 100s multi .70 .25
**1240** A394 200s Church tower, book 1.25 .60

College of St. Mariana, cent.

A395

Tourism: No. 100s, No. 1244c, Iguana. 200s, No. 1244b, La Compania Church, Quito. 300s, No. 1244a, Old man from Vilcabamba. No. 1244d, Locomotive.

**1990, Sept. 7** **Litho.** ***Perf. 13½***
**1241** A395 100s multi .85 .25
**1242** A395 200s multi, vert. 1.75 .55
**1243** A395 300s multi 2.50 .75

**Size: 111x90mm**

***Perf. 12½ on 2 sides***

**1244** Block of 4 7.50 3.25
*a.-d.* A395 100s any single .35 .25
*Nos. 1241-1244 (4)* 12.60 4.80

A396

National Census: 100s, No. 1248a, People and house. 200s, No. 1248b, Map. 300s, No. 1248c, Census breakdown, pencil.

**1990, Sept. 1** ***Perf. 13½***
**1245** A396 100s multicolored .60 .25
**1246** A396 200s multicolored, horiz. 1.25 .55
**1247** A396 300s multicolored 1.75 .75

**Size: 109x88mm**
***Perf. 12½ on 2 sides***
**1248** Block of 3 1.90 1.90
***a.-c.*** A396 100s any single .30 .30
*Nos. 1245-1248 (4)* 5.50 3.45

A397

**1990, Nov. 2** **Litho.** ***Perf. 14***
**1249** A397 200s Flags 1.25 .55
**1250** A397 300s shown 1.90 .75

Organization of Petroleum Exporting Countries (OPEC), 30th anniv.

A398

**1990, Oct. 31** ***Perf. 13½x14***
**1251** A398 200s Emblem 1.25 .55
**1252** A398 300s Wooden parrots 1.90 .75

**Size: 92x110mm**
***Imperf***
**1253** A398 200s Wooden parrots, diff. 2.10 2.10
*Nos. 1251-1253 (3)* 5.25 3.40

Artisans' Organization, 25th anniv.

Flowers — A399

**Wmk. 395**
**1990, Nov. 12** **Litho.** ***Perf. 13½***
**1254** A399 100s Sobralia 1.25 .25
**1255** A399 100s Blakea, vert. 1.25 .25
**1256** A399 100s Cattleya, vert. 1.25 .25
**1257** A399 100s Loasa, vert. 1.25 .25
*Nos. 1254-1257 (4)* 5.00 1.00

Discovery of America, 500th Anniv. (in 1992) A400

**1990, Dec. 31** **Litho.** ***Perf. 13½***
**1258** A400 100s Ancient dwelling .70 .25
**1259** A400 200s Mangrove swamp 1.60 .35

Natl. Union of Journalists, 50th Anniv. A401

**1991, Feb. 28**
**1260** A401 200s shown 1.10 .70
**1261** A401 300s Eugenio Espejo, writer 1.75 .80
**1262** A401 400s Union emblem 1.90 1.10
*Nos. 1260-1262 (3)* 4.75 2.60

Radio Quito, 50th Anniv. A402

Designs: 200s, Man with microphone, vert. 500s, Family listening to radio.

**1991, Apr. 10**
**1263** A402 200s multicolored .85 .35
**1264** A402 500s multicolored 1.75 .95

Dr. Pablo A. Suarez, Birth Cent. — A403

**1991, Sept. 16** **Wmk. 395**
**1265** A403 70s multicolored .45 .25

Dated 1990.

For surcharge see note following No. 1177. Value $20.

America Issue A404

UPAEP emblem and: 200s, Columbus' ships. 500s, Columbus, landing in America.

**1991, Oct. 18** **Litho.** ***Perf. 13½x13***
**1266** A404 200s multicolored 1.25 .65
**1267** A404 500s multicolored 2.25 1.25

A405

Designs: Cultural artifacts.

**Wmk. 395**
**1991, Nov. 14** **Litho.** ***Perf. 13½***
**1268** A405 100s Cat censer .50 .25
**1269** A405 200s Statue of old man's head 1.00 .35
**1270** A405 300s Zoomorphic statue 1.75 .60
*Nos. 1268-1270 (3)* 3.25 1.20

Dated 1990. See No. 1291.

A406

Design: 500s, Woman in profile.

**1991** ***Perf. 13***
**1271** A406 300s shown 1.00 .55
**1272** A406 500s multicolored 1.90 1.00

Day of Non-violence Toward Women.

Jacinto Jijon y Caamano, Archaeologist, Birth Cent. — A407

**1991, Dec. 11** ***Perf. 13½***
**1273** A407 200s Portrait, vert. .70 .35
**1274** A407 300s shown 1.10 .55

Pres. Rodrigo Borja, Ecuador and Pres. Jaime Paz Zamora, Bolivia — A408

**1991, Dec. 10** ***Perf. 14x13½***
**1275** A408 500s multicolored 2.00 1.00

Pres. Rodrigo Borja's Visit to the UN — A409

**Wmk. 395**
**1992, Jan. 24** **Litho.** ***Perf. 14***
**1276** A409 100s multicolored .40 .25
**1277** A409 1000s Flags, world map 3.00 1.60

Battle of Jambeli, 50th Anniv. — A410

No. 1278, Gunboat Calderon and Capt. Raphael Moran Valverde. No. 1279, Dispatch boat Atahualpa and Ens. Victor Naranjo Fiallo. No. 1280, Valverde, Fiallo and ships.

**1992, Apr. 7**
**1278** A410 300s multicolored .55 .40
**1279** A410 500s multicolored 1.25 .90

**Size: 110x90mm**
***Imperf***
**1280** A410 500s multicolored 2.75 2.40
*Nos. 1278-1280 (3)* 4.55 3.70

Galapagos Islands Wildlife — A411

Designs: No. 1281, Giant tortoise. No. 1282, Galapagos penguin, vert. No. 1283, Zalophus californianus, vert. No. 1284, Swallow-tailed gull. No. 1285, Fregata minor. No. 1286, Land iguana.

**1992, Apr. 10** **Litho.** ***Perf. 13½***
**1281** A411 100s multicolored 1.75 .80
**1282** A411 100s multicolored 1.75 .80
**1283** A411 100s multicolored 1.75 .80
**1284** A411 100s multicolored 1.75 .80
**1285** A411 100s multicolored 1.75 .80
**1286** A411 100s multicolored 1.75 .80
*Nos. 1281-1286 (6)* 10.50 4.80

Vicente Rocafuerte National College, 150th Anniv. (in 1991) A412

***Perf. 14x13½***
**1992, Apr. 29** **Litho.** **Wmk. 395**
**1287** A412 200s shown .85 .35
**1288** A412 400s Vicente Rocafuerte 1.40 .65

Eloy Alfaro (1842-1912), President — A413

Designs: 300s, Portrait, vert.

***Perf. 13½x14, 14x13½***
**1992, Aug. 26** **Litho.** **Wmk. 395**
**1289** A413 300s multicolored .90 .70
**1290** A413 700s multicolored 1.60 1.00

**Cultural Artifacts Type of 1991**
**1992, Sept. 6** **Litho.** ***Perf. 13½***
**1291** A405 400s Ceremonial mask 1.40 .75

Dated 1990.

Discovery of America, 500th Anniv. A414

**Wmk. 395**
**1992, Oct. 15** **Litho.** ***Perf. 13½***
**1292** A414 200s Sailing ship .75 .50
**1293** A414 400s Columbus, map, vert. 1.40 .85

Andres F. Cordova (b. 1892) A415

**1992, Nov. 17** **Litho.** ***Perf. 13½***
**1294** A415 300s multicolored 1.10 .60

Beatification of Narcisa of Jesus — A416

**1992, Nov. 30** ***Perf. 13½***
**1295** A416 100s multicolored .45 .30

A417

Christmas: 300s, Infant Jesus of Saqueo, 18th cent. 600s, Stable scene, Infant Jesus asleep on hay.

**1992, Dec. 14** *Perf. 13½*
**1296** A417 300s multicolored 1.10 .60
**1297** A417 600s multicolored 1.90 1.25

A418

**1992, Dec. 29**
**1298** A418 200s multicolored .80 .45

Father Juan de Velasco, Death Bicent.

Frogs — A419

No. 1299, Agalychnis spurelli. No. 1300, Atelopus bomolochos. No. 1301, Gastrotheca plumbea. No. 1302, Hyla picturata. No. 1303, Dendrobates sp. No. 1304, Sphaenorhyncus lacteus.

*Perf. 13½x14*
**1993, Jan. 28 Litho. Wmk. 395**
**1299** A419 300s multi .85 .35
**1300** A419 300s multi .85 .35
**1301** A419 600s multi 2.00 .90
**1302** A419 600s multi 2.00 .90
**1303** A419 900s multi 2.75 1.40
**1304** A419 900s multi 2.75 1.40
*Nos. 1299-1304 (6)* 11.20 5.30

A420

**1993, Feb. 16 Litho.** *Perf. 13x13½*
**1305** A420 300s blue .80 .25

J. Roberto Paez, (1893-1983), co-founder of social security.

Francisco Robles (1811-93) — A421

**1993, Mar. 16** *Perf. 13½x14*
**1306** A421 500s No. 168 1.50 .55

National Police — A422

*Perf. 13½x14*
**1993, Mar. 25 Litho. Wmk. 395**
**1307** A422 300s multicolored 1.00 .60

Pres. Jose Maria Velasco Ibarra (1893-1979) A423

*Perf. 14x13½*
**1993, Mar. 31 Litho. Wmk. 395**
**1308** A423 500s multicolored 1.50 .55

Insects — A424

150s, Fulgora laternaria. 200s, Semiotus ligneus. 300s, Taeniotes pulverulenta. 400s, Danaus plexippus. 600s, Erotylus onagga. 700s, Xylocopa darwini.

**Wmk. 395**
**1993, May 27 Litho.** *Perf. 13½*
**1309** A424 150s multi .75 .25
**1310** A424 200s multi 1.00 .25
**1311** A424 300s multi 1.50 .45
**1312** A424 400s multi 2.00 .60
**1313** A424 600s multi 3.00 .95
**1314** A424 700s multi 3.25 1.10
*Nos. 1309-1314 (6)* 11.50 3.60

A425

**Wmk. 395**
**1993, May 31 Litho.** *Perf. 13½*
**1315** A425 1000s multicolored 3.00 1.50

Pedro Fermin Cevallos Villacreces (1812-93), historian and founder of Academy of Language.

First Latin-American Children's Peace Assembly, Quito — A426

**1993, June 7**
**1316** A426 300s multicolored .80 .45

Juan Benigno Vela Hervas (1843-97), Jurist A427

*Perf. 13x13½*
**1993, July 8 Litho. Wmk. 395**
**1317** A427 2000s multicolored 5.00 3.00

Guillermo Bustamante, Birth Cent. A428

**1993, Sept. 23** *Perf. 13½*
**1318** A428 1500s multicolored 4.00 1.75

University of Ecuador School of Medicine, 300th Anniv. A429

*Perf. 14x13½*
**1993, Sept. 7 Litho. Wmk. 395**
**1319** A429 300s multicolored .80 .45

Maldonado-La Condamine Amazon Expedition, 250th Anniv. — A430

Designs: 150s, Cinchona cordifolia. 200s, Pedro V. Maldonado, 1500s, Charles La Condamine (1701-74), explorer.

**1993, Aug. 20**
**1320** A430 150s multicolored .35 .25
**1321** A430 200s multicolored .50 .25
**1322** A430 1500s multicolored 4.25 2.10
*Nos. 1320-1322 (3)* 5.10 2.60

A431

**Wmk. 395**
**1993, Nov. 27 Litho.** *Perf. 13*
**1323** A431 500s multicolored 1.10 .55

Dr. Carlos A. Arroyo del Rio, birth cent.

Endangered Species — A432

400s, Dinomys branickii, horiz. 800s, Ara severa.

**1993, Oct. 15** *Perf. 13½x13, 13x13½*
**1324** A432 400s multicolored 2.00 .60
**1325** A432 800s multicolored 3.00 1.25

America issue.

Christmas A433

600s, Holy Family, 18th cent. Tagua miniatures. 900s, Mother and child, vert.

**Wmk. 395**
**1993, Dec. 1 Litho.** *Perf. 13*
**1326** A433 600s multicolored 1.40 .90
**1327** A433 900s multicolored 2.25 1.40

Intl. Year of the Family — A434

**Wmk. 395**
**1994, Jan. 18 Litho.** *Perf. 13*
**1328** A434 300s grn, blk & org .40 .35

A435

**1994, Jan. 25**
**1329** A435 500s multicolored 1.75 .90

Dr. Julio Tobar Donoso, birth cent.

Orchids — A436

No. 1330, Dracula hirtzii. No. 1331, Sobralia dichotoma. No. 1332, Encyclia pulcherrima. No. 1333, Lepanthes delhierroi. No. 1334, Masdevallia rosea. No. 1335, Telipogon andicola.

**Wmk. 395**
**1994, Feb. 7 Litho.** *Perf. 13½*
**1330** A436 150s multicolored .35 .25
**1331** A436 150s multicolored .35 .25
**1332** A436 300s multicolored .85 .40
**1333** A436 300s multicolored .85 .40
**1334** A436 600s multicolored 1.75 .90
**1335** A436 600s multicolored 1.75 .90
*Nos. 1330-1335 (6)* 5.90 3.10

First Convention on the Conservation of Andean Orchids.

Federico Gonzalez Suarez (1844-1917) A437

**1994, Apr. 12** *Perf. 13*
**1336** A437 200s multicolored .55 .25

Scouting in Ecuador — A438

**1994, Jan. 11**
**1337** A438 400s multicolored 1.25 .60

Dr. Miguel Egas Cabezas (1823-94) A439

**Wmk. 395**

**1994, Mar. 10 Litho.** *Perf. 13*

**1338** A439 100s multicolored .50 .25

Father Aurelio Espinosa, Birth Cent. — A440

**1994, July 12**

**1339** A440 200s multicolored .70 .45

A441

Nos. 1341, 1343d, Mascot. 900s, Player.
No. 1343: a, Emblem. b, "COPA MUNDIAL FUTBOL '94," emblem. c, "COPA MUNDIAL, USA 94."

**Wmk. 395**

**1994, June 10 Litho.** *Perf. 13*

**1340** A441 300s shown 1.25 .60
**1341** A441 600s Mascot 2.40 1.25
**1342** A441 900s Soccer player 3.75 1.75

***Perf. 12 on 2 Sides***

**1343** A441 600s Block of 4, #a.-d. 9.75 7.50
*Nos. 1340-1343 (4)* 17.15 11.10

1994 World Cup Soccer Championships, US.
No. 1343 contains two 50x25mm stamps, two 50x51mm stamps.

Ecuador in Antarctica A442

**1994, July 19** *Perf. 13*

**1344** A442 600s Outpost 2.25 1.10
**1345** A442 900s Ship, B/1 Orion 3.50 1.75

ILO, 75th Anniv. A443

**1994 Litho. Wmk. 395** *Perf. 13*

**1346** A443 100s multicolored .50 .25

Ecuadorian Culture Center, 50th Anniv. A444

**1994**

**1347** A444 700s Benjamin Carrion, vert. 2.40 1.40
**1348** A444 900s Cultural center 3.50 1.60

Natl. Lottery, Cent. A445

**1994**

**1349** A445 1000s multicolored 3.75 1.75

Junior World Cycling Championships, Quito — A446

**Wmk. 395**

**1994, June 22 Litho.** *Perf. 13*

**1350** A446 300s shown .75 .35
**1351** A446 400s Stylized cyclist, vert. 1.00 .50

Postal Transportation A447

America Issue: No. 1352, Van, airplane, ship, horiz. No. 1353, Airplane, mail bag.

**1994**

**1352** A447 600s multicolored .80 .40
**1353** A447 600s multicolored 1.00 .50

Christmas — A448

No. 1354, Simulated stamp showing globe circled by envelope, horiz. No. 1355, Nativity.

**1994**

**1354** A448 600s multicolored 1.10 .75
**1355** A448 900s multicolored 1.60 .85

Juan Leon Mera, Death Cent.
A449 A450

**Wmk. 395**

**1994, Dec. 21 Litho.** *Perf. 13*

**1356** A449 600s Mera's home 1.00 .65
**1357** A450 900s multicolored 2.25 1.40

Gen. Antonio Jose de Sucre (1795-1830) — A451

*Perf. 14x13½*

**1995, Mar. 14 Litho. Wmk. 395**

**1358** A451 1500s shown 3.75 1.75
**1359** A451 2000s Portrait at right 5.00 2.50

**Size: 80x105**

***Imperf***

**1360** A451 3000s In military uniform 5.50 5.50
*Nos. 1358-1360 (3)* 14.25 9.75

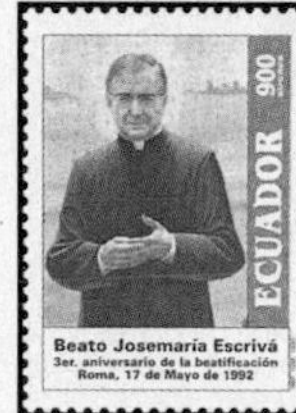


Beatification of Josemaria Escriva, 3rd Anniv. — A452

**1995, May 17** *Perf. 13x13½*

**1361** A452 900s multicolored 1.50 .90

Gen. Eloy Alfaro (1842-1912), Alfarista Revolution, Cent. A453

**1995, June 5** *Perf. 13½x13*

**1362** A453 800s multicolored 1.40 .80

A454

Conflict Between Ecuador & Peru — A455

Designs: 200s, Soldier writing to children. 400s, Hand holding flag of Ecuador. 800s, Soldier in wilderness.

**1995, July** *Perf. 13½, 13 (#1364)*

**1363** A454 200s multicolored .50 .25
**1364** A455 400s multicolored 1.00 .45
**1365** A454 800s multicolored 1.75 .90
*Nos. 1363-1365 (3)* 3.25 1.60

CARE, 50th Anniv. — A456

**1995, July 14** *Perf. 13½*

**1366** A456 400s Girl, vert. .60 .30
**1367** A456 800s shown 1.75 1.00

CAF (Andes Development Corporation), 25th Anniv. — A457

**1995, Aug. 22** *Perf. 13*

**1368** A457 1000s multicolored 3.00 1.25

Virgin of Cisne — A458

**1995, Sept. 2 Litho.** *Perf. 13*

**1369** A458 500s multi .75 .50

A459

**1995, Sept. 28**

**1370** A459 400s multicolored .85 .45

Natl. Institute of Children and Families (INNFA), 35th anniv.

UN, 50th Anniv. A460

**Wmk. 395**

**1995, Oct. 6 Litho.** *Perf. 13*

**1371** A460 1000s bl, blk & bis 2.00 1.00

Intl. Decade for Natural Disaster Reduction A461

Civil defense emblem and: No. 1372, House surrounded by flood waters. No. 1373, Family leaving site of erupting volcano. No. 1374, People under table during earthquake. No. 1375, Couple planting seedlings on hillside. No. 1376, Man reading instruction booklet for natural disaster preparation.

**1995, Oct. 11**

**1372** A461 1000s multicolored 2.00 1.00
**1373** A461 1000s multicolored 2.00 1.00
**1374** A461 1000s multicolored 2.00 1.00
**1375** A461 1000s multicolored 2.00 1.00
**1376** A461 1000s multicolored 2.00 1.00
*Nos. 1372-1376 (5)* 10.00 5.00

FAO, 50th Anniv. A462

**1995, Oct. 16**

**1377** A462 1300s multicolored 2.75 1.50

Women's Culture Club, 50th Anniv. A463

**1995, Oct. 20**
**1378** A463 1500s multicolored 2.75 1.50

29th Assembly of Inter-America Philatelic Federation, Quito — A464

**1995, Nov. 11**
**1379** A464 1000s blue & red 1.75 1.00

A465

Christmas: 2000s, Santa, sleigh, reindeer on top of world. 2600s, Man on decorated horse, children.

**Wmk. 395**
**1995, Dec. Litho. *Perf. 13***
**1380** A465 2000s multicolored 5.00 2.40
**1381** A465 2600s multicolored 6.00 2.40

A466

Indigenous Birds: No. 1382, Aglaiocercus kingi.

No. 1383: a, Coeligena torquata. b, Phaethornis superciliosus. c, Ocreatus underwoodii. d, Oreotrochilus chimborazo. e, Aglaiocercus coelestis.

**1995, Dec.**
**1382** A466 1000s multicolored 2.25 .85
**1383** A466 1000s Strip of 5, #a.-e. 11.25 6.25

Ecuadoran Air Force, 75th Anniv. A467

**1995, Dec.**
**1384** A467 1000s multicolored 2.00 .95

Year of Folk Music — A468

2000s, Julio Jaramillo (1935-78), musician, composer. 3000s, Jaramillo, wall.

**1996, Jan. 16 Litho. *Perf. 13***
**1385** A468 2000s multicolored 3.75 2.00

***Imperf***
**1386** A468 3000s multicolored 5.00 4.25

Advancement of Ecuador, 4 Year Program A469

Designs show symbols for: 1500s, Mail delivery. 2000s, Customs crossing. 2600s, Telecommunications. 3000p, Ports.

**Wmk. 395**
**1996, July 23 Litho. *Perf. 13***
**1387** A469 1000s multicolored 1.75 .80
**1388** A469 1500s multicolored 2.75 1.25
**1389** A469 2000s multicolored 3.25 1.75
**1390** A469 2600s multicolored 4.50 1.90
*a.* Pair, #1388, #1390 8.00 8.00
*b.* Pair, #1389, #1390 8.50 8.50
**1391** A469 3000s multicolored 5.50 3.00
*a.* Pair, #1387, #1391 8.00 8.00
*b.* Pair, #1389, #1391 9.50 9.50
*Nos. 1387-1391 (5)* 17.75 8.70
*Nos. 1390a-1391b (4)* 34.00 34.00

Nos. 1387-1391 were issued in strips of 2 each.

Esmeraldas '96, 8th National Games A470

Mascot depicting two sports on each stamp: No. 1392, Tennis, boxing. No. 1393, Basketball, socccer. 600s, Racketball, swimming. 800s, Weight lifting, karate. 1000s, Volleyball, gymnastics. 1200s, Athletics, judo. No. 1398, Chess, wrestling.

No. 1399, Mascot holding flag, emblem, surrounded by flags.

**1996, July 30**
**1392** A470 400s multicolored .55 .25
**1393** A470 400s multicolored .55 .25
**1394** A470 600s multicolored .90 .45
*a.* Pair, #1392, #1394 1.50 1.50
**1395** A470 800s multicolored 1.25 .60
*a.* Pair, #1394-1395 2.25 2.25
**1396** A470 1000s multicolored 1.60 .75
*a.* Pair, #1393, #1396 2.40 2.40
*b.* Pair, #1395-1396 3.00 3.00
**1397** A470 1200s multicolored 1.75 .95
**1398** A470 2000s multicolored 3.25 1.40
*Nos. 1392-1398 (7)* 9.85 4.65
*Nos. 1394a-1396b (4)* 9.15 9.15

**Size: 120x100mm**
**1399** A470 2000s multicolored 4.00 3.50

Nos. 1392-1396 were printed in strips of 2 each.

Civil Aviation, 50th Anniv. A471

**1996, Aug. 8**
**1400** A471 2000s multicolored 3.00 1.25

1996 Summer Olympic Games, Atlanta A472

Atlanta Games emblem and: 1000s, Mascot carrying torch. No. 1402, Emblem of Olympic Committee of Ecuador. 3000s, Jefferson Perez, vert.

No. 1404, Perez, gold medalist, 20-kilometer walk, walking.

**1996**
**1401** A472 1000s multicolored 2.00 .75
**1402** A472 2000s multicolored 4.00 2.25
*a.* Pair, #1401-1402 6.00 6.00
**1403** A472 3000s multicolored 5.00 2.50
*Nos. 1401-1403 (3)* 11.00 5.50

**Size: 100x120mm**
***Imperf***
**1404** A472 2000s multicolored 4.50 3.50

Fight Against Drug Abuse — A473

**1996 Litho. Wmk. 395 *Perf. 13***
**1408** A473 2000s multicolored 4.00 2.00

Dr. Eduardo Salazar Gomez, Birth Cent. — A474

**1996**
**1409** A474 1000s multicolored 2.50 1.25

Catholic University, Quito, 50th Anniv. — A475

Designs: 400s, Outside view of building, horiz. 800s, Entrance.

**1996**
**1410** A475 400s multicolored .90 .45
**1411** A475 800s multicolored 1.75 .85

Junior Chamber International A476

2000s, Children's faces, horiz.

**1996**
**1412** A476 2000s multi 4.50 2.75
**1413** A476 2600s shown 5.50 3.50

Catholic University, Quito, 50th Anniv. A477

**1996, Nov.**
**1414** A477 2000s multicolored 4.00 2.00

The Universe Daily Newspaper, 75th Anniv. — A478

**1996, Dec.**
**1415** A478 2000s multicolored 4.00 2.00

Private Technical University, Loja — A479

**1996, Dec. 9**
**1416** A479 4700s multicolored 11.00 5.50

UNICEF, 50th Anniv. A480

**1996, Dec. 11**
**1417** A480 2000s multicolored 4.50 2.25

Christmas A481

Children's paintings: 600s, Merry Chrismas All Over the World. 800s, World of Peace and Love. 2000s, Christmas.

**1996, Dec. 19**
**1418** A481 600s multicolored 1.50 1.00
**1419** A481 800s multicolored 2.00 1.25

**Size: 51x31mm**
***Perf. 13½***
**1420** A481 2000s multicolored 5.00 2.50
*Nos. 1418-1420 (3)* 8.50 4.75

Preserving the Ecological System A482

America '95: 1000s, Voltur grypus. 1500s, Harpia harpyja, vert.

**1996, Dec. 30 *Perf. 13***
**1421** A482 1000s multicolored 2.50 1.50
**1422** A482 1500s multicolored 3.75 2.00

Typical Children's Costumes — A483

America '96: No. 1423, "Bordando" girl, Zuleta. No. 1424, Girl from Otavalo.

**1996, Dec. 30**
**1423** A483 2600s multicolored 5.00 1.75
**1424** A483 2600s multicolored 5.00 4.25
*a.* Pair, #1423-1424 12.50 12.50

Mejia Natl. Institute, Cent. A484

Design: Jose Mejia Lequerica, building.

**1997, Jan. 10**
**1425** A484 1000s multicolored 2.25 1.25

Army Polytechnical School, 75th Anniv. A485

**Wmk. 395**

**1997, June 16 Typo. *Perf. 13***
**1426** A485 400s multicolored 1.10 .75

Natl. Experimental College, Ambato, 50th Anniv. A486

**1997, June 20**
**1427** A486 600s multicolored 1.50 1.00

Vicente Rocafuerte (1783-1847), First Constitutional President of Ecuador — A487

**1997, July 1**
**1428** A487 400s multicolored 1.25 .75

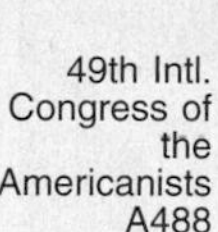

49th Intl. Congress of the Americanists A488

**1997, July 3**
**1429** A488 2000s multicolored 5.00 3.25

Butterflies A489

Designs: 400s, Actinote equatoria. 600s, Dismorphia amphione. 800s, Marpesia corinna. 2000s, Marpesia berania. 2600s, Morpho helenor.

**1997, July 21**
**1430** A489 400s multicolored 1.25 .80
**1431** A489 600s multicolored 1.50 1.00
**1432** A489 800s multicolored 2.00 1.25
**1433** A489 2000s multicolored 5.00 3.25
**1434** A489 2600s multicolored 7.00 4.75
*Nos. 1430-1434 (5)* 16.75 11.05

Air Club of Ecuador, 66th Anniv. A490

**1997, July 23**
**1435** A490 2600s multicolored 6.00 3.00

Orchids — A491

400s, Epidendrum secundum. 600s, Epidendrum. 800s, Oncidium cultratrum. 2000s, Oncidium sp mariposa. 2600s, Pleurothalis corrulensis.

**1997, Aug. 14 Litho. *Perf. 13***
**1436** A491 400s multicolored 1.25 .80
**1437** A491 600s multicolored 1.50 1.00
**1438** A491 800s multicolored 2.00 1.25
**1439** A491 2000s multicolored 5.00 3.25
**1440** A491 2600s multicolored 7.00 4.75
*Nos. 1436-1440 (5)* 16.75 11.05

Rocks and Minerals — A492

**1997, Oct. 6 Litho. *Perf. 13***
**1441** A492 400s Quartz 1.25 .80
**1442** A492 600s Chalcopyrite 1.50 1.00
**1443** A492 800s Gold 2.00 1.25
**1444** A492 2000s Petrified wood 5.00 3.25
**1445** A492 2600s Pyrite 7.00 4.75
*Nos. 1441-1445 (5)* 16.75 11.05

A493

Christmas (Children's designs): 400s, Santa as postman delivering letters over world. 2600s, Star on Christmas tree reaching for letters, airplane under tree. 3000s, Child dreaming of angels carrying letters.

**1997, Dec. 22 Litho. *Perf. 13***
**1446** A493 400s multicolored 1.25 .80
**1447** A493 2600s multicolored 7.00 4.75
**1448** A493 3000s multicolored 8.25 5.50
*Nos. 1446-1448 (3)* 16.50 11.05

America Issue — A494

**1997, Dec. 29**
**1449** A494 800s Life of a Postman 2.00 1.00
**1450** A494 2000s On bicycle 5.00 2.50

Intl. Women's Day — A495

Matilde Hidalgo de Procel (1889-1974), physician, social reformer.

**1998, Mar. 6 Litho. *Perf. 13***
**1451** A495 2000s multicolored 4.75 3.25

Dr. Misael Acosta Solis, Botanist — A496

**Wmk. 395**

**1998, Apr. 22 Litho. *Perf. 13***
**1452** A496 2000s multicolored 8.25 5.50

Organization of American States (OAS), 50th Anniv. A497

**1998, Apr. 30**
**1453** A497 2600s multicolored 5.00 3.25

1998 World Cup Soccer Championships, France — A498

Designs: 2600s, Trophy, mascot, vert. 3000s, Two players, trophy.

**1998, May**
**1454** A498 2000s multicolored 4.00 2.25
**1455** A498 2600s multicolored 5.00 2.75
**1456** A498 3000s multicolored 6.00 3.25
*Nos. 1454-1456 (3)* 15.00 8.25

Flowers — A499

600s, Gypsophila paniculata. 800s, Banana flowers. 2000s, Roses. 2600s, Asters.

**1998, June**
**1457** A499 600s multicolored 1.40 .60
**1458** A499 800s multicolored 1.75 .90
**1459** A499 2000s multicolored 4.00 2.25
**1460** A499 2600s multicolored 5.00 2.75
*Nos. 1457-1460 (4)* 12.15 6.50

Galapagos Flora — A500

Designs: 600s, Jasminocereus thouarsii. 1000s, Cordia lutea lamarck. 2600s, Momordica charantia.

**1998, July**
**1461** A500 600s multicolored 1.10 .60
**1462** A500 1000s multicolored 1.90 1.00
**1463** A500 2600s multicolored 5.00 2.75
*Nos. 1461-1463 (3)* 8.00 4.35

Tourism A501

Designs: 600s, St. Augustine Church, Quito. 800s, Monument to the Heroes of the Independence, Guayaquil. 2000s, Equator Monument, Quito. 2600s, Mojanda Lake.

**1998, July**
**1464** A501 600s multi, vert. 1.25 .60
**1465** A501 800s multi, vert. 1.50 .90
**1466** A501 2000s multi 3.50 2.25
**1467** A501 2600s multi 4.50 2.75
*Nos. 1464-1467 (4)* 10.75 6.50

Emiliano Ortega Espinosa (1898-1974), Educator A502

***Perf. 13¼x13, 13x13¼***

**1998 Litho. Wmk. 395**
**1468** A502 400s shown .90 .50
**1469** A502 4700s Portrait, vert. 11.00 8.25

Carlos Cueva Tamariz (1898-1991), Educator — A503

***Perf. 13x13¼***

**1998, Nov. Litho. Wmk. 395**
**1470** A503 2600s multicolored 5.00 3.50

Radio Club of Guayaquil, 75th Anniv. — A504

**Wmk. 395**

**1998, Nov. 20 Litho. *Perf. 13***
**1471** A504 600s multicolored 1.25 .90

6th South American Games — A505

Designs: 400s, Mascot. 1000s, Games poster, tennis rackets, hurdles, sailing, hammer throw, bowling, boxing. 2600s, Mascot, parallel bars, wrestling, judo, fencing, running, swimming, shooting, cycling.

**1998**
**1472** A505 400s multicolored 1.10 .50
**1473** A505 1000s multicolored 1.90 1.00
**1474** A505 2600s multicolored 5.00 2.75
*Nos. 1472-1474 (3)* 8.00 4.25

Paintings by Eduardo Kingman (1913-85) A506

Designs: 600s, Ecuadoran Woman, vert. 800s, World Without Answers.

**1998, Dec. 10**
**1475** A506 600s multicolored 1.25 .65
**1476** A506 800s multicolored 1.90 1.00

Manuela Sáenz (1797-1856), Mistress of Simon Bolívar — A507

**1999, Jan. 19**
**1477** A507 1000s multicolored 2.00 .95

America issue. Exists imperf.

Christmas A508

Children's drawings: 1000s, Santa posting letters on tree. 2600s, People holding up giant letter, vert. 3000s, Santas parachuting with letters, nativity scene, tree, vert.

**1998, Dec. 22**
**1478** A508 1000s multicolored 1.75 .95
**1479** A508 2600s multicolored 4.50 2.50
**1480** A508 3000s multicolored 5.00 2.75
*Nos. 1478-1480 (3)* 11.25 6.20

Los Tayos Caves A509

**1999, Feb. 25 Litho. *Perf. 13***
**1481** A509 1000s Man in cave, vert. 1.75 .90
**1482** A509 2600s shown 4.75 2.50

Napal, the Age of Wrath, by Oswaldo Guayasamin (1919-99) — A510

**Wmk. 395**
**1999, May 12 Litho. *Perf. 13***
**1483** A510 2000s multicolored 4.25 2.10

Iberoamerica art exhibition.

Universal Day of Human Rights A511

**1999, May 28**
**1484** A511 4000s multicolored 7.50 4.50

Eloy Alfaro Superior Military College, Cent. A512

5200s, Cannon, monument, flags, buildings. 9400s, Honor Guard, modern building.

**1999, June 4**
**1485** A512 5200s multicolored 10.50 7.00
**1486** A512 9400s multicolored 17.50 11.50

Puyo, 100th Anniv. — A513

Designs: a, Bromeliad. b, Ara chloroptera.

**1999, June 2**
**1487** A513 4000s Pair, #a.-b. 14.50 10.00

Dr. Rafael Barahona Andrade (1827-98) A514

***Perf. 13¼x13***
**1999, June 17 Litho. Wmk. 395**
**1488** A514 5200s multi 9.00 4.50

Generals — A515

Designs: 2000s, Manuel Antonio de Luzarraga y Echezurria (1776-1859). 4000s, Tomas Carlos Wright (1799-1868).

**1999, Aug. 11 *Perf. 13x13¼***
**1489-1490** A515 Set of 2 11.00 6.00

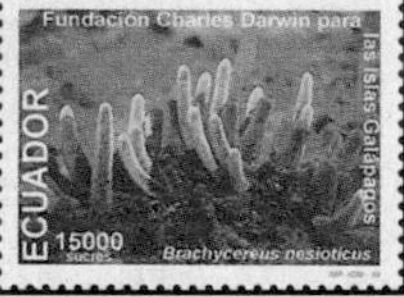


Galapagos Islands Flora and Fauna A516

No. 1491, vert.: a, Phoenicopterus ruber. b, Buteo galapagoensis. c, Amblyrhynchus cristatus. d, Conolophus subcristatus. e, Opuntia galapageia. f, Pyrocephalus rubinus. g, Sula nebouxii. h, Sula dactylatra. i, Scalesia villosa. j, G. elephantopus abingdoni.

No. 1492: a, Brachycereus nesioticus. b, Dendroica petechia. c, Nannopterum harrisi. d, Tursiops truncatus. e, Pentaceraster cumingi. f, G. elephantopus porteri. g, Microlophus albemarlensis. h, Arctocephalus galapagoensis. i, Spheniscus mendiculus. j, Geospiza scandens.

***Perf. 13x13¼, 13¼x13***
**1999, Sept. 3 Litho. Wmk. 395**
**1491** Strip of 10 *90.00 75.00*
*a.-j.* A516 7000s Any single *5.50 1.75*
**1492** Strip of 10 *175.00 125.00*
*a.-j.* A516 15,000s Any single *12.00 5.00*

Intl. Year of Older Persons A517

Designs: No. 1493, 1000s, Hands of child and old person. No. 1494, 1000s, Emblem.

***Perf. 13¼x13***
**1999, Sept. 22 Litho. Wmk. 395**
**1493-1494** A517 Set of 2 3.00 1.75

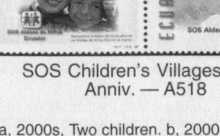

SOS Children's Villages, 50th Anniv. — A518

a, 2000s, Two children. b, 2000s, One child.

**1999, Sept. 30**
**1495** A518 Pair, #a-b 5.00 2.50

America Issue, A World Without Arms — A519

No. 1496: a, World map. b, Tree, bird, Earth.

***Perf. 13¼x13***
**1999, Dec. 11 Litho. Wmk. 395**
**1496** A519 4000s Pair, #a-b *14.50 10.00*

UPU, 125th Anniv. A520

Designs: 1000s, Ecuadorian Postal Service mascot, vert. 4000s, Dove with letter, vert. 8000s, UPU emblem.

***Perf. 13¼x12¾***
**1999, Dec. 11 Litho. Wmk. 395**
**1497** A520 1000s multi .90 .45
**1498** A520 4000s multi 3.50 1.75
**1499** A520 8000s multi 7.00 4.00
*Nos. 1497-1499 (3)* 11.40 6.20

Ecuador as Secretary General of Permanent South Pacific Commission A521

***Perf. 13x13¼***
**1999, Dec. 21 Litho. Wmk. 395**
**1500** A521 7000s multi *7.50 5.50*

Machala Tourism A522

Designs: No. 1501, Banana flower and city. No. 1502, vert.: a, Monument to banana plantation workers. b, City Hall.

**1999, Dec. 28 *Perf. 13¼x13, 13x13¼***
**1501** A522 3000s multi *3.25 1.60*
**1502** A522 3000s Pair, #a-b *6.50 3.25*

EMELEC Soccer Team — A523

No. 1503: a, Jorge Bolanos. b, Carlos Raffo. No. 1504, EMELEC team photo, 1957. No. 1505, Player, vert.

***Perf. 13x13¼, 13¼x13***
**2000, Jan. 7 Litho.**
**1503** A523 1000s Pair, #a-b *3.00 2.25*
**1504** A523 2000s multi *3.00 1.50*
**1505** A523 2000s multi *3.00 1.50*

Guayas Philanthropic Society, 150th Anniv. A524

Designs: 1000s, Building. 2000s, Founder Juan Maria Martinez Coello. 4000s, Emblem.

***Perf. 13¼x13***
**2000, Jan. 19 Litho. Wmk. 395**
**1506-1508** A524 Set of 3 *3.00 1.50*

Dual Nationality Day — A525

**2000, Jan. 24 *Perf. 13x13¼***
**1509** A525 7000s multi *3.00 1.50*

Cuenca, World Heritage Site — A526

No. 1510: a, Buildings. b, Puente Roto and Tomebamba River. c, Church bell gable, Concepcion Monastery. d, Cathedral and city skyline. e, San José Church.

**2000, Mar. 24 *Perf. 13¼x13***
**1510** Strip of 5 *7.00 6.00*
*a.-e.* A526 4000s Any single *.75 .50*

Nicolas Lapentti, Tennis Player — A527

**2000, Mar. 26 *Perf. 13x13¼***
**1511** A527 8000s multi *3.00 1.50*

Birds — A528

No. 1512: a, Diglossa cyanea. b, Oreotrochilus chimborazo. c, Trogon personatus. d, Colibri coruscans. e, Atlapetes rufinucha.

**2000, Apr. 7**
**1512** Horiz. strip of 5 *13.00 11.50*
*a.-e.* A528 8000s Any single *2.25 1.50*

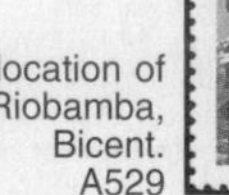

Relocation of Riobamba, Bicent. A529

Designs: No. 1513, Mt. Chimborazo.

No. 1514: a, Riobamba Cathedral. b, Statue of Pedro Vicente Maldonado.

**2000, Apr. 13** ***Perf. 13¼x13, 13x13¼***
**1513** A529 8000s multi 2.75 1.00
**1514** A529 8000s Pair, #a-b 5.25 3.50

Gen. Eloy Alfaro, Founder of Natl. Music Conservatory A530

**2000, Apr. 19** ***Perf. 13x13¼***
**1515** A530 10,000s multi 4.00 1.60

Natl. Music Conservatory, cent.

Climbing of Mt. Everest by Ivan Vallejo Ricaurte A531

**2000, May 23** ***Perf. 13¼x13***
**1516** A531 8000s multi 3.50 2.00

**100 Cents=1 Dollar**

Dolores Sucre Fiscal College, 50th Anniv. — A532

***Perf. 13x13¼***
**2000** **Litho.** **Wmk. 395**
**1517** A532 32c multi 2.50 1.25

Training Ship Guayas — A533

**2000, July 5** ***Perf. 13x13¼***
**1518** A533 68c multi 1.60 .80

***Imperf***
**Size: 90x110mm**
**1519** A533 $1 multi 7.00 3.25

Battle of Jambeli, 59th Anniv., Navy Day — A534

**2000** ***Perf. 13¼x13***
**1520** A534 16c multi 1.50 .25

Guayaquil Civic Renovation A535

**2000, July** ***Perf. 13x13¼***
**1521** A535 84c multi 7.50 3.75

Megaptera Novaeangliae — A536

**2000, Aug. 3** ***Perf. 13¼x13***
**1522** A536 84c multi 8.50 4.25

***Imperf***
**Size: 90x110mm**
**1523** A536 $1 Two whales 11.50 5.75

American and Caribbean Dog Show, Quito A537

**2000, Aug.** ***Perf. 13¼x13***
**1524** A537 68c multi 4.50 2.25

Guayaquil Tennis Club, 90th Anniv. A538

**2000, Aug.** **Wmk. 395**
**1525** A538 84c multi 5.50 2.50

Alberto Spencer, Soccer Player — A539

**2000** ***Perf. 13x13¼***
**1526** A539 68c multi 5.00 2.50

***Imperf***
**Size: 69x99mm**
**1527** A539 $1 Spencer, crowd 9.00 4.50

2000 Summer Olympics, Sydney — A540

Ecuadoran team emblem, Games emblem and: 32c Mascots. 68c, Runner Jefferson Perez Marchista. 84c, Weight lifter Boris Burov, Olympic flag, horiz.

**2000, Sept.** ***Perf. 13x13¼, 13¼x13***
**1528-1530** A540 Set of 3 12.00 6.00

Salinas Yacht Club, 60th Anniv. A541

Designs: No. 1531a, Lighthouse, vert. Nos. 1531b, 1533, Sailboat, vert. 68c, Sailboats, fisherman, waterskier, scuba diver.

**2000, Oct.** ***Perf. 13x13¼***
**1531** A541 32c Horiz. pair, #a-b 5.50 2.75

***Perf. 13¼x13***
**1532** A541 68c multi 5.75 2.75

***Imperf***
**Size: 69x100mm**
**1533** A541 $1 multi 9.00 4.50

Inter-American Development Bank, 40th Anniv. — A542

Designs: No. 1534a, 68c, No. 1536a, 25c, Salsipuedes Bridge, Felipe Herrera. No. 1534b, 68c, No. 1536b, 25c, Daule-Peripa Dam, Antonio Ortiz Mena. No. 1535a, 84c, No. 1536c, 25c, Enrique Iglesias, Ucubamba Water Treatment Plant. No. 1535b, 84c, No. 1536d, 25c, Bank emblem, History Museum, Quito.

**2000, Oct. 27** ***Perf. 13¼x13***
**Horiz. Pairs, #a-b**
**1534-1535** A542 Set of 2 20.00 10.00

***Rouletted 14 on 2 sides***
**1536** A542 25c Sheet of 4, #a-d 7.50 3.75

Size of Nos. 1536a-1536b, 75x48mm; Nos. 1536c-1536d, 75x42mm.

National Union of Journalists A543

**2000, Nov. 1** ***Perf. 13¼x13***
**1537** A543 16c multi 1.25 .25

Civil Registry, Cent. — A544

No. 1538: a, People, flag, computer. b, Fingerprint, family.

**2000, Oct. 27** ***Perf. 13x13¼***
**1538** A544 68c Horiz. pair, #a-b 9.00 4.50

Mama Negra Festival, Latacunga — A545

No. 1539: a, Mama Negra with doll. b, Man in Moor King costume.

**2000, Nov.** ***Perf. 13x13¼***
**1539** A545 32c Horiz. pair, #a-b 5.50 2.75

***Imperf***
**Size: 100x68mm**
**1540** A545 $1 Mama Negra, doll, diff. 6.50 3.00

Ministry of Labor, 75th Anniv. — A546

**2000, Nov. 15** ***Perf. 13x13¼***
**1541** A546 68c multi 4.75 2.25

Intl. Fruits and Flowers Festival, Ambato, 50th Anniv. — A547

No. 1542, horiz.: Design inside "0" of 50 — a, Tungurahua Volcano. b, Aerial view of Ambato.
No. 1544, horiz.: Design inside "0" of 50 — a, Flower. b. Fruit.

**2000, Nov.** ***Perf. 13¾***
**1542** A547 32c Vert. pair, #a-b 4.25 2.10
**1543** A547 84c shown 5.75 2.75
**1544** A547 84c Vert. pair, #a-b 12.00 6.00
*Nos. 1542-1544 (3)* 22.00 10.85

***Imperf***
**Size: 68x100mm**
**1545** A547 $1 Ambato 6.25 3.00

Christmas — A548

Children's art by — No. 1546, 68c: a, Giannina Rhor Isaias. b, Josue Remache Romero.
No. 1547, 84c: a, Maria Cedeño Bazurtto. b, Juan Alban Salazar.
$1, Walther Carvache.

**2000, Dec. 15** ***Perf. 13¼x13***
**Horiz. Pairs, #a-b**
**1546-1547** A548 Set of 2 21.50 11.00

***Imperf***
**Size: 100x69mm**
**1548** A548 $1 multi 6.25 3.00

Expoflores Flower Producer and Exporter Association A549

**2000** ***Perf. 13x13¼***
**1549** A549 68c multi 5.00 2.50

Man's Chapel, Guayasamin A550

**2000** ***Perf. 13¼x13***
**1550** A550 16c multi 1.25 .25

Spanish Chamber of Commerce in Ecuador, 80th Anniv. — A551

**2000, Dec.** ***Perf. 13x13¼***
**1551** A551 16c multi 1.25 .25

Intl. Volunteers Year — A552

**2000** **Wmk. 395**
**1552** A552 16c multi 1.25 .25

Restoration of Bolivar Theater, Quito — A553

Designs: 16c, Piano, banquet room. 32c, Stage, orchestra, horiz.

**2000, Dec.** ***Perf. 13x13¼, 13¼x13***
**1553-1554** A553 Set of 2 3.75 1.75

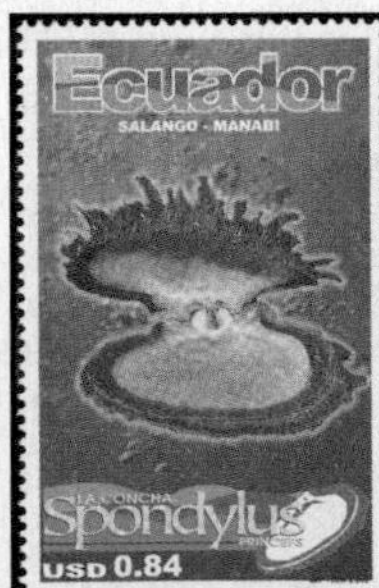


Spondylus Princeps A554

**2000, Dec. 16** ***Perf. 13¾***
**1555** A554 84c multi 6.00 3.00

***Imperf***

**Size: 69x99mm**

**1556** A554 $1 multi 7.00 3.50

America Issue, Fight Against AIDS — A555

No. 1557: a, Strands. b, Earth.

**2000** ***Perf. 13x13¼***
**1557** A555 84c Horiz. pair, #a-b 15.00 7.50

Guayas Province Red Cross, 90th Anniv. A556

**2000** ***Perf. 13¼x13***
**1558** A556 16c multi 1.25 .60

Guayas Sports Federation, 78th Anniv. — A557

**2000, Dec.** ***Perf. 13x13¼***
**1559** A557 16c multi 1.25 .60

Landscapes A557a

Designs: No. 1559A, 16c, Andean region. No. 1559B, 16c, Pacific coast. 32c, Tourism emblem. 68c, Amazonia. 84c, Galápagos Islands.

***Perf. 13¼x12¾***

**2001, Jan. 24** **Litho.** **Wmk. 395**

| | | | | |
|---|---|---|---|---|
| **1559A** | A557a | 16c multi | 1.25 | .60 |
| **1559B** | A557a | 16c multi | 1.25 | .60 |
| **1559C** | A557a | 32c multi | 2.50 | 1.10 |
| **1559D** | A557a | 68c multi | 4.75 | 2.40 |
| **1559E** | A557a | 84c multi | 4.75 | 2.40 |
| | *Nos. 1559A-1559E (5)* | | 14.50 | 7.10 |

Guayas Soccer Team, 50th Anniv. A558

**2001, Mar. 8** ***Perf. 13¼x13***
**1560** A558 68c multi 5.00 2.50

Census — A558a Census — A558b

***Perf. 12¾x13¼***

**2001, Mar. 12** **Litho.** **Wmk. 395**
**1560A** A558a 68c multi 4.50 4.50
**1560B** A558b 68c multi 4.50 4.50
*c.* Horiz. pair, #1560A-1560B 10.00 10.00

Dr. Raúl Clemente Huerta A559

**2001, Apr. 4** ***Perf. 13¼x13***
**1561** A559 68c multi 5.50 2.75

Dr. Antonio J. Quevedo, Birth Cent. A560

**2001, Apr. 5** **Litho.**
**1562** A560 84c multi 6.50 3.25

Military Geographic Institute A560a

No. 1562A: b, Soldier, building. c, Computer, printing press.

***Perf. 13¼x12¾***

**2001, Apr. 11** **Litho.** **Wmk. 395**
**1562A** A560a 68c Vert. pair, #b-c 12.00 6.00

Automobile Club of Ecuador, 50th Anniv. A561

**2001, May 15** **Wmk. 395**
**1563** A561 84c multi 6.50 3.25

San Francisco de Peleusí Church, Azogues — A561a

***Perf. 12¾x13¼***

**2001, May** **Litho.** **Wmk. 395**
**1563A** A561a 84c multi 6.50 3.25

Women's Training Institute — A562

**2001, Apr. 10** ***Perf. 13x13¼***
**1564** A562 84c multi 6.50 3.25

Intl. Women's Day A563

No. 1565: a, Woman, child, corn. b, Woman, emblem.

**2001, Apr. 2** ***Perf. 13¼x13***
**1565** A563 84c Vert. pair, #a-b 12.50 6.25

Secular Education at Manuela Cañizares University, Cent. A564

**2001, Mar. 29** **Wmk. 395**
**1566** A564 84c multi 6.50 3.25

Ecuador Merchant Marines, Cent. — A565

**2001, Jan. 2001** ***Perf. 13x13¼***
**1567** A565 16c multi 1.25 .60

Ambato Technical University, 32nd Anniv. A566

No. 1568: a, Building. b, Painting.

**2001** ***Perf. 13¼x13***
**1568** A566 32c Vert. pair, #a-b 5.50 2.75

Galapagos Islands Scenes — A567

No. 1569: a, Española Island (shown). b, San Cristobal Island. c, Bartolome Island. d, Española Island, diff. e, Bartolome and Santiago Islands.

$1, Bird on rock, Española Island.

**2001, Feb. 17** ***Perf. 13¾***
**1569** Horiz. strip of 5 6.00 3.00
*a.-e.* A567 16c Any single .50 .25

***Imperf***

**Size: 100x70mm**

**1570** A567 $1 multi 8.00 4.00

Alexander von Humboldt (1769-1859), Naturalist — A568

***Perf. 13x13¼***

**2001, June 14** **Litho.** **Wmk. 395**
**1571** A568 84c multi 6.00 3.00

Ecuadorian Atomic Energy Commission A568a

**2001, Aug. 3 Litho.** ***Perf. 12¾x13¼***
**1571A** A568a 70c multi 5.50 2.75

Lebanese Union, 80th Anniv. — A569

No. 1572: a, Building and emblem. b, Emblem.

**2001, Aug. 30** ***Perf. 13¼x13***
**1572** A569 16c Horiz. pair, #a-b 3.00 1.50

Manta Port Authority — A570

No. 1573: a, Emblem. b, Ships in port.

**2001, Sept. 28**
**1573** A570 68c Horiz. pair, #a-b 10.00 5.00

Esmereldas Province Tourism — A571

No. 1574: a, Beach. b, Musicians and dancers on beach.

**2001**
**1574** A571 86c Horiz. pair, #a-b 12.50 6.25

Latin American Writers — A572

No. 1575: a, Claudia Lars (1899-1974), Salvadoran poet. b, Federico Proaño (1848-94), Ecuadoran journalist.

**2001, Aug. 28** ***Perf. 13x13¼***
**1575** A572 86c Horiz. pair, #a-b 13.50 6.75

Andean Condor Preservation — A573

No. 1576: a, Condor and chick. b, Condor heads, FRAPZOO emblem.
$1, Condor in flight, FRAPZOO emblem.

**2001, July 23** ***Perf. 13x13¼***
**1576** A573 86c Horiz. pair, #a-b 12.50 6.25

***Imperf***
**Size: 68x99mm**

**1577** A573 $1 multi 7.50 3.75

Ecuador — Peru Peace Accords A574

No. 1578: a, Map of Ecuador and Peru. b, Soldier. c, Flags of military obeservers. d, Amazon River. e, Men in field.

**2001, May 22** ***Perf. 13¼x13***
**1578** Horiz. strip of 5 22.50 11.00
*a.-e.* A574 68c Any single 4.00 2.00

Archidona Canton — A575

No. 1579: a, Phragmipedium orchid. b, Saimiri sciureus. c, B. macrophylla. d, Church. e, Kichwa Indian family.

**2001, Apr. 28** ***Perf. 13x13¼***
**1579** Vert. strip of 5 30.00 15.00
*a.-e.* A575 84c Any single 5.00 2.40

Ecotourism in Baños A576

No. 1580: a, Orchid. b, Basilica, Baños. c, Tungurahua Volcano. d, Pailon del Diablo Waterfall. e, Statue of Virgin of Rosario de Agua Santa.
$1, Pailon del Diablo Waterfall, orchid.

**2001** ***Perf. 13¼x13***
**1580** Horiz. strip of 5 27.50 13.50
*a.-e.* A576 86c Any single 5.00 2.40

***Imperf***
**Size: 68x99mm**

**1581** A576 $1 multi 7.50 3.75

Guayas Educational Journalists Association, 30th Anniv. A577

***Perf. 13¼x13***
**2001, Oct. 15 Litho. Wmk. 395**
**1582** A577 16c multi 1.25 .60

Foundation for Development of Cattle Ranching, 15th Anniv. — A578

**2001, Aug. 15** ***Perf. 13x13¼***
**1583** A578 16c multi 1.25 .60

City Gates, Loja — A579

**2001** ***Perf. 13¼x13***
**1584** A579 32c multi 2.50 1.25

Quito Municipal District Directorate of Security A580

**2001, Nov. 26**
**1585** A580 68c multi 5.00 2.50

Salvador Bustamante Celi (1876-1935), Musician A581

**2001**
**1586** A581 68c multi 5.50 2.75

Marcel Laniado de Wind (1927-98), First Pres. of Natl. Modernization Council — A582

**2001, Aug. 6** ***Perf. 13x13¼***
**1587** A582 70c multi 5.50 2.75

Bernardino Cardinal Echeverria (1912-2000) A583

**2001, Nov. 14**
**1588** A583 84c multi 6.50 3.25

José Joaquin Olmedo (1780-1847), Statesman and Poet — A584

**2001, Nov. 8**
**1589** A584 84c multi 6.50 3.25

El Angel Ecological Reserve — A585

No. 1590: a, Paja de Paramo. b, Frailejón.

**2001** ***Perf. 13¼x13***
**1590** A585 16c Horiz. pair, #a-b 2.75 1.40

Yahuarcocha Race Track — A586

No. 1591: a, Race track and lake. b, Lake.

**2001, Nov. 30**
**1591** A586 68c Horiz. pair, #a-b 10.00 5.00

World Food Day — A587

No. 1592: a, Wheat ears. b, Food baskets.

**2001, Nov. 5**
**1592** A587 84c Horiz. pair, #a-b 12.50 6.25

Art of Voroshilov Bazante A588

No. 1593: a, Spatial composition. b, Abstract, artists name at LR. c, Urban landscape. d, Abstract, diff., "Abstracto" at UL, denomination at LL. e, Abstract, denomination at LR.

**2001, Nov.**
**1593** Horiz. strip of 5 27.50 12.50
*a.-e.* A588 84c Any single 5.00 2.50

Wilson Popenoe Private Foundation A589

**2001, Nov. 19 Litho.** ***Perf. 13¼x13***
**1594** A589 16c multi 1.25 .60

FAO Food Program A590

**2001, Aug. 15**
**1595** A590 84c multi 6.50 3.25

Rotary District 4400, 75th Anniv. — A591

**2001, Nov. 30** ***Perf. 13x13¼***
**1596** A591 84c multi 6.50 3.25

Pres. Camilo Ponce Enriquez (1912-76) — A592

**2001**
**1597** A592 84c multi 6.50 3.25

Pedro Vicente Maldonado (1702-48), Geographer A593

**2001, Dec. 12**
**1598** A593 84c multi 6.50 3.25

Otonga Foundation — A595

No. 1599: a, Frog on branch. b, Mustela frenata.

**2001, Oct. 31**
**1599** A595 16c Horiz. pair, #a-b 2.75 1.40

Tourism in Zaruma — A596

No. 1600: a, Virgen del Carmen. b, Orchid.

**2001, Dec. 12** ***Perf. 13¼x13***
**1600** A596 68c Horiz. pair, #a-b 10.00 5.00

Radio HCJB, 70th Anniv. — A597

No. 1601: a, Microphone. b, Announcer.

**2001, Dec. 21**
**1601** A597 68c Horiz. pair, #a-b 10.00 5.00

Tennis A598

No. 1602: a, Davis Cup. b, K. Lapentti, G. Lapentti, L.A. Morejón, A. Intriago and R. Viver. c, Francisco Guzman and Miguel Olvera. d, Pancho Segura. e, Andres Gomez.

**2001, Nov. 1**
**1602** Horiz. strip of 5 24.00 12.00
***a.-e.*** A598 68c Any single 4.50 2.25

Church Paintings of Wilfrido Martínez — A599

No. 1603: a, San Francisco (artist's name is vert.). b, Guapulo. c, San Francisco (artist's name is horiz.). d, La Compania. e, El Rosario.

**2002, Apr. 9** ***Perf. 13¾***
**1603** Horiz. strip of 5 27.00 13.50
***a.-e.*** A599 90c Any single 5.00 2.50

First Judicial Summit of the Americas, Quito A600

***Perf. 13¼x13***
**2002, Jan. 8 Litho. Wmk. 395**
**1604** A600 68c multi 5.00 2.50

Union Club, Guayaquil — A601

**2002, Apr. 25** ***Perf. 13x13¼***
**1605** A601 90c multi 5.75 2.75

South American Soccer Confederation A602

Designs: 25c, Confederation Pres. Nicolás Leoz. 40c, Confederation emblem, soccer players. 70c, Emblem of Emelec team.

**2002, Jan. 29**
**1606-1608** A602 Set of 3 10.00 5.00

World Conservation Union — A603

Designs: 70c, Fish, man's head. 85c, Leopard, man, horiz.
$1, Bird, animals, women and children, horiz.

**2002, Feb. 21** ***Perf. 13x13¼, 13¼x13***
**1609-1610** A603 Set of 2 11.50 5.75

***Imperf***
**Size: 100x70mm**
**1611** A603 $1 multi 7.50 3.75

UN High Commissioner for Refugees — A604

Designs: 70c, Emblem. 85c, Child.
$1, Refugees carrying belongings, horiz.

**2002, Feb. 28** ***Perf. 13x13¼***
**1612-1613** A604 Set of 2 11.50 5.75

***Imperf***
**Size: 100x70mm**
**1614** A604 $1 multi 7.50 3.75

Ecuadorian Educational Credit and Scholarship Institute — A605

No. 1615: a, Student using microscope. b, Emblem.

**2002, Apr. 30** ***Perf. 13x13¼***
**1615** A605 25c Horiz. pair, #a-b 3.00 1.50

Cuenca Soccer Team — A606

No. 1616: a, Team photo. b, Emblem, player dribbling.

**2002, Apr. 19** ***Perf. 13¼x13***
**1616** A606 25c Horiz. pair, #a-b 3.00 1.50

Imbabura Province History — A607

No. 1617: a, Building. b, Statue.

**2002, Mar. 27** ***Perf. 13x13¼***
**1617** A607 40c Horiz. pair, #a-b 6.00 3.00

Crucita — A608

No. 1618: a, Parachutist with sun on horizon. b, Prachutist above beach.

**2002, Mar. 28** ***Perf. 13¼x13***
**1618** A608 40c Horiz. pair, #a-b 6.00 3.00

Mountains A609

No. 1619: a, Mt. Altar (trees in foreground). b, Mt. Chimborazo. c, Mt. Carihuayrazo. d, Mt. Altar (lake in foreground). e, Mt. Cubillin.

**2002, Apr. 19**
**1619** Horiz. strip of 5 29.00 15.00
***a.-e.*** A609 90c Any single 5.00 2.25

Endangered Frogs A610

No. 1620: a, Atelopus bomolochos. b, Atelopus longirostris. c, Atelopus pachydermus. d, Atelopus arthuri. e, Atelopus sp.
$1, Atelopus ignescens.

**2002, Mar. 25** ***Perf. 13¼x13***
**1620** Horiz. strip of 5 29.00 15.00
***a.-e.*** A610 $1.05 Any single 5.00 2.25

***Imperf***
**Size: 100x70mm**
**1621** A610 $1 multi 10.00 8.00

National Anti-narcotics Police — A611

No. 1622: a, Policeman and dog. b, Emblem.

***Perf. 13x13¼***
**2002, Apr. 23 Litho. Wmk. 395**
**1622** A611 40c Horiz. pair, #a-b 6.00 3.00

2002 World Cup Soccer Championships, Japan and Korea — A612

Designs: 90c, Ecuadorian Soccer Federation emblem, vert. $1.05, $2, Emblem, team photo, players in action.

**2002, Apr. 28** ***Perf. 13x13¼, 13¼x13***
**1623-1624** A612 Set of 2 9.00 4.50

***Imperf***
**Size: 100x70mm**
**1625** A612 $2 multi 9.00 4.50

Dr. Servio Aguirre Villamagua, Forest Conservationist — A613

No. 1626: a, Aguirre. b, Plant.

**2002, May 22** ***Perf. 13¼x13***
**1626** A613 40c Horiz. pair, #a-b 4.00 2.00

Food and Agriculture Organization in Ecuador, 50th Anniv. A614

**2002, May 30**
**1627** A614 $1.05 multi 5.00 2.50

Galapagos Islands Fauna A615

No. 1628: a, Grapsus grapsus. b, Conolophus subcristatus.
No. 1629, vert.: a, Sula sula websteri. b, Phoenicopterus ruber.
No. 1630, Amblyrhynchus cristatus.
No. 1631, vert.: a, Pair of Zalophus californianus wollebacki. b, One Zalophus californianus wollebacki.
No. 1632, Sula nebouxxi excisa, vert.
No. 1633, vert.: a, Sula dactylatra granti. b, Emblem of Iberoamerican Summit on Tourism and Environment.
$2, Bird, tourists, tourist ship.

**2002, May 31** ***Perf. 13¼x13, 13x13¼***

| | | | | |
|---|---|---|---|---|
| **1628** A615 | 25c Horiz. pair, #a-b | 3.00 | 1.50 |
| **1629** A615 | 40c Horiz. pair, #a-b | 4.00 | 2.00 |
| **1630** A615 | 90c multi | 6.00 | 3.00 |
| **1631** A615 | 90c Horiz. pair, #a-b | 9.00 | 4.50 |
| **1632** A615 | $1.05 multi | 5.00 | 2.50 |
| **1633** A615 | $1.05 Horiz. pair, #a-b | 10.00 | 5.00 |
| | *Nos. 1628-1633 (6)* | 37.00 | 18.50 |

***Imperf***

**Size: 100x68mm**

**1634** A615 $2 multi 11.50 7.00

Ministry of Foreign Relations — A616

**2002, June 5** ***Perf. 13x13¼***

**1635** A616 90c multi 4.50 2.25

Army Polytechnic School, 80th Anniv. A617

**2002, June 13** ***Perf. 13¼x13***

**1636** A617 25c multi 1.75 .90

Military Engineers, Cent. A618

Designs: No. 1637, 40c, Castle of Engineering. No. 1638, 40c, Castle of Engineering, Military engineers in action, vert.

$2, Castle of Engineering, engineers in action, emblems of military groups.

***Perf. 13¼x13, 13x13¼***

**2002, June 19**

**1637-1638** A618 Set of 2 4.00 2.00

***Imperf***

**Size: 100x68mm**

**1639** A618 $2 multi 9.00 4.50

Dr. Alfredo Pérez Guerrero (1901-66), Academic — A619

**2002, July 4** ***Perf. 13x13¼***

**1640** A619 25c multi 1.75 .90

20th Anniv. of Ecuador's Second Place Finish In World Taekwondo Championships — A620

**2002, July 18** ***Perf. 13¼x13***

**1641** A620 40c multi 2.00 1.00

Orellana Province — A621

No. 1642: a, Three native men. b, Man in tree.

**2002, July 30** **Wmk. 395**

**1642** A621 25c Horiz. pair, #a-b 3.00 1.50

CARE in Ecuador, 40th Anniv. — A622

No. 1643: a, Two children. b, Boy.

**2002, July 30** ***Perf. 13x13¼***

**1643** A622 90c Horiz. pair, #a-b 9.00 4.50

Macará Region A623

**2002, Aug. 10** ***Perf. 13¼x13***

**1644** A623 40c multi 2.00 1.00

Intl. Organization for Migration, 50th Anniv. — A624

**2002, Aug. 18** ***Perf. 13x13¼***

**1645** A624 $1.05 multi 5.00 2.50

Quito Philharmonic Society, 50th Anniv. — A625

**2002, Aug. 29**

**1646** A625 25c multi 1.75 .90

Comptroller General, 75th Anniv. — A625a

***Perf. 13x13¼***

**2002, Sept. 26** **Litho.** **Wmk. 395**

**1646A** A625a 40c multi 2.00 1.00

Second World Meeting of Mountain People — A626

No. 1647 — Emblem of World Meeting and: a, Mountain. b, Group of people. c, Houses in valley. d, Town. e, Other emblems.

**2002, Sept. 18**

**1647** Horiz. strip of 5 22.50 11.00

*a.-e.* A626 90c Any single 4.00 2.00

Pujili Dancer — A627

***Perf. 13x13¼***

**2002, Oct. 14** **Litho.** **Wmk. 395**

**1648** A627 $1.05 multi 5.00 2.50

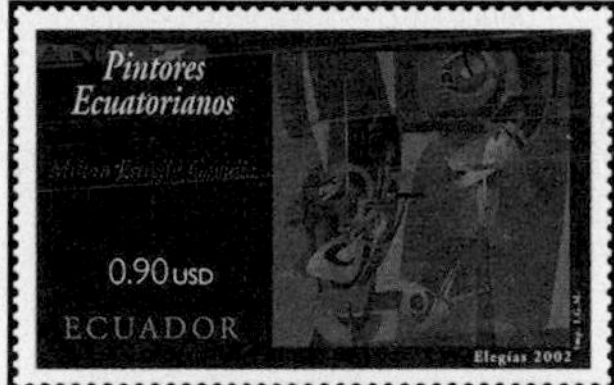

Paintings of Milton Estrella Gavidia — A628

No. 1649 — Various paintings with background colors of: a, Blue violet. b, Brown violet. c, Olive green. d, Blue. e, Gray lilac.

**Wmk. 395**

**2002, May 17** **Litho.** ***Perf. 13¾***

**1649** Horiz. strip of 5 22.50 11.00

*a.-e.* A628 90c Any single 4.00 2.00

Paintings of Leonardo Hidalgo A629

No. 1650: a, La Dolorosa. b, El Hombre Cargando su Fruto. c, Frida Kahlo. d, El Hombre Fuerte del Mar. e, Jesus.

**Wmk. 395**

**2002, Oct. 3** **Litho.** ***Perf. 13¾***

**1650** Horiz. strip of 5 22.50 11.00

*a.-e.* A629 90c Any single 4.00 2.00

Pan-American Health Organization, Cent. — A630

**2002, Dec. 2** ***Perf. 13¼x12¾***

**1651** A630 $1.05 multi 5.00 2.50

Lo Nuestro Art Exhibition — A631

No. 1652: a, Wall with six works of art. b, Walls with 16 works of art.

**2002, Dec. 15**

**1652** A631 25c Horiz. pair, #a-b 2.50 1.25

Catholic University, 40th Anniv. A632

**2002, Dec. 18**

**1653** A632 40c multi 2.00 1.00

America Issue — UNESCO World Heritage Sites — A633

No. 1654: a, Cupola of San Blas Church, Cuenca. b, Society of Jesus Church, Quito.

**2002, Dec. 18** ***Perf. 12¾x13¼***

**1654** A633 25c Horiz. pair, #a-b 3.00 1.50

Dated 2001.

America Issue — Youth, Education and Literacy — A634

No. 1655: a, Students and blackboard. b, Toddler and books.

**2002, Dec. 18** ***Perf. 13¼x12¾***

**1655** A634 25c Horiz. pair, #a-b 3.00 1.50

Second Meeting of South American Presidents, Guayaquil — A635

No. 1656: a, Meeting emblem. b, Emblem, presidents and flags.

**2003, Jan. 13**

**1656** A635 $1.05 Horiz. pair, #a-b 8.00 4.00

Papal Benediction for Ecuadorian Emigrants — A636

**2003, Jan. 24** ***Perf. 12¾x13¼***

**1657** A636 $1.05 multi 4.50 2.25

**Size: 68x100mm**

***Imperf***

**1658** A636 $2 multi 9.00 4.50

World Vision — A637

**2003, Feb. 6** *Perf. 12¾x13¼*
**1659** A637 40c multi 1.90 .95

Intl. Women's Day — A638

**2003, Mar. 8** **Wmk. 395**
**1660** A638 $1.05 multi 5.00 2.50

Agustin Cueva Vallejo (1820-73), Physician — A639

**2003, Mar. 13** **Litho.**
**1661** A639 40c multi 1.90 .95

Blasco Moscoso Cuesta, Founder of Pichincha Sports Writers Association — A640

**2003, Mar. 14**
**1662** A640 25c multi 1.50 .75

Cuenca Artisan Products A641

No. 1663: a, Azuay University domes. b, Tinware. c, Jewelry. d, Fireworks. e, Saddles.
No. 1664: a, Engraving. b, Metallurgy. c, Baskets. d, Embroidery. e, Ceramics.
$2, Assorted products.

**2003, Mar. 27** *Perf. 13¼x12¾*
**1663** Horiz. strip of 5 6.00 3.00
*a.-e.* A641 25c Any single 1.00 .50
**1664** Horiz. strip of 5 22.50 11.00
*a.-e.* A641 $1.05 Any single 4.00 2.00

**Size: 100x68mm**

***Imperf***

**1665** A641 $2 multi 9.00 4.50

Flora and Fauna A642

No. 1666: a, Curculionidae. b, Lycidae. c, Acridoidea. d, Aracnidae. e, Liliacea.

**2003, Apr. 4** *Perf. 13¼x12¾*
**1666** Horiz. strip of 5 22.50 11.00
*a.-e.* A642 $1.05 Any single 4.00 2.00

Military Geographic Institute, 75th Anniv. A643

Designs: No. 1667, 40c, No. 1669, $2, Painting by Eduardo Kingman. No. 1668, 40c, Institute emblem, vert.

*Perf. 13¼x12¾, 12¾x13¼*

**2003, Apr. 11**
**1667-1668** A643 Set of 2 3.50 1.75

**Size: 100x68mm**

***Imperf***

**1669** A643 $2 multi 9.00 4.50

Galápagos Marine Reserve — A644

Designs: 40c, Stylized butterfly.
No. 1671, $1.05, horiz.: a, Sphyrna lewini. b, Chelonia mydas agassisi.
No. 1672, $1.05, horiz.: a, Xanthichthys mento. b, Zanclus cornutus.
$2, Tubastrea coccinea, horiz.

*Perf. 12¾x13¼, 13¼x12¾*

**2003, May 9**
**1670** A644 40c multi 1.75 .90

**Horiz. Pairs, #a-b**

**1671-1672** A644 Set of 2 17.50 8.75

**Size: 100x68mm**

***Imperf***

**1673** A644 $2 multi 9.00 4.50

Intl. Tourism Trade Fair of Ecuador A645

No. 1674: a, Monkey in tree. b, Birds. c, Embroidery. d, Mountain. e, Hat seller on beach.

**2003, May 14** *Perf. 13¼x12¾*
**1674** Vert. strip of 5 6.00 3.00
*a.-e.* A645 25c Any single 1.00 .50

Artifacts of Pre-Columbian Cultures — A646

No. 1675, 25c: a, Gold bell with monkey. b, Amphora.
No. 1676, 25c: a, Sculpture of a man. b, Three-footed pot.

*Perf. 13x13¼*

**2003, May 16** **Litho.** **Wmk. 395**

**Horiz. pairs, #a-b**

**1675-1676** A646 Set of 2 4.50 2.25

Central Bank of Ecuador A647

No. 1677, vert.: a, Tolita Culture mask. b, Guayaquil Historic Park.
$1.05, Pumapungo Museum.

*Perf. 13x13¼, 13¼x13*

**2003, June 5** **Litho.**
**1677** A647 25c Horiz. pair, #a-b 1.50 .75
**1678** A647 $1.05 multi 2.75 1.40

Philately and Guayaquil A648

No. 1679, horiz.: a, British consular cover to Veracruz with British stamp and cancel. b, Stampless cover.
No. 1680, horiz.: a, SCADTA first flight cover. b, French consular cover to Lima with French stamps and cancels.
$1.05, Philatelic magazines.
$2, Guayaquil Philatelic Club emblem, Ecuadoran stamps, horiz.

**2003, July 22** *Perf. 13¾*
**1679** A648 40c Vert. pair, #a-b 3.25 1.60
**1680** A648 40c Vert. pair, #a-b 3.25 1.60
**1681** A648 $1.05 multi 4.00 2.00
*Nos. 1679-1681 (3)* 10.50 5.20

**Size: 100x69mm**

***Imperf***

**1682** A648 $2 multi 9.00 4.50

Guayaquil Urban Renewal A649

No. 1683: a, Punta Cerro Santa Ana. b, Plaza Colón. c, Malecón Gardens. d, Crystal Palace. e, Plaza de San Francisco.

**2003, July 26** *Perf. 13¼x13*
**1683** Horiz. strip of 5 19.00 9.50
*a.-e.* A649 90c Any single 3.50 1.75

World Bird Festival A650

Designs: No. 1684, $1.05, Geranoaetus melanoleucus. No. 1685, $1.05, Harpia harpyja, vert.

**2003, Sept. 2** *Perf. 13¼x13, 13x13¼*
**1684-1685** A650 Set of 2 9.00 4.50

Zamora-Chinchipe Province, 50th Anniv. — A651

No. 1686: a, Shown. b, Eira barbara. c, Boa constrictor. d, Tapirus terrestris. e, Psophia crepitans.

**2003, Nov. 7** *Perf. 13¼x13*
**1686** Vert. strip of 5 6.00 3.00
*a.-e.* A651 25c Any single 1.00 .50

America Issue — Flora and Fauna — A652

No. 1687: a, Semnornis ramphastinus. b, Bomarea glaucescens.

*Perf. 13x13¼*

**2003, Nov. 1** **Litho.** **Wmk. 395**
**1687** A652 $1.05 Horiz. pair, #a-b 7.50 3.75

Selection of Quito as World Heritage Site, 25th Anniv. A653

Churches: 40c, El Sagrario. No. 1689a, La Compañia de Jesus. No. 1689b, Santa Barbara. $1.05, San Francisco, vert.

**2003, Nov. 1** *Perf. 13¼x13, 13x13¼*
**1688** A653 40c multi 1.25 .60
**1689** A653 90c Horiz. pair, #a-b 6.00 3.00
**1690** A653 $1.05 multi 3.75 1.90
*Nos. 1688-1690 (3)* 11.00 5.50

Christmas A654

Children's art by: No. 1691a, Stephanie Pacheco. No. 1691b, Sebastián Tejada. 40c, María Claudia Iturralde, vert. 90c, Luis Antonio Ortega. $1.05, Angel Andrés Castro, vert.

**2003, Nov. 1**
**1691** A654 25c Horiz. pair, #a-b 1.90 .95
**1692** A654 40c multi 1.50 .75
**1693** A654 90c multi 3.50 1.75
**1694** A654 $1.05 multi 3.75 1.90
*Nos. 1691-1694 (4)* 10.65 5.35

Treasures of Guayaquil Municipal Museum A655

No. 1695: a, Santiago de Guayaquil Act of Independence. b, Punaes ceremonial stone. c, Proclamation of Mariano Donoso. d, Tzantzas. e, Manteño-Huancavilca totem.

**2003, Dec. 1** *Perf. 13¼x13*
**1695** Horiz. strip of 5 7.00 3.50
*a.-e.* A655 40c Any single 1.25 .65

Selection of Galapagos Islands as World Heritage Site, 25th Anniv. — A656

No. 1696: a, Zalophus californianus wollebacki. b, Fregata minor palmerstoni. c, Sula nebouxxi excisa. d, Isla Bartolomé. e, Two Sula nebouxxi excisa shaped as "25."

**2003, Nov. 26** *Perf. 13x13¼*
**1696** Horiz. strip of 5 7.00 3.50
*a.-e.* A656 40c Any single 1.25 .65

Army Aviation Instruction, 50th Anniv. — A657

No. 1697, 40c: a, Mountain, airplanes, emblem. b, Airplane in flight, men on ground.
No. 1698, 40c, horiz.: a, Helicopter and soldiers. b, Airplanes, mountain, people.

**2004, Jan. 21** ***Perf. 13x13¼, 13¼x13***
**Horiz. pairs, #a-b**
**1697-1698** A657 Set of 2 6.00 3.00

Military Geographical Institute's Role in National Development — A658

**2004, Apr. 14** ***Perf. 13¼x13***
**1699** A658 $1.05 multi 3.25 1.90

Commander Rafael Morán Valverde, Military Hero — A659

**2004, Apr. 5** ***Perf. 13x13¼***
**1700** A659 $1.05 multi 3.75 1.90

Intl. Philately Day — A660

No. 1701: a, Ecuador #2, Greece #1. b, Cover with six stamps.
$2, Various stamps, tongs, magnifying glass, stamp catalogues.

**2004, May 6** ***Perf. 13¼x13***
**1701** A660 75c Horiz. pair, #a-b 6.00 3.00

***Imperf***
**Size: 100x68mm**
**1702** A660 $2 multi 7.50 3.75

Ecuadorian Volleyball Federation A661

***Perf. 13x13¼***
**2004, May 27** **Litho.** **Wmk. 395**
**1703** A661 75c multi 3.00 1.50

2004 Miss Universe Pageant A662

**2004, May 29** ***Perf. 13¾***
**1704** A662 75c multi 3.00 1.50

Sculpture by Mario Tapia A663

No. 1705: a, Adolescencia. b, Beato Chaminade. c, Delfín de Galapagos. d, Pelícano. e, Homenaje a Carlo Vidano.
$2, Similar to No. 1705b.

**2004, June 1** ***Perf. 13¼x13***
**1705** Horiz. strip of 5 16.00 8.00
*a.-e.* A663 90c Any single 2.25 1.10

***Imperf***
**Size: 100x69mm**
**1706** A663 $2 multi 9.00 4.50

Pedro Vicente Maldonado (1704-48), Cartographer A664

**2004, June 25** ***Perf. 13x13¼***
**1707** A664 90c multi 3.00 1.50

Dr. Agustín Cueva Tamariz (1903-79) — A665

**2004, June 30** **Litho.**
**1708** A665 90c multi 3.00 1.50

34th General Assembly of the Organization of American States — A666

**2004, July 4** **Wmk. 395**
**1709** A666 75c multi 3.00 1.50

Dr. Angel Felicísmo Rojas (b. 1909), Writer — A667

**2004, July 11**
**1710** A667 50c multi 2.00 1.00

Ecuadoran and Spanish Postal Money Orders A668

**2004, Aug. 3** ***Perf. 13¼x13***
**1711** A668 $1.05 multi 3.25 1.90

2004 Summer Olympics, Athens — A669

No. 1712 — 2004 Summer Olympics emblem, Ecuadoran Olympic Committee emblem and: a, 2004 Olympics mascots. b, Alexandra Escobar Guerrero.

**2004, Aug. 3** ***Perf. 13x13¼***
**1712** A669 $1.05 Horiz. pair, #a-b 7.50 3.75

Ecuador Orchid Association, 30th Anniv. — A670

Designs: 25c, Cattleya maxima. $1.05, Epidendrum bracteolatum.

**2004, Sept. 30**
**1713-1714** A670 Set of 2 5.00 2.50

Guayaquil Symphony Orchestra — A671

***Perf. 13x13¼***
**2004, Nov. 19** **Litho.** **Wmk. 395**
**1715** A671 90c multi 3.00 1.50

Christmas — A672

Children's art: 40c, Christmas stocking with envelopes. $1.05, Santa Claus giving letter to Christmas tree, horiz.

**2004, Dec. 12** ***Perf. 13x13¼, 13¼x13***
**1716-1717** A672 Set of 2 5.00 2.50

America Issue - Environmental Protection — A673

Designs: 40d, Buddha and trees. $1.05, Mother Earth.

**2004, Dec. 23** ***Perf. 13x13¼***
**1718-1719** A673 Set of 2 5.00 2.50

Galapagos Islands Fauna A674

Designs: 40c, Chelonoidis abingdonii. 90c, Amblyfhynchus cristatus, vert. $2.15, Sula granti. $3, Fregata magnifiscens.
$2, Creagrus furcatus, vert.

**2005, Feb. 18** ***Perf. 13¼x13, 13x13¼***
**1720-1723** A674 Set of 4 24.00 12.00

***Imperf***
**Size: 68x98mm**
**1724** A674 $2 multi 7.50 3.75

El Mercurio Newspaper, 80th Anniv. A675

Designs: $1.25, Masthead. $2, Dr. Nicanor Merchan Bermeo, newspaper co-founder. $2.25, Miguel Merchan Ochoa.

**2005, Mar. 4** ***Perf. 13¼x13, 13x13¼***
**1725-1727** A675 Set of 3 22.50 11.00

Tourism A676

**2005, Mar. 22** ***Perf. 13¼x13***
**1728** A676 $3.75 multi 14.00 7.00

Ecuadorian Chess Federation, 25th Anniv. — A677

**2005, Apr. 1** ***Perf. 13x13¼***
**1729** A677 $1.25 multi 5.00 2.50

Ecuadorian Olympic Academy, 25th Anniv. — A678

*Perf. 13x13¼*

**2005, June 20 Litho. Wmk. 395**

**1730** A678 $1.25 shown 5.00 2.50

***Imperf***

**Size: 69x100mm**

**1731** A678 $2 Emblems 9.00 4.50

Rotary International, Cent. A679

Rotary emblem and: 40c, Man on Mt. Chimborazo. 90c, People on Mt. Cotopaxi. $2, Man on Mt. Shisha Pangma, Nepal.

**2005, June 29** ***Perf. 13¼x13***

**1732-1734** A679 Set of 3 12.50 6.25

Guayaquil Conference, 183rd Anniv. — A680

No. 1735 — Guayaquil Philatelic Club emblem and: a, José de San Martín, Argentina #1. b, Simón Bolívar, Venezuela #1.
$2, Bolívar, San Martín, monument.

**2005, July 22** ***Perf. 13¼x13***

**1735** A680 90c Horiz. pair, #a-b 7.50 3.75

***Imperf***

**Size:98x68mm**

**1736** A680 $2 multi 9.00 4.50

Intl. Year of Books and Reading — A681

*Perf. 13x13¼*

**2005, July 22 Litho. Wmk. 395**

**1737** A681 25c multi 1.25 .60

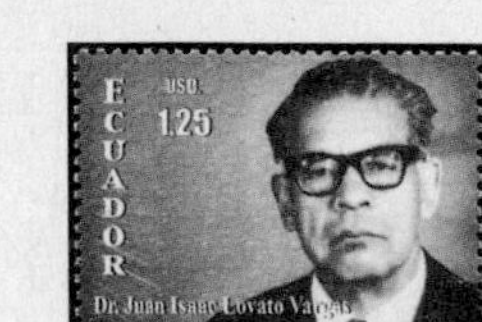


Dr. Juan Isaac Lovato Vargas (1904-2001), Judge — A682

*Perf. 13¼x13*

**2005, July 28 Litho. Wmk. 395**

**1738** A682 $1.25 multi 6.00 3.00

Mountain and Eastern Cattleman's Association — A683

No. 1739 — Emblem and: a, Mountains. b, Head of cow.

**2005, Aug. 4** ***Perf. 13x13¼***

**1739** A683 40c Horiz. pair, #a-b 3.00 3.00

University Sports League of Quito, 75th Anniv. A684

No. 1740: a, University Sports League Stadium. b, 1969 University Sports League soccer team. c, Emblem. d, Children playing at school. e, Statue of emblem, League Country Club.
$2, Soccer shirt, vert.

**2005, Aug. 4** ***Perf. 13¼x13***

**1740** Horiz. strip of 5 8.00 4.00
*a.-e.* A684 40c Any single 1.40 .70

***Imperf***

**Size: 68x98mm**

**1741** A684 $2 multi 9.00 4.50

15th Bolivarian Games, Armenia and Pereira A685

**2005, Aug. 8** ***Perf. 13¼x13***

**1742** A685 25c multi 1.25 .60

1938 South American Swimming Champions, Trophy and Swimming Federation Emblem A686

**2005, Aug. 8 Litho.**

**1743** A686 25c multi 1.25 .60

First Ecuadoran victory in international sports competition.

Virgin of Cisne — A687

**2005, Sept. 6** ***Perf. 13¾***

**1744** A687 $1.25 multi 6.00 3.00

History of the Ecuadoran Army A688

No. 1745: a, Troops in Esmeraldas, 1916. b, Military school cadets, 1928. c, Cayambe Battalion. d, Arms and Grandsons of Gen. Eloy Alfaro. e, Imbabura Battalion.
$2, Battle for emancipation of Guayaquil.

**2005, Sept. 15** ***Perf. 13¼x13***

**1745** Horiz. strip of 5 8.00 4.00
*a.-e.* A688 40c Any single 1.00 .50

***Imperf***

**Size: 98x67mm**

**1746** A688 $2 multi 9.00 4.50

Carchi Province Arms — A689

No. 1747: a, Tulcán Canton. b, Bolívar Canton.
No. 1748: a, Carchi Province. b, Huaca Canton. c, Mira Canton. d, Espejo Canton. e, Montúfar Canton.

**2005, Sept. 26** ***Perf. 13x13¼***

**1747** Horiz. pair 3.00 1.50
*a.-b.* A689 40c Either single 1.40 .70

**1748** Horiz. strip of 5 7.50 3.75
*a.-e.* A689 40c Any single 1.40 .70

Tourism — A690

No. 1749: a, Cerro Santa Ana, Guayaquil. b, Esmereldas. c, Misahualli. d, Tsunki Shuar, Pastaza.
No. 1750: a, Cisne Church, Loja. b, Ingapirca Ruins. c, Seal, Galapagos Islands. d, Sea turtle, Galapagos Islands.

*Perf. 13¼x13*

**2005, Sept. 26 Litho. Wmk. 395**

**1749** A690 30c Block of 4, #a-d 5.00 2.50

**1750** A690 40c Block of 4, #a-d 6.50 3.25

St. Mariana de Jesús Paredes y Flores A691

**2005, Oct. 19**

**1751** A691 25c multi 1.25 .60

Popes Reigning in 2005 — A692

No. 1752: a, $1.25, Pope John Paul II (1920-2005). b, $2, Pope Benedict XVI.

**2005, Oct. 19**

**1752** A692 Horiz. pair, #a-b 12.50 6.25

Cenepa War With Peru, 10th Anniv. — A693

No. 1753: a, Mirage F1-JA airplanes. b, Cessna A-37B airplanes. c, Kfir-C2 airplanes. d, Lt. Col. Carlos Uscategui and airplane.

**2005, Oct. 26**

**1753** A693 $1.25 Block of 4, #a-d 22.50 11.00

First Guayaquil to Cuenca Airmail Flight, 85th Anniv. — A694

No. 1754: a, 25c, Tail of Telegrafo I airplane, flight manager José Abel Castillo. b, $1, Front of Telegrafo I airplane, pilot Elia Liut.

**2005, Nov. 12**

**1754** A694 Horiz. pair, #a-b 5.50 2.75

Ecuadorian Armed Forces in United Nations Peacekeeping Forces — A695

No. 1755: a, Female soldier. b, Two soldiers wearing helmets. c, Soldiers with flags. d, United Nations and Ecuadorian flags, beret of Peacekeeping forces.

**2005, Nov. 25** ***Perf. 13x13¼***

**1755** A695 75c Block of 4, #a-d 12.00 6.00

Christmas — A696

No. 1756 — Children's drawings by: a, Pamela Alejandra Castillo Rocha. b, Kira Cedeño. c, Silvia Moran Burgos. d, Carol Garcia.

**2005, Nov. 25**

**1756** A696 $1.25 Block of 4, #a-d 22.50 11.00

19th Cent. Watercolors of Ecuadorians A697

No. 1757: a, Water bearer. b, Indian governor's wife. c, Dancer. d, Cuenca Indian. e, Municipal council piper. f, Indian carrying skyrockets. g, Woman (Mina gigante). h, Majordomo. i, Society woman (Chola pinganilla). j, Street sweeper.

**2005, Nov. 30** ***Perf. 13¾***
**1757** Block of 10 12.50 6.25
*a.-j.* A697 25c Any single 1.00 .50

Publication of Don Quixote, 400th Anniv. — A698

No. 1758 — Drawings of Don Quixote and: a, Windmills. b, Tree.

**2005, Dec. 7** ***Perf. 13x13¼***
**1758** A698 $2 Horiz. pair, #a-b 17.00 8.50

Colonial Religious Art — A699

Colonial Religious Art — A700

No. 1759: a, St. Joseph and Baby Jesus. b, Resurrected Christ. c, Virgin of Quito. d, St. Augustine.
No. 1760: $2, The Divine Shepherd.

**2005, Dec. 9**
**1759** A699 40c Block of 4, #a-d 6.00 3.00

**Souvenir Sheet**
***Imperf***

**1760** A700 $2 multi 9.00 4.50

El Comercio Newspaper, Cent. (in 2006) A701

"100" and: No. 1761, Statue at LL, newspaper masthead. No. 1762a, Statue at LR. No. 1762b, Statue in "0." No. 1763, Statue in seal. No. 1764, Statue at LL, newspaper masthead, simulated perforations.

***Perf. 13¼x13***

**2006, Jan. 2** **Litho.** **Wmk. 395**
**1761** A701 40c multi 1.75 .85
**1762** A701 40c Horiz. pair, #a-b 3.25 1.60

**Size: 55x35mm**
***Perf. 13¾***

**1763** A701 50c multi 2.00 1.00
*Nos. 1761-1763 (3)* 7.00 3.45

**Size: 100x69mm**
***Imperf***

**1764** A701 $2 multi 8.00 4.00

Dated 2006.

Quito Tourism A702

**2006, Jan. 11** ***Perf. 13¼x13***
**1765** A702 25c multi 1.25 .60

Dated 2005.

35th Latin American and Caribbean Lions' Club Forum, Quito — A703

Color of oceans: 90c, White. $2, Orange.

**2006, Jan. 19** ***Perf. 13x13¼***
**1766** A703 90c multi 4.00 2.00

**Size: 68x99mm**
***Imperf***

**1767** A703 $2 multi 8.00 4.00

Biodiversity of Puyo A704

Designs: $1, Cromacris sp. $1.20, Desmodus rotundus.

**2006, Mar. 22** ***Perf. 13¼x13***
**1768-1769** A704 Set of 2 10.00 5.00

America Issue, Fight Against Poverty A705

Various Pre-Columbian Guayasamin figurines: 40c, 80c, $1, $1.20.

**2006, Feb. 12**
**1770-1773** A705 Set of 4 14.50 7.25

Benito Juarez (1806-72), President of Mexico — A706

**2006, Mar. 21** ***Perf. 13x13¼***
**1774** A706 $1.20 multi 5.00 2.50

Manteña Raft A707

**2006, Mar. 23** ***Perf. 13¼x13***
**1775** A707 $1 multi 4.50 2.25

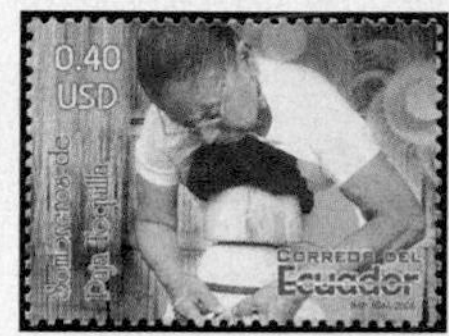

Straw Hat Makers A708

Designs: No. 1776, 40c, Hat maker. No. 1777, 40c, Hat maker wearing hat, vert.

**2006, Apr. 8** ***Perf. 13¼x13, 13x13¼***
**1776-1777** A708 Set of 2 3.75 1.90

Federation of University Students — A709

**2006, Apr. 21** ***Perf. 13x13¼***
**1778** A709 30c multi 1.25 .60

Miracle of Colegio San Gabriel, Cent. — A710

**2006, Apr. 21** **Wmk. 395**
**1779** A710 80c multi 3.75 1.90

Ibarra, 400th Anniv. A711

**2006, Apr. 28** ***Perf. 13¼x13***
**1780** A711 20c shown .80 .25

**Size: 68x100mm**
***Imperf***

**1781** A711 $2.50 Painting, diff. 11.00 5.50

Baltazara Calderon — A712

**2005, May 16** ***Perf. 13x13¼***
**1782** A712 $1 multi 4.50 2.25

18th Cent. Military Uniforms A713

No. 1783: a, Compañia Fija de Quito. b, Dragones de Quito. c, Infanteria de Quito. d, Dragones de Guayaquil (gray horse). e, Dragones de Guayaquil (brown horse).

**2006, May 18** ***Perf. 13¾***
**1783** Horiz. strip of 5 4.25 2.10
*a.-e.* A713 20c Any single .70 .25

Mushrooms and Fauna of Podocarpus Park — A714

Designs: 20c, Basidiomicetes. 25c, Tremarctus ornatus. 90c, Harpya harpyja, vert.

***Perf. 13¼x13, 13x13¼***

**2006, May 22** **Litho.** **Wmk. 395**
**1784-1786** A714 Set of 3 6.00 3.00

Wolfgang Amadeus Mozart (1756-91), Composer A715

**2006, May 31** ***Perf. 13¼x13***
**1787** A715 20c multi .80 .25

UNICEF, 60th Anniv. A716

Designs: 75c, Child, butterfly, and sun. $1, Children and books.

***Perf. 13¼x13***

**2006, June 1** **Litho.** **Wmk. 395**
**1788-1789** A716 Set of 2 8.00 4.00

Eloy Alfaro Military School A717

**2006, June 5**
**1790** A717 80c multi 3.75 1.90

Banco Pichincha, Cent. A718

Designs: No. 1791, 1906 1-sucre banknote. No. 1792 — First bank building: a, Denomination at left. b, Denomination at right.

**2006, June 8**

| | | | |
|---|---|---|---|
| **1791** A718 40c shown | | 1.80 | .90 |
| **1792** A718 40c Horiz. pair, #a-b | | 3.75 | 1.90 |

2006 World Cup Soccer Championships, Germany — A719

FIFA emblem and: 40c, World Cup. 80c, 2006 World Cup emblem. $1, Mascot. $1.20, World Cup and flags of competing countries.

*Perf. 13¼x13*

**2006, June 9 Litho. Wmk. 395**

| | | |
|---|---|---|
| **1793-1796** A719 Set of 4 | 14.50 | 7.25 |

**World Cup Type of 2006**

*Perf. 13¼x13*

**2006, June 9 Litho. Wmk. 395**

**Stamps Without FIFA Emblem With Inscription "COPA MONDIAL de la FIFA"**

| | | | | |
|---|---|---|---|---|
| **1797** | A719 | 80c Like #1794 | *5.25* | *5.25* |
| **1797A** | A719 | $1 Like #1795 | *6.75* | *6.75* |
| **1797B** | A719 | $1.20 Like #1795 | *8.00* | *8.00* |
| | | *Nos. 1797-1797B (3)* | *20.00* | *20.00* |

Designs: No. 1797C, Like #1796. No. 1797D, Similar to #1796, but with scores of Ecuador team's first round victories.

**2006 Litho. Wmk. 395 *Imperf.***

**Size: 60x40mm**

| | | |
|---|---|---|
| **1797C** A719 $2 multi | 8.00 | 4.00 |
| **1797D** A719 $2 multi | 8.00 | 4.00 |

A720

Plaza de Mayo Mothers of Argentina — A721

*Perf. 13¼x13*

**2006, June 19 Litho. Wmk. 395**

| | | |
|---|---|---|
| **1798** A720 80c multi | 3.75 | 1.90 |

***Imperf***

| | | |
|---|---|---|
| **1799** A721 $2.50 multi | 11.00 | 5.50 |

Machala Canton, 182nd Anniv. A722

**2006, June 20 *Perf. 13¼x13***

| | | |
|---|---|---|
| **1800** A722 30c multi | 1.25 | .60 |

Machala Canton, 182nd Anniv. — A723

Flags of 2006 World Cup Soccer Championship participants, FIFA emblem and: No. 1801, Flag of Ecuador. No. 1802, Soccer shoes and ball.

**2006 Litho. Wmk. 395 *Imperf.***

| | | |
|---|---|---|
| **1801** A723 $2 multi | 8.00 | 4.00 |
| **1802** A723 $2 multi | 8.00 | 4.00 |

2006 World Cup Soccer Championships, Germany.

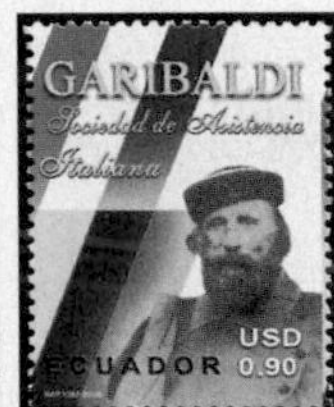

Garibaldi Italian Assistance Society — A724

**2006, July 7 *Perf. 13x13¼***

| | | |
|---|---|---|
| **1803** A724 90c multi | 4.00 | 2.00 |

Municipal Railroads A725

Designs: No. 1804, $1, Steam locomotive. No. 1805, $1, Steam locomotive, vert.

*Perf. 13¼x13, 13x13¼*

**2006, July 20 Litho. Wmk. 395**

| | | |
|---|---|---|
| **1804-1805** A725 Set of 2 | *8.00* | *8.00* |

Souvenir Sheet

Municipal Railroads — A726

**Wmk. 395**

**2006, July 20 Litho. *Imperf.***

| | | |
|---|---|---|
| **1806** A726 $2 multi | 8.00 | 4.00 |

Simón Bolívar Experimental College — A727

Bolívar A728

**2006, July 25 Litho. *Perf. 13x13¼***

| | | |
|---|---|---|
| **1807** A727 20c multi | .80 | .25 |

***Imperf***

| | | |
|---|---|---|
| **1808** A728 $10 multi | 40.00 | 20.00 |

Spondylus Shell Carvings in National Institute of Cultural Heritage A729

Designs: 25c, Necklace.
No. 1810, vert.: a, Figurine of trader. b, Figurine of fishermen in boat.

**2006, July 26 *Perf. 13¼x13, 13x13¼***

| | | |
|---|---|---|
| **1809** A729 25c multi | 1.50 | .75 |
| **1810** A729 $1 Horiz. pair, #a-b | 8.00 | 8.00 |

Indian Postal Runner and Ecuador Post Emblem — A730

Background colors: 25c, White. 30c, Dark blue. 40c, Black. 60c, Beige. 80c, Olive green

**2006, Aug. 5 *Perf. 13x13¼***

| | | |
|---|---|---|
| **1811-1815** A730 Set of 5 | 10.00 | 5.00 |

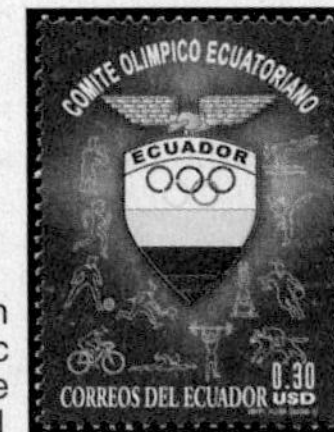

Ecuadorian Olympic Committee A731

**2006, Aug. 15 Litho.**

| | | |
|---|---|---|
| **1816** A731 30c multi | 1.25 | .60 |

Writers — A732

Designs: $1, Jorge Icaza (1906-78). $1.20, Pablo Palacio (1906-47).

**2006, Sept. 18 Wmk. 395**

| | | |
|---|---|---|
| **1817-1818** A732 Set of 2 | 10.00 | 5.00 |

Ecuadorian Food — A733

No. 1819: a, Bandera Manabi. b, Viche de Manabi.

**2006, Sept. 23 *Perf. 13¼x13***

| | | |
|---|---|---|
| **1819** A733 $1 Horiz. pair, #a-b | 8.50 | 4.25 |

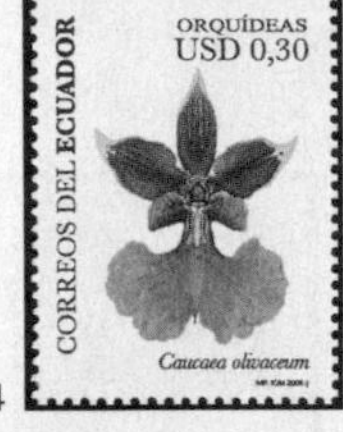

Orchids — A734

No. 1820: a, Caucaea olivaceum. b, Cyrtochilum macranthum. c, Miltoniopsis vexillaria. d, Odontoglossum harryanum. e, Cyrtochilum pastasae. f, Cyrtochilum loxense. g, Cyrtochilum eduardii. h, Odontoglossum epidendroides. i, Cyrtochilum retusum. j, Cyrtochilum geniculatum.
$2, Cyrtochilum macranthum, diff.

**2006, Sept. 29 *Perf. 13x13¼***

| | | |
|---|---|---|
| **1820** Block of 10 | 13.00 | 6.50 |
| *a.-j.* A734 30c Any single | 1.25 | .60 |

***Imperf***

**Size: 66x95mm**

| | | |
|---|---|---|
| **1821** A734 $2 multi | 8.50 | 4.25 |

America Issue, Energy Conservation — A735

Background color: $1, Brown. $1.20, Blue.

**2006, Oct. 4 *Perf. 13¼x13***

| | | |
|---|---|---|
| **1822-1823** A735 Set of 2 | 10.00 | 5.00 |

Natural Fiber Art, by Giti Neuman — A736

Designs: No. 1824, En la Ventana.
No. 1825: a, Forma en Movimiento. b, Caminantes.
No. 1826, horiz.: a, Caminando. b, Cabezas Huecas.

**2006, Oct. 4 *Perf. 13x13¼, 13¼x13***

| | | |
|---|---|---|
| **1824** A736 30c multi | 1.25 | .60 |
| **1825** A736 30c Vert. pair, #a-b | 2.75 | 1.40 |
| **1826** A736 30c Horiz. pair, #a-b | 2.75 | 1.40 |
| *Nos. 1824-1826 (3)* | 6.75 | 3.40 |

Tourism in Otavalo A737

Designs: 25c, El Lechero tree. 30c, El Jordan Church. 75c, Young girl, vert. $1, Costume for El Coraza Festival, vert.

**2006, Oct. 18** ***Perf. 13¼x13, 13x13¼***
**1827-1830** A737 Set of 4 10.50 5.25

Eruption of Tungurahua Volcano — A738

No. 1831: a, Ash cloud above volcano. b, Lava flowing down volcano.

**2006, Oct. 20** ***Perf. 13x13¼***
**1831** A738 $1 Horiz. pair, #a-b 8.50 4.25

Urban Renewal of Guayaquil A739

No. 1832: a, Municipal Palace, denomination at left. b, Municipal Palace, denomination at right. c, Vulcan forge. d, José Joaquín de Olmedo Airport. e, Bus station.

**2006, Oct. 24** ***Perf. 13¼x13***
**1832** Horiz. strip of 5 21.50 11.00
***a.-e.*** A739 $1 Any single 3.75 1.90

Radio Station HCJB, 75th Anniv. A740

**2006, Oct. 26** **Wmk. 395**
**1833** A740 $1 multi 4.50 2.25

Millennium Development Objectives of the United Nations — A741

**2006, Oct. 27** ***Perf. 13¾***
**1834** A741 $2 multi 8.50 4.25

Pres. Galo Plaza Lasso (1906-87) — A742

Designs: 40c, Photograph. 80c, Tree.

**2006, Oct. 27** ***Perf. 13x13¼***
**1835-1836** A742 Set of 2 5.00 2.50

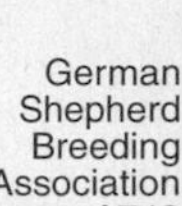

German Shepherd Breeding Association A743

**2006, Oct. 28** **Litho.** ***Perf. 13¼x13***
**1837** A743 $1 multi 4.50 2.25

Military Parachuting, 50th Anniv. A744

Designs: 20c, Soldiers. 40c, Soldiers and airplane. 60c, Soldier and troop emblem. 80c, Paratrooper in air.

***Perf. 13¼x13, 13x13¼***
**2006, Oct. 31** **Litho.** **Wmk. 395**
**1838-1841** A744 Set of 4 8.50 4.25

Galapagos Islands Fauna — A745

No. 1842, horiz.: a, Sea turtle. b, Sea gull. c, Marine iguana. d, Blue-footed boobies. e, Sea lion.
80c, Flamingo. $1, Crab. $1.20, Fish.

**2006, Nov. 1**
**1842** A745 30c Horiz. strip of 5, #a-e 6.50 3.25
**1843** A745 80c multi 3.25 1.60
**1844** A745 $1 multi 4.00 2.00
**1845** A745 $1.20 multi 5.00 2.50
*Nos. 1842-1845 (4)* 18.75 9.35

Christmas — A746

**2006, Nov. 28** ***Perf. 13x13¼***
**1846** A746 80c multi 3.25 1.60

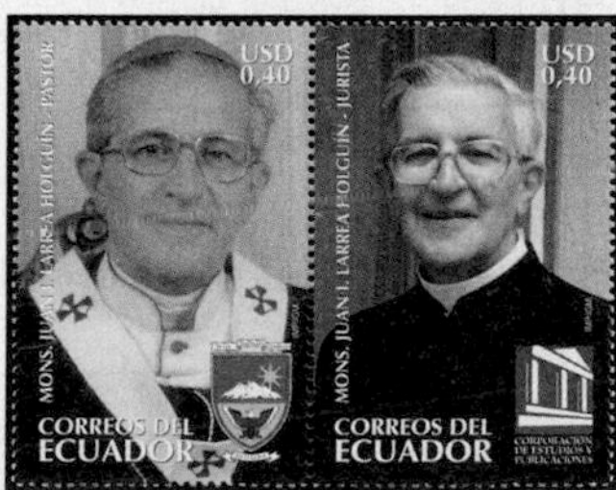


Monsignor Juan I. Larrea Holguín (1927-2006) — A747

No. 1847: a, In bishop's robes. b, In judicial robes.

**2006, Dec. 8** ***Perf. 13¾***
**1847** A747 40c Horiz. pair, #a-b 3.75 1.90

Freemasonry A748

Designs: 25c, Masonic altar, beehive. 40c, Compass and square.

**2006, Dec. 11** ***Perf. 13x13¼***
**1848-1849** A748 Set of 2 3.00 1.50

Quito Zoo Animals — A749

No. 1850: a, Parrot. b, Frog.
No. 1851: a, Harpy eagle. b, Jaguar.
$2, Parrot on branch.

**2006, Dec. 11** ***Perf. 13x13¼***
**1850** A749 60c Horiz. pair, #a-b 4.75 2.40
**1851** A749 80c Horiz. pair, #a-b 6.50 3.25

***Imperf***

**Size: 40x65mm**

**1852** A749 $2 multi 8.50 4.25

Erotic and Fertility Figurines — A750

Designs: 10c, Nursing mother. 20c, Copulating couple. $1.20, Pregnant woman. $2, Man with erect penis.

**2006, Dec. 12** ***Perf. 13x13¼***
**1853-1856** A750 Set of 4 15.00 7.50

Admiral Juan Illingworth Naval Museum — A751

Emblem of Ecuador Navy and Illingworth: 20c, On rope ladder, 1880. 25c, As Marine Guard, 1854.

**2006, Dec. 15** **Litho.**
**1857-1858** A751 Set of 2 2.00 1.00

Colors of Ecuador Flag — A752

**2006, Dec. 15** **Wmk. 395**
**1859** A752 $10 multi 37.50 19.00

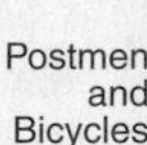

Postmen and Bicycles A753

Color of photograph: 20c, Gray brown. 40c, Gray blue. 80c, Red.

**2006, Dec. 17** ***Perf. 13¼x13***
**1860-1862** A753 Set of 3 6.00 3.00

Pets A754

Designs: 25c, Puppy. 40c, Dog, vert. 50c, Cat with brown and blue eyes, vert. 80c, Dog running. $1, Cat with blue eyes, vert.

**2006, Dec. 17** ***Perf. 13¼x13, 13x13¼***
**1863-1867** A754 Set of 5 12.00 6.00

Cuenca Biennale A755

Art by: 5c, Alexander Apóstol. 15c, Ricardo González Elias, vert.

**2006, Dec. 20**
**1868-1869** A755 Set of 2 .55 .25

Independence Monument, 50th Anniv. — A756

No. 1870: a, Head of statue. b, Entire statue.

**2006, Dec. 21** ***Perf. 13¾***
**1870** A756 20c Horiz. pair, #a-b 1.80 .90

Quito Fair — A757

Designs: No. 1871, Matador Manolo Caena.
No. 1872 — Matadors: a, Sebastián Castella. b, El Juli.
No. 1873, horiz. — Quito Bull Ring: a, At right. b, At left.
$3, Sculpture of Jesus, horiz.

***Perf. 13x13¼, 13¼x13***
**2006, Dec. 27** **Litho.**
**1871** A757 50c multi 2.50 1.25
**1872** A757 50c Horiz. pair, #a-b 4.25 2.10
**1873** A757 50c Horiz. pair, #a-b 4.25 2.10
*Nos. 1871-1873 (3)* 11.00 5.45

**Litho. With Foil Application**

***Imperf***

**Size: 65x40mm**

**1874** A757 $3 multi 13.00 6.50

Pirates
A758

No. 1875, vert.: a, Jolly Roger flag, ship, sea lions. b, Sea lions, ships. c, Ships, Jolly roger flag. d, Armed pirate on ship. e, Ship, Jolly Roger flag.

No. 1876: a, Map of Galapagos Islands, Jolly Roger flag, Sir Francis Drake. b, Ship, map, skull.

$1, Ship, map, skull, William Dampier.

***Perf. 13x13¼, 13¼x13***

**2006, Dec. 27** **Litho.**

**1875** A758 30c Horiz. strip of 5, #a-e 7.25 3.50
**1876** A758 40c Horiz. pair, #a-b 3.75 1.90
**1877** A758 $1 multi 5.00 2.50
*Nos. 1875-1877 (3)* 16.00 7.90

SEK International University, Quito
A759

***Perf. 13¼x13***

**2006, Dec. 29** **Wmk. 395**

**1878** A759 10c multi .50 .40

Scouting, Cent. — A760

Scout emblem and: 25c, Circles. $2, Scout and circles.

***Perf. 13x13¼***

**2007, Mar. 29** **Litho.** **Wmk. 395**

**1879-1880** A760 Set of 2 8.00 4.00

Hispanic-American Poetry Festival — A761

**2007, Apr. 19**

**1881** A761 10c multi .40 .30

Cuenca, 450th Anniv. — A762

Designs: 40c, Casa de los Arcos (Arch House). 75c, Vergel Plaza. 80c, Tomebamba River Gorge, horiz. $3, Cathedral of the Immaculate Conception.

**2007, Apr. 27** ***Perf. 13x13¼, 13¼x13***

**1882-1885** A762 Set of 4 17.50 8.75

Prehistoric Animals — A763

Designs: No. 1886, 80c, Megatherium. No. 1887, 80c, Smilodon, horiz.

**2007, May 10**

**1886-1887** A763 Set of 2 5.75 3.75

Beetles
A764

Designs: No. 1888, Golopha eaucus.

No. 1889: a, Chrysophora chrysochlora. b, Dynastes hercules.

**2007, May 10** ***Perf. 13¼x13***

**1888** A764 40c multi 1.50 .75
**1889** A764 40c Horiz. pair, #a-b 3.00 1.50

Guayaquil Rotary Club, 80th Anniv.
A765

**2007, June 1** **Wmk. 395**

**1890** A765 25c multi .90 .45

America Issue, Education For All — A766

Designs: 40c, Children on school bus. 80c, Girl doing geometry work. $1, Children flying kites, vert. $1.20, Student in wheelchair, vert. $2, Girl and handprints, vert.

**2007, June 6** ***Perf. 13¼x13, 13x13¼***

**1891-1894** A766 Set of 4 12.00 6.00

***Imperf***

**Size: 40x65mm**

**1895** A766 $2 multi 7.50 3.75

Naval Institute of Oceanography, 75th Anniv. — A767

Antarctic research: 10c, Penguin, ship. $3, Scientists and scientific equipment, horiz.

**2007, July 18** ***Perf. 13x13¼***

**1896** A767 10c multi .40 .30

***Perf. 12***

**Size: 52x32mm**

**1897** A767 $3 multi 11.00 5.50

Central Bank of Ecuador, 80th Anniv. — A768

**2007, Aug. 28** ***Perf. 12***

**1898** A768 $2 multi 7.50 3.75

Guayaquil Firefighters
A769

Various firefighters at fires: 5c, 10c, 15c, 25c, $1. 25c and $1 are horiz.

**2007, Oct. 10** ***Perf. 13x13¼, 13¼x13***

**1899-1903** A769 Set of 5 5.50 2.75

Breast Cancer Prevention
A770

**2007, Oct. 15** ***Perf. 13¼x13***

**1904** A770 $3 multi 11.00 5.50

Guayaquil Tourism — A771

Designs: 5c, Las Peñas. 10c, Lighthouse, Santa Ana Hill. 15c, El Velero Bridge. 25c, Mercado Sur, horiz. $1, June 5 Bridge, horiz.

**2007, Oct. 23** ***Perf. 13x13¼, 13¼x13***

**1905-1909** A771 Set of 5 5.50 2.25

Cuenca Chamber of Industries, 70th Anniv.
A772

**2007, Oct. 25** ***Perf. 13¼x13***

**1910** A772 $1.20 multi 4.25 2.10

Operation Smile
A773

**2007, Nov. 16** **Litho.**

**1911** A773 $1 multi 3.75 1.90

Vistazo Magazine, 50th Anniv.
A774

**2007, Nov. 29** ***Perf. 12***

**1912** A774 20c multi .75 .25

Galapagos Islands Fauna
A775

Designs: 40c, Sea turtle. 80c, Penguin. $1, Dolphin. $1.20, Tropicbird.

**2007, Nov. 30** ***Perf. 13¼x13***

**1913-1916** A775 Set of 4 12.00 6.00

Compare with type A780.

Comptroller General, 80th Anniv.
A776

**2007, Dec. 3** ***Perf. 12***

**1917** A776 20c multi .75 .25

2007 Pan American Games, Rio de Janeiro — A777

No. 1918 — Athletes and text noting gold medalists: a, Alexandra Escobar. b, Seledina Nieve. c, Jefferson Perez. d, Xavier Moreno. e, Under-18 soccer team.

**2007, Dec. 18** ***Perf. 13x13¼***

**1918** Horiz. strip of 5 7.25 3.00
***a.-e.*** A777 40c Any single 1.25 .60

Christmas — A778

No. 1919: a, The Annunciation. b, The Three Magi. c, Nativity. d, Flight into Egypt.

**2007, Dec. 20** ***Perf. 13¼x13***

**1919** A778 20c Block of 4, #a-d 2.75 1.40

Guayas Province Transit Commission, 60th Anniv. — A779

*Perf. 13x13¼*

**2008, Jan. 29 Litho. Wmk. 395**

**1920** A779 $1 multi 3.75 1.90

Galapagos Islands A780

Map of islands and: 40c, Pelecanus occidentalis. 80c, Aetobatus narinari. $1, Carcharhinus galapagensis. $1.20, San Cristóbal Windmill Project.

**2008, Mar. 18** ***Perf. 13¼x13***

**1921-1924** A780 Set of 4 12.00 6.00

Compare with Type A775.

Free Maternity and Infant Care — A781

**2008, Mar. 28** ***Perf. 12***

**1925** A781 $1 multi 3.75 1.90

Guayaquil Port Authority, 50th Anniv. A782

**2008, Apr. 8**

**1926** A782 20c multi .75 .25

Tungurahua Chamber of Industry, 80th Anniv. — A783

**Wmk. 395**

**2008, Apr. 24 Litho.** ***Perf. 12***

**1927** A783 $3 multi 11.00 5.50

Father Carlos Crespi (1891-1982) — A784

**2008, Apr. 30**

**1928** A784 $2 multi 7.25 3.00

Santiago de Guayaquil Medallion A785

**2008, June 3**

**1929** A785 30c multi 1.10 .55

Intl. Philately Day.

Jorge Pérez Concha, Historian and Diplomat, Birth Cent. — A786

**2008, June 4**

**1930** A786 $3 multi 11.00 5.50

Los Pinos College, Quito, 40th Anniv. A787

**2008, June 6**

**1931** A787 20c multi .75 .25

Guayaquil-Quito Railway, Cent. — A788

Ecuador No. 174 and: 56c, Steam locomotive. $5, Steam locomotives, Gabriel García Moreno and Gen. Eloy Alfaro.

**2008, June 23** ***Perf. 12***

**1932** A788 56c multi 2.00 1.00

***Imperf***

**Size: 100x70mm**

**1933** A788 $5 multi 18.00 9.00

Polytechnic School of the Coast, 50th Anniv. — A789

**Wmk. 395**

**2008, July 28 Litho.** ***Perf. 12***

**1934** A789 32c multi 1.10 .55

Latin American Youth Year — A790

**2008, Aug. 20**

**1935** A790 30c multi 1.10 .55

Ecuadorian Cacao — A791

No. 1936: a, Cacao pod, UL corner of #306. b, Cacao flower, UR corner of #306. c, Cacao processing, LL corner of #306. d, Cacao pods and beans, chocolate candy, LR corner of #306.

**2008, Oct. 1** ***Perf. 13¼x13***

**1936** A791 56c Block of 4, #a-d 8.00 4.00

Meridiano Newspaper, 25th Anniv. — A792

**2008, Oct. 22** ***Perf. 13x13¼***

**1937** A792 60c multi 2.00 1.00

Intl. Swimming Federation, Cent. A793

No. 1938: a, World Map. b, Ecuadorian swimmer.
30c, Swimmer from underwater.

**2008, Oct. 31** ***Perf. 13¼x13***

**1938** A793 24c Horiz. pair, #a-b 1.25 .60
**1939** A793 30c multi .70 .30

Office of the Procurator General, 80th Anniv. — A794

**2008, Nov. 11** ***Perf. 13x13¼***

**1940** A794 25c multi .60 .25

Guayaquil Chamber of Construction, 40th Anniv. A795

**2008, Nov. 27** ***Perf. 13¼x13***

**1941** A795 $1 multi 2.25 1.10

New Constitution — A796

Flag and: 32c, Sun behind clouds. $5, People, vert.

**2008, Nov. 29** ***Perf. 12***

**1942** A796 32c multi .75 .30

**Size: 66x95mm**

***Imperf***

**1943** A796 $5 multi 12.00 6.00

Santiago de Guayaquil Municipal Museum, Cent. A797

No. 1944: a, Old musuem building. b, New museum building with murals.
$2, Entrance to old musuem building.

**2008, Dec. 16** ***Perf. 13¼x13***

**1944** A797 60c Horiz. pair, #a-b 3.00 1.50
**1945** A797 $2 multi 5.00 2.50

Friendship Between Ecuador and Japan, 90th Anniv. — A798

No. 1945: a, Cotopaxi Volcano, Ecuador. b, Mt. Fuji, Japan.

**2008, Dec. 17**

**1946** A798 30c Horiz. pair, #a-b 1.50 .75

America Issue, National Festivals — A799

No. 1947 — Festival of Sts. Peter and Paul: a, Dancers. b, Guitarist.
No. 1948, vert. — Diablada Pillareña: a, Figure with red mask. b, Figure with black mask.

**2008, Dec. 23** *Perf. 13¼x13*

**1947** A799 20c Horiz. pair, #a-b 1.00 .50

*Perf. 13x13¼*

**1948** A799 $1 Horiz. pair, #a-b 5.00 2.50

Christmas A800

Various creche figurines of Holy Family and animals with background color of: 30c, Blue. No. 1949: a, Green. b, Yellow brown.

**2008, Dec. 23** *Perf. 13¼x13*

**1949** A800 30c multi .75 .30
**1950** A800 80c Horiz. pair, #a-b 4.00 2.00

A801

A802

A803

A804

Jacchigua National Folk Ballet A805

*Perf. 13¼x13*

**2009, Feb. 18 Litho. Wmk. 395**

**1951** Horiz. strip of 5 12.00 6.00
*a.* A801 $1 multi 2.00 1.00
*b.* A802 $1 multi 2.00 1.00
*c.* A803 $1 multi 2.00 1.00
*d.* A804 $1 multi 2.00 1.00
*e.* A805 $1 multi 2.00 1.00

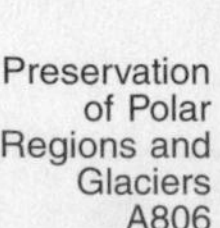

Preservation of Polar Regions and Glaciers A806

Designs: 20c, Feet of polar bear. 80c, Earth in water.

**2009, Mar. 31**

**1952-1953** A806 Set of 2 2.50 1.25

A807

Tourism — A808

Designs: No. 1954, Babahoyo River, Los Ríos Province. No. 1955, Ingapirca Ruins, Cañar Province. No. 1956, Rafters on Quijos River, Napo Province. No. 1957, Marimba group, Esmeraldas Province. $1.25, Tulcán cemetery, Carchi Province. $2, Train and Mt. Chimborazo, Chimborazo Province. $3, Alcea rosea flowers, Morona-Santiago Province. $5, Acrocinus longimanus, Sucumbíos Province.

No. 1962: a, Like #1954. b, Like #1957. c, Like #1958. d, Like #1955. e, Like #1959. f, Like #1956. g, Like #1960. h, Like #1961.

No. 1963: a, Equator Monument, Pichincha Province. b, Colorado Indians, Santo Domingo de los Tsáchilas Province. c, Los Frailes Beach, Manabí Province. d, Banana plantation, El Oro Province. e, Arctocephalus galapagoensis, Galápagos Province. f, Cuicocha Lake, Imbabura Province. g, Harpia harpyja, Pastaza Province. h, Shuar community, Orellana Province.

No. 1964: a, Bolívar and San Martín Monument, Guayas Province. b, The Lovers of Sumpa, Santa Elena Province. c, Pillaro devil, Tungurahua Province. d, Mt. Cotopaxi, Cotopaxi Province. e, Guaranga Indian Monument, Bolívar Province. f, Virgin of Cisne, Loja Province. g, Tomebamba River, Azuay Province. h, Leopardus pardalis, Zamora Province.

*Perf. 13¼x13*

**2009 Litho. Wmk. 395**

**1954** A807 25c multi .60 .25
**1955** A807 50c multi 1.25 .60
**1956** A807 75c multi 1.75 .90
**1957** A807 $1 multi 2.50 1.25
**1958** A807 $1.25 multi 3.00 1.50
**1959** A807 $2 multi 4.75 2.40
**1960** A807 $3 multi 7.25 3.50
**1961** A807 $5 multi 12.00 6.00
*Nos. 1954-1961 (8)* 33.10 16.40

**Booklet Stamps**
**Self-Adhesive**
***Die Cut***
**Unwmk.**

**1962** Booklet pane of 8 + 2 labels 12.50
*a.-b.* A808 25c Either single .60 .25
*c.-d.* A808 50c Either single 1.25 .50
*e.-f.* A808 75c Either single 1.75 .75
*g.-h.* A808 $1 Either single 2.50 1.00
**1963** Booklet pane of 8 + 2 labels 12.50
*a.-b.* A808 25c Either single .60 .25
*c.-d.* A808 50c Either single 1.25 .50
*e.-f.* A808 75c Either single 1.75 .75
*g.-h.* A808 $1 Either single 2.50 1.00
**1964** Booklet pane of 8 + 2 labels 12.50
*a.-b.* A808 25c Either single .60 .25
*c.-d.* A808 50c Either single 1.25 .50
*e.-f.* A808 75c Either single 1.75 .75
*g.-h.* A808 $1 Either single 2.50 1.00
*Nos. 1962-1964 (3)* 37.50

Issued: Nos. 1954-1961, 4/29; Nos. 1962-1964, July.

See Nos. 1985-2000, 2021-2022.

Intl. Philately Day — A809

*Perf. 13¼x13*

**2009, May 6 Wmk. 395**

**1965** A809 75c multi 1.75 .90

Icons of Santa Clara Monastery A810

No. 1966: a, Angel. b, Jesus Christ. c, Pensive child. d, Protective Virgin. e, Virgin of Quito.

**2009, June 9** *Perf. 13x13¼*

**1966** Horiz. strip of 5 12.00 6.00
*a.-e.* A810 $1 Any single 2.00 1.00

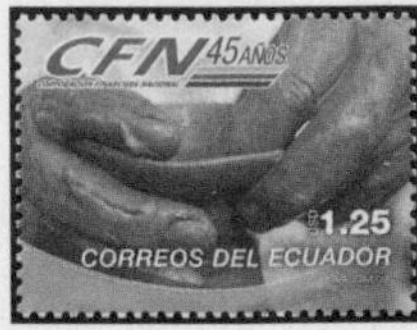

National Finance Corporation, 45th Anniv. A811

**2009, June 22** *Perf. 13¼x13*

**1967** A811 $1.25 multi 3.00 1.50

Ambato Electric Company, 50th Anniv. A812

**2009, June**

**1968** A812 $1 multi 2.50 1.25

Paute-Molino Dam, 25th Anniv. A813

**2009, July 22**

**1969** A813 $2 multi 5.00 2.50

El Telégrafo Newspaper, 125th Anniv. A814

**2009, July 30** *Perf. 12*

**1970** A814 $1.75 multi 4.25 2.10

Call for Independence, Bicent. — A815

Nos. 1971 and 1972 — Doves, butterflies, bell and: a, Open mouth. b, Monument.

**2009, Aug. 14** *Perf. 13¼x13*

**1971** A815 $3 Horiz. pair, #a-b 14.50 7.25

**Souvenir Sheet**
**With Horizontal Blue Stripe Added to Middle of Stamps**

**1972** A815 $3 Sheet of 2, #a-b 14.50 7.25

Call for Independence, Bicent. — A816

***Serpentine Die Cut 12½x12¼***

**2009, Aug. 14 Litho. Unwmk.**
**Self-Adhesive**
**Printed on Cork**

**1973** A816 $3.50 multi 8.50 4.25

Chinese Benevolent Society, Cent. — A817

No. 1974: a, Galápagos tortoise. b, Giant panda.

*Perf. 13¼x13*

**2009, Aug. 18 Wmk. 395**

**1974** A817 25c Horiz. pair, #a-b 1.25 .60

Famous People A818

No. 1975: a, Carlos Silva Pareja (1909-68), musician. b, Tránsito Amaguaña (1909-2009), Indian rights advocate. c, Demetrio Aguilera Malta (1909-81), writer, diplomat. d, Carlos Zevallos Menéndez (1909-81), archaeologist. e, Humberto Salvador Guerra (1909-82), writer.

**2009, Aug. 28 Litho.**

**1975** Horiz. strip of 5 3.00 1.50
*a.-e.* A818 25c Any single .50 .25

Ecuadorian Olympic Committee, 50th Anniv. A819

Designs: No. 1976, 25c, Shooting, cycling, equestrian, wrestling, archery, and basketball. No. 1977, 25c, Diving, running, weight lifting, tennis, boxing and soccer, vert.

**2009, Oct. 17** *Perf. 13¼x13, 13x13¼*

**1976-1977** A819 Set of 2 1.25 .60

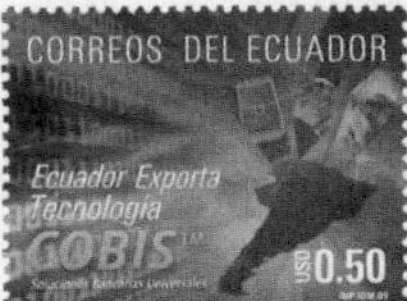

Exportation of Cooperative Open Banking Information System A820

*Perf. 13¼x13*

**2009, Nov. 5 Litho. Wmk. 395**

**1978** A820 50c multi 1.25 1.00

Loja National University, 150th Anniv. — A821

**Wmk. 395**

**2009, Nov. 27 Litho.** *Perf. 12*

**1979** A821 $2 multi 5.00 2.50

Independence, Bicent. — A822

No. 1980: a, Juan Pío Montúfar (1758-1818), Chairman of Supreme Council of Government. b, José Mejía Lequerica (1777-1813), representative to Cortes of Cadiz. c, Eugenio Espejo (1747-95), journalist, medical pioneer. d, Manuela Cañizares (1769-1814), patriot. e, Bicentenary emblem.

**2009, Nov. 28**

**1980** Horiz. strip of 5 9.00 4.50
*a.-e.* A822 75c Any single 1.50 .75

A823

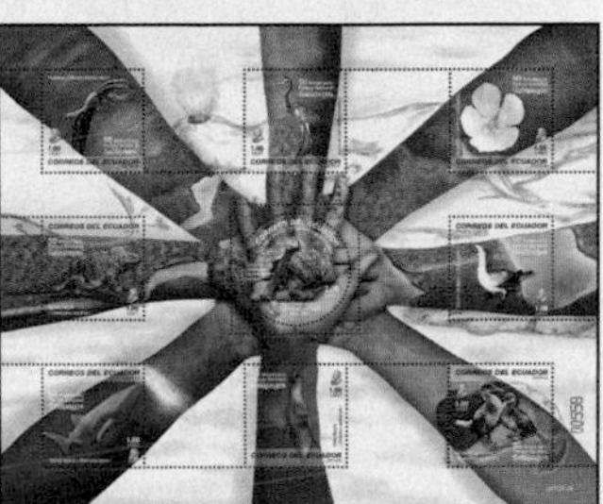

Charles Darwin (1809-82), Naturalist — A824

No. 1982 — Darwin and: a, Phoenicopterus ruber. b, Ardea herodias. c, Calandria galapagosa. d, Conolopus marthae. e, Sula granti. f, Rhincodon typus. g, Zalophus wollebaeki. h, Phalacrocorax harrisi. i, Geochelone nigra abingdoni. Nos. 1982a-1982h are 35x35mm, No. 1982i is 38mm diameter.

***Perf. 13¾x14***

**2009, Nov. 30** **Unwmk.**

**Granite Paper**

**1981** A823 $5 multi 12.00 6.00

***Perf. 13¼ ($1), 13¾ ($2)***

**1982** A824 Sheet of 9 24.00 12.00
*a.-h.* $1 Any single 2.00 1.00
*i.* $2 multi 4.00 2.00

Christmas A825

***Perf. 13¼x13***

**2009, Dec. 10** **Wmk. 395**

**1983** A825 $1 multi 2.50 1.25

America Issue, Toys and Games — A826

No. 1984: a, Paddle and ball. b, Go-cart.

**2009, Dec. 18**

**1984** A826 $1 Horiz. pair, #a-b 5.00 2.50

**Tourism Type of 2009**

Designs: No. 1985, The Lovers of Sumpa, Santa Elena Province. No. 1986, Colorado Indians, Santo Domingo de los Tsáchilas Province. No. 1987, Shuar community, Orellana Province. No. 1988, Guaranga Indian Monument, Bolívar Province. No. 1989, Banana plantation, El Oro Province. No. 1990, Virgin of Cisne, Loja Province. No. 1991, Pillaro devil, Tungurahua Province. No. 1992, Equator Monument, Pichincha Province. No. 1993, Cuicocha Lake, Imbabura Province. $1.75, Bolívar and San Martín Monument, Guayas Province. No. 1995, Tomebamba River, Azuay Province. No. 1996, Leopardus pardalis, Zamora Province. No. 1997, Los Frailes Beach, Manabí Province. No. 1998, Harpia harpyja, Pastaza Province. No. 1999, Arctocephalus galapagoensis, Galápagos Province. $5, Mt. Cotopaxi, Cotopaxi Province.

**Wmk. 395, 377 (#1986-1987, 1989, 1992, 1993, 1997-1999)**

**2010-11** **Litho.** ***Perf. 13¼x13***

| | | | | | |
|---|---|---|---|---|---|
| **1985** | A807 | 25c | multi | .50 | .25 |
| **1986** | A807 | 25c | multi | .50 | .25 |
| **1987** | A807 | 25c | multi | .50 | .25 |
| **1988** | A807 | 50c | multi | 1.00 | .50 |
| **1989** | A807 | 50c | multi | 1.00 | .50 |
| **1990** | A807 | $1 | multi | 2.00 | 1.00 |
| **1991** | A807 | $1.25 | multi | 2.50 | 1.25 |
| **1992** | A807 | $1.25 | multi | 2.50 | 1.25 |
| **1993** | A807 | $1.25 | multi | 2.50 | 1.25 |
| **1994** | A807 | $1.75 | multi | 3.50 | 1.75 |
| **1995** | A807 | $2 | multi | 4.00 | 2.00 |
| **1996** | A807 | $2 | multi | 4.00 | 2.00 |
| **1997** | A807 | $2 | multi | 4.00 | 2.00 |
| **1998** | A807 | $3 | multi | 6.00 | 3.00 |
| **1999** | A807 | $3 | multi | 6.00 | 3.00 |
| **2000** | A807 | $5 | multi | 10.00 | 5.00 |
| | *Nos. 1985-2000 (16)* | | | 50.50 | 25.25 |

Issued: Nos. 1985, 1988, 1991, 1995, 1/20; Nos. 1990, 1994, 1996, 2000, 4/12; Nos. 1986, 1992, 1997, 1998, 9/30; Nos. 1987, 1989, 1993, 1999, 1/24/11.

Miniature Sheet

First Unmanned Ecuadorian Airship — A827

No. 2001: a, $1, Pilot with remote-control device (40x18mm). b, $1, Airship over coastline (40x18mm). c, $1, Airship and mountain (40x18mm). d, $3, Airship (115x42mm).

**Wmk. 395**

**2010, Feb. 7** **Litho.** ***Perf. 14***

**2001** A827 Sheet of 4, #a-d 12.00 6.00

Ecuadorian Red Cross, Cent. — A828

No. 2002: a, Old ambulance, blood drop inscribed "Ayuda." b, New ambulance, blood drop inscribed "Cuida." c, Modern Red Cross hard hat, blood drop inscribed "Salva." d, Old Red Cross hard hat, blood drop inscribed "Vida."

***Perf. 13¼x13***

**2010, Mar. 18** **Wmk. 395**

**2002** A828 50c Block of 4, #a-d 4.00 2.00

Birds — A829

No. 2003: a, Tachycineta albiventer. b, Momotus momota. c, Semnornis ramphastinus. d, Aulacorhynchus haematopygus.

No. 2004, horiz.: a, Ramphocelus carbo. b, Tangara vitriolina.

**2010, Apr. 16** **Wmk. 395** ***Perf. 14***

**2003** A829 25c Block of 4, #a-d 2.00 1.00

**Souvenir Sheet**

***Perf. 13¼x13***

**2004** A829 $1.50 Sheet of 2, #a-b 6.00 3.00

No. 2004 contains two 38x27mm stamps. Birdpex 2010, Antwerp, Belgium (No. 2004).

Tall Ships in Velas Sudamérica 2010 — A830

No. 2005, vert. (27x38mm) — Various knots, ships and flags: a, Cisne Branco, Brazil. b, Libertad, Argentina. c, Sagres, Portugal. d, Capitán Miranda, Uruguay. e, Europa, Netherlands. f, Esmerelda, Chile. g, Gloria, Colombia. h, Simón Bolívar, Venezuela. i, Cuauhtémoc, Mexico. j, Juan Sebastián Elcano, Spain.

$1, Training Ship Guayas, Ecuador.

***Perf. 13x13¼***

**2010, May 7** **Wmk. 377**

**2005** Block of 10 15.00 7.50
*a.-j.* A830 75c Any single 1.50 .75

***Perf. 12***

**2006** A830 $1 shown 2.00 1.00

Miniature Sheet

Manuela Sáenz (c. 1797-1856), Mistress of Simón Bolívar — A831

**Litho. with Foil Application**

**2010, May 24** ***Imperf.***

**2007** A831 $3 multi 6.00 3.00

See Venezuela No. 1707.

2010 World Cup Soccer Championships, South Africa — A832

No. 2008 — Emblem of 2010 World Cup, soccer player, ball and: a, Lion. b, Elephant. c, Zebra.

$5, Mascot of 2010 World Cup, giraffe.

**2010, June 9** **Litho.** ***Perf. 13¼x13***

**2008** Horiz. strip of 3 6.00 3.00
*a.-c.* A832 $1 Any single 2.00 1.00

**Souvenir Sheet**

***Imperf***

**2009** A832 $5 multi 10.00 5.00

No. 2009 contains one 45x36mm stamp with simulated perforations. Animals on No. 2009 have blurred appearance, but have a three-dimensional appearance when seen through 3-D glasses.

Creation of Tungurahua Province, 150th Anniv. — A833

No. 2010: a, Atelopus ignescens. b, Mt. Tungurahua, flag at Parque de la Familia. c, Casa del Portal Museum.

***Perf. 13¼x13***

**2010, July 1** **Wmk. 377**

**2010** Horiz. strip of 3 1.50 .75
*a.-c.* A833 25c Any single .50 .25

Las Floristas, by Camilo Egas — A834

**2010, July 21** ***Perf. 12***

**2011** A834 $1.25 multi 2.50 1.25

Campaign against illegal trafficking in historical objects.

Souvenir Sheet

Massacre of Patriots, Bicent. — A835

No. 2012: a, Soldier with sword threatening woman, man and child. b, Soldier threatening to shoot man.

**2010, Aug. 2** ***Perf. 13x13¼***

**2012** A835 $2 Sheet of 2, #a-b, + central label 8.00 4.00

Souvenir Sheet

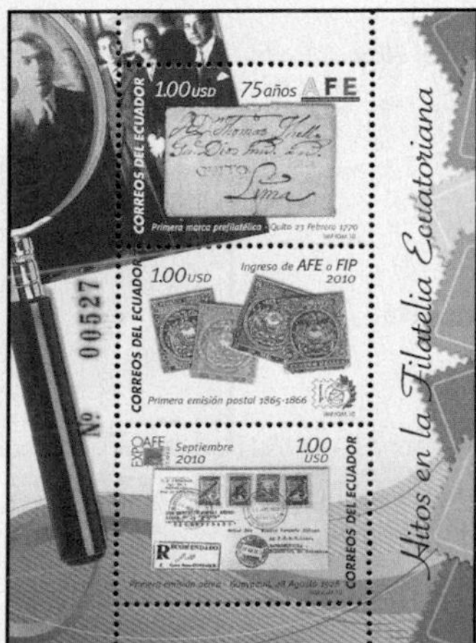


Philatelic Firsts of Ecuador — A836

No. 2013: a, First postmark of Ecuador, 1770, emblem of Philatelic Association of Ecuador. b, First Ecuadorian stamps (#2, 3, 5, 6), emblem of Intl. Federation of Philately. c, Cover from first SCADTA flight, 1928, emblem of 2010 Philatelic Association of Ecuador Expo.

**2010, Aug. 25** ***Perf. 13¼x13***

**2013** A836 $1 Sheet of 3, #a-c 6.00 3.00

Philatelic Association of Ecuador, 75th anniv., and its admission to Intl. Federation of Philately.

Organization of Petroleum Exporting Countries, 50th Anniv. A837

**2010, Sept. 14 Wmk. 377 *Perf. 12***

2014 A837 50c multi 1.00 .50

Citigroup in Ecuador, 50th Anniv. A838

**2010, Oct. 7 *Perf. 13¼x13***

2015 A838 $1 multi 2.00 1.00

General Directorate of Civil Registration, Identification and Certification — A839

**2010, Oct. 29 Litho. *Perf. 12***

2016 A839 50c multi 1.00 .50

America Issue, National Symbols A840

No. 2017 — National: a, Flag. b, Coat of arms. c, Anthem.

**2010, Nov. 24 *Perf. 13¼x13***

2017 Horiz. strip of 3 6.00 3.00
*a.-c.* A840 $1 Any single 2.00 1.00

Christmas — A841

**2010, Dec. 3 *Perf. 13x13¼***

2018 A841 $2 multi 4.00 2.00

San José-La Salle College, Guayaquil, Cent. — A842

**2010, Dec. 16 Litho. Wmk. 377**

2019 A842 25c multi .50 .25

Children's Christmas Parade, Cuenca A843

**2010, Dec. 21 *Perf. 13¼x13***

2020 A843 50c multi 1.00 .50

**Tourism Type of 2009**

No. 2021 — Galapagos Islands fauna: a, Fregata magnificens. b, Sula dactylatra. c, Sphenisciforme. d, Sula nebouxi. e, Conolophus subcristatus. f, Geochelone nigra. g, Chelonia mydas agassisi. h, Oxycirrhites typus.

No. 2022 — Galapagos Islands sites and fauna: a, Bartolomé Island, denomination at L. b, Bartolomé Island, denomination at R. c, Zoluphus wallebaeki, denomination at L. d, Zoluphus wallebaeki, denomination at R. e, Darwin's Arch, denomination at L. f, Darwin's Arch, denomination at R. g, Amblyrhynchus cristatus, denomination at L. h, Amblyrhynchus cristatus, denomination at R.

**2011, Mar. 18 Unwmk. *Die Cut***
**Self-Adhesive**

2021 Booklet pane of 8 + 2 labels 10.00
*a.-b.* A808 25c Either single .50 .25
*c.-d.* A808 50c Either single 1.00 .50
*e.-f.* A808 75c Either single 1.50 .75
*g.-h.* A808 $1 Either single 2.00 1.00
*i.* Booklet pane of 8, #a-h, with lilac pane margins 10.00
2022 Booklet pane of 8 + 2 labels 10.00
*a.-b.* A808 25c Either single .50 .25
*c.-d.* A808 50c Either single 1.00 .50
*e.-f.* A808 75c Either single 1.50 .75
*g.-h.* A808 $1 Either single 2.00 1.00
*i.* Booklet pane of 8, #a-h, with lilac pane margins 10.00

Issued: Nos. 2021i, 2022i, 1/13/12. Nos. 2021 and 2022 have gray pane margins.

Souvenir Sheet

Postal Union of the Americas, Spain and Portugal (UPAEP), Cent. — A844

**2011, Mar. 18 Wmk. 377 *Perf. 12***

2023 A844 $3 multi 6.00 3.00

Souvenir Sheet

Yuri Gagarin, First Man in Space, 50th Anniv. — A845

**2011, May 6 *Perf. 13x13¼***

2024 A845 $5 multi 10.00 5.00

Intl. Year of Forests — A846

No. 2025, 50c: a, Chinchona officinalis. b, Ceiba tichistandra.

No. 2026, 75c, horiz.: a, Jacaranda sp. b, Prosopis sp.

**2011, May 19 *Perf. 13x13¼, 13¼x13***
**Horiz. pairs, #a-b**

2025-2026 A846 Set of 2 5.00 2.50

Pichincha Chamber of Industries and Production, 75th Anniv. — A847

**Wmk. 377**
**2011, June 16 Litho. *Perf. 12***

2027 A847 $2 multi 4.00 4.00

Christopher Columbus College, Guayaquil, Cent. A848

**2011, July 7 *Perf. 13¼x13***

2028 A848 $1 multi 2.00 2.00

National Telecommunications Day — A849

No. 2029: a, First Bell telephone, 1876. b, Western Electric magneto wall telephone, 1894. c, Ericsson wall pay telephone, 1970. d, Apple iPhone, 2011.

**2011, July 8**

2029 A849 50c Block of 4, #a-d 4.00 4.00

Miniature Sheet

Seven Wonders of Quito — A850

No. 2030: a, Basilica of the National Vow. b, Virgin of the Panecillo. c, Chimbacalle Railway Station. d, San Francisco Convent. e, Independence Plaza. f, Church of the Society of Jesus. g, Sanctuary of the Virgin of El Quinche.

**2011, Sept. 8**

2030 A850 75c Sheet of 7, #a-g, + label 10.50 10.50

Quito, 2011 American Capital of Culture.

Yasuni- ITT Initiative — A851

No. 2031 — Reptiles: a, Chelonoidis denticulata. b, Anolis trachyderma. c, Thecadactylus solimoensis. d, Epicrates cenchria. e, Dendropsophus bifurcus. f, Osteocephalus taurinus. g, Ranitomeya ventrimaculata. h, Melanosuchus niger.

No. 2032: a, Clavija procera. b, Duguetia hadrantha. c, Hymenaea oblongifolia. d, Connarus ruber. e, Fungi. f, Theobroma speciosum. g, Brownea gradiceps. h, Apeiba membranacea.

**Unwmk.**
**2011, Sept. 20 Litho. *Die Cut***
**Self-Adhesive**

2031 Booklet pane of 8 + 2 labels 10.00
*a.-b.* A851 25c Either single .50 .25
*c.-d.* A851 50c Either single 1.00 .50
*e.-f.* A851 75c Either single 1.50 .75
*g.-h.* A851 $1 Either single 2.00 1.00
2032 Booklet pane of 8 + 2 labels 10.00
*a.-b.* A851 25c Either single .50 .25
*c.-d.* A851 50c Either single 1.00 .50
*e.-f.* A851 75c Either single 1.50 .75
*g.-h.* A851 $1 Either single 2.00 1.00

See Nos. 2061-2062.

Intl. Year For People of African Descent — A852

No. 2033 — Musical instruments: a, Marimba. b, Guasá. c, Maracas. d, Cununos.

***Perf. 13¼x13***
**2011, Sept. 26 Litho. Wmk. 395**

2033 A852 $1 Block of 4, #a-d 8.00 4.00

Flowers — A853

Designs: 25c, Passiflora manicata. $2, Passiflora pinnatistipula. $3, Herrania balaensis. $5, Passiflora arborea.

***Perf. 13x13¼***
**2011, Sept. 26 Litho. Wmk. 377**

2034-2037 A853 Set of 4 20.50 20.50

Trains — A854

Railroad Stations — A855

No. 2038 — Locomotives: a, 1992 GEC Alsthon. b, 1900 Baldwin. c, 1900 Baldwin, diff. d, 1935 Baldwin. e, 1992 GEC Alsthon on hillside. f, Front of 1992 GEC Alsthon. g, 1953 Baldwin. h, Baldwin XXXX.

No. 2039 — Stations at: a, Machachi. b, Latacunga. c, Sibambe. d, Durán. e, El Tambo. f, Riobamba. g, Chimbacalle. h, Boliche.

**2011, Oct. 3 Unwmk. *Die Cut***
**Self-Adhesive**

2038 Booklet pane of 8 + 2 labels 10.00
*a.-b.* A854 25c Either single .50 .25
*c.-d.* A854 50c Either single 1.00 .50
*e.-f.* A854 75c Either single 1.50 .75
*g.-h.* A854 $1 Either single 2.00 1.00
2039 Booklet pane of 8 + 2 labels 10.00
*a.-b.* A855 25c Either single .50 .25
*c.-d.* A855 50c Either single 1.00 .50
*e.-f.* A855 75c Either single 1.50 .75
*g.-h.* A855 $1 Either single 2.00 1.00

Exports — A856

No. 2040: a, Wicker basket. b, Chocolate. c, Wooden automobile. d, Hats. e, Textiles. f, Leather goods. g, Filigree. h, Tagua carvings.

*Perf. 13¼x13*

**2011, Oct. 11** **Wmk. 395**

**2040** A856 50c Block of 8, #a-h, + central label 8.00 8.00

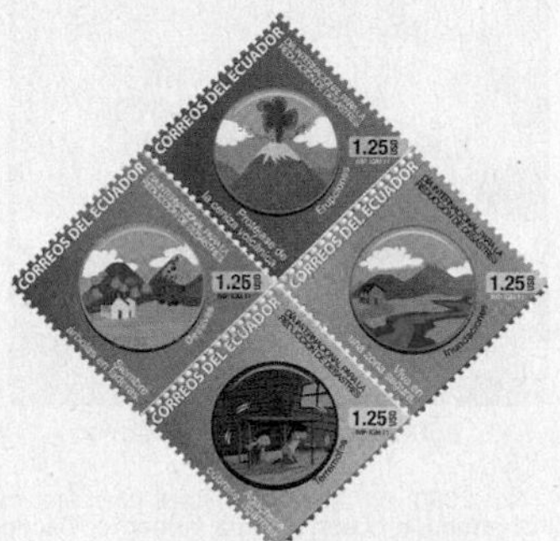

Intl. Day for Disaster Reduction — A857

No. 2041: a, Volcano eruption. b, Landslide. c, Flood, d, Earthquake.

**2011, Oct. 12** *Perf. 13¼*

**2041** A857 $1.25 Block of 4, #a-d 10.00 10.00

Mail Boxes and Postal Transportation — A858

Designs: No. 2042, $1.75, 1928 mailbox, bicycle. No. 2043, $1.75, 2011 mailbox, motorcycle.

$5, Mailbox, Post Office Bay, Galápagos Islands, vert.

*Perf. 13½x13¾*

**2011, Nov. 28** **Wmk. 377**

**2042-2043** A858 Set of 2 7.00 7.00

**Souvenir Sheet**

*Perf. 13x13¼*

**2044** A858 $5 multi 10.00 10.00

America issue. No. 2044 contains one 28x38mm stamp.

Christmas — A859

No. 2045: a, Holy Family. b, Angel.

**2011, Nov. 29** *Perf. 13½x13¾*

**2045** A859 $1 Horiz. pair, #a-b 4.00 4.00

2011 Pan-American Games, Guadalajara, Mexico — A860

Emblem, sports equipment and athletes: a, Karate. b, Weight lifting. c, Kayaking. d, Boxing. e, Rollerblading.

**2011, Nov. 30**

**2046** Horiz. strip of 5 2.50 2.50
*a.-e.* A860 25c Any single .50 .50

Guayaquil Chamber of Industries, 75th Anniv. — A861

**2011, Dec. 14** **Wmk. 377**

**2047** A861 $2 multi 4.00 4.00

Ecuador Cancer Society, 60th Anniv. — A862

**2011, Dec. 19** *Perf. 13¼x13*

**2048** A862 75c multi 1.50 .75

Pres. Luis Cordero (1833-1912) A864

**2012, Mar. 1** *Perf. 13¾x13½*

**2051** A864 $1 multi 2.00 2.00

Flowers — A865

Designs: $1, Barnadesia spinosa. $2, Bixa orellana. $3, Espeletia pycnophylla. $5, Brugmansia sanguinea.

*Perf. 13½x13¾*

**2012, Mar. 28** **Unwmk.**

**2052-2055** A865 Set of 4 22.00 22.00

**Souvenir Sheets**

Sinking of the Titanic, Cent. — A866

Designs: No. 2056, $4, Titanic, sepia-toned image. No. 2056, $4, Titanic and Olympic at dock.

*Perf. 13¾x13½*

**2012, Apr. 20** **Wmk. 377**

**2056-2057** A866 Set of 2 16.00 16.00

Bananas — A867

*Perf. 13½x13¾*

**2012, May 17** **Litho.** **Wmk. 377**

**2058** A867 $2 multi 4.00 4.00

Banco de Machala, 50th anniv.

Catholic University of Santiago, Guayaquil, 50th Anniv. A868

**2012, May 31** *Perf. 13¾*

**2059** A868 $1 multi 2.00 2.00

**Miniature Sheet**

Guayaquil Tourist Attractions — A869

No. 2060: a, Hemiciclo la Rotonda (monument honoring meeting of Simón Bolívar and José de San Martín). b, Malecón del ío Guayas (Guayas River Walk). c, Metropolitan Cathedral. d, Torre del Reloj (Clock Tower). e, Malecón del Salado (Salado Walk). f, Edificio del Municipio (City Hall). g, Las Peñas Cerro Santa Ana (Santa Ana Hill).

**2012, June 8** **Wmk. 377**

**2060** A869 75c Sheet of 7, #a-g, + label 10.50 10.50

**Yasuni-ITT Type of 2011**

No. 2061 — Flora and fauna: a, Dasypodidae. b, Saimiri sciureus. c, Tettigoniidae. d, Automeris postalbida. e, Brownea sp. f, Aristolochia sp. g, Hypsiboas sp. h, Hypsiboas geographicus.

No. 2062 — Birds: a, Morphnus guianensis. b, Sarcoramphus papa. c, Ara ararauna. d, Harpia harpyja. e, Trochilidae sp. f, Ramphastos tucanus. g, Pteroglossus pluricinctus. h, Pionus menstruus.

**2012, June 11** **Unwmk.** ***Die Cut***

**Self-Adhesive**

**2061** Booklet pane of 8 + 2 labels 10.00
*a.-b.* A851 25c Either single .50 .50
*c.-d.* A851 50c Either single 1.00 1.00
*e.-f.* A851 75c Either single 1.50 1.50
*g.-h.* A851 $1 Either single 2.00 2.00

**2062** Booklet pane of 8 + 2 labels 10.00
*a.-b.* A851 25c Either single .50 .50
*c.-d.* A851 50c Either single 1.00 1.00
*e.-f.* A851 75c Either single 1.50 1.50
*g.-h.* A851 $1 Either single 2.00 2.00

Galapagos Islands Landscapes and Fauna — A870

No. 2063: a, Rocks in surf. b, Head of Amblyrhynchus cristatus. c, Numenius phaeopus. d, South Plaza Island. e. Pinnacle Rock, Bartolomé Island. f, Sula nebouxi. g, Chelonoidis sp. h, Kicker Rock (Leon Dormido), San Cristóbal Island.

No. 2064: a, Zalophus wollebaeki. b, Geospiza magnirostris. c, Sula granti. d, Fregata magnificens. e, Microlophus bivittatus. f, Spheniscus mendiculus. g, Anas bahamensis. h, Sphyrna lewini.

**2012, July 11** **Unwmk.** ***Die Cut***

**Self-Adhesive**

**Water Droplets on Blue Depicted in Frames Around Stamps**

**2063** Booklet pane of 8 10.00
*a.-b.* A870 25c Either single .50 .25
*c.-d.* A870 50c Either single 1.00 .50
*e.-f.* A870 75c Either single 1.50 .75
*g.-h.* A870 $1 Either single 2.00 1.00
*i.* Booklet pane of 8, #a-h, with pane margins depicting rocks 10.00

**2064** Booklet pane of 8 10.00
*a.-b.* A870 25c Either single .50 .25
*c.-d.* A870 50c Either single 1.00 .50
*e.-f.* A870 75c Either single 1.50 .75
*g.-h.* A870 $1 Either single 2.00 1.00
*i.* Booklet pane of 8, #a-h, with pane margins depicting rocks 10.00

Issued: Nos. 2063i, 2064i, 10/8. See Nos. 2094-2095.

Guayas Sports Federation, 90th Anniv. A871

No. 2065: a, Shooting (tiro). b, Wrestling (lucha). c, Kayaking (canotaje). d, Boxing (boxeo). e, Weight lifting (pesas).

*Perf. 13¾x13½*

**2012, July 25** **Wmk. 377**

**2065** Horiz. strip of 5 5.00 2.50
*a.-e.* A871 50c Any single 1.00 .50

A872

Legacy of the Revolution of 1895 — A873

No. 2066: a, Ecuador #129, Matilde Huerta, first Ecuadoran female postal official, 1895. b, Bolívar College, Tulcán, first lay college, 1896. c, Civil Registration Law, 1900. d, School of Fine Arts, Quito, 1904. e, Opening of Guayaquil-Quito Railroad, 1908. f, Founding of Guayaquil Worker's Society, 1903. g, Creation of Independence Plaza, Quito, 1909. h, Map of South America, José Martí, Eloy Alfaro, and Augusto César Sandino, 1911.
$3, Alfaro, locomotive.

**2012, July 31** ***Perf. 13¾x13½***
**2066** A872 25c Sheet of 8, #a-h 4.00 2.00

**Souvenir Sheet**

***Imperf***

**2067** A873 $3 multi 6.00 3.00

Enrique Gil Gilbert (1912-73), Writer A874

**2012, Aug. 8** ***Perf. 13¾x13½***
**2068** A874 $1 multi 2.00 1.00

**Souvenir Sheet**

Steamship Ecuador — A875

No. 2069 — Emblem of 2012 Ecuador Philatelic Society Stamp Exposition and: a, Ship's stern and flag. b, Ship's bow.

**Litho. (Foil Application in Margin)**

**2012, Aug. 16** ***Perf. 13½x13¾***
**2069** A875 $3 Sheet of 2, #a-b, gold inscription in sheet margin 12.00 6.00
*c.* As #2069, silver inscription in sheet margin 12.00 6.00
*d.* As #2069, red metallic inscription in sheet margin 12.00 6.00

**Miniature Sheet**

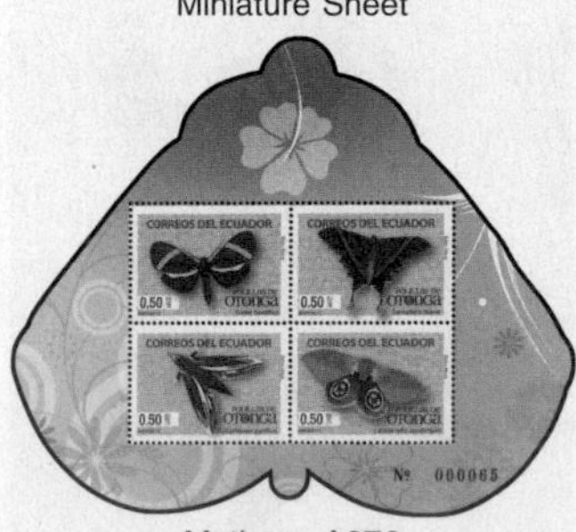

Moths — A876

No. 2070: a, Getta baetifica. b, Sematura diana. c, Xylophanes pyrrhus. d, Leucanella contempta.

***Perf. 13¾x13½***

**2012, Aug. 28** **Litho.**
**2070** A876 50c Sheet of 4, #a-d 4.00 2.00

Quito Chamber of Construction, 50th Anniv. — A877

Construction materials: No. 2071, $1, Timber (madera). No. 2072, $1, Bamboo (guadua). No. 2073, $1, Wattle (bahareque). No. 2074, $1, Compacted mud (tapial).

**2012, Sept. 4** ***Perf. 13½x13¾***
**2071-2074** A877 Set of 4 8.00 4.00

America Issue A878

Myths and legends: No. 2075, $2, Legend of Ayer. No. 2076, $2, Legend of the Rooster of the Cathedral, vert.

***Perf. 13¾x13½, 13½x13¾***

**2012, Sept. 17**
**2075-2076** A878 Set of 2 8.00 4.00

Nelson Estupiñán Bass (1912-2002), Writer — A879

**2012, Sept. 20** ***Perf. 13¾x13½***
**2077** A879 $2 multi 4.00 2.00

Alexander von Humboldt (1769-1859), Naturalist A880

Denominations: 50c, $2.

**2012, Sept. 26** **Wmk. 377**
**2078-2079** A880 Set of 2 5.00 2.50

Friendship between Ecuador and Germany, 125th anniv.

A881

Trains — A882

No. 2080: a, Baldwin No. 3 Ingenio Valdez. b, Baldwin No. 2 Inés María. c, Baldwin No. 12 C.F.F.E. d, Baldwin No. 37 G&Q. e. Baldwin No. 7 G&Q. f, Baldwin No. 3 Quito-Esmeraldas train. g, Baldwin No. 2 Yaguachi train. h, Baldwin No. 1 Curaray train.

No. 2081: a, Baldwin No. 53. b, Gec Alsthom No. 2408. c, Gec Alsthom No. 2405. d, Baldwin No. 17. e, Baldwin No. 58. f, Gec Alsthom No. 2407 and station. g, Gec Alsthom No. 2404. h, Gec Alsthom No. 2407.

No. 2082: a, Baldwin No. 58, diff. b, Gec Alsthom No. 2404, diff. c, Gec Alsthom No. 2406. d, Baldwin No. 53, diff. e, Gec Alsthom No. 2402. f, Baldwin No. 58 on bridge. g, Baldwin No. 17, diff. h, Gec Alsthom No. 2405, diff.

**2012, Oct. 8** **Unwmk.** ***Die Cut***

**Self-Adhesive**

**2080** Booklet pane of 8 10.00
*a.-b.* A881 25c Either single .50 .25
*c.-d.* A881 50c Either single 1.00 .50
*e.-f.* A881 75c Either single 1.50 .75
*g.-h.* A881 $1 Either single 2.00 1.00
**2081** Booklet pane of 8 10.00
*a.-b.* A882 25c Either single .50 .25
*c.-d.* A882 50c Either single 1.00 .50
*e.-f.* A882 75c Either single 1.50 .75
*g.-h.* A882 $1 Either single 2.00 1.00
**2082** Booklet pane of 8 10.00
*a.-b.* A882 25c Either single .50 .25
*c.-d.* A882 50c Either single 1.00 .50
*e.-f.* A882 75c Either single 1.50 .75
*g.-h.* A882 $1 Either single 2.00 1.00

Jesuit Institutions A883

Schools: No. 2083, $1, Unidad Educativa Borja, 75th anniv. No. 2084, $1, Unidad Educativa San Felipe Neri, 175th anniv. No. 2085, $1.25, Colegio San Gabriel, 150th anniv.
$5, Jesuit church and emblem.

***Perf. 13¾x13½***

**2012, Oct. 29** **Wmk. 377**
**2083-2085** A883 Set of 3 6.50 3.25

**Size: 100x70mm**

***Imperf***

**2086** A883 $5 multi 10.00 10.00

Permanent return of Jesuits to Ecuador, 150th anniv.

Renovation of Guayas Government Palace — A884

**2012, Nov. 6** ***Perf. 13½x13¾***
**2087** A884 $5 multi 10.00 10.00

Ecuadorian Army's Communications Group, 50th Anniv. — A885

No. 2088: a, Indian messenger. b, Men and wagon transporting radiotelegraphic station, 1924. c, Bicycle messengers, 1932. d, Communication transmission school building, 1942.

**2012, Nov. 14**
**2088** Horiz. strip of 4 2.00 2.00
*a.-d.* A885 25c Any single .50 .50

Guayaquil Beneficence Council, 125th Anniv. — A886

**2012, Nov. 27** ***Perf. 13¾x13½***
**2089** A886 $3 multi 6.00 6.00

**Miniature Sheet**

Guayas Tourism — A887

No. 2090: a, Crucifix. b, Rock climbers. c, Fishermen in boats. d, Rice farmer. e, Cacao farmer. f, Sugar processing.

**2012, Nov. 29**
**2090** A887 75c Sheet of 6, #a-f, + 2 labels 9.00 9.00

Christmas A888

Icons: No. 2091, $1, Bethlehem Portal, Concepción Monastery, Quito. No. 2092, $1, Mystery, Carmen Alto Monastery, Quito.

**2012, Dec. 3** **Wmk. 377**
**2091-2092** A888 Set of 2 4.00 4.00

Military Leaders A889

No. 2093: a, Gen. Eloy Alfaro (1842-1912). b, Col. Carlos Concha Torres (1864-1919). c, Col. Luis Vargas Torres (1855-87).

**2012, Dec. 14** ***Rouletted 13½***
**2093** Horiz. strip of 3 7.50 7.50
*a.-c.* A889 $1.25 Any single 2.50 2.50

**Galapagos Islands Type of 2012**

No. 2094: a, Rock with carving of face, Isla Floreana. b, Phoebastria irrorata. c, Carcharhinus galapagensis. d, Chelonia mydas. e, Pterophyllum scalare. f, Sleeping Lion Rock, San Cristóbal. g, Flower. h, Isla Plaza Sur.

No. 2095: a, Fregata magnificens. b, Post barrel, Post Office Bay, Isla Floreana. c, Camarhynchus pallidus. d, Pyrocephalus rubinus. e, Buteo galapagoensis. f, Isla

Bartolomé. g, Red reef fish. h, Vicente Roca Point.

**2013, Jan. 16 Unwmk. *Die Cut***
**Self-Adhesive**

| | | | |
|---|---|---|---|
| 2094 | Booklet pane of 8 | 10.00 | |
| *a.-b.* | A870 25c Either single | .50 | .50 |
| *c.-d.* | A870 50c Either single | 1.00 | 1.00 |
| *e.-f.* | A870 75c Either single | 1.50 | 1.50 |
| *g.-h.* | A870 $1 Either single | 2.00 | 2.00 |
| 2095 | Booklet pane of 8 | 10.00 | |
| *a.-b.* | A870 25c Either single | .50 | .50 |
| *c.-d.* | A870 50c Either single | 1.00 | 1.00 |
| *e.-f.* | A870 75c Either single | 1.50 | 1.50 |
| *g.-h.* | A870 $1 Either single | 2.00 | 2.00 |

Miniature Sheet

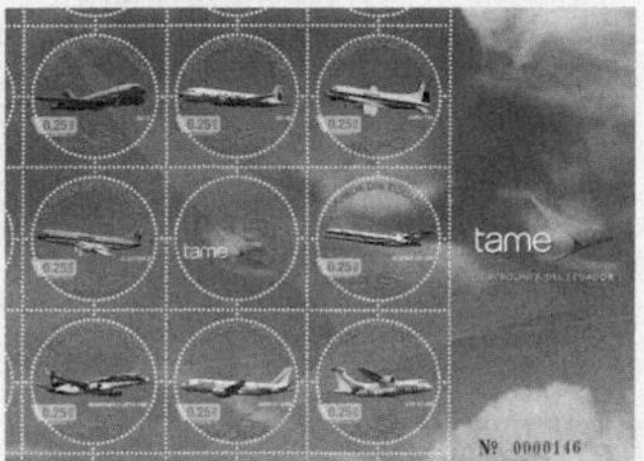


TAME Airlines, 50th Anniv. — A890

No. 2096: a, DC-3. b, DC-6B. c, Avro 748. d, Electra II. e, Boeing 727-200. f, Embraer E-190. g, Airbus A320. h, ATR 42-500.

**2013, Feb. 8 Wmk. 377 *Perf. 13½***
**2096** A890 25c Sheet of 8, #a-h, + central label 4.00 4.00

Hat Making — A891

No. 2097: a, Unfinished hats (orange panel). b, Hat maker (blue panel). c, Hat maker, diff. (red panel).

**2013, Mar. 18 *Perf. 13¼***
**2097** Horiz. strip of 3 3.00 3.00
*a.-c.* A891 50c Any single 1.00 1.00

Scout Group No. 14, Guayaquil, 50th Anniv. — A892

**Litho. With Foil Application**
***Perf. 13½x13¾***
**2013, June 21 Wmk. 377**
**2098** A892 $1 multi 2.00 2.00

Launch of Pegasus NEE-01 (First Ecuadorian Satellite) A893

***Perf. 13¾x13½***
**2013, June 28 Litho.**
**2099** A893 $2 multi 4.00 4.00

Diplomatic Relations Between Dominican Republic and Ecuador, 75th Anniv. — A894

**2013, July 2 *Perf. 13½x13¾***
**2100** A894 $1 multi 2.00 2.00

Popes Francis and Benedict XVI — A895

**Litho. With Foil Application**
**2013, July 3 Wmk. 377**
**2101** A895 $5 multi 10.00 10.00

June 24, 2012 Death of Pinta Island Tortoise, Lonesome George — A896

Lonesome George and: $3, Surf spray. $25, Trees.

**Litho. With Grit Affixed**
***Perf. 13½x13¼***
**2013, July 4 Unwmk.**
**2102** A896 $3 multi 6.00 6.00

**Litho.**
**Wmk. 377**
**Size: 91x71mm**
***Imperf***
**2103** A896 $25 multi 50.00 50.00

Dr. Ricardo Descalzi (1912-90), Writer and Physician — A897

***Perf. 13½x13¾***
**2013, Aug. 1 Litho. Wmk. 377**
**2104** A897 $3 multi 6.00 6.00

Volcanos A898

No. 2105: a, Mt. Chimborazo. b, Mt. Cotopaxi. c, Mt. Tungurahua.

***Perf. 13¾x13½***
**2013, Aug. 21 Litho. Wmk. 377**
**2105** Horiz. strip of 3 1.50 1.50
*a.-c.* A898 25c Any single .50 .50

Flower With Black and White Faces, Dr. Martin Luther King, Jr. — A899

***Perf. 13¾x13½***
**2013, Oct. 22 Litho. Wmk. 377**
**2106** A899 $1 multi 2.00 2.00

America issue (campaign against discrimination).

Royal Audience of Quito, 450th Anniv. — A900

Designs: 25c, Hernando de Santillán y Figueroa (1519-75), First President of the Royal Audience of Quito. $5, Map of the Royal Audience of Quito.

***Perf. 13¾x13½***
**2013, Nov. 13 Litho. Wmk. 377**
**2107** A900 25c multi .50 .50

**Size: 74x94mm**
***Imperf***
**2108** A900 $5 multi 10.00 10.00

Ecuadorian Presence in the Antarctic, 25th Anniv. — A901

No. 2109: a, Pygoscelis papua. b, Leptonychotes weddellii. c, Catharacta lonnbergi.

**Wmk. 377**
**2013, Nov. 21 Litho. *Perf. 13½***
**2109** Horiz. strip of 3 3.00 3.00
*a.-c.* A901 50c Any single 1.00 1.00

Miniature Sheet

Christmas — A902

No. 2110: a, Annunciation (Primer día). b, Visitation of St. Elizabeth (Segundo día). c, St. Joseph's dream (Tercer día). d, Journey to Bethlehem (Cuarto día). e, Arrival at the inn (Quinto día). f, Star of Bethlehem (Sexto día). g, Shepherds (Séptimo día). h, Angels (Octavo día). i, Holy Family (Noveno día).

***Perf. 13½x13¼***
**2013, Nov. 29 Litho. Wmk. 377**
**2110** A902 25c Sheet of 9, #a-i 4.50 4.50

Intl. Year of Quinoa A903

No. 2111: a, Chenopodium quinoa. b, Amaranthus caudatus. c, Lupinus mutabilis.

***Perf. 13¾x13½***
**2013, Dec. 16 Litho. Wmk. 377**
**2111** Horiz. strip of 3 12.00 12.00
*a.-c.* A903 $2 Any single 4.00 4.00

Imbabura Textile Mill — A904

No. 2112: a, Workers near weaving machines. b, Workers near machines with thread spools.

***Rouletted 12¼***
**2014, Jan. 27 Litho. Wmk. 377**
**2112** A904 $1 Horiz. pair, #a-b 4.00 4.00

Resolution of Ecuador-Peru Border Dispute, 15th Anniv. — A905

***Rouletted 12¼***
**2014, Jan. 30 Litho. Wmk. 377**
**2113** A905 $5 multi 10.00 10.00

Presidents of Ecuador — A906

No. 2114: a, Juan Jose Flores A. (1800-64). b, Vicente Rocafuerte B. (1783-1847). c, Vicente Roca R. (1792-1858). d, Diego Noboa A, (1789-1870). e, José M. Urbina V. (1808-91). f, Francisco Robles G. (1811-93). g, Gabriel García M. (1821-75). h, Jerónimo Carrión P. (1804-73). i, Javier Espinosa E. (1815-70). j, Antonio Borrero C. (1827-1911). k, Ignacio de Vientemilla V. (1828-1908). l, José M. Camaño (1837-1900). m, Antonio Flores J. (1833-1915). n, Luis Cordero C. (1833-1912). o, Eloy Alfaro D. (1842-1912). p, Leonidas Plaza G. (1865-1932). q, Lizardo García S. (1844-1937). r, Emilio Estrada C. (1855-1911). s, Alfredo Baquerizo M. (1859-1951). t, José L. Tamayo T. (1858-1947). u, Gonzalo S. córdova R. (1863-1928). v, Isidro Ayora C. (1879-1978). w, Juan D. Martínez M. (1875-1955). x, José M. Velasco I. (1893-1979). y, Aurelio Mosquera N. (1883-1939). z, Carlos A. Arroyo (1893-1969). aa, Mariano Suárez V. (1897-1980). ab, Carlos J. Arosemena T. (1888-1952). ac, Galo Plaza L. (1906-87). ad, Camilo Ponce E. (1912-76). ae, Carlos J. Arosemena M. (1919-2004). af, Otto Arosemena G. (1925-84). ag, Jaime Roldós A. (1940-81). ah, León Febres Cordero R. (1931-2008).

***Perf. 13¾x13½***
**2014, Apr. 1 Litho. Wmk. 377**
**2114** Sheet of 34 + label 17.00 17.00
*a.-ah.* A906 25c Any single .50 .50

Hugo R. Chávez (1954-2013), President of Venezuela A907

*Perf. 13¾x13½*

**2014, Apr. 14 Litho. Wmk. 377**

**2115** A907 50c multi 1.00 1.00

Parade of Tall Ships, Manabí — A908

No. 2116 — Ship and national flag: a, Cisne Branco, Brazil. b, Cuauhtémoc, Mexico. c, Gloria, Colombia. d, Libertad, Argentina. e, Esmerelda, Chile. f, Guayas, Ecuador. g, Simón Bolívar, Venezuela.

*Perf. 13½x13¾*

**2014, May 3 Litho. Wmk. 377**

**2116** Sheet of 7 + label 10.50 10.50

*a.-g.* A908 75c Any single 1.50 1.50

Intl. Philately Day — A909

Magnifying glass over: $2, Ecuadorian stamps. $3, Text from *El Nacional.*

**2014, May 22 Litho.** *Perf. 13½x13¾*

**2117** A909 $2 multi 4.00 4.00

**Size: 90x70mm**

**Wmk. 395**

***Imperf***

**2118** A909 $3 multi 6.00 6.00

Regional Platform for Disaster Risk Reduction in the Americas, Guayaquil — A910

*Perf. 13½x13¾*

**2014, May 27 Litho. Wmk. 377**

**2119** A910 $1 multi 2.00 2.00

2014 World Cup Soccer Championships, Brazil — A911

Designs: 50c, Stadium and stylized Ecuador soccer player. $3, Stylized Ecuador soccer player in stadium, Christ the Redeemer Statue, Rio de Janeiro, horiz.
$5, Soccer player and field, horiz.

*Perf. 13½x13¾, 13¾x13½*

**2014, June 18 Litho. Wmk. 377**

**2120-2121** A911 Set of 2 7.00 7.00

**Size: 55x35mm**

***Imperf***

**2122** A911 $5 multi 10.00 10.00

Pancho Segura, Ecuadorian-born Tennis Player — A912

Designs: 25c, Segura on tennis court as young man. $5, Segura, tennis ball and racquet, Ecuadoran flag.

*Perf. 13½x13¾*

**2014, July 25 Litho. Wmk. 377**

**2123-2124** A912 Set of 2 10.50 10.50

Intl. Year of Family Farming A913

Designs: 75c, Woman near tree. $1, Woman spinning yarn from wool. $2, Man pulling down cacao pod from tree.

*Perf. 13¾x13½*

**2014, Aug. 11 Litho. Wmk. 377**

**2125-2127** A913 Set of 3 7.50 7.50

2014 Latin American Integration Association Expo, Montevideo, Uruguay — A914

*Perf. 13½x13¾*

**2014, Aug. 28 Litho. Wmk. 377**

**2128** A914 $3 multi 6.00 6.00

Mural by Oswaldo Guayasamín — A915

No. 2129: a, Denomination at left. b, Denomination at right.

*Perf. 13¾x13½*

**2014, Aug. 29 Litho. Wmk. 377**

**2129** A915 25c Horiz. pair, #a-b 1.00 1.00

Latin American Parliament, 50th anniv.

Luis Vernaza Hospital, 450th Anniv. — A916

No. 2130: a, Hospital building. b, Doctor examining patient.

*Perf. 13½x13¾*

**2014, Sept. 10 Litho. Wmk. 377**

**2130** A916 50c Horiz. pair, #a-b 2.00 2.00

Miniature Sheet

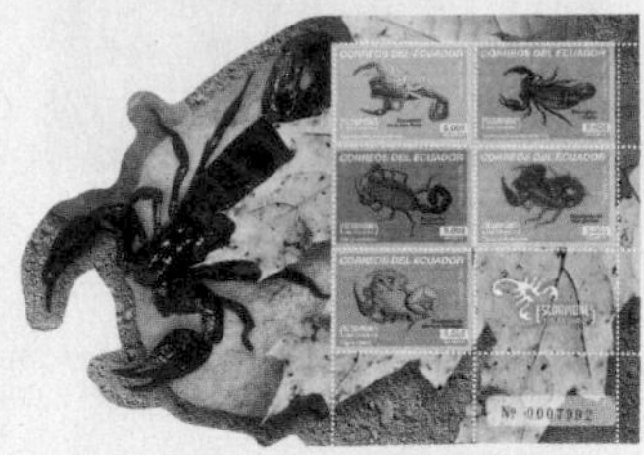

Scorpions — A917

No. 2131: a, Centruroides margaritatus. b, Teuthraustes atramentarius. c, Tityus asthenes. d, Tityus crassicauda. e, Tityus ythieri.

*Perf. 13¾x13½*

**2014, Sept. 30 Litho. Wmk. 377**

**2131** A917 $5 Sheet of 5, #a-e, + label 50.00 50.00

Yachay University Buildings — A918

No. 2132: a, Capitular Building, b, Library.

*Perf. 13¾x13½*

**2014, Oct. 21 Litho. Wmk. 377**

**2132** A918 $2 Horiz. pair, #a-b 8.00 8.00

Oryx Leucoryx, Vultur Gryphus, Flags of Ecuador and Qatar — A919

**Litho. With Foil Application**

*Perf. 13½x13¾*

**2014, Oct. 22 Wmk. 377**

**2133** A919 $10 multi 20.00 20.00

See Qatar No. 1101.

Manuela Espejo (c. 1757-c. 1829), Writer — A920

**Litho. With Foil Application**

*Perf. 13½x13¾*

**2014, Oct. 28 Wmk. 377**

**2134** A920 $5 metallic blue & blue 10.00 10.00

America issue.

Electricity Generation Projects — A921

Designs: 75c, Baba Dam. $1.25, Wind generators, Villonaco. $2, Mazar Dam.

*Perf. 13½x13¾*

**2014, Oct. 31 Litho. Wmk. 377**

**2135-2137** A921 Set of 3 8.00 8.00

Fall of the Berlin Wall, 25th Anniv. — A922

*Perf. 13¾x13½*

**2014, Nov. 10 Litho. Wmk. 377**

**2138** A922 75c multi 1.50 1.50

Christmas A923

Designs: 50c, Ivory creche figurines, 18th cent. $1, Wood carving of Infant Jesus, by Caspicara, vert.

*Perf. 13¾x13½, 13½x13¾*

**2014, Nov. 25 Litho. Wmk. 377**

**2139-2140** A923 Set of 2 3.00 3.00

Miniature Sheet

Cuenca Tourist Attractions — A924

No. 2141: a, Rio Tomebamba. b, Mayor's office (Alcaldía). c, Benigno Malo College. d, Interamerican Artisans Center. e, New Cathedral. f, Azuay Provincial Court. g, Plaza de las Flores.

*Perf. 13¾x13½*

**2014, Dec. 2 Litho. Wmk. 377**

**2141** A924 75c Sheet of 7, #a-g, + label 10.50 10.50

Miniature Sheet

First Ecuadorian Postage Stamps, 150th Anniv. — A925

No. 2142: a, Emilia Rivadeneira (1839-1916), engraver. b, Printing press, Ecuador #3. c, Printing press, Ecuador #2. d, Printing press, Ecuador #5. e, Manuel Rivadeneira (1814-94), printer.

**Litho. With Foil Application**

*Perf. 13¾x13½*

**2015, Mar. 19 Wmk. 377**

**2142** A925 $5 Sheet of 5, #a-e, + 4 labels 50.00 50.00

Insects — A926

No. 2143: a, Antianthe expansa. b, Heteronotus abbreviatus. c, Cyphonia clavata. d, Guayaquila gracilicornis. e, Stegaspis fronditia. f, Thuris depressus. g, Tritropidia galeata. h, Membracis mexicana.

**Unwmk.**

**2015, Apr. 21 Litho.** ***Die Cut***

**Self-Adhesive**

| | | | |
|---|---|---|---|
| **2143** | Booklet pane of 8 | 10.00 | |
| *a.-b.* | A926 25c Either single | .50 | .50 |
| *c.-d.* | A926 50c Either single | 1.00 | 1.00 |
| *e.-f.* | A926 75c Either single | 1.50 | 1.50 |
| *g.-h.* | A926 $1 Either single | 2.00 | 2.00 |

Pres. Sixto Durán Ballén and Dove — A927

***Perf. 13½x13¾***

**2015, May 15 Litho. Wmk. 377**

**2144** A927 $1.25 multi 2.50 2.50

Insects — A928

No. 2145: a, Alchisme grossa. b, Membracis foliata. c, Cladonota apicalis. d, Cyphonia trifida. e, Adippe histrio.

***Perf. 13½x13¾***

**2015, May 28 Litho. Wmk. 377**

| | | | |
|---|---|---|---|
| **2145** | Horiz. strip of 5 | 30.00 | 30.00 |
| *a.-e.* | A928 $3 Any single | 6.00 | 6.00 |

Cattle — A929

Breeds: 75c, Aberdeen Angus. $1.25, Brahman. $3, Holstein Friesian.

***Perf. 13½x13¾***

**2015, June 2 Litho. Wmk. 377**

**2146-2148** A929 Set of 3 10.00 10.00

Eradication of hoof-and-mouth disease in Ecuador.

Renovation of San Francisco Monastery, Quito — A930

Designs: 25c, Friar Jodoco Ricke baptizing indigenous people. 50c, Icon of Jesus, San Francisco Church. $1, San Francisco Church and Plaza. $1.75, Franciscan monk making beer. $2, Religious procession.

***Perf. 13½x13¾***

**2015, June 11 Litho. Wmk. 377**

**2149-2153** A930 Set of 5 11.00 11.00

Birds — A931

Designs: 25c, Grallaria ridgelyi. 50c, Amazona lilacina. $1, Atlapetes pallidiceps. $2, Pyrrhura albipectus. $3, Chaetocercus berlepschi.

***Perf. 13½x13¾***

**2015, June 16 Litho. Wmk. 377**

**2154-2158** A931 Set of 5 13.50 13.50

Visit of Pope Francis to Ecuador A932

***Perf. 13¾x13½***

**2015, June 30 Litho. Wmk. 377**

**2159** A932 $3 multi 6.00 6.00

**Litho. With Foil Application**

**Size: 100x70mm**

***Imperf***

**2160** A932 $5 Pope Francis, diff. 10.00 10.00

Official Registrar, 120th Anniv. A933

***Perf. 13¾x13½***

**2015, Sept. 1 Litho. Wmk. 377**

**2161** A933 $1.50 multi 3.00 3.00

Famous People A934

No. 2162: a, Antonio Bastidas y Carranza (1615-81), poet. b, Raúl Clemente Huerta (1915-91), politician. c, Morayma Ofyr Carvajal (1915-51), writer. d, José Modesto Espinosa (1833-1915), writer. e, José Cuero y Caicedo (1735-1815), bishop of Quito.

***Perf. 13¾x13½***

**2015, Sept. 22 Litho. Wmk. 377**

| | | | |
|---|---|---|---|
| **2162** | Horiz. strip of 5 | 12.50 | 12.50 |
| *a.-e.* | A934 $1.25 Any single | 2.50 | 2.50 |

Miniature Sheet

ExpoAFE,150th Anniv. — A935

No. 2163: a, Argentina #594, flag of Argentina. b, Unissued Bolivia stamp of 1863, flag of Bolivia. c, Brazil #3252c, flag of Brazil. d, Canada #322, flag of Canada. e, Chile #348A, flag of Chile. f, Colombia #C56, flag of Colombia. g, Costa Rica #1, flag of Costa Rica. h, Cuba #432, flag of Cuba. i, Ecuador #306, flag of Ecuador. j, El Salvador #509, flag of El Salvador. k, Cover of *El Coleccionista Ecuatoriano*, emblem of Ecuadorian Philatelic Association. l, Block of six of Ecuador #2, ExpoAFE 80th anniv. emblem. m, Cover to Lima, emblem of ExpopAFE thematic stamp exhibition. n, Cover depicting airplane, emblem of FIAF thematic stamp exhibition. o, Postal card, FIAF emblem. p, Spain #345, flag of Spain. q, United States #C3a, flag of United States. r, Guatemala #21, flag of Guatemala. s, Mexico #246, flag of Mexico. t, Panama #214, flag of Panama. u, Paraguay #407, flag of Paraguay. v, Peru #C338, flag of Peru. w, St. Pierre & Miquelon #136, flag of St. Pierre & Miquelon. x, Uruguay #1167, flag of Uruguay. y, Venezuela #C9, flag of Venezuela.

***Perf. 13½x13¾***

**2015, Sept. 29 Litho. Wmk. 377**

| | | | |
|---|---|---|---|
| **2163** | A935 Sheet of 25 | 37.50 | 37.50 |
| *a.-y.* | 75c Any single | 1.50 | 1.50 |

Birds — A936

No. 2164: a, Tangara florida. b, Acropternis orthonyx. c, Piprcola jucunda. d, Pionopsitta pyrilia. e, Semnornis ramphastinus. f, Trogon chionurus. g, Pipra filicauda. h, Dacnis egregia.

No. 2165: a, Thryothorus nigricapillus. b, Neomorphus radiolosus. c, Phoenicircus nigricollis. d, Tangara gyrola. e, Aegolius harrisii. f, Grallaricula lineifrons. g, Melanopareia elegans. h, Piculus rivolii.

**Unwmk.**

**2015, Oct. 20 Litho.** ***Die Cut***

**Self-Adhesive**

| | | | |
|---|---|---|---|
| **2164** | Booklet pane of 8 | 10.00 | |
| *a.-b.* | A936 25c Either single | .50 | .50 |
| *c.-d.* | A936 50c Either single | 1.00 | 1.00 |
| *e.-f.* | A936 75c Either single | 1.50 | 1.50 |
| *g.-h.* | A936 $1 Either single | 2.00 | 2.00 |
| **2165** | Booklet pane of 8 | 10.00 | |
| *a.-b.* | A936 25c Either single | .50 | .50 |
| *c.-d.* | A936 50c Either single | 1.00 | 1.00 |
| *e.-f.* | A936 75c Either single | 1.50 | 1.50 |
| *g.-h.* | A936 $1 Either single | 2.00 | 2.00 |

Don Quixote in Art — A937

No. 2166, $1 — Depictions of Don Quixote by: a, Carlos Monsalve. b, Ernesto Saá Sevilla.

No. 2167, $1.50 — Depictions of Don Quixote by: a, Oswaldo Viteri. b, Vilma Vargas.

No. 2168, $1.75, horiz. — Depictions of Don Quixote by: a, Joaquín Pinto. b, Karlomán Villota.

***Perf. 13½x13¾, 13¾x13½***

**2015, Oct. 30 Litho. Wmk. 377**

**Horiz. Pairs, #a-b**

**2166-2168** A937 Set of 3 17.00 17.00

A938

A939

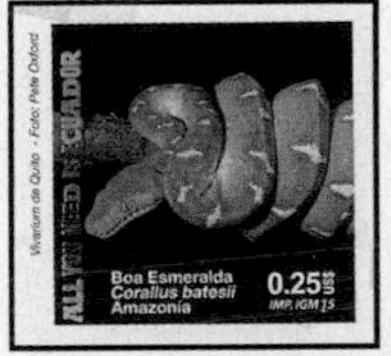


Tourism A940

No. 2169: a, Chelonia mydas. b, Vicugna vicugna. c, Paleosuchus trigonatus. d, Megaptera novaeangliae. e, Marine iguana.

$5, Tortoise, caiman, whale, condor.

No. 2171: a, Corallus batesii. b, San Rafael Waterfall. c, Dasyatis brevis. d, Gardner Bay Beach, Española Island, Galapagos Islands. e, Ceratophrys stolzmanni. f, Ship on Guayas River. g, Coeligena torquata. h, El Vado, Cuenca.

No. 2172: a, Hippocampus ingens. b, Amblyrhynchus cristatus. c, Prionurus laticlavius. d, Fregata magnificens. e, Spheniscus mendiculus. f, Boats near Isabela Island, Galapagos Islands. g, Roca Pináculo, Bartolomé Island, Galapagos Islands. h, Boats near Plaza Islands, Galapagos Islands.

***Perf. 13¾x13½***

**2015, Nov. 11 Litho. Wmk. 377**

| | | | |
|---|---|---|---|
| **2169** | Horiz. strip of 5 | 10.00 | 10.00 |
| *a.-e.* | A938 $1 Any single | 2.00 | 2.00 |

***Imperf***

**2170** A939 $5 multi 10.00 10.00

**Self-Adhesive**

**Unwmk.**

***Die Cut***

| | | | |
|---|---|---|---|
| **2171** | Booklet pane of 8 | 10.00 | |
| *a.-b.* | A940 25c Either single | .50 | .50 |
| *c.-d.* | A940 50c Either single | 1.00 | 1.00 |
| *e.-f.* | A940 75c Either single | 1.50 | 1.50 |
| *g.-h.* | A940 $1 Either single | 2.00 | 2.00 |
| **2172** | Booklet pane of 8 | 10.00 | |
| *a.-b.* | A940 25c Either single | .50 | .50 |
| *c.-d.* | A940 50c Either single | 1.00 | 1.00 |
| *e.-f.* | A940 75c Either single | 1.50 | 1.50 |
| *g.-h.* | A940 $1 Either single | 2.00 | 2.00 |

Campaign to End Violence Against Women A941

*Perf. 13¾x13½*

**2015, Nov, 25 Litho. Wmk. 377**

**2173** A941 $5 multi 10.00 10.00

See Dominican Republic No. 1583, Guatemala No. 717, El Salvador No. 1747, Venezuela No. 1731.

Campaign Against Human Trafficking — A942

*Perf. 13½x13¾*

**2015, Nov. 22 Litho. Wmk. 377**

**2174** A942 $1.50 multi 3.00 3.00

America Issue.

Christmas — A943

*Perf. 13½x13¾*

**2015, Dec. 3 Litho. Wmk. 377**

**2175** A943 $2 multi 4.00 4.00

Yachay, City of Knowledge A944

*Perf. 13¾x13½*

**2016, Mar. 31 Litho. Wmk. 377**

**2176** A944 $2 multi 4.00 4.00

Amphibians A945

No. 2177: a, Epipedobates anthonyi. b, Hyloscirtus princecharlesi, c, Oophaga sylvatica. d, Ceratophrys stolzmanni. e, Gastrotheca riobambae. f, Hyalinobatrachium aureoguttatum. g, Hypsiboas picturatus. h, Atelopus balios.

**Unwmk.**

**2016, Mar. 31 Litho. *Die Cut***

**Self-Adhesive**

**2177** Booklet pane of 8 10.00
*a.-b.* A945 25c Either single .50 .50
*c.-d.* A945 50c Either single 1.00 1.00
*e.-f.* A945 75c Either single 1.50 1.50
*g.-h.* A945 $1 Either single 2.00 2.00

Quito Central Lions Club, 70th Anniv. — A946

*Perf. 13½x13¾*

**2016, Apr. 27 Litho. Wmk. 377**

**2178** A946 $5 multi 10.00 10.00

Ecuador Postal Service, 185th Anniv. — A947

No. 2179: a, Chasqui (relay messenger). b, Postman on bicycle. c, Postal worker on motorcycle. d, Old Quito Post Office, 185th anniv. emblem.

*Perf. 13½x13¾*

**2016, May 25 Litho. Wmk. 377**

**2179** A947 10c Block of 4, #a-d .80 .80

Miniature Sheet

2016 Summer Olympics, Rio de Janeiro — A948

No. 2180: a, Swimming. b, Running, c, Weight lifting. d, Boxing.

*Perf. 13¾x13½*

**2016, Aug. 16 Litho. Wmk. 377**

**2180** A948 $1.25 Sheet of 4, #a-d 10.00 10.00

Colegio Intisana, Quito, 50th Anniv. — A949

*Perf. 13½x13¾*

**2016, Oct. 24 Litho. Wmk. 377**

**2181** A949 $2 multi 4.00 4.00

Jamaica Letter, by Simón Bolívar, 200th Anniv. (in 2015) — A950

No. 2182: a, Portrait of Bolívar, by Antonio Salguero. b, Jamaica Letter, ribbon in colors of Ecuadorian flag.

*Perf. 13½x13¾*

**2016, Oct. 28 Litho. Wmk. 377**

**2182** A950 $10 Horiz. pair, #a-b 40.00 40.00

Coca Codo Sinclair Hydroelectric Project A951

Designs: $1.25, Dam. $1.50, Compensating reservoir. $1.75, Generators.

*Perf. 13¾x13½*

**2016, Oct. 25 Litho. Wmk. 377**

**2183-2185** A951 Set of 3 9.00 9.00

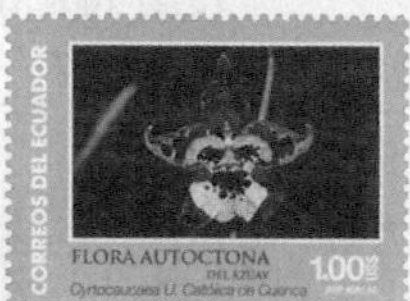


Flowers A952

No. 2186: a, Cyrtocaucaea. b, Masdevallia. c, Hippeastrum sp. d, Gentianella hirculus. e, Bomarea caldasii.

*Perf. 13¾x13½*

**2016, Nov. 12 Litho. Wmk. 395**

**2186** Horiz. strip of 5 10.00 10.00
*a.-e.* A952 $1 Any single 2.00 2.00

Third French-Ecuadorian Geodesic Mission — A953

No. 2187: a, Drawing of people near globe. b, Mt. Chimborazo.

*Perf. 13¾x13½*

**2016, Nov. 14 Litho. Wmk. 377**

**2187** A953 10c Horiz. pair, #a-b .40 .40

Society for Protection of Children — A954

*Perf. 13½x13¾*

**2016, Nov. 22 Litho. Wmk. 377**

**2188** A954 $5 multi 10.00 10.00

Santa Elena Petroleum Ancón Oil Well — A955

*Perf. 13¾x13½*

**2016, Nov. 30 Litho. Wmk. 377**

**2189** A955 30c multi .60 .60

Christmas A956

No. 2190: a, Shepherd and sheep, volcano. b, Star of Bethlehem, Andean village. c, Annunciation, Galapagos turtle. d, Three Magi in Ecuadorian Indian costumes. e, Afro-American Holy Family.

*Perf. 13¾x13½*

**2016, Dec. 12 Litho. Wmk. 377**

**2190** Horiz. strip of 5 20.00 20.00
*a.-e.* A956 $2 Any single 4.00 4.00

Union of South American Nations Summit, Quito A957

*Perf. 13¾x13½*

**2016, Dec. 22 Litho. Wmk. 377**

**2191** A957 $3 multi 6.00 6.00

Ecuadorian Institute for Promotion of Exportation and Investment — A958

No. 2192: a, Dam, emblem for 2016 Ecuador Investment Summit. b, Spiral and "love life." c, Hats. d, Cacao pods. e, Onions, bananas, herbs, shrimp.

*Perf. 13½x13¾*

**2016, Dec. 29 Litho. Wmk. 377**

**2192** Horiz. strip of 5 10.00 10.00
*a.-e.* A958 $1 Any single 2.00 2.00

A959

Schools — A960

No. 2193: a, Hands, emblem of Ecuador University of Arts. b, Book, quill pen, emblem of National University of Ecuador.

No. 2194: a, Buckminsterfullerene molecule, emblem for Yachay Tech. b, Frog, emblem for Amazon Regional University.

*Perf. 13½x13¾*

**2016, Dec. 30 Litho. Wmk. 377**

**2193** A959 $3 Horiz. pair, #a-b 12.00 12.00
**2194** A960 $3 Horiz. pair, #a-b 12.00 12.00

Carnival, Guaranda — A961

No. 2195: a, Aerial view of Guaranda. b, Guitarist.

*Perf. 13¾x13½*

**2017, Feb. 24** **Litho.**

**2195** A961 $1 Horiz. pair, #a-b 4.00 4.00

Ants — A962

No. 2196: a, Atta cephalotes (Hormiga arriera). b, Eciton hamatum (Hormiga legionaria). c, Daceton armigerum (Hormiga cazadora). d, Acanthoponera minor (Conga enana). e, Ectatomma tuberculatum (Hormiga rugosa). f, Gigantiops destructor (Hormiga ojona). g, Neoponera villosa (Hormiga peluda). h, Cephalotes atratus (Cabezona negra).

No. 2197: a, Cephalotes spinosus (Hormiga paracaidista). b, Odontomachus hastatus (Hormiga mandibula). c, Pheidole xanthogaster (Hormiga zanahoria). d, Myrmelachista ruszkii (Hormiga limón). e, Leptogenys pucuna (Hormiga de Lattke). f, Eciton rapax (Hormiga rapaz). g, Paraponera clavata (Conga). h, Camponotus sericeiventris (Hormiga aterciopelada).

**Unwmk.**

**2017, Mar. 31** **Litho.** ***Die Cut***

**Self-Adhesive**

**2196** Booklet pane of 8 10.00
*a.-b.* A962 25c Either single .50 .50
*c.-d.* A962 50c Either single 1.00 1.00
*e.-f.* A962 75c Either single 1.50 1.50
*g.-h.* A962 $1 Either single 2.00 2.00
**2197** Booklet pane of 8 10.00
*a.-b.* A962 25c Either single .50 .50
*c.-d.* A962 50c Either single 1.00 1.00
*e.-f.* A962 75c Either single 1.50 1.50
*g.-h.* A962 $1 Either single 2.00 2.00

Miniature Sheet

World Philately Day — A963

No. 2198: a, Emblem of Olympic and Sports Philatelic Association of Ecuador. b, 1883 cover with Ecuador #18. c, 1895 cover with Guaranda provisional surcharge stamps. d, 1896 cover with bisected Seebeck stamp and other Ecuador stamps.

**Litho., Litho With Foil Application (#2198a)**

*Perf. 13¾x13½*

**2017, May 18** **Wmk. 377**

**2198** A963 $2.50 Sheet of 4, #a-d 20.00 20.00

---

## SEMI-POSTAL STAMPS

**Nos. 423-428 Surcharged in Carmine or Blue**

**1944, May 9** **Unwmk.** ***Perf. 12***

**B1** A171 10c + 10c yel grn (C) .60 .30
**B2** A171 20c + 20c rose pink .60 .30
**B3** A171 30c + 20c dk gray brn .60 .30
**B4** A171 50c + 20c dp red lil 1.20 .60
**B5** A171 1s + 50c ol gray (C) 2.00 1.00
**B6** A171 10s + 2s red orange 7.00 3.50
*Nos. B1-B6 (6)* 12.00 6.00

The surtax aided Mendez Hospital.

---

## AIR POST STAMPS

In 1928-30, the internal airmail service of Ecuador was handled by the Sociedad Colombo-Alemana de Transportes Aereos ("SCADTA") under government sanction. During this period SCADTA issued stamps which were the only legal franking for airmail service except that handled under contract with Pan American-Grace Airways. SCADTA issues are Nos. C1-C6, C16-C25, CF1-CF2.

Colombia Air Post Stamps of 1923 Surcharged in Carmine

**"Provisional" at 45 degree Angle**

*Perf. 14x14½*

**1928, Aug. 28** **Wmk. 116**

**C1** AP6 50c on 10c green 110.00 70.00
**C2** AP6 75c on 15c car 210.00 160.00
**C3** AP6 1s on 20c gray 70.00 42.50
**C4** AP6 1½s on 30c blue 45.00 35.00
**C5** AP6 3s on 60c brown 85.00 52.50
*Nos. C1-C5 (5)* 520.00 360.00

**"Provisional" at 41 degree Angle**

**1929, Mar. 20**

*C1a* AP6 50c on 10c green 125.00 110.00
*C2a* AP6 75c on 15c carmine 225.00 175.00
*C3a* AP6 1s on 20c gray 225.00 175.00
*Nos. C1a-C3a (3)* 575.00 460.00

**C6** AP6 50c on 10c green *700.00 1,700.*

A 75c on 15c carmine with "Cts." between the surcharged numerals exists. There is no evidence that it was regularly issued or used.

For overprints see Nos. CF1-CF1a.

Plane over River Guayas — AP1

**Unwmk.**

**1929, May 5** **Engr.** ***Perf. 12***

**C8** AP1 2c black .40 .25
**C9** AP1 5c carmine rose .40 .25
**C10** AP1 10c deep brown .40 .25
**C11** AP1 20c dark violet .90 .25
**C12** AP1 50c deep green 1.60 .45
**C13** AP1 1s dark blue 6.00 2.75
**C14** AP1 5s orange yellow 25.00 11.00
**C15** AP1 10s orange red 135.00 57.50
*Nos. C8-C15 (8)* 169.70 72.70

Establishment of commercial air service in Ecuador. The stamps were available for all forms of postal service and were largely used for franking ordinary letters.

Nos. C13-C15 show numerals in color on white background. Counterfeits of No. C15 exist.

See Nos. C26-C31. For overprints and surcharge see Nos. C32-C38, C287, CO1-CO12.

Jesuit Church La Compania AP2

Mount Chimborazo AP3

**Wmk. 127**

**1929, Apr. 1** **Litho.** ***Perf. 14***

**C16** AP2 50c red brown 4.50 2.25
**C17** AP2 75c green 4.50 2.25
**C18** AP2 1s rose 7.00 2.25
**C19** AP2 1½s gray blue 7.00 2.25
**C20** AP2 2s violet 11.50 4.50
**C21** AP2 3s brown 11.50 4.50
**C22** AP3 5s lt blue 50.00 15.00
**C23** AP3 10s lt red 100.00 32.50
**C24** AP3 15s violet 160.00 65.00
**C25** AP3 25s olive green 225.00 75.00
*Nos. C16-C25 (10)* 581.00 205.50

For overprint see No. CF2.

**Plane Type of 1929**

**1930-44** **Unwmk.** **Engr.** ***Perf. 12***

**C26** AP1 1s carmine lake 6.50 .55
**C27** AP1 1s green ('44) 1.00 .25
**C28** AP1 5s olive green 10.00 3.75
**C29** AP1 5s purple ('44) 2.00 .25
**C30** AP1 10s black 30.00 5.50
**C31** AP1 10s brt ultra ('44) 4.50 .30
*Nos. C26-C31 (6)* 54.00 10.60

Nos. C26-C31 show numerals in color on white background.

For surcharge see No. C287.

Nos. C26, C28, C30 Ovptd. in Various Colors

**1930, June 4**

**C32** AP1 1s car lake (Bk) 22.50 22.50
*a.* Double ovpt. (R Br + Bk) 75.00
**C33** AP1 5s olive grn (Bl) 22.50 22.50
**C34** AP1 10s black (R Br) 22.50 22.50
*Nos. C32-C34 (3)* 67.50 67.50

Flight of Capt. Benjamin Mendez from Bogota to Quito, bearing a crown of flowers for the tomb of Grand Marshal Sucre.

Air Post Official Stamps of 1929-30 Ovptd. in Various Colors or Srchd. Similarly in Upper & Lower Case

**1935, July 24**

**C35** AP1 50c deep green (Bl) 12.50 5.00
**C36** AP1 50c olive brn (R) 12.50 5.00
**C37** AP1 1s on 5s ol grn (Bk) 12.50 5.00
*a.* Double surcharge 95.00
**C38** AP1 2s on 10s black (R) 12.50 5.00
*Nos. C35-C38 (4)* 50.00 20.00

Unveiling of a monument to Bolivar at Quito, July 24th, 1935.

AP5

**1935, Oct. 13** **Photo.** ***Perf. 11½x11***

**C38A** AP5 5c ultra & red .25 *.30*
**C38B** AP5 10c brown & black .25 *.50*
**C38C** AP5 50c green & red .25 *.50*
**C38D** AP5 1S carmine & blue .80 *1.20*
**C38E** AP5 5S gray grn & red 1.20 *2.40*
*Nos. C38A-C38E (5)* 2.75 *4.90*

Columbus Day. Nos. 338A-338E and C38A-C38E were prepared by the Sociedad Colombista Panamericana and were sold by the Ecuadorian post office through Oct. 30. Nos. C38B-C38E exist imperf.

**Geodesical Mission Issue**

Nos. 349-351 Overprinted in Blue or Black and Type of Regular issue

**1936, July 3** ***Perf. 12½***

**C39** A136 10c deep orange (Bl) .60 .25
**C40** A136 20c violet (Bk) .60 .25
**C41** A136 50c dark red (Bl) .60 .25
**C42** A136 70c black 1.25 .35
*Nos. C39-C42 (4)* 3.05 1.10

For surcharge see No. RA42.

**Philatelic Exhibition Issue**

Type of Regular Issue Overprinted "AEREA"

**1936, Oct. 20** ***Perf. 13½x14***

**C43** A137 2c rose 5.00 5.00
**C44** A137 5c brown orange 5.00 5.00
**C45** A137 10c brown 5.00 5.00
**C46** A137 20c ultra 5.00 5.00
**C47** A137 50c red violet 5.00 5.00
**C48** A137 1s green 5.00 5.00
*Nos. C43-C48 (6)* 30.00 30.00

Condor and Plane — AP6

*Perf. 13½*

**C49** AP6 70c orange brown 2.25 .50
**C50** AP6 1s dull violet 2.25 .50

Nos. C43-C50 were issued for the 1st Intl. Phil. Exhib. at Quito.

Condor over "El Altar" — AP7

**1937-46** ***Perf. 11½, 12***

**C51** AP7 10c chestnut 5.00 .25
**C52** AP7 20c olive black 6.50 .25
**C53** AP7 40c rose car ('46) 6.50 .25
**C54** AP7 70c black brown 9.00 .25
**C55** AP7 1s gray black 14.00 .25
**C56** AP7 2s dark violet 24.00 .65
*Nos. C51-C56 (6)* 65.00 1.90

Issue dates: 40c, Oct. 7; others, Aug. 19.

For overprints see Nos. 463-464, CO13-CO17.

Portrait of Washington, American Eagle and Flags — AP8

**Engraved and Lithographed**

**1938, Feb. 9** ***Perf. 12***

**Center Multicolored**

**C57** AP8 2c brown .40 .25
**C58** AP8 5c black .40 .25
**C59** AP8 10c brown .40 .25
**C60** AP8 20c dark blue .80 .25
**C61** AP8 50c violet 1.75 .25
**C62** AP8 1s black 3.25 .25
**C63** AP8 2s violet 7.50 .90
*Nos. C57-C63 (7)* 14.50 2.40

150th anniv. of the US Constitution.

In 1947, Nos. C61-C63 were overprinted in dark blue: "Primero la Patria!" and plane. These revolutionary propaganda stamps were later renounced by decree. Value $20.

For overprints see Nos. C102-C104, C139-C141.

No. RA35 Surcharged in Red

**1938, Nov. 16** *Perf. 13½*

| | | | | |
|---|---|---|---|---|
| **C64** | PT12 | 65c on 3c ultra | .40 | .25 |

A national airmail concession was given to the Sociedad Ecuatoriano de Transportes Aereos (SEDTA) in July, 1938. No. RA35 was surcharged for SEDTA postal requirements. SEDTA operated through 1940.

Army Horseman — AP9

Woman Runner — AP10

Tennis — AP11

Boxing — AP12

Olympic Fire — AP13

**1939, Mar. Engr.** *Perf. 12*

| | | | | |
|---|---|---|---|---|
| **C65** | AP9 | 5c lt green | 1.60 | .25 |
| **C66** | AP10 | 10c salmon | 2.25 | .25 |
| **C67** | AP11 | 50c redsh brown | 11.50 | .25 |
| **C68** | AP12 | 1s black brown | 13.50 | .45 |
| **C69** | AP13 | 2s rose carmine | 17.00 | 1.10 |
| | | *Nos. C65-C69 (5)* | 45.85 | 2.30 |

First Bolivarian Games (1938).

Plane over Chimborazo AP14

**1939, May 1** *Perf. 13x12½*

| | | | | |
|---|---|---|---|---|
| **C70** | AP14 | 1s yellow brown | .40 | .25 |
| **C71** | AP14 | 2s rose violet | .70 | .25 |
| **C72** | AP14 | 5s black | 1.90 | .25 |
| | | *Nos. C70-C72 (3)* | 3.00 | .75 |

Golden Gate Bridge and Mountain Peak — AP15

**1939** *Perf. 12½x13*

| | | | | |
|---|---|---|---|---|
| **C73** | AP15 | 2c black | .40 | .25 |
| **C74** | AP15 | 5c rose red | .40 | .25 |
| **C75** | AP15 | 10c indigo | .40 | .25 |
| **C76** | AP15 | 50c rose violet | .40 | .25 |
| **C77** | AP15 | 1s chocolate | .80 | .25 |
| **C78** | AP15 | 2s yellow brown | 1.00 | .25 |
| **C79** | AP15 | 5s emerald | 2.00 | .25 |
| | | *Nos. C73-C79 (7)* | 5.40 | 1.75 |

Golden Gate International Exposition.
For surcharge & overprint see Nos. 434, CO18.

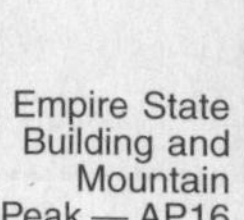

Empire State Building and Mountain Peak — AP16

**1939**

| | | | | |
|---|---|---|---|---|
| **C80** | AP16 | 2c brown orange | .65 | .30 |
| **C81** | AP16 | 5c dark carmine | .65 | .25 |
| **C82** | AP16 | 10c indigo | .65 | .30 |
| **C83** | AP16 | 50c slate green | .65 | .30 |
| **C84** | AP16 | 1s deep orange | 1.30 | .30 |
| **C85** | AP16 | 2s dk red violet | 1.50 | .30 |
| **C86** | AP16 | 5s dark gray | 3.50 | .30 |
| | | *Nos. C80-C86 (7)* | 8.90 | 2.05 |

New York World's Fair.
For surcharge see No. 435.

Map of the Americas and Airplane — AP17

**1940, July 9**

| | | | | |
|---|---|---|---|---|
| **C87** | AP17 | 10c red org & blue | .45 | .25 |
| **C88** | AP17 | 70c sepia & blue | .45 | .25 |
| **C89** | AP17 | 1s copper brn & blue | .90 | .25 |
| **C90** | AP17 | 10s black & blue | 3.50 | .95 |
| | | *Nos. C87-C90 (4)* | 5.30 | 1.70 |

Pan American Union, 50th anniversary.

**Journalism Type**

**1941, Dec. 15**

| | | | | |
|---|---|---|---|---|
| **C91** | A157 | 3s rose carmine | 5.75 | .25 |
| **C92** | A157 | 10s yellow orange | 12.00 | .45 |

See note after No. 399.

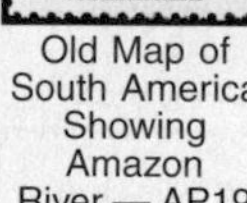

Old Map of South America Showing Amazon River — AP19

Panoramic View of Amazon River — AP20

Designs: 70c, Gonzalo de Pineda. 5s, Painting of the expedition.

**1942, Jan. 30**

| | | | | |
|---|---|---|---|---|
| **C93** | AP19 | 40c black & buff | 1.90 | .25 |
| **C94** | AP19 | 70c olive | 2.90 | .25 |
| **C95** | AP20 | 2s dark green | 3.25 | .25 |
| **C96** | AP19 | 5s rose | 4.00 | 1.10 |
| | | *Nos. C93-C96 (4)* | 12.05 | 1.85 |

See note after No. 403.

**Remigio Crespo Toral Type**

**1942, Sept. 1** *Perf. 13½*

| | | | | |
|---|---|---|---|---|
| **C97** | A162 | 10c dull violet | 1.25 | .50 |

**Alfaro Types**

70c, Gen. Eloy Alfaro. 1s, Devils's Nose. 3s, Military College. 5s, Montecristi, Alfaro's birthplace.

**1943, Feb. 16** *Perf. 12*

| | | | | |
|---|---|---|---|---|
| **C98** | A166 | 70c dk rose & blk | 1.90 | .25 |
| **C99** | A167 | 1s ol blk & red brn | 3.25 | .75 |
| **C100** | A167 | 3s ol gray & grn | 4.50 | 1.10 |
| **C101** | A167 | 5s slate & salmon | 6.75 | 1.30 |
| | | *Nos. C98-C101 (4)* | 16.40 | 3.40 |

**Nos. C61-C63 Overprinted in Red Brown**

**1943, Apr. 15** *Perf. 11½*

**Center Multicolored**

| | | | | |
|---|---|---|---|---|
| **C102** | AP8 | 50c violet | 2.75 | 1.50 |
| **C103** | AP8 | 1s black | 3.25 | 1.60 |
| **C104** | AP8 | 2s violet | 4.00 | 2.50 |
| | | *Nos. C102-C104 (3)* | 10.00 | 5.60 |

Visit of US Vice-Pres. Henry A. Wallace.

**Nos. 374-376 Overprinted "AEREO LOOR A BOLIVIA JUNIO 11-1943" (like Nos. C111-C113)**

**1943, June 11** *Perf. 13*

| | | | | |
|---|---|---|---|---|
| **C105** | A146 | 50c dp red violet | .40 | .25 |
| **C106** | A147 | 1s copper red | .60 | .25 |
| **C107** | A148 | 2s dark green | .70 | .25 |
| | | *Nos. C105-C107 (3)* | 1.70 | .75 |

Visit of Pres. Eurique Penaranda of Bolivia.
Vertical overprints on Nos. C105-C106.

**Nos. 374-376 Overprinted "AEREO LOOR A PARAGUAY JULIO 5-1943" (like Nos. C111-C113)**

**1943, July 5**

| | | | | |
|---|---|---|---|---|
| **C108** | A146 | 50c dp red violet | .45 | .25 |
| *a.* | | Double overprint | 75.00 | |
| **C109** | A147 | 1s copper red | 1.10 | .50 |
| **C110** | A148 | 2s dark green | 1.50 | .70 |
| | | *Nos. C108-C110 (3)* | 3.05 | 1.45 |

Visit of Pres. Higinio Morinigo of Paraguay.
Vertical overprints on Nos. C108-C109.

Nos. 374-376 Overprinted in Black

**1943, July 23**

| | | | | |
|---|---|---|---|---|
| **C111** | A146 | 50c dp red violet | .45 | .25 |
| **C112** | A147 | 1s copper red | .65 | .25 |
| **C113** | A148 | 2s dark green | .75 | .25 |
| | | *Nos. C111-C113 (3)* | 1.85 | .75 |

Issued to commemorate the visit of President Isaias Medina Angarita of Venezuela.
Vertical overprint on Nos. C111-C112.
See Nos. C105-C110.

President Arroyo del Rio Addressing US Congress — AP26

**1943, Oct. 9** *Perf. 12*

| | | | | |
|---|---|---|---|---|
| **C114** | AP26 | 50c dark brown | 1.00 | .50 |
| **C115** | AP26 | 70c brt rose | 1.30 | .50 |
| **C116** | AP26 | 3s dark blue | 1.50 | .65 |
| **C117** | AP26 | 5s dark green | 3.50 | 1.20 |
| **C118** | AP26 | 10s olive black | 13.00 | 4.25 |
| | | *Nos. C114-C118 (5)* | 20.30 | 7.10 |

Good will tour of Pres. Arroyo del Rio in 1942.
For surcharges see Nos. CB1-CB5.

**1944, Feb. 7**

| | | | | |
|---|---|---|---|---|
| **C119** | AP26 | 50c dp red lilac | .90 | .65 |
| **C120** | AP26 | 70c red brown | 1.75 | .65 |
| **C121** | AP26 | 3s turq green | 1.75 | .65 |
| **C122** | AP26 | 5s brt ultra | 2.90 | 1.40 |
| **C123** | AP26 | 10s scarlet | 3.50 | 1.60 |
| | | *Nos. C119-C123 (5)* | 10.80 | 4.95 |
| | | *Nos. C114-C123 (10)* | 31.10 | 12.05 |

Church of San Francisco, Quito — AP27

**1944, Feb. 13**

| | | | | |
|---|---|---|---|---|
| **C124** | AP27 | 70c turq green | 1.90 | .45 |
| **C125** | AP27 | 1s olive | 1.90 | .45 |
| **C126** | AP27 | 3s red orange | 4.25 | 1.10 |
| **C127** | AP27 | 5s carmine rose | 5.25 | 1.30 |
| | | *Nos. C124-C127 (4)* | 13.30 | 3.30 |

See note after No. 433.

**Palace Type**

**1944 Engr.** *Perf. 11*

| | | | | |
|---|---|---|---|---|
| **C128** | A173 | 3s orange | 1.00 | .25 |
| **C129** | A173 | 5s dark brown | 1.75 | .25 |
| **C130** | A173 | 10s dark red | 4.00 | .25 |
| | | *Nos. C128-C130 (3)* | 6.75 | .75 |

See No. C221. For overprints and surcharges see Nos. 541, C136-C138, C210-C213, C218-C220, C223-C224, C277-C279.

**Red Cross Type**

**1945, Apr. 25 Unwmk.** *Perf. 12*

**Cross in Rose**

| | | | | |
|---|---|---|---|---|
| **C131** | A174 | 2s deep blue | 4.00 | 1.10 |
| **C132** | A174 | 3s green | 4.50 | 1.25 |
| **C133** | A174 | 5s dark violet | 6.50 | 1.75 |
| **C134** | A174 | 10s carmine rose | 21.00 | 5.75 |
| | | *Nos. C131-C134 (4)* | 36.00 | 9.85 |

No. RA55 Surcharged in Black

**1945, June 8**

| | | | | |
|---|---|---|---|---|
| **C135** | PT21 | 40c on 5c blue | 1.00 | .25 |
| *a.* | | Double surcharge | 10.00 | |

Counterfeits exist.

Nos. C128-C130 Overprinted in Green

**1945, Sept. 6** *Perf. 11*

| | | | | |
|---|---|---|---|---|
| **C136** | A173 | 3s orange | 1.00 | .50 |
| *a.* | | Inverted overprint | 50.00 | |
| *b.* | | Double overprint | 50.00 | |
| **C137** | A173 | 5s dark brown | 1.25 | .65 |
| **C138** | A173 | 10s dark red | 3.25 | 1.25 |
| | | *Nos. C136-C138 (3)* | 5.50 | 2.40 |

**Nos. C61-C63 Overprinted in Dark Blue and Gold like Nos. 444-446**

**1945, Oct. 2** *Perf. 12*

**Center Multicolored**

| | | | | |
|---|---|---|---|---|
| **C139** | AP8 | 50c violet | 1.40 | .25 |
| **C140** | AP8 | 1s black | 1.60 | 1.50 |
| **C141** | AP8 | 2s violet | 2.50 | 1.90 |
| | | *Nos. C139-C141 (3)* | 5.50 | 3.65 |

Visit of Pres. Juan Antonio Rios of Chile.

Monument to Liberty — AP30

**1945, Nov. 14** **Engr.**

| | | | | |
|---|---|---|---|---|
| **C142** | AP30 | 30c blue | .45 | .25 |
| **C143** | AP30 | 40c rose carmine | .45 | .25 |
| **C144** | AP30 | 1s dull violet | 1.30 | .55 |

**C145** AP30 3s gray black 2.50 1.40
**C146** AP30 5s purple brown 3.50 1.90
*Nos. C142-C146 (5)* 8.20 4.35

Gen. Antonio Jose de Sucre, 150th birth anniv.

**Catalogue values for unused stamps in this section, from this point to the end of the section, are for Never Hinged items.**

### Highway Type

**1946, Apr. 22** **Unwmk.**
**C147** A176 1s carmine rose .65 .40
**C148** A176 2s violet .80 .55
**C149** A176 3s turq green 1.40 .60
**C150** A176 5s red orange 1.75 .80
**C151** A176 10s dark blue 2.75 .80
*Nos. C147-C151 (5)* 7.35 3.15

### Revolution Types

**1946, Aug. 9** ***Perf. 12½***
**C152** A177 40c deep claret .25 .25
**C153** A178 1s sepia .25 .25
**C154** A179 2s indigo .60 .25
**C155** A180 3s olive green 1.10 .45
*Nos. C152-C155 (4)* 2.20 1.20

National Union of Journalists, Initials and Quill Pen — AP36

**1946, Sept. 16**
**C156** AP36 50c dull purple .75 .30
**C157** AP36 70c dark green .90 .45
**C158** AP36 3s red 1.50 .60
**C159** AP36 5s indigo 2.00 .75
**C160** AP36 10s chocolate 6.50 1.25
*Nos. C156-C160 (5)* 11.65 3.35

Campaign for adult education.

The Blessed Mariana Teaching Children — AP37

"Lily of Quito" — AP38

**1946, Nov. 28** **Unwmk.**
**C161** AP37 40c chocolate .30 .25
**C162** AP37 60c deep blue .40 .35
**C163** AP38 3s orange yellow .80 .60
**C164** AP38 5s green 2.00 .85
*Nos. C161-C164 (4)* 3.50 2.05

300th anniv. of the death of the Blessed Mariana de Jesus Paredes y Flores.

### Rocafuerte Type

60c-1.10s, Jual de Velasco. 1.30s-2s, Riobamba Irrigation Canal.

**1947, Nov. 27** ***Perf. 12***
**C165** A185 60c dark green .25 .25
**C166** A185 70c purple .25 .25
**C167** A185 1s black brown .25 .25
**C168** A185 1.10s car rose .25 .25
**C169** A185 1.30s deep blue .35 .25
**C170** A185 1.90s olive bister 1.00 .25
**C171** A185 2s olive green 1.20 .25
*Nos. C165-C171 (7)* 3.55 1.75

For overprints & surcharges see Nos. C175, C181, C207-C209, C215, C216-C217, C222, C235.

### Bello Type

**1948, Apr. 21** ***Perf. 13***
**C172** A188 60c magenta .40 .25
**C173** A188 1.30s dk blue grn .70 .25
**C174** A188 1.90s dk rose car .60 .25
*Nos. C172-C174 (3)* 1.70 .75

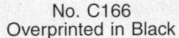

No. C166 Overprinted in Black

**1948, May 24** ***Perf. 12***
**C175** A185 70c purple .65 .35

Columbus — AP42

**1948, May 26** ***Perf. 14***
**C176** AP42 50c olive green .25 .25
**C177** AP42 70c rose carmine .50 .40
**C178** AP42 3s ultra 1.60 1.10
**C179** AP42 5s brown 2.60 1.60
**C180** AP42 10s deep violet 8.00 2.00
*Nos. C176-C180 (5)* 12.95 5.35

See note after No. 495.

### No. C169 Overprinted in Carmine like No. 496 (MANANA reads up)

**1948, Aug. 26** **Unwmk.** ***Perf. 12***
**C181** A185 1.30s deep blue .40 .25

National Fair of Today and Tomorrow, 1948.

Elia Liut and Telegrafo I — AP43

**1948, Sept. 10** ***Perf. 12½***
**C182** AP43 60c rose red .80 .25
**C183** AP43 1s green .80 .25
**C184** AP43 1.30s deep claret .80 .25
**C185** AP43 1.90s deep violet .80 .25
**C186** AP43 2s dark brown 1.20 .30
**C187** AP43 5s blue 2.40 .50
*Nos. C182-C187 (6)* 6.80 1.80

25th anniv. (in 1945) of the 1st postal flight in Ecuador.

Teacher and Pupils — AP44

**1948, Oct. 12** ***Perf. 14***
**C188** AP44 50c violet 1.50 .50
**C189** AP44 70c deep blue 1.50 .50
**C190** AP44 3s dark green 2.50 1.00
**C191** AP44 5s red 4.00 1.50
**C192** AP44 10s brown 7.50 2.00
*Nos. C188-C192 (5)* 17.00 5.50

Campaign for adult education.

AP45

Franklin D. Roosevelt and Two of "Four Freedoms" — AP46

**1948, Oct. 24** ***Perf. 12½***
**C193** AP45 60c emer & org brn .40 .25
**C194** AP45 1s car rose & slate .60 .30
**C195** AP46 1.50s grn & red brn .75 .55
**C196** AP46 2s red & black .80 .30
**C197** AP46 5s ultra & blk 1.75 .30
*Nos. C193-C197 (5)* 4.30 1.70

### Maldonado Types

**1948, Nov. 17**
**C198** A196 60c dp org & rose car .80 .25
**C199** A197 90c red & gray blk .80 .25
**C200** A196 1.30s pur & dp org 1.00 .25
**C201** A197 2s dp bl & dull grn 1.00 .25
*Nos. C198-C201 (4)* 3.60 1.00

See note after No. 519.

Juan Montalvo and Cervantes AP47

Don Quixote — AP48

**1949, May 2** **Engr.** ***Perf. 12½x12***
**C202** AP47 1.30s ol brn & ultra 3.00 2.50
**C203** AP48 1.90s grn & rose car 1.00 .30
**C204** AP47 3s vio & org brn 1.50 .30
**C205** AP48 5s red & gray blk 2.75 .25
**C206** AP47 10s red lil & aqua 4.00 .25
*Nos. C202-C206 (5)* 12.25 3.60

400th anniv. of the birth of Miguel de Cervantes Saavedra, novelist, playwright and poet, and the 60th anniv. of the death of Juan Montalvo (1832-89), Ecuadorean writer.

For surcharges see Nos. C225-C226.

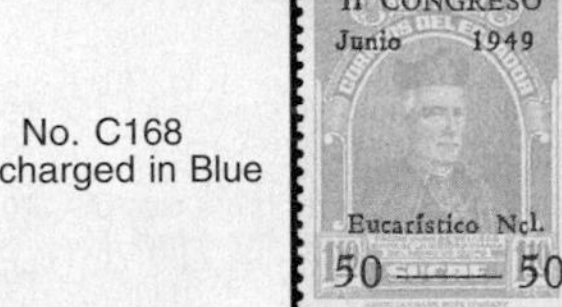

No. C168 Surcharged in Blue

**1949, June 15** ***Perf. 12***
**C207** A185 50c on 1.10s car rose .45 .25
**C208** A185 60c on 1.10s car rose .45 .25
**C209** A185 90c on 1.10s car rose .65 .25
*Nos. C207-C209 (3)* 1.55 .75

2nd Eucharistic Cong., Quito, June 1949.

No. C128 Surcharged in Black

**1949, Oct. 11** ***Perf. 11***
**C210** A173 60c on 3s orange .75 .40
*a.* Double surcharge 30.00
**C211** A173 90c on 3s orange .80 .30
**C212** A173 1s on 3s orange 1.00 .40
**C213** A173 2s on 3s orange 1.75 .40
*Nos. C210-C213 (4)* 4.30 1.50

"SUCRE(S)" in capitals on Nos. C212-C213.
75th anniv. of the UPU.

Type of 1949 Surcharged in Black

**1950** **Unwmk.** ***Perf. 12***
**C214** R1 60c on 50c gray .75 .25
*a.* Double surcharge 15.00

### No. C170 Surcharged with New Value in Black

**C215** A185 90c on 1.90s ol bis .75 .25

Nos. C168, C128-C129 and Type of 1944 Srchd. or Ovptd. in Black or Carmine

**1950, Feb. 10** ***Perf. 12***
**C216** A185 50c on 1.10s 1.75 1.75
**C217** A185 70c on 1.10s 2.25 1.75

***Perf. 11***
**C218** A173 3s orange 3.25 3.00
**C219** A173 5s dark brown (C) 5.00 2.50
**C220** A173 10s violet (C) 7.50 3.00
*Nos. C216-C220 (5)* 19.75 12.00

Issued to publicize adult education.
For overprint see No. 541.

### Govt. Palace Type of 1944

**1950, May 15** **Engr.** ***Perf. 11***
**C221** A173 10s violet 2.00 .25

For surcharges see Nos. C277-C279.

### No. C169 Surcharged with New Value in Black

**1950** ***Perf. 12***
**C222** A185 90c on 1.30s dp blue .30 .25

See No. C235.

Nos. C128-C129 Overprinted in Black

**1951, July 28** **Unwmk.** ***Perf. 11***
**C223** A173 3s orange 1.25 .90
**C224** A173 5s dark brown 2.50 1.25

20,000th crossing of the equator by Pan American-Grace Airways planes.

### Nos. C202-C203 Surcharged in Black

**1951** **Unwmk.** ***Perf. 12½x12***
**C225** AP47 60c on 1.30s .30 .25
**C226** AP48 1s on 1.90s .30 .25
*a.* Inverted surcharge 20.00

Issued to publicize adult education.

St. Mariana de Jesus — AP50

**1952, Feb. 15** **Engr.**

| | | | | |
|---|---|---|---|---|
| C227 | AP50 | 60c plum & aqua | .60 | .30 |
| C228 | AP50 | 90c dk grn & lt ultra | .80 | .30 |
| C229 | AP50 | 1s car & dk grn | .90 | .30 |
| C230 | AP50 | 2s indigo & rose lil | 1.00 | .30 |
| | | *Nos. C227-C230 (4)* | 3.30 | 1.20 |

Canonization of Mariana de Jesus Paredes y Flores.

**Plaza Visit to US Issue**

3s, as No. 558. 5s, as No. 559.

**1952, Mar. 26** ***Perf. 12***

| | | | | |
|---|---|---|---|---|
| C231 | A205 | 3s lilac & bl grn | .70 | .45 |
| C232 | A205 | 5s red brn & ol gray | 2.00 | 1.75 |
| a. | | Souv. sheet of 2, #C231-C232 | 4.50 | 9.00 |

**Consular Service Stamps Surcharged in Black**

**1952** **Unwmk.** ***Perf. 12***

| | | | | |
|---|---|---|---|---|
| C233 | R2 | 60c on 1s green | .30 | .25 |
| C234 | R2 | 1s on 1s green | .30 | .25 |

Type R2 illustrated above No. 545.

**No. C169 Surcharged with New Value in Carmine**

| | | | | |
|---|---|---|---|---|
| C235 | A185 | 90c on 1.30s dp bl | .30 | .25 |
| | | *Nos. C233-C235 (3)* | .90 | .75 |

See No. C222.

Pres. José M. Urvina and Allegory of Freedom — AP52

***Hyphen-hole Perf. 7x6½***

**1952, Nov. 18** **Litho.**

| | | | | |
|---|---|---|---|---|
| C236 | AP52 | 60c rose red & blue | 3.50 | .45 |
| C237 | AP52 | 90c lilac & red | 3.50 | .60 |
| C238 | AP52 | 1s orange & green | 3.50 | .30 |
| C239 | AP52 | 2s red brn & blue | 3.50 | .45 |
| | | *Nos. C236-C239 (4)* | 14.00 | 1.80 |

Centenary of abolition of slavery in Ecuador. Counterfeits exist.

Torch of Knowledge AP53

Design: 2s, Aged couple studying alphabet.

**Unwmk.**

**1953, Apr. 13** **Engr.** ***Perf. 12***

| | | | | |
|---|---|---|---|---|
| C240 | AP53 | 1s dark blue | 1.20 | .25 |
| C241 | AP53 | 2s red orange | 1.50 | .25 |

1952 adult education campaign.

Globe Showing Part of Western Hemisphere AP54

**1953, June 5** ***Perf. 12½x12***

| | | | | |
|---|---|---|---|---|
| C242 | AP54 | 60c orange yellow | .30 | .25 |
| C243 | AP54 | 90c dark blue | .40 | .30 |
| C244 | AP54 | 3s carmine | .70 | .45 |
| | | *Nos. C242-C244 (3)* | 1.40 | 1.00 |

Issued to publicize the crossing of the equator by the Pan-American highway.

**Consular Service Stamps Surcharged in Black**

a

b

**1953-54** ***Perf. 12***

| | | | | | |
|---|---|---|---|---|---|
| C245 | R1 | (a) | 60c on 2s brown | .35 | .25 |
| C246 | R2 | (a) | 60c on 5s sep ('54) | .35 | .25 |
| C247 | R2 | (a) | 70c on 5s sep ('54) | .35 | .25 |
| C248 | R2 | (a) | 90c on 50c car rose ('54) | .35 | .25 |
| C249 | R1 | (b) | 1s on 2s brown | .35 | .25 |
| C250 | R1 | (a) | 1s on 2s brn ('54) | .35 | .25 |
| C251 | R1 | (a) | 2s on 2s brn ('54) | .65 | .25 |
| C252 | R1 | (a) | 3s on 5s vio ('54) | .90 | .25 |
| | | | *Nos. C245-C252 (8)* | 3.65 | 2.00 |

Surcharge is horizontal on Nos. C245-C248.

Carlos Maria Cardinal de la Torre — AP55

**1954, Jan. 13** **Photo.** ***Perf. 8½***

**Center in Black**

| | | | | |
|---|---|---|---|---|
| C253 | AP55 | 60c rose lilac | .50 | .30 |
| C254 | AP55 | 90c green | .80 | .30 |
| C255 | AP55 | 3s orange | 1.20 | .45 |
| | | *Nos. C253-C255 (3)* | 2.50 | 1.05 |

1st anniv. of the elevation of Archbishop de la Torre to Cardinal.

Queen Isabella I — AP56

**1954, Apr. 22**

| | | | | |
|---|---|---|---|---|
| C256 | AP56 | 60c dk grn & grn | .50 | .40 |
| C257 | AP56 | 90c lil rose | .50 | .40 |
| C258 | AP56 | 1s blk & pale lil | .50 | .40 |
| C259 | AP56 | 2s blk brn & pale bl | .70 | .40 |
| C260 | AP56 | 5s blk brn & buff | 1.75 | .40 |
| | | *Nos. C256-C260 (5)* | 3.95 | 2.00 |

See note with No. 585.

Post Office, Guayaquil AP57

**1954, May 19** **Engr.** ***Perf. 12½x12***

**Black Surcharge**

| | | | | |
|---|---|---|---|---|
| C261 | AP57 | 80c on 20c red | .30 | .25 |
| C262 | AP57 | 1s on 20c red | .30 | .25 |

25th anniversary of Pan American-Grace Airways' operation in Ecuador.

Plane, Gateway and Wheel — AP58

**Unwmk.**

**1954, Aug. 2** **Litho.** ***Perf. 11***

| | | | | |
|---|---|---|---|---|
| C263 | AP58 | 80c blue | .35 | .25 |

Day of the Postal Employee.

San Pablo Lagoon AP59

**1954, Sept. 24** **Photo.**

| | | | | |
|---|---|---|---|---|
| C264 | AP59 | 60c orange | .30 | .25 |
| C265 | AP59 | 70c rose pink | .30 | .25 |
| C266 | AP59 | 90c dp grn | .30 | .25 |
| C267 | AP59 | 1s dk gray grn | .30 | .25 |
| C268 | AP59 | 2s blue | .40 | .25 |
| C269 | AP59 | 3s yel brn | .75 | .25 |
| | | *Nos. C264-C269 (6)* | 2.35 | 1.50 |

Glorification of Abdon Calderon Garaicoa AP60

Capt. Calderon — AP61

**1954, Oct. 1**

| | | | | |
|---|---|---|---|---|
| C270 | AP60 | 80c rose pink | .45 | .25 |
| C271 | AP61 | 90c blue | .45 | .25 |

150th anniversary of the birth of Capt. Abdon Calderon Garaicoa.

El Cebollar College AP62

Brother Miguel Instructing Boys — AP63

Designs: 90c, Francisco Febres Cordero (Brother Miguel). 2.50s, Tomb of Brother Miguel. 3s, Monument to Brother Miguel.

**1954, Dec. 3** **Unwmk.** ***Perf. 11***

| | | | | |
|---|---|---|---|---|
| C272 | AP62 | 70c dk grn | .25 | .25 |
| C273 | AP63 | 80c dk brn | .25 | .25 |
| C274 | AP63 | 90c dk gray bl | .25 | .25 |
| C275 | AP63 | 2.50s indigo | .45 | .25 |
| C276 | AP62 | 3s lil rose | .55 | .35 |
| | | *Nos. C272-C276 (5)* | 1.75 | 1.35 |

Centenary of the birth of Francisco Febres Cordero (Brother Miguel).

No. C221 Surcharged in Various Colors

**1955, May 25**

| | | | | |
|---|---|---|---|---|
| C277 | A173 | 1s on 10s vio (Bk) | .30 | .25 |
| C278 | A173 | 1.70s on 10s vio (C) | .40 | .25 |
| C279 | A173 | 4.20s on 10s vio (Br) | .65 | .35 |
| | | *Nos. C277-C279 (3)* | 1.35 | .85 |

Denomination in larger type on No. C279. National Exhibition of Daily Periodicals.

"La Rotonda," Guayaquil, and Rotary Emblem AP64

Design: 90c, Eugenio Espejo hospital, Quito, and Rotary emblem.

**1955, July 9** **Engr.** ***Perf. 12½***

| | | | | |
|---|---|---|---|---|
| C280 | AP64 | 80c dark brown | .30 | .25 |
| C281 | AP64 | 90c dark green | .50 | .35 |

50th anniv. of the founding of Rotary Intl.

José Abel Castillo AP65

2s, 5s, José Abel Castillo, Map of Ecuador.

**1955, Oct. 19** ***Perf. 11x11½***

| | | | | |
|---|---|---|---|---|
| C282 | AP65 | 60c chocolate | 1.10 | .25 |
| C283 | AP65 | 90c light olive green | 1.25 | .25 |
| C284 | AP65 | 1s lilac | 1.40 | .25 |
| C285 | AP65 | 2s vermilion | 1.75 | .30 |
| C286 | AP65 | 5s ultra | 3.50 | .55 |
| | | *Nos. C282-C286 (5)* | 9.00 | 1.60 |

See note after No. 595.

No. C29 Surcharged in Black

**1955, Oct. 24** ***Perf. 12***

| | | | | |
|---|---|---|---|---|
| C287 | AP1 | 1s on 5s purple | .65 | .25 |

A similar surcharge on No. C29, set in two lines with letters 5mm high and no X's or black-out line of squares, was privately applied.

San Pablo, Imbabura — AP66

50s, Rumichaca Caves. 1.30s, Virgin of Quito. 1.50s, Cotopaxi Volcano. 1.70s, Tungurahua Volcano, Tungurahua. 1.90s, Guanacos. 2.40s, Mat market. 2.50s, Ruins at Ingapirca. 4.20s, El Carmen, Cuenca, Azuay. 4.80s, Santo Domingo Church.

**1956, Jan. 2** **Photo.** ***Perf. 13***

| | | | | |
|---|---|---|---|---|
| C288 | AP66 | 50c slate blue | 2.75 | .25 |
| C289 | AP66 | 1s ultra | 2.75 | .25 |
| C290 | AP66 | 1.30s crimson | 4.25 | .25 |
| C291 | AP66 | 1.50s dp grn | 2.75 | .25 |
| C292 | AP66 | 1.70s yel brn | 1.75 | .25 |
| C293 | AP66 | 1.90s olive | 3.50 | .25 |
| C294 | AP66 | 2.40s red org | 3.75 | .25 |
| C295 | AP66 | 2.50s violet | 3.75 | .25 |
| C296 | AP66 | 4.20s black | 4.75 | .25 |
| C297 | AP66 | 4.80s yel org | 7.50 | .30 |
| | | *Nos. C288-C297 (10)* | 37.50 | 2.55 |

See Nos. C310-C311. For surcharges see Nos. 766A, 766G.

Honorato Vazquez — AP67

**1956, May 28** **Engr.**

**Various Portraits**

| | | | | |
|---|---|---|---|---|
| C298 | AP67 | 1s yellow green | .50 | .25 |
| C299 | AP67 | 1.50s red | .50 | .25 |
| C300 | AP67 | 1.70s bright blue | .50 | .25 |
| C301 | AP67 | 1.90s slate blue | .50 | .25 |
| | | *Nos. C298-C301 (4)* | 2.00 | 1.00 |

Birth centenary (in 1955) of Honorato Vazquez, statesman.

Title Page of First Book — AP68

**1956, Aug. 27 Unwmk. *Perf. 13½***

**C302** AP68 1s black .60 .25
**C303** AP68 1.70s slate bl .60 .25
**C304** AP68 2s blk brn .60 .25
**C305** AP68 3s redsh brn .60 .25
*Nos. C302-C305 (4)* 2.40 1.00

Bicentenary of printing in Ecuador.

Hands Reaching for UN Emblem AP69

**1956, Oct. 24 *Perf. 14***

**C307** AP69 1.70s red org 1.10 .25

10th anniv. of the UN (in 1955).
See No. C319. For overprint see No. C426.

Coat of Arms and Basketball Player — AP70

Designs: 1.70s, Map of South America with flags and girl basketball players.

**1956, Dec. 28 Photo. *Perf. 14½x14***

**C308** AP70 1s red lilac .65 .25
**C309** AP70 1.70s deep green 1.00 .25

6th South American Women's Basketball Championship, Aug. 1956.

**Scenic Type of 1956**

**1957, Jan. 2 *Perf. 13***

**C310** AP66 50c bl grn 1.75 .25
**C311** AP66 1s orange 1.75 .25

**Type of Regular Issue, 1957**

Designs: 50c, Map of Cuenca, 16th century. 80c, Cathedral of Cuenca. 1s, Modern City Hall.

**Unwmk.**

**1957, Apr. 7 Photo. *Perf. 12***

**C312** A219 50c brn, *cr* .30 .25
*a.* Souvenir sheet of 4 1.00 1.00
**C313** A219 80c red, *bluish* .30 .25
**C314** A219 1s pur, *yel* .30 .25
*a.* Souvenir sheet of 3 2.00 2.00
*Nos. C312-C314 (3)* .90 .75

No. C312a contains 4 imperf. 50c stamps similar to No. 613, but inscribed "AEREO" and printed in green. The sheet is printed on white ungummed paper.

No. C314a contains 3 imperf. stamps in designs similar to Nos. C312-C314, but with colors changed to orange (50c), brown (80c), violet (1s). The sheet is printed on white ungummed paper.

Gabriela Mistral — AP71

**Unwmk.**

**1957, Sept. 18 Litho. *Perf. 14***

**C315** AP71 2s lt bl, blk & red .55 .25

Issued to honor Gabriela Mistral (1889-1957), Chilean poet and educator.
See Nos. C406-C407.

Arms of Espejo, Carchi — AP72

Arms of Cantons: 2s, Montufar. 4.20s, Tulcan.

**1957, Nov. 16 *Perf. 14½x13½***

**Coat of Arms Multicolored**

**C316** AP72 1s carmine .55 .25
**C317** AP72 2s black .55 .25
**C318** AP72 4.20s ultra 1.00 .25
*Nos. C316-C318 (3)* 2.10 .75

Province of Carchi.
See Nos. C334-C337, C355-C364, C392-C395. For surcharge see No. 766.

**Redrawn UN Type of 1956**

**1957, Dec. 10 Engr. *Perf. 14***

**C319** AP69 2s greenish blue .55 .25

Honoring the UN. Dates, as on No. C307, are omitted; inscribed: "Homenaje a las Naciones Unidas."

Mater Dolorosa, San Gabriel College — AP73

No. C321, 1s, Door of San Gabriel College, Quito.

**1958, Apr. 27 Engr. *Perf. 14***

**C320** AP73 30c rose cl, *dp rose* .30 .25
**C321** AP73 30c rose cl, *dp rose* .30 .25
*a.* Pair, #C320-C321 .75 .60
**C322** AP73 1s dk bl, *lt bl* .30 .25
**C323** AP73 1.70s dk bl, *lt bl* .30 .25
*a.* Pair, #C322-C323 .75 .60

Miracle of San Gabriel College, Quito, 50th anniv.

Rafael Maria Arizaga (1858-1933), Writer — AP74

**1958, July 21 Litho.**

**C324** AP74 1s multi .45 .30

See Nos. C343, C350, C412.

Daule River Bridge AP75

**1958, July 25 Engr. *Perf. 13½x14***

**C325** AP75 1.30s green .50 .25

Issued to commemorate the opening of the River Daule bridge in Guayas province.
See Nos. C367-C369.

Basketball Player — AP76

**1958, Sept. 1 Photo. *Perf. 14x13½***

**C326** AP76 1.30s dk grn & lt brn .55 .45

South American basketball championships.
For surcharge see No. 774A.

Symbolical of the Eucharist — AP77

Design: 60c, Cathedral of Guayaquil.

**1958, Sept. 25 Litho. Unwmk.**

**C327** AP77 10c vio & buff .40 .30
**C328** AP77 60c org & vio brn .40 .30
**C329** AP77 1s brn & lt bl .40 .30
*Nos. C327-C329 (3)* 1.20 .90

**Souvenir Sheet**

Symbolical of the Eucharist — AP78

***Perf. 13½x14***

**C330** AP78 Sheet of 4 2.75 2.25
*a.-d.* 40c dark blue, any single .25 .25

3rd National Eucharistic Congress.

Stamps of 1865 and 1920 — AP79

Designs: 2s, Stamps of 1920 and 1948. 4.20s, Municipal museum and library.

**1958, Oct. 8 Photo. *Perf. 11½***

**Granite Paper**

**C331** AP79 1.30s grn & brn red .35 .25
**C332** AP79 2s bl & vio .70 .30
**C333** AP79 4.20s dk brn .90 .40
*Nos. C331-C333 (3)* 1.95 .95

National Philatelic Exposition (EXFIGUA), Guayaquil, Oct. 4-14.
For surcharge see No. 774.

**Coat of Arms Type of 1957**

Province of Imbabura

Arms of Cantons: 50c, Cotacachi. 60c, Antonio Ante. 80c, Otavalo. 1.10s, Ibarra.

**1958, Nov. 9 Litho. *Perf. 14½x13½***

**Coats of Arms Multicolored**

**C334** AP72 50c blk & red .50 .25
**C335** AP72 60c blk, bl & red .50 .25
**C336** AP72 80c blk & yel .50 .25
**C337** AP72 1.10s blk & red .50 .25
*Nos. C334-C337 (4)* 2.00 1.00

Charles V AP80

**Engr. & Photo.**

**1958, Dec. 12 *Perf. 14x13½***

**C338** AP80 2s brn red & dk brn .45 .30
**C339** AP80 4.20s dk gray & red brn .55 .45

400th anniv. of the death of Charles V, Holy Roman Emperor.

Paul Rivet — AP81

**1958, Dec. 29 Photo. *Perf. 11½***

**Granite Paper**

**C340** AP81 1s brown .45 .30

Issued in honor of Paul Rivet (1876-1958), French anthropologist.

**1959, May 6**

Portrait: 2s, Alexander von Humboldt.

**C341** AP81 2s slate .35 .25

Cent. of the death of Alexander von Humboldt, German naturalist and geographer.

Front Page of "El Telegrafo" — AP82

**1959, Feb. Litho. *Perf. 13½***

**C342** AP82 1.30s bl grn & blk .35 .25

75th anniv. of Ecuador's oldest newspaper.

**Portrait Type of 1958**

José Luis Tamayo (1858-1947), lawyer.

**1959, June 26 Unwmk. *Perf. 14***

**Portrait Multicolored**

**C343** AP74 1.30s lt grn, bl & sal .45 .30

El Sagrario & House of Manuela Canizares AP83

Condor — AP84

Designs: 80c, Hall at San Agustin. 1s, First words of the constitutional act. 2s, Entrance to Cuartel Real. 4.20s, Allegory of Liberty.

**Unwmk.**

**1959, Aug. 28 Photo. *Perf. 14***

**C344** AP83 20c ultra & lt brn .25 .25
**C345** AP83 80c brt bl & dp org .25 .25
**C346** AP83 1s dk red & dk ol .25 .25
**C347** AP84 1.30s brt bl & org .25 .25
**C348** AP84 2s ultra & org brn .25 .25
**C349** AP84 4.20s scar & brt bl .65 .45
*Nos. C344-C349 (6)* 1.90 1.70

Sesquicentennial of the revolution.

### Portrait Type of 1958

1s, Alfredo Baquerizo Moreno (1859-1951), statesman.

**1959, Sept. 26 Litho. *Perf. 14***

**C350** AP74 1s gray, red & salmon .45 .30

Pope Pius XII — AP85

**1959, Oct. 9 Unwmk. *Perf. 14½***

**C351** AP85 1.30s multi .45 .30

Issued in memory of Pope Pius XII.

Flags of Argentina, Bolivia, Brazil, Guatemala, Haiti, Mexico and Peru — AP86

Flags of: 80c, Chile, Costa Rica, Cuba, Dominican Republic, Panama, Paraguay, United States. 1.30s, Colombia, Ecuador, Honduras, Nicaragua, Salvador, Uruguay, Venezuela.

**1959, Oct. 12 *Perf. 13½.***

**C352** AP86 50c multi .25 .25
**C353** AP86 80c yel, red & bl .30 .25
**C354** AP86 1.30s multi .40 .25
*Nos. C352-C354 (3)* .95 .75

Organization of American States.
For overprints see Nos. C423-C425, CO19-CO21.

### Arms of the Cantons Type of 1957
Province of Pichincha

10c, Rumiñahui. 40c, Pedro Moncayo. 1s, Mejia. 1.30s, Cayambe. 4.20s, Quito.

***Perf. 14½x13½***

**1959-60 Unwmk. Litho.**

**Coat of Arms Multicolored**

**C355** AP72 10c blk & dk red ('60) .50 .30
**C356** AP72 40c blk & yel .50 .30
**C357** AP72 1s blk & brn ('60) .50 .30
**C358** AP72 1.30s blk & grn ('60) .50 .30
**C359** AP72 4.20s blk & org .50 .30
*Nos. C355-C359 (5)* 2.50 1.50

### Province of Cotopaxi

40c, Pangua. 60c, Pujili. 70c, Saquisili. 1s, Salcedo. 1.30s, Latacunga.

**1960 Coat of Arms Multicolored**

**C360** AP72 40c blk & car .30 .25
**C361** AP72 60c blk & bl .30 .25
**C362** AP72 70c blk & turq .30 .25
**C363** AP72 1s blk & red org .30 .25
**C364** AP72 1.30s blk & org .35 .25
*Nos. C360-C364 (5)* 1.55 1.25

Flags of American Nations — AP87

**1960, Feb. 23 *Perf. 13x12½***

**C365** AP87 1.30s multi .30 .25
**C366** AP87 2s multi .30 .25

11th Inter-American Conference, Feb. 1960.

### Bridge Type of 1958.

Bridges: No. C367, Juntas. No. C368, Saracay. 2s, Railroad bridge, Ambato.

**1960 Litho. *Perf. 13½***

**C367** AP75 1.30s chocolate .30 .25

**Photo. *Perf. 12½***

**C368** AP75 1.30s emerald .30 .25
**C369** AP75 2s brown .50 .25
*Nos. C367-C369 (3)* 1.10 .75

Building of three new bridges.

Bahia-Chone Road — AP88

Pres. Camilo Ponce Enriquez AP89

Designs: 4.20s, Public Works Building, Cuenca. 5s, El Coca airport. 10s, New Harbor, Guayaquil.

**1960, Aug. Litho. *Perf. 14***

**C370** AP88 1.30s blk & dl yel .30 .25
**C371** AP88 4.20s rose car & lt grn .45 .45
**C372** AP88 5s dk brn & yel .65 .55
**C373** AP88 10s dk bl & bl 1.50 .55

***Perf. 11x11½***

**C374** AP89 2s org brn & blk 2.25 .30
*Nos. C370-C374 (5)* 5.15 2.10

Nos. C370-C374 publicize the achievements of Pres. Camilo Ponce Enriquez (1956-1960).
Issued: Nos. C370-C373, 8/24; No. C374, 8/31.

Red Cross Building, Quito and Henri Dunant AP90

**1960, Oct. 5 Unwmk. *Perf. 13x14***

**C375** AP90 2s rose vio & car .60 .25

Centenary (in 1959) of Red Cross idea.
For overprint see No. C408.

El Belen Church, Quito — AP91

**1961, Jan. 14 *Perf. 12½***

**C376** AP91 3s multi .50 .25

Ecuador's participation in the 1960 Barcelona Philatelic Congress.

Map of Ecuador and Amazon River System AP92

**1961, Feb. 27 Litho. *Perf. 10½***

**C377** AP92 80c salmon, claret & grn .35 .25
**C378** AP92 1.30s gray, slate & grn .55 .25
**C379** AP92 2s beige, red & grn .75 .25
*Nos. C377-C379 (3)* 1.65 .75

Amazon Week, and the 132nd anniversary of the Battle of Tarqui against Peru.

Juan Montalvo, Juan Leon Mera, Juan Benigno Vela — AP93

**1961, Apr. 13 Unwmk. *Perf. 13***

**C380** AP93 1.30s salmon & blk .50 .25

Centenary of Tungurahua province.

Hugo Ortiz G. — AP94

Design: No. C382, Ortiz monument.

**1961, May 25 *Perf. 14x14½***

**C381** AP94 1.30s grnsh bl, blk & yel .35 .25
**C382** AP94 1.30s grnsh bl, pur, ol & brn .35 .25

Lt. Hugo Ortiz G., killed in battle 8/2/41.

Condor and Airplane Stamp of 1936 AP95

1.30s, Map of South America and stamp of 1865. 2s, Bolivar monument stamp of 1930.

***Perf. 10½***

**1961, May 25 Litho. Unwmk.**

**Size: 41x28mm**

**C383** AP95 80c org & vio .50 .25

**Size: 41x34mm**

**C384** AP95 1.30s bl, yel, ol & car .80 .35

**Size: 40½x37mm**

**C385** AP95 2s car rose & blk 1.25 .35
*Nos. C383-C385 (3)* 2.55 .95

Third National Philatelic Exhibition, Quito, May 25-June 3, 1961.

Arms of Los Rios and Egret — AP96

**1961, May 27 *Perf. 14½x13½***

**Coat of Arms Multicolored**

**C386** AP96 2s bl & blk .50 .30

Centenary (in 1960) of Los Rios province.

Gabriel Garcia Moreno — AP97

**1961, Sept. 24 Unwmk. *Perf. 12***

**C387** AP97 1s bl, brn & buff .45 .25

Centenary of the restoration of national integrity.

Remigio Crespo Toral — AP98

**1961, Nov. 3 Unwmk. *Perf. 14***

**C388** AP98 50c multi .35 .25

Centenary of the birth of Remigio Crespo Toral, poet laureate of Ecuador.

### Galapagos Islands Nos. LC1-LC3 Overprinted in Black or Red (Similar to #684-686)
"ESTACION DE BIOLOGIA MARITIMA DE GALAPAGOS" and " UNESCO 1961"

**1961, Oct. 31 Photo. *Perf. 12***

**C389** A1 1s dp bl 1.75 .25
*a.* "de Galapagos" on top line 6.00 6.00
**C390** A1 1.80s rose vio 2.40 .40
*a.* UNESCO emblem omitted 6.00 6.00
**C391** A1 4.20s blk (R) 3.50 .60
*Nos. C389-C391 (3)* 7.65 1.25

Establishment of maritime biological stations on Galapagos Islands by UNESCO.

### Arms of the Cantons Type of 1957
Province of Tungurahua

50c, Pillaro. 1s, Pelileo. 1.30s, Baños. 2s, Ambato.

***Perf. 14½x13½***

**1962, Mar. 30 Litho. Unwmk.**

**Coats of Arms Multicolored**

**C392** AP72 50c black .25 .25
**C393** AP72 1s black .35 .25
**C394** AP72 1.30s black .45 .25
**C395** AP72 2s black .75 .25
*Nos. C392-C395 (4)* 1.80 1.00

AP99

Designs: 1.30s, 2s, Pres. Arosemena and Prince Philip, Arms of Ecuador and Great Britain and Equator Monument.

*Perf. 14x13½*

**1962, Feb. 17 Wmk. 340**

**C396** AP99 1.30s bl, sepia, red & yel .30 .25
**C397** AP99 2s multi .50 .25

Visit of Prince Philip, Duke of Edinburgh, to Ecuador, Feb. 17-20, 1962.

Mountain Farming — AP100

*Perf. 12½*

**1963, Mar. 21 Unwmk. Litho.**

**C398** AP100 30c emer, yel & blk .30 .25
**C399** AP100 3s dl red, grn & org .70 .25
**C400** AP100 4.20s bl, blk & yel 1.10 .55
*Nos. C398-C400 (3)* 2.10 1.05

FAO "Freedom from Hunger" campaign. Exist imperf. Value $32.50.

Mosquito and Malaria Eradication Emblem AP101

**1963, Apr. 17 Unwmk. *Perf. 12½***

**C401** AP101 50c multi .25 .25
**C402** AP101 80c multi .25 .25
**C403** AP101 2s multi .40 .25
*Nos. C401-C403 (3)* .90 .75

WHO drive to eradicate malaria.

Stagecoach and Jet Plane AP102

**1963, May 7 Litho.**

**C404** AP102 2s org & car rose .40 .30
**C405** AP102 4.20s claret & ultra .70 .50

1st Intl. Postal Conference, Paris, 1863.

**Type of 1957 Inscribed "Islas Galapagos," Surcharged with New Value and Overprinted "Ecuador" in Black or Red**

**1963, June 19 Unwmk. *Perf. 14***

**C406** AP71 5s on 2s gray, dk bl & red 1.10 .80
**C407** AP71 10s on 2s gray, dk bl & red (R) 2.00 1.60

The basic 2s exists without surcharge and overprint. No. C407 exists with "ECUADOR" omitted, and with both "ECUADOR" and "10 SUCRES" double.

**No. C375 Overprinted: "1863-1963/Centenario/de la Fundación/ de la Cruz Roja/Internacional"**

**1963, June 21 Photo. *Perf. 13x14***

**C408** AP90 2s rose vio & car .40 .25

Intl. Red Cross, centenary.

**Type of Regular Issue, 1963**

Arosemena and: 70c, Flags of Ecuador. 2s, Flags of Ecuador, Panama. 4s, Flags of Ecuador, US.

**1963, July 1 Litho. *Perf. 14***

**C409** A238 70c pale bl & multi .25 .25
**C410** A238 2s pink & multi .50 .25
**C411** A238 4s lt bl & multi 1.10 .35
*Nos. C409-C411 (3)* 1.85 .85

Imperfs exist. Value $15.

**Portrait Type of 1958**

Portrait: 2s, Dr. Mariano Cueva (1812-82).

**Unwmk.**

**1963, July 4 Litho. *Perf. 14***

**C412** AP74 2s lt grn & multi .45 .25

Social Insurance Symbol — AP103

**1963, July 9 Litho.**

**C413** AP103 10s brn & multi 1.10 .90

25th anniversary of Social Insurance. Exists imperf. Value $9.

Mother and Child — AP104

**1963, July 28 *Perf. 12½***

**C414** AP104 1.30s org, dk bl & blk .30 .25
**C415** AP104 5s gray, red & brn .60 .60

7th Pan-American and South American Pediatrics Congresses, Quito.

Simon Bolivar Airport, Guayaquil AP105

**1963, July 25 *Perf. 14***

**C416** AP105 60c gray .25 .25
**C417** AP105 70c dl grn .30 .25
**C418** AP105 5s brn vio .50 .35
*Nos. C416-C418 (3)* 1.05 .85

Opening of Simon Bolivar Airport, Guayaquil, July 15, 1962. Exist imperf. Value $4.50.

**Nos. 638, 640-641 Overprinted "AEREO"**

**1964 *Perf. 12***

**Flags in National Colors**

**C419** A223 1.80s dl vio .60 .35
**C420** A224 2s dk brn .60 .35
**C421** A223 2.20s blk brn .60 .35
*Nos. C419-C421 (3)* 1.80 1.05

On 1.80s and 2.20s, "AEREO" is vertical, reading down.

**No. 650 Overprinted in Gold: "FARO DE COLON / AEREO"**

**1964 Photo. *Perf. 14x13½***

**C422** A229 1.80s dk bl 3.00 2.00

**Nos. C352-C354 Overprinted**

**1964 Litho. *Perf. 13½***

**C423** AP86 50c bl & multi .80 .45
**C424** AP86 80c yel & multi .80 .45
**C425** AP86 1.30s pale grn & multi .80 .45
*Nos. C423-C425 (3)* 2.40 1.35

**No. C307 Overprinted: "DECLARACION / DERECHOS HUMANOS / 1964 / XV-ANIV"**

**Unwmk.**

**1964, Sept. 29 Engr. *Perf. 14***

**C426** AP69 1.70s red org .40 .25

15th anniversary (in 1963) of the Universal Declaration of Human Rights.

**Banana Type**

**1964, Oct. 26 Litho. *Perf. 12½x12***

**C427** A241 4.20s blk, bis & gray ol .40 .30
**C428** A241 10s blk, scar & gray ol .70 .50
*a.* Souv. sheet of 4 3.25 3.00

No. C428a contains imperf. stamps similar to Nos. 720-721 and C427-C428.

John F. Kennedy, Flag-draped Coffin and John Jr. — AP106

**1964, Nov. 22 Litho. *Perf. 14***

**C429** AP106 4.20s multi 1.25 .95
**C430** AP106 5s multi 1.60 1.25
**C431** AP106 10s multi 3.00 1.60
*a.* Souv. sheet of 3 10.00 10.00
*Nos. C429-C431 (3)* 5.85 3.80

President John F. Kennedy (1917-63).

No. C431a contains stamps similar to Nos. C429-C431, imperf.

**Olympic Type**

1.30s, Gymnast, vert. 1.80s, Hurdler. 2s, Basketball.

*Perf. 13½x14, 14x13½*

**1964, Dec. 16 Unwmk.**

**C432** A243 1.30s vio bl, ver & brn .45 .25
**C433** A243 1.80s vio bl & multi .45 .25
**C434** A243 2s red & multi .45 .25
*a.* Souv. sheet of 4 3.25 3.25
*Nos. C432-C434 (3)* 1.35 .75

No. C434a contains stamps similar to Nos. 725 and C432-C434, imperf.

**Sports Type**

Torch and Athletes: 2s, 3s, Diver, gymnast, wrestlers and weight lifter. 2.50s, 4s, Bicyclists. 3.50s, 5s, Jumpers.

**1965, Nov. 20 Litho. *Perf. 12x12½***

**C435** A247 2s bl, gold & blk .60 .25
**C436** A247 2.50s org, gold & blk .60 .25
**C437** A247 3s brt pink, gold & blk .60 .25
**C438** A247 3.50s lt vio, gold & bl .65 .65
**C439** A247 4s brt yel grn, gold & blk .65 .25
**C440** A247 5s red org, gold & blk .75 .35
*a.* Souv. sheet of 12 12.00 12.00
*Nos. C435-C440 (6)* 3.85 2.00

No. C440a contains 12 imperf. stamps similar to Nos. 738-743 and C435-C440.

For surcharges see Nos. 766B, C449.

**Bird Type**

Birds: 1s, Yellow grosbeak. 1.30s, Black-headed parrot. 1.50s, Scarlet tanager. 2s, Sapphire quail-dove. 2.50s, Violet-tailed sylph. 3s, Lemon-throated barbet. 4s, Yellow-tailed oriole. 10s, Collared puffbird.

**1966, June 17 Litho. *Perf. 13½***

**Birds in Natural Colors**

**C441** A249 1s lt red brn & blk 1.10 .25
**C442** A249 1.30s pink & blk 1.10 .25
**C443** A249 1.50s pale grn & blk 1.10 .25
**C444** A249 2s sal & blk 2.75 .45
**C445** A249 2.50s lt yel grn & blk 2.75 .45
**C446** A249 3s sal & blk 3.75 .65
**C447** A249 4s gray & blk 5.00 .85
**C448** A249 10s beige & blk 7.75 2.10
*Nos. C441-C448 (8)* 25.30 5.25

For surcharges see Nos. 766E-766F, C450, C455-C457.

**Nos. C436 and C443 Surcharged**

**1967**

**C449** A247 80c on 2.50s multi .40 .35
**C450** A249 80c on 1.50s multi .40 .25

Old denomination on No. C449 is obliterated with heavy bar; the surcharge on No. C450 includes "Resello" and an ornament over old denomination.

Peñaherrera Monument, Quito — AP107

Design: 2s, Peñaherrera statue.

**1967, Dec. 29 Litho. *Perf. 12x12½***

**C451** AP107 1.30s blk & org .30 .25
**C452** AP107 2s blk & lt ultra .30 .25

See note after No. 767B.

**Arosemena Type**

1.30s, Inauguration. 2s, Pres. Arosemena speaking in Punta del Este.

**1968, May 9 Litho. *Perf. 13½x14***

**C453** A251 1.30s multi .25 .25
**C454** A251 2s multi .30 .25

No. C448 Srchd. in Plum, Dark Blue or Green

**1969, Jan. 9 Litho. *Perf. 13½***

**Bird in Natural Colors**

**C455** A249 80c on 10s beige (P) .50 .25
**C456** A249 1s on 10s beige (DBl) .50 .25
**C457** A249 2s on 10s beige (G) .50 .25
*Nos. C455-C457 (3)* 1.50 .75

"Operation Friendship" AP108

**1969-70 Typo. *Perf. 13½***

**C458** AP108 2s yel, blk, red & lt bl .30 .25
*a.* Perf. 12½ .30 .25
**C459** AP108 2s bl, blk, car & yel ('70) .30 .25

Friendship campaign. Medallion background on Nos. C458 and C458a is blue; on No. C459, yellow.

No. C459 exists imperf. Value $5.

**No. 639 Surcharged in Gold "S/. 5 AEREO" and Bar**

**1969, Nov. 25 Litho. *Perf. 12***

**C460** A224 5s on 2s multi 2.00 .75

**Butterfly Type**

Butterflies: 1.30s, Morpho peleides. 1.50s, Anartia amathea.

**1970 Litho. *Perf. 12½***

**C461** A255 1.30s multi 3.50 .25
**C462** A255 1.50s pink & multi 3.50 .25

**Same, White Background**

**1970 *Perf. 13½***

**C463** A255 1.30s multi 3.50 .25
**C464** A255 1.50s multi 3.50 .25

**Arms Type**

Provincial Arms and Flags: 1.30s, El Oro. 2s, Loja. 3s, Manabi. 5s, Pichincha. 10s, Guayas.

**1971 Litho. *Perf. 10½***

**C465** A258 1.30s pink & multi .25 .25
**C466** A258 2s multi .35 .25
**C467** A258 3s multi .50 .30

| | | | | |
|---|---|---|---|---|
| **C468** | A258 | 5s multi | .65 | .30 |
| **C469** | A258 | 10s multi | 1.25 | .40 |
| | | *Nos. C465-C469 (5)* | 3.00 | 1.50 |

Presentation of the Virgin — AP109

Art of Quito: 1.50s, Blessed Anne at Prayer. 2s, St. Theresa de Jesus. 2.50s, Altar of Carmen, horiz. 3s, Descent from the Cross. 4s, Christ of St. Mariana de Jesus. 5s, Shrine of St. Anthony. 10s, Cross of San Diego.

**1971** ***Perf. 11½***

**Inscriptions in Black**

| | | | | |
|---|---|---|---|---|
| **C473** | AP109 | 1.30s multi | .25 | .25 |
| **C474** | AP109 | 1.50s multi | .25 | .25 |
| **C475** | AP109 | 2s multi | .25 | .25 |
| **C476** | AP109 | 2.50s multi | .40 | .25 |
| **C477** | AP109 | 3s multi | .50 | .25 |
| **C478** | AP109 | 4s multi | .65 | .25 |
| **C479** | AP109 | 5s multi | .65 | .35 |
| **C480** | AP109 | 10s multi | 1.25 | .65 |
| | | *Nos. C473-C480 (8)* | 4.20 | 2.50 |

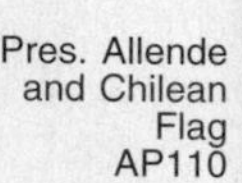

Pres. Allende and Chilean Flag AP110

2.10s, Pres. José M. Velasco Ibarra of Ecuador, Pres. Salvador Allende of Chile, national flags.

**1971, Aug. 24** ***Perf. 12½***

| | | | | |
|---|---|---|---|---|
| **C481** | AP110 | 2s multi | .25 | .25 |
| **C482** | AP110 | 2.10s multi | .25 | .25 |

Visit of Pres. Salvador Allende of Chile, Aug. 24.

Globe and Emblem AP111

**1971**

| | | | | |
|---|---|---|---|---|
| **C483** | AP111 | 5s black | 1.10 | .45 |
| **C484** | AP111 | 5.50s dl pur & blk | 1.10 | .45 |

Opening of Postal Museum, Aug. 24, 1971. Exist imperf. Value $7.50.

**Pazmiño Type**

**1971, Sept. 16** ***Perf. 12x11½***

| | | | | |
|---|---|---|---|---|
| **C485** | A260 | 1.50s grn & multi | .25 | .25 |
| **C486** | A260 | 2.50s grn & multi | .35 | .25 |

AP112

Designs: 5s, Map of Americas. 10s, Converging roads and map. 20s, Map of Americas and Equator. 50s, Mountain road and monument on Equator.

**1971** ***Perf. 11½***

| | | | | |
|---|---|---|---|---|
| **C487** | AP112 | 5s org & multi | .80 | .30 |
| **C488** | AP112 | 10s org & blk | 1.25 | .55 |
| **C489** | AP112 | 20s blk, bl & brt rose | 2.00 | 1.00 |
| **C490** | AP112 | 50s bl, blk & gray | 3.25 | 1.50 |
| | | *Nos. C487-C490 (4)* | 7.30 | 3.35 |

11th Pan-American Road Congress. Issued: 5s, 10s, 50s, 11/15; 20s, 11/22.

No. C488 exists imperf. Value $8.

AP113

Design: 3s, Arms of Ecuador and Argentina. 5s, Presidents José M. Velasco Ibarra and Alejandro Agustin Lanusse.

**1972**

| | | | | |
|---|---|---|---|---|
| **C491** | AP113 | 3s blk & multi | .25 | .25 |
| **C492** | AP113 | 5s blk & multi | .50 | .30 |

Visit of Lt. Gen. Alejandro Agustin Lanusse, president of Argentina, Jan. 25.

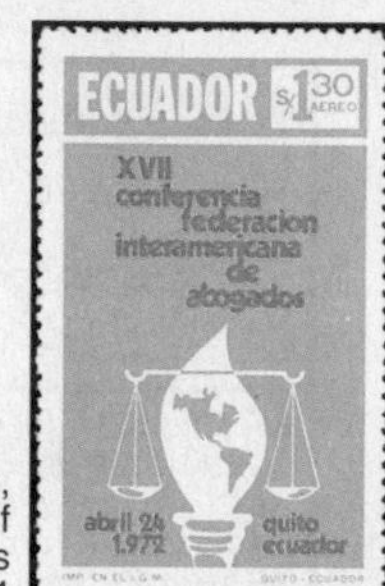


Flame, Scales, Map of Americas AP114

**1972, Apr. 24** **Litho.** ***Perf. 12½***

| | | | | |
|---|---|---|---|---|
| **C493** | AP114 | 1.30s bl & red | .50 | .25 |

17th Conference of the Interamerican Federation of Lawyers, Quito, Apr. 24.

**Religious Paintings Type of Regular Issue**

Ecuadorian Paintings: 3s, Virgin of the Flowers, by Miguel de Santiago. 10s, Virgin of the Rosary, by Quito School.

**1972, Apr. 24** ***Perf. 14x13½***

| | | | | |
|---|---|---|---|---|
| **C494** | A263 | 3s blk & multi | .35 | .35 |
| **C495** | A263 | 10s blk & multi | 1.10 | .55 |
| *a.* | | Souv. sheet of 2, #C494-C495 | 1.90 | 1.90 |

**1972, May 4**

Ecuadorian Statues: 3s, St. Dominic, Quito School. 10s, St. Rosa of Lima, by Bernardo de Legarda.

| | | | | |
|---|---|---|---|---|
| **C496** | A263 | 3s blk & multi | .35 | .35 |
| **C497** | A263 | 10s blk & multi | 1.00 | .55 |
| *a.* | | Souv. sheet of 2, #C496-C497 | 2.50 | 2.10 |

Letters of "Ecuador" 3mm high on Nos. C496-C497, 7mm high on Nos. C494-C495.

**Portrait Type**

Designs (Generals, from Paintings): 1.30s, José Maria Saenz. 3s, Tomás Wright. 4s, Antonio Farfan. 5s, Antonio José de Sucre. 10s, Simon Bolivar. 20s, Arms of Ecuador.

**1972, May 24**

| | | | | |
|---|---|---|---|---|
| **C498** | A264 | 1.30s bl & multi | .25 | .25 |
| **C499** | A264 | 3s bl & multi | .25 | .25 |
| **C500** | A264 | 4s bl & multi | .35 | .25 |
| **C501** | A264 | 5s bl & multi | .55 | .30 |
| **C502** | A264 | 10s bl & multi | 1.00 | .55 |
| **C503** | A264 | 20s bl & multi | 2.00 | 1.00 |
| | | *Nos. C498-C503 (6)* | 4.40 | 2.60 |

**Artisan Type**

Handicraft of Ecuador: 2s, Woman wearing flowered poncho. 3s, Striped poncho. 5s, Poncho with roses. 10s, Gold sunburst sculpture.

**1972, July** **Photo.** ***Perf. 13***

| | | | | |
|---|---|---|---|---|
| **C504** | A265 | 2s multi | .25 | .25 |
| **C505** | A265 | 3s multi | .50 | .25 |
| **C506** | A265 | 5s multi | .80 | .40 |
| **C507** | A265 | 10s org red & multi | 1.40 | .90 |
| *a.* | | Souv. sheet of 4, #C504-C507 | 4.00 | 4.00 |
| | | *Nos. C504-C507 (4)* | 2.95 | 1.80 |

Epidendrum Orchid — AP115

**1972** **Photo.** ***Perf. 12½***

| | | | | |
|---|---|---|---|---|
| **C508** | AP115 | 4s shown | .90 | .90 |
| **C509** | AP115 | 6s Canna | 1.40 | 1.40 |
| **C510** | AP115 | 10s Jimson weed | 2.00 | 2.00 |
| *a.* | | Souv. sheet of 3, #C508-C510 | 6.00 | 6.00 |
| | | *Nos. C508-C510 (3)* | 4.30 | 4.30 |

Exists imperf.

Oil Drilling Towers — AP116

**1972, Oct. 17** **Litho.** ***Perf. 11½***

| | | | | |
|---|---|---|---|---|
| **C511** | AP116 | 1.30s bl & multi | .50 | .25 |

Ecuadorian oil industry.

Coat of Arms — AP117

**Arms Multicolored**

**1972, Nov. 18** **Litho.** ***Perf. 11½***

| | | | | |
|---|---|---|---|---|
| **C512** | AP117 | 2s black | .25 | .25 |
| **C513** | AP117 | 3s black | .25 | .25 |
| **C514** | AP117 | 4s black | .30 | .25 |
| **C515** | AP117 | 4.50s black | .30 | .25 |
| **C516** | AP117 | 6.30s black | .75 | .30 |
| **C517** | AP117 | 6.90s black | .75 | .30 |
| | | *Nos. C512-C517 (6)* | 2.60 | 1.60 |

**Pichincha Type**

Designs: 2.40s, Corridor, San Agustin. 4.50s, La Merced Convent. 5.50s, Column base. 6.30s, Chapter Hall, San Agustin. 6.90s, Interior, San Agustin. 7.40s, Crucifixion, Cantuña Chapel. 7.90s, Decorated ceiling, San Agustin.

**1972, Dec. 6** **Wmk. 367**

| | | | | |
|---|---|---|---|---|
| **C518** | A266 | 2.40s yel & multi | .25 | .25 |
| **C519** | A266 | 4.50s yel & multi | .45 | .30 |
| **C520** | A266 | 5.50s yel & multi | .45 | .30 |
| **C521** | A266 | 6.30s yel & multi | .60 | .35 |
| **C522** | A266 | 6.90s yel & multi | .60 | .35 |
| **C523** | A266 | 7.40s yel & multi | .90 | .55 |
| **C524** | A266 | 7.90s yel & multi | .90 | .55 |
| | | *Nos. C518-C524 (7)* | 4.15 | 2.65 |

UN Emblem — AP118

**1973, Mar. 23** **Unwmk.**

| | | | | |
|---|---|---|---|---|
| **C525** | AP118 | 1.30s lt bl & blk | .30 | .25 |

25th anniversary of the Economic Committee for Latin America (CEPAL).

OAS Emblem — AP119

**1973, Apr. 14** **Wmk. 367**

| | | | | |
|---|---|---|---|---|
| **C526** | AP119 | 1.50s multi | .30 | .25 |
| *a.* | | Unwatermarked | .30 | .25 |

Day of the Americas and "Philately for Peace."

**Bird Type**

**1973** **Unwmk.** ***Perf. 11½x11***

| | | | | |
|---|---|---|---|---|
| **C527** | A268 | 1.30s Blue-footed booby | 2.10 | .25 |
| **C528** | A268 | 3s Brown pelican | 2.10 | .25 |

Presidents Lara and Caldera AP120

**1973, June 15** **Wmk. 367**

| | | | | |
|---|---|---|---|---|
| **C529** | AP120 | 3s multi | .45 | .30 |

Visit of Venezuela Pres. Rafael Caldera, Feb. 5-7.

Silver Coin, 1934 — AP121

Ecuadorian Coins: 10s, Silver coin, obverse. 50s, Gold coin, 1928.

**Unwmk.**

**1973, Dec. 14** **Photo.** ***Perf. 14***

| | | | | |
|---|---|---|---|---|
| **C530** | AP121 | 5s multi | .60 | .40 |
| **C531** | AP121 | 10s multi | 1.00 | .60 |
| **C532** | AP121 | 50s multi | 4.50 | 2.50 |
| *a.* | | Souvenir sheet of 3 | 7.25 | 7.25 |
| | | *Nos. C530-C532 (3)* | 6.10 | 3.50 |

No. C532a contains one each of Nos. C530-C532; Dated "1972." Exists imperf. Value, same.

A gold marginal overprint was applied in 1974 to No. C532a (perf. and imperf.): "X Campeonato Mundial de Football / Munich - 1974." Value, each $75.

A carmine overprint was applied in 1974 to No. C532a (perf. and imperf.): "Seminario de Telecommunicaciones Rurales, / Septiembre-1974 / Quito-Ecuador" and ITU emblem. Value, each $10.

Globe, OPEC Emblem, Oil Derrick — AP122

**1974, June 15** **Litho.** ***Perf. 11½***

| | | | | |
|---|---|---|---|---|
| **C533** | AP122 | 2s multi | .45 | .30 |

Meeting of Organization of Oil Exporting Countries, Quito, June 15-24.

Ecuadorian Flag, UPU Emblem — AP123

**1974, July 15** **Litho.** ***Perf. 11½***
**C534** AP123 1.30s multi .30 .25

Centenary of Universal Postal Union.
Two 25s souvenir sheets exist. These were sold on a restricted basis. Value, each $75.

Teodoro Wolf AP124

Capt. Edmundo Chiriboga AP125

**1974** **Litho.** ***Perf. 12x11½***
**C535** AP124 1.30s blk & ultra .25 .25
**C536** AP125 1.50s gray .30 .25

Teodoro Wolf, geographer; Edmundo Chiriboga, national hero.
Issued: No. C535, 11/29; No. C536, 12/4.

Congress Emblem AP126

**1974, Dec. 8** **Litho.** ***Perf. 11½x12***
**C537** AP126 5s bl & multi .45 .30

8th Inter-American Postmasters' Cong., Quito.

Map of Americas and Coat of Arms — AP127

**1975, Feb. 1** ***Perf. 12x11½***
**C538** AP127 3s bl & multi .45 .30

EXFIGUA Stamp Exhibition and 5th General Assembly of Federation Inter-Americana de Filatelia, Guayaquil, Nov. 1973.

Prominent Ecuadorians AP128

No. C539, Manuel J. Calle, Journalist. No. C540, Leopoldo Benites V., president of UN General Assembly, 1973-74; No. C541, Adolfo H. Simmonds G. (1892-1969), journalist; No. C542, Juan de Dios Martinez Mera, President of Ecuador, birth centenary.

**1975** ***Perf. 12x11½***
**C539** AP128 5s lilac rose .60 .30
**C540** AP128 5s gray .60 .30
**C541** AP128 5s violet .60 .30
**C542** AP128 5s blk & rose red .60 .30
*Nos. C539-C542 (4)* 2.40 1.20

Pres. Guillermo Rodriguez Lara — AP129

**1975** **Unwmk.** ***Perf. 12***
**C546** AP129 5s vermilion & blk .60 .30

State visit of Pres. Guillermo Rodriguez Lara to Algeria, Romania and Venezuela.

### Meeting Type of 1975

1.50s, Rafael Rodriguez Palacios & Argelino Duran Quintero meeting at border in Rumichaca. 2s, Signing border agreement.

**1975, Apr. 1** **Litho.** ***Perf. 12x11½***
**C547** A273 1.50s multi .30 .25
**C548** A273 2s multi .30 .25

Sacred Heart (Painting) AP130

Quito Cathedral AP131

Design: 2s, Monstrance.

**1975, Apr. 28** **Litho.** ***Perf. 12x11½***
**C549** AP130 1.30s yel & multi .25 .25
**C550** AP130 2s bl & multi .30 .25
**C551** AP131 3s multi .40 .25
*Nos. C549-C551 (3)* .95 .75

3rd Bolivarian Eucharistic Congress, Quito, June 9-16, 1974.

J. Delgado Panchana with Trophy — AP132

J. Delgado Panchana Swimming AP133

***Perf. 12x11½, 11½x12***
**1975, June 12** **Unwmk.**
**C552** AP132 1.30s bl & multi .25 .25
**C553** AP133 3s blk & multi .30 .25

Jorge Delgado Panchana, South American swimming champion, 1971 and 1974.

### Sports Type of 1975

**1975, Sept. 11** **Litho.** ***Perf. 11½***
**C554** A276 1.30s Tennis .40 .25
**C555** A276 2s Target shooting .55 .25
**C556** A276 2.80s Volleyball .65 .25
**C557** A276 3s Raft with sails .65 .25
**C558** A276 5s Mask 1.10 .25
*Nos. C554-C558 (5)* 3.35 1.25

### Flower Type of 1975

**1975, Nov. 18** **Litho.** ***Perf. 11½x12***
**C559** A277 1.30s Pitcairnia pungens .35 .25
**C560** A277 2s Scarlet sage .55 .25
**C561** A277 3s Amaryllis .75 .40
**C562** A277 4s Opuntia quitense 1.10 .55
**C563** A277 5s Bomarea 1.60 .75
*Nos. C559-C563 (5)* 4.35 2.20

Tail Assemblies and Emblem — AP134

Planes over Map of Ecuador — AP135

**1975, Dec. 17** **Litho.** ***Perf. 11½***
**C564** AP134 1.30s bl & multi .45 .30
**C565** AP135 3s multi .55 .30

TAME, Military Transport Airline, 13th anniv.

Benalcázar Statue — AP136

**1976, Feb. 6** **Litho.** ***Perf. 11½***
**C566** AP136 2s multi .35 .25
**C567** AP136 3s multi .35 .25

Sebastián de Benalcázar (1495-1550), Spanish conquistador, founder of Quito.

### Archaeology Type of 1975

1.30s, Seated man, Carchi Culture. 2s, Funerary urn, Tuncahuan Culture. 3s, Priest, Bahia de Caraquez Culture. 4s, Snail's shell, Cuasmal Culture. 5s, Bowl supported by figurines, Guangala Culture.

**1976, Feb. 12** **Litho.** ***Perf. 11½***
**C568** A278 1.30s multi .35 .25
**C569** A278 2s multi .45 .25
**C570** A278 3s multi .65 .45
**C571** A278 4s multi .95 .45
**C572** A278 5s multi 1.25 .45
*Nos. C568-C572 (5)* 3.65 1.85

### Fruit Type of 1976

**1976, Mar. 30**
**C573** A280 2s Apples .40 .25
**C574** A280 5s Rose .80 .40

Lufthansa Jet — AP137

**1976, June 25** **Litho.** ***Perf. 12***
**C575** AP137 10s bl & multi 1.50 .50

Lufthansa, 50th anniversary.
An imperf. 20s miniature sheet exists, similar to No. C575 enlarged, with overprinted black bar covering line below "Lufthansa." Size: 90x115mm.

Projected PO, Quito — AP138

**1976, Aug. 10** **Litho.** ***Perf. 12***
**C576** AP138 5s blk & multi .40 .25

Design for new General Post Office, Quito.

Fruit Peddler — AP139

No. C578, Longshoreman. No. C579, Cerros del Carmen & Santa Ana, hills of Guayaquil, horiz. No. C580, Sebastián de Belalcázar. No. C581, Francisco de Orellana. No. C582, Chief Guayas & his wife Quila.

**1976, July 25**
**C577** AP139 1.30s red & multi .25 .25
**C578** AP139 1.30s red & multi .25 .25
**C579** AP139 1.30s red & multi .25 .25
**C580** AP139 2s red & multi .25 .25
**C581** AP139 2s red & multi .25 .25
**C582** AP139 2s red & multi .25 .25
*Nos. C577-C582 (6)* 1.50 1.50

Founding of Guayaquil, 441st anniversary.

Emblem and Laurel AP140

**1976, Aug. 9**
**C583** AP140 1.30s yel & multi .35 .25

Bolivarian Soc. of Ecuador, 50th anniv.

Western Hemisphere and Equator Monument AP141

**1976, Sept. 6**
**C584** AP141 2s multi .35 .25

### Souvenir Sheet
### *Imperf*

**C585** AP141 5s multi 4.00 4.00

3rd Conf. of Pan-American Transport Ministers, Quito, Sept. 6-11. No. C585 contains design similar to No. C584 with black denomination and red control number in margin.

Congress Emblem — AP142

**1976, Sept. 27** **Litho.** ***Perf. 11½***
**C586** AP142 1.30s bl & multi .40 .25
**C587** AP142 3s bl & multi .50 .30

### Souvenir Sheet
### *Imperf*

**C588** AP142 10s bl & multi 1.75 1.00

10th Inter-American Congress of the Construction Industry, Quito, Sept. 27-30.

George Washington AP143

American Bicentennial: 5s, Naval battle, Sept. 23, 1779, in which the Bonhomme Richard, commanded by John Paul Jones, defeated and captured the Serapis, British man-of-war, off Yorkshire coast, horiz.

**1976, Oct. 18 Litho. *Perf. 12***

**C589** AP143 3s blk & multi .65 .30
**C590** AP143 5s red brn & yel 1.25 .60

Dr. Hideyo Noguchi — AP144

**1976 Litho. *Perf. 11½***

**C591** AP144 3s yel & multi .40 .25

Dr. Hideyo Noguchi (1876-1928), bacteriologist (at Rockefeller Institute). A 10s imperf. miniature sheet in same design exists without "Aereo." Size: 95x114mm. Value $6.

Luis Cordero — AP145

**1976, Dec. Litho. *Perf. 11½***

**C592** AP145 2s multi .35 .25

Luis Cordero (1833-1912), president of Ecuador.

Mariuxi Febres Cordero — AP146

**1976, Dec. *Perf. 11½***

**C593** AP146 3s multi .35 .25

Mariuxi Febres Cordero, South American swimming champion.

Flags and Monument AP147

**1976, Nov. 9 *Perf. 12***

**C594** AP147 3s multi .35 .25

### Miniature Sheet
### *Imperf*

**C595** AP147 5s multi 2.50 1.50

2nd Meeting of the Agriculture Ministers of the Andean Countries, Quito, Nov. 8-10.

Sister Catalina — AP148

**1977, June 17 Litho. *Perf. 12x11½***

**C596** AP148 1.30s blk & pale salmon .45 .30

Sister Catalina de Jesus Herrera (1717-1795), writer.

Congress Hall, Quito — AP149

**1977, Aug. 15 Litho. *Perf. 12x11½***

**C597** AP149 5s multi .60 .30
*a.* 10s souvenir sheet 2.00 2.00

11th General Assembly of Pan-American Institute of Geography and History, Quito, Aug. 15-30. No. C597a contains the designs of types A282 and AP149 without denominations and with simulated perforations.

Pres. Alfonso López Michelsen, Flag of Colombia — AP150

Designs: 5s, Pres. López Michelsen of Colombia, Pres. Alfredo Poveda Burbano of Ecuador and aide. 7s, as 5s, vert. 9s, 10s, Presidents with aides.

**1977, Sept. 13 *Perf. 12***

**C598** AP150 2.60s multi .50 .25
**C599** AP150 5s multi .75 .30
**C600** AP150 7s multi .90 .40
**C601** AP150 9s multi 1.25 .60

### *Imperf*

**C602** AP150 10s multi 1.25 1.00
*Nos. C598-C602 (5)* 4.65 2.55

Meeting of the Presidents of Ecuador and Colombia and Declaration of Putumayo, Feb. 25, 1977. Nos. C598-C602 are overprinted in multiple fluorescent, colorless rows: INSTITUTO GEOGRAFICO MILITAR GOBIERNO DEL ECUADOR.

Ceramic Figure, Tolita Culture AP151

9s, Divine Shepherdess, sculpture by Bernardo de Legarda. 11s, The Fruit Seller, sculpture by Legarda. 20s, Sun God, pre-Columbian gold mask.

**1977, Aug. 24 *Perf. 12***

**C603** AP151 7s gold & multi 1.20 .30
**C604** AP151 9s gold & multi 1.50 .35
**C605** AP151 11s gold & multi 2.00 .70
*Nos. C603-C605 (3)* 4.70 1.35

### Souvenir Sheet
### Gold Embossed
### *Imperf*

**C606** AP151 20s vio, bl, blk & gold 8.50 3.50

Central Bank of Ecuador, 50th anniversary. Nos. C603-C605 overprinted like Nos. C598-C602.

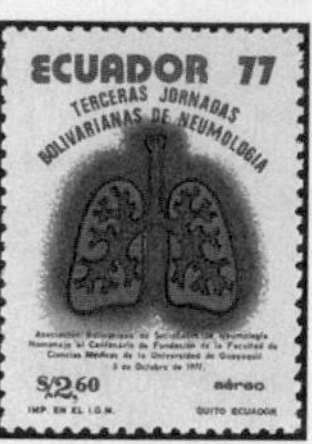

Lungs — AP152

**1977, Oct. 5 Litho. *Perf. 12x11½***

**C607** AP152 2.60s multi .35 .25

3rd Cong. of the Bolivarian Pneumonic Soc. and cent. of the founding of the medical faculty of the University of Guayaquil.

Brother Miguel, St. Peter's, Rome — AP153

**1977**

**C608** AP153 2.60s multi .35 .25

Beatification of Brother Miguel.

### Peralta Type

2.60s, Titles of works by Peralta & his bookmark.

**1977 *Perf. 11½***

**C609** A284 2.60s multi .40 .25

Broadcast Tower — AP154

**1977, Dec. 2 Litho. *Perf. 12x11½***

**C610** AP154 5s multi .45 .45

9th World Telecommunications Day.

Remigio Romero y Cordero (1895-1967), Poet — AP155

**1978, Mar. 2 Litho. *Perf. 12½x11½***

**C611** AP155 3s multi .40 .25
**C612** AP155 10.60s multi .55 .30

### *Imperf*

**C612A** AP155 10s multi 1.40 1.40
*Nos. C611-C612A (3)* 2.35 1.95

No. C612A contains a vignette similar to Nos. C611-C612.

Dr. Vicente Corral Moscoso — AP156

5s, Hospital emblem with Caduceus.

**1978, Apr. 12 Litho. *Imperf.***

**C613** AP156 5s multi .55 .25

### *Perf. 12x11½*

**C614** AP156 7.60s multi 1.10 .50

Inauguration (in 1977) of Dr. Vicente Corral Moscoso Regional Hospital, Cuenca.

Faces — AP157

Designs: 9s, Emblems and flags of Ecuador. 10s, 11s, Hands reaching for light.

**1978, Mar. 17**

**C615** AP157 7s multicolored .70 .25
**C616** AP157 9s multicolored 1.00 .25
**C617** AP157 11s multicolored 1.25 .25

### *Imperf*

**C618** AP157 10s multicolored 1.25 1.25
*Nos. C615-C618 (4)* 4.20 2.00

Ecuadorian Social Security Institute, 50th anniv.

### Geographical Institute Type

7.60s, Plane over map of Ecuador with mountains.

**1978, Apr. 12 Litho. *Perf. 11½***

**C619** A287 7.60s multi 1.10 .55

### *Imperf*

**C620** A287 10s multi 1.75 1.75

No. C620 contains 2 vignettes with simulated perforations in designs of Nos. 967 and C619.

### Lions Type

**1978 *Perf. 11½***

**C621** A288 5s multi .75 .25
**C622** A288 6.20s multi .90 .40

### *Imperf*

**C623** A288 10s multi 2.50 1.25
*Nos. C621-C623 (3)* 4.15 1.90

No. C623 contains a vignette similar to Nos. C621-C622.

San Martin — AP158

**1978, Apr. 13 Litho. *Perf. 12***

**C624** AP158 10.60s multi 1.60 .50

### *Imperf*

**C625** AP158 10s multi 1.75 1.75

Gen. José de San Martin (1778-1850), soldier and statesman. No. C625 contains a vignette similar to No. C624.

### Bank Type

Design: 5s, Bank emblem.

**1978, Sept. Litho. *Perf. 11½***

**C626** A289 5s gray & multi .45 .30

**Soccer Type**

Designs: 2.60s, "Gauchito" and Games' emblem. 5s, "Gauchito." 7s, Soccer ball. 9s, Games' emblem, vert. 10s, Games' emblem.

**1978, Nov. 1** *Perf. 12*

| | | | | |
|---|---|---|---|---|
| **C627** | A290 | 2.60s multi | .30 | .25 |
| **C628** | A290 | 7s multi | .80 | .40 |
| **C629** | A290 | 9s multi | 1.10 | .65 |

***Imperf***

| | | | | |
|---|---|---|---|---|
| **C630** | A290 | 5s blk & bl | 6.00 | 6.00 |
| **C631** | A290 | 10s blk & bl | 6.00 | 6.00 |
| | *Nos. C627-C631 (5)* | | 14.20 | 13.30 |

Bernardo O'Higgins AP159

**1978, Nov. 11 Litho.** *Perf. 12x11½*

| | | | | |
|---|---|---|---|---|
| **C632** | AP159 | 10.60s multi | .80 | .30 |

***Imperf***

| | | | | |
|---|---|---|---|---|
| **C633** | AP159 | 10s multi | 1.50 | .90 |

Gen. Bernardo O'Higgins (1778-1842), Chilean soldier and statesman. No. C633 contains a vignette similar to No. C632.

Old Men of Vilcabamba AP160

**1978, Nov. 11** *Perf. 12x11½*

| | | | | |
|---|---|---|---|---|
| **C634** | AP160 | 5s multi | .50 | .30 |

Vilcabamba, valley of longevity.

Humphrey AP161

**1978, Nov. 27 Litho.** *Perf. 12x11½*

| | | | | |
|---|---|---|---|---|
| **C635** | AP161 | 5s multi | .50 | .30 |

Hubert H. Humphrey (1911-1978), Vice President of the US.

Virgin and Child — AP162

Children's Drawings: 4.60s, Holy Family. 6.20s, Candle and children.

**1978**

| | | | | |
|---|---|---|---|---|
| **C636** | AP162 | 2.20s multi | .30 | .25 |
| **C637** | AP162 | 4.60s multi | .50 | .25 |
| **C638** | AP162 | 6.20s multi | .85 | .40 |
| | *Nos. C636-C638 (3)* | | 1.65 | .90 |

Christmas 1978.

Village, by Anibal Villacis AP163

Ecuadorian Painters: No. C640, Mountain Village, by Gilberto Almeida. No. C641, Bay, by Roura Oxandaberro. No. C642, Abstract, by Luis Molinari. No. C643, Statue, by Oswaldo Viteri. No. C644, Tools, by Enrique Tabara.

**1978, Dec. 9** *Perf. 12*

| | | | | |
|---|---|---|---|---|
| **C639** | AP163 | 5s multi | .60 | .25 |
| **C640** | AP163 | 5s multi | .60 | .25 |
| **C641** | AP163 | 5s multi | .60 | .25 |
| **C642** | AP163 | 5s multi | .60 | .25 |
| **C643** | AP163 | 5s multi | .60 | .25 |
| **C644** | AP163 | 5s multi | .60 | .25 |
| | *Nos. C639-C644 (6)* | | 3.60 | 1.50 |

House and Monument AP164

Design: 3.40s, Monument, vert.

**1979, Feb. 27 Litho.** *Perf. 12*

| | | | | |
|---|---|---|---|---|
| **C645** | AP164 | 2.40s multi | .30 | .25 |
| **C646** | AP164 | 3.40s multi | .30 | .25 |

***Imperf***

| | | | | |
|---|---|---|---|---|
| **C647** | AP164 | 10s multi | .90 | .90 |
| | *Nos. C645-C647 (3)* | | 1.50 | 1.40 |

Sesquicentennial of Battle of Portete and Tarqui. No. C647 contains vignettes similar to #C645-C646.

Fish and Ship — AP165

7s, Map of Ecuador & Galapagos showing territorial waters. 9s, Map of South America with west-coast territorial waters.

***Perf. 12x11½, 11½x12***

**1979, July 23 Litho. Wmk. 367**

| | | | | |
|---|---|---|---|---|
| **C648** | AP165 | 5s multi | .75 | .25 |
| **C649** | AP165 | 7s multi, horiz. | 1.00 | .35 |
| **C650** | AP165 | 9s multi | 1.40 | .50 |
| | *Nos. C648-C650 (3)* | | 3.15 | 1.10 |

Declaration of 200-mile territorial limit, 25th anniversary.

**National Heritage Type**

Designs: 10.60s, Bells in Quito clock tower, horiz. 13.60s, Aerial view of Galapagos coast.

**1979, Aug. 3** *Perf. 12x11½*

| | | | | |
|---|---|---|---|---|
| **C651** | A293 | 10.60s multi | 1.25 | .60 |
| **C652** | A293 | 13.60s multi | 1.40 | .75 |

**Size: 115x91mm**

***Imperf***

**Unwmk.**

| | | | | |
|---|---|---|---|---|
| **C653** | A293 | 10s multi | 5.00 | 2.10 |
| | *Nos. C651-C653 (3)* | | 7.65 | 3.45 |

National heritage: Quito and Galapagos Islands. No. C653 contains vignettes similar to Nos. 977, C651-C652.

Flags of Ecuador and U.S. — AP166

**1979, Aug. Wmk. 367** *Perf. 11½x12*

| | | | | |
|---|---|---|---|---|
| **C654** | AP166 | 7.60s multi | .50 | .50 |
| **C655** | AP166 | 10.60s multi | .75 | .75 |

**Size: 115x91mm**

***Imperf***

**Unwmk.**

| | | | | |
|---|---|---|---|---|
| **C656** | AP166 | 10s multi | .90 | .75 |
| | *Nos. C654-C656 (3)* | | 2.15 | 2.00 |

5th anniv. of Ecuador-US Chamber of Commerce. No. C656 contains vignettes similar to Nos. C654-C655.

Smiling Girl, IYC Emblem — AP167

***Perf. 12x11½***

**1979, Sept. 7 Litho. Wmk. 367**

| | | | | |
|---|---|---|---|---|
| **C657** | AP167 | 10s multi | .85 | .40 |

International Year of the Child.

Citizens and Flag of Ecuador AP168

Design: 10.60s, Pres. Jaime Roldos Aguilera, flag of Ecuador, vert.

***Perf. 11½***

**1979, Sept. 27 Litho. Unwmk.**

| | | | | |
|---|---|---|---|---|
| **C658** | AP168 | 7.60s multi | 1.00 | .45 |

**Wmk. 367**

| | | | | |
|---|---|---|---|---|
| **C659** | AP168 | 10.60s multi | 1.25 | .40 |

Restoration of democracy to Ecuador.

Ecuador Coat of Arms, Olympic Rings and Eagle — AP169

***Perf. 12x11½***

**1979, Nov. 23 Unwmk.**

| | | | | |
|---|---|---|---|---|
| **C660** | AP169 | 28s multi | 2.00 | 1.25 |

5th National Games, Cuenca.

CIESPAL Building, Quito AP170

***Perf. 11½x12½***

**1979, Dec. 26 Wmk. 367**

| | | | | |
|---|---|---|---|---|
| **C661** | AP170 | 10.60s multi | .80 | .40 |

Opening of Ecuadorian Institute of Engineers building.

**Olmedo Type**

***Perf. 12x11½***

**1980, Apr. 29 Litho. Unwmk.**

| | | | | |
|---|---|---|---|---|
| **C662** | A294 | 10s multi | 1.25 | .65 |

**Tribal Chief Type**

Indo-American Tribal Chiefs: No. C663, Cuauhtemoc, Mexico. No. C664, Lempira, Honduras. No. C665, Nicaragua. No. C666, Lambaré, Paraguay. No. C667, Urraca, Panama. No. C668, Anacaona, Haiti. #C669, Caupolican, Chile. No. C670, Tacun-Uman, Guatemala. No. C671, Calarca, Colombia. No. C672, Garabito, Costa Rica. No. C673, Hatuey, Cuba. No. C674, Cmarao, Brazil. No. C675, Tehuelche, Argentina. No. C676, Tupaj Katri, Bolivia. 17.80s, Sequoyah, US. 22.80s, Ruminahui, Ecuador.

**Wmk. 367 (#C663, C667), Unwmkd.**

**1980, May 12**

| | | | | |
|---|---|---|---|---|
| **C663** | A295 | 7.60s multi | 1.50 | .35 |
| **C664** | A295 | 7.60s multi | 1.50 | .35 |
| **C665** | A295 | 7.60s multi | 1.50 | .35 |
| **C666** | A295 | 10s multi | 1.90 | .40 |
| **C667** | A295 | 10s multi | 1.90 | .40 |
| **C668** | A295 | 10.60s multi | 1.90 | .40 |
| **C669** | A295 | 10.60s multi | 1.90 | .40 |
| **C670** | A295 | 10.60s multi | 1.90 | .40 |
| **C671** | A295 | 12.80s multi | 2.50 | .55 |
| **C672** | A295 | 12.80s multi | 2.50 | .55 |
| **C673** | A295 | 12.80s multi | 2.50 | .55 |
| **C674** | A295 | 13.60s multi | 2.50 | .55 |
| **C675** | A295 | 13.60s multi | 2.50 | .55 |
| **C676** | A295 | 13.60s multi | 2.50 | .55 |
| **C677** | A295 | 17.80s multi | 3.00 | .65 |
| **C678** | A295 | 22.80s multi | 3.50 | 1.25 |
| | *Nos. C663-C678 (16)* | | 35.50 | 8.25 |

**Royal Visit Type**

***Perf. 11½x12***

**1980, May 18 Unwmk.**

| | | | | |
|---|---|---|---|---|
| **C679** | A296 | 10.60s multi | .75 | .40 |

Pichincha Provincial Development Council Building — AP171

**1980, June 1** *Perf. 12x11½*

| | | | | |
|---|---|---|---|---|
| **C680** | AP171 | 10.60s multi | 1.25 | .60 |

Progress in Pichincha Province.

**Indian Type**

**1980, June 10 Litho.** *Perf. 12x11½*

| | | | | |
|---|---|---|---|---|
| **C681** | A297 | 7.60s Salasaca boy, Tungurahua | 1.00 | .75 |
| **C682** | A297 | 10s Amula woman, Chimborazo | 1.25 | .85 |
| **C683** | A297 | 10.60s Canar woman, Canar | 1.50 | .90 |
| **C684** | A297 | 13.60s Colorado Indian, Pichincha | 1.75 | 1.25 |
| | *Nos. C681-C684 (4)* | | 5.50 | 3.75 |

**Virgin of Mercy Type**

**1980, July 7 Litho.** *Perf. 11½*

| | | | | |
|---|---|---|---|---|
| **C685** | A298 | 7.60s Cupola, cloisters | 1.00 | .50 |
| **C686** | A298 | 7.60s Gold screen | 1.00 | .50 |
| **C687** | A298 | 7.60s Quito from basilica tower | 1.00 | .50 |
| **C688** | A298 | 10.60s Retable | 1.25 | .60 |
| **C689** | A298 | 10.60s Pulpit | 1.25 | .60 |
| **C690** | A298 | 13.60s Cupola | 1.75 | .90 |
| **C691** | A298 | 13.60s Statue of Virgin | 1.75 | .90 |
| | *Nos. C685-C691 (7)* | | 9.00 | 4.50 |

Nos. C685-C691 are vert.

UPU Monument AP172

Design: 17.80s, Mail box, 1880.

**1980, July 7** *Perf. 12*
**C692** AP172 10.60s multi 1.50 .75
**C693** AP172 17.80s multi 2.50 1.25

**Souvenir Sheet**

**C694** AP172 25s multi 3.50 3.00

UPU membership cent. No. C694 contains designs of C692 and C693, horiz., perf. 11½.

**Olympic Type.**

Design: 10.60s, 13.60s, Moscow '80 emblem, Olympic rings.

*Perf. 12x11½*

**1980, July 19** **Wmk. 395**
**C695** A299 10.60s multi .90 .65
**C696** A299 13.60s multi 1.25 .85

**Souvenir Sheet**

**C697** A299 30s multi 7.00 7.00

No. C697 contains vignettes in designs of Nos. 991 and C695.

Marshal Sucre, by Marco Sales — AP173

**1980**
**C698** AP173 10.60s multi .90 .60

Marshal Antonio Jose de Sucre, death sesquicentennial.

Rotary International, 75th Anniversary AP174

**1980, Aug. 4** *Perf. 11½*
**C699** AP174 10s multi 1.40 .50

**Riobamba Type**

Design: 7.60s, 10.60s, Monstrance, Riobamba Cathedral, vert.

**1980, Sept. 20** **Litho.** *Perf. 11½*
**C700** A301 7.60s multi .70 .30
**C701** A301 10.60s multi .95 .40

**Souvenir Sheet**

*Imperf*

**C702** A301 30s multi 2.25 2.25

No. C702 contains vignettes in designs of Nos. 996 and C701.

**Democracy Type**

7.60s, 10.60s, Pres. Aguilera and voter.

*Perf. 12x11½*

**1980, Oct. 9** **Litho.** **Wmk. 395**
**C703** A302 7.60s multi .90 .45
**C704** A302 10.60s multi 1.20 .50

**Souvenir Sheet**

*Imperf*

**C705** A302 15s multi 1.50 1.50

No. C705 contains vignettes in designs of Nos. 999 and C703.

**OPEC Type**

20th Anniversary of OPEC: 7.60s, Men holding OPEC emblem, vert.

**1980, Nov. 8** *Perf. 11½x12*
**C706** A303 7.60s multi .60 .45

**Carchi Province Type**

10.60s, Governor's Palace, vert. 17.80s, Victory Museum, Central Square, vert.

**1980, Nov. 21** *Perf. 13*
**C707** A304 10.60c multi 1.25 .50
**C708** A304 17.80s multi 1.90 .80

**Orchid Type**

*Perf. 12x11½, 11½x12*

**1980, Nov. 22**
**C709** A305 7.60s Anguloa uniflora 2.25 .60
**C710** A305 10.60s Scuticaria salesiana 3.25 .35
**C711** A305 50s Helcia sanguinolenta, vert. 5.75 1.10
**C712** A305 100s Anguloa virginalis 7.50 2.25
*Nos. C709-C712 (4)* 18.75 4.30

**Souvenir Sheets**

*Imperf*

**C713** A305 20s multi 7.50 5.25
**C714** A305 20s multi 7.50 5.25

Nos. C713-C714 contain vignettes in designs of Nos. C709, C711 and C710, C712 respectively.

**Christmas Type**

7.60s, Pope blessing crowd. 10.60s, Portrait.

**1980, Dec. 27** *Perf. 12*
**C715** A306 7.60s multi, vert. 1.00 .50
**C716** A306 10.60s multi, vert. 1.25 .60

Isidro Cueva — AP175

**1980, Nov. 20** *Perf. 13*
**C717** AP175 18.20s multi 2.50 1.25

Dr. Isidro Ayora Cueva, former president, birth centenary.

Simon Bolivar, by Marco Salas — AP176

**1980, Dec. 17** *Perf. 11½*
**C718** AP176 13.60s multi 2.00 1.00

Simon Bolivar death sesquicentennial.

Turtle, Galapagos Islands AP177

100s, Oldest Ecuadorian mail box, 1793.

**1981, Feb. 12** **Litho.** *Perf. 13*
**C719** AP177 50s multi 6.50 4.00
**C720** AP177 100s multi, vert. 8.00 5.00

**HCJB Type**

**1981** **Litho.** *Perf. 13*
**C721** A311 7.60s Emblem, horiz. 1.25 .65
**C722** A311 10.60s Emblem, diff. 1.75 .90

Soccer Players — AP178

**1981, July 8**
**C723** AP178 7.60s Emblem .90 .45
**C724** AP178 10.60s shown 1.20 .45
**C725** AP178 13.60s World Cup 1.40 .75
*Nos. C723-C725 (3)* 3.50 1.65

**Souvenir Sheets**

**C726** AP178 20s multi 3.50 3.50
**C727** AP178 20s multi 3.50 3.50

1982 World Cup Soccer Championship. Nos. C726-C727 contain vignettes in designs of Nos. C723 and C725 respectively.

**Picasso Type**

7.60s, Still-life. 10.60s, First Communion, vert. 13.60s, Las Meninas, vert.

**1981, Oct. 26** **Litho.** *Perf. 13*
**C728** A313a 7.60s multi .90 .45
**C729** A313a 10.60s multi 1.25 .60
**C730** A313a 13.60s multi 1.40 .70

**Size: 110x90mm**

*Imperf*

**C731** A313a 20s multi 3.00 3.00
*Nos. C728-C731 (4)* 6.55 4.75

No. C731 contains designs of Nos. C730, C729.

**World Food Day Type**

**1981, Dec. 31** **Litho.** *Perf. 13x13½*
**C732** A314 10.60s Farming, vert. 1.40 .70

**IYD Type**

**1982, Feb. 25** **Litho.** *Perf. 13*
**C733** A316 7.60s Emblem .70 .30
**C734** A316 10.60s Man with crutch .90 .55

**Montalvo Type**

**1982** **Litho.** *Perf. 13*
**C735** A318 5s Home, horiz. 1.25 .65

**Swimming Type**

**1982, July 30**
**C736** A320 10.20s Emblem, vert. .95 .45
**C737** A320 14.20s Diving, vert. 1.25 .60

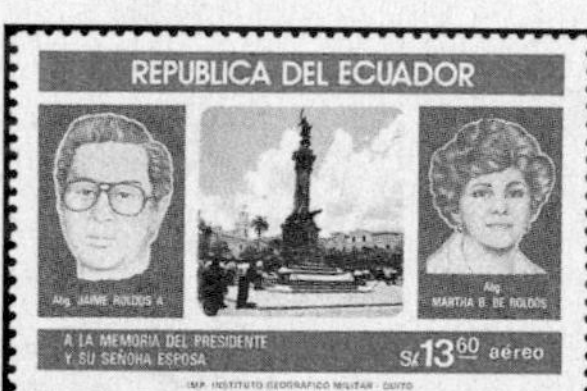


Pres. Jaime Roldos, (1940-81), Mrs. Martha Roldos, Independence Monument, Quito — AP179

**1983, May 25** **Litho.** *Perf. 12*
**C738** AP179 13.60s multi .65 .50

**Souvenir Sheet**

*Imperf*

**C739** AP179 20s multi 2.00 2.00

## AIR POST SEMI-POSTAL STAMPS

**Nos. C119-C123 Surcharged in Blue or Red**

**1944, May 9** **Unwmk.** *Perf. 12*
**CB1** AP26 50c + 50c 7.00 3.50
**CB2** AP26 70c + 30c 7.00 3.50
**CB3** AP26 3s + 50c (R) 7.00 3.50
**CB4** AP26 5s + 1s (R) 7.00 3.50
**CB5** AP26 10s + 2s 7.00 3.50
*Nos. CB1-CB5 (5)* 35.00 17.50

The surtax aided Mendez Hospital.

## AIR POST REGISTRATION STAMPS

**Issued by Sociedad Colombo-Alemana de Transportes Aereos (SCADTA)**

Nos. C3 and C3a Overprinted in Carmine

**1928-29** **Wmk. 116** *Perf. 14x14½*
**CF1** AP6 1s on 20c (#C3) 110.00 100.00
*a.* 1s on 20c (#C3a) ('29) 140.00 110.00

No. C18 Overprinted in Black

**1929, Apr. 1** **Wmk. 127** *Perf. 14*
**CF2** AP2 1s rose 85.00 55.00

## AIR POST OFFICIAL STAMPS

Nos. C8-C15 Overprinted in Red or Black

**1929, May** **Unwmk.** *Perf. 12*
**CO1** AP1 2c black (R) 1.00 .50
**CO2** AP1 5c carmine rose 1.00 .50
**CO3** AP1 10c deep brown 1.00 .50
**CO4** AP1 20c dark violet 1.00 .50
**CO5** AP1 50c deep green 4.00 2.00
**CO6** AP1 1s dark blue 4.00 2.00
*a.* Inverted overprint 240.00
**CO7** AP1 5s orange yellow 18.00 7.75
**CO8** AP1 10s orange red 210.00 75.00
*Nos. CO1-CO8 (8)* 240.00 88.75

Establishment of commercial air service in Ecuador.

Counterfeits of No. CO8 exist.

See Nos. CO9-CO12. For overprints and surcharges see No. C35.

**1930, Jan. 9**
**CO9** AP1 50c olive brown 3.50 1.75
**CO10** AP1 1s carmine lake 4.50 2.25
**CO11** AP1 5s olive green 11.00 5.50
**CO12** AP1 10s black 21.00 10.50
*Nos. CO9-CO12 (4)* 40.00 20.00

For surcharges and overprint see Nos. C32-C34, C36-C38.

Air Post Stamps of 1937 Overprinted in Black

**1937, Aug. 19**
**CO13** AP7 10c chestnut .50 .25
**CO14** AP7 20c olive black .50 .25
**CO15** AP7 70c black brown .60 .25
**CO16** AP7 1s gray black .70 .25
**CO17** AP7 2s dark violet .70 .30
*Nos. CO13-CO17 (5)* 3.00 1.30

For overprints see Nos. 463-464.

No. C79 Overprinted in Black

**1940, Aug. 1** *Perf. 12½x13*

| | | | | |
|---|---|---|---|---|
| **CO18** | AP15 | 5s emerald | 2.00 | .60 |

**Catalogue values for unused stamps in this section, from this point to the end of the section, are for Never Hinged items.**

**Nos. C352-C354 Overprinted**

**1964** *Perf. 13½*

| | | | | |
|---|---|---|---|---|
| **CO19** | AP86 | 50c multi | 2.00 | .85 |
| **CO20** | AP86 | 80c multi | 2.00 | .85 |
| **CO21** | AP86 | 1.30s multi | 2.00 | .85 |
| | | *Nos. CO19-CO21 (3)* | 6.00 | 2.55 |

## SPECIAL DELIVERY STAMPS

SD1

SD1a

**1928** **Unwmk.** *Perf. 12*

| | | | | |
|---|---|---|---|---|
| **E1** | SD1 | 2c on 2c blue | 8.00 | *9.00* |
| *a.* | | "DOS CVTOS." inverted | 35.00 | *37.50* |
| **E2** | SD1a | 5c on 2c blue | 7.00 | *9.00* |
| **E3** | SD1a | 10c on 2c blue | 7.00 | 6.00 |
| *a.* | | "10 CENTAVOS" inverted | 21.00 | *25.00* |
| **E4** | SD1a | 20c on 2c blue | 10.00 | 9.00 |
| **E5** | SD1a | 50c on 2c blue | 12.00 | 9.00 |
| | | *Nos. E1-E5 (5)* | 44.00 | *42.00* |

No. E1 surcharge reads "CTVOS". Nos. E2-E5 surcharge reads "CENTAVOS".

No. RA49A Surcharged in Red

**1945**

| | | | | |
|---|---|---|---|---|
| **E6** | PT18 | 20c on 5c green | 3.00 | 2.00 |

## LATE FEE STAMP

No. RA49A Surcharged in Black

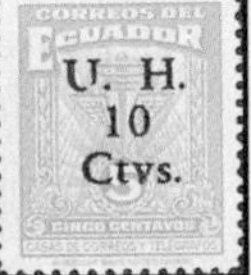


**1945** **Unwmk.** *Perf. 12*

| | | | | |
|---|---|---|---|---|
| **I1** | PT18 | 10c on 5c green | 1.00 | 1.00 |

## POSTAGE DUE STAMPS

Numeral — D1

**1896** **Engr.** **Wmk. 117** *Perf. 12*

| | | | | |
|---|---|---|---|---|
| **J1** | D1 | 1c blue green | 6.00 | *6.50* |
| **J2** | D1 | 2c blue green | 6.00 | *6.50* |
| **J3** | D1 | 5c blue green | 6.00 | *6.50* |
| **J4** | D1 | 10c blue green | 6.00 | *6.50* |
| **J5** | D1 | 20c blue green | 6.00 | *8.50* |
| **J6** | D1 | 50c blue green | 6.00 | *13.00* |
| **J7** | D1 | 100c blue green | 6.00 | *17.00* |
| | | *Nos. J1-J7 (7)* | 42.00 | *64.50* |

*Reprints are on very thick paper with distinct watermark and vertical paper-weave direction. Value 15c each.*

**Unwmk.**

| | | | | |
|---|---|---|---|---|
| **J8** | D1 | 1c blue green | *5.00* | *6.00* |
| **J9** | D1 | 2c blue green | *5.00* | *6.00* |
| **J10** | D1 | 5c blue green | *5.00* | *6.00* |
| **J11** | D1 | 10c blue green | *5.00* | *6.00* |
| **J12** | D1 | 20c blue green | *5.00* | *7.50* |
| **J13** | D1 | 50c blue green | *5.00* | *10.50* |
| **J14** | D1 | 100c blue green | *5.00* | *15.00* |
| | | *Nos. J8-J14 (7)* | 35.00 | *57.00* |

Coat of Arms — D2

**1929**

| | | | | |
|---|---|---|---|---|
| **J15** | D2 | 5c deep blue | .40 | .40 |
| **J16** | D2 | 10c orange yellow | .40 | .40 |
| **J17** | D2 | 20c red | .60 | .60 |
| | | *Nos. J15-J17 (3)* | 1.40 | 1.40 |

Numeral — D3

*Perf. 13½*

**1958, Nov.** **Unwmk.** **Litho.**

| | | | | |
|---|---|---|---|---|
| **J18** | D3 | 10c bright lilac | .50 | .40 |
| **J19** | D3 | 50c emerald | .50 | .40 |
| **J20** | D3 | 1s maroon | .60 | .40 |
| **J21** | D3 | 2s red | .70 | .40 |
| | | *Nos. J18-J21 (4)* | 2.30 | 1.60 |

## OFFICIAL STAMPS

Regular Issues of 1881 and 1887 Handstamped in Black

**1886** **Unwmk.** *Perf. 12*

| | | | | |
|---|---|---|---|---|
| **O1** | A5 | 1c yellow brown | 2.50 | 2.50 |
| **O2** | A6 | 2c lake | 3.00 | 3.00 |
| **O3** | A7 | 5c blue | 6.75 | *8.75* |
| **O4** | A8 | 10c orange | 5.25 | 3.25 |
| **O5** | A9 | 20c gray violet | 5.25 | 5.25 |
| **O6** | A10 | 50c blue green | 15.00 | 11.50 |
| | | *Nos. O1-O6 (6)* | 37.75 | 34.25 |

**1887**

| | | | | |
|---|---|---|---|---|
| **O7** | A12 | 1c green | 3.25 | 2.50 |
| **O8** | A13 | 2c vermilion | 3.25 | 3.25 |
| **O9** | A14 | 5c blue | 5.25 | 2.50 |
| **O10** | A15 | 80c olive green | 17.50 | 10.00 |
| | | *Nos. O7-O10 (4)* | 29.25 | 18.25 |

Nos. O1-O10 are known with red handstamp but these are believed to be speculative.

The overprint on the 1886-87 issues is handstamped and is found in various positions.

Flores — O1

**1892** **Carmine Overprint**

| | | | | |
|---|---|---|---|---|
| **O11** | O1 | 1c ultramarine | .25 | *.40* |
| **O12** | O1 | 2c ultramarine | .25 | *.40* |
| **O13** | O1 | 5c ultramarine | .25 | *.40* |
| **O14** | O1 | 10c ultramarine | .25 | *.60* |
| **O15** | O1 | 20c ultramarine | .25 | *.90* |
| **O16** | O1 | 50c ultramarine | .25 | *.90* |
| **O17** | O1 | 1s ultramarine | .35 | *1.00* |
| | | *Nos. O11-O17 (7)* | 1.85 | 4.60 |

Arms — O1a

**1894**

| | | | | |
|---|---|---|---|---|
| **O18** | O1a | 1c slate green (R) | 15.00 | |
| **O19** | O1a | 2c lake (Bk) | 20.00 | |

Nos. O18 and O19 were not placed in use.

Rocafuerte — O2

**Dated "1894"**

**1894** **Carmine Overprint**

| | | | | |
|---|---|---|---|---|
| **O20** | O2 | 1c gray black | .60 | *1.00* |
| **O21** | O2 | 2c gray black | .60 | .60 |
| **O22** | O2 | 5c gray black | .60 | .60 |
| **O23** | O2 | 10c gray black | .75 | *1.00* |
| **O24** | O2 | 20c gray black | 1.00 | 1.00 |
| **O25** | O2 | 50c gray black | 3.75 | 3.75 |
| **O26** | O2 | 1s gray black | 6.00 | 6.00 |
| | | *Nos. O20-O26 (7)* | 13.30 | 13.95 |

**Dated "1895"**

**1895** **Carmine Overprint**

| | | | | |
|---|---|---|---|---|
| **O27** | O2 | 1c gray black | 5.25 | 5.25 |
| **O28** | O2 | 2c gray black | 7.50 | 7.50 |
| **O29** | O2 | 5c gray black | 1.50 | 1.50 |
| **O30** | O2 | 10c gray black | 7.50 | 7.50 |
| **O31** | O2 | 20c gray black | 11.00 | 10.50 |
| **O32** | O2 | 50c gray black | *75.00* | *75.00* |
| **O33** | O2 | 1s gray black | 3.75 | 3.75 |
| | | *Nos. O27-O33 (7)* | *111.50* | *111.00* |

Reprints of 1894-95 issues are on very thick paper with paper weave found both horizontal and vertical for all denominations. Values: Nos. O20-O26, 35c each; O27-O33, 20c each. Generally they are blacker than originals.

*For overprints see Nos. O50-O91.*

Types of 1896 Overprinted in Carmine

**1896** **Wmk. 117**

| | | | | |
|---|---|---|---|---|
| **O34** | A21 | 1c olive bister | 1.00 | 1.00 |
| **O35** | A22 | 2c olive bister | 1.00 | 1.00 |
| **O36** | A23 | 5c olive bister | 1.00 | 1.00 |
| **O37** | A24 | 10c olive bister | 1.00 | 1.00 |
| **O38** | A25 | 20c olive bister | 1.00 | 1.00 |
| **O39** | A26 | 50c olive bister | 1.00 | 1.00 |
| **O40** | A27 | 1s olive bister | 3.00 | 3.00 |
| **O41** | A28 | 5s olive bister | 6.00 | 6.00 |
| | | *Nos. O34-O41 (8)* | 15.00 | 15.00 |

*Reprints of Nos. O34-O41 are on thick paper with vertical paper weave direction.*

**Unwmk.**

| | | | | |
|---|---|---|---|---|
| **O42** | A21 | 1c olive bister | 3.00 | 3.00 |
| **O43** | A22 | 2c olive bister | 3.00 | 3.00 |
| **O44** | A23 | 5c olive bister | 3.00 | 3.00 |
| **O45** | A24 | 10c olive bister | 3.00 | 3.00 |
| **O46** | A25 | 20c olive bister | 3.00 | 3.00 |
| **O47** | A26 | 50c olive bister | 3.00 | *3.00* |
| **O48** | A27 | 1s olive bister | 7.50 | 7.50 |
| **O49** | A28 | 5s olive bister | 10.50 | 10.50 |
| | | *Nos. O42-O49 (8)* | 36.00 | 36.00 |

*Reprints of Nos. O42-O49 all have overprint in black. Value 20 cents each.*

Nos. O20-O26 Overprinted

**1897-98**

| | | | | |
|---|---|---|---|---|
| **O50** | O2 | 1c gray black | *20.00* | *20.00* |
| **O51** | O2 | 2c gray black | *35.00* | *35.00* |
| **O52** | O2 | 5c gray black | *200.00* | *200.00* |
| **O53** | O2 | 10c gray black | *30.00* | *30.00* |
| **O54** | O2 | 20c gray black | *20.00* | *20.00* |
| **O55** | O2 | 50c gray black | *35.00* | *35.00* |
| **O56** | O2 | 1s gray black | *55.00* | *55.00* |
| | | *Nos. O50-O56 (7)* | *395.00* | *395.00* |

Nos. O20-O26 Overprinted

| | | | | |
|---|---|---|---|---|
| **O57** | O2 | 1c gray black | *4.00* | *4.00* |
| **O58** | O2 | 2c gray black | *9.00* | *9.00* |
| **O59** | O2 | 5c gray black | *90.00* | *90.00* |
| **O60** | O2 | 10c gray black | *100.00* | *100.00* |
| **O61** | O2 | 20c gray black | *25.00* | *25.00* |
| **O62** | O2 | 50c gray black | *15.00* | *15.00* |
| **O63** | O2 | 1s gray black | *165.00* | *165.00* |
| | | *Nos. O57-O63 (7)* | *408.00* | *408.00* |

Nos. O20-O26 Overprinted

| | | | | |
|---|---|---|---|---|
| **O64** | O2 | 1c gray black | *40.00* | *40.00* |
| **O65** | O2 | 2c gray black | *40.00* | *40.00* |
| **O66** | O2 | 5c gray black | *40.00* | *40.00* |
| **O67** | O2 | 10c gray black | *40.00* | *40.00* |
| **O68** | O2 | 20c gray black | *40.00* | *40.00* |
| **O69** | O2 | 50c gray black | *40.00* | *40.00* |
| **O70** | O2 | 1s gray black | *40.00* | *40.00* |
| | | *Nos. O64-O70 (7)* | *280.00* | *280.00* |

**Nos. O27-O33 Overprinted in Black like Nos. O50-O56**

| | | | | |
|---|---|---|---|---|
| **O71** | O2 | 1c gray black | *20.00* | *20.00* |
| **O72** | O2 | 2c gray black | *20.00* | *20.00* |
| **O73** | O2 | 5c gray black | *20.00* | *20.00* |
| **O74** | O2 | 10c gray black | *20.00* | *20.00* |
| **O75** | O2 | 20c gray black | *30.00* | *30.00* |
| **O76** | O2 | 50c gray black | *275.00* | *275.00* |
| **O77** | O2 | 1s gray black | *100.00* | *100.00* |
| | | *Nos. O71-O77 (7)* | *485.00* | 485.00 |

Nos. O27-O33 Overprinted

| | | | | |
|---|---|---|---|---|
| **O78** | O2 | 1c gray black | *35.00* | *35.00* |
| **O79** | O2 | 2c gray black | *30.00* | *30.00* |
| **O80** | O2 | 5c gray black | *30.00* | *30.00* |
| **O81** | O2 | 10c gray black | *32.50* | *32.50* |
| **O82** | O2 | 20c gray black | *42.50* | *42.50* |
| **O83** | O2 | 50c gray black | *30.00* | *30.00* |
| **O84** | O2 | 1s gray black | *30.00* | *30.00* |
| | | *Nos. O78-O84 (7)* | *230.00* | *230.00* |

**Nos. O27-O33 Overprinted like #O64-O70**

| | | | | |
|---|---|---|---|---|
| **O85** | O2 | 1c gray black | *90.00* | *90.00* |
| **O86** | O2 | 2c gray black | *20.00* | *20.00* |
| **O87** | O2 | 5c gray black | *80.00* | *80.00* |
| **O88** | O2 | 10c gray black | *80.00* | *80.00* |
| **O89** | O2 | 20c gray black | *140.00* | *140.00* |
| **O90** | O2 | 50c gray black | *85.00* | *85.00* |
| **O91** | O2 | 1s gray black | *165.00* | *165.00* |
| | | *Nos. O85-O91 (7)* | *660.00* | *660.00* |

Many forged overprints of Nos. O50-O91 exist, made on the original stamps and reprints.

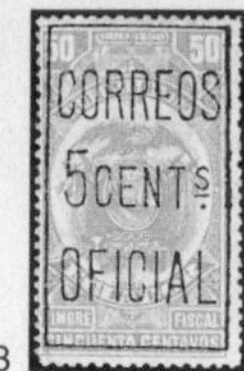

O3

**1898-99** *Perf. 15, 16*

**Black Surcharge**

**O92** O3 5c on 50c lilac 10.00 10.00
*a.* Inverted surcharge 25.00 25.00
**O93** O3 10c on 20s org 15.00 15.00
*a.* Double surcharge 40.00 30.00
**O94** O3 10c on 50c lilac *140.00 140.00*
**O95** O3 20c on 50c lilac 30.00 30.00
**O96** O3 20c on 50s green 30.00 30.00
*Nos. O92-O96 (5) 225.00 225.00*

**Green Surcharge**

**O97** O3 5c on 50c lilac 10.00 10.00
*a.* Double surcharge 5.00
*b.* Double surcharge, blk and grn 12.00
*c.* Same as "b," blk surch. invtd. 5.00

**1899** **Red Surcharge**

**O98** O3 5c on 50c lilac 10.00 10.00
*a.* Double surcharge 20.00
*b.* Dbl. surch., blk and red 25.00
**O99** O3 20c on 50s green 15.00 15.00
*a.* Inverted surcharge 40.00
*b.* Dbl. surch., red and blk 60.00

**Similar Surcharge in Black Value in Words in Two Lines**

**O100** O3 1c on 5c blue *650.00*

**Red Surcharge**

**O101** O3 2c on 5c blue *1,150.*
**O102** O3 4c on 20c blue *800.00*

Types of Regular Issue of 1899 Ovptd. in Black

**1899** *Perf. 14, 15*

**O103** A37 2c orange & blk .70 *1.60*
**O104** A39 10c orange & blk .70 *1.60*
**O105** A40 20c orange & blk .50 *2.50*
**O106** A41 50c orange & blk .50 *3.25*
*Nos. O103-O106 (4)* 2.40 *8.95*

For overprint see No. O167.

The above overprint was applied to remainders of the postage stamps of 1904 with the idea of increasing their salability. They were never regularly in use as official stamps.

Regular Issue of 1911-13 Overprinted in Black

**1913** *Perf. 12*

**O107** A71 1c scarlet & blk 3.50 3.50
**O108** A72 2c blue & blk 3.50 3.50
**O109** A73 3c orange & blk 2.25 2.25
**O110** A74 5c scarlet & blk 4.50 4.50
**O111** A75 10c blue & blk 4.50 4.50
*Nos. O107-O111 (5)* 18.25 18.25

Regular Issue of 1911-13 Overprinted

**1916-17** **Overprint 22x3½mm**

**O112** A72 2c blue & blk 25.00 18.00
**O113** A74 5c scarlet & blk 25.00 18.00
**O114** A75 10c blue & blk 15.00 12.00
*Nos. O112-O114 (3)* 65.00 48.00

**Overprint 25x4mm**

**O115** A71 1c scarlet & blk 1.10 1.10
**O116** A72 2c blue & blk 1.60 1.60
*a.* Inverted overprint 5.00 5.00
**O117** A73 3c orange & blk 1.00 1.00
**O118** A74 5c scarlet & blk 1.60 1.60
**O119** A75 10c blue & blk 1.60 1.60
*Nos. O115-O119 (5)* 6.90 6.90

**Same Overprint On Regular Issue of 1915-17**

**O120** A71 1c orange 1.40 1.40
**O121** A72 2c green 1.40 1.40
**O122** A73 3c black 2.25 2.25
**O123** A78 4c red & blk 2.25 2.25
*a.* Inverted overprint 15.00
**O124** A74 5c violet 1.40 1.40
**O125** A75 10c blue 2.75 2.75
**O126** A79 20c green & blk 15.00 15.00
*Nos. O120-O126 (7)* 26.45 26.45

Regular Issues of 1911-17 Overprinted in Black or Red

**O127** A71 1c orange .90 .90
**O128** A72 2c green .70 .70
**O129** A73 3c black (Bk) .90 .90
**O130** A73 3c black (R) .90 .70
*a.* Inverted overprint
**O131** A78 4c red & blk .90 .90
**O132** A74 5c violet 1.75 .90
**O133** A75 10c blue & blk 4.50 1.75
**O134** A75 10c blue .90 .90
**O135** A79 20c green & blk 4.50 1.75
*Nos. O127-O135 (9)* 15.95 9.40

Regular Issue of 1920 Overprinted

**1920**

**O136** A86 1c green 1.25 1.25
*a.* Inverted overprint 17.00 —
**O137** A86 2c carmine 1.00 1.00
**O138** A86 3c yellow brn 1.25 1.25
**O139** A86 4c dark green 2.00 2.00
*a.* Inverted overprint 17.00 —
**O140** A86 5c blue 2.00 2.00
**O141** A86 6c orange 1.25 1.25
**O142** A86 7c brown 2.00 2.00
**O143** A86 8c yellow green 2.50 2.50
**O144** A86 9c red 3.25 3.25
**O145** A95 10c blue 2.00 2.00
**O146** A86 15c gray 11.00 11.00
**O147** A86 20c deep violet 14.50 14.50
**O148** A86 30c violet 17.00 17.00
**O149** A86 40c dark brown 21.00 21.00
**O150** A86 50c dark green 14.50 14.50
**O151** A86 60c dark blue 17.00 17.00
**O152** A86 70c gray 17.00 17.00
**O153** A86 80c yellow 21.00 21.00
**O154** A104 90c green 21.00 21.00
**O155** A86 1s blue 45.00 45.00
*Nos. O136-O155 (20)* 217.50 217.50

Cent. of the independence of Guayaquil.

Stamps of 1911 Overprinted

**1922**

**O156** A71 1c scarlet & blk 9.00 9.00
**O157** A72 2c blue & blk 4.50 4.50

**Revenue Stamps of 1919-1920 Overprinted like Nos. O156 and O157**

**1924**

**O158** PT3 1c dark blue 2.00 2.00
**O159** PT3 2c green 12.50 12.50

Regular Issues of 1911-17 Overprinted

**1924**

**O160** A71 1c orange 7.00 7.00
*a.* Inverted overprint 15.00

Overprinted in Black or Red

**O161** A72 2c green .60 .60
**O162** A73 3c black (R) .80 .80
**O163** A78 4c red & blk 1.25 1.25
**O164** A74 5c violet 1.25 1.25
**O165** A75 10c deep blue 1.25 1.25
**O166** A76 1s green & blk 7.00 7.00
*Nos. O160-O166 (7)* 19.15 19.15

No. O106 with Additional Overprint

**1924** *Perf. 14, 15*

**O167** A41 50c orange & blk 2.25 2.25

Nos. O160-O167 exist with inverted overprint.

No. 199 Overprinted

**1924** *Perf. 12*

**O168** A71 1c orange 5.50 5.50

Regular Issues of 1911-25 Overprinted

**1925**

**O169** A71 1c scarlet & blk 10.00 4.25
*a.* Inverted overprint 15.00
**O170** A71 1c orange .60 .60
*a.* Inverted overprint 4.00
**O171** A72 2c green .60 .60
*a.* Inverted overprint 4.00
**O172** A73 3c black (Bk) .60 .60
**O173** A73 3c black (R) 1.10 1.10
**O174** A78 4c red & blk .60 .60
**O175** A74 5c violet .80 .80
**O176** A74 5c rose .80 .80
**O177** A75 10c deep blue .60 .60
*Nos. O169-O177 (9)* 15.70 9.95

Regular Issues of 1916-25 Ovptd. Vertically Up or Down

**1927, Oct.**

**O178** A71 1c orange 2.00 2.00
**O179** A86 2c carmine 2.00 2.00
**O180** A86 3c yellow brown 2.00 2.00
**O181** A86 4c myrtle green 2.00 2.00
**O182** A86 5c pale blue 2.00 2.00
**O183** A75 10c yellow green 2.00 2.00
*Nos. O178-O183 (6)* 12.00 12.00

Regular Issues of 1920-27 Overprinted

**1928**

**O184** A71 1c lt blue 1.25 1.25
**O185** A86 2c carmine 1.25 1.25
**O186** A86 3c yellow brown 1.25 1.25
*a.* Inverted overprint 5.00
**O187** A86 4c myrtle green 1.25 1.25
**O188** A86 5c lt blue 1.25 1.25
**O189** A75 10c yellow green 1.25 1.25
**O190** A109 20c violet 11.00 2.50
*a.* Overprint reading up 3.50 2.25
*Nos. O184-O190 (7)* 18.50 10.00

The overprint is placed vertically reading down on No. O190.

Regular Issue of 1936 Overprinted in Black

**1936** *Perf. 14*

**O191** A131 5c olive green 1.50 1.50
**O192** A132 10c brown 1.50 1.50
**O193** A133 20c dark violet 1.90 .70
**O194** A134 1s dark carmine 2.25 1.10
**O195** A135 2s dark blue 2.50 1.75
*Nos. O191-O195 (5)* 9.65 6.55

Regular Postage Stamps of 1937 Overprinted in Black

**1937** *Perf. 11½*

**O196** A139 2c green .40 .40
**O197** A140 5c deep rose .40 .40
**O198** A141 10c blue .40 .40
**O199** A142 20c deep rose .40 .40
**O200** A143 1s olive green .40 .40
*Nos. O196-O200 (5)* 2.00 2.00

**Catalogue values for unused stamps in this section, from this point to the end of the section, are for Never Hinged items.**

**Tobacco Stamp, Overprinted in Black**

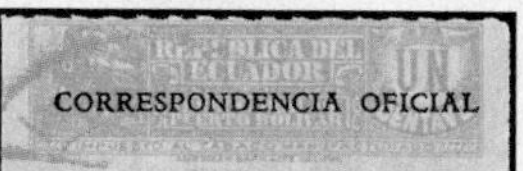


**1946** **Unwmk.** ***Rouletted***

**O201** PT7 1c rose red 1.75 1.75

Communications Building, Quito — O4

**1947 Unwmk. Litho. *Perf. 11***

**O202** O4 30c brown .60 .40
**O203** O4 30c greenish blue .60 .40
*a.* Imperf., pair
**O204** O4 30c purple .60 .40
*Nos. O202-O204 (3)* 1.80 1.20

Nos. O202 to O204 overprinted "Primero la Patria!" and plane in dark blue were issued in August, 1947, by a revolutionary group. They were later repudiated by decree.

### No. 719 with Additional Diagonal Overprint

**1964 *Perf. 14x13***

**O205** A231 80c block of 4 6.00 6.00

The "OEA" overprint covers four stamps, the "oficial" overprint is applied to every stamp.

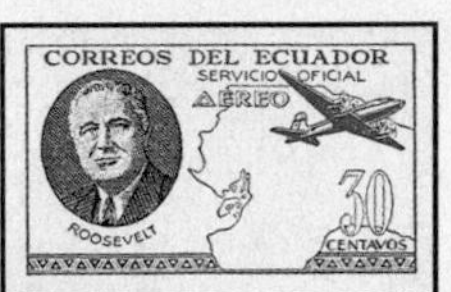


A set of 20 imperforate items in the above Roosevelt design, some overprinted with the initials of various government ministries, was released in 1949. Later that year a set of 8 miniature sheets, bearing the same design plus a marginal inscription, "Presidencia (or Vicepresidencia) de la Republica," and a frame-line were released. In the editors' opinion, information justifying the listing of these issues has not been received.

## POSTAL TAX STAMPS

Roca — PT1

**1920 Unwmk. *Perf. 12***

**RA1** PT1 1c orange .75 .30

PT2

PT3

**RA2** PT2 1c red & blue 1.10 .25
*a.* "de" inverted 10.50 5.25
*b.* Double overprint 10.00 .60
*c.* Inverted overprint 10.00 .60
**RA3** PT3 1c deep blue 1.25 .25
*a.* Inverted overprint 6.00 1.00
*b.* Double overprint 6.00 1.00

For overprints see Nos. O158-O159.

PT4

PT5

### Red or Black Surcharge or Overprint

**Stamp Dated 1911-1912**

**RA4** PT4 20c deep blue — 30.00

**Stamp Dated 1913-1914**

**RA5** PT4 20c deep blue (R) 2.25 .35

**Stamp Dated 1917-1918**

**RA6** PT4 20c olive green (R) 6.50 .55
*a.* Dated 1919-20 25.00
**RA7** PT5 1c on 2c green .90 .25

**Stamp Dated 1911-1912**

**RA8** PT5 1c on 5c green .90 .25
*a.* Double surcharge

**Stamp Dated 1913-1914**

**RA9** PT5 1c on 5c green 8.00 .55
*a.* Double surcharge 12.00 4.00

On Nos. RA7, RA8 and RA9 the surcharge is found reading upward or downward.
For surcharges see Nos. RA15-RA16.

Post Office — PT6

**1920-24 Engr.**

**RA10** PT6 1c olive green .40 .25
**RA11** PT6 2c deep green .40 .25
**RA12** PT6 20c bister brn ('24) 1.75 .25
**RA13** PT6 2s violet 11.50 3.25
**RA14** PT6 5s blue 20.00 5.75
*Nos. RA10-RA14 (5)* 34.05 9.75

For overprints and surcharge see Nos. 259, 266-268, 273, 302, RA17, RA28.

Revenue Stamps of 1917-18 Srchd. Vertically in Red reading up or down

**1921-22**

**RA15** PT5 20c on 1c dk blue 55.00 6.50
**RA16** PT5 20c on 2c green 55.00 6.50

No. RA12 Surcharged in Green

**1924**

**RA17** PT6 2c on 20c bis brn .60 .25
*a.* Inverted surcharge 14.00 5.00
*b.* Double surcharge 4.00 2.00

PT7

**1924 *Rouletted 7***

**RA18** PT7 1c rose red .90 .25
*a.* Inverted overprint 3.50

**Similar Design, Eagle at left**

***Perf. 12***

**RA19** PT7 2c blue .90 .25
*a.* Inverted overprint 3.50 1.75

For overprints and surcharges see Nos. 346, O201, RA32, RA34, RA37, RA44-RA45, RA47.

PT8

**Inscribed "Timbre Fiscal"**

**1924**

**RA20** PT8 1c yellow 4.50 .85
**RA21** PT8 2c dark blue 1.40 .35

**Inscribed "Region Oriental"**

**RA22** PT8 1c yellow .70 .30
**RA23** PT8 2c dark blue 1.40 .35
*Nos. RA20-RA23 (4)* 8.00 1.85

Overprint on No. RA22 reads down or up.

Revenue Stamp Overprinted in Blue

**1934**

**RA24** 2c green .50 .25
*a.* Blue overprint inverted 3.50 1.75
*b.* Blue ovpt. dbl., one invtd. 4.00 1.25

**Postage Stamp of 1930 Overprinted in Red**

***Perf. 12½***

**RA25** A119 20c ultra & yel .50 .25

Telegraph Stamp Overprinted in Red, like No. RA24, and Surcharged diagonally in Black

**1934 *Perf. 14***

**RA26** 2c on 10c olive brn .70 .25
*a.* Double surcharge 5.50

**Overprint Blue, Surcharge Red**

**RA27** 2c on 10c olive brn .70 .25

PT9

**1934-36 *Perf. 12***

**RA28** PT9 2c green .60 .25
*a.* Both overprints in red ('36) .60 .25

Postal Tax stamp of 1920-24, overprinted in red "POSTAL" has been again overprinted "CASA de Correos y Teleg. de Guayaquil" in black.

PT10

***Perf. 14½x14***

**1934 Photo. Wmk. 233**

**RA29** PT10 2c yellow green .50 .25

For the rebuilding of the GPO at Guayaquil.
For surcharge see No. RA31.

Symbols of Post and Telegraph Service PT11

**1935**

**RA30** PT11 20c claret .50 .25

For the rebuilding of the GPO at Guayaquil.

No. RA29 Surcharged in Red and Overprinted in Black

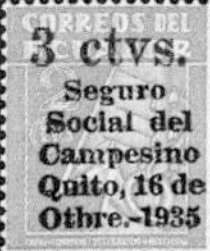


**1935**

**RA31** PT10 3c on 2c yel grn .40 .25
*a.* Double surcharge

Social and Rural Workers' Insurance Fund.

**Tobacco Stamp Surcharged in Black**

**1936 Unwmk. *Rouletted 7***

**RA32** PT7 3c on 1c rose red .60 .25
*a.* Lines of words reversed 2.00 .25
*b.* Horiz. pair, imperf. vert.

Issued for the Social and Rural Workers' Insurance Fund.

No. 310 Overprinted in Black

**1936 *Perf. 12½***

**RA33** A119 20c ultra & yel .60 .25
*a.* Double overprint

**Tobacco Stamp Surcharged in Black**

**1936 *Rouletted 7***

**RA34** PT7 3c on 1c rose red .60 .25

Social and Rural Workers' Insurance Fund.

Worker — PT12

**1936 Engr. *Perf. 13½***

**RA35** PT12 3c ultra .40 .25

Social and Rural Workers' Insurance Fund.
For surcharges see Nos. C64, RA36, RA53-RA54.

Surcharged in Black

**1936**

RA36 PT13 5c on 3c ultra .60 .25

This combines the 2c for the rebuilding of the post office with the 3c for the Social and Rural Workers' Insurance Fund.

### National Defense Issue
### Tobacco Stamp Surcharged in Black

**1936** *Rouletted 7*

RA37 PT7 10c on 1c rose .90 .25
- *a.* Double surcharge

Symbolical of Defense — PT14

**1937-42** *Perf. 12½*

RA38 PT14 10c deep blue .90 .25

A 1s violet and 2s green exist in type PT14.
For surcharge see No. RA40.

### Overprinted or Surcharged in Black

PT15

**1937** **Engr. & Typo.** *Perf. 13½*

RA39 PT15 5c lt brn & red 2.00 .25
- *d.* Inverted overprint 20.00

**1942** *Perf. 12, 11½*

RA39A PT15 20c on 5c rose pink & red 75.00 20.00

RA39B PT15 20c on 1s yel brn & red 75.00 20.00
- *e.* Surcharge omitted —

RA39C PT15 20c on 2s grn & red 75.00 20.00

*Nos. RA39A-RA39C (3)* 225.00 60.00

A 50c dark blue and red exists.

No. RA38 Surcharged in Red

**1937** **Engr.** *Perf. 12½*

RA40 PT14 5c on 10c dp blue 1.10 .25

Map of Ecuador — PT16

**1938** *Perf. 14x13½*

RA41 PT16 5c carmine rose .70 .25

Social and Rural Workers' Insurance Fund.

### No. C42 Surcharged in Red

**1938** *Perf. 12½*

RA42 A136 20c on 70c black 1.10 .25

No. 307 Surcharged in Red

**1938**

RA43 A116 5c on 6c yel & red .40 .25

This stamp was obligatory on all mail from Nov. 23rd to 30th, 1938. The tax was for the Intl. Union for the Control of Cancer.

### Tobacco Stamp Surcharged in Black

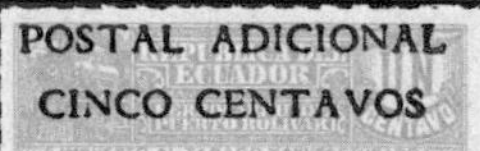


**1939** *Rouletted*

RA44 PT7 5c on 1c rose .70 .25
- *a.* Double surcharge
- *b.* Triple surcharge

### Tobacco Stamp Surcharged in Blue

**1940**

RA45 PT7 5c on 1c rose red 1.00 .25
- *a.* Double surcharge 3.50 3.50

### No. 370 Surcharged in Carmine

**1940** *Perf. 11½*

RA46 A144 20c on 50c blk & multi .50 .25
- *a.* Double surcharge, one inverted

### Tobacco Stamp Surcharged in Black

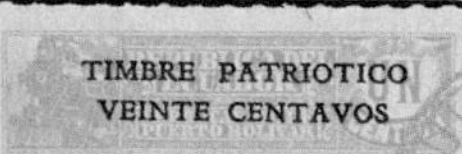


**1940** *Rouletted*

RA47 PT7 20c on 1c rose red 6.00 .50

Farmer Plowing — PT17

**1940** *Perf. 13x13½*

RA48 PT17 5c carmine rose .70 .25

Communication Symbols — PT18

**1940-43** *Perf. 12*

RA49 PT18 5c copper brown .70 .25

RA49A PT18 5c green ('43) .70 .25

For overprint and surcharges see #534, E6, I1.

Pursuit Planes — PT19

**1941** *Perf. 11½x13*

RA50 PT19 20c ultra 1.10 .25

The tax was used for national defense.

Warrior Shielding Women — PT20

**1942-46** **Engr.** *Perf. 12*

RA51 PT20 20c dark blue 1.10 .25

RA51A PT20 40c blk brn ('46) 1.10 .25

The tax was used for national defense.
A 20c carmine, 20c brown and 30c gray exist lithographed in type PT20.

### No. 370 Surcharged in Carmine

**1942** *Perf. 11½*

RA52 A144 20c on 50c multi 1.10 .25
- *a.* Double surcharge 10.00

No. RA35 Surcharged in Red

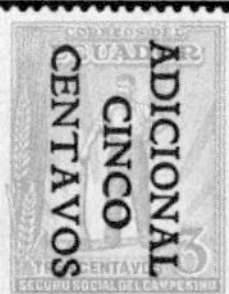


**1943** *Perf. 13½*

RA53 PT12 5c on 3c ultra .60 .25

No. RA53 with Additional Surcharge in Black

**1943**

RA54 PT12 5c on 5c on 3c ultra 1.10 .25

Peons — PT21

**1943** *Perf. 12*

RA55 PT21 5c blue .90 .25

The tax was for farm workers.
For overprint & surcharge see #535, C135.

Revenue Stamp (as No. RA64) Overprinted or Surcharged in Black

**1943** *Perf. 12½*

RA56 20c red orange 75.00 1.50

Revenue Stamp (as No. RA64) Overprinted or Surcharged in Black

**1943** *Perf. 12*

RA57 20c on 10c orange 2.25 .25
- *a.* Double surcharge

Coat of Arms — PT22

**1943** *Perf. 12½*

RA58 PT22 20c orange red .70 .25

The tax was for national defense.

No. RA58 Surcharged in Black

**1944**

RA59 PT22 30c on 20c org red .70 .25
- *a.* Double surcharge

**Catalogue values for unused stamps in this section, from this point to the end of the section, are for Never Hinged items.**

Consular Service Stamps Surcharged in Black

**1951** **Unwmk.** *Perf. 12*

RA60 R1 20c on 1s red .60 .25

RA61 R1 20c on 2s brown .60 .25

RA62 R1 20c on 5s violet .60 .25

*Nos. RA60-RA62 (3)* 1.80 .75

Teacher and Pupils in Schoolyard — PT23

**1952 Engr. *Perf. 13***

**RA63** PT23 20c blue green .60 .25

Revenue Stamp Overprinted — PT24

**1952 *Perf. 12***

**RA64** PT24 40(c) olive green 1.10 .25

For overprints & surcharges see #RA56-RA57

Woman Holding Flag — PT25

**1953 *Perf. 12½***

**RA65** PT25 40c ultra 1.25 .25

Telegraph Stamp Surcharged in Black — PT26

**1954 Unwmk. *Perf. 13***

**RA66** PT26 20c on 30c red brn 1.00 .25

**Revenue Stamps Surcharged or Overprinted Horizontally in Black**

PT26a

10 ctvs. 10
PRO
TURISMO
1 9 5 4
Diez Centavos

PT26b

PT26c

**1954 Unwmk. *Perf. 12***

**RA67** PT26a 10c on 25c blue 1.25 .25

**RA68** PT26b 10c on 50c org red 1.25 .25

**RA69** PT26c 10c carmine 1.25 .25

*Nos. RA67-RA69 (3)* 3.75 .75

Telegraph Stamp Surcharged — PT27

**1954 *Perf. 13***

**RA70** PT27 10c on 30c red brn 2.25 .25

Revenue Stamp Overprinted in Black

**1954 *Perf. 12***

**RA71** R3 20c olive black 1.75 .25

Consular Service Stamp Surcharged in Black

**1954**

**RA72** R1 20c on 10s gray 1.75 .25

Young Student at Desk — PT28

**Imprint: "Heraclio Fournier.-Vitoria"**

**1954 Photo. *Perf. 11***

**RA73** PT28 20c rose pink 1.25 .25

See No. RA76.

Globe, Ship, Plane — PT29

**1954 Engr. *Perf. 12***

**RA74** PT29 10c dp magenta 2.25 .25

Soldier Kissing Flag — PT30

**1955 Photo. *Perf. 11***

**RA75** PT30 40c blue 2.25 .25

See No. RA77.

**Types of 1954-55 Redrawn.**
**Imprint: "Thomas de la Rue & Co. Ltd."**

**1957 Unwmk. *Perf. 13***

**RA76** PT28 20c rose pink 1.10 .25

***Perf. 14x14½***

**RA77** PT30 40c blue 2.25 .25

No. RA77 is inscribed "Republica del Ecuador."

The above stamp is believed to have been used only for fiscal purposes.

## AIR POST POSTAL TAX STAMPS

No. 438 Surcharged in Black or Carmine

**1945 Unwmk. *Perf. 11***

**RAC1** A173 20c on 10c dk grn .75 .25

*a.* Pair, one without surcharge 90.00

**RAC2** A173 20c on 10c dk grn (C) .75 .25

Obligatory on letters and parcel post carried on planes in the domestic service.

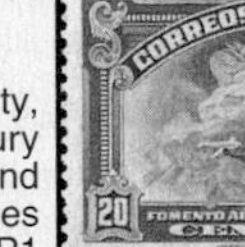

Liberty, Mercury and Planes PTAP1

**1946 Engr. *Perf. 12***

**RAC3** PTAP1 20c orange brown .75 .25

## GALAPAGOS ISLANDS

Issued for use in the Galapagos Islands (Columbus Archipelago), a province of Ecuador, but were commonly used throughout the country.

**Catalogue values for unused stamps in this section are for Never Hinged items.**

Sea Lions — A1

Map — A2

Design: 1s, Marine iguana.

**Unwmk.**

**1957, July 15 Photo. *Perf. 12***

**L1** A1 20c dark brown 1.50 .30

**L2** A2 50c violet 1.00 .30

**L3** A1 1s dull olive green 4.75 .80

*Nos. L1-L3 (3)* 7.25 1.40

*Nos. L1-L3,LC1-LC3 (6)* 18.50 3.65

125th anniv. of Ecuador's possession of the Galapagos Islands, and publicizing the islands.

See Nos. LC1-LC3. For overprints see Nos. 684-686, C389-C391.

## GALAPAGOS AIR POST STAMPS

**Type of Regular Issue**

1s, Santa Cruz Island. 1.80s, Map of Galapagos archipelago. 4.20s, Galapagos giant tortoise.

**Unwmk.**

**1957, July 19 Photo. *Perf. 12***

**LC1** A1 1s deep blue 1.25 .30

**LC2** A1 1.80s rose violet 2.50 .70

**LC3** A1 4.20s black 7.50 1.25

*Nos. LC1-LC3 (3)* 11.25 2.25

For overprints see Nos. C389-C391.

**Redrawn Type of Ecuador, 1956**

**1959, Jan. 3 Engr. *Perf. 14***

**LC4** AP69 2s lt olive green 1.25 .70

Issued to honor the United Nations. See note after No. C407.

# EGYPT

'ē-jəpt

LOCATION — Northern Africa, bordering on the Mediterranean and the Red Sea
GOVT. — Republic
AREA — 386,900 sq. mi.
POP. — 61,404,000 (1997 est.)
CAPITAL — Cairo

Modern Egypt was a part of Turkey until 1914 when a British protectorate was declared over the country and the Khedive was deposed in favor of Hussein Kamil under the title of sultan. In 1922 the protectorate ended and the reigning sultan was declared king of the new monarchy. Egypt became a republic on June 18, 1953. Egypt merged with Syria in 1958 to form the United Arab Republic. Syria left this union in 1961. In 1971 Egypt took the name of Arab Republic of Egypt.

40 Paras = 1 Piaster
1000 Milliemes = 100 Piasters = 1 Pound (1888)
1000 Milliemes = 1 Pound (1953)
1000 Milliemes = 100 Piasters = 1 Pound (1982)

**Catalogue values for unused stamps in this country are for Never Hinged items, beginning with Scott 241 in the regular postage section, Scott B1 in the semi-postal section, Scott C38 in the airpost section, Scott CB1 in the airpost semi-postal section, Scott E5 in the special delivery section, Scott J40 in the postage due section, Scott M16 in the military stamps section, Scott O60 in the officials section, Scott N1 in the occupation section, Scott NC1 in the occupation airpost section, Scott NE1 in the occupation special delivery section, and Scott NJ1 in the occupation postage due section.**

## Watermarks

Wmk. 118 — Pyramid and Star

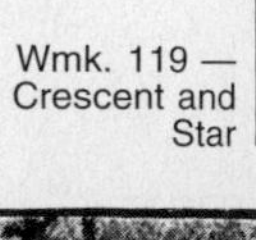
Wmk. 119 — Crescent and Star

Wmk. 120 — Triple Crescent and Star

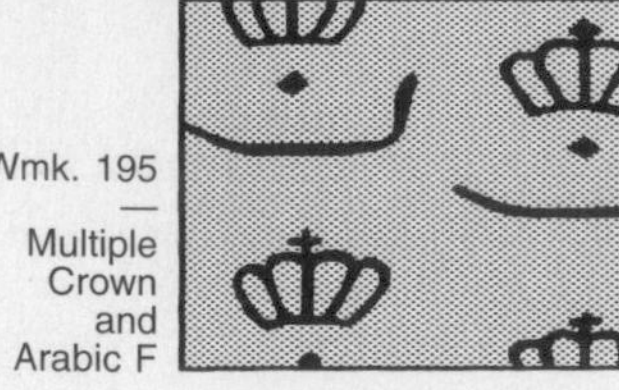
Wmk. 195 — Multiple Crown and Arabic F

"F" in watermark stands for Fuad.

Wmk. 315 — Multiple Eagle

Wmk. 318 — Multiple Eagle and "Misr"

Wmk. 328 — U A R

Wmk. 342 — Coat of Arms, Multiple

Values for unused stamps are for examples with original gum as defined in the catalogue introduction. Very fine examples of Nos. 1-15 will have perforations that are clear of the framelines but with the design noticeably off center. Well centered stamps are extremely scarce and will command substantial premiums.

Turkish Numerals

## Turkish Suzerainty

A1

A2

A3

A4

A5

A6

A7

### Surcharged in Black

**Wmk. 118**

**1866, Jan. 1 — Litho. — *Perf. 12½***

| No. | Type | Description | Unused | Used |
|---|---|---|---|---|
| 1 | A1 | 5pa greenish gray | 62.50 | 37.50 |
| *a.* | | Imperf., pair | 250.00 | |
| *b.* | | Pair, imperf. between | 400.00 | |
| *c.* | | Perf. 12½x13 | 82.50 | 62.50 |
| *d.* | | Perf. 13 | 325.00 | 365.00 |
| 2 | A2 | 10pa brown | 75.00 | 37.50 |
| *a.* | | Imperf., pair | 210.00 | |
| *b.* | | Pair, imperf. between | 525.00 | |
| *c.* | | Perf. 13 | 290.00 | *325.00* |
| *d.* | | Perf. 12½x15 | 325.00 | *350.00* |
| *e.* | | Perf. 12½x13 | 100.00 | 62.50 |
| 3 | A3 | 20pa blue | 105.00 | 40.00 |
| *a.* | | Imperf., pair | 300.00 | |
| *b.* | | Pair, imperf. between | 500.00 | |
| *c.* | | Perf. 12½x13 | 140.00 | 95.00 |
| *d.* | | Perf. 13 | 575.00 | 375.00 |
| 4 | A4 | 2pi yellow | 125.00 | 52.50 |
| *a.* | | Imperf. | *150.00* | *125.00* |
| *b.* | | Imperf. vert. or horiz., pair | 500.00 | 425.00 |
| *c.* | | Perf. 12½x15 | 210.00 | |
| *d.* | | Diagonal half used as 1pi on cover | | *3,000.* |
| *e.* | | Perf. 12½x13, 13x12½ | 200.00 | 75.00 |
| *f.* | | Pair, imperf. between | 625.00 | 525.00 |
| 5 | A5 | 5pi rose | 325.00 | 250.00 |
| *a.* | | Imperf. | 425.00 | 375.00 |
| *b.* | | Imperf. vert. or horiz., pair | *1,250.* | |
| *d.* | | Inscription of 10pi, imperf. | 1,100. | 950.00 |
| *e.* | | Perf. 12½x13, 13x12½ | 350.00 | 275.00 |
| *f.* | | As "d," perf. 12½x15 | 1,050. | 1,000. |
| *g.* | | Perf. 13 | 825.00 | |
| 6 | A6 | 10pi slate bl | 375.00 | 325.00 |
| *a.* | | Imperf. | *550.00* | 450.00 |
| *b.* | | Pair, imperf. between | *2,500.* | |
| *c.* | | Perf. 12½x13, 13x12½ | 550.00 | 550.00 |
| *d.* | | Perf. 13 | *2,000.* | |

**Unwmk.**

**Typo.**

| No. | Type | Description | Unused | Used |
|---|---|---|---|---|
| 7 | A7 | 1pi rose lilac | 80.00 | 5.50 |
| *a.* | | Imperf. | 125.00 | |
| *b.* | | Horiz. pair, imperf. vert. | 500.00 | |
| *c.* | | Perf. 12½x13, 13x12½ | 110.00 | 25.00 |
| *d.* | | Perf. 13 | 450.00 | 300.00 |
| *e.* | | Perf. 12½x15 | *350.00* | |
| | | *Nos. 1-7 (7)* | 1,148. | 748.00 |

Single imperforates of types A1-A10 are sometimes simulated by trimming wide-margined examples of perforated stamps.

No. 4d must be dated between July 16 and July 31, 1867.

Proofs of Nos. 1-7 are on smooth white paper, unwatermarked and imperforate. Proofs of No. 7 are on thinner paper than No. 7a.

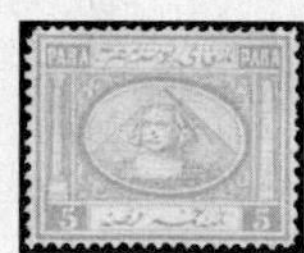
Sphinx and Pyramid — A8

***Perf. 15x12½***

**1867 — Litho. — Wmk. 119**

| No. | Type | Description | Unused | Used |
|---|---|---|---|---|
| 8 | A8 | 5pa orange | 42.50 | *11.00* |
| *a.* | | Imperf. | 250.00 | — |
| *b.* | | Horiz. pair, imperf between | 190.00 | |
| *c.* | | Vert. pair, imperf between | — | |
| 9 | A8 | 10pa lilac ('69) | 70.00 | 11.00 |
| *a.* | | 10pa violet | 95.00 | 14.00 |
| *b.* | | Half used as 5pa on newspaper piece | | 850.00 |
| 11 | A8 | 20pa yellow green ('69) | 135.00 | 14.00 |
| *a.* | | 20pa blue green | 135.00 | 17.00 |
| 13 | A8 | 1pi rose red | 27.50 | 1.10 |
| *a.* | | Imperf, pair | 150.00 | |
| *b.* | | Pair, imperf. between | 300.00 | |
| *d.* | | Rouletted | 70.00 | |
| *e.* | | 1pi lake red | 175.00 | 32.50 |
| 14 | A8 | 2pi blue | 150.00 | 18.00 |
| *a.* | | Imperf. | 325.00 | |
| *b.* | | Horiz. pair, imperf. vert. | 500.00 | |
| *d.* | | Perf. 12½ | 275.00 | |
| 15 | A8 | 5pi brown | 375.00 | 200.00 |
| | | *Nos. 8-15 (6)* | 800.00 | 255.10 |

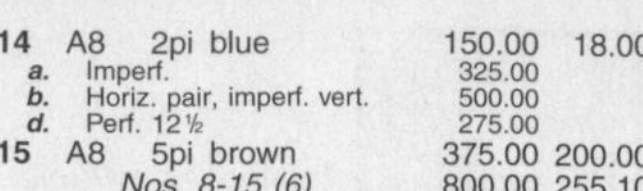

There are 4 types of each value, so placed that any block of 4 contains all types.

A9

### Clear Impressions
### Thick Opaque Paper

**Typographed by the Government at Boulac**

***Perf. 12½x13½ Clean-cut***

**1872 — Wmk. 119**

| No. | Type | Description | Unused | Used |
|---|---|---|---|---|
| 19 | A9 | 5pa brown | 10.00 | 5.50 |
| 20 | A9 | 10pa lilac | 9.00 | 3.75 |
| 21 | A9 | 20pa blue | 67.50 | 4.75 |
| 22 | A9 | 1pi rose red | 72.50 | 2.25 |
| *h.* | | Half used as 20pa on cover | | 750.00 |
| 23 | A9 | 2pi dull yellow | 100.00 | 15.00 |
| *j.* | | Half used as 1p on cover | | 1,200. |
| 24 | A9 | 2½pi dull violet | 95.00 | 25.00 |
| 25 | A9 | 5pi green | 325.00 | 42.50 |
| *i.* | | Tête bêche pair | *8,000.* | |
| | | *Nos. 19-25 (7)* | 679.00 | 98.75 |

***Perf. 13½ Clean-cut***

| No. | Type | Description | Unused | Used |
|---|---|---|---|---|
| *19a* | A9 | 5pa brown | 27.50 | 10.00 |
| *20a* | A9 | 10pa dull lilac | 7.00 | 3.50 |
| *21a* | A9 | 20pa blue | 95.00 | 22.00 |
| *22a* | A9 | 1pi rose red | 95.00 | 4.00 |
| *23a* | A9 | 2pi dull yellow | 20.00 | 4.50 |
| *24a* | A9 | 2½pi dull violet | 800.00 | 225.00 |
| *25a* | A9 | 5pi green | 325.00 | 62.50 |

**Litho.**

| No. | Type | Description | Unused | Used |
|---|---|---|---|---|
| *21m* | A9 | 20pa blue, perf. 12½x13½ | 160.00 | 80.00 |
| *21n* | A9 | 20pa blue, perf. 13½ | 250.00 | 65.00 |
| *21p* | A9 | 20pa blue, imperf. | — | |
| *21q* | A9 | 20pa blue, pair, imperf. between | — | 2,000. |
| *22m* | A9 | 1pi rose red, perf. 12½x13½ | 550.00 | 20.00 |
| *22n* | A9 | 1pi rose red, perf. 13½ | 875.00 | 50.00 |

A10

### Blurred Impressions
### Thinner Paper

***Perf. 12½ Rough***

**1874-75 — Typo. — Wmk. 119**

| No. | Type | Description | Unused | Used |
|---|---|---|---|---|
| 26 | A10 | 5pa brown ('75) | 22.50 | 3.75 |
| *e.* | | Imperf. | 200.00 | 200.00 |
| *f.* | | Vert. pair, imperf. horiz. | 1,000. | — |
| *g.* | | Tête bêche pair | 45.00 | 45.00 |
| *20b* | A9 | 10pa gray lilac | 16.00 | 3.75 |
| *g.* | | Tête bêche pair | 225.00 | 225.00 |
| *21b* | A9 | 20pa gray blue | 105.00 | 4.00 |
| *k.* | | Half used as 10pa on cover | | — |
| *22b* | A9 | 1pi vermilion | 12.00 | 1.75 |
| *f.* | | Imperf. | — | 150.00 |
| *g.* | | Tête bêche pair | 150.00 | 125.00 |
| *23b* | A9 | 2pi yellow | 90.00 | 5.75 |
| *i.* | | Tête bêche pair | 600.00 | 600.00 |
| *24b* | A9 | 2½pi deep violet | 9.25 | 6.25 |
| *e.* | | Imperf. | — | — |
| *f.* | | Tête bêche pair | 600.00 | 600.00 |
| *25b* | A9 | 5pi yellow green | 65.00 | 22.50 |
| *e.* | | Imperf. | 400.00 | — |

No. 26f normally occurs tête-bêche.

***Perf. 13½x12½ Rough***

| No. | Type | Description | Unused | Used |
|---|---|---|---|---|
| *26c* | A10 | 5pa brown | 24.00 | 4.50 |
| *i.* | | Tête bêche pair | 62.50 | 62.50 |
| *20c* | A9 | 10pa gray lilac | 37.50 | 3.50 |
| *i.* | | Tête bêche pair | 225.00 | *225.00* |
| *21c* | A9 | 20pa gray blue | 11.00 | 3.75 |
| *h.* | | Pair, imperf. between | 350.00 | |
| *22c* | A9 | 1pi vermilion | 90.00 | 3.25 |
| *i.* | | Tête bêche pair | 500.00 | 500.00 |
| *23c* | A9 | 2pi yellow | 10.00 | 6.25 |
| *g.* | | Tête bêche pair | 500.00 | 500.00 |
| *k.* | | Half used as 1pi on cover | | *4,000.* |

***Perf. 12½x13½ Rough***

| No. | Type | Description | Unused | Used |
|---|---|---|---|---|
| *23d* | A9 | 2pi yellow ('75) | 80.00 | 17.00 |
| *h.* | | Tête bêche pair | *1,250.* | |
| *24d* | A9 | 2½pi dp violet ('75) | 80.00 | 20.00 |
| *i.* | | Tête bêche pair | *1,150.* | *800.00* |
| *25d* | A9 | 5pi yel green ('75) | 375.00 | 300.00 |

Nos. 24b, 24d Surcharged in Black

**1879, Jan. 1** *Perf. 12½ Rough*

27 A9 5pa on 2½pi dull vio 10.00 *12.00*
- a. Imperf. 450.00 450.00
- b. Tête bêche pair *7,500.*
- c. Inverted surcharge 125.00 75.00
- d. Perf. 12½x13½ rough 12.00 *12.00*
- e. As "d," tête bêche pair 7,500.
- f. As "d," inverted surcharge 150.00 150.00

28 A9 10pa on 2½pi dull vio 12.50 12.50
- a. Imperf. 400.00 400.00
- b. Tête bêche pair *2,500.*
- c. Inverted surcharge 125.00 82.50
- d. Perf. 12½x13½ rough 17.00 17.00
- e. As "d," tête bêche pair 3,000.
- f. As "d," inverted surcharge 150.00 125.00

A11

A12

A13

A14

A15

A16

**1879-1902** **Typo.** *Perf. 14x13½*

**Ordinary Paper**

29 A11 5pa brown 4.25 1.25
30 A12 10pa violet 57.50 5.00
31 A12 10pa lilac rose ('81) 70.00 10.00
32 A12 10pa gray ('82) 8.00 1.75
33 A12 10pa green ('84) 2.50 2.00
34 A13 20pa ultra 67.50 2.25
35 A13 20pa rose ('84) 22.00 1.25
36 A14 1pi rose 42.50 .30
37 A14 1pi ultra ('84) 5.75 .30
38 A15 2pi orange yel 42.50 1.50
39 A15 2pi orange brn 27.50 .50
40 A16 5pi green 77.50 11.50
41 A16 5pi gray ('84) 25.00 .50
*Nos. 29-41 (13)* 452.50 38.10

Nos. 29-31, 35-41 imperf are proofs.

Nos. 37, 39, 41, exist on both ordinary and chalky paper. See *Scott Classic Specialized Catalogue of Stamps & Covers* for detailed listings.

For overprints see Nos. 42, O6-O7.

A17

**1884, Feb. 1**

42 A17 20pa on 5pi green 14.00 2.25
- a. Inverted surcharge 70.00 62.50
- b. Double surcharge —

A18

A19

A20

A21

A22

A23

**1888-1906** **Ordinary Paper**

43 A18 1m pale brown ('02) 3.50 .25
44 A19 2m green ('02) 3.00 .25
45 A20 3m maroon ('92) 8.00 2.25
46 A20 3m yel org ('02) 5.75 .25
48 A22 5m carmine rose 6.50 .25
49 A23 10p purple ('89) 35.00 1.00
*Nos. 43-49 (6)* 61.75 4.25

**Chalky Paper**

43a A18 1m pale brown ('02) 4.00 .25
44a A19 2m green ('02) 1.25 .25
46a A20 3m yel org ('02) 3.00 .25
47 A21 4m brown red ('06) 4.75 .25
- a. Half used as 2m on cover —

48b A22 5m rose ('02) 3.00 .25
49b A23 10p mauve ('02) 22.50 .55

Nos. 43-44, 47-48 imperf are proofs.

For overprints see Nos. O2-O5, O8-O10, O14-O15.

Boats on Nile
A24

Cleopatra
A25

Ras-el-Tin Palace
A26

Giza Pyramids
A27

Sphinx
A28

Colossi of Thebes
A29

Pylon of Karnak and Temple of Khonsu — A30

Citadel at Cairo — A31

Rock Temple of Abu Simbel — A32

Aswan Dam — A33

*Perf. 13½x14*

**1914, Jan. 8** **Wmk. 119**

**Chalk-surfaced Paper**

50 A24 1m olive brown 1.25 *.80*
51 A25 2m dp green 3.75 .25
52 A26 3m orange 3.50 .50
53 A27 4m red 4.50 .75
54 A28 5m lake 4.25 .25
- a. Booklet pane of 6 250.00

55 A29 10m dk blue 7.50 .40

*Perf. 14*

56 A30 20m olive grn 8.00 .70
57 A31 50m red violet 24.00 1.10
58 A32 100m black 25.00 1.40
59 A33 200m plum 42.50 4.00
*Nos. 50-59 (10)* 124.25 10.15

All values of this issue exist imperforate on both watermarked and unwatermarked paper but are not known to have been issued in that condition.

See Nos. 61-69, 72-74. For overprints and surcharge see Nos. 60, 78-91, O11-O13, O16-O27, O30.

**British Protectorate**

No. 52 Surcharged

**1915, Oct. 15**

60 A26 2m on 3m orange 1.25 2.25
- a. Inverted surcharge 250.00 250.00

**Scenic Types of 1914 and**

Statue of Ramses II
A34 A35

**1921-22** **Wmk. 120** *Perf. 13½x14*

**Chalk-surfaced Paper**

61 A24 1m olive brown 1.50 *3.00*
62 A25 2m dp green 9.00 4.75
63 A25 2m red ('22) 6.00 2.50
64 A26 3m orange 9.00 6.00
65 A27 4m green ('22) 8.00 *6.50*
66 A28 5m lake 7.00 1.75
67 A28 5m pink 14.00 .25
68 A29 10m dp blue 12.00 .70
69 A29 10m lake ('22) 3.50 .70
70 A34 15m indigo ('22) 10.00 .30
71 A35 15m indigo ('22) 40.00 5.00

*Perf. 14*

72 A30 20m olive green 12.50 .40
73 A31 50m maroon 10.00 1.25
74 A32 100m black 95.00 7.50
*Nos. 61-74 (14)* 237.50 40.60

For overprints see Nos. O28-O29.

**Independent Kingdom**

Stamps of 1921-22 Overprinted

**1922, Oct. 10**

78 A24 1m olive brown 1.50 1.10
- a. Inverted overprint 475.00 450.00
- b. Double overprint 225.00 —

79 A25 2m red 1.10 .65
- a. Double overprint 225.00 —

80 A26 3m orange 2.25 1.10
81 A27 4m green 1.50 1.00
- b. Inverted overprint 225.00 —

82 A28 5m pink 2.75 .25
83 A29 10m lake 2.75 .25
84 A34 15m indigo 5.75 1.10
85 A35 15m indigo 4.50 1.10

*Perf. 14*

86 A30 20m olive green 6.00 1.10
- a. Inverted overprint 200.00 —
- b. Double overprint 300.00 —

87 A31 50m maroon 9.00 1.10
- a. Inverted overprint 400.00 500.00

88 A32 100m black 22.50 1.25
- a. Inverted overprint 500.00 160.00
- b. Double overprint 400.00 250.00

*Nos. 78-88 (11)* 59.60 10.00

**Same Overprint on Nos. 58-59**

**Wmk. Crescent and Star (119)**

90 A32 100m black 90.00 50.00
91 A33 200m plum 30.00 1.60

Proclamation of the Egyptian monarchy.

The overprint signifies "The Egyptian Kingdom, March 15, 1922." It exists in four types, one lithographed and three typographed on Nos. 78-87, but lithographed only on Nos. 88-91.

A36

King Fuad — A37

**Wmk. 120**

**1923-24** **Photo.** *Perf. 13½*

**Size 18x22½mm**

92 A36 1m orange .35 .25
93 A36 2m black 1.10 .25
94 A36 3m brown 1.00 .65
- a. Imperf., pair 225.00

95 A36 4m yellow grn .90 .50
96 A36 5m orange brn .45 .25
- a. Imperf., pair 50.00

97 A36 10m rose 2.00 .25
98 A36 15m ultra 3.25 .25

*Perf. 14*

**Size: 22x28mm**

99 A36 20m dk green 6.25 .25
100 A36 50m myrtle grn 10.00 .25
101 A36 100m red violet 25.00 .55
102 A36 200m violet ('24) 45.00 2.00
- a. Imperf., pair 325.00

103 A37 £1 ultra & dk vio ('24) 175.00 27.50
- a. Imperf., pair 1,750.

*Nos. 92-103 (12)* 270.30 32.95

For overprints & surcharge see Nos. 167, O31-O38.

Thoth Carving Name of King Fuad — A38

**1925, Apr.** **Litho.** *Perf. 11*

105 A38 5m brown 11.00 6.00
106 A38 10m rose 22.50 12.50
107 A38 15m ultra 22.50 14.00
*Nos. 105-107 (3)* 56.00 32.50

International Geographical Congress, Cairo.

Nos. 106-107 exist with both white and yellowish gum.

Oxen Plowing A39

**1926** **Wmk. 195** *Perf. 13x13½*

108 A39 5m lt brown 3.00 2.00
109 A39 10m brt rose 2.75 2.00
110 A39 15m dp blue 3.00 2.00
111 A39 50m Prus green 14.00 5.00
112 A39 100m brown vio 22.50 8.00
113 A39 200m brt violet 32.50 17.50
*Nos. 108-113 (6)* 77.75 36.50

12th Agricultural and Industrial Exhibition at Gezira.

For surcharges see Nos. 115-117.

King Fuad — A40

*Perf. 14x14½*

**1926, Apr. 2** **Photo.** **Wmk. 120**

114 A40 50p brn vio & red vio 140.00 22.50

58th birthday of King Fuad.

For overprint and surcharge see Nos. 124, 166.

**Nos. 111-113 Surcharged**

*Perf. 13x13½*

**1926, Aug. 24** **Wmk. 195**

**115** A39 5m on 50m Prus green 2.50 2.50
**116** A39 10m on 100m brown vio 2.50 2.50
**117** A39 15m on 200m brt violet 2.50 2.50
*a.* Double surcharge 300.00
*Nos. 115-117 (3)* 7.50 7.50

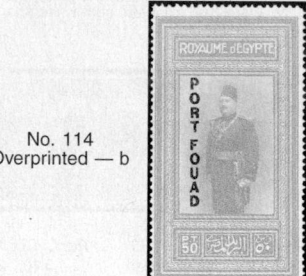

Ship of Hatshepsut — A41

**1926, Dec. 9** **Litho.** ***Perf. 13x13½***

**118** A41 5m brown & blk 3.00 1.40
**119** A41 10m dp red & blk 3.50 1.50
**120** A41 15m dp blue & blk 4.00 1.50
*Nos. 118-120 (3)* 10.50 4.40

International Navigation Congress, Cairo.
For overprints see Nos. 121-123.

Nos. 118-120, 114 Overprinted — a

No. 114 Overprinted — b

**1926, Dec. 21**

**121** A41 (a) 5m 300.00 250.00
**122** A41 (a) 10m 300.00 250.00
**123** A41 (a) 15m 300.00 250.00

*Perf. 14x14½*
**Wmk. 120**

**124** A40 (b) 50p 1,600. *875.00*

Inauguration of Port Fuad opposite Port Said.
Nos. 121-123 have a block over "Le Caire" at lower left.
Forgeries of Nos. 121-124 exist.

Branch of Cotton A42

*Perf. 13x13½*

**1927, Jan. 25** **Wmk. 195**

**125** A42 5m dk brown & sl grn 1.75 .80
**126** A42 10m dp red & slate grn 2.75 1.50
**127** A42 15m dp blue & slate grn 3.50 1.50
*Nos. 125-127 (3)* 8.00 3.80

International Cotton Congress, Cairo.

King Fuad
A43 A44

A45

A46

Type I Type II

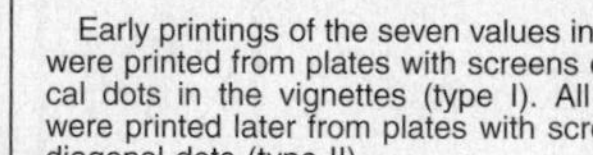

Early printings of the seven values indicated were printed from plates with screens of vertical dots in the vignettes (type I). All values were printed later from plates with screens of diagonal dots (type II).

*Perf. 13x13½*

**1927-37** **Wmk. 195** **Photo.**

**Type II**

**128** A43 1m orange .35 .25
*a.* Type I 3.25 .60
**129** A43 2m black .35 .25
*a.* Type I 11.00 6.00
**130** A43 3m olive brn .35 .55
*a.* Type I 2.50 1.00
**131** A43 3m dp green ('30) .65 .25
**132** A43 4m yellow grn 1.25 1.10
*a.* Type I 65.00 12.50
**133** A43 4m brown ('30) 1.10 .55
**134** A43 4m dp green ('34) .85 .40
**135** A43 5m dk red brn ('29) .95 .40
*a.* Type I 3.50 1.00
**136** A43 10m dk red ('29) 1.40 .25
*a.* 10m orange red, type I 2.50 .45
**137** A43 10m purple ('34) 3.75 .25
**138** A43 13m car rose ('32) 1.50 .40
**139** A43 15m ultra 2.50 .25
*a.* Type I 12.00 .65
**140** A43 15m dk violet ('34) 5.25 .25
**141** A43 20m ultra ('34) 9.25 .30

*Perf. 13½x14*

**142** A44 20m olive grn 3.25 .40
**143** A44 20m ultra ('32) 7.50 .25
**144** A44 40m olive brn ('32) 4.25 .25
**145** A44 50m Prus green 3.50 .25
*a.* 50m greenish blue 6.00 .35
**146** A44 100m brown vio 10.00 .35
*a.* 100m claret 14.00 .50
**147** A44 200m deep violet 9.00 1.25

Printings of Nos. 142, 145 and 146, made in 1929 and later, were from new plates with stronger impressions and darker colors.

*Perf. 13x13½*

**148** A45 500m choc & Prus bl, entirely photo ('32) 100.00 25.00
*a.* Frame litho, vignette photo 125.00 11.50
**149** A46 £1 dk grn & org brn, entirely photo ('37) 125.00 8.25
*a.* Frame litho, vignette photo 140.00 7.00
*Nos. 128-149 (22)* 292.00 41.45

Statue of Amenhotep, Son of Hapu — A47

**1927, Dec. 29** **Photo.** ***Perf. 13½x13***

**150** A47 5m orange brown 1.50 1.00
**151** A47 10m copper red 2.00 1.00
**152** A47 15m deep blue 3.25 1.00
*Nos. 150-152 (3)* 6.75 3.00

Statistical Congress, Cairo.

Imhotep — A48 Mohammed Ali Pasha — A49

**1928, Dec. 15**

**153** A48 5m orange brown 1.10 .65
**154** A49 10m copper red 1.25 .65

Intl. Congress of Medicine at Cairo and the cent. of the Faculty of Medicine at Cairo.

Prince Farouk — A50

**1929, Feb. 11** **Litho.**

**155** A50 5m choc & gray 2.00 1.40
**156** A50 10m dull red & gray 3.00 1.50
**157** A50 15m ultra & gray 3.00 1.50
**158** A50 20m Prus blue & gray 3.50 1.50
*Nos. 155-158 (4)* 11.50 5.90

Ninth birthday of Prince Farouk.
Nos. 155-158 with black or brown centers are trial color proofs. They were sent to the UPU, but were never placed on sale to the public, although some are known used.

Tomb Fresco at El-Bersheh — A51

**1931, Feb. 15** ***Perf. 13x13½***

**163** A51 5m brown 1.50 1.00
**164** A51 10m copper red 2.50 1.75
**165** A51 15m dark blue 3.50 2.00
*Nos. 163-165 (3)* 7.50 4.75

14th Agricultural & Industrial Exhib., Cairo.

**Nos. 114 and 103 Surcharged in Black**

**1932** **Wmk. 120** ***Perf. 14x14½***

**166** A40 50m on 50p 20.00 3.00

***Perf. 14***

**167** A37 100m on £1 250.00 190.00

Locomotive of 1852 — A52

*Perf. 13x13½*

**1933, Jan. 19** **Litho.** **Wmk. 195**

**168** A52 5m shown 14.00 8.00
**169** A52 13m 1859 21.00 12.00
**170** A52 15m 1862 21.00 12.00
**171** A52 20m 1932 21.00 12.00
*Nos. 168-171 (4)* 77.00 44.00

International Railroad Congress, Heliopolis.

Commercial Passenger Airplane — A56

Dornier Do-X A57

Graf Zeppelin A58

**1933, Dec. 20** **Photo.**

**172** A56 5m brown 7.50 4.00
**173** A56 10m brt violet 17.50 12.00
**174** A57 13m brown car 20.00 15.00
**175** A57 15m violet 20.00 13.00
**176** A58 20m blue 25.00 20.00
*Nos. 172-176 (5)* 90.00 64.00

International Aviation Congress, Cairo.

A59

Khedive Ismail Pasha — A60

**1934, Feb. 1** ***Perf. 13½***

**177** A59 1m dp orange .60 *1.10*
**178** A59 2m black .60 *1.10*
**179** A59 3m brown .75 *1.25*

180 A59 4m blue green 1.25 .40
181 A59 5m red brown 1.40 .25
182 A59 10m violet 2.50 .35
183 A59 13m copper red 4.00 2.25
184 A59 15m dull violet 4.50 1.75
185 A59 20m ultra 3.00 .40
186 A59 50m Prus blue 9.50 .65
187 A59 100m olive grn 9.50 1.25
188 A59 200m dp violet 75.00 7.25

***Perf. 13½x13***

189 A60 50p brown 225.00 95.00
190 A60 £1 Prus blue 400.00 150.00
*Nos. 177-190 (14)* 737.60 263.00

10th Congress of UPU, Cairo.

King Fuad — A61

**1936-37** ***Perf. 13½***

191 A61 1m dull orange .55 *.90*
192 A61 2m black 1.75 .25
193 A61 4m dk green 2.00 .25
194 A61 5m chestnut 1.40 .55
195 A61 10m purple ('37) 2.50 .35
196 A61 15m brown violet 2.75 .50
197 A61 20m sapphire 3.25 .35
*Nos. 191-197 (7)* 14.20 3.15

Entrance to Agricultural Building — A62

Agricultural Building — A63

Design: 15m, 20m, Industrial Building.

**1936, Feb. 15** ***Perf. 13½x13***

198 A62 5m brown 1.75 1.25

***Perf. 13x13½***

199 A63 10m violet 2.00 1.50
200 A63 13m copper red 3.25 2.50
201 A63 15m dark violet 1.75 1.25
202 A63 20m blue 3.75 2.25
*Nos. 198-202 (5)* 12.50 8.75

15th Agricultural & Industrial Exhib., Cairo.

Signing of Treaty — A65

**1936, Dec. 22** ***Perf. 11***

203 A65 5m brown .80 .80
204 A65 15m dk violet 1.00 1.00
205 A65 20m sapphire 1.75 1.75
*Nos. 203-205 (3)* 3.55 3.55

Signing of Anglo-Egyptian Treaty, Aug. 26, 1936.

King Farouk — A66

**1937-44** **Wmk. 195** ***Perf. 13x13½***

206 A66 1m brown org .30 .25
207 A66 2m vermilion .30 .25
208 A66 3m brown .30 .25
209 A66 4m green .30 .25
210 A66 5m red brown .50 .25
211 A66 6m lt yel grn ('40) .60 .25
212 A66 10m purple .30 .25
213 A66 13m rose car .60 .35
214 A66 15m dk vio brn .50 .25
215 A66 20m blue .75 .35
216 A66 20m lil gray ('44) .75 .25
*Nos. 206-216 (11)* 5.20 2.95

For overprints see Nos. 301, 303, 345, 348, 360E, N3, N6, N8, N22, N25, N27.

Medal for Montreux Conf. — A67

**1937, Oct. 15** ***Perf. 13½x13***

217 A67 5m red brown .75 .55
218 A67 15m dk violet 1.25 1.10
219 A67 20m sapphire 1.50 1.25
*Nos. 217-219 (3)* 3.50 2.90

Intl. Treaty signed at Montreux, Switzerland, under which foreign privileges in Egypt were to end in 1949.

Eye of Ré — A68

**1937, Dec. 8** ***Perf. 13x13½***

220 A68 5m brown 1.25 .80
221 A68 15m dk violet 1.50 .90
222 A68 20m sapphire 1.75 1.00
*Nos. 220-222 (3)* 4.50 2.70

15th Ophthalmological Congress, Cairo, December, 1937.

King Farouk, Queen Farida — A69

**1938, Jan. 20** ***Perf. 11***

223 A69 5m red brown 6.50 5.00

Royal wedding of King Farouk and Farida Zulficar.

**Inscribed: "11 Fevrier 1938"**

**1938, Feb. 11**

224 A69 £1 green & sepia 200.00 *150.00*

King Farouk's 18th birthday.
No. 224 is valued CTO; postally used examples: Value, $300.

Cotton Picker — A70

**1938, Jan. 26** ***Perf. 13½x13***

225 A70 5m red brown .75 .75
226 A70 15m dk violet 2.25 1.50
227 A70 20m sapphire 2.00 1.75
*Nos. 225-227 (3)* 5.00 4.00

18th International Cotton Congress at Cairo.

Pyramids of Giza and Colossus of Thebes A71

**1938, Feb. 1** ***Perf. 13x13½***

228 A71 5m red brown 1.40 1.00
229 A71 15m dk violet 2.00 1.25
230 A71 20m sapphire 2.25 1.25
*Nos. 228-230 (3)* 5.65 3.50

Intl. Telecommunication Conf., Cairo.

Branch of Hydnocarpus — A72

**1938, Mar. 21** ***Perf. 13x13½***

231 A72 5m red brown 1.50 1.25
232 A72 15m dk violet 2.25 1.25
233 A72 20m sapphire 2.50 1.25
*Nos. 231-233 (3)* 6.25 3.75

International Leprosy Congress, Cairo.

King Farouk and Pyramids — A73

King Farouk
A74 A75

Backgrounds: 40m, Hussan Mosque. 50m, Cairo Citadel. 100m, Aswan Dam. 200m, Cairo University.

**1939-46** **Photo.** ***Perf. 14x13½***

234 A73 30m gray .75 .25
*a.* 30m slate gray .75 .25
234B A73 30m ol grn ('46) .80 .25
235 A73 40m dk brown .85 .25
236 A73 50m Prus green 1.00 .25
237 A73 100m brown vio 1.40 .50
238 A73 200m dk violet 5.00 .50

***Perf. 13½x13***

239 A74 50p green & sep 11.00 4.00
240 A75 £1 dp bl & dk brn 26.00 7.00
*Nos. 234-240 (8)* 46.80 13.00

For £1 with A77 portrait, see No. 269D. See Nos. 267-269D. For overprints see Nos. 310-314, 316, 355-358, 360, 363-364, N13-N19, N32-N38.

**Catalogue values for unused stamps in this section, from this point to the end of the section, are for Never Hinged items.**

King Fuad — A76

**1944, Apr. 28** ***Perf. 13½x13***

241 A76 10m dk violet .50 .25

8th anniv. of the death of King Fuad.

King Farouk — A77

**1944-50** **Wmk. 195** ***Perf. 13x13½***

242 A77 1m yellow brn ('45) .45 .25
243 A77 2m red org ('45) .45 .25
244 A77 3m sepia ('46) 1.00 1.00
245 A77 4m dp green ('45) .45 .25
246 A77 5m red brown ('46) .45 .25
247 A77 10m dp violet .45 .25
247A A77 13m rose red ('50) 12.00 4.25
248 A77 15m dk violet ('45) 1.25 .25
249 A77 17m olive grn 1.25 .25
250 A77 20m dk gray ('45) 1.40 .25
251 A77 22m dp blue ('45) 1.40 .25
*Nos. 242-251 (11)* 20.55 7.50

For overprints see Nos. 299-300, 302, 304-309, 343-344, 346-347, 349-354, 360B, 361-362, N1-N2, N4-N5, N7, N9-N12, N20-N21, N23-N24, N26, N28-N31.

King Farouk — A78

**1945, Feb. 10** ***Perf. 13½x13***

252 A78 10m deep violet .40 .25

25th birthday of King Farouk.

Khedive Ismail Pasha — A79

**1945, Mar. 2** **Photo.**

253 A79 10m dark olive .35 .25

50th anniv. of death of Khedive Ismail Pasha.

Flags of Arab Nations — A80

**1945, July 29**

254 A80 10m violet .35 .25
255 A80 22m dp yellow grn .45 .25

League of Arab Nations Conference, Cairo, Mar. 22, 1945.

Flags of Egypt and Saudi Arabia A81

***Perf. 13x13½***

**1946, Jan. 10** **Wmk. 195**

256 A81 10m dp yellow grn .35 .25

Visit of King Ibn Saud, Jan. 1946.

Citadel, Cairo A82

**1946, Aug. 9**

257 A82 10m yel brn & dp yel grn .40 .25

Withdrawal of British troops from Cairo Citadel, Aug. 9, 1946.

King Farouk and Inchas Palace, Cairo A83

2m, Prince Abdullah, Yemen. 3m, Pres. Bechara el-Khoury, Lebanon. 4m, King Abdul Aziz ibn Saud, Saudi Arabia. 5m, King Faisal II, Iraq. 10m, Amir Abdullah ibn Hussein, Jordan. 15m, Pres. Shukri el Kouatly, Syria.

**1946, Nov. 9**

| | | | | |
|---|---|---|---|---|
| 258 | A83 | 1m dp yellow grn | .60 | .25 |
| 259 | A83 | 2m sepia | .60 | .25 |
| 260 | A83 | 3m deep blue | .60 | .25 |
| 261 | A83 | 4m brown orange | .60 | .25 |
| 262 | A83 | 5m brown red | .60 | .25 |
| 263 | A83 | 10m dark gray | .75 | .25 |
| 264 | A83 | 15m deep violet | .75 | .25 |
| | | *Nos. 258-264 (7)* | 4.50 | 1.75 |

Arab League Cong. at Cairo, May 28, 1946.

Parliament Building, Cairo — A84

**1947, Apr. 7** **Photo.**

265 A84 10m green .35 .25

36th conf. of the Interparliamentary Union, Apr. 1947.

Raising Egyptian Flag over Kasr-el-Nil Barracks — A85

**1947, May 6** ***Perf. 13½x13***

266 A85 10m dp plum & yel grn .40 .25

Withdrawal of British troops from the Nile Delta.

**Farouk Types 1939 Redrawn and**

King Farouk — A85a

**1947-51** **Wmk. 195** ***Perf. 14x13½***

| | | | | |
|---|---|---|---|---|
| 267 | A73 | 30m olive green | .75 | .25 |
| 268 | A73 | 40m dk brown | .60 | .25 |
| 269 | A73 | 50m Prus grn ('48) | .90 | .25 |
| 269A | A73 | 100m dk brn vio ('49) | 6.00 | .90 |
| 269B | A73 | 200m dk violet ('49) | 14.00 | 1.40 |

***Perf. 13½x13***

| | | | | |
|---|---|---|---|---|
| 269C | A85a | 50p green & sep ('51) | 27.50 | 9.50 |
| 269D | A75 | £1 dp bl & dk brn ('50) | 37.50 | 3.75 |
| | | *Nos. 267-269D (7)* | 87.25 | 16.30 |

The king faces slightly to the left and clouds have been added in the sky on Nos. 267-269B. Backgrounds as in 1939-46 issue. Portrait on £1 as on type A77.

For overprints see Nos. 315, 359.

Field and Branch of Cotton — A86

***Perf. 13½x13***

**1948, Apr. 1** **Wmk. 195**

270 A86 10m olive green .65 .25

Intl. Cotton Cong. held at Cairo in Apr. 1948.

Map and Infantry Column — A87

**1948, June 15** ***Perf. 11½x11***

271 A87 10m green 1.40 .25

Arrival of Egyptian troops at Gaza, 5/15/48.

Ibrahim Pasha (1789-1848) — A88

**1948, Nov. 10** ***Perf. 13x13½***

272 A88 10m brn red & dp grn .40 .25

Statue, "The Nile" A89

Protection of Industry and Agriculture — A90

***Perf. 13x13½***

**1949, Mar. 1** **Photo.** **Wmk. 195**

| | | | | |
|---|---|---|---|---|
| 273 | A89 | 1m dk green | .40 | .25 |
| 274 | A89 | 10m purple | 1.00 | .25 |
| 275 | A89 | 17m crimson | 1.00 | .25 |
| 276 | A89 | 22m deep blue | 1.00 | .45 |

***Perf. 11½x11***

| | | | | |
|---|---|---|---|---|
| 277 | A90 | 30m dk brown | 1.50 | .60 |
| | | *Nos. 273-277 (5)* | 4.90 | 1.80 |

**Souvenir Sheets**

**Photo. & Litho.**

***Imperf***

| | | |
|---|---|---|
| 278 Sheet of 4 | 3.75 | 3.75 |
| *a.* A89 1m red brown | .75 | .75 |
| *b.* A89 10m dark brown | .75 | .75 |
| *c.* A89 17m brown orange | .75 | .75 |
| *d.* A89 22m dark Prussian green | .75 | .75 |
| 279 Sheet of 2 | 3.75 | 3.75 |
| *a.* A90 10m violet gray | 1.60 | 1.60 |
| *b.* A90 30m red orange | 1.60 | 1.60 |

16th Agricultural & Industrial Expo., Cairo.

Mohammed Ali and Map — A93

***Perf. 11½x11***

**1949, Aug. 2** **Photo.** **Wmk. 195**

280 A93 10m orange brn & grn .60 .25

Centenary of death of Mohammed Ali.

Globe — A94

**1949, Oct. 9** ***Perf. 13½x13***

| | | | | |
|---|---|---|---|---|
| 281 | A94 | 10m rose brown | 1.00 | .60 |
| 282 | A94 | 22m violet | 2.00 | .90 |
| 283 | A94 | 30m dull blue | 2.75 | 1.20 |
| | | *Nos. 281-283 (3)* | 5.75 | 2.70 |

75th anniv. of the UPU.

Scales of Justice A95

**1949, Oct. 14** ***Perf. 13x13½***

284 A95 10m deep olive green .40 .25

End of the Mixed Judiciary System, 10/14/49.

Desert Scene A96

**1950, Dec. 27**

285 A96 10m violet & red brn .90 .75

Opening of the Fuad I Institute of the Desert.

Fuad I University A97

**1950, Dec. 27**

286 A97 22m dp green & claret .90 .75

Founding of Fuad I University, 25th anniv.

Globe and Khedive Ismail Pasha A98

**1950, Dec. 27**

287 A98 30m claret & dp grn .90 .75

75th anniv. of Royal Geographic Society of Egypt.

Picking Cotton — A99

**1951, Feb. 24**

290 A99 10m olive green .40 .35

International Cotton Congress, 1951.

King Farouk and Queen Narriman — A100

**1951, May 6** **Photo.** ***Perf. 11x11½***

| | | | | |
|---|---|---|---|---|
| 291 | A100 | 10m green & red brn | 3.00 | 2.25 |
| | *a.* | Souvenir sheet | 17.50 | *19.00* |

Marriage of King Farouk and Narriman Sadek, May 6, 1951.

Stadium Entrance A101

Arms of Alexandria and Olympic Emblem — A102

King Farouk A103

**1951, Oct. 5** ***Perf. 13x13½, 13½x13***

**292** A101 10m brown 1.10 1.10
**293** A102 22m dp green 1.40 1.40
**294** A103 30m blue & dp grn 1.40 1.40
*a.* Souvenir sheet of 3, #292-294 14.00 *16.00*
*Nos. 292-294 (3)* 3.90 3.90

Issued to publicize the first Mediterranean Games, Alexandria, Oct. 5-20, 1951.

Winged Figure and Map — A105

Designs: 22m, King Farouk and Map. 30m, King Farouk and Flag.

**Dated "16 Oct. 1951"**

**1952, Feb. 11** ***Perf. 13½x13***

**296** A105 10m dp green .75 .40
**297** A105 22m plum & dp grn 1.00 .75
**298** A105 30m green & brown 1.25 .95
*a.* Souvenir sheet of 3, #296-298 14.00 14.00
*Nos. 296-298 (3)* 3.00 2.10

Abrogation of the Anglo-Egyptian treaty.

Stamps of 1937-51 Overprinted in Various Colors

***Perf. 13x13½***

**1952, Jan. 17** **Wmk. 195**

**299** A77 1m yellow brown .85 .25
**300** A77 2m red org (Bl) .35 .25
**301** A66 3m brown (Bl) .35 .50
**302** A77 4m dp green (RV) .35 .25
**303** A66 6m lt yel grn (RV) 1.25 1.25
**304** A77 10m dp vio (C) .45 .25
**305** A77 13m rose red (Bl) 1.75 1.60
**306** A77 15m dk violet (C) 2.75 1.75
**307** A77 17m olive grn (C) 2.00 .35
**308** A77 20m dk gray (RV) 1.60 .35
**309** A77 22m dp blue (C) 3.00 3.00

No. 244, the 3m sepia, exists with this overprint but was not regularly issued or used.

Same Overprint, 24½mm Wide, on Nos. 267 to 269B

**310** A73 30m olive grn (DkBl) 3.75 .25
*a.* Black overprint 2.25 1.00
**311** A73 40m dk brown (G) .90 .25
**312** A73 50m Prus grn (C) 1.75 .25
**313** A73 100m dk brn vio (C) 3.00 .50
**314** A73 200m dk violet (C) 15.00 2.25

Same Overprint, 19mm Wide, on Nos. 269C-269D

**315** A85a 50p grn & sep (C) 25.00 8.00
**316** A75 £1 dp bl & dk brn (Bl) 45.00 9.00
*Nos. 299-316 (18)* 109.10 30.30

The overprint translates: King of Egypt and the Sudan, Oct. 16, 1951.

Overprints in colors other than as listed are color trials.

Egyptian Flag — A106

***Perf. 13½x13***

**1952, May 6** **Photo.** **Wmk. 195**

**317** A106 10m org yel, dp bl & dp grn 1.00 .25
*a.* Souvenir sheet of 1 7.50 5.25

Issued to commemorate the birth of Crown Prince Ahmed Fuad, Jan. 16, 1952.

"Dawn of New Era" A107

Symbolical of Egypt Freed — A108

Designs: 10m, "Egypt" with raised sword. 22m, Citizens marching with flag.

**Dated: "23 Juillet 1952"**

***Perf. 13x13½, 13½x13***

**1952, Nov. 23**

**318** A107 4m dp green & org .35 .25
**319** A107 10m dp grn & cop brn .35 .75
**320** A108 17m brn org & dp grn .75 .90
**321** A108 22m choc & dp grn 1.25 .60
*Nos. 318-321 (4)* 2.70 2.50

Change of government, July 23, 1952.

**Republic**

Farmer A109

Soldier A110

Mosque of Sultan Hassan — A111

Queen Nefertiti — A112

**1953-56** ***Perf. 13x13½***

**322** A109 1m red brown .50 .25
**323** A109 2m dk lilac .35 .25
**324** A109 3m brt blue .50 .45
**325** A109 4m dk green .35 .25
**326** A110 10m dk brown ("Defence") .40 .40
**327** A110 10m dk brown ("Defense") .80 .25
**328** A110 15m gray .55 .25
**329** A110 17m dk grnsh blue .75 .25
**330** A110 20m purple .35 .25

***Perf. 13½***

**331** A111 30m dull green .35 .25
**332** A111 32m brt blue .90 .25
**333** A111 35m violet ('55) 1.10 .25
**334** A111 37m gldn brn ('56) 1.75 .60
**335** A111 40m red brown .90 .25
**336** A111 50m violet brn 1.75 .25
**337** A112 100m henna brn 2.75 .30
**338** A112 200m dk grnsh blue 4.50 .75
**339** A112 500m purple 12.00 1.75

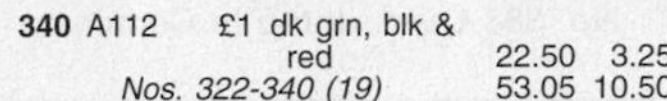

**340** A112 £1 dk grn, blk & red 22.50 3.25
*Nos. 322-340 (19)* 53.05 10.50

Nos. 327-330 are inscribed "Defense."

See No. 490. For overprints and surcharges see Nos. 460, 500, N44-N56, N72.

Stamps of 1939-51 Overprinted in Black

**1953** ***Perf. 13x13½, 13½x13***

**343** A77 1m yellow brn .35 .25
**344** A77 2m red orange .35 .25
**345** A66 3m brown .75 .75
**346** A77 3m sepia .35 .25
**347** A77 4m dp green .35 .25
**348** A66 6m lt yellow grn .35 .25
**349** A77 10m dp violet .35 .25
**350** A77 13m rose red 1.00 1.00
**351** A77 15m dk violet .75 .25
**352** A77 17m olive grn .75 .25
**353** A77 20m dk gray .90 .25
**354** A77 22m deep blue 1.25 .25
**355** A73 30m ol grn (#267) .75 .35
**356** A73 50m Prus grn (#269) 1.20 .35
**357** A73 100m dk brn vio (#269A) 2.00 .75
**358** A73 200m dk violet (#269B) 7.50 1.60
**359** A85a 50p grn & sepia 19.00 7.00
**360** A75 £1 dp bl & dk brn (#269D) 24.00 4.75
*Nos. 343-360 (18)* 61.95 19.05

No. 206 with this overprint is a forgery.

**Same Overprint on Nos. 300, 303-305, 311 and 314**

**360B** A77 2m red orange .40 .25
**360E** A66 6m lt yel grn *35.00*
**361** A77 10m dp violet 4.00 4.00
**362** A77 13m rose red 1.25 .75
**363** A73 40m dk brown 6.00 .75
**364** A73 200m dk violet 4.00 .90
*Nos. 360B,361-364 (5)* 15.65 6.65

Practically all values of Nos. 343-364 exist with double overprint. Other values of the 1952 overprinted issue are known only with counterfeit bars.

Symbols of Electronic Progress A113

**1953, Nov. 23** **Photo.** ***Perf. 13x13½***

**365** A113 10m brt blue .75 .50

Electronics Exposition, Cairo, Nov. 23.

Crowd Acclaiming the Republic — A114

Design: 30m, Crowd, flag and eagle.

***Perf. 13½x13***

**1954, June 18** **Wmk. 195**

**366** A114 10m brown .55 .25
**367** A114 30m deep blue .90 .60

Proclamation of the republic, 1st anniv.

Farmer — A115

**1954-55** ***Perf. 13x13½***

**368** A115 1m red brown .35 .25
**369** A115 2m dark lilac .35 .25
**370** A115 3m brt blue .35 .25
**371** A115 4m dk green ('55) 1.25 .95
**372** A115 5m dp car ('55) .35 .25
*Nos. 368-372 (5)* 2.65 1.95

For overprints see Nos. N39-N43.

Egyptian Flag, Map — A116

Design: 35m, Bugler, soldier and map.

**1954, Nov. 4** ***Perf. 13½x13***

**373** A116 10m rose vio & grn .50 .30
**374** A116 35m ver, blk & bl grn .80 .70

Agreement of Oct. 19, 1954, with Great Britain for the evacuation of the Suez Canal zone by British troops.

**Arab Postal Union Issue**

Globe — A117

**1955, Jan. 1**

**375** A117 5m yellow brn .60 .30
**376** A117 10m green .60 .50
**377** A117 37m violet 1.25 .95
*Nos. 375-377 (3)* 2.45 1.75

Founding of the Arab Postal Union, 7/1/54.

For overprints see Nos. 381-383.

Paul P. Harris and Rotary Emblem — A118

35m, Globe, wings and Rotary emblem.

***Perf. 13½x13***

**1955, Feb. 23** **Wmk. 195**

**378** A118 10m claret 1.10 .35
**379** A118 35m blue 1.50 .75

50th anniv. of the founding of Rotary Intl.

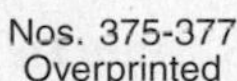

Nos. 375-377 Overprinted

**1955, Nov. 1**

**381** A117 5m yellow brown 1.00 .80
**382** A117 10m green 1.25 1.00
**383** A117 37m violet 1.75 1.25
*Nos. 381-383 (3)* 4.00 3.05

Arab Postal Union Congress held at Cairo, Mar. 15, 1955.

Map of Africa and Asia, Olive Branch and Rings A119

Globe, Torch, Dove and Olive Branch — A120

**1956, July 29** ***Perf. 13x13½, 13½x13***
**384** A119 10m chestnut & green .40 .25
**385** A120 35m org yel & dull pur 1.00 .70

Afro-Asian Festival, Cairo, July, 1956.

Map of Suez Canal and Ship — A121

***Perf. 11½x11***
**1956, Sept. 26** **Wmk. 195**
**386** A121 10m blue & buff .60 .60

Nationalization of the Suez Canal, July 26, 1956. See No. 393.

Queen Nefertiti — A122

**1956, Oct. 15** ***Perf. 13½x13***
**387** A122 10m dark green 1.40 1.25

Intl. Museum Week (UNESCO), Oct. 8-14.

Egyptians Defending Port Said — A123

**1956, Dec. 20** **Litho.** ***Perf. 11x11½***
**388** A123 10m brown violet 1.00 .75

Honoring the defenders of Port Said.

**No. 388 Overprinted in Carmine Rose**

**1957, Jan. 14**
**389** A123 10m brown violet 1.00 .60

Evacuation of Port Said by British and French troops, Dec. 22, 1956.

Old and New Trains A124

**1957, Jan. 30** **Photo.** ***Perf. 13x13½***
**390** A124 10m red violet & gray 1.10 1.00

100th anniv. of the Egyptian Railway System (in 1956).

Mother and Children A125

**1957, Mar. 21**
**391** A125 10m crimson .90 .35

Mother's Day, 1957.

Battle Scene A126

***Perf. 13x13½***
**1957, Mar. 28** **Wmk. 195**
**392** A126 10m bright blue .40 .35

Victory over the British at Rosetta, 150th anniv.

**Type of 1956; New Inscriptions in English**

**1957, Apr. 15** ***Perf. 11½x11***
**393** A121 100m blue & yel grn 1.60 1.25

Reopening of the Suez Canal.
No. 393 is inscribed: "Nationalisation of Suez Canal Co. Guarantees Freedom of Navigation" and "Reopening 1957."

Map of Gaza Strip — A127

***Perf. 13½x13***
**1957, May 4** **Photo.** **Wmk. 195**
**394** A127 10m Prus blue 1.50 .70

"Gaza Part of Arab Nation."
For overprint see No. N57.

Al Azhar University A128

**1957, Apr. 27** ***Perf. 13x13½***
**New Arabic Date in Red**
**395** A128 10m brt violet .50 .40
**396** A128 15m violet brown .80 .60
**397** A128 20m dark gray 1.30 .90
*Nos. 395-397 (3)* 2.60 1.90

Millenary of Al Azhar University, Cairo.

Shepheard's Hotel, Cairo — A129

***Perf. 13½x13***
**1957, July 20** **Wmk. 195**
**398** A129 10m brt violet .70 .45

Reopening of Shepheard's Hotel, Cairo.

Gate, Palace and Eagle — A130

***Perf. 11½x11***
**1957, July 22** **Wmk. 315**
**399** A130 10m yellow & brown .70 .40

First meeting of New National Assembly.

Amasis I in Battle of Avaris, 1580 B.C. A131

Designs: No. 401, Sultan Saladin, Hitteen, 1187 A. D. No. 402, Louis IX of France in chains, Mansourah, 1250, vert. No. 403, Map of Middle East, Ein Galout, 1260. No. 404, Port Said, 1956.

**Inscribed: "Egypt Tomb of Aggressors 1957"**

**1957, July 26** ***Perf. 13x13½, 13½x13***
**400** A131 10m carmine rose 1.50 1.50
**401** A131 10m dk olive grn 1.50 1.50
**402** A131 10m brown violet 1.50 1.50
**403** A131 10m grnsh blue 1.50 1.50
**404** A131 10m yellow brown 1.50 1.50
*Nos. 400-404 (5)* 7.50 7.50

No. 400 exists with Wmk. 195.

Ahmed Arabi Speaking to the Khedive A132

***Perf. 13x13½***
**1957, Sept. 16** **Wmk. 315**
**405** A132 10m deep violet .80 .25

75th anniversary of Arabi Revolution.

Hafez Ibrahim — A133

Portrait: No. 407, Ahmed Shawky.

**1957, Oct. 14** ***Perf. 13½x13***
**406** A133 10m dull red brn .30 .25
**407** A133 10m olive green .30 .25
*a.* Pair, #406-407 1.00 *1.00*

25th anniv. of the deaths of Hafez Ibrahim and Ahmed Shawky, poets.

MiG and Ilyushin Planes A134

Design: No. 409, Viscount plane.

**1957, Dec. 19** ***Perf. 13x13½***
**408** A134 10m ultra .70 .50
**409** A134 10m green .70 .50
*a.* Pair, #408-409 1.60 1.60

25th anniv. of the Egyptian Air Force and of Misrair, the Egyptian airline.

Pyramids, Dove and Globe A135

**1957, Dec. 26** **Photo.** **Wmk. 315**
**410** A135 5m brown orange .60 .40
**411** A135 10m green .60 .30
**412** A135 15m brt violet .50 .40
*Nos. 410-412 (3)* 1.70 1.10

Afro-Asian Peoples Conf., Cairo, 12/26-1/2.

Farmer's Wife A136

Ramses II A137

**1957-58** **Wmk. 315** ***Perf. 13½***
**413** A136 1m blue green ('58) .30 .25
**414** A137 10m violet .30 .25

"Industry" — A138

**1958** **Wmk. 318**
**415** A136 1m lt blue green .30 .25
**416** A138 5m brown .35 .25
**417** A137 10m violet .60 .25
*Nos. 413-417 (5)* 1.85 1.25

See Nos. 438-444, 474-488, 535. For overprints see Nos. N58-N63, N66-N68, N75, N77-N78.

Cyclists — A139

*Perf. 13½x13*

**1958, Jan. 12** **Wmk. 315**

**418** A139 10m lt red brown .65 .45

5th Intl. Bicycle Race, Egypt, Jan. 12-26.

Mustafa Kamel — A140

**1958, Feb. 10** **Photo.** **Wmk. 318**

**419** A140 10m blue gray .80 .25

50th anniversary of the death of Mustafa Kamel, orator and politician.

**United Arab Republic**

Linked Maps of Egypt and Syria — A141

*Perf. 11½x11*

**1958, Mar. 22** **Wmk. 318**

**436** A141 10m yellow & green .75 .25

Birth of United Arab Republic. See No. C90. See also Syria-UAR Nos. 1 and C1.

Cotton — A142

**1958, Apr. 5** ***Perf. 13½x13***

**437** A142 10m Prussian blue .35 .25

Intl. Fair for Egyptian Cotton, Apr., 1958.

**Types of 1957-58 Inscribed "U.A.R. EGYPT" and**

Princess Nofret — A143

Designs: 1m, Farmer's wife. 2m, Ibn-Tulun's Mosque. 4m, 14th century glass lamp (design lacks "1963" of A217). 5m, "Industry" (factories and cogwheel). 10m, Ramses II. 35m, "Commerce" (eagle, ship and cargo).

**1958** ***Perf. 13½x14***

| | | | | | |
|---|---|---|---|---|---|
| **438** | A136 | 1m | crimson | .30 | .30 |
| **439** | A138 | 2m | blue | .25 | .25 |
| **440** | A143 | 3m | dk red brown | .25 | .25 |
| **441** | A217 | 4m | green | .30 | .25 |
| **442** | A138 | 5m | brown | .30 | .25 |
| **443** | A137 | 10m | violet | .85 | .30 |
| **444** | A138 | 35m | lt ultra | 3.75 | .45 |
| | | | *Nos. 438-444 (7)* | 6.00 | 2.05 |

See Nos. 474-488, 532-533, N62-N68, N75-N78.

Qasim Amin — A144

**1958, Apr. 23** ***Perf. 13½x13***

**445** A144 10m deep blue .60 .25

50th anniversary of the death of Qasim Amin, author of "Emancipation of Women."

Doves, Broken Chain and Globe — A145

**1958, June 18**

**446** A145 10m violet .60 .25

5th anniv. of the republic and to publicize the struggle of peoples and individuals for freedom.

For overprint see No. N69.

Cement Industry — A146

UAR Flag — A147

Industries: No. 448, Textile. No. 449, Iron & steel. No. 450, Petroleum (Oil). No. 451, Electricity and fertilizers.

*Perf. 13½x13*

**1958, July 23** **Photo.** **Wmk. 318**

| | | | | | |
|---|---|---|---|---|---|
| **447** | A146 | 10m | red brown | .40 | .25 |
| **448** | A146 | 10m | blue green | .40 | .25 |
| **449** | A146 | 10m | bright red | .40 | .25 |
| **450** | A146 | 10m | olive green | .40 | .25 |
| **451** | A146 | 10m | dark blue | .40 | .25 |
| *a.* | | | Strip of 5, #447-451 | 2.75 | 2.75 |

**Souvenir Sheet**

***Imperf***

**452** A147 50m grn, dp car & blk 16.00 14.00

Revolution of July 23, 1952, 6th anniv.

Sayed Darwich — A148

**1958, Sept. 15** ***Perf. 13½x13***

**453** A148 10m violet brown .50 .25

35th anniv. of the death of Sayed Darwich, Arab composer.

Hand Holding Torch, Broken Chain and Flag — A149

**1958, Oct. 14** **Photo.** **Wmk. 318**

**454** A149 10m carmine rose .40 .25

Establishment of the Republic of Iraq. See Syria-UAR No. 13.

Maps and Cogwheels — A150

**1958, Dec. 8** ***Perf. 13x13½***

**455** A150 10m blue .50 .25

Issued to publicize the Economic Conference of Afro-Asian Countries, Cairo, Dec. 8.

**Ovptd. in Red in English and Arabic in 3 Lines "Industrial and Agricultural Production Fair"**

**1958, Dec. 9**

**456** A150 10m lt red brown .50 .25

Issued to publicize the Industrial and Agricultural Production Fair, Cairo, Dec. 9.

Dr. Mahmoud Azmy and UN Emblem A151

**1958, Dec. 10**

| | | | | | |
|---|---|---|---|---|---|
| **457** | A151 | 10m | dull violet | .45 | .25 |
| **458** | A151 | 35m | green | 1.00 | .75 |

10th anniv. of the signing of the Universal Declaration of Human Rights.

For overprints see Nos. N70-N71.

University Building, Sphinx, "Education" and God Thoth — A152

**1958, Dec. 21** **Photo.** **Wmk. 318**

**459** A152 10m grnsh black .40 .25

50th anniversary of Cairo University.

No. 337 Surcharged

**1959, Jan. 20** **Wmk. 195** ***Perf. 13½***

**460** A112 55m on 100m henna brn 3.00 .75

For overprint see No. N72.

Emblem A153

**1959, Feb. 2** ***Perf. 13x13½***

**461** A153 10m lt olive green .35 .25

Afro-Asian Youth Conf., Cairo, Feb. 2.

See Syria UAR issues for stamps of designs A141, A149, A154, A156, A157, A162, A170, A172, A173, A179 with denominations in piasters (p).

Arms of UAR — A154

*Perf. 13½x13*

**1959, Feb. 22** **Photo.** **Wmk. 318**

**462** A154 10m green, blk & red .35 .25

First anniversary, United Arab Republic. See Syria UAR No. 17.

Nile Hilton Hotel A155

**1959, Feb. 22** ***Perf. 13x13½***

**463** A155 10m dark gray .35 .25

Opening of the Nile Hilton Hotel, Cairo.

Globe, Radio and Telegraph A156

**1959, Mar. 1**

**464** A156 10m violet .40 .25

Arab Union of Telecommunications. See Syria-UAR Nos. C20-C21.

**United Arab States Issue**

Flags of UAR and Yemen A157

**1959, Mar. 8**

**465** A157 10m sl grn, car & blk .35 .25

First anniversary of United Arab States. See Syria-UAR No. 16.

Oil Derrick and Pipe Line — A158

*Perf. 13½x13*

**1959, Apr. 16 Litho. Wmk. 318**

| | | | | |
|---|---|---|---|---|
| **466** | A158 | 10m lt bl & dk bl | .65 | .25 |

First Arab Petroleum Congress, Cairo.

Railroad A159

Designs: No. 468, Bus on highway. No. 469, River barge. No. 470, Ocean liner. No. 471, Telecommunications on map. No. 472, Stamp printing building, Heliopolis. No. 472A, Ship, train, plane and motorcycle mail carrier.

**1959, July 23 Photo. *Perf. 13x13½***

**Frame in Gray**

| | | | | |
|---|---|---|---|---|
| **467** | A159 10m maroon | | 1.10 | .50 |
| **468** | A159 10m green | | 1.10 | .50 |
| **469** | A159 10m violet | | 1.10 | .50 |
| **470** | A159 10m dark blue | | 1.10 | .50 |
| **471** | A159 10m dull purple | | 1.10 | .50 |
| **472** | A159 10m scarlet | | 1.10 | .50 |
| | *Nos. 467-472 (6)* | | 6.60 | 3.00 |

**Souvenir Sheet**

***Imperf***

| | | | |
|---|---|---|---|
| **472A** | A159 50m green & red | *12.00* | *12.00* |

No. 472A for the 7th anniv. of the Egyptian revolution of 1952 and was sold only with 5 sets of Nos. 467-472.

Globe, Swallows and Map — A160

**1959, Aug. 8 *Perf. 13½x13***

| | | | | |
|---|---|---|---|---|
| **473** | A160 | 10m maroon | .40 | .25 |

Convention of the Assoc. of Arab Emigrants in the US.

**Types of 1953-58 without "Egypt" and**

St. Simon's Gate, Bosra, Syria — A161

Designs: 1m, Farmer's wife. 2m, Ibn-Tulun's Mosque. 3m, Princess Nofret. 4m, 14th century glass lamp (design lacks "1963" of A217). 5m, "Industry" (factories and cogwheel). 10m, Ramses II. 15m, Omayyad Mosque, Damascus. 20m, Lotus vase, Tutankhamun treasure. 35m, Eagle, ship and cargo. 40m, Scribe statue. 45m, Saladin's citadel, Aleppo. 55m, Eagle, cotton and wheat. 60m, Dam and factory. 100m, Eagle, hand, cotton and grain. 200m, Palmyra ruins, Syria. 500m, Queen Nefertiti, inscribed "UAR" (no ovpt.).

*Perf. 13½x14, 14x13½*

**1959-60 Wmk. 328 Photo.**

| | | | | |
|---|---|---|---|---|
| **474** | A136 | 1m vermilion | .25 | .25 |
| **475** | A138 | 2m dp blue ('60) | .25 | .25 |
| **476** | A143 | 3m maroon | .25 | .25 |
| **477** | A217 | 4m green ('60) | .25 | .25 |
| **478** | A138 | 5m black ('60) | .25 | .25 |
| **479** | A137 | 10m dk ol grn | .30 | .25 |
| **480** | A138 | 15m deep claret | .30 | .25 |
| **481** | A138 | 20m crimson ('60) | .90 | .25 |
| **482** | A161 | 30m brown vio | .65 | .25 |
| **483** | A138 | 35m lt vio bl ('60) | .75 | .25 |
| **484** | A143 | 40m sepia | 1.10 | .25 |
| **485** | A161 | 45m lil gray ('60) | 2.25 | .35 |
| **486** | A138 | 55m brt blue grn | 2.00 | .25 |
| **487** | A138 | 60m dp purple ('60) | 2.75 | .25 |
| **488** | A138 | 100m org & sl grn ('60) | 2.25 | .30 |
| **489** | A161 | 200m lt blue & mar | 4.50 | .50 |
| **490** | A112 | 500m dk gray & red ('60) | 14.00 | 1.60 |
| | | *Nos. 474-490 (17)* | 33.00 | 6.00 |

See Nos. 532-535.

Shield and Cogwheel — A162

*Perf. 13½x13*

**1959, Oct. 20 Photo. Wmk. 328**

| | | | | |
|---|---|---|---|---|
| **491** | A162 | 10m brt car rose | .35 | .25 |

Issued for Army Day, 1959.
See Syria-UAR No. 32.

Cairo Museum A163

**1959, Nov. 18 *Perf. 13x13½***

| | | | | |
|---|---|---|---|---|
| **492** | A163 | 10m olive gray | .40 | .25 |

Centenary of Cairo museum.

Abu Simbel Temple of Ramses II — A164

**1959, Dec. 22 *Perf. 11x11½***

| | | | | |
|---|---|---|---|---|
| **493** | A164 | 10m lt red brn, *pnksh* | .70 | .30 |

Issued as propaganda to save historic monuments in Nubia threatened by the construction of Aswan High Dam.

Postrider, 12th Century A165

**1960, Jan. 2 *Perf. 13x13½***

| | | | | |
|---|---|---|---|---|
| **494** | A165 | 10m dark blue | .35 | .25 |

Issued for Post Day, Jan. 2.

Hydroelectric Power Station, Aswan Dam — A166

**1960, Jan. 9**

| | | | | |
|---|---|---|---|---|
| **495** | A166 | 10m violet blk | .35 | .25 |

Inauguration of the Aswan Dam hydroelectric power station, Jan. 9.

A167

10m, Arabic and English Description of Aswan High Dam. 35m, Architect's Drawing of Aswan High Dam.

**1960, Jan. 9 *Perf. 11x11½***

| | | | |
|---|---|---|---|
| **496** | 10m claret | .75 | .60 |
| **497** | 35m claret | 1.10 | .75 |
| *a.* | A167 Pair, #496-497 | 2.00 | 2.00 |

Start of work on the Aswan High Dam.

Symbols of Agriculture and Industry — A169

**1960, Jan. 16 *Perf. 13½x13***

| | | | | |
|---|---|---|---|---|
| **498** | A169 | 10m gray grn & sl grn | .35 | .25 |

Industrial and Agricultural Fair, Cairo.

Arms and Flag — A170

**1960, Feb. 22 Photo. Wmk. 328**

| | | | | |
|---|---|---|---|---|
| **499** | A170 | 10m green, blk & red | .35 | .25 |

2nd anniversary of the proclamation of the United Arab Republic.
See Syria-UAR No. 38.

No. 340 Overprinted in Red

**1960 Wmk. 195 *Perf. 13½***

| | | | | |
|---|---|---|---|---|
| **500** | A112 | £1 dk grn, blk & red | 19.00 | 4.25 |

"Art" — A171

*Perf. 13½x13*

**1960, Mar. 1 Wmk. 328**

| | | | | |
|---|---|---|---|---|
| **501** | A171 | 10m brown | .35 | .25 |

Issued to publicize the 3rd Biennial Exhibition of Fine Arts in Alexandria.

Arab League Center, Cairo A172

**1960, Mar. 22 Photo. *Perf. 13x13½***

| | | | | |
|---|---|---|---|---|
| **502** | A172 | 10m dull grn & blk | .35 | .25 |

Opening of Arab League Center and Arab Postal Museum, Cairo.
See Syria-UAR No. 40.

Refugees Pointing to Map of Palestine A173

**1960, Apr. 7**

| | | | | |
|---|---|---|---|---|
| **503** | A173 | 10m orange ver | .55 | .30 |
| **504** | A173 | 35m Prus blue | .80 | .65 |

World Refugee Year, 7/1/59-6/30/60.
See Nos. N73-N74. See also Syria-UAR Nos. 43-44.

Weight Lifter — A174

Stadium, Cairo — A175

Sports: No. 506, Basketball. No. 507, Soccer. No. 508, Fencing. No. 509, Rowing. 30m, Steeplechase, horiz. 35m, Swimming, horiz.

*Perf. 13½x13*

**1960, July 23 Photo. Wmk. 328**

| | | | | |
|---|---|---|---|---|
| **505** | A174 | 5m gray | .60 | .30 |
| **506** | A174 | 5m brown | .60 | .30 |
| **507** | A174 | 5m dp claret | .60 | .30 |
| **508** | A174 | 10m brt carmine | .60 | .30 |
| **509** | A174 | 10m gray green | .60 | .30 |
| *a.* | | Vert. or horiz. strip, #505-509 | 3.75 | |
| **510** | A174 | 30m purple | .85 | .50 |
| **511** | A174 | 35m dark blue | 1.10 | .60 |
| | | *Nos. 505-511 (7)* | 4.95 | 2.60 |

**Souvenir Sheet**

***Imperf***

| | | | | |
|---|---|---|---|---|
| **512** | A175 | 100m car & brown | 3.25 | 3.25 |

Nos. 505-511 for the 17th Olympic Games, Rome, Aug. 25-Sept. 11.

Dove and UN Emblem — A176

35m, Lights surrounding UN emblem, horiz.

***Perf. 13½x13***

**1960, Oct. 24** **Wmk. 328**

**513** A176 10m purple .25 .25
**514** A176 35m brt rose .50 .30

15th anniversary of United Nations.

Abu Simbel Temple of Queen Nefertari — A177

***Perf. 11x11½***

**1960, Nov. 14** **Photo.** **Wmk. 328**

**515** A177 10m ocher, *buff* .80 .50

Issued as propaganda to save historic monuments in Nubia and in connection with the UNESCO meeting, Paris, Nov. 14.

Model Post Office A178

**1961, Jan. 2** ***Perf. 13x13½***

**516** A178 10m brt car rose .40 .25

Issued for Post Day, Jan. 2.

Eagle, Fasces and Victory Wreath — A179

**1961, Feb. 22** ***Perf. 13½x13***

**517** A179 10m dull violet .35 .25

3rd anniversary of United Arab Republic. See Syria-UAR No. 50.

Wheat and Globe Surrounded by Flags — A180

**1961, Mar. 21** **Wmk. 328**

**518** A180 10m vermilion .35 .25

Intl. Agricultural Exhib., Cairo, 3/21-4/20.

Patrice Lumumba and Map — A181

**1961, Mar. 30** ***Perf. 13½x13***

**519** A181 10m black .35 .25

Africa Day, Apr. 15 and 3rd Conf. of Independent African States, Cairo, Mar. 25-31.

Reading Braille and WHO Emblem — A182

**1961, Apr. 6** **Photo.**

**520** A182 10m red brown .35 .25

WHO Day. See Nos. B21, N80.

Tower of Cairo — A183

**1961, Apr. 11** ***Perf. 13½x13***

**521** A183 10m grnsh blue .35 .25

Opening of the 600-foot Tower of Cairo, on island of Gizireh. See No. C95.

Arab Woman and Son, Palestine Map — A184

**1961, May 15** **Wmk. 328**

**522** A184 10m brt green .45 .30

Issued for Palestine Day. See No. N79.

Symbols of Industry and Electricity A185

Chart and Workers — A186

No. 524, New buildings and family. No. 525, Ship, train, bus and radio. No. 526, Dam, cotton and field. No. 527, Hand holding candle and family.

**1961, July 23** **Photo.** ***Perf. 13x13½***

**523** A185 10m dp carmine .65 .30
**524** A185 10m brt blue .65 .30
**525** A185 10m dk vio brown .65 .30
**526** A185 35m dk green .85 .40
**527** A185 35m brt purple .85 .40
*Nos. 523-527 (5)* 3.65 1.70

**Souvenir Sheet**

***Imperf***

**528** A186 100m red brown 4.00 3.75

9th anniv. of the revolution.

Map of Suez Canal and Ships — A187

***Perf. 11½x11***

**1961, July 26** **Unwmk.**

**529** A187 10m olive .50 .30

Suez Canal Co. nationalization, 5th anniv.

Various Enterprises of Misr Bank — A188

***Perf. 13x13½***

**1961, Aug. 22** **Wmk. 328**

**530** A188 10m red brn, *pnksh* .35 .25

The 41st anniversary of Misr Bank.

Flag, Ship's Wheel and Battleship — A189

**1961, Aug. 29** **Photo.** ***Perf. 13½x13***

**531** A189 10m deep blue .45 .25

Issued for Navy Day.

**Type A136 Redrawn, Type A138, Type A217 and**

Eagle of Saladin over Cairo — A190

Designs: 1m, Farmer's wife. 4m, 14th cent. glass lamp. 35m, "Commerce."

**1961, Aug. 31** **Unwmk.** ***Perf. 11½***

**532** A136 1m blue .25 .25
**533** A217 4m olive .25 .25
**534** A190 10m purple .40 .25
**535** A138 35m slate blue .70 .25
*Nos. 532-535 (4)* 1.60 1.00

Smaller of two Arabic inscriptions in new positions: 1m, at right above Egyptian numeral; 4m, upward to spot beside waist of lamp; 35m, upper left corner below "UAR." On 4m, "UAR" is 2mm deep instead of 1mm. "Egypt" omitted as in 1959-60.

UN Emblem, Book, Cogwheel, Corn — A191

Design: 35m, Globe and cogwheel, horiz.

***Perf. 13½x13***

**1961, Oct. 24** **Photo.** **Wmk. 328**

**536** A191 10m black & ocher .30 .25
**537** A191 35m blue grn & brn .65 .35

UN Technical Assistance Program and 16th anniv. of the UN.
See Nos. N81-N82.

Trajan's Kiosk, Philae — A192

**1961, Nov. 4** **Unwmk.** ***Perf. 11½***

**Size: 60x27mm**

**538** A192 10m dp vio blue .85 .40

15th anniv. of UNESCO, and to publicize UNESCO's help in safeguarding the monuments of Nubia.

Palette, Brushes, Map of Mediterranean A193

**1961, Dec. 14** **Wmk. 328** ***Perf. 13½***

**539** A193 10m dk red brown .35 .25

Issued to publicize the 4th Biennial Exhibition of Fine Arts in Alexandria.

Atom and Educational Symbols — A194

**1961, Dec. 18**

**540** A194 10m dull purple .35 .25

Issued to publicize Education Day.
See No. N83.

Arms of UAR A195

**1961, Dec. 23** **Unwmk.** ***Perf. 11½***

**541** A195 10m brt pink, brt grn & blk .35 .25

Victory Day. See No. N84.

Sphinx at Giza — A196

**1961, Dec. 27** *Perf. 11x11½*
542 A196 10m black .55 .35

Issued to publicize the "Sound and Light" Project, the installation of floodlights and sound equipment at the site of the Pyramids and Sphinx.

Post Office Printing Plant, Nasser City A197

**1962, Jan. 2** **Photo.** *Perf. 11½x11*
543 A197 10m dk brown .40 .25

Issued for Post Day, Jan. 2.

Map of Africa, King Mohammed V of Morocco and Flags — A198

**1962, Jan. 4** *Perf. 11x11½*
544 A198 10m indigo .35 .25

African Charter, Casablanca, 1st anniv.

Girl Scout Saluting and Emblem A199

*Perf. 13x13½*

**1962, Feb. 22** **Wmk. 328**
545 A199 10m bright blue .95 .30

Egyptian Girl Scouts' 25th anniversary.

Arab Refugees, Flag and Map — A200

**1962, Mar. 7** *Perf. 13½x13*
546 A200 10m dark slate green .40 .25

5th anniv. of the liberation of the Gaza Strip. See No. N85.

Mother and Child — A201

**1962, Mar. 21** **Photo.**
547 A201 10m dk violet brn .40 .25

Issued for Arab Mother's Day, Mar. 21.

Map of Africa and Post Horn — A202

**1962, Apr. 23** **Wmk. 328**
548 A202 10m crimson & ocher .40 .30
549 A202 50m dp blue & ocher .80 .55

Establishment of African Postal Union.

Cadets on Parade and Academy Emblem A203

**1962, June 18** *Perf. 13x13½*
550 A203 10m green .35 .25

Egyptian Military Academy, 150th anniv.

Malaria Eradication Emblem — A204

**1962, June 20** *Perf. 13½x13*
551 A204 10m dk brown & red .25 .25
552 A204 35m dk green & blue .70 .50

WHO drive to eradicate malaria. See Nos. N87-N88.

Theodor Bilharz — A205

**1962, June 24** *Perf. 11x11½*
553 A205 10m brown orange .55 .25

Dr. Theodor Bilharz (1825-1862), German physician who first described bilharziasis, an endemic disease in Egypt.

Patrice Lumumba and Map of Africa — A206

**1962, July 1** **Photo.** **Wmk. 342**
554 A206 10m rose & red .35 .25

Issued in memory of Patrice Lumumba (1925-61), Premier of Congo.

Hand on Charter — A207

**1962, July 10** *Perf. 11x11½*
555 A207 10m brt blue & dk brn .35 .25

Proclamation of the National Charter.

"Birth of the Revolution" A208

Symbolic Designs: No. 557, Proclamation (Scroll and book). No. 558, Agricultural Reform (Farm and crescent). No. 559, Bandung Conference (Dove, globe and olive branch). No. 560, Birth of UAR (Eagle and flag). No. 561, Industrialization (cogwheel, factory, ship and bus). No. 562, Aswan High Dam. No. 563, Social Revolution (Modern buildings and emblem). 100m, Arms of UAR, emblems of Afro-Asian and African countries and UN.

**1962, July 23** *Perf. 11½*
556 A208 10m brn, dk red brn & pink .40 .30
557 A208 10m dk blue & sepia .40 .30
558 A208 10m sepia & brt bl .40 .30
559 A208 10m olive & dk ultra .40 .30
560 A208 10m grn, blk & red .40 .30
561 A208 10m brn org & indigo .40 .30
562 A208 10m brn org & vio blk .40 .30
563 A208 10m orange & blk .40 .30
*Nos. 556-563 (8)* 3.20 2.40

**Souvenir Sheets**

*Perf. 11½*

564 A208 100m grn, pink, red & blk 2.75 2.50

10th anniv. of the revolution. No. 564 exists imperf. Same value.

Mahmoud Moukhtar, Museum and Sculpture A209

**1962, July 24** *Perf. 11½x11*
565 A209 10m lt vio bl & olive .40 .25

Opening of the Moukhtar Museum, Island of Gezireh. The sculpture is "La Vestale de Secrets" by Moukhtar.

Flag of Algeria and Map of Africa Showing Algeria — A210

**1962, Aug. 15** *Perf. 11x11½*
566 A210 10m multicolored .35 .25

Algeria's independence, July 1, 1962.

Rocket, Arms of UAR and Atom Symbol — A211

**1962, Sept. 1** **Photo.** **Wmk. 342**
567 A211 10m brt grn, red & blk .45 .25

Launching of UAR rockets.

Rifle and Target — A212

Map of Africa, Table Tennis Paddle, Net and Ball — A213

**1962, Sept. 18** *Perf. 11½*
568 A212 5m green, blk & red .55 .45
569 A213 5m green, blk & red .55 .45
a. Pair, #568-569 1.25 1.25
570 A212 10m bister, bl & dk grn .65 .55
571 A213 10m bister, bl & dk grn .65 .55
a. Pair, #570-571 1.50 1.50
572 A212 35m dp ultra, red & blk 1.50 1.50
573 A213 35m dp ultra, red & blk 1.50 1.50
a. Pair, #572-573 3.25 3.25
*Nos. 568-573 (6)* 5.40 5.00

38th World Shooting Championships and the 1st African Table Tennis Tournament. Types A212 and A213 are printed se-tenant at the base.

Dag Hammarskjold and UN Emblem — A214

*Perf. 11½x11*

**1962, Oct. 24** **Photo.** **Wmk. 342**

**Portrait in Slate Blue**

574 A214 5m deep lilac .65 .25
575 A214 10m olive .75 .25
576 A214 35m deep ultra 1.10 .50
*Nos. 574-576 (3)* 2.50 1.00

Dag Hammarskjold, Secretary General of the UN, 1953-61, and 17th anniv. of the UN. See Nos. N89-N91.

Queen Nefertari Crowned by Isis and Hathor — A215

**1962, Oct. 31** ***Perf. 11½***

**577** A215 10m blue & ocher 1.25 .40

Issued to publicize the UNESCO campaign to safeguard the monuments of Nubia.

Jet Trainer, Hawker Hart Biplane and College Emblem
A216

**1962, Nov. 2** ***Perf. 11½x11***

**578** A216 10m bl, dk bl & crim .40 .25

25th anniversary of Air Force College.

14th Century Glass Lamp and "1963" — A217

**1963, Feb. 20** ***Perf. 11x11½***

**579** A217 4m dk brn, grn & car .35 .25

Issued for use on greeting cards.
See Nos. 441, 477, 533, N76, N92. For overprint see No. N65.

Yemen Flag and Hand with Torch — A218

**1963, Mar. 14 Photo. Wmk. 342**

**580** A218 10m olive & brt car .45 .25

Establishment of Yemen Arab Republic.

Tennis Player, Pyramids and Globe A219

***Perf. 11½x11***

**1963, Mar. 20 Unwmk.**

**581** A219 10m gray, blk & brn .75 .30

Intl. Lawn Tennis Championships, Cairo.

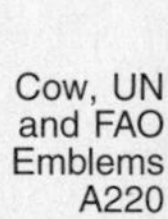

Cow, UN and FAO Emblems A220

Designs: 10m, Corn, wheat and emblems, vert. 35m, Wheat, corn and emblems.

***Perf. 11½x11, 11x11½***

**1963, Mar. 21 Wmk. 342**

**582** A220 5m violet & dp org .45 .30
**583** A220 10m ultra & yel .55 .30
**584** A220 35m blue, yel & blk .75 .75
*Nos. 582-584 (3)* 1.75 1.35

FAO "Freedom from Hunger" campaign.
See Nos. N93-N95.

Centenary Emblem — A221

Design: 35m, Globe and emblem.

**1963, May 8 Unwmk.** ***Perf. 11x11½***

**585** A221 10m lt blue, red & mar .30 .25
**586** A221 35m lt blue & red .85 .85

Centenary of the Red Cross.
See Nos. N96-N97.

Arab Socialist Union Emblem A222

50m, Tools, torch & symbol of National Charter.

**Wmk. 342**

**1963, July 23 Photo.** ***Perf. 11½***

**587** A222 10m slate & rose pink .35 .25

**Souvenir Sheets**

***Perf. 11½***

**588** A222 50m vio bl & org yel 2.25 2.25

11th anniv. of the revolution and to publicize the Arab Socialist Union.
No. 588 exists imperf. Same value.

Television Station, Cairo, and Screen A223

**1963, Aug. 1** ***Perf. 11½x11***

**589** A223 10m dk blue & yel .35 .25

2nd Intl. Television Festival, Alexandria, 9/1-10.

Queen Nefertari — A224

Designs: 10m, Great Hypostyle Hall, Abu Simbel. 35m, Ramses in moonlight.

**Size: 25x42mm (5m, 35m); 28x61mm (10m)**

**Wmk. 342**

**1963, Oct. 1 Photo.** ***Perf. 11***

**590** A224 5m brt vio blue & yel .65 .40
**591** A224 10m gray, blk & red org .75 .45
**592** A224 35m org yel & blk 1.60 .85
*Nos. 590-592 (3)* 3.00 1.70

UNESCO world campaign to save historic monuments in Nubia.
See Nos. N98-N100.

Swimmer and Map of Suez Canal — A225

**1963, Oct. 15**

**593** A225 10m blue & sal rose .35 .25

Intl. Suez Canal Swimming Championship.

Ministry of Agriculture — A226

***Perf. 11½x11***

**1963, Nov. 20 Wmk. 342**

**594** A226 10m multicolored .35 .25

50th anniv. of the Ministry of Agriculture.

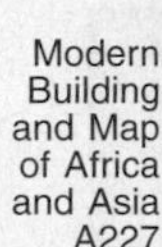

Modern Building and Map of Africa and Asia A227

**1963, Dec. 7**

**595** A227 10m multicolored .35 .25

Afro-Asian Housing Congress, Dec. 7-12.

Scales, Globe, UN Emblem A228

**1963, Dec. 10**

**596** A228 5m dk green & yel .30 .25
**597** A228 10m blue, gray & blk .35 .25
**598** A228 35m rose red, pink & red .85 .45
*Nos. 596-598 (3)* 1.50 .95

15th anniv. of the Universal Declaration of Human Rights.
See Nos. N101-N103.

Sculpture, Arms of Alexandria and Palette with Flags — A229

**1963, Dec. 12** ***Perf. 11x11½***

**599** A229 10m pale bl, dk bl & brn .35 .25

Issued to publicize the 5th Biennial Exhibition of Fine Arts in Alexandria.

Lion and Nile Hilton Hotel — A230

Vase, 13th Century — A231

Pharaoh Userkaf (5th Dynasty) A232

Designs: 1m, Vase, 14th century. 2m, Ivory headrest. 3m, Pharaonic calcite boat. 4m, Minaret and gate. 5m, Nile and Aswan High Dam. 10m, Eagle of Saladin over pyramids. 15m, Window, Ibn Tulun's mosque. No. 608, Mitwalli Gate, Cairo. 35m, Nefertari. 40m, Tower Hotel. 55m, Sultan Hassan's Mosque. 60m, Court-yard, Al Azhar University. 200m, Head of Ramses II. 500m, Funerary mask of Tutankhamun.

**1964-67 Unwmk. Photo.** ***Perf. 11***

**Size: Nos. 608, 612, 19x24mm; others, 24x29mm**

| No. | Type | Denomination / Color | Unused | Used |
|---|---|---|---|---|
| **600** | A231 | 1m citron & ultra | .25 | .25 |
| **601** | A230 | 2m magenta & bis | .25 | .25 |
| **602** | A230 | 3m sal, org & bl | .25 | .25 |
| **603** | A235 | 4m och, blk & ultra | .35 | .25 |
| **604** | A230 | 5m brn & brt blue | .25 | .25 |
| *a.* | | 5m brown & dark blue | .50 | .25 |
| **605** | A231 | 10m green, dk brn & lt brn | .30 | .25 |
| **606** | A230 | 15m ultra & yel | .30 | .25 |
| **607** | A230 | 20m brn org & blk | .90 | .25 |
| **608** | A231 | 20m lt olive grn ('67) | 1.60 | .25 |
| **609** | A231 | 30m yellow & brown | .75 | .25 |
| **610** | A231 | 35m sal, och & ultra | .90 | .25 |
| **611** | A231 | 40m ultra & yellow | 1.75 | .40 |
| **612** | A231 | 55m brt red lil ('67) | 2.00 | .25 |
| **613** | A231 | 60m grnsh bl & yel brn | 1.25 | .55 |
| | | **Wmk. 342** | | |
| **614** | A232 | 100m dk vio brn & sl | 3.50 | .85 |
| **615** | A232 | 200m bluish blk & yel brn | 8.00 | 1.00 |
| **616** | A232 | 500m ultra & dp org | 17.50 | 3.25 |
| | | *Nos. 600-616 (17)* | 40.10 | 9.05 |

Nos. 603 & N107 lack the vertically arranged dates which appear at lower right on No. 619.
See Nos. N104-N116.

HSN Commission Emblem — A233

***Perf. 11x11½***

**1964, Jan. 10 Wmk. 342**

**617** A233 10m dull bl, dk bl & yel .35 .25

1st conf. of the Commission of Health, Sanitation and Nutrition.

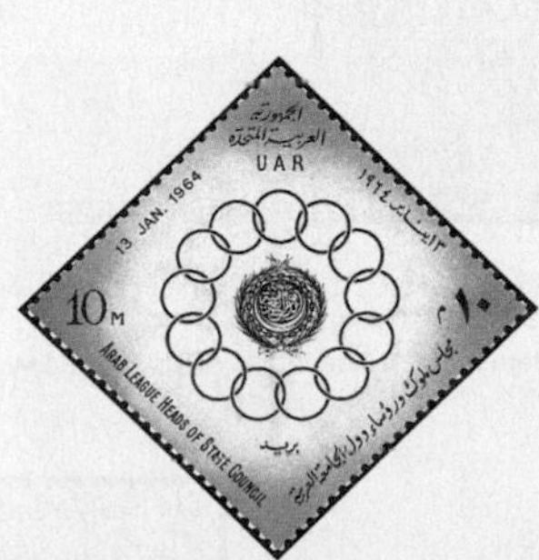


Arab League Emblem — A234

**1964, Jan. 13** ***Perf. 11***

**618** A234 10m brt green & blk .35 .25

1st meeting of the Heads of State of the Arab League, Cairo, January.
See No. N117.

Minaret at Night — A235

**1964 Unwmk. *Perf. 11***

**619** A235 4m emerald, blk & red .35 .25

Issued for use on greeting cards.
See Nos. 603, N107, N118.

Old and New Dwellings and Map of Nubia A236

***Perf. 11½x11***

**1964, Feb. 27 Photo. Wmk. 342**

**620** A236 10m dull vio & yel .35 .25

Resettlement of Nubian population.

Map of Africa and Asia and Train A237

**1964, Mar. 21**

**621** A237 10m dull bl, dk bl & yel .90 .50

Asian Railway Conference, Cairo, Mar. 21.

Ikhnaton and Nefertiti with Children — A238

**1964, Mar. 21 *Perf. 11x11½***

**622** A238 10m dk brown & ultra .90 .30

Issued for Arab Mother's Day, Mar. 21.

APU Emblem — A239

**1964, Apr. 1 Photo. Wmk. 342**

**623** A239 10m org brn & bl, *sal* .35 .25

Permanent Office of the APU, 10th anniv.
See No. N119.

WHO Emblem — A240

**1964, Apr. 7**

**624** A240 10m dk blue & red .35 .25

World Health Day (Anti-Tuberculosis).
See No. N120.

Statue of Liberty, World's Fair Pavilion and Pyramids A241

**1964, Apr. 22 *Perf. 11½x11***

**625** A241 10m brt green & ol, *grysh* .35 .25

New York World's Fair, 1964-65.

Nile and Aswan High Dam A242

**1964, May 15 Unwmk. *Perf. 11½***

**626** A242 10m black & blue .35 .25

The diversion of the Nile.

"Land Reclamation" — A243

Design: No. 628, "Electricity," Aswan High Dam hydroelectric station.

**1964, July 23 *Perf. 11½***

**627** A243 10m yellow & emer .35 .25
**628** A243 10m green & blk .35 .25

Land reclamation and hydroelectric power due to the Aswan High Dam.

An imperf. souvenir sheet, issued July 23, contains two 50m black and blue stamps showing Aswan High Dam before and after diversion of the Nile. Value $2.

Map of Africa and 34 Flags — A244

**1964, July 17 Photo.**

**629** A244 10m brn, brt bl & blk .40 .25

Assembly of Heads of State and Government of the Organization for African Unity at Cairo in July.

Jamboree Emblem — A245

Design: No. 631, Emblem of Air Scouts.

**1964, Aug. 28 Unwmk. *Perf. 11½***

**630** A245 10m red, grn & blk .60 .40
**631** A245 10m green & red .60 .40
*a.* Pair, #630-631 2.50 2.50

The 6th Pan Arab Jamboree, Alexandria.

Flag of Algeria A246

**1964, Sept. 5 *Perf. 11½x11***

**Flags in Original Colors**

**632** A246 10m Algeria .75 .40
**633** A246 10m Iraq .75 .40
**634** A246 10m Jordan .75 .40
**635** A246 10m Kuwait .75 .40
**636** A246 10m Lebanon .75 .40
**637** A246 10m Libya .75 .40
**638** A246 10m Morocco .75 .40
**639** A246 10m Saudi Arabia .75 .40
**640** A246 10m Sudan .75 .40
**641** A246 10m Syria .75 .40
**642** A246 10m Tunisia .75 .40
**643** A246 10m UAR .75 .40
**644** A246 10m Yemen .75 .40
*Nos. 632-644 (13)* 9.75 5.20

2nd meeting of the Heads of State of the Arab League, Alexandria, Sept. 1964.

World Map, Dove, Olive Branches and Pyramids — A247

**1964, Oct. 5 *Perf. 11½***

**645** A247 10m slate blue & yel .35 .25

Conference of Heads of State of Non-Aligned Countries, Cairo, Oct. 1964.

Pharaonic Athletes A248

Designs from ancient decorations: 10m, Four athletes, vert. 35m, Wrestlers, vert. 50m, Pharaoh in chariot hunting.

***Perf. 11½x11, 11x11½***

**1964, Oct. 10 Photo. Unwmk.**

**Sizes: 39x22mm, 22x39mm**

**646** A248 5m lt green & org .40 .25
**647** A248 10m slate bl & lt brn .45 .25
**648** A248 35m dull vio & lt brn 1.10 .75

**Size: 58x24mm**

**649** A248 50m ultra & brn org 1.75 1.00
*Nos. 646-649 (4)* 3.70 2.25

18th Olympic Games Tokyo, Oct. 10-25.

Emblem, Map of Africa and Asia — A249

**1964, Oct. 10 *Perf. 11x11½***

**650** A249 10m violet & yellow .35 .25

First Afro-Asian Medical Congress.

Map of Africa, Communication Symbols — A250

**1964, Oct. 24**

**651** A250 10m green & blk .35 .25

Pan-African and Malagasy Posts and Telecommunications Cong., Cairo, Oct. 24-Nov. 6.

Horus and Facade of Nefertari Temple, Abu Simbel A251

Ramses II — A252

Designs: 35m, A god holding rope of life, Abu Simbel. 50m, Isis of Kalabsha, horiz.

**1964, Oct. 24 *Perf. 11½, 11x11½***

**652** A251 5m grnsh bl & yel brn .70 .35
**653** A252 10m sepia & brt yel 1.10 .40
**654** A251 35m brown org & indigo 2.50 1.25
*Nos. 652-654 (3)* 4.30 2.00

**Souvenir Sheet**

***Imperf***

**655** A252 50m olive & vio blk 15.00 15.00

"Save the Monuments of Nubia" campaign. No. 655 contains one horiz. stamp.

Emblems of Cooperation, Rural Handicraft and Women's Work — A253

***Perf. 11½x11***

**1964, Dec. 8 Photo. Unwmk.**

**656** A253 10m yellow & dk blue .35 .25

25th anniv. of the Ministry of Social Affairs.

UN, UNESCO Emblems, Pyramids — A254

**1964, Dec. 24 *Perf. 11x11½***

**657** A254 10m ultra & yellow .35 .25

Issued for UNESCO Day.

Minaret, Mardani Mosque — A255

**1965, Jan. 20** **Photo.** ***Perf. 11***

**658** A255 4m blue & dk brown .35 .25

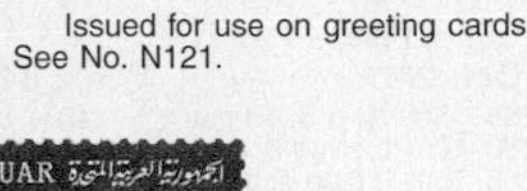

Issued for use on greeting cards. See No. N121.

Police Emblem over City — A256

***Perf. 11x11½***

**1965, Jan. 25** **Wmk. 342**

**659** A256 10m black & yellow .85 .40

Issued for Police Day.

Oil Derrick and Emblem — A257

**1965, Mar. 16** **Photo.**

**660** A257 10m dk brown & yellow .45 .25

5th Arab Petroleum Congress and the 2nd Arab Petroleum Exhibition.

Flags and Emblem of the Arab League — A258

Design: 20m, Arab League emblem, horiz.

**1965, Mar. 22** **Wmk. 342**

**661** A258 10m green, red & blk .80 .40
**662** A258 20m ultra & brown 1.00 .55

20th anniversary of the Arab League. See Nos. N122-N123.

Red Crescent and WHO Emblem — A259

**1965, Apr. 7** **Photo.**

**663** A259 10m blue & crimson .55 .35

World Health Day (Smallpox: Constant Alert). See No. N124.

Dagger in Map of Palestine — A260

**1965, Apr. 9** ***Perf. 11x11½***

**664** A260 10m black & red 1.50 .35

Deir Yassin massacre, Apr. 9, 1948. See No. N125.

ITU Emblem, Old and New Communication Equipment — A261

**1965, May 17** ***Perf. 11½x11***

**665** A261 5m violet blk & yel .40 .30
**666** A261 10m red & yellow .65 .30
**667** A261 35m dk blue, ultra & yel 1.75 .80
*Nos. 665-667 (3)* 2.80 1.40

Cent. of the ITU. See Nos. N126-N128.

Library Aflame and Lamp A262

**1965, June 7** **Photo.** **Wmk. 342**

**668** A262 10m black, grn & red .60 .25

Burning of the Library of Algiers, 6/7/62.

Sheik Mohammed Abdo (1850-1905), Mufti of Egypt — A263

**1965, July 11** ***Perf. 11x11½***

**669** A263 10m Prus blue & bis brn .35 .25

Pouring Ladle (Heavy Industry) A264

President Gamal Abdel Nasser and Emblems of Arab League, African Unity Organization, Afro-Asian Countries and UN — A265

No. 670, Search for off-shore oil. No. 672, Housing, construction in Nasser City (diamond shaped).

**1965, July 23** ***Perf. 11½***

**670** A264 10m indigo & lt blue .85 .50
**671** A264 10m brown & yellow .85 .50
**672** A264 10m yel brn & blk .85 .50
**673** A265 100m lt green & blk 5.75 3.25
*Nos. 670-673 (4)* 8.30 4.75

13th anniversary of the revolution.

The 100m was printed in sheets of six, consisting of two singles and two vertical pairs. Margins and gutters contain multiple UAR coat of arms in light green. Size: 240x330mm.

4th Pan Arab Games Emblem A266

Map and Emblems of Previous Games — A267

No. 675, Swimmers Zeitun & Abd el Gelil, arms of Alexandria. 35m, Race horse "Saadoon."

***Perf. 11½x11; 11½ (#676)***

**1965, Sept. 2** **Photo.** **Wmk. 342**

**674** A266 5m blue & red .40 .40
**675** A266 10m dp blue & dk brn .65 .30
**676** A267 10m org brn & dp bl .80 .45
**677** A266 35m green & brown 1.40 1.00
*Nos. 674-677 (4)* 3.25 2.15

4th Pan Arab Games, Cairo, Sept. 2-11. No. 675 for the long-distance swimming competition at Alexandria, a part of the Games.

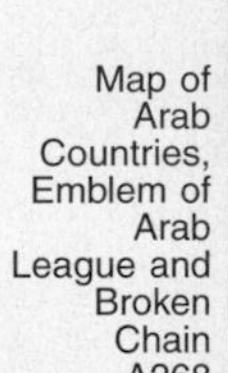

Map of Arab Countries, Emblem of Arab League and Broken Chain A268

**1965, Sept. 13** **Photo.** ***Perf. 11½***

**678** A268 10m brown & yellow .40 .25

3rd Arab Summit Conf., Casablanca, 9/13.

Land Forces Emblem and Sun — A269

***Perf. 11x11½***

**1965, Oct. 20** **Wmk. 342**

**679** A269 10m bister brn & blk .65 .30

Issued for Land Forces Day.

Map of Africa, Torch and Olive Branches — A270

**1965, Oct. 21** ***Perf. 11½***

**680** A270 10m dull pur & car rose .40 .25

Assembly of Heads of State of the Organization for African Unity.

Ramses II, Abu Simbel, and ICY Emblem A271

Pillars, Philae, and UN Emblem — A272

Designs: 35m, Two Ramses II statues, Abu Simbel and UNESCO emblem. 50m, Cartouche of Ramses II and ICY emblem, horiz.

**Wmk. 342**

**1965, Oct. 24** **Photo.** ***Perf. 11½***

**681** A271 5m yellow & slate grn 1.00 .50
**682** A272 10m blue & black 2.00 .50
**683** A271 35m dk violet & yel 3.75 2.00
*Nos. 681-683 (3)* 6.75 3.00

**Souvenir Sheet**

***Imperf***

**684** A272 50m brt ultra & dk brn 5.00 4.00

Intl. cooperation in saving the Nubian monuments. No. 684 also for the 20th anniv. of the UN. No. 684 contains one 42x25mm stamp.

Al-Maqrizi, Buildings and Books
A273

*Perf. 11½x11*

**1965, Nov. 20 Photo. Wmk. 342**

**685** A273 10m olive & dk slate grn .40 .25

Ahmed Al-Maqrizi (1365-1442), historian.

Flag of UAR, Arms of Alexandria and Art Symbols — A274

**1965, Dec. 16** ***Perf. 11x11½***

**686** A274 10m multicolored .40 .25

6th Biennial Exhibition of Fine Arts in Alexandria, Dec. 16, 1965-Mar. 31, 1966.

Parchment Letter, Carrier Pigeon and Postrider
A275

**1966, Jan. 2 Wmk. 342** ***Perf. 11½***

**687** A275 10m multicolored .80 .25

*Nos. 687,CB1-CB2 (3)* 8.30 6.50

Post Day, Jan. 2.

Lamp and Arch — A276

**1966, Jan. 10 Unwmk.** ***Perf. 11***

**688** A276 4m violet & dp org .40 .25

Issued for use on greeting cards.

Exhibition Poster — A277

*Perf. 11x11½*

**1966, Jan. 27 Wmk. 342**

**689** A277 10m lt blue & blk .40 .25

Industrial Exhibition, Jan. 29-Feb.

Arab League Emblem — A278

**1966, Mar. 22 Photo. Wmk. 342**

**690** A278 10m brt yellow & pur .40 .25

Arab Publicity Week, Mar. 22-28.

Printed Page and Torch — A279

**1966, Mar. 25** ***Perf. 11x11½***

**691** A279 10m dp orange & sl blue .40 .25

Centenary of the national press.

Traffic Signal at Night — A280

**1966, May 4 Photo. Wmk. 342**

**692** A280 10m green & red .85 .25

Issued for Traffic Day.

Hands Holding Torch, Flags of UAR & Iraq — A281

**1966, May 26** ***Perf. 11x11½***

**693** A281 10m dp claret, rose red & brt grn .40 .25

Friendship between UAR and Iraq.

Workers and UN Emblem
A282

*Perf. 11½x11*

**1966, June 1 Photo. Wmk. 342**

**694** A282 5m blue grn & blk .35 .25

**695** A282 10m brt rose lil & grn .40 .25

**696** A282 35m orange & black 1.25 .85

*Nos. 694-696 (3)* 2.00 1.35

50th session of the ILO.

Mobilization Dept. Emblem, People and City — A283

**1966, June 30** ***Perf. 11x11½***

**697** A283 10m dull pur & brn .35 .25

Population sample, May 31-June 16.

"Salah el Din," Crane and Cogwheel
A284

Present-day Basket Dance and Pharaonic Dance — A285

No. 699, Transfer of first stones of Abu Simbel. No. 700, Development of Sinai (map of Red Sea area and Sinai Peninsula). No. 701, El Maadi Hospital and nurse with patient.

**Wmk. 342**

**1966, July 23 Photo.** ***Perf. 11½***

**698** A284 10m orange & multi .65 .30

**699** A284 10m brt green & multi .65 .30

**700** A284 10m yellow & multi .65 .30

**701** A284 10m lt blue & multi .65 .30

*Nos. 698-701 (4)* 2.60 1.20

**Souvenir Sheet**

***Imperf***

**702** A285 100m multicolored 5.00 3.75

14th anniv. of the revolution.

Suez Canal Headquarters, Ships and Map of Canal — A286

**1966, July 26** ***Perf. 11½***

**703** A286 10m blue & crimson 1.10 .50

Suez Canal nationalization, 10th anniv.

Cotton, Farmers with Plow and Tractor
A287

*Perf. 11½x11*

**1966, Sept. 9 Photo. Wmk. 342**

**704** A287 5m shown .35 .25

**705** A287 10m Rice .35 .25

**706** A287 35m Onions 1.10 .90

*Nos. 704-706 (3)* 1.80 1.40

Issued for Farmer's Day.

WHO Headquarters, Geneva — A288

Designs: 10m, UN refugee emblem. 35m, UNICEF emblem.

*Perf. 11½x11*

**1966, Oct. 24 Wmk. 342**

**707** A288 5m olive & brt pur .40 .25

**708** A288 10m orange & brt pur .40 .25

**709** A288 35m lt blue & brt pur .90 .80

*Nos. 707-709 (3)* 1.70 1.30

21st anniversary of the United Nations. See Nos. N129-N131.

World Map and Festival Emblem
A289

**1966, Nov. 8 Photo.**

**710** A289 10m brt purple & yellow .55 .25

5th Intl. Television Festival, Nov. 1-10.

Arms of UAR, Rocket and Pylon
A290

**1966, Dec. 23 Wmk. 342** ***Perf. 11½***

**711** A290 10m brt grn & car rose .55 .25

Issued for Victory Day. See No. N132.

Jackal
A291

35m, Alabaster head from Tutankhamun treasure.

**1967, Jan. 2 Photo.**

**712** A291 10m slate, yel & brn 1.50 .35

**713** A291 35m bl, dk vio & ocher 2.75 .70

Issued for Post Day, Jan. 2.

Carnations — A292

**1967, Jan. 10 Unwmk.** ***Perf. 11***

**714** A292 4m citron & purple .50 .25

Issued for use on greeting cards.

Workers Planting Tree — A293

**Perf. 11x11½**

**1967, Mar. 15 Wmk. 342**

**715** A293 10m brt green & blk vio .40 .25

Issued to publicize the Tree Festival.

Gamal el-Dine el-Afaghani and Arab League Emblem — A294

**1967, Mar. 22 Photo. Wmk. 342**

**716** A294 10m dp green & dk brn .40 .25

Arab Publicity Week, Mar. 22-28.
See No. N133.

Census Emblem, Man, Woman and Factory A295

**1967, Apr. 23 Perf. 11½x11**

**717** A295 10m black & dp org .40 .25

First industrial census.

Brickmaking Fresco, Tomb of Rekhmire, Thebes, 1504-1450 B.C. — A296

**1967, May 1 Photo. Wmk. 342**

**718** A296 10m olive & orange .55 .30

Issued for Labor Day, 1967.
See No. N134.

Ramses II and Queen Nefertari — A297

Design: 35m, Shooting geese, frieze from tomb of Atet at Meidum, c. 2724 B. C.

**Perf. 11½x11**

**1967, June 7 Photo. Wmk. 342**

**719** A297 10m multicolored 1.00 .50
**720** A297 35m dk green & org 4.25 1.40
*Nos. 719-720,C113-C115 (5)* 13.60 6.15

Issued for International Tourist Year, 1967.

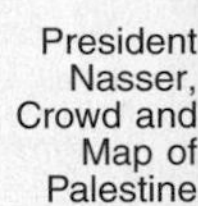

President Nasser, Crowd and Map of Palestine A298

**1967, June 22 Perf. 11½**

**721** A298 10m dp org, yel & ol 2.75 1.50

Issued to publicize Arab solidarity for "the defense of Palestine."

Souvenir Sheet

National Products — A299

**1967, July 23 Wmk. 342 Imperf.**

**722** A299 100m multicolored 4.00 3.50

15th anniv. of the revolution.

Salama Higazi — A300

**Perf. 11x11½**

**1967, Oct. 14 Photo. Wmk. 342**

**723** A300 20m brown & dk blue .80 .40

50th anniversary of the death of Salama Higazi, pioneer of Egyptian lyric stage.

Stag on Ceramic Disk A301

Design: 55m, Apse showing Christ in Glory, Madonna and Saints, Coptic Museum, and UNESCO Emblem.

**1967, Oct. 24 Perf. 11½**

**724** A301 20m dull rose & dk bl .95 .40
**725** A301 55m dk slate grn & yel 1.75 .85
*Nos. 724-725,C117 (3)* 4.20 2.15

22nd anniv. of the UN.

Savings Bank and Postal Authority Emblems A302

**1967, Oct. 31 Perf. 11½x11**

**726** A302 20m sal pink & dk blue .60 .30

International Savings Day.

Rose — A303

**Unwmk.**

**1967, Dec. 15 Photo. Perf. 11**

**727** A303 5m green & rose lilac .50 .25

Issued for use on greeting cards.

Pharaonic Dress — A304

Designs: Various pharaonic dresses from temple decorations.

**Perf. 11x11½**

**1968, Jan. 2 Wmk. 342**

**728** A304 20m brown, grn & buff 1.40 .35
**729** A304 55m lt grn, yel & sepia 2.25 .85
**730** A304 80m dk brn, bl & brt rose 3.75 1.25
*Nos. 728-730 (3)* 7.40 2.45

Issued for Post Day, Jan. 2.
See Nos. 752-755.

Aswan High Dam and Power Lines — A305

**1968, Jan. 9**

**731** A305 20m yel, bl & dk brn .35 .25

1st electricity generated by the Aswan Hydroelectric Station.

Alabaster Vessel, Tutankhamun Treasure — A306

Capital of Coptic Limestone Pillar A307

**Perf. 11x11½, 11½**

**1968, Jan. 20 Photo. Wmk. 342**

**732** A306 20m dk ultra, yel & brn .75 .30
**733** A307 80m lt grn, dk pur & ol grn 1.60 1.00

2nd International Festival of Museums.

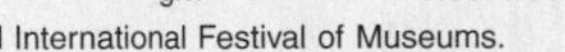

Girl, Moon and Paint Brushes — A308

**1968, Feb. 15 Perf. 11x11½**

**734** A308 20m brt blue & black .40 .30

7th Biennial Exhibition of Fine Arts, Alexandria, Feb. 15.

Cattle and Veterinarian — A309

**Perf. 11½x11**

**1968, May 4 Photo. Wmk. 342**

**735** A309 20m brown, yel & grn .75 .25

8th Arab Veterinary Congress, Cairo.

Human Rights Flame — A310

**Perf. 11x11½**

**1968, July 1 Photo. Wmk. 342**

**736** A310 20m citron, crim & grn .50 .25
**737** A310 60m sky blue, crim & grn 1.00 .90

International Human Rights Year, 1968.

Open Book with Symbols of Science, Victory Election Result A311

Workers, Cogwheel with Coat of Arms and Open Book — A312

**1968, July 23 Perf. 11½**

**738** A311 20m rose red & sl grn .50 .25

**Souvenir Sheet**

***Imperf***

**739** A312 100m lt grn, org & pur 3.25 3.00

16th anniversary of the revolution.

Imhotep and WHO Emblem A313

No. 741, Avicenna and WHO emblem.

*Perf. 11½x11*

**1968, Sept. 1 Photo. Wmk. 342**

| | | | | |
|---|---|---|---|---|
| **740** | A313 | 20m blue, yel & brn | 1.10 | .55 |
| **741** | A313 | 20m yellow, bl & brn | 1.10 | .55 |
| *a.* | | Pair, #740-741 | 3.00 | 3.00 |

20th anniv. of the WHO. Nos. 740-741 printed in checkerboard sheets of 50 (5x10).

Table Tennis — A314

*Perf. 11x11½*

**1968, Sept. 20 Photo. Wmk. 342**

| | | | | |
|---|---|---|---|---|
| **742** | A314 | 20m lt green & dk brn | .90 | .35 |

First Mediterranean Table Tennis Tournament, Alexandria, Sept. 20-27.

Factories and Fair Emblem A315

**1968, Oct. 20 Wmk. 342 *Perf. 11½***

| | | | | |
|---|---|---|---|---|
| **743** | A315 | 20m bl gray, red & sl bl | .45 | .25 |

Cairo International Industrial Fair.

Temples of Philae — A316

Refugees, Map of Palestine, Refugee Year Emblem A317

55m, Temple at Philae & UNESCO emblem.

**1968, Oct. 24 Photo.**

| | | | | |
|---|---|---|---|---|
| **744** | A316 | 20m multicolored | 1.25 | .30 |
| **745** | A317 | 30m multicolored | 1.75 | .85 |
| **746** | A317 | 55m lt blue, yel & blk | 3.00 | 1.10 |
| | | *Nos. 744-746 (3)* | 6.00 | 2.25 |

Issued for United Nations Day, Oct. 24.

Egyptian Boy Scout Emblem — A318

**1968, Nov. 1**

| | | | | |
|---|---|---|---|---|
| **747** | A318 | 10m dull org & vio bl | .80 | .30 |

50th anniversary of Egyptian Boy Scouts.

Pharaonic Sports A319

Design: 30m, Pharaonic sports, diff.

**1968, Nov. 1**

| | | | | |
|---|---|---|---|---|
| **748** | A319 | 20m pale ol, pale sal & blk | .80 | .25 |
| **749** | A319 | 30m pale blue, buff & pur | 1.25 | .75 |

19th Olympic Games, Mexico City, 10/12-27.

Aly Moubarak — A320

**1968, Nov. 9 *Perf. 11½***

| | | | | |
|---|---|---|---|---|
| **750** | A320 | 20m green, brn & bister | .55 | .25 |

Aly Moubarak (1823-93), founder of the modern educational system in Egypt.

Lotus — A321

**1968, Dec. 11 Photo. Wmk. 342**

| | | | | |
|---|---|---|---|---|
| **751** | A321 | 5m brt blue, grn & yel | .55 | .25 |

Issued for use on greeting cards.

Ramses IV — A322

Pharaonic Dress: No. 753, Ramses III. No. 754, Girl carrying basket on her head. 55m, Queen of the New Empire in transparent dress.

**1969, Jan. 2 Photo. *Perf. 11½***

| | | | | |
|---|---|---|---|---|
| **752** | A322 | 5m blue & multi | .75 | .30 |
| **753** | A322 | 20m blue & multi | 1.25 | .50 |
| **754** | A322 | 20m blue & multi | 1.50 | .60 |
| **755** | A322 | 55m blue & multi | 3.75 | 1.75 |
| | | *Nos. 752-755 (4)* | 7.25 | 3.15 |

Issued for Post Day, Jan. 2.

Hefni Nassef — A323

Portrait: No. 757, Mohammed Farid.

*Perf. 11x11½*

**1969, Mar. 2 Photo. Wmk. 342**

| | | | | |
|---|---|---|---|---|
| **756** | A323 | 20m purple & brown | .55 | .30 |
| **757** | A323 | 20m emerald & brown | .55 | .30 |
| *a.* | | Pair, #756-757 | 1.25 | 1.25 |

50th anniv. of the death of Hefni Nassef (1860-1919) writer and government worker, and Mohammed Farid (1867-1919), lawyer and Speaker of the Nationalist Party.

Teacher and Children — A324

**1969, Mar. 2 *Perf. 11x11½***

| | | | | |
|---|---|---|---|---|
| **758** | A324 | 20m multicolored | .55 | .25 |

Arab Teacher's Day.

ILO Emblem and Factory Chimneys — A325

**1969, Apr. 11 Photo. Wmk. 342**

| | | | | |
|---|---|---|---|---|
| **759** | A325 | 20m brown, ultra & car | .55 | .25 |

50th anniv. of the ILO.

Flag of Algeria, Africa Day and Tourist Year Emblems A326

*Perf. 11½x11*

**1969, May 25 Litho. Wmk. 342**

| | | | | |
|---|---|---|---|---|
| **760** | A326 | 10m Algeria | .95 | .55 |
| **761** | A326 | 10m Botswana | .95 | .55 |
| **762** | A326 | 10m Burundi | .95 | .55 |
| **763** | A326 | 10m Cameroun | .95 | .55 |
| **764** | A326 | 10m Cent. Afr. Rep. | .95 | .55 |
| **765** | A326 | 10m Chad | .95 | .55 |
| **766** | A326 | 10m Congo (Brazzaville) | .95 | .55 |
| **767** | A326 | 10m Congo (Kinshassa) | .95 | .55 |
| **768** | A326 | 10m Dahomey | .95 | .55 |
| **769** | A326 | 10m Equatorial Guinea | .95 | .55 |
| **770** | A326 | 10m Ethiopia | .95 | .55 |
| **771** | A326 | 10m Gabon | .95 | .55 |
| **772** | A326 | 10m Gambia | .95 | .55 |
| **773** | A326 | 10m Ghana | .95 | .55 |
| **774** | A326 | 10m Guinea | .95 | .55 |
| **775** | A326 | 10m Ivory Coast | .95 | .55 |
| **776** | A326 | 10m Kenya | .95 | .55 |
| **777** | A326 | 10m Lesotho | .95 | .55 |
| **778** | A326 | 10m Liberia | .95 | .55 |
| **779** | A326 | 10m Libya | .95 | .55 |
| **780** | A326 | 10m Malagasy | .95 | .55 |
| **781** | A326 | 10m Malawi | .95 | .55 |
| **782** | A326 | 10m Mali | .95 | .55 |
| **783** | A326 | 10m Mauritania | .95 | .55 |
| **784** | A326 | 10m Mauritius | .95 | .55 |
| **785** | A326 | 10m Morocco | .95 | .55 |
| **786** | A326 | 10m Niger | .95 | .55 |
| **787** | A326 | 10m Nigeria | .95 | .55 |
| **788** | A326 | 10m Rwanda | .95 | .55 |
| **789** | A326 | 10m Senegal | .95 | .55 |
| **790** | A326 | 10m Sierra Leone | .95 | .55 |
| **791** | A326 | 10m Somalia | .95 | .55 |
| **792** | A326 | 10m Sudan | .95 | .55 |
| **793** | A326 | 10m Swaziland | .95 | .55 |
| **794** | A326 | 10m Tanzania | .95 | .55 |
| **795** | A326 | 10m Togo | .95 | .55 |
| **796** | A326 | 10m Tunisia | .95 | .55 |
| **797** | A326 | 10m Uganda | .95 | .55 |
| **798** | A326 | 10m UAR | .95 | .55 |
| **799** | A326 | 10m Upper Volta | .95 | .55 |
| **800** | A326 | 10m Zambia | .95 | .55 |
| | | *Nos. 760-800 (41)* | 38.95 | 22.55 |

El Fetouh Gate, Cairo A327

Sculptures from the Egyptian Museum, Cairo — A328

Millenary of Cairo — A329

No. 802, Al Azhar University. No. 803, The Citadel. No. 805, Sculptures, Coptic Museum. No. 806, Glass plate and vase, Fatimid dynasty, Islamic Museum.

No. 807: a, Islamic coin. b, Fatimist era jewelry. c, Copper vase. d, Coins and plaque.

*Perf. 11½x11*

**1969, July 23 Photo. Wmk. 342**

| | | | | |
|---|---|---|---|---|
| **801** | A327 | 10m dk brown & multi | .55 | .25 |
| **802** | A327 | 10m green & multi | .55 | .25 |
| **803** | A327 | 10m blue & multi | .55 | .25 |

*Perf. 11½*

| | | | | |
|---|---|---|---|---|
| **804** | A328 | 20m yellow grn & multi | .95 | .40 |
| **805** | A328 | 20m dp ultra & multi | .95 | .40 |
| **806** | A328 | 20m brown & multi | .95 | .40 |
| | | *Nos. 801-806 (6)* | 4.50 | 1.95 |

**Souvenir Sheet**

| | | | | |
|---|---|---|---|---|
| **807** | A329 | Sheet of 4 | 15.00 | 14.00 |
| *a.* | | 20m dark blue & multi | 2.50 | 2.00 |
| *b.* | | 20m lilac & multi | 2.50 | 2.00 |
| *c.* | | 20m yellow & multi | 2.50 | 2.00 |
| *d.* | | 20m dark green & multi | 2.50 | 2.00 |

Millenium of the founding of Cairo.

African Development Bank Emblem — A330

*Perf. 11x11½*

**1969, Sept. 10 Photo. Wmk. 342**

| | | | | |
|---|---|---|---|---|
| **808** | A330 | 20m emerald, yel & vio | .40 | .25 |

African Development Bank, 5th anniv.

Pharaonic Boat and UN Emblem A331

Temple of Philae Inundated and UNESCO Emblem A332

Design: 5m, King and Queen from Abu Simbel Temple and UNESCO Emblem (size: 21x38mm).

*Perf. 11x11½, 11½x11*

**1969, Oct. 24 Photo. Wmk. 342**

**809** A332 5m brown & multi .45 .30
**810** A331 20m yellow & ultra 1.40 .55

*Perf. 11½*

**811** A332 55m yellow & multi 1.60 .75
*Nos. 809-811 (3)* 3.45 1.60

Issued for United Nations Day.

Ships of 1869 and 1967 and Maps of Africa and Suez Canal — A333

**1969, Nov. 15** ***Perf. 11½x11***

**812** A333 20m lt blue & multi 1.50 .55

Centenary of the Suez Canal.

Cairo Opera House and Performance of Aida — A334

**1969, Nov. 15**

**813** A334 20m multicolored 1.00 .45

Centenary of the Cairo Opera House.

Crowd with Egyptian and Revolutionary Flags — A335

**1969, Nov. 15** ***Perf. 11½x11***

**814** A335 20m brt grn, dull lil & red 1.00 .45

Revolution of 1919.

Ancient Arithmetic and Computer Cards A336

*Perf. 11½x11*

**1969, Dec. 17 Photo. Wmk. 342**

**815** A336 20m multicolored .55 .30

Intl. Congress for Scientific Accounting, Cairo, Dec. 17-19.

Poinsettia — A337

**1969, Dec. 24 Unwmk.** ***Perf. 11***

**816** A337 5m yellow, grn & car .30 .25

Issued for use on greeting cards.

Sakkara Step Pyramid — A338

El Fetouh Gate, Cairo — A339

Fountain, Sultan Hassan Mosque, Cairo — A340

King Khafre (Ruled c. 2850 B.C.) A341

Designs: 5m, Al Azhar Mosque. 10m, Luxor Temple. 50m, Qaitbay Fort, Alexandria.

**Wmk. 342 (20m, £1), Unwmkd.**
**Photo.; Engr. (20m, 55m)**

**1969-70** ***Perf. 11***

**817** A338 1m multi ('70) .30 *.40*
**818** A338 5m multi ('70) .50 .25
**819** A338 10m multi ('70) .50 .25
**820** A339 20m dark brown 2.25 .35
**821** A338 50m multi ('70) 2.25 .50
**822** A340 55m slate green 3.50 .30

*Perf. 11½*
**Photo. & Engr.**

**823** A341 £1 org & sl grn ('70) 40.00 9.50
*Nos. 817-823 (7)* 49.30 11.55

See Nos. 889-891, 893-897, 899, 901-902, 904.

Veiled Women, by Mahmoud Said — A342

*Perf. 11x11½*

**1970, Jan. 2 Photo. Wmk. 342**

**824** A342 100m blue & multi 3.50 3.00

Post Day. Sheet of 8 with 2 panes of 4.

Parliament, Scales, Globe and Laurel — A343

**1970, Feb. 2** ***Perf. 11½x11***

**825** A343 20m blue, vio bl & ocher .75 .25

Intl. Conf. of Parliamentarians on the Middle East Crisis, Cairo, Feb. 2-5.

Map of Arab League Countries, Flag and Emblem A344

*Perf. 11½x11*

**1970, Mar. 22 Photo. Wmk. 342**

**826** A344 30m brn org, grn & dk pur .65 .40

Arab League, 25th anniv. See No. B42.

Mena House and Sheraton Hotel — A345

**1970, Mar. 23**

**827** A345 20m olive, org & bl .55 .25

Centenary of Mena House and the inauguration of the Cairo Sheraton Hotel.

Manufacture of Medicine — A346

**1970, Apr. 20**

**828** A346 20m brown, yel & bl 1.25 .35

Production of medicines in Egypt, 30th anniv.

Mermaid — A347

**1970, Apr. 20** ***Perf. 11x11½***

**829** A347 20m orange, blk & ultra .65 .25

8th Biennial Exhibition of Fine Arts, Alexandria, March 12.

Misr Bank and Talaat Harb — A348

**1970, May 7 Photo. Wmk. 342**

**830** A348 20m multicolored .65 .25

50th anniversary of Misr Bank.

ITU Emblem — A349

**1970, May 17** ***Perf. 11x11½***

**831** A349 20m dk brn, yel & dull bl .65 .25

World Telecommunications Day.

UPU Headquarters, Bern — A350

**1970, May 20** ***Perf. 11½x11***

**832** A350 20m multicolored .80 .35

Inauguration of the UPU Headquarters in Bern. See No. C128.

Basketball Player and Map of Africa — A351

UPU, UN and U.P.A.F. Emblems A352

No. 834, Soccer player, map of Africa & cup, horiz.

*Perf. 11x11½, 11½x11*

**1970, May 25 Photo. Wmk. 342**

**833** A351 20m lt blue, yel & brn 1.25 .40
**834** A351 20m yellow & multi .80 .35
**835** A352 20m ocher, grn & blk .70 .25
*Nos. 833-835 (3)* 2.75 1.00

Africa Day. No. 833 also for the 5th African basketball championship for men; No. 834 the annual African Soccer championship; No. 835 publicizes the African Postal Union seminar.

Fist and Freed Bird — A353

**1970, July 23 Photo.** ***Perf. 11***

**836** A350 20m lt green, org & blk .95 .25

**Souvenir Sheet**
***Imperf***

**837** A353 100m lt blue, dp org & blk 3.25 2.40

18th anniv. of the revolution.

Al Aqsa Mosque on Fire — A354

**1970, Aug. 21 Wmk. 342** ***Perf. 11***

**838** A354 20m multicolored 1.25 .40
**839** A354 60m brt blue & multi 2.75 1.60

1st anniv. of the burning of Al Aqsa Mosque, Jerusalem.

Standardization Emblems — A355

**1970, Oct. 14 Wmk. 342 *Perf. 11***

840 A355 20m yellow, ultra & grn .75 .25

World Standards Day and 25th anniv. of the Intl. Standardization Organization, ISO.

UN Emblem, Scales and Dove — A356

Temple at Philae A357

Child, Education Year and UN Emblems A358

Designs: 10m, UN emblem. No. 845, 2nd Temple at Philae (denomination at left).

***Perf. 11 (5m), 11½ (others)***

**1970, Oct. 24 Photo. Wmk. 342**

841 A356 5m lt bl, rose lil & sl .25 .25
842 A357 10m yel, brn & lt bl .25 .25
843 A358 20m slate & multi .65 .30
844 A357 55m brn, bl & ocher 1.10 .75
845 A357 55m brn, bl & ocher 1.10 .75
a. Strip of 3, #842, 844-845 4.00 4.00
*Nos. 841-845,B43 (6)* 4.25 3.10

25th anniv. of the UN. No. 843 also for Intl. Education Year; Nos. 842, 844-845, the work of UNESCO in saving the Temples of Philae. No. 845a printed in sheets of 35 (15 No. 842, 10 each Nos. 844-845). Nos. 844-845 show continuous picture of the Temples at Philae.

Gamal Abdel Nasser — A359

**1970, Nov. 6 Wmk. 342 *Perf. 11***

846 A359 5m sky blue & blk .25 .25
847 A359 20m gray green & blk .55 .25
*Nos. 846-847,C129-C130 (4)* 4.55 2.15

Gamal Abdel Nasser (1918-70), Pres. of Egypt.

Medical Association Building — A360

No. 849, Old & new National Library. No. 850, Egyptian Credo (Nasser quotation). No. 851, Engineering Society, old & new buildings. No. 852, Government Printing Offices, old & new buildings.

**1970, Dec. 20 Photo. *Perf. 11***

848 A360 20m yel, grn & brn .80 .40
849 A360 20m green & multi .80 .40
850 A360 20m lt blue & brn .80 .40
851 A360 20m blue, yel & brn .80 .40
852 A360 20m blue, yel & brn .80 .40
a. Strip of 5, #848-852 4.50 4.25

50th anniv. of Egyptian Medical Assoc. (No. 848); cent. of Natl. Library (No. 849); Egyptian Engineering Assoc. (No. 851); sesqui. of Government Printing Offices (No. 852).

Map and Flags of UAR, Libya, Sudan A361

**1970, Dec. 27 *Perf. 11½***

853 A361 20m lt grn, car & blk .75 .25

Signing of the Charter of Tripoli affirming the unity of UAR, Libya & the Sudan, 12/27/70.

Qalawun Minaret — A362

Designs (Minarets): 10m, As Saleh. 20m, Isna. 55m, Al Hakim.

**1971, Jan. 2 Wmk. 342 *Perf. 11***

854 A362 5m green & multi .60 .25
855 A362 10m green & multi 1.25 .40
856 A362 20m green & multi 2.50 .80
857 A362 55m green & multi 4.00 2.25
a. Strip of 4, #854-857 + label 10.00 9.00

Post Day, 1971.
See Nos. 905-908, 932-935.

Gamal Abdel Nasser A363

**Photogravure and Engraved**

**1971 Wmk. 342 *Perf. 11½***

858 A363 200m brn vio & dk bl 5.00 1.25
859 A363 500m blue & black 12.00 3.25

**Souvenir Sheet**

Design: Portrait facing right.

***Imperf***

860 Sheet of 2 13.00 13.00
a. A363 100m light green & black 4.00 2.75
b. A363 200m blue & black 6.00 4.50

No. 860 commemorates inauguration of the Aswan High Dam, which is shown in margin. Issued: No. 860, 1/15; Nos. 858-859, 2/1. See No. 903.

Cotton and Globe A364

**1971, Mar. 6 Photo. *Perf. 11½x11***

861 A364 20m lt green, blue & brn .65 .25

Egyptian cotton.

Arab Countries, and Arab Postal Union Emblem A365

**1971, Mar. 6 Wmk. 342**

862 A365 20m lt bl, org & sl grn .65 .25

9th Arab Postal Cong., Cairo, 3/6-25. See No. C131.

Cairo Fair Emblem — A366

**1971, Mar. 6 *Perf. 11x11½***

863 A366 20m plum, blk & org .65 .25

Cairo International Fair, March 2-23.

Nesy Ra, Apers Papyrus and WHO Emblem A367

***Perf. 11½x11***

**1971, Apr. 30 Photo. Wmk. 342**

864 A367 20m yellow bis & pur 1.25 .30

World Health Organization Day.

Gamal Abdel Nasser — A368

**1971, May 1 *Perf. 11***

865 A368 20m purple & bl gray .90 .30
866 A368 55m blue & purple 2.75 .95

Map of Africa, Telecommunications Symbols — A369

**1971, May 17 *Perf. 11½x11***

867 A369 20m blue & multi .65 .25

Pan-African telecommunications system.

Wheelwright A370

Hand Holding Wheat and Laurel A371

Candle Lighting Africa — A372

***Perf. 11x11½***

**1971, July 23 Photo. Wmk. 342**

868 A370 20m yellow & multi .60 .25
869 A371 20m tan, grn & ocher .60 .25

**Souvenir Sheet**

***Imperf***

870 A372 100m blue & multi 6.00 4.75

19th anniv. of the July Revolution. No. 870 contains one stamp with simulated perforations in gold.

Arab Postal Union Emblem A373

**1971, Aug. 3 *Perf. 11½***

871 A373 20m black, yel & grn .65 .25

25th anniv. of the Conf. of Sofar, Lebanon, establishing the APU. See No. C135.

## Arab Republic of Egypt

Three Links A374

***Perf. 11½x11***

**1971, Sept. 28 Photo. Wmk. 342**

872 A374 20m gray, org brn & blk .65 .30

Confederation of Arab Republics (Egypt, Syria and Libya). See No. C136.

Gamal Abdel Nasser — A375

**1971, Sept. 28 *Perf. 11x11½***

873 A375 5m slate grn & vio brn .45 .25
874 A375 20m violet brn & ultra .65 .25
875 A375 30m ultra & brown 1.25 .75
876 A375 55m brown & emerald 2.10 1.10
*Nos. 873-876 (4)* 4.45 2.35

Death of Pres. Gamal Abdel Nasser, 1st anniv.

Blood Donation — A376

**1971, Oct. 24**

877 A376 20m green & carmine 1.10 .25

"Blood Saves Lives."

Princess Nursing Child, UNICEF Emblem A377

Submerged Pillar, Philae, UNESCO Emblem A379

Equality Year Emblem A378

***Perf. 11x11½, 11½x11***

**1971, Oct. 24 Photo. Wmk. 342**

**878** A377 5m buff, blk & org brn .55 .30
**879** A378 20m red brn, grn, yel & blk .90 .30
**880** A379 55m black, lt bl, yel & brn 2.25 .30
*Nos. 878-880,C137 (4)* 5.45 1.35

UN Day. No. 878 honors UN Intl. Children's Fund; No. 879 for Intl. Year Against Racial Discrimination; No. 880 honors UNESCO.

Postal Traffic Center, Alexandria A380

**1971, Oct. 31** ***Perf. 11½x11***

**881** A380 20m blue & bister 1.00 .30

Opening of Postal Traffic Center in Alexandria.

Sunflower — A381

**1971, Nov. 13** ***Perf. 11***

**882** A381 5m lt blue & multi .45 .25

For use on greeting cards.

Abdalla El Nadim — A382

**1971, Nov. 14** ***Perf. 11x11½***

**883** A382 20m green & brown .65 .25

Abdalla El Nadim (1845-1896), journalist, publisher, connected with Orabi Revolution.

Section of Earth's Crust, Map of Africa on Globe A383

**1971, Nov. 27** ***Perf. 11½x11***

**884** A383 20m ultra, yel & brn 1.25 .25

75th anniv. of Egyptian Geological Survey and Intl. Conference, Nov. 27-Dec. 1.

Postal Union Emblem, Letter and Dove A384

55m, African Postal Union emblem and letter.

**1971, Dec. 2**

**885** A384 5m multicolored .45 .25
**886** A384 20m olive, blk & org .90 .25
**887** A384 55m red, blk & blue 2.00 1.10
*Nos. 885-887,C138 (4)* 4.75 2.00

10th anniversary of African Postal Union.

Money and Safe Deposit Box A385

**1971, Dec. 23** ***Perf. 11½***

**888** A385 20m rose, brn & grn .85 .30

70th anniversary of Postal Savings Bank.

**Types of 1969-70, 1971 Inscribed "A. R. Egypt" and**

Ramses II — A385a

Designs as before and: No. 894, King Citi I. No. 897, View of Alexandria. No. 898, Queen Nefertari. No. 900, Sphinx and Middle Pyramid. 100m, Cairo Mosque. 200m, Head of Pharaoh Userkaf.

**Wmk. 342 (892A, 901-904)**

**1972-76 Photo. Unwmk.** ***Perf. 11***

| No. | Type | Denom. | Description | Unused | Used |
|---|---|---|---|---|---|
| **889** | A338 | 1m | multi | .25 | .25 |
| **890** | A338 | 1m | dk brn ('73) | .30 | .25 |
| **891** | A338 | 5m | multi | .40 | .25 |
| **892** | A385a | 5m | olive ('73) | .45 | .25 |
| **892A** | A385a | 5m | bister ('76) | .45 | .25 |
| **893** | A338 | 10m | multi | .70 | .25 |
| **894** | A338 | 10m | lt brn ('73) | .70 | .25 |
| **895** | A339 | 20m | olive | 1.10 | .25 |
| **896** | A339 | 20m | purple ('73) | 1.10 | .25 |
| **897** | A338 | 50m | multi | 2.25 | .30 |
| **898** | A385a | 50m | dull bl ('73) | 2.25 | .30 |
| **899** | A340 | 55m | red lilac | 4.00 | .90 |
| **900** | A340 | 55m | green ('74) | 2.00 | .50 |
| **901** | A339 | 100m | lt blue, dp org & blk | 3.00 | .70 |

***Perf. 11½***

**Photo. & Engr.**

| No. | Type | Denom. | Description | Unused | Used |
|---|---|---|---|---|---|
| **902** | A341 | 200m | yel grn & brn | 6.75 | 1.50 |
| **903** | A363 | 500m | bl & choc | 17.50 | 4.00 |
| **904** | A341 | £1 | orange & sl grn | 32.50 | 9.00 |
| | | | *Nos. 889-904 (17)* | 75.70 | 19.45 |

**Minaret Type of 1971**

5m, West Minaret, Nasser Mosque. 20m, East Minaret, Nasser Mosque. 30m, Minaret, Al Gawli Mosque. 55m, Minaret, Ibn Tulun Mosque.

**Wmk. 342**

**1972, Jan. 2 Photo.** ***Perf. 11***

**905** A362 5m dk green & multi .45 .25
**906** A362 20m dk green & multi 1.25 .25
**907** A362 30m dk green & multi 2.75 .50
**908** A362 55m dk green & multi 3.75 1.50
*a.* Strip of 4, #905-908 + label 11.00 3.50

Post Day, 1972.

Police Emblem and Activities — A386

**1972, Jan. 25** ***Perf. 11½***

**909** A386 20m dull blue, brn & yel 2.25 .35

Police Day 1972.

UNESCO, UN and Book Year Emblems — A387

**1972, Jan. 25** ***Perf. 11x11½***

**910** A387 20m lt yel grn, vio bl & yel 1.10 .25

International Book Year 1972.

Alexandria Biennale A388

**1972, Feb. 15 Wmk. 342** ***Perf. 11½***

**911** A388 20m black, brt rose & yel .85 .30

9th Biennial Exhibition of Fine Arts, Alexandria, Mar., 1972.

Fair Emblem — A389

**1972, Mar. 5** ***Perf. 11x11½***

**912** A389 20m blue, org & yel grn 1.10 .30

International Cairo Fair.

Abdel Moniem Riad — A390

**1972, Mar. 21 Photo. Wmk. 342**

**913** A390 20m blue & brown 1.25 .30

In memory of Brig. Gen. Abdel Moniem Riad (1919-1969), military hero.

Bird Feeding Young A391

**1972, Mar. 21** ***Perf. 11½***

**914** A391 20m yellow & multi 1.00 .25

Mother's Day.

Tutankhamun — A392

Design: 55m, Back of chair with king's name and symbols of eternity.

**1972, May 22 Unwmk.**

**915** A392 20m gray, blk & ocher 2.25 .65
**916** A392 55m purple & yellow 6.25 1.75
*Nos. 915-916,C142-C143 (4)* 28.50 13.40

Discovery of the tomb of Tutankhamun by Howard Carter & Lord Carnarvon, 50th anniv. See No. C144.

Queen Nefertiti A393

**Wmk. 342**

**1972, May 22 Photo.** ***Perf. 11½***

**917** A393 20m red, blk & gold 1.25 .30

Soc. of the Friends of Art, 50th anniv.

Map of Africa — A394

**1972, May 25** ***Perf. 11x11½***

**918** A394 20m purple, bl & brn .75 .30

Africa Day.

Atom Symbol, "Faith and Science" A395

Design: No. 920, Egyptian coat of arms.

**1972, July 23** *Perf. 11½*

**919** A395 20m blue, claret & blk 1.10 .30
**920** A395 20m ol grn, gold & blk 1.10 .30

20th anniversary of the revolution.

Boxing, Olympic and Motion Emblems — A396

Designs (Olympic and Motion Emblems and): 10m, Wrestling. 20m, Basketball.

**1972, Aug. 17** *Perf. 11½x11*

**921** A396 5m blue & multi .35 .25
**922** A396 10m yellow & multi .50 .25
**923** A396 20m ver & multi .60 .30
*Nos. 921-923,C149-C152 (7)* 6.65 3.70

20th Olympic Games, Munich, 8/26-9/11.

Flag of Confederation of Arab Republics — A397

**1972, Sept. 1** **Wmk. 342** *Perf. 11½*

**924** A397 20m carmine, bis & blk .85 .30

Confederation of Arab Republics, 1st anniv.

Red Crescent, TB and UN Emblems — A398

Heart and WHO Emblem A399

Refugees, UNRWA Emblem, Map of Palestine — A400

Design: 55m, Inundated Temple of Philae, UNESCO emblem.

*Perf. 11x11½ (#925), 11½ (#926, 928), 11 (#927)*

**1972, Oct. 24** **Photo.**

**925** A398 10m brn org, red & bl .55 .30
**926** A399 20m green, yel & blk 1.00 .40
**927** A400 30m lt bl, pur & lt brn 3.00 .75
**928** A399 55m brn, gold & bluish gray 3.25 1.00
*Nos. 925-928 (4)* 7.80 2.45

UN Day. No. 925 is for the 14th Regional Tuberculosis Conf., Cairo, 1972; No. 926 World Health Month; No. 927 publicizes aid to refugees and No. 928 the UN campaign to save the Temples at Philae.

Morning Glory — A401

**1972, Oct. 24** *Perf. 11*

**929** A401 10m yel, lilac & grn .65 .25

For use on greeting cards.

"Seeing Eye" A402

**1972, Nov. 30** *Perf. 11½*

**930** A402 20m multicolored 1.00 .25

Social Work Day.

Sculling Race, View of Luxor — A403

**1972, Dec. 17** **Wmk. 342** *Perf. 11*

**931** A403 20m blue & brown 1.40 .40

3rd Nile Intl. Rowing Festival, Dec. 1972.

**Minaret Type of 1971**

10m, Al Maridani, 1338. 20m, Bashtak, 1337. 30m, Qusun, 1330. 55m, Al Gashankir, 1306.

**1973, Jan. 2**

**Frame in Bright Yellow Green**

**932** A362 10m multicolored .80 .25
**933** A362 20m multicolored 1.25 .30
**934** A362 30m multicolored 2.75 .75
**935** A362 55m multicolored 3.75 2.00
*a.* Strip of 4, #932-935 + Label 11.00 10.00

Post Day, 1973.

Cairo Fair Emblem A404

*Perf. 11½x11*

**1973, Mar. 21** **Photo.** **Wmk. 342**

**936** A404 20m gray & multi .55 .25

International Cairo Fair.

Family — A405

**1973, Mar. 21** *Perf. 11x11½*

**937** A405 20m multicolored .65 .25

Family planning.

Sania Girls' School and Hoda Sharawi A406

*Perf. 11½x11*

**1973, July 15** **Photo.** **Wmk. 342**

**938** A406 20m ultra & green .65 .25

Centenary of education for girls and 50th anniversary of the Egyptian Women's Union, founded by Hoda Sharawi.

Rifaa el Tahtawi — A407

**1973, July 15** *Perf. 11x11½*

**939** A407 20m brt green, ol & brn .70 .30

Centenary of the death of Rifaa el Tahtawi, champion of democracy and principal of language school.

Omar Makram A408

Abdel Rahman al Gabarti, Historian A409

"Reconstruction and Battle" — A410

No. 941, Mohamed Korayem, martyr.

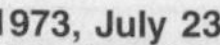

**1973, July 23**

**940** A408 20m yel grn, bl & brn .65 .30
**941** A408 20m lt grn, bl & brn .65 .30
**942** A409 20m ocher & brown .65 .30
*Nos. 940-942 (3)* 1.95 .90

**Souvenir Sheet**

***Imperf***

**943** A410 110m gold, bl & blk 3.25 3.00

Revolution establishing the republic, 21st anniv.

Grain, Cow, FAO Emblem A411

*Perf. 11½x11*

**1973, Oct. 24** **Wmk. 342**

**944** A411 10m brn, dk bl & yel grn .65 .25

10th anniv. of the World Food Org.

Inundated Temples at Philae A412

**1973, Oct. 24** *Perf. 11½*

**945** A412 55m blue, pur & org 4.00 1.40

UNESCO campaign to save the temples at Philae.

Bank Building A413

**1973, Oct. 24**

**946** A413 20m brn org, grn & blk .75 .30

75th anniv. of the National Bank of Egypt.

Rose — A414

**1973, Oct. 24** *Perf. 11*

**947** A414 10m blue & multi .55 .25

For use on greeting cards.

Human Rights Flame — A415

*Perf. 11x11½*

**1973, Dec. 8** **Photo.** **Wmk. 342**

**948** A415 20m yel grn, dk bl & car .75 .25

25th anniversary of the Universal Declaration of Human Rights.

Taha Hussein — A416

**1973, Dec. 10**
949 A416 20m dk blue, brn & emer .75 .25

Dr. Taha Hussein (1893-1973), "Father of Education" in Egypt, writer, philosopher.

Pres. Sadat, Flag and Battle of Oct. 6 — A417

**1973, Dec. 23** ***Perf. 11x11½***
950 A417 20m yellow, blk & red 1.25 .60

October War against Israel (crossing of Suez Canal by Egyptian forces, Oct. 6, 1973). See No. 959.

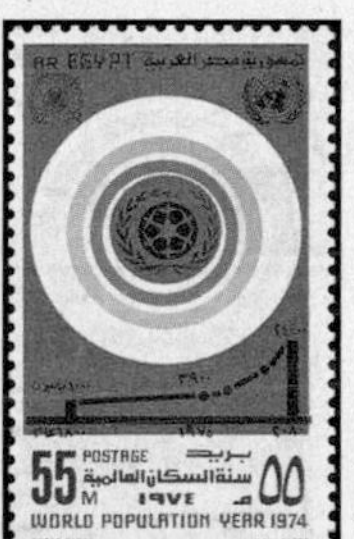

WPY Emblem and Chart — A418

**1974, Mar. 21** **Wmk. 342** ***Perf. 11***
951 A418 55m org, grn & dk bl 1.10 .50

World Population Year.

Cairo Fair Emblem — A419

**1974, Mar. 21** **Photo.**
952 A419 20m blue & multi .65 .25

Cairo International Fair.

Nurse and Medal of Angels of Ramadan 10 — A420

**1974, May 15** ***Perf. 11½***
953 A420 55m multicolored 2.00 .65

Nurses' and World Hospital Day.

Workers, Relief Carving from Queen Tee's Tomb, Sakhara — A421

**1974, May 15** ***Perf. 11***
954 A421 20m yellow, blue & brn .85 .30

Workers' Day.

Pres. Sadat, Troops Crossing Suez Canal — A422

"Reconstruction," Map of Suez Canal and New Building — A423

Sheet of Aluminum A424

Design: 110m, Pres. Sadat's "October Working Paper," symbols of science and development.

**1974, July 23** **Photo.** ***Perf. 11x11½***
955 A422 20m multicolored .75 .40
956 A423 20m blue, gold & blk .75 .40

***Perf. 11½***
957 A424 20m plum & silver .75 .40
*Nos. 955-957 (3)* 2.25 1.20

**Souvenir Sheet**
***Imperf***
958 A424 110m green & multi 3.75 3.75

22nd anniv. of the revolution establishing the republic and for the end of the October War. No. 958 contains one 52x59mm stamp.

Pres. Sadat and Flag — A425

***Perf. 11x11½***
**1974, Oct. 6** **Wmk. 342**
959 A425 20m yellow, blk & red 1.50 .75

1st anniv. of Battle. See No. 950.

Palette and Brushes A426

**1974, Oct. 6** ***Perf. 11½***
960 A426 30m purple, yel & blk 1.00 .40

6th Exhibition of Plastic Art.

Teachers and Pupils — A427

**1974, Oct. 6** ***Perf. 11x11½***
961 A427 20m multicolored .75 .25

Teachers' Day.

Souvenir Sheet

UPU Monument, Bern — A428

**1974, Oct. 6** ***Imperf.***
962 A428 110m gold & multi 5.50 5.00

Cent. of the UPU.

Emblems, Cogwheel and Calipers — A429

Refugee Camp under Attack and UN Refugee Organization Emblem — A430

Child and UNICEF Emblem A431

Temple of Philae — A432

**1974, Oct. 24** ***Perf. 11½, 11x11½***
963 A429 10m black, bl & yel .55 .25
964 A430 20m dp org, bl & blk .85 .25
965 A431 30m green, bl & brn 1.25 .40
966 A432 55m black, bl & yel 3.00 .85
*Nos. 963-966 (4)* 5.65 1.75

UN Day. World Standards Day (10m); Palestinian refugee repatriation (20m); Family Planning (30m); Campaign to save Temple of Philae (55m).

Calla Lily — A433

**1974, Nov. 7** ***Perf. 11***
967 A433 10m ultra & multi .55 .25

For use on greeting cards.

10m-coins, Smokestacks and Grain — A434

**1974, Nov. 7** ***Perf. 11½x11***
968 A434 20m yel grn, dk bl & sil .60 .25

International Savings Day.

Organization Emblem and Medical Services — A435

**1974, Nov. 7** ***Perf. 11½***
969 A435 30m vio, red & gold .90 .30

Health Insurance Organization, 10th anniv.

Mustafa Lutfy El Manfalouty A436

Abbas Mahmoud El Akkad A437

*Perf. 11x11½*

**1974, Dec. 8 Photo. Wmk. 342**

**970** A436 20m blue blk & brn .55 .30
**971** A437 20m brown & bl blk .55 .30
*a.* Pair, #970-971 1.30 1.30

Arab writers; El Manfalouty (1876-1924) and El Akkad (1889-1964).

Goddess Maat Facing God Thoth — A438

Fish-shaped Vase — A439

Pharaonic Golden Vase — A440

Sign of Life, Mirror — A441

**Wmk. 342**

**1975, Jan. 2 Photo. *Perf. 11½***

**972** A438 20m silver & multi 1.00 .30
**973** A439 30m multicolored 1.25 .30
**974** A440 55m multicolored 1.75 1.00
**975** A441 110m blue & multi 3.00 1.75
*Nos. 972-975 (4)* 7.00 3.35

Post Day 1975. Egyptian art works from 12th-5th centuries B.C.

Om Kolthoum — A442

*Perf. 11½*

**1975, Mar. 3 Photo. Unwmk.**

**976** A442 20m brown .85 .25

In memory of Om Kolthoum, singer.

Crescent, Globe, Al Aqsa and Kaaba — A443

**1975, Mar. 25**

**977** A443 20m multicolored .85 .25

Mohammed's Birthday.

Cairo Fair Emblem — A444

*Perf. 11x11½*

**1975, Mar. 25 Wmk. 342**

**978** A444 20m multicolored .65 .25

International Cairo Fair.

Kasr El Ainy Hospital WHO Emblem A445

*Perf. 11½x11*

**1975, May 7 Photo. Wmk. 342**

**979** A445 20m dk brown & blue .85 .25

World Health Organization Day.

Children Reading Book — A446

Children and Line Graph — A447

**1975, May 7 *Perf. 11x11½***

**980** A446 20m multicolored 1.00 .40
**981** A447 20m multicolored 1.00 .40

Science Day.

Suez Canal, Globe, Ships, Pres. Sadat — A448

**1975, June 5 *Perf. 11½***

**982** A448 20m blue, brn & blk .85 .30
*Nos. 982,C166-C167 (3)* 5.35 2.90

Reopening of the Suez Canal, June 5.

Belmabgoknis Flowers — A449

**1975, July 30 Photo. Wmk. 342**

**983** A449 10m green & blue .65 .25

For use on greeting cards.

Sphinx and Pyramids Illuminated — A450

Rural Electrification — A451

Map of Egypt with Tourist Sites — A452

**1975, July 23**

**984** A450 20m black, org & grn .75 .25
**985** A451 20m dk blue & brown .75 .25

***Perf. 11***

**986** A452 110m multicolored 5.75 5.00
*Nos. 984-986 (3)* 7.25 5.50

23rd anniversary of the revolution establishing the republic. No. 986 printed in sheets of 6 (2x3). Size: 71x80mm.

Volleyball — A453

No. 988, Running. No. 989, Torch and flag bearers. No. 990, Basketball. No. 991, Soccer.

**1975, Aug. 2 Photo. *Perf. 11x11½***

**987** A453 20m shown .90 .45
**988** A453 20m multicolored .90 .45
**989** A453 20m multicolored .90 .45
**990** A453 20m multicolored .90 .45
**991** A453 20m multicolored .90 .45
*a.* Strip of 5, #987-991 5.75 5.75

6th Arab School Tournament.

Egyptian Flag and Tanks A454

**1975 Photo. Unwmk. *Perf. 11½***

**992** A454 20m multicolored 1.40 .40

**Two-line Arabic Inscription in Bottom Panel, "M" over "20"**

**992A** A454 20m multicolored 1.40 .40

No. 992 for 2nd anniv. of October War against Israel, "The Spark;" No. 992A, the Intl. Symposium on October War against Israel 1973, Cairo University, Oct. 27-31.

Issue dates: No. 992, Oct. 6; No. 992A, Oct. 24.

Arrows Pointing to Fluke, and Emblems A455

Submerged Wall and Sculpture, UNESCO Emblem A456

*Perf. 11x11½*

**1975, Oct. 24 Wmk. 342**

**993** A455 20m multicolored .95 .40
**994** A456 55m multicolored 2.50 1.25

UN Day. 20m for Intl. Conf. on Schistosomiasis (Bilharziasis); 55m for UNESCO help in saving temples at Philae. See Nos. C169-C170.

Pharaonic Gate, University Emblem — A457

**1975, Nov. 15 Photo. Wmk. 342**

**995** A457 20m multicolored .55 .25

Ain Shams University, 25th anniversary.

Al Biruni — A458

Arab Philosophers: No. 997, Al Farabi and lute. No. 998, Al Kanady, book and compass.

**1975, Dec. 23 Photo. *Perf. 11x11½***

**996** A458 20m blue, brn & grn 1.50 .50
**997** A458 20m blue, brn & grn 1.50 .50
**998** A458 20m blue, brn & grn 1.50 .50
*Nos. 996-998 (3)* 4.50 1.50

Ibex (Prow) — A459

Post Day (from Tutankhamun's Tomb): 30m, Lioness. 55m, Cow's head (Goddess Hawthor). 110m, Hippopotamus' head (God Horus).

**1976, Jan. 2 Unwmk. *Perf. 11½***

**999** A459 20m multicolored 4.75 2.00

**Wmk. 342**

**1000** A459 30m brown, gold & ultra 7.50 2.50
**1001** A459 55m multicolored 12.50 6.50
**1002** A459 110m multicolored 18.00 13.50
*Nos. 999-1002 (4)* 42.75 24.50

Lake, Aswan Dam, Industry and Agriculture — A460

***Perf. 11½x11***

**1976, Jan. 27 Photo. Wmk. 342**

**1003** A460 20m multicolored .90 .25

Filling of lake formed by Aswan High Dam.

Fair Emblem — A461

**1976, Mar. 15 *Perf. 11x11½***

**1004** A461 20m orange & purple .50 .25

9th International Cairo Fair, Mar. 8-27.

Commemorative Medal — A462

**1976, Mar. 15 Wmk. 342**

**1005** A462 20m olive, yel & blk .60 .25

11th Biennial Exhibition of Fine Arts, Alexandria.

Hands Shielding Invalid A463

**1976, Apr. 7 Photo. *Perf. 11½***

**1006** A463 20m dk grn, lt grn & yel .65 .30

Founding of Faithfulness and Hope Society.

Eye and WHO Emblem A464

**1976, Apr. 7**

**1007** A464 20m dk brn, yel & grn .85 .25

World Health Day: "Foresight prevents blindness."

Pres. Sadat, Legal Department Emblem — A465

***Perf. 11½x11***

**1976, May 15 Photo. Wmk. 342**

**1008** A465 20m olive & multi .65 .30

Centenary of State Legal Department.

Scales of Justice — A466

**1976, May 15 *Perf. 11x11½***

**1009** A466 20m carmine, blk & grn .60 .30

5th anniversary of Rectification Movement.

Al-Ahram Front Page, First Issue A467

***Perf. 11½x11***

**1976, June 25 Photo. Wmk. 342**

**1010** A467 20m bister & multi .65 .30

Centenary of Al-Ahram newspaper.

World Map, Pres. Sadat and Emblems — A468

**1976, July 23 *Perf. 11x11½***

**1011** A468 20m bl, blk & yel .85 .35

**Size: 240x216mm**

***Imperf***

**1012** A468 110m bl, brn & yel 7.00 6.75

24th anniv. of the revolution. No. 1012 design is similar to No. 1011.

Scarborough Lily — A469

**1976, Sept. 10 Photo. *Perf. 11***

**1013** A469 10m multicolored .55 .25

For use on greeting cards.

Reconstruction of Sinai by Irrigation — A470

Abu Redice Oil Wells and Refinery — A471

Unknown Soldier, Memorial Pyramid for October War — A472

**1976, Oct. 6 *Perf. 11x11½***

**1014** A470 20m multicolored .85 .40
**1015** A471 20m multicolored .85 .40

**Size: 65x77mm**

**1016** A472 110m grn, bl & blk 7.50 7.00

October War against Israel, 3rd anniv.

Papyrus with Children's Animal Story — A473

Al Aqsa Mosque, Palestinian Refugees — A474

55m, Isis, from Philae Temple, UNESCO emblem, vert. 110m, UNESCO emblem & "30."

***Perf. 11½, 11½x11***

**1976, Oct. 24 Photo. Wmk. 342**

**1017** A473 20m dk bl, bis & brn .65 .30
**1018** A474 30m brn, grn & blk .80 .35
**1019** A473 55m dk blue & bister 1.50 .50
**1020** A474 110m lt grn, vio bl & red 2.50 1.40
*Nos. 1017-1020 (4)* 5.45 2.55

30th anniversary of UNESCO.

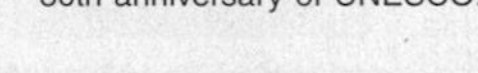

Census Chart A475

**1976, Nov. 22 Photo. *Perf. 11½x11***

**1021** A475 20m multicolored .65 .25

10th General Population and Housing Census.

A476

Nile and commemorative medal.

**1976, Nov. 22 *Perf. 11x11½***

**1022** A476 20m green & brown .65 .25

Geographical Soc. of Egypt, cent. (in 1975).

A477

Post Day: 20m, Akhnaton. 30m, Akhnaton's daughter. 55m, Nefertiti, Akhnaton's wife. 110m, Akhnaton, front view.

**1977, Jan. 2 Photo. *Perf. 11x11½***

**1023** A477 20m multicolored .65 .30
**1024** A477 30m multicolored .65 .35
**1025** A477 55m multicolored 1.10 .55
**1026** A477 110m multicolored 3.50 1.50
*Nos. 1023-1026 (4)* 5.90 2.70

Policeman, Emblem and Emergency Car — A478

*Perf. 11½x11*

**1977, Feb. 25 Photo. Wmk. 342**

**1027** A478 20m multicolored 1.10 .30

Police Day.

Map of Africa, Arab League Emblem — A479

**1977, Mar 7** ***Perf. 11x11½***

**1028** A479 55m multicolored .90 .50

First Afro-Arab Summit Conference, Cairo.

Fair Emblem, Pharaonic Ship A480

**1977, Mar. 7** ***Perf. 11½x11***

**1029** A480 20m green, blk & red .65 .30

10th International Cairo Fair.

King Faisal — A481

**1977, Mar. 22 Photo.** ***Perf. 11x11½***

**1030** A481 20m indigo & brown .65 .25

King Faisal Ben Abdel-Aziz Al Saud of Saudi Arabia (1906-1975).

Healthy and Crippled Children — A482

**1977, Apr. 12 Wmk. 342**

**1031** A482 20m multicolored .95 .30

National campaign to fight poliomyelitis.

APU Emblem, Members' Flags A483

**1977, Apr. 12** ***Perf. 11½***

**1032** A483 20m blue & multi .45 .25

**1033** A483 30m gray & multi .65 .25

25th anniv. of Arab Postal Union (APU).

Children's Village A484

***Perf. 11½x11***

**1977, May 7 Photo. Wmk. 342**

**1034** A484 20m multicolored .55 .35

**1035** A484 55m multicolored 1.25 .70

Inauguration of Children's Village, Cairo.

Loom, Spindle and Factory A485

**1977, May 7**

**1036** A485 20m multicolored .55 .25

Egyptian Spinning and Weaving Company, El Mehalla el Kobra, 50th anniv.

Satellite, Globe, ITU Emblem — A486

**1977, May 17** ***Perf. 11x11½***

**1037** A486 110m dk blue & multi 2.00 .50

World Telecommunications Day.

Flag and "25" A487

Egyptian Flag and Eagle — A488

***Perf. 11½x11***

**1977, July 23 Photo. Wmk. 342**

**1038** A487 20m silver, car & blk .65 .25

***Perf. 11x11½***

**1039** A488 110m multicolored 3.00 3.00

25th anniversary of July 23rd Revolution. No. 1039 printed in sheets of six. Size: 75x83mm.

Saad Zaghloul — A489

***Perf. 11x11½***

**1977, Aug. 23 Photo. Wmk. 342**

**1040** A489 20m dk green & dk brn .40 .25

Saad Zaghloul, leader of 1919 Revolution, 50th death anniversary.

Archbishop Capucci, Map of Palestine — A490

**1977, Sept. 1**

**1041** A490 45m emerald & blue 1.10 .50

Palestinian Archbishop Hilarion Capucci, jailed by Israel in 1974.

Bird-of-Paradise Flower — A491

**1977, Sept. 3**

**1042** A491 10m multicolored .45 .25

For use on greeting cards.

Proclamation Greening the Land — A492

***Perf. 11x11½***

**1977, Sept. 25 Photo. Wmk. 342**

**1043** A492 20m multicolored .50 .25

Agrarian Reform Law, 25th anniversary.

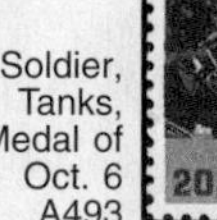

Soldier, Tanks, Medal of Oct. 6 A493

Anwar Sadat — A494

**1977, Oct. 6** ***Perf. 11½x11***

**1044** A493 20m multicolored .55 .25

**Unwmk.**

***Perf. 11***

**1045** A494 140m dk brn, gold & red 8.50 8.50

October War against Israel, 4th anniv. No. 1045 printed in sheets of 16.

Refugees Looking at Al Aqsa Mosque A495

Goddess Taueret and Spirit of Flight (Horus) A496

Mural Relief, Temple of Philae — A497

**Wmk. 342**

**1977, Oct. 24 Photo.** ***Perf. 11***

**1046** A495 45m grn, red & blk .80 .35

**1047** A496 55m dp blue & yel 1.50 .45

**1048** A497 140m ol bis & dk brn 2.50 1.25

*Nos. 1046-1048 (3)* 4.80 2.05

United Nations Day.

Electric Trains, First Egyptian Locomotive — A498

**1977, Oct. 22**

**1049** A498 20m multicolored 1.75 .40

125th anniversary of Egyptian railroads.

Film and Eye A499

**1977, Nov. 16** ***Perf. 11½x11***

**1050** A499 20m gray, blk & gold .75 .25

50th anniversary of Egyptian cinema.

Natural Gas Well and Refinery — A500

**1977, Nov. 17 Photo.**

**1051** A500 20m multicolored 1.25 .30

National Oil Festival, celebrating the acquisition of Sinai oil wells.

Pres. Sadat and Dome of the Rock A501

***Perf. 11½x11***

**1977, Dec. 31 Photo. Wmk. 342**

**1052** A501 20m green, brn & blk .60 .25
**1053** A501 140m green, blk & brn 2.00 .80

Pres. Sadat's peace mission to Israel.

Ramses II — A502

Post Day: 45m, Queen Nefertari, bas-relief.

**1978, Jan. 2** ***Perf. 11½***

**1054** A502 20m green, blk & gold .85 .40
**1055** A502 45m orange, blk & ol 1.75 .90

Post Day 1978.

Water Wheels, Fayum — A503

Flying Duck, from Floor in Ikhnaton's Palace A504

5m, Birdhouse, 10m, Statue of Horus. 20m, 30m, Al Rifa'i Mosque, Cairo. 50m, Monastery, Wadi al-Natrun. 55m, Ruins of Edfu Temple. 70m, 80m, Bridge of Oct. 6. 85m, Medum pyramid. 100m, Facade, El Morsi Mosque, Alexandria. 200m, Column, Alexandria, Sphinx. 500m, Arabian stallion.

**Wmk. 342, Unwmkd. (30m, 70m, 80m)**

**1978-85** ***Perf. 11½***

**1056** A503 1m slate blue .25 .25
*a.* Unwmkd. ('79) .25 .25
*b.* 1m gray ('83) .25 .25
*c.* 1m gray, unwmkd. ('83) .25 .25
**1057** A503 5m bister brn .25 .25
*a.* 5m dull brn, unwmkd. (79) .25 .25
**1058** A503 10m brt green .25 .25
*a.* Unwmkd. ('79) .25 .25
**1059** A503 20m dk brown .25 .25
*b.* Unwmkd. ('79) .25 .25
**1059A** A503 30m sepia .60 .50
*c.* Wmk. 342 ('82) — —
**1060** A503 50m Prus blue .25 .25
*a.* Unwmkd. ('79) .25 .25
*b.* Unwmkd., brt blue ('87) .25 .25
**1061** A503 55m olive .25 .25
**1062** A503 70m olive ('79) .40 .25
**1062A** A503 80m olive ('82) .50 .30
**1063** A503 85m dp purple .70 .30
*a.* Unwmkd. ('85) .70 .35
**1064** A503 100m brown .95 .30
*a.* Unwmkd. ('85) 1.25 .40
**1065** A503 200m bl & indigo 2.25 .80
*a.* Unwmkd. ('85) 2.25 .85
**1066** A504 500m multicolored 7.00 2.00
*a.* Unwmkd. ('85) 7.00 2.00
**1067** A504 £1 multicolored 11.00 4.00
*a.* Unwmkd. ('85) 11.00 4.00
*Nos. 1056-1067 (14)* 24.90 9.95

Issued: 500m, £1, 2/27/78; 70m, 8/22/79; others, 7/23/78.

Fair Emblem and Wheat A505

**1978, Mar. 15** ***Perf. 11½***

**1072** A505 20m multicolored .45 .25

11th Cairo International Fair, Mar. 11-25.

Emblem, Kasr El Ainy School A506

**1978, Mar. 18** ***Perf. 11½x11***

**1073** A506 20m lt blue, blk & gold .55 .25

Kasr El Ainy School of Medicine, 150th anniv.

A507

No. 1074, Soldiers and Emblem. No. 1075, Youssef El Sebai.

**1978, Mar. 30** ***Perf. 11x11½***

**1074** 20m multicolored .50 .30
**1075** 20m bister brown .50 .30
*a.* A507 Pair, #1074-1075 1.25 1.25

Youssef El Sebai, newspaper editor, assassinated on Cyprus and in memory of the commandos killed in raid on Cyprus.

Biennale Medal, Statue for Entrance to Port Said A509

**1978, Apr. 1** ***Perf. 11½***

**1076** A509 20m blue, grn & blk .55 .25

12th Biennial Exhibition of Fine Arts, Alexandria.

Child with Smallpox, UN Emblem A510

**1978, Apr. 7 Photo.** ***Perf. 11½***

**1077** A510 20m multicolored .55 .35

Eradication of smallpox.

Heart & Arrow, UN Emblem — A511

**1978, Apr. 7 Wmk. 342**

**1078** A511 20m multicolored .55 .35

Fight against hypertension.

Anwar Sadat — A512

**1978, May 15 Photo.** ***Perf. 11½x11***

**1079** A512 20m grn, brn & gold .65 .30

7th anniversary of Rectification Movement.

Social Security Emblem — A513

**1978, May 16** ***Perf. 11***

**1080** A513 20m lt green & dk brn .35 .25

General Organization of Insurance and Pensions (Social Security), 25th anniversary.

New Cities on Map of Egypt — A514

Map of Egypt and Sudan, Wheat — A515

**Wmk. 342**

**1978, July 23 Photo.** ***Perf. 11½***

**1081** A514 20m multicolored .85 .30
**1082** A515 45m multicolored 1.75 .50

26th anniversary of July 23rd revolution.

Symbols of Egyptian Ministries — A516

**1978, Aug. 28 Photo.** ***Perf. 11½x11***

**1083** A516 20m multicolored .65 .30

Centenary of Egyptian Ministerial System.

Pres. Sadat and "Spirit of Egypt" Showing Way — A517

**1978, Oct. 6 Photo.** ***Perf. 11x11½***

**1084** A517 20m multicolored .85 .30

October War against Israel, 5th anniv.

Fight Against Racial Discrimination Emblem — A518

Kobet al Sakra Mosque, Refugee Camp A519

Dove and Human Rights Emblem — A520

UN Day: 55m, Sanctuary of Isis at Philae and UNESCO emblem, horiz.

***Perf. 11, 11½ (45m)***

**1978, Oct. 24 Photo. Wmk. 342**

**1085** A518 20m multicolored .45 .25
**1086** A519 45m multicolored .90 .50
**1087** A518 55m multicolored 1.00 .60
**1088** A520 140m multicolored 2.25 1.00
*Nos. 1085-1088 (4)* 4.60 2.35

Pilgrims, Mt. Arafat and Holy Kaaba — A521

**1978, Nov. 7 Photo. *Perf. 11***
**1089** A521 45m multicolored 1.00 .40

Pilgrimage to Mecca.

Tahtib Horse Dance — A522

**1978, Nov. 7**
**1090** A522 10m multicolored .50 .25
**1091** A522 20m multicolored .50 .25

For use on greeting cards.

UN Emblem, Globe and Grain A523

**1978, Nov. 11 Photo. *Perf. 11½***
**1092** A523 20m green, dk bl & yel .45 .25

Technical Cooperation Among Developing Countries Conf., Buenos Aires, Sept. 1978.

Pipes, Map and Emblem of Sumed Pipeline A524

**1978, Nov. 11**
**1093** A524 20m brown, bl & yel .65 .25

Inauguration of Sumed pipeline from Suez to Alexandria, 1st anniversary.

Mastheads — A525

**1978, Dec. 24 *Perf. 11x11½***
**1094** A525 20m brown & black .65 .25

El Wakea el Masriya newspaper, 150th anniv.

Abu el Walid — A526

**1978, Dec. 24**
**1095** A526 45m brt grn & indigo .85 .30

800th death anniv. of Abu el Walid ibn Rashid.

Helwan Observatory and Sky — A527

**1978, Dec. 30 Wmk. 342**
**1096** A527 20m multicolored .95 .35

Helwan Observatory, 75th anniversary.

Second Daughter of Ramses II A528

Ramses Statues, Abu Simbel, and Cartouches — A529

**1979, Jan. 2 Photo. *Perf. 11***
**1097** A528 20m brown & yellow .65 .30

***Perf. 11½x11***

**1098** A529 140m multicolored 2.25 .80

Post Day 1979.

Book, Reader and Globe A530

***Perf. 11½x11***

**1979, Feb. 1 Photo. Wmk. 342**
**1099** A530 20m yel grn & brn .45 .25

Cairo 11th International Book Fair.

Wheat, Globe, Fair Emblem — A531

***Perf. 11x11½***

**1979, Mar. 17 Photo. Unwmk.**
**1100** A531 20m blue, org & blk .50 .25

12th Cairo International Fair, Mar.-Apr.

Skull, Poppy, Agency Emblem — A532

**1979, Mar. 20 *Perf. 11***
**1101** A532 70m multicolored 1.90 .65

Anti-Narcotics General Administration, 50th anniv.

Isis Holding Horus — A533

**1979, Mar. 21**
**1102** A533 140m multicolored 3.25 1.00

Mother's Day.

World Map and Book — A534

***Perf. 11x11½***

**1979, Mar. 22 Wmk. 342**
**1103** A534 45m yellow, bl & brn .55 .25

Cultural achievements of the Arabs.

Pres. Sadat's Signature, Peace Doves A535

**Wmk. 342**

**1979, Mar. 31 Photo. *Perf. 11½***
**1104** A535 70m brt green & red 1.25 .45
**1105** A535 140m yel grn & red 2.25 1.00

Signing of Peace Treaty between Egypt and Israel, Mar. 26.

**1979, May 26 Photo. *Perf. 11½***
**1106** A535 20m yellow & dk brn .55 .30

Return of Al Arish to Egypt.

Honeycomb with Food Symbols A536

**1979, May 15**
**1107** A536 20m multicolored .35 .25

8th anniversary of movement to establish food security.

Coins, 1959, 1979 A537

***Perf. 11½x11***

**1979, June 1 Wmk. 342 Photo.**
**1108** A537 20m yellow & gray .45 .25

25th anniversary of the Egyptian Mint.

Egypt No. 1104 under Magnifying Glass — A538

**1979, June 1 *Perf. 11***
**1109** A538 20m green, blk & brn .55 .25

Philatelic Society of Egypt, 50th anniversary.

Book, Atom Symbol, Rising Sun — A539

"23 July," "Revolution" and "Peace" — A540

***Perf. 11½x11***

**1979, July 23 Wmk. 342**
**1110** A539 20m multicolored .50 .25

**Miniature Sheet**

***Imperf***

**1111** A540 140m multicolored 3.75 3.75

27th anniversary of July 23rd revolution.

Musicians — A541

**1979, Aug. 22** ***Perf. 11½***
**1112** A541 10m multicolored .25 .25

For use on greeting cards.

Dove over Map of Suez Canal A542

**Wmk. 342**

**1979, Oct. 6** **Photo.** ***Perf. 11½***
**1113** A542 20m blue & brown .65 .30

October War against Israel, 6th anniv.

Prehistoric Mammal Skeleton, Map of Africa — A543

***Perf. 11½x11***

**1979, Oct. 9** **Photo.** **Wmk. 342**
**1114** A543 20m multicolored 2.00 .35

Egyptian Geological Museum, 75th anniv.

T Square on Drawing Board — A544

**1979, Oct. 11** ***Perf. 11***
**1115** A544 20m multicolored .65 .25

Engineers Day.

Human Rights Emblem Over Globe — A545

Boy Balancing IYC Emblem — A546

***Perf. 11½***

**1979, Oct. 24** **Photo.** **Unwmk.**
**1116** A545 45m multicolored .65 .30
**1117** A546 140m multicolored 1.50 1.25

UN Day and Intl. Year of the Child.

International Savings Day — A547

**1979, Oct. 31**
**1118** A547 70m multicolored 1.00 .45

A548

Design: Shooting championship emblem.

**1979, Nov. 16**
**1119** A548 20m multicolored .65 .25

20th International Military Shooting Championship, Cairo.

International Palestinian Solidarity Day — A549

**1979, Nov. 29** ***Perf. 11x11½***
**1120** A549 45m multicolored .85 .30

Dove Holding Olive Branch, Rotary Emblem, Globe A550

**1979, Dec. 3** **Photo.** ***Perf. 11½***
**1121** A550 140m multicolored 1.60 1.00

Rotary Intl., 75th anniv,; Cairo Rotary Club, 50th anniv.

Arms Factories, 25th Anniversary — A551

***Perf. 11½x11***

**1979, Dec. 23** **Photo.** **Wmk. 342**
**1122** A551 20m lt olive grn & brn .55 .25

Aly El Garem (1881-1949) — A552

Poets: No. 1124, Mahmoud Samy El Baroudy (1839-1904).

**1979, Dec. 25** ***Perf. 11x11½***
**1123** A552 20m dk brn & yel brn .50 .30
**1124** A552 20m brn & dk brn .50 .30
*a.* Pair, #1123-1124 1.25 1.25

Pharaonic Capital — A553

Post Day: Various Pharaonic capitals.

**1980, Jan. 2** **Unwmk.** ***Perf. 11½***
**1125** A553 20m multicolored .45 .30
**1126** A553 45m multicolored .65 .65
**1127** A553 70m multicolored 1.00 .75
**1128** A553 140m multicolored 2.75 1.50
*a.* Strip of 4, #1125-1128 6.50 .650

Golden Goddess of Writing, Fair Emblem — A554

**1980, Feb. 2** **Photo.** ***Perf. 11½***
**1129** A554 20m multicolored 1.10 .25

12th Cairo Intl. Book Fair, Jan. 24-Feb. 4.

Exhibition Catalogue and Medal — A555

**1980, Feb. 2**
**1130** A555 20m multicolored .60 .30

13th Biennial Exhibition of Fine Arts, Alexandria.

13th Cairo International Fair — A556

**1980, Mar. 8** **Photo.** ***Perf. 11x11½***
**1131** A556 20m multicolored .60 .25

Kiosk of Trajan — A557

a, Kiosk of Trajan. b, Temple of Korasy, entry at right. c, Temple of Ksalabsha, carvings on frame. d, Temple of Philae, 5 columns..

**1980, Mar. 10** ***Perf. 11½***
**1132** Strip of 4 + label 5.50 5.50
*a.-d.* A557 70m, any single 1.10 .85

UNESCO campaign to save Nubian monuments, 20th anniversary. Shown on stamps are Temples of Philae, Kalabsha, Korasy.

Physicians' Day — A558

**1980, Mar. 18** ***Perf. 11x11½***
**1133** A558 20m multicolored .60 .25

Rectification Movement, 9th Anniversary — A559

***Perf. 11½x11***

**1980, May 15** **Photo.** **Wmk. 342**
**1134** A559 20m multicolored .60 .25

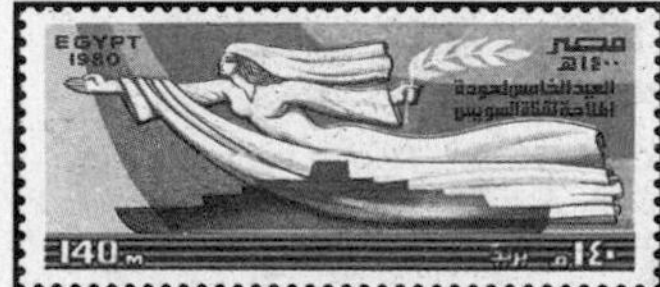
Re-opening of Suez Canal, 5th Anniversary — A560

**1980, June 5** ***Perf. 11½***
**1135** A560 140m multicolored 1.50 1.00

Prevention of Cruelty to Animals Week
A561

**1980, June 5**

**1136** A561 20m lt yel grn & gray .85 .25

Industry Day
A562

***Perf. 11½x11***

**1980, July 12 Photo. Wmk. 342**

**1137** A562 20m multicolored .55 .25

Leaf with Text
A563

Family Protection Emblem — A564

**1980, July 23** ***Perf. 11½***

**1138** A563 20m multicolored .60 .25

**Souvenir Sheet**

***Imperf***

**1139** A564 140m multicolored 3.75 3.75

July 23rd Revolution, 28th anniv.; Social Security Year.

Erksous Seller and Nakrazan Player — A565

***Perf. 11½***

**1980, Aug. 8 Unwmk. Photo.**

**1140** A565 10m multicolored .50 .25

For use on greeting cards.

October War Against Israel, 7th Anniv. — A566

**1980, Oct. 6 Litho.**

**1141** A566 20m multicolored .75 .25

Islamic and Coptic Columns
A567

International Telecommunications Union Emblem — A568

**Wmk. 342**

**1980, Oct. 24 Photo.** ***Perf. 11½***

**1142** A567 70m multicolored .80 .60

**1143** A568 140m multicolored 1.60 1.25

UN Day. Campaign to save Egyptian monuments (70m), Intl. Telecommunications Day (140m).

Hegira (Pilgrimage Year)
A569

**1980, Nov. 9 Litho.** ***Perf. 11x11½***

**1144** A569 45m multicolored .70 .30

Opening of Suez Canal Third Branch
A570

***Perf. 11½x11***

**1980, Dec. 16 Photo. Wmk. 342**

**1145** A570 70m multicolored 1.10 .60

Mustafa Sadek El-Rafai (1880-1927), Writer — A571

No. 1147, Ali Mustafa Mousharafa (1898-1950), mathematician (with glasses). No. 1148, Ali Ibrahim (1880-1947), surgeon.

**1980, Dec. 23** ***Perf. 11x11½***

**1146** A571 20m green & brown .50 .30

**1147** A571 20m green & brown .50 .30

**1148** A571 20m green & brown .50 .30

*a.* Strip of 3, #1146-1148 2.00 2.00

See Nos. 1178-1179.

Ladybug Scarab Emblem — A572

***Perf. 11½***

**1981, Jan. 2 Photo. Unwmk.**

**1149** A572 70m shown 1.25 .50

**1150** A572 70m Scarab, reverse 1.25 .50

Post Day.

von Stephan, UPU — A573

***Perf. 11x11½***

**1981, Jan. 7 Wmk. 342**

**1151** A573 140m grnsh bl & dk brn 1.75 .70

Heinrich von Stephan (1831-97), founder of UPU.

13th Cairo International Book Fair — A574

**1981, Feb. 1** ***Perf. 11½x11***

**1152** A574 20m multicolored .60 .25

14th Cairo International Fair, Mar. 14-28 — A575

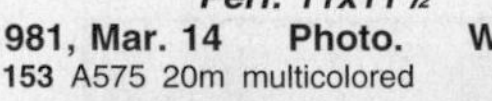

***Perf. 11x11½***

**1981, Mar. 14 Photo. Wmk. 342**

**1153** A575 20m multicolored .60 .25

Rural Electrification Authority, 10th Anniversary — A576

**1981, Mar. 18**

**1154** A576 20m multicolored .60 .25

Veterans' Day — A577

**1981, Mar. 26**

**1155** A577 20m multicolored .60 .25

Intl. Dentistry Conf., Cairo — A578

***Perf. 11x11½***

**1981, Apr. 14 Photo. Wmk. 342**

**1156** A578 20m red & olive .60 .25

Trade Union Emblem — A579

***Perf. 11x11½***

**1981, May 1 Photo. Wmk. 342**

**1157** A579 20m brt blue & dk brn .60 .25

International Confederation of Arab Trade Unions, 25th anniv.

Nurses' Day — A580

**1981, May 12**

**1158** A580 20m multicolored .60 .25

Irrigation Equipment (Electrification Movement) — A581

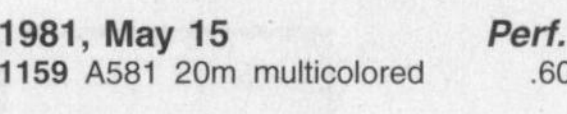

**1981, May 15** ***Perf. 11½***

**1159** A581 20m multicolored .60 .25

Air Force Day — A582

*Perf. 11x11½*

**1981, June 30 Photo. Wmk. 342**

**1160** A582 20m multicolored .60 .25

Flag Surrounding Map of Suez Canal — A583

**Wmk. 342**

**1981, July 23 Photo. *Perf. 11½***

**1161** A583 20m multicolored .60 .25
**1162** A583 20m Emblems .60 .25

July 23rd Revolution, 29th anniv.; Social Defense Year.

Lotus — A584

**Wmk. 342**

**1981, July 29 Photo. *Perf. 11***

**1163** A584 10m multicolored .60 .25

For use on greeting cards.

Kemal Ataturk — A585

**1981, Aug. 10 *Perf. 11x11½***

**1164** A585 140m dp bluish grn, brn 2.25 1.25

Orabi Revolution Centenary — A586

20m, Orabi Pasha, Leader of Egyptian Force.

*Perf. 11x11½*

**1981, Sept. 9 Photo. Wmk. 342**

**1165** A586 20m dp bluish grn, brn .60 .25

A587

**1981, Sept. 14**

**1166** A587 45m ochre, blk, brn .85 .25

World Muscular Athletics Championships, Cairo.

A588

*Perf. 11x11½*

**1981, Sept. 26 Photo. Wmk. 342**

**1167** A588 45m multicolored .60 .25

Ministry of Industry and Mineral Resources, 25th anniv.

20th Intl. Occupational Health Congress, Cairo — A589

**1981, Sept. 28 *Perf. 11½x11***

**1168** A589 20m multicolored .60 .25

October War Against Israel, 8th Anniv. A590

**1981, Oct. 6**

**1169** A590 20m multicolored .65 .25

World Food Day A591

13th World Telecommunications Day — A592

Intl. Year of the Disabled — A593

Fight Against Apartheid A594

*Perf. 11½x11, 11x11½*

**1981, Oct. 24 Photo. Wmk. 342**

**1170** A591 10m multicolored .45 .25
**1171** A592 20m multicolored .60 .25
**1172** A593 45m multicolored .80 .55
**1173** A594 230m multicolored 3.75 1.10
*Nos. 1170-1173 (4)* 5.60 2.15

United Nations Day.

Pres. Anwar Sadat (1917-81) — A595

*Perf. 11x11½*

**1981, Nov. 14 Unwmk.**

**1174** A595 30m multicolored 1.25 .75
**1175** A595 230m multicolored 5.50 3.00

Establishment of Shura Council — A596

*Perf. 11½x11*

**1981, Dec. 12 Photo. Wmk. 342**

**1176** A596 45m purple & yellow .60 .30

Agricultural Credit and Development Bank, 50th Anniv. — A597

**1981, Dec. 15 *Perf. 11x11½***

**1177** A597 20m multicolored .50 .25

**Famous Men Type of 1980**

30m, Ali el-Ghayati (1885-1956), journalist. 60m, Omar Ebn sl-Fared (1181-1234), Sufi poet.

*Perf. 11x11½*

**1981, Dec. 21 Photo. Wmk. 342**

**1178** A571 30m green & brown .40 .30
**1179** A571 60m green & brown .65 .45
*a.* Pair, #1178-1179 1.50 1.50

20th Anniv. of African Postal Union A598

**1981, Dec. 21 *Perf. 11½x11***

**1180** A598 60m multicolored .95 .35

14th Cairo Intl. Book Fair — A599

**1982, Jan. 28**

**1181** A599 3p brown & yellow .65 .25

Arab Trade Union of Egypt, 25th Anniv. — A600

**1982, Jan. 30**

**1182** A600 3p multicolored .45 .25

Khartoum Branch of Cairo University, 25th Anniv. A601

*Perf. 11½x11*

**1982, Mar. 4 Wmk. 342**

**1183** A601 6p blue & green .75 .35

15th Cairo Intl. Fair — A602

**1982, Mar. 13 *Perf. 11x11½***

**1184** A602 3p multicolored .60 .25

50th Anniv. of Al-Ghardaka Marine Biological Station — A603

Fish of the Red Sea: 10m, Lined butterfly fish. 30m, Blue-banded sea perch. 60m, Bat-fish. 230m, Blue-spotted boxfish.

**1982, Apr. 24 Litho. *Perf. 11½x11***

**1185** 10m multicolored .90 .60
**1186** 30m multicolored 1.10 .70
**1187** 60m multicolored 1.50 .90
**1188** 230m multicolored 3.50 2.00
*a.* A603 Block of 4, #1185-1188 7.50 7.50

Liberation of the Sinai — A604

**1982, Apr. 25 Photo.** ***Perf. 11x11½***
**1189** A604 3p multicolored .65 .25

50th Anniv. of Egypt Air A605

**1982, May 7 Photo.** ***Perf. 11½x11***
**1190** A605 23p multicolored 3.25 2.25

Minaret — A606

Al Azhar Mosque — A607

a, shown. b, Two terraces. c, Three terraces. d, Two turrets at top.

***Perf. 11x11½***
**1982, June 28 Photo. Wmk. 342**
**1191** Strip of 4 + label 5.00 5.00
***a.-d.*** A606 6p any single, multi .75 .55

**Souvenir Sheet**
**Unwmk.** ***Imperf.***
**1192** A607 23p multicolored 6.25 6.25

Al Azhar Mosque millennium.
No. 1192 airmail.

Dove — A608

Flower in Natl. Colors — A609

***Perf. 11x11½***
**1982, July 23 Photo. Wmk. 342**
**1193** A608 3p multicolored .50 .25

**Souvenir Sheet**
***Imperf***
**1194** A609 23p multicolored 4.00 4.00

30th anniv. of July 23rd Revolution.

World Tourism Day A610

Design: Sphinx, pyramid of Cheops, St. Catherine's Tower.

***Perf. 11½x11***
**1982, Sept. 27 Photo. Wmk. 342**
**1195** A610 23p multicolored 3.50 2.25

October War Against Israel, 9th Anniv. A611

**1982, Oct. 6**
**1196** A611 3p Memorial, map .65 .25

Biennale of Alexandria Art Exhibition — A612

**1982, Oct. 17** ***Perf. 11x11½***
**1197** A612 3p multicolored .60 .25

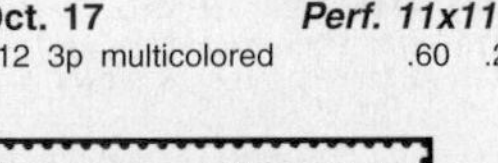

10th Anniv. of UN Conference on Human Environment — A613

2nd UN Conference on Peaceful Uses of Outer Space, Vienna, Aug. 9-21 — A614

Scouting Year A615

TB Bacillus Centenary A616

***Perf. 11½x11, 11½ (A615)***
**1982, Oct. 24**
**1198** A613 3p multicolored .50 .35
**1199** A614 6p multicolored .80 .55
**1200** A615 6p multicolored 1.10 .55
**1201** A616 8p multicolored 1.25 .75
*Nos. 1198-1201 (4)* 3.65 2.20

United Nations Day.

50th Anniv. of Air Force A617

**1982, Nov. 2** ***Perf. 11½x11***
**1202** A617 3p Jet, plane .70 .25

Ahmed Chawki (1868-1932) and Hafez Ibrahim (1871-1932), Poets — A618

***Perf. 11½x11***
**1982, Nov. 25 Photo. Wmk. 342**
**1203** A618 6p multicolored .65 .50

Natl. Research Center, 25th Anniv. — A619

**1982, Dec. 12 Photo.** ***Perf. 11x11½***
**1204** A619 3p red & blue .70 .30

50th Anniv. of Arab Language Society A620

**1982, Dec. 25** ***Perf. 11½x11***
**1205** A620 6p multicolored .80 .50

Year of the Aged — A621

**1982, Dec. 25** ***Perf. 11x11½***
**1206** A621 23p multicolored 3.25 2.00

Post Day A622

**1983, Jan. 2** ***Perf. 11½***
**1207** A622 3p multicolored .60 .25

15th Cairo Intl. Book Fair — A623

***Perf. 11x11½***
**1983, Jan. 25 Photo. Wmk. 342**
**1208** A623 3p blue & red .65 .25

Police Day A624

**1983, Jan. 25** ***Perf. 11½x11***
**1209** A624 3p multicolored .65 .25

16th Cairo Intl. Fair — A625

***Perf. 11x11½***
**1983, Mar. 2 Photo. Wmk. 342**
**1210** A625 3p multicolored .65 .30

5th UN African Map Conf., Cairo — A626

**1983, Mar. 2**
**1211** A626 3p lt green & blue .70 .30

African Ministers of Transport, Communications and Planning, 3rd Conference — A627

**1983, Mar. 8** ***Perf. 11½x11***

**1212** A627 23p green & blue 1.75 1.00

Victory in African Soccer Cup — A628

**1983, Mar. 20** ***Perf. 11x11½***

**1213** A628 3p Heading .55 .30
**1214** A628 3p Kick .55 .30
*a.* Pair, #1213-1214 1.25 1.25

World Health Day and Natl. Blood Donation Campaign — A629

***Perf. 11x11½***

**1983, Apr. 2 Photo. Wmk. 342**

**1215** A629 3p olive & red .70 .25

Org. of African Trade Union Unity A630

***Perf. 11½x11***

**1983, Apr. 21 Photo. Wmk. 342**

**1216** A630 3p multicolored .65 .30

1st Anniv. of Sinai Liberation — A631

**1983, Apr. 25** ***Perf. 11x11½***

**1217** A631 3p multicolored .70 .30

75th Anniv. of Entomology Society — A632

3p, Emblem (Holy Scarab).

**1983, May 23**

**1218** A632 3p blue & black .70 .30

Chrysanthemums A633

**1983, June 11 Photo.** ***Perf. 11½x11***

**1219** A633 20m green & org red .40 .25

For use on greeting cards.

5th African Handball Championship, Cairo — A634

***Perf. 11½x11***

**1983, July 22 Photo. Wmk. 342**

**1220** A634 6p brown & dk grn .65 .30

31st Anniv. of Revolution A635

**1983, July 23** ***Perf. 11½***

**1221** A635 3p multicolored .45 .25

Simon Bolivar (1783-1830) — A636

**1983, Aug.** ***Perf. 11x11½***

**1222** A636 23p brown & dull grn 1.75 1.00

Centenary of Arrival of Natl. Hero Orabi in Ceylon A637

3p, Map, Orabi, El-Zahra School.

***Perf. 11½x11***

**1983, Aug. 25 Photo. Wmk. 342**

**1223** A637 3p multicolored .55 .25

Islamic Vase, Museum Building A638

**1983, Sept. 14 Photo.** ***Perf. 11½x11***

**1224** A638 3p yel brn & dk brn .85 .30

Reopening of Islamic Museum.

October War Against Israel, 10th Anniv. — A639

**1983, Oct. 6** ***Perf. 11½***

**1225** A639 3p multicolored .70 .25

2nd Pharaonic Race — A640

**1983, Oct. 17** ***Perf. 11½***

**1226** A640 23p multicolored 2.25 1.25

United Nations Day — A641

**1983, Oct. 24 Photo.** ***Perf. 11***

**1227** A641 3p IMO, ships, horiz. .60 .25
**1228** A641 6p ITU, UPU .75 .50
**1229** A641 6p FAO, UN, grain .75 .50
**1230** A641 23p UN, ocean 2.50 1.75
*Nos. 1227-1230 (4)* 4.60 3.00

4th World Karate Championship, Cairo — A642

**1983, Nov. Photo.** ***Perf. 13***

**1231** A642 3p multicolored .70 .30

Intl. Palestinian Cooperation Day — A643

**1983, Nov. 29 Photo.** ***Perf. 13x13½***

**1232** A643 6p Dome of the Rock 1.00 .30

75th Anniv. of Faculty of Fine Arts, Cairo A644

**1983, Nov. 30** ***Perf. 13***

**1233** A644 3p multicolored .55 .25

75th Anniv. of Cairo University — A645

**1983, Nov. 30** ***Perf. 11x11½***

**1234** A645 3p multicolored .55 .25
*a.* Perf. 13¼x12¾

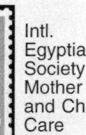

Intl. Egyptian Society of Mother and Child Care A646

**1983, Nov. 30** ***Perf. 11½x11***

**1235** A646 3p multicolored .55 .25

Org. of African Unity, 20th Anniv. — A647

***Perf. 11x11½***

**1983, Dec. 20 Photo. Wmk. 342**

**1236** A647 3p multicolored .55 .25

World Heritage Convention, 10th Anniv. — A648

**1983, Dec. 24**

**1237** A648 Strip of 3 2.25 2.25
*a.* 3p Wood carving, Islamic .70 .45
*b.* 3p Coptic tapestry .70 .45
*c.* 3p Ramses II Thebes .70 .45

Post Day A649

Restored Forts: 6p, Quatbay. 23p, Mosque, Salah El-Din.

**1984, Jan. 2** ***Perf. 13***

**1238** A649 6p multicolored .80 .45
**1239** A649 23p multicolored 2.50 1.25

Misr Insurance Co., 50 Anniv. A650

**1984, Jan. 14** ***Perf. 11½x11***

**1240** A650 3p multicolored .55 .30

16th Cairo Intl. Book Fair — A651

*Perf. 13½x13*

**1984, Jan. 26 Photo. Wmk. 342**

**1241** A651 3p multicolored .55 .25

17th Cairo Intl. Fair A652

*Perf. 11½x11*

**1984, Mar. 10 Photo. Wmk. 342**

**1242** A652 3p multicolored .55 .30

25th Anniv. of Asyut University — A653

**1984, Mar. 10** *Perf. 11x11½*

**1243** A653 3p multicolored .55 .25

75th Anniv. of Cooperative Unions — A654

**1984, Mar. 17**

**1244** A654 3p multicolored .55 .25

World Theater Day — A655

Mahmoud Mokhtar (1891-1934), Sculptor — A656

*Perf. 11x11½, 11½x11*

**1984, Mar. 27 Photo. Unwmk.**

**1245** A655 3p Masks .55 .25

**1246** A656 3p Pride of the Nile .55 .25

World Health Day and Fight Against Polio — A657

*Perf. 11½x11*

**1984, Apr. 7 Photo. Wmk. 342**

**1247** A657 3p Polio vaccine 1.00 .30

2nd Anniv. of Sinai Liberation — A658

**1984, Apr. 25**

**1248** A658 3p Doves, map .55 .25

Africa Day A659

*Perf. 12½x13½*

**1984, May 25 Photo. Wmk. 342**

**1249** A659 3p Map, UN emblem .55 .25

Satellite, Waves — A660

**1984, May 31** *Perf. 11x11½*

**1250** A660 3p multicolored .55 .25

Radio broadcasting in Egypt, 50th anniv.

Carnations — A661

**1984, June 1**

**1251** A661 2p red & green .45 .25

For use on greeting cards.

Intl. Cairo Arab Arts Biennale — A662

**1984, June 1** *Perf. 13½x12½*

**1252** A662 3p multicolored .55 .25

July Revolution, 32nd Anniv. — A663

3p, Atomic energy, agriculture.

**Wmk. 342**

**1984, July 23 Photo.** *Perf. 11*

**1253** A663 3p multicolored .55 .25

A664

1984 Summer Olympics: a, Boxing. b, Basketball. c, Volleyball. d, Soccer.

**1984, July 28**

**1254** Strip of 4 + label 5.75 5.75

*a.-d.* A664 3p any single .45 .25

**Size: 130x80mm**

***Imperf***

**1255** A664 30p like No. 1254 4.25 4.25

A665

**Wmk. 342**

**1984, Aug. 13 Photo.** *Perf. 11*

**1256** A665 3p bl & multi .55 .25

**1257** A665 23p grn & multi 2.50 1.40

2nd Genl. Conference of Egyptians Abroad, Aug. 11-15, Cairo.

Youth Hostels, 30th Anniv. — A666

*Perf. 11x11½*

**1984, Sept. 22 Photo. Wmk. 342**

**1258** A666 3p Youths, emblem .55 .25

Egypt Tour Co., 50th Anniv. — A667

**1984, Sept. 27**

**1259** A667 3p Emblem, sphinx .60 .25

October War Against Israel, 11th Anniv. — A668

**1984, Oct. 6**

**1260** A668 3p Map, eagle .55 .25

Egypt-Sudan Unity — A669

**1984, Oct. 12**

**1261** A669 3p Map of Nile, arms .55 .25

UN Day — A670

*Perf. 13½x12½*

**1984, Oct. 24 Photo. Wmk. 342**

**1262** A670 3p UNICEF Emblem, child .55 .25

UN campaign for infant survival.

Tanks, Emblem — A671

**1984, Nov. 10**

**1263** A671 3p multicolored .60 .25

Military Equipment Exhibition, Cairo, Nov. 10-14.

Tolon Mosque, Egypt A672

**1984, Dec. 23 Photo.** *Perf. 11½x11*

**1264** A672 3p multicolored .65 .25

Ahmed Ebn Tolon (A.D. 835-884), Gov. of Egypt, founder of Kataea City.

A673

**1984, Dec. 23** *Perf. 11x11½*

**1265** A673 3p multicolored .55 .25

Kamel el-Kilany (1897-1959), author.

Globe and Congress Emblem — A674

*Perf. 11x11½*

**1984, Dec. 26 Photo. Wmk. 342**

1266 A674 3p lt blue, ver & blk .65 .25

29th Intl. Congress on the History of Medicine, Dec. 27, 1984-Jan. 1, 1985, Cairo.

Academy of the Arts, 25th Anniv. A675

**1984, Dec. 31** ***Perf. 13***

1267 A675 3p Emblem in spotlights .60 .25

Pharaoh Receiving Message, Natl. Postal Museum, Cairo A676

**1985, Jan. 2** ***Perf. 11½x11***

1268 A676 3p brown, lt bl & ver .65 .25

Postal Museum, 50th anniv.

Intl. Union of Architects, 15th Conference, Jan. 14-Feb. 15 — A677

**1985, Jan. 20**

1269 A677 3p multicolored .60 .25

Seated Pharaonic Scribe — A678

**1985, Jan. 22** ***Perf. 11x11½***

1270 A678 3p brt org & dk blue grn .70 .30

17th Intl. Book Fair, Jan. 22-Feb. 3, Cairo.

Wheat, Cogwheels, Fair Emblem — A679

**1985, Mar. 9** ***Perf. 13½x13***

1271 A679 3p multicolored .60 .25

18th Intl. Fair, Mar. 9-22, Cairo.

Return of Sinai to Egypt, 3rd Anniv. — A680

**1985, Apr. 25 Wmk. 342 Litho.**

1272 A680 5p multicolored 1.00 .30

Ancient Artifacts — A681

A681a

Designs: 1p, God Mout, limestone sculpture, 360-340 B.C. 2p, No. 1281, Five wading birds, bas-relief. 3p, No. 1276, Seated statue, Ramses II, Temple of Luxor. No. 1276A, Vase. 8p, 15p, Slave bearing votive fruit offering, mural. 10p, Double-handled flask. 11p, Sculpted head of woman. No. 1282, Pitcher. 30p, 50p, Decanter. 35p, Temple of Karnak carved capitals. £1, Mosque.

**1985-90 Photo. Unwmk. *Perf. 11½***

| | | | | | |
|---|---|---|---|---|---|
| 1273 | A681 | 1p | brown olive | .40 | .25 |
| 1274 | A681 | 2p | brt grnsh bl | .40 | .25 |
| 1275 | A681 | 3p | yel brn | .40 | .25 |
| 1276 | A681 | 5p | dk violet | .50 | .25 |
| 1276A | A681 | 6p | lemon | .40 | .25 |
| 1277 | A681 | 8p | pale ol grn, sep & brn | .75 | .25 |
| 1278 | A681 | 10p | dk vio & bl | .60 | .25 |
| 1279 | A681 | 11p | dk violet | .90 | .30 |
| 1280 | A681 | 15p | pale yel, sep & brn | 1.40 | .30 |
| 1281 | A681 | 20p | yel grn | .60 | .30 |
| 1282 | A681 | 20p | dk grn & yel | .60 | .30 |
| 1283 | A681 | 30p | ol bis & buff | .70 | .30 |
| 1284 | A681 | 35p | sep & pale yel | 1.00 | .60 |
| 1285 | A681 | 50p | pur & buff | 1.25 | .50 |
| 1285A | A681a | £1 | brn & buff | 3.00 | 1.25 |
| 1286 | A681a | £2 | sepia & yel | 6.00 | 2.00 |
| | *Nos. 1273-1286 (16)* | | | 18.90 | 7.60 |

Issued: 1p, 2p, 3p, No. 1276, 8p, 11p, 15p, 5/1/85; 35p, 7/7/85; No. 1281, 4/1/86; 10p, 10/1/89; £2, 12/1/89; No. 1282, 2/1/90; 30p, 50p, 2/5/90; £1, 2/8/90; No. 1276A, 12/15/90.

No. 1276A is 18x23mm.

No. 1278 exists dated "1990."

See Nos. 1467, 1470, 1472.

Helwan University School of Music, 50th Anniv. A682

**1985, May 15**

1287 A682 5p multicolored .75 .30

El-Moulid Bride, Folk Doll — A683

**1985**

1288 A683 2p orange & multi .50 .25

1289 A683 5p red & multi .60 .30

Festivals 1985. Issued: 2p, 6/11; 5p, 8/10.

For use on greeting cards.

A684

Winning teams: a, b, Cairo Sports Stadium. c, El-Zamalek Club, white uniform, 1983. d, Natl. Club, red uniform, 1984. e, El-Mokawiloon Club (Arab Contractor Club), orange uniform, 1984.

**1985, June 17** ***Perf. 13½x13***

1290 Strip of 5 5.50 5.50

*a.-e.* A684 5p any single .80 .50

1985 Africa Cup Soccer Championships. Cairo Sports Stadium, 25th anniv. Nos. 1290a-1290b have continuous design.

A685

**1985, July 23** ***Perf. 11½x11***

1291 A685 5p blue, brn & yel .80 .30

Egyptian Television, 25th anniv. Egyptian Revolution, 33rd anniv.

Suez Canal Reopening, 10th Anniv. — A686

*Perf. 13x13½*

**1985, July 23 Litho. Wmk. 342**

1292 A686 5p multicolored .80 .30

Egyptian Revolution, 33rd anniv.

Ahmed Hamdi Memorial Underwater Tunnel — A687

**1985, July 23** ***Perf. 13½x13***

1293 A687 5p blue, vio & org .60 .25

Egyptian Revolution, 33rd anniv.

Souvenir Sheet

Aswan High Dam, 25th Anniv. — A688

**Wmk. 342**

**1985, July 23 Photo.** ***Imperf.***

1294 A688 30p multicolored 4.00 4.00

Heart, Map, Olive Laurel, Conference Emblem — A689

**1985, Aug. 10 Litho.** ***Perf. 13½x13***

1295 A689 15p multicolored 1.25 .85

Egyptian Emigrants, 3rd general conference, Aug. 10-14, Cairo.

Natl. Tourism Ministry, 50th Anniv. — A690

**1985, Sept. 10** ***Perf. 13x13½***

1296 A690 5p multicolored .55 .30

October War Against Israel, 12th Anniv. — A691

**1985, Oct. 6**

1297 A691 5p multicolored .60 .30

Air Scouts Assoc., 30th Anniv. — A692

**1985, Oct. 15 Photo.** *Perf. 11½*
**1298** A692 5p Emblem .80 .30

UN Day, Meteorology Day — A693

5p, UN emblem, weather map.

**1985, Oct. 24**
**1299** A693 5p multicolored .55 .25

UN, 40th Anniv. — A694

**1985, Oct. 24**
**1300** A694 15p multicolored 1.25 .85

Intl. Youth Year — A695

**1985, Oct. 24**
**1301** A695 5p multicolored .55 .25

A696

**1985, Oct. 24**
**1302** A696 15p blue & int blue 1.25 .85

Intl. Communications Development Program.

2nd Intl. Dentistry Conference — A697

Emblem, hieroglyphics of Hassi Raa, 1st known dentist.

**1985, Oct. 29** *Perf. 11x11½*
**1303** A697 5p beige & pale bl vio .75 .30

Emblem, Squash Player — A698

**1985, Nov. 18 Photo.** *Perf. 11½*
**1304** A698 5p multicolored .65 .25

1985 World Squash Championships, Nov. 18-Dec. 4.

A699

**1985, Nov. 2 Litho.** *Perf. 13½x13*
**1305** A699 5p multicolored .55 .30

4th Intl. Conference on the Biography and Sunna of Mohammed.

A700

**1985, Dec. 1 Photo.** *Perf. 11x11½*
**1306** A700 5p multicolored .55 .25

1st Conference on the Development of Vocational Training.

Natl. Olympic Committee, 75th Anniv. — A701

**1985, Dec. 28 Photo.** *Perf. 13x13½*
**1307** A701 5p multicolored .60 .30

18th Intl. Book Fair, Cairo — A702

**1986, Jan. 21** *Perf. 11x11½*
**1308** A702 5p Pharaonic scribe .55 .25

CODATU III — A703

**1986, Jan. 26** *Perf. 11½*
**1309** A703 5p lt ol grn, ver & grnsh bl .55 .25

3rd Intl. Conference on Urban Transportation in Developing Countries, Cairo.

Central Bank, 25th Anniv. — A704

**1986, Jan. 30** *Perf. 13x13½*
**1310** A704 5p multicolored .55 .25

Cairo Postal Traffic Center Inauguration — A705

**1986, Jan. 30** *Perf. 11½x11*
**1311** A705 5p blue & dk brown .55 .25

Pharaonic Mural, Btah Hotteb's Tomb at Saqqara A706

**1986, Feb. 27 Photo.** *Perf. 11½x11*
**1312** A706 5p yel, gldn brn & brn .70 .35

Faculty of Commerce, Cairo Univ., 75th anniv.

Cairo Intl. Fair, Mar. 8-21 — A707

**1986, Mar. 8 Litho.** *Perf. 13½x13*
**1313** A707 5p multicolored .55 .25

Queen Nefertiti, Sinai — A708

*Perf. 13x13½*
**1986, Apr. 25 Litho. Wmk. 342**
**1314** A708 5p multicolored .70 .30

Return of the Sinai to Egypt, 4th anniv.

Ministry of Health, 50th Anniv. — A709

**1986, Apr. 10** *Perf. 13½x13*
**1315** A709 5p multicolored .55 .30

1986 Census — A710

**1986, May 26 Photo.** *Perf. 11½*
**1316** A710 15p brn, grnsh bl & yel bis 1.00 .50

Egypt, Winner of African Soccer Cup — A711

No. 1317, English inscription below cup. No. 1318, Arabic inscription below cup.

**1986, May 31** *Perf. 13½x13*
**1317** A711 5p multicolored .65 .45
**1318** A711 5p multicolored .65 .45
*a.* Pair, #1317-1318 1.50 1.50

Festivals, Roses — A712

**1986, June 2** *Perf. 11½*
**1319** A712 5p multicolored .55 .25

For use on greeting cards.

World Environment Day — A713

15p, Emblem, smokestacks.

**1986, June 5** ***Perf. 13½x13***
**1320** A713 15p multicolored 1.25 .50

July 23rd Revolution, 34th Anniv. A714

**1986, July 23** **Litho.** ***Perf. 13***
**1321** A714 5p gray grn, scar & yel bis .60 .25

6th African Roads Conference, Cairo, Sept. 22-26 — A715

***Perf. 13½x13***
**1986, Sept. 21** **Litho.** **Wmk. 342**
**1322** A715 15p multicolored 1.25 .55

October War Against Israel, 13th Anniv. A716

**1986, Oct. 6** **Litho.** ***Perf. 13***
**1323** A716 5p multicolored 1.00 .30

Engineers' Syndicate, 40th Anniv. A717

**1986, Oct. 11** **Photo.** ***Perf. 11½***
**1324** A717 5p lt blue, brn & pale grn .55 .25

Workers' Cultural Education Assoc., 25th Anniv. — A718

**1986, Oct. 11** ***Perf. 11x11½***
**1325** A718 5p orange & rose vio .55 .25

Intl. Peace Year — A719

**1986, Oct. 24**
**1326** A719 5p blue, grn & pale sal .55 .25

First Oil Well in Egypt, Cent. — A720

**1986, Nov. 7** **Photo.** ***Perf. 11½***
**1327** A720 5p dull grn, blk & pale yel .65 .25

UN Child Survival Campaign A721

**1986, Nov. 20** **Litho.** ***Perf. 13***
**1328** A721 5p multicolored .60 .25

Ahmed Amin, Philosopher A722

**1986, Dec. 20** ***Perf. 11½***
**1329** A722 5p pale grn, pale yel & brn .55 .25

National Theater, 50th Anniv. — A723

**1986, Dec. 20** ***Perf. 13½x13***
**1330** A723 5p multicolored .55 .25

Post Day A724

Step Pyramid, Saqqara, King Zoser.

***Perf. 13x13½***
**1987, Jan. 2** **Litho.** **Wmk. 342**
**1331** A724 5p multicolored .65 .30

19th Intl. Book Fair, Cairo A725

**1987, Jan. 25** **Litho.** ***Perf. 13***
**1332** A725 5p multicolored .60 .30

5th World Conference on Islamic Education A726

**Wmk. 342**
**1987, Mar. 8** **Litho.** ***Perf. 13***
**1333** A726 5p multicolored .55 .25

20th Intl. Fair, Cairo — A727

5p, Good workers medal.

**1987, Mar. 21** **Photo.** ***Perf. 11½***
**1334** A727 5p multicolored .55 .25

Veteran's Day A728

**1987, Mar. 26**
**1335** A728 5p multicolored .55 .30

Intl. Gardens Inauguration, Nasser City — A729

**1987, Mar. 30** **Litho.** ***Perf. 13***
**1336** A729 15p multicolored 1.10 .60

World Health Day A730

No. 1337, Mother feeding child. No. 1338, Oral rehydration therapy.

**1987, Apr. 7** **Photo.** ***Perf. 11½***
**1337** A730 5p multicolored .55 .30

**Litho.**
***Perf. 13***
**1338** A730 5p multicolored .55 .30

A731

Natl. Team Victory at 1986 Intl. Soccer Championships — A732

Trophies: No. 1339a, Al Ahly Cup. No. 1339b, National Cup. No. 1339c, Al Zamalek Cup. No. 1340, Natl. flag, Cairo Stadium and trophies pictured on No. 1339.

**1987, Apr. 19** **Litho.** ***Perf. 13½x13***
**1339** Strip of 3 1.75 1.75
*a.-c.* A731 5p any single .55 .30

**Size: 115x85mm**
***Imperf***
**1340** A732 30p multicolored 4.00 4.00

A733

Salah El Din Citadel, Pharoah's Is., Sinai.

**1987, Apr. 25**
**1341** A733 5p sky blue & lt brown .65 .30

Return of the Sinai to Egypt, 5th anniv.

Festivals — A734

**1987, May 21 Photo. *Perf. 11½***
**1342** A734 5p Dahlia .55 .25

Cultural Heritage Exhibition — A735

**1987, June 17 Litho. *Perf. 13x13½***
**1343** A735 15p multicolored 1.00 1.00

Tourism Year — A736

a, Column and Sphinx, Alexandria. b, St. Catherine's Monastery, Mt. Sinai. c, Colossi of Thebes. d, Temple of Theban Triad, Luxor.

**1987, June 18**
**1344** Block of 4 5.25 5.25
*a.-d.* A736 15p any single 1.10 .90

See No. C187.

Loyalty Day A737

**1987, June 26 *Perf. 13***
**1345** A737 5p multicolored .55 .25

General Intelligence Service, 32nd anniv.

Industry-Agriculture Exhibition — A738

**1987, July 23 Photo. *Perf. 11½***
**1346** A738 5p grn, dull org & blk .55 .25

Intl. Year of Shelter for the Homeless A739

**1987, Sept. 2 Litho. *Perf. 13***
**1347** A739 5p multicolored .55 .25

World Architects' Day.

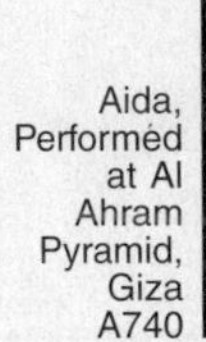

Aida, Performed at Al Ahram Pyramid, Giza A740

Radamis and troops returning from Ethiopia.

**1987, Sept. 21**
**1348** A740 15p multicolored 1.50 .65

**Size: 70x70mm**

***Imperf***

**1349** A740 30p multicolored 10.00 10.00

Greater Cairo Subway Inauguration — A741

**1987, Sept. 27 *Perf. 13x13½***
**1350** A741 5p multicolored 1.20 .30

Industry Day A742

**1987, Oct. 1 *Perf. 13***
**1351** A742 5p multicolored .55 .25

Battle of Hettin, 800th Anniv. — A743

**1987, Oct. 6 Photo. *Perf. 11x11½***
**1352** A743 5p multicolored .70 .30

UPU Emblem A744

***Perf. 11½***

**1987, Oct. 24 Unwmk. Photo.**
**1353** A744 5p multicolored .55 .25

UN Executive Council, 40th anniv.; UPU Consultative Council, 30th anniv.

16th Art Biennial of Alexandria A745

**1987, Nov. 7 Litho. *Perf. 13½x13***
**1354** A745 5p multicolored .55 .25

Second Intl. Defense Equipment Exhibition, Cairo, Nov. 9-13 — A746

***Perf. 13x13½***

**1987, Nov. 9 Litho. Unwmk.**
**1355** A746 5p multicolored .60 .25

2nd Pan-Arab Congress on Anaesthesia and Intensive Care — A747

**Unwmk.**

**1987, Dec. 1 Litho. *Perf. 13***
**1356** A747 5p multicolored .65 .30

Intl. Orthopedic and Traumatology Conference A748

**1987, Dec. 1 *Perf. 13½x13***
**1357** A748 5p gray, red brn & bl .55 .25

Selim Hassan (1887-1961), Egyptologist, and Hieroglyphs A749

Abdel Hamid Badawi (1887-1965), Jurist, and Scales of Justice — A750

***Perf. 13½x13***

**1987, Dec. 30 Litho. Unwmk.**
**1358** A749 5p multicolored .55 .25
**1359** A750 5p multicolored .55 .25

Stamp Day 1988 — A751

Pyramids of the Pharaohs and: a, Cheops. b, Chefren. c, Mycerinus. No. 1360 has a continuous design.

**1988, Jan. 2**
**1360** A751 Strip of 3 5.50 5.50
*a.-c.* 15p, any single 1.40 .90

Afro-Asian Peoples Solidarity Organization, 30th Anniv. — A752

**1988, Jan. 10 *Perf. 13x13½***
**1361** A752 15p multicolored 1.00 .55

20th Intl. Book Fair, Cairo — A753

**1988, Jan. 26** ***Perf. 13½x13***
**1362** A753 5p multicolored .55 .25

Martrans (Natl. Shipping Line), 25th Anniv. A754

**Unwmk.**
**1988, Mar. 3** **Litho.** ***Perf. 13***
**1363** A754 5p multicolored .85 .25

Cairo Intl. Fair A755

**1988, Mar. 12** **Photo.** ***Perf. 11½x11***
**1364** A755 5p multicolored .55 .25

World Health Day 1988: Diabetes — A756

***Perf. 11x11½***
**1988, Apr. 7** **Photo.** **Unwmk.**
**1365** A756 5p multicolored .55 .25

Prince, Fig Tree — A757

**1988, Apr. 17** ***Perf. 11½***
**1366** A757 5p grn, brn org & brn .55 .25

1988 Festival. For use on greeting cards.

African Postal Union, 25th Anniv. — A758

**1988, Apr. 23** **Litho.** ***Perf. 13x13½***
**1367** A758 15p brt blue 1.00 1.00

Oppose Racial Discrimination — A759

**1988, May 25** **Photo.** ***Perf. 11½***
**1368** A759 5p multicolored .50 .25

Taw Fek-Hakem (1902-1987), Playwright, Novelist — A760

**1988, Aug. 5** **Photo.** ***Perf. 11½***
**1369** A760 5p brt grn bl & org brn .60 .25

See Nos. 1383-1384, 1479-1480, 1486, 1500-1502, 1543-1546.

Faculty of Art Education, 50th Anniv. A761

***Perf. 11½***
**1988, Sept. 10** **Photo.** **Unwmk.**
**1370** A761 5p multicolored .50 .25

A762

1988 Summer Olympics, Seoul — A763

**1988, Sept. 17** **Litho.** ***Perf. 13***
**1371** A762 15p multicolored 1.25 1.25

**Size: 96x91mm**

***Imperf.***
**1372** A763 30p multicolored 6.25 6.25

No. 1371 is airmail.

October War Against Israel, 15th Anniv. — A764

***Perf. 13x13½***
**1988, Oct. 6** **Litho.** **Unwmk.**
**1373** A764 5p multicolored .55 .35

A765

Opening of the Opera House — A766

**1988, Oct. 10** ***Perf. 11½***
**1374** A765 5p multicolored .55 .30

**Size: 112x75mm**

***Imperf***
**1375** A766 50p multicolored 3.50 3.50

Intl. Red Cross and Red Crescent Organizations, 125th Annivs. — A767

***Perf. 11½***
**1988, Oct. 24** **Photo.** **Unwmk.**
**1376** A767 5p green, blk & red .50 .25

WHO, 40th Anniv. — A768

**1988, Oct. 24** ***Perf. 11x11½***
**1377** A768 20p multicolored 1.25 1.10

Naguib Mahfouz, 1988 Nobel Prize Winner for Literature — A769

**1988, Nov. 7** **Litho.** ***Perf. 13x13½***
**1378** A769 5p multicolored .50 .25

See No. C190.

Arab Scouting Organization, 75th Anniv. — A770

**1988, Nov. 10**
**1379** A770 25p multicolored 1.25 1.25

Return of Taba to Egypt — A771

**1988, Nov. 15**
**1380** A771 5p multicolored .50 .25

Intl. Conference on Orthopedic Surgery, Cairo, Nov. 15-18 — A772

**1988, Nov. 15** **Photo.** ***Perf. 11½x11***
**1381** A772 5p pale yel, brt yel grn & brn .60 .25

A773

**1988, Dec. 3** ***Perf. 11½***
**1382** A773 5p multicolored .50 .25

Ministry of Agriculture, 75th anniv.

A774

Famous Men: No. 1383, Mohamed Hussein Hekal (1888-1956), author, politician. No. 1384, Ahmed Lotfi El Sayed (1872-1963), educator, politician.

***Perf. 13½x13***
**1988, Dec. 29** **Litho.** **Unwmk.**
**1383** A774 5p green & red brn .45 .25
**1384** A774 5p green & red brn .45 .25
*a.* Pair, #1383-1384 1.00 1.00

Stamp Day — A775

Statues: 5p, Statue of K. Abr, a priest, 5th cent. No. 1386, Queen Nefert, 4th Dynasty. No. 1387, King Ra Hoteb, 4th Dynasty.

**1989, Jan. 2**

| | | | |
|---|---|---|---|
| 1385 | A775 5p multicolored | .50 | .30 |
| 1386 | A775 25p multicolored | 1.60 | 1.00 |
| 1387 | A775 25p multicolored | 1.60 | 1.00 |
| *a.* | Pair, #1386-1387 | 3.50 | 3.50 |
| | *Nos. 1385-1387 (3)* | 3.70 | 2.30 |

A776

**1989, Jan. 10**

| | | | |
|---|---|---|---|
| 1388 | A776 5p dull green | .55 | .25 |

Jawaharlal Nehru (1889-1964), 1st Prime Minister of independent India.

Nile Hilton Hotel, 30th Anniv. — A777

**1989, Feb. 22 Litho.** ***Perf. 13x13½***

| | | | |
|---|---|---|---|
| 1389 | A777 5p multicolored | .45 | .25 |

Return of Taba to Egypt A778

**Unwmk.**

**1989, Mar. 15 Litho.** ***Perf. 13***

| | | | |
|---|---|---|---|
| 1390 | A778 5p multicolored | .45 | .25 |

2nd Stage of Cairo Subway A779

**1989, Apr. 12 Litho.** ***Perf. 13***

| | | | |
|---|---|---|---|
| 1391 | A779 5p multicolored | 1.00 | .30 |

Lantern — A780

**1989, May 4 Photo.** ***Perf. 11½***

| | | | |
|---|---|---|---|
| 1392 | A780 5p multicolored | .45 | .25 |

1989 Festival. For use on greeting cards.

1st Arab Olympic Day A781

**1989, May 24**

| | | | |
|---|---|---|---|
| 1393 | A781 5p tan, blk & dull grn | .50 | .25 |

Interparliamentary Union, Cent. — A782

Pyramids and the Parliament Building, Cairo.

**1989, June 29 Litho.** ***Perf. 13x13½***

| | | | |
|---|---|---|---|
| 1394 | A782 25p shown | 1.60 | 1.25 |

**Size: 87x76mm**

***Imperf***

| | | | |
|---|---|---|---|
| 1395 | A782 25p multi, diff. | 2.75 | 2.75 |

French Revolution, Bicent. — A783

**1989, July 14 Photo.** ***Perf. 11½***

| | | | |
|---|---|---|---|
| 1396 | A783 25p multicolored | 1.50 | 1.25 |

No. 1396 is an airmail issue.

African Development Bank, 25th Anniv. — A784

***Perf. 11½***

**1989, Oct. 1 Photo. Unwmk.**

| | | | |
|---|---|---|---|
| 1397 | A784 10p multicolored | .45 | .25 |

A785

October War Against Israel, 16th Anniv. — A786

**1989, Oct. 6** ***Perf. 13***

| | | | |
|---|---|---|---|
| 1398 | Strip of 3 | 1.50 | 1.50 |
| *a.* | A785 10p shown | .50 | .25 |
| *b.* | A786 10p shown | .50 | .25 |
| *c.* | A785 10p Battle scene | .50 | .25 |

See No. 1424.

Aga Khan Award for Architecture A788

***Perf. 11½***

**1989, Oct. 15 Photo. Unwmk.**

| | | | |
|---|---|---|---|
| 1400 | A788 35p multicolored | 1.25 | .60 |

Natl. Health Insurance Plan, 25th Anniv. A789

**1989, Oct. 24**

| | | | |
|---|---|---|---|
| 1401 | A789 10p blk, gray & ver | .50 | .25 |

World Post Day — A790

**1989, Oct. 24** ***Perf. 11x11½***

| | | | |
|---|---|---|---|
| 1402 | A790 35p blue, blk & brt yel | 1.00 | .50 |

Statues of Memnon, Thebes — A791

***Perf. 11½***

**1989, Nov. 12 Photo. Unwmk.**

| | | | |
|---|---|---|---|
| 1403 | A791 10p lt vio, blk & brt yel grn | .50 | .25 |

Intl. Cong. & Convention Assoc. (ICCA) annual convention, Nov. 11-18, Cairo.

Cairo University School of Agriculture, Cent. — A792

**1989, Nov. 15**

| | | | |
|---|---|---|---|
| 1404 | A792 10p pale grn, blk & brt yel | .45 | .25 |

Cairo Intl. Conference Center — A793

**1989, Nov. 20** ***Perf. 11½x11***

| | | | |
|---|---|---|---|
| 1405 | A793 5p multicolored | .45 | .25 |

Road Safety Soc., 20th Anniv. — A794

**1989, Nov. 20** ***Perf. 11½***

| | | | |
|---|---|---|---|
| 1406 | A794 10p multicolored | .45 | .25 |

Alexandria University, 50th Anniv. — A795

**1989, Nov. 30** ***Perf. 11x11½***

| | | | |
|---|---|---|---|
| 1407 | A795 10p pale blue & tan | .45 | .25 |

Portrait of Pasha, Monument in Opera Square, Cairo A796

***Perf. 11½x11***

**1989, Dec. 31 Photo. Unwmk.**

| | | | |
|---|---|---|---|
| 1408 | A796 10p multicolored | .45 | .25 |

Ibrahim Pasha (d. 1838), army commander from 1825 to 1828.

Famous Men

A797 A798

**1989, Dec. 31** ***Perf. 11x11½***

| | | | |
|---|---|---|---|
| 1409 | A797 10p grn & dk ol grn | .45 | .25 |
| 1410 | A798 10p golden brown | .45 | .25 |

Abd El-Rahman El-Rafei (b. 1889), historian (No. 1409); Abdel Kader El Mazni (b. 1889), man of letters (No. 1410).

See Nos. 1431-1432.

Statue of Priest Ranofr — A799

Relief Sculpture of Betah Hoteb — A800

**1990, Jan. 2** *Perf. 13½x13*
**1411** A799 30p multicolored 1.00 .40
**1412** A800 30p multicolored 1.00 .40
*a.* Pair, #1411-1412 2.75 2.75

Stamp Day.

Arab Cooperation Council, 1st Anniv. — A801

*Perf. 13x13½*
**1990, Feb. 16** **Photo.** **Unwmk.**
**1413** A801 10p multicolored .45 .25
**1414** A801 35p multicolored 1.25 .60

Emblem, Conference Center — A802

*Perf. 13½x13*
**1990, Mar. 10** **Litho.** **Unwmk.**
**1415** A802 10p brt yel grn, red & blk .50 .25

**Size: 80x59mm**
***Imperf***
**1416** A802 30p multicolored 1.50 1.50

African Parliamentary Union 13th general conference, Mar. 10-15.

Road Safety Emblems — A803

**1990, Mar. 19** **Photo.** *Perf. 11x11½*
**1417** A803 10p multicolored .60 .25

Intl. Conference on Road Safety & Accidents in Developing Countries, Mar. 19-22.

Egyptian Wild Daisies — A804

**1990, Apr. 24** *Perf. 11½*
**1418** A804 10p multicolored .45 .25

1990 Festival. For use on greeting cards.

Sinai Liberation, 8th Anniv. A805

**1990, Apr. 25**
**1419** A805 10p blue, blk & yel grn .50 .25

World Cup Soccer Championships, Italy — A806

**1990, May 26** **Litho.** *Perf. 13½x13*
**1420** A806 10p multicolored .40 .25

**Souvenir Sheet**
***Imperf***
**1421** A806 50p Flags, trophy 2.25 2.25

World Basketball Championships, Argentina — A807

**1990, Aug. 8** *Perf. 13x13½*
**1422** A807 10p multicolored .50 .25

Natl. Population Council, 5th Anniv. — A808

**1990, Sept. 15** *Perf. 13½x13*
**1423** A808 10p brown & yel grn .50 .25

**October War Against Israel Type**
**1990, Oct. 6** **Litho.** *Perf. 13x13½*
**1424** Strip of 3 1.75 1.75
*a.* A785 10p Bunker, tank .40 .25
*b.* A786 10p like #1398b .40 .25
*c.* A785 10p Troops with flag, flame thrower .40 .25

Egyptian Postal Service, 125th Anniv. — A809

**1990, Oct. 9**
**1425** A809 10p lt blue, blk & red .50 .25

Dar El Eloum Faculty, Cent. A810

**1990, Oct. 13** **Litho.** *Perf. 13*
**1426** A810 10p multicolored .45 .25

UN Development Program, 40th Anniv. — A811

ITU, 125th Anniv. — A812

**1990, Oct. 24** *Perf. 11½*
**1427** A811 30p yel, bl grn & yel grn .90 .30

*Perf. 13*
**1428** A812 30p multicolored .90 .30

UN Day.

Ras Mohammed Natl. Park — A813

Designs: a, Crown butterfly fish. b, Lionfish. c, Twobar anemone fish. d, Grouper.

**1990, Dec. 22** **Litho.** *Perf. 13*
**1429** A813 Block of 4 3.50 3.50
*a.-b.* 10p any single .50 .30
*c.-d.* 20p any single .80 .40

Day of the Disabled — A814

**1990. Dec. 15** **Photo.** *Perf. 11*
**1430** A814 10p multicolored .50 .25

Mohamed Fahmy Abdel Meguid Bey, Medical Reformer A815

Nabaweya Moussa (1890-1951), Educator A816

*Perf. 11x11½*
**1990, Dec. 30** **Unwmk.**
**1431** A815 10p Prus bl, brn & org .40 .25
**1432** A816 10p grn, org brn & blk .40 .25

Stamp Day — A817

**1991, Jan. 1** **Litho.** *Perf. 13½x13*
**1433** A817 5p No. 1 .30 .25
**1434** A817 10p No. 2 .45 .25
**1435** A817 20p No. 3 .60 .40
*a.* Strip of 3, #1433-1435 1.75 1.75

See Nos. 1443-1446, 1459-1460.

Veterinary Surgeon Syndicate, 50th Anniv. — A818

**1991, Feb. 28 Photo. *Perf. 11½***
**1436** A818 10p multicolored .45 .25

Syndicate of Journalists, 50th Anniv. — A819

**1991, Apr. Photo. *Perf. 11½***
**1437** A819 10p multicolored .40 .25

Narcissus — A820

**1991, Apr. 13**
**1438** A820 10p multicolored .40 .25

1991 Festival. For use on greeting cards.

Giza Zoo, Cent. — A821

**1991, June 15 Litho. *Imperf.***
**Size: 80x63mm**
**1439** A821 50p multicolored 4.00 4.00

Mahmoud Mokhtar (1891-1934), Sculptor — A822

Mohamed Nagi (1888-1956), Painter — A823

***Perf. 13x13½, 13½x13***
**1991, June 11 Litho.**
**1440** A822 10p multicolored .40 .25
**1441** A823 10p multicolored .40 .25

Faculty of Engineering — A824

**1991, June 30 *Perf. 13x13½***
**1442** A824 10p multicolored .40 .25

**Stamp Day Type**

Designs: No. 1443, No. 5. No. 1444, No. 4. No. 1445, No. 7. No. 1446, Sphinx, pyramid, No. 6.

**1991, July 23 *Perf. 13***
**1443** A817 10p orange & blk .40 .25
**1444** A817 10p yellow & blk .40 .25
**1445** A817 10p lilac & blk .40 .25
*a.* Strip of 3, #1443-1445 1.40 1.40

**Size: 80x60mm**
***Imperf***
**1446** A817 50p multicolored 2.25 1.75
*Nos. 1443-1446 (4)* 3.45 2.50

Mohamed Abdel el Wahab, Musician A825

**1991, Aug. 28 *Perf. 13***
**1447** A825 10p multicolored .55 .25

5th Africa Games, Cairo — A826

No. 1448, Karate, judo. No. 1449, Table tennis, field hockey, tennis. No. 1450, Running, gymnastics, swimming. No. 1451, Soccer, basketball, shooting. No. 1452, Boxing, wrestling, weightlifting. No. 1453, Handball, cycling, volleyball. No. 1454, Games mascot, vert. No. 1455, Mascot, emblem, torch.

***Perf. 13x13½***
**1991, Sept. Litho. Unwmk.**
**1448** A826 10p multicolored .40 .25
**1449** A826 10p multicolored .40 .25
*a.* Pair, #1448-1449 .90 .90
**1450** A826 10p multicolored .40 .25
**1451** A826 10p multicolored .40 .25
*a.* Pair, #1450-1451 .90 .90
**1452** A826 10p multicolored .40 .25
**1453** A826 10p multicolored .40 .25
*a.* Pair, #1452-1453 .90 .90

***Perf. 13½x13***
**1454** A826 10p multicolored .45 .25

**Size: 80x60mm**
***Imperf***
**1455** A826 50p multicolored 1.75 1.75
*Nos. 1448-1455 (8)* 4.60 3.50

Intl. Statistics Institute, 48th Session A827

**1991, Sept. 9**
**1456** A827 10p multicolored .40 .25

Opening of Dar Al Eftaa Religious Center — A828

**1991, Oct. 1 Litho. *Perf. 13***
**1457** A828 10p multicolored .40 .25

October War Against Israel, 18th Anniv. — A829

**1991, Oct. 6 *Perf. 13x13½***
**1458** A829 10p multicolored .55 .25

**Stamp Day Type**

Designs: 10p, No. 6. £1, Stamp exhibition emblem, hieroglyphics, pyramids, sphinx.

**1991, Oct. 7 *Perf. 13***
**1459** A817 10p blue & black .50 .25

**Size: 90x60mm**
***Imperf***
**1460** A817 £1 multicolored *5.50 5.50*

Natl. Philatelic Exhibition, Cairo, 10/7-12 (No. 1460). No. 1460 sold only with £1 admission ticket at exhibition.

**Ancient Artifacts Type of 1985**
***Perf. 11½x11***
**1990-92 Unwmk. Photo.**
**Size: 18x23mm**
**1467** A681 10p like #1278 .60 .25
**1470** A681 30p like #1283 1.00 1.00
**1472** A681 50p like #1285 1.75 1.75
*Nos. 1467-1472 (3)* 3.35 3.00

Issued: 10p, 1/20/90; 30p, 9/1/91; 50p, 7/11/92.

United Nations Day — A830

No. 1477, Brick hands housing people. No. 1478, Woman learning to write, fingerprint, vert.

***Perf. 13x13½, 13½x13***
**1991, Oct. 24 Litho.**
**1476** A830 10p shown .40 .25
**1477** A830 10p multicolored .40 .25
**1478** A830 10p multicolored .40 .25
*Nos. 1476-1478 (3)* 1.20 .75

**Famous Men Type of 1988**
Inscribed "1991"

Designs: No. 1479, Dr. Zaki Mubarak (1891-1952), writer and poet. No. 1480, Abd El Kader Hamza (1879-1941), journalist.

**1991, Dec. 23 Photo. *Perf. 13½x13***
**1479** A760 10p olive brown .40 .25
**1480** A760 10p gray .40 .25

A831

Post Day — A832

**1992, Jan. 2 Litho. *Perf. 13***
**1481** A831 10p shown .40 .25
**1482** A831 45p Bird mosaic 1.00 1.00

***Perf. 14***
**1483** A832 70p shown 1.75 1.75
*Nos. 1481-1483 (3)* 3.15 3.00

Nos. 1482-1483 are airmail.

Police Day — A833

**1992, Jan. 25 *Perf. 14***
**1484** A833 10p multicolored .40 .25

25th Cairo Intl. Fair A834

**1992, Feb. 15 Litho. *Perf. 14***
**1485** A834 10p multicolored .40 .25

**Famous Men Type of 1988**
Inscribed "1992"

10p, Sayed Darwish (1882-1923), musician.

**1992, Mar. 17 Photo. *Perf. 14x13½***
**1486** A760 10p dull org & olive .40 .25

Festivals — A835

**1992, Mar. 18 *Perf. 11½***
**1487** A835 10p Egyptian hoopoe .40 .25

For use on greeting cards.

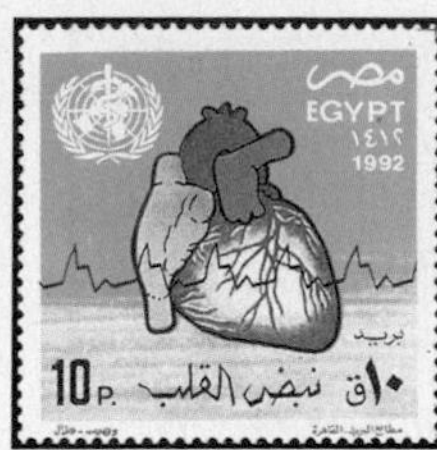


World Health Day
A836

**1992, Apr. 20 Litho. *Perf. 13***

**1488** A836 10p multicolored .50 .25

Aswan Dam, 90th Anniv.
A837

**1992, July Litho. *Perf. 13***

**1489** A837 10p No. 487 .50 .25

20th Arab Scout Jamboree — A838

**1992, July 10 *Perf. 13x13½***

**1490** A838 10p multicolored .50 .25

A839

70p, Summer Games' emblem.

**1992, July 20 *Perf. 13½x13***

**1491** A839 10p multicolored .45 .25

**Size: 80x60mm**

***Imperf***

**1492** A839 70p multicolored 5.00 2.50

1992 Summer Olympics, Barcelona.

El Helal Magazine, Cent. — A840

**1992, Sept. 14 Litho. *Perf. 13½x13***

**1493** A840 10p multicolored .45 .25

Alexandria World Festival — A841

**1992, Sept. 27 *Perf. 13x13½***

**1494** A841 70p multicolored 1.60 1.60

Congress of Federation of World and American Travel Companies, Cairo — A842

**1992, Sept. 20**

**1495** A842 70p multicolored 1.50 1.50

World Post Day
A843

**1992, Oct. 9 Litho. *Perf. 13***

**1496** A843 10p dk bl, lt bl & blk .45 .25

Children's Day — A844

**1992, Oct. 24 Litho. *Perf. 13½x13***

**1497** A844 10p multicolored .55 .25

Intl. Conference on Food, Agriculture and World Health
A845

**1992, Oct. 24 *Perf. 13***

**1498** A845 70p multicolored 1.50 1.50

A846

**1992, Nov. 21 *Perf. 13½x13***

**1499** A846 10p multicolored .50 .25

20th Arab Scout Conference, Cairo.

**Famous Men Type of 1988**

Inscribed "1992"

No. 1500, Talaat Harb, economist. No. 1501, Mohamed Taymour, writer. No. 1502, Dr. Ahmed Zaki Abu Shadi (with glasses), physician & poet.

**1992, Dec. 23 Photo. *Perf. 13½x13***

**1500** A760 10p blue & brown .40 .25
**1501** A760 10p citron & blue gray .40 .25
**1502** A760 10p citron & blue gray .40 .25
*a.* Pair, #1501-1502 .90 .90
*Nos. 1500-1502 (3)* 1.20 .75

A847

Pharaohs: 10p, Sesostris I. 45p, Amenemhet III. 70p, Hur I.

**1993, Jan. 2 Litho. *Perf. 13½x13***

**1503** A847 10p brown & yellow .45 .25
**1504** A847 45p brown & yellow .75 .65
**1505** A847 70p brown & yellow 1.20 1.00
*a.* Strip of 3, #1503-1505 3.00 3.00

Post Day.

25th Intl. Book Fair, Cairo — A848

**1993, Jan. 26 Litho. *Perf. 13½x13***

**1506** A848 15p multicolored .40 .25

A849

A849a

A849b

A849c

A849d

A849e

A849f

A849g

A849h

Artifacts: A849, Bust. A849a, Sphinx. A849b, Bust of princess. A849c, Ramses II. A849d, Queen Ti. A849e, Horemheb. A849f, As A849b. A849g, Amenhotep III. £1, Head of a woman. £2, Woman wearing headdress. £5, Pharaonic capital.

**Photo., Litho. (#1511)**

**1993-99 Unwmk. *Perf. 11½x11,***

**1507** A849 5p multi .55 .25
**1508** A849a 15p brn & bis .55 .25
**1509** A849a 15p brn & bis .30 .25
**1510** A849b 25p brn & org brn .35 .25
**1511** A849c 55p blk & bl .90 .50

**Size: 21x25mm**

***Perf. 11¼***

**1512** A849 5p dp cl & brick red .50 .25
**1513** A849d 5p brown .30 .25
*a.* Wmk. 342 .30 .25
**1514** A849a 15p brn & bis .50 .25
**1515** A849e 20p blk & gray .30 .25
*a.* Wmk. 342 .30 .25
**1516** A849f 25p brn & org brn .70 .30
**1517** A849f 25p black brown .30 .25
**1518** A849c 55p blk & lt bl .60 .60
**1519** A849g 75p blk & brn .90 .80

***Perf. 11½***

**1520** A849h £1 slate & blk 2.25 2.25
**1521** A849h £2 brn & grn 5.00 5.00
**1521A** A849h £5 brn & gold 10.00 10.00
*Nos. 1507-1521A (16)* 24.00 21.70

*Warning: Avoid using watermark fluid on Nos. 1513-1513a and 1515-1515a. Images will be adversely affected.*

Body of Sphinx on Nos. 1509, 1514 stops above value, and extends through value on No. 1508.

Issued: Nos. 1507-1508, 2/1; No. 1509, 3/10; £1, £2, 4/1; No. 1511, 7/1/93; £5, 8/1/93; Nos. 1512, 1514, 1518, 10/30/94; No. 1516, 6/25/94; 20p, 2/1/97; 75p, 3/25/97; No. 1517, 1998; Nos. 1513a, 1515a, 1999.

See Nos. C204-C206.

Architects' Association, 75th Anniv. — A850

**1993, Feb. 28 Litho. *Perf. 13x13½***

**1522** A850 15p multicolored .45 .25

New Building for Ministry of Foreign Affairs
A851

**1993, Mar. 15 *Perf. 13***

**1523** A851 15p multicolored .45 .25
**1524** A851 80p multicolored 1.50 1.50

Diplomacy Day (No. 1523). No. 1524 is airmail.

Feasts — A852

**1993, Mar. 20 Litho.** ***Perf. 13x13½***

**1525** A852 15p Opuntia .45 .25

For use on greeting cards.

Newspaper, Le Progres Egyptien, Cent. — A853

**1993, Apr. 15 Litho.** ***Perf. 13x13½***

**1526** A853 15p multicolored .40 .25

A854

**1993, May 15 Litho.** ***Perf. 13½x13***

**1527** A854 15p multicolored .50 .25

World Telecommunications Day.

A855

**1993, June 15 Litho.** ***Perf. 13½x13***

**1528** A855 15p multicolored .45 .25

UN Conference on Human Rights, Vienna.

Organization of African Unity — A856

**1993, June 26** ***Perf. 13***

**1529** A856 15p yel grn & multi .45 .25

**1530** A856 80p red violet & multi 1.10 1.10

No. 1530 is airmail.

World PTT Conference, Cairo — A857

**1993, Sept. 4 Litho.** ***Perf. 13***

**1531** A857 15p multicolored .45 .25

Salah El-Din El Ayubi (1137-1193), Dome of the Rock — A858

**1993, Sept. 4**

**1532** A858 55p multicolored 1.10 1.10

A859

**1993, Oct. 6**

**1533** A859 15p multicolored .50 .25

October War Against Israel, 20th Anniv.

A860

**1993, Oct. 12** ***Perf. 13½x13***

**1534** A860 15p cream & multi .45 .25

**1535** A860 55p silver & multi 1.10 .55

**1536** A860 80p gold & multi 1.50 .85

***Imperf***

**Size: 90x70mm**

**1537** A860 80p multicolored 2.00 2.00

*Nos. 1534-1537 (4)* 5.05 3.65

Pres. Mohamed Hosni Mubarak, Third Term.

Reduction of Natural Disasters A861

**1993, Oct. 24 Litho.** ***Perf. 13***

**1538** A861 80p multicolored 1.10 1.10

Electricity in Egypt, Cent. — A862

**1993, Oct. 24** ***Perf. 13½x13***

**1539** A862 15p multicolored .45 .25

Intl. Conference on Big Dams, Cairo — A863

**1993, Nov. 19 Litho.** ***Perf. 13***

**1540** A863 15p multicolored .45 .25

35th Military Intl. Soccer Championship — A864

**1993, Dec. 1 Litho.** ***Perf. 13x13½***

**1541** A864 15p orange & multi .40 .25

**1542** A864 15p Trophy, emblem .40 .25

9th Men's Junior World Handball Championship (No. 1542).

**Famous Men Type of 1988**

**Inscribed "1993"**

No. 1543, Abdel Azis Al-Bishry. No. 1544, Mohammad Farid Abu Hadid. No. 1545, Mahmud Beyram el-Tunsi. No. 1546, Ali Moubarak.

**1993, Dec. 25** ***Perf. 13½x13***

**1543** A760 15p blue .40 .25

**1544** A760 15p blue black .40 .25

**1545** A760 15p light violet .40 .25

**1546** A760 15p green .40 .25

*Nos. 1543-1546 (4)* 1.60 1.00

Post Day — A865

15p, Amenhotep III. 55p, Queen Hatshepsut. 80p, Thutmose III.

**1994, Jan. 2**

**1547** A865 15p multicolored .45 .25

**1548** A865 55p multicolored 1.10 .30

**1549** A865 80p multicolored 1.75 .40

*Nos. 1547-1549 (3)* 3.30 .95

Congress of Egyptian Sedimentary Geology Society — A866

**1994, Jan. 4 Litho.** ***Perf. 13x13½***

**1550** A866 15p multicolored .45 .25

Birds A867

**1994, Mar. 3 Litho.** ***Perf. 13***

**1551** A867 Block of 4, #a.-d. 2.75 2.75

*a.* 15p Egyptian swallow .45 .30

*b.* 15p Fire crest .45 .30

*c.* 15p Rose-ringed parrot .45 .30

*d.* 15p Goldfinch .45 .30

Festivals 1994.

Arab Scouting, 40th Anniv. — A868

**1994, Mar. 25** ***Perf. 13½x13***

**1552** A868 15p multicolored .45 .25

27th Cairo Intl. Fair — A869

**1994, Apr. 9 Litho.** ***Perf. 13½x13***

**1553** A869 15p multicolored .45 .25

A870

**1994, Apr. 15 Litho.** ***Perf. 13***

**1554** A870 15p green & brown .45 .25

1994 African Telecommunications Exhibition, Cairo.

A871

**1994, Apr. 30 Litho. *Perf. 13***
**1555** A871 15p grn, blk & blue .45 .25

Natl. Afforestation Campaign.

5th Arab Energy Conference, Cairo. — A872

**1994, July 5 Litho. *Perf. 13***
**1556** A872 15p multicolored .45 .25

Signing of Washington Accord for Palestinian Self-Rule in Gaza and Jericho — A873

**1994, May 4 Litho. *Perf. 13***
**1557** A873 15p multicolored .60 .25

18th Biennial Art Exhibition, Alexandria — A874

**1994, May 21**
**1558** A874 15p yel, blk & gray .45 .25

Organization of African Unity — A875

**1994, May 25**
**1559** A875 15p multicolored .45 .25

Natl. Reading Festival — A876

**1994, June 15**
**1560** A876 15p multicolored .45 .25

ILO, 75th Anniv. — A877

**1994, June 28 Litho. *Perf. 13½x13***
**1561** A877 15p multicolored .45 .25

Intl. Conference on Population and Development, Cairo — A878

15p, Conference, UN emblems. 80p, Drawings, hieroglyphics, conference emblem.

**1994, Sept. 5 Litho. *Perf. 13***
**1562** A878 15p multi .45 .25
**1563** A878 80p multi, vert. 1.10 .75

No. 1563 is airmail.

World Junior Squash Championships — A879

**1994, Sept. 14 Litho. *Perf. 13***
**1564** A879 15p multicolored .45 .25

World Post Day A880

**1994, Oct. 9 Litho. *Perf. 13***
**1565** A880 15p multicolored .50 .25

Intl. Red Cross & Red Crescent Societies, 75th Anniv. — A881

**1994, Oct. 24**
**1566** A881 80p multicolored 1.50 .90

Akhbar El-Yom Newspaper, 50th Anniv. — A882

**1994, Nov. 11**
**1567** A882 15p multicolored .45 .25

African Field Hockey Club Championships — A883

**1994, Nov. 14 Litho. *Perf. 13***
**1568** A883 15p multicolored .45 .25

A884

Opera Aida, by Verdi — A885

**1994, Nov. 26**
**1569** A884 15p multicolored .45 .25

***Imperf***

**Size: 58x69mm**

**1570** A885 80p multicolored 2.25 2.25

No. 1570 is airmail.

Intl. Olympic Committee, Cent. — A886

**1994, Dec. 10 *Perf. 13***
**1571** A886 15p multicolored .45 .25

Egyptian Youth Hostels Assoc., 40th Anniv. — A887

**1994, Dec. 24**
**1572** A887 15p multicolored .45 .25

Intl. Speed Ball Federation, 10th Anniv. — A888

**1994, Dec. 25**
**1573** A888 15p multicolored .45 .25

African Development Bank, 30th Anniv. — A889

**1994, Dec. 26**
**1574** A889 15p multicolored .45 .25

Opening of Suez Canal, 125th Anniv. — A890

Design: 80p, Map, inaugural ceremony.

**1994, Dec. 27**
**1575** A890 15p multicolored .65 .25
**1576** A890 80p multicolored 1.25 .75

No. 1576 is airmail.

Famous Men — A891

No. 1577, Hassan Fathy, engineer. No. 1578, Mahmoud Taimour, writer.

**1994, Dec. 29**
**1577** A891 15p multicolored .40 .25
**1578** A891 15p multicolored .40 .25

Post Day — A892

15p, Statue of Akhenaton. 55p, Golden mask of King Tutankhamun. 80p, Statue of Nefertiti.

**1995, Jan. 2 Litho.** ***Perf. 13½x13***

| | | | | |
|---|---|---|---|---|
| **1579** | A892 15p multicolored | .50 | .25 |
| **1580** | A892 55p multicolored | 1.10 | .40 |
| **1581** | A892 80p multicolored | 1.50 | .50 |
| | *Nos. 1579-1581 (3)* | 3.10 | 1.15 |

World Tourism Organization, 20th Anniv. — A893

**1995, Jan. 2** ***Perf. 13x13½***

**1582** A893 15p multicolored .45 .25

Festivals — A894

**1995, Feb. 25 Litho.** ***Perf. 13x13½***

**1583** A894 15p multicolored .45 .25

For use on greeting cards.

Egyptian Women's Day — A895

**1995, Mar. 16 Litho.** ***Perf. 13x13½***

**1584** A895 15p multicolored .45 .25

Arab League, 50th Anniv. — A896

**1995, Mar. 22** ***Perf. 13½x13***

| | | | |
|---|---|---|---|
| **1585** | A896 15p blue & multi | .45 | .25 |
| **1586** | A896 55p green & multi | .75 | .75 |

Sheraton Hotel, Cairo, 25th Anniv. — A897

**1995, Mar. 28** ***Perf. 13x13½***

**1587** A897 15p multicolored .45 .25

Misr Bank, 75th Anniv. — A898

**1995, May 7 Litho.** ***Perf. 13½x13***

**1588** A898 15p multicolored .50 .25

World Telecommunications Day — A899

**1995, May 31** ***Perf. 13x13½***

**1589** A899 80p multicolored 1.00 .50

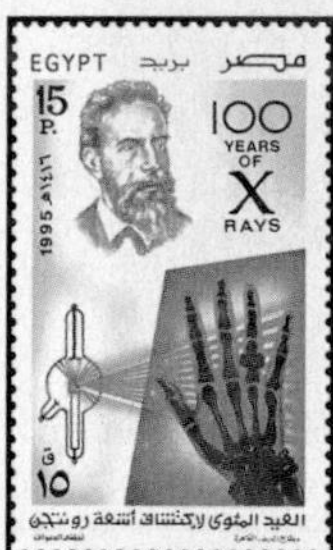

Wilhelm Roentgen (1845-1923), Discovery of the X-Ray, Cent. — A900

**1995, May Litho.** ***Perf. 13½x13***

**1590** A900 15p multicolored .50 .25

Membership in World Heritage Committee, 20th Anniv. (in 1994) — A901

Artifacts from the Shaft of Luxor: No. 1591, Goddess Hathor. No. 1592, God Atoum. 80p, God Amon and Horemheb.

**1995, July 23 Litho.** ***Perf. 13½x13***

| | | | |
|---|---|---|---|
| **1591** | 15p multicolored | .45 | .25 |
| **1592** | 15p multicolored | .45 | .25 |
| *a.* | A901 Pair, #1591-1592 | 1.10 | 1.10 |
| **1593** | A901 80p multicolored | 1.10 | 1.10 |
| | *Nos. 1591-1593 (3)* | 2.00 | 1.60 |

No. 1592a is a continuous design. No. 1593 is airmail.

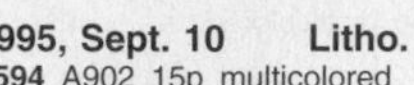

21st Intl. Conference on Pediatrics, Cairo A902

**1995, Sept. 10 Litho.** ***Perf. 13***

**1594** A902 15p multicolored .50 .25

Intl. Ozone Day — A903

**1995, Sept. 16 Litho.** ***Perf. 13x12½***

| | | | |
|---|---|---|---|
| **1595** | A903 15p green & multi | .45 | .25 |
| **1596** | A903 55p brown & multi | .90 | .45 |
| **1597** | A903 80p blue & multi | 1.40 | .55 |
| | *Nos. 1595-1597 (3)* | 2.75 | 1.25 |

See Nos. 1622-1623.

World Tourism Day A904

**1995, Sept. 25** ***Perf. 12½x13***

**1598** A904 15p multicolored 1.00 .25

Government Printing House, 175th Anniv. — A905

**1995, Sept. 27**

**1599** A905 15p multicolored .45 .25

Sun Verticality on Abu Simbel Temple A906

**1995, Oct. 22 Litho.** ***Perf. 12½x13***

**1600** A906 15p multicolored .95 .30

Opening of New Esna Dam — A907

**1995, Nov. 25** ***Perf. 12½***

**1601** A907 15p multicolored .75 .30

Egyptian Engineers Assoc., 75th Anniv. A908

**1995, Dec. 20** ***Perf. 13***

**1602** A908 15p multicolored .45 .25

A909

Famous entertainers.

**1995, Dec. 9 Litho.** ***Perf. 13x12½***

| | | | |
|---|---|---|---|
| **1603** | A909 15p Abdel Halim Hafez | .40 | .25 |
| **1604** | A909 15p Youssef Wahbi | .40 | .25 |
| **1605** | A909 15p Naquib el-Rihani | .40 | .25 |
| | *Nos. 1603-1605 (3)* | 1.20 | .75 |

A910

**1995, Dec. 23 Litho.** ***Perf. 13x12½***

**1606** A910 15p multicolored .45 .25

Motion Pictures, cent.

Post Day A911

Ancient paintings: 55p, Man facing right. 80p, Man facing left. 100p, Playing flute, dancers.

**1996, Jan. 2 Litho.** ***Perf. 13½x13***

| | | | |
|---|---|---|---|
| **1607** | 55p multicolored | 1.10 | .60 |
| **1608** | 80p multicolored | 1.50 | .90 |
| *a.* | A911 Pair, Nos. 1607-1608 | 2.75 | 2.75 |

***Imperf***

**Size: 88x72mm**

**1609** A911 100p multicolored 3.00 3.00

Nos. 1607-1608 are airmail.

Feasts — A912

**1996, Feb. 15** ***Perf. 12½***

| | | | |
|---|---|---|---|
| **1610** | A912 15p Blue convolvulus | .45 | .25 |
| **1611** | A912 15p Red poppies | .45 | .25 |
| *a.* | Pair, No. 1610-1611 | .95 | .95 |

For use on greeting cards.

A913

**1996, Mar. 13 Litho.** ***Perf. 13x12½***

**1612** A913 15p pink & multi .40 .25
**1613** A913 80p brown & multi .90 .60

Summit of Peace Makers, Sharm al-Sheikh. No. 1613 is airmail.

A914

**1996, Mar. 16**

**1614** A914 15p multicolored .45 .25

29th Intl. Fair, Cairo.

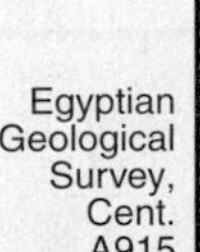

Egyptian Geological Survey, Cent. A915

**1996, Mar. 18** ***Perf. 12½x13***

**1615** A915 15p multicolored .45 .25

A916

**1996, Apr. 11 Litho.** ***Perf. 13x12½***

**1616** A916 15p blue & multi .45 .25
**1617** A916 80p pink & multi .95 .50

Signing of African Nuclear Weapon-Free Zone Treaty.

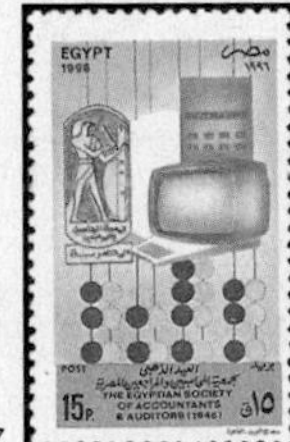


A917

**1996, Apr. 20 Litho.** ***Perf. 13x12½***

**1618** A917 15p multicolored .45 .25

Egyptian Society of Accountants and Auditors, 50th anniv.

General Census — A918

**1996, May 4**

**1619** A918 15p multicolored .45 .25

A919

1996 Summer Olympics, Atlanta: 15p, Atlanta 1996 emblem. £1, Emblem surrounded by sports pictograms.

**1996, July 15 Litho.** ***Perf. 13x12½***

**1620** A919 15p lilac & multi .50 .25

**Size: 63x103mm**

***Imperf***

**1621** A919 £1 black & multi 2.75 2.75

No. 1621 is airmail.

**Intl. Ozone Day Type of 1995**

**1996, Sept. 16 Litho.** ***Perf. 13x12½***

**1622** A903 15p pink & multi .40 .25
**1623** A903 80p gray & multi 1.10 .55

No. 1623 is airmail.

A920

**1996, Sept. 19**

**1624** A920 80p multicolored .75 .45

2nd Alexandria World Festival.

A921

**1996, Sept. 21**

**1625** A921 15p grn, blk & bl .45 .25

Scientific Research and Technology Academy, 25th anniv.

Opening of 2nd Line of Greater Cairo Subway System
A922

**1996, Oct. 7** ***Perf. 12½x13***

**1626** A922 15p multicolored .50 .25

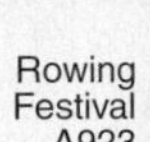

Rowing Festival A923

**1996, Sept. 27**

**1627** A923 15p multicolored .75 .25

Intl. Tourism Day. See Nos. C215-C216.

Courts of the State Council, 50th Anniv. A924

**1996, Nov. 2 Litho.** ***Perf. 12½x13***

**1628** A924 15p blue & claret .45 .25

A925

**1996, Nov. 4** ***Perf. 13x12½***

**1629** A925 15p yel, blk & blue .40 .25

25th World Conference of Intl. Federation of Training and Development Organizations.

A926

Cairo Economic Summit (MENA): £1, Graph, earth, gear, olive branch, wheat.

**1996, Nov. 12 Litho.** ***Perf. 13x12½***

**1630** A926 15p shown .45 .25

**Size: 65x45mm**

***Imperf***

**1631** A926 £1 multicolored 1.75 1.75

No. 1631 is airmail.

A927

**1996, Nov. 13** ***Perf. 13x12½***

**1632** A927 15p multicolored .45 .25

1996 World Food Summit, Rome.

A928

National Day of El-Gharbia Governorate: Al Sayd Ahmed El-Badawy mosque, Tanta.

**1996, Nov. 16**

**1633** A928 15p multicolored .45 .25

A929

Famous artists: No. 1634, Ali El-Kassar. No. 1635, George Abyad. No. 1636, Mohamed Kareem. No. 1637, Fatma Roshdi.

**1996, Dec. 28 Litho.** ***Perf. 13x12½***

**1634** A929 20p black .45 .25
**1635** A929 20p red brown .45 .25
**1636** A929 20p brown .45 .25
**1637** A929 20p black .45 .25
*Nos. 1634-1637 (4)* 1.80 1.00

See Nos. 1666-1669.

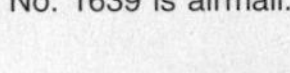

A930

**1997, Jan. 2**

**1638** A930 20p multicolored .45 .25

**Size: 61x80mm**

***Imperf***

**1639** A930 £1 multicolored 2.00 2.00

Post Day; Discovery of Tutankhamun's tomb, 75th anniv.
No. 1639 is airmail.

Police Day A931

**1997, Jan. 25 Litho.** ***Perf. 13x13½***

**1640** A931 20p multicolored .45 .25

Feasts — A932

**1997, Feb. 1** ***Perf. 13***

**1641** A932 20p Pink asters .40 .25
**1642** A932 20p White asters .40 .25
*a.* Pair, #1641-1642 .95 .95

For use on greeting cards.

World Civil Defense Day A933

**1997, Mar. 10 Litho.** ***Perf. 13x13½***

**1643** A933 20p multicolored .45 .25

30th Cairo Intl. Fair — A934

**1997, Mar. 19** ***Perf. 13½x13***
**1644** A934 20p multicolored .45 .25

Mahmoud Said, Photographer, Artist, Birth Cent. — A935

The City, By Mahmoud Said — A936

**1997, Apr. 12** **Litho.** ***Perf. 12½***
**1645** A935 20p multicolored .45 .25

**Size: 80x60mm**

***Imperf***

**1646** A936 £1 multicolored 1.25 1.25

No. 1646 is airmail.

Institute of African Research and Studies, 50th Anniv. — A937

**1997, May 27** **Litho.** ***Perf. 13***
**1647** A937 75p multicolored .65 .65

New Headquarters of State Information Service — A938

**1997, Aug. 16** **Litho.** ***Perf. 12½***
**1648** A938 20p multicolored .45 .25

A939

£1, Mascot, soccer ball, playing field, emblems.

**1997, Sept. 4** ***Perf. 13x12½***
**1649** A939 20p multicolored .45 .25
**1650** AP81 75p multicolored .70 .65

**Size: 75x55mm**

***Imperf***

**1651** A939 £1 multicolored 1.75 1.75

Nos. 1650-1651 are airmail. Under 17 FIFA World Soccer Championships, Egypt.

A940

**1997, Sept. 16** ***Perf. 13***
**1652** A940 20p lt bl grn & multi .60 .30
**1653** A940 £1 pink & multi 1.60 1.25

Montreal Protocol on Substances that Deplete the Ozone Layer, 10th anniv. No. 1653 is airmail.

Completion of Second Stage of Metro Line No. 2 — A941

**1997, Sept. 27** ***Perf. 12½x13***
**1654** A941 20p multicolored .45 .25

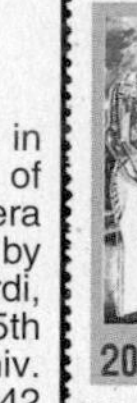

Premiere in Egypt of Opera Aida, by Verdi, 125th Anniv. A942

**1997, Oct. 12** ***Perf. 13***
**1655** A942 20p multicolored .60 .25

**Size: 80x75mm**

***Imperf***

**1656** A942 £1 like #1655 4.00 4.00

No. 1656 is airmail.

Queen Nefertari — A943

**1997, Oct. 25** **Litho.** ***Perf. 13***
**1657** A943 £1 multicolored 1.25 1.25
*a.* Perf. 14¼x14 — —

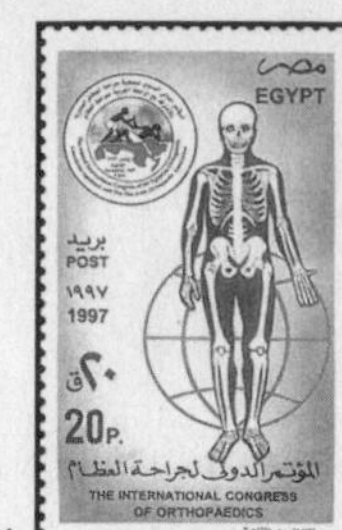


A944

**1997, Nov. 17** **Litho.** ***Perf. 13***
**1658** A944 20p multicolored .50 .25

Intl. Congress of Orthopedics, Cairo.

A945

Designs: 20p, Goddess Selket. £1, Scarab, baboon pendant.

**1997, Nov. 22** ***Perf. 13x12½***
**1659** A945 20p black & gold .50 .25

**Size: 73x62mm**

***Imperf***

**1660** A945 £1 multicolored 1.50 1.50

No. 1660 is airmail. Discovery of King Tutanhkamen's tomb, 75th anniv.

Inauguration of Nubia Monument Museum — A946

**1997, Nov. 23** ***Perf. 13***
**1661** A946 20p multicolored .95 .25

Arab Land Bank, 50th Anniv. — A947

**1997, Dec. 10** ***Perf. 12½***
**1662** A947 20p multicolored .60 .25

5th Pan Arab Congress on Anesthesia and Intensive Care — A948

**1997, Dec. 9** **Litho.** ***Perf. 13***
**1663** A948 20p multicolored .45 .25

El Salaam Canal — A949

**1997, Dec. 28**
**1664** A949 20p multicolored .60 .25

Liberation of Sinai, 15th anniv.

**Famous Artists Type of 1996 and**

A950

**1997, Dec. 23** **Litho.** ***Perf. 13x12½***
**1665** A950 20p blue .40 .25
**1666** A929 20p Zaky Tolaimat .40 .25
**1667** A929 20p Ismael Yassen .40 .25
**1668** A929 20p Zaky Roustom .40 .25
**1669** A929 20p Soliman Naguib .40 .25
*a.* Strip of 5, #1665-1669 2.00 2.00

A951

Post Day: 20p, King Tutankhamun's guard. 75p, King Ramses III. £1, Cover of King Tutankhamun's coffin.

**1998, Jan. 2** ***Perf. 13***
**1670** A951 20p multicolored .45 .25
**1671** A951 75p multicolored 1.10 .65

**Size: 26x43mm**

**1672** A951 £1 multicolored 1.75 .85

Nos. 1671-1672 are airmail.

Feasts — A952

**1998, Jan. 20**
**1673** 20p multicolored .40 .25
**1674** 20p multicolored .40 .25
*a.* A952 Pair, #1673-1674 .80 .80

For use on greeting cards.

Intl. Cairo Fair — A954

**1998, Mar. 11** **Litho.** ***Perf. 13***
**1675** A954 20p multicolored .50 .25

Natl. Bank of Egypt, Cent. — A955

**1998, Mar. 12**
**1676** A955 20p multicolored .50 .25

Tutankhamun A956

Thutmose IV A957

**1998 Litho.** ***Perf. 13½x12½***
**1077** A956 £2 pink & multi 1.75 1.75
**1677A** A956 £2 Like #1677, with white background — —
*b.* Perf. 14x14¼ — —
**1678** A957 £5 purple & black 5.00 3.75
*Nos. 1677-1678 (3)* 6.75 5.50

Issued: £2, 4/23; £5, 3/23.

A958

**1998, Apr. 14** ***Perf. 13***
**1679** A958 20p green & multi .45 .25
**1680** A958 75p blue & multi 1.10 .75

**Size: 70x52mm**

***Imperf***

**1681** A958 £1 Natl. flags, map, trophy 1.50 1.00

Egypt, winners of 21st African Cup of Nations soccer competition.
Nos. 1680-1681 are airmail.

Egyptian Satellite "Nile Sat" — A959

**1998, May 30 Litho.** ***Perf. 13***
**1682** A959 20p multicolored .50 .25

World Environment Day — A960

**1998, June 5**
**1683** A960 20p shown .60 .25

**Size: 43x62mm**

***Imperf***

**1684** A960 £1 Fauna, emblems 3.75 3.75

No. 1684 is airmail.

A961

**1998, June 14**
**1685** A961 20p blue & black .40 .25
**1686** A961 £1 yel, grn & blk 1.10 .80

Dr. Ahmed Zewail, winner of Franklin Institute award.
No. 1686 is airmail.

A962

Imam Sheikh Mohamed Metwalli Al-Shaarawi.

**1998, July 15**
**1687** A962 20p buff & multi .40 .25
**1688** A962 £1 green & multi 1.10 .80

No. 1688 is airmail.

Day of the Nile Flood — A963

**1998, Sept. 12 Litho.** ***Perf. 13***
**1689** A963 20p multicolored .50 .25

A964

**1998, Sept. 30 Litho.** ***Perf. 13***
**1690** A964 20p multicolored .50 .25

Chemistry Administration, cent.

October War Against Israel, 25th Anniv. — A965

**1998, Oct. 6 Litho.** ***Perf. 13***
**1691** A965 20p multicolored .60 .25

**Size: 50x70mm**

***Imperf***

**1692** A965 £2 like No. 1691 3.25 3.25

No. 1692 is airmail.

Egyptian Survey Authority, Cent. — A966

**1998, Oct. 15** ***Perf. 13***
**1693** A966 20p multicolored .50 .25

Cairo University, 90th Anniv. — A967

**1998, Dec. 7 Litho.** ***Perf. 13***
**1694** A967 20p multicolored .50 .25

A968

**1998, Dec. 17 Litho.** ***Perf. 13***
**1695** A968 20p multicolored .45 .25

Egyptian trade unions, cent.

A970

Post Day (19th Dynasty): 20p, Queen Nefertari, Goddess Isis. 125p, God Osiris, Goddess Isis.

**1999, Jan. 2 Litho.** ***Perf. 13***
**1696** A970 20p multicolored .50 .25

**Size: 41x61mm**

***Imperf***

**1697** A970 125p multicolored 2.00 2.00

No. 1697 is airmail.

Feasts — A971

**1999, Jan. 5** ***Perf. 13***
**1698** 20p multicolored 1.00 .30
**1699** 20p multicolored .40 .25
*a.* A971 Pair, #1698-1699 1.75 *1.75*

For use on greeting cards.

Intl. Women's Day — A973

**1999, Mar. 7 Litho.** ***Perf. 13***
**1700** A973 20p multicolored .50 .25

Cairo Intl. Fair — A974

**1999, Mar. 9**
**1701** A974 20p multicolored .50 .25

Opening of Metro Line Beneath Nile River — A975

**1999, Apr. Litho.** ***Perf. 13***
**1702** A975 20p multicolored .60 .25

A976

UPU, 125th Anniv. — A977

**1999, Apr. 21**
**1703** A976 20p shown .45 .25
**1704** A976 £1 multi 1.25 .85
**1705** A977 125p shown 1.50 1.20

**Size: 50x70mm**

***Imperf***

**1706** A977 125p multi 2.10 2.10
*Nos. 1703-1706 (4)* 5.30 4.40

Nos. 1704-1706 are airmail.

A978

**1999, May 8** *Perf. 13*
1707 A978 20p green & multi .45 .25
1708 A978 125p buff, red & multi 1.25 1.00

Geneva Conventions, 50th anniv. No. 1708 is airmail.

A980

**1999, May 20 Litho.** *Perf. 13x12¾*
1710 A980 20p green & multi .45 .25
1711 A980 £1 buff & multi .95 .85

African Development Bank, 35th Meeting, Cairo. No. 1711 is airmail.

16th Men's Handball World Championship — A981

20p, Stylized player with ball, pyramids. 1£, Mascot with ball, Sphinx, pyramids, globe. 125p, Mascot with ball, goalie, pyramids.

**1999, June 1** *Perf. 13*
1712 A981 20p multicolored .45 .25
1713 A981 £1 multicolored .90 .85
1714 A981 125p multicolored 1.10 1.00
*Nos. 1712-1714 (3)* 2.45 2.10

Nos. 1713-1714 are airmail.

Goddess Selket — A982

**1999, June 23 Litho.** *Perf. 13*
1715 A982 25p multicolored .40 .25

See Nos. 1750, 1754.

SOS Children's Village, 50th Anniv. — A983

**1999, June 23** *Perf. 12¾x13¼*
1716 A983 20p grn, blk & blue .45 .25
1717 A983 125p pale yel, blk & bl 1.25 1.10

No. 1717 is airmail.

A984

No. 1718, Sameera Moussa (1917-52), Physicist. No. 1719, Aisha Abdul Rahman (1913-98), writer. No. 1720, Ahmed Eldemerdash Touny (1907-97), member of Intl. Olympic Committee.

**1999 Litho.** *Perf. 13x12¾*
1718 A984 20p multicolored .45 .25
1719 A984 20p multicolored .45 .25
1720 A984 20p multicolored .45 .25
*Nos. 1718-1720 (3)* 1.35 .75

Issued: Nos. 1718-1719, 7/23; No. 1720, 8/13.
See Nos. 1730-1733.

A985

**1999, Oct. 5 Litho.** *Perf. 13x12¾*
1721 A985 20p org & multi .45 .25
1722 A985 £1 silver & multi .90 .85
1723 A985 125p gold & multi 1.10 1.00

***Imperf***

1724 A985 125p multicolored 2.00 2.00
*Nos. 1721-1724 (4)* 4.45 4.10

Pres. Hosni Mubarak, 4th term.
Nos. 1722-1724 are airmail.

A986

**1999, Nov. 15 Litho.** *Perf. 13¼x13*
**Background Color**
1725 A986 20p green .45 .25
1726 A986 £1 red vio .90 .85
1727 A986 125p purple 1.10 1.00
*Nos. 1725-1727 (3)* 2.45 2.10

Intl. Year of the Elderly. Nos. 1726-1727 are airmail.

A987

**1999, Nov. 20**
1728 A987 20p multi .50 .25

Children's Day.

**Famous People Type of 1999**

No. 1730, Farid El Attrash (1913-76), singer, movie star. No. 1731, Laila Mourad (1918-95), singer, movie star. No. 1732, Anwar Wagdi (1911-55), actor, director. No. 1733, Asia Dagher (1901-86), actor, producer.

**1999, Dec. 30 Litho.** *Perf. 13x12¾*
1730 A984 20p lt bl & blk .40 .25
1731 A984 20p lt bl & blk .40 .25
1732 A984 20p lt bl & blk .40 .25
1733 A984 20p lt bl & blk .40 .25
*Nos. 1730-1733 (4)* 1.60 1.00

Millennium A989

20p, "1999" & "2000." 125p, Countdown of years. £2, Holy Family, Virgin Tree.

**2000, Jan. 1** *Perf. 13x12¾*
1734 A989 20p multi .45 .25
1735 A989 125p multi 1.25 1.10

**Size: 70x50mm**

***Imperf***

1736 A989 £2 multi, horiz. 4.00 4.00
*Nos. 1734-1736 (3)* 5.70 5.35

Nos. 1735-1736 are airmail.

A990

Post Day — A991

**2000, Jan. 2** *Perf. 13¼x12¾*
1737 A990 20p multi .50 .25
1738 A991 20p multi .50 .25
*a.* Pair, #1737-1738 1.25 1.25

**Size: 70x50mm**

***Imperf***

1739 A991 125p Chariot, horiz. 2.00 2.00
*Nos. 1737-1739 (3)* 3.00 2.50

Ain Shams University, 50th Anniv. — A992

**2000, Jan. 3** *Perf. 13¼x13*
1740 A992 20p multi .50 .25

Festivals
A993 A994

**2000, Jan. 5** *Perf. 13x13¼*
1741 A993 20p multi .40 .25
1742 A994 20p multi .40 .25
*a.* Pair, #1741-1742 .90 .90

For use on greeting cards.

A995

**2000, Jan. 20** *Perf. 13¼x13*
1743 A995 20p multi .50 .25

Islamic Development Bank, 25th anniv.

A996

**2000, Feb. 28** *Perf. 13¼x12¾*
1744 A996 125p multi 1.25 1.25

Common Market for Eastern and Southern Africa Economic Conference.

Death of Om Kolthoum, 25th Anniv. — A997

**2000, Mar. 11** *Perf. 13¼x13*
1745 A997 20p multi .50 .25

8th Intl. Congress of Egyptologists — A998

**2000, Mar. 28** *Perf. 13x13¼*
1746 A998 20p multi .50 .25

Europe-Africa Summit, Cairo — A999

**2000, Apr. 3** ***Perf. 13¼x13***

**1747** A999 125p multi 1.25 1.25

Group of 15 Developing Nations, 10th Summit, Cairo — A1000

***Perf. 12¾x13¼***

**2000, June 19** **Litho.**

**1748** A1000 125p multi 1.25 1.25

**Goddess Selket Type of 1999 and**

Scene from 20th Dynasty A1003

Nofret, Wife of Rahotep A1004

King Seostris A1005

Princess Merit Aton A1006

20th Dynasty — A1007

Pyramid at Snefru A1008

Wife of Sheikh-el-Balad A1009

King Psusennes I A1010

King Tutankhamun A1011

Obelisk of Ramses II A1011a

Temple of Karnak A1012

***Perf. 12¾x13¼, 11¼ (#1750A, 1752-1755, 1757), 11x11½ (#1758-1760), 13¼x12¾ (#1756, 1761, 1763)***

**Photo., Litho. (#1750, 1750A, 1751, 1754, 1754A, 1761, 1763)**

**2000-2002**

| | | | | |
|---|---|---|---|---|
| **1750** | A982 | 10p multi, type I | .40 | .25 |
| **1750A** | A982 | 10p multi, Type II | *3.00* | *3.00* |
| **1751** | A1003 | 10p multi | .40 | .25 |
| **1752** | A1004 | 20p multi | .40 | .25 |
| *a.* | | With dot pattern in headdress and on chest and face ('07) | — | — |
| **1753** | A1005 | 25p multi | .40 | .25 |
| **1754** | A982 | 30p multi, Type I | .60 | .45 |
| **1754A** | A982 | 30p multi, Type II | — | — |
| **1755** | A1006 | 30p multi | .50 | .35 |
| **1756** | A1007 | 50p multi | .65 | .45 |
| **1757** | A1008 | £1 multi | .60 | .25 |
| **1758** | A1009 | 110p multi | 1.25 | .95 |
| **1759** | A1010 | 125p multi | 1.40 | 1.00 |
| **1760** | A1011 | 150p multi | 1.75 | 1.25 |
| **1761** | A1011a | 225p multi | 2.75 | 2.00 |
| **1763** | A1012 | £5 multi | 5.75 | 5.50 |
| *a.* | | Perf. 14x14¼ | — | — |
| | | *Nos. 1750-1763 (15)* | 19.85 | 16.20 |

Issued: 20p, 6/25; No. 1750, 3/25/01; No. 1750A, 2001 (?); 30p, 6/11/01. Nos. 1751, 1755, 225p, 5/25/02; 110p, 6/4/02; 125p, 6/20/02; 150p, 6/15/02; £5, 6/1/02. 30p, 50p, £1, 6/30/02.

Type I (Nos. 1750, 1754), has "Goddess" in smaller type than "Silakht." Type II (No. 1750A, 1754A), has "Goddess" and "Silakht" in type the same height.

Intl. Day Against Drug Abuse — A1013

***Perf. 12¾x13¼***

**2000, June 26** **Litho.**

**1764** A1013 20p multi .50 .25

See No. 1796.

Natl. Insurance Company, Cent. — A1014

125p, Emblem, building, horiz.

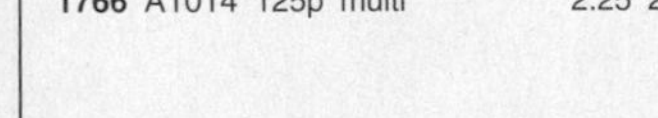

***Perf. 13¼x12¾***

**2000, Aug. 20** **Litho.**

**1765** A1014 20p shown .50 .25

***Imperf***

**Size: 96x75mm**

**1766** A1014 125p multi 2.25 2.25

2000 Summer Olympics, Sydney A1015

Background colors: 20p, Light blue. 125p, Pink.

**2000, Sept. 9** ***Perf. 13¼x12¾***

**1767-1768** A1015 Set of 2 1.75 1.50

No. 1768 is airmail.

Productive Cooperative Union, 25th Anniv. — A1016

**2000, Sept. 15** ***Perf. 12¾x13¼***

**1769** A1016 20p multi .50 .25

Opening of Fourth Stage of Second Cairo Subway Line — A1017

**2000, Oct. 7**

**1770** A1017 20p multi .60 .25

World Post Day — A1018

**2000, Oct. 9**

**1771** A1018 125p multi 1.40 1.40

Solidarity with Palestinians — A1019

Palestinian Authority flag and: 20p, Dome of the Rock, Jerusalem, vert. No. 1773, 125p, shown. No. 1774, 125p, Dome of the Rock, father and boy, vert.

***Perf. 13¼x12¾, 12¾x13¼***

**2000, Nov. 29**

**1772-1774** A1019 Set of 3 3.25 3.25

No. 1774 is airmail.

Opening of El-Ferdan Railway Bridge — A1020

**2000, Dec. 2** ***Perf. 12¾x13¼***

**1775** A1020 20p multi .70 .25

Disabled Person's Day — A1021

**2000, Dec. 9** ***Perf. 13¼x12¾***

**1776** A1021 20p multi .50 .25

Opening of Al-Azhar Professorial Building — A1022

**2000, Dec. 10** ***Perf. 12¾x13¼***

**1777** A1022 20p multi .50 .25

Famous Egyptians A1023

No. 1778: a, Karem Mahmoud, artist (yellow background). b, Mahmoud El-Miligi, artist (green background). c, Mohamed Fawzi, musician (pink background). d, Hussein Riyad, artist (lilac background). e, Abdel Wares Asser, artist (light blue background).

**2000, Dec. 24** ***Perf. 13¼x12¾***

**1778** Horiz. strip of 5 2.00 2.00

*a.-e.* A1023 20p Any single .40 .25

Feasts — A1024

a, Red and yellow flowers. b, Purple flowers.

***Perf. 12¾x13¼***

**2000, Dec. 23** **Litho.**

**1779** A1024 20p Pair, #a-b .90 .90

For use on greeting cards.

Jerusalem, City of Peace — A1025

**2001, Jan. 1** *Imperf.*
**1780** A1025 £2 multi 2.00 2.00

Post Day — A1026

Ancient Egyptian art: 20p, 8 standing figures. No. 1782, 125p, 3 large standing figures.

**2001, Jan. 2** *Perf. 12¾x13¼*
**1781-1782** A1026 Set of 2 1.75 1.75

***Imperf***

**Size: 80x60mm**

**1783** A1026 125p Chariot 2.00 2.00

No. 1782 is airmail.

Arab Labor Organization, 36th Anniv. — A1027

*Perf. 13¼x12¾*

**2001, Feb. 10** **Litho.**
**1784** A1027 20p multi .50 .25

Postal Savings Bank, Cent. — A1028

**2001, Mar. 1**
**1785** A1028 20p multi .50 .25

Natl. Council for Women, 1st Anniv. — A1029

Background colors: 30p, Pink. 125p, Blue.

**2001, Mar. 16** *Perf. 12¾x13¼*
**1786-1787** A1029 Set of 2 2.00 1.40

No. 1787 is airmail.

Cairo Intl. Fair — A1030

**2001, Mar. 21** *Perf. 13¼x12¾*
**1788** A1030 30p multi .50 .25

Helwan University, 25th Anniv. — A1031

**2001, May 4** *Perf. 12¾x13¼*
**1789** A1031 30p multi .50 .25

Inauguration of Alexandria Library — A1032

**2001, May 20**
**1790** A1032 125p multi 1.40 1.25

African Conference on the Future of Children A1033

Background color: 30p, Blue. 125p, Red.

**2001, May 28** *Perf. 13¼x12¾*
**1791-1792** A1033 Set of 2 1.75 1.40

No. 1792 is airmail.

World Environment Day — A1034

**2001, June 5** **Litho.** *Perf. 13¼x12¾*
**1793** A1034 125p multi 1.40 1.25

World Military Soccer Championships A1035

Designs: 30p, Emblem. 125p, Emblem and map.

*Perf. 13¼x12¾*

**2001, June 21** **Litho.**
**1794-1795** A1035 Set of 2 1.75 1.50

**Intl. Day Against Drug Abuse Type of 2000**

**2001, June 26** *Perf. 12¾x13¼*
**1796** A1013 30p multi .50 .25

Egypt's Victory in World Military Soccer Championships — A1036

**2001, July 6** **Litho.** *Imperf.*
**1797** A1036 125p multi 1.75 1.75

Egyptian Railways, 150th Anniv. — A1037

**2001, July 12** *Perf. 12¾x13¼*
**1798** A1037 30p multi .75 .25

Poets — A1038

No. 1799: a, Aziz Abaza Pasha (1898-73), blue background. b, Ahmed Rami (1892-1981), pink background.

**2001, July 28** *Perf. 13¼x12¾*
**1799** A1038 30p Horiz. pair, #a-b .80 .80

Intl. Volunteers Year — A1039

**2001, Aug. 18**
**1800** A1039 125p multi 1.40 1.10

Ismailia Folklore Festival — A1040

**2001, Aug. 20**
**1801** A1040 30p multi .60 .25

Satellite Telecommunications Ground Stations, 25th Anniv. — A1041

**2001, Sept. 8** *Perf. 12¾x13¼*
**1802** A1041 30p multi .60 .25

Year of Dialogue Among Civilizations A1042

Designs: No. 1803, 125p, Emblem. No. 1804, 125p, UN emblem, globe, symbols of various civilizations, horiz.

*Perf. 13¼x12¾, 12¾x13¼*

**2001, Oct. 9**
**1803-1804** A1042 Set of 2 3.00 2.50

Opening of Suez Canal Bridge — A1043

No. 1805: a, 30p, Bridge, ship. b, 125p, Bridge, road.

No. 1806, Bridge, ship and flags of Egypt and Japan.

**2001, Oct. 10** *Perf. 12¾x13¼*
**1805** A1043 Horiz. pair, #a-b 1.75 1.75

***Imperf***

**Size: 81x60mm**

**1806** A1043 125p multi 2.00 2.00

Ancient Gold Masks — A1044

Designs: No. 1807, 30p, Mask of San Xing Dui, China, green background. No. 1808, 30p, Funerary mask of King Tutankhamun, brown background.

**2001, Oct. 12** ***Perf. 12¾x13¼***
**1807-1808** A1044 Set of 2 .80 .60

See People's Republic of China 3141-3142.

Opening of Azhar Tunnels, Cairo — A1045

**2001, Oct. 28** ***Perf. 13¼x12¾***
**1809** A1045 30p multi .60 .25

El-Menoufia University, 25th Anniv. — A1046

**2001, Nov. 25**
**1810** A1046 30p multi .60 .25

Feasts — A1047

No.1811: a, Black and white bird on branch. b, Sea gulls. c, Parrot. d, Blue bird on branch.

**2001, Dec. 5**
**1811** A1047 30p Block of 4, #a-d 2.50 2.00

For use on greeting cards.

Musicians — A1048

No. 1812: a, Zakaria Ahmed (1896-1961) with scarf around neck (4). b, Riyadh El-Sonbati (1908-81) with glasses with rectangular lenses (3). c, Mahmoud El-Sherif (1912-90) (2). d, Mohamed El-Kasabgi (1898-1966) with glasses with round lenses (1). Stamp numbers, shown in parentheses, are found at the bottom center in Arabian script.

**2001, Dec.**
**1812** A1048 30p Horiz. strip of 4 2.00 1.40

Painting From Tomb of Anhur Khawi — A1049

Painting from Tomb of Irinefer — A1050

**2002, Jan. 2** **Litho.** ***Perf. 12¾x13¼***
**1813** A1049 30p multi .45 .25

***Imperf***

**Size: 79x60mm**

**1814** A1050 125p multi 2.25 2.25

Post Day.

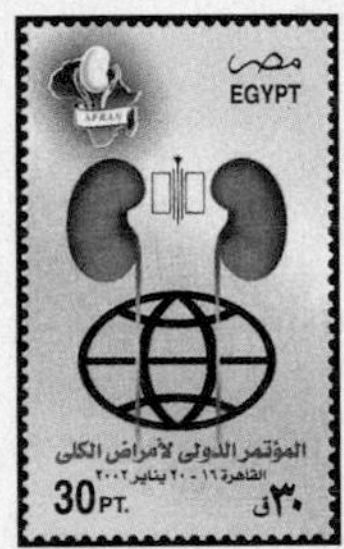

Intl. Nephrology Congress A1051

**2002, Jan. 16** **Litho.** ***Perf. 13¼x12¾***
**1815** A1051 30p multi .45 .25

Police Day, 50th Anniv. A1052

**2002, Jan. 25** ***Perf. 12¾x13¼***
**1816** A1052 30p multi .45 .25

***Imperf***

**Size: 79x50mm**

**1817** A1052 30p multi 1.60 1.50

Return of Sinai to Egypt, 20th Anniv. — A1053

**2002, Apr. 25** ***Perf. 13¼x12¾***
**1818** A1053 30p multi .60 .25

Cairo Bank, 50th Anniv. — A1054

**2002, May 15**
**1819** A1054 30p multi .50 .25

Weight Lifters — A1055

No. 1820: a, Ibrahim Shams, 1948 (weights over head). b, Khidre el Touney, 1936 (weights at knees).

**2002, June 1**
**1820** A1055 30p Horiz. pair, #a-b .80 .80

Al Akhbar Newspaper, 50th Anniv. — A1056

**2002, June 15** ***Perf. 12¾x13¼***
**1821** A1056 30p multi .45 .25

Nos. 318-321 and Egyptian Arms — A1057

**2002, July 23** **Litho.** ***Imperf.***
**1822** A1057 125p multi 1.40 1.40

July 23rd Revolution, 50th anniv.

Aswan Dam, Cent. — A1058

No. 1823: a, Dam. b, Dam and buildings.

**2002, Aug. 15** ***Perf. 12¾x13¼***
**1823** A1058 30p Horiz. pair, #a-b .90 .90

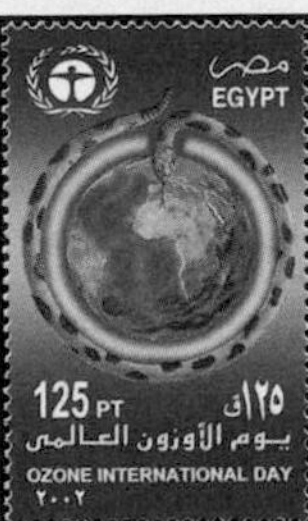

Intl. Day for Preservation of the Ozone Layer — A1059

**2002, Sept. 16** ***Perf. 13¼x12¾***
**1824** A1059 125p multi 1.40 1.25

18th Intl. Conference on Road Safety, Cairo — A1060

**2002, Sept. 22**
**1825** A1060 30p multi .50 .25

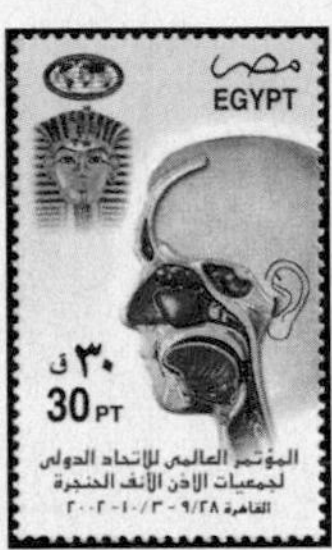

17th Congress of Intl. Federation of Otorhinolaryngological Societies, Cairo — A1061

**2002, Sept. 28**
**1826** A1061 30p multi .50 .25

World Post Day — A1062

**2002, Oct. 9**
**1827** A1062 125p multi 1.10 1.10

Opening of Alexandria Library — A1063

Ancient Alexandria Library — A1064

Designs: 30p, Library exterior. 125p, Pillar, sun on horizon, vert.

***Perf. 12¾x13¼, 13¼x12¾***

**2002, Oct. 16**
**1828-1829** A1063 Set of 2 1.75 1.50

**Size: 60x80mm**

***Imperf***

**1830** A1064 125p multi 1.60 1.60

Hassan Faek, Actor — A1065

Aziza Amir, Actress — A1066

Farid Shawki, Actor — A1067

Mary Mounib, Actress — A1068

**2002, Nov. 23** ***Perf. 13¼x12¾***

| | | | |
|---|---|---|---|
| **1831** | Horiz. strip of 4 | 1.75 | 1.60 |
| *a.* | A1065 30p tan & black | .40 | .25 |
| *b.* | A1066 30p tan & black | .40 | .25 |
| *c.* | A1067 30p tan & black | .40 | .25 |
| *d.* | A1068 30p tan & black | .40 | .25 |

A1069

A1070

A1071

Birds — A1072

**2002, Dec. 3** ***Perf. 13¼x12¾***

| | | | |
|---|---|---|---|
| **1832** | Block of 4 | 1.75 | 1.60 |
| *a.* | A1069 30p multi | .40 | .25 |
| *b.* | A1070 30p multi | .40 | .25 |
| *c.* | A1071 30p multi | .40 | .25 |
| *d.* | A1072 30p multi | .40 | .25 |

Egyptian Museum, Cent. — A1073

125p, Entrance, statue of Cheops.

**2002, Dec. 11** ***Perf. 12¾x13¼***
**1833** A1073 30p shown .50 .25

**Size: 80x60mm**

***Imperf***

**1834** A1073 125p multi 1.40 1.40

Opening of Aswan Suspension Bridge — A1074

No. 1835: a, Bridge and support cables. b, Bridge towers.

**2002, Dec. 17** ***Perf. 12¾x13¼***
**1835** A1074 30p Horiz. pair, #a-b .90 .90

Suez Canal University, 25th Anniv. — A1075

**2002, Dec. 29** ***Perf. 13¼x12¾***
**1836** A1075 30p multi .45 .25

Toshka Land Reclamation Project — A1076

**2002, Dec. 31** ***Perf. 12¾x13¼***
**1837** A1076 30p multi .45 .25

A1077

A1078

Post Day — A1079

**2003, Jan. 2**

| | | | |
|---|---|---|---|
| **1838** | A1077 30p multi | .45 | .25 |
| **1839** | A1078 30p multi | .45 | .25 |
| **1840** | A1079 125p multi | 1.10 | 1.00 |
| | *Nos. 1838-1840 (3)* | 2.00 | 1.50 |

Cairo Intl. Communications and Information Technology Fair — A1080

**2003, Jan. 12 Litho.** ***Perf. 13¼x12¾***
**1841** A1080 30p multi .50 .25

Intl. Nile Children's Song Festival — A1081

Background color: 30p, Brown. 125p, Green.

**2003, Jan. 28** ***Perf. 12¾x13¼***
**1842-1843** A1081 Set of 2 1.50 1.25

Intl. Table Tennis Championships — A1082

Background color: 30p, Blue. 125p, Orange.

**2003, Feb. 3**
**1844-1845** A1082 Set of 2 1.50 1.25

Tenth Intl. Building and Construction Conference A1083

Background color: 30p, Orange. 125p, Blue.

**2003, Apr. 1** ***Perf. 13¼x12¾***
**1846-1847** A1083 Set of 2 1.50 1.10

Arab Lawyer's Union, 60th Anniv. — A1084

Background color: 30p, Blue. 125p, Lilac.

**2003, Apr. 25** ***Perf. 12¾x13¼***
**1848-1849** A1084 Set of 2 1.40 1.10

Inauguration of First Phase of Smart Village Project — A1085

Denomination color: 30p, White. 125p, Yellow. £1, White.

**2003, July 1** ***Perf. 12¾x13¼***
**1850-1851** A1085 Set of 2 1.50 1.50

**Size: 79x59mm**

***Imperf***

**1852** A1085 £1 multi 1.50 1.50

Writers — A1086

No. 1853: a, Ihsan Abdul Qudous (1919-90) (wearing checked tie). b, Youssef Idris (1927-91) (wearing solid tie).

**2003, July 28** ***Perf. 13¼x12¾***
**1853** A1086 30p Horiz. pair, #a-b .90 .90

African Men's Basketball Championships A1087

Background color: 30p, Black. 125p, Blue.

**2003, Aug. 12**
**1854-1855** A1087 Set of 2 1.50 1.10

Natl. Institute of Astronomical and Geophysical Research, Cent. — A1088

**2003, Sept. 7** ***Perf. 12¾x13¼***
**1856** A1088 30p multi .60 .30

World Tourism Day — A1089

Denomination color: 30p, White. 125p, Red.

***Perf. 12¾x13¼***
**2003, Sept. 27** **Litho.**
**1857-1858** A1089 Set of 2 1.50 1.10

Egypt's Bid for Hosting 2010 World Cup Soccer Championships — A1090

Designs: 30p, Emblem, vert. 125p, Emblem, funerary mask of King Tutankhamun.

***Perf. 13¼x12¾, 12¾x13¼***
**2003, Sept. 27**
**1859-1860** A1090 Set of 2 1.50 1.10

October War Against Israel, 30th Anniv. — A1091

**2003, Oct. 6** ***Perf. 13¼x12¾***
**1861** A1091 30p multi 1.00 .30

World Post Day — A1092

**2003, Oct. 9**
**1862** A1092 125p multi 1.00 .80

National Bar Association, 91st Anniv. — A1093

**2003, Oct. 30**
**1863** A1093 30p multi .60 .25

Festivals — A1094

No. 1864: a, Pink orchids. b, White rose. c, Red rose. d, Sunflower.

**2003, Nov. 23** ***Perf. 14***
**1864** A1094 30p Block of 4, #a-d 1.50 1.50

For use on greeting cars.

Film Directors — A1095

No. 1865: a, Salah Abou Seif (balding man with open collar). b, Kamal Selim (round eyeglasses) c, Henri Barakat (square eyeglasses). d, Hassan El Emam.

**2003, Dec. 1** ***Perf. 13¼x12¾***
**1865** A1095 30p Horiz. strip of 4, #a-d 1.50 1.50

El Gomhoreya Newspaper, 50th Anniv. — A1096

**2003, Dec. 7**
**1866** A1096 30p multi .50 .25

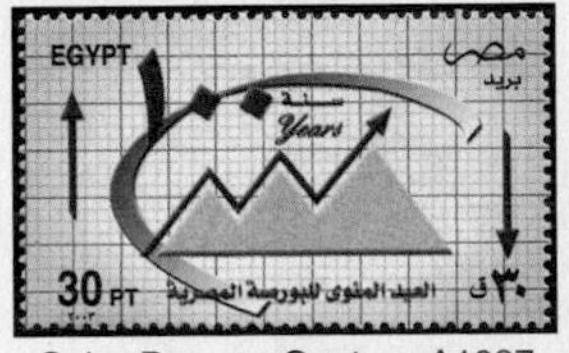
Cairo Bourse, Cent. — A1097

**2003, Dec. 7** ***Perf. 12¾x13¼***
**1867** A1097 30p multi .45 .25

Mrs. Suzanne Mubarak, Emblems of Fifth E-9 Ministerial Review Meeting and UNESCO — A1098

Background color: 30p, Blue. 125p, Orange. £2, Blue.

***Perf. 12¾x13¼***
**2003, Dec. 18** **Litho.**
**1868-1869** A1098 Set of 2 1.50 1.10

***Imperf***
**Size: 79x60mm**
**1870** A1098 £2 multi 2.00 2.00

Delta International Bank, 25th Anniv. — A1099

Background color: 30p, Green. 125p, Blue. £2, Green and blue, horiz.

**2004, Jan. 1** ***Perf. 12¾x13¼***
**1871-1872** A1099 Set of 2 1.40 1.00

***Imperf***
**Size: 80x60mm**
**1873** A1099 £2 multi 2.00 2.00

Post Day A1100

Denominations: 30p, 125p.

**2004, Jan. 2** ***Perf. 12¾x13¼***
**1874-1875** A1100 Set of 2 1.50 1.25

Eighth Intl. Telecommunications Conference — A1101

**2004, Jan. 17**
**1876** A1101 30p multi .80 .30

Treasures of Egypt A1102

No. 1877: a, Sinai. b, Pyramids at dusk. c, Egyptian Bedouin. d, Red Sea corals. e, Suez Canal, Ferdinand-Marie de Lesseps, Khedive Ismail. f, Ramadan lanterns. g, Nile felucca. h, White Western Desert. i, Maydum Pyramid.

No. 1878: a, St. Catherine Monastery, Sinai. b, Icon of Sts. Paul and Anthony. c, Mosque of Muhammad Ali. d, Lamp, Old Cairo. e, Emblem of Sultan Qaytbay. f, Minaret, Cairo. g, Mosque of al-Azhar. h, Coptic priest and icon, Cairo. i, Ben Ezra Synagogue.

No. 1879: a, Ankh. b, Rosetta Stone. c, Sarcophagus of Ahmes Meritamun. d, Stela of Amenmhat. e, Sphinx. f, Udjat. g, Canopic jars of Tutankhamun. h, Cartouche of Tutankhamun. i, Egyptian scribe.

No. 1880: a, Sphinx, diff. b, Queen Nefertiti. c, Tutankhamun.

**2004, Jan. 22** **Litho.** ***Perf. 13x13¼***
**1877** Booklet pane of 9 2.25 —
*a.-i.* A1102 30p Any single .40 .25
**1878** Booklet pane of 9 8.25 —
*a.-i.* A1102 125p Any single .90 .80

**Litho. & Embossed, Litho. & Embossed With Foil Application (£10)**

**1879** Booklet pane of 9 13.50 —
*a.-i.* A1102 £2 Any single 1.50 1.25

***Perf. 13¼***
**1880** Booklet pane of 3 15.00 —
*a.-b.* A1102 £5 Either single, 38x51mm 3.75 3.75
*c.* A1102 £10 gold & multi, 38x51mm 7.00 7.00
Complete booklet, #1877-1880 39.00

Complete booklet sold for £80.

Morkos Hanna — A1103

Ahmed Lotfi — A1104

Mahmoud Abu el Nasr — A1105

Abd el Aziz Fahmy — A1106

Ibrahim el Helbawi — A1107

Makram Ebeid — A1108

Mohammad Naguib el Gharabli — A1109

Mohammad Bassiouni A1110

Mohammad Hafez Ramadan A1111

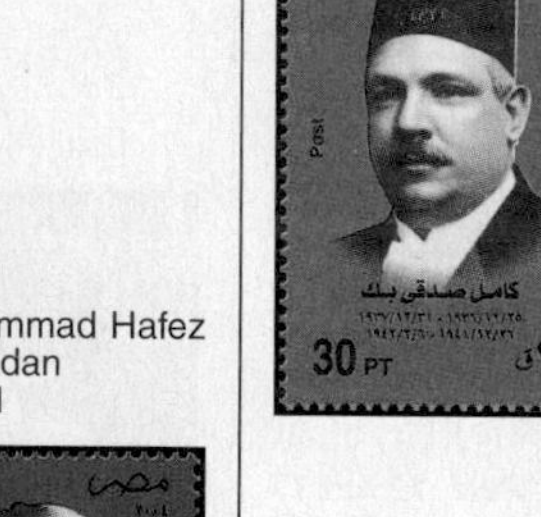

Mohammad Abu Shadi — A1112

Mahmoud Fahmi Goundia — A1113

Kamel Youssof Saleh — A1114

Abd el Hamid Abd el Hakk — A1115

Mohammad Ali Allouba — A1116

Kamel Sedki Beck — A1117

Bar Association Emblem — A1118

Abd el Rahman el Rafei — A1119

Abd el Fattah el Shalkany A1120

Mohammad Sabri Abu Alam — A1121

Omar Omar — A1122

Sameh Ashour — A1123

Ahmed el Khawaga A1124

Abd el Aziz el Shorgabi A1125

Mostafa el Baradei — A1126

**2004, Feb. Litho. *Perf. 13¼x12¾***

| | | | |
|---|---|---|---|
| **1881** | Block of 25 | 8.75 | 8.75 |
| *a.* | A1103 30p bright blue & black | .35 | .25 |
| *b.* | A1104 30p bright blue & black | .35 | .25 |
| *c.* | A1105 30p bright blue & black | .35 | .25 |
| *d.* | A1106 30p bright blue & black | .35 | .25 |
| *e.* | A1107 30p bright blue & black | .35 | .25 |
| *f.* | A1108 30p pink & black | .35 | .25 |
| *g.* | A1109 30p pink & black | .35 | .25 |
| *h.* | A1110 30p pink & black | .35 | .25 |
| *i.* | A1111 30p pink & black | .35 | .25 |
| *j.* | A1112 30p pink & black | .35 | .25 |
| *k.* | A1113 30p orange & black | .35 | .25 |
| *l.* | A1114 30p orange & black | .35 | .25 |
| *m.* | A1115 30p orange & black | .35 | .25 |
| *n.* | A1116 30p orange & black | .35 | .25 |
| *o.* | A1117 30p orange & black | .35 | .25 |
| *p.* | A1118 30p green & multi | .35 | .25 |
| *q.* | A1119 30p green & black | .35 | .25 |
| *r.* | A1120 30p green & black | .35 | .25 |
| *s.* | A1121 30p green & black | .35 | .25 |
| *t.* | A1122 30p green & black | .35 | .25 |
| *u.* | A1118 30p dark blue & multi | .35 | .25 |
| *v.* | A1123 30p dark blue & black | .35 | .25 |
| *w.* | A1124 30p dark blue & black | .35 | .25 |
| *x.* | A1125 30p dark blue & black | .35 | .25 |
| *y.* | A1126 30p dark blue & black | .35 | .25 |

National Bar Association, 92nd anniv.

IBM Corporation in Egypt, 50th Anniv. — A1127

**2004, Feb. 24**
**1882** A1127 30p multi .60 .25

Cairo Rotary Club, 75th Anniv. — A1128

**2004, Mar. 11**
**1883** A1128 30p multi .60 .25

Egyptian Victory in Regional Computer Programming and Information Technology Competition A1129

**2004, Mar. 15**
**1884** A1129 30p multi .60 .25

National Women's Day — A1130

Background colors: 30p, Blue. 125p, Red orange.

**2004, Mar. 16** **Litho.**
**1885-1886** A1130 Set of 2 1.50 1.00

Anti-Narcotics General Administration, 75th Anniv. — A1131

**2004, Mar. 20** ***Perf. 12¾x13¼***
**1887** A1131 30p multi .75 .30

***Imperf***

**Size: 80x60mm**

**1888** A1131 125p multi 1.50 1.50

Orphan's Day — A1132

**2004, Apr. 2** ***Perf. 13¼x12¾***
**1889** A1132 30p multi .60 .25

Compare with Types A1169 and A1199.

Telecom Africa Fair and Conference, Cairo — A1133

**2004, May 4** ***Perf. 12¾x13¼***
**1890** A1133 30p multi .60 .25

Egyptian Philatelic Society, 75th Anniv. — A1134

Designs: 30p, Emblem. 125p, Emblem, stamp, magnifying glass, tongs.

**2004, May 20** ***Perf. 13¼x12¾***
**1891** A1134 30p multi .60 .25

***Imperf***

**Size: 80x60mm**

**1892** A1134 125p multi 1.50 1.50

State Information Service, 50th Anniv. — A1135

**2004, May 30** ***Perf. 12¾x13¼***
**1893** A1135 30p multi .75 .25

Tenth Radio and Television Festival, Cairo — A1136

Designs: 30p, Festival emblem, green background. £1, Fesitval emblem, brown background. 125p, Sphinx, festival emblem, film, horiz.
£2, Like 125p, horiz.

***Perf. 13¼x12¾, 12¾x13¼***

**2004, June 1**
**1894-1896** A1136 Set of 3 2.00 2.00

***Imperf***

**Size: 80x60mm**

**1897** A1136 £2 multi 2.00 2.00

Pres. Hosni Mubarak, "Education for All" Arab Regional Conference Emblem — A1137

Stylized Children, Emblems A1138

***Perf. 12¾x13¼, 13¼x12¾***

**2004, June 1**
**1898** A1137 30p yel & multi .35 .25
**1899** A1137 125p red org & multi .60 .60
**1900** A1138 125p multi .60 .60
*Nos. 1898-1900 (3)* 1.55 1.45

***Imperf***

**Size: 80x60mm**

**1901** A1137 £2 blue & multi 1.75 1.75

Construction and Housing Bank, 25th Anniv. — A1139

**2004, June 24** ***Perf. 13¼x12¾***
**1902** A1139 30p multi .60 .25

2004 Summer Olympics, Athens — A1140

Background color: 30p, Gray. 150p, Orange yellow.

***Perf. 13¼x12¾***

**2004, Aug. 13** **Litho.**
**1903-1904** A1140 Set of 2 1.50 1.40

Scouting in Egypt, 90th Anniv. — A1141

**2004, Aug. 15** ***Perf. 12¾x13¼***
**1905** A1141 30p multi .80 .30

14th Intl. Folklore Festival, Ismailia — A1142

**2004, Aug. 24** ***Perf. 13¼x12¾***
**1906** A1142 30p multi .70 .25

Administrative Attorneys, 50th Anniv. — A1143

**2004, Sept. 16** ***Perf. 13¼x12¾***
**1907** A1143 30p multi .60 .25

***Imperf***

**Size: 60x80mm**

**1908** A1143 £1 multi 1.50 1.50

Egyptian National Archives, 50th Anniv. — A1144

**2004, Sept. 20** ***Perf. 12¾x13¼***
**1909** A1144 30p multi .75 .25

Light and Hope Society, 50th Anniv. — A1145

**2004, Sept. 26**
**1910** A1145 30p multi .70 .25

General Arab Journalists Union, 10th Conference A1146

**2004, Oct. 2** ***Perf. 13¼x12¾***
**1911** A1146 125p multi 1.00 .80

Telecom Egypt, 150th Anniv. A1146a

**2004, Oct. 3** **Litho.** ***Perf. 12¾x13¼***
**1911A** A1146a 30p multi *18.50 18.50*

No. 1911A was withdrawn from sale after a few days as anniversary emblem was incorrect.

Military Production Day, 50th Anniv. — A1147

**2004, Oct. 6** ***Perf. 12¾x13¼***
**1912** A1147 30p multi .90 .30

World Post Day — A1148

**2004, Oct. 9**
**1913** A1148 150p multi 1.10 1.00

Egyptian Youth Hostels Association, 50th Anniv. — A1149

**2004, Oct. 20** *Perf. 13¼x12¾*

**1914** A1149 30p multi .80 .25

Rose — A1150

Songbird A1151

*Perf. 12¾x13¼*

**2004, Nov. 10** **Litho.**

**1915** A1150 30p multi .50 .25

*Perf. 13¼x12¾*

**1916** A1151 30p multi .50 .25

24th Arab Scouting Congress — A1152

**2004, Nov. 27** *Perf. 12¾x13¼*

**1917** A1152 30p multi .65 .25

Arab Scouting Organization, 50th Anniv. — A1153

**2004, Dec. 4**

**1918** A1153 30p multi .65 .25

Islamic Art Museum Foundation, Cent. — A1154

**2004, Dec. 15** *Perf. 13¼x12¾*

**1919** A1154 30p multi .65 .25

FIFA (Fédération Internationale de Football Association), Cent. — A1155

**2004, Dec. 15** *Perf. 12¾x13¼*

**1920** A1155 150p multi 1.25 1.00

Fekri Abaza (1896-1979), Journalist A1156

Abd El Rahman El Sharqawi (1920-87), Journalist A1157

**2004, Dec. 28** *Perf. 13¼x12¾*

**1921** A1156 30p multi .40 .25

**1922** A1157 30p multi .40 .25

Telecom Egypt, 150th Anniv. — A1158

Color of central panel: 30p, White. 125p, Gray.

**2004, Dec. 30** *Perf. 12¾x13¼*

**1923-1924** A1158 Set of 2 1.50 1.10

First Sale of Natural Gas to Jordan — A1159

**2005, Jan. 1**

**1925** A1159 30p multi .90 .30

Post Day — A1160

**2005, Jan. 2** *Perf. 13¼x12¾*

**1926** A1160 30p multi .80 .30

Opening of Om El Massrean — El Moneib Subway Line, Cairo — A1161

**2005, Jan. 16** *Perf. 12¾x13¼*

**1927** A1161 30p multi .65 .30

***Imperf***

**Size: 80x59mm**

**1928** A1161 150p multi 1.40 1.40

Police Day — A1162

Pres. Hosni Mubarak and flag stripes aligned: 30p, Vertically. £1, Horizontally.

**2005, Jan. 25** *Perf. 13¼x12¾*

**1929** A1162 30p multi .60 .25

***Imperf***

**Size: 80x59mm**

**1930** A1162 £1 multi 1.25 1.25

El Mohandes Insurance Company, 25th Anniv. — A1163

**2005, Jan. 26** *Perf. 13¼x12¾*

**1931** A1163 30p multi .65 .30

9th Intl. Telecommunications and Information Conference, Cairo — A1164

**2005, Feb. 1**

**1932** A1164 30p multi .65 .25

7th University Youth Week — A1165

**2005, Feb. 5**

**1933** A1165 30p multi .65 .25

Rotary International, Cent. — A1166

**2005, Feb. 23** **Litho.**

**1934** A1166 30p multi .75 .30

38th Intl. Fair, Cairo — A1167

**2005, Mar. 15**

**1935** A1167 30p multi .50 .25

Arab League, 60th Anniv. — A1168

**2005, Mar. 22**

**1936** A1168 30p multi .55 .25

Orphan's Day — A1169

**2005, Apr. 2**

**1937** A1169 30p multi .70 .30

Compare with Types A1132 and A1199. See also Nos. 2035, 2053.

Heliopolis Foundation, Cent. — A1170

**2005, May 5** *Perf. 12¾x13¼*
1938 A1170 30p multi .65 .25

National Center of Social and Criminological Research, 50th Anniv. — A1171

**2005, May 22 Litho.** *Perf. 13¼x12¾*
1939 A1171 30p multi .70 .30

Egyptian-European Association Agreement, 1st Anniv. — A1172

**2005, June 1**
1940 A1172 150p multi .90 .50

World Environment Day — A1173

**2005, June 5** *Perf. 12¾x13¼*
1941 A1173 30p multi .80 .30

World Summit on the Information Society, Tunis — A1174

**2005, July 31 Litho.** *Perf. 13¼x12¾*
1942 A1174 150p multi 1.40 1.40

Ministry of Youth, 50th Anniv. — A1175

Background colors: 30p, Green. 125p, Olive green.

**2005, Aug. 13**
1943-1944 A1175 Set of 2 1.25 1.10

Presidential Elections A1176

**2005, Sept. 7**
1945 A1176 30p multi .65 .30

13th World Psychiatry Congress, Cairo — A1177

Designs: 30p, Emblem. 150p, Emblem and funerary mask of King Tutankhamun, horiz.

**2005, Sept. 10** *Perf. 13¼x12¾*
1946 A1177 30p multi .65 .30

*Imperf*

**Size: 80x60mm**

1947 A1177 150p multi 1.90 1.90

World Literacy Day — A1178

**2005, Sept. 24** *Perf. 12¾x13¼*
1948 A1178 30p multi .70 .30

Re-election of Pres. Hosni Mubarak A1179

**2005, Sept. 27** *Perf. 13¼x12¾*
1949 A1179 30p multi .60 .25

Mohamed El-Baradei, Director General of Intl. Atomic Energy Agency — A1180

Background colors: 30p, Blue green. 150p, Rose lilac.

**2005, Oct. 8**
1950-1951 A1180 Set of 2 1.75 1.50

Awarding of 2005 Nobel Peace Prize to El-Baradei and IAEA.

World Post Day — A1181

Denominations: 30p, 150p.

**2005, Oct. 9**
1952-1953 A1181 Set of 2 1.40 1.25

Intl. Year of Sports and Physical Education A1182

**2005, Oct. 24**
1954 A1182 150p multi 1.25 1.00

United Nations, 60th Anniv. — A1183

**2005, Oct. 24** *Perf. 12¾x13¼*
1955 A1183 150p multi 1.25 1.00

Festivals A1184

**2005, Nov. 1** *Perf. 13¼x12¾*
1956 A1184 30p multi .70 .30

Alexandria Biennale, 50th Anniv. — A1185

**2005, Dec. 1**
1957 A1185 30p multi .65 .30

K-8 Training Airplane — A1186

Denominations: 30p, 150p.

*Perf. 12¾x13¼*

**2005, Dec. 26** **Litho.**
1958-1959 A1186 Set of 2 2.00 1.50

Sayed Mekawi, Musician A1187

Mohamed El Mogi (1923-95), Musician A1188

Kamal El Taweel, Composer A1189

Ali Ismael (1921-75), Composer A1190

Mohamed Roshdi, Folk Singer — A1191

**2005, Dec. 31** ***Perf. 13¼x12¾***

| | | | |
|---|---|---|---|
| **1960** | Horiz. strip of 5 | 1.75 | 1.75 |
| *a.* | A1187 30p green & multi | .30 | .25 |
| *b.* | A1188 30p blue & multi | .30 | .25 |
| *c.* | A1189 30p lilac & black | .30 | .25 |
| *d.* | A1190 30p org & black | .30 | .25 |
| *e.* | A1191 30p brt org & black | .30 | .25 |

Post Day — A1192

**2006, Jan. 2**

**1961** A1192 30p multi .75 .30

25th Africa Cup of Nations Soccer Tournament A1193

**2006, Jan. 20**

**1962** A1193 30p multi .60 .25

Arab University Youth Week — A1194

**2006, Feb. 4** ***Perf. 12¾x13¼***

**1963** A1194 30p multi .55 .25

Intl. Telecommunications, Information and Networking Exhibition, Cairo — A1195

**2006, Feb. 5** ***Perf. 13¼x12¾***

**1964** A1195 30p multi .55 .25

Pres. Hosni Mubarak Holding African Cup of Nations — A1196

**2006, Feb. 10** ***Perf. 12¾x13¼***

**1965** A1196 30p multi .75 .35

**Size: 80x60mm**

***Imperf***

**1966** A1196 150p multi 1.75 1.60

Information and Decision Support Center, 20th Anniv. — A1197

**2006, Mar. 27** ***Perf. 13¼x12¾***

**1967** A1197 30p multi .55 .25

Total Solar Eclipse of March 29, 2006 — A1198

**2006, Mar. 29** ***Perf. 12¾x13¼***

**1968** A1198 30p multi .55 .35

**Size: 82x60mm**

***Imperf***

**1969** A1198 150p multi 2.25 1.90

Orphan's Day — A1199

**2006, Apr. 2** ***Perf. 13¼x12¾***

**1970** A1199 30p multi .70 .30

Compare with types A1132 and A1169. See also Nos. 2035, 2053.

Gamal Hemdan (1928-93), Geographical Historian A1200

**2006, Apr. 16**

**1971** A1200 30p lilac & black .55 .30

Abd El-Rahman ibn Khaldun (1332-1406), Historian A1201

**2006, May 27**

**1972** A1201 30p multi .70 .30

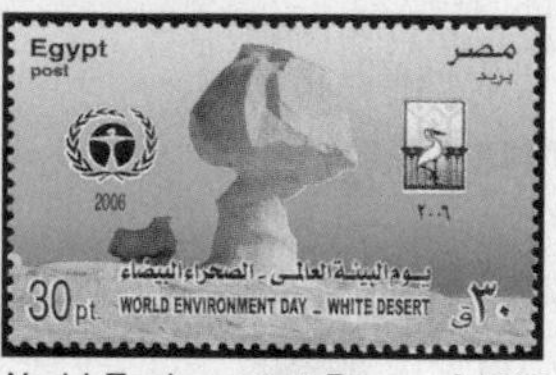

World Environment Day — A1202

Designs: 30p, Stone pillar in White Desert. 150p, Trees in desert.

**2006, June 5** ***Perf. 12¾x13¼***

**1973-1974** A1202 Set of 2 1.50 1.25

Diplomatic Relations Between Egypt and People's Republic of China, 50th Anniv. — A1203

No. 1975, £1.50: a, Abu Simbel Temple, Egypt. b, South Gate Pavilion, China.

**2006, July 13** **Litho.** ***Perf. 12***

| | | | |
|---|---|---|---|
| **1975** | A1203 Horiz. pair, #a-b, + central label | 1.75 | 1.75 |
| *c.* | Souvenir sheet, #1975 | *25.00* | *25.00* |

Military Academy Headquarters, Heliopolis, 50th Anniv. — A1204

**2006, July 19** ***Perf. 12¾x13¼***

**1976** A1204 30p multi .70 .30

Nationalization of the Suez Canal, 50th Anniv. — A1205

**2006, July 26** ***Perf. 13¼x12¾***

**1977** A1205 30p multi .55 .25

World Post Day — A1206

Denominations: 30p, 150p.

**2006, Oct. 9**

**1978-1979** A1206 Set of 2 1.50 1.25

China - Africa Summit — A1206a

No. 1979A: b, Chinese mask. c, African mask.

**2006, Nov. 5** **Litho.** ***Perf. 12***

| | | | |
|---|---|---|---|
| **1979A** | A1206a Horiz. pair with central label | 2.25 | 2.25 |
| *b.-c.* | £1.50 Either single | .80 | .60 |

National Housing Census — A1207

**2006, Nov. 21** **Litho.** ***Perf. 13¼x13***

**1980** A1207 30p multi .55 .25

Al-Ahram Newspaper — A1208

No. 1981: a, Newspaper headquarters. b, Newspaper emblem.

150p, Headquarters and emblem.

**2006, Nov. 26** ***Perf. 13x13¼***

**1981** A1208 30p Horiz. pair, #a-b, + central label 1.00 1.00

***Imperf***

**Size: 80x60mm**

**1982** A1208 150p multi 1.00 1.00

Egyptian Initiative to Support Lebanon — A1209

**2006, Dec. 27** ***Perf. 13x13¼***

**1983** A1209 150p multi 1.00 1.00

Feasts — A1210

**2006, Dec. 30**
1984 A1210 30p multi .45 .25

Post Day — A1211

**2007, Jan. 2**
1985 A1211 30p multi .45 .25

Ali El Kassar (1888-1957), Artist — A1212

**2007, Jan. 15** ***Perf. 13¼x13***
1986 A1212 30p multi .45 .25

Automobile and Touring Club of Egypt — A1213

**2007, Jan. 14 Litho.** ***Perf. 12¾x13¼***
1987 A1213 30p multi .55 .30

***Imperf***

**Size: 80x60mm**
1988 A1213 150p multi 1.50 1.50

Police Day — A1214

**2007, Jan. 25** ***Perf. 12¾x13¼***
1989 A1214 30p multi .55 .30

***Imperf***

**Size: 80x60mm**
1990 A1214 150p multi 1.00 1.00

Rededication of National Library — A1215

**2007, Feb. 25** ***Perf. 12¾x13¼***
1991 A1215 30p multi .55 .30

Arabic Language Academy, 75th Anniv. — A1216

**2007, Mar. 17** ***Perf. 13¼x12¾***
1992 A1216 30p multi .55 .30

World Health Day — A1217

**2007, Apr. 7 Litho.** ***Perf. 12¾x13¼***
1993 A1217 30p multi .55 .30

Egyptian Trade Union Federation, 50th Anniv. — A1218

**2007, May 1** ***Perf. 13¼x12¾***
1994 A1218 30p multi .45 .25

Egypt Air, 75th Anniv. — A1219

Anniversary emblem and: 30p, Biplane. 150p, Biplane and jet.

**2007, May 7** ***Perf. 12¾x13¼***
1995-1996 A1219 Set of 2 1.00 .75

Return of Sinai to Egypt, 25th Anniv. — A1220

No. 1997: a, Monastery of St. Catherine. b, Salah el Din Castle. c, Sharm el-Sheikh. d, Oasis of Nabq.

**2007, Apr. 25 Litho.** ***Perf. 12¾x13¼***
1997 A1220 30p Block of 4, #a-d 1.90 1.25

Mevlana Jalal ad-Din Rumi (1207-73), Islamic Philosopher A1221

**2007, May 8** ***Perf. 13¼x12¾***
1998 A1221 150p multi .55 .30

World Environment Day — A1222

Designs: 30p, Sinai baton blue butterfly. 150p, Melting ice, horiz.

***Perf. 13¼x12¾, 12¾x13¼***

**2007, June 5**
1999-2000 A1222 Set of 2 1.50 .75

Scouting, Cent. — A1223

**2007, June 6** ***Perf. 12¾x13¼***
2001 A1223 150p multi 1.25 .80

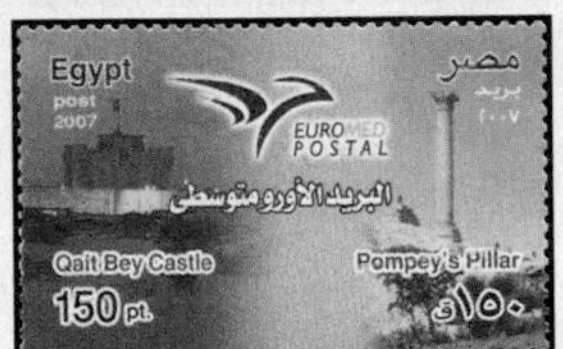

EuroMed Postal Conference, Marseille, France — A1224

**2007, July 9**
2002 A1224 150p multi 1.10 .75

Diplomatic Relations Between Egypt and Nepal, 50th Anniv. — A1225

**2007, July 16**
2003 A1225 150p multi 1.10 .75

Egyptian Air Force, 75th Anniv. — A1226

**2007, Oct. 14 Litho.** ***Perf. 13x13¼***
2004 A1226 30p multi .55 .25

A1227

11th Arab Games — A1228

**2007, Oct. 26 Litho.** ***Perf. 13¼x12¾***
2005 A1227 150p multi 1.25 .90

***Imperf***

**Size: 95x75mm**
2006 A1228 150p multi 1.25 1.00

Assiut University, 50th Anniv. — A1229

**2007, Nov. 27** ***Perf. 13¼x12¾***
2007 A1229 30p brn & blk .45 .25

Hafez Ibrahim (1872-1932), Poet — A1230

Ahmed Shawky (1868-1932), Poet — A1231

**2007, Dec. 16**

| | | | | |
|---|---|---|---|---|
| **2008** | A1230 | 30p multi | .45 | .25 |
| **2009** | A1231 | 30p multi | .45 | .25 |

A 150p stamp issued in December 2007 depicting riders on horses on a beach with a se-tenant label was created exclusively for the Utopia Resort in Marsa Alam. The resort sold the stamps to its guests.

Egyptian Handball Federation, 50th Anniv. — A1232

**2007, Dec. 30**

| | | | | |
|---|---|---|---|---|
| **2010** | A1232 | 30p multi | .50 | .25 |

Musicians — A1233

**2008, Jan. 1** ***Perf. 12¾x13¼***

| | | | | |
|---|---|---|---|---|
| **2011** | A1233 | 30p multi | .45 | .25 |

Post Day — A1234

**2008, Feb. 7** **Litho.** ***Imperf.***

| | | | | |
|---|---|---|---|---|
| **2012** | A1234 | 150p multi | 1.00 | 1.00 |

Africa Cup of Nations Soccer Championships, Ghana — A1235

**2008, Feb. 10** ***Perf. 13¼x13***

| | | | | |
|---|---|---|---|---|
| **2013** | A1235 | 30p multi | .45 | .25 |

Wadi El-Hitan UNESCO World Heritage Site — A1236

No. 2014: a, Whale bones on ground. b, Reconstructed whale skeleton.

**2008, Feb. 10** ***Perf. 13x13¼***

| | | | | |
|---|---|---|---|---|
| **2014** | | Horiz. pair with central label | 1.00 | 1.00 |
| *a.-b.* | A1236 | 30p Either single | .45 | .25 |

Cairo University, Cent. — A1237

**2008, Apr. 14** ***Perf. 13¼x13***

| | | | | |
|---|---|---|---|---|
| **2015** | A1237 | 30p multi | .45 | .25 |

Land Mine Clearance in Northwest Egypt — A1238

No. 2016 — Map and: a, Amputee surrounded by land mines. b, Hand, "no land mines" symbol, vert.

***Perf. 13x13¼, 13¼x13 (#2016b)***

**2008, Apr. 22**

| | | | | |
|---|---|---|---|---|
| **2016** | A1238 | 150p Pair, #a-b | 1.10 | 1.10 |

Telecom Africa Conference A1239

**2008, May 12** ***Perf. 13¼x13***

| | | | | |
|---|---|---|---|---|
| **2017** | A1239 | 30p multi | .45 | .25 |

World Environment Day — A1240

Background colors: 30p, Blue. 150p, Lilac.

**2008, June 5**

| | | | | |
|---|---|---|---|---|
| **2018-2019** | A1240 | Set of 2 | 1.00 | .70 |

Faculty of Fine Arts, Cent. — A1241

No. 2020 — Background color: a, 30p, Blue. b, 150p, Green.

**2008, June 21** **Litho.** ***Perf. 13¼x13***

| | | | | |
|---|---|---|---|---|
| **2020** | A1241 | Horiz. pair, #a-b | 1.25 | 1.25 |

Pan African Postal Union Plenipotentiary Conference, Cairo — A1242

**2008, June 28** ***Perf. 13x13¼***

| | | | | |
|---|---|---|---|---|
| **2021** | A1242 | 150p multi | 1.25 | .60 |

Egypt Air Joining Star Alliance — A1243

**2008, July 11**

| | | | | |
|---|---|---|---|---|
| **2022** | A1243 | 150p multi | 1.25 | .85 |

Alexandria, 2008 Islamic Cultural Capital — A1244

**2008, July 26**

| | | | | |
|---|---|---|---|---|
| **2023** | A1244 | 150p multi | .85 | .60 |

Arab Post Day — A1245

No. 2024 — Emblem and: a, World map, pigeon. b, Camel caravan.

**2008, Aug. 3**

| | | | | |
|---|---|---|---|---|
| **2024** | | Horiz. pair | 2.00 | 2.00 |
| *a.-b.* | A1245 | 150p Either single | .75 | .60 |

24th Universal Postal Union Congress, Geneva, Switzerland — A1246

**2008, Aug. 4** **Litho.** ***Perf. 12¾x13¼***

| | | | | |
|---|---|---|---|---|
| **2025** | A1246 | 150p multi | 1.00 | .75 |

Men's Sports Education Faculty, 50th Anniv. — A1247

**2008, Oct. 15** **Litho.** ***Perf. 13¼x13***

| | | | | |
|---|---|---|---|---|
| **2026** | A1247 | 30p multi | .50 | .30 |

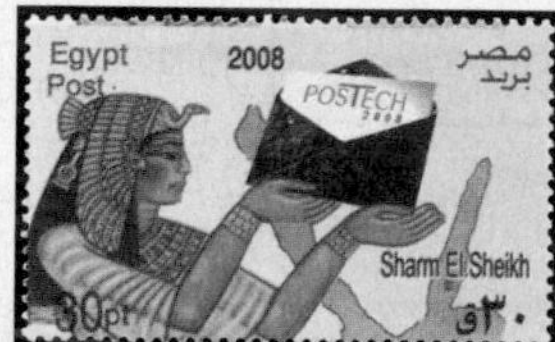


Postech 2008 Intl. Postal Technology Conference, Sharm El-Sheikh — A1248

Map and: 30p, Queen Nefertari holding Postech 2008 emblem. 150p, Statue of King Tutankhamun, hand holding Postech emblem.

***Perf. 12¾x13¼***

**2008, Nov. 17** **Litho.**

| | | | | |
|---|---|---|---|---|
| **2027-2028** | A1248 | Set of 2 | 1.40 | .90 |

Egyptian Cooperative Movement, Cent. — A1249

**2008, Dec. 22** ***Perf. 13¼x12¾***

| | | | | |
|---|---|---|---|---|
| **2029** | A1249 | 30p multi | .45 | .25 |

Natl. Telecommunications Institute, 25th Anniv. — A1250

**2008, Dec. 31** ***Perf. 12¾x13¼***

| | | | | |
|---|---|---|---|---|
| **2030** | A1250 | 30p multi | .55 | .30 |

Natl. Sports Council — A1251

**2009, Mar. 3** ***Perf. 13¼x12¾***
**2031** A1251 150p multi .95 .75

Constitutional Judiciary, 40th Anniv. — A1252

Designs: 30p, Emblem, text below. 150p, Emblem, text at right, horiz.

**2009, Mar. 7** ***Perf. 13¼x12¾***
**2032** A1252 30p multi .65 .40

**Size:80x60mm**

***Imperf***

**2033** A1252 150p multi 1.00 1.00

Intl. Francophone Day — A1253

**2009, Mar. 20** ***Perf. 12¾x13¼***
**2034** A1253 150p multi .95 .55

Orphan's Day — A1254

**2009, Apr. 3** ***Perf. 13¼x12¾***
**2035** A1254 150p multi 1.00 .60

Compare with Types A1132, A1169 and A1199. See also No. 2053.

Intl. Labor Organization, 90th Anniv. — A1255

**2009, Apr. 21** ***Perf. 12¾x13¼***
**2036** A1255 150p multi .90 .60

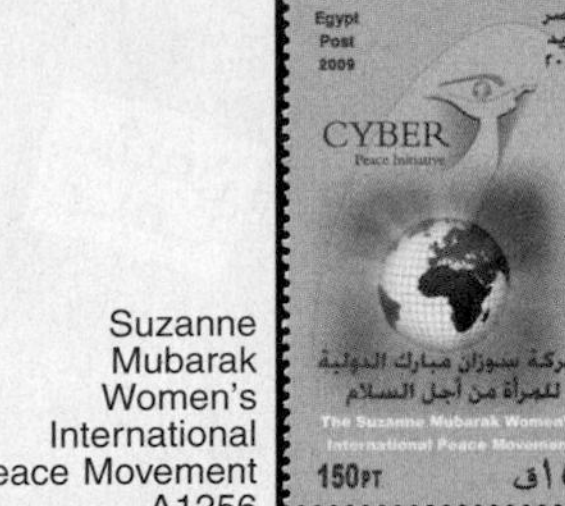
Suzanne Mubarak Women's International Peace Movement A1256

**2009, May 14** ***Perf. 13¼x12¾***
**2037** A1256 150p multi .75 .55

Yehia Hakki (1905-92), Writer — A1257

**2009, May 11 Litho.** ***Perf. 12¾x13¼***
**2038** A1257 150p multi .95 .55

Nobel Laureates From Africa — A1258

No. 2039: a, Ahmed Zewail, Chemistry, 1999. b, Bishop Desmond Tutu, Peace, 1984. c, Wangari Maathai, Peace 2004. d, Anwar al-Sadat, Peace, 1978. e, Naguib Mahfouz, Literature, 1988. f, Allan M. Cormack, Physiology or Medicine, 1979. g, Nelson Mandela, Peace, 1993. h, Wole Soyinka, Literature, 1986. i, Sydney Brenner, Physiology or Medicine, 2002. j, F.W. de Klerk, Peace, 1993. k, Nadine Gordimer, Literature, 1991. l, Max Theiler, Physiology or Medicine, 1951. m, Mohamed El Baradei, Peace, 2005. n, Albert Luthuli, Peace, 1960. o, Kofi Annan, Peace, 2001. p, J.M. Coetzee, Literature, 2003.

**2009, June 9**
**2039** Sheet of 16, #a-p, + 9 labels 22.50 22.50
*a.-p.* A1258 150p Any single .95 .75

Fourth Extraordinary Session of the Pan-African Postal Union Plenipotentiary Conference, Cairo.

Fifteenth Non-Aligned Movement Summit, Sharm el-Sheikh A1259

**2009, July 15** ***Perf. 13¼x12¾***
**2040** A1259 150p multi .55 .55

Opening of Mubarak Public Library, Damanhour — A1260

**2009, May 7 Litho.** ***Perf. 13x13¼***
**2041** A1260 150p multi .95 .70

Jerusalem, Capital of Arab Culture — A1261

**2009, Aug. 3** ***Perf. 13¼x13***
**2042** A1261 150p multi .95 .75

FIFA Under-20 World Cup Soccer Championships, Egypt — A1262

No. 2042 — Tournament emblem, trophy and flag of participating team: a, Paraguay. b, Brazil. c, Uruguay. d, Germany. e, Nigeria. f, South Korea. g, Venezuela. h, Ghana. i, United Arab Emirates. j, South Africa. k, Egypt. l, Spain. m, Italy. n, Hungary. o, Czech Republic. p, Costa Rica.

**2009, Oct. 5** ***Perf. 13x13¼***
**2043** Sheet of 16, #a-p, + 9 labels 19.50 19.50
*a.-p.* A1262 150p Any single .95 .75

Fourth Ministerial Conference of Forum on China-African Cooperation, Sharm El Sheikh — A1263

**2009, Nov. 8**
**2044** A1263 150p multi .95 .75

Fourth Meeting of Internet Governance Forum, Sharm El Sheikh — A1264

**2009, Nov. 15**
**2045** A1264 150p multi .95 75

Luxor Governate — A1264a

**2009, Dec. 9 Litho.** ***Perf. 12¾x13¼***
**2045A** A1264a 250p multi 1.25 1.25

Egyptian Society of Political Economy, Statistics and Legislation, Cent. — A1265

**2009, Dec. 19**
**2046** A1265 150p multi .95 .95

Pharmaceutical Industry Drug Holding Company, 75th Anniv. — A1266

Background colors: 30p, Pink, yellow and pale green. 150p, Green.

**2009, Dec. 19** ***Perf. 13¼x13***
**2047-2048** A1266 Set of 2 .95 .95

Egyptian Stock Exchange, 125th Anniv. — A1267

Stock Exchange Building with anniversary emblem at left in: 30p, Gold and white. 150p, Gold (75x30mm).

**2009, Dec. 21** ***Perf. 13x13¼***
**2049-2050** A1267 Set of 2 .95 .95

Pan-African Postal Union, 30th Anniv. — A1268

**2010, Jan. 18**
**2051** A1268 150p multi .85 .85

National Council for Women, 10th Anniv. — A1269

**2010, Mar. 16**
**2052** A1269 30p multi .65 .65

Orphan's Day — A1270

**2010, Jan. 4 Litho.** ***Perf. 13¼x12¾***
**2053** A1270 30p multi .55 .55

Compare with Types A1132, A1169 and A1199. See also No. 2035.

Edfu Temple — A1271

**2010, Jan. 5** ***Perf. 12¾x13¼***
**2054** A1271 250p multi 1.50 1.50

Aswan High Dam, 50th Anniv. — A1272

No. 2055 — Part of dam: a, 30p. b, £1.

**2010, Jan. 15**
**2055** A1272 Horiz. pair, #a-b 1.50 1.50

Arab League Center, 50th Anniv. — A1273

**2010, Mar. 22**
**2056** A1273 200p multi 1.25 1.25

Egyptian Soccer Team, 2010 Winner of African Cup of Nations — A1274

No. 2057 — Pyramid, African Cup of Nations, tournament emblems and: a, 30p, Crocodile mascot. b, 200p, Eagle mascot. c, 250p, Antelope mascot.

No. 2058, 250p, Soccer players, African Cup of nations, years of Egyptian championships, horiz.

**2010, Jan. 31 Litho.** ***Perf. 13¼x12¾***
**2057** A1274 Horiz. strip of 3, #a-c 4.50 4.50

**Size: 80x60mm**

***Imperf***

**2058** A1274 250p multi 1.50 1.50

Egyptian Gazette, 130th Anniv. — A1275

**2010, Apr. 20** ***Perf. 13¼x12¾***
**2059** A1275 30p multi .55 .55

Egypt Pavilion, Expo 2010, Shanghai — A1276

**2010, May 1 Litho.** ***Perf. 12¾x13¼***
**2060** A1276 £2.50 multi 1.75 1.75

Opening of Road to Red Sea — A1277

**2010, May 27** ***Perf. 13¼x12¾***
**2061** A1277 £1 multi .95 .95

World Environment Day — A1278

**2010, June 5** ***Perf. 12¾x13¼***
**2062** A1278 £2.50 multi 1.50 1.50

Tawfiq al-Hakim (1898-1987), Writer — A1279

**2010, June 6 Litho.** ***Perf. 13¼x12¾***
**2063** A1279 150p multi .95 .95

Second Egyptian Post Innovation Meeting.

Reading for All, 20th Anniv. — A1280

**2010, June 21**
**2064** A1280 £1 multi .95 .95

Egyptian Television, 50th Anniv. — A1281

**2010, July 21**
**2065** A1281 £1.50 multi 1.25 1.25

Alexandria, 2010 Captial of Arab Tourism — A1282

**2010, July 22** ***Perf. 12¾x13¼***
**2066** A1282 150p multi 1.25 1.25

2010 Asia-Pacific Broadcasting Union Robotics Competition, Cairo — A1283

**2010, Sept. 19**
**2067** A1283 £2.50 multi 1.50 1.50

2010 Euromed Postal Conference, Alexandria — A1284

**2010, Sept. 28**
**2068** A1284 £2.50 multi 1.75 1.75

Alabaster Canopic Jar — A1285

**2010, Oct. 8** ***Perf. 13¼x12¾***
**2069** A1285 £2.50 multi 1.75 1.75

See Slovakia No. 601.

Second Arab University Games, Cairo — A1286

**2010, Oct. 17** ***Perf. 13¼x12¾***
**2070** A1286 30p multi .55 .55

World Statistics Day — A1287

**2010, Oct. 20**
**2071** A1287 30p multi .55 .55

Reopening of Museum of Islamic Art, Cairo — A1288

No. 2072: a, 30p, Goblet. £2, Bas-relief. £2.50, Plate with antelope design.

**2010, Oct. 25**
**2072** A1288 Horiz. strip of 3, #a-c 2.50 2.50

Egyptian Olympic Committee, Cent. — A1289

**2010, Dec. 11**
**2073** A1289 30p multi .60 .60

Information and Decision Support Center, 25th Anniv. — A1290

**2010, Dec. 20** ***Perf. 12¾x13¼***
**2074** A1290 30p multi .55 .55

Cairo Stadium, 50th Anniv. — A1291

**2010, Dec. 30** ***Imperf.***
**2075** A1291 £2.50 multi 1.50 1.50

Post Day A1292

No. 2076 — Egyptian stamps: a, #3. b, #57. c, #107. d, #183. e, #271. f, #321. g, #386. h, #389. i, #873. j, #C1.

**2011, Jan. 2** ***Perf. 13***
**2076** Block of 10 5.50 5.50
***a.-h.*** A1292 30p Any single .40 .30
***i.*** A1292 £2 multi 1.00 .75
***j.*** A1292 £2.50 multi 1.25 1.00

Cairo Tower, 50th Anniv. — A1293

No. 2077 — Tower: a, 30p, In daylight. b, £2.50, At night.

**2011, Apr. 11** ***Perf. 13¼x12¾***
**2077** A1293 Horiz. pair, #a-b 2.25 2.25

World Environment Day — A1294

**2011, June 5**
**2078** A1294 £2.50 multi 1.50 1.50

War Academy, 200th Anniv. — A1295

**2011, July 20** ***Perf. 12¾x13¼***
**2079** A1295 30p multi .80 .80

Rivers — A1296

No. 2080: a, 30p, Pyramids, Nile River. b, 30p, Downtown Singapore, Singapore River. c, £2, Ancient Egyptian boat, Nile River. d, £2, Modern boat, Singapore River. e, £2.50, Cairo skyline, yellow flowers, Nile River. f, £2.50, Singapore buildings, pink flowers, Singapore River.

**2011, Oct. 17**
**2080** A1296 Block of 6, #a-f 3.25 3.25

See Singapore Nos. 1513-1515.

Post Day — A1297

No. 2081: a, Dove, flowers, Egypt Post emblem. b, Post office, air mail envelopes. c, Eye of Horus, flowers, Egypt Post emblem.

**2012, Jan. 2** ***Perf. 13¼x12¾***
**2081** A1297 £2.50 Horiz. strip of 3, #a-c 2.50 2.50

Temple — A1297a

**2011** **Litho.** ***Perf. 11¼***
**2081D** A1297a £2.50 multi — —

January 25 Revolution, 1st Anniv. — A1298

**2012, Jan. 25** ***Imperf.***
**2082** A1298 £2.50 multi .85 .85

Pope Shenouda III of Alexandria (1923-2012) — A1299

**2012, Mar. 17** ***Imperf.***
**2083** A1299 £5 multi 1.75 1.75

Diplomatic Relations Between Egypt and Azerbaijan, 20th Anniv. — A1300

No. 2084: a, Arches and Maiden Tower, Baku, Azerbaijan. b, Sphinx and Pyramids, Egypt.

**2012, May 28** ***Perf. 12¾x13¼***
**2084** A1300 £2.50 Horiz. pair, #a-b 1.75 1.75

Environment Day — A1301

**2012, June 5** ***Perf. 13¼x12¾***
**2085** A1301 £2 multi .70 .70

A1302

Overthrow of King Farouk by Gamal Abdel Nasser, 60th Anniv. — A1303

**2012, July 23** ***Perf. 12¾x13¼***
**2086** A1302 £2 multi .65 .65
***Imperf***
**2087** A1303 £4 multi 1.40 1.40

2012 Summer Olympics, London — A1304

No. 2088 — Mascot and: a, Cycling. b, Running. c, Emblem of 2012 Summer Olympics. d, Basketball. e, Soccer.

**2012, July 27** ***Perf. 13¼x12¾***
**2088** Horiz. strip of 5 4.25 4.25
***a.-e.*** A1304 £2.50 Any single .85 .85

Arab Postal Day — A1305

**2012, Aug. 3** ***Perf. 12¾x13¼***
**2089** A1305 £3 multi 1.00 1.00

Festivals — A1306

No. 2090: a, Rider on blue gray horse, heads of white and black horses. b, Two riders, black horse, head of brown horse. c, Rider on brown horse.

**2012, Aug. 18** ***Perf. 13¼x12¾***
**2090** A1306 £1 Horiz. strip of 3, #a-c 1.00 1.00

Lawyers Trade Union, Cent. — A1307

**2012, Sept. 12** ***Perf. 12¾x13¼***
**2091** A1307 £1 multi .35 .35

Tourism and Sustainable Energy — A1308

**2012, Sept. 27** ***Perf. 13¼x12¾***
**2092** A1308 £1 multi .35 .35

Helwan University Art Education Faculty, 75th Anniv. — A1309

**2012, Nov. 12** **Litho.**
**2093** A1309 £2 multi .65 .65

Post Day — A1310

No. 2094: a, Ancient Egyptian art with Isis seated at right, envelopes. b, Lotus flowers. funerary mask of King Tutankhamun. c, Anceint Egyptian art with Isis seated at left.

**2013, Jan. 2** ***Perf. 13¼x13***
**2094** A1310 £3 Horiz. strip of 3, #a-c 3.00 3.00

January 25th Revolution, 2nd Anniv. — A1311

**2013, Jan. 25** ***Perf. 13x13¼***
**2095** A1311 £1 multi .30 .30

Victory of Egyptian Team at African Cup of Nations Youth Soccer Championships A1312

**2013, Apr. 24** ***Perf. 13¼x13***
**2096** A1312 £3 multi .90 .90

Return of Sinai to Egypt, 31st Anniv. — A1313

No. 2097 — Various tourist attractions and Sinai Peninsula map showing: a, Northwestern section. b, Northeastern section. c, Southwestern section. d, Southeastern section.

**2013, Apr. 25** ***Perf. 13x13¼***
**2097** A1313 £2 Block of 4, #a-d 2.40 2.40

World Environment Day — A1314

**2013, June 5** ***Perf. 13¼x13***
**2098** A1314 £3 multi .85 .85

July 23rd Revolution, 61st Anniv. — A1315

**2013, July 23** **Litho.** ***Perf. 12¾x13¼***
**2099** A1315 £3 multi .85 .85

Day of the Nile Inundation — A1316

**2013, Aug. 25** **Litho.** ***Imperf.***
**2100** A1316 £4 multi 1.25 1.25

Intl. Islamic Council for Da'wa and Relief — A1317

***Perf. 13¼x12¾***

**2013, Sept. 21** **Litho.**
**2101** A1317 £2 multi .60 .60

World Tourism Day — A1318

***Perf. 13¼x12¾***

**2013, Sept. 27** **Litho.**
**2102** A1318 £3 multi .90 .90

A1319

October War Against Israel, 40th Anniv. — A1320

**2013, Oct. 6** **Litho.** ***Perf. 12¾x13¼***
**2103** A1319 £1 multi .30 .30
**2104** A1320 £4 multi 1.25 1.25

Sculptures of Egyptian Pharaohs
A1321 A1322

Designs: Nos. 2105, 2106, Thutmosis III. £1, Senusret I. £3, Ramesses II. £4, Akhenaten.

**2013, Oct. 7** **Litho.** ***Perf. 11¼***
**2105** A1321 50p org & multi .25 .25
**2106** A1321 50p grn & multi .25 .25

***Perf. 11x11½***
**2107** A1322 £1 multi .30 .30
**2108** A1322 £3 lil & multi .90 .90
**2108A** A1322 £3 blue & multi — —
**2109** A1322 £4 brn & multi 1.25 1.25
**2109A** A1322 £4 rose brn & multi — —
*Nos. 2105-2109A (7)* 2.95 2.95

World Post Day — A1323

**2013, Oct. 9** **Litho.** ***Perf. 12¾x13¼***
**2110** A1323 £4 multi 1.25 1.25

Tourists on Horseback, Utopia Resort, Marsa Alam — A1324

Old Town, Hurghada — A1325

Madinat Makadi Resort, Hurghada — A1326

***Perf. 12¾x13¼***

**2013, Dec. 17** **Litho.**
**2111** A1324 £4 multi 1.25 1.25
**2112** A1325 £4 multi 1.25 1.25
**2113** A1326 £4 multi 1.25 1.25
*Nos. 2111-2113 (3)* 3.75 3.75

Nile Meter, by. M. Sabry — A1327

**2014, Jan. 2** **Litho.** ***Imperf.***
**2114** A1327 £4 multi 1.25 1.25

Post Day.

January 25th Revolution, 3rd Anniv. — A1328

**2014, Jan. 25** **Litho.** ***Perf. 12¾x13¼***
**2115** A1328 £2 multi .60 .60

Intl. Women's Day — A1329

**2014, Mar. 8** **Litho.** ***Perf. 12¾x13¼***
**2116** A1329 £2 multi .60 .60

World Heritage Day — A1330

No. 2117: a, Two women. b, Men and camel. c, Men playing board game. d, Man, pottery in windows.

**2014, Apr. 18** **Litho.** ***Perf. 12¾x13¼***
**2117** A1330 £1 Block of 4 #a-d 1.25 1.25

Diversion of the Nile River, 50th Anniv. — A1331

**2014, May 15** **Litho.** ***Imperf.***
**2118** A1331 £4 multi 1.10 1.10

African Regional Postal Training Center — A1332

**2014, June 1 Litho. *Perf. 12¾x13¼***
**2119** A1332 £2 multi .55 .55

Day of the African Child — A1333

***Perf. 12¾x13¼***
**2014, June 17 Litho.**
**2120** A1333 £3 multi .85 .85

Euromed Postal Emblem and Mediterranean Sea — A1334

**2014, July 9 Litho. *Perf. 13x13¼***
**2121** A1334 £4 multi 1.10 1.10

July 23rd Revolution, 62nd Anniv. — A1335

**2014, July 23 Litho. *Perf. 13¼x13***
**2122** A1335 £2 multi .55 .55

Start of Construction on Second Suez Canal — A1336

No. 2123: a, Suez Canal emblem, ship, map of northern portion of canal. b, Map of central portion of canal, ships near locks of Panama Canal. c, Map of southern portion of canal, Administration building, ship.

**2014, Aug. 5 Litho. *Perf. 13¼x13***
**2123** A1336 £2 Horiz. strip of 3, #a-c *55.00 37.50*

No. 2123 was withdrawn shortly after the error in stamp design (the Suez Canal has no locks) was made known to Egypt Post.

General Arab Insurance Federation, 50th Anniv. — A1337

50th anniversary emblem: No. 2124, Above map of Arab countries. No. 2125, To left of map of Arab countries.

**2014, Sept. 1 Litho. *Perf. 13¼x13***
**2124** A1337 £4 multi 1.10 1.10

***Imperf***

**Size: 90x70mm**

**2125** A1337 £4 multi 1.10 1.10

Start of Construction on New Suez Canal — A1338

No. 2126: a, Map of canal, Adminisration Building, ship in canal. b, Map of canal, ship approaching canal. c, Suez Canal emblem, ship in canal.

**2014, Sept. 16 Litho. *Perf. 13¼x13***
**2126** A1338 £2 Horiz. strip of 3, #a-c 1.75 1.75

No. 2126 replaces the hastily withdrawn No. 2123. First day covers of No. 2126 show the Aug. 5 first day cancel of No. 2123, though the stamps were printed after the discovery of the design error on No. 2123.

Shali Siwa Oasis — A1339

***Perf. 12¾x13¼***
**2014, Sept. 27 Litho.**
**2127** A1339 £4 multi 1.10 1.10

October War Against Israel, 41st Anniv. — A1340

**2014, Oct. 6 Litho. *Perf. 12¾x13¼***
**2128** A1340 £2 multi .55 .55

World Post Day — A1341

**2014, Oct. 9 Litho. *Perf. 13¼x12¾***
**2129** A1341 £4 multi 1.10 1.10

Scouting in Egypt, Cent. — A1342

**2014, Oct. 15 Litho. *Perf. 12¾x13¼***
**2130** A1342 £1.25 multi .35 .35

Arabic Calligraphy — A1343

**2014, Dec. 6 Litho. *Imperf.***
**2131** A1343 £5 multi 1.40 1.40

Central Agency for Public Mobilization and Statistics, Cent. — A1344

**2014, Dec. 8 Litho. *Perf. 13¼x12¾***
**2132** A1344 £3 multi .85 .85

Birds — A1345

No. 2133, £1.25: a, Palm dove. b, Hoopoe. c, Roller. d, Bee-eater. e, Sooty falcon. f, Golden oriole.

***Perf. 13¼x12¾***
**2014, Dec. 10 Litho.**
**2133** A1345 Block of 6, #a-f, + 3 central labels 2.10 2.10

Re-opening of National Theater — A1346

***Perf. 12¾x13¼***
**2014, Dec. 20 Litho.**
**2134** A1346 £1.50 multi .45 .45

Amenhotep, Son of Hapu — A1347

**2015 Litho. *Perf. 11¼***
**2135** A1347 £3 multi .85 .85

A1348

Egyptian Post, 150th Anniv. — A1349

**2015, Jan. 2 Litho. *Perf. 12¾x13¼***
**2136** A1348 £1.50 multi .45 .45

***Imperf***

**2137** A1349 £4 multi 1.10 1.10

January 25 Revolution, 4th Anniv. — A1350

**2015, Jan. 25 Litho. *Perf. 12¾x13¼***
**2138** A1350 £2 multi .55 .55

Faten Hamama (1931-2015), Actress — A1351

**2015, Mar. 8 Litho. *Perf. 13¼x12¾***
**2139** A1351 £3 black .80 .80

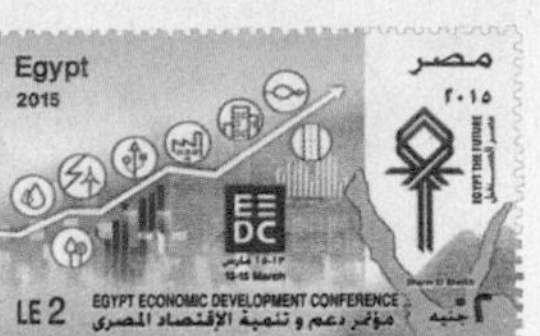


Egypt Economic Development Conference — A1352

***Perf. 12¾x13¼***
**2015, Mar. 13 Litho.**
**2140** A1352 £2 multi .55 .55

26th Arab Summit, Sharm el-Sheikh
A1353

***Perf. 13¼x12¾***

**2015, Mar. 23** **Litho.**
**2141** A1353 £3 multi .80 .80

International Telecommunication Union, 150th Anniv. — A1354

**2015, May 17 Litho. *Perf. 12¾x13¼***
**2142** A1354 £4 multi 1.10 1.10

Dar al-Ifta al-Misriyyah Educational Institute, 120th Anniv. — A1355

**2015, June 1 Litho. *Perf. 12¾x13¼***
**2143** A1355 £2 multi .55 .55

July 23rd Revolution, 63rd Anniv. — A1356

**2015, July 23 Litho. *Perf. 12¾x13¼***
**2144** A1356 £2 multi .55 .55

Campaign to Save the Nile River — A1357

**2015, July 25 Litho. *Perf. 12¾x13¼***
**2145** A1357 £2 multi .55 .55

A1358

New Suez Canal — A1359

**2015, Aug. 6 Litho. *Perf. 12¾x13¼***
**2146** Horiz. strip of 3 2.40 2.40
*a.* A1358 £3 lilac & multi .80 .80
*b.* A1358 £3 beige & multi .80 .80
*c.* A1358 £3 lt blue green & multi .80 .80

***Imperf***

**2147** A1359 £4 multi 1.10 1.10

Poets — A1360

No. 2148: a, Fouad Hadad (1927-85). b, Salah Jaheen (1930-86). c, Abd el Rahman El Abnody (1938-2015).

***Perf. 13¼x12¾***

**2015, Aug. 10** **Litho.**
**2148** A1360 £2 Horiz. strip of 3, #a-c 1.60 .80

Food and Agricultural Organization, 70th Anniv. — A1361

**2015, Oct. 1 Litho. *Perf. 12¾x13¼***
**2149** A1361 £3 multi .80 .40

October War With Israel, 42nd Anniv. — A1362

**2015, Oct. 6 Litho. *Perf. 12¾x13¼***
**2150** A1362 £2 multi .50 .25

A1363

Federation of Afro-Asian Insurers and Reinsurers, 50th Anniv. — A1364

**2015, Oct. 12 Litho. *Perf. 13¼x12¾***
**2151** A1363 £4 multi 1.00 .50

***Imperf***

**2152** A1364 £4 multi 1.00 .50

World Statistics Day — A1365

**2015, Oct. 20 Litho. *Perf. 12¾x13¼***
**2153** A1365 £3 multi .75 .35

Yacht "Mahrousa," 150th Anniv. — A1366

***Perf. 12¾x13¼***

**2015, Dec. 15** **Litho.**
**2154** A1366 £2 multi .55 .55

Al-Ahram Newspaper, 140th Anniv. — A1367

***Perf. 13¼x12¾***

**2015, Dec. 20** **Litho.**
**2155** A1367 £2 multi .55 .55

Helwan University Faculty of Applied Arts, 175th Anniv. — A1368

***Perf. 12¾x13¼***

**2015, Dec. 31** **Litho.**
**2156** A1368 £2 multi .55 .55

A1369

First Egyptian Postage Stamps, 150th Anniv. — A1370

No. 2157: a, Egypt #4-7, dove, boat. b, Egyptian man on donkey. c, Egypt #1-3, Egyptian man on camel.

£4, Emblem of Philatelic Society of Egypt, dove, boat, train, mail carrier on bicycle, mail box.

**2016, Jan. 1 Litho. *Perf. 13¼x12¾***
**2157** A1369 £2 Horiz. strip of 3, #a-c 1.60 1.60

***Imperf***

**2158** A1370 £4 multi 1.10 1.10

Syndicate of Journalists, 75th Anniv. — A1371

***Perf. 13¼x12¾***

**2016, Mar. 31** **Litho.**
**2159** A1371 £3 multi .70 .70

Famous Men — A1372

No. 2160: a, United Nations emblem and Boutros Boutros-Ghali (1922-2016), United Nations Secretary-General. b, Muhammad Husayn Haykal (1888-1956), Minister of Education.

**2016, May 31 Litho. *Perf. 13¼x12¾***
**2160** A1372 £2 Horiz. pair, #a-b .90 .90

World Day to Combat Drugs — A1373

***Perf. 12¾x13¼***

**2016, June 26** **Litho.**
**2161** A1373 £2 multi .45 .45

Egypt Nos. 356, 374, 386, 388 and 393 — A1374

**2016, July 23 Litho. *Imperf.***
**2162** A1374 £4 multi .90 .90

July 23 Revolution, 64th anniv.

Arab Postal Day — A1375

No. 2163 — Area behind denomination in: a, White. b, Green.

**2016, Aug. 3 Litho. *Perf. 12¾x13¼***
**2163** A1375 £3 Horiz. pair, #a-b 1.40 1.40

Gezera Youth Center — A1376

***Perf. 13¼x12¾***
**2016, Aug. 15 Litho.**
**2164** A1376 £2 multi .45 .45

Relocation of Abu Simbel Temples, 50th Anniv. — A1377

No. 2165: a, Moving of statues. b, Man wearing glasses. c, Face of Ramesses II statue.

***Perf. 13¼x12¾***
**2016, Aug. 18 Litho.**
**2165** A1377 £2 Horiz. strip of 3, #a-c 1.40 1.40

World Tourism Day — A1378

No. 2166: a, Hanging Church, Cairo. b, Al-Moez Street, Cairo. c, Philae Temple, Aswan. d, Qaitbay Castle, Alexandria.

***Perf. 12¾x13¼***
**2016, Sept. 27 Litho.**
**2166** A1378 £2 Block of 4, #a-d 1.90 1.90

October War Against Israel, 43rd Anniv. — A1379

**2016, Oct. 6 Litho. *Perf. 12¾x13¼***
**2167** A1379 £2 multi .45 .45

Egyptian Parliament, 150th Anniv. — A1380

**2016, Oct. 22 Litho. *Perf. 12¾x13¼***
**2168** A1380 £2 multi + label .45 .45

Ahmed Zewail (1946-2016), 1999 Nobel Laureate in Chemistry — A1381

**2016, Oct. 25 Litho. *Perf. 12¾x13¼***
**2169** A1381 £2 multi .45 .45

Actors — A1382

No. 2170: a, Mahmoud Abd El-Aziz (1946-2016). b, Nour El-Sherif (1946-2015). c, Ahmed Zaki (1949-2005).

***Perf. 13¼x12¾ Syncopated***
**2016, Nov. 27 Litho.**
**2170** A1382 £2 Horiz. strip of 3, #a-c .70 .70

Miniature Sheet

Giza Zoo, 125th Anniv. — A1383

No. 1383: a, Barbary sheep. b, Giraffe. c, Elephant. d, Crocodile. e, Hippopotamus. f, Pelicans. g, Lion. h, Tiger.

**2016, Dec. 2 Litho. *Perf. 12¾x13¼***
**2171** A1383 £2 Sheet of 8, #a-h 1.90 1.90

World Day of the Arabic Language — A1384

No. 2172: a, £1, Arabic calligraphy. b, £2, Arabic calligraphy, diff., circle arc at left. c, £2, Arabic calligraphy, diff., circle arc at right.

**2016, Dec. 18 Litho. *Perf. 11½***
**2172** A1384 Horiz. strip of 3, #a-c .55 .55

National Circus, 50th Anniv. — A1385

**2016, Dec. 25 Litho. *Imperf.***
**2173** A1385 £4 multi .45 .45

Central Agency for Public Mobilization and Statistics A1386

***Perf. 13¼x12¾ Syncopated***
**2017, Apr. 10 Litho.**
**2177** A1386 £2 multi .25 .25

Modern Egypt Heritage, 150th Anniv. — A1387

***Perf. 12¾x13¼ Syncopated***
**2017, July 5 Litho.**
**2178** A1387 £2 multi .25 .25

July 23 Revolution, 65th Anniv. — A1388

***Perf. 12¾x13¼ Syncopated***
**2017, July 23 Litho.**
**2179** A1388 £4 multi .45 .45

General Sports Union for Businesses, 50th Anniv. — A1389

***Perf. 13¼x12¾ Syncopated***
**2017, Sept. 14 Litho.**
**2180** A1389 £2 multi .25 .25

## SEMI-POSTAL STAMPS

**Catalogue values for unused stamps in this section are for Never Hinged items.**

Princess Ferial — SP1

***Perf. 13½x14***
**1940, May 17 Photo. Wmk. 195**
**B1** SP1 5m + 5m copper brown 4.50 1.25

No. B1 Overprinted in Green

**1943, Nov. 17**
**B2** SP1 5m + 5m 14.00 9.00
*a.* Arabic date "1493" 300.00 300.00

The surtax on Nos. B1 and B2 was for the children's fund.

First Postage Stamp of Egypt SP2

King Fuad SP3

No. B4, Khedive Ismail Pasha. No. B6, King Farouk.

***Perf. 13x13½***
**1946, Feb. 28 Wmk. 195**

| | | | | |
|---|---|---|---|---|
| **B3** | SP2 | 1m + 1m gray | .40 | .25 |
| **B4** | SP3 | 10m + 10m violet | .50 | .25 |
| **B5** | SP3 | 17m + 17m brown | .50 | .40 |
| **B6** | SP3 | 22m + 22m yel grn | .75 | .60 |
| *a.* | | Souv. sheet, #B3-B6, perf. 8½ | 85.00 | 85.00 |
| *b.* | | As "a," imperf. | 85.00 | 85.00 |
| | | *Nos. B3-B6 (4)* | 2.15 | 1.50 |

80th anniv. of Egypt's 1st postage stamp. Nos. B6a, B6b measure 129x171mm.

Goddess Hathor, King Men-kau-Re (Mycerinus) and Jackalheaded Goddess — SP7

Ramesseum, Thebes — SP8

Queen Nefertiti SP9

Funerary Mask of King Tutankhamun SP10

*Perf. 13½x13*

**1947, Mar. 9** **Wmk. 195**

**B9** SP7 5m + 5m slate 1.75 .80
**B10** SP8 15m + 15m dp blue 2.00 1.00
**B11** SP9 30m + 30m henna brn 2.50 1.75
**B12** SP10 50m + 50m brown 3.50 2.25
*Nos. B9-B12 (4)* 9.75 5.80

Intl. Exposition of Contemporary Art, Cairo.

Boy Scout Emblem — SP11

Scout Emblems: 20m+10m, Sea Scouts. 35m+15m, Air Explorers.

**1956, July 25** **Photo.** ***Perf. 13½x13***

**B13** SP11 10m + 10m green 1.00 .55
**B14** SP11 20m + 10m ultra 1.50 .85
**B15** SP11 35m + 15m blue 2.00 1.25
*Nos. B13-B15 (3)* 4.50 2.65

2nd Arab Scout Jamboree, Alexandria-Aboukir, 1956.

Souvenir sheets, perf. and imperf., contain one each of Nos. B13-B15. Size: 118x158mm. Values: $1,750 unused each, $1,100 used each.

Ambulance — SP12

**1957, May 13** ***Perf. 13x13½***

**B16** SP12 10m + 5m rose red .80 .55

50th anniv. of the Public Aid Society.

**United Arab Republic**

Eye and Map of Africa, Europe and Asia — SP13

*Perf. 13½x13*

**1958, Mar. 1** **Photo.** **Wmk. 318**

**B17** SP13 10m + 5m orange 1.25 1.00

1st Afro-Asian Cong. of Ophthalmology, Cairo.

The surtax was for centers to aid the blind.

Postal Emblem — SP14

**1959, Jan. 2**

**B18** SP14 10m + 5m bl grn, red & blk .40 .30

Post Day. The surtax went to the social fund for postal employees.

See Syria UAR issues No. B1 for similar stamp with denominations in piasters (p).

Children and UN Emblem — SP15

**1959, Oct. 24** **Wmk. 328**

**B19** SP15 10m + 5m brown lake .60 .30
**B20** SP15 35m + 10m dk blue .90 .40

Issued for International Children's Day and to honor UNICEF.

**Braille Type of Regular Issue, 1961**

**1961, Apr. 6** ***Perf. 13½x13***

**B21** A182 35m + 15m yel & brn .80 .50

Arab League Building, Cairo, and Emblem — SP16

**1962, Mar. 22** **Photo.** **Wmk. 328**

**B22** SP16 10m + 5m gray .60 .40

Arab Publicity Week, Mar. 22-28.

See No. N86.

Postal Emblem — SP17

Stamp of 1866 — SP18

**1963, Jan. 2** **Wmk. 342** ***Perf. 11½***

**B23** SP17 20m +10m brt grn, red & blk 1.25 1.25
**B24** SP18 40m +20m blk & brn org 1.75 1.75
**B25** SP18 40m +20m brn org & blk 1.75 1.75
*a.* Pair, #B24-B25 4.00 4.00
*Nos. B23-B25 (3)* 4.75 4.75

Post Day, Jan. 2 and 1966 exhibition of the FIP.

Arms of UAR and Pyramids SP19

**1964, Jan. 2** **Wmk. 342** ***Perf. 11***

**B26** SP19 10m + 5m org yel & grn 1.75 1.00
**B27** SP19 80m + 40m grnsh bl & blk 3.00 1.75
**B28** SP19 115m + 55m org brn & blk 4.00 2.25
*Nos. B26-B28 (3)* 8.75 5.00

Issued for Post Day. Jan. 2.

**Type of 1963 and**

SP20

Postal Emblem — SP20a

No. B30, Emblem of Postal Secondary School. 80m+40m, Postal emblem, gear-wheel, laurel wreath.

*Perf. 11½*

**1965, Jan. 2** **Unwmk.** **Photo.**

**B29** SP20 10m + 5m lt grn & car 1.00 .50
**B30** SP20 10m + 5m ultra, car & blk 1.00 .50
*a.* Pair, #B29-B30 2.50 2.00
**B31** SP20a 80m + 40m rose, brt grn & blk 2.75 2.00
*Nos. B29-B31 (3)* 4.75 3.00

Issued for Post Day, Jan. 2. No. B31 also publicizes the Stamp Centenary Exhibition.

Souvenir Sheet

Stamps of Egypt, 1866 — SP21

**1966, Jan. 2** **Wmk. 342** ***Imperf.***

**B32** SP21 140m + 60m blk, sl bl & rose 4.50 4.50

Post Day, 1966, and cent. of the 1st Egyptian postage stamps.

Pharaonic "Mediator" — SP22

Design: 115m+40m, Pharaonic guard.

**1967, Jan. 2** **Wmk. 342** ***Perf. 11½***

**B33** SP22 80m + 20m multi 3.75 2.75
**B34** SP22 115m + 40m multi 6.00 3.50

Issued for Post Day, Jan. 2.

Grand Canal, Doges' Palace, Venice, and Santa Maria del Fiore, Florence — SP23

115m+30m, Piazetta and Campanile, Venice, and Palazzo Vecchio, Florence.

*Perf. 11½x11*

**1967, Dec. 9** **Photo.** **Wmk. 342**

**B35** SP23 80m + 20m grn, yel & brn 1.75 1.25
**B36** SP23 115m + 30m ol, yel & sl bl 2.75 2.00

The surtax was to help save the cultural monuments of Venice and Florence, damaged in the 1966 floods.

Boy and Girl — SP24

Design: No. B38, Five children and arch.

**Wmk. 342**

**1968, Dec. 11** **Photo.** ***Perf. 11***

**B37** SP24 20m + 10m car, bl & lt brn .80 .60
**B38** SP24 20m + 10m vio bl, sep & lt grn .80 .60

Children's Day & 22nd anniv. of UNICEF.

Emblem and Flags of Arab League — SP25

**1969, Mar. 22** ***Perf. 11x11½***

**B39** SP25 20m + 10m multi .80 .60

Arab Publicity Week, Mar. 22-28.

Refugee Family SP26

**1969, Oct. 24 Photo. *Perf. 11½***

| | | | |
|---|---|---|---|
| **B40** SP26 30m + 10m multi | | .80 | .60 |

Issued for United Nations Day.

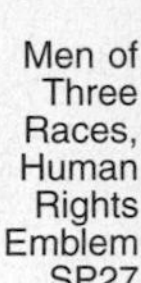

Men of Three Races, Human Rights Emblem SP27

**1970, Mar. 21 *Perf. 11½x11***

| | | |
|---|---|---|
| **B41** SP27 20m + 10m multi | 1.00 | .75 |

Issued to publicize the International Day for the Elimination of Racial Discrimination.

**Arab League Type**

**1970, Mar. 22 Wmk. 342**

| | | |
|---|---|---|
| **B42** A344 20m + 10m bl, grn & brn | .90 | .60 |

Map of Palestine and Refugees SP28

***Perf. 11½x11***

**1970, Oct. 24 Photo. Wmk. 342**

| | | |
|---|---|---|
| **B43** SP28 20m + 10m multi | .90 | .80 |

25th anniv. of the UN and to draw attention to the plight of the Palestinian refugees.

**Arab Republic of Egypt**

Blind Girl, WHO and Society Emblems — SP29

**1973, Oct. 24 Photo. *Perf. 11x11½***

| | | |
|---|---|---|
| **B44** SP29 20m + 10m blue & gold | .85 | .75 |

25th anniv. of WHO and for the Light and Hope Soc., which educates and helps blind girls.

Map of Africa, OAU Emblem — SP30

***Perf. 11x11½***

**1973, Dec. 8 Photo. Wmk. 342**

| | | |
|---|---|---|
| **B45** SP30 55m + 20m multi | 2.25 | 1.50 |

Organization for African Unity, 10th anniv.

Social Work Day Emblem — SP31

**1973, Dec. 8**

| | | |
|---|---|---|
| **B46** SP31 20m + 10m multi | .75 | .65 |

Social Work Day.

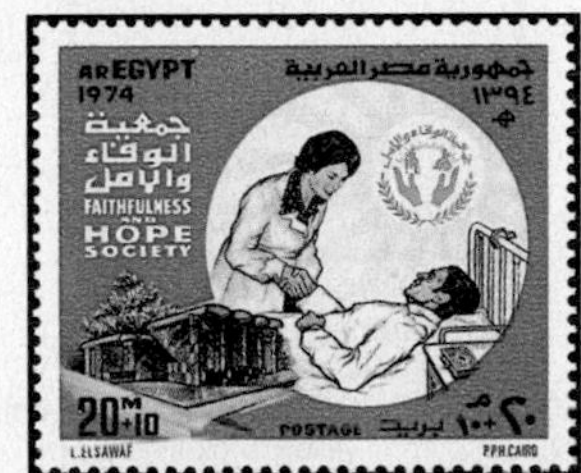


Jihan al Sadat Consoling Wounded Man — SP32

**1974, Mar. 21 Wmk. 342 *Perf. 11***

| | | |
|---|---|---|
| **B47** SP32 20m + 10m multi | 1.25 | .90 |

Faithfulness and Hope Society.

Afghan Solidarity SP33

**Wmk. 342**

**1981, July 15 Photo. *Perf. 11½***

| | | |
|---|---|---|
| **B48** SP33 20m + 10m multi | 1.00 | .75 |

**Size: 30x25mm**

**1981 Photo. *Perf. 11½***

| | | |
|---|---|---|
| **B49** SP33 20m + 10m multi | 4.25 | 3.75 |

Map of Sudan, Dunes, Dead Tree — SP34

**1986, Mar. 25 Photo. *Perf. 13x13½***

| | | |
|---|---|---|
| **B50** SP34 15p + 5p multi | 1.75 | 1.25 |

Fight against drought and desertification of the Sudan. Surtax for drought relief.

Organization of African Unity, 25th Anniv. — SP35

**1988, May 25 Litho. *Perf. 13***

| | | |
|---|---|---|
| **B51** SP35 15p +10p multi | 1.25 | 1.00 |

## AIR POST STAMPS

Mail Plane in Flight AP1

***Perf. 13x13½***

**1926, Mar. 10 Wmk. 195 Photo.**

| | | |
|---|---|---|
| **C1** AP1 27m deep violet | 32.50 | 32.50 |

**1929, July 17**

| | | |
|---|---|---|
| **C2** AP1 27m orange brown | 10.00 | 2.50 |

**Zeppelin Issue**

**No. C2 Surcharged in Blue or Violet**

**1931, Apr. 6**

| | | |
|---|---|---|
| **C3** AP1 50m on 27m (Bl) | 90.00 | 77.50 |
| *a.* "1951" instead of "1931" | 125.00 | 115.00 |
| **C4** AP1 100m on 27m (V) | 90.00 | *82.50* |

Airplane over Giza Pyramids AP2

**1933-38 Litho. *Perf. 13x13½***

| | | | | |
|---|---|---|---|---|
| **C5** | AP2 | 1m orange & blk | .30 | .50 |
| **C6** | AP2 | 2m gray & blk | .80 | 1.50 |
| **C7** | AP2 | 2m org red & blk ('38) | 2.75 | 2.00 |
| **C8** | AP2 | 3m ol brn & blk | .60 | .35 |
| **C9** | AP2 | 4m green & blk | .90 | .90 |
| **C10** | AP2 | 5m dp brown & blk | .75 | .25 |
| **C11** | AP2 | 6m dk green & blk | 1.50 | 1.25 |
| **C12** | AP2 | 7m dk blue & blk | 1.25 | 1.00 |
| **C13** | AP2 | 8m violet & blk | .80 | .25 |
| **C14** | AP2 | 9m dp red & blk | 2.00 | 1.50 |
| **C15** | AP2 | 10m violet & brn | .75 | .70 |
| **C16** | AP2 | 20m dk green & brn | .60 | .25 |
| **C17** | AP2 | 30m dull blue & brn | .75 | .25 |
| **C18** | AP2 | 40m dp red & brn | 15.00 | .60 |
| **C19** | AP2 | 50m orange & brn | 13.00 | .25 |
| **C20** | AP2 | 60m gray & brn | 6.00 | 1.10 |
| **C21** | AP2 | 70m dk blue & bl grn | 3.50 | 1.00 |
| **C22** | AP2 | 80m ol brn & bl grn | 3.50 | 1.00 |
| **C23** | AP2 | 90m org & bl grn | 4.00 | 1.00 |
| **C24** | AP2 | 100m vio & bl grn | 9.00 | .80 |
| **C25** | AP2 | 200m dp red & bl grn | 15.00 | 1.75 |
| | | *Nos. C5-C25 (21)* | 82.75 | 18.20 |

See #C34-C37. For overprint see #C38.

**Type of 1933**

**1941-43 Photo.**

| | | | | |
|---|---|---|---|---|
| **C34** | AP2 | 5m copper brn ('43) | .30 | .30 |
| **C35** | AP2 | 10m violet | .55 | .30 |
| **C36** | AP2 | 25m dk vio brn ('43) | .55 | .30 |
| **C37** | AP2 | 30m green | .70 | .30 |
| | | *Nos. C34-C37 (4)* | 2.10 | 1.20 |

**Catalogue values for unused stamps in this section, from this point to the end of the section, are for Never Hinged items.**

**No. C37 Overprinted in Black**

**1946, Oct. 1**

| | | |
|---|---|---|
| **C38** AP2 30m green | .85 | .40 |
| *a.* Double overprint | 425.00 | — |
| *b.* Inverted overprint | 425.00 | — |

Middle East Intl. Air Navigation Congress, Cairo, Oct. 1946.

King Farouk, Delta Dam and DC-3 Plane AP3

***Perf. 13x13½***

**1947, Feb. 19 Photo. Wmk. 195**

| | | | | |
|---|---|---|---|---|
| **C39** | AP3 | 2m red orange | .30 | *.85* |
| **C40** | AP3 | 3m dk brown | .30 | *1.00* |
| **C41** | AP3 | 5m red brown | .30 | .30 |
| **C42** | AP3 | 7m dp yellow org | .60 | .30 |
| **C43** | AP3 | 8m green | .60 | *.90* |
| **C44** | AP3 | 10m violet | .60 | .30 |
| **C45** | AP3 | 20m brt blue | .90 | .30 |
| **C46** | AP3 | 30m brown violet | 1.20 | .30 |
| **C47** | AP3 | 40m carmine rose | 2.00 | .75 |
| **C48** | AP3 | 50m Prus green | 2.50 | .85 |
| **C49** | AP3 | 100m olive green | 5.00 | 2.50 |
| **C50** | AP3 | 200m dark gray | 11.00 | 5.00 |
| | | *Nos. C39-C50 (12)* | 25.30 | 13.35 |

For overprints see Nos. C51-C64, C67-C89, NC1-NC30.

**Nos. C49 and C50 Surcharged in Black**

**1948, Aug. 23**

| | | |
|---|---|---|
| **C51** AP3 13m on 100m | .60 | .55 |
| **C52** AP3 22m on 200m | .85 | *.85* |
| *a.* Date omitted | | |

Inaugural flights of "Services Aeriens Internationaux d'Egypte" from Cairo to Athens and Rome, Aug. 23, 1948.

**Nos. C39 to C50 Overprinted in Various Colors**

**Overprint 27mm Wide**

**1952, Jan. Wmk. 195 *Perf. 13x13½***

| | | | | |
|---|---|---|---|---|
| **C53** | AP3 | 2m red orange (Bl) | .45 | .30 |
| **C54** | AP3 | 3m dark brown (RV) | 1.60 | 1.25 |
| **C55** | AP3 | 5m red brown | .55 | .55 |
| **C56** | AP3 | 7m dp yel org (Bl) | .85 | .50 |
| **C57** | AP3 | 8m green (RV) | 2.50 | 1.60 |
| **C58** | AP3 | 10m violet (G) | 1.75 | 1.60 |
| **C59** | AP3 | 20m brt blue (RV) | 4.25 | 2.50 |
| **C60** | AP3 | 30m brown vio (G) | 1.90 | 1.60 |
| **C61** | AP3 | 40m carmine rose | 4.00 | 2.50 |
| **C62** | AP3 | 50m Prus green (RV) | 4.25 | 2.75 |
| **C63** | AP3 | 100m olive green | 7.50 | 3.75 |
| **C64** | AP3 | 200m dark gray (RV) | 15.00 | 7.50 |
| | | *Nos. C53-C64 (12)* | 44.60 | 26.40 |

See notes after No. 316.

Delta Dam and Douglas DC-3
AP4

**1953** **Photo.**

**C65** AP4 5m red brown .60 .60
**C66** AP4 15m olive green 1.50 1.25

For overprints see Nos. NC31-NC32.

**Nos. C39-C49 Overprinted in Black**

**1953**

**C67** AP3 2m red orange 3.00 3.00
**C68** AP3 3m dk brown 1.25 1.25
**C69** AP3 5m red brown 1.60 1.60
**C70** AP3 7m dp yellow org .60 .60
**C71** AP3 8m green 2.00 2.00
**C72** AP3 10m violet *32.50 37.50*
**C73** AP3 20m brt blue 2.10 .60
**C74** AP3 30m brown violet 3.00 1.60
**C75** AP3 40m carmine rose 3.00 1.90
**C76** AP3 50m Prus green 5.00 2.00
**C77** AP3 100m olive green 9.25 4.75
**C77A** AP3 200m gray *55.00*

No. C77A is in question. It is not known postally used.

**Nos. C53-C64 Overprinted in Black with Three Bars to Obliterate Portrait**

**1953**

**C78** AP3 2m red orange .90 .50
**C79** AP3 3m dark brown 1.90 1.60
**C80** AP3 5m red brown .50 .35
**C82** AP3 8m green 1.10 *2.50*
**C83** AP3 10m violet .90 *2.00*
**C85** AP3 30m brown violet 2.00 2.00
**C87** AP3 50m Prus green 4.25 1.60
**C88** AP3 100m olive green 6.25 3.75
**C89** AP3 200m dark gray 12.50 12.50
*Nos. C78-C89 (9)* 30.30 26.80

Practically all values of Nos. C67-C89 exist with double overprint. The 7m, 20m and 40m with this overprint have been considered forgeries. Values: 7m, $8 mint and used; 20m, $5 mint and used; 40m, $20 mint, $25 used.

**United Arab Republic**
**Type of Regular Issue**

***Perf. 11½x11***

**1958, Mar. 22** **Photo.** **Wmk. 318**

**C90** A141 15m ultra & red brn .65 .30

Pyramids at Giza
AP5

Al Azhar University
AP6

Designs: 15m, Colossi of Memnon, Thebes. 90m, St. Catherine Monastery, Mt. Sinai.

**1959-60** **Wmk. 328** ***Perf. 13x13½***

**C91** AP5 5m bright red .35 .25
**C92** AP5 15m dk dull violet .40 .35
**C93** AP6 60m dk green .95 .60
**C94** AP5 90m brown car ('60) 2.00 1.25
*Nos. C91-C94 (4)* 3.70 2.45

Nos. C91-C93 exist imperf. See Nos. C101, C105, NC33.

**Tower of Cairo Type, Redrawn**

**1961, May 1** ***Perf. 13½x13***

**C95** A183 50m bright blue 1.10 .55

Top inscription has been replaced by two airplanes.

Weather Vane, Anemometer and UN World Meteorological Organization Emblem — AP7

***Perf. 11½x11***

**1962, Mar. 23** **Photo.** **Unwmk.**

**C96** AP7 60m yellow & dp blue 2.00 1.00

2nd World Meteorological Day, Mar. 23.

Patrice Lumumba and Map of Africa — AP8

***Perf. 13½x13***

**1962, July 1** **Wmk. 328**

**C97** AP8 35m multicolored .65 .40

Patrice Lumumba (1925-61), Premier of Congo.

Maritime Station, Alexandria — AP9

Designs: 30m, International Airport, Cairo. 40m, Railroad Station, Luxor.

**1963, Mar. 18** ***Perf. 13x13½***

**C98** AP9 20m dark brown .70 .30
**C99** AP9 30m carmine rose .95 .40
**C100** AP9 40m black 1.50 1.00
*Nos. C98-C100 (3)* 3.15 1.70

**Type of 1959-60 and**

Temple of Queen Nefertari, Abu Simbel
AP10

Arch and Tower of Cairo — AP11

Designs: 80m, Al Azhar University seen through arch. 140m, Ramses II, Abu Simbel.

***Perf. 11½x11, 11x11½***

**1963-65** **Photo.** **Wmk. 342**

**C101** AP6 80m vio blk & brt bl 3.75 1.60
**C102** AP10 115m brown & yel 4.00 1.50
**C103** AP10 140m pale vio, blk & org red 4.00 2.00

**Unwmk.**

**C104** AP11 50m yel brn & brt bl 2.25 1.00
**C105** AP6 80m vio bl & lt bl 3.75 1.60
*Nos. C101-C105 (5)* 17.75 7.70

Issued: 50m, 11/2/64; No. C105, 2/13/65; others, 10/24/63.
See Nos. NC34-NC36.

Weather Vane, Anemometer and WMO Emblem — AP12

***Perf. 11½x11***

**1965, Mar. 23** **Wmk. 342**

**C106** AP12 80m dk blue & rose lil 2.75 1.50

Fifth World Meteorological Day.
See No. NC37.

Game Board from Tomb of Tutankhamun — AP13

**1965, July 1** **Photo.** **Unwmk.**

**C107** AP13 10m yellow & dk blue 2.00 .45

See No. NC38.

Temples at Abu Simbel — AP14

**1966, Apr. 28** **Wmk. 342** ***Perf. 11½***

**C108** AP14 20m multicolored 1.10 .55
**C109** AP14 80m multicolored 2.50 1.75

Issued to commemorate the transfer of the temples of Abu Simbel to a hilltop, 1963-66.

Scout Camp and Jamboree Emblem
AP15

**1966, Aug. 10** ***Perf. 11½x11***

**C110** AP15 20m olive & rose 1.60 .50

7th Pan-Arab Boy Scout Jamboree, Good Daim, Libya, Aug. 12.

St. Catherine Monastery, Mt. Sinai — AP16

**1966, Nov. 30** **Photo.** **Wmk. 342**

**C111** AP16 80m multicolored 2.25 1.75

St. Catherine Monastery, Sinai, 1400th anniv.

Cairo Airport
AP17

**1967, Apr. 26** ***Perf. 11½x11***

**C112** AP17 20m sky bl, sl grn & lt brn 1.00 .40

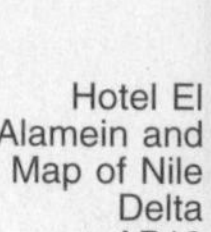

Hotel El Alamein and Map of Nile Delta
AP18

Intl. Tourist Year: 80m, The Virgin's Tree, Virgin Mary and Child. 115m, Fishing in the Red Sea.

**1967, June 7** **Wmk. 342** ***Perf. 11½***

**C113** AP18 20m dull pur, sl grn & dl org 1.10 .50
**C114** AP18 80m blue & multi 2.50 1.50
**C115** AP18 115m brown, org & bl 4.75 2.25
*Nos. C113-C115 (3)* 8.35 4.25

Oil Derricks, Map of Egypt
AP19

**1967, July 23** **Photo.**

**C116** AP19 50m org & bluish blk 1.25 .85

15th anniversary of the revolution.

**Type of Regular Issue, 1967**

Design: 80m, Back of Tutankhamun's throne and UNESCO emblem.

**1967, Oct. 24** **Wmk. 342** ***Perf. 11½***

**C117** A301 80m blue & yellow 1.50 .90

Koran — AP20

**1968, Mar. 25** **Wmk. 342** ***Perf. 11½***

**C118** AP20 30m lilac, bl & yel 1.25 1.00
**C119** AP20 80m lilac, bl & yel 2.25 1.25
*a.* Pair, #C118-C119 + label 4.50 3.50

1400th anniv. of the Koran. Nos. C118-C119 are printed in miniature sheets of 4 containing 2 each of Nos. C118-C119.

St. Mark and St. Mark's Cathedral — AP21

**1968, June 25** **Wmk. 342** ***Perf. 11½***

**C120** AP21 80m brt grn, dk brn & dp car 1.75 1.00

Martyrdom of St. Mark, 1900th anniv. and the consecration of St. Mark's Cathedral, Cairo.

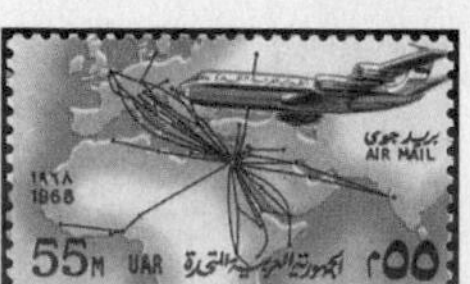

Map of United Arab Airlines and Boeing 707
AP22

Design: No. C122, Ilyushin 18 and routes of United Arab Airlines.

**1968-69 Photo. *Perf. 11½x11***

**C121** AP22 55m blue, ocher & car 1.75 .90
**C122** AP22 55m bl, yel & vio blk ('69) 1.25 .90

1st flights of a Boeing 707 and an Ilyushin 18 for United Arab Airlines.

Mahatma Gandhi, Arms of India and UAR — AP23

**1969, Sept. 10 *Perf. 11x11½***

**C123** AP23 80m lt blue, ocher & brn 4.00 1.75

Mohandas K. Gandhi (1869-1948), leader in India's fight for independence.

Imam El Boukhary — AP24

**1969, Dec. 27 Photo. Wmk. 342**

**C124** AP24 30m lt ol & dk brn .70 .25

1100th anniv. of the death of the Imam El Boukhary (824-870), philosopher and writer.

Azzahir Beybars Mosque AP25

**1969, Dec. 27 Engr. *Perf. 11½x11***

**C125** AP25 30m red lilac .70 .25

700th anniv. of the founding of the Azzahir Beybars Mosque, Cairo.

Lenin (1870-1924) — AP26

***Perf. 11x11½***

**1970, Apr. 22 Photo. Wmk. 342**

**C126** AP26 80m lt grn & brn 2.00 1.25

Phantom Fighters and Destroyed Factory AP27

**1970, May 1 *Perf. 11½x11***

**C127** AP27 80m yel, grn & dk vio brn 2.00 1.00

Issued to commemorate the destruction of the Abu-Zaabal factory by Israeli planes.

**UPU Type of Regular Issue**

**1970, May 20 Photo. Wmk. 342**

**C128** A350 80m multicolored 1.40 .85

Nasser and Burial Mosque — AP28

**1970, Nov. 6 Wmk. 342 *Perf. 11***

**C129** AP28 30m olive & blk 1.00 .40
**C130** AP28 80m brown & blk 2.75 1.25

Gamal Abdel Nasser (1918-70), Pres. of Egypt.

**Postal Congress Type**

***Perf. 11½x11***

**1971, Mar. 6 Photo. Wmk. 342**

**C131** A365 30m lt ol, org & sl grn .90 .45

Nasser, El Rifaei and Sultan Hussein Mosques AP29

Designs: 85m, Nasser and Ramses Square, Cairo. 110m, Nasser, Sphinx and pyramids.

***Perf. 11½x11***

**1971, July 1 Photo. Wmk. 342**

**C132** AP29 30m multicolored 2.50 .80
**C133** AP29 85m multicolored 4.50 1.25
**C134** AP29 110m multicolored 5.75 2.50
*Nos. C132-C134 (3)* 12.75 4.55

**APU Type of Regular Issue**

**1971, Aug. 3 Wmk. 342 *Perf. 11½***

**C135** A373 30m brown, yel & bl 1.40 .50

**Arab Republic of Egypt Confederation Type**

***Perf. 11½x11***

**1971, Sept. 28 Photo. Wmk. 342**

**C136** A374 30m gray, sl grn & dk pur 1.25 .50

Al Aqsa Mosque and Woman AP30

**Wmk. 342**

**1971, Oct. 24 Photo. *Perf. 11½***

**C137** AP30 30m bl, yel, brn & grn 1.75 .45

25th anniv. of the UN (in 1970) and return of Palestinian refugees.

**Postal Union Type**

30m, African Postal Union emblem & letter.

**1971, Dec. 2 *Perf. 11½x11***

**C138** A384 30m green, blk & bl 1.40 .40

Aida, Triumphal March AP31

**1971, Dec. 23 Wmk. 342 *Perf. 11½***

**C139** AP31 110m dk brn, yel & sl grn 5.75 3.00

Centenary of the first performance of the opera Aida, by Giuseppe Verdi.

Globe, Glider, Rocket Club Emblem — AP32

**1972, Feb. 11 *Perf. 11x11½***

**C140** AP32 30m blue, ocher & yel 1.50 .50

International Aerospace Education Conference, Cairo, Jan. 11-13.

St. Catherine's Monastery on Fire — AP33

***Perf. 11½x11***

**1972, Feb. 15 Unwmk.**

**C141** AP33 110m dp car, org & blk 4.75 4.00

The burning of St. Catherine's Monastery in Sinai Desert, Nov. 30, 1971.

Tutankhamun in Garden — AP34

Tutankhamun, from 2nd Sarcophagus — AP35

Design: No. C143, Ankhesenamun.

**1972, May 22 Photo. *Perf. 11½***

**C142** 110m brn org, bl & grn 10.00 5.50
**C143** 110m brn org, bl & grn 10.00 5.50
*a.* AP34 Pair, #C142-C143 26.00 22.50

**Souvenir Sheet**

***Imperf***

**C144** AP35 200m gold & multi 32.50 32.50

50th anniv. of the discovery of the tomb of Tutankhamun.

Souvenir Sheet

Flag of Confederation of Arab Republics — AP36

**1972, July 23 Photo. *Imperf.***

**C145** AP36 110m gold, dp car & blk 4.50 4.25

20th anniversary of the revolution.

Temples at Abu Simbel AP37

Designs: 30m, Al Azhar Mosque and St. George's Church. 110m, Pyramids at Giza.

**1972 Wmk. 342 *Perf. 11½x11***

**C146** AP37 30m blue, brn & buff 2.50 .40
**C147** AP37 85m bl, brn & ocher 3.50 1.75
**C148** AP37 110m multicolored 5.25 1.75
*Nos. C146-C148 (3)* 11.25 3.90

Issued: Nos. C146, C148, 11/22; No. C147, 8/1.

**Olympic Type of Regular Issue**

Olympic and Motion Emblems and: No. C149, Handball. No. C150, Weight lifting. 50m, Swimming. 55m, Gymnastics. All vertical.

**1972, Aug. 17 *Perf. 11x11½***

**C149** A396 30m multicolored .80 .40
**C150** A396 30m yellow & multi .80 .40
**C151** A396 50m blue & multi 1.60 1.00
**C152** A396 55m multicolored 2.00 1.10
*Nos. C149-C152 (4)* 5.20 2.90

Champollion, Rosetta Stone, Hieroglyphics — AP38

**1972, Oct. 16**

**C153** AP38 110m gold, grn & blk 7.50 2.50

Sesquicentennial of the deciphering of Egyptian hieroglyphics by Jean-François Champollion.

World Map, Telephone, Radar, ITU Emblem — AP39

**1973, Mar. 21 Photo. *Perf. 11***

**C154** AP39 30m lt bl, dk bl & blk .90 .25

5th World Telecommunications Day.

Karnak Temple, Luxor — AP40

**1973, Mar. 21**
**C155** AP40 110m dp ultra, blk & rose 4.75 2.50

Sound and light at Karnak.

Hand Dripping Blood and Falling Plane — AP41

**1973, May 1** ***Perf. 11x11½***
**C156** AP41 110m multicolored 6.25 3.00

Israeli attack on Libyan civilian plane, Feb. 1973.

WMO Emblem, Weather Vane — AP42

**1973, Oct. 24** ***Perf. 11x11½***
**C157** AP42 110m blue, gold & pur 3.00 1.75

Cent. of intl. meteorological cooperation.

Refugees, Map of Palestine AP43

**1973, Oct. 24** ***Perf. 11½***
**C158** AP43 30m dk brn, yel & bl 1.60 .50

Plight of Palestinian refugees.

INTERPOL Emblem — AP44

***Perf. 11x11½***

**1973, Dec. 8 Photo. Wmk. 342**
**C159** AP44 110m black & multi 3.75 2.00

Intl. Criminal Police Organization, 50th anniv.

Postal and UPU Emblems — AP45

Post Day (UPU Emblems and): 30m, APU emblem. 55m, African Postal Union emblem. 110m, UPU emblem.

**Size: 26x46½mm**

**1974, Jan. 2 Unwmk.** ***Perf. 11***
**C160** AP45 20m gray, red & blk .45 .25
**C161** AP45 30m sal, blk & pur .65 .25
**C162** AP45 55m emerald, blk & brt mag 1.25 .85

**Size: 37x37½mm**

***Perf. 11½***

**C163** AP45 110m lt bl, blk & gold 1.75 1.50
*Nos. C160-C163 (4)* 4.10 2.85

Solar Bark of Khufu (Cheops) — AP46

**Wmk. 342**

**1974, Mar. 21 Photo.** ***Perf. 11½***
**C164** AP46 110m blue, gold & brn 3.75 2.25

Solar Bark Museum.

Hotel Meridien AP47

**1974, Oct. 6** ***Perf. 11½x11***
**C165** AP47 110m multicolored 2.25 1.25

Opening of Hotel Meridien, Cairo.

**Suez Canal Type of 1975**

**1975, June 5** ***Perf. 11½***
**C166** A448 30m bl, yel grn & ind 1.75 .60
**C167** A448 110m indigo & blue 2.75 2.00

Irrigation Commission Emblem — AP48

**1975, July 20**
**C168** AP48 110m orange & dk grn 2.25 1.25

9th Intl. Congress on Irrigation and Drainage, Moscow, and 25th anniv. of the Intl. Commission on Irrigation and Drainage.

Refugees and UNWRA Emblem — AP49

Woman and IWY Emblem — AP50

***Perf. 11x11½***

**1975, Oct. 24 Photo. Wmk. 342**
**C169** AP49 30m multicolored 1.40 .50

**Unwmk.**

**C170** AP50 110m olive, org & blk 3.50 2.00

UN Day. 30m publicizes UN help for refugees; 110m is for Intl. Women's Year 1975.

Step Pyramid, Sakhara, and Entrance Gate AP51

Designs: 45m, 60m, Plane over Giza Pyramids. 140m, Plane over boats on Nile.

***Perf. 11½x11***

**1978-82 Photo. Wmk. 342**
**C171** AP51 45m yel & brown .60 .25
*b.* Unwatermarked — —
**C171A** AP51 60m olive 2.00 1.00
*c.* Unwatermarked — —
**C172** AP51 115m blue & brown 1.10 .55
**C173** AP51 140m blue & purple 2.00 1.00
**C173A** AP51 185m bl, sep & gray brn 5.00 2.25
*Nos. C171-C173A (5)* 10.70 5.05

Issued: 60m, 1/15/82; 185m, 1982; others, 1/1/78.

Flyer and UN ICAO Emblem — AP52

***Perf. 11x11½***

**1978, Dec. 30 Photo. Wmk. 342**
**C174** AP52 140m blue, blk & brn 2.50 1.25

75th anniversary of 1st powered flight.

Seeing Eye Medallion AP53

***Perf. 11½x11***

**1981, Oct. 1 Photo. Wmk. 342**
**C175** AP53 230m multicolored 2.50 1.25

Hilton Ramses Hotel Opening — AP54

***Perf. 11x11½***

**1982, Mar. 15 Photo. Wmk. 342**
**C176** AP54 18½p multi 2.00 1.00

Temple of Horus, Edfu AP55

Designs: 15p, like 6p. 18½p, 25p, Statue of Akhnaton, Thebes, hieroglyphics, vert. 23p, 30p, Giza pyramids.

***Perf. 11½x11, 11x11½***

**1985 Photo. Wmk. 342**
**C177** AP55 6p lt blue & dk bl grn 1.00 .40
**C178** AP55 15p grnsh bl & brn 1.75 .50
*a.* Unwatermarked — —
**C179** AP55 18½p grn, sep & dp yel 2.00 1.25
**C180** AP55 23p grnsh bl, sep & yel bis 2.50 1.50
**C181** AP55 25p lt bl, sep & yel bis 2.10 .95
*a.* Unwmkd. ('87) 2.75 1.10
**C182** AP55 30p grnsh bl, sep & org yel 2.10 .85
*a.* Unwmkd. ('87) 2.75 1.10
*Nos. C177-C182 (6)* 11.45 5.45

Issued: 6p, 18½p, 23p, 3/1; 15p, 25p, 30p, 5/1.

See No. C236.

Post Day — AP56

Narmer Board, oldest known hieroglyphic inscriptions: No. C183a, Tablet obverse. No. C183b, Reverse.

**1986, Jan. 2 Photo.** ***Perf. 13½x13***
**C183** AP56 Pair 2.50 2.50
*a.-b.* 15p any single 1.10 1.00

Map, Jet, AFRAA Emblem AP57

**1986, Apr. 7 Photo.** ***Perf. 11½***
**C184** AP57 15p blue, yel & blk 1.25 .50

African Airlines Assoc., 18th General Assembly, Cairo, Apr. 7-10.

World Food Day AP58

UNESCO, 40th Anniv. — AP59

*Perf. 13½x13, 13x13½*

**1986, Oct. 24 Litho.**

| | | | | | |
|---|---|---|---|---|---|
| C185 | AP58 | 15p multicolored | 1.00 | 1.00 |
| C186 | AP59 | 15p multicolored | 1.00 | 1.00 |

UN Day.

Tourism Year — AP60

Design: Column and Sphinx in Alexandria, St. Catherine's Monastery in Mt. Sinai, Colossi of Thebes and Temple of Theban Triad in Luxor.

**Unwmk.**

**1987, Sept. 30 Litho. *Imperf.***

**Size: 140x90mm**

C187 AP60 30p multicolored 4.25 4.25

See No. 1344.

Palestinian Uprising — AP61

**1988, Sept. 28 Litho. *Perf. 12x13½***

C188 AP61 25p multicolored 1.60 1.40

UN Day AP62

**1988, Oct. 20 Litho. *Perf. 13x13½***

C189 AP62 25p multicolored 1.60 1.40

**Nobel Prize Type of 1988**

**1988, Nov. 7**

C190 A769 25p multicolored 1.60 1.40

Arab Cooperation Council — AP63

**1989, May 10 Litho. *Perf. 13½x13***

C191 AP63 25p Flags 1.25 .55

**Size: 89x80mm**

***Imperf***

C192 AP63 50p Flags, seal 3.50 3.50

Architecture and Art — AP64

**1989-91 Photo. *Perf. 11x11½***

| | | | | |
|---|---|---|---|---|
| C193 | AP64 20p Balcony | .75 | .45 |
| C194 | AP64 25p Brazier | 1.10 | .60 |
| C195 | AP64 35p shown | 1.25 | .75 |
| C196 | AP64 45p Tapestry | 1.60 | .75 |
| C197 | AP64 45p like #C195 | 1.40 | .40 |
| C198 | AP64 50p Stag (dish) | 2.00 | 1.00 |
| C199 | AP64 55p 4 animals (plate) | 1.90 | .90 |
| C200 | AP64 60p like #C198 | 2.25 | 1.25 |
| C201 | AP64 65p like #C198 | 2.50 | 1.50 |
| C202 | AP64 70p like #C193 | 2.50 | 1.50 |
| C203 | AP64 85p like #C199 | 3.00 | 1.75 |
| | *Nos. C193-C203 (11)* | 20.25 | 10.85 |

Issued: 35p, 60p, 10/1/89; 55p, 1/1/90; No. C197, C202, 1/25/91; 65p, 85p, 7/20/91; others, 4/1/89.

AP65

Funerary Mask of King Tutankhamun — AP66

King Tutankhamun AP66a

No. C205, 21mm between "EGYPT" and Arabic text at top.

No. C205A, 17mm between "Egypt" and Arabic text at top ('00).

**1993-2000 Litho. *Perf. 11½***

| | | | | |
|---|---|---|---|---|
| C204 | AP65 | 55p black & sepia | 2.00 | .95 |
| C205 | AP66 | 80p black & drab | 3.25 | 1.25 |
| C205A | AP66 | 80p black & sepia | — | — |

**Photo.**

***Perf. 11x11¼***

| | | | | |
|---|---|---|---|---|
| C206 | AP66a | £1 black & brown | 1.50 | 1.25 |
| *b.* | | Wmk. 342 | 2.00 | 1.25 |
| | | *Nos. C204-C206 (4)* | 6.75 | 3.45 |

Issued: 55p, 80p, 3/1/93; £1, 1997; No. C206b, 1999.

See No. C231.

ICAO, 50th Anniv. — AP67

**1994, Sept. 16 Litho. *Perf. 13***

C207 AP67 80p multicolored 1.00 .45

Intl. Year of the Family — AP68

**1994, Oct. 24 Litho. *Perf. 13***

C208 AP68 80p multicolored 1.50 1.00

Arab League for Education, Culture, & Science Organization — AP69

**1995, July 25 Litho. *Perf. 13x13½***

C209 AP69 55p multicolored .80 .50

UN Organizations, 50th Anniv. — AP70

*Perf. 12½x13, 13x12½*

**1995, Oct. 24 Litho.**

| | | | | |
|---|---|---|---|---|
| C210 | AP70 80p UN | 2.00 | 1.00 |
| C211 | AP70 80p FAO | 2.00 | 1.00 |
| C212 | AP70 80p UNESCO, vert. | 2.00 | 1.00 |
| | *Nos. C210-C212 (3)* | 6.00 | 3.00 |

Arab Summit, Cairo — AP71

**1996, June 21 Litho. *Perf. 13x12½***

C213 AP71 55p multicolored .70 .30

16th Intl. Conference on Irrigation and Drainage, Cairo — AP72

**1996, Sept. 15 Litho. *Perf. 12½x13***

C214 AP72 80p multicolored 1.10 1.10

Intl. Tourism Day — AP73

**1996, Sept. 27 *Perf. 13***

C215 AP73 80p multicolored 1.50 .60

Arabian Horse Day — AP74

**1996, Sept. 27 *Perf. 13x12½***

C216 AP74 55p grn, blk & gray 1.00 .35

World Post Day — AP75

**1996, Oct. 9 Litho. *Perf. 13x12½***

C217 AP75 80p multicolored 1.25 .60

AP76

**1996, Oct. 24**

C218 AP76 55p multicolored .70 .40

Cairo, Arab cultural capital of 1996.

UNICEF, 50th Anniv. — AP77

**1996, Oct. 24**

C219 AP77 80p multicolored 1.10 .55

World Meteorological Day — AP78

**1997, Mar. 23 Litho. *Perf. 13x12½***

C220 AP78 £1 multicolored 1.75 1.00

Thutmose III — AP79

**1997, Mar. 25 Photo.** ***Perf. 11x11½***
**C221** AP79 75p blk, bl & gray 1.10 1.10

Heinrich von Stephan (1831-97) — AP80

**1997, Apr. 15 Litho.** ***Perf. 13***
**C222** AP80 £1 multicolored 1.60 1.25

AP81

**1997, Sept. 11**
**C223** AP81 £1 multicolored 1.00 .90

98th Intl. Parliamentary Conference, Cairo.

AP82

**1997, Sept. 10 Litho.** ***Perf. 13***
**C224** AP82 75p multicolored 1.00 .90

1997 Egyptian Team, top medal winners of 8th Pan Arab Games, Beirut, Lebanon.

AP83

**1997, Sept. 27** ***Perf. 13x12½***
**C225** AP83 £1 multicolored 1.90 1.00

Sarabas (180-211), mumified Egyptian.

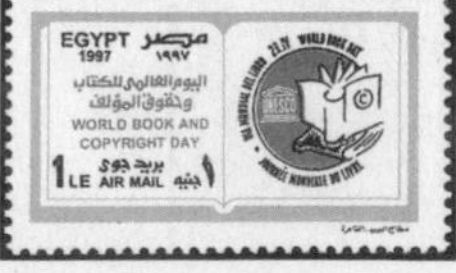


World Book and Copyright Day AP84

**1997, Oct. 24 Litho.** ***Perf. 12½x13***
**C226** AP84 £1 multicolored 1.75 1.00

African Ministries of Transport and Communications, 11th Conference — AP85

**1997, Nov. 22 Litho.** ***Perf. 13x12½***
**C227** AP85 75p multicolored .80 .70

Arab Scout Movement, 85th Anniv. — AP86

**1997, Nov. 24** ***Perf. 12½x13***
**C228** AP86 75p multicolored 1.00 .90

8th G-15 Summit Meeting — AP87

**1998, May 11 Litho.** ***Perf. 13***
**C229** AP87 £1 multicolored 1.10 .90

Lighthouse of Alexandria AP88

**1998, May 20 Litho.** ***Perf. 13***
**C230** AP88 £1 multicolored 1.75 1.00

**King Tut Type of 1997**

**1998, July 25 Litho.** ***Perf. 11x11¼***
**C231** AP66a 125p Tutankhamun 1.75 1.25
*a.* Wmk. 342 ('99) 5.50 4.00

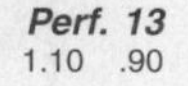

Arab Post Day — AP90

**1998, Aug. 3** ***Perf. 13***
**C232** AP90 £1 multicolored 1.10 .90

World Post Day — AP91

**1998, Oct. 9 Litho.** ***Perf. 13***
**C233** AP91 125p multicolored 1.40 1.25

67th Interpol Meeting, Cairo — AP92

**1998, Oct. 22**
**C234** AP92 125p multicolored 1.40 1.25

AP93

**1998, Oct. 24**
**C235** AP93 125p multicolored 1.40 1.25

Universal Declaration of Human Rights, 50th anniv.

**Statue of Akhnaton Type of 1985**

**1998 Litho.** ***Perf. 13***
**C236** AP55 25p lt bl, brn & tan 1.75 1.00

AP94

**1999, Oct. 12 Litho.** ***Perf. 13x12¾***
**C237** AP94 125p multicolored 2.25 1.75

Performance of opera "Aida" at the Pyramids.

AP95

**1999, Oct. 16**
**C238** AP95 125p multicolored 2.50 1.75

Discovery of the Rosetta Stone, bicent.

World Tourism Day — AP96

***Perf. 13¼x12¾***

**2000, Sept. 27 Litho.**
**C239** AP96 125p multi 1.50 1.25

Awarding of Nobel Prize for Chemistry to Dr. Ahmed Zewail — AP97

**1999, Dec. 10** ***Imperf.***
**C240** AP97 125p multi 2.00 2.00

UN High Commissioner for Refugees, 50th Anniv. — AP98

**2000, Dec. 13**
**C241** AP98 125p multi 1.50 1.25

---

## AIR POST SEMI-POSTAL STAMPS

**Catalogue values for unused stamps in this section are for Never Hinged items.**

**United Arab Republic**

Pharaonic Mail Carriers and Papyrus Plants SPAP1

Design: 115m+55m, Jet plane, world map and stamp of Egypt, 1926 (No. C1).

**Wmk. 342**

**1966, Jan. 2 Photo. *Perf. 11½***

**CB1** SPAP1 80m + 40m multi 3.25 2.75
**CB2** SPAP1 115m + 55m multi 4.25 3.50
*a.* Pair, #CB1-CB2 10.00 8.00

Post Day, Jan. 2.

## SPECIAL DELIVERY STAMPS

Motorcycle Postman — SD1

***Perf. 13x13½***

**1926, Nov. 28 Photo. Wmk. 195**

**E1** SD1 20m dark green 35.00 9.50

**1929, Sept.**

**E2** SD1 20m brown red & black 6.75 1.75

**Inscribed "Postes Expres"**

**1943-44 Litho.**

**E3** SD1 26m brn red & gray blk 6.75 *6.75*
**E4** SD1 40m dl brn & pale gray ('44) 6.00 4.00

For overprints see Nos. E5, NE1.

**Catalogue values for unused stamps in this section, from this point to the end of the section, are for Never Hinged items.**

**No. E4 Overprinted in Black**

**1952, Jan. Overprint 27mm Wide**

**E5** SD1 40m dl brn & pale gray 3.50 2.00

See notes after No. 316.

## POSTAGE DUE STAMPS

D1

**Wmk. Crescent and Star (119)**

**1884, Jan. 1 Litho. *Perf. 10½***

**J1** D1 10pa red 57.50 9.50
*a.* Horiz. pair, imperf. vert. 150.00
**J2** D1 20pa red 175.00 50.00
**J3** D1 1pi red 145.00 52.50
**J4** D1 2pi red 240.00 12.50
**J5** D1 5pi red 20.00 *60.00*
*Nos. J1-J5 (5)* 637.50 184.50

**1886, Aug. 1 Unwmk.**

**J6** D1 10pa red 75.00 17.50
*a.* Horiz. pair, imperf. vert. 135.00
**J7** D1 20pa red 260.00 50.00
**J8** D1 1pi red 37.50 10.00
*a.* Pair, imperf. between 200.00 135.00
**J9** D1 2pi red 37.50 5.00
*a.* Pair, imperf. between 175.00
*Nos. J6-J9 (4)* 410.00 82.50

D2

**1888, Jan. 1 *Perf. 11½***

**J10** D2 2m green 22.50 *27.50*
*a.* Horiz. pair, imperf. between 225.00 200.00
**J11** D2 5m rose red 45.00 27.50
**J12** D2 1pi blue 145.00 40.00
*a.* Pair, imperf. between 300.00
**J13** D2 2pi yellow 155.00 20.00
**J14** D2 5pi gray 240.00 210.00
*a.* Period after "PIASTRES" 325.00 250.00
*Nos. J10-J14 (5)* 607.50 325.00

Excellent counterfeits of #J1-J14 are plentiful.

There are 4 types of each of Nos. J1-J14, so placed that any block of 4 contains all types.

D3

***Perf. 14x13½***

**1889 Wmk. 119 Typo.**

**J15** D3 2m green 10.00 .70
*a.* Half used as 1m on cover 350.00
**J16** D3 4m maroon 3.75 .70
**J17** D3 1pi ultra 7.75 .70
**J18** D3 2pi orange 7.50 1.00
*a.* Half used as 1p on cover —
*Nos. J15-J18 (4)* 29.00 3.10

Nos. J15-J18 exist on both ordinary and chalky paper. Imperf. examples of Nos. J15-J17 are proofs.

**Black Surcharge**

Type I — D4

**1898**

**J19** D4 3m on 2pi orange 2.10 *6.25*
*a.* Inverted surcharge 65.00 *82.50*
*b.* Pair, one without surcharge —
*f.* Double surcharge 225.00 —

There are two types of this surcharge. In type I, the spacing between the last two Arabic characters at the right is 2mm. In type II, this spacing is 3mm, and there is an added sign on top of the second character from the right. See *Scott Classic Specialized Catalogue of Stamps & Covers* for detailed listing.

D5

D6

**1921 Wmk. 120 *Perf. 14x13½***

**J20** D5 2m green 3.75 *6.75*
**J21** D5 4m vermilion 7.50 *19.00*
**J22** D6 10m deep blue 12.50 *25.00*
*Nos. J20-J22 (3)* 23.75 50.75

**1921-22**

**J23** D5 2m vermilion 1.00 *2.25*
**J24** D5 4m green 6.00 2.00
**J25** D6 10m lake ('22) 6.50 1.50
*Nos. J23-J25 (3)* 13.50 5.75

Nos. J18, J23-J25 Overprinted

**1922, Oct. 10 Wmk. 119**

**J26** D3 2pi orange 7.50 *10.50*
*a.* Overprint right side up 30.00 *30.00*

**Wmk. 120**

**J27** D5 2m vermilion 1.00 *3.00*
**J28** D5 4m green 1.60 *3.00*
**J29** D6 10m lake 2.50 1.90
*Nos. J26-J29 (4)* 12.60 18.40

Overprint on Nos. J26-J29 is inverted.

Arabic Numeral — D7

***Perf. 13x13½***

**1927-56 Litho. Wmk. 195**

**Size: 18x22½mm**

**J30** D7 2m slate .85 .50
**J31** D7 2m orange ('38) 1.00 1.10
**J32** D7 4m green .85 .55
**J33** D7 4m ol brn ('32) 8.00 5.25
**J34** D7 5m brown 4.25 1.10
**J35** D7 6m gray grn ('41) 2.75 2.10
**J36** D7 8m brn vio 1.60 .65
**J37** D7 10m brick red ('29) 1.25 .35
*a.* 10m deep red 1.90 1.00
**J38** D7 12m rose lake ('41) 1.90 *3.75*
**J38A** D7 20m dk red ('56) 2.50 2.50

***Perf. 13½x14***

**Size: 22x28mm**

**J39** D7 30m purple 5.25 3.75
*Nos. J30-J39 (11)* 30.20 21.60

See Nos. J47-J59. For overprints see Nos. J40-J46, NJ1-NJ7.

**Catalogue values for unused stamps in this section, from this point to the end of the section, are for Never Hinged items.**

Postage Due Stamps and Type of 1927 Overprinted in Various Colors

**1952, Jan. 16 *Perf. 13x13½***

**J40** D7 2m orange (Bl) 1.60 1.60
**J41** D7 4m green 1.60 1.60
**J42** D7 6m gray grn (RV) 1.90 1.90
**J43** D7 8m brn vio (Bl) 2.50 2.50
**J44** D7 10m dl rose (Bl) 4.25 3.50
*a.* 10m brown red (Bk) 4.00 3.75
**J45** D7 12m rose lake (Bl) 2.10 2.10

***Perf. 14***

**J46** D7 30m purple (C) 3.50 3.50
*Nos. J40-J46 (7)* 17.45 16.70

See notes after No. 316.

**United Arab Republic**

**1960 Wmk. 318 *Perf. 13x13½***

**Size: 18x22½mm**

**J47** D7 2m orange 1.00 1.00
**J48** D7 4m light green 1.50 1.50
**J49** D7 6m green 2.50 2.50
**J50** D7 8m brown vio 5.00 5.00
**J51** D7 12m rose brown 12.00 10.00
**J52** D7 20m dull rose brn 2.00 .50

***Perf. 14***

**Size: 22x28mm**

**J53** D7 30m violet 12.00 6.00
*Nos. J47-J53 (7)* 36.00 26.50

**1962 Wmk. 328 *Perf. 13x13½***

**Size: 18x22½mm**

**J54** D7 2m salmon 1.00 1.00
**J55** D7 4m light green 1.50 1.50
**J56** D7 10m red brown 2.50 2.50
**J57** D7 12m rose brown 5.00 5.00
**J58** D7 20m dull rose brn 11.00 11.00

***Perf. 14***

**Size: 22x28mm**

**J59** D7 30m light violet 16.00 16.00
*Nos. J54-J59 (6)* 37.00 37.00

D8

**1965 Unwmk. Photo. *Perf. 11***

**J60** D8 2m org & vio blk 1.25 1.00
**J61** D8 8m lt bl & dk bl 1.50 1.50
**J62** D8 10m yel & emer 2.25 1.50
**J63** D8 20m lt bl & vio blk 2.75 2.25
**J64** D8 40m org & emer 4.75 2.00
*Nos. J60-J64 (5)* 12.50 8.25

## MILITARY STAMPS

The "British Forces" and "Army post" stamps were special issues provided at a reduced rate for the purchase and use by the British military forces in Egypt and their families for ordinary letters sent to Great Britain and Ireland by a concessionary arrangement made with the Egyptian government. From Nov. 1, 1932 to Feb. 29, 1936, in order to take advantage of the concessionary rate, it was mandatory to use #M1-M11 by affixing them to the backs of envelopes. An "Egypt Postage Prepaid" handstamp was applied to the face of the envelopes. Envelopes bearing these stamps were to be posted only at British military post boxes. Envelopes bearing the 1936-39 "Army Post" stamps (#M12-M15, issued by the Egyptian Postal Administration) also were sold at the concessionary rate and also were to be posted only at British military post boxes. The "Army Post" stamps were withdrawn in 1941, but the concession continued without the use of special stamps. The concession was finally canceled in 1951.

Imperf examples of Nos. M1-M4, M6, M9 (without overprint) and M10 are proofs.

M1

**Unwmk.**

**1932, Nov. 1 Typo. *Perf. 11***

**M1** M1 1pi red & blue 70.00 4.50

For similar design see No. M3.

M2

**1932, Nov. 26 Typo. *Perf. 11½***

**M2** M2 3m blk, *sage grn* 57.50 *80.00*

See Nos. M4, M6, M10.

M3

**1933, Aug. Typo. *Perf. 11***

**M3** M3 1pi red & blue 47.50 1.10

**Camel Type of 1932**

**1933, Nov. 13 Typo. *Perf. 11½***

**M4** M2 3m brown lake 40.00 *57.50*

M4

**1934, June 1 Photo. *Perf. 14½x14***

**M5** M4 1pi bright carmine 40.00 1.25

See Nos. M7-M8. For overprint and surcharge see Nos. M9, M11.

**Camel Type of 1932**

**1934, Nov. 17 Typo. *Perf. 11½***

**M6** M2 3m deep blue 30.00 *30.00*

**Type of 1934**

**1934, Dec. 5 Photo. *Perf. 14½x14***

**M7** M4 1pi green 6.00 6.00

**Type of 1934**

**1935, Apr. 24 *Perf. 13½x14***

**M8** M4 1pi bright carmine 2.90 *3.75*

### Type of 1934 Overprinted in Red

**1935, May 6** *Perf. 14*
M9 M4 1pi ultramarine 350.00 275.00

### Camel Type of 1932

**1935, Nov. 23 Typo.** *Perf. 11½*
M10 M2 3m vermilion 30.00 *45.00*

### No. M8 Surcharged

**1935, Dec. 16 Photo.** *Perf. 13½x14*
M11 M4 3m on 1pi brt car 40.00 *100.00*

### Fuad Type of 1927

Inscribed "Army Post" — M5

**1936, Mar. 1** **Wmk. 195**
M12 M5 3m green 2.50 2.50
M13 M5 10m carmine 7.00 .25

King Farouk — M6

**1939, Dec. 16** *Perf. 13x13½*
M14 M6 3m green 6.00 *12.00*
M15 M6 10m carmine rose 8.00 .25

**Catalogue values for unused stamps in this section, from this point to the end of the section, are for Never Hinged items.**

### United Arab Republic

Arms of UAR and Military Emblems — M7

*Perf. 11x11½*
**1971, Apr. 15 Photo. Wmk. 342**
M16 M7 10m purple .75 .50

## OFFICIAL STAMPS

O1

**Wmk. Crescent and Star (119)**
**1893, Jan. 1 Typo.** *Perf. 14x13½*
O1 O1 orange brown 3.75 .25

No. O1 exists on ordinary and chalky paper. Imperf. examples of No. O1 are proofs.

Regular Issues of 1884-93 Overprinted

**1907**
O2 A18 1m brown 2.40 .35
O3 A19 2m green 4.25 .25
O4 A20 3m orange 4.75 1.25
O5 A22 5m car rose 7.75 .25
O6 A14 1pi ultra 4.75 .25
O7 A16 5pi gray 17.00 6.00
*Nos. O2-O7 (6)* 40.90 8.35

Nos. O2-O3, O5-O7 imperf. are proofs.

No. 48 Overprinted

**1913**
O8 A22 5m carmine rose 9.50 .70
a. Inverted overprint 90.00
b. No period after "S" 65.00 19.00

Regular Issues Overprinted

**1914-15 On Issues of 1888-1906**
O9 A19 2m green 5.00 *10.00*
a. Inverted overprint 42.50 42.50
b. Double overprint 450.00
c. No period after "S" 16.00 16.00
O10 A21 4m brown red 7.50 5.50
a. Inverted overprint 225.00 160.00

**On Issue of 1914**
O11 A24 1m olive brown 2.50 *5.00*
a. No period after "S" 14.00 *30.00*
O12 A26 3m orange 3.75 *6.00*
a. No period after "S" 16.00 *30.00*
O13 A28 5m lake 4.75 2.75
a. No period after "S" 17.50 *26.00*
b. Two periods after "S" 17.50 *26.00*
*Nos. O9-O13 (5)* 23.50 29.25

Regular Issues Overprinted

**1915, Oct. On Issues of 1888-1906**
O14 A19 2m green 5.50 *5.00*
a. Inverted overprint 24.00 24.00
b. Double overprint 30.00
O15 A21 4m brown red 11.00 *11.00*

**On Issue of 1914**
O16 A28 5m lake 15.00 1.75
a. Pair, one without overprint 325.00
*Nos. O14-O16 (3)* 31.50 17.75

Nos. 50, 63, 52, 67 Overprinted

**1922** **Wmk. 120**
O17 A24 1m olive brown 4.25 *16.00*
O18 A25 2m red 10.00 *24.00*
O19 A26 3m orange 77.50 *150.00*
O20 A28 5m pink 21.00 6.00
*Nos. O17-O20 (4)* 112.75 196.00

Regular Issues of 1921-22 Overprinted

**1922**
O21 A24 1m olive brn 1.50 *3.25*
O22 A25 2m red 2.00 *4.50*
O23 A26 3m orange 3.25 *5.00*
O24 A27 4m green 7.00 *9.00*
a. Two periods after "H" none after "S" 175.00 175.00
O25 A28 5m pink 4.00 1.00
a. Two periods after "H" none after "S" 75.00 75.00
O26 A29 10m deep blue 7.00 *8.00*
O27 A29 10m lake ('23) 10.00 4.00
a. Two periods after "H" none after "S" 100.00 100.00
O28 A34 15m indigo 8.00 7.00
O29 A35 15m indigo 160.00 160.00
a. Two periods after "H" none after "S" 250.00 250.00
O30 A31 50m maroon 20.00 18.00

Regular Issue of 1923 Overprinted in Black or Red

**1924** *Perf. 13½x14*
O31 A36 1m orange 2.10 *2.25*
O32 A36 2m gray (R) 2.75 *3.50*
O33 A36 3m brown 6.75 *6.75*
O34 A36 4m yellow green 8.50 8.50
O35 A36 5m orange brown 2.00 1.05
O36 A36 10m rose 5.50 4.00
O37 A36 15m ultra 9.25 6.75

*Perf. 14*
O38 A36 50m myrtle green 25.00 13.50
*Nos. O31-O38 (8)* 61.85 46.30

O2

*Perf. 13x13½*
**1926-35 Litho. Wmk. 195**
**Size: 18½x22mm**
O39 O2 1m lt orange 1.05 .55
O40 O2 2m black .70 .40
O41 O2 3m olive brn 2.00 1.35
O42 O2 4m lt green 1.75 1.60
O43 O2 5m brown 2.10 .55
O44 O2 10m dull red 5.25 .55
O45 O2 10m brt vio ('34) 3.00 .60
O46 O2 15m dp blue 5.25 1.25
O47 O2 15m brown vio ('34) 5.25 1.10
O48 O2 20m dp blue ('35) 5.50 1.60

*Perf. 13½*
**Size: 22½x27½mm**
O49 O2 20m olive green 7.50 2.75
O50 O2 50m myrtle green 10.00 2.00
*Nos. O39-O50 (12)* 49.35 14.30

O3

**1938, Dec.** **Size: 22½x19mm**
O51 O3 1m orange .35 .35
O52 O3 2m red .35 .35
O53 O3 3m olive brown 1.60 1.60
O54 O3 4m yel green 1.00 1.00
O55 O3 5m brown .50 .50
O56 O3 10m brt violet .60 .60
O57 O3 15m rose violet 1.60 1.60
O58 O3 20m blue 1.60 1.60

*Perf. 14x13½*
**Size: 26½x22mm**
O59 O3 50m myrtle green 3.75 3.00
*Nos. O51-O59 (9)* 11.35 10.60

**Catalogue values for unused stamps in this section, from this point to the end of the section, are for Never Hinged items.**

Nos. O51 to O59 Overprinted in Various Colors

### Overprint 19mm Wide

**1952, Jan.** *Perf. 13x13½*
O60 O3 1m orange (Br) 2.10 2.10
O61 O3 2m red (Br) 2.10 2.10
O62 O3 3m olive brn (Bl) 2.50 2.50
O63 O3 4m yel green (Bl) 2.50 2.50
O64 O3 5m brown (Bl) 2.50 2.50
O65 O3 10m brt violet (Bl) 2.50 2.50
O66 O3 15m rose violet (Bl) 3.00 3.00
O67 O3 20m blue 3.75 3.75

### Overprint 24½mm Wide

*Perf. 14x13½*
O68 O3 50m myrtle grn (RV) 8.00 8.00
*Nos. O60-O68 (9)* 28.95 28.95

See notes after No. 316.

### United Arab Republic

O4

*Perf. 13x13½*
**1959 Litho. Wmk. 318**
O69 O4 10m brown violet .65 .25
O70 O4 35m chalky blue 1.75 .30

**1962-63** **Wmk. 328**
O71 O4 1m orange ('63) .30 .30
O72 O4 4m yel grn ('63) .60 .60
O73 O4 5m brown .60 .25
O74 O4 10m dk brown .75 .30
O75 O4 35m dark blue 2.25 .50
O76 O4 50m green 3.50 .60
O77 O4 100m violet ('63) 7.00 1.75
O78 O4 200m rose red ('63) 15.00 8.00
O79 O4 500m gray ('63) 22.50 15.00
*Nos. O71-O79 (9)* 52.50 27.30

Arms of UAR — O5

*Perf. 11½x11*
**1966-68 Unwmk. Photo.**
O80 O5 1m ultra .25 .25
O81 O5 4m brown .25 .25
O82 O5 5m olive .30 .25
O83 O5 10m brown blk 1.00 .35
O84 O5 20m magenta .60 .30
O85 O5 35m dk purple 1.00 .35
O86 O5 50m orange 1.10 .25
O87 O5 55m dk purple 1.10 .45

**Wmk. 342**
O88 O5 100m brt grn & brick red 2.25 1.00
O89 O5 200m blue & brick red 4.50 2.00
O90 O5 500m olive & brick red 10.00 6.25
*Nos. O80-O90 (11)* 22.35 11.90

**1969** **Wmk. 342**
O91 O5 10m magenta 1.10 .65

### Arab Republic of Egypt

Arms of Egypt — O6

**Wmk. 342**
**1972, June 30 Photo.** *Perf. 11*
O92 O6 1m black & vio blue .30 .25
a. 1m black & light blue ('75) .25 .25
O93 O6 10m black & car .65 .30
a. 10m black & rose red ('76) .25 .25
O94 O6 20m black & olive .90 .40
O95 O6 50m black & orange .60 .55
O96 O6 55m black & purple 3.00 1.00

**1973**
O97 O6 20m lilac & sepia .90 .40
a. 20m purple & light brown ('76) 2.50 .75
O98 O6 70m black & grn ('79) .85 .45

**1982 Photo. Unwmk.** *Perf. 11*
O99 O6 30m purple & brown .60 .30
O100 O6 60m black & orange .70 .30
O101 O6 80m black & green .95 .35
*Nos. O92-O101 (10)* 9.45 4.30

Issued: 30m, 2/12; 60m, 2/24; 80m, 2/18.

Arms of Egypt — O7

**1985-89 Photo. *Perf. 11½***
**Size: 21x25mm**

| No. | Type | Description | Unused | Used |
|---|---|---|---|---|
| O102 | O7 | 1p vermilion | .25 | .25 |
| O103 | O7 | 2p brown | .25 | .25 |
| O104 | O7 | 3p sepia | .25 | .25 |
| O105 | O7 | 5p orange yel | .35 | .30 |
| O106 | O7 | 8p green | .70 | .35 |
| O107 | O7 | 10p brown olive | .25 | .25 |
| O108 | O7 | 15p dull violet | 1.50 | .70 |
| O109 | O7 | 20p blue | .85 | .80 |
| O110 | O7 | 25p red | 1.50 | 1.00 |
| O111 | O7 | 30p dull violet | .90 | .70 |
| O112 | O7 | 50p green | 2.25 | 2.25 |
| O113 | O7 | 60p myrtle green | 2.00 | 1.40 |
| | | *Nos. O102-O113 (12)* | 11.05 | 8.50 |

Issued: 1p, 3p, 5p, 8p, 15p, 5/1/85; 20p, 50p, 4/88; 10p, 30p, 60p, 12/1/89; 2p, 25p, 1989.

**1991-99 Wmk. 342 *Perf. 11½x11***
**Size: 18x22mm**

| No. | Type | Description | Unused | Used |
|---|---|---|---|---|
| O114 | O7 | 5p orange yellow | .25 | .25 |
| O115 | O7 | 10p brown violet | .25 | .25 |
| O116 | O7 | 15p brown | .25 | .25 |
| O117 | O7 | 20p blue | .35 | .25 |
| O118 | O7 | 20p violet | .25 | .25 |
| O119 | O7 | 25p purple | .45 | .25 |
| O120 | O7 | 30p dk violet | .50 | .25 |
| O121 | O7 | 50p green | .80 | .60 |
| O122 | O7 | 55p red | .70 | .55 |
| O123 | O7 | 75p brown | .75 | .55 |
| O124 | O7 | £1 green blue | 1.25 | .75 |
| O125 | O7 | £2 green | 2.50 | 1.50 |
| | | *Nos. O114-O125 (12)* | 8.30 | 5.70 |

Issued: 10p, 30p, 7/1/91; 50p, 12/1/91; 55p, 4/1/93; £1, £2, 3/22/94; No. O123, 75p, 2/1/97; No. O118, 4/11/99.

**Arms Type of 1985-89**
***Perf. 11½x11***
**2001-02? Photo. Unwmk.**
**Size: 18x22mm**

| No. | Type | Description | Unused | Used |
|---|---|---|---|---|
| O126 | O7 | 5p orange yellow | — | — |
| O127 | O7 | 10p brown | 2.75 | .50 |
| O128 | O7 | 20p dark blue | — | — |
| O129 | O7 | 25p purple | — | — |
| O130 | O7 | 30p violet | 3.75 | .60 |
| O131 | O7 | 75p olive brown | — | — |
| O132 | O7 | £1 greenish blue | — | — |

Issued: Nos. O126-O129, O131-O132, 3/25/01; No. O130, 2002?.

## OCCUPATION STAMPS

**Catalogue values for unused stamps in this section are for Never Hinged items.**

### For Use in Palestine

Stamps of 1939-46 Overprinted in Red, Green or Black — a

***Perf. 13x13½, 13½x13***
**1948, May 15 Wmk. 195**

| No. | Type | Description | Unused | Used |
|---|---|---|---|---|
| N1 | A77 | 1m yellow brn (G) | .35 | .35 |
| N2 | A77 | 2m red org (G) | .35 | .35 |
| N3 | A66 | 3m brown (G) | .35 | .35 |
| N4 | A77 | 4m dp green | .35 | .35 |
| N5 | A77 | 5m red brown (Bk) | .35 | .35 |
| N6 | A66 | 6m lt yel grn (Bk) | .35 | .35 |
| N7 | A77 | 10m dp violet | .35 | .35 |
| N8 | A66 | 13m rose car (G) | 2.00 | *2.50* |
| N9 | A77 | 15m dk violet | .45 | .45 |
| N10 | A77 | 17m olive green | .45 | .45 |
| N11 | A77 | 20m dk gray | .45 | .45 |
| N12 | A77 | 22m deep blue | .50 | .50 |
| N13 | A74 | 50pi green & sep | 30.00 | 30.00 |
| N14 | A75 | £1 dp bl & dk brn | 50.00 | 50.00 |

The two lines of the overprint are more widely separated on Nos. N13 and N14.

Nos. 267-269, 237 and 238 Ovptd. in Red — b

***Perf. 14x13½***

| No. | Type | Description | Unused | Used |
|---|---|---|---|---|
| N15 | A73 | 30m olive green | 1.25 | 1.25 |
| N16 | A73 | 40m dark brown | 1.60 | 1.60 |
| N17 | A73 | 50m Prus green | 3.00 | 3.00 |
| N18 | A73 | 100m brown violet | 5.00 | 5.00 |
| N19 | A73 | 200m dark violet | 15.00 | 15.00 |
| | | *Nos. N1-N19 (19)* | 112.15 | 112.65 |

Overprint arranged to fit size of stamps.

**Nos. N1-N19 Overprinted in Black with Three Bars to Obliterate Portrait**

***Perf. 13x13½, 13½x13, 14x13½***
**1953 Wmk. 195**

| No. | Type | Description | Unused | Used |
|---|---|---|---|---|
| N20 | A77 | 1m yellow brown | .70 | .70 |
| N21 | A77 | 2m red orange | .70 | .70 |
| N22 | A66 | 3m brown | .70 | .70 |
| N23 | A77 | 4m deep green | .70 | .70 |
| N24 | A77 | 5m red brown | .70 | .70 |
| N25 | A66 | 6m lt yel grn | .80 | .80 |
| N26 | A77 | 10m deep violet | .85 | .85 |
| N27 | A66 | 13m rose carmine | .90 | .90 |
| N28 | A77 | 15m dark violet | .95 | .95 |
| N29 | A77 | 17m olive green | .95 | .95 |
| N30 | A77 | 20m dark gray | 1.10 | 1.10 |
| N31 | A77 | 22m deep blue | 1.45 | 1.45 |
| N32 | A73 | 30m olive green | 1.45 | 1.45 |
| N33 | A73 | 40m dark brown | 2.60 | 2.60 |
| N34 | A73 | 50m Prus green | 8.00 | 8.00 |
| N35 | A73 | 100m brown violet | 17.00 | 17.00 |
| N36 | A73 | 200m dark violet | 40.00 | 40.00 |
| N37 | A74 | 50pi green & sepia | 80.00 | 75.00 |
| N38 | A75 | £1 dp bl & dk brn | 170.00 | 170.00 |
| | | *Nos. N20-N38 (19)* | 329.55 | 324.55 |

**Regular Issue of 1953-55 Overprinted Type "a" in Blue or Red**

**1954-56 *Perf. 13x13½***

| No. | Type | Description | Unused | Used |
|---|---|---|---|---|
| N39 | A115 | 1m red brown | .45 | .45 |
| N40 | A115 | 2m dark lilac | .45 | .45 |
| N41 | A115 | 3m brt blue (R) | .45 | .45 |
| N42 | A115 | 4m dark green (R) | .45 | .45 |
| N43 | A115 | 5m deep carmine | .45 | .45 |
| N44 | A110 | 10m dark brown | .45 | .45 |
| N45 | A110 | 15m gray (R) | .45 | .45 |
| N46 | A110 | 17m dk grnsh bl (R) | .45 | .45 |
| N47 | A110 | 20m purple (R) ('54) | .60 | .60 |

Nos. 331-333 and 335-340 Overprinted in Blue or Red — c

***Perf. 13½***

| No. | Type | Description | Unused | Used |
|---|---|---|---|---|
| N48 | A111 | 30m dull green (R) | .85 | .85 |
| N49 | A111 | 32m brt blue (R) | .95 | .95 |
| N50 | A111 | 35m violet (R) | 1.25 | 1.25 |
| N51 | A111 | 40m red brown | 1.90 | 1.90 |
| N52 | A111 | 50m violet brown | 2.25 | 2.25 |
| N53 | A112 | 100m henna brown | 5.50 | 5.50 |
| N54 | A112 | 200m dk grnsh bl (R) | 20.00 | 20.00 |
| N55 | A112 | 500m purple (R) | 70.00 | 70.00 |
| N56 | A112 | £1 dk grn, blk & red (R) ('56) | 115.00 | 115.00 |
| | | *Nos. N39-N56 (18)* | 221.90 | 221.90 |

Type of 1957 Overprinted in Red — d

**1957 Wmk. 195 *Perf. 13½x13***

| No. | Type | Description | Unused | Used |
|---|---|---|---|---|
| N57 | A127 | 10m blue green | 5.00 | 5.00 |

**Nos. 414-417 Overprinted Type "d" in Red**

**1957-58 Wmk. 315 *Perf. 13½***

| No. | Type | Description | Unused | Used |
|---|---|---|---|---|
| N58 | A137 | 10m violet | 3.00 | 3.00 |

**Wmk. 318**

| No. | Type | Description | Unused | Used |
|---|---|---|---|---|
| N59 | A136 | 1m lt bl grn ('58) | .60 | .60 |
| N60 | A138 | 5m brown ('58) | .60 | .60 |
| N61 | A137 | 10m violet ('58) | .90 | .90 |
| | | *Nos. N58-N61 (4)* | 5.10 | 5.10 |

### United Arab Republic

Nos. 438-444 Overprinted in Red or Green

***Perf. 13½x14***
**1958 Wmk. 318 Photo.**

| No. | Type | Description | Unused | Used |
|---|---|---|---|---|
| N62 | A136 | 1m crimson | .35 | .35 |
| N63 | A138 | 2m blue | .35 | .35 |
| N64 | A143 | 3m dk red brn (G) | .35 | .35 |
| N65 | A217 | 4m green | .35 | .35 |
| N66 | A138 | 5m brown | .35 | .35 |
| N67 | A137 | 10m violet | .45 | .35 |
| N68 | A138 | 35m lt ultra | 3.50 | 3.25 |
| | | *Nos. N62-N68 (7)* | 5.70 | 5.35 |

Freedom Struggle Type of 1958 Overprint in Red

**1958 *Perf. 13½x13***

| No. | Type | Description | Unused | Used |
|---|---|---|---|---|
| N69 | A145 | 10m dark brown | 2.00 | 2.00 |

**Declaration of Human Rights Type of 1958 Overprinted in Green**

**1958 *Perf. 13x13½***

| No. | Type | Description | Unused | Used |
|---|---|---|---|---|
| N70 | A151 | 10m rose violet | 3.00 | 3.00 |
| N71 | A151 | 35m red brown | 8.00 | 8.00 |

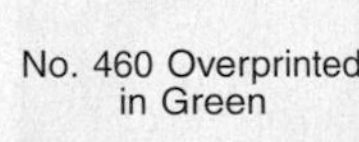

No. 460 Overprinted in Green

**1959 Wmk. 195 *Perf. 13½***

| No. | Type | Description | Unused | Used |
|---|---|---|---|---|
| N72 | A112 | 55m on 100m henna brn | 4.00 | 4.00 |

**World Refugee Year Type "PALESTINE" Added in English and Arabic to Stamps of Egypt**

OS1

**1960 Wmk. 328 *Perf. 13x13½***

| No. | Type | Description | Unused | Used |
|---|---|---|---|---|
| N73 | OS1 | 10m orange brown | .75 | .75 |
| N74 | OS1 | 35m dk blue gray | 1.75 | 1.50 |

**Type of Regular Issue 1957-63**

**1960 *Perf. 13½x14***

| No. | Type | Description | Unused | Used |
|---|---|---|---|---|
| N75 | A136 | 1m brown orange | .35 | .35 |
| N76 | A217 | 4m olive gray | .35 | .35 |
| N77 | A138 | 5m dk dull pur | .35 | .35 |
| N78 | A137 | 10m dk olive grn | .35 | .35 |
| | | *Nos. N75-N78 (4)* | 1.40 | 1.40 |

**Palestine Day Type**

**1961, May 15 *Perf. 13½x13***

| No. | Type | Description | Unused | Used |
|---|---|---|---|---|
| N79 | A184 | 10m purple | 1.00 | 1.00 |

**WHO Day Type**

**1961 Wmk. 328 *Perf. 13½x13***

| No. | Type | Description | Unused | Used |
|---|---|---|---|---|
| N80 | A182 | 10m blue | 1.25 | .75 |

**U.N.T.A.P. Type**

**1961, Oct. 24**

| No. | Type | Description | Unused | Used |
|---|---|---|---|---|
| N81 | A191 | 10m dk blue & org | .50 | .50 |
| N82 | A191 | 35m vermilion & blk | .75 | .75 |

**Education Day Type**

**1961, Dec. 18 Photo. *Perf. 13½***

| No. | Type | Description | Unused | Used |
|---|---|---|---|---|
| N83 | A194 | 10m red brown | .50 | .50 |

**Victory Day Type**

**1961, Dec. 23 Unwmk. *Perf. 11½***

| No. | Type | Description | Unused | Used |
|---|---|---|---|---|
| N84 | A195 | 10m brn org & brn | .40 | .40 |

**Gaza Strip Type**

***Perf. 13½x13***
**1962, Mar. 7 Wmk. 328**

| No. | Type | Description | Unused | Used |
|---|---|---|---|---|
| N85 | A200 | 10m red brown | .40 | .40 |

**Arab Publicity Week Type**

**1962, Mar. 22 *Perf. 13½x13***

| No. | Type | Description | Unused | Used |
|---|---|---|---|---|
| N86 | SP16 | 10m dark purple | .30 | .30 |

**Anti-Malaria Type**

**1962, June 20 Photo.**

| No. | Type | Description | Unused | Used |
|---|---|---|---|---|
| N87 | A204 | 10m brn & dk car rose | .45 | .45 |
| N88 | A204 | 35m black & yellow | .55 | .55 |

**Hammarskjold Type**

***Perf. 11½x11***
**1962, Oct. 24 Wmk. 342**
**Portrait in Slate Blue**

| No. | Type | Description | Unused | Used |
|---|---|---|---|---|
| N89 | A214 | 5m bright rose | .35 | .35 |
| N90 | A214 | 10m brown | .45 | .45 |
| N91 | A214 | 35m blue | .75 | .75 |
| | | *Nos. N89-N91 (3)* | 1.55 | 1.55 |

**Lamp Type of Regular Issue**

***Perf. 11x11½***
**1963, Feb. 20 Unwmk.**

| No. | Type | Description | Unused | Used |
|---|---|---|---|---|
| N92 | A217 | 4m dk brn, org & ultra | .35 | .35 |

**"Freedom from Hunger" Type**

***Perf. 11½x11, 11x11½***
**1963, Mar. 21 Wmk. 342**

| No. | Type | Description | Unused | Used |
|---|---|---|---|---|
| N93 | A220 | 5m lt grn & dp org | .35 | .35 |
| N94 | A220 | 10m olive & yellow | .45 | .45 |
| N95 | A220 | 35m dull pur, yel & blk | .65 | .65 |
| | | *Nos. N93-N95 (3)* | 1.45 | 1.45 |

**Red Cross Centenary Type**

Designs: 10m, Centenary emblem, bottom panel added. 35m, Globe and emblem, top and bottom panels added.

**1963, May 8 Unwmk. *Perf. 11x11½***

| No. | Type | Description | Unused | Used |
|---|---|---|---|---|
| N96 | A221 | 10m dk blue & crim | .35 | .35 |
| N97 | A221 | 35m crim & dk blue | .60 | .60 |

**"Save Abu Simbel" Type, 1963**

**1963, Oct. 15 Wmk. 342 *Perf. 11***

| No. | Type | Description | Unused | Used |
|---|---|---|---|---|
| N98 | A224 | 5m black & yellow | .40 | .40 |
| N99 | A224 | 10m gray, blk & yellow | .50 | .50 |
| N100 | A224 | 35m org yel & violet | 1.25 | .95 |
| | | *Nos. N98-N100 (3)* | 2.15 | 1.85 |

**Human Rights Type**

**1963, Dec. 10 Photo. *Perf. 11½x11***

| No. | Type | Description | Unused | Used |
|---|---|---|---|---|
| N101 | A228 | 5m dk brown & yellow | .35 | .35 |
| N102 | A228 | 10m dp claret, gray & blk | .40 | .40 |
| N103 | A228 | 35m lt grn, pale grn & blk | .95 | .95 |
| | | *Nos. N101-N103 (3)* | 1.70 | 1.70 |

**Types of Regular Issue**

**1964 Unwmk. *Perf. 11***

| No. | Type | Description | Unused | Used |
|---|---|---|---|---|
| N104 | A231 | 1m citron & lt vio | .40 | .40 |
| N105 | A230 | 2m orange & slate | .40 | .40 |
| N106 | A230 | 3m blue & ocher | .40 | .40 |
| N107 | A235 | 4m ol gray, ol, brn & rose | .40 | .40 |
| N108 | A230 | 5m rose & brt blue | .40 | .40 |
| *a.* | | 5m rose & dark blue | 1.25 | 1.25 |
| N109 | A231 | 10m ol, rose & brn | .40 | .40 |
| N110 | A230 | 15m lilac & yellow | .50 | .50 |
| N111 | A230 | 20m brown blk & ol | .80 | .80 |
| N112 | A231 | 30m dp org & ind | 1.60 | 1.60 |

**N113** A231 35m buff, ocher & emer 1.40 1.40
**N114** A231 40m ultra & emer 1.75 1.75
**N115** A231 60m grnsh bl & brn org 2.50 2.50

**Wmk. 342**

**N116** A232 100m bluish blk & yel brn 3.50 3.50
*Nos. N104-N116 (13)* 14.45 14.45

### Arab League Council Type

**1964, Jan. 13 Photo.**
**N117** A234 10m olive & black .35 .35

### Minaret Type

**1964 Unwmk. *Perf. 11***
**N118** A235 4m ol, red brn & red .35 .35

### Arab Postal Union Type

**1964, Apr. 1 Wmk. 342 *Perf. 11***
**N119** A239 10m emer & ultra, *lt grn* .35 .35

### WHO Type

**1964, Apr. 7**
**N120** A240 10m violet blk & red .35 .35

### Minaret Type

**1965, Jan. 20 Unwmk. *Perf. 11***
**N121** A255 4m green & dk brn .35 .35

### Arab League Type

**1965, Mar. 22 Wmk. 342 *Perf. 11***
**N122** A258 10m green, red & blk .35 .35
**N123** A258 20m green & brown .35 .35

### World Health Day Type

**1965, Apr. 7 Wmk. 342 *Perf. 11***
**N124** A259 10m brt green & crim .35 .35

### Massacre Type

**1965, Apr. 9 Photo.**
**N125** A260 10m slate blue & red .60 .60

### ITU Type

**1965, May 17 Wmk. 342 *Perf. 11***
**N126** A261 5m sl grn, sl bl & yel .40 .40
**N127** A261 10m car, rose red & gray .50 .50
**N128** A261 35m vio bl, ultra & yel 1.40 .95
*Nos. N126-N128 (3)* 2.30 1.85

### United Nations Type

5m, WHO Headquarters Building, Geneva. 10m, UN Refugee emblem. 35m, UNICEF emblem.

**1966, Oct. 24 Wmk. 342 *Perf. 11***
**N129** A288 5m rose & brt pur .35 .35
**N130** A288 10m yel brn & brt pur .40 .40
**N131** A288 35m brt green & brt pur .80 .80
*Nos. N129-N131 (3)* 1.55 1.55

### Victory Day Type

**Wmk. 342**

**1966, Dec. 23 Photo. *Perf. 11½***
**N132** A290 10m olive & car rose .40 .40

### Arab Publicity Week Type

***Perf. 11x11½***

**1967, Mar. 22 Photo. Wmk. 342**
**N133** A294 10m vio blue & brn .35 .35

### Labor Day Type

***Perf. 11½x11***

**1967, May 1 Photo. Wmk. 342**
**N134** A296 10m olive & sepia .35 .35

---

## OCCUPATION AIR POST STAMPS

**Catalogue values for unused stamps in this section are for Never Hinged items.**

### Nos. C39-C50 Overprinted Type "b" in Black, Carmine or Red

***Perf. 13x13½***

**1948, May 15 Wmk. 195**
**NC1** AP3 2m red org (Bk) .75 .75
**NC2** AP3 3m dk brn (C) .75 .75
**NC3** AP3 5m red brn (Bk) .75 .75
**NC4** AP3 7m dp yel org (Bk) 1.05 1.05
**NC5** AP3 8m green (C) 1.05 1.05
**NC6** AP3 10m violet 1.20 1.20
**NC7** AP3 20m brt bl 1.90 1.90
**NC8** AP3 30m brn vio (Bk) 4.50 4.50
**NC9** AP3 40m car rose (Bk) 3.00 3.00
**NC10** AP3 50m Prus grn 4.00 4.00
**NC11** AP3 100m olive grn 6.75 6.75
**NC12** AP3 200m dark gray 34.00 34.00
*Nos. NC1-NC12 (12)* 59.70 59.70

### Nos. NC1-NC12 Overprinted in Black with Three Bars to Obliterate Portrait

**1953**
**NC13** AP3 2m red org 1.90 1.90
**NC14** AP3 3m dk brn 1.20 1.20
**NC15** AP3 5m red brn 20.00 20.00
**NC16** AP3 7m dp yel org 1.25 1.25
**NC17** AP3 8m green 3.75 3.75
**NC18** AP3 10m violet 3.75 3.75
**NC19** AP3 20m brt bl 3.75 3.75
**NC20** AP3 30m brn vio 3.75 3.75
**NC21** AP3 40m car rose 6.75 6.75
**NC22** AP3 50m Prus grn 28.00 28.00
**NC23** AP3 100m olive grn 115.00 115.00
**NC24** AP3 200m dk gray 15.00 15.00
*Nos. NC13-NC24 (12)* 204.10 204.10

### Nos. NC1-NC3, NC6, NC10, NC11 with Additional Overprint in Various Colors

**1953**
**NC25** AP3 2m red org (Bk + Bl) 1.00 1.00
**NC26** AP3 3m dk brn (Bk + RV) 19.00 19.00
**NC27** AP3 5m red brn (Bk) 2.75 2.75
**NC28** AP3 10m vio (R + G) 28.00 28.00
**NC29** AP3 50m Prus grn (R + RV) 8.75 8.75
**NC30** AP3 100m ol grn (R + Bk) 62.50 62.50
*Nos. NC25-NC30 (6)* 122.00 122.00

### Nos. C65-C66 Overprinted Type "b" in Black or Red

**1955 Wmk. 195 *Perf. 13x13½***
**NC31** AP4 5m red brn 7.00 5.75
**NC32** AP4 15m ol grn (R) 10.00 8.25

### United Arab Republic

OAP1

Designs: 80m, Al Azhar University. 115m, Temple of Queen Nefertari, Abu Simbel. 140m, Ramses II, Abu Simbel.

***Perf. 11½x11***

**1963, Oct. 24 Photo. Wmk. 342**
**NC33** OAP1 80m blk & brt bl 2.50 2.50
**NC34** OAP1 115m blk & yel 3.50 3.50
**NC35** OAP1 140m bl, ultra & org red 4.00 4.00
*Nos. NC33-NC35 (3)* 10.00 10.00

### Cairo Tower Type, 1964

**1964, Nov. 2 Unwmk. *Perf. 11x11½***
**NC36** AP11 50m dl vio & lt bl 1.25 1.25

### World Meteorological Day Type

**1965, Mar. 23 Wmk. 342 *Perf. 11***
**NC37** AP12 80m dk bl & org 3.00 3.00

### Tutankhamun Type of 1965

**1965, July 1 Photo. *Perf. 11***
**NC38** AP13 10m brn org & brt grn 1.75 1.75

---

## OCCUPATION SPECIAL DELIVERY STAMP

**Catalogue values for unused stamps in this section are for Never Hinged items.**

### No. E4 Overprinted Type "b" in Carmine

**1948 Wmk. 195 *Perf. 13x13½***
**NE1** SD1 40m dl brn & pale gray 12.50 12.50

---

## OCCUPATION POSTAGE DUE STAMPS

**Catalogue values for unused stamps in this section are for Never Hinged items.**

### Postage Due Stamps of Egypt, 1927-41, Overprinted Type "a" in Black or Rose

**1948 Wmk. 195 *Perf. 13x13½***
**NJ1** D7 2m orange 2.25 *2.40*
**NJ2** D7 4m green (R) 1.60 *2.00*
**NJ3** D7 6m gray green 1.60 *2.00*
**NJ4** D7 8m brown violet 1.60 *2.00*
**NJ5** D7 10m brick red 1.60 *2.00*
**NJ6** D7 12m rose lake 1.60 *2.00*

### Overprinted Type "b" in Red

***Perf. 14***

**Size: 22x28mm**

**NJ7** D7 30m purple 5.00 *9.00*
*Nos. NJ1-NJ7 (7)* 15.25 *21.40*

---

# ELOBEY, ANNOBON & CORISCO

ˌel-ə-ˈbā, ˌan-ə-ˈbän and kə-ˈris-ˌkō

LOCATION — A group of islands near the Guinea Coast of western Africa.
GOVT. — Spanish colonial possessions administered as part of the Continental Guinea District. A second district under the same governor-general included Fernando Po.
AREA — 13¾ sq. mi.
POP. — 2,950 (estimated 1910)
CAPITAL — Santa Isabel

100 Centimos = 1 Peseta

King Alfonso XIII — A1

**1903 Unwmk. Typo. *Perf. 14***
**Control Numbers on Back**

**1** A1 ¼c carmine .75 .55
**2** A1 ½c dk violet .75 .55
**3** A1 1c black .75 .55
**4** A1 2c red .75 .55
**5** A1 3c dk green .75 .55
**6** A1 4c dk blue grn .75 .55
**7** A1 5c violet .75 .55
**8** A1 10c rose lake 1.50 1.60
**9** A1 15c orange buff 4.50 1.75
**10** A1 25c dark blue 7.75 6.00
**11** A1 50c red brown 9.00 10.50
**12** A1 75c black brn 9.00 *14.50*
**13** A1 1p orange red 15.00 *20.00*
**14** A1 2p chocolate 40.00 *60.00*
**15** A1 3p dp olive grn 60.00 *75.00*
**16** A1 4p claret 140.00 100.00
**17** A1 5p blue green 165.00 110.00
**18** A1 10p dull blue 300.00 165.00
*Nos. 1-18 (18)* 757.00 568.20
Set, never hinged 1,500.

### Dated "1905"

**1905 Control Numbers on Back**
**19** A1 1c carmine 1.25 .70
**20** A1 2c dp violet 5.00 .70
**21** A1 3c black 1.25 .70
**22** A1 4c dull red 1.25 .70
**23** A1 5c dp green 1.25 .70
**24** A1 10c blue grn 4.50 .90
**25** A1 15c violet 5.00 4.75
**26** A1 25c rose lake 5.00 4.75
**27** A1 50c orange buff 9.00 7.25
**28** A1 75c dark blue 9.00 7.25
**29** A1 1p red brown 18.50 16.00
**30** A1 2p black brn 20.00 22.50
**31** A1 3p orange red 20.00 23.00
**32** A1 4p dk brown 150.00 72.50
**33** A1 5p bronze grn 160.00 80.00
**34** A1 10p claret 350.00 225.00
*Nos. 19-34 (16)* 761.00 467.40
Set, never hinged 1,500.

Nos. 19-22 Surcharged in Black or Red

**1906**
**35** A1 10c on 1c rose (Bk) 11.50 6.50
*a.* Inverted surcharge 11.50 6.50
*b.* Value omitted 30.00 16.00
*c.* Frame omitted 16.00 7.50
*d.* Double surcharge 11.50 6.50
*e.* Surcharged "15 cents" 30.00 16.00
*f.* Surcharged "25 cents" 52.50 22.50
*g.* Surcharged "50 cents" 37.50 22.50
*h.* "1906" omitted 17.50 7.50
**36** A1 15c on 2c dp vio (R) 11.50 6.50
*a.* Frame omitted 12.50 6.50
*b.* Surcharged "25 cents" 16.00 9.00
*c.* Inverted surcharge 11.50 6.50
*d.* Double surcharge 11.50 6.50
**37** A1 25c on 3c blk (R) 11.50 6.50
*a.* Inverted surcharge 11.50 6.50
*b.* Double surcharge 11.50 6.50
*c.* Surcharged "15 cents" 16.00 6.50
*d.* Surcharged "50 cents" 25.00 11.00
**38** A1 50c on 4c red (Bk) 11.50 6.50
*a.* Inverted surcharge 11.50 6.50
*b.* Value omitted 35.00 17.50
*c.* Frame omitted 17.50 8.00
*e.* Double surcharge 11.50 6.50
*f.* "1906" omitted 17.50 8.00
*g.* Surcharged "10 cents" 32.50 16.00
*h.* Surcharged "25 cents" 32.50 16.00
*Nos. 35-38 (4)* 46.00 26.00

Eight other surcharges were prepared but not issued: 10c on 50c, 75c, 1p, 2p and 3p; 15c on 50c and 5p; 50c on 5c.

Exist with surcharges in different colors; #35 in blue, red or violet, #36 in black or violet, #37 in black or violet, #38 in blue, violet or red. Value, set of 10, $135.

King Alfonso XIII — A2

**1907 Control Numbers on Back**
**39** A2 1c dk violet .55 .45
**40** A2 2c black .55 .45
**41** A2 3c red orange .55 .45
**42** A2 4c dk green .55 .45
**43** A2 5c blue green .55 .45
**44** A2 10c violet 6.00 5.50
**45** A2 15c carmine 1.75 1.75
**46** A2 25c orange 1.75 1.75
**47** A2 50c blue 1.75 1.75
**48** A2 75c brown 6.50 2.75
**49** A2 1p black brn 10.00 4.75
**50** A2 2p orange red 13.50 8.00
**51** A2 3p dk brown 13.00 9.00
**52** A2 4p bronze grn 20.00 8.50
**53** A2 5p claret 25.00 10.00
**54** A2 10p rose 50.00 27.50
*Nos. 39-54 (16)* 152.00 83.50
Set, never hinged 350.00

Stamps of 1907 Surcharged

**1908-09 Black Surcharge**
**55** A2 5c on 3c red org ('09) 2.25 1.25
**56** A2 5c on 4c dk grn ('09) 2.25 1.25
**57** A2 5c on 10c violet 4.50 5.00
**58** A2 25c on 10c violet 30.00 15.00
*Nos. 55-58 (4)* 39.00 22.50

**1910 Red Surcharge**
**59** A2 5c on 1c dark violet 1.75 .90
**60** A2 5c on 2c black 1.75 .90

Nos. 55-60 exist with surcharge inverted (value set, $125 unused or used); with double surcharge, one black, one red (value set, $300 unused or used); with "PARA" omitted (value set, $150.00 unused or used)

The same 5c surcharge was also applied to Nos. 45-54, but these were not issued (value set, $250).

In 1909, stamps of Spanish Guinea replaced those of Elobey, Annobon and Corisco.

Revenue stamps surcharged as above were unauthorized although some were postally used.

For postally valid examples similar to the item shown above see Rio de Oro Nos. 44-45 and Spanish Guinea Nos. 98-101C.

For revenue stamps with the arms at the left surcharged for postal use see Spanish Guinea Nos. 8A-8J.

# EPIRUS

i-'pī-rəs

LOCATION — A region of southeastern Europe, now divided between Greece and Albania.

During the First Balkan War (1912-13), this territory was occupied by the Greek army, and the local Greek majority wished to be united with Greece. Italy and Austria-Hungary favored its inclusion in the newly created Albania, however, which both powers expected to dominate. Greek forces were withdrawn subsequently in early 1914. The local population resisted inclusion in Albania and established the Autonomous Republic of Northern Epirus on Feb. 28, 1914. Resistance to Albanian control continued until October, when Greece reoccupied the country. Northern Epirus was administered as an integral part of Greece, and it was expected that Greece's annexation of the territory would become official following World War I. Instead, in 1916, Italian pressure and its own military reverses in Anatolia caused Greece to withdraw from Epirus and to formally cede the territory to Albania.

100 Lepta = 1 Drachma

### Chimarra Issue

Double-headed Eagle, Skull and Crossbones — A1

**Handstamped**

**1914, Feb. 10 Unwmk. *Imperf.***

**Control Mark in Blue**

**Without Gum**

| | | | | |
|---|---|---|---|---|
| **1** | A1 | 1 l black & blue | *475.00* | 250.00 |
| *a.* | | Tête-bêche pair | | 3,000. |
| **2** | A1 | 5 l blue & red | *475.00* | 250.00 |
| *a.* | | Horiz. pair, #4A, 4B | | 35.00 |
| **3** | A1 | 10 l red & blk | *475.00* | 250.00 |
| **4** | A1 | 25 l blue & red | *475.00* | 250.00 |
| | | *Nos. 1-4 (4)* | *1,900.* | 1,000. |

All values exist without control mark. This mark is a solid blue oval, about 12x8mm, containing the colorless Greek letters "SP," the first two letters of Spiromilios, the Chimarra commander.

All four exist with denomination inverted and the 1 l, 5 l and 10 l with denomination double.

The values above are for the first printing on somewhat transparent shiny, white, thin, wove paper, which is sometimes known as "rice paper."

A second printing was made from original handstamps, on similar thin wove paper, but not transluscent, known as "Spetsiotis Reprints." Value, unused or canceled to order, each $55. Later printings were made from original handstamps on other papers, generally thicker and whiter, sometimes surfaced. Value, unused or canceled to order, each $45.

Values above are for genuine stamps expertized by knowledgeable authorities. Most of the stamps offered as Nos. 1-4 in the marketplace are forgeries. Most resemble the stamps from the second reprinting, but the designs differ in details of the lettering, monogram and skull. Such forgeries have only nominal commercial value.

Some experts question the official character of this issue.

### Argyrokastro Issues

Stamps of Turkey surcharged "AUTONOMOUS EPIRUS" and new denominations in several formats in Greek currency.

### On Turkish stamps of 1908

No. 4A

No. 4B

**1914, Mar. 2**

| | | | | |
|---|---|---|---|---|
| **4A** | A19 | 1d on 2½pi (#137) | 11.00 | 12.50 |
| **4B** | A19 | 2d on 2½pi (#137) | 11.00 | 12.50 |

No. 4C

No. 4D

| | | | | |
|---|---|---|---|---|
| **4C** | A19 | 5d on 25pi (#140) | 80.00 | 92.50 |
| **4D** | A19 | 5d on 50pi (#141) | 127.50 | 140.00 |

### On Turkish stamps of 1909-10

| | | | | |
|---|---|---|---|---|
| **4E** | A21 | 5 l on 5pa (#151) | 80.00 | — |

No. 4F

No. 4G

| | | | | |
|---|---|---|---|---|
| **4F** | A21 | 5 l on 10pa (#152) | 3.50 | *4.00* |
| **4G** | A21 | 10 l (oval "O") on 20pa (#153) | 2.50 | *2.75* |
| *a.* | | Double surcharge | 80.00 | |

No. 4H

No. 4I

| | | | | |
|---|---|---|---|---|
| **4H** | A21 | 10 l (round "O") on 20pa (#153) | 2.50 | *2.75* |
| *a.* | | Double surcharge | 80.00 | |
| **4I** | A21 | 20 l on 1pi (#154) | 2.50 | *2.75* |
| *a.* | | Double surcharge | 80.00 | |

No. 4J

No. 4K

| | | | | |
|---|---|---|---|---|
| **4J** | A21 | 25 l on 1pi (#154) | 2.50 | *2.75* |
| *a.* | | Double surcharge | 80.00 | |
| **4K** | A21 | 40 l on 2pi (#155) | 3.50 | *3.75* |

No. 4L

No. 4M

| | | | | |
|---|---|---|---|---|
| **4L** | A21 | 80 l on 2pi (#155) | 3.50 | *3.75* |
| **4M** | A21 | 1d on 5pi (#157) | 13.00 | *14.00* |

No. 4N

No. 4O

| | | | | |
|---|---|---|---|---|
| **4N** | A21 | 2d on 5pi (#157) | 13.00 | 14.00 |
| **4O** | A21 | 5d on 10pi (#158) | 80.00 | *92.50* |
| *a.* | | Double surcharge | | |
| **4P** | A21 | 5d on 10pa (#152) | 135.00 | *170.00* |
| **4Q** | A21 | 5d on 20pa (#153) | 135.00 | *170.00* |
| **4R** | A21 | 5d on 1pi (#154) | 135.00 | *170.00* |
| **4RR** | A21 | 5d on 2½pi (#156) | 135.00 | *170.00* |
| **4S** | A21 | 5d on 50pi (#160) | 135.00 | *170.00* |

### On Turkish stamps of 1909-11 (with "Béhié")

| | | | | |
|---|---|---|---|---|
| **4T** | A21 | 5 l on 10pa (#161) | 80.00 | |
| **4U** | A21 | 10 l (oval "O") on 20pa (#162) | 80.00 | |
| **4V** | A21 | 10 l (round "O") on 20pa (#162) | 80.00 | |
| **4W** | A21 | 20 l on 1pi (#163) | 80.00 | |
| **4X** | A21 | 25 l on 1pi (#163) | 80.00 | |
| **4Y** | A21 | 40 l on 2pi (#164) | 80.00 | |
| **4Z** | A21 | 80 l on 2pi (#164) | 80.00 | |
| **4AA** | A21 | 5d on 10pa (#161) | 135.00 | |
| **4BB** | A21 | 5d on 20pa (#162) | 135.00 | |
| **4CC** | A21 | 5d on 1pi (#163) | 135.00 | |
| **4CA** | A21 | 5d on 2pi (#164) | 135.00 | |

### On Turkish Printed Matter stamps of 1910-11

No. 4DD

No. 4EE

| | | | | |
|---|---|---|---|---|
| **4DD** | A21 | 30 l on 2pa on 5pa (#P67) | 87.50 | |
| **4EE** | A21 | 50 l on 2pa on 5pa (#P67) | 87.50 | |

No. 4FF

| | | | | |
|---|---|---|---|---|
| **4FF** | A21 | 30 l on 2pa (#P68) | 2.50 | *2.75* |
| **4GG** | A21 | 50 l on 2pa (#P68) | 2.50 | *2.75* |

### Provisional Government Issues

Infantryman with Rifle
A2 A3

***Serrate Roulette 13½***

**1914, Mar. Litho.**

| | | | | |
|---|---|---|---|---|
| **5** | A2 | 1 l orange | .50 | 1.00 |
| *a.* | | Imperf., pair | 60.00 | |
| **6** | A2 | 5 l green | .50 | 1.00 |
| *a.* | | Imperf., pair | 60.00 | |
| **7** | A3 | 10 l carmine | .50 | 1.00 |
| **8** | A3 | 25 l deep blue | .50 | 1.00 |
| **9** | A2 | 50 l brown | 1.50 | 1.50 |
| **10** | A2 | 1d violet | 2.25 | 2.50 |
| **11** | A2 | 2d blue | 14.00 | 14.00 |
| **12** | A2 | 5d gray green | 18.00 | 19.00 |
| | | *Nos. 5-12 (8)* | 37.75 | 41.00 |

Issue dates: 10 l, 25 l, Mar. 5; balance of set, Mar. 26.

Flag of Epirus — A5

**1914, Aug. 28**

| | | | | |
|---|---|---|---|---|
| **15** | A5 | 1 l brown & blue | .35 | *.40* |
| **16** | A5 | 5 l green & blue | .35 | *.40* |
| **17** | A5 | 10 l rose red & blue | .40 | *.65* |
| **18** | A5 | 25 l dk blue & blue | 1.00 | 1.10 |
| **19** | A5 | 50 l violet & blue | 1.00 | 1.10 |
| **20** | A5 | 1d carmine & blue | 5.75 | *6.50* |
| **21** | A5 | 2d orange & blue | 1.50 | *2.25* |
| *a.* | | Double impression, one inverted | *1,000.* | |
| **22** | A5 | 5d dk green & blue | 9.50 | 11.00 |
| *a.* | | Double impression | | 1,000. |
| | | *Nos. 15-22 (8)* | 19.85 | *23.40* |

Nos. 16 and 21 exist with the blue color inverted.

### Koritsa Issue

A7

**1914, Sept. 25**

| | | | | |
|---|---|---|---|---|
| **26** | A7 | 25 l dk blue & blue | 6.00 | 5.25 |
| **27** | A7 | 50 l violet & blue | 12.00 | *13.50* |

Nos. 26 and 27 were issued at Koritsa (Korce) to commemorate that city's occupation by Epirot forces.

### Chimarra Issues

King Constantine I — A8

**1914, Oct.**

| | | | | |
|---|---|---|---|---|
| **28** | A8 | 1 l yellow green | 135.00 | 77.50 |
| **29** | A8 | 2 l red | 120.00 | 42.50 |
| **30** | A8 | 5 l dark blue | 120.00 | 77.50 |
| **31** | A8 | 10 l orange brown | 80.00 | 30.00 |
| **32** | A8 | 20 l carmine | 87.50 | 62.50 |
| **33** | A8 | 25 l gray blue | 115.00 | 77.50 |
| **33A** | A8 | 50 l yellow green | 170.00 | 90.00 |
| **33B** | A8 | 1d carmine | 170.00 | 90.00 |
| **33C** | A8 | 2d pale yellow green | 255.00 | 125.00 |
| **33D** | A8 | 5d orange brown | 425.00 | 290.00 |
| | | *Nos. 28-33D (10)* | 1,678. | 962.50 |

Nos. 28-33D were printed by Papachrysanthou, Athens. The papermaker's watermark "PARCHIMINE JOHANNOT" appears on some stamps in the set.

1911-23 Issues of Greece Overprinted

**1914, Aug. 24 *Perf. Perf. 11 ½***

| | | | | |
|---|---|---|---|---|
| **34** | A24 | 1 l green | 55.00 | 62.50 |
| **35** | A25 | 2 l carmine | 45.00 | 52.50 |
| **36** | A24 | 3 l vermilion | 45.00 | 52.50 |
| **37** | A26 | 5 l green | 45.00 | 52.50 |
| **38** | A24 | 10 l carmine | 60.00 | 65.00 |
| **39** | A25 | 20 l slate | 80.00 | 87.50 |
| **40** | A25 | 25 l blue | 175.00 | 185.00 |
| **41** | A26 | 50 l violet brn | 220.00 | 225.00 |
| | | *Nos. 34-41 (8)* | 725.00 | 782.50 |

The 2 l and 3 l are engraved stamps of the 1911-21 issue; the others are lithographed stamps of the 1912-23 issue.

Overprint reads: "Greek Chimarra 1914."

Stamps of this issue are with or without a black monogram (S.S., for S. Spiromilios) in manuscript. Counterfeits are plentiful.

### Moschopolis Issue

Arms
A9

Ancient Epirot Coins/Medals
A10

| 1914, Sept. | | Engr. | Perf. 14 ½ | |
|---|---|---|---|---|
| 42 | A9 | 1 l yellow brown | .75 | *3.50* |
| 43 | A9 | 2 l black | .75 | *3.50* |
| 44 | A9 | 3 l yellow | .75 | *3.50* |
| 45 | A9 | 5 l green | .75 | *3.50* |
| 46 | A9 | 10 l red | .75 | *3.50* |
| 47 | A9 | 25 l deep blue | .75 | *3.50* |
| 48 | A9 | 30 l violet | .75 | *3.50* |
| 49 | A9 | 40 l olive gray | .75 | *3.50* |
| 50 | A9 | 50 l violet black | .75 | *3.50* |
| 51 | A10 | 1d yellow brown & olive | 5.00 | *11.50* |
| 52 | A10 | 2d carmine & gray | 5.00 | *11.50* |
| 53 | A10 | 3d gray green & red brown | 5.00 | *11.50* |
| 54 | A10 | 5d olive & yellow brown | 5.00 | *11.50* |
| 55 | A10 | 10d orange & blue | 5.00 | *14.50* |
| 56 | A10 | 25d violet & black | 5.00 | *20.00* |
| | | *Nos. 42-56 (15)* | 36.75 | *112.00* |

Nos. 42-56 were privately printed in early 1914. In June 1914, the Epirots occupied Moschopolis (Voskopoj), and these stamps were authorized for use by the local military commander in Sept. After the occupation of Moschopolis by Greek forces in Nov., remaining stocks of this issue were sent to Athens, where they were destroyed in 1931.

All values exist imperf., and all but the 5 l and 10 l stamps exist in different colors. For details, see the *Scott Classic Specialized Catalogue of Stamps and Covers.*

The 1d exists with center omitted. Value $100. The 1d, 2d, 10d and 25d exist with center inverted. Values, each $65.

Stamps of the following designs were locals, privately produced. Issued primarily for propaganda and for philatelic purposes, their postal use is in dispute. The 1917 and 1920 designs are fantasy items, created long after Epirus was annexed by Albania.

From 1914: 1st design, 3 varieties. 2nd design, 6 varieties. 3rd design, 7 varieties.

From 1917: 4th design, 8 varieties, + 1 surcharged; perforated and imperforate.

From 1920: 5th design, 4 varieties.

## OCCUPATION STAMPS

### Issued under Greek Occupation

Greek Occupation Stamps of 1913 Overprinted Horizontally

***Serrate Roulette 13½***

| 1914-15 | | Black Overprint | Unwmk. | |
|---|---|---|---|---|
| N1 | O1 | 1 l brown | .90 | .90 |
| *b.* | | Inverted overprint | 25.00 | 25.00 |
| *c.* | | Double overprint | 25.00 | 25.00 |
| *d.* | | Double overprint, one inverted | 25.00 | 25.00 |
| N2 | O2 | 2 l red | .90 | .90 |
| *b.* | | 2 l rose | 1.35 | 1.35 |
| *c.* | | As #N2, inverted overprint | 25.00 | 25.00 |
| *d.* | | As "b", inverted overprint | 32.50 | 32.50 |
| *e.* | | As #N2, double overprint | 26.00 | *32.50* |
| *f.* | | As "b", double overprint | 32.50 | 32.50 |
| *g.* | | As #N2, double overprint, one inverted | 25.00 | 25.00 |
| N4 | O2 | 3 l orange | .90 | .90 |
| *b.* | | Inverted overprint | 20.00 | 17.50 |
| *c.* | | Double overprint | 20.00 | 17.50 |
| *d.* | | Double overprint, one inverted | 26.00 | 26.00 |
| N5 | O1 | 5 l green | 2.50 | 2.50 |
| *b.* | | Inverted overprint | 37.50 | 37.50 |
| N6 | O1 | 10 l rose red | 3.00 | 3.00 |
| *a.* | | Inverted overprint | 52.50 | 52.50 |
| *b.* | | Double overprint | 52.50 | 52.50 |
| N7 | O1 | 20 l violet | 7.00 | 7.00 |
| *a.* | | Inverted overprint | 52.50 | 52.50 |
| *b.* | | Double overprint | 67.50 | 67.50 |
| N8 | O2 | 25 l pale blue | 3.00 | 3.25 |
| N9 | O1 | 30 l gray green | 14.50 | 15.00 |
| N10 | O2 | 40 l indigo | 19.50 | 21.00 |
| N11 | O1 | 50 l dark blue | 22.00 | 24.00 |
| N12 | O2 | 1d violet brown | 140.00 | 150.00 |
| *a.* | | Inverted overprint | 325.00 | *225.00* |
| *b.* | | Double overprint | 400.00 | *300.00* |
| | | *Nos. N1-N12 (11)* | 214.20 | 228.45 |

**Red Overprint**

| | | | |
|---|---|---|---|
| *N1a* | O1 | 1 l brown | 5.75 |
| *N2a* | O2 | 2 l red | 5.75 |
| *N4a* | O2 | 3 l orange | 5.75 |
| *N5a* | O1 | 5 l green | 5.75 |

Nos. N1a-N5a were not issued. Exist canceled.

Regular Issues of Greece, 1911-23, Ovptd. Reading Up

**On Issue of 1911-21**

| 1916 | | | Engr. | |
|---|---|---|---|---|
| N17 | A24 | 3 l vermilion | 11.50 | 11.50 |
| *a.* | | Overprint reading down | 15.00 | |
| N18 | A26 | 30 l carmine rose | 52.50 | 40.00 |
| *a.* | | Overprint reading down | 225.00 | |
| N19 | A27 | 1d ultra | 85.00 | 85.00 |
| N20 | A27 | 2d vermilion | 95.00 | 95.00 |
| N21 | A27 | 3d carmine rose | 130.00 | 130.00 |
| N22 | A27 | 5d ultra | — | — |
| *a.* | | Double overprint | 1,950. | 1,950. |
| *b.* | | Overprint reading down | 725.00 | |
| | | *Nos. N17-N22 (6)* | 374.00 | 361.50 |

**On Issue of 1912-23**

| 1916 | | | Litho. | |
|---|---|---|---|---|
| N23 | A24 | 1 l green | 2.75 | 2.75 |
| *a.* | | Overprint reading down | 9.50 | |
| N24 | A25 | 2 l carmine | 2.75 | 2.75 |
| *a.* | | Overprint reading down | 9.50 | |
| N25 | A24 | 3 l vermilion | 2.75 | 2.75 |
| *a.* | | Overprint reading down | 14.00 | |
| N26 | A26 | 5 l green | 2.75 | 2.75 |
| *a.* | | Overprint reading down | 14.00 | |
| N27 | A24 | 10 l carmine | 2.75 | 2.75 |
| *a.* | | Overprint reading down | 27.50 | |
| N28 | A25 | 20 l slate | 2.75 | 2.75 |
| N29 | A25 | 25 l blue | 3.75 | 3.75 |
| N30 | A26 | 30 l rose | 22.00 | 22.00 |
| *a.* | | Overprint reading down | 250.00 | |
| N31 | A25 | 40 l indigo | 16.50 | 16.50 |
| *a.* | | Overprint reading down | 475.00 | |
| N32 | A26 | 50 l violet brown | 26.50 | 26.50 |
| | | *Nos. N23-N32 (10)* | 85.25 | 85.25 |

In each sheet, there are two varieties in the overprint. For listings, see the *Scott Classic Catalogue.*

Counterfeits exist of Nos. N1-N32.

Postage stamps issued in 1940-41, during Greek occupation, are listed under Greece.

# EQUATORIAL GUINEA

ˌē-kwə-ˈtō-ē-əl ˈgi-nē

LOCATION — Gulf of Guinea, West Africa
GOVT. — Republic
AREA — 10,832 sq. mi.
POP. — 465,746 (1999 est.)
CAPITAL — Malabo

The Spanish provinces Fernando Po and Rio Muni united and became independent as the Republic of Equatorial Guinea, Oct. 12, 1968.

100 Centimos = 1 Peseta
100 centimos = 1 ekuele, bipkwele is plural (1973)
100 centimes = 1 CFA franc (1985)

**Catalogue values for all unused stamps in this country are for Never Hinged items.**

Clasped Hands and Laurel — A1

**Unwmk.**

| 1968, Oct. 12 | | Photo. | Perf. 13 | |
|---|---|---|---|---|
| 1 | A1 | 1p dp bl, gold & sep | .30 | .30 |
| 2 | A1 | 1.50p dk grn, gold & brn | .30 | .30 |
| 3 | A1 | 6p cop red, gold & brn | .30 | .30 |
| | | *Nos. 1-3 (3)* | .90 | .90 |

Attainment of independence, Oct. 12, 1968.

Pres. Francisco Macias Nguema — A2

| 1970, Jan. 27 | | | Perf. 13x12½ | |
|---|---|---|---|---|
| 4 | A2 | 50c dl org, brn & crim | .25 | .25 |
| 5 | A2 | 1p pink, grn & lil | .25 | .25 |
| 6 | A2 | 1.50p pale ol, brn & bl grn | .25 | .25 |
| 7 | A2 | 2p buff, grn & ol | .25 | .25 |
| 8 | A2 | 2.50p pale grn, dk grn & dk bl | .30 | .25 |
| 9 | A2 | 10p bis, Prus bl & vio brn | 1.00 | .25 |
| 10 | A2 | 25p gray, blk & brn | 2.10 | .25 |
| | | *Nos. 4-10 (7)* | 4.40 | 1.75 |

Pres. Macias Nguema and Cock — A3

| 1971, Apr. | | Photo. | Perf. 13 | |
|---|---|---|---|---|
| 11 | A3 | 3p lt bl & multi | .25 | .25 |
| 12 | A3 | 5p buff & multi | .30 | .25 |
| 13 | A3 | 10p pale lilac & multi | .75 | .25 |
| 14 | A3 | 25p pale grn & multi | 1.50 | .35 |
| | | *Nos. 11-14 (4)* | 2.80 | 1.10 |

2nd anniv. of independence, Oct. 12, 1970.

Torch, Bow and Arrows — A4

| 1972 | | Photo. | Perf. 11½ | |
|---|---|---|---|---|
| 15 | A4 | 50p ocher & multi | 1.50 | .50 |

"3rd Triumphal Year."

**Upon achieving independence from Spain in 1968, Francisco Macias Nguema was elected the first president of Equatorial Guinea. By May 1971, Nguema controlled a government that essentially performed no functions except internal security. From 1972 to 1979, the country's main post office was padlocked and completely inoperative. Nonetheless, European agents continued to produce postage stamps for Equatorial Guinea that were promoted by so-called press releases from Madrid, Spain.**

**With the exception of Nos. 16-25, the editors question whether any of the stamps described below could have reached Equatorial Guinea or been placed on sale in that country. As such, they do not meet the criteria for listing in the Scott catalogue. See the Catalogue Listing Policy section in the catalogue introduction for additional details.**

Apollo 15, set of seven, 1p, 3p, 5p, 8p, 10p, airmail 15p, 25p, plus two airmail semi-postal gold foil perf. 200p+25p, imperf. 250p+50p, and two souv. sheets, perf. 25p+200p, imperf. 50p+250p, issued Jan. 28. Nos. 7201-7211.

1972 Winter Olympics, Sapporo, set of seven, 1p, 2p, 3p, 5p, 8p, airmail 15p, 50p, plus two airmail semi-postal gold foil perf., imperf., 200p+25p, 250p+50p, and two souv. sheets, perf. 200p+25p, imperf. 250p+50p, issued Feb. 3, 1972. Nos. 7212-7222.

Christmas, paintings, set of seven, 1p, 3p, 5p, 8p, 10p, airmail 15p, 25p, plus two airmail semi-postal gold foil perf. 200p+25p, imperf. 250p+50p, and two souv. sheets, perf. 25p+200p, imperf. 50p+250p (Virgin and Child by da Vinci, Murillo, Raphael, Mabuse, van der Weyden, Durer), issued Feb. 20. Nos. 7223-7233.

Easter, set of seven, 1p, 3p, 5p, 8p, 10p, airmail 15p, 25p, plus two airmail semi-postal gold foil perf., imperf., 200p+25p, 250p+50p (designs by Velazquez and El Greco), two souv. sheets, perf. (25p, 200p), and imperf. 250p+50p, issued Apr. 28. Nos. 7234-7244.

1972 Summer Olympics, Munich, set of seven, 1p, 2p, 3p, 5p, 8p, airmail 15p, 50p, plus two airmail semi-postal souv. sheets, perf. 200p+25p, imperf. 250p+50p, and presentation folder with two gold foil, perf. 200p+25p, imperf. 250p+50p, issued May 5, 1972. Nos. 7245-7255.

Gold Medal Winners, Sapporo, set of seven, 1p, 2p, 3p, 5p, 8p, airmail 15p, 50p, plus 12 airmail semi-postal gold foil perf. 200p+25p (6), imperf. 250p+50p (6), imperf. souv. sheet 250p+50p, and perf. souv. sheet of two (25p, 200p), issued May 25. Nos. 7256-7276.

Black Gold Medal Winners, Munich, set of seven, 1p, 2p, 3p, 5p, 8p, airmail 15p, 50p, plus 18 gold foil airmail semi-postal perf. 200p+25p (9), imperf. 250p+50p (9), and two souv. sheets, perf. 200p+25p, imperf. 250p+50p, issued June 26. Nos. 7277-72103.

Olympic Games, Regatta in Kiel and Oberschleissheim, set of seven, 1p, 2p, 3p, 5p, 8p, airmail 15p, 50p, plus four airmail semi-postal gold foil, perf. 200p+25p (2), imperf. 250p+50p (2), and two souv. sheets, perf. 200p+25p, imperf. 250p+50p, issued July 25. Nos. 72104-72116.

1972 Summer Olympics, Munich, set of seven, 1p, 2p, 3p, 5p, 8p, airmail 15p, 50p, plus two airmail semi-postal souv. sheets, perf. 200p+25p, imperf, 250p+50p, issued Aug. 10, 1972; and 20 gold foil, perf. 200p+25p (10), imperf. 250+50p (10), issued Aug. 17. Nos. 72117-72145.

Olympic Equestrian Events, set of seven, 1p, 2p, 3p, 5p, 8p, airmail 15p, 50p, plus two airmail semi-postal souv. sheets, perf. 200p+25p, imperf. 250p+50p, two gold foil, perf. 200p+25p, imperf. 250p+50p, four gold foil souv. sheets of two, 200p+25p (2 perf., 2 imperf.), and 16 souv. sheets, perf. 200p+25p (8), imperf. 250p+50p (8), issued Aug. 24. Nos. 72146-72176.

Japanese Railroad Cent. (locomotives), set of seven, 1p, 3p, 5p, 8p, 10p, airmail 15p, 25p, plus 2 airmail semi-postal souv. sheets, perf. 200p+25p, imperf. 250p+50p, 11 gold foil souv. sheets of 1, perf. 200p+25p (9), imperf. 200p+25p (2), and 2 souv. sheets of 2, perf., imperf., 200p+25p, issued Sept. 21. Nos. 72177-72198.

Gold Medal Winners, Munich, set of seven, 1p, 2p, 3p, 5p, 8p, airmail 15p, 50p, plus two airmail semi-postal souv. sheets, perf. 200p+25p, imperf. 250p+50p, and four gold foil souv. sheets, perf. 200p+25p (2), imperf. 250p+50p (2), issued Oct. 30. Nos. 72199-72211.

Christmas and 500th Birth Anniv. of Lucas Cranach, Madonnas and Christmas seals, set of seven, 1p, 3p, 5p, 8p, 10p, airmail 15p, 25p (Giotto, Schongauer, Fouquet, de Morales, Fini, David, Sassetta), plus two airmail semi-postal souv. sheets, perf. 200p+25p, imperf. 250p+50p, 12 gold foil souv. sheets, perf. 200p+25p (6), imperf. 250p+50p (6), two souv. sheets of two, perf., imperf., 200p+25p, and ovptd. 200p+25p stamp, issued Nov. 22. Nos. 72212-72234.

---

American and Russian Astronaut Memorial, set of seven, 1p, 3p, 5p, 8p, 10p, airmail 15p, 25p, plus two airmail semi-postal souv. sheets, perf. 200p+25p, imperf. 250p+50p, and four gold foil ovptd. "Apollo 16 and 17" perf. 200p+25p (2), imperf. 250p+50p (2), issued Dec. 14. Nos. 72235-72247.

---

United Natl. Workers' Party Emblem — A5

| 1973 | | Litho. | *Perf. 13½x13* | |
|---|---|---|---|---|
| **16** | A5 | 1p multi | .25 | .25 |
| **17** | A5 | 1.50p multi | .25 | .25 |
| **18** | A5 | 2p multi | .25 | .25 |
| **19** | A5 | 4p multi | .30 | .25 |
| **20** | A5 | 5p multi | .40 | .25 |
| | | *Nos. 16-20 (5)* | 1.45 | 1.25 |

Natl. Independence, 4th Anniv. — A6

Pres. Macias Nguema and: 1.50p, Agriculture. 2p, 4p, Education. 3p, 5p, Natl. defense.

| 1973 | | | *Perf. 13½* | |
|---|---|---|---|---|
| **21** | A6 | 1.50p multi | .25 | .25 |
| **22** | A6 | 2p multi | .25 | .25 |
| **23** | A6 | 3p multi | .35 | .25 |
| **24** | A6 | 4p multi | .40 | .25 |
| **25** | A6 | 5p multi | .60 | .35 |
| | | *Nos. 21-25 (5)* | 1.85 | 1.35 |

---

**1973**

Transatlantic Yacht Race, set of seven, 1p, 2p, 3p, 5p, 8p, airmail 15p, 50p, and two airmail semi-postal souv. sheets, perf. 200p+25p, imperf. 250p+50p, issued Jan. 22. Nos. 7301-7309.

---

Renoir paintings, set of seven, 1p, 2p, 3p, 5p, 8p, airmail 15p, 50p, plus two airmail semi-postal gold foil, perf. 200p+25p, imperf. 250p+50p, and two souv. sheets, perf. 200p+25p, imperf. 250p+50p, issued Feb. 22. Nos. 7310-7320.

Conquest of Venus (spacecraft), set of seven, 1p, 3p, 5p, 8p, 10p, airmail 5p, 25p, and two airmail semi-postal souv. sheets, perf. 200p+25p, imperf. 250p+50p, issued Mar. 22. Nos. 7321-7329.

Apollo 11-17 Flights, gold foil airmail semi-postal souv. sheets, perf. 200p+25p (7), 250p+50p (7), and four souv. sheets of two, perf. 200p+25p (2), imperf. 250p+50p (2), issued Mar. 22. Nos. 7330-7347.

Easter, paintings, set of seven, 1p, 3p, 5p, 8p, 10p, airmail 15p, 25p (Verrocchio, Perugino, Tintoretto, Witz, Pontormo), plus two airmail semi-postal souv. sheets, perf. 200p+25p, imperf. 250p+50p, and four gold foil issue of 1972 souv. sheets ovptd., perf. 200p+25p (2), imperf. 250p+50p (2), issued Apr. 25. Nos. 7348-7360.

Copernicus, 500th birth anniv. (US and USSR space explorations), four gold foil airmail semi-postal souv. sheets, perf. 200p+25p (2), imperf. 250p+50p (2), issued May 15. Nos. 7361-7364.

Tour de France bicycle race, set of seven, 1p, 2p, 3p, 5p, 8p, airmail 15p, 50p, and two airmail semi-postal souv. sheets, perf. 200p+25p, imperf. 250p+50p, issued May 22. Nos. 7365-7373.

Paintings, set of seven, 1p, 2p, 3p, 5p, 8p, airmail 15p, 50p, and two airmail semi-postal souv. sheets, 200p+25p, imperf. 250p+50p, issued June 29. Nos. 7374-7382.

1974 World Cup Soccer Championships, Munich, set of nine, 5c, 10c, 15c, 20c, 25c, 55c, 60c, airmail 5p, 70p, and two airmail souv. sheets, perf. 130p, imperf. 200p, issued Aug. 30. Nos. 7383-7393.

Rubens paintings, set of seven, 1p, 2p, 3p, 5p, 8p, airmail 15p, 50p, and two airmail semi-postal souv. sheets, perf. (25p, 200p), imperf. (50p, 250p), issued Sept. 23. Nos. 7394-73102.

1974 World Cup Soccer Championships, Munich, four gold foil airmail souv. sheets, perf. 130e (2), imperf. 200e (2), and two souv. sheets of two, perf. 130e, imperf. 200e, issued Oct. 24. Nos. 73103-73108.

Christmas, paintings, set of seven, 1p, 3p, 5p, 8p, 10p, airmail 15p, 25p, and two airmail semi-postal souv. sheets, perf. 200p+25p, imperf. 250p+50p (Nativity, by van der Weyden, Bosco, de Carvajal, Mabuse, Lucas Jordan, P. Goecke, Maino, Fabriano, Lochner), issued Oct. 30. Nos. 73109-73117.

Apollo Program and J.F. Kennedy, two gold foil airmail semi-postals, perf. 200p+25p, imperf. 250p+50p, and two souv. sheets, perf. 200p+25p, imperf. 250p+50p, issued Nov. 10. Nos. 73118-73121.

World Cup Soccer (famous players), set of nine, 30c, 35c, 40c, 45c, 50c, 65c, 70c, airmail 8p, 60p, and two airmail souv. sheets, perf. 130p, imperf. 200p, issued Nov. 20. Nos. 73122-73132.

Princess Anne's Wedding, six gold foil airmail souv. sheets, perf., imperf., two sheets of one, each 250e, one sheet of two 250e, issued Dec. 17. Nos. 73133-73141.

Pablo Picasso Memorial (Blue Period paintings), set of seven, 30c, 35c, 40c, 45c, 50c, airmail 8e, 60e, and two airmail souv. sheets, perf. 130e, imperf. 200e, issued Dec. 20. Nos. 73142-73150.

**1974**

Copernicus, 500th birth anniv., set of seven, 5c, 10c, 15c, 20c, 4e, airmail 10e, 70e, two airmail souv. sheets, perf. 130e, imperf. 200e, issued Feb. 8, 1974; eight gold foil airmail souv. sheets, perf. 130e (3), 250e, imperf. 200e (3), 300e, and four souv. sheets of two, perf. 250e (2), imperf. 250e (2), issued Apr. 10. Nos. 7401-7421.

World Cup Soccer Championships (final games), set of nine, 75c, 80c, 85c, 90c, 95c, 1e, 1.25e, airmail 10e, 50e, and two airmail souv. sheets, perf. 130e, imperf. 200e, issued Feb. 28. Nos. 7422-7432.

Easter, paintings, set of seven, 1p, 3p, 5p, 8p, 10p, airmail 15p, 25p (Fra Angelico, Castagno, Allori, Multscher, della Francesca, Pleydenwurff, Correggio), and two airmail semi-postal souv. sheets, perf. 200p+25p, imperf. 250p+50p, issued Mar. 27. Nos. 7433-7441.

Holy Year 1975 (famous churches), set of seven, 5c, 10c, 15c, 20c, 3.50e, airmail 10e, 70e, and two airmail souv. sheets, perf. 130e, imperf. 200e, issued Apr. 11. Nos. 7442-7450.

World Cup Soccer (contemporary players), set of nine, 1.50, 1.75, 2, 2.25, 2.50, 3, 3.50e, airmail 10, 60e, and 2 airmail souv. sheets of 2, perf. (2x65e), imperf. (2x100e), issued Apr. 30. Nos. 7451-7461.

UPU Cent. (transportation from messenger to rocket), set of seven, 60c, 70c, 80c, 1e, 1.50e, airmail 30e, 50e, and two airmail souv. sheets, perf. 225e, imperf. (150e, 150e), issued May 30; three airmail deluxe souv. sheets, 130e, and 2x130e, issued June 8. Nos. 7462-7472A.

Picasso Memorial (Pink Period paintings), set of seven, 55c, 60c, 65c, 70c, 75c, airmail 10e, 50e, and two airmail souv. sheets, perf. 130e, imperf. 200e, issued June 28. Nos. 7473-7481.

World Cup Soccer Championships, gold foil airmail souv. sheets, four sheets of one, 130e (2), 250e (2), two sheets of two (2x130e; 2x250e), issued July 8. Nos. 7482-7487.

Aleksander Solzhenitsyn, two gold foil airmail souv. sheets, perf. 250e, imperf. 300e, issued July 25. Nos. 7488-7489.

Opening of American West, set of seven, 30c, 35c, 40c, 45c, 50c, airmail 8p, 60p, and two souv. sheets, perf. 130p, imperf. 200p, issued July 30. Nos. 7490-7498.

Flowers, set of 14, 5c, 10c, 15c, 20c, 25c, 1p, 3p, 5p, 8p, 10p, airmail 5p, 15p, 25p, 70p, and 4 airmail souv. sheets, perf. 130p, 25p+200p, imperf. 200p, 50p+250p, issued Aug. 20. Nos. 7499-74116.

Christmas, set of seven, 60c, 70c, 80c, 1e, 1.50e, airmail 30e, 50e, and two souv. sheets, perf. 225e, imperf. 300e, issued Sept. 16. Nos. 74117-74125.

Barcelona Soccer Team, 75th anniv., set of seven, 1e, 3e, 5e, 8e, 10e, airmail 15e, 60e, miniature sheet of seven plus label, two airmail souv. sheets, perf. 200e, imperf. 300e, and two gold foil airmail souv. sheets, perf., imperf., 200e each, issued Sept. 25. Nos. 74126-74137.

UPU Cent. and ESPANA 75, set of seven, 1.25e, 1.50e, 1.75e, 2e, 2.25e, airmail 35e, 60e, and 2 airmail souv. sheets, perf. 225e, imperf. 300e, issued Oct. 9; 6 gold foil sheets, perf. 250e, 250e, 2x250e, imperf. 300e, 300e, 2x300e, issued Oct. 14. Nos. 74138-74152.

**Nature Protection**

Australian Animals, set of seven, 80c, 85c, 90c, 95c, 1e, airmail 15e, 40e, and two airmail souv. sheets, perf. 130e, imperf. 200e, issued Oct. 25. Nos. 74153-74161.

African Animals, set of seven, 55c, 60c, 65c, 70c, 75c, airmail 10e, 70e, and two airmail souv. sheets, perf. 130e, imperf. 200e, issued Nov. 6. Nos. 74162-74170.

Australian and South American Birds, set of 14, 1.25p, 1.50p, 1.75p, 2p, 2.25p, 2.50p, 2.75p, 3p, 3.50p, 4p, airmail 20p, 25p, 30p, 35p, and four souv. sheets, perf. 130p (2), imperf. 200p (2), issued Nov. 26. Nos. 74171-74188.

Endangered Species, set of 15, 10c, 15c, 20c, 25c, 30c, 35c, 40c, 45c, 50c, 55c, 60c, 1e, 2e, airmail 10e, 70e, se-tenant in sheet of 15, issued Dec. 17. Nos. 74189-74203.

Monkeys, various species, set of 16, 5c, 10c, 15c, 20c, 25c, 30c, 35c, 40c, 45c, 50c, 55c, 60c, 1e, 2e, airmail 10e, 70e, se-tenant in sheet of 16, issued Dec. 27. Nos. 74204-74219.

Cats, various species, set of 16, 5c, 10c, 15c, 20c, 25c, 30c, 35c, 40c, 45c, 50c, 55c, 60c, 1e, 2e, airmail 10e, 70e, se-tenant in sheet of 16, issued Dec. 27. Nos. 74220-74235.

Fish, various species, set of 16, 5c, 10c, 15c, 20c, 25c, 30c, 35c, 40c, 45c, 50c, 55c, 60c, 1e, 2e, airmail 10e, 70e, se-tenant in sheet of 16, issued Dec. 27. Nos. 74236-74251.

Butterflies, various species, set of 16, 5c, 10c, 15c, 20c, 25c, 30c, 35c, 40c, 45c, 50c, 55c, 60c, 1e, 2e, airmail 10e, 70e, se-tenant in sheet of 16, issued Dec. 27. Nos. 74252-74267.

**1975**

Picasso Memorial (paintings from last period), set of seven, 5c, 10c, 15c, 20c, 25c, airmail 5e, 70e, and two souv. sheets, perf. 130e, imperf. 200e, issued Jan. 27. Nos. 7501-7509.

ARPHILA 75 Phil. Exhib., Paris, 8 gold foil airmail souv. sheets: perf. 3 sheets of 1 250e, 1 sheet of 2 250e, imperf. 3 sheets of 1 300e, 1 sheet of 2 300e, issued Jan. 27. Nos. 7510-7517.

Easter and Holy Year 1975, set of seven, 60c, 70c, 80c, 1e, 1.50e, airmail 30e, 50e, and two airmail souv. sheets, perf. 225e, imperf. 300e, issued Feb. 15. Nos. 7518-7526.

1976 Winter Olympics, Innsbruck, set of 11, 5c, 10c, 15c, 20c, 25c, 30c, 35c, 40c, 45c, 25e, 70e, two airmail souv. sheets, perf. 130e, imperf. 200e, and two gold foil airmail souv. sheets, 1 sheet of 1 250e, 1 sheet of 2 250e, issued Mar. 10. Nos. 7527-7541.

Don Quixote, set of seven, 30c, 35c, 40c, 45c, 50c, airmail 25e, 60e, and two airmail souv. sheets, perf. 130e, imperf. 200e, issued Apr. 4. Nos. 7542-7550.

American Bicent. (1st issue), set of nine, 5c, 20c, 40c, 75c, 2e, 5e, 8e, airmail 25e, 30e, and two airmail souv.

sheets, perf. 130e, imperf. 200e, issued Apr. 30. Nos. 7551-7561.

American Bicent. (2nd issue), set of nine, 10c, 30c, 50c, 1e, 3e, 6e, 10e, airmail 12e, 40e, and two airmail souv. sheets, perf. 130e, imperf. 200e, issued Apr. 30. Nos. 7562-7572.

American Bicent. (Presidents), set of 18, 5c, 10c, 20c, 30c, 40c, 50c, 75c, 1e, 2e, 3e, 5e, 6e, 8e, 10e, airmail 12e, 25e, 30e, 40e, four airmail souv. sheets, perf. 225e (2), imperf. 300e (2), and six embossed gold foil airmail souv. sheets, perf. 200e, 200e, 2x200e, imperf. 300e, 300e, 2x300e, issued July 4. Nos. 7573-75100.

Bull Fight, set of seven, 80c, 85c, 90c, 95c, 8e, airmail 35e, 40e, and two airmail souv. sheets, perf. 130e, imperf. 200e, issued May 26. Nos. 75101-75109.

Apollo-Soyuz Space Project, set of 11, 1e, 2e, 3e, 5e, 5.50e, 7e, 7.50e, 9e, 15e, airmail 20e, 30e, and two airmail souv. sheets, perf. 225e, imperf. 300e, issued June 20, 1975; airmail souv. sheet, perf. 250e, issued July 17. Nos. 75110-75123.

Famous Painters, Nudes, set of 16, 5c, 10c, 15c, 20c, 25c, 30c, 35c, 40c, 45c, 50c, 55c, 60c, 1e, 2e, airmail 10e, 70e (Egyptian Greek, Homan, Indian art, Goes, Durer, Liss, Beniort, Renoir, Gauguin, Stenlen, Picasso, Modigliani, Matisse, Padua), se-tenant in sheet of 16, and 20 airmail embossed gold foil souv. sheetlets, perf. 200p+25p (10), imperf. 250p+50p (10), issued Aug. 10. Nos. 75124-75159.

Conquerors of the Sea, set of 14, 30c, 35c, 40c, 45c, 50c, 55c, 60c, 65c, 70c, 75c, airmail 8p, 10p, 50p, 60p, and four airmail souv. sheets, perf. 130p (2), imperf. 200p (2), issued Sept. 5. Nos. 75160-75177.

Christmas and Holy Year, 1975, set of seven, 60c, 70c, 80c, 1e, 1.50e, airmail 30e, 50e (Jordan, Barocci, Vereycke, Rubens, Mengs, Del Castillo, Cavedone), two airmail souv. sheets, perf. 225e, imperf. 300e, plus four embossed gold foil souv. sheets, perf. 200e (2), imperf. 300e (2), and two gold foil miniature sheets of two, perf. 200e+200e, imperf. 300e+300e, issued Oct. Nos. 75178-75192.

President Macias, IWY, set of eight, 1.50e, 3e, 3.50e, 5e, 7e, 10e, airmail 100e, 300e, and two imperf. airmail souv. sheets (world events), 100e (US 2c Yorktown), 300e, issued Dec. 25. Nos. 75193-75202.

**1976**

Cavalry Uniforms, set of seven, 5c, 10c, 15c, 20c, 25c, airmail 5p, 70p, and two airmail souv. sheets, perf. 130p, imperf. 200p, issued Feb. 2. Nos. 7601-7609.

1976 Winter Olympics, Innsbruck, set of 11, 50c, 55c, 60c, 65c, 70c, 75c, 80c, 85c, 90c, airmail 35e, 60e, and two airmail souv. sheets, perf. 130e, imperf. 200e, issued Feb. Nos. 7610-7622.

1976 Summer Olympics, Montreal, Ancient to Modern Games, set of seven, 50c, 60c, 70c, 80c, 90c, airmail 35e, 60e, and two airmail souv. sheets, perf. 225e, imperf. 300e, issued Feb. Nos. 7623-7631.

1976 Summer Olympics, Montreal, set of seven, 50c, 60c, 70c, 80c, 90c, airmail 30e, 60e, plus two airmail souv. sheets, perf. 225e, imperf. 300e, four embossed gold foil airmail souv. sheets, per. 250e (2), imperf. 300e (2), and two imperf. miniature sheets of two, perf. 2x250e, imperf. 2x300e, issued Mar. 5. Nos. 7632-7646.

El Greco, paintings, set of seven, 1e, 3e, 5e, 8e, 10e, airmail 15e, 25e, and two airmail semi-postal souv. sheets, perf. 200e+25e, imperf. 250e+50e, issued Apr. 5. Nos. 7647-7655.

1976 Summer Olympics, modern games, set of 11, 50c, 55c, 60c, 65c, 70c, 75c, 80c, 85c, 90c, airmail 35e, 60e, plus two airmail souv. sheets, perf. 225e, imperf. 300e, four embossed gold foil airmail souv. sheets, perf. 250e (2), imperf. 300e (2), and two miniature sheets of two, perf. 2x250e, imperf. 2x300e, issued May 7. Nos. 7656-7674.

UN 30th Anniv., airmail souv. sheet, 250e, issued June. No. 7675.

Contemporary Automobiles, set of seven, 1p, 3p, 5p, 8p, 10p, airmail 15p, 25p, and two airmail semi-postal souv. sheets, perf. 200p+25p, imperf. 250p+50p, issued June 10. Nos. 7675-7684.

**Nature Protection**

European Animals, set of seven, 5c, 10c, 15c, 20c, 25c, airmail 5p, 70p, and two airmail souv. sheets, perf. 130p, imperf. 200p, issued July 1. Nos. 7685-7693.

Asian Animals, set of seven, 30c, 35c, 40c, 45c, 8p, airmail 50c, 60p, and two airmail souv. sheets, perf. 130p, imperf. 200p, issued Sept. 20. Nos. 7694-74102.

Asian Birds, set of seven, 55c, 60c, 65c, 70c, 75c, airmail 10p, 50p, and two airmail souv. sheets, perf. 130p, imperf. 200p, issued Sept. 20. Nos. 76103-76111.

European Birds, set of seven, 5c, 10c, 15c, 20c, 25c, airmail 5p, 70p, and two airmail souv. sheets, perf. 130p, imperf. 200p, issued Sept. 20. Nos. 76112-76120.

North American Birds, set of seven, 80c, 85c, 90c, 95c, 1p, airmail 15p, 40p, and two airmail souv. sheets, perf. 130p, imperf. 200p, issued Sept. 20. Nos. 76121-76129.

Motorcycle Aces, set of 16, two each 1e, 2e, 3e, 4e, 5e, 10e, 30e, 40e, in se-tenant blocks of eight diff. values, issued July 22. Nos. 76130-76145.

1976 Summer Olympics, Montreal, set of five, 10e, 25e se-tenant strip of 3, airmail 200e, and imperf. airmail souv. sheet, 300e, issued Aug. 7. Nos. 76146-76151.

South American Flowers, set of seven, 30c, 35c, 40c, 45c, 50c, airmail 8p, 60p, and two airmail souv. sheets, perf. 130p, imperf. 200p, issued Aug. 16. Nos. 76152-76160.

Oceania, set of seven, 80c, 85c, 90c, 95c, 1p, airmail 15p, 40p, and two airmail souv. sheets, perf. 130p, imperf. 200p, issued 1976. Nos. 76161-76169.

**1977**

Butterflies, set of seven, 80c, 85c, 90c, 95c, 8e, airmail 35e, 40e, and two airmail souv. sheets, perf. 130e, imperf. 200e, issued Jan. Nos. 7701-7709.

Madrid Real, 75th Anniv., set of nine, 2e, 4e, 5e, 8e, 10e, 15e, airmail 20e, 35e, 150e, issued Jan. Nos. 7710-7718.

Ancient Carriages, set of 16, 5c, 10c, 15c, 20c, 25c, 30c, 35c, 40c, 45c, 50c, 55c, 60c, 1e, 2e, airmail 10e, 70e, issued Feb. Nos. 7719-7734.

Chinese Art, set of seven, 60c, 70c, 80c, 1e, 1.50e, airmail 30e, 50e, and two airmail souv. sheets, perf. 130e, imperf. 200e, issued Feb. Nos. 7735-7743.

African Masks, set of seven, 5c, 10c, 15c, 20c, 25c, airmail 5e, 70e, and two airmail souv. sheets, perf. 130e, imperf. 200e, issued Mar. Nos. 7744-7752.

North American Animals, set of seven, 1.25e, 1.50e, 1.75e, 2e, 2.25e, airmail 20e, 50e, and two airmail souv. sheets, perf. 130e, imperf. 200e, issued 1977. Nos. 7753-7761.

World Cup Soccer Championships, Argentina '78 (famous players), set of eight, 2e, 4e, 5e, 8e, 10e, 15e, airmail 20e, 35e, and two airmail souv. sheets, perf. 150e, imperf. 250e, issued July 25. Nos. 7762-7771.

World Cup Soccer (famous teams), se-tenant set of eight, 2e, 4e, 5e, 8e, 10e, 15e, airmail 20e, 35e, and two gold foil embossed souv. sheets, 500e (AMPHILEX '77, Cutty Sark, Concorde), airmail 500e (World Cup), issued Aug. 25.Nos. 7772-7781.

Napoleon, Life and Battle Scenes, se-tenant sheet of 16, 5c, 10c, 15c, 20c, 25c, 30c, 35c, 40c, 45c, 50c, 55c, 60c, 1e, 2e, airmail 10e, 70e, issued Aug. 20. Nos. 7782-7797.

Napoleon, Military Uniforms, se-tenant sheet of 16, 5c, 10c, 15c, 20c, 25c, 30c, 35c, 40c, 45c, 50c, 55c, 60c, 1e, 2e, airmail 10e, 70e, issued Aug. 20. Nos. 7798-77113.

South American Animals, set of seven, 2.50e, 2.75e, 3e, 3.50e, 4e, airmail 25e, 35e, and two airmail souv. sheets, perf. 130e, imperf. 200e, issued Aug. Nos. 77114-77122.

USSR Space Program, 20th Anniv., set of eight, 2e, 4e, 5e, 8e, 10e, 15e, airmail 20e, 35e, and two airmail souv. sheets, imperf. 150e, perf. 250e, issued Dec. 15. Nos. 77123-77132.

**1978**

Ancient Sailing Ships, set of 12, 5c, 10c, 15c, 20c, 25c, airmail 5e, 70e, also 5e, 10e, 20e, 25e, 70e, plus four airmail souv. sheets, perf. 150c, 225e, imperf. 250e, 300e, and two embossed gold foil airmail souv. sheets, perf., imperf., 500e, issued Jan. 6. Nos. 7801-7818.

1980 Winter Olympics, Lake Placid, set of five, 5e, 10e, 20e, 25e, airmail 70e, two airmail souv. sheets, perf. 150e, imperf. 250e, and two embossed gold foil airmail souv. sheets, perf., imperf., 500e, issued Jan. 17. Nos. 7819-7827.

1980 Summer Olympics, Moscow, set of eight, 2e, 3e, 5e, 8e, 10e, 15e, airmail 30e, 50e, two airmail souv. sheets, perf. 150e, imperf. 250e, and two embossed gold foil airmail souv. sheets, perf., imperf., 500e, issued Jan. 17. Nos. 7828-7839.

1980 Summer Olympic Water Games, Tallinn, set of five, 5e, 10e, 20e, 25e, airmail 70e, two airmail souv. sheets, perf. 150e, imperf. 250e, and two embossed gold foil airmail souv. sheets, perf., imperf., 500e, issued Jan. 17. Nos. 7840-7848.

Eliz. II Coronation, 25th Anniv., set of eight, 2e, 5e, 8e, 10e, 12e, 15e, airmail 30e, 50e, and two airmail souv. sheets, perf. 150e, imperf. 250e, issued Apr. 25. Nos. 7849-7858.

English Knights of 1200-1350 A.D., set of seven, 5e, 10e, 15e, 20e, 25e, airmail 15e, 70e, and two airmail souv. sheets, perf. 130e, imperf. 200e, issued Apr. 25. Nos. 7859-7867.

Old Locomotives, set of seven, 1e, 2e, 3e, 5e, 10e, airmail 25e, 70e, and two airmail souv. sheets, perf. 150e, imperf. 250e, issued Aug. Nos. 7868-7876.

Prehistoric Animals, set of seven, 30e, 35e, 40e, 45e, 50e, airmail 25e, 60e, and airmail souv. sheets, 130e, 200e, issued Aug. Nos. 7877-7884, 7884A.

Francisco Goya, "Maja Vestida," airmail souv. sheet, 150e, issued Aug. No. 7885.

Peter Paul Rubens — UNICEF, airmail souv. sheet, 250e, issued Aug. No. 7886.

Europa — CEPT — Europhila '78, airmail souv. sheet, 250e, issued Aug. No. 7887.

30th Intl. Stamp Fair, Riccione, airmail souv. sheet, 150e, issued Aug. Nos. 7888.

Eliz. II Coronation, 25th anniv., airmail souv. sheet of three, 150e, issued

CEPT, airmail souv. sheet, 250e, issued Aug. Nos. 7890.

World Cup Soccer Championships, Argentina '78 and Spain '82, airmail souv. sheet, 150e, issued Aug. Nos. 7891.

Christmas, Titian painting, "The Virgin," airmail souv. sheet, 150e, issued Aug. Nos. 7892.

Natl. Independence, 5th Anniv. (in 1973) — A7

| **1979** | | | *Perf. 13x13½* | |
|---|---|---|---|---|
| **26** | A7 | 1e Ekuele coin | 1.10 | .25 |

Natl. Independence, 5th Anniv. (in 1973) — A8

1e, Port Bata. 1.50e, State Palace. 2b, Central Bank, Bata. 2.50b, Nguema Biyogo Bridge. 3b, Port, palace, bank, bridge.

| **1979** | | | | | |
|---|---|---|---|---|---|
| **27** | A8 | 1e | multicolored | .25 | .25 |
| **28** | A8 | 1.50e | multicolored | .25 | .25 |
| **29** | A8 | 2b | multicolored | .30 | .30 |
| **30** | A8 | 2.50b | multicolored | .35 | .35 |
| **31** | A8 | 3b | multicolored | .60 | .60 |
| | | | *Nos. 27-31 (5)* | 1.75 | 1.75 |

Pres. Nguema — A9

| **1979** | | | *Perf. 13½x13* | |
|---|---|---|---|---|
| **32** | A9 | 1.50e multi | .50 | .35 |

United Natl. Workers's Party (PUNT), 3rd Congress.

Independence Martyrs — A10

1e, Enrique Nvo. 1.50e, Salvador Ndongo Ekang. 2b, Acacio Mane.

**1979**

**33** A10 1e multicolored .25 .25
**34** A10 1.50e multicolored .30 .30
**35** A10 2b multicolored .40 .40
*Nos. 33-35 (3)* .95 .95

Agricultural Experiment Year A11

**1979** *Perf. 13x13½*

**36** A11 1e multi .65 .25
**37** A11 1.50e multi, diff. .95 .35

Independence Martyrs — A12

Natl. Coat of Arms — A13

5b, Obiang Esono Nguema. 15b, Fermando Nvara Engonga. 25b, Ela Edjodjomo Mangue. 35b, Obiang Nguema Mbasogo, president. 50b, Hipolito Micha Eworo.

**1981, Mar.** **Photo.** *Perf. 13½x12½*

**38** A12 5b multicolored .55 .25
**39** A12 15b multicolored .55 .25
**40** A12 25b multicolored .55 .25
**41** A12 35b multicolored .75 .25
**42** A12 50b multicolored 1.10 .25
**43** A13 100b multicolored 2.25 .35
*Nos. 38-43 (6)* 5.75 1.60

Dated 1980.

Christmas 1980 A14

**1981, Mar. 30** *Perf. 13½*

**44** A14 8b Cathedral, infant .25 .25
**45** A14 25b Bells, youth .30 .25

Dated 1980.

Souvenir Sheet

Pres. Obiang Nguema Mbasogo — A15

**1981, Aug. 30** **Litho.** *Imperf.*

**46** A15 400b multi 5.50 2.25

State Visit of King Juan Carlos of Spain — A16

50b, Government reception. 100b, Arrival at airport. 150b, King, Pres. Mbasogo, vert.

*Perf. 13x13½, 13½x13*

**1981, Nov. 30**

**47** A16 50b multicolored 1.00 .25
**48** A16 100b multicolored 2.00 .50
**49** A16 150b multicolored 3.00 .75
*Nos. 47-49 (3)* 6.00 1.50

State Visit of Pope John Paul II — A17

100b, Papal and natl. arms. 200b, Pres. Mbasogo greeting Pope. 300b, Pope, vert.

**1982, Feb. 18**

**50** A17 100b multicolored 1.50 .70
**51** A17 200b multicolored 3.25 1.40
**52** A17 300b multicolored 4.75 2.10
*Nos. 50-52 (3)* 9.50 4.20

Christmas 1981 A18

**1982, Feb. 25** **Photo.**

**53** A18 100b Carolers, vert. 1.25 .35
**54** A18 150b Magi, African youth 1.90 .60

Dated 1981.

1982 World Cup Soccer Championships, Spain — A19

40b, Emblem. 60b, Naranjito character trademark. 100b, World Cup trophy. 200b, Players, palm tree, emblem.

**1982, June 13** *Perf. 13½*

**55** A19 40b multicolored .55 .25
**56** A19 60b multicolored .90 .35
**57** A19 100b multicolored 1.50 .70
**58** A19 200b multicolored 3.00 1.25
*Nos. 55-58 (4)* 5.95 2.55

Fauna A20

**1983, Feb. 4** **Litho.**

**59** A20 40b Gorilla .75 .25
**60** A20 60b Hippopotamus 1.25 .40
**61** A20 80b Atherurus africanus 1.75 .55
**62** A20 120b Felis pardus 2.75 .85
*Nos. 59-62 (4)* 6.50 2.05

Dated 1982.

Christmas 1982 A21

**1983, Feb. 25** **Photo.**

**63** A21 100b Stars .95 .35
**64** A21 200b King offering frankincense 2.25 .75

Dated 1982.

World Communications Year — A22

**1983, July 18** **Litho.**

**65** A22 150b Postal runner 1.00 .45
**66** A22 200b Microwave station, drummer 2.40 1.00

Banana Trees A23

**1983, Oct. 8**

**67** A23 300b shown 3.25 1.00
**68** A23 400b Forest, vert. 4.50 1.40

Christmas 1983 A24

**1984**

**69** A24 80b Folk dancer, musical instruments 1.00 .35
**70** A24 100b Holy Family 1.25 .50

Dated 1983.

Constitution of State Powers — A25

Scales of justice, fundamental lawbook and various maps.

**1984, Feb. 15**

**71** A25 50b Annobon and Bioko .75 .40
**72** A25 100b Mainland regions 1.75 .75

Inscription at the UR on No. 71 reads "Region Insular". No. 71 also exists with inscription reading "Regiones Insulares".

Turtle Hunting, Rio Muni — A26

**1984, May 1**

**73** A26 125b Hunting Whales, horiz. 1.75 .75
**74** A26 150b shown 2.00 .85

World Food Day — A27

**1984, Sept.**

**75** A27 60b Papaya 1.25 .50
**76** A27 80b Malanga 1.50 .65

Abstract Wood-Carved Figurines and Art — A28

Designs: 25b, *Black Gazelle* and *Anxiety.* 30b, *Black Gazelle,* diff., and *Woman.* 60b, *Man and woman,* vert. 75b, *Poster,* vert. 100b, *Mother and Child,* vert. 150b, *Man and Woman,* diff., and *Bust of a Woman.*

**1984, Nov. 15**

**77** A28 25b multi .25 .25
**78** A28 30b multi .35 .25
**79** A28 60b multi .75 .35
**80** A28 75b multi 1.00 .40
**81** A28 100b multi 1.50 .50
**82** A28 150b multi 2.00 .90
*Nos. 77-82 (6)* 5.85 2.65

Christmas A29

**1984, Dec. 24**

**83** A29 60b Mother and child, vert. .75 .25
**84** A29 100b Musical instruments 1.25 .55

Immaculate Conception Missions, Cent. — A30

50fr, Emblem, vert. 60fr, Map, nun and youths, vert. 80fr, First Guinean nuns. 125fr, Missionaries landing at Bata Beach, 1885.

**1985, Apr.** *Perf. 14*

**85** A30 50fr multi .45 .25
**86** A30 60fr multi .60 .25
**87** A30 80fr multi .90 .30
**88** A30 125fr multi 1.40 .60
*Nos. 85-88 (4)* 3.35 1.40

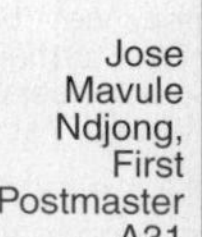

Jose Mavule Ndjong, First Postmaster A31

**1985, July** *Perf. 13½*

**89** A31 50fr Postal emblem, vert. .95 .25
**90** A31 80fr shown 1.60 .45

Equatorial Guinea Postal Service.

Christmas A32

**1985, Dec.**
**91** A32 40fr Nativity .65 .25
**92** A32 70fr Folk band, dancers, mother and child 1.10 .35

Nature Conservation — A33

15fr, Crab, snail. 35fr, Butterflies, bees, birds. 45fr, Flowering plants. 65fr, Spraying and harvesting cacao.

**1985**
**93** A33 15fr multicolored .85 .25
**94** A33 35fr multicolored 2.25 .75
**95** A33 45fr multicolored 2.25 .75
**96** A33 65fr multicolored 3.25 .80
*Nos. 93-96 (4)* 8.60 2.55

Folklore — A34

10fr, Ndowe dance, Mekuyo, horiz. 50fr, Fang dance, Mokom. 65fr, Cacha Bubi, Bisila. 80fr, Fang dance, Ndong-Mba.

**1986, Apr. 15**
**97** A34 10fr multicolored .25 .25
**98** A34 50fr multicolored .60 .25
**99** A34 65fr multicolored .90 .30
**100** A34 80fr multicolored 1.00 .50
*Nos. 97-100 (4)* 2.75 1.30

A35

1986 World Cup Soccer Championships, Mexico: Various soccer plays.

**1986, June 25**
**101** A35 50fr multi, horiz. .25 .25
**102** A35 100fr multi, horiz. .75 .25
**103** A35 150fr multi 1.10 .40
**104** A35 200fr multi 1.40 .55
*Nos. 101-104 (4)* 3.50 1.45

Christmas — A36

**1986, Dec. 12**
**105** A36 100fr Musical instruments, horiz. 1.10 .35
**106** A36 150fr Holy Family, lamb 1.60 .60

Conf. of the Union of Central African States — A37

**1986, Dec. 29**
**107** A37 80fr Flags, map .90 .35
**108** A37 100fr Emblem, map, horiz. 1.25 .40

Campaign Against Hunger A38

**1987, June 5**
**109** A38 60fr Chicken .65 .25
**110** A38 80fr Fish .95 .35
**111** A38 100fr Wheat 1.25 .45
*Nos. 109-111 (3)* 2.85 1.05

Intl. Peace Year A39

**1987, July 15 Litho. *Perf. 13½***
**112** A39 100fr shown .75 .40
**113** A39 200fr Hands holding dove 1.60 .80

Stamp Day 1987 A40

**1987, Oct. 5 Litho. *Perf. 13½***
**114** A40 150fr shown 1.25 .50
**115** A40 300fr Posting envelope 2.25 .85

Christmas 1987 — A41

Mother and child (wood carvings).

**1987, Dec. 22 Litho. *Perf. 13½***
**116** A41 80fr multi 1.00 .35
**117** A41 100fr multi, diff. 1.40 .55

Climbing Palm Tree — A42

75fr, Woman carrying fish. 150fr, Chopping down trees.

**1988, May 4 Litho. *Perf. 13½***
**118** A42 50fr shown .50 .25
**119** A42 75fr multicolored .70 .35
**120** A42 150fr multicolored 1.50 .75
*Nos. 118-120 (3)* 2.70 1.35

Democratic Party — A43

40fr, Crest. 75fr, Torch, motto, horiz. 100fr, Torch, flag, weaving, horiz.

**1988, Nov. 16**
**121** A43 40fr multicolored .35 .25
**122** A43 75fr multicolored .60 .30
**123** A43 100fr multicolored .85 .40
*Nos. 121-123 (3)* 1.80 .95

Cultural Revolution Day — A44

Geometric shapes.

**1988, June 4**
**124** A44 35fr shown .25 .25
**125** A44 50fr Squares, sphere .35 .25
**126** A44 100fr Bird .75 .50
*Nos. 124-126 (3)* 1.35 1.00

Christmas — A45

**1988, Dec. 22**
**127** A45 50fr shown .45 .25
**128** A45 100fr Mother and child .95 .40

Natl. Independence, 20th Anniv. — A46

Designs: 10fr, Lumber on truck. 35fr, Folk dancers. 45fr, Officials on dais.

**1989, Apr. 14 Litho. *Perf. 14***
**129** A46 10fr multicolored .35 .25
**130** A46 35fr multicolored .40 .35
**131** A46 45fr multicolored .55 .40
*Nos. 129-131 (3)* 1.30 1.00

Youths Bathing, Ilachi Falls — A47

25fr, Waterfall in the jungle. 60fr, Boy drinking from fruit, boys swimming at Luba Beach.

**1989, July 7 *Perf. 13½***
**132** A47 15fr shown .45 .25
**133** A47 25fr multicolored .50 .25
**134** A47 60fr multicolored .75 .50
*Nos. 132-134 (3)* 1.70 1.00

1st Congress of the Democratic Party of Equatorial Guinea A48

**1989, Oct. 23 Litho. *Perf. 13½***
**135** A48 25fr shown .30 .25
**136** A48 35fr Torch, vert. .50 .25
**137** A48 40fr Pres. Nguema, vert. .60 .25
*Nos. 135-137 (3)* 1.40 .75

Christmas — A49

**1989, Dec. 18 Litho. *Perf. 13½***
**138** A49 150fr shown 1.60 .75
**139** A49 300fr Nativity, horiz. 2.00 1.00

Boy Scouts A50

**1990, Mar. 23 Litho. *Perf. 13***
**140** A50 100fr Lord Baden-Powell 1.50 .50
**141** A50 250fr Salute 3.50 1.10
**142** A50 350fr Bugler 4.75 1.50
*Nos. 140-142 (3)* 9.75 3.10

World Cup Soccer Championships, Italy — A51

**1990, June 8 Litho. *Perf. 13***
**143** A51 100fr Soccer player, map .60 .35
**144** A51 250fr Goalkeeper 1.50 .65
**145** A51 350fr Trophy 2.00 1.00
*Nos. 143-145 (3)* 4.10 2.00

Musical Instruments of the Ndowe People — A52

Instruments of the: 250fr, Fang. 350fr, Bubi.

**1990, June 19**
**146** A52 100fr multicolored .90 .30
**147** A52 250fr multicolored 1.75 .75
**148** A52 350fr multicolored 2.75 1.00
*Nos. 146-148 (3)* 5.40 2.05

Discovery of America, 500th Anniv. (in 1992) A53

**1990, Oct. 10**

**149** A53 170fr Arrival in New World 1.75 .60
**150** A53 300fr Columbus' fleet 2.25 1.00

Christmas — A54

**1990, Dec. 23 Litho. *Perf. 13½***

**151** A54 170fr shown 1.00 .45
**152** A54 300fr Bubi tribesman 2.00 .90

1992 Summer Olympics, Barcelona A55

**1991, Apr. 22 Litho. *Perf. 13½x14***

**153** A55 150fr Tennis 2.50 .90
**154** A55 250fr Cycling 4.25 1.50

**Souvenir Sheet**

**155** A55 500fr Equestrian 13.50 6.00

La Maja Desnuda by Goya A56

Designs: 250fr, Eve by Durer, vert. 350fr, The Three Graces by Rubens, vert.

**1991, May 6 Litho. *Perf. 14***

**156** A56 100fr shown 1.50 .50
**157** A56 250fr multicolored 2.75 1.00
**158** A56 350fr multicolored 3.75 1.25
*Nos. 156-158 (3)* 8.00 2.75

Madrillus Sphinx — A57

**1991, July 1 Litho. *Perf. 13½x14***

**159** A57 25fr shown 2.50 1.25
**160** A57 25fr Face 2.50 1.25
**161** A57 25fr Seated 2.50 1.25
**162** A57 25fr Walking, horiz. 2.50 1.25
*Nos. 159-162 (4)* 10.00 5.00

World Wildlife Fund.

Discovery of America, 500th Anniv. A58

Captains, ships: 150fr, Vicente Yanez Pinzon, Nina. 260fr, Martin Alonso Pinzon, Pinta. 350fr, Christopher Columbus, Santa Maria.

**1991 Litho. *Perf. 13½x14***

**163** A58 150fr multicolored 1.50 .60
**164** A58 250fr multicolored 2.75 1.00
**165** A58 350fr multicolored 3.75 1.50
*Nos. 163-165 (3)* 8.00 3.10

Locomotives — A59

150fr, Electric, Japan, 1932. 250fr, Steam, US, 1873. 500fr, Steam, Germany, 1841.

**1991, Sept. 10**

**166** A59 150fr multicolored 1.50 .65
**167** A59 250fr multicolored 3.00 .75

**Souvenir Sheet**

**168** A59 500fr multicolored 19.00 6.00

1992 Summer Olympics, Barcelona A60

**1992, Feb. 12 Litho. *Perf. 13½x14***

**169** A60 200fr Basketball 1.75 .75
**170** A60 300fr Swimming 2.50 1.10

**Souvenir Sheet**

**171** A60 400fr Baseball 19.00 12.50

Souvenir Sheet

Discovery of America, 500th Anniv. — A61

Columbus: a, 300fr, Departing from Palos, Spain. b, 500fr, Landing in New World.

**1992, Apr. 8**

**172** A61 Sheet of 2, #a.-b. 22.50 12.50

Motion Pictures, Cent. A61a

Scenes from movies: 100fr, Humphrey Bogart, Ingrid Bergman, Dooley Wilson in "Casablanca," 1942. 250fr, "Viridiana," 1961. 350fr, Laurel and Hardy in "Sons of the Desert," 1933.

**1992, Sept. Litho. *Perf. 14***

**172C** A61a 100fr multicolored 2.00 .75
**172D** A61a 250fr multicolored 3.00 1.25
**172E** A61a 350fr multicolored 5.00 1.75
*Nos. 172C-172E (3)* 10.00 3.75

Mushrooms A62

75fr, Termitomyces globulus. 125fr, Termitomyces le testui. 150fr, Termitomyces robustus.

**1992, Nov. Litho. *Perf. 14x13½***

**173** A62 75fr multicolored 1.00 .25
**174** A62 125fr multicolored 1.50 .50
**175** A62 150fr multicolored 2.00 .65
*Nos. 173-175 (3)* 4.50 1.40

A62a

Wildlife Protection: 150fr, Halcyon malimbicus. 250fr, Corythaeola cristata. 500fr, Mariposa nymphalidae, horiz.

**1992 Litho. *Perf. 14x13½***

**175A** A62a 150fr multicolored 2.75 1.00
**175B** A62a 250fr multicolored 4.75 1.50

**Souvenir Sheet**

***Perf. 13½x14***

**175C** A62a 500fr multicolored 17.50 8.00

Virgin and Child with Virtuous Saints, by Claudio Coello (c. 1635-1693) — A63

Paintings, by Jacob Jordaens (1593-1678): 300fr, Apollo Conquering Marsias. 400fr, Meleager and Atalanta.

**1993, Mar. Litho. *Perf. 13½x14***

**176** A63 200fr multicolored 2.25 .75
**177** A63 300fr multicolored 3.25 1.25

**Souvenir Sheet**

**178** A63 400fr multicolored 15.00 8.00

1992 Olympic Gold Medalists A64

Designs: 100fr, Quincy Watts, 400-meter dash, US. 250fr, Martin Lopez Zubero, swimming, Spain. 350fr, Petra Kronberger, women's slalom, Austria. 400fr, Flying Dutchman class yachting, Spain.

**1993 Litho. *Perf. 13½x14***

**179** A64 100fr multicolored .90 .35
**180** A64 250fr multicolored 2.25 .75
**181** A64 350fr multicolored 3.25 1.00
**182** A64 400fr multicolored 4.00 1.25
*Nos. 179-182 (4)* 10.40 3.35

Scene from Romeo and Juliet, by Tchaikovsky — A65

Design: 200fr, Scene from Faust, by Charles-Francois Gounod (1818-93).

**1993, June Litho. *Perf. 13½x14***

**183** A65 100fr multicolored 1.10 .50
**184** A65 200fr multicolored 2.00 .80

First Ford Gasoline Engine, Cent. A66

**1993 *Perf. 13½x14, 14x13½***

**185** A66 200fr First Ford vehicle 3.00 1.00
**186** A66 300fr Ford Model T 4.00 1.25
**187** A66 400fr Henry Ford, vert. 6.00 1.50
*Nos. 185-187 (3)* 13.00 3.75

25th Anniv. of Independence — A67

Designs: 150fr, Pres. Obiang Nguema Mbasogo, vert. 250fr, Cargo ship, map, communications . 300fr, Hydroelectric plant, Riaba. 350fr, Bridge.

***Perf. 14x13½, 13½x14***

**1993, Oct. 12 Litho.**

**188** A67 150fr multicolored 1.00 .50
**189** A67 250fr multicolored 1.75 .75
**190** A67 300fr multicolored 2.25 .85
**191** A67 350fr multicolored 2.75 .95
*Nos. 188-191 (4)* 7.75 3.05

1994 World Cup Soccer Championships, US — A68

Designs: 200fr, German team, 1990 champions. 300fr, Rose Bowl Stadium, Pasadena, Calif. 500fr, Player kicking ball, vert.

**1994 Litho. *Perf. 13½x14, 14x13½***

**192** A68 200fr multicolored 1.25 .45
**193** A68 300fr multicolored 1.75 .65
**194** A68 500fr multicolored 3.25 1.10
*Nos. 192-194 (3)* 6.25 2.20

First Manned Moon Landing, 25th Anniv. A69

Designs: 500fr, Lunar module, Eagle. 700fr, "Buzz" Aldrin, Michael Collins, Neil Armstrong. 900fr, Footprint on moon, astronaut.

**1994 *Perf. 13½x14***

**195** A69 500fr multicolored 2.75 .70
**196** A69 700fr multicolored 4.25 1.00
**197** A69 900fr multicolored 6.50 1.75
*Nos. 195-197 (3)* 13.50 3.45

Dinosaurs A70

Designs: 300fr, Chasmosaurus. 500fr, Tyrannosaurus rex. 700fr, Triceratops. 800fr, Styracosaurus, deinonychus.

**1994**

**198** A70 300fr multicolored 2.00 .65
**199** A70 500fr multicolored 3.25 1.10
**200** A70 700fr multicolored 6.00 1.60
*Nos. 198-200 (3)* 11.25 3.35

**Souvenir Sheet**

**201** A70 800fr multicolored 19.00 17.50

Famous Men
A71

Designs: 300fr, Jean Renoir (1894-1979), French film director. 500fr, Ferdinand de Lesseps (1805-94), French diplomat, promoter of Suez Canal. 600fr, Antoine de Saint Exupery (1900-44), French aviator, writer. 700fr, Walter Gropius (1883-1969), architect.

**1994 Litho. *Perf. 13½x14***

**202** A71 300fr multicolored 2.25 .75
**203** A71 500fr multicolored 3.75 1.40
**204** A71 600fr multicolored 4.50 1.50
**205** A71 700fr multicolored 5.50 2.00
*Nos. 202-205 (4)* 16.00 5.65

Establishment of The Bauhaus, 75th anniv. (#205).

Minerals
A72

**1994 Litho. *Perf. 13½x14***

**206** A72 300fr Aurichalcite 2.50 1.00
**207** A72 400fr Pyromorphite 3.50 1.40
**208** A72 600fr Fluorite 5.00 1.90
**209** A72 700fr Halite 6.00 2.25
*Nos. 206-209 (4)* 17.00 6.55

Domestic Animals
A73

Designs: a, Cat. b, Dog. c, Pig.

**1995 Litho. *Perf. 13½x14***

**210** Strip of 3, #a.-c. 9.50 9.50
***a.-c.*** A73 500fr Any single 1.75 1.50

Butterflies & Orchids
A74

a, Hypolimnas salmacis. b, Myrina silenus. c, Palla ussheri. d, Pseudacraea boisduvali.

**1995**

**211** Strip of 4, #a.-d. 14.00 14.00
***a.-d.*** A74 400fr Any single 2.75 1.60

Anniversaries — A75

Designs: a, 350fr, End of World War II, 50th Anniv. b, 450fr, UN, 50th anniv. c, 600fr, Sir Rowland Hill, birth bicent.

**1995 Litho. *Perf. 13½x14***

**212** Strip of 3, #a.-c. 11.00 11.00
***a.*** A75 350fr multi 2.50 1.25
***b.*** A75 450fr multi 3.25 1.50
***c.*** A75 600fr multi 4.00 2.25

Trains
A76

Designs: No. 213a, English steam engine. b, German diesel engine. c, Japanese Shinkansen train.
800fr, Swiss electric locomotive.

**1995**

**213** Strip of 3, #a.-c. 12.00 12.00
***a.-c.*** A76 500fr Any single 2.50 2.00

**Souvenir Sheet**

**214** A76 800fr multicolored 10.00 9.00

Formula 1 Driving Champions
A77

Designs: a, Juan Manuel Fangio. b, Ayrton Senna. c, Jim Clark. d, Jochen Rindt.

**1995 Litho. *Perf. 14***

**215** Strip of 4, #a.-d. 12.00 12.00
***a.-d.*** A77 400fr Any single 2.25 1.50

Motion Pictures, Cent.
A78

Designs: a, Marilyn Monroe. b, Elvis Presley. c, James Dean. d, Vittorio de Sica.

**1996 Litho. *Perf. 14***

**216** Strip of 4, #a.-d. 9.00 9.00
***a.-d.*** A78 350fr Any single 1.50 1.50

Famous People
A79

Designs: a, Alfred Nobel (1833-96), inventor, philanthropist. b, Anton Bruckner (1824-96), composer. c, Abraham and Three Angels, by Giovanni B. Tiepolo (1696-1770).
800fr, Family of Charles IV, by Francisco de Goya, (1746-1828).

**1996**

**217** Strip of 3, #a.-c. 13.50 13.50
***a.-c.*** A79 500fr Any single 2.75 2.00

**Souvenir Sheet**

**218** A79 800fr multicolored 8.00 7.75

Chess
A80

Designs: a, World Chess Festival for youth and children, Minorca, Spain. b, Women's World Chess Championship, Jaén, Spain. c, Men's World Chess Championship, Karpov versus Kamsky, Elista, Kalmyk. d, Chess Olympiad, Yerevan, Armenia.

**1996 Litho. *Perf. 14***

**219** Strip of 4, #a.-d. 14.00 14.00
***a.-d.*** A80 400fr Any single 3.00 1.50

1996 Summer Olympic Games, Atlanta
A81

Designs: a, Olympic Stadium, Athens, 1896. b, Cycling. c, Tennis. d, Equestrian show jumping.

**1996 Litho. *Perf. 14***

**220** Strip of 4, #a.-d. 10.00 10.00
***a.-d.*** A81 400fr Any single 1.75 1.50

Ships
A82

Designs: a, Paddle steamer with sails, 19th cent. b, Bark "Galatea," 1896. c, Modern ferry.

**1996**

**221** Strip of 3, #a.-c. 12.00 12.00
***a.-c.*** A82 500fr Any single 2.75 2.00

Franz Schubert (1797-1828), Composer — A83

Miguel de Cervantes (1547-1616), Novelist — A84

Designs: a, shown. b, Chinese Lunar New Year, 1997, (Year of the Ox). c, Johannes Brahms (1833-97), composer.

**1997, Apr. 23 Litho. *Perf. 14***

**222** Strip of 3, #a.-c. 10.00 10.00
***a.-c.*** A83 500fr Any single 2.50 2.00

**Souvenir Sheet**

**223** A84 800fr multicolored 5.50 5.50

Mushrooms — A85

a, Sparassis laminosa. b, Amanita pantherina. c, Morchella esculenta. d, Aleuria aurantia.

**1997**

**224** Strip of 4, #a.-d. 13.50 13.50
***a.-d.*** A85 400fr Any single 2.25 1.75

1998 World Cup Soccer Championships, France — A86

Designs: a, Players with ball on field. b, Stadium. c, Kicking ball.

**1997 Litho. *Perf. 14***

**225** Strip of 3, #a.-c. 7.00 7.00
***a.-c.*** A86 300fr Any single 1.50 1.10

Fauna
A88

a, Snake. b, Snail. c, Turtle. d, Monitor lizard.

**1998 Litho. *Perf. 14***

**230** Strip of 4, #a.-d. 14.00 14.00
***a.-d.*** A88 400fr Any single 2.25 1.50

A89

Military Uniforms: a, Alsace Regiment, French Infantry, 18th cent. b, English Marine, 18th cent. c, Georgian Hussars Regiment, Russian Calvary, 18th cent. d, Prussian Artillery, 19th cent.

**1998**

**231** Strip of 4, #a.-d. 11.00 11.00
***a.-d.*** A89 400fr Any single 1.75 1.50

A90

Easter (Museum paintings): a, Crucifixion of Christ, by Velázquez. b, Adoration of the Magi, by Rubens. c, Holy Family, by Michelangelo.

**1999 Litho. *Perf. 14***

**232** Strip of 3, #a.-c. 10.00 10.00
***a.-c.*** A90 500fr Any single 2.25 2.00

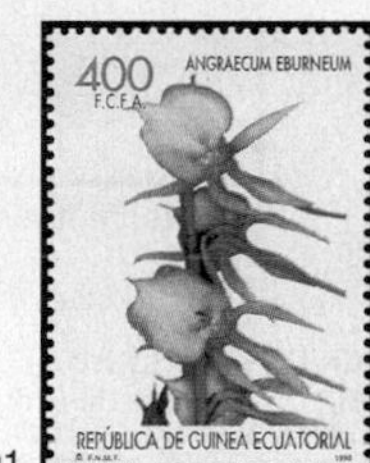


Orchids — A91

Designs: a, Angraecum eburneum. b, Paphiopedilum insigne. c, Ansellia africana. d, Cattleya leopoldii.

**1999**

**233** Strip of 4, #a.-d. 16.00 16.00
***a.-d.*** A91 400fr Any single 3.00 1.50

Birth and Death Anniversaries
A92

No. 234: a, 750fr, Portrait of Frederic Chopin (1810-49), by Eugene Delacroix. b, 100fr, Christ Crowned With Thorns, by Anthony Van Dyck (1599-1641). c, 250fr, Portrait of Johann Wolfgang von Goethe (1749-1832), by Joseph Carl Stieler. d, 500fr, Jacques-Etienne Montgolfiere (1745-1799) and balloon.

**1999 Litho. *Perf. 14x13¾***

**234** Horiz. strip of 4, #a-d 11.00 11.00
***a.*** A92 750fr multi 4.00 3.00
***b.*** A92 100fr multi .45 .35
***c.*** A92 250fr multi 1.25 1.10
***d.*** A92 500fr multi 2.75 2.00

Parrots — A93

No. 235: a, Aratinga guarouba. b, Ara ambigua. c, Anodorhynchus hyacinthinus.
800fr, Alisterus amboinensis.

**1999**

**235** Vert. strip of 3, #a-c 11.50 11.50
*a.-c.* A93 500fr any single 2.75 2.00

**Souvenir Sheet**

**236** A93 800fr multi 8.50 7.50

Economic and Monetary Community of Central Africa Week — A93a

Designs: 100fr, Map of Africa, flags of member nations.

**1999 Litho. *Perf. 14½***

**236A** A93a 100fr multi —

An additional stamp was issued in this set. The editors would like to examine any example.

Locomotives — A94

No. 237: a, Swiss. b, German. c, Japanese.

**2000 Litho. *Perf. 13¾x14***

**237** Horiz. strip of 3 11.00 11.00
*a.-c.* A94 500fr Any single 2.75 2.25

**Souvenir Sheet**

**238** A94 800fr AVE Train 5.00 5.00

Butterflies A95

a, Fabriciana niobe. b, Palaeochrysophanus hippothoe. c, Inachis io. d, Apatura iris.

**2000**

**239** Horiz. strip of 4 16.00 16.00
*a.-d.* A95 400fr Any single 3.00 1.75

UPU, 125th Anniv. (in 1999) A96

**2000 Litho. *Perf. 13¾***

**240** A96 400fr multi 2.00 1.75

Mushrooms A97

No. 241: a, Gyroporus cyanescens. b, Terfezia arenaria. c, Battarrea stevenii. d, Amanita muscaria.

**2001 Litho. *Perf. 13¾***

**241** Horiz. strip of 4 11.00 11.00
*a.-d.* A97 400fr Any single 2.00 1.60

Fire Trucks A98

No. 242: a, Truck, 1915. b, Tanker, 1943. c, Ladder truck, 1966. d, Merryweather pumper, 1888.

**2001**

**242** Horiz. strip of 4 12.00 12.00
*a.-d.* A98 400fr Any single 2.25 1.75

Soldiers — A99

No. 243: a, Infantry officer, 1700. b, Harquebusier, 1534. c, Musketeer, 17th cent. d, Fusilier, 1815.

**2001 Litho. *Perf. 14x13¾***

**243** Horiz. strip of 4 11.00 11.00
*a.-d.* A99 400fr Any single 2.25 1.60

Prehistoric Animals A100

No. 244: a, Carnotaurus sastrei. b, Iberomesornis romerali. c, Troodon.
800fr, Diplodocus carnegiei.

**2001 *Perf. 13¾x14***

**244** Horiz. strip of 3 8.25 8.25
*a.-c.* A100 500fr Any single 2.25 2.00

**Souvenir Sheet**

**245** A100 800fr multi 5.75 4.00

Millennium A101

Designs: No. 246, 200fr, Intl. Conference Center. No. 247, 200fr, Offshore petroleum exploration. No. 248, 200fr, Women's Plaza, Malabo.
400fr, Statue at Intl. Conference Center, vert.

**2001 Litho. *Perf. 13¾x14***

**246-248** A101 Set of 3 3.50 3.50

**Souvenir Sheet**

***Perf. 14x13¾***

**249** A101 400fr multi 1.75 1.75

Flora — A102

No. 250: a, Alstonia congensis. b, Harongana madagascariensis. c, Caloncoba glauca. d, Cassia occidentalis.

**2002 *Perf. 14x13¾***

**250** Horiz. strip of 4 8.50 8.50
*a.-d.* A102 400fr Any single 2.00 1.60

Automobiles — A103

No. 251: a, 1924 Rochet Schneider 20,000. b, 1930 Bugatti T49. c, 1931 Ford Model A. d, 1925 Alfa Romeo RLSS.

**2002 *Perf. 13¾x14***

**251** Vert. strip of 4 9.00 9.00
*a.-d.* A103 400fr Any single 2.00 1.60

Butterflies A104

No. 252: a, Papilio menestheus canui. b, Papilio policenes. c, Papilio tynderaeus. d, Papilio zalmoxis.

**2002**

**252** Strip of 4 9.00 9.00
*a.-d.* A104 400fr Any single 2.00 1.60

Famous Men A105

No. 253: a, Victor Hugo (1802-85), writer. b, Santiago Ramón y Cajal (1852-1934), histologist. c, Emile Zola (1840-1902), writer.

**2002**

**253** Horiz. strip of 3 6.50 6.50
*a.-c.* A105 400fr Any single 1.75 1.60

2002 World Cup Soccer Championships, Japan and Korea — A106

No. 254: a, Player with yellow shirt with knee on ground. b, Stadium. c, Player with yellow shirt on ground.

**2002**

**254** Horiz. strip of 3 8.00 8.00
*a.-c.* A106 500fr Any single 2.25 2.10

Souvenir Sheet

2002 Chess Olympiad, Bled, Slovenia — A107

**2002**

**255** A107 800fr multi 5.75 5.75

Anniversaries and Events — A108

No. 256: a, Painting by Henri de Toulouse-Lautrec (1864-1901). b, Year of Dialogue Among Civilizations. c, Giuseppe Verdi (1813-1901), composer.

**2004 ? Litho. *Perf. 14x13¾***

**256** Vert. strip of 3 6.50 6.50
*a.-c.* A108 400fr Any single 2.00 1.75

Dated 2001. Stamps did not appear in philatelic market until 2004.

Anniversaries and Events — A109

No. 257: a, Tour de France bicycle race, cent. b, Painting by Vincent van Gogh (1853-90). c, Wright Brothers and Wright Flyer.

**2004 ? *Perf. 13¾x14***

**257** Horiz. strip of 3 8.50 8.50
*a.* A109 400fr multi 2.25 2.25
*b.* A109 500fr multi 2.75 2.75
*c.* A109 600fr multi 3.50 3.50

Dated 2003. Stamps did not appear in philatelic market until 2004.

Minerals A110

**2004 ?**

**258** Vert. strip of 4 9.50 9.50
*a.* A110 400fr Realgar 1.75 1.75
*b.* A110 450fr Gypsum 2.25 2.00
*c.* A110 550fr Red quartz 2.50 2.25
*d.* A110 600fr Chrysoberyl 2.75 2.50

Dated 2003. Stamps did not appear in philatelic market until 2004.

Lighthouses A111

Designs: a, Marina Lighthouse, Luba, Equatorial Guinea. b, La Plata Lighthouse, Spain. c, Prodecao Lighthouse, Luba. d, Torre de Hércules, Spain.

**2004 ? *Perf. 14x13¾***

**259** Horiz. strip of 4 12.50 12.50
*a.* A111 400fr multi 2.50 2.25
*b.* A111 450fr multi 2.75 2.50
*c.* A111 550fr multi 3.00 2.75
*d.* A111 600fr multi 3.75 3.50

Dated 2003. Stamps did not appear in philatelic market until 2004.

Space Shuttle Columbia Accident — A112

No. 260: a, Rocket lift-off. b, Rocket on launch pad. c, Flight crew patch.
1000fr, View of earth from outer space.

**2004 ?**

**260** Vert. strip of 3 9.00 9.00
*a.* A112 500fr multi 2.50 2.25
*b.* A112 600fr multi 2.75 2.50
*c.* A112 700fr multi 3.25 3.00

**Souvenir Sheet**

**261** A112 1000fr multi 5.00 5.00

Dated 2003. Stamps did not appear in philatelic market until 2004.

Motorcycles — A113

No. 262: a, 1944-47 Soriano Tigre. b, 1970 Derbi 50 Grand Prix. c, 1938 DKW 250 with sidecar.
1000fr, Harley-Davidson VRSCA V-Rod.

**2004 ?** ***Perf. 13¾x14***

**262** Horiz. strip of 3 8.50 8.50
*a.* A113 450fr multi 2.00 1.90
*b.* A113 500fr multi 2.50 2.25
*c.* A113 550fr multi 3.00 2.75

**Souvenir Sheet**

**263** A113 1000fr multi 6.50 6.50

Dated 2003. Stamps did not appear in philatelic market until 2004.

Souvenir Sheet

Wedding of Spanish Prince Felipe and Letizia Ortiz Rocasolano — A114

**2004** **Litho.** ***Perf. 13¾x14***

**264** A114 1400fr multi 6.00 6.00

2004 Summer Olympics, Athens A115

**2004**

**265** Horiz. strip of 4 8.25 8.25
*a.* A115 400fr Basketball 1.60 1.60
*b.* A115 450fr Track 1.90 1.90
*c.* A115 550fr Tennis 2.25 2.25
*d.* A115 600fr Cycling 2.50 2.50

2004 Anniversaries A116

No. 266: a, FIFA (Fédération Internationale de Football Association), cent. b, Pablo Neruda (1904-73), poet. c, Anton Dvorak (1841-1904), composer.

**2005 ?** **Litho.** ***Perf. 14x13¾***

**266** Vert. strip of 3 6.75 6.75
*a.* A116 450fr multi 1.90 1.90
*b.* A116 500fr multi 2.10 2.10
*c.* A116 550fr multi 2.40 2.40

Dated 2004. Stamps did not appear in philatelic marketplace until 2005.

Airplanes A117

No. 267: a, Concorde. b, Airbus A340-600. c, Boeing 747-400. d, Eurofighter C-16 Typhoon.

**2005 ?** ***Perf. 13¾x14***

**267** Vert. strip of 4 8.50 8.50
*a.* A117 400fr multi 1.60 1.60
*b.* A117 450fr multi 1.90 1.90
*c.* A117 500fr multi 2.10 2.10
*d.* A117 600fr multi 2.50 2.50

Dated 2004. Stamps did not appear in philatelic marketplace until 2005.

Churches — A118

No. 268: a, Cathedral, Pisa, Italy. b, Notre-Dame-la-Grande Church, Poitiers, France. c, Speyer Cathedral, Germany. d, Cathedral, Santiago de Compostela, Spain.

**2005** ***Perf. 14x13¾***

**268** Horiz. strip of 4 9.00 9.00
*a.* A118 400fr multi 1.60 1.60
*b.* A118 450fr multi 1.90 1.90
*c.* A118 550fr multi 2.40 2.40
*d.* A118 600fr multi 2.50 2.50

Paintings by Salvador Dali (1904-89) — A119

Various unnamed paintings.

**2005** ***Perf. 14x13¾***

**269** Vert. strip of 3 8.00 8.00
*a.* A119 500fr multi 2.00 2.00
*b.* A119 600fr multi 2.50 2.50
*c.* A119 700fr multi 2.75 2.75

**Souvenir Sheet**

**270** A119 1000fr multi 4.50 4.50

Art and Architecture — A120

No. 271: a, Statue of African Woman, Malabo. b, Building, Bioko Sur. c, Eyi Muan Ndong, troubador.

**2005** **Litho.** ***Perf. 13¾x14***

**271** Horiz. strip of 3 7.25 7.25
*a.* A120 450fr multi 2.00 2.00
*b.* A120 550fr multi 2.40 2.40
*c.* A120 600fr multi 2.75 2.75

Trains A121

No. 272: a, Tren Basculante. b, Tren Talgo Pendular. c, Tren Electrotrén. d, Tren T. A. F.

**2005** ***Perf. 13¾x14***

**272** Strip of 4 9.00 9.00
*a.* A121 400fr multi 1.75 1.75
*b.* A121 450fr multi 1.90 1.90
*c.* A121 550fr multi 2.40 2.40
*d.* A121 600fr multi 2.50 2.50

Publication of Don Quixote, 400th Anniv. — A122

No. 273: a, Emblem. b, Don Quixote and Sancho Panza riding. c, Quixote catching falling Panza. d, Quixote on horse, windmill.

**2005** ***Perf. 14x13¾***

**273** Horiz. strip of 4 9.00 9.00
*a.* A122 400fr multi 1.75 1.75
*b.* A122 450fr multi 1.90 1.90
*c.* A122 550fr multi 2.40 2.40
*d.* A122 600fr multi 2.50 2.50

Famous People A123

No. 274: a, Christopher Columbus (1451-1506), explorer. b, Federico Garcia Lorca (1898-1936), poet. c, Wolfgang Amadeus Mozart (1756-91), composer.

**2006** ***Perf. 13¾x14***

**274** Horiz. strip of 3 7.25 7.25
*a.* A123 450fr multi 2.00 2.00
*b.* A123 550fr multi 2.25 2.25
*c.* A123 600fr multi 2.50 2.50

Pope Benedict XVI A124

No. 275: a, Coat of Arms. b, St. Peter's Basilica.
1000fr, Pope Benedict XVI.

**2006**

**275** Vert. pair 4.50 4.50
*a.* A124 450fr multi 2.00 2.00
*b.* A124 550fr multi 2.40 2.40

**Souvenir Sheet**

**276** A124 1000fr multi 6.50 6.50

Tourism A125

No. 277: a, Road from Boloko to Luba. b, Malabo Intl. Airport Terminal. c, Sculpture, Avenida de Juan Pablo II. d, National Parliament.

**2006** **Litho.** ***Perf. 13¾x14***

**277** Strip of 4 8.00 8.00
*a.* A125 400fr multi 1.60 1.60
*b.* A125 450fr multi 1.75 1.75
*c.* A125 550fr multi 2.25 2.25
*d.* A125 600fr multi 2.40 2.40

Spain, 2006 World Basketball Champions A126

No. 278: a, Emblem of Spanish Basketball Federation. b, Basketball and hoop. c, Players.

**2006** ***Perf. 14x13¾***

**278** Vert. strip of 3 7.00 7.00
*a.* A126 450fr multi 1.75 1.75
*b.* A126 550fr multi 2.25 2.25
*c.* A126 600fr multi 2.40 2.40

Christmas A127

No. 279 — Baby and: a, People and drummer. b, People. c, People and airplane.

**2006** ***Perf. 13¾x14***

**279** Horiz. strip of 3 6.75 6.75
*a.* A127 450fr multi 1.75 1.75
*b.* A127 550fr multi 2.25 2.25
*c.* A127 600fr multi 2.40 2.40

European Economic Community, 50th Anniv. — A128

No. 280: a, Orchard, Spain. b, Mountain, France. c, Farm fields, Italy. d, Village, Germany.

**2007** **Litho.** ***Perf. 13¾x14***

**280** Horiz. strip of 4 11.50 11.50
*a.* A128 400fr multi 2.00 1.75
*b.* A128 500fr multi 2.50 2.25
*c.* A128 550fr multi 2.75 2.50
*d.* A128 600fr multi 3.00 2.75

Locomotives in Madrid Train Museum — A129

No. 281: a, Steam locomotive 242F-2009. b, Diesel locomotive 1615. c, Electric locomotive 6101. d, Talgo II train.
1000fr, Steam locomotive, diff.

**2007**

**281** Strip of 4 11.50 11.50
*a.* A129 450fr multi 2.00 2.00
*b.* A129 550fr multi 2.50 2.50

*c.* A129 600fr multi 3.00 2.75
*d.* A129 650fr multi 3.25 3.00

**Souvenir Sheet**

**282** A129 1000fr multi 5.75 5.75

Native Toys A130

**2007 Litho. *Perf. 13¾x14***

**283** Horiz. strip of 4 8.50 8.50
*a.* A130 400fr Airplane 1.75 1.75
*b.* A130 450fr Car 2.00 2.00
*c.* A130 500fr Scooter 2.25 2.25
*d.* A130 550fr Songo game 2.50 2.50

Flora A131

No. 284: a, Artocarpus communis. b, Hibiscus sabdariffa. c, Spathodea campanulata. d, Theobroma cacao.

**2007 Litho. *Perf. 13¾x14***

**284** Horiz. strip of 4 9.00 9.00
*a.* A131 400fr multi 1.75 1.75
*b.* A131 450fr multi 2.00 2.00
*c.* A131 550fr multi 2.50 2.50
*d.* A131 600fr multi 2.75 2.75

African Children A132

No. 285: a, Child and basket. b, Five children and toy cars. c, Six children and net.

**2008 Litho. *Perf. 13¾***

**285** Horiz. strip of 3 6.50 6.50
*a.* A132 400fr multi 1.90 1.90
*b.* A132 450fr multi 2.10 2.10
*c.* A132 500fr multi 2.40 2.40

2008 African Cup of Nations Soccer Championships, Ghana — A133

No. 286 — Emblem and: a, Soccer ball and player's foot. b, Soccer ball being caught. c, Goalie. d, Goalie, diff.

**2008**

**286** Horiz. strip of 4 9.25 9.25
*a.* A133 400fr multi 1.90 1.90
*b.* A133 450fr multi 2.10 2.10
*c.* A133 500fr multi 2.40 2.40
*d.* A133 600fr multi 2.75 2.75

Flora and Fauna A134

No. 287: a, Sitatunga. b, Passiflora quadrangularis. c, Pachylobus edulis.

**2008**

**287** Horiz. strip of 3 6.25 6.25
*a.* A134 450fr multi 1.75 1.75
*b.* A134 500fr multi 2.00 2.00
*c.* A134 600fr multi 2.40 2.40

Intl. Year of Planet Earth A135

No. 288: a, Seedlings. b, Parched earth. c, Waterfall.

**2008**

**288** Horiz. strip of 3 5.50 5.50
*a.* A135 400fr multi 1.60 1.60
*b.* A135 450fr multi 1.75 1.75
*c.* A135 550fr multi 2.10 2.10

Declaration of the Rights of Children, 50th Anniv. — A136

No. 289: a, Child drinking glass of milk. b, Children playing with ball. c, Children reading. d, Child coloring.

**2009, Mar. 27 Litho. *Perf. 14x13¾***

**289** Horiz. strip of 4 8.50 8.50
*a.* A136 400fr multi 1.60 1.60
*b.* A136 500fr multi 2.10 2.10
*c.* A136 550fr multi 2.25 2.25
*d.* A136 600fr multi 2.50 2.50

Women's Soccer A137

No. 290: a, Cheering crowd. b, Soccer ball hitting net. c, Players battling for ball. d, Corner of field.

**2009, May 14 Litho. *Perf. 13¾***

**290** Vert. strip of 4 9.75 9.75
*a.* A137 450fr multi 1.90 1.90
*b.* A137 550fr multi 2.40 2.40
*c.* A137 600fr multi 2.60 2.60
*d.* A137 650fr multi 2.75 2.75

Medicinal Plants — A138

No. 291: a, Asystasia gangetica. b, Bryophyllum pinnatum. c, Solanum torvum. 1000fr, Cassia alata.

**2009, Aug. 14**

**291** Vert. strip of 3 6.25 6.25
*a.* A138 400fr multi 1.75 1.75
*b.* A138 450fr multi 2.00 2.00
*c.* A138 550fr multi 2.40 2.40

**Souvenir Sheet**

**292** A138 1000fr multi 4.50 4.50

Christmas — A139

No. 293 — Paintings: a, Birth of Christ, by Federico Barocci. b, Adoration of the Kings, by J. B. Maíno. c, Adoration of the Shepherds, by Maíno. d, Nativity, by Master of Sopetrán.

**2009, Sept. 25**

**293** Horiz. strip of 4 8.50 8.50
*a.* A139 400fr multi 1.75 1.75
*b.* A139 450fr multi 2.00 2.00
*c.* A139 500fr multi 2.25 2.25
*d.* A139 550fr multi 2.50 2.50

Paintings by Joaquin Sorolla y Bastida A140

No. 294: a, Paseo a Orillas del Mar. b, El Balandrito. c, La Hora del Baño. d, Self-portrait.

***Perf. 13¾x13¼***

**2010, Mar. 15 Litho.**

**294** Horiz. strip of 4 9.75 9.75
*a.* A140 475fr multi 2.00 2.00
*b.* A140 575fr multi 2.40 2.40
*c.* A140 625fr multi 2.60 2.60
*d.* A140 675fr multi 2.75 2.75

Architecture — A141

No. 295: a, La Paz Medical Center, Bata. b, Gepetrol Building, Malabo. c, Gecotel Building, Bata. d, Central African Economic and Monetary Community Parliament Building, Malabo.

**2010, June 15**

**295** Horiz. strip of 4 9.25 9.25
*a.* A141 475fr multi 1.90 1.90
*b.* A141 575fr multi 2.25 2.25
*c.* A141 625fr multi 2.40 2.40
*d.* A141 675fr multi 2.60 2.60

2010 World Cup Soccer Championships, South Africa — A142

No. 296: a, Emblem of 2010 tournament. b, Mascot. c, World Cup. d, Colors of Spain, World Cup champions.

**2010 Litho. *Perf. 13¼x13¾***

**296** Horiz. strip of 4 9.75 9.75
*a.* A142 475fr multi 2.00 2.00
*b.* A142 575fr multi 2.40 2.40
*c.* A142 625fr multi 2.60 2.60
*d.* A142 675fr multi 2.75 2.75

**Miniature Sheet**

Christmas — A143

No. 297: a, 375fr, Adoration of the Shepherds, by Anton Rafael Mengs. b, 425fr, Adoration of the Magi, by Diego Velázquez. c, 475fr, Nativity, by Hans Memling. d, 525fr, Adoration of the Shepherds, by El Greco.

**2010**

**297** A143 Sheet of 4, #a-d 7.50 7.50

Intl. Women's Day, Cent. A144

No. 298 — Stylized woman as: a, Doctor. b, Police officer. c, Chemist. d, Chef.

**2011 *Perf. 13¾x14***

**298** Horiz. strip of 4 11.50 11.50
*a.* A144 525fr black 2.40 2.40
*b.* A144 625fr green 2.75 2.75
*c.* A144 675fr red violet 3.00 3.00
*d.* A144 725fr blue 3.25 3.25

Intl. Year of Chemistry — A145

No. 299 — Emblem and: a, Chemical glassware. b, Molecular model and textbook. c, Children in school. d, Water.

**2011 *Perf. 14x13¾***

**299** Horiz. strip of 4 11.50 11.50
*a.* A145 525fr multi 2.40 2.40
*b.* A145 625fr multi 2.75 2.75
*c.* A145 675fr multi 3.00 3.00
*d.* A145 725fr multi 3.25 3.25

Gustavo Adolfo Bécquer (1836-70), Poet — A146

No. 300: a, Drawing of Woman. b, Windows of Veruela Monastery. c, Portrait of Bécquer by his brother, Valeriano.

**2011**

**300** Horiz. strip of 3 7.75 7.75
*a.* A146 525fr multi 2.25 2.25
*b.* A146 625fr multi 2.60 2.60
*c.* A146 675fr multi 2.75 2.75

Christmas A147

No. 301 — Christmas-themed paintings by: a, Nicolás Francés. b, Fra Angelico. c, Luca di Tommè. d, Jaume Serra.

**2011 *Perf. 13¾x14***

**301** Horiz. strip of 4 11.00 11.00
*a.* A147 525fr multi 2.25 2.25
*b.* A147 625fr multi 2.60 2.60
*c.* A147 675fr multi 2.75 2.75
*d.* A147 725fr multi 3.00 3.00

Paintings by Juan Gris (1887-1927) A148

Various paintings.

**2012** *Perf. 14x13¾*

| | | | |
|---|---|---|---|
| **302** | Horiz. strip of 4 | 9.75 | 9.75 |
| *a.* | A148 525fr multi | 2.00 | 2.00 |
| *b.* | A148 625fr multi | 2.40 | 2.40 |
| *c.* | A148 675fr multi | 2.60 | 2.60 |
| *d.* | A148 725fr multi | 2.75 | 2.75 |

Spices — A149

No. 303: a, Xylopia aethiopica. b, Piper guineense. c, Capsicum frutescens. d, Zingiber officinale.

**2012**

| | | | |
|---|---|---|---|
| **303** | Horiz. strip of 4 | 10.50 | 10.50 |
| *a.* | A149 525fr multi | 2.10 | 2.10 |
| *b.* | A149 625fr multi | 2.50 | 2.50 |
| *c.* | A149 675fr multi | 2.75 | 2.75 |
| *d.* | A149 725fr multi | 3.00 | 3.00 |

Sports A150

No. 304: a, Gymnastics. b, Table tennis. c, Running. d, Kayaking.

**2012** *Perf. 14x13¾*

| | | | |
|---|---|---|---|
| **304** | Horiz. strip of 4 | 10.50 | 10.50 |
| *a.* | A150 525fr multi | 2.10 | 2.10 |
| *b.* | A150 625fr multi | 2.50 | 2.50 |
| *c.* | A150 675fr multi | 2.75 | 2.75 |
| *d.* | A150 725fr multi | 3.00 | 3.00 |

Christmas A151

No. 305 — Religious painting by: a, Pietro de Lignis. b, Francisco and Rodrigo de Osona. c, Pietro da Cortona. d, Hans Memling.

**2012** *Perf. 14x13¾*

| | | | |
|---|---|---|---|
| **305** | Horiz. strip of 4 | 10.50 | 10.50 |
| *a.* | A151 525fr multi | 2.10 | 2.10 |
| *b.* | A151 625fr multi | 2.50 | 2.50 |
| *c.* | A151 675fr multi | 2.75 | 2.75 |
| *d.* | A151 725fr multi | 3.00 | 3.00 |

Tourist Areas A152

No. 306: a, Sipopo. b, Luba. c, Mbini. d, Bata.

**2013** *Perf. 13¾x13¼*

| | | | |
|---|---|---|---|
| **306** | Horiz. strip of 4 | 10.00 | 10.00 |
| *a.* | A152 550fr multi | 2.25 | 2.25 |
| *b.* | A152 600fr multi | 2.40 | 2.40 |
| *c.* | A152 650fr multi | 2.60 | 2.60 |
| *d.* | A152 700fr multi | 2.75 | 2.75 |

Intl. Red Cross, 150th Anniv. A153

No. 307: a, Students in classroom. b, Man carrying large pot on head. c, Red Cross worker. d, Flags on building.

**2013** *Perf. 13¾x14*

| | | | |
|---|---|---|---|
| **307** | Horiz. strip of 4 | 10.00 | 10.00 |
| *a.* | A153 550fr multi | 2.25 | 2.25 |
| *b.* | A153 600fr multi | 2.40 | 2.40 |
| *c.* | A153 650fr multi | 2.60 | 2.60 |
| *d.* | A153 700fr multi | 2.75 | 2.75 |

Pope John XXIII (1881-1963) A154

No. 307: a, Pope John XXIII. b, Pope John XXIII, diff. c, Pope John XXIII, diff. d, Arms of Pope John XXIII.

**2013** *Perf. 13¼x13¾*

| | | | |
|---|---|---|---|
| **308** | Horiz. strip of 4 | 10.50 | 10.50 |
| *a.* | A154 550fr multi | 2.25 | 2.25 |
| *b.* | A154 600fr multi | 2.50 | 2.50 |
| *c.* | A154 650fr multi | 2.75 | 2.75 |
| *d.* | A154 700fr multi | 3.00 | 3.00 |

Christmas — A155

No. 308: a, Nativity. b, Adoration of the Magi. c, Nativity, diff. d, Nativity, diff.

**2013** *Perf. 13¼x13¾*

| | | | |
|---|---|---|---|
| **309** | Horiz. strip of 4 | 10.50 | 10.50 |
| *a.* | A155 550fr multi | 2.25 | 2.25 |
| *b.* | A155 600fr multi | 2.50 | 2.50 |
| *c.* | A155 650fr multi | 2.75 | 2.75 |
| *d.* | A155 700fr multi | 3.00 | 3.00 |

Bolondo-Mbini Bridge — A156

Various views of bridge.

**2014** **Litho.** *Perf. 13¼x13¾*

| | | | |
|---|---|---|---|
| **310** | Horiz. strip of 4 | 11.50 | 11.50 |
| *a.* | A156 600fr multi | 2.50 | 2.50 |
| *b.* | A156 650fr multi | 2.75 | 2.75 |
| *c.* | A156 700fr multi | 3.00 | 3.00 |
| *d.* | A156 750fr multi | 3.25 | 3.25 |

Intl. Year of Family Farms A157

No. 311: a, Hands leveling earth. b, Woman tending cows. c, Woman tending goats. d, Farmer inspecting crops.

**2014** **Litho.** *Perf. 13¾x13¼*

| | | | |
|---|---|---|---|
| **311** | Horiz. strip of 4 | 11.50 | 11.50 |
| *a.* | A157 600fr multi | 2.50 | 2.50 |
| *b.* | A157 650fr multi | 2.75 | 2.75 |
| *c.* | A157 700fr multi | 3.00 | 3.00 |
| *d.* | A157 750fr multi | 3.25 | 3.25 |

Religious Paintings by El Greco (1541-1614) A158

No. 312: a, St. Andrew and St. Francis. b, Christ Carrying the Cross. c, St. Peter. d, The Disrobing of Christ.

**2014** **Litho.** *Perf. 13¼x13¾*

| | | | |
|---|---|---|---|
| **312** | Horiz. strip of 4 | 10.50 | 10.50 |
| *a.* | A158 600fr multi | 2.25 | 2.25 |
| *b.* | A158 650fr multi | 2.50 | 2.50 |
| *c.* | A158 700fr multi | 2.75 | 2.75 |
| *d.* | A158 750fr multi | 3.00 | 3.00 |

Christmas A159

No. 313: a, Adoration of the Shepherds, by Bartolomé Esteban Murillo. b, Adoration of the Magi, by Peter Paul Rubens. c, Adoration of the Magi, by Luis de Morales. d, Adoration of the Shepherds, by de Morales.

**2014** **Litho.** *Perf. 13¼x13¾*

| | | | |
|---|---|---|---|
| **313** | Horiz. strip of 4 | 10.50 | 10.50 |
| *a.* | A159 600fr multi | 2.25 | 2.25 |
| *b.* | A159 650fr multi | 2.50 | 2.50 |
| *c.* | A159 700fr multi | 2.75 | 2.75 |
| *d.* | A159 750fr multi | 3.00 | 3.00 |

Sipopo Congresws Center, Malabo — A160

No. 314: a, Seats and video screen in meeting hall (29x41mm). b, Seats in auditorium (29x41mm). c, Building exterior (29x41mm). d, Building entrance (58x41mm).

**2015** **Litho.** *Perf. 13¼x13¾*

| | | | |
|---|---|---|---|
| **314** | Horiz. strip of 4 | 14.50 | 14.50 |
| *a.* | A160 650fr multi | 2.25 | 2.25 |
| *b.* | A160 700fr multi | 2.40 | 2.40 |
| *c.* | A160 750fr multi | 2.60 | 2.60 |
| *d.* | A160 2100fr multi | 7.25 | 7.25 |

Paintings of Women by Federico de Madrazo y Kuntz (1815-94) — A161

No. 315 — Various women wearing: a, Blue dress. b, White dress. c, Lilac dress. d, Black dress.

**2015** **Litho.** *Perf. 13¾*

| | | | |
|---|---|---|---|
| **315** | Horiz. strip of 4 | 9.25 | 9.25 |
| *a.* | A161 600fr multi | 2.00 | 2.00 |
| *b.* | A161 650fr multi | 2.25 | 2.25 |
| *c.* | A161 700fr multi | 2.40 | 2.40 |
| *d.* | A161 750fr multi | 2.60 | 2.60 |

International Year of Light — A162

No. 316: a, Fiber optic cord connector. b, Ends of optical fibers. c, Ends of optical fibers, diff. d, Close-up of ends of bound optical fibers.

**2015** **Litho.** *Perf. 13¾x13¼*

| | | | |
|---|---|---|---|
| **316** | Horiz. strip of 4 | 8.75 | 8.75 |
| *a.* | A162 600fr multi | 2.00 | 2.00 |
| *b.* | A162 650fr multi | 2.10 | 2.10 |
| *c.* | A162 700fr multi | 2.25 | 2.25 |
| *d.* | A162 750fr multi | 2.40 | 2.40 |

Christmas — A163

No. 317 — Various Nativity paintings by unknown artists from: a, Prado, Madrid. b, Museum of Fine Arts, Bilbao. c, Prado, diff. d, Museum of Fine Arts, diff.

**2015** **Litho.** *Perf. 13¼x13¾*

| | | | |
|---|---|---|---|
| **317** | Horiz. strip of 4 | 8.75 | 8.75 |
| *a.* | A163 600fr multi | 2.00 | 2.00 |
| *b.* | A163 650fr multi | 2.10 | 2.10 |
| *c.* | A163 700fr multi | 2.25 | 2.25 |
| *d.* | A163 750fr multi | 2.40 | 2.40 |

Paintings by Hieronymus Bosch (c.1450-1516) A164

No. 318 — Details of paintings: a, Garden of Earthly Delights (left panel). b, Garden of Earthly Delights (center panel). c, The Hay Wagon (center panel). d, St. John the Baptist in the Wilderness.

**2016** **Litho.** *Perf. 13¾*

| | | | |
|---|---|---|---|
| **318** | Horiz. strip of 4 | 8.75 | 8.75 |
| *a.* | A164 600fr multi | 2.00 | 2.00 |
| *b.* | A164 650fr multi | 2.25 | 2.25 |
| *c.* | A164 700fr multi | 2.40 | 2.40 |
| *d.* | A164 750fr multi | 2.60 | 2.60 |

Miguel de Cervantes (1547-1616), Writer — A165

No. 319 — Various paintings from Prado Museum, Madrid.

**2016** **Litho.** *Perf. 13¾*

| | | | |
|---|---|---|---|
| **319** | Horiz. strip of 4 | 8.75 | 8.75 |
| *a.* | A165 600fr multi | 2.00 | 2.00 |
| *b.* | A165 650fr multi | 2.25 | 2.25 |
| *c.* | A165 700fr multi | 2.40 | 2.40 |
| *d.* | A165 750fr multi | 2.60 | 2.60 |

Flora and Fauna A166

No. 320: a, Hibisco (hibiscus). b, Geranio de la jungla (jungle geranium). c, Pangolín arborícola (tree pangolin). d, Barbasco guineano (Vogel's tephrosia).

**2016 Litho. *Perf. 13¾x14***

**320** Horiz. strip of 4 8.75 8.75
*a.* A166 600fr multi 1.90 1.90
*b.* A166 650fr multi 2.10 2.10
*c.* A166 700fr multi 2.25 2.25
*d.* A166 750fr multi 2.40 2.40

Christmas — A167

Various paintings depicting the Nativity from the Prado Museum, Madrid.

**2016 Litho. *Perf. 14x13¾***

**321** Horiz. strip of 4 8.75 8.75
*a.* A167 600fr multi 1.90 1.90
*b.* A167 650fr multi 2.10 2.10
*c.* A167 700fr multi 2.25 2.25
*d.* A167 750fr multi 2.40 2.40

International Year for Sustainable Tourism for Development — A168

No. 322: a, Bicyclist walking bicycle. b, Boat near dock. c, Cyclist on trail. d, Canoers.

**2017 Litho. *Perf. 13¾***

**322** Horiz. strip of 4 9.50 9.50
*a.* A168 600fr multi 2.10 2.10
*b.* A168 650fr multi 2.25 2.25
*c.* A168 700fr multi 2.40 2.40
*d.* A168 750fr multi 2.60 2.60

Paintings by Bartolomé Esteban Murillo (1617-82) — A169

No. 323: a, Leander and St. Bonaventure. b, Saints Justa and Rufina. c, Christ the Good Shepherd. d, Immaculate Conception.

**2017 Litho. *Perf. 13¾***

**323** Horiz. strip of 4 9.50 9.50
*a.* A169 600fr multi 2.10 2.10
*b.* A169 650fr multi 2.25 2.25
*c.* A169 700fr multi 2.40 2.40
*d.* A169 750fr multi 2.60 2.60

Malabo National Park A170

No. 324: a, Bridge. b, Sculptures. c, Island. d, Park entrance.

**2017 Litho. *Perf. 13¾***

**324** Horiz. strip of 4 10.00 10.00
*a.* A170 600fr multi 2.25 2.25
*b.* A170 650fr multi 2.40 2.40
*c.* A170 700fr multi 2.60 2.60
*d.* A170 750fr multi 2.75 2.75

Christmas — A171

Various unattributed Nativity paintings from the Prado Museum.

**2017 Litho. *Perf. 13¾***

**325** Horiz. strip of 4 10.00 10.00
*a.* A171 600fr multi 2.25 2.25
*b.* A171 650fr multi 2.40 2.40
*c.* A171 700fr multi 2.60 2.60
*d.* A171 750fr multi 2.75 2.75

---

## SPECIAL DELIVERY STAMPS

Archer with Crossbow — SD1

**1971, Oct. 12 Photo. *Perf. 12½x13***

**E1** SD1 4p blue & multi 1.00 .25
**E2** SD1 8p rose & multi 1.50 .35

3rd anniversary of independence.

---

# ERITREA

ˌer-ə-ˈtrē-ə

LOCATION — In northeast Africa, bordering on the Red Sea, Sudan, Ethiopia and Djibouti.
GOVT. — Independent state
AREA — 45,300 (?) sq. mi.
POP. — 3,984,723 (1999 est.)
CAPITAL — Asmara

Formerly an Italian colony, Eritrea was incorporated as a State of Italian East Africa in 1936.

Under British occupation (1941-52) until it became part of Ethiopia as its northernmost region. Eritrea became independent May 24, 1993.

100 Centesimi = 1 Lira
100 cents = 1 birr (1991)
100 cents = 1 nakfa (1997)

**Catalogue values for unused stamps in this country are for Never Hinged items, beginning with Scott 200 in the regular postage section.**

**All used values to about 1916 are for postally used stamps. From 1916-1934, used values in italics are for postally used stamps. CTO's, for stamps valued postally used, sell for about the same as unused, hinged stamps.**

**Watermark**

Wmk. 140 — Crown

**Stamps of Italy Overprinted**

a

b

**1892 Wmk. 140 *Perf. 14***

**Overprinted Type "a" in Black**

**1** A6 1c bronze grn 10.00 10.00
*a.* Inverted overprint 675.00 675.00
*b.* Double overprint 1,900.
Never hinged 2,400.
*c.* Vert. pair, one without overprint 4,500.
Never hinged 5,750.
**2** A7 2c org brn 5.00 5.00
*a.* Inverted overprint 600.00 600.00
*b.* Double overprint 1,900.
Never hinged 2,400.
**3** A33 5c green 160.00 17.50
*a.* Inverted overprint 8,000. 4,500.
Never hinged 10,000.

**Overprinted Type "b" in Black**

**4** A17 10c claret 210.00 17.50
**5** A17 20c orange 375.00 12.00
**6** A17 25c blue 1,450. 55.00
**7** A25 40c brown 13.50 *32.50*
**8** A26 45c slate grn 13.50 *32.50*
**9** A27 60c violet 13.50 72.50
**10** A28 1 l brn & yel 65.00 *80.00*
**11** A38 5 l bl & rose 650.00 550.00
*Nos. 1-11 (11)* *2,966.* *884.50*
Set, never hinged *7,300.*

**1895-99**

**Overprinted type "a" in Black**

**12** A39 1c brown ('99) 22.50 12.00
**13** A40 2c org brn ('99) 4.75 2.40
**14** A41 5c green 4.75 2.40
*a.* Inverted overprint 525.00 *4,250.*

**Overprinted type "b" in Black**

**15** A34 10c claret ('98) 4.75 2.40
**16** A35 20c orange 4.75 3.25
**17** A36 25c blue 4.75 4.75
**18** A37 45c olive grn 37.50 *27.50*
*Nos. 12-18 (7)* *83.75* *54.70*
Set, never hinged 215.00

**1903-28**

**Overprinted type "a" in Black**

**19** A42 1c brown 1.60 *1.25*
*a.* Inverted overprint 125.00 125.00
**20** A43 2c orange brn 1.60 .60
**21** A44 5c blue green 120.00 .60
**22** A45 10c claret 140.00 .60
**23** A45 20c orange 6.50 1.25
**24** A45 25c blue 1,200. 18.00
*a.* Double overprint 1,100. —
**25** A45 40c brown 1,300. 30.00
**26** A45 45c olive grn 8.00 *10.00*
**27** A45 50c violet 475.00 32.50
**28** A46 75c dk red & rose ('28) 80.00 20.00
**29** A46 1 l brown & grn 8.00 .85
**30** A46 1.25 l bl & ultra ('28) 40.00 20.00
**31** A46 2 l dk grn & org ('25) 87.50 *100.00*
**32** A46 2.50 l dk grn & org ('28) 175.00 72.50
**33** A46 5 l blue & rose 55.00 *45.00*
*Nos. 19-33 (15)* *3,698.* 353.15
Set, never hinged 9,250.

Surcharged in Black

**1905**

**34** A45 15c on 20c orange 80.00 20.00
Never hinged 200.00

**1908-28**

**Overprinted type "a" in Black**

**35** A48 5c green 1.20 1.00
**36** A48 10c claret ('09) 1.20 1.00
**37** A48 15c slate ('20) 22.50 14.50
**38** A49 20c green ('25) 16.00 11.00
**39** A49 20c lilac brn ('28) 8.00 3.25
**40** A49 25c blue ('09) 6.50 2.25
**41** A49 30c gray ('25) 16.00 14.50
**42** A49 40c brown ('16) 55.00 40.00
**43** A49 50c violet ('16) 16.00 2.10
**44** A49 60c brown car ('18) 27.50 *28.00*
*a.* Printed on both sides *1,750.*
**45** A49 60c brown org ('28) 110.00 *225.00*
**46** A51 10 l gray grn & red ('16) 425.00 *775.00*
*Nos. 35-46 (12)* 704.90 *1,118.*
Set, never hinged 1,750.

See No. 53.

A1

Government Building at Massaua — A2

**1910-29 Unwmk. Engr. *Perf. 13½***

**47** A1 15c slate 390.00 30.00
*a.* Perf. 11 ('29) 40.00 *55.00*
Never hinged 100.00
**48** A2 25c dark blue 7.25 *17.50*
*a.* Perf. 12 875.00 875.00

For surcharges see Nos. 51-52.

A3

Farmer Plowing — A4

**1914-28**

**49** A3 5c green 1.20 *2.50*
*a.* Perf. 11 ('28) 210.00 75.00
Never hinged 525.00
**50** A4 10c carmine 4.75 *4.25*
*a.* Perf. 11 ('28) 12.00 *47.50*
Never hinged 30.00
*b.* Perf. 13½x14 62.50 62.50

**No. 47 Surcharged in Red or Black**

**1916**

**51** A1 5c on 15c slate (R) 8.75 *15.00*
**52** A1 20c on 15c slate 4.00 4.25
*a.* "CEN" for "CENT" 47.50 47.50
*b.* "CENT" omitted 190.00 190.00
*c.* "ENT" 47.50 *47.50*
Set, never hinged 32.00

Italy No. 113 Overprinted in Black — f

**1921 Wmk. 140 *Perf. 14***

**53** A50 20c brown orange 4.75 *15.00*
Never hinged 12.00

### Victory Issue

**Italian Victory Stamps of 1921 Overprinted type "f" 13mm long**

**1922**

54 A64 5c olive green 2.00 *7.25*
55 A64 10c red 2.00 *7.25*
56 A64 15c slate green 2.00 *11.00*
57 A64 25c ultra 2.00 *11.00*
*Nos. 54-57 (4)* 8.00 *36.50*
Set, never hinged 20.00

Somalia Nos. 10-16 Overprinted In Black g

**1922** **Wmk. 140**

58 A1 2c on 1b brn 4.75 *17.50*
a. Pair, one missing "ERITREA" 2,250.
59 A1 5c on 2b bl grn 4.75 *13.00*
60 A2 10c on 1a claret 4.75 2.40
61 A2 15c on 2a brn org 4.75 2.40
62 A2 25c on 2½a blue 4.75 2.40
63 A2 50c on 5a yellow 22.50 13.50
a. "ERITREA" double *1,600.*
64 A2 1 l on 10a lilac 22.50 22.50
a. "ERITREA" double 1,600. 1,600.
b. Pair, one missing "ERITREA" *3,000.*
*Nos. 58-64 (7)* 68.75 *73.70*
Set, never hinged 170.00

See Nos. 81-87.

### Propagation of the Faith Issue

Italy Nos. 143-146 Overprinted

**1923**

65 A68 20c ol grn & brn org 12.00 *52.50*
66 A68 30c claret & brn org 12.00 *52.50*
67 A68 50c vio & brn org 8.00 *60.00*
68 A68 1 l bl & brn org 8.00 *92.50*
*Nos. 65-68 (4)* 40.00 *257.50*
Set, never hinged 100.00

### Fascisti Issue

Italy Nos. 159-164 Overprinted in Red or Black — j

**1923** **Unwmk.** ***Perf. 14***

69 A69 10c dk green (R) 11.00 *20.00*
70 A69 30c dk violet (R) 11.00 *20.00*
71 A69 50c brown carmine 11.00 *27.50*

**Wmk. 140**

72 A70 1 l blue 11.00 *52.50*
73 A70 2 l brown 11.00 *65.00*
74 A71 5 l black & blue (R) 11.00 *95.00*
*Nos. 69-74 (6)* 66.00 *280.00*
Set, never hinged 165.00

### Manzoni Issue

Italy Nos. 165-170 Overprinted in Red

**1924** ***Perf. 14***

75 A72 10c brown red & blk 12.00 *80.00*
76 A72 15c blue grn & blk 12.00 *80.00*
77 A72 30c black & slate 12.00 *80.00*
78 A72 50c org brn & blk 12.00 *80.00*
79 A72 1 l blue & blk 72.50 *475.00*
80 A72 5 l violet & blk 475.00 *3,250.*
*Nos. 75-80 (6)* 595.50 *4,045.*
Set, never hinged 1,500.

On Nos. 79 and 80 the overprint is placed vertically at the left side.

**Somalia Nos. 10-16 Overprinted type "g" in Blue or Red**

**1924**

**Bars over Original Values**

81 A1 2c on 1b brn 17.50 *27.50*
a. Pair, one without "ERITREA" 2,400.
82 A1 5c on 2b bl grn (R) 17.50 *17.50*
83 A2 10c on 1a rose red 9.50 *16.00*
84 A2 15c on 2a brn org 9.50 *16.00*
a. Pair, one without "ERITREA" 2,400.
b. "ERITREA" inverted 1,750. 1,750.
85 A2 25c on 2½a bl (R) 9.50 *11.00*
a. Double surcharge 1,200.
86 A2 50c on 5a yellow 9.50 *20.00*
87 A2 1 l on 10a lil (R) 9.50 *27.50*
*Nos. 81-87 (7)* 82.50 *135.50*
Set, never hinged 200.00

**Stamps of Italy, 1901-08 Overprinted type "j" in Black**

**1924**

88 A42 1c brown 9.50 *9.50*
a. Inverted overprint 325.00
b. Vertical pair, one without ovpt. 1,750.
89 A43 2c orange brown 6.50 *8.00*
b. Vertical pair, one without ovpt. 1,750.
90 A48 5c green 9.50 *8.75*
*Nos. 88-90 (3)* 25.50 *26.25*
Set, never hinged 60.00

### Victor Emmanuel Issue

Italy Nos. 175-177 Overprinted — k

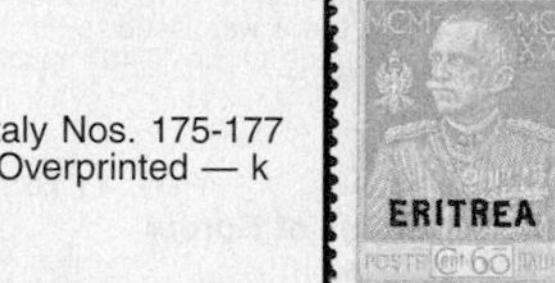


**1925-26** **Unwmk.** ***Perf. 11***

91 A78 60c brown car 2.40 *9.50*
a. Perf. 13½ 13.00 40.00
92 A78 1 l dark blue 2.40 *14.50*
a. Perf. 13½ *24,000.* *9,500.*
Never hinged *36,000.*

***Perf. 13½***

93 A78 1.25 l dk blue ('26) 4.00 *32.50*
a. Perf. 11 8.00 *40.00*
*Nos. 91-93 (3)* 8.80 *56.50*
Set, never hinged 22.00

### Saint Francis of Assisi Issue

Italian Stamps of 1926 Overprinted

**1926** **Wmk. 140** ***Perf. 14***

94 A79 20c gray green 2.40 *14.00*
95 A80 40c dark violet 2.40 *14.00*
96 A81 60c red violet 2.40 *26.00*

**Overprinted in Red**

**Unwmk.** ***Perf. 11***

97 A82 1.25 l dark blue 2.40 *36.00*

***Perf. 14***

98 A83 5 l + 2.50 l ol grn 8.00 *72.50*
*Nos. 94-98 (5)* 17.60 *162.50*
Set, never hinged 44.00

**Italian Stamps of 1926 Overprinted type "f" in Black**

**1926** **Wmk. 140** ***Perf. 14***

99 A46 75c dk red & rose 80.00 20.00
a. Double overprint 450.00
100 A46 1.25 l blue & ultra 40.00 20.00
101 A46 2.50 l dk green & org 175.00 72.50
*Nos. 99-101 (3)* 295.00 112.50
Set, never hinged 725.00

### Volta Issue

Type of Italy, 1927, Overprinted — o

**1927**

102 A84 20c purple 6.50 *40.00*
103 A84 50c deep orange 9.50 *27.50*
a. Double overprint 200.00
104 A84 1.25 l brt blue 14.00 *65.00*
*Nos. 102-104 (3)* 30.00 *132.50*
Set, never hinged 75.00

**Italian Stamps of 1925-28 Overprinted type "a" in Black**

**1928-29**

105 A86 7½c lt brown ('29) 24.00 *72.50*
106 A86 50c brt violet 87.50 65.00
Set, never hinged 270.00

**Italian Stamps of 1927-28 Overprinted type "f"**

**1928-29**

107 A86 50c brt violet 72.50 *60.00*
Never hinged 175.00

**Unwmk.** ***Perf. 11***

107A A85 1.75 l deep brown 95.00 52.50
Never hinged 240.00

**Italy No. 192 Overprinted type "o"**

**1928** **Wmk. 140** ***Perf. 14***

108 A85 50c brown & slate 24.00 12.00
Never hinged 60.00

### Monte Cassino Issue

Types of 1929 Issue of Italy Overprinted in Red or Blue

**1929** ***Perf. 14***

109 A96 20c dk green (R) 6.50 *22.50*
110 A96 25c red orange (Bl) 6.50 *22.50*
111 A98 50c + 10c crim (Bl) 6.50 *24.00*
112 A98 75c + 15c ol brn (R) 6.50 *24.00*
113 A96 1.25 l + 25c dl vio (R) 14.50 *45.00*
114 A98 5 l + 1 l saph (R) 14.50 *47.50*

Overprinted in Red

**Unwmk.**

115 A100 10 l + 2 l gray brn 14.50 *72.50*
*Nos. 109-115 (7)* 69.50 *258.00*
Set, never hinged 170.00

### Royal Wedding Issue

Type of Italian Stamps of 1930 Overprinted

**1930** **Wmk. 140**

116 A101 20c yellow green 3.25 *9.50*
117 A101 50c + 10c dp orange 2.40 *9.50*
118 A101 1.25 l + 25c rose red 2.40 *19.00*
*Nos. 116-118 (3)* 8.05 *38.00*
Set, never hinged 20.00

Lancer — A5

Scene in Massaua A6

2c, 35c, Lancer. 5c, 10c, Postman. 15c, Lineman. 25c, Askari (infantryman). 2 l, Railroad viaduct. 5 l, Asmara Deghe Selam. 10 l, Camels.

**1930** **Wmk. 140** **Litho.** ***Perf. 14***

119 A5 2c brt bl & blk 4.75 *20.00*
120 A5 5c dk vio & blk 8.00 2.40
121 A5 10c yel brn & blk 8.00 1.25
122 A5 15c dk grn & blk 8.00 1.60
123 A5 25c gray grn & blk 8.00 1.25
124 A5 35c red brn & blk 12.50 *35.00*
125 A6 1 l dk bl & blk 8.00 1.25
126 A6 2 l choc & blk 12.50 *40.00*
127 A6 5 l ol grn & blk 24.00 *52.50*
128 A6 10 l dl bl & blk 32.50 *100.00*
*Nos. 119-128 (10)* 126.25 *255.25*
Set, never hinged 310.00

### Ferrucci Issue

**Types of Italian Stamps of 1930 Overprinted type "f" in Red or Blue**

**1930**

129 A102 20c violet (R) 6.50 *6.50*
130 A103 25c dk green (R) 6.50 *6.50*
131 A103 50c black (R) 6.50 *12.00*
132 A103 1.25 l dp blue (R) 6.50 *22.50*
133 A104 5 l + 2 l dp car (Bl) 14.50 *47.50*
*Nos. 129-133 (5)* 40.50 *95.00*
Set, never hinged 99.00

### Virgil Issue

**Types of Italian Stamps of 1930 Overprinted in Red or Blue**



**1930** **Photo.**

134 A106 15c violet black 1.25 *12.00*
135 A106 20c orange brown 1.25 *4.75*
136 A106 25c dark green 1.25 *4.75*
137 A106 30c lt brown 1.25 *4.75*
138 A106 50c dull violet 1.25 *4.75*
139 A106 75c rose red 1.25 *9.50*
140 A106 1.25 l gray blue 1.25 *12.00*

**Unwmk.** **Engr.**

141 A106 5 l + 1.50 l dk vio 4.75 *47.50*
142 A106 10 l + 2.50 l ol brn 4.75 *72.50*
*Nos. 134-142 (9)* 18.25 *172.50*
Set, never hinged 44.00

### Saint Anthony of Padua Issue

**Types of Italian Stamps of 1931 Overprinted type "f" in Blue, Red or Black**

**1931** **Photo.** **Wmk. 140**

143 A116 20c brown (Bl) 1.60 *22.50*
144 A116 25c green (R) 1.60 *8.00*
145 A118 30c gray brn (Bl) 1.60 *8.00*
146 A118 50c dl violet (Bl) 1.60 *8.00*
147 A120 1.25 l slate bl (R) 1.60 *40.00*

**Unwmk.** **Engr.**

148 A121 75c black (R) 1.60 *22.50*
149 A122 5 l + 2.50 l dk brn (Bk) 11.00 *80.00*
*Nos. 143-149 (7)* 20.60 *189.00*
Set, never hinged 55.00

Victor Emmanuel III — A13

**1931 Photo. Wmk. 140**

150 A13 7½c olive brown 1.60 *6.50*
151 A13 20c slate bl & car 1.60 .25
152 A13 30c ol grn & brn vio 1.60 .25
153 A13 40c bl & yel grn 2.40 .25
154 A13 50c bis brn & ol 1.60 .25
155 A13 75c carmine rose 4.75 .25
156 A13 1.25 l violet & indigo 6.50 6.50
157 A13 2.50 l dull green 6.50 14.50
*Nos. 150-157 (8)* 26.55 28.75
Set, never hinged 65.00

Camel A14

Temple Ruins — A18

Designs: 2c, 10c, Camel. 5c, 15c, Shark fishery. 25c, Baobab tree. 35c, Pastoral scene. 2 l, African elephant. 5 l, Eritrean man. 10 l, Eritrean woman.

**1934 Photo. Wmk. 140**

158 A14 2c deep blue 2.40 *4.75*
159 A14 5c black 4.00 .40
160 A14 10c brown 4.00 .35
161 A14 15c orange brn 4.75 *1.60*
162 A14 25c gray green 4.00 .35
163 A14 35c purple 12.50 *9.50*
164 A18 1 l dk blue gray .80 .35
165 A14 2 l olive black 35.00 3.25
166 A18 5 l carmine rose 19.00 6.50
167 A18 10 l red orange 27.50 *22.50*
*Nos. 158-167 (10)* 113.95 *49.55*
Set, never hinged 275.00

**Abruzzi Issue**

Types of 1934 Issue Overprinted in Black or Red

**1934**

168 A14 10c dull blue (R) 22.50 *32.50*
169 A14 15c blue 16.00 *32.50*
170 A14 35c green (R) 9.50 *32.50*
171 A18 1 l copper red 9.50 *32.50*
172 A14 2 l rose red 27.50 *32.50*
173 A18 5 l purple (R) 19.00 *55.00*
174 A18 10 l olive grn (R) 19.00 *72.50*
*Nos. 168-174 (7)* 123.00 *290.00*
Set, never hinged 300.00

Grant's Gazelle A22

**1934 Photo.**

175 A22 5c ol grn & brn 5.50 *22.50*
176 A22 10c yel brn & blk 5.50 *22.50*
177 A22 20c scar & indigo 5.50 *20.00*
178 A22 50c dk vio & brn 5.50 *20.00*
179 A22 60c org brn & ind 5.50 *27.50*
180 A22 1.25 l dk bl & grn 5.50 *47.50*
*Nos. 175-180 (6)* 33.00 *160.00*
Set, never hinged 80.00

Second Colonial Arts Exhibition, Naples. See Nos. C1-C6.

---

Between 1981 and 1986 unofficial labels appeared showing such non-Eritrean subjects as the British royal weddings, Queen Mother, Queen's birthday, and the Duke & Duchess of York. These labels are not listed.

---

In 1978, two sets of stamps were issued for use within liberated areas of Eritrea and to publicize the liberation effort. A May 26 set of 5c, 10c, 80c and 1b commemorated the 8th anniv. of the Eritrean People's Liberation Front (EPLF). An August 1 set of 80c, 1b, 1.50b featured the Future of Eritrea theme. A September 1, 1991 set of 5c, 15c and 20c was issued with a Freedom Fighter design in orange and black almost identical to design A24. Although the 80c from the 1st 1978 issue was available at the Asmara post office in late 1992 and early 1993, there is no evidence that any of these stamps were available at the time of independence. Thus these stamps are more properly considered locals and provisionals.

---

A23

Freedom Fighter with EPLF Flags

**1991, Jan. 16 Typo. *Perf. 11 rough***

192 A23 5c lt bl, blk & org *30.00 40.00*
193 A23 15c pale green, blk & org *30.00 40.00*
194 A23 20c pale yel, blk & org *30.00 40.00*
195 A23 3b silver, blk & org *25.00 25.00*
196 A23 5b gold, blk & org *25.00 25.00*

See footnotes following No. 199.

A24

**1993, Feb. 1 Litho. *Perf. 10***

197 A24 5c lt bl, blk & org *25.00 25.00*
198 A24 15c pale grn, blk & org *25.00 25.00*
199 A24 20c pale yel, blk & org *25.00 25.00*

Nos. 192-199 commemorate 30 years of the war for national liberation.

Nos. 192-199 were issued for local use, and became valid for international mail on Sept. 13, 1993.

**Catalogue values for unused stamps in this section, from this point to the end of the section, are for Never Hinged items.**

Referendum for Independence A25

Designs: 15c, Placing ballot in box. 60c, Group of arrows pointing right, one pointing left. 75c, Signs indicating "yes" & "no." 1b, Candle burning. 2b, Peace dove, horn over country map.

***Perf. 14x15***

**1993, Apr. 22 Litho. Wmk. 373**

200 A25 15c multicolored *1.50 1.50*
201 A25 60c multicolored *2.75 2.75*
202 A25 75c multicolored *4.00 4.00*
203 A25 1b multicolored *7.50 7.50*
204 A25 2b multicolored *10.00 10.00*
*Nos. 200-204 (5)* *25.75 25.75*

Natl. Flag — A26

**1993 Litho. *Perf. 11 rough***
**Blue Border**

205 A26 5c multicolored *2.50 .50*
206 A26 20c multicolored — —
207 A26 35c multicolored *4.25 2.00*
208 A26 50c multicolored *11.00 2.50*
209 A26 70c multicolored *3.50 3.50*
210 A26 80c multicolored *3.50 4.00*

The border of the 40c, No. 215, is similar to that of this issue but it was issued with next set. And the type face of the "0.40" matches that set.

**1994 Litho. *Perf. 11 rough***
**Color of Border**

211 A26 5c brown *2.00 1.50*
212 A26 15c red *2.00 1.50*
213 A26 20c gold *15.00*
214 A26 25c lt blue *2.00 1.50*
215 A26 40c blue *15.00 15.00*
216 A26 60c yellow *3.00 2.00*
217 A26 70c purple *3.00 2.25*
218 A26 3b light green *7.50 6.00*
219 A26 5b silver *9.00 6.00*

Flag & Map — A27

**1994, Sept. 2 Litho. *Perf. 13½x14***
**Color of Border**

220 A27 5c deep yellow *.45 .40*
221 A27 10c yellow green *.50 .45*
222 A27 20c salmon *.70 .65*
223 A27 25c red *1.25 1.25*
224 A27 40c lilac rose *1.40 1.25*
225 A27 60c blue green *1.50 1.25*
226 A27 70c dark green *1.60 1.50*
227 A27 1b yellow *1.60 1.50*
228 A27 2b orange *1.75 1.50*
229 A27 3b blue violet *1.90 1.75*
230 A27 5b red lilac *2.25 2.00*
231 A27 10b pale violet *3.75 3.50*
*Nos. 220-231 (12)* *18.65 17.00*

See Nos. 277A-277D.

World Tourism Organization, 20th Anniv. — A29

***Perf. 14x13½, 13½x14***

**1995, Jan. 2 Litho.**

232 A29 10c Fishing from boat *1.50 1.50*
233 A29 35c Monument, vert. *1.50 1.50*
234 A29 85c Winding road *3.00 3.00*
235 A29 2b Stone dwelling, vert. *5.00 5.00*
*Nos. 232-235 (4)* *11.00 11.00*

Fish — A30

Designs: 30c, Horned butterflyfish. 55c, Gonochaetodon larvatus. 70c, Shrimp lobster. 1b, Bluestripe snapper.

**1995, Apr. 1 *Perf. 14x13½***

236 A30 30c multicolored *.60 .60*
237 A30 55c multicolored *.85 .85*
238 A30 70c multicolored *1.25 1.25*
239 A30 1b multicolored *1.50 1.50*
*Nos. 236-239 (4)* *4.20 4.20*

Independence Day — A31

Designs: 25c, Breaking chains, mountain, buildings, animals. 40c, Raising natl. flag, vert. 70c, Three men, holding natl. flag, sword, vert. 3b, Natl. flag, fireworks, vert.

***Perf. 14x13½, 13½x14***

**1995, May 23 Litho.**

240 A31 25c multicolored *.40 .40*
241 A31 40c multicolored *.45 .45*
242 A31 70c multicolored *.70 .70*
243 A31 3b multicolored *1.40 1.40*
*Nos. 240-243 (4)* *2.95 2.95*

Future Development Plan — A32

**1995, Aug. 28 Litho. *Perf. 13***

244 A32 60c Building bridge *.60 .60*
245 A32 80c Trees *.75 .75*
246 A32 90c Rural village *.90 .90*
247 A32 1b Camels *1.00 1.00*
*Nos. 244-247 (4)* *3.25 3.25*

A33

**1995, Oct. 23 *Perf. 13½x14***

248 A33 40c shown *.30 .30*
249 A33 60c Tree, emblem *.40 .40*
250 A33 70c Dove, "50," emblem *.50 .50*
251 A33 2b like No. 248 *2.25 2.25*
*Nos. 248-251 (4)* *3.45 3.45*

UN, 50th anniv.

A34

COMESA, Committee for Economic Growth and Development in Southern Africa: 40c, Map of African member countries. 50c, Tree with country names on branches. 60c, Emblem, 3b, Emblem surrounded by country flags, horiz.

**1995, Oct. 2** *Perf. 13½x14, 14x13½*

| | | | | |
|---|---|---|---|---|
| **252** A34 40c multicolored | | | .30 | .30 |
| **253** A34 50c multicolored | | | .50 | .50 |
| **254** A34 60c multicolored | | | .60 | .60 |
| **255** A34 3b multicolored | | | 2.25 | 2.25 |
| *Nos. 252-255 (4)* | | | 3.65 | 3.65 |

FAO, 50th Anniv. — A35

5c, Food bowl with world map on it, spoon. 25c, Men with tractor. 80c, Mother bird feeding chicks. 3b, Vegetables in horn of plenty.

**1995, Dec. 18** **Litho.** *Perf. 13x14*

| | | |
|---|---|---|
| **256** A35 5c multicolored | .40 | .40 |
| **257** A35 25c multicolored | .40 | .40 |
| **258** A35 80c multicolored | .80 | .80 |
| **259** A35 3b multicolored | 2.50 | 2.50 |
| *Nos. 256-259 (4)* | 4.10 | 4.10 |

Endangered Fauna — A36

No. 260: a, Green monkey. b, Aardwolf. c, Dugong. d, Maned rat.

Beisa oryx: No. 261: a, With young. b, One facing left. c, Two with heads together. d, One facing right.

White-eyed gull: No. 262: a, Preening. b, In flight. c, Two standing. d, One facing right.

**1996, July 15** **Litho.** *Perf. 14*

**260-262** A36 3b Set of 3 strips 26.00 26.00

Nos. 260-262 were each issued in sheets of 12 stamps, containing three strips of four stamps, Nos. a.-d. No. 261 for World Wildlife Fund.

Martyrs Day — A37

**1996, June 17** **Litho.** *Perf. 13½x14*

| | | |
|---|---|---|
| **263** A37 40c People, flag | .40 | .40 |
| **264** A37 60c At grave | .40 | .40 |
| **265** A37 70c Mother, child | .80 | .80 |
| **266** A37 80c Planting crops | 1.00 | 1.00 |
| *Nos. 263-266 (4)* | 2.60 | 2.60 |

1996 Summer Olympic Games, Atlanta A38

No. 267, Cycling. No. 268, Basketball, vert. No. 269, Volleyball, vert. No. 270, Soccer.

No. 271, vert: a, Volleyball. b, Laurel wreath. c, Basketball. d, Torch. e, Cycling, yellow shirt. f, Torch, diff. g, Cycling, green shirt. h, Gold medal. i, Soccer.

Each 10b: No. 272, Soccer, vert. No. 273, Cycling, vert.

**1996, Nov. 20** **Litho.** *Perf. 14*

| | | |
|---|---|---|
| **267-270** A38 3b Set of 4 | 7.50 | 7.50 |
| **271** A38 2b Sheet of 9, #a.-i. | 11.00 | 11.00 |

**Souvenir Sheets**

**272-273** A38 Set of 2 11.00 11.00

UNICEF, 50th Anniv. A39

UNICEF emblem and: 40c, Mother with child. 55c, Nurse helping child. 60c, Weighing baby. 95c, Boy with one leg walking with crutch.

**1996, Dec. 9** **Litho.** *Perf. 14x13½*

| | | |
|---|---|---|
| **274** A39 40c multicolored | .45 | .45 |
| **275** A39 55c multicolored | .45 | .45 |
| **276** A39 60c multicolored | 1.00 | 1.00 |
| **277** A39 95c multicolored | 1.00 | 1.00 |
| *Nos. 274-277 (4)* | 2.90 | 2.90 |

**Flag and Map Type of 1994 Redrawn With Islands Added on Map at Lower Right**

**1996, Dec. 25** **Litho.** *Perf. 13½x14*

**Color of Border**

| | | |
|---|---|---|
| **277A** A27 20c salmon | — | — |
| **277B** A27 40c lilac rose | — | — |
| **277C** A27 60c blue green | — | — |
| **277D** A27 3b blue violet | — | — |

Revival of Eritrea Railway A40

Designs: 40c, Repairing track. 55c, Steam train arriving at station. 60c, Train shuttle transporting people. 95c, Train tunnel.

**1997, Jan. 10**

| | | |
|---|---|---|
| **278** A40 40c multicolored | .50 | .50 |
| **279** A40 55c multicolored | .50 | .50 |
| **280** A40 60c multicolored | .50 | .50 |
| **281** A40 95c multicolored | 1.50 | 1.50 |
| *Nos. 278-281 (4)* | 3.00 | 3.00 |

National Service A41

40c, Service members, speaker's platform, flags, vert. 55c, People looking over mountainside, vert. 60c, People digging ditches. 95c, Man standing on mountain top, overlooking valley, lake.

**1996, Dec. 28** *Perf. 13½x14, 14x13½*

| | | |
|---|---|---|
| **282** A41 40c multicolored | .75 | .75 |
| **283** A41 55c multicolored | .75 | .75 |
| **284** A41 60c multicolored | 1.25 | 1.25 |
| **285** A41 95c multicolored | 2.00 | 2.00 |
| *Nos. 282-285 (4)* | 4.75 | 4.75 |

Butterflies and Moths A42

1b, Pieris napi. 2b, Heliconius melpomerie. 4b, Ornithoptera goliath. 8b, Heliconius astraea.

No. 290, vert, each 3b: a, Psaphis eusehemoides. b, Papilio brookiana. c, Parnassius charitonius. d, Morpho cypris. e, Dariaus plexippus. f, Precis octavia. g, Teinopalpus imperialis. h, Samia gloreri. i, Automeris nyctimene.

No. 291, each 3b: a, Papilio polymnestar. b, Ornithoptera paradiseo. c, Graphium marcellus. d, Panaxia quadripunctaria. e, Cardui japonica. f, Papilio childrence. g, Philosamea cynthis. h, Actias luna. i, Heticopis acit.

Each 10b: No. 292, Papilio glaucus. No. 293, Parnassius phoebus.

**1997, June 16** **Litho.** *Perf. 14*

**286-289** A42 Set of 4 12.00 12.00

**Sheets of 9**

**290-291** A42 3b Set of 2 Sheets, #a.-i. 30.00 30.00

**Souvenir Sheets**

**292-293** A42 10b Set of 2 Sheets 15.00 15.00

Environmental Protection — A43

**1997, Aug. 15** **Litho.** *Perf. 14x13½*

| | | |
|---|---|---|
| **294** A43 60c Irrigation | .90 | .90 |
| **295** A43 90c Reforestation | .90 | .90 |
| **296** A43 95c Preventing erosion | 2.00 | 2.00 |
| *Nos. 294-296 (3)* | 3.80 | 3.80 |

Marine Life A44

No. 297, each 3n: a, Sergeant major, white tipped reef shark. b, Hawksbill turtle, devil ray (e). c, Surgeonfish. d, Red sea houndfish, humpback whale (a, g). e, Devil ray (b, f, h). f, Devil ray (e, c), two-banded clownfish. g, Long-nosed butterflyfish. h, Red sea houndfish (g), yellow sweetlips (i). i, White moray eel.

No. 298, each 3n: a, Masked butterflyfish. b, Suckerfish (a), whale shark (a). c, Sunrise dottyback, bluefin trevally. d, Moon wrasse (a), purple moon angel (a), two-banded anemonefish. e, Lionfish (b, f). f, White tipped shark, sand diver fish. g, Golden jacks (d), lunar tailed grouper. h, Batfish (e, i). i, Black triggerfish.

Each 10n: No. 299, Powder-blue surgeonfish. No. 300, Twin-spot wrasse.

**1997, Dec. 29** **Litho.** *Perf. 14*

**Sheets of 9, #a.-i.**

**297-298** A44 Set of 2 20.00 20.00

**Souvenir Sheets**

**299-300** A44 Set of 2 Sheets 12.50 12.50

A45

Natl. Constitution: 10c, Speaker, crowd seated beneath tree. 40c, Dove, scales of justice. 85c, Hands holding constitution.

**1997, Oct. 24** **Litho.** *Perf. 13½x14*

**301-303** A45 Set of 3 3.50 3.50

A46

Birds — No. 304, each 3n: a, African darter (b, d, e). b, White-headed vulture (e). c, Egyptian vulture (f). d, Yellow-billed hornbill (g). e, Helmeted guineafowl (d, f). f, Secretary bird (d, e, i). g, Martial eagle (h). h, Bateleur eagle (i). i, Red-billed queleas.

No. 305, each 3n: a, Black-headed weaver. b, Abyssinian roller (c, f). c, Abyssinian ground hornbill (b, e, f). d, Lichtenstein's sandgrouse. e, Erckel's francolin (d, g, h). f, Arabian bustard (e, i). g, Chestnut-backed finch-lark. h, Desert lark. i, Bifasciated lark.

Each 10n: #306, Peregrine falcon. #307, Hoopoe.

**1998, Mar. 16** **Litho.** *Perf. 14*

**Sheets of 9, #a.-i.**

**304-305** A46 Set of 2 25.00 25.00

**Souvenir Sheets**

**306-307** A46 Set of 2 Sheets 12.00 12.00

Dwellings — A47

**1998, July 1** **Litho.** *Perf. 13½x14*

| | | |
|---|---|---|
| **308** A47 50c Highlanders | 1.50 | 1.50 |
| **309** A47 60c Lowlanders | 1.50 | 1.50 |
| **310** A47 85c Danakils (Afars) | 1.50 | 1.50 |
| *Nos. 308-310 (3)* | 4.50 | 4.50 |

Traditional Hair Styles — A48

**1998, Nov. 23** **Litho.** *Perf. 13½x14*

| | | |
|---|---|---|
| **311** A48 10c Cunama | .30 | .30 |
| **312** A48 50c Tignnys | .60 | .60 |
| **313** A48 85c Bllen | 1.00 | 1.00 |
| **314** A48 95c Tigre | 1.25 | 1.25 |
| *Nos. 311-314 (4)* | 3.15 | 3.15 |

Dated 1997.

A49

Traditional Musical Instruments: 15c, Chirawata. 60c, Imbilta, malaket, shambeko. 75c, Kobero. 85c, K'rar.

**1998, Dec. 28** **Litho.** *Perf. 13½x14*

| | | |
|---|---|---|
| **315** A49 15c multicolored | .35 | .35 |
| **316** A49 60c multicolored | .60 | .60 |
| **317** A49 75c multicolored | .80 | .80 |
| **318** A49 85c multicolored | 1.00 | 1.00 |
| *Nos. 315-318 (4)* | 2.75 | 2.75 |

A50

**1999, May 25** **Litho.** *Perf. 13¼x14*

| | | |
|---|---|---|
| **319** A50 60c green & multi | .60 | .60 |
| **320** A50 1n red & multi | 1.00 | 1.00 |
| **321** A50 3n blue & multi | 4.00 | 4.00 |
| *Nos. 319-321 (3)* | 5.60 | 5.60 |

Independence, 8th Anniv.

1997 Introduction of Nakfa Currency — A51

Bank notes: 10c, 1 Nakfa. 60c, 5 Nakfa. 80c, 10 Nakfa. 1n, 20 Nakfa. 2n, 50 Nakfa. 3n, 100 Nakfa.

**1999, Nov. 8 Litho. *Perf. 13¼***

| | | | | |
|---|---|---|---|---|
| **322** | A51 | 10c multicolored | .45 | .45 |
| **323** | A51 | 60c multicolored | .60 | .60 |
| **324** | A51 | 80c multicolored | .75 | .75 |
| **325** | A51 | 1n multicolored | 1.00 | 1.00 |
| **326** | A51 | 2n multicolored | 2.00 | 2.00 |
| **327** | A51 | 3n multicolored | 3.50 | 3.50 |
| | | *Nos. 322-327 (6)* | 8.30 | 8.30 |

Natl. Union of Eritrean Women, 20th Anniv. A52

Designs: 5c, Woman and child, vert. 10c, Three women. 25c, Women and flag. 1n, Woman with binoculars.

***Perf. 13¼x14, 14x13¼***

**1999, Nov. 26**

| | | | | |
|---|---|---|---|---|
| **328** | A52 | 5c multicolored | .35 | .35 |
| **329** | A52 | 10c multicolored | .35 | .35 |
| **330** | A52 | 25c multicolored | .50 | .50 |
| **331** | A52 | 1n multicolored | .75 | .75 |
| | | *Nos. 328-331 (4)* | 1.95 | 1.95 |

A53

Marine Life A54

No. 332, each 3n: a, Coachwhip ray. b, Sulfur damselfish. c, "Gray moray." d, Sabre squirrelfish. e, Rusty parrotfish. f, "Striped eel catfish."

No. 333, each 3n: a, Spangled emperor. b, Devil scorpionfish. c, Crown squirrelfish. d, Vanikoro sweeper. e, Sergeant major. f, Giant manta.

No. 334, each 3n: a, Chilomycterus spilostylus. b, Dascyllus marginatus. c, Balistapus undulatus. d, Pomacanthus semicirculatus. e, Rhinecanthus assasi. f, Millepora.

No. 335, each 3n: a, Epinephalus fasciata. b, Pygoplites diacanthus. c, Cephalopholis miniata. d, Centropyge eibli. e, Ostracion cubicus. f, Heniochus acuminatus.

Each 10n: No. 336, Centropyge flavissimus. No. 337, Larabicus quadrilineatus. No. 338, Anthias squamipinnis. 15n, Pomacanthus maculosus.

**2000, Apr. 17 Litho. *Perf. 14***

**Sheets of 6, #a.-f.**

| | | | | |
|---|---|---|---|---|
| **332-333** | A53 | Set of 2 | 13.50 | 13.50 |
| **334-335** | A54 | Set of 2 | 13.50 | 13.50 |

**Souvenir Sheets**

| | | | | |
|---|---|---|---|---|
| **336-338** | A54 | Set of 3 | 15.00 | 15.00 |
| **339** | A54 | 15n multi | 6.00 | 6.00 |

Illustrations on Nos. 332c and 332f were switched.

A55

Flag and: 5c, Man with sword. 10c, Ship Denden Assab. 25c, Independence Day festivities. 60c, Soldiers and barracks. 1n, Finger, heart and map. 2n, People under tree. 3n, Ballot box. 5n, Eritrean seal, military plane, tank, ship. 7n, Seal. 10n, Ten-nakfa note.

***Perf. 13¾x13¼***

**2000, Mar. 17 Litho.**

**Denominations in Sans-Serif Type**

| | | | | |
|---|---|---|---|---|
| **340-349** | A55 | Set of 10 | 16.00 | 16.00 |

See Nos. 363A-363F.

Worldwide Fund for Nature (WWF) — A56

Proteles cristatus: a, Laying down. b. Pair in den. c, Walking. d, Close-up.

**2001, Oct. 1 Litho. *Perf. 14***

| | | | | |
|---|---|---|---|---|
| **350** | A56 | 3n Block or strip of 4, #a-d | 4.50 | 4.50 |

Wild Animals — A57

No. 351, 3n: a, Salt's dik-dik. b, Klipspringer. c, Greater kudu. d, Soemmering's gazelle. e, Dorcas gazelle. f, Somali wild ass.

No. 352, 3n: a, Aardvark. b, Black-backed jackal. c, Striped hyena. d, Spotted hyena. e, East African leopard. f, African elephant.

**2001, Oct. 29**

**Sheets of 6, #a-f**

| | | | | |
|---|---|---|---|---|
| **351-352** | A57 | Set of 2 | 10.00 | 10.00 |

Struggle for Independence, 10th Anniv. — A58

Designs: 20c, Women, flag, jewelry. 60c, Doves, stylized flag, vert. 1n, Bees, honeycomb, flag, vert. 3n, Men with sticks, vert.

***Perf. 13x13¼, 13¼x13***

**2001, May 23 Litho.**

| | | | | |
|---|---|---|---|---|
| **353-356** | A58 | Set of 4 | 3.00 | 3.00 |

Liberation of Nakfa, 25th Anniv. A59

Designs: 50c, Denden. 1n, Town of Nakfa, 1977 (77x27mm). 3n, First Organizational Congress of the Eritrean People's Liberation Front (77x27mm).

**2002, Mar. 23 Litho. *Perf. 14x13¼***

| | | | | |
|---|---|---|---|---|
| **357-359** | A59 | Set of 3 | 2.00 | 2.00 |

Martyr's Day — A60

Designs: 1n, People and map. 2n, Hand, map of Badma area, and flag. 3n, Map and ship. 5n, Dove, map and dead man (49x29mm, triangular).

***Perf. 14x13¼, 13½ (5n)***

**2002, June 20**

| | | | | |
|---|---|---|---|---|
| **360-363** | A60 | Set of 4 | 4.50 | 4.50 |

**Type of 2000 Redrawn**

Flag and: 30c, People under tree. 45c, Man with sword. 50c, Independence Day festivities. 60c, Soldiers and barracks. 75c, Ship Denden Assab. 3n, Ballot box.

**2002, Oct. 21 Litho. *Perf. 13¼x14¼***

**Denominations in Serifed Type**

| | | | | |
|---|---|---|---|---|
| **363A** | A55 | 30c multi | | — |
| **363B** | A55 | 45c multi | — | — |
| **363C** | A55 | 50c multi | — | — |
| **363D** | A55 | 60c multi | — | — |
| **363E** | A55 | 75c multi | — | — |
| **363F** | A55 | 3n multi | — | — |

Denominations on Nos. 340-349 are in sans-serif type.

Dr. Fred C. Hollows (1929-93), Ophthalmologist A61

Designs: 50c, Portrait. 1n, Hollows wearing ophthalmological equipment. 2n, Hollows with man.

**2003, Feb. 10 *Perf. 13¼x14***

| | | | | |
|---|---|---|---|---|
| **364-366** | A61 | Set of 3 | 2.00 | 2.00 |

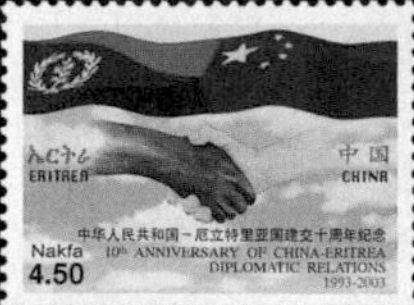

Eritrea — People's Republic of China Diplomatic Relations, 10th Anniv. A62

**2003, May 24 *Perf. 12***

| | | | | |
|---|---|---|---|---|
| **367** | A62 | 4.50n multi | 2.50 | 2.50 |

Eritrean postal authorities have declared "illegal" the following items:

Sheetlet of nine 5n stamps depicting Trains;

Sheetlets of nine 3n stamps depicting Marilyn Monroe (two different), Dogs, The Beatles "Yellow Submarine," September 11 firefighters, Brigitte Bardot, Grace Kelly, Sophia Loren, Golf etiquette, Sexy actresses, Sexy models, Boris Vallejo nudes, Dorian Cleavenger, Michael Möbius, Olivia, Ricky Carralero, Concorde;

Sheetlets of six stamps with various denominations depicting Lighthouses (with Rotary emblem) (two different), Hopper paintings (two different), Vettriano paintings (two different), Marilyn Monroe (two different), Elvgren pin-ups (two different), Teddy bears (two different);

Sheetlets of six 3n stamps depicting Van Gogh paintings, Paintings of nudes;

Sheetlets of five 3n stamps depicting Corot paintings, Pisarro paintings, Renoir paintings, Elvis Presley, Marilyn Monroe;

Sheetlets of four stamps with various denominations depicting Pandas (with Scouting emblem), Crocodiles (with Scouting emblem), Buffalos (with Rotary emblem), Elephants (with Rotary emblem), Monkeys (with Scouting emblem), Lizards (with Scouting emblem), Snakes (with Scouting Emblem), Turtles (with Rotary emblem), Wild cats (with Scouting emblem), Birds of prey (with Rotary emblem), Fowl (with Rotary emblem), Parrots (with Scouting emblem), Penguins (with Rotary emblem), Fish (with Rotary emblem), Marine life (with Scouting emblem), Mushrooms (with Rotary emblem), Butterflies (with Scouting emblem), Bees (with Scouting emblem), Spiders (with Scouting emblem);

Sheetlets of four 3n stamps depicting Dinosaurs (with Scouting emblem), Dinosaurs (with Rotary emblem) Elephants (with Scouting emblem), Elephants (with Rotary emblem), Horses (with Scouting emblem), Horses (with Rotary emblem), Birds (with Scouting emblem), Birds (with Rotary emblem), Penguins (with Scouting emblem), Penguins (with Rotary emblem), Orchids (with Scouting emblem), Orchids (with Rotary emblem), Butterflies (with Scouting emblem), Butterflies (with Rotary emblem), Cars (with Scouting emblem), Cars (with Rotary emblem), Motorcycles (with Scouting emblem), Motorcycles (with Rotary emblem), Trains (with Scouting emblem), Trains (with Rotary emblem);

Sheetlets of three 5n stamps depicting Dinosaurs (with Rotary emblem) (two different), Pandas;

Strips of three 5n stamps depicting Steam trains (four different);

Souvenir sheet with one 8n stamp depicting Steam Trains (with Rotary emblem) (two different), Dinosaurs (with Rotary emblem), Pandas (with Scouting emblem), Elephants (with Scouting emblem), Tigers (with Scouting emblem), Birds of prey (with Scouting emblem);

Souvenir sheets with one 5n stamp depicting Marilyn Monroe (six different), Lighthouses (with Rotary emblem) (four different), Teddy bears (four different), Hopper paintings (two different), Vettriano paintings (two different).

Eritrean Railway A63

Independence Celebrations A63a

Massawa A63b

**2003 Litho. *Perf. 14x13¼***

**Denomination Color**

| | | | | | |
|---|---|---|---|---|---|
| **368** | A63 | 5c Prussian blue | .25 | .25 |
| **369** | A63 | 10c greenish blk | .25 | .25 |
| **370** | A63 | 15c lilac | .25 | .25 |
| **371** | A63 | 35c violet | .25 | .25 |
| **372** | A63 | 50c orange | .25 | .25 |
| **373** | A63 | 90c olive green | .25 | .25 |
| **374** | A63 | 1n red | .25 | .25 |
| **375** | A63 | 2n blue violet | .55 | .55 |
| **376** | A63 | 10n red | 2.75 | 2.75 |
| **376A** | A63a | 50n white | 12.00 | 12.00 |
| **376B** | A63b | 75n white | 18.00 | 18.00 |
| **376C** | A63 | 100n white | 24.00 | 24.00 |
| | | *Nos. 368-376C (12)* | 59.05 | 59.05 |

Issued: 50n, 75n, 100n, 8/29.

Liberation of Massawa, 14th Anniv. A64

Designs: 40c, Tanks as fountains. 50c, Boat with soldiers.

No. 379: a, 3n, Crashed airplane, people, soldiers in shallow water. b, 3n, Tank, soldier, flag, boat. c, 4n, People, buildings at shore.

**2004**

**377-378** A64 Set of 2 1.00 1.00

**Miniature Sheet**

**379** A64 Sheet of 3, #a-c 4.00 4.00

Man and Camels — A65

Man and Cattle A66

Highland Woman, Child and Camel — A67

**2004, July 12 Litho. *Perf. 12***

**Frame Color**

| | | | | |
|---|---|---|---|---|
| **380** | A65 | 20c violet blue | .25 | .25 |
| **381** | A65 | 25c red violet | .25 | .25 |
| **382** | A65 | 40c brown | .25 | .25 |
| **383** | A66 | 50c red | .25 | .25 |
| **384** | A66 | 55c green | .25 | .25 |
| **385** | A66 | 60c light blue | .25 | .25 |
| **386** | A67 | 80c olive green | .50 | .50 |
| **387** | A67 | 1n orange | .50 | .50 |
| **388** | A67 | 4.50n blue | 1.25 | 1.25 |
| | | *Nos. 380-388 (9)* | 3.75 | 3.75 |

A68

A69

Monuments and Statues — A70

***Perf. 13¼x14, 14x13¼***

**2006, Jan. 5 Litho.**

| | | | | |
|---|---|---|---|---|
| **389** | A68 | 1.50n multi | .25 | .25 |
| **390** | A69 | 6n multi | .80 | .80 |
| **391** | A70 | 25n multi | 3.50 | 3.50 |
| | | *Nos. 389-391 (3)* | 4.55 | 4.55 |

China - Africa Cooperation Forum, Beijing — A71

**2006, Nov. 3 Litho. *Perf. 12***

**392** A71 7n multi .95 .95

African Soccer Confederation, 50th Anniv. — A72

Anniversary emblem and: 3n, Eritrean soccer players and flags. 5n, Soccer field. 10n, Soccer players in action.

**2007, May 29 Litho. *Perf. 13x13¼***

**393-395** A72 Set of 3 2.40 2.40

Soldiers Carrying Flag — A73

**2008, Dec. 31 Litho. *Perf. 14x13¼***

**Denomination Color**

| | | | | |
|---|---|---|---|---|
| **396** | A73 | 15c dark blue | .25 | .25 |
| **397** | A73 | 35c green | .25 | .25 |
| **398** | A73 | 50c orange | .25 | .25 |
| **399** | A73 | 70c red | .25 | .25 |
| **400** | A73 | 75c blue | .25 | .25 |
| **401** | A73 | 90c brown | .25 | .25 |
| **402** | A73 | 1.50n red violet | .25 | .25 |
| **403** | A73 | 2n indigo | .25 | .25 |
| **404** | A73 | 3n org yellow | .40 | .40 |
| **405** | A73 | 5n gray | .65 | .65 |
| **406** | A73 | 10n yel green | 1.25 | 1.25 |
| | | *Nos. 396-406 (11)* | 4.30 | 4.30 |

Eritrean National Festival A74

Ethnic groups in costume: 5c, Afars. 10c, Bilens. 30c, Hedarebs. 95c, Kunamas. 1n, Naras. 1.50n, Rashaidas. 4n, Sahos. 7n, Tigres. 8n, Tigrinyas.

**2010, Nov. 15**

**407-415** A74 Set of 9 4.25 4.25

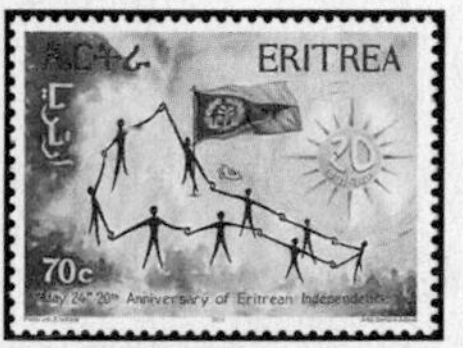

Independence, 20th Anniv. — A75

Designs: 70c, Eritrean flag, stylized people defining border. 95c, Map of Eritrea, hand holding torch, vert. 8n, Map of Africa, flag of Eritrea, vert.

**2011, Mar. 24 *Perf. 14x13¼, 13¼x14***

**416-418** A75 Set of 3 2.00 2.00

Eritrean Martyr's Day, 20th Anniv. — A76

Designs: 80c, Eritreans and woman holding shining square. 9n, Woamn and child lighting candles

**2011, June 17 *Perf. 13¾x13¼***

**419-420** A76 Set of 2 2.10 2.10

Eritrean Armed Struggle, 50th Anniv. — A77

Designs: 1.50n, Arm holding rifle, "50," flame, stylized people. 7n, Flame, arms holding rifles.

**2011, Sept. 3 *Perf. 13¼x14***

**421-422** A77 Set of 2 1.75 1.75

Miniature Sheet

Diplomatic Relations Between Eritrea and People's Republic of China, 20th Anniv. — A78

No. 423: a, 1n, Mosque, Nakfa, Eritrea. b, 1n, Harbor, Massawa, Eritrea. c, 1.50n, Pagoda and bridge, Yan'an, People's Republic of China. d, 1.50n, Harbor, Qingdao, People's Republic of China. e, 7n, Buildings, Asmara, Eritrea. f, 7n, Camels. g, 10n, Buildings, Datong, People's Republic of China. h, 10n, Antelopes.

**2013, May 27 Litho. *Perf. 12***

**423** A78 Block of 8, #a-h 8.50 8.50

*i.* Souvenir sheet of 8, #423a-423h 8.50 8.50

Gelaalo A79

**2013, June 27 Litho. *Perf. 13x13¼***

**Frame Color**

| | | | | |
|---|---|---|---|---|
| **424** | A79 | 55c orange yellow | .50 | .50 |
| **425** | A79 | 60c green | .55 | .55 |
| **426** | A79 | 70c purple | .60 | .60 |
| **427** | A79 | 80c blue | .70 | .70 |
| **428** | A79 | 90c red | .80 | .80 |
| **429** | A79 | 95c olive yellow | .85 | .85 |
| **430** | A79 | 1.50n yellow brown | 1.40 | 1.40 |
| **431** | A79 | 50n light blue | 42.50 | 42.50 |
| | | *Nos. 424-431 (8)* | 47.90 | 47.90 |

Operation Fenkil, 25th Anniv. — A80

Designs: 3n, Soldiers watching man in water. 7n, Tank in Massawa. 10n, Soldiers watching people in boats.

***Perf. 13¼x13¾***

**2015, Feb. 10 Litho.**

**432-434** A80 Set of 3 4.25 4.25

A81

Liberation of Eritrea, 25th Anniv. A82

**2016 Litho. *Perf. 14x14¼***

**435** A81 7n multi 1.40 1.40
**436** A82 8n multi 1.60 1.60

Souvenir Sheet

Liberation of Eritrea, 25th Anniv. — A83

No. 437: a, 3n, Eritrean flag. b, 4n, Flagbearer and camel's head. c, 5n, Body of camel.

**2016 Litho. *Perf. 14x13½***

**437** A83 Sheet of 3, #a-c 2.75 2.75

## SEMI-POSTAL STAMPS

Many issues of Italy and Italian Colonies include one or more semipostal denominations. To avoid splitting sets, these issues are generally listed as regular postage, airmail, etc., unless all values carry a surtax.

### Italy Nos. B1-B3 Overprinted type "f"

**1915-16 Wmk. 140 *Perf. 14***

**B1** SP1 10c + 5c rose 4.00 *16.00*
*a.* "EPITREA" 32.50 *45.00*
*b.* Inverted overprint 800.00 800.00
**B2** SP2 15c + 5c slate 32.50 *27.50*
**B3** SP2 20c + 5c orange 4.75 *35.00*
*a.* "EPITREA" 80.00 *110.00*
*b.* Inverted overprint 800.00 800.00
*c.* Pair, one without ovpt. — *4,500.*
*Nos. B1-B3 (3)* 41.25 *78.50*
Set, never hinged 102.00

No. B2 Surcharged

**1916**

**B4** SP2 20c on 15c+5c slate 32.50 *35.00*
Never hinged 80.00
*a.* "EPITREA" 80.00 *110.00*
*b.* Pair, one without overprint 2,000.
Never hinged 2,500.

Counterfeits exist of the minor varieties of Nos. B1, B3-B4.

### Holy Year Issue
### Italy Nos. B20-B25 Overprinted in Black or Red

**1925 *Perf. 12***

**B5** SP4 20c + 10c dk grn & brn 4.00 *24.00*
**B6** SP4 30c + 15c dk brn & brn 4.00 *27.50*
*a.* Double overprint
**B7** SP4 50c + 25c vio & brn 4.00 *24.00*
**B8** SP4 60c + 30c dp rose & brn 4.00 *32.50*
*a.* Inverted overprint
**B9** SP8 1 l + 50c dp bl & vio (R) 4.00 *40.00*
**B10** SP8 5 l + 2.50 l org brn & vio (R) 4.00 *60.00*
*Nos. B5-B10 (6)* 24.00 *208.00*
Set, never hinged 60.00

### Colonial Institute Issue

"Peace" Substituting Spade for Sword — SP1

**1926 Typo. *Perf. 14***

**B11** SP1 5c + 5c brown 1.20 *9.50*
**B12** SP1 10c + 5c olive grn 1.20 *9.50*
**B13** SP1 20c + 5c blue grn 1.20 *9.50*
**B14** SP1 40c + 5c brown red 1.20 *9.50*
**B15** SP1 60c + 5c orange 1.20 *9.50*
**B16** SP1 1 l + 5c blue 1.20 *20.00*
*Nos. B11-B16 (6)* 7.20 *67.50*
Set, never hinged 18.00

The surtax of 5c on each stamp was for the Italian Colonial Institute.

Italian Semi-Postal Stamps of 1926 Overprinted

**1927 Unwmk. *Perf. 11½***

**B17** SP10 40c + 20c dk brn & blk 4.00 *45.00*
**B18** SP10 60c + 30c brn red & ol brn 4.00 *45.00*
**B19** SP10 1.25 l + 60c dp bl & blk 4.00 *65.00*
**B20** SP10 5 l + 2.50 l dk grn & blk 6.50 *100.00*
*Nos. B17-B20 (4)* 18.50 *255.00*
Set, never hinged 46.00

The surtax on these stamps was for the charitable work of the Voluntary Militia for Italian National Defense.

Fascism and Victory — SP2

**1928 Wmk. 140 Typo. *Perf. 14***

**B21** SP2 20c + 5c blue grn 3.25 *14.00*
**B22** SP2 30c + 5c red 3.25 *14.00*
**B23** SP2 50c + 10c purple 3.25 *24.00*
**B24** SP2 1.25 l + 20c dk blue 4.00 *32.50*
*Nos. B21-B24 (4)* 13.75 *84.50*
Set, never hinged 34.00

The surtax was for the Society Africana d'Italia, whose 46th anniv. was commemorated by the issue.

### Types of Italian Semi-Postal Stamps of 1928 Overprinted type "f"

**1929 Unwmk. *Perf. 11***

**B25** SP10 30c + 10c red & blk 4.75 *27.50*
**B26** SP10 50c + 20c vio & blk 4.75 *30.00*
**B27** SP10 1.25 l + 50c brn & bl 7.25 *52.50*
**B28** SP10 5 l + 2 l olive grn & blk 7.25 *100.00*
*Nos. B25-B28 (4)* 24.00 *210.00*
Set, never hinged 60.00

Surtax for the charitable work of the Voluntary Militia for Italian Natl. Defense.

### Types of Italian Semi-Postal Stamps of 1930 Overprinted type "f" in Black or Red

**1930 *Perf. 14***

**B29** SP10 30c + 10c dk grn & bl grn (Bk) 35.00 *65.00*
**B30** SP10 50c + 10c dk grn & vio 35.00 *100.00*
**B31** SP10 1.25 l + 30c ol brn & red brn 35.00 *100.00*
**B32** SP10 5 l + 1.50 l ind & grn 120.00 *275.00*
*Nos. B29-B32 (4)* 225.00 *540.00*
Set, never hinged 560.00

Surtax for the charitable work of the Voluntary Militia for Italian Natl. Defense.

Agriculture — SP3

**1930 Photo. Wmk. 140**

**B33** SP3 50c + 20c ol brn 4.00 *25.00*
**B34** SP3 1.25 l + 20c dp bl 4.00 *25.00*
**B35** SP3 1.75 l + 20c green 4.00 *27.50*
**B36** SP3 2.55 l + 50c purple 9.50 *45.00*
**B37** SP3 5 l + 1 l dp car 9.50 *67.50*
*Nos. B33-B37 (5)* 31.00 *190.00*
Set, never hinged 76.00

Italian Colonial Agricultural Institute, 25th anniv. The surtax aided that institution.

## AIR POST STAMPS

Desert Scene AP1

Design: 80c, 1 l, 2 l, Plane and globe.

**Wmk. Crowns (140)**

**1934, Oct. 17 Photo. *Perf. 14***

**C1** AP1 25c sl bl & org red 5.50 *22.50*
**C2** AP1 50c grn & indigo 5.50 *20.00*
**C3** AP1 75c brn & org red 5.50 *20.00*
**C4** AP1 80c org brn & ol grn 5.50 *22.50*
**C5** AP1 1 l scar & ol grn 5.50 *27.50*
**C6** AP1 2 l dk bl & brn 5.50 *47.50*
*Nos. C1-C6 (6)* 33.00 *160.00*
Set, never hinged 81.00

Second Colonial Arts Exhibition, Naples.

Plowing AP3

Plane and Cacti AP6

Designs: 25c, 1.50 l, Plowing. 50c, 2 l, Plane over mountain pass. 60c, 5 l, Plane and trees. 75c, 10 l, Plane and cacti. 1 l, 3 l, Bridge.

**1936 Photo.**

**C7** AP3 25c deep green 4.75 *4.75*
**C8** AP3 50c dark brown 3.25 .35
**C9** AP3 60c brown orange 6.50 *16.00*
**C10** AP6 75c orange brown 4.75 1.60
**C11** AP3 1 l deep blue 1.60 .35
**C12** AP3 1.50 l purple 6.50 .85
**C13** AP3 2 l gray blue 6.50 *3.25*
**C14** AP3 3 l copper red 25.00 27.50
**C15** AP3 5 l green 19.00 8.00
**C16** AP6 10 l rose red 45.00 27.50
*Nos. C7-C16 (10)* 122.85 90.15
Set, never hinged 300.00

## AIR POST SEMI-POSTAL STAMPS

King Victor Emmanuel III — SPAP1

**1934 Wmk. 140 Photo. *Perf. 14***

**CB1** SPAP1 25c + 10c 9.50 *27.50*
**CB2** SPAP1 50c + 10c 9.50 *27.50*
**CB3** SPAP1 75c + 15c 9.50 *27.50*
**CB4** SPAP1 80c + 15c 9.50 *27.50*
**CB5** SPAP1 1 l + 20c 9.50 *27.50*
**CB6** SPAP1 2 l + 20c 9.50 *27.50*
**CB7** SPAP1 3 l + 25c 27.50 *125.00*
**CB8** SPAP1 5 l + 25c 27.50 *125.00*
**CB9** SPAP1 10 l + 30c 27.50 *125.00*
**CB10** SPAP1 25 l + 2 l 27.50 *125.00*
*Nos. CB1-CB10 (10)* 167.00 *665.00*
Set, never hinged 410.00

65th birthday of King Victor Emmanuel III and the nonstop flight from Rome to Mogadiscio. Used values are for stamps canceled to order.

## AIR POST SEMI-POSTAL OFFICIAL STAMP

### Type of Air Post Semi-Postal Stamps, 1934, Overprinted in Black

**1934 Wmk. 140 *Perf. 14***

**CBO1** SPAP1 25 l + 2 l cop red *2,800.*
Never hinged *5,500.*

## SPECIAL DELIVERY STAMPS

### Special Delivery Stamps of Italy, Overprinted type "a"

**1907 Wmk. 140 *Perf. 14***

**E1** SD1 25c rose red 24.00 20.00
Never hinged 60.00
*a.* Double overprint — —

**1909**

**E2** SD2 30c blue & rose 145.00 *240.00*
Never hinged 375.00

**1920**

**E3** SD1 50c dull red 4.00 *24.00*
Never hinged 10.00

"Italia" SD1

**1924 Engr. Unwmk.**

E4 SD1 60c dk red & brn 6.50 *24.00*
a. Perf. 13½ 14.00 *40.00*
E5 SD1 2 l dk blue & red 17.50 *27.50*
Set, never hinged 59.00

For surcharges see Nos. E6-E8.

### Nos. E4 and E5 Surcharged in Dark Blue or Red

v

w

**1926**

E6 SD1 70c on 60c (Bl) 6.50 *16.00*
E7 SD1 2.50 l on 2 l (R) 17.50 *27.50*
Set, never hinged 60.00

### Type of 1924 Surcharged in Blue or Black

**1927-35 *Perf. 11***

E8 SD1 1.25 l on 60c dk red & brn (Bl) 16.00 4.00
Never hinged 40.00
a. Perf. 14 (Bl) ('35) 110.00 24.00
Never hinged 275.00
b. Perf. 11 (Bk) ('35) *9,500.* 1,250.
Never hinged *14,500.*
c. Perf. 14 (Bk) ('35) 400.00 65.00
Never hinged 1,000.

## AUTHORIZED DELIVERY STAMP

### Authorized Delivery Stamp of Italy, No. EY2, Overprinted Type "f" in Black

**1939-41 Wmk. 140 *Perf. 14***

EY1 AD2 10c dk brown ('41) .80 —
Never hinged 2.00
a. 10c reddish brown 27.50 *47.50*
Never hinged 72.50

On No. EY1a, which was used in Italian East Africa, the overprint hits the figures "10." On No. EY1, which was sold in Rome, the overprint falls above the 10's.

## POSTAGE DUE STAMPS

### Postage Due Stamps of Italy Overprinted type "a" at Top

**1903 Wmk. 140 *Perf. 14***

J1 D3 5c buff & mag 24.00 *47.50*
a. Double overprint 550.00
J2 D3 10c buff & mag 16.00 *47.50*
J3 D3 20c buff & mag 16.00 *32.50*
J4 D3 30c buff & mag 24.00 *35.00*
J5 D3 40c buff & mag 80.00 *72.50*
J6 D3 50c buff & mag 87.50 72.50
J7 D3 60c buff & mag 24.00 *72.50*
J8 D3 1 l blue & mag 16.00 *40.00*
J9 D3 2 l blue & mag 200.00 *180.00*
J10 D3 5 l blue & mag 325.00 340.00
J11 D3 10 l blue & mag 3,600. 875.00
Never hinged 7,200.
Set, #J1-J10, never hinged 1,600.

### Same with Overprint at Bottom

**1920-22**

*J1b* D3 5c buff & magenta 4.75 *16.00*
c. Numeral and ovpt. inverted 550.00 550.00
*J2a* D3 10c buff & magenta 8.00 *16.00*
*J3a* D3 20c buff & magenta 950.00 475.00
*J4a* D3 30c buff & magenta 65.00 65.00
*J5a* D3 40c buff & magenta 47.50 52.50
*J6a* D3 50c buff & magenta 24.00 *47.50*
*J7a* D3 60c buff & magenta 24.00 *47.50*
*J8a* D3 1 l blue & magenta 40.00 47.50
*J9a* D3 2 l blue & magenta 1,900. 1,450.
*J10a* D3 5 l blue & magenta 475.00 350.00
*J11a* D3 10 l blue & magenta 47.50 *100.00*
Set, never hinged 7,125.

**1903 Wmk. 140**

J12 D4 50 l yellow 875.00 300.00
J13 D4 100 l blue 475.00 180.00
Set, never hinged 2,700.

**1927**

J14 D3 60c buff & brown 160.00 *240.00*
Never hinged 325.00

### Postage Due Stamps of Italy, 1934, Overprinted type "j" in Black

**1934**

J15 D6 5c brown .80 *16.00*
J16 D6 10c blue .80 *3.25*
J17 D6 20c rose red 4.00 *4.75*
a. Inverted overprint — —
J18 D6 25c green 4.00 *6.50*
J19 D6 30c red orange 4.00 *16.00*
J20 D6 40c black brown 4.00 *16.00*
J21 D6 50c violet 4.00 2.40
J22 D6 60c black 8.00 *24.00*
J23 D7 1 l red orange 4.00 3.25
a. Inverted overprint 550.00 —
J24 D7 2 l green 16.00 *47.50*
J25 D7 5 l violet 28.00 *55.00*
J26 D7 10 l blue 32.50 *65.00*
J27 D7 20 l carmine rose 40.00 *72.50*
a. Inverted overprint 550.00
*Nos. J15-J27 (13)* 150.10 *332.15*
Set, never hinged 375.00

## PARCEL POST STAMPS

These stamps were used by affixing them to the way bill so that one half remained on it following the parcel, the other half staying on the receipt given the sender. Most used halves are right halves. Complete stamps were obtainable canceled, probably to order. Both unused and used values are for complete stamps.

### Parcel Post Stamps of Italy, 1914-17, Overprinted type "j" in Black on Each Half

**1916 Wmk. 140 *Perf. 13½***

Q1 PP2 5c brown 145.00 *225.00*
Q2 PP2 10c deep blue *2,600.* *4,250.*
Never hinged 5,250.
Q3 PP2 25c red 290.00 *350.00*
Q4 PP2 50c orange 72.50 *225.00*
Q5 PP2 1 l violet 145.00 *225.00*
Q6 PP2 2 l green 110.00 *225.00*
Q7 PP2 3 l bister 875.00 *625.00*
Q8 PP2 4 l slate 875.00 *625.00*
Set #Q1, Q3 Q0, never hinged 5,200.

### Halves Used, Each

Q1 4.25
Q2 85.00
Q3 5.50
Q4 3.00
Q5 3.00
Q6 8.50
Q7 19.00
Q8 19.00

### Overprinted type "f" on Each Half

**1917-24**

Q9 PP2 5c brown 3.25 *8.00*
Q10 PP2 10c deep blue 3.25 *8.00*
Q11 PP2 20c black 3.25 *8.00*
Q12 PP2 25c red 3.25 *8.00*
Q13 PP2 50c orange 6.50 *12.00*
Q14 PP2 1 l violet 6.50 *12.00*
Q15 PP2 2 l green 6.50 *12.00*
Q16 PP2 3 l bister 6.50 *12.00*
Q17 PP2 4 l slate 6.50 *20.00*
Q18 PP2 10 l rose lil ('24) 87.50 *190.00*
Q19 PP2 12 l red brn ('24) 240.00 *375.00*
Q20 PP2 15 l olive grn ('24) 240.00 *375.00*
Q21 PP2 20 l brn vio ('24) 325.00 *525.00*
*Nos. Q9-Q21 (13)* 938.00 *1,565.*
Set, never hinged 1,860.

### Halves Used, Each

Q9 1.20
Q10 1.20
Q11 1.20
Q12 1.20
Q13 1.20
Q14 1.20
Q15 1.60
Q16 4.25
Q17 4.25
Q18 8.50
Q19 12.50
Q20 12.50
Q21 17.00

### Parcel Post Stamps of Italy, 1927-39, Overprinted type "f" on Each Half

**1927-37**

Q21A PP3 10c dp blue ('37) *8,750.* 1,250.
Never hinged *13,500.*
Q22 PP3 25c red ('37) 550.00 72.50
Q23 PP3 30c ultra ('29) 4.00 *24.00*
Q24 PP3 50c orange ('36) 725.00 47.50
Q25 PP3 60c red ('29) 4.00 *24.00*
Q26 PP3 1 l brown vio ('36) 325.00 47.50
a. 1 l lilac 400.00 47.50
Q27 PP3 2 l green ('36) 325.00 47.50
Q28 PP3 3 l bister 9.50 *40.00*
Q29 PP3 4 l gray 9.50 *40.00*
Q30 PP3 10 l rose lilac ('36) 525.00 800.00
Q31 PP3 20 l lilac brn ('36) 525.00 800.00
*Nos. Q22-Q31 (10)* 3,002.
Set, never hinged 6,000.
*Nos. Q21A-Q31 (11)* 3,193.

### Halves Used, Each

Q21A 27.50
Q22 1.20
Q23 .65
Q24 1.70
Q25 .85
Q26 1.25
Q26a 1.25
Q27 1.25
Q28 1.25
Q29 1.25
Q30 37.50
Q31 37.50

# ESTONIA

e-ˈstō-nē-ə

LOCATION — Northern Europe, bordering on the Baltic Sea and the Gulf of Finland
GOVT. — Independent republic
AREA — 17,462 sq. mi.
POP. — 1,408,523 (1999 est.)
CAPITAL — Tallinn

Formerly a part of the Russia empire, Estonia declared its independence in 1918. In 1940 it was incorporated in the Union of Soviet Socialist Republics.

Estonia declared the restoration of its independence from the USSR on Aug. 20, 1991. Estonian independence was recognized by the Soviet Union on Sept. 6, 1991.

100 Kopecks = 1 Ruble (1918, 1991)
100 Penni = 1 Mark (1919)
100 Sents = 1 Kroon (1928, 1992)

**Catalogue values for unused stamps in this country are for Never Hinged items, beginning with Scott 200 in the regular postage section, Scott B60 in the semi-postal section, and Scott F1 in the registration section.**

### Watermark

Wmk. 207 — Arms of Finland in the Sheet

Watermark covers a large part of sheet.

A1

A2

**1918-19 Unwmk. Litho. *Imperf.***

1 A1 5k pale red .95 .80
2 A1 15k bright blue .95 .80
3 A2 35p brown ('19) .80 .80
a. Printed on both sides 200.00
b. 35p olive 80.00 80.00
4 A2 70p olive grn ('19) 1.60 *2.00*
*Nos. 1-4 (4)* 4.30 4.40

Nos. 1-4 exist privately perforated.

Russian Stamps of 1909-17 Handstamped in Violet or Black

**1919, May 7 *Perf. 14, 14½x15, 13½***

8 A14 1k orange *8,000.* *8,000.*
9 A14 2k green 45.00 *45.00*
10 A14 3k red 52.50 *52.50*
11 A14 5k claret 45.00 *45.00*
12 A15 10k dk bl (Bk) 85.00 *85.00*
13 A15 10k dk bl 500.00 *500.00*
14 A14 10k on 7k lt bl *2,400.* *2,400.*
15 A11 15k red brn & bl 67.50 *67.50*
16 A11 25k grn & vio 80.00 *80.00*
17 A11 35k red brn & grn *7,000.* *7,000.*
18 A8 50k vio & grn 190.00 190.00
19 A9 1r pale brn, brn & org 325.00 325.00
20 A13 10r scar, yel & gray *12,000.* *12,000.*

***Imperf***

21 A14 1k orange 62.50 *62.50*
22 A14 2k green *2,000.* *2,000.*
23 A14 3k red 85.00 85.00
24 A9 1r pale brn, brn & red org *475.00* *475.00*
25 A12 3½r maroon & grn *2,000.* *2,000.*
26 A13 5r dk bl, grn & pale bl *2,750.* *2,750.*

Provisionally issued at Tallinn. This overprint has been extensively counterfeited. Values are for genuine examples competently expertized. No. 20 is always creased.

Gulls — A3

**1919, May 13 *Imperf.***

27 A3 5p yellow 2.50 *5.50*

A4

A5

A6

A7

Viking Ship — A8

**1919-20** *Perf. 11½*
**28** A4 10p green .45 .80

*Imperf*

**29** A4 5p orange .25 .25
**30** A4 10p green .25 .25
**31** A5 15p rose .25 .30
**32** A6 35p blue .25 .30
**33** A7 70p dl vio ('20) .25 .30
**34** A8 1m bl & blk brn 4.25 1.60
*a.* Gray granite paper ('20) 1.60 .80
**35** A8 5m yel & blk 6.25 4.75
*a.* Gray granite paper ('20) 3.25 1.25
**36** A8 15m yel grn & vio ('20) 4.00 2.40
**37** A8 25m ultra & blk brn ('20) 6.50 5.50
*Nos. 28-37 (10)* 22.70 16.45
Set, never hinged 32.50

The 5m exists with inverted center. Not a postal item.

See Nos. 76-77. For surcharges see Nos. 55, 57.

Skyline of Tallinn — A9

**1920-24** **Pelure Paper** *Imperf.*
**39** A9 25p green .30 .40
**40** A9 25p yellow ('24) .30 .30
**41** A9 35p rose .40 .40
**42** A9 50p green ('21) .60 .25
**43** A9 1m vermilion 1.25 .80
**44** A9 2m blue .80 .40
**45** A9 2m ultramarine 1.00 1.25
**46** A9 2.50m blue 1.25 .80
*Nos. 39-46 (8)* 5.90 4.60
Set, never hinged 16.50

Nos. 39-46 with sewing machine perforation are unofficial.

For surcharge see No. 56.

**Stamps of 1919-20 Surcharged**

**1920** *Imperf.*
**55** A5 1m on 15p rose .50 .50
**56** A9 1m on 35p rose .70 .80
**57** A7 2m on 70p dl vio .85 .80
*Nos. 55-57 (3)* 2.05 2.10
Set, never hinged 4.25

Weaver
A10

Blacksmith
A11

**1922-23** **Typo.** *Imperf.*
**58** A10 ½m orange ('23) 2.75 *8.00*
**59** A10 1m brown ('23) 4.75 *11.00*
**60** A10 2m yellow green 4.75 *8.00*
**61** A10 2½m claret 5.50 *8.00*
**62** A11 5m rose 8.00 8.00
**63** A11 9m red ('23) 12.00 *24.00*
**64** A11 10m deep blue 5.50 *16.00*
*Nos. 58-64 (7)* 43.25 83.00
Set, never hinged 110.00

**1922-25** *Perf. 14*
**65** A10 ½m orange ('23) 1.25 .80
**66** A10 1m brown ('23) 2.40 .80
**67** A10 2m yellow green 2.40 .40
**68** A10 2½m claret 4.75 .80
**69** A10 3m blue green ('24) 2.00 .40
**70** A11 5m rose 2.75 .40
**71** A11 9m red ('23) 4.75 1.60
**72** A11 10m deep blue 6.00 .40
**73** A11 12m red ('25) 6.00 1.75
**74** A11 15m plum ('25) 8.00 1.40
**75** A11 20m ultra ('25) 22.00 .80
*Nos. 65-75 (11)* 62.30 9.55
Set, never hinged 130.00

See No. 89. For surcharges see Nos. 84-88.

**Viking Ship Type of 1920**

**1922, June 8** *Perf. 14x13½*
**76** A8 15m yel grn & vio 20.00 .80
**77** A8 25m ultra & blk brn 20.00 3.25
Set, never hinged 80.00

Map of Estonia — A13

**1923-24** **Paper with Lilac Network**
**78** A13 100m ol grn & bl 24.00 3.50

**Paper with Buff Network**
**79** A13 300m brn & bl ('24) 80.00 17.50
Set, never hinged 210.00

For surcharges see Nos. 106-107.

National Theater, Tallinn — A14

**Paper with Blue Network**

**1924, Dec. 9** *Perf. 14x13½*
**81** A14 30m violet & blk 10.00 4.00

**Paper with Rose Network**
**82** A14 70m car rose & blk 15.00 8.00
Set, never hinged 50.00

For surcharge see No. 105.

Vanemuine Theater, Tartu — A15

**Paper with Lilac Network**

**1927, Oct. 25**
**83** A15 40m dp bl & ol brn 10.00 3.50
Never hinged 20.00

Stamps of 1922-25 Surcharged in New Currency in Red or Black

**1928** *Perf. 14*
**84** A10 2s yellow green 1.25 1.25
**85** A11 5s rose red (B) 1.25 1.25
**86** A11 10s deep blue 2.40 1.25
*a.* Imperf., pair *2,000.* *16,000.*
**87** A11 15s plum (B) 3.75 1.25
**88** A11 20s ultra 3.75 1.25
*Nos. 84-88 (5)* 12.40 6.25
Set, never hinged 30.00

10th anniversary of independence.

**3rd Philatelic Exhibition Issue**
**Blacksmith Type of 1922-23**

**1928, July 6**
**89** A11 10m gray 3.00 *6.00*
Never hinged 6.00

Sold only at Tallinn Philatelic Exhibition. Exists imperf. Value $1,000.

Arms — A16

**Paper with Network in Parenthesis**

**1928-40** *Perf. 14, 14½x14*
**90** A16 1s dk gray (bl) .50 .25
*a.* Thick gray-toned laid paper ('40) 10.00 *27.50*
**91** A16 2s yel grn (org) .50 .25
**92** A16 4s grn (brn) ('29) 1.10 .25
**93** A16 5s red (grn) .70 .25
*a.* 5 feet on lowest lion 45.00 32.50
**94** A16 8s vio (buff) ('29) 2.75 .25
**95** A16 10s lt bl (lilac) 1.75 .25
**96** A16 12s crimson (grn) 1.75 .25
**97** A16 15s yel (blue) 2.75 .25
**98** A16 15s car (gray) ('35) 12.00 1.50
**99** A16 20s slate bl (red) 3.75 .25
**100** A16 25s red vio (grn) ('29) 9.00 .25
**101** A16 25s bl (brn) ('35) 10.00 1.50
**102** A16 40s red org (bl) ('29) 5.75 .80
**103** A16 60s gray (brn) ('29) 10.00 .80
**104** A16 80s brn (bl) ('29) 12.00 1.60
*Nos. 90-104 (15)* 74.30 8.70
Set, never hinged 160.00

**Types of 1924 Issues Surcharged**

**1930, Sept. 1** *Perf. 14x13½*
**Paper with Green Network**
**105** A14 1k on 70m car & blk 16.00 5.50

**Paper with Rose Network**
**106** A13 2k on 300m brn & bl 32.50 16.00

**Paper with Blue Network**
**107** A13 3k on 300m brn & bl 60.00 27.50
*Nos. 105-107 (3)* 108.50 49.00
Set, never hinged 215.00

University Observatory
A17

University of Tartu
A18

**Paper with Network as in Parenthesis**

**1932, June 1** *Perf. 14*
**108** A17 5s red (yellow) 6.00 .80
**109** A18 10s light bl (lilac) 4.00 .80
**110** A17 12s car (blue) 10.00 4.00
**111** A18 20s dk bl (green) 6.00 1.60
*Nos. 108-111 (4)* 26.00 7.20
Set, never hinged 57.50

University of Tartu tercentenary.

Narva Falls — A19

**1933, Apr. 1** **Photo.** *Perf. 14x13½*
**112** A19 1k gray black 6.50 3.00
Never hinged 14.00

See No. 149.

Ancient Bard Playing Harp — A20

**Paper with Network as in Parenthesis**

**1933, May 29** **Typo.** *Perf. 14*
**113** A20 2s green (orange) 1.60 .30
**114** A20 5s red (green) 2.75 .30
**115** A20 10s blue (lilac) 3.50 .30
*Nos. 113-115 (3)* 7.85 .90
Set, never hinged 17.00

Tenth National Song Festival.
Nos. 113-115 exist imperf. Value $125.

Woman Harvester — A21

**1935, Mar. 1** **Engr.** *Perf. 13½*
**116** A21 3k black brown .80 *6.50*
Never hinged 1.75

Pres. Konstantin Päts — A22

**1936-40** **Typo.** *Perf. 14*
**117** A22 1s chocolate .80 .40
**118** A22 2s yellow green .80 .40
**119** A22 3s dp org ('40) 8.00 8.00
**120** A22 4s rose vio 1.60 .80
**121** A22 5s lt blue grn 2.00 .40
**122** A22 6s rose lake 1.60 .40
**123** A22 6s dp green ('40) 40.00 *55.00*
**124** A22 10s greenish blue 2.00 .40
**125** A22 15s crim rose ('37) 2.40 .40
**126** A22 15s dp bl ('40) 4.00 3.25
**127** A22 18s dp car ('39) 17.50 6.25
**128** A22 20s brt vio 4.00 .40
**129** A22 25s dk bl ('38) 12.00 1.60
**130** A22 30s bister ('38) 18.00 1.60
**131** A22 30s ultra ('39) 24.00 6.25
**132** A22 50s org brn 8.75 1.60
**133** A22 60s brt pink 20.00 5.50
*Nos. 117-133 (17)* 167.45 92.65
Set, never hinged 340.00

St. Brigitta Convent Entrance
A23

Ruins of Convent, Pirita River
A24

Front View of Convent — A25

Seal of Convent — A26

### Paper with Network as in Parenthesis

**1936, June 10** *Perf. 13½*
**134** A23 5s green (buff) .60 *1.60*
**135** A24 10s blue (lil) .60 *1.60*
**136** A25 15s red (org) 1.75 *4.75*
**137** A26 25s ultra (brn) 3.00 *8.00*
*Nos. 134-137 (4)* 5.95 *15.95*
Set, never hinged 12.00

St. Brigitta Convent, 500th anniversary.

Harbor at Tallinn — A27

**1938, Apr. 11** **Engr.** *Perf. 14*
**138** A27 2k blue .80 *8.00*
Never hinged 1.75

Friedrich R. Faehlmann A28

Friedrich R. Kreutzwald A29

**1938, June 15** **Typo.** *Perf. 13½*
**139** A28 5s dark green .40 *.80*
**140** A29 10s deep brown .40 *.80*
**141** A29 15s dark carmine .80 *5.50*
**142** A28 25s ultra 1.25 *7.25*
*a.* Sheet of 4, #139-142 10.00 *80.00*
*Nos. 139-142 (4)* 2.85 *14.35*
Set, never hinged 8.00

Society of Estonian Scholars centenary.

Hospital at Pärnu — A30

Beach Hotel — A31

**1939, June 20** **Typo.** *Perf. 14x13½*
**144** A30 5s dark green 1.60 1.60
**145** A31 10s deep red violet .80 1.60
**146** A30 18s dark carmine 1.25 *5.50*
**147** A31 30s deep blue 1.60 *7.25*
*a.* Sheet of 4, #144-147 16.00 *87.50*
*Nos. 144-147 (4)* 5.25 15.95
Set, never hinged 11.00

Cent. of health resort and baths at Pärnu.

### Narva Falls Type of 1933

**1940, Apr. 15** **Engr.**
**149** A19 1k slate green 1.40 *12.00*
Never hinged 2.75

The sky consists of heavy horizontal lines and the background consists of horizontal and vertical lines.

Carrier Pigeon and Plane — A32

**1940, July 30** **Typo.**
**150** A32 3s red orange .25 .25
**151** A32 10s purple .25 .25
**152** A32 15s rose brown .25 .25
**153** A32 30s dark blue 1.60 1.25
*Nos. 150-153 (4)* 2.35 2.00
Set, never hinged 4.75

Centenary of the first postage stamp.
The 15s exists imperf. Value $6.25.

**Catalogue values for unused stamps in this section, from this point to the end of the section, are for Never Hinged items.**

Natl. Arms — A40

**1991, Oct. 1** **Litho.** *Perf. 13x12½*
**200** A40 5k salmon & red .30 .30
**201** A40 10k lt grn & dk bl grn .30 .30
**202** A40 15k lt bl & dk bl .30 .30
**203** A40 30k vio & gray .35 .35
**204** A40 50k org & brn .40 .40
**205** A40 70k pink & purple .50 .50
**206** A40 90k pur & rose lilac .60 .60

**Size: 20½x27mm**
**Engr.**
***Perf. 12½ Horiz.***

**207** A40 1r dark brown .75 .75
**208** A40 2r lt bl & dk bl 1.50 1.50
*Nos. 200-208 (9)* 5.00 5.00

See Nos. 211-213, 215, 216, 230, 299-301, 314-314A, 317, 333-334, 339-340. For surcharge, see No. 217.

A41

***Perf. 13½x14, 14x13½***

**1991, Nov. 1** **Litho.**
**209** A41 1.50r Flag, vert. 1.10 1.10
**210** A41 2.50r shown 1.90 1.90

National Arms — A42

**1992, Mar. 16** **Litho.** *Perf. 13x12½*
**211** A42 E (1r) lemon .25 .25
**212** A42 I (20r) blue green .85 .85
**213** A42 A (40r) blue 1.90 1.90
*Nos. 211-213 (3)* 3.00 3.00

No. 211 was valid for postage within Estonia. No. 212 was valid for postage within Europe. No. 213 was valid for overseas mail. See Nos. 214, 219, 220, 224-229.

### Arms Types of 1991-1992 and

No. 202 Surcharged

Natl. Arms — A42a

***Perf. 14, 13x12½ (#214, 217, 219-220)***

**1992-96**
**214** A42 E (10s) orange .25 .25
**215** A40 10s blue & gray .25 .25
**216** A40 50s gray & brt bl .25 .25
*a.* Perf. 13x13¼ —
**217** A40 60s on 15k #202 .25 .25
**218** A40 60s lilac & olive .25 .25
**219** A42 I (1k) emerald .75 .75
**220** A42 A (2k) violet blue 1.50 1.50
**221** A42a 5k bis & red vio 1.25 1.25
*a.* 5k yel orange & red violet 2.75 2.75
**222** A42a 10k blue & olive 2.50 2.50
**223** A42a 20k pale lilac & slate grn 4.25 4.25
*Nos. 214-223 (10)* 11.50 11.50

### Coil Stamps

**Engr.**
**Size: 20½x27mm**
***Perf. 12½ Horiz.***

**224** A42 X (10s) brown .30 .30
**225** A42 X (10s) olive .30 .30
**226** A42 X (10s) black .30 .30
**227** A42 Z (30s) red lilac .30 .30
**228** A42 Z (30s) red .30 .30
**229** A42 Z (30s) dark blue .30 .30

**Litho.**

**230** A40 60s lilac brown .30 .30
*Nos. 224-230 (7)* 2.10 2.10

Issued: Nos. 214, 219-220, 6/22; No. 224, 8/29; No. 225, 9/25; No. 226, 10/31; No. 227, 11/16; No. 228, 12/1; No. 229, 12/22; No. 230, 1/8/93; No. 217, 3/5/93; 10s, 50s, 3/23 1993; 10k, 5/25/93; 5k, 7/7/93; No. 218, 8/5/93; 20k, 9/8/93; No. 221a, 9/19/96; No. 216a, 3/5/96.
See note after No. 213. Nos. 224-229 were valid for postage within Estonia.
See No. F1.

A44

Birds of the Baltic shores.

**1992, Oct. 3** **Litho. & Engr.** *Perf. 13*

### Booklet Stamps

**231** A44 1k Pandion haliaetus .65 *.65*
**232** A44 1k Limosa limosa .65 *.65*
**233** A44 1k Mergus merganser .65 *.65*
**234** A44 1k Tadorna todorna .65 *.65*
*a.* Booklet pane of 4, #231-234 2.60 2.60

See Latvia Nos. 332-335a, Lithuania Nos. 427-430a and Sweden Nos. 1975-1978a.

A45

**1992, Dec. 15** **Litho.** *Perf. 14*
**235** A45 30s gray & multi .30 .30
**236** A45 2k light brown & multi .70 .70

Christmas.
Exist on ordinary and fluorescent paper. Values are for former. Value for set on fluorescent paper, $30.

Friendship A46

**1993, Feb. 8** **Litho.** *Perf. 14*
**237** A46 1k multicolored .30 .30
*a.* Booklet pane of 6 1.80

See Finland No. 906.

First Republic, 75th Anniv. — A47

**1993, Feb. 16** *Perf. 13x13½*
**238** A47 60s black & multi .25 .25
**239** A47 1k violet & multi .25 .25
**240** A47 2k blue & multi .50 .50
*Nos. 238-240 (3)* 1.00 1.00

First Baltic Sea Games — A48

60s, Wrestling. 1k +25s, Viking ship, map. 2k, Shot put with rock.

**1993, June 9** **Litho.** *Perf. 13½x14*
**241** A48 60s multi .25 .25
**242** A48 1k +25s multi .30 .30
**243** A48 2k multi .45 .45
*Nos. 241-243 (3)* 1.00 1.00

Tallinn Castle — A49

Designs: 1k, Toolse Castle. No. 245, Paide Castle, vert. No. 246, Purtse Castle. No. 247, Haapsalu Castle and Cathedral. 2.70k, Narva Fortress. 2.90k, Haapsalu Cathedral. 3k, Monks' Tower, Kiiu. 3.20k, Rakvere Castle. 4k, Kuressaare Castle. 4.80k, Viljandi Castle.

**1993-97** **Litho.** *Perf. 14*
**244** A49 1k gray & black .45 .45
**245** A49 2k tan & brown .45 .45
**246** A49 2.50k lt vio & dk vio .55 .55
**247** A49 2.50k gray .55 .55
**248** A49 2.70k lt blue & dk blue .55 .55
**249** A49 2.90k lt grn & dk grn .60 .60
**250** A49 3k rose & brown .60 .60
**251** A49 3.20k lt grn & dk grn .85 .85
**252** A49 4k lt gray vio & gray vio .90 .90
**253** A49 4.80k dull org & brn .95 .95
*Nos. 244-253 (10)* 6.45 6.45

Issued: 1k, 2/22/94; 2k, 10/12/93; 2.70k, 12/10/93; 2.90k, 12/23/93; 3k, 3/31/94; 3.20, 12/28/94; 4k, 9/20/94; No. 246, 1/25/96; 247, 7/25/96; 4.80k, 1/21/97.

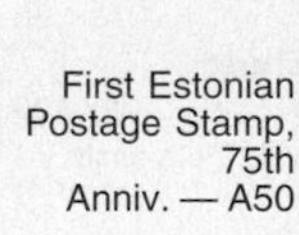


First Estonian Postage Stamp, 75th Anniv. — A50

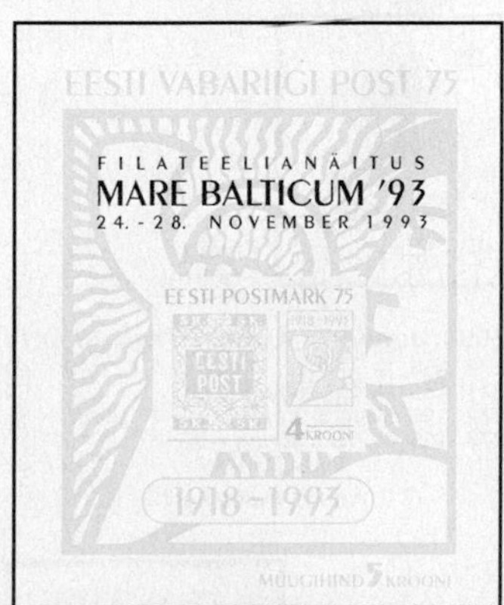


No. 260a

**1993, Nov. 13** **Litho.** *Perf. 14*
**259** A50 1k multicolored .40 .40

### Souvenir Sheet

***Imperf***

**260** A50 4k multicolored 3.00 3.00
*a.* Ovptd. in sheet margin 11.50 11.50

No. 260 sold for 5k.

Christmas A51

80s, Haapsalu Cathedral. 2k, Tallinn Church.

**1993, Nov. Litho. *Perf. 14***

**261** A51 80s red .25 .25
**262** A51 2k blue, vert. .40 .40

See Nos. 279-280.

Lydia Koidula — A52

**1993, Dec. 14 Litho. *Perf. 14***

**263** A52 1k multicolored .35 .35

1994 Winter Olympics, Lillehammer — A53

**1994, Jan. 26**

**264** A53 1k +25s Ski jumping .40 .40
**265** A53 2k Speed skating .50 .50

Festival Badges — A54

1k+25s, Tartu, 1869. 2k, Tallinn, 1923. 3k, Tallinn, 1969.
15k, Anniversary badge.

**1994, May 31 Litho. *Perf. 13½x14***

**266** A54 1k +25s olive & multi .25 .25
**267** A54 2k blue & brown .45 .45
**268** A54 3k brown, buff & bister .60 .60
*Nos. 266-268 (3)* 1.30 1.30

**Souvenir Sheet**

**269** A54 15k multicolored 3.00 3.00

All Estonian Song Festival, 125th anniv.

Flying Squirrel — A55

**1994, June 27 Litho. *Perf. 13½x14***

**270** A55 1k shown .40 .40
**271** A55 2k On leafy branch .50 .50
**272** A55 3k In fir tree .85 .85
**273** A55 4k With young 1.10 1.10
*Nos. 270-273 (4)* 2.85 2.85

World Wildlife Fund.

A56

Europa (Estonian Inventions): 1k, Rotating horizontal millstones, by Aleksander Mikiver. 2.70k, First mini-camera, by Walter Zapp.

**1994, July 19**

**274** A56 1k multicolored *.25 .25*
**275** A56 2.70k multicolored *.50 .50*

Folk Costumes — A57

**1994, Aug. 23 Litho. *Perf. 14***

**276** A57 1k Jamaja .25 .25
**277** A57 1k Mustjala .25 .25

See Nos. 286-287, 303-304, 325-326, 347-348, 369-370, 476-477, 497-498, 524-525.

Estonian Art Museum, 75th Anniv. — A58

**1994, Sept. 27 Litho. *Perf. 13½***

**278** A58 1.70k multicolored .35 .35

**Christmas Type of 1993**

Designs: 1.20k, Ruhnu Church, vert. 2.50k, Urvaste Church.

**1994, Nov. 15 Litho. *Perf. 14***

**279** A51 1.20k brown .30 .30
**280** A51 2.50k green .55 .55

For surcharge see No. B63.

Intl. Year of the Family — A59

**1994, Oct. 18**

**281** A59 1.70k multicolored .40 .40

A60

Gustavus II Adolphus (1594-1632), King of Sweden.

**1994, Dec. 9**

**282** A60 2.50k lilac 1.00 1.00

Matsalu Nature Reserve — A61

**1995, Jan. 26 Litho. *Perf. 14***

**283** A61 1.70k Branta leucopsis .35 .35
**284** A61 3.20k Anser anser .60 .60

FAO, 50th Anniv. — A62

Farm Laborer's Family at Table, by Efraim Allsalu.

**1995, Feb. 28 Litho. *Perf. 14***

**285** A62 2.70k multicolored .55 .55

**Folk Costumes Type of 1994**

**1995, Mar. 30 Litho. *Perf. 14***

**286** A57 1.70k Muhu couple .40 .40
**287** A57 1.70k Three Muhu girls .40 .40

A63

Via Baltica Highway Project: Nos. 288, 289a, Beach Hotel, Parnu. No. 289b, Castle, Bauska, Latvia. No. 289c, Kaunas, Lithuania.

**1995, Apr. 20 Litho. *Perf. 14***

**288** A63 1.70k multicolored .45 .45

**Souvenir Sheet**

**289** A63 3.20k Sheet of 3, #a.-c. 2.00 2.00

See Latvia Nos. 394-395, Lithuania Nos. 508-509.

A64

**1995, Apr. 20 Litho. *Perf. 14***

**290** A64 2.70k multicolored *.75 .75*

Europa. Liberation of Nazi Concentration Camps, 50th anniv.

UN, 50th Anniv. — A65

**1995, June 1 Litho. *Perf. 14***

**291** A65 4k multicolored .75 .75

Pakri Lighthouse A66

**1995, July 5 Litho. *Perf. 14***

**292** A66 1.70k multicolored .45 .45

See Nos. 309, 318, 338, 356, 388-389, 408, 434, 452, 501-502.

Vanemuine Theater, 125th Anniv. — A67

**1995, Aug. 14 Litho. *Perf. 14***

**293** A67 1.70k multicolored .45 .45

Louis Pasteur (1822-95) A68

**1995, Sept. 20 Litho. *Perf. 14***

**294** A68 2.70k multicolored .60 .60

Miniature Sheet

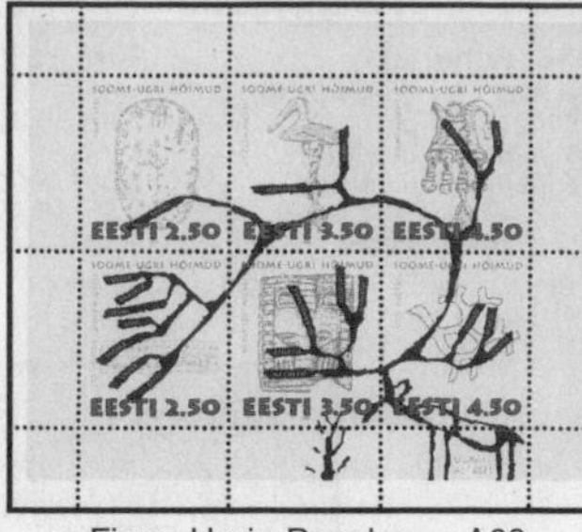

Finno-Ugric Peoples — A69

Ethnographic object, languages: a, 2.50k, Drawing on shaman's drum, Saami. b, 3.50k, Duck-shaped brooch, Mordva, Mari. c, 4.50k, Duck-feet necklace pendant, Udmurdi, Komi. d, 2.50k, Khanty band ornament, Ungari, Mansi, Handi. e, 3.50k, Bronze amulet, Neenetsi, Eenetsi, Nganassaani, Solkupi, Kamassi. f, 4.50k, Karelian writing on birchbark, Eesti, Vadia, Soome, Liivi, Isuri, Karjala, Vespa.

**1995, Oct. 17 Litho. *Perf. 14***

**295** A69 Sheet of 6, #a.-f. 4.00 4.00

Aleksander Kunileid (1845-75), Composer — A70

**1995, Nov. 1 Engr. *Perf. 12½ Horiz.***

**296** A70 2k dark blue black .45 .45

Christmas — A71

Churches: 2k, St. Martin's, Türi. 3.50k, Charles' Church of the Toompea Congregation, Tallinn.

**1995, Nov. 15 Litho. *Perf. 14***

**297** A71 2k yellow orange .55 .55
**298** A71 3.50k dull carmine .95 .95

See Nos. 315-316, 331.

**Natl. Arms Type of 1991**

**1995, Oct. 26 Litho. *Perf. 14***

**299** A40 20s blue green & black .25 .25
**300** A40 30s gray & magenta .25 .25
**301** A40 80s lilac & blue black .25 .25
***a.*** Perf. 13 .25 .25
*Nos. 299-301 (3)* .75 .75

No. 301a issued in 1996.

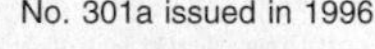

Submarine *Lembit* — A72

**1996, Feb. 29 Litho. *Perf. 14***

**302** A72 2.50k multicolored .65 .65

See No. 308, 328.

**Folk Costume Type of 1994**

**1996, Mar. 26 Litho. *Perf. 14***

**303** A57 2.50k Emmaste .65 .65
**304** A57 2.50k Reigi .65 .65

A73

Designs: a, 2.50k, First gold medal, 1896. b, 3.50k, Alfred Neuland, weight lifter, first to win gold medal for Estonia, 1920. c, 4k, Cyclist.

**1996, Apr. 25** **Litho.** ***Perf. 14***
**305** A73 Sheet of 3, #a.-c. 2.00 2.00

Modern Olympic Games, Cent. & 1996 Summer Olympics, Atlanta.

A74

Europa: Marie Under (1883-1980), poet.

**1996, May 10**
**306** A74 2.50k multicolored *1.00 1.00*

Radio, Cent. — A75

**1996, June 27** **Litho.** ***Perf. 14***
**307** A75 3.50k Guglielmo Marconi .90 .90

### Ship Type of 1996

Design: Icebreaker, Suur Toll.

**1996, Aug. 30** **Litho.** ***Perf. 14***
**308** A72 2.50k multicolored .65 .65

### Lighthouse Type of 1995

**1996, Sept. 25** **Litho.** ***Perf. 14***
**309** A66 2.50k Vaindloo .70 .70

Estonian Narrow Gauge Railway, Cent. — A76

Designs: 3.20k, Class Gk steam locomotive. 3.50k, DeM 1 diesel motor wagon. 4.50k, Class Sk steam locomotive.

**1996, Oct. 17** **Litho.** ***Perf. 14***
**310** A76 3.20k multicolored .70 .70
**311** A76 3.50k multicolored .75 .75
**312** A76 4.50k multicolored .85 .85
*Nos. 310-312 (3)* 2.30 2.30

See No. 397.

Christmas A77

**1996, Nov. 27** **Litho.** ***Perf. 14***
**313** A77 2.50k multicolored .60 .60

### Natl. Arms Type of 1991

**1996-97** ***Perf. 14***
**314** A40 3.30k lilac and claret 1.25 1.25

***Perf. 13x13¼***

**314A** A40 3.30k blue & lt claret 1.25 1.25

Issued: No. 314, 12/2; No. 314A, 12/10/97.

### Church Type of 1995

Christmas: 3.30k, Harju-Madise Church. 4.50k, Holy Spirit Church, Tallinn.

**1996, Dec. 12**
**315** A71 3.30k blue .70 .70
**316** A71 4.50k pink .85 .85

### Natl. Arms Type of 1991

**1996, Oct. 24** **Litho.** ***Perf. 13½***
**317** A40 2.50k grn & dark grn 1.25 1.25

### Lighthouse Type of 1995

**1997, Feb. 11** **Litho.** ***Perf. 14***
**318** A66 3.30k Ruhnu .75 .75

Tallinn Zoo — A78

a, Haliaeetus pelagicus. b, Mustela lutreola. c, Aegypius monachus. d, Panthera pardus orientalis. e, Diceros bicornis. f, Capra cylindricornis.

**1997, Mar. 26** **Litho.** ***Perf. 14***
**319** A78 3.30k Sheet of 6, #a.-f. 3.50 3.50

Heinrich von Stephan (1831-97), Founder of UPU — A79

**1997, Apr. 8** **Litho.** ***Perf. 14***
**320** A79 7k black & bister 1.25 1.25

A80

**1997, May 5** **Litho.** ***Perf. 14***
**321** A80 4.80k Goldspinners Fairy Tale *1.00 1.00*

Europa.

A81

No. 323: a, like #322. b, Linijkugis, 17th cent. c, Kurenas, 16th cent.

**1997, May 10**
**322** A81 3.30k multicolored .70 .70

***Perf. 14x14½***

**323** A81 4.50k Sheet of 3, #a.-c. 5.25 5.25

Maasilinn ship, 16th cent.
See Latvia Nos. 443-444, Lithuania Nos. 571-572.

### Folk Costume Type of 1994

**1997, June 10** **Litho.** ***Perf. 14***
**325** A57 3.30k Ruhnu .55 .55
**326** A57 3.30k Vormsi .55 .55

One Kroon Coin — A82

**1997, June 12** **Litho.** ***Perf. 14***
**327** A82 50k bl grn, blk & gray 9.00 9.00

See Nos. 345, 363, 391.

### Ship Type of 1996

Design: Four-masted barkentine, Tormilind.

**1997, July 2**
**328** A72 5.50k multicolored .90 .90

Stone Bridge, Tartu — A83

**1997, Sept. 16** **Litho.** ***Perf. 14***
**329** A83 3.30k multicolored .65 .65

Wastne Testament, Estonian Bible Translation, 1686 — A84

**1997, Oct. 14** **Litho.** ***Perf. 14***
**330** A84 3.50k multicolored .65 .65

### Church Type of 1995

Christmas: St. Anne's, Halliste.

**1997, Nov. 27** **Litho.** ***Perf. 14***
**331** A71 3.30k brown .65 .65

Christmas A85

**1997, Dec. 3**
**332** A85 2.90k Elves .60 .60

### Natl. Arms Type of 1991

**1998, Jan. 19** **Litho.** ***Perf. 13x13½***
**333** A40 3.10k lt violet & rose .60 .60
**334** A40 3.60k lt blue & ultra .70 .70
*a.* 3.60k gray & vio bl .80 .80

Issued: No. 334a, 8/4/98.

1998 Winter Olympic Games, Nagano — A86

**1998, Jan. 28** **Litho.** ***Perf. 14***
**335** A86 3.60k multicolored .70 .70

Republic of Estonia, 80th Anniv. — A87

**1998, Feb. 6** **Litho.** ***Imperf.***
**336** A87 7k Proclamation, arms 1.40 1.40

Eduard Wiiralt (1898-1954), Print Artist — A88

Various sections of print, "Hell," showing faces: a, 3.60k, shown. b, 3.60k, Explosion coming from center figure. c, 5.50k, Cat on top of one figure's head. d, 5.50k, Faces within faces.

**1998, Feb. 18** ***Perf. 14***
**337** A88 Sheet of 4, #a.-d. 4.00 4.00

### Lighthouse Type of 1995

**1998, Mar. 12** **Litho.** ***Perf. 14***
**338** A66 3.60k Kunda .70 .70

### Natl. Arms Type of 1991

**1998, Mar. 16** ***Perf. 13***
**339** A40 10s grn bl & brn blk .25 .25
**340** A40 4.50k pale orange & brick red .80 .80

Issued: 10s, 3/25/97; 4.50k, 3/16/98.

A88a

**1998, Apr. 16** **Litho.** ***Perf. 14***
**341** A88a 7k multicolored 1.30 1.30

1998 World Cup Soccer Championship, France.

A89

**1998, May 5** **Litho.** ***Perf. 14***
**342** A89 5.20k St. John's Day *1.25 1.25*

Europa.

Use of Lübeck Charter in Tallinn, 750th Anniv. — A90

**1998, June 1**
**343** A90 4.80k multicolored .95 .95

Beautiful Homes Year — A91

**1998, June 16** **Litho.** ***Perf. 14***
**344** A91 3.60k multicolored .85 .85

**One Kroon Coin Type of 1997**

**1998, June 18**
**345** A82 25k green, gray & black 4.75 4.75

A92

**1998, Aug. 4** **Litho.** ***Perf. 14***
**346** A92 5.50k multicolored 1.00 1.00

470 Class World Yachting Championships.

**Folk Costume Type of 1994**

**1998, Aug. 21** **Litho.** ***Perf. 14***
**347** A57 3.60k Kihnu couple .65 .65
**348** A57 3.60k Kihnu family .65 .65

A93

**1998, Sept. 3**
**349** A93 3.60k yel, blue & blk .70 .70

Juhan Jaik (1899-1948), author.

Tallinn Zoo — A94

Design: Panthera tigris altaica.

**1998, Sept. 17**
**350** A94 3.60k multicolored .70 .70

See No. 357.

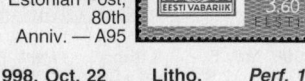

Estonian Post, 80th Anniv. — A95

**1998, Oct. 22** **Litho.** ***Perf. 14***
**351** A95 3.60k multicolored .75 .75

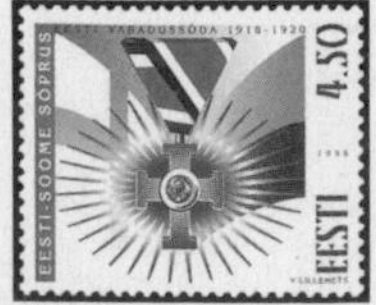

Military Aid from Finland, 90th Anniv. — A96

**1998, Nov. 5** **Litho.** ***Perf. 14***
**352** A96 4.50k Freedom Cross .85 .85

Christmas A97

**1998, Nov. 26** **Litho.** ***Perf. 14***
**353** A97 3.10k Santa, child, vert. .60 .60
**354** A97 5k shown .90 .90

Friedrich Robert Faehlmann, Founder of Learned Estonian Society, Birth Bicent. — A98

**1998, Dec. 2**
**355** A98 3.60k multicolored .70 .70

**Lighthouse Type of 1995**

**1999, Jan. 20** **Litho.** ***Perf. 14***
**356** A66 3.60k Vilsandi .70 .70

**Tallinn Zoo Type of 1998**

**1999, Feb. 18** **Litho.** ***Perf. 14***
**357** A94 3.60k Uncia uncia .70 .70

Council of Europe, 50th Anniv. — A99

**1999, Mar. 24** **Litho.** ***Perf. 14***
**358** A99 5.50k multicolored 1.00 1.00

Estonian Pres. Lennart Meri, 70th Birthday A100

**1999, Mar. 29**
**359** A100 3.60k multicolored .70 .70

Tolkuse Bog — A101

**1999, Apr. 27** **Litho.** ***Perf. 14***
**360** A101 5.50k multicolored *1.25 1.25*

Europa.

Bank of Estonia, 80th Anniv. — A102

**1999, May 3** **Litho.** ***Perf. 14***
**361** A102 5k multicolored 1.00 1.00

Olustvere Manor — A103

**1999, June 1**
**362** A103 3.60k multicolored .70 .70

See Nos. 395, 414, 433, 456, 490, 520, 551, 562, 603, 627, 648.

**One Kroon Coin Type of 1997**

**1999, June 18** **Litho.** ***Perf. 14***
**363** A82 100k bl, bister & blk 17.00 17.00

Estonian Natl. Anthem — A104

**1999, June 30** **Litho.** ***Perf. 14***
**364** A104 3.60k multicolored .70 .70

No. 364 is printed se-tenant with label.

Tower on Suur Munamägi, Highest Point in Baltic Countries A105

**1999, July 17**
**365** A105 5.20k multicolored 1.00 1.00

A106

Families holding hands and: 3.60k, Estonian flag.

No. 367: a, like #366. b, Latvian flag. c, Lithuanian flag.

**1999, Aug. 23** **Litho.** ***Perf. 14***
**366** A106 3.60k multicolored .70 .70

**Souvenir Sheet**

**367** A106 5.50k Sheet of 3, #a.-c. 3.00 3.00

Baltic Chain, 10th Anniv.

See Latvia Nos.493-494, Lithuania Nos. 639-640.

A107

**1999, Sept. 23** **Litho.** ***Perf. 14x13¾***
**368** A107 7k multicolored 1.40 1.40

UPU, 125th Anniv.

**Folk Costumes Type of 1994**

**1999, Oct. 12** **Litho.** ***Perf. 13¾x14***
**369** A57 3.60k Setu couple .65 .65
**370** A57 5k Setu man, boy .90 .90


Three Lions — A108

***Perf. 13x13¼, 13¾x14 (#371, 373, 374, 378-382)***

**1999-2002** **Litho.**

**371** A108 10s brn & dk brn .30 .30
**372** A108 30s lt bl & dk bl .30 .30
*a.* Perf. 13¾x14 .30 .30
**373** A108 30s blue & slate blue, dated 2003 .30 .30
**374** A108 50s olive & dk grn .30 .30
**375** A108 1k brown & fawn .30 .30
**376** A108 2k gray .50 .50
**377** A108 3.60k sky bl & dk bl .75 .75
*a.* Bright blue green ('00) .75 .75
**378** A108 4.40k grn & bl grn 1.00 .80
*a.* Inscribed "2001" 1.00 .80
*b.* Inscribed "2002" 1.00 .80
**379** A108 4.40k bl grn & brt bl grn, wide 2001 date 1.00 .30
**380** A108 4.40k Prus bl & lt bl, narrow 2001 date 1.00 .30
**381** A108 4.40k green & lt grn, dated 2002 1.00 .30
**382** A108 4.40k grn & apple grn, dated 2002 1.00 .30
**382A** A108 4.40k ol grn & apple grn, dated 2003 1.00 .35
**382B** A108 5k grn & lt grn, dated "2001" 1.30 1.30
*a.* Inscribed "2002" 1.20 1.20
*b.* Inscribed "2004" .75 .75
**382C** A108 6k bis & yel 1.50 1.50
**382D** A108 6.50k bis & org 1.50 1.50
**382E** A108 8k lake & pink 1.75 1.75
*Nos. 371-382E (17)* 14.80 11.15

Issued: 30s, 2k, 11/4; No. 377, 10/22; No. 377a, 3/31/00; No. 378, 8/21/00; 6k, 10/12/00; 6.50k, 10/5/00; 8k, 10/19/00; No. 372a: 4/17/01; 1k, 5k, 8/28/01; 10s, 2/2/02. 50s, 1/7/03; No. 373, 3/11/03; No. 379, 4/17/01; No. 380, 9/24/01; No. 381, 2/2/02; No. 382, 11/14/02; No. 382A, 3/11/03.

The background color of No. 379 is bolder than that on No. 380.

See Nos. 467, 472-474.

Christmas A109

**1999, Nov. 25** **Litho.** ***Perf. 14x13¾***
**383** A109 3.10k multicolored .60 .60

A110

**1999, Nov. 25** ***Perf. 13¾x14***
**384** A110 7k multicolored 1.25 1.25

1st public Christmas tree in Tallinn, 1441.

Christmas Lottery A110a

**1999, Dec. 1** **Litho.** ***Perf. 14x13¾***
**384A** A110a 3.10k + 1.90k multi 1.75 1.75

A111

**1999, Dec. 14 Litho.** ***Perf. 13¾x14***
**385** A111 5.50k Millennium 1.10 1.10

2000 Census — A112

**2000, Jan. 5**
**386** A112 3.60k multicolored .70 .70

Tartu Peace Treaty, 80th Anniv. — A113

**2000, Feb. 2 Litho.** ***Perf. 14x13¾***
**387** A113 3.60k multi .70 .70

**Lighthouse Type of 1995**

**2000, Feb. 25**
**388** A66 3.60k Ristna .65 .65
**389** A66 3.60k Kopu .65 .65
*a.* Pair, #388-389 1.30 1.30

Congress, 10th Anniv. — A114

**2000, Mar. 9** ***Perf. 13¾x14***
**390** A114 3.60k multi .65 .65

**One Kroon Coin Type of 1997**

**2000, Mar. 14** ***Perf. 14x13¾***
**391** A82 10k red, sil & blk 1.75 1.75

Cornflower (Natl. Flower) — A115

**2000, Apr. 7**
**392** A115 4.80k multi .85 .85

Natl. Book Year — A116

**2000, Apr. 22** ***Perf. 13¾x14***
**393** A116 3.60k multi .65 .65

First book printed in Estonian language, 475th anniv.

**Europa, 2000**
Common Design Type

**2000, May 9**
**394** CD17 4.80k multi *1.25 1.25*

**Manor Type of 1999**

**2000, May 23 Litho.** ***Perf. 14x13¾***
**395** A103 3.60k Palmse Hall .70 .70

Tallinn Zoo — A117

**2000, June 13 Litho.** ***Perf. 14x13¾***
**396** A117 3.60k Naemorhedus caudatus .70 .70

**Railway Type of 1996**

4.50k, Viljandi-Tallinn Railway, cent.

**2000, June 30**
**397** A76 4.50k multi .80 .80

9th Intl. Finno-Ugric Congress A118

**2000, Aug. 1**
**398** A118 5k multi 1.00 1.00

2000 Summer Olympics, Sydney — A119

**2000, Sept. 5 Litho.** ***Perf. 13¾x14***
**399** A119 8k multi 1.50 1.50

**Folk Costume Type of 1994**

Designs: 4.40k, Hargla. 8k, Polva.

**2000, Sept. 12**
**400-401** A57 Set of 2 2.25 2.25

August Mälk (1900-87), Writer — A120

**2000, Sept. 20** ***Perf. 14x13¾***
**402** A120 4.40k multi .80 .80

Lake Peipus Fish — A121

No. 403: a, Osmerus eperlanus spirinchus. b, Stizostedion lucioperka.

**2000, Oct. 25**
**403** Horiz. pair + central label 2.50 2.50
*a.-b.* A121 6.50k Any single 1.10 1.10

See Russia No. 6607.

Souvenir Sheet

Estonian Bookplates, Cent. — A122

Various bookplates. Denominiations in: a, LR. b, UR.

**2000, Nov. 11** ***Perf. 13¾x14***
**404** A122 6k Sheet of 2, #a-b 2.25 2.25

Christmas A123

3.60k, Horn and bow. 6k, Ornament.

**2000, Nov. 29** ***Perf. 14x13¾***
**405-406** A123 Set of 2 1.60 1.60

Erki Nool, Olympic Decathlon Champion A124

**2001, Jan. 10 Litho.** ***Perf. 14x13¾***
**407** A124 4.40k multi .75 .75

**Lighthouse Type of 1995**

**2001, Jan. 24**
**408** A66 4.40k Mohni .80 .80

Valentine's Day — A125

**2001, Feb. 6 Litho.** ***Perf. 13¾x14***
**409** A125 4.40k multi .80 .80

Stenbock House, Seat of Government A126

**2001, Feb. 20** ***Perf. 14x13¾***
**410** A126 6.50k multi 1.10 1.10

Souvenir Sheet

Paintings of Johann Köler (1826-99) — A127

No. 411: a, Girl on the Spring, 1858-62. b, Eve of the Pomegranate, 1879-80.

**2001, Feb. 27**
**411** A127 4.40k Sheet of 2, #a-b 1.50 1.50

European Year of Languages A128

**2001, Mar. 6**
**412** A128 4.40k multi .85 .85

Vanellus Vanellus A129

**2001, Apr. 4** ***Perf. 12¾x13***
**413** A129 4.40k multi .85 .85

See No. 435.

**Manor Type of 1999**

**2001, Apr. 17** ***Perf. 14x13¾***
**414** A103 4.40k Laupa Hall .80 .80

Europa — A130

**2001, May 9** ***Perf. 13¾x14***
**415** A130 6.50k multi *1.30 1.30*

Kalev Sports Association, Cent. — A131

**2001, May 24**
**416** A131 6.50k multi 1.25 1.25

Pärnu, 750th Anniv. — A132

**2001, June 5 Litho. *Perf. 14x13¾***
417 A132 4.40k multi .85 .85

Illustrations from Pokuland, by Edgar Valter — A133

Characters and — No. 418: a, Lake. b, Owl. c, Crane. d, Bird in nest.

No. 419: a, Fence. b, Flowers. c, Dog. d, Moon.

**2001, June 19**
418 Booklet pane of 4 2.75
*a.-d.* A133 3.60k Any single .75 .75
419 Booklet pane of 4 3.75
*a.-d.* A133 4.40k Any single .90 .90
Booklet, #418-419 7.25

Entire booklet sold for 35k, 3k of which went to the Pokuland Project of the Estonian Nature Fund.

Restoration of Independence, 10th Anniv. — A134

**2001, Aug. 7 *Perf. 13¾x14***
420 A134 4.40k multi .85 .85

Establishment of St. Mary's Land, 800th Anniv. — A135

**2001, Aug. 15 *Perf. 14x13¾***
421 A135 6.50k multi 1.25 1.25

Resumption of Issuing Stamps, 10th Anniv. — A136

**2001, Sept. 4 *Perf. 13¾x14***
422 A136 4.40k #200 .85 .85

Baltic Coast Landscapes A137

Designs: 4.40k, No. 424a, Lahemaa. No. 424b, Vidzeme. No. 424c, Palanga.

**2001, Sept. 15 *Perf. 14x13¾***
423 A137 4.40k multi .90 .90

**Souvenir Sheet**

***Perf. 13¼x13½***

424 Sheet of 3 3.50 3.50
*a.-c.* A137 6k Any single 1.10 1.10

No. 424 contains three 35x29mm stamps. See Lithuania Nos.

See Latvia Nos. 534-535, Lithuania Nos. 698-699.

Tallinn Zoo — A138

**2001, Oct. 4 *Perf. 14x13¾***
425 A138 4.40k Alligator sinensis .90 .90

Estonia 26/9 Racing Car — A139

**2001, Oct. 23**
426 A139 6k multi 1.15 1.15

**Folk Costume Type of 1994**

Designs: 4.40k, Paistu woman. 7.50k, Tarvastu man.

**2001, Nov. 7 Litho. *Perf. 13¾x14***
427-428 A57 Set of 2 2.25 2.25

A140

Christmas A141

***Perf. 13¾x14, 14x13¾***

**2001, Nov. 22**
429 A140 3.60k multi .70 .70
430 A141 6.50k multi 1.40 1.40

Radio Broadcasting in Estonia, 75th Anniv. — A142

**2001, Dec. 4 *Perf. 14x13¾***
431 A142 4.40k multi .90 .90

2002 Winter Olympics, Salt Lake City — A143

**2002, Jan. 10 Litho. *Perf. 14x13¾***
432 A143 8k multi 1.40 1.40

**Manor Type of 1999**

**2002, Jan. 22**
433 A103 4.40k Sangaste Hall .80 .80

**Lighthouse Type of 1995**

**2002, Feb. 20**
434 A66 4.40k Laidunina .80 .80

**Bird Type of 2001**

Design: Passer domesticus and Passer montanus.

**2002, Mar. 7 *Perf. 12¾x13***
435 A129 4.40k multi .80 .80

Spring Flowers — A144

**2002, Mar. 20 *Perf. 14x13¾***
436 A144 4.40k multi .80 .80

Estonian Puppet Theater, 50th Anniv. — A145

**2002, Mar. 27 *Perf. 13¾x14***
437 A145 4.40k multi + label .80 .80

PTO-4 Training Airplane — A146

**2002, Apr. 10 *Perf. 14x13¾***
438 A146 6k multi 1.10 1.10

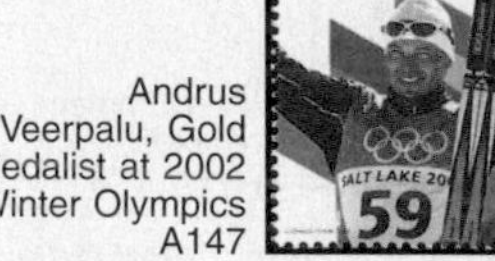
Andrus Veerpalu, Gold Medalist at 2002 Winter Olympics A147

**2002, Apr. 12**
439 A147 4.40k multi .80 .80

Tartu University Anniversaries — A148

No. 440: a, Main building, 1806-09, founding act of 1632. b, University Library, 1982, text from Biblia Latina.

**2002, Apr. 24**
440 A148 4.40k Horiz. pair, #a-b, + central label 2.25 2.25

Europa A149

**2002, May 9 *Perf. 12¾x13***
441 A149 6.50k multi *1.60 1.60*

Re-adoption of Constitution, 10th Anniv. — A150

**2002, May 23 *Perf. 13¾x14***
442 A150 4.40k multi .80 .80

Adoption of Lübeck Charter by Town of Rakvere, 700th Anniv. — A151

**2002, June 5**
443 A151 4.40k multi .80 .80

**Souvenir Sheet**

Re-introduction of the Kroon, 10th Anniv. — A152

No. 444 — Portraits from bank notes: a, Lydia Koidula, poet. b, Carl Rober Jakobson, journalist.

**2002, June 10 *Perf. 14x13¾***
444 A152 4.40k Sheet of 2, #a-b 2.00 2.00

**Souvenir Sheet**

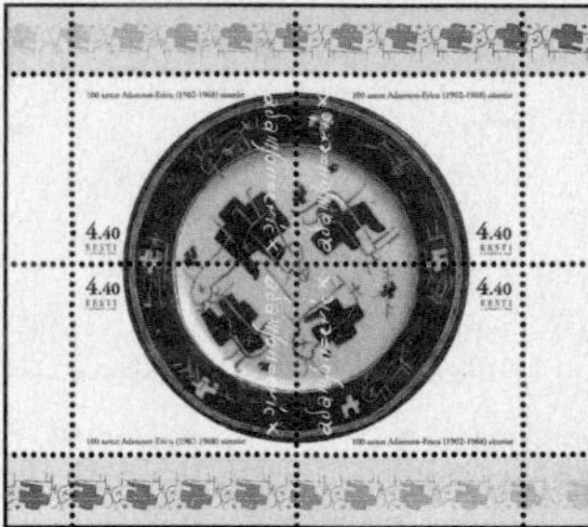
Adamson-Eric (1902-68), Painter — A153

Denomination at: a, LL. b, LR. c, UL. d, UR.

**2002, Aug. 8 Litho. *Perf. 14x13¾***
445 A153 4.40k Sheet of 4, #a-d 3.00 3.00

Sus Scrofa A154

**2002, Aug. 21 *Perf. 12¾x13***
446 A154 4.40k multi .80 .80

Limestone, Estonia's National Stone
A155

**2002, Sept. 18**
**447** A155 4.40k multi .80 .80

### Folk Costume Type of 1994

Designs: 4.40k, Kolga-Jaani women. 5.50k, Suure-Jaani boy and girl.

**2002, Oct. 1** ***Perf. 13¾x14***
**448-449** A57 Set of 2 1.60 1.60

A156

Christmas — A157

***Perf. 14x13¾, 13¾x14***
**2002, Nov. 20** **Litho.**
**450** A156 3.60k Reindeer .60 .60
**451** A157 6.50k Christmas tree 1.15 1.15

### Lighthouse Type of 1995

**2003, Jan. 15** ***Perf. 14x13¾***
**452** A66 4.40k Keri .80 .80

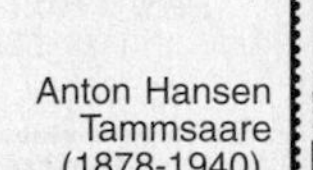

Anton Hansen Tammsaare (1878-1940), Novelist — A158

**2003, Jan. 30** **Litho.** ***Perf. 14x13¾***
**453** A158 4.40k multi .80 .80

Pica Pica
A159

**2003, Feb. 13** ***Perf. 12¾x13***
**454** A159 4.40k multi .80 .80

See Nos. 485, 509, 540, 566, 595, 625.

Spring Flowers — A160

No. 455: a, Tulips. b, Helleborus purpurascens. c, Narcissus poeticus. d, Crocus vernus.

**2003, Mar. 20** ***Perf. 13¾x14***
**455** A160 4.40k Sheet of 4, #a-d 7.00 7.00
*e.* Booklet pane, like #455, without date in margin 3.25 —
Complete booklet, #455e 3.25

See No. 484.

### Manor Type of 1999

**2003, Apr. 9** ***Perf. 14x13¾***
**456** A103 4.40k Alatskivi Hall .80 .80

Pres. Arnold Rüütel, 75th Birthday — A161

**2003, Apr. 24**
**457** A161 4.40k multi + label .90 .90

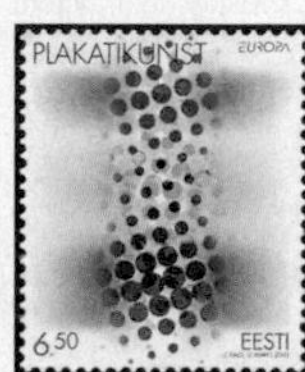

Europa — A162

**2003, May 8** ***Perf. 13¾x14***
**458** A162 6.50k multi *1.60 1.60*

Tartu University Botanical Gardens, Bicent. — A163

**2003, June 11** **Litho.** ***Perf. 14x13¾***
**459** A163 4.40k multi .90 .90

14th Junior World Orienteering Championships
A164

**2003, June 27**
**460** A164 7.50k multi 1.25 1.25

Circumnavigation of Adam Johann von Krusenstern (1770-1846) — A165

**2003, Aug. 6** ***Perf. 12½***
**461** A165 8k multi 1.40 1.40

Phoca Hispida
A166

**2003, Aug. 27** ***Perf. 12¾x13***
**462** A166 4.40k multi .80 .80

Adm. Fabian Gottlieb von Bellingshausen (1778-1852) — A167

**2003, Sept. 10**
**463** A167 8k multi 1.75 1.75

Ancient Trade Routes — A168

Map and: No. 464, 6.50k, Silver coin of Prince Volodymyr Sviatoslavovych, Slavic warship with sail. No. 465, 6.50k, Arrival of Scandinavian Seamen, coin of Danish King Svend Estridsen.

**2003, Sept. 10** ***Perf. 11½***
**464-465** A168 Set of 2 2.10 2.10

See Ukraine No. 524.

### Three Lions Type of 1999-2002

**2003-04** **Litho.** ***Perf. 13¾x14***
**467** A108 20s blk & gray .30 .30
**472** A108 4.40k ol grn & apple grn .80 .80
**473** A108 5k dk grn & apple grn, dated 2004 .90 .90
**474** A108 5.50k dk grn & yel grn 1.00 1.00

Issued: 20s, 4.40k, 8/22; 5k, 1/20/04; 5.50k, 3/25/04.

### Folk Costume Type of 1994

Designs: 4.40k, Aksi woman and girl. 6.50k, Otepää man, woman and girl.

**2003, Oct. 9** **Litho.** ***Perf. 13¾x14***
**476-477** A57 Set of 2 1.90 1.90

A169

Christmas
A170

**2003, Nov. 26** ***Perf. 14x13¾***
**478** A169 3.60k multi .70 .70
**479** A170 6k multi .90 .90

Souvenir Sheet

Friedrich Reinhold Kreutzwald (1803-82), Writer — A171

No. 480: a, 4.40k, Illustration by Kristjan Raud of "Voyage to the End of the World," from "Kalevipoeg," by Kreutzwald. b, 6.50k, Portrait of Kreutzwald.

**2003, Dec. 4** ***Perf. 13x12¾***
**480** A171 Sheet of 2, #a-b 2.10 2.10

### Lighthouse Type of 1995

**2004, Jan. 7** **Litho.** ***Perf. 14x13¾***
**481** A66 4.40k Sorgu .85 .85

Canis Lupus
A172

**2004, Feb. 3** ***Perf. 12¾x13***
**482** A172 4.40k multi .85 .85

Voyage Around Cape Horn of the Hioma, 150th Anniv. — A173

**2004, Feb. 18** ***Perf. 13¾x14***
**483** A173 8k multi 1.50 1.50

### Spring Flowers Type of 2003

No. 484: a, Viola riviniana. b, Anemone nemorosa. c, Hepatica nobilis. d, Trollius europaeus.

**2004, Mar. 17**
**484** A160 4.40k Sheet of 4, #a-d 3.25 3.25
*e.* Booklet pane, like #484 without date in margin 3.25
Complete booklet, #484e 3.25

### Bird Type of 2003

**2004, Apr. 6** ***Perf. 12¾x13***
**485** A159 4.40k Ciconia ciconia .80 .80

Admission to European Union
A174

**2004, May 1** ***Perf. 13¼x13***
**486** A174 6.50k multi 1.25 1.25

Europa — A175

**2004, May 4** ***Perf. 13***
**487** A175 6.50k multi *1.25 1.25*

Tallinn Town Hall, 600th Anniv.
A176

**2004, May 13** **Litho.** ***Perf. 12¾x13***
**488** A176 4.40k multi .80 .80

Consecration of Estonian Flag, 120th Anniv. — A177

**2004, June 4** ***Perf. 13¾x14***
**489** A177 4.40k multi .80 .80

### Manor Type of 1999

**2004, June 15** ***Perf. 14x13¾***
**490** A103 4.40k Vasalemma Hall .80 .80

Admission to NATO — A178

**2004, June 28** *Perf. 13¾x14*
**491** A178 6k multi 1.10 1.10

2004 Summer Olympics, Athens — A179

**2004, July 15 Litho.** *Perf. 13¾x14*
**492** A179 8k multi 1.40 1.40

Dragon Class Yachting European Championships — A180

**2004, Aug. 17** *Perf. 14x13¾*
**493** A180 6k multi 1.10 1.10

Taraxacum Officinale — A181

***Serpentine Die Cut 12½***
**2004, Sept. 14 Self-Adhesive**
**494** A181 30s multi .40 .40

See Nos. 547, 560, 572.

County Arms — A182

**2004, Sept. 28 Self-Adhesive**
**495** A182 4.40k Harjumaa .80 .80
**496** A182 4.40k Hiiumaa .80 .80

See Nos. 506-507, 518-519, 532-533, 536, 552, 561, 573, 588, 594, 608.

**Folk Costumes Type of 1994**

Designs: 4.40k, Viru-Jaagupi boy and girl. 7.50k, Jõhvi woman and girl.

**2004, Oct. 5 Litho.** *Perf. 13¾x14*
**497-498** A57 Set of 2 2.10 2.10

A183

Christmas A184

**2004, Nov. 23** *Perf. 13¾x14*
**499** A183 4.40k multi .90 .90

*Perf. 14x13¾*
**500** A184 6.50k multi 1.00 1.00

**Lighthouse Type of 1995**

Norrby Lighthouse with: 4.40k, White top, vert. 6.50k, Red top, vert.

**2005, Jan. 11 Litho.** *Perf. 14*
**501-502** A66 Set of 2 1.75 1.75

Castor Fiber A185

**2005, Jan. 25** *Perf. 12¾x13*
**503** A185 4.40k multi .70 .70

Rotary International, Cent. — A186

**2005, Feb. 11** *Perf. 13¾x14*
**504** A186 8k multi 1.25 1.25

Flag Over Pikk Hermann Tower, Tallinn — A187

***Serpentine Die Cut 12½***
**2005, Feb. 22 Self-Adhesive**
**505** A187 5k multi .90 .90

See Nos. 530, 559, 574.

**County Arms Type of 2004**

**2005 Self-Adhesive Litho.**
**506** A182 4.40k Ida-Virumaa .80 .80
**507** A182 4.40k Järvamaa .80 .80

Issued: No. 506, 3/8; No. 507, 3/15.

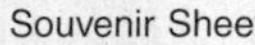

Souvenir Sheet

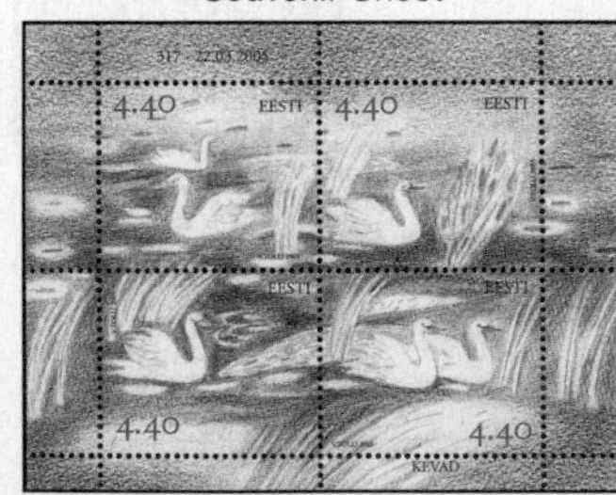


Spring — A188

No. 508: a, Two swans, denomination at UL. b, One swan, denomination at UL. c, One swan, denomination at LL. d, Two swans, denomination at LR.

**2005, Mar. 22 Litho.** *Perf. 14x13¾*
**508** A188 4.40k Sheet of 4, #a-d 2.75 2.75

**Bird Type of 2003**

**2005, Apr. 5** *Perf. 12¾x13*
**509** A159 4.40k Accipiter gentilis .80 .80

Mother's Day — A189

**2005, Apr. 20** *Perf. 14x13¾*
**510** A189 4.40k multi .80 .80

Europa — A190

Designs: 6k, Vegetable wrap. 6.50k, Tomato, carrots, egg yolk, parsley, fish, onion, beet.

**2005, May 3**
**511-512** A190 Set of 2 *2.25 2.25*

Eduard Tubin (1905-82), Composer A191

**2005, May 18**
**513** A191 6k multi 1.00 1.00

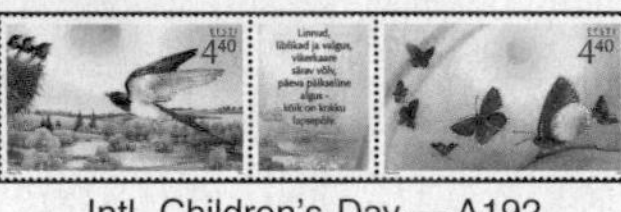

Intl. Children's Day — A192

No. 514: a, Birds. b, Butterflies.

**2005, June 1** *Perf. 13¼x13¾*
**514** A192 4.40k Horiz. pair, #a-b, + central label 1.50 1.50

Orchids — A193

Designs: 4.40k, Epipactis palustris. 8k, Epipogium aphyllum.

**2005, June 16 Litho.** *Perf. 13¾x14*
**515-516** A193 Set of 2 2.50 2.50

Restoration of St. John's Cathedral, Tartu — A194

**2005, June 29**
**517** A194 4.40k multi .80 .80

Tartu, 975th anniv.

**County Arms Type of 2004**

***Serpentine Die Cut 12½***
**2005 Self-Adhesive Litho.**
**518** A182 4.40k Jõgevamaa .75 .75
**519** A182 4.40k Läänemaa .75 .75

Issued: No. 518, 7/5; No. 519, 7/8.

**Manor Type of 1999**

**2005, July 12** *Perf. 14x13¾*
**520** A103 4.40k Kiltsi Hall .75 .75

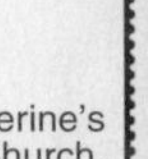


St. Catherine's Church, Karja — A195

**2005, Sept. 20**
**521** A195 4.40k multi .75 .75

Souvenir Sheet

Sculptures by Amandus Adamson (1855-1929) — A196

No. 522: a, Igavesti Voidutsev Armastus, 1889. b, Lüüriline Muusika, 1891. c, Memento Mori, 1907. d, Koit ja Hämarik, 1895.

**2005, Oct. 12** *Perf. 13½*
**522** A196 650s Sheet of 4, #a-d 4.00 4.00

Dogs — A197

No. 523: a, Kazakh hound (Kasaahi hurt). b, Estonian hound (Eesti hagijas).

**2005, Oct. 19** *Perf. 14x13¾*
**523** A197 6.50k Horiz. pair, #a-b 2.10 2.10

See Kazakhstan No. 495.

**Folk Costumes Type of 1994**

Designs: 4.40k, Ambla man, woman and girl. 8k, Türi women.

**2005, Oct. 28** *Perf. 13¾x14*
**524-525** A57 Set of 2 2.25 2.25

New Year's Goat — A198

Adoration of the Magi — A199

**2005, Nov. 22**
**526** A198 4.40k multi .80 .80
**527** A199 8k sil & red lil 1.45 1.45

Christmas and New Year's Day.

Due to the postponed conversion to the euro, originally scheduled for Jan. 1, 2007, Estonian stamps issued between 2006 and 2010 show denominations in kroons and the at-that-time-uncirculating euros.

Europa Stamps, 50th Anniv. — A200

CEPT emblem and: 6k, Superimposed letters. 6.50k, Map of Europe.

**2006, Jan. 4 Litho.** *Perf. 14x13¾*
**528** A200 6k multi .95 .95

**Souvenir Sheet**

**529** A200 6.50k multi 1.00 1.00

### Flag Over Pikk Hermann Tower Type of 2005 With Euro Denominations Added

**2006, Jan. 11** *Die Cut Perf. 12½*

**Self-Adhesive**

**530** A187 11k multi 1.75 1.75

2006 Winter Olympics, Turin, Italy — A201

**2006, Jan. 18** *Perf. 14x13¾*

**531** A201 8k multi 1.25 1.25

### County Arms Type of 2004 With Euro Denominations Added

**2006** *Die Cut Perf. 12½*

**Self-Adhesive**

**532** A182 4.40k Lääne-Virumaa .70 .70
**533** A182 4.40k Polvamaa .70 .70

Issued: No. 532, 1/25; No. 533, 2/8.

Alces Alces A202

**2006, Feb. 1** *Perf. 12¾x13*

**534** A202 4.40k multi .75 .75

Opening of KUMU Art Museum — A203

**2006, Feb. 17 Litho.** *Perf. 13¾x14*

**535** A203 4.40k multi .75 .75

### County Arms Type of 2004 With Euro Denominations Added

**2006, Mar. 8** *Die Cut Perf. 12½*

**Self-Adhesive**

**536** A182 4.40k Pärnumaa .85 .85

Souvenir Sheet

National Opera, Cent. — A204

No. 537: a, Characters from Vikerlased, first opera staged in 1928. b, Ballerina.

**2006, Mar. 27** *Perf. 13¾x14*

**537** A204 6.50k Sheet of 2, #a-b, + central label 2.25 2.25

A205

Gold Medalists at 2006 Winter Olympics — A206

No. 539: a, Andrus Veerpalu. b, Kristina Smigun.

**2006, Mar. 30** *Perf. 14x13¾*

**538** A205 4.40k multi .75 .75

**Souvenir Sheet**

**539** A206 8k Sheet of 2, #a-b 2.50 2.50

### Bird Type of 2003 With Euro Denominations Added

**2006, Apr. 5** *Perf. 12¾x13*

**540** A159 4.40k multi .75 .75

Lighthouses A207

Designs: 4.40k, Tallinn Bay lower lighthouse. 6.50k, Tallinn Bay upper lighthouse.

**2006, Apr. 12** *Perf. 13¾x14*

**541-542** A207 Set of 2 1.75 1.75

See Nos. 564, 587, 624.

Estonian Shooting Sport Federation, 75th Anniv. — A208

**2006, Apr. 26**

**543** A208 4.40k car & sil .75 .75

Europa — A209

**2006, May 3**

**544** A209 6.50k multi 1.25 1.25

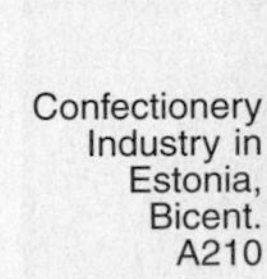

Confectionery Industry in Estonia, Bicent. A210

**2006, May 18** *Perf. 14x13¾*

**545** A210 4.40k multi .75 .75

Posthorns — A211

**2006, May 22** *Die Cut Perf. 10*

**Self-Adhesive**

**546** A211 4.40k gray brn + label .75 .75

Labels could be personalized.

See No. 563.

### Flower Type of 2004 with Euro Denominations Added

**2006, May 24** *Die Cut Perf. 12½*

**Self-Adhesive**

**547** A181 30s Hepatica nobilis .35 .35

Souvenir Sheet

Tori Stud Farm, 150th Anniv. — A212

No. 548: a, Three horses, denomination at UL. b, Pony and three horses, denomination at UR.

**2006, June 7** *Perf. 14x13¾*

**548** A212 4.40k Sheet of 2, #a-b 1.40 1.40

Victory Day — A213

**2006, June 23**

**549** A213 4.40k multi .75 .75

20th Intl. Organ Music Festival, Tallinn — A214

**2006, July 28 Litho.** *Perf. 14x13¾*

**550** A214 4.40k multi .75 .75

### Manor Type of 1999 With Added Euro Denomination

**2006, Aug. 16**

**551** A103 4.40k Taagepera Hall .75 .75

### County Arms Type of 2004 With Added Euro Denomination

**2006, Sept. 6** *Die Cut Perf. 12½*

**Self-Adhesive**

**552** A182 4.40k Haplamaa .75 .75

St. Lawrence's Church, Noo — A215

**2006, Sept. 20** *Perf. 13¾x14*

**553** A215 4.40k multi .75 .75

Betti Alver (1906-89), Writer — A216

**2006, Oct. 11** *Perf. 13*

**554** A216 4.40k multi .75 .75

Antarctic Wildlife — A217

No. 555 — Estonian and Chilean flags and: a, Aptenodytes forsteri. b, Balaenoptera acutorostrata.

**2006, Oct. 25** *Perf. 13½*

**555** A217 8k Pair, #a-b 2.50 2.50

See Chile No. 1468.

A218

Christmas — A219

**2006, Nov. 22 Litho.** *Perf. 13¾x14*

**556** A218 4.40k multi .70 .70
**557** A219 6k multi .95 .95

Lotte From Gadgetville A220

**2007, Jan. 4** *Perf. 14x13¾*

**558** A220 4.40k multi .85 .85

### Flag Over Pikk Hermann Tower Type of 2005 With Euro Denomination Added

**2007, Jan. 11** *Die Cut Perf. 12½*

**Self-Adhesive**

**559** A187 5k tan & multi .85 .85

### Flower Type of 2004 With Euro Denomination Added

**2007, Jan. 17** *Die Cut Perf. 12½*

**Self-Adhesive**

**560** A181 30s Leucanthemum vulgare .30 .30

### County Arms Type of 2004 With Euro Denomination Added

**2007, Jan. 25** *Die Cut Perf. 12½*

**Self-Adhesive**

**561** A182 4.40k Saaremaa .85 .85

### Manor Type of 1999 With Euro Denomination Added

**2007, Feb. 14** *Perf. 14x13¾*

**562** A103 5.50k Sagadi Hall .95 .95

**Posthorns Type of 2006**

**2007, Feb. 22** ***Die Cut Perf. 10***

**Self-Adhesive**

**563** A211 5.50k bl grn + label 1.00 1.00

Labels could be personalized.

**Lighthouse Type of 2006**

**2007, Mar. 8** ***Perf. 14x13¾***

**564** A207 6k Juminda, horiz. 1.00 1.00

Meles Meles A221

**2007, Mar. 22** ***Perf. 12¾x13***

**565** A221 4.40k multi .90 .90

**Bird Type of 2003 With Euro Denomination Added**

**2007, Apr. 5** ***Perf. 12¾x13***

**566** A159 4.40k Cygnus bewickii .90 .90

Miniature Sheet

Summer Flowers — A222

No. 567: a, Paeonia officinalis. b, Lilium lancifolium. c, Rosa ecae Golden Chersonese. d, Iris latifolia.

**2007, Apr. 19** ***Perf. 13¾x14***

**567** A222 4.40k Sheet of 4, #a-d 3.25 3.25

Europa — A223

**2007, May 3** ***Perf. 12½***

**568** A223 20.50k multi 3.50 3.50

Scouting, cent.

Intl. Children's Day — A224

**2007, June 1** **Litho.** ***Perf. 13½***

**569** A224 10k multi 1.75 1.75

Souvenir Sheet

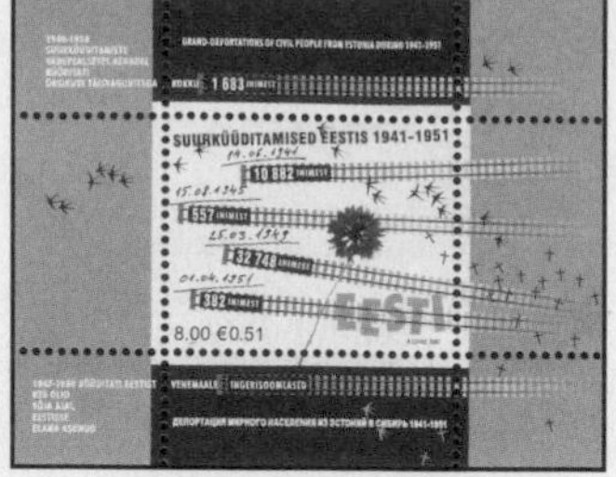

1941-51 Deportation of Estonians — A225

**2007, June 14** ***Perf. 13***

**570** A225 8k multi 1.40 1.40

Pirita Convent, 600th Anniv. — A226

**2007, June 15** **Litho.** ***Perf. 12½***

**571** A226 5.50k multi 1.00 1.00

**Flower Type of 2004 With Euro Denominations Added**

**2007, July 2** ***Die Cut Perf. 12½***

**Self-Adhesive**

**572** A181 1.10k Centaurea phrygia .30 .30

**County Arms Type of 2004 With Euro Denominations Added**

**2007, July 2** **Self-Adhesive**

**573** A182 5.50k Tartumaa 1.00 1.00

**Flag Over Pikk Hermann Tower Type of 2005 With Euro Denominations Added**

**2007, Aug. 1** **Self-Adhesive**

**574** A187 10k multi 1.75 1.75

Hellenurme Mill — A227

**2007, Aug. 9** ***Perf. 14x13¾***

**575** A227 5.50k multi 1.00 1.00

Hirvepark Demonstration, 20th Anniv. — A228

**2007, Aug. 23** ***Perf. 14x14¼***

**576** A228 5.50k multi 1.00 1.00

Souvenir Sheet

Matthias Johann Eisen (1857-1934), Folklorist — A229

**2007, Sept. 14** ***Imperf.***

**577** A229 10k multi 1.75 1.75

No. 577 has simulated perforations.

Ragnar Nurkse (1907-59), Economist — A230

**2007, Oct. 5** ***Perf. 13***

**578** A230 10k multi 1.75 1.75

St. John's Church, Kanepi — A231

**2007, Oct. 11** ***Perf. 13¾x14***

**579** A231 5.50k multi 1.00 1.00

Arms of Viljandi — A232

**2007, Oct. 25** **Litho.** ***Perf. 13¾x14***

**580** A232 5.50k multi 1.00 1.00

A233

Christmas A234

***Die Cut Perf. 11¼ Syncopated***

**2007, Nov. 22** **Self-Adhesive**

**581** A233 5.50k multi .90 .90

**582** A234 8k multi 1.40 1.40

Post Horn — A235

**2008** **Litho.** ***Die Cut Perf. 12½***

**Self-Adhesive**

**583** A235 5.50k brt orange 1.00 1.00

**584** A235 6.50k brt yel green 1.15 1.15

**585** A235 9k blue 1.60 1.60

*Nos. 583-585 (3)* 3.75 3.75

Issued: 5.50k, 1/10; 6.50k, 3/6; 9k, 4/1.

See Nos. 600, 638, 649, 658-662, 675-677, 682-684, 696-697, 708, 719-721.

Gustav Ernesaks (1908-93), Composer A236

**2008, Jan. 17** **Litho.** ***Perf. 13***

**586** A236 5.50k multi 1.00 1.00

**Lighthouse Type of 2006**

**2008, Jan. 24** ***Perf. 14x13¾***

**587** A207 5.50k Mehikoorma, horiz. 1.00 1.00

**County Arms Type of 2004 With Euro Denominations Added**

**2008, Feb. 7** ***Die Cut Perf. 12½***

**Self-Adhesive**

**588** A182 5.50k Valgamaa 1.00 1.00

Plecotus Auritus A237

**2008, Feb. 14** ***Perf. 12¾x13***

**589** A237 5.50k multi 1.00 1.00

Oak Tree — A238

**2008, Feb. 23** ***Perf. 13***

**590** A238 5.50k multi 1.00 1.00

Republic of Estonia, 90th anniv.

Kristjan Palusalu (1908-87), Olympic Wrestling Gold Medalist — A239

**2008, Mar. 10** ***Perf. 12½***

**591** A239 10k multi 1.75 1.75

State Awards of the Baltic Countries — A240

Designs: Nos. 592, 593a, Order of the National Coat of Arms, Estonia. No. 593b, Order of Three Stars, Latvia. No. 593c, Order of Vytautas the Great, Lithuania.

**2008, Mar. 15 Litho. *Perf. 13¾***
**592** A240 5.50k multi 1.00 1.00

**Souvenir Sheet**

**593** A240 10k Sheet of 3, #a-c, + label 5.25 5.25

See Latvia Nos. 701-702, Lithuania Nos. 862-863.

**County Arms Type of 2004 With Euro Denominations Added**

**2008, Mar. 27 *Die Cut Perf. 12½***
**Self-Adhesive**

**594** A182 5.50k Viljandimaa 1.00 1.00

**Bird Type of 2003 With Euro Denomination Added**

**2008, Apr. 3 *Perf. 12¾x13***
**595** A159 5.50k Tetrao tetrix 1.10 1.10

Europa A241

**2008, Apr. 30 *Perf. 14x14¼***
**596** A241 9k multi 1.60 1.60

Otto Strandman (1875-1941), Statesman — A242

**2008, May 9 Litho. *Perf. 13¾x14***
**597** A242 5.50k brown 1.00 1.00

Wavy Lines — A243

**2008, May 22 *Serpentine Die Cut 10***
**Self-Adhesive**

**598** A243 9k multi + label 1.75 1.75

The label shown is generic. Labels could be personalized for a fee.

Peasant War at Mahtra, 150th Anniv. — A244

**2008, May 31 *Perf. 14x13¾***
**599** A244 5.50k multi 1.00 1.00

**Posthorn Type of 2008**
***Die Cut Perf. 12½***

**2008, May 31 Litho.**
**Self-Adhesive**

**600** A235 50s gray .35 .35

2008 Summer Olympics, Beijing — A245

**2008, Aug. 8 Litho. *Perf. 13¾x14***
**601** A245 9k multi 1.60 1.60

Polma Windmill A246

**2008, Aug. 28 *Perf. 14x13¾***
**602** A246 5.50k multi 1.00 1.00

**Manor Type of 1999 With Euro Denomination Added**

**2008, Sept. 18 Litho. *Perf. 14x13¾***
**603** A103 5.50k Kalvi Hall 1.00 1.00

Gerd Kanter, Olympic Discus Champion A247

**2008. Sept. 25 *Perf. 13½***
**604** A247 5.50k multi 1.00 1.00

Church of the Holy Cross, Audru — A248

**2008, Oct. 16 Litho. *Perf. 13¾x14***
**605** A248 5.50k multi 1.00 1.00

**County Arms Type of 2004 With Euro Denominations Added**

**2008, Oct. 30 *Die Cut Perf. 12½***
**Self-Adhesive**

**606** A182 5.50k Vorumaa 1.00 1.00

Estonia Post, 90th Anniv. — A249

**2008, Nov. 13 *Perf. 13¾x14***
**607** A249 5.50k multi 1.00 1.00

Christmas A250

Designs: 5.50k, Gift on skis. 9k, Snowman on gift.

***Die Cut Perf. 11¼ Syncopated***

**2008, Nov. 20 Litho.**
**Booklet Stamps Self-Adhesive**

**608** A250 5.50k multi .90 .90
*a.* Booklet pane of 10 8.25
**609** A250 9k multi 1.60 1.60
*a.* Booklet pane of 10 13.50

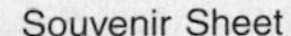

Souvenir Sheet

International Polar Year — A251

No. 610 — Antarctic glacier with snowflake emblem in: a, White. b, Blue.

**2009, Jan. 15 Litho. *Perf. 13x12¾***
**610** A251 15k Sheet of 2, #a-b 5.50 5.50

Battle of Paju, 90th Anniv. A252

**2009, Jan. 29 *Perf. 12¾x13***
**611** A252 5.50k multi 1.00 1.00

Gen. Johan Laidoner (1884-1953) — A253

**2009, Feb. 12 Litho. *Perf. 13***
**612** A253 5.50k multi 1.00 1.00

Ants Piip (1884-1942), Prime Minister — A254

**2009, Feb. 26 *Perf. 14***
**613** A254 5.50k maroon 1.00 1.00

Pres. Lennart Meri (1929-2006) A255

**2009, Mar. 26 Litho. *Perf. 14***
**614** A255 5.50k blue 1.00 1.00

Estonian National Museum, Cent. — A256

**2009, Apr. 14 *Perf. 13***
**615** A256 5.50k multi 1.00 1.00

Estonian Parliament, 90th Anniv. — A257

**2009, Apr. 23 *Perf. 14***
**616** A257 5.50k multi 1.00 1.00

Europa — A258

No. 617: a, Galaxies and hexagonal cells. b, Galaxy and hexagonal cells at left.

**2009, May 5 Litho. *Perf. 13¾x14***
**617** A258 9k Horiz. pair, #a-b 3.25 3.25

Intl. Year of Astronomy.

Räpina Paper Mill, 275th Anniv. — A259

**2009, May 14**
**618** A259 5.50k multi 1.00 1.00

Estonian Flag, 125th Anniv. — A260

***Die Cut Perf. 11¼ Syncopated***

**2009, June 5**
**Booklet Stamp Self-Adhesive**

**619** A260 9k multi 1.50 1.50
*a.* Booklet pane of 10 15.00

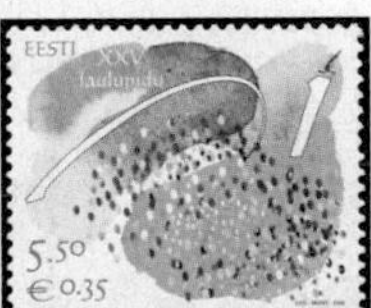

25th Song Festival — A261

**2009, June 18 *Perf. 14x13¾***
**620** A261 5.50k multi 1.00 1.00

Alexander Church, Narva, 125th Anniv. — A262

**2009, July 10 Litho. *Perf. 13¾x14***
**621** A262 5.50k multi *1.50 1.50*

Ursus Arctos A263

**2009, Sept. 10** *Perf. 12¾x13*
622 A263 5.50k multi 1.00 1.00

First Track and Field Competition in Estonia, Cent. — A264

**2009, Sept. 22** *Perf. 14x13¾*
623 A264 5.50k multi 1.10 1.10

**Lighthouse Type of 2006**

**2009, Sept. 24** *Perf. 14x13¾*
624 A207 5.50k Hara Tuletorn, horiz. 1.10 1.10

**Bird Type of 2003 With Euro Denomination Added**

**2009, Oct. 8 Litho.** *Perf. 12¾x13*
625 A159 5.50k Strix aluco 1.10 1.10

Windmill, Angla — A265

**2009, Oct. 22** *Perf. 13¾x14*
626 A265 5.50k multi 1.10 1.10

**Manor Type of 1999 With Euro Denomination Added**

**2009, Nov. 5** *Perf. 14x13¾*
627 A103 5.50k Saku Hall 1.10 1.10

A266

Christmas A267

***Die Cut Perf. 11¼ Syncopated***
**2009, Nov. 19**
**Booklet Stamps Self-Adhesive**
628 A266 5.50k multi .95 .95
a. Booklet pane of 10 9.50
629 A267 9k multi 1.60 1.60
a. Booklet pane of 10 16.00

Fabric Design — A268

***Die Cut Perf. 11¼ Syncopated***
**2010, Jan. 7 Litho.**
**Booklet Stamp Self-Adhesive**
630 A268 50k orange & multi 8.50 8.50
a. Booklet pane of 10 85.00

See Nos. 646, 650.

Jüri Jaakson (1870-1942), Politician — A269

**2010, Jan. 15** *Perf. 14*
631 A269 5.50k multi .95 .95

2010 European Figure Skating Championships, Tallinn — A270

**2010, Jan. 19** *Perf. 12¾x13*
632 A270 9k multi 1.50 1.50
a. Tete-beche pair 3.00 3.00

Tartu Peace Treaty, 90th Anniv. A271

**2010, Feb. 2** *Perf. 13*
633 A271 5.50k multi 1.00 1.00

**Post Horn Type of 2008**

**2010, Feb. 4** *Die Cut Perf. 12½*
**Self-Adhesive**
634 A235 9k deep blue 1.50 1.50

Dated 2010. Compare with No. 585.

2010 Winter Olympics, Vancouver — A272

**2010, Feb. 4** *Perf. 14*
635 A272 9k multi 1.60 1.60

Platanthera Bifolia — A273

**2010, Feb. 19**
636 A273 5.50k multi 1.00 1.00

Estonia Pavilion, Expo 2010, Shanghai A274

**2010, Mar. 11**
637 A274 9k multi 1.50 1.50

**Posthorn Type of 2008**

***Die Cut Perf. 12½***
**2010, Mar. 23 Litho.**
**Self-Adhesive**
638 A235 5.50k bright pink 1.00 1.00

St. Catherine's Church, Pärnu — A275

**2010, Mar. 23** *Perf. 13¾x14*
639 A275 6.50k multi 1.10 1.10

Juhan Kukk (1885-1942), State Elder — A276

**2010, Apr. 13**
640 A276 5.50k olive brown 1.00 1.00

**Lighthouses Type of 2006**

Designs: 6.50k, Suurupi front lighthouse. 8k, Suurupi rear lighthouse.

**2010, Apr. 22**
641-642 A207 Set of 2 2.50 2.50

Europa — A277

Children's book illustrations: No. 643, 9k, Family of mice, by Jüri Mildeberg. No. 644, 9k, Skaters in snow, by Viive Noor.

**2010, May 6** *Perf. 14x13¾*
643-644 A277 Set of 2 2.50 2.50

**Bird Type of 2003 With Euro Denominations Added**

**2010, May 13** *Perf. 12¾x13*
645 A159 5.50k Lanius collurio 1.00 1.00

**Fabric Design Type of 2010**

***Die Cut Perf. 11¼ Syncopated***
**2010, June 1**
**Booklet Stamp Self-Adhesive**
646 A268 26k brt yel grn & multi 4.50 4.50
a. Booklet pane of 10 45.00

Intl. Children's Day — A278

**2010, June 1 Litho.**
**Booklet Stamp Self-Adhesive**
647 A278 5.50k multi 1.00 1.00
a. Booklet pane of 10 10.00

**Manor Type of 1999 With Euro Denominations Added**

**2010, Aug. 5 Litho.** *Perf. 14x13¾*
648 A103 5.50k Suuremõisa Hall .95 .95

**Posthorn Type of 2008**

**2010, Aug. 18** *Die Cut Perf. 12*
**Self-Adhesive**
649 A235 9k bright yellow 1.50 1.50

**Fabric Design Type of 2010**

***Die Cut Perf. 11¼ Syncopated***
**2010, Aug. 18**
**Booklet Stamp Self-Adhesive**
650 A268 26k lilac & multi 4.50 4.50
a. Booklet pane of 10 45.00

Tallinn, 2011 European Capital of Culture — A279

**2010, Sept. 9 Litho.**
**Self-Adhesive**
651 A279 5.50k multi 1.00 1.00

Eliomys Quercinus A280

**2010, Sept. 23** *Perf. 12¾x13*
652 A280 5.50k multi .75 .75

A281

A282

A283

Worldwide Fund for Nature (WWF) — A284

Various views of Triturus cristatus.

**2010, Oct. 14** *Perf. 14x13¾*
653 Horiz. strip of 4 6.50 6.50
a. A281 9k multi 1.60 1.60
b. A282 9k multi 1.60 1.60
c. A283 9k multi 1.60 1.60
d. A284 9k multi 1.60 1.60
e. Sheet of 8 stamps with two tete-beche strips 13.00 13.00

Lennuk, by Nikolai Triik — A285

**2010, Nov. 17 Litho. *Perf. 14***

654 A285 9k multi 1.60 1.60

A286

Christmas — A287

***Die Cut Perf. 11¼ Syncopated***

**2010, Nov. 25**

**Booklet Stamps**
**Self-Adhesive**

655 A286 5.50k multi .95 .95
a. Booklet pane of 10 9.50
656 A287 9k multi 1.60 1.60
a. Booklet pane of 10 16.00

Stamps in No. 655a are tete-beche in relation to adjacent stamps. Vertical pairs of stamps in No. 656a are tete-beche.

100 Cents = 1 Euro

Introduction of Euro Currency A288

***Die Cut Perf. 11¼ Syncopated***

**2011, Jan. 1**

**Booklet Stamp**
**Self-Adhesive**

657 A288 €1 multi 2.75 2.75
a. Booklet pane of 10 27.50

**Post Horn Type of 2008 with Euro Denominations Only**

**2011, Jan. 3 *Die Cut Perf. 12½***

**Self-Adhesive**

658 A235 1c orange .25 .25
659 A235 5c salmon pink .25 .25
660 A235 10c lilac .25 .25
661 A235 50c blue 1.40 1.40
662 A235 65c green 1.75 1.75
*Nos. 658-662 (5)* 3.90 3.90

New Year 2011 (Year of the Rabbit) A289

**2011, Feb. 3 Litho. *Perf. 12¾x13***

663 A289 58c multi 1.60 1.60

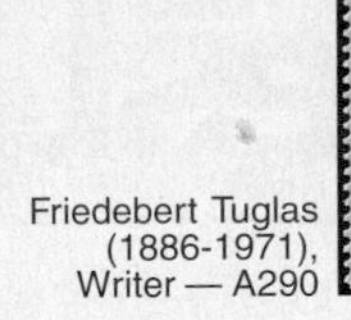

Friedebert Tuglas (1886-1971), Writer — A290

**2011, Mar. 2 *Perf. 13¾x14***

664 A290 58c multi 1.60 1.60

Villem Reiman (1861-1917), Historian — A291

**2011, Mar. 9**

665 A291 35c multi 1.00 1.00

Peony A292

**2011, Mar. 24 *Perf. 13x12¾***

666 A292 58c multi 1.75 1.75

Printed in sheets of 4 having each stamp rotated 90 degrees in relation to each other.

Folk Costumes — A293

Designs: 35c, Man and woman from Rapla. 58c, Two women from Joelähtme.

**2011, Apr. 14 *Perf. 13¾x14***

667-668 A293 Set of 2 2.50 2.50

Hirundo Rustica A294

**2011, Apr. 21 *Perf. 12¾x13***

669 A294 35c multi 1.00 1.00

Europa A295

Designs: No. 670, 58c, Elk in forest. No. 671, 58c, Cut logs.

**2011, Apr. 28 *Perf. 13***

670-671 A295 Set of 2 3.00 3.00

Intl. Year of Forests.

Souvenir Sheet

Struve Geodetic Arc — A296

No. 672 — Map of arc and: a, Friedrch Georg Wilhelm Struve (1793-1864), astronomer. b, Tartu Observatory.

**2011, May 6 *Perf. 14x13¾***

672 A296 58c Sheet of 2, #a-b 3.25 3.25

Lepus Europaeus A297

**2011, May 19 *Perf. 12¾x13***

673 A297 35c multi 1.00 1.00

Vergi Lighthouse A298

**2011, June 2 *Perf. 14x13¾***

674 A298 35c multi 1.00 1.00

**Posthorn Type of 2008 With Euro Denominations Only**

**2011 *Die Cut Perf. 12½***

**Self-Adhesive**

675 A235 35c brt yel grn 1.00 1.00
676 A235 58c lt purple 1.75 1.75
677 A235 58c green 1.60 1.60

Issued: 35c, No. 676, 6/2. No. 677, 8/25.

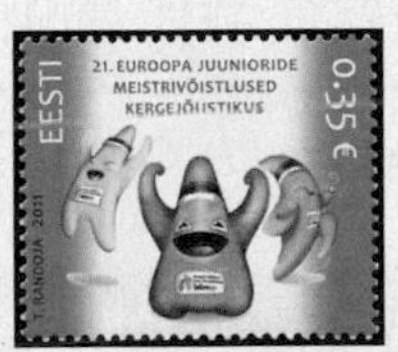

21st European Junior Track and Field Championships, Tallinn — A299

**2011, July 20 Litho. *Perf. 14x13¾***

678 A299 35c multi 1.00 1.00

Restoration of Independence, 20th Anniv. — A300

**2011, Aug. 20 *Perf. 13¾x14¼***

679 A300 35c multi 1.00 1.00

St. Margaret's Church, Karuse — A301

**2011, Aug. 25 *Perf. 14x13¾***

680 A301 35c multi 1.00 1.00

Friedrich Karl Akel (1871-1941), State Elder — A302

**2011, Sept. 5 *Perf. 13¾x14***

681 A302 35c brown 1.00 1.00

**Posthorn Type of 2008 With Euro Denominations Only**

**2011 *Die Cut Perf. 12½***

**Self-Adhesive**

682 A235 10c sage green .30 .30
683 A235 35c cerise .95 .95
684 A235 45c rose 1.25 1.25
*Nos. 682-684 (3)* 2.50 2.50

Issued: 10c, 45c, 11/1; 35c, 9/15.

Heinrich Mark (1911-2004), Prime Minister — A303

**2011, Sept. 30 *Perf. 13¾x14***

685 A303 35c blue .95 .95

Michael Andreas Barclay de Tolly (1761-1818), Military Leader — A304

**2011, Oct. 20 *Perf. 14x13¾***

686 A304 €1 multi 2.75 2.75

10-Cent and 2-Euro Coins — A305

***Die Cut Perf. 11¼ Syncopated***

**2011, Nov. 1**

**Booklet Stamp**
**Self-Adhesive**

687 A305 €2.10 multi 5.50 5.50
a. Booklet pane of 10 55.00

Market, Painting by Henn-Olavi Roode (1924-74) A306

**2011, Nov. 17** *Perf. 14*
**688** A306 €1 multi 2.75 2.75

Christmas — A307

*Die Cut Perf. 11¼ Syncopated*
**2011, Nov. 24**

**Booklet Stamps**
**Self-Adhesive**

**689** A307 45c Angel 1.25 1.25
*a.* Booklet pane of 10 12.50
**690** A307 €1 Ornament 2.75 2.75
*a.* Booklet pane of 10 27.50

Vertical pairs of stamps in Nos. 689a and 690a are tete-beche.

Oskar Luts (1887-1953), Writer — A308

**2012, Jan. 7** **Litho.** *Perf. 13*
**691** A308 45c multi 1.25 1.25

Population and Housing Census — A309

*Die Cut Perf. 11¼x11½ Syncopated*
**2012, Jan. 12** **Self-Adhesive**
**692** A309 45c multi 1.25 1.25

New Year 2012 (Year of the Dragon) A310

**2012, Jan. 23** *Perf. 12¾x13*
**693** A310 €1.10 multi 3.00 3.00

Capreolus Capreolus A311

**2012, Feb. 16** *Perf. 12¾x13*
**694** A311 45c multi 1.25 1.25

Heino Eller (1887-1970), Composer A312

**2012, Mar. 7** *Perf. 14x13¾*
**695** A312 45c multi 1.25 1.25

**Posthorn Type of 2008 With Euro Denominations Only**

**2012, Mar. 29** *Die Cut Perf. 12½*

**Self-Adhesive**
**Dated "2012"**

**696** A235 10c dull blue green .25 .25
**697** A235 50c pale yel grn 1.40 1.40

Compare Nos. 696 and 750.

Personalized Stamp — A313

*Die Cut Perf. 8¾ Syncopated*
**2012, Mar. 29** **Self-Adhesive**
**698** A313 45c multi 1.25 1.25

The generic vignette shown, depicting a map of Saaremaa, could be personalized for an additional fee.
See No. 773.

Folk Costumes — A314

Designs: 45c, Woman and girl from Hageri. €1, Woman from Nissi.

**2012, Apr. 14** **Litho.** *Perf. 13¾x14*
**699-700** A314 Set of 2 4.00 4.00

Charadrius Dubius A315

**2012, Apr. 19** *Perf. 12¾x13*
**701** A315 45c multi 1.25 1.25

Johannes Pääsuke (1892-1918), Creator of First Estonian Film in 1912 — A316

**2012, Apr. 30**
**702** A316 45c multi 1.25 1.25

Europa A317

Inscriptions: No. 703, €1, "wild est." No. 704, €1, "smart est."

**2012, May 3** *Perf. 14x13¾*
**703-704** A317 Set of 2 5.25 5.25

Church of St. Simeon and the Prophet Anne, Tallinn — A318

**2012, May 17** *Perf. 13¾x14*
**705** A318 45c multi 1.25 1.25

2012 Summer Olympics, London A319

**2012, June 1** *Perf. 14x13¾*
**706** A319 €1.10 multi 2.75 2.75

Martin Klein (1884-1947), First Estonian Olympic Medalist — A320

**2012, July 13** *Perf. 14x14¼*
**707** A320 €1 multi 2.50 2.50

**Posthorn Type of 2008 With Euro Denominations Only**

**2012, Aug. 10** *Die Cut Perf. 12½*

**Self-Adhesive**

**708** A235 45c citron 1.25 1.25

One-Euro Coin — A321

*Die Cut Perf. 11¼ Syncopated*
**2012, Aug. 10** **Self-Adhesive**
**709** A321 €1 multi 2.60 2.60

Amanita Virosa — A322

**2012, Aug. 30** *Perf. 13¾x14*
**710** A322 45c red & black 1.25 1.25

Käsmu Lighthouse A323

**2012, Sept. 13** *Perf. 14x13¾*
**711** A323 45c multi 1.25 1.25

Jaan Teemant (1872-1941), State Elder — A324

**2012, Sept. 24** *Perf. 13¾x14*
**712** A324 45c brown 1.25 1.25

Railway Bridges A325

Train and: Nos. 713, 714a, Narva Bridge, Estonia. No. 714b, Carnikava Bridge, Latvia. No. 714c, Lyduvenai Bridge, Lithuania.

**2012, Oct. 25** *Perf. 13¼*
**713** A325 45c multi 1.25 1.25

**Souvenir Sheet**

**714** A325 €1 Sheet of 3, #a-c 8.00 8.00

See Latvia Nos. 815-816, Lithuania Nos. 985-986.

Scouting in Estonia, Cent. — A326

**2012, Nov. 7** *Perf. 14x13¾*
**715** A326 45c multi 1.25 1.25

Still Life with Mandolin, by Lepo Mikko — A327

**2012, Nov. 16** *Perf. 14*
**716** A327 €1.10 multi 3.00 3.00

Santa Claus on Skis — A328

Poinsettia A329

*Die Cut Perf. 11¼ Syncopated*

**2012, Nov. 22** **Self-Adhesive**

**717** A328 45c multi 1.25 1.25
**718** A329 €1 multi 2.60 2.60

Christmas.

**Posthorn Type of 2008 With Euro Denominations Only Self-Adhesive**

**2013, Jan. 10** ***Die Cut Perf. 12½***

**719** A235 5c light blue .30 .30
**720** A235 50c green 1.40 1.40
**721** A235 65c red violet 1.75 1.75
*Nos. 719-721 (3)* 3.45 3.45

Kiipsaare Lighthouse A330

**2013, Jan. 31** ***Perf. 14x13¾***

**722** A330 45c multi 1.25 1.25

New Year 2013 (Year of the Snake) A331

**2013, Feb. 8** ***Perf. 12¾x13***

**723** A331 €1.10 multi 3.00 3.00

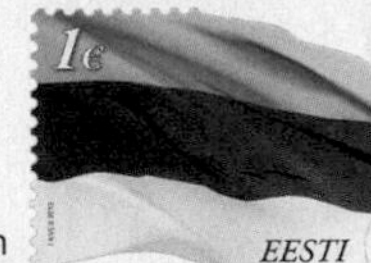

Estonian Flag — A332

*Die Cut Perf. 11¼ Syncopated*

**2013, Feb. 22**

**Self-Adhesive**

**724** A332 €1 multi 2.60 2.60
*a.* Dated "2014" 2.75 2.75

See No. 754.
Issued No. 724a, 5/22/14.

Perdix Perdix A333

**2013, Mar. 7** ***Perf. 12¾x13***

**725** A333 45c multi 1.25 1.25

Arms of Sindi — A333a

*Die Cut Perf. 12½*

**2013, Mar. 28** **Litho.**

**Self-Adhesive**

**725A** A333a 45c multi 1.75 1.75

Folk Costumes — A334

Man and woman from: 45c, Kihelkonna. €1, Karja.

**2013, Apr. 12** ***Perf. 13¾x14***

**726-727** A334 Set of 2 4.00 4.00

Icebreaker "Tarmo" — A335

**2013, Apr. 25** ***Perf. 14x13¾***

**728** A335 €1 multi 2.75 2.75

Europa — A336

No. 729 — Postal vehicles: a, Horse-drawn stagecoach, 1840s. b, Modern van.

**2013, May 2** **Litho.**

**729** A336 €1 Horiz. pair, #a-b 5.25 5.25

Souvenir Sheet

Estcube-1 Satellite — A337

**2013, May 2**

**730** A337 €1.10 multi 3.00 3.00

Kuressaare, 450th Anniv. A338

**2013, May 8** ***Perf. 14x14¼***

**731** A338 45c multi 1.40 1.40

Kaarel Eenpalu (1888-1942), State Elder and Prime Minister — A339

**2013, May 28** ***Perf. 13¾x14***

**732** A339 45c dk brn violet 1.25 1.25

Mustela Nivalis A340

**2013, June 6** ***Perf. 12¾x13***

**733** A340 45c multi 1.25 1.25

St. Catherine's Church, Voru — A341

**2013, July 24** ***Perf. 13¾x14***

**734** A341 45c multi 1.25 1.25

Souvenir Sheet

Cultural Heritage Year — A342

**2013, Aug. 3** ***Perf.***

**735** A342 €1.10 multi 3.00 3.00

Finn Class Sailing World Championships, Tallinn — A343

**2013, Aug. 23** ***Perf. 14¼x13¾***

**736** A343 €1.10 multi 3.00 3.00

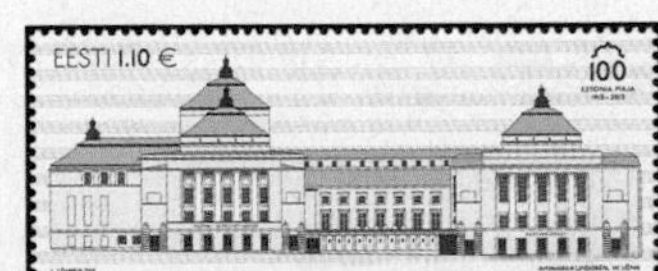

Estonia Theater and Concert House, Tallinn, Cent. — A344

**2013, Sept. 6** ***Perf. 13***

**737** A344 €1.10 multi 3.00 3.00

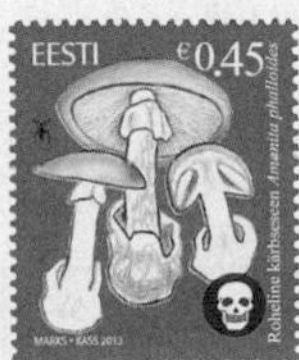

Amanita Phalloides — A345

**2013, Sept. 12** ***Perf. 13¾x14***

**738** A345 45c multi 1.25 1.25

Raimond Valgre (1913-49), Composer — A346

**2013, Oct. 7** **Litho.** ***Perf. 13***

**739** A346 45c multi 1.25 1.25

Arms of Moisaküla — A347

*Die Cut Perf. 12½*

**2013, Oct. 31** **Litho.**

**Self-Adhesive**

**740** A347 45c sil & black 1.50 1.50

Regular Postal Services in Estonia, 375th Anniv. A348

*Perf. 14¼x13¾*

**2013, Nov. 13** **Litho.**

**741** A348 45c multi 1.50 1.50

Aadu (Ado) Birk (1883-1942), Prime Minister — A349

**2013, Nov. 14** **Litho.** ***Perf. 13¾x14***

**742** A349 45c dull brown 1.25 1.25

After Dinner, by Elmar Kits (1913-72) A350

**2013, Nov. 15** **Litho.** ***Perf. 14***

**743** A350 €1.10 multi 2.50 2.50

A351

Christmas A352

*Serpentine Die Cut 11¼ Syncopated*

**2013, Nov. 22** **Litho.**

**Self-Adhesive**

**744** A351 45c multi 1.25 1.25
**745** A352 €1 multi 2.75 2.75

Estonian Olympic Committee, 90th Anniv. — A353

**2013, Dec. 9 Litho. *Perf. 13¾x14***
**746** A353 45c multi 1.50 1.50

Jaan Tonisson (1888-c. 1941), Prime Minister — A354

**2013, Dec. 20 Litho. *Perf. 13¾x14***
**747** A354 45c brown 1.25 1.25

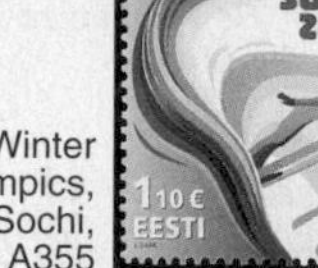

2014 Winter Olympics, Sochi, Russia — A355

**2014, Jan. 16 Litho. *Perf. 14x13¾***
**748** A355 €1.10 multi 3.00 3.00

New Year 2014 (Year of the Horse) A356

**2014, Jan. 31 Litho. *Perf. 12¾x13***
**749** A356 €1.10 multi 3.00 3.00

**Post Horn Type of 2008 With Euro Denomination Only**
***Die Cut Perf. 12½***
**2014, Feb. 19 Litho.**
**Self-Adhesive**
**Dated "2014"**
**750** A235 10c brt bl grn .35 .35
*a.* Dated "2015" .35 .35

Issued: No. 750a, 10/16/15. Compare with No. 696.

Estonian History Museum, 150th Anniv. A357

**2014, Feb. 19 Litho. *Perf. 12¾x13***
**751** A357 45c multi 1.25 1.25

Pres. Konstantin Päts (1874-1956) A358

**2014, Feb. 21 Litho. *Perf. 13¾x14***
**752** A358 45c blue 1.25 1.25

Arms of Voru — A359

***Die Cut Perf. 12½***
**2014, Mar. 5 Litho.**
**Self-Adhesive**
**753** A359 45c multi 1.25 1.25

**Estonian Flag Type of 2013**
***Die Cut Perf. 11¼ Syncopated***
**2014, Mar. 5 Litho.**
**Self-Adhesive**
**754** A332 €2 multi 5.50 5.50

Alcedo Atthis A360

**2014, Mar. 20 Litho. *Perf. 12¾x13***
**755** A360 45c multi 1.25 1.25

Folk Costumes — A361

Designs: 45c, Man and woman from Mihkli. €1, Women from Vigala.

**2014, Apr. 12 Litho. *Perf. 13¾x14***
**756-757** A361 Set of 2 4.00 4.00

Juhan Liiv (1864-1913), Poet — A362

**2014, Apr. 30 Litho. *Perf. 13***
**758** A362 45c multi 1.25 1.25

Inachis Io — A363

***Serpentine Die Cut 12½***
**2014, May 2 Litho.**
**Booklet Stamp**
**Self-Adhesive**
**759** A363 45c multi 1.40 1.40
*a.* Booklet pane of 4 5.60

Europa A364

Musical instruments: No. 760, €1, Väikekannel (zither). No. 761, €1, Lootspill (accordion).

**2014, May 8 Litho. *Perf. 14x13¾***
**760-761** A364 Set of 2 5.00 5.00

Erinaceus Europaeus A365

**2014, May 30 Litho. *Perf. 12¾x13***
**762** A365 45c multi 1.25 1.25

Estonian Herdbook, Cent. A366

**2014, July 19 Litho. *Perf. 14x13½***
**Textured and Flocked Granite Paper**
**763** A366 €1 multi 2.75 2.75

Baltic Chain Demonstration, 25th Anniv. — A367

Designs: 55c, Man and child.
No. 765: a, Five adults and one child. b, Three women. c, Like #764

**2014, Aug. 23 Litho. *Perf. 13¼***
**764** A367 55c multi 1.50 1.50

**Souvenir Sheet**
**765** A367 €1 Sheet of 3, #a-c 8.00 8.00

See Latvia Nos. 883-884; Lithuania No. 1031.

Souvenir Sheet

Tallinn Zoo, 75th Anniv. — A368

No. 766: a, Gypaetus barbatus. b, Panthera pardus orientalis.

***Perf. 14¼x13¾***
**2014, Aug. 25 Litho.**
**766** A368 55c Sheet of 2, #a-b 3.00 3.00

Estonian Academy of Arts, Cent. — A369

**2014, Sept. 1 Litho. *Perf. 14x13¾***
**767** A369 55c multi 1.50 1.50

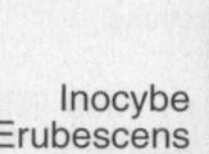

Inocybe Erubescens A370

**2014, Sept. 11 Litho. *Perf. 13¾x14***
**768** A370 55c red & black 1.40 1.40

Arms of Saue — A371

***Die Cut Perf. 12½***
**2014, Sept. 11 Litho.**
**Self-Adhesive**
**769** A371 55c multi 1.40 1.40

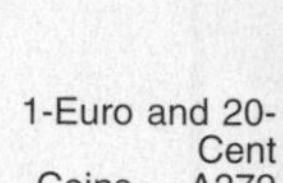

1-Euro and 20-Cent Coins — A372

***Die Cut Perf. 11¼ Syncopated***
**2014, Oct. 2 Litho.**
**Self-Adhesive**
**770** A372 €1.20 multi 3.00 3.00

Lighthouses A373

Designs: 55c, Northern Soru Lighthouse. €1.30, Southern Soru Lighthouse.

**2014, Oct. 17 Litho. *Perf. 13¾x14***
**771-772** A373 Set of 2 5.00 5.00

**Personalized Stamp Type of 2012**
***Die Cut Perf. 8¾ Syncopated***
**2014, Nov. 17 Litho.**
**Self-Adhesive**
**773** A313 55c multi 1.40 1.40

The generic vignette, depicting a map of Hüumaa, could be personalized for an additional fee.

Courtyard, by Herbert Lukk (1892-1919) A374

**2014, Nov. 17 Litho. *Perf. 14***
**774** A374 €1.30 multi 3.50 3.50

Christmas A375

Christmas tree, ornaments and: 55c, Ribbon. €1.20, Pine cone.

***Die Cut Perf. 11¼ Syncopated***
**2014, Nov. 20 Litho.**
**Self-Adhesive**
**775-776** A375 Set of 2 4.50 4.50

Jüri Uluots (1890-1945), Prime Minister — A376

**2015, Jan. 13 Litho.** ***Perf. 13¾x14***
**777** A376 55c blue 1.25 1.25

Johannes Kotkas (1915-88), Wrestler — A377

**2015, Feb. 3 Litho.** ***Perf. 12½***
**778** A377 55c multi 1.25 1.25

New Year 2015 (Year of the Ram) A378

**2015, Feb. 19 Litho.** ***Perf. 12¾x13***
**779** A378 €1.30 multi 3.00 3.00

Eduard Vilde (1865-1933), Writer — A379

**2015, Mar. 4 Litho.** ***Perf. 13***
**780** A379 55c multi 1.25 1.25

Arms of Elva — A380

***Die Cut Perf. 12½***
**2015, Mar. 12 Litho.**
**Self-Adhesive**
**781** A380 55c multi 1.25 1.25

Souvenir Sheet

Seal and Map of Baltic Sea — A381

**2015, Mar. 12 Litho.** ***Perf.***
**782** A381 €2.55 multi 6.25 6.25

Folk Costumes — A382

Designs: 55c, Man, woman and girl from Lihula. €1.20, Women from Kirbla.

**2015, Apr. 14 Litho.** ***Perf. 13¾x14***
**783-784** A382 Set of 2 4.00 4.00

Europa A383

Designs: No. 785, €1.20, Toy horses. No. 786, €1.20, Stuffed animals.

**2015, May 6 Litho.** ***Perf. 14***
**785-786** A383 Set of 2 5.50 5.50

Pernis Apivorus A384

**2015, May 21 Litho.** ***Perf. 12¾x13***
**787** A384 55c multi 1.25 1.25

Characters From Animated Film *Lotte From Gadgetville* — A385

No. 788: a, Bruno the Kitten. b, Albert the Bunny. c, Bruno, Albert and Lotte. d, Lotte the Puppy.

***Serpentine Die Cut 5x6***
**2015, May 30 Litho.**
**Self-Adhesive**
**788** A385 Booklet pane of 4 + 6 stickers 5.50
*a.-d.* 55c Any single 1.35 1.35

Giraffe With Head Above Cloud — A386

***Serpentine Die Cut 5x6***
**2015, June 4 Litho.**
**Booklet Stamp**
**Self-Adhesive**
**789** A386 €1.20 multi 2.75 2.75
*a.* Booklet pane of 4 11.00

Aleksander Warma (1890-1970), Prime Minister — A387

**2015, June 22 Litho.** ***Perf. 13¾x14***
**790** A387 55c Prus grn 1.25 1.25

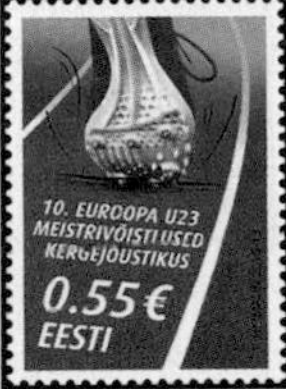

European Under-23 Track and Field Championships, Tallinn — A388

**2015, July 1 Litho.** ***Perf. 14x13¾***
**791** A388 55c multi 1.25 1.25

Estonian Business Innovations — A389

No. 792: a, Fortumo. b, GrabCAD. c, Skype. d, TransferWise.

***Die Cut Perf. 12½***
**2015, July 6 Litho.**
**Self-Adhesive**
**792** A389 Booklet pane of 4 12.00
*a.-d.* €1.30 Any single 3.00 3.00

Lutra Lutra A390

**2015, Aug. 25 Litho.** ***Perf. 12¾x13***
**793** A390 55c multi 1.35 1.35

Arms of Paide — A391

***Die Cut Perf. 12½***
**2015, Sept. 10 Litho.**
**Self-Adhesive**
**794** A391 55c multi 1.25 1.25

Cortinarius Rubellus — A392

**2015, Sept. 10 Litho.** ***Perf. 13¾x14***
**795** A392 55c multi 1.35 1.35

Tahkuna Lighthouse A393

**2015, Oct. 16 Litho.** ***Perf. 14x13¾***
**796** A393 55c multi 1.25 1.25

Penny Black, 175th Anniv. — A394

**2015, Nov. 13 Litho.** ***Perf. 13½***
**797** A394 55c multi 1.25 1.25

A Girl and the Moon, by Karl Pärsimägi (1902-42) — A395

**2015, Nov. 17 Litho.** ***Perf. 14***
**798** A395 55c multi 1.25 1.25

A396

Christmas — A397

***Die Cut Perf. 11¼ Syncopated***
**2015, Nov. 19 Litho.**
**Self-Adhesive**
**799** A396 55c multi 1.25 1.25
**800** A397 €1.20 multi 2.60 2.60

Arthur Jochim von Oettingen (1836-1920), Meteorologist, and Tartu University Meteorological Observatory — A398

**2015, Dec. 2 Litho. *Perf. 14¼x13¾***

**801** A398 65c multi 1.60 1.60

Tartu University Meteorological Observatory, 150th anniv.

Paul Keres (1916-75), Chess Player — A399

**2016. Jan. 7 Litho. *Perf. 12½***

**802** A399 65c multi 1.50 1.50

Souvenir Sheet

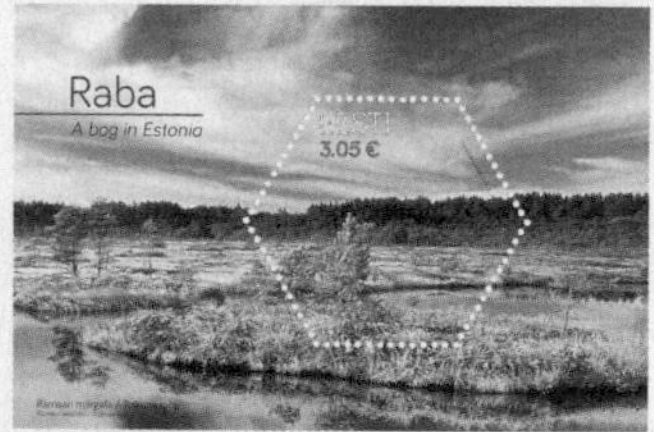

Tolkuse Bog — A400

**2016, Feb. 2 Litho. *Perf. 13***

**803** A400 €3.05 multi 7.25 7.25

New Year 2016 (Year of the Monkey) A401

**2016, Feb. 8 Litho. *Perf. 12¾x13***

**804** A401 €1.50 multi 3.25 3.25

Arms of Keila — A402

***Die Cut Perf. 12½***

**2016, Feb. 10 Litho.**

**Self-Adhesive**

**805** A402 65c multi 1.40 1.40

Posthorn — A403

***Die Cut Perf. 12½***

**2016, Feb. 10 Litho.**

**Self-Adhesive**

**806** A403 €1.40 multi 3.00 3.00

*a.* Dated "2017" 3.00 3.00

Issued: No. 806a, 1/18/17.

See Nos. 816-818, 832-833.

Parus Major A404

**2016, Feb. 17 Litho. *Perf. 12¾x13***

**807** A404 65c multi 1.40 1.40

Architecture — A405

No. 808: a, Tartu University Narva College, Narva (magenta background). b, Snail Tower, Tartu (green background). c, Estonian Embassy, Beijing (yellow brown background). d, Rotermann Quarter, Tallinn (turquoise green background).

**2016, Mar. 17 Litho. *Perf. 14***

**808** A405 65c Block of 4, #a-d 6.00 6.00

*e.* Booklet pane of 4, #808a-808d 6.00 —

Complete booklet, #808e 6.00

August Rei (1886-1963), Chairman of Estonian National Council — A406

**2016, Mar. 22 Litho. *Perf. 13¾x14***

**809** A406 65c brown 1.50 1.50

Otepää, 900th Anniv. — A407

**2016, Apr. 1 Litho. *Perf. 13¼x12¾***

**810** A407 65c multi 1.50 1.50

Folk Costumes — A408

Designs: 65c, Man and woman from Audru. €1.50, Girl and woman from Tostamaa.

**2016, Apr. 14 Litho. *Perf. 13¾x14***

**811-812** A408 Set of 2 5.00 5.00

Self-Portrait of Ants Laikmaa (1866-1942), Painter — A409

**2016, May 5 Litho. *Perf. 12¾x13***

**813** A409 65c multi 1.50 1.50

A410

Europa A411

**2016, May 9 Litho. *Perf. 14***

**814** A410 €1.40 multi 3.25 3.25

**815** A411 €1.40 multi 3.25 3.25

Think Green Issue.

**Posthorn Type of 2016**

***Die Cut Perf. 12½***

**2016, May 19 Litho.**

**Self-Adhesive**

**Background Color**

**816** A403 5c yel & pale yel .25 .25

**817** A403 20c mag & pale mag .45 .45

**818** A403 40c brt grn & pale grn .90 .90

*Nos. 816-818 (3)* 1.60 1.60

2016 Summer Olympics, Rio de Janeiro — A412

**2016, June 9 Litho. *Perf. 13¾x14¼***

**819** A412 €1.50 multi 3.50 3.50

Souvenir Sheet

Oil Shale Mining in Estonia, Cent. — A413

***Perf. 13¼x13½***

**2016, June 15 Litho.**

**820** A413 €2.95 multi 6.75 6.75

2016 Veterans' World Orienteering Championships, Tallinn and Harju County — A414

**2016, Aug. 5 Litho. *Perf. 12¾x13***

**821** A414 €1.50 multi 3.50 3.50

Tonis Kint (1896-1991), Deputy Prime Minister of Exile Government A415

**2016, Aug. 17 Litho. *Perf. 13¾x14***

**822** A415 65c blue green 1.50 1.50

Sicista Betulina A416

**2016, Aug. 25 Litho. *Perf. 12¾x13***

**823** A416 65c multi 1.50 1.50

Amanita Muscaria — A417

**2016, Sept. 8 Litho. *Perf. 13¾x14***

**824** A417 65c multi 1.50 1.50

National Museum — A418

**2016, Oct. 1 Litho. *Perf. 13***

**825** A418 €1.50 multi 3.50 3.50

Virtsu Lighthouse A419

**2016, Oct. 27 Litho. *Perf. 14x13¾***

**826** A419 65c multi 1.50 1.50

Baltic Assembly, 25th Anniv. — A420

**2016, Nov. 8 Litho. *Perf. 13½***

**Stamp With White Frame**

**827** A420 65c multi 1.50 1.50

**Souvenir Sheet**

**Stamp With Multicolored Frame**

**828** A420 €1.40 multi 3.25 3.25

See Latvia Nos. 948-949, Lithuania Nos. 1088-1089.

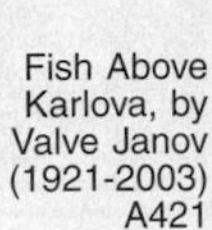

Fish Above Karlova, by Valve Janov (1921-2003) A421

**2016, Nov. 17 Litho. *Perf. 14***

**829** A421 65c multi 1.50 1.50

Cookies A422

Stylized Christmas Tree A423

***Die Cut Perf. 13½x14***

**2016, Nov. 18 Litho.**

**Self-Adhesive**

**830** A422 65c multi 1.50 1.50
**831** A423 €1.40 multi 3.25 3.25

Christmas. No. 830 is impregnated with a gingerbread scent.

**Posthorn Type of 2016**

***Die Cut Perf. 12½***

**2017, Jan. 18 Litho.**

**Self-Adhesive**

**Background Color**

**832** A403 10c org & pale org .30 .30
**833** A403 65c bl grn & pale bl 1.50 1.50

New Year 2017 (Year of the Rooster) A424

**2017, Jan. 28 Litho. *Perf. 12¾x13***

**834** A424 €1.50 multi 3.50 3.50

Streptopelia Turtur — A425

**2017, Feb. 9 Litho. *Perf. 12¾x13***

**835** A425 65c multi 1.50 1.50

Baltic Herring — A426

**2017, Feb. 23 Litho. *Perf. 13***

**836** A426 65c multi 1.50 1.50

Ships Built in Estonia — A427

No. 837: a, Patrol 4500 WP patrol vessel. b, AC600PVDB fish feeding barge. c, Saare 46 yacht. d, Koidula ferry.

**2017, Mar. 30 Litho. *Perf. 14***

**837** A427 65c Block of 4, #a-d 6.00 6.00
*e.* Booklet pane of 4, #837a-837d 6.00 —
Complete booklet, #837e 6.00

No. 837 was printed in sheets containing two blocks that are tete-beche in relation to each other.

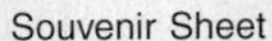

**Souvenir Sheet**

Figure Skating in Estonia, Cent. — A428

**2017, Apr. 15 Litho. *Perf. 13¼***

**838** A428 €3.05 multi + 2 labels 7.00 7.00

Lions Clubs International, Cent. — A429

**2017, Apr. 29 Litho. *Perf. 13***

**839** A429 65c multi 1.50 1.50

Europa A430

Designs: No. 840, €1.40, Keila-Joa Castle, lion. No. 841, €1.40, Maarjamäe Castle, eagle.

**2017, May 8 Litho. *Perf. 12¾x13***

**840-841** A430 Set of 2 6.50 6.50

Estonian Presidency of the European Union Council in 2017 — A431

**2017, May 13 Litho. *Perf. 14¼x14***

**842** A431 €1.40 multi 3.25 3.25

Statue of Martin Luther — A432

**2017, May 27 Litho. *Perf. 13¾x14***

**843** A432 65c multi 1.50 1.50

Protestant Reformation, 500th anniv.

Republic of Estonia, Cent. (in 2018) — A433

***Die Cut Perf. 11¼ Syncopated***

**2017, June 1 Litho.**

**Self-Adhesive**

**844** A433 €1.50 multi 3.50 3.50

Gustav Boesberg (1867-1922), Weight Lifter — A434

**2017, June 19 Litho. *Perf. 12½***

**845** A434 65c multi 1.50 1.50

Constitution of Republic of Estonia, 25th Anniv. — A435

**2017, June 28 Litho. *Perf. 14x13¾***

**846** A435 65c multi 1.50 1.50

World Orienteering Championships, Estonia — A436

**2017, July 1 Litho. *Perf. 13¾x14***

**847** A436 €1.50 multi 3.50 3.50

Orjaku Lighthouses A438

Designs: 65c, Lighthouse 26mm tall. €1.40, Lighthouse 29mm tall.

**2017, Sept. 8 Litho. *Perf. 13¾x14***

**849-850** A438 Set of 2 5.00 5.00

Lynx Lynx A439

**2017, Sept. 11 Litho. *Perf. 12¾x13***

**851** A439 65c multi 1.60 1.60

Pres. Kersti Kaljulaid — A441

**2017, Oct. 10 Litho. *Perf. 13¾x14***

**853** A441 65c multi 1.50 1.50

---

## SEMI-POSTAL STAMPS

Assisting Wounded Soldier — SP1

Offering Aid to Wounded Hero — SP2

**1920, June Unwmk. Litho. *Imperf.***

**B1** SP1 35p + 10p red & ol grn .50 2.00
**B2** SP2 70p + 15p dp bl & brn .50 2.00

Surcharged

**1920**

**B3** SP1 1m on No. B1 .35 .30
**B4** SP2 2m on No. B2 .35 .30

Nurse and Wounded Soldier — SP3

**1921, Aug. 1 *Imperf.***

**B5** SP3 2½ (3½)m org, brn & car 2.00 8.00
**B6** SP3 5 (7)m ultra, brn & car 2.00 8.00

**1922, Apr. 26 *Perf. 13½x14***

**B7** SP3 2½ (3½)m org, brn & car 2.00 8.00
*a.* Vert. pair, imperf. horiz. 30.00 95.00
**B8** SP3 5 (7)m ultra, brn & car 2.00 8.00
*a.* Vert. pair, imperf. horiz. 30.00 95.00

Nos. B5-B8 Overprinted

**1923, Oct. 8** ***Imperf.***

| | | | |
|---|---|---|---|
| **B9** | SP3 2½ (3½)m | 60.00 | *160.00* |
| **B10** | SP3 5 (7)m | 60.00 | *160.00* |

***Perf. 13½x14***

| | | | |
|---|---|---|---|
| **B11** | SP3 2½ (3½)m | 60.00 | *160.00* |
| *a.* | Vert. pair, imperf. horiz. | 300.00 | *1,000.* |
| **B12** | SP3 5 (7)m | 60.00 | *160.00* |
| *a.* | Vert. pair, imperf. horiz. | 300.00 | *1,000.* |
| | *Nos. B9-B12 (4)* | 240.00 | 640.00 |

Excellent forgeries are plentiful.

Nos. B7 and B8 Surcharged

**1926, June 15**

| | | | |
|---|---|---|---|
| **B13** | SP3 5 (6)m on #B7 | 3.75 | *9.50* |
| *a.* | Vert. pair, imperf. horiz. | 32.50 | *120.00* |
| **B14** | SP3 10 (12)m on #B8 | 4.50 | *9.50* |
| *a.* | Vert. pair, imperf. horiz. | 32.50 | *120.00* |

Nos. B5-B14 had the franking value of the lower figure. They were sold for the higher figure, the excess going to the Red Cross Society.

Kuressaare Castle SP4

Tartu Cathedral SP5

Tallinn Castle SP6

Narva Fortress SP7

View of Tallinn — SP8

**Laid Paper**

***Perf. 14½x14***

**1927, Nov. 19 Typo. Wmk. 207**

| | | | |
|---|---|---|---|
| **B15** | SP4 5m + 5m bl grn & ol, *grysh* | .60 | *9.50* |
| **B16** | SP5 10m + 10m dp bl & brn, *cream* | .60 | *9.50* |
| **B17** | SP6 12m + 12m rose red & ol grn, *bluish* | .60 | *9.50* |

***Perf. 14x13½***

| | | | |
|---|---|---|---|
| **B18** | SP7 20m + 20m bl & choc, *gray* | .60 | *9.50* |
| **B19** | SP8 40m + 40m org brn & slate, *buff* | .60 | *9.50* |
| | *Nos. B15-B19 (5)* | 3.00 | *47.50* |

The money derived from the surtax was donated to the Committee for the commemoration of War for Liberation.

**Red Cross Issue**

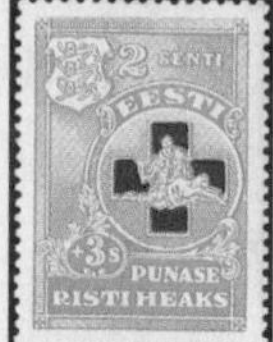
Symbolical of Succor to Injured — SP9

Symbolical of "Light of Hope" — SP10

**1931, Aug. 1 Unwmk. *Perf. 13½***

| | | | |
|---|---|---|---|
| **B20** | SP9 2s + 3s grn & car | 10.00 | 9.50 |
| **B21** | SP10 5s + 3s red & car | 10.00 | 9.50 |
| **B22** | SP10 10s + 3s lt bl & car | 10.00 | 9.50 |
| **B23** | SP9 20s + 3s dk bl & car | 12.00 | *20.00* |
| | *Nos. B20-B23 (4)* | 42.00 | 48.50 |
| | Set, never hinged | 85.00 | |

Nurse and Child SP11

Taagepera Sanatorium SP12

Lorraine Cross and Flower — SP13

**Paper with Network as in Parenthesis**

**1933, Oct. 1 *Perf. 14, 14½***

| | | | |
|---|---|---|---|
| **B24** | SP11 5s + 3s ver (grn) | 8.00 | *8.00* |
| **B25** | SP12 10s + 3s lt bl & red (vio) | 8.00 | *8.00* |
| **B26** | SP13 12s + 3s rose & red (grn) | 10.00 | *12.00* |
| **B27** | SP12 20s + 3s dk bl & red (org) | 12.00 | *16.00* |
| | *Nos. B24-B27 (4)* | 38.00 | 44.00 |
| | Set, never hinged | 75.00 | |

The surtax was for a fund to combat tuberculosis.

**Coats of Arms**

Narva — SP14

Pärnu — SP15

Tartu — SP16

Tallinn — SP17

**Paper with Network as in Parenthesis**

**1936, Feb. 1 *Perf. 13½***

| | | | |
|---|---|---|---|
| **B28** | SP14 10s + 10s grn & ultra (gray) | 2.50 | *8.00* |
| **B29** | SP15 15s + 15s car & bl (gray) | 4.00 | *12.00* |
| **B30** | SP16 25s + 25s gray bl & red (brn) | 4.50 | *16.00* |
| **B31** | SP17 50s + 50s blk & dl org (ol) | 18.00 | *52.50* |
| | *Nos. B28-B31 (4)* | 29.00 | *88.50* |
| | Set, never hinged | 57.50 | |

Paide SP18

Rakvere SP19

Valga SP20

Viljandi SP21

**Paper with Network as in Parenthesis**

**1937, Jan. 2 *Perf. 13½x14***

| | | | |
|---|---|---|---|
| **B32** | SP18 10s + 10s grn (gray) | 2.50 | *9.50* |
| **B33** | SP19 15s + 15s red brn (gray) | 3.50 | *9.50* |
| **B34** | SP20 25s + 25s dk bl (lil) | 4.00 | *14.50* |
| **B35** | SP21 50s + 50s dk vio (gray) | 10.00 | *24.00* |
| | *Nos. B32-B35 (4)* | 20.00 | *57.50* |
| | Set, never hinged | 40.00 | |

Baltiski — SP22

Võru — SP23

Haapsalu SP24

Kuressaare SP25

**Designs are the armorial bearings of various cities**

**1938, Jan. 21**

**Paper with Gray Network**

| | | | |
|---|---|---|---|
| **B36** | SP22 10s + 10s dk brn | 2.00 | *8.00* |
| **B37** | SP23 15s + 15s car & grn | 2.00 | *12.00* |
| **B38** | SP24 25s + 25s dk bl & car | 4.00 | *20.00* |
| **B39** | SP25 50s + 50s blk & org yel | 12.00 | *40.00* |
| *a.* | Sheet of 4, #B36-B39 | 30.00 | *95.00* |
| | *Nos. B36-B39 (4)* | 20.00 | *80.00* |
| | Set, never hinged | 40.00 | |

Annual charity ball, Tallinn, Jan. 2, 1938.

Viljandimaa SP27

Pärnumaa SP28

Tartumaa SP29

Harjumaa SP30

**Designs are the armorial bearings of various cities**

**1939, Jan. 10 *Perf. 13½***

**Paper with Gray Network**

| | | | |
|---|---|---|---|
| **B41** | SP27 10s + 10s dk bl grn | 2.00 | *8.00* |
| **B42** | SP28 15s + 15s carmine | 2.00 | *8.00* |
| **B43** | SP29 25s + 25s dk blue | 6.00 | *20.00* |
| **B44** | SP30 50s + 50s brn lake | 16.00 | *47.50* |
| *a.* | Sheet of 4, #B41-B44 | 45.00 | *175.00* |
| | *Nos. B41-B44 (4)* | 26.00 | *83.50* |
| | Set, never hinged | 52.50 | |

Võrumaa SP32

Järvamaa SP33

Läänemaa SP34

Saaremaa SP35

**Designs are the armorial bearings of various cities**

**1940, Jan. 2 Typo. *Perf. 13½***

**Paper with Gray Network**

| | | | |
|---|---|---|---|
| **B46** | SP32 10s + 10s dp grn & ultra | 2.00 | *12.00* |
| **B47** | SP33 15s + 15s dk car & ultra | 2.00 | *16.00* |
| **B48** | SP34 25s + 25s dk bl & scar | 3.00 | *24.00* |
| **B49** | SP35 50s + 50s ocher & ultra | 8.00 | *32.50* |
| | *Nos. B46-B49 (4)* | 15.00 | *84.50* |
| | Set, never hinged | 30.00 | |

**Catalogue values for unused stamps in this section, from this point to the end of the section, are for Never Hinged items.**

1992 Summer Olympics, Barcelona — SP40

**1992, June 22 Litho. *Perf. 14***

| | | | |
|---|---|---|---|
| **B60** | SP40 1r +50k red | .40 | .40 |
| **B61** | SP40 3r +1.50r green | 1.75 | 1.75 |
| **B62** | SP40 5r +2.50r blue & blk | .80 | .80 |
| | *Nos. B60-B62 (3)* | 2.95 | 2.95 |

While face values are shown in kopecks and rubles, the stamps were sold in the new currency at the rate of 1 ruble = 10 sents.

No. 280 Surcharged

**1994, Nov. 18 Litho. *Perf. 14***

| | | | |
|---|---|---|---|
| **B63** | A51 2.50k +20k green | *6.00* | *6.00* |

Surtax for benefit of survivors of sinking of ferry "Estonia."

Haliaeetus Albicilla — SP41

**1995, Aug. 29 Litho. *Perf. 14***

| | | | | |
|---|---|---|---|---|
| **B64** | SP41 | 2k +25k black & blue | .45 | .45 |

Surtax for Keep the Estonian Sea Clean Assoc.

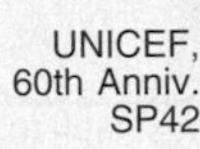
UNICEF, 60th Anniv. SP42

**2006, June 1 Litho. *Perf. 13½***

| | | | | |
|---|---|---|---|---|
| **B65** | SP42 | 4.40k +1k multi | 1.00 | 1.00 |

## AIR POST STAMPS

Airplane AP1

**Unwmk.**

**1920, Mar. 13 Typo. *Imperf.***

| | | | | |
|---|---|---|---|---|
| **C1** | AP1 | 5m yel, blk & lt grn | 2.50 | *6.50* |
| | | Never hinged | 7.00 | |

### No. C1 Overprinted "1923" in Red

**1923, Oct. 1**

| | | | | |
|---|---|---|---|---|
| **C2** | AP1 | 5m multicolored | 8.00 | *32.50* |
| | | Never hinged | 16.00 | |

### No. C1 Surcharged in Red

**1923, Oct. 1**

| | | | | |
|---|---|---|---|---|
| **C3** | AP1 | 15m on 5m multi | 16.00 | *47.50* |
| | | Never hinged | 32.50 | |

Pairs of No. C1 Surcharged in Black or Red

**1923, Oct.**

| | | | | |
|---|---|---|---|---|
| **C4** | AP1 | 10m on 5m+5m (B) | 10.00 | *35.00* |
| **C5** | AP1 | 20m on 5m+5m | 20.00 | *55.00* |
| **C6** | AP1 | 45m on 5m+5m | 60.00 | *200.00* |

***Rough Perf. 11½***

| | | | | |
|---|---|---|---|---|
| **C7** | AP1 | 10m on 5m+5m (B) | *650.00* | *1,600.* |
| **C8** | AP1 | 20m on 5m+5m | *275.00* | *725.00* |
| | | *Nos. C4-C8 (5)* | *1,015.* | *2,615.* |
| | | Set, never hinged | *1,850.* | |

The pairs comprising Nos. C7 and C8 are imperforate between. Forged surcharges and perforations abound. Authentication is required.

Monoplane in Flight — AP2

Designs: Various views of planes in flight.

**1924, Feb. 12 *Imperf.***

| | | | | |
|---|---|---|---|---|
| **C9** | AP2 | 5m yellow & blk | 1.60 | *8.00* |
| **C10** | AP2 | 10m blue & blk | 1.60 | *8.00* |
| **C11** | AP2 | 15m red & blk | 1.60 | *8.00* |
| **C12** | AP2 | 20m green & blk | 1.60 | *8.00* |
| **C13** | AP2 | 45m violet & blk | 1.60 | *16.00* |
| | | *Nos. C9-C13 (5)* | 8.00 | *48.00* |
| | | Set, never hinged | 16.00 | |

The paper is covered with a faint network in pale shades of the frame colors. There are four varieties of the frames and five of the pictures.

**1925, July 15 *Perf. 13½***

| | | | | |
|---|---|---|---|---|
| **C14** | AP2 | 5m yellow & blk | 1.25 | *8.00* |
| **C15** | AP2 | 10m blue & blk | 1.25 | *8.00* |
| **C16** | AP2 | 15m red & blk | 1.25 | *8.00* |
| **C17** | AP2 | 20m green & blk | 1.25 | *8.00* |
| **C18** | AP2 | 45m violet & blk | 1.25 | *16.00* |
| | | *Nos. C14-C18 (5)* | 6.25 | *48.00* |
| | | Set, never hinged | 12.00 | |

Counterfeits of Nos. C1-C18 are plentiful.

## REGISTRATION STAMP

**Catalogue values for unused stamps in this section are for Never Hinged items.**

### Arms Type of 1992

**1992, Mar. 16 Litho. *Perf. 13x12½***

| | | | | |
|---|---|---|---|---|
| **F1** | A42 | R (10r) pink & red | *.60* | *.60* |

## OCCUPATION STAMPS

### Issued under German Occupation

For Use in Tartu (Dorpat)

Russian Stamps of 1909-12 Surcharged

**1918 Unwmk. *Perf. 14x14½***

| | | | | |
|---|---|---|---|---|
| **N1** | A15 | 20pf on 10k dk bl | 40.00 | *160.00* |
| **N2** | A8 | 40pf on 20k bl & car | 40.00 | *160.00* |
| | | Set, Never Hinged | 250.00 | |

Forged overprints exist.

Estonian Arms and Swastika — OS1

***Perf. 11½***

**1941, Aug. Typo. Unwmk.**

| | | | | |
|---|---|---|---|---|
| **N3** | OS1 | 15k brown | 8.00 | *16.00* |
| **N4** | OS1 | 20k green | 5.50 | *14.50* |
| **N5** | OS1 | 30k dark blue | 5.50 | *14.50* |
| | | *Nos. N3-N5 (3)* | 19.00 | *45.00* |
| | | Set, never hinged | 45.00 | |

Exist imperf. Value, set $200.

Nos. N3-N5 were issued on both ordinary paper with colorless gum and thick chalky paper with yellow gum. Value, set on chalky paper $22.50.

## OCCUPATION SEMI-POSTAL STAMPS

Castle Tower, Tallinn — OSP1

Designs: 20k+20k, Stone Bridge, Tartu, horiz. 30k+30k, Narva Castle, horiz. 50k+50k, Tallinn view, horiz. 60k+60k, Tartu University. 100k+100k, Narva Castle, close view.

### Paper with Gray Network

***Perf. 11½***

**1941, Sept. 29 Photo. Unwmk.**

| | | | | |
|---|---|---|---|---|
| **NB1** | OSP1 | 15k + 15k dk brn | .60 | *4.75* |
| **NB2** | OSP1 | 20k + 20k red lil | .60 | *4.75* |
| **NB3** | OSP1 | 30k + 30k dk bl | .60 | *4.75* |
| **NB4** | OSP1 | 50k + 50k bluish grn | .70 | *9.50* |
| **NB5** | OSP1 | 60k + 60k car | 1.00 | *8.00* |
| **NB6** | OSP1 | 100k + 100k gray | 1.50 | *9.50* |
| | | *Nos. NB1-NB6 (6)* | 5.00 | *41.25* |
| | | Set, never hinged | 10.00 | |

Nos. NB1-NB6 exist imperf. Value, set unused $70, used $200.

A miniature sheet containing one each of Nos. NB1-NB6, imperf., exists in various colors. Value, mint $40, used $60. It was not postally valid. Reproductions are common.

# ETHIOPIA

ˌē-thē-ˈō-pē-ə

(Abyssinia)

LOCATION — Northeastern Africa
GOVT. — Republic (1988)
AREA — 426,260 sq. mi.
POP. — 59,680,383 (1999 est.)
CAPITAL — Addis Ababa

During the Italian occupation (1936-1941) Nos. N1-N7 were used, also stamps of Italian East Africa, Eritrea and Somalia.

During the British administration (1941-42) stamps of Great Britain and Kenya were used when available.

16 Guerche = 1 Menelik Dollar or 1 Maria Theresa Dollar
100 Centimes = 1 Franc (1905)
40 Paras = 1 Piaster (1908)
16 Mehalek = 1 Thaler or Talari (1928)
100 Centimes = 1 Thaler (1936)
100 Cents = 1 Ethiopian Dollar (1946)
100 Cents = 1 Birr (1978)

**Catalogue values for unused stamps in this country are for Never Hinged items, beginning with Scott 247 in the regular postage section, Scott B6 in the semi-postal section, Scott C18 in the airpost section, Scott E1 in the special delivery section, and Scott J57 in the postage due section.**

### Watermarks

Wmk. 140 — Crown

Wmk. 282 — Ethiopian Star and Amharic Characters, Multiple

Excellent forgeries of Nos. 1-86 exist.

Very Fine examples of Nos. 1-86 and J1-J42 will have perforations touching the design on one or more sides due to the narrow spacing of the stamps on the plates and imperfect perforating methods. Stamps with margins clear on all sides are scarce and command high premiums.

On March 9, 1894 Menelik II awarded Alfred Ilg a concession to develop a railway, including postal service. Ilg's stamps, Nos. 1-79, were valid locally and to Djibouti. Mail to other countries had to bear stamps of Obock, Somali Coast, etc.

Ethiopia joined the UPU Nov. 1, 1908.

Menelik II A1

Lion of Judah A2

Amharic numeral "8"

***Perf. 14x13½***

**1895, Jan. Unwmk. Typo.**

| | | | | |
|---|---|---|---|---|
| **1** | A1 | ¼g green | 4.00 | 2.00 |
| **2** | A1 | ½g red | 4.00 | 2.00 |
| **3** | A1 | 1g blue | 4.00 | 2.00 |
| **4** | A1 | 2g dark brown | 4.00 | 2.00 |
| **5** | A2 | 4g lilac brown | 4.00 | 2.00 |
| **6** | A2 | 8g violet | 4.00 | 2.00 |
| **7** | A2 | 16g black | 4.00 | 2.00 |
| | | *Nos. 1-7 (7)* | 28.00 | 14.00 |

For 4g, 8g and 16g stamps of type A1, see Nos. J3a, J4a and J7a.

Earliest reported use is Jan. 29, 1895.

Forged cancellations are plentiful.

For overprints see Nos. 8-86, J8-J28, J36-J42. For surcharges see Nos. 94-100, J29-J35.

Nos. 1-7 Handstamped in Violet or Blue

### Overprint 9¼x2½mm, Serifs on "E"

**1901, July 18**

| | | | | |
|---|---|---|---|---|
| **8** | A1 | ¼g green | 27.50 | 27.50 |
| **9** | A1 | ½g red | 27.50 | 27.50 |
| **10** | A1 | 1g blue | 27.50 | 27.50 |
| **11** | A1 | 2g dark brown | 27.50 | 27.50 |
| **12** | A2 | 4g lilac brown | 32.50 | 32.50 |
| **13** | A2 | 8g violet | 47.50 | 47.50 |
| **14** | A2 | 16g black | 60.00 | 60.00 |
| | | *Nos. 8-14 (7)* | 250.00 | 250.00 |

Violet overprints were issued July 18, 1901, for postal use, while the blue overprints were issued in Jan. 5 1902 for philatelic purposes. The blue overprints were not used in the mails. Values for unused stamps are for examples with blue overprints. The blue overprints became valid for postage in 1908 only. Unused stamps with violet overprints are worth much more.

Overprints 8¼mm wide are unofficial reproductions.

Nos. 1-7 Handstamped in Violet, Blue or Black

### Overprint 11x3mm, Low Colons

**1902, Apr. 1**

| No. | Type | Description | Unused | Used |
|---|---|---|---|---|
| **15** | A1 | ¼g green | 6.00 | 6.00 |
| **16** | A1 | ½g red | 9.00 | 7.00 |
| **17** | A1 | 1g blue | 10.00 | 10.00 |
| **18** | A1 | 2g dark brown | 14.00 | 14.00 |
| **19** | A2 | 4g lilac brown | 24.00 | 24.00 |
| **20** | A2 | 8g violet | 30.00 | 30.00 |
| **21** | A2 | 16g black | 55.00 | 55.00 |
| | | *Nos. 15-21 (7)* | 148.00 | 146.00 |

The handstamp reads "Bosta" (Post).

Overprints 10¾mm and 11mm wide with raised colons are unofficial reproductions.

Nos. 1-7 Handstamped in Black

**1903, Jan. 9** **Overprint 16x3¾mm**

| No. | Type | Description | Unused | Used |
|---|---|---|---|---|
| **22** | A1 | ¼g green | 7.50 | 7.50 |
| **23** | A1 | ½g red | 12.00 | 12.00 |
| **24** | A1 | 1g blue | 15.00 | 15.00 |
| **25** | A1 | 2g dark brown | 19.00 | 19.00 |
| **26** | A2 | 4g lilac brown | 27.50 | 27.50 |
| **27** | A2 | 8g violet | 37.50 | 37.50 |
| **28** | A2 | 16g black | 57.50 | 57.50 |
| | | *Nos. 22-28 (7)* | 176.00 | 176.00 |

The handstamp reads "Malekt." (Also "Melekt," message).

Original stamps have blurred colons. Unofficial reproductions have clean colons.

Nos. 22-28 have black overprints only. All other colors are fakes.

Nos. 1-7 Handstamped in Violet or Blue

### Overprint 18¼mm Wide

**1904, Dec.**

| No. | Type | Description | Unused | Used |
|---|---|---|---|---|
| **36** | A1 | ¼g green | 15.00 | 15.00 |
| **37** | A1 | ½g red | 20.00 | |
| **38** | A1 | 1g blue | 25.00 | |
| **39** | A1 | 2g dark brown | 27.50 | |
| **40** | A2 | 4g lilac brown | 35.00 | |
| **41** | A2 | 8g violet | 57.50 | |
| **42** | A2 | 16g black | 75.00 | |
| | | *Nos. 36-42 (7)* | 255.00 | |

The handstamp reads "Malekathe" (message). This set was never issued.

### Preceding Issues Surcharged with New Values in French Currency in Blue, Violet, Rose or Black

a

b

### On Nos. 1-7

**1905, Jan. 1** **Overprint 3mm High**

| No. | Type | Description | Unused | Used |
|---|---|---|---|---|
| **43** | A1 (a) | 5c on ¼g | 10.00 | 10.00 |
| **44** | A1 (a) | 10c on ½g | 10.00 | 10.00 |
| **45** | A1 (a) | 20c on 1g | 10.00 | 10.00 |
| **46** | A1 (a) | 40c on 2g | 11.00 | 11.00 |
| **47** | A2 (a) | 80c on 4g | 21.00 | 21.00 |
| **48** | A2 (b) | 1.60fr on 8g | 22.50 | 22.50 |
| **49** | A2 (b) | 3.20fr on 16g | 40.00 | 40.00 |
| | | *Nos. 43-49 (7)* | 124.50 | 124.50 |

Nos. 48-49 exist with period or comma.

**1905, Feb.**

**On No. 8, "Ethiopie" in Blue**

| No. | Type | Description | Unused | Used |
|---|---|---|---|---|
| **50** | A1 (a) | 5c on ¼g | 120.00 | 100.00 |

**On No. 15, "Bosta" in Black**

| No. | Type | Description | Unused | Used |
|---|---|---|---|---|
| **51** | A1 (a) | 5c on ¼g | 40.00 | 40.00 |

**On No. 22, "Malekt" in Black**

| No. | Type | Description | Unused | Used |
|---|---|---|---|---|
| **52** | A1 (a) | 5c on ¼g | 140.00 | 75.00 |

Unofficial reproductions exist of Nos. 50, 51, 52. The 5c on No. 36, 10c, 20c, 40c, 80c, and 1.60fr surcharges exist as unofficial reproductions only.

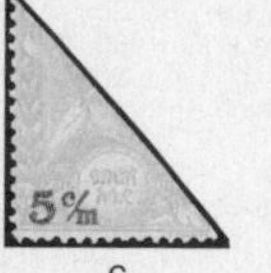


c

d

**1905** **On No. 2**

| No. | Type | Description | Unused | Used |
|---|---|---|---|---|
| **54** | A1 (c) | 5c on half of ½g | 10.00 | 10.00 |

**On No. 21, "Bosta" in Black**

| No. | Type | Description | Unused | Used |
|---|---|---|---|---|
| **55** | A2 (d) | 5c on 16g blk | 200.00 | 100.00 |

On No. 55, "Bosta" is in black.

**On No. 28, "Malekt" in Black**

| No. | Type | Description | Unused | Used |
|---|---|---|---|---|
| **56** | A2 (d) | 5c on 16g blk | 250.00 | 250.00 |
| | | *Nos. 54-56 (3)* | 460.00 | 360.00 |

No. 54 issued in March. Nos. 55-56 issued Mar. 30.

The overprints and surcharges on Nos. 8 to 56 inclusive were handstamped, the work being very roughly done.

As is usual with handstamped overprints and surcharges there are many inverted and double, but most of them are fakes or unofficial reproductions.

Surcharged with New Values in Various Colors and in Violet

### Overprint 14¾x3½mm

**1906, Jan. 1**

| No. | Type | Description | Unused | Used |
|---|---|---|---|---|
| **57** | A1 | 5c on ¼g green | 10.00 | 10.00 |
| **58** | A1 | 10c on ½g red | 12.00 | 12.00 |
| **59** | A1 | 20c on 1g blue | 12.00 | 12.00 |
| **60** | A1 | 40c on 2g dk brn | 12.00 | 12.00 |
| **61** | A2 | 80c on 4g lilac brn | 18.00 | 18.00 |
| **62** | A2 | 1.60fr on 8g violet | 27.50 | 27.50 |
| **63** | A2 | 3.20fr on 16g black | 45.00 | 45.00 |
| | | *Nos. 57-63 (7)* | 136.50 | 136.50 |

Two types of the 4-character overprint ("Menelik"): 14x¾x3½mm and 16x4mm.

Surcharged in Violet Brown

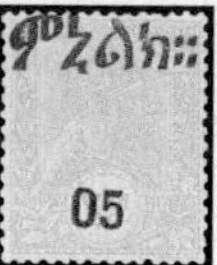


**1906, July 1** **Overprint 16x4¼mm**

| No. | Type | Description | Unused | Used |
|---|---|---|---|---|
| **64** | A1 | 5c on ¼g grn | 9.25 | 9.25 |
| *a.* | | Surcharged "20" | 75.00 | 75.00 |
| **65** | A1 | 10c on ½g red | 11.00 | 11.00 |
| **66** | A1 | 20c on 1g blue | 17.50 | 17.50 |
| **67** | A1 | 40c on 2g dk brn | 17.50 | 17.50 |
| **68** | A2 | 80c on 4g lil brn | 25.00 | 25.00 |
| **69** | A2 | 1.60fr on 8g vio | 25.00 | 25.00 |
| **70** | A2 | 3.20fr on 16g blk | 60.00 | 60.00 |
| | | *Nos. 64-70 (7)* | 165.25 | 165.25 |

The control overprint reads "Menelik."

### Surcharged in Violet

e

f

**1907, June 21**

| No. | Type | Description | Unused | Used |
|---|---|---|---|---|
| **71** | A1 (e) | ¼ on ¼g grn | 8.75 | 8.75 |
| **72** | A1 (e) | ½ on ½g red | 8.75 | 8.75 |
| **73** | A1 (f) | 1 on 1g blue | 11.00 | 11.00 |
| **74** | A1 (f) | 2 on 2g dk brn | 12.00 | 12.00 |
| *a.* | | Surcharged "40" | 65.00 | |
| **75** | A2 (f) | 4 on 4g lil brn | 13.00 | 13.00 |
| *a.* | | Surcharged "80" | 57.50 | |
| **76** | A2 (f) | 8 on 8g vio | 30.00 | 30.00 |
| **77** | A2 (f) | 16 on 16g blk | 37.50 | 37.50 |
| | | *Nos. 71-77 (7)* | 121.00 | 121.00 |

Nos. 71-72 are also found with stars farther away from figures.

The control overprint reads "Dagmawi" ("Second"), meaning Emperor Menelik II.

On stamps with "1" in surcharge, genuine examples have straight serifs, forgeries have curved serifs.

Nos. 2, 23 Surcharged in Bluish Green

**1908, Aug. 14**

| No. | Type | Description | Unused | Used |
|---|---|---|---|---|
| **78** | A1 | 1pi on ½g red (#2) | 15.00 | 15.00 |
| **79** | A1 | 1pi on ½g red (#23) | *850.00* | — |

Official reproductions exist. Value, set $25. Forgeries exist.

The surcharges on Nos. 57-78 are handstamped and are found double, inverted, etc.

Surcharged in Black

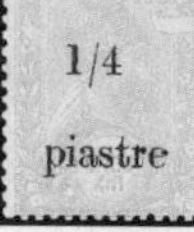


**1908, Nov. 1**

| No. | Type | Description | Unused | Used |
|---|---|---|---|---|
| **80** | A1 | ¼p on ¼g grn | 1.50 | 1.50 |
| **81** | A1 | ½p on ½g red | 1.50 | 1.50 |
| **82** | A1 | 1p on 1g blue | 2.25 | 2.25 |
| **83** | A1 | 2p on 2g dk brn | 3.75 | 3.75 |
| **84** | A2 | 4p on 4g lil brn | 5.25 | 5.25 |
| **85** | A2 | 8p on 8g vio | 12.50 | 12.50 |
| **86** | A2 | 16p on 16g blk | 18.00 | 18.00 |
| | | *Nos. 80-86 (7)* | 44.75 | 44.75 |

Surcharges on Nos. 80-85 are found double, inverted, etc. Forgeries exist.

These are the 1st stamps valid for international mail.

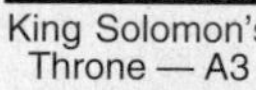

King Solomon's Throne — A3

Menelik in Native Costume — A4

Menelik in Royal Dress — A5

**1909, Jan. 29** ***Perf. 11½***

| No. | Type | Description | Unused | Used |
|---|---|---|---|---|
| **87** | A3 | ¼g blue green | 1.10 | .85 |
| **88** | A3 | ½g rose | 1.25 | .85 |
| **89** | A3 | 1g green & org | 6.25 | 2.50 |
| **90** | A4 | 2g blue | 4.75 | 3.00 |
| **91** | A4 | 4g green & car | 7.00 | 5.50 |
| **92** | A5 | 8g ver & dp grn | 15.00 | 10.00 |
| **93** | A5 | 16g ver & car | 22.50 | 16.50 |
| | | *Nos. 87-93 (7)* | 57.85 | 39.20 |

For overprints see Nos. 101-115, J43-J49, J55-J56. For surcharges see Nos. 116-119.

Nos. 1-7 Handstamped and Surcharged in ms.

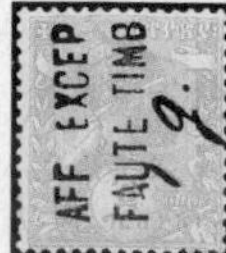


**1911, Oct. 1** ***Perf. 14x13½***

| No. | Type | Description | Unused |
|---|---|---|---|
| **94** | A1 | ¼g on ¼g grn | 50.00 |
| **95** | A1 | ½g on ½g red | 50.00 |
| **96** | A1 | 1g on 1g blue | 50.00 |
| **97** | A1 | 2g on 2g dk brn | 50.00 |
| **98** | A2 | 4g on 4g lil brn | 50.00 |
| **99** | A2 | 8g on 8g violet | 50.00 |
| **100** | A2 | 16g on 16g black | 50.00 |
| | | *Nos. 94-100 (7)* | 350.00 |

Nos. 94-100 were produced as a philatelic speculation by the postmaster at Dire-Dawa.

The overprint is abbreviated from "Affranchissement Exceptionnel Faute Timbres" (Special Franking Lacking Stamps). The overprints and surcharges were applied to stamps on cover and then canceled. These covers were then sold to dealers in Europe. No. 98 is known postally used on a small number of commercial covers.

Nos. 94-100 without surcharge are forgeries.

### Stamps of 1909 Handstamped in Violet or Black

Nos. 101-102

Nos. 104-107

**1917, Mar. 30** ***Perf. 11½***

| No. | Type | Description | Unused | Used |
|---|---|---|---|---|
| **101** | A3 | ¼g blue grn (V) | 7.50 | 6.75 |
| **102** | A3 | ½g rose (V) | 7.50 | 6.75 |
| **104** | A4 | 2g blue (Bk) | 10.00 | 8.25 |
| **105** | A4 | 4g grn & car (Bk) | 15.00 | 17.00 |
| **106** | A5 | 8g ver & dp grn (Bk) | 25.00 | 22.50 |
| **107** | A5 | 16g ver & car (Bk) | 40.00 | 35.00 |
| | | *Nos. 101-107 (6)* | 105.00 | 96.25 |

Coronation of Empress Zauditu and appointment of Prince Tafari as Regent and Heir to the throne.

Exist with overprint inverted and double.

### Stamps of 1909 Overprinted in Blue, Black or Red

Nos. 108-111

Nos. 112-115

**1917, Apr. 5-Oct. 1**

| No. | Type | Description | Unused | Used |
|---|---|---|---|---|
| **108** | A3 | ¼g blue grn (Bl) | 1.25 | 1.25 |
| **109** | A3 | ½g rose (Bl) | 1.25 | 1.25 |
| **110** | A3 | 1g grn & org (Bl) | 2.25 | 2.25 |
| **111** | A4 | 2g blue (R) | 82.50 | 87.25 |
| **112** | A4 | 2g blue (Bk) | 1.25 | 1.25 |
| **113** | A4 | 4g grn & car (Bl) | 1.25 | 1.25 |
| *a.* | | Black overprint | 11.00 | 11.00 |
| **114** | A5 | 8g ver & dp grn (Bl) | 1.25 | 1.25 |
| **115** | A5 | 16g ver & car (Bl) | 2.25 | 2.25 |
| | | *Nos. 108-115 (8)* | 93.25 | 98.00 |

Coronation of Empress Zauditu.

Nos. 108-115 all exist with double overprint, inverted overprint, double overprint, one inverted, and various combinations.

### Nos. 114-115 with Additional Surcharge

k

l

m

n

**1917, May 28**

| No. | Type | Description | Unused | Used |
|---|---|---|---|---|
| 116 | A5 (k) | ¼g on 8g | 5.00 | 4.00 |
| 117 | A5 (l) | ½g on 8g | 5.00 | 4.00 |
| 118 | A5 (m) | 1g on 16g | 11.00 | 8.00 |
| 119 | A5 (n) | 2g on 16g | 12.00 | 9.00 |
| | | *Nos. 116-119 (4)* | 33.00 | 25.00 |

Nos. 116-119 all exist with the numerals double and inverted and No. 116 with the Amharic surcharge missing.

Sommering's Gazelle — A6

Prince Tafari — A9

Cathedral of St. George A12

Empress Waizeri Zauditu — A18

¼g, Giraffes. ½g, Leopard. 2g, Prince Tafari, diff. 4g, Prince Tafari, diff. 8g, White rhinoceros. 12g, Somali ostriches. 1t, African elephant. 2t, Water buffalo. 3t, Lions. 5t, 10t, Empress Zauditu.

**1919, June 16 Typo. *Perf. 11½***

| No. | Type | Description | Unused | Used |
|---|---|---|---|---|
| 120 | A6 | ⅛g violet & brn | .25 | .25 |
| 121 | A6 | ¼g bl grn & drab | .25 | .25 |
| 122 | A6 | ½g scar & ol grn | .25 | .25 |
| 123 | A9 | 1g rose lil & gray grn | .25 | .25 |
| 124 | A9 | 2g dp ultra & fawn | .25 | .25 |
| 125 | A9 | 4g turq bl & org | .25 | *2.50* |
| 126 | A12 | 6g lt blue & org | .25 | .25 |
| 127 | A12 | 8g ol grn & blk brn | .35 | .25 |
| 128 | A12 | 12g red vio & gray | .50 | .30 |
| 129 | A12 | 1t rose & gray blk | .90 | .40 |
| 130 | A12 | 2t black & brown | 2.50 | |
| 131 | A12 | 3t grn & dp org | 2.50 | 1.90 |
| 132 | A18 | 4t brn & lil rose | 3.00 | 2.50 |
| 133 | A18 | 5t carmine & gray | 4.00 | 4.00 |
| 134 | A18 | 10t gray grn & bis | 8.00 | 5.25 |
| | | *Nos. 120-134 (15)* | 23.50 | |
| | | *Nos. 120-129,131-134 (14)* | | 18.25 |

No. 130 was not issued.

For overprints see Nos. J50-J54. For surcharges see Nos. 135-154.

*Reprints have brownish gum that is cracked diagonally. Originals have smooth, white gum. Reprints exist imperf. and some values with inverted centers. Value for set, unused or canceled, $5.*

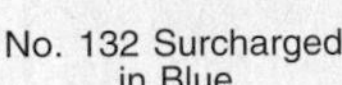

No. 132 Surcharged in Blue

**1919, July**

| No. | Type | Description | Unused | Used |
|---|---|---|---|---|
| 135 | A18 | 4g on 4t brn & lil rose | 3.50 | 3.50 |

Nos. 135-154

The Amharic surcharge indicates the new value and, therefore, varies on Nos. 135-154. There are numerous defective letters and figures, several types of the "2" of "½," the errors "guerhce," "gnerche," etc.

Many varieties of surcharge, such as double, inverted, lines transposed or omitted, and inverted "2" in "½," exist.

There are many irregularly produced settings in imitation of Nos. 136-154 which differ slightly from the originals. These may be essays or proofs.

Stamps of 1919 Surcharged

**1921**

| No. | Type | Description | Unused | Used |
|---|---|---|---|---|
| 136 | A6 | ½g on ⅛g vio & brn | 1.00 | 1.00 |
| 137 | A6 | 1g on ¼g grn & db | 2.50 | 1.00 |
| 138 | A9 | 2g on 1g lil brn & gray grn | 1.00 | 1.50 |
| 139 | A18 | 2g on 4t brn & lil rose | 35.00 | 15.00 |
| 140 | A6 | 2½g on ½g scar & ol grn | 1.00 | *1.50* |
| 141 | A9 | 4g on 2g ultra & fawn | 1.00 | *1.25* |
| | | *Nos. 136-141 (6)* | 41.50 | 21.25 |

Forgeries of No. 139 exist.

Stamps and Type of 1919 Surcharged

**1925-26**

| No. | Type | Description | Unused | Used |
|---|---|---|---|---|
| 142 | A12 | ½g on 1t rose & gray blk ('26) | 1.00 | 1.00 |
| *a.* | | Without colon ('26) | 12.50 | 12.50 |
| 143 | A18 | ½g on 5t car & gray ('26) | 2.00 | 1.00 |
| 144 | A12 | 1g on 6g bl & org | 1.00 | 1.00 |
| 145 | A12 | 1g on 12g lil & gray | 450.00 | 400.00 |
| 146 | A12 | 1g on 3t grn & org ('26) | 22.50 | 16.00 |
| 147 | A18 | 1g on 10t gray grn & bis ('26) | 1.00 | *1.00* |
| | | *Nos. 142-147 (6)* | 477.50 | 420.00 |

On No. 142 the surcharge is at the left side of the stamp, reading upward. On No. 142a it is at the right, reading downward. The two surcharges are from different, though similar, settings. On No. 146 the surcharge is at the right, reading upward. See note following No. 154.

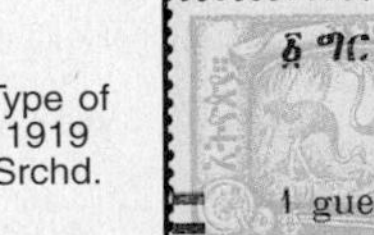


Type of 1919 Srchd.

**1925, Oct.**

| No. | Type | Description | Unused | Used |
|---|---|---|---|---|
| 147A | A12 | 1g on 12g lil & gray | 400.00 | |

Forgeries exist.

Nos. 126-128 Srchd.

**1926**

| No. | Type | Description | Unused | Used |
|---|---|---|---|---|
| 148 | A12 | ½g on 8g | 3.00 | 1.25 |
| 149 | A12 | 1g on 6g | 80.00 | 50.00 |
| 150 | A12 | 1g on 12g | 350.00 | |
| | | *Nos. 148-150 (3)* | 433.00 | 51.25 |

The Amharic line has 7 (½g) or 6 characters (1g).

Nos. 126-128, 131 Srchd.

**1925-27**

| No. | Type | Description | Unused | Used |
|---|---|---|---|---|
| 151 | A12 | ½g on 8g ('27) | 1.50 | 1.50 |
| 152 | A12 | 1g on 6g ('27) | 60.00 | 40.00 |
| 153 | A12 | 1g on 12g ('27) | 5.00 | 1.50 |
| 154 | A12 | 1g on 3t | 375.00 | |
| | | *Nos. 151-154 (4)* | 441.50 | 43.00 |

The Amharic line has 7 (½g) or 4 characters (1g). No. 152 has the lines closer together than do the others.

Forgeries of No. 154 exist.

Ras Tafari — A22

Empress Zauditu — A23

**1928, Sept. 5 Typo. *Perf. 13½x14***

| No. | Type | Description | Unused | Used |
|---|---|---|---|---|
| 155 | A22 | ⅛m org & lt bl | 1.50 | 1.40 |
| 156 | A23 | ¼m ind & red org | .90 | *1.40* |
| 157 | A22 | ½m gray grn & blk | 1.50 | 1.40 |
| 158 | A23 | 1m dk car & blk | .90 | *1.40* |
| 159 | A22 | 2m dk bl & blk | .90 | *1.40* |
| 160 | A23 | 4m yel & olive | .90 | *1.40* |
| 161 | A22 | 8m vio & olive | 2.40 | 1.40 |
| 162 | A23 | 1t org brn & vio | 2.75 | 1.40 |
| 163 | A22 | 2t grn & bister | 4.25 | 3.25 |
| 164 | A23 | 3t choc & grn | 6.75 | 3.75 |
| | | *Nos. 155-164 (10)* | 22.75 | 18.20 |

For overprints and surcharges see Nos. 165-209, 217-230, C1-C10.

Preceding Issue Overprinted in Black, Violet or Red

**1928, Sept. 1**

| No. | Type | Description | Unused | Used |
|---|---|---|---|---|
| 165 | A22 | ⅛m (Bk) | 3.25 | 3.25 |
| 166 | A23 | ¼m (V) | 3.25 | 3.25 |
| 167 | A22 | ½m (V) | 3.25 | 3.25 |
| 168 | A23 | 1m (V) | 3.25 | 3.25 |
| 169 | A22 | 2m (R) | 3.25 | 3.25 |
| 170 | A23 | 4m (Bk) | 3.25 | 3.25 |
| 171 | A22 | 8m (R) | 3.25 | 3.25 |
| 172 | A23 | 1t (Bk) | 4.50 | 4.50 |
| 173 | A22 | 2t (R) | 6.00 | 6.00 |
| 174 | A23 | 3t (R) | 6.00 | 6.00 |
| | | *Nos. 165-174 (10)* | 39.25 | 39.25 |

Opening of General Post Office, Addis Ababa.

Exist with overprint inverted, double, double, one inverted, etc.

Nos. 155, 157, 159, 161, 163 Handstamped in Violet, Red or Black

**1928, Oct. 7**

| No. | Type | Description | Unused | Used |
|---|---|---|---|---|
| 175 | A22 | ⅛m (V) | 4.25 | 4.25 |
| 176 | A22 | ½m (R) | 4.25 | 4.25 |
| 177 | A22 | 2m (R) | 4.25 | 4.25 |
| 178 | A22 | 8m (Bk) | 4.25 | 4.25 |
| 179 | A22 | 2t (V) | 4.25 | 4.25 |
| | | *Nos. 175-179 (5)* | 21.25 | 21.25 |

Crowning of Prince Tafari as king (Negus) on Oct. 7, 1928.

Nos. 175-177 exist with overprint vertical, inverted, double, etc.

Forgeries exist.

Nos. 155-164 Overprinted in Red or Green

**1930, Apr. 3**

| No. | Type | Description | Unused | Used |
|---|---|---|---|---|
| 180 | A22 | ⅛m org & lt bl (R) | 1.40 | 1.40 |
| 181 | A23 | ¼m ind & red org (G) | 1.40 | 1.40 |
| 182 | A22 | ½m gray grn & blk (R) | 1.40 | 1.40 |
| 183 | A23 | 1m dk car & blk (G) | 1.40 | 1.40 |
| 184 | A22 | 2m dk bl & blk (R) | 1.40 | 1.40 |
| 185 | A23 | 4m yel & ol (R) | 2.10 | 2.10 |
| 186 | A22 | 8m vio & ol (R) | 3.00 | 3.00 |
| 187 | A23 | 1t org brn & vio (R) | 5.00 | 5.00 |
| 188 | A22 | 2t grn & bis (R) | 6.00 | 6.00 |
| 189 | A23 | 3t choc & grn (R) | 8.00 | 8.00 |
| | | *Nos. 180-189 (10)* | 31.10 | 31.10 |

Proclamation of King Tafari as King of Kings of Abyssinia under the name "Haile Selassie."

A similar overprint, set in four vertical lines, was printed on all denominations of the 1928 issue. It was not considered satisfactory and was rejected. The trial impressions were not placed on sale to the public, but some stamps reached private hands and have been passed through the post.

Nos. 155-164 Overprinted in Red or Olive Brown

**1930, Apr. 3**

| No. | Type | Description | Unused | Used |
|---|---|---|---|---|
| 190 | A22 | ⅛m orange & lt bl | 1.40 | 1.40 |
| 191 | A23 | ¼m ind & red org (OB) | 1.40 | 1.40 |
| 192 | A22 | ½m gray grn & blk | 1.40 | 1.40 |
| 193 | A23 | 1m dk car & blk (OB) | 1.40 | 1.40 |
| 194 | A22 | 2m dk blue & blk | 1.40 | 1.40 |
| 195 | A23 | 4m yellow & ol | 2.10 | 2.10 |
| 196 | A22 | 8m violet & ol | 3.00 | 3.00 |
| 197 | A23 | 1t org brn & vio | 5.00 | 5.00 |
| 198 | A22 | 2t green & bister | 6.00 | 6.00 |
| 199 | A23 | 3t chocolate & grn | 8.00 | 8.00 |
| | | *Nos. 190-199 (10)* | 31.10 | 31.10 |

Proclamation of King Tafari as Emperor Haile Selassie.

All stamps of this series exist with "H" of "HAILE" omitted and with many other varieties.

Nos. 155-164 Handstamped in Violet or Red

**1930, Nov. 2**

| No. | Type | Value | Unused | Used |
|---|---|---|---|---|
| **200** | A22 | ⅛m (V) | 1.10 | 1.10 |
| **201** | A23 | ¼m (V) | 1.10 | 1.10 |
| **202** | A22 | ½m (R) | 1.10 | 1.10 |
| **203** | A23 | 1m (V) | 1.10 | 1.10 |
| **204** | A22 | 2m (R) | 1.10 | 1.10 |
| **205** | A23 | 4m (V) | 1.10 | 1.10 |
| **206** | A22 | 8m (V or R) | 1.90 | 1.90 |
| **207** | A23 | 1t (V) | 3.00 | 3.00 |
| **208** | A22 | 2t (V or R) | 4.50 | 4.50 |
| **209** | A23 | 3t (V or R) | 6.50 | 6.50 |
| | | *Nos. 200-209 (10)* | 22.50 | 22.50 |

Coronation of Emperor Haile Selassie, Nov. 2, 1930.

Haile Selassie Coronation Monument, Symbols of Empire — A24

**1930, Nov. Engr. *Perf. 12½***

| No. | Type | Value | Unused | Used |
|---|---|---|---|---|
| **210** | A24 | 1g orange | 1.00 | 1.00 |
| **211** | A24 | 2g ultra | 1.00 | 1.00 |
| **212** | A24 | 4g violet | 1.00 | 1.00 |
| **213** | A24 | 8g dull green | 1.00 | 1.00 |
| **214** | A24 | 1t brown | 1.25 | 1.25 |
| **215** | A24 | 3t green | 2.00 | 2.00 |
| **216** | A24 | 5t red brown | 2.00 | 2.00 |
| | | *Nos. 210-216 (7)* | 9.25 | 9.25 |

Coronation of Emperor Haile Selassie. Issued: 4g, 11/2; others, 11/23.

*Reprints of Nos. 210 to 216 exist. Colors are more yellow and the ink is thicker and slightly glossy. Ink on the originals is dull and granular. Value 35c each.*

**Nos. 158-160, 164 Surcharged in Green, Red or Blue**

Type I

Type II

**1931 *Perf. 13½x14***

| No. | Type | Value | Unused | Used |
|---|---|---|---|---|
| **217** | A23 | ⅛m on 1m | .80 | .80 |
| **218** | A22 | ⅛m on 2m (R) | .80 | .80 |
| **219** | A23 | ⅛m on 4m | .80 | .80 |
| **220** | A23 | ¼m on 1m (Bl) | .80 | .80 |
| **221** | A22 | ¼m on 2m (R) | 1.50 | 1.50 |
| **222** | A23 | ¼m on 4m | 1.50 | 1.50 |
| **225** | A23 | ½m on 1m (Bl) | 1.50 | 1.50 |
| **226** | A22 | ½m on 2m (R) | 1.50 | 1.50 |
| **227** | A23 | ½m on 4m, type II | 1.50 | 1.50 |
| *a.* | | ½m on 4m, type I | 10.00 | 10.00 |
| **228** | A23 | ½m on 3t (R) | 12.00 | 12.00 |
| **230** | A22 | 1m on 2m (R) | 3.00 | 3.00 |
| | | *Nos. 217-230 (11)* | 25.70 | 25.70 |

The ½m on ⅛m orange & light blue and ½m on ¼m indigo & red orange were clandestinely printed and never sold at the post office.

No. 230 with double surcharge in red and blue is a color trial.

Many varieties exist.

Issued: 1m, Apr.; others, 3/20.

Ras Makonnen A25

Empress Menen A27

View of Hawash River and Railroad Bridge A26

Designs: 2g, 8g, Haile Selassie (profile). 4g, 1t, Statue of Menelik II. 3t, Empress Menen (full face). 5t, Haile Selassie (full face).

***Perf. 12½, 12x12½, 12½x12***

**1931, June 27 Engr.**

| No. | Type | Value | Unused | Used |
|---|---|---|---|---|
| **232** | A25 | ⅛g red | .40 | .40 |
| **233** | A26 | ¼g olive green | 1.10 | 1.10 |
| **234** | A25 | ½g dark violet | 1.10 | 1.10 |
| **235** | A27 | 1g red orange | 1.10 | 1.10 |
| **236** | A27 | 2g ultra | 1.10 | 1.10 |
| **237** | A25 | 4g violet | 1.25 | 1.25 |
| **238** | A27 | 8g blue green | 2.00 | 2.00 |
| **239** | A25 | 1t chocolate | 24.00 | 10.00 |
| **240** | A27 | 3t yellow green | 7.00 | 3.00 |
| **241** | A27 | 5t red brown | 12.00 | 5.50 |
| | | *Nos. 232-241 (10)* | 51.05 | 26.55 |

For overprints see Nos. B1-B5. For surcharges see Nos. 242-246.

*Reprints of Nos. 232-236, 238-240 are on thinner and whiter paper than the originals. On originals the ink is dull and granular. On reprints, heavy, caked and shiny. Value 20c each.*

**Nos. 232-236 Surcharged in Blue or Carmine**

**1936, Jan. 29 *Perf. 12x12½, 12½x12***

| No. | Type | Value | Unused | Used |
|---|---|---|---|---|
| **242** | A25 | 1c on ⅛g red | 2.00 | 1.00 |
| **243** | A26 | 2c on ¼g ol grn (C) | 2.00 | 1.00 |
| **244** | A25 | 3c on ½g dk vio | 2.00 | 1.10 |
| **245** | A27 | 5c on 1g red org | 2.50 | 1.50 |
| **246** | A27 | 10c on 2g ultra (C) | 3.25 | 1.90 |
| | | *Nos. 242-246 (5)* | 11.75 | 6.50 |

**Catalogue values for unused stamps in this section, from this point to the end of the section, are for Never Hinged items.**

Haile Selassie I — A32

**1942, Mar. 23 Litho. *Perf. 14x13½***

| No. | Type | Value | Unused | Used |
|---|---|---|---|---|
| **247** | A32 | 4c lt bl grn, ind & blk | .80 | .40 |
| **248** | A32 | 10c rose, indigo & blk | 2.50 | .75 |
| **249** | A32 | 20c dp ultra, ind & blk | 5.00 | 1.25 |
| | | *Nos. 247-249 (3)* | 8.30 | 2.40 |

Haile Selassie I — A33

**1942-43 Unwmk.**

| No. | Type | Value | Unused | Used |
|---|---|---|---|---|
| **250** | A33 | 4c lt bl grn & indigo | .90 | .25 |
| **251** | A33 | 8c yel org & indigo | 1.00 | .25 |
| **252** | A33 | 10c rose & indigo | 1.25 | .25 |
| **253** | A33 | 12c dull vio & indigo | 1.25 | .30 |
| **254** | A33 | 20c dp ultra & indigo | 2.00 | .50 |
| **255** | A33 | 25c dull grn & indigo | 2.50 | .70 |
| **256** | A33 | 50c dull brn & indigo | 4.75 | 1.25 |
| **257** | A33 | 60c lilac & indigo | 7.25 | 1.50 |
| | | *Nos. 250-257 (8)* | 20.90 | 5.00 |

Issued: 25c, 50c, 60c, 4/1/43; others, 6/22/42.

For surcharges see Nos. 258-262, 284, C18-C20.

Nos. 250-254 Surcharged in Black or Brown

**1943, Nov. 3**

| No. | Type | Value | Unused | Used |
|---|---|---|---|---|
| **258** | A33 | 5c on 4c | 85.00 | 85.00 |
| **259** | A33 | 10c on 8c | 85.00 | 85.00 |
| **260** | A33 | 15c on 10c | 85.00 | 85.00 |
| **261** | A33 | 20c on 12c (Br) | 85.00 | 85.00 |
| **262** | A33 | 30c on 20c (Br) | 85.00 | 85.00 |
| | | *Nos. 258-262 (5)* | 425.00 | 425.00 |

Restoration of the Obelisk in Myazzia Place, Addis Ababa, and the 13th anniv. of the coronation of Emperor Haile Selassie.

No. 258 exists with inverted "5" in surcharge. Value $150. On No. 262, "3" is surcharged on "2" of "20" to make "30."

Approximately 40 sets exist with a somewhat different handstamped surcharge. Value, set *$2,000*. Forgeries exist.

Palace of Menelik II A34

Menelik II — A35

Statue — A36

50c, Mausoleum. 65c, Menelik II (with scepter).

**1944, Dec. 31 Litho. *Perf. 10½***

| No. | Type | Value | Unused | Used |
|---|---|---|---|---|
| **263** | A34 | 5c green | 1.25 | .65 |
| **264** | A35 | 10c red lilac | 2.25 | 1.10 |
| **265** | A36 | 20c deep blue | 4.00 | 2.25 |
| **266** | A34 | 50c dull purple | 5.25 | 2.25 |
| **267** | A35 | 65c bister brown | 9.25 | 3.50 |
| | | *Nos. 263-267 (5)* | 22.00 | 9.75 |

Cent. of the birth of Menelik II, 8/18/44. Printed on gum-impregnated paper.

**Unissued Semi-Postal Stamps Overprinted in Carmine**

Nurse & Baby — A39

**Various Designs Inscribed "Croix Rouge"**

**1945, Aug. 7 Photo. *Perf. 11½***

| No. | Type | Value | Unused | Used |
|---|---|---|---|---|
| **268** | A39 | 5c brt green | 1.50 | .75 |
| **269** | A39 | 10c brt red | 1.50 | .75 |
| **270** | A39 | 25c brt blue | 1.50 | .75 |
| **271** | A39 | 50c dk yellow brn | 8.50 | 3.50 |
| **272** | A39 | 1t brt violet | 13.50 | 4.50 |
| | | *Nos. 268-272 (5)* | 26.50 | 10.25 |

Nos. 268-272 without overprint were ordered printed in Switzerland before Ethiopia fell to the invading Italians, so were not delivered to Addis Ababa. After the country's liberation, the set was overprinted "V" and issued for ordinary postage. These stamps exist without overprint, but were not issued. Value $1.25.

Some values exist inverted or double.

Forged overprints exist.

For surcharges see Nos. B11-B15, B36-B40.

Lion of Judah — A44

Menelik II — A45

Mail Transport, Old and New A46

Designs: 50c, Old Post Office, Addis Ababa. 70c, Menelik II and Haile Selassie.

**1947, Apr. 18 Engr. *Perf. 13***

| No. | Type | Value | Unused | Used |
|---|---|---|---|---|
| **273** | A44 | 10c yellow org | 3.50 | .75 |
| **274** | A45 | 20c deep blue | 5.75 | 1.10 |
| **275** | A46 | 30c orange brn | 9.50 | 1.75 |
| **276** | A46 | 50c dk slate grn | 22.50 | 3.75 |
| **277** | A46 | 70c red violet | 37.50 | 7.50 |
| | | *Nos. 273-277 (5)* | 78.75 | 14.85 |

50th anniv. of Ethiopia's postal system.

Haile Selassie and Franklin D. Roosevelt — A49

Design: 65c, Roosevelt and US Flags.

**Engraved and Photogravure**

**1947, May 23 Unwmk. *Perf. 12½***

| No. | Type | Value | Unused | Used |
|---|---|---|---|---|
| **278** | A49 | 12c car lake & bl grn | 2.75 | 3.00 |
| **279** | A49 | 25c dk blue & rose | 2.75 | 3.00 |
| **280** | A49 | 65c blk, red & dp bl | 6.00 | 6.50 |
| | | *Nos. 278-280,C21-C22 (5)* | 41.50 | 42.50 |

King Sahle Selassie Reclining A50

King Sahle Selassie — A52

Design: 30c, View of Ankober.

**1947, May 1 Engr. *Perf. 13***

**281** A50 20c deep blue 4.25 .90
**282** A50 30c dark purple 6.25 1.25
**283** A52 $1 deep green 15.00 3.50
*Nos. 281-283 (3)* 25.50 5.65

150th anniversary of Selassie dynasty.

No. 255 Surcharged in Orange

**1947, July 14 *Perf. 14x13½***

**284** A33 12c on 25c 85.00 85.00

Amba Alaguie A53

Designs: 2c, Trinity Church. 4c, Debra Sina. 5c, Mecan, near Achanguie. 8c, Lake Tana. 12c, 15c, Parliament Building, Addis Ababa. 20c, Aiba, near Mai Cheo. 30c, Bahr Bridge over Blue Nile. 60c, 70c, Canoe on Lake Tana. $1, Omo Falls. $3, Mt. Alamata. $5, Ras Dashan Mountains.

***Perf. 13x13½***

**1947-53 Engr. Wmk. 282**

**285** A53 1c rose violet .25 .25
**286** A53 2c blue violet .25 .25
*a.* Unwatermarked ('51) 37.50 15.00
**287** A53 4c green .35 .25
**288** A53 5c dark green .35 .25
**289** A53 8c deep orange .65 .25
**290** A53 12c red .80 .25
**290A** A53 15c dk ol brn ('53) .75 .25
**291** A53 20c blue 1.10 .40
**292** A53 30c orange brown 1.90 .55
**292A** A53 60c red ('51) 2.25 .95
**293** A53 70c rose lilac 3.25 .70
**294** A53 $1 dk carmine rose 5.25 .70
**295** A53 $3 bright blue 14.00 2.75
**296** A53 $5 olive 22.50 5.50
*Nos. 285-296 (14)* 53.65 13.30

Issue dates: 15c, May 25, 1953; 60c, Feb. 10, 1951; others, Aug. 23, 1947.
Shades exist.
For overprints see Nos. 355-356. For surcharges see Nos. B6-B10, B16-B20.

Empress Waizero Menen and Emperor Haile Selassie A54

**1949, May 5 Wmk. 282 *Perf. 13***

**297** A54 20c blue 3.50 .85
**298** A54 30c yellow org 3.50 1.10
**299** A54 50c purple 8.00 2.10
**300** A54 80c green 12.00 2.50
**301** A54 $1 red 14.00 3.50
*Nos. 297-301 (5)* 41.00 10.05

Central ornaments differ on each denomination.
8th anniv. of Ethiopia's liberation from Italian occupation.

Dejach Balcha Hospital A55

Abuna Petros — A56

Designs: 20c, Haile Selassie raising flag. 30c, Lion of Judah statue. 50c, Empress Waizero Menen, Haile Selassie and building.

***Perf. 13x13½, 13½x13***

**1950, Nov. 2 Engr. Wmk. 282**

**302** A55 5c purple 1.60 .35
**303** A56 10c deep plum 3.00 .70
**304** A56 20c deep carmine 6.50 .90
**305** A56 30c green 9.50 2.00
**306** A55 50c deep blue 16.00 3.50
*Nos. 302-306 (5)* 36.60 7.45

20th anniv. of the coronation of Emperor Haile Selassie and Empress Menen.

Abbaye Bridge — A57

**1951, Jan. 1 Unwmk. *Perf. 14***

**308** A57 5c dk green & dk brn 4.25 .50
**309** A57 10c dp orange & blk 5.75 .50
**310** A57 15c dp blue & org brn 8.25 .50
**311** A57 30c olive & lil rose 15.00 .80
**312** A57 60c brown & dp bl 37.50 2.00
**313** A57 80c purple & green 50.00 3.00
*Nos. 308-313 (6)* 120.75 7.30

Opening of the Abbaye Bridge over the Blue Nile.

Tomb of Ras Makonnen A58

**1951, Mar. 2 Center in Black**

**314** A58 5c dark green 3.25 .65
**315** A58 10c deep ultra 3.25 .40
**316** A58 15c blue 5.50 .40
**317** A58 30c claret 11.00 1.50
**318** A58 80c rose carmine 17.00 2.25
**319** A58 $1 orange brown 22.50 2.25
*Nos. 314-319 (6)* 62.50 7.45

55th anniversary of the Battle of Adwa.

Emperor Haile Selassie — A59

**1952, July 23 *Perf. 13½***

**320** A59 5c dark green .85 .25
**321** A59 10c red orange 1.25 .25
**322** A59 15c black 2.00 .40
**323** A59 25c ultra 2.50 .40
**324** A59 30c violet 3.25 .65
**325** A59 50c rose red 5.00 .90
**326** A59 65c chocolate 10.00 1.60
*Nos. 320-326 (7)* 24.85 4.45

60th birthday of Haile Selassie.

Open Road to Sea A60

Designs: 25c, 50c, Road and broken chain. 65c, Map. 80c, Allegory: Reunion. $1, Haile Selassie raising flag. $2, Ethiopian flag and seascape. $3, Haile Selassie addressing League of Nations.

**Wmk. 282**

**1952, Sept. 11 Engr. *Perf. 13***

**327** A60 15c brown carmine .85 .25
**328** A60 25c red brown 1.10 .40
**329** A60 30c yellow brown 2.00 .60
**330** A60 50c purple 3.00 1.25
**331** A60 65c gray 5.75 1.40
**332** A60 80c blue green 6.50 .95
**333** A60 $1 rose carmine 13.00 2.00
**334** A60 $2 deep blue 22.50 3.25
**335** A60 $3 magenta 47.50 5.50
*Nos. 327-335 (9)* 102.20 15.60

Issued to celebrate Ethiopia's federation with Eritrea, effected Sept. 11, 1952.

Haile Selassie and New Ethiopian Port A61

15c, 30c, Haile Selassie on deck of ship.

**1953, Oct. 4**

**337** A61 10c red & dk brn 4.75 1.75
**338** A61 15c blue & dk grn 5.00 1.75
**339** A61 25c orange & dk brn 9.00 3.50
**340** A61 30c red brn & dk grn 16.00 5.00
**341** A61 50c purple & dk brn 25.00 6.75
*Nos. 337-341 (5)* 59.75 18.75

Federation of Ethiopia and Eritrea, 1st anniv.

Princess Tsahai at a Sickbed A62

***Perf. 13x13½***

**1955, July 8 Engr. Wmk. 282**

**Cross Typo. in Red**

**342** A62 15c choc & ultra 2.50 1.25
**343** A62 20c green & orange 3.75 1.50
**344** A62 30c ultra & green 6.25 1.90
*Nos. 342-344 (3)* 12.50 4.65

Ethiopian Red Cross, 20th anniv.
For surcharges see Nos. B33-B35.

Promulgating the Constitution — A63

Bishops' Consecration by Archbishop — A64

25c, Kagnew Battalion. 35c, Reunion with the Motherland. 50c, "Progress." 65c, Empress Waizero Menen & Emperor Haile Selassie.

***Perf. 12½***

**1955, Nov. 3 Unwmk. Engr.**

**345** A63 5c green & choc 1.25 .55
**346** A64 20c carmine & brn 2.50 .90
**347** A64 25c magenta & gray 3.50 1.40
**348** A63 35c brown & red org 4.75 1.75
**349** A64 50c dk brn & ultra 7.00 2.50
**350** A64 65c violet & car 9.75 4.00
*Nos. 345-350 (6)* 28.75 11.10

Silver jubilee of the coronation of Emperor Haile Selassie and Empress Waizero Menen.

Emperor Haile Selassie and Fair Emblem — A65

**1955, Nov. 5 Wmk. 282**

**351** A65 5c green & ol grn 1.00 .25
**352** A65 10c car & dp ultra 1.50 .40
**353** A65 15c vio blk & grn 2.00 .60
**354** A65 50c mag & red brn 3.00 1.50
*Nos. 351-354 (4)* 7.50 2.75

Silver Jubilee Fair, Addis Ababa.

**Nos. 291 and 292A Overprinted**

**1960, Apr. 7 *Perf. 13x13½***

**355** A53 20c blue 1.75 1.25
**356** A53 60c red 3.00 2.40

WRY, July 1, 1959-June 30, 1960.
The 60c without serifs is a trial printing.

Map of Africa, "Liberty" and Haile Selassie — A66

***Perf. 13½***

**1960, June 14 Engr. Unwmk.**

**357** A66 20c orange & green 1.25 .85
**358** A66 80c orange & violet 3.50 .85
**359** A66 $1 orange & maroon 4.00 1.10
*Nos. 357-359 (3)* 8.75 2.80

2nd Conf. of Independent African States at Addis Ababa. Issued in sheets of 10.

Emperor Haile Selassie — A67

**1960, Nov. 2 Wmk. 282 *Perf. 14***

| | | | | |
|---|---|---|---|---|
| **360** | A67 | 10c brown & blue | .90 | .25 |
| **361** | A67 | 25c violet & emerald | 1.75 | .55 |
| **362** | A67 | 50c dk bl & org yel | 3.25 | 1.75 |
| **363** | A67 | 65c slate grn & sal pink | 4.25 | 1.75 |
| **364** | A67 | $1 indigo & rose vio | 7.25 | 2.75 |
| | | *Nos. 360-364 (5)* | 17.40 | 7.05 |

30th anniv. of the coronation of Emperor Haile Selassie.

Africa Hall, UN Economic Commission for Africa — A68

**1961, Apr. 15 Wmk. 282 *Perf. 14***

| | | | | |
|---|---|---|---|---|
| **365** | A68 | 80c ultra | 3.75 | 1.40 |

Africa Freedom Day, Apr. 15. Sheets of 10.

Map of Ethiopia, Olive Branch A69

**1961, May 5 *Perf. 13x13½***

| | | | | |
|---|---|---|---|---|
| **366** | A69 | 20c green | .40 | .25 |
| **367** | A69 | 30c violet blue | .60 | .25 |
| **368** | A69 | $1 brown | 3.25 | 1.10 |
| | | *Nos. 366-368 (3)* | 4.25 | 1.60 |

20th anniv. of Ethiopia's liberation from Italian occupation.

African Wild Ass A70

**1961, June 16 Wmk. 282 *Perf. 14***

| | | | | |
|---|---|---|---|---|
| **369** | A70 | 5c shown | 1.10 | .25 |
| **370** | A70 | 15c Eland | 1.10 | .25 |
| **371** | A70 | 25c Elephant | 1.25 | .40 |
| **372** | A70 | 35c Giraffe | 3.00 | .50 |
| **373** | A70 | 50c Beisa | 3.00 | .50 |
| **374** | A70 | $1 Lion | 6.00 | 1.50 |
| | | *Nos. 369-374 (6)* | 15.45 | 3.40 |

Issued in sheets of 10. Used values are for CTO's.

Emperor Haile Selassie and Empress Waizero Menen — A71

**1961, July 27 Unwmk. *Perf. 11***

| | | | | |
|---|---|---|---|---|
| **375** | A71 | 10c green | 1.25 | .45 |
| **376** | A71 | 50c violet blue | 2.25 | .80 |
| **377** | A71 | $1 carmine rose | 4.25 | 1.60 |
| | | *Nos. 375-377 (3)* | 7.75 | 2.85 |

Golden wedding anniv. of the Emperor and Empress.

Warlike Horsemanship (Guks) — A72

15c, Hockey. 20c, Bicycling. 30c, Soccer. 50c, 1960 Olympic marathon winner, Abebe Bikila.

**Photogravure and Engraved**

**1962, Jan. 14 *Perf. 12x11½***

| | | | | |
|---|---|---|---|---|
| **378** | A72 | 10c yel grn & car | .35 | .25 |
| **379** | A72 | 15c pink & dk brn | .35 | .25 |
| **380** | A72 | 20c red & black | 1.20 | .25 |
| **381** | A72 | 30c ultra & dl pur | 2.00 | .25 |
| **382** | A72 | 50c yellow & green | 4.00 | .25 |
| | | *Nos. 378-382 (5)* | 7.90 | 1.25 |

Third Africa Football (soccer) Cup, Addis Ababa, Jan. 14-22.

Malaria Eradication Emblem, World Map and Mosquito — A73

**Wmk. 282**

**1962, Apr. 7 Engr. *Perf. 13½***

| | | | | |
|---|---|---|---|---|
| **383** | A73 | 15c black | .40 | .25 |
| **384** | A73 | 30c purple | 1.60 | .25 |
| **385** | A73 | 60c red brown | 2.40 | .65 |
| | | *Nos. 383-385 (3)* | 4.40 | 1.15 |

WHO drive to eradicate malaria.

Abyssinian Ground Hornbill A74

Birds: 15c, Abyssinian roller. 30c, Bateleur, vert. 50c, Double-toothed barbet, vert. $1, Didric cuckoo.

***Perf. 11½***

**1962, May 5 Unwmk. Photo.**

**Granite Paper**

| | | | | |
|---|---|---|---|---|
| **386** | A74 | 5c multicolored | 1.40 | .25 |
| **387** | A74 | 15c emer, brn & ultra | 2.40 | .50 |
| **388** | A74 | 30c lt brn, blk & red | 2.75 | 1.75 |
| **389** | A74 | 50c multicolored | 5.25 | 1.50 |
| **390** | A74 | $1 multicolored | 12.00 | 2.50 |
| | | *Nos. 386-390 (5)* | 23.80 | 6.50 |

See Nos. C77-C81, C97-C101, C107-C111.

Assab Hospital A75

15c, School at Assab. 20c, Church at Massawa. 50c, Mosque at Massawa. 60c, Assab port.

**Wmk. 282**

**1962, Sept. 11 Engr. *Perf. 13½***

| | | | | |
|---|---|---|---|---|
| **391** | A75 | 3c purple | .25 | .25 |
| **392** | A75 | 15c dark blue | .25 | .25 |
| **393** | A75 | 20c green | .40 | .25 |
| **394** | A75 | 50c brown | 1.50 | .40 |
| **395** | A75 | 60c carmine rose | 1.60 | .50 |
| | | *Nos. 391-395 (5)* | 4.00 | 1.65 |

Federation of Ethiopia and Eritrea, 10th anniv.

King Bazen, Madonna and Stars over Bethlehem — A76

15c, Ezana, obelisks & temple. 20c, Kaleb & sailing fleet. 50c, Lalibela, rock-church and frescoes, vert. 60c, King Yekuno Amlak & Abuna Tekle Haimanot preaching in Ankober. 75c, King Zara Yacob & Maskal celebration. $1, King Lebna Dengel & battle against Mohammed Gragn.

***Perf. 14½***

**1962, Nov. 2 Unwmk. Photo.**

| | | | | |
|---|---|---|---|---|
| **396** | A76 | 10c multicolored | .35 | .25 |
| **397** | A76 | 15c multicolored | .50 | .25 |
| **398** | A76 | 20c multicolored | .70 | .25 |
| **399** | A76 | 50c multicolored | 1.10 | .25 |
| **400** | A76 | 60c multicolored | 1.25 | .50 |
| **401** | A76 | 75c multicolored | 2.00 | .85 |
| **402** | A76 | $1 multicolored | 3.00 | 1.25 |
| | | *Nos. 396-402 (7)* | 8.90 | 3.60 |

32nd anniv. of the coronation of Emperor Haile Selassie and to commemorate ancient kings and saints.

Map of Ethiopian Telephone Network — A77

Designs: 50c, Radio mast and waves. 60c, Telegraph pole and rising sun.

***Perf. 13½x14***

**1963, Jan. 1 Engr. Wmk. 282**

| | | | | |
|---|---|---|---|---|
| **403** | A77 | 10c dark red | .50 | .25 |
| **404** | A77 | 50c ultra | 2.25 | .50 |
| **405** | A77 | 60c brown | 2.75 | .60 |
| | | *Nos. 403-405 (3)* | 5.50 | 1.35 |

10th anniv. of the Imperial Board of Telecommunications.

Wheat Emblem — A78

**1963, Mar. 21 Unwmk. *Perf. 13½***

| | | | | |
|---|---|---|---|---|
| **406** | A78 | 5c deep rose | .25 | .25 |
| **407** | A78 | 10c rose carmine | .25 | .25 |
| **408** | A78 | 15c violet blue | .25 | .25 |
| **409** | A78 | 30c emerald | 1.25 | .25 |
| | | *Nos. 406-409 (4)* | 2.00 | 1.00 |

FAO "Freedom from Hunger" campaign.

Abuna Salama — A79

Spiritual Leaders: 15c, Abuna Aregawi. 30c, Abuna Tekle Haimanot. 40c, Yared. 60c, Zara Yacob.

**1964, Jan. 3 Unwmk. *Perf. 13½***

| | | | | |
|---|---|---|---|---|
| **410** | A79 | 10c blue | .45 | .25 |
| **411** | A79 | 15c dark green | .75 | .25 |
| **412** | A79 | 30c brown red | 1.90 | .45 |
| **413** | A79 | 40c dark blue | 2.50 | .75 |
| **414** | A79 | 60c brown | 3.75 | 1.40 |
| | | *Nos. 410-414 (5)* | 9.35 | 3.10 |

Queen of Sheba — A80

Ethiopian Empresses: 15c, Helen. 50c, Seble Wongel. 60c, Mentiwab. 80c, Taitu, consort of Menelik II.

**Granite Paper**

**1964, Mar. 2 Photo. *Perf. 11½***

| | | | | |
|---|---|---|---|---|
| **415** | A80 | 10c multicolored | 1.10 | .30 |
| **416** | A80 | 15c multicolored | 2.25 | .50 |
| **417** | A80 | 50c multicolored | 2.50 | 1.00 |
| **418** | A80 | 60c multicolored | 5.00 | 1.75 |
| **419** | A80 | 80c multicolored | 6.50 | 2.50 |
| | | *Nos. 415-419 (5)* | 17.35 | 6.05 |

Priest Teaching Alphabet to Children — A81

10c, Classroom. 15c, Woman learning to read. 40c, Students in chemistry laboratory. 60c, Graduation procession.

**1964, June 1 Unwmk. *Perf. 11½***

**Granite Paper**

| | | | | |
|---|---|---|---|---|
| **420** | A81 | 5c brown | .25 | .25 |
| **421** | A81 | 10c emerald | .25 | .25 |
| **422** | A81 | 15c rose vio, vert. | .25 | .25 |
| **423** | A81 | 40c vio blue, vert. | 1.00 | .30 |
| **424** | A81 | 60c dark pur, vert. | 1.50 | .55 |
| | | *Nos. 420-424 (5)* | 3.25 | 1.60 |

Issued to publicize education.

Eleanor Roosevelt (1884-1962) — A82

**1964, Oct. 11 Photo.**

**Granite Paper**

**Portrait in Slate Blue**

| | | | | |
|---|---|---|---|---|
| **425** | A82 | 10c yellow bister | .25 | .25 |
| **426** | A82 | 60c orange brown | 2.00 | .75 |
| **427** | A82 | 80c green & gold | 3.00 | 1.00 |
| | | *Nos. 425-427 (3)* | 5.25 | 2.00 |

King Serse Dengel and View of Gondar, 1563 A83

Ethiopian Leaders: 10c, King Fasiladas and Gondar in 1632. 20c, King Yassu the Great and Gondar in 1682. 25c, Emperor Theodore II and map of Ethiopia. 60c, Emperor John IV and Battle of Gura, 1876. 80c, Emperor Menelik II and Battle of Adwa, 1896.

**1964, Dec. 12 Photo. *Perf. 14½x14***

| | | | | |
|---|---|---|---|---|
| **428** | A83 | 5c multicolored | .40 | .25 |
| **429** | A83 | 10c multicolored | .40 | .25 |
| **430** | A83 | 20c multicolored | 1.00 | .25 |
| **431** | A83 | 25c multicolored | 1.50 | .25 |
| **432** | A83 | 60c multicolored | 2.75 | .95 |
| **433** | A83 | 80c multicolored | 3.75 | 1.25 |
| | | *Nos. 428-433 (6)* | 9.80 | 3.20 |

Ethiopian Rose — A84

Flowers: 10c, Kosso tree. 25c, St.-John's-wort. 35c, Parrot's-beak. 60c, Maskal daisy.

**1965, Mar. 30** *Perf. 12x13½*

**434** A84 5c multicolored .35 .25
**435** A84 10c multicolored .35 .25
**436** A84 25c multicolored 1.20 .25
**437** A84 35c multicolored 2.50 .50
**438** A84 60c green, yel & org 3.00 .80
*Nos. 434-438 (5)* 7.40 2.05

ITU Emblem, Old and New Communication Symbols — A85

*Perf. 13½x14½*

**1965, May 17** **Litho.** **Unwmk.**

**439** A85 5c blue, indigo & yel .25 .25
**440** A85 10c blue, indigo & org .55 .25
**441** A85 60c blue, indigo & lil rose 2.00 .95
*Nos. 439-441 (3)* 2.80 1.45

Cent. of the ITU.

Laboratory A86

Designs: 5c, Textile spinning mill. 10c, Sugar factory. 20c, Mountain road. 25c, Autobus. 30c, Diesel locomotive and bridge. 35c, Railroad station, Addis Ababa.

**1965, July 19** **Photo.** *Perf. 11½*

**Granite Paper**

**Portrait in Black**

**442** A86 3c sepia .25 .25
**443** A86 5c dull pur & buff .25 .25
**444** A86 10c black & gray .65 .25
**445** A86 20c green & pale yel .95 .25
**446** A86 25c dk brown & yel 1.40 .25
**447** A86 30c maroon & gray 2.25 .35
**448** A86 35c dk blue & gray 2.50 .50
*Nos. 442-448 (7)* 8.25 2.10

For overprints see Nos. 609-612.

ICY Emblem A87

**1965, Oct. 24** **Unwmk.** *Perf. 11½*

**Granite Paper**

**449** A87 10c blue & red brn .50 .25
**450** A87 50c dp blue & red brn 1.40 .75
**451** A87 80c vio blue & red brn 2.25 1.10
*Nos. 449-451 (3)* 4.15 2.10

International Cooperation Year, 1965.

National Bank Emblem A88

Designs: 10c, Commercial Bank emblem. 60c, Natl. and Commercial Bank buildings.

**1965, Nov. 2** **Photo.** *Perf. 13*

**452** A88 10c dp car, blk & indigo .40 .25
**453** A88 30c ultra, blk & indigo .85 .40
**454** A88 60c black, yel & indigo 1.50 .65
*Nos. 452-454 (3)* 2.75 1.30

Natl. and Commercial Banks of Ethiopia.

"Light and Peace" Press Building A89

**1966, Apr. 5** **Engr.** *Perf. 13*

**455** A89 5c pink & black .25 .25
**456** A89 15c lt yel grn & blk .60 .25
**457** A89 30c orange yel & blk 1.10 .55
*Nos. 455-457 (3)* 1.95 1.05

Opening of the "Light and Peace" Printing Press building.

Kabaro Drum — A90

Musical Instruments: 10c, Bagana harp. 35c, Messenko guitar. 50c, Krar lyre. 60c, Wachent flutes.

**1966, Sept. 9** **Photo.** *Perf. 13½*

**458** A90 5c brt green & blk .25 .25
**459** A90 10c dull blue & blk .25 .25
**460** A90 35c orange & blk 1.25 .50
**461** A90 50c yellow & blk 2.25 .70
**462** A90 60c rose car & blk 2.75 1.25
*Nos. 458-462 (5)* 6.75 2.95

Emperor Haile Selassie — A91

**1966, Nov. 1** **Unwmk.** *Perf. 12*

**463** A91 10c black, gold & grn .40 .25
**464** A91 15c black, gold & dp car .70 .25
**465** A91 40c black & gold 2.00 .65
*Nos. 463-465 (3)* 3.10 1.15

50 years of leadership of Emperor Haile Selassie.

UNESCO Emblem and Map of Africa A92

**Wmk. 282**

**1966, Nov. 30** **Litho.** *Perf. 13½*

**466** A92 15c blue car & blk .50 .25
**467** A92 60c olive, brn & dk bl 2.50 .60

20th anniv. of UNESCO.

WHO Headquarters, Geneva — A93

**1966, Nov. 30**

**468** A93 5c olive, ultra & brn .80 .25
**469** A93 40c brown, pur & emer 2.50 .35

Opening of WHO Headquarters, Geneva.

Expo '67 Ethiopian Pavilion and Columns of Axum (Replica) — A94

*Perf. 12x13½*

**1967, May 2** **Photo.** **Unwmk.**

**470** A94 30c brt blue & multi .65 .30
**471** A94 45c multicolored .85 .40
**472** A94 80c gray & multi 1.50 .60
*Nos. 470-472 (3)* 3.00 1.30

EXPO '67, Intl. Exhibition, Montreal, Apr. 28-Oct. 27, 1967.

Diesel Train and Map — A95

**1967, June 7** **Photo.** *Perf. 12*

**473** A95 15c multicolored 1.10 .55
**474** A95 30c multicolored 2.75 1.40
**475** A95 50c multicolored 3.75 1.75
*Nos. 473-475 (3)* 7.60 3.70

Djibouti-Addis Ababa railroad, 50th anniv.

Papilionidae Aethiops — A96

Various Butterflies.

*Perf. 13½x13*

**1967, June 30** **Photo.** **Unwmk.**

**476** A96 5c buff & multi .60 .25
**477** A96 10c lilac & multi 2.00 .40
**478** A96 20c multicolored 2.75 .75
**479** A96 35c blue & multi 4.75 1.50
**480** A96 40c multicolored 7.75 2.00
*Nos. 476-480 (5)* 17.85 4.90

Emperor Haile Selassie and Lion of Judah A97

**1967, July 21** *Perf. 11½*

**Granite Paper**

**481** A97 10c dk brn, emer & gold .45 .25
**482** A97 15c dk brn, yel & gold .80 .25
**483** A97 $1 dk brn, red & gold 3.50 1.50
*Nos. 481-483 (3)* 4.75 2.00

**Souvenir Sheet**

**484** A97 $1 dk brn, pur & gold 15.00 15.00

75th birthday of Emperor Haile Selassie.

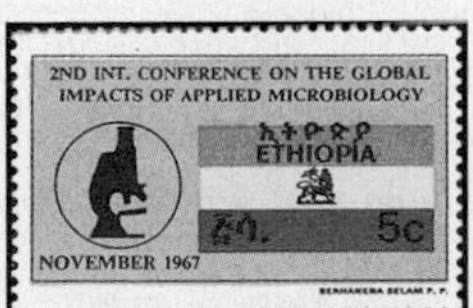


Microscope and Ethiopian Flag — A98

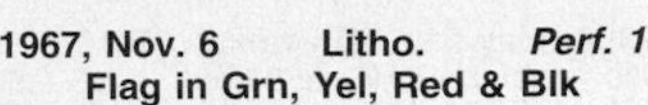

**1967, Nov. 6** **Litho.** *Perf. 13*

**Flag in Grn, Yel, Red & Blk**

**485** A98 5c blue .25 .25
**486** A98 30c ocher 1.00 .30
**487** A98 $1 violet 2.75 .95
*Nos. 485-487 (3)* 4.00 1.50

2nd Intl. Conf. on the Global Impact of Applied Microbiology, Addis Ababa, 11/6-12.

Wall Painting from Debre Berhan Selassie Church, Gondar, 17th Century — A99

ITY Emblem and: 25c, Votive throne from Atsbe Dera, 4th Cent. B.C., vert. 35c, Prehistoric cave painting, Harar Province. 50c, Prehistoric stone tools, Melke Kontoure, vert.

**1967, Nov. 20** **Photo.** *Perf. 14½*

**488** A99 15c multicolored 2.75 1.40
**489** A99 25c yel grn, buff & blk 3.00 1.40
**490** A99 35c green, brn & blk 2.75 1.75
**491** A99 50c yellow & blk 5.00 2.75
*Nos. 488-491 (4)* 13.50 7.30

International Tourist Year, 1967.

A100

Crosses of Lalibela: 5c, Processional Bronze Cross, Biet-Maryam Church. 10c, Processional copper cross. 15c, Copper cross, Biet-Maryam church. 20c, Lalibela-style cross. 50c, Chiseled copper cross, Madhani Alem church.

**1967, Dec. 7** **Photo.** *Perf. 14½*

**Crosses in Silver**

**492** A100 5c yellow & blk .40 .25
**493** A100 10c red orange & blk .40 .25
**494** A100 15c violet & blk .50 .25
**495** A100 20c brt rose & blk .95 .25
**496** A100 50c orange yel & blk 3.00 .60
*Nos. 492-496 (5)* 5.25 1.60

A101

Designs: 10c, Emperor Theodore (1818?-1868). 20c, Emperor Theodore and lions, horiz. 50c, Imperial crown.

*Perf. 14x13½*

**1968, Apr. 18** **Litho.** **Unwmk.**

**497** A101 10c lt vio, ocher & brn .55 .25
**498** A101 20c lilac, brn & dk vio 1.25 .25
**499** A101 50c dk grn, org & rose cl 2.75 .75
*Nos. 497-499 (3)* 4.55 1.25

Human Rights Flame A102

**1968, May 31** **Unwmk.** ***Perf. 14½***

**500** A102 15c pink, red & blk .55 .55
**501** A102 $1 lt bl, brt bl & blk 2.40 2.40

International Human Rights Year, 1968.

Shah Mohammed Reza Pahlavi, Emperor and Flags — A103

**1968, June 3** **Litho.** ***Perf. 13½***

**502** A103 5c multicolored .25 .25
**503** A103 15c multicolored .30 .30
**504** A103 30c multicolored 1.25 1.25
*Nos. 502-504 (3)* 1.80 1.80

Visit of Shah Mohammed Riza Pahlavi of Iran.

Emperor Haile Selassie Appealing to League of Nations, 1935 — A104

35c, African Unity Building and map of Africa. $1, World map, symbolizing intl. relations.

**1968, July 22** **Photo.** ***Perf. 14x13½***

**505** A104 15c bl, red, blk & gold .40 .25
**506** A104 35c blk, emer, red & gold .75 .75
**507** A104 $1 dk bl, lil, blk & gold 2.50 2.75
*Nos. 505-507 (3)* 3.65 3.75

Ethiopia's struggle for peace. Issued with tabs on bottom row. Value, set $10.

WHO Emblem A105

***Perf. 14x13½***

**1968, Aug. 30** **Litho.** **Unwmk.**

**508** A105 15c brt green & blk .35 .35
**509** A105 60c red lilac & blk 1.90 1.90

20th anniv. of the WHO.

Abebe Bikila, Marathon Runner A106

**1968, Oct. 12** ***Perf. 11½***

**510** A106 10c shown .25 .25
**511** A106 15c Soccer .40 .40
**512** A106 20c Boxing .50 .50
**513** A106 40c Basketball 1.25 1.25
**514** A106 50c Bicycling 1.90 1.90
*Nos. 510-514 (5)* 4.30 4.30

19th Olympic Games, Mexico City, 10/12-27.

Arrussi Woman — A107

Regional Costumes: 15c, Man from Gemu Gefa. 20c, Gojam man. 30c, Kefa man. 35c, Harar woman. 50c, Ilubabor grass coat. 60c, Woman from Eritrea.

***Perf. 13½x13***

**1968, Dec. 10** **Photo.** **Unwmk.**

**515** A107 5c silver & multi .65 .25
**516** A107 15c silver & multi .65 .25
**517** A107 20c silver & multi .65 .25
**518** A107 30c silver & multi .85 .55
**519** A107 35c silver & multi 1.00 .65
**520** A107 50c silver & multi 2.00 1.10
**521** A107 60c silver & multi 2.75 1.60
*Nos. 515-521 (7)* 8.55 4.65

See Nos. 575-581.

Message Stick and Amharic Postal Emblem A108

**1969, Mar. 10** **Litho.** ***Perf. 14***

**522** A108 10c emerald, blk & brn .70 .70
**523** A108 15c yellow, blk & brn .70 .70
**524** A108 35c multicolored 1.25 1.25
*Nos. 522-524 (3)* 2.65 2.65

Ethiopian postal service, 75th anniv.

ILO Emblem A109

**1969, Apr. 11** **Litho.** ***Perf. 14½***

**525** A109 15c orange & blk .50 .50
**526** A109 60c emerald & blk 2.00 2.00

50th anniv. of the ILO.

Dove, Red Cross, Crescent, Lion and Sun Emblems A110

**1969, May 8** **Wmk. 282** ***Perf. 13***

**527** A110 5c lt ultra, blk & red .25 .25
**528** A110 15c lt ultra, grn & red .65 .65
**529** A110 30c lt ultra, vio bl & red 1.40 1.40
*Nos. 527-529 (3)* 2.30 2.30

League of Red Cross Societies, 50th anniv.

Endybis Silver Coin, 3rd Century — A111

Ancient Ethiopian Coins: 10c, Gold of Ezana, 4th cent. 15c, Gold of Kaleb, 6th cent. 30c, Bronze of Armah, 7th cent. 40c, Bronze of Wazena, 7th cent. 50c, Silver of Gersem, 8th cent.

**1969, June 19** **Photo.** ***Perf. 14½***

**530** A111 5c ultra, blk & sil .25 .25
**531** A111 10c brt red, blk & gold .45 .45
**532** A111 15c brown, blk & gold .70 .70
**533** A111 30c dp car, blk & brnz 1.25 1.25
**534** A111 40c dk green, blk & brnz 1.50 1.50
**535** A111 50c dp violet, blk & sil 2.40 2.40
*Nos. 530-535 (6)* 6.55 6.55

Zebras and Tourist Year Emblem A112

Designs: 10c, Camping. 15c, Fishing. 20c, Water skiing. 25c, Mountaineering, vert.

***Perf. 13x13½, 13½x13***

**1969, Aug. 29** **Litho.** **Unwmk.**

**536** A112 5c multicolored .40 .40
**537** A112 10c multicolored .40 .40
**538** A112 15c multicolored 1.10 1.25
**539** A112 20c multicolored 2.25 2.50
**540** A112 25c multicolored 2.50 3.50
*Nos. 536-540 (5)* 6.65 8.05

International Year of African Tourism.

Stylized Bird and UN Emblem A113

UN 25th anniv.: 30c, Stylized flowers, UN and peace emblems, vert. 60c, Stylized bird, UN emblem and plane.

**1969, Oct. 24** **Unwmk.** ***Perf. 11½***

**541** A113 10c lt blue & multi .25 .25
**542** A113 30c lt blue & multi .80 .80
**543** A113 60c lt blue & multi 2.00 2.00
*Nos. 541-543 (3)* 3.05 3.05

Ancient Cross and Holy Family A114

Designs: Various ancient crosses.

***Perf. 14½x13½***

**1969, Dec. 10** **Photo.**

**544** A114 5c black, yel & dk bl .25 .25
**545** A114 10c black & yellow .25 .30
**546** A114 25c black, yel & grn 1.10 1.40
**547** A114 60c black & ocher 2.75 3.00
*Nos. 544-547 (4)* 4.35 4.95

Ancient Figurines — A115

Ancient Ethiopian Pottery: 20c, Vases, Yeha period, 4th-3rd centuries B.C. 25c, Vases and jugs, Axum, 4th-6th centuries A.D. 35c, Bird-shaped jug and jugs, Matara, 4th-6th centuries A.D. 60c, Decorated pottery, Adulis, 6th-7th centuries A.D.

**1970, Feb. 6** **Photo.** ***Perf. 14½***

**548** A115 10c black & multi .55 .55
**549** A115 20c black & multi .55 .55
**550** A115 25c black & multi .55 .55
**551** A115 35c black & multi 1.25 1.25
**552** A115 60c black & multi 2.25 2.25
*Nos. 548-552 (5)* 5.15 5.15

Medhane Alem Church — A116

Rock Churches of Lalibela, 12th-13th Centuries: 10c, Bieta Emmanuel. 15c, The four Rock Churches of Lalibela. 20c, Bieta Mariam. 50c, Bieta Giorgis.

**1970, Apr. 15** **Unwmk.** ***Perf. 13***

**553** A116 5c brown & multi .25 .25
**554** A116 10c brown & multi .25 .25
**555** A116 15c brown & multi .40 .40
**556** A116 20c brown & multi .65 .65
**557** A116 50c brown & multi 1.50 1.50
*Nos. 553-557 (5)* 3.05 3.05

Sailfish Tang A117

Tropical Fish: 10c, Undulate triggerfish. 15c, Orange butterflyfish. 25c, Butterflyfish. 50c, Imperial Angelfish.

**1970, June 19** **Photo.** ***Perf. 12½***

**558** A117 5c multicolored .25 .25
**559** A117 10c multicolored .25 .25
**560** A117 15c multicolored .60 .60
**561** A117 25c multicolored 1.50 1.50
**562** A117 50c multicolored 3.00 3.00
*Nos. 558-562 (5)* 5.60 5.60

Education Year Emblem — A118

**1970, Aug. 14** **Unwmk.** ***Perf. 13½***

**563** A118 10c multicolored .25 .25
**564** A118 20c gold, ultra & emer .45 .45
**565** A118 50c gold, emer & org 1.40 1.40
*Nos. 563-565 (3)* 2.10 2.10

Issued for International Education Year.

Map of Africa — A119

30c, Flag of Organization of African Unity. 40c, OAU Headquarters, Addis Ababa.

**1970, Sept. 21** **Photo.** ***Perf. 13½***

**566** A119 20c multicolored .55 .55
**567** A119 30c multicolored .70 .70
**568** A119 40c green & multi 1.00 1.00
*Nos. 566-568 (3)* 2.25 2.25

Africa Unity Day and Organization of African Unity.

Emperor Haile Selassie — A120

**1970, Oct. 30 Unwmk. *Perf. 14½***

**569** A120 15c Prus bl & multi .30 .30
**570** A120 50c multicolored 1.40 1.40
**571** A120 60c multicolored 2.00 2.00
*Nos. 569-571 (3)* 3.70 3.70

Coronation, 40th anniv.

Buildings — A121

**1970, Dec. 30 Litho. *Perf. 13½***

**572** A121 10c ver & multi .25 .25
**573** A121 50c brown & multi 1.25 1.25
**574** A121 80c multicolored 2.00 2.00
*Nos. 572-574 (3)* 3.50 3.50

Opening of new Posts, Telecommunications and General Post Office buildings.

### Costume Type of 1968

Regional Costumes: 5c, Warrior from Begemdir and Semien. 10c, Woman from Bale. 15c, Warrior from Welega. 20c,Woman from Shoa. 25c, Man from Sidamo. 40c, Woman from Tigre. 50c, Man from Welo.

**1971, Feb. 17 Photo. *Perf. 11½***
**Granite Paper**

**575** A107 5c gold & multi .35 .35
**576** A107 10c gold & multi .35 .35
**577** A107 15c gold & multi .70 .70
**578** A107 20c gold & multi .85 .85
**579** A107 25c gold & multi 1.10 1.10
**580** A107 40c gold & multi 1.60 1.60
**581** A107 50c gold & multi 3.00 3.00
*Nos. 575-581 (7)* 7.95 7.95

Plane's Tail with Emblem — A122

Designs: 10c, Ethiopian scenes. 20c, Nose of Boeing 707. 60c, Pilots in cockpit, and engine. 80c, Globe with routes shown.

**1971, Apr. 8 *Perf. 14½x14***

**582** A122 5c multicolored .70 .70
**583** A122 10c multicolored .70 .70
**584** A122 20c multicolored .90 .90
**585** A122 60c multicolored 1.75 1.75
**586** A122 80c multicolored 4.00 4.00
*Nos. 582-586 (5)* 8.05 8.05

Ethiopian Airlines, 25th anniversary. Issued with tabs on bottom row. Value, set $11.

Fountain of Life, 15th Century Gospel Book — A123

Ethiopian Paintings: 10c, King David, 15th cent. manuscript. 25c, St. George, 17th cent. painting on canvas. 50c, King Lalibela, 18th cent. painting on wood. 60c, Yared singing before King Kaleb. Mural in Axum Cathedral.

**1971, June 15 Photo. *Perf. 11½***
**Granite Paper**

**587** A123 5c tan & multi .25 .25
**588** A123 10c pale sal & multi .25 .25
**589** A123 25c lemon & multi .60 .60
**590** A123 50c yellow & multi 1.60 1.60
**591** A123 60c gray & multi 2.50 2.50
*Nos. 587-591 (5)* 5.20 5.20

Black and White Heads, Globes A124

Designs: 60c, Black and white hand holding globe. 80c, Four races, globes.

**1971, Aug. 31 Unwmk.**

**592** A124 10c org, red brn & blk .45 .45
**593** A124 60c green, bl & blk 1.40 1.40
**594** A124 80c bl, org, yel & blk 2.25 2.25
*Nos. 592-594 (3)* 4.10 4.10

Intl. Year Against Racial Discrimination.

Emperor Menelik II and Reading of Treaty of Ucciali A125

Contemporary Paintings: 30c, Menelik II on horseback gathering the tribes. 50c, Ethiopians and Italians in Battle of Adwa. 60c, Menelik II and Taitu at head of their armies.

**1971, Oct. 20 Litho. *Perf. 13½***

**595** A125 10c multicolored .35 .35
**596** A125 30c multicolored .95 .95
**597** A125 50c multicolored 1.40 1.40
**598** A125 60c multicolored 2.40 2.40
*Nos. 595-598 (4)* 5.10 5.10

75th anniversary of victory of Adwa over the Italians, March 1, 1896.

Two telephones, 1897, Menelik II and Ras Makonnen — A126

Designs: 10c, Haile Selassie Broadcasting and Map of Ethiopia. 30c, Ethiopians around television set. 40c, Telephone microwave circuits. 60c, Map of Africa on globe and telephone dial.

**1971, Nov. 2**

**599** A126 5c brown & multi .35 .35
**600** A126 10c yellow & multi .35 .35
**601** A126 30c vio bl & multi .65 .65
**602** A126 40c black & multi 1.40 1.40
**603** A126 60c vio bl & multi 2.75 2.75
*Nos. 599-603 (5)* 5.50 5.50

Telecommunications in Ethiopia, 75th anniv.

UNICEF Emblem, Mother and Child — A127

UNICEF Emblem and: 10c, Children drinking milk. 15c, Man holding sick child. 30c, Kindergarten class. 50c, Father and son.

**1971, Dec. 15 Unwmk.**

**604** A127 5c yellow & multi .35 .35
**605** A127 10c pale brn & multi .35 .35
**606** A127 15c rose & multi .75 .75
**607** A127 30c violet & multi 1.50 1.50
**608** A127 50c green & multi 2.00 2.00
*Nos. 604-608 (5)* 4.95 4.95

25th anniv. of UNICEF.

Nos. 445-448 Overprinted

**1972, Jan. 28 Photo. *Perf. 11***
**Portrait in Black**

**609** A86 20c grn & pale yel .55 .55
**610** A86 25c dk brn & yel 1.00 1.00
**611** A86 30c maroon & gray 3.75 3.75
**612** A86 35c dk blue & gray 3.75 3.75
*Nos. 609-612 (4)* 9.05 9.05

1st meeting of UN Security Council in Africa.

River Boat on Lake Haik — A128

**1972, Feb. 7 Litho. *Perf. 11½***
**Granite Paper**

**613** A128 10c shown .45 .45
**614** A128 20c Boats on Lake Abaya .85 .85
**615** A128 30c on Lake Tana 1.60 1.60
**616** A128 60c on Baro River 2.75 2.75
*Nos. 613-616 (4)* 5.65 5.65

Proclamation of Cyrus the Great — A129

**1972, Mar. 28 Photo. *Perf. 14x14½***

**617** A129 10c red & multi .50 .50
**618** A129 60c emerald & multi 2.00 2.00
**619** A129 80c gray & multi 3.00 3.00
*Nos. 617-619 (3)* 5.50 5.50

2500th anniversary of the founding of the Persian empire by Cyrus the Great.

Houses, Sidamo Province A130

Ethiopian Architecture: 10c, Tigre Province. 20c, Eritrea Province. 40c, Addis Ababa. 80c, Shoa Province.

**1972, Apr. 11 Litho. *Perf. 13½***

**620** A130 5c black & multi .30 .30
**621** A130 10c black, gray & brn .30 .30
**622** A130 20c black & multi .65 .65
**623** A130 40c black, bl grn & brn 1.10 1.10
**624** A130 80c black, brn & red brn 2.75 2.75
*Nos. 620-624 (5)* 5.10 5.10

Hands Holding Map of Ethiopia — A131

10c, Hands shielding Ethiopians. 25c, Map of Africa, hands reaching for African Unity emblem. 50c, Brown & white hands clasped, UN emblem. 60c, Hands protecting dove. Each denomination shows different portrait of the Emperor.

***Perf. 14½x14***

**1972, July 21 Litho. Unwmk.**

**625** A131 5c scarlet & multi .35 .35
**626** A131 10c ultra & multi .35 .35
**627** A131 25c vio bl & multi .60 .60
**628** A131 50c lt blue & multi 1.25 1.25
**629** A131 60c brown & multi 1.50 1.50
*Nos. 625-629 (5)* 4.05 4.05

80th birthday of Emperor Haile Selassie.

Running, Flags of Mexico, Japan, Italy — A132

**1972, Aug. 25 *Perf. 13½x13***

**630** A132 10c shown .45 .45
**631** A132 30c Soccer 1.00 1.00
**632** A132 50c Bicycling 1.90 1.90
**633** A132 60c Boxing 2.75 2.75
*Nos. 630-633 (4)* 6.10 6.10

20th Olympic Games, Munich, Germany, Aug. 26-Sept. 11.

Open Bible, Cross and Orbit A133

Designs: 50c, First and 1972 headquarters of the British and Foreign Bible Society, vert. 80c, First Amharic Bible.

**1972, Sept. 25 Photo. *Perf. 13½***

**634** A133 20c deep red & multi .60 .60
**635** A133 50c deep red & multi 2.10 2.10
**636** A133 80c deep red & multi 2.75 2.75
*Nos. 634-636 (3)* 5.45 5.45

United Bible Societies World Assembly, Addis Ababa, Sept. 1972.

Security Council Meeting A134

Designs: 60c, Building where Security Council met. 80c, Map of Africa with flags of participating members.

**1972, Nov. 1 Litho. *Perf. 13½***

**637** A134 10c lt bl & vio bl .25 .25
**638** A134 60c multicolored 1.25 1.25
**639** A134 80c multicolored 2.00 2.00
*Nos. 637-639 (3)* 3.50 3.50

First United Nations Security Council meeting, Addis Ababa, Jan. 28-Feb. 4, 1972.

Fish in Polluted Sea A135

Designs: 30c, Fisherman, beacon, family. 80c, Polluted seashore.

**1973, Feb. 23 Photo. *Perf. 13½***

**640** A135 20c gold & multi .50 .50
**641** A135 30c gold & multi .85 .85
**642** A135 80c gold & multi 2.00 2.00
*Nos. 640-642 (3)* 3.35 3.35

World message from the sea, Ethiopian anti-pollution campaign.

INTERPOL and Ethiopian Police Emblems — A136

50c, INTERPOL emblem & General Secretariat, Paris. 60c, INTERPOL emblem.

**1973, Mar. 20 Photo. *Perf. 13½***

**643** A136 40c dull orange & blk 1.25 1.25
**644** A136 50c blue, blk & yel 1.75 1.75
**645** A136 60c dk carmine & blk 2.00 2.00
*Nos. 643-645 (3)* 5.00 5.00

50th anniversary of International Criminal Police Organization (INTERPOL).

Virgin of Emperor Zara Yaqob — A137

Ethiopian Art: 15c, Crucifixion, Zara Yaqob period. 30c, Virgin and Child, from Entoto Mariam Church. 40c, Christ, contemporary mosaic. 80c, The Evangelists, contemporary bas-relief.

**1973, May 15 Photo. *Perf. 11½***
**Granite Paper**

**646** A137 5c brown & multi .30 .30
**647** A137 15c dp blue & multi .55 .55
**648** A137 30c gray grn & multi 1.10 1.10
**649** A137 40c multicolored 1.40 1.40
**650** A137 80c slate & multi 3.50 3.50
*Nos. 646-650 (5)* 6.85 6.85

Free African States in 1963 and 1973 A138

Designs (Map of Africa and): 10c, Flags of OAU members. 20c, Symbols of progress. 40c, Dove and people. 80c, Emblems of various UN agencies.

**1973 May 25 *Perf. 14½x14***

**651** A138 5c red & multi .25 .25
**652** A138 10c ol gray & multi .30 .30
**653** A138 20c green & multi .45 .45
**654** A138 40c sepia & multi 1.25 1.25
**655** A138 80c lt blue & multi 2.50 2.50
*Nos. 651-655 (5)* 4.75 4.75

OAU, 10th anniv.

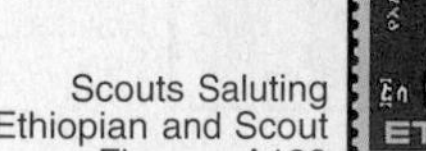


Scouts Saluting Ethiopian and Scout Flags — A139

Designs: 15c, Road and road sign. 30c, Girl Scout reading to old man. 40c, Scout and disabled people. 60c, Ethiopian Boy Scout.

**1973, July 10 Photo. *Perf. 11½***
**Granite Paper**

**656** A139 5c blue & multi .45 .45
**657** A139 15c lt green & multi .65 .65
**658** A139 30c yellow & multi 1.25 1.25
**659** A139 40c crimson & multi 1.60 1.60
**660** A139 60c violet & multi 3.50 3.50
*Nos. 656-660 (5)* 7.45 7.45

24th Boy Scout World Conference, Nairobi, Kenya, July 16-21.

WMO Emblem A140

50c, WMO emblem, anemometer. 60c, Weather satellite over earth, WMO emblem.

**1973, Sept. 4 Photo. *Perf. 13½***

**661** A140 40c black, bl & dl bl 1.20 1.20
**662** A140 50c dull blue & blk 1.50 1.50
**663** A140 60c dull blue & multi 2.40 2.40
*Nos. 661-663 (3)* 5.10 5.10

Cent. of intl. meteorological cooperation. Printed with tabs at top of sheet inscribed in Amharic and tabs at bottom with "ETHIOPIA."

Ras Makonnen, Duke of Harar — A141

5c, Old wall of Harar. 20c, Operating room. 40c, Boy Scouts learning 1st aid & hospital. 80c, Prince Makonnen & hospital.

**1973, Nov. 1 Unwmk. *Perf. 14½***

**664** A141 5c gray & multi .30 .30
**665** A141 10c red brn & multi .30 .30
**666** A141 20c green & multi 1.10 1.10
**667** A141 40c brown red & multi 2.50 2.50
**668** A141 80c ultra & multi 4.50 4.50
*Nos. 664-668 (5)* 8.70 8.70

Opening of Ras Makonnen Memorial Hospital.

Human Rights Flame — A142

***Perf. 11½***
**1973, Nov. 16 Photo. Unwmk.**
**Granite Paper**

**669** A142 40c yel, gold & dk grn .70 .70
**670** A142 50c lt grn, gold & dk grn 1.00 1.00
**671** A142 60c org, gold & dk grn 1.25 1.25
*Nos. 669-671 (3)* 2.95 2.95

25th anniversary of the Universal Declaration of Human Rights.

Emperor Haile Selassie — A143

**1973, Nov. 5 Photo. *Perf. 11½***

**672** A143 5c yellow & multi .35 .30
**673** A143 10c brt blue & multi .35 .30
**674** A143 15c green & multi .45 .40
**675** A143 20c dull yel & multi .55 .40
**676** A143 25c multicolored .65 .40
**677** A143 30c multicolored .80 .40
**678** A143 35c multicolored .85 .40
**679** A143 40c ultra & multi .95 .40
**680** A143 45c multicolored 1.10 .50
**681** A143 50c orange & multi 1.25 .50
**682** A143 55c magenta & multi 1.60 .85
**683** A143 60c multicolored 1.75 1.10
**684** A143 70c red org & multi 2.10 1.25
**685** A143 90c brt vio & multi 2.75 1.40
**686** A143 $1 multicolored 3.25 1.90
**687** A143 $2 orange & multi 6.25 3.25
**688** A143 $3 multicolored 10.50 5.00
**689** A143 $5 multicolored 17.00 8.25
*Nos. 672-689 (18)* 52.50 27.00

Wicker Furniture A144

Designs: Various wicker baskets, wall hangings, dinnerware.

**1974, Jan. 31 Photo. *Perf. 11½***
**Granite Paper**

**690** A144 5c violet bl & multi .25 .25
**691** A144 10c violet bl & multi .30 .30
**692** A144 30c violet bl & multi .90 .90
**693** A144 50c violet bl & multi 1.40 1.40
**694** A144 60c violet bl & multi 1.75 1.75
*Nos. 690-694 (5)* 4.60 4.60

Cow, Calf, Syringe — A145

Designs: 15c, Inoculation of cattle. 20c, Bullock and syringe. 50c, Laboratory technician, cow's head, syringe. 60c, Map of Ethiopia, cattle, syringe.

**1974, Feb. 20 Litho. *Perf. 13½x13***

**695** A145 5c sepia & multi .25 .25
**696** A145 15c ultra & multi .40 .40
**697** A145 20c ultra & multi .50 .50
**698** A145 50c orange & multi 1.40 1.40
**699** A145 60c gold & multi 1.75 1.75
*Nos. 695-699 (5)* 4.30 4.30

Campaign against cattle plague.

Umbrella Makers A146

Designs: 30c, Weaving. 50c, Child care. 60c, Foundation headquarters.

**1974, Apr. 17 Photo. *Perf. 14½***

**700** A146 10c lt lilac & multi .30 .30
**701** A146 30c multicolored .45 .45
**702** A146 50c multicolored 1.10 1.10
**703** A146 60c blue & multi 1.25 1.25
*Nos. 700-703 (4)* 3.10 3.10

20th anniv. of Haile Selassie Foundation.

Ceremonial Robe — A147

Designs: Ceremonial robes.

**1974, June 26 Litho. *Perf. 13***

**704** A147 15c multicolored .40 .40
**705** A147 25c ocher & multi .60 .60
**706** A147 35c green & multi 1.10 1.10
**707** A147 40c lt brown & multi 1.25 1.25
**708** A147 60c gray & multi 2.50 2.50
*Nos. 704-708 (5)* 5.85 5.85

World Population Statistics — A148

Designs: 50c, "Larger families-lower living standard." 60c, Rising population graph.

**1974, Aug. 19 Photo. *Perf. 14½***

**709** A148 40c yellow & multi 1.10 1.10
**710** A148 50c violet & multi 1.25 1.25
**711** A148 60c green & multi 1.50 1.50
*Nos. 709-711 (3)* 3.85 3.85

World Population Year 1974.

UPU Emblem, Letter Carrier's Staff — A149

UPU Emblem and: 50c, Letters and flags. 60c, Globe. 70c, Headquarters, Bern.

**1974, Oct. 9 Photo. *Perf. 11½***
**Granite Paper**

**712** A149 15c yellow & multi .50 .30
**713** A149 50c multicolored 1.35 .85
**714** A149 60c ultra & multi 1.75 1.10
**715** A149 70c multicolored 2.00 1.25
*Nos. 712-715 (4)* 5.60 3.50

Centenary of Universal Postal Union.

Celebration Around "Damara" Pillar — A150

5c, Site of Gishen Mariam Monastery. 20c, Cross and festivities. 80c, Torch (Chibos) Parade.

**1974, Dec. 17 Photo. *Perf. 14x14½***

**716** A150 5c yellow & multi .40 .40
**717** A150 10c yellow & multi .45 .45
**718** A150 20c yellow & multi .55 .55
**719** A150 80c yellow & multi 2.25 2.25
*Nos. 716-719 (4)* 3.65 3.65

Meskel Festival, Sept. 26-27, commemorating the finding in the 4th century of the True Cross, of which a fragment is kept at Gishen Mariam Monastery in Welo Province.

Precis Clelia — A151

Butterflies: 25c, Charaxes achaemenes. 45c, Papilio dardanus. 50c, Charaxes druceanus. 60c, Papilio demodocus.

**1975, Feb. 18 Photo. *Perf. 12x12½***

**720** A151 10c silver & multi 1.00 .35
**721** A151 25c gold & multi 1.50 .75
**722** A151 45c purple & multi 3.00 1.75
**723** A151 50c green & multi 3.50 2.50
**724** A151 60c brt blue & multi 5.00 3.00
*Nos. 720-724 (5)* 14.00 8.35

Adoration of the Kings — A152

10c, Baptism of Jesus. 15c, Jesus teaching in the Temple. 30c, Jesus giving sight to the blind. 40c, Crucifixion. 80c, Resurrection.

**Granite Paper**

**1975, Apr. 23 Photo. *Perf. 11½***

| | | | | |
|---|---|---|---|---|
| **725** | A152 | 5c brown & multi | .35 | .35 |
| **726** | A152 | 10c black & multi | .40 | .40 |
| **727** | A152 | 15c dk brown & multi | .45 | .45 |
| **728** | A152 | 30c dk brown & multi | .70 | .70 |
| **729** | A152 | 40c black & multi | 1.25 | 1.25 |
| **730** | A152 | 80c slate & multi | 2.40 | 2.40 |
| | | *Nos. 725-730 (6)* | 5.55 | 5.55 |

Murals from Ethiopian churches.

Wild Animals A153

**1975, May 27 Photo. *Perf. 11½***

**Granite Paper**

| | | | | |
|---|---|---|---|---|
| **731** | A153 | 5c Warthog | .75 | .75 |
| **732** | A153 | 10c Aardvark | .75 | .75 |
| **733** | A153 | 20c Semien wolf | 1.10 | 1.10 |
| **734** | A153 | 40c Gelada baboon | 2.10 | 2.10 |
| **735** | A153 | 80c Civet | 4.25 | 4.25 |
| | | *Nos. 731-735 (5)* | 8.95 | 8.95 |

"Peace," Dove, Globe, IWY Emblem — A154

50c, Symbols of development. 90c, Equality between men and women.

**1975, June 30 Litho. *Perf. 14x14½***

| | | | | |
|---|---|---|---|---|
| **736** | A154 | 40c blue & black | .70 | .70 |
| **737** | A154 | 50c salmon & multi | .90 | .90 |
| **738** | A154 | 90c multicolored | 1.75 | 1.75 |
| | | *Nos. 736-738 (3)* | 3.35 | 3.35 |

International Women's Year 1975.

Postal Museum A155

Various interior views of Postal Museum.

**1975, Aug. 19 Photo. *Perf. 13x12½***

| | | | | |
|---|---|---|---|---|
| **739** | A155 | 10c ocher & multi | .35 | .30 |
| **740** | A155 | 30c pink & multi | .65 | .50 |
| **741** | A155 | 60c multicolored | 1.50 | 1.10 |
| **742** | A155 | 70c lt green & multi | 1.75 | 1.25 |
| | | *Nos. 739-742 (4)* | 4.25 | 3.15 |

Ethiopian Natl. Postal Museum, opening.

Map of Ethiopia and Sun — A156

**1975, Sept. 11 Photo. *Perf. 11½***

**Granite Paper**

| | | | | |
|---|---|---|---|---|
| **743** | A156 | 5c lilac & multi | .25 | .25 |
| **744** | A156 | 10c ultra & multi | .25 | .25 |
| **745** | A156 | 25c brown & multi | .35 | .35 |
| **746** | A156 | 50c yellow & multi | .90 | .90 |
| **747** | A156 | 90c brt green & multi | 1.75 | 1.75 |
| | | *Nos. 743-747 (5)* | 3.50 | 3.50 |

1st anniv. of Ethiopian revolution.

UN Emblem A157

**1975, Oct. 24 Photo. *Perf. 11½***

| | | | | |
|---|---|---|---|---|
| **748** | A157 | 40c lilac & multi | .90 | .90 |
| **749** | A157 | 50c multicolored | 1.00 | 1.00 |
| **750** | A157 | 90c blue & multi | 2.00 | 2.00 |
| | | *Nos. 748-750 (3)* | 3.90 | 3.90 |

United Nations, 30th anniversary.

Regional Hair Styles — A158

**1975, Dec. 15 Photo. *Perf. 11½***

| | | | | |
|---|---|---|---|---|
| **751** | A158 | 5c Ilubabor | .30 | .30 |
| **752** | A158 | 15c Arusi | .40 | .40 |
| **753** | A158 | 20c Eritrea | .60 | .60 |
| **754** | A158 | 30c Bale | .85 | .85 |
| **755** | A158 | 35c Kefa | 1.00 | 1.00 |
| **756** | A158 | 50c Begemir | 1.40 | 1.40 |
| **757** | A158 | 60c Shoa | 1.75 | 1.75 |
| | | *Nos. 751-757 (7)* | 6.30 | 6.30 |

See Nos. 832-838.

Delphinium Wellbyi — A159

Flowers: 10c, Plectocephalus varians. 20c, Brachystelma asmarensis, horiz. 40c, Ceropegia inflata. 80c, Erythrina brucei.

**1976, Jan. 15 Photo. *Perf. 11½***

| | | | | |
|---|---|---|---|---|
| **758** | A159 | 5c multicolored | .35 | .35 |
| **759** | A159 | 10c multicolored | .40 | .40 |
| **760** | A159 | 20c multicolored | .60 | .60 |
| **761** | A159 | 40c multicolored | 1.50 | 1.50 |
| **762** | A159 | 80c multicolored | 2.50 | 2.50 |
| | | *Nos. 758-762 (5)* | 5.35 | 5.35 |

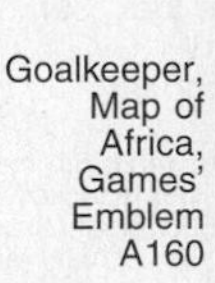

Goalkeeper, Map of Africa, Games' Emblem A160

Designs: Various scenes from soccer, map of Africa and ball.

**1976, Feb. 27 Photo. *Perf. 14½***

| | | | | |
|---|---|---|---|---|
| **763** | A160 | 5c orange & multi | .25 | .25 |
| **764** | A160 | 10c yellow & multi | .35 | .35 |
| **765** | A160 | 25c lilac & multi | .70 | .70 |
| **766** | A160 | 50c green & multi | 1.50 | 1.50 |
| **767** | A160 | 90c brt grn & multi | 3.00 | 3.00 |
| | | *Nos. 763-767 (5)* | 5.80 | 5.80 |

10th African Cup of Nations, Addis Ababa and Dire Dawa, Feb. 29-Mar. 14.

Telephones, 1876 and 1976 — A161

Designs: 60c, Alexander Graham Bell. 90c, Transmission tower.

**1976, Mar. 10 Litho. *Perf. 12x13½***

| | | | | |
|---|---|---|---|---|
| **768** | A161 | 30c lt ocher & multi | .85 | .75 |
| **769** | A161 | 60c emerald & multi | 1.75 | 1.25 |
| **770** | A161 | 90c ver, blk & buff | 2.75 | 2.00 |
| | | *Nos. 768-770 (3)* | 5.35 | 4.00 |

Centenary of first telephone call by Alexander Graham Bell, Mar. 10, 1876.

Ethiopian Jewelry — A162

Designs: Women wearing various kinds of Ethiopian jewelry.

**Granite Paper**

**1976, May 14 Photo. *Perf. 11½***

| | | | | |
|---|---|---|---|---|
| **771** | A162 | 5c blue & multi | .25 | .25 |
| **772** | A162 | 10c plum & multi | .35 | .25 |
| **773** | A162 | 20c gray & multi | .75 | .50 |
| **774** | A162 | 40c green & multi | 1.25 | .90 |
| **775** | A162 | 80c orange & multi | 2.50 | 1.75 |
| | | *Nos. 771-775 (5)* | 5.10 | 3.65 |

Boxing — A163

Designs (Montreal Olympic Emblem and): 80c, Runner and maple leaf. 90c, Bicycling.

**1976, July 15 Litho. *Perf. 12½x12***

| | | | | |
|---|---|---|---|---|
| **776** | A163 | 10c multicolored | .50 | .40 |
| **777** | A163 | 80c brt red, blk & grn | 2.25 | 1.75 |
| **778** | A163 | 90c brt red & multi | 2.75 | 2.00 |
| | | *Nos. 776-778 (3)* | 5.50 | 4.15 |

21st Olympic Games, Montreal, Canada, July 17-Aug. 1.

Hands Holding Map of Ethiopia — A164

**1976, Aug. 5 Photo. *Perf. 14½***

| | | | | |
|---|---|---|---|---|
| **779** | A164 | 5c rose & multi | .25 | .25 |
| **780** | A164 | 10c olive & multi | .30 | .25 |
| **781** | A164 | 25c orange & multi | .40 | .30 |
| **782** | A164 | 50c multicolored | .95 | .70 |
| **783** | A164 | 90c dk blue & multi | 1.75 | 1.40 |
| | | *Nos. 779-783 (5)* | 3.65 | 2.90 |

Development through cooperation.

Revolution Emblem: Eye and Map A165

**1976, Sept. 9 Photo. *Perf. 13½***

| | | | | |
|---|---|---|---|---|
| **784** | A165 | 5c multicolored | .25 | .25 |
| **785** | A165 | 10c multicolored | .30 | .25 |
| **786** | A165 | 25c multicolored | .40 | .30 |
| **787** | A165 | 50c yellow & multi | .95 | .70 |
| **788** | A165 | 90c green & multi | 1.60 | 1.25 |
| | | *Nos. 784-788 (5)* | 3.50 | 2.75 |

2nd anniversary of the revolution.

Sunburst Around Crest — A166

**1976, Sept. 13 Photo. *Perf. 11½***

| | | | | |
|---|---|---|---|---|
| **789** | A166 | 5c green, gold & blk | .25 | .25 |
| **790** | A166 | 10c org, gold & blk | .25 | .25 |
| **791** | A166 | 15c grnsh bl, gold & blk | .40 | .25 |
| **792** | A166 | 20c lilac, gold & blk | .50 | .25 |
| **793** | A166 | 25c brt grn, gold & blk | .60 | .25 |
| **794** | A166 | 30c car, gold & blk | .75 | .25 |
| **795** | A166 | 35c yel, gold & blk | .90 | .25 |
| **796** | A166 | 40c ol, gold & blk | 1.00 | .40 |
| **797** | A166 | 45c brt grn, gold & blk | 1.10 | .50 |
| **798** | A166 | 50c car rose, gold & blk | 1.25 | .70 |
| **799** | A166 | 55c ultra, gold & blk | 1.50 | .90 |
| **800** | A166 | 60c fawn, gold & blk | 1.75 | .90 |
| **801** | A166 | 70c rose, gold & blk | 2.00 | .90 |
| **802** | A166 | 90c blue, gold & blk | 2.25 | .90 |
| **803** | A166 | $1 dull grn, gold & blk | 2.75 | 1.00 |
| **804** | A166 | $2 gray, gold & blk | 6.00 | 2.00 |
| **805** | A166 | $3 brn vio, gold & blk | 8.00 | 3.25 |
| **806** | A166 | $5 slate bl, gold & blk | 12.00 | 5.00 |
| | | *Nos. 789-806 (18)* | 43.25 | 18.20 |

**Denomination Expressed as "BIRR"**

**1983, June 16**

| | | | | |
|---|---|---|---|---|
| **806A** | A166 | 1b dull grn, gold & blk | 15.00 | 2.25 |
| **806B** | A166 | 2b gray, gold & blk | 37.50 | 4.50 |
| **806C** | A166 | 3b brn vio, gold & blk | 45.00 | 6.25 |

Plane Over Man with Donkey — A167

10c, Globe showing routes. 25c, Crew and passengers forming star. 50c, Propeller and jet engine. 90c, Airplanes surrounding map of Ethiopia.

**1976, Oct. 28 Litho. *Perf. 12x12½***

| | | | | |
|---|---|---|---|---|
| **807** | A167 | 5c dull bl & multi | .40 | .30 |
| **808** | A167 | 10c lilac & multi | .50 | .35 |
| **809** | A167 | 25c multicolored | .70 | .50 |
| **810** | A167 | 50c orange & multi | 1.40 | 1.25 |
| **811** | A167 | 90c olive & multi | 2.75 | 2.25 |
| | | *Nos. 807-811 (5)* | 5.75 | 4.65 |

Ethiopian Airlines, 30th anniversary.

Tortoises — A168

Reptiles: 20c, Chameleon. 30c, Python. 40c, Monitor lizard. 80c, Nile crocodiles.

**1976, Dec. 15 Photo. *Perf. 14½***

| | | | | |
|---|---|---|---|---|
| **812** | A168 | 10c multicolored | .50 | .40 |
| **813** | A168 | 20c multicolored | .75 | .50 |
| **814** | A168 | 30c multicolored | 1.00 | .80 |
| **815** | A168 | 40c multicolored | 1.50 | 1.10 |
| **816** | A168 | 80c multicolored | 3.00 | 2.25 |
| | | *Nos. 812-816 (5)* | 6.75 | 5.05 |

Hand Holding Makeshift Hammer — A169

Designs: 5c, Hands holding bowl and plane dropping food. 45c, Infant with empty bowl, and bank note. 60c, Map of affected area, footprints and tire tracks. 80c, Film strip, camera and Ethiopian sitting between eggshells.

**1977, Jan. 20 Litho. *Perf. 12½***

| | | | | |
|---|---|---|---|---|
| **817** | A169 | 5c multicolored | .30 | .25 |
| **818** | A169 | 10c multicolored | .45 | .40 |
| **819** | A169 | 45c multicolored | 1.25 | .85 |
| **820** | A169 | 60c multicolored | 1.75 | 1.00 |
| **821** | A169 | 80c multicolored | 1.90 | 1.60 |
| | | *Nos. 817-821 (5)* | 5.65 | 4.10 |

Ethiopian Relief and Rehabilitation Commission for drought and disaster areas.

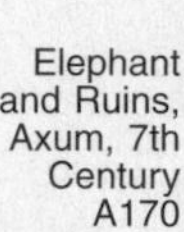

Elephant and Ruins, Axum, 7th Century A170

Designs: 10c, Ibex and temple, 5th century, B.C., Yeha. 25c, Megalithic dolmen and pottery, Sourre Kabanawa. 50c, Awash Valley, stone axe, Acheulean period. 80c, Omo Valley, hominid jawbone.

**1977, Mar. 15 Photo. *Perf. 13½***

| | | | | |
|---|---|---|---|---|
| **822** | A170 | 5c gold & multi | .50 | .35 |
| **823** | A170 | 10c gold & multi | .60 | .45 |
| **824** | A170 | 25c gold & multi | .75 | .65 |
| **825** | A170 | 50c gold & multi | 1.25 | 1.10 |
| **826** | A170 | 80c gold & multi | 2.25 | 1.50 |
| | | *Nos. 822-826 (5)* | 5.35 | 4.05 |

Archaeological sites and finds in Ethiopia.

Map of Africa with Trans-East Highway — A171

**1977, Mar. 30 *Perf. 14***

| | | | | |
|---|---|---|---|---|
| **827** | A171 | 10c gold & multi | .40 | .35 |
| **828** | A171 | 20c gold & multi | .50 | .40 |
| **829** | A171 | 40c gold & multi | 1.25 | .80 |
| **830** | A171 | 50c gold & multi | 1.50 | 1.00 |
| **831** | A171 | 60c gold & multi | 1.90 | 1.25 |
| | | *Nos. 827-831 (5)* | 5.55 | 3.80 |

Addis Ababa to Nairobi Highway and projected highways to Cairo, Egypt, and Gaborone, Botswana.

**Hairstyle Type of 1975**

**1977, Apr. 28 Photo. *Perf. 11½***

| | | | | |
|---|---|---|---|---|
| **832** | A158 | 5c Welega | .25 | .25 |
| **833** | A158 | 10c Gojam | .30 | .25 |
| **834** | A158 | 15c Tigre | .40 | .35 |
| **835** | A158 | 20c Harar | .70 | .65 |
| **836** | A158 | 25c Gemu Gefa | .85 | .70 |
| **837** | A158 | 40c Sidamo | 1.40 | 1.25 |
| **838** | A158 | 50c Welo | 1.75 | 1.50 |
| | | *Nos. 832-838 (7)* | 5.65 | 4.95 |

Addis Ababa A172

Towns of Ethiopia: 10c, Asmara. 25c, Harar. 50c, Jima. 90c, Dese.

**1977, June 20 Photo. *Perf. 14½***

| | | | | |
|---|---|---|---|---|
| **839** | A172 | 5c silver & multi | .30 | .25 |
| **840** | A172 | 10c silver & multi | .40 | .35 |
| **841** | A172 | 25c silver & multi | .60 | .55 |
| **842** | A172 | 50c silver & multi | 1.25 | 1.00 |
| **843** | A172 | 90c silver & multi | 2.25 | 1.50 |
| | | *Nos. 839-843 (5)* | 4.80 | 3.65 |

Terebratula Abyssinica A173

Fossil Shells: 10c, Terebratula subalata. 25c, Cuculloea lefeburiaua. 50c, Ostrea plicatissima. 90c, Trigonia cousobrina.

**1977, Aug. 15 Photo. *Perf. 14x13½***

| | | | | |
|---|---|---|---|---|
| **844** | A173 | 5c multicolored | .75 | .25 |
| **845** | A173 | 10c multicolored | 1.25 | .50 |
| **846** | A173 | 25c multicolored | 1.50 | .85 |
| **847** | A173 | 50c multicolored | 2.50 | 1.50 |
| **848** | A173 | 90c multicolored | 4.00 | 2.50 |
| | | *Nos. 844-848 (5)* | 10.00 | 5.60 |

Fractured Imperial Crown — A174

Designs: 10c, Symbol of the Revolution (spade, axe, torch). 25c, Warriors, hammer and sickle, map of Ethiopia. 60c, Soldier, farmer and map. 80c, Map and emblem of revolutionary government.

**1977, Sept. 9 Litho. *Perf. 15***

| | | | | |
|---|---|---|---|---|
| **849** | A174 | 5c multicolored | .25 | .25 |
| **850** | A174 | 10c multicolored | .40 | .35 |
| **851** | A174 | 25c multicolored | .50 | .45 |
| **852** | A174 | 60c multicolored | 1.25 | 1.00 |
| **853** | A174 | 80c multicolored | 1.50 | 1.25 |
| | | *Nos. 849-853 (5)* | 3.90 | 3.30 |

Third anniversary of the revolution.

Cicindela Petitii — A175

Insects: 10c, Heliocopris dillonii. 25c, Poekilocerus vignaudii. 50c, Pepsis heros. 90c, Pepsis dedjaz.

**1977, Sept. 30 Photo. *Perf. 14x13½***

| | | | | |
|---|---|---|---|---|
| **854** | A175 | 5c multicolored | .40 | .40 |
| **855** | A175 | 10c multicolored | .50 | .50 |
| **856** | A175 | 25c multicolored | 1.00 | 1.00 |
| **857** | A175 | 50c multicolored | 2.50 | 2.50 |
| **858** | A175 | 90c multicolored | 3.75 | 3.75 |
| | | *Nos. 854-858 (5)* | 8.15 | 8.15 |

Lenin, Globe, Map of Ethiopia and Emblem — A176

**1977, Nov. 15 Litho. *Perf. 12***

| | | | | |
|---|---|---|---|---|
| **859** | A176 | 5c orange & multi | .40 | .25 |
| **860** | A176 | 10c multicolored | .45 | .35 |
| **861** | A176 | 25c salmon & multi | .50 | .40 |
| **862** | A176 | 50c lt blue & multi | 1.00 | .85 |
| **863** | A176 | 90c yellow & multi | 1.75 | 1.25 |
| | | *Nos. 859-863 (5)* | 4.10 | 3.10 |

60th anniv. of Russian October Revolution.

Chondrostoma Dilloni — A177

Salt-water Fish: 10c, Ostracion cubicus. 25c, Serranus summana. 50c, Serranus luti. 90c, Tetraodon maculatus.

**1978, Jan. 20 Litho. *Perf. 15½***

| | | | | |
|---|---|---|---|---|
| **864** | A177 | 5c multicolored | .65 | .65 |
| **865** | A177 | 10c multicolored | .75 | .75 |
| **866** | A177 | 25c multicolored | 1.25 | 1.25 |
| **867** | A177 | 50c multicolored | 2.25 | 2.25 |
| **868** | A177 | 90c multicolored | 4.00 | 4.00 |
| | | *Nos. 864-868 (5)* | 8.90 | 8.90 |

Domestic Animals — A178

**1978, Mar. 27 Litho. *Perf. 13½x14***

| | | | | |
|---|---|---|---|---|
| **869** | A178 | 5c Cattle | .25 | .25 |
| **870** | A178 | 10c Mules | .40 | .25 |
| **871** | A178 | 25c Goats | .75 | .55 |
| **872** | A178 | 50c Dromedaries | 1.50 | 1.25 |
| **873** | A178 | 90c Horses | 2.75 | 2.25 |
| | | *Nos. 869-873 (5)* | 5.65 | 4.55 |

Weapons and Shield, Map of Ethiopia — A179

"Call of the Motherland." (Map of Ethiopia and): 10c, Civilian fighters. 25c, Map of Africa. 60c, Soldiers. 80c, Red Cross nurse and wounded man.

**1978, May 13 Litho. *Perf. 15½***

| | | | | |
|---|---|---|---|---|
| **874** | A179 | 5c multicolored | .30 | .25 |
| **875** | A179 | 10c multicolored | .40 | .35 |
| **876** | A179 | 25c multicolored | .70 | .60 |
| **877** | A179 | 60c multicolored | 1.25 | 1.00 |
| **878** | A179 | 80c multicolored | 2.25 | 1.50 |
| | | *Nos. 874-878 (5)* | 4.90 | 3.70 |

Bronze Ibex, 5th Century B.C. — A180

Ancient Bronzes: 10c, Lion, Yeha, 5th cent. B.C., horiz. 25c, Lamp with ibex attacked by dog, Matara, 1st cent. B.C. 50c, Goat, Axum, 3rd cent. A.D., horiz. 90c, Ax, chisel and sickle, Yeha, 5th-4th centuries B.C.

**1978, June 21 Litho. *Perf. 15½***

| | | | | |
|---|---|---|---|---|
| **879** | A180 | 5c multicolored | .25 | .25 |
| **880** | A180 | 10c multicolored | .35 | .30 |
| **881** | A180 | 25c multicolored | .60 | .50 |
| **882** | A180 | 50c multicolored | 1.50 | 1.25 |
| **883** | A180 | 90c multicolored | 2.50 | 1.75 |
| | | *Nos. 879-883 (5)* | 5.20 | 4.05 |

See Nos. 1024-1027.

Globe and Argentina '78 Emblem A181

20c, Soccer player kicking ball. 30c, Two players embracing, net and ball. 55c, World map and ball. 70c, Soccer field, vert.

***Perf. 14x13½, 13½x14***

**1978, July 19 Litho.**

| | | | | |
|---|---|---|---|---|
| **884** | A181 | 5c multicolored | .45 | .40 |
| **885** | A181 | 20c multicolored | .70 | .50 |
| **886** | A181 | 30c multicolored | 1.00 | .65 |
| **887** | A181 | 55c multicolored | 1.75 | 1.25 |
| **888** | A181 | 70c multicolored | 2.25 | 1.75 |
| | | *Nos. 884-888 (5)* | 6.15 | 4.55 |

11th World Cup Soccer Championship, Argentina, June 1-25.

Map of Africa, Oppressed African — A182

Namibia Day: 10c, Policeman pointing gun. 25c, Sniper with gun. 60c, African caught in net. 80c, Head of free man.

**1978, Aug. 25 *Perf. 12½x13½***

| | | | | |
|---|---|---|---|---|
| **889** | A182 | 5c multicolored | .30 | .25 |
| **890** | A182 | 10c multicolored | .50 | .45 |
| **891** | A182 | 25c multicolored | .60 | .50 |
| **892** | A182 | 60c multicolored | 1.50 | 1.00 |
| **893** | A182 | 80c multicolored | 2.25 | 1.50 |
| | | *Nos. 889-893 (5)* | 5.15 | 3.70 |

Soldiers, Guerrilla and Jets A183

Design: 1b, People looking toward sun, crushing snake, flags.

**1978, Sept. 8 Photo. *Perf. 14***

| | | | | |
|---|---|---|---|---|
| **894** | A183 | 80c multicolored | 1.75 | 1.25 |
| **895** | A183 | 1b multicolored | 2.50 | 1.75 |

4th anniversary of revolution.

Hand and Globe with Tools — A184

Designs: 15c, Symbols of energy, communications, education, medicine, agriculture and industry. 25c, Cogwheels and world map. 60c, Globe and hands passing wrench. 70c, Flying geese and turtle over globe.

**1978, Nov. 14 Litho. *Perf. 12x12½***

| | | | | |
|---|---|---|---|---|
| **896** | A184 | 10c multicolored | .30 | .25 |
| **897** | A184 | 15c multicolored | .35 | .30 |
| **898** | A184 | 25c multicolored | .55 | .50 |
| **899** | A184 | 60c multicolored | 1.40 | 1.00 |
| **900** | A184 | 70c multicolored | 1.75 | 1.25 |
| | | *Nos. 896-900 (5)* | 4.35 | 3.30 |

Technical Cooperation Among Developing Countries Conference, Buenos Aires, Argentina, Sept. 1978.

Human Rights Emblem — A185

**1978, Dec. 7 Photo. *Perf. 12½x13½***

| | | | | |
|---|---|---|---|---|
| **901** | A185 | 5c multicolored | .30 | .25 |
| **902** | A185 | 15c multicolored | .30 | .25 |
| **903** | A185 | 25c multicolored | .45 | .40 |
| **904** | A185 | 35c multicolored | .75 | .70 |
| **905** | A185 | 1b multicolored | 2.25 | 1.75 |
| | | *Nos. 901-905 (5)* | 4.05 | 3.35 |

Declaration of Human Rights, 30th anniv.

Broken Chain, Anti-Apartheid Emblem — A186

**1978, Dec. 28 Litho. *Perf. 12½x12***

**906** A186 5c multicolored .30 .25
**907** A186 20c multicolored .45 .40
**908** A186 30c multicolored .75 .65
**909** A186 55c multicolored 1.25 1.00
**910** A186 70c multicolored 1.50 1.25
*Nos. 906-910 (5)* 4.25 3.55

Anti-Apartheid Year.

Stele from Osole — A187

Ancient Carved Stones, Soddo Region: 10c, Anthropomorphous stele, Gorashino. 25c, Leaning stone, Wado. 60c, Round stones, Ambeut. 80c, Bas-relief, Tiya.

**1979, Jan. 25 *Perf. 14***

**911** A187 5c multicolored .30 .25
**912** A187 10c multicolored .40 .30
**913** A187 25c multicolored .65 .50
**914** A187 60c multicolored 1.75 1.25
**915** A187 80c multicolored 2.25 1.75
*Nos. 911-915 (5)* 5.35 4.05

Cotton Plantation A188

Shemma Industry: 10c, Women spinning cotton yarn. 20c, Man reeling cotton. 65c, Weaver. 80c, Shemma (Natl. dress).

**1979, Mar. 15 Litho. *Perf. 15½***

**916** A188 5c multicolored .40 .25
**917** A188 10c multicolored .45 .35
**918** A188 20c multicolored .60 .40
**919** A188 65c multicolored 1.75 1.25
**920** A188 80c multicolored 2.25 1.50
*Nos. 916-920 (5)* 5.45 3.75

Ethiopian Trees — A189

**1979, Apr. 26 Photo. *Perf. 13½x14***

**921** A189 5c Grar .35 .25
**922** A189 10c Weira .45 .30
**923** A189 25c Tidh .65 .40
**924** A189 50c Shola 1.25 1.00
**925** A189 90c Zigba 2.00 1.50
*Nos. 921-925 (5)* 4.70 3.45

Agricultural Development A190

Revolutionary Development Campaign: 15c, Industry. 25c, Transportation and communication. 60c, Education and health. 70c, Commerce.

**1979, July 3 Litho. *Perf. 12x12½***

**926** A190 10c multicolored .30 .25
**927** A190 15c multicolored .45 .30
**928** A190 25c multicolored .60 .50
**929** A190 60c multicolored 1.25 1.00
**930** A190 70c multicolored 1.75 1.50
*Nos. 926-930 (5)* 4.35 3.55

IYC Emblem — A191

Intl. Year of the Child: 15c, Adults leading children. 25c, Adult helping child. 60c, IYC emblem surrounded by children. 70c, Adult and children embracing.

**1979, Aug. 16 Litho. *Perf. 12x12½***

**931** A191 10c multicolored .40 .35
**932** A191 15c multicolored .50 .40
**933** A191 25c multicolored .75 .65
**934** A191 60c multicolored 1.75 1.40
**935** A191 70c multicolored 2.00 1.75
*Nos. 931-935 (5)* 5.40 4.55

Guerrilla Fighters — A192

15c, Soldiers. 25c, Map of Africa within cog-wheel, star. 60c, Students with book, torch. 70c, Family, hammer & sickle emblem.

**1979, Sept. 11 Photo. *Perf. 14***

**936** A192 10c multicolored .40 .35
**937** A192 15c multicolored .50 .45
**938** A192 25c multicolored .75 .65
**939** A192 60c multicolored 1.75 1.25
**940** A192 70c multicolored 2.25 1.75
*Nos. 936-940 (5)* 5.65 4.45

Fifth anniversary of revolution.

Telephone Receiver — A193

Telecom Emblem and: 5c, Symbolic waves. 35c, Satellite beaming to earth. 45c, Dish antenna. 65c, Television cameraman.

**1979, Sept. 20 Photo. *Perf. 11½***

**941** A193 5c multicolored .35 .30
**942** A193 30c multicolored .75 .60
**943** A193 35c multicolored .95 .75
**944** A193 45c multicolored 1.50 1.00
**945** A193 65c multicolored 2.25 1.50
*Nos. 941-945 (5)* 5.80 4.15

3rd World Telecommunications Exhibition, Geneva, Sept. 20-26.

Incense Container — A194

**1979, Nov. 15 Litho. *Perf. 15***

**946** A194 5c shown .45 .30
**947** A194 10c Vase .85 .45
**948** A194 25c Earthenware cover 1.25 .75
**949** A194 60c Milk container 3.25 1.25
**950** A194 80c Storage container 3.75 1.75
*Nos. 946-950 (5)* 9.55 4.50

Wooden Grain Bowl — A195

**1980, Jan. 3 Litho. *Perf. 13½x13***

**951** A195 5c shown .50 .35
**952** A195 30c Chair, stool .90 .50
**953** A195 35c Mortar, pestle 1.00 .75
**954** A195 45c Buckets 1.75 1.25
**955** A195 65c Storage jars 2.75 2.00
*Nos. 951-955 (5)* 6.90 4.85

Lappet-faced Vulture — A196

Birds of Prey: 15c, Long-crested hawk eagle. 25c, Secretary bird. 60c, Abyssinian long-eared owl. 70c, Lanner falcon.

**1980, Feb. 12 *Perf. 13½x14***

**956** A196 10c multicolored 1.25 1.25
**957** A196 15c multicolored 1.50 1.50
**958** A196 25c multicolored 2.25 2.25
**959** A196 60c multicolored 4.00 4.00
**960** A196 70c multicolored 6.00 6.00
*Nos. 956-960 (5)* 15.00 15.00

Fight Against Cigarette Smoking — A197

**1980, Apr. 7 Photo. *Perf. 13x13½***

**961** A197 20c shown 1.25 1.00
**962** A197 60c Cigarette 1.75 1.25
**963** A197 1b Respiratory system 3.00 2.50
*Nos. 961-963 (3)* 6.00 4.75

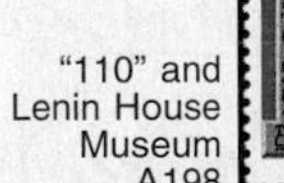

"110" and Lenin House Museum A198

Lenin, 110th "Birthday" (Paintings): 15c, In hiding. 20c, As a young man. 40c, Returning to Russia. 1b, Speaking on the Goelro Plan.

**1980, Apr. 22 Litho. *Perf. 12x12½***

**964** A198 5c multicolored .35 .30
**965** A198 15c multicolored .40 .35
**966** A198 20c multicolored .50 .45
**967** A198 40c multicolored 1.20 .80
**968** A198 1b multicolored 2.50 2.00
*Nos. 964-968 (5)* 4.95 3.90

Grévy's Zebras A199

**1980, June 10 Litho. *Perf. 12½x12***

**969** A199 10c shown .75 .75
**970** A199 15c Gazelles 1.00 1.00
**971** A199 25c Wild hunting dogs 1.50 1.50
**972** A199 60c Swayne's hartebeests 2.75 2.75
**973** A199 70c Cheetahs 6.00 6.00
*Nos. 969-973 (5)* 12.00 12.00

Runner, Moscow '80 Emblem — A200

**1980, July 19 Photo. *Perf. 11½x12***

**974** A200 30c shown 1.00 1.00
**975** A200 70c Cycling 2.25 2.25
**976** A200 80c Boxing 3.00 3.00
*Nos. 974-976 (3)* 6.25 6.25

22nd Summer Olympic Games, Moscow, July 19-Aug. 3.

Removing Blindfold — A201

40c, Revolutionary. 50c, Woman breaking chain. 70c, Russian & Ethiopian flags.

**1980, Sept. 10 Photo. *Perf. 14x13½***

**977** A201 30c shown .75 .50
**978** A201 40c multicolored 1.00 .65
**979** A201 50c multicolored 1.50 1.00
**980** A201 70c multicolored 2.25 1.25
*Nos. 977-980 (4)* 5.50 3.40

6th anniversary of revolution.

Bamboo Folk Craft — A202

**1980, Oct. 23 Litho. *Perf. 14***

**981** A202 5c Bamboo food basket .30 .25
**982** A202 15c Lamp shade .40 .35
**983** A202 25c Stool .75 .60
**984** A202 35c Fruit basket 1.25 1.00
**985** A202 1b Lamp shade 2.75 1.75
*Nos. 981-985 (5)* 5.45 3.95

Mekotkocha (Used in Weeding) A203

Traditional Harvesting Tools: 15c, Layda (grain separator). 40c, Mensh (fork). 45c, Mededekia (soil turner). 70c, Mofer & Kenber (plow and yoke).

**1980, Dec. 18 Litho. *Perf. 12½x12***

**986** A203 10c multicolored .30 .25
**987** A203 15c multicolored .35 .30
**988** A203 40c multicolored 2.00 .75
**989** A203 45c multicolored 2.25 1.00
**990** A203 70c multicolored 3.25 1.75
*Nos. 986-990 (5)* 8.15 4.05

Baro River Bridge Opening A204

**1981, Feb. 28 Photo. *Perf. 13½x13***

**991** A204 15c Canoes and ferry .50 .40
**992** A204 65c Bridge construction 2.75 1.25
**993** A204 1b shown 4.75 2.25
*Nos. 991-993 (3)* 8.00 3.90

Semien National Park — A205

World Heritage Year: 5c, Wawel Castle, Poland. 15c, Quito Cathedral, Ecuador. 20c, Old Slave Quarters, Goree Island, Senegal. 30c, Mesa Verde Indian Village, US. 1b, L'Anse aux Meadows excavation, Canada.

*Perf. 11x11½, 11½x11*

**1981, Mar. 10** **Photo.**

**994** A205 5c multicolored .40 .30
**995** A205 15c multicolored .55 .45
**996** A205 20c multicolored .70 .55
**997** A205 30c multicolored 1.40 .75
**998** A205 80c multicolored 3.50 1.50
**999** A205 1b multicolored 4.50 2.25
*Nos. 994-999 (6)* 11.05 5.80

**1981, June 16** **Photo.**

10c, Biet Medhanialem Church, Ethiopia. 15c, Nahanni Natl. Park, Canada. 20c, Yellowstone River Lower Falls, U.S. 30c, Aachen Cathedral, Germany. 80c, Kicker Rock, San Cristobal Island, Ecuador. 1b, The Lizak corridor, Holy Cross Chapel, Cracow, Poland.

**1000** A205 10c multi .45 .30
**1001** A205 15c multi .55 .45
**1002** A205 20c multi 1.00 .60
**1003** A205 30c multi 1.75 .80
**1004** A205 80c multi 4.50 2.25
**1005** A205 1b multi, vert. 5.50 2.75
*Nos. 1000-1005 (6)* 13.75 7.15

Ancient Drinking Vessel A206

**1981, May 5** **Litho.** ***Perf. 12½x12***

**1006** A206 20c shown .60 .30
**1007** A206 25c Spice container 1.00 .40
**1008** A206 35c Jug 1.25 .75
**1009** A206 40c Cooking pot holder 1.50 1.10
**1010** A206 60c Animal figurine 2.25 1.60
*Nos. 1006-1010 (5)* 6.60 4.15

Intl. Year of the Disabled — A207

**1981, July 16** **Photo.** ***Perf. 11½x12***

**1011** A207 5c Prostheses .50 .25
**1012** A207 15c Boys writing .50 .25
**1013** A207 20c Activities .75 .50
**1014** A207 40c Knitting 1.50 1.00
**1015** A207 1b Weaving 3.75 2.25
*Nos. 1011-1015 (5)* 7.00 4.25

7th Anniv. of Revolution A208

**1981, Sept. 10** ***Perf. 14***

**1016** A208 20c Children's Center .65 .35
**1017** A208 60c Heroes' Center 1.25 1.00
**1018** A208 1b Serto Ader (state newspaper) 2.25 1.75
*Nos. 1016-1018 (3)* 4.15 3.10

World Food Day — A209

**1981, Oct. 15** **Litho.** ***Perf. 13½x12½***

**1019** A209 5c Wheat airlift .25 .25
**1020** A209 15c Plowing .30 .25
**1021** A209 20c Malnutrition .70 .30
**1022** A209 40c Agriculture education 1.50 .70
**1023** A209 1b Cattle, corn 4.00 1.75
*Nos. 1019-1023 (5)* 6.75 3.25

**Ancient Bronze Type of 1978**

**1981, Dec. 15** **Litho.** ***Perf. 14x13½***

**1024** A180 15c Pitcher .35 .35
**1025** A180 45c Tsenatsil (musical instrument) 1.00 1.00
**1026** A180 50c Pitcher, diff. 1.25 1.25
**1027** A180 70c Pot 1.50 1.50
*Nos. 1024-1027 (4)* 4.10 4.10

Horn Artifacts — A210

**1982, Feb. 18** **Photo.** ***Perf. 12x12½***

**1028** A210 10c Tobacco containers .25 .25
**1029** A210 15c Cup .35 .30
**1030** A210 40c Container, diff. .90 .70
**1031** A210 45c Goblet 1.25 .95
**1032** A210 70c Spoons 1.75 1.25
*Nos. 1028-1032 (5)* 4.50 3.45

Coffee Cultivation A211

**1982, May, 6** **Photo.** ***Perf. 13½***

**1033** A211 5c Plants .25 .25
**1034** A211 15c Bushes .35 .30
**1035** A211 25c Mature bushes 1.25 1.10
**1036** A211 35c Picking beans 2.25 1.50
**1037** A211 1b Drinking coffee 2.25 1.75
*Nos. 1033-1037 (5)* 6.35 4.90

1982 World Cup — A212

Various soccer plays.

*Perf. 13½x12½*

**1982, June 10** **Litho.**

**1038** A212 5c multicolored .25 .25
**1039** A212 15c multicolored .40 .30
**1040** A212 20c multicolored .55 .50
**1041** A212 40c multicolored 1.25 1.10
**1042** A212 1b multicolored 2.50 2.25
*Nos. 1038-1042 (5)* 4.95 4.40

TB Bacillus Centenary A213

**1982, July 12** **Litho.** ***Perf. 13½x12½***

**1043** A213 15c Cow .50 .40
**1044** A213 20c Magnifying glass .60 .50
**1045** A213 30c Koch, microscope 1.00 .90
**1046** A213 35c Koch 1.25 1.00
**1047** A213 80c Man coughing 2.50 2.25
*Nos. 1043-1047 (5)* 5.85 5.05

8th Anniv. of Revolution — A214

Designs: Symbols of justice.

**1982, Sept. 10** ***Perf. 12½x13½***

**1048** A214 80c multicolored 2.00 1.50
**1049** A214 1b multicolored 2.25 1.75

World Standards Day — A215

**1982, Oct. 14** **Litho.** ***Perf. 13½x12½***

**1050** A215 5c Hand, foot, square .25 .25
**1051** A215 15c Scales .40 .30
**1052** A215 20c Rulers .50 .40
**1053** A215 40c Weights 1.00 .80
**1054** A215 1b Emblem 2.50 1.75
*Nos. 1050-1054 (5)* 4.65 3.50

10th Anniv. of UN Conference on Human Environment A216

5c, Wildlife conservation. 15c, Environmental health and settlement. 20c, Forest protection. 40c, Natl. literacy campaign. 1b, Soil and water conservation.

**1982, Dec. 13** **Litho.** ***Perf. 12***

**1055** A216 5c multicolored .25 .25
**1056** A216 15c multicolored .40 .35
**1057** A216 20c multicolored .60 .45
**1058** A216 40c multicolored 1.00 .90
**1059** A216 1b multicolored 3.00 2.00
*Nos. 1055-1059 (5)* 5.25 3.95

Cave of Sof Omar A217

Various views.

**1983, Feb. 10** **Photo.** ***Perf. 13½***

**1060** A217 5c multicolored .25 .25
**1061** A217 10c multicolored .30 .25
**1062** A217 15c multicolored .95 .35
**1063** A217 70c multicolored 2.00 1.10
**1064** A217 80c multicolored 2.25 1.50
*Nos. 1060-1064 (5)* 5.75 3.45

A218

**1983, Apr. 29** **Photo.** ***Perf. 14***

**1065** A218 80c multicolored 2.00 1.50
**1066** A218 1b multicolored 2.25 2.00

25th Anniv. of Economic Commission for Africa.

A219

*Perf. 12½x11½*

**1983, June 3** **Photo.**

**1067** A219 85c Emblem 1.60 1.25
**1068** A219 1b Lighthouse, ship 3.25 2.25

25th Anniv. of Intl. Maritime Org.

WCY — A220

**1983, July 22** **Litho.**

**1069** A220 25c UPU emblem .70 .60
**1070** A220 55c Dish antenna, emblems 2.25 2.10
**1071** A220 1b Bridge, tunnel 5.00 3.50
*Nos. 1069-1071 (3)* 7.95 6.20

9th Anniv. of Revolution — A221

**1983, Sept. 10** **Litho.** ***Perf. 14½***

**1072** A221 25c Dove .50 .40
**1073** A221 55c Star 1.40 1.00
**1074** A221 1b Emblems 2.00 1.60
*Nos. 1072-1074 (3)* 3.90 3.00

Musical Instruments — A222

**1983, Oct. 17** **Litho.** ***Perf. 12½x13½***

**1075** A222 5c Hura .25 .25
**1076** A222 15c Dinke .45 .40
**1077** A222 20c Meleket .75 .65
**1078** A222 40c Embilta 1.25 1.00
**1079** A222 1b Tom 2.75 2.00
*Nos. 1075-1079 (5)* 5.45 4.30

Charaxes Galawadiwosi A223

15c, Epiphora elianae. 55c, Batuana rougeoti. 1b, Achaea saboeareginae.

**1983, Dec. 13** **Photo.** ***Perf. 14***

**1080** A223 10c shown 1.25 1.00
**1081** A223 15c multicolored 1.75 1.50
**1082** A223 55c multicolored 4.75 3.00
**1083** A223 1b multicolored 9.00 7.50
*Nos. 1080-1083 (4)* 16.75 13.00

Intl. Anti-Apartheid Year (1983) — A224

*Perf. 13½x12½*

**1984, Feb. 10** **Litho.**

**1084** A224 5c multicolored .35 .30
**1085** A224 15c multicolored .55 .50
**1086** A224 20c multicolored .75 .65
**1087** A224 40c multicolored 1.25 1.00
**1088** A224 1b multicolored 2.50 2.00
*Nos. 1084-1088 (5)* 5.40 4.45

Local Flowers — A225

5c, Protea gaguedi. 25c, Sedum epidendrum. 50c, Echinops amplexicaulis. 1b, Canarina eminii.

**1984, Apr. 13** **Litho.** ***Perf. 13½***

**1089** A225 5c multi .30 .25
**1090** A225 25c multi 1.25 .90
**1091** A225 50c multi 2.50 1.75
**1092** A225 1b multi 5.00 3.25
*Nos. 1089-1092 (4)* 9.05 6.15

Traditional Houses — A226

**1984, June 13** **Photo.**

**1093** A226 15c Konso .55 .40
**1094** A226 65c Dorze 2.40 1.40
**1095** A226 1b Harer 3.75 2.50
*Nos. 1093-1095 (3)* 6.70 4.30

10th Anniv. of the Revolution A227

**1984, Sept. 10** **Photo.** ***Perf. 11½***

**1096** A227 5c Sept. 12, 1974 .25 .25
**1097** A227 10c Mar. 4, 1975 .35 .25
**1098** A227 15c Apr. 20, 1976 .45 .35
**1099** A227 20c Feb. 11, 1977 .60 .50
**1100** A227 25c Mar. 1978 .75 .60
**1101** A227 40c July 8, 1980 1.10 .80
**1102** A227 45c Dec. 17, 1980 1.40 1.00
**1103** A227 50c Sept. 15, 1980 1.75 1.25
**1104** A227 70c Sept. 18, 1981 2.00 1.50
**1105** A227 1b June 6, 1983 2.75 2.00
*Nos. 1096-1105 (10)* 11.40 8.50

Traditional Sports A228

**1984, Dec. 7** **Photo.** ***Perf. 14***

**1106** A228 5c Gugs .25 .25
**1107** A228 25c Tigil 1.00 .50
**1108** A228 50c Genna 2.50 1.50
**1109** A228 1b Gebeta 4.75 3.50
*Nos. 1106-1109 (4)* 8.50 5.75

Birds — A229

**1985, Jan. 4** **Photo.** ***Perf. 14½***

**1110** A229 5c Francolinus harwoodi .50 .40
**1111** A229 15c Rallus rougetti 1.00 .75
**1112** A229 80c Merops pusillus 5.00 3.00
**1113** A229 85c Malimbus rubriceps 5.25 3.50
*Nos. 1110-1113 (4)* 11.75 7.65

Indigenous Fauna A230

20c, Hippopotamus amphibius. 25c, Litocranius walleri. 40c, Sylvicapra grimmia. 1b, Rhynchotragus guentheri.

**1985, Feb. 4** **Litho.** ***Perf. 12½x12***

**1114** A230 20c multicolored .90 .75
**1115** A230 25c multicolored 1.25 1.00
**1116** A230 40c multicolored 2.00 1.50
**1117** A230 1b multicolored 4.50 3.25
*Nos. 1114-1117 (4)* 8.65 6.50

Freshwater Fish — A231

10c, Barbus degeni. 20c, Labeo cylindricus. 55c, Protopterus annectens. 1b, Alestes dentex.

**1985, Apr. 3** ***Perf. 13½***

**1118** A231 10c multicolored .45 .40
**1119** A231 20c multicolored 1.25 .60
**1120** A231 55c multicolored 2.75 1.50
**1121** A231 1b multicolored 6.00 3.25
*Nos. 1118-1121 (4)* 10.45 5.75

Medicinal Plants A232

10c, Securidaca longepedunculata. 20c, Plumbago zeylanicum. 55c, Brucea antidysenteric. 1b, Dorstenia barminiana.

**1985, May 23** ***Perf. 11½x12½***

**1122** A232 10c multicolored .40 .30
**1123** A232 20c multicolored .90 .45
**1124** A232 55c multicolored 2.10 1.25
**1125** A232 1b multicolored 5.00 2.75
*Nos. 1122-1125 (4)* 8.40 4.75

Ethiopian Red Cross Soc., 50th Anniv. — A233

**1985, Aug. 6** **Litho.** ***Perf. 13½x13***

**1126** A233 35c multicolored .90 .75
**1127** A233 55c multicolored 2.25 1.25
**1128** A233 1b multicolored 4.50 2.50
*Nos. 1126-1128 (3)* 7.65 4.50

Ethiopian Revolution, 11th Anniv. A234

10c, Kombolcha Mills, Welo Region. 80c, Muger Cement Factory, Mokoda, Shoa. 1b, Relocating famine and drought victims.

**1985, Sept. 10** **Litho.** ***Perf. 13½***

**1129** A234 10c multicolored .30 .25
**1130** A234 80c multicolored 2.25 2.00
**1131** A234 1b multicolored 3.00 2.50
*Nos. 1129-1131 (3)* 5.55 4.75

UN 40th Anniv. — A235

**1985, Nov. 22** **Litho.** ***Perf. 13½x14***

**1132** A235 25c multicolored .90 .75
**1133** A235 55c multicolored 1.75 1.50
**1134** A235 1b multicolored 3.25 2.50
*Nos. 1132-1134 (3)* 5.90 4.75

Anti-Polio Campaign A236

**1986, Jan. 10** **Litho.** ***Perf. 11½x12½***

**1135** A236 5c Boy, prosthesis .40 .25
**1136** A236 10c Boy on crutches .55 .30
**1137** A236 20c Nurse, boy 1.00 .50
**1138** A236 55c Man, sewing machine 2.75 1.25
**1139** A236 1b Nurse, mother, child 4.50 2.50
*Nos. 1135-1139 (5)* 9.20 4.80

Indigenous Trees A237

10c, Millettia ferruginea. 30c, Syzygium guineense. 50c, Cordia africana. 1b, Hagenia abyssinica.

**1986, Feb. 10** ***Perf. 13½x14½***

**1140** A237 10c multicolored .40 .35
**1141** A237 30c multicolored 1.25 .75
**1142** A237 50c multicolored 2.00 1.25
**1143** A237 1b multicolored 4.25 2.75
*Nos. 1140-1143 (4)* 7.90 5.10

Spices — A238

10c, Zingiber officinale rosc. 15c, Ocimum bacilicum. 55c, Sinapsis alba. 1b, Cuminum cyminum.

**1986, Mar. 10** ***Perf. 13½***

**1144** A238 10c multicolored .50 .40
**1145** A238 15c multicolored 1.10 .50
**1146** A238 55c multicolored 2.50 1.50
**1147** A238 1b multicolored 5.00 3.00
*Nos. 1144-1147 (4)* 9.10 5.40

Current Coins, Obverse and Reverse A239

**1986, May 9** **Litho.** ***Perf. 13½x14***

**1148** A239 5c 1-cent .25 .25
**1149** A239 10c 25-cent .50 .35
**1150** A239 35c 5-cent 1.60 1.00
**1151** A239 50c 50-cent 2.00 1.25
**1152** A239 1b 10-cent 4.00 2.50
*Nos. 1148-1152 (5)* 8.35 5.35

Discovery of 3.5 Million Year-old Hominid Skeleton, "Lucy" — A240

**1986, July 4** ***Perf. 13½***

**1153** A240 2b multicolored 11.00 11.00

Ethiopian Revolution, 12th Anniv. — A241

Designs: 20c, Military service. 30c, Tiglachin monument. 55c, Delachin Exhibition emblem. 85c, Food processing plant, Merti.

**1986, Sept. 10** **Litho.** ***Perf. 14***

**1154** A241 20c multicolored .75 .40
**1155** A241 30c multicolored 1.10 .60
**1156** A241 55c multicolored 2.10 1.00
**1157** A241 85c multicolored 2.75 1.75
*Nos. 1154-1157 (4)* 6.70 3.75

Ethiopian Airlines, 40th Anniv. — A242

**1986, Oct. 14**

**1158** A242 10c DC-7 .65 .30
**1159** A242 20c DC-3 1.00 .50
**1160** A242 30c Personnel, jet tail 1.60 .75
**1161** A242 40c Engine 2.00 1.00
**1162** A242 1b DC-7, map 4.50 2.25
*Nos. 1158-1162 (5)* 9.75 4.80

Intl. Peace Year — A243

**1986, Nov. 13** ***Perf. 13½***

**1163** A243 10c multicolored .40 .30
**1164** A243 80c multicolored 2.25 2.00
**1165** A243 1b multicolored 3.00 2.50
*Nos. 1163-1165 (3)* 5.65 4.80

UN Child Survival Campaign — A244

**1986, Dec. 11** *Perf. 12½*

1166 A244 10c Breast feeding .60 .30
1167 A244 35c Immunization 1.75 .75
1168 A244 50c Hygiene 2.25 1.00
1169 A244 1b Growth monitoring 4.50 2.00
*Nos. 1166-1169 (4)* 9.10 4.05

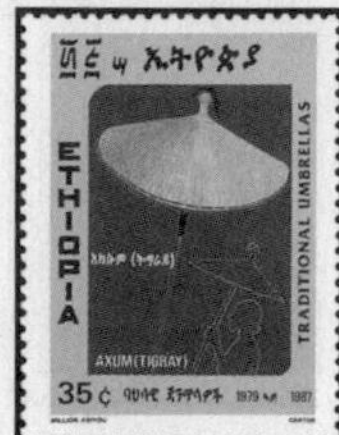


Umbrellas A245

**1987, Feb. 10** *Perf. 13½*

1170 A245 35c Axum 1.20 .85
1171 A245 55c Negele-Borena 1.75 1.25
1172 A245 1b Jimma 3.50 2.50
*Nos. 1170-1172 (3)* 6.45 4.60

Artwork by Afewerk Tekle (b. 1932) A246

Designs: 50c, Defender of His Country — Afar, stained glass window. 2b, Defender of His Country — Adwa, painting.

**1987, Mar. 19** **Litho.** *Perf. 13½*

1173 A246 50c multicolored 1.75 1.00
1174 A246 2b multicolored 6.25 4.50

Stained Glass Windows by Afewerk Tekle — A247

**1987, June 16** **Photo.** *Perf. 11½x12*

**Granite Paper**

1175 A247 50c multicolored *8.00* *4.00*

**Size: 26x38mm**

1176 A247 80c multicolored *10.00* *5.50*
1177 A247 1b multicolored *15.00* *8.00*
*Nos. 1175-1177 (3)* *33.00* *17.50*

Struggle of the African People.
Sold out in Addis Ababa on date of issue.

Simien Fox A248

**1987, June 29** **Litho.** *Perf. 13½*

1178 A248 5c multicolored .25 .25
1179 A248 10c multicolored .60 .25
1180 A248 15c multicolored .90 .40
1181 A248 20c multicolored 1.10 .50
1182 A248 25c multicolored 1.50 .75
1183 A248 45c multicolored 2.25 1.00
1184 A248 55c multicolored 2.75 1.50
*Nos. 1178-1184 (7)* 9.35 4.65

For overprints see Nos. 1234-1237. For similar design see A294a.

Ethiopian Revolution, 13th Anniv. A249

**1987, Sept. 10** *Perf. 12½*

1185 A249 5c Constitution, freedom of press .50 .30
1186 A249 10c Popular elections .65 .40
1187 A249 80c Referendum 2.50 1.50
1188 A249 1b Bahir Dar Airport, map 3.75 2.00
*Nos. 1185-1188 (4)* 7.40 4.20

Addis Ababa, Cent. A251

"100" and views: 5c, Emperor Menelik II, Empress Taitu and city. 10c, Traditional buildings. 80c, Central Addis Ababa. 1b, Aerial view of city.

**1987, Sept. 7** *Perf. 13½*

1193 A251 5c multicolored .50 .30
1194 A251 10c multicolored .65 .40
1195 A251 80c multicolored 2.75 1.50
1196 A251 1b multicolored 3.50 2.00
*Nos. 1193-1196 (4)* 7.40 4.20

Wooden Spoons A252

**1987, Nov. 30**

1197 A252 85c Hurso, Harerge 3.75 3.75
1198 A252 1b Borena, Sidamo 4.25 4.25

Intl. Year of Shelter for the Homeless A253

10c, Village revitalization program. 35c, Resettlement program. 50c, Urban improvement. 1b, Cooperative and government housing.

**1987, Dec. 12** **Litho.** *Perf. 13*

1199 A253 10c multicolored .70 .40
1200 A253 35c multicolored 1.40 .90
1201 A253 50c multicolored 1.75 1.00
1202 A253 1b multicolored 2.75 1.50
*Nos. 1199-1202 (4)* 6.60 3.80

October Revolution, Russia, 70th Anniv. (in 1987) — A254

Painting: 1b, Lenin receiving Workers' Council delegates in the Smolny Institute.

**1988, Feb. 17** *Perf. 12½x12*

1203 A254 1b multicolored 2.50 1.75

Traditional Hunting Methods and Prey — A255

**1988, Mar. 30** **Litho.** *Perf. 13½*

1204 A255 85c Bow and arrow 3.25 2.25
1205 A255 1b Double-pronged spear 3.75 3.50

A256

**1988, May 6**

1206 A256 85c multicolored 2.50 1.50
1207 A256 1b multicolored 3.50 1.75

Intl. Red Cross and Red Crescent Organizations, 125th annivs.

A257

**1988, June 7** **Photo.** *Perf. 11½x12*

1208 A257 2b multicolored 3.50 2.25

Organizaton of African Unity, 25th anniv.

Ethiopian Revolution, 14th Anniv. A258

Design: Various details of *The Victory of Ethiopia,* six-panel mural by Afewerk Tekle (b. 1932) in the museum of the Heroes Center, Debre Zeit.

**1988, June 28** **Litho.** *Perf. 13½x13*

1209 A258 10c Jet over farm, vert. .40 .30
1210 A258 20c Farm workers on road, vert. .50 .35
1211 A258 35c Allegory of unity, vert. .80 .50
1212 A258 55c Jet over industry 1.40 1.00
1213 A258 80c Steel works 1.90 1.25
1214 A258 1b Weaving 2.50 2.00
*Nos. 1209-1214 (6)* 7.50 5.40

Nos. 1209-1211 vert.

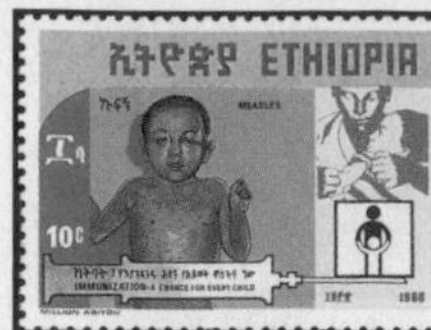


Women, Bracelets and Maps A259

**1988, July 27** **Litho.** *Perf. 13x13½*

1215 A259 15c Sidamo .40 .30
1216 A259 85c Arsi 1.75 1.25
1217 A259 1b Harerge 2.50 2.00
*Nos. 1215-1217 (3)* 4.65 3.55

Immunize Every Child A260

**1988, June 14** **Litho.** *Perf. 13x13½*

1218 A260 10c Measles .45 .25
1219 A260 35c Tetanus .95 .60
1220 A260 50c Whooping cough 1.60 1.00
1221 A260 1b Diphtheria 3.00 1.75
*Nos. 1218-1221 (4)* 6.00 3.60

Intl. Fund for Agricultural Development (IFAD), 10th Anniv. — A261

**1988, Aug. 16** *Perf. 13½*

1222 A261 15c Monetary aid .30 .25
1223 A261 85c Farming activities 1.50 1.10
1224 A261 1b Harvest 2.25 1.25
*Nos. 1222-1224 (3)* 4.05 2.60

People's Democratic Republic of Ethiopia, 1st Anniv. — A262

5c, 1st Session of the natl. Shengo (congress). 10c, Mengistu Haile-Mariam, 1st president of the republic. 80c, Natl. crest, flag & crowd. 1b, State assembly building.

**1988, Sept. 9** *Perf. 14*

1225 A262 5c multicolored .25 .25
1226 A262 10c multicolored .30 .25
1227 A262 80c multicolored 1.75 1.50
1228 A262 1b multicolored 2.25 2.00
*Nos. 1225-1228 (4)* 4.55 4.00

Bank Notes A263

**1988, Nov. 10** **Photo.** *Perf. 13*

1229 A263 5c 1-Birr .35 .25
1230 A263 10c 5-Birr .50 .30
1231 A263 20c 10-Birr 1.00 .50
1232 A263 75c 50-Birr 2.50 1.50
1233 A263 85c 100-Birr 3.25 2.00
*Nos. 1229-1233 (5)* 7.60 4.55

Nos. 1181-1184 Ovptd. in Two Languages

**1988, Dec. 1** **Litho.** *Perf. 13½*

1234 A248 20c multicolored *4.75* *4.50*
1235 A248 25c multicolored *6.25* *5.50*
1236 A248 45c multicolored *12.50* *10.50*
1237 A248 55c multicolored *13.00* *11.00*
*Nos. 1234-1237 (4)* *36.50* *31.50*

Intl. Day for the Fight Against AIDS.

WHO, 40th Anniv. A264

**1988, Dec. 30 Litho. Perf. 14**

1238 A264 50c multicolored 1.40 .80
1239 A264 65c multicolored 1.90 1.00
1240 A264 85c multicolored 2.50 1.50
*Nos. 1238-1240 (3)* 5.80 3.30

Traditional Musical Instruments A265

**1989, Feb. 9 Perf. 13x13½**

1241 A265 30c Gere .85 .45
1242 A265 40c Fanfa 1.10 .65
1243 A265 50c Chancha 1.40 .90
1244 A265 85c Negarcet 2.00 1.25
*Nos. 1241-1244 (4)* 5.35 3.25

Ethiopian Shipping Lines, 25th Anniv. A266

**1989, Mar. 27 Litho. Perf. 14**

1245 A266 15c *Abyot* .45 .30
1246 A266 30c *Wolwol* .85 .60
1247 A266 55c *Queen of Sheba* 1.60 1.25
1248 A266 1b *Abbay Wonz* 3.00 2.25
*Nos. 1245-1248 (4)* 5.90 4.40

Birds — A267

10c, Yellow-fronted parrot. 35c, White-winged cliff chat. 50c, Yellow-throated seed eater. 1b, Black-headed forest oriole.

**1989, May 18 Litho. Perf. 13½x13**

1249 A267 10c multicolored .65 .30
1250 A267 35c multicolored 2.00 1.00
1251 A267 50c multicolored 2.75 1.25
1252 A267 1b multicolored 4.50 2.25
*Nos. 1249-1252 (4)* 9.90 4.80

Production of Early Manuscripts — A268

**1989, June 16 Litho. Perf. 13½**

1253 A268 5c Preparing vellum .35 .25
1254 A268 10c Ink horns, pens .40 .25
1255 A268 20c Scribe .70 .40
1256 A268 75c Book binding 2.10 1.25
1257 A268 85c Illuminated manuscript 2.75 1.75
*Nos. 1253-1257 (5)* 6.30 3.90

Indigenous Wildlife — A269

**1989, July 18**

1258 A269 30c Greater kudu 1.00 .75
1259 A269 40c Lesser kudu 1.25 1.00
1260 A269 50c Roan antelope 1.50 1.25
1261 A269 85c Nile lechwe 2.50 2.00
*Nos. 1258-1261 (4)* 6.25 5.00

People's Democratic Republic of Ethiopia, 2nd Anniv. A270

Designs: 15c, Melka Wakana Hydroelectric Power Station. 75c, Adea Berga Dairy Farm. 1b, Pawe Hospital.

**1989, Sept. 8**

1262 A270 15c multicolored .35 .25
1263 A270 75c multicolored 1.50 1.25
1264 A270 1b multicolored 3.00 2.00
*Nos. 1262-1264 (3)* 4.85 3.50

African Development Bank, 25th Anniv. — A271

**1989, Nov. 10 Litho. Perf. 13½x13**

1265 A271 20c multicolored .35 .30
1266 A271 80c multicolored 2.25 1.25
1267 A271 1b multicolored 2.75 2.00
*Nos. 1265-1267 (3)* 5.35 3.55

Pan-African Postal Union, 10th Anniv. — A272

**1990, Jan. 18 Litho. Perf. 13½**

1268 A272 50c multicolored 1.00 .75
1269 A272 70c multicolored 1.75 1.25
1270 A272 80c multicolored 2.00 1.75
*Nos. 1268-1270 (3)* 4.75 3.75

UNESCO World Literacy Year — A273

15c, Illiterate man holding newspaper upside down. 85c, Adults learning alphabet in school. 1b, Literate man holding newspaper upright.

**1990, Mar. 13**

1271 A273 15c multicolored .65 .40
1272 A273 85c multicolored 2.25 1.50
1273 A273 1b multicolored 3.25 2.25
*Nos. 1271-1273 (3)* 6.15 4.15

Abebe Bikila, Marathon Runner A274

5c, Race. 10c, Flag bearer, Olympic team. 20c, Race, Rome Olympics. 75c, Race, Tokyo Olympics. 85c, Bikila, trophies, vert.

**1990, Apr. 17**

1274 A274 5c multicolored .35 .25
1275 A274 10c multicolored .40 .25
1276 A274 20c multicolored .80 .50
1277 A274 75c multicolored 2.40 1.50
1278 A274 85c multicolored 3.00 2.00
*Nos. 1274-1278 (5)* 6.95 4.50

Flag — A275

**1990, Apr. 30 Litho. Perf. 13½x13**

1279 A275 5c multicolored .35 .25
1280 A275 10c multicolored .35 .25
1281 A275 15c multicolored .40 .25
1282 A275 20c multicolored .55 .30
1283 A275 25c multicolored .65 .35
1284 A275 30c multicolored .80 .40
1285 A275 35c multicolored .90 .45
1286 A275 40c multicolored 1.10 .50
1287 A275 45c multicolored 1.25 .65
1288 A275 50c multicolored 1.40 .65
1289 A275 55c multicolored 1.60 .70
1290 A275 60c multicolored 1.75 .80
1291 A275 70c multicolored 1.90 .90
1292 A275 80c multicolored 2.00 1.00
1293 A275 85c multicolored 2.10 1.10
1294 A275 90c multicolored 2.25 1.25
1295 A275 1b multicolored 2.50 1.25
1296 A275 2b multicolored 5.25 2.75
1297 A275 3b multicolored 7.75 4.00
*Nos. 1279-1297 (19)* 34.85 17.80

Dated 1989.

Sowing of Teff A276

**1990, May 18 Litho. Perf. 13½**

1298 A276 5c shown .25 .25
1299 A276 10c Harvesting .25 .25
1300 A276 20c Threshing .50 .40
1301 A276 75c Storage, preparation 1.75 1.50
1302 A276 85c Consumption 2.25 2.00
*Nos. 1298-1302 (5)* 5.00 4.40

Walia Ibex — A277

**1990, June 18 Perf. 14x13½**

1303 A277 5c multi .55 .35
1304 A277 15c multi 1.25 .75
1305 A277 20c multi 1.90 1.10
1306 A277 1b multi, horiz. 7.50 4.25
*Nos. 1303-1306 (4)* 11.20 6.45

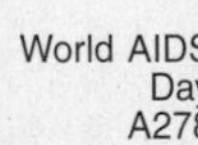

World AIDS Day A278

**1991, Jan. 31 Litho. Perf. 14**

1307 A278 15c Stages of disease .65 .30
1308 A278 85c Education 2.75 1.50
1309 A278 1b Causes, preventatives 3.50 2.00
*Nos. 1307-1309 (3)* 6.90 3.80

Intl. Decade for Natural Disaster Reduction A279

Map of disaster-prone African areas and: 5c, Volcano. 10c, Earthquake. 15c, Drought. 30c, Flood. 50c, Red Cross health education. 1b, Red Cross assisting fire victims.

**1991, Apr. 9 Litho. Perf. 14**

1310 A279 5c multicolored .40 .25
1311 A279 10c multicolored .40 .25
1312 A279 15c multicolored .45 .25
1313 A279 30c multicolored .90 .50
1314 A279 50c multicolored 1.90 1.00
1315 A279 1b multicolored 3.50 2.00
*Nos. 1310-1315 (6)* 7.55 4.25

The Cannon of Tewodros A280

Designs: 15c, Villagers receiving cannon 85c, Warriors leaving with cannon. 1b, Hauling cannon up mountainside.

**1991, June 18 Litho. Perf. 13½**

1316 A280 15c multicolored .65 .40
1317 A280 85c multicolored 2.25 1.50
1318 A280 1b multicolored 2.75 2.00
*Nos. 1316-1318 (3)* 5.65 3.90

Fish A281

**1991, Sept. 6 Litho. Perf. 13½**

1319 A281 5c Lacepede .60 .30
1320 A281 15c Black-finned butterflyfish .75 .40
1321 A281 80c Regal angelfish 2.75 1.75
1322 A281 1b Bleeker 3.75 2.50
*Nos. 1319-1322 (4)* 7.85 4.95

A282

Traditional Ceremonial Robes: Various robes.

**1992, Jan. 1 Litho. Perf. 13½x14**

1323 A282 5c yellow & multi .45 .25
1324 A282 15c orange & multi .55 .25
1325 A282 80c yel green & multi 2.25 1.50
1326 A282 1b blue & multi 2.75 1.75
*Nos. 1323-1326 (4)* 6.00 3.75

A283

Flowers: 5c, Cissus quadrangularis. 15c, Delphinium dasycaulon. 80c, Epilobium hirsutum. 1b, Kniphofia foliosa.

**1992, Mar. 5 Litho. *Perf. 13½x14***

**1327** A283 5c multicolored .40 .30
**1328** A283 15c multicolored .50 .40
**1329** A283 80c multicolored 2.25 1.75
**1330** A283 1b multicolored 2.75 2.00
*Nos. 1327-1330 (4)* 5.90 4.45

Traditional Homes A284

**1992, May 14 Litho. *Perf. 12½x12***

**1331** A284 15c Afar .55 .30
**1332** A284 35c Anuak 1.10 .60
**1333** A284 50c Gimira 1.35 .90
**1334** A284 1b Oromo 3.00 1.75
*Nos. 1331-1334 (4)* 6.00 3.55

A285

Pottery.

**1992, July 7 Litho. *Perf. 13x13½***

**1335** A285 15c Cover .75 .55
**1336** A285 85c Jug 3.00 2.40
**1337** A285 1b Tall jar 4.25 3.50
*Nos. 1335-1337 (3)* 8.00 6.45

A286

**1992, Sept. 29 *Perf. 14x13½***

**1338** A286 20c multicolored .60 .30
**1339** A286 80c multicolored 2.25 1.25
**1340** A286 1b multicolored 3.00 1.75
*Nos. 1338-1340 (3)* 5.85 3.30

Pan-African Rinderpest campaign.

Musical Instruments A287

**1993, Feb. 16 Litho. *Perf. 14x13½***

**1341** A287 15c Catchel .45 .30
**1342** A287 35c Huldudwa .90 .55
**1343** A287 50c Dita 1.20 .75
**1344** A287 1b Atamo 3.00 2.00
*Nos. 1341-1344 (4)* 5.55 3.60

Birds — A288

**1993, Apr. 22 Litho. *Perf. 14x13½***

**1345** A288 15c Banded barbet .60 .60
**1346** A288 35c Ruppell's chat 1.10 1.00
**1347** A288 50c Abyssinian catbird 1.75 1.40
**1348** A288 1b White-billed starling 4.00 3.00
*Nos. 1345-1348 (4)* 7.45 6.00

Animals A289

**1993, May 14 *Perf. 13½x14***

**1349** A289 15c Honey badger .45 .35
**1350** A289 35c Spotted necked otter .75 .60
**1351** A289 50c Rock hyrax .80 .60
**1352** A289 1b White-tailed mongoose 1.50 1.25
*Nos. 1349-1352 (4)* 3.50 2.80

Herbs — A290

**1993, June 10 *Perf. 14x13½***

**1353** A290 5c Caraway seed .65 .50
**1354** A290 15c Garlic .75 .60
**1355** A290 80c Turmeric 1.50 1.00
**1356** A290 1b Capsicum peppers 2.50 2.25
*Nos. 1353-1356 (4)* 5.40 4.35

Butterflies A291

20c, Papilio echeriodes. 30c, Papilio rex. 50c, Graphium policenes. 1b, Graphium leonidas.

**1993, July 9 Litho. *Perf. 14x13½***

**1357** A291 20c multicolored 1.00 .85
**1358** A291 30c multicolored 1.25 1.00
**1359** A291 50c multicolored 1.75 1.40
**1360** A291 1b multicolored 3.50 2.50
*Nos. 1357-1360 (4)* 7.50 5.75

Insects — A292

**1993, Aug. 10**

**1361** A292 15c C. Variabilis .45 .35
**1362** A292 35c Lycus trabeatus .70 .60
**1363** A292 50c Malachius bifasciatus .95 .80
**1364** A292 1b Homoeogryllus xanthographus 1.90 1.45
*Nos. 1361-1364 (4)* 4.00 3.20

Trees A293

15c, Euphorbia ampliphylla. 35c, Erythrina brucei. 50c, Dracaena steudneri. 1b, Allophylus abyssinicus.

**1993, Oct. 12 Litho. *Perf. 13½x14***

**1365** A293 15c multicolored .35 .35
**1366** A293 35c multicolored .50 .40
**1367** A293 50c multicolored .90 .70
**1368** A293 1b multicolored 1.75 1.25
*Nos. 1365-1368 (4)* 3.50 2.70

Lakes A294

**1993, Dec. 14**

**1369** A294 15c Wonchi .35 .35
**1370** A294 35c Zuquala .50 .40
**1371** A294 50c Ashengi .90 .70
**1372** A294 1b Tana 1.75 1.25
*Nos. 1369-1372 (4)* 3.50 2.70

Simien Fox A294a

***Rough Perf. 13½***

**1994, Jan. 18 Litho.**

**Color of Border**

**1372A** A294a 5c violet — .25
**1372B** A294a 10c brown — .25
**1372C** A294a 15c lemon — .25
**1372D** A294a 20c salmon — .25
**1372E** A294a 40c pale rose — .25
**1372F** A294a 55c dull green — .35
**1372G** A294a 60c dark blue — .35
**1372H** A294a 80c bright blue — .45
**1372I** A294a 85c gray green — .50
**1372J** A294a 1b bright green — .75
*Nos. 1372A-1372J (10)* *300.00* 3.65

Nos. 1372A-1372J have rough perforations and a poor quality printing impression. Dated "1991."

See Nos. 1393A-1393T.

A295

Transitional government: 15c, First anniversary of EPRDF's control of Addis Ababa. 35c, Transition Conference. 50c, National, regional elections. 1b, Coat of arms of Transitional Government.

**1994, Mar. 31 Litho. *Perf. 14***

**1373** A295 15c multicolored .35 .25
**1374** A295 35c multicolored .40 .30
**1375** A295 50c multicolored .75 .35
**1376** A295 1b multicolored 1.40 .55
*Nos. 1373-1376 (4)* 2.90 1.45

A296

**1994, May 17 *Perf. 13½***

**1377** A296 15c blue & multi .50 .25
**1378** A296 85c green & multi .85 .40
**1379** A296 1b violet & multi 1.10 .50
*Nos. 1377-1379 (3)* 2.45 1.15

Intl. Year of the Family.

Ethiopian Postal Service, Cent. A297

Designs: 60c, Early, modern postal workers, Scott Type A1. 75c, Early letter carriers. 80c, Older building, methods of transportation. 85c, People, mail buses. 1b, Modern methods of transportation, modern high-rise building.

**1994, July 4 Litho. *Perf. 13½***

**1380** A297 60c multicolored .75 .55
**1381** A297 75c multicolored .90 .60
**1382** A297 80c multicolored 1.15 .70
**1383** A297 85c multicolored 1.20 .75
**1384** A297 1b multicolored 1.45 1.05
*a.* Souvenir sheet, #1380-1384 + label 10.00 8.00
*Nos. 1380-1384 (5)* 5.45 3.65

Enset Plant — A298

**1994, Aug. 3**

**1385** A298 10c shown .25 .25
**1386** A298 15c Young plants, hut .35 .30
**1387** A298 25c Root, women processing leaves .40 .35
**1388** A298 50c Mature plants .75 .40
**1389** A298 1b Uses as food 1.50 .65
*Nos. 1385-1389 (5)* 3.25 1.95

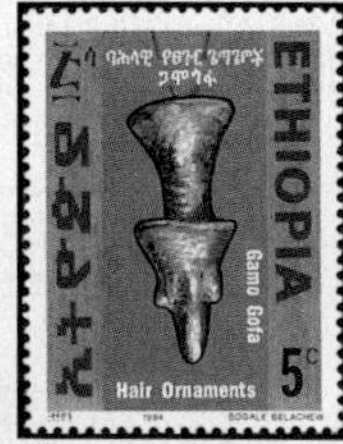

Hair Ornaments A299

**1994, Sept. 2**

**1390** A299 5c Gamo gofa .40 .30
**1391** A299 15c Sidamo .50 .35
**1392** A299 80c Gamo gofa, diff. .90 .50
**1393** A299 1b Wello 1.20 .65
*Nos. 1390-1393 (4)* 3.00 1.80

**Simien Fox Type of 1994**
**Size: 39x25mm**
**Color of Border**

**1994, Oct. 18 Litho. *Perf. 14***

**1393A** A294a 5c dull lilac — *.35*
**1393B** A294a 10c brown — *.45*
**1393C** A294a 15c lemon — *.55*
**1393D** A294a 20c salmon — *.65*
**1393E** A294a 25c lemon — *.75*
**1393F** A294a 30c yel brn — *1.00*
**1393G** A294a 35c orange — *1.25*
**1393H** A294a 40c pale rose — *1.50*
**1393I** A294a 45c pale red org — *1.75*
**1393J** A294a 50c rose lilac — *2.00*
**1393K** A294a 55c pale grn — *2.25*

| | | | | |
|---|---|---|---|---|
| **1393L** | A294a 60c dark blue | — | *2.50* |
| **1393M** | A294a 65c pale lilac | — | *2.75* |
| **1393N** | A294a 70c brt grn | — | *3.00* |
| **1393O** | A294a 75c pale bl grn | — | *3.25* |
| **1393P** | A294a 80c bright blue | — | *3.50* |
| **1393Q** | A294a 85c dk grnsh blue | — | *3.75* |
| **1393R** | A294a 90c pale brn | — | *4.00* |
| **1393S** | A294a 1b grnsh blue | — | *5.00* |
| **1393T** | A294a 2b yel brn | — | *9.00* |
| | *Nos. 1393A-1393T (20)* | | *49.25* |
| | *Nos. 1393A-1393T (20)* | *800.00* | |

Nos. 1393A-1393T have sharp impressions, Questa imprint, clean perforations. Dated "1993."

For overprints see Nos. 1393U-1393X, 1396A-1396D.

**Nos. 1393L, 1393P-1393Q, 1393S Ovptd. in Blue**

**1994, Oct. 20 Litho. *Perf. 14***

| | | | |
|---|---|---|---|
| **1393U** | A294a 60c on #1393L | 27.50 | 4.25 |
| **1393V** | A294a 80c on #1393P | 35.00 | 5.50 |
| **1393W** | A294a 85c on #1393Q | 72.50 | 10.50 |
| **1393X** | A294a 1b on #1393S | 80.00 | 9.50 |
| | *Nos. 1393U-1393X (4)* | 215.00 | 29.75 |

UNFPA, 50th anniv.

ICAO, 50th Anniv. A300

**1994, Dec. 7 Litho. *Perf. 13½***

| | | | |
|---|---|---|---|
| **1394** | A300 20c mag, lt bl & yel | .55 | .50 |
| **1395** | A300 80c yel & lt bl | .85 | .60 |
| **1396** | A300 1b dk bl, lt bl & yel | 1.10 | .95 |
| | *Nos. 1394-1396 (3)* | 2.50 | 2.05 |

**Nos. 1393M-1393O, 1393R Ovptd.**

**1994, Dec. 20 Litho. *Perf. 14***

| | | | |
|---|---|---|---|
| **1396A** | A294a 65c on #1393M | 27.50 | 4.25 |
| **1396B** | A294a 70c on #1393N | 35.00 | 5.50 |
| **1396C** | A294a 75c on #1393O | 72.50 | 10.50 |
| **1396D** | A294a 90c on #1393R | 80.00 | 9.50 |
| | *Nos. 1396A-1396D (4)* | 215.00 | 29.75 |

African Development Bank, 30th anniv.

Baskets for Serving Food A301

**1995, June 7 Litho. *Perf. 13½***

| | | | |
|---|---|---|---|
| **1397** | A301 30c Erbo | .30 | .25 |
| **1398** | A301 70c Sedieka | .80 | .55 |
| **1399** | A301 1b Tirar | 1.25 | .80 |
| | *Nos. 1397-1399 (3)* | 2.35 | 1.60 |

Traditional Hair Styles — A302

**1995, July 5 Litho. *Perf. 13½***

| | | | |
|---|---|---|---|
| **1400** | A302 25c Kuncho | .25 | .25 |
| **1401** | A302 75c Gamme | .75 | .55 |
| **1402** | A302 1b Sadulla | 1.25 | .80 |
| | *Nos. 1400-1402 (3)* | 2.25 | 1.60 |

FAO, 50th Anniv. A303

**1995, Aug. 29 Litho. *Perf. 13½***

| | | | |
|---|---|---|---|
| **1403** | A303 20c green & multi | .25 | .25 |
| **1404** | A303 80c blue & multi | .95 | .65 |
| **1405** | A303 1b brown & multi | 1.75 | .90 |
| | *Nos. 1403-1405 (3)* | 2.95 | 1.80 |

Cultivating Tools A304

**1995, Sept. 7**

| | | | |
|---|---|---|---|
| **1406** | A304 15c Dangora | .30 | .25 |
| **1407** | A304 35c Gheso | .45 | .40 |
| **1408** | A304 50c Akafa | .75 | .55 |
| **1409** | A304 1b Ankasse | 1.00 | .85 |
| | *Nos. 1406-1409 (4)* | 2.50 | 2.05 |

UN, 50th Anniv. — A305

**1995, Oct. 18 Litho. *Perf. 13½***
**Color of UN Emblem**

| | | | |
|---|---|---|---|
| **1410** | A305 20c black | .65 | .55 |
| **1411** | A305 80c bister | .75 | .65 |
| **1412** | A305 1b blue | 1.10 | 1.00 |
| | *Nos. 1410-1412 (3)* | 2.50 | 2.20 |

Intergovernmental Authority on Drought and Development (IGADD), 10th Anniv. — A306

Flags of member nations and: 15c, Seedling being planted in arid region. 35c, People carrying supplies through desert. 50c, Person picking fruit. 1b, Map of member nations.

**1995, Dec. 27 Litho. *Perf. 13½***

| | | | |
|---|---|---|---|
| **1413** | A306 15c multicolored | .45 | .35 |
| **1414** | A306 35c multicolored | .55 | .45 |
| **1415** | A306 50c multicolored | .70 | .60 |
| **1416** | A306 1b multicolored | 1.10 | 1.00 |
| | *Nos. 1413-1416 (4)* | 2.80 | 2.40 |

Victory at Battle of Adwa, Cent. — A307

Designs: 40c, Battle sites. 50c, Map of Africa focused at Ethiopia. 60c, Troops, ship. 70c, Warriors, soldiers in two battle scenes. 80c, Italians surrendering, Ethiopian troops, cannons. 1b, Emperor Menelik II, constitution, Empress Taitu.

**1996, Mar. 2 Litho. *Perf. 13½x14½***

| | | | |
|---|---|---|---|
| **1417** | A307 40c multicolored | .35 | .35 |
| **1418** | A307 50c multicolored | .40 | .35 |
| **1419** | A307 60c multicolored | .60 | .45 |
| **1420** | A307 70c multicolored | .75 | .55 |
| **1421** | A307 80c multicolored | 1.00 | .80 |
| **1422** | A307 1b multicolored | 1.40 | 1.10 |
| *a.* | Souvenir sheet, #1417-1422 | 5.50 | 5.50 |
| | *Nos. 1417-1422 (6)* | 4.50 | 3.60 |

UN Volunteers, 25th Anniv. A308

Designs: 20c, People, temporary housing huts. 30c, Planting seedlings. 50c, Instructing students. 1b, Caring for infant.

**1996, June 6 Litho. *Perf. 13½***

| | | | |
|---|---|---|---|
| **1423** | A308 20c multicolored | .25 | .25 |
| **1424** | A308 30c multicolored | .35 | .25 |
| **1425** | A308 50c multicolored | .50 | .40 |
| **1426** | A308 1b multicolored | 1.40 | 1.25 |
| | *Nos. 1423-1426 (4)* | 2.50 | 2.15 |

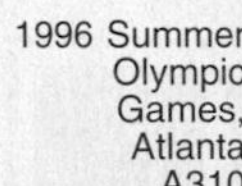

1996 Summer Olympic Games, Atlanta A310

**1996, Aug. 1 Litho. *Perf. 12½x12***
**Overprint in Black**

| | | | |
|---|---|---|---|
| **1427** | A310 15c Boxing | .75 | .55 |
| **1428** | A310 20c Swimming | .85 | .65 |
| **1429** | A310 40c Cycling | .95 | .75 |
| **1430** | A310 85c Athletics | 1.25 | 1.10 |
| **1431** | A310 1b Soccer | 1.60 | 1.40 |
| | *Nos. 1427-1431 (5)* | 5.40 | 4.45 |

Nos. 1427-1431 were originally prepared for the 1984 Summer Olympic Games in Los Angeles, but were not released due to the Soviet-led boycott. Nos. 1427-1431 exist without overprint. Value, set $100.

A311

UNICEF, 50th Anniv.: 10c, Emblems. 15c, Mother, child receiving vaccination. 25c, Woman carrying water, boy drinking from faucet. 50c, Children studying. 1b, Mother breastfeeding infant.

**1996, Sept. 10 Litho. *Perf. 13½***

| | | | |
|---|---|---|---|
| **1432** | A311 10c multicolored | .35 | .35 |
| **1433** | A311 15c multicolored | .40 | .35 |
| **1434** | A311 25c multicolored | .50 | .40 |
| **1435** | A311 50c multicolored | .85 | .65 |
| **1436** | A311 1b multicolored | 1.40 | 1.05 |
| | *Nos. 1432-1436 (5)* | 3.50 | 2.80 |

A312

Creation of Federal Democratic Republic of Ethiopia: 10c, People discussing new Constitution, approved Dec. 8, 1994. 20c, Ballot boxes, hand placing ballot in box. 30c, Marking ballot, placing into box, tower building, items from country's environment. 40c, Building, ballot, assembly hall. 1b, Natl. flag, transition of power.

**1996, Dec. 26 Litho. *Perf. 13½***

| | | | |
|---|---|---|---|
| **1437** | A312 10c multicolored | .50 | .50 |
| **1438** | A312 20c multicolored | .50 | .50 |
| **1439** | A312 30c multicolored | .60 | .50 |
| **1440** | A312 40c multicolored | .95 | .75 |
| **1441** | A312 1b multicolored | 1.90 | 1.45 |
| | *Nos. 1437-1441 (5)* | 4.45 | 3.70 |

Traditional Baskets — A313

**1997, Feb. 20 Litho. *Perf. 13½***

| | | | |
|---|---|---|---|
| **1442** | A313 5c Jimma | 1.20 | .85 |
| **1443** | A313 15c Wello | 1.20 | .85 |
| **1444** | A313 80c Welega | 2.00 | .95 |
| **1445** | A313 1b Shewa | 2.50 | 1.40 |
| | *Nos. 1442-1445 (4)* | 6.90 | 4.05 |

Traditional Baskets A314

**1997, May 22 Litho. *Perf. 13½***

| | | | |
|---|---|---|---|
| **1446** | A314 35c Arssi | 1.25 | 1.00 |
| **1447** | A314 65c Gojam | 2.25 | 1.90 |
| **1448** | A314 1b Harer | 3.50 | 3.00 |
| | *Nos. 1446-1448 (3)* | 7.00 | 5.90 |

See Nos. 1464-1466.

UN Decade Against Drug Abuse & Illicit Trafficking A315

**1997, Sept. 9 Litho. *Perf. 14***

| | | | |
|---|---|---|---|
| **1449** | A315 20c green & multi | .70 | .50 |
| **1450** | A315 80c brown & multi | .95 | .75 |
| **1451** | A315 1b blue & multi | 1.40 | 1.10 |
| | *Nos. 1449-1451 (3)* | 3.05 | 2.35 |

Historic Buildings, Addis Ababa A316

45c, Bitwoded Haile Giorgis' house. 55c, Alfred Ilg's house, vert. 3b, Menelik's Elfign.

***Perf. 14½x14, 14x14½***

**1997, Dec. 23** **Litho.**

| | | | | |
|---|---|---|---|---|
| **1452** | A316 | 45c multicolored | .50 | .45 |
| **1453** | A316 | 55c multicolored | .65 | .60 |
| **1454** | A316 | 3b multicolored | 2.25 | 1.75 |
| | | *Nos. 1452-1454 (3)* | 3.40 | 2.80 |

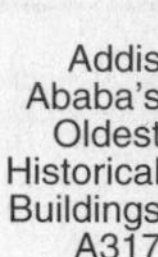

Addis Ababa's Oldest Historical Buildings A317

Designs: 60c, Ras Biru W/Gabriel's house. 75c, Sheh Hojele Alhassen's house. 80c, Fitawrari H/Giorgis Dinegde's house. 85c, Etege Taitu Hotel. 1b, Dejazmach Wube Atnafseged's house.

**1997, Dec. 30** **Litho.** ***Perf. 14½x14***

| | | | | |
|---|---|---|---|---|
| **1455** | A317 | 60c multicolored | .55 | .45 |
| **1456** | A317 | 75c multicolored | .60 | .55 |
| **1457** | A317 | 80c multicolored | .70 | .60 |
| **1458** | A317 | 85c multicolored | .75 | .70 |
| **1459** | A317 | 1b multicolored | 1.15 | .90 |
| | | *Nos. 1455-1459 (5)* | 3.75 | 3.20 |

Pan African Postal Union, 18th Anniv. A318

Union's emblem and wildlife: 45c, Deculla bushback. 55c, Soemmering's gazelle. 1b, Defassa waterbuck. 2b, Black buffalo.

**1998, Mar. 25** **Litho.** ***Perf. 14½x14***

| | | | | |
|---|---|---|---|---|
| **1460** | A318 | 45c multicolored | .50 | .35 |
| **1461** | A318 | 55c multicolored | .55 | .45 |
| **1462** | A318 | 1b multicolored | 1.00 | .65 |
| **1463** | A318 | 2b multicolored | 2.00 | 1.25 |
| | | *Nos. 1460-1463 (4)* | 4.05 | 2.70 |

**Traditional Basket Type of 1997**

**1998, May 21** **Litho.** ***Perf. 13½***

| | | | | |
|---|---|---|---|---|
| **1464** | A314 | 45c Gonder | .45 | .45 |
| **1465** | A314 | 55c Harere | .65 | .55 |
| **1466** | A314 | 3b Tigray | 2.75 | 2.50 |
| | | *Nos. 1464-1466 (3)* | 3.85 | 3.50 |

Golden-Backed Woodpecker A319

**1998, Jan. 12** **Photo.** ***Perf. 11½***

**Granite Paper**

**Panel Color**

| | | | | |
|---|---|---|---|---|
| **1467** | A319 | 5c green blue | .45 | .30 |
| **1468** | A319 | 10c yellow | .45 | .30 |
| **1469** | A319 | 15c blue | .45 | .30 |
| **1470** | A319 | 20c light brown | *15.00* | .30 |
| **1471** | A319 | 25c violet | .45 | .30 |
| **1472** | A319 | 30c light blue | .45 | .30 |
| **1473** | A319 | 35c salmon rose | .45 | .30 |
| **1474** | A319 | 40c lilac | .45 | .30 |
| **1475** | A319 | 45c green | .45 | .30 |
| **1476** | A319 | 50c salmon | .45 | .35 |
| **1477** | A319 | 55c blue | .45 | .35 |
| **1478** | A319 | 60c brick red | .45 | .40 |
| **1479** | A319 | 65c light gray | .45 | .45 |
| **1480** | A319 | 70c bright yellow | .45 | .50 |
| **1481** | A319 | 75c pale violet | .70 | .65 |
| **1482** | A319 | 80c apple green | .75 | .70 |
| **1483** | A319 | 85c gray | .80 | .75 |
| **1484** | A319 | 90c orange | .90 | .80 |
| **1485** | A319 | 1b yellow green | 1.25 | .95 |
| **1486** | A319 | 2b pale rose | 1.50 | 1.25 |
| **1487** | A319 | 3b lilac rose | 2.50 | 2.00 |
| **1488** | A319 | 5b bister | 3.50 | 3.00 |
| **1489** | A319 | 10b orange yellow | 7.00 | 6.00 |
| | | *Nos. 1467-1489 (23)* | 39.75 | 20.85 |

Agreement for Return of Axum Obelisk from Italy — A320

45c, Map of Italy, pieces of obelisk. 55c, Obelisk in Rome. 3b, Map of E. Africa, obelisk, ruins of Axum.

**1998, Sept. 3** **Litho.** ***Perf. 13½***

| | | | | |
|---|---|---|---|---|
| **1490** | A320 | 45c multicolored | .75 | .45 |
| **1491** | A320 | 55c multicolored | .95 | .85 |
| **1492** | A320 | 3b multicolored | 3.00 | 2.50 |
| | | *Nos. 1490-1492 (3)* | 4.70 | 3.80 |

Ethiopia-Djibouti Railway, Cent. — A321

Designs: 45c, Men carrying rails during construction. 55c, Early steam train, CFE 404. 1b, Terminal building. 2b, Modern train, BB 1212.

**1998, Nov. 24** **Litho.** ***Perf. 11½***

**Granite Paper**

| | | | | |
|---|---|---|---|---|
| **1493** | A321 | 45c multicolored | .55 | .35 |
| **1494** | A321 | 55c multicolored | .70 | .45 |
| **1495** | A321 | 1b multicolored | 1.20 | .75 |
| **1496** | A321 | 2b multicolored | 2.50 | 1.25 |
| | | *Nos. 1493-1496 (4)* | 4.95 | 2.80 |

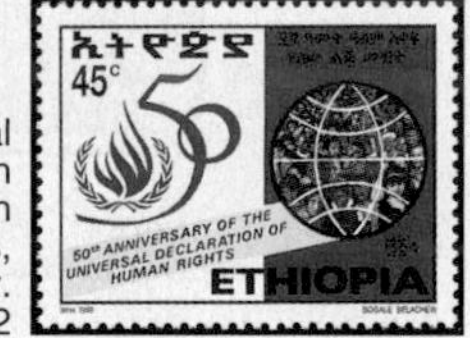


Universal Declaration of Human Rights, 50th Anniv. A322

**1998, Dec. 23** **Litho.** ***Perf. 13x13½***

| | | | | |
|---|---|---|---|---|
| **1497** | A322 | 45c red & multi | .45 | .25 |
| **1498** | A322 | 55c yellow & multi | .45 | .30 |
| **1499** | A322 | 1b green & multi | .75 | .50 |
| **1500** | A322 | 2b blue & multi | 1.10 | .75 |
| | | *Nos. 1497-1500 (4)* | 2.75 | 1.80 |

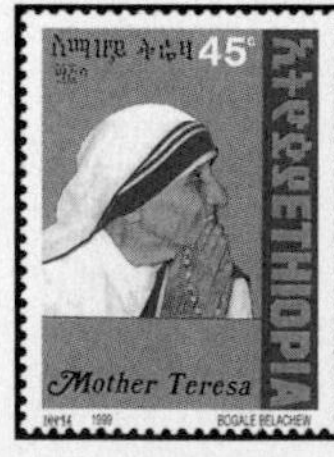


Mother Teresa (1910-97) — A323

Various portraits.

**1999, Mar. 9** **Litho.** ***Perf. 13½x13***

| | | | | |
|---|---|---|---|---|
| **1501** | A323 | 45c brown & multi | 1.05 | .35 |
| **1502** | A323 | 55c green & multi | 1.15 | .45 |
| **1503** | A323 | 1b yel org & multi | 1.40 | .60 |
| **1504** | A323 | 2b blue & multi | 3.25 | 1.25 |
| | | *Nos. 1501-1504 (4)* | 6.85 | 2.65 |

Intl. Year of the Ocean A324

**1999, May 6** **Litho.** ***Perf. 13½x13¼***

| | | | | |
|---|---|---|---|---|
| **1505** | A324 | 45c black & multi | .80 | .25 |
| **1506** | A324 | 55c red & multi | 1.00 | .30 |
| **1507** | A324 | 1b blue & multi | 1.35 | .50 |
| **1508** | A324 | 2b green & multi | 2.75 | 1.00 |
| | | *Nos. 1505-1508 (4)* | 5.90 | 2.05 |

World Environment Day — A325

**1999, June 17** **Litho.** ***Perf. 13½***

| | | | | |
|---|---|---|---|---|
| **1509** | A325 | 45c pink & multi | .55 | .30 |
| **1510** | A325 | 55c vio & multi | .70 | .40 |
| **1511** | A325 | 1b yel org & multi | 1.10 | .70 |
| **1512** | A325 | 2b grn & multi | 1.90 | 1.00 |
| | | *Nos. 1509-1512 (4)* | 4.25 | 2.40 |

National Parks — A326

45c, Abijata, Shalla Lakes. 70c, Nechisar. 85c, Bale Mountains. 2b, Awash.

***Perf. 13¾x13¼, 13¼x13¾***

**1999, Sept. 8** **Litho.**

| | | | | |
|---|---|---|---|---|
| **1513** | A326 | 45c multi, vert. | .75 | .50 |
| **1514** | A326 | 70c multi, vert. | 1.10 | .70 |
| **1515** | A326 | 85c multi, vert. | 1.40 | .90 |
| **1516** | A326 | 2b multi | 3.50 | 1.50 |
| | | *Nos. 1513-1516 (4)* | 6.75 | 3.60 |

See Nos. 1521-1524.

UPU, 125th Anniv. — A327

**1999, Oct. 28** ***Perf. 13¼x13***

| | | | | |
|---|---|---|---|---|
| **1517** | A327 | 20c multicolored | .55 | .25 |
| **1518** | A327 | 80c multicolored | .70 | .35 |
| **1519** | A327 | 1b multicolored | 1.25 | .60 |
| **1520** | A327 | 2b multicolored | 1.75 | .80 |
| | | *Nos. 1517-1520 (4)* | 4.25 | 2.00 |

**National Parks Type of 1999**

Designs: 50c, Omo, vert. 70c, Mago, vert. 80c, Yangudi-Rassa, vert. 2b, Gambella.

**1999, Nov. 30** **Litho.** ***Perf. 13¼***

| | | | | |
|---|---|---|---|---|
| **1521-1524** | A326 | Set of 4 | 7.50 | 2.50 |

Intl. Year of Older Persons A328

45c, Woman attending to sick man. 70c, Older people gardening. 85c, Four men, bench. 2b, Older man, two young people.

**1999, Dec. 30** ***Perf. 13¾x13¼***

| | | | | |
|---|---|---|---|---|
| **1525-1528** | A328 | Set of 4 | 5.00 | 3.75 |

Alexander Pushkin, Writer, Birth Bicent. (in 1999) — A329

Various portraits: 45c, 70c, 85c, 2b.

**2000, Mar. 9** **Litho.** ***Perf. 13¾x13¼***

| | | | | |
|---|---|---|---|---|
| **1529-1532** | A329 | Set of 4 | 3.25 | 2.50 |

Worldwide Fund for Nature (WWF) — A330

Grevy's zebra: a, Grazing. b, Running. c, Resting. d, Head.

**2001, Jan. 30** **Litho.** ***Perf. 13¼x13¾***

| | | | | |
|---|---|---|---|---|
| **1533** | | Strip of 4 | *7.50* | *5.00* |
| *a.* | | A330 45c multi | *.60* | *.45* |
| *b.* | | A330 55c multi | *.75* | *.55* |
| *c.* | | A330 1b multi | *1.40* | *1.00* |
| *d.* | | A330 3b multi | *4.25* | *3.00* |

Operation Sunset — A331

Designs: 45c, President Meles Zenawi, Parliament. 55c, Soldiers, flag ceremony. 1b, People, house. 2b, Agriculture, construction.

**2000, June 27** ***Perf. 13¾***

| | | | | |
|---|---|---|---|---|
| **1534-1537** | A331 | Set of 4 | 4.50 | 2.50 |

Flags A332

Designs: 25c, Harar Region. 30c, Oromia Region. 50c, Amhara Region. 60c, Tigre Region. 70c, Benishangi Region. 80c, Somalia Region. 90c, Peoples of the South Region. 95c, Gambella Region. 1b, Afar Region. 2b, Ethiopia.

**2000, Oct. 26** ***Perf. 13¼x13¾***

| | | | | |
|---|---|---|---|---|
| **1538-1547** | A332 | Set of 10 | 7.00 | 4.50 |

Afro Ayigeba, Cross of St. Lalibela A333

**2000, Apr. 27** ***Perf. 13¾x13¼***
**1548** A333 4b multi 3.50 2.25

Menelik's Bushbuck A334

***Perf. 13¾x13¼***

**2000, June 19** **Litho.**

**Frame Color**

| No. | Type | Value | Color | Unused | Used |
|---|---|---|---|---|---|
| **1548A** | A334 | 5c | dk Prus blue | *1.50* | .25 |
| **1549** | A334 | 10c | lilac | *1.50* | .25 |
| **1549A** | A334 | 15c | blue | *1.50* | .25 |
| **1549B** | A334 | 20c | yellow bister | *1.50* | .25 |
| **1549C** | A334 | 25c | purple | *1.50* | .25 |
| **1549D** | A334 | 30c | lt Prus blue | *1.50* | .25 |
| **1549E** | A334 | 35c | brt red | *1.50* | .25 |
| **1549F** | A334 | 40c | lilac | *1.50* | .25 |
| **1549G** | A334 | 45c | emerald | *1.50* | .25 |
| **1549H** | A334 | 50c | red | *1.60* | .25 |
| **1549I** | A334 | 55c | blue | *1.75* | .25 |
| **1549J** | A334 | 60c | yellow orange | *1.90* | .25 |
| **1549K** | A334 | 65c | deep blue | *2.00* | .25 |
| **1549L** | A334 | 70c | dull blue | *2.00* | .25 |
| **1549M** | A334 | 75c | orange yellow | *2.50* | .35 |
| **1549N** | A334 | 80c | carmine | *2.50* | .35 |
| **1549O** | A334 | 85c | light blue | *2.50* | .40 |
| **1550** | A334 | 90c | ocher | *2.50* | .40 |
| **1551** | A334 | 1b | green | *3.00* | .50 |
| **1552** | A334 | 2b | red violet | *7.50* | .75 |
| **1553** | A334 | 3b | purple | *12.50* | .90 |
| **1554** | A334 | 5b | dark carmine | *22.50* | 1.75 |
| **1555** | A334 | 10b | light carmine | *30.00* | 4.00 |
| | | | *Nos. 1548A-1555 (23)* | 108.25 | 12.90 |

Haile Gebreselassie, Runner — A335

Gebreselassie : No. 1557, 50c, Running. No. 1557A, 60c, Running, diff. No. 1557B, 90c, Running, diff. No. 1558, 2b, With arms raised.

**2000, Nov. 9** **Litho.** ***Perf. 13½***
**1557-1558** A335 Set of 4 4.25 2.00

World Meteorological Organization, 50th Anniv. — A336

Color of inscriptions: 40c, Gray. 75c, Green. 85c, Brown. 2b, Blue.

**2000, Oct. 10** **Litho.** ***Perf. 13½***
**1559-1562** A336 Set of 4 3.25 2.50

Addis Ababa University, 50th Anniv. — A337

**2000, Nov. 30** ***Perf. 13½x14¼***
**1563** A337 4b multi 3.25 2.50

UN High Commissioner for Refugees, 50th Anniv. — A338

Frame color: 40c, Brown. 75c, Green. 85c, Blue. 2b, Gold.

**2000 Dec. 14** ***Perf. 13½x14***
**1564-1567** A338 Set of 4 4.00 2.50

Freshwater Fish — A340

Designs: 45c, Catfish. 55c, Tilapia. 3b, Nile perch.

**2001, July 26** **Litho.** ***Perf. 14¼***
**1572-1574** A340 Set of 3 5.00 2.75

Traditional Means of Transportation — A341

Designs: 40c, Man on horseback, horse-drawn cart. 60c, Camel caravan. 1b, Man on horseback, horse carrying load. 2b, Man on donkey, donkeys carrying goods.

**2001, Aug. 30** ***Perf. 13¼x13½***
**1575-1578** A341 Set of 4 5.00 2.75

Year of Dialogue Among Civilizations A342

Color of country name: 25c, Light blue. 75c, White. 1b, Light yellow. 2b, Pink.

**2001, Oct. 9** ***Perf. 14***
**1579-1582** A342 Set of 4 4.00 2.25

Birds — A343

Designs: 50c, White-tailed swallow. 60c, Spot-breasted plover. 90c, Abyssinian long-claw. 2b, Prince Ruspoli's turaco.

**2001, Nov. 29** ***Perf. 14¼***
**1583-1586** A343 Set of 4 6.00 3.00

Traditional Beehives A344

Various beehives: 40c, 70c, 90c, 2b.

**2002, Jan. 24** **Litho.** ***Perf. 14***
**1587-1590** A344 Set of 4 5.00 2.75

Traditional Grain Storage — A345

Designs: 30c, Gota. 70c, Bekollo Gotera. 1b, Gotera. 2b, Gotera, diff.

**2002, Mar. 28** ***Perf. 13½x14***
**1591-1594** A345 Set of 4 5.00 3.00

Lions Club Intl. — A346

Lions Club Intl. emblem and: 45c, Quality emblem. 55c, Woman at pump. 1b, Eye doctor treating patient. 2b, Man in wheelchair.

**2002, Apr. 26** **Litho.** ***Perf. 13x13¼***
**1595-1598** A346 Set of 4 6.00 4.50

Trees A347

Designs: 50c, Acacia abyssinica. 60c, Boswellia papyrifera, vert. 90c, Aningeria adolfi-freiderici, vert. 2b, Prunus africana, vert.

***Perf. 13½x13¼, 13¼x13½***

**2002, June 27**
**1599-1602** A347 Set of 4 6.00 4.50

Traditional Beehives A348

Various beehives with panel colors of: 45c, Pink. 55c, Yellow. 1b, Light blue. 2b, Light green.

**2002, Sept. 19** **Litho.** ***Perf. 13¼x13***
**1603-1606** A348 Set of 4 5.00 3.50

Granite — A349

Designs: 45c, Sidamo. 55c, Harrar. 1b, Tigray. 2b, Wollega.

**2002, Oct. 24** ***Perf. 13x13¼***
**1607-1610** A349 Set of 4 5.50 4.00

Konso Waka A350

Various wooden sculptures with background colors of: 40c, Green. 60c, Blue. 1b, Yellow. 2b, Red.

**2002, Nov. 28** ***Perf. 14***
**1611-1614** A350 Set of 4 4.75 3.00

Menelik's Bushbuck — A351

**2002, Dec. 12** ***Perf. 13½x13¾***

**Frame Color**

| No. | Type | Value | Color | Unused | Used |
|---|---|---|---|---|---|
| **1615** | A351 | 5c | brt grn blue | .25 | .25 |
| **1616** | A351 | 10c | lilac | .25 | .25 |
| **1617** | A351 | 15c | bright blue | .25 | .25 |
| **1618** | A351 | 20c | brn orange | .25 | .25 |
| **1619** | A351 | 25c | purple | .25 | .25 |
| **1620** | A351 | 30c | bright blue | .25 | .25 |
| **1621** | A351 | 35c | carmine | .25 | .25 |
| **1622** | A351 | 40c | purple | .25 | .25 |
| **1623** | A351 | 45c | emerald | .25 | .25 |
| **1624** | A351 | 50c | red | .25 | .25 |
| **1625** | A351 | 55c | blue | .25 | .25 |
| **1626** | A351 | 60c | bright yel | .35 | .25 |
| **1627** | A351 | 65c | red | .35 | .25 |
| **1628** | A351 | 70c | light blue | .35 | .25 |
| **1629** | A351 | 75c | bright yel | .40 | .35 |
| **1630** | A351 | 80c | carmine | .40 | .35 |
| **1631** | A351 | 85c | bright blue | .50 | .40 |
| **1632** | A351 | 90c | orange brn | .50 | .40 |
| **1633** | A351 | 95c | green | .50 | .40 |
| **1634** | A351 | 1b | red violet | .60 | .50 |
| **1635** | A351 | 2b | purple | .85 | .75 |
| **1636** | A351 | 3b | blue | 1.00 | .90 |
| **1637** | A351 | 5b | dull red | 2.00 | 1.50 |
| **1638** | A351 | 10b | light green | 6.00 | 3.00 |
| **1639** | A351 | 20b | rose pink | 10.00 | 6.00 |
| | | | *Nos. 1615-1639 (25)* | 26.55 | 18.05 |

Oil Crops A352

Designs: 40c, Abyssinian mustard. 60c, Linseed. 3b, Niger seed.

**2002, Dec. 31** **Litho.** ***Perf. 13¼x13***
**1640-1642** A352 Set of 3 3.00 2.50

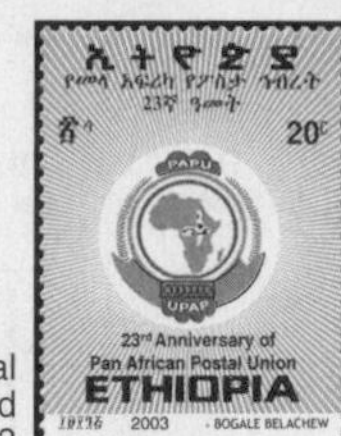


Pan-African Postal Union, 23rd Anniv. — A353

Background color: 20c, Green. 80c, Blue green. 1b, Orange brown. 2b, Purple.

**2003, Feb. 18** *Perf. 13x13¼*
**1643-1646** A353 Set of 4 3.50 2.00

Opals — A354

Designs: 45c, Milk opal. 60c, Brown precious opal. 95c, Fire opal. 2b, Yellow precious opal.

**2003, May 8** *Perf. 14*
**1647-1650** A354 Set of 4 5.00 3.00

Emperor Tewodros's Amulet — A355

Various views with frame color of: 40c, Green. 60c, Yellow orange. 3b, Red.

**2003, Sept. 4 Litho.** *Perf. 13x13¼*
**1651-1653** A355 Set of 3 4.50 2.50

Flowers — A356

Designs: 45c, Kniphofia isoetfolia. 55c, Kniphofia insignis. 1b, Crinum bambusetum. 2b, Crinum abyssinicum, horiz.

**2003, Nov. 27 Litho.** *Perf. 13x13¼*
**1654-1657** A356 Set of 4 4.25 3.50

Konso Terracing System A357

Designs: 40c, Village, crops. 60c, Man and woman, ears of grains. 1b, Terraces, tool. 2b, Farmers working on terraces, crops.

**2003, Dec. 30** *Perf. 13¼x13¾*
**1658-1661** A357 Set of 4 4.00 2.00

Amaranths A358

Designs: 20c, Seeds. 80c, White amaranth. 1b, Red amaranth. 2b, Amaranth bread.

**2004, Mar. 11 Litho.** *Perf. 13¼x14*
**1662-1665** A358 Set of 4 4.50 2.25

Marble A359

Designs: 25c, Sabian multicolored marble. 75c, Eshet blue marble. 1b, Sabian rose green marble. 2b, Sabian purple marble.

**2004, July 27** *Perf. 14*
**1666-1669** A359 Set of 4 2.25 2.25

FIFA (Fédération Internationale de Football Association), Cent. — A360

Soccer field, "100" and: 5c, FIFA emblem. 95c, Old soccer ball. 1b, Cleats. 2b, Modern soccer ball.

**2004, Sept. 7 Litho.** *Perf. 14*
**1670-1673** A360 Set of 4 2.25 2.25

2004 Summer Olympics, Athens A361

Designs: 20c, Track. 35c, Hammer throw. 45c, Boxing. 3b, Cycling.

**2004, Dec. 7**
**1674-1677** A361 Set of 4 2.25 2.25



Gesho — A362

Designs: 40c, Chopped plant. 60c, Plants, horiz. 1b, Cut logs. 2b, Branch with berries.

**2004, Dec. 28**
**1678-1681** A362 Set of 4 2.25 2.25

Black Rhinoceros A363

**2005, June 20 Litho.** *Perf. 14*

**Background Color**

| | | | | |
|---|---|---|---|---|
| **1682** | A363 | 5c bright blue | .25 | .25 |
| **1683** | A363 | 10c lilac | .25 | .25 |
| **1684** | A363 | 15c dark blue | .25 | .25 |
| **1685** | A363 | 20c bister | 1.00 | 1.00 |
| **1686** | A363 | 25c dark purple | 1.00 | 1.00 |
| **1687** | A363 | 30c blue | 1.00 | 1.00 |
| **1688** | A363 | 35c red | 1.00 | 1.00 |
| **1689** | A363 | 40c purple | 1.00 | 1.00 |
| **1690** | A363 | 45c green | 1.00 | 1.00 |
| **1691** | A363 | 4b bright red | 4.25 | 4.25 |
| | | *Nos. 1682-1691 (10)* | 11.00 | 11.00 |

Sabean Inscriptions — A364

Various inscriptions with background colors of: 15c, Green. 40c, Red, vert. 45c, Orange, vert. 3b, Blue, vert.

*Perf. 13¾x14, 14x13¾*

**2005, Aug. 20** **Litho.**
**1692-1695** A364 Set of 4 2.00 2.00

Surma Hairstyles A365

Various hairstyles with background colors of: 15c, Red. 40c, Green. 45c, Blue. 3b, Lilac.

**2005, Dec. 20** *Perf. 14x13¾*
**1696-1699** A365 Set of 4 2.00 2.00

Flowers A366

Designs: 45c, Chlorophytum neghellense. 55c, Aloe bertemariae, vert. 3b, Aloe schelpei, vert.

*Perf. 13¾x14, 14x13¾*

**2006, June 6** **Litho.**
**1700-1702** A366 Set of 3 2.00 2.00

Ethiopian Airlines, 60th Anniv. A367

Designs: 15c, Douglas C-47A Dakota III. 40c, Douglas DC-6B Super Cloudmaster. 45c, Boeing 720-060B. 1b, Boeing 767-300ER. 2b, Boeing 787 Dreamliner.

**2006, Sept. 28** *Perf. 13x13¼*
**1703-1707** A367 Set of 5 2.00 2.00

Intl. Year of Deserts and Desertification — A368

Emblem and: 15c, United Nations emblem. 40c, Map of Ethiopia showing desertification vulnerability. 45c, Map of Africa showing climate types. 3b, Map of world showing climate types.

**2006, Oct. 31** *Perf. 14x13½*
**1708-1711** A368 Set of 4 2.00 2.00

Ethiopian Millennium A369

Panel color: 40c, Pink. 60c, Buff. 3b, Green.

**2007, Nov. 15 Litho.** *Perf. 13¾*
**1712-1714** A369 Set of 3 2.00 2.00

Minerals A370

Designs: 40c, Gypsum. 60c, Quartz. 1b, Ambo sandstone. 2b, Feldspar.

**2007, Dec. 25** *Perf. 14*
**1715-1718** A370 Set of 4 2.00 2.00

Onslaught Martyrs Memorial A371

Designs: 40c, Martyrs Memorial Center. 60c, Emblem of Association for the Erection of the Martyrs Memorial Monument, vert. 3b, Woman, jail cell, gun, vert.

**2008, Aug. 26 Litho.** *Perf. 14*
**1719-1721** A371 Set of 3 .85 .85

Catha Edulis — A372

Designs: 45c, Red leaves. 55c, Harvesting of plant. 3b, Plant.

**2008, Sept. 8** *Perf. 13¾*
**1722-1724** A372 Set of 3 .85 .85

Diplomatic Relations Between Ethiopia and India, 60th Anniv. A373

"60" and: 30c, Ethiopian and Indian flowers. 70c, Rock church, Lalibela, and Taj Mahal, India. 3b, Symbols of India and Ethiopia.

**2008, Dec. 30 Litho.** *Perf. 14x13¼*
**1725-1727** A373 Set of 3 .80 .80

Pan-African Tsetse and Trypanosomiasis Eradication Campaign A374

Designs: 15c, Campaign emblem. 40c, Tsetse fly. 45c, Tsetse fly and blood drop, horiz. 3b, Tsetse fly, cow, silhouette of human, map of Africa, horiz.

***Perf. 13½x14, 14x13½***

**2009, July 21** **Litho.**
**1728-1731** A374 Set of 4 .70 .70

Addis Ababa Monuments — A375

Designs: 45c, Arat Kilo, Miazia 27 Square Monument. 55c, Sidist Kilo, Yekatit 12 Square Monument. 3b, Abune Petros Monument, vert.

**2009, Sept. 17** **Litho.** ***Perf. 13¾***
**1732-1734** A375 Set of 3 .65 .65

Eradication of Rinderpest in Ethiopia A376

Designs: 15c, First laboratory in Addis Ababa where rinderpest vaccine was produced. 40c, Certificate from World Organization for Animal Health. 45c, Dead cattle. 3b, Dr. Alemework Beyene, monument to Dr. Engueda Johannes, veterinarians.

**2009, Dec. 31** ***Perf. 14***
**1735-1738** A376 Set of 4 .65 .65

Pan-African Postal Union, 30th Anniv. — A377

Background color: 45c, Green. 55c, Yellow. 3b, Rose.

**2010, Apr. 6** **Litho.** ***Perf. 13¼x14***
**1739-1741** A377 Set of 3 .60 .60

Writers — A378

Designs: No. 1742, 1b, Tsegaye Gebremedhin (1936-2006). No. 1743, 1b, Dr. Sindehu Gebru (1915-2009). No. 1744, 1b, Dr. Haddis Alemayehu (1910-2003). No. 1745, 1b, Dr. Kebede Michael (1915-98).

**2010, Aug. 6** ***Perf. 14***
**1742-1745** A378 Set of 4 .60 .60

Ethiopian Red Cross, 75th Anniv. A379

75th anniversary emblem and: 45c, Ambulance, Red Cross workers and truck. 55c, Bags of blood, boy receiving transfusion. 1b, Amharic letters, vert. 2b, Red Cross building.

**2010, Oct. 12** **Litho.** ***Perf. 14***
**1746-1749** A379 Set of 4 .50 .50

Mosques A380

Designs: 20c, Goze Mosque. 80c, Al-Nejashi Mosque. 3b, Sheh Hussein Mosque, Dire.

**2011, May 24** **Litho.** ***Perf. 14***
**1750-1752** A380 Set of 3 .50 .50

Monasteries and Churches — A381

Designs: 35c, Zoz Amba St. George's Monastery, Gonder. 65c, Meskele Kiristonse Church, Wollo, vert. 3b, Debre Damo Abuna Aregawi Monastery, Tigrai, vert.

**2011, June 9**
**1753-1755** A381 Set of 3 .50 .50

Bridges A382

Designs: 20c, Tezeke Bridge No. 3. 80c, Hidassie Bridge. 1b, Beshela River Bridge. 2b, Blue Nile Bridge.

**2011, Sept. 2** **Litho.** ***Perf. 14x13¼***
**1756-1759** A382 Set of 4 .50 .50

Martyr's Monuments A383

Designs: 40c, Amhara Region Martyr's Monument, Bahir Dar. 60c, Oromo Martyr's Monument, Adama. 3b, Tigrai Region Martyr's Monument, Mekelle, horiz.

**2011, Sept. 9** ***Perf. 13¼x13, 13x13¼***
**1760-1762** A383 Set of 3 .50 .50

Coffee Ceremony A384

Designs: 20c, Coffee pots. 80c, Preparation of coffee. 1b, Bean roasting. 2b, Pouring of coffee into cups.

**2011, Dec. 20** ***Perf. 13¼x14***
**1763-1766** A384 Set of 4 .50 .50

Medicinal Plants A385

Designs: 20c, Lippia adoensis. 35c, Artemisia absinthium. 45c, Thymus schimperi. 3b, Ocimum lamiifolium.

**2012, Apr. 10** ***Perf. 14x13¼***
**1767-1770** A385 Set of 4 .45 .45

Addis Ababa Monuments — A386

Designs: 40c, Lion of Judah Monument. 60c, Ras Mekonen Monument. 1b, Lion of Judah Monument, vert. 2b, Menelik II Monument, vert.

**2012, July 5** ***Perf. 14x13¼, 13¼x14***
**1771-1774** A386 Set of 4 .45 .45

Writers — A387

Designs: 20c, Temesgen Gebre. 80c, Hiruy Woldeslassie. 1b, Yoftahe Nigussie. 2b, Afework Gebreyesus.

**2012, Sept. 7** ***Perf. 13¼x14***
**1775-1778** A387 Set of 4 .45 .45

Addis Ababa, 125th Anniv. (in 2011) — A388

Various views of Addis Ababa: 15c, 35c, 2b, 4b.

***Perf. 13¾x13½***

**2013, Aug. 20** **Litho.**
**1779-1782** A388 Set of 4 .70 .70

Dated 2012.

African Union, 50th Anniv. — A389

African Union emblem, "50," and: 10c, Year of Pan-Africanism emblem, building. 40c, Building, diff. 2b, Assembly hall. 4b, Map of Africa, doves, airplane, road, farm field.

**2013, Dec. 3** **Litho.** ***Perf. 13¼x14***
**1783-1786** A389 Set of 4 .70 .70

Ethio Telecom A390

Designs: 10c, Man holding wireless telephone console. 40c, Woman holding mobile telephone, woman using wall-mounted telephone, old dial telephone, vert. 2b, Man and woman using computer. 4b, Satellite, satellite dish, map, vert.

***Perf. 14x13¼, 13¼x14***

**2014, May 13** **Litho.**
**1787-1790** A390 Set of 4 .70 .70

Traditional Costumes of Southern Ethiopian People A391

Map and costumes of the: 15c, Karo. 35c, Erbore. 2b, Hamer. 4b, Daasanach.

**2014, May 27** **Litho.** ***Perf. 14x13¼***
**1791-1794** A391 Set of 4 .70 .70

Ethiopian Orthodox Tewahedo Churches and Monasteries — A392

Designs: 50c, Orra Kidanemihiret Zege (monastery), Tana Island. 1b, Kibran Gebriel (monastery), Tana Island. 2b, Debrebirihan Silassie (church), Gonder, vert. 3b, Tsion Mariam Church, Axum.

***Perf. 14x13¼, 13¼x14***

**2014, June 12** **Litho.**
**1795-1798** A392 Set of 4 .70 .70

Rift Valley Sites A393

Designs: 5c, Salt deposits, Dallol. 25c, Sulfur deposits, Dallol. 30c, Brine ponds, Dallol. 45c, Erta Ale Volcano erupting. 65c, Ash plume over Erta Ale Volcano. 4b, Erta Ale caldera.

**2014, Aug. 26** **Litho.** ***Perf. 14***
**1799-1804** A393 Set of 6 .60 .60

University of Gondar, 60th Anniv. — A394

Designs: 5c, Millennium Steps, Referral Hospital, Health team training group on horses in 1964, new campus. 45c, President's office. 2b, Main gate. 4b, 60th anniv. emblem, vert.

**2014, Dec. 2 Litho. *Perf. 13½***
**1805-1808** A394 Set of 4 .65 .65

Ethiopian Airlines A395

Designs: 15c, Boeing 777-F6N cargo plane. 35c, Boeing 777-200R passenger plane. 2b, Ethiopian Airlines Star Alliance jet. 4b, Boeing 787 Dreamliner.

**2014, Dec. 25 Litho. *Perf. 13x13¼***
**1809-1812** A395 Set of 4 .65 .65
*1812a* Booklet pane of 16, 4 each #1809-1812, perf. 13x13¼ on 3 sides 2.60 —
Complete booklet, #1812a 2.60

Ethiopian Visual Artists Association — A396

Painters and their works: 10c, Yegezu Bisrat (1926-79). 40c, Emealaf Hiruy (1907-71). 2b, Belachew Yimer (1869-1957). 4b, Agegnehu Engida (1905-50).

**2015, Nov. 10 Litho. *Perf. 13¼***
**1813-1816** A396 Set of 4 .65 .65

Ethiopian National Archives and Libraries Agency, 70th Anniv. — A397

Designs: 10c, Sea of Computs. 15c, Ethiopian Cultural Medicine Book. 25c, Letter from Ethiopian King Theodros to Queen Victoria of Great Britain, 19th cent. 1b, Four Gospels Bible, 14th cent. 2b, Book of Enoch, 15th cent., horiz. 3b, National Archives, horiz.

***Perf. 13¼x13½, 13½x13¼***
**2016, Jan. 28 Litho.**
**1817-1822** A397 Set of 6 .65 .65

Palaces — A398

Designs: 10c, Emperor Menelik Palace, Fit Ber Gate. 40c, Emperor Menelik Palace, Entoto. 2b, Guenete Leul Palace and gate, Addis Ababa. 4b, National Palace, Addis Ababa.

***Perf. 13¼x13½***
**2016, Feb. 18 Litho.**
**1823-1826** A398 Set of 4 .65 .65

Haramaya University, 60th Anniv. A399

Designs: 5c, Parking lot and Administration building. 45c, Agricultural research plot, dairy production. 2b, Main gate. 4b, 60th anniv. emblem, vert.

***Perf. 13½x13¼, 13¼x13½***
**2016, Apr. 21 Litho.**
**1827-1830** A399 Set of 4 .60 .60

Waterfalls A400

Designs: 10c, Habera River Falls, Bale. 40c, Sor Waterfalls, Ilu Abba Bora. 2b, Blue Nile Falls, Gojam. 4b, Ajora Falls, Wolaitta.

***Perf. 13½x13¼***
**2016, June 14 Litho.**
**1831-1834** A400 Set of 4 .60 .60

Ministry of Urban Development and Housing — A401

Designs: 50c, Building under construction. 1b, Housing complexes and bricks. 2b, Main office. 3b, Emblem.

***Perf. 13½x13¼***
**2016, Sept. 28 Litho.**
**1835-1838** A401 Set of 4 .60 .60

Snakes A402

Designs: 50c, Ethiopian house snake. 1b, Abyssinian house snake. 2b, Ethiopian blind snake. 3b, Ethiopian mountain adder.

**2016, Oct. 27 Litho. *Perf. 13½x13¼***
**1839-1842** A402 Set of 4 .60 .60

Defeat of Italy In East African Campaign, 75th Anniv. — A403

Designs: No. 1843, 1b, People on gallows, statue at left, monuments, four Ethiopians in foreground, green frame. No. 1844, 1b, Four Ethiopians, monument at center, green frame. No. 1845, 1b, Ethiopians planting flag in ground, monument, train, dam, tractor, red frame. No. 1846, 1b, Eight Ethiopians, monument at center, gray green frame. No. 1847, 1b, Six Ethiopians, monument at center, blue frame. 1.50b, Two Ethiopians, monument at center, blue frame.

**2016, Nov. 6 Litho. *Perf. 13½x13¾***
**1843-1848** A403 Set of 6 .60 .60

Fish A404

Map and: 5c, Labeobarbus marcophtalmus. 45c, Labeobarbus gorguari. 1b, Labeobarbus acutirostris. 5b, Labeobarbus osseensis.

***Perf. 13½x13¼***
**2017, Mar. 21 Litho.**
**1849-1852** A404 Set of 4 .60 .60

Dated 2016.

---

## SEMI-POSTAL STAMPS

Types of 1931, Overprinted in Red at Upper Left

***Perf. 12x12½, 12½x12***
**1936, Feb. 24 Unwmk.**
**B1** A27 1g light green .60 .60
**B2** A27 2g rose .60 .60
**B3** A25 4g blue .60 .60
**B4** A27 8g brown .85 .85
**B5** A25 1t purple .85 .85
*Nos. B1-B5 (5)* 3.50 3.50

Nos. B1-B5 were sold at twice face value, the surtax going to the Red Cross.

**Catalogue values for unused stamps in this section, from this point to the end of the section, are for Never Hinged items.**

### Nos. 289, 290, 292-294 Surcharged in Blue

***Perf. 13x13½***
**1949, June 13 Wmk. 282**
**B6** A53 8c + 8c deep org 2.50 2.50
**B7** A53 12c + 5c red 2.50 2.50
**B8** A53 30c + 15c org brn 4.00 4.00
**B9** A53 70c + 70c rose lilac 25.00 25.00
**B10** A53 $1 + 80c dk car rose 32.50 32.50
*Nos. B6-B10 (5)* 66.50 66.50

No. B10 exists with "80+" error.
See Nos. B16-B20.

Type A39 Surcharged in Red or Carmine

***Perf. 11½***
**1950, May 8 Unwmk. Photo.**
**Various Designs**
**Inscribed "Croix Rouge"**
**B11** A39 5c + 10c brt grn 1.50 2.00
**B12** A39 10c + 10c brt red 2.00 2.25
**B13** A39 25c + 10c brt bl 2.75 3.50
**B14** A39 50c + 10c dk yel brn 7.00 5.50
**B15** A39 1t + 10c brt vio 14.00 15.00
*Nos. B11-B15 (5)* 27.25 28.25

The surtax was for the Red Cross.

The surcharge includes two dots which invalidate the original surtax. The original surcharge with uneven cross was red, a 1951 printing with even cross was carmine. Forgeries exist.

### Nos. B6-B10 Overprinted in Black

***Perf. 13x13½***
**1951, Nov. 17 Wmk. 282**
**B16** A53 8c + 8c dp org .70 .70
**B17** A53 12c + 5c red .70 .70
**B18** A53 30c + 15c org brn 1.25 1.25
**B19** A53 70c + 70c rose lilac 12.00 12.00
**B20** A53 $1 + 80c dk car rose 20.00 20.00
*Nos. B16-B20 (5)* 34.65 34.65

No. B20 exists with "80 +" error.

Tree, Staff and Snake — SP1

**Wmk. 282**
**1951, Nov. 25 Engr. *Perf. 13***
**Lower Panel in Red**
**B21** SP1 5c + 2c dp bl grn .50 .25
**B22** SP1 10c + 3c orange .70 .30
**B23** SP1 15c + 3c dp bl .90 .50
**B24** SP1 30c + 5c red 2.00 1.25
**B25** SP1 50c + 7c red brn 5.00 3.00
**B26** SP1 $1 + 10c purple 10.00 5.00
*Nos. B21-B26 (6)* 19.10 10.30

The surtax was for anti-tuberculosis work.

**1958, Dec. 1**
**Lower Panel in Red**
**B27** SP1 20c + 3c dl pur .40 .30
**B28** SP1 25c + 4c emerald .50 .35
**B29** SP1 35c + 5c rose vio .75 .40
**B30** SP1 60c + 7c vio bl 1.50 .80
**B31** SP1 65c + 7c violet 3.00 1.75
**B32** SP1 80c + 9c car rose 5.00 3.00
*Nos. B27-B32 (6)* 11.15 6.60
*Nos. B21-B32 (12)* 26.85 15.35

The surtax was for anti-tuberculosis work.

Nos. B21-B32 were the only stamps on sale from Dec. 1-25, 1958.

### Type of Regular Issue, 1955, Overprinted and Surcharged

**Engr.; Cross Typo. in Red**
**1959, May 30 Wmk. 282**
**B33** A62 15c + 2c olive bister & rose red .70 .70
**B34** A62 20c + 3c vio & emer 1.00 1.00
**B35** A62 30c + 5c rose car & grnsh bl 1.75 1.75
*Nos. B33-B35 (3)* 3.45 3.45

Cent. of the Intl. Red Cross idea. Surtax for the Red Cross.

The overprint includes the cross, "RED CROSS CENTENARY" and date in two languages. The surcharge includes the date in Amharic and the new surtax. The surcharge was applied locally.

Design A39 Surcharged

*Perf. 11½*

**1960, May 7 Photo. Unwmk.**

| No. | Type | Value | Description | Unused | Used |
|---|---|---|---|---|---|
| **B36** | A39 | 5c + 1c | brt green | .85 | .85 |
| **B37** | A39 | 10c + 2c | brt red | 1.25 | 1.00 |
| **B38** | A39 | 25c + 3c | brt blue | 1.90 | 1.25 |
| **B39** | A39 | 50c + 4c | dk yel brn | 3.00 | 2.50 |
| **B40** | A39 | 1t + 5c | brt vio | 5.00 | 4.50 |
| | | | *Nos. B36-B40 (5)* | 12.00 | 10.10 |

25th anniversary of Ethiopian Red Cross. Forgeries exist.

Crippled Boy on Crutches — SP2

**Wmk. 282**

**1963, July 23 Engr. *Perf. 13½***

| No. | Type | Value | Description | Unused | Used |
|---|---|---|---|---|---|
| **B41** | SP2 | 10c + 2c | ultra | .40 | .40 |
| **B42** | SP2 | 15c + 3c | red | .60 | .45 |
| **B43** | SP2 | 50c + 5c | brt green | 1.90 | 1.60 |
| **B44** | SP2 | 60c + 5c | red lilac | 2.75 | 2.00 |
| | | | *Nos. B41-B44 (4)* | 5.65 | 4.45 |

The surtax was to aid the disabled.

## AIR POST STAMPS

Regular Issue of 1928 Handstamped in Violet, Red, Black or Green

*Perf. 13½x14*

**1929, Aug. 17 Unwmk.**

| No. | Type | Value | Description | Unused | Used |
|---|---|---|---|---|---|
| **C1** | A22 | ⅛m | orange & lt bl | .90 | *1.00* |
| **C2** | A23 | ¼m | ind & red org | .90 | *1.00* |
| **C3** | A22 | ½m | gray grn & blk | .90 | *1.00* |
| **C4** | A23 | 1m | dk car & blk | .90 | *1.00* |
| **C5** | A22 | 2m | dk blue & blk | 1.00 | *1.25* |
| **C6** | A23 | 4m | yellow & olive | 1.00 | *1.25* |
| **C7** | A22 | 8m | violet & olive | 1.00 | *1.25* |
| **C8** | A23 | 1t | org brn & vio | 1.25 | *1.25* |
| **C9** | A22 | 2t | green & bister | 1.60 | *2.00* |
| **C10** | A23 | 3t | choc & grn | 1.75 | *2.00* |
| | | | *Nos. C1-C10 (10)* | 11.20 | *13.00* |

The overprint signifies "17 August 1929-Airplane of the Ethiopian Government." The stamps commemorate the arrival at Addis Ababa of the 1st airplane of the Ethiopian Government.

There are 3 types of the overprint: (I) 19½mm high; "colon" at right of bottom word. (II) 20mm high; same "colon." (III) 19½mm high; no "colon." Many errors exist.

Symbols of Empire, Airplane and Map — AP1

**1931, June 17 Engr. *Perf. 12½***

| No. | Type | Value | Description | Unused | Used |
|---|---|---|---|---|---|
| **C11** | AP1 | 1g | orange red | .25 | *.25* |
| **C12** | AP1 | 2g | ultra | .25 | *.30* |
| **C13** | AP1 | 4g | violet | .25 | *.40* |
| **C14** | AP1 | 8g | blue green | .50 | *.80* |
| **C15** | AP1 | 1t | olive brown | 1.25 | *1.00* |
| **C16** | AP1 | 2t | carmine | 2.25 | *3.75* |
| **C17** | AP1 | 3t | yellow green | 3.25 | *5.00* |
| | | | *Nos. C11-C17 (7)* | 8.00 | *11.50* |

Nos. C11 to C17 exist imperforate.

*Reprints of C11 to C17 exist. Paper is thinner and gum whiter than the originals and the ink is heavy and shiny. Originals have ink that is dull and granular. Reprints usually sell at about one-tenth of above values.*

**Catalogue values for unused stamps in this section, from this point to the end of the section, are for Never Hinged items.**

**Nos. 250, 255 and 257 Surcharged in Black**

a

b

*Perf. 14x13½*

**1947, Mar. 20 Unwmk.**

| No. | Type | Value | Description | Unused | Used |
|---|---|---|---|---|---|
| **C18** | A33 (a) | 12c | on 4c | 77.50 | 77.50 |
| **C19** | A33 (b) | 50c | on 25c | 72.50 | 72.50 |
| *a.* | | | "26-12-46" | 275.00 | |
| **C20** | A33 (b) | $2 | on 60c | 125.00 | 125.00 |
| *a.* | | | "26-12-46" | 340.00 | |
| | | | *Nos. C18-C20 (3)* | 275.00 | 275.00 |
| | | | Set, hinged | 175.00 | |

Resumption of airmail service, 12/29/46.

Franklin D. Roosevelt AP2

Design: $2, Haile Selassie.

**Engraved and Photogravure**

**1947, May 23 *Perf. 12½***

| No. | Type | Value | Description | Unused | Used |
|---|---|---|---|---|---|
| **C21** | AP2 | $1 | dk purple & sepia | 12.50 | 12.50 |
| **C22** | AP2 | $2 | carmine & dp blue | 17.50 | 17.50 |

Farmer Plowing AP3

Designs: 10c, 25c, Zoquala, extinct volcano. 30c, 35c, Tesissat Falls, Abai River. 65c, 70c, Amba Alaguie. $1, Sacala, source of Nile. $3, Gorgora and Dembia, Lake Tana. $5, Magdala, former capital. $10, Ras Dashan, mountain peak.

*Perf. 13x13½*

**1947-55 Wmk. 282 Engr.**

| No. | Type | Value | Description | Unused | Used |
|---|---|---|---|---|---|
| **C23** | AP3 | 8c | purple brown | .30 | .30 |
| **C24** | AP3 | 10c | bright green | .30 | .30 |
| **C25** | AP3 | 25c | dull pur ('52) | .45 | .30 |
| **C26** | AP3 | 30c | orange yellow | .95 | .30 |
| **C27** | AP3 | 35c | blue ('55) | .95 | .45 |
| **C28** | AP3 | 65c | purple ('55) | 1.10 | .80 |
| **C29** | AP3 | 70c | red | 1.75 | .80 |
| **C30** | AP3 | $1 | deep blue | 2.00 | .95 |
| **C31** | AP3 | $3 | rose lilac | 7.75 | 4.75 |
| **C32** | AP3 | $5 | red brown | 15.00 | 6.75 |
| **C33** | AP3 | $10 | rose violet | 30.00 | 17.50 |
| | | | *Nos. C23-C33 (11)* | 60.55 | 33.20 |

For overprints see Nos. C64-C70.

UPU Monument, Bern — AP4

**1950, Apr. 3 Unwmk. *Perf. 12½***

| No. | Type | Value | Description | Unused | Used |
|---|---|---|---|---|---|
| **C34** | AP4 | 5c | green & red | .25 | .25 |
| **C35** | AP4 | 15c | dk sl grn & car | 1.40 | 1.40 |
| **C36** | AP4 | 25c | org yel & grn | 1.75 | 1.40 |
| **C37** | AP4 | 50c | carmine & ultra | 4.25 | 3.25 |
| | | | *Nos. C34-C37 (4)* | 7.65 | 6.30 |

75th anniv. of the UPU.

No. C34 exists in the colors of Nos. C35-C37. These are considered to be trial color proofs.

Convair Plane over Mountains AP5

**Engraved and Lithographed**

**1955, Dec. 30 Unwmk. *Perf. 12½***

**Center Multicolored**

| No. | Type | Value | Description | Unused | Used |
|---|---|---|---|---|---|
| **C38** | AP5 | 10c | gray green | 1.25 | .30 |
| **C39** | AP5 | 15c | carmine | 1.60 | .80 |
| **C40** | AP5 | 20c | violet | 2.50 | 1.25 |
| | | | *Nos. C38-C40 (3)* | 5.35 | 2.35 |

10th anniversary of Ethiopian Airlines.

Promulgating the Constitution — AP6

*Perf. 14x13½*

**1956, July 16 Engr. Wmk. 282**

| No. | Type | Value | Description | Unused | Used |
|---|---|---|---|---|---|
| **C41** | AP6 | 10c | redsh brn & ultra | .60 | .70 |
| **C42** | AP6 | 15c | dk car rose & ol grn | .95 | 1.00 |
| **C43** | AP6 | 20c | blue & org red | 1.25 | 1.00 |
| **C44** | AP6 | 25c | purple & green | 1.40 | 1.60 |
| **C45** | AP6 | 30c | dk grn & red brn | 2.40 | 2.50 |
| | | | *Nos. C41-C45 (5)* | 6.60 | 6.80 |

25th anniversary of the constitution.

Aksum AP7

Ancient Capitals: 10c, Lalibela. 15c, Gondar. 20c, Mekele. 25c, Ankober.

**1957, Feb. 7 *Perf. 14***

**Centers in Green**

| No. | Type | Value | Description | Unused | Used |
|---|---|---|---|---|---|
| **C46** | AP7 | 5c | red brown | .75 | .40 |
| **C47** | AP7 | 10c | rose carmine | .75 | .40 |
| **C48** | AP7 | 15c | red orange | .90 | .50 |
| **C49** | AP7 | 20c | ultramarine | 1.40 | .70 |
| **C50** | AP7 | 25c | claret | 2.10 | 1.00 |
| | | | *Nos. C46-C50 (5)* | 5.90 | 3.00 |

Amharic "A" — AP8

Designs: Various Amharic characters and views of Addis Ababa. The characters, arranged by values, spell Addis Ababa.

**1957, Feb. 14 Engr.**

**Amharic Letters in Scarlet**

| No. | Type | Value | Description | Unused | Used |
|---|---|---|---|---|---|
| **C51** | AP8 | 5c | ultra, *sal pink* | .35 | .35 |
| **C52** | AP8 | 10c | ol grn, *pink* | .35 | .35 |
| **C53** | AP8 | 15c | dl pur, *yel* | .55 | .35 |
| **C54** | AP8 | 20c | grn, *buff* | .90 | .40 |
| **C55** | AP8 | 25c | plum, *pale bl* | 2.50 | .55 |
| **C56** | AP8 | 30c | red, *pale grn* | 1.75 | .60 |
| | | | *Nos. C51-C56 (6)* | 6.40 | 2.60 |

70th anniversary of Addis Ababa.

Map, Rock Church at Lalibela and Obelisk AP9

**1958, Apr. 15 Wmk. 282 *Perf. 13½***

| No. | Type | Value | Description | Unused | Used |
|---|---|---|---|---|---|
| **C57** | AP9 | 10c | green | .25 | .25 |
| **C58** | AP9 | 20c | rose red | 1.10 | .25 |
| **C59** | AP9 | 30c | bright blue | 1.75 | .90 |
| | | | *Nos. C57-C59 (3)* | 3.10 | 1.40 |

Conf. of Independent African States, Accra, Apr. 15-22.

Map of Africa and UN Emblem AP10

**1958, Dec. 29 *Perf. 13***

| No. | Type | Value | Description | Unused | Used |
|---|---|---|---|---|---|
| **C60** | AP10 | 5c | emerald | .25 | .25 |
| **C61** | AP10 | 20c | carmine rose | .55 | .25 |
| **C62** | AP10 | 25c | ultramarine | .75 | .55 |
| **C63** | AP10 | 50c | pale purple | 1.50 | .75 |
| | | | *Nos. C60-C63 (4)* | 3.05 | 1.80 |

1st session of the UN Economic Conf. for Africa, opened in Addis Ababa Dec. 29.

**Nos. C23-C29 Overprinted**

*Perf. 13x13½*

**1959, Aug. 16 Engr. Wmk. 282**

| No. | Type | Value | Description | Unused | Used |
|---|---|---|---|---|---|
| **C64** | AP3 | 8c | purple brown | .50 | .30 |
| **C65** | AP3 | 10c | brt green | .70 | .35 |
| **C66** | AP3 | 25c | dull purple | 1.05 | .40 |
| **C67** | AP3 | 30c | orange yellow | 1.15 | .60 |
| **C68** | AP3 | 35c | blue | 1.40 | .65 |
| **C69** | AP3 | 65c | purple | 2.25 | 1.00 |
| **C70** | AP3 | 70c | red | 2.75 | 1.25 |
| | | | *Nos. C64-C70 (7)* | 9.80 | 4.55 |

30th anniv. of Ethiopian airmail service.

Ethiopian Soldier and Map of Congo — AP11

***Perf. 11½***

**1962, July 23 Unwmk. Photo.**

**Granite Paper**

| | | | | |
|---|---|---|---|---|
| **C71** | AP11 | 15c org, bl, brn & grn | .25 | .25 |
| **C72** | AP11 | 50c pur, bl, brn & grn | .75 | .65 |
| **C73** | AP11 | 60c red, bl, brn & grn | 1.40 | .80 |
| | | *Nos. C71-C73 (3)* | 2.40 | 1.70 |

2nd anniv. of the Ethiopian contingent of the UN forces in the Congo and in honor of the 70th birthday of Emperor Haile Selassie.

Globe with Map of Africa — AP12

**1963, May 22 Granite Paper**

| | | | | |
|---|---|---|---|---|
| **C74** | AP12 | 10c magenta & blk | .35 | .35 |
| **C75** | AP12 | 40c emerald & blk | 1.75 | 1.00 |
| **C76** | AP12 | 60c blue & blk | 2.75 | 1.25 |
| | | *Nos. C74-C76 (3)* | 4.85 | 2.60 |

Conf. of African heads of state for African Unity, Addis Ababa.

**Bird Type of Regular Issue**

Birds: 10c, Black-headed forest oriole. 15c, Broad-tailed paradise whydah, vert. 20c, Lammergeier, vert. 50c, White-checked touraco. 80c, Purple indigo bird.

**1963, Sept. 12 *Perf. 11½***

**Granite Paper**

| | | | | |
|---|---|---|---|---|
| **C77** | A74 | 10c multicolored | .60 | .25 |
| **C78** | A74 | 15c multicolored | .75 | .25 |
| **C79** | A74 | 20c blue, blk & ocher | 1.50 | .60 |
| **C80** | A74 | 50c lemon & multi | 2.40 | 1.10 |
| **C81** | A74 | 80c ultra, blk & brn | 4.75 | 1.90 |
| | | *Nos. C77-C81 (5)* | 10.00 | 4.10 |

Swimming AP13

Sport: 10c, Basketball, vert. 15c, Javelin. 80c, Soccer game in stadium.

***Perf. 14x13½***

**1964, Sept. 15 Litho. Unwmk.**

| | | | | |
|---|---|---|---|---|
| **C82** | AP13 | 5c multicolored | .30 | .25 |
| **C83** | AP13 | 10c multicolored | .30 | .25 |
| **C84** | AP13 | 15c multicolored | .85 | .55 |
| **C85** | AP13 | 80c multicolored | 3.00 | 1.10 |
| | | *Nos. C82-C85 (4)* | 4.45 | 2.15 |

18th Olympic Games, Tokyo, Oct. 10-25.

Queen Elizabeth II and Emperor Haile Selassie — AP14

**1965, Feb. 1 Photo. *Perf. 11½***

**Granite Paper**

| | | | | |
|---|---|---|---|---|
| **C86** | AP14 | 5c multicolored | .45 | .45 |
| **C87** | AP14 | 35c multicolored | 1.40 | 1.40 |
| **C88** | AP14 | 60c multicolored | 2.10 | 1.40 |
| | | *Nos. C86-C88 (3)* | 3.95 | 3.25 |

Visit of Queen Elizabeth II, Feb. 1-8.

Koka Dam and Power Plant — AP15

Designs: 15c, Sugar cane field. 50c, Blue Nile Bridge. 60c, Gondar castles. 80c, Coffee tree. $1, Cattle at water hole. $3, Camels at well. $5, Ethiopian Air Lines jet plane.

**1965, July 19 Unwmk. *Perf. 11½***

**Granite Paper**

**Portrait in Black**

| | | | | |
|---|---|---|---|---|
| **C89** | AP15 | 15c vio brn & buff | .25 | .25 |
| **C90** | AP15 | 40c vio bl & lt bl | .45 | .30 |
| **C91** | AP15 | 50c grn & lt bl | .70 | .35 |
| **C92** | AP15 | 60c claret & yel | 1.20 | .60 |
| **C93** | AP15 | 80c grn, yel & red | 1.50 | .70 |
| **C94** | AP15 | $1 brn & lt bl | 1.75 | .85 |
| **C95** | AP15 | $3 claret & pink | 6.00 | 2.25 |
| **C96** | AP15 | $5 ultra & lt bl | 12.75 | 4.25 |
| | | *Nos. C89-C96 (8)* | 24.60 | 9.55 |

**Bird Type of Regular Issue**

Birds: 10c, White-collared kingfisher. 15c, Blue-breasted bee-eater. 25c, African paradise flycatcher. 40c, Village weaver. 60c, White-collared pigeon.

**1966, Feb. 15 Photo. *Perf. 11½***

**Granite Paper**

| | | | | |
|---|---|---|---|---|
| **C97** | A74 | 10c dull yel & multi | .90 | .25 |
| **C98** | A74 | 15c lt blue & multi | 1.20 | .25 |
| **C99** | A74 | 25c gray & multi | 2.50 | .80 |
| **C100** | A74 | 40c pink & multi | 4.75 | 1.10 |
| **C101** | A74 | 60c multicolored | 5.50 | 1.75 |
| | | *Nos. C97-C101 (5)* | 14.85 | 4.15 |

Black Rhinoceros — AP16

Animals: 10c, Leopard. 20c, Black-and-white colobus (monkey). 30c, Mountain nyala. 60c, Nubian ibex.

**1966, June 20 Litho. *Perf. 13***

| | | | | |
|---|---|---|---|---|
| **C102** | AP16 | 5c dp grn, blk & gray | .25 | .25 |
| **C103** | AP16 | 10c grn, blk & ocher | .55 | .25 |
| **C104** | AP16 | 20c cit, blk & grn | 1.10 | .25 |
| **C105** | AP16 | 30c yel grn, blk & ocher | 1.75 | .25 |
| **C106** | AP16 | 60c yel grn, blk & dk brn | 3.25 | .65 |
| | | *Nos. C102-C106 (5)* | 6.90 | 1.65 |

**Bird Type of Regular Issue**

Birds: 10c, Blue-winged goose, vert. 15c, Yellow-billed duck. 20c, Wattled ibis. 25c, Striped swallow. 40c, Black-winged lovebird, vert.

**1967, Sept. 29 Photo. *Perf. 11½***

**Granite Paper**

| | | | | |
|---|---|---|---|---|
| **C107** | A74 | 10c lt ultra & multi | .25 | .25 |
| **C108** | A74 | 15c green & multi | 1.40 | .25 |
| **C109** | A74 | 20c yellow & multi | 1.60 | .25 |
| **C110** | A74 | 25c salmon & multi | 2.75 | .25 |
| **C111** | A74 | 40c pink & multi | 5.75 | 1.60 |
| | | *Nos. C107-C111 (5)* | 11.75 | 2.60 |

## SPECIAL DELIVERY STAMPS

**Catalogue values for unused stamps in this section are for Never Hinged items.**

Motorcycle Messenger — SD1

Addis Ababa Post Office SD2

**Unwmk.**

**1947, Apr. 24 Engr. *Perf. 13***

| | | | | |
|---|---|---|---|---|
| **E1** | SD1 | 30c orange brown | 5.00 | 1.25 |
| **E2** | SD2 | 50c blue | 9.00 | 3.50 |

**1954-62 Wmk. 282**

| | | | | |
|---|---|---|---|---|
| **E3** | SD1 | 30c org brown ('62) | 5.75 | 3.75 |
| **E4** | SD2 | 50c blue | 3.75 | 1.40 |

## POSTAGE DUE STAMPS

Very Fine examples of Nos. J1-J42 will have perforations touching the design on one or more sides.

Nos. 1-4 and unissued values Overprinted

***Perf. 14x13½***

**1896, June 10 Unwmk.**

**Black Overprint**

| | | | |
|---|---|---|---|
| **J1** | A1 | ¼g green | 1.45 |
| **J2** | A1 | ½g red | 1.45 |
| **J3** | A1 | 4g lilac brown | 1.00 |
| | *a.* | Without overprint | 1.00 |
| **J4** | A1 | 8g violet | 1.00 |
| | *a.* | Without overprint | 1.00 |

**Red Overprint**

| | | | |
|---|---|---|---|
| **J5** | A1 | 1g blue | 1.45 |
| **J6** | A1 | 2g dark brown | 1.45 |
| **J7** | A1 | 16g black | 1.00 |
| | *a.* | Without overprint | 1.00 |
| | | *Nos. J1-J7 (7)* | 8.80 |

Nos. J1-J7 were not issued. Forgeries exist.

**Nos. 1-7 Handstamped in Various Colors**

a

**1905, Apr.**

| | | | | |
|---|---|---|---|---|
| **J8** | A1 (a) | ¼g green | 55.00 | 55.00 |
| **J9** | A1 (a) | ½g red | 55.00 | 55.00 |
| **J10** | A1 (a) | 1g blue | 55.00 | 55.00 |
| **J11** | A1 (a) | 2g dk brown | 55.00 | 55.00 |
| **J12** | A2 (a) | 4g lilac brown | 55.00 | 55.00 |
| **J13** | A2 (a) | 8g violet | 55.00 | 55.00 |
| **J14** | A2 (a) | 16g black | 55.00 | 55.00 |
| | | *Nos. J8-J14 (7)* | 385.00 | 385.00 |

b

**1905, Aug.**

| | | | | |
|---|---|---|---|---|
| **J15** | A1 (b) | ¼g green | 55.00 | 55.00 |
| **J16** | A1 (b) | ½g red | 55.00 | 55.00 |
| **J17** | A1 (b) | 1g blue | 55.00 | 55.00 |
| **J18** | A1 (b) | 2g dark brown | 55.00 | 55.00 |
| **J19** | A2 (b) | 4g lilac brown | 55.00 | 55.00 |
| **J20** | A2 (b) | 8g violet | 55.00 | 55.00 |
| **J21** | A2 (b) | 16g black | 55.00 | 55.00 |
| | | *Nos. J15-J21 (7)* | 385.00 | 385.00 |

Excellent forgeries of Nos. J8-J42 exist.

Nos. 1-7 Handstamped in Blue or Violet

**1905, Sept.**

| | | | | |
|---|---|---|---|---|
| **J22** | A1 | ¼g green | 14.50 | 14.50 |
| **J23** | A1 | ½g red | 14.50 | 14.50 |
| **J24** | A1 | 1g blue | 14.50 | 14.50 |
| **J25** | A1 | 2g dark brown | 14.50 | 14.50 |
| **J26** | A2 | 4g lilac brown | 14.50 | 14.50 |
| **J27** | A2 | 8g violet | 21.00 | 21.00 |
| **J28** | A2 | 16g black | 25.00 | 25.00 |
| | | *Nos. J22-J28 (7)* | 118.50 | 118.50 |

Nos. J22-J27 exist with inverted overprint, also No. J22 with double overprint.

Forgeries exist.

**With Additional Surcharge of Value Handstamped as on Nos. 71-77**

**1907, July 1**

| | | | | |
|---|---|---|---|---|
| **J29** | A1 (e) | ¼ on ¼g grn | 14.00 | 14.00 |
| **J30** | A1 (e) | ½ on ½g red | 14.00 | 14.00 |
| **J31** | A1 (f) | 1 on 1g blue | 14.00 | 14.00 |
| **J32** | A1 (f) | 2 on 2g dk brown | 14.00 | 14.00 |
| **J33** | A2 (f) | 4 on 4g lilac brn | 14.00 | 14.00 |
| **J34** | A2 (f) | 8 on 8g violet | 14.00 | 14.00 |
| **J35** | A2 (f) | 16 on 16g blk | 22.50 | 22.50 |
| | | *Nos. J29-J35 (7)* | 106.50 | 106.50 |

Nos. J30-J35 exist with inverted surcharge. Nos. J30, J33-J35 exist with double surcharge.

Nos. 1-7 Handstamped in Black

**1908, Dec. 1**

| | | | | |
|---|---|---|---|---|
| **J36** | A1 | ¼g green | 1.40 | 1.25 |
| **J37** | A1 | ½g red | 1.40 | 1.25 |
| **J38** | A1 | 1g blue | 1.40 | 1.25 |
| **J39** | A1 | 2g dark brown | 1.75 | 1.50 |
| **J40** | A2 | 4g lilac brown | 2.50 | 2.50 |
| **J41** | A2 | 8g violet | 5.50 | 6.25 |
| **J42** | A2 | 16g black | 17.50 | 20.00 |
| | | *Nos. J36-J42 (7)* | 31.45 | 34.00 |

Nos. J36 to J42 exist with inverted overprint and Nos. J36, J37, J38 and J40 with double overprint.

Forgeries of Nos. J36-J56 exist.

**Same Handstamp on Nos. 87-93**

**1912, Dec. 1 *Perf. 11½***

| | | | | |
|---|---|---|---|---|
| **J43** | A3 | ¼g blue green | 1.75 | 1.25 |
| **J44** | A3 | ½g rose | 1.75 | 1.50 |

**1913, July 1**

| | | | | |
|---|---|---|---|---|
| **J45** | A3 | 1g green & org | 6.00 | 4.25 |
| **J46** | A4 | 2g blue | 7.00 | 6.00 |
| **J47** | A4 | 4g green & car | 11.00 | 7.00 |
| **J48** | A5 | 8g ver & dp grn | 14.00 | 11.00 |
| **J49** | A5 | 16g ver & car | 35.00 | 27.50 |
| | | *Nos. J43-J49 (7)* | 76.50 | 58.50 |

Nos. J43-J49, all exist with inverted, double and double, one inverted overprint.

**Same Handstamp on Nos. 120-124 in Blue Black**

**1925-27 *Perf. 11½***

| | | | | |
|---|---|---|---|---|
| **J50** | A6 | ⅛g violet & brn | *18.00* | *18.00* |
| **J51** | A6 | ¼g bl grn & db | *18.00* | *18.00* |
| **J52** | A6 | ½g scar & ol grn | *20.00* | *20.00* |
| **J53** | A9 | 1g rose lil & gray grn | *20.00* | *20.00* |
| **J54** | A9 | 2g dp ultra & fawn | *20.00* | *20.00* |
| | | *Nos. J50-J54 (5)* | *96.00* | *96.00* |

**Same Handstamp on Nos. 110, 112**

**1917 (?)**

| | | | | |
|---|---|---|---|---|
| **J55** | A3 (i) | 1g green & org | *30.00* | *30.00* |
| **J56** | A4 (j) | 2g blue | *30.00* | *30.00* |

The status of Nos. J55-J56 is questioned.

**Catalogue values for unused stamps in this section, from this point to the end of the section, are for Never Hinged items.**

D2

*Perf. 11½*

**1951, Apr. 2 Unwmk. Litho.**

**J57** D2 1c emerald .35 .25
**J58** D2 5c rose red .75 .25
**J59** D2 10c violet 1.40 .55
**J60** D2 20c ocher 2.00 1.25
**J61** D2 50c bright ultra 3.75 2.75
**J62** D2 $1 rose lilac 7.75 3.75
*Nos. J57-J62 (6)* 16.00 8.80

Nos. J57-J62 were reissued in 1968 on slightly yellowish paper.

## OCCUPATION STAMPS

**Issued under Italian Occupation**

100 Centesimi = 1 Lira

OS1

Emperor Victor Emmanuel III — OS2

**1936 Wmk. 140 *Perf. 14***

**N1** OS1 10c org brn 16.00 9.50
**N2** OS1 20c purple 14.50 4.00
**N3** OS2 25c dark green 9.50 .80
**N4** OS2 30c dark brown 9.50 1.60
**N5** OS2 50c rose car 4.00 .40
**N6** OS1 75c deep orange 36.00 8.00
**N7** OS1 1.25 l deep blue 36.00 12.00
*Nos. N1-N7 (7)* 125.50 36.30
Set, never hinged 300.00

Issued: Nos. N3-N5, May 22; others Dec. 5.

For later issues see Italian East Africa.

# FALKLAND ISLANDS

ˈfol-klənd ˈī-ləndz

LOCATION — A group of islands about 300 miles east of the Straits of Magellan at the southern limit of South America

GOVT. — British Crown Colony

AREA — 4,700 sq. mi.

POP. — 2,607 (1996)

CAPITAL — Stanley

Dependencies of the Falklands are South Georgia and South Sandwich. In March 1962, three other dependencies — South Shetland Islands, South Orkneys and Graham Land—became the new separate colony of British Antarctic Territory. In 1985 South Georgia and the South Sandwich Islands became a separate colony.

12 Pence = 1 Shilling
20 Shillings = 1 Pound
100 Pence = 1 Pound (1971)

**Catalogue values for unused stamps in this country are for Never Hinged items, beginning with Scott 97 in the regular postage section, Scott B1 in the semi-postal section, Scott J1 in the postage due section, Scott 1L1 in Falkland Island Dependencies regular issues, Scott 1LB1 in Falkland Island Dependencies semi-postals, and Scott 2L1, 3L1, 4L1, 5L1 in the Issues for Separate Islands.**

Values for unused stamps are for examples with original gum as defined in the catalogue introduction.

Nos. 1-4, 7-8, and some printings of Nos. 5-6, exist with straight edges on one or two sides, being the imperforate margins of the sheets. This occurs in 24 out of 60 stamps. Catalogue values are for stamps with perforations on all sides.

Queen Victoria — A1

**1878-79 Unwmk. Engr. *Perf. 14***

**1** A1 1p claret 850.00 500.00
**2** A1 4p dark gray ('79) 1,400. 200.00
**3** A1 6p green 125.00 85.00
**4** A1 1sh bister brown 85.00 80.00

**1883-95 Wmk. 2**

**5** A1 1p brt claret ('94) 130.00 95.00
*a.* 1p claret 425.00 190.00
*b.* Horiz. pair, imperf. vert. *90,000.*
*c.* 1p red brown ('91) 300.00 95.00
*d.* Diag. half of #5c used as ½p on cover *4,250.*
**6** A1 4p ol gray ('95) 14.00 27.50
*a.* 4p gray black 750.00 100.00
*b.* 4p olive gray black ('89) 200.00 65.00
*c.* 4p brownish black ('94) 1,300. 400.00

No. 6c has watermark reversed.

For surcharge see No. 19E.

**1886 Wmk. 2 Sideways**

**7** A1 1p claret 95.00 65.00
*a.* 1p brownish claret 125.00 80.00
*b.* Diagonal half of #7a used as ½p on cover *4,250.*
**8** A1 4p olive gray 525.00 60.00
*a.* 4p pale gray black 850.00 90.00

For surcharge see No. 19.

**1891-1902 Wmk. 2**

**9** A1 ½p green ('92) 19.00 18.00
*a.* ½p blue green 28.00 *32.50*
**10** A1 ½p yel green ('99) 3.25 *3.50*
**11** A1 1p orange brown 130.00 85.00
*a.* Diagonal half used as ½p on cover *4,250.*
**11B** A1 1p pale red ('99) 9.00 3.50
**12** A1 1p org red ('02) 17.50 4.75
*a.* 1p Venetian red ('95) 32.50 20.00
**13** A1 2p magenta ('96) 7.00 14.00
**14** A1 2½p deep blue ('94) 275.00 160.00
**15** A1 2½p ultra ('94) 50.00 14.00
*a.* 2½p pale ultra ('98) 70.00 20.00
*b.* 2½p dull blue 350.00 35.00
*c.* 2½p deep ultra ('01) 50.00 42.50
*d.* 2½p pale chalky ultra 275.00 60.00
**16** A1 6p yellow ('96) 55.00 55.00
*a.* 6p orange ('92) 325.00 225.00
**17** A1 9p ver ('95) 60.00 *65.00*
*a.* 9p salmon ('96) 65.00 *70.00*
**18** A1 1sh gray brn ('95) 80.00 65.00
*a.* 1sh bis brn ('96) 75.00 55.00
*Nos. 9-18 (11)* 705.75 487.75

Nos. 7 and 5a Surcharged in Black

**1891 Wmk. 2 Sideways**

**19** A1 ½p on half of 1p, #7 725.00 360.00
*d.* Unsevered pair 4,000. 1,600.

**Wmk. 2**

**19E** A1 ½p on half of 1p, #5a 825.00 325.00
*f.* Unsevered pair 5,000. 1,800.

Genuine used bisects should be canceled with a segmented circular cork cancel. Any other cancel must be linked by date to known mail ship departures. This surcharge exists on "souvenir" bisects, including examples of No. 11, and can be found inverted, double and sideways.

A3

A4

**1898 Wmk. 1**

**20** A3 2sh6p dark blue 290.00 290.00
**21** A4 5sh brown red 260.00 260.00

A5

A6

King Edward VII

**1904-07 Wmk. 3 *Perf. 14***

**22** A5 ½p yellow green 9.00 1.75
**23** A5 1p red, wmk. sideways ('07) 1.50 *4.25*
*a.* Wmk. upright ('04) 17.00 *1.75*
**24** A5 2p dull vio ('04) 25.00 *32.50*
**25** A5 2½p ultramarine 35.00 10.00
*a.* 2½p deep blue 300.00 200.00
**26** A5 6p orange ('05) 50.00 *57.50*
**27** A5 1sh bis brn ('05) 50.00 40.00
**28** A6 3sh gray green 180.00 160.00
**29** A6 5sh dull red ('05) 240.00 160.00
*Nos. 22-29 (8)* 590.50 466.00

A7

A8

King George V

**1912-14 *Perf. 13¾x14, 14 (#36-40)***

**30** A7 ½p yel grn 3.00 3.75
**31** A7 1p red 5.50 2.75
**32** A7 2p brn vio 30.00 *24.00*
**33** A7 2½p deep ultra 27.50 *25.00*
**34** A7 6p orange 17.50 *22.50*
**35** A7 1sh bis brn 40.00 *37.50*
**36** A8 3sh dark green 100.00 *95.00*
**37** A8 5sh brown red 120.00 *120.00*
**38** A8 5sh plum ('14) 300.00 *300.00*
**39** A8 10sh red, *green* 200.00 *275.00*
**40** A8 £1 black, *red* 550.00 *600.00*
*Nos. 30-40 (11)* 1,394. *1,506.*

For overprints see Nos. MR1-MR3.

**1921-29 Wmk. 4 *Perf. 14***

| | | | | |
|---|---|---|---|---|
| 41 | A7 | ½p yellow green | 3.50 | 4.50 |
| 42 | A7 | 1p red ('24) | 6.00 | 2.10 |
| 43 | A7 | 2p brown vio ('23) | 26.00 | 8.50 |
| 44 | A7 | 2½p dark blue | 24.00 | 20.00 |
| *a.* | | 2½p Prussian blue ('29) | 375.00 | 550.00 |
| 45 | A7 | 2½p vio, *yel* ('23) | 6.00 | 42.50 |
| 46 | A7 | 6p orange ('25) | 11.00 | 45.00 |
| 47 | A7 | 1sh bister brown | 24.00 | 57.50 |
| 48 | A8 | 3sh dk green ('23) | 100.00 | 190.00 |
| | | *Nos. 41-48 (8)* | 200.50 | 370.10 |

Some specialists call into question No. 44a. The editors would like to see authenticated evidence of its existence.

No. 43 Surcharged

**1928**

| | | | | |
|---|---|---|---|---|
| 52 | A7 | 2½p on 2p brn vio | 1,300. | 1,400. |
| *a.* | | Double surcharge | 60,000. | |

Beware of forged surcharges.

King George V — A9

**1929-31 *Perf. 14***

| | | | | |
|---|---|---|---|---|
| 54 | A9 | ½p green | 1.40 | 4.25 |
| 55 | A9 | 1p scarlet | 4.50 | .90 |
| 56 | A9 | 2p gray | 6.00 | 3.75 |
| 57 | A9 | 2½p blue | 6.00 | 2.50 |
| 58 | A9 | 4p deep orange | 23.00 | 15.00 |
| 59 | A9 | 6p brown violet | 24.00 | 19.00 |
| 60 | A9 | 1sh black, *green* | 32.50 | 37.50 |
| *a.* | | 1sh black, *emerald* | 27.50 | 37.50 |
| 61 | A9 | 2sh6p red, *blue* | 70.00 | 70.00 |
| 62 | A9 | 5sh green, *yel* | 105.00 | 120.00 |
| 63 | A9 | 10sh red, *green* | 225.00 | 275.00 |

**Wmk. 3**

| | | | | |
|---|---|---|---|---|
| 64 | A9 | £1 black, *red* | 350.00 | 425.00 |
| | | *Nos. 54-64 (11)* | 847.40 | 972.90 |

Issue dates: 4p, 1931, others, Sept. 2.

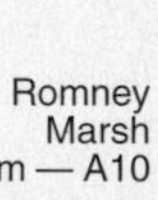

Romney Marsh Ram — A10

Iceberg A11

Whaling Ship — A12

Port Louis A13

Map of the Islands A14

South Georgia A15

Blue Whale A16

Government House A17

Battle Memorial — A18

King Penguin — A19

Coat of Arms — A20

King George V — A21

**1933, Jan. 2 Wmk. 4 *Perf. 12***

| | | | | |
|---|---|---|---|---|
| 65 | A10 | ½p grn & blk | 4.00 | 13.00 |
| 66 | A11 | 1p dl red & blk | 3.75 | 2.75 |
| 67 | A12 | 1½p lt bl & blk | 21.00 | 27.50 |
| 68 | A13 | 2p ol brn & blk | 17.50 | 32.50 |
| 69 | A14 | 3p dl vio & blk | 28.00 | 35.00 |
| 70 | A15 | 4p org & blk | 26.00 | 28.00 |
| 71 | A16 | 6p gray & blk | 75.00 | 95.00 |
| 72 | A17 | 1sh ol grn & blk | 75.00 | 100.00 |
| 73 | A18 | 2sh6p dp vio & blk | 250.00 | 400.00 |
| 74 | A19 | 5sh yel & blk | 950.00 | 1,500. |
| *a.* | | 5sh yellow orange & black | 3,250. | 3,750. |
| 75 | A20 | 10sh lt brn & blk | 850.00 | 1,500. |
| 76 | A21 | £1 rose & blk | 2,500. | 3,500. |
| | | *Nos. 65-76 (12)* | 4,800. | 7,234. |

Cent. of the permanent occupation of the islands as a British colony.

Common Design Types pictured following the introduction.

### Silver Jubilee Issue

Common Design Type

**1935, May 7 *Perf. 11x12***

| | | | | |
|---|---|---|---|---|
| 77 | CD301 | 1p car & blue | 3.50 | .50 |
| 78 | CD301 | 2½p ultra & brn | 12.50 | 2.25 |
| 79 | CD301 | 4p indigo & grn | 24.00 | 8.00 |
| 80 | CD301 | 1sh brn vio & ind | 15.00 | 4.00 |
| | | *Nos. 77-80 (4)* | 55.00 | 14.75 |
| | | Set, never hinged | 75.00 | |
| | | Set (4), Ovptd. "SPECIMEN" | | 500.00 |

### Coronation Issue

Common Design Type

**1937, May 12 *Perf. 11x11½***

| | | | | |
|---|---|---|---|---|
| 81 | CD302 | ½p deep green | .25 | .25 |
| 82 | CD302 | 1p dark carmine | .75 | .55 |
| 83 | CD302 | 2½p deep ultra | 1.90 | 1.50 |
| | | *Nos. 81-83 (3)* | 2.90 | 2.30 |
| | | Set, never hinged | 4.00 | |
| | | Set (3), Ovptd. "SPECIMEN" | 450.00 | |

Whale Jawbones (Centennial Monument) — A22

Nos. 85, 86A, Black-necked swan. Nos. 85B, 86, Battle memorial. 2½p, 3p, Flock of sheep. 4p, Upland goose. 6p, R.R.S. "Discovery II." 9p, R.R.S. "William Scoresby." 1sh, Mt. Sugar Top. 1sh3p, Turkey vultures. 2sh6p, Gentoo penguins. 5sh, Sea lions. 10sh, Deception Island. £1, Arms of Colony.

**1938-46 *Perf. 12***

| | | | | |
|---|---|---|---|---|
| 84 | A22 | ½p green & blk | .25 | .75 |
| 85 | A22 | 1p red & black | 2.50 | 1.00 |
| *a.* | | 1p rose carmine & black | 22.50 | 1.00 |
| 85B | A22 | 1p dk vio & blk ('41) | 2.00 | 2.00 |
| 86 | A22 | 2p dk vio & blk | 1.30 | 1.00 |
| 86A | A22 | 2p rose car & black ('41) | 1.40 | 4.50 |
| 87 | A22 | 2½p ultra & blk | 1.00 | .50 |
| 87A | A22 | 3p blue & blk ('41) | 5.50 | 8.50 |
| *c.* | | 3p dp blue & blk | 12.50 | 4.50 |
| 88 | A22 | 4p rose vio & black | 2.75 | 2.00 |
| 89 | A22 | 6p sepia & blk | 7.50 | 4.25 |
| 90 | A22 | 9p sl bl & blk | 15.00 | 6.00 |
| 91 | A22 | 1sh lt dl blue | 30.00 | 19.00 |
| 92 | A22 | 1sh3p car & blk | 2.00 | 1.60 |
| 93 | A22 | 2sh6p gray black | 40.00 | 22.50 |
| 94 | A22 | 5sh org brn & ultra | 75.00 | 95.00 |
| *a.* | | 5sh yel brown & indigo | 650.00 | 150.00 |
| 95 | A22 | 10sh org & blk | 100.00 | 65.00 |
| 96 | A22 | £1 dk vio & blk | 75.00 | 75.00 |
| | | *Nos. 84-96 (16)* | 361.20 | 308.60 |
| | | Set, never hinged | 600.00 | |
| | | Set (16), perf. "SPECIMEN" | | 2,500. |

Issued: Nos. 85B, 86A, 3p, 7/14/41; 1sh3p, 12/10/46; No. 94a, 1942; others, 1/3/38.

See Nos. 101-102. For overprints see Nos. 2L1-2L8, 3L1-3L8, 4L1-4L8.

**Catalogue values for unused stamps in this section, from this point to the end of the section, are for Never Hinged items.**

### Peace Issue

Common Design Type

***Perf. 13½x14***

**1946, Oct. 7 Engr. Wmk. 4**

| | | | | |
|---|---|---|---|---|
| 97 | CD303 | 1p purple | .35 | .80 |
| 98 | CD303 | 3p deep blue | .55 | .55 |

### Silver Wedding Issue

Common Design Types

**1948, Nov. 1 Photo. *Perf. 14x14½***

| | | | | |
|---|---|---|---|---|
| 99 | CD304 | 2½p bright ultra | 2.10 | 1.10 |

**Engr.; Name Typo.**

***Perf. 11½x11***

| | | | | |
|---|---|---|---|---|
| 100 | CD305 | £1 purple | 110.00 | 75.00 |

### Types of 1938-46

2½p, Upland goose. 6p, R.R.S. "Discovery II."

***Perf. 12***

**1949, June 15 Engr. Wmk. 4**

| | | | | |
|---|---|---|---|---|
| 101 | A22 | 2½p dp blue & black | 7.50 | 8.50 |
| 102 | A22 | 6p gray black | 6.75 | 5.50 |

### UPU Issue

Common Design Types

**Engr.; Name Typo. on 3p, 1sh3p**

**1949, Oct. 10 *Perf. 13½, 11x11½***

| | | | | |
|---|---|---|---|---|
| 103 | CD306 | 1p violet | 1.75 | 1.10 |
| 104 | CD307 | 3p indigo | 5.00 | 5.00 |
| 105 | CD308 | 1sh3p green | 3.50 | 2.50 |
| 106 | CD309 | 2sh blue | 3.75 | 8.50 |
| | | *Nos. 103-106 (4)* | 14.00 | 17.10 |

Sheep A35

Arms of the Colony — A36

Designs: 1p, R.M.S. Fitzroy. 2p Upland goose. 2½p, Map. 4p, Auster plane. 6p, M.S.S. John Biscoe. 9p, "Two Sisters" peaks. 1sh, Gentoo penguins. 1sh 3p, Kelp goose and gander. 2sh 6p, Sheep shearing. 5sh, Battle memorial. 10sh, Sea lion and clapmatch. £1, Hulk of "Great Britain."

***Perf. 13½x13, 13x13½***

**1952, Jan. 2 Engr. Wmk. 4**

| | | | | |
|---|---|---|---|---|
| 107 | A35 | ½p green | 1.25 | 1.00 |
| 108 | A35 | 1p red | 2.40 | .55 |
| 109 | A35 | 2p violet | 4.50 | 3.00 |
| 110 | A35 | 2½p ultra & blk | 2.00 | .70 |
| 111 | A36 | 3p deep ultra | 2.25 | 1.10 |
| 112 | A35 | 4p claret | 12.50 | 1.75 |
| 113 | A35 | 6p yellow brn | 12.00 | 1.10 |
| 114 | A35 | 9p orange yel | 9.00 | 2.25 |
| 115 | A36 | 1sh black | 24.00 | 1.10 |
| 116 | A35 | 1sh3p red orange | 18.00 | 7.00 |
| 117 | A36 | 2sh6p olive | 22.50 | 12.50 |
| 118 | A36 | 5sh red violet | 20.00 | 11.00 |
| 119 | A35 | 10sh gray | 30.00 | 20.00 |
| 120 | A35 | £1 black | 40.00 | 27.00 |
| | | *Nos. 107-120 (14)* | 200.40 | 90.05 |

### Coronation Issue

Common Design Type

**1953, June 4 *Perf. 13½x13***

| | | | | |
|---|---|---|---|---|
| 121 | CD312 | 1p car & black | .90 | 1.50 |

### Types of 1952 with Portrait of Queen Elizabeth II

**1955-57 *Perf. 13½x13, 13x13½***

| | | | | |
|---|---|---|---|---|
| 122 | A35 | ½p green ('57) | 1.00 | 1.50 |
| 123 | A35 | 1p red ('57) | 1.25 | 1.25 |
| 124 | A35 | 2p violet ('56) | 3.25 | 4.75 |
| 125 | A35 | 6p light brown | 9.00 | .70 |
| 126 | A35 | 9p ocher ('57) | 10.50 | 17.00 |
| 127 | A36 | 1sh black | 12.00 | 2.50 |
| | | *Nos. 122-127 (6)* | 37.00 | 27.70 |

Marsh Starling A37

Birds: ½p, Falkland Islands Thrush. 1p, Dominican gull. 2p, Gentoo penguins. 3p, Upland geese. 4p, Steamer ducks. 5½p, Rock-hopper penguin. 6p, black-browed albatross. 9p, Silver grebe. 1sh, Pied oystercatchers. 1sh3p, Yellow-billed teal. 2sh, Kelp geese, 5sh, King shag. 10sh, Guadelupe caracara. £1, Black-necked swan.

***Perf. 13½x13***

**1960, Feb. 10 Engr. Wmk. 314**

**Center in Black**

| | | | | |
|---|---|---|---|---|
| 128 | A37 | ½p green | 5.00 | 2.25 |
| *a.* | | Wmk. sideways ('66) | .45 | .40 |
| 129 | A37 | 1p rose red | 3.00 | 2.00 |
| 130 | A37 | 2p blue | 4.50 | 1.25 |
| 131 | A37 | 2½p bister brn | 2.50 | 1.00 |
| 132 | A37 | 3p olive | 1.25 | .50 |
| 133 | A37 | 4p rose car | 1.50 | 1.25 |
| 134 | A37 | 5½p violet | 3.25 | 2.50 |
| 135 | A37 | 6p sepia | 3.50 | .30 |
| 136 | A37 | 9p orange | 2.50 | 1.25 |
| 137 | A37 | 1sh dull purple | 1.25 | .40 |
| 138 | A37 | 1sh3p ultra | 12.50 | 14.00 |
| 139 | A37 | 2sh brown car | 30.00 | 2.50 |
| 140 | A37 | 5sh grnsh blue | 27.50 | 11.00 |
| 141 | A37 | 10sh rose lilac | 42.60 | 22.00 |
| 142 | A37 | £1 yellow org | 45.00 | 27.00 |
| | | *Nos. 128-142 (15)* | 185.85 | 89.20 |

Morse Key — A38

**1962, Oct. 5 Photo. *Perf. 11½x11***
**143** A38 6p dp org & dk red .85 .50
**144** A38 1sh brt ol grn & dp green .95 .50
**145** A38 2sh brt ultra & violet 1.25 *1.75*
*Nos. 143-145 (3)* 3.05 2.75

Falkland Islands radio station, 50th anniv.

### Freedom from Hunger Issue
Common Design Type

**1963, June 4 *Perf. 14x14½***
**146** CD314 1sh ultramarine 10.50 2.50

### Red Cross Centenary Issue
Common Design Type
**Wmk. 314**

**1963, Sept.2 Litho. *Perf. 13***
**147** CD315 1p black & red 2.00 .75
**148** CD315 1sh ultra & red 16.00 4.75

### Shakespeare Issue
Common Design Type

**1964, Apr. 23 Photo. *Perf. 14x14½***
**149** CD316 6p black 1.60 .50

H.M.S. Glasgow A39

6p, H.M.S. Kent. 1sh, H.M.S. Invincible. 2sh, Falkland Islands Battle Memorial, vert.

**1964, Dec. 8 Engr. *Perf. 13***
**150** A39 2½p ver & black 9.00 3.75
**151** A39 6p blue & black .55 .30
*a.* "Glasgow" vignette *30,000.*
**152** A39 1sh carmine & blk .55 *1.00*

***Perf. 13x14***
**153** A39 2sh dk blue & blk .55 .75
*Nos. 150-153 (4)* 10.65 5.80

Battle of the Falkland Islands between the British and German navies, 50th anniv.

### ITU Issue
Common Design Type
***Perf. 11x11½***

**1965, May 26 Litho. Wmk. 314**
**154** CD317 1p blue & dl dk bl .50 .40
**155** CD317 2sh lilac & dl yel 6.25 2.75

### Intl. Cooperation Year Issue
Common Design Type

**1965, Oct. 25 *Perf. 14½***
**156** CD318 1p blue grn & claret 1.25 .40
**157** CD318 1sh lt violet & grn 4.75 1.25

### Churchill Memorial Issue
Common Design Type

**1966, Jan. 24 Photo. *Perf. 14***
**Design in Black, Gold and Carmine Rose**
**158** CD319 ½p bright blue .75 *2.25*
**159** CD319 1p green 2.00 .30
**160** CD319 1sh brown 5.50 3.00
**161** CD319 2sh violet 4.50 4.00
*Nos. 158-161 (4)* 12.75 9.55

Human Rights Flame and Globe A40

***Perf. 14x14½***

**1968, July 4 Photo. Wmk. 314**
**162** A40 2p brt rose & multi .40 .25
**163** A40 6p brt green & multi .45 .25
**164** A40 1sh orange & multi .55 .30
**165** A40 2sh ultra & multi .65 .35
*Nos. 162-165 (4)* 2.05 1.15

International Human Rights Year.

Dusty Miller — A41

Falkland Islands flora: 1½p, Pig vine, horiz. 2p, Pale maiden. 3p, Dog orchid. 3½p, Sea cabbage, horiz. 4½p, Vanilla daisy. 5½p, Arrowleaf marigold, horiz. 6p, Diddle-dee, horiz. 1sh, Scurvy grass, horiz. 1sh6p, Prickly burr. 2sh, Fachine. 3sh, Lavender. 5sh, Felton's flower, horiz. £1, Yellow orchid.

**1968, Oct. 9 Photo. *Perf. 14***
**166** A41 ½p multicolored .25 *1.75*
**167** A41 1½p multicolored .45 .25
**168** A41 2p multicolored .60 .25
**169** A41 3p multicolored 6.00 1.00
**170** A41 3½p multicolored .35 *1.00*
**171** A41 4½p multicolored 1.60 *2.00*
**172** A41 5½p multicolored 1.60 *2.00*
**173** A41 6p multicolored .85 *.30*
**174** A41 1sh multicolored 1.00 *1.50*
**175** A41 1sh6p multicolored 5.00 *15.00*
**176** A41 2sh multicolored 5.50 6.25
**177** A41 3sh multicolored 7.75 8.00
**178** A41 5sh multicolored 27.00 13.00
**179** A41 £1 multicolored 11.50 3.25
*Nos. 166-179 (14)* 69.45 55.55

See Nos. 210-222. For surcharges see Nos. 197-209.

Beaver DHC 2 Seaplane A42

Designs: 6p, Norseman seaplane. 1sh, Auster plane. 2sh, Falkland Islands arms.

**1969, Apr. 8 Litho. *Perf. 14***
**180** A42 2p multicolored .45 .30
**181** A42 6p multicolored .65 .35
**182** A42 1sh multicolored .65 .40
**183** A42 2sh multicolored 1.20 *2.00*
*Nos. 180-183 (4)* 2.95 3.05

21st anniv. of Government Air Service.

Bishop Stirling A43

2p, Holy Trinity Church, 1869. 6p, Christ Church Cathedral, 1969. 2sh, Bishop's miter.

**1969, Oct. 30 *Perf. 14***
**184** A43 2p emerald & black .40 .60
**185** A43 6p red orange & black .50 .60
**186** A43 1sh lilac & black .50 .60
**187** A43 2sh yellow & multi .60 .75
*Nos. 184-187 (4)* 2.00 2.55

Consecration of Waite Hocking Stirling (1829-1923), as first Bishop of the Bishopric of the Falkland Islands, cent.

Gun Emplacement — A44

2p, Volunteer on horseback, vert. 1sh, Volunteer in dress uniform, vert. 2sh, Defense Force badge.

***Perf. 13½x13, 13x13½***

**1970, Apr. 30 Litho. Wmk. 314**
**188** A44 2p ultra & multi 1.15 .70
**189** A44 6p multicolored 1.40 .80
**190** A44 1sh buff & multi 2.25 .80
**191** A44 2sh yellow & multi 3.25 1.00
*Nos. 188-191 (4)* 8.05 3.30

Falkland Islands Defense Force, 50th anniv.

The Great Britain, 1843 A45

The Great Britain in: 4p, 1845. 9p, 1876. 1sh, 1886. 2sh, 1970.

**1970, Oct. 30 Litho. *Perf. 14½***
**192** A45 2p lemon & multi 1.00 .50
**193** A45 4p lilac & multi 1.25 .90
**194** A45 9p bister & multi 1.50 .90
**195** A45 1sh org brn & multi 1.50 .90
**196** A45 2sh multicolored 2.00 1.10
*Nos. 192-196 (5)* 7.25 4.30

Nos. 166-178 Surcharged

**1971, Feb. 15 Photo. *Perf. 14***
**197** A41 ½p on ½p multi .40 .40
**198** A41 1p on 1½p multi .25 .25
*a.* 5p on 1½p (error) 750.00
**199** A41 1½p on 2p multi .35 .35
**200** A41 2p on 3p multi .55 .55
**201** A41 2½p on 3½p multi .30 .30
**202** A41 3p on 4½p multi .35 .35
**203** A41 4p on 5½p multi .40 .40
**204** A41 5p on 6p multi .70 .70
**205** A41 6p on 1sh multi 6.00 7.00
**206** A41 7½p on 1sh6p multi 8.00 8.00
**207** A41 10p on 2sh multi 8.00 3.50
**208** A41 15p on 3sh multi 3.50 2.75
**209** A41 25p on 5sh multi 4.50 3.75
*Nos. 197-209 (13)* 33.30 28.30

### Flower Type of 1968 "p" instead of "d"

Designs as before. 1p, 2½p, 4p, 5p, 6p, 25p, horizontal.

**Wmk. 314, Sideways on Vert. Stamps**

**1972, June 1 *Perf. 14***
**210** A41 ½p Dusty miller .75 *4.75*
*a.* Wmk. upright ('74) *15.00 32.50*
*b.* Wmk. 373 ('75) 3.25 *3.50*
**211** A41 1p Pig vine .40 .40
**212** A41 1½p Pale maiden .55 *4.50*
**213** A41 2p Dog orchid 6.00 1.50
*a.* Wmk. upright ('74) 30.00 3.25
**214** A41 2½p Sea cabbage .70 *4.50*
**215** A41 3p Vanilla daisy .75 *1.40*
**216** A41 4p Arrowleaf marigold 1.00 *1.10*
**217** A41 5p Diddle-dee 1.10 .75
**218** A41 6p Scurvy grass 18.00 9.50
*a.* Wmk. sideways ('74) 2.10 *2.50*
**219** A41 7½p Prickly burr 2.00 3.75
**220** A41 10p Fachine 10.00 4.00
**221** A41 15p Lavender 4.00 4.50
**222** A41 25p Felton's flower 8.00 6.00
*Nos. 210-222 (13)* 53.25 46.65

### Silver Wedding Issue, 1972
Common Design Type

Design: Queen Elizabeth II, Prince Philip, Romney Marsh sheep and giant sea lions.

**1972, Nov 20 Photo. *Perf. 14x14½***
**223** CD324 1p sl grn & multi .30 .30
**224** CD324 10p ultra & multi .70 *.85*

### Princess Anne's Wedding Issue
Common Design Type

**1973, Nov. 14 Litho. *Perf. 14***
**225** CD325 5p lilac & multi .25 .25
**226** CD325 15p citron & multi .45 .35

Fur Seals A46

Tourist Publicity: 4p, Trout fishing. 5p, Rockhopper penguins. 15p, Military starling.

**1974, Mar. 6 Litho. Wmk. 314**
**227** A46 2p lt ultra & multi 2.25 2.00
**228** A46 4p brt blue & multi 3.25 1.50
**229** A46 5p yellow & multi 10.50 2.50
**230** A46 15p lt ultra & multi 12.00 5.00
*Nos. 227-230 (4)* 28.00 11.00

Early 19th Cent. Mail Coach, UPU Emblem — A47

UPU Cent.: 5p, Packet, 1841. 8p, First British mail planes, 1911. 16p, Catapult mail, 1920's.

**1974, July 31 *Perf. 14***
**231** A47 2p multicolored .25 .25
**232** A47 5p multicolored .30 *.45*
**233** A47 8p multicolored .35 *.55*
**234** A47 16p multicolored .55 *.75*
*Nos. 231-234 (4)* 1.45 *2.00*

Churchill, Parliament and Big Ben A48

Design: 20p, Churchill and warships.

**1974, Nov. 30 *Perf. 13x13½***
**235** A48 16p multicolored 1.00 1.00
**236** A48 20p multicolored 1.50 1.50
*a.* Souvenir sheet of 2, #235-236 8.00 8.00

Sir Winston Churchill (1874-1965).

HMS Exeter A49

Battleships: 6p, HMNZS Achilles. 8p, Admiral Graf Spee. 16p, HMS Ajax.

**1974, Dec. 13 *Perf. 14***
**237** A49 2p multicolored 2.50 1.75
**238** A49 6p multicolored 4.25 3.50
**239** A49 8p multicolored 5.25 4.50
**240** A49 16p multicolored 10.00 14.00
*Nos. 237-240 (4)* 22.00 23.75

35th anniv. of the Battle of the River Plate between British ships and the German battleship Graf Spee.

Seal and Flag Badge — A50

7½p, Coat of arms, 1925. 10p, Arms, 1948. 16p, Arms (Falkland Islands Dependencies), 1952.

**1975, Oct. 28 Litho. Wmk. 373**

| | | | | | |
|---|---|---|---|---|---|
| **241** | A50 | 2p | multicolored | 1.00 | .50 |
| **242** | A50 | 7½p | multicolored | 1.60 | 1.50 |
| **243** | A50 | 10p | multicolored | 1.75 | 1.75 |
| **244** | A50 | 16p | multicolored | 2.50 | *3.25* |
| | | | *Nos. 241-244 (4)* | 6.85 | 7.00 |

Falkland Islands heraldic arms, 50th anniv.

½p-Coin and Trout A51

New Coinage: 5½p, 1p-coin and gentoo penguins, 8p, 2p-coin and upland geese. 10p, 5p-coin and black-browed albatross. 16p, 10p-coin and sea lions.

**1975, Dec. 31 Litho. Wmk. 373**

| | | | | | |
|---|---|---|---|---|---|
| **245** | A51 | 2p | copper & multi | .75 | .50 |
| **246** | A51 | 5½p | copper & multi | 1.75 | 1.50 |
| **247** | A51 | 8p | copper & multi | 2.00 | 1.75 |
| **248** | A51 | 10p | silver & multi | 2.50 | 2.00 |
| **249** | A51 | 16p | silver & multi | 3.00 | 3.00 |
| | | | *Nos. 245-249 (5)* | 10.00 | 8.75 |

Gathering Sheep — A52

Sheep Farming: 7½p, Shearing. 10p, Dipping sheep. 20p, Motor Vessel Monsunen collecting wool.

**1976, Apr. 28 Litho. *Perf. 13½***

| | | | | | |
|---|---|---|---|---|---|
| **250** | A52 | 2p | multicolored | .90 | .75 |
| **251** | A52 | 7½p | multicolored | 1.25 | 1.25 |
| **252** | A52 | 10p | multicolored | 1.60 | 1.60 |
| **253** | A52 | 20p | multicolored | 2.50 | *3.50* |
| | | | *Nos. 250-253 (4)* | 6.25 | 7.10 |

Prince Philip, 1957 Visit A53

11p, Queen, ampulla and spoon. 33p, Queen awaiting anointment, and Knights of the Garter.

**1977, Feb. 7 *Perf. 13½x14***

| | | | | | |
|---|---|---|---|---|---|
| **254** | A53 | 6p | multicolored | .35 | .35 |
| | *a.* | | Booklet pane of 4, wmk. 314 | 6.00 | |
| | *b.* | | Single stamp from #254a | 1.50 | *4.00* |
| **255** | A53 | 11p | multicolored | .60 | .60 |
| | *a.* | | Booklet pane of 4 | 2.40 | |
| **256** | A53 | 33p | multicolored | 1.50 | 1.50 |
| | *a.* | | Booklet pane of 4 | 6.00 | |
| | | | *Nos. 254-256 (3)* | 2.45 | 2.45 |

25th anniv. of the reign of Elizabeth II.

Map of West and East Falkland with Communications Centers — A54

Telecommunications: 11p, Ship to shore communications at Fox Bay. 40p, Globe with Telex tape and telephone.

**1977, Oct. 24 Litho. *Perf. 14½x14***

| | | | | | |
|---|---|---|---|---|---|
| **257** | A54 | 3p | yel brown & multi | .90 | .25 |
| **258** | A54 | 11p | lt ultra & multi | 1.60 | .60 |
| **259** | A54 | 40p | rose & multi | 2.50 | 2.00 |
| | | | *Nos. 257-259 (3)* | 5.00 | 2.85 |

A.E.S., 1957-1974 — A55

Designs: Mail ships.

**1978, Jan. 25 Wmk. 373 *Perf. 14***

**No Date Inscription**

| | | | | | |
|---|---|---|---|---|---|
| **260** | A55 | 1p | shown | .25 | .25 |
| **261** | A55 | 2p | Darwin, 1957-75 | .35 | .25 |
| **262** | A55 | 3p | Merak-N 1951-53 | .25 | *1.50* |
| **263** | A55 | 4p | Fitzroy, 1936-57 | .25 | *1.50* |
| **264** | A55 | 5p | Lafonia 1936-41 | .25 | *.30* |
| **265** | A55 | 6p | Fleurus, 1924-33 | .30 | *.40* |
| **266** | A55 | 7p | S.S. Falkland, 1914-34 | .40 | *2.75* |
| **267** | A55 | 8p | Oravia, 1900-12 | .45 | *1.25* |
| **268** | A55 | 9p | Memphis, 1890-97 | .45 | *1.00* |
| **269** | A55 | 10p | Black Hawk, 1873-80 | .60 | .50 |
| **270** | A55 | 20p | Foam, 1963-72 | 1.00 | *1.50* |
| **271** | A55 | 25p | Fairy, 1857-61 | 1.00 | *3.25* |
| **272** | A55 | 50p | Amelia, 1852-54 | 1.50 | *3.50* |
| **273** | A55 | £1 | Nautilus, 1846-48 | 2.50 | *5.50* |
| **274** | A55 | £3 | Hebe, 1842-46 | 9.00 | *13.00* |
| | | | *Nos. 260-274 (15)* | 18.55 | *36.45* |

The 1p, 3p, 5p, 6p and 10p were also issued in booklet panes of 4.

For overprints see Nos. 352-353.

**1982, Dec. 1 Inscribed "1982"**

| | | | | | |
|---|---|---|---|---|---|
| *260a* | A55 | 1p | shown | .40 | *2.00* |
| *261a* | A55 | 2p | Darwin, 1957-75 | .50 | *2.00* |
| *262a* | A55 | 3p | Merak-N 1951-53 | .60 | *2.00* |
| *263a* | A55 | 4p | Fitzroy, 1936-57 | .60 | *2.00* |
| *264a* | A55 | 5p | Lafonia 1936-41 | .70 | *2.00* |
| *265a* | A55 | 6p | Fleurus, 1924-33 | .70 | *2.00* |
| *266a* | A55 | 7p | S.S. Falkland, 1914-34 | .75 | *2.00* |
| *267a* | A55 | 8p | Oravia, 1900-12 | .75 | *2.00* |
| *268a* | A55 | 9p | Memphis, 1890-97 | .80 | *2.00* |
| *269a* | A55 | 10p | Black Hawk, 1873-80 | .85 | *2.00* |
| *270a* | A55 | 20p | Foam, 1963-72 | 1.50 | *3.25* |
| *271a* | A55 | 25p | Fairy, 1857-61 | 1.50 | *3.25* |
| *272a* | A55 | 50p | Amelia, 1852-54 | 1.75 | *4.00* |
| *273a* | A55 | £1 | Nautilus, 1846-48 | 3.25 | *5.00* |
| *274a* | A55 | £3 | Hebe, 1842-46 | 5.00 | *10.00* |
| | | | *Nos. 260a-274a (15)* | 19.65 | *45.50* |

**Elizabeth II Coronation Anniversary Issue**

Souvenir Sheet

Common Design Type

**1978, June 2 Unwmk. *Perf. 15***

| | | | | |
|---|---|---|---|---|
| **275** | | Sheet of 6 | 4.00 | *5.50* |
| | *a.* | CD326 25p Red Dragon of Wales | .60 | .85 |
| | *b.* | CD327 25p Elizabeth II | .60 | .85 |
| | *c.* | CD328 25p Hornless ram | .60 | .85 |

No. 275 contains 2 se-tenant strips of Nos. 275a-275c, separated by horizontal gutter with commemorative and descriptive inscriptions.

Short Sunderland Mark III — A56

Design: 33p, Plane in flight and route Southampton to Stanley.

**1978, Apr. 28 Wmk. 373 *Perf. 14***

| | | | | | |
|---|---|---|---|---|---|
| **276** | A56 | 11p | multicolored | 2.75 | 2.25 |
| **277** | A56 | 33p | multicolored | 4.00 | 3.25 |

First direct flight Southampton, England to Stanley, Falkland Islands, 26th anniv.

First Fox Bay PO and No. 1 — A57

Designs: 11p, Second Stanley Post Office and #2. 15p, New Island Post Office and #3. 22p, 1st Stanley Post Office and #4.

**1978, Aug. 8 Litho. *Perf. 13½x13***

| | | | | | |
|---|---|---|---|---|---|
| **278** | A57 | 3p | multicolored | .25 | .25 |
| **279** | A57 | 11p | multicolored | .30 | *.40* |
| **280** | A57 | 15p | multicolored | .40 | .50 |
| **281** | A57 | 22p | multicolored | .70 | *.85* |
| | | | *Nos. 278-281 (4)* | 1.65 | 2.00 |

Falkland Islands postage stamps, cent.

Macrocystis Pyrifera — A58

Kelp: 7p, Durvillea. 11p, Lessoniae, horiz. 15p, Callophyllis, horiz. 25p, Iridea.

**1979, Feb. 19 Litho. *Perf. 14***

| | | | | | |
|---|---|---|---|---|---|
| **282** | A58 | 3p | multicolored | .40 | .40 |
| **283** | A58 | 7p | multicolored | .45 | .45 |
| **284** | A58 | 11p | multicolored | .55 | .55 |
| **285** | A58 | 15p | multicolored | .80 | .80 |
| **286** | A58 | 25p | multicolored | .95 | 1.10 |
| | | | *Nos. 282-286 (5)* | 3.15 | 3.30 |

Britten-Norman Islander over Map — A59

Opening of Stanley Airport: 11p, Fokker F27 over map. 15p, Fokker F28 over Stanley. 25p, Cessna 172 Skyhawk, Islander and Fokkers F27, F28 over runway.

**1979, May 1 Litho. *Perf. 13½***

| | | | | | |
|---|---|---|---|---|---|
| **287** | A59 | 3p | multicolored | .45 | .25 |
| **288** | A59 | 11p | multicolored | .85 | .65 |
| **289** | A59 | 15p | multicolored | 1.00 | .65 |
| **290** | A59 | 25p | multicolored | 1.50 | 1.00 |
| | | | *Nos. 287-290 (4)* | 3.80 | 2.55 |

Rowland Hill and No. 121 A60

Sir Rowland Hill (1795-1879), originator of penny postage, and: 11p, Falkland Islands No. 1, vert. 25p, Penny Black. 33p, Falkland Islands No. 37, vert.

**1979, Aug. 27 *Perf. 14***

| | | | | | |
|---|---|---|---|---|---|
| **291** | A60 | 3p | multicolored | .25 | .25 |
| **292** | A60 | 11p | multicolored | .40 | .40 |
| **293** | A60 | 25p | multicolored | .75 | .75 |
| | | | *Nos. 291-293 (3)* | 1.40 | 1.40 |

**Souvenir Sheet**

| | | | | | |
|---|---|---|---|---|---|
| **294** | A60 | 33p | multicolored | 1.50 | 1.50 |

Mail Delivery by Air, UPU Emblem A61

UPU Membership Cent. (Modes of Mail Delivery): 11p, Horseback. 25p, Schooner Gwendolin.

**1979, Nov. 26**

| | | | | | |
|---|---|---|---|---|---|
| **295** | A61 | 3p | multicolored | .25 | .25 |
| **296** | A61 | 11p | multicolored | .45 | *.55* |
| **297** | A61 | 25p | multicolored | .65 | *1.10* |
| | | | *Nos. 295-297 (3)* | 1.35 | *1.90* |

Commerson's Dolphin — A62

**1980, Feb. 25 Wmk. 373 *Perf. 14***

| | | | | | |
|---|---|---|---|---|---|
| **298** | A62 | 3p | Peale's porpoise, vert. | .40 | .40 |
| **299** | A62 | 6p | shown | .60 | .60 |
| **300** | A62 | 7p | Hour-glass dolphin | .60 | .60 |
| **301** | A62 | 11p | Spectacled porpoise, vert. | .70 | .70 |
| **302** | A62 | 15p | Dusky dolphin | .80 | .80 |
| **303** | A62 | 25p | Killer whale | .90 | *1.50* |
| | | | *Nos. 298-303 (6)* | 4.00 | 4.60 |

Miniature Sheet

A63

Designs: a, Falkland Islands Cancel, 1878. b, New Islds., 1915. c, Falklands Islds., 1901. d, Port Stanley, 1935. e, Port Stanley airmail, 1952. f, Fox Bay, 1934.

**1980, May 6 Litho. *Perf. 14***

| | | | | |
|---|---|---|---|---|
| **304** | A63 | Sheet of 6 | 1.60 | 1.60 |
| | *a.-f.* | 11p any single | .25 | .25 |

London 1980 Intl. Stamp Exhib., May 6-14.

**Queen Mother Elizabeth Birthday**

Common Design Type

**1980, Aug. 4 Litho. *Perf. 14***

| | | | | |
|---|---|---|---|---|
| **305** | CD330 | 11p multicolored | .40 | .40 |

Striated Caracara A64

**1980, Aug. 11 Wmk. 373 *Perf. 13½***

| | | | | | |
|---|---|---|---|---|---|
| **306** | A64 | 3p | shown | .60 | .30 |
| **307** | A64 | 11p | Red-backed buzzard | .75 | .55 |
| **308** | A64 | 15p | Crested caracara | .85 | .65 |
| **309** | A64 | 25p | Cassin's falcon | 1.00 | 1.00 |
| | | | *Nos. 306-309 (4)* | 3.20 | 2.50 |

Port Egmont, Early Settlement — A65

**1980, Dec. 22 Litho. *Perf. 14***

| | | | | | |
|---|---|---|---|---|---|
| **310** | A65 | 3p | Stanley | .25 | .25 |
| **311** | A65 | 11p | shown | .35 | .35 |
| **312** | A65 | 25p | Port Louis | .75 | .75 |
| **313** | A65 | 33p | Mission House, Keppel Island | .95 | .95 |
| | | | *Nos. 310-313 (4)* | 2.30 | 2.30 |

Polwarth Sheep A66

**1981, Jan. 19 Litho. *Perf. 14***

| | | | | | |
|---|---|---|---|---|---|
| **314** | A66 | 3p | shown | .25 | .25 |
| **315** | A66 | 11p | Frisian cow and calf | .35 | .30 |
| **316** | A66 | 25p | Horse | .70 | *1.00* |
| **317** | A66 | 33p | Welsh collies | .80 | *1.25* |
| | | | *Nos. 314-317 (4)* | 2.10 | 2.80 |

Map of Falkland Islands, Bowles and Carver, 1779 A67

**1981, May 22 Litho. *Perf. 14***
318 A67 3p shown .25 .25
319 A67 10p Hawkin's Mainland, 1773 .30 .35
320 A67 13p New Isles, 1747 .35 .35
321 A67 15p French & British Islands .45 .35
322 A67 25p Falklands, 1771 .60 .50
323 A67 26p Falklands, 1764 .65 .50
*Nos. 318-323 (6)* 2.60 2.30

**Royal Wedding Issue**
Common Design Type

**1981, July 22 Litho. *Perf. 13½x13***
324 CD331 10p Bouquet .25 .25
325 CD331 13p Charles .40 .45
326 CD331 52p Couple 1.00 1.00
*Nos. 324-326 (3)* 1.65 1.70

Duke of Edinburgh's Awards, 25th Anniv. — A68

**1981, Sept. 28 Litho. *Perf. 14***
327 A68 10p Spinning .25 .25
328 A68 13p Camping .25 .25
329 A68 15p Kayaking .35 .35
330 A68 26p Duke of Edinburgh .55 .55
*Nos. 327-330 (4)* 1.40 1.40

The Holy Virgin, by Guido Reni (1575-1642) A69

Christmas: 3p, Adoration of the Holy Child, 16th cent. Dutch. 13p, Holy Family in an Italian Landscape, 17th cent. Italian.

**1981, Nov. 9 Litho. *Perf. 14***
331 A69 3p multicolored .25 .25
332 A69 13p multicolored .50 .50
333 A69 26p multicolored .75 .75
*Nos. 331-333 (3)* 1.50 1.50

This set was issued Nov. 2 in London by the Crown Agents.

Rock Cod — A70

Designs: Shelf fish. 5p, 15p, 25p horiz.

**1981, Dec. 7**
334 A70 5p Falkland herring .25 .25
335 A70 13p shown .30 *.35*
336 A70 15p Patagonian hake .35 *.40*
337 A70 25p Southern blue whiting .55 *.75*
338 A70 26p Gray-tailed skate .55 *.75*
*Nos. 334-338 (5)* 2.00 *2.50*

Shipwrecks — A71

**1982, Feb. 15 Wmk. 373 *Perf. 14½***
339 A71 5p Lady Elizabeth, 1913 .35 .35
340 A71 13p Capricorn, 1882 .45 .45
341 A71 15p Jhelum, 1870 .50 .50
342 A71 25p Snowsquall, 1864 .70 .70
343 A71 26p St. Mary, 1890 .70 .70
*Nos. 339-343 (5)* 2.70 2.70

Sesquicentennial of Charles Darwin's Visit — A72

**1982, Apr. 19 Litho. *Perf. 14***
344 A72 5p Darwin .45 .45
345 A72 17p Microscope .55 .55
346 A72 25p Warrah .85 .85
347 A72 34p Beagle 1.10 1.10
*Nos. 344-347 (4)* 2.95 2.95

**Princess Diana Issue**
Common Design Type

**1982, July 5 Wmk. 373 *Perf. 13***
348 CD333 5p Arms .30 .30
349 CD333 17p Diana .60 .60
350 CD333 37p Wedding .90 .90
351 CD333 50p Portrait 1.15 1.15
*Nos. 348-351 (4)* 2.95 2.95

**Nos. 264, 271 Overprinted**

**1982, Oct. 7 Litho. *Perf. 14***
352 A55 5p multicolored .25 *.30*
353 A55 25p multicolored .50 *1.00*

12th Commonwealth Games, Brisbane, Australia, Sept. 30-Oct. 9.

Tussock Bird — A73

**1982, Dec. 6 *Perf. 15x14½***
354 A73 5p shown .40 .40
355 A73 10p Black-chinned siskin .50 .50
356 A73 13p Grass wren .50 .50
357 A73 17p Black-throated finch .50 .50
358 A73 25p Falkland-correndera pipit .60 .60
359 A73 34p Dark-faced ground-tyrant .70 .70
*Nos. 354-359 (6)* 3.20 3.20

British Occupation Sesquicentennial — A74

1p, Raising the Standard, Port Louis, 1833. 2p, Chelsea pensioners & barracks, 1849. 5p, Wool trade, 1874. 10p, Ship repairing trade, 1850-90. 15p, Government House, early 20th cent. 20p, Battle of the Falkland Islands, 1914. 25p, Whalebone Arch centenary, 1933. 40p, Contribution to World War II effort, 1939-45. 50p, Visit of Duke of Edinburgh, 1957. £1, Royal Marines, 1933, 1983, vert. £2, Queen Elizabeth II.

**1983, Jan. 1 Litho. *Perf. 14***
360 A74 1p multi, vert. .35 .35
361 A74 2p multi .40 .40
362 A74 5p multi, vert. .40 .40
363 A74 10p multi .55 .70
364 A74 15p multi .55 .80
365 A74 20p multi, vert. .75 *1.25*
366 A74 25p multi .75 *1.25*
367 A74 40p multi, vert. .80 *1.25*
368 A74 50p multi .95 *1.25*
369 A74 £1 multi 1.25 *1.75*
370 A74 £2 multi, vert. 2.50 *3.00*
*Nos. 360-370 (11)* 9.25 *12.40*

For surcharges see Nos. 402-403.

A75

**1983, Mar. 14**
371 A75 5p No. 69 .25 .25
372 A75 17p No. 65 .45 .45
373 A75 34p No. 75, vert. .70 *1.00*
374 A75 50p No. 370, vert. .90 *1.00*
*Nos. 371-374 (4)* 2.30 2.70

Commonwealth Day.

First Anniv. of Liberation A76

**1983, June 14 Wmk. 373 *Perf. 14***
375 A76 5p Army .30 .30
376 A76 13p Merchant Navy .40 .40
377 A76 17p Royal Air Force .60 .60
378 A76 50p Royal Navy 1.20 *1.75*
*a.* Souvenir sheet of 4, #375-378 2.50 *2.75*
*Nos. 375-378 (4)* 2.50 3.05

Local Fruit A77

**1983, Oct. 10 Litho. *Perf. 14***
379 A77 5p Diddle dee .25 .25
380 A77 17p Tea berries .35 *.40*
381 A77 25p Mountain berries .50 *.60*
382 A77 34p Native strawberries .70 *.80*
*Nos. 379-382 (4)* 1.80 *2.05*

Britten-Norman Islander — A78

**1983, Nov. 14 Litho. *Perf. 14***
383 A78 5p shown .25 .25
384 A78 13p DHC-2 Beaver .35 *.40*
385 A78 17p Noorduyn Norseman .45 *.50*
386 A78 50p Auster 1.00 *1.25*
*Nos. 383-386 (4)* 2.05 *2.40*

Green Spider A79

Insects and Spiders.

**1984, Jan. 1 Litho. *Perf. 14***
387 A79 1p shown .30 *.80*
388 A79 2p Ichneumon-Fly 2.75 2.50
*a.* Inscribed "1986" 4.00 3.25
389 A79 3p Brocade Moth .65 *.85*
390 A79 4p Black Beetle .50 *.85*
391 A79 5p Fritillary .50 *.85*
392 A79 6p Green Spider, diff. .50 *.85*
393 A79 7p Ichneumon-Fly, diff. .50 *.70*
394 A79 8p Ochre Shoulder .50 *.70*
395 A79 9p Clocker Weevil .50 *.70*
396 A79 10p Hover Fly .50 *.70*
397 A79 20p Weevil 2.75 1.10
398 A79 25p Metallic Beetle .65 *1.10*
399 A79 50p Camel Cricket 1.10 *1.75*
400 A79 £1 Beauchene Spider 1.40 *2.50*
401 A79 £3 Southern Painted Lady 4.00 *6.50*
*Nos. 387-401 (15)* 17.10 *22.45*

**Nos. 364, 366 Surcharged**

**1984, Jan. 3 Litho. *Perf. 14***
402 A74 17p on 15p multi .65 .90
403 A74 22p on 25p multi .35 .45

**Lloyd's List Issue**
Common Design Type

**1984, May 7 Wmk. 373 *Perf. 14½***
404 CD335 6p Wavertree .60 .50
405 CD335 17p Port Stanley, 1910 .90 .65
406 CD335 22p Oravia .90 .75
407 CD335 52p Cunard Countess 1.10 *1.75*
*Nos. 404-407 (4)* 3.50 3.65

Great Grebe — A80

**1984, Aug. 6 *Perf. 14½x14***
408 A80 17p shown 1.25 1.25
409 A80 22p Silver grebe 1.50 1.50
410 A80 52p Rolland's grebe 2.25 *3.25*
*Nos. 408-410 (3)* 5.00 6.00

See Nos. 450-453.

1984 UPU Congress A81

**1984, June 25 Litho. *Perf. 14***
411 A81 22p Emblem, jet, ship .60 *.75*

Wildlife Conservation A82

**1984, Nov. 5 Litho. *Perf. 14½***
412 A82 6p Birds 1.00 1.00
413 A82 17p Plants .90 .70
414 A82 22p Mammals 1.00 .80
415 A82 52p Marine Life 1.60 *2.25*
*a.* Souvenir sheet of 4, #412-415 7.00 *7.75*
*Nos. 412-415 (4)* 4.50 4.75

Camber Railway, 1915-1927
A83

**1985, Feb. 18 Litho. *Perf. 14***
**416** A83 7p multicolored .35 .35
**417** A83 22p multicolored .65 .65
**418** A83 27p multicolored .70 *.85*

**Size: 77x26mm**

**419** A83 54p multicolored 1.40 *1.75*
*Nos. 416-419 (4)* 3.10 3.60

**Queen Mother 85th Birthday**
Common Design Type

Designs: 7p, Commonwealth Visitor's Reception. 22p, With Prince Charles, Mark Phillips, Princess Anne. 27p, 80th birthday celebration. 54p, Holding Prince Henry. £1, In coach with Princess Diana.

***Perf. 14½x14***
**1985, June 7 Litho. Wmk. 384**
**420** CD336 7p multicolored .35 .35
**421** CD336 22p multicolored .90 .70
**422** CD336 27p multicolored 1.00 1.00
**423** CD336 54p multicolored 1.10 *1.60*
*Nos. 420-423 (4)* 3.35 3.65

**Souvenir Sheet**

**424** CD336 £1 multicolored 4.00 3.00

Mount Pleasant Airport Opening
A84

**1985, May 12 Litho. *Perf. 14½***
**425** A84 7p Pioneer camp, docked ship .75 .40
**426** A84 22p Construction site 1.00 1.00
**427** A84 27p Runway layout 1.30 1.30
**428** A84 54p Aircraft landing 1.75 *2.40*
*Nos. 425-428 (4)* 4.80 5.10

Captain J. McBride, HMS Jason, 1765 — A85

18th-19th century naval explorers: 22p, Commodore J. Byron, HMS Dolphin and Tamar, 1765. 27p, Vice-Adm. R. Fitzroy, HMS Beagle, 1831. 54p, Adm. Sir B.J. Sulivan, HMS Philomel, 1842.

**1985, Sept. 23**
**429** A85 7p multicolored .75 .45
**430** A85 22p multicolored 1.25 .90
**431** A85 27p multicolored 1.35 1.15
**432** A85 54p multicolored 2.50 2.25
*Nos. 429-432 (4)* 5.85 4.75

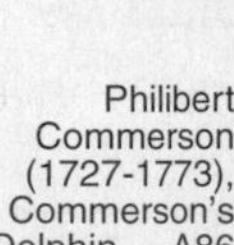

Philibert Commerson (1727-1773), Commerson's Dolphin — A86

Naturalists, endangered species: 22p, Rene Primevere Lesson (1794-1849), kelp. 27p, Joseph Paul Gaimard (1796-1858), diving petrel. 54p, Charles Darwin (1803-1882), Calceolaria darwinii.

**1985, Nov. 4 *Perf. 14½***
**433** A86 7p multicolored .85 .30
**434** A86 22p multicolored 1.10 1.10
**435** A86 27p multicolored 2.00 2.00
**436** A86 54p multicolored 2.25 2.25
*Nos. 433-436 (4)* 6.20 5.65

Seashells
A87

**1986, Feb. 10 Wmk. 384 *Perf. 14½***
**437** A87 7p Painted keyhole limpet .95 .95
**438** A87 22p Magellanic volute 1.50 1.50
**439** A87 27p Falkland scallop 1.60 *1.90*
**440** A87 54p Rough thorn drupe 2.75 *3.25*
*Nos. 437-440 (4)* 6.80 7.60

**Queen Elizabeth II 60th Birthday**
Common Design Type

Designs: 10p, With Princess Margaret at St. Paul's, Waldenbury, 1932. 24p, Christmas broadcast from Sandringham, 1958. 29p, Order of the Thistle, St. Giles Cathedral, Edinburgh, 1962. 45p, Royal reception on the Britannia, US visit, 1976. 58p, Visiting Crown Agents' offices, 1983.

**1986, Apr. 21 Litho. *Perf. 14x14½***
**441** CD337 10p scar, blk & sil .30 .30
**442** CD337 24p ultra, blk & sil .55 *.65*
**443** CD337 29p green & multi .60 *.85*
**444** CD337 45p violet & multi 1.25 *1.40*
**445** CD337 58p rose vio & multi 1.25 *1.75*
*Nos. 441-445 (5)* 3.95 *4.95*

AMERIPEX '86 — A88

SS Great Britain's arrival in the Falkland Isls., Cent.: 10p, Maiden voyage, crossing the Atlantic, 1845. 24p, Wreck in Sparrow Cove, 1937. 29p, Refloating wreck, 1970. 58p, Restored vessel, Bristol, 1986.

**1986, May 22**
**446** A88 10p multicolored .50 .50
**447** A88 24p multicolored .60 *.90*
**448** A88 29p multicolored .75 *1.10*
**449** A88 58p multicolored 1.10 *2.25*
*a.* Souvenir sheet of 4, #446-449 3.75 3.75
*Nos. 446-449 (4)* 2.95 *4.75*

**Bird Type of 1984**

Rockhopper Penguins.

**1986, Aug. 25 Wmk. 373 *Perf. 14½***
**450** A80 10p Adult 1.00 .75
**451** A80 24p Adults swimming 1.90 1.90
**452** A80 29p Adults, diff. 2.10 2.10
**453** A80 58p Adult and young 3.25 *4.25*
*Nos. 450-453 (4)* 8.25 9.00

Wedding of Prince Andrew and Sarah Ferguson — A90

Various photographs: 17p, Presenting Queen's Polo Cup, Windsor, 1986. 22p, Open carriage, wedding. 29p, Andrew wearing military fatigues.

**1986, Nov. 10 Wmk. 384 *Perf. 14½***
**454** A90 17p multicolored .70 .70
**455** A90 22p multicolored .90 .90
**456** A90 29p multicolored 1.25 1.25
*Nos. 454-456 (3)* 2.85 2.85

Royal Engineers, 200th Anniv.
A91

10p, Surveying Sapper Hill. 24p, Explosives disposal. 29p, Boxer Bridge, Pt. Stanley. 58p, Postal services, Stanley Airport.

**1987, Feb. 9 Litho. *Perf. 14½***
**457** A91 10p multicolored 1.35 .90
**458** A91 24p multicolored 2.40 1.50
**459** A91 29p multicolored 2.10 *2.50*
**460** A91 58p multicolored 3.50 *4.25*
*Nos. 457-460 (4)* 9.35 9.15

Seals
A92

**1987, Apr. 27**
**461** A92 10p Southern sea lion 1.25 1.25
**462** A92 24p Falkland fur seal 2.00 2.00
**463** A92 29p Southern elephant seal 2.25 2.25
**464** A92 58p Leopard seal 3.00 *4.50*
*Nos. 461-464 (4)* 8.50 10.00

Hospitals
A93

Designs: 10p, Victorian Cottage Home, c. 1912. 24p, King Edward VII Memorial Hospital, c. 1914. 29p, Churchill Wing, 1953. 58p, Prince Andrew Wing, 1987.

**1987, Dec. 8 *Perf. 14***
**465** A93 10p multicolored .65 .50
**466** A93 24p multicolored 1.10 .90
**467** A93 29p multicolored 1.25 1.00
**468** A93 58p multicolored 2.00 1.50
*Nos. 465-468 (4)* 5.00 3.90

Fungi — A94

**1987, Sept. 14 Litho. *Perf. 14½***
**469** A94 10p Suillus luteus 2.50 1.75
**470** A94 24p Mycena 3.50 3.00
**471** A94 29p Camarophyllus adonis 4.00 3.50
**472** A94 58p Gerronema schusteri 5.00 *5.50*
*Nos. 469-472 (4)* 15.00 13.75

1940 Morris Truck, Fitzroy
A95

Classic automobiles: 24p, 1929 Citroen Kegresse, San Carlos. 29p, 1933 Ford 1-Ton Truck, Port Stanley. 58p, 1935 Ford Model T Saloon, Darwin.

**1988, Apr. 11 Litho. *Perf. 14***
**473** A95 10p multicolored .65 .35
**474** A95 24p multicolored 1.10 .65
**475** A95 29p multicolored 1.25 .75
**476** A95 58p multicolored 1.90 1.50
*Nos. 473-476 (4)* 4.90 3.25

Geese
A96

**1988, July 25**
**477** A96 10p Kelp 2.50 .60
**478** A96 24p Upland 3.25 .90
**479** A96 29p Ruddy-headed 3.50 1.10
**480** A96 58p Ashy-headed 5.75 2.50
*Nos. 477-480 (4)* 15.00 5.10

**Lloyds of London, 300th Anniv.**
Common Design Type

Designs: 10p, Lloyd's Nelson Collection silver service. 24p, Hydroponic Gardens, horiz. 29p, Supply ship A.E.S., horiz. 58p, Wreck of the Charles Cooper near the Falklands, 1866.

**1988, Nov. 14 Litho. Wmk. 373**
**481** CD341 10p multicolored .45 .45
**482** CD341 24p multicolored .85 .85
**483** CD341 29p multicolored 1.75 1.05
**484** CD341 58p multicolored 2.40 1.50
*Nos. 481-484 (4)* 5.45 3.85

Ships of Cape Horn
A97

**1989, Feb. 28**
**485** A97 1p Padua 1.75 .85
**486** A97 2p Priwall, vert. 1.40 1.40
*a.* Wmk. 384 1.20 1.20
**487** A97 3p Passat 1.40 1.40
*a.* Wmk. 384 1.20 1.20
**488** A97 4p Archibald Russell, vert. 2.40 .85
**489** A97 5p Pamir, vert. 2.40 .85
**490** A97 6p Mozart 1.90 1.90
*a.* Wmk. 384 1.90 1.90
**491** A97 7p Pommern 2.40 .95
**492** A97 8p Preussen 2.40 .95
**493** A97 9p Fennia 1.90 1.90
*a.* Wmk. 384 2.50 2.50
**494** A97 10p Cassard 2.40 .95
**495** A97 20p Lawhill 3.50 1.90
**496** A97 25p Garthpool 3.75 1.90
**497** A97 50p Grace Harwar 4.25 3.00
**498** A97 £1 Criccieth Castle 5.00 4.75
*a.* Wmk. 384 6.00 6.00
**499** A97 £3 Cutty Sark, vert. 15.00 10.00
**500** A97 £5 Flying Cloud 27.50 11.50
*Nos. 485-500 (16)* 79.35 45.05

Nos. 486a, 487a, 490a, 493a, 498a are dated "1991."

Whales — A98

**1989, May 15 Wmk. 384 *Perf. 14***
**501** A98 10p Southern right 1.50 .85
**502** A98 24p Minke 2.50 1.25
**503** A98 29p Humpback 3.25 2.00
**504** A98 58p Blue 4.75 3.00
*Nos. 501-504 (4)* 12.00 7.10

Sports Assoc. Activities
A99

Children's drawings.

**1989, Sept. 16**
**505** A99 5p Gymkhana .30 .30
**506** A99 10p Steer Riding .35 .35
**507** A99 17p Sheep shearing .55 .55
**508** A99 24p Dog trial .70 .70
**509** A99 29p Horse racing .95 .95
**510** A99 45p Sack race 1.25 1.25
*Nos. 505-510 (6)* 4.10 4.10

Battles — A100

Commanders, ships and ship crests: 10p, Vice-Adm. Sturdee, HMS *Invincible.* 24p, Vice-Adm. Von Spee, SMS *Scharnhorst.* 29p, Commodore Harwood, HMS *Ajax.* 58p, Capt. Langsdorff, *Admiral Graff Spee.*

**1989, Dec. 8** ***Perf. 14x13½***
**511** A100 10p multicolored 1.35 .35
**512** A100 24p multicolored 2.25 .80
**513** A100 29p multicolored 2.25 1.00
**514** A100 58p multicolored 3.25 2.50
*Nos. 511-514 (4)* 9.10 4.65

Battle of the Falklands, 75th anniv. (10p, 24p); Battle of the River Plate, 50th anniv. (29p, 58p).

Emblems and Presentation Spitfires, 1940 — A101

**1990, May 3** **Wmk. 373** ***Perf. 14***
**515** A101 12p No. 92 Squadron 1.00 1.00
**516** A101 26p No. 611 Squadron 1.40 1.40
**517** A101 31p No. 92 Squadron, diff. 1.75 1.75
**518** A101 62p Spitfires scramble 3.00 3.00
*Nos. 515-518 (4)* 7.15 7.15

**Souvenir Sheet**

**519** A101 £1 Battle of Britain 7.00 7.00

Stamp World London '90.
For souvenir sheet similar to No. 519, see No. 530.

A102

**1990, Apr. 1** **Wmk. 384** ***Perf. 14½***
**520** A102 12p Kidney Is. .80 .55
**521** A102 26p Beauchene Is. 1.25 .55
**522** A102 31p Bird Is. 1.50 1.25
**523** A102 62p Elephant Jason Is. 2.25 2.75
*Nos. 520-523 (4)* 5.80 5.10

Nature reserves and bird sanctuaries.

**Queen Mother, 90th Birthday**
Common Design Types

26p, Queen Mother in Dover. £1, Steering the "Queen Elizabeth," 1946.

**1990, Aug. 4** **Wmk. 384** ***Perf. 14x15***
**524** CD343 26p multicolored 1.00 1.00

***Perf. 14½***

**525** CD344 £1 multicolored 3.75 3.75

A103

**Wmk. 384**

**1990, Oct. 3** **Litho.** ***Perf. 14***
**526** A103 12p Black browed albatross 1.00 .75
**527** A103 26p Adult bird 1.90 1.25
**528** A103 31p Adult, chick 2.25 1.50
**529** A103 62p Bird in flight 3.50 3.50
*Nos. 526-529 (4)* 8.65 7.00

**Battle of Britain Type of 1990 inscribed "SECOND VISIT OF / HRH THE DUKE OF EDINBURGH"**
Souvenir Sheet

**1991, Mar. 7**
**530** A101 £1 multicolored 13.00 13.00

Orchids — A104

**1991, Mar. 18** **Wmk. 373**
**531** A104 12p Gavilea australis 1.60 1.00
**532** A104 26p Codonorchis lessonii 1.90 1.50
**533** A104 31p Chlorea gaudichaudii 2.25 1.75
**534** A104 62p Gavilea littoralis 3.50 *4.00*
*Nos. 531-534 (4)* 9.25 8.25

King Penguin — A105

2p, Two adults crossing bills. 6p, Two adults, one brooding. 12p, Adult with two young. 20p, Adult swimming. 31p, Adult feeding young. 62p, Two adults, diff.

**1991, Aug. 26** **Wmk. 384**
**535** A105 2p multi 1.10 1.10
**536** A105 6p multi 1.60 1.60
**537** A105 12p multi 2.00 2.00
**538** A105 20p multi 2.25 2.25
**539** A105 31p multi 2.25 2.25
**540** A105 62p multi 3.25 3.25
*Nos. 535-540 (6)* 12.45 12.45

World Wildlife Fund.


Falkland Islands Bisects, Cent. A106

**1991, Sept. 10** **Wmk. 384** ***Perf. 14½***
**541** A106 12p #9, #15 1.00 .90
**542** A106 26p On cover 1.90 1.50
**543** A106 31p Unsevered pair 1.50 1.50
**544** A106 62p S.S. Isis 2.50 *3.25*
*Nos. 541-544 (4)* 6.90 7.15

Discovery of America, 500th Anniv. (in 1992) — A107

Sailing ships: 14p, STV Eye of the Wind. 29p, STV Soren Larsen. 34p, Nina, Santa Maria, Pinta. 68p, Columbus and Santa Maria.

**1991, Dec. 12** **Wmk. 373** ***Perf. 14***
**545** A107 14p multicolored .90 .90
**546** A107 29p multicolored 2.00 1.75
**547** A107 34p multicolored 2.25 2.00
**548** A107 68p multicolored 3.50 *4.25*
*Nos. 545-548 (4)* 8.65 8.90

World Columbian Stamp Expo '92, Chicago and Genoa '92 Intl. Philatelic Exhibitions.

**Queen Elizabeth II's Accession to the Throne, 40th Anniv.**
Common Design Type

**1992, Feb. 6**
**549** CD349 7p multicolored .65 .50
**550** CD349 14p multicolored .90 .90
**551** CD349 29p multicolored 1.00 1.10
**552** CD349 34p multicolored 1.40 1.40
**553** CD349 68p multicolored 2.00 2.00
*Nos. 549-553 (5)* 5.95 5.90

Christ Church Cathedral, Cent. — A108

**1992, Feb. 21** **Wmk. 384** ***Perf. 14½***
**554** A108 14p Laying foundation stone 1.00 .75
**555** A108 29p Interior, 1920 2.00 1.25
**556** A108 34p Bishop's chair 2.25 1.50
**557** A108 68p Without tower c. 1900, horiz. 3.00 2.75
*Nos. 554-557 (4)* 8.25 6.25

First Sighting of Falkland Islands by Capt. John Davis, 400th Anniv. A109

Designs: 22p, Capt. John Davis using backstaff. 29p, Capt. Davis working on chart. 34p, Queen Elizabeth I, Queen Elizabeth II. 68p, The Desire sights Falkland Islands.

**1992, Aug. 14** **Wmk. 373**
**558** A109 22p multicolored 1.60 1.10
**559** A109 29p multicolored 2.00 1.50
**560** A109 34p multicolored 2.10 1.90
**561** A109 68p multicolored 3.50 *5.00*
*Nos. 558-561 (4)* 9.20 9.50

Falkland Islands Defense Force and West Yorkshire Regiment — A110

7p, Private, Falkland Islands Volunteers, 1892. 14p, Officer, Falkland Islands Defense Corps, 1914. 22p, Officer, Falkland Islands Defense Force, 1920. 29p, Private, Falkland Islands Defense Force, 1939-45. 34p, Officer, West Yorkshire Regiment, 1942. 68p, Private, West Yorkshire Regiment, 1942.

**1992, Oct. 1** ***Perf. 14***
**562** A110 7p multicolored .60 .60
**563** A110 14p multicolored .90 .90
**564** A110 22p multicolored 1.25 .90
**565** A110 29p multicolored 1.50 1.25
**566** A110 34p multicolored 1.90 1.60
**567** A110 68p multicolored 3.00 *3.75*
*Nos. 562-567 (6)* 9.15 9.00

Gulls and Terns A111

***Perf. 14x14½***

**1993, Jan. 2** **Litho.** **Wmk. 384**
**568** A111 15p South American tern 1.40 1.00
**569** A111 31p Pink breasted gull 1.90 1.50
**570** A111 36p Dolphin gull 2.50 2.25
**571** A111 72p Dominican gull 3.50 *5.50*
*Nos. 568-571 (4)* 9.30 10.25

Souvenir Sheet

Visit of Liner QE II to Falkland Islands — A112

**Wmk. 373**

**1993, Jan. 22** **Litho.** ***Perf. 14***
**572** A112 £2 multicolored 10.00 10.00

**Royal Air Force, 75th Anniv.**
Common Designs Type

Designs: No. 573, Lockheed Tristar. No. 574, Lockheed Hercules. No. 575, Boeing Vertol Chinook. No. 576, Avro Vulcan.
No. 577a, Hawker Siddeley Andover. b, Westland Wessex. c, Panavia Tornado F3. d, McDonnell Douglas Phantom.

**Wmk. 373**

**1993, Apr. 3** **Litho.** ***Perf. 14***
**573** CD350 15p multicolored 1.15 1.15
**574** CD350 15p multicolored 1.15 1.15
**575** CD350 15p multicolored 1.15 1.15
**576** CD350 15p multicolored 1.15 1.15
*Nos. 573-576 (4)* 4.60 4.60

**Souvenir Sheet of 4**

**577** CD350 36p #a.-d. 6.25 6.25

Fisheries A113

Designs: 15p, Short-finned squid. 31p, Stern haul of whiptailed hake. 36p, Fishery Patrol Vessel Falklands Protector. 72p, Aerial surveillance by Britten-Norman Islander.

**Wmk. 384**

**1993, July 1** **Litho.** ***Perf. 14***
**578** A113 15p multicolored .85 .85
**579** A113 31p multicolored 1.75 1.75
**580** A113 36p multicolored 2.10 2.10
**581** A113 72p multicolored 3.25 *5.00*
*Nos. 578-581 (4)* 7.95 9.70

Launch of SS Great Britain, 150th Anniv. — A114

***Perf. 14x13½***

**1993, July 19** **Litho.** **Wmk. 384**
**582** A114 8p In drydock, Bristol .80 .50
**583** A114 £1 At sea 4.25 *5.50*

Cruise Ships and Penguins A115

16p, Explorer. 34p, Rockhopper penguins. 39p, World Discoverer. 78p, Columbus Caravelle.

**Wmk. 373**

**1993, Oct. 1 Litho. *Perf. 14***

**584** A115 16p multicolored 1.60 .80
**585** A115 34p multicolored 2.50 1.60
**586** A115 39p multicolored 2.75 2.00
**587** A115 78p multicolored 3.75 *7.50*
*Nos. 584-587 (4)* 10.60 11.90

Pets — A116

***Perf. 14x14½***

**1993, Dec. 1 Litho. Wmk. 384**

**588** A116 8p Pony .90 .90
**589** A116 16p Lamb 1.10 1.10
**590** A116 34p Puppy, kitten 2.25 1.50

***Perf. 14½x14***

**591** A116 39p Kitten, vert. 2.75 2.00
**592** A116 78p Collie, vert. 3.75 *5.75*
*Nos. 588-592 (5)* 10.75 11.25

**Ovptd. with Hong Kong '94 Emblem**

**1994, Feb. 18**

**593** A116 8p on #588 1.00 *1.25*
**594** A116 16p on #589 1.25 *1.50*
**595** A116 34p on #590 2.75 *3.00*
**596** A116 39p on #591 3.00 *4.00*
**597** A116 78p on #592 4.00 *6.50*
*Nos. 593-597 (5)* 12.00 *16.25*

Inshore Marine Life A117

**Wmk. 384**

**1994, Apr. 4 Litho. *Perf. 14***

**598** A117 1p Goose barnacles, vert. 1.00 .75
**599** A117 2p Painted shrimp 1.75 .75
**600** A117 8p Common limpet 2.00 1.00
**601** A117 9p Mullet 2.00 1.00
**602** A117 10p Sea anemones 2.00 .75
**603** A117 20p Rock eel 2.75 1.00
**604** A117 25p Spider crab 2.75 1.00
**605** A117 50p Lobster krill, vert. 2.75 2.75
**606** A117 80p Falkland skate 2.75 2.75
**607** A117 £1 Centollon crab 2.75 3.00
*a.* Souv. sheet of 1, wmk. 373 6.75 6.75
**608** A117 £3 Rock cod 12.00 8.00
**609** A117 £5 Octopus, vert. 18.00 14.00
*Nos. 598-609 (12)* 52.50 36.75

No. 607a for return of Hong Kong to China. Issued 7/1/97.

See No. 671.

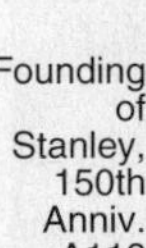

Founding of Stanley, 150th Anniv. A118

9p, Blacksmith's shop, dockyard, Sir James Clark Ross, explorer. 17p, James Leith Mody, 1st colonial chaplain, home at 21 Fitzroy Road. 30p, Stanley cottage, Dr. Henry J. Hamblin, 1st colonial surgeon. 35p, Pioneer row, Sergeant Major Henry Felton. 40p, Government House, Governor R. C. Moody R.E. 65p, View of Stanley, Edward Stanley, 14th Earl of Derby, Secretary of State for Colonies.

**Wmk. 373**

**1994, July 1 Litho. *Perf. 14***

**610** A118 9p multicolored .85 .75
**611** A118 17p multicolored 1.25 1.00
**612** A118 30p multicolored 2.00 1.25
**613** A118 35p multicolored 2.25 1.75
**614** A118 40p multicolored 2.50 2.00
**615** A118 65p multicolored 3.00 *3.50*
*Nos. 610-615 (6)* 11.85 10.25

Methods of Transportation — A119

17p, Tristar over Gypsy Cove. 35p, Cruise ship, Sea Lion Island. 40p, FIGAS Islander, Pebble Island Beach. 65p, Land Rover, Volunteer Beach.

**Wmk. 384**

**1994, Oct. 24 Litho. *Perf. 14***

**616** A119 17p multicolored 1.10 .75
**617** A119 35p multicolored 2.10 1.50
**618** A119 40p multicolored 2.75 2.75
**619** A119 65p multicolored 3.25 *4.25*
*Nos. 616-619 (4)* 9.20 9.25

South American Missionary Society, 150th Anniv. — A120

Designs: 5p, Mission House, Keppel Island. 17p, Thomas Bridges, compiler of Yahgan dictionary. 40p, Fuegian Indians. 65p, Schooner Allen Gardiner, Capt. Allen Gardiner.

**1994, Dec. 1**

**620** A120 5p multicolored .30 .30
**621** A120 17p multicolored .85 .85
**622** A120 40p multicolored 1.75 1.75
**623** A120 65p multicolored 2.75 *3.50*
*Nos. 620-623 (4)* 5.65 6.40

Flowering Shrubs — A121

Designs: 9p, Lupinus arboreus. 17p, Boxwood. 30p, Fuchsia magellanica. 35p, Berberis ilicifolia. 40p, Gorse. 65p, Veronica.

***Perf. 14½x14***

**1995, Jan. 3 Litho. Wmk. 384**

**624** A121 9p multicolored .90 .65
**625** A121 17p multicolored 1.10 .80
**626** A121 30p multicolored 1.45 1.45
**627** A121 35p multicolored 1.75 1.45
**628** A121 40p multicolored 1.90 1.60
**629** A121 65p multicolored 3.25 4.25
*Nos. 624-629 (6)* 10.35 10.20

Shore Birds A122

Designs: 17p, Magellanic oystercatcher. 35p, Rufous chested dotterel. 40p, Black oystercatcher. 65p, Two banded plover.

**Wmk. 373**

**1995, Mar. 1 Litho. *Perf. 13½***

**630** A122 17p multicolored 1.75 .90
**631** A122 35p multicolored 2.50 1.50
**632** A122 40p multicolored 2.75 1.75
**633** A122 65p multicolored 4.00 7.00
*Nos. 630-633 (4)* 11.00 11.15

**End of World War II, 50th Anniv.**
Common Design Types

17p, Falkland Islands Victory Parade contingent. 35p, Governor Sir Alan Wolsey Cardinall on Bren gun carrier. 40p, HMAS Esperance Bay, 1942. 65p, HMS Exeter, 1939.

£1, Reverse of War Medal 1939-45.

**Wmk. 373**

**1995, May 8 Litho. *Perf. 14***

**634** CD351 17p multicolored 1.50 .90
**635** CD351 35p multicolored 2.40 1.50
**636** CD351 40p multicolored 2.75 2.00
**637** CD351 65p multicolored 4.75 *5.50*
*Nos. 634-637 (4)* 11.40 9.90

**Souvenir Sheet**

**638** CD352 £1 multicolored 7.25 7.25

Transporting Peat — A123

**Wmk. 384**

**1995, Aug. 1 Litho. *Perf. 14***

**639** A123 17p Ox, cart .80 .80
**640** A123 35p Horse, cart 1.75 1.25
**641** A123 40p Tractor, sledge 2.00 1.50
**642** A123 65p Truck, peat bank 3.50 *4.00*
*Nos. 639-642 (4)* 8.05 7.55

Miniature Sheet of 6

Wildlife — A124

Designs: a, Kelp geese. b, Albatross. c, Cormorants. d, Magellanic penguins. e, Fur seals. f, Rockhopper penguins.

**1995, Sept. 11**

**643** A124 35p #a.-f. 19.00 19.00

No. 643 is a continuous design.

Wild Animals A125

**1995, Nov. 6 Wmk. 373**

**644** A125 9p Rabbit 1.00 .90
**645** A125 17p Hare 1.60 1.10
**646** A125 35p Guanaco 2.50 1.75
**647** A125 40p Fox 3.00 2.00
**648** A125 65p Otter 4.00 *5.00*
*Nos. 644-648 (5)* 12.10 10.75

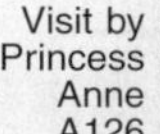

Visit by Princess Anne A126

Princess Anne and: 9p, Government House. 19p, San Carlos Cemetery. 30p, Christ Church Cathedral. 73p, Goose Green.

**1996, Jan. 30 *Perf. 14½***

**649** A126 9p multicolored 1.00 .60
**650** A126 19p multicolored 1.35 1.00
**651** A126 30p multicolored 1.75 1.50
**652** A126 73p multicolored 6.00 *7.50*
*Nos. 649-652 (4)* 10.10 10.60

**Queen Elizabeth II, 70th Birthday**
Common Design Type

Various portraits of Queen, scenes from Falkland Islands: 17p, Steeple Jason. 40p, Ship, KV Tamar. 45p, New Island with shipwreck on beach. 65p, Community School.

£1, Queen in formal dress at Sandringham Ball.

**1996, Apr. 21 *Perf. 13½***

**653** CD354 17p multicolored .90 .70
**654** CD354 40p multicolored 2.25 1.35
**655** CD354 45p multicolored 2.40 1.90
**656** CD354 65p multicolored 3.00 2.25
*Nos. 653-656 (4)* 8.55 6.20

**Souvenir Sheet**

**657** CD354 £1 multicolored 5.00 5.00

CAPEX '96 A127

Mail delivery: 9p, Horseback, 1890. 40p, Norseman floatplane. 45p, Inter-island ship. 76p, Beaver floatplane.

£1, LMS Jubilee Class 4-6-0 locomotive.

**1996, June 8 Wmk. 384 *Perf. 14***

**658** A127 9p multicolored .90 .65
**659** A127 40p multicolored 2.40 1.50
**660** A127 45p multicolored 2.50 1.60
**661** A127 76p multicolored 3.50 *4.00*
*Nos. 658-661 (4)* 9.30 7.75

**Souvenir Sheet**

**662** A127 £1 multicolored 4.25 4.25

No. 662 contains one 48x32mm stamp.

Beaked Whales — A128

Designs: 9p, Southern bottlenose whale. 30p, Cuvier's beaked whale. 35p, Straptoothed beaked whale. 75p, Gray's beaked whale.

**Wmk. 373**

**1996, Sept. 2 Litho. *Perf. 14***

**663** A128 9p multicolored .80 .60
**664** A128 30p multicolored 1.60 1.50
**665** A128 35p multicolored 1.90 1.75
**666** A128 75p multicolored 4.00 4.00
*Nos. 663-666 (4)* 8.30 7.85

Magellanic Penguins — A129

Designs: 17p, Two adults. 35p, Young in nest. 40p, Chick, adult. 65p, Swimming.

**Wmk. 373**

**1997, Jan. 2 Litho. *Perf. 14***

**667** A129 17p multicolored 2.00 .75
**668** A129 35p multicolored 3.00 1.25
**669** A129 40p multicolored 3.25 1.50
**670** A129 65p multicolored 4.50 3.25
*Nos. 667-670 (4)* 12.75 6.75

**Fish Type of 1994**
Souvenir Sheet

**Wmk. 373**

**1997, Feb. 3 Litho. *Perf. 14***

**671** A117 £1 Smelt 5.50 5.50

Hong Kong '97.

Ferns — A130

*Perf. 14½x14*

**1997, Mar. 3 Litho. Wmk. 373**

**672** A130 17p Coral 1.75 .60
**673** A130 35p Adder's tongue 2.50 1.25
**674** A130 40p Fuegian tall 2.50 1.50
**675** A130 65p Small fern 3.50 3.00
*Nos. 672-675 (4)* 10.25 6.35

Lighthouses — A131

**Wmk. 373**

**1997, July 1 Litho. Perf. 14**

**676** A131 9p Bull Point 3.25 1.00
**677** A131 30p Cape Pembroke 4.50 2.00
**678** A131 £1 Cape Meredith 10.50 5.00
*Nos. 676-678 (3)* 18.25 8.00

Queen Elizabeth II and Prince Philip, 50th Wedding Anniv. — A132

No. 679, Queen holding flowers. No. 680, Prince with horse. No. 681, Queen riding in open carriage. No. 682, Prince in uniform. No. 683, Queen in red coat & hat, Prince. No. 684, Princes William and Harry on horseback.
£1.50, Queen, Prince riding in open carriage.

**1997 Wmk. 384 Perf. 14½x14**

**679** 9p multicolored 1.00 .75
**680** 9p multicolored 1.00 .75
*a.* A132 Pair, #679-680 2.75 2.75
**681** 17p multicolored 1.75 1.00
**682** 17p multicolored 1.75 1.00
*a.* A132 Pair, #681-682 4.00 4.00
**683** 40p multicolored 3.00 1.50
**684** 40p multicolored 3.00 1.50
*a.* A132 Pair, #683-684 8.00 8.00
*Nos. 679-684 (6)* 11.50 6.50

**Souvenir Sheet**

**685** A132 £1.50 multicolored 9.00 9.00

Endangered Species — A133

Designs: 17p, Phalcoboenus australis. 19p, Otaria flavescens. 40p, Calandrinia feltonii. 73p, Aplochiton zebra.

**Wmk. 373**

**1997, Oct. 16 Litho. Perf. 14½**

**686** A133 17p multicolored 3.75 1.75
**687** A133 19p multicolored 2.75 2.25
**688** A133 40p multicolored 4.50 3.00
**689** A133 73p multicolored 7.50 *8.50*
*Nos. 686-689 (4)* 18.50 15.50

Fire Service in Falkland Islands, Cent. — A134

Equipment, manufacturer: 9p, Greenwich Gem, Merryweather & Son. 17p, Hatfield trailer pump, Merryweather & Son. 40p, Godiva trailer pump, Coventry Climax. 65p, Water tender type B, Carmichael Bedford.

**Wmk. 384**

**1998, Feb. 26 Litho. Perf. 14½**

**690** A134 9p multicolored 3.25 1.50
**691** A134 17p multicolored 3.75 1.50
**692** A134 40p multicolored 6.00 3.00
**693** A134 65p multicolored 8.00 *9.25*
*Nos. 690-693 (4)* 21.00 15.25

**Diana, Princess of Wales (1961-97)**
Common Design Type

Portraits: a, Looking left. b, In red dress. c, Hand on cheek. d, Investigating land mines.

*Perf. 14½x14*

**1998, Mar. 31 Wmk. 373**

**694** CD355 30p Sheet of 4, #a-d 5.00 5.00

No. 694 sold for £1.20 + 20p, with surtax from international sales being donated to the Princess Diana Memorial Fund and surtax from national sales being donated to designated local charity.

Birds A135

1p, Tawny-throated dotterel. 2p, Hudsonian godwit. 5p, Eared dove. No. 698, Great grebe. No. 699, Roseate spoonbill. 10p, Southern lapwing. 16p, Buff-necked ibis. 17p, Astral parakeet. 30p, Ashy-headed goose. 35p, American kestrel. 65p, Red-legged shag. 88p, Red shoveler. £1, Red-fronted coot. £3, Chilean flamingo. £5, Fork-tailed flycatcher.

**Wmk. 373**

**1998, July 14 Litho. Perf. 14**

**695** A135 1p multicolored 1.00 *1.25*
**696** A135 2p multicolored 1.00 *1.25*
**697** A135 5p multicolored 1.00 *1.25*
**698** A135 9p multicolored 1.50 1.00
**699** A135 9p multicolored 6.00 *9.50*
**700** A135 10p multicolored 2.25 1.00
**701** A135 16p multicolored 2.25 2.25
**702** A135 17p multicolored 1.25 *2.25*
*a.* Booklet pane, 2 #699, 8 #702 + 2 labels 22.00
Complete booklet, #702a 22.00
**703** A135 30p multicolored 2.50 1.75
**704** A135 35p multicolored 3.00 *4.00*
Complete booklet, 6 #704 18.00
**705** A135 65p multicolored 4.00 2.50
**706** A135 88p multicolored 4.25 *6.25*
**707** A135 £1 multicolored 4.50 4.50
**708** A135 £3 multicolored 11.00 *15.00*
**709** A135 £5 multicolored 15.00 *22.50*
*Nos. 695-709 (15)* 60.50 76.25

Boats — A136

Boat, country flag, year: 17p, Penelope, Germany, 1926. 35p, Ilen, Italy, 1926. 40p, Weddell, Chilo, 1940. 65p, Lively, Scotland, 1940.

**Wmk. 373**

**1998, Sept. 30 Litho. Perf. 14**

**710** A136 17p multicolored 2.50 1.00
**711** A136 35p multicolored 3.50 2.00
**712** A136 40p multicolored 3.75 2.25

**Size: 29x18mm**

**713** A136 65p multicolored 5.50 *6.00*
*Nos. 710-713 (4)* 15.25 11.25

FIGAS (First Medivac Air Ambulance Service), 50th Anniv. — A137

17p, Man carrying patient, airplane. £1, Airplane, map of Islands, float plane.

**Wmk. 373**

**1998, Dec. 1 Litho. Perf. 14**

**714** A137 17p multicolored 3.00 1.25
**715** A137 £1 multicolored 12.50 12.50

Military Uniforms — A138

Uniform, background location: 17p, Marine Private, 1776, The Block House at Port Egmont, Saunders Island. 30p, Marine Officer, 1833, Port Louis, East Falkland. 35p, Royal Marine Corporal, 1914, HMS Kent. 65p, Royal Marine Bugler, 1976, Government House.

**Wmk. 373**

**1998, Dec. 8 Litho. Perf. 14½**

**716** A138 17p multicolored 3.00 1.00
**717** A138 30p multicolored 4.00 2.50
**718** A138 35p multicolored 4.25 2.50
**719** A138 65p multicolored 6.50 *9.50*
*Nos. 716-719 (4)* 17.75 15.50

St. Mary's Church, Cent. A139

**Wmk. 373**

**1999, Feb. 12 Litho. Perf. 14**

**720** A139 17p Inside view 2.40 .90
**721** A139 40p Outside view 3.75 3.00
**722** A139 75p Laying corner-stone, 1899 7.75 *2.75*
*Nos. 720-722 (3)* 13.90 6.65

Australia '99, World Stamp Expo A140

25p, HMS Beagle. 35p, HMAS Australia. 40p, SS Canberra. No. 726, SS Great Britain. No. 727, All-England Eleven visit Australia, 1861-62.

**1999, Mar. 5 Wmk. 384**

**723** A140 25p multicolored 3.25 2.00
**724** A140 35p multicolored 3.50 2.50
**725** A140 40p multicolored 4.75 2.75
**726** A140 50p multicolored 4.50 *7.00*
**727** A140 50p multicolored 4.50 *7.00*
*a.* Pair, #726-727 9.00 *14.00*
*Nos. 723-727 (5)* 20.50 21.25

1999 Visit of HRH Prince of Wales — A141

*Perf. 14x13½*

**1999, Mar. 13 Litho. Wmk. 384**

**728** A141 £2 multicolored 16.00 16.00

**Wedding of Prince Edward and Sophie Rhys-Jones**
Common Design Type

*Perf. 13¾x14*

**1999, June 15 Litho. Wmk. 384**

**729** CD356 80p Separate portraits 6.00 6.00
**730** CD356 £1.20 Couple 8.00 8.00

PhilexFrance '99, World Philatelic Exhibition — A142

Designs: 35p, French cruiser, Jeanne d'Arc, Port Stanley, 1931. 40p, CAMS 37/11 Flying Boat's first flight.
£1, CAMS 37 Flying Boat over Port Stanley, 1931.

**1999, June 21 Wmk. 373 Perf. 14**

**731** A142 35p multicolored 5.25 5.25
**732** A142 40p multicolored 5.75 5.75

**Souvenir Sheet**

**733** A142 £1 multicolored 13.00 *14.00*

No. 733 contains one 48x31mm stamp.

**Queen Mother's Century**
Common Design Type

Queen Mother: 9p, With King George VI at Port of London. 20p, With Queen Elizabeth at Women's Institute, Sandringham. 30p, With Princes Charles, William and Harry at Clarence House, 95th birthday. 67p, As Colonel-in-Chief of the Queen's Royal Hussars.
£1.40, With Ernest Shackleton, Robert F. Scott and Edward A. Wilson.

**Wmk. 384**

**1999, Aug. 18 Litho. Perf. 13½**

**734** CD358 9p multi 2.00 1.00
**735** CD358 20p multi 3.00 1.50
**736** CD358 30p multi 3.50 1.75
**737** CD358 67p multi 5.50 *8.00*
*Nos. 734-737 (4)* 14.00 12.25

**Souvenir Sheet**

**738** CD358 £1.40 multi 16.00 16.00

For overprint see No. 767.

Waterfowl A143

*Perf. 14¼x14½*

**1999, Sept. 9 Litho. Wmk. 384**

**739** A143 9p Chiloe wigeon 2.50 1.75
**740** A143 17p Crested duck 3.25 2.00
**741** A143 30p Brown pintail 4.00 3.25
**742** A143 35p Silver teal 4.25 3.50
**743** A143 40p Yellow billed teal 4.75 4.00
**744** A143 65p Flightless steamer duck 7.00 *9.50*
*Nos. 739-744 (6)* 25.75 24.00

California Gold Rush A144

Designs: 9p, Vicar of Bray, 1999. 35p, Gold panning, 1849. 40p, Gold rocking cradle, 1849. 80p, Vicar of Bray, 1849.
£1, Vicar of Bray in San Francisco Harbor, 1849.

**Wmk. 373**

**1999, Nov. 3 Litho. Perf. 14**

**745** A144 9p multicolored 1.10 1.10
**746** A144 35p multicolored 4.25 4.25
**747** A144 40p multicolored 4.75 4.75
**748** A144 80p multicolored 10.00 *12.00*
*Nos. 745-748 (4)* 20.10 22.10

**Souvenir Sheet**

*Perf. 13¾*

**749** A144 £1 multicolored 15.00 15.00

No. 749 contains one 48x31mm stamp.

Millennium
A145

Designs: No. 750, Kelp gull. No. 751, Upland goose. No. 752, Christchurch Cathedral. No. 753, Night heron. No. 754, King penguin. No. 755, Christmas at home.

**1999, Dec. 6** ***Perf. 14x14½***

| | | | | | |
|---|---|---|---|---|---|
| **750** | A145 | 9p multicolored | | 2.75 | 2.75 |
| **751** | A145 | 9p multicolored | | 2.75 | 2.75 |
| **752** | A145 | 9p multicolored | | 2.75 | 2.75 |
| **753** | A145 | 30p multicolored | | 4.75 | 4.75 |
| **754** | A145 | 30p multicolored | | 4.75 | 4.75 |
| **755** | A145 | 30p multicolored | | 4.75 | 4.75 |
| | | *Nos. 750-755 (6)* | | 22.50 | 22.50 |

Visit of Princess Alexandra
A146

Designs: 9p, Princess in patterned dress, trees. £1, Princess in blue dress, trees.

***Perf. 13¼x13¾***

**2000, Feb. 1** **Litho.** **Wmk. 373**

| | | | | |
|---|---|---|---|---|
| **756** | A146 | 9p multi | 2.00 | 2.00 |
| **757** | A146 | £1 multi | 9.50 | 9.50 |

Sir Ernest Shackleton (1874-1922), Polar Explorer — A147

17p, Ship Endurance, discovery of the Caird Coast. 45p, Endurance trapped in pack ice. 75p, Shackleton, Chilean tugboat Yelcho.

**2000, Feb. 10** **Wmk. 373** ***Perf. 14***

| | | | | |
|---|---|---|---|---|
| **758** | A147 | 17p multi | 5.00 | 2.00 |
| **759** | A147 | 45p multi | 8.50 | 4.50 |
| **760** | A147 | 75p multi | 12.50 | *14.00* |
| | | *Nos. 758-760 (3)* | 26.00 | 20.50 |

See British Antarctic Territory Nos. 285-287, South Georgia and South Sandwich Islands Nos. 254-256.

British Monarchs — A148

a, Elizabeth I. b, James II. c, George I. d, William IV. e, Edward VIII. f, Elizabeth II.

**2000, Feb. 29** **Wmk. 373** ***Perf. 14***

| | | | | |
|---|---|---|---|---|
| **761** | A148 | 40p Sheet of 6, #a.-f. | 17.00 | 17.00 |

The Stamp Show 2000, London.

**Prince William, 18th Birthday**
Common Design Type

William: 10p, As toddler with fireman's helmet, vert. 20p, In checked suit and in navy suit, vert. 37p, With blue shirt. 43p, In gray suit and in navy suit holding flowers. 50p, As child with dog.

***Perf. 13¾x14¼, 14¼x13¾***

**2000, June 21** **Litho.** **Wmk. 373**

**Stamps with White Border**

| | | | | |
|---|---|---|---|---|
| **762** | CD359 | 10p multi | 1.50 | 1.25 |
| **763** | CD359 | 20p multi | 2.10 | 1.50 |
| **764** | CD359 | 37p multi | 3.00 | 2.75 |
| **765** | CD359 | 43p multi | 4.00 | 3.00 |
| | | *Nos. 762-765 (4)* | 10.60 | 8.50 |

**Souvenir Sheet**

**Stamps Without White Border**

***Perf. 14¼***

| | | | |
|---|---|---|---|
| **766** | Sheet of 5 | 14.00 | 14.00 |
| *a.* | CD359 10p multi | 1.00 | 1.00 |
| *b.* | CD359 20p multi | 1.50 | 1.50 |
| *c.* | CD359 37p multi | 2.50 | 2.50 |
| *d.* | CD359 43p multi | 3.00 | 3.00 |
| *e.* | CD359 50p multi | 5.00 | 5.00 |

**No. 738 Ovptd. in Gold**

**Wmk. 384**

**2000, Aug. 4** **Litho.** ***Perf. 13½***

| | | | | |
|---|---|---|---|---|
| **767** | CD358 | £1.40 multi | 17.00 | 17.00 |

Bridges
A149

Bridges over: 20p, Malo River. 37p, Bodie Creek. 43p, Fitzroy River.

**2000, Oct. 16** ***Perf. 14¼x14½***

| | | | | |
|---|---|---|---|---|
| **768-770** | A149 | Set of 3 | 17.00 | 17.00 |

Christmas — A150

Designs: 10p, Shepherd, sheep. 20p, Shepherds, sheep, angel. 33p, Holy family, shepherds, Magus, donkey, sheep. 43p, Angel, two Magi. 78p, Camel.

**2000, Nov. 1** **Wmk. 373**

| | | | | |
|---|---|---|---|---|
| **771-775** | A150 | Set of 5 | 15.50 | 15.50 |
| *775a* | | Souvenir sheet, #771-775 | 17.50 | 17.50 |

Sunrises and Sunsets
A151

Various photos: 10p, 20p, 37p, 43p.

**2001, Jan. 10** ***Perf. 14½x14¼***

| | | | | |
|---|---|---|---|---|
| **776-779** | A151 | Set of 4 | 15.00 | 15.00 |

Souvenir Sheet

New Year 2001 (Year of the Snake) — A152

Birds: a, Striated caracara. b, Mountain hawk eagle.

***Perf. 14½x14¼***

**2001, Feb. 1** **Litho.** **Wmk. 373**

| | | | | |
|---|---|---|---|---|
| **780** | A152 | 37p Sheet of 2, #a-b | 10.50 | *12.00* |

Hong Kong 2001 Stamp Exhibition.

Age of Victoria — A153

Designs: 3p, Falkland Islands #1. 10p, S.S. Great Britain, horiz. 20p, Stanley Harbor, 1888, horiz. 43p, Cape Pembroke Lighthouse, telephones, 1897. 93p, Royal Marines, 1900. £1.50, Queen Victoria, by Franz Xavier Winterhalter, 1859.

£1, Funeral procession for Queen Victoria.

**2001, May 24** ***Perf. 14***

| | | | | |
|---|---|---|---|---|
| **781-786** | A153 | Set of 6 | 24.50 | 24.50 |

**Souvenir Sheet**

| | | | | |
|---|---|---|---|---|
| **787** | A153 | £1 multi | 10.50 | 10.50 |

Royal Navy Connections to Falkland Islands — A154

Designs: 10p, Welfare, ship that made first recorded landing, 1690. 17p, HMS Invincible, ship in Battle of the Falklands, 1914. 20p, HMS Exeter, ship in Battle of the River Plate, 1939. 37p, SN.R6 Hovercraft, 1967. 43p, Antarctic patrol ship HMS Protector and Wasp helicopter, 1955. 68p, Desire, ship that made first sighting, 1592.

**2001, July 24**

| | | | | |
|---|---|---|---|---|
| **788-793** | A154 | Set of 6 | 27.50 | 27.50 |

Carcass Island and its Flora and Fauna — A155

No. 794, 37p: a, Yellow violet. b, Tussac bird.

No. 795, 43p: a, Carcass Island settlement. b, Black-crowned night heron.

**Wmk. 373**

**2001, Sept. 28** **Litho.** ***Perf. 13¾***

**Pairs, #a-b**

| | | | | |
|---|---|---|---|---|
| **794-795** | A155 | Set of 2 | 19.00 | 19.00 |

Gentoo Penguins — A156

Designs: 10p, Birds flapping wings. 33p, Feeding young. 37p, Bird with beak open. 43p, Four birds walking.

**2001, Oct. 26** ***Perf. 14½x14¼***

| | | | | |
|---|---|---|---|---|
| **796-799** | A156 | Set of 4 | 10.00 | 10.00 |

Falkland Islands Company, 150th Anniv.
A157

Designs: 10p, Company coat of arms, and gathering of cattle. 20p, Company flag, and ship Amelia. 43p, Manager F. E. Cobb, and company buildings. £1, Sheep farmer William Wickham Bertrand, sheep dip.

**Wmk. 373**

**2002, Jan. 10** **Litho.** ***Perf. 14***

| | | | | |
|---|---|---|---|---|
| **800-803** | A157 | Set of 4 | 16.00 | 16.00 |

**Reign Of Queen Elizabeth II, 50th Anniv. Issue**
Common Design Type

Designs: Nos. 804, 808a, 20p, Princess Elizabeth reading, 1945. Nos. 805, 808b, 37p, In 1977. Nos. 806, 808c, 43p, Holding Prince Charles, 1949. Nos. 807, 808d, 50p, At Garter ceremony, 1994. No. 808e, 50p, 1955 portrait by Annigoni (38x50mm).

***Perf. 14¼x14½, 13¾ (#808e)***

**2002, Feb. 6** **Litho.** **Wmk. 373**

**With Gold Frames**

| | | | | |
|---|---|---|---|---|
| **804** | CD360 | 20p multicolored | 1.75 | 1.00 |
| **805** | CD360 | 37p multicolored | 2.25 | 2.00 |
| **806** | CD360 | 43p multicolored | 3.50 | 3.50 |
| **807** | CD360 | 50p multicolored | 4.00 | 4.00 |
| | | *Nos. 804-807 (4)* | 11.50 | 10.50 |

**Souvenir Sheet**

**Without Gold Frames**

| | | | | |
|---|---|---|---|---|
| **808** | CD360 | Sheet of 5, #a-e | 11.50 | 11.50 |

Falkland Islands War, 20th Anniv. — A158

No. 809, 22p: a, HMS Hermes, 1982. b, Fishery patrol vessel, 2002.

No. 810, 40p: a, Troops landing, 1982. b, Mine clearing, 2002.

No. 811, 45p: a, RAF Harrier on HMS Hermes, 1982. b, RAF Tristar, 2002.

**Wmk. 373**

**2002, June 14** **Litho.** ***Perf. 14***

**Horiz. pairs, #a-b**

| | | | | |
|---|---|---|---|---|
| **809-811** | A158 | Set of 3 | 20.00 | 20.00 |

**Queen Mother Elizabeth (1900-2002)**
Common Design Type

Designs: 22p, Wearing hat and scarf (black and white photograph). 25p, Wearing blue hat with polka dots. Nos. 814, 816a, 95p, Wearing feathered hat (black and white photograph). Nos. 815, 816b, £1.20, Wearing blue hat.

**Wmk. 373**

**2002, Aug. 5** **Litho.** ***Perf. 14¼***

**With Purple Frames**

| | | | | |
|---|---|---|---|---|
| **812** | CD361 | 22p multicolored | 1.00 | 1.00 |
| **813** | CD361 | 25p multicolored | 1.25 | 1.25 |
| **814** | CD361 | 95p multicolored | 5.00 | 5.00 |
| **815** | CD361 | £1.20 multicolored | 6.75 | 6.75 |
| | | *Nos. 812-815 (4)* | 14.00 | 14.00 |

**Souvenir Sheet**

**Without Purple Frames**

***Perf. 14½x14¼***

| | | | | |
|---|---|---|---|---|
| **816** | CD361 | Sheet of 2, #a-b | 14.50 | 14.50 |

Worldwide Fund for Nature (WWF) — A159

Penguins: 36p, Rockhopper. 40p, Magellanic. 45p, Gentoo. 70p, Macaroni.

**Wmk. 373**

**2002, Aug. 30** **Litho.** ***Perf. 14¼***

| | | | | |
|---|---|---|---|---|
| **817-820** | A159 | Set of 4 | 11.50 | 11.50 |
| *a.* | | Horiz. strip of 4, #817-820 | 13.00 | 13.00 |

West Point Island and its Flora and Fauna — A160

No. 821, 40p: a, Felton's flower. b, Black-browed albatross.
No. 822, 45p: a, Rockhopper penguin. b, Island settlement.

***Perf. 14¼x14½***

**2002, Oct. 31 Litho. Wmk. 373**
**Horiz. Pairs, #a-b**

**821-822** A160 Set of 2 15.00 15.00

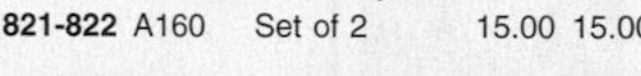

Visit of Prince Andrew — A161

No. 823: a, 22p, In uniform. b, £1.52, In suit and tie.

**2002, Nov. 11** ***Perf. 13¼x13½***

**823** A161 Horiz. pair, #a-b 14.50 14.50

Shepherds' Houses — A162

Designs: 10p, Gun Hill shanty, Little Chartres. 22p, Paragon House, Lafonia. 45p, Dos Lomas, Lafonia. £1, Old House, Shallow Bay Farm.

**Wmk. 373**

**2003, Mar. 31 Litho.** ***Perf. 14***

**824-827** A162 Set of 4 12.00 12.00

**Head of Queen Elizabeth II**
Common Design Type
**Wmk. 373**

**2003, June 2 Litho.** ***Perf. 13¾***

**828** CD362 £2 multi 9.00 9.00

**Prince William, 21st Birthday**
Common Design Type

Color photographs: a, In suit at right. b, With Prince Harry at left.

**Wmk. 373**

**2003, June 21 Litho.** ***Perf. 14¼***

**829** Horiz. pair 13.50 13.50
***a.-b.*** CD364 95p Either single 5.50 5.50

Birds — A163

Designs: 1p, Chiloe widgeon. 2p, Dolphin gull, vert. 5p, Falkland flightless steamer duck. 10p, Black-throated finch, vert. 22p, White-tufted grebe. 25p, Rufous-chested dotterel, vert. 45p, Upland goose. 50p, Dark-faced ground-tyrant, vert. 95p, Black-crowned night heron. £1, Red-backed hawk, vert. £3, Black-necked swan. £5, Short-eared owl, vert.

***Perf. 13x13¼, 13¼x13***

**2003, July 21 Litho. Wmk. 373**

| | | | | |
|---|---|---|---|---|
| **830** | A163 | 1p multi | .60 | *1.25* |
| **831** | A163 | 2p multi | .90 | *1.50* |
| **832** | A163 | 5p multi | 1.25 | *1.50* |
| **833** | A163 | 10p multi | 1.50 | 1.50 |
| **834** | A163 | 22p multi | 1.75 | 1.25 |
| **835** | A163 | 25p multi | 2.00 | 1.25 |
| **836** | A163 | 45p multi | 2.50 | 2.00 |
| **837** | A163 | 50p multi | 3.00 | 3.00 |
| **838** | A163 | 95p multi | 4.25 | *5.25* |
| **839** | A163 | £1 multi | 4.50 | *5.25* |
| **840** | A163 | £3 multi | 12.00 | *13.00* |
| **841** | A163 | £5 multi | 18.00 | *20.00* |
| | *Nos. 830-841,C1 (13)* | | 54.75 | 59.25 |

See Nos. 917-919, C1.

Bird Life International A164

Black-browed albatross: No. 842, Adult on nest, facing right. No. 843, Chick. 40p, Heads of two adults, vert. £1, Adult on nest, facing left, vert.
16p, In flight.

***Perf. 14¼x13¾, 13¾x14¼***

**2003, Sept. 26**

| | | | | |
|---|---|---|---|---|
| **842** | A164 22p multi | | 1.75 | 1.75 |
| *a.* | Perf. 14¼x14½ | | 1.75 | 1.75 |
| **843** | A164 22p multi | | 1.75 | 1.75 |
| *a.* | Perf. 14¼x14½ | | 1.75 | 1.75 |
| **844** | A164 40p multi | | 2.75 | 2.75 |
| *a.* | Perf. 14½x14¼ | | 2.75 | 2.75 |
| **845** | A164 £1 multi | | 7.25 | 7.25 |
| *a.* | Perf. 14½x14¼ | | 7.25 | 7.25 |
| | *Nos. 842-845 (4)* | | 13.50 | 13.50 |

**Souvenir Sheet**

**846** Sheet, #842a-846a 16.50 16.50
*a.* A164 16p multi, perf. 14¼x14½ 1.40 1.40

New Island and its Flora and Fauna A165

No. 847, 40p: a, Striated caracara. b, Lady's slipper.
No. 848, 45p: a, Stone Cottage. b, King penguin.

**Wmk. 373**

**2003, Oct. 24 Litho.** ***Perf. 13¾***
**Pairs, #a-b**

**847-848** A165 Set of 2 18.00 18.00

Christmas — A166

Various depictions of Pale maiden flower: 16p, 30p, 40p, 95p.

**2003, Nov. 3** ***Perf. 14x14¼***

**849-852** A166 Set of 4 16.50 16.50

Sheep Farming A167

Designs: 19p, Traditional hand shearing. 22p, Driving the sheep. 45p, Big House, Hill Cove. 70p, The early years. £1, Wool collection, SS Fitzroy.

**Unwmk.**

**2004, Apr. 30 Litho.** ***Perf. 14***

**853-857** A167 Set of 5 22.50 22.50

Wildlife Conservation in Falkland Islands, 25th Anniv. — A168

Designs: 20p, Man planting tussac grass. 24p, People cleaning beach. 50p, Satellite tracking of rockhopper penguins. £1, Weighing of albatross chick.

**2004, June 17 Litho.** ***Perf. 14***

**858-861** A168 Set of 4 18.00 18.00

Sir Rowland Hill (1795-1879) and Falkland Islands Postage Stamps — A169

Hill and: 24p, #20. 50p, #74. 75p, #94. £1, #151a.

**2004, Aug. 31 Litho.** ***Perf. 13¼***

**862-865** A169 Set of 4 19.00 19.00

Sea Lion Island and its Flora and Fauna — A170

No. 866, 42p: a, King cormorant. b, Dog orchid.
No. 867, 50p: a, Magellanic penguin. b, Sea Lion Lodge.

**2004, Sept. 15** ***Perf. 13¾***
**Pairs, #a-b**

| | | | | |
|---|---|---|---|---|
| **866-867** | A170 | Set of 2 | 19.50 | 19.50 |
| *866c* | As #866a, dated "2005" | | *2.25* | — |
| *866d* | As #866b, dated "2005" | | *2.25* | — |
| *866e* | Pair, #866c-866d | | *7.00* | — |

Owls — A171

Designs: 18p, Head of short-eared owl. 45p, Short-eared owl. 50p, Barn owl in flight. £1.50, Barn owl.
£2, Barn owl in flight, horiz.

**2004, Oct. 25**

**868-871** A171 Set of 4 18.00 18.00

**Souvenir Sheet**

**872** A171 £2 multi 12.00 12.00

Battle of the Falkland Islands, 90th Anniv. A172

No. 873: a, HMS Kent, HMS Inflexible, half of HMS Carnarvon, half of HMS Cornwall. b, British Navy flag, HMS Glasgow, half of HMS Carnarvon, half of HMS Cornwall, half of HMS Invincible. c, Medals, half of HMS Invincible.
No, 874: a, Medals, half of SMS Scharnhorst. b, German imperial war ensign, SMS Dresden, half of SMS Scharnhorst, half of SMS Leipzig. c, SMS Nürnberg, SMS Gneisenau, half of SMS Leipzig.

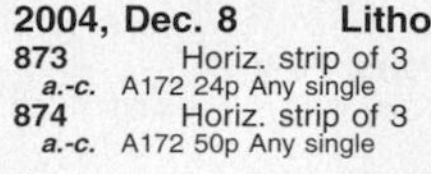

**2004, Dec. 8 Litho.** ***Perf. 14***

| | | | |
|---|---|---|---|
| **873** | Horiz. strip of 3 | 9.50 | 9.50 |
| ***a.-c.*** | A172 24p Any single | 2.40 | 1.90 |
| **874** | Horiz. strip of 3 | 17.50 | 17.50 |
| ***a.-c.*** | A172 50p Any single | 4.25 | 3.25 |

Camber Railway, 90th Anniv. — A173

Designs: 3p, Old track bed. 24p, Kerr Stuart Wren Class locomotive at Camber Depot, horiz. 50p, Kerr Stuart Wren Class locomotive Falkland Islands Express, horiz. £2, Camber sailing wagon.

**2005, Feb. 28** ***Perf. 13¾***

**875-878** A173 Set of 4 17.00 17.00

Wedding of Prince Charles and Camilla Parker Bowles A174

Designs: 24p, Couple. 50p, Couple in formal wear, vert.
£2, Couple, Windsor Castle.

**2005, Apr. 29** ***Perf. 14***

**879-880** A174 Set of 2 5.00 5.00

**Souvenir Sheet**

**881** A174 £2 multi 10.50 10.50

End of World War II, 60th Anniv. — A175

No. 882, 24p: a, Walrus reconnaissance seaplane. b, Presentation Spitfire X4616.
No. 883, 80p: a, HMS Exeter at Port Stanley. b, Governor, King Edward Memorial Hospital staff, Rear Admiral Harwood and Capt. Bell.
No. 884, £1: a, Fitzroy. b, HMS William Scoresby.

***Perf. 13¼x13½***

**2005, June 29 Litho.**
**Horiz. Pairs, #a-b**

**882-884** A175 Set of 3 28.00 28.00

Maritime Heritage A176

Designs: 24p, Snow Squall escaping CSS Tuscaloosa, 1863. No. 886, 55p, Jhelum, 1870. No. 887, 55p, Charles Cooper, 1866. £1.20, SS Imo colliding with the Mont Blanc, Halifax Harbor, 1917.

**2005, Aug. 29 Litho.** ***Perf. 14***

**885-888** A176 Set of 4 13.00 13.00

Pebble Island and its Flora and Fauna — A177

No. 889, 45p: a, Gentoo penguin. b, Falkland lavender.
No. 890, 55p: a, Pebble Island Lodge. b, Black-necked swan.

**2005, Sept. 12** *Perf. 13¾*

**Pairs, #a-b**

**889-890** A177 Set of 2 14.00 14.00

Souvenir Sheet

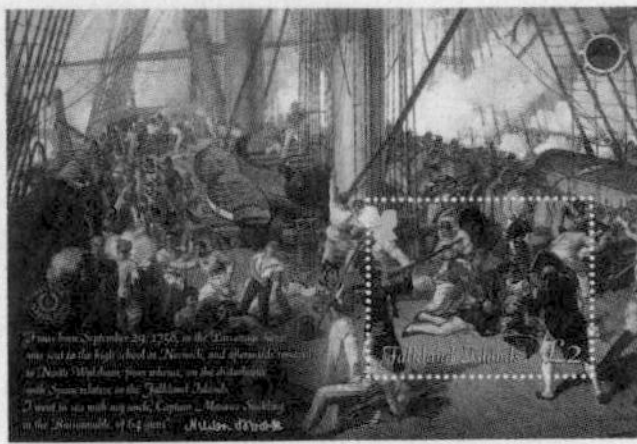

The Fall of Nelson, Battle of Trafalgar, 21 October 1805, by Denis Dighton — A178

**2005, Oct. 21**

**891** A178 £2 multi 12.00 12.00

Battle of Trafalgar, bicent.

Hans Christian Andersen (1805-75), Author — A179

Stories: 18p, The Little Mermaid. 30p, The Snowman. 45p, The Ugly Duckling. £1, Thumbelina.

**2005, Oct. 28** *Perf. 14*

**892-895** A179 Set of 4 11.50 11.50

Stanley Infant and Junior School, 50th anniv.

Black-crowned Night Heron — A180

Designs: 24p, Head. 55p, Bird on one leg. 80p, Juvenile standing. £1, Head of juvenile.

**2006, Feb. 10** **Litho.** *Perf. 13¾*

**896-899** A180 Set of 4 13.00 13.00

Queen Elizabeth II, 80th Birthday — A181

Queen wearing: 24p, Yellow hat. 55p, Green hat. 80p, Blue hat. £1, Red hat.
£2, Tiara and white hat, horiz.

**2006, Apr. 21** *Perf. 14*

**900-903** A181 Set of 4 13.00 13.00

**Souvenir Sheet**

**904** A181 £2 multi 11.00 11.00

SS Great Britain — A182

View of: 24p, Bow. 55p, Stern. £1.50, Deck and masts.

**2006, May 19** *Perf. 13¾x13¼*

**905-907** A182 Set of 3 13.00 13.00

Birds A183

Designs: No. 908, 25p, Gentoo penguin chicks. No. 909, 25p, King cormorants. No. 910, 60p, King penguin. No. 911, 60p, Wandering albatross.

**2006, Aug. 30** **Litho.** *Perf. 14¼x14*

**908-911** A183 Set of 4 11.00 11.00

Bleaker Island and its Flora and Fauna — A184

No. 912, 50p: a, Woolly Falkland ragwort. b, Macaroni penguin.
No. 913, 60p: a, The Outlook and sheep. b, Long-tailed meadowlark.

**2006, Sept. 18** *Perf. 13¼x13*

**Pairs, #a-b**

**912-913** A184 Set of 2 15.00 15.00

Victoria Cross, 150th Anniv. — A185

Designs: Nos. 914, 916a, 60p, Lt. Col. H. Jones. Nos. 915, 916b, 60p, Sgt. Ian McKay. No. 916c, £1, Victoria Cross.

**2006, Nov. 11** *Perf. 13¼*

**Stamps With White Frames**

**914-915** A185 Set of 2 7.00 7.00

**Souvenir Sheet**

**Stamps Without White Frames**

**916** A185 Sheet of 3, #a-c 7.00 7.00

**Bird Type of 2003**

Designs: 20p, Black-browed albatross, vert. 25p, Rufous-chested dotterel, vert. £5, Short-eared owl, vert.

*Perf. 13¼x13*

**2006, Nov. 15** **Litho.** **Unwmk.**

| | | | |
|---|---|---|---|
| **917** A163 20p multi | | 2.50 | 2.00 |
| **918** A163 25p multi | | 2.75 | 2.50 |
| **919** A163 £5 multi | | 22.50 | *24.00* |
| *Nos. 917-919 (3)* | | 27.75 | 28.50 |

Nos. 918-919 differ from Nos. 835 and 841 by having less color around the Queen's head. Nos. 917-919 are dated "2006."

Worldwide Fund for Nature (WWF) A186

Striated caracara: 25p, Heads of two birds. 50p, Bird in flight. 60p, Bird standing. 85p, Bird eating shellfish.

**2006, Dec. 20** **Litho.** *Perf. 13¾*

**920-923** A186 Set of 4 10.00 10.00

*923a* Miniature sheet, 4 each #920-923 47.50 47.50

Fisheries, 20th Anniv. A187

Designs: 3p, Fishermen at sea. 11p, Fishing boat at night. 25p, Fishermen leaving boat. 30p, Japanese jigger. 60p, Fishery protection boat Dorada. £1.05, Trawler transferring fish to a freezer container ship.

**2007, Feb. 24** *Perf. 14¼*

**924-929** A187 Set of 6 13.50 13.50

HMS Plymouth A188

HMS Plymouth: 25p, Joining Falkland Islands Task Force. 40p, Supporting SBS. 60p, Under attack by Argentine fighters. £1.05, Docked at Port Stanley.

**2007, Mar. 27**

**930-933** A188 Set of 4 17.50 17.50

Souvenir Sheet

Falkland Islands War, 25th Anniv. — A189

No. 934: a, Avro Vulcan prototype VX770. b, Avro Vulcan XM597. c, Avro Vulcan XM607. d, Vulcan in the Sky Project.

**2007, May 25** **Litho.** *Perf. 13¼*

**934** A189 60p Sheet of 4, #a-d 14.00 14.00

Miniature Sheets

British and Falkland Islander Casualties of the Falkland Islands War — A190

No. 935, 25p — Casualties beginning with: a, Doreen Bonner. b, G. W. J. Batt. c, J. R. Carlyle. d, S. J. Dixon. e, I. R. Farrell. f, G. C. Grace. g, R. R. Heath. h, A. S. James.
No. 936, 60p: a, D. Lee. b, P. B. McKay. c, G. T. Nelson. d, J. B. Pashley. e, M. Sambles. f, D. A. Strickland. g, R. G. Thomas. h, P. A. West.

**2007, June 14** **Litho.** *Perf. 14¼*

**Sheets of 8, #a-h**

**935-936** A190 Set of 2 30.00 30.00

Scouting, Cent. — A191

Designs: 10p, Scouts on ladder of RRS Discovery. 20p, Dignitaries on ship's deck. 25p, Dignitaries, diff. £2, RRS Discovery.

**2007, July 23** **Litho.** *Perf. 13½x13¼*

**937-940** A191 Set of 4 12.00 12.00

Voyage of RRS Discovery from Falkland Islands for presentation to British Scout Association, 70th anniv.

Princess Diana (1961-97) — A192

**2007, Aug. 31** *Perf. 14*

**941** A192 60p multi 3.75 3.75

Printed in sheets of 8 stamps + 2 labels.

Saunders Island and its Flora and Fauna — A193

No. 942, 50p: a, Rockhopper penguin. b, Dusty miller.
No. 943, 55p: a, Crested caracara. b, Earliest British settlement at Port Egmont.

**2007, Sept. 28** **Litho.** *Perf. 13¾*

**Pairs, #a-b**

**942-943** A193 Set of 2 15.00 15.00

Wedding of Queen Elizabeth II and Prince Philip, 60th Anniv. A194

**2007, Nov. 20** **Litho.** *Perf. 14*

**944** A194 £1 multi 6.00 6.00

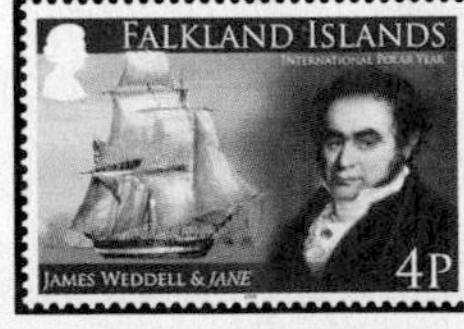


Polar Explorers and Their Ships A195

Explorers and ships: 4p, James Weddell (1787-1834), and Jane. 25p, James Clark Ross (1800-62), and HMS Erebus. 85p, William Spiers Bruce (1867-1921), and Scotia. £1.61, James Marr (1902-65), and Discovery II.

**2008, Apr. 7**

**945-948** A195 Set of 4 13.00 13.00

Southern Elephant Seals A196

Designs: 27p, Seal pup. 55p, Male and female. 65p, Seals play fighting. £1.10, Seal and tussock bird.

**2008, July 15** **Litho.** *Perf. 14*

**949-952** A196 Set of 4 14.00 14.00

Aircraft A197

Designs: 1p, Taylorcraft Auster Mk 5. 2p, Boeing 747-300. 5p, De Havilland Canada DHC-6 Twin Otter. 10p, Lockheed C-130 Hercules. 27p, De Havilland Canada DHC-2 Beaver. 55p, Airbus A320. 65p, Lockheed L-1011-385-3 Tristar C2. 90p, Avro Vulcan B2. £1, Britten-Norman BN-2 Islander. £2, Panavia Tornado F3. £3, De Havilland Canada DHC-7-110 Dash 7. £5, BAE Sea Harrier.

**2008, Aug. 1 Litho. *Perf. 14***

| | | | | |
|---|---|---|---|---|
| **953** | A197 | 1p multi | .40 | *.75* |
| **954** | A197 | 2p multi | .40 | *.75* |
| **955** | A197 | 5p multi | .75 | .85 |
| **956** | A197 | 10p multi | .90 | .90 |
| **957** | A197 | 27p multi | 1.75 | 1.75 |
| **958** | A197 | 55p multi | 2.25 | 2.25 |
| **959** | A197 | 65p multi | 2.75 | 2.75 |
| **960** | A197 | 90p multi | 3.50 | 3.50 |
| **961** | A197 | £1 multi | 4.00 | 4.00 |
| **962** | A197 | £2 multi | 7.25 | *8.00* |
| **963** | A197 | £3 multi | 10.00 | *11.00* |
| **964** | A197 | £5 multi | 16.00 | *18.00* |
| | | *Nos. 953-964 (12)* | 49.95 | 54.50 |

**Souvenir Sheet**

**Stamps With Royal Air Force 90th Anniv. Emblem Added**

| | | | |
|---|---|---|---|
| **965** | Sheet of 4 | 14.50 | 14.50 |
| *a.* | A197 10p Like #956 | .40 | .40 |
| *b.* | A197 65p Like #959 | 2.60 | 2.60 |
| *c.* | A197 90p Like #960 | 3.50 | 3.50 |
| *d.* | A197 £2 Like #962 | 8.00 | 8.00 |

Port Louis, 175th Anniv. — A198

Designs: 27p, Sailor raising British flag. 65p, Royal Marines, British flag.
£2, Capt. Onslow of HMS Clio, British flag.

**2008, Sept. 22 Litho. *Perf. 14***
**966-967** A198 Set of 2 4.75 4.75

**Souvenir Sheet**

**968** A198 £2 multi 9.00 9.00

Islands and Rocks A199

Designs: 22p, The Slipper. 40p, Kidney Island. 60p, Stephens Bluff and Castle Rock. £1, The Colliers.

**2008, Oct. 1 Litho. *Perf. 13¾***
**969-972** A199 Set of 4 10.00 10.00

See Nos. 986-989, 1025-1028.

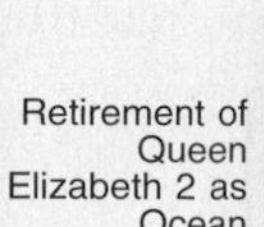

Retirement of Queen Elizabeth 2 as Ocean Liner — A200

Designs: 23p, Launch of Queen Elizabeth 2. 27p, Service of Queen Elizabeth 2 as troop ship in Falkland Islands War. 65p, Queen Elizabeth 2, Palm Jumeirah, Dubai. £2, Queen Elizabeth 2 (70x34mm).

**2008, Nov. 21 Litho. *Perf. 13¼***
**973-976** A200 Set of 4 13.00 13.00

Charles Darwin (1809-82), Naturalist — A201

Designs: 4p, Darwin seated. 27p, Warrah. 65p, HMS Beagle in Berkeley Sound, 1834. £1.10, Darwin encountering a Magellanic penguin.

**2009, Apr. 23 Litho. *Perf. 14***
**977-980** A201 Set of 4 8.00 8.00

Naval Aviation, Cent. A202

Royal Navy aircraft and ships: 30p, Westland/Aerospatiale Gazelle AH1 helicopter. 50p, Westland Lynx HAS2 helicopter. 65p, Westland Wessex HU5 helicopter. £1.10, Westland Sea King HAS5 helicopter.
£2, BAe Sea Harrier, HMS Hermes.

**2009, May 7 Litho. *Perf. 14***
**981-984** A202 Set of 4 11.00 11.00

**Souvenir Sheet**

**985** A202 £2 multi 7.50 7.50

**Islands and Rocks Type of 2008**

Designs: 27p, Seal Rocks. 40p, Beauchene Island. 65p, Jason East Cay, Steeple Jason. £1.50, Horse Block.

**2009, Aug. 14 Litho. *Perf. 13¾***
**986-989** A199 Set of 4 11.50 11.50

Albatrosses A203

Designs: 22p, Black-browed albatross. 27p, Gray-headed albatross. 60p, Light-mantled sooty albatross. 90p, Wandering albatross.

**2009, Oct. 19 Litho. *Perf. 13¾***
**990-993** A203 Set of 4 8.50 8.50

Cobb's Wren A204

Designs: Nos. 994, 994a, 27p, Wren on seaweed. Nos. 995, 998b, 65p, Wrens at nest. Nos. 996, 998c, 90p, Wren on rock. Nos. 997, 998d, £1.10, Two wrens.

**2009, Nov. 10 *Perf. 13¾***

**Stamps With WWF Emblem**

**994-997** A204 Set of 4 10.00 10.00
*997a* Sheet of 16, 4 each #994-997 52.50 52.50

**Souvenir Sheet**

**Stamps With Falklands Conservation Emblem**

**998** A204 Sheet of 4, #a-d 10.00 10.00

Ships Named HMS Exeter A205

Ship used from: 4p, 1931-42. 20p, 1931-42, with helicopter. 30p, 1980-2009, with helicopter. £1.66, 1980-2009, with helicopter, diff.

**2009, Dec. 8 Litho. *Perf. 14***
**999-1002** A205 Set of 4 7.50 7.50

Skies in Four Seasons A206

Designs: 27p, Carcass Island in spring. 55p, Beach on New Island in summer. 65p, Rainbow over Stanley in autumn. £1.10, Islands in winter.

**2010, Jan. 25 Litho. *Perf. 13***
**1003-1006** A206 Set of 4 8.00 8.00

Restoration of the SS Great Britain A207

SS Great Britain: 27p, On pontoon near jetty in Stanley. 50p, Beached at Sparrow Cove. 65p, Bow. £1.10, Mast and rigging.

**2010, Apr. 12 *Perf. 13¼***
**1007-1010** A207 Set of 4 8.00 8.00

**Miniature Sheet**

Battle of Britain, 70th Anniv. — A208

No. 1011 — Airplanes: a, Hawker Hurricane P2961. b, Supermarine Spitfire P9398. c, Hawker Hurricane P3854. d, Supermarine Spitfire P7350. e, Hawker Hurricane V6665. f, Supermarine Spitfire L1036. g, Hawker Hurricane P3576. h, Supermarine Spitfire X4620.

**2010, May 7 Litho. *Perf. 14x14¼***
**1011** A208 65p Sheet of 8, #a-h 15.00 15.00

London 2010 Festival of Stamps.

Birds A209

Designs: Nos. 1012, 1016a, 27p, Sooty shearwater. Nos. 1013, 1016b, 70p, White-chinned petrel. Nos. 1014, 1016c, 95p, Southern giant petrel. Nos. 1015, 1016d, £1.15, Greater shearwater.

**2010, July 8 Litho. *Perf. 13¾***

**Stamps With White Frames**

**1012-1015** A209 Set of 4 9.50 9.50

**Souvenir Sheet**

**Stamps Without White Frames**

**1016** A209 Sheet of 4, #a-d 11.50 11.50

Flowering Shrubs A210

Designs: 27p, Fuchsia. 70p, Boxwood. 95p, Gorse. £1.15, Honeysuckle.

**2010, Oct. 27 Litho. *Perf. 13¼x13***
**1017-1020** A210 Set of 4 10.00 10.00

Royal Air Force Search and Rescue Force, 70th Anniv. — A211

Anniversary emblem and: 27p, Helicopter on ground. 70p, Helicopter in flight. 95p, Crew in helicopter cockpit. £1.15, Helicopter in flight with open door.

**2011, Mar. 9 *Perf. 13¼***
**1021-1024** A211 Set of 4 10.00 10.00

**Islands and Rocks Type of 2008**

Designs: 3p, Bird Island. 27p, Eddystone Rock. 70p, Round Island and Sail Rock. £1.71, Direction Island.

**2011, Apr. 11 *Perf. 13¼x13***
**1025-1028** A199 Set of 4 8.50 8.50

Wedding of Prince William and Catherine Middleton — A212

**2011, Apr. 29 *Perf. 13¼***
**1029** A212 £2 multi 6.75 6.75

Worldwide Fund for Nature (WWF) — A213

Southern sea lions: 27p, Males and females on beach. 40p, Pod in water. 70p, Males on beach. £1.15, Head.

**2011, May 30 *Perf. 13¾***
**1030-1033** A213 Set of 4 8.75 8.75
*1033a* Miniature sheet of 16, 4 each #1030-1033 35.00 35.00

Queen Elizabeth II, 85th Birthday — A214

Queen Elizabeth II wearing: 27p, Red violet hat with flower. 30p, Fur hat. 70p, White hat with pink and white ribbons. £1.50, White hat with feather.

**2011, June 11** *Perf. 13¾*
**1034-1037** A214 Set of 4 8.50 8.50

Souvenir Sheet

Queen Elizabeth II — A215

**2011, Aug. 8 Litho.** *Perf. 14¼x15*
**1038** A215 £2 multi 6.75 6.75

Commonwealth Parliamentary Association, cent.

Wildlife A216

Designs: 27p, Gentoo penguins. 70p, Leopard seal. 95p, Gonatus squid. £1.15, Gentoo penguins, diff.

**2011, Nov. 16** *Perf. 13¾*
**1039-1042** A216 Set of 4 10.00 10.00

Marine Life A217

Designs: 27p, Sea anemone. 50p, Jellyfish. 70p, Starfish. £1.15, Nudibranch.

**2012, Apr. 11** *Perf. 13¼x13½*
**1043-1046** A217 Set of 4 8.00 8.00

Reign of Queen Elizabeth II, 60th Anniv. — A218

Photograph of Queen Elizabeth II in: 27p, 1952. 30p, 1977. 70p, 2002. £1.71, 2012.
£3, Queen Elizabeth II wearing tiara, 1955.

**2012, May 10** *Perf. 13½x13¼*
**1047-1050** A218 Set of 4 9.00 9.00

**Souvenir Sheet**

***Perf. 13¼***

**1051** A218 £3 multi 9.00 9.00

No. 1051 contains one 30x48mm stamp.

Liberation of the Falkland Islands, 30th Anniv. — A219

Designs: No. 1052, 30p, Ferry MV Concordia Bay. No. 1053, 30p, Liberation Monument, Stanley. No. 1054, 75p, School, Stanley. No. 1055, 75p, Wind turbines. £1, Sign and houses near Stanley Harbor. £1.20, Children and penguins.

**2012, June 14** *Perf. 14*
**1052-1057** A219 Set of 6 12.50 12.50

Coastal Landscapes — A220

Designs: 30p, Surf Bay, East Falkland Island. 75p, Cliffs, New Island. £1, Mountain, Steeple Jason Island. £1.20, Deaths Head and Grave Cove, West Falkland Island.

**2012, July 12** *Perf. 13*
**1058-1061** A220 Set of 4 9.25 9.25

Sinking of the P.S.N.C. Oravia, Cent. A221

Designs: 30p, Oravia at sea. 75p, Passengers and crew wearing life vests. £1, Passengers filling lifeboats. £1.20 Oravia and the Samson.

**2012, Aug. 28** *Perf. 14*
**1062-1065** A221 Set of 4 12.00 12.00

Souvenir Sheet

Sinking of the Titanic, Cent. — A222

**2012, Aug. 28** *Perf. 14x14¾*
**1066** A222 £2 multi 9.00 9.00

Dolphins and Whales — A223

Designs: 1p, Southern right whale dolphins. 2p, Minke whale. 5p, Peale's dolphin. 10p, Dusky dolphin. 30p, Southern right whale. 50p, Fin whale. 75p, Hourglass dolphin. £1, Long-finned pilot whale. £1.20, Killer whales. £2, Sperm whale. £3.50, Commerson's dolphin. £5, Sei whale.

**2012, Nov. 9** *Perf. 13¼*

| | | | | |
|---|---|---|---|---|
| **1067** | A223 | 1p multi | .25 | .25 |
| **1068** | A223 | 2p multi | .25 | .25 |
| **1069** | A223 | 5p multi | .25 | .25 |
| **1070** | A223 | 10p multi | .30 | .30 |
| **1071** | A223 | 30p multi | .95 | .95 |
| **1072** | A223 | 50p multi | 1.60 | 1.60 |
| **1073** | A223 | 75p multi | 2.40 | 2.40 |
| **1074** | A223 | £1 multi | 3.25 | 3.25 |
| **1075** | A223 | £1.20 multi | 4.00 | 4.00 |
| **1076** | A223 | £2 multi | 6.50 | 6.50 |
| **1077** | A223 | £3.50 multi | 11.00 | 11.00 |
| **1078** | A223 | £5 multi | 14.00 | 14.00 |
| | *Nos. 1067-1078 (12)* | | 44.75 | 44.75 |

See No. 1172.

Color in Nature — A224

No. 1079: a, Night heron. b, Diddle-dee berries.
No. 1080: a, Short-eared owl. b, Scurvy grass flowers.

**2012, Dec. 14** *Perf. 13*

| | | | |
|---|---|---|---|
| **1079** | Pair | 2.00 | 2.00 |
| *a.-b.* | A224 30p Either single | 1.00 | 1.00 |
| **1080** | Pair | 4.50 | 4.50 |
| *a.-b.* | A224 75p Either single | 2.25 | 2.25 |

See Nos. 1108-1109, 1122-1123, 1136-1137.

2013 Referendum on Political Status A225

Map, of Falkland Island, hand and ballot box with denomination color of: 3p, Deep blue. 40p, Red violet. 75p, Green. £1.76, Red brown.
£3, Purple.

**2013, Feb. 15**
**1081-1084** A225 Set of 4 8.75 8.75

**Souvenir Sheet**

***Perf. 13½x13¼***

**1085** A225 £3 multi 9.00 9.00

No. 1085 contains one 56x45mm stamp.

Wildlife A226

Designs: 30p, Johnny rook. 75p, Rockhopper penguins. £1, Rockhopper penguin swimming. £1.20, Lobster krill.

**2013, Mar. 28** *Perf. 13¾*
**1086-1089** A226 Set of 4 10.00 10.00

Lady Margaret Thatcher (1925-2013), British Prime Minister — A227

Lady Thatcher: 30p, And husband, Denis arriving at 10 Downing Street, 1979. 75p, Inspecting Falkland Islands minefield, 1983. £1, With flag at celebration of 10th anniversary of Falkland Islands liberation, 1992. £1.20, Holding Falkland Islands coin commemorating 25th anniversary of the liberation, 2007.

**2013, May 16** *Perf. 13¾*
**1090-1093** A227 Set of 4 10.00 10.00

Sir Rex Hunt (1926-2012), Governor of Falkland Islands — A228

Falkland Islands coat of arms and Hunt: 30p, As Civil Commissioner, 1982. 75p, In uniform next to Governor's car. £1, With flag of Falkland Islands, 1992. £1.20, Talking to Queen Elizabeth II, 2000.

**2013, June 11** *Perf. 14*
**1094-1097** A228 Set of 4 10.00 10.00

Coronation of Queen Elizabeth II, 60th Anniv. — A229

Queen Elizabeth II: 30p, Wearing coronation gown. 75p, With crown and orb. £1, Waving. £1.20, With Prince Philip.

**2013, July 22** *Perf. 13½x13¼*
**1098-1101** A229 Set of 4 10.00 10.00

Shallow Marine Surveys Group A230

Marine life: Nos. 1102, 1106a, 30p, Saffron sea cucumber. Nos. 1103, 1106b, 75p, Stalked jellyfish. Nos. 1104, 1106c, £1, Scythe-edged serolis. Nos. 1105, 1106d, £1.20, Naked sea urchin.
No. 1107a, £1, Painted shrimp, vert.

**2013, Aug. 29** *Perf. 13¼x13½*

**Stamps With White Frames**

**1102-1105** A230 Set of 4 10.50 10.50

**Stamps Without White Frames**

**1106** A230 Strip of 4, #a-d 10.50 10.50

**Souvenir Sheet**

***Perf. 13½x13¼***

| | | | |
|---|---|---|---|
| **1107** | A230 Sheet of 3 (see footnote) | 9.75 | 9.75 |
| *a.* | A230 £1 multi | 3.25 | 3.25 |

No. 1107 contains No. 1107a, Ascension No. 1104a and South Georgia and South Sandwich Islands No. 485a. This sheet was sold in Ascension, Falkland Islands and South Georgia and South Sandwich Islands.

**Color in Nature Type of 2012**

No. 1108: a, Macaroni penguin. b, Purple cap fungi.
No. 1109: a, Crested duck. b, Southern painted lady butterfly.

**2013, Oct. 3** *Perf. 13¼*

| | | | |
|---|---|---|---|
| **1108** | Pair | 1.90 | 1.90 |
| *a.-b.* | A224 30p Either single | .95 | .95 |
| **1109** | Pair | 4.80 | 4.80 |
| *a.-b.* | A224 75p Either single | 2.40 | 2.40 |

Wildlife A231

Designs: 30p, King penguin and chick. 75p, Gaptooth lanternfish. £1, Southern sea lion. £1.20, King penguins, diff.

**2014, Mar. 25 Litho.** *Perf. 13¼*
**1110-1113** A231 Set of 4 11.00 11.00

Mushrooms A232

Designs: 30p, False chanterelle. 75p, Red wax cap. £1, Clustered domecap. £1.20, Shaggy inkcap.

**2014, Apr. 15 Litho. *Perf. 13¼***
**1114-1117** A232 Set of 4 10.00 10.00

Royal Christenings A233

Photograph from christening of: 30p, Queen Elizabeth II. 75p, Prince Charles. £1, Prince William. £1.20, Prince George.

**2014, May 21 Litho. *Perf. 13¼***
**1118-1121** A233 Set of 4 10.00 10.00

### Color in Nature Type of 2012

No. 1122: a, King penguins. b, Marsh marigolds.
No. 1123: a, Black oystercatcher. b, Vanilla daisies.

**2014, Sept. 16 Litho. *Perf. 13¼***

| | | | |
|---|---|---|---|
| **1122** | Pair | 2.00 | 2.00 |
| *a.-b.* | A224 30p Either single | 1.00 | 1.00 |
| **1123** | Pair | 5.00 | 5.00 |
| *a.-b.* | A224 75p Either single | 2.50 | 2.50 |

Battle of the Falkland Islands, Cent. — A234

Designs: 30p, SMS Scharnhorst. 75p, HMS Invincible. £1, British and German flags, poppies. £1.20, Sailor, Battle of the Falkland Islands Monument.

**2014, Dec. 8 Litho. *Perf. 13¾***
**1124-1127** A234 Set of 4 10.00 10.00

Type 42 Destroyers — A235

Designs: 30p, HMS Sheffield. 75p, HMS Exeter. £1, HMS Liverpool. £1.20, HMS Edinburgh.

**2014, Dec. 22 Litho. *Perf. 14***
**1128-1131** A235 Set of 4 9.00 9.00

Birds — A236

Adult and chicks: 30p, Pied oystercatchers. 75p, Gentoo penguins. £1, Black-browed albatrosses. £1.20, Falkland skuas.

**2015, Feb. 11 Litho. *Perf. 13¾***
**1132-1135** A236 Set of 4 10.00 10.00

### Color in Nature Type of 2012

No. 1136: a, Black-throated finch. b, Fuegian ferns.
No. 1137: a, Dolphin gulls. b, Yellow daisies.

**2015, May 12 Litho. *Perf. 13¼***

| | | | |
|---|---|---|---|
| **1136** | Pair | 1.90 | 1.90 |
| *a.-b.* | A224 30p Either single | .95 | .95 |
| **1137** | Pair | 4.50 | 4.50 |
| *a.-b.* | A224 75p Either single | 2.25 | 2.25 |

Magna Carta, 800th Anniv. A237

Designs: 30p, King John, Magna Carta and barons. 75p, Courtroom. £1, Gilbert House, Stanley. £1.20, King John, arms of Falkland Islands.

**2015, June 15 Litho. *Perf. 14***
**1138-1141** A237 Set of 4 10.50 10.50

Wildlife A238

Designs: 30p, Magellanic penguin. 75p, Falkland sprats. £1, Falkland skua. £1.20, Heads of two magellanic penguins.

**2015, Aug. 21 Litho. *Perf. 13¾***
**1142-1145** A238 Set of 4 10.00 10.00

Queen Elizabeth II, Longest-Reigning British Monarch — A239

Queen Elizabeth II and events during her reign: 30p, Publications reporting on her coronation, 1953. 75p, Arrival of first Land Rovers in the Falkland Islands, 1950s. £1, Coach used for Golden Jubilee, 2012. £1.25, Falkland Islands referendum, 2013.

**2015, Sept. 9 Litho. *Perf. 14***
**1146-1149** A239 Set of 4 10.00 10.00

Elephant Seal Research Group, 20th Anniv. — A240

No. 1150, 30p: a, Seal in water. b, Researcher with equipment near seal.
No. 1151, 75p: a, Pod of seals on beach. b, Researcher approaching seal.
No. 1152, £1: a, Seal and penguins. b, Researcher holding measuring stick above seal.

**2015, Nov. 30 Litho. *Perf. 13***
**Horiz. Pairs, #a-b**
**1150-1152** A240 Set of 3 12.50 12.50

Clouds — A241

Designs: 31p, Asperitas. 76p, Altocumulus. £1.01, Altocumulus lenticularis. £1.22, Cumulonimbus and Stratocumulus.

**2015, Dec. 9 Litho. *Perf. 13¼***
**1153-1156** A241 Set of 4 9.75 9.75

Birds of Prey — A242

Designs: No. 1157, 31p, Barn owl. No. 1158, 31p, Short-eared owl. No. 1159, 76p, Red-backed buzzard. No. 1160, 76p, Crested caracara. £1.01, Peregrine falcon. £1.22, Striated caracara.

**2016, Jan. 13 Litho. *Perf. 13¾***
**1157-1162** A242 Set of 6 13.00 13.00

Items at Historic Dockyard Museum — A243

Designs: 31p, Traditional horse gear. 76p, Peat-burning stove. £1.01, Warrah skull. £1.22, Antarctic exploration hut.

**2016, Mar. 30 Litho. *Perf. 13¾***
**1163-1166** A243 Set of 4 9.50 9.50

Queen Elizabeth II, 90th Birthday — A244

Photographs of Queen Elizabeth from: 31p, 1977. 76p, 1982. £1.01, 1953. £1.22, 2014. £3, Queen Elizabeth II in 1962.

**2016, Apr. 21 Litho. *Perf. 14***
**1167-1170** A244 Set of 4 9.75 9.75

**Souvenir Sheet**

**1171** A244 £3 multi 9.00 9.00

### Dolphins and Whales Type of 2012

**2016, Aug. 1 Litho. *Perf. 13¼***
**1172** A223 31p Southern right whale .85 .85

Endemic Plants A245

Designs: No. 1173, 31p, Falkland rock-cress. No. 1174, 31p, Lady's slipper. No. 1175, 76p, False-plantain. No. 1176, 76p, Silvery buttercup. No. 1177, £1.01, Snakeplant. No. 1178, £1.01, Falkland nassauvia.
No. 1179, 66p: a, Like No. 1173. b, Like No. 1174. c, Like No. 1175. d, Like No. 1176. e, Like No. 1177. f, Like No. 1178.

**2016, Nov. 21 Litho. *Perf. 13¾***
**1173-1178** A245 Set of 6 11.00 11.00

**Miniature Sheet**

**1179** A245 66p Sheet of 6, #a-f 10.00 10.00

No. 1179 has cream colored margins around the stamps.

Shipwrecks A246

Designs: 31p, Acteon. 76p, Charles Cooper. £1.01, Afterglow. £1.22, Capricorn.

**2017, Mar. 27 Litho. *Perf. 13***
**1180-1183** A246 Set of 4 8.25 8.25

Falkland Islands Journal, 50th Anniv. — A247

Journal cover from: 31p, 2010. 76p, 2013r. £1.01, 2014. £1.22, 2016.

**2017, July 5 Litho. *Perf. 13½x13¼***
**1184-1187** A247 Set of 4 8.50 8.50

A248

Birds — A249

Designs: 1p, Tussacbird. 2p, Long-tailed meadowlark. 5p, Black-chinned siskin. 10p, Falkland pipit, above white flowers. 20p, Cobb's wren. 50p, White-bridled finch. 76p, Falkland thrush. £1, Two-banded plover. £1.20, Falkland grass wren. £2, Dark-faced ground tyrant. £3.50, Rufous-chested dotterel. £5, Magellanic snipe.
(31p), Falkland pipit, above red flowers.

**2017, Aug. 14 Litho. *Perf. 13***

| | | | | |
|---|---|---|---|---|
| **1188** | A248 | 1p multi | .25 | .25 |
| **1189** | A248 | 2p multi | .25 | .25 |
| **1190** | A248 | 5p multi | .25 | .25 |
| **1191** | A248 | 10p multi | .30 | .30 |
| **1192** | A248 | 20p multi | .55 | .55 |
| **1193** | A248 | 50p multi | 1.40 | 1.40 |
| **1194** | A248 | 76p multi | 2.00 | 2.00 |
| **1195** | A248 | £1 multi | 2.75 | 2.75 |
| **1196** | A248 | £1.20 multi | 3.25 | 3.25 |
| **1197** | A248 | £2 multi | 5.25 | 5.25 |
| **1198** | A248 | £3.50 multi | 9.25 | 9.25 |
| **1199** | A248 | £5 multi | 13.50 | 13.50 |
| | *Nos. 1188-1199 (12)* | | 39.00 | 39.00 |

**Booklet Stamp**
**Self-Adhesive**

***Serpentine Die Cut 13***

| | | | |
|---|---|---|---|
| **1200** | A249 (31p) multi | .85 | .85 |
| *a.* | Booklet pane of 10 | 8.50 | |

Falkland Islands Fisheries, 30th Anniv. — A250

Designs: 31p, Toothfish and CFL Hunter. 76p, FPV Protegat and fishery RIB. £1.01, Argos Vigo and Frank Wild. £1.22, Robin M. Lee and Falkland calamari.

**2017, Oct. 23 Litho. *Perf. 13½x13¼***
**1201-1204** A250 Set of 4 8.75 8.75

70th Wedding Anniversary of Queen Elizabeth II and Prince Philip A251

Photograph of Queen Elizabeth II and Prince Philip from: 31p, 1952. 76p, 1961. £1.22, 1972. £1.78, 2016.

**2017, Nov. 20 Litho. *Perf. 13¼x13***

| | | | | |
|---|---|---|---|---|
| **1205-1208** | A251 | Set of 4 | 11.00 | 11.00 |

Christ Church Cathedral, Stanley, 125th Anniv. A252

Various views of Cathedral: 31p, 76p, £1.01, £1.22.

**2017, Dec. 18 Litho. *Perf. 13¼x13***

| | | | | |
|---|---|---|---|---|
| **1209-1212** | A252 | Set of 4 | 9.00 | 9.00 |

## SEMI-POSTAL STAMPS

**Catalogue values for unused stamps in this section are for Never Hinged items.**

Rebuilding after Conflict with Argentina — SP1

**Wmk. 373**

**1982, Sept. 13 Litho. *Perf. 11***

| | | | | |
|---|---|---|---|---|
| **B1** | SP1 | £1 + £1 Battle sites | 3.00 | 3.00 |

Liberation of Falkland Islands, 10th Anniv. — SP2

Designs: 14p+6p, San Carlos Cemetery. 29p+11p, 1982 War Memorial, Port Stanley. 34p+16p, South Atlantic Medal. 68p+32p, Government House, Port Stanley.

**Wmk. 373**

**1992, June 14 Litho. *Perf. 14***

| | | | | |
|---|---|---|---|---|
| **B2** | SP2 | 14p + 6p multicolored | 1.00 | *1.60* |
| **B3** | SP2 | 29p + 11p multicolored | 1.75 | 2.00 |
| **B4** | SP2 | 34p + 16p multicolored | 2.00 | 2.25 |
| **B5** | SP2 | 68p + 32p multicolored | 2.75 | *3.50* |
| *a.* | | Souvenir sheet of 4, #B2-B5 | 8.50 | 8.50 |
| | | *Nos. B2-B5 (4)* | 7.50 | 9.35 |

Surtax for Soldiers', Sailors' and Airmen's Families Association.

## AIR POST STAMPS

### Bird Type of 2003

Design: Rockhopper penguins, vert.

**Booklet Stamp**

***Serpentine Die Cut 6x6½ Syncopated***

**2003, Sept. 19 Litho.**

**Self-Adhesive**

| | | | | |
|---|---|---|---|---|
| **C1** | A163 (40p) multi | | 2.50 | 2.50 |
| *a.* | Booklet pane of 8 | | 20.00 | |

Penguins — AP1

Designs: No. C2, (55p), King penguin. No. C3, (55p), Macaroni penguin. No. C4, (55p), Magellanic penguin. No. C5, (55p), Rockhopper penguin. No. C6, (55p), Gentoo penguin. No. C7, (55p), Albino rockhopper penguin.

**2008, Dec. 1 Litho. *Perf. 13¼***

| | | | | |
|---|---|---|---|---|
| **C2-C7** | AP1 | Set of 6 | 19.00 | 19.00 |
| *C7a* | | Souvenir sheet, #C2-C7 | 19.00 | 19.00 |

Penguins — AP2

Designs: Nos. C8, C14a, (70p), King penguin. Nos. C9, C14b, (70p), Macaroni penguin. Nos. C10, C14c, (70p), Rockhopper penguins. Nos. C11, C14d, (70p), Albino and normal rockhopper penguins. Nos. C12, C14e, (70p), Magellanic penguin. Nos. C13, C14f, (70p), Gentoo penguins.

**2010, Sept. 29 Litho. *Perf. 13¾***

**Stamps With White Frames**

| | | | | |
|---|---|---|---|---|
| **C8-C13** | AP2 | Set of 6 | 13.50 | 13.50 |

**Stamps Without White Frames**

| | | | | |
|---|---|---|---|---|
| **C14** | AP2 | (70p) Sheet of 6, #a-f | 13.50 | 13.50 |

Albino and Normal Rockhopper Penguins AP3

Gentoo Penguins AP4

Magellanic Penguin AP5

Rockhopper Penguins AP6

King Penguins AP7

Macaroni Penguins AP8

**2013, Nov. 21 Litho. *Perf. 13¼***

**Stamps With White Frames**

| | | | | |
|---|---|---|---|---|
| **C15** | AP3 | (65p) multi | 2.10 | 2.10 |
| **C16** | AP4 | (65p) multi | 2.10 | 2.10 |
| **C17** | AP5 | (65p) multi | 2.10 | 2.10 |
| **C18** | AP6 | (65p) multi | 2.10 | 2.10 |
| **C19** | AP7 | (65p) multi | 2.10 | 2.10 |
| **C20** | AP8 | (65p) multi | 2.10 | 2.10 |
| | | *Nos. C15-C20 (6)* | 12.60 | 12.60 |

**Souvenir Sheet**

**Stamps Without White Frames**

| | | | | |
|---|---|---|---|---|
| **C21** | | Sheet of 6 | 14.00 | *16.00* |
| *a.* | AP3 | (65p) multi | 2.25 | *2.60* |
| *b.* | AP4 | (65p) multi | 2.25 | *2.60* |
| *c.* | AP5 | (65p) multi | 2.25 | *2.60* |
| *d.* | AP6 | (65p) multi | 2.25 | *2.60* |
| *e.* | AP7 | (65p) multi | 2.25 | *2.60* |
| *f.* | AP8 | (65p) multi | 2.25 | *2.60* |

## POSTAGE DUE STAMPS

**Catalogue values for unused stamps in this section are for never hinged items.**

Penguin — D1

***Perf. 14½x14***

**1991, Jan. 7 Litho. Wmk. 373**

| | | | | |
|---|---|---|---|---|
| **J1** | D1 | 1p lilac rose & lake | .25 | *.60* |
| **J2** | D1 | 2p buff & brown org | .25 | *.60* |
| **J3** | D1 | 3p yel & orange yel | .25 | *.60* |
| **J4** | D1 | 4p lt bl grn & dk bl grn | .25 | *.60* |
| **J5** | D1 | 5p sky blue & Prus bl | .25 | *.60* |
| **J6** | D1 | 10p lt blue & dk blue | .35 | *.70* |
| **J7** | D1 | 20p lt violet & dk vio | .90 | *1.50* |
| **J8** | D1 | 50p brt yel grn & dk yel green | 2.00 | *3.00* |
| | | *Nos. J1-J8 (8)* | 4.50 | *8.20* |

Penguins D2

Various penguins.

**2005, Dec. 2 Litho. *Perf. 13¾***

| | | | | |
|---|---|---|---|---|
| **J9** | D2 | 1p multi | .25 | .25 |
| **J10** | D2 | 3p multi | .25 | .25 |
| **J11** | D2 | 5p multi | .25 | .25 |
| **J12** | D2 | 10p multi | .45 | .45 |
| **J13** | D2 | 20p multi | .85 | .85 |
| **J14** | D2 | 50p multi | 1.90 | 1.90 |
| **J15** | D2 | £1 multi | 3.75 | 3.75 |
| **J16** | D2 | £2 multi | 7.50 | 7.50 |
| **J17** | D2 | £3 multi | 11.00 | 11.00 |
| **J18** | D2 | £5 multi | 17.00 | 17.00 |
| | | *Nos. J9-J18 (10)* | 43.20 | 43.20 |

## WAR TAX STAMPS

Regular Issue of 1912-14 Overprinted

**1918-20 Wmk. 3 *Perf. 14***

| | | | | |
|---|---|---|---|---|
| **MR1** | A7 | ½p dp ol grn | .55 | *7.25* |
| **MR2** | A7 | 1p org ver ('19) | .55 | *4.00* |
| *a.* | | Double overprint | *4,250.* | |
| **MR3** | A7 | 1sh bis brn | 6.50 | *52.50* |
| *a.* | | Pair, one without overprint | 18,000. | |
| *b.* | | Double ovpt., one albino | 2,250. | |
| *c.* | | 1sh brn, thick grayish paper ('20) | 6.00 | 50.00 |
| *d.* | | As "c," double ovpt., one albino | 2,000. | |
| | | *Nos. MR1-MR3 (3)* | 7.60 | *63.75* |

No. MR3a probably is caused by a foldover and is not constant.

## FALKLAND ISLANDS DEPENDENCIES

**Catalogue values for unused stamps in this section are for Never Hinged items.**

Map of Falkland Islands — A1

**Engr., Center Litho. in Black**

**1946, Feb. 1 Wmk. 4 *Perf. 12***

| | | | | |
|---|---|---|---|---|
| **1L1** | A1 | ½p yellow green | 1.10 | *3.50* |
| **1L2** | A1 | 1p blue violet | 1.30 | *2.00* |
| **1L3** | A1 | 2p deep carmine | 1.30 | *2.60* |
| **1L4** | A1 | 3p ultramarine | 1.90 | *5.25* |
| **1L5** | A1 | 4p deep plum | 2.40 | *5.00* |
| **1L6** | A1 | 6p orange yellow | 3.75 | *5.25* |
| **1L7** | A1 | 9p brown | 2.25 | *4.00* |
| **1L8** | A1 | 1sh rose violet | 3.00 | *4.50* |
| | | *Nos. 1L1-1L8 (8)* | 17.00 | *32.10* |

Nos. 1L1-1L8 were reissued in 1948, printed on more opaque paper with the lines of the map finer and clearer. Value for set, unused or used $130.

See No. 1L13.

Common Design Types pictured following the introduction.

### Peace Issue

Common Design Type

**1946, Oct. 4 *Perf. 13½x14***

| | | | | |
|---|---|---|---|---|
| **1L9** | CD303 | 1p purple | .50 | .50 |
| **1L10** | CD303 | 3p deep blue | .80 | .50 |

### Silver Wedding Issue

Common Design Types

**1948, Dec. 6 Photo. *Perf. 14x14½***

| | | | | |
|---|---|---|---|---|
| **1L11** | CD304 | 2½p brt ultra | 1.75 | *3.25* |

***Perf. 11½x11***

**Engr.**

| | | | | |
|---|---|---|---|---|
| **1L12** | CD305 | 1sh blue violet | 2.50 | *2.75* |

### Type of 1946

**1949, Mar. 6 *Perf. 12***

**Center Litho. in Black**

| | | | | |
|---|---|---|---|---|
| **1L13** | A1 | 2½p deep blue | 9.00 | 4.25 |

### UPU Issue

Common Design Types

**Engr.; Name Typo. on 2p, 3p**

**1949, Oct. 10 *Perf. 13½, 11x11½***

| | | | | |
|---|---|---|---|---|
| **1L14** | CD306 | 1p violet | 1.10 | *4.00* |
| **1L15** | CD307 | 2p deep carmine | 5.00 | 4.00 |
| **1L16** | CD308 | 3p indigo | 3.75 | 2.25 |
| **1L17** | CD309 | 6p red orange | 4.75 | 4.25 |
| | | *Nos. 1L14-1L17 (4)* | 14.60 | 14.50 |

### Coronation Issue

Common Design Type

**1953, June 4 *Perf. 13½x13***

| | | | | |
|---|---|---|---|---|
| **1L18** | CD312 | 1p purple & black | 1.80 | 1.40 |

John Biscoe — A2

Trepassey — A3

Ships: 1½p, Wyatt Earp. 2p, Eagle. 2½p, Penola. 3p, Discovery II. 4p, William Scoresby. 6p, Discovery. 9p, Endurance. 1sh, Deutschland. 2sh, Pourquoi-pas? 2sh6p, Français. 5sh, Scotia. 10sh, Antarctic. £1, Belgica.

**1954, Feb. 1 Engr. *Perf. 12½***

**Center in Black**

| | | | | |
|---|---|---|---|---|
| **1L19** | A2 | ½p blue green | .25 | *2.00* |
| **1L20** | A3 | 1p sepia | 1.75 | 1.50 |
| **1L21** | A3 | 1½p olive | 2.00 | 1.75 |
| **1L22** | A3 | 2p rose red | 1.25 | 2.50 |
| **1L23** | A3 | 2½p yellow | 1.25 | .35 |
| **1L24** | A3 | 3p ultra | 1.25 | .35 |

| | | | | | |
|---|---|---|---|---|---|
| **1L25** | A3 | 4p | red violet | 3.00 | 1.75 |
| **1L26** | A2 | 6p | rose violet | 3.50 | 1.75 |
| **1L27** | A2 | 9p | black | 3.50 | 2.00 |
| **1L28** | A3 | 1sh | org brown | 3.50 | 2.00 |
| **1L29** | A3 | 2sh | lilac rose | 18.00 | 10.00 |
| **1L30** | A2 | 2sh6p | blue gray | 19.00 | 7.00 |
| **1L31** | A2 | 5sh | violet | 40.00 | 7.50 |
| **1L32** | A3 | 10sh | brt blue | 55.00 | 18.00 |
| **1L33** | A2 | £1 | black | 85.00 | 47.50 |
| | | | *Nos. 1L19-1L33 (15)* | 238.25 | 105.95 |

Nos. 20, 23-24, 26 Ovptd. in Black

**1956, Jan 30** **Center in Black**

| | | | | | |
|---|---|---|---|---|---|
| **1L34** | A3 | 1p | sepia | .30 | .30 |
| **1L35** | A3 | 2½p | yellow | .55 | .55 |
| **1L36** | A3 | 3p | ultramarine | .65 | .65 |
| **1L37** | A2 | 6p | rose violet | .75 | .75 |
| | | | *Nos. 1L34-1L37 (4)* | 2.25 | 2.25 |

Trans-Antarctic Expedition, 1955-1958.

A4

1p, Map of Dependencies. 2p, Shag Rocks. 3p, Bird and Willis Islands. 4p, Gulbrandsen Lake. 5p, King Edward Point. 6p, Shackleton's Memorial Cross. 7p, Shackleton's grave. 8p, Grytviken Church. 9p, Coaling Hulk "Louise". 10p, Clerke Rocks. 20p, Candlemas Island. 25p, Twitcher Rock, Cook Island. 50p, "John Biscoe". £1, "Bransfield". £3, "Endurance".

**Wmk. 373**

**1980, May 5** **Litho.** ***Perf. 13½***

| | | | | | |
|---|---|---|---|---|---|
| **1L38** | A4 | 1p | multicolored | .25 | .25 |
| **1L39** | A4 | 2p | multicolored | .25 | .25 |
| **1L40** | A4 | 3p | multicolored | .25 | .25 |
| **1L41** | A4 | 4p | multicolored | .25 | .25 |
| **1L42** | A4 | 5p | multicolored | .25 | .25 |
| **1L43** | A4 | 6p | multicolored | .25 | .25 |
| **1L44** | A4 | 7p | multicolored | .25 | .25 |
| **1L45** | A4 | 8p | multicolored | .25 | .25 |
| **1L46** | A4 | 9p | multicolored | .25 | .30 |
| **1L47** | A4 | 10p | multicolored | .25 | .30 |
| **1L48** | A4 | 20p | multicolored | .45 | .55 |
| **1L49** | A4 | 25p | multicolored | .60 | .70 |
| **1L50** | A4 | 50p | multicolored | 1.10 | 1.25 |
| **1L51** | A4 | £1 | multicolored | 2.25 | 2.75 |
| **1L52** | A4 | £3 | multicolored | 5.50 | 7.00 |
| | | | *Nos. 1L38-1L52 (15)* | 12.40 | 14.85 |

Nos. 38-50 exist dated 1984; issued May 3, 1984. Value, set $16.

**1985, Nov. 18** **Wmk. 384**

| | | | | |
|---|---|---|---|---|
| *1L48a* | A4 | 20p | 3.25 | *4.50* |
| *1L49a* | A4 | 25p | 3.25 | *4.50* |
| *1L50a* | A4 | 50p | 3.25 | *4.50* |
| *1L51a* | A4 | £1 | 3.25 | *4.50* |
| *1L52a* | A4 | £3 | 7.50 | 6.50 |
| | | *Nos. 1L48a-1L52a (5)* | 20.50 | *24.50* |

Magellanic Clubmoss — A5

**1981, Feb. 5** **Litho.** ***Perf. 14***

| | | | | | |
|---|---|---|---|---|---|
| **1L53** | A5 | 3p | shown | .25 | .25 |
| **1L54** | A5 | 6p | Alpine cat's-tail | .25 | .25 |
| **1L55** | A5 | 7p | Greater burnet | .25 | .25 |
| **1L56** | A5 | 11p | Antarctic bed-straw | .35 | .35 |
| **1L57** | A5 | 15p | Brown rush | .45 | .45 |
| *a.* | | | Brown missing | *3,750.* | |
| **1L58** | A5 | 25p | Antarctic hair grass | .65 | .65 |
| | | | *Nos. 1L53-1L58 (6)* | 2.20 | 2.20 |

**Royal Wedding Issue**

Common Design Type

**1981, July 22** **Litho.** ***Perf. 14***

| | | | | | |
|---|---|---|---|---|---|
| **1L59** | CD331 | 10p | Bouquet | .25 | .25 |
| **1L60** | CD331 | 13p | Charles | .35 | .35 |
| **1L61** | CD331 | 52p | Couple | .85 | .85 |
| | | | *Nos. 1L59-1L61 (3)* | 1.45 | 1.45 |

Reindeer in Spring — A6

**1982, Jan. 29** **Litho.** ***Perf. 14***

| | | | | | |
|---|---|---|---|---|---|
| **1L62** | A6 | 5p | shown | .25 | *.60* |
| **1L63** | A6 | 13p | Autumn | .35 | *.75* |
| **1L64** | A6 | 25p | Winter | .45 | *1.00* |
| **1L65** | A6 | 26p | Late winter | .50 | *1.00* |
| | | | *Nos. 1L62-1L65 (4)* | 1.55 | *3.35* |

Gamasellus Racovitzai — A7

10p, Alaskozetes antarcticus. 13p, Cryptopygus antarcticus. 15p, Notiomaso australis. 25p, Hydromedion sparsutum. 26p, Parochlus steinenii.

**1982, Mar. 16** **Litho.** ***Perf. 14***

| | | | | | |
|---|---|---|---|---|---|
| **1L66** | A7 | 5p | shown | .25 | .25 |
| **1L67** | A7 | 10p | multicolored | .25 | .35 |
| **1L68** | A7 | 13p | multicolored | .30 | .40 |
| **1L69** | A7 | 15p | multicolored | .35 | .40 |
| **1L70** | A7 | 25p | multicolored | .40 | .50 |
| **1L71** | A7 | 26p | multicolored | .45 | .50 |
| | | | *Nos. 1L66-1L71 (6)* | 2.00 | 2.40 |

**Princess Diana Issue**

Common Design Type

**1982, July 1** **Litho.** ***Perf. 14x14½***

| | | | | | |
|---|---|---|---|---|---|
| **1L72** | CD333 | 5p | Arms | .25 | .25 |
| **1L73** | CD333 | 17p | Diana | .35 | .45 |
| *a.* | | | Perf. 14 | 2.50 | *2.75* |
| **1L74** | CD333 | 37p | Wedding | .90 | .90 |
| **1L75** | CD333 | 50p | Portrait | 1.00 | 1.00 |
| | | | *Nos. 1L72-1L75 (4)* | 2.50 | 2.60 |

Crustacea — A8

5p, Euphausia superba. 17p, Glyptonotus antarcticus. 25p, Epimeria monodon. 34p, Serolis pagenstecheri.

***Perf. 14½x14***

**1984, Mar. 23** **Wmk. 373**

| | | | | | |
|---|---|---|---|---|---|
| **1L76** | A8 | 5p | multicolored | .30 | .30 |
| **1L77** | A8 | 17p | multicolored | .40 | .40 |
| **1L78** | A8 | 25p | multicolored | .70 | .70 |
| **1L79** | A8 | 34p | multicolored | 1.10 | 1.10 |
| | | | *Nos. 1L76-1L79 (4)* | 2.50 | 2.50 |

Manned Flight Bicentenary — A9

**1983, Dec. 23** **Litho.** ***Perf. 14***

| | | | | | |
|---|---|---|---|---|---|
| **1L80** | A9 | 5p | Westland Whirlwind | .25 | .25 |
| **1L81** | A9 | 13p | Westland Wasp | .45 | .45 |
| **1L82** | A9 | 17p | Saunders-Roe Walrus | .55 | .55 |
| **1L83** | A9 | 50p | Auster | 1.75 | 1.75 |
| | | | *Nos. 1L80-1L83 (4)* | 3.00 | 3.00 |

South Sandwich Islds. Volcanoes — A10

6p, Zavodovski Island. 17p, Mt. Michael, Saunders Island. 22p, Bellingshausen Island. 52p, Bristol Island.

**1984, Nov. 8** **Wmk. 373** ***Perf. 14½***

| | | | | | |
|---|---|---|---|---|---|
| **1L84** | A10 | 6p | multicolored | .60 | .60 |
| **1L85** | A10 | 17p | multicolored | 1.40 | 1.40 |
| **1L86** | A10 | 22p | multicolored | 2.00 | 2.00 |
| **1L87** | A10 | 52p | multicolored | 3.50 | 3.50 |
| | | | *Nos. 1L84-1L87 (4)* | 7.50 | 7.50 |

Albatrosses — A11

7p, Diomedea chrysostoma. 22p, Diomedea melanophris. 27p, Diomedea exulans. 54p, Phoebetria palpebrata.

**1985, May 5** **Wmk. 384** ***Perf. 14½***

| | | | | | |
|---|---|---|---|---|---|
| **1L88** | A11 | 7p | multicolored | .80 | .80 |
| **1L89** | A11 | 22p | multicolored | 2.25 | 2.25 |
| **1L90** | A11 | 27p | multicolored | 2.50 | 2.50 |
| **1L91** | A11 | 54p | multicolored | 4.75 | 4.75 |
| | | | *Nos. 1L88-1L91 (4)* | 10.30 | 10.30 |

**Queen Mother 85th Birthday**

Common Design Type

Designs: 7p, 14th birthday celebration. 22p, With Princess Anne, Lady Sarah Armstrong-Jones, Prince Edward. 27p, Queen Mother. 54p, Holding Prince Henry. £1, On the Britannia.

**1985, June 23** ***Perf. 14½x14***

| | | | | | |
|---|---|---|---|---|---|
| **1L92** | CD336 | 7p | multicolored | .25 | .25 |
| **1L93** | CD336 | 22p | multicolored | .75 | .75 |
| **1L94** | CD336 | 27p | multicolored | 1.00 | 1.00 |
| **1L95** | CD336 | 54p | multicolored | 2.00 | 2.00 |
| | | | *Nos. 1L92-1L95 (4)* | 4.00 | 4.00 |

**Souvenir Sheet**

| | | | | | |
|---|---|---|---|---|---|
| **1L96** | CD336 | £1 | multicolored | 4.00 | 4.00 |

**Falkland Islands Naturalists Type of 1985**

Naturalists, endangered species: 7p, Dumont d'Urville (1790-1842), kelp. 22p, Johann Reinhold Forster (1729-1798), king penguin. 27p, Johann Georg Adam Forster (1754-1794), tussock grass. 54p, Sir Joseph Banks (1743-1820), dove prion.

**1985, Nov. 4** ***Perf. 13½x14***

| | | | | | |
|---|---|---|---|---|---|
| **1L97** | A86 | 7p | multicolored | .75 | .75 |
| **1L98** | A86 | 22p | multicolored | 1.60 | 1.60 |
| **1L99** | A86 | 27p | multicolored | 2.00 | 2.00 |
| **1L100** | A86 | 54p | multicolored | 3.75 | 3.75 |
| | | | *Nos. 1L97-1L100 (4)* | 8.10 | 8.10 |

## SEMI-POSTAL STAMP

**Rebuilding Type of Falkland Islands**

**Wmk. 373**

**1982, Sept. 13** **Litho.** ***Perf. 11***

| | | | | | |
|---|---|---|---|---|---|
| **1LB1** | SP1 | £1 | Map of So. Georgia | 2.75 | 2.75 |

## ISSUES FOR THE SEPARATE ISLANDS

### Graham Land

**Nos. 84, 85B, 86A, 87A, 88-91 Overprinted in Red**

**1944, Feb. 12** **Wmk. 4** ***Perf. 12***

| | | | | | |
|---|---|---|---|---|---|
| **2L1** | A22 | ½p | green & black | .45 | *2.25* |
| **2L2** | A22 | 1p | dk vio & black | .45 | *1.10* |
| **2L3** | A22 | 2p | rose car & blk | .55 | *1.10* |
| **2L4** | A22 | 3p | deep bl & blk | .55 | *1.10* |
| **2L5** | A22 | 4p | rose vio & blk | 1.90 | 1.75 |
| **2L6** | A22 | 6p | brown & black | 19.00 | 2.75 |
| **2L7** | A22 | 9p | slate bl & blk | 1.25 | *1.50* |
| **2L8** | A22 | 1sh | dull blue | 1.25 | *1.50* |
| | | | *Nos. 2L1-2L8 (8)* | 25.40 | *13.05* |

### South Georgia

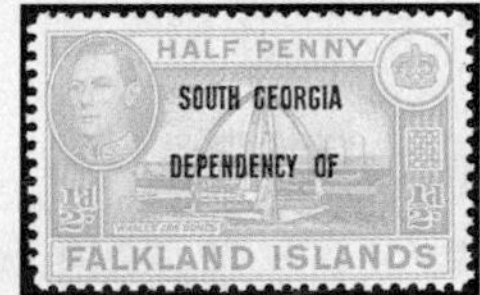


**1944, Apr. 3** **Wmk. 4** ***Perf. 12***

| | | | | | |
|---|---|---|---|---|---|
| **3L1** | A22 | ½p | green & black | .35 | *2.25* |
| **3L2** | A22 | 1p | dark vio & blk | .35 | *1.10* |
| **3L3** | A22 | 2p | rose car & blk | .55 | *1.10* |
| **3L4** | A22 | 3p | deep bl & blk | .55 | *1.10* |
| **3L5** | A22 | 4p | rose vio & blk | 1.90 | 1.75 |
| **3L6** | A22 | 6p | brown & black | 19.00 | 2.50 |
| **3L7** | A22 | 9p | slate bl & blk | 1.25 | *1.50* |
| **3L8** | A22 | 1sh | dull blue | 1.25 | *1.50* |
| | | | *Nos. 3L1-3L8 (8)* | 25.20 | *12.80* |

### South Orkneys

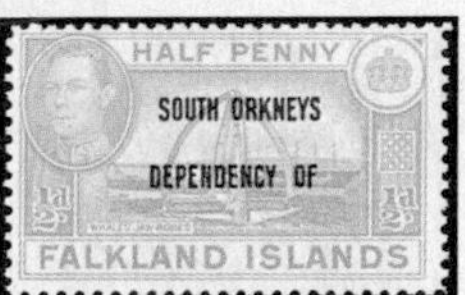


**1944, Feb. 21** **Wmk. 4** ***Perf. 12***

| | | | | | |
|---|---|---|---|---|---|
| **4L1** | A22 | ½p | green & black | .45 | *2.25* |
| **4L2** | A22 | 1p | dark vio & blk | .45 | *1.10* |
| **4L3** | A22 | 2p | rose car & blk | .75 | *1.10* |
| **4L4** | A22 | 3p | deep bl & blk | .75 | *1.10* |
| **4L5** | A22 | 4p | rose vio & blk | 1.75 | 1.75 |
| **4L6** | A22 | 6p | brown & black | 19.00 | 2.50 |
| **4L7** | A22 | 9p | slate bl & blk | 1.25 | *1.50* |
| **4L8** | A22 | 1sh | dull blue | 1.25 | *1.50* |
| | | | *Nos. 4L1-4L8 (8)* | 25.65 | *12.80* |

### South Shetlands

**1944** **Wmk. 4** ***Perf. 12***

| | | | | | |
|---|---|---|---|---|---|
| **5L1** | A22 | ½p | green & black | .45 | *2.25* |
| **5L2** | A22 | 1p | dark vio & blk | .45 | *1.10* |
| **5L3** | A22 | 2p | rose car & blk | .55 | *1.10* |
| **5L4** | A22 | 3p | deep bl & blk | .55 | *1.10* |
| **5L5** | A22 | 4p | rose vio & blk | 1.25 | 1.75 |
| **5L6** | A22 | 6p | brown & black | 19.00 | 2.50 |
| **5L7** | A22 | 9p | slate bl & blk | 1.25 | *1.50* |
| **5L8** | A22 | 1sh | dull blue | 1.25 | *1.50* |
| | | | *Nos. 5L1-5L8 (8)* | 24.75 | *12.80* |

# FAR EASTERN REPUBLIC

'fär 'ē-stərn ri-'pə-blik

LOCATION — In Siberia east of Lake Baikal
GOVT. — Republic
AREA — 900,745 sq. mi.
POP. — 1,560,000 (approx. 1920)
CAPITAL — Chita

A short-lived independent government was established here in 1920.

100 Kopecks = 1 Ruble

### Watermark

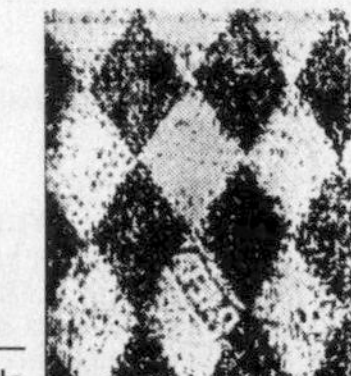

Wmk. 171 — Diamonds

### Vladivostok Issue
### Russian Stamps Surcharged or Overprinted

a

b

c

### On Stamps of 1909-17

*Perf. 14, 14½x15, 13½*

| 1920 | | | Unwmk. | |
|---|---|---|---|---|
| 2 | A14(a) | 2k green | 10.00 | 15.00 |
| 3 | A14(a) | 3k red | 10.00 | 10.00 |
| 4 | A11(b) | 3k on 35k red brn & grn | 40.00 | 50.00 |
| 5 | A15(a) | 4k carmine | 10.00 | 12.00 |
| 6 | A11(b) | 4k on 70k brn & org | 10.00 | 15.00 |
| 8 | A11(b) | 7k on 15k red brn & bl | 2.00 | 2.00 |
| a. | | Inverted surcharge | 100.00 | |
| b. | | Pair, one ovptd. "DBP" only | 100.00 | |
| 9 | A15(a) | 10k dark blue | 75.00 | 55.00 |
| a. | | Overprint on back | 90.00 | |
| 10 | A12(c) | 10k on 3½r mar & lt grn | 25.00 | 25.00 |
| 11 | A11(a) | 14k blue & rose | 50.00 | 35.00 |
| 12 | A11(a) | 15k red brn & bl | 30.00 | 25.00 |
| 13 | A8(a) | 20k blue & car | 150.00 | 100.00 |
| 14 | A11(b) | 20k on 14k bl & rose | 10.00 | 8.00 |
| a. | | Surcharge on back | 30.00 | |
| 15 | A11(a) | 25k green & vio | 25.00 | 15.00 |
| 16 | A11(a) | 35k red brn & grn | 50.00 | 35.00 |
| 17 | A8(a) | 50k brn vio & grn | 10.00 | 12.00 |
| 18 | A9(a) | 1r pale brn, dk brn & org | 750.00 | 750.00 |

### On Stamps of 1917
*Imperf*

| | | | | |
|---|---|---|---|---|
| 21 | A14(a) | 1k orange | 25.00 | 10.00 |
| 22 | A14(a) | 2k gray grn | 20.00 | 10.00 |
| 23 | A14(a) | 3k red | 20.00 | 10.00 |
| 25 | A11(b) | 7k on 15k red brn & dp bl | 2.00 | 5.00 |
| a. | | Pair, one without surcharge | 100.00 | |
| b. | | Pair, one ovptd. "DBP" only | 100.00 | |
| 26 | A12(c) | 10k on 3½r mar & lt grn | 27.50 | 15.00 |
| 27 | A9(a) | 1r pale brn, brn & red org | 40.00 | 20.00 |

### On Stamps of Siberia 1919
*Perf. 14, 14½x15*

| | | | | |
|---|---|---|---|---|
| 30 | A14(a) | 35k on 2k green | 5.00 | 8.00 |
| a. | | "DBP" on back | 25.00 | 50.00 |

*Imperf*

| | | | | |
|---|---|---|---|---|
| 31 | A14(a) | 35k on 2k green | 35.00 | 25.00 |
| 32 | A14(a) | 70k on 1k orange | 7.50 | 10.00 |

Counterfeit surcharges and overprints abound, including digital forgeries.

### On Russia Nos. AR2, AR3

A1

*Perf. 14½x15*
**Wmk. 171**

| | | | | |
|---|---|---|---|---|
| 35 | A1(b) | 1k on 5k green, *buff* | 30.00 | 20.00 |
| 36 | A1(b) | 2k on 10k brown, *buff* | 40.00 | 30.00 |

The letters on these stamps resembling "DBP," are the Russian initials of "Dalne Vostochnaya Respublika" (Far Eastern Republic).

### Chita Issue

A2

A2a

| 1921 | Unwmk. | Typo. | *Imperf.* | |
|---|---|---|---|---|
| 38 | A2 | 2k gray green | 1.50 | 1.50 |
| 39 | A2a | 4k rose | 3.00 | 3.00 |
| 40 | A2 | 5k claret | 3.00 | 3.00 |
| 41 | A2a | 10k blue | 2.50 | 2.50 |
| | | *Nos. 38-41 (4)* | 10.00 | 10.00 |

For overprints see Nos. 62-65.

### Blagoveshchensk Issue

A3

| 1921 | | Litho. | *Imperf.* | |
|---|---|---|---|---|
| 42 | A3 | 2r red | 2.75 | 2.00 |
| 43 | A3 | 3r dark green | 2.75 | 2.00 |
| 44 | A3 | 5r dark blue | 2.75 | 2.00 |
| a. | | Tête bêche pair | 45.00 | 50.00 |
| 45 | A3 | 15r dark brown | 2.75 | 2.00 |
| 46 | A3 | 30r dark violet | 2.75 | 2.00 |
| a. | | Tête bêche pair | 35.00 | 15.00 |
| | | *Nos. 42-46 (5)* | 13.75 | 10.00 |

Remainders of Nos. 42-46 were canceled in colored crayon or by typographed bars. These sell for half of foregoing values.

### Chita Issue

A4

A5

| 1922 | | Litho. | *Imperf.* | |
|---|---|---|---|---|
| 49 | A4 | 1k orange | 1.00 | .85 |
| 50 | A4 | 3k dull red | .40 | .45 |
| 51 | A5 | 4k dp rose & buff | .40 | .45 |
| 52 | A4 | 5k orange brown | .80 | .45 |
| 53 | A4 | 7k light blue | 1.50 | 1.50 |
| a. | | Perf. 11½ | 2.00 | 2.50 |
| b. | | Rouletted 9 | 3.00 | 3.00 |
| c. | | Perf. 11½x rouletted | 6.50 | 6.50 |
| 54 | A5 | 10k dk blue & red | .60 | .65 |
| 55 | A4 | 15k dull rose | .80 | 1.10 |
| 56 | A5 | 20k blue & red | .80 | 1.10 |
| 57 | A5 | 30k green & red org | 1.25 | 1.10 |
| 58 | A5 | 50k black & red org | 3.00 | 2.25 |
| | | *Nos. 49-58 (10)* | 10.55 | 9.90 |

The 4k exists with "4" omitted. Value $100.

### Vladivostok Issue

Stamps of 1921 Overprinted in Red

1917
7 XI
1922

| 1922 | | | *Imperf.* | |
|---|---|---|---|---|
| 62 | A2 | 2k gray green | 35.00 | 25.00 |
| a. | | Inverted overprint | 250.00 | |
| 63 | A2a | 4k rose | 35.00 | 25.00 |
| a. | | Inverted overprint | 250.00 | |
| b. | | Double overprint | 250.00 | |
| 64 | A2 | 5k claret | 35.00 | 35.00 |
| a. | | Inverted overprint | 100.00 | |
| b. | | Double overprint | 350.00 | |
| 65 | A2a | 10k blue | 35.00 | 35.00 |
| a. | | Inverted overprint | 250.00 | |
| | | *Nos. 62-65 (4)* | 140.00 | 120.00 |

Russian revolution of Nov. 1917, 5th anniv.

Once in the setting the figures "22" of 1922 have the bottom stroke curved instead of straight. Value, each $75.

No. 63 exists in a block with overprints missing on some stamps.

### Vladivostok Issue

Russian Stamps of 1922-23 Surcharged in Black or Red

Д. В.
коп. 1 коп.
ЗОЛОТОМ

| 1923 | | | *Imperf.* | |
|---|---|---|---|---|
| 66 | A50 | 1k on 100r red | .40 | 1.00 |
| a. | | Inverted surcharge | 60.00 | |
| 67 | A50 | 2k on 70r violet | .40 | .75 |
| 68 | A49 | 5k on 10r blue (R) | .40 | .75 |
| 69 | A50 | 10k on 50r brown | .90 | 1.25 |
| a. | | Inverted surcharge | 250.00 | |

*Perf. 14½x15*

| | | | | |
|---|---|---|---|---|
| 70 | A50 | 1k on 100r red | .90 | 1.25 |
| | | *Nos. 66-70 (5)* | 3.00 | 5.00 |

## OCCUPATION STAMPS

### Issued under Occupation of General Semenov
### Chita Issue
### Russian Stamps of 1909-12 Surcharged

a

b

c

| 1920 | | Unwmk. | *Perf. 14, 14x15½* | |
|---|---|---|---|---|
| N1 | A15 (a) | 1r on 4k car | 150.00 | 100.00 |
| N2 | A8 (b) | 2r50k on 20k bl & car | 40.00 | 30.00 |
| N3 | A14 (c) | 5r on 5k claret | 25.00 | 50.00 |
| a. | | Double surcharge | 200.00 | |
| N4 | A11 (a) | 10r on 70k brn & org | 20.00 | 25.00 |
| | | *Nos. N1-N4 (4)* | 235.00 | 205.00 |

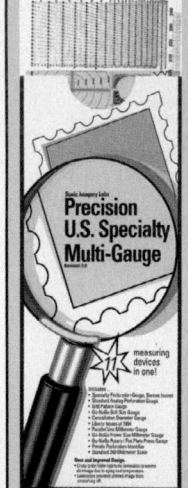

## FAROE ISLANDS

ˈfar-ˌō ˈī-ləndz

(The Faroes)

LOCATION — North Atlantic Ocean
GOVT. — Self-governing part of Kingdom of Denmark
AREA — 540 sq. mi.
POP. — 41,059 (1999 est.)
CAPITAL — Thorshavn

100 Ore = 1 Krone

**Catalogue values for unused stamps in this country are for Never Hinged items, beginning with Scott 7.**

Denmark No. 97 Handstamp Surcharged

**1919, Jan. Typo. *Perf. 14x14½***

| | | | | |
|---|---|---|---|---|
| 1 | A16 2o on 5o green | | 1,400. | 475.00 |

Counterfeits of surcharge exist.

Denmark No. 88a, the bisect, was used with Denmark No. 97 in Faroe Islands Jan. 3-23, 1919.

**Denmark Nos. 220, 224, 238A, 224C Surcharged in Blue or Black**

Nos. 2, 5-6

No. 3

No. 4

**1940-41 Engr. *Perf. 13***

| | | | |
|---|---|---|---|
| 2 | A32 20o on 1o ('41) | 40.00 | 110.00 |
| 3 | A32 20o on 5o ('41) | 40.00 | 35.00 |
| 4 | A30 20o on 15o (Bk) | 60.00 | 22.50 |
| 5 | A32 50o on 5o (Bk) | 275.00 | 90.00 |
| 6 | A32 60o on 6o (Bk) | 125.00 | *250.00* |
| | *Nos. 2-6 (5)* | 540.00 | 507.50 |
| | Set, never hinged | 1,150. | |

Issued during British administration.

**Catalogue values for unused stamps in this section, from this point to the end of the section, are for Never Hinged items.**

Map of Islands, 1673 — A1

Map of North Atlantic, 1573 — A2

West Coast, Sandoy — A3

Vidoy and Svinoy, by Eyvindur Mohr — A4

Designs: 200o, like 70o. 250o, 300o, View of Streymoy and Vagar. 450o, Houses, Nes, by Ruth Smith. 500o, View of Hvitanes and Skalafjordur, by S. Joensen-Mikines.

**Unwmk.**

**1975, Jan. 30 Engr. *Perf. 13***

| | | | |
|---|---|---|---|
| 7 | A1 5o sepia | .25 | .25 |
| 8 | A2 10o emer & dark blue | .25 | .25 |
| 9 | A1 50o graysh green | .25 | .25 |
| 10 | A2 60o brown & dark blue | .80 | .80 |
| 11 | A3 70o vio bl & slate grn | .80 | .80 |
| 12 | A2 80o ocher & dark blue | .45 | .45 |
| 13 | A1 90o red brown | .80 | .80 |
| 14 | A2 120o brt bl & dark bl | .60 | .40 |
| 15 | A3 200o vio bl & slate grn | .60 | .60 |
| 16 | A3 250o multicolored | .60 | .60 |
| 17 | A3 300o multicolored | 5.00 | 1.60 |

**Photo.**

***Perf. 12½x13***

| | | | |
|---|---|---|---|
| 18 | A4 350o multicolored | .80 | .80 |
| 19 | A4 450o multicolored | .80 | .80 |
| 20 | A4 500o multicolored | 1.00 | 1.00 |
| | *Nos. 7-20 (14)* | 13.00 | 9.40 |

Faroe Boat — A5

Faroe Flag — A6

Faroe Mailman — A7

***Perf. 12½x13, 12 (A6)***

**1976, Apr. 1 Engr.; Litho. (A6)**

| | | | |
|---|---|---|---|
| 21 | A5 125o copper red | 1.60 | 1.25 |
| 22 | A6 160o multicolored | .45 | .45 |
| 23 | A7 800o olive | 1.75 | 1.25 |
| | *Nos. 21-23 (3)* | 3.80 | 2.95 |

Faroe Islands independent postal service, Apr. 1, 1976.

Motor Fishing Boat — A8

Faroese Fishing Vessels and Map of Islands: 125o, Inland fishing cutter. 160o, Modern seine fishing vessel. 600o, Deep-sea fishing trawler.

**1977, Apr. 28 Photo. *Perf. 14½x14***

| | | | |
|---|---|---|---|
| 24 | A8 100o green & black | 4.50 | 3.75 |
| 25 | A8 125o carmine & black | .65 | .65 |
| 26 | A8 160o blue & black | .90 | .65 |
| 27 | A8 600o brown & black | 1.60 | 1.10 |
| | *Nos. 24-27 (4)* | 7.65 | 6.15 |

Common Snipe A9

**Photogravure & Engraved**

**1977, Sept. 29 *Perf. 14½x14***

| | | | |
|---|---|---|---|
| 28 | A9 70o shown | .25 | .25 |
| 29 | A9 180o Oystercatcher | .55 | .55 |
| 30 | A9 250o Whimbrel | .65 | .65 |
| | *Nos. 28-30 (3)* | 1.45 | 1.45 |

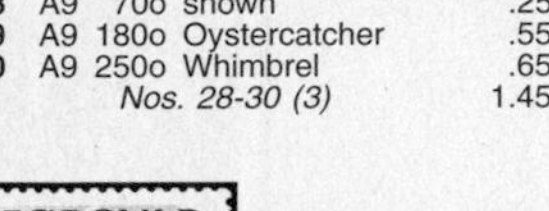

North Coast, Puffins — A10

Mykines Village — A11

Mykines Island: 140o, Coast. 150o, Aerial view. 180o, Map.

***Perf. 13x13½, 13½x13***

**1978, Jan. 26 Photo.**

**Size: 21x28mm, 28x21mm**

| | | | |
|---|---|---|---|
| 31 | A10 100o multicolored | .25 | .25 |
| 32 | A11 130o multicolored | .45 | .45 |
| 33 | A11 140o multicolored | .55 | .55 |
| 34 | A10 150o multicolored | .55 | .55 |

**Size: 37x26mm**

***Perf. 14½x14***

| | | | |
|---|---|---|---|
| 35 | A11 180o multicolored | .55 | .55 |
| | *Nos. 31-35 (5)* | 2.35 | 2.35 |

Sea Birds — A12

**Lithographed and Engraved**

**1978, Apr. 13 *Perf. 12x12½***

| | | | |
|---|---|---|---|
| 36 | A12 140o Gannets | .45 | .45 |
| 37 | A12 180o Puffins | .55 | .55 |
| 38 | A12 400o Guillemots | 1.40 | 1.10 |
| | *Nos. 36-38 (3)* | 2.40 | 2.10 |

Old Library — A13

**1978, Dec. 7 *Perf. 13***

| | | | |
|---|---|---|---|
| 39 | A13 140o shown | .45 | .45 |
| 40 | A13 180o New library | .55 | .55 |

Completion of New Library Building.

Girl Guide, Tent and Fire — A14

**1978, Dec. 7 Photo. *Perf. 13½***

| | | | |
|---|---|---|---|
| 41 | A14 140o multicolored | .45 | .45 |

Faroese Girl Guides, 50th anniversary.

Ram — A15

**Lithographed and Engraved**

**1979, Mar. 19 *Perf. 12***

| | | | |
|---|---|---|---|
| 42 | A15 25k multicolored | 6.00 | 6.00 |

Denmark No. 88a — A16

Europa: 180o, Faroe Islands No. 1.

**1979, May 7 *Perf. 12½***

| | | | |
|---|---|---|---|
| 43 | A16 140o yellow & blue | *.45* | *.45* |
| 44 | A16 180o rose, grn & blk | *.55* | *.55* |

Girl Wearing Festive Costume — A17

Children's Drawings and IYC Emblem: 150o, Fisherman. 200o, Two friends.

**1979, Oct. 1 *Perf. 12***

| | | | |
|---|---|---|---|
| 45 | A17 110o multicolored | .45 | .45 |
| 46 | A17 150o multicolored | .45 | .45 |
| 47 | A17 200o multicolored | .55 | .55 |
| | *Nos. 45-47 (3)* | 1.45 | 1.45 |

International Year of the Child.

Sea Plantain — A18

**1980, Mar. 17 Photo. *Perf. 12x11½***

| | | | |
|---|---|---|---|
| 48 | A18 90o shown | .25 | .25 |
| 49 | A18 110o Glacier buttercup | .45 | .45 |
| 50 | A18 150o Purple saxifrage | .55 | .55 |
| 51 | A18 200o Starry saxifrage | .55 | .55 |
| 52 | A18 400o Lady's mantle | .90 | .90 |
| | *Nos. 48-52 (5)* | 2.70 | 2.70 |

Jakob Jakobsen (1864-1918), Linguist — A19

Europa: 200o, Vensel Ulrich Hammershaimb (1819-1909), theologian, linguist and folklorist.

**1980, Oct. 6 Engr. *Perf. 11½***

| | | | |
|---|---|---|---|
| 53 | A19 150o dull green | *.40* | *.40* |
| 54 | A19 200o dull red brown | *.60* | *.60* |

Perf. 13 bicolored examples of Nos. 53-54 are rejected stamps never put on sale that were to have been burned, but which escaped destruction.

Coat of Arms, Virgin and Child, Gothic Pew Gable — A20

Kirkjubour Pew Gables, 15th Century: 140o, Norwegian coat of arms, John the Baptist. 150o, Christ's head, St. Peter. 200o, Hand in halo, Apostle Paul.

**Photo. & Engr.**

**1980, Oct. 6** *Perf. 13½*

**55** A20 110o multicolored .45 .45
**56** A20 140o multicolored .45 .45
**57** A20 150o multicolored .45 .45
**58** A20 200o multicolored .55 .55
*Nos. 55-58 (4)* 1.90 1.90

See Nos. 102-105, 389-392

A21

Sketches of Old Torshavn by Ingalzur Reyni.

**1981, Mar. 2** **Engr.**

**59** A21 110o dark green .45 .45
**60** A21 140o black .45 .45
**61** A21 150o dark brown .45 .45
**62** A21 200o dark blue .55 .55
*Nos. 59-62 (4)* 1.90 1.90

The Ring Dance A22

Europa: 200o, The garter dance.

**1981, June 1** **Engr.** *Perf. 13x14*

**63** A22 150o pale rose & grn *.35 .35*
**64** A22 200o pale yel grn & dk brn *.55 .55*

Rune Stones, 800-1000 AD — A23

Historic Writings: 1k, Folksong, 1846. 3k, Sheep Letter excerpt, 1298. 6k, Seal and text, 1533. 10k, Titlepage from Faeroae et Faeroa, by Lucas Jacobson Debes, library.

**Photo. & Engr.**

**1981, Oct. 19** *Perf. 11½*

**65** A23 10o multicolored .25 .25
**66** A23 1k multicolored .25 .25
**67** A23 3k multicolored 1.00 .65
**68** A23 6k multicolored 1.60 1.25
**69** A23 10k multicolored 2.75 2.75
*Nos. 65-69 (5)* 5.85 5.15

Nos. 70-80 not assigned.

Europa 1982 — A24

1.50k, Viking North Atlantic routes. 2k, Viking house foundation.

**1982, Mar. 15** **Engr.** *Perf. 13½*

**81** A24 1.50k dk blue & blue .45 .45
**82** A24 2k gray & blk .55 .55

View of Gjogv, by Ingalvur av Reyni A25

**1982, June 7** **Litho.** *Perf. 12½x13*

**83** A25 180o shown .45 .45
**84** A25 220o Hvalvik 1.00 .75
**85** A25 250o Kvivik .65 .65
*Nos. 83-85 (3)* 2.10 1.85

Ballad of Harra Paetur and Elinborg — A26

Scenes from the medieval ballad of chivalry.

**1982, Sept. 27** **Litho.**

**86** A26 220o multicolored .65 .65
**87** A26 250o multicolored .75 .75
**88** A26 350o multicolored 1.00 1.00
**89** A26 450o multicolored 1.20 1.20
*Nos. 86-89 (4)* 3.60 3.60

Cargo Ships A27

**1983, Feb. 21** **Litho.** *Perf. 14x14½*

**90** A27 220o Arcturus, 1856 .65 .65
**91** A27 250o Laura, 1882 .90 .90
**92** A27 700o Thyra, 1866 2.00 2.00
*Nos. 90-92 (3)* 3.55 3.55

Chessmen, by Pol i Buo (1791-1857) — A28

**1983, May 2** **Engr.** *Perf. 13 Vert.*

**Booklet Stamps**

**93** 250o King 2.25 2.25
**94** 250o Queen 2.25 2.25
*a.* Bklt. pane of 6, 3 each #93-94 16.00
*b.* A28 Pair, #93-94 5.50 5.50

Europa 1983 — A29

Nobel Prizewinners in Medicine: 250o, Niels R. Finsen (1860-1903), ultraviolet radiation pioneer. 400o, Alexander Fleming (1881-1955), discoverer of penicillin.

**1983, June 6** **Engr.** *Perf. 12x11½*

**95** A29 250o dark blue *.65 .65*
**96** A29 400o red brown *1.10 1.10*

A30

**1983, Sept. 19** **Litho.** *Perf. 12½x13*

**97** A30 250o Tusk .65 .65
**98** A30 280o Haddock .85 .85
**99** A30 500o Halibut 1.60 1.60
**100** A30 900o Catfish 2.50 2.50
*Nos. 97-100 (4)* 5.60 5.60

Souvenir Sheet

Traditional Costumes — A31

Various national costumes.

**1983, Nov. 4** **Litho.** *Perf. 12*

**101** A31 Sheet of 3 10.00 11.00
*a.-c.* 250o multicolored 2.75 2.75

Nordic House Cultural Center opening. Margin shows Scandinavian flags.

**Pew Gables Type of 1980**

Designs: 250o, John, shield with three crowns. 300o, St. Jacob, shield with crossed keys. 350o, Thomas, shield with crossbeam. 400o, Judas Taddeus, Toulouse cross halo.

**Photo. & Engr.**

**1984, Jan. 30** *Perf. 14x13½*

**102** A20 250o lil, pur & dk brn .75 .75
**103** A20 300o red brn, dk buff & dk brn .85 .85
**104** A20 350o blk, lt gray & dk brn 1.00 1.00
**105** A20 400o ol grn, pale yel & dk brn 1.10 1.10
*Nos. 102-105 (4)* 3.70 3.70

Europa (1959-84) A33

**1984, Apr. 2** **Engr.** *Perf. 13½*

**106** A33 250o red *.60 .60*
**107** A33 500o dark blue *1.40 1.40*

Sverri Patursson (1871-1960), Writer — A34

Poets: 2.50k, Joannes Patursson (1866-1946). 3k, J. H. O. Djurhuus (1881-1948). 4.50k, H.A. Djurhuus (1883-1951).

**1984, May 28** **Engr.** *Perf. 13½*

**108** A34 2k olive green .55 .55
**109** A34 2.50k red .65 .65
**110** A34 3k dark blue .85 .85
**111** A34 4.50k violet 1.25 1.25
*Nos. 108-111 (4)* 3.30 3.30

Faroese Smack (Fishing Boat) — A35

*Perf. 12½x13, 13x12½*

**1984, Sept. 10** **Engr.**

**112** A35 280o shown .75 .75
**113** A35 300o Fishermen, vert. .85 .85
**114** A35 12k Helmsman, vert. 3.75 3.75
*Nos. 112-114 (3)* 5.35 5.35

Fairytale Illustrations by Elinborg Lutzen — A36

**1984, Oct. 29** **Litho.** *Perf. 13 Vert.*

**Booklet Stamps**

**115** A36 140o Beauty of the Veils 5.00 5.00
**116** A36 280o Veils, diff. 5.00 5.00
**117** A36 280o Girl Shy Prince 5.00 5.00
**118** A36 280o The Glass Sword 5.00 5.00
**119** A36 280o Little Elin 5.00 5.00
**120** A36 280o The Boy and the Ox 5.00 5.00
*a.* Booklet pane of 6, #115-120 30.00

View of Torshavn and the Forts, by Edward Dayes A37

Dayes' Landscapes, 1789: 280o, Skaeling. 550o, View Towards the North Seen from the Hills Near Torshavn in Stremoy, Faroes. 800o, The Moving Stones in Eysturoy, Faroes.

**Litho. & Engr.**

**1985, Feb. 4** *Perf. 13*

**121** A37 250o multicolored .65 .65
**122** A37 280o multicolored .85 .85
**123** A37 550o multicolored 2.00 2.00
**124** A37 800o multicolored 2.50 2.50
*Nos. 121-124 (4)* 6.00 6.00

Europa 1985 — A38

Children taking music lessons.

**1985, Apr. 1** **Litho.** *Perf. 13½x14½*

**125** A38 280o multicolored *.85 .85*
**126** A38 550o multicolored *1.90 1.90*

Paintings, Faroese Museum of Art A39

Designs: 280o, The Garden, Hoyvik, 1973, by Thomas Arge (1942-78). 450o, Self-Portrait, 1952, by Ruth Smith (1913-58), vert. 550o, Winter's Day in Nolsoy, 1959, by Steffan Danielsen (1922-76).

**Litho. & Engr.**

**1985, June 3** *Perf. 12½*

**127** A39 280o multicolored 1.25 1.25
**128** A39 450o multicolored 1.75 1.75
**129** A39 550o multicolored 2.50 2.50
*Nos. 127-129 (3)* 5.50 5.50

Lighthouses — A40

**1985, Sept. 23** **Litho.** *Perf. 13½x14*

**130** A40 270o Nolsoy, 1893 .85 .85
**131** A40 320o Thorshavn, 1909 1.25 1.25
**132** A40 350o Mykines, 1909 1.25 1.25
**133** A40 470o Map of locations 1.60 1.60
*Nos. 130-133 (4)* 4.95 4.95

Passenger Aviation in the Faroes, 22nd Anniv. A41

*Perf. 13½ Horiz.*

**1985, Oct. 28 Photo.**

**Booklet Stamps**

**134** A41 300o Douglas DC-3 2.75 2.75
**135** A41 300o Fokker Friendship 2.75 2.75
**136** A41 300o Boeing 737 2.75 2.75
**137** A41 300o Interisland LM-IKB 2.75 2.75
**138** A41 300o Helicopter Snipan 2.75 2.75
*a.* Booklet pane of 5, #134-138 14.00 14.00

Skrimsla, Ancient Folk Ballad — A42

**1986, Feb. 3 Litho. *Perf. 12½x13***

**139** A42 300o Peasant in woods .80 .80
**140** A42 420o Meets Giant 1.20 1.20
**141** A42 550o Giant loses game 1.40 1.40
**142** A42 650o Giant grants Peasant's wish 1.60 1.60
*Nos. 139-142 (4)* 5.00 5.00

Europa 1986 — A43

**1986, Apr. 7 Litho. *Perf. 13½***

**143** A43 3k shown *1.60 1.60*
**144** A43 5.50k Sea pollution *2.25 2.25*

Amnesty Intl., 25th Anniv. — A44

Winning design competition artwork.

**1986, June 2 *Perf. 14x13½***

**145** A44 3k Olivur vid Neyst 1.25 1.25
**146** A44 4.70k Eli Smith 1.90 1.90
**147** A44 5.50k Ranna Kunoy 2.40 2.40
*Nos. 145-147 (3)* 5.55 5.55

Nos. 145-146 horiz.

Souvenir Sheet

HAFNIA '87, Copenhagen — A45

Design: East Bay of Torshavn, watercolor, 1782, by Christian Rosenmeyer (1728-1802).

**1986, Aug. 29 Litho. *Perf. 13x13½***

**148** A45 Sheet of 3 8.75 8.75
*a.* 3k multicolored 2.75 2.75
*b.* 4.70k multicolored 2.75 2.75
*c.* 6.50k multicolored 2.75 2.75

Sold for 20k.

Old Stone Bridges A46

2.70k, Glyvrar on Eysturoy. 3k, Leypanagjogv on Vagar, vert. 13k, Skaelinger on Streymoy.

***Perf. 13½x14½, 14½x13½***

**1986, Oct. 13 Engr.**

**149** A46 2.70k dp brown vio 1.75 1.75
**150** A46 3k bluish blk 1.40 1.40
**151** A46 13k gray green 3.00 3.00
*Nos. 149-151 (3)* 6.15 6.15

Farmhouses — A47

Traditional architecture: 300o, Depil on Borooy, 1814. 420o, Depil, diff. 470o, Frammi vio Gjonna on Streymoy, c. 1814. 650o, Frammi, diff.

**1987, Feb. 9 Engr. *Perf. 13x14½***

**152** A47 300o pale blue & blue .90 .90
**153** A47 420o buff & brown 1.40 1.40
**154** A47 470o pale grn & dp grn 1.75 1.75
**155** A47 650o pale gray & black 2.25 2.25
*Nos. 152-155 (4)* 6.30 6.30

Europa 1987 — A48

Nordic House.

**1987, Apr. 6 *Perf. 13x14***

**156** A48 300o Exterior *.85 .85*
**157** A48 550o Interior *1.90 1.60*

Fishing Trawlers A49

**1987, June 1 Litho. *Perf. 14x13½***

**158** A49 3k Joannes Patursson .90 .90
**159** A49 5.50k Magnus Heinason 1.90 1.90
**160** A49 8k Sjurdarberg 4.00 4.00
*Nos. 158-160 (3)* 6.80 6.80

Hestur (Horse) Island A50

**Litho. & Engr.**

**1987, Sept. 7 *Perf. 13***

**161** A50 270o Map .80 .80
**162** A50 300o Seaport .75 .75
**163** A50 420o Bird cliff 1.60 1.60
**164** A50 470o Pasture, sheep 1.75 1.75
**165** A50 550o Seashore 1.75 1.75
*Nos. 161-165 (5)* 6.65 6.65

Nos. 161, 163 and 165 vert.

Collages by Zacharias Heinesen A51

West Bay of Torshavn, Watercolor by Rosenmeyer — A52

**1987, Oct. 16 Litho. *Perf. 13½x14***

**166** A51 4.70k Eystaravag 1.25 1.25
**167** A51 6.50k Vestarvag 1.75 1.75

**Souvenir Sheet**

***Perf. 13½x13***

**168** A52 3k multicolored 3.50 3.50

HAFNIA '87. Sold for 4k.

Flowers — A53

**1988, Feb. 8 Litho. *Perf. 11½***

**Granite Paper**

**169** A53 2.70k Bellis perennis 1.10 1.10
**170** A53 3k Dactylorchis maculata .65 .65
**171** A53 4.70k Potentilla erecta 1.75 1.75
**172** A53 9k Pinguicula vulgaris 2.50 2.50
*Nos. 169-172 (4)* 6.00 6.00

Europa — A54

Communication and transport: 3k, Satellite dish, satellite. 5.50k, Fork lift, crane, ship.

**1988, Apr. 11 Photo. *Perf. 11½***

**173** A54 3k multi *.90 .90*
**174** A54 5.50k multi *1.50 1.50*

A55

Writers: 270o, Jorgen-Frantz Jacobsen (1900-38). 300o, Christian Matras (b. 1900). 470o, William Heinesen (b. 1900). 650o, Hedin Bru (1901-87).

**1988, June 6 Engr. *Perf. 13½***

**175** A55 270o myrtle green 1.40 1.40
**176** A55 300o rose lake .85 .85
**177** A55 470o dark blue 2.00 2.00
**178** A55 650o brown black 2.25 2.25
*Nos. 175-178 (4)* 6.50 6.50

A56

Text, illustrations and cameo portraits of organizers: 3k, Announcement and Djoni Geil, Enok Baerentsen and H.H. Jacobsen. 3.20k, Meeting, Rasmus Effersoe, C.L. Johannesen and Samal Krakusteini. 12k, Oystercatcher and lyrics of *Now the Hour Has Come,* by poet Sverri Patursson (1871-1960), Just A. Husum, Joannes Patursson and Jens Olsen.

**Granite Paper**

**1988, Sept. 5 Photo. *Perf. 12***

**179** A56 3k multicolored .80 .80
**180** A56 3.20k multicolored 1.20 1.20
**181** A56 12k multicolored 4.50 4.50
*Nos. 179-181 (3)* 6.50 6.50

1888 Christmas meeting to preserve cultural traditions and the natl. language, cent.

Kirkjubour Cathedral Ruins A57

270o, Exterior. 300o, Arch. 470o, Crucifixion, bas-relief. 550o, Interior.

**1988, Oct. 17 Engr. *Perf. 13***

**182** A57 270o dark green 1.40 1.40
**183** A57 300o dark bl, vert. 1.10 1.10
**184** A57 470o dark brn, vert. 1.60 1.60
**185** A57 550o dark violet 1.60 1.60
*Nos. 182-185 (4)* 5.70 5.70

Havnar Church, Torshavn, 200th Anniv. A58

Designs: 350o, Church exterior. 500o, Crypt, vert. 15k, Bell, vert.

**1989, Feb. 6 Engr. *Perf. 13***

**186** A58 350o dark green 1.00 1.00
**187** A58 500o dark brown 1.75 1.75
**188** A58 15k deep blue 3.50 3.50
*Nos. 186-188 (3)* 6.25 6.25

Folk Costumes — A59

**Photo. & Engr.**

**1989, Apr. 10 *Perf. 13½***

**189** A59 350o Man 1.00 1.00
**190** A59 600o Woman 2.00 2.00

Europa 1989 — A60

Wooden children's toys.

**1989, Apr. 10 Photo. *Perf. 12x11½***

**Granite Paper**

**191** A60 3.50k Boat *1.00 1.00*
**192** A60 6k Horse *1.50 1.50*

Island Games, July 5-13 — A61

**1989, June 5 Photo. *Perf. 12½***
**Granite Paper**

**193** A61 200o Rowing .75 .75
**194** A61 350o Handball 1.25 1.25
**195** A61 600o Soccer 1.75 1.75
**196** A61 700o Swimming 2.25 2.25
*Nos. 193-196 (4)* 6.00 6.00

A62

Bird cliffs of Suduroy.

**1989, Oct. 2 Engr. *Perf. 14x13½***

**197** A62 320o Tvoran 1.00 1.00
**198** A62 350o Skuvanes 1.40 1.40
**199** A62 500o Beinisvord 1.75 1.75
**200** A62 600o Asmundarstakkur 2.00 2.00
*Nos. 197-200 (4)* 6.15 6.15

A63

Modern fish factory (filleting station).

**1990, Feb. 5 Litho. *Perf. 14x13½***

**201** A63 3.50k Unloading fish 1.00 1.00
**202** A63 3.70k Cleaning and sorting 1.00 1.00
**203** A63 5k Filleting 1.25 1.25
**204** A63 7k Packaged frozen fish 2.00 2.00
*Nos. 201-204 (4)* 5.25 5.25

Europa 1990 — A64

Post offices.

**1990, Apr. 9 Litho. *Perf. 13½x14***

**205** A64 3.50k Gjogv *1.00 1.00*
**206** A64 6k Klaksvik *1.75 1.75*

Souvenir Sheet

Recognition of the Merkid, Flag of the Faroes, by the British, 50th Anniv. — A65

Designs: a, Flag. b, Fishing trawler *Nyggjaberg,* disappeared, 1942. c, Sloop *Saana,* sunk by the Germans, 1942.

**1990, Apr. 9 Photo. *Perf. 12***
**Granite Paper**

**207** A65 Sheet of 3 4.50 4.50
*a.-c.* 3.50k any single 1.60 1.60

Whales A66

**1990, June 6 Photo. *Perf. 11½***
**Granite Paper**

**208** A66 320o Mesoplodon bidens 1.25 1.25
**209** A66 350o Balaena mysticetus 1.50 1.50
**210** A66 600o Eubalaena glacialis 2.25 2.25
**211** A66 700o Hyperoodon ampullatus 2.50 2.50
*Nos. 208-211 (4)* 7.50 7.50

Nolsoy Island by Steffan Danielsen A67

**1990, Oct. 8 Photo. *Perf. 11½***
**Granite Paper**

**212** A67 50o shown .25 .25
**213** A67 350o Coastline 1.10 1.10
**214** A67 500o Town 1.50 1.50
**215** A67 1000o Coastline, cliffs 3.00 3.00
*Nos. 212-215 (4)* 5.85 5.85

Flora and Fauna — A68

**1991, Feb. 4 Litho. *Perf. 13***

**216** A68 3.70k Plantago lanceolata 1.00 1.00
**217** A68 4k Rumex longifolius 1.20 1.20
**218** A68 4.50k Amara aulica 1.50 1.50
**219** A68 6.50k Lumbricus terrestris 2.00 2.00
*Nos. 216-219 (4)* 5.70 5.70

Europa — A69

Designs: 3.70k, Weather satellite. 6.50k, Celestial navigation.

**1991, Apr. 4 Litho. *Perf. 13***

**220** A69 3.70k multicolored *1.00 1.00*
**221** A69 6.50k multicolored *1.75 1.75*

Town of Torshavn, 125th Anniv. — A70

**1991, Apr. 4 *Perf. 14x13½***

**222** A70 3.70k Town Hall 1.25 1.25
**223** A70 3.70k View of town 1.25 1.25

Birds — A71

**1991, June 3 Litho. *Perf. 13½***

**224** A71 3.70k Rissa tridactyla 1.20 1.20
**225** A71 3.70k Sterna paradisaea 1.20 1.20
*a.* Bklt. pane, 3 each #224-225 9.00

Village of Saksun A72

**1991, June 3**

**226** A72 370o shown 1.00 1.00
**227** A72 650o Cliffs of Vestmanna 1.75 1.75

Samal Joensen-Mikines (1906-1979), Painter — A73

**1991, Oct. 7 Litho. *Perf. 13½***

**228** A73 340o Funeral Procession 1.00 1.00
**229** A73 370o The Farewell 1.10 1.10
**230** A73 550o Handanagarthur 1.60 1.60
**231** A73 1300o Winter morning 3.75 3.75
*Nos. 228-231 (4)* 7.45 7.45

Mail Boats A74

**1992, Feb. 10 Litho. *Perf. 13½x14***

**232** A74 200o Ruth .70 .70
**233** A74 370o Ritan 1.00 1.00
**234** A74 550o Sigmundur 1.50 1.50
**235** A74 800o Masin 2.50 2.50
*Nos. 232-235 (4)* 5.70 5.70

Europa A75

Designs: 3.70k, Map of North Atlantic, Viking ship. 6.50k, Map of Central Atlantic region, one of Columbus' ships.

**1992, Apr. 6 Litho. *Perf. 13½x14***

**236** A75 3.70k multicolored *1.10 1.10*
**237** A75 6.50k multicolored *2.00 2.00*

**Souvenir Sheet**

**238** A75 Sheet of 2, #236-237 *8.50 8.50*

First landing in the Americas by Leif Erikson (No. 236). Discovery of America by Christopher Columbus, 500th anniv. (No. 237).

Seals A76

**1992, June 9 Litho. *Perf. 14x13½***

**239** A76 3.70k Halichoerus grypus 1.40 1.40
**240** A76 3.70k Phoca vitulina 1.40 1.40
*a.* Bklt. pane, 3 #239, 3 #240 *17.50*

Minerals — A77

**1992, June 9 Photo. *Perf. 12***
**Granite Paper**

**241** A77 370o Stilbite 1.25 1.25
**242** A77 650o Mesolite 2.25 2.25

Traditional Houses A78

**1992, Oct. 5 Litho. *Perf. 13½***

**243** A78 3.40k Hja Glyvra Hanusi 1.00 1.00
**244** A78 3.70k I Nordragotu 1.10 1.10
**245** A78 6.50k Blasastova 2.00 2.00
**246** A78 8k Jakupsstova 2.40 2.40
*Nos. 243-246 (4)* 6.50 6.50

Nordic House Entertainers — A79

**1993, Feb. 8 Litho. *Perf. 13½***

**247** A79 400o Dancers 1.10 1.10
**248** A79 400o Pianist 1.10 1.10
**249** A79 400o Trio 1.10 1.10
*a.* Souv. sheet, #247-249, perf 12½ 4.00 4.00
*Nos. 247-249 (3)* 3.30 3.30

Village of Gjogv A80

**1993, Apr. 5**

**250** A80 4k View toward sea 1.50 1.50
**251** A80 4k Ravine, village 1.50 1.50
*a.* Booklet pane, 3 each #250-251 9.00

Europa — A81

Sculptures by Hans Pauli Olsen: 4k, Movement. 7k, Reflection.

**1993, Apr. 5**

**252** A81 4k multicolored *1.50 1.50*
**253** A81 7k multicolored *2.00 2.00*

Horses — A82

*Perf. 13½x13, 13x13½*

**1993, June 7** **Engr.**
254 A82 400o shown 1.10 1.10
255 A82 20k Mare, foal, horiz. 5.50 5.50

Butterflies A83

**1993, Oct. 4** **Litho.** ***Perf. 14½***
256 A83 350o Apamea zeta 1.10 1.10
257 A83 400o Hepialus humuli 1.25 1.25
258 A83 700o Vanessa atalanta 2.10 2.10
259 A83 900o Perizoma albulata 2.75 2.75
*Nos. 256-259 (4)* 7.20 7.20

Fish — A84

**1994, Feb. 7** **Litho.** ***Perf. 14½***
260 A84 10o Gasterosteus aculeatus .25 .25
261 A84 4k Neocyttus helgae 1.25 1.25
262 A84 7k Salmo trutta fario 2.25 2.25
263 A84 10k Hoplostethus atlanticus 3.00 3.00
*Nos. 260-263 (4)* 6.75 6.75

Voyages of St. Brendan (484-577) A85

Europa: 4k, St. Brendan on island with sheep, Irish monks in boat. 7k, St. Brendan, monks sailing past volcano.

**1994, Apr. 18** **Litho.** ***Perf. 14½x14***
264 A85 4k multicolored *1.25 1.25*
265 A85 7k multicolored *2.40 2.00*
a. Miniature sheet of 2, #264-265 *4.50 4.50*

Nos. 264-265 have designers name below the design. Stamps in No. 265a do not.
See Iceland Nos. 780-781; Ireland Nos. 923-924.

Sheepdogs — A86

Design: No. 267, Dog watching over sheep.

**1994, June 6** **Litho.** ***Perf. 13½***
266 A86 4k multicolored 1.40 1.40

**Size: 39x25mm**

267 A86 4k multicolored 1.40 1.40
a. Booklet pane, 3 each #266-267 8.50
Complete booklet, #267a 9.50

School of Navigation A87

Designs: 3.50k, Man using sextant, schooner. 7k, Ship, man at computer.

**1994, June 6**
268 A87 3.50k multicolored 1.00 1.00
269 A87 7k multicolored 2.50 2.50

Brusajokil's Lay — A88

Scenes, verses of the ballad: 1k, Ship at sea. 4k, Asbjorn entering Brusajokil's cave. 6k, Ormar with cat, trolls. 7k, Ormar pulling Brusajokil's beard.

**1994, Sept. 19** **Litho.** ***Perf. 14***
270 A88 1k multicolored .35 .35
271 A88 4k multicolored 1.40 1.40
272 A88 6k multicolored 1.75 1.75
273 A88 7k multicolored 2.25 2.25
*Nos. 270-273 (4)* 5.75 5.75

Twelve Days of Christmas A89

No. 274, Goats, men, deer, hides. No. 275, Ducks, cattle, sheep, horses, banners, barrels.

**1994, Oct. 31** **Litho.** ***Perf. 14x13***
274 A89 4k multicolored 1.10 1.10
275 A89 4k multicolored 1.10 1.10
a. Bklt. pane, 3 each #274-275 7.00
Complete booklet, #275a 7.00

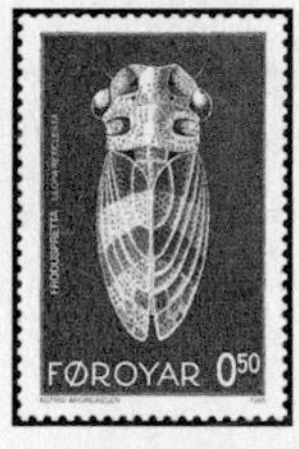
Leafhoppers — A90

Designs: 50o, Ulopa reticulata. 4k, Streptanus sordidus. 5k, Anoscopus flavostriatus. 13k, Macrosteles alpinus.

**1995, Feb. 6** **Litho.** ***Perf. 14***
276 A90 50o multicolored .25 .25
277 A90 4k multicolored 1.00 1.60
278 A90 5k multicolored 1.60 1.60
279 A90 13k multicolored 4.50 4.50
*Nos. 276-279 (4)* 7.95 7.95

Tourism A91

**1995, Apr. 10** **Litho.** ***Perf. 13½x14***
280 A91 4k Village of Famjin 1.50 1.50
281 A91 4k Vatnsdalur valley 1.50 1.50

Peace & Freedom A92

Europa: 4k, Island couple, "Vidar, vali og baldur." 7k, Couple looking toward sun, "Liv og livtrasir."

**1995, Apr. 10** ***Perf. 13x14***
282 A92 4k multicolored *1.20 1.20*
283 A92 7k multicolored *2.50 2.50*

Nordic Art — A93

Designs: 2k, Museum of Art, Torshavn. 4k, Woman, by Frimod Joensen, vert. 5.50k, Self-portrait, by Joensen, vert.

***Perf. 13½x14, 14x13½***

**1995, June 12** **Litho.**
284 A93 2k multicolored .65 .65
285 A93 4k multicolored 1.40 1.40
286 A93 5.50k multicolored 1.90 1.90
*Nos. 284-286 (3)* 3.95 3.95

Corvus Corax A94

**1995, June 12** ***Perf. 13½x14***
287 A94 4k Black raven 1.40 1.40
288 A94 4k White-speckled raven 1.40 1.40
a. Booklet pane, 5 each #287-288 14.00
Complete booklet, #288a 14.00

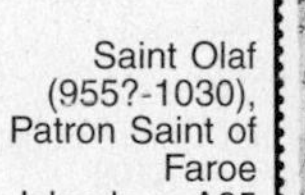
Saint Olaf (955?-1030), Patron Saint of Faroe Islands — A95

**Litho. & Engr.**

**1995, Sept. 12** ***Perf. 13½x13***
289 A95 4k multicolored 1.60 1.60

See Aland Islands No. 119.

Early Folk Life A95a

4k, Dairy maids carrying buckets. 6k, Peasants fleecing sheep. 15k, Schooners, saltfish being brought ashore, vert.

**1995, Sept. 12** **Engr.** ***Perf. 12½***
290 A95a 4k dark green 1.50 1.50
291 A95a 6k dark brn, vert. 2.25 2.25
292 A95a 15k dark blue 5.00 5.00
*Nos. 290-292 (3)* 8.75 8.75

Church of Mary Catholic Church — A96

Designs: No. 293, Stained glass window. No. 294, Exterior view of church.

**1995, Nov. 9** **Litho.** ***Perf. 13½***
293 A96 4k multicolored 1.40 1.40
294 A96 4k multicolored 1.40 1.40
a. Booklet pane, 5 ea #293-294 14.00
Complete booklet, #294a 14.00

Rocky Coastline — A97

**1996, Jan. 1** **Litho.** ***Perf. 14***
295 A97 4.50k multicolored 1.40 1.40

Seaweed — A98

4k, Ptilota plumosa. 5.50k, Fucus spiralis. 6k, Ascophyllum nodosum. 9k, Laminaria hyperborea.

**1996, Feb. 12** ***Perf. 15***
296 A98 4k multicolored 1.10 1.10
297 A98 5.50k multicolored 1.40 1.40
298 A98 6k multicolored 1.60 1.60
299 A98 9k multicolored 2.75 2.75
*Nos. 296-299 (4)* 6.85 6.85

Birds — A99

**1996, Apr. 15** **Litho.** ***Perf. 14x15***
300 A99 4.50k Laxia curvirostra 1.40 1.40
301 A99 4.50k Bombycilla garrulus 1.40 1.40
a. Booklet pane, 5 each #300-301 14.00
Complete booklet, #301a 14.00

See Nos. 313-314.

A100

Europa (Wives of Faroese Seamen): 4.50k, Woman standing beside sea coast. 7.50k, Portrait of a woman, vert.

**1996, Apr. 15** ***Perf. 15x14½, 14½x15***
302 A100 4.50k multicolored *1.50 1.50*
303 A100 7.50k multicolored *2.00 2.00*

A101

Nordatlantex '96 (Children's drawings): a, Boy playing with hoop, stick, by Bugvi. b, Two girls on steet, road sign, by Gudrid. c, Girl on bicycle, car on street, by Herborg.

**1996, June 7** **Litho.** ***Perf. 14½***

**Souvenir Sheet of 3**

304 A101 4.50k #a.-c. 3.50 3.50

A102

Sea bed off the Faroes.

**Litho. & Engr.**

**1996, June 7** *Perf. 13*

| | | | | |
|---|---|---|---|---|
| **305** | A102 | 10k violet & multi | 2.50 | 2.50 |
| **306** | A102 | 16k green & multi | 4.00 | 4.00 |

See Nos. 319-320, 343, 377-378.

Janus Kamban (b. 1913), Sculptor, Graphic Artist A103

Works of art: 4.50k, Flock of Sheep. 6.50k, Fisherman on the Way Home. 7.50k, View from Tórshavn's Old Quarter.

**1996, Sept. 16 Litho.** *Perf. 14*

| | | | | |
|---|---|---|---|---|
| **307** | A103 | 4.50k multicolored | 1.40 | 1.40 |
| **308** | A103 | 6.50k multicolored | 1.60 | 1.60 |
| **309** | A103 | 7.50k multicolored | 2.25 | 2.25 |
| | | *Nos. 307-309 (3)* | 5.25 | 5.25 |

A104

Christianschurch, Klaksvík — A105

**1996, Nov. 4 Litho.** *Perf. 14x15*

| | | | | |
|---|---|---|---|---|
| **310** | A104 | 4.50k Exterior | 1.40 | 1.40 |
| **311** | A105 | 4.50k Interior, altar fresco | 1.40 | 1.40 |
| *a.* | | Booklet pane, 6 #310, 4 #311 | 14.00 | |
| | | Complete booklet, #311a | 14.00 | |

Christmas.

Souvenir Sheet

Reign of Queen Margaret II, 25th Anniv. — A106

**1997, Jan. 14 Litho.** *Perf. 14½*

| | | | | |
|---|---|---|---|---|
| **312** | A106 | 4.50k multicolored | 1.25 | 1.25 |

**Bird Type of 1996**

**1997, Feb. 27 Litho.** *Perf. 14x15*

| | | | | |
|---|---|---|---|---|
| **313** | A99 | 4.50k Pyrrhula pyrrhula | 1.25 | 1.25 |
| **314** | A99 | 4.50k Carduelis flammea | 1.25 | 1.25 |
| *a.* | | Booklet pane, 5 each #313-314 | 12.50 | — |
| | | Complete booklet, #314a | 12.50 | |

Mushrooms — A107

Designs: 4.50k, Hygrocybe helobia. 6k, Hygrocybe chlorophana. 6.50k, Hygrocybe virginea. 7.50k, Hygrocybe psittacina.

**1997, Feb. 17** *Perf. 14½*

| | | | | |
|---|---|---|---|---|
| **315** | A107 | 4.50k multicolored | 1.10 | 1.10 |
| **316** | A107 | 6k multicolored | 1.60 | 1.60 |
| **317** | A107 | 6.50k multicolored | 1.60 | 1.60 |
| **318** | A107 | 7.50k multicolored | 2.00 | 2.00 |
| | | *Nos. 315-318 (4)* | 6.30 | 6.30 |

**Map Type of 1996**

**Litho. & Engr.**

**1997, May 20** *Perf. 13*

| | | | | |
|---|---|---|---|---|
| **319** | A102 | 11k red & multi | 2.90 | 2.90 |
| **320** | A102 | 18k claret & multi | 4.50 | 4.50 |

Europa — A108

Legends illustrated by William Heinesen: 4.50k, The Temptations of Saint Anthony. 7.50k, The Merman sitting at bottom of sea eating fish bait.

**1997, May 20 Litho.** *Perf. 14½*

| | | | | |
|---|---|---|---|---|
| **321** | A108 | 4.50k multicolored | *1.40* | *1.40* |
| **322** | A108 | 7.50k multicolored | *2.25* | *2.25* |

Kalmar Union, 600th Anniv. — A109

**1997, May 20 Engr.** *Perf. 12½*

| | | | | |
|---|---|---|---|---|
| **323** | A109 | 4.50k deep blue violet | 1.50 | 1.50 |

A110

Barbara, Film Shot in Faroe Islands (Scenes from film): 4.50k, Danish theologian Poul Aggerso arriving at Faroe Islands. 6.50k, Barbara and Poul. 7.50k, Barbara with men on boat. 9k, Barbara in row boat, sailing ship.

**1997, Sept. 15 Litho.** *Perf. 14*

| | | | | |
|---|---|---|---|---|
| **324** | A110 | 4.50k multicolored | 1.25 | 1.25 |
| **325** | A110 | 6.50k multicolored | 1.60 | 1.60 |
| **326** | A110 | 7.50k multicolored | 2.00 | 2.00 |
| **327** | A110 | 9k multicolored | 2.25 | 2.25 |
| | | *Nos. 324-327 (4)* | 7.10 | 7.10 |

A111

Hvalvik church.

**1997, Sept. 15**

| | | | | |
|---|---|---|---|---|
| **328** | A111 | 4.50k Interior | 1.25 | 1.25 |
| **329** | A111 | 4.50k Exterior | 1.25 | 1.25 |
| *a.* | | Booklet pane, 5 each #328-329 | 12.50 | — |
| | | Complete booklet, #329a | 12.50 | |

Birds — A112

**1998, Feb. 23 Litho.** *Perf. 14x14½*

| | | | | |
|---|---|---|---|---|
| **330** | A112 | 4.50k Sturnus vulgaris | 1.25 | 1.25 |
| **331** | A112 | 4.50k Turdus merula | 1.25 | 1.25 |
| *a.* | | Bklt. pane, 5 each #330-331 | 12.50 | |
| | | Complete booklet, #331a | 12.50 | |

A113

Scenes from the Sigurd poem "Brynhild's Ballad": 4.50k, King Buole, daughter Brynhild. 6.50k, Sigurd riding through wall of fire on horseback. 7.50k, Sigurd, Brynhild together. 10k, Guthrun alone leading horse.

**1998, Feb. 23** *Perf. 14*

| | | | | |
|---|---|---|---|---|
| **332** | A113 | 4.50k multicolored | 1.25 | 1.25 |
| **333** | A113 | 6.50k multicolored | 1.60 | 1.60 |
| **334** | A113 | 7.50k multicolored | 1.90 | 1.90 |
| **335** | A113 | 10k multicolored | 2.50 | 2.50 |
| | | *Nos. 332-335 (4)* | 7.25 | 7.25 |

Europa — A114

**1998, May 18 Litho.** *Perf. 14*

| | | | | |
|---|---|---|---|---|
| **336** | A114 | 4.50k Parade | *1.25* | *1.25* |
| **337** | A114 | 7.50k Processional | *1.25* | *1.25* |

Olavsoka, Natl. Festival of Faroe Islands.

A115

**1998, May 18** *Perf. 14½*

| | | | | |
|---|---|---|---|---|
| **338** | A115 | 7.50k multicolored | 1.90 | 1.90 |

UN Declaration of Human Rights, 50th anniv.

Intl. Year of the Ocean A116

Toothed whales: 4k, Lagenorhynchus acutus. 4.50k, Orcinus orca. 7k, Tursiops truncatus. 9k, Delphinapterus leucas.

**1998, May 18** *Perf. 14½x14*

| | | | | |
|---|---|---|---|---|
| **339** | A116 | 4k multicolored | 1.00 | 1.00 |
| **340** | A116 | 4.50k multicolored | 1.10 | 1.10 |
| **341** | A116 | 7k multicolored | 1.75 | 1.75 |
| **342** | A116 | 9k multicolored | 2.25 | 2.25 |
| | | *Nos. 339-342 (4)* | 6.10 | 6.10 |

**Map Type of 1996**

**Litho. & Engr.**

**1998, Sept. 14** *Perf. 13*

| | | | | |
|---|---|---|---|---|
| **343** | A102 | 14k multicolored | 3.75 | 3.75 |

Frederickschurch A117

**1998, Sept. 14 Litho.** *Perf. 14*

| | | | | |
|---|---|---|---|---|
| **344** | A117 | 4.50k Exterior, coastline | 1.25 | 1.25 |
| **345** | A117 | 4.50k Interior | 1.25 | 1.25 |
| *a.* | | Bklt. pane, 5 each #344-345 | 12.50 | |
| | | Complete booklet, #345a | 12.50 | |

A118

Paintings by Hans Hansen (1920-70): 4.50k, Fell-field, 1966. 5.50k, Village Interior, 1965. 6.50k, Portrait of Farmer Ólavur í Utistovu from Mikladalur, 1968. 8k, Self-portrait, 1968.

***Perf. 13½x14, 14x13½***

**1998, Sept. 14**

| | | | | |
|---|---|---|---|---|
| **346** | A118 | 4.50k multi | 1.25 | 1.25 |
| **347** | A118 | 5.50k multi | 1.50 | 1.50 |
| **348** | A118 | 6.50k multi, vert. | 1.60 | 1.60 |
| **349** | A118 | 8k multi, vert. | 2.25 | 2.25 |
| | | *Nos. 346-349 (4)* | 6.60 | 6.60 |

Birds — A119

**1999, Feb. 22 Litho.** *Perf. 13½*

| | | | | |
|---|---|---|---|---|
| **350** | A119 | 4.50k Passer domesticus | 1.25 | 1.25 |
| **351** | A119 | 4.50k Troglodytes troglodytes | 1.25 | 1.25 |
| *a.* | | Bklt. pane, 5 each #350-351 | 12.50 | |
| | | Complete booklet, #351a | 12.50 | |

Ships Named "Smyril" A120

**1999, Feb. 22** *Perf. 14½x14*

| | | | | |
|---|---|---|---|---|
| **352** | A120 | 4.50k 1895 | 1.25 | 1.25 |
| **353** | A120 | 5k 1932 | 1.40 | 1.40 |
| **354** | A120 | 8k 1967 | 2.25 | 2.25 |
| **355** | A120 | 13k 1975 | 3.50 | 3.50 |
| | | *Nos. 352-355 (4)* | 8.40 | 8.40 |

Northern Islands A121

**1999, May 25 Litho.** *Perf. 13½*

| | | | | |
|---|---|---|---|---|
| **356** | A121 | 50o Kalsoy | .25 | .25 |
| **357** | A121 | 100o Vithoy | .25 | .25 |
| **358** | A121 | 400o Svinoy | 1.10 | 1.10 |
| **359** | A121 | 450o Fugloy | 1.25 | 1.25 |

360 A121 600o Kunoy 1.60 1.60
361 A121 800o Borthoy 2.10 2.10
*Nos. 356-361 (6)* 6.55 6.55

See Nos. 383-386.

Waterfalls — A122

Europa: 6k, Svartifossur. 8k, Foldarafossur.

**1999, May 25** *Perf. 14x14½*
362 A122 6k multicolored *1.60 1.60*
363 A122 8k multicolored *2.25 2.25*

Abstract Paintings of Ingálvur av Reyni — A123

**1999, Sept. 27 Litho.** *Perf. 12½*
364 A123 4.50k Bygd 1.25 1.25
365 A123 6k Húsavík 1.60 1.60
366 A123 8k Roytt regn 2.10 2.10
367 A123 20k Genta 5.25 5.25
*Nos. 364-367 (4)* 10.20 10.20

Bible Stories — A124

**1999, Sept. 27** *Perf. 14½x14*
368 A124 450o John 1:1-5 1.25 1.25
a. Booklet pane of 6 7.50
Complete booklet, #368a 7.50
369 A124 600o Luke 1:26-28 1.60 1.60
a. Booklet pane of 6 10.00
Complete booklet, #369a 10.00

See Nos. 387-388, 407-408.

A125

Christianity in the Faroes, 1000th Anniv.: 4.50k, Man on rocks in ocean. 5.50k, Monk with cross, man with sword. 8k, People, flags. 16k, Cross in sky.

*Perf. 13½x13¼*
**2000, Feb. 21** **Litho.**
370 A125 4.50k multi 1.25 1.25
371 A125 5.50k multi 1.40 1.40
372 A125 8k multi 2.10 2.10
373 A125 16k multi 4.25 4.25
*Nos. 370-373 (4)* 9.00 9.00

A126

School and: No. 374, Sanna av Skarthi, Anna Suffia Rasmussen, wives of founders. No. 375, Rasmus Rasmussen (1871-1962), Símun av Skarthi (1872-1942), school founders.

**2000, Feb. 21**
374 A126 4.50k multi 1.25 1.25
375 A126 4.50k multi 1.25 1.25
a. Bklt. pane, 4 ea #374-375 10.00
Complete booklet, #375a 10.00

Faroese Folk High School, cent.

**Europa, 2000**
Common Design Type

**2000, May 9 Litho.** *Perf. 13¼x13*
376 CD17 8k multi *2.40 2.40*

**Map Type of 1996**
**Litho. & Engr.**

**2000, May 22** *Perf. 13¼x13*
377 A102 15k multi 3.75 3.75
378 A102 22k multi 5.75 5.75

Stampin' The Future Children's Stamp Design Contest Winners A127

Art by: 4k, Katrin Mortensen. 4.50k, Sigga Andreassen. 6k, Steingrímur Joensen. 8k, Dion Dam Frandsen.

**2000, May 22 Litho.** *Perf. 13x13¼*
379 A127 4k multi 1.10 1.10
380 A127 4.50k multi 1.25 1.25
381 A127 6k multi 1.60 1.60
382 A127 8k multi 2.25 2.25
*Nos. 379-382 (4)* 6.20 6.20

**Island Type of 1999**

**2000, Sept. 18 Litho.** *Perf. 13½*
383 A121 200o Skúvoy .65 .65
384 A121 650o Hestoy 1.60 1.60
385 A121 750o Koltur 1.90 1.90
386 A121 1000o Nólsoy 2.50 2.50
*Nos. 383-386 (4)* 6.65 6.65

**Bible Story Type of 1999**

**2000, Sept. 18 Litho.** *Perf. 13x13¼*
387 A124 4.50k Micah 5:1 1.25 1.25
a. Booklet pane of 6 7.50
Booklet, #387a 7.50
388 A124 6k John 1:14 1.60 1.60
a. Booklet pane of 6 10.00
Booklet, #388a 10.00

**Pew Gables Type of 1980**

Kirkjubour pew gables: 430o, St. Andrew with cross. 650o, St. Bartholomew. 800o, Unknown apostle. 18k, Unknown apostle, diff.

**Photo. & Engr.**

**2001, Feb. 12** *Perf. 12¾x12½*
389 A20 450o multi 1.25 1.25
390 A20 650o multi 1.60 1.60
391 A20 800o multi 2.10 2.10
392 A20 18k multi 4.50 4.50
*Nos. 389-392 (4)* 9.45 9.45

Faroese Red Cross, 75th Anniv. A128

Designs: 4.50k, Old person. 6k, Relief worker.

**2001, Feb. 12 Litho.** *Perf. 14½x14*
393 A128 4.50k multi 1.25 1.25
a. Booklet pane of 6 7.50
Booklet, #393a 7.50
394 A128 6k multi 1.60 1.60
a. Booklet pane of 6 10.00
Booklet, #394a 10.00

Souvenir Sheet

Faroe Islands Postal Service, 25th Anniv. — A129

No. 395: a, Boat for interisland mail transport, 19th cent. b, Tórshavn post office, 1906. c, Simon Pauli Poulsen (Morkabóndin), mail carrier.

**Photo. & Engr.**

**2001, Apr. 1** *Perf. 13x13¼*
395 A129 4.50k Sheet of 3, #a-c 5.00 5.00

Nordic Myths and Legends About Light and Darkness — A130

No. 396: a, The Death of Hogni. b, The Tree of the Year. c, The Harp. d, Gram and Grane. e, The Ballad of Nornagest. f, Gudrun's Evil Magic.

**Litho. with Foil Application**

**2001, Apr. 1** *Perf. 13½x13¼*
396 A130 6k Sheet of 6, #a-f 10.00 10.00

Hafnia 2001 Philatelic Exhibition, Copenhagen.

Paintings by Zacharias Heinesen A131

Designs: 4k, The Artist's Mother, 1992. 4.50k, Uti á Reyni, 1974. 10k, Ur Vágunum, 2000. 15k, Sunrise, 1975.

**2001, June 11 Litho.** *Perf. 13¼x13*
397 A131 4k multi 1.10 1.10
398 A131 4.50k multi 1.25 1.25
399 A131 10k multi 2.75 2.75
400 A131 15k multi 4.00 4.00
*Nos. 397-400 (4)* 9.10 9.10

Europa A132

Hydroelectric power stations: 6k, Fossáverkith. 8k, Eithisverkith.

**2001, June 11** *Perf. 13x13½*
401 A132 6k multi *1.60 1.60*
402 A132 8k multi *2.25 2.25*

Whales — A133

Designs: 4.50k, Physeter macrocephalus. 6.50k, Balaenoptera physalus. 9k, Balaenoptera musculus. 20k, Balaenoptera borealis.

*Perf. 13¾x13¼*
**2001, Sept. 17** **Litho.**
403 A133 4.50k multi 1.25 1.25
404 A133 6.50k multi 1.60 1.60
405 A133 9k multi 2.25 2.25
406 A133 20k multi 5.50 5.50
*Nos. 403-406 (4)* 10.60 10.60

**Bible Stories Type of 1999**

**2001, Sept. 17** *Perf. 13*
407 A124 5k Luke 2:34-35 1.40 1.40
a. Booklet pane of 6 8.50 —
Booklet, #407a 8.50
408 A124 6.50k Matthew 2:18 1.60 1.60
a. Booklet pane of 6 10.00 —
Booklet, #408a 10.00

Mollusks — A134

Designs: 5k, Sepiola atlantica. 7k, Modiolus modiolus. 7.50k, Polycera faeroensis. 18k, Buccinum undatum.

**2002, Feb. 11 Litho.** *Perf. 13*
409 A134 5k multi 1.40 1.40
410 A134 7k multi 1.75 1.75
411 A134 7.50k multi 1.90 1.90
412 A134 18k multi 4.50 4.50
*Nos. 409-412 (4)* 9.55 9.55

Portions of the designs were applied by a thermographic process producing a shiny, raised effect.

Souvenir Sheet

Viking Voyages — A135

No. 413: a, Navigation tool. b, Viking sailor on boat. c, Viking boat.

**Litho. & Engr.**

**2002, Feb. 11** *Perf. 13*
413 A135 6.50k Sheet of 3, #a-c 5.00 5.00

Europa A136

Designs: 6.50k, Clowns. 8k, Various circus performers.

**2002, Apr. 8 Litho.** *Perf. 13¼x13½*
414 A136 6.50k multi *1.60 1.60*
415 A136 8k multi *2.10 2.10*

Art by Tróndur Patursson A137

Designs: 5k, Bládypi. 6.50k, Kosmiska Rúmith.

**2002, Apr. 8**

**416** A137 5k multi 1.40 1.40
**417** A137 6.50k multi 1.60 1.60
*a.* Booklet pane of 8, 4 each #416-417 13.00 —
Booklet, #417a 13.00

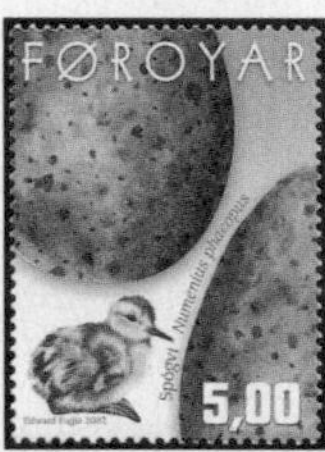
Eggs and Chicks — A138

Designs: 5k, Numenius phaeopus. 7.50k, Gallinago gallinago. 12k, Haematopus ostralegus. 20k, Pluvialis apricaria.

**2002, June 17** *Perf. 14x14½*

**418** A138 5k multi 1.40 1.40
**419** A138 7.50k multi 1.90 1.90
**420** A138 12k multi 3.00 3.00
**421** A138 20k multi 5.25 5.25
*Nos. 418-421 (4)* 11.55 11.55

Souvenir Sheet

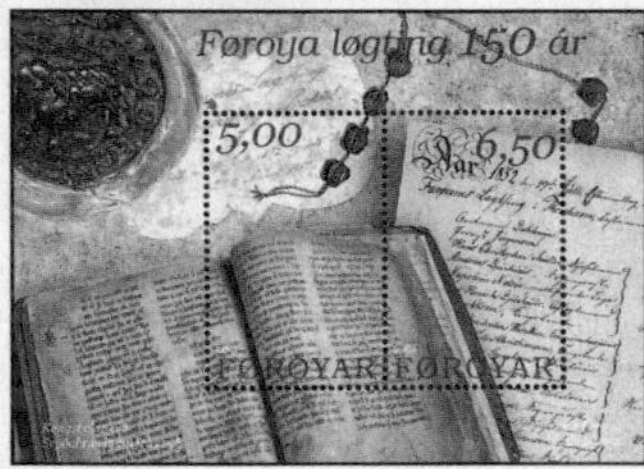
Faroese Representative Council, 150th Anniv. — A139

Designs: 5k, Royal book and seal. 6.50k, Royal book, Protocol of 1852.

**2002, June 17** *Perf. 14*

**422** A139 Sheet of 2, #a-b 4.00 4.00

Falco Columbarius Subaesalon — A140

**Litho. & Embossed**

**2002, Sept. 23** *Perf. 13¼*

**423** A140 30k multi 8.25 8.25

Gota Church — A141

**2002, Sept. 23 Litho.** *Perf. 12½*

**424** A141 5k Exterior 1.40 1.40
**425** A141 6.50k Interior 1.60 1.60
*a.* Booklet pane, 5 each #424-425 15.00 —
Booklet, #425a 15.00

Souvenir Sheet

Intl. Council for the Exploration of the Sea, Cent. — A142

No. 426: a, Micromesistius poutassou and island. b, Exploration ship Magnus Heinason and fish.

**Litho. & Engr.**

**2002, Sept. 23** *Perf. 13*

**426** A142 8k Sheet of 2, #a-b 4.50 4.50

See Denmark Nos. 1237-1238, Greenland Nos. 401-402.

Opening of Vagár-Streymoy Tunnel, Nov. 2002 — A143

Designs: No. 427, Wheeled tunneling machine at right. No. 428, Workers in red uniforms at left.

**2003, Feb. 24 Litho.** *Perf. 13¼x13*

**427** A143 5k multi 1.40 1.40
**428** A143 5k multi 1.40 1.40
*a.* Booklet pane, 5 each #427-428 14.00 —
Complete booklet, #428a 14.00

Voluspá, Ancient Norse Poem — A144

No. 429: a, Seeress Heid holding staff. b, Heid sees animal and man in vision. c, Nude man and woman. d, Scribe and horseman. e, Battle between group with swords and man with hammer. f, Horseman and warriors. g, Men, large sword. h, Longboat. i, Attack on man holding spear, fire. j, Two figures with staffs, winged serpent.

**2003, Feb. 24** *Perf. 14*

**429** A144 Sheet of 10 17.50 17.50
*a.-j.* 6.50k Any single 1.60 1.60

Europa — A145

Poster art for Nordic House: 6.50k, Fish Tree, by Astrid Andreasen, 1991. 8k, Ceramics by Guthrith Poulsen, 1997.

**2003, Apr. 14** *Perf. 13½x13¼*

**430** A145 6.50k multi *1.60 1.60*
**431** A145 8k multi *2.10 2.10*

Children's Songs — A146

No. 432: a, Woman playing hopscotch (26x44mm). b, Boy on rocks, moon (26x44mm). c, Girl with missing teeth (26x26mm). d, Boy with toy sailboat (26x26mm). e, Cat, horse and girl (26x26mm). f, Butterfly and fly (26x26mm). g, Girl in bed, boy with stars (44x26mm). h, Cat on stairs, mouse (26x36mm). i, Man playing drums (26x26mm). j, King and queen in longboat (44x26mm).

***Perf. 13¼, 13¼x13¼x13¼x14 (#432g, 432j), 13¼x14 (#432h)***

**2003, Apr. 14**

**432** A146 Sheet of 10 14.00 14.00
*a.-j.* 5k Any single 1.25 1.25

Small Towns A147

**2003, June 10 Litho.** *Perf. 13x13¼*

**433** A147 5k Bour 1.40 1.40
**434** A147 5k Gásadalur 1.40 1.40

Communities With Post Offices 100 Years Old — A148

No. 435: a, Fuglafjorthur. b, Strendur. c, Sandur. d, Eithi. e, Vestmanna. f, Vágur. g, Mithvágur. h, Hvalba.

**2003, June 10** *Perf. 13¼x13*

**435** A148 Sheet of 8 11.00 11.00
*a.-h.* 5k Any single 1.25 1.25

Theologians — A149

Designs: 5k, Jesper Rasmussen Brochmand (1585-1652). 6.50k, Thomas Kingo (1634-1703).

**2003, Sept. 22** *Perf. 13x13¼*

**436** A149 5k multi 1.40 1.40
**437** A149 6.50k multi 1.60 1.60
*a.* Booklet pane, 5 each #436-437 15.00 —
Complete booklet, #437a 15.00

Souvenir Sheet

Dancing in the Inn's Smoking Room, by Emil Krause — A150

**Litho. & Engr.**

**2003, Sept. 22** *Perf. 12¼*

**438** A150 25k multi 7.50 7.50

100th Faroese stamp engraved by Czeslaw Slania.

**Islands Type of 1999**

**2004, Jan. 26 Litho.** *Perf. 13½*

**439** A121 550o Stóra Dímun 1.40 1.40
**440** A121 700o Lítla Dímun 1.90 1.90

Suthuroy Island — A151

No. 441: a, Sigmundargjogv, Sandvik. b, Fiskieithi, Hvalba. c, A Hamri, Frothba. d, Tjaldavíkshólmur, Oravík. e, Fossurin Stóri, Fámjin. f, Hovsfjorthur, Hov. g, I Eystrum, Porkeri. h, A Okrum. i, I Horg, Sumba. j, I Akrabergi.

**2004, Jan. 26** *Perf. 13x13¼*

**441** A151 5k Sheet of 10, #a-j 14.00 14.00

1854 Cruise of Yacht "Maria" — A152

No. 442: a, Gáshólmur and Tindhólmur. b, Framvith "Diamantunum." c, Hús av tí betra slagnum. d, Mylingur sunnanífrá. e, Mylingur northanífrá. f, Kalsoyggin northanífrá. g, Raetha teir infoddu. h, Sunnari endi av Kunoynni.

**2004, Mar. 26 Litho.** *Perf. 13*

**442** A152 6.50k Sheet of 8, #a.-h. 14.00 14.00

Souvenir Sheet

Norse Gods — A153

No. 443: a, Thor, in boat, fighting Midgard serpent. b, Ran in fishing net.

**2004, Mar. 26**

**443** A153 6.50k Sheet of 2, #a.-b. 4.50 4.50

Souvenir Sheet

Wedding of Crown Prince Frederik and Mary Donaldson — A154

**Litho. & Photo.**

**2004, May 14** *Perf. 13¼*

**444** A154 Sheet of 2 + central label 4.00 4.00
*a.* 5k Couple facing right 1.60 1.60
*b.* 6.50k Couple facing left 2.25 2.25

Soccer Organization Centenaries A155

Soccer players and emblems of: 5k, Klaksvík and Tórshavn teams. 6.50k, FIFA (Fédération Internationale de Football Association).

**2004, May 24 Litho.** *Perf. 13¼x13*

**445** A155 5k multi 1.40 1.40
**446** A155 6.50k multi 1.60 1.60
*a.* Booklet pane, 4 each #445-446 12.00 —
Complete booklet, #446a 12.00

Europa A156

Designs: 6.50k, Tourists in gorge, Hestur. 8k, Tourists at shore, Stóra Dímun.

**2004, May 24** *Perf. 13x13¼*

**447** A156 6.50k multi *1.60 1.60*
**448** A156 8k multi *2.25 2.25*

Churches A157

**2004, Sept. 20 Litho.** *Perf. 13¼x13*

**449** A157 5.50k Vágur 1.40 1.40
**450** A157 7.50k Tvoroyri 2.00 2.00
*a.* Booklet pane, 4 each #449-450 14.00 —
Complete booklet, #450a 14.00

Poems by Janus Djurhuus (1881-1948) — A158

No. 451: a, Atlantis. b, Grímur Kamban. c, Gandkvaethi Tróndar. d, Til Foroya I-III. e, Mín sorg. f, Loki. g, I búri og Slatur. h, Heimferth Nólsoyar Páls. i, Móses á Sinai fjalli. j, Cello.

**2004, Sept. 20** *Perf. 13*

**451** A158 Sheet of 10 20.00 20.00
*a.-j.* 7.50k Any single 2.00 2.00

Souvenir Sheet

Life of the Vikings — A159

No. 452: a, Men tending sheep. b, Men with farm implements. c, Women weaving and woman milking cow.

**Litho. & Engr.**

**2005, Feb. 7** *Perf. 13*

**452** A159 Sheet of 3 6.00 6.00
*a.-c.* 7.50k Any single 2.00 2.00

Miniature Sheet

Vágar Island — A160

No. 453: a, Víkar. b, Gásadalur. c, Bour. d, Slaettanes. e, Kvígandalsá. f, Sorvágur. g, Sandavágur. h, Vatnsoyrar. i, Fjallavatn. j, Mithvágur.

**2005, Feb. 7 Litho.** *Perf. 13x13¼*

**453** A160 Sheet of 10 15.00 15.00
*a.-j.* 5.50k Any single 1.50 1.50

Lepus Timidus — A161

**2005, Apr. 18** *Perf. 13¼x13½*

**454** A161 5.50k shown 1.60 1.60
**455** A161 5.50k Brown fur 1.60 1.60
*a.* Booklet pane, 4 each #454-455 13.00 —
Complete booklet, #455a 13.00

Europa — A162

Various traditional foods with: 7.50k, Brown panel. 10k, Green panel.

**2005, Apr. 18** *Perf. 13¼x13*

**456** A162 7.50k multi *2.00 2.00*
**457** A162 10k multi *2.75 2.75*

Worldwide Fund for Nature (WWF) A163

Petrels: 8.50k, Oceanodroma leucorhoa. 9k, Hydrobates pelagicus. 12k, Oceanodroma leucorhoa on ground. 20k, Hydrobates pelagicus on ground.

**2005, June 6** *Perf. 13*

**458** A163 8.50k multi 1.60 1.60
**459** A163 9k multi 2.75 2.75
**460** A163 12k multi 3.25 3.25
**461** A163 20k multi 5.50 5.50
*Nos. 458-461 (4)* 13.10 13.10

Miniature Sheet

Landscapes by Jógvan Waagstein (1879-1949) — A164

No. 462: a, Path and wall at LL, denomination in red, year date in black in grass. b, Path and wall at LL, denomination in white, year date in black on wall. c, Stone hut at left, denomination in red, year date in black. d, Path at right, denomination in red, year date in black. e, Two large rocks at right, denomination in red, year date in black. f, Rocks at LL, denomination in red, year date in white. g, Path at center, denomination in white, year date in black on path. h, Buildings at LL, denomination in red, year date in black in path. i, Churches, denomination in white, year date in black in water.

**2005, Sept. 19 Litho.** *Perf. 14x14¼*

**462** A164 Sheet of 9 17.00 17.00
*a.-i.* 7.50k Any single 1.90 1.90

End of British Occupation In World War II, 60th Anniv. A165

Soldiers with: 5.50k, Arms. 9k, Children.

**2005, Sept. 19** *Perf. 14*

**463** A165 5.50k blue & blk 1.40 1.40
**464** A165 9k yel & blk 2.40 2.40

Christmas — A166

Ballads: 5.50k, Jólavísan. 7.50k, Rudisar Vísa.

**2005, Nov. 7** *Perf. 13½x13¼*

**465** A166 5.50k multi 1.40 1.40
**466** A166 7.50k multi 2.00 2.00
*a.* Booklet pane, 5 each #465-466 17.00 —
Complete booklet, #466a 17.00

Villages A167

**2006, Feb. 13 Litho.** *Perf. 13¾*

**467** A167 7k Sythrugota 1.90 1.90
**468** A167 12k Fuglafjorthur 2.50 2.50
**469** A167 20k Leirvík 5.00 5.00
*Nos. 467-469 (3)* 9.40 9.40

Miniature Sheet

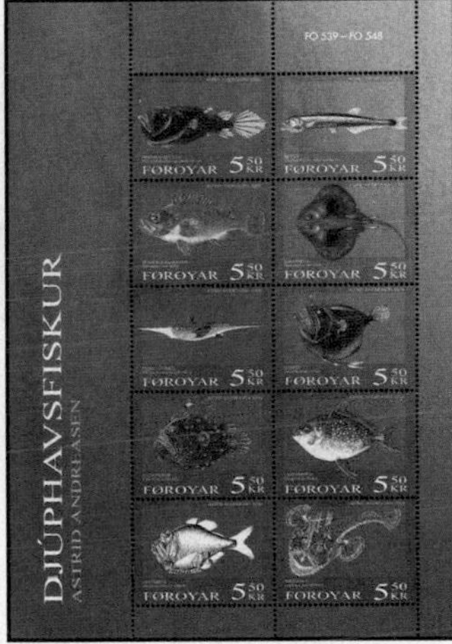


Fish — A168

No. 470: a, Himantolophus groenlandicus. b, Gonostoma elongatum. c, Sebastes mentella. d, Neoraja caerulea. e, Rhinochimaera atlantica. f, Linophryne lucifer. g, Ceratias holboelli. h, Lampris guttatus. i, Argyropelecus olfersi. j, Lophius piscatorius.

**2006, Feb. 13** *Perf. 14*

**470** A168 Sheet of 10 15.00 15.00
*a.-j.* 5.50k Any single 1.40 1.40

Souvenir Sheet

Norse Folklore — A169

No. 471: a, Norns surrounding sleeping child. b, Sea ghost.

**2006, Mar. 29** *Perf. 13*

**471** A169 7.50k Sheet of 2, #a-b 4.00 4.00

Miniature Sheet

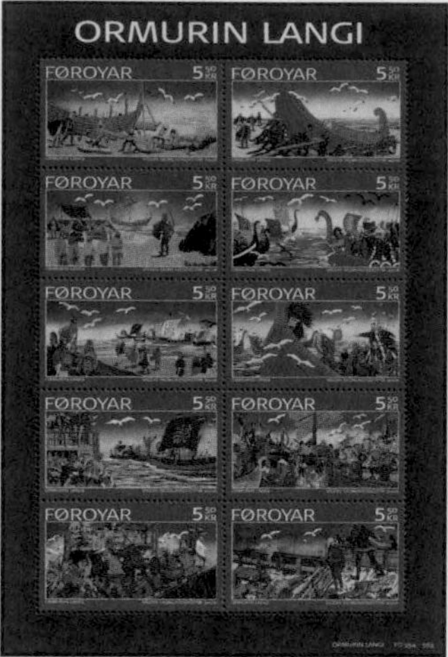


Ballad of the Long Serpent, by Jens Christian Djurhuus — A170

No. 472: a, Building of ship. b, Launch of ship. c, King on throne. d, King's fleet at sea (brown ship at LL, blue ship at LR). e, King and sailors on shore. f, King pointing. g, Ship with red sail at R. h, Battle scene (injured men falling into water). i, Battle scene (men with shields jumping from ship to ship). j, Dead men on ship's deck.

**2006, Mar. 29** ***Perf. 13¼x13***
**472** A170 Sheet of 10 15.00 15.00
*a.-j.* 5.50k Any single 1.40 1.40

Opening of Northoy Tunnel — A171

Tunnel and: No. 473, Fish. No. 474, Canoe.

**2006, June 12** ***Perf. 13¼***
**473** A171 5.50k multi 1.40 1.40
**474** A171 5.50k multi 1.40 1.40
*a.* Booklet pane, 4 each #473-474 11.00 —
Complete booklet, #474a 11.00

Europa A172

**2006, June 12** ***Perf. 13¾***
**475** A172 7.50k shown 2.00 2.00
**476** A172 10k Hands, diff. 2.75 2.75

Miniature Sheet

Sandoy Island — A173

No. 477: a, Sunnan fyri Skopun. b, Dalur. c, Soltuvík. d, Skálavík. e, Skopun. f, Sandur. g, Skarvanes. h, Húsavík.

**2006, Sept. 18 Litho.** ***Perf. 13x13¼***
**477** A173 Sheet of 8 16.00 16.00
*a.-h.* 7.50k Any single 2.00 2.00

Sandur Church A174

Designs: 5.50k, Building exterior, steeple cross. 7.50k, Interior.

**2006, Sept. 18** ***Perf. 14***
**478** A174 5.50k multi 1.40 1.40
**479** A174 7.50k multi 2.00 2.00
*a.* Booklet pane, 4 each #478-479 14.00 —
Complete booklet, #479a 14.00

Wave Energy A175

**2007, Feb. 12 Litho.** ***Perf. 12½x13***
**480** A175 7.50k multi 2.00 2.00

Art From 1838 La Recherche Expedition A176

Art by Barthélemy Lauvergne: 5.50k, La Recherche off Nólsoy. 7.50k, Skaelingsfjall.

**2007, Feb. 12**
**481** A176 5.50k multi 1.40 1.40
**482** A176 7.50k multi 2.00 2.00
*a.* Booklet pane, 4 each #481-482 12.00 —
Complete booklet, #482a 12.00

Miniature Sheet

Legend of the Seal Woman — A177

No. 483: a, Man, head of white seal. b, Woman and seals in ring. c, Man, nude woman, seals. d, Man and nude woman seated on chest. e, Ship and two seals. f, Children, seal woman nursing child. g, Seal woman and man. h, Sleeping man and seal woman with hands open. i, Man and dead seals. j, Seal woman.

**2007, Feb. 12** ***Perf. 14***
**483** A177 Sheet of 10 15.00 15.00
*a.-j.* 5.50k Any single 1.50 1.50

Miniature Sheet

The Old Man and His Sons, Novel by Hethin Brú — A178

No. 484: a, Ketil cutting whale's throat. b, Men carrying injured Klávus on log. c, Kálvur and fiancee, Klávusardóttir with pot and kettle. d, Ketil and Kálvur in fishing boat. e, Ketil's wife arguing with daughter-in-law. f, Ketil catching flying northern fulmars. g, Kálvur and stone fence. h, Ketil, Kálvur and cow.

**2007, Apr. 10 Litho.** ***Perf. 13x12½***
**484** A178 Sheet of 8 16.00 16.00
*a.-h.* 7.50k Any single 2.00 2.00

Europa — A179

Design: 5.50k, Scout holding bird. 10k, Tent.

**2007, Apr. 10**
**485** A179 5.50k multi 1.40 1.40
**486** A179 10k multi 2.75 2.75

Scouting, cent.

Souvenir Sheet

Bible Translators — A180

No. 487: a, Jákup Dahl (1878-1944). b, Kristian O. Videro (1906-91). c, Victor Danielsen (1894-1961).

**2007, June 11 Litho.** ***Perf. 13x12½***
**487** A180 Sheet of 3 5.00 5.00
*a.-c.* 5.50k Any single 1.60 1.60

Domesticated Birds — A181

Designs: 9k, Chickens and rooster. 20k, Ducks. 25k, Geese.

**2007, June 11** ***Perf. 12½x13***
**488** A181 9k multi 2.40 2.40
**489** A181 20k multi 5.00 5.00
**490** A181 25k multi 6.50 6.50
*Nos. 488-490 (3)* 13.90 13.90

Hoyvík — A182

**2007, Oct. 1** ***Perf. 13½***
**491** A182 7.50k multi 2.00 2.00

Wooden Religious Statues of Kirkjubour Cathedral — A183

**2007, Oct. 1** ***Perf. 13x12½***
**492** A183 5.50k Jesus 1.40 1.40
**493** A183 7.50k Mary 2.00 2.00
*a.* Booklet pane, 4 each #492-493 14.00 —
Complete booklet, #493a 14.00

Miniature Sheet

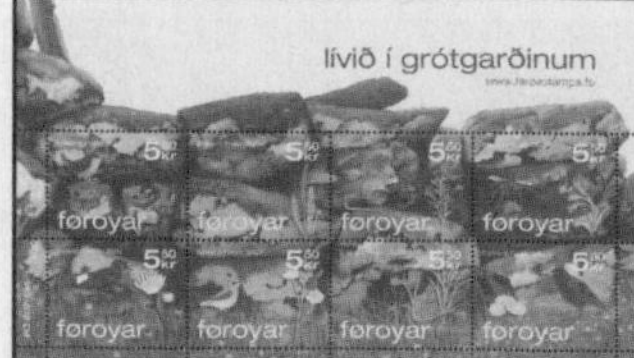


Stone Fence and Wildlife — A184

No. 494: a, Bird, worm. b, Two red beetles, fern. c, Mouse, purple flowers. d, Mosquito, pink flowers. e, Large black and white bird, dandelions. f, Bird with black wings, buttercups. g, Earwigs, grass. h, Bird and eggs.

**2007, Oct. 1** ***Perf. 13½x14¼***
**494** A184 Sheet of 8 12.00 12.00
*a.-h.* 5.50k Any single 1.40 1.40

Klaksvík, Cent. — A185

**Litho. & Embossed**

**2008, Feb. 11** ***Perf. 14***
**495** A185 5.50k multi 1.40 1.40

Tinganes A186

**2008, Feb. 11 Litho.** ***Perf. 13¼***
**496** A186 14k multi 3.50 3.50

Hoydalar Tuberculosis Sanatorium, Cent. — A187

Lungs and: 5.50k, Patients, buildings. 9k, Dr. Vilhelm Magnussen examining patient, child.

**2007, Feb. 11** ***Perf. 12½x13***
**497** A187 5.50k multi 1.40 1.40
**498** A187 9k multi 2.50 2.50
*a.* Booklet pane, 4 each #497-498 16.00
Complete booklet, #498a 16.00

Miniature Sheet

Prints by Elinborg Lützens — A188

No. 499: a, Houses below mountain. b, Milk maids (30x30mm). c, Houses. d, Underwater scene. e, Chicken (30x30mm). f, Person and bird near wooden bucket.

**2008, Feb. 11** ***Perf. 13¼***
**499** A188 Sheet of 6 16.00 16.00
*a.-f.* 10k Any single 2.60 2.60

Souvenir Sheet

Mythical Places — A189

No. 500: a, Alvheyggur. b, Klovningasteinur.

**2008, Mar. 27 Litho.** ***Perf. 12½x13***

| | | | |
|---|---|---|---|
| **500** | A189 Sheet of 2 | 4.00 | 4.00 |
| *a.-b.* | 7.50k Either single | 2.00 | 2.00 |

Caltha Palustris A190

**2008, May 19** ***Perf. 13¼***

| | | | |
|---|---|---|---|
| **501** | A190 30k multi | 8.00 | 8.00 |

Europa A191

Designs: 550o, Heart and "Teg." 750o, Posthorn with "@" symbol and "Hey."

**2008, May 19** ***Perf. 13¼x13***

| | | | |
|---|---|---|---|
| **502** | A191 550o multi | 1.40 | 1.40 |
| **503** | A191 750o multi | 2.00 | 2.00 |

Miniature Sheet

Famous People — A192

No. 504: a, Niels Winther (1822-92), politician and newspaper publisher. b, Súsanna Helena Patursson (1864-1916), writer and newspaper publisher. c, Rasmus C. Effersoe (1857-1916), writer and newspaper editor. d, Jógvan Poulsen (1854-1941), religious and school book writer. e, Frithrikur Petersen (1853-1917), poet. f, Andreas Christian Evensen (1874-1917), magazine publisher and school book writer.

**2008, May 19** ***Perf. 13½x13¼***

| | | | |
|---|---|---|---|
| **504** | A192 Sheet of 6 | 9.00 | 9.00 |
| *a.-f.* | 5.50k Any single | 1.40 | 1.40 |

Miniature Sheet

Ferns — A193

No. 505: a, Gymnocarpium dryopteris. b, Polypodium vulgare. c, Dryopteris dilatata. d, Asplenium adiantum-nigrum. e, Athyrium filix-femina. f, Dryopteris filix-mas. g, Cystopteris fragilis. h, Phegopteris connectilis. i, Polystichum lonchitis. j, Asplenium trichomanes.

**2008, Sept. 22 Litho.** ***Perf. 13x13½***

| | | | |
|---|---|---|---|
| **505** | A193 Sheet of 10 | 25.00 | 25.00 |
| *a.-j.* | 800o Any single | 2.40 | 2.40 |

Christmas — A194

**2008, Sept. 22** ***Perf. 13x12½***

| | | | |
|---|---|---|---|
| **506** | A194 6k shown | 1.60 | 1.60 |
| **507** | A194 10k Wooden cross | 2.75 | 2.75 |
| *a.* | Booklet pane of 8, 4 each #506-507 | 17.00 | — |
| | Complete booklet, #507a | 17.00 | |

Global Warming — A195

Designs: 6k, Earth and "No entry" sign. 8k, Earth in shape of water droplet.

**2009, Feb. 23 Litho.** ***Perf. 13¾x14***

| | | | |
|---|---|---|---|
| **508** | A195 6k multi | 1.60 | 1.60 |
| **509** | A195 8k multi | 2.10 | 2.10 |
| *a.* | Souvenir sheet, #508-509 | 3.75 | 3.75 |

Portions of the designs were applied by a thermographic process producing a shiny raised effect.

Miniature Sheet

Scenes From *The Lost Musicians,* by William Heinesen — A196

No. 510: a, People, stylized harp. b, Ring of silhouetted dancers. c, Woman on roof of house, kneeling people and standing woman near house. d, Silhouetted man approaching woman on park bench. e, Women and seated cellist. f, Violinist and two silhouetted men. g, Man in bed. h, People in rowboat.

**2009, Feb. 23** ***Perf. 13½***

| | | | |
|---|---|---|---|
| **510** | A196 Sheet of 8 | 19.00 | 19.00 |
| *a.-h.* | 8k Any single | 2.25 | 2.25 |

Europa — A197

Designs: 10k, Trollhovdi Island and Saturn. 12k, Heygadrangur Island, Jupiter and one of its moons, Europa.

**2009, May 25 Litho.** ***Perf. 13x12½***

| | | | |
|---|---|---|---|
| **511** | A197 10k multi | 2.75 | 2.75 |
| **512** | A197 12k multi | 3.25 | 3.25 |

Intl. Year of Astronomy.

Miniature Sheet

Geological Formation of the Faroe Islands — A198

No. 513: a, Large volcano spewing lava, trees. b, Smaller volcano spewing ash, dead tree, lava on landscape. c, Map of area 60 million years ago. d, Map of area 15 million years ago. e, Map of Faroe Isands, map of Faroe Islands and area nearby. f, Glacier, rock pinnacles.

**2009, May 25** ***Perf. 12½x13***

| | | | |
|---|---|---|---|
| **513** | A198 Sheet of 6 | 18.00 | 18.00 |
| *a.-f.* | 10k Any single | 3.00 | 3.00 |

Thorshavn Gymnastics Club, Cent. — A199

Gymnasts: 6k, Male lifting female. 10k, Female doing handstand. 26k, Male on rings.

**2009, May 25** ***Perf. 14***

| | | | |
|---|---|---|---|
| **514** | A199 6k multi | 1.75 | 1.75 |
| **515** | A199 10k multi | 3.00 | 3.00 |
| **516** | A199 26k multi | 7.75 | 7.75 |
| | *Nos. 514-516 (3)* | 12.50 | 12.50 |

***Serpentine Die Cut 14***

**Booklet Stamps**

**Self-Adhesive**

| | | | |
|---|---|---|---|
| **517** | A199 6k multi | 2.00 | 2.00 |
| **518** | A199 10k multi | 3.00 | 3.00 |
| *a.* | Booklet pane of 8, 4 each #517-518 | 20.00 | |

Leynar — A200

**2009, Sept. 16** ***Perf. 12¾***

| | | | |
|---|---|---|---|
| **519** | A200 10k multi | 3.00 | 3.00 |

Rock Pigeons A201

Designs: 14k, Two pigeons on rocks. 36k, Head of pigeon, two pigeons in flight.

**2009. Sept. 16** ***Perf. 13***

| | | | |
|---|---|---|---|
| **520** | A201 14k multi | 4.00 | 4.00 |
| **521** | A201 36k multi | 11.00 | 11.00 |

Altarpiece at Vestmanna Church — A202

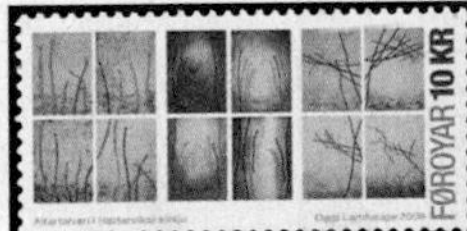


Altarpiece at Hattarvik Church A203

**2009, Sept. 16** ***Perf. 13¾x13¼***

| | | | |
|---|---|---|---|
| **522** | A202 6k multi | 1.75 | 1.75 |
| *a.* | Perf. 13¾ vert. | 1.75 | 1.75 |
| **523** | A203 10k multi | 3.25 | 3.25 |
| *a.* | Perf. 14¼x13¾ on 3 sides | 3.25 | 3.25 |
| *b.* | Booklet pane of 8, 4 each #522a, 523a | 20.00 | — |
| | Complete booklet, #523b | 20.00 | |

Christmas.

Globicephala Melas — A204

**2010, Feb. 22 Litho.** ***Perf. 14¾***

| | | | |
|---|---|---|---|
| **524** | A204 50k multi | 15.00 | 15.00 |

Marine Flora and Fauna — A205

Various photographs.

**2010, Feb. 22** ***Perf. 13¼x13½***

| | | | |
|---|---|---|---|
| **525** | A205 1k multi | .35 | .35 |
| **526** | A205 6k multi | 1.75 | 1.75 |
| **527** | A205 8k multi | 2.50 | 2.50 |
| **528** | A205 12k multi | 3.50 | 3.50 |
| | *Nos. 525-528 (4)* | 8.10 | 8.10 |

Butterflies and Moths A206

Designs: 6k, Inachis io. 8k, Vanessa cardui. 14k, Agrius convolvuli. 16k, Acherontia atropos.

**2010, Feb. 22** *Perf. 13x12¾*

**529** A206 6k multi 1.75 1.75
**530** A206 8k multi 2.50 2.50
**531** A206 14k multi 4.25 4.25
**532** A206 16k multi 5.00 5.00
*Nos. 529-532 (4)* 13.50 13.50

Souvenir Sheet

Aquaculture — A207

No. 533: a, Fish, net. b, Fisherman holding net.

*Perf. 14¼x14½*

**2010, Mar. 24** **Litho.**

**533** A207 Sheet of 2 6.00 6.00
*a.-b.* 10k Either single 3.00 3.00

Paintings by Eli Smith — A208

Various paintings.

**2010, Apr. 26** *Perf. 14½*

**534** A208 18k multi 5.50 5.50
**535** A208 24k multi 7.50 7.50

Europa A209

Scenes from children's books: 10k, A Dog, A Cat and A Mouse, by Bárthur Oskarsson. 12k, Moss Mollis's Journey, by Janus á Húsagarthi.

**2010, Apr. 26** *Perf. 13¾*

**536** A209 10k multi 3.00 3.00
**537** A209 12k multi 3.50 3.50

**Booklet Stamps**
**Self-Adhesive**
***Serpentine Die Cut 14***

**538** A209 10k multi 3.00 3.00
**539** A209 12k multi 3.50 3.50
*a.* Booklet pane of 8, 4 each #538-539 26.00 26.00

Jens Christian Svabo (1746-1824), Writer and Lexicographer — A210

Writings of Svabo and Svabo: 6k, Holding walking stick. 12k, At desk. 14k, Holding book. 22k, With sheaf of papers, pen and inkwell.

*Perf. 13¼x13¾*

**2010, Sept. 20** **Litho. & Engr.**

**540** A210 6k multi 1.75 1.75
**541** A210 12k multi 3.75 3.75
**542** A210 14k multi 4.50 4.50
**543** A210 22k multi 7.00 7.00
*Nos. 540-543 (4)* 17.00 17.00

Vegetables — A211

**2010, Sept. 20** **Litho.** *Perf. 13x13¼*

**544** A211 6k Potatoes 1.75 1.75
**545** A211 8k Turnips 2.50 2.50

Christmas — A212

Carols: 6k, My Little Sweet Brownie (Lítla Fitta Nissa Mín). 10k, In My Early Childhood (A Barnaárum Ungu).

**2010, Sept. 20** *Perf. 13x12½*

**546** A212 6k multi 1.75 1.75
**547** A212 10k multi 3.25 3.25
*a.* Booklet pane of 8, 4 each #546-547 20.00 —
Complete booklet, #547a 20.00

See Nos. 570-571, 592-593.

Intl. Women's Day, Cent. A213

**2011, Feb. 21** **Litho.** *Perf. 14*

**548** A213 10k multi 3.00 3.00

Traditional Women's Professions — A214

Designs: 6k, Nurses with patient and child. 16k, Midwives holding babies.

**2011, Feb. 21** *Perf. 13x13¼*

**549** A214 6k multi 1.75 1.75
**550** A214 16k multi 5.00 5.00

Cats — A215

Color of cat: 6k, Black and white. 10k, Brown and white.

**2011, Feb. 21** *Perf. 13¾*

**551** A215 6k multi 1.75 1.75
**552** A215 10k multi 3.25 3.25

**Booklet Stamps**
**Self-Adhesive**
***Serpentine Die Cut 14***

**553** A215 6k multi 1.75 1.75
**554** A215 10k multi 3.25 3.25
*a.* Booklet pane of 8, 4 each #553-554 20.00

Souvenir Sheet

Legend of Annika od Dímun — A216

No. 555 — Annika: a, With chalice. b, With guards. c, With bound hands in water.

**2011, Feb. 21** *Perf. 14¾*

**555** A216 Sheet of 3 9.00 9.00
*a.-c.* 10k Any single 3.00 3.00

Paintings by Bergithe Johannessen (1905-95) — A217

Designs: 2k, Skerjut Strond (Glowing Beach). 24k, Ur Nólsoy (From Nólsoy).

**2011, Apr. 26** *Perf. 12½x13*

**556** A217 2k multi .65 .65
**557** A217 24k multi 7.50 7.50

Paintings by Frida Zachariassen (1912-92) — A218

Designs: 6k, Urtagardhur (The Garden). 26k, Kona (Woman).

**2011, Apr. 26** *Perf. 13*

**558** A218 6k multi 1.75 1.75
**559** A218 26k multi 7.50 7.50

Europa A219

Tree plantations on: 10k, Tórshavn. 12k, Kunoy, vert.

**2011, Apr. 26** *Perf. 12½*

**560** A219 10k multi 3.25 3.25
**561** A219 12k multi 3.75 3.75

Intl. Year of Forests.

Flowers — A220

Designs: 14k, Silene dioica. 20k, Geranium sylvaticum.

**2011, Apr. 26** *Perf. 13¼*

**562** A220 14k multi 4.50 4.50
**563** A220 20k multi 6.00 6.00

Berries — A221

Designs: 50o, Juniperus communis subsp. alpina. 6.50k, Empetrum nigrum. subsp. hermaphroditum.

**2011, Sept. 1** **Litho.** *Perf. 12¾x13½*

**564** A221 50o multi .25 .25
**565** A221 6.50k multi 2.00 2.00

Stóridrangur — A222

**2011, Sept. 28** *Perf. 12½x13*

**566** A222 10.50k multi 3.25 3.25

Old Motor Vehicles A223

Designs: No. 567, Black Ford TT truck, first vehicle on Faroe Islands. No. 568, Red Morris bus. No. 569, White De Luxe Model, automobile built on Faroe Islands.

**2011, Sept. 28** *Perf. 13½x12¾*

**567** A223 13k multi 4.00 4.00
**568** A223 13k multi 4.00 4.00
**569** A223 13k multi 4.00 4.00
*a.* Souvenir sheet of 3, #567-569 12.50 12.50
*Nos. 567-569 (3)* 12.00 12.00

**Christmas Type of 2010**

Carols: 6.50k, I Can't Wait for Christmas to Come (Eg Eri So Spent Til Jóla). 10.50k, I Rejoice Every Christmas Eve (Eg Gledist So Hvort Jólakvold).

**2011, Sept. 28** *Perf. 13x12½*

**570** A212 6.50k multi 2.00 2.00
**571** A212 10.50k multi 3.25 3.25
*a.* Booklet pane of 8, 4 each #570-571 21.00 —
Complete booklet, #571a 21.00

Reign of Queen Margrethe II, 40th Anniv. — A224

**Litho. & Engr.**

**2012, Jan. 4** *Perf. 13¼*

**572** A224 10.50k multi 3.00 3.00
*a.* Souvenir sheet of 1 3.00 3.00

Extinct Animals — A225

Designs: 13k, Pinguinis impennis. 21k, Dimun sheep (Ovis aries), horiz.

**2012, Feb. 20 Litho. *Perf. 13¼x13***
**573** A225 13k multi 4.00 4.00

***Perf. 13x13¼***
**574** A225 21k multi 6.00 6.00

Sea Anemones A226

Various sea anemones.

**2012, Feb. 20 *Perf. 14***
**575** A226 3k multi .90 .90
**576** A226 6.50k multi 2.00 2.00
**577** A226 8.50k multi 2.40 2.40
**578** A226 10.50k multi 3.00 3.00
*Nos. 575-578 (4)* 8.30 8.30

**Booklet Stamps Self-Adhesive**

***Serpentine Die Cut 14***
**579** A226 6.50k multi 2.00 2.00
**580** A226 10.50k multi 3.00 3.00
*a.* Booklet pane of 8, 4 each #579-580 20.00

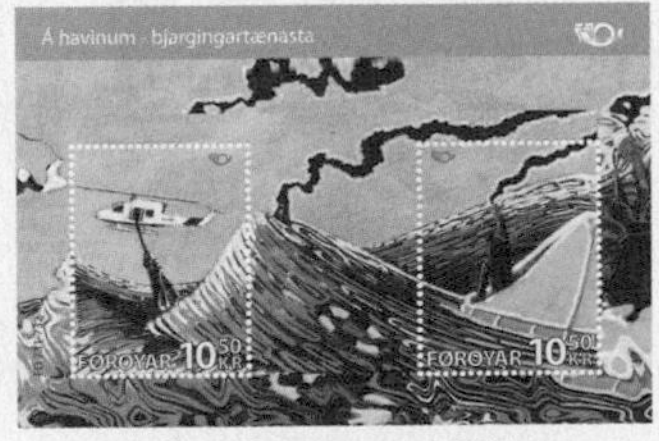

Sea Rescue — A227

No. 581: a, Helicopter. b, Life raft.

**2012, Mar. 21 *Perf. 14¼x13½***
**581** A227 Sheet of 2 6.00 6.00
*a.-b.* 10.50k Either single 3.00 3.00

Europa — A228

Designs: 6.50k, Tourists on boat near Suthuroy Island cliffs. 10.50k, Hikers on rocks.

**2012, Apr. 30 *Perf. 12½x13***
**582** A228 6.50k multi 2.00 2.00
**583** A228 10.50k multi 3.00 3.00

Monsters A229

Designs: 6.50k, Gryla. 11k, Marra. 17k, Nithagrisur. 19k, Fjorutroll.

**2012, Apr. 30 *Perf. 13***
**584** A229 6.50k multi 2.00 2.00
**585** A229 11k multi 3.25 3.25
**586** A229 17k multi 4.75 4.75
**587** A229 19k multi 5.50 5.50
*Nos. 584-587 (4)* 15.50 15.50

Old Pharmacy, Klaksvík — A230

**2012, Sept. 24 *Perf. 12½x13***
**588** A230 8.50k multi 2.40 2.40

Contemporary Art — A231

Designs: 13k, Mr. Walker on the Faroes, by Jan Hafström. 21k, Egg Procession, by Edward Fuglo.

**2012, Sept. 24 *Perf. 13***
**589** A231 13k multi 3.50 3.50
**590** A231 21k multi 5.75 5.75

Miniature Sheet

Legend of Regin the Blacksmith — A232

No. 591: a, Hjordis attends to dying husband, Sigmund, on battlefield. b, Sigurd on horse. c, Regin hammering sword. d, Sigurd on horseback encounters Odin. e, Sigurd attacks serpent. f, Birds watching Sigurd cooking serpent's heart.

**Litho., Litho & Embossed (#591e)**

**2012, Sept. 24 *Perf. 13¼x13***
**591** A232 Sheet of 6 20.00 20.00
*a.-f.* 11k Any single 3.25 3.25

**Christmas Type of 2010**

Carols: 6.50k, Why is Everything So Cozy Tonight? (Hví Man Tadh Vera?) 12.50k, Silent Night (Gledhilig Jól).

**2012, Sept. 24 Litho. *Perf. 13x12½***
**592** A212 6.50k multi 2.00 2.00
**593** A212 12.50k multi 4.00 4.00
*a.* Booklet pane of 8, 4 each #592-593 24.00 24.00
Complete booklet, #593a 24.00 24.00

Lambs — A233

**2013, Feb. 25 *Perf. 13¼x13¾***
**594** A233 12.50k multi 4.00 4.00

Crustaceans — A234

Designs: 7k, Cancer pagurus. 9k, Chaceon affinis. 23k, Pandalus borealis. 34k, Nephrops norvegicus.

**2013, Feb. 25 *Perf. 12½x13***
**595** A234 7k multi 2.50 2.50
**596** A234 9k multi 3.25 3.25
**597** A234 23k multi 8.00 8.00
**598** A234 34k multi 12.00 12.00
*Nos. 595-598 (4)* 25.75 25.75

Miniature Sheet

Traditional Faroese Rowboat — A235

No. 599: a, Tollur og homluband (oarlock and strap, 26x23mm). b, Arar (oars, 66x23mm). c, Rodhur og rodhurarmur (rudder, 26x23mm). d, Kumpass (compass, 26x23mm). e, Seksmannafar (hull of six-man boat, 66x23mm). f, Kaggi (barrel, 26x23mm). g, Eyskar (bailing scoop, 26x23mm). h, Mastur og vrá vidh segli (mast and sail, 66x23mm). i, Nogla og togendi (bung and rope, 26x23mm).

**Litho. & Engr.**

**2013, Feb. 25 *Perf. 13¼***
**599** A235 Sheet of 9 20.00 20.00
*a.-i.* 7k Any single 2.00 2.00

Soren Kierkegaard (1813-55), Philosopher A266

**2013, Mar. 4 *Perf. 12¼***
**600** A266 35k multi 11.00 11.00

Europa A267

Designs: 7k, Postal van. 12.50k, Postal truck.

**2013, Apr. 29 Litho. *Perf. 14***
**601** A267 7k multi 2.25 2.25
**602** A267 12.50k multi 4.00 4.00

**Booklet Stamps Self-Adhesive**

***Serpentine Die Cut 14***
**603** A267 7k multi 2.25 2.25
**604** A267 12.50k multi 4.00 4.00
*a.* Booklet pane of 8, 4 each #603-604 27.00

Rodents — A268

Designs: 11k, Rattus norvegicus. 12.50k, Mus domesticus.

**2013, Apr. 29 *Perf. 13¾x13¼***
**605** A268 11k multi 3.50 3.50
**606** A268 12.50k multi 4.00 4.00

Paintings by Olivur Vith Neyst — A269

Designs: 19k, Sólskin (Sunshine). 38k, Vestaravág (West Harbor).

**2013, Sept. 23 *Perf. 12½***
**607** A269 19k multi 5.50 5.50
**608** A269 38k multi 11.00 11.00

Souvenir Sheet

Nordafar Fishery, Foroyinghavn, Greenland — A270

No. 609: a, Fishing boat, white building in background. b, Fishermen on dock. c, Fishing boats, red buildings in background.

***Perf. 13¼x13¾***

**2013, Sept. 23 Litho. & Engr.**
**609** A270 Sheet of 3 8.50 8.50
*a.-c.* 9k Any single 2.75 2.75

See Greenland No. 652.

Christmas — A271

Designs: 7k, Manger. 12.50k, Holy Family.

**2013, Sept. 23 Litho. *Perf. 12¾***
**610** A271 7k multi 2.25 2.25
**611** A271 12.50k multi 3.75 3.75
*a.* Booklet pane of 8, 4 each #610-611 24.00 —
Complete booklet, #611a 24.00

See Nos. 632-633, 651-652.

Rosa Mollis — A272

**2014, Feb. 26 Litho. *Perf. 12½x13***
**612** A272 14.50k multi 4.75 4.75

Jellyfish — A273

Designs: 8k, Aurelia aurita. 15.50k, Cyanea capillata. 18.50k, Pelagia noctiluca. 26k, Beroe cucumis.

**2014, Feb. 26 Litho. *Perf. 13***
**613** A273 8k multi 2.50 2.50
**614** A273 15.50k multi 4.75 4.75
**615** A273 18.50k multi 5.75 5.75
**616** A273 26k multi 7.50 7.50
*Nos. 613-616 (4)* 20.50 20.50

Souvenir Sheet

Legend of the Lady of Húsavik — A274

No. 617: a, Woman holding horn of Viking chief. b, Woman and nykur (mythical beast). c, Woman on throne.

**2014, Feb. 26 Litho. *Perf. 13x13½***

| | | | | |
|---|---|---|---|---|
| **617** | A274 | Sheet of 3 | 10.00 | 10.00 |
| *a.-c.* | | 10k Any single | 3.25 | 3.25 |

Souvenir Sheet

Ferry MS Norröna — A275

No. 618: a, Ship's stern. b, Ship's bow.

**2014, Mar. 17 Litho. *Perf. 13x13¼***

| | | | | |
|---|---|---|---|---|
| **618** | A275 | Sheet of 2 | 9.00 | 9.00 |
| *a.-b.* | | 14.50k Either single | 4.25 | 4.25 |

Europa A276

Designs: 14.50k, Faroese Symphony Orchestra. 19.50k, Bass players, vert.

**2014, Apr. 28 Litho. *Perf. 13x13¼***

| | | | |
|---|---|---|---|
| **619** A276 14.50k multi | | 4.50 | 4.50 |

***Perf. 13¼x13***

| | | | |
|---|---|---|---|
| **620** A276 19.50k multi | | 6.00 | 6.00 |

Lighthouses — A277

Designs: 14.50k, Akraberg Lighthouse. 15.50k, Dímun Lighthouse. 17k, Toftir Lighthouse.

**2014, Apr. 28 Litho. *Perf. 14***

| | | | |
|---|---|---|---|
| **621** A277 | 14.50k multi | 4.50 | 4.50 |
| **622** A277 | 15.50k multi | 4.75 | 4.75 |
| **623** A277 | 17k multi | 5.25 | 5.25 |
| | *Nos. 621-623 (3)* | 14.50 | 14.50 |

**Booklet Stamps**
**Self-Adhesive**

***Serpentine Die Cut 14***

| | | | |
|---|---|---|---|
| **624** A277 | 14.50k multi | 4.50 | 4.50 |
| **625** A277 | 15.50k multi | 4.75 | 4.75 |
| **626** A277 | 17k multi | 5.25 | 5.25 |
| *a.* | Booklet pane of 6, 2 each #624-626 | 29.00 | |
| | *Nos. 624-626 (3)* | 14.50 | 14.50 |

Prince Henrik, 80th Birthday A278

***Perf. 13½x13¼***

**2014, June 11 Litho.**

| | | | |
|---|---|---|---|
| **627** A278 14.50k multi | | 4.50 | 4.50 |

**Booklet Stamp**
**Self-Adhesive**

***Die Cut Perf. 13½x13¼***

| | | | |
|---|---|---|---|
| **628** A278 14.50k multi | | 4.50 | 4.50 |
| *a.* | Booklet pane of 4 | 18.00 | |

Roger Casement, Boats, Congolese Natives, and Daniel J. Danielsen — A279

***Perf. 13¼x13½***

**2014, Sept. 24 Litho.**

| | | | |
|---|---|---|---|
| **629** A279 25k multi | | 7.50 | 7.50 |

Danielsen (1871-1916), missionary to the Congo, and documenter of human rights abuses reported on in Casement's 1904 report to the British Government.

Captain Vilhelm Reinert-Joensen (1891-1949), Ships Used in D-Day Invasion — A280

***Perf. 13¼x13½***

**2014, Sept. 24 Litho.**

| | | | |
|---|---|---|---|
| **630** A280 26k multi | | 7.50 | 7.50 |

D-Day, 70th anniv.

Miniature Sheet

World War I, Cent. — A281

No. 631: a, Newspaper headlines, map of Europe, man in rowboat. b, Children, ration coupons, national leaders of the World War I combattants. c, Faroese boat attacked by German submarine, map of Faroe islands and British Isles. d, Map of Vimy Ridge, Faroese-Canadian soldier Christian L. Petersen, soldiers.

***Perf. 13¼x13½***

**2014, Sept. 24 Litho.**

| | | | | |
|---|---|---|---|---|
| **631** | A281 | Sheet of 4 | 10.00 | 10.00 |
| *a.-d.* | | 8k Any single | 2.50 | 2.50 |
| *e.* | | Like #631, with "In Memoriam" and poppies added in red in sheet margin | 9.00 | 9.00 |

Issued: No. 631e, 5/13/15.

**Christmas Type of 2013**

Designs: 8k, Angels. 14.50k, Shepherds.

**2014, Sept. 24 Litho. *Perf. 12¾***

| | | | |
|---|---|---|---|
| **632** A271 | 8k multi | 2.50 | 2.50 |
| **633** A271 | 14.50k multi | 4.50 | 4.50 |
| *a.* | Booklet pane of 8, 4 each #632-633 | 28.00 | — |
| | Complete booklet, #633a | 28.00 | |

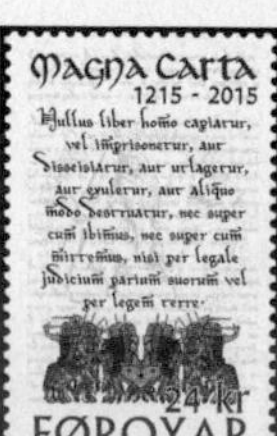

Magna Carta, 800th Anniv. — A282

**2015, Feb. 23 Litho. *Perf. 13½***

| | | | |
|---|---|---|---|
| **634** A282 24k multi | | 7.00 | 7.00 |

Woman Suffrage, Cent. A283

**2015, Feb. 23 Litho. *Perf. 13x13¼***

| | | | |
|---|---|---|---|
| **635** A283 36k multi | | 11.00 | 11.00 |

Opening of New Terminal at Vagar Airport A284

Designs: 8.50k, Airplanes on ground. 15k, New terminal.

**2015, Feb. 23 Litho. *Perf. 13x13¼***

| | | | |
|---|---|---|---|
| **636** A284 | 8.50k multi | 2.60 | 2.60 |
| **637** A284 | 15k multi | 4.50 | 4.50 |
| *a.* | Booklet pane of 8, 4 each #636-637 | 28.50 | — |
| | Complete booklet, #637a | 28.50 | |

Miniature Sheet

1833 Expedition of George Clayton Atkinson to Faroe Islands — A285

No. 638 — Paintings by Thomas Miles Richarson of: a, Vatnmylla (watermill). b, Tórshavn. c, Waterfall on Vágar, Koltur and Hestur Islands. d, Trollkonufingur.

**2015, Feb. 23 Litho. *Perf. 13x13¼***

| | | | | |
|---|---|---|---|---|
| **638** | A285 | Sheet of 4 | 10.50 | 10.50 |
| *a.-d.* | | 8.50k Any single | 2.60 | 2.60 |

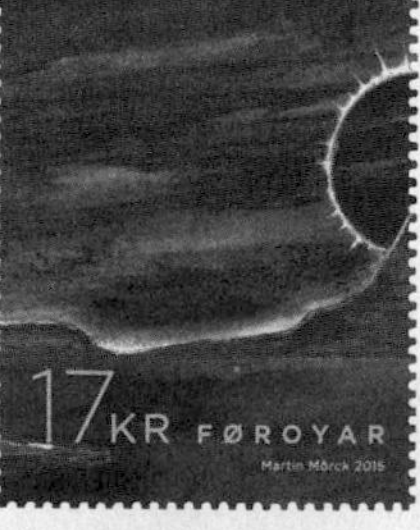

March 20, 2015 Total Solar Eclipse A286

Eclipse at: 17k, Right. 19k, Left.

**2015, Mar. 11 Litho. *Perf. 12***

| | | | |
|---|---|---|---|
| **639** A286 | 17k multi | 5.00 | 5.00 |
| **640** A286 | 19k multi | 5.75 | 5.75 |
| *a.* | Souvenir sheet of 2, #639-640 | 11.00 | 11.00 |

**Booklet Stamps**
**Self-Adhesive**

***Die Cut Perf. 11½***

| | | | |
|---|---|---|---|
| **641** A286 | 17k multi | 5.00 | 5.00 |
| *a.* | Booklet pane of 4 | 20.00 | |
| **642** A286 | 19k multi | 5.75 | 5.75 |
| *a.* | Booklet pane of 4 | 23.00 | |

Faroe Islands Flag, 75th Anniv. — A287

Designs: 11k, Arne Vatnhamar holding Faroe Islands flag on Mt. Everest. 12k, Map and flag of Faroe Islands.

**2015, Apr. 14 Litho. *Perf. 13½***

| | | | |
|---|---|---|---|
| **643** A287 | 11k multi | 3.50 | 3.50 |
| **644** A287 | 12k multi | 3.75 | 3.75 |

Europa — A288

Old toys: 17k, Rag doll. 22k, Hoop made of ram's horn.

**2015, Apr. 14 Litho. *Perf. 13½***

| | | | |
|---|---|---|---|
| **645** A288 | 17k multi | 5.25 | 5.25 |
| **646** A288 | 22k multi | 6.75 | 6.75 |

Knitted Art by Randi Samsonsen — A289

**2015, Sept. 28 Litho. *Perf. 13x12¾***

| | | | |
|---|---|---|---|
| **647** A289 17k multi | | 5.25 | 5.25 |

H. N. Jacobsen's Bookstore, 150th Anniv. A290

Designs: 17k, Bookstore exterior. 26k, Bookstore interior, book covers, bindery machinery.

**2015, Sept. 28 Litho. *Perf. 12½***

| | | | |
|---|---|---|---|
| **648** A290 | 17k multi | 5.25 | 5.25 |
| **649** A290 | 26k multi | 8.00 | 8.00 |

Souvenir Sheet

Christian Artifacts of the Viking Era — A291

No. 650 — Inscriptions: a, Krossteinur úr Olansgardhi í Skúvoy (stone with crucifix from Olansgardhi). b, Botnur úr laggadhum traeílati (cross on wooden bucket bottom). c, Vadhsteinur vidh ihogdum St. Hanskrossi (stone fishing sinkers with St. Hans crucifix).

**Litho. & Engr.**

**2015, Sept. 28 *Perf. 12¾x13***

| | | | | |
|---|---|---|---|---|
| **650** | A291 | Sheet of 3 | 11.50 | 11.50 |
| *a.-c.* | | 12k Any single | 3.75 | 3.75 |

**Christmas Type of 2013**

Designs: 8.50k, Magi on camels. 17k, Holy Family fleeing to Egypt.

**2015, Sept. 28 Litho. *Perf. 12¾***

| | | | |
|---|---|---|---|
| **651** A271 | 8.50k multi | 2.60 | 2.60 |
| **652** A271 | 17k multi | 5.25 | 5.25 |
| *a.* | Booklet pane of 8, 4 each #651-652 | 32.00 | — |
| | Complete booklet, #652a | 32.00 | |

Oystercatchers in Flight — A292

*Perf. 13¼x13¾*

**2016, Feb. 22** **Litho.**

**653** A292 17k multi 5.25 5.25

Grounding of the Westerbeek off Lopra, 274th Anniv. — A293

Designs: 17k, Chest and the Westerbeek. 19k, Grounding of the Westerbeek.

*Perf. 13¾x13½*

**2016, Feb. 22** **Litho.**

**654** A293 17k multi 5.25 5.25
**655** A293 19k multi 5.75 5.75
*a.* Souvenir sheet of 2, #654-655 11.00 11.00

Fire Fighting Equipment A294

Designs: 1k, Fire pump, 1776. 15k, 1948 Bedford K fire truck. 19k, 1937 Triangle fire truck.

**2016, Feb. 22** **Litho.** *Perf. 13*

**656** A294 1k multi .30 .30
**657** A294 15k multi 4.75 4.75
**658** A294 19k multi 5.75 5.75
*Nos. 656-658 (3)* 10.80 10.80

**Booklet Stamps Self-Adhesive**

***Serpentine Die Cut 13¼***

**659** A294 1k multi .30 .30
**660** A294 15k multi 4.75 4.75
**661** A294 19k multi 5.75 5.75
*a.* Booklet pane of 6, 2 each #659-661 22.00
*Nos. 659-661 (3)* 10.80 10.80

Faroe Islands Mailboxes A295

Designs: 9k, Blue Postverk Foroya mailbox used 1976-present. 17k, Red Danish Postal Service mailbox used until 1976.

**2016, Apr. 1** **Litho.** *Perf. 14¼*

**662** A295 9k multi 2.75 2.75

**Souvenir Sheet**

**663** Sheet of 2, #662, 663a 8.00 8.00
*a.* A295 19k multi 5.25 5.25

Postverk Foroya (Faroe Islands Postal Service), 40th anniv.

Foods in Faroese Drying Shed — A296

**2016, Apr. 26** **Litho.** *Perf. 13½*

**664** A296 9k multi 2.75 2.75

Nólsoyar Páll (1766-1808 or 1809), National Hero — A297

**Litho. & Engr.**

**2016, Apr. 26** *Perf. 13*

**665** A297 24k blk & brn lake 7.50 7.50

A298

Europa A299

**2016, May 9** **Litho.** *Perf. 13½x13*

**666** A298 9k green 2.75 2.75
**667** A299 17k multi 5.25 5.25

Think Green Issue.

Cod A300

**Litho. & Engr.**

**2016, Sept. 26** *Perf. 13x13¼*

**668** A300 50k multi 15.00 15.00

A square of tanned cod skin with engraved text is affixed to No. 668. The square of cod skin has a fish odor and may detach from the stamp if soaked.

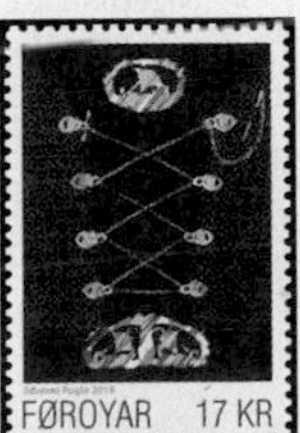


Traditional Woman's Blouse A301

Traditional Men's Waistcoat A302

**2016, Sept. 26** **Litho.** *Perf. 13x13½*

**669** A301 17k multi 5.25 5.25
**670** A302 20k multi 6.00 6.00

Miniature Sheet

Life of Jesus — A303

No. 671 — Wood carvings by Edward Fuglo depicting: a, Annunciation. b, Adoration of the Shepherds. c, Jesus as child in temple. d, Baptism of Jesus. e, Jesus feeding the multitude. f, Jesus healing lepers. g, Jesus calming storm at sea. h, Entry into Jerusalem. i, Jesus carrying cross. j, Resurrection.

**2016, Sept. 26** **Litho.** *Perf. 13x12½*

**671** A303 Sheet of 10 27.50 27.50
*a.-j.* 9k Any single 2.75 2.75

House Near Skorá River Waterfall — A304

**2017, Feb. 27** **Litho.** *Perf. 13*

**672** A304 9.50k multi 2.75 2.75

Leitisvatn Lake — A305

Lakeside: 17k, Cliffs. 19k, Buildings.

*Perf. 13½x13¼*

**2017, Feb. 27** **Litho.**

**673** A305 17k multi 5.00 5.00
**674** A305 19k multi 5.50 5.50

Somateria Mollissima Faeroensis — A306

Eider facing: 18k, Right. 27k, Left.

*Perf. 13½x13¾*

**2017, Feb. 27** **Litho.**

**675** A306 18k multi 5.25 5.25
**676** A306 27k multi 7.75 7.75

Miniature Sheet

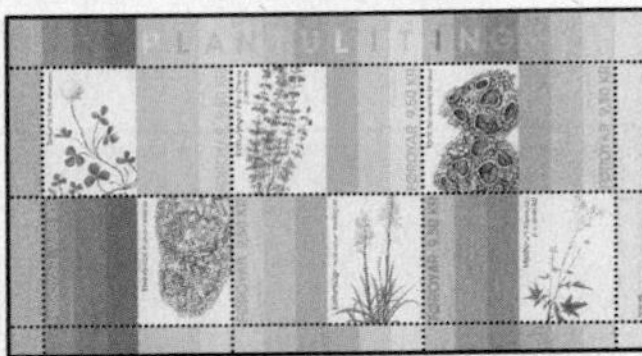

Natural Dyes — A307

No. 677: a, Trifolium repens. b, Erica cinerea. c, Ochrolechia tartarea. d, Parmelia saxatilis. e, Narthecium ossifragum. f, Filipendula ulmaria.

**2017, Feb. 27** **Litho.** *Perf. 13x12½*

**677** A307 Sheet of 6 16.50 16.50
*a.-f.* 9.50k Any single 2.75 2.75

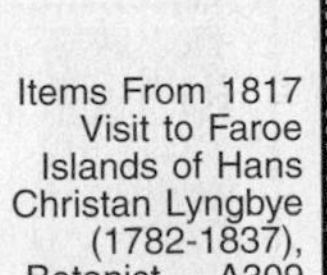

Europa — A308

Legend of the Princess of Nólsoy: 9.50k, Ship and castle. 17k, Ship, Princess and her husband.

**2017, May 15** **Litho.** *Perf. 14*

**678** A308 9.50k multi 3.00 3.00
**679** A308 17k multi 5.25 5.25

Items From 1817 Visit to Faroe Islands of Hans Christan Lyngbye (1782-1837), Botanist — A309

Designs: 9.50k, Carex lyngbyei. 13k, Illustrations of seaweeds from Lyngbye's book, *Tentamen Hydrophytologiae Danicae*, horiz. 19k, Illustrations by Lyngbye of Faroese baptismal fonts and rocking stones, horiz. 22k, Seaweed from Lyngbye's herbarium, horiz.

**2017, May 15 Litho. *Perf. 13¼x13***

| | | | | |
|---|---|---|---|---|
| **682** | A309 | 9.50k multi | 3.00 | 3.00 |

***Perf. 13x13¼***

| | | | | |
|---|---|---|---|---|
| **683** | A309 | 13k multi | 4.00 | 4.00 |
| **684** | A309 | 19k multi | 5.75 | 5.75 |
| **685** | A309 | 22k multi | 6.75 | 6.75 |
| | | *Nos. 682-685 (4)* | 19.50 | 19.50 |

Souvenir Sheet

Queen Margrethe II and Prince Henrik, 50th Wedding Anniversary — A310

**2017, May 15 Litho. *Perf. 13½***

| | | | | |
|---|---|---|---|---|
| **686** | A310 | 50k gold & multi | 15.00 | 15.00 |

See Denmark No. 1777, Greenland No. 754.

Legend of the Seven Swans A311

Designs: 9.50k, Men turning into swans. 19k, Woman near stake.

***Perf. 13¾x13¼***

**2017, Sept. 8 Litho. & Engr.**

| | | | | |
|---|---|---|---|---|
| **687** | A311 | 9.50k multi | 3.00 | 3.00 |
| **688** | A311 | 19k multi | 6.00 | 6.00 |
| *a.* | | Souvenir sheet of 2, #687-688 | 9.00 | 9.00 |

Traditional Clothing — A312

Designs: 9.50k, Women's dress, apron and shoes. 17k, Men's breeches, stockings and shoes.

**2017, Oct. 2 Litho. *Perf. 12¾x13½***

| | | | | |
|---|---|---|---|---|
| **689** | A312 | 9.50k multi | 3.00 | 3.00 |
| **690** | A312 | 17k multi | 5.50 | 5.50 |

Martin Luther Nailing 95 Theses to Church Door — A313

**2017, Oct. 2 Litho. *Perf. 13¼x13***

| | | | | |
|---|---|---|---|---|
| **693** | A313 | 18k multi | 5.75 | 5.75 |
| *a.* | | Souvenir sheet of 1 | 5.75 | 5.75 |

Protestant Reformation, 500th anniv.

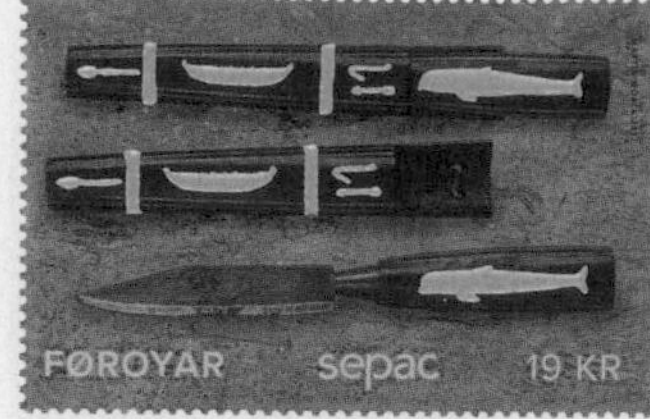


Faroese Knives and Sheaths — A314

**Litho. & Embossed With Foil Application**

**2017, Oct. 2 *Perf. 13¼x13***

**Inscribed "sepac"**

| | | | | |
|---|---|---|---|---|
| **694** | A314 | 19k gold & multi | 6.00 | 6.00 |

**Souvenir Sheet Without "sepac" Inscription**

| | | | | |
|---|---|---|---|---|
| **695** | A314 | 19k gold & multi | 6.00 | 6.00 |

## FERNANDO PO

fər-ˈnan-ₒdō ˈpō

LOCATION — An island in the Gulf of Guinea off west Africa.
GOVT. — Former province of Spain
AREA — 800 sq. mi.
POP. — 62,612 (1960)
CAPITAL — Santa Isabel

Together with the islands of Elobey, Annobon and Corisco, Fernando Po came under the administration of Spanish Guinea. Postage stamps of Spanish Guinea were used until 1960.

The provinces of Fernando Po and Rio Muni united Oct. 12, 1968, to form the Republic of Equatorial Guinea.

100 Centimos = 1 Escudo = 2.50 Pesetas
100 Centimos = 1 Peseta
1000 Milesimas = 100 Centavos = 1 Peso (1882)

**Catalogue values for unused stamps in this country are for Never Hinged items, beginning with Scott 181 in the regular postage section and Scott B1 in the semi-postal section.**

Isabella II — A1

**1868 Unwmk. Typo. *Perf. 14***

| | | | | |
|---|---|---|---|---|
| **1** | A1 | 20c brown | 400.00 | 140.00 |
| *a.* | | 20c red brown | 525.00 | 140.00 |

No. 1 is valued in the grade of fine, as illustrated. Examples with very fine centering are uncommon and sell for more.

Forgeries exist.

Alfonso XII — A2

**1879 Centimos de Peseta**

| | | | | |
|---|---|---|---|---|
| **2** | A2 | 5c green | 57.50 | 15.00 |
| **3** | A2 | 10c rose | 42.50 | 15.00 |
| **4** | A2 | 50c blue | 100.00 | 15.00 |
| | | *Nos. 2-4 (3)* | 200.00 | 45.00 |

**1882-89 Centavos de Peso**

| | | | | |
|---|---|---|---|---|
| **5** | A2 | 1c green | 9.50 | 5.50 |
| **6** | A2 | 2c rose | 18.00 | 8.75 |
| **7** | A2 | 5c gray blue | 60.00 | 12.00 |
| **8** | A2 | 10c dk brown ('89) | 82.50 | 6.75 |
| | | *Nos. 5-8 (4)* | 170.00 | 33.00 |

Nos. 5-7 Handstamp Surcharged in Blue, Black or Violet — a

**1884-95**

| | | | | |
|---|---|---|---|---|
| **9** | A2 | 50c on 1c green ('95) | 120.00 | 19.00 |
| **11** | A2 | 50c on 2c rose | 32.00 | 6.00 |
| **12** | A2 | 50c on 5c blue ('87) | 150.00 | 25.00 |
| | | *Nos. 9-12 (3)* | 302.00 | 50.00 |

Values above are for examples surcharged in black. Stamps surcharged in violet or blue are worth about 25% more.

Inverted and double surcharges exist. No. 12 exists overprinted in carmine. Value $100.

King Alfonso XIII — A4

**1894-97 *Perf. 14***

| | | | | |
|---|---|---|---|---|
| **13** | A4 | ⅛c slate ('96) | 22.00 | 3.00 |
| **14** | A4 | 2c rose ('96) | 15.50 | 2.50 |
| **15** | A4 | 5c blue grn ('97) | 16.00 | 2.50 |
| **16** | A4 | 6c dk violet ('96) | 13.00 | 3.00 |
| **17** | A4 | 10c blk vio ('94) | 450.00 | 115.00 |
| **17A** | A4 | 10c dark brown ('94) | 30.00 | 5.00 |
| **18** | A4 | 10c lake ('95) | 50.00 | 8.75 |
| **19** | A4 | 10c org brn ('96) | 10.50 | 2.50 |
| **20** | A4 | 12½c dk brown ('96) | 11.50 | 3.00 |
| **21** | A4 | 20c slate bl ('96) | 11.50 | 3.00 |
| **22** | A4 | 25c claret ('96) | 23.00 | 3.00 |
| | | *Nos. 13-22 (10)* | 623.00 | 146.25 |

Most exist imperf. Value, set, pairs Nos. 13-16 and Nos. 18-22, $2,500.

**Stamps of 1894-97 Handstamped in Blue, Black or Red**

b

c

**Type "b" Surcharge**

**1896-98**

| | | | | |
|---|---|---|---|---|
| **22A** | A4 | 5c on ⅛c slate (Bl) | 100.00 | 27.50 |
| **23** | A4 | 5c on 2c rose (Bl) | 50.00 | 16.50 |
| **23A** | A4 | 5c on 6c dk vio (Bl) | 180.00 | 45.00 |
| **24** | A4 | 5c on 10c brn vio (Bl) | 180.00 | 45.00 |
| **24A** | A4 | 5c on 10c org brn (Bl) | 180.00 | 45.00 |
| **24B** | A4 | 5c on 10c dk brn (Bk) | 67.50 | 27.50 |
| **25** | A4 | 5c on 12½c brn (Bl) | 37.50 | 13.00 |
| *a.* | | Black surcharge | 37.50 | 13.00 |
| **25B** | A4 | 5c on 20c sl bl (R) | 180.00 | 45.00 |
| **25C** | A4 | 5c on 25c claret (Bk) | 180.00 | 35.00 |
| | | *Nos. 22A-25C (9)* | 1,155. | 299.50 |

**Type "c" Surcharge**

| | | | | |
|---|---|---|---|---|
| **26** | A4 | 5c on ⅛c slate (Bk) | 32.50 | 6.75 |
| **27** | A4 | 5c on 2c rose (Bl) | 32.50 | 6.75 |
| *a.* | | Black surcharge | 32.50 | 6.75 |
| **28** | A4 | 5c on 5c green (R) | 160.00 | 22.00 |
| **29** | A4 | 5c on 6c dk vio (R) | 23.00 | 14.00 |
| *a.* | | Violet surcharge | 24.00 | 15.50 |
| **30** | A4 | 5c on 10c org brn (Bk) | 210.00 | 27.50 |
| **30A** | A4 | 5c on 10c dk brn (Bk) | 160.00 | 26.00 |
| **30B** | A4 | 5c on 10c lake (Bl) | 400.00 | 110.00 |
| **31** | A4 | 5c on 12½c brn (R) | 70.00 | 11.00 |
| **32** | A4 | 5c on 20c sl bl (R) | 40.00 | 10.50 |
| **33** | A4 | 5c on 25c claret (Bk) | 37.50 | 11.00 |
| *a.* | | Blue surcharge | 37.50 | 13.50 |
| | | *Nos. 26-33 (10)* | 1,166. | 245.50 |

Exist surcharged in other colors.

**Type "a" Srch. in Blue or Black**

**1898-99**

| | | | | |
|---|---|---|---|---|
| **34** | A4 | 50c on 2c rose | 92.50 | 11.50 |
| **35** | A4 | 50c on 10c brn vio | 220.00 | 33.00 |
| **36** | A4 | 50c on 10c lake | 230.00 | 33.00 |
| **37** | A4 | 50c on 10c org brn | 220.00 | 33.00 |
| **38** | A4 | 50c on 12½c brn (Bk) | 190.00 | 22.00 |

The "a" surch. also exists on ⅛c, 5c & 25c. Values, $325, $225 and $210, respectively.

**Revenue Stamps Privately Handstamped in Blue**

Arms

A5 A6

**1897-98 *Imperf.***

| | | | | |
|---|---|---|---|---|
| **39** | A5 | 5c on 10c rose | 28.00 | 12.50 |
| **40** | A6 | 10c rose | 24.00 | 11.00 |

**Revenue Stamps Handstamped in Black or Red**

A7

A8

A9

Arms — A9a

**1899 *Imperf.***

| | | | | |
|---|---|---|---|---|
| **41** | A7 | 15c on 10c green | 45.00 | 23.00 |
| *a.* | | Blue surcharge, vertical | 39.00 | 21.00 |
| **42** | A8 | 10c on 25c green | 120.00 | 65.00 |
| **43** | A9 | 15c on 25c green | 190.00 | 120.00 |
| **43A** | A9a | 15c on 25c green (R) | *1,800.* | *1,100.* |
| *b.* | | Black surcharge | *1,800.* | *1,100.* |

Surcharge on No. 41 is either horizontal, inverted or vertical.

On No. 42 "CORREOS" is ovptd. in red.

On Nos. 43A and 43Ab, the signature is always in black.

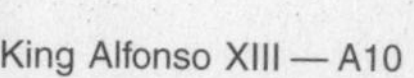

King Alfonso XIII — A10

Double-lined shaded letters at sides.

**1899** *Perf. 14*

**44** A10 1m orange brn 2.40 .45
**45** A10 2m orange brn 2.40 .45
**46** A10 3m orange brn 2.40 .45
**47** A10 4m orange brn 2.40 .45
**48** A10 5m orange brn 2.40 .45
**49** A10 1c black vio 2.40 .45
**50** A10 2c dk blue grn 2.40 .45
**51** A10 3c dk brown 2.40 .45
**52** A10 4c orange 13.00 1.10
**53** A10 5c carmine rose 2.50 .45
**54** A10 6c dark blue 2.50 .45
**55** A10 8c gray brn 8.00 .45
**56** A10 10c vermilion 5.25 .45
**57** A10 15c slate grn 5.25 .45
**58** A10 20c maroon 14.50 1.10
**59** A10 40c violet 100.00 19.00
**60** A10 60c black 100.00 19.00
**61** A10 80c red brown 100.00 19.00
**62** A10 1p yellow grn 325.00 92.50
**63** A10 2p slate blue 325.00 95.00
*Nos. 44-63 (20)* 1,020. 252.55

Nos. 44-63 exist imperf. Value for set, $3,500.

See Nos. 66-85. For surcharges see Nos. 64-65, 88-88B.

**1900** **Surcharged type "a"**

**64** A10 50c on 20c maroon 16.00 2.50
*a.* Blue surcharge 32.00 4.75

**Surcharged type "b"**

**64B** A10 5c on 20c maroon 300.00 40.00

**Surcharged type "c"**

**65** A10 5c on 20c maroon 9.50 2.40
*Nos. 64-65 (3)* 325.50 44.90

**1900** **Dated "1900"**

Solid letters at sides.

**66** A10 1m black 3.00 .50
**67** A10 2m black 3.00 .50
**68** A10 3m black 3.00 .50
**69** A10 4m black 3.00 .50
**70** A10 5m black 3.00 .50
**71** A10 1c green 3.00 .50
**72** A10 2c violet 3.00 .50
**73** A10 3c rose 3.00 .50
**74** A10 4c black brn 3.00 .50
**75** A10 5c blue 3.00 .50
**76** A10 6c orange 3.00 .50
**77** A10 8c bronze grn 3.00 .50
**78** A10 10c claret 3.00 .50
**79** A10 15c dk violet 3.00 .50
**80** A10 20c olive brn 3.00 .50
**81** A10 40c brown 7.75 2.25
**82** A10 60c green 16.50 2.50
**83** A10 80c dark blue 17.50 3.75
**84** A10 1p red brown 110.00 30.00
**85** A10 2p orange 190.00 62.50
*Nos. 66-85 (20)* 386.75 108.50
Set, never hinged 750.00

Nos. 66-85 exist imperf. Value, set *$3,500.*

**Revenue Stamps Overprinted or Surcharged with Handstamp in Red or Black**

A11

A12

**1900** *Imperf.*

**86** A11 10c blue (R) 37.50 17.50
**87** A12 5c on 10c blue 100.00 40.00
Set, never hinged 175.00

**Nos. 52 and 80 Surcharged type "a" in Violet or Black**

**1900**

**88** A10 50c on 4c orange (V) 14.00 4.00
*a.* Green surcharge 22.50 12.00
**88B** A10 50c on 20c ol brn 14.00 3.50
Set, never hinged 37.50

A13

**1901** *Perf. 14*

**89** A13 1c black 3.00 .90
**90** A13 2c orange brn 3.00 .90
**91** A13 3c dk violet 3.00 .90
**92** A13 4c lt violet 3.00 .90
**93** A13 5c orange red 1.75 .90
**94** A13 10c violet brn 1.75 .90
**95** A13 25c dp blue 1.75 .90
**96** A13 50c claret 3.00 .90
**97** A13 75c dk brown 2.25 .90
**98** A13 1p blue grn 67.50 7.50
**99** A13 2p red brown 42.50 10.00
**100** A13 3p olive grn 42.50 14.00
**101** A13 4p dull red 42.50 14.00
**102** A13 5p dk green 52.50 14.00
**103** A13 10p buff 125.00 40.00
*Nos. 89-103 (15)* 395.00 107.60
Set, never hinged 850.00

**Dated "1902"**

**1902** **Control Numbers on Back**

**104** A13 5c dk green 2.60 .45
**105** A13 10c slate 2.90 .50
**106** A13 25c claret 6.25 1.00
**107** A13 50c violet brn 15.00 3.25
**108** A13 75c lt violet 15.00 3.25
**109** A13 1p car rose 18.50 4.00
**110** A13 2p olive grn 40.00 9.50
**111** A13 5p orange red 57.50 20.00
*Nos. 104-111 (8)* 157.75 41.95
Set, never hinged 250.00

Exist imperf. Value for set, *$1,500.*

A14

**Dated "1903"**

**1903** *Perf. 14*

**Control Numbers on Back**

**112** A14 ¼c dk violet .45 .25
**113** A14 ½c black .45 .25
**114** A14 1c scarlet .45 .25
**115** A14 2c dk green .45 .30
**116** A14 3c blue grn .45 .30
**117** A14 4c violet .45 .30
**118** A14 5c rose lake .50 .30
**119** A14 10c orange buff .60 .45
**120** A14 15c blue green 2.50 1.00
**121** A14 25c red brown 2.75 1.25
**122** A14 50c black brn 4.50 2.00
**123** A14 75c carmine 16.50 3.50
**124** A14 1p dk brown 25.00 6.00
**125** A14 2p dk olive grn 32.50 7.50
**126** A14 3p claret 32.50 7.50
**127** A14 4p dark blue 40.00 12.50
**128** A14 5p dp dull blue 60.00 16.00
**129** A14 10p dull red 130.00 27.50
*Nos. 112-129 (18)* 350.05 87.15
Set, never hinged 600.00

**Dated "1905"**

**1905** **Control Numbers on Back**

**136** A14 1c dp violet .40 .30
**137** A14 2c black .40 .30
**138** A14 3c vermilion .40 .30
**139** A14 4c dp green .40 .30
**140** A14 5c blue grn .45 .35
**141** A14 10c violet 1.60 .75
**142** A14 15c car lake 1.60 .75
**143** A14 25c orange buff 12.50 2.25
**144** A14 50c green 8.00 2.75
**145** A14 75c red brown 11.00 7.50
**146** A14 1p dp gray brn 12.50 7.50
**147** A14 2p carmine 20.00 12.50
**148** A14 3p deep brown 32.50 14.00
**149** A14 4p bronze grn 40.00 18.00
**150** A14 5p claret 62.50 25.00
**151** A14 10p deep blue 90.00 35.00
*Nos. 136-151 (16)* 294.25 127.55
Set, never hinged 600.00

King Alfonso XIII — A15

**1907** **Control Numbers on Back**

**152** A15 1c blue black .30 .25
**153** A15 2c car rose .30 .25
**154** A15 3c dp violet .40 .25
**155** A15 4c black .40 .25
**156** A15 5c orange buff .40 .25
**157** A15 10c maroon 2.00 .80
**158** A15 15c bronze grn .55 .35
**159** A15 25c dk brown 65.00 15.00
**160** A15 50c blue green .45 .30
**161** A15 75c vermilion .45 .30
**162** A15 1p dull blue 3.00 .60
**163** A15 2p brown 11.00 4.00
**164** A15 3p lake 11.00 4.00
**165** A15 4p violet 11.00 4.00
**166** A15 5p black brn 11.00 4.00
**167** A15 10p orange brn 11.00 4.00
*Nos. 152-167 (16)* 128.25 38.60
Set, never hinged 350.00

No. 157 Handstamp Surcharged in Black, Blue or Red

**1908**

**168** A15 5c on 10c mar (Bk) 2.75 2.00
*a.* Blue surcharge 10.00 5.50
*b.* Red surcharge 30.00 10.00
**169** A15 25c on 10c mar (Bk) 60.00 20.00
Set, never hinged 77.50

The surcharge on Nos. 168-169 exist inverted, double, etc. The surcharge also exists on other stamps.

Seville-Barcelona Issue of Spain, 1929, Overprinted in Blue or Red

**1929** *Perf. 11*

**170** A52 5c rose lake .25 .25
**171** A53 10c green (R) .25 .25
*a.* Perf. 14 .65 .65
**172** A50 15c Prus bl (R) .25 .25
**173** A51 20c purple (R) .25 .25
**174** A50 25c brt rose .25 .25
**175** A52 30c black brn .25 .25
**176** A53 40c dk blue (R) .50 .50
**177** A51 50c dp orange 1.10 1.10
**178** A52 1p blue blk (R) 4.25 4.25
**179** A53 4p deep rose 22.50 22.50
**180** A53 10p brown 27.50 27.50
*Nos. 170-180 (11)* 57.35 57.35
Set, never hinged 100.00

**Catalogue values for unused stamps in this section, from this point to the end of the section, are for Never Hinged items.**

Virgin Mary — A16

**1960** **Unwmk.** **Photo.** *Perf. 13x12½*

**181** A16 25c dull gray vio .50 .25
**182** A16 50c brown olive .50 .25
**183** A16 75c violet brn .50 .25
**184** A16 1p orange ver .50 .25
**185** A16 1.50p lt blue grn .50 .25
**186** A16 2p red lilac .50 .25
**187** A16 3p dark blue 5.00 .80
**188** A16 5p lt red brn .75 .25
**189** A16 10p lt olive grn .90 .30
*Nos. 181-189 (9)* 9.65 2.85

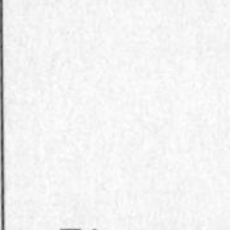

Tricorn and Windmill from "The Three-Cornered Hat" by Falla — A17

Manuel de Falla A18

**1960** *Perf. 13x12½, 12½x13*

**190** A17 35c slate green .60 .60
**191** A18 80c Prus green .70 .70

Issued to honor Manuel de Falla (1876-1946), Spanish composer.

See Nos. B1-B2.

Map of Fernando Po — A19

General Franco A20

Designs: 70c, Santa Isabel Cathedral.

*Perf. 13x12½, 12½x13*

**1961, Oct. 1** **Photo.** **Unwmk.**

**192** A19 25c gray violet .35 .35
**193** A20 50c olive brown .35 .35
**194** A19 70c brt green .40 .40
**195** A20 1p red orange .45 .45
*Nos. 192-195 (4)* 1.55 1.55

25th anniv. of the nomination of Gen. Francisco Franco as Chief of State.

Ocean Liner A21

Design: 50c, S.S. San Francisco.

**1962, July 10** *Perf. 12½x13*

**196** A21 25c dull violet .30 .30
**197** A21 50c gray olive .35 .35
**198** A21 1p orange brn .35 .35
*Nos. 196-198 (3)* 1.00 1.00

Mailman — A22

Mail Transport Symbols A23

*Perf. 13x12½, 12½x13*

**1962, Nov. 23** **Unwmk.**

**199** A22 15c dark green .30 .30
**200** A23 35c lilac rose .35 .35
**201** A22 1p brown .35 .35
*Nos. 199-201 (3)* 1.00 1.00

Issued for Stamp Day.

Fetish — A24

**1963, Jan. 29** *Perf. 13x12½*
**202** A24 50c olive gray .30 .30
**203** A24 1p deep magenta .35 .35

Issued to help victims of the Seville flood.

Nuns A25

Design: 50c, Nun and child, vert.

*Perf. 12½x13, 13x12½*
**1963, July 6** **Photo.** **Unwmk.**
**204** A25 25c bright lilac .30 .30
**205** A25 50c dull green .35 .35
**206** A25 1p red orange .35 .35
*Nos. 204-206 (3)* 1.00 1.00

Issued for child welfare.

Child and Arms A26

**1963, July 12** *Perf. 12½x13*
**207** A26 50c brown olive .30 .30
**208** A26 1p carmine rose .35 .35

Issued for Barcelona flood relief.

Governor Chacon A27

Orange Blossoms — A28

**1964, Mar. 6** *Perf. 12½x13, 13x12½*
**209** A27 25c violet black .30 .30
**210** A28 50c dark olive .35 .35
**211** A27 1p brown red .35 .35
*Nos. 209-211 (3)* 1.00 1.00

Issued for Stamp Day 1963.

Men in Dugout Canoe — A29

Design: 50c, Pineapple.

**1964, June 1** **Photo.** *Perf. 13x12½*
**212** A29 25c purple .30 .30
**213** A28 50c dull olive .35 .35
**214** A29 1p deep claret .35 .35
*Nos. 212-214 (3)* 1.00 1.00

Issued for child welfare.

Ring-necked Francolin — A30

Designs: 15c, 70c, 3p, Ring-necked francolin. 25c, 1p, 5p, Two mallards. 50c, 1.50p, 10p, Head of great blue touraco.

**1964, July 1**
**215** A30 15c chestnut .35 .30
**216** A30 25c dull violet .35 .30
**217** A30 50c dk olive grn .35 .30
**218** A30 70c green .35 .30
**219** A30 1p brown orange .40 .30
**220** A30 1.50p grnsh blue .45 .35
**221** A30 3p violet blue .75 .35
**222** A30 5p dull purple 1.75 .40
**223** A30 10p bright green 2.75 1.00
*Nos. 215-223 (9)* 7.50 3.60

The Three Kings A31

Designs: 50c, 1.50p, Caspar, vert.

*Perf. 13x12½, 12½x13*
**1964, Nov. 23** **Unwmk.**
**224** A31 50c green .35 .35
**225** A31 1p orange ver .40 .35
**226** A31 1.50p deep green .45 .35
**227** A31 3p ultra 1.75 1.40
*Nos. 224-227 (4)* 2.95 2.45

Issued for Stamp Day, 1964.

Boy — A32

Woman Fruit Picker — A33

1.50p, Girl learning to write, and church.

**1964, Mar. 1** **Photo.** *Perf. 13x12½*
**228** A32 50c indigo .30 .30
**229** A33 1p dark red .35 .30
**230** A33 1.50p grnsh blue .40 .35
*Nos. 228-230 (3)* 1.05 .95

Issued to commemorate 25 years of peace.

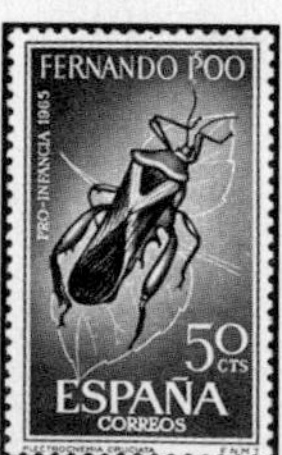

Plectrocnemia Cruciata — A34

Design: 1p, Metopodontus savagei, horiz.

*Perf. 13x12½, 12½x13*
**1965, June 1** **Photo.** **Unwmk.**
**231** A34 50c slate green .45 .35
**232** A34 1p rose red .45 .35
**233** A34 1.50p Prus blue .45 .35
*Nos. 231-233 (3)* 1.35 1.05

Issued for child welfare.

Pole Vault A35

Arms of Fernando Po — A36

*Perf. 12½x13, 13x12½*
**1965, Nov. 23** **Photo.** **Unwmk.**
**234** A35 50c yellow green .30 .30
**235** A36 1p brt org brn .35 .30
**236** A35 1.50p brt blue .40 .35
*Nos. 234-236 (3)* 1.05 .95

Issued for Stamp Day, 1965.

Children Reading A37

1.50p, St. Elizabeth of Hungary, vert.

*Perf. 12½x13, 13x12½*
**1966, June 1** **Photo.** **Unwmk.**
**237** A37 50c dark green .30 .30
**238** A37 1p brown red .35 .30
**239** A37 1.50p dark blue .35 .35
*Nos. 237-239 (3)* 1.00 .95

Issued for child welfare.

White-nosed Monkey — A38

Stamp Day: 40c, 4p, Head of moustached monkey, vert.

**1966, Nov. 23** **Photo.** *Perf. 13*
**240** A38 10c dk blue & yel .35 .30
**241** A38 40c lt brn, bl & blk .40 .30
**242** A38 1.50p ol bis, brn org & blk .45 .40
**243** A38 4p sl grn, brn org & blk .55 .45
*Nos. 240-243 (4)* 1.75 1.45

Flowers — A39

Designs: 40c, 4p, Six flowers.

**1967, June 1** **Photo.** *Perf. 13*
**244** A39 10c brt car & pale grn .30 .30
**245** A39 40c red brn & org .35 .30
**246** A39 1.50p red lil & lt red brn .40 .35
**247** A39 4p dk blue & lt grn .45 .40
*Nos. 244-247 (4)* 1.50 1.35

Issued for child welfare.

Linsang — A40

Stamp Day: 1.50p, Needle-clawed galago, vert. 3.50p, Fraser's scaly-tailed flying squirrel.

**1967, Nov. 23** **Photo.** *Perf. 13*
**248** A40 1p black & bister .35 .30
**249** A40 1.50p brown & olive .40 .35
**250** A40 3.50p rose lake & dl grn .50 .40
*Nos. 248-250 (3)* 1.25 1.05

Stamp of 1868, No. 1, and Arms of San Carlos A41

Fernando Po No. 1 and: 1.50p, Arms of Santa Isabel. 2.50p, Arms of Fernando Po.

**1968, Feb. 4** **Photo.** *Perf. 13*
**251** A41 1p brt plum & brn org .30 .30
**252** A41 1.50p dp blue & brn org .40 .30
**253** A41 2.50p brn & brn org .50 .40
*Nos. 251-253 (3)* 1.20 1.00

Centenary of the first postage stamp.

Signs of the Zodiac — A42

**1968, Apr. 25** **Photo.** *Perf. 13*
**254** A42 1p Libra .30 .30
**255** A42 1.50p Leo .40 .35
**256** A42 2.50p Aquarius .50 .40
*Nos. 254-256 (3)* 1.20 1.05

Issued for child welfare.

---

## SEMI-POSTAL STAMPS

**Catalogue values for unused stamps in this section are for Never Hinged items.**

### Types of Regular Issue, 1960

Designs: 10c+5c, Manuel de Falla. 15c+5c, Dancers from "Love, the Magician."

*Perf. 12½x13, 13x12½*
**1960** **Photo.** **Unwmk.**
**B1** A18 10c + 5c maroon .35 .30
**B2** A17 15c + 5c dk brn & bister .35 .35

The surtax was for child welfare.

Whale SP1

Design: Nos. B4, B6, Harpooning whale.

**1961** *Perf. 12½x13*
**B3** SP1 10c + 5c rose brown .35 .30
**B4** SP1 20c + 5c dk slate grn .35 .30
**B5** SP1 30c + 10c olive brn .40 .30
**B6** SP1 50c + 20c dark brn .45 .30
*Nos. B3-B6 (4)* 1.55 1.20

Issued for Stamp Day, 1960.

Hand Blessing Woman — SP2

Design: 25c+10c, Boy making sign of the cross, and crucifix.

**1961, June 21** ***Perf. 13x12½***

**B7** SP2 10c + 5c rose brn .40 .30
**B8** SP2 25c + 10c gray vio .40 .30
**B9** SP2 80c + 20c dk grn .50 .35
*Nos. B7-B9 (3)* 1.30 .95

The surtax was for child welfare.

Ethiopian Tortoise SP3

Stamp Day: 25c+10c, 1p+10c, Native carriers, palms and shore.

**1961, Nov. 23** ***Perf. 12½x13***

**B10** SP3 10c + 5c rose red .35 .30
**B11** SP3 25c + 10c dk pur .40 .30
**B12** SP3 30c + 10c vio brn .40 .30
**B13** SP3 1p + 10c red org .50 .40
*Nos. B10-B13 (4)* 1.65 1.30

## FIJI

ˈfē-ˌjē

LOCATION — Group of 332 islands (106 inhabited) in the South Pacific Ocean east of Vanuatu
GOVT. — Independent nation in British Commonwealth
AREA — 7,078 sq. mi.
POP. — 812,918 (1999 est.)
CAPITAL — Suva

A British colony since 1874, Fiji became fully independent in 1970.

12 Pence = 1 Shilling
20 Shillings = 1 Pound
100 Cents = 1 Dollar (1872-74, 1969)

**Syncopated Perforations**

**Type A (1st stamp #873):** On shorter sides, the seventh hole from the larger side is an oval hole equal in width to three holes.

**Catalogue values for unused stamps in this country are for Never Hinged items, beginning with Scott 137 in the regular postage section and Scott B1 in the semi-postal section.**

Values for unused stamps are for examples with original gum as defined in the catalogue introduction except for Nos. 1-10 which are valued without gum. Additionally, Nos. 1-10 are valued with roulettes showing on two or more sides, but expect small faults that do not detract from the appearance of the stamps. Very few examples of Nos. 1-10 will be found free of faults, and these will command substantial premiums.

**Watermark**

Wmk. 17 — FIJI POSTAGE Across Center Row of Sheet

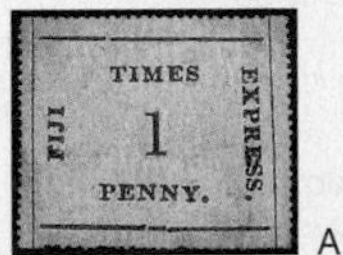


A1

**1870 Unwmk. Typeset** ***Rouletted***
**Thin Quadrille Paper**

**1** A1 1p black, *pink* 4,500. 4,750.
**2** A1 3p black, *pink* 5,500. 5,000.
*a.* Comma after "EXPRESS" *8,000. 8,000.*
**3** A1 6p black, *pink* 3,500. 3,500.
**5** A1 1sh black, *pink* 2,250. 2,500.

**1871 Thin Vertically Laid Paper**

**6** A1 1p black, *pink* 1,150. 2,100.
**7** A1 3p black, *pink* 1,900. 3,400.
**8** A1 6p black, *pink* 1,600. 2,100.
**9** A1 9p black, *pink* 3,400. 4,000.
**10** A1 1sh black, *pink* 1,900. 1,900.

This service was established by the *Fiji Times*, a weekly newspaper, for the delivery of the newspaper. Since there was no postal service to the other islands, delivery of letters to agents of the newspaper on the islands was offered to the public.

Nos. 1-5 were printed in the same sheet, one horizontal row of 6 of each (6p, 1sh, 1p, 3p). Nos. 6-10 were printed from the same plate with three 9p replacing three 3p.

Most used examples have pen cancels.

*Up to three sets of imitations exist. One on pink laid paper, pin-perforated, measuring 22½x16mm. Originals measure 22½x18½mm. A later printing was made on pink wove paper.*

Forgeries also exist plus fake cancellations.

Crown and "CR" (Cakobau Rex)
A2 A3
A4

**1871 Typo. Wmk. 17** ***Perf. 12½***
**Wove Paper**

**15** A2 1p blue 62.50 140.00
**16** A3 3p green 160.00 400.00
**17** A4 6p rose 170.00 325.00
*Nos. 15-17 (3)* 392.50 865.00

Sheets of 50 (10x5).

For overprints and surcharges see Nos. 18-39.

Forgeries exist.

Stamps of 1871 Surcharged in Black

**1872, Jan. 13**

**18** A2 2c on 1p blue 60.00 *65.00*
**19** A3 6c on 3p green 90.00 90.00
**20** A4 12c on 6p rose 125.00 90.00
*Nos. 18-20 (3)* 275.00 245.00

**Nos. 18-20 with Additional Overprint in Black**

b

c

**1874, Oct. 10**

**21** A2(b) 2c on 1p blue 1,250. 340.00
*a.* No period after "R" 3,250. 1,150.
**22** A2(c) 2c on 1p blue 1,150. 300.00
*a.* Invtd. "A" instead of "V" 3,250. 1,350.
*b.* Period after "R" is a Maltese Cross 3,250. 1,350.
*c.* No period after "R" 3,250. 1,350.
*d.* Round raised period after "V" 3,250. 1,350.
*e.* Round raised period after "V" and "R" 3,250. 1,350.
**23** A3(b) 6c on 3p green 3,250. 1,000.
*a.* No period after "R" 5,500. 2,000.
**24** A3(c) 6c on 3p green 2,500. 750.00
*a.* Inverted "A" 5,500. 2,000.
*b.* Period after "R" is a Maltese Cross 5,500. 2,000.
*c.* No period after "R" 5,500. 2,000.
*d.* Round raised period after "V" 5,500. 2,000.
*e.* Round raised period after "V" and "R" 5,500. 2,000.
**25** A4(b) 12c on 6p rose 1,050. 260.00
*a.* "V.R." inverted 7,500.
*b.* No period after "R" 3,000. 1,150.
**26** A4(c) 12c on 6p rose 1,000. 250.00
*a.* Inverted "A" 3,000. 1,350.
*b.* Period after "R" is a Maltese Cross 3,000. 1,350.
*c.* "V.R." inverted — 7,000.
*d.* No period after "R" 3,000. 1,350.
*e.* Round raised period after "V" 3,000. 1,350.
*f.* Round raised period after "V" and "R" 3,000. 1,350.

Forged overprints exist on both forged stamps and on genuine stamps.

Types "b" and "c" were in the same sheet.

Nos. 23-26 with Additional Surcharge in Black or Red

**1875**

**27** A3(b) 2p on 6c on 3p 2,750. 800.00
*a.* Period btwn. "2" and "d" 4,500. 1,600.
*b.* "V.R." double 5,500. 4,500.
*c.* No period after "R" 4,500. 1,600.
**28** A3(b) 2p on 6c on 3p (R) 900.00 300.00
*a.* Period btwn. "2" and "d" 2,250. 850.00
*b.* No period after "R" 2,250. 900.00
**29** A3(c) 2p on 6c on 3p 1,900. 600.00
*a.* Inverted "A" 4,750. 1,600.
*b.* Period after "R" is a Maltese Cross 4,750. 1,600.
*c.* No period after "2d" 4,750. 1,600.
*d.* No period after "R" 4,750. 1,600.
*e.* Round raised period after "V" 4,750. 1,600.
*f.* Round raised period after "V" and "R" 4,750. 1,600.
**30** A3(c) 2p on 6c on 3p (R) 750.00 250.00
*a.* Inverted "A" 2,100. 850.00
*b.* Period after "R" is a Maltese Cross 2,250. 875.00
*c.* No period after "2d" 2,250. 875.00
*d.* No period after "R" 2,250. 875.00
*e.* Round raised period after "V" 2,250. 875.00
*f.* Round raised period after "V" and "R" 2,250. 875.00
**31** A4(b) 2p on 12c on 6p 3,250. 1,000.
*a.* Period btwn. "2" and "d"
*b.* No period after "2d"
*c.* "2d, VR" double 5,500.
**32** A4(c) 2p on 12c on 6p 3,000. 900.00
*a.* Inverted "A" 4,500. 1,400.
*b.* No period after "2d" — 2,250.
*c.* "2d, VR" double 5,500.
*d.* Round raised period after "R" — 1,600.
*e.* Round raised period after "R" 4,250. 1,200.
*f.* As "a," with raised period after "V" 4,750. 1,500.

Forged overprints exist on both forged stamps and on genuine stamps.

**Types of 1871 Overprinted or Surcharged in Black**

e

f

**1876, Jan. 31** **Unwmk.**
**Wove Paper**

**33** A2(e) 1p ultramarine 60.00 60.00
*a.* Inverted surcharge
*b.* Dbl. impression of stamp 1,000.
*c.* Horiz. pair, imperf vert. 1,000.
**34** A3(e+f) 2p on 3p dk grn 60.00 *65.00*
*a.* Dbl. surch. "Two Pence"
**35** A4(e) 6p rose 70.00 65.00
*b.* Surcharge inverted
*c.* Dbl. impression of stamp 2,850.
*Nos. 33-35 (3)* 190.00 190.00

**1877** **Laid Paper**

**36** A2(e) 1p ultramarine 32.50 *50.00*
*a.* Horiz. pair, imperf. vert. 1,100.
**37** A3(e+f) 2p on 3p dk grn 75.00 *85.00*
*b.* Perf 10 400.00
*c.* Perf 11 375.00
*d.* Horiz. pair, imperf. vert. 1,100.
*e.* Horiz. pair, imperf. between 1,000.
**38** A3(e+f) 4p on 3p lilac 110.00 27.50
*a.* Horiz. pair, imperf. vert. 1,000.
**39** A4(e) 6p rose 60.00 42.50
*a.* Horiz. pair, imperf. vert. 800.00
*Nos. 36-39 (4)* 277.50 205.00

Many of the preceding stamps are known imperforate. They are printer's waste and were never issued.

A12

A13

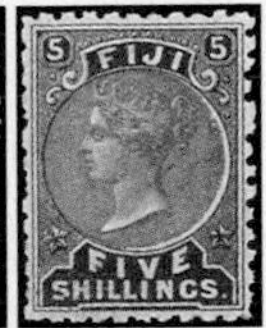


Queen Victoria
A14 A15

***Perf. 10-13½ & Compound***

**1878-90 Wove Paper Typo.**

**40** A12 1p ultra ('79) 20.00 20.00
*a.* 1p blue 65.00 6.50
**41** A12 2p green 40.00 1.75
*b.* 2p ultramarine (error) *40,000.*
**42** A12 4p brt vio ('90) 16.00 9.00
*a.* 4p mauve 27.50 12.00
**43** A13 6p brt rose ('80) 16.00 4.75
*a.* Printed on both sides 2,500. 2,000.
**44** A14 1sh yel brn ('81) 60.00 12.50
*a.* 1sh deep brown 100.00 32.50

**Litho. & Typo.**

**45** A15 5sh blk & red brn ('82) 75.00 50.00
*Nos. 40-45 (6)* 227.00 98.00

No. 41b was not put on sale. All examples were supposed to be destroyed.

A quantity of No. 45 was sold as remainders, canceled-to-order with the following Suva dates: 15.DEC.00; 22.DE.1900; 28.DEC.1900; 12.DEC.01; 15.DEC.01; 16.DE.1901; 21.JUN.02; 15.DEC.02; 15. DE. 1902; and 21.DE.1902. Examples so canceled are worth less than postally used examples.

No. 45 imperf was sold only as a remainder, canceled "Suva, 15.DEC.00."

A late printing of the 5sh, made from an electrotyped plate, exists in gray black and red orange, perf 10, differing from No. 45 in many details. It was also sold only as a remainder, canceled "Suva, 15.DEC.00." It is scarce.

For surcharges see Nos. 46-52.

Nos. 40-45 exist with sheetmaker's watermark. Watermarked stamps are scarcer than unwatermarked.

**1881-90** ***Perf. 10***

*40d* A12 1p ultramarine 30.00 3.50

**Surcharged type "f" in Black**

**1878-90 Typo.**

**46** A12 2p on 3p green 12.00 *42.50*
**47** A12 4p on 1p vio ('90) 75.00 60.00
**48** A12 4p on 2p lilac ('83) 100.00 16.00
*Nos. 46-48 (3)* 187.00 118.50

**Nos. 40-43 Surcharged in Black**

g h

j

k

**1891-92** ***Perf. 10***

**49** A12(g) ½p on 1p ('92) 62.50 *80.00*
**50** A12(h) 2½p on 2p 52.50 *55.00*
*a.* Wider space (2mm) between "2" and "½" 150.00 *150.00*

51 A12(j) 5p on 4p ('92) 62.50 *80.00*
52 A13(k) 5p on 6p ('92) 67.50 *75.00*
a. "FIVE" and "PENCE" 3mm apart 75.00 *85.00*
*Nos. 49-52 (4)* 245.00 *290.00*

No. 50a resulted from loose type, sometimes printing narrow, sometimes wide. Intermediate spacing is known.

A18

A20

Fijian Canoe — A19

**1891-96** ***Perf. 10-12 & Compound***
53 A18 ½p grnsh blk ('92) 2.75 7.00
a. ½p gray 3.75 7.00
54 A19 1p black ('93) 18.00 8.50
55 A19 1p lilac rose ('96) 5.00 1.10
56 A19 2p green ('93) 9.00 .85
a. Perf. 10x12 ('94) 800.00 425.00
57 A20 2½ red brown 6.50 5.50
58 A19 5p ultra ('93) 25.00 8.00
*Nos. 53-58 (6)* 66.25 30.95

Edward VII — A22

**1903, Feb. 1** **Wmk. 2** ***Perf. 14***
59 A22 ½p gray grn & pale grn 3.25 2.25
60 A22 1p vio & blk, *red* 20.00 .65
61 A22 2p vio & orange 4.50 1.40
62 A22 2½p vio & ultra, *bl* 15.00 2.50
63 A22 3p vio & red vio 1.60 *2.75*
64 A22 4p violet & blk 1.60 *2.75*
65 A22 5p vio & green 1.60 *2.50*
66 A22 6p vio & car rose 1.60 *2.00*
67 A22 1sh grn & car rose 18.00 *80.00*
68 A22 5sh green & blk 85.00 *170.00*
69 A22 £1 gray & ultra 400.00 *475.00*
Revenue cancel 75.00
*Nos. 59-68 (10)* 152.15 *266.80*

Numerals of 2p, 4p, 6p and 5sh of type A22 are in color on plain tablet.

**1904-12** **Ordinary Paper** **Wmk. 3**
70 A22 ½p grn & pale grn ('04) 18.50 3.25
70A A22 ½p green ('08) 15.00 3.50
71 A22 1p vio & black, *red* ('04) 40.00 .25
72 A22 1p carmine ('06) 25.00 .25
73 A22 2½p ultra ('10) 7.50 *10.00*

**Chalky Paper**

74 A22 6p violet ('10) 30.00 *50.00*
75 A22 1sh grn & car rose ('09) 32.50 *42.50*
76 A22 1sh black, *green* ('11) 11.00 *16.00*
77 A22 5sh grn & scarlet, *yel* ('11) 72.50 *105.00*
78 A22 £1 vio & black, *red* ('12) 300.00 275.00
*Nos. 70-77 (9)* 252.00 *230.75*

George V — A23

**Die I**

For description of Dies I and II see "Dies of British Colonial Stamps" in Table of Contents.

**1912-23** **Ordinary Paper**
79 A23 ¼p brown ('16) 2.75 .40
80 A23 ½p green 4.50 .60
81 A23 1p scarlet 2.75 .50
a. 1p carmine ('16) 3.50 .25
82 A23 2p gray ('14) 2.00 .25
83 A23 2½p ultra ('14) 3.50 3.75
84 A23 3p violet, *yel* 4.50 *12.50*
a. Die II ('21) 3.25 *32.00*
85 A23 4p black & red, *lem* ('21) 3.25 *17.50*
a. Die II ('23) 3.25 *35.00*

**Chalky Paper**

86 A23 5p dl vio & ol grn ('14) 5.50 *12.50*
87 A23 6p dl vio & red vio ('14) 2.40 *6.00*
88 A23 1sh black, *green* 1.30 *14.50*
a. 1sh black, *blue green, ol back* 3.25 *11.00*
b. 1sh black, *emerald* ('21) 5.50 *67.50*
c. Die II ('22) 3.25 *40.00*
89 A23 2sh 6p black & red, *blue* 37.50 *35.00*
90 A23 5sh grn & scar, *yellow* 37.50 *45.00*
91 A23 £1 vio & black, *red* 300.00 325.00
a. Die II ('21) 300.00 325.00
Revenue cancel 52.50

**Surface-colored Paper**

92 A23 1sh black, *green* 1.25 *14.50*
*Nos. 79-90,92 (13)* 108.70 *163.00*

Numerals of ¼p, 1½p, 2p, 4p, 6p, 2sh, 2sh6p and 5sh of type A23 are in color on plain tablet.

For overprints see Nos. MR1-MR2.

**Die II**

**1922-27** **Wmk. 4** **Ordinary Paper**
93 A23 ¼p dark brown 3.75 *27.50*
94 A23 ½p green 1.10 *1.50*
95 A23 1p rose red 6.50 1.00
96 A23 1p violet ('27) 1.40 .25
97 A23 1½p rose red ('27) 4.50 1.50
98 A23 2p gray 1.40 .25
a. "2d" and value tablet omitted 28,000.
99 A23 3p ultra ('23) 3.00 1.20
100 A23 4p blk & red, *yel* 16.00 7.00
101 A23 5p dl vio & ol green 1.75 *2.25*
102 A23 6p dl vio & red violet 2.40 1.50

**Chalky Paper**

103 A23 1sh blk, *emerald* 14.00 3.00
104 A23 2sh vio & ultra, *bl* ('27) 30.00 *72.50*
105 A23 2sh6p blk & red, *bl* 12.50 *35.00*
106 A23 5sh grn & scar, *yellow* 55.00 *90.00*
*Nos. 93-106 (14)* 153.30 *244.45*

The only known example of No. 98a is the center stamp of an unused block of nine.

Common Design Types pictured following the introduction.

**Silver Jubilee Issue**
Common Design Type

**1935, May 6** ***Perf. 13½x14***
110 CD301 1½p carmine & blue 1.00 *9.00*
111 CD301 2p gray blk & ultra 1.50 .40
112 CD301 3p blue & brown 2.75 *4.50*
113 CD301 1sh brt vio & indigo 10.00 *14.00*
*Nos. 110-113 (4)* 15.25 27.90
Set, never hinged 24.00

**Coronation Issue**
Common Design Type

**1937, May 12** ***Perf. 11x11½***
114 CD302 1p dark violet .50 *1.25*
115 CD302 2p gray black .50 *2.25*
116 CD302 3p indigo .50 *2.25*
*Nos. 114-116 (3)* 1.50 *5.75*
Set, never hinged 2.00

Outrigger Canoe — A24

Fijian Village — A25

Outrigger Canoe A26

Map of Fiji Islands A27

Government Buildings — A27a

Canoe and Arms of Fiji — A28

Sugar Cane — A29

Spear Fishing at Night — A30

Arms of Fiji — A31

Suva Harbor — A32

River Scene — A33

Fijian House — A34

Papaya Tree — A35

Bugler — A36

8p, 1sh5p, 1sh6p, Arms of Fiji.

***Perf. 13½, 12½ (1p)***
**1938-55** **Engr.** **Wmk. 4**
117 A24 ½p green .25 .75
c. Perf. 14 ('41) 15.50 5.75
d. Perf. 12 ('48) 1.00 *3.00*
118 A25 1p blue & brn .45 .25
119 A26 1½p rose car (empty canoe) 12.00 .35
120 A27 2p grn & org brn (no "180 degree") 27.00 .40
121 A27a 2p mag & grn .45 *.60*
a. Perf. 12 ('46) 1.75 .70

***Perf. 12½, 13x12 (6p), 14 (8p)***
122 A28 3p dp ultra 1.50 .30
123 A29 5p rose red & blue 28.00 12.00
124 A29 5p rose red & yel grn .25 .30
125 A27 6p blk (no "180 degree") 40.00 10.00
126 A31 8p rose car 2.25 *3.00*
a. Perf. 13 ('50) 1.75 *2.75*
127 A30 1sh black & yel 2.00 .75

***Perf. 14***
128 A31 1sh5p car & black .25 .25
128A A31 1sh6p ultra 2.75 2.75
b. Perf. 13 ('55) 1.00 *17.50*

***Perf. 12½***
129 A32 2sh vio & org 2.75 .40
130 A33 2sh6p brn & grn 5.25 1.50
131 A34 5sh dk vio & grn 5.25 2.50
131A A35 10sh emer & brn org 28.00 *52.50*
131B A36 £1 car & ultra 37.50 *65.00*
*Nos. 117-131B (18)* 195.90 *153.60*

Issued: 1sh5p, 6/13/40; 5p, 10/1/40; No. 121, 5/19/42; 8p, 11/15/48; 10sh, £1, 3/13/50; 1sh6p, 8/1/50; others, 4/5/38.

**Types of 1938-40 Redrawn**

Man in Canoe — A36a

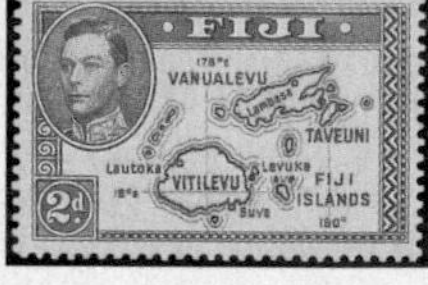
180 Degree Added to the Lower Right Hand Corner of the Design — A36b

***Perf. 13½ (1½p, 2p, 6p), 14 (2½p)***
**1940-49** **Wmk. 4**
132 A36a 1½p rose carmine 2.25 3.00
a. Perf. 12 ('49) 2.50 1.25
b. Perf. 14 ('42) 21.50 17.50
133 A36b 2p grn & org brn ("180 degree") 16.00 15.00
134 A36b 2½p grn & org brn 2.75 .75
a. Perf. 12 ('48) 1.75 .50
b. Perf. 13½ ('42) 2.00 .75
135 A36b 6p blk ("180 degree") 6.00 1.25
a. Perf. 12 ('47) 2.75 1.00
*Nos. 132-135 (4)* 27.00 20.00

Issued: 2½p, Jan. 6, 1942; others Oct. 1, 1940.

No. 133 Surcharged in Black

**1941, Feb. 10** ***Perf. 13½***
136 A27 2½p on 2p grn & org brn 1.50 1.00
Never hinged 2.50

**Catalogue values for unused stamps in this section, from this point to the end of the section, are for Never Hinged items.**

**Peace Issue**
Common Design Type

**1946, Aug. 17** ***Perf. 13½***
137 CD303 2½p bright green .25 *1.50*
138 CD303 3p deep blue .25 .25

**Silver Wedding Issue**
Common Design Types

**1948, Dec. 17** **Photo.** ***Perf. 14x14½***
139 CD304 2½p dark green .50 2.50

**Engr.; Name Typo.**
***Perf. 11½x11***
140 CD305 5sh blue violet 16.50 9.00

### UPU Issue
Common Design Types
**Engr.; Name Typo. on 3p, 8p**
***Perf. 13½, 11x11½***

**1949, Oct. 10** **Wmk. 4**
**141** CD306 2p red violet .35 .75
**142** CD307 3p indigo 2.25 6.50
**143** CD308 8p dp carmine .35 *4.50*
**144** CD309 1sh6p blue .40 *3.00*
*Nos. 141-144 (4)* 3.35 14.75

### Coronation Issue
Common Design Type

**1953, June 2** ***Perf. 13½x13***
**145** CD312 2½p dk green & blk 1.00 .60
*Nos. 145 (1)* 1.00 .60

### Type of 1938-40 with Portrait of Queen Elizabeth II Inscribed: "Royal Visit 1953"

**1953, Dec. 16** ***Perf. 13***
**146** A31 8p carmine lake .65 .35

Visit of Queen Elizabeth II and the Duke of Edinburgh, 1953.

### Types of 1938-50 with Portrait of Queen Elizabeth II, and

A39

Loading Copra A40

Designs: 1sh6p, Sugar cane train. 2sh, Bananas for export. 5sh, Gold industry.

***Perf. 11½ (A24, A27, A39); 11½x11 (A40); 12 (A27, 2p); 12½ (A30, A33, A35, A36); 13 (A31)***

**1954-56** **Engr.**
**147** A24 ½p green 1.00 *1.60*
**148** A39 1p grnsh blue 1.90 .25
**149** A39 1½p brown 3.00 .70
**150** A27a 2p mag & green 1.35 .40
**151** A39 2½p blue vio 3.25 .25
**152** A40 3p purple & brn 5.00 .25
**154** A27 6p black 2.75 .90
**155** A31 8p carmine lake 8.50 1.90
**156** A30 1sh black & yel 3.25 .25
**157** A40 1sh6p grn & dp ultra 17.00 1.05
**158** A40 2sh brt car & black 5.00 .65
**159** A33 2sh6p brn & bl grn 1.90 .25
**160** A40 5sh dp ultra & yel 8.50 1.30
**161** A35 10sh emer & brn org 8.00 *15.00*
**162** A36 £1 car & ultra 35.00 11.00
*Nos. 147-162 (15)* 105.40 35.75

Issued: 2p, 1sh, 2sh6p, 2/1/54; ½p, 6p, 8p, 10sh, £1, 7/1/54; 1p, 6/1/56; 1½p, 2½p, 3p, 1sh6p, 2sh, 5sh, 10/1/56.

### Types of 1954-56 and

Nautilus Shells — A41

Hibiscus — A42

Kandavu Parrot A43

½p, 2p, 2½p, Queen Elizabeth II (A39). 1p, Queen, turtles in bottom panels. 6p, Fijian beating drum (lali). 10p, Yaqona ceremony. 1sh, South Pacific map. 2sh6p, Nadi Airport. 10sh, Cutting sugar cane. £1, Arms of Fiji.

***Perf. 11½ (A39, A41); 11½x11 (A40); 14½x14 (A42); 14x14½ (A43)***
**Engr. (A39, A40, A41); others Photo.**

**1959-63** **Wmk. 4**
**163** A39 ½p green ('61) .25 *2.60*
**164** A41 1p dk blue ('62) 3.75 2.60
**165** A41 1½p dk brown ('62) 3.75 2.60
**166** A39 2p crim rose ('61) 1.60 .25
**167** A39 2½p brown org ('62) 3.25 *5.00*
**168** A40 6p blk & car rose ('61) 1.90 .25
**169** A42 8p gray, red, yel & grn ('61) .55 .30
**170** A40 10p car & brn ('63) 2.60 .65
**171** A40 1sh dk bl & bl ('61) 1.60 .25
**172** A40 2sh6p pur & blk ('61) 9.50 .25
**173** A43 4sh dk grn, red, bl & emer 3.00 1.30
**174** A40 10sh sep & emer ('61) 2.75 1.30
**175** A40 £1 org & blk ('61) 5.75 3.75
*Nos. 163-175 (13)* 40.25 21.10

Issued: 4sh, 7/13; 8p, 8/1; ½p, 2p, 6p, 1sh, 2sh6p, 10sh, £1, 11/14; 1p, 1½p, 2½p, 12/3; 10p, 4/1.
For type overprinted see No. 205.

### Types of 1954-63 and

Elizabeth II — A44

1sh6p, 180th meridian and Intl. Date Line. 2sh, White orchids. 5sh, Orange dove.

***Perf. 11½ (A41); 12½ (A44); 11½x11 (A40); 14x14½ (A43)***
**Engr. (A40, A41); others Photo.**

**1962-67** **Wmk. 314**
**176** A41 1p dark blue ('64) 1.00 *3.75*
**177** A39 2p crim rose ('65) .50 .25
**178** A44 3p rose cl & multi .25 .25
**179** A40 6p blk & car rose ('64) 1.50 .25
**180** A42 9p ultra, red, yel & grn ('63) .90 .65
**181** A40 10p car & brn ('64) .60 .50
**182** A40 1sh dk bl & bl ('66) 2.25 .45
**183** A43 1sh6p dk bl & multi 1.50 .60
**184** A42 2sh gold, yel grn & grn 10.00 3.50
**185** A40 2sh6p pur & blk ('65) 5.50 1.25
**186** A43 4sh grn & multi, wmk. sideways ('67) 4.25 1.00
*a.* As #186, wmk. upright ('64) 7.50 2.00
*b.* 4sh dark green & multi ('66) 6.00 2.50
**187** A43 5sh dk gray, yel & red 10.00 .35
**188** A40 10sh sep & emer ('64) 7.50 2.50
**189** A40 £1 org & blk ('64) 14.00 7.00
*Nos. 176-189 (14)* 59.75 22.30

Issued: 3p, 1sh6p, 2sh, 5sh, 12/3; 9p, No. 186a, 4/1; 1p, 10p, 10sh, 1/14; 6p, £1, 6/9; 2p, 2sh6p, 8/3; No. 186b, 3/1; No. 186, 2/16.

### Nos. 178 and 171 Overprinted

**1963, Feb. 1**
**196** A44 3p multicolored .50 .35
**197** A40 1sh dark blue & blue .65 .35

Visit of Elizabeth II & Prince Philip, Feb. 3.

### Freedom from Hunger Issue
Common Design Type

**1963, June 4** **Photo.** ***Perf. 14x14½***
**198** CD314 2sh ultramarine 3.50 2.25

Running A45

9p, Throwing the discus, vert. 1sh, Field hockey, vert. 2sh6p, Women's high jump.

***Perf. 14½x14, 14x14½***

**1963, Aug. 6** **Wmk. 314**
**199** A45 3p yel, blk & brn .45 .25
**200** A45 9p violet, blk & brn .45 1.00
**201** A45 1sh green, blk & brn .45 .25
**202** A45 2sh6p blue, blk & brn 1.10 .95
*Nos. 199-202 (4)* 2.45 2.45

1st So. Pacific Games, Suva, 8/29-9/7.

### Red Cross Centenary Issue
Common Design Type

**1963, Sept. 2** **Litho.** ***Perf. 13***
**203** CD315 2p black & red 1.00 .30
**204** CD315 2sh ultra & red 2.25 2.50

Type of 1959-63 Overprinted

**1963, Dec. 2** **Engr.** ***Perf. 11½x11***
**205** A40 1sh dark blue & blue 1.00 .35

Opening of the Commonwealth Pacific (telephone) Cable service, COMPAC.

Fiji Scout Badge — A46

Scouts of India, Fiji and Europe Tying Knot — A47

**1964, Aug. 3** **Photo.** ***Perf. 12½***
**206** A46 3p multicolored .50 .50
**207** A47 1sh ocher & purple .65 .65

50th anniv. of the founding of the Fiji Boy Scouts.

Amphibian "Aotearoa," 1939 — A48

Map of Fiji and Tonga Islands and Plane A49

Design: 6p, Heron plane.

**1964, Oct. 24** ***Perf. 12½, 14½***
**208** A48 3p brt red & black .50 .35
**209** A48 6p ultra & red .85 .85
**210** A49 1sh grnsh blue & black .85 .85
*Nos. 208-210 (3)* 2.20 2.05

Fiji-Tonga airmail service, 25th anniv.

### ITU Issue
Common Design Type
***Perf. 11x11½***

**1965, May 17** **Litho.** **Wmk. 314**
**211** CD317 3p blue & rose red .50 .30
**212** CD317 2sh yel & bister 1.50 .75

### Intl. Cooperation Year Issue
Common Design Type

**1965, Oct. 25** ***Perf. 14½***
**213** CD318 2p blue grn & claret .35 .25
**214** CD318 2sh6p lt vio & grn 1.60 1.00

### Churchill Memorial Issue
Common Design Type

**1966, Jan. 24** **Photo.** ***Perf. 14***
**Design in Black, Gold and Carmine Rose**
**215** CD319 3p brt blue .75 .25
**216** CD319 9p green 1.10 1.25
**217** CD319 1sh brown 1.10 .25
**218** CD319 2sh6p violet 1.45 1.25
*Nos. 215-218 (4)* 4.40 3.00

### World Cup Soccer Issue
Common Design Type

**1966, July 1** **Litho.** ***Perf. 14***
**219** CD321 2p multicolored .30 .25
**220** CD321 2sh multicolored 1.40 .35

H.M.S. Pandora and Split Island, Rotuma A50

Designs: 10p, Rotuma chiefs, Pandora, and Rotuma's position in Pacific. 1sh6p, Rotuma islanders welcoming Pandora.

**1966, Aug. 29** **Photo.** ***Perf. 14x13***
**221** A50 3p multicolored .40 .25
**222** A50 10p multicolored .40 .25
**223** A50 1sh6p multicolored .65 .95
*Nos. 221-223 (3)* 1.45 1.45

175th anniv. of the discovery of Rotuma, a group of eight islands forming part of the colony of Fiji.

### WHO Headquarters Issue
Common Design Type

**1966, Sept. 20** **Litho.** ***Perf. 14***
**224** CD322 6p multicolored 1.45 .30
**225** CD322 2sh6p multicolored 3.25 3.00
*Nos. 224-225 (2)* 4.70 3.30

Woman Runner A51

Designs: 9p, Shot put, vert. 1sh, Diver.

**1966, Dec. 8** **Photo.** ***Perf. 14x14½***
**226** A51 3p ol, black & lt brn .25 .25
**227** A51 9p brt blue, blk & brn .35 .35
**228** A51 1sh blue green & multi .40 .40
*Nos. 226-228 (3)* 1.00 1.00

2nd South Pacific Games, Noumea, New Caledonia, Dec. 8-18.

Military Band A52

Intl. Tourist Year: 9p, Reef diving. 1sh, Beqa fire walkers. 2sh, Liner Oriana and Mt. Rama volcano.

**1967, Oct. 20** ***Perf. 14x13***
**229** A52 3p multi & gold .60 .25
**230** A52 9p multi & silver .30 .25
**231** A52 1sh multi & gold .30 .25
**232** A52 2sh multi & silver .60 .30
*Nos. 229-232 (4)* 1.80 1.05

Admiral Bligh, H.M.S. Providence and Old Map of "Feejee" A53

Designs: 1sh, Bligh's longboat being chased by double canoe and map of Fiji Islands. 2sh6p, Bligh's tomb, St. Mary's Cemetery, Lambeth, London.

***Perf. 15x14, 12½x13 (1sh)***

**1967, Dec. 7 Photo. Wmk. 314**

**Size: 35x21mm**

**233** A53 4p emer, blk & yel .25 .25

**Size: 54x20mm**

**234** A53 1sh brt bl, brn org & blk .40 .25

**Size: 35x21mm**

**235** A53 2sh6p sepia & multi .40 .30
*Nos. 233-235 (3)* 1.05 .80

150th anniv. of the death of Adm. William Bligh (1754-1817), captain of the Bounty and principal discoverer of the Fiji Islands.

Simmonds "Spartan" Seaplane — A54

Designs: 6p, Fiji Airways Hawker-Siddeley H748 and emblems of various airlines. 1sh, Fokker "Southern Cross," Capt. Charles Kingsford-Smith, his crew and Southern Cross constellation. 2sh, Lockheed Altair "Lady Southern Cross."

***Perf. 14x14½***

**1968, June 5 Wmk. 314**

**236** A54 2p green & black .25 .25
**237** A54 6p brt blue, car & blk .25 .25
**238** A54 1sh dp violet & green .30 .25
**239** A54 2sh orange brn & dk blue .50 .25
*Nos. 236-239 (4)* 1.30 1.00

40th anniv. of the first Trans-Pacific Flight through Fiji under Capt. Charles Kingsford-Smith.

Fijian Bures — A55

Eastern Reef Heron — A56

1p, Passion fruit flowers. 2p, Nautilus pompilius shell. 4p, Hawk moth. 6p, Reef butterflyfish. 9p, Bamboo raft (bilibili). 10p, Tiger moth. 1sh, Black marlin. 1sh6p, Orange-breasted honey eaters. 2sh, Ringed sea snake, horiz. 2sh6p, Outrigger canoes (takia), horiz. 3sh, Golden cowrie shell. 4sh, Emperor gold mine and gold ore. 5sh, Bamboo orchids, horiz. 10sh, Tabua (ceremonial whale's tooth). £1, Coat of Arms and Queen Elizabeth II, horiz.

***Perf. 13½ (A55), 14 (A56)***

**1968, July 15 Photo. Wmk. 314**

**240** A55 ½p multicolored .25 .25
**241** A55 1p multicolored .25 .25
**242** A55 2p multicolored .25 .25
**243** A56 3p multicolored .45 .25
**244** A55 4p multicolored .95 1.60
**245** A55 6p multicolored .30 .25
**246** A55 9p multicolored .25 1.60
**247** A55 10p multicolored 1.50 .25
**248** A56 1sh multicolored .25 .25
**249** A56 1sh6p multicolored 5.50 4.50
**250** A56 2sh multicolored .90 1.60
**251** A56 2sh6p multicolored .90 .30
**252** A55 3sh multicolored 1.90 4.75
**253** A56 4sh multicolored 4.25 2.25
**254** A56 5sh multicolored 2.40 1.25
**255** A56 10sh multicolored 1.25 2.40
**256** A56 £1 red & multi 1.50 2.40
*Nos. 240-256 (17)* 23.05 24.40

See Nos. 260-276.

WHO Emblem, Map of Fiji and Nurses — A57

WHO Emblem and: 9p, Medical team loading patient on stretcher on dinghy and medical ship "Vuniwai." 3sh, People playing on beach.

**1968, Dec. 9 Litho. *Perf. 14***

**257** A57 3p blue green & multi .25 .25
**258** A57 9p brt blue & multi .40 .40
**259** A57 3sh dk blue & multi .60 .60
*Nos. 257-259 (3)* 1.25 1.25

WHO, 20th anniv.

## Types of 1968 Values in Cents and Dollars

Designs: 1c, Passion fruit flowers. 2c, Nautilus pompilius shell. 3c, Reef heron. 4c, Hawk moth. 5c, Reef butterflyfish. 6c, Fijian bures. 8c, Bamboo raft. 9c, Tiger moth. 10c, Black marlin. 15c, Orange-breasted honey-eater. 20c, Ringed sea snake, horiz. 25c, Outrigger canoes (takia), horiz. 30c, Golden cowrie shell. 40c Emperor gold mine and gold ore. 50c, Bamboo orchids, horiz. $1, Tabua (ceremonial whale's tooth). $2, Coat of Arms and Queen Elizabeth II, horiz.

***Perf. 13½ (A55), 14 (A56)***

**1969, Jan. 13 Photo. Wmk. 314**

**260** A55 1c multicolored .25 .25
**261** A55 2c multicolored .25 .25
**262** A56 3c multicolored 1.25 1.00
**263** A55 4c multicolored 1.50 1.00
**264** A55 5c multicolored .25 .25
**265** A55 6c multicolored .25 .25
**266** A55 8c multicolored .25 .25
**267** A55 9c multicolored 1.50 *2.25*
**268** A56 10c multicolored .25 .25
**269** A56 15c multicolored 6.50 6.00
**270** A56 20c multicolored 1.25 .80
**271** A56 25c multicolored 1.00 .25
**272** A55 30c multicolored 3.50 1.50
**273** A56 40c multicolored 7.50 4.00
**274** A56 50c multicolored 2.00 .25
**275** A56 $1 multicolored 1.50 .40
**276** A56 $2 red & multi 3.00 1.50
*Nos. 260-276 (17)* 32.00 20.45

For overprints & surcharges see Nos. 286-288, B5-B6.

Nos. 274 and 275 exist on glazed paper. Values, set: $15 unused, $5 used.

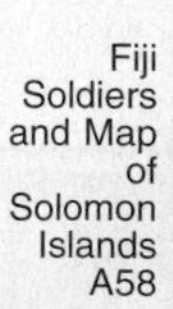

Fiji Soldiers and Map of Solomon Islands A58

Designs: 10c, Flags of Fiji Military Force, soldiers in full and battle dress. 25c, Cpl. Sefanaia Sukanaivalu and Victoria Cross.

**1969, June 23 Wmk. 314 *Perf. 14***

**277** A58 3c emerald & multi .50 .25
**278** A58 10c red & multi .55 .25
**279** A58 25c black & multi .85 .45
*Nos. 277-279 (3)* 1.90 .95

25th anniv. of the Fiji Military Forces campaign in the Solomon Islands and of the posthumous award of the Victoria Cross to Cpl. Sefanaia Sukanaivalu.

Yachting — A59

Designs: 4c, Javelin. 20c, Winners and South Pacific Games medal.

**1969, Aug. 18 Photo. *Perf. 14½x14***

**280** A59 4c red, brown & blk .30 .30
**281** A59 8c blue & black .40 .40
**282** A59 20c olive grn, blk & ocher .50 .50
*Nos. 280-282 (3)* 1.20 1.20

3rd South Pacific Games, Port Moresby, Papua New Guinea, Aug. 13-23.

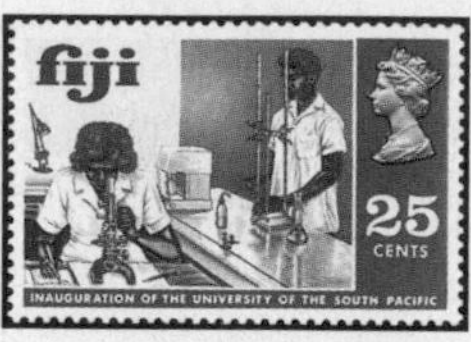


Students in Laboratory — A60

2c, Map of South Pacific and mortarboard. 8c, Site of University at Royal New Zealand Air Force Seaplane Station, Laucala Bay, RNZAF badge and Sunderland flying boat.

**1969, Nov. 10 *Perf. 14x14½***

**283** A60 2c multicolored .25 .25
**284** A60 8c red & multi .35 .35
**285** A60 25c dk green & multi .80 .75
*Nos. 283-285 (3)* 1.40 1.35

Inauguration of the University of the South Pacific, Laucala Bay, Suva.

Nos. 261, 268 and 271 Overprinted

**1970, Mar. 4 *Perf. 13½, 14***

**286** A55 2c multicolored .30 *.40*
**287** A56 10c multicolored .40 .30
**288** A55 25c multicolored .80 .80
*Nos. 286-288 (3)* 1.50 1.50

Visit of Queen Elizabeth II, Prince Philip and Princess Anne, Mar. 4-5.

Nuns Sitting under Chaulmoogra Tree, and Chaulmoogra Fruit — A61

Designs: 10c, Paintings by Semisi Maya (former patient). No. 290, Cascade, vert. No. 291, Sea urchins, vert. 30c, Aerial view of Makogai Hospital.

***Perf. 14x14½, 14½x14***

**1970, May 25 Photo. Wmk. 314**

**289** A61 2c brt pink & multi .25 .55
**290** A61 10c gray green & blk .50 .55
**291** A61 10c blue, car & blk .50 .55
*a.* Pair, #290-291 1.00 1.10
**292** A61 30c orange & multi 1.00 .60
*Nos. 289-292 (4)* 2.25 2.25

Closing of the Leprosy Hospital on Makogai Island in 1969.

Abel Tasman and Ship's Log, 1643 — A62

3c, Capt. James Cook & "Endeavour." 8c, Capt. William Bligh & longboat, 1789. 25c, Man of Fiji & Fijian ocean-going canoe.

**1970, Aug. 18 Litho. *Perf. 13x12½***

**293** A62 2c blue green & multi .75 .55
**294** A62 3c gray green & multi 1.25 .55
**295** A62 8c multicolored 1.25 .45
**296** A62 25c dull lilac & multi .75 .45
*Nos. 293-296 (4)* 4.00 2.00

Discoverers and explorers of Fiji Islands.

King Cakobau and Cession Stone at Lavuka A63

Designs: 3c, Chinese, Fijian, Indian and European children. 10c, Prime Minister Ratu Sir Kamisese Mara and flag of Fiji. 25c, Fijian male dancer and Indian female dancer.

**1970, Oct. 10 Wmk. 314 *Perf. 14***

**297** A63 2c multicolored .25 .25
**298** A63 3c multicolored .25 .25
**299** A63 10c multicolored 1.10 .25
**300** A63 25c multicolored .30 .30
*Nos. 297-300 (4)* 1.90 1.05

Fijian independence.

Fiji Nos. 1 and 3 — A64

15c, Fiji #15, 44, 59, 81, 127, 166. 20c, Fiji Times Office, Levuka, & G. P. O., Suva.

**1970, Nov. 2 Photo. *Perf. 14½x14***

**Size: 35x21mm**

**301** A64 4c multicolored .30 .25

**Size: 60x21½mm**

**302** A64 15c multicolored .75 .30

**Size: 35x21mm**

**303** A64 20c multicolored .75 .30
*Nos. 301-303 (3)* 1.80 .85

Centenary of first postage stamps of Fiji.

Gray-backed White Eyes — A65

Yellow-breasted Musk Parrots — A66

Designs: 1c, Cirrhopetalum umbellatum. 2c, Cardinal honey eaters. 3c, Calanthe furcata.4c, Bulbophyllum. 6c, Phaius tancarvilliae. 8c,Blue-crested broadbills. 10c, Acanthephippiumvitiense. 15c, Dendrobium tokai. 20c, Slaty flycatchers. 25c, Kandavu honey eaters. 30c, Dendrobium gordonii. 50c, White-throated pigeon. $1, Collared lories (kula). $2, Dendrobium platygastrium. (Orchids shown on 1c, 3c, 4c, 6c, 10c, 15c, 30c, $2.)

**Wmk. 314 Upright**

**1971-72 Litho. *Perf. 13½x14***

**305** A65 1c blk & multi ('72) .25 .30
**306** A65 2c carmine & multi .45 .25
**307** A65 3c multi ('72) .85 .25
**308** A65 4c blk & multi ('72) .65 1.75
**309** A65 5c brown & multi .35 .25
**310** A65 6c lt bl & multi ('72) 4.75 6.00
**311** A65 8c black & multi .35 .25
**312** A65 10c multi ('72) .35 .25
**313** A65 15c multi ('72) 4.75 1.00
**314** A65 20c gray & multi 1.35 .30

***Perf. 14***

**315** A66 25c sepia & multi 3.75 .25
**316** A66 30c grn & multi ('72) 8.75 .85
**317** A66 40c blue & multi 4.00 .45
**318** A66 50c gray & multi 2.60 .45
**319** A66 $1 red & multi 3.50 .85
**320** A66 $2 multi ('72) 2.75 8.00
*Nos. 305-320 (16)* 39.45 21.45

Issued: 5c, 20c, 40c, 50c, 8/6; 2c, 8c, 25c, $1, 11/22; 1c, 10c, 30c, $2, 1/4; 3c, 4c, 6c, 15c, 6/23.

**1972-74 Wmk. 314 Sideways**

*306c* A65 2c ('73) .40 *9.00*
*307a* A65 3c ('73) 2.25 .50
*308a* A65 4c ('73) 5.50 .85
*309a* A65 5c ('73) 7.75 3.75
*310a* A65 6c ('73) 9.75 1.40
*311a* A65 8c ('73) 3.50 .80
*313a* A65 15c ('73) 5.00 2.50
*314a* A65 20c 13.50 2.10
*315a* A66 25c ('73) 1.75 .95
*317a* A66 40c ('74) 2.75 *9.50*

*318a* A66 50c ('74) 2.75 *4.00*
*319a* A66 $1 2.75 *4.50*
*320a* A66 $2 2.75 *4.50*
*Nos. 306c-320a (13)* 60.40 44.35

Issued: 20c, $1, $2, 11/17; 3c, 5c, 3/8; 4c, 6c, 8c, 15c, 25c, 4/11; 2c, 12/12; 40c, 50c, 3/15.

**1975-77 Wmk. 373**

*305b* A65 1c 1.00 *4.50*
*306d* A65 2c .80 *4.50*
*307b* A65 3c .45 *4.50*
*308b* A65 4c ('76) 3.50 .25
*309b* A65 5c 1.30 *4.75*
*310b* A65 6c ('76) 2.90 .25
*311b* A65 8c ('76) .35 .25
*312b* A65 10c .40 *2.50*
*313b* A65 15c ('76) 2.60 .50
*314b* A65 20c ('77) 3.75 .60
*316b* A66 30c ('76) 5.00 1.10
*317b* A66 40c ('76) 4.50 .65
*318b* A66 50c ('76) 3.00 .65
*319b* A66 $1 ('76) 3.00 1.05
*320b* A66 $2 ('76) 1.45 1.05
*Nos. 305b-320b (15)* 34.00 27.10

Issued: 1c, 2c, 3c, 5c, 10c, 4/9; 20c, 7/15; others, 9/3.

Women's Basketball — A67

**1971, Sept. 6 Wmk. 314 *Perf. 14***

**321** A67 8c shown .25 .25
**322** A67 10c Running .50 .50
**323** A67 25c Weight lifting 1.00 .95
*Nos. 321-323 (3)* 1.75 1.70

4th South Pacific Games, Papeete, French Polynesia, Sept. 8-19.

Community Education — A68

Designs: 4c, Public health. 50c, Economic growth (farm scenes).

**1972, Feb. 7**

**324** A68 2c bright rose & multi .25 .25
**325** A68 4c gray & multi .25 .25
**326** A68 50c bright blue & multi 1.05 1.05
*Nos. 324-326 (3)* 1.55 1.55

South Pacific Commission, 25th anniv.

Rugby — A70

**1973, Mar. 9 Litho. *Perf. 14***

**330** A70 2c shown .40 .40
**331** A70 8c Tackle .80 .80
**332** A70 25c Kicking ball 1.05 1.05
*Nos. 330-332 (3)* 2.25 2.25

60th anniversary of Fiji Rugby Union.

Forestry Development — A71

Development projects: 8c, Irrigation of rice field. 10c, Low income housing. 25c, Highway construction.

**1973, July 23 *Perf. 14***

**333** A71 5c multicolored .25 *.45*
**334** A71 8c multicolored .35 .25
**335** A71 10c multicolored .40 .25
**336** A71 25c multicolored .70 *.75*
*Nos. 333-336 (4)* 1.70 1.70

Holy Family — A72

Festivals: 10c, Diwali (Candles; Indian New Year). 20c, Id-Ul-Fitar (Friendly greeting and mosque; Moslem, Ramadan). 25c, Chinese New Year (dragon dance).

**1973, Oct. 26 *Perf. 14x14½***

**337** A72 3c blue & multi .30 .25
**338** A72 10c purple & multi .30 .25
**339** A72 20c emerald & multi .55 *.60*
**340** A72 25c red & multi .55 *.60*
*Nos. 337-340 (4)* 1.70 1.70

Festivals celebrated by various groups in Fiji.

Runners — A73

**1974, Jan. 7**

**341** A73 3c shown .40 .25
**342** A73 8c Boxing .40 .25
**343** A73 50c Lawn bowling 1.20 *1.50*
*Nos. 341-343 (3)* 2.00 2.00

10th British Commonwealth Games, Christchurch, N.Z., Jan. 24-Feb. 2.

Centenary of Cricket in Fiji — A74

Designs: 3c, Bowler. 25c, Batsman and wicketkeeper. 40c, Fielder, horiz.

***Perf. 14x14½, 14½x14***

**1974, Feb. 21 Litho.**

**344** A74 3c multicolored 1.10 .25
**345** A74 25c multicolored 1.35 .25
**346** A74 40c multicolored 1.60 *2.25*
*Nos. 344-346 (3)* 4.05 2.75

Mailman and UPU Emblem A75

UPU Emblem and: 8c, Loading mail on ship. 30c, Post office and truck. 50c, Jet.

**1974, May 22 Wmk. 314 *Perf. 14***

**347** A75 3c orange & multi .25 .25
**348** A75 8c multicolored .30 .25
**349** A75 30c lt blue & multi .45 .40
**350** A75 50c multicolored .90 *1.00*
*Nos. 347-350 (4)* 1.90 1.90

Centenary of the Universal Postal Union.

Cub Scouts A76

Designs: 10c, Boy Scouts reading map. 40c, Scouts and Fiji flag, vert.

**1974, Aug. 30**

**351** A76 3c multicolored .25 .25
**352** A76 10c multicolored .50 .25
**353** A76 40c multicolored 1.25 1.80
*Nos. 351-353 (3)* 2.00 2.30

First National Boy Scout Jamboree, Lautoka, Viti Levu Island.

Cakobau Club and Flag — A77

King Cakobau, Queen Victoria A78

Design: 50c, Signing ceremony at Levuka.

**1974, Oct. 9 Litho. *Perf. 13½x13***

**354** A77 3c multicolored .25 .25
**355** A78 8c multicolored .25 .25
**356** A78 50c multicolored .60 .60
*Nos. 354-356 (3)* 1.10 1.10

Deed of Cession, cent. and 4th anniv. of independence.

Diwali, Hindu Festival of Lights — A79

Designs: 15c, Id-Ul-Fitar (women exchanging greetings under moon). 25c, Chinese New Year (girl twirling streamer, and fireworks). 30c, Christmas (man and woman singing hymns, and star).

**1975, Oct. 31 Wmk. 373 *Perf. 14***

**357** A79 3c black & multi .25 .25
**358** A79 15c black & multi .45 .25
**359** A79 25c black & multi .85 .25
**360** A79 30c black & multi 1.10 1.90
*a.* Souvenir sheet of 4, #357-360 4.50 4.50
*Nos. 357-360 (4)* 2.65 2.65

Festivals celebrated by various groups in Fiji.

Steam Locomotive No. 21 — A80

Sugar mill trains: 15c, Diesel locomotive No. 8. 20c, Diesel locomotive No. 1. 30c, Free passenger train.

**1976, Jan. 26 Litho. *Perf. 14½***

**361** A80 4c yellow & multi .45 .25
**362** A80 15c salmon & multi .85 .40
**363** A80 20c multicolored .95 1.00
**364** A80 30c blue & multi 1.20 1.80
*Nos. 361-364 (4)* 3.45 3.45

Fiji Blind Society and Rotary Emblems A81

Rotary Intl. of Fiji, 40th Anniv.: 25c, Ambulance and Rotary emblems.

***Perf. 13x13½***

**1976, Mar. 26 Wmk. 373**

**365** A81 10c lt green, brn, ultra .25 .25
**366** A81 25c multicolored .65 .65

De Havilland Drover — A82

Planes: 15c, BAC One-Eleven. 25c, Hawker-Siddeley 748. 30c, Britten Norman Trislander.

**1976, Sept. 1 Litho. *Perf. 14***

**367** A82 4c multicolored .60 .25
**368** A82 15c multicolored 1.10 1.10
**369** A82 25c multicolored 1.25 1.25
**370** A82 30c multicolored 1.40 *1.75*
*Nos. 367-370 (4)* 4.35 4.35

Fiji air service, 25th anniversary.

Queen's Visit, 1970 — A83

**Silver Wedding Issue, 1972**

Common Design Type

Queen Elizabeth II, Prince Philip, flowers, shells.

**1972, Nov. 20 Photo. *Perf. 14x14½***

**328** CD324 10c slate grn & multi .25 .25
**329** CD324 25c red lilac & multi .45 .45
*a.* Blue omitted *550.00*

On No. 329a, Prince Philip's coat is brown instead of blue.

Designs: 25c, King Edward's Chair. 30c, Queen wearing cloth-of-gold supertunica.

**1977, Feb. 7 Litho. *Perf. 14x13½***

**371** A83 10c silver & multi .25 .25
**372** A83 25c silver & multi .30 .25
**373** A83 30c silver & multi .40 .30
*Nos. 371-373 (3)* .95 .80

25th anniv. of reign of Elizabeth II.

World Map, Sinusoidal Projection — A84

Design: 30c, Map showing Fiji Islands.

**Wmk. 373**

**1977, Apr. 12 Litho. *Perf. 14½***

**374** A84 4c multicolored .25 .25
**375** A84 30c multicolored .60 .60

First Joint Council of Ministers Conference of the European Economic Community (EEC) and of African, Caribbean and Pacific States (ACP).

Hibiscus A85

**1977, Aug. 27 Wmk. 373 *Perf. 14***

**376** A85 4c red .25 .25
**377** A85 15c orange .25 .25
**378** A85 30c pink .45 .30
**379** A85 35c yellow .75 *.90*
*Nos. 376-379 (4)* 1.70 1.70

Fiji Hibiscus Festival, 21st anniversary.

Drua, Double Canoe A86

Canoes: 15c, Tabilai. 25c, Takia, dugout outrigger canoe. 40c, Camakau.

**1977, Nov. 7 Litho. *Perf. 14½***

**380** A86 4c multicolored .25 .25
**381** A86 15c multicolored .35 .30
**382** A86 25c multicolored .50 .45
**383** A86 40c multicolored .60 *.70*
*Nos. 380-383 (4)* 1.70 1.70

**Elizabeth II Coronation Anniversary Issue**

Common Design Types
Souvenir Sheet

**Unwmk.**

**1978, Apr. 21 Litho. *Perf. 15***

**384** Sheet of 6 1.75 1.75
*a.* CD326 25c White hart of Richard II .25 .25
*b.* CD327 25c Elizabeth II .25 .25
*c.* CD328 25c Banded iguana .25 .25

No. 384 contains 2 se-tenant strips of Nos. 348a-348c, separated by horizontal gutter.

Southern Cross on Naselai Beach — A87

4c, Fiji Defence Force surrounding Southern Cross. 25c, Wright Flyer. 30c, Bristol F2B.

**1978, June 26 Wmk. 373 *Perf. 14½***

**385** A87 4c multicolored .25 .25
**386** A87 15c multicolored .40 .30
**387** A87 25c multicolored .75 .60
**388** A87 30c multicolored 1.10 .75
*Nos. 385-388 (4)* 2.50 1.90

50th anniv. of Kingsford-Smith's Trans-Pacific flight, May 31-June 10, 1928 (4c, 15c); 75th anniv. of Wright brothers' first powered flight, Dec. 17, 1903 (25c); 60th anniv. of Royal Air Force, Apr. 1, 1918 (30c).

Necklace of Sperm Whale Teeth A88

Fiji artifacts: 4c, Wooden oil dish in shape of man, vert. 25c, Twin water bottles. 30c, Carved throwing club (Ula), vert.

**1978, Aug. 14 Litho. *Perf. 14***

**389** A88 4c multicolored .25 .25
**390** A88 15c multicolored .25 .25
**391** A88 25c multicolored .30 .30
**392** A88 30c multicolored .45 .45
*Nos. 389-392 (4)* 1.25 1.25

Christmas Wreath and Candles A89

Festivals: 15c, Diwali (oil lamps). 25c, Id-Ul-Fitr (fruit, coffeepot and cups). 40c, Chinese New Year (paper dragon).

**1978, Oct. 30 *Perf. 14***

**393** A89 4c multicolored .25 .25
**394** A89 15c multicolored .25 .25
**395** A89 25c multicolored .35 .35
**396** A89 40c multicolored .55 .55
*Nos. 393-396 (4)* 1.40 1.40

Banded Iguana A90

Endangered species and Wildlife Fund emblem: 15c, Tree frog. 25c, Long-legged warbler. 30c, Pink-billed parrot finch.

**1979, Mar. 19 Litho. Wmk. 373**

**397** A90 4c multicolored 1.25 .50
**398** A90 15c multicolored 2.00 1.00
**399** A90 25c multicolored 8.75 1.50
**400** A90 30c multicolored 8.75 5.00
*Nos. 397-400 (4)* 20.75 8.00

Indian Women Making Music A91

15c, Indian men sitting around kava bowl. 30c, Indian sugar cane, houses. 40c, Sailing ship Leonidas, map of South Pacific.

**1979, May 11 Wmk. 373 *Perf. 14***

**401** A91 4c multicolored .25 .25
**402** A91 15c multicolored .25 .25
**403** A91 30c multicolored .35 .35
**404** A91 40c multicolored .50 .50
*Nos. 401-404 (4)* 1.35 1.35

Arrival of Indians as indentured laborers, cent.

Soccer A92

Games Emblem and: 15c, Rugby. 30c, Tennis. 40c, Weight lifting.

**1979, July 2 Litho. *Perf. 14***

**405** A92 4c multicolored .30 .25
**406** A92 15c multicolored .40 .30
**407** A92 30c multicolored .80 .65
**408** A92 40c multicolored .95 1.25
*Nos. 405-408 (4)* 2.45 2.45

6th South Pacific Games.

Old Town Hall, Suva A93

2c, Dudley Church, Suva. 3c, Telecommunications building, Suva. 4c, 5c, Lautoka Mosque. 6c, GPO, Suva. 8c, 12c, Levuka Public School. 10c, Visitors' Bureau, Suva. 15c, Colonial War Memorial Hospital Suva. 18c, Labasa Sugar Mill. 20c, Rewa Bridge, Nausori. 30c Sacred Heart Cathedral, Suva. 35c Grand Pacific Hotel, Suva. 45c, Shiva Temple, Suva. 50c Serua Island Village. $1, Solo Lighthouse. $2, Baker memorial Hall, Nausori. $5, Government House.

**Without Inscribed Date, except #411B (1991)**

**Chalky Paper (#409-411, 414, 416, 418-419, 425)**

**Ordinary Paper (#412-413, 415, 417, 420-424)**

**1979-94 Wmk. 373 *Perf. 14***

**409** A93 1c multicolored .30 .60
*a.* Ordinary paper 1.75 2.00
*b.* Inscribed "1994" 2.00 3.00
**410** A93 2c multicolored .90 .75
*a.* Ordinary paper 1.75 2.00
*b.* Inscribed "1983" 1.00 .50
*c.* Inscribed "1986" 1.50 .25
*d.* Inscribed "1991" .75 .75
*e.* Inscribed "1993" 3.50 3.50
*f.* Inscribed "1994" 1.00 1.50
**411** A93 3c multicolored .75 .75
*a.* Ordinary paper 2.00 2.00
*b.* Inscribed "1993" 4.50 4.50
**411B** A93 4c multicolored 1.50 1.50
*a.* Inscribed "1993" 6.00 6.00
*b.* Inscribed "1994" 3.50 5.50
**412** A93 5c multicolored .25 .25
*a.* Inscribed "1983" .60 .25
**413** A93 6c multicolored .25 .75
*a.* Inscribed "1983" .30 .25
**414** A93 10c multicolored .40 .25
*a.* Ordinary paper 2.00 1.75
*b.* Inscribed "1991" 2.75 3.00
**415** A93 12c multicolored .40 2.75
*a.* Inscribed "1993" 3.50 4.00
*b.* Inscribed "1994" 2.00 3.50
**416** A93 15c multicolored .75 .60
*a.* Ordinary paper 1.75 1.75
*b.* Inscribed "1991" 3.50 3.00
**417** A93 18c multicolored .30 .25
**418** A93 20c multicolored 1.00 .30
*a.* Ordinary paper 2.50 2.00
*b.* Inscribed "1993" 3.75 3.75
*c.* Inscribed "1994" 3.50 3.50
**419** A93 30c multi, vert. 1.25 .50
*a.* Ordinary paper .60 1.75
**420** A93 35c multicolored .60 *1.50*
**421** A93 45c multicolored .45 .45
**422** A93 50c multicolored .60 .40
*a.* Inscribed "1994" 3.50 4.00

***Perf. 14x13½, 13½x14***

**Size: 45x29mm, 29x45mm (#423)**

**423** A93 $1 multi, vert. 1.50 *2.50*
**424** A93 $2 multicolored 1.50 *1.75*
**425** A93 $5 multicolored 2.50 *2.75*
*Nos. 409-425 (18)* 15.20 18.60

Issued: 5c, 6c, 12c, 18c, 35c-$2, 12/22/80; No. 411B, 11/1991; others, 11/11/79.

**1986-92 Wmk. 384**

**With Date Inscription**

**1986**

*410g* A93 2c multicolored 1.25 1.25
**413B** A93 8c multicolored 4.50 4.50

**1988**

*410h* A93 2c multicolored 1.00 1.00
*411h* A93 3c multicolored 1.00 1.00
*411Bh* A93 4c multicolored 1.00 1.00
*418h* A93 20c multicolored 2.00 2.00

**1990**

*414i* A93 10c multicolored 1.50 1.50
*418i* A93 20c multicolored 2.00 2.00

**1991**

*409j* A93 1c multicolored 1.75 3.50
*410j* A93 2c multicolored 1.00 1.00
*411j* A93 3c multicolored 1.75 1.75
*411Bj* A93 4c multicolored 1.00 1.00
*414j* A93 10c multicolored 2.00 2.00
*416j* A93 15c multicolored 1.00 1.00
*420j* A93 35c multicolored 2.75 2.75
*422j* A93 50c multicolored 3.75 3.75
*423j* A93 $1 multi, vert. 9.00 9.00

**1992**

*409k* A93 1c multicolored 2.00 2.00
*411k* A93 3c multicolored 3.75 3.75
*411Bk* A93 4c multicolored 3.75 3.75
*416k* A93 15c multicolored 2.75 2.75
*418k* A93 20c multicolored 5.50 5.50
*420k* A93 35c multicolored 5.50 5.50
*422k* A93 50c multicolored 5.50 5.50
*423k* A93 $1 multi, vert. 11.00 11.00

Southern Cross, 1873, London 1980 Emblem A94

**1980, Apr. 28 Wmk. 373 *Perf. 13½***

**426** A94 6c shown .25 .25
**427** A94 20c Levuka, 1910 .35 .25
**428** A94 45c Matua, 1936 .70 .50
**429** A94 50c Oronsay, 1951 .70 *1.00*
*Nos. 426-429 (4)* 2.00 2.00

London 80 Intl. Stamp Exhib., May 6-14.

Sovi Bay A95

**1980, Aug. 18 *Perf. 13½x14***

**430** A95 6c shown .25 .25
**431** A95 20c Yanuca Island, evening scene .25 .25
**432** A95 45c Dravuni Beach .40 .40
**433** A95 50c Wakaya Island .40 .40
*Nos. 430-433 (4)* 1.30 1.30

Opening of Parliament, 1979 — A96

**1980, Oct. 6 Litho. *Perf. 13***

**434** A96 6c shown .25 .25
**435** A96 20c Coat of arms, vert. .35 .25
**436** A96 45c Fiji flag .50 .50
**437** A96 50c Elizabeth II, vert. .60 .65
*Nos. 434-437 (4)* 1.70 1.65

Independence, 10th anniversary.

Coastal Scene, by Semisi Maya A97

Intl. Year of the Disabled: Paintings and portrait of disabled artist Semisi Maya.

**1981, Apr. 21 Wmk. 373 *Perf. 14***

**438** A97 6c shown .25 .25
**439** A97 35c Underwater Scene .35 .35
**440** A97 50c Maya Painting, vert. .45 .45
**441** A97 60c Peacock, vert. .50 .50
*Nos. 438-441 (4)* 1.55 1.55

**Royal Wedding Issue**

Common Design Type

**1981, July 22 Wmk. 373 *Perf. 14***

**442** CD331 6c Bouquet .25 .25
**443** CD331 45c Charles .40 .25
**444** CD331 $1 Couple .70 *.85*
*Nos. 442-444 (3)* 1.35 1.35

Operator Assistance Center — A98

35c, Microwave station, map. 50c, Satellite earth station. 60c, Cableship Retriever.

**1981, Aug. 7 Litho. *Perf. 14***
**445** A98 6c shown .25 .25
**446** A98 35c multicolored .50 .50
**447** A98 50c multicolored .60 .60
**448** A98 60c multicolored .75 .75
*Nos. 445-448 (4)* 2.10 2.10

World Food Day — A99

**1981, Sept. 21 Litho. *Perf. 14½x14***
**449** A99 20c multicolored .45 .25

Ratu Sir Lala Sukuna, First Legislative Council Speaker — A100

**1981, Oct. 19 Litho. *Perf. 14***
**450** A100 6c shown .25 .25
**451** A100 35c Mace, flag .40 .40
**452** A100 50c Suva Civic Center .60 .60
*Nos. 450-452 (3)* 1.25 1.25

**Souvenir Sheet**

**453** A100 60c Emblem, participants' flags 1.10 1.10

27th Commonwealth Parliamentary Assoc. Conf., Suva.

World War II Aircraft A101

6c, Bell P-39 Aircobra. 18c, Consolidated PBY-5 Catalina. 35c, Curtiss P-40 Warhawk. 60c, Short Singapore.

**1981, Dec. 7 Litho. *Perf. 14***
**454** A101 6c multi 1.50 .25
**455** A101 18c multi 2.40 .30
**456** A101 35c multi 3.25 .65
**457** A101 60c multi 3.50 5.00
*Nos. 454-457 (4)* 10.65 6.20

Scouting Year A102

**1982, Feb. 22 Litho. *Perf. 14½***
**458** A102 6c Building .35 .25
**459** A102 20c Sailing, vert. .60 .35
**460** A102 45c Campfire .75 .50
**461** A102 60c Baden-Powell, vert. 1.00 1.00
*Nos. 458-461 (4)* 2.70 2.10

Disciplined Forces — A103

**1982, May 10 Wmk. 373 *Perf. 14***
**462** A103 12c UN checkpoint .60 .25
**463** A103 30c Construction project .70 .55
**464** A103 40c Police, car 2.00 1.00
**465** A103 70c Navy ship 2.00 *3.50*
*Nos. 462-465 (4)* 5.30 5.30

1982 World Cup A104

**1982, June 15 Litho. *Perf. 14***
**466** A104 6c Fiji Soccer Assoc. emblem .25 .25
**467** A104 18c Flag, ball .35 .25
**468** A104 50c Stadium .85 .50
**469** A104 90c Emblem 1.25 1.60
*Nos. 466-469 (4)* 2.70 2.60

**Princess Diana Issue**
Common Design Type

**1982, July 1 *Perf. 14½x14***
**470** CD333 20c Arms .35 .35
**471** CD333 35c Diana .50 .35
**472** CD333 45c Wedding .65 .50
**473** CD333 $1 Portrait 1.75 1.75
*Nos. 470-473 (4)* 3.25 2.95

October Royal Visit — A105

**1982, Nov. 1 Litho. *Perf. 14***
**474** A105 6c Duke of Edinburgh .30 .30
**475** A105 45c Elizabeth II 1.10 1.10

**Souvenir Sheet**

**476** Sheet of 3 3.50 3.50
*c.* A105 $1 Britannia 1.00 1.00

No. 476 contains Nos. 474-475 and 476c.

Christmas A106

**1982, Nov. 22 *Perf. 14x14½***
**477** A106 6c Holy Family .25 .25
**478** A106 20c Adoration of the Kings .40 .40
**479** A106 35c Carolers .70 .70
*Nos. 477-479 (3)* 1.35 1.35

**Souvenir Sheet**

**480** A106 $1 Faith, from The Three Virtues, by Raphael 2.00 2.00

Red-throated Lory — A107

Parrots.

**1983, Feb. 14 Litho. *Perf. 14***
**481** A107 20c shown 2.00 .30
**482** A107 40c Blue-crowned lory 2.50 .60
**483** A107 55c Sulphur-breasted musk parrot 3.00 1.75
**484** A107 70c Red-breasted musk parrot 3.25 *5.25*
*Nos. 481-484 (4)* 10.75 7.90

A108

**1983, Mar. 14**
**485** A108 8c Traditional house .25 .25
**486** A108 25c Barefoot firewalkers .30 .30
**487** A108 50c Sugar cane crop .50 .50
**488** A108 80c Kava Yagona ceremony .65 .65
*Nos. 485-488 (4)* 1.70 1.70

Commonwealth Day.

Manned Flight Bicentenary — A109

**1983, July 18 Wmk. 373 *Perf. 14***
**489** A109 8c Montgolfiere, 1783 .45 .25
**490** A109 20c Wright Flyer .55 .35
**491** A109 25c DC-3 .65 .40
**492** A109 40c DeHavilland Comet 1.00 .70
**493** A109 50c Boeing 747 1.15 .85
**494** A109 58c Columbia space shuttle 1.35 1.00
*Nos. 489-494 (6)* 5.15 3.55

Cordia Subcordata — A110

Flowers.

**1983, Sept. 26 Litho. *Perf. 14***
**495** A110 8c shown .25 .25
**496** A110 25c Gmelina vitiensis .45 .30
**497** A110 40c Carruthersia scandens .55 .45
**498** A110 $1 Amylotheca insularum .90 1.15
*Nos. 495-498 (4)* 2.15 2.15

See Nos. 505-508.

Earth Satellite Station, Fijian Playing Lali — A111

**Perf. 14x13½**
**1983, Nov. 7 Wmk. 373**
**499** A111 50c multicolored .75 .75

Dacryopinax Spathularia A112

Various fungi: 15c, Podoscypha involuta. 40c, Lentinus squarrosulus. 50c, Scleroderma flavidum. $1, Phillipsia domingensis.

**1984, Jan. 9 *Perf. 14x13½, 13½x14***
**500** A112 8c shown 1.25 .25
**501** A112 15c multicolored 1.50 .45
**502** A112 40c multicolored 2.50 1.10
**503** A112 50c multicolored 2.50 1.50
**504** A112 $1 multicolored 3.75 3.50
*Nos. 500-504 (5)* 11.50 6.80

**Flower Type of 1983**

**1984 Litho. *Perf. 14x14½***
**505** A110 15c Pseuderanthemum laxiflorum .40 .25
**506** A110 20c Storkiella vitiensis .50 .30
**507** A110 50c Paphia vitiensis .70 .80
**508** A110 70c Elaeocarpus storkii .80 *1.05*
*Nos. 505-508 (4)* 2.40 2.40

**Lloyd's List Issue**
Common Design Type
***Perf. 14½x14***

**1984, May 7 Wmk. 373**
**509** CD335 8c Tui Lau on reef .80 .25
**510** CD335 40c Tofua 1.50 .90
**511** CD335 55c Canberra 1.50 1.50
**512** CD335 60c Suva Wharf 1.50 2.25
*Nos. 509-512 (4)* 5.30 4.90

Souvenir Sheet

1984 UPU Congress — A113

**1984, June 14 Litho. *Perf. 14½***
**513** A113 25c Map 2.50 2.50

Ausipex '84 — A114

***Perf. 14x14½***
**1984, Sept. 17 Wmk. 373**
**514** A114 8c Yalavou cattle .25 .25
**515** A114 25c Wailoa Power Station, vert. .50 .55
**516** A114 40c Boeing 737 1.90 .95
**517** A114 $1 Cargo ship Fua Kavenga 1.50 *2.40*
*Nos. 514-517 (4)* 4.15 4.15

No. 515 is perf. 14½x14

Christmas A115

**1984, Nov. 5 Litho. *Perf. 14***
**518** A115 8c Church on hill .25 .25
**519** A115 20c Sailing .50 .25
**520** A115 25c Santa, children, tree .50 .25
**521** A115 40c Going to church .50 .60
**522** A115 $1 Family, tree, vert. .95 *1.35*
*Nos. 518-522 (5)* 2.70 2.70

Butterflies A116

**1985, Feb. 4 *Perf. 14***
**523** A116 8c Monarch 2.00 .25
**524** A116 25c Common eggfly 3.25 .80
**525** A116 40c Long-tailed blue, vert. 4.00 1.40

**526** A116 $1 Meadow argus, vert. 5.75 *6.50*
*Nos. 523-526 (4)* 15.00 8.95

EXPO '85, Tsukuba, Japan — A117

**1985, Mar. 18 Litho. *Perf. 14***
**527** A117 20c Outrigger canoe, Toberua Isl. .90 .40
**528** A117 25c Wainivula Falls 1.20 .50
**529** A117 50c Mana Island 1.35 1.25
**530** A117 $1 Sawa-I-Lau Caves 1.60 *2.50*
*Nos. 527-530 (4)* 5.05 4.65

**Queen Mother 85th Birthday Issue**
Common Design Type
***Perf. 14½x14***
**1985, June 7 Wmk. 384**
**531** CD336 8c Holding Prince Andrew .25 .25
**532** CD336 25c With Prince Charles .40 .40
**533** CD336 40c On Oaks Day, Epsom Races 1.00 .80
**534** CD336 50c Holding Prince Henry 1.00 *1.20*
*Nos. 531-534 (4)* 2.65 2.65

**Souvenir Sheet**
**535** CD336 $1 In Royal Wedding Cavalcade, 1981 3.50 3.50

Shallow Water Fish A118

**1985, Sept. 23 *Perf. 14½***
**536** A118 40c Horned squirrel fish 1.50 .75
**537** A118 50c Yellow-banded goatfish 1.75 1.00
**538** A118 55c Fairy cod 2.00 1.50
**539** A118 $1 Peacock rock cod 2.75 *4.50*
*Nos. 536-539 (4)* 8.00 7.75

Sea Birds — A119

**1985, Nov. 4 *Perf. 14***
**540** A119 15c Collared petrel 2.50 .45
**541** A119 20c Lesser frigate bird 2.50 .50
**542** A119 50c Brown booby 4.75 4.00
**543** A119 $1 Crested tern 7.25 *8.00*
*Nos. 540-543 (4)* 17.00 12.95

**Queen Elizabeth II 60th Birthday Issue**
Common Design Type

20c, With the Duke of York at the Royal Tournament, 1936. 25c, On Buckingham Palace balcony, wedding of Princess Margaret and Anthony Armstrong-Jones, 1960. 40c, Inspecting the Guard of Honor, Suva, 1982. 50c, State visit to Luxembourg, 1976. $1, Visiting Crown Agents' offices, 1983.

***Perf. 14x14½***
**1986, Apr. 21 Wmk. 384**
**544** CD337 20c scar, blk & sil .40 .30
**545** CD337 25c ultra & multi .40 .30
**546** CD337 40c green & multi .65 .50
**547** CD337 50c violet & multi .75 .75
**548** CD337 $1 rose vio & multi .80 *1.15*
*Nos. 544-548 (5)* 3.00 3.00

Intl. Peace Year — A120

**1986, June 23 Wmk. 373 *Perf. 14½***
**549** A120 8c shown .50 .25
**550** A120 40c Dove .85 *1.10*

Halley's Comet — A121

**1986, July 7 *Perf. 13½***
**551** A121 25c Newton's reflector telescope 2.00 .55
**552** A121 40c Comet over Lomaiviti 2.25 .95
**553** A121 $1 Comet nucleus, Giotto probe 2.75 *5.50*
*Nos. 551-553 (3)* 7.00 7.00

Reptiles and Amphibians — A122

**1986, Aug. 1 *Perf. 14½***
**554** A122 8c Ground frog 1.05 .25
**555** A122 20c Burrowing snake 1.50 .30
**556** A122 25c Spotted gecko 1.50 .35
**557** A122 40c Crested iguana 1.60 .85
**558** A122 50c Blotched skink 1.60 *2.50*
**559** A122 $1 Speckled skink 2.00 *5.50*
*Nos. 554-559 (6)* 9.25 9.75

Ancient War Clubs — A123

**1986, Nov. 10 Wmk. 384 *Perf. 14***
**560** A123 25c Gatawaka .95 .35
**561** A123 40c Siriti 1.25 .60
**562** A123 50c Bulibuli 1.40 *1.60*
**563** A123 $1 Culacula 2.50 *3.00*
*Nos. 560-563 (4)* 6.10 5.55

Cone Shells — A124

**1987, Feb. 26 Litho. *Perf. 14x14½***
**564** A124 15c Weasel 1.25 .25
**565** A124 20c Pertusus 1.25 .30
**566** A124 25c Admiral 1.40 .30
**567** A124 40c Leaden 1.50 1.00
**568** A124 50c Imperial 1.75 *2.25*
**569** A124 $1 Geography 2.00 *5.00*
*Nos. 564-569 (6)* 9.15 9.10

**Souvenir Sheet**

Tagimoucia Flower — A125

**1987, Apr. 23 Wmk. 373 *Perf. 14½***
**570** A125 $1 multicolored 4.75 3.75

**No. 570 Overprinted**

**1987, June 13**
**571** A125 $1 multicolored *40.00 40.00*

Intl. Year of Shelter for the Homeless A126

**1987, July 20 *Perf. 14***
**572** A126 55c Hut .65 .65
**573** A126 70c Government housing .85 .85

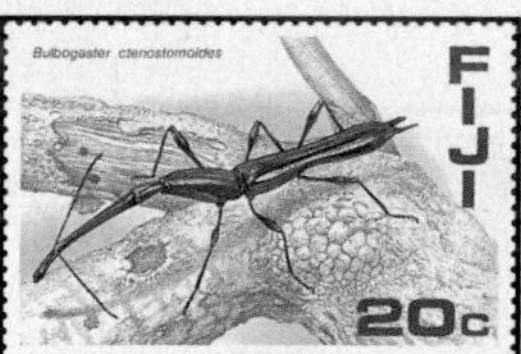

Beetles — A127

**1987, Sept. 7 Wmk. 384**
**574** A127 20c Bulbogaster ctenostomoides 2.50 .45
**575** A127 25c Paracupta flaviventris 2.50 .55
**576** A127 40c Cerambyrhynchus schoenherri 3.00 1.75
**577** A127 50c Rhinoscapha lagopyga 3.25 *3.50*
**578** A127 $1 Xixuthrus heros 4.00 *8.50*
*Nos. 574-578 (5)* 15.25 14.75

Christmas — A128

**1987, Nov. 19**
**579** A128 8c Holy Family, vert. 1.00 .25
**580** A128 40c Shepherds see star 2.25 .65
**581** A128 50c Three Kings follow star 2.75 1.50
**582** A128 $1 Adoration of the Magi 3.75 *5.00*
*Nos. 579-582 (4)* 9.75 7.40

World Expo '88, Apr. 30-Oct. 30, Brisbane, Australia A129

**1988, Apr. 27 Litho. *Perf. 14***
**583** A129 30c Windsurfing 1.60 1.60

Intl. Council of Women, Cent. A130

**1988, June 14**
**584** A130 45c Fiji Nouna 1.30 1.30

Pottery A131

**Wmk. 384, 373 (69c)**
**1988, Aug. 29 Litho. *Perf. 13½***
**585** A131 9c Lapita (bowl) .25 .25
**586** A131 23c Kuro (cooking pot) .40 .25
**587** A131 58c Saqa (ritual drinking vessel) .80 .80
**588** A131 63c Saqa, diff. .90 .90
**589** A131 69c Ramarama (oil lamp) .95 *1.00*
**590** A131 75c Kuro, diff., vert. 1.10 *1.20*
*Nos. 585-590 (6)* 4.40 4.40

Fiji Tree Frog — A132

**1988, Oct. 3 Wmk. 384 *Perf. 14***
**591** A132 18c multi 4.50 3.00
**592** A132 23c multi, diff. 5.00 3.00
**593** A132 30c multi, diff. 5.75 5.75
**594** A132 45c multi, diff. 6.50 *10.00*
*Nos. 591-594 (4)* 21.75 21.75

World Wildlife Fund.

Indigenous Flowering Plants — A133

**1988, Nov. 21 Wmk. 373**
**595** A133 9c Dendrobium mohlianum .85 .25
**596** A133 30c Dendrobium cattilare 1.25 .45
**597** A133 45c Degeneria vitiensis .95 *1.35*
**598** A133 $1 Degeneria roseiflora 1.75 *2.75*
*Nos. 595-598 (4)* 4.80 4.80

Intl. Red Cross and Red Crescent Orgs., 125th Anniv. — A134

**1989, Feb. 6** **Wmk. 384**

**599** A134 58c Battle of Solferino, 1859 1.75 1.00
**600** A134 63c Jean-Henri Dunant, vert. 1.75 1.10
**601** A134 69c Medicine 2.25 1.40
**602** A134 $1 Anniv. emblem, vert. 2.75 1.90
*Nos. 599-602 (4)* 8.50 5.40

Epic Voyage of William Bligh A135

Designs: 45c, Plans (line drawing) of the Bounty's launch. 58c, Diary and inscription on artifacts "The cup I eat my miserable allowance out of." 80c, Silhouette, lightning, quote "O Almighty God, relieve us. . ." $1, Map of Bligh's Islands, launch and compass rose.

**1989, Apr. 28** ***Perf. 14½***

**603** A135 45c multicolored 2.10 .70
**604** A135 58c multicolored 2.25 1.50
**605** A135 80c multicolored 3.50 3.25
**606** A135 $1 multicolored 4.75 3.50
*Nos. 603-606 (4)* 12.60 8.95

Coral A136

**1989, Aug. 21** **Wmk. 373** ***Perf. 14***

**607** A136 46c Platygyra daedalea 2.00 1.00
**608** A136 60c Caulastrea furcata 2.50 2.00
**609** A136 75c Acropora echinata 3.00 2.50
**610** A136 90c Acropora humilis 3.75 3.00
*Nos. 607-610 (4)* 11.25 8.50

Nos. 609-610 vert.

1990 World Cup Soccer Championships, Italy — A137

Various Fijian soccer players.

**1989, Sept. 25** **Wmk. 384** ***Perf. 14½***

**611** A137 35c shown 1.35 .75
**612** A137 63c multi, diff. 2.40 2.40
**613** A137 70c multi, diff. 2.60 2.60
**614** A137 85c multi, diff. 2.90 3.00
*Nos. 611-614 (4)* 9.25 8.75

Christmas A138

**1989, Nov. 1** **Wmk. 373**

**615** A138 9c Church service .40 .25
**616** A138 45c *Delonix regia* tree 1.00 .25
**617** A138 $1 Holy family 2.00 2.10
**618** A138 $1.40 Tree, Fijian children 2.25 3.00
*Nos. 615-618 (4)* 5.65 5.60

Fish A139

**1990, Apr. 23** **Litho.** **Wmk. 384**

**619** A139 50c Mangrove jack 2.60 1.00
**620** A139 70c Orange-spotted therapon perch 3.50 3.50
**621** A139 85c Spotted scat 3.75 3.75
**622** A139 $1 Flagtail 4.25 4.25
*Nos. 619-622 (4)* 14.10 12.50

**Souvenir Sheet**

Stamp World London '90 — A140

**1990, May 1**

**623** A140 Sheet of 2 12.50 9.50
*a.* $1 No. 243 3.75 2.60
*b.* $2 No. 249 8.00 6.00

Soil Conservation — A141

50c, Vertiver grass contours. 70c, Mulching. 90c, Contour cultivation. $1, Proper land use.

**1990, July 23** **Litho.** **Wmk. 373**

**625** A141 50c multi 1.25 .65
**626** A141 70c multi 1.75 1.75
**627** A141 90c multi 1.90 *2.25*
**628** A141 $1 multi, vert. 2.00 *2.50*
*Nos. 625-628 (4)* 6.90 7.15

Trees — A142

25c, Dacrydium nidulum. 35c, Decussocarpus vitiensis. $1, Agathis vitiensis. $1.55, Santalum yasi.

**1990, Oct. 2**

**629** A142 25c multi .90 .25
**630** A142 35c multi 1.00 .35
**631** A142 $1 multi 3.00 3.00
**632** A142 $1.55 multi 4.25 *5.50*
*Nos. 629-632 (4)* 9.15 9.10

Christmas — A143

Christmas carols: 10c, Hark! The Herald Angels Sing. 35c, Silent Night. 65c, Joy to the World! $1, The Race that Long in Darkness Pined.

**1990, Nov. 26** **Wmk. 373** ***Perf. 14***

**633** A143 10c multicolored .40 .25
**634** A143 35c multicolored 1.00 .35
**635** A143 65c multicolored 1.60 *1.75*
**636** A143 $1 multicolored 2.50 *2.75*
*Nos. 633-636 (4)* 5.50 5.10

Scenic Views — A144

**1991, Feb. 25** **Wmk. 384**

**637** A144 35c Sigatoka sand dunes 1.35 .35
**638** A144 50c Monu, Monuriki Islands 2.25 1.25
**639** A144 65c Ravilevu Nature Reserve 2.60 *2.75*
**640** A144 $1 Colo-I-Suva Forest Park 4.00 *4.50*
*Nos. 637-640 (4)* 10.20 8.85

Discovery of Rotuma Island, Bicent. A145

**1991, Aug. 8** **Wmk. 373** ***Perf. 14***

**641** A145 54c HMS Pandora 2.75 1.25
**642** A145 70c Map of Rotuma Island 3.00 3.00
**643** A145 75c Natives 3.00 3.00
**644** A145 $1 Mt. Solroroa, Uea Island 4.75 4.75
*Nos. 641-644 (4)* 13.50 12.00

Crabs A146

Designs: 38c, Scylla serrata. 54c, Metopograpsus messor. 96c, Parasesarma erythrodactyla. $1.65, Cardisoma carnifex.

**1991, Sept. 26** ***Perf. 14½x14***

**645** A146 38c multicolored 1.15 .45
**646** A146 54c multicolored 1.75 .75
**647** A146 96c multicolored 2.90 2.75
**648** A146 $1.65 multicolored 4.00 5.50
*Nos. 645-648 (4)* 9.80 9.45

Christmas A147

Designs: 11c, Mary, Joseph travelling to Bethlehem. 75c, Manger scene. 96c, Jesus being blessed at temple in Jerusalem. $1, Baby Jesus.

**1991, Oct. 31** **Wmk. 384** ***Perf. 14***

**649** A147 11c multicolored .65 .25
**650** A147 75c multicolroed 2.00 .75
**651** A147 96c multicolored 2.10 2.50
**652** A147 $1 multicolored 2.25 2.50
*Nos. 649-652 (4)* 7.00 6.00

No. 649 exists with wmk. 373.

Air Pacific, 40th Anniv. A148

Airplanes: 54c, Dragon Rapide, Harold Gatty, founder. 75c, Douglas DC3. 96c, ATR 42. $1.40, Boeing 767.

**1991, Nov. 18** ***Perf. 14½***

**653** A148 54c multicolored 2.40 1.25
**654** A148 75c multicolored 3.25 2.50
**655** A148 96c multicolored 3.50 3.50
**656** A148 $1.40 multicolored 4.75 *5.00*
*Nos. 653-656 (4)* 13.90 12.25

Expo '92, Seville A149

Designs: 27c, Traditional dance and costumes. 75c, Faces of people. 96c, Train and gold bars. $1.40, Cruise ship in port.

***Perf. 14½x14***

**1992, Mar. 23** **Litho.** **Wmk. 373**

**657** A149 27c multicolored .75 .50
**658** A149 75c multicolored 1.75 1.75
**659** A149 96c multicolored 8.25 5.50
**660** A149 $1.40 multicolored 8.75 8.25
*Nos. 657-660 (4)* 19.50 16.00

Inter-Islands Shipping — A150

**1992, June 22** ***Perf. 14***

**661** A150 38c Tabusoro 2.75 .75
**662** A150 54c Degei II 3.25 1.50
**663** A150 $1.40 Dausoko 5.50 4.50
**664** A150 $1.65 Nivanga 5.50 4.50
*Nos. 661-664 (4)* 17.00 11.25

1992 Summer Olympics, Barcelona — A151

**1992, July 30** ***Perf. 13½***

**665** A151 20c Running 1.00 .25
**666** A151 86c Yachting 3.00 2.50
**667** A151 $1.34 Swimming 3.50 4.00
**668** A151 $1.50 Judo 3.50 4.00
*Nos. 665-668 (4)* 11.00 10.75

Levuka A152

30c, European War Memorial. 42c, Map. 59c, Beach Street. 77c, Sacred Heart Church, vert. $2, Deed of Cession Site, vert.

**1992, Sept. 21** ***Perf. 14½***

**669** A152 30c multicolored .45 .30
**670** A152 42c multicolored .65 .50
**671** A152 59c multicolored .95 .95
**672** A152 77c multicolored 1.20 *1.25*
**673** A152 $2 multicolored 2.50 *2.75*
*Nos. 669-673 (5)* 5.75 5.75

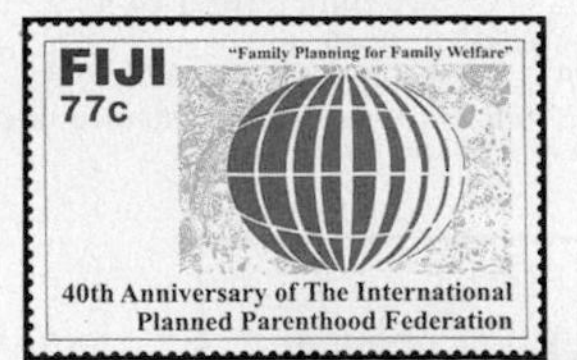


Intl. Planned Parenthood Federation, 40th Anniv. — A153

**1992, Nov. 2** *Perf. 15x14½*

**674** A153 77c Globe 1.35 1.00
**675** A153 $2 Family 3.50 3.50

Christmas — A154

Bible interpretations: 12c, "God so loved the world..." 77c, "We love because God first loved us." 83c, "It is more blessed to give..." $2, "Every good gift..."

**1992, Nov. 17**

**676** A154 12c multicolored .75 .25
**677** A154 77c multicolored 2.25 1.75
**678** A154 83c multicolored 2.50 2.00
**679** A154 $2 multicolored 4.00 5.50
*Nos. 676-679 (4)* 9.50 9.50

Peace Corps in Fiji, 25th Anniv. A155

Designs: 59c, Voluntary service. 77c, Fiji/US friendship. $1, Education. $2, Income generating business through volunteer help.

**Wmk. 373**

**1993, Feb. 22 Litho.** *Perf. 14½*

**680** A155 59c multicolored 1.40 .75
**681** A155 77c multicolored 1.90 1.00
**682** A155 $1 multicolored 2.00 1.50
**683** A155 $2 multicolored 3.50 5.00
*Nos. 680-683 (4)* 8.80 8.25

Hong Kong Rugby Sevens — A156

Designs: 77c, Players performing traditional Cibi Dance. $1.06, Two players, map of Fiji, Hong Kong, and Australia. $2, Stadium, players in scrum.

*Perf. 14x15*

**1993, Mar. 26 Litho. Wmk. 384**

**684** A156 77c multicolored 1.75 1.50
**685** A156 $1.06 multicolored 4.00 2.50
**686** A156 $2 multicolored 4.25 5.50
*Nos. 684-686 (3)* 10.00 9.50

## Royal Air Force, 75th Anniv.

Common Design Type

Designs: 59c, Gloster Gauntlet. 77c, Armstrong Whitworth Whitley. 83c, Bristol F2b. $2, Hawker Tempest.

No. 691: a, Vickers Vildebeest. b, Handley Page Hampden. c, Vickers Vimy. d, British Aerospace Hawk.

**1993, Apr. 1** *Perf. 14*

**687** CD350 59c multicolored 1.50 .75
**688** CD350 77c multicolored 1.75 1.40
**689** CD350 83c multicolored 2.25 1.75
**690** CD350 $2 multicolored 3.50 4.75
*Nos. 687-690 (4)* 9.00 8.65

**Souvenir Sheet of 4**

**691** CD350 $1 #a.-d. 8.75 8.75
*e.* Overprinted in sheet margin 9.75 9.75

Overprint on No. 691e is exhibition emblem for Hong Kong '94.

Nudibranchs A157

12c, Chromodoris fidelis. 42c, Halgerda carlsoni. 53c, Chromodoris lochi. 83c, Glaucus atlanticus. $1, Phyllidia bourguini. $2, Hexabranchus sanguineus.

**Wmk. 373**

**1993, July 27 Litho.** *Perf. 14*

**692** A157 12c multicolored .80 .25
**693** A157 42c multicolored 1.60 .50
**694** A157 53c multicolored 1.75 1.00
**695** A157 83c multicolored 2.50 2.25
**696** A157 $1 multicolored 2.90 2.25
**697** A157 $2 multicolored 4.00 *6.50*
*Nos. 692-697 (6)* 13.55 12.75

Tropical Fruit — A158

**Wmk. 373**

**1993, Oct. 25 Litho.** *Perf. 13½*

**698** A158 30c Mango 1.90 .50
**699** A158 42c Guava 2.10 1.00
**700** A158 $1 Lemon 3.75 3.00
**701** A158 $2 Soursop 6.00 8.00
*Nos. 698-701 (4)* 13.75 12.50

Souvenir Sheet

Hong Kong '94 — A159

Butterflies: a, Caper white. b, Blue branded king crow. c, Vagrant. d, Glasswing.

*Perf. 14½x13*

**1994, Feb. 18 Litho. Wmk. 373**

**702** A159 $1 Sheet of 4, #a.-d. 9.00 9.00

Easter A160

59c, The Last Supper. 77c, The Crucifixion. $1, The Resurrection. $2, Jesus showing his wounds to his disciples.

*Perf. 14x15, 15x14*

**1994, Mar. 31 Litho. Wmk. 373**

**703** A160 59c multi 1.35 .50
**704** A160 77c multi, vert. 1.75 .75
**705** A160 $1 multi 2.00 1.75
**706** A160 $2 multi, vert. 3.75 5.25
*Nos. 703-706 (4)* 8.85 8.25

Edible Seaweeds A161

42c, Codium bulbopilum. 83c, Coulerpa racemosa. $1, Hypnea pannosa. $2, Gracilaria.

**Wmk. 384**

**1994, June 6 Litho.** *Perf. 14*

**707** A161 42c multicolored 1.10 .40
**708** A161 83c multicolored 2.25 1.60
**709** A161 $1 multicolored 2.75 1.90
**710** A161 $2 multicolored 4.00 6.25
*Nos. 707-710 (4)* 10.10 10.15

Souvenir Sheet

White-Collared Kingfisher — A162

Designs: a, On branch. b, In flight.

**Wmk. 373**

**1994, Aug. Litho.** *Perf. 13½*

**711** A162 $1.50 Sheet of 2, #a.-b. 11.50 11.50
*c.* Overprinted in sheet margin 11.50 11.50

Overprint on No. 711c consists of exhibition emblem and "JAKARTA '95."

Issued: #711, 8/16; #711c, 8/19.

Souvenir Sheet

Singpex '94 — A163

Neoveitchia storckii: a, Complete tree. b. Fruits, inflorescence.

**1994, Aug. 31 Wmk. 384** *Perf. 14*

**712** A163 $1.50 Sheet of 2, #a.-b. 9.00 9.00

First Catholic Missionaries in Fiji, 150th Anniv. — A164

**Wmk. 373**

**1994, Dec. 16 Litho.** *Perf. 14*

**713** A164 23c Father Ioane Batita .50 .25
**714** A164 31c Local catechist .60 .25
**715** A164 44c Sacred Heart Cathedral .80 .60
**716** A164 63c Lomary Church 1.10 1.00
**717** A164 81c Pope Gregory XVI 1.50 1.50
**718** A164 $2 Pope John Paul II 4.00 *4.75*
*Nos. 713-718 (6)* 8.50 8.35

Souvenir Sheet

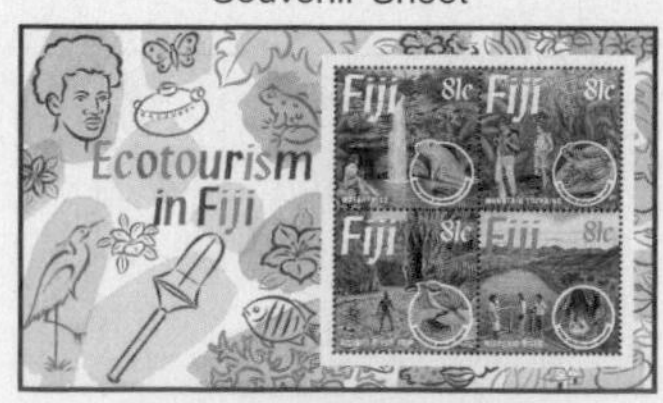


Ecotourism in Fiji — A165

Designs: a, Waterfalls, banded iguana. b, Mountain trekking, Fiji tree frog. c, Bilibili River trip, kingfisher. d, Historic sites, flying fox.

**Wmk. 373**

**1995, Mar. 27 Litho.** *Perf. 14*

**719** A165 81c Sheet of 4, #a.-d. 8.25 8.25

## End of World War II, 50th Anniv.

Common Design Types

Designs: 13c, Fijian regiment guarding crashed Japanese Zero Fighter. 63c, Kameli Airstrip, Solomon Islands, built by Fijian regiment. 87c, Corp. Sukanaivalu VC, Victoria Cross. $1.12, HMS Fiji.

$2, Reverse side of War Medal 1939-45.

**Wmk. 373**

**1995, May 8 Litho.** *Perf. 13½*

**720** CD351 13c multicolored 1.25 .25
**721** CD351 63c multicolored 2.75 1.75
**722** CD351 87c multicolored 3.25 2.75
**723** CD351 $1.12 multicolored 3.75 3.25
*Nos. 720-723 (4)* 11.00 8.00

**Souvenir Sheet**

*Perf. 14*

**724** CD352 $2 multicolored 6.50 6.50

Birds — A166

1c, Red-headed parrotfinch. 2c, Golden whistler. 3c, Ogea flycatcher. 4c, Peale's pigeon. 6c, Blue-crested broadbill. 13c, Island thrush. 23c, Many-colored fruit dove. 31c, Mangrove heron. 44c, Purple swamphen. 63c, Fiji goshawk. 81c, Kadavu fantail. 87c, Collared lory. $1, Scarlet robin. $2, Peregrine falcon. $3, Barn owl. $5, Yellow-breasted musk parrot.

**1995 Litho. Wmk. 373** *Perf. 13*

**725** A166 1c multi 1.00 1.75
**726** A166 2c multi 1.00 1.75
**727** A166 3c multi 1.00 1.75
**728** A166 4c multi 1.00 1.75
**729** A166 6c multi 1.00 1.75
**730** A166 13c multi .75 .25
**731** A166 23c multi .75 .30
**732** A166 31c multi .85 .35
**733** A166 44c multi 1.00 .40
**734** A166 63c multi 1.50 .50
**735** A166 81c multi 1.75 .65
**736** A166 87c multi 2.00 .75
**737** A166 $1 multi 2.00 .85
**738** A166 $2 multi 3.00 1.75
**739** A166 $3 multi 4.25 3.75
**739A** A166 $5 multi 4.50 *5.50*
*Nos. 725-739A (16)* 27.35 23.80

Issued: 13c, 23c, 31c, 44c, 63c, 81c, $2, $3, 7/25; 1c, 2c, 3c, 4c, 6c, 87c, $1, $5, 11/7.

See No. 1011.

For surcharges, see Nos. 1149-1160, 1191-1197C, 1214-1223A, 1249-1254E, 1314-1317.

Souvenir Sheet

Singapore '95 — A167

Orchids: a, Arundina graminifolia. b, Phaius tankervilliae.

**Wmk. 373**

**1995, Sept. 1 Litho.** *Perf. 14*

**740** A167 $1 Sheet of 2, #a.-b. 7.50 7.50

Independence, 25th Anniv. — A168

Designs: 81c, Pres. Kamisese Mara, Parliament Building. 87c, Fijian youth. $1.06, Playing rugby. $2, Air Pacific Boeing 747.

**Wmk. 373**

**1995, Oct. 4 Litho. *Perf. 14***

| No. | Type | Value | Description | Unused | Used |
|---|---|---|---|---|---|
| **741** | A168 | 81c | multicolored | 1.50 | 1.10 |
| **742** | A168 | 87c | multicolored | 1.35 | 1.35 |
| **743** | A168 | $1.06 | multicolored | 2.10 | 2.25 |
| **744** | A168 | $2 | multicolored | 4.25 | *4.50* |
| | | | *Nos. 741-744 (4)* | 9.20 | 9.20 |

Christmas — A169

Paintings: 10c, Praying Madonna with the Crown of Stars, from Correggio Workshop. 63c, Madonna and Child with Crowns on porcelain. 87c, The Holy Virgin with the Holy Child and St. John, after Titian. $2, The Holy Family and St. John, from Rubens Workshop.

**Wmk. 373**

**1995, Nov. 22 Litho. *Perf. 13***

| No. | Type | Value | Description | Unused | Used |
|---|---|---|---|---|---|
| **745** | A169 | 10c | multicolored | .30 | .25 |
| **746** | A169 | 63c | multicolored | 1.20 | 1.00 |
| **747** | A169 | 87c | multicolored | 1.60 | 1.50 |
| **748** | A169 | $2 | multicolored | 3.50 | 3.75 |
| | | | *Nos. 745-748 (4)* | 6.60 | 6.50 |

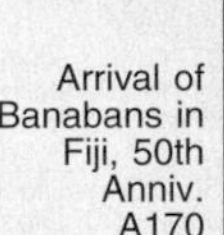

Arrival of Banabans in Fiji, 50th Anniv. A170

***Perf. 14x14½, 14½x14***

**1996, Jan. 24 Litho. Wmk. 373**

| No. | Type | Value | Description | Unused | Used |
|---|---|---|---|---|---|
| **749** | A170 | 81c | Trolling lure | 2.25 | 1.25 |
| **750** | A170 | 87c | Canoes | 2.50 | 1.25 |
| **751** | A170 | $1.12 | Warrior, vert. | 2.75 | 2.00 |
| **752** | A170 | $2 | Frigate bird, vert. | 5.25 | 7.00 |
| | | | *Nos. 749-752 (4)* | 12.75 | 11.50 |

A171

Radio, Cent.: 44c, L2B portable tape recorder. 63c, Fiji Broadcasting Center. 81c, Communications satellite in orbit. $3, Marconi.

**Wmk. 373**

**1996, Mar. 11 Litho. *Perf. 14½***

| No. | Type | Value | Description | Unused | Used |
|---|---|---|---|---|---|
| **753** | A171 | 44c | multicolored | .90 | .50 |
| **754** | A171 | 63c | multicolored | 1.25 | .75 |
| **755** | A171 | 81c | multicolored | 1.60 | 1.25 |
| **756** | A171 | $3 | multicolored | 5.25 | *6.50* |
| | | | *Nos. 753-756 (4)* | 9.00 | 9.00 |

A172

Ancient Chinese artifacts: 63c, Bronze monster mask and ring, c. 450 BC. 81c, Archer, 210 BC. $1, Plate, Hsuan Te Period, 1426-35. $2, Central Asian horseman, dated 706.
30c, Yan Deng Mountain.

**Wmk. 384**

**1996, Apr. 25 Litho. *Perf. 13½***

| No. | Type | Value | Description | Unused | Used |
|---|---|---|---|---|---|
| **757** | A172 | 63c | multicolored | 1.25 | .50 |
| **758** | A172 | 81c | multicolored | 1.60 | 1.00 |
| **759** | A172 | $1 | multicolored | 2.00 | 1.50 |
| **760** | A172 | $2 | multicolored | 3.50 | *4.25* |
| | | | *Nos. 757-760 (4)* | 8.35 | 7.25 |

**Souvenir Sheet**

***Perf. 13½x13***

| No. | Type | Value | Description | Unused | Used |
|---|---|---|---|---|---|
| **761** | A172 | 30c | multicolored | 2.50 | 2.50 |

No. 761 contains one 48x76mm stamp.
CHINA '96, 9th Asian Intl. Philatelic Exhibition.

A173

**Wmk. 373**

**1996, June 18 Litho. *Perf. 14***

| No. | Type | Value | Description | Unused | Used |
|---|---|---|---|---|---|
| **762** | A173 | 31c | Hurdling | .65 | .25 |
| **763** | A173 | 63c | Judo | 1.50 | 1.00 |
| **764** | A173 | 87c | Sailboarding | 2.10 | 1.75 |
| **765** | A173 | $1.12 | Swimming | 2.40 | *2.50* |
| | | | *Nos. 762-765 (4)* | 6.65 | 5.50 |

**Souvenir Sheet**

| No. | Type | Value | Description | Unused | Used |
|---|---|---|---|---|---|
| **766** | A173 | $2 | Athlete, 1896 | 3.75 | 3.75 |

Modern Olympic Games, cent.

A174

31c, Computerized telephone exchange, horiz. 44c, Mail being unloaded, horiz. 81c, Manual switchboard operator. $1, Mail delivery.
No. 771: a, #117, b, #527.

**1996, July 1**

| No. | Type | Value | Description | Unused | Used |
|---|---|---|---|---|---|
| **767** | A174 | 31c | multicolored | .60 | .35 |
| **768** | A174 | 44c | multicolored | .85 | .75 |
| **769** | A174 | 81c | multicolored | 1.20 | *1.50* |
| **770** | A174 | $1 | multicolored | 2.10 | 2.10 |
| | | | *Nos. 767-770 (4)* | 4.75 | 4.70 |

**Souvenir Sheet of 2**

| No. | Type | Value | Description | Unused | Used |
|---|---|---|---|---|---|
| **771** | A174 | $1.50 | #a.-b. | 8.25 | 8.25 |

Creation of independent Postal, Telecommunications Companies.

UNICEF, 50th Anniv. A175

Designs: 81c, "Our children, our future." 87c, Village scene. $1, "Living in harmony the world over." $2, "Their future."

**Wmk. 384**

**1996, Aug. 13 Litho. *Perf. 14***

| No. | Type | Value | Description | Unused | Used |
|---|---|---|---|---|---|
| **772** | A175 | 81c | multicolored | 2.00 | 1.50 |
| **773** | A175 | 87c | multicolored | 2.00 | 1.50 |
| **774** | A175 | $1 | multicolored | 2.10 | 1.60 |
| **775** | A175 | $2 | multicolored | 3.25 | *4.75* |
| | | | *Nos. 772-775 (4)* | 9.35 | 9.35 |

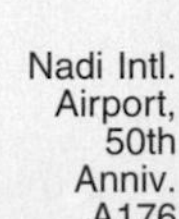

Nadi Intl. Airport, 50th Anniv. A176

Designs: 31c, First airplane in Fiji, 1921. 44c, Nadi Airport commences Commercial Operations, 1946. 63c, First jet in Fiji, 1959. 87c, Airport entrance. $1, Control tower, 1996. $2, Global positioning system, first commercial use, 1994.

**Wmk. 373**

**1996, Oct. 1 Litho. *Perf. 14***

| No. | Type | Value | Description | Unused | Used |
|---|---|---|---|---|---|
| **776** | A176 | 31c | multicolored | .80 | .35 |
| **777** | A176 | 44c | multicolored | 1.00 | .50 |
| **778** | A176 | 63c | multicolored | 1.60 | 1.15 |
| **779** | A176 | 87c | multicolored | 1.75 | 1.60 |
| **780** | A176 | $1 | multicolored | 2.10 | 1.90 |
| **781** | A176 | $2 | multicolored | 3.50 | 5.00 |
| | | | *Nos. 776-781 (6)* | 10.75 | 10.50 |

Christmas — A177

Scene from the Christmas story and native story or scene: 13c, Angel Gabriel & Mary, beating of Lali. 81c, Shepherds with sheep, Fijian canoe. $1, Wise men on camels, multiracial Fiji. $3, Mary, Christ Child in stable, blowing of conch shell.

**1996, Nov. 20 Wmk. 373**

| No. | Type | Value | Description | Unused | Used |
|---|---|---|---|---|---|
| **782** | A177 | 13c | multicolored | .50 | .25 |
| **783** | A177 | 81c | multicolored | 1.90 | 1.00 |
| **784** | A177 | $1 | multicolored | 2.10 | 1.50 |
| **785** | A177 | $3 | multicolored | 6.25 | 7.25 |
| | | | *Nos. 782-785 (4)* | 10.75 | 10.00 |

Hong Kong '97 A178

Cattle: a, Brahman. b, Freisian (Holstein). c, Hereford. d, Fiji draught bullock.

**1997, Feb. 12**

| No. | Type | Value | Description | Unused | Used |
|---|---|---|---|---|---|
| **786** | A178 | $1 | Sheet of 4, #a.-d. | 8.50 | 8.50 |

**Souvenir Sheet**

Black-Faced Shrikebill — A179

**1997, Feb. 21 *Perf. 14x15***

| No. | Type | Value | Description | Unused | Used |
|---|---|---|---|---|---|
| **787** | A179 | $2 | multicolored | 4.25 | 4.25 |

Singpex '97.

Orchids — A180

Designs: 81c, Dendrobium biflorum. 87c, Dendrobium dactylodes. $1.06, Spathoglottis pacifica. $2, Dendrobium macropus.

**Wmk. 384**

**1997, Apr. 22 Litho. *Perf. 14***

| No. | Type | Value | Description | Unused | Used |
|---|---|---|---|---|---|
| **788** | A180 | 81c | multicolored | 2.40 | 1.50 |
| **789** | A180 | 87c | multicolored | 2.40 | 1.50 |

**Wmk. 373**

| No. | Type | Value | Description | Unused | Used |
|---|---|---|---|---|---|
| **790** | A180 | $1.06 | multicolored | 2.75 | 2.50 |
| **791** | A180 | $2 | multicolored | 4.50 | 4.50 |
| | | | *Nos. 788-791 (4)* | 12.05 | 10.00 |

**Souvenir Sheet**

Hawksbill Turtle — A181

Designs: a, 63c, Female laying eggs. b, 81c, Baby turtles emerging from nest. c, $1.06 Young turtles in water. d, $2, One adult in water, coral.

**1997, May 26 Wmk. 373**

| No. | Type | Value | Description | Unused | Used |
|---|---|---|---|---|---|
| **792** | A181 | | Sheet of 4, #a.-d. | 10.00 | 10.00 |

Coral A182

Designs: 63c, Branching hard coral 87c, Massive hard coral. $1, Soft coral, sinularia. $3, Soft coral, dendronephthya.

**Wmk. 373**

**1997, July 16 Litho. *Perf. 14***

| No. | Type | Value | Description | Unused | Used |
|---|---|---|---|---|---|
| **793** | A182 | 63c | multicolored | 1.25 | .50 |
| **794** | A182 | 87c | multicolored | 1.90 | 1.00 |
| **795** | A182 | $1 | multicolored | 2.10 | 1.50 |
| **796** | A182 | $3 | multicolored | 5.25 | *7.50* |
| | | | *Nos. 793-796 (4)* | 10.50 | 10.50 |

Fijian Monkey-faced Bat — A183

63c, With nose pointed downward. 81c, Hanging below flower. $2, Between leaves on tree branch.

***Perf. 13½***

**1997, Oct. 15 Litho. Unwmk.**

| No. | Type | Value | Description | Unused | Used |
|---|---|---|---|---|---|
| **797** | A183 | 44c | multicolored | 1.00 | .50 |
| **798** | A183 | 63c | multicolored | 1.40 | .75 |
| **799** | A183 | 81c | multicolored | 1.75 | 1.15 |
| **800** | A183 | $2 | multicolored | 3.50 | *4.50* |
| *a.* | | | Sheet, 2 each #797-800 | 15.50 | 15.50 |
| | | | *Nos. 797-800 (4)* | 7.65 | 6.90 |

World Wildlife Fund.

Christmas A184

Designs: 13c, Angel, shepherd. 31c, Birth of Jesus. 87c, Magi. $3, Madonna and Child.

***Perf. 14x14½***

**1997, Nov. 18 Wmk. 373**

| No. | Type | Value | Description | Unused | Used |
|---|---|---|---|---|---|
| **801** | A184 | 13c | multicolored | .35 | .25 |
| **802** | A184 | 31c | multicolored | .75 | .25 |
| **803** | A184 | 87c | multicolored | 1.75 | .85 |
| **804** | A184 | $3 | multicolored | 4.25 | *5.75* |
| | | | *Nos. 801-804 (4)* | 7.10 | 7.10 |

A185

1997 Rugby World Cup Sevens Champions: a, 50c, Waisale Serevi, captain, highest point scorer. b, 50c, Taniela Qauqau. c, 50c, Jope Tuikabe. d, 50c, Leveni Duvuduvukula. e, 50c, Inoke Maraiwai. f, 50c, Aminiasi Naituyaga. g, 50c, Lemeki Koroi. h, 50c, Marika Vunibaka, highest try scorer. i, 50c, Luke Erenavula. j, 50c, Manasa Bari. k, $1, Entire team.

**Wmk. 373**

**1997, Oct. 30 Litho. *Perf. 14***

**805** A185 Sheet of 11, #a.-k. 14.50 14.50

No. 805k is 53x39mm.

A186

Chief's Traditional Costumes: 81c, War dress. 87c, Formal dress. $1.12, Presentation dress. $2, Highland war dress.

**Wmk. 373**

**1998, Jan. 20 Litho. *Perf. 14***

**806** A186 81c multicolored 1.25 .75
**807** A186 87c multicolored 1.25 1.00
**808** A186 $1.12 multicolored 1.50 1.50
**809** A186 $2 multicolored 2.75 *3.50*
*Nos. 806-809 (4)* 6.75 6.75

Asian and Pacific Decade of Disabled Persons, 1993-2000 A187

63c, Mastering modern technology. 87c, Assisting the will to overcome. $1, Using natural born skills. $2, Competing to win.

**Wmk. 373**

**1998, Mar. 18 Litho. *Perf. 13***

**810** A187 63c multicolored 1.25 .60
**811** A187 87c multicolored 1.50 .75
**812** A187 $1 multicolored 1.50 1.40
**813** A187 $2 multicolored 2.75 *4.25*
*Nos. 810-813 (4)* 7.00 7.00

**Royal Air Force, 80th Anniv.**

Common Design Type of 1993 Re-Inscribed

Designs: 44c, R34 Airship. 63c, Handley Page Heyford. 87c, Supermarine Swift FR.5. $2, Westland Whirlwind.

No. 818: a, Sopwith Dolphin. b, Avro 504K. c, Vickers Warwick V. d, Shorts Belfast.

**1998, Apr. 1 *Perf. 13½x14***

**814** CD350 44c multicolored 1.00 .50
**815** CD350 63c multicolored 1.25 .75
**816** CD350 87c multicolored 1.75 1.50
**817** CD350 $2 multicolored 3.00 3.00
*Nos. 814-817 (4)* 7.00 5.75

**Souvenir Sheet of 4**

**818** CD350 $1 #a.-d. 7.00 7.00

**Diana, Princess of Wales (1961-97)**

Common Design Type

Design: No. 819, Wearing plaid jacket.

No. 820: a, Wearing blue jacket. b, In high-collared blouse. c, Holding flowers.

**1998, Mar. 31 Litho. *Perf. 14x14½***

**819** CD355 81c multicolored 1.00 1.00
**820** CD355 81c Sheet of 4, #819, a.-c. 4.25 4.25

No. 820 sold for $3.24 + 50c, with surtax from international sales being donated to the Princess Diana Memorial Fund and surtax from national sales being donated to designated local charity.

Sperm Whale A188

**Wmk. 373**

**1998, June 22 Litho. *Perf. 14***

**821** A188 63c shown 1.75 .75
**822** A188 81c Adult, calf 1.90 1.00
**823** A188 87c Breaching 2.25 1.25
**824** A188 $2 Sperm whale tooth 3.00 *4.00*
*a.* Souvenir sheet 5.50 5.50
*Nos. 821-824 (4)* 8.90 7.00

16th Commonwealth Games, Kuala Lumpur, Malaysia — A189

**Wmk. 384**

**1998, Sept. 11 Litho. *Perf. 14***

**825** A189 44c Athletics .85 .35
**826** A189 63c Lawn bowls 1.00 .50
**827** A189 81c Javelin 1.40 1.15
**828** A189 $1.12 Weight lifting 1.75 *2.50*
*Nos. 825-828 (4)* 5.00 4.50

**Souvenir Sheet**

**829** A189 $2 Waisale Serevi, rugby sevens 4.25 4.25

Maritime Heritage A190

Designs: 13c, Takia, hollowed-out log with outrigger. 44c, Camakau, sailing canoe. 87c, Drua, twin-hulled sailing canoe. $3, MV Pioneer motor yacht.

$1.50, Camakau, map of Fiji.

**Wmk. 384**

**1998, Oct. 26 Litho. *Perf. 13½***

**830** A190 13c multicolored .45 .25
**831** A190 44c multicolored .75 .35
**832** A190 87c multicolored 1.40 1.00
**833** A190 $3 multicolored 5.00 *6.00*
*Nos. 830-833 (4)* 7.60 7.60

**Souvenir Sheet**

**834** A190 $1.50 multicolored 3.75 3.75

Australia '99, World Stamp Expo (#834). See Nos. 843-847.

Christmas A191

Children's drawings: 13c, "Jesus in a Manger." 50c, "A Time for Family and Friends." $1, "What Christmas Means to Me," vert. $2, "The Joy of Christmas," vert.

**1998, Nov. 23 Wmk. 373**

**835** A191 13c multicolored .50 .25
**836** A191 50c multicolored 1.20 .45
**837** A191 $1 multicolored 2.00 1.10
**838** A191 $2 multicolored 2.60 *4.50*
*Nos. 835-838 (4)* 6.30 6.30

Traditional Dances — A192

Designs: 13c, Vakamalolo (women's sitting dance). 81c, Mekeiwau (club dance). 87c, Seasea (women's fan dance). $3, Meke ni yaqona (Kava serving dance).

**Wmk. 373**

**1999, Jan. 20 Litho. *Perf. 14½***

**839** A192 13c multicolored .75 .25
**840** A192 81c multicolored 1.75 1.25
**841** A192 87c multicolored 1.75 1.25
**842** A192 $3 multicolored 5.25 *6.75*
*Nos. 839-842 (4)* 9.50 9.50

**Maritime Heritage Type of 1998**

Designs: 63c, SS Toufua, 1920-30's. 81c, MF Adi Beti, 1920-30's. $1, SS Niagara, 1920-30's. $2, MV Royal Viking Sun, 1990's.

$1.50, SS. Makatea, 1920's.

**1999, Mar. 19 Wmk. 384 *Perf. 13½***

**843** A190 63c multicolored 1.60 .50
**844** A190 81c multicolored 1.75 .75
**845** A190 $1 multicolored 1.90 1.50
**846** A190 $2 multicolored 3.00 *4.00*
*Nos. 843-846 (4)* 8.25 6.75

**Souvenir Sheet**

**847** A190 $1.50 multicolored 4.00 4.00

Australia '99, World Stamp Exhibition (#847).

Souvenir Sheet

Ducks — A193

a, Wandering whistling. b, Pacific black.

**1999, Apr. 27 Wmk. 373**

**848** A193 $2 Sheet of 2, #a.-b. 6.25 6.25

IBRA '99, Intl. Philatelic Exhibition, Nuremberg.

Orchids — A194

Designs: 44c, Calanthe ventilabrum. 63c, Dendrobium prasinum. 81c, Dendrobium macrophyllum. $3, Dendrobium tokai.

**1999, June 28**

**849** A194 44c multicolored 1.00 .50
**850** A194 63c multicolored 1.25 .90
**851** A194 81c multicolored 1.75 1.00
**852** A194 $3 multicolored 4.00 *5.00*
*Nos. 849-852 (4)* 8.00 7.40

**1st Manned Moon Landing, 30th Anniv.**

Common Design Type

13c, Astronaut waves goodbye. 87c, Stage 3 fires towards moon. $1, Aldrin walks on lunar surface. $2, Command module fires towards earth.

$2, Looking at earth from moon.

***Perf. 14x13¾***

**1999, July 20 Wmk. 384**

**853** CD357 13c multicolored .60 .25
**854** CD357 87c multicolored 1.35 1.10
**855** CD357 $1 multicolored 1.45 1.25
**856** CD357 $2 multicolored 2.60 2.60
*Nos. 853-856 (4)* 6.00 5.20

**Souvenir Sheet**

***Perf. 14***

**857** CD357 $2 multicolored 3.25 3.25

No. 857 contains one circular stamp 40mm in diameter.

**Queen Mother's Century**

Common Design Type

Queen Mother: 13c, Visiting Hull to see bomb damage. 63c, With Prince Charles. 81c, As Colonel-in-Chief of Light Infantry. $3, With Prince Charles at Clarence House.

$2, With crowd on Armistice Day.

**Wmk. 384**

**1999, Aug. 18 Litho. *Perf. 13½***

**858** CD358 13c multicolored .80 .50
**859** CD358 63c multicolored 1.25 .75
**860** CD358 81c multicolored 2.00 1.75
**861** CD358 $3 multicolored 4.00 *5.50*
*Nos. 858-861 (4)* 8.05 8.50

**Souvenir Sheet**

**862** CD358 $2 multicolored 4.75 4.75

UPU, 125th Anniv. A195

Sugar Mills rolling stock: 50c, Diesel locomotive. 87c, Steam locomotive. $1, Diesel locomotive, diff. $2, Free passenger train.

**Wmk. 373**

**1999, Oct. 26 Litho. *Perf. 13¾***

**863** A195 50c multicolored .85 .40
**864** A195 87c multicolored 1.25 .75
**865** A195 $1 multicolored 1.40 1.10
**866** A195 $2 multicolored 2.50 *3.75*
*Nos. 863-866 (4)* 6.00 6.00

Christmas — A196

Designs: 13c, Giving gifts. 31c, Angels and star. 63c, Bible, Magi, Holy family. 87c, Joseph, mary, donkey, vert. $1, Mary, Jesus, animals, vert. $2, Children, Santa, vert.

***Perf. 13¼x13***

**1999, Nov. 29 Litho. Wmk. 373**

**867** A196 13c multicolored .25 .25
**868** A196 31c multicolored .60 .35
**869** A196 63c multicolored .95 .50
**870** A196 87c multicolored 1.15 .75
**871** A196 $1 multicolored 1.30 .85
**872** A196 $2 multicolored 2.25 *3.50*
*Nos. 867-872 (6)* 6.50 6.20

Millennium A197

Designs: No. 873, Outstretched hands, islands (arch at top). No. 874, Map, flag (arch at right). No. 875, Globe, warrior beating lali, temple (arch at bottom). No. 876, Globe, drua, red line (arch at left).

No. 877: a, Fiji petrel (arch at top). b, Crested iguana, islands (arch at top). c, Red prawns (arch at bottom). d, Tagimaucia (arch at bottom).

***Perf. 13¼ Syncopated Type A***
**Litho. with Foil Application**

**2000, Jan. 1 Unwmk.**
**873** A197 $5 gold & multi 7.00 7.00
**874** A197 $5 gold & multi 7.00 7.00
**875** A197 $5 gold & multi 7.00 7.00
**876** A197 $5 gold & multi 7.00 7.00
*Nos. 873-876 (4)* 28.00 28.00

**Souvenir Sheet**

**877** A197 $10 Sheet of 4, #a-d 60.00 60.00

Beetles — A198

Designs: 15c, Paracupta sulcata. 87c, Agrilus sp. $1.06, Cyphogastra abdominalis. $2, Paracupta sp.

***Perf. 13¾x14***

**2000, Mar. 14 Litho. Wmk. 373**
**878** A198 15c multi .40 .25
**879** A198 87c multi 1.20 .75
**880** A198 $1.06 multi 1.45 *1.50*
**881** A198 $2 multi 2.40 *3.00*
*Nos. 878-881 (4)* 5.45 5.50

Sesame Street — A199

No. 882: a, Big Bird. b, Oscar the Grouch. c, Cookie Monster. d, Grover. e, Elmo. f, Ernie. g, Zoe. h, The Count. i, Bert.

No. 883, Big Bird, Elmo and Ernie, horiz. No. 884, Cookie Monster, Bert and Ernie, horiz.

***Perf. 14½x14¾***

**2000, Apr. 20 Litho. Wmk. 373**
**882** A199 50c Sheet of 9, #a-i 7.75 7.75

**Souvenir Sheets**

***Perf. 14¾x14½***

**883** A199 $2 multi 3.25 3.25
**884** A199 $2 multi 3.25 3.25

The Stamp Show 2000, London (#882).

Pres. Ratu Sir Kamisese Mara, 80th Birthday — A200

President with: 15c, Lumberjack, timber truck. 81c, Women. $1, Workers in cane field. $3, Ships.

**2000, May 13 *Perf. 14x13¾***
**885** A200 15c multi .35 .25
**886** A200 81c multi .95 .65
**887** A200 $1 multi 1.05 .75
**888** A200 $3 multi 4.50 5.00
*Nos. 885-888 (4)* 6.85 6.65

**Prince William, 18th Birthday**
Common Design Type

William: Nos. 889, 893a, As child, wearing fireman's helmet, vert. Nos. 890, 893b, Wearing navy suit, vert. Nos. 891, 893c, Wearing scarf. Nos. 892, 893d, Wearing suit and wearing blue shirt. No. 893e, As child, wearing camouflage and beret.

***Perf. 13¾x14¼, 14¼x13¾***

**2000, June 21 Wmk. 373**

**Stamps With White Border**

**889** CD359 $1 multi 1.35 1.35
**890** CD359 $1 multi 1.35 1.35
**891** CD359 $1 multi 1.35 1.35
**892** CD359 $1 multi 1.35 1.35
*Nos. 889-892 (4)* 5.40 5.40

**Souvenir Sheet**
**Stamps Without White Border**
***Perf. 14¼***

**893** CD359 $1 Sheet of 5, #a-e 7.50 7.50

2000 Summer Olympics, Sydney — A201

**Wmk. 373**

**2000, Aug. 8 Litho. *Perf. 13¾***
**894** A201 44c Swimming, vert. .75 .50
**895** A201 87c Judo, vert. 1.15 .75
**896** A201 $1 Running 1.25 1.25
**897** A201 $2 Windsurfing 2.25 2.90
*Nos. 894-897 (4)* 5.40 5.40

Souvenir Sheet

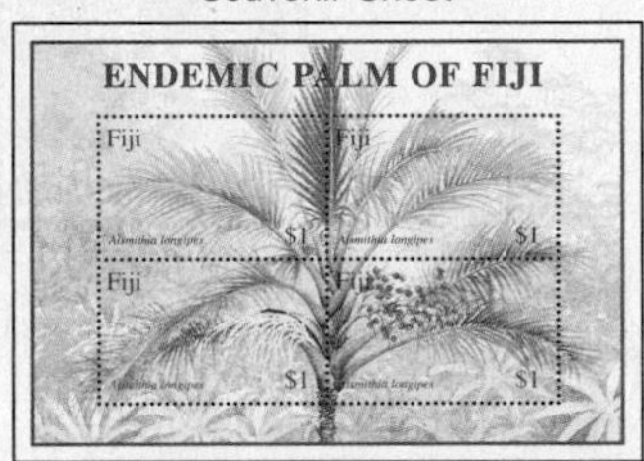

Alsmithia Longipes — A202

No. 898: a, Red frond at R. b, Red frond at L. c, Yellow frond. d, Fruit.

**Wmk. 373**

**2000, Sept. 12 Litho. *Perf. 13½***
**898** A202 $1 Sheet of 4, #a-d 6.50 6.50

Lapita Pottery Shards and Discovery Sites — A203

44c, Yanuca Island. 63c, Mago Island. $1, Ugaga Island. $2, Sigatoka sand dunes.

**2000, Oct. 24 *Perf. 13¾***
**899-902** A203 Set of 4 5.75 5.75

Christmas A204

Designs: 15c, Jungle. 81c, Cliffside trail. 87c, Coastal village. $3, Outrigger canoe.

**2000, Nov. 21**
**903-906** A204 Set of 4 6.25 6.25

Souvenir Sheet

Taveuni Rain Forest — A205

Designs: a, Orange dove. b, Xixuthrus heyrovskyi.

***Perf. 13¾x13½***

**2001, Feb. 1 Litho. Unwmk.**
**907** A205 $2 Sheet of 2, #a-b 6.00 6.00

Moths A206

Designs: 17c, Macroglossum hirundo vitiensis. 48c, Hippotion celerio. 69c, Gnathothlibus erotus eras. 89c, Theretra pinastrina intersecta. $1.17, Deilephila placida torenia. $2, Psilogramma jordana.

**2001, Mar. 20 *Perf. 13¼x13***
**908-913** A206 Set of 6 6.75 6.75

Souvenir Sheet

Gallus Gallus — A207

Designs: a, Hen. b, Rooster.

**2001, May 22 *Perf. 13¾x14***
**914** A207 $2 Sheet of 2, #a-b 7.00 7.00

Society for Prevention of Cruelty — A208

Designs: 34c, Girl, cat. 96c, Boy, dogs. $1.23, Girl, cat, diff. $2, Boy, dog.

***Perf. 14x13¾***

**2001, June 26 Litho. Unwmk.**
**915-918** A208 Set of 4 6.50 6.50

Pigeons — A209

Designs: 69c, White-throated. 89c, Pacific, vert. $1.23, Peal's, vert. $2, Rock.

**2001, July 20 *Perf. 14x14¾, 14¾x14***
**919-922** A209 Set of 4 7.25 7.25

Westpac Pacific Bank, 100th Anniv. in Fiji — A210

Bank office in: 48c, 1901. 96c, 1916. $1, 1934. $2, 2001.

**2001, Aug. 10 *Perf. 13¼x13¾***
**923-926** A210 Set of 4 5.00 5.00

Fish A211

Designs: 50c, Yellowfin tuna. 96c, Wahoo. $1.17, Dolphin fish. $2, Pacific blue marlin.

**2001, Aug. 23**
**927-930** A211 Set of 4 5.50 5.50

Christmas A212

Designs: 17c, Angel appears to Mary. 34c Nativity. 48c, Adoration of the shepherds. 69c, Adoration of the Magi. 89c, Flight to Egypt. $2, Fijian Chirst child.

**2001, Oct. 29 Litho. *Perf. 13¾x13¼***
**931-936** A212 Set of 6 6.75 6.75

Colonial Financial Services Group, 125th Anniv. in Fiji — A213

Designs: 17c, Bank office. 48c, Women using automatic teller machine. $1, Suva Private Hospital. $3, Hoisting of British flag.

**2001, Nov. 16 Litho. *Perf. 13¼***
**937-940** A213 Set of 4 6.75 6.75

Air Pacific, 50th Anniv. — A214

No. 941: a, De Havilland Drover. b, Hawker Siddley HS-748. c, Douglas DC-10-30. d, Boeing 747-200.

**2001, Nov. 30 Litho. *Perf. 13***
**941** Horiz. strip of 4 7.50 7.50
***a.*** A214 89c multi 1.50 1.50
***b.*** A214 96c multi 1.75 1.75
***c.*** A214 $1 multi 1.75 1.75
***d.*** A214 $2 multi 2.25 2.25

Spices — A215

Designs: 69c, Pepper. 89c, Nutmeg. $1, Vanilla. $2, Cinnamon.

**2002, Mar. 12 Litho.** ***Perf. 13¼***
**942-945** A215 Set of 4 6.25 6.25

Souvenir Sheet

Balaka Palm — A216

Palm and: a, Bird, butterfly, beetle. b, Lizard, butterfly

**2002, Apr. 29**
**946** A216 $2 Sheet of 2, #a-b 6.75 6.75

Freshwater Fish — A217

Designs: 48c, Redigobius sp. 96c, Spotted flagtail. $1.23, Silverstripe mudskipper. $2, Snakehead gudgeon.

**2002, May 13**
**947-950** A217 Set of 4 6.50 6.50

Fruit — A218

Designs: 25c, Breadfruit. 34c, Wi. $1, Jakfruit. $3, Avocado.

**2002, July 25 Litho.** ***Perf. 13¾x13¼***
**951-954** A218 Set of 4 6.25 6.25

Murex Shells — A219

Designs: 69c, Saul's murex. 96c, Caltrop murex. $1, Purple Pacific drupe. $2, Ramose murex.

**2002, Aug. 20** ***Perf. 13¾***
**955-958** A219 Set of 4 7.00 7.00

Fiji Goshawk A220

Designs: 48c, Goshawk and eggs. 89c, Chicks in nest. $1, Juvenile on branch. $3, Adult.

**2002, Sept. 10**
**959-962** A220 Set of 4 8.25 8.25

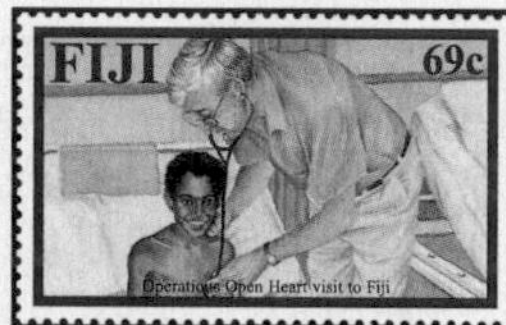
2002 Operation Open Heart Visit to Fiji — A221

Designs: 34c, Doctors performing operation, vert. 69c, Doctor listening to patient's heart with stethoscope. $1.17, Technician administering echocardiogram. $2, Administration of anesthesia to patient, vert.

**2002, Oct. 30** ***Perf. 13¼***
**963-966** A221 Set of 4 7.25 7.25

Fiji Natural Artesian Water — A222

Designs: 25c, Bottle of water, flowers, vert. 48c, Bottling plant. $1, Delivery truck. $3, Children with bottled water, vert.

**2002, Nov. 5**
**967-970** A222 Set of 4 7.50 7.50

Christmas — A223

Designs: 17c, Christian church. 89c, Mosque. $1, Hindu temple. $3, Christian church, diff.

**2002, Nov. 20**
**971-974** A223 Set of 4 7.50 7.50

Post Fiji, Ltd. Improvements — A224

Designs: 48c, General Post Office. 96c, Post Fiji Mail Center. $1, Post Fiji Logistics Center. $2, Smart Mail.

**2003, Mar. 19 Litho.** ***Perf. 13¼***
**975-978** A224 Set of 4 6.75 6.75

Souvenir Sheet

Intl. Year of Fresh Water — A225

No. 979: a, Top of waterfall, flowers. b, Base of waterfall, butterfly.

**2003, Apr. 22**
**979** A225 $2 Sheet of 2, #a-b 7.25 7.25

2003 South Pacific Games, Suva — A226

Designs: 10c, Track athlete with arms raised. 14c, Baseball. 20c, Netball. No. 983, $5, Shot put.
No. 984, $5, Flags of participating nations, venues, volleyball players.

**2003** ***Perf. 13¼***
**980-983** A226 Set of 4 7.25 7.25

**Size: 120x85mm**

***Imperf***

**984** A226 $5 multi 6.75 6.75

Issued: Nos. 980-983, 5/26; No. 984, 6/28.

Fish A227

Siganus uspi: 58c, Fish, crab and coral. 83c, Two fish and coral. $1.15, Two fish, coral, and other fish species. $3, Fish and coral.

**2003, Aug. 12** ***Perf. 13¼***
**985-988** A227 Set of 4 8.50 8.50

Bird Life International A228

Designs: 41c, Long-legged warbler. 60c, Silktail. $1.07, Red-throated lorikeet. $3, Pink-billed parrot finch.

**2003, Sept. 16**
**989-992** A228 Set of 4 13.00 13.00

Geckos A229

Designs: 83c, Pacific slender-toed gecko. $1.07, Indopacific tree gecko. $1.15, Mann's gecko. $2, Voracious gecko.

**2003, Oct. 21 Litho.** ***Perf. 13¼***
**993-996** A229 Set of 4 9.75 9.75

Christmas — A230

Children's art: 18c, Children, Christmas tree. 41c, Children, flag of Fiji. 58c, Children, Santa Claus, reindeer pulling sleighs, vert. 83c, Santa Claus on chimney, gifts, children, Christmas tree, vert. $1.07, Children with candles, Christmas tree, vert. $1.15, Santa Claus, children, bell, rainbow, vert.
$1.41, Handshake.

**2003, Nov. 26 Litho.** ***Perf. 13¼***
**997-1002** A230 Set of 6 7.25 7.25

**Souvenir Sheet**

**1003** A230 $1.41 multi 3.50 3.50

Tagimoucia — A231

**2003, Dec. 1 Litho.** ***Perf. 14½x14***
**1004** A231 50c multi + label *5.00 5.00*

Sold in sheets of 10 stamps + 10 labels that could be personalized for $15 per sheet.

Xixuthrus Heyrovskyi, Longest Beetle in the World — A232

**2003, Feb. 27** ***Imperf.***
**1005** A232 $5 multi 7.50 7.50

Miniature Sheet

Worldwide Fund for Nature (WWF) — A233

No. 1006: a, 58c, Skipjack tuna. b, 83c, Albacore tuna. c, $1.07, Yellowfin tuna. d, $3, Bigeye tuna.

**2004, Apr. 7** *Perf. 13¼*
**1006** A233 Sheet of 4, #a-d 8.50 8.50
*e.* Like #1006, with artist's name at LL of each stamp 8.50 8.50

Land Snails A234

Designs: 18c, Malleated placostyle. 41c, Kandavu placostyle. $1.15, Fragile orpiella. $3, Thin Fijian placostyle.

**2004, May 28**
**1007-1010** A234 Set of 4 7.25 7.25

**Bird Type of 1995 and**

No. 1011A

*Perf. 13¼x13*
**2004, June 26** **Unwmk.**
**1011** A166 18c Island thrush 1.90 1.90
**1011A** A166 4c on 18c #1011 *250.00 250.00*

No. 1011A issued Aug. 2008. Surcharge on No. 1011A exists only inverted. Values are for stamps with surcharge at top, as shown. Value, with surcharge centered $400.

Coral Reef Shrimp — A235

Designs: 58c, Boxer shrimp. 83c, Bumblebee shrimp. $1.07, Mantis shrimp. $3, Anemone shrimp.

**2004, June 30** *Perf. 13¼*
**1012-1015** A235 Set of 4 7.25 7.25

Birds A236

Designs: 41c, Wandering tattler. 58c, Whimbrel. $1.15, Pacific golden plover. $3, Bristle-thighed curlew.

**2004, July 28**
**1016-1019** A236 Set of 4 10.00 10.00

2004 Summer Olympics, Athens A237

Designs: 41c, Swimming. 58c, Judo, vert. $1.40, Weight lifting, vert. $2, Makelesi Bulikiobo, runner.

**2004, Aug. 12**
**1020-1023** A237 Set of 4 7.25 7.25

Musket Cove to Port Vila Yacht Race, 25th Anniv. — A238

Various yachts: 83c, $1.07, $1.15, $2. $1.07 and $2 are vert.

**2004, Sept. 18** *Perf. 14¼*
**1024-1027** A238 Set of 4 8.00 8.00
*1027a* Souvenir sheet of 1 4.25 4.25

See Vanuatu Nos. 858-861.

Souvenir Sheet

Coconut Crab — A239

**2004, Oct. 20** **Litho.** *Perf. 14*
**1028** A239 $5 multi 7.50 7.50

Papilio Schmeltzii — A240

Designs: 58c, Newly-emerged adult, vert. 83c, Larva. $1.41, Adult. $3, Pupa, vert.

*Perf. 14x14½, 14½x14*
**2004, Nov. 10**
**1029-1032** A240 Set of 4 9.50 9.50

Christmas A241

Designs: 18c, Annunciation. 58c, Infant in manger. $1.07, Madonna and child. $3, Adoration of the Shepherds.

**2004, Dec. 1** **Litho.** *Perf. 13¼*
**1033-1036** A241 Set of 4 9.00 9.00

Birds — A242

No. 1037: a, Little heron. b, Great white egret. c, White-faced heron. d, Pacific reef heron.

**2005, Jan. 26**
**1037** Horiz. strip of 4 9.25 9.25
*a.-d.* A242 $1 Any single 2.25 2.25

Flowers For Perfume — A243

Designs: 58c, Cananga odorata. $1.15, Euodia hortensis. $1.41, Pandanus tecorius. $2, Santalum yasi.

**2005, Feb. 20** *Perf. 14x14½*
**1038-1041** A243 Set of 4 7.50 7.50

Peregrine Falcons — A244

Designs: 41c, Head of falcon. 83c, Adult at nest. $1.07, Chicks. $3, Adult on rock.

**2005, Mar. 14** **Litho.** *Perf. 14½x14*
**1042-1045** A244 Set of 4 9.50 9.50

Triggerfish — A245

Designs: 58c, Whitebanded triggerfish. 83c, Yellow-spotted triggerfish. $1.15, Orange-lined triggerfish. $2, Clown triggerfish.

**2005, Apr. 27**
**1046-1049** A245 Set of 4 8.00 8.00

European Philatelic Cooperation, 50th Anniv. (in 2006) — A246

Color of arches: 58c, Red. 83c, Blue green. $1.41, Purple. $4, Yellow bister.

**2005, June 1** *Perf. 13¾*
**1050-1053** A246 Set of 4 10.00 10.00
*1053a* Souvenir sheet, #1050-1053 10.00 10.00

Europa stamps, 50th anniv. (in 2006).

Miniature Sheet

End of World War II, 60th Anniv. — A247

No. 1054: a, HMNZS Achilles. b, Japanese Yokosuka E14Y "Glen" over Suva Harbor. c, Fijian South Pacific Scouts in Solomon Islands. d, USS Chicago. e, Patrol vessel HMS Viti. f, British Prime Minister Winston Churchill. g, HMS Hood. h, Dambusters Raid. i, German King Tiger tank in Ardennes. j, Gen. Dwight D. Eisenhower.

**2005, June 27** **Litho.** *Perf. 13¾*
**1054** A247 83c Sheet of 10, #a-j 12.75 12.75

Game Fish A248

Designs: 41c, Great barracuda. 58c, Narrow-barred Spanish mackerel. $1.07, Giant trevally. $3, Indo-Pacific sailfish.

**2005, July 27** **Litho.** *Perf. 14½x14*
**1055-1058** A248 Set of 4 8.75 8.75

Pope John Paul II (1920-2005) A249

**2005, Aug. 18** *Perf. 14*
**1059** A249 $1 multi 2.50 2.50

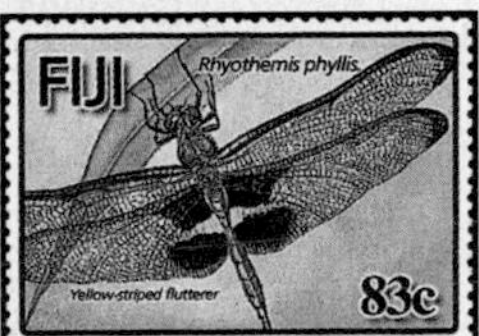


Dragonflies — A250

Designs: 83c, Yellow-striped flutterer. $1.07, Agrionoptera insignis. $1.15, Green skimmer. $2, Common percher.

**2005, Aug. 30** **Litho.** *Perf. 13¼*
**1060-1063** A250 Set of 4 7.50 7.50

Albert Einstein (1879-1955), Physicist — A251

Einstein: 83c, As a child. $1.07, In 1905. $1.15, And blackboard. $2, And galaxies.

**2005, Sept. 27** **Litho.** *Perf. 14¼x14*
**1064-1067** A251 Set of 4 9.25 9.25

Intl. Year of Physics.

Root Crops — A252

Designs: 41c, Manihot utilissima. 83c, Ipomoea satatas. $1.41, Colocasia esculenta. $2, Dioscorea sativa.

**2005, Oct. 13** *Perf. 13¼*
**1068-1071** A252 Set of 4 7.25 7.25

Tall Ships A253

Designs: 83c, Eliza of Province. $1.15, Elbe. $1.41, HMS Rosario. $2, L'Astrolabe.

**2005, Nov. 21 Litho. *Perf. 14x14¼***
**1072-1075** A253 Set of 4 9.00 9.00

Barn Owls — A254

Owl: 18c, And eggs. $1.15, Juvenile. $1.41, With prey. $2, Perched.

**2006, Jan. 10 Litho. *Perf. 14¼x14***
**1076-1079** A254 Set of 4 9.75 9.75

Platymantis Vitianus — A255

Various depictions: 50c, 83c, $1.15, $2.

**2006, Feb. 8 Litho. *Perf. 14x14¼***
**1080-1083** A255 Set of 4 8.00 8.00

Skinks A256

Designs: 18c, Pygmy snake-eyed skink. 58c, Brown-tailed copper striped skink. $1.15, Pacific black skink. $3, Pacific blue-tailed skink.

**2006, Mar. 22**
**1084-1087** A256 Set of 4 7.50 7.50

Queen Elizabeth II, 80th Birthday A257

Designs: 50c, As child. 65c, Wearing tiara. 90c, Wearing blue hat. $3, Wearing blue hat, diff.

No. 1092: a, Like 65c. b, Like 90c.

**2006, Apr. 21 Litho. *Perf. 14***
**With White Frames**
**1088-1091** A257 Set of 4 7.00 7.00

**Souvenir Sheet**
**Without White Frames**
**1092** A257 $2 Sheet of 2, #a-b 5.75 5.75

Miniature Sheet

Vijay Singh, Golfer — A258

No. 1097 — Singh: a, Head. b, With arm raised. c, Leaning on golf club. d, Hitting ball from sand trap. e, Holding trophy (60x87mm).

***Perf. 14x14¼***
**2006, May 26 Litho. Unwmk.**
**1097** A258 $1 Sheet of 5, #a-e 8.50 8.50

2006 World Cup Soccer Championships, Germany — A259

Various players: 65c, 90c, $1.20, $2.

**2006, June 9 *Perf. 14¼x14***
**1098-1101** A259 Set of 4 7.50 7.50

Souvenir Sheet

Purple Swamphen — A260

No. 1102: a, Swamphen and flowers. b, Swamphen on nest.

**2006, July 20 *Perf. 14½x14***
**1102** A260 $2 Sheet of 2, #a-b 6.50 6.50

Extinct Species A261

Designs: 50c, Brachylophus vitiensis. $1.10, Natunaornis gigoura, vert. $1.20, Vitirallus watlingi, vert. $1.50, Platymantis megabotoniviti.

***Perf. 14x14¼, 14¼x14***
**2006, Aug. 15 Litho.**
**1103-1106** A261 Set of 4 7.00 7.00

Phasmids — A262

Designs: 10c, Hermarchus apollonius. $1.10, Cotylosoma dipneusticum. $1.20, Chitoniscus feejeeanus. $2, Graeffea crouanii.

**2006, Sept. 7 *Perf. 14½x14***
**1107-1110** A262 Set of 4 7.00 7.00

Honey Production A263

Designs: 18c, Bees and honeycomb. 40c, Apiarist examining honeycomb, horiz. $1, Woman and beehives, horiz. $3, Man and bottle of honey.

**2006, Oct. 16 *Perf. 14x14½, 14½x14***
**1111-1114** A263 Set of 4 7.50 7.50

Christmas A264

Flowering plants: 18c, Decaspermum vitiense. 65c, Quisqualis indica. 90c, Mussaendra raiateensis. $3, Delonix regia.

**2006, Dec. 5 *Perf. 14x14½***
**1115-1118** A264 Set of 4 7.50 7.50

Anemonefish — A265

Designs: 18c, Spine-cheek anemonefish. 60c, Pink anemonefish. 90c, Orange-fin anemonefish. $3, Dusky anemonefish.

***Perf. 14½x14, 14x14½***
**2006, Nov. 7 Litho.**
**1119-1122** A265 Set of 4 7.50 7.50

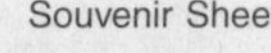

Souvenir Sheet

Thalassina Anomala — A266

**2007, Jan. 24 *Perf. 13½***
**1123** A266 $4 multi 5.50 5.50

Traditional Architecture — A267

Designs: 20c, Coastal dwelling. 65c, Inland dwelling. $1.10, Temple, Bau. $3, Lauan-style house.

**2007, Mar. 20 Litho. *Perf. 13¼***
**1124-1127** A267 Set of 4 7.25 7.25

Freshwater Gobies — A268

Designs: 20c, Sicyopterus lagocephalus. $1.10, Stiphodon rutilaureus. $1.20, Sicyopus zosterophorum. $2, Stiphodon sp.

**2007, Apr. 5 Litho. *Perf. 13¼***
**1128-1131** A268 Set of 4 6.25 6.25

Birds Introduced to Fiji — A269

Designs: 50c, Red-vented bulbul. 65c, Spotted dove, horiz. $1.50, Australian magpie, horiz. $2, Java sparrow.

**2007, May 22**
**1132-1135** A269 Set of 4 7.50 7.50

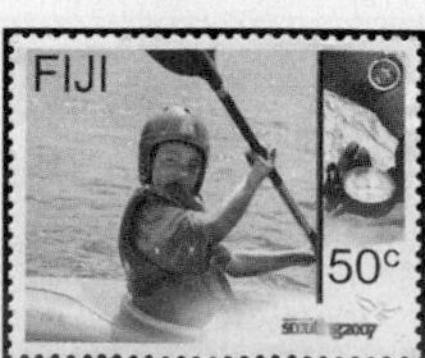

Scouting, Cent. A270

Designs: 50c, Scout in kayak, hand holding compass. 90c, Three Scouts wearing helmets, hands tying knot. No. 1138, $1.50, Scout in harness climbing, Scout saluting. $2, Scout writing observation notes, hands tying neckerchief.

No. 1140, $1.50, vert.: a, Scout emblem. b, Lord Robert Baden-Powell.

**2007, July 9 *Perf. 13¾***
**1136-1139** A270 Set of 4 7.00 7.00

### Souvenir Sheet

**1140** A270 $1.50 Sheet of 2, #a-b 4.75 4.75

Snails A271

Designs: 40c, Clithon diadema. 90c, Neritina variegata. $1.20, Fijidoma maculata. $2, Neritina squamaepicta.

**2007, Aug. 18** ***Perf. 14x14¼***
**1141-1144** A271 Set of 4 6.50 6.50

Orchids — A272

Designs: 20c, Liparis layardii. 65c, Dendrobium catillare, horiz. $1.10, Dendrobium mohlianum, horiz. $3, Glomera montana.

***Perf. 14¼x14, 14x14¼***

**2007, Aug. 21**
**1145-1148** A272 Set of 4 7.25 7.25

### Nos. 725 and 729 Surcharged

No. 1149

No. 1150

### Methods, Types and Watermarks As Before

**2006-08**
**1149** A166 1c on 6c #729 1.50 1.50
**1150** A166 1c on 6c #729 *7.00 7.00*

No. 1149 exists with inverted surcharge. Value, $90. No. 1149 also exists with double surcharge, one inverted. Value, $150. No. 1149 also exists with normal surcharge shifted 75% upward. Value, $50.

No. 1151

No. 1152

No. 1152c

**1151** A166 2c on 1c #725 *4.50 4.50*
**1152** A166 2c on 1c #725, larger font *2.50 2.50*
*c.* 1½mm gap between "2" and "c" (position 67) *60.00 60.00*

No. 1152 exists with normal surcharge shifted 50% upward. Value, $50.

No. 1152A

No. 1152Ab

No. 1152Ac

**1152A** A166 2c on 1c #725, 4mm between "c" and obliterator *200.00 200.00*
*b.* 5mm between "c" and obliterator *200.00 200.00*
*c.* 3mm between "c" and obliterator —

No. 1152Ab exists with inverted surcharge. Value, $375.

No. 1153

No. 1153a

No. 1153c

**1153** A166 2c on 6c #729, 4mm between "c" and obliterator 1.25 1.25
*a.* 5mm between "c" and obliterator 1.25 1.25
*c.* 1½mm gap between "2" and "c" (position 57) *60.00 60.00*

No. 1153a exists with inverted surcharge. Value, $110. No. 1153a also exists with double surcharge, one inverted. Value, $150.

No. 1153B

No. 1154

No. 1154A

**1153B** A166 2c on 6c #729 *550.00 550.00*
**1154** A166 3c on 1c #725 1.25 1.25
**1154A** A166 3c on 1c #725, larger font *650.00 650.00*

No. 1154 exists with inverted surcharge. Value, $275. No. 1154 exists with double surcharge, one inverted. Value, $225.

No. 1155

No. 1155a

**1155** A166 4c on 1c #725 1.50 1.50
*a.* 1½mm gap between "4" and "c" (position 57) *60.00 60.00*

No. 1156

No. 1156a

**1156** A166 4c on 6c #729, 4mm between "c" an obliterator 1.25 1.25
*a.* 5mm between "c" and obliterator 1.25 1.25

No. 1156a exists with inverted surcharge. Value, $110. No. 1156a also exists with double surcharge, one inverted. Value, $150. No. 1156a also exists with normal surcharge shifted 75% upward and 50% upward. Values, each $50.

No. 1156B

No. 1157

**1156B** A166 6c on 6c #729 *650.00 650.00*
**1157** A166 18c on 6c #729, 4mm between "c" and obliterator *6.50 6.50*

No. 1157 exists with double surcharge, one with normal 4mm between "c" and obliterator and the other with 2½mm between "c" and obliterator. One surcharge is shifted 75% upward. Half of the errors have the normal separation between "c" and obliterator at top and half have it at bottom. Each error variety is equally scarce. Value, each $130. No. 1157 exists with double surcharge, both with 4mm between "c" and obliterator. Value, $150.

No. 1157 also exists with normal surcharge shifted 75% upward but with no second surcharge. Value, $50.

No. 1158

No. 1158a

**1158** A166 18c on 6c #729, 2½mm between "c" and obliterator *11.00 11.00*
*a.* 4mm between "c" and obliterator *22.00 22.00*

No. 1158 exists with double surcharge. Value, $150. No. 1158 also exists with double surcharge, both inverted. Value, $225.

No. 1159

No. 1159a

**1159** A166 20c on 6c #729, 2½mm between "c" and obliterator *6.50 6.50*
*a.* 4mm between "c" and obliterator *14.50 14.50*

No. 1159 exists with inverted surcharge. Value, $110.

No. 1160

No. 1160a

No. 1160b

**1160** A166 20c on 6c #729, 4mm between "c" and obliterator *30.00 30.00*
*a.* 1½mm between "c" and obliterator *60.00 60.00*
*b.* No gap between "c" and obliterator *475.00 475.00*
*Nos. 1149-1160 (16) 2,125. 2,125.*

No. 1160a exists with double surcharge. Value, $150.

Issued: No. 1149, 5/30/07; No. 1150, 9/19/07; No. 1151, 4/3; No. 1152, 11/13; No. 1152A, July 2007, No. 1152Ab, 8/20/08; Nos. 1153, 1153B 2/19/07; No. 1153a, 2/27/07; No. 1154, 3/13; No. 1155, 6/27; No. 1156, 6/6/07; No. 1156a, 2/19/08; No. 1156B, Feb. 2007; No. 1157, 6/8; No. 1158, 9/8; No. 1158a, Aug. 2007; No. 1159, 1/19/07; No. 1159a, Jan. 2007; No. 1160, 3/8/07; No. 1160a, 4/12/08.

Fish A273

Designs: 50c, Coronation trout. 90c, Roving coral trout. $1.50, Squaretail coral trout. $2, Chinese footballer.

**2007, Oct. 15** **Litho.** ***Perf. 13¼***
**1161-1164** A273 Set of 4 7.75 7.75

Butterflies — A274

Designs: 20c, Polyura caphontis. $1.10, Hypolimnas bolina, horiz. $1.20, Doleschallia bisaltide, horiz. $2, Danaus hamata.

**2007, Nov. 20** **Litho.** ***Perf. 13¼***
**1165-1168** A274 Set of 4 6.00 6.00

### Souvenir Sheet

Barred-winged Rail — A275

No. 1169: a, Head of adult. b, Chick.

**2007, Dec. 3**
**1169** A275 $2 Sheet of 2, #a-b 5.50 5.50

National Medals — A276

Designs: 50c, Medal of the Order of Fiji. 65c, Member of the Order of Fiji. $1.20, Officer of the Order of Fiji. $2, Companion of the Order of Fiji.

**2008, Feb. 20 Litho. *Perf. 13¼***
**1170-1173** A276 Set of 4 6.25 6.25

Souvenir Sheet

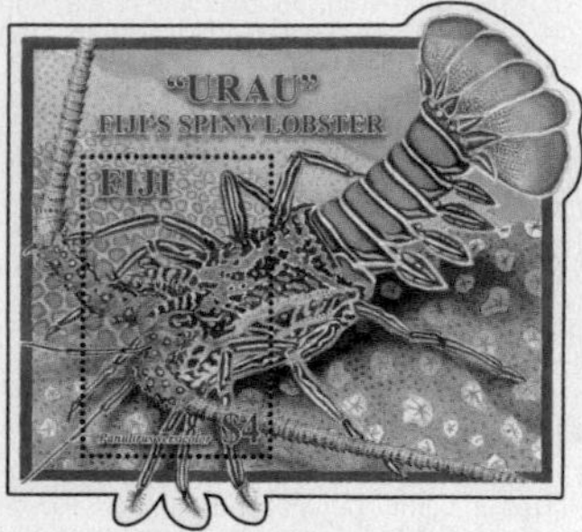

Spiny Lobster — A277

**2008, Apr. 22 Litho. *Perf. 14x14½***
**1174** A277 $4 multi 5.25 5.25

First Trans-Pacific Flight of the Southern Cross, 80th Anniv. — A278

Southern Cross: 20c, Over Fiji. 90c, In Albert Park, Suva. $1.50, Surrounded by police guard. $2, With crew.

**2008, June 13 *Perf. 13½***
**1175-1178** A278 Set of 4 5.75 5.75

2008 Summer Olympics, Beijing A279

Designs: 20c, Bamboo, Running. 65c, Dragon, Judo. 90c, Lanterns, Shooting. $1.50, Carp, Swimming.

**2008, May 5 Litho. *Perf. 13¼***
**1179-1182** A279 Set of 4 4.25 4.25

Red-breasted Musk Parrot Varieties — A280

Prosopeia tabuensis: 65c, Koroensis. 90c, Atrogularis, horiz. $1.50, Taviunensis, horiz. $2, Splendens.

**2008, Mar. 25 Litho. *Perf. 13½***
**1183-1186** A280 Set of 4 6.75 6.75

Humpback Whales — A281

Humpback whale: 20c, Pair underwater. 50c, Breaching water's surface. $1.10, Reentering water. $3, Flukes.

**2008, July 17 Litho. *Perf. 14½x14***
**1187-1190** A281 Set of 4 6.00 6.00

### Nos. 729-731 Surcharged Like Nos. 1149-1160

No. 1191

No. 1191A

No. 1191Ab

### Methods, Perfs and Watermarks As Before

**2007-09**

**1191** A166 1c on 13c #730, 5mm between "c" and obliterator 1.50 1.50
*b.* 4mm between "c" and obliterator (positions 3 and 89) *50.00 50.00*

**1191A** A166 1c on 23c #731, 4mm between "c" and obliterator 1.00 1.00
*b.* 5mm between "c" and obliterator 1.00 1.00
*c.* Pair, Nos. 1191Ab and 1191A (positions 3 and 89) *50.00 50.00*

No. 1191 exists with double surcharge, one inverted. Value, $150. No. 1191 exists with double surcharge: one upright with "XX" obliterator, the other inverted with "xxx" obliterator. Value, $175. No. 1191A exists with inverted surcharge. Value, $160. No. 1191A exists with a "2c" surcharge having a 1½mm gap between the "2" and the "c" (position 57). Value, $100. No. 1191Ab exists with inverted surcharge. Value, $160. No. 1191Ab also exists with double surcharge, one inverted. Value, $175.

No. 1191C

No. 1192

**1191C** A166 2c on 6c #729 *175.00 175.00*
*d.* 1½mm gap between "2" and "c" (position 57) —

**1192** A166 2c on 6c #729 *175.00 175.00*
*c.* 2½mm gap between pair of double bars of obliterator *400.00 400.00*
*d.* 4mm between "c" and obliterator *325.00 325.00*

No. 1192 exists with obliterator of three double bars and with obliterator of four double bars. Value, each $500. No. 1192 exists with obliterator of two double bars and a single bar. Value, $400. No. 1192 exists with obliterator omitted. Value, $750.

No. 1192A

No. 1192Ab

No. 1193

No. 1193a

No. 1193B

No. 1193C

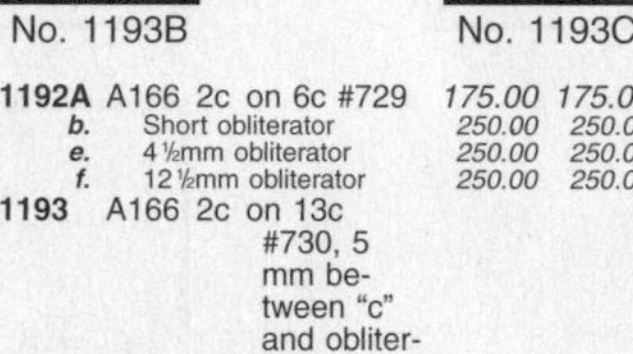

**1192A** A166 2c on 6c #729 *175.00 175.00*
*b.* Short obliterator *250.00 250.00*
*e.* 4½mm obliterator *250.00 250.00*
*f.* 12½mm obliterator *250.00 250.00*

**1193** A166 2c on 13c #730, 5 mm between "c" and obliterator 1.50 1.50
*a.* 4mm between "c" and obliterator (positions 3 and 89) *50.00 50.00*

**1193B** A166 2c on 23c #731, 5 mm between "c" and obliterator *125.00 125.00*
*a.* 4mm between "c" and obliterator (positions 3 and 89) *200.00 200.00*

**1193C** A166 3c on 13c #730 *175.00 175.00*

No. 1192A has an 8mm obliterator. Two lines comprise the obliterator on No. 1192Ab: one long, one short. The obliterator on No. 1192Af extends into the right margin and must be collected with right selvage attached to show the entire obliterator.

No. 1193 exists with double surcharge, one inverted. Value, $150. No. 1193 exists with double surcharge: one upright with "XX" obliterator, the other inverted with "xxx" obliterator. Value, $175. No. 1193 exists with a period after the "2c." Value, $500.

No. 1194

No. 1194a

No. 1195

No. 1195b

**1194** A166 4c on 13c #730, 5mm between "c" and obliterator 1.50 1.50
*a.* 4mm between "c" and obliterator (positions 3 and 89) *50.00 50.00*
*b.* 1½mm gap between "4" and "c" *225.00 225.00*

**1195** A166 20c on 6c #729 *100.00 100.00*
*b.* No gap between "c" and obliterator *550.00 550.00*

No. 1194 exists with double surcharge, one inverted at top of stamp. Value, $200. No. 1194 exists with double surcharge, one inverted in center of stamp. Value, $200.

No. 1195A

**1195A** A166 20c on 23c #731 *400.00 400.00*
*c.* 3½mm between "c" and obliterator *400.00 400.00*

No. 1195A exists with normal surcharge shifted 75% upward. Value, $300. No. 1195A also exists with inverted surcharge. Value, $350. No. 1195A also exists with "c" of surcharge omitted. Value, $400.

No. 1196

No. 1196a

**1196** A166 20c on 23c #731 *2.00 2.00*
*a.* No gap between "c" and obliterator (position 70) *35.00 35.00*

No. 1196 exists with inverted surcharge. Value, $90. No. 1196 also exists with double surcharge and with double surcharge, one inverted. Value, each $150. No. 1196 also exists surcharged on gum side only; the surcharge is always inverted. Value, $200. No. 1196 also exists surcharged on both sides. Value, $180.

No. 1197

No. 1197a

No. 1197d

No. 1197e

No. 1197f

**1197** A166 20c on 23c #731, 1½mm between "c" and obliterator *200.00 200.00*
*a.* 2½mm between "c" and obliterator *90.00 90.00*
*d.* 3mm between "c" and obliterator *100.00 100.00*
*e.* 4mm between "c" and obliterator *90.00 90.00*
*f.* 5mm between "c" and obliterator *175.00 175.00*

No. 1197 exists with surcharge shifted 75% upward. Value, $175. No. 1197d exists with inverted surcharge. Value, $150.

No. 1197B

No. 1197C

**1197B** A166 20c on 23c #731 *35.00 35.00*
*a.* No gap between "c" and obliterator (positions 70 and 79) *100.00 100.00*
*c.* 3mm between "c" and obliterator *70.00 70.00*

**1197C** A166 20c on 23c #731 175.00 175.00
*a.* No gap between "c" and obliterator 450.00 450.00
*Nos. 1191-1197C (15)* 1,743. 1,743.

No. 1197B exists with inverted surcharge. Value, $150. No. 1197C exists with inverted surcharge. Value, $350. No 1197C exists with obliterator of two double bars with a dash between them. Value, $450.

Issued: No. 1191, 8/22/08; No. 1191A, 12/18/08; No. 1191Ab, 1/23/09; No. 1191C, 1192, 1192A, 2/19/07; Nos. 1193, 1194, 8/20/08; No. 1195, 4/28/08; No. 1195A, Apr. 2008; Nos. 1196, 4/12/08; Nos. 1197, 1197a, 1197d, 1197e, 1197f. Apr. 2008; 1197B, 4/12/08; 1197C, Apr. 2008.

Bananas — A282

Various banana varieties: 65c, $1.10, $1.20, $2.

**2008, Sept. 23** **Litho.** ***Perf. 14x14½***
**1198-1201** A282 Set of 4 5.50 5.50

Eels A283

Designs: 50c, Anguilla obscura. 90c, Anguilla marmorata. $1.50, Anguilla obscura, diff. $2, Gymnothorax potyuranodon.

**2008, Oct. 15** ***Perf. 14½x14***
**1202-1205** A283 Set of 4 5.50 5.50

Christmas — A284

Various choirs: 20c, 50c, 65c, $3.

**2008, Dec. 10** **Litho.** ***Perf. 14½x14***
**1206-1209** A284 Set of 4 4.50 4.50

Fruit Doves — A285

Designs: 50c, Many-colored fruit dove. 65c, Crimson-crowned fruit dove. 90c, Whistling dove. $3, Orange dove.

**2009, Feb. 17** **Litho.** ***Perf. 14x14½***
**1210-1213** A285 Set of 4 5.50 5.50

### Nos. 729-731 Surcharged Like Nos. 1149-1160

No. 1214

No. 1214B

No. 1215

No. 1215A

### Methods, Perfs and Watermarks As Before

**2009-12**

**1214** A166 1c on 13c #730 45.00 45.00
*a.* 2½mm gap between "c" and obliterator (positions 3 and 89) 120.00 120.00
**1214B** A166 1c on 13c #730, small font 90.00 90.00
**1215** A166 1c on 23c #731 1.25 1.25
*b.* 2½mm gap between "c" and obliterator (positions 3 and 89) 50.00 50.00
**1215A** A166 1c on 23c #731, small font 1.00 1.00

No. 1215 exists with inverted surcharge. Value, $90. No. 1215A exists with inverted surcharge. Value, $90. No. 1215A also exists with "xx" obliterator (position 70). Value, $200.

No. 1216

No. 1216A

No. 1216B

No. 1216D

**1216** A166 2c on 6c #729 100.00 100.00
*e.* 2½mm gap between "c" and obliterator (positions 3 and 89) 175.00 175.00
**1216A** A166 2c on 13c #730 45.00 45.00
*c.* 2½mm gap between "c" and obliterator (positions 3 and 89) 120.00 120.00
**1216B** A166 2c on 23c #731 175.00 175.00
**1216D** A166 2c on 13c #730, small font 175.00 175.00

No. 1216D has a 2½mm gap between "c" and obliterator.

No. 1217

No. 1217A

**1217** A166 2c on 23c #731 20.00 20.00
*b.* 2½mm between "c" and obliterator (positions 3 and 89) 50.00 50.00
**1217A** A166 2c on 23c #731, small font 1.00 1.00

No. 1217 exists with inverted surcharge. Value, $175. No. 1217A exists with inverted surcharge. Value, $90. No. 1217A also exists with double surcharge, one inverted. Value, $120. No. 1217A also exists with "xx" obliterator (position 70). Value, $200.

No. 1218

No. 1218A

**1218** A166 3c on 23c #731 45.00 45.00
*b.* 2½mm between "c" and obliterator (positions 3 and 89) 140.00 140.00
**1218A** A166 3c on 23c #731, small font 1.00 1.00

No. 1218 exists with "3" of surcharge omitted. Most of the known singles have irregular perforations from being roughly removed from sheets. Value thus, $100. Errors with intact perforations are extremely scarce. Value, $300. Value of single error in pair with normal stamp, $350.

No. 1218A exists with double surcharge. Value, $150. No. 1218A exists with inverted surcharge. Value, $100. No. 1218A exists with double surcharge, one inverted. Value, $130. No. 1218A exists with "xx" obliterator (position 70). Value, $200.

No. 1219

No. 1219B

No. 1220

No. 1220B

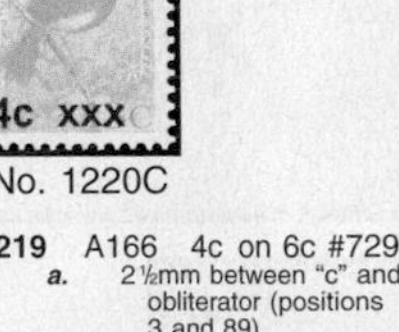
No. 1220C

No. 1220D

**1219** A166 4c on 6c #729 70.00 70.00
*a.* 2½mm between "c" and obliterator (positions 3 and 89) 100.00 100.00
**1219B** A166 40c on 6c #729 100.00 100.00
*a.* No gap between "c" and obliterator (position 70) 200.00 200.00
**1219C** A166 4c on 6c #729, small font 85.00 85.00
**1220** A166 4c on 13c #730 45.00 45.00
*a.* 2½mm gap between "c" and obliterator (positions 3 and 89) 120.00 120.00
**1220B** A166 5c on 13c #730 160.00 130.00
**1220C** A166 4c on 13c #730, small font 90.00 90.00
**1220D** A166 40c on 13c #730 400.00 400.00
*a.* No gap between "c" and obliterator (position 70) — —

Nos. 1219 and 1219a exist with inverted surcharge. Value, each $200. No. 1219C exists with inverted surcharge. Value, $175. No. 1219C also exists with double surcharge, one inverted. Value, $225. No. 1220C exists with inverted surcharge. Value, $100.

No. 1221

No. 1222

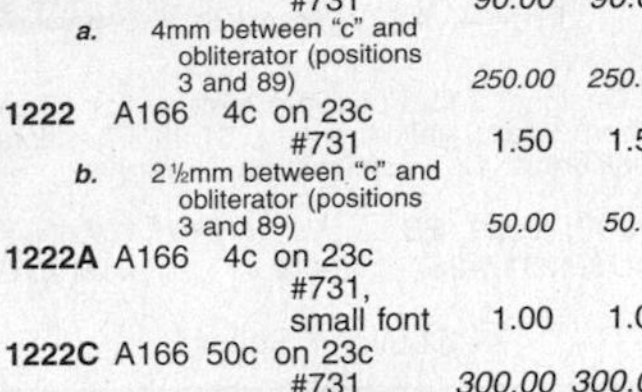
No. 1222A

No. 1222C

**1221** A166 4c on 23c #731 90.00 90.00
*a.* 4mm between "c" and obliterator (positions 3 and 89) 250.00 250.00
**1222** A166 4c on 23c #731 1.50 1.50
*b.* 2½mm between "c" and obliterator (positions 3 and 89) 50.00 50.00
**1222A** A166 4c on 23c #731, small font 1.00 1.00
**1222C** A166 50c on 23c #731 300.00 300.00
*a.* No gap between "c" and obliterator (position 70) 1,000.

No. 1221 exists with inverted surcharge. Value, $150.

No. 1222 exists with inverted surcharge. Value, $90. No. 1222 exists with double surcharge, one inverted. Value, $130. No. 1222 exists with double surcharge, one with normal 4mm between "c" and obliterator and the other with 2½mm between "c" and obliterator. Value, $150.

No. 1222A exists with inverted surcharge. Value, $100. No. 1222A exists with double surcharge, one inverted. Value, $120. No. 1222A exists with double surcharge. Value, $150.

No. 1223

No. 1223b

No. 1223c

No. 1223A

**1223** A166 5c on 23c #731, 4mm between "c" and obliterator 1.50 1.50
*b.* 2½mm between "c" and obliterator (positions 3 and 89) 50.00 50.00
*c.* No obliterator 325.00 325.00
**1223A** A166 5c on 23c #731, small font 1.00 1.00
*Nos. 1214-1223A (23)* 1,644. 1,614.

No. 1223 exists with surcharge shifted 50% upward. Value, $60. No. 1223 also exists with inverted surcharge and with double surcharge, one inverted. Values, $100 and $150, respectively. No. 1223A exists with inverted surcharge. Value, $90.

On Nos. 1215, 1217, 1218, 1219, 1222 and 1223, the "c" and obliterator are 4mm apart.

Issued: Nos. 1214, 1215, 1215b, Mar. 10; Nos. 1215A, 1217A, 1218A, 8/5/10; No. 1216A, Mar. 30; Nos. 1216, 1216B, Mar.; Nos. 1217, 1217b, Mar. 30; No. 1218, Aug. 27; No. 1219, 1220, 1221, 1222, Mar. 10; No. 1222A, 8/3/10; No. 1223, July 8; No. 1223A, 8/6/10.

Weddings in Fiji — A286

Designs: 20c, Chinese wedding. 40c, Muslim wedding. $1.50, Indian wedding. $3, Fijian wedding, vert.

***Perf. 14¼x14, 14x14½***
**2009, Aug. 17** **Litho.** **Unwmk.**
**1224-1227** A286 Set of 4 6.00 6.00

Passion Fruit — A287

Designs: 20c, Passiflora foetida. 65c, Passiflora edulis (yellow green). $1.20, Passiflora maliformis. $2, Passiflora edulis (purple).

**2009, Sept. 29** ***Perf. 14x14¼***
**1228-1231** A287 Set of 4 6.00 6.00

Souvenir Sheet

People's Republic of China, 60th Anniv. — A288

**2009, Oct. 1** ***Perf. 13¼***
**1232** A288 $5 multi 6.00 6.00

Ferns — A289

Designs: 20c, Cyathea lunulata. 40c, Asplenium australasicum. $1.50, Diplazium proliferum. $3, Nephrolepsis biserrata.

**2009, Dec. 15** ***Perf. 14x14½***
**1233-1236** A289 Set of 4 6.00 6.00

Snakes — A290

Designs: 20c, Yellow-bellied sea snake. 90c, Fiji burrowing snake. $1.10, Banded sea krait. $2, Pacific boa.

**2010, Mar. 30** **Litho.** ***Perf. 14½x14***
**1237-1240** A290 Set of 4 4.50 4.50

Peonies — A291

No. 1241: a, 20c, Pink peony. b, 40c, Red peony.

**2010, Apr. 8** **Litho.** ***Perf. 13¼***
**1241** A291 Horiz. pair, #a-b 13.00 13.00

Raiateana Knowlesi — A292

No. 1242: a, 20c, Newly-emerged insect. b, $1.50, Mature insect.

***Perf. 14x14½***
**2010, June 30** **Unwmk.**
**1242** A292 Vert. pair, #a-b 2.00 2.00

A293

A294

A295

Worldwide Fund for Nature (WWF) — A296

**2010, Oct. 27** ***Perf. 14¼x14***
**1243** Horiz. strip of 4 9.00 9.00
*a.* A293 $2 multi 2.25 2.25
*b.* A294 $2 multi 2.25 2.25
*c.* A295 $2 multi 2.25 2.25
*d.* A296 $2 multi 2.25 2.25

Fruit — A297

Designs: 20c, Citrus maxima. 40c, Barringtinia edulis. 65c, Pometia pinnata. $1.20, Musa troglogytarum. $10, Syzygium malacensis.

**2010, Dec. 2** ***Perf. 14¼***
**1244-1248** A297 Set of 5 14.50 14.50

No. 1249

No. 1249A

No. 1249Ab

No. 1254

No. 1254a

No. 1254C

No. 1254G

### Methods, Perfs and Watermarks As Before

**2011-14**
**1249** A166 1c on 31c #732 1.00 1.00
*c.* 3½mm between "c" and obliterator *75.00 75.00*
*d.* 1½mm between "c" and obliterator *125.00 125.00*
*e.* 4mm between "c" and obliterator, larger font *50.00 50.00*
*f.* 2¼mm between "c" and obliterator *100.00 100.00*
*g.* 2½mm between "c" and obliterator *75.00 75.00*
**1249A** A166 1c on 31c #732 *80.00 80.00*
*b.* Extra large "XX" (position 51) *275.00 275.00*
**1250** A166 2c on 31c #732 1.00 1.00
*a.* 4mm between "c" and obliterator *95.00 95.00*
*b.* 3mm between "c" and obliterator (positions 3 and 89) *185.00 185.00*
**1251** A166 3c on 31c #732 1.00 1.00
**1252** A166 4c on 31c #732 1.00 1.00
*a.* 4mm between "c" and obliterator *95.00 95.00*
*b.* 3mm between "c" and obliterator (positions 3 and 89) *185.00 185.00*
**1253** A166 5c on 31c #732 1.00 1.00
*a.* 3½mm between "c" and obliterator *75.00 75.00*
*b.* 1½mm between "c" and obliterator *100.00 100.00*
*c.* 2¼mm between "c" and obliterator *100.00 100.00*
**1254** A166 20c on 31c #732 2.00 2.00
*a.* Larger font *50.00 50.00*
*b.* As "a," 2½mm between "c" and obliterator *100.00 100.00*
*d.* As No. 1254, no gap between "c" and obliterator (position 70) *35.00 35.00*
*f.* As "a," no gap between "c" and obliterator *250.00 250.00*
**1254C** A166 20c on 31c #732 *125.00 125.00*
**1254E** A166 40c on 31c #732 3.00 3.00
*a.* No gap between "c" and obliterator *50.00 50.00*
**1254G** A166 20c on 31c #732 *180.00 180.00*
*a.* No gap between "c" and obliterator *225.00 225.00*
*Nos. 1249A-1254G (10)* *395.00 395.00*

Nos. 1249-1253 have 2½mm between "c" and obliterator. No. 1249A has 3½mm spacing. Nos. 1249Ab, 1254, 1254a, 1254E and 1254G have 1½mm spacing.

No. 1249 exists with inverted surcharge. Value, $90. No. 1249 exists with double surcharge. Value, $120; and with double surcharge, one inverted, value, $130. No. 1249A exists with denomination omitted (position 77). Value, $500.

No. 1250 exists with inverted surcharge. Value, $90. No. 1250 exists with double surcharge. Value, $120. No. 1250 exists with double surcharge, one inverted. Value, $130. No. 1250a exists with double surcharge. Value, $200.

No. 1251 exists with inverted surcharge. Value, $100. No. 1251 exists with double surcharge. Value, $120. No. 1251 exists with double surcharge, one inverted. Value, $130. No. 1251 exists with surcharge shifted 50% upward. Value, $50. No. 1252 exists with inverted surcharge. Value, $90. No. 1252 exists with double surcharge. Value, $120. No. 1252 with double surcharge, one inverted. Value, $130.

No. 1253 exists with inverted surcharge. Value, $90. No. 1253 exists with double surcharge, with double surcharge, one shifted 50% upward, and with double surcharge, one inverted, value, each $130. No. 1253 exists with surcharge shifted 50% upward. Value, $50.

No. 1254 exists with inverted surcharge. Value, $100. No. 1254 exists with inverted surcharge. Value, $100. No. 1254 exists with double surcharge. Value, $65. No. 1254 exists with double surcharge, one with large "20," the other with small "20." Value, $175. No. 1254 exists with double surcharge, one inverted: one with large "20," the other with small "20." Value, $175. No. 1254 exists with double surcharge, one inverted (top surcharge inverted, bottom shifted 50% upward). Value, $110. No. 1254 exists with surcharge shifted 50% upward. Value, $50. No. 1254 exists with double surcharge, one shifted 50% upward. Value, $100. No. 1254 exists with double surcharge, one shifted 50% upward; both with no gap between "c" and obliterator. Value, $300. No. 1254a exists with surcharge shifted 50% upward. Value, $80. No. 1254a exists with surcharge inverted and shifted 50% upward. Value, $130. No. 1254a exists with "c" omitted. Value, $150. No. 1254f exists with surcharge shifted 50% upward. Value, $250.

No. 1254E exists with inverted surcharge. Value, $90. No. 1254E exists with double surcharg. Value, $120. No. 1254E exists with double surcharge, one inverted. Value, $130. No. 1254E exists with surcharge shifted 45% upward. Value, $50.

No. 1254G exists with inverted surcharge. Value, $225. No. 1254G also exists with "c" of "20c" omitted. Value, $325.

Issued: No. 1249, 6/6; No. 1249A, 7/30/14; Nos. 1250, 1253, 3/24; No. 1250a, 3/2014; No. 1251, 7/8; No. 1252, 5/20; No. 1252a, 2/2014; No. 1254, 5/4; Nos. 1254a, 1254b, 2011; No. 1254d, 5/4; Nos. 1254E, 1254Ea, 12/7/12.

Souvenir Sheet

Wedding of Prince William and Catherine Middleton — A298

***Perf. 14¾x14¼***
**2011, Apr. 29** **Litho.** **Wmk. 406**
**1255** A298 $10 multi 11.50 11.50

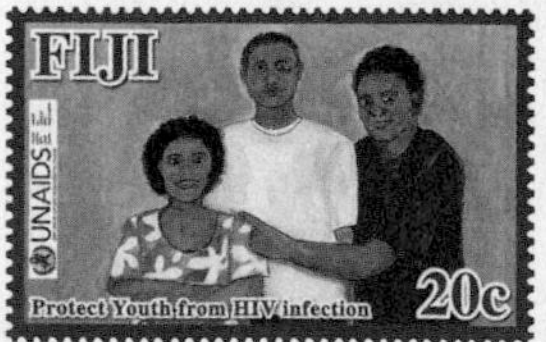


Campaign Against AIDS — A299

People, UNAIDS emblem and slogan: 20c, Protect youth from HIV infection. 40c, Zero new HIV infections, vert. 65c, Stop mothers & babies from being infected with HIV, vert. $5, Zero discrimination.

***Perf. 14½x14, 14x14½***
**2011, June 22** **Unwmk.**
**1256-1259** A299 Set of 4 7.25 7.25

Frangipani Flowers — A300

Designs: 50c, Plumeria rubra bud. 90c, Plumeria rubra f. rubra flower. $1.50, Plumeria rubra f. lutea. $3, Plumeria obtusa.

**2011, July 12** ***Perf. 14½x14***
**1260-1263** A300 Set of 4 6.75 6.75

Pomegranate Tree Branches and Birds — A301

No. 1264: a, 65c, Bird on branch. b, $1.20, Bird in flight near branch.

**2011, Aug. 15** ***Perf. 13¼x13¾***
**1264** A301 Horiz. pair, #a-b 2.25 2.25

No. 1264 was printed in sheets containing three pairs.

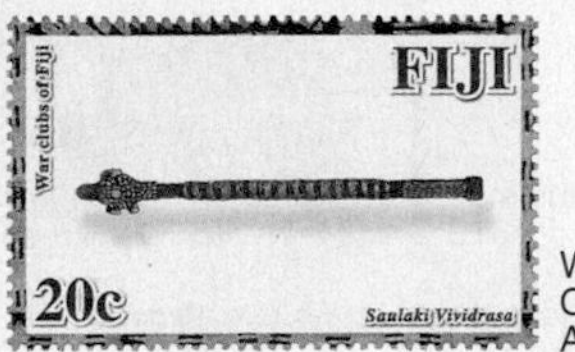


War Clubs A302

Designs: 20c, Saulaki vividrasa. 65c, Cali. $1.20, Totokia. $10, I ula tavatava.

**2011, Aug. 15** ***Perf. 14½x14***
**1265-1268** A302 Set of 4 14.00 14.00

Intl. Year of Volunteers — A303

Volunteers for: 40c, St. John Ambulance Association. 90c, Suva City Council, vert. $1.10, Red Cross, vert. $10, National Blood Bank.

***Perf. 14½x14, 14x14½***

**2011, Nov. 25**
**1269-1272** A303 Set of 4 14.50 14.50

Christmas — A304

Designs: 20c, Fijian with gift box. 65c, Fijian with pottery. $1.20, Fijian with necklace. $2, Holy Family.

**2011, Dec. 16** ***Perf. 14½x14***
**1273-1276** A304 Set of 4 4.50 4.50

New Year 2012 (Year of the Dragon) A305

**2012, Jan. 23** ***Perf. 14¼***
**1277** A305 $3 multi 3.50 3.50

No. 1277 was printed in sheets of 4.

Endangered Flora — A306

Designs: 20c, Fijian acmopyle. 65c, Lau fan palm. $1.20, Cycad. $2, Fiji magnolia.

**2012, Apr. 26** ***Perf. 14½x14***
**1278-1281** A306 Set of 4 4.50 4.50

Intl. Year of Sustainable Energy For All — A307

Designs: 20c, Water power. 50c, Biomass. $1.20, Wind energy. $3, Solar power.

**2012, June 25**
**1282-1285** A307 Set of 4 5.50 5.50

A308

A309

A310

Worldwide Fund for Nature (WWF) A311

**2012, July 11** ***Perf. 14¼x14***

| | | | |
|---|---|---|---|
| **1286** | Horiz. strip of 4 | 9.00 | 9.00 |
| *a.* | A308 $2 multi | 2.25 | 2.25 |
| *b.* | A309 $2 multi | 2.25 | 2.25 |
| *c.* | A310 $2 multi | 2.25 | 2.25 |
| *d.* | A311 $2 multi | 2.25 | 2.25 |

Christmas — A312

Designs: 20c, Journey to Bethlehem. 40c, Holy Family. 65c, Adoration of the Shepherds. $1.20, Adoration of the Shepherds, diff. $5, Adoration of the Magi.

**2012, Dec. 14** **Litho.** ***Perf. 14½x14***
**1287-1291** A312 Set of 5 8.50 8.50

Birth of Prince George of Cambridge A313

Prince George and: 40c, Duke and Duchess of Cambridge. 65c, Duchess of Cambridge. $1.20, Duke and Duchess of Cambridge, diff. $5, Duke of Cambridge.

**2013, Aug. 28** **Litho.** ***Perf. 13½***
**1292-1295** A313 Set of 4 7.75 7.75

Mangrove Protection A314

Designs: 50c, Mangroves. 65c, Mangrove, jellyfish, starfish. $1.20, Fish and underwater root system of mangrove. $10, People planting mangroves.

**2013, Oct. 30** **Litho.** ***Perf. 13½***
**1296-1299** A314 Set of 4 13.50 13.50

Christmas — A315

Bell-shaped Christmas ornament with: 40c, Cathedral. 65c, Flowers. $1.20, Fijian family walking on beach. $3, Fijian children with Christmas gifts.

**2013, Dec. 2** **Litho.** ***Perf. 13½***
**1300-1303** A315 Set of 4 5.75 5.75

Submarine Cable Between Fiji and Vanuatu — A316

No. 1304: a, Workers, ship and cable with floats. b, Diver examining cable. c, Electronic cables plugged into machine.

### Litho. With Foil Application

**2014, Jan. 15** ***Perf. 14½x14***

| | | | |
|---|---|---|---|
| **1304** | Horiz. strip of 6 + central label, #1304a-1304c, Vanuatu #1070a-1070c | 14.50 | 14.50 |
| *a.* | A316 65c multi | .70 | .70 |
| *b.* | A316 $1.20 multi | 1.25 | 1.25 |
| *c.* | A316 $6 multi | 6.50 | 6.50 |

No. 1304 sold for $13.30 in Fiji and 750v in Vanuatu. See Vanuatu No. 1070.

Sharks A317

Designs: 50c, Blacktip reef shark. 90c, Silky shark. $1.20, Oceanic whitetip shark. $5, Big-eye thresher shark.

**2014, July 28** **Litho.** ***Perf. 13¾x13¼***
**1305-1308** A317 Set of 4 8.25 8.25

Grand Pacific Hotel, Cent. A318

Designs: 40c, Hotel driveway and entrance. 65c, Sofas and tables. 90c, Swimming pool. $1.20, Dining area. $5, Entrance, diff.

**2014, Aug. 8** **Litho.** ***Perf. 13¾x13¼***
**1309-1313** A318 Set of 5 8.75 8.75

### Nos. 732-733 Surcharged

No. 1313A

No. 1314

No. 1314b

No. 1315

No. 1315B

No. 1316

No. 1317

### Methods, Perfs and Watermarks As Before

**2014-15**

| | | | | |
|---|---|---|---|---|
| **1313A** | A166 | 1c on 44c #733 | 4.00 | 4.00 |
| *b.* | | 2¼mm between "c" and obliterator | *50.00* | *50.00* |
| *c.* | | 4¼mm between "c" and obliterator | *40.00* | *40.00* |
| **1314** | A166 | 20c on 44c #733 | 1.50 | 1.50 |
| *a.* | | No gap between "c" and obliterator (position 70) | *50.00* | *50.00* |
| *b.* | | Large "20" | *30.00* | *30.00* |
| *c.* | | As "b," no gap between "c" and obliterator (positions 70 and 79) | *75.00* | *75.00* |
| *d.* | | As "b," 3mm between "c" and obliterator (positions 31, 41, 61, 71, 81 and 91) | *50.00* | *50.00* |

*e.* 3¾mm between "c" and obliterator (position 3) *175.00 175.00*

**1315** A166 40c on 44c #733 2.00 2.00

*a.* No gap between "c" and obliterator (position 70) *60.00 60.00*

**1315B** A166 50c on 3c #727 450.00 450.00

*c.* No gap between "c" and obliterator (position 70) — —

**1316** A166 50c on 31c #732 6.00 6.00

*a.* No gap between "c" and obliterator (position 70) *50.00 50.00*

**1317** A166 50c on 44c #733 3.00 3.00

*a.* No gap between "c" and obliterator (position 70) *65.00 65.00*

*Nos. 1313A-1317 (6)* 466.50 466.50

No. 1313A exists with double surcharge. Value, $120. No. 1313A also exists with inverted surcharge. Value, $110.

No. 1314 exists with surcharge shifted 50% upward. Value, $25. No. 1314 exists with surcharge inverted. Value, $60. No. 1314a exists with surcharge shifted 50% upward. Value, $75. No. 1314b exists with surcharge inverted. Value, $100. No. 1314b exists with double surcharge. Value, $120.

No. 1315 exists with surcharge shifted 50% upward. Value, $25. No. 1315a exists with surcharge shifted 50% upward. Value, $80.

No. 1316 exists with double surcharge. Value, $70. Nos. 1316 and 1316a exist with inverted surcharge. Value, both $120.

No. 1317 exists with surcharge shifted 50% upward. Value, $30. No. 1317a exists with surcharge shifted 50% upward. Value, $90.

Issued: No. 1313A, 8/28/15; No. 1314, 6/11; No. 1314b, 7/31; Nos. 1315, 1317, 6/10. No. 1316, 3/5.

Christmas — A319

Houses of worship: 40c, The Church of Jesus Christ of Latter-day Saints, Suva. 65c, Holy Redeemer Anglican Church, Levuka. $3, Baker Memorial Methodist Church, Nausori. $10, St. Francis Xavier Church, Navunibitu.

*Perf. 13½*

**2014, Dec. 4 Litho. Unwmk.**

**1320-1323** A319 Set of 4 14.00 14.00

Souvenir Sheet

Blue Coral — A320

No. 1324 — Heliopora coerulea: a, 65c. b, $5.

*Perf. 13½x13¼*

**2015, Feb. 23 Litho.**

**1324** A320 Sheet of 2, #a-b 5.50 5.50

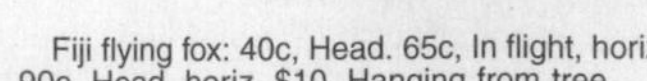

Fiji Flying Fox — A321

Fiji flying fox: 40c, Head. 65c, In flight, horiz. 90c, Head, horiz. $10, Hanging from tree.

*Perf. 13¼x13¾, 13¾x13¼*

**2015, Apr. 30 Litho.**

**1325-1328** A321 Set of 4 13.50 13.50

Levuka UNESCO World Heritage Site A322

Designs: 50c, Fiji Times Building, Beach Street, c. 1894. 65c, Sacred Heart Church, c. 1902, vert. 90c, Levuka Public School, c. 1884, vert. $5, Public Office, Nasova, c. 1877-82.

**2015, June 16 Litho.** *Perf. 13½*

**1329-1332** A322 Set of 4 6.75 6.75

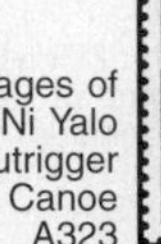

Voyages of Uto Ni Yalo Outrigger Canoe A323

Uto Ni Yalo: 40c, Near shore with white and black sails. 65c, Near Sydney Harbour Bridge and Sydney Opera House. $1.50, Near Golden Gate Bridge. $10, Near shore with red and black sails.

*Perf. 13¾x13¼*

**2015, Aug. 31 Litho.**

**1333-1336** A323 Set of 4 11.50 11.50

Medicinal Plants A324

Designs: 40c, Scaevola sericea. 65c, Vigna marina. 90c, Ipomoea pes-caprae subsp. brasiliensis. $1.20, Clerodendrum inerme. $5, Morinda citrifolia.

**2015, Oct. 21 Litho.** *Perf. 13¾x13¼*

**1337-1341** A324 Set of 5 7.75 7.75

Christmas — A325

Archangels: 40c, St. Uriel. 65c, St. Gabriel. 90c, St. Raphael. $10, St. Michael.

**2015, Dec. 7 Litho.** *Perf. 13¼x13¾*

**1342-1345** A325 Set of 4 11.50 11.50

Nos. 735 Surcharged

Nos. 734 Surcharged

**Methods, Perfs. and Watermarks As Before**

**2015-16**

**1346** A166 1c on 81c #735 *7.50 7.50*

*a.* 2¼mm between and obliterator (positions 1 and 2) *125.00 125.00*

*b.* 4¼mm between "c" and obliterator (position 51) *175.00 175.00*

**1347** A166 20c on 63c #734 *20.00 20.00*

*a.* No gap between "c" and obliterator (position 70) *120.00 120.00*

*b.* 3¼mm between "c" and obliterator (position 3) *120.00 120.00*

*c.* Large "20" *120.00 120.00*

No. 1346 has 3¼mm between "c" and obliterator. No. 1347 has 1½mm between "c" and obliterator.

Issued: No. 1346, 1/29/16; No. 1347, 12/31.

New Year 2016 (Year of the Monkey) A326

No. 1348: a, Macaca arctoides, bananas. b, Rhinopithecus, peonies. c, Rhesus macaque, coconut palm trees. d, White-headed langur, hibiscus flowers.

*Perf. 13½x13¼*

**2016, Mar. 30 Litho. Unwmk.**

**1348** Horiz. strip of 4 + central label 11.50 11.50

*a.* A326 38c multi .40 .40

*b.* A326 47c multi .45 .45

*c.* A326 85c multi .85 .85

*d.* A326 $10 multi 9.75 9.75

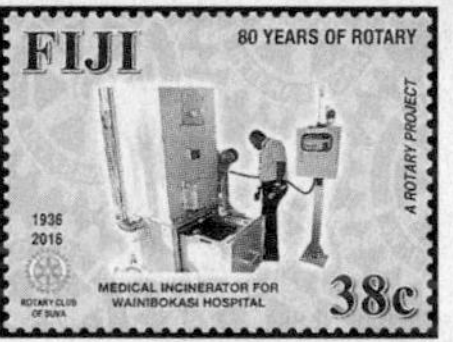

Rotary International in Fiji, 80th Anniv. — A327

Designs: 38c, Medical incinerator for Wainibokasi Hospital. 62c, Dialysis machine for Kidney Foundation of Fiji, vert. $1.04, Emergency Response Kit label, vert. $5, Braille machine for Fiji Society for the Blind.

*Perf. 13½x13¼, 13¼x13½*

**2016, May 19 Litho. Unwmk.**

**1349-1352** A327 Set of 4 6.75 6.75

**No. 733 Surcharged**

No. 1353

No. 1354

No. 1355

No. 1356

**Methods, Perfs. and Watermarks As Before**

**2016**

**1353** A166 3c on 44c #733 *3.00 3.00*

**1354** A166 4c on 44c #733 *3.00 3.00*

**1355** A166 5c on 44c #733 *3.00 3.00*

**1356** A166 23c on 44c #733 *4.50 4.50*

*Nos. 1353-1356 (4) 13.50 13.50*

No. 1355 exists with double surcharge. Value, $800.

Issued: No. 1353, 6/13; No. 1354, 6/15; No. 1355, 8/26; No. 1356, 10/25.

Thatched Structures at Navala Village A328

Designs: 38c, Dwelling. 47c, Home for the elderly. 85c, Meeting house. $10, Chief's home.

*Perf. 13½x13¼*

**2016, July 27 Litho. Unwmk.**

**1357-1360** A328 Set of 4 11.50 11.50

Flowers — A329

Designs: 47c, Pink Hibiscus rosa-sinensis. 58c, Abelmoschus esculentus (okra). 85c, Red Hibiscus rosa-sinensis. $1.04, Thespesia populnea. $15, Hibiscus tiliaceus.

*Perf. 13¼x13½*

**2016, Aug. 12 Litho. Unwmk.**

**1361-1365** A329 Set of 5 17.50 17.50

Christmas A330

Designs: 40c, Carolers. 90c, People preparing lovo for feast. $1.20, Family going to church. $10, Exchanging gifts.

*Perf. 13½x13¼*

**2016, Dec. 5 Litho. Unwmk.**

**1366-1369** A330 Set of 4 12.00 12.00

**No. 733 Surcharged**

No. 1370 No. 1371

**Methods, Perfs. and Watermarks As Before**

**2016-17**

**1370** A166 2c on 44c #733 *3.00 3.00*

**1371** A166 50c on 44c #733 *24.00 24.00*

Issued: No. 1370, 2016; No. 1371, 2017.

Compare No. 1371 with No. 1317.

## SEMI-POSTAL STAMPS

**Catalogue values for unused stamps in this section are for Never Hinged items.**

Children at Play — SP1

Rugby Player — SP2

***Perf. 13x13½***

| **1951, Sept. 17** | **Engr.** | **Wmk. 4** | |
|---|---|---|---|
| **B1** | SP1 1p + 1p brown | .30 | *1.60* |
| **B2** | SP2 2p + 1p deep green | .45 | *1.10* |

Bamboo River Raft — SP3

Design: 2½p+½p, Cross of Lorraine.

| **1954, Apr. 1** | | ***Perf. 11x11½*** | |
|---|---|---|---|
| **B3** | SP3 1½p + ½p green & brn | .25 | *1.10* |
| **B4** | SP3 2½p + ½p black & org | .30 | .30 |

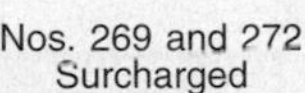

Nos. 269 and 272 Surcharged

| **1972, Dec. 4** | **Photo.** | ***Perf. 14, 13½*** | |
|---|---|---|---|
| **B5** | A56 15c + 5c multi | .40 | .35 |
| **B6** | A55 30c + 10c multi | 1.10 | .35 |

Indian Boy, Map of Fiji SP4

Map of Fiji and: 15c+2c, European girl. 30c+3c, Chinese girl. 40c+4c, Fijian boy.

**Wmk. 373**

| **1979, Sept. 17** | **Litho.** | ***Perf. 14½*** | |
|---|---|---|---|
| **B7** | SP4 4c + 1c multicolored | .25 | .25 |
| **B8** | SP4 15c + 2c multicolored | .25 | .25 |
| **B9** | SP4 30c + 3c multicolored | .40 | .40 |
| **B10** | SP4 40c + 4c multicolored | .60 | .60 |
| | *Nos. B7-B10 (4)* | 1.50 | 1.50 |

The surtax was for IYC fund.

Iliesa Delana, Gold Medalist at 2012 Paralympic Games — SP5

Delana: 40c+10c, High jumping. 65c+10c, Standing and waving flag of Fiji, vert. $1.20+10c, Wearing gold medal, vert. $2+10c, Going around track waving flag of Fiji.

| **2013, Mar. 7** | ***Perf. 14½x14, 14x14½*** | | |
|---|---|---|---|
| **B11-B14** | SP5 Set of 4 | 5.25 | 5.25 |

Surtax for Fiji Paralympic Committee.

## POSTAGE DUE STAMPS

D1

D2

D3

**1917 Unwmk. Typeset *Perf. 11***

**Laid Papers; Without Gum**

| | | | |
|---|---|---|---|
| **J1** | D1 ½p black | 1,400. | 500.00 |
| **J2** | D2 ½p black | 550.00 | 300.00 |
| **J3** | D3 1p black | 500.00 | 140.00 |
| *a.* | Narrow setting | 375.00 | 150.00 |
| **J4** | D3 2p black | 350.00 | 80.00 |
| *a.* | Narrow setting | 1,250. | 700.00 |
| **J5** | D3 3p black | 900.00 | 120.00 |
| **J6** | D3 4p black | 1,250. | 550.00 |
| *a.* | Strip of 8, 3 #J3, 1 ea. #J1 and #J6, and 3 #J5 | *19,000.* | |
| | *Nos. J1-J6 (6)* | 4,950. | 1,690. |

There were two printings of this issue. In the first printing, the 2d was printed in sheets of 84 (7x12), and the other four values were printed together in sheets of 96 (8x12), with each row consisting of three 1p, one ½p, one 4p and three 3p values. Setenant multiples exist. Sheets were not perforated on the margins, so that marginal stamps were not perforated on the outer edge. Examples from the first printing are 25mm wide (including margins).

In the second printing, the ½p, 1p and 2p were printed in separate sheets of 84 (7x12). The clichés were set a little closer, so that examples of this printing are 23mm wide.

D4

***Perf. 14***

| **1918, June 1** | **Typo.** | **Wmk. 3** | |
|---|---|---|---|
| **J7** | D4 ½p black | 3.25 | *30.00* |
| **J8** | D4 1p black | 3.75 | *5.50* |
| **J9** | D4 2p black | 3.50 | *8.00* |
| **J10** | D4 3p black | 3.50 | *52.50* |
| **J11** | D4 4p black | 6.50 | *30.00* |
| | *Nos. J7-J11 (5)* | 20.50 | *126.00* |

D5

| **1940** | **Wmk. 4** | ***Perf. 12½*** | |
|---|---|---|---|
| **J12** | D5 1p bright green | 5.00 | *72.50* |
| **J13** | D5 2p bright green | 10.00 | *72.50* |
| **J14** | D5 3p bright green | 11.00 | *80.00* |
| **J15** | D5 4p bright green | 12.00 | *85.00* |
| **J16** | D5 5p bright green | 14.00 | *90.00* |
| **J17** | D5 6p bright green | 15.00 | *90.00* |
| **J18** | D5 1sh dk carmine | 15.00 | *115.00* |
| **J19** | D5 1sh6p dk carmine | 15.00 | *260.00* |
| | *Nos. J12-J19 (8)* | 97.00 | *865.00* |
| | Set, never hinged | 140.00 | |

## WAR TAX STAMPS

Regular Issue of 1912-16 Overprinted

**Die I**

| **1916** | **Wmk. 3** | ***Perf. 14*** | |
|---|---|---|---|
| **MR1** | A23 ½p green | 1.90 | *9.00* |
| *a.* | Inverted overprint | 700.00 | |
| *b.* | Double overprint | | |
| **MR2** | A23 1p scarlet | 4.50 | .80 |
| *a.* | 1p carmine | 45.00 | 26.00 |
| *b.* | Pair, one without ovpt. | *8,000.* | |
| *c.* | Inverted overprint | 800.00 | |

Most examples of #MR2b are within horiz. strips of 12.

# FINLAND

'fin-lənd

(Suomi)

LOCATION — Northern Europe bordering on the Gulfs of Bothnia and Finland
GOVT. — Republic
AREA — 130,119 sq. mi.
POP. — 5,147,349 (1997)
CAPITAL — Helsinki

Finland was a Grand Duchy of the Russian Empire from 1809 until December 1917, when it declared its independence.

100 Kopecks = 1 Ruble
100 Pennia = 1 Markka (1866)
100 Cents = 1 Euro (2002)

**Catalogue values for unused stamps in this country are for Never Hinged items, beginning with Scott 220 in the regular postage section, Scott B39 in the semi-postal section, Scott C2 in the air-post section, Scott M1 in the military stamp section, and Scott Q6 in the parcel post section.**

Unused stamps are valued with original gum as defined in the catalogue introduction except for Nos. 1-3B which are valued without gum. Used values for Nos. 1-3B are for pen-canceled examples. Very fine examples of the serpentine rouletted issues, Nos. 4-13c, will have roulettes cutting the design slightly on one or more sides and will have all "teeth" complete and intact. Stamps with roulettes clear of the design on all four sides are extremely scarce and sell for substantial premiums. Stamps with teeth entirely missing or with several short roulettes are worth much less. See *Scott Classic Specialized Catalogue* for values for used stamps with one or two short roulettes.

**Watermarks**

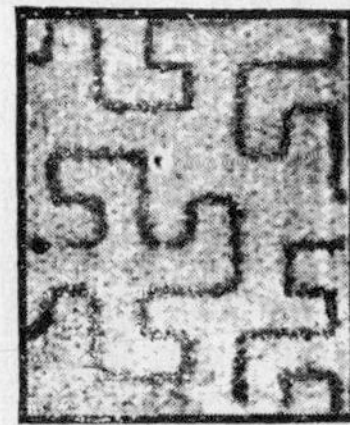

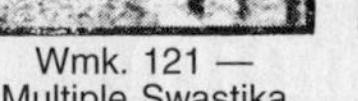

Wmk. 121 — Multiple Swastika

Wmk. 208 — Post Horn

Wmk. 168 — Wavy Lines and Letters

Wmk. 273 — Roses

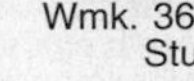

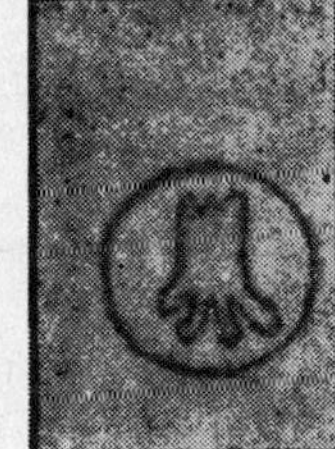

Wmk. 363 — Tree Stump

**Syncopated Perforations**

Type A (1st stamp #1065): On one longer side, groups of five holes are separated by an oval hole equal in width to eight holes.

Type B (1st stamp, #1142): On the top groups of 3 holes at left and right and a middle group of 4 holes separated by rectangular perforations equal in width to 4 holes.

**Issues under Russian Empire**

Coat of Arms — A1

**1856-58 Unwmk. Typo. *Imperf.***

**Small Pearls in Post Horns**

**Wove Paper**

| | | | |
|---|---|---|---|
| **1** | A1 5k blue | *6,750.* | 1,600. |
| | Pen and town cancellation | | 1,900. |
| | Town cancellation | | 3,250. |
| *a.* | Tête bêche pair | *80,000.* | *80,000.* |
| | Pen and town cancellation | | *75,000.* |
| **2** | A1 10k rose | 8,750. | 400. |
| | Pen and town cancellation | | 575. |
| | On cover | | 1,850. |
| | Town cancellation | | 925. |
| | On cover | | 2,850. |
| *a.* | Tête bêche pair | *80,000.* | *65,000.* |
| | Pen and town cancellation | | *75,000.* |

**Cut to shape**

| | | | |
|---|---|---|---|
| *1* | A1 5k blue | | 150. |
| | Pen and town cancellation | | 200. |
| | Town cancellation | | 250. |
| *2* | A1 10k rose | | 65. |
| | Pen and town cancellation | | 90. |
| | Town cancellation | | 100. |

**Wide Vertically Laid Paper**

| | | | |
|---|---|---|---|
| **2C** | A1 10k rose ('58) | — | 1,400. |
| | Pen and town cancellation | | 1,800. |
| | Town cancellation | | 2,500. |
| *d.* | Tête bêche pair | | — |

**Cut to shape**

| | | | |
|---|---|---|---|
| *2C* | A1 10k rose | | 200. |
| | Pen and town cancellation | | 250. |
| | Town cancellation | | 300. |

**Narrow Vertically Laid Paper**

| | | | |
|---|---|---|---|
| *2C* | A1 10k carmine | | 625. |
| | Pen and town cancellation | | 800. |
| | Town cancellation | | 1,100. |

The wide vertically laid paper has 13-14 distinct lines per 2 centimeters. The narrow laid paper has lines that sometimes are indistinct.

A 5k blue with small pearls exists on narrow vertically laid paper. It is rare.

Stamps on diagonally laid paper are envelope cut squares. Envelope cut squares also exist on unwatermarked wove paper.

### Large Pearls in Post Horns

**1858** **Wove Paper**

**3** A1 5k blue 11,000. 1,800.
Pen and town cancellation 1,550.
Town cancellation 2,500.
*a.* Tête bêche pair 60,000.
Pen and town cancellation 65,000.

### Cut to shape

*3* A1 5k blue 125.00
Pen and town cancellation 150.00
Town cancellation 200.00

**1859** **Wide Vertically Laid Paper**

**3B** A1 5k blue — 18,000.
Pen and town cancellation 25,000.

### Cut to shape

*3B* A1 5k blue 2,000.
Pen and town cancellation 2,500.

*Reprints of Nos. 2 and 3, made in 1862, are on brownish paper, on vertically laid paper, and in tête bêche pairs on normal and vertically laid paper. Reprints of 1871, 1881 and 1893 are on yellowish or white paper. Value for least costly of each, $85.*

*In 1956, Nos. 2 and 3 were reprinted for the Centenary with post horn watermark and gum. Value, $85 each.*

Values for rouletted stamps with one or two short teeth are considerably less than the values shown, which are for stamps with all teeth full and intact. See the *Scott Classic Specialized Catalogue* for greater detail. Stamps with several short teeth or teeth entirely missing sell for very small percentages of the values shown.

Coat of Arms — A2

I — Depth 1-1 ¼mm

II — Depth 1 ½-1 ¾mm

III — Depth 2-2 ¼mm

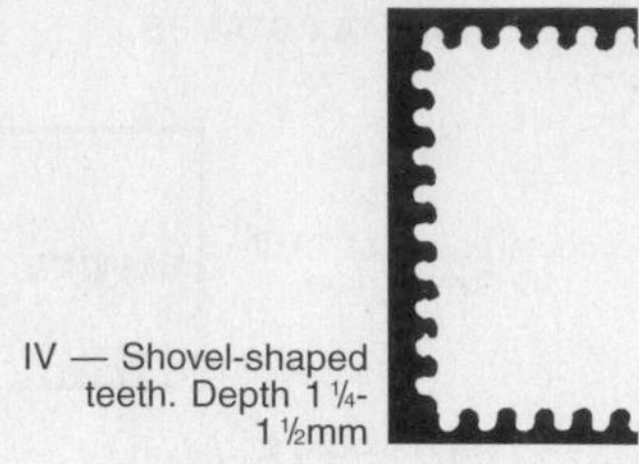
IV — Shovel-shaped teeth. Depth 1 ¼-1 ½mm

### Wove Paper

**1860** ***Serpentine Roulette 7½, 8***

**4** A2 5k blue, *bluish*, I 850.00 200.00
*a.* Roulette II 800.00 225.00
*b.* Perf. vert.
**5** A2 10k rose, *pale rose*, I 575.00 57.50
*a.* Roulette II 1,150. 160.00

A3

A4

**1866-74** ***Serpentine Roulette***

**6** A3 5p pur brn, *lil*, I ('73) 375.00 170.00
*a.* Roulette II 5,000.
*b.* 5p red brn, *lil*, III ('71) 350.00 180.00
**7** A3 8p blk, *grn*, III ('67) 275.00 170.00
*a.* Ribbed paper, III ('72) 1,150. 925.00
*b.* Roulette II ('74) 340.00 275.00
*c.* As "b," ribbed paper ('74) 340.00 225.00
*d.* Roulette I ('73) 525.00 325.00
*e.* As "d," ribbed paper 1,050. 400.00
*f.* Serpentine roulette 10½ ('67) 13,500.
**8** A3 10p blk, *yel*, III ('70) 675.00 350.00
*a.* 10p blk, *buff*, II 800.00 450.00
*b.* 10p blk, *buff*, I ('73) 750.00 375.00
**9** A3 20p bl, *bl*, III 575.00 57.50
*a.* Roulette II 575.00 90.00
*b.* Roulette I ('73) 675.00 115.00
*c.* Roulette IV ('74) — 1,150.
*d.* Perf. horiz. —
*e.* Printed on both sides (40p blue on back) 10,500.
**10** A3 40p rose, *lil rose*, III 525.00 67.50
*a.* Ribbed paper, III ('73) 675.00 200.00
*b.* Roulette II 525.00 85.00
*c.* As "b," ribbed paper ('73) 675.00 170.00
*d.* Roulette I 750.00 170.00
*e.* As "d," ribbed paper 675.00 115.00
*f.* Roulette IV — 2,275.
*g.* As "f," ribbed paper — —
*h.* Serpentine roulette 10½ —
**11** A4 1m yel brn, III ('67) 2,250. 850.00
*a.* Roulette II 2,850. 1,700.

Nos. 7f and 10h are private roulettes and are also known in compound serpentine roulette 10½ and 7½.

*Nos. 4-11 were reprinted in 1893 on thick wove paper. Colors differ from originals. Roulette type IV. Value for Nos. 4-5, each $40, Nos. 6-10, each $50. Value for No. 11, $55.*

### Thin or Thick Laid Paper

**12** A3 5p red brn, *lil*, III 290.00 160.00
*a.* Roulette II 300.00 300.00
*b.* Roulette I 290.00 300.00
*d.* 5p blk, *buff*, roul. III (error) 20,000.
*e.* Tête bêche pair —

**13** A3 10p black, *buff*, III 675.00 290.00
*a.* 10p black, *yel*, II 850.00 290.00
*b.* 10p black, *yel*, I 1,150. 750.00
*c.* 10p red brown, *lil*, III (error) 8,000. 7,000.

Forgeries of No. 13c exist.

A5

**1875** ***Perf. 14x13½***

**16** A5 32p lake 2,400. 425.00

Forgeries exist of No. 16 that have been created by perforating cut squares.

**1875-82** ***Perf. 11***

**17** A5 2p gray 62.50 70.00
**18** A5 5p orange 140.00 15.00
*a.* 5p yellow org 160.00 18.00
**19** A5 8p blue green 300.00 90.00
*a.* 8p yellow green 275.00 70.00
**20** A5 10p brown ('81) 700.00 70.00
**21** A5 20p ultra 175.00 3.50
*a.* 20p blue 175.00 5.00
*b.* 20p Prussian blue 400.00 45.00
*c.* Tête bêche pair 3,500.
**22** A5 25p carmine ('79) 350.00 17.00
*a.* 25p rose ('82) 475.00 75.00
**23** A5 32p carmine 400.00 60.00
*a.* 32p rose 450.00 62.50
**24** A5 1m violet ('77) 1,000. 160.00
*Nos. 17-24 (8)* 3,128. 485.50

A souvenir card issued in 1974 for NORDIA 1975 reproduced a block of four of the unissued "1 MARKKAA" design.

*Nos. 19, 23 were reprinted in 1892-93, perf. 12½. Value $25.00 each.* They exist imperf.

**1881-83** ***Perf. 12½***

**25** A5 2p gray 20.00 20.00
*a.* Imperf., pair 600.00 600.00
**26** A5 5p orange 62.50 6.25
*a.* Tête bêche pair 8,250. 4,750.
*b.* Imperf. vert., pair —
*c.* Imperf. horiz., pair —
**27** A5 10p brown 100.00 27.00
**28** A5 20p ultra 65.00 2.00
*a.* 20p blue 65.00 2.00
*b.* Tête bêche pair — 2,500.
*c.* Imperf., pair —
**29** A5 25p rose ('82) 55.00 12.00
*a.* 25p carmine 55.00 21.00
*b.* Tête bêche pair 15,000. —
**30** A5 1m violet ('82) 450.00 55.00
*Nos. 25-30 (6)* 752.50 122.25

*Nos. 27-29 were reprinted in 1893 in deeper shades, perf. 12½. Value $40 each.*

Most examples of No. 28c are from printer's waste.

**1881** ***Perf. 11x12½***

*26d* A5 5p orange 450.00 90.00
*27a* A5 10p brown 925.00 225.00
*28d* A5 20p ultra 575.00 42.50
*28e* A5 20p blue 575.00 42.50
*29c* A5 25p rose 675.00 190.00
*29d* A5 25p carmine 650.00 125.00
*30a* A5 1m violet 1,450.

**1881** ***Perf. 12½x11***

*26e* A5 5p orange 450.00 90.00
*27b* A5 10p brown — 325.00
*28f* A5 20p ultra 575.00 45.00
*28g* A5 20p blue 575.00 45.00
*29e* A5 25p rose — 290.00
*29f* A5 25p carmine 575.00 115.00

**1885** ***Perf. 12½***

**31** A5 5p emerald 20.00 8.00
*a.* 5p yellow green 24.00 1.10
*b.* Tête bêche pair 14,000. 11,000.
**32** A5 10p carmine 30.00 3.50
*a.* 10p rose 50.00 3.50
**33** A5 20p orange 35.00 .65
*a.* 20p yellow 47.50 2.50
*b.* Tête bêche pair — 3,500.
**34** A5 25p ultra 70.00 4.25
*a.* 25p blue 70.00 3.00
**35** A5 1m gray & rose 37.50 25.00
**36** A5 5m green & rose 500.00 500.00
**37** A5 10m brown & rose 625.00 750.00

Denomination on No. 35 is spelled "MARKKA". Denomination on Nos. 36-37 is spelled "MARKKAA".

A6

**1889-92** ***Perf. 12½***

**38** A6 2p slate ('90) .75 1.25
**39** A6 5p green ('90) 40.00 .50
**40** A6 10p carmine ('90) 70.00 .50
*a.* 10p rose ('90) 90.00 .75
*b.* Imperf. 110.00
**41** A6 20p orange ('92) 95.00 .50
*a.* 20p yellow ('89) 95.00 1.25
**42** A6 25p ultra ('91) 80.00 .85
*a.* 25p blue 80.00 1.15
**43** A6 1m slate & rose ('92) 6.00 3.25
*a.* 1m brnsh gray & rose ('90) 35.00 4.00
**44** A6 5m green & rose ('90) 32.50 77.50
**45** A6 10m brown & rose ('90) 40.00 90.00
*Nos. 38-45 (8)* 364.25 174.35

The 2p slate, perf. 14x13, is believed to be an essay.

See Nos. 60-63.

See Russia for types similar to A7-A18.

Finnish stamps have "dot in circle" devices or are inscribed "Markka," "Markkaa," "Pen." or "Pennia."

Imperial Arms of Russia
A7 A8 A9

A10

A11

### Laid Paper

**1891-92** **Wmk. 168** ***Perf. 14½x15***

**46** A7 1k orange yel 6.50 11.00
**47** A7 2k green 6.50 11.00
**48** A7 3k carmine 12.00 18.00
**49** A8 4k rose 14.00 18.00
**50** A7 7k dark blue 8.00 2.25
**51** A8 10k dark blue 17.50 18.00
**52** A9 14k blue & rose 20.00 30.00
**53** A8 20k blue & car 20.00 24.00
**54** A9 35k violet & grn 30.00 60.00
**55** A8 50k violet & grn 35.00 42.50

***Perf. 13½***

**56** A10 1r brown & org 90.00 67.50
**57** A11 3½r black & gray 325.00 550.00
*a.* 3½r black & yellow (error) 15,000. 18,000.
**58** A11 7r black & yellow 250.00 350.00
*Nos. 46-58 (13)* 834.50 1,202.

Forgeries of Nos. 57, 57a, 58 exist.

### Type of 1889-90
### Wove Paper

**1895-96** **Unwmk.** ***Perf. 14x13***

**60** A6 5p green .80 .50
**61** A6 10p carmine .80 .50
**62** A6 20p orange .80 .50
*b.* Imperf. 160.00 —
**63** A6 25p ultra 1.25 .70
*a.* 25p blue 1.25 .70
*b.* Imperf. 125.00 —
*Nos. 60-63 (4)* 3.65 2.20

A12

A13

A14

A15

**1901 Litho. *Perf. 14½x15***

**Chalky Paper**

**64** A12 2p yellow 6.00 8.00
**65** A12 5p green 12.50 2.00
**66** A13 10p carmine 27.50 3.25
**67** A12 20p dark blue 70.00 1.50
**68** A14 1m violet & grn 350.00 10.00

***Perf. 13½***

**69** A15 10m black & gray 325.00 350.00
*Nos. 64-69 (6)* 791.00 374.75

Imperf sheets of 10p and 20p, stolen during production, were privately perforated 11½ to defraud the P.O. Uncanceled imperfs. of Nos. 65-68 are believed to be proofs.

See Nos. 70-75, 82.

**Types of 1901 Redrawn**

No. 64

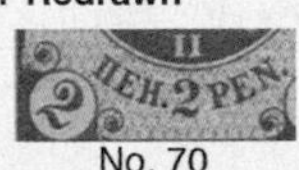
No. 70

2p. On No. 64, the "2" below "II" is shifted slightly leftward. On No. 70, the "2" is centered below "II."

No. 65

No. 71

5p. On No. 65, the frame lines are very close. On No. 71, a clear white space separates them.

Nos. 66, 67

Nos. 72, 73

10p, 20p. On Nos. 66-67, the horizontal central background lines are faint and broken. On Nos. 72-73, they are clear and solid, though still thin.

20p. On No. 67, "H" close to "2" with period midway. On No. 73 they are slightly separated with period close to "H."

No. 68

Nos. 74, 74a

1m. On No. 68, the "1" following "MARKKA" lacks serif at base. On Nos. 74-74a, this "1" has serif.

No. 69

No. 75

10m. On No. 69, the serifs of "M" and "A" in top and bottom panels do not touch. On No. 75, the serifs join.

***Perf. 14¼x14¾, 14¼x14***

**1901-14 Typo. Ordinary Paper**

**70** A12 2p orange 1.00 1.50
**71** A12 5p green 2.00 .60
*a.* Perf 14¼x14 ('06) 3.50 .75
Never hinged 4.00
**72** A13 10p carmine 14.00 .60
*a.* Perf 14¼x14 ('07) 90.00 .95
Never hinged 92.50
*b.* Background inverted, perf 14¼x14¾ 17.50 5.00
*c.* Background inverted, perf 14¼x14 95.00 2.75
**73** A12 20p dark blue 10.00 .60
*a.* Perf 14¼x14 ('06) 82.50 1.25
Never hinged 115.00
**74** A14 1m lil & grn, perf. 14¼x14 ('14) 1.10 .60
*a.* 1m violet & blue green, perf. 14¼x14¾ ('02) 10.00 .90
Never hinged 22.50
*Nos. 70-74 (5)* 28.10 3.90
Set, never hinged 45.00

***Perf. 13½***

**75** A15 10m blk & drab ('03) 160.00 60.00
Never hinged 275.00

**Imperf Pairs**

*70a* A12 2p 375.00 *525.00*
*71b* A12 5p 100.00 *200.00*
*72d* A13 10p 110.00 *225.00*
*73b* A12 20p 200.00 *225.00*
*74b* A14 1m 190.00 *210.00*
*Nos. 70a-74b (5)* 975.00 1,385.

A16 A17 A18

**1911-16 *Perf. 14, 14¼x14¾***

**77** A16 2p orange .30 *.90*
**78** A16 5p green .35 .40
*a.* Imperf. —
*b.* Perf. 14¼x14¾ 1,400. 140.00
Never hinged 675.00
**79** A17 10p rose ('15) .30 .75
*a.* Imperf. 110.00 225.00
*b.* Perf. 14¼x14¾ ('16) 3.50 *5.50*
Never hinged 9.50
**80** A16 20p deep blue .40 *.60*
*a.* Imperf. 180.00 140.00
*b.* Perf. 14¼x14¾ 27.50 3.50
Never hinged 21.00
**81** A18 40p violet & blue .40 .40
*a.* Perf. 14¼x14¾ 6,000. 4,000.
*Nos. 77-81 (5)* 1.75 3.05
Set, never hinged 3.00

There are three minor types of No. 79. Values are for the least expensive type.

***Perf. 14½***

**82** A15 10m blk & grnsh gray ('16) 160.00 210.00
Never hinged 275.00
*a.* Horiz. pair, imperf. vert. 3,900.

**Republic**
**Helsinki Issue**

Arms of the Republic — A19

Type I

Type II

Two types of the 40p.
Type I — Thin figures of value.
Type II — Thick figures of value.

***Perf. 14, 14¼x14¾***

**1917-30 Unwmk.**

**83** A19 5p green .35 .35
**84** A19 5p gray ('19) .35 .35
**85** A19 10p rose .35 *.45*
*a.* Imperf., pair 250.00 *400.00*
**86** A19 10p green ('19) 1.50 .55
*a.* Perf. 14¼x14¾ *3,000.*
**87** A19 10p brt blue ('21) .40 *.45*
**88** A19 20p buff .40 *.50*
**89** A19 20p rose ('20) .40 *.45*
**90** A19 20p brown ('24) 1.00 *.90*
*a.* Perf. 14¼x14¾ .65 *25.00*
Never hinged 1.50
**91** A19 25p blue .40 *.45*
**92** A19 25p lt brown ('19) .40 .40
**93** A19 30p green ('23) .40 *.55*
**94** A19 40p violet (I) .40 .35
*a.* Perf. 14¼x14¾ 400.00 27.50
Never hinged 850.00
**95** A19 40p bl grn (II) ('29) .50 *3.00*
*a.* Type I ('24) 14.00 6.00
Never hinged 24.00
*b.* Perf. 14¼x14¾ 1.25 *21.00*
Never hinged 2.50
**96** A19 50p orange brn .45 *.45*
**97** A19 50p dp blue ('19) 4.00 .45
*a.* Perf. 14¼x14¾ 2,200.
**98** A19 50p green ('21) 4.50 .40
*a.* Perf. 14¼x14¾ .40 *1.50*
Never hinged .50
**99** A19 60p red vio ('21) .60 .40
*a.* Imperf., pair — —
**100** A19 75p yellow ('21) .40 *.75*
**101** A19 1m dull rose & blk 16.00 .30
**102** A19 1m red org ('25) 9.00 *30.00*
*a.* Perf. 14 ('30) .25 *550.00*
Never hinged .65
**103** A19 1½m bl grn & red vio ('29) .25 *2.50*
*a.* Perf. 14¼x14¾ .40 *1.25*
Never hinged .65
**104** A19 2m green & blk ('21) 3.50 .70
**105** A19 2m dk blue & ind ('22) 2.50 .45
*a.* Perf. 14¼x14¾ .65 *4.00*
Never hinged 1.50
**106** A19 3m blue & blk ('21) 25.00 .50
**107** A19 5m red vio & blk 17.50 .45
**108** A19 10m brn & gray blk, perf. 14 1.00 *1.25*
*a.* 10m light brown & black, perf. 14¼x14¾ ('29) 3.50 *400.00*
Never hinged 7.00
**110** A19 25m dull red & yel ('21) .90 *26.00*
*Nos. 83-108,110 (27)* 92.45 *73.35*
Set, never hinged 260.00

Examples of a 2½p gray of this type exist. They are proofs from the original die which were distributed through the UPU. No plate was made for this denomination.

See Nos. 127-140, 143-152. For surcharge and overprints see Nos. 119-126, 153-154.

**Vasa Issue**

Arms of the Republic — A20

**1918 Litho. *Perf. 11½***

**111** A20 5p green .75 *1.25*
**112** A20 10p red .75 *1.25*
**113** A20 30p slate 1.25 *4.50*
**114** A20 40p brown vio .70 *1.75*
**115** A20 50p orange brn .75 *5.00*
**116** A20 70p gray brown 2.25 *32.50*
**117** A20 1m red & gray .75 *2.50*
**118** A20 5m red violet & gray 45.00 *125.00*
*Nos. 111-118 (8)* 52.20 *173.75*
Set, never hinged 92.50

Nos. 111-118 exist imperforate but were not regularly issued in that condition.

Sheet margin examples, perf. on 3 sides, imperf. on margin side, were sold by post office.

Stamps and Type of 1917-29 Surcharged

**1919 *Perf. 14***

**119** A19 10p on 5p green .50 .55
**120** A19 20p on 10p rose .50 .55
**121** A19 50p on 25p blue 1.00 .55
**122** A19 75p on 20p orange .50 *.85*
*Nos. 119-122 (4)* 2.50 2.50
Set, never hinged 5.75

**Stamps and Type of 1917-29 Surcharged**

Nos. 123-125

No. 126

**1921**

**123** A19 30p on 10p green .65 .65
**124** A19 60p on 40p red violet 3.75 1.25
**125** A19 90p on 20p rose .40 .50
**126** A19 1½m on 50p blue 1.40 .50
*a.* Thin "2" in "½" 12.50 11.00
*b.* Imperf., pair 300.00 *500.00*
*Nos. 123-126 (4)* 6.20 2.90
Set, never hinged 13.00

**Arms Type of 1917-29**

***Perf. 14, 14¼x14¾***

**1925-29 Wmk. 121**

**127** A19 10p ultra ('27) .50 *2.75*
**128** A19 20p brown .50 *2.00*
**129** A19 25p brn org ('29) 1.00 *90.00*
**130** A19 30p yel green .40 *.95*
*a.* Perf. 14¼x14¾ 7.00 1.50
Never hinged 7.50
**131** A19 40p blue grn (I) ('26) 9.50 1.40
*a.* Perf. 14¼x14¾ ('26) 9.50 1.40
Never hinged 15.00
*b.* Type II ('28) *140.00* *82.50*
Never hinged 290.00
*c.* As "b," perf. 14¼x14¾ ('28) 9.50 1.40
Never hinged 13.50
**132** A19 50p gray grn ('26) 1.25 .80
*a.* Perf. 14¼x14¾ ('26) .55 *.55*
Never hinged 2.00
**133** A19 60p red violet .40 *.95*
**134** A19 1m dp orange 7.00 .40
*a.* Perf. 14¼x14¾ 100.00 1.25
Never hinged 250.00

**Perf. 14¼x14¾**

**135** A19 1½m blue green & red violet ('26) 6.25 .60
*a.* Perf. 14 ('26) 60.00 .50
Never hinged 80.00
**136** A19 2m dk blue & indigo ('27) 1.00 *.50*
*a.* Perf. 14 1.00 .50
Never hinged 2.25
**137** A19 3m chlky blue & blk ('26) 1.00 .50
**138** A19 5m red violet & blk ('27) .50 .50
*a.* Perf. 14 1.25 .50
Never hinged 2.75
**139** A19 10m lt brn & blk ('27) 4.00 *32.50*
**140** A19 25m dp org & yel ('27) 20.00 *400.00*
*Nos. 127-140 (14)* 53.30 *533.85*
Set, never hinged 100.00

No. 130a is not known cancelled during the period in which it was valid for postal use.

A21

**Wmk. 208**

**1927, Dec. 6 Typo. *Perf. 14***

**141** A21 1½m deep violet .30 *.60*
**142** A21 2m deep blue .30 *2.00*

10th anniv. of Finnish independence.

**Arms Type of 1917-29**

***Perf. 14, 14¼x14¾***

**1927-29 Wmk. 208**

**143** A19 20p lt brown ('29) 2.00 *40.00*
**144** A19 40p bl grn (II) ('28) .40 *.65*
**145** A19 50p gray grn ('28) .40 *.75*
**146** A19 1m dp orange .40 *1.00*
*a.* Imperf., pair 115.00 *200.00*
*b.* Perf. 14 1.25 1.25
**147** A19 1½m bl grn & red vio ('28) 3.00 .70
*a.* Perf. 14 1,000. 26.00
**148** A19 2m dk bl & ind ('28) .45 *.65*
**149** A19 3m chlky bl & blk .50 *.65*
*a.* Perf. 14 1.60 *5.00*
**150** A19 5m red vio & blk ('28) .50 .60
**151** A19 10m lt brown & blk 2.00 *35.00*
**152** A19 25m brown org & yel 2.25 *400.00*
*Nos. 143-152 (10)* 11.90 *480.00*

Nos. 146-147 Overprinted

**1928, Nov. 10 Litho. Wmk. 208**

**153** A19 1m deep orange 10.00 *19.00*
**154** A19 1½m bl grn & red vio 10.00 *19.00*
Set, never hinged 35.00

Nos. 153 and 154 were sold exclusively at the Helsinki Philatelic Exhibition, Nov. 10-18, 1928, and were valid only during that period.

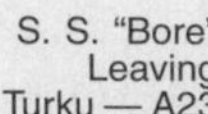

S. S. "Bore" Leaving Turku — A23

Turku Cathedral — A24

Turku Castle — A25

**Wmk. 208**

**1929, May 22 Typo. *Perf. 14***

| No. | Type | Description | Unused | Used |
|---|---|---|---|---|
| **155** | A23 | 1m olive green | 1.50 | *5.00* |
| **156** | A24 | 1½m chocolate | 2.25 | *4.00* |
| **157** | A25 | 2m dark gray | .45 | *4.50* |
| | | *Nos. 155-157 (3)* | 4.20 | *13.50* |
| | | Set, never hinged | 12.50 | |

Founding of the city of Turku (Abo), 700th anniv.

A26

**1930-46 Unwmk. *Perf. 14***

| No. | Type | Description | Unused | Used |
|---|---|---|---|---|
| **158** | A26 | 5p chocolate | .50 | *.50* |
| **159** | A26 | 10p dull violet | .50 | .50 |
| **160** | A26 | 20p yel grn | .50 | *.50* |
| **161** | A26 | 25p yel brn | .50 | .50 |
| **162** | A26 | 40p blue grn | 2.00 | .25 |
| **163** | A26 | 50p yellow | .50 | .50 |
| **164** | A26 | 50p blue grn ('32) | .45 | .45 |
| *b.* | | Imperf., pair | 150.00 | *200.00* |
| **165** | A26 | 60p dark gray | .50 | *.65* |
| **165A** | A26 | 75p dp org ('42) | .55 | *.75* |
| **166** | A26 | 1m red org | .50 | .50 |
| **166B** | A26 | 1m yel grn ('42) | .50 | .50 |
| **167** | A26 | 1.20m crimson | .55 | *1.75* |
| **168** | A26 | 1.25m yel ('32) | .50 | .50 |
| **169** | A26 | 1½m red vio | 2.00 | .50 |
| **170** | A26 | 1½m car ('32) | .50 | .50 |
| **170A** | A26 | 1½m sl ('40) | .50 | .50 |
| **170B** | A26 | 1.75m org yel ('40) | .90 | .70 |
| **171** | A26 | 2m indigo | .50 | .50 |
| **172** | A26 | 2m dp vio ('32) | 6.00 | .50 |
| **173** | A26 | 2m car ('36) | .50 | .50 |
| | | Complete booklet, panes of 4 #161, 164, 166, 168, 173 | 5.75 | |
| **173B** | A26 | 2m yel org ('42) | .50 | .50 |
| **173C** | A26 | 2m blue grn ('45) | .50 | .50 |
| **174** | A26 | 2½m brt blue ('32) | 4.75 | .55 |
| **174A** | A26 | 2½m car ('42) | .50 | .50 |
| **174B** | A26 | 2.75m rose vio ('40) | .50 | .50 |
| **175** | A26 | 3m olive blk | 35.00 | .65 |
| **175B** | A26 | 3m car ('45) | 1.00 | .50 |
| **175C** | A26 | 3m yel ('45) | .50 | *.80* |
| **176** | A26 | 3½m brt bl ('36) | 9.00 | .50 |
| **176A** | A26 | 3½m olive ('42) | .50 | .50 |
| **176B** | A26 | 4m olive ('45) | 1.10 | .50 |
| **176C** | A26 | 4½m saph ('42) | .50 | .50 |
| **176D** | A26 | 5m saph ('45) | .50 | .50 |
| **176E** | A26 | 5m pur ('45) | 1.50 | .50 |
| *j.* | | Imperf., pair | 150.00 | *200.00* |
| **176F** | A26 | 5m yel ('46) | 1.25 | .55 |
| *k.* | | Imperf., pair | 150.00 | *200.00* |
| **176G** | A26 | 6m car ('45) | 1.20 | .50 |
| *m.* | | Imperf., pair | 200.00 | *275.00* |
| **176H** | A26 | 8m pur ('46) | .50 | .50 |
| **176I** | A26 | 10m saph ('45) | 1.75 | .50 |
| | | *Nos. 158-176I (38)* | 80.00 | 21.10 |

See Nos. 257-262, 270-274, 291-296, 302-304. For surcharges and overprints see Nos. 195-196, 212, 221-222, 243, 250, 275, M2-M3.

Stamps of types A26-A29 overprinted "ITA KARJALA" are listed under Karelia, Nos. N1-N15.

Castle in Savonlinna A27

Lake Saima — A28

Woodchopper A29

**1930 Engr.**

| No. | Type | Description | Unused | Used |
|---|---|---|---|---|
| **177** | A27 | 5m blue | 1.50 | *.65* |
| **178** | A28 | 10m gray lilac | 55.00 | 4.75 |
| **179** | A29 | 25m black brown | 1.00 | .50 |
| | | *Nos. 177-179 (3)* | 57.50 | 5.90 |
| | | Set, never hinged | 150.00 | |

See Nos. 205, 305. For overprint see No. C1.

Elias Lönnrot — A30

Seal of Finnish Literary Society — A31

**1931, Jan. 1 Typo.**

| No. | Type | Description | Unused | Used |
|---|---|---|---|---|
| **180** | A30 | 1m olive brown | 2.50 | *5.75* |
| **181** | A31 | 1½m dull blue | 12.50 | 6.25 |
| | | Never hinged | 45.00 | |

Centenary of Finnish Literary Society.

A32

**1931, Feb. 28**

| No. | Type | Description | Unused | Used |
|---|---|---|---|---|
| **182** | A32 | 1½m red | 2.75 | *9.50* |
| | | Never hinged | 6.00 | |
| **183** | A32 | 2m blue | 2.75 | *11.50* |
| | | Never hinged | 6.00 | |

1st use of postage stamps in Finland, 75th anniv.

Nos. 162-163 Surcharged

**1931, Dec.**

| No. | Type | Description | Unused | Used |
|---|---|---|---|---|
| **195** | A26 | 50p on 40p blue grn | 2.75 | 1.20 |
| | | Never hinged | 8.50 | |
| **196** | A26 | 1.25m on 50p yellow | 4.00 | 3.50 |
| | | Never hinged | 13.00 | |

Svinhufvud — A33

**1931, Dec. 15**

| No. | Type | Description | Unused | Used |
|---|---|---|---|---|
| **197** | A33 | 2m gray blue & blk | 1.50 | *3.25* |
| | | Never hinged | 5.25 | |

Pres. Pehr Eyvind Svinhufvud, 70th birthday.

**Lake Saima Type of 1930**

**1932-43 Re-engraved**

| No. | Type | Description | Unused | Used |
|---|---|---|---|---|
| **205** | A28 | 10m red violet ('43) | .70 | .50 |
| | | Never hinged | 1.60 | |
| *a.* | | 10m dark violet | 20.00 | .70 |
| | | Never hinged | 40.00 | |

On Nos. 205 and 205a the lines of the islands, the clouds and the foliage are much deeper and stronger than on No. 178.

Alexis Kivi — A34

**1934, Oct. 10 Typo.**

| No. | Type | Description | Unused | Used |
|---|---|---|---|---|
| **206** | A34 | 2m red violet | 2.25 | *4.50* |
| | | Never hinged | 5.50 | |

Alexis Kivi, Finnish poet (1834-1872).

Bards Reciting the "Kalevala" A35

Goddess Louhi, As Eagle Seizing Magic Mill — A36

Kullervo — A37

**1935, Feb. 28 Engr.**

| No. | Type | Description | Unused | Used |
|---|---|---|---|---|
| **207** | A35 | 1¼m brown lake | 2.00 | *2.50* |
| | | Never hinged | 4.00 | |
| **208** | A36 | 2m black | 4.50 | 2.00 |
| | | Never hinged | 12.50 | |
| **209** | A37 | 2½m blue | 3.00 | 3.00 |
| | | Never hinged | 10.00 | |
| | | *Nos. 207-209 (3)* | 9.50 | 7.50 |
| | | Set, never hinged | 26.50 | |

Cent. of the publication of the "Kalevala" (Finnish National Epic).

No. 170 Surcharged in Black

**1937, Feb.**

| No. | Type | Description | Unused | Used |
|---|---|---|---|---|
| **212** | A26 | 2m on 1½m car | 8.00 | 1.40 |
| | | Never hinged | 14.00 | |

Gustaf Mannerheim — A38

**1937, June 4 Photo. *Perf. 14***

| No. | Type | Description | Unused | Used |
|---|---|---|---|---|
| **213** | A38 | 2m ultra | 1.00 | *1.45* |
| | | Never hinged | 2.50 | |

70th birthday of Field Marshal Baron Carl Gustaf Mannerheim, June 4th, 1937.

Swede-Finn Co-operation in Colonization A39

**1938, June 1**

| No. | Type | Description | Unused | Used |
|---|---|---|---|---|
| **214** | A39 | 3½m dark brown | .90 | *2.75* |
| | | Never hinged | 3.00 | |

Tercentenary of the colonization of Delaware by Swedes and Finns.

Early Post Office — A40

Designs: 1¼m, Mail delivery in 1700. 2m, Modern mail plane. 3½m, Helsinki post office.

**1938, Sept. 6 Photo. *Perf. 14***

| No. | Type | Description | Unused | Used |
|---|---|---|---|---|
| **215** | A40 | 50p green | .35 | .55 |
| | | Never hinged | .65 | |
| **216** | A40 | 1¼m dk blue | 1.15 | *3.25* |
| | | Never hinged | 3.25 | |
| **217** | A40 | 2m scarlet | 1.15 | 1.25 |
| | | Never hinged | 6.25 | |
| **218** | A40 | 3½m slate black | 3.25 | *8.00* |
| | | Never hinged | 8.75 | |
| | | *Nos. 215-218 (4)* | 5.90 | 13.05 |
| | | Set, never hinged | 19.00 | |

300th anniv. of the Finnish Postal System.

Margin strips of each denomination (3 of No. 215, 2 each of Nos. 216, 217, 218) were pasted on to advertising sheets and stapled into a booklet. Value, $120.

Post Office, Helsinki — A44

**1939-42 Photo.**

| No. | Type | Description | Unused | Used |
|---|---|---|---|---|
| **219** | A44 | 4m brown black | .40 | *.45* |
| | | Never hinged | 1.10 | |
| | | **Engr.** | | |
| **219A** | A44 | 7m black brn ('42) | .50 | *.45* |
| | | Never hinged | 1.90 | |
| **219B** | A44 | 9m rose lake ('42) | .60 | .50 |
| | | Never hinged | 1.60 | |
| | | *Nos. 219-219B (3)* | 1.50 | 1.40 |
| | | Set, never hinged | 3.50 | |

See No. 248.

**Catalogue values for unused stamps in this section, from this point to the end of the section, are for Never Hinged items.**

University of Helsinki — A45

**1940, May 1 Photo.**

| No. | Type | Description | Unused | Used |
|---|---|---|---|---|
| **220** | A45 | 2m dp blue & blue | .75 | *.90* |

300th anniv. of the founding of the University of Helsinki.

Nos. 168 and 173 Surcharged in Black

**1940, June 16** **Typo.**
221 A26 1.75m on 1.25m yel 4.00 *3.25*
222 A26 2.75m on 2m carmine 10.00 .90

President Kallio Reviewing Military Band — A46

**1941, May 24** **Engr.**
223 A46 2.75m black .75 *1.00*

Pres. Kyösti Kallio (1873-1940).

Castle at Viborg — A47

**1941, Aug. 30** **Typo.**
224 A47 1.75m yellow orange .50 *.60*
225 A47 2.75m rose violet .50 *.60*
226 A47 3.50m blue .90 *1.25*

Field Marshal Mannerheim — A48

**1941, Dec. 31** **Engr.** **Wmk. 273**
227 A48 50p dull green 1.75 *2.75*
228 A48 1.75m deep brown 1.75 *2.75*
229 A48 2m dark red 2.75 2.75
230 A48 2.75m dull vio brn 2.75 2.75
231 A48 3.50m deep blue 1.75 *2.00*
232 A48 5m slate blue 1.75 *2.00*
*Nos. 227-232 (6)* 12.50 *15.00*

Pres. Risto Ryti — A49

233 A49 50p dull green 1.60 *2.25*
234 A49 1.75m deep brown 1.60 *2.25*
235 A49 2m dark red 1.60 *2.25*
236 A49 2.75m dull vio brn 1.60 *3.50*
237 A49 3.50m deep blue 1.60 *2.25*
238 A49 5m slate blue 1.60 *2.25*
*Nos. 233-238 (6)* 9.60 *14.75*

Types A48-A49 overprinted "ITA KARJALA" are listed under Karelia, Nos. N16-N27.

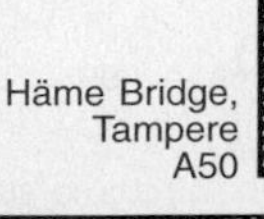

Häme Bridge, Tampere A50

South Harbor, Helsinki — A51

**1942** **Unwmk.**
239 A50 50m dull brown vio 3.25 .45
240 A51 100m indigo 5.00 .40

See No. 350.

Altar and Open Bible — A52

17th Century Printer — A53

**1942, Oct. 10**
241 A52 2.75m dk brown .90 *1.40*
242 A53 3.50m violet blue 1.00 *3.50*

300th anniv. of the printing of the 1st Bible in Finnish.

No. 174B Surcharged in Black

**1943, Feb. 1**
243 A26 3.50m on 2.75m rose vio .85 .70

Minna Canth (1844-96), Author and Playwright — A54

**1944, Mar. 20**
244 A54 3.50m dk olive grn .60 *1.00*

Pres. P. E. Svinhufvud — A55

**1944, Aug. 1**
245 A55 3.50m black .90 *1.25*

Death of President Svinhufvud (1861-1944).

K. J. Stahlberg — A56

**1945, May 16** **Engr.** ***Perf. 14***
246 A56 3.50m brown vio .60 *.75*

80th birthday of Dr. K. J. Stahlberg.

Castle in Savonlinna A57

**1945, Sept. 4**
247 A57 15m lilac rose 2.75 .60
248 A44 20m sepia 1.75 .60

For a 35m of type A57, see No. 280.

Jean Sibelius — A58

**1945, Dec. 8**
249 A58 5m dk slate green 1.00 .55

Jean Sibelius (1865-1957), composer.

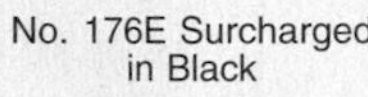

No. 176E Surcharged in Black

**1946, Mar. 16**
250 A26 8(m) on 5m purple .75 .50

Victorious Athletes — A59

**1946, June 1** **Engr.** ***Perf. 13½***
251 A59 8m brown violet .60 *.75*

3rd Sports Festival, Helsinki, June 27-30, 1946.

Lighthouse at Uto — A60

**1946, Sept. 19**
252 A60 8m deep violet .75 *.70*

250th anniv. of the Finnish Department of Pilots and Lighthouses.

Post Bus — A61

**1946-47** **Unwmk.** ***Perf. 14***
253 A61 16m gray black .85 *.75*
253A A61 30m gray black ('47) 3.00 .50

Issue dates: 16m, Oct. 16, 30m, Feb. 10.

Old Town Hall, Porvoo — A62

Cathedral, Porvoo — A63

**1946, Dec. 3**
254 A62 5m gray black .60 *.75*
255 A63 8m deep claret .60 *.75*

600th anniv. of the founding of the city of Porvoo (Borga).

Waterfront, Tammisaari A64

**1946, Dec. 14**
256 A64 8m grnsh black .60 *.75*

400th anniv. of the founding of the town of Tammisaari (Ekenas).

**Lion Type of 1930**

**1947** **Typo.** ***Perf. 14***
257 A26 2½m dark green .65 .50
258 A26 3m slate gray .75 .50
259 A26 6m deep orange 2.00 .50
260 A26 7m carmine 1.50 .45
261 A26 10m purple 5.00 .45
262 A26 12m deep blue 4.50 .45
*Nos. 257-262 (6)* 14.40 2.85

Issued: 3m, 6/9; 7m, 12m, 2/10; others, 1/20.

Pres. Juho K. Paasikivi — A65

**1947, Mar. 15** **Engr.**
263 A65 10m gray black .65 .50

Postal Savings Emblem — A66

**1947, Apr. 1**
264 A66 10m brown violet .50 .50

60th anniv. of the foundation of the Finnish Postal Savings Bank.

Ilmarinen, the Plowman — A67

**1947, June 2**
265 A67 10m gray black .50 .50

2nd year of peace following WW II.

Girl and Boy Athletes — A68

**1947, June 2**
266 A68 10m bright blue .70 *.75*

Finnish Athletic Festival, Helsinki, June 29-July 3, 1947.

Wheat and Savings Bank Assoc. Emblem — A69

**1947, Aug. 21**

**267** A69 10m red brown .80 *.75*

Finnish Savings Bank Assoc., 125th anniv.

Sower — A70

**1947, Nov. 1**

**268** A70 10m gray black .75 .70

150th anniv. of Finnish Agricultural Societies.

Koli Mountain and Lake Pielisjärvi A71

**1947, Nov. 1**

**269** A71 10m indigo .90 *.75*

60th anniv. of the Finnish Touring Assoc.

**Lion Type of 1930**

**1948 Typo. *Perf. 14***

| | | | | |
|---|---|---|---|---|
| **270** | A26 | 3m dark green | 4.50 | .45 |
| **271** | A26 | 6m yellow green | 1.25 | .65 |
| **272** | A26 | 9m carmine | 1.25 | .50 |
| **273** | A26 | 15m dark blue | 8.00 | .50 |
| **274** | A26 | 24m brown lake | 2.75 | .50 |
| | | *Nos. 270-274 (5)* | 17.75 | 2.60 |

Issued: 3m, 2/9; 24m, 4/26; others, 9/13.

No. 261 Surcharged in Black

**1948, Feb. 9**

**275** A26 12(m) on 10m purple 2.00 .50

Statue of Michael Agricola — A72

12m, Agricola translating New Testament.

**1948, Oct. 2 Engr. *Perf. 14***

| | | | | |
|---|---|---|---|---|
| **276** | A72 | 7m rose violet | 1.25 | *2.25* |
| **277** | A72 | 12m gray blue | 1.25 | *2.25* |

400th anniv. of publication of the Finnish translation of the New Testament, by Michael Agricola.

Sveaborg Fortress A73

**1948, Oct. 15**

**278** A73 12m deep green 1.60 *2.00*

200th anniv. of the construction of Sveaborg Fortress on the Gulf of Finland.

Post Rider — A74

**1948, Oct. 27**

**279** A74 12m green 9.00 *17.50*

Helsinki Philatelic Exhibition. Sold only at exhibition for 62m, of which 50m was entrance fee.

**Castle Type of 1945**

**1949**

**280** A57 35m violet 9.00 .50

Sawmill and Cellulose Plant — A75

Pine Tree and Globe — A76

**1949, June 15**

| | | | | |
|---|---|---|---|---|
| **281** | A75 | 9m brown | 3.00 | *4.50* |
| **282** | A76 | 15m dull green | 3.00 | *4.50* |

Issued to publicize the Third World Forestry Congress, Helsinki, July 10-20, 1949.

Woman with Torch — A77

**1949, July 16 Engr. *Perf. 14***

| | | | | |
|---|---|---|---|---|
| **283** | A77 | 5m dull green | 5.50 | *11.50* |
| **284** | A77 | 15m red *(Worker)* | 5.50 | *11.50* |

50th anniv. of the Finnish labor movement.

Harbor of Lappeenranta (Willmanstrand) — A78

Raahe (Brahestad) — A79

**1949**

| | | | | |
|---|---|---|---|---|
| **285** | A78 | 5m dk blue grn | 2.00 | 1.50 |
| **286** | A79 | 9m brown carmine | 2.00 | *2.00* |
| **287** | A78 | 15m brt blue *(Kristi-inan-kaupunki)* | 2.75 | *4.50* |
| | | *Nos. 285-287 (3)* | 6.75 | 8.00 |

300th anniv. of the founding of Willmanstrand, Brahestad and Kristinestad (Kristiinankaupunki).

Issued: 5m, 8/6; 9m, 8/13; 15m, 7/30.

Technical High School Badge — A80

**1949, Sept. 13**

**288** A80 15m ultra 1.40 *1.60*

Founding of the technical school, cent.

Hannes Gebhard — A81

**1949, Oct. 2**

**289** A81 15m dull green 1.40 *1.60*

Establishment of Finnish cooperatives, 50th anniv.

Finnish Lake Country — A82

**1949, Oct. 8**

**290** A82 15m blue 1.40 *1.60*

75th anniv. of the UPU.

**Lion Type of 1930**

**1950, Jan. 9 Typo. *Perf. 14***

| | | | | |
|---|---|---|---|---|
| **291** | A26 | 8m brt green | 2.25 | 1.75 |
| **292** | A26 | 9m red orange | 2.40 | .60 |
| **293** | A26 | 10m violet brown | 7.25 | .50 |
| **294** | A26 | 12m scarlet | 2.00 | .50 |
| **295** | A26 | 15m plum | 25.00 | .50 |
| **296** | A26 | 20m deep blue | 10.00 | .50 |
| | | *Nos. 291-296 (6)* | 48.90 | 4.35 |

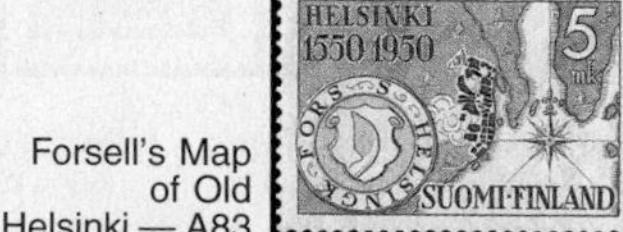

Forsell's Map of Old Helsinki — A83

J. A. Ehrenstrom and C. L. Engel — A84

City Hall — A85

**1950, June 11 Engr.**

| | | | | |
|---|---|---|---|---|
| **297** | A83 | 5m emerald | 1.00 | *.90* |
| **298** | A84 | 9m brown | 1.25 | *1.50* |
| **299** | A85 | 15m deep blue | .90 | *1.10* |
| | | *Nos. 297-299 (3)* | 3.15 | 3.50 |

400th anniv. of the founding of Helsinki.

J. K. Paasikivi — A86

**1950, Nov. 27**

**300** A86 20m deep ultra .70 .50

80th birthday of Pres. J. K. Paasikivi.

View of Kajaani — A87

**1951, July 7 Unwmk. *Perf. 14***

**301** A87 20m red brown 2.00 *1.00*

Tercentenary of Kajaani.

**Lion and Chopper Types of 1930**

**1952, Jan. 18 Typo.**

| | | | | |
|---|---|---|---|---|
| **302** | A26 | 10m emerald | 4.50 | .40 |
| **303** | A26 | 15m red | 4.25 | .45 |
| **304** | A26 | 25m blue | 7.00 | .40 |
| | | **Engr.** | | |
| **305** | A29 | 40m black brown | 4.25 | .50 |
| | | *Nos. 302-305 (4)* | 20.00 | 1.75 |

Arms of Pietarsaari — A88

**1952, June 19 Unwmk. *Perf. 14***

**306** A88 25m blue 1.40 1.10

300th anniv. of the founding of Pietarsaari (Jacobstad).

Rooftops of Vaasa — A89

**1952, Aug. 3**

**307** A89 25m brown 2.25 1.10

Centenary of the burning of Vaasa.

Chess Symbols — A90

**1952, Aug. 10**

**308** A90 25m gray 3.00 *3.00*

10th Chess Olympics, Helsinki, 8/10-31/52.

Torch Bearers — A91

**1953, Jan. 27**

**309** A91 25m blue 1.60 1.10

Temperance movement in Finland, cent.

Air View of Hamina (Fredrikshamn) A92

**1953, June 20**

**310** A92 25m dk gray green 2.10 1.10

Tercentenary of Hamina.

Ivar Wilskman — A93

**1954, Feb. 26**

**311** A93 25m blue 1.10 1.00

Centenary of the birth of Prof. Ivar Wilskman, "father of gymnastics in Finland."

Arms of Finland — A94

**1954-59** ***Perf. 11½***

| | | | | |
|---|---|---|---|---|
| **312** | A94 | 1m red brown ('55) | .40 | .25 |
| **313** | A94 | 2m green ('55) | .40 | .25 |
| **314** | A94 | 3m deep orange | .40 | .25 |
| **314A** | A94 | 4m gray ('58) | .75 | .50 |
| **315** | A94 | 5m violet blue | .80 | .25 |
| **316** | A94 | 10m blue green | 1.25 | .25 |
| *a.* | | Bklt. pane of 5 (vert. strip) | 22.50 | 22.50 |
| | | Complete booklet, #316a | 25.00 | |
| **317** | A94 | 15m rose red | 4.50 | .25 |
| **318** | A94 | 15m yellow org ('57) | 8.25 | .25 |
| **319** | A94 | 20m rose lilac | 14.00 | .25 |
| **320** | A94 | 20m rose red ('56) | 2.40 | .25 |
| **321** | A94 | 25m deep blue | 4.50 | .25 |
| **322** | A94 | 25m rose lilac ('59) | 12.00 | .25 |
| **323** | A94 | 30m lt ultra ('56) | 2.40 | .25 |
| | | *Nos. 312-323 (13)* | 52.05 | 3.50 |

See Nos. 398, 400-405A, 457-459A, 461A-462, 464-464B.

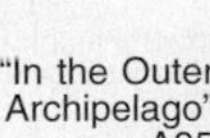

"In the Outer Archipelago" A95

**1954, July 21** ***Perf. 14***

**324** A95 25m black .90 .70

Cent. of the birth of Albert Edelfelt, painter.

J. J. Nervander A96

**1955, Feb. 23**

**325** A96 25m blue 1.70 1.00

150th anniv. of the birth of J. J. Nervander, astronomer and poet.

Composite of Finnish Public Buildings — A97

**1955, Mar. 30** **Engr.** ***Perf. 14***

**326** A97 25m gray 17.00 *24.00*

Sold for 125m, which included the price of admission to the Natl. Postage Stamp Exhibition, Helsinki, Mar. 30-Apr. 3, 1955.

Bishop Henrik with Foot on Lalli, his Murderer — A98

25m, Arrival of Bishop Henrik and monks.

**1955, May 19**

**327** A98 15m rose brown 1.25 1.00
**328** A98 25m green 1.25 1.00

Adoption of Christianity in Finland, 800th anniv.

Conference Hall, Helsinki — A99

**1955, Aug. 25**

**329** A99 25m bluish green 1.25 *2.00*

44th conf. of the Interparliamentarian Union, Helsinki, Aug. 25-31, 1955.

Sailing Vessel and Merchant A100

**1955, Sept. 2**

**330** A100 25m sepia 2.40 2.10

350th anniv. of founding of Oulu.

Town Hall, Lahti — A101

**1955, Nov. 1** ***Perf. 14x13½***

**331** A101 25m violet blue 1.50 *2.50*

50th anniversary of founding of Lahti.

Radio Sender, Map of Finland — A102

Designs: 15m, Otto Nyberg. 25m, Telegraph wires and pines under snow.

**Inscribed: Lennatin 1855-1955 Telegrafen**

**1955, Dec. 10** ***Perf. 14***

**332** A102 10m green 3.00 *2.40*
**333** A102 15m dull violet 3.00 1.25
**334** A102 25m lt ultra 4.50 2.00
*Nos. 332-334 (3)* 10.50 5.65

Cent. of the telegraph in Finland.

A103

**1956, Jan. 26** **Unwmk.** ***Perf. 14***

**335** A103 25m Lighthouse, Porkkala Peninsula 1.10 *1.40*

Return of the Porkkala Region to Finland by Russia, Jan. 1956.

A104

30m, 50m, Church at Lammi. 40m, House of Parliament. 60m, Fortress of Olavinlinna (Olofsborg).

**1956-57** ***Perf. 11½***

| | | | | |
|---|---|---|---|---|
| **336** | A104 | 30m gray olive | 1.25 | .30 |
| **337** | A104 | 40m dull purple | 2.75 | .30 |
| **338** | A104 | 50m gray ol ('57) | 8.25 | .30 |
| **338A** | A104 | 60m pale pur ('57) | 12.00 | .30 |
| | | *Nos. 336-338A (4)* | 24.25 | 1.20 |

Issued: 30m, 3/4; 40m, 3/11; 50m, 3/3; 60m, 4/7. See Nos. 406-408A.

Johan V. Snellman — A105

**1956, May 12** **Engr.** ***Perf. 14***

**339** A105 25m dk violet brn .85 *1.00*

Johan V. Snellman (1806-81), statesman.

Gymnast and Athletes — A106

**1956, June 28**

**340** A106 30m violet blue 1.60 1.25

Finnish Gymnastic and Sports Games, Helsinki, June 28-July 1, 1956.

A107

**Wmk. 208**

**1956, July 7** **Typo.** ***Rouletted***

**341** A107 30m deep ultra 4.00 *6.50*
*a.* Tête bêche pair 10.00 *15.00*
*b.* Pane of 10 50.00 *75.00*

Issued to publicize the FINLANDIA Philatelic Exhibition, Helsinki, July 7-15, 1956.

Printed in sheets containing four 2x5 panes, with white margins around each group. The stamps in each double row are printed tete-beche, making the position of the watermark differ in the vertical row of each pane of ten.

Sold for 155m, price including entrance ticket to exhibition.

Town Hall at Vasa — A108

**Unwmk.**

**1956, Oct. 2** **Engr.** ***Perf. 14***

**342** A108 30m bright blue 1.60 1.25

350th anniversary of Vasa.

**Northern Countries Issue**

Whooper Swans — A108a

**1956, Oct. 30** ***Perf. 12½***

**343** A108a 20m rose red 1.50 1.40
**344** A108a 30m ultra 5.00 1.40

See footnote after Denmark No. 362.

University Clinic, Helsinki A109

**1956, Dec. 17** ***Perf. 11½***

**345** A109 30m dull green 1.75 1.10

Public health service in Finland, bicent.

Scout Sign, Emblem and Globe — A110

**1957, Feb. 22** ***Perf. 14***

**346** A110 30m ultra 3.00 1.40

50th anniversary of Boy Scouts.

Arms Holding Hammers and Laurel — A111

Design: 20m, Factories and cogwheel.

**1957** **Engr.** ***Perf. 13½***

**347** A111 20m dark blue 1.10 1.10
**348** A111 30m carmine 2.50 1.40

50th anniv.: Central Fed. of Finnish Employers (20m, issued 9/27); Finnish Trade Union Movement (30m, issued 4/15).

"Lex" from Seal of Parliament — A112

**1957, May 23** ***Perf. 14***

**349** A112 30m olive gray 1.50 1.10

50th anniv. of the Finnish parliament.

**Harbor Type of 1942**

**1957** **Unwmk.** ***Perf. 14***

**350** A51 100m grnsh blue 12.50 .35

Ida Aalberg — A114

**1957, Dec. 4** ***Perf. 14***
**351** A114 30m vio gray & mar 1.50 *.90*

Birth cent. of Ida Aalberg, Finnish actress.

Arms of Finland A115

**1957, Dec. 6** ***Perf. 11½***
**352** A115 30m blue 1.40 *1.00*

40th anniv. of Finland's independence.

Jean Sibelius — A116

**1957, Dec. 8** ***Perf. 14***
**353** A116 30m black 2.75 1.10

Jean Sibelius (1865-1957), composer.

Ski Jump — A117

Design: 30m, Skier, vert.

**1958, Feb. 1** **Engr.** ***Perf. 11½***
**354** A117 20m slate green 1.10 *1.60*
**355** A117 30m blue 1.10 .80

Nordic championships of the Intl. Ski Federation, Lahti.

"March of the Bjorneborgienses," by Edelfelt — A118

**1958, Mar. 8**
**356** A118 30m violet gray 1.75 .95

400th anniv. of the founding of Pori (Bjorneborg).

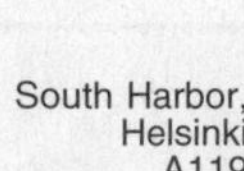

South Harbor, Helsinki A119

**1958, June 2** **Unwmk.** ***Perf. 11½***
**357** A119 100m bluish green 17.50 .35

See No. 410.

Seal of Jyväskylä Lyceum A120

**1958, Oct. 1** ***Perf. 11½***
**358** A120 30m rose carmine 1.75 1.10

Cent. of the founding of the 1st Finnish secondary school.

Chrismon and Globe — A121

**1959, Jan. 19**
**359** A121 30m dull violet .75 .65

Finnish Missionary Society, cent.

Diet at Porvoo, 1809 — A122

**1959, Mar. 22** ***Perf. 11½***
**360** A122 30m dk blue gray .75 .65

150th anniv. of the inauguration of the Diet at Porvoo.

Saw Cutting Log — A123

**1959, May 13** **Engr.**
**361** A123 10m shown .95 .95
**362** A123 30m Forest .95 .95

No. 361 for the cent. of the establishment of the 1st steam saw-mill in Finland; No. 362, the cent. of the Dept. of Forestry.

Pyhakoski Power Station — A124

**1959, May 24**
**363** A124 75m gray 5.75 .40

See No. 409.

Oil Lamp — A125

**1959, Dec. 19**
**364** A125 30m blue .90 .75

Cent. of the liberation of the country trade.

Woman Gymnast A126

**1959, Nov. 14** **Unwmk.**
**365** A126 30m rose lilac 1.10 .75

Finnish women's gymnastics and the cent. of the birth of Elin Oihonna Kallio, pioneer of Finnish women's physical education.

Arms of Six New Towns — A127

**1960, Jan. 2** ***Perf. 14***
**366** A127 30m light violet 1.75 1.00

Issued to commemorate the founding of new towns in Finland: Hyvinkaa, Kouvola, Riihimaki, Rovaniemi, Salo and Seinajoki.

Type of 1860 Issue A128

**1960, Mar. 25** **Typo.** ***Rouletted 4½***
**367** A128 30m blue & gray 5.50 9.75

Cent. of Finland's serpentine roulette stamps, and in connection with HELSINKI 1960, 40th anniv. exhib. of the Federation of Philatelic Societies of Finland, Mar. 25-31. Sold only at the exhibition for 150m including entrance ticket.

Mother and Child, Waiting Crowd and Uprooted Oak Emblem A129

**1960, Apr. 7** **Engr.** ***Perf. 11½***
**368** A129 30m rose claret .80 .80
**369** A129 40m dark blue .80 .80

World Refugee Year, 7/1/59-6/30/60.

Johan Gadolin — A130

**1960, June 4** ***Perf. 11½***
**370** A130 30m dark brown 1.10 .75

Bicent. of the birth of Gadolin, chemist.

Hj. Nortamo — A131

**1960, June 13** **Unwmk.**
**371** A131 30m gray green 1.10 .75

Cent. of the birth of Hj. Nortamo (Hjalmar Nordberg), writer.

Symbolic Tree and Cuckoo A132

**1960, June 18**
**372** A132 30m vermilion 1.40 .80

Karelian Natl. Festival, Helsinki, June 18-19.

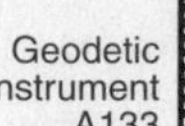

Geodetic Instrument A133

Design: 30m, Aurora borealis and globe.

**1960, July 26** **Unwmk.** ***Perf. 13½***
**373** A133 10m blue & pale brn 1.00 .65
**374** A133 30m ver & rose car 1.25 .65

12th General Assembly of the Intl. Union of Geodesy and Geophysics, Helsinki.

Urho Kekkonen — A134

**1960, Sept. 3** **Engr.** ***Perf. 11½***
**375** A134 30m violet blue .90 .40

Issued to honor President Urho Kekkonen on his 60th birthday.

Common Design Types pictured following the introduction.

**Europa Issue, 1960**
Common Design Type

**1960, Sept. 19** ***Perf. 13½***
**Size: 30½x21mm.**
**376** CD3 30m dk bl & Prus bl *.90* .90
**377** CD3 40m dk brn & plum *.80* *.90*

A 30m gray similar to No. 376 was printed with simulated perforations in a non-valid souvenir sheet privately released in London for STAMPEX 1961.

Uno Cygnaeus — A135

**1960, Oct. 13** ***Perf. 11½***
**378** A135 30m dull violet .80 .80

150th anniv. of the birth of Pastor Uno Cygnaeus, founder of elementary schools.

"Pommern" and Arms of Mariehamn A136

**1961, Feb. 21** ***Perf. 11½***
**379** A136 30m grnsh blue 2.75 2.00

Centenary of the founding of Mariehamn.

Lake and Rowboat A137

Turku Castle — A138

**1961** **Engr.** **Unwmk.**

| | | | |
|---|---|---|---|
| **380** | A137 5m green | .40 | .30 |
| **381** | A138 125m slate green | 20.00 | .35 |

See Nos. 399, 411.

Postal Savings Bank Emblem — A139

**1961, May 24**

| | | | |
|---|---|---|---|
| **382** | A139 30m Prus green | .75 | .45 |

75th anniv. of Finland's Postal Savings Bank.

Symbol of Standardization — A140

**1961, June 5** **Litho.** ***Perf. 14x13½***

| | | | |
|---|---|---|---|
| **383** | A140 30m dk sl grn & org | .75 | .45 |

Meeting of the Intl. Organization for Standardization (ISO), Helsinki, June 5.

Juhani Aho — A141

***Perf. 11½***

**1961, Sept. 11** **Unwmk.** **Engr.**

| | | | |
|---|---|---|---|
| **384** | A141 30m red brown | .75 | .65 |

Juhani Aho (1861-1921), writer.

Various Buildings — A142

**1961, Oct. 16** ***Perf. 11½***

| | | | |
|---|---|---|---|
| **385** | A142 30m slate | .75 | .65 |

150 years of the Central Board of Buildings.

Arvid Jarnefelt A143

**1961, Nov. 16**

| | | | |
|---|---|---|---|
| **386** | A143 30m deep claret | .75 | .65 |

Cent. of the birth of Arvid Jarnefelt, writer.

Bank of Finland — A144

**1961, Dec. 12** **Engr.** ***Perf. 11½***

| | | | |
|---|---|---|---|
| **387** | A144 30m brown violet | .75 | .65 |

150th anniversary of Bank of Finland.

First Finnish Locomotive A145

30m, Steam locomotive & timber car. 40m, Diesel locomotive & passenger train.

**1962, Jan. 31** **Unwmk.** ***Perf. 11½***

| | | | |
|---|---|---|---|
| **388** | A145 10m gray green | 1.75 | .60 |
| **389** | A145 30m violet blue | 2.50 | .60 |
| **390** | A145 40m dull red brown | 6.00 | .60 |
| | *Nos. 388-390 (3)* | 10.25 | 1.80 |

Centenary of the Finnish State Railways.

Mora Stone — A146

**1962, Feb. 15**

| | | | |
|---|---|---|---|
| **391** | A146 30m gray brown | .75 | .70 |

Issued to commemorate 600 years of political rights of the Finnish people.

Senate Place, Helsinki A147

**1962, Apr. 8** **Unwmk.** ***Perf. 11½***

| | | | |
|---|---|---|---|
| **392** | A147 30m violet brown | .75 | .70 |

Sesquicentennial of the proclamation of Helsinki as capital of Finland.

Customs Emblem A148

**1962, Apr. 11**

| | | | |
|---|---|---|---|
| **393** | A148 30m red | .75 | .70 |

Finnish Board of Customs, sesquicentennial.

Staff of Mercury — A149

**1962, May 21** **Engr.**

| | | | |
|---|---|---|---|
| **394** | A149 30m bluish green | .65 | .60 |

Cent. of the 1st commercial bank in Finland.

Santeri Alkio — A150

**1962, June 17** **Unwmk.** ***Perf. 11½***

| | | | |
|---|---|---|---|
| **395** | A150 30m brown carmine | 1.20 | .80 |

Cent. of the birth of Santeri Alkio, writer and pioneer of the young people's societies in Finland.

Finnish Labor Emblem and Conveyor Belt — A151

**1962, Oct. 19**

| | | | |
|---|---|---|---|
| **396** | A151 30m chocolate | .75 | .40 |

National production progress.

Survey Plane and Compass — A152

**1962, Nov. 14**

| | | | |
|---|---|---|---|
| **397** | A152 30m yellow green | .95 | .75 |

Finnish Land Survey Board, 150th anniv.

**Types of 1954-61 and**

House of Parliament — A152a

Church at Lammi — A152b

Fortress of Olavinlinna — A152c

Log Floating A153

Parainen Bridge — A154

Farm on Lake Shore — A155

Aerial View of Punkaharju — A155a

A155b

Ristikallio in Kuusamo A156

**1963-67** **Engr.** ***Perf. 11½***

| | | | | | |
|---|---|---|---|---|---|
| **398** | A94 | 5p | violet blue | .50 | .25 |
| *a.* | | | Booklet pane of 2 (vert. pair) | 22.50 | 20.00 |
| *b.* | | | Bklt. pane of 2 (horiz. pair) | 12.00 | 10.00 |
| **399** | A137 | 5p | green | .50 | .25 |
| **400** | A94 | 10p | blue green | 2.00 | .25 |
| *a.* | | | Booklet pane of 2 (vert. pair) | 22.50 | 20.00 |
| **401** | A94 | 15p | yellow org | 4.25 | .25 |
| **402** | A94 | 20p | rose red | 3.00 | .25 |
| *a.* | | | Booklet pane of 2 (vert. pair) | 24.00 | |
| | | | Complete booklet, #398a, 400a, 402a | 85.00 | |
| *b.* | | | Bklt. pane, 2 #400, 1 #402 + label; horiz. strip | 45.00 | 35.00 |
| | | | Complete booklet, #398b, 402b | 100.00 | |
| *c.* | | | Bklt. pane, 2 #398, 2 #400, 1 #402; horiz. strip | 3.50 | 3.50 |
| | | | Complete booklet, #402c | 5.00 | |
| **403** | A94 | 25p | rose lilac | 4.00 | .25 |
| **404** | A94 | 30p | lt ultra | 6.00 | .25 |
| **404A** | A94 | 30p | blue gray ('65) | 6.25 | .25 |
| **405** | A94 | 35p | blue | 1.50 | .25 |
| **405A** | A94 | 40p | ultra ('67) | 1.75 | .35 |
| **406** | A152a | 40p | dull purple | 3.50 | .35 |
| **407** | A152b | 50p | gray olive | 5.75 | .50 |
| **408** | A152c | 60p | pale purple | 8.25 | .50 |
| **408A** | A152c | 65p | pale pur ('67) | 1.20 | .25 |
| **409** | A124 | 75p | gray | 2.25 | .50 |
| **410** | A119 | 1m | bluish grn | 2.00 | .25 |
| **411** | A138 | 1.25m | slate grn | 2.00 | .50 |
| **412** | A153 | 1.50m | dk grnsh gray | 2.00 | .25 |
| **413** | A154 | 1.75m | blue | 2.00 | .50 |
| **414** | A155 | 2m | green ('64) | 12.00 | .25 |
| **414A** | A155a | 2.50m | ultra & yel grn ('67) | 11.00 | .65 |
| **414B** | A155b | 2.50m | ultra, dk grn & yel grn ('69) | 8.00 | .40 |
| **415** | A156 | 5m | dk slate grn ('64) | 21.00 | .50 |
| | | | *Nos. 398-415 (23)* | 110.70 | 8.00 |

Pennia denominations expressed: "0.05," "0.10," etc.

Four stamps of type A94 (5p, 10p, 20p, 25p) come in two types: I. Four vertical lines in "O" of SUOMI. II. Three lines in "O."

For similar designs see Nos. 457-470A.

Mother and Child — A157

**1963, Mar. 21** **Unwmk.** ***Perf. 11½***

| | | | |
|---|---|---|---|
| **416** | A157 40p red brown | .55 | .40 |

FAO "Freedom from Hunger" campaign.

"Christ Today" — A158

Design: 10p, Crown of thorns and medieval cross of consecration.

**1963, July 30 Engr. *Perf. 11½***
**417** A158 10p maroon .50 .45
**418** A158 30p dark green .50 .45

4th assembly of the Lutheran World Federation, Helsinki, July 30-Aug. 8.

**Europa Issue, 1963**
Common Design Type

**1963, Sept. 16 Size: 30x20mm**
**419** CD6 40p red lilac *1.25 .55*

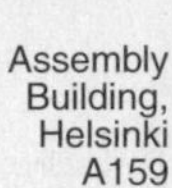

Assembly Building, Helsinki A159

**1963, Sept. 18**
**420** A159 30p violet blue .70 .40

Representative Assembly of Finland, cent.

Convair Metropolitan A160

Design: 40p, Caravelle jetliner.

**1963, Nov. 1**
**421** A160 35p slate green 1.00 .60
**422** A160 40p brt ultra 1.10 .50

40th anniversary of Finnish air traffic.

M. A. Castrén — A161

**1963, Dec. 2 Unwmk.**
**423** A161 35p violet blue .70 .45

Matthias Alexander Castrén (1813-52), ethnologist and philologist.

Stone Elk's Head, 2000 B.C. — A162

**1964, Feb. 5 Litho. *Perf. 14***
**424** A162 35p ocher & slate grn .70 .45

Cent. of the Finnish Artists' Association. The soapstone sculpture was found at Huittinen.

Emil Nestor Setälä — A163

**1964, Feb. 27 Engr. *Perf. 11½***
**425** A163 35p dk red brown .80 .50

Emil Nestor Setälä (1864-1946), philologist, minister of education and foreign affairs and chancellor of Abo University.

Staff of Aesculapius A164

**1964, June 13 Unwmk. *Perf. 11½***
**426** A164 40p slate green 1.10 .45

18th General Assembly of the World Medical Association, Helsinki, June 13-19, 1964.

Ice Hockey — A165

**1965, Jan. 4 Engr.**
**427** A165 35p dark blue 1.10 .60

World Ice Hockey Championships, Finland, March 3-14, 1965.

Design from Centenary Medal — A166

**1965, Feb. 6 Unwmk. *Perf. 11½***
**428** A166 35p olive gray .70 .40

Centenary of communal self-government in Finland.

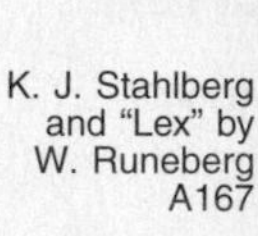

K. J. Stahlberg and "Lex" by W. Runeberg A167

**1965, Mar. 22 Engr.**
**429** A167 35p brown .70 .40

Kaarlo Juho Stahlberg (1865-1952), 1st Pres. of Finland.

International Cooperation Year Emblem A168

**1965, Apr. 2 Litho. *Perf. 14***
**430** A168 40p bis, dull red, blk & grn .70 .40

UN International Cooperation Year.

"Fratricide" by Gallen-Kallela A169

35p, Girl's Head by Akseli Gallen-Kallela.

**1965, Apr. 26 *Perf. 13½x14***
**431** A169 25p multicolored 1.40 .65
**432** A169 35p multicolored 1.40 .65

Centenary of the birth of the painter Aksell Gallen-Kallela.

Sibelius, Piano and Score — A170

Design: 35p, Musical score and bird.

**1965, May 15 Engr. *Perf. 11½***
**433** A170 25p violet 1.40 .80
**434** A170 35p dull green 1.40 .40

Jean Sibelius (1865-1957), composer.

Antenna for Satellite Telecommunication — A171

**1965, May 17**
**435** A171 35p blue .70 .50

Cent. of the ITU.

"Winter Day" by Pekka Halonen — A172

***Perf. 14x13½***

**1965, Sept. 23 Litho. Unwmk.**
**436** A172 35p gold & multi .70 .40

Centenary of the birth of the painter Pekka Halonen.

**Europa Issue, 1965**
Common Design Type
**Engraved and Lithographed**

**1965, Sept. 27 *Perf. 13½x14***
**437** CD8 40p bister, red brn, dk bl & grn *1.25 .55*

"Growth" — A173

**1966, May 11 Litho. *Perf. 14***
**438** A173 35p vio blue & blue .70 .40

Centenary of the promulgation of the Elementary School Decree.

Old Post Office — A174

**1966, June 11 Litho. *Perf. 14***
**439** A174 35p ocher, yel, dk bl & blk 4.50 *7.00*

Cent. of the 1st postage stamps in Finnish currency, and in connection with the NORDIA Stamp Exhibition, Helsinki, June 11-15. The stamp was sold only to buyers of a 1.25m exhibition entrance ticket.

UNESCO Emblem and World Map — A175

**Lithographed and Engraved**

**1966, Oct. 9 *Perf. 14***
**440** A175 40p grn, yel, blk & brn org .65 .30

20th anniv. of UNESCO.

Finnish Police Emblem — A176

**1966, Oct. 15**
**441** A176 35p dp ultra, blk & sil .65 .30

Issued to honor the Finnish police.

Insurance Sesquicentennial Medal — A177

**1966, Oct. 28 Engr. & Photo.**
**442** A177 35p maroon, olive & blk .65 .30

150th anniv. of the Finnish insurance system.

UNICEF Emblem A178

**1966, Nov. 14**
**443** A178 15p lt ultra, pur & grn .30 .30

Activities of UNICEF.

"FINEFTA," Finnish Flag and Circle — A179

**1967, Feb. 15 Engr. *Perf. 14***
**444** A179 40p ultra .65 .30

European Free Trade Association, EFTA. See note after Denmark No. 431.

Windmill and Arms of Uusikaupunki A180

**Lithographed and Engraved**

**1967, Apr. 19 *Perf. 14***
**445** A180 40p multicolored .65 .30

350th anniv. of Uusikaupunki (Nystad).

Mannerheim Monument by Aimo Tukiainen — A181

**1967, June 4 *Perf. 14***
**446** A181 40p violet & multi .65 .30

Cent. of the birth of Field Marshal Carl Gustav Emil Mannerheim.

Double Mortise Corner — A182

**1967, June 16 Litho. & Photo.**
**447** A182 40p multicolored .65 .30

Issued to honor Finnish settlers in Sweden.

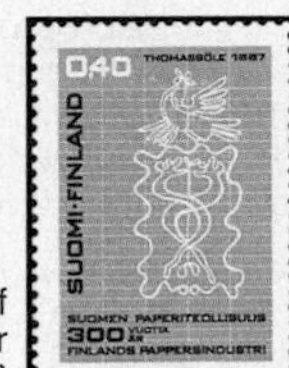

Watermark of Thomasböle Paper Mill — A183

**1967, Sept. 6 *Perf. 14***
**448** A183 40p olive & black .65 .30

300th anniv. of the Finnish paper industry.

Martin Luther, by Lucas Cranach A184

**Photogravure and Engraved**
**1967, Nov. 4 *Perf. 14***
**449** A184 40p bister & brown .65 .30

450th anniversary of the Reformation.

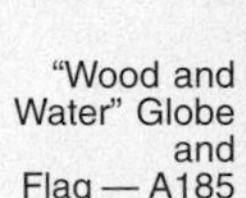

"Wood and Water" Globe and Flag — A185

Designs (Globe, Flag and): 25p, Flying swan. 40p, Ear of wheat.

**1967, Dec. 5 *Perf. 11½***
**450** A185 20p green & blue .65 .30
**451** A185 25p ultra & blue .65 .30
**452** A185 40p magenta & bl .65 .30
*Nos. 450-452 (3)* 1.95 .90

50th anniv. of Finland's independence.

Zachris Topelius and Blue Bird — A186

**1968, Jan. 14 Litho. *Perf. 14***
**453** A186 25p blue & multi 1.10 .50

Topelius (1818-98), writer and educator.

Skiers and Ski Lift — A187

**1968, Feb. 19 Photo. *Perf. 14***
**454** A187 25p multicolored .85 .70

Winter Tourism in Finland.

Paper Making, by Hannes Autere — A188

**1968, Mar. 12 Litho. Wmk. 363**
**455** A188 45p dk red, brn & org .70 .45

Finnish paper industry and 150th anniv. of the oldest Finnish paper mill, Tervakoski, whose own watermark was used for this stamp.

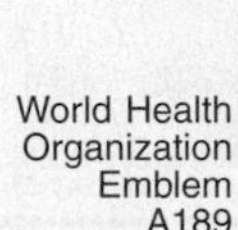

World Health Organization Emblem A189

**Lithographed and Photogravure**
**1968, Apr. 6 Unwmk. *Perf. 14***
**456** A189 40p red org, dk blue & gold .65 .30

To honor World Health Organization.

**Lion Type of 1954-58 and**

Market Place and Mermaid Fountain, Helsinki A190

Keuru Wooden Church, 1758 — A191

Häme Bridge, Tampere A192

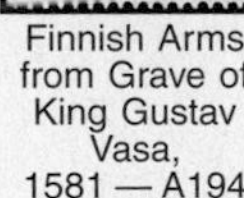

Finnish Arms from Grave of King Gustav Vasa, 1581 — A194

A194a

25p, Post bus. 30p, Aquarium-Planetarium, Tampere. No. 463, P.O., Tampere. No. 465, National Museum, Helsinki, vert. No. 467A, like 70p. 1.30m, Helsinki railroad station.

**Engr. (type A94, except #459A); Litho. (#459A, 465 & type A190); Engr. & Litho. (others)**
***Perf. 11½; 12½ (#466, 467A); 13 (#465); 13½ (#470); 14 (#463, 470A)***
**1968-78**

| | | | | | |
|---|---|---|---|---|---|
| **457** | A94 | 1p | lt red brn | .40 | *.50* |
| **458** | A94 | 2p | gray green | .40 | *.65* |
| **459** | A94 | 4p | gray | .50 | *.65* |
| **459A** | A94 | 5p | violet blue | 2.00 | *3.00* |
| **460** | A192 | 25p | multi ('71) | .50 | .25 |
| **461** | A191 | 30p | multi ('71) | 1.25 | .25 |
| **461A** | A94 | 35p | dull org ('74) | .55 | *.40* |
| *b.* | | | Bklt. pane of 4, #459A, 461A, 400, 464A + label | 2.50 | 2.50 |
| | | | Complete booklet, #461b | 3.50 | |
| **462** | A94 | 40p | orange ('73) | .90 | .65 |
| *a.* | | | Bklt. pane of 3, #462, 2 #404A + 2 labels | 6.00 | *8.00* |
| | | | Complete booklet, #462a | 8.00 | |
| **463** | A192 | 40p | multi ('73) | 1.00 | .25 |
| **464** | A94 | 50p | lt ultra ('70) | 3.00 | .25 |
| *c.* | | | Bklt. pane of 5, #401, 403, 464, 2 #459A + 5 labels | 13.00 | *14.50* |
| | | | Complete booklet, #464c | 14.00 | |
| **464A** | A94 | 50p | rose lake ('74) | .80 | .25 |
| *d.* | | | Bklt. pane of 4, #400, 464A, 2 #402 + label | 1.75 | 1.75 |
| | | | Complete booklet, #464Ad | 2.00 | |
| **464B** | A94 | 60p | blue ('73) | 1.10 | .25 |
| **465** | A191 | 60p | multi ('73) | 1.25 | .25 |
| **466** | A190 | 70p | multi ('73) | .95 | .25 |
| **467** | A191 | 80p | multi ('70) | 5.25 | .25 |
| **467A** | A190 | 80p | multi ('76) | .50 | .50 |
| **468** | A192 | 90p | multi | 2.00 | .50 |
| **469** | A191 | 1.30m | multi ('71) | 1.25 | .50 |
| **470** | A194 | 10m | multi ('74) | 5.25 | .50 |
| **470A** | A194a | 20m | multi ('78) | 11.00 | .50 |
| | *Nos. 457-470A (20)* | | | 39.85 | 10.60 |

Issued: 5p, 6/72.

Infantry Monument, Vaasa — A195

Designs: 25p, War Memorial (cross), Hietaniemi Cemetery. 40p, Soldier, 1968.

**1968, June 4 Photo. *Perf. 14***
**471** A195 20p lt violet & multi 1.10 .35
**472** A195 25p lt blue & multi 1.10 .35
**473** A195 40p orange & multi 1.10 .35
*Nos. 471-473 (3)* 3.30 1.05

To honor Finnish national defense.

Camping Ground A196

**1968, June 10 Litho.**
**474** A196 25p multicolored .60 .40

Issued to publicize Finland for summer vacations.

Paper, Pulp and Pine — A197

**Lithographed and Embossed**
**1968, July 2 Unwmk. *Perf. 14***
**475** A197 40p multicolored .70 .40

Finnish wood industry.

Mustola Lock, Saima Canal — A198

**1968, Aug. 5 Litho. *Perf. 14***
**476** A198 40p multicolored .70 .40

Opening of the Saima Canal.

Oskar Merikanto and Pipe Organ — A199

**1968, Aug. 5 Unwmk.**
**477** A199 40p vio, silver & lt brn 1.10 .40

Centenary of the birth of Oskar Merikanto, composer.

Ships in Harbor and Emblem of Central Chamber of Commerce A200

**1968, Sept. 13 Litho. *Perf. 14***
**478** A200 40p lt bl, brt bl & blk .70 .40

Publicizing economic development and for the 50th anniv. of the Central Chamber of Commerce of Finland.

Welder — A201

**1968, Oct. 11 Litho. *Perf. 14***
**479** A201 40p blue & multi .70 .40

Finnish metal industry.

Lyre, Students' Emblem — A202

**Lithographed and Engraved**
**1968, Nov. 24 *Perf. 14***
**480** A202 40p ultra, vio bl & gold .70 .40

Issued to publicize the work of the student unions in Finnish social life.

**Nordic Cooperation Issue**

Five Ancient Ships — A203

**1969, Feb. 28 Engr. *Perf. 11½***
**481** A203 40p lt ultra 2.00 .40

50th anniv. of the Nordic Society and centenary of postal cooperation among the northern countries. The design is taken from a coin found at the site of Birka, an ancient Swedish town. See also Denmark Nos. 454-455, Iceland Nos. 404-405, Norway Nos. 523-524 and Sweden Nos. 808-810.

Town Hall and Arms of Kemi — A203a

**1969, Mar. 5 Photo. *Perf. 14***
**482** A203a 40p multicolored .70 .40

Centenary of the town of Kemi.

### Europa Issue, 1969
Common Design Type

**1969, Apr. 28 Photo. *Perf. 14***
**Size: 30x20mm**

**483** CD12 40p dl rose, vio bl & dk bl *3.50* .75

ILO Emblem A204

### Lithographed and Engraved

**1969, June 2 *Perf. 11½***

**484** A204 40p dp rose & vio blue .70 .40

50th anniv. of the ILO.

Armas Järnefelt — A205

**1969, Aug. 14 Photo. *Perf. 14***

**485** A205 40p multicolored 1.40 .40

Järnefelt (1869-1958), composer and conductor. Portrait on stamp by Vilho Sjöström.

Emblems and Flag — A206

**1969, Sept. 19 Photo. *Perf. 14***

**486** A206 40p lt bl, blk, grn & lil .70 .40

Publicizinge the importance of National and International Fairs in Finnish economy.

Johannes Linnankoski — A207

**1969, Oct. 18 Litho.**

**487** A207 40p dk brn red & multi .70 .40

Linnankoski (1869-1913), writer.

Educational Symbols A208

### Lithographed and Engraved

**1969, Nov. 24 *Perf. 11½***

**488** A208 40p gray, vio & grn .70 .40

Centenary of the Central School Board.

DC-8-62 CF Plane and Helsinki Airport — A209

**1969, Dec. 22 Photo. *Perf. 14***

**489** A209 25p sky blue & multi 1.10 .75

Golden Eagle — A210

**1970, Feb. 10 Litho. *Perf. 14***

**490** A210 30p multicolored 3.50 1.10

Year of Nature Conservation, 1970.

Swatches in Shape of Factories A211

**1970, Mar. 9 Litho. *Perf. 14***

**491** A211 50p multicolored .85 .40

Finnish textile industry.

Molecule Diagram and Factories A212

**1970, Mar. 26 Photo. *Perf. 14***

**492** A212 50p multicolored .85 .40

Finnish chemical industry.

UNESCO Emblem and Lenin — A213

Atom Diagram and Laurel — A214

UN Emblem and Globe — A215

**1970 Litho. and Engr.**

**493** A213 30p gold & multi .70 .40
**494** A214 30p red & multi .70 .40

### Photogravure and Gold Embossed

**495** A215 50p bl, vio bl & gold .70 .40
*Nos. 493-495 (3)* 2.10 1.20

25th anniv. of the UN. No. 493 also publicizes the UNESCO-sponsored Lenin Symposium, Tampere, Apr. 6-10. No. 494 also publicizes the Nuclear Data Conf. of the Atomic Energy Commission, Otaniemi (Helsinki), June 15-19.

Issued: No. 493, 4/6; No. 494, 6/15; No. 495, 10/24.

Handicapped Volleyball Player — A216

**1970, June 27 Litho. *Perf. 14***

**496** A216 50p orange, red & blk 1.00 .40

Issued to publicize the position of handicapped civilians and war veterans in society and their potential contributions to it.

Meeting of Auroraseura Society — A217

**1970, Aug. 15 Photo. *Perf. 14***

**497** A217 50p multicolored .70 .40

200th anniv. of the Auroraseura Soc., dedicated to the study of Finnish history, geography, economy and language. The design of the stamp is after a painting by Eero Jarnefelt.

Uusikaarlepyy Arms, Church and 17th Cent. Building A218

Design: No. 499, Arms of Kokkola, harbor, Sports Palace and 17th century building.

**1970 *Perf. 14***

**498** A218 50p multicolored .70 .40
**499** A218 50p multicolored .70 .40

Towns of Uusikaarlepyy and Kokkola, 350th anniv.

Issued: No. 498, Aug. 21; No. 499, Sept. 17.

Urho Kekkonen, Medal by Aimo Tukiainen — A219

**1970, Sept. 3 Litho. & Engr.**

**500** A219 50p ultra, sil & blk .70 .40

70th birthday of Pres. Urho Kekkonen.

Globe, Maps of US, Finland, USSR — A220

### Lithographed and Gold Embossed

**1970, Nov. 2**

**501** A220 50p blk, bl, pink & gold .70 .40

Strategic Arms Limitation Talks (SALT) between the US & USSR, Helsinki, 11/2-12/18.

Pres. Paasikivi by Essi Renavall — A221

**1970, Nov. 27 Photo. *Perf. 14***

**502** A221 50p gold, brt bl & slate .70 .40

Centenary of the birth of Juho Kusti Paasikivi (1870-1956), President of Finland.

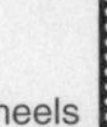

Cogwheels A222

**1971, Jan. 28 Litho. *Perf. 14***

**503** A222 50p multicolored .70 .40

Finnish industry.

### Europa Issue, 1971
Common Design Type

**1971, May 3 Litho. *Perf. 14***
**Size: 30x20mm**

**504** CD14 50p dp rose, yel & blk *5.00* .75

Tornio Church — A223

**1971, May 12 Litho. *Perf. 14***

**505** A223 50p multicolored 1.00 .40

350th anniversary of the town of Tornio.

Front Page, January 15, 1771 — A224

**1971, June 1 Litho. *Perf. 14***

**506** A224 50p multicolored .70 .40

Bicentenary of the Finnish press.

Athletes in Helsinki Stadium A225

50p, Running & javelin in Helsinki Stadium.

**1971, July 5 Litho. *Perf. 14***

**507** A225 30p multicolored 1.50 .85
**508** A225 50p multicolored 2.50 .85

European Athletic Championships.

Sailboats A226

**1971, July 14**

**509** A226 50p multicolored 1.25 .60

International Lightning Class Championships, Helsinki, July 14-Aug. 1.

Silver Tea Pot, Guild's Emblem, Tools — A227

**1971, Aug. 6**

**510** A227 50p lilac & multi .70 .40

600th anniv. of Finnish goldsmiths' art.

"Plastic Buttons and Houses" A228

**Photogravure and Embossed**

**1971, Oct. 20** *Perf. 14*
**511** A228 50p multicolored .70 .40

Finnish plastics industry.

**Europa Issue 1972**
Common Design Type

**1972, May 2 Litho. *Perf. 14***
**Size: 20x30mm**
**512** CD15 30p dk red & multi *2.50 .70*
**513** CD15 50p lt brn & multi *4.50 .70*

Finnish National Theater A229

**1972, May 22. Litho. *Perf. 14***
**514** A229 50p lt violet & multi .70 .40

Centenary of the Finnish National Theater, founded by Kaarlo and Emilie Bergbom.

Globe, US and USSR Flags — A230

**1972, June 2**
**515** A230 50p multicolored 1.25 .40

Strategic Arms Limitation Talks (SALT), final meeting, Helsinki, Mar. 28-May 26; treaty signed, Moscow, May 26.

Map and Arms of Aland — A231

**1972, June 9**
**516** A231 50p multicolored 3.25 .85

1st Provincial Meeting of Aland, 50th anniv.

Training Ship Suomen Joutsen — A232

**1972, June 19**
**517** A232 50p orange & multi 1.25 .40

Tall Ships' Race 1972, Helsinki, Aug. 20.

Costume from Perni, 12th Cent. — A233

No. 519, Couple, Tenhola, 18th cent. No. 520, Girl, Nastola, 19th cent. No. 521, Man, Voyni, 19th cent. No. 522, Lapps, Inari, 19th cent.

**1972, Nov. 19 Litho. *Perf. 13***
**518** A233 50p shown 2.50 .65
**519** A233 50p multicolored 2.50 .65
**520** A233 50p multicolored 2.50 .65
**521** A233 50p multicolored 2.50 .65
**522** A233 50p multicolored 2.50 .65
*a.* Strip of 5, #518-522 12.50 14.50
Complete booklet, 2 each #518-522 30.00

Regional costumes.
See Nos. 533-537.

Circle Surrounding Map of Europe — A234

**1972, Dec. 11** *Perf. 14x13½*
**523** A234 50p multicolored 2.25 .55

Preparatory Conference on European Security and Cooperation.

Book, Finnish and Soviet Colors — A235

**Litho.; Gold Embossed**

**1973, Apr. 6** *Perf. 14*
**524** A235 60p gold & multi .55 .40

Soviet-Finnish Treaty of Friendship, 25th anniv.

Kyösti Kallio (1873-1940), Pres. of Finland — A236

**1973, Apr. 10 Litho. *Perf. 13***
**525** A236 60p multicolored .55 .40

**Europa Issue 1973**
Common Design Type

**1973, Apr. 30 Photo. *Perf. 14***
**Size: 31x21mm**
**526** CD16 60p bl, brt bl & emer 1.25 .55

**Nordic Cooperation Issue**

Nordic House, Reykjavik A236a

**1973, June 26 Engr. *Perf. 12½***
**527** A236a 60p multicolored 1.00 .40
**528** A236a 70p multicolored 1.00 .40

A century of postal cooperation among Denmark, Finland, Iceland, Norway and Sweden, and in connection with the Nordic Postal Conference, Reykjavik.

Map of Europe, "EUROPA" as a Maze — A237

**Litho. & Embossed**

**1973, July 3** *Perf. 13*
**529** A237 70p multicolored .75 .40

Conference for European Security and Cooperation, Helsinki, July 1973.

Paddling A238

**1973, July 18 Litho. *Perf. 14***
**530** A238 60p multicolored .75 .40

Canoeing World Championships, Tampere, July 26-29.

Radiosonde, WMO Emblem — A239

**1973, Aug. 6 Litho. *Perf. 14***
**531** A239 60p multicolored .55 .40

Cent. of intl. meteorological cooperation.

Eliel Saarinen and Design for Parliament, Helsinki A240

**1973, Aug. 20** *Perf. 12½x13*
**532** A240 60p multicolored .55 .40

Eliel Saarinen (1873-1950), architect.

**Costume Type of 1972**

**1973, Oct. 10 Litho. *Perf. 13***
**533** A233 60p Woman, Kaukola 2.75 .40
**534** A233 60p Woman, Jaaski 2.75 .40
**535** A233 60p Married couple, Koivisto 2.75 .40
**536** A233 60p Mother and son, Sakyla 2.75 .40
**537** A233 60p Girl, Hainavesi 2.75 .40
*a.* Strip of 5, #533-537 16.00 19.00

Regional costumes.

DC10-30 Jet — A241

**1973, Nov. 1 Litho. *Perf. 14***
**538** A241 60p multicolored .80 .40

50th anniv. of regular air service, Finnair.

Santa Claus in Reindeer Sleigh — A242

**1973, Nov. 15 Litho. *Perf. 14***
**539** A242 30p multicolored .95 .40

Christmas 1973.

"The Barber of Seville" A243

**1973, Nov. 21**
**540** A243 60p multicolored .55 .40

Centenary of opera in Finland.

Production of Porcelain Jug — A244

**1973, Nov. 23**
**541** A244 60p blue & multi .55 .40

Finnish porcelain.

Nurmi, by Waino Aaltonen — A245

**1973, Dec. 11**
**542** A245 60p multicolored .85 .40

Paavo Nurmi (1897-1973), runner, Olympic winner, 1920-1924-1928.

Arms, Map and Harbor of Hanko — A246

**1974, Jan. 10 Litho. *Perf. 14***
**543** A246 60p blue & multi .75 .40

Centenary of the town of Hanko.

Ice Hockey A247

**1974, Mar. 5 Litho. *Perf. 14***
**544** A247 60p multicolored .90 .40

European and World Ice Hockey Championships, held in Finland.

Seagulls (7 Baltic States) A248

**1974, Mar. 18** *Perf. 12½*
**545** A248 60p multicolored 1.00 .40

Protection of marine environment of the Baltic Sea.

Goddess of Freedom, by Waino Aaltonen — A249

**1974, Apr. 29 Litho.** *Perf. 13x12½*
**546** A249 70p multicolored *5.00 .50*

Europa.

Ilmari Kianto and Old Pine — A250

**1974, May 7** *Perf. 13*
**547** A250 60p multicolored .55 .40

Ilmari Kianto (1874-1970), writer.

Society Emblem, Symbol A251

**Lithographed and Embossed**

**1974, June 12** *Perf. 13½x14*
**548** A251 60p gold & multi .55 .40

Centenary of Adult Education.

Grid — A252

**1974, June 14** **Litho.** *Perf. 14x13½*
**549** A252 60p multicolored .55 .40

Rationalization Year in Finland, dedicated to economic and business improvements.

UPU Emblem — A253

**1974, Oct. 10** **Litho.** *Perf. 13½x14*
**550** A253 60p multicolored .55 .40
**551** A253 70p multicolored .55 .40

Centenary of Universal Postal Union.

Elves Distributing Gifts — A254

**1974, Nov. 16** **Litho.** *Perf. 14x13½*
**552** A254 35p multicolored 1.75 .35

Christmas 1974.

Concrete Bridge and Granite Bridge, Aunessilta — A255

**Litho. & Engr.**

**1974, Dec. 17** *Perf. 14*
**553** A255 60p multicolored 1.25 .70

Royal Finnish Directorate of Roads and Waterways, 175th anniversary.

Coat of Arms, 1581 — A256

Chimneyless Log Sauna — A256a

Cheese Frames A257

Carved Wooden Distaffs A258

Kirvu Weather Vane A258a

1.50m, Wood-carved high drinking bowl, 1542.

***Perf. 11½; 14 (2m, 5m)***

**1975-90** **Engr.**

| | | | | | |
|---|---|---|---|---|---|
| **555** | A256 | 10p | red lilac ('78) | .25 | *.50* |
| *a.* | Bklt. pane of 4 (#555, 2 #556, #559) + label | | | 2.25 | 2.25 |
| | Complete booklet, #555a | | | 2.50 | |
| *b.* | Bklt. pane of 5 (2 #555, #557, #563, #564) | | | 2.50 | 2.25 |
| | Complete booklet, #555b | | | 3.00 | |
| *c.* | As "a," no label | | | 2.50 | 2.50 |
| | Complete booklet, #555c | | | 3.00 | |
| *d.* | Perf. 13x12½ | | | .35 | .25 |
| **556** | A256 | 20p | olive ('77) | .40 | *.30* |
| *a.* | 20p yellow bister ('85) | | | 1.10 | 1.40 |
| *b.* | As "a," perf. 13x12½ | | | 1.25 | 1.25 |
| **557** | A256 | 30p | carmine ('77) | 2.25 | 1.50 |
| **557A** | A256 | 30p | car, litho. | 5.50 | 3.00 |
| **558** | A256 | 40p | orange | .40 | .30 |
| *a.* | Perf. 13x12½ | | | 1.75 | 1.50 |
| **559** | A256 | 50p | green ('76) | .50 | .30 |
| *a.* | Perf. 13x12½ | | | 2.00 | 1.25 |
| **560** | A256 | 60p | blue | .60 | .30 |
| *a.* | Perf. 13x12½ | | | 2.50 | 1.50 |
| **561** | A256 | 70p | sepia | .50 | .25 |
| **562** | A256 | 80p | dl red & bl grn ('76) | .50 | .50 |
| *a.* | Perf. 13x12½ | | | 4.25 | 4.00 |
| **563** | A256 | 90p | vio bl ('77) | .45 | .40 |
| **564** | A256 | 1.10m | yellow ('79) | .45 | .35 |
| **565** | A256 | 1.20m | dk blue ('79) | .70 | .60 |
| **566** | A258 | 1.50m | multi ('76) | 1.10 | .25 |

**Litho.**

| | | | | | |
|---|---|---|---|---|---|
| **567** | A256a | 2m | multi ('77) | 1.25 | .30 |

**Lithographed and Engraved**

| | | | | | |
|---|---|---|---|---|---|
| **568** | A257 | 2.50m | multi ('76) | 1.25 | .50 |
| *a.* | Perf. 14 | | | 2.25 | 1.00 |
| **569** | A258 | 4.50m | multi ('76) | 2.40 | .40 |
| *a.* | Perf. 14 | | | 3.25 | 2.50 |
| **570** | A258a | 5m | multi ('77) | 2.25 | .30 |
| | *Nos. 555-570 (17)* | | | 20.75 | 10.05 |

Some denominations of design A256 exist in up to three engraving types.

Nos. 560a and 562a was only issued within the booklet panes Nos. 713a and 715a.

Issued: No. 557A, 6/3/80; No. 560a, 7/25/88; No. 555d, 7/25/89; No. 562a, 3/1/90; No. 558a, 8/18/94; No. 568a, 12/28/88; No. 569a, 9/26/88; No. 556b, 4/3/98.

See Nos. 629, 631-633, 711-715, 861.

Finland No. 16 — A259

**Lithographed and Typographed**

**1975, Apr. 26** *Perf. 13*
**571** A259 70p multicolored 2.75 4.50

Nordia 75 Philatelic Exhibition, Helsinki, Apr. 26-May 1. Sold only at exhibition for 3m including entrance ticket.

Girl Combing Hair, by Magnus Enckell — A260

Europa: 90p, Washerwoman, by Tyko Sallinen (1879-1955).

**1975, Apr. 28** **Litho.** *Perf. 13x12½*
**572** A260 70p gray & multi *2.50 .40*
**573** A260 90p tan & multi *2.50 .40*

Balance of Justice, Sword of Legality — A261

**1975, May 7** *Perf. 14*
**574** A261 70p vio blue & multi .55 .40

Sesquicentennial of State Economy Comptroller's Office.

Rescue Boat and Sinking Ship — A262

**1975, June 2** **Litho.** *Perf. 14*
**575** A262 70p multicolored .85 .40

12th Intl. Salvage Conf., Finland, stressing importance of coordinating sea, air and communications resources in salvage operations.

Safe and Unsafe Levels of Drugs — A263

**1975, July 21** **Litho.** *Perf. 14*
**576** A263 70p multicolored .55 .40

Importance of pharmacological studies and for the 6th Intl. Pharmacology Cong., Helsinki.

Olavinlinna Castle A264

**1975, July 29** *Perf. 13*
**577** A264 70p multicolored .55 .40

500th anniversary of Olavinlinna Castle.

Swallows over Finlandia Hall — A265

**1975, July 30**
**578** A265 90p multicolored .70 .40

European Security and Cooperation Conference, Helsinki, July 30-Aug. 1. (The swallows of the design represent freedom, mobility and continuity.) See No. 709.

"Men and Women Working for Peace" — A266

**1975, Oct. 24** **Litho.** *Perf. 13x12½*
**579** A266 70p multicolored .55 .40

International Women's Year 1975.

"Continuity and Growth" — A267

**1975, Oct. 29** *Perf. 13*
**580** A267 70p brown & multi .55 .40

Industrial Art and for the centenary of the Finnish Society of Industrial Art.

Boys as Three Kings and Herod — A268

**1975, Nov. 8** *Perf. 14*
**581** A268 40p blue & multi 1.10 .35

Christmas 1975.

Top Border of State Debenture A269

**Lithographed and Engraved**

**1976, Jan. 9** *Perf. 11½*
**582** A269 80p multicolored .55 .40

Centenary of State Treasury.

Glider over Lake Region A270

**1976, Jan. 13** **Litho.** *Perf. 14*
**583** A270 80p multicolored .90 .40

15th World Glider Championships, Rayskala, June 13-27.

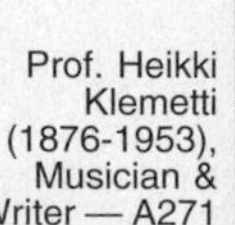

Prof. Heikki Klemetti (1876-1953), Musician & Writer — A271

**1976, Feb. 14** **Litho.** *Perf. 13*
**584** A271 80p green & multi .55 .40

Map with Areas of Different Dialects — A272

**1976, Mar. 10 Litho. *Perf. 13***
**585** A272 80p multicolored .55 .40

Finnish Language Society, centenary.

Aino Ackté, by Albert Edelfelt — A273

**1976, Apr. 23**
**586** A273 70p yellow & multi .70 .40

Aino Ackté (1876-1944), opera singer.

### Europa Issue

Knife from Voyri, Sheath and Belt — A274

**1976, May 3 Litho. *Perf. 13***
**587** A274 80p violet bl & multi *3.25 .50*

Radio and Television A275

**1976, Sept. 9 Litho. *Perf. 13***
**588** A275 80p multicolored .55 .40

Radio broadcasting in Finland, 50th anniv.

Christmas Morning Ride to Church A276

**1976, Oct. 23 Litho. *Perf. 14***
**589** A276 50p multicolored .90 .40

Christmas 1976.

Turku Chapter Seal (Virgin and Child) A277

**1976, Nov. 1 Litho. *Perf. 12½***
**590** A277 80p buff, brn & red .55 .40

Cathedral Chapter of Turku, 700th anniv.

Alvar Aalto, Finlandia Hall, Helsinki A278

**1976, Nov. 4**
**591** A278 80p multicolored .55 .40

Hugo Alvar Henrik Aalto (1898-1976), architect.

Ice Dancers — A280

**1977, Jan. 25 Litho. *Perf. 13***
**592** A280 90p multicolored .65 .40

European Figure Skating Championships, Finland, Jan. 25-29.

Five Water Lilies — A281

### Photogravure and Engraved

**1977, Feb. 2 *Perf. 12½***
**593** A281 90p brt green & multi 1.00 .40
**594** A281 1m ultra & multi 1.00 .40

Nordic countries cooperation for protection of the environment and 25th Session of Nordic Council, Helsinki, Feb. 19.

Icebreaker Rescuing Merchantman A282

**1977, Mar. 2 Litho. *Perf. 13***
**595** A282 90p multicolored 1.00 .40

Winter navigation between Finland and Sweden, centenary.

Nuclear Reactor A283

**1977, Mar. 3 *Perf. 12½x13***
**596** A283 90p multicolored .55 .40

Opening of nuclear power station on Hästholmen Island.

### Europa Issue

Autumn Landscape, Northern Finland — A284

**1977, May 2 Litho. *Perf. 12½x13***
**597** A284 90p multicolored *3.25 .45*

Tree, Birds and Nest — A285

**1977, May 4 *Perf. 13x12½***
**598** A285 90p multicolored .55 .40

75th anniversary of cooperative banks.

Orthodox Church, Valamo Cloister — A286

**1977, May 31 Litho. *Perf. 14***
**599** A286 90p multicolored .55 .40

Consecration festival of new Orthodox Church at Valamo Cloister, Heinävesi; 800th anniversary of introduction of orthodoxy in Karelia and of founding of Valamo Cloister.

Paavo Ruotsalainen (1777-1852), Lay Leader of Pietists in Finland — A287

**1977, July 8 Litho. *Perf. 13***
**600** A287 90p multicolored .55 .40

People Fleeing Fire and Water — A288

**1977, Sept. 14 Litho. *Perf. 14***
**601** A288 90p multicolored .55 .40

Civil defense for security.

Volleyball — A289

**1977, Sept. 15**
**602** A289 90p multicolored .70 .40

European Women's Volleyball Championships, Finland, Sept. 29-Oct. 2.

Children Bringing Water for Sauna — A290

**1977, Oct. 25**
**603** A290 50p multicolored 1.10 .40

Christmas 1977.

Finnish Flag — A291

**1977, Dec. 5 Litho. *Perf. 14***
**Size: 31x21mm**
**604** A291 80p multicolored .70 .40
**Size: 37x25mm**
***Perf. 13***
**605** A291 1m multicolored 1.00 .40

Finland's declaration of independence, 60th anniv.

Wall Telephone, 1880, New Telephone — A292

**1977, Dec. 9 *Perf. 14***
**606** A292 1m multicolored .60 .40

Centenary of first telephone in Finland.

Harbor, Sunila Factory, Kotka Arms — A293

**1978, Jan. 2 Litho. *Perf. 14***
**607** A293 1m multicolored .60 .40

Centenary of founding of Kotka.

Paimio Sanitarium by Alvar Aalto — A294

Europa: 1.20m, Hvittrask studio house, 1902, horiz.

**1978, May 2 Litho. *Perf. 13***
**608** A294 1m multicolored *7.50 1.00*
**609** A294 1.20m multicolored *9.50 11.50*

Rural Bus Service A295

**1978, June 8 Litho. *Perf. 14***
**610** A295 1m multicolored .60 .40

Eino Leino and Eagle — A296

**1978, July 6** **Litho.** ***Perf. 13***

**611** A296 1m multicolored .60 .40

Eino Leino (1878-1926), poet.

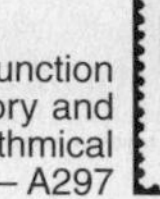

Function Theory and Rhythmical Lines — A297

**1978, Aug. 15** **Litho.** ***Perf. 14***

**612** A297 1m multicolored .60 .40

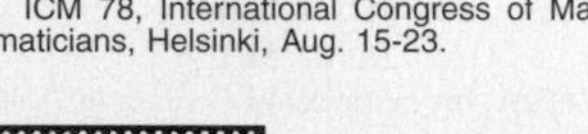

ICM 78, International Congress of Mathematicians, Helsinki, Aug. 15-23.

Child Feeding Birds — A298

**1978, Oct. 23** **Litho.** ***Perf. 14***

**613** A298 50p multicolored 1.00 .40

Christmas 1978.

A299

**1979, Jan. 2** **Litho.** ***Perf. 13***

**614** A299 1.10m multicolored .75 .40

International Year of the Child.

A300

**1979, Feb. 7** **Litho.** ***Perf. 14***

**615** A300 1.10m Runner .55 .40

8th Orienteering World Championships, Finland, Sept. 1-4.

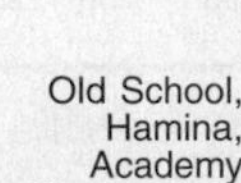

Old School, Hamina, Academy Flag — A301

**1979, Mar. 20** **Litho.** ***Perf. 14***

**616** A301 1.10m multicolored .55 .40

200th anniv. of Finnish Military Academy.

A302

Design: Turku Cathedral and Castle, Prinkkala house, Brahe statue.

**1979, Mar. 31**

**617** A302 1.10m multicolored .55 .40

A303

**1979, May 2** **Litho.** ***Perf. 14***

**618** A303 1.10m Streetcar, Helsinki .55 .30

Non-polluting urban transportation.

View of Tampere, 1779 — A304

**1979, May 2**

**619** A304 90p multicolored .55 .40

View of Tampere, 1979 — A305

**1979, Oct. 1** ***Perf. 13***

**620** A305 1.10m multicolored .55 .40

Bicentenary of founding of Tampere.

Optical Telegraph, 1796, Map of Islands A306

Europa: 1.10m, Letter of Queen Christina to Per Brahe, 1638, establishing postal service.

**1979, May 2** ***Perf. 13***

**621** A306 1.10m multi *3.00 .80*

**622** A306 1.30m multi, horiz. *4.50 1.40*

Shops and Merchants' Signs — A307

**1979, Sept. 26** ***Perf. 14***

**623** A307 1.10m multicolored .55 .40

Business and industry regulation centenary.

Old and New Cars, Street Crossing A308

**1979, Oct. 1**

**624** A308 1.10m multicolored .55 .40

Road safety.

Elves Feeding Horse — A309

**1979, Oct. 24**

**625** A309 60p multicolored .90 .40

Christmas 1979.

Korppi House, Lapinjarvi A310

Farm houses, First Row: Syrjala House, Tammela, 2 stamps in continuous design; Murtovaara House, Valtimo; Antila House, Lapua. Second row: Lofts, Pohjanmaa; Courtyard gate, Kanajarvi House, Kalvola; Main door, Havuselka House, Kauhajoki; Maki-Rasinpera House and dinner bell tower; Gable and eaves, Rasula Kuortane granary.

**1979, Oct. 27** **Litho.** ***Perf. 13***

**626** Booklet pane of 10 8.00 6.00
*a.-j.* A310 1.10m single stamp .60 .35
Complete booklet, #626 8.00

See design A349a.

**Type of 1975 and**

Kauhaneva Swamp A315

Hame Castle, Hameenlinna A316

Windmill, Harrstrom A318

Multiharju Forest, Seitseminen Natl. Park — A319

Shuttle, Raanu Designs A322

Kaspaikka Towel Design — A323

Bridal Rug, Teisko, 1815 — A324

Iron-forged Door, Hollola Church — A325

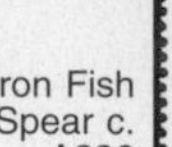

Iron Fish Spear c. 1100 — A326

Design: 1.80m, Eastern Gulf natl. park.

**Litho. & Engr., Litho., Engr.**

**1979-98** ***Perf. 14, 11½ (A256, A318)***

| | | | | | |
|---|---|---|---|---|---|
| **627** | A315 | 70p | multicolored | .40 | .25 |
| **628** | A316 | 90p | brown red | .30 | .30 |
| **629** | A256 | 1m | red brown | .40 | .30 |
| *a.* | | | Perf. 13x12½ ('98) | 1.25 | 1.25 |
| **630** | A318 | 1m | bl & red brn | .40 | .30 |
| **631** | A256 | 1.30m | dk green | .60 | .60 |
| **631A** | A256 | 1.30m | dk green, litho. | 1.00 | 1.10 |
| *b.* | | | Booklet pane, #555-556, 557A, 560, 631A | 3.00 | 3.00 |
| | | | Complete booklet, #631Ab | 3.25 | |
| **632** | A256 | 1.40m | purple | .65 | .60 |
| **633** | A256 | 1.50m | grnsh blue | .80 | .80 |
| **634** | A319 | 1.60m | multicolored | 1.20 | .40 |
| **635** | A315 | 1.80m | multicolored | 2.00 | .50 |
| **636** | A322 | 3m | multicolored | 1.40 | .40 |
| **637** | A323 | 6m | multicolored | 2.50 | .30 |
| **638** | A324 | 7m | multicolored | 3.00 | .60 |
| **639** | A325 | 8m | multicolored | 3.50 | .40 |
| **640** | A326 | 9m | blk & dk bl | 4.00 | .90 |
| | | | *Nos. 627-640 (15)* | 22.15 | 7.75 |

**Coil Stamps**

***Perf. 11½ Vert.***

**641** A316 90p brown red .85 1.00

***Perf. 12½ Horiz.***

**642** A318 1m blue & red brn 1.10 .50

Issued: 3m, 10/27/79; 6m, 4/9/80; No. 629, 1/2/81; 70p, 1/12/81; 90p, 9/1/82; 1.60m, 2/8/82; 7m, 2/15/82; No. 631, 1/3/83; Nos. 630, 642, 1/12/83; 1.80m, 8m, 2/10/83; 1.40m, 9m, 1/2/84; 1.50m, 1/2/85; No. 631A, 11/1/85.

Maria Jotuni (1880-1943), Writer — A327

**1980, Apr. 9** **Litho.**

**643** A327 1.10m multicolored .55 .40

Frans Eemil Sillanpaa (1888-1964), Writer — A328

Europa: 1.30m, Artturi Ilmari Virtanen (1895-1973), chemist, vert.

**1980, Apr. 28** ***Perf. 13***

**644** A328 1.10m multicolored *2.25 .40*

**645** A328 1.30m multicolored *2.50 1.25*

Pres. Urho Kekkonen, 80th Birthday — A329

**1980, Sept. 3** **Litho.** ***Perf. 13***

**646** A329 1.10m multicolored .55 .40

**Nordic Cooperation Issue**

Back-piece Harness, 19th century A330

**1980, Sept. 9** *Perf. 14*
647 A330 1.10m shown .55 .40
648 A330 1.30m Collar harness, vert. .55 .40

Biathlon A331

**1980, Oct. 17 Litho.** *Perf. 14*
649 A331 1.10m multicolored .55 .40

World Biathlon Championship, Lahti, Feb. 10-15, 1981.

Pull the Roller, Weighing out the Salt — A332

Christmas 1980 (Traditional Games): 1.10m, Putting out the shoemaker's eye.

**1980, Oct. 27**
650 A332 60p multicolored 1.10 .50
651 A332 1.10m multicolored 1.10 .50

Boxing Match — A333

**1981, Feb. 28 Litho.** *Perf. 14*
652 A333 1.10m multicolored .45 .40

European Boxing Championships, Tampere, May 2-10.

Glass Blowing A334

**1981, Mar. 12**
653 A334 1.10m multicolored .45 .40

Glass industry, 300th anniversary.

Mail Boat Furst Menschikoff, 1836 — A335

**Litho & Engr.**

**1981, May 6** *Perf. 13*
654 A335 1.10m brown & tan 3.25 4.50

Nordia '81 Stamp Exhibition, Helsinki, May 6-10. Sold only at exhibition for 3m including entrance ticket.

**Europa Issue**

Rowing to Church A336

**1981, May 18 Litho.** *Perf. 13*
655 A336 1.10m shown *.75* *.30*
656 A336 1.50m Midsummer's Eve dance *1.50* *.50*

Traffic Conference Emblem — A337

**1981, May 26 Litho.** *Perf. 14*
657 A337 1.10m multicolored .45 .40

European Conference of Ministers of Transport, May 25-28.

Boy and Girl Riding Pegasus A338

**1981, June 11**
658 A338 1m multicolored .45 .40

Youth associations centenary.

Intl. Year of the Disabled — A339

**1981, Sept. 2 Litho.** *Perf. 13*
659 A339 1.10m multicolored .45 .40

Christmas 1981 — A340

70p, Children, Christmas tree. 1.10m, Decorating tree, vert.

**1981, Oct. 27 Litho.** *Perf. 14*
660 A340 70p multicolored .85 .30
661 A340 1.10m multicolored .85 .30

"Om Konsten att Ratt Behaga" First Issue (Periodicals Bicentenary) A341

**1982, Jan. 15**
662 A341 1.20m multicolored .45 .40

Kuopio Bicentenary — A343

**1982, Mar. 4 Litho.** *Perf. 14*
664 A343 1.20m multicolored .45 .40

Score, String Instrument Neck — A344

**1982, Mar. 11** *Perf. 13*
665 A344 1.20m multicolored 1.20 .45

Centenaries of Sibelius Academy of Music and Helsinki Orchestra.

Electric Power Plant Centenary A345

**1982, Mar. 15** *Perf. 14*
666 A345 1.20m multicolored .85 .40

Gardening A346

**1982, Apr. 16 Litho.** *Perf. 14*
667 A346 1.10m multicolored .45 .40

Europa — A347

1.20m, Publication of Abckiria (1st Finnish book), 1543 (Sculpture of Mikael Agricola, translator, by Oskari Jauhiainen, 1951). 1.50m, Turku Academy, 1st Finnish university (Turku Academy Inaugural Procession, 1640, after Albert Edelfelt).

**1982, Apr. 29 Litho.** *Perf. 13x12½*
668 A347 1.20m multicolored *1.50* *.45*

**Size: 47x31mm**

***Perf. 12½***

669 A347 1.50m multicolored *1.90* *.60*

Intl. Monetary Fund and World Bank Emblems A348

**1982, May 12** *Perf. 14*
670 A348 1.60m multicolored .55 .50

IMF Interim Committee and IMF-WB Joint Development Committee Meeting, Helsinki, May 12-14.

75th Anniv. of Unicameral Parliament A349

2.40m, Future, by Waino Aaltonen, Parliament.

**1982, May 25**
671 A349 2.40m ultra & blk .85 .70

Manor Houses A349a

1st Row: a, Kuitia, Parainen, 1490. b, Louhisaari, Askainen, 1655. c, Frugard, Joroinen, 1780. d, Jokioinen, 1798. e, Moisio, Elimaki, 1820.

2nd Row: f, Sjundby, Siuntio, 1560. g, Fagervik, Inkoo, 1773. h, Mustio, Karjaa, 1792. i, Fiskars, Pohja, 1818. j, Kotkaniemi, Vihti, 1836.

**1982, June 14 Litho.** *Perf. 13x13½*
672 Booklet pane of 10 12.00 12.00
*a.-j.* A349a 1.20m single stamp 1.20 .50
Complete booklet, #672 12.00 12.00

See design A310.

Christmas 1982 — A350

**1982, Oct. 25**
673 A350 90p Feeding forest animals .70 .40
674 A350 1.20m Children eating porridge .70 .40

Nordic Cooperation A351

**1983, Mar. 24 Litho.** *Perf. 14*
675 A351 1.20m Panning for gold .55 .40
676 A351 1.30m Kitkajoki River rapids .55 .40

World Communications Year — A352

**1983, Apr. 9 Litho.** *Perf. 13*
677 A352 1.30m Postal services .55 .40
678 A352 1.70m Sound waves, optical cables .65 .45

Europa 1983 A353

1.30m, Flash smelting method. 1.70m, Temppeliaukio Church.

**1983, May 2 Litho.** *Perf. 12½x13*
679 A353 1.30m multicolored *5.00* *.45*
680 A353 1.70m multicolored *6.00* *.90*

Pres. Lauri Kristian Relander (1883-1942) — A354

**1983, May 31 Litho.** *Perf. 14*
681 A354 1.30m multicolored .45 .40

Running — A355

**1983, June 6**

682 A355 1.20m Javelin, horiz. .45 .40
683 A355 1.30m shown .45 .40

First World Athletic Championships, Helsinki, Aug. 7-14.

Toivo Kuula (1883-1918), Composer — A356

**1983, July 7** ***Perf. 14***

684 A356 1.30m multicolored .55 .40

Christmas 1983 — A357

Childrens drawings: 1m, Santa, reindeer, sled and gifts by Eija Myllyviita. 1.30m, Two candles by Camilla Lindberg.

**Engr., Litho.**

**1983, Nov. 4** ***Perf. 12, 14***

685 A357 1m dark blue .85 .40
686 A357 1.30m multi, vert. .85 .40

A358

**1983, Nov. 25 Litho.** ***Perf. 14***

687 A358 1.30m brt blue & blk .45 .40

President Mauno Henrik Koivisto, 60th birthday.

A360

1.10m, Letters (2nd class rate). 1.40m, Automated sorting (1st class rate), vert.

**1984, Mar. 1 Engr.** ***Perf. 12***

689 A360 1.10m multicolored .90 .50

**Photo. & Engr.**

690 A360 1.40m multicolored .70 .50

Inauguration of Nordic postal rates.

Museum Pieces — A361

Work and Skill — A362

Designs: No. 691, Pottery, 3200 B.C.; Silver chalice, 1416; Crossbow, 16th cent. No. 692, Kaplan hydraulic turbine.

**1984, Apr. 30 Litho.** ***Perf. 13½***

691 A361 1.40m multicolored .50 .40
692 A362 1.40m multicolored .50 .40

Europa (1959-84) A363

**1984, May 7** ***Perf. 12½x13***

693 A363 1.40m multicolored *4.00* .25
694 A363 2m multicolored *4.00* *.80*

Dentistry — A364

**1984, Aug. 27 Litho.** ***Perf. 14***

695 A364 1.40m Dentist, teeth .80 .50

Astronomy A365

**1984, Sept. 12**

696 A365 1.10m Observatory, planets, sun 1.00 .55

Aleksis Kivi (1934-72), Writer — A366

**1984, Oct. 10 Litho.** ***Perf. 14***

697 A366 1.40m Song of my Heart .80 .40

Christmas 1984 — A367

**Litho. & Engr.**

**1984, Nov. 30** ***Perf. 12***

698 A367 1.10m Father Christmas, brownie 1.40 .40

Common Law of 1734 — A368

**1984, Dec. 6** ***Perf. 14***

699 A368 2m Statute Book 1.20 .70

25th Anniv. of EFTA — A369

**1985, Feb. 2** **Litho.**

700 A369 1.20m multicolored .50 .40

100th Anniv. of Society of Swedish Literature in Finland A370

**1985, Feb. 5** **Litho.**

701 A370 1.50m Johan Ludvig Runeberg .50 .35

A371

**1985, Feb. 18 Litho.** ***Perf. 11½x12***

702 A371 1.50m Icon .50 .40

Order of St. Sergei and St. Herman, 100th anniv.

150th Anniv. of Kalevala — A372

**Litho. & Engr.**

**1985, Feb. 28** ***Perf. 13x12½***

703 A372 1.50m Pedri Shemeikka .80 .40
704 A372 2.10m Larin Paraske 1.20 .75

A373

**Litho. & Engr.**

**1985, May 15** ***Perf. 13***

705 A373 1.50m Mermaid and sea lions 4.50 *6.25*

NORDIA 1985 philatelic exhibition, May 15-19. Sold for 10m, which included admission ticket.

A374

Finnish Banknote Cent.: banknotes of 1886, 1909, 1922, 1945 and 1955.

**Photo. & Engr.**

**1985, May 18** ***Perf. 11½***

706 A374 Booklet pane of 8 7.50 7.50
*a.-h.* 1.50m any single .90 .70
Complete booklet, #706 7.50

A375

Europa: 1.50m, Children playing the recorder. 2.10m, Excerpt "Ramus Virens Olivarum" from the "Piae Cantiones," 1582.

**1985, June 17 Litho.** ***Perf. 13***

707 A375 1.50m multicolored *5.50* *.50*
708 A375 2.10m multicolored *6.50* *1.10*

### Security Conference Type of 1975

**1985, June 19** **Litho.**

**709** A265 2.10m multicolored .75 .60

European Security and Cooperation Conference, 10th Anniv.

A376

**1985, Sept. 5** **Litho.** ***Perf. 14***

**710** A376 1.50m Provincial arms, Count's seal 1.20 .35

Provincial Administration Established by Count Per Brahe, 350th Anniv.

### Arms Type of 1975 and

Kerimaki Church A376a

Urho Kekkonen Natl. Park — A376b

Tulip Damask Table Cloth, 18th Cent. A377

Postal Service A377a

Brown Bear — A377b

***Perf. 11½, 13x12½ (2m)***

**1985-90** **Engr.**

**711** A256 1.60m vermilion .80 .60
**712** A256 1.70m black 1.20 .50
*a.* Bklt. pane, #558, 560, 2 each #555, 556a, 712 + 2 labels 9.00 *11.00*
Complete booklet, #712a 10.00
**713** A256 1.80m olive green 1.25 .70
*a.* Bklt. pane, 2 ea #555d, 560a, 713b 3.50 3.00
Complete booklet, #713a 3.50
*b.* Perf. 13x12½ 2.50 1.50
**714** A256 1.90m brt orange 1.10 .30
**715** A256 2m blue grn, bklt. stamp 2.50 .90
*a.* Bklt. pane, #562a, 2 ea #715, 555d 7.00 7.00
Complete booklet, #715a 7.00

**Litho.** ***Perf. 14***

**716** A376a 2.20m multi 1.10 .30
**717** A376b 2.40m multi 1.40 .40
**718** A377 12m multi 7.00 1.00

**Litho. & Engr.**

***Perf. 13x12½***

**719** A377b 50m blk, grn & lt red brn 24.00 8.50
*Nos. 711-719 (9)* 40.35 13.20

No. 712a contains two labels inscribed to publicize FINLANDIA '88.

Issued: 12m, 9/13/85; 1.60m, 1/2/86; 1.70m, 1/2/87; No. 712a, 8/10/87; 1.80m, 1/4/88; 2.20m, 2.40m, 1/20/88; No. 713b, 7/25/88; 1.90m, 1/2/89; 2m, 1/19/90; 50m, 8/30/89.

### Booklet Stamps

No. 720, Telephone, mailbox. No. 721, Postal truck, transport plane. No. 722, Transport plane, fork lift. No. 723, Postman delivering letter. No. 724, Woman accepting letter.

***Perf. 12½ on 3 Sides***

**1988, Feb. 1** **Litho.**

**720** A377a 1.80m multi 1.50 .50
**721** A377a 1.80m multi 1.50 .50
**722** A377a 1.80m multi 1.50 .50
**723** A377a 1.80m multi 1.50 .50
**724** A377a 1.80m multi 1.50 .50
*a.* Bklt. pane, 2 each #720-724 16.00 10.50
Complete booklet, #724a 16.00
*Nos. 720-724 (5)* 7.50 2.50

Nos. 721-722 and 723-724 printed se-tenant in continuous designs. No. 724c sold for 14m to households on mainland Finland. Each household entitled to buy 2 booklets at discount price from Feb. 1 to May 31, with coupon.

Miniature Sheet

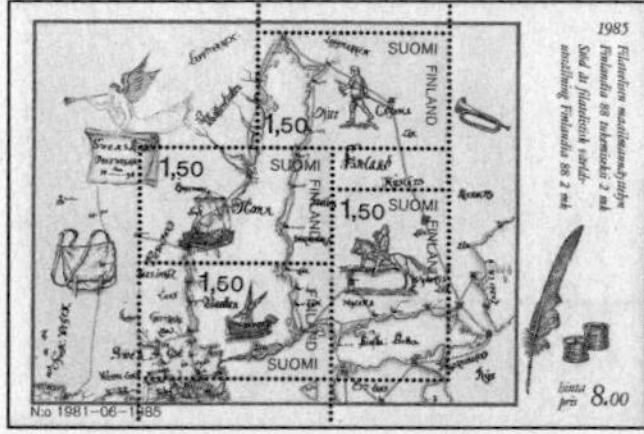

Postal Map, 1698 — A378

Designs: a, Postman on foot. b, Postal Map, 1698. c, Sailing vessel, diff. d, Postrider, vert.

**Litho. & Engr.**

**1985, Oct. 16** ***Perf. 14***

**728** A378 Sheet of 4 8.00 10.00
*a.-d.* 1.50m any single 2.00 2.50

FINLANDIA '88, 350th anniv. of Finnish Postal Service, founded in 1638 by Gov.-Gen. Per Brahe. Sheet sold for 8m.

Intl. Youth Year — A379

**1985, Nov. 1** **Litho.** ***Perf. 13***

**729** A379 1.50m multicolored .70 .35

Christmas — A380

No. 730, Bird, tulips. No. 731, Cross of St. Thomas, hyacinths.

**1985, Nov. 29** ***Perf. 14***

**730** A380 1.20m multicolored 1.10 .40
**731** A380 1.20m multicolored 1.10 .40

Natl. Geological Society, Cent. — A390

**1986, Feb. 8** **Litho.** ***Perf. 14***

**732** A390 1.30m Orbicular granite .90 .40
**733** A390 1.60m Rapaviki 1.00 .40
**734** A390 2.10m Veined gneiss 1.25 .60
*Nos. 732-734 (3)* 3.15 1.40

Europa 1986 A391

1.60m, Saimaa ringed seal. 2.20m, Environmental conservation.

**1986, Apr. 10** ***Perf. 12½x13***

**735** A391 1.60m multicolored *2.50* .40
**736** A391 2.20m multicolored *5.50* .80

Conference Palace, Baghdad, 1982 — A392

Natl. Construction Year. b, Lahti Theater, 1983. c, Kuusamo Municipal Offices, 1978. d, Hamina Court Building, 1983. e, Finnish Embassy, New Delhi, 1986. f, Western Sakyla Daycare Center, 1980.

**1986, Apr. 19** ***Perf. 14***

**737** Booklet pane of 6 5.75 6.00
*a.-f.* A392 1.60m, any single .90 .70
Complete booklet, #737 5.75

Nordic Cooperation Issue 1986 — A393

Sister towns.

**1986, May 27** **Litho.** ***Perf. 14***

**738** A393 1.60m Joensuu .70 .40
**739** A393 2.20m Jyvaskyla .90 .75

Souvenir Sheet

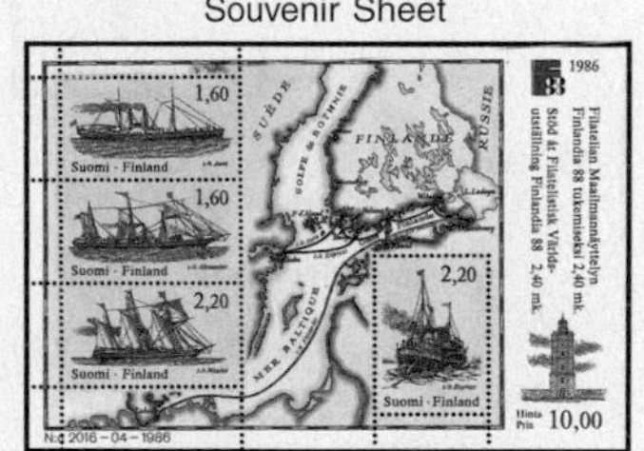

FINLANDIA '88 — A394

Postal ships: a, Iron paddle steamer Aura, Stockholm-St. Petersburg, 1858. b, Screw vessel Alexander, Helsinki-Tallinn-Lubeck, 1859. c, Steamship Nicolai, Helsinki-Tallinn-St. Petersburg, 1858. d, 1st Ice steamship Express II, Helsinki-Stockholm, 1877-98, vert.

**Litho. & Engr.**

**1986, Aug. 29** ***Perf. 13***

**740** A394 Sheet of 4 14.00 14.00
*a.-b.* 1.60m, any single 3.25 3.25
*c.-d.* 2.20m, any single 3.25 3.25

Sold for 10k.

Pierre-Louis Moreau de Maupertuis (1698-1759) — A395

**1986, Sept. 5** **Litho.** ***Perf. 12½x13***

**741** A395 1.60m multicolored .80 .40

Lapland Expedition, 250th anniv., proved Earth's poles are flattened.

See France No. 2016.

Urho Kaleva Kekkonen (1900-86), Pres. — A396

**1986, Sept. 30** **Engr.** ***Perf. 14***

**742** A396 5m black 2.25 2.00

Intl. Peace Year — A397

**1986, Oct. 13** **Litho.** ***Perf. 13***

**743** A397 1.60m multicolored .70 .40

A398

Christmas A399

**Photo. & Engr.**

**1986, Oct. 31** ***Perf. 12***

**744** 1.30m Denomination at L .70 .45
**745** 1.30m Denomination at R 1.50 .40
*a.* A398 Pair, #744-745 3.00 2.40
**746** A399 1.60m Elves 1.25 .40
*Nos. 744-746 (3)* 3.45 1.25

No. 745a has a continuous design.

Postal Savings Bank, Cent. — A400

**1987, Jan. 2** **Litho.** ***Perf. 14***

**747** A400 1.70m multicolored .70 .40

Natl. Tourism, Cent. — A401

**1987, Feb. 4** **Litho.** ***Perf. 14***

**748** A401 1.70m Winter .65 .40
**749** A401 2.30m Summer .85 .60

A402

**1987, Feb. 4** ***Perf. 14***

**750** A402 1.40m multicolored .70 .40

Metric system in Finland, cent.

A403

**1987, Feb. 17 Litho. *Perf. 14***
**751** A403 2.10m multicolored 1.10 .50

Leevi Madetoja (1887-1947), composer.

European Wrestling Championships A404

**1987, Feb. 17**
**752** A404 1.70m multicolored .80 .40

1987 World Bowling Championships A405

**1987, Apr. 13**
**753** A405 1.70m multicolored .80 .40

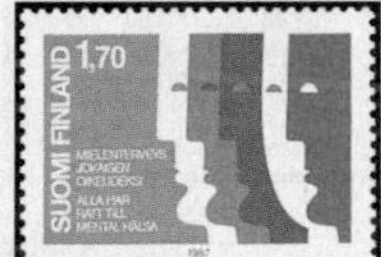
Mental Health — A406

**1987, Apr. 13**
**754** A406 1.70m multicolored .70 .40

Souvenir Sheet

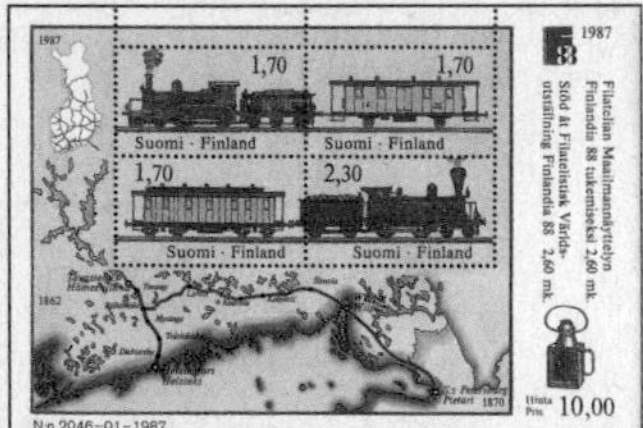
FINLANDIA '88 — A407

Locomotives and mail cars: a, Steam locomotive, 6-wheeled tender. b, 4-window mail car. c, 7-window mail car.

**Litho. & Engr.**
**1987, May 8 *Perf. 12½x13***
**755** A407 Sheet of 4 15.00 15.00
*a.-c.* 1.70m any single 4.00 4.00
*d.* 2.30m multicolored 4.00 4.00

Sold for 10m.

Europa 1987 A408

Modern architecture: 1.70m, Tampere Main Library, 1986, designed by Raili and Reima Pietila. 2.30m, Stoa Monument, Helsinki, c. 1981, by sculptor Hannu Siren.

**1987, May 15 Litho. *Perf. 13***
**756** A408 1.70m multicolored *5.25* .25
**757** A408 2.30m multicolored *5.25* *.90*

Natl. Art Museum, Ateneum, Cent. — A409

Paintings: a, Strawberry Girl, by Nils Schillmark (1745-1804). b, Still-life on a Lady's Work Table, by Ferdinand von Wright (1822-1906). c, Old Woman with Basket, by Albert Edelfelt (1854-1906). d, Boy and Crow, by Akseli Gallen-Kallela (1865-1931). e, Late Winter, by Tyko Sallinen (1879-1955).

**1987, May 15**
**758** Booklet pane of 5 8.50 8.50
*a.-e.* A409 1.70m any single 1.60 .90
Complete booklet, #758 9.00

A410

**1987, Aug. 12 *Perf. 14***
**759** A410 1.70m multicolored .70 .40

European Physics Soc. 7th gen. conf., Helsinki, Aug. 10-14.

A411

**1987, Oct. 12**
**760** A411 1.70m ultra, sil & pale lt gray .70 .40

**Size: 30x41mm**

**761** A411 10m dark ultra, lt blue & sil 4.00 2.00

Natl. independence, 70th anniv.

Ylppo, Child and Lastenlinna Children's Hospital A412

**1987, Oct. 27**
**762** A412 1.70m multicolored .70 .40

Arvo Ylppo (b. 1887), pediatrics pioneer.

Christmas — A413

**1987, Oct. 30**
**763** A413 1.40m Santa Claus, youths, horiz. 1.00 .40
**764** A413 1.70m shown 1.00 .40

Finnish News Agency (STT), Cent. — A414

**1987, Nov. 1**
**765** A414 2.30m multicolored .95 .80

Lauri "Tahko" Pihkala (1888-1981), Promulgator of Sports and Physical Education A415

**1988, Jan. 5 Litho. *Perf. 14***
**766** A415 1.80m blk, chalky blue & brt blue .80 .40

A416

**1988, Mar. 14 Litho.**
**767** A416 1.40m multicolored .70 .40

Meteorological Institute, 150th anniv.

Settlement of New Sweden in America, 350th Anniv. — A417

Design: 17th Century European settlers negotiating with 3 American Indians, map of New Sweden, the Swedish ships Kalmar Nyckel and Fogel Grip, based on an 18th cent. illustration from a Swedish book about the American Colonies.

**Litho. & Engr.**
**1988, Mar. 29 *Perf. 13***
**768** A417 3m multicolored 1.25 .80

See US No. C117 and Sweden No. 1672.

FINLANDIA '88, June 1-12, Helsinki Fair Center — A418

Agathon Faberge (1876-1951), famed philatelist, & rarities from his collection.

**Booklet Stamp**
**1988, May 2 Litho. *Perf. 13***
**769** A418 5m Pane of 1+2 labels 14.00 *17.50*
Complete booklet, #769 15.00

350th Anniv. of the Finnish Postal Service. No. 769 sold for 30m to include the price of adult admission to the exhibition.

Achievements of Finnish Athletes at the 1988 Winter Olympics, Calgary — A419

Design: Matti Nykanen, gold medalist in all 3 ski jumping events at the '88 Games.

**1988, Apr. 6 *Perf. 14***
**770** A419 1.80m multicolored .90 .40

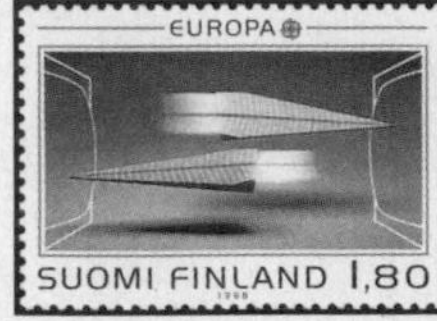
Europa 1988 A420

Communication and transport.

**1988, May 23 Litho. *Perf. 13***
**771** A420 1.80m shown *5.00* *.25*
**772** A420 2.40m Horse-drawn tram, 1890 *5.00* *.90*

Souvenir Sheet

FINLANDIA '88 — A421

1st airmail flights: a, Finnish air force Breguet 14 biplane transporting mail from Helsinki to Tallinn, Feb. 12, 1920. b, AERO Junkers F-13 making 1st airmail night flight from Helsinki to Copenhagen, May 15, 1930. c, AERO Douglas DC-3, 1st intl. route, Helsinki-Norrkoping-Copenhagen-Amsterdam, 1947. d, Douglas DC 10-30, 1975-88, inauguration of Helsinki-Beijing route, June 2, 1988.

**Litho. & Engr.**
**1988, June 2 *Perf. 13½***
**773** A421 Sheet of 4 15.00 16.00
*a.-c.* 1.80m any single 3.75 4.00
*d.* 2.40m multicolored 3.75 4.00

Sold for 11m.

Turku Fire Brigade, 150th Anniv. — A422

Design: 1902 Horse-drawn, steam-driven fire pump, preserved at the brigade.

**1988, Aug. 15 Litho. *Perf. 14***
**774** A422 2.20m multicolored .95 .55

A423

*Missale Aboense*, the 1st printed book in Finland, 500th anniv.

**1988, Aug. 17**
**775** A423 1.80m multicolored .90 .40

A424

Finnish Postal Service, 350th Anniv.: No. 776, Postal tariff issued by Queen Christina of Sweden, Sept. 6, 1638. No. 777, Postal cart, c. 1880. #778, Leyland Sherpa 185 mail van, 1976. No. 779, Malmi P.O. interior. #780,

Skier using mobile telephone, c. 1970. No. 781, Telecommunications satellite in orbit.

**Booklet Stamps**

**1988, Sept. 6 Litho. *Perf. 13***

**776** A424 1.80m multicolored .90 .65
**777** A424 1.80m multicolored .90 .65
**778** A424 1.80m multicolored .90 .65
**779** A424 1.80m multicolored .90 .65
**780** A424 1.80m multicolored .90 .65
**781** A424 1.80m multicolored .90 .65
*a.* Booklet pane of 6, #776-781 5.50 6.50
Complete booklet, #781a 5.50

Children's Playgroups (Preschool) A425

**1988, Oct. 10 *Perf. 14***

**782** A425 1.80m multicolored .80 .40

Christmas A426

**1988, Nov. 4 Litho.**

**783** A426 1.40m multicolored 1.40 .35
**784** A426 1.80m multicolored 1.75 .55

Hameenlinna Township, 350th Anniv. — A427

Design: Market square, coat of arms and 17th century plan of the town.

**1989, Jan. 19 Litho.**

**785** A427 1.90m multicolored .80 .40

1989 Nordic Ski Championships, Lahti, Feb. 17-26 — A428

**1989, Jan. 25**

**786** A428 1.90m multicolored .80 .40

Salvation Army in Finland, Cent. — A429

**1989, Feb. 6 Litho.**

**787** A429 1.90m multicolored .80 .40

Photography, 150th Anniv. — A430

1.50m, Photographer, box camera, c.1900.

**1989, Feb. 6**

**788** A430 1.50m brn, buff, cream .75 .55

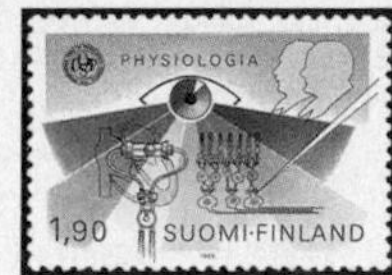


31st Intl. Physiology Congress, Basel, July 9-14 — A431

Design: Congress emblem, silhouettes of Robert Tigerstedt and Ragnar Granit, eye, flowmeter measuring flow of blood through heart, color-sensitive retinal cells and microelectrode.

**1989, Mar. 2**

**789** A431 1.90m multicolored .80 .40

Sports — A432

**1989, Mar. 10 Booklet Stamps**

**790** A432 1.90m Skiing 1.00 .50
**791** A432 1.90m Jogging 1.00 .50
**792** A432 1.90m Cycling 1.00 .50
**793** A432 1.90m Canoeing 1.00 .50
*a.* Booklet pane of 4, #790-793 4.25 4.25
Complete booklet, #793a 4.50

**Souvenir Sheet**

Finnish Kennel Club, Cent. — A433

Dogs: a, Lapponian herder. b, Finnish spitz. c, Karelian bear dog. d, Finnish hound.

**1989, Mar. 17 Litho. *Perf. 14***

**794** A433 Sheet of 4 4.00 4.00
*a.-d.* 1.90m any single 1.00 .70

Europa — A434

**1989, Mar. 31 *Perf. 13***

**795** A434 1.90m Hopscotch *2.50* *.25*
**796** A434 2.50m Sledding *2.50* *.65*

A435

Nordic Cooperation Year: Folk Costumes.

**1989, Apr. 20 *Perf. 14***

**797** A435 1.90m Sakyla (man) 1.10 .45
**798** A435 2.50m Veteli (woman) 1.10 .65

Finnish Pharmacies, 300th Anniv. — A436

Foxglove, distilling apparatus, mortar, flask.

**1989, June 2 Litho.**

**799** A436 1.90m multicolored .90 .35

A437

**1989, June 2**

**800** A437 1.90m multicolored .90 .35

Savonlinna Municipal Charter, 350th anniv.

Helsinki Zoo, Cent. — A438

No. 801, Panthera uncia. No. 802, Capra falconeri

**1989, June 12**

**801** A438 1.90m multi .90 .45
**802** A438 2.50m multi 1.10 .70

Vocational Training, 150th Anniv. — A439

Interparliamentary Union, Cent. — A440

Council of Europe, 40th Anniv. — A441

**1989, Sept. 4 Litho. *Perf. 14***

**803** A439 1.50m multicolored .70 .70
**804** A440 1.90m multicolored .90 .35
**805** A441 2.50m multicolored 1.25 .90
*Nos. 803-805 (3)* 2.85 1.95

Admission of Finland to the Council of Europe (2.50m).

A442

**1989, Oct. 9 Litho.**

**806** A442 1.90m multicolored .90 .35

Hannes Kolehmainen (1889-1966) winning the 5000-meter race at the Stockholm Olympics, 1912.

A443

**1989, Oct. 20**

**807** A443 1.90m multicolored .90 .35

Continuing Education in Finland, cent.

A444

Christmas: 1.90m, Sodankyla Church, Siberian jays in snow.

**1989, Nov. 3**

**808** A444 1.50m shown 1.10 .40
**809** A444 1.90m multicolored 1.10 .40

A445

**1990, Jan. 19 Litho. *Perf. 13x13½***

**810** A445 1.90m multicolored 1.40 1.10
**811** A445 2.50m multicolored 1.60 1.25

Incorporation of the State Posts and Telecommunications Services.

Emblem of the corporation was produced by holography. Soaking may affect the design.

Musical Soc. of Turku and Finnish Orchestras, 200th Annivs. A446

**1990, Jan. 26 *Perf. 14***

**812** A446 1.90m multicolored 1.10 .40

Disabled Veteran's Assoc., 50th Anniv. — A447

**1990, Mar. 13 Litho.**

**813** A447 2m multicolored .90 .35

End of the Winter (Russo-Finnish) War, 50th Anniv. — A448

**1990, Mar. 13**

**814** A448 2m blue .90 .35

University of Helsinki, 350th Anniv. — A449

University crest and: 2m, Queen Christina on horseback. 3.20m, Degree ceremony procession in front of the main university building.

**1990, Mar. 26 Litho. *Perf. 13***

**815** A449 2m multicolored .85 .40
**816** A449 3.20m multicolored 1.25 .70

Europa 1990 A450

Post Offices: 2m, Lapp man, P.O. at Nuvvus, Mt. Nuvvus Ailigas. 2.70m, Turku main P.O.

| **1990, Mar. 26** | | | *Perf. 12½x13* | |
|---|---|---|---|---|
| **817** A450 | 2m | multicolored | *6.00* | *.25* |
| **818** A450 | 2.70m | multicolored | *6.00* | *.65* |

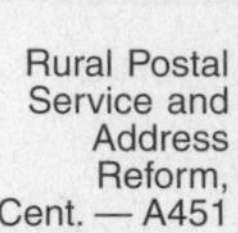

Rural Postal Service and Address Reform, Cent. — A451

| **1990, Apr. 19** | **Litho.** | *Perf. 13* | |
|---|---|---|---|
| **819** A451 2m multicolored | | .90 | .35 |

"Ali Baba and the Forty Thieves" A452

"Story of the Great Musician" A453

"Story of the Giants, the Witches and the Daughter of the Sun" A454

"The Golden Bird, the Golden Horse and the Princess" A455

"Lamb Brother" A456

"The Snow Queen" A457

Fairy tale illustrations by Rudolf Koivu.

**Booklet Stamps**

***Perf. 14 on 3 sides***

| **1990, Aug. 29** | | | **Litho.** | |
|---|---|---|---|---|
| **820** A452 | 2m | multicolored | 1.60 | .65 |
| **821** A453 | 2m | multicolored | 1.60 | .65 |
| **822** A454 | 2m | multicolored | 1.60 | .65 |
| **823** A455 | 2m | multicolored | 1.60 | .65 |
| **824** A456 | 2m | multicolored | 1.60 | .65 |
| **825** A457 | 2m | multicolored | 1.60 | .65 |
| *a.* | Booklet pane of 6, #820-825 | | 10.00 | 8.00 |
| | Complete booklet, #825a | | 10.00 | |

**Souvenir Sheet**

Horse Care — A458

a, Feeding. b, Riding. c, Watering. d, Currying.

| **1990, Oct. 10** | **Litho.** | *Perf. 14* | |
|---|---|---|---|
| **826** A458 Sheet of 4 | | 4.50 | 4.25 |
| *a.-d.* 2m any single | | 1.10 | .75 |

Christmas A459

| **1990, Nov. 2** | | | | |
|---|---|---|---|---|
| **827** A459 | 1.70m | Santa's elves | 1.70 | .40 |
| **828** A459 | 2m | Santa, reindeer | 1.70 | .40 |

**Provincial Flowers**

A460

A460a

A460b

A460c

A460d

A460e

A460f

A460g

A460h

A460i

A460j

A460k

2m, Wood anemone. 2.10m, Rowan. 2.70m, Heather. 2.90m, Sea buckthorn. 3.50m, Oak. No. 834, Globeflower. No. 835, Hepatica. No. 836, Iris. No. 838, Rosebay willowherb. No. 839, Labrador tea. No. 840, Karelian rose. No. 841, Daisy. No. 842, Water lily. No. 843, Bird cherry. No. 844, Harebell. No. 845, Cowslip.

| **1990-99** | | | | *Perf. 13x12½* | |
|---|---|---|---|---|---|
| **829** A460 | 2m | multi | | 1.10 | .25 |
| **830** A460 | 2.10m | multi | | 1.10 | .25 |
| **831** A460 | 2.70m | multi | | 1.40 | .40 |
| **832** A460 | 2.90m | multi | | 1.50 | .40 |
| **833** A460 | 3.50m | multi | | 2.00 | .50 |
| **834** A460a | 2 | multi | | 2.25 | .50 |
| **835** A460b | 1 | multi | | 2.50 | .30 |
| | *Nos. 829-835 (7)* | | | 11.85 | 2.60 |

**Self-Adhesive**

***Die Cut***

| | | | | | |
|---|---|---|---|---|---|
| **836** A460c | 2 | multi | | 2.25 | .30 |
| *a.* | Booklet pane of 20 | | | 45.00 | 27.50 |
| **837** A460 | 2.10m | like #830 | | 1.40 | .30 |
| **838** A460d | 1 | multi | | 2.50 | .35 |
| **839** A460e | 1 | multi | | 2.50 | .35 |
| *a.* | Booklet pane of 10 | | | 24.50 | 7.50 |
| **840** A460f | 1 | multi | | 2.50 | .40 |
| **841** A460g | 1 | multi | | 2.50 | .35 |
| **842** A460h | 1 | multi | | 2.50 | .35 |
| **843** A460i | 1 | multi | | 2.50 | .45 |
| **844** A460j | 1 | multi | | 2.50 | .45 |
| **845** A460k | 1 | multi | | 2.50 | .45 |
| | *Nos. 836-845 (10)* | | | 23.65 | 3.75 |

Issued: 2m, 2.70m, 1/19/90; No. 830, 2.90m, 3.50m, 2/5/90; 2.10m, 1991; Nos. 834-835, 3/2/92; No. 838, 10/9/92; No. 836, 3/1/93; No. 839, 6/14/93; No. 840, 5/5/94; No. 841, 3/15/95; No. 842, 6/3/96; No. 843, 3/18/97; No. 844, 3/12/98; No. 845, 4/28/99.

No. 834 sold for 1.60m, No. 836 sold for 1.90m, Nos. 835, 838 for 2.10m, Nos. 839-840 for 2.30m, Nos. 841-844 sold for 2.80m, No. 845 sold for 3m at time of release.

Nos. 837-838, 840-845 issued in sheets of 10. Nos. 836a and 839a were issued as complete booklets. The peelable backing serves as a booklet cover.

The numbers on the stamps represent the class of mail for which each was intended at time of release.

A461

| **1991, Mar. 1** | *Perf. 14* | |
|---|---|---|
| **846** A461 2.10m multicolored | 1.10 | .40 |

World Hockey Championships, Turku.

A462

| **1991, Mar. 1** | | |
|---|---|---|
| **847** A462 2.10m Cooking class | .80 | .40 |

Home economics teacher education, cent.

**Sauna Type of 1977 and**

Birds — A463

No. 848, Great tit. No. 849, Wagtail. No. 850, Aegolius funereus. No. 850A, Phoenicurus phoenicurus. No. 851, Chaffinches. No. 852, Robin. No. 856, Bullfinch. No. 857, Waxwing. No. 859, Dendrocopos leucotos.

***Perf. 13x12½, 14 (#861)***

**1991-99** **Litho.**

**Booklet Stamps (#848-859)**

| | | | | | |
|---|---|---|---|---|---|
| **848** | A463 | 10p | multi | .40 | .35 |
| **849** | A463 | 10p | multi | .40 | .25 |
| **850** | A463 | 10p | multi | .90 | .60 |
| **850A** | A463 | 20p | multi | 10.00 | 5.00 |
| **851** | A463 | 60p | multi | 6.00 | .65 |
| **852** | A463 | 60p | multi | 7.00 | 1.25 |
| **856** | A463 | 2.10m | multi | .90 | .40 |
| *a.* | Bklt. pane, #851, 2 each #848, 856 | | | 7.50 | 7.50 |
| | Complete booklet, #856a | | | 8.00 | |
| **857** | A463 | 2.10m | multi | .90 | .40 |
| *a.* | Bklt. pane, #852, 2 each #849, 857 | | | 6.25 | 6.25 |
| | Complete booklet, #857a | | | 6.75 | |
| **859** | A463 | 2.30m | multi | 1.00 | .50 |
| *a.* | Booklet pane of #850A, 2 each #850, #859 + 1 label | | | 7.50 | 7.50 |
| | Complete booklet, #859a | | | 8.00 | |

**Sheet Stamp**

| | | | | | |
|---|---|---|---|---|---|
| **861** | A256a | 4.80m | multi | 2.00 | 1.25 |
| | *Nos. 848-861 (10)* | | | 29.50 | 10.65 |

Issued: Nos. 848, 851, 856, 3/20/91; Nos. 849, 852, 857, 4/22/92; Nos. 850, 850A, 859, 6/4/93. 861, 7/1/99.

"SUOMI" is in upper left on Nos. 849, 852, 857.

Fishing — A464

Designs: a, Fly fisherman, trout. b, Perch, bobber. c, Crayfish, trap. d, Trawling for herring. e, Stocking powan.

| **1991, Mar. 20** | *Perf. 14* | |
|---|---|---|
| **863** Booklet pane of 5 | 6.00 | 6.00 |
| *a.-e.* A464 2.10m any single | 1.20 | .45 |
| Complete booklet, #863 | 6.50 | |

Tourism — A465

2.10m, Seurasaari Island. 2.90m, Steamship, Lake Saimaa.

| **1991, June 4** | **Litho.** | | *Perf. 14* | |
|---|---|---|---|---|
| **864** A465 | 2.10m | multi | 1.00 | .25 |
| **865** A465 | 2.90m | multi | 1.10 | .70 |

Europa A466

European map and: 2.10m, Human figures. 2.90m, Satellites, dish antennae.

| **1991, June 7** | **Litho.** | | *Perf. 12½x13* | |
|---|---|---|---|---|
| **866** A466 | 2.10m | multicolored | *5.50* | *.25* |
| **867** A466 | 2.90m | multicolored | *5.50* | *.70* |

Alfred W. Finch (1854-1930) A467

Designs: 2.10m, Iris, ceramic vase. 2.90m, Painting, The English Coast at Dover.

| **1991, Sept. 7** | **Litho.** | | *Perf. 13* | |
|---|---|---|---|---|
| **868** A467 | 2.10m | multicolored | 1.10 | .25 |
| **869** A467 | 2.90m | multicolored | 2.25 | .70 |

See Belgium No. 1410.

Finnish Candy Industry, Cent. — A468

| **1991, Sept. 17** | **Photo.** | *Perf. 11½* | |
|---|---|---|---|
| **870** A468 2.10m multicolored | | 1.00 | .50 |

**Souvenir Sheets**

Children's Stamp Designs — A469

a, Sun. b, Rainbow. c, Cows grazing.

| **1991, Sept. 17** | **Litho.** | *Perf. 13½* | |
|---|---|---|---|
| **871** A469 Sheet of 3 | | 3.00 | 3.00 |
| *a.-c.* 2.10m any single | | 1.00 | .65 |

Skiing — A470

Color of skisuit: a, red. b, green. c, yellow. d, blue.

**1991, Oct. 4** *Perf. 14*
**872** A470 Sheet of 4 4.00 4.00
*a.-d.* 2.10m any single 1.00 .65

Town Status for Iisalmi, Cent. — A471

**1991, Oct. 18** **Litho.** *Perf. 14*
**873** A471 2.10m multicolored .90 .50

Christmas A472

1.80m, Santa, animals carrying candles. 2.10m, Reindeer pulling Santa's sleigh.

**1991, Nov. 1** **Litho.** *Perf. 14*
**874** A472 1.80m multi 1.75 .45
**875** A472 2.10m multi, vert. 1.75 .45

Chemists' Club, Finnish Chemists' Society, Cent. — A473

**1991, Nov. 1**
**876** A473 2.10m multi 1.10 .40
**877** A473 2.10m multi, diff. 1.10 .40
*a.* Pair, #876-877 + label 3.00 3.00

Second and third vertical branches merge while second and third branches below almost touch in the upper left part of camphor molecular structure on No. 877. Nos. 876-877 are designed to produce a three dimensional effect when viewed together.

1992 Olympic Games A474

Designs: No. 878, Skier, Albertville. No. 879, Swimmer, Barcelona.

**1992, Feb. 4** **Litho.** *Perf. 14*
**878** A474 2.10m multicolored 1.00 .40
**879** A474 2.90m multicolored 1.40 .75

Expo '92, Seville — A475

**1992, Mar. 20** **Litho.** *Perf. 14*
**880** A475 3.40m multicolored 1.50 .75

Conference on Security and Cooperation in Europe, Helsinki A476

**1992, Mar. 20** *Perf. 14½x15*
**881** A476 16m multicolored 6.00 3.50

Town of Rauma, 550th Anniv. — A477

**1992, Mar. 27** *Perf. 14*
**882** A477 2.10m multicolored 1.40 .40

Healthy Brains — A478

**1992, Mar. 27**
**883** A478 3.50m multicolored 1.40 1.00

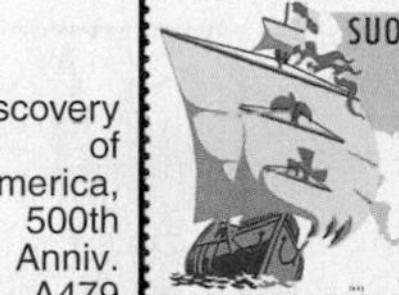

Discovery of America, 500th Anniv. A479

**1992, May 8** **Litho.** *Perf. 12½x13*
**884** A479 2.10m Santa Maria, map *2.25 .30*
**885** A479 2.10m Map, Columbus *2.25 .30*
*a.* Pair, #884-885 *4.50 5.00*

Europa.

Finnish Technology A480

Hologram of trees and: 2.10m, Drawing of blowing machine. 2.90m, Schematic of electronic circuits. 3.40m, Triangles and grid.

**1992, May 8** *Perf. 13x12½*
**886** A480 2.10m multicolored 1.10 .60
**887** A480 2.90m multicolored 1.40 .75
**888** A480 3.40m multicolored 1.75 1.20
*Nos. 886-888 (3)* 4.25 2.55

First Finnish patent granted, sesqui. (No. 886), Finnish chairmanship of Eureka (No. 887), Government Technology Research Center, 50th anniv. (No. 888).

Nos. 886-888 have holographic images. Soaking in water may affect the hologram.

Natl. Board of Agriculture, Cent. — A481

**1992, June 4** **Litho.** *Perf. 14*
**889** A481 2.10m Currant harvesting 1.00 .40

Finnish Women A482

No. 890, Aurora Karamzin (1808-1902), founder of Deaconesses' Institution of Helsinki. No. 891, Baroness Sophie Mannerheim (1863-1928), reformer of nursing education. No. 892, Laimi Leidenius (1877-1938), physician and educator. No. 893, Miina Sillanpaa (1866-1952), Minister for social affairs. No. 894, Edith Sodergran (1892-1923), poet. No. 895, Kreeta Haapasalo (1813-1893), folk singer.

**Litho. & Engr.**

**1992, June 8** *Perf. 14*

**Booklet Stamps**

**890** A482 2.10m multicolored 1.00 .55
**891** A482 2.10m multicolored 1.00 .55
**892** A482 2.10m multicolored 1.00 .55
**893** A482 2.10m multicolored 1.00 .55
**894** A482 2.10m multicolored 1.00 .55
**895** A482 2.10m multicolored 1.00 .55
*a.* Booklet pane of 6, #890-895 6.00 7.25
Complete booklet, #895a 6.00

Child's Painting A483

Independence, 75th Anniv. — A484

**1992, Oct. 5** **Litho.** *Perf. 13*
**896** A483 2.10m multicolored 1.00 .40

**Souvenir Sheet**

*Perf. 13½*

**897** A484 2.10m multicolored 1.90 1.20

Nordia '93 — A485

Illustrations depicting "Moomin" characters, by Tove Jansson: No. 898, Winter scene, ice covered bridges. No. 899, Winter scene in forest. No. 900, Boats in water. No. 901, Characters on beach.

***Perf. 13 on 3 Sides***

**1992, Oct. 9** **Litho.**

**Booklet Stamps**

**898** A485 2.10m multicolored 2.75 .55
**899** A485 2.10m multicolored 2.75 .55
**900** A485 2.10m multicolored 2.75 .55
**901** A485 2.10m multicolored 2.75 .55
*a.* Booklet pane of 4, #898-901 11.00 11.50
Complete booklet, #901a 11.00

A486

**1992, Oct. 20** **Litho.** *Perf. 13*
**902** A486 2.10m multicolored 1.00 .40

Printing in Finland, 350th anniv.

Christmas A487

Designs: 1.80m, Church of St. Lawrence, Vantaa. 2.10m, Stained glass window of nativity scene, Karkkila Church, vert.

**1992, Oct. 30** **Litho.** *Perf. 14*
**903** A487 1.80m multicolored 1.25 .45
**904** A487 2.10m multicolored 1.25 .45

Central Chamber of Commerce, 75th Anniv. — A488

**1993, Feb. 8** **Litho.** *Perf. 14*
**905** A488 1.60m multicolored .75 .50

Friendship A489

**1993, Feb. 8** **Litho.** *Perf. 14*
**906** A489 1 multicolored 2.50 .40
*a.* Booklet pane of 5 + label 14.00 7.50
Complete booklet, 2 #906a 28.00

No. 906 sold for 2m at time of release. See note following No. 845.
See Estonia No. 237.

Alopex Lagopus — A490

a, Adult with winter white coat. b, Face, full view, winter white coat. c, Mother, kits, summer coat. d, Two on rock, summer coat.

**1993, Mar. 19** **Litho.** *Perf. 12½x13*
**907** A490 Block of 4 5.50 5.50
*a.-d.* 2.30m Any single 1.40 .45

World Wildlife Fund.

Sculptures A491

Europa: 2m, Rumba, by Martti Aiha. 2.90m, Complete Works, by Kari Caven.

**1993, Apr. 26** *Perf. 13*
**908** A491 2m multicolored *1.90 .25*
**909** A491 2.90m multicolored *1.40 .60*

Organized Philately in Finland, Cent. — A492

**1993, May 6** *Perf. 13x12½*
**910** A492 2.30m Rosa pimpinellifolia 1.10 .70

Vyborg Castle, 700th Anniv. A493

**1993, May 6** *Perf. 13½*
**911** A493 2.30m multicolored 2.00 .40

Tourism
A494

**1993, May 7** ***Perf. 13x12½***

**912** A494 2.30m Naantali 1.00 .25
**913** A494 2.90m Imatra 1.25 .70

550th anniv. of Naantali (No. 912).

A495

Independent Finland Defense Forces, 75th Anniv.: 2.30m, Finnish landscape in form of soldier's silhouette. 3.40m, UN checkpoint of Finnish battalion, Middle East.

**1993, June 4** **Litho.** ***Perf. 14***

**914** A495 2.30m multicolored .85 .25
**915** A495 3.40m multicolored 1.40 1.00

A496

Art by Martta Wendelin (1893-1986): No. 916, Boy on skis, 1936. No. 917, Mother, daughter knitting, 1931. No. 918, Children building snowman, 1931. No. 919, Mother, children at fence, 1935. #920, Girl with lamb, 1936.

**Booklet Stamps**

**1993, June 14** **Litho.** ***Perf. 12½x13***

**916** A496 2.30m multicolored 1.50 .45
**917** A496 2.30m multicolored 1.50 .45
**918** A496 2.30m multicolored 1.50 .45
**919** A496 2.30m multicolored 1.50 .45
**920** A496 2.30m multicolored 1.50 .45
*a.* Booklet pane of 5, #916-920 7.50 8.00
Complete booklet, #920a 9.50

Water Birds — A497

No. 921, Flock of gavia arctica. No. 922, Pair of gavia arctica. No. 923, Mergus merganser. No. 924, Anas platyrhynchos. No. 925, Mergus serrator.

***Perf. 12½x13 on 3 or 4 Sides***

**1993, Sept. 20** **Litho.**

**Booklet Stamps**

**921** A497 2.30m multicolored 1.10 .75
**922** A497 2.30m multicolored 1.10 .75

**Size: 26x40mm**

**923** A497 2.30m multicolored 1.10 .75
**924** A497 2.30m multicolored 1.10 .75
**925** A497 2.30m multicolored 1.10 .75
*a.* Booklet pane of 5, #921-925 5.50 5.50
Complete booklet, #925a 7.50

Physical Education in Finnish Schools, 150th Anniv. — A498

**1993, Oct. 8** ***Perf. 14***

**926** A498 2.30m multicolored .90 .35

Souvenir Sheet

New Opera House, Helsinki — A499

Operas and ballet: a, 2.30m, Ostrobothnians, by Leevi Madetoja. b, 2.30m, The Faun (four dancers), by Claude Debussy. c, 2.90m, Giselle, by Adolphe Adam. d, 3.40m, The Magic Flute, by Wolfgang Amadeus Mozart.

**1993, Oct. 8** ***Perf. 13***

**927** A499 Sheet of 4 6.00 7.00
*a.-b.* 2.30m Either single 1.10 .70
*c.* 2.90m multi 1.75 1.75
*d.* 3.40m multi 1.75 *2.25*

Christmas — A500

**1993, Nov. 5** **Litho.** ***Perf. 14***

**928** A500 1.80m Christmas tree, elves 1.25 .40
*a.* Booklet pane of 10 16.00 16.00
Complete booklet, #928a 16.00
**929** A500 2.30m Three angels 1.25 .40

Pres. Mauno Koivisto, 70th Birthday — A501

**1993, Nov. 25**

**930** A501 2.30m multicolored .80 .40

Friendship — A502

Moomin characters: No. 931, Two standing. No. 932, Seven running.

**1994, Jan. 27** **Litho.** ***Perf. 12½x13***

**Booklet Stamps**

**931** A502 1 multicolored 2.50 .40
**932** A502 1 multicolored 2.50 .40
*a.* Bklt. pane, 4 each #931-932 20.00 10.00
Complete booklet, #932a 20.00

Nos. 931-932 each sold for 2.30m at time of release. See note following No. 845.

Souvenir Sheet

Intl. Olympic Committee, Cent. — A503

Winter Olympics medalists from Finland: a, Marja-Liisa Kirvesniemi, Marjo Matikainen, cross-country skiing. b, Clas Thunberg, speed skating. c, Veikko Kankkonen, ski jumping. d, Veikko Hakulinen, cross-country skiing.

**1994, Jan. 27** ***Perf. 13***

**933** A503 4.20m Sheet of 4, #a-d 8.00 9.50

See No. 939.

A504

Waino Aaltonen (1894-1966), Sculptor — A505

**1994, Mar. 8**

**934** A504 2m "Peace" 1.00 .40
**935** A505 2m "Muse" 1.00 .40
*a.* Pair, #934-935 2.10 2.10

Postal Service Civil Servants' Federation, Cent. — A506

**1994, Mar. 11**

**936** A506 2.30m multicolored .85 .45

Finnish Technology A507

Europa: 2.30m, Paper roll, nitrogen fixation, safety lock, ice breaker MS Fennica. 4.20m, Radiosonde, fishing lure, mobile phone, wind power plant.

**1994, Mar. 18**

**937** A507 2.30m multicolored *1.40* *.25*
**938** A507 4.20m multicolored *1.90* *1.10*

**Olympic Athlete Type of 1994**

Souvenir Sheet

Finnish athletes: a, Riitta Salin, Pirjo Haggman, runners. b, Lasse Viren, runner. c, Tiina Lillak, javelin thrower. d, Pentti Nikula, pole vaulter.

**1994, May 5** **Litho.** ***Perf. 13***

**939** A503 4.20m Sheet of 4, #a-d 8.00 8.00

European Track & Field Championships, Finlandia '95.

Finlandia '95, Helsinki — A508

Coccinella septempunctata.

**1994, May 10** ***Perf. 13½x13***

**940** A508 16m multi 9.00 8.00

See Nos. 962, 1009.

Miniature Sheet

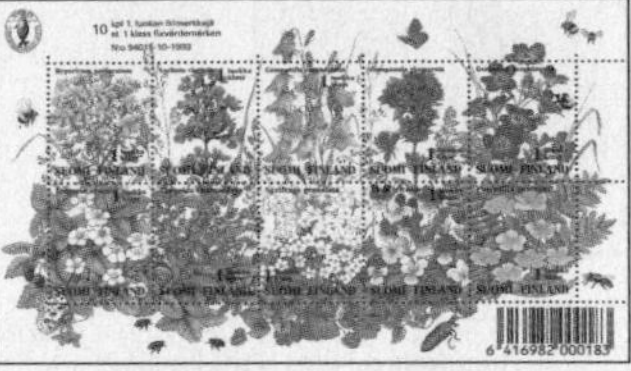
Wildflowers — A509

Designs: a, Hypericum perforatum (b). b, Lychnis viscaria. c, Campanula rotundifolia. d, Campanula glomerata. e, Geranium sanguineum (d). f, Fragaria vesca. g, Veronica chamaedrys (f, h). h, Saxifraga granulata (c, i). i, Viola tricolor (j). j, Potentilla anserina.

**1994, June 1** ***Perf. 12***

**941** A509 1 Sheet of 10 25.00 22.50
*a.-j.* Any single 2.50 .40

No. 941 sold for 23m at time of release. See note following No. 845.

Finland-Sweden Track and Field Meet — A510

No. 942, Seppo Raty, Finland, javelin. No. 943, Patrick Sjoberg, Sweden, high jump.

**1994, Aug. 26** **Litho.** ***Perf. 12½***

**Booklet Stamps**

**942** A510 2.40m multicolored 1.10 .60
**943** A510 2.40m multicolored 1.10 .60
*a.* Booklet pane, 2 each #942-943 4.50 4.50
Complete booklet, #943a 4.50

See Sweden Nos. 2091-2092.

Population Registers, 450th Anniv. — A511

**1994, Sept. 1**

**944** A511 2.40m multicolored 1.10 .35

Intl. Year of the Family — A512

**1994, Sept. 1**

**945** A512 3.40m multicolored 1.40 .90

Souvenir Sheet

Letter Writing Day — A513

Dog Hill Kids in the Post Office: a, At Post Office window. b, Standing in doorway, mail cart. c, Blowing horn, pig. d, Putting letters in mailbox.

**1994, Oct. 7 Litho. *Perf. 14***

**946** A513 2.80m Sheet of 4, #a-d 5.00 5.00

Christmas A514

2.10m, Reindeer, bullfinches on antlers. 2.80m, Elves among snow-covered trees.

**1994, Nov. 4**

**947** A514 2.10m multi 1.25 .25
*a.* Booklet pane of 10 16.00 16.00
Complete booklet, #947a 18.00
**948** A514 2.80m multi, vert. 1.40 .50

Greetings — A515

"Dog Hill Kids," sending/receiving greetings: No. 949, Delivering mail to Moon, spaceman. No. 950, Cat writing letter, clown. No. 951, Receiving mail from postman, baby. No. 952, Writing in bed, friend. No. 953, Winter scene at mailbox, characters at beach. No. 954, On bus, girl friend. No. 955, Standing at microphone with guitar, fan. No. 956, Baby in play pen, teddy bear.

***Perf. 13 on 3 Sides***

**1995, Jan. 30 Litho.**

**Booklet Stamps**

**949** A515 2.80m multicolored 1.75 .75
**950** A515 2.80m multicolored 1.75 .75
**951** A515 2.80m multicolored 1.75 .75
**952** A515 2.80m multicolored 1.75 .75
**953** A515 2.80m multicolored 1.75 .75
**954** A515 2.80m multicolored 1.75 .75
**955** A515 2.80m multicolored 1.75 .75
**956** A515 2.80m multicolored 1.75 .75
*a.* Booklet pane, #949-956 14.00 14.00
Complete booklet, 956a 14.00

Nos. 949-952 are printed tete beche with Nos. 953-956. Soaking in water may affect the holographic images on Nos. 949-956.

Souvenir Sheet

Team Sports — A516

a, Paivi Ikola, pesapallo. b, Jari Kurri, ice hockey. c, Jari Litmanen, soccer. d, Lea Hakala, basketball.

**1995, Jan. 30 *Perf. 13***

**957** A516 3.40m Sheet of 4, #a-d 7.00 7.00

See No. 961.

Membership in European Union — A517

**1995, Jan. 30 *Perf. 14***

**958** A517 3.50m multicolored 1.75 .90

Peace & Liberty — A518

Europa: 2.90m, Stylized parachutists.

**1995, Mar. 1 Litho. *Perf. 14***

**959** A518 2.90m multicolored *1.90 .45*

Endangered Species — A519

Designs: a, Felis lynx. b, Lake, forest. c, Rocks, lake. d, Pusa hispida.

**1995, Mar. 1 *Perf. 13***

**960** Block of 4 5.50 5.50
*a.-d.* A519 2.90m Any single 1.40 1.00

Nos. 960a-960b, 960c-960d are continuous designs. See Russia No. 6249.

**Athlete Type of 1995**

Souvenir Sheet

Motor sports drivers in cars, on motorcycles: a, Timo Makinen. b, Juha Kankkunen. c, Tommi Ahvala. d, Heikki Mikkola.

**1995, May 10 Litho. *Perf. 13***

**961** A516 3.50m Sheet of 4, #a.-d. 6.50 6.50

**Insect Type of 1994**

**1995, May 11**

**962** A508 19m Geotrupes stercorarius 12.50 12.50

Tourism — A520

Designs: 2.80m, Linnanmaki amusement park, Helsinki. 2.90m, Town of Mantyharju.

**1995, May 12**

**963** A520 2.80m multicolored 1.75 .50
**964** A520 2.90m multicolored 1.75 .70

Town of Loviisa, 250th Anniv. — A521

**1995, June 30 Litho. *Perf. 14***

**965** A521 3.20m multicolored 1.40 1.00

Intl. Union of Forestry Research Organizations, 20th World Congress, Tampere — A522

Designs: No. 966, Betula pendula. No. 967, Pinus sylvestris. No. 968, Picea abies. No. 969, Research, tree grown from needle.

***Perf. 14 on 2 or 3 Sides***

**1995, Aug. 8 Litho.**

**Booklet Stamps**

**966** A522 2.80m multicolored 1.25 .50
**967** A522 2.80m multicolored 1.25 .50
**968** A522 2.80m multicolored 1.25 .50
**969** A522 2.80m multicolored 1.25 .50
*a.* Booklet pane of 4, #966-969 5.25 5.25
Complete booklet, #969a 5.25

Wilhelm Roentgen (1845-1923), Discovery of the X-Ray, Cent. — A523

**1995, Aug. 8 *Perf. 14***

**970** A523 4.30m multicolored 1.90 1.25

Cats — A525

**1995, Oct. 9 Litho. *Perf. 13½***

**972** A525 2.80m Somali 1.75 .65
**973** A525 2.80m Siamese 1.75 .65
**974** A525 2.80m Norwegian forest 1.75 .65
**975** A525 2.80m Persian 1.75 .65

**Size: 59x35mm**

**976** A525 2.80m European domestic female 1.75 .65
**977** A525 2.80m Three kittens, frog 1.75 .65
*a.* Booklet pane of 6, #972-977 11.00
Complete booklet, #977a 11.00

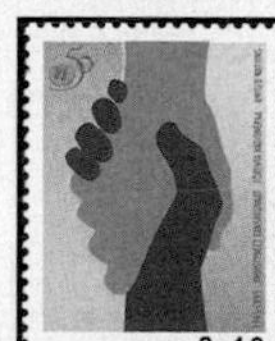


UN, 50th Anniv. — A526

**1995, Oct. 20 *Perf. 14***

**978** A526 3.40m multicolored 1.40 .90

A527

Christmas A528

**1995, Nov. 3 Litho. *Perf. 14***

**979** A527 2m Santa on skates 1.10 .25
**980** A528 2.80m Poinsettias 1.10 .60

Letter Stamps — A529

**1996, Feb 2 Litho. *Perf. 13½x14***

**Booklet Stamps**

**981** A529 1m "M" .65 .65
**982** A529 1m "O" .65 .65
**983** A529 1m "I" .65 .65
**984** A529 1m "H" .65 .65
**985** A529 1m "E" .65 .65
**986** A529 1m "J" .65 .65
**987** A529 1m "A" .65 .65
**988** A529 1m "N" .65 .65
**989** A529 1m "T" .65 .65
**990** A529 1m "P" .65 .65
**991** A529 1m "U" .65 .65
**992** A529 1m "S" .65 .65
*a.* Booklet pane of 12, #981-992 7.75 7.75
Complete booklet, No. 992a 7.75

UNICEF, 50th Anniv. — A530

**1996, Feb. 2 *Perf. 14***

**993** A530 2.80m multicolored 1.10 .55

Women's Gymnastics in Finland, Cent. — A531

**1996, Feb. 26 Litho. *Perf. 13***

**994** A531 2.80m multicolored 1.10 .55

Woman Suffrage, 90th Anniv. A532

**Litho. & Engr.**

**1996, Mar. 8 *Perf. 13***

**995** A532 3.20m multicolored *1.25 .75*

Europa.

Cinema, Cent. — A533

Finnish films: No. 996, "Juha," 1937. No. 997, "Laveata Tieta," 1931. No. 998, "Tuntematon Sotilas," 1935. No. 999, Oldest known photo of a motion picture show, 1896. No. 1000, "Jäniksen Vuosi," 1977. No. 1001, "Valkoinen Peura," 1952. No. 1002, "Kaikki Rakastavat," 1935. No. 1003, "Varjoja Paratiisissa," 1986.

**1996, Apr. 1 Litho. *Perf. 14x13½***

**Booklet Stamps**

**996** A533 2.80m multicolored 1.40 .70
**997** A533 2.80m multicolored 1.40 .70
**998** A533 2.80m multicolored 1.40 .70
**999** A533 2.80m multicolored 1.40 .70
**1000** A533 2.80m multicolored 1.40 .70
**1001** A533 2.80m multicolored 1.40 .70
**1002** A533 2.80m multicolored 1.40 .70
**1003** A533 2.80m multicolored 1.40 .70
*a.* Bklt. pane of 8, #996-1003 11.50 11.50
Complete booklet, #1003a 11.50

Radio, Cent. — A534

**1996, Apr. 25** *Perf. 14*
1004 A534 4.30m multicolored 1.80 1.10

1996 Summer Olympic Games, Atlanta — A535

**1996, June 3 Litho. *Perf. 12 Vert.***
**Booklet Stamps**

1005 A535 3.40m Kayaking 1.75 1.75
1006 A535 3.40m Sailing 1.75 1.75
1007 A535 3.40m Rowing 1.75 1.75
1008 A535 3.40m Swimming 1.75 1.75
*a.* Booklet pane of 4, #1005-1008 7.00 7.00
Complete booklet, #1008a 9.00

**Insect Type of 1994**

**1996, July 1 Litho.** *Perf. 13*
1009 A508 19m Dytiscus marginalis 11.00 11.00

Shore Birds — A536

No. 1010, Gallinago gallinago. No. 1011, Haematopus ostralegus. No. 1012, Scolopax rusticola. No. 1013, Vanellus vanellus. No. 1014, Numenius arquata.

***Perf. 13½ on 3 Sides***
**1996, Sept. 6 Litho. & Engr.**

1010 A536 2.80m multicolored 1.40 .70
1011 A536 2.80m multicolored 1.40 .70
1012 A536 2.80m multicolored 1.40 .70
1013 A536 2.80m multicolored 1.40 .70

**Size: 30x52mm**

1014 A536 2.80m multicolored 1.40 .70
*a.* Sheet of 5, #1010-1014 7.00 7.00

Finnish Comic Strips — A537

No. 1015, "Professor Itikainen" examining plant with magnifying glass, by Ilmari Vainio. No. 1016, "Pekka Puupää (Peter Blockhead)" taking letter from mailbox, by Ola Fogelberg. No. 1017, "Joonas" holding drawing pencil, by Veikko Savolainen. No. 1018, "Mämmilä" wearing helmet, by Tarmo Koivisto. No. 1019, "Rymy-Eetu" smoking pipe, by Erkki Tanttu. No. 1020, "Kieku" writing letter, by Asmo Alho. No. 1021, "Pikku Risunen" with animal, by Riitta Uusitalo. No. 1022, "Kiti" holding up pencil, by Kati Kovács.

**1996, Oct. 9 Litho.** *Perf. 13½*
**Booklet Stamps**

1015 A537 2.80m black & red 1.40 .75
1016 A537 2.80m black & red 1.40 .75
1017 A537 2.80m red & black 1.40 .75
1018 A537 2.80m black & red 1.40 .75
1019 A537 2.80m black & red 1.40 .75
1020 A537 2.80m red & black 1.40 .75
1021 A537 2.80m red & black 1.40 .75
1022 A537 2.80m red & black 1.40 .75
*a.* Bklt. pane of 8, #1015-1022 11.00 11.00
Complete booklet, #1022a 11.00

Christmas A538

2m, Snowman, Santa, gnome playing musical instruments. 2.80m, Rabbit, reindeer watching northern lights. 3.20m, Santa reading letters.

**1996, Nov. 1 Litho.** *Perf. 14*
1023 A538 2m multi 1.75 .50
1024 A538 2.80m multi 1.75 .55
1025 A538 3.20m multi, vert. 2.75 .85
*Nos. 1023-1025 (3)* 6.25 1.90

Greetings Stamps — A539

End of 19th cent.: No. 1026, Two angels. No. 1027, Flowers in basket. No. 1028, Hand reaching through garland, bluebird. No. 1029, Boy, girl dancing. No. 1030, Boy, envelope, shamrocks. No. 1031, Clasping hands through heart-shaped garlands. No. 1032, Roses. No. 1033, Angel.

***Perf. 13x12½ on 3 Sides***
**1997, Jan. 30 Litho.**
**Booklet Stamps**

1026 A539 1 multicolored 2.50 .65
1027 A539 1 multicolored 2.50 .65
1028 A539 1 multicolored 2.50 .65
1029 A539 1 multicolored 2.50 .65
1030 A539 1 multicolored 2.50 .65
1031 A539 1 multicolored 2.50 .65
1032 A539 1 multicolored 2.50 .65
1033 A539 1 multicolored 2.50 .65
*a.* Bklt. pane of 8, #1026-1033 20.00 20.00
Complete booklet, #1033a 20.00

Nos. 1026-1033 sold for 2.80m on day of issue.

Number on stamp represents class of mail.

Mail Order Sales in Finland, Cent. — A540

**1997, Jan. 30** *Perf. 13½x14*
1034 A540 2.80m multicolored 1.10 .45

1997 Ice Hockey World Championships, Helsinki — A541

**1997, Jan. 30**
1035 A541 2.80m multicolored 1.20 .50

On each stamp from the right vertical row of the sheet, No. 1035 exists without the thin, curved black line at the center right edge of the stamp. Value, single stamp $3.00.

Lepus Timidus A542

**1997, Mar. 4 Litho.** *Perf. 14*
1036 A542 2.80m multicolored 1.10 .40

Saami Folktale, "Girl Who Turned into a Golden Merganser" — A543

Europa: 3.20m, Duck, girl, prince. 3.40m, Girl falling into crevice.

**1997, Mar. 4** *Perf. 13*
1037 A543 3.20m multicolored *1.50 .50*
1038 A543 3.40m multicolored *2.00 1.00*

Paavo Nurmi (1897-1973), Winner of 9 Olympic Gold Medals — A544

**1997, Mar. 18** *Perf. 14*
1039 A544 3.40m multicolored 1.40 1.20

Southwest Archipelago Natl. Park — A545

**Litho. & Engr.**
**1997, Apr. 25** *Perf. 14*
1040 A545 4.30m multicolored 1.75 1.10

Tango — A546

**1997, May 19 Litho.**
1041 A546 1 multicolored 2.50 .40
Complete booklet of 5 12.50

No. 1041 sold for 2.80m on day of release. Number on stamp represents class of mail.

A547

Sailing Ships: No. 1042, Astrid. No. 1043, Jacobstads Wapen. No. 1044, Tradewind. No. 1045, Merikokko. No. 1046, Suomen Joutsen. No. 1047, Sigyn.

**Booklet Stamps**

**1997, May 19** *Perf. 13½*
1042 A547 2.80m multicolored 1.25 .60
1043 A547 2.80m multicolored 1.25 .60
1044 A547 2.80m multicolored 1.25 .60
1045 A547 2.80m multicolored 1.25 .60

**Size: 48x25½mm**

1046 A547 2.80m multicolored 1.25 .60
1047 A547 2.80m multicolored 1.25 .60
*a.* Booklet pane of 6, #1042-1047 7.50
Complete booklet, #1047a 7.50

Pres. Martti Ahtisaari, 60th Birthday A548

**1997, June 23 Litho.** *Perf. 14*
1048 A548 2.80m multicolored 1.10 .40

Independence, 80th Anniv. — A549

Four seasons: No. 1049, Spring, lily-of-the-valley (natl. flower). No. 1050, Summer, white clouds. No. 1051, Fall, colorful leaves. No. 1052, Winter, snow crystals.

***Perf. 13x12½ on 2 or 3 Sides***
**1997, June 23 Booklet Stamps**

1049 A549 2.80m multicolored 1.10 .65
1050 A549 2.80m multicolored 1.10 .65
1051 A549 2.80m multicolored 1.10 .65
1052 A549 2.80m multicolored 1.10 .65
*a.* Booklet pane, #1049-1052 4.50 4.50
Complete booklet, #1052a 4.50

**Souvenir Sheet**

A550

Grus Grus (Cranes): a, With young. b, With frog. c, Performing mating dance. d, In flight.

**1997, Aug. 19 Litho.** *Perf. 14*
1053 A550 2.80m Sheet of 4, #a.-d. 5.00 5.00

A551

Finnish Writers Assoc. (Covers from books): No. 1054, "Seven Brothers," by Aleksis Kivi. No. 1055, "Sinuhe the Egyptian," by Mika Waltari. No. 1056, "Täällä Pohjantähden alla I," by Väinö Linna. No. 1057, "Hyvästi Iijoki," by Kalle Päätalo. No. 1058, "Haukka, minum rakkaani," by Kaari Utrio. No. 1059, "Juhannustanssit," by Hannu Salama. No. 1060, "Manillaköysi," by Veijo Meri. No. 1061, "Uppo-Nalle ja Kumma," by Elina Karjalainen.

**Booklet Stamps**

**1997, Oct. 9 Litho.** *Perf. 14¼, 14½*
1054 A551 2.80m multicolored 1.25 .75
1055 A551 2.80m multicolored 1.25 .75
1056 A551 2.80m multicolored 1.25 .75
1057 A551 2.80m multicolored 1.25 .75
1058 A551 2.80m multicolored 1.25 .75
1059 A551 2.80m multicolored 1.25 .75
1060 A551 2.80m multicolored 1.25 .75
1061 A551 2.80m multicolored 1.25 .75
*a.* Booklet pane, #1054-1061 10.00 10.00
Complete booklet, #1061a 10.00

No. 1056 exists perf 14½x14¼. The other values also should exist thus. The editors would like to examine such stamps.

Christmas A552

**1997, Oct. 31**
1062 A552 2m Village 1.00 .40
1063 A552 2.80m Candelabra, vert. 1.00 .40
1064 A552 3.20m Church, vert. 1.25 .65
*Nos. 1062-1064 (3)* 3.25 1.45

Wildlife A553

2nd, Stizostedion lucioperca. 1st, Turdus merula.

***Die Cut Perf. 10 Horiz. Syncopated***

**1998, Jan. 15 Litho.**

**Self-Adhesive**

**Coil Stamps**

**1065** A553 2 multicolored 2.75 .40
**1066** A553 1 multicolored 2.00 .35

Nos. 1065-1066 were valued at 2.40m and 2.80m, respectively, on date of issue. Number on stamp represents class of mail.

See Nos. 1099-1100.

A554

Moomin Cartoon Characters, by Tove Jansson: No. 1067, Boy Moomin drawing with pad and pencil. No. 1068, Girl Moomin in sunshine. No. 1069, Organ grinder. No. 1070, Boy Moomin giving flower to girl Moomin.

**1998, Jan. 15** ***Perf. 13 on 3 Sides***

**Booklet Stamps**

**1067** A554 1 multicolored 2.90 .60
**1068** A554 1 multicolored 2.90 .60
**1069** A554 1 multicolored 2.90 .60
**1070** A554 1 multicolored 2.90 .60
*a.* Booklet pane, #1067-1070 12.00 12.00
Complete booklet, #1070a 12.00

Nos. 1067-1070 each sold for 2.80m on day of issue. Number on stamp represents class of mail.

See No. 1127.

A555

**1998, Feb. 3** ***Perf. 14***

**1071** A555 2.80m multicolored 1.20 .30

Finnish Federation of Nurses, cent.

A556

Valentine's Day Surprise Stamps. (Designs beneath scratch-off heart): a, Musical notes, two dogs. b, Elephant, mouse and flowers. c, Puppy, sealed envelope. d, Kittens, kittens hugging. e, Dog with nose in air, bouquet of flowers. f, Flowers, two rodents.

**1998, Feb. 3** ***Perf. 12***

**1072** 1 Sheet of 6 15.00 9.50
*a.-f.* A556 Any single, unscratched 2.50 .75

Nos. 1072a-1072f were each valued at 2.80m on day of issue. Number on stamp represents class of mail. Unused values are for singles with attached selvage. Inscriptions are shown in selvage above or below each stamp.

Each stamp bears a heart-shaped, golden scratch-off overlay. Values are for unscratched examples. Scratched stamps, with hearts partially or fully removed, sell for about 20 percent less.

Tussilago Farfara — A557

**1998, Mar. 27 Litho.** ***Perf. 14***

**1073** A557 2.80m multi 1.20 .30

National Festivals A558

Europa: 3.20m, Boy and girl, balloons, "Vappu" (May Day). 3.40m, Boy and girl in a dream floating over water, Midsummer Festival.

**1998, Mar. 27** ***Perf. 14x14½***

**1074** A558 3.20m multicolored *2.00* .30
**1075** A558 3.40m multicolored *2.75* .80

Finnish Marine Research Institute, 80th Anniv. — A559

Designs: 2.80m, Research vessel, "Aranda." 3.20m, "Vega," chart showing route of Nils Adolf Erik Nordenskjold's expedition.

**Litho. & Engr.**

**1998, May 7** ***Perf. 14x13***

**1076** A559 2.80m multicolored 1.40 .40
**1077** A559 3.20m multicolored 1.50 .60

First Performance of National Anthem, 150th Anniv. — A560

**1998, May 7** ***Perf. 13***

**1078** A560 5m multicolored 2.00 1.00

Puppies A561

No. 1079, Bernese Mountain dog. No. 1080, Puli. No. 1081, Boxer. No. 1082, Bichon Frisé. No. 1083, Finnish lapphound. No. 1084, Wirehaired dachshund. No. 1085, Scottish cairn terrier. No. 1086, Labrador retriever.

***Perf. 13½x13 on 2 or 3 Sides***

**1998, June 4 Litho.**

**Booklet Stamps**

**1079** A561 1 multicolored 2.50 .60
**1080** A561 1 multicolored 2.50 .60
**1081** A561 1 multicolored 2.50 .60
**1082** A561 1 multicolored 2.50 .60
**1083** A561 1 multicolored 2.50 .60
**1084** A561 1 multicolored 2.50 .60
**1085** A561 1 multicolored 2.50 .60
**1086** A561 1 multicolored 2.50 .60
*a.* Booklet pane, #1079-1086 20.00 20.00
Complete booklet, #1086a 20.00

Nos. 1079-1086 each sold for 2.80m on day of issue. Number on stamp represents class of mail.

Owls — A562

Designs: a, Bubo bubo. b, Wing of bubo bubo. c, Bubo bubo, aegolius funereus. d, Strix nebulosa. e, Nyctea scandiaca.

**1998, Sept. 4 Litho.** ***Perf. 13½***

**1087** Sheet of 5 + label 6.00 6.00
*a.-e.* A562 3m any single 1.20 1.20

No. 1087b is 52x27mm; Nos. 1087c-1087d, 26x44mm; No. 1087e, 30x44mm.

See No. 1113.

Cycling — A563

**1998, Sept. 4** ***Perf. 14***

**1088** A563 3m multicolored 1.25 1.25

Finnish Design — A564

No. 1089, Savoy vases, by Alvar Aalto. No. 1090, Karuselli chair, by Yrjö Kukkapuro. No. 1091, Tasaraita knitwear, designed by Annika Rimala for Marimekko. No. 1092, Kilta tableware set, by Kaj Franck. No. 1093, Cast iron pot, by Timo Sarpaneva. No. 1094, Carelia cutlery set, by Bertel Gardberg.

***Perf. 13½ on 3 Sides***

**1998, Oct. 9 Litho.**

**Booklet Stamps**

**1089** A564 3m multicolored 1.40 .75
**1090** A564 3m multicolored 1.40 .75
**1091** A564 3m multicolored 1.40 .75
**1092** A564 3m multicolored 1.40 .75
**1093** A564 3m multicolored 1.40 .75
**1094** A564 3m multicolored 1.40 .75
*a.* Booklet pane, #1089-1094 8.00 8.00
Complete booklet, #1094a 8.00

Nos. 1090-1091, 1093-1094 are 29x34mm.

Christmas A565

Designs: 2m, Christmas tree, children, vert. 3m, Children, dog riding sled. 3.20m, Winter scene of cottage in center of island.

**1998, Oct. 30** ***Perf. 14***

**1095** A565 2m multicolored 1.25 .55
**1096** A565 3m multicolored 1.40 .40
**1097** A565 3.20m multicolored 1.50 .65
*Nos. 1095-1097 (3)* 4.15 1.60

Souvenir Sheet

Mika Häkkinen, Formula 1 Driving Champion — A566

**1999, Jan. 15** ***Perf. 13½***

**1098** A566 3m multicolored 3.00 3.00

**Native Wildlife Type of 1998**

2, Salmo salar. 1, Luscinia svecica.

***Die Cut Perf. 10 Horiz. Syncopated***

**1999, Jan. 27 Litho.**

**Coil Stamps**

**Self-Adhesive**

**1099** A553 2 multi 2.00 .60

***Die Cut Perf. 10 Vert. Syncopated***

**1100** A553 1 multi, vert. 2.75 .60

Nos. 1099-1100 were valued at 2.40m and 3m, respectively, on day of issue. Number on stamp represents class of mail.

Friendship A567

Animals' tails: No. 1101, Zebra, lion. No. 1102, Dog, cat.

**Booklet Stamps**

***Serpentine Die Cut Perf. 13 Horiz.***

**1999, Jan. 27 Self-Adhesive**

**1101** A567 3m multicolored 1.25 1.20
**1102** A567 3m multicolored 1.25 1.20
*a.* Bklt. pane, 3 each #1101-1102 8.50 8.00

No. 1102a is a complete booklet.

Finnish Labor Movement, Cent. — A568

**1999, Jan. 27** ***Perf. 13½***

**1103** A568 4.50m multicolored 1.80 1.80

Finland's Roads — A569

No. 1104, Snow-covered landscape, Arctic Ocean Road. No. 1105, Freeway interchanges, Jyväsjtkä Lakeshore Road. No. 1106, Raippaluoto Bridge. No. 1107, Wooded drive, Kitee.

**1999, Feb. 15 Litho.** ***Perf. 14 Horiz.***

**Booklet Stamps**

**1104** A569 3m multicolored 1.25 .75
*a.* Perf. 12¾ horiz. *75.00* *13.00*
**1105** A569 3m multicolored 1.25 .75
*a.* Perf. 12¾ horiz. *75.00* *13.00*
**1106** A569 3m multicolored 1.25 .75
*a.* Perf. 12¾ horiz. *75.00* *13.00*
**1107** A569 3m multicolored 1.25 .75
*a.* Booklet pane, #1104-1107 5.00
Complete booklet, #1107a 6.00
*b.* Perf. 12¾ horiz. *75.00* *13.00*
*c.* Booklet pane, #1104a, 1105a, 1106a, 1107b *300.00* *300.00*
Complete booklet, #1107c *325.00*

A570

Women's Kalevala-style brooches: a, Horse clasp. b, Bird clasp. c, Virusmäki clasp.

**1999, Feb. 15** *Perf. 13½x14*
**1108** Sheet of 3 3.75 3.75
*a.-c.* A570 3m any single 1.25 1.10

1st Publication of Legend of the Kalevala, 150th Anniv.

Crocus Vernus — A571

**1999, Mar. 15** *Perf. 13x13½*
**1109** A571 3m multi 1.25 .60

Martha Organization, Cent. — A572

**1999, Mar. 15** *Perf. 13½x13*
**1110** A572 3m multicolored 1.25 .60

Europa A573

**1999, Mar. 15** *Perf. 13½x14*
**1111** A573 2.70m Esplanade Park *1.75 .50*
**1112** A573 3.20m Ruissalo Park *3.00 .60*

**Bird Type of 1998**

Designs: a, Luscinia luscinia. b, Cuculus canorus. c, Botaurus stellaris. d, Caprimulgus europaeus. e, Crex crex.

**1999, May 18** *Perf. 13½*
**1113** Sheet of 5 + label 6.00 6.00
*a.-e.* A562 3m any single 1.10 .75

No. 1113b is 25x43mm. No. 1113c is 45x30mm. No. 1113d-1113e are 26x37mm.

Finland's Presidency of European Union — A574

**1999, July 1 Litho.** *Perf. 13¾x13½*
**1114** A574 3.50m multicolored 1.40 .60

Finnish Entertainers A575

a, Harmony Sisters, Vera (1914-97), Maire (1916-95) & Raija (1918-97) Valtonen. b, Olavi Virta (1915-72), singer. c, Georg Malmstén (1902-81), composer, conductor. d, Topi Kärki (1915-22), composer, and Reino (Repe) Helismaa (1913-65), lyricist. e, Tapio Rautavaara (1915-79), singer. f, Esa Parkarinen (1911-89), musician, actor.

*Perf. 13¼ on 3 Sides*

**1999, Sept. 6 Litho.**
**1115** Booklet pane of 6 8.50
*a.-f.* A575 3.50m any single 1.40 .75
Complete booklet, #1115 8.50

Nos. 1115a, 1115d are each 60x34mm.

Finnish Commercial Product Design — A576

a, Fiskars cutting tools. b, Zoel/Versoul guitars. c, Ergo II/Silenta hearing protectors. d, Ponsse Cobra HS 10 tree harvester. e, Suunto compass. f, Exel Avanti QLS ski pole.

*Perf. 13¼ on 3 Sides*

**1999, Oct 8 Litho.**
**1116** Booklet pane of 6 8.00
*a.-f.* A576 3.50m any single 1.40 .75
Complete booklet, #1116 10.50

Size of b, c, e, f: 30x35mm.

"The Nativity," by Giorgio di Chirico (1888-1978) A577

Rabbits, Birds — A578

**1999, Nov. 5** *Perf. 14*
**1117** A578 2.50m Santa Claus, vert. .90 .40
**1118** A577 3m multicolored 1.20 1.20
**1119** A578 3.50m multicolored 1.60 .60
*Nos. 1117-1119 (3)* 3.70 2.20

Christmas. See Italy Nos. 2314-2315.

Sveaborg Fortress — A579

**2000, Jan. 12 Litho.** *Perf. 13¾x13½*
**1120** A579 7.20m multi 3.00 1.75

Helsinki, 450th Anniv. A580

Designs: No. 1121, Baltic herring market (designer's name at UL).

No. 1122: a, Museum of Contemporary Art (blue building), vert. b, Cathedral, Senate Square (green building). c, Finlandia Hall (orange building). d, Glass Palace Film and Media Center (red building), vert.

No. 1123: a, Quest for the Lost Crown, Sveaborg Fortress (children and arch), vert. b, Like No. 1121, no designer's name. c, Forces of Light City Festival. d, Cellist at outdoor concert, Kaivopuisto Park.

**2000, Jan. 12** *Perf. 14*
**1121** A580 3.50m multi 1.40 .70

*Perf. 14½x14¾ (vert. stamps), 14¾x14½*

**1122** Booklet pane of 4 6.50 6.50
*a.-d.* A580 3.50m Any single 1.60 1.60
**1123** Booklet pane of 4 6.50 6.50
*a.-d.* A580 3.50m Any single 1.60 1.60
Complete booklet, #1122-1123 13.00

Valentine's Day — A581

Designs: a, Earth as backpack. b, Painters on ladder. c, Birds in balloon. d, Alien with magnet. e, Boy with heart-shaped balloon. f, Polar bear and igloo.

*Perf. 13x12¾ on 3 sides*

**2000, Jan. 12**
**1124** Bklt. pane of 6 + 4 labels 8.50
*a.-f.* A581 3.50m Any single 1.40 .70
Complete booklet, #1124 8.50

Souvenir Sheet of 2

Tommi Mäkinen, 1999 Rally World Champion — A582

a, Mäkinen behind wheel. b, Race car.

**2000, Mar. 3** *Perf. 13x13¼*
**1125** A582 3.50m #a.-b. 3.00 3.00

Easter — A583

**2000, Mar. 15** *Perf. 13¾x13¼*
**1126** A583 3.50m Caltha palustris 1.40 .70

**Moomin Type of 1998**

a, Rat with broom looking at Moomins. b, Moomin with uniform, figures sprouting from ground. c, Moomin with hat in forest. d, Moomin with hat, children, in front of stove.

*Perf. 13x12¾ on 3 Sides*

**2000, Mar. 15**
**1127** Booklet pane of 4 27.50 27.50
*a.-d.* A554 1 Any single 6.50 2.50
Complete booklet, #1127 30.00 12.00
*e.* As #1127, perf. 13¼ on 3 sides 12.00
*f.-i.* As #a-d, perf. 13¼ on 3 sides 2.75 .65
Booklet, #1127e 12.50

Nos. 1127a-1127d sold for 3.50m on day of issue. Number on stamp represents class of mail.

Issued: No. 1127e, 7/10/00.

Jubilee Year — A584

Turku Cathedral: a, Nave. b, Woman, votive candles. c, Christ on the Mount of Transfiguration, alterpiece. d, Infant baptism.

**2000, Mar. 15 Litho.** *Perf. 14 Vert.*
**1128** Booklet pane of 4 6.00 3.50
*a.-d.* A584 3.50m Any single 1.50 .60
Complete booklet, #1128 6.00

**Europa, 2000**
Common Design Type

**2000, May 9** *Perf. 13¼x13*
**1129** CD17 3.50m multi 2.00 .60

**Provincial Flowers**

Spring Anemone A585

Blue Cornflower A586

Pulsatilla Patens — A587

*Die Cut Perf. 13x12½*

**2000-01 Litho.**

**Booklet Stamps Self-Adhesive**

**1130** A585 1 multi 2.50 .50
*a.* Booklet pane of 10 16.00

*Die Cut Perf. 14¾x13½*

**1131** A586 1 multi 2.50 .50
**1132** A587 1 multi 2.50 .50
*a.* Booklet pane, 5 each #1131-1132 25.00

Number on stamp represents class of mail. No. 1130 sold for 3.50m at time of release. Nos. 1131-1132 each sold for 3.60m on day of issue. No. 1132a was issued in two printings. The white box containing the stamps on the original printing is 114mm wide and on the 2003 printing, the box is 110mm wide.

Issued: No. 1130, 5/9. Nos. 1131-1132, 5/16/01.

Souvenir Sheet

Science — A595

Designs: a, Children, molecuar model (triangular stamp). b, Man's face, DNA strand (rhomboid stamp). c, Man's face, Sierpinski triangles (square stamp).

**2000, May 30** *Perf. 14¼*
**1140** A595 3.50m Sheet of 3, #a.-c. 4.25 4.25

No. 1140 has holographic image. Soaking in water may affect the hologram.

Finnish Design — A596

No. 1141: a, Rug, by Akseli Gallen-Kallela (1865-1931). b, Pearl Bird, by Birger Kaipiainen (1915-88). c, Pot, by Kyllikki Salmenhaara (1915-81). d, Leaf, by Tapio Wirkkala (1915-85). e, Detail from damask, by Dora Jung (1906-80). f, Glass vase, by Valter Jung (1879-1946).

***Perf. 13¼ on 3 Sides***

**2000, Sept. 5** **Litho.**

**1141** Booklet pane of 6 8.00 8.00
***a.-f.*** A596 3.50m Any single 1.50 1.00
Booklet, #1141 8.00

Size of b, c, e, f: 30x35mm.

Coregonus Lavaretus A597

Lagopus Lagopus A598

**Coil Stamps**

***Die Cut Perf. 10 Horiz. Syncopated***

**2000, Sept. 5** **Self-Adhesive**

**1142** A597 2 multi 2.50 .50
**1143** A598 1 multi 2.50 .50

Nos. 1142-1143 sold for 3m and 3.50m respectively on day of sale.

On modern stamps bearing the "denominations" "1" or "2," the number represents the class of mail.

Christmas A599

2.50m, Costumed Tiernapojat carol singers. 3.50m, Bullfinch on door ornament, vert.

***Serpentine Die Cut 14¼***

**2000, Nov. 3** **Photo.**

**Self-Adhesive**

**1144-1145** A599 Set of 2 3.00 .90

**Litho.**

***Serpentine Die Cut 13¾***

**1146** A599 3.50m multi + label 7.00 5.25

No. 1146 issued in sheets of 20 that sold for 120m, together with a separate sheet of stickers that could be affixed on the label. The labels attached to the stamps are separated by a row of interrupted serpentine die cutting. Labels could be personalized with photographs taken at some sale sites.

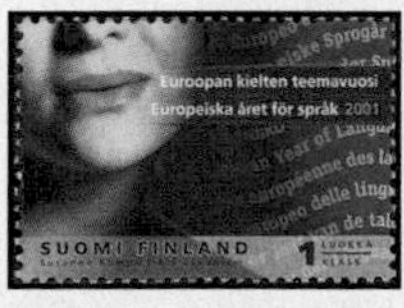


European Year of Languages A600

**2001, Jan. 17** **Litho.** ***Perf. 13¼***

**1147** A600 1 multi 2.50 .75

No. 1147 sold for 3.50m on day of sale.

World Ski Championships, Lahti — A601

No. 1148: a, Ski jumper Janne Ahonen (yellow helmet). b, Skier Mika Myllylä.

**2001, Jan. 17**

**1148** A601 3.50m Horiz. pair, #a-b 2.75 2.75

Valentine's Day — A602

No. 1149: a, Oval wreath. b, Basket of flowers, letter. c, Heart-shaped wreath. d, Bouquet of flowers, letter. e, Flowers, tea set. f, Flowers, heart-shaped pastry.

***Serpentine Die Cut 11½x11¾ on 3 Sides***

**2001, Jan. 17** **Photo.**

**Self-Adhesive**

**1149** Booklet pane of 6 15.00 10.00
***a.-f.*** A602 1 Any single 2.50 .75
Booklet, #1149 15.00

Nos. 1149a-1149f each sold for 3.50m on day of issue.

Souvenir Sheet

Donald Duck Comics in Finland, 50th Anniv. — A603

No. 1150: a, Mickey Mouse, Donald Duck, Santa Claus, Goofy. b, First comics, silhouette of boy. c, Tin soldier with Finnish flag, Chip and Dale (25x30mm). d, Finnish epic hero Väinämöinen, silhouette of Donald Duck. e, Helsinki Cathedral, Donald Duck.

***Perf. 7¾ on 3 or 4 Sides***

**2001, Mar. 13** **Litho.**

**1150** A603 1 Sheet of 5, #a-e 12.50 8.00

Nos. 1150a-1150e sold for 3.50m each on day of issue.

Santa Claus and Sleigh — A604

**2001-04** ***Serpentine Die Cut 14½x14***

**Self-Adhesive**

**1151** A604 1 multi 2.50 .75
***a.*** Serpentine die cut 13¾x13¼ ('04) 2.75 .80

No. 1151 sold for 3.60m on day of issue. No. 1151a sold for 65c on day of issue.
No. 1151, 4/2/01. No. 1151a, 12/04.

Europa A605

**2001, Apr. 2** ***Perf. 13x13½***

**1152** A605 5.40m multi 3.00 3.00

Easter — A606

No. 1153: a, Chick. b, Decorated egg.

**2001, Apr. 2** ***Perf. 13¼***

**1153** A606 3.60m Horiz. pair, #a-b 2.75 2.50

Souvenir Sheet

Verla Mill, UNESCO World Heritage Site — A607

Denominations in: a, UL. b, UR. c, LL. d, LR.

**2001, Apr. 2**

**1154** A607 3.60m Sheet of 4, #a-d 5.50 4.00

Orienteering World Championships, Tampere — A608

**2001, May 16**

**1155** A608 3.60m multi 1.75 .75

Values are for stamps with surrounding selvage.

Souvenir Sheet

Woodpeckers — A609

No. 1156: a, Dendrocopos minor (32x36mm). b, Picoides tridactylus (29x36mm). c, Dendrocopos leucotos (32x42mm). d, Dendrocopos major (29x42mm). e, Picus canus (32x41mm). f, Dryocopus martius (29x41mm).

***Perf. 14½x14¼ on 2, 3 or 4 Sides***

**2001, May 16**

**1156** A609 3.60m Sheet of 6, #a-f 10.00 8.00

Marine Life — A610

No. 1157: a, Lampetra fluviatilis. b, Aspius aspius. c, Coregonus albula.

***Die Cut Perf. 10 Horiz. Syncopated***

**2001, Sept. 6** **Photo.**

**Self-Adhesive**

**Coil Stamps**

**1157** Horiz. strip of 3 7.00 5.00
***a.-c.*** A610 2 Any single 2.25 .35

Nos. 1157a-1157c were sold in boxes of 100 stamps that sold at a discount price of 270m on day of sale. The franking value on the day of sale for each stamp was 3m.

Birds A611

No. 1158: a, Parus caeruleus. b, Motacilla alba. c, Oriolus oriolus.

***Die Cut Perf. 10 Horiz. Syncopated***

**2001, Sept. 6** **Photo.**

**Self-Adhesive**

**Coil Stamps**

**1158** Horiz. strip of 3 7.00 4.75
***a.-c.*** A611 1 Any single 2.25 .35

Nos. 1158a-1158c were sold in boxes of 100 stamps that sold at a discount price of 330m on day of sale. The franking value on the day of sale for each stamp was 3.60m.

History of Gulf of Finland A612

No. 1159: a, Utö Lighthouse. b, Wreck of the St. Mikael. c, Diver exploring St. Mikael. d, Opossum shrimp, isopod. e, Ship's cabin and nautical chart (32x55mm).

***Perf. 13¼x13¾ on 2 or 3 Sides***

**2001, Sept. 6** **Litho.**

**1159** Booklet pane of 5 12.50 9.50
***a.-e.*** A612 1 Any single 2.50 1.00
Booklet, #1159 12.50

Nos. 1159a-1159e each sold for 3.60m on day of sale.

See No. 1177.

Christmas A613

Designs: 2.50m, Elf reading Santa's book, candle. 3.60m, Elf delivering package on sled, horiz.

***Serpentine Die Cut 14¼***

**2001, Oct. 26** **Photo.**

**Self-Adhesive**

**1160** A613 2.50m multi 1.10 .40
**1161** A613 3.60m multi 1.40 .65

Slightly larger examples of Nos. 1160-1161 serpentine die cut 14 are known on first day and other covers produced by the postal service. They were not sold unused to the public.

**100 Cents = 1 Euro (€)**

Flowers — A614

National Symbols A615

Heraldic Lion — A616

Type A614 — No. 1162, Myosotis scorpioides: a, Forty-one flowers. b, Four flowers, five buds. c, One flower, four buds. d, Entire plant. e, Five flowers.

No. 1163, Convallaria majallis: a, Leaf, stem with five flowers. b, Two leaves, stem with eight flowers. c, Two flowers. d, Two leaves, stem with five flowers. e, Entire plants.

Type A615: 50c, Swan, vert. 60c, Birch. 1, Flag and bird. 90c, Kymintehtaalta, by Victor Westerholm. €1.30, Granite cliff. €2.50, Spruce. €3.50, Pine.

***Die Cut Perf. 15***

**2002, Jan. 1 Photo.**

**Self-Adhesive**

**1162** Vert. strip of 5 .80 .80
*a.-e.* A614 5c Any single .25 .25
*f.* As #1162, die cut perf 14 .80
*g.-k.* A614 5c Any single, die cut perf 14 .25 .25

***Die Cut Perf. 14***

**1163** Vert. strip of 5 1.75 1.75
*a.-e.* A614 10c Any single .35 .25
**1164** A615 50c multi 1.60 .40
**1165** A615 60c multi 2.00 .40

***Die Cut Perf. 13¾***

**1166** A615 1 multi 2.50 .40
*a.* Booklet pane of 10 25.00
Booklet, #1166a 25.00

***Die Cut Perf. 14¾x15***

**1167** A615 90c multi 3.00 .65

***Die Cut Perf. 12 Syncopated***

**1168** A616 €1 blue & multi 3.25 .65

***Die Cut Perf. 14¾x15***

**1169** A615 €1.30 multi 4.00 1.20
*a.* Die cut perf 14 ('04) 4.50 1.20

***Die Cut Perf. 14***

**1170** A615 €2.50 multi 8.00 1.25
**1171** A615 €3.50 multi 11.00 1.75

***Die Cut Perf. 12 Syncopated***

**1172** A616 €5 red & multi 16.00 5.00
*Nos. 1162-1172 (11)* 53.90 14.25

No. 1166 sold for 60c on day of issue.

Die cut perf 14 examples of No. 1167 exist on first day and other covers produced by the postal service. They were not sold unused to the public.

No. 1169a issued 7/04. No. 1169a has a duller blue panel and a duller black denomination than that found on No. 1169, and a die cut perf. 14 version of No. 1169 that was available only on first day covers with 1/1/02 cancels, and which was not made available to the public unused. Nos. 1169 and 1169a were produced by different printers.

Nos. 1162f-1162k were printed and put on first day and other covers in 2002 but were not sold to the public until 2006.

See Nos. 1179-1180, 1383-1384.

Easter — A617

***Die Cut Perf. 14***

**2002, Mar. 6 Photo.**

**Self-Adhesive**

**1173** A617 60c multi 1.90 .75

Souvenir Sheet

Elias Lönnrot (1802-84), Botanist, Linguist — A618

No. 1174: a, Plantain. b, Opening lines of "Kalevala" (denomination at UL). c, Closing lines of "Kalevala" (denomination at UR). d, Portrait.

***Perf. 13¼ on 3 or 4 Sides***

**2002, Mar. 6 Litho.**

**1174** A618 60c Sheet of 4, #a-d 7.50 5.50

Souvenir Sheet

Old Rauma, UNESCO World Heritage Site — A619

Denominations at: a, UL. b, UR. c, LL. d, LR.

**2002, Mar. 6** ***Perf. 13½***

**1175** A619 60c Sheet of 4, #a-d 7.50 5.50

Europa — A620

**2002, Apr. 15** ***Perf. 13***

**1176** A620 60c multi *2.50 1.25*

**Gulf of Finland Type of 2001**

No. 1177: a, Birds, fish. b, Sailboat, plankton. c, Flounder on sea bed. d, Shrimp, herring. e, Tvärminne Zoological Station, ship, isopod, oceanographic equipment, mussels (32x55mm).

***Perf. 13¼x13¾ on 2 or 3 Sides***

**2002, Apr. 15**

**1177** Booklet pane of 5 12.50 9.00
*a.-e.* A612 1 Any single 2.50 1.25
Booklet, #1177 12.50

Nos. 1177a-1177e each sold for 60c on day of issue.

Sibelius Monument, Helsinki, by Eila Hiltunen A621

**2002, May 3** ***Perf. 13***

**1178** A621 60c multi 1.90 .50

**National Symbols Type of 2002 Without Finland Post Emblem**

Designs: 60c, Juniperus communis. 1, Reindeer in Lapland.

***Die Cut Perf. 14***

**2002, Oct. 9 Photo.**

**Self-Adhesive**

**1179** A615 60c multi 1.90 .50
**1180** A615 1 multi 2.50 .50

No. 1180 sold for 60c on day of issue.

Christmas A622

Designs: 45c, Horse-drawn sleigh. 60c, Angel with trumpet, vert.

***Serpentine Die Cut 14¼***

**2002, Nov. 1 Self-Adhesive**

**1181-1182** A622 Set of 2 3.75 1.50

Fish — A623

No. 1183: a, Abramis brama. b, Salmo trutta lacustris. c, Esox lucius.

***Syncopated Die Cut Perf. 10 Horiz.***

**2003, Jan. 15 Self-Adhesive**

**Coil Stamps**

**1183** Horiz. strip of 3 8.00 8.00
*a.-c.* A623 2 Any single 2.50 2.50

Nos. 1183a-1183c were sold in boxes of 100 that sold at a discount price of €47 on day of issue. The franking value on the day of issue for each stamp was 50c.

Birds — A624

No. 1184: a, Cuculus canorus. b, Alauda arvensis. c, Perisoreus infaustus.

***Syncopated Die Cut Perf. 10 Horiz.***

**2003, Jan. 15 Self-Adhesive**

**Coil Stamps**

**1184** Horiz. strip of 3 8.00 8.00
*a.-c.* A624 1 Any single 2.50 2.50

Nos. 1184a-1184c were sold in boxes of 100 that sold at a discount price of €57 on day of issue. The franking value on the day of issue for each stamp was 60c.

Viivi and Wagner, by Jussi Tuomola — A625

No. 1185: a, Viivi and Wagner running. b, Viivi and Wagner dancing. c, Viivi writing love letter. d, Wagner and Viivi in bed. e, Viivi and Wagner kissing. f, Wagner reading love letter.

***Serpentine Die Cut 11½x11¾ on 3 Sides***

**2003, Jan. 15 Self-Adhesive**

**1185** Booklet pane of 6 15.00
*a.-f.* A625 1 Any single 2.50 1.25
Booklet, #1185 15.00

Nos. 1185a-1185f each sold for 60c on day of issue.

Ice Hockey World Championships — A626

**2003, Mar. 3 Litho.** ***Perf. 13¼x13¾***

**1186** A626 65c multi 2.00 .75

St. Bridget (1303-73) — A627

**2003, Mar. 3** ***Perf. 13***

**1187** A627 65c multi 2.00 .75

Viola Wittrockiana — A628

***Die Cut Perf. 13¾x14***

**2003, Mar. 3 Photo.**

**Self-Adhesive**

**1188** A628 65c multi 2.00 1.25

Fighting Wood Grouses, by Ferdinand von Wright — A629

**2003, Mar. 3** ***Die Cut Perf. 13¾***

**Self-Adhesive**

**1189** A629 90c multi 3.00 1.25

Airplanes A630

No. 1190: a, Super Caravelle. b, Airbus 320. c, Junkers Ju 52/3m. d, Douglas DC-3.

***Perf. 14x14½ on 3 Sides***

**2003, Mar. 3**

**1190** Booklet pane of 4 + 4 etiquettes 8.00 —
*a.-d.* A630 65c Any single 2.00 1.00
Complete booklet, #1190 8.00

Finnair, 80th anniv.; Powered flight, cent.

Europa A631

No. 1191 — Posters by Lasse Hietala: a, Woman with newspaper. b, Hearts.

**2003, May 7 Litho.** ***Perf. 13¾x13¼***

**1191** A631 Pair *4.25 3.75*
*a.-b.* 65c Either single 1.90 1.50

Souvenir Sheet

Flora and Fauna Seen in Summer — A632

No. 1192: a, Moth, flowers (35x29mm). b, Dragonfly, grasshopper (44x35mm). c, Grasshopper, caterpillar, thistle (35x25mm). d, Frog, flowers, butterfly, insects (44x36mm). e, Magpie, snail, flowers (35x46mm). f, Hedgehog, bee, ant, spider, flowers (44x29mm).

*Perf. 14½ on 2 or 3 Sides*

**2003, May 7**

**1192** A632 Sheet of 6 12.00 10.00
*a.-f.* 65c Any single 2.00 1.75

Moomins A633

No. 1193: a, Moomin ancestors. b, Moomins around stove. c, Moomin standing on hands in water. d, Moomin and fox. e, Moomin looking at film negative. f, Moomin with hat, flowers.

*Serpentine Die Cut 11½x11¾ on 3 Sides*

**2003, May 7 Photo.**

**Self-Adhesive**

**1193** Booklet pane of 6 15.00 —
*a.-f.* A633 1 Any single 2.50 .75
Complete booklet, #1193 15.00

Nos. 1193a-1193f each sold for 65c on day of issue.

Cupid A634

*Serpentine Die Cut 11½ Syncopated*

**2003, May 14 Litho.**

**Self-Adhesive**

**1194** A634 1 multi 2.50 1.50

No. 1194 could be personalized. It sold for 65c on day of issue.

Lingonberries — A635

*Serpentine Die Cut 14*

**2003, Sept. 10 Photo.**

**Self-Adhesive**

**1195** A635 65c multi 2.00 .75

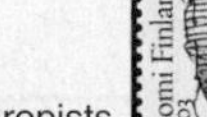

Philanthropists A636

No. 1196: a, Juho (1852-1913) and Maria (1858-1923) Lallukka. b, Emil Aaltonen (1869-1949), vert. c, Heikki Huhtamäki (1900-70), vert. d, Antti (1883-1962) and Jenny Wihuri. e, Alfred Kordelin (1868-1917), vert. f, Amos Anderson (1878-1961), vert.

*Perf. 13¼x13¾, 13¾x13¼ on 3 Sides*

**2003, Sept. 10 Litho.**

**1196** Booklet pane of 6 15.00 15.00
*a.-f.* A636 65c Any single 2.50 2.50
Complete booklet, #1196 11.50

Lighthouses — A637

No. 1197: a, Bengtskär. b, Russarö. c, Rönnskär. d, Harmaja Grahara. e, Söderskär.

**2003, Sept. 10** *Perf. 13¼x13¾*

**1197** A637 Sheet of 5 12.50 9.50
*a.-e.* 1 Any single 2.50 .85

Nos. 1197a-1197e sold for 65c on day of issue. Size of No. 1197a, 28x45mm; Nos. 1197b-1197e, 21x36mm.

Christmas A638

Designs: 45c, Elf mailing letter. 65c, Elf with ginger biscuit on baking pan, vert.

*Serpentine Die Cut 14x14¼, 14¼x14*

**2003, Oct. 31 Photo.**

**Self-Adhesive**

**1198-1199** A638 Set of 2 4.00 2.10

Slightly larger versions of No. 1198 with a serpentine die cutting of 13¼x13¾ and of No. 1199 with a serpentine die cutting of 13¾x13¼ exist only on first day and other covers produced by the postal service. They were not sold unused to the public.

Apples A639

*Serpentine Die Cut 11½ Syncopated*

**2003, Oct. 31 Litho.**

**Self-Adhesive**

**1200** A639 1 multi 2.50 1.50

No. 1200 could be personalized. It sold for 65c on day of issue.

Pres. Tarja Halonen, 60th Birthday — A640

**2003, Dec. 1 Litho.** *Perf. 13*

**1201** A640 65c multi 2.00 .75

Linnaea Borealis — A641

*Die Cut Perf. 14*

**2004, Jan. 14 Photo.**

**Self-Adhesive**

**1202** A641 30c multi 1.00 .60

Souvenir Sheet

Johan Ludvig Runeberg (1804-77), Poet — A642

No. 1203: a, Title page of *Tales of Ensign Stahl.* b, Sven Dufva with gun. c, Illustration for "Our Country." d, Sculpture of Runeberg.

*Perf. 13½x13¼ on 3 or 4 Sides*

**2004, Jan. 14 Litho.**

**1203** A642 65c Sheet of 4, #a-d 8.00 6.00

Jean Sibelius (1865-1957), Composer A643

No. 1204: a, Satu, and Sibelius, paintings by Akseli Gallen-Kallela. b, Hands of Sibelius on piano keyboard. c, Swans, musical score by Sibelius.

No. 1205: a, Sibelius' house, Ainola. b, Sibelius and wife, Aino. c, Score of "Voces Intimae."

*Die Cut Perf. 10 Horiz. Syncopated*

**2004, Jan. 14 Photo.**

**Coil Stamps**

**Self-Adhesive**

**1204** Horiz. strip of 3 12.00 —
*a.-c.* A643 2 Any single 3.00 1.50
**1205** Horiz. strip of 3 12.00
*a.-c.* A643 1 Any single 3.00 1.50

Nos. 1204a-1204c each sold for 55c on day of issue and have two short syncopations; Nos. 1205a-1205c each sold for 65c on day of issue, and have one large syncopation.

Love — A644

Text and: a, Rose. b, Man kissing. c, Woman's eye. d, Man and woman embracing. e, Elderly woman. f, Hand pulling petal from daisy.

*Serpentine Die Cut 11½x11¾ on 3 Sides*

**2004, Jan. 14 Self-Adhesive**

**1206** Booklet pane of 6 15.00 —
*a.-f.* A644 1 Any single 2.50 .75

Nos. 1206a-1206f each sold for 65c on day of issue.

Ursus Arctos — A645

**2004, Mar. 1** *Die Cut Perf. 14*

**Self-Adhesive**

**1207** A645 2 multi 2.25 1.00
*a.* Pale yellow background, animal name 8mm long 4.00 4.00

No. 1207 sold for 55c on day of issue. No. 1207 has a pale pink background and animal name is 6mm long.

Issued: No. 1207a, 2009.

Rose — A646

**2004, Mar. 1 Booklet Stamp**

**Self-Adhesive**

**1208** A646 1 multi 2.50 1.40
*a.* Booklet pane of 10 25.00

No. 1208 sold for 65c on day of issue. Booklet pane was sold folded.

Easter Flowers — A647

*Die Cut Perf. 14*

**2004, Mar. 1 Self-Adhesive Litho.**

**1209** A647 65c multi 2.00 .60

**Heraldic Lion Type of 2002**

*Die Cut Perf. 12 Syncopated*

**2004, Mar. 1 Self-Adhesive**

**1210** A616 €3 multi 9.50 3.75

Swallows A648

Orchid A649

*Serpentine Die Cut 11½ Syncopated*

**2004, Mar. 26 Self-Adhesive**

**1211** A648 1 multi 2.50 2.00
**1212** A649 1 multi 2.50 2.00

Nos. 1211-1212 each sold for 65c on day of issue, and they could be personalized.

Souvenir Sheet

Norse Gods — A650

No. 1213: a, Head of Luonnotar (33x30mm). b, Luonnotar with arms extended (22x42mm).

*Perf. 14¼x14½ (#1213a), 14½x14 (#1213b)*

**2004, Mar. 26**

**1213** A650 65c Sheet of 2, #a-b 6.25 6.25

Forest Animals — A651

No. 1214: a, Red squirrel (40x40mm). b, Raven (40x31mm). c, Variable hare (40x34mm). d, Stoat (40x37mm). e, Lizard (40x34mm). f, Red fox (40x40mm).

***Perf. 13¼x14 on 2 or 3 Sides***

**2004, Apr. 28**

**1214** A651 Sheet of 6 14.00 11.50
*a.-f.* 65c Any single 2.25 1.25

Fragaria Vesca — A652

***Die Cut Perf. 14***

**2004, Apr. 28** **Photo.**

**Self-Adhesive**

**1215** A652 65c multi 2.00 1.40

Luxembourg Gardens, by Albert Edelfelt (1854-1905) A653

**2004, Apr. 28** **Self-Adhesive**

**1216** A653 1 multi 2.50 .75

No. 1216 sold for 65c on day of issue.

Europa — A654

No. 1217: a, People around campfire. b, Family in rowboat.

**2004, Apr. 28** **Litho.** ***Perf. 13***

**1217** A654 65c Horiz. pair, #a-b *4.00 3.75*

Snufkin and Moomintroll A655

**Litho. & Embossed**

**2004, Sept. 8** ***Perf. 13***

**Flocked Paper**

**1218** A655 1 multi *7.00* 2.00

No. 1218 sold for 65c on day of issue.

Shipwreck Treasures A656

No. 1219: a, Tankard. b, Fabric seal. c, Gold watch. d, Powder keg. e, Figurehead (23x40mm).

***Perf. 14¼x13 on 3 or 4 Sides***

**2004, Sept. 8**

**1219** Booklet pane of 5 12.50 8.00
*a.-e.* A656 1 Any single 2.50 1.60
Complete booklet, #1219 12.50

Stamps sold for 65c each on day of issue.

Souvenir Sheet

Sammallahdenmäki, UNESCO World Heritage Site — A657

No. 1220: a, Stone wall and trees. b, Lichen-covered rocks.

**2004, Sept. 8** **Litho.** ***Perf. 14¾x14¼***

**1220** A657 65c Sheet of 2, #a-b 4.00 3.75

Rights of the Child — A658

No. 1221: a, Two girls. b, Boy painting.

**2004, Oct. 29** ***Perf. 13***

**1221** A658 65c Horiz. pair, #a-b 6.25 3.75

Christmas A659

Designs: 45c, Boy writing Santa Claus. 65c, Christmas tree branch, candle, ornaments, vert.

***Serpentine Die Cut 13¼x13¾, 13¾x13¼***

**2004, Oct. 29** **Photo.**

**Self-Adhesive**

**1222-1223** A659 Set of 2 3.50 2.50

Rotary International, Cent. — A660

**2005, Jan. 14** **Litho.** ***Perf. 13***

**1224** A660 65c blue & gold 2.00 1.00

Lahti, Cent. — A661

No. 1225: a, Sibelius Concert Hall. b, Illuminated radio towers.

**2005, Jan. 14**

**1225** A661 65c Pair, #a-b 4.00 3.25

Oulo, 400th Anniv. — A662

No. 1226: a, Child with pail and shovel. b, Woman riding bicycle.

**2005, Jan. 14**

**1226** A662 65c Horiz. pair, #a-b 4.00 3.25

Publishing of First Finnish Almanac, 300th Anniv. — A663

***Die Cut Perf. 14***

**2005, Jan. 14** **Photo.**

**Self-Adhesive**

**1227** A663 65c multi 2.00 .75

Children's Toys — A664

No. 1228: a, Stuffed lion and tiger. b, Stuffed elephant and dog. c, Airplane, train and car. d, Stuffed bear and rabbit.

***Serpentine Die Cut 9¼x8½ on 3 Sides***

**2005, Jan. 14** **Self-Adhesive**

**1228** Booklet pane of 4 10.00 —
*a.-d.* A664 1 Any single 2.50 1.25

Stamps sold for 65c each on day of issue.

End of Winter War, 65th Anniv. — A665

**2005, Mar. 2** **Litho.** ***Perf. 13***

**1229** A665 65c multi 2.00 1.25

Easter — A666

**2005, Mar. 2** ***Serpentine Die Cut 14***

**Self-Adhesive**

**1230** A666 65c multi 2.00 1.00

Apple Blossom — A667

***Die Cut Perf. 14***

**2005, Mar. 2** **Photo.**

**Booklet Stamp**

**Self-Adhesive**

**1231** A667 1 multi 2.50 1.40
*a.* Booklet pane of 10 25.00

No. 1231 sold for 65c on day of issue.

Door Decoration, by Eliel Saarinen A668

Copper Stove Door — A669

Chair Back — A670

Stained Glass Window, by Olga Gummerus-Ehrström — A671

Dining Room — A672

Exterior of Hvitträsk A673

***Die Cut Perf. 10 Horiz. Syncopated***

**2005, Mar. 2** **Litho.**

**Self-Adhesive**

**Coil Stamps**

**1232** Horiz. strip of 3 10.00
*a.* A668 2 multi 2.75 .90
*b.* A669 2 multi 2.75 .90
*c.* A670 2 multi 2.75 .90

**1233** Horiz. strip of 3 10.00
*a.* A671 1 multi 2.75 .90
*b.* A672 1 multi 2.75 .90
*c.* A673 1 multi 2.75 .90

Hvitträsk, home and studio of architects Eliel Saarinen, Armas Lindgren and Herman Gesellius. Nos. 1232a-1232c each sold for 55c on day of issue and have two short syncopations. Nos. 1233a-1233c each sold for 65c on day of issue and have one large syncopation.

Miniature Schnauzer A674

***Serpentine Die Cut 11½ Syncopated***

**2005, Apr. 6**

**1234** A674 1 multi 2.50 1.90

Sold for 65c on day of issue. Sheets could be personalized.

Europa — A675

No. 1235 — Plates with: a, Whitefish and beetroot tartare on lettuce. b, Sauteed reindeer and grouse breast.

**2005, May 11** ***Perf. 13***

**1235** A675 65c Pair, #a-b *4.00 3.50*

Souvenir Sheet

Golf — A676

No. 1236: a, Man driving ball (44x31mm). b, Boy holding flag, vert. (30x44mm). c, Boy putting, vert. (33x44mm). d, Putter and golf ball (44x32mm).

***Perf. 13¼ on 3 or 4 Sides***

**2005, May 11**

**1236** A676 65c Sheet of 4, #a-d 8.00 6.50

World Track Championships, Helsinki — A677

***Serpentine Die Cut 12½***

**2005, May 11** **Self-Adhesive**

**1237** A677 65c multi 2.00 1.00

Buses in Finland, Cent. A678

***Die Cut Perf. 14***

**2005, May 11** **Photo.**

**Self-Adhesive**

**1238** A678 65c brown & black 2.00 1.00

Horses — A679

No. 1239: a, Icelandic horse with saddle. b, White Welsh Mountain pony. c, New Forest pony with blanket. d, Shetland Pony.

***Serpentine Die Cut 9¼x8½ on 3 Sides***

**2005, May 11** **Self-Adhesive**

**1239** Booklet pane of 4 10.00

***a.-d.*** A679 1 Any single 2.50 1.00

Stamps sold for 65c each on day of issue.

Cloudberries — A680

***Die Cut Perf. 14***

**2005, Sept. 7** **Photo.**

**Self-Adhesive**

**1240** A680 1 multi 2.50 1.40

Sold for 65c on day of issue.

Fruits I, by Kari Huhtamo A681

***Die Cut Perf. 11½ Syncopated***

**2005, Sept. 7** **Litho.**

**Self-Adhesive**

**1241** A681 90c multi 3.00 2.00

Sheets could be personalized.

Souvenir Sheet

Petäjävesi Church, UNESCO World Heritage Site — A682

No. 1242: a, Bell tower (26x47mm). b, Church (34x39mm). c, Angel (26x39mm). d, Chandelier (27x39mm).

**2005, Sept. 7** **Litho.** ***Perf. 13***

**1242** A682 65c Sheet of 4, #a-d 8.00 6.00

Icebreakers — A683

No. 1243: a, Urho, 1975. b, Otso, 1986. c, Fennica, 1993. d, Botnica, 1998.

**2005, Sept. 7** ***Perf. 13¼ Horiz.***

**1243** Booklet pane of 4 10.00 —

***a.-d.*** A683 1 Any single 2.50 1.00

Each stamp sold for 65c on day of issue.

Souvenir Sheet

Imperial Winter Egg, by Carl Fabergé — A684

No. 684: a, Flowers in egg. b, Frost detail of egg.

**Litho. & Embossed with Foil Application**

**2005, Oct. 28** ***Perf. 13***

**1244** A684 €3.50 Sheet of 2, #a-b 22.50 20.00

A limited quantity of 2,500 numbered sheets, which sold for €30, exist. Value, $100.

Christmas — A685

Designs: 50c, Santa Claus reading letters. 1, Santa Claus and wife dancing, horiz.

***Serpentine Die Cut 13¾x13¼, 13¼x13¾***

**2005, Oct. 28** **Photo.**

**Self-Adhesive**

**1245-1246** A685 Set of 2 4.00 1.50

No. 1246 sold for 65c on day of issue.

Postal Employees Union, Cent. — A686

**2006, Jan. 11** **Litho.** ***Perf. 13***

**1247** A686 65c multi 2.00 .75

Heart — A687

**2006, Jan. 11** ***Die Cut***

**Self-Adhesive**

**1248** A687 65c bright pink 2.00 .75

Renaming of Helsinki University Library as National Library of Finland — A688

**2006, Jan. 11** ***Die Cut Perf. 14x13¾***

**Self-Adhesive**

**1249** A688 1 multi 2.50 1.40

Sold for 65c on day of issue.

Forest in Winter — A689

**2006, Jan. 11** **Photo.**

**Self-Adhesive**

**1250** A689 1 multi 2.50 1.40

Sold for 65c on day of issue.

Taxis, Cent. — A690

No. 1251: a, Women passengers in taxi, 1906. b, Driver standing in front of 1929 Chevrolet taxi. c, Driver leaning on 1957 Pobeda taxi. d, Driver on phone at taxi stand next to Mercedes-Benz taxi.

***Serpentine Die Cut 11¼ Vert.***

**2006, Jan. 11** **Litho.**

**Self-Adhesive**

**1251** Booklet pane of 4 8.00 —

***a.-d.*** A690 65c Any single 2.00 .75

Souvenir Sheet

Johan Vilhelm Snellman (1806-81), Philosopher — A691

No. 1252: a, Caricature of Snellman, masthead of his newspaper "Saima." b, Snellman's portrait on 1940 five thousand mark note. c, Snellman and European railway map. d, Ilmarinen, first Finnish locomotive, and European railway map.

**2006, Jan. 11** ***Perf. 13¼x13¾***

**1252** A691 65c Sheet of 4, #a-d 8.00 8.00

Parliament, Cent. — A692

***Serpentine Die Cut 14***

**2006, Feb. 3** **Litho.**

**Self-Adhesive**

**1253** A692 1 multi 2.50 1.40

Sold for 65c on day of sale.

Flag — A693

**2006, Mar. 1** **Self-Adhesive**

**1254** A693 1 multi 2.50 1.40

Sold for 65c on day of sale.

Lilacs — A694

*Die Cut Perf. 13¾x14*

**2006, Mar. 1 Photo.**

**Self-Adhesive**

**1255** A694 1 multi 2.50 1.40

Sold for 65c on day of sale.

Easter — A695

**2006, Mar. 1 Litho. *Die Cut***

**Self-Adhesive**

**1256** A695 65c multi 2.00 1.00

Fortune Teller, by Helene Schjerfbeck — A696

*Die Cut Perf. 13¾x14*

**2006, Mar. 1 Photo.**

**Self-Adhesive**

**1257** A696 95c multi 3.00 2.25

Bil-Bol Poster A697

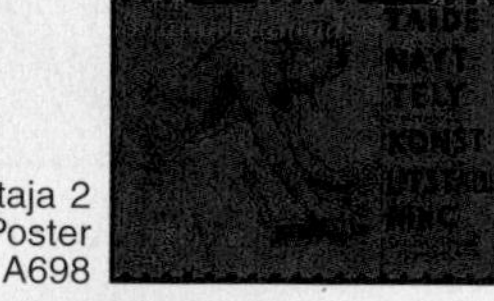
Errotaja 2 Poster A698

Concert Finnois Poster A699

Madonna A700

Self-Portrait A701

Home of Artist Akseli Gallen-Kallela, Tarvaspää — A702

*Die Cut Perf. 10 Horiz. Syncopated*

**2006, Mar. 1 Self-Adhesive**

**Coil Stamps**

**1258** Horiz. strip of 3 6.75 —
*a.* A697 2 multi 2.25 2.25
*b.* A698 2 multi 2.25 2.25
*c.* A699 2 multi 2.25 2.25

*Die Cut Perf. 10 Vert. Syncopated*

**1259** Vert. strip of 3 6.75 —
*a.* A700 1 multi 2.25 .75
*b.* A701 1 multi 2.25 .75
*c.* A702 1 multi 2.25 .75

Akseli Gallen-Kallela (1865-1931), artist. Nos. 1258a-1258c each sold for 55c and Nos. 1259a-1259c each sold for 65c on day of issue.

Souvenir Sheet

Norse Mythology — A703

No. 1260 — Fairy tale book cover illustrations by Rudolf Koivu: a, Fairy. b, Fairy dancing with Santa Claus, vert.

*Perf. 13½x13¼, 13¼x13½ (#1260b)*

**2006, Mar. 29 Litho.**

**1260** A703 65c Sheet of 2, #a-b 4.00 4.00

Europa A704

**2006, May 4 *Perf. 13***

**1261** A704 65c multi 2.00 1.00

Vaasa, 400th Anniv. — A705

**2006, May 4**

**1262** A705 1 multi 2.50 1.00

Sold for 65c on day of issue.

A706

*Serpentine Die Cut 10 Syncopated*

**2006, May 4 Booklet Stamp**

**Self-Adhesive**

**1263** A706 1 multi 2.50 1.50
*a.* Booklet pane of 8 20.00

No. 1263 sold for 65c on day of issue. Design portion of stamp could be personalized.

Summer Activities A707

No. 1264: a, Woman fishing. b, Children making flower garlands. c, Man making sauna whisk. d, Woman weeding flower garden.

*Serpentine Die Cut 11¼ Vert.*

**2006, May 4 Self-Adhesive**

**1264** Booklet pane of 4 10.00
*a.-d.* A707 1 Any single 2.50 1.00

Nos. 1264a-1264d each sold for 65c on day of issue.

Cats — A708

No. 1265: a, Striped house cat. b, British shorthair (gray cat). c, Ragdoll cat (brown and white). d, Chocolate Persian cat.

**2006, May 4 Self-Adhesive**

**1265** Booklet pane of 4 10.00
*a.-d.* A708 1 Any single 2.50 1.00

Nos. 1265a-1265d each sold for 65c on day of issue.

Suomenlinna (Sveaborg) Fortress, Helsinki — A709

No. 1266: a, Ship without oars. b, Ship with oars facing fortress. c, Ship with oars, windmill.

**Litho. & Engr.**

**2006, May 4 *Perf. 13x12¾***

**1266** A709 Booklet pane of 3 7.50 —
*a.-c.* 1 Any single 2.50 1.00
Complete booklet, #1266 7.50

Nos. 1266a-1266c each sold for 65c on day of issue. See Sweden No. 2530.

Blueberries and Blueberry Pie — A710

*Die Cut Perf. 14*

**2006, Aug. 24 Photo.**

**Self-Adhesive**

**1267** A710 1 multi 2.50 1.40

Sold for 70c on day of issue.

Miniature Sheet

Family Life — A711

No. 1268: a, Family watching television. b, Woman writing letter to husband.

**2006, Aug. 24 *Die Cut***

**Self-Adhesive**

**1268** A711 1 Sheet of 2, #a-b 5.00 2.50

Nos. 1268a-1268b each sold for 70c on day of issue.

Newspaper Journalism — A712

*Die Cut Perf. 14*

**2006, Sept. 22 Litho.**

**Self-Adhesive**

**1269** A712 70c multi 2.25 1.00

Points, Textile Art by Ritva Puotila — A713

*Serpentine Die Cut 11½ Syncopated*

**2006, Sept. 22 Self-Adhesive**

**1270** A713 1 multi 2.50 1.75

Sold for 70c on day of issue.

Dryas Octopetala A714

*Serpentine Die Cut 14*

**2006, Sept. 22 Photo.**

**Self-Adhesive**

**1271** A714 1 multi 2.50 1.00

Sold for 70c on day of issue.

Art of Snow and Ice — A715

No. 1272: a, Horse. b, Kemi Snow Castle. c, Wall of ice tiles. d, Snowball lantern.

***Serpentine Die Cut 11¾ Vert.***

**2006, Sept. 22** **Self-Adhesive**

**1272** Booklet pane of 4 10.00
*a.-d.* A715 1 Any single 2.50 2.50

Nos. 1272a-1272d each sold for 70c on day of issue. Denominations are printed in thermographic ink that changes color when warmed.

Miniature Sheet

Finnish Postage Stamps, 150th Anniv. — A716

No. 1273: a, 70c, Heraldic lion and fleurons in white. b, 95c, Part of vignette of type A1. c, €1.40, Heraldic lion in gold, fleurons in red.

**Litho. & Embossed With Foil Application**

**2006, Oct. 27** ***Perf. 13½x13***

**1273** A716 Sheet of 3, #a-c 9.50 9.50

A717

Christmas — A718

***Serpentine Die Cut 13¼x13¾***

**2006, Oct. 27** **Photo.**

**Self-Adhesive**

**1274** A717 50c multi 1.40 .90

***Serpentine Die Cut 13¾x13¼***

**1275** A718 1 multi 2.75 .90

No. 1275 sold for 70c on day of issue.

Television Broadcasting in Finland, 50th Anniv. — A719

***Die Cut Perf. 14***

**2007, Jan. 24** **Litho.**

**Self-Adhesive**

**1276** A719 70c multi 2.25 1.50

Faces — A720

**2007, Jan. 24** **Self-Adhesive**

**1277** A720 70c multi 2.25 1.50

Winter Landscape, Haminalahti, by Ferdinand von Wright A721

**2007, Jan. 24** **Photo.**

**Booklet Stamp**

**Self-Adhesive**

**1278** A721 1 multi 2.50 1.50
*a.* Booklet pane of 10 25.00

Sold for 70c on day of issue.

Sun Setting Over Flower Field — A722

**2007, Jan. 24** **Litho.**

**Self-Adhesive**

**1279** A722 €1.40 multi 4.50 3.00

Souvenir Sheet

Intl. Polar Year — A723

No. 1280: a, Snowflake. b, Aurora borealis.

***Perf. 13 Syncopated (#1280a), 13 (#1280b)***

**Litho. With Hologram Affixed**

**2007, Jan. 24**

**1280** A723 70c Sheet of 2, #a-b + label 4.50 4.00

Truck Transport — A724

No. 1281: a, Log truck. b, Milk truck. c, Dump truck. d, Tractor trailer.

***Serpentine Die Cut 12¼ Horiz.***

**2007, Jan. 24** **Litho.**

**Self-Adhesive**

**1281** Booklet pane of 4 9.00 6.00
*a.-d.* A724 70c Any single 2.25 1.40

Central Organization of Finnish Trade Unions — A725

**2007, Mar. 7** ***Perf. 13***

**1282** A725 70c multi 2.25 1.50

Soccer Association of Finland, Cent. — A726

**2007, Mar. 7** ***Die Cut***

**Self-Adhesive**

**1283** A726 70c multi 2.25 1.50

Easter — A727

**2007, Mar. 7** ***Die Cut Perf. 14***

**Self-Adhesive**

**1284** A727 1 multi 2.50 1.50

Sold for 70c on day of issue. Portions of design were applied by a thermographic process producing a shiny, raised effect.

Lilium Enchantment A728

**2007, Mar. 7** **Litho.**

**Booklet Stamp**

**Self-Adhesive**

**1285** A728 1 multi 2.50 1.50
*a.* Booklet pane of 10 25.00

No. 1285 sold for 70c on day of issue.

Souvenir Sheet

Bishop Michael Agricola (1509-57) — A729

No. 1286: a, Text and open book. b, Agricola preaching.

**2007, Mar. 7** ***Perf. 13½***

**1286** A729 70c Sheet of 2, #a-b 4.50 4.00

Tampere Cathedral, Cent. — A730

**2007, May 9** ***Perf. 13¼***

**1287** A730 70c multi 2.25 1.25

Europa — A731

No. 1288: a, Scouts on sailboat. b, Scouts around campfire.

**2007, May 9** ***Perf. 12½x13***

**1288** A731 Horiz. pair 4.50 4.50
*a.-b.* 70c Either single 2.25 2.25

Scouting, cent.

Helsinki Public Transportation — A732

No. 1289: a, Commuter train in station. b, Tram on street. c, Subway train on bridge. d. People in Kamppi Bus Station.

***Serpentine Die Cut 12¼ Horiz.***

**2007, May 9** **Self-Adhesive**

**1289** Booklet pane of 4 10.00 8.00
*a.-d.* A732 1 Any single 2.50 1.50

Nos. 1289a-1289d each sold for 70c on day of issue.

Moomins A733

No. 1290: a, Little My in water. b, Moomintroll running across rocks. c, Moominpappa at typewriter. d, Snork Maiden picking flowers. e, Moominmamma making pancakes. f, Snufkin amid flowers.

***Serpentine Die Cut 11¾ Vert.***

**2007, May 9** **Photo.**

**Self-Adhesive**

**1290** Booklet pane of 6 15.00
*a.-f.* A733 1 Any single 2.50 1.25

Nos. 1290a-1290f each sold for 70c on day of issue.

Souvenir Sheet

2007 Eurovision Song Contest, Helsinki — A734

No. 1291: a, Eurovision Song Contest emblem. b, Finnish singers Laila Kinnunen, Marion Rung, Kirka Babitzin and Katri Helena. c, 2006 Finnish contest-winning band, Lordi. d, Lead singer of Lordi.

**Litho. With Foil Application**

**2007, May 9** ***Die Cut***

**Self-Adhesive**

**1291** A734 70c Sheet of 4, #a-d 9.00 9.00

A735

*Serpentine Die Cut 11½ Syncopated*

**2007, Aug. 24 Litho.**

**Self-Adhesive**

**1292** A735 1 multi 2.50 1.25

No. 1292 sold for 70c on day of issue. Design portion of stamp could be personalized.

Home Furnishings — A736

No. 1293 — Picture frame and: a, Empire-style chair, "Porvoo Garland" wallpaper, 19th cent. (country name at LR). b, Paimio chair, "2+3" wallpaper, 20th cent. (country name at LL).

*Die Cut Perf. 14*

**2007, Aug. 24 Litho.**

**Self-Adhesive**

**1293** Pair 5.00
*a.-b.* A736 1 Either single 2.50 1.25

Nos. 1293a-1293b each sold for 70c on day of issue.

Raspberries and Raspberry Cake — A737

*Die Cut Perf. 14*

**2007, Aug. 24 Photo.**

**Self-Adhesive**

**Booklet Stamp**

**1294** A737 1 multi 2.50 1.25

No. 1294 sold for 70c on day of issue.

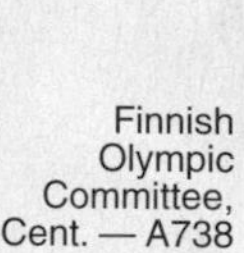

Finnish Olympic Committee, Cent. — A738

**2007, Aug. 24 Litho.**

**Self-Adhesive**

**Booklet Stamp**

**1295** A738 1 multi 2.50 1.25

No. 1295 sold for 70c on day of issue.

Butterflies — A739

No. 1296: a, Apatura iris. b, Scolitantides orion. c, Colias palaeno.

*Die Cut Perf. 10 Vert., Syncopated at Right*

**2007, Aug. 24 Self-Adhesive**

**Coil Stamps**

**1296** Vert. strip of 3 7.50
*a.-c.* A739 1 Any single 2.50 2.50

Nos. 1296a-1296c had a franking value of 70c on day of issue. A roll of 100 stamps sold for €68.

Miniature Sheet

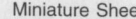

Independence, 90th Anniv. — A740

No. 1297 — Photographs of people at work and play: a, Man and horse hauling wood. b, Girl blowing horn. c, Four boys with skis. d, People at coffee break. e, People near bonfire. f, Boy ski jumping. g, Boy diving. h, Ice fisherman. Nos. 1297a-1297d are black and white photos.

**2007, Nov. 2** ***Perf. 13¼***

**1297** A740 Sheet of 8 18.00 16.50
*a.-h.* 70c Any single 2.25 1.50

Souvenir Sheet

Woodwork — A741

No. 1298: a, Zitan armchair with dragon design, China (denomination at left). b, Modern Finnish bowls (denomination at right).

**2007, Nov. 2** ***Perf. 13¼x14¼***

**1298** A741 Sheet of 2 4.50 4.50
*a.-b.* 70c Either single 2.25 1.75

See Hong Kong Nos. 1298-1299.

A742

Christmas — A743

*Serpentine Die Cut 13¼x13¾*

**2007, Nov. 2 Photo.**

**Self-Adhesive**

**1299** A742 55c multi 1.75 1.25

*Serpentine Die Cut 13¾x13¼*

**1300** A743 1 multi 2.50 1.75

No. 1300 sold for 70c on day of issue.

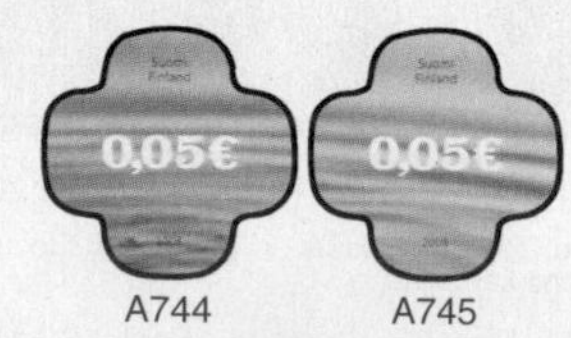

A744 A745

Water — A746

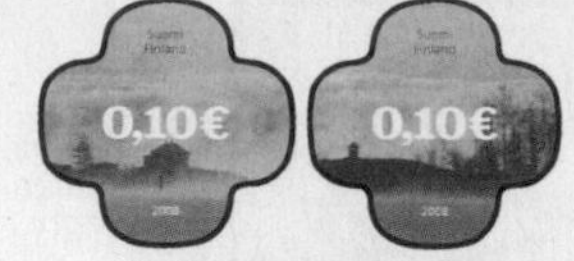

A747 A748

Islands — A749

**2008, Jan. 24 Photo.** ***Die Cut***

**Self-Adhesive**

**1301** Horiz. strip of 3 .45
*a.* A744 5c multi .25 .25
*b.* A745 5c multi .25 .25
*c.* A746 5c multi .25 .25
**1302** Horiz. strip of 3 .90
*a.* A747 10c multi .30 .30
*b.* A748 10c multi .30 .30
*c.* A749 10c multi .30 .30

Souvenir Sheet

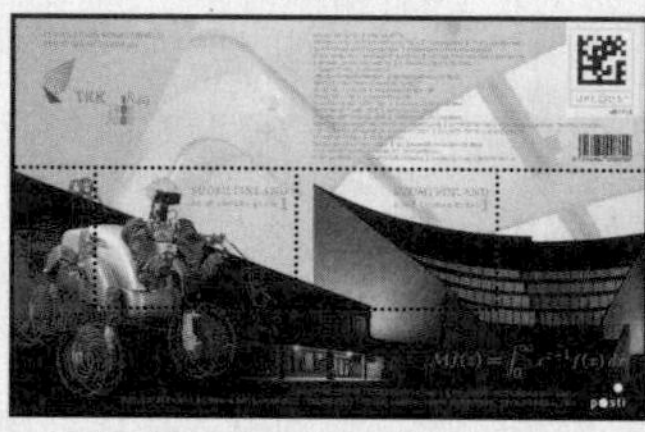

Helsinki University of Technology, Cent. — A750

No. 1303: a, Robot. b, University building.

**2008, Jan. 24 Litho.** ***Perf. 13½x13¼***

**1303** A750 Sheet of 2 5.00 4.25
*a.-b.* 1 Any single 2.50 1.25

Nos. 1303a-1303b each sold for 70c on day of issue.

Miniature Sheet

Love — A751

No. 1304: a, Airplane pulling heart banner. b, Carrier pigeon with envelope. c, Heart-shaped smoke signals. d, Heart and cell phone. e, Bottle with hearts.

**2008, Jan. 24** ***Die Cut***

**Self-Adhesive**

**1304** A751 Sheet of 5 12.50 10.50
*a.-e.* 1 Any single 2.50 1.25

Nos. 1304a-1304e each sold for 70c on day of issue.

Miniature Sheet

Snow Sports — A752

No. 1305: a, Matti Räty in yellow ski suit. b, Antti Autti (snowboarder) in air in red ski suit. c, Tapio Saarimaki in red ski suit. d, Tanja Poutiainen in white and green ski suit.

**Litho. With Three-Dimensional Plastic Affixed**

*Serpentine Die Cut 9 Syncopated*

**2008, Jan. 24 Self-Adhesive**

**1305** A752 Sheet of 4 10.00 9.00
*a.-d.* 1 Any single 2.50 1.25

Nos. 1305a-1305d each sold for 70c on day of issue.

Clock and Lamp on Desk — A753

*Die Cut Perf. 13¾*

**2008, Feb. 27 Litho.**

**Booklet Stamp**

**Self-Adhesive**

**1306** A753 €1.05 multi 3.50 2.60
*a.* Booklet pane of 10 35.00

Finnish Book Publishers Association, 150th Anniv. — A754

*Serpentine Die Cut 13¼*

**2008, Feb. 27 Self-Adhesive**

**1307** A754 1 multi 2.50 1.75

No. 1307 sold for 70c on day of issue.

Lathyrus Odoratus — A755

*Die Cut Perf. 13¾*

**2008, Feb. 27 Photo.**

**Self-Adhesive**

**1308** A755 1 multi 2.50 1.75

No. 1308 sold for 70c on the day of issue and has Braille dots applied by a thermographic process.

Easter — A756

**Litho. With Foil Application**

*Serpentine Die Cut 13¾*

**2008, Feb. 27 Self-Adhesive**

**1309** A756 1 multi 2.50 1.75

No. 1309 sold for 70c on day of issue.

Fauna Associated With Weather Forecasting Folk Beliefs — A757

No. 1310: a, Perch. b, Lambs. c, Frogs. d, Swallows. e, Snail.

***Serpentine Die Cut 12¼ Horiz.***

**2008, Feb. 27** **Litho.**

**Self-Adhesive**

**1310** Booklet pane of 5 12.50 11.00
***a.-e.*** A757 1 Any single 2.50 1.25

Nos. 1310a-1310e each sold for 70c on day of issue.

Souvenir Sheet

Mythical Places — A758

No. 1311: a, Cliff resembling human face, Astuvansalmi. b, Amber carving of head found at Astuvansalmi.

**2008, Mar. 27** ***Perf. 13½***

**1311** A758 Sheet of 2 4.75 4.25
***a.-b.*** 70c Either single 2.25 2.00

Europa — A759

No. 1312 — Handwritten letters and portraits by Pekka Halonen of: a, Himself. b, His wife, Maija.

**2008, May 9** ***Perf. 13***

**1312** A759 Horiz. pair 5.25 5.25
***a.-b.*** 70c Either single 2.50 2.10

Kvarken Archipelago UNESCO World Heritage Site — A760

***Serpentine Die Cut 13¾***

**2008, May 9** **Self-Adhesive**

**1313** A760 €1.50 blk & red 5.50 4.50

Moths — A761

No. 1314: a, Arctia caja. b, Aglia tau. c. Deilephila elpenor.

***Die Cut Perf. 10 Syncopated***

**2008, May 9** **Photo.**

**Coil Stamps**

**Self-Adhesive**

**1314** Vert. strip of 3 7.75 7.00
***a.-c.*** A761 1 Any single 2.50 1.25

Nos. 1314a-1314c each sold for 70c on day of issue.

Psychedelic Art — A762

No. 1315: a, Melting mushrooms and teardrops. b, Guitars. c, Flying fish. d, Flowers and woman's legs in high heels. e, Six balloons.

***Serpentine Die Cut 12½ Horiz.***

**2008, May 9** **Litho.**

**Self-Adhesive**

**1315** Booklet pane of 5 13.00
***a.-e.*** A762 1 Any single 2.60 1.25

Nos. 1315a-1315e each sold for 70c on day of issue.

Modern Art — A763

No. 1316: a, Sinistä ja Punaista, by Sam Vanni. b, Merirosvolaiva, by Kimmo Kaivanto. c, Hiljaisuuden Kuuntelija, by Juhani Linnovaara. d, Odotan Kevään Tuloa, by Göran Augustson. e, Minä, by Carolus Enckell. f, Pöytä, by Reino Hietanen.

***Serpentine Die Cut 11¾ Vert.***

**2008, May 9** **Self-Adhesive**

**1316** Booklet pane of 6 16.00 14.00
***a.-f.*** A763 1 Any single 2.60 1.25

Nos. 1316a-1316f each sold for 70c on day of issue.

Personalized Stamp — A764

***Serpentine Die Cut 10***

**2008, Sept. 5** **Litho.**

**Self-Adhesive**

**1317** A764 1 multi 2.50 2.00

No. 1317 sold for 80c on day of issue. The generic design portion of the stamp shown could be personalized.

Dogs — A765

No. 1318: a, Spitz with open mouth, facing forward. b, Rough collie, with open mouth, facing right. c, Boxer, facing left. d, Finnish hound, facing left. e, Cavalier King Charles spaniel, facing right. f, Jack Russell terrier, looking over shoulder.

***Serpentine Die Cut 11¾ Vert.***

**2008, Sept. 5** **Self-Adhesive**

**1318** Booklet pane of 6 15.00 13.50
***a.-f.*** A765 1 Any single 2.50 1.25

Nos. 1318a-1318f each sold for 80c on day of issue.

Souvenir Sheet

Mika Waltari (1908-79), Writer — A766

No. 1319: a, Waltari. b, Cover of Waltari's book, *Komisario Palmun Erehyds.*

**2008, Sept. 5** ***Perf. 14x13½***

**1319** A766 Sheet of 2 5.00 4.50
***a.-b.*** 80c Either single 2.50 2.25

Souvenir Sheet

Kimi Räikkönen, 2007 Formula 1 Racing Champion — A767

No. 1320: a, Räikkönen (24x30mm). b, Räikkönen's Ferrari Formula 1 race car (74x30mm).

***Die Cut Perf. 11x11½ on 2 Sides (#1320a), 11½ Vert. (#1320b)***

**2008, Sept. 5** **Self-Adhesive**

**1320** A767 Sheet of 2 5.00 4.50
***a.-b.*** 1 Either single 2.50 2.25

Nos. 1320a-1320b each sold for 80c on day of issue.

Souvenir Sheet

Adolf Erik Nordenskiöld (1832-1901), Arctic Explorer — A768

No. 1321: a, Nordenskiöld (29x34mm). b, Ship Sofia (58x34mm).

**Litho. & Engr.**

**2008, Oct. 20** ***Perf. 13x13¼***

**1321** A768 Sheet of 2 5.00 4.50
***a.-b.*** 1 Either single 2.50 2.25

Nos. 1321a-1321b each sold for 80c on day of issue. See Greenland Nos. 527-528.

A769

A770

Christmas A771

***Die Cut Perf. 14***

**2008, Nov. 6** **Litho.**

**Self-Adhesive**

**1322** A769 60c multi 1.75 .75

***Serpentine Die Cut 13¼x13¾***

**Photo.**

**1323** A770 1 multi 2.75 2.75

**Printed On Plastic**

***Die Cut Perf. 13¾***

**1324** A771 1 multi 3.00 2.00
*Nos. 1322-1324 (3)* 7.50 5.50

On day of issue, Nos. 1323 and 1324 each sold for 80c.

Pres. Martti Ahtisaari, 2008 Nobel Peace Laureate A772

**2008, Dec. 10** **Litho.** ***Perf. 13***

**1325** A772 80c light blue 2.50 1.25

Hospital Work — A773

**2009, Jan. 22** **Litho.** ***Perf. 13***

**1326** A773 80c multi 2.25 1.75

Pallas-Yllästunturi National Park — A774

**2009, Jan. 22** ***Die Cut Perf. 14***

**Self-Adhesive**

**1327** A774 1 multi 2.50 1.40

No. 1327 sold for 80c on day of issue and has Braille dots applied in varnish.

Peony — A775

***Die Cut Perf. 14***

**2009, Jan. 22** **Photo.**

**Self-Adhesive**

**1328** A775 €1.10 multi 3.00 2.25

Children's Dream Occupations A776

No. 1329 — Child dressed as: a, Policeman. b, Doctor. c, Firefighter. d, Skier. e, Construction worker.

*Serpentine Die Cut 12¼ Vert.*

**2009, Jan. 22 Litho.**

**Self-Adhesive**

**1329** Booklet pane of 5 12.50 10.00
*a.-e.* A776 1 Any single 2.50 1.40

Nos. 1329a-1329e each sold for 80c on day of issue.

Miniature Sheet

Finland as Grand Duchy of Russia, 200th Anniv. — A777

No. 1330: a, Tsar Alexander I (1777-1825), facing left with blue sash. b, Count Georg Magnus Sprengtporten (1740-1819), with red sash and gold epaulets. c, Count Carl Erik Mannerheim (1759-1837), without epaulets. d, Count Gustaf Mauritz Armfelt (1757-1814), facing right, with blue sash. Names are on sheet margin.

**Litho. & Embossed With Foil Application**

**2009, Jan. 22** ***Perf. 13¾***

**1330** A777 80c Sheet of 4, #a-d 9.00 9.00

Miniature Sheet

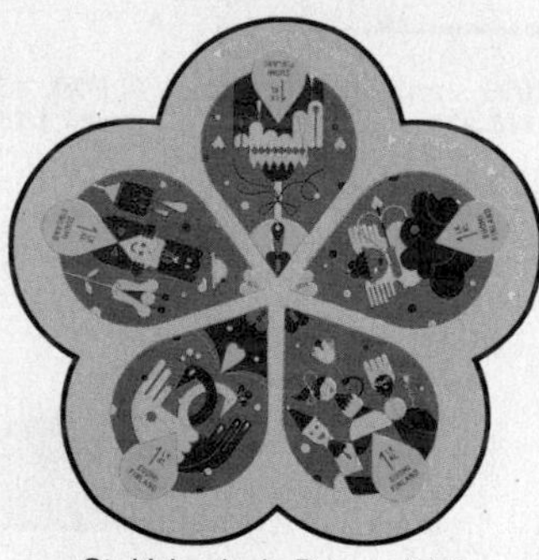

St. Valentine's Day — A778

No. 1331: a, Birthday cake and candle. b, Cupid. c, Three people, flower. d, Swans. e, Teddy bear hugging heart.

**2009, Jan. 22 Litho.** ***Die Cut***

**Self-Adhesive**

**1331** A778 1 Sheet of 5, #a-e 12.50 10.00

Nos. 1331a-1331e each sold for 80c on day of issue.

Rose — A779

*Die Cut Perf. 14*

**2009, Mar. 18 Litho.**

**Self-Adhesive**

**1332** A779 1 multi 2.50 2.00

No. 1332 sold for 80c on day of issue.

Easter — A780

**2009, Mar. 18 Self-Adhesive**

**1333** A780 1 multi 2.50 2.00

No. 1333 sold for 80c on day of issue.

Souvenir Sheet

Preservation of Polar Regions and Glaciers — A781

No. 1334: a, Sky, blue emblem. b, Sea and ice, silver emblem.

**Litho. With Foil Application**

**2009, Mar. 18** ***Perf.***

**1334** A781 Sheet of 2 5.00 3.75
*a.-b.* 1 Either single 2.50 1.90

Nos. 1334a-1334b each sold for 80c on day of issue.

Greetings A782

No. 1335: a, Gift and tulips. b, Chocolate-covered strawberries, cake. c, Flowers. d, Coffee cup, letter and rose. e, Dove and apples.

*Serpentine Die Cut 10¼ Horiz.*

**2009, Mar. 18 Litho.**

**Self-Adhesive**

**1335** Booklet pane of 5 + 5 labels 12.50
*a.-e.* A782 1 Any single 2.50 1.25

Nos. 1335a-1335e each sold for 80c on day of issue.

Europa — A783

No. 1336: a, Lake, birds, Moon, stars and other heavenly bodies. b, Lake, comet, Saturn, stars and other heavenly bodies.

**2009, May 6** ***Perf. 13***

**1336** A783 Horiz. pair 5.00 5.00
*a.-b.* 80c Either single 2.50 1.75

Intl. Year of Astronomy.

Sauna — A784

No. 1337: a, Towels, scrubber, bucket of birch branches (55x23mm). b, People in sauna (55x23mm). c, Waterside sauna (55x23mm). d, Birch whisk (27x45mm). e, Water tubs and window (27x45mm).

*Serpentine Die Cut 11¾ Horiz.*

**2009, May 6 Self-Adhesive**

**1337** Booklet pane of 5 12.50
*a.-e.* A784 1 Any single 2.50 1.40

Nos. 1337a-1337e each sold for 80c on day of issue. No. 1337d is impregnated with a birch scent.

Moomins — A785

No. 1338: a, Moomin carrying purse. b, Moominpappa with hat holding paper. c, Little My holding large pair of glasses. d, Moomin at mirror. e, Moomin and Snufkin fishing. f, Moominpappa slipping down hill.

*Serpentine Die Cut 11¾ Horiz.*

**2009, May 6 Self-Adhesive**

**1338** Booklet pane of 6 15.00
*a.-f.* A785 1 Any single 2.50 1.25

Nos. 1338a-1338f each sold for 80c on day of issue.

Miniature Sheet

Women's Fashion — A786

No. 1339: a, Dress by Anna and Tuomas Laitinen (30x45mm). b, Dress by Jasmin Santanen (30x45mm). c, Handbag by Lumi (30x35mm). d, Red shoes by Minna Parikka (30x25mm). e, Shoes by Julia Lundsten (30x30mm).

*Serpentine Die Cut 14¼x13¾*

**2009, May 6 Self-Adhesive**

**1339** A786 Sheet of 5 12.50 9.50
*a.-e.* 1 Any single 2.50 1.25

Nos. 1339a-1339e each sold for 80c on day of issue.

Gustavian Style Clock, Table and Candle Holder — A787

*Die Cut Perf. 13¾*

**2009, Sept. 9 Litho.**

**Self-Adhesive**

**1340** A787 1 multi 2.50 1.25
*a.* Booklet pane of 10 25.00

No. 1340 sold for 80c on day of issue.

Aurora Borealis — A788

No. 1341 — Various pictures of Aurora Borealis taken at: a, 65 degrees, 1 minute, 17.03 seconds north; 25 degrees, 39 minutes, 31.26 seconds east. b, 65 degrees, 57.16 seconds north; 25 degrees, 39 minutes, 41.01 seconds east. c, 67 degrees, 45 minutes, 2.44 seconds north; 23 degrees, 36 minutes, 41.53 seconds east.

*Die Cut Perf. 10 Vert., Syncopated at Right*

**2009, Sept. 9 Self-Adhesive**

**Coil Stamps**

**1341** Vert. strip of 3 7.50
*a.-c.* A788 1 Any single 2.50 1.25

Nos. 1341a-1341c each sold for 80c on day of issue.

Paintings of Flowers — A789

No. 1342: a, Snapdragons, by Helene Schjerfbeck. b, Blooming Irises, by Wäinö Aaltonen. c, Burnet Roses, by Eero Järnefelt. d, Lone Calla, by Ester Helenius. e, Amaryllis, by Birger Carlstedt. f, Still Life with Carnations, by Tuomas von Boehm.

*Serpentine Die Cut 11¾ Horiz.*

**2009, Sept. 9 Self-Adhesive**

**1342** Booklet pane of 6 15.00
*a.-f.* A789 1 Any single 2.50 1.25

Nos. 1342a-1342f each sold for 80c on day of issue.

Wreath — A790

Girl and Basket of Apples — A791

Amaryllis A792

Personalized Stamp — A793

*Die Cut Perf. 14*

**2009, Nov. 6 Litho.**

**Self-Adhesive**

**1343** Horiz. pair 3.75
*a.* A790 60c multi 1.75 .50
*b.* A791 60c multi 1.75 .50
**1344** A792 1 multi 2.50 2.25

*Serpentine Die Cut 11½x11¾ Syncopated*

**1345** A793 1 multi 2.50 2.25

Nos. 1344 and 1345 each sold for 80c on day of issue. The generic design portion of No. 1345, shown, could be personalized.

Antennaria Dioica — A794

*Die Cut Perf. 11 Syncopated*

**2010, Jan. 25 Litho.**

**Self-Adhesive**

**1346** A794 1 multi 2.75 2.25

No. 1346 sold for 80c on day of issue.

Miniature Sheet

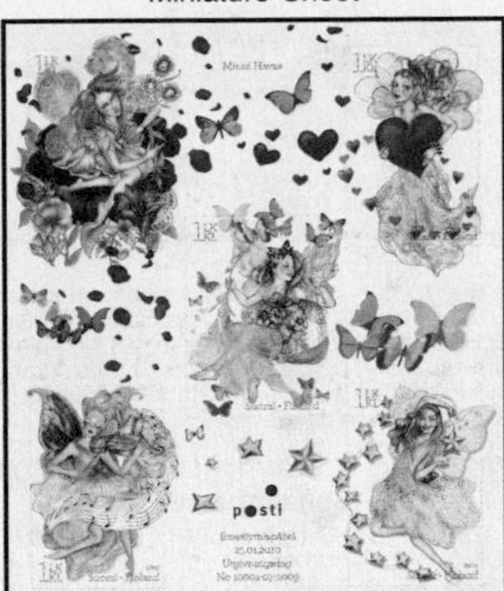

Fairies — A795

No. 1347 — Fairy: a, Holding flowers. b, Holding heart. c, On swing. d, Holding violin. e, With stars.

***Serpentine Die Cut 14½x14***
**Litho. & Silk-screened**

**2010, Jan. 25 Self-Adhesive**

**1347** A795 Sheet of 5 13.50 10.50
*a.-e.* 1 Any single 2.50 1.25

Nos. 1347a-1347e each sold for 80c on day of issue.

Rock Stars A796

No. 1348: a, Eppu Normaali (45x33mm). b, Yö (41x31mm). c, Popeda (40x28mm). d, Dingo (44x33mm). e, Maarit (34x41mm). f, Mamba (38x36mm).

***Die Cut Perf. 8½***

**2010, Jan. 25 Litho.**
**Self-Adhesive**

**1348** Booklet pane of 6 17.00 12.50
*a.-f.* A796 1 Any single 3.25 2.10

Nos. 1348a-1348f each sold for 80c on day of issue.

A797

Easter — A798

***Serpentine Die Cut 12½***

**2010, Mar. 8 Litho. & Embossed**
**Self-Adhesive**

**1349** A797 1 multi 11.00 8.50

**Litho.**
***Die Cut Perf. 14***

**1350** A798 1 multi 2.75 2.25

Nos. 1349 and 1350 each sold for 80c on day of issue.

Rural Life — A799

No. 1351: a, Mussels, children lifting caught fish. b, Children on swing, strawberries, flowers, horse in meadow. c, Farmer on tractor, farmhouses. d, Milk cans, girl milking cow. e, Musicians and dancers.

***Serpentine Die Cut 10¼ Horiz.***

**2010, Mar. 8 Litho.**
**Self-Adhesive**

**1351** Booklet pane of 5 13.50 10.00
*a.-e.* A799 1 Any single 2.50 1.25

Nos. 1351a-1351e each sold for 80c on day of issue.

Famous Women — A800

No. 1352: a, Ritva-Liisa Pohjalainen, jewelry and clothing designer. b, Elina Haavio-Mannila, sociologist. c, Aira Samulin, dance instructor. d, Maria-Liisa Nevala, director of National Theater. e, Laila Hirvisaari, writer. f, Leena Palotie (1952-2010), geneticist.

***Serpentine Die Cut 11 Horiz. Syncopated***
**Litho. & Silk-screened**

**2010, Mar. 8 Self-Adhesive**

**1352** Booklet pane of 6 17.00 12.00
*a.-f.* A800 1 Any single 2.75 1.40

Nos. 1352a-1352f each sold for 80c on day of issue.

Vegetables A801

No. 1353: a, Tomato (38x33mm). b, Onions (47x34mm). c, Pumpkin (34x36mm). d, Cucumber (27x43mm). e, Eggplant (42x41mm). f, Carrot (29x44mm). g, Broccoli (43x35mm). h, Potato (40x30mm).

**2010, Mar. 8 Litho. *Die Cut***
**Self-Adhesive**

**1353** Booklet pane of 8 22.00
*a.-h.* A801 1 Any single 2.75 1.40

Nos. 1353a-1353h each sold for 80c on day of issue.

Souvenir Sheet

Kotka Harbor — A802

No. 1354: a, Vellamo Maritime Center, museum ship Tarmo, crane. b, Sailboat, Wooden Boat Center, vert.

**2010, Mar. 24 *Perf. 13¾***

**1354** A802 Sheet of 2 5.50 5.50
*a.-b.* 1 Either single 2.75 2.10

Nos. 1354a-1354b each sold for 80c on day of issue.

Europa — A803

No. 1355 — Children, books, characters and background in: a, Orange. b, Blue green.

**2010, May 4 *Perf. 14x13¼***

**1355** A803 Horiz. pair 4.75 4.25
*a.-b.* 80c Either single 2.25 1.50

Personalized Stamp — A804

***Serpentine Die Cut 11¾ Syncopated***

**2010, May 4 Self-Adhesive**

**1356** A804 1 multi 2.75 1.40

No. 1356 sold for 80c on day of issue. The generic design part of the stamp shown could be personalized.

Sculpture — A805

No. 1357: a, Hymy, by Kain Tapper (28x33mm). b, Hefaistos, by Laila Pullinen (28x33mm). c, Cyclist, by Pekka Aarnio (28x33mm). d, Construction, by Kari Huhtamo (28x33mm). e, Salvos, by Mauno Hartman, horiz. (56x29mm). f, Joy, by Miina Akkijyrkka, horiz. (56x29mm).

***Serpentine Die Cut 11¾ Horiz.***

**2010, May 4 Self-Adhesive**

**1357** Booklet pane of 6 17.00 13.00
*a.-f.* A805 1 Any single 2.75 2.10

Nos. 1357a-1357f each sold for 80c on day of issue.

Souvenir Sheet

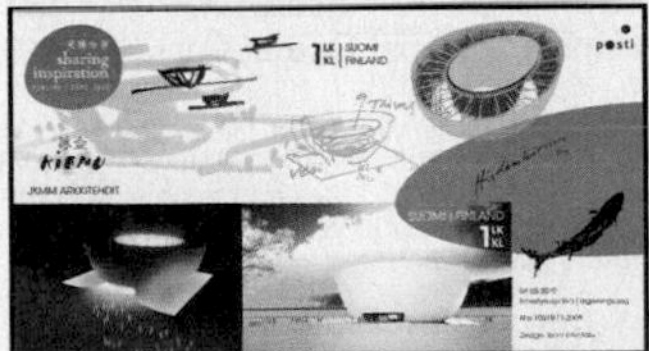

Finnish Pavilion, Expo 2010, Shanghai — A806

No. 1358: a, Aerial view of model and drawing. b, Side view of model.

***Serpentine Die Cut 4½ At Bottom***

**2010, May 4 Self-Adhesive**

**1358** A806 Sheet of 2 5.50 4.25
*a.-b.* 1 Either single 2.75 2.10

Nos. 1358a-1358b each sold for 80c on day of issue.

Miniature Sheet

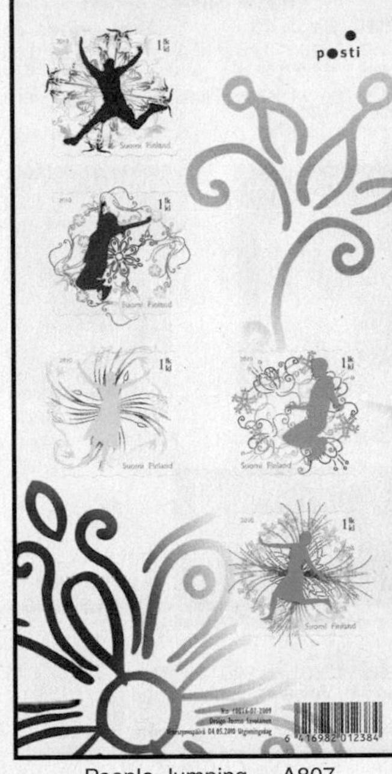

People Jumping — A807

No. 1359 — Jumpers in: a, Purple. b, Red. c, Yellow. d, Blue. e, Green.

**2010, May 4 *Serpentine Die Cut 5***
**Self-Adhesive**

**1359** A807 Sheet of 5 13.50 10.50
*a.-e.* 1 Any single 2.60 2.10

Nos. 1359a-1359e each sold for 80c on day of issue.

Torronsuo National Park — A808

***Die Cut Perf. 14***

**2010, Sept. 13 Litho.**
**Self-Adhesive**

**1360** A808 1 multi 2.75 2.10

No. 1360 sold for 75c on day of issue.

1960s-1970s Era Room Furnishings A809

**2010, Sept. 13 Booklet Stamp**
**Self-Adhesive**

**1361** A809 1 multi 2.75 2.10
*a.* Booklet pane of 10 27.50

No. 1361 sold fo 75c on day of issue.

Souvenir Sheet

Autumn — A810

No. 1362 — Forest and: a, Crayfish. b, Ducks. c, Elk.

***Serpentine Die Cut 12¾x13¼ Syncopated***

**Litho. & Silk-screened**

**2010, Sept. 13** **Self-Adhesive**

**1362** A810 Sheet of 3 8.25 6.50
*a.-c.* 1 Any single 2.75 2.10

On day of issue, Nos. 1362a-1362c each sold for 75c.

Santa Claus — A811

Reindeer and Moon — A812

Sleigh of Santa Claus Over Lapland A813

No. 1365: a, Star and Santa Claus with sack. b, Poinsettias, ribbon and bell. c, Sleigh of Santa Claus over church. d, Heart-shaped wreath. e, Reindeer and Aurora Borealis.

***Die Cut Perf. 14***

**2010, Nov. 5** **Litho.**

**Self-Adhesive**

**1363** Horiz. pair 3.50 3.25
*a.* A811 55c multi 1.75 1.60
*b.* A812 55c multi 1.75 1.60
**1364** A813 1 multi 2.75 2.10

**Souvenir Sheet**

**1365** Sheet of 5 8.50 7.75
*a.* A811 55c multi 1.60 1.50
*b.* A811 55c multi 1.60 1.50
*c.* A813 55c multi 1.60 1.50
*d.* A811 55c multi 1.60 1.50
*e.* A811 55c multi 1.60 1.50

Christmas. No. 1364 sold for 75c on day of issue. See Japan No. 3269.

Birch Bud A814

Birch Leaves A815

**2011, Jan. 24** **Litho.** ***Die Cut***

**Self-Adhesive**

**1366** A814 20c multi .60 .55
**1367** A815 30c multi .90 .85

Flag of Finland A816

**2011, Jan. 24** **Litho. & Embossed**

**Self-Adhesive**

**1368** A816 2 gray & blue 2.50 1.75

No. 1368 sold for 60c on day of issue.

Birds and Flowers — A817

No. 1369: a, Bird on branch, country name in red circle. b, Bird in flight, country name in blue circle. c, Flowers, country name in red circle. d, Bird on branch, country name in blue circle. e, Bird in flight, country name in red circle.

***Serpentine Die Cut 10¼ Horiz.***

**2011, Jan. 24** **Litho.**

**Self-Adhesive**

**1369** Booklet pane of 5 12.50 8.00
*a.-e.* A817 2 Any single 2.50 1.60

Nos. 1369a-1369e each sold for 60c on day of issue.

Mailboxes — A818

No. 1370: a, Mailbox mounted on tire. b, Snow-covered mailbox. c, Child opening mailbox. d, Mailbox next to sauna. e, Mailbox with posthorn and Finnish lion.

***Die Cut Perf. 10 Vert. Syncopated at Right***

**2011, Jan. 24** **Self-Adhesive**

**Coil Stamps**

**1370** Strip of 5 12.50 8.50
*a.-e.* A818 2 Any single 2.50 1.75

Nos. 1370a-1370e each sold for 60c on day of issue.

Miniature Sheet

Finnish National Opera, Cent. — A819

No. 1371: a, Male and female performers dancing, men in helmets. b, Man with hat and red ribbon, vert. c, Male and female performers in embrace. d, Woman in red dress in water, vert.

***Serpentine Die Cut 15½ Horiz.***

**2011, Jan. 24** **Self-Adhesive**

**1371** A819 Sheet of 4 10.00 6.50
*a.-d.* 2 Any single 2.50 1.60

Nos. 1371a-1371d each sold for 60c on day of issue.

Miniature Sheet

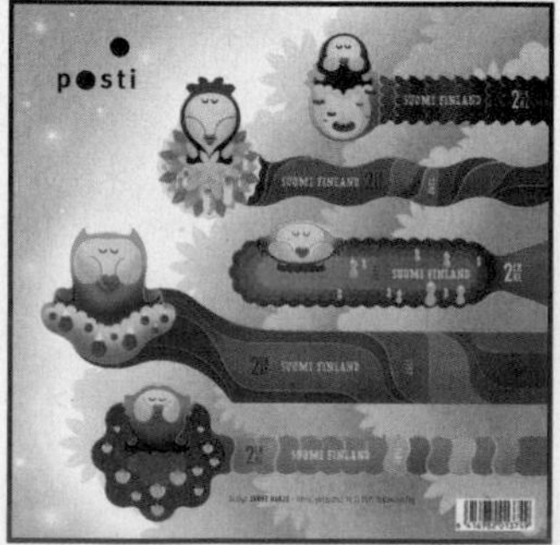

Birds in Trees — A820

No. 1372 — Various stylized birds with tree leaves in: a, Green (53x24mm). b, Blue (64x32mm). c, Orange (70x20mm). d, Yellow brown (89x39mm). e, Red violet (78x31mm).

**2011, Jan. 24** ***Die Cut***

**Self-Adhesive**

**1372** A820 Sheet of 5 12.50 8.00
*a.-e.* 2 Any single 2.50 1.60

Nos. 1372a-1372e each sold for 60c on day of issue.

Tulips — A821

**2011, Apr. 1** ***Die Cut Perf. 13¾***

**Self-Adhesive**

**1373** A821 2 multi 2.50 1.75

No. 1373 sold for 60c on day of issue.

Dahlias — A822

**2011, Apr. 1** ***Die Cut***

**Self-Adhesive**

**Color of Country Name**

**1374** A822 1 red violet 2.75 .75
**1375** A822 1 gray green 2.75 .75
*a.* Horiz. pair, #1374-1375 5.50

Nos. 1374-1375 each sold for 75c on day of issue.

Miniature Sheet

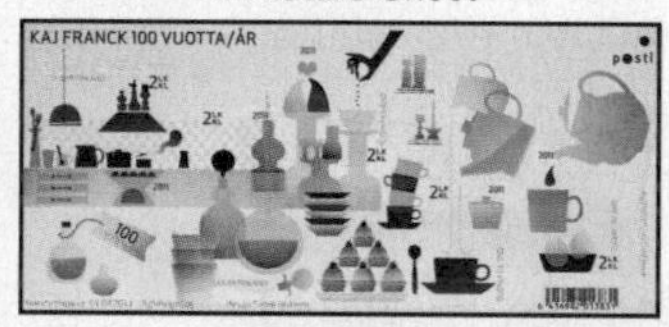

Kitchen — A823

No. 1376: a, Lamp, counter, pitcher, stove with pots (32x22mm, serpentine die cut 10x10¾). b, Bottles with stoppers (19x46mm, serpentine die cut 9¾x10). c, Hand dropping seasonings into bowl (24x32mm, serpentine die cut 10x10¼). d, Cup, saucer, bowl with lid (22x32mm, serpentine die cut 9½x10¼). e, Cup, eggs in bowl (24x32mm, serpentine die cut 9¾x10).

**2011, Apr. 1** ***Serpentine Die Cut***

**Self-Adhesive**

**1376** A823 Sheet of 5 12.50 8.50
*a.-e.* 2 Any single 2.50 1.60

Nos. 1376a-1376e each sold for 60c on day of issue.

Government Buildings — A824

No. 1377: a, House of the Estates, Helsinki, 1890. b, Finnish Embassy, New Delhi, India, 1985. c, Helsinki Music Center, 2011. d, Government Palace, Helsinki, 1828. e, Malmi Airport, Helsinki, 1938. f, Finnish Forest Research Institute Research Center, Joensuu, 2004.

**2011, Apr. 1** ***Die Cut Perf. 13¼***

**Self-Adhesive**

**1377** Booklet pane of 6 15.00 10.50
*a.-f.* A824 2 Any single 2.50 1.75

Nos. 1377a-1377f each sold for 60c on day of issue.

National Council of Women, Cent. A825

No. 1378 — Comic strip characters Maisa and Kaarina, by Tiina Paju and Sari Luhtanen: a, Holding star-tipped wands. b, Knitting blanket with stars. c, Playing tennis. d, Posing and taking picture. e, Wearing stars on dresses. f, Placing star on cake.

**2011, Apr. 1** ***Serpentine Die Cut 11***

**Self-Adhesive**

**1378** Booklet pane of 6 15.00 10.50
*a.-f.* A825 2 Any single 2.50 1.75

Nos. 1378a-1378f each sold for 60c on day of issue.

Europa — A826

No. 1379 — Trees in: a, Spring and summer. b, Autumn and winter.

**2011, May 6** ***Perf. 12¾x13¼***

**Self-Adhesive**

**1379** A826 Horiz. pair 5.00 3.00
*a.-b.* 2 Either single 2.50 1.25

Intl. Year of Forests. Nos. 1379a-1379b each sold for 60c on day of issue.

Moomin — A827

Mymble — A828

Little My — A829

Moominmamma and Moomin — A830

Hemulen A831

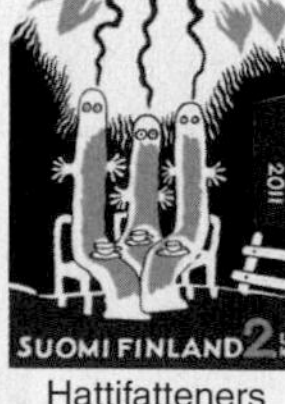

Hattifatteners A832

**2011, May 6** ***Die Cut***

**Self-Adhesive**

**1380** Booklet pane of 6 15.00 10.00
*a.* A827 2 multi 2.50 1.60
*b.* A828 2 multi 2.50 1.60
*c.* A829 2 multi 2.50 1.60
*d.* A830 2 multi 2.50 1.60
*e.* A831 2 multi 2.50 1.60
*f.* A832 2 multi 2.50 1.60

Nos. 1380a-1380f each sold for 60c on day of issue.

Souvenir Sheet

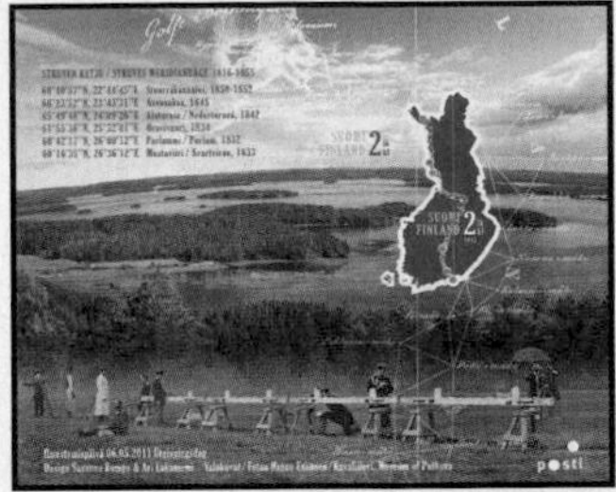

Struve Geodetic Arc — A833

No. 1381: a, Land, water, geodetic arc triangulations. b, Map of Finland with path of triangulations.

**2011, May 6** *Die Cut*
**Self-Adhesive**

**1381** A833 Sheet of 2 5.00 3.50
*a.-b.* 2 Either single 2.50 1.75

Nos. 1381a-1381b each sold for 60c on day of issue.

Miniature Sheet

Tree of Happiness — A834

No. 1382: a, Balloons and gifts (32mm diameter). b, Birds on branch (32mm diameter). c, Cake with Finnish flags (34x29mm oval). d, Bird in birdhouse (34x29mm oval). e, Boy and girl on branch (32mm diameter).

**2011, May 6** *Die Cut*
**Self-Adhesive**

**1382** A834 Sheet of 5 12.50 8.50
*a.-e.* 2 Any single 2.50 1.60

Nos. 1382a-1382e each sold for 60c on day of issue.

**Heraldic Lion Type of 2002**
***Die Cut Perf. 12 Syncopated***
**2011, Sept. 5** **Litho.**
**Self-Adhesive**

**1383** A616 €2 green & multi 5.75 5.50
**1384** A616 €4 pur & multi 11.50 11.00

Souvenir Sheet

Juhani Aho (1861-1921), Writer — A835

No. 1385: a, Stack of paper, trees. b, Aho on skis.

**Litho. & Embossed**
**2011, Sept. 5** ***Perf. 13½***
**Self-Adhesive**

**1385** A835 Sheet of 2 5.00 3.50
*a.-b.* 2 Either single 2.50 1.75

Nos. 1385a-1385b each sold for 60c on day of issue.

Miniature Sheet

Finnish Comics, Cent. — A836

No. 1386: a, Kili ja Possu, by Olavi Vikainen, 1950s. b, Unto Uneksija, by Joonas (Veikko Savolainen), 1960s. c, Herra Kerhonen, by Gösta Thilén, 1930s. d, Antti Puuhaara, by Aarne Nopsanen, 1940s. e, Janne Ankkanen, by Ola Fogelberg, 1910s. f, Olli Pirteä, by Hjalmar Löfving, 1920s.

***Die Cut Perf. 8½***
**2011, Sept. 5** **Litho.**
**Self-Adhesive**

**1386** A836 Sheet of 6 15.00 10.00
*a.-f.* 2 Any single 2.50 2.00

Nos. 1386a-1386f each sold for 60c on day of issue.

Houses with Snow-covered Roofs — A837

**2011, Nov. 7** ***Die Cut Perf. 14***
**Booklet Stamp**
**Self-Adhesive**

**1387** A837 1 multi 2.75 2.10
*a.* Booklet pane of 10 + 10 etiquettes 27.50

No. 1387 sold for 75c on day of issue.

Personalized Stamp — A838

***Serpentine Die Cut 11¾ Syncopated***
**2011, Nov. 7** **Self-Adhesive**

**1388** A838 2 multi 2.50 1.75

No. 1388 sold for 60c on day of issue. The generic design part of the stamp shown could be personalized.

A839

Christmas — A840

***Die Cut Perf. 14***
**2011, Nov. 7** **Self-Adhesive**

**1389** A839 55c multi 1.75 1.50
**1390** A840 2 multi 2.50 1.75

No. 1390 sold for 60c on day of issue.

Miniature Sheet

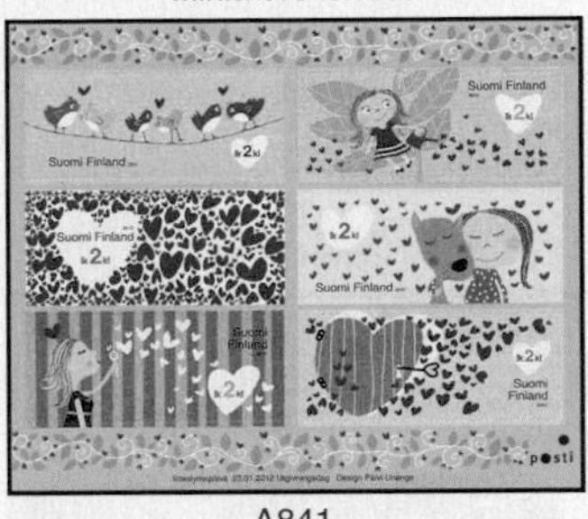

A841

No. 1391: a, Birds on wire. b, Girl with watering can. c, Hearts. d, Girl and dog. e, Woman blowing heart-shaped bubbles. f, Heart-shaped door and key.

**2012, Jan. 23** ***Die Cut Perf. 13¼x13***
**Self-Adhesive**

**1391** A841 Sheet of 6 15.00 9.50
*a.-f.* 2 Any single 2.50 1.20

Nos. 1391a-1391f each sold for 60c on day of issue.

Miniature Sheet

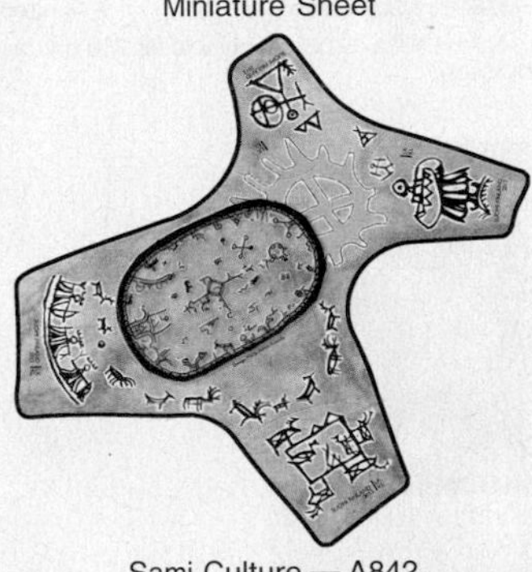

Sami Culture — A842

No. 1392: a, Stick-figure man holding forked stick. b, Stick figure of woman. c, Reindeer at sides of rectangle. d, Three daughters of Sami's mother god and reindeer. Stamps are of various sizes.

**2012, Jan. 23** ***Die Cut***
**Self-Adhesive**

**1392** A842 Sheet of 4 11.00 8.00
*a.-d.* 1 Any single 2.75 2.00

Nos. 1392a-1392d each sold for 75c on day of issue.

The School Girl II — A843

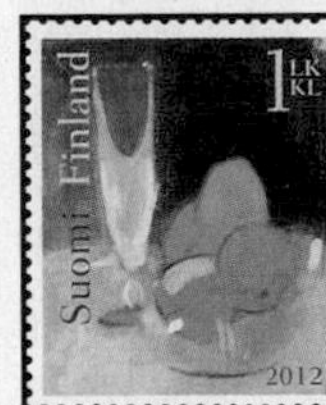

Green Apples and Champagne Glass — A844

Self-Portrait on Black — A845

Silk Shoes A846

***Die Cut Perf. 13, 12¾x13¼ (#1393b), 13¼ (#1393c)***
**2012, Jan. 23** **Self-Adhesive**

**1393** Booklet pane of 4 11.00 8.00
*a.* A843 1 multi 2.75 2.00
*b.* A844 1 multi 2.75 2.00
*c.* A845 1 multi 2.75 2.00
*d.* A846 1 multi 2.75 2.00

Paintings by Helene Schjerfbeck (1862-1946). Nos. 1393a-1393d each sold for 75c on day of issue.

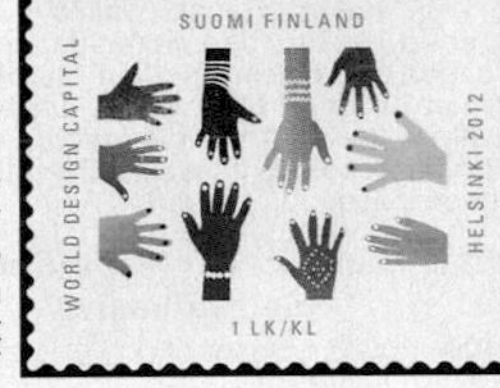

Winning Designs in Future City Stamp Design Contest A847

Designs: No. 1394, Hands, by Varpu Kangas. No. 1395, Shapes and dots, by Kangas. No. 1396, Future City is Diversity, by Chloé Chapeaublanc. No. 1397, Buildings, balloons, and inverted umbrella on tree branch, by Sini Henttonen. No. 1398, Children's drawingin red, blue, and black, by Daniel Kallström, vert. No. 1399, Children's drawing of animal under sun, by Elias Ollila, vert. No. 1400, Rabbits, by Katja Hynninen. No. 1401, Cat's head and heavy man on bicycle, by Ville Korhonen.

**Booklet Stamps**

***Serpentine Die Cut 8¾x9 (#1394, 1400), Rectangle and Arc Die Cut (#1395-1396), Arc Die Cut 12¾ (#1397, 1401), Sawtooth Die Cut 15½x15¼ (#1398-1399)***
**2012, Jan. 23** **Self-Adhesive**

**1394** A847 1 multi 2.75 2.75
**1395** A847 1 multi 2.75 2.75
*a.* Booklet pane of 2, #1394-1395 5.50 4.00
**1396** A847 1 multi 2.75 2.75
**1397** A847 1 multi 2.75 2.75
*a.* Booklet pane of 2, #1396-1397 5.50 4.00
**1398** A847 1 multi 2.75 2.75
**1399** A847 1 multi 2.75 2.75
*a.* Booklet pane of 2, #1398-1399 5.50 4.00
**1400** A847 1 multi 2.75 2.75
**1401** A847 1 multi 2.75 2.75
*a.* Booklet pane of 2, #1400-1401 5.50 4.00
Complete booklet, #1395a, 1397a, 1399a, 1401a 22.00 16.00
*Nos. 1394-1401 (8)* 22.00 22.00

Nos. 1394-1401 each sold for 75c on day of issue.

Wedding Rings — A848

***Die Cut Perf. 14***
**2012, Mar. 5** **Litho. & Engr.**
**Self-Adhesive**

**1402** A848 1 multi 2.75 2.00

No. 1402 sold for 75c on day of issue.

Easter A849

*Serpentine Die Cut 8¼ Vert.*

**2012, Mar. 5** **Litho.**

**Self-Adhesive**

**1403** A849 1 multi 2.75 2.00

No. 1403 sold for 75c on day of issue.

Souvenir Sheet

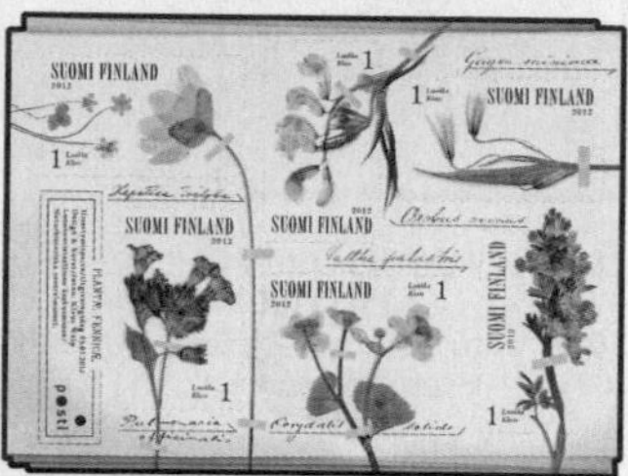

Flowers — A850

No. 1404: a, Hepatica triloba (three small yellow flowers at L, large yellow flower at R, denomination al LL). b, Orobus virnus (six yellow and white flowers on stem, denomination at UR), vert. c, Gagea minima (two partially opened buds, denomination at UL). d, Pulmonaria officinalis (four purple flowers, denomination at LR), vert. e, Caltha palastris (yellow flowers, denoimination at UR). f, Corydalis solida (cluster of purple flowers, denomination at LL), vert.

**2012, Mar. 5** ***Die Cut Perf. 10***

**Self-Adhesive**

**1404** A850 Sheet of 6 17.00 12.00
***a.-f.*** 1 Any single 2.75 2.00

Nos. 1404a-1404f each sold for 75c on day of issue.

Intl. Women's Day A851

No. 1405: a, Woman and hearts. b, Women's hands with glasses of fruit, vert. c, Women's legs and shoes, vert. d, Women and musical notes.

**2012, Mar. 5** ***Die Cut Perf. 12½***

**Self-Adhesive**

**1405** Booklet pane of 4 11.00 8.00
***a.-d.*** A851 1 Any single 2.75 2.00

Nos. 1405a-1405d each sold for 75c on day of issue.

Railroads in Finland, 150th Anniv. — A852

No. 1406: a, Train engineer, steam locomotive. b, Train, ticket. c, Railroad warning sign, train in snow. d, Passenger car and passengers at platform, clock. e, Railway worker, modern train. f, Train, lake, statue.

*Serpentine Die Cut 9½ Horiz.*

**2012, Mar. 5** **Self-Adhesive**

**1406** Booklet pane of 6 17.00 12.00
***a.-f.*** A852 1 Any single 2.75 2.00

Nos. 1406a-1406f each sold for 75c on day of issue.

2012 Men's Ice Hockey World Cup Tournament, Finland and Sweden A853

**2012, Mar. 21** ***Die Cut Perf. 14***

**Self-Adhesive**

**1407** A853 1 multi 2.75 2.00

No. 1407 sold for 75c on day of issue.

Souvenir Sheet

Rescue Boats — A854

No. 1408: a, Jenny Wihuri (red and white boat). b, Merikarhu (green, orange and white boat).

**2012, Mar. 21** ***Perf. 13½x13***

**Self-Adhesive**

**1408** A854 Sheet of 2 5.50 4.00
***a.-b.*** 1 Either single 2.75 2.00

Nos. 1408a-1408b each sold for 75c on day of issue.

Europa — A855

No. 1409: a, Ship on lake. b, People at beach.

**2012, May 7** ***Perf. 13¼x12¾***

**Self-Adhesive**

**1409** A855 1 Vert. pair, #a-b 5.50 3.75

Nos. 1409a-1409b each sold for 75c on day of issue.

Bothnian Sea National Park — A856

**2012, May 7** ***Die Cut Perf. 14***

**Self-Adhesive**

**1410** A856 1 multi 2.75 2.00

No. 1410 sold for 75c on day of issue.

A857

Sunflowers — A858

**2012, May 7** ***Die Cut Perf. 17***

**Self-Adhesive**

**1411** A857 1 multi 2.75 2.00
**1412** A858 1 multi 2.75 2.00

Nos. 1411-142 each sold for 75c on day of issue.

A859

A860

Clouds A861

*Die Cut Perf. 10 Horiz., Syncopated at Bottom*

**2012, May 7** **Self-Adhesive**

**Coil Stamps**

**1413** Horiz. strip of 3 8.25
***a.*** A859 1 multi 2.75 1.40
***b.*** A860 1 multi 2.75 1.40
***c.*** A861 1 multi 2.75 1.40

Nos. 1413a-1413c each sold for 75c on day of issue.

Souvenir Sheet

Disabled Athletes — A862

No. 1414: a, Leo-Pekka Tahti, cyclist. b, Saana-Maria Sinisalo, archer.

*Die Cut Perf. 11¼x11½*

**Litho. & Silk-screened**

**2012, May 7** **Self-Adhesive**

**1414** A862 1 Sheet of 2, #a-b 5.50 4.00

Nos. 1414a-1414b each sold for 75c on day of issue.

Miniature Sheet

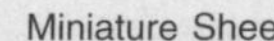

Autumn Dreams — A863

No. 1415: a, Hot-air balloon (36x46mm). b, Moon, lanterns in tree (37x39mm). c, Flying geese (28x36mm). d, Scarecrow and hay rolls (29x46mm). e, Girl feeding carrots to horse (44x34mm).

*Serpentine Die Cut 4 to 7*

**2012, Sept. 3** **Litho.**

**Self-Adhesive**

**1415** A863 Sheet of 5 13.50 10.00
***a.-e.*** 1 Any single 2.60 2.00

On day of issue, Nos. 1415a-1415e each sold for 80c.

Recording Stars of the 1990s A864

No. 1416: a, Kaija Koo. b, Jari Sillanpää. c, Laura Voutilainen. d, Yölintu. e, Agents. f, Anna Eriksson.

**2012, Sept. 3** ***Die Cut Perf. 8½***

**Self-Adhesive**

**1416** Booklet pane of 6 17.00 12.00
***a.-f.*** A864 1 Any single 2.75 2.00

On day of issue, Nos. 1416a-1416f each sold for 80c.

Pets — A865

No. 1417: a, Cat, inscriptions in red. b, White rabbit facing left. c, Gray rabbit facing right. d, Dachshund puppy, year date at LR. e, Jack Russell terrier puppy, year date at LL. f, Kitten, inscriptions in green.

*Serpentine Die Cut 11¾ Horiz.*

**2012, Sept. 3** **Self-Adhesive**

**1417** Booklet pane of 6 17.00 12.00
***a.-f.*** A865 1 Any single 2.75 2.00

On day of issue, Nos. 1417a-1417f each sold for 80c.

Christmas Tree — A866

Stable Lantern — A867

**2012, Nov. 5** *Serpentine Die Cut 9½*

**Self-Adhesive**

1418 A866 60c multi 1.75 1.60

*Serpentine Die Cut 10*

1419 A867 1 multi 2.75 1.75

Christmas. No. 1419 sold for 80c on day of issue.

Sledders A868

**Self-Adhesive**

**2013, Jan. 21** *Die Cut Perf. 14*

1420 A868 1 multi 2.75 1.40

No. 1420 sold for 80c on day of issue.

Coilostylis Parkinsoniana A869

**Self-Adhesive**

**2013, Jan. 21** *Die Cut Perf. 14*

1421 A869 €1.10 multi 2.75 1.40

See No. 1442.

Miniature Sheet

St.Valentine's Day — A870

No. 1422: a, Polar bears. b, Whale. c, Parrots. d, Elephants. e, Chameleon. f, Monkey.

**2013, Jan. 21** *Die Cut*

**Self-Adhesive**

1422 A870 Sheet of 6 + 4 labels 17.00 12.00
*a.-f.* 1 Any single 2.75 2.00

Nos. 1422a-1422f each sold for 80c on day of issue.

Actors and Actresses — A871

No. 1427: a, Ritva Valkama. b, Esko Salminen. c, Outi Mäenpää. d, Martti Suosalo. e, Krista Kosonen. f, Aku Hirviniemi.

*Die Cut Perf. 6¾ Vert. Syncopated*

**2013, Mar. 4**

**Self-Adhesive**

1423 Booklet pane of 6 17.00 12.00
*a.-f.* A871 1 Any single 2.75 2.00

Finnish Actors Federation, cent. On day of issue, Nos. 1423a-1423f each sold for 80c.

Easter Rooster — A872

**2013, Mar. 8** *Die Cut Perf. 14*

**Self-Adhesive**

1424 A872 1 multi 2.75 2.00

No. 1424 sold for 80c on day of issue.

Roses — A873

**2013, Mar. 8** **Self-Adhesive**

1425 A873 1 multi 2.75 2.00

No. 1425 sold for 80c on day of issue.

Blackberries A874

Gooseberry A875

Red Currants A876

*Die Cut Perf. 10 Horiz. Syncopated*

**2013, Mar. 8** **Self-Adhesive**

**Coil Stamps**

1426 Horiz. strip of 3 8.50 6.00
*a.* A874 1 multi 2.75 2.00
*b.* A875 1 multi 2.75 2.00
*c.* A876 1 multi 2.75 2.00

On day of issue, Nos. 1426a-1426c each sold for 80c.

A877

A878

A879

Outhouses A880

**2013, Mar. 8** *Die Cut Perf. 12*

**Self-Adhesive**

1427 Booklet pane of 4 11.50
*a.* A877 2 multi 2.75 2.00
*b.* A878 2 multi 2.75 2.00
*c.* A879 2 multi 2.75 2.00
*d.* A880 2 multi 2.75 2.00

On day of issue, Nos. 1527a-1527d each sold for 70c.

Flower Bouquet — A881

**2013, May 6** *Die Cut Perf. 14*

**Self-Adhesive**

1428 A881 1 multi 2.75 1.40

No. 1428 sold for 80c on day of issue.

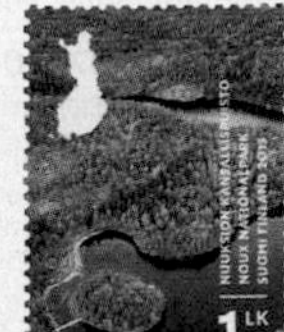

Nuuksio Natl. Park — A882

**2013, May 6** **Litho.**

**Self-Adhesive**

1429 A882 1 multi 2.75 1.40

No. 1429 sold for 80c on day of issue.

2012 Ford Transit Connect Mail Van — A883

1933 Volvo LV-70 Mail Truck A884

**2013, May 6** *Die Cut Perf. 12½x13¼*

**Self-Adhesive**

1430 Horiz. pair 5.50
*a.* A883 1 multi 2.75 2.00
*b.* A884 1 multi 2.75 2.00

Europa. On day of issue, Nos. 1430a-1430b each sold for 80c.

Miniature Sheet

Odd Finnish Sports and Activities — A885

No. 1431: a, Man carrying wife. b, Boot throwing. c, Air guitarist. d, Woman pushing man in milk cart. e, Man sitting on ant hill. f, Swamp soccer.

**2013, May 6** *Die Cut Perf. 10*

**Self-Adhesive**

1431 A885 Sheet of 6 + 6 etiquettes 17.50
*a.-f.* 1 Any single 2.75 2.00

On day of issue, Nos. 1431a-1431f each sold for 80c.

Moomins — A886

No. 1432: a, Moominpappa holding drink (red background, 30x34mm). b, Moomintroll jumping (blue background, 33x31mm). c, Moominmamma with purse (green background, 33x34mm). d, Little My with basket on head (yellow orange background, 32x33mm). e, Snorkmaiden and piece of paper (red violet background, 30x35mm). f, Snufkin (brown orange background, 32x36mm).

**2013, May 6** *Die Cut*

**Self-Adhesive**

1432 Booklet pane of 6 + 6 etiquettes 17.00
*a.-f.* A886 1 Any single 2.75 2.00

On day of issue, Nos. 1432a-1432f each sold for 80c.

Personalized Stamp — A891

*Serpentine Die Cut 11¾ Syncopated*

**2013, Aug. 12** **Litho.**

**Self-Adhesive**

1437 A891 1 black 4.50 4.50

No. 1437 had a franking value of 85c on the day of issue. The vignette shown for No. 1437 is a generic image depicting a Volvo PV 444 police vehicle and is one of ten different police vehicles depicted in the image portion of stamps in a sheet of ten stamps having the same common "frame" that sold for €16.50. Customers purchasing sheets of No. 1437 could also download vignette images from an online library of images on the stamp creation website or use their own downloaded images.

Pres. Sauli Niinistö, 65th Birthday A895

*Die Cut Perf. 12 Syncopated*

**2013, Aug. 23** **Litho.**

**Self-Adhesive**

1441 A895 1 blk & gray 2.75 1.40

No. 1441 sold for 85c on day of issue.

**Coilostylis Parkinsoniana Type of 2013**

*Die Cut Perf. 14*

**2013, Aug. 23** **Litho.**

**Self-Adhesive**

1442 A869 €1.20 multi 2.75 1.40

Souvenir Sheet

Paintings by Eero Järnefelt (1863-1937) — A896

No. 1443: a, Metsämaisema (Forest Scene) (34x49mm). b, Raatajat Rahanalaiset (Under the Yoke - Burning the Brushwood) (44x40mm).

*Serpentine Die Cut 14½*

**2013, Sept. 9 Litho.**

**Self-Adhesive**

| | | | | |
|---|---|---|---|---|
| **1443** | A896 | Sheet of 2 | 5.50 | 4.25 |
| ***a.-b.*** | | 1 Either single | 2.75 | 2.10 |

On day of issue, Nos. 1443a-1443b each sold for 85c.

Postcrossing — A897

No. 1444 — Stylized postal card and: a, Hand holding pencil. b, Blackboard. c, Heart-shaped Earth. d, Open mouth.

*Serpentine Die Cut 12¼*

**2013, Sept. 9 Litho.**

**Self-Adhesive**

| | | | | |
|---|---|---|---|---|
| **1444** | | Booklet pane of 4 + 4 etiquettes | 11.00 | |
| ***a.-d*** | A897 | 1 Any single | 2.75 | 1.10 |

On day of issue Nos. 1444a-1444d each sold for 85c.

Miniature Sheet

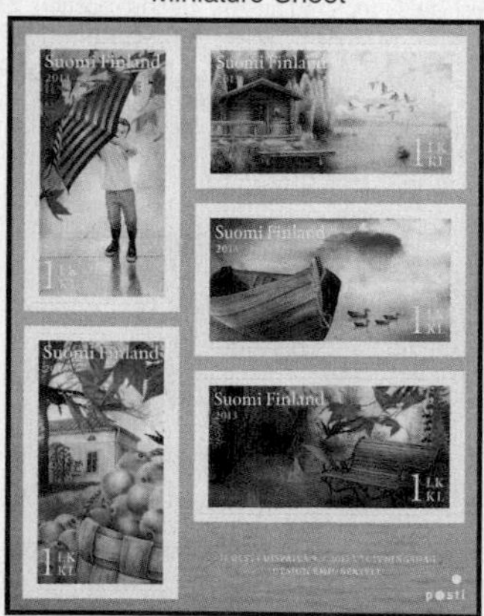

Autumn Scenes — A898

No. 1445: a, Boy with umbrella, falling leaves. b, Lakeside sauna, geese in flight, buoy, horiz. c, Rowboat and ducks, horiz. d, Apples in basket, house, falling leaves. e, Park bench, falling leaves, horiz.

*Serpentine Die Cut 14x14¼, 14¼x14*

**2013, Sept. 9 Litho.**

**Self-Adhesive**

| | | | | |
|---|---|---|---|---|
| **1445** | A898 | Sheet of 5 | 11.50 | |
| ***a.-e.*** | | 1 Any single | 2.25 | 2.25 |

On day of issue, Nos. 1445a-1445e each sold for 85c.

Miniature Sheet

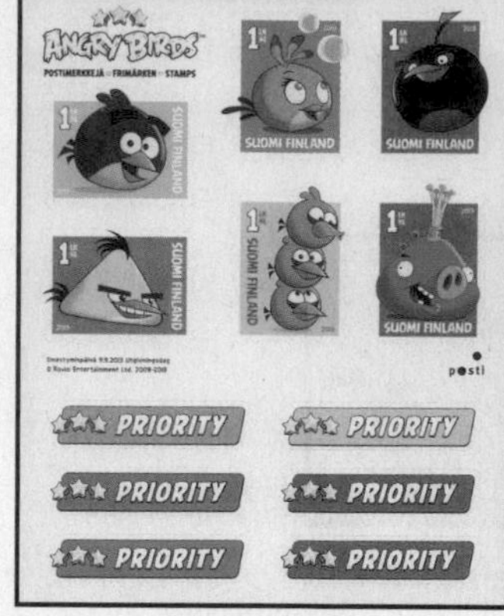

Angry Birds Characters — A899

No. 1446: a, Red Bird. b, Pink Bird, vert. c, Black Bird, vert. d, Yellow Bird. e, Blue Birds, vert. f, King Pig, vert.

*Die Cut Perf. 8¼*

**2013, Sept. 9 Litho.**

**Self-Adhesive**

| | | | | |
|---|---|---|---|---|
| **1446** | A899 | Sheet of 6 + 6 etiquettes | 13.50 | |
| ***a.-f.*** | | 1 Any single | 2.25 | 2.25 |

On day of issue, Nos. 1446a-1446f each sold for 85c.

Finnish Parliament, 150th Anniv. — A900

*Die Cut Perf. 14*

**2013, Sept. 17 Litho.**

**Self-Adhesive**

| | | | | |
|---|---|---|---|---|
| **1447** | A900 | 1 multi | 2.40 | 2.40 |

No. 1447 sold for 85c on day of issue.

Finnish School System — A901

No. 1448: a, Girl receiving school lunch, apple, lettuce, pitcher and plate. b, Boy receiving medical examination, posture diagrams. c, Girl practicing writing on blackboard, letters in Finnish alphabet. d, Uno Cygnaeus (1810-88), founder of Finnish school system, map of Finland. e, Children in physical education class, children skiing. f, Teacher watching boys writing at desk, orrery, sun and planet.

*Die Cut Perf. 6¾ Horiz. At Top*

**2013, Nov. 14 Litho.**

**Self-Adhesive**

| | | | | |
|---|---|---|---|---|
| **1448** | | Booklet pane of 6 | 13.50 | |
| ***a.-f.*** | A901 | 1 Any single | 2.25 | 2.25 |

On day of issue, Nos. 1448a-1448f each sold for 85c.

Children Hugging A902

Angel A903

Boy with Christmas Trees — A904

*Die Cut Perf. 14*

**2013, Nov. 4 Litho.**

**Self-Adhesive**

| | | | | |
|---|---|---|---|---|
| **1449** | A902 | 65c multi | 1.75 | 1.75 |
| **1450** | A903 | 2 multi | 2.00 | 2.00 |
| **1451** | A904 | 1 multi | 2.25 | 2.25 |
| | | *Nos. 1449-1451 (3)* | 6.00 | 6.00 |

Christmas. On day of issue, No. 1450 sold for 75c; No. 1451, 85c.

Snowmen A905

*Serpentine Die Cut 10¼*

**2014, Jan. 20 Litho.**

**Self-Adhesive**

| | | | | |
|---|---|---|---|---|
| **1452** | A905 | 1 multi | 2.75 | 2.75 |

No. 1452 sold for €1 on day of issue.

Miniature Sheet

Teddy Bears — A906

No. 1453: a, Teddy bear writing with quill pen. b, Teddy bear pushing another on sled, horiz. c, Two Teddy bears and flower. d, Two Teddy bears dancing. e, Teddy bear sleeping in slipper, horiz. f, Two Teddy bears playing musical instruments.

*Serpentine Die Cut 16*

**2014, Jan. 20 Litho.**

**Self-Adhesive**

| | | | | |
|---|---|---|---|---|
| **1453** | A906 | Sheet of 6 + 4 stickers | 16.50 | |
| ***a.-f.*** | | 1 Any single | 2.75 | 2.75 |

Nos. 1453a-1453f each sold for €1 on day of issue.

Castles — A907

No. 1454: a, Turun Linna (Turku Castle) (34x50mm). b, Hämeen Linna (Häme Castle) (34x50mm). c, Raaseporin Linna (Raseborg Castle) (34x50mm). d, Suomenlinna (Sveaborg Fortress) (34x58mm). e, Olavinlinna (Olavinlinna Castle) (34x50mm). f, Kastelholma (Kastelholma Castle) (50x34mm).

*Die Cut Perf. 7½*

**2014, Jan. 20 Litho.**

**Self-Adhesive**

| | | | | |
|---|---|---|---|---|
| **1454** | | Booklet pane of 6 | 16.50 | |
| ***a.-f.*** | A907 | 1 Any single | 2.75 | 2.75 |

Nos. 1454a-1454f each sold for €1 on day of issue.

Souvenir Sheet

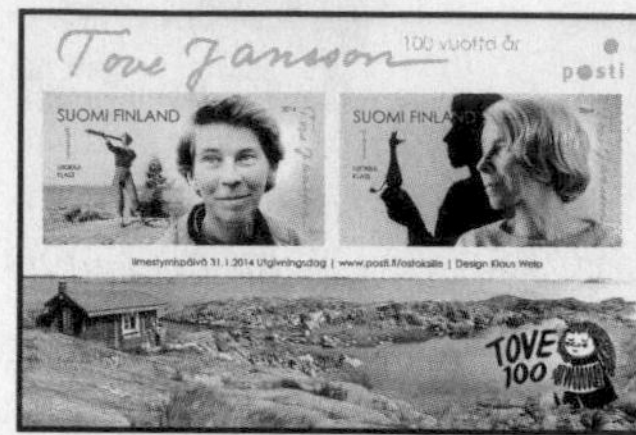

Tove Jansson (1914-2001), Creator of *Moomins* Characters — A908

No. 1456: a, Jansson with telescope. b, Silhouette of Jansson and Moomin character, Sniff.

*Die Cut Perf. 12½*

**2014, Jan. 31 Litho.**

**Self-Adhesive**

| | | | | |
|---|---|---|---|---|
| **1455** | A908 | Sheet of 2 | 5.50 | |
| ***a.-b.*** | | 1 Either single | 2.75 | 2.75 |

Nos. 1455a-1455b each sold for €1 on day of issue.

Easter A909

*Die Cut Perf. 9¾ Horiz.*

**2014, Mar. 3 Litho.**

**Self-Adhesive**

| | | | | |
|---|---|---|---|---|
| **1456** | A909 | 1 multi | 2.75 | 2.75 |

No. 1456 sold for €1 on day of issue.

Sami Jauhojärvi and Iivo Niskanen, 2014 Winter Olympic Cross-Country Team Sprint Gold Medalists — A909a

*Serpentine Die Cut 11¾ Syncopated*

**2014, Mar. 3 Litho.**

**Self-Adhesive**

| | | | | |
|---|---|---|---|---|
| **1456A** | A909a | 1 multi | 5.00 | 5.00 |

No. 1456A was printed in sheets of 10 that sold for €18. No. 1456 had a franking value of €1 on day of issue.

Fruits and Blossoms — A910

No. 1457: a, Pears (light green background). b, Apples (yellow background). c, Cherries (pink background).

*Die Cut Perf. 10 Vert. Syncopated*

**2014, Mar. 3** **Litho.**

**Coil Stamps**

**Self-Adhesive**

**1457** Vert. strip of 3 7.50
*a.-c.* A910 2 Any single 2.50 2.50

Nos. 1457a-1457c each sold for 90c on day of issue.

A911

Congratulations A912

No. 1458: a, Cat, cake with strawberries. b, Butterflies and flower. c, Squirrel and flowers. d, Strrawberries, blueberries and flower. e, Basket of flowers.

*Serpentine Die Cut 13¾x13½ (A911), 14½x15¼ (A912)*

**2014, Mar. 3** **Litho.**

**Self-Adhesive**

**1458** Booklet pane of 5 14.00
*a.-b.* A911 1 Either single 2.75 2.75
*c.-e.* A912 1 Any single 2.75 2.75

Nos. 1458a-1458e each sold for €1 on day of issue.

Souvenir Sheet

Finnjet Ferry — A913

No. 1459 — Ferry with posthorn at: a, Left. b, Right.

*Serpentine Die Cut 13½*

**2014, Mar. 17** **Litho.**

**Self-Adhesive**

**1459** A913 Sheet of 2 5.50
*a.-b.* 1 Either single 2.75 2.75

Nos. 1459a-1459b each sold for €1 on day of issue.

Violas — A914

**2014, May 5** **Litho.** ***Die Cut Perf. 14***

**Self-Adhesive**

**1460** A914 1 multi 2.75 2.75

No. 1460 sold for €1 on day of issue.

Linnansaari National Park — A915

**2014, May 5** **Litho.** ***Die Cut Perf. 14***

**Self-Adhesive**

**1461** A915 1 multi 2.75 2.75

No. 1461 sold for €1 on day of issue.

Europa A916

No. 1462: a, Man playing accordion. b, Woman playing kantele.

*Irregular Serpentine Die Cut*

**2014, May 5** **Litho.**

**Self-Adhesive**

**1462** Horiz. pair 5.50
*a.-b.* A916 1 Either single 2.75 2.75

Nos. 1462a-1462b each sold for €1 on day of issue.

A917

A918

A919

A920

A921

A922

*Die Cut Perf. 13½*

**2014, May 5** **Litho.**

**Self-Adhesive**

**1463** Booklet pane of 6 16.50
*a.* A917 1 multi 2.75 2.75
*b.* A918 1 multi 2.75 2.75
*c.* A919 1 multi 2.75 2.75
*d.* A920 1 multi 2.75 2.75
*e.* A921 1 multi 2.75 2.75
*f.* A922 1 multi 2.75 2.75

Nos. 1463a-1463f each sold for €1 on day of issue.

Miniature Sheet

Caricatures of Dudesons Television Show Cast Members — A923

No. 1464 — Dudeson: a, On snowboard. b, With red cap. c, Wearing shirt with target. d, Running naked, holding book.

*Crenellated Die Cut 5*

**2014, Sept. 1** **Litho.**

**Self-Adhesive**

**1464** A923 Sheet of 4 11.00
*a.-d.* 1 Any single 2.75 2.75

Nos. 1464a-1464d each sold for €1 on day of issue.

A924

A925

A926

Watercolors of Yards and Gardens by Urpo Martikainen A927

*Die Cut Perf. 13*

**2014, Sept. 8** **Litho.**

**Self-Adhesive**

**1465** Booklet pane of 4 11.00
*a.* A924 1 multi 2.75 2.75
*b.* A925 1 multi 2.75 2.75
*c.* A926 1 multi 2.75 2.75
*d.* A927 1 multi 2.75 2.75

Nos. 1465a-1465d each sold for €1 on day of issue.

Celestial and Meteorological Objects — A928

No. 1466: a, Saturn (45x40mm). b, Moon (36x36mm). c, Sun (40x38mm). d, Cloud and lightning bolt (40x51mm). e, Earth and Moon (35x41mm). f, Comet (40x45mm). g, Cloud (48x42mm). h, Rainbow (40x38mm).

*Serpentine Die Cut 9¼ on 1 or 2 Sides*

**2014, Sept. 8** **Litho.**

**Self-Adhesive**

**1466** Booklet pane of 8 22.00
*a.-h.* A928 1 Any single 2.75 2.75

Nos. 1466a-1466h each sold for €1 on day of issue.

Souvenir Sheet

Art by Tom of Finland (Touko Laaksonen) (1920-91) — A929

No. 1467: a, Man wearing police cap smoking cigarette (43x32mm). b, Man's head between legs of another man (45x33mm). c, Man's head and buttocks (36x33mm).

*Die Cut Perf. 5½*

**2014, Sept. 8** **Litho.**

**Self-Adhesive**

**1467** Sheet of 3 8.25
*a.-c.* A929 1 Any single 2.75 2.75

Nos. 1467a-1467c each sold for €1 on day of issue.

A930

A931

A932

A933

A934

A935

A936

A937

A938

Bridges A939

*Die Cut Perf. 8½ Horiz.*

**2014, Oct. 23 Litho.**

**Coil Stamps**

**Self-Adhesive**

| | | | | |
|---|---|---|---|---|
| 1468 | A930 | 1 multi + etiquette | 2.50 | 2.50 |
| 1469 | A931 | 1 multi + etiquette | 2.50 | 2.50 |
| 1470 | A932 | 1 multi + etiquette | 2.50 | 2.50 |
| 1471 | A933 | 1 multi + etiquette | 2.50 | 2.50 |
| 1472 | A934 | 1 multi + etiquette | 2.50 | 2.50 |
| 1473 | A935 | 1 multi + etiquette | 2.50 | 2.50 |
| 1474 | A936 | 1 multi + etiquette | 2.50 | 2.50 |
| 1475 | A937 | 1 multi + etiquette | 2.50 | 2.50 |
| 1476 | A938 | 1 multi + etiquette | 2.50 | 2.50 |
| 1477 | A939 | 1 multi + etiquette | 2.50 | 2.50 |
| *a.* | | Horiz. strip of 10, #1468-1477, + 10 etiquettes | 25.00 | |
| | | *Nos. 1468-1477 (10)* | 25.00 | 25.00 |

On day of issue, Nos. 1468-1477 had a franking value of €1. A complete roll of 100 stamps sold for €97.50 on the day of issue,

Changes in Everyday Items — A940

No. 1478: a, Computer keyboard, computer storage disks, computer, dial telephone, computer chip, television, computer mouse, compact disk and video cassette tapes (54x30mm). b, Potatoes, olives, cookies, cracker, sushi, shrimp, fish, pizza slice (54x30mm). c, Satellite, vacuum cleaner, chest freezer, coffee maker, stove, refrigerator, toaster, washing machine (54x30mm). d, Hay bales, cattle, tractor, storage shed, boarded windows, apartment house, automobiles, house (54x30mm). e, Radio, phonograph record, cassette tape player and headphones, mirrored ball, aerosol cans, electronic piano, dresses, make-up (54x30mm). f, Automobiles, rowboat, bus, scooter, sled, bicycle, cart, train (44x35mm).

**2014, Oct. 23 Litho. *Die Cut***

**Self-Adhesive**

| | | | | |
|---|---|---|---|---|
| 1478 | | Booklet pane of 6 | 15.00 | |
| *a.-f.* | A940 | 1 Any single | 2.50 | 2.50 |

Nos. 1478a-1478f each sold for €1 on day of issue.

A941

Christmas — A942

*Die Cut Perf. 13*

**2014, Oct. 23 Litho.**

**Self-Adhesive**

| | | | | |
|---|---|---|---|---|
| 1479 | A941 | 75c multi | 1.90 | 1.90 |
| 1480 | A942 | 1 multi | 2.50 | 2.50 |

No. 1480 sold for €1 on day of issue.

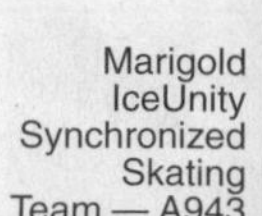

Marigold IceUnity Synchronized Skating Team — A943

*Die Cut Perf. 14*

**2015, Jan. 19 Litho.**

**Self-Adhesive**

**Textured Paper**

| | | | | |
|---|---|---|---|---|
| 1481 | A943 | 1 multi | 2.25 | 2.25 |

No. 1481 sold for €1 on day of issue.

Miniature Sheet

St. Valentine's Day — A944

No. 1482 — Smiling: a, Snowflakes. b, Trees, snowflakes and bird. c, Mouse and snow angel. d, Birds in nest. e, Berry plants. f, Fox and rabbit.

*Serpentine Die Cut 7*

**2015, Jan. 19 Litho.**

**Self-Adhesive**

| | | | | |
|---|---|---|---|---|
| 1482 | A944 | Sheet of 6 + 6 etiquettes | 13.50 | |
| *a.-f.* | | 1 Any single | 2.25 | 2.25 |

Nos. 1482a-1482f each sold for €1 on day of issue.

Artists' Assocition of Finland, 150th Anniv. A945

No. 1483: a, Line Form, by Anneli Hilli (36x36mm). b, Point, by Mika Natri (36x36mm). c, Artist's Rollercoaster, by Marjo Suikkanen (36x40mm). d, Dance from the Bride, by Mayumi Niiranen-Hisatomi (32x40mm oval). e, Flight, by Laura Konttinen (36x30mm). f, You Will Know Them By Their Fruits, by Kalevi Karlsson (36x30mm).

*Serpentine Die Cut 10¼*

**2015, Jan. 19 Litho.**

**Self-Adhesive**

| | | | | |
|---|---|---|---|---|
| 1483 | | Booklet pane of 6 + 6 etiquettes | 13.50 | |
| *a.-f.* | A945 | 1 Any single | 2.25 | 2.25 |

Nos. 1483a-1483f each sold for €1 on day of issue.

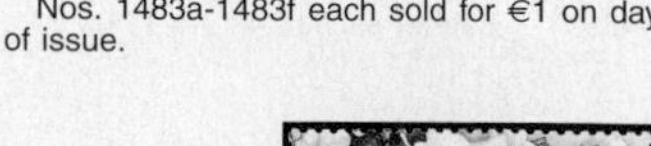

Flowers A946

*Die Cut Perf. 13¾*

**2015, Mar. 2 Litho.**

**Self-Adhesive**

| | | | | |
|---|---|---|---|---|
| 1484 | A946 | 1 multi | 2.50 | 2.50 |

No. 1484 sold for €1.10 on day of issue.

Easter — A947

*Serpentine Die Cut 8¾*

**2015, Mar. 2 Litho.**

**Self-Adhesive**

| | | | | |
|---|---|---|---|---|
| 1485 | A947 | 1 multi | 2.50 | 2.50 |

No. 1485 sold for €1.10 on day of issue.

Student's Cap — A948

*Die Cut Perf. 14¼*

**2015, Mar. 2 Litho.**

**Self-Adhesive**

| | | | | |
|---|---|---|---|---|
| 1486 | A948 | 1 multi | 2.50 | 2.50 |

No. 1486 sold for €1.10 on day of issue.

A949

A950

A951

International Women's Day — A952

**2015, Mar. 2 Litho. *Die Cut***

**Self-Adhesive**

| | | | | |
|---|---|---|---|---|
| 1487 | | Booklet pane of 4 | 10.00 | |
| *a.* | A949 | 1 multi | 2.50 | 2.50 |
| *b.* | A950 | 1 multi | 2.50 | 2.50 |
| *c.* | A951 | 1 multi | 2.50 | 2.50 |
| *d.* | A952 | 1 multi | 2.50 | 2.50 |

Nos. 1487a-1487d each sold for €1.10 on day of issue.

Souvenir Sheet

Toivo Kärki (1915-92), Composer — A953

No. 1488 — Kärki and: a, Record album (44mm diameter). b, Score (45x32mm). c, Accordion, silhouette of man and woman (45x32mm).

*Die Cut (#1488a), Die Cut Perf. 5¼*

**2015, Mar. 2 Litho.**

**Self-Adhesive**

| | | | | |
|---|---|---|---|---|
| 1488 | A953 | Sheet of 3 | 7.50 | |
| *a.-c.* | | 1 Any single | 2.50 | 2.50 |

Nos. 1488a-1488c each sold for €1.10 on day of issue.

Rugosa Roses — A954

Orchids A955

*Die Cut Perf. 13¾*

**2015, May 8 Litho.**

**Self-Adhesive**

| | | | | |
|---|---|---|---|---|
| 1489 | | Horiz. pair | 4.50 | |
| *a.* | A954 | 2 multi | 2.25 | 2.25 |
| *b.* | A955 | 2 multi | 2.25 | 2.25 |

Nos. 1489a-1489b each sold for €1 on day of issue.

Swan A956

**Litho. With Foil Application**

**2015, May 8 *Die Cut Perf. 13½***

**Self-Adhesive**

| | | | | |
|---|---|---|---|---|
| 1490 | A956 | 1 multi | 2.50 | 2.50 |

A957

Moomin Toys A958

*Serpentine Die Cut 9¾*

**2015, May 8 Self-Adhesive Litho.**

| | | | | |
|---|---|---|---|---|
| 1491 | | Horiz. pair | 5.00 | |
| *a.* | A957 | 1 multi | 2.50 | 2.50 |
| *b.* | A958 | 1 multi | 2.50 | 2.50 |

Europa. Nos. 1491a-1491b each sold for €1.10 on day of issue.

Miniature Sheet

Sights of Summer — A959

No. 1492: a, Strawberry, ladybug and ant (22x30mm). b, Man and woman in rowboat (62x30mm). c, Bicycle (41x30mm). d, Woman with ice cream cone (30x50mm). e, Woman diving into water (30x45mm).

***Serpentine Die Cut 9¼x11 (#1492a), 7½x6¼ (#1492b), 8x8¼ (#1492c), 7x6½ (#1492d), 7x7¼ (#1492e)***

**2015, May 8 Self-Adhesive Litho.**

**1492** A959 Sheet of 5 12.50
*a.-e.* 1 Any single 2.50 2.50

Nos. 1492a-1492e each sold for €1.10 on day of issue.

Miniature Sheet

Scenes From Imaginary Town — A960

No. 1493: a, Woman riding giraffe (20x33mm). b, Woman with shopping bag (38x21mm). c, Sailboat and swan (30mm diameter). d, House and horse (41x24mm). e, Rabbits in front of building with clock (34x21mm). f, Birds and flowers in pots (18x35mm).

***Serpentine Die Cut 7¾ on 2 Opposite Sides, Die Cut (#1493c, 1493d)***

**2015, Sept. 11 Litho.**

**Self-Adhesive**

**1493** A960 Sheet of 6 15.00
*a.-f.* 1 Any single 2.50 2.50

Nos. 1493a-1493f each sold for €1.10 on day of issue.

Miniature Sheet

Art — A961

No. 1494: a, Horse running. b, Head and arm of woman. c, Woman unzipping dress. d, Woman's legs with high-heeled shoes.

**Litho. With Foil Application**

***Serpentine Die Cut 6¾***

**2015, Sept. 11 Self-Adhesive**

**1494** A961 Sheet of 4 10.00
*a.-d.* 1 Any single 2.50 2.50

Nos. 1494a-1494d each sold for €1.10 on day of issue.

A962

A963

Jean Sibelius (1865-1957), Composer
A964

***Serpentine Die Cut 10¼***

**2015, Sept. 11 Litho.**

**Self-Adhesive**

**1495** Booklet pane of 3 + 3 etiquettes 7.50
*a.* A962 1 multi 2.50 2.50
*b.* A963 1 multi 2.50 2.50
*c.* A964 1 multi 2.50 2.50

Nos. 1495a-1495c each sold for €1.10 on day of issue.

The Rasmus
A965

HIM
A966

Apocalyptica
A967

Children of Bodom
A968

Hanoi Rocks — A969

Nightwish
A970

***Serpentine Die Cut 10¼x10 (#1496a-1496b), 9¾x10 (#1496c), 10¼x9½ (#1496d), 9½x10 (#1496e), 10¼x9¼ (#1496f)***

**2015, Sept. 11 Litho.**

**Self-Adhesive**

**1496** Booklet pane of 6 + 6 etiquettes 15.00
*a.* A965 1 multi 2.50 2.50
*b.* A966 1 multi 2.50 2.50
*c.* A967 1 multi 2.50 2.50
*d.* A968 1 multi 2.50 2.50
*e.* A969 1 multi 2.50 2.50
*f.* A970 1 multi 2.50 2.50

Rock bands. Nos. 1496a-1496f each sold for €1.10 on day of issue.

Finnish Design — A971

No. 1497: a, Marimekko Kukkuluuruu fabric design, by Sanna Annukka (28x45mm). b, Ultima Thule drinking glass, by Tapio Wirkkala (27x27mm). c, Block lamp, by Harri Koskinen (32x27mm). d, Paratiisi plate, by Birger Kaipiainen (27x33mm). e, Mademoiselle lounge chair, by Ilmari Tapiovaara (28x45mm). f, Solifer moped, by Richard Lindh (36x27mm).

***Die Cut Perf. 13¼***

**2015, Sept. 11 Litho.**

**1497** Booklet pane of 6 15.00
*a.-f.* A971 1 Any single 2.50 2.50

Nos. 1497a-1497f each sold for €1.10 on day of issue.

Pertti Kurikan Nimipälvät
A972

***Die Cut Perf. 11½ Syncopated***

**2015, Apr. 28 Litho.**

**Self-Adhesive**

**1498** A972 1 multi 2.50 2.50

Eurovision Song Contest. No. 1498 sold for €1.10 on day of issue.

Tomatoes
A973

Basil
A974

Peppers — A975

***Die Cut Perf. 9¾ Vert. Syncopated***

**2015, Nov. 6 Litho.**

**Coil Stamps**

**Self-Adhesive**

**1499** A973 1 multi + etiquette 2.50 2.50
**1500** A974 1 multi + etiquette 2.50 2.50
**1501** A975 1 multi + etiquette 2.50 2.50
*a.* Vert. strip of 3, #1499-1501, + 3 etiquettes 7.50
*Nos. 1499-1501 (3)* 7.50 7.50

Nos. 1499-1501 each sold for €1.10 on day of issue.

Miniature Sheet

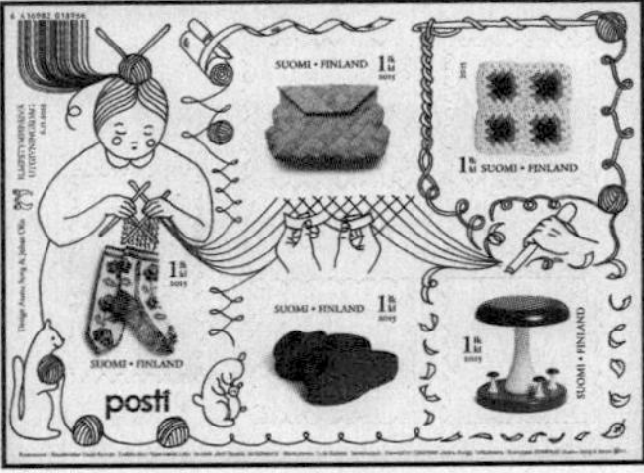


Craft Items — A976

No. 1502: a, Purse made of tree bark (40x36mm). b, Crocheted square (35x35mm). c, Socks (32x50mm). d, Dancing shoes (38x35mm). e, Mushroom-shaped wooden stool (37x34mm).

***Various Die Cuts***

**2015, Nov. 6 Litho.**

**Self-Adhesive**

**1502** A976 Sheet of 5 12.50
*a.-e.* 1 Any single 2.50 2.50

On day of issue, Nos. 1502a-1502e each sold for €1.10.

Father and Son Dragging Christmas Tree Past Church — A977

Child Looking at Christmas Ornament — A978

***Die Cut Perf. 11 Syncopated***

**2015, Nov. 6 Litho.**

**Self-Adhesive**

**1503** A977 1 multi 2.50 2.50

**Booklet Stamp**

**1504** A978 80c multi 1.90 1.90
*a.* Booklet pane of 20 38.00

No. 1503 sold for €1.10 on day of issue and was printed in sheets of 10 + 10 etiquettes.

Victory of Finnish Team in World Junior Ice Hockey Championships — A979

***Die Cut Perf. 11½ Syncopated***

**2016, Jan. 15 Litho.**

**Self-Adhesive**

**1505** A979 1 multi 2.40 2.40

No. 1505 sold for €1.10 on day of issue.

Snowflake — A980

**Litho. With Holographic Foil**
***Die Cut Perf. 9¾ Horiz.***

**2016, Jan. 22 Self-Adhesive**

**1506** A980 1 multi + etiquette 2.40 2.40

No. 1506 sold for €1.10 on day of issue.

Karelian Pasties — A981

***Serpentine Die Cut 8 Syncopated***

**2016, Jan. 22 Litho.**

**Self-Adhesive**

**1507** A981 1 multi + etiquette 2.40 2.40

No. 1507 sold for €1.10 on day of issue.

Deer and Bird A982

Birds A983

Horse and Dog A984

Bird and Butterfly — A985

Cat and Dog A986

***Serpentine Die Cut 6½***

**2016, Jan. 22 Litho.**

**Self-Adhesive**

**1508** Booklet pane of 5 + 5 etiquettes 12.00

| | | | |
|---|---|---|---|
| *a.* | A982 1 multi | 2.40 | 2.40 |
| *b.* | A983 1 multi | 2.40 | 2.40 |
| *c.* | A984 1 multi | 2.40 | 2.40 |
| *d.* | A985 1 multi | 2.40 | 2.40 |
| *e.* | A986 1 multi | 2.40 | 2.40 |

On day of issue, Nos. 1508a-1508e each sold for €1.10.

Rabbit and Easter Basket — A987

***Die Cut Perf. 13¾***

**2016, Feb. 26 Litho.**

**Self-Adhesive**

**1509** A987 1 multi + etiquette 2.60 2.60

No. 1509 sold for €1.20 on day of issue.

Siberian Iris — A988

***Die Cut Perf. 13¾***

**2016, Feb. 26 Litho.**

**Self-Adhesive**

**1510** A988 1 multi 2.60 2.60

No. 1510 sold for €1.20 on day of issue.

Nuuksio National Park — A989

Birch Tree A990

***Die Cut Perf. 11 Horiz.***

**2016, Feb. 26 Litho.**

**Self-Adhesive**

**1511** A989 €1.30 multi + etiquette 3.00 3.00

**1512** A990 €1.30 multi + etiquette 3.00 3.00

*a.* Horiz. pair, #1511-1512, + 2 etiquettes 6.00

Bird in Flight — A991

***Die Cut Perf. 13¾***

**2016, Feb. 26 Litho.**

**Self-Adhesive**

**1513** A991 €1.80 multi 4.00 4.00

Package With Legs — A992

Bird Carrying Letter A993

Angel Blowing Trumpet A994

Birthday Cake — A995

Boot and Flowers — A996

**2016, Feb. 26 Litho. *Die Cut***

**Self-Adhesive**

**1514** Booklet pane of 5 + 5 etiquettes and 5 stickers 13.00

| | | | |
|---|---|---|---|
| *a.* | A992 1 multi | 2.60 | 2.60 |
| *b.* | A993 1 multi | 2.60 | 2.60 |
| *c.* | A994 1 multi | 2.60 | 2.60 |
| *d.* | A995 1 multi | 2.60 | 2.60 |
| *e.* | A996 1 multi | 2.60 | 2.60 |

On day of issue, Nos, 1514a-1514e each sold for €1.20.

Feather A997

***Die Cut Perf. 13¾***

**2016, May 6 Litho.**

**Self-Adhesive**

**1515** A997 50c multi 1.10 1.10

Europa A998

***Serpentine Die Cut 12¼ Syncopated***

**2016, May 6 Litho.**

**Self-Adhesive**

**1516** A998 1 multi + etiquette 2.75 2.75

Think Green Issue.

No. 1516 sold for €1.20 on day of issue.

Vacation Scenes A999

No. 1517: a, Woman's crossed feet in sandals, women in park. b, Feet of skateboarder, buildings and cranes. c, Men and women, umbrella and bicycle. d, People at beach. e, Woman at market stall.

**2016, May 6 Litho. *Die Cut Perf. 13***

**Self-Adhesive**

**1517** Booklet pane of 5 + 5 etiquettes 14.00

*a.-e.* A999 1 Any single 2.75 2.75

Nos. 1517a-1517e each sold for €1.20 on day of issue.

A1000

A1001

A1002

A1003

Barns A1004

***Die Cut Perf. 9¼ Syncopated***

**2016, May 6 Litho.**

**Self-Adhesive**

**1518** Booklet pane of 5 + 5 etiquettes 14.00

| | | | |
|---|---|---|---|
| *a.* | A1000 1 multi | 2.75 | 2.75 |
| *b.* | A1001 1 multi | 2.75 | 2.75 |
| *c.* | A1002 1 multi | 2.75 | 2.75 |
| *d.* | A1003 1 multi | 2.75 | 2.75 |
| *e.* | A1004 1 multi | 2.75 | 2.75 |

Nos. 1518a-1518e each sold for €1.20 on day of issue.

Worldwide Fund for Nature (WWF) — A1005

No. 1519: a, Pusa hispida saimensis. b, Nehalennia speciosa. c, Anser erythropus.

***Serpentine Die Cut 4¼ at Top***

**2016, Sept. 9 Litho.**

**Self-Adhesive**

**1519** Vert. strip of 3 + 3 etiquettes 8.25

*a.-c.* A1005 1 Any single + etiquette 2.75 2.75

Nos. 1519a-1519c each sold for €1.20 on day of issue.

Mushrooms A1006

No. 1520: a, Russula paludosa. b, Tricholoma matsutake. c, Craterellus cornucopioides. d, Cantharellus cibarius. e, Lactarius deterrimus.

***Serpentine Die Cut 14¼x13¾***

**2016, Sept. 9 Litho.**

**Self-Adhesive**

**1520** Booklet pane of 5 + 5 etiquettes 14.00

*a.-e.* A1006 1 Any single 2.75 2.75

Nos. 1520a-1520e each sold for €1.20 on day of issue.

People Enjoying Nature A1007

No. 1521: a, Flower picking. b, Ice fishing. c, Berry harvesting. d, Boating. e, Camping. f, Skiing.

*Die Cut Perf. $8\frac{3}{4}$ on 1 Side*

**2016, Sept. 9** **Litho.**

**Self-Adhesive**

**1521** Booklet pane of 6 + 6 etiquettes 16.50
*a.-f.* A1007 1 Any single 2.75 2.75

Nos. 1521a-1521f each sold for €1.20 on day of issue.

Miniature Sheet

Art by Ville Andersson and Eeva-Riitta Eerola — A1008

Various unnamed works, as shown.

*Serpentine Die Cut $6\frac{3}{4}$*

**2016, Sept. 9** **Litho.**

**Self-Adhesive**

**1522** A1008 Sheet of 4 11.00
*a.-d.* 1 Any single 2.75 2.75

Nos. 1522a-1522d each sold for €1.20 on day of issue.

Church, Soini A1011

Wooden Pauper Statue, Soini — A1012

Wooden Pauper Statue, Alajärvi — A1013

Church, Alajärvi — A1014

Church, Hauho A1015

Wooden Pauper Statue, Hauho A1016

*Sawtooth Die Cut 6*

**2016, Nov. 10** **Litho.**

**Self-Adhesive**

**1525** Booklet pane of 6 16.00
*a.* A1011 (€1.20) multi 2.60 2.60
*b.* A1012 (€1.20) multi 2.60 2.60
*c.* A1013 (€1.20) multi 2.60 2.60
*d.* A1014 (€1.20) multi 2.60 2.60
*e.* A1015 (€1.20) multi 2.60 2.60
*f.* A1016 (€1.20) multi 2.60 2.60

Reindeer A1017

Girl and Squirrel With Cookies A1018

Snow-covered House A1019

*Die Cut Perf. $7\frac{3}{4}$*

**2016, Nov. 10** **Litho.**

**Self-Adhesive**

**1526** A1017 (90c) multi 1.90 1.90

*Die Cut Perf. $7\frac{3}{4}$x$7\frac{1}{2}$*

**1527** A1018 (€1.20) multi 2.60 2.60

*Die Cut Perf. 14*

**1528** A1019 (€1.30) multi 2.75 2.75
*Nos. 1526-1528 (3)* 7.25 7.25

Etiquettes are found to the sides of No. 1528 in the sheet margin.

Flag of Finland A1020

*Die Cut Perf. $5\frac{3}{4}$ Horiz.*

**2017, Jan. 20** **Litho.**

**Self-Adhesive**

**1529** A1020 (€1.20) multi 2.60 2.60

Snow Castle A1021

*Die Cut Perf. $8\frac{3}{4}$ Horiz.*

**2017, Jan. 20** **Litho.**

**Self-Adhesive**

**1530** A1021 (€1.20) multi 2.60 2.60

Europa.

Hearts A1022

No. 1531: a, One heart. b, Four hearts. c, 39 hearts. d, Two hearts upright. e, Two hearts sideways.

*Die Cut Perf. $9\frac{1}{2}$ Vert.*

**2017, Jan. 20** **Litho.**

**Self-Adhesive**

**1531** Booklet pane of 5 13.00
*a.-e.* A1022 (€1.20) Any single 2.60 2.60

Souvenir Sheet

Lions Clubs International, Cent. — A1023

No. 1532 — Various Lions pins and Lions International emblem, with map of Finland at: a, LL. b, UL.

*Die Cut Perf. $12\frac{3}{4}$x$12\frac{1}{4}$*

**2017, Jan. 20** **Litho.**

**Self-Adhesive**

**1532** A1023 Sheet of 2 5.25
*a.-b.* (€1.20) Either single 2.60 2.60

Flowers in Cup A1024

*Die Cut Perf. $12\frac{1}{2}$*

**2017, Feb. 24** **Litho.**

**Self-Adhesive**

**1533** A1024 (€1.20) multi 2.60 2.60

Pussy Willows — A1025

*Die Cut Perf. $8\frac{1}{2}$x$8\frac{1}{4}$*

**2017, Feb. 24** **Litho.**

**Self-Adhesive**

**1534** A1025 (€1.20) multi 2.60 2.60

Carousel — A1026

*Die Cut Perf. $8\frac{1}{2}$x$8\frac{1}{4}$*

**2017, Feb. 24** **Litho.**

**Self-Adhesive**

**1535** A1026 (€1.20) multi 2.60 2.60

Fishermen in Boat — A1027

Reflection of Clouds in Lake A1028

Swans A1029

*Die Cut Perf. Horiz.*

**2017, Feb. 24** **Litho.**

**Self-Adhesive**

**1536** Vert. strip of 3 + 3 etiquettes 8.25
*a.* A1027 (€1.30) multi + etiquette 2.75 2.75
*b.* A1028 (€1.30) multi + etiquette 2.75 2.75
*c.* A1029 (€1.30) multi + etiquette 2.75 2.75

Miniature Sheet

Arctic Birds — A1030

No. 1538: a, Clangula hyemalis (27x27mm). b, Melanitta fusca (27x27mm). c, Branta bernicla (27x39mm). d, Branta leucopsis (27x39mm).

*Die Cut Perf. $13\frac{1}{4}$*

**2017, May 9** **Litho.**

**Self-Adhesive**

**1538** A1030 Sheet of 4 6.75
*a.* 10c multi .25 .25
*b.* 20c multi .45 .45
*c.-d.* (€1.30) Either single 3.00 3.00

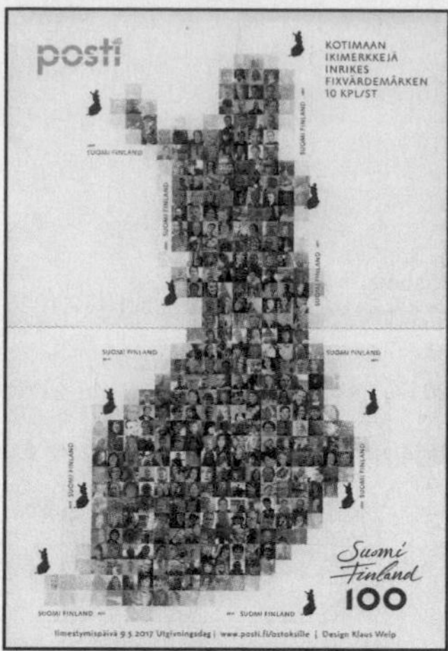


Faces of People Making Up Map of Finland — A1031

No. 1539 — Approximate areas of map of Finland: a, Northwestern Lappi Province. b, Northeastern Lappi Province, vert. c, Southwestern Lappi Province and upper Gulf of Bothnia, vert. d, Southeastern Lappi Province and northeastern Oulu Province, vert. e, Southwestern Oulu Province and northern Vaasa Province. f, Eastern Oulu Province. g, Southern Vaasa Province and northern Turku ja Pori Province. h, Mikkeli Province and southern Kuopio and Pohjois-Karjala Provinces. i, Aland Islands and Southern Turku ja Pori Province. j, Uusimaa and Kymi Provinces.

**2017, May 9 Litho. *Die Cut Perf. 13***

**Self-Adhesive**

**1539** A1031 Booklet pane of 10 30.00
*a.-j.* (€1.30) Any single 3.00 3.00

Independence, cent.

Sauna — A1032

Sauna — A1033

Sauna — A1034

Sauna — A1035

Sauna Bucket and Birch Branch Whisk — A1036

***Die Cut Perf. 6 Horiz.***

**2017, May 24 Litho.**

**Self-Adhesive**

**1540** Booklet pane of 5 15.00
*a.* A1032 (€1.30) multi 3.00 3.00
*b.* A1033 (€1.30) multi 3.00 3.00
*c.* A1034 (€1.30) multi 3.00 3.00
*d.* A1035 (€1.30) multi 3.00 3.00
*e.* A1036 (€1.30) multi 3.00 3.00

See Aland Islands Nos. 396-397.

A1037

A1038

A1039

A1040

Moomin Characters — A1041

***Die Cut Perf. 7 Horiz.***

**2017, May 24 Litho.**

**Self-Adhesive**

**1541** Booklet pane of 5 + 5 etiquettes 16.50
*a.* A1037 (€1.40) multi 3.25 3.25
*b.* A1038 (€1.40) multi 3.25 3.25
*c.* A1039 (€1.40) multi 3.25 3.25
*d.* A1040 (€1.40) multi 3.25 3.25
*e.* A1041 (€1.40) multi 3.25 3.25

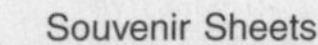

Souvenir Sheets

A1042

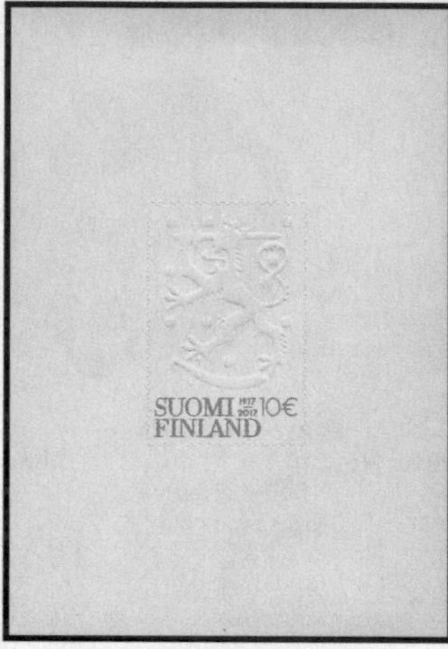


Coat of Arms — A1043

***Die Cut Perf. 10***

**2017, May 24 Litho.**

**Self-Adhesive**

**1542** A1042 Sheet of 2 6.00
*a.* (€1.30) green 3.00 3.00
*b.* (€1.30) blue 3.00 3.00

**Souvenir Sheet**

**Embossed With Foil Application**

***Die Cut Perf. 13¼***

**1543** A1043 €10 gold 22.50 22.50

Independence, cent. Finlandia 2017 Stamp Exhibition, Tampere (No. 1542).

Pres. Mauno Koivisto (1923-2017) A1045

***Die Cut Perf. 13¾***

**2017, June 9 Litho.**

**Self-Adhesive**

**1545** A1045 (€1.30) multi 3.00 3.00

A1047

A1048

Figurines A1049

***Die Cut Perf. 8½***

**2017, Sept. 6 Litho.**

**Self-Adhesive**

**1547** Strip of 3 9.75
*a.* A1047 (€1.30) multi 3.25 3.25
*b.* A1048 (€1.30) multi 3.25 3.25
*c.* A1049 (€1.30) multi 3.25 3.25

City Parks — A1050

No. 1548 — Park in: a, Porvoo. b, Hämeenlinna. c, Turku.

***Die Cut Perf. 10¼***

**2017, Sept. 6 Litho.**

**Self-Adhesive**

**1548** Strip of 3 9.75
*a.-c.* A1050 (€1.30) Any single 3.25 3.25

Flower in Spring A1051

Boat on Shore in Summer A1052

Lake in Autumn A1053

Ice in Winter A1054

***Die Cut Perf. 9½ Horiz.***

**2017, Sept. 6 Litho.**

**Coil Stamps**

**Self-Adhesive**

**1549** A1051 (€1.30) multi 3.25 3.25
**1550** A1052 (€1.30) multi 3.25 3.25
**1551** A1053 (€1.30) multi 3.25 3.25
**1552** A1054 (€1.30) multi 3.25 3.25
*a.* Horiz. strip of 4, #1549-1552 13.00
*Nos. 1549-1552 (4)* 13.00 13.00

## SEMI-POSTAL STAMPS

Arms — SP1

**Unwmk.**

**1922, May 15 Typo. *Perf. 14***

**B1** SP1 1m + 50p gray & red .90 *10.00*
Never hinged 2.00
*a.* Perf. 13x13½ *11.00*
Never hinged *22.50*

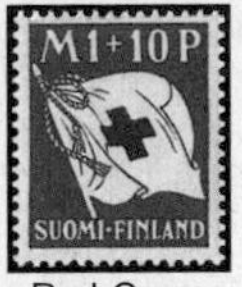

Red Cross Standard SP2

Symbolic SP3

Ship of Mercy — SP4

**1930, Feb. 6**

B2 SP2 1m + 10p red org & red 1.75 *11.50*
Never hinged 4.50
B3 SP3 1½m + 15p grysh grn & red 1.10 *11.50*
Never hinged 3.25
B4 SP4 2m + 20p dk bl & red 3.00 *50.00*
Never hinged 6.25
*Nos. B2-B4 (3)* 5.85 *73.00*
Set, never hinged 14.00

The surtax on this and subsequent similar issues was for the benefit of the Red Cross Society of Finland.

Church in Hattula — SP5

Designs: 1½m+15p, Castle of Hameenlinna. 2m+20p, Fortress of Viipuri.

**1931, Jan. 1 Cross in Red Engr.**

B5 SP5 1m + 10p gray grn 1.90 *14.00*
Never hinged 4.25
B6 SP5 1½m + 15p lil brn 11.50 *16.50*
Never hinged 35.00
B7 SP5 2m + 20p dull bl 1.90 *35.00*
Never hinged 3.50
*Nos. B5-B7 (3)* 15.30 *65.50*
Set, never hinged 42.50

SP8

**1931, Oct. 15 Typo. *Rouletted 4, 5***

B8 SP8 1m + 4m black 12.50 *45.00*
Never hinged 20.00

The surtax was to assist the Postal Museum of Finland in purchasing the Richard Granberg collection of entire envelopes.

Helsinki University Library SP9

Nikolai Church at Helsinki SP10

2½m+25p, Parliament Building, Helsinki.

**1932, Jan. 1 *Perf. 14***

B9 SP9 1¼m + 10p ol bis & red 1.50 *12.50*
Never hinged 4.75
B10 SP10 2m + 20p dp vio & red .40 *6.50*
Never hinged 1.00
B11 SP9 2½m + 25p lt blue & red 1.00 *25.00*
Never hinged 2.50
*Nos. B9-B11 (3)* 2.90 *44.00*
Set, never hinged 8.25

Bishop Magnus Tawast SP12

Michael Agricola SP13

Design: 2½m+25p, Isacus Rothovius.

**1933, Jan. 20 Engr.**

B12 SP12 1¼m + 10p blk brn & red 3.25 *16.00*
Never hinged 11.00
B13 SP13 2m + 20p brn vio & red 1.25 *4.50*
Never hinged 2.75
B14 SP13 2½m + 25p indigo & red 1.25 *8.75*
Never hinged 2.75
*Nos. B12-B14 (3)* 5.75 *29.25*
Set, never hinged 16.50

Evert Horn — SP15

Designs: 2m+20p, Torsten Stalhandske. 2½m+25p, Jakob (Lazy Jake) de la Gardie.

**1934, Jan. Cross in Red**

B15 SP15 1¼m + 10p brown 1.10 *4.50*
Never hinged 2.75
B16 SP15 2m + 20p gray lil 2.10 *8.00*
Never hinged 11.00
B17 SP15 2½m + 25p gray 1.10 *4.50*
Never hinged 2.75
*Nos. B15-B17 (3)* 4.30 *17.00*
Set, never hinged 16.50

Mathias Calonius — SP18

Designs: 2m+20p, Henrik C. Porthan. 2½m+25p, Anders Chydenius.

**1935, Jan. 1 Cross in Red**

B18 SP18 1¼m + 15p brown .90 *3.25*
Never hinged 2.10
B19 SP18 2m + 20p gray lil 2.00 *5.75*
Never hinged 5.75
B20 SP18 2½m + 25p gray bl .75 *3.25*
Never hinged 1.75
*Nos. B18-B20 (3)* 3.65 *12.25*
Set, never hinged 9.60

Robert Henrik Rehbinder — SP21

2m+20p, Count Gustaf Mauritz Armfelt. 2½m+25p, Count Arvid Bernard Horn.

**1936, Jan. 1 Cross in Red**

B21 SP21 1¼m + 15p dk brn .75 *2.40*
Never hinged 1.35
B22 SP21 2m + 20p vio brn 3.00 *7.25*
Never hinged 9.00
B23 SP21 2½m + 25p blue .75 *3.50*
Never hinged 1.60
*Nos. B21-B23 (3)* 4.50 *13.15*
Set, never hinged 12.00

Type "Uusimaa" SP24

Type "Turunmaa" SP25

Design: 3½m+35p, Type "Hameenmaa."

**1937, Jan. 1 Cross in Red**

B24 SP24 1¼m + 15p brown .70 *3.00*
Never hinged 2.00
B25 SP25 2m + 20p brn lake 13.00 9.00
Never hinged 50.00
B26 SP24 3½m + 35p indigo 1.00 *3.50*
Never hinged 2.75
*Nos. B24-B26 (3)* 14.70 15.50
Set, never hinged 54.00

Aukuste Makipeska — SP27

Designs: 1¼m+15p, Robert Isidor Orn. 2m+20p, Edward Bergenheim. 3½m+35p, Johan Mauritz Nordenstam.

**1938, Jan. 5 Cross in Red Engr.**

B27 SP27 50p + 5p dk grn .50 *1.35*
Never hinged .95
B28 SP27 1¼m + 15p dk brn .80 *2.25*
Never hinged 2.00
B29 SP27 2m + 20p rose lake 7.00 *7.50*
Never hinged 15.00
B30 SP27 3½m + 35p dk blue .55 *3.50*
Never hinged 1.25
*Nos. B27-B30 (4)* 8.85 *14.60*
Set, never hinged 19.00

Skiing — SP31

Designs: 2m+1m, Ski jumper. 3.50m+1.50m, Skier.

**1938, Jan. 18**

B31 SP31 1.25m + 75p sl grn 3.00 *13.00*
Never hinged 7.50
B32 SP31 2m + 1m dk car 3.00 *13.00*
Never hinged 7.50
B33 SP31 3.50m + 1.50m dk blue 3.00 *13.00*
Never hinged 7.50
*Nos. B31-B33 (3)* 9.00 *39.00*
Set, never hinged 22.50

Ski championships held at Lahti.

Soldier — SP34

**1938, May 16**

B34 SP34 2m + ½m blue 1.40 *5.00*
Never hinged 4.00

Victory of the White Army over the Red Guards. The surtax was for the benefit of the members of the Union of the Finnish Front.

Battlefield at Solferino SP35

**1939, Jan. 2 Cross in Scarlet**

B35 SP35 50p + 5p dk grn .85 *2.10*
Never hinged 1.75
B36 SP35 1¼m + 15p dk brn 1.00 *2.75*
Never hinged 1.50
B37 SP35 2m + 20p lake 14.00 *17.50*
Never hinged 32.50
B38 SP35 3½m + 35p dk bl .85 *3.50*
Never hinged 1.75
*Nos. B35-B38 (4)* 16.70 25.85
Set, never hinged 37.50

Intl. Red Cross Soc., 75th anniv.

**Catalogue values for unused stamps in this section, from this point to the end of the section, are for Never Hinged items.**

Soldiers with Crossbows — SP36

1¼m+15p, Cavalryman. 2m+20p, Soldier of Charles XII of Sweden. 3½m+35p, Officer and soldier of War with Russia, 1808-1809.

**1940, Jan. 3 Cross in Red**

B39 SP36 50p + 5p dk grn 1.40 *1.75*
B40 SP36 1¼m + 15p dk brn 3.50 3.00
B41 SP36 2m + 20p lake 5.50 3.50
B42 SP36 3½m + 35p dp ultra 3.50 *4.25*
*Nos. B39-B42 (4)* 13.90 12.50

The surtax aided the Finnish Red Cross.

Arms of Finland — SP40

**1940, Feb. 15 Litho.**

B43 SP40 2m +2m indigo .50 *1.75*

The surtax was given to a fund for the preservation of neutrality.

Mason — SP41

1.75m+15p, Farmer plowing. 2.75m+25p, Mother and child. 3.50m+35p, Finnish flag.

**1941, Jan. 2 Cross in Red Engr.**

B44 SP41 50p + 5p green .60 .55
B45 SP41 1.75m + 15p brown 1.75 *2.40*
B46 SP41 2.75m + 25p brn car 9.00 *9.50*
B47 SP41 3.50m + 35p dp ultra 2.00 *3.25*
*Nos. B44-B47 (4)* 13.35 15.70

See Nos. B65-B68.

Soldier's Emblem — SP45

**1941, May 24 Unwmk.**

B48 SP45 2.75m + 25p brt ultra .85 1.25

The surtax was for the aid of the soldiers who fought in the Russo-Finnish War.

Aland Arms — SP46

Coats of Arms: 1.75m+15p, Nyland. 2.75m+25p, Finland's first arms. 3.50m+35p, Karelia. 4.75m+45p, Satakunta.

**1942, Jan. 2** *Perf. 14*

**Cross in Red**

| | | | | |
|---|---|---|---|---|
| **B49** | SP46 | 50p + 5p green | 1.40 | 1.25 |
| **B50** | SP46 | 1.75m + 15p brown | 2.10 | *3.25* |
| **B51** | SP46 | 2.75m + 25p dark red | 4.50 | *3.25* |
| **B52** | SP46 | 3.50m + 35p deep ultra | 3.50 | *4.25* |
| **B53** | SP46 | 4.75m + 45p dk sl grn | 2.75 | *3.50* |
| | | *Nos. B49-B53 (5)* | 14.25 | *15.50* |

The surtax aided the Finnish Red Cross.

Lapland Arms — SP51

Coats of Arms: 2m+20p, Hame. 3.50m+35p, Eastern Bothnia. 4.50m+45p, Savo.

**Cross in Red**

**1943, Jan. 6** **Inscribed "1943"**

| | | | | |
|---|---|---|---|---|
| **B54** | SP51 | 50p + 5p green | .70 | *1.40* |
| **B55** | SP51 | 2m + 20p brown | 1.50 | *2.25* |
| **B56** | SP51 | 3.50m + 35p dark red | 1.75 | *2.25* |
| **B57** | SP51 | 4.50m + 45p brt ultra | 4.25 | *9.50* |
| | | *Nos. B54-B57 (4)* | 8.20 | *15.40* |

The surtax aided the Finnish Red Cross.

Soldier's Helmet and Sword — SP55

Mother and Children — SP56

**1943, Feb. 1** *Perf. 13*

| | | | | |
|---|---|---|---|---|
| **B58** | SP55 | 2m + 50p dk brown | .70 | *1.20* |
| **B59** | SP56 | 3.50m + 1m brown red | .70 | *1.20* |

The surtax was for national welfare.

Red Cross Train — SP57

2m+50p, Ambulance. 3.50m+75p, Red Cross Hospital, Helsinki. 4.50m+1m, Hospital plane.

**1944, Jan. 2** **Cross in Red** *Perf. 14*

| | | | | |
|---|---|---|---|---|
| **B60** | SP57 | 50p + 25p green | .45 | *.50* |
| **B61** | SP57 | 2m + 50p sepia | .85 | *1.50* |
| **B62** | SP57 | 3.50m + 75p ver | .70 | *1.25* |
| **B63** | SP57 | 4.50m + 1m brt ultra | 1.75 | *4.75* |
| | | *Nos. B60-B63 (4)* | 3.75 | *8.00* |

The surtax aided the Finnish Red Cross.

Symbols of Peace — SP61

**1944, Dec. 1**

| | | | | |
|---|---|---|---|---|
| **B64** | SP61 | 3.50m + 1.50m dk red brn | .55 | *1.10* |

The surtax was for national welfare.

**Type of 1941 Inscribed "1945"**

**1945, May 2** **Photo. & Engr.**

**Cross in Red**

| | | | | |
|---|---|---|---|---|
| **B65** | SP41 | 1m + 25p green | .40 | *.50* |
| **B66** | SP41 | 2m + 50p brown | .40 | *1.00* |
| **B67** | SP41 | 3.50m + 75p brn car | .40 | *.70* |
| **B68** | SP41 | 4.50m + 1m dp ultra | .85 | *2.40* |
| | | *Nos. B65-B68 (4)* | 2.05 | 4.60 |

The surtax was for the Finnish Red Cross.

Wrestling — SP62

2m+1m, Gymnast. 3.50m+1.75m, Runner. 4.50m+2.25m, Skier. 7m+3.50m, Javelin thrower.

**1945, Apr. 16** **Engr.** *Perf. 13½*

| | | | | |
|---|---|---|---|---|
| **B69** | SP62 | 1m + 50p bluish grn | .40 | *1.20* |
| **B70** | SP62 | 2m + 1m dp red | .40 | *1.20* |
| **B71** | SP62 | 3.50m + 1.75m dull vio | .40 | *1.20* |
| **B72** | SP62 | 4.50m + 2.25m ultra | .75 | *1.50* |
| **B73** | SP62 | 7m + 3.50m dull brn | 1.00 | *2.50* |
| | | *Nos. B69-B73 (5)* | 2.95 | 7.60 |

Fishing — SP67

Designs: 3m+75p, Churning. 5m+1.25m, Reaping. 10m+2.50m, Logging.

**Engraved; Cross Typo. in Red**

**1946, Jan. 7**

| | | | | |
|---|---|---|---|---|
| **B74** | SP67 | 1m + 25p dull grn | .55 | *.70* |
| **B75** | SP67 | 3m + 75p lilac brn | .55 | *.70* |
| **B76** | SP67 | 5m + 1.25m rose red | .55 | *.70* |
| *a.* | | Red cross omitted | *850.00* | 850.00 |
| **B77** | SP67 | 10m + 2.50m ultra | .70 | *1.25* |
| | | *Nos. B74-B77 (4)* | 2.35 | *3.35* |

The surtax was for the Finnish Red Cross.

Nurse and Children — SP71

Design: 8m+2m, Doctor examining infant.

**1946, Sept. 2** **Engr.**

| | | | | |
|---|---|---|---|---|
| **B78** | SP71 | 5m + 1m green | .50 | *.75* |
| **B79** | SP71 | 8m + 2m brown vio | .50 | *.75* |

The surtax was for the prevention of tuberculosis.

**Nos. B78 and B79 Surcharged with New Values in Black**

**1947, Apr. 1**

| | | | | |
|---|---|---|---|---|
| **B80** | SP71 | 6m + 1m on 5m + 1m | .75 | *1.10* |
| **B81** | SP71 | 10m + 2m on 8m + 2m | .75 | *1.10* |

The surtax was for the prevention of tuberculosis.

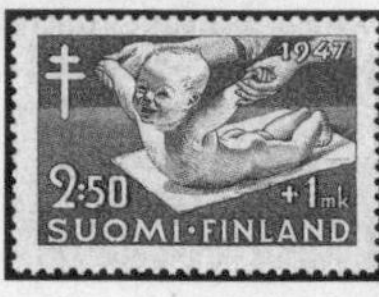


SP73

Medical Examination of Infants — SP74

Designs: 10m+2.50m, Infant held by the feet. 12m+3m, Mme. Alli Paasikivi and a child. 20m+5m, Infant standing.

**1947, Sept. 15** **Engr.**

| | | | | |
|---|---|---|---|---|
| **B82** | SP73 | 2.50m + 1m green | .55 | *1.40* |
| **B83** | SP74 | 6m + 1.50m dk red | .70 | *2.10* |
| **B84** | SP74 | 10m + 2.50m red brn | 1.10 | *2.10* |
| **B85** | SP73 | 12m + 3m dp blue | 1.40 | *2.75* |
| **B86** | SP74 | 20m + 5m dk red vio | 2.10 | *3.50* |
| | | *Nos. B82-B86 (5)* | 5.85 | *11.85* |

The surtax was for the prevention of tuberculosis.

For surcharges see Nos. B91-B93.

Zachris Topelius — SP78

7m+2m, Fredrik Pacius. 12m+3m, Johan L. Runeberg. 20m+5m, Fredrik Cygnaeus.

**Engraved; Cross Typo. in Red**

**1948, May 10** **Unwmk.** *Perf. 14*

| | | | | |
|---|---|---|---|---|
| **B87** | SP78 | 3m + 1m green | .50 | *.75* |
| **B88** | SP78 | 7m + 2m rose red | .65 | *1.50* |
| **B89** | SP78 | 12m + 3m brt blue | .75 | *1.50* |
| **B90** | SP78 | 20m + 5m dk vio | .90 | *2.00* |
| | | *Nos. B87-B90 (4)* | 2.80 | 5.75 |

The surtax was for the Finnish Red Cross.

**Nos. B83, B84 and B86 Surcharged with New Values and Bars in Black**

**1948, Sept. 13** **Engr.** *Perf. 13½*

| | | | | |
|---|---|---|---|---|
| **B91** | SP74 | 7m + 2m on #B83 | 2.25 | *3.50* |
| **B92** | SP74 | 15m + 3m on #B84 | 2.25 | *3.50* |
| **B93** | SP74 | 24m + 6m on #B86 | 2.50 | *5.25* |
| | | *Nos. B91-B93 (3)* | 7.00 | 12.25 |

The surtax was for the prevention of tuberculosis.

Tying Birch Boughs — SP79

9m+3m, Bathers in Sauna house. 15m+5m, Rural bath house. 30m+10m, Cold plunge in lake.

**Engraved; Cross Typo. in Red**

**1949, May 5** *Perf. 13½x14*

| | | | | |
|---|---|---|---|---|
| **B94** | SP79 | 5m + 2m dull grn | .50 | *.80* |
| **B95** | SP79 | 9m + 3m dk car | .90 | *1.40* |
| **B96** | SP79 | 15m + 5m dp blue | .90 | *1.40* |
| **B97** | SP79 | 30m + 10m dk vio brn | 2.00 | *3.25* |
| | | *Nos. B94-B97 (4)* | 4.30 | 6.85 |

The surtax was for the Finnish Red Cross.

Wood Anemone — SP83

**1949, June 2** **Engr.**

**Inscribed: "1949"**

| | | | | |
|---|---|---|---|---|
| **B98** | SP83 | 5m + 2m shown | .80 | *1.10* |
| **B99** | SP83 | 9m + 3m Wild rose | 1.00 | *1.25* |
| **B100** | SP83 | 15m + 5m Coltsfoot | 1.00 | *1.50* |
| | | *Nos. B98-B100 (3)* | 2.80 | 3.85 |

The surtax was for the prevention of tuberculosis.

**Similar to Type of 1949**

Designs: 5m+2m, Water lily. 9m+3m, Pasqueflower. 15m+5m, Bell flower cluster.

**1950, Apr. 1** **Inscribed: "1950"**

| | | | | |
|---|---|---|---|---|
| **B101** | SP83 | 5m + 2m emer | 3.25 | 2.75 |
| **B102** | SP83 | 9m + 3m rose car | 2.40 | 2.00 |
| **B103** | SP83 | 15m + 5m blue | 2.40 | 2.00 |
| | | *Nos. B101-B103 (3)* | 8.05 | 6.75 |

The surtax was for the prevention of tuberculosis.

Hospital Entrance, Helsinki SP84

Blood Donor's Medal SP86

Design: 12m+3m, Giving blood.

**Engraved; Cross Typo. in Red**

**1951, Mar. 17** **Unwmk.** *Perf. 14*

| | | | | |
|---|---|---|---|---|
| **B104** | SP84 | 7m + 2m chocolate | 1.10 | *2.10* |
| **B105** | SP84 | 12m + 3m bl vio | 1.75 | *2.75* |
| **B106** | SP86 | 20m + 5m car | 2.00 | *3.50* |
| | | *Nos. B104-B106 (3)* | 4.85 | *8.35* |

The surtax was for the Finnish Red Cross.

Capercaillie — SP87

Designs: 12m+3m, European cranes. 20m+5m, Caspian terns.

**1951, Oct. 26** **Engr.**

| | | | | |
|---|---|---|---|---|
| **B107** | SP87 | 7m + 2m dk grn | 3.75 | *4.00* |
| **B108** | SP87 | 12m + 3m rose brn | 3.75 | *4.00* |
| **B109** | SP87 | 20m + 5m blue | 3.75 | *4.00* |
| | | *Nos. B107-B109 (3)* | 11.25 | *12.00* |

The surtax was for the prevention of tuberculosis.

Diver — SP88

Soccer Players
SP89

No. B112, Stadum, Helsinki. No. B113, Runners.

**1951-52**

**B110** SP88 12m + 2m rose car 2.10 1.75
**B111** SP89 15m + 2m grn ('52) 2.50 2.25
**B112** SP88 20m + 3m deep blue 2.10 2.00
**B113** SP89 25m + 4m brn ('52) 2.75 *3.00*
*Nos. B110-B113 (4)* 9.45 9.00

XV Olympic Games, Helsinki, 1952. The surtax was to help finance the games.

Issued: B110, B112, 11/16; B111, B113, 2/15/52.

Margin blocks of four of each denomination were cut from regular or perf-through-margin sheets and pasted by the selvage, overlapping, in a printed folder to create a kind of souvenir booklet. Value $60.

Field Marshal
Mannerheim — SP90

**Engraved; Cross Typo. in Red**

**1952, Mar. 4**

**B114** SP90 10m + 2m gray 2.40 *2.50*
**B115** SP90 15m + 3m rose vio 2.40 *2.50*
**B116** SP90 25m + 5m blue 2.40 *2.50*
*Nos. B114-B116 (3)* 7.20 *7.50*

The surtax was for the Red Cross.

Great
Titmouse — SP91

Designs: 15m+3m, Spotted flycatchers and nest. 25m+5m, Swift.

**1952, Dec. 4** **Engr.**

**B117** SP91 10m + 2m green 3.75 *3.50*
**B118** SP91 15m + 3m plum 3.75 *3.50*
**B119** SP91 25m + 5m deep blue 3.75 *3.50*
*Nos. B117-B119 (3)* 11.25 *10.50*

The surtax was for the prevention of tuberculosis.

See Nos. B148-B150.

European Red
Squirrel
SP92

No. B121, Brown bear. No. B122, European elk.

**Unwmk.**

**1953, Nov. 16** **Engr.** ***Perf. 14***

**B120** SP92 10m + 2m red brown 3.75 *4.25*
**B121** SP92 15m + 3m violet 3.75 *4.25*
**B122** SP92 25m + 5m dark grn 3.75 *4.25*
*Nos. B120-B122 (3)* 11.25 *12.75*

Surtax for the prevention of tuberculosis.

Children Receiving
Parcel from Welfare
Worker — SP93

Designs: 15m+3m, Aged woman knitting. 25m+5m, Blind basket-maker and dog.

**Engraved; Cross Typo. in Red**

**1954, Mar. 8** ***Perf. 11½***

**B123** SP93 10m + 2m dk ol grn 1.50 *2.00*
**B124** SP93 15m + 3m dk blue 1.50 *2.00*
**B125** SP93 25m + 5m dk brown 1.50 *2.00*
*Nos. B123-B125 (3)* 4.50 *6.00*

The surtax was for the Finnish Red Cross.

Bumblebees,
Dandelions — SP94

15m+3m, Butterfly. 25m+5m, Dragonfly.

**Engraved; Cross Typo. in Red**

**1954, Dec. 7** ***Perf. 14***

**B126** SP94 10m + 2m brown 2.75 2.10
**B127** SP94 15m + 3m carmine 3.25 2.75
**B128** SP94 25m + 5m blue 3.25 2.75
*Nos. B126-B128 (3)* 9.25 7.60

The surtax was for the prevention of tuberculosis.

European
Perch — SP95

Designs: 15m+3m, Northern pike. 25m+5m, Atlantic salmon.

**Engraved; Cross Typo. in Red**

**1955, Sept. 26** ***Perf. 14***

**B129** SP95 10m + 2m dl grn 2.00 2.10
**B130** SP95 15m + 3m vio brn 2.50 2.10
**B131** SP95 25m + 5m dk bl 3.25 2.10
*Nos. B129-B131 (3)* 7.75 6.30

Surtax for the Anti-Tuberculosis Society.

Gen. von Dobeln in
Battle of Juthas,
1808 — SP96

Illustrations by Albert Edelfelter from J. L. Runeberg's "Tales of Ensign Stal": 15m+3m, Col. J. Z. Duncker holding flag. 25m+5m, Son of fallen Soldier.

**Engraved; Cross Typo. in Red**

**1955, Nov. 24**

**B132** SP96 10m + 2m dp ultra 1.75 *2.00*
**B133** SP96 15m + 3m dk red brn 1.75 *2.00*
**B134** SP96 25m + 5m green 1.75 *2.00*
*Nos. B132-B134 (3)* 5.25 6.00

The surtax was for the Red Cross.

Waxwing — SP97

Birds: 20m+3m, Eagle owl. 30m+5m, Mute swan.

**Engraved; Cross Typo. in Red**

**1956, Sept. 25** ***Perf. 11½***

**B135** SP97 10m + 2m dl red brn 2.10 1.25
**B136** SP97 20m + 3m bl grn 2.75 2.10
**B137** SP97 30m + 5m blue 3.75 2.10
*Nos. B135-B137 (3)* 8.60 5.45

Surtax for the Anti-Tuberculosis Society.

Pekka Aulin — SP98

Portraits: 10m+2m, Leonard von Pfaler. 20m+3m, Gustaf Johansson. 30m+5m, Viktor Magnus von Born.

**Engraved; Cross Typo. in Red**

**1956, Nov. 26** **Unwmk.**

**B138** SP98 5m + 1m grysh grn 1.00 1.25
**B139** SP98 10m + 2m brown 1.50 1.50
**B140** SP98 20m + 3m magenta 2.25 2.25
**B141** SP98 30m + 5m lt ultra 2.25 2.25
*Nos. B138-B141 (4)* 7.00 7.25

The surtax was for the Red Cross.

Wolverine
(Glutton) — SP99

20m+3m, Lynx. 30m+5m, Reindeer.

**Engraved; Cross Typo. in Red**

**1957, Sept. 5** ***Perf. 11½***

**B142** SP99 10m + 2m dull purple 2.00 1.50
**B143** SP99 20m + 3m sepia 3.00 2.40
**B144** SP99 30m + 5m dark blue 3.00 2.40
*Nos. B142-B144 (3)* 8.00 6.30

The surtax was for the Anti-Tuberculosis Society. See Nos. B160-B165.

Red Cross
Flag — SP100

**1957, Nov. 25** **Engr.** ***Perf. 14***

**Cross in Red**

**B145** SP100 10m + 2m ol grn 1.75 2.40
**B146** SP100 20m + 3m maroon 2.00 3.50
**B147** SP100 30m + 5m dull blue 2.00 3.50
*Nos. B145-B147 (3)* 5.75 9.40

80th anniv. of the Finnish Red Cross.

**Type of 1952**

Flowers: 10m+2m, Lily of the Valley. 20m+3m, Red clover. 30m+5m, Hepatica.

**Engraved; Cross Typo. in Red**

**1958, May 5** **Unwmk.** ***Perf. 14***

**B148** SP91 10m + 2m green 2.40 1.60
**B149** SP91 20m + 3m lilac rose 2.75 2.60
**B150** SP91 30m + 5m ultra 3.00 2.60
*Nos. B148-B150 (3)* 8.15 6.80

Surtax for the Anti-Tuberculosis Society.

Raspberry — SP101

20m+3m, Cowberry. 30m+5m, Blueberry.

**Engraved; Cross Typo. in Red**

**1958, Nov. 20** ***Perf. 11½***

**B151** SP101 10m + 2m orange 2.40 1.75
**B152** SP101 20m + 3m red 2.75 2.25
**B153** SP101 30m + 5m dk blue 2.75 2.25
*Nos. B151-B153 (3)* 7.90 6.25

The surtax was for the Red Cross.

Daisy — SP102

20m+5m, Primrose. 30m+5m, Cornflower.

**Engraved; Cross Typo. in Red**

**1959, Sept. 7** **Unwmk.**

**B154** SP102 10m + 2m green 4.00 2.00
**B155** SP102 20m + 3m lt brown 4.50 3.00
**B156** SP102 30m + 5m blue 4.50 3.00
*Nos. B154-B156 (3)* 13.00 8.00

Surtax for the Anti-Tuberculosis Society.

Reindeer
SP103

No. B158, Lapp & lasso. No. B159, Mountains.

**Engraved; Cross Typo. in Red**

**1960, Nov. 24** ***Perf. 11½***

**B157** SP103 10m + 2m dk gray 1.50 1.50
**B158** SP103 20m + 3m gray vio 2.25 2.25
**B159** SP103 30m + 5m rose vio 2.25 2.25
*Nos. B157-B159 (3)* 6.00 6.00

The surtax was for the Red Cross.

**Animal Type of 1957**

Designs: 10m+2m, Muskrat. 20m+3m, Otter. 30m+5m, Seal.

**Engr.; Cross at right, Typo. in Red**

**1961, Sept. 4**

**B160** SP99 10m + 2m brn car 1.75 1.40
**B161** SP99 20m + 3m slate bl 2.50 2.00
**B162** SP99 30m + 5m bl grn 2.50 2.00
*Nos. B160-B162 (3)* 6.75 5.40

Surtax for the Anti Tuberculosis Society.

**Animal Type of 1957**

Designs: 10m+2m, Hare. 20m+3m, Pine marten. 30m+5m, Ermine.

**Engraved; Cross Typo. in Red**

**1962, Oct. 1**

**B163** SP99 10m + 2m gray 1.90 1.90
**B164** SP99 20m + 3m dl red brn 2.50 2.25
**B165** SP99 30m + 5m vio bl 2.50 2.25
*Nos. B163-B165 (3)* 6.90 6.40

The surtax was for the Anti-Tuberculosis Society.

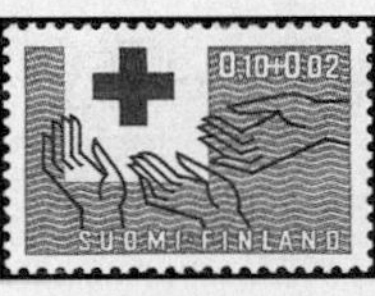

Cross and
Outstretched
Hands
SP104

**Engraved; Cross Typo. in Red**

**1963, May 8** **Unwmk.** ***Perf. 11½***

**B166** SP104 10p + 2p red brn .75 1.00
**B167** SP104 20p + 3p violet 1.25 1.50
**B168** SP104 30p + 5p green 1.25 1.50
*Nos. B166-B168 (3)* 3.25 4.00

The surtax was for the Red Cross.

Attending the
Wounded
SP105

Red Cross Activities: 25p+4p, Hospital ship. 35p+5p, Prisoner-of-war health examination. 40p+7p, Gift parcel distribution.

**Engraved; Cross Typo. in Red**

**1964, May 26** *Perf. 11½*
**B169** SP105 15p + 3p vio bl 1.25 .70
**B170** SP105 25p + 4p green 1.50 1.10
**B171** SP105 35p + 5p vio brn 1.50 1.10
**B172** SP105 40p + 7p dk ol grn 1.50 1.10
*Nos. B169-B172 (4)* 5.75 4.00

The surtax was for the Red Cross.

Finnish Spitz — SP106

Designs: 25p+4p, Karelian bear dog. 35p+5p, Finnish hunting dog.

**Engraved; Cross Typo. in Red**

**1965, May 10** *Perf. 11½*
**B173** SP106 15p + 3p org brn 2.00 1.50
**B174** SP106 25p + 4p black 3.00 2.25
**B175** SP106 35p + 5p gray brn 3.00 2.25
*Nos. B173-B175 (3)* 8.00 6.00

Surtax for Anti-Tuberculosis Society.

Artificial Respiration — SP107

First Aid: 25p+4p, Skin diver rescuing occupants of submerged car. 35p+5p, Helicopter rescue in winter.

**1966, May 7** **Litho.** *Perf. 14*
**B176** SP107 15p + 3p multi 1.10 1.25
**B177** SP107 25p + 4p multi 1.25 1.50
**B178** SP107 35p + 5p multi 1.25 1.50
*Nos. B176-B178 (3)* 3.60 4.25

The surtax was for the Red Cross.

Birch — SP108

Trees: 25p+4p, Pine. 40p+7p, Spruce.

**1967, May 12** **Litho.** *Perf. 14*
**B179** SP108 20p + 3p multi 1.00 1.00
**B180** SP108 25p + 4p multi 1.00 1.00
**B181** SP108 40p + 7p multi 1.00 1.00
*Nos. B179-B181 (3)* 3.00 3.00

Surtax for Anti-Tuberculosis Society. See Nos. B185-B187.

Horse-drawn Ambulance SP109

25p+4p, Ambulance, 1967. 40p+7p, Red Cross.

**Cross in Red**

**1967, Nov. 24** **Litho.** *Perf. 14*
**B182** SP109 20p + 3p dl yel, grn & blk 1.10 1.10
**B183** SP109 25p + 4p vio & blk 1.10 1.10
**B184** SP109 40p + 7p dk grn, blk & dk ol 1.10 1.10
*Nos. B182-B184 (3)* 3.30 3.30

The surtax was for the Red Cross.

**Tree Type of 1967**

Trees: 20p+3p, Juniper. 25+4p, Aspen. 40p+7p, Chokecherry.

**1969, May 12** **Litho.** *Perf. 14*
**B185** SP108 20p + 3p multi .90 1.10
**B186** SP108 25p + 4p multi .90 1.10
**B187** SP108 40p + 7p multi .90 1.10
*Nos. B185-B187 (3)* 2.70 3.30

Surtax for Anti-Tuberculosis Society.

"On the Lapp's Magic Rock" SP110

Designs: 30p+6p, Juhani blowing horn on Impivaara Rock, vert. 50p+10p, The Pale Maiden. The designs are from illustrations by Askeli Gallen-Kallelas for "The Seven Brothers" by Aleksis Kivi.

**1970, May 8** **Litho.** *Perf. 14*
**B188** SP110 25p + 5p multi .70 .70
**B189** SP110 30p + 6p multi .85 .90
**B190** SP110 50p + 10p multi .85 .90
*Nos. B188-B190 (3)* 2.40 2.50

The surtax was for the Red Cross.

Cutting and Loading Timber SP111

Designs: 30p+6p, Floating logs downstream. 50p+10p, Sorting logs at sawmill.

**1971, Apr. 25** **Litho.** *Perf. 14*
**B191** SP111 25p + 5p multi .90 1.00
**B192** SP111 30p + 6p multi .90 1.00
**B193** SP111 50p + 10p multi 1.00 1.00
*Nos. B191-B193 (3)* 2.80 3.00

Surtax for Anti-Tuberculosis Society.

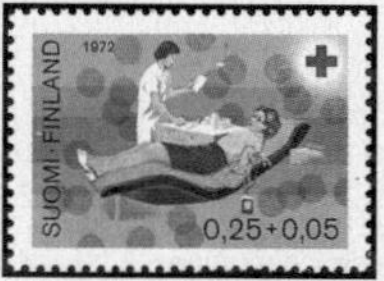

Blood Donor and Nurse SP112

30p+6p, Blood research (microscope, slides), vert. 50p+10p, Blood transfusion.

**1972, Oct. 23**
**B194** SP112 25p + 5p multi .70 .85
**B195** SP112 30p + 6p multi 1.10 1.10
**B196** SP112 50p + 10p multi 1.10 1.10
*Nos. B194-B196 (3)* 2.90 3.05

Surtax was for the Red Cross.

Girl with Lamb, by Hugo Simberg — SP113

Paintings: 40p+10p, Summer Evening, by Vilho Sjöström. 60p+15p, Woman at Mountain Fountain, by Juho Rissanen.

**1973, Sept. 12** **Litho.** *Perf. 13x12½*
**B197** SP113 30p + 5p multi 1.25 1.25
**B198** SP113 40p + 10p multi 1.75 1.75
**B199** SP113 60p + 15p multi 1.75 1.75
*Nos. B197-B199 (3)* 4.75 4.75

Surtax for the Finnish Anti-Tuberculosis Assoc. Birth centenaries of featured artists.

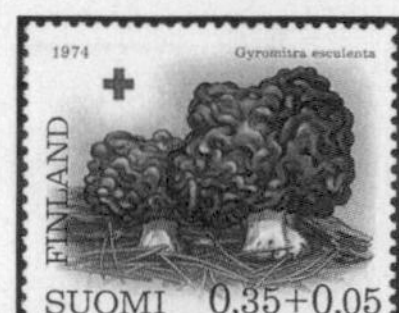

Morel SP114

Mushrooms: 50p+10p, Chanterelle. 60p+15p, Boletus edulis.

**1974, Sept. 24** **Litho.** *Perf. 12½x13*
**B200** SP114 35p + 5p multi 2.50 1.50
**B201** SP114 50p + 10p multi 2.25 1.50
**B202** SP114 60p + 15p multi 2.25 1.50
*Nos. B200-B202 (3)* 7.00 4.50

Finnish Red Cross.

Echo, by Ellen Thesleff (1869-1954) SP115

Paintings: 60p+15p, Hilda Wiik, by Maria Wiik (1853-1928). 70p+20p, At Home (old woman in chair), by Helene Schjerfbeck (1862-1946).

**1975, Sept. 30** **Litho.** *Perf. 13x12½*
**B203** SP115 40p + 10p multi 1.10 1.10
**B204** SP115 60p + 15p multi 1.25 1.25
**B205** SP115 70p + 20p multi 1.25 1.25
*Nos. B203-B205 (3)* 3.60 3.60

Finnish Red Cross. In honor of International Women's Year paintings by women artists were chosen.

Disabled Veterans' Emblem SP116

**Lithographed and Photogravure**

**1976, Jan. 15** *Perf. 14*
**B206** SP116 70p + 30p multi .80 .80

The surtax was for hospitals for disabled war veterans.

Wedding Procession SP117

Designs: 70p+15p, Wedding dance, vert. 80p+20p, Bride, groom, matron and pastor at wedding dinner.

**1976, Sept. 15** **Litho.** *Perf. 13*
**B207** SP117 50p + 10p multi .85 .95
**B208** SP117 70p + 15p multi 1.10 1.10
**B209** SP117 80p + 20p multi 1.10 1.10
*Nos. B207-B209 (3)* 3.05 3.15

Surtax for Anti-Tuberculosis Society.

Disaster Relief SP118

Designs: 80p+15p, Community work. 90p+20p, Blood transfusion service.

**1977, Jan. 19** **Litho.** *Perf. 14*
**B210** SP118 50p + 10p multi .65 .65
**B211** SP118 80p + 15p multi .80 .80
**B212** SP118 90p + 20p multi .80 .80
*Nos. B210-B212 (3)* 2.25 2.25

Finnish Red Cross centenary.

Long-distance Skiing SP119

Design: 1m+50p, Ski jump.

**1977, Oct. 5** **Litho.** *Perf. 13*
**B213** SP119 80p + 40p multi 2.50 3.75
**B214** SP119 1m + 50p multi 2.00 2.00

Surtax was for World Ski Championships, Lahti, Feb. 17-26, 1978.

Saffron Milkcap SP120

Edible Mushrooms: 80p+15p, Parasol, vert. 1m+20p, Gypsy.

**1978, Sept. 13** **Litho.** *Perf. 13*
**B215** SP120 50p + 10p multi 1.75 1.10
**B216** SP120 80p + 15p multi 2.00 2.00
**B217** SP120 1m + 20p multi 2.00 2.00
*Nos. B215-B217 (3)* 5.75 5.10

Surtax was for Red Cross. See Nos. B221-B223.

Pehr Kalm, 1716-1779 SP121

Finnish Scientists: 90p+15p, Title page of Pehr Adrian Gadd's (1727-97) book, vert. 1.10m+20p, Petter Forsskal (1732-63).

***Perf. 12½x13, 13x12½***

**1979, Sept. 26** **Litho.**
**B218** SP121 60p + 10p multi .65 .80
**B219** SP121 90p + 15p multi .85 .85
**B220** SP121 1.10m + 20p multi .85 .85
*Nos. B218-B220 (3)* 2.35 2.50

Surtax for Finnish Anti-Tuberculosis Assoc.

**Mushroom Type of 1978**

Edible Mushrooms: 60p+10p, Woolly milkcap. 90p+15p, Orange-cap boletus, vert. 1.10m+20p, Russula paludosa.

**1980, Apr. 19** **Litho.** *Perf. 13*
**B221** SP120 60p + 10p multi 1.50 1.10
**B222** SP120 90p + 15p multi 2.00 2.00
**B223** SP120 1.10m + 20p multi 2.00 2.00
*Nos. B221-B223 (3)* 5.50 5.10

Surtax was for Red Cross.

Fuchsia — SP122

No. B225, African violet. No. B226, Geranium.

**1981, Aug. 24** **Litho.** *Perf. 13*
**B224** SP122 70p + 10p shown 1.10 1.10
**B225** SP122 1m + 15p multi 1.10 1.10
**B226** SP122 1.10m + 20p multi 1.10 1.10
*Nos. B224-B226 (3)* 3.30 3.30

Surtax for Finnish Anti-Tuberculosis Assoc.

Garden Dormouse SP123

No. B228, Flying squirrels. No. B229, European minks.

**1982, Aug. 16 Litho. *Perf. 13***
**B227** SP123 90p + 10p shown 1.10 1.00
**B228** SP123 1.10m + 15p multi 1.10 1.10
**B229** SP123 1.20m + 20p multi 1.25 1.10
*Nos. B227-B229 (3)* 3.45 3.20

Surtax was for Red Cross. No. B228 vert.

Forest and Wetland Plants SP124

1m+20p, Chickweed wintergreen. 1.20m+25p, Marsh violet. 1.30m+30p, Marsh marigold.

**1983, July 7 Litho. *Perf. 13***
**B230** SP124 1m + 20p multi 1.00 1.00
**B231** SP124 1.20m + 25p multi 1.00 1.00
**B232** SP124 1.30m + 30p multi 1.00 1.00
*Nos. B230-B232 (3)* 3.00 3.00

Surtax for Finnish Anti-Tuberculosis Assoc.

Globe Puzzle — SP125

2m+40p, Symbolic world communication.

**1984, May 28 Litho. *Perf. 13***
**B233** SP125 1.40m + 35p multi .80 .75
**B234** SP125 2m + 40p multi 1.25 1.10

Surtax for Red Cross.

Butterflies SP126

No. B235, Anthocharis cardamines. No. B236, Nymphalis antiopa. No. B237, Parnassius apollo.

**1986, May 22 Litho. *Perf. 13***
**B235** SP126 1.60m + 40p multi 1.25 .85
**B236** SP126 2.10m + 45p multi 1.90 1.50
**B237** SP126 5m + 50p multi 4.00 4.00
*Nos. B235-B237 (3)* 7.15 6.35

Surtax for Red Cross.

Festivals SP127

**1988, Mar. 14 Litho. *Perf. 13***
**B238** SP127 1.40m +40p Christmas 1.10 .85
**B239** SP127 1.80m +45p Easter 1.25 .90
**B240** SP127 2.40m +50p Midsummer 1.25 1.25
*Nos. B238-B240 (3)* 3.60 3.00

Surtax for the Red Cross.

*Heodes virgaureae* on Goldrod Plant SP128

Butterflies and plants: No. B242, *Agrodiaetus amandus* on meadow vetchling. No. B243, *Inachis io* on tufted vetch.

**1990, Apr. 6 Photo. *Perf. 12x11½***
**B241** SP128 1.50m +40p multi 1.00 1.00
**B242** SP128 2m +50p multi 1.25 1.25
**B243** SP128 2.70m +60p multi 1.50 1.50
*Nos. B241-B243 (3)* 3.75 3.75

Surtax for the natl. Red Cross Soc.

Paintings by Helene Schjerfbeck — SP129

Designs: No. B244a, The Little Convalescent, No. B244b, Green Still-Life.

**1991, Mar. 8 Litho. *Perf. 13***
**B244** SP129 Pair 3.00 3.00
*a.-b.* 2.10m +50p any single 1.40 1.40

Surtax for philately.

Butterflies SP130

No. B245, Xestia brunneopicta. No. B246, Acerbia alpina. No. B247, Baptria tibiale.

**Litho. & Embossed**

**1992, Apr. 22 *Perf. 13***
**B245** SP130 1.60m +40p multi .90 .90
**B246** SP130 2.10m +50p multi 1.20 1.20
**B247** SP130 5m +60p multi 2.25 2.75
*Nos. B245-B247 (3)* 4.35 4.85

Surtax for Finnish Red Cross. Embossed "Arla 100" in braille for Arla Institute, training center for the blind, cent.

Autumn Landscape of Lake Pielisjarvi, by Eero Jarnefelt — SP131

a, Tree-covered hill. b, Lake shoreline.

**1993, Mar. 19 Litho. *Perf. 13***
**B248** SP131 2.30m + 70p Pair, #a.-b. 3.00 3.00

Surtax for philately.

Finnhorses SP132

**1994, Mar. 11 Litho. *Perf. 13***
**B249** SP132 2m +40p Draft horses 1.00 1.00
**B250** SP132 2.30m +50p Trotter 1.50 1.50
**B251** SP132 4.20m +60p War horses, vert. 2.25 2.25
*Nos. B249-B251 (3)* 4.75 4.75

Surtax for Finnish Red Cross.

Paintings, by Albert Edelfelt (1854-1905) — SP133

No. B252, Playing Boys on the Shore. No. B253, Queen Blanche.

**1995, Mar. 1 Litho. *Perf. 13½***
**B252** 2.40m +60p multi 2.25 1.50

**Size: 22x31mm**

**B253** 2.40m +60p multi 2.25 1.50
*a.* SP133 Pair, #B252-B253 4.50 4.50

Surtax for philately.

Chickens SP134

**1996, Mar. 18 Litho. *Perf. 13***
**B254** SP134 2.80m +60p Chicks 1.90 2.40
**B255** SP134 3.20m +70p Hens 1.90 1.90
**B256** SP134 3.40m +70p Rooster, vert. 2.00 3.50
*Nos. B254-B256 (3)* 5.80 7.80

Surtax for Finnish Red Cross.

The Aino Myth, by Akseli Gallen-Kallela (1865-1931) SP135

Designs: No. B257, Väinämöinen proposing marriage to Aino in forest. No. B258, Aino jumping into water to escape Väinämöinen. No. B259, Aino at shore for bath.

**1997, Sept. 5 Litho. *Perf. 13½x13***
**Booklet Stamps**
**B257** SP135 2.80m +60p multi 2.25 2.25
**B258** SP135 2.80m +60p multi 2.25 2.25
**B259** SP135 2.80m +60p multi 2.25 2.25
*a.* Booklet pane, #B257-B259 6.75 6.75
Complete booklet, #B259a 6.75

No. B258 is 33x46mm.
Surtax for philately.

Pigs — SP136

2.80m+60p, Sow, piglets. 3.20m+70p, Three piglets. 3.40m+70p, Pig's head.

**1998, Mar. 12 Litho. *Perf. 13***
**B260** SP136 2.80m +60p multi 1.60 1.60
**B261** SP136 3.20m +70p multi 1.90 1.90
**B262** SP136 3.40m +70p multi 2.00 2.00
*Nos. B260-B262 (3)* 5.50 5.50

Surtax for Finnish Red Cross.

Paintings by Hugo Simberg (1873-1917) SP137

a, Garden of Death. b, Wounded Angel.

***Perf. 13¼x13¾***

**1999, Sept. 24 Litho.**
**B263** Booklet pane of 2 4.25 4.25
*a.-b.* SP137 3.50m +50p any single 2.00
Complete booklet, #B263 4.25

Surtax for philately.

Cow and Calf — SP138

***Perf. 13¾x13¼***

**2000, Mar. 15 Litho.**
**B264** SP138 3.50m +70p Bull, vert. 1.50 1.20

***Perf. 13¼x13¾***

**B265** SP138 4.80m +80p shown 2.25 2.00

Surtax for Finnish Red Cross.

Post Horn SP139

**2010, May 4 Litho. *Perf. 14½x14¼***
**B266** SP139 1 +5c multi 2.75 2.60

No. B266 had a franking value of 80c on day of issue. Surtax for construction of Finland's first solar energy plant.

## AIR POST STAMPS

No. 178 Overprinted in Red

**1930, Sept. 24 Unwmk. *Perf. 14***
**C1** A28 10m gray lilac 140.00 *290.00*
*a.* 1830 for 1930 2,500. *12,000.*

Overprinted expressly for use on mail carried in "Graf Zeppelin" on return flight from Finland to Germany on Sept. 24, 1930, after which trip the stamps ceased to be valid for postage. Forgeries are almost always on No. 205, rather than No. 178.

**Catalogue values for unused stamps in this section, from this point to the end of the section, are for Never Hinged items.**

Douglas DC-2 — AP1

**1944 Engr.**
**C2** AP1 3.50m dark brown .70 *1.40*

Air Transport Service anniv, 1923-43.

Douglas DC-6 Over Winter Landscape — AP2

**1950, Feb. 13**

| | | | | |
|---|---|---|---|---|
| **C3** | AP2 | 300m blue | 17.50 | 7.00 |

Available also for ordinary postage.

**Redrawn**

**1958, Jan. 20** *Perf. 11½*

| | | | | |
|---|---|---|---|---|
| **C4** | AP2 | 300(m) blue | 32.50 | .80 |

On No. C4 "mk" is omitted.
See Nos. C9-C9a.

Convair 440 over Lakes — AP3

**1958, Oct. 31 Unwmk.** *Perf. 11½*

| | | | | |
|---|---|---|---|---|
| **C5** | AP3 | 34m blue | 1.25 | .75 |

No. C5 Surcharged

**1959, Apr. 5**

| | | | | |
|---|---|---|---|---|
| **C6** | AP3 | 45m on 34m blue | 2.50 | 2.25 |

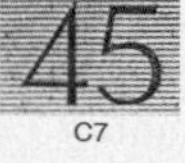

C7

C8

**1959, Nov. 2**

| | | | | |
|---|---|---|---|---|
| **C7** | AP3 | 45m blue | 3.00 | 1.50 |

**1963, Feb. 15**

| | | | | |
|---|---|---|---|---|
| **C8** | AP3 | 45p blue | 2.00 | .40 |

On No. C7 the denomination is "45." On No. C8 it is "0.45."

DC-6 Type, Comma After "3" — AP5

Type I — 16 lines in numeral "0"
Type II — 13 lines in numeral "0"

**1963, Oct. 10**

| | | | | |
|---|---|---|---|---|
| **C9** | AP5 | 3m blue, Type II ('73) | 3.25 | .30 |
| *a.* | | Type I | 40.00 | .40 |

**Convair Type of 1958**

**1970, July 15**

| | | | | |
|---|---|---|---|---|
| **C10** | AP3 | 57p ultra | 2.00 | 1.25 |

## MILITARY STAMPS

**Catalogue values for unused stamps in this section are for Never Hinged items.**

M1

**Unwmk.**

**1941, Nov. 1 Typo.** *Imperf.*

| | | | | |
|---|---|---|---|---|
| **M1** | M1 (4m) | blk, *dk org* | .80 | *.90* |

#M1 has simulated roulette printed in black.

Type of 1930-46 Overprinted in Black

**1943, Oct. 16** *Perf. 14*

| | | | | |
|---|---|---|---|---|
| **M2** | A26 | 2m deep orange | .65 | *1.10* |
| **M3** | A26 | 3½m greenish blue | .65 | *1.10* |

Post Horn and Sword — M2

**1943, July 1 Size: 29½x19½mm**

| | | | | |
|---|---|---|---|---|
| **M4** | M2 | (2m) green | .90 | .75 |
| **M5** | M2 | (3m) rose violet | 1.10 | .75 |

**1944, Feb. 16 Size: 20x16mm**

| | | | | |
|---|---|---|---|---|
| **M6** | M2 | (2m) green | .75 | .60 |
| **M7** | M2 | (3m) rose violet | .75 | .60 |

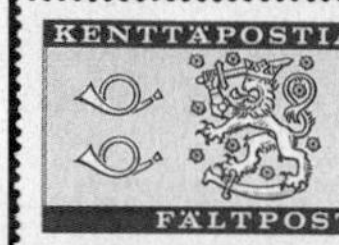

Post Horns and Arms of Finland — M3

**1963, Sept. 26 Litho.** *Perf. 14*

| | | | | |
|---|---|---|---|---|
| **M8** | M3 | violet blue | *160.00* | *175.00* |

Used during maneuvers Sept. 30-Oct. 5, 1963. Valid from Sept. 26.

**No. M8 Overprinted "1983"**

**1983, Apr. 20**

| | | | | |
|---|---|---|---|---|
| **M9** | M3 | violet blue | *250.00* | *175.00* |

Used during maneuvers Apr. 24-30.

## PARCEL POST STAMPS

PP1

**Wmk. Rose & Triangles Multiple**
***Rouletted 6 on 2 or 3 Sides***

**1949-50 Typo.**

| | | | | |
|---|---|---|---|---|
| **Q1** | PP1 | 1m brt grn & blk | 1.90 | *5.00* |
| **Q2** | PP1 | 5m red & blk | 20.00 | *32.50* |
| **Q3** | PP1 | 20m org & blk | 30.00 | *55.00* |
| **Q4** | PP1 | 50m bl & blk ('50) | 12.00 | *17.50* |
| **Q5** | PP1 | 100m brn & blk ('50) | 12.50 | *17.50* |
| | | *Nos. Q1-Q5 (5)* | 76.40 | *127.50* |
| | | Set, never hinged | 130.00 | |

**Catalogue values for unused stamps in this section, from this point to the end of the section, are for Never Hinged items.**

Mail Bus — PP2

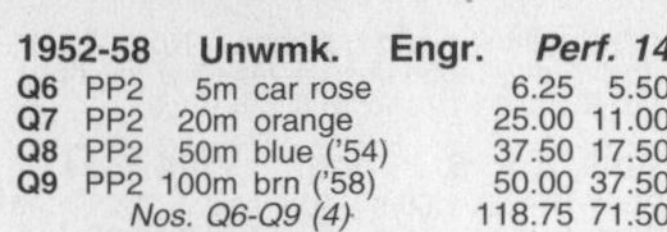

**1952-58 Unwmk. Engr.** *Perf. 14*

| | | | | |
|---|---|---|---|---|
| **Q6** | PP2 | 5m car rose | 6.25 | 5.50 |
| **Q7** | PP2 | 20m orange | 25.00 | 11.00 |
| **Q8** | PP2 | 50m blue ('54) | 37.50 | 17.50 |
| **Q9** | PP2 | 100m brn ('58) | 50.00 | 37.50 |
| | | *Nos. Q6-Q9 (4)* | 118.75 | 71.50 |

Mail Bus — PP3

**1963** *Perf. 12*

| | | | | |
|---|---|---|---|---|
| **Q10** | PP3 | 5p red & blk | 3.50 | 5.00 |
| **Q11** | PP3 | 20p org & blk | 18.00 | 8.50 |
| **Q12** | PP3 | 50p blue & blk | 10.50 | 8.25 |
| **Q13** | PP3 | 1m brn & blk | 14.50 | 8.75 |
| | | *Nos. Q10-Q13 (4)* | 46.50 | 30.50 |

Nos. Q1-Q13 were issued only in booklets: panes of 6 for Nos. Q1-Q5, 10 for Nos. Q6-Q9 and 5 for Nos. Q10-Q13.

Used values are for regular postal or mail-bus cancels. Pen strokes, cutting or other cancels sell for half as much.

1981 SISU Bus — PP4

**Photo. & Engr.**

**1981, Dec. 7** *Perf. 12 Horiz.*

| | | | | |
|---|---|---|---|---|
| **Q14** | PP4 | 50p dk bl & blk | 2.75 | *5.75* |
| **Q15** | PP4 | 1m dk brn & blk | 3.25 | *5.75* |
| **Q16** | PP4 | 5m grn & blk | 4.00 | *16.00* |
| **Q17** | PP4 | 10m red & blk | 7.25 | *32.50* |
| | | *Nos. Q14-Q17 (4)* | 17.25 | *60.00* |

Parcel post stamps invalid after Jan. 9, 1985.

# ALAND ISLANDS

LOCATION — A group of 6,554 islands at the mouth of the Gulf of Bothnia, between Finland and Sweden.
GOVT. — Province of Finland
AREA — 590 sq. mi.
POP. — 23,761
CAPITAL — Mariehamn

The province of Aland was awarded to Finland in 1921 by the League of Nations. The Swedish language is spoken and the province has a considerable amount of self-determination.

**Catalogue values for unused stamps in this country are for Never Hinged items.**

**Most Aland Island issues exist favor canceled, and used values are for such cancellations. Postally used examples are worth 30 to 40% more than the values shown.**

Gaff-rigged Sloop — A1

Aland Flag — A2

Midsummer Pole — A3

Landscapes — A4

Map of Scandinavia — A5

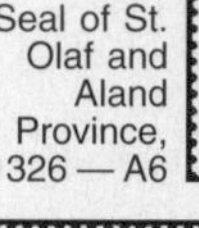

Seal of St. Olaf and Aland Province, 1326 — A6

Artifacts — A7

Sea Birds — A8

Gothic Tower, Jomala Church, 12th Cent. — A9

Mariehamn Town Hall, Designed by Architect Lars Sonck — A9a

Designs: 1.50m, Statue of Frans Petter von Knorring, vicar from 1834 to 1875, and St. Michael's Church, Finstrom, 12th cent. 1.60m, Burial site, clay hands. 1.70m, Somateria mollissima. 2.20m, Bronze Staff of Finby, apostolic decoration. 2.30m, Aythya fuligula. 5m, Outer Aland Archipelago. 8m, Farm and windmill. 12m, Melantha fusca. 20m, Ancient court site, contemporary monument.

**1984-90 Engr. Unwmk.** *Perf. 12*

| | | | | |
|---|---|---|---|---|
| **1** | A1 | 10p magenta | .25 | .25 |
| **2** | A1 | 20p brown olive | .25 | .25 |
| **3** | A1 | 50p bright green | .35 | .25 |
| **4** | A1 | 1.10m deep blue | .70 | .70 |
| **5** | A1 | 1.20m black | .55 | .50 |
| **6** | A1 | 1.30m dark green | 1.00 | .60 |

**Litho.**

***Perf. 14, 13x14 (#8)***

| | | | | |
|---|---|---|---|---|
| **7** | A2 | 1.40m multi | .75 | .30 |
| **8** | A9 | 1.40m multi | 2.00 | 1.20 |
| **9** | A3 | 1.50m multi, I | 2.00 | 1.00 |
| **9A** | A3 | 1.50m multi, II | 1.00 | .80 |
| **10** | A9 | 1.50m multi | 2.00 | 1.25 |

***Perf. 13, 14 (#13)***

| | | | | |
|---|---|---|---|---|
| **11** | A7 | 1.60m multi, vert. | 2.00 | 1.75 |
| **12** | A8 | 1.70m multi | 8.00 | 8.00 |
| **13** | A9a | 1.90m multi | 2.00 | 1.50 |
| **14** | A4 | 2m multi | 2.00 | 2.00 |
| **15** | A7 | 2.20m multi, vert. | 2.00 | 1.00 |
| **16** | A8 | 2.30m multi | 4.00 | 4.00 |
| **17** | A5 | 3m multi | 3.50 | 1.50 |
| **18** | A4 | 5m multi, horiz. | 3.00 | 2.75 |
| **19** | A4 | 8m multi, horiz. | 5.50 | 3.75 |

**Litho. & Engr.**

| | | | | |
|---|---|---|---|---|
| **20** | A6 | 10m multi | 5.50 | 4.00 |

**Litho.**

| | | | | |
|---|---|---|---|---|
| **21** | A8 | 12m multi | 8.00 | 8.00 |
| **22** | A7 | 20m multi | 10.50 | 10.50 |
| | | *Nos. 1-22 (23)* | 66.85 | 55.85 |

On No. 9A (type II) "Aland" is 10½mm long, figure support is 2mm wide, pole supports are thinner, diagonal black highlighting lines in pole greenery and horizontal black line on support under the man removed.

Issued: Nos. 2-4, 7, 17, 20, 3/1/84; Nos. 1, 5, 6, 9, 1/2/85; Nos. 14, 18-19, 9/16/85; Nos. 11, 15, 22, 4/4/86; Nos. 12, 16, 21, 1/2/87; No. 8, 8/26/88; No. 13, 1/2/89; No. 10, 9/4/89; No. 9A, 5/21/90.

See Nos. 39-42, 87-92, 178-179, 195-196.

A10

Bark Pommern and car ferries, Mariehamn West Harbor

**1984, Mar. 1 Litho. *Perf. 14***
**23** A10 2m multicolored 8.50 3.00

A11

**1986, Jan. 2 Litho. *Perf. 14***
**24** A11 1.60m multicolored 3.00 2.00

1986 Nordic Orienteering Championships, Aug. 30-31.

Onningeby Artists' Colony, Cent. — A12

Design: Pallette, pen and ink drawing of Onningeby landscape, 1891, by Victor Westerholm (1860-1919), founder.

**1986, Sept. 1 Litho.**
**25** A12 3.70m multicolored 3.00 *2.00*

Mariehamn Volunteer Fire Brigade, Cent. — A13

**1987, Apr. 27 Litho. *Perf. 14***
**26** A13 7m multicolored 4.00 3.00

Farjsund Bridge, 50th Anniv., Rebuilt in 1980 — A14

**1987, Apr. 27 Engr. *Perf. 13x13½***
**27** A14 1m greenish black .75 .60

Municipal Meeting, Finstrom, 1917 — A15

**1987, Aug. 20 Litho. *Perf. 14***
**28** A15 1.70m multicolored 1.00 1.00

Movement for reunification with Sweden, 70th anniv.

Loading of Mail Barrels on Sailboat, Post Office, Eckero — A16

**1988, Jan. 4 Litho. *Perf. 14***
**29** A16 1.80m multicolored 3.00 2.50

Postal Service, 350th anniv. From Feb. I to May 31, Alanders were entitled to buy 20 stamps for 28m with a discount coupon.

New Aland Farm School, Horse-Drawn Plow — A17

**1988, Mar. 29 Litho. *Perf. 14***
**30** A17 2.20m multicolored 2.25 *1.75*

Haga Farm School, cent.; Aland Farm School, 75th anniv.; 50th anniv. of experimental farming on Aland.

Sailing Ships — A18

**1988, June 4 Litho. *Perf. 13***
**31** A18 1.80m Albanus, 1904, vert. 2.50 1.50
**32** A18 2.40m Ingrid, c. 1900 4.00 4.00
**33** A18 11m Pamir, c. 1900 10.00 10.00
*Nos. 31-33 (3)* 16.50 15.50

**Type of 1988 and**

Orchids — A19

Fish
A20

Handicrafts
A21

Fresco, St. Anna's Church of Kumlinge
A22

Mammals
A23

Geological Formations
A24 A25

Designs: 10p, Boulder field, Geta. No. 35, *Dactylorhiza sambucina*. No. 36, *Clupea harengus membras*. No. 37, *Erinaceus europauus*. No. 38, Drumlin, Finstrom. 1.70m, St. Andrew Church, Lumparland. No. 40, Vardo Church. No. 41, Hammarland Church. No. 42, Sottunga Church. No. 43, *Esox lucius*. No. 45, Diabase dike, Sottunga, Basskar. 2.10m, *Sciurus vulgaris*. 2.50m, *Cephalanthera longifolia*. No. 48, *Platichthys flesus*. No. 49, Pillow lava, Kumlinge, western Varpskar. No. 50, *Capreolus capreolus*. No. 51, Rouche Moutonne, Roda Kon, Lumparn. 6m, Folded gneiss, Sottunga, Gloskar. 13m, Tapestry, 1793. 14m, *Cypripedium calceolus*.

***Perf. 13, 14 (Nos. 39-42, 44, 53), 15x14½ (10p, Nos. 38, 45, 49, 51-52)***

**1989-94 Litho.**

| | | | | | |
|---|---|---|---|---|---|
| **34** | A25 | 10p | multicolored | .25 | .25 |
| **35** | A19 | 1.50m | multicolored | 1.40 | 2.25 |
| **36** | A20 | 1.50m | multicolored | 1.60 | 1.20 |
| **37** | A23 | 1.60m | multicolored | 1.40 | 1.00 |
| **38** | A25 | 1.60m | multicolored | 1.50 | 1.10 |
| **39** | A9 | 1.70m | multicolored | 1.50 | 1.20 |
| **40** | A9 | 1.80m | multicolored | 1.40 | 1.10 |
| **41** | A9 | 1.80m | multicolored | 1.25 | 1.25 |
| **42** | A9 | 1.80m | multicolored | 1:25 | 1.25 |
| **43** | A20 | 2m | multicolored | 1.60 | 1.20 |
| **44** | A22 | 2m | multicolored | 1.10 | .90 |
| **45** | A24 | 2m | multicolored | .90 | .80 |
| **46** | A23 | 2.10m | multicolored | 1.40 | 1.00 |
| **47** | A19 | 2.50m | multicolored | 2.00 | 2.00 |
| **48** | A20 | 2.70m | multicolored | 1.60 | 1.20 |
| **49** | A24 | 2.70m | multicolored | 1.25 | 1.00 |
| **50** | A23 | 2.90m | multicolored | 1.60 | 1.10 |
| **51** | A25 | 2.90m | multicolored | 2.50 | 1.75 |
| **52** | A24 | 6m | multicolored | 2.50 | 2.50 |
| **53** | A21 | 13m | multicolored | 6.75 | 5.75 |
| **54** | A19 | 14m | multicolored | 9.00 | 9.00 |
| | | | *Nos. 34-54 (21)* | 43.75 | 38.80 |

Issued: 2.50m, 14m, No. 35, 4/10/89; 2.70m, No. 36, 43, 3/1/90; 13m, 4/19/90; 1.70m, No. 44, 9/10/90; 1.60m, 2.10m, No. 50, 3/3/91; No. 40, 10/9/91; No. 41 10/5/92; Nos. 45, 49, 52, 9/3/93; No. 42, 10/8/93; 10p, Nos. 38, 51, 2/1/94.

See Nos. 96, 102, 105.

Educational System of the Province, 350th Anniv. — A33

**1989, May 31 Litho. *Perf. 14***
**57** A33 1.90m multicolored 1.50 .90

Souvenir Sheet

1991 Aland Island Games — A34

a, Volleyball. b, Shooting. c, Soccer. d, Running.

**1991, Apr. 5 Litho. *Perf. 13x12½***
**58** A34 2.10m Sheet of 4, #a.-d. 5.00 5.00

Autonomy of Aland, 70th Anniv. — A35

**1991, June 4 *Perf. 13***
**59** A35 16m multicolored 8.25 6.25

Kayaking
A36

**1991, June 4 *Perf. 14***
**60** A36 2.10m shown 1.25 .75
**61** A36 2.90m Cycling 1.75 1.25

Rev. Frans Peter Von Knorring (1792-1875), Educator — A37

Cape Horn Congress, Mariehamn, June 8-11 — A38

**1992, Mar. 2 Litho. *Perf. 13***
**62** A37 2 multicolored 1.40 1.00

**Litho. & Engr.**
***Perf. 13½x14***
**63** A38 1 multicolored 3.00 2.25

No. 62 sold for 1.60m, No. 63 for 2.10m.

On stamps bearing the "denominations" "1" or "2," the number represents the class of mail.

Lighthouses A39

**1992, May 8 Litho. *Perf. 13***

**Booklet Stamps**

| | | | | |
|---|---|---|---|---|
| **64** | A39 2.10m Ranno | | 7.75 | 4.50 |
| **65** | A39 2.10m Salskar | | 7.75 | 4.50 |
| **66** | A39 2.10m Lagskar | | 7.75 | 4.50 |
| **67** | A39 2.10m Market | | 7.75 | 4.50 |
| *a.* | Booklet pane of 4, #64-67 | | 30.00 | 22.50 |

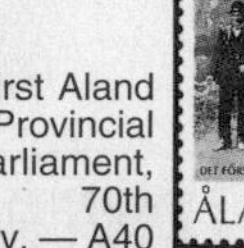

First Aland Provincial Parliament, 70th Anniv. — A40

**1992, June 8 Litho. *Perf. 13***

| | | | |
|---|---|---|---|
| **68** | A40 3.40m multicolored | 1.75 | 1.75 |

Joel Pettersson (1892-1937), Painter — A41

**1992, June 8**

| | | | |
|---|---|---|---|
| **69** | A41 2.90m Landscape from Lemland | 1.50 | 1.25 |
| **70** | A41 16m Self-Portrait | 8.50 | 7.00 |

Arms of Aland — A42

**1993, Mar. 1 Litho. *Perf. 14***

| | | | |
|---|---|---|---|
| **71** | A42 1.60m gray, sepia & blue | 1.20 | .90 |

Autonomy Act, Jan. 1.

Souvenir Sheet

Autonomous Postal Administration — A43

Designs: a, Inscriptions from old letter canceled in Kastelholm, vert. b, Mariehamn post office. c, Ferry, mail truck. d, New post office emblem, vert.

***Perf. 12½x13, 14 (#b.-c.)***

**1993, Mar. 1 Litho., Engr. (#b.-c.)**

| | | | |
|---|---|---|---|
| **72** | A43 1.90m Sheet of 4, #a.-d. | 3.00 | 3.00 |

Fiddler, Jan Karlsgarden Museum — A44

2.30m, Boat Shed, Jan Karlsgarden Museum.

***Perf. 13x12½, 12½x13***

**1993, May 7 Litho.**

| | | | |
|---|---|---|---|
| **73** | A44 2m multicolored | 1.40 | 1.00 |
| **74** | A44 2.30m multi, horiz. | 1.40 | 1.00 |

Folk Dresses — A45

Clothing from: 1.90m, Saltvik. 3.50m, Brando, Eckero, Mariehamn. 17m, Finstrom.

**1993, June 1 *Perf. 12½***

| | | | |
|---|---|---|---|
| **75** | A45 1.90m multicolored | 1.25 | 1.25 |
| **76** | A45 3.50m multicolored | 2.00 | 1.50 |
| **77** | A45 17m multicolored | 9.00 | 6.75 |
| | *Nos. 75-77 (3)* | 12.25 | 9.50 |

Butterflies A46

No. 78, Melitaea cinxia. No. 79, Quercusia querqus. No. 80, Parnassius mnemosyne. No. 81, Hesperia comma.

***Perf. 14 on 3 Sides***

**1994, Mar. 1 Litho.**

**Booklet Stamps**

| | | | |
|---|---|---|---|
| **78** | A46 2.30m multicolored | 1.60 | 1.25 |
| **79** | A46 2.30m multicolored | 1.60 | 1.25 |
| **80** | A46 2.30m multicolored | 1.60 | 1.25 |
| **81** | A46 2.30m multicolored | 1.60 | 1.25 |
| *a.* | Booklet pane, 2 each #78-81 | 13.00 | *11.00* |
| | *Nos. 78-81 (4)* | 6.40 | 5.00 |

A47

Europa, Inventions and Discoveries: 2.30m, Diagram showing transmission of von Willebrand's Disease, discovered by E. A. von Willebrand. 2.90m, Purification of heparin, by Erik Jorpes.

**1994, May 5 Litho. *Perf. 13***

| | | | |
|---|---|---|---|
| **82** | A47 2.30m multicolored | *2.75* | *2.25* |
| **83** | A47 2.90m multicolored | *1.90* | *1.60* |

**Types of 1989-93 and**

Ice Age Survivors — A48

Fossils — A49

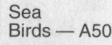

Sea Birds — A50

Bronze Age — A51

Stone Age — A52

Ships — A53

Lichens — A54

Primula Veris — A55

30p, Saduria entomon, mysis relicta. 40p, Trilobita asaphus. 1.80m, Sterna paradisaea. No. 87, Church of Mariehamn. No. 88, Church of Eckerö. No. 89, St. Bridget's Church, Lemland. No. 90, Church of St. John the Baptist, Sund. No. 91, St. George Church, Geta. No. 92, Church of Brando. No. 93, Bronze sword, bronze dagger. No. 94, Ship tumulus grave. No. 95, Larus canus. 2.30m, Pitcher of Kallskar. No. 97, Pottery. No. 98, Myoxocephalus quadricornis. 2.60m, Larus marinus. No. 100, Stone tools. No. 101, SS Thornbury. 3.40m, Erratic boulders. 3.50m, SS Osmo. 4.30m, Phoca hispida. 7m, Potholes. 9m, Gastropoda euomophalus. 18m, Settlement. 2, Hypogmnia physodes. 1, Xanthoria parietina.

***Perf. 13 (A48, A50, A52, A54), 15x14½ (No. 89), 14½x15 (Nos. 101-103, 105), 14½ (40p, Nos. 88, 93-94, 96), 14 (Nos. 87, 90-92), 15 (No. 106)***

**1994-2000 Engr.**

| | | | | |
|---|---|---|---|---|
| **84** | A48 | 30p multi | .25 | .25 |
| **85** | A49 | 40p multi | .25 | .50 |
| **86** | A50 | 1.80m multi | .80 | .70 |
| **87** | A9 | 1.90m multi | 1.00 | .90 |
| **88** | A9 | 1.90m multi | 1.00 | .90 |
| **89** | A9 | 1.90m multi | .75 | .90 |
| **90** | A9 | 2m multi | 1.25 | 1.00 |
| **91** | A9 | 2m multi | 1.25 | 1.25 |
| **92** | A9 | 2m multi | 1.25 | 1.00 |
| **93** | A51 | 2m multi | .85 | .75 |
| **94** | A51 | 2.20m multi, vert. | 1.00 | .85 |
| **95** | A50 | 2.20m multi, vert. | .90 | .70 |
| **96** | A24 | 2.30m multi | 1.10 | 1.00 |
| **97** | A52 | 2.40m multi, vert. | 1.90 | 1.50 |
| **98** | A48 | 2.40m multi | 1.50 | .90 |
| **99** | A50 | 2.60m multi | 1.25 | .90 |
| **100** | A52 | 2.80m multi, vert. | 1.50 | 1.20 |
| **101** | A53 | 2.80m multi | 1.10 | 1.00 |
| **102** | A24 | 3.40m multi, horiz. | 1.75 | 1.50 |
| **103** | A53 | 3.50m multi | 1.75 | 2.25 |
| **104** | A48 | 4.30m multi | 2.25 | 1.90 |
| **105** | A24 | 7m multi, horiz. | 3.25 | 2.75 |
| **106** | A49 | 9m multi | 5.00 | 4.00 |
| **107** | A52 | 18m multi | 9.25 | 6.00 |

***Perf. 13***

| | | | | |
|---|---|---|---|---|
| **107A** | A54 | 2 multi | 1.10 | .90 |
| **107B** | A54 | 1 multi | 1.10 | .90 |

**Self-Adhesive**

***Serpentine Die Cut Perf. 10***

| | | | | |
|---|---|---|---|---|
| **108** | A55 | 2.40m multi | 1.00 | 1.10 |
| | | *Nos. 84-108 (27)* | 45.35 | 37.50 |

No. 108 was issued in sheets of 10.

Nos. 107A-107B sold for 2m and 2.40m, respectively, on day of issue.

Issued: Nos. 97, 100, 18m, 8/16/94; No. 90, 10/7/94; 2.30m, 3.40m, 7m, 1/2/95; No. 91, 9/15/95; 40p, No. 92, 9m, 10/9/96; 30p, No. 98, 4.30m, 2/3/97; Nos. 101, 103, 9/8/97; No. 87, 10/9/97; No. 88, 10/9/98; Nos. 93-94, 2/1/99; No. 108, 4/28/99; Nos. 107A-107B, 9/25/99; No. 89, 10/8/99; 1.80m, No. 95, 2.60m, 1/3/00.

Cargo Vessels — A58

***Perf. 14 on 3 Sides***

**1995, Mar. 1 Litho.**

**Booklet Stamps**

| | | | |
|---|---|---|---|
| **109** | A58 2.30m Skuta | 1.10 | 1.25 |
| **110** | A58 2.30m Sump | 1.10 | 1.25 |
| **111** | A58 2.30m Storbat | 1.10 | 1.25 |
| **112** | A58 2.30m Jakt | 1.10 | 1.25 |
| *a.* | Booklet pane, 2 each #109-112 | 9.00 | *11.00* |
| | Complete booklet, #112a | 9.50 | |
| | *Nos. 109-112 (4)* | 4.40 | 5.00 |

Entry into European Union — A59

**1995, Mar. 1 Litho. *Perf. 13x14***

| | | | |
|---|---|---|---|
| **113** | A59 2.90m multicolored | 1.50 | *1.75* |

Europa — A60

**1995, May 5 Litho. *Perf. 13x14***

| | | | |
|---|---|---|---|
| **114** | A60 2.80m shown | *1.40* | *1.25* |
| **115** | A60 2.90m Dove, island in sea | *1.40* | *1.25* |

Tourism — A61

**1995, May 12**

| | | | |
|---|---|---|---|
| **116** | A61 2 Golf | 1.00 | 1.20 |
| **117** | A61 1 Fishing | 1.25 | .75 |

Nos. 116-117 sold for value 2m and 2.30m, respectively.

Optimist Dinghy World Championships — A62

**1995, June 2 Litho. *Perf. 13½x14***

| | | | |
|---|---|---|---|
| **118** | A62 3.40m multicolored | 1.75 | 1.50 |

St. Olaf (995?-1030), Patron Saint of Aland — A63

**Litho. & Engr.**

**1995, Sept. 15 *Perf. 13½x13***

| | | | |
|---|---|---|---|
| **119** | A63 4.30m multicolored | 2.25 | 2.00 |

See Faroe Islands No. 289

A64

Greeting Stamps (stylized designs): No. 120, Fish with natl. flag, "Hälsningar fran Aland." No. 121, Yellow bird with flower, "Grattis."

**1996, Feb. 14 Litho. *Perf. 13x14***

**120** A64 1 multicolored 1.20 1.00
**121** A64 1 multicolored 1.20 .80

Nos. 120-121 had a face value of 2.30m on day of issue.

A65

Eagle owl (bubo bubo): No. 122, Landing on tree branch over lake. No. 123, Perched on branch over lake. No. 124, Male, darker feathers. No. 125, Female, lighter feathers.

**Booklet Stamps**

**1996, Mar. 1 *Perf. 14 on 3 Sides***

**122** A65 2.40m multicolored 1.20 1.25
**123** A65 2.40m multicolored 1.20 1.25
**124** A65 2.40m multicolored 1.20 1.25
**125** A65 2.40m multicolored 1.20 1.25
*a.* Booklet pane, 2 ea #122-125 9.00 10.00
Complete booklet, No. 125a 9.50
*Nos. 122-125 (4)* 4.80 5.00

World Wildlife Fund.

Famous Women A66

Europa: 2.80m, Sally Salminen (1906-76), writer. 2.90m, Fanny Sundström (1883-1944), politician.

**1996, May 6 Litho. *Perf. 14x13***

**126** A66 2.80m multicolored *1.40 2.00*
**127** A66 2.90m multicolored *1.40 2.00*

A67

**1996, June 7 Litho. *Perf. 13½x14***

**128** A67 2.40m multicolored 1.25 1.10

Aland '96 Song and Music Festival.

A68

"Haircut," by Karl Emanuel Jansson (1846-74).

**1996, June 7 *Perf. 13***

**129** A68 18m multicolored 9.00 8.00

Spring Flowers — A69

Designs: No. 130, Tussilago farfara. No. 131, Hepatica nobilis. No. 132, Anemone nemorosa. No. 133, Anemone ranunculoides.

**1997, Feb. 3 Litho. *Perf. 14***

**Booklet Stamps**

**130** A69 2.40m multicolored 1.10 1.10
**131** A69 2.40m multicolored 1.10 1.10
**132** A69 2.40m multicolored 1.10 1.10
**133** A69 2.40m multicolored 1.10 1.10
*a.* Booklet pane, 2 each #130-133 9.00 *10.00*
Complete booklet, #133a 9.50

A70

**1997, May 3 Litho. *Perf. 14x13½***

**134** A70 3.40m multicolored 1.50 1.25

1st Floorball World Championships, Aland.

Europa — A71

Devil's Dance with Clergyman's Wife.

**1997, May 9 *Perf. 13x14***

**135** A71 2.90m multicolored *2.50* 1.25

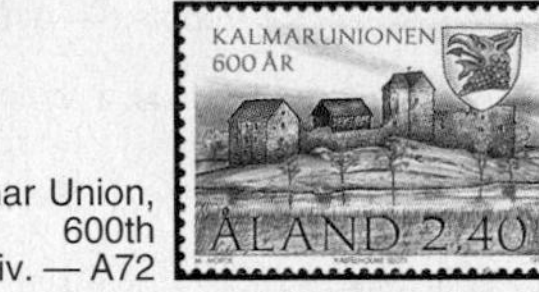
Kalmar Union, 600th Anniv. — A72

Design: Kastelholm Castle, arms of Lord High Chancellor Bo Jonsson Grip.

**1997, May 30 Litho. *Perf. 14x13***

**136** A72 2.40m multicolored 1.25 1.10

**Souvenir Sheet**

Autonomy, 75th Anniv. — A73

**1997, June 9 *Perf. 13***

**137** A73 20m multicolored 10.00 *11.00*

No. 137 contains a holographic image. Soaking in water may affect the hologram.

Horticulture A74

**1998, Feb. 2 Litho. *Perf. 14½x15***

**138** A74 2m Apples .75 .75
**139** A74 2.40m Cucumbers 1.10 .85

Youth Activities A75

No. 140, Riding moped. No. 141, Computer. No. 142, Listening to music. No. 143, Aerobics.

**1998, Mar. 28 *Perf. 14 on 3 Sides***

**Booklet Stamps**

**140** A75 2.40m multicolored 1.10 1.25
**141** A75 2.40m multicolored 1.10 1.25
**142** A75 2.40m multicolored 1.10 1.25
**143** A75 2.40m multicolored 1.10 1.25
*a.* Booklet pane, 2 each #140-143 9.00 *10.00*
Complete booklet, #143a 9.50

Midsummer Celebration in Aland — A76

**1998, Apr. 27 Litho. *Perf. 14***

**144** A76 4.20m multicolored *1.75 1.50*

Europa.

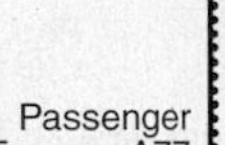
Passenger Ferry — A77

**1998, May 8 *Perf. 14½***

**145** A77 2.40m multicolored 1.25 1.00

Intl. Year of the Ocean — A78

**1998, May 8**

**146** A78 6.30m multicolored 2.75 2.10

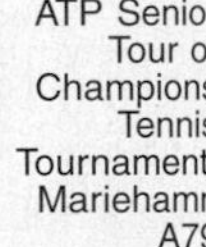

ATP Senior Tour of Champions Tennis Tournament, Mariehamn A79

***Serpentine Die Cut***

**1998, June 25 Litho.**

**Self-Adhesive**

**147** A79 2.40m multicolored 1.25 1.40

Issued in sheets of 10.

Scouting — A80

**1998, Aug. 1 *Perf. 14***

**148** A80 2.80m multicolored 1.25 1.00

Foyers — A81

Homesteads: 1.60m, Seffers. 2m, Labbas. 2.90m, Abras.

**1998, Sept. 11 Litho. *Perf. 14½***

**149** A81 1.60m multicolored .75 .70
**150** A81 2m multicolored .90 .70
**151** A81 2.90m multicolored 1.25 .85
*Nos. 149-151 (3)* 2.90 2.25

18th Century Furniture Ornamentation A82

***Perf. 14 on 3 Sides***

**1999, Feb. 1 Litho.**

**Booklet Stamps**

**152** A82 2.40m Wardrobe 1.50 1.25
**153** A82 2.40m Distaff 1.50 1.25
**154** A82 2.40m Chest 1.50 1.25
**155** A82 2.40m Spinning wheel 1.50 1.25
*a.* Booklet pane, 2 each #152-155 12.00
Complete booklet, #155a 12.50

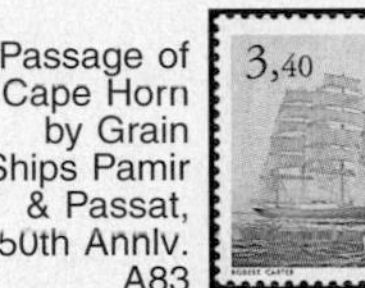
Passage of Cape Horn by Grain Ships Pamir & Passat, 50th Anniv. A83

**1999, Mar. 19 Litho. *Perf. 14½***

**156** A83 3.40m multicolored 1.50 1.50

Beginning with No. 157, denominations are indicated on many stamps in both Markkas and Euros. The value shown is in Markkas.

Nature Reserve, Kökar — A84

**1999, Apr. 28 Litho. *Perf. 13***

**157** A84 2.90m multicolored *1.25 1.20*

Europa.

Match Sailboat Racing — A85

**1999, Aug. 5 Litho. *Perf. 14½x15***

**158** A85 2.70m multicolored 1.10 1.00

UPU, 125th Anniv. A86

**1999, Sept. 25**

**159** A86 2.90m multicolored 1.20 1.00

Finnish Cross-Country Championships, Mariehamn — A87

**1999, Oct. 9 Litho. *Perf. 14¾x14½***

**160** A87 3.50m multicolored 1.40 1.20

Souvenir Sheet

Peace Symbol, Aland Flag — A88

Background colors: a, Yellow. b, Red. c, Blue. d, White.

**Litho. & Embossed**

**2000, Jan. 3** *Perf. 13*

| | | | | |
|---|---|---|---|---|
| **161** | A88 | 3.40m Sheet of 4, #a.-d. | 6.00 | 6.00 |

Elk — A89

Elk in: No. 162, Spring. No. 163, Summer. No. 164, Autumn. No. 165, Winter.

*Perf. 11¾on 3 sides*

**2000, Mar. 1** **Litho.**

**Booklet Stamps**

| | | | | |
|---|---|---|---|---|
| **162** | A89 | 2.60m multicolored | 1.10 | 1.10 |
| **163** | A89 | 2.60m multicolored | 1.10 | 1.10 |
| **164** | A89 | 2.60m multicolored | 1.10 | 1.10 |
| **165** | A89 | 2.60m multicolored | 1.10 | 1.10 |
| *a.* | | Block of 4, #162-165 | 4.50 | 4.50 |
| *b.* | | Booklet pane, 2 #165a | 9.00 | *10.50* |
| | | Complete booklet, #165b | 9.50 | |

**Europa, 2000**

Common Design Type

**2000, May 9** *Perf. 13*

| | | | | |
|---|---|---|---|---|
| **166** | CD17 | 3m multicolored | *2.00* | *1.10* |

A90

**Self-Adhesive**

**Coil Stamp**

**2000, June 9** *Die Cut Perf. 13x13¼*

| | | | | |
|---|---|---|---|---|
| **167** | A90 | 2.60m multicolored | 1.75 | 1.40 |

Gymnastics Festival, Mariehamn.

A91

**2000, July 21** **Litho.** *Perf. 13½x13¼*

| | | | | |
|---|---|---|---|---|
| **168** | A91 | 3.40m multicolored | 1.50 | 1.20 |

Cutty Sark Tall Ships race to Mariehamn.

Vikings From Aland — A92

**2000, July 28**

| | | | | |
|---|---|---|---|---|
| **169** | A92 | 4.50m multicolored | 2.00 | 1.75 |

Recreation of Viking market, Saltvik.

Architecture by Hilda Hongell (1867-1952) A93

**2000, Aug. 25** *Perf. 13¼x13¾*

| | | | | |
|---|---|---|---|---|
| **170** | A93 | 3.80m shown | 1.75 | 1.25 |
| **171** | A93 | 10m House, diff. | 4.75 | 4.00 |

Christianity, 2000th Anniv. — A94

**2000, Oct. 9** *Perf. 13*

| | | | | |
|---|---|---|---|---|
| **172** | A94 | 3m multicolored | 1.40 | 1.10 |

**Church Type of 1984-90 and**

Swamp Plants — A95

Swamp plants: 1.90m, Equisetum fluviatile. 2.80m, Lycopodium annotinum. 3.50m, Polypodium vulgare.

Churches: No. 179, Föglö Church, Föglö. 2m, Kökar Church, Kökar.

*Perf. 13x13¼, 13 (#178)*

**2000-01** **Litho.**

| | | | | |
|---|---|---|---|---|
| **177** | A95 | 1.90m multicolored | 1.00 | 1.10 |
| **178** | A9 | 2m multicolored | 1.25 | 1.00 |
| **179** | A9 | 2m multi | .90 | .70 |
| **180** | A95 | 2.80m multicolored | 1.25 | 1.40 |
| **182** | A95 | 3.50m multicolored | 1.75 | 1.90 |
| | | *Nos. 177-182 (5)* | 6.15 | 6.10 |

These stamps are part of an ongoing definitive set. Numbers have been reserved for additional stamps.

Issued: 2m, 10/9; 1.90m, 2.80m, 3.50m, 1/2/01; No. 179, 10/9/01.

Worldwide Fund for Nature (WWF) — A100

Polysticta stelleri: a, Pair in flight. b, Pair on rock. c, Pair in water. d, Male in water.

*Perf. 13¼ on 3 sides*

**2001, Jan. 2** **Litho.**

**Booklet Stamps**

| | | | | |
|---|---|---|---|---|
| **185** | A100 | Block of 4 | 5.00 | 5.50 |
| *a.-d.* | | 2.70m any single | 1.25 | 1.40 |
| *e.* | | Booklet pane, 2 #185 | 10.00 | *11.00* |
| | | Booklet, #185e | 11.00 | |

Valentine's Day — A101

**2001, Feb. 14** *Perf. 14½x14¾*

| | | | | |
|---|---|---|---|---|
| **186** | A101 | 3.20m multicolored | 1.40 | 1.10 |

Europa A102

**2001, May 9** **Litho.** *Perf. 14½x14¾*

| | | | | |
|---|---|---|---|---|
| **187** | A102 | 3.20m multi | *1.60* | *1.25* |

Windmills A103

Windmill types: 3m, Archipelago. 7m, Timbered, horiz. 20m, Nest, horiz.

*Perf. 13¾x14¼, 14¼x13¾*

**2001, June 8**

| | | | | |
|---|---|---|---|---|
| **188-190** | A103 | Set of 3 | 13.00 | 11.50 |

Puppies — A104

Designs: 2, Golden retriever. 1, Wire-haired dachshund.

**2001, Sept. 3** *Perf. 13¼*

| | | | | |
|---|---|---|---|---|
| **191-192** | A104 | Set of 2 | 2.75 | 2.00 |

Nos. 191-192 sold for 2.30m and 2.70m respectively on day of issue.

100 Cents = 1 Euro (€)

**Church Type of 1998 with Euro Denominations and**

Fauna — A105

Post Terminal — A106

Mushrooms A107

Designs: 5c, Coronella austriaca. 10c, Chanterelle mushroom. 35c, Saltviks Church. 40c, Kumlinge Church. 50c, King Bolete mushroom. 70c, Triturus cristatus. €1, Post Terminal. €2.50, Parasol mushroom.

*Perf. 12½, 13 (#193, 196), 13¼ (#198), 14¾x14 (#195)*

**2002-03** **Litho.**

| | | | | |
|---|---|---|---|---|
| **193** | A105 | 5c multi | .25 | .25 |
| **194** | A107 | 10c multi | .30 | .30 |
| **195** | A9 | 35c multi | 1.00 | 1.00 |
| **196** | A9 | 40c multi | 1.10 | 1.10 |
| **197** | A107 | 50c multi | 1.75 | 1.40 |
| **198** | A105 | 70c multi | 2.00 | 1.50 |
| **199** | A106 | €1 multi | 2.75 | 2.10 |
| **200** | A107 | €2.50 multi | 8.75 | 6.00 |
| | | *Nos. 193-200 (8)* | 17.90 | 13.65 |

Issue dates: 5c, 70c, 1/2/02; €1, 2/28/02; 35c, 10/9/02; 10c, 50c, €2.50, 1/2/03. No. 196, 10/9/03.

This is an expanding set. Numbers may change.

Introduction of the Euro — A108

**2002, Jan. 2** **Litho.** *Perf. 12½*

| | | | | |
|---|---|---|---|---|
| **201** | A108 | 60c multi | 1.60 | 1.25 |

St. Canute's Day — A109

**2002, Jan. 2**

| | | | | |
|---|---|---|---|---|
| **202** | A109 | €2 multi | 3.75 | 3.25 |

Cuisine — A110

Flowers and: a, Gravlax, boiled potatoes. b, Fried herring, beets, mashed potatoes. c, Black bread, cheese, butter. d, Pancake with prune sauce and whipped cream, coffee.

*Perf. 13½x13¼ on 3 Sides*

**2002, Feb. 28** **Litho.**

| | | | | |
|---|---|---|---|---|
| **203** | A110 | Block of 4 | 7.00 | 5.50 |
| *a.-d.* | | 1 Any single | 1.75 | 1.40 |
| *e.* | | Booklet pane, 2 #203 | 14.00 | |
| | | Booklet, #203e | 14.00 | |

Nos. 203a-203d each sold for 55c on day of issue.

Europa — A111

**2002, May 3** *Perf. 13¼*

| | | | | |
|---|---|---|---|---|
| **204** | A111 | 40c multi | *1.40* | *1.00* |

Radar II, Sculpture by Stefan Lindfors A112

**2002, May 3** *Perf. 13*

| | | | | |
|---|---|---|---|---|
| **205** | A112 | €3 multi | 8.00 | 7.00 |

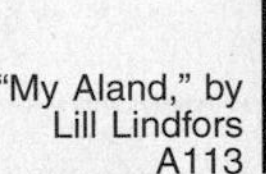
"My Aland," by Lill Lindfors
A113

**2002, Aug. 12** **Litho.** ***Perf. 13¼***
**206** A113 90c multi 2.50 2.00

Iron Age Artifacts — A114

Designs: No. 207, 2, Buckle found in Persby. No. 208, 1, Ornamental pin found in Syllöda.

**2002, Sept. 2** ***Perf. 13x13¼***
**207-208** A114 Set of 2 3.00 2.75

Nos. 207-208 sold for 45c and 55c respectively on day of issue.

Janne Holmén, Marathon Gold Medalist in European Track and Field Championships
A115

**2002, Nov. 1** ***Perf. 12½***
**209** A115 1 multi 1.75 1.50

Sold for 55c on day of issue.

House Cats — A116

**2003, Mar. 14** **Litho.** ***Perf. 13¼***
**210** A116 2 Tovis 1.25 .85
**211** A116 1 Randi, horiz. 1.75 .95

Nos. 210-211 sold for 45c and 55c respectively on day of issue.

Landscape in Summer, by Elin Danielson-Gambogi (1861-1919) — A117

No. 212: a, Woman at fence. b, Tree without leaves. c, Sun. d, Boat.

**2003, Mar. 28** ***Perf. 14 Vert.***

**Booklet Stamps**

**212** A117 Horiz. strip of 4 6.25 6.25
*a.-d.* 1 Any single 1.50 1.50
*e.* Booklet pane, 2 #212 12.50 12.50
Complete booklet, #212e 13.00

Nos. 212a-212d each sold for 55c on day of issue.

Europa — A118

**2003, May 9** ***Perf. 13¼***
**213** A118 45c multi *1.25 1.00*

Museum Ship "Pommern," Cent.
A119

**2003, June 6** ***Die Cut Perf. 9¼x9½***

**Booklet Stamp**

**Self-Adhesive**

**214** A119 55c multi 1.50 1.40
*a.* Booklet pane of 4 12.00 12.00
Complete booklet, 2 #214a 25.00

Mark and Stephen Levengood on Beach — A120

**2003, June 18** ***Perf. 12½***
**215** A120 55c multi 1.50 1.40

Aland Folk Music Association, 50th Anniv. — A121

**2003, Aug. 1** ***Perf. 14¼***
**216** A121 €1.10 buff & black 3.00 2.25

St. Lucia's Day Celebrations
A122

**2003, Oct. 9** **Litho.** ***Perf. 12½***
**217** A122 60c multi 1.60 1.50

Mammals — A123

Designs: 20c, Mustela erminea. 60c, Vulpes vulpes. €3, Martes martes.

**2004, Feb. 2** **Litho.** ***Perf. 14½x14¼***
**218** A123 20c multi .65 .60
**219** A123 60c multi 2.00 1.50
**220** A123 €3 multi 8.75 7.75
*Nos. 218-220 (3)* 11.40 9.85

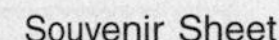
Souvenir Sheet

Norse Gods Fenja and Menja — A124

**2004, Mar. 26** ***Perf. 14¼x14¾***
**221** A124 55c multi 2.25 2.40

Aland Flag, 50th Anniv. — A125

***Serpentine Die Cut 12½***

**2004, Apr. 23** **Booklet Stamp**

**Self-Adhesive**

**222** A125 1 multi 2.00 1.75
*a.* Booklet pane of 4 8.00 6.75
Complete booklet, 2 #222a 20.00

No. 222a was reprinted in 2007 with a hole for a pegboard hook. See No. 296.

Finnish Pres. Mauno Koivisto and Guests on Boat — A126

**2004, Apr. 23** ***Perf. 12½***
**223** A126 90c multi 2.50 2.50

Europa — A127

**2004, May 10** ***Perf. 13¾x14¼***
**224** A127 75c multi *2.00 1.75*

Destruction of Bomarsund Fortress, 150th Anniv. — A128

No. 225: a, Fortress, six ships in harbor. b, Fortress, three ships in harbor. c, Three soldiers in foreground. d, Six soldiers in foreground.

**2004, June 9** ***Perf. 13***
**225** Booklet pane of 4 8.50 8.50
*a.-d.* A128 75c Any single 2.10 2.10
Complete booklet, 2 #225 18.00

2004 Summer Olympics, Athens
A183

**2004, Aug. 13** **Litho.** ***Perf. 14¼***
**226** A183 80c multi 2.25 2.25

Landscapes
A184

Designs: 2, Storklynkan, Brändö. 1, Prästgardsnäset Nature Reserve, Finström.

**2004, Aug. 13** ***Perf. 12½***
**227-228** A184 Set of 2 3.00 3.00

Nos. 227-228 sold for 50c and 60c respectively on day of issue.

See Nos. 252-253, 260.

Christmas
A185

**2004, Oct. 8** ***Perf. 14½x14¾***
**229** A185 45c multi 2.50 1.75

Birds — A186

Designs: 15c, Phalacrocorax carbo sinensis. 65c, Cygnus cygnus. €4, Ardea cinerea, vert.

**2005, Jan. 14** **Litho.** ***Perf. 13¼***
**230** A186 15c multi .55 .55
**231** A186 65c multi 1.75 1.75
**232** A186 €4 multi 11.00 9.00
*Nos. 230-232 (3)* 13.30 11.30

Automobiles — A187

No. 233: a, 1928 Oakland Sport Cabriolet. b, 1939 Ford V8. c, 1957 Buick Super 4D HT. d, 1964 Volkswagen 1200.

**2005, Mar. 4** ***Perf. 13¼ Horiz.***

**Booklet Stamps**

**233** Vert. strip of 4 7.00 7.25
*a.-d.* A187 1 Any single 1.75 1.75
*e.* Booklet pane, 2 #233 14.00 —
Complete booklet, #233e 14.00

Stamps sold for 60c each on day of issue.

Europa A188

**2005, Apr. 29** *Perf. 13¼*
234 A188 90c multi 2.50 2.10

Walpurgis Night Bonfire A189

*Serpentine Die Cut 12½*

**2005, Apr. 29** **Booklet Stamp**

**Self-Adhesive**

235 A189 2 multi 1.50 1.40
*a.* Booklet pane of 4 5.75
Complete booklet, 2 #235a 11.50

Stamp sold for 50c on day of issue.

Tennis Player Bjorn Borg — A190

**2005, May 26** *Perf. 12½*
236 A190 55c multi 1.50 1.50

Mr. Black and Mr. Smith at Bomarsund, by Fritz von Dardel A191

**2005, Aug. 12** **Litho.** *Perf. 13¾*
237 A191 €1.30 multi 3.50 3.50

Schooner Linden — A192

**2005, Aug. 26** *Perf. 13¼*
238 A192 60c multi 1.75 1.75

**Landscapes Type of 2004**

Designs: 70c, Pine tree on Sandö Island. 80c, Cliffs, Gröndal.

**2005, Aug. 26** *Perf. 12½*
239-240 A184 Set of 2 4.00 4.00

Christmas — A193

**Litho. with Hologram Applied**

**2005, Oct. 10** *Perf. 13*
241 A193 45c multi 1.50 1.40

Stars in hologram differ on each stamp.

Beetles A194

Designs: 40c, Potosia cuprea. 65c, Coccinella septempunctata. €2, Oryctes nasicornis.

**Litho. & Embossed**

**2006, Jan. 2** *Perf. 13½*
242 A194 40c multi 1.10 1.10
243 A194 65c multi 1.75 1.60
244 A194 €2 multi 5.25 4.75
*Nos. 242-244 (3)* 8.10 7.45

Woman Suffrage in Finland, Cent. — A195

**2006, Mar. 8** **Litho.** *Perf. 12½*
245 A195 85c multi 2.50 2.25

Demilitarization of Aland, 150th Anniv. — A196

**2006, Mar. 29** *Perf. 13¾*
246 A196 €1.50 multi 4.00 3.75

Souvenir Sheet

Lettesgubbe, Mythological Being — A197

**2006, Mar. 29** *Perf. 12½x13*
247 A197 85c multi 2.50 3.00

Europa — A198

**2006, May 4**
248 A198 €1.30 multi 3.50 3.50

A199

*Serpentine Die Cut 10 Syncopated*

**2006, May 26**
249 A199 1 multi 1.75 1.50
*a.* Booklet pane of 8 14.00 14.50

No. 249 sold for 65c on day of issue. Design portion of stamp could be personalized at €10.40 per booklet with a minimum purchase of three booklets. The label design shown is a generic vignette. Other generic vignettes were created for sale at stamp shows beginning in 2008.

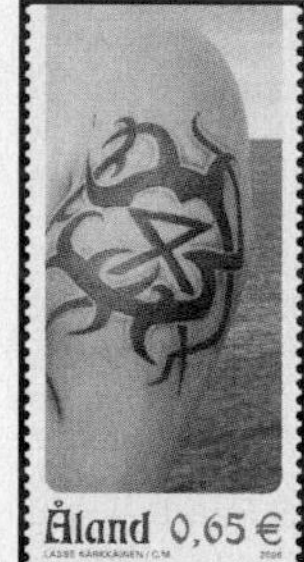

Tattoos — A200

No. 250: a, Tribal tattoo on man's biceps. b, Sailor's tattoo on man's forearm. c, Flower tattoo, on woman's torso.

**2006, Sept. 7** *Perf. 14 Vert.*

**Booklet Stamps**

250 Horiz. strip of 3 5.25 5.25
*a.-c.* A200 65c Any single 1.75 1.75
*d.* Booklet pane, 3 #250 16.00
Complete booklet, #250d 16.00

Fishing Boat From Television Film Directed by Ake Lindman A201

**2006, Aug. 4** **Litho.** *Perf. 12½*
251 A201 75c multi 2.00 1.75

**Landscapes Type of 2004**

Designs: 55c, Foggy grove, windmill and houses, Söderby, Lemland. €1.20, Rocks, Norra Essvik, Sottunga.

**2006, Aug. 4**
252-253 A184 Set of 2 4.75 4.50

Christmas A202

**Litho. With Holograms Affixed**

**2006, Oct. 9** *Perf. 13*
254 A202 (50c) multi 1.40 1.40

Flowers A203

Designs: 80c, Tripolium vulgare. 90c, Lythrum salicaria. €5, Angelica archangelica.

**2007, Feb. 1** **Litho.** *Perf. 12½x13*
255 A203 80c multi 2.50 2.00
256 A203 90c multi 2.75 2.50
257 A203 €5 multi 13.50 13.00
*Nos. 255-257 (3)* 18.75 17.50

Mail Planes A204

Designs: 2, Junkers F13. 1, Saab 340.

**2007, Mar. 1** *Perf. 12½*
258-259 A204 Set of 2 3.50 3.25

No. 258 sold for 55c, and No. 259 sold for 70c on day of issue.

**Landscapes Type of 2004**

**2007, Mar. 13**
260 A184 2 Skaftö, Kumlinge 1.60 1.50

Sold for 55c on day of issue.

Untitled Painting by Tove Jansson A205

**2007, Apr. 18** *Perf. 13¼x13¾*
261 A205 85c multi 2.40 2.40

Europa — A206

**2007, May 9** *Perf. 12½x13¼*
262 A206 70c multi 2.00 1.75

Scouting, cent.

Contemporary Crafts — A207

Designs: No. 263, Bridal crown, by Titti Sundblom. No. 264, Floral textile design, by Maria Korpi-Gordon and Adam Gordon. No. 265, Cups, bowl and plate, by Judy Kuyitunen.

**2007, May 18** *Perf. 13 Horiz.*

**Booklet Stamps**

263 A207 1 multi 2.00 2.25
264 A207 1 multi 2.00 2.25
265 A207 1 multi 2.00 2.25
*a.* Booklet pane, 3 each #263-265 18.00 18.50
Complete booklet, #265a 18.00

Nos. 263-265 each sold for 70c on day of issue.

A208

***Serpentine Die Cut 10 Syncopated***

**2007, June 7 Booklet Stamp**

**Self-Adhesive**

**266** A208 1 multi 2.00 1.75
*a.* Booklet pane of 8 16.00 14.00
Complete booklet, #266a 16.00

No. 266 sold for 70c on day of issue. Design portion of stamp could be personalized at €10.40 per booklet with a minimum purchase of three booklets.

Emigration to America A209

**2007, Aug. 9 Litho. *Perf. 13¼x12½***

**267** A209 75c multi 2.25 2.10

Kjusan, Hammarland A210

**2007, Oct. 1 *Perf. 12½***

**268** A210 1 multi 2.10 2.00

No. 268 sold for 70c on day of issue.

Christmas — A211

**2007, Oct. 9 *Perf. 14***

**269** A211 (50c) multi 1.75 1.40

Fish A212

Designs: 45c, Perca fluviatilis. €4.50, Sander lucioperca.

**2008, Feb. 1 Litho. *Perf. 13¼x13***

**270** A212 45c multi 1.75 1.50
**271** A212 €4.50 multi 14.50 13.50

Souvenir Sheet

Mythical Princess Signhild at Drottningkleven — A213

***Perf. 12½x13¼***

**2008, Mar. 27 Litho.**

**272** A213 (85c) multi 3.00 3.00

Badhusberget, Mariehamn — A214

Langvikshagen, Lumparland — A215

**2008, Apr. 15 *Perf. 13x12½***

**273** A214 (70c) multi 2.40 2.25
**274** A215 (70c) multi 2.40 2.25

2008 Summer Olympics, Beijing A216

**2008, May 9 *Perf. 13¾***

**275** A216 (90c) multi 3.00 3.00

Europa A217

**2008, May 9 *Perf. 13¼x13***

**276** A217 €1 multi 3.50 3.25

Lighthouses A218

No. 277: a, Marhällan Lighthouse. b, Gustaf Dalén Lighthouse. c, Kökarsören Lighthouse. d, Bogskär Lighthouse.

**Litho., Litho & Engr (#277c-277d)**

**2008, June 6 *Perf. 12¾ on 3 Sides***

**Booklet Stamps**

**277** Block or strip of 4 10.00 9.75
*a.-d.* A218 (75c) Any single 2.50 2.40
*e.* Booklet pane, 2 #277 20.00 —
Complete booklet, #277e 20.00

Within the booklet pane, stamps in one row are tete-beche in relation to stamps in the adjacent row.

Gravel Road and Profiles of Marcus Grönholm, Rally Driver, and Christoph Treier, Trainer A219

**2008, July 26 Litho. *Perf. 13½***

**278** A219 (90c) multi 2.75 2.50

Particles of granite were applied to portions of the design using a thermographic process.

Aland Peasant Bride, by Karl Emanuel Jansson — A220

**2008, Aug. 15 *Perf. 13x13¼***

**279** A220 €1.50 multi 5.00 4.75

Christmas A221

**Litho. With Hologram Applied**

**2008, Oct. 9 *Perf. 13¾x13¼***

**280** A221 (55c) multi 1.50 1.25

Personalized Stamp — A222

***Serpentine Die Cut 10 Syncopated***

**2008, Oct. 9 Litho.**

**Booklet Stamp**

**Self-Adhesive**

**281** A222 (75c) multi 2.00 1.75
*a.* Booklet pane of 8 16.00 14.00
Complete booklet, #281a 16.00

The generic design portion of the stamp shown could be personalized. Other generic vignettes were created for sale at stamp shows in 2009 and 2010.

1810 Boundary Post — A223

**Litho. & Embossed With Foil Application**

**2009, Jan. 22 *Perf. 14¼***

**282** A223 (80c) multi 2.25 2.00

Souvenir Sheet

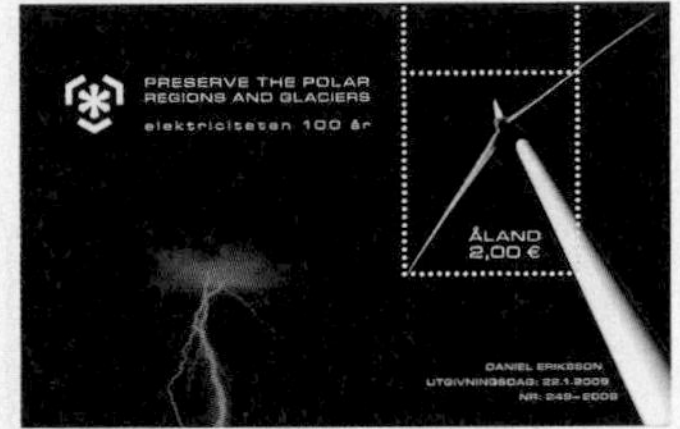


Electricity on Aland Islands, Cent. — A224

**Litho. & Embossed**

**2009, Jan. 22 *Perf. 12½x13¼***

**283** A224 €2 black 6.00 6.50

Writers — A225

No. 284: a, Ulla-Lena Lundberg and ship. b, Anni Blomqvist (1909-90), sailboat and dockside shack. c, Valdemar Nyman (1904-98), flowers, cattle.

**2009, Mar. 21 Litho. *Perf. 13 Horiz.***

**Booklet Stamps**

**284** Vert. strip of 3 6.75 7.00
*a.-c.* A225 (80c) Any single 2.25 2.25
*d.* Booklet pane, 3 #284 21.00 —
Complete booklet, #284d 21.00

Movie Theaters in Aland, Cent. — A226

**2009, Apr. 6 *Perf. 12½x13¼***

**285** A226 €1.60 multi 4.50 4.00

Divers at Plus Shipwreck A227

**2009, May 8**

**286** A227 (75c) multi 2.25 2.10

Europa A228

**2009, May 8 *Perf. 13***

**287** A228 (80c) multi 2.25 2.25

Intl. Year of Astronomy. Star-shaped holes are die cut in stamp.

Passenger Ferries A229

Designs: (75c), SS Viking. (80c), New Viking Line ferry, 2009.

**2009, June 1** **Litho.** ***Perf. 13***
**288-289** A229 Set of 2 4.75 4.50

See Nos. 301-302, 311-312, 325-326, 339, 347, 351-352.

Personalized Stamp — A230

**Booklet Stamp**

***Serpentine Die Cut 10 Syncopated***

**2009, June 27** **Self-Adhesive**
**290** A230 (90c) multi 2.75 2.50
*a.* Booklet pane of 8 22.00
Complete booklet, #290a 22.00

The generic design portion of the stamp shown could be personalized.

Cliffs, Föglö A231

Islets, Saltvik A232

**2009, Sept. 16** ***Perf. 12½***
**291** A231 (75c) multi 2.40 2.00
**292** A232 (80c) multi 2.50 2.25

Honeymoon Cabin of Finland President Martti Ahtisaari A233

**2009, Sept. 29** ***Perf. 13x12½***
**293** A233 (90c) multi 2.75 2.50

Christmas A234

Poinsettia and: (60c), Man and woman. (90c), Woman with scroll.

**2009, Oct. 9** ***Perf. 13¾***
**294-295** A234 Set of 2 4.75 4.25

**Flag Type of 2004 Inscribed "Inrikes"**

***Serpentine Die Cut 12½***

**2009, July 1** **Litho.**

**Booklet Stamp**

**Self-Adhesive**

**296** A125 (75c) multi 2.10 2.10
*a.* Booklet pane of 4 8.50
Complete booklet, 2 #296a 17.00

Mail Jetty at Eckerö, Painting by Victor Westerholm — A235

**2010, Jan. 4** ***Perf. 13***
**297** A235 (80c) multi 2.60 1.50

Jesus Christ, Painting by Warner Sallman — A236

**Litho. With Foil Application**

**2010, Mar. 24** ***Perf. 14x14¼***
**298** A236 (90c) multi 2.75 1.60

Souvenir Sheet

Kobba Klintar Pilot Station — A237

**2010, Mar. 24** **Litho.** ***Perf. 12½***
**299** A237 (90c) multi 2.75 3.00

Europa — A238

**2010, Apr. 19** ***Perf. 12½x13***
**300** A238 (85c) multi 2.50 1.50

**Ferries Type of 2009**

Designs: 75c, MS Skandia. €3.50, MS Prinsessan.

**2010, May 3** **Litho.** ***Perf. 13***
**301-302** A229 Set of 2 12.50 12.00

Plastic Toys Made By Plasto — A239

No. 303: a, Scooter. b, Dump truck. c, Ducks.

**2010, May 10** ***Perf. 13¾ Horiz.***

**Booklet Stamps**

**303** Vert. strip of 3 7.50 8.00
*a.-c.* A239 (85c) Any single 2.50 2.60
*d.* Booklet pane, 3 #303 22.50 23.00
Complete booklet, #303d 22.50

Farmhand Delivering Mail — A240

**2010, June 12** ***Perf. 12½x13¼***
**304** A240 (75c) multi 2.25 2.00

Personalized Stamp — A241

**2010, June 12** ***Perf. 12½***
**305** A241 (85c) black 2.50 2.25

No. 305 was printed in sheets of 8. The generic design portion of the stamp shown could be personalized for an extra fee.

Stained-Glass Windows — A242

Stained-glass window from church in Jomala: 80c, St. Olaf. €1.60, St. Olaf and other figures, horiz.

**2010, Aug. 30** **Litho.** ***Perf. 13***
**306** A242 80c multi 2.75 2.40

**Souvenir Sheet**

**307** A242 €1.60 multi 5.25 5.50

See Macao Nos. 1317-1318.

Shoreline, Eckerö A243

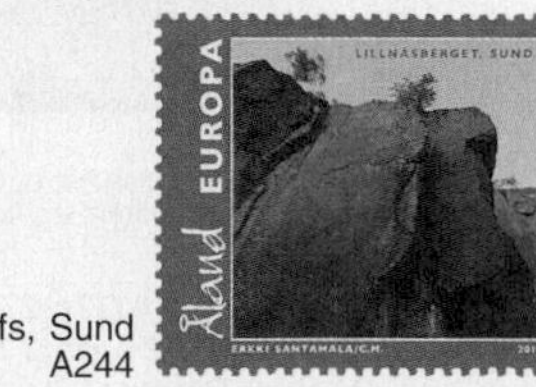


Cliffs, Sund A244

**2010, Sept. 16** ***Perf. 12½***
**308** A243 80c multi 2.40 2.25
**309** A244 (85c) multi 2.40 2.40

Christmas A245

**2010, Oct. 8** ***Perf. 13***
**310** A245 (65c) multi 1.90 1.75

**Ferries Type of 2009**

Designs: 80c, MS Alandia. €1.50, MS Apollo.

**2011, Feb. 1** **Litho.** ***Perf. 13***
**311-312** A229 Set of 2 6.75 6.25

Souvenir Sheet

Princess Maria Alexandrovna of Russia (1824-80) — A246

**2011, Feb. 21** ***Perf.***
**313** A246 €1 multi 3.00 3.25

City of Mariehamn, 150th anniv. A limited edition of No. 313 with gold embossing sold for €15. See Russia No. 7255.

Georg August Wallin (1811-52), Explorer of Arabia — A247

**2011, Apr. 1** ***Perf. 14x14¼***
**314** A247 (90c) multi 2.75 2.50

Europa A248

**2011, May 9** ***Perf. 13***
**315** A248 (85c) multi 2.75 2.50

Intl. Year of Forests.

Comic Book Superheroes Created by Paul Gustafson (1916-77) A249

No. 316: a, The Arrow. b, Fantom of the Fair. c, Alias the Spider.

**2011, May 9** ***Perf. 13***

**Booklet Stamps**

**316** Horiz. strip of 3 8.50 8.00
*a.-c.* A249 (90c) Any single 2.75 2.60
*d.* Tete-beche block of 6 18.00 18.00
*e.* Booklet pane of 3 #316 25.00 24.00
Complete booklet, #316e 25.00

Champagne Bottles From 1840s Shipwreck A250

**2011, June 3** **Litho.** ***Perf. 13½***
**317** A250 (90c) multi 2.75 2.50

Chips Ab Potato Chips — A251

**2011, June 7** ***Perf. 13¾***
**318** A251 85c multi 2.60 2.50

Strömma Apples — A252

**2011, June 7** **Litho.**
**319** A252 5c shown .25 .25
**320** A252 €4 Apples, diff. 12.50 12.50

Personalized Stamp — A253

**2011, Aug. 16** ***Perf. 13¾x14¼***
**321** A253 (95c) blk & grn 3.00 3.00

No. 321 was printed in sheets of 8. The generic design portion of the stamp shown could be personalized for an extra fee.

Kökar A254

Jomala A255

**2011, Sept. 20** **Litho.** ***Perf. 12½***
**322** A254 (85c) multi 2.50 2.25
**323** A255 (90c) multi 2.60 2.40

Christmas A256

**2011, Oct. 7** ***Perf. 14½***
**324** A256 (55c) multi 1.60 1.40

**Ferries Type of 2009**

Designs: 55c, SS Birger Jarl. (75c), MS Sally Albatross.

**2012, Feb. 1** ***Perf. 13¼***
**325-326** A229 Set of 2 3.75 3.50

No. 326 is inscribed "Lokalpost."

Souvenir Sheet

Fishermen at Sea — A257

**2012, Mar. 21** ***Perf. 13¼x13***
**327** A257 (€1) multi 2.75 3.00

Sinking of the Titanic, Cent. — A258

**2012, Apr. 16** ***Perf. 12¾x13¼***
**328** A258 €1.80 multi 5.00 4.75

See Belgium No. 2562.

The Man at the Wheel, Sculpture by Emil Cedercreutz A259

**Litho. & Engr.**

**2012, Apr. 26** ***Perf. 13¼x13***
**329** A259 €3 multi 8.50 8.25

Europa A260

**2012, May 9** **Litho.** ***Perf. 13¾***
**330** A260 (95c) multi 2.75 2.00

Personalized Stamp — A261

**2012, June 4** ***Perf. 14¼x13¾***
**331** A261 (95c) multi 2.75 2.00

Printed in sheets of 8. The design portion of this stamp could be personalized. The design shown is a generic vignette. Other generic vignettes were created for sale at stamp shows beginning in 2013.

Dragonflies A262

Designs: (75c), Aeshna cyanea. (95c), Sympetrum sanguineum.

**2012, June 4** ***Perf. 14¼***
**332-333** A262 Set of 2 4.75 4.75

No. 332 is inscribed "Lokalpost;" No. 333, "Europa."

Architecture — A263

No. 334: a, Miramar. b, Societetshusen. c, Badhotellet.

**2012, Aug. 23** ***Perf. 13¾ Horiz.***

**Booklet Stamps**

| | | | |
|---|---|---|---|
| **334** | Vert. strip of 3 | 8.00 | 8.50 |
| ***a.-c.*** | A263 (€1) Any single | 2.60 | 2.75 |
| ***d.*** | Booklet pane of 9, 3 each #334a-334c | 24.00 | — |
| | Complete booklet, #334d | 24.00 | |

Nos. 334a-334c are each inscribed "Världen."

Public Transportation — A264

Designs: No. 335, (95c), 1954 Volvo L224 bus. No. 336, (95c), 1924 Ford TT bus.

**2012, Sept. 19** ***Perf. 13¾x13½***
**335-336** A264 Set of 2 5.50 5.25

No. 335 is inscribed "Inrikes." No. 336 is inscribed "Europa."

Christmas A265

**2012, Oct. 9** ***Perf. 13***
**337** A265 (60c) multi 1.75 1.75

Yearning, Painting by Guy Frisk — A266

**2013, Jan. 15** ***Perf. 13¾x13¼***
**338** A266 (€1.10) multi 3.25 3.00

Aland Art Museum, 50th anniv.

**Ferries Type of 2009**

Design: (80c), SS Alandsfärjan.

**2013, Feb. 19** ***Perf. 13***
**339** A229 (80c) multi 2.25 2.25

Worldwide Fund for Nature (WWF) — A267

No. 340: a, Gavia arctica. b, Gavia stellata. c, Podiceps auritus. d, Podiceps cristatus.

**2013, Apr. 5** ***Perf. 12½x12¾***

**Booklet Stamps**

| | | | |
|---|---|---|---|
| **340** | A267 Block of 4 | 11.00 | 11.50 |
| ***a.-d.*** | (€1) Any single | 2.75 | 2.75 |
| ***e.*** | Booklet pane of 8, 2 each #340a-340d | 22.00 | 23.00 |
| | Complete booklet, #340e | 22.00 | |

Europa A268

**2013, May 6** ***Perf. 13¾x13¼***
**341** A268 (€1) multi 2.75 2.75

Personalized Stamp — A269

**2013, May 6** ***Perf. 12½***
**342** A269 (€1.10) ol grn & blk 3.25 3.00

No. 342 was printed in sheets of 8. The generic design portion of the stamp shown could be personalized for an extra fee. Other generic vignettes were created for sale at stamp shows beginning in 2014.

Water Lilies A270

Designs: (€1), Nymphaea alba. €2.50, Nuphar lutea.

**2013, June 4** ***Perf. 13x13¼***
**343-344** A270 Set of 2 9.50 9.50

Crowd at Rockoff Music Festival A271

Woman at Island in the Sun Music Festival — A272

**2013, July 12** **Litho.** ***Perf. 13¾***
**345** A271 (80c) multi 2.10 2.10
**346** A272 (€1.10) multi 3.25 3.00

**Ferries Type of 2009**

Design: €2, MS Princess Anastasia.

**2013, Aug. 5** **Litho.** ***Perf. 13***
**347** A229 €2 multi 5.50 5.50

See Russia No. 7468.

Inachis Io — A273

**2013, Aug. 20 Litho. *Perf. 13¾***
348 A273 (€1.10) multi 3.00 3.00

Christmas A274

Paintings by Pinturicchio: No. 349, Adoration of the Magi. No. 350, Nativity.

**2013, Nov. 8 Litho. *Perf. 13¼x13¾***
349 A274 (65c) multi 1.75 1.75
350 A274 65c multi 1.75 1.75

No. 350 was printed in sheets of 8 + central label. See Vatican City Nos. 1549-1550.

**Ferries Type of 2009**

Designs: No. 351, MS Birka Princess. No. 352, MS Viking Grace.

**2014, Feb. 7 Litho. *Perf. 13¾***
351 A229 (€1.10) multi 3.00 3.00
352 A229 (€1.10) multi 3.00 3.00

No. 351 is inscribed "Inrikes"; No. 352, "Europa."

Mariehamn Theater Society, Cent. — A275

**2014, Feb. 7 Litho. *Perf. 13¼***
353 A275 €1.50 multi 4.25 4.25

Souvenir Sheet

Bridge of a Freighter and Horizon — A276

**2014, Mar. 17 Litho. *Perf. 13¼***
354 A276 €3 multi 8.25 8.25

Grand Piano of Alie Lindberg (1849-1933), Concert Pianist — A277

**2014, May 8 Litho. *Perf. 13¼x13***
355 A277 (€1.10) multi 3.00 3.00

Europa.

Campanula Trachelium A278

**2014, May 8 Litho. *Perf. 12½***
356 A278 (€1.10) multi 3.00 3.00

Kenta Sandvik, Weight Lifter A279

**2014, May 31 Litho. *Perf. 13x13¼***
357 A279 (90c) multi 2.50 2.50

Personalized Stamp — A280

**2014, May 31 Litho. *Perf. 12½***
358 A280 (€1.10) multi 3.00 3.00

No. 358 was printed in sheets of 8. The generic design portion of the stamp shown could be personalized for an extra fee. Other generic vignettes were created for sale at stamp shows beginning in 2015.

Robert Helenius, Professional Boxer, and Family on Aland Island — A281

**2014, June 9 Litho. *Perf. 13x13¼***
359 A281 €2.30 multi 6.25 6.25

Musical Groups of the 1960s — A282

No. 360: a, Hitch Hikers. b, Stockdoves. c, Anacondas.

**2014, Aug. 25 Litho. *Perf. 13x12¼***
**Booklet Stamps**
360 Vert. strip of 3 7.25 7.25
*a.-c.* A282 (90c) Any single 2.40 2.40
*d.* Booklet pane of 9, 3 each #360a-360c 22.00 —
Complete booklet, #360d 22.00

Christmas A283

**Litho. With Foil Application**
**2014, Oct. 9 *Perf. 13¾x13¼***
361 A283 (70c) multi 1.75 1.75

New Year 2015 (Year of the Ram) A284

No. 362: a, Ram, ewe and lamb. b, Ram's head.

**Litho. & Engr.**
**2014, Nov. 5 *Perf. 13x12¾***
362 A284 Pair 4.00 4.00
*a.-b.* 80c Either single 2.00 2.00

Printed in sheets containing two pairs.

Ships A285

Designs: 85c, Schooner Lemland. (€1.20), Barquentine Leo.

**2015, Feb. 2 Litho. *Perf. 13x13¼***
363-364 A285 Set of 2 4.75 4.75

See Nos. 377-378.

Campanula Persicifolia A286

**2015, Apr. 10 Litho. *Perf. 14¼***
365 A286 85c multi 1.90 1.90

Midvinterblot, Painting by Carl Larsson (1853-1919) — A287

**2015, Apr. 10 Litho. *Perf. 14x14¼***
366 A287 €3 multi 6.75 6.75

Race Horse Indian Silver A288

**2015, May 1 Litho. *Perf. 14***
367 A288 (95c) multi 2.25 2.25

Europa A289

**2015, May 8 Litho. *Perf. 14¼***
368 A289 (€1.20) multi 2.75 2.75

Personalized Stamp — A290

**2015, May 8 Litho. *Perf. 12½***
369 A290 (€1.20) multi 2.75 2.75

Printed in sheets of 8. The design portion of this stamp could be personalized. The design shown is a generic vignette.

Julius Sundblom (1865-1945), Politician — A291

**2015, June 22 Litho. *Perf. 13***
370 A291 (€1.20) multi 2.75 2.75

Silver Jewelry — A292

Designs: (€1.20), Buckle from Aland Islands. €2, Brooch from Bern, Switzerland.

**Litho. & Embossed**
**2015, Sept. 3 *Perf. 13***
371 A292 (€1.20) multi 2.75 2.75
372 A292 €2 multi 4.50 4.50

See Switzerland Nos. 1568-1569.

Dogs — A293

No. 373: a, Finnish hound (Finsk stövare). b, Gray Norwegian elkhound (Norsk älghund gra). c, Wire-haired dachshund (Strävharig tax).

**2015, Sept. 3 Litho. *Perf. 13***
**Booklet Stamps**
373 Horiz. strip of 3 8.25 8.25
*a.-c.* A293 (€1.20) Any single 2.75 2.75
*d.* Booklet pane of 9, 3 each #373a-373c 25.00 —
Complete booklet, #373d 25.00

A294

Christmas
A295

**2015, Oct. 9 Litho. *Perf. 13***

**374** A294 (70c) multi 1.60 1.60
**375** A295 (€1.20) multi 2.75 2.75

Aland Sea Rescue Society, 50th Anniv. — A296

**2015, Oct. 30 Litho. *Perf. 13***

**376** A296 (95c) multi 2.10 2.10

**Ships Type of 2015**

Designs: 10c, Brig Altai. €10, Barque Pehr Brahe.

**2016, Feb. 2 Litho. *Perf. 13x13¼***

**377-378** A285 Set of 2 22.00 22.00

Buckthorn Dessert Made by Chef Michael Björklund
A297

**2016, Mar. 18 Litho. *Perf. 14¼***

**379** A297 (€1.30) multi 3.00 3.00

Witch Trials, 350th Anniv. — A298

**2016, Apr. 8 Litho. *Perf. 13***

**380** A298 (€1.30) multi 3.00 3.00

A299

Europa
A300

**2016, May 9 Litho. *Perf. 13***

**381** A299 (€1.30) multi 3.00 3.00
**382** A300 (€1.30) multi 3.00 3.00

Think Green Issue.

Medicinal Plants — A301

No. 383: a, Hyoscyamus niger. b, Digitalis purpurea. c, Tanacetum vulgare.

**2016, May 9 Litho. *Perf. 12 Horiz.***

**Booklet Stamps**

**383** Vert. strip of 3 9.00 9.00
*a.-c.* A301 (€1.30) Any single 3.00 3.00
*d.* Booklet pane of 9, 3 each #383a-383c 27.00 —
Complete booklet, #383d 27.00

Lilla Aland Chair Designed by Carl Malmsten — A302

**2016, May 27 Litho. *Perf. 11½***

**384** A302 €2.50 multi 5.75 5.75

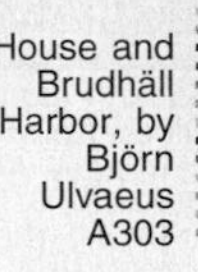


House and Brudhäll Harbor, by Björn Ulvaeus
A303

**2016, July 8 Litho. *Perf. 11½***

**385** A303 (€1.30) multi 3.00 3.00

Apple and Blossom
A304

**2016, Aug. 12 Litho. *Perf. 12½***

**386** A304 (€1.30) multi 3.00 3.00

Elves Decorating Christmas Tree — A305

Elf, Reindeer and Gifts — A306

**2016, Oct. 10 Litho. *Perf. 13***

**387** A305 (70c) multi 1.60 1.60
**388** A306 (€1.30) multi 3.00 3.00

Christmas.

Souvenir Sheet

New Year 2017 (Year of the Rooster) — A307

No. 389 — Rooster and: a, Flower. b, Rowboat.

**2016, Nov. 11 Litho. *Perf. 13***

**389** A307 Sheet of 2 9.00 9.00
*a.-b.* €2 Either single 4.50 4.50

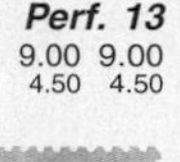

Mermerus
A308

Mariehamn
A309

**2017, Feb. 2 Litho. *Perf. 13x13¼***

**390** A308 20c multi .45 .45
**391** A309 (€1.10) multi 2.40 2.40

Personalized Stamp — A310

**2017, Mar. 14 Litho. *Perf. 12½***

**392** A310 (€1.30) multi 3.00 3.00

No. 392 was printed in sheets of 8. The generic design portion of the stamp shown could be personalized for an extra fee.

Pinus Sylvestris and Salvadora Oleoides
A311

**2017, Mar. 14 Litho. *Perf. 13x13¼***

**393** A311 (€1.30) multi 3.00 3.00

Cultural Diversity.

Kastelholm Castle
A312

**2017, May 9 Litho. *Perf. 13x13¼***

**394** A312 (€1.40) multi 3.25 3.25

Europa.

Independence of Finland, Cent. — A313

**Litho. & Embossed With Foil Application**

**2017, May 24 *Perf. 13x13¼***

**395** A313 €5 multi 11.50 11.50

Sauna Bench, Bucket and Whisk
A314

Exterior of Sauna
A315

**2017, May 24 Litho. *Perf. 13¼x13½***

**396** A314 (€1.40) multi 3.25 3.25
**397** A315 (€1.40) multi 3.25 3.25
*a.* Souvenir sheet of 2, #396-397 6.50 6.50

See Finland No. 1540.

Handcrafted Jewelry Made From Recycled Items — A316

**2017, Aug. 17 Litho. *Perf. 13x13¼***

**398** A316 €1 multi 2.40 2.40

Mammals
A317

No. 399: a, Lepus timidus. b, Mustela nivalis. c, Nyctereutes procyonoides.

***Perf. 14¼x14½***

**2017, Sept. 15 Litho.**

**Booklet Stamps**

**399** Horiz. strip of 3 8.00 8.00
*a.-c.* A317 (€1.10) Any single 2.60 2.60
*d.* Booklet pane of 9, 3 each #399a-399c 24.00 —
Complete booklet, #399d 24.00

A318

Gingerbread Houses
A319

**2017, Oct. 9 Litho. *Perf. 13¼***

**400** A318 (70c) multi 1.60 1.60
**401** A319 (€1.40) multi 3.25 3.25

Christmas.

Souvenir Sheet

New Year 2018 (Year of the Dog) — A320

No. 402 — China dog at: a, Right. b, Left.

**2017, Nov. 10 Litho.** ***Perf. 13¼x13***

| | | | | |
|---|---|---|---|---|
| **402** | A320 | €1 Sheet of 2, #a-b | 4.75 | 4.75 |

## ALAND ISLANDS

### SEMI-POSTAL STAMPS

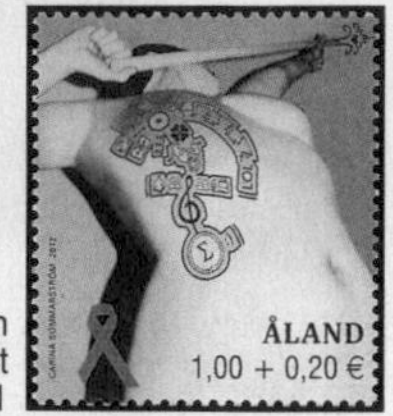


Campaign Against Breast Cancer — SP1

**2012, Oct. 1 Litho.** ***Perf. 13½x13¾***

| | | | | |
|---|---|---|---|---|
| **B1** | SP1 | €1+20c multi | 3.25 | 3.25 |

Surtax for Aland Cancer Society.

Sculpture of Gnome by Hakan Sandberg SP2

**2013, Sept. 2 Litho.** ***Perf. 13¾x13½***

| | | | | |
|---|---|---|---|---|
| **B2** | SP2 | €1+20c multi | 3.25 | 3.25 |

Surtax for Aland Cancer Society.

Zero Tolerance Program Against Drug Abuse — SP3

**Litho. & Embossed**

**2014, Apr. 11** ***Perf. 14¾***

| | | | | |
|---|---|---|---|---|
| **B3** | SP3 | €1.10 +20c black | 3.75 | 3.75 |

## FIUME

ˈfyü-ˌmā

LOCATION — A city and surrounding territory on the Adriatic Sea

GOVT. — Formerly a part of Italy

AREA — 8 sq. mi.

POP. — 44,956 (estimated 1924)

Fiume was under Hapsburg rule after 1466 and was transferred to Hungarian control after 1870. Of mixed Italian and Croatian population and strategically important, it was Hungary's only international seaport. Following World War I, Fiume was disputed between Italy and the newly created Kingdom of the Serbs, Croats and Slovenes (later Yugoslavia). A force of Allied troops occupied the city in Nov. 1918, while its future status was negotiated at the Paris Peace Conference.

In Sept. 1919, the Italian nationalist poet Gabriele d'Annunzio organized his legionnaires and seized Fiume, together with the islands of Arbe, Carnaro and Veglia, in the name of Italy. D'Annunzio established an autonomous administration, which soon came into conflict with the Italian government. There followed several years of instability, with three Italian interventions after 1920. In Jan. 1924, the Treaty of Rome between Italy and Yugoslavia established formal Italian sovereignty over Fiume, and Fiume stamps were replaced by those of Italy after March 31, 1924.

100 Filler = 1 Korona
100 Centesimi = 1 Corona (1919)
100 Centesimi = 1 Lira

See note on FIUME-KUPA Zone, Italian Occupation, after Yugoslavia No. NJ22.

The overprints on Nos. 1-23a have been extensively forged. Even the inexpensive values are difficult to find with genuine overprints. Forgeries of many later issues also exist, most created for the packet trade in the 1920s. Values are for genuine stamps. Collectors should be aware that stamps sold "as is" are likely to be forgeries, and unexpertized collections should be assumed to consist of mostly forged stamps. Education plus working with knowledgeable dealers is mandatory in this collecting area. More valuable stamps should be expertized.

Hungarian Stamps of 1916-18 Typograph Overprinted, Bold Sans Serif Letters

**1918, Dec. 2 Wmk. 137** ***Perf. 15***

**On Stamps of 1916**

**Colored Numerals**

| | | | | |
|---|---|---|---|---|
| **1A** | A9 | 20f gray brown | 4,000. | 2,500. |

Hungarian Stamps of 1916-18 Typograph Overprinted

**On Stamps of 1916**

**White Numerals**

| | | | | |
|---|---|---|---|---|
| **1** | A8 | 10f rose | — | — |
| *b.* | | Handstamped overprint | 100.00 | *47.50* |
| **2** | A8 | 15f violet | 47.50 | 40.00 |

Value for No. 1a is for handstamped overprint. Value for No. 2 is for typographed overprint.

**On Stamps of 1916-18**

**Colored Numerals**

| | | | | |
|---|---|---|---|---|
| **3** | A9 | 2f brown orange | 4.75 | 2.40 |
| **4** | A9 | 3f red violet | 4.75 | 2.40 |
| **5** | A9 | 5f green | 4.75 | 2.40 |
| **6** | A9 | 6f grnsh blue | 4.75 | 2.40 |
| **7a** | A9 | 10f rose red | 72.50 | 27.50 |
| **8** | A9 | 15f violet | 4.75 | 2.40 |
| **9** | A9 | 20f gray brown | 4.75 | 2.40 |
| **10** | A9 | 25f deep blue | 16.00 | 3.25 |
| **11** | A9 | 35f brown | 9.50 | 4.75 |
| **12a** | A9 | 40f olive green | 45.00 | 24.00 |

**White Numerals**

| | | | | |
|---|---|---|---|---|
| **13** | A10 | 50f red vio & lil | 6.50 | 4.00 |
| **14** | A10 | 75f brt bl & pale bl | 13.00 | 4.75 |
| **15** | A10 | 80f grn & pale grn | 13.00 | 4.00 |
| **16** | A10 | 1k red brn & claret | 40.00 | 9.50 |
| **17** | A10 | 2k ol brn & bis | 6.50 | 4.50 |
| **18** | A10 | 3k dk vio & ind | 55.00 | 27.50 |
| **19** | A10 | 5k dk brn & lt brn | 145.00 | 27.50 |
| **20a** | A10 | 10k vio brn & vio | 475.00 | 240.00 |

Inverted or double overprints exist on most of Nos. 4-15.

**On Stamps of 1918**

| | | | | |
|---|---|---|---|---|
| **21** | A11 | 10f scarlet | 4.00 | 4.00 |
| **22** | A11 | 20f dark brown | 3.25 | 2.40 |
| **23a** | A12 | 40f olive green | 37.50 | 20.00 |

The overprint on Nos. 3-23a was applied by 2 printing plates and 6 handstamps. Values are for the less costly. Values of Nos. 7a, 12a, 20a and 23a are for handstamps. See the *Scott Specialized Catalogue of Stamps and Covers* for detailed listings.

Postage Due Stamps of Hungary, 1915-20 Ovptd. & Surcharged in Black

**1919, Jan.**

| | | | | |
|---|---|---|---|---|
| **24** | D1 | 45f on 6f green & red | 20.00 | 16.00 |
| **25** | D1 | 45f on 20f green & red | 60.00 | 16.00 |
| | | Set, never hinged | 200.00 | |

**Hungarian Savings Bank Stamp Surcharged in Black**

A2

**1919, Jan. 29**

| | | | | |
|---|---|---|---|---|
| **26** | A2 | 15f on 10f dk violet | 24.00 | 20.00 |
| | | Never hinged | 60.00 | |

Overprints on Nos. 24-26 are typographed.

"Italy" — A3

Italian Flag on Clock-Tower in Fiume — A4

"Revolution" A5

Sailor Raising Italian Flag at Fiume (1918) A6

Nos. 30-43 exist on three types of paper: (A) grayish, porous paper, printed in sheets of 70 stamps (Jan, Feb. printings); (B) translucent or semi-translucent good quality white paper, printed in sheets of 70 stamps (March printing); and (C) good quality medium white paper, plain and opaque, sometimes grayish or yellowish, printed in sheets of 100 (April printing). Values are for the least expensive variety. See the *Scott Specialized Catalogue of Stamps and Covers* for detailed listings.

***Perf. 11½***

**1919, April Unwmk. Litho.**

| | | | | |
|---|---|---|---|---|
| **27** | A3 | 2c dull blue | 2.40 | 2.40 |
| **28** | A3 | 3c gray brown | 2.40 | 2.40 |
| **29** | A3 | 5c yellow green | 2.40 | 2.40 |
| **30a** | A4 | 10c rose | 25.00 | 16.00 |
| **31** | A4 | 15c violet | 2.40 | 2.40 |
| **32a** | A4 | 20c emerald green | 4.00 | *4.00* |
| **33** | A5 | 25c dark blue | 3.25 | 2.40 |
| **34** | A6 | 30c deep violet | 3.25 | 2.40 |
| **35** | A5 | 40c brown | 3.25 | 2.40 |
| **36** | A5 | 45c orange | 3.25 | 2.40 |
| **37** | A6 | 50c yellow green | 3.25 | 2.40 |
| **38** | A6 | 60c claret | 3.25 | 2.40 |
| **39** | A6 | 1cor brown orange | 4.75 | 2.40 |
| **40** | A6 | 2cor brt blue | 4.75 | 2.40 |
| **41** | A6 | 3cor orange red | 6.50 | 2.40 |
| **42** | A6 | 5cor deep brown | 40.00 | 40.00 |
| **43a** | A6 | 10cor olive green | 47.50 | *80.00* |
| | | *Nos. 27-43a (17)* | 161.60 | 171.20 |

The earlier printings of Jan. and Feb. are on thin grayish paper, the Mar. printing is on semi-transparent white paper, all in sheets of 70. An Apr. printing is on white paper of medium thickness in sheets of 100. Part-perf. examples of most of this series are known.

For surcharges see Nos. 58, 60, 64, 66-69.

A7

A8

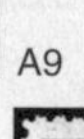


A9

A10

**1919, July 28** ***Perf. 11½***

| | | | | |
|---|---|---|---|---|
| **46** | A7 | 5c yellow green | 2.40 | 1.60 |
| **47** | A8 | 10c rose | 2.40 | 1.60 |
| **48** | A9 | 30c violet | 11.00 | 4.00 |
| **49** | A10 | 40c yellow brown | 2.40 | *2.40* |
| **50** | A10 | 45c orange | 11.00 | 8.00 |
| **51** | A9 | 50c yellow green | 11.00 | 8.00 |
| **52** | A9 | 60c claret | 11.00 | 8.00 |
| *a.* | | Perf. 13x12½ | 190.00 | |
| | | Never hinged | 475.00 | |
| *b.* | | Perf. 10½ | 350.00 | |
| | | Never hinged | 875.00 | |
| **53** | A9 | 10cor olive green | 11.00 | *22.50* |
| *a.* | | Perf. 13x12½ | 65.00 | *105.00* |
| | | Never hinged | 160.00 | |
| *b.* | | Perf. 10½ | 350.00 | *375.00* |
| | | Never hinged | 875.00 | |
| | | *Nos. 46-53 (8)* | 62.20 | 56.10 |
| | | Set, never hinged | 145.00 | |

Five other denominations (25c, 1cor, 2cor, 3cor and 5cor) were not officially issued. Some examples of the 25c are known canceled.

For surcharges see Nos. 59, 61-63, 65, 70.

Stamps and Types of 1919 Handstamp Surcharged

**1919-20**

| | | | | |
|---|---|---|---|---|
| **58** | A4 | 5c on 20c grn ('20) | 2.40 | 2.40 |
| **59** | A9 | 5c on 25c blue | 2.40 | 2.40 |
| **60** | A5 | 10c on 45c orange | 2.40 | 2.40 |
| **61** | A9 | 15c on 30c vio ('20) | 2.40 | 2.40 |
| **62** | A10 | 15c on 45c orange | 2.40 | 2.40 |
| **63** | A9 | 15c on 60c cl ('20) | 2.40 | 2.40 |
| **64** | A6 | 25c on 50c yel grn ('20) | 20.00 | *35.00* |
| **65** | A9 | 25c on 50c yel grn ('20) | 2.40 | 2.40 |
| **66** | A6 | 55c on 1cor brn org | 40.00 | 40.00 |
| **67** | A6 | 55c on 2cor brt bl | 6.50 | *9.50* |
| **68** | A6 | 55c on 3cor org red | 6.50 | 8.00 |
| **69** | A6 | 55c on 5cor dp brn | 6.50 | 8.00 |
| **70** | A9 | 55c on 10cor ol grn | 32.50 | 35.00 |
| | | *Nos. 58-70 (13)* | 128.80 | *152.30* |
| | | Set, never hinged | 300.00 | |

**Semi-Postal Stamps of 1919 Surcharged**

a

b 

**1919-20**

73 SP6(a) 5c on 5c green 2.40 2.40
74 SP6(a) 10c on 10c rose 2.40 2.40
75 SP6(a) 15c on 15c gray 2.40 2.40
76 SP6(a) 20c on 20c org 2.40 2.40
77 SP9(a) 25c on 25c bl ('20) 2.40 2.40
78 SP7(b) 45c on 45c ol grn 4.00 4.00
79 SP7(b) 60c on 60c rose 4.00 4.00
80 SP7(b) 80c on 80c violet 2.40 2.40
81 SP7(b) 1cor on 1cor sl 4.00 4.00
82 SP8(a) 2cor on 2cor red brn 6.50 6.50
83 SP8(a) 3cor on 3cor blk brn 8.00 8.00
84 SP8(a) 5cor on 5cor yel brn 9.50 9.50
85 SP8(a) 10cor on 10cor dk vio ('20) 4.00 4.00
*Nos. 73-85 (13)* 54.40 54.40
Set, never hinged 120.00

Double or inverted surcharges, or imperf. varieties, exist on most of Nos. 73-85.

There were three settings of the surcharges on Nos. 73-85 except No. 77 which is known only with one setting.

Gabriele d'Annunzio — A11

**1920, Sept. 12 Typo. *Perf. 11½***

**Pale Buff Background**

86 A11 5c green 2.40 2.40
87 A11 10c carmine 2.40 2.40
88 A11 15c dark gray 2.40 2.40
89 A11 20c orange 2.40 2.40
90 A11 25c dark blue 3.25 3.25
91 A11 30c red brown 3.25 3.25
92 A11 45c olive gray 4.75 4.75
93 A11 50c lilac 4.75 4.75
94 A11 55c bister 4.75 4.75
95 A11 1 l black 20.00 *27.50*
96 A11 2 l red violet 20.00 *27.50*
97 A11 3 l dark green 20.00 *27.50*
98 A11 5 l brown 80.00 55.00
99 A11 10 l gray violet 20.00 *27.50*
*Nos. 86-99 (14)* 190.35 *195.35*
Set, never hinged 450.00

The background print, pale buff, also exists doubly printed or shifted on several denominations.

Counterfeits of Nos. 86 to 99 are plentiful.

For overprints see Nos. 134-148.

Severing the Gordian Knot — A12

Designs: 10c, Ancient emblem of Fiume. 20c, Head of "Fiume." 25c, Hands holding daggers.

**1920, Sept. 12**

100 A12 5c green 42.50 27.50
a. Imperf. 145.00
b. Horiz. pair, imperf. between 375.00
101 A12 10c deep rose 27.50 22.50
a. Imperf. 95.00
102 A12 20c brown orange 42.50 22.50
103 A12 25c indigo 27.50 *47.50*
a. Imperf. 180.00
b. Double impression, imperf. 1,075.
c. Horiz. pair, imperf. between 550.00
d. 25c blue 95.00 *100.00*
e. As "d," imperf. 400.00
f. As "d," horiz. pair, imperf. between 1,075.
*Nos. 100-103 (4)* 140.00 120.00
Set, never hinged 440.00

Anniv. of the occupation of Fiume by d'Annunzio. They were available for franking the correspondence of the legionnaires on the day of issue only, Sept. 12, 1920.

Counterfeits of Nos. 100-103 are plentiful.

For overprints and surcharges see Nos. 104-133, E4-E9.

Nos. 100-103 Overprinted or Surcharged in Black or Red

**1920, Nov. 20**

104 A12 1c on 5c green 2.40 2.40
a. Inverted overprint 55.00 55.00
b. Double overprint 200.00
105 A12 2c on 25c indigo (R) 2.40 2.40
a. Inverted overprint 55.00 55.00
b. Double overprint 72.50 72.50
c. 2c on 25c blue (R) 80.00 80.00
106 A12 5c green 20.00 2.40
a. Inverted overprint 47.50 47.50
b. Double overprint 72.50 72.50
107 A12 10c rose 20.00 2.40
a. Inverted overprint 55.00 55.00
b. Double overprint 72.50 72.50
108 A12 15c on 10c rose 2.40 2.40
a. Inverted overprint 65.00 65.00
b. Double overprint 72.50 72.50
109 A12 15c on 20c brn org 2.40 *2.40*
a. Inverted overprint 65.00 65.00
b. Double overprint 72.50 72.50
110 A12 15c on 25c indigo (R) 2.40 *2.40*
a. Inverted overprint 65.00 65.00
b. Double overprint 72.50 72.50
c. 15c on 25c blue (R) 225.00 225.00
111 A12 20c brown orange 2.40 2.40
a. Inverted overprint 27.50 27.50
b. Double overprint 125.00 125.00
112 A12 25c indigo (R) 2.40 2.40
a. Inverted overprint 24.00 24.00
b. 25c blue (R) 8.00 8.00
113 A12 25c indigo (Bk) 175.00 175.00
a. Inverted overprint 450.00 350.00
b. 25c blue (Bk) 240.00 240.00
c. As "b," inverted overprint 725.00
114 A12 25c on 10c rose 2.40 4.75
a. Double overprint 72.50 72.50
115 A12 50c on 20c brn org 5.00 2.40
a. Double overprint 72.50 72.50
116 A12 55c on 5c green 21.00 4.75
a. Inverted overprint 95.00 95.00
b. Double overprint 72.50 72.50
117 A12 1 l on 10c rose 47.50 40.00
a. Inverted overprint 275.00 275.00
b. Double overprint 275.00
118 A12 1 l on 25c indigo (R) 100.00 100.00
a. 1 l on 25c blue (R) 600.00 600.00
b. As "a," inverted overprint 875.00 725.00
119 A12 2 l on 5c green 47.50 40.00
a. Inverted overprint 325.00
b. Double overprint 200.00
120 A12 5 l on 10c rose 225.00 *240.00*
a. Inverted overprint 725.00 725.00
b. Double overprint 725.00
121 A12 10 l on 20c brn org 700.00 550.00
a. Inverted overprint 1,600. 800.00
b. Double overprint 1,600. 800.00
*Nos. 104-121 (18)* 1,380. 1,179.
Set, never hinged 3,850.

The Fiume Legionnaires of d'Annunzio occupied the islands of Arbe and Veglia in the Gulf of Carnaro Nov. 13, 1920-Jan. 5, 1921.

Varieties of overprint or surcharge exist for most of Nos. 104-121.

Nos. 113, 117-121, 125, 131 have a backprint.

Nos. 106-107, 111, 113, 115-116 Overprinted or Surcharged at top

**1920, Nov. 28**

122 A12 5c green 35.00 24.00
123 A12 10c rose 45.00 *52.50*
124 A12 20c brown org 87.50 52.50
125 A12 25c deep blue 52.50 *52.50*
126 A12 50c on 20c brn org 95.00 52.50
127 A12 55c on 5c green 95.00 52.50
*Nos. 122-127 (6)* 410.00 286.50
Set, never hinged 1,000.

The overprint on Nos. 122-125 comes in two widths: 11mm and 14mm. Values are for the 11mm width.

Nos. 106-107, 111, 113, 115-116 Overprinted or Surcharged at top

**1920, Nov. 28**

128 A12 5c green 35.00 24.00
129 A12 10c rose 45.00 *52.50*
130 A12 20c brown orange 87.50 52.50
131 A12 25c deep blue 52.50 *52.50*
132 A12 50c on 20c brn org 95.00 52.50
133 A12 55c on 5c green 95.00 52.50
*Nos. 128-133 (6)* 410.00 286.50
Set, never hinged 1,000.

Nos. 86-99 Overprinted

**1921, Feb. 2**

**"Provvisorio" 20mm wide**

**Space between lines 3mm**

**Pale Buff Background**

134 A11 5c green 2.40 2.40
a. Inverted overprint 27.50 27.50
b. Double overprint 52.50 52.50
135 A11 10c carmine 2.40 2.40
a. Inverted overprint 27.50 27.50
b. Double overprint 52.50 52.50
136 A11 15c dark gray 2.40 *2.40*
a. Inverted overprint 27.50 27.50
b. Double overprint 52.50 52.50
137 A11 20c orange 4.00 4.00
a. Inverted overprint 27.50 27.50
b. Double overprint 27.50 27.50
138 A11 25c dark blue 4.00 4.00
a. Inverted overprint 27.50 27.50
b. Double overprint 52.50 52.50
139 A11 30c red brown 4.00 4.00
a. Inverted overprint 27.50 27.50
b. Double overprint 27.50 27.50
140 A11 45c olive gray 2.40 2.40
a. Inverted overprint 55.00 55.00
b. Double overprint 40.00 40.00
141 A11 50c lilac 4.00 4.00
a. Inverted overprint 27.50 27.50
142 A11 55c bister 4.00 4.00
a. Inverted overprint 16.00 16.00
143 A11 1 l black 145.00 *180.00*
a. Inverted overprint 350.00 350.00
144 A11 2 l red violet 95.00 95.00
145 A11 3 l dark green 95.00 95.00
146 A11 5 l brown 95.00 95.00
147 A11 10 l gray violet 95.00 95.00

With Additional Surcharge

148 A11 1 l on 30c red brown 2.50 2.50
a. Inverted overprint 27.50 27.50
b. Double overprint 55.00 55.00
*Nos. 134-148 (15)* 557.10 592.10
Set, never hinged 1,400.

Most of Nos. 134-143, 148 and E10-E11 exist with inverted or double overprint.

See Nos. E10-E11.

**Second Printing, Milan**

**"Provvisorio" 21mm wide**

**Space between overprint lines 4mm**

**1921, Dec. 18**

148A A11 5c yellow green 50.00 *57.50*
Never hinged 125.00
On cover 300.00
148B A11 10c carmine 135.00 40.00
Never hinged 340.00
On cover 300.00
c. Vert. pair, imperf. between *650.00*

**First Constituent Assembly**

Nos. B4-B15 Overprinted

**1921, Apr. 24**

149 SP6 5c blue green 6.50 4.75
150 SP6 10c rose 6.50 4.75
a. Inverted overprint 65.00 65.00
151 SP6 15c gray 6.50 4.75
152 SP6 20c orange 6.50 4.75
153 SP7 45c olive green 17.50 12.00
154 SP7 60c car rose 17.50 12.00
a. Inverted overprint 47.50 47.50
155 SP7 80c brt violet 27.50 24.00

**With Additional Overprint "L"**

156 SP7 1 l on 1cor dk slate 32.50 *35.00*
a. Inverted overprint 80.00 80.00
157 SP8 2 l on 2cor red brn 120.00 4.25
a. Inverted overprint 325.00 160.00
158 SP8 3 l on 3cor black brn 120.00 *130.00*
159 SP8 5 l on 5cor yel brn 120.00 4.25
160 SP8 10 l on 10cor dk vio 175.00 175.00
a. Inverted overprint 475.00 400.00
*Nos. 149-160 (12)* 656.00 415.50
Set, never hinged 1,625.

The overprint exists inverted on several denominations.

**Second Constituent Assembly**

"Constitution" Issue of 1921 With Additional Overprint "1922"

**1922**

161 SP6 5c blue green 4.75 3.25
a. Inverted overprint 24.00 24.00
162 SP6 10c rose 2.40 *2.40*
a. Inverted overprint 24.00 24.00
b. Double overprint, one inverted 40.00 40.00
163 SP6 15c gray 20.00 12.00
164 SP6 20c orange 2.40 2.40
a. Inverted overprint 32.50 32.50
b. Double overprint 40.00 40.00
c. Double overprint, one inverted — —
165 SP7 45c olive grn 13.00 12.00
a. Double overprint 40.00 40.00
166 SP7 60c car rose 2.40 *3.25*
167 SP7 80c brt violet 2.40 *3.25*
168 SP7 1 l on 1cor dk slate 2.40 *2.40*
a. Inverted overprint 55.00 55.00
b. Double overprint 40.00 40.00
169 SP8 2 l on 2cor red brn 20.00 16.00
170 SP8 3 l on 3cor blk brn 2.50 *3.25*
171 SP8 5 l on 5cor yel brn 2.50 *3.25*
*Nos. 161-171 (11)* 74.75 63.45
Set, never hinged 170.00

Nos. 161-171 have the overprint in heavier type than Nos. 149-160 and "IV" in Roman instead of sans-serif numerals.

The overprint exists inverted or double on almost all values.

Venetian Ship — A16

Roman Arch — A17

St. Vitus — A18

Rostral Column — A19

**1923, Mar. 23** *Perf. 11½*

**Pale Buff Background**

**172** A16 5c blue green 2.40 2.40
**173** A16 10c violet 2.40 2.40
**174** A16 15c brown 2.40 2.40
**175** A17 20c orange red 2.40 2.40
**176** A17 25c dark gray 2.40 2.40
**177** A17 30c dark green 2.40 2.40
**178** A18 50c dull blue 2.40 2.40
**179** A18 60c rose 4.00 *4.00*
**180** A18 1 l dark blue 4.00 *4.00*
**181** A19 2 l violet brown 65.00 20.00
**182** A19 3 l olive bister 55.00 45.00
**183** A19 5 l yellow brown 55.00 52.50
*Nos. 172-183 (12)* 199.80 142.30
Set, never hinged 465.00

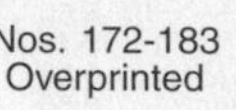
Nos. 172-183 Overprinted

**1924, Feb. 22**

**Pale Buff Background**

**184** A16 5c blue green 2.40 *12.00*
*a.* Inverted overprint 20.00 *40.00*
*b.* Double overprint 130.00
**185** A16 10c violet 2.40 *12.00*
*a.* Inverted overprint 16.00 *40.00*
**186** A16 15c brown 2.40 *12.00*
*a.* Inverted overprint 17.00 *40.00*
**187** A17 20c orange red 2.40 *12.00*
*a.* Inverted overprint 21.00 *40.00*
*b.* Double overprint 260.00
**188** A17 25c dk gray 2.40 *12.00*
**189** A17 30c dk green 2.40 *12.00*
*a.* Inverted overprint 42.50
**190** A18 50c dull blue 2.40 *12.00*
*a.* Inverted overprint 42.50 42.50
**191** A18 60c red 2.40 *12.00*
*a.* Inverted overprint 87.50
**192** A18 1 l dark blue 2.40 *12.00*
*a.* Inverted overprint 21.00 *40.00*
**193** A19 2 l violet brown 4.00 *32.50*
*a.* Inverted overprint 130.00 *160.00*
**194** A19 3 l olive 6.00 *40.00*
**195** A19 5 l yellow brown 6.00 *40.00*
*Nos. 184-195 (12)* 37.60 *220.50*
Set, never hinged 80.00

The overprint exists inverted on almost all values.

Nos. 172-183 Overprinted

**1924, Mar. 1**

**Pale Buff Background**

**196** A16 5c blue green 2.40 *20.00*
**197** A16 10c violet 2.40 *20.00*
**198** A16 15c brown 2.40 *20.00*
**199** A17 20c orange red 2.40 *20.00*
**200** A17 25c dark gray 2.40 *20.00*
**201** A17 30c dark green 2.40 *20.00*
**202** A18 50c dull blue 2.40 *20.00*
**203** A18 60c red 2.40 *20.00*
**204** A18 1 l dark blue 2.40 *20.00*
**205** A19 2 l violet brown 4.00 *27.50*
**206** A19 3 l olive 4.00 *27.50*
**207** A19 5 l yellow brown 4.00 *27.50*
*Nos. 196-207 (12)* 33.60 *262.50*
Set, never hinged 62.50

Postage stamps of Fiume were superseded by stamps of Italy.

## SEMI-POSTAL STAMPS

Semi-Postal Stamps of Hungary, 1916-17 Overprinted

**1918, Dec. 2** **Wmk. 137** *Perf. 15*

**B1** SP3 10f + 2f rose 8.00 8.00
*a.* Inverted overprint 72.50 40.00
*b.* Double overprint 240.00 120.00
**B2** SP4 15f + 2f dl vio 8.00 8.00
*a.* Inverted overprint 145.00 40.00
*b.* Double overprint 145.00 47.50
**B3** SP5 40f + 2f brn car 14.50 8.00
*a.* Inverted overprint 87.50 37.50
*Nos. B1-B3 (3)* 30.50 24.00
Set, never hinged 72.50

Examples of Nos. B1-B3 with overprint handstamped sell for higher prices.

Statue of Romulus and Remus Being Suckled by Wolf — SP6

Venetian Galley — SP7

Church of St. Mark's, Venice — SP8

*Perf. 11½*

**1919, May 18** **Unwmk.** **Typo.**

**B4** SP6 5c +5 l bl grn 47.50 32.50
**B5** SP6 10c +5 l rose 47.50 32.50
**B6** SP6 15c +5 l dk gray 47.50 32.50
**B7** SP6 20c +5 l orange 47.50 32.50
**B8** SP7 45c +5 l ol grn 47.50 32.50
**B9** SP7 60c +5 l car rose 47.50 32.50
**B10** SP7 80c +5 l lilac 47.50 32.50
**B11** SP7 1cor +5 l dk slate 47.50 32.50
**B12** SP8 2cor +5 l red brn 47.50 32.50
**B13** SP8 3cor +5 l blk brn 47.50 32.50
**B14** SP8 5cor +5 l yel brn 47.50 32.50
**B15** SP8 10cor +5 l dk vio 47.50 32.50
*Nos. B4-B15 (12)* 570.00 390.00
Set, never hinged 1,450.

200th day of peace. The surtax aided Fiume students in Italy. "Posta di Fiume" is printed on the back of Nos. B4-B16.

The surtax is shown on the stamps as "LIRE 5" but actually was 5cor.

For surcharges and overprints see Nos. 73-76, 78-85, 149-171, J15-J26.

Dr. Antonio Grossich — SP9

**1919, Sept. 20**

**B16** SP9 25c + 2 l blue 3.25 3.25
Never hinged 8.00

Surtax for the Dr. Grossich Foundation. For overprint and surcharge, see No. 77.

## SPECIAL DELIVERY STAMPS

1916 Special Delivery Stamp of Hungary Overprinted

**1918, Dec. 2** **Wmk. 137** *Perf. 15*

**Typographed Overprint**

**E1** SD1 2f gray green & red 4.75 4.75
Never hinged 12.00
*a.* Double overprint 190.00 175.00

Handstamped overprints sell for more.

SD3

*Perf. 11½*

**1920, Sept. 12** **Unwmk.** **Typo.**

**E2** SD3 30c slate blue 25.00 25.00
**E3** SD3 50c rose 25.00 25.00
Set, never hinged 125.00

For overprints see Nos. E10-E11.

Nos. 102 and 100 Surcharged

**1920, Nov.**

**E4** A12 30c on 20c brn org 190.00 175.00
*a.* Inverted overprint 625.00
*b.* Double overprint 625.00
**E5** A12 50c on 5c green 290.00 125.00
*a.* Inverted overprint 1,000.
*b.* Double overprint 1,000.
*c.* Double overprint, one inverted 1,100.

Nos. E4-E5 have a backprint.

**Same Surcharge as on Nos. 124, 122**

**E6** A12 30c on 20c brn org 275.00 180.00
**E7** A12 50c on 5c green 210.00 180.00
*a.* Double overprint 950.00

Overprint on Nos. E6-E7 is 11mm wide.

**Same Surcharge as on Nos. 130, 128**

**E8** A12 30c on 20c brn org 275.00 180.00
**E9** A12 50c on 5c green 210.00 180.00
*a.* Double overprint 950.00 950.00
*Nos. E4-E9 (6)* 1,450. 1,020.
Set, never hinged 2,900.

Overprint on Nos. E8-E9 is 17mm wide.

**Nos. E2 and E3 Overprinted**

**1921, Feb. 2**

**E10** SD3 30c slate blue 11.00 12.00
*a.* Inverted overprint 120.00 120.00
*b.* Double overprint 40.00 40.00
**E11** SD3 50c rose 15.00 12.00
*a.* Inverted overprint 27.50 27.50
*b.* Double overprint 105.00 105.00
Set, never hinged 62.50

Fiume in 16th Century SD4

**1923, Mar. 23** *Perf. 11, 11½*

**E12** SD4 60c rose & buff 24.00 24.00
**E13** SD4 2 l dk bl & buff 24.00 24.00
Set, never hinged 120.00

**Nos. E12-E13 Overprinted**

**1924, Feb. 22**

**E14** SD4 60c car & buff 3.25 *20.00*
**E15** SD4 2 l dk bl & buff 3.25 *20.00*
*a.* Inverted overprint 130.00 *160.00*
Set, never hinged 16.00

**Nos. E12-E13 Overprinted**

**1924, Mar. 1**

**E16** SD4 60c car & buff 4.00 *80.00*
**E17** SD4 2 l dk bl & buff 4.00 *80.00*
Set, never hinged 20.00

## POSTAGE DUE STAMPS

Postage Due Stamps of Hungary, 1915-1916, Overprinted

**1918, Dec.** **Wmk. 137** *Perf. 15*

*J1c* D1 6f green & black 190.00 105.00
*d.* Double overprint — 1,450.
*J2c* D1 12f green & black 180.00 72.50
*d.* Double overprint 1,450.
*J3c* D1 50c green & black 65.00 35.00
*d.* Double overprint 1,450.

*J4c* D1 1f green & red 40.00 24.00
*d.* Inverted overprint 425.00
*e.* Double overprint 525.00 190.00
**J5** D1 2f green & red 6.50 6.50
*a.* Inverted overprint 52.50 45.00
*b.* Double overprint 175.00
*J6c* D1 5f green & red 40.00 47.50
*d.* Inverted overprint 320.00 440.00
*e.* Double overprint 525.00 525.00
**J7** D1 6f green & red 6.50 6.50
*a.* Inverted overprint 25.00 25.00
*b.* Double overprint 27.50
*J8c* D1 10f green & red 32.50 32.50
*d.* Inverted overprint 475.00 475.00
**J9** D1 12f green & red 6.50 6.50
*J10c* D1 15f green & red 32.50 32.50
*d.* Inverted overprint 800.00
*e.* Double overprint 440.00 440.00
**J11** D1 20f green & red 6.50 6.50
*a.* Double overprint 45.00 32.50
*J12c* D1 30f green & red 32.50 32.50
*d.* Inverted overprint 900.00
*e.* Double overprint 950.00 950.00
*Nos. J1c-J12 (12)* 638.50 407.50
Set, never hinged 1,275.

Overprint was applied by press or handstamp. Six minor varieties of the handstamp exist. Some are sought by specialists at much higher values. Excellent forgeries exist. For more detailed listings, see *Scott Classic Specialized Catalogue of Stamps and Covers 1840-1940.*

Eagle — D2

*Perf. 11½*

**1919, July 28** **Unwmk.** **Typo.**

**J13** D2 2c brown 2.40 2.40
**J14** D2 5c brown 2.40 2.40
Set, never hinged 12.00

Semi-Postal Stamps of 1919 Overprinted and Surcharged

**1921, Mar. 21**

| | | | | |
|---|---|---|---|---|
| **J15** | SP6 | 2c on 15c gray | 6.50 | 6.50 |
| **J16** | SP6 | 4c on 10c rose | 4.75 | 4.75 |
| **J17** | SP9 | 5c on 25c blue | 4.75 | 4.75 |
| **J18** | SP6 | 6c on 20c orange | 4.75 | 4.75 |
| **J19** | SP6 | 10c on 20c orange | 6.50 | 6.50 |

Nos. B8-B11 Surcharged

| | | | | |
|---|---|---|---|---|
| **J20** | SP7 | 20c on 45c olive grn | 2.40 | *4.75* |
| **J21** | SP7 | 30c on 1cor dk slate | 12.00 | *12.00* |
| **J22** | SP7 | 40c on 80c violet | 4.75 | *6.50* |
| **J23** | SP7 | 50c on 60c carmine | 4.75 | *6.50* |
| **J24** | SP7 | 60c on 45c olive grn | 2.40 | *4.75* |
| **J25** | SP7 | 80c on 45c olive grn | 2.40 | *4.75* |

**Surcharged like Nos. J15-J19**

| | | | | |
|---|---|---|---|---|
| **J26** | SP8 | 1 l on 2cor red brown | 24.00 | *24.00* |
| | | *Nos. J15-J26 (12)* | 79.95 | *90.50* |
| | | Set, never hinged | 190.00 | |

See note below No. 85 regarding settings of "Valore Globale" overprint.

## NEWSPAPER STAMPS

**Newspaper Stamp of Hungary, 1914, Overprinted like Nos. 1-23**

**1918, Dec. 2 Wmk. 137 *Imperf.***

| | | | | |
|---|---|---|---|---|
| **P1** | N5 (2f) orange | | 4.75 | 3.25 |
| | Never hinged | | 15.00 | |
| *a.* | Inverted overprint | | 55.00 | 52.50 |
| *b.* | Double overprint | | 210.00 | 190.00 |

Handstamped overprints sell for more.

Eagle
N1

**1919 Unwmk. *Perf. 11½***

| | | | |
|---|---|---|---|
| **P2** | N1 2c deep buff | 9.50 | *14.50* |

**Re-engraved**

| | | | |
|---|---|---|---|
| **P3** | N1 2c deep buff | 9.50 | *14.50* |
| | Set, never hinged | 48.00 | |

In the re-engraved stamp the top of the "2" is rounder and broader, the feet of the eagle show clearly and the diamond at bottom has six lines instead of five.

Steamer — N2

**1920, Sept. 12**

| | | | |
|---|---|---|---|
| **P4** | N2 1c gray green | 4.00 | 3.25 |
| | Never hinged | 10.00 | |
| *a.* | Imperf | 24.00 | 24.00 |

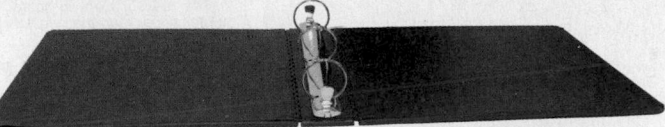

# FRANCE

ˈfran(t)s

LOCATION — Western Europe
GOVT. — Republic
AREA — 210,033 sq. mi.
POP. — 58,978,172 (1999 est.)
CAPITAL — Paris

100 Centimes = 1 Franc
100 Cents = 1 Euro (2002)

**Catalogue values for unused stamps in this country are for Never Hinged items, beginning with Scott 299 in the regular postage section, Scott B42 in the semi-postal section, Scott C18 in the airpost section, Scott CB1 in the airpost semi-postal section, Scott J69 in the postage due section, Scott M10 in the military stamps section, Scott 1O1 in the section for official stamps for the Council of Europe, Scott 2O1 for the section for UNESCO, Scott S1 for franchise stamps, Scott N27 for occupation stamps, and Scott 2N1 for AMG stamps.**

### Watermarks

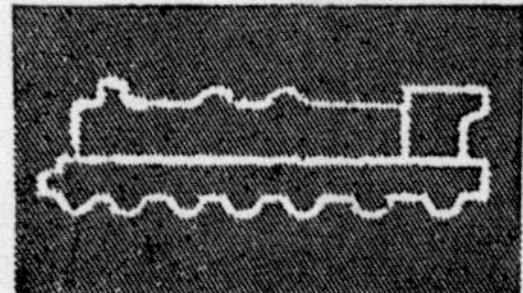

Wmk. 407

Ceres — A1

**FORTY CENTIMES**

40 Type I — 40 Type II

**1849-50 Typo. Unwmk. *Imperf.***

1 A1 10c bis, *yelsh* ('50) 1,500. 210.00
  a. 10c dark bister, *yelsh* 1,825. 240.00
  b. 10c greenish bister 2,350. 600.00
  d. As #1, tête beche pair *85,000.* *18,000.*
2 A1 15c green, *grnsh* 21,500. 800.00
  a. 15c yellow green, *grnsh* 20,000. 700.00
  c. Tête bêche pair —
3 A1 20c blk, *yelsh* 340.00 34.00
  a. 20c black 375.00 50.00
  b. 20c black, *buff* 1,100. 135.00
  c. Tête bêche pair *9,250.* *6,500.*
4 A1 20c dark blue *2,400.*
  a. 20c blue, *bluish* *2,050.*
  b. 20c blue, *yelsh* *2,750.*
  c. Tête bêche pair *60,000.*
6 A1 25c lt bl, *bluish* 5,400. 30.00
  a. 25c blue, *bluish* ('50) 5,400. 30.00
  b. 25c blue, *yelsh* 6,250. 40.00
  c. Tête bêche pair *155,000.* *12,500.*
7 A1 40c org, *yelsh* (I) ('50) 2,950. 360.00
  a. 40c org ver, *yelsh* (I) 3,500. 475.00
  b. 40c orange, *yelsh* (II) 20,750. 5,250.
  c. Pair, types I and II *31,000.* *12,500.*
  g. Vertical half used as 20c on cover *260,000.*
8 A1 1fr vermilion, *yelsh* *92,500.* *13,750.*
  a. 1fr dull orange red *95,000.* *17,000.*
  c. 1fr pale ver ("Vervelle") *20,000.*
  d. As "c," tête bêche pair *450,000.*
9 A1 1fr light carmine 8,750. 650.00
  a. Tête bêche pair *200,000.* *23,250.*
  b. 1fr brown carmine 10,000. 800.00
  c. 1fr dark carmine, *yelsh* 12,250. 1,075.

No. 4 was printed but not yet gummed when the rate change to 25c made them unnecessary. An essay with a red "25" surcharge on No. 4 was rejected.

An ungummed sheet of No. 8c was found in 1895 among the effects of Anatole A. Hulot, the printer. It was sold to Ernest Vervelle, a Parisian dealer, by whose name the stamps are known.

See Nos. 329-329e, 612-613, 624.

**Nos. 1, 4a, 6a, 7 and 13 are of similar designs and colors to French Colonies Nos. 9, 11, 12, 14, and 8. There are numerous shades of each. Identification by those who are not experts can be difficult, though cancellations can be used as a guide for used stamps.**

**Because of the date of issue the Colonies stamps are similar in shades and papers to the perforated French stamps, Nos. 23a, 54, 57-59, and are not as clearly printed. Except for No. 13, unused, the French Colonies stamps sell for much less than the values shown here for properly identified French versions.**

**Expertization of these stamps is recommended.**

**1862 Re-issue**

1g A1 10c bister 435.
2d A1 15c yellow green 560.
3d A1 20c black, *yellowish* 375.
4d A1 20c blue 340.
6d A1 25c blue 400.
7d A1 40c orange (I) 575.
7e A1 40c orange (II) *11,000.*
  h. Pair, types I and II *15,000.*
9d A1 1fr pale lake 600.

*The re-issues are fine impressions in lighter colors and on whiter paper than the originals. An official imitation of the essay, 25c on 20c blue, also in a lighter shade and on whiter paper, was made at the same time as the re-issues.*

President Louis Napoleon — A2

**1852**

10 A2 10c pale bister, *yelsh* *30,000.* 450.00
  a. 10c dark bister, *yelsh* *30,000.* 525.00
11 A2 25c blue, *bluish* *2,450.* 32.50
  b. 25c dark blue, *bluish* *2,900.* 50.00

**1862 Re-issue**

10b A2 10c bister 525.00
11a A2 25c blue 350.00

*The re-issues are in lighter colors and on whiter paper than the originals.*

Emperor Napoleon III — A3

Die I. The curl above the forehead directly below "R" of "EMPIRE" is made up of two lines very close together, often appearing to form a single thick line. There is no shading across the neck.

Die II. The curl is made of two distinct, more widely separated lines. There are lines of shading across the upper neck.

**1853-60 *Imperf.***

12 A3 1c ol grn, *pale bl* ('60) 165.00 62.50
  a. 1c bronze grn, *pale bluish* 155.00 67.50
13 A3 5c grn, *grnsh* (I) ('54) 630.00 62.50
14 A3 10c bis, *yelsh* (I) 360.00 6.50
  a. 10c yellow, *yelsh* (I) 1,200. 27.50
  b. 10c bister brn, *yelsh* (I) 450.00 18.50
  c. 10c bister, *yelsh* (II) ('60) 450.00 19.00
15 A3 20c bl, *bluish* (I) ('54) 150.00 1.35
  a. 20c dark bl, *bluish* (I) 220.00 1.35
  b. 20c milky blue (I) 225.00 10.00
  c. 20c blue, *lilac* (I) 4,250. 62.50
  d. 20c blue, *bluish* (II) ('60) 285.00 4.00
  e. Half used as 10c on cover *16,000.*
  f. Tête bêche pair *155,000.*
16 A3 20c bl, *grnsh* (II) *5,250.* 150.00
  a. 20c blue, *greenish* (I) *4,250.* 100.00
17 A3 25c bl, *bluish* (I) 2,050. 165.00
18 A3 40c org, *yelsh* (I) 2,000. 10.00
  a. 40c org ver, *yellowish* *2,850.* 16.00
  b. Half used as 20c on cover *110,000.*
19 A3 80c lake, *yelsh* (I) ('54) 2,800. 40.00
  a. Tête bêche pair *340,000.* *22,000.*
  b. Half used as 40c on cover *50,000.*
20 A3 80c rose, *pnksh* (I) ('60) 1,875. 42.50
  a. Tête-bêche pair *49,500.* *10,000.*
21 A3 1fr lake, *yelsh* (I) *7,450.* *2,475.*
  a. Tête bêche pair *300,000.* *135,000.*

Most values of the 1853-60 issue are known privately rouletted, pin-perf., perf. 7 and percé en scie.

**1862 Re-issue**

17c A3 25c blue (I) 450.
19c A3 80c lake (I) 1,800.
21c A3 1fr lake (I) 1,500.
  d. Tête bêche pair *27,500.*

*The re-issues are in lighter colors and on whiter paper than the originals.*

**1862-71 *Perf. 14x13½***

22 A3 1c ol grn, *pale bl* (II) 140.00 30.00
  a. 1c bronze grn, *pale bl* (II) 140.00 35.00
  On cover 175.00
  On cover, single franking 325.00
23 A3 5c yel grn, *grnsh* (I) 190.00 10.00
  a. 5c deep green, *grnsh* (I) 225.00 12.50
24 A3 5c grn, *pale bl* ('71) (I) 1,800. 110.00
25 A3 10c bis, *yelsh* (II) 1,350. 3.75
  a. 10c yel brn, *yelsh* (II) 1,750. 8.50
26 A3 20c bl, *bluish* (II) 200.00 1.25
  a. Tête bêche pair (II) 4,000. 1,000.
27 A3 40c org, *yelsh* (I) 1,200. 6.50

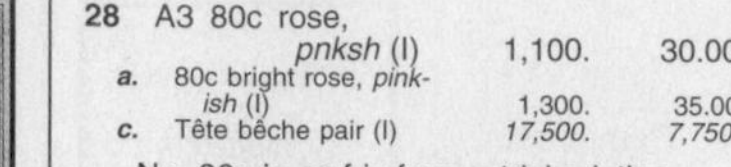

28 A3 80c rose, *pnksh* (I) 1,100. 30.00
  a. 80c bright rose, *pinkish* (I) 1,300. 35.00
  c. Tête bêche pair (I) *17,500.* *7,750.*

No. 26a imperf is from a trial printing.

A4 A5

Napoleon III — A6

**1863-70 *Perf. 14x13½***

29 A4 1c brnz grn, *pale bl* ('70) 37.50 16.00
  a. 1c olive green, *pale blue* 37.50 16.00
30 A4 2c red brn, *yelsh* 105.00 25.00
  b. Half used as 1c on cover *36,000.*
31 A4 4c gray 165.00 37.50
  a. Tete beche pair *17,500.* *11,000.*
  d. Half used as 2c on cover *50,000.*
32 A5 10c bis, *yelsh* ('67) 215.00 5.00
  c. Half used as 5c on cover with other stamps *3,750.*
33 A5 20c bl, *bluish* ('67) 175.00 1.55
  c. Half used as 10c on cover *62,500.*
  e. 20c dark blue ('67) 275.00 3.25
  No gum 140.00
  On cover, single franking 4.00
34 A5 30c brn, *yelsh* ('67) 625.00 12.50
  a. 30c dk brn, *yellowish* 1,000. 30.00
35 A5 40c pale org, *yelsh* 700.00 8.00
  a. 40c org, *yelsh* ('68) 700.00 8.00
  c. Half used as 20c on cover *35,000.*
36 A5 80c rose, *pnksh* ('68) 800.00 20.00
  a. 80c carmine, *yellowish* 950.00 24.00
  d. Half used as 40c on cover *42,500.*
  e. Quarter used as 20c on cover *50,000.*
37 A6 5fr gray lil, *lav* ('69) *6,000.* 750.00

**Values for blocks of 4**
**Original Issue Imperfs**

31c A4 4c gray 270.00 —
32b A5 10c bis, *yelsh* 360.00 —
33b A5 20c bl, *bluish* 270.00 —
36c A5 80c rose, *pnksh* — —
37b A6 5fr gray lil, *lav* *7,800.*

**Imperfs, "Rothschild" Re-issue**
**Paper Colors are the Same**

29b A4 1c olive green 1,050.
30a A4 2c pale red brown 200.00
31b A4 4c pale gray 185.00
32a A5 10c pale bister 160.00
33a A5 20c pale blue 250.00
34c A5 30c pale brown 190.00
35b A5 40c pale orange 225.00
36b A5 80c rose 400.00

*The re-issues constitute the "Rothschild Issue." These stamps were authorized exclusively for the banker to use on his correspondence. Used examples exist.*

Ceres

A7 A8

A9

A10

A11

### Bordeaux Issue

On the lithographed stamps, except for type I of the 20c, the shading on the cheek and neck is in lines or dashes, not in dots. On the typographed stamps the shading is in dots. The 2c, 5c, 10c and 20c (types II and III) occur in two or more types. The most easily distinguishable are:

2c — Type A. To the left of and within the top of the left "2" are lines of shading composed of dots.

2c — Type B. These lines of dots are replaced by solid lines.

5c — Type A. The head and hairline merge with the background of the medallion, without a distinct separation.

5c — Type B. A white line separates the contour of the head and hairline from the background of the medallion.

10c — Type A. The inner frame lines are of the same thickness as all other frame lines.

10c — Type B. The inner frame lines are much thicker than the others.

Three Types of the 20c.

A9 — The inscriptions in the upper and lower labels are small and there is quite a space between the upper label and the circle containing the head. There is also very little shading under the eye and in the neck.

A10 — The inscriptions in the labels are similar to those of the first type, the shading under the eye and in the neck is heavier and the upper label and circle almost touch.

A11 — The inscriptions in the labels are much larger than those of the two preceding types, and are similar to those of the other values of the same type in the set.

**1870-71 Litho. *Imperf.***

38 A7 1c ol grn, *pale bl* 125.00 1.00
a. 1c bronze green, *pale blue* 160.00 155.00
39 A7 2c red brn, *yelsh* (B) 225.00 225.00
a. 2c brick red, *yelsh* (B) 800.00 700.00
b. 2c chestnut, *yelsh* (B) 1,350. 700.00
c. 2c chocolate, *yelsh* (A) 750.00 700.00
40 A7 4c gray 250.00 200.00
41 A8 5c yel green, *greenish* (B) 250.00 160.00
a. 5c grn, *grnsh* (B) 325.00 175.00
b. 5c emerald, *greenish* (B) 3,500. 1,250.
c. 5c yellowish green, *greenish* (A) 2,400. 3,250.
42 A8 10c bis, *yelsh* (A) 825.00 60.00
a. 10c bister, *yellowish* (B) 825.00 90.00
43 A9 20c bl, *bluish* *21,500.* 550.00
a. 20c dark blue, *bluish* *25,000.* 725.00
44 A10 20c bl, *bluish* 950.00 45.00
a. 20c dark blue, *bluish* 1,150. 85.00
b. 20c ultra, *bluish* *20,000.* *3,100.*
45 A11 20c bl, *bluish* ('71) 825.00 16.00
a. 20c ultra, *bluish* 2,200. 675.00
46 A8 30c brn, *yelsh* 325.00 200.00
a. 30c blk brn, *yelsh* 1,750. 675.00
47 A8 40c org, *yelsh* 425.00 100.00
a. 40c yel orange, *yelsh* 1,250. 225.00
b. 40c red orange, *yelsh* 625.00 190.00
c. 40c scarlet, *yelsh* *1,250.* *675.00*
48 A8 80c rose, *pinkish* 600.00 250.00
a. 80c dull rose, *pinkish* 600.00 275.00

All values of the 1870 issue are known privately rouletted, pin-perf and perf. 14.

See Nos. 50-53.

A12

### Dark Blue Surcharge

**1871 Typo. *Perf. 14x13½***

49 A12 10c on 10c bister 1,400.
a. Pale blue surcharge 1,900.

No. 49 was never placed in use. Counterfeits exist.

A13

Two types of the 40c as in the 1849-50 issue.

**1870-73 Typo. *Perf. 14x13½***

50 A7 1c ol grn, *pale bl* 40.00 11.50
a. 1c bronze grn, *pale bl* ('72) 47.50 14.00
51 A7 2c red brn, *yelsh* ('70) 80.00 13.50
52 A7 4c gray ('70) 250.00 40.00
53 A7 5c yel grn, *pale bl* ('72) 150.00 7.50
a. 5c green 150.00 7.50
54 A13 10c bis, *yelsh* 540.00 55.00
a. Tête beche pair *5,500.* *2,250.*
b. Half used as 5c on cover *4,500.*
55 A13 10c bis, *rose* ('73) 265.00 9.50
a. Tête bêche pair 3,750. 1,750.
56 A13 15c bis, *yelsh* ('71) 300.00 4.50
a. Tête bêche pair *37,500.* *12,000.*
57 A13 20c dl bl, *bluish* 225.00 6.75
a. 20c bright blue, *bluish* 350.00 8.00
b. Tête bêche pair 3,750. 1,450.
c. Half used as 10c on cover *55,000.*
d. Quarter used as 5c on cover *52,500.*
58 A13 25c bl, *bluish* ('71) 110.00 1.10
a. 25c dk bl, *bluish* 135.00 1.10
b. Tête bêche pair *6,750.* *3,000.*
59 A13 40c org, *yelsh* (I) 475.00 6.00
a. 40c orange yel, *yelsh* (I) 575.00 9.00
b. 40c orange, *yelsh* (II) 3,150. 130.00
c. 40c orange yel, *yelsh* (II) 3,150. 130.00
d. Pair, types I and II *6,500.* 525.00
f. Half used as 20c on circular *20,000.*
g. Half used as 20c on cover *40,000.*

No. 58 exists in three main plate varieties, differing in one or another of the flower-like corner ornaments.

Margins on this issue are extremely small.

*Nos. 54, 57 and 58 were reprinted imperf. in 1887. See note after No. 37.*

### Imperf.

*50b A7 1c 270.00*
*51a A7 2c 350.00*
*52a A7 4c 450.00*
*53b A7 5c yel grn, pale bl 260.00*
*55b A13 10c 350.00*
*56b A13 15c 375.00*

A14

**1872-75 *Perf. 14x13½***

### Larger Numerals

60 A14 10c bis, *rose* ('75) 325.00 11.00
a. Cliché of 15c in plate of 10c *3,750.* *4,250.*
b. Pair, #60, 60a *6,750.* *8,500.*
61 A14 15c bister ('73) 320.00 3.25
62 A14 30c brn, *yelsh* 550.00 5.25
63 A14 80c rose, *pnksh* 640.00 11.50

### Imperf.

*62a A14 30c 475.00*
*63a A14 80c 650.00*

Peace and Commerce ("Type Sage") — A15

Type I. The "N" of "INV" is under the "B" of "REPUBLIQUE."

Type II. The "N" of "INV" is under the "U" of "REPUBLIQUE."

### Type I

**1876-78 *Perf. 14x13½***

64 A15 1c grn, *grnsh* 125.00 70.00
65 A15 2c grn, *grnsh* 1,425. 240.00
66 A15 4c grn, *grnsh* 145.00 55.00
67 A15 5c grn, *grnsh* 650.00 45.00
68 A15 10c grn, *grnsh* 800.00 21.00
69 A15 15c gray lil, *grysh* 800.00 17.50
70 A15 20c red brn, *straw* 575.00 17.50
71 A15 20c bl, *bluish* *27,500.*
72 A15 25c ultra, *bluish* *7,750.* 55.00
73 A15 30c brn, *yelsh* 425.00 8.25
74 A15 40c red, *straw* ('78) 600.00 35.00
75 A15 75c car, *rose* 950.00 12.50
76 A15 1fr brnz grn, *straw* 925.00 10.00

No. 71 was never put into use.

*The reprints of No. 71 are type II. They are imperforate or with forged perforation.*

For overprints and surcharges see Offices in China Nos. 1-17, J7-J10, J20-J22, Offices in Egypt, Alexandria 1-15, Port Said 1-17, Offices in Turkish Empire 1-7, Cavalle 1-8, Dedeagh 1-8, Port Lagos 1-5, Vathy 1-9, Offices in Zanzibar 1-33, 50-54, French Morocco 1-8, and Madagascar 14-27.

### Imperf.

*64a A15 1c 150.00*
*65a A15 2c 1,000.*
*66a A15 4c 160.00*
*67a A15 5c 525.00*
*68a A15 10c 575.00*
*69a A15 15c 575.00*
*70a A15 20c 375.00*
*73a A15 30c 275.00*
*74a A15 40c 250.00*
*75a A15 75c 550.00*
*76a A15 1fr 400.00*

Beware of French Colonies Nos. 24-29.

### Type II

**1876-77 *Perf. 14x13½***

77 A15 2c grn, *grnsh* 115.00 19.00
78 A15 5c grn, *grnsh* 25.00 .60
a. Imperf. 175.00
79 A15 10c grn, *grnsh* 1,100. 240.00
80 A15 15c gray lil, *grysh* 675.00 1.90
81 A15 25c ultra, *bluish* 425.00 1.00
a. 25c blue, *bluish* 475.00 1.50
b. Pair, types I & II *60,000.* *17,500.*
c. Imperf. 325.00
82 A15 30c yel brn, *yelsh* 82.50 1.40
a. 30c brown, *yellowish* 90.00 1.40
b. Imperf. 525.00
83 A15 75c car, *rose* ('77) 1,775. 110.00
84 A15 1fr brnz grn, *straw* ('77) 145.00 7.50
a. Imperf. 1,100.

Beware of French Colonies Nos. 31, 35.

**1877-80**

86 A15 1c blk, *lil bl* 3.75 1.65
a. 1c black, *gray blue* 3.75 1.65
b. Imperf. 75.00
87 A15 1c blk, *Prus bl* ('80) *11,000.* *4,350.*

Values for No. 87 are for examples with the perfs touching the design on at least one side.

88 A15 2c brn, *straw* 4.50 1.90
a. 2c brown, *yellow* 4.50 1.90
b. Imperf. 210.00
89 A15 3c yel, *straw* ('78) 200.00 42.50
a. Imperf. 150.00
90 A15 4c claret, *lav* 5.00 1.90
a. 4c vio brown, *lavender* 8.25 4.50
b. Imperf. 60.00
91 A15 10c blk, *lavender* 35.00 1.00
a. 10c black, *rose lilac* 37.50 1.00
b. 10c black, *lilac* 37.50 1.00
c. Imperf. 70.00
92 A15 15c blue ('78) 22.50 .60
a. Imperf. 95.00
b. 15c blue, *bluish* 435.00 15.00
93 A15 25c blk, *red* ('78) 1,075. 25.00
a. Imperf. 675.00
94 A15 35c blk, *yel* ('78) 525.00 35.00
a. 35c blk, *yel org* 525.00 35.00
b. Imperf. 250.00
95 A15 40c red, *straw* ('80) 90.00 2.10
a. Imperf. 240.00
96 A15 5fr vio, *lav* 440.00 70.00
a. As #96, imperf. 750.00
b. 5fr red lilac, *lavender* 650.00 100.00

Beware of French Colonies Nos. 38-40, 42, 44.

**1879-90**

97 A15 3c gray, *grysh* ('80) 3.00 1.65
a. Imperf. 67.50
98 A15 20c red, *yel grn* 37.50 4.25
a. 20c red, *deep green* ('84) 72.50 6.00
b. Imperf. 100.00
99 A15 25c yel, *straw* 340.00 5.00
a. Imperf. 250.00
100 A15 25c blk, *pale rose* ('86) 72.50 1.00
a. Imperf. 155.00
101 A15 50c rose, *rose* ('90) 210.00 2.65
a. 50c carmine, *rose* 225.00 3.50
102 A15 75c dp vio, *org* ('90) 215.00 35.00
a. 75c deep violet, *yellow* 265.00 45.00
*Nos. 97-102 (6)* 878.00 49.55

Beware of French Colonies No. 43.

**1892 Quadrille Paper**

103 A15 15c blue 12.50 .35
a. Imperf. 175.00

**1898-1900 Ordinary Paper**

104 A15 5c yel grn 16.00 1.30
a. Imperf. 82.50

### Type I

105 A15 5c yel grn 14.00 1.30
a. Imperf. 575.00
106 A15 10c blk, *lavender* 21.00 2.50
a. Imperf. 275.00
107 A15 50c car, *rose* 200.00 30.00
108 A15 2fr brn, *azure* ('00) 110.00 40.00
b. Imperf. 2,250.
*Nos. 104-108 (5)* 361.00 75.10

See No. 226.

*Reprints of A15, type II, were made in 1887 and left imperf. See note after No. 37. Value for set of 27, $4,000.*

Liberty, Equality, Fraternity
A16

"The Rights of Man"
A17

Liberty and Peace
A18

**1900-29 *Perf. 14x13½***

109 A16 1c gray .55 .40
110 A16 2c violet brn .70 .25
111 A16 3c orange .45 .45
a. 3c red 19.00 7.50
112 A16 4c yellow brn 3.00 1.60
113 A16 5c green 2.00 .35
b. Booklet pane of 10 330.00
114 A16 7½c lilac ('26) .60 .45
115 A16 10c lilac ('29) 4.00 .60
116 A17 10c carmine 25.00 1.50
a. Numerals printed separately 24.00 10.00
117 A17 15c orange 8.00 .60
118 A17 20c brown vio 55.00 9.25
119 A17 25c blue 125.00 1.65
a. Numerals printed separately 115.00 9.25
120 A17 30c violet 70.00 6.00
121 A18 40c red & pale bl 15.00 .85
122 A18 45c green & bl ('06) 29.00 2.10
123 A18 50c bis brn & gray 100.00 1.65
124 A18 60c vio & ultra ('20) 1.00 1.15

| | | | | |
|---|---|---|---|---|
| **125** | A18 | 1fr claret & ol grn | 26.50 | .85 |
| **126** | A18 | 2fr gray vio & yel | 625.00 | 75.00 |
| **127** | A18 | 2fr org & pale bl ('20) | 42.50 | .60 |
| **128** | A18 | 3fr vio & bl ('25) | 27.50 | 7.50 |
| **129** | A18 | 3fr brt vio & rose ('27) | 55.00 | 2.80 |
| **130** | A18 | 5fr dk bl & buff | 85.00 | 5.00 |
| **131** | A18 | 10fr grn & red ('26) | 125.00 | 17.00 |
| **132** | A18 | 20fr mag & grn ('26) | 200.00 | 37.50 |
| | | *Nos. 109-132 (24)* | 1,626. | 175.10 |

In the 10c and 25c values, the first printings show the numerals to have been impressed by a second operation, whereas, in later printings, the numerals were inserted in the plates. Two operations were used for all 20c and 30c, and one operation for the 15c.

No. 114 was issued precanceled only. Values for precanceled stamps in first column are for those which have not been through the post and have original gum. Values in the second column are for postally used, gumless stamps.

See Offices in China Nos. 34, 40-44, Offices in Crete 1-5, 10-15, Offices in Egypt, Alexandria 16-20, 26-30, 77, 84-86, Port Said 18-22, 28-32, 83, 90-92, Offices in Turkish Empire 21-26, 31-33, Cavalle 9, Dedeagh 9.

For overprints and surcharge see Nos. 197, 246, C1-C2, M1, P7. Offices in China 57, 62-65, 71, 73, 75, 83-85, J14, J27, Offices in Crete 17-20, Offices in Egypt, Alexandria 31-32, 34-35, 40-48, 57-64, 66, 71-73, Port Said 33, 35-40, 43, 46-57, 59, 65-71, 73, 78-80, Offices in Turkish Empire 35-38, 47-49, Cavalle 13-15, Dedeagh 16-18, Offices in Zanzibar 39, 45-49, 55, Offices in Morocco 11-15, 20-22, 26-29, 35-41, 49-54, 72-76, 84-85, 87-89, B6.

### Imperf.

| | | | | | |
|---|---|---|---|---|---|
| *109a* | A16 | 1c | | 55.00 | |
| *110a* | A16 | 2c | | 67.50 | 60.00 |
| *111b* | A16 | 3c | | 55.00 | |
| *112a* | A16 | 4c | | 150.00 | |
| *113a* | A16 | 5c | | 75.00 | |
| *116b* | A17 | 10c | #116 or 116a | 235.00 | *135.00* |
| *117a* | A17 | 15c | | 190.00 | *165.00* |
| *119b* | A17 | 25c | #119 or 119a | 500.00 | |
| *121a* | A18 | 40c | | 190.00 | *155.00* |
| *122a* | A18 | 45c | | 260.00 | |
| *123a* | A18 | 50c | | 375.00 | *375.00* |
| *124a* | A18 | 60c | | 525.00 | |
| *125a* | A18 | 1fr | | 250.00 | *225.00* |
| *126a* | A18 | 2fr | No gum | *1,300.* | |
| *127a* | A18 | 2fr | | 475.00 | |
| *128a* | A18 | 3fr | | *725.00* | 500.00 |
| *129a* | A18 | 3fr | | 425.00 | |
| *130a* | A18 | 5fr | | 950.00 | |

Flat Plate & Rotary Press

The following stamps were printed by both flat plate and rotary press: Nos. 109-113, 144-146, 163, 166, 168, 170, 175, 177-178, 185, 192 and P7.

"Rights of Man" — A19

### 1902

| | | | | |
|---|---|---|---|---|
| **133** | A19 | 10c rose red | 32.50 | .90 |
| **134** | A19 | 15c pale red | 11.00 | .60 |
| **135** | A19 | 20c brown violet | 82.50 | 14.00 |
| **136** | A19 | 25c blue | 100.00 | 2.25 |
| **137** | A19 | 30c lilac | 250.00 | 14.50 |
| | | *Nos. 133-137 (5)* | 476.00 | 32.25 |

### Imperf.

| | | | | |
|---|---|---|---|---|
| *133a* | A19 | 10c rose red | 450.00 | *275.00* |
| *134a* | A19 | 15c pale red | 450.00 | *325.00* |
| *135a* | A19 | 20c brown violet | 800.00 | *475.00* |
| *136a* | A19 | 25c blue | 950.00 | *625.00* |
| *137a* | A19 | 30c lilac | *1,100.* | 675.00 |

See Offices in China Nos. 35-39, Offices in Crete 6-10, Offices in Egypt, Alexandria 21-25, 81-82, Port Said 23-27, 87-88, Offices in Turkish Empire 26-30, Cavalle 10-11, Dedeagh 10-11.

For overprints and surcharges see Nos. M2, Offices in China 45, 58-61, 66-70, 76-82, J15-J16, J28-J30, Offices in Crete 16, Offices in Egypt, Alexandria 33, 36-39, 49-50, 52-56, 65, 67-70, B1-B4, Port Said 34, 41-42, 44-45, 57, 60-64, 77, 74-77, B1-B4, Offices in Turkish Empire 34, 39, Cavalle 12, Dedeagh 15, Offices in Zanzibar 40-44, 56-59, Offices in Morocco 16-19, 30-34, 42-48, 77-83, 86, B1-B5, B7, B9.

Sower — A20

### 1903-38

| | | | | |
|---|---|---|---|---|
| **138** | A20 | 10c rose | 8.00 | .40 |
| **139** | A20 | 15c slate grn | 4.00 | .25 |
| *b.* | | Booklet pane of 10 | 450.00 | |
| **140** | A20 | 20c violet brn | 67.50 | 1.90 |
| **141** | A20 | 25c dull blue | 75.00 | 1.40 |
| **142** | A20 | 30c violet | 175.00 | 5.25 |
| **143** | A20 | 45c lt violet ('26) | 6.00 | 1.90 |
| **144** | A20 | 50c dull blue ('21) | 27.50 | 1.90 |
| **145** | A20 | 50c gray grn ('26) | 6.25 | 1.25 |
| **146** | A20 | 50c vermilion ('26) | 1.25 | .25 |
| *a.* | | Booklet pane of 10 | 40.00 | |
| **147** | A20 | 50c grnsh bl ('38) | 1.00 | .35 |
| **148** | A20 | 60c lt vio ('24) | 6.25 | 2.10 |
| **149** | A20 | 65c rose ('24) | 3.00 | 1.75 |
| **150** | A20 | 65c gray grn ('27) | 6.50 | 2.10 |
| **151** | A20 | 75c rose lil ('26) | 5.25 | .60 |
| **152** | A20 | 80c ver ('25) | 26.50 | 9.50 |
| **153** | A20 | 85c ver ('24) | 13.50 | 3.25 |
| **154** | A20 | 1fr dull blue ('26) | 6.00 | .75 |
| | | *Nos. 138-154 (17)* | 438.50 | 34.40 |
| | | Set, never hinged | 940.00 | |

See Nos. 941, 942A. For surcharges and overprints see Nos. 229-230, 232-233, 236, 256, B25, B29, B32, B36, B40, M3-M4, M6, Offices in Turkish Empire 46, 54.

### Imperf.

| | | | | | |
|---|---|---|---|---|---|
| *138a* | A20 | 10c | | 175.00 | |
| *139a* | A20 | 15c | | 140.00 | 55.00 |
| *140a* | A20 | 20c | | 300.00 | 160.00 |
| *141a* | A20 | 25c | | 350.00 | |
| *142a* | A20 | 30c | | 625.00 | |
| *144a* | A20 | 50c | | 140.00 | |
| *145a* | A20 | 50c | | 125.00 | |
| *146b* | A20 | 50c | No gum | 70.00 | |
| *147a* | A20 | 50c | | 67.50 | |
| *149a* | A20 | 65c | | 300.00 | |
| *151a* | A20 | 75c | | 450.00 | |
| *154a* | A20 | 1fr | | *1,000.* | |

Ground — A21

### 1906, Apr. 13
### With Ground Under Feet of Figure

| | | | | |
|---|---|---|---|---|
| **155** | A21 | 10c red | 2.50 | 1.75 |
| *a.* | | Imperf., pair, no gum | 275.00 | 225.00 |
| | | As "a," with gum | 450.00 | |

No Ground — A22

TEN AND THIRTY-FIVE CENTIMES

Type I — Numerals and letters of the inscriptions thin.

Type II — Numerals and letters thicker.

### No Ground Under the Feet

### 1906-37

| | | | | |
|---|---|---|---|---|
| **156** | A22 | 1c olive bis ('33) | .25 | .30 |
| **157** | A22 | 2c dk green ('33) | .25 | .30 |
| **158** | A22 | 3c ver ('33) | .25 | .30 |
| **159** | A22 | 5c green ('07) | 1.50 | .25 |
| *a.* | | Imperf., pair | 40.00 | 30.00 |
| *b.* | | Booklet pane of 10 | 100.00 | |
| **160** | A22 | 5c orange ('21) | 1.25 | .30 |
| *a.* | | Booklet pane of 10 | 72.50 | |
| **161** | A22 | 5c cerise ('34) | .25 | .25 |
| **162** | A22 | 10c red (II) ('07) | 1.50 | .25 |
| *a.* | | Imperf., pair | 37.50 | 115.00 |
| *b.* | | 10c red (I) ('06) | 8.25 | 1.00 |
| *c.* | | As #162b, imperf., pair | 37.50 | 115.00 |
| *d.* | | Booklet pane of 10 (I) | 125.00 | |
| *e.* | | Booklet pane of 10 (II) | 75.00 | |
| *f.* | | Booklet pane of 6 (II) | 240.00 | |
| **163** | A22 | 10c grn (II) ('21) | 1.00 | .55 |
| *a.* | | 10c green (I) ('27) | 32.50 | 37.50 |
| *b.* | | Booklet pane of 10 (I, "Phena") | 350.00 | |
| *c.* | | Booklet pane of 10 (I, "Mineraline") | 3,200. | |
| **164** | A22 | 10c ultra ('32) | 1.40 | .25 |
| **165** | A22 | 15c red brn ('26) | .25 | .25 |
| *a.* | | Booklet pane of 10 | 27.50 | |
| **166** | A22 | 20c brown | 3.00 | .65 |
| *a.* | | Imperf., pair | 82.50 | 100.00 |
| *b.* | | 20c black brown | 6.00 | 2.00 |
| **167** | A22 | 20c red vio ('26) | .25 | .25 |
| *a.* | | Booklet pane of 10 | 7.50 | |
| **168** | A22 | 25c blue | 2.40 | .25 |
| *a.* | | Booklet pane of 10 | 37.50 | |
| *b.* | | Imperf, pair (dark blue) | 45.00 | 60.00 |
| **169** | A22 | 25c yel brown ('27) | .25 | .25 |
| *a.* | | 25c red brown | .30 | .25 |
| **170** | A22 | 30c orange | 13.50 | 1.40 |
| *a.* | | Imperf, pair | 200.00 | 175.00 |
| **171** | A22 | 30c red ('21) | 6.50 | 2.25 |
| **172** | A22 | 30c cerise ('25) | 1.25 | .80 |
| *a.* | | Booklet pane of 10 | 13.50 | |
| *b.* | | Imperf, pair | 575.00 | |
| **173** | A22 | 30c lt blue ('25) | 3.75 | .60 |
| *a.* | | Booklet pane of 10 | 35.00 | |
| *b.* | | Imperf, pair | 2,200. | |
| **174** | A22 | 30c cop red ('37) | .25 | .30 |
| *a.* | | Booklet pane of 10 | 9.00 | |
| **175** | A22 | 35c vio (II) ('07) | 8.25 | .90 |
| *a.* | | Imperf, pair | 150.00 | 120.00 |
| *b.* | | 35c violet (I) ('06) | 150.00 | 7.50 |
| *c.* | | As "b," Imperf, pair, no gum | *575.00* | |
| **176** | A22 | 35c grn ('37) | .50 | .55 |
| *a.* | | Imperf, pair | 750.00 | |
| **177** | A22 | 40c olive ('25) | 1.40 | .55 |
| *b.* | | Booklet pane of 10 | 30.00 | |
| **178** | A22 | 40c ver ('26) | 2.50 | .80 |
| *a.* | | Booklet pane of 10 | 25.00 | |
| **179** | A22 | 40c violet ('27) | 2.00 | .90 |
| **180** | A22 | 40c lt ultra ('28) | 1.25 | .50 |
| **181** | A22 | 1.05fr ver ('25) | 9.50 | 5.25 |
| **182** | A22 | 1.10fr cerise ('27) | 11.50 | 2.50 |
| **183** | A22 | 1.40fr cerise ('26) | 20.00 | 22.50 |
| **184** | A22 | 2fr Prus grn ('31) | 14.00 | 1.75 |
| | | *Nos. 156-184 (29)* | 109.95 | 45.95 |
| | | Set, never hinged | 225.00 | |

The 10c and 35c, type I, were slightly retouched by adding thin white outlines to the sack of grain, the underside of the right arm and the back of the skirt. It is difficult to distinguish the retouches except on clearly-printed copies. The white outlines were made stronger on the stamps of type II.

Stamps of types A16, A18, A20 and A22 were printed in 1916-20 on paper of poor quality, usually grayish and containing bits of fiber. This is called G. C. (Grande Consommation) paper.

Nos. 160, 162b, 163, 175b and 176 also exist imperf.

See Nos. 241-241b. For surcharges and overprint see Nos. 227-228, 234, 238, 240, 400, B1, B24, B28, B31, B35, B37, B39, B41, M5, P8, Offices in Turkish Empire 40-45, 52, 55.

Louis Pasteur — A23

### 1923-26

| | | | | |
|---|---|---|---|---|
| **185** | A23 | 10c green | .55 | .30 |
| *a.* | | Booklet pane of 10 | 15.00 | |
| **186** | A23 | 15c green ('24) | 1.40 | .30 |
| **187** | A23 | 20c green ('26) | 2.75 | .90 |
| **188** | A23 | 30c red | .90 | *1.50* |
| **189** | A23 | 30c green ('26) | .55 | .50 |
| **190** | A23 | 45c red ('24) | 1.90 | 2.10 |
| **191** | A23 | 50c blue | 4.50 | .50 |
| **192** | A23 | 75c blue ('24) | 3.75 | 1.00 |
| *a.* | | Imperf., pair | 250.00 | |
| **193** | A23 | 90c red ('26) | 11.00 | 3.50 |
| **194** | A23 | 1fr blue ('25) | 21.00 | .50 |
| **195** | A23 | 1.25fr blue ('26) | 25.00 | 8.00 |
| **196** | A23 | 1.50fr blue ('26) | 5.25 | .50 |
| | | *Nos. 185-196 (12)* | 78.55 | 19.60 |
| | | Set, never hinged | 150.00 | |

Nos. 185, 188 and 191 were issued to commemorate the cent. of the birth of Pasteur.

For surcharges and overprint see Nos. 231, 235, 257, B26, B30, B33, C4.

No. 125 Overprinted in Blue

### 1923, June 15

| | | | | |
|---|---|---|---|---|
| **197** | A18 | 1fr claret & ol grn | 440.00 | 500.00 |
| | | Never hinged | 825.00 | |

Allegory of Olympic Games at Paris A24

The Trophy A25

Milo of Crotona — A26

Victorious Athlete — A27

### 1924, Apr. 1 — *Perf. 14x13½, 13½x14*

| | | | | |
|---|---|---|---|---|
| **198** | A24 | 10c gray grn & yel grn | 2.25 | 1.25 |
| **199** | A25 | 25c rose & dk rose | 3.00 | .80 |
| **200** | A26 | 30c brn red & blk | 9.50 | 11.00 |
| **201** | A27 | 50c ultra & dk bl | 26.00 | 5.75 |
| | | *Nos. 198-201 (4)* | 40.75 | 18.80 |
| | | Set, never hinged | 125.00 | |

### Imperf Singles

| | | | | |
|---|---|---|---|---|
| *198a* | A24 | 10c | 1,000. | |
| *199a* | A25 | 25c | 1,000. | *725.* |
| *200a* | A26 | 30c | 1,000. | |
| *201a* | A27 | 50c | 1,000. | 1,000. |

8th Olympic Games, Paris.

Pierre de Ronsard (1524-85), Poet — A28

### 1924, Oct. 6 — *Perf. 14x13½*

| | | | | |
|---|---|---|---|---|
| **219** | A28 | 75c blue, *bluish* | 1.90 | 1.40 |
| | | Never hinged | 2.75 | |

"Light and Liberty" Allegory A29

Majolica Vase — A30

Potter Decorating Vase — A31

Terrace of Château A32

### 1924-25 — *Perf. 14x13½, 13½x14*

| | | | | |
|---|---|---|---|---|
| **220** | A29 | 10c dk grn & yel ('25) | .55 | .75 |
| **221** | A30 | 15c ind & grn ('25) | .55 | .85 |
| *a.* | | Imperf. | *400.00* | |
| | | Never hinged | *640.00* | |
| **222** | A31 | 25c vio brn & garnet | .80 | .50 |
| **223** | A32 | 25c gray bl & vio ('25) | 1.60 | .65 |
| *a.* | | Imperf. | *450.00* | 150.00 |
| | | Never hinged | *700.00* | |
| **224** | A31 | 75c indigo & ultra | 3.50 | 2.25 |
| **225** | A29 | 75c dk bl & lt bl ('25) | 18.00 | 6.50 |
| *a.* | | Imperf. | *375.00* | |
| | | Never hinged | *650.00* | |
| | | *Nos. 220-225 (6)* | 25.00 | 11.50 |
| | | Set, never hinged | 52.50 | |

Intl. Exhibition of Decorative Modern Arts at Paris, 1925.

### Philatelic Exhibition Issue
Souvenir Sheet

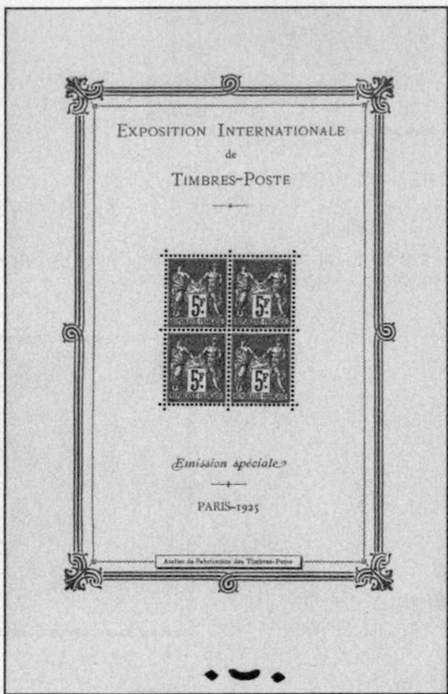


A32a

**1925, May 2** *Perf. 14x13½*

| No. | Type | Description | Unused | Used |
|---|---|---|---|---|
| **226** | A32a | Sheet of 4, A15 II | 1,100. | 1,100. |
| | | Never hinged | 3,750. | |
| *a.* | | Imperf. sheet | 5,000. | 1,750. |
| | | Never hinged | 7,750. | |
| *b.* | | 5fr carmine, perf. | 125.00 | 140.00 |
| | | Never hinged | 225.00 | |
| *c.* | | 5fr carmine, imperf. | 900.00 | |
| | | Never hinged | 1,325. | |

These were on sale only at the Intl. Phil. Exhib., Paris, May, 1925. Size: 140x220mm.

Nos. 148-149, 152-153, 173, 175, 181, 183, 192, 195 Surcharged

**1926-27**

| No. | Type | Description | Unused | Used |
|---|---|---|---|---|
| **227** | A22 | 25c on 30c lt bl | .25 | .50 |
| *a.* | | Pair, one without surcharge | 1,050. | 925.00 |
| **228** | A22 | 25c on 35c violet | .25 | .50 |
| *a.* | | Double surcharge | 525.00 | 350.00 |
| *b.* | | Pair, one without surcharge | 550.00 | *925.00* |
| **229** | A20 | 50c on 60c lt vio ('27) | 1.40 | 1.10 |
| *a.* | | Pair, one without surcharge | 525.00 | *925.00* |
| **230** | A20 | 50c on 65c rose ('27) | .75 | .55 |
| *a.* | | Inverted surcharge | *1,225.* | *1,400.* |
| *b.* | | Pair, one without surcharge | 675.00 | *925.00* |
| **231** | A23 | 50c on 75c blue | 3.25 | 1.50 |
| **232** | A20 | 50c on 80c ver ('27) | 1.25 | 1.10 |
| *a.* | | Pair, one without surcharge | 475.00 | *925.00* |
| **233** | A20 | 50c on 85c ver ('27) | 2.25 | 1.00 |
| **234** | A22 | 50c on 1.05fr ver | 1.25 | .75 |
| *a.* | | Pair, one without surcharge | 475.00 | *925.00* |
| **235** | A23 | 50c on 1.25fr blue | 2.75 | 2.25 |
| *a.* | | Pair, one without surcharge | 525.00 | *925.00* |
| **236** | A20 | 55c on 60c lt vio | 125.00 | 52.50 |
| **238** | A22 | 90c on 1.05fr ver ('27) | 2.25 | 2.75 |
| *a.* | | Pair, one without surcharge | *1,000.* | 925.00 |
| **240** | A22 | 1.10fr on 1.40fr cer | 1.00 | 1.10 |
| *a.* | | Pair, one without surcharge | 575.00 | *925.00* |
| | | *Nos. 227-240 (12)* | 141.65 | 65.60 |
| | | Set, never hinged | 275.00 | |

Issue dates: Nos. 229-230, 232 234, 1927.

No. 236 is known only precanceled. See second note after No. 132.

Nos. 229, 230, 234, 238 and 240 have three bars instead of two. The 55c surcharge has thinner, larger numerals and a rounded "c." Width, including bars, is 17mm, instead of 13mm.

The 55c was used only precanceled at the Magasins du Louvre department store in Paris, August 1926.

### Strasbourg Exhibition Issue
Souvenir Sheet

A32b

**1927, June 4**

| No. | Type | Description | Unused | Used |
|---|---|---|---|---|
| **241** | A32b | Sheet of 2 | 1,000. | 1,000. |
| | | Never hinged | 2,300. | |
| *a.* | | 5fr light ultra (A22) | 250.00 | 250.00 |
| | | Never hinged | 400.00 | |
| *b.* | | 10fr carmine rose (A22) | 250.00 | 250.00 |
| | | Never hinged | 400.00 | |

Sold at the Strasbourg Philatelic Exhibition as souvenirs. Size: 111x140mm.

Marcelin Berthelot (1827-1907), Chemist and Statesman — A33

**1927, Sept. 7**

| No. | Type | Description | Unused | Used |
|---|---|---|---|---|
| **242** | A33 | 90c dull rose | 1.90 | .60 |
| | | Never hinged | 3.00 | |

For surcharge see No. C3.

Lafayette, Washington, S. S. Paris and Airplane "Spirit of St. Louis" — A34

**1927, Sept. 15**

| No. | Type | Description | Unused | Used |
|---|---|---|---|---|
| **243** | A34 | 90c dull red | 1.25 | 1.75 |
| *a.* | | Value omitted | 2,000. | 1,725. |
| **244** | A34 | 1.50fr deep blue | 4.00 | 2.50 |
| *a.* | | Value omitted | 1,450. | |
| | | Set, never hinged | 10.00 | |

Visit of American Legionnaires to France, September, 1927. Exist imperf.

Joan of Arc — A35

**1929, Mar.**

| No. | Type | Description | Unused | Used |
|---|---|---|---|---|
| **245** | A35 | 50c dull blue | 1.90 | .25 |
| | | Never hinged | 2.75 | |
| *a.* | | Booklet pane of 10 | 50.00 | |
| *b.* | | Imperf. | 140.00 | |

500th anniv. of the relief of Orleans by the French forces led by Joan of Arc.

No. 127 Overprinted in Blue

**1929, May 18**

| No. | Type | Description | Unused | Used |
|---|---|---|---|---|
| **246** | A18 | 2fr org & pale bl | 600.00 | 600.00 |
| | | Never hinged | 1,325. | |

Sold exclusively at the Intl. Phil. Exhib., Le Havre, May, 1929, for 7fr, which included a 5fr admission ticket.

Excellent counterfeits of No. 246 exist.

Reims Cathedral — A37

Die I, II, III

Die IV

Die I Die II Die III

Die I — The window of the 1st turret on the left is made of 2 lines. The horizontal line of the frame surrounding 3F is continuous.

Die II — Same as Die I but the line under 3F is not continuous.

Die III — Same as Die II but there is a deeply cut line separating 3 and F.

Die IV — Same as Die III but the window of the first turret on the left is made of three lines.

Mont-Saint-Michel — A38

Die I

Die II

Die I — The line at the top of the spire is broken.

Die II — The line is unbroken.

Port of La Rochelle A39

Dies I & II

Die III

Die I — The top of the "E" of "POSTES" has a serif. The oval of shading inside the "0" of "10 fr" and the outer oval are broken at their bases.

Die II — The same top has no serif. Interior and exterior of "0" broken as in Die I.

Die III — Top of "E" has no serif. Interior and exterior of "0" complete.

Pont du Gard, Nimes A40

Dies I & II

Die III

Die I — Shading of the first complete arch in the left middle tier is made of horizontal lines. Size 36x20¾mm. Perf. 13½.

Die II — Same, size 35½x21mm. Perf. 11.

Die III — Shading of same arch is made of three diagonal lines. Thin paper. Perf. 13.

**1929-33** **Engr.** ***Perf. 11, 13, 13½***

| No. | Type | Description | Unused | Used |
|---|---|---|---|---|
| **247** | A37 | 3fr dk gray ('30) (I) | 62.50 | 2.40 |
| | | Never hinged | 115.00 | |
| **247A** | A37 | 3fr dk gray ('30) (II) | 125.00 | 3.50 |
| | | Never hinged | 200.00 | |
| **247B** | A37 | 3fr dk gray ('30) (III) | 375.00 | 24.00 |
| | | Never hinged | 600.00 | |
| **248** | A37 | 3fr bluish sl ('31) (IV) | 60.00 | 2.40 |
| | | Never hinged | 115.00 | |
| **249** | A38 | 5fr brn ('30) (I) | 24.00 | 4.25 |
| | | Never hinged | 40.00 | |
| **250** | A38 | 5fr brn ('31) (II) | 21.00 | .75 |
| | | Never hinged | 32.50 | |
| **251** | A39 | 10fr lt ultra (I) | 95.00 | 15.00 |
| | | Never hinged | 160.00 | |
| **251A** | A39 | 10fr ultra (II) | 140.00 | 26.00 |
| | | Never hinged | 225.00 | |
| **252** | A39 | 10fr dk ultra ('31) (III) | 70.00 | 6.50 |
| | | Never hinged | 140.00 | |
| **253** | A40 | 20fr red brown (I) | 275.00 | 40.00 |
| | | Never hinged | 500.00 | |
| **254** | A40 | 20fr brt red brn ('30) (II) | 1,000. | 350.00 |
| | | Never hinged | 1,650. | |
| **254A** | A40 | 20fr org brn ('31) (III) | 250.00 | 35.00 |
| | | Never hinged | 450.00 | |
| | | *Nos. 247-254A (12)* | 2,498. | 509.80 |

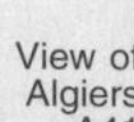

View of Algiers A41

**1929, Jan. 1** **Typo.**

| No. | Design | Description | Unused | Used |
|---|---|---|---|---|
| 255 | A41 | 50c blue & rose red | 2.40 | .50 |
| | | Never hinged | 5.50 | |

Cent. of the 1st French settlement in Algeria.

Nos. 146 and 196 Overprinted

**1930, Apr. 23** ***Perf. 14x13½***

| No. | Design | Description | Unused | Used |
|---|---|---|---|---|
| 256 | A20 | 50c vermilion | 3.00 | 3.25 |
| 257 | A23 | 1.50fr blue | 20.00 | 14.50 |
| | | Set, never hinged | 47.50 | |

Intl. Labor Bureau, 48th Congress, Paris.

**Colonial Exposition Issue**

Fachi Woman — A42

French Colonials A43

**1930-31** **Typo.** ***Perf. 14x13½***

| No. | Design | Description | Unused | Used |
|---|---|---|---|---|
| 258 | A42 | 15c gray black | 1.10 | .30 |
| 259 | A42 | 40c dark brown | 2.40 | .30 |
| 260 | A42 | 50c dark red | .65 | .25 |
| *a.* | | Booklet pane of 10 | 12.50 | |
| 261 | A42 | 1.50fr deep blue | 9.00 | .65 |

***Perf. 13½***

**Photo.**

| No. | Design | Description | Unused | Used |
|---|---|---|---|---|
| 262 | A43 | 1.50fr dp blue ('31) | 45.00 | 2.75 |
| | | *Nos. 258-262 (5)* | 58.15 | 4.25 |
| | | Set, never hinged | 125.00 | |

No. 260 has two types: type 1 shows four short downward hairlines near top of head, type 2 has no lines. Booklet stamps are type 2.

Arc de Triomphe A44

**1931** **Engr.** ***Perf. 13***

| No. | Design | Description | Unused | Used |
|---|---|---|---|---|
| 263 | A44 | 2fr red brown | 40.00 | 1.25 |
| | | Never hinged | 80.00 | |

Peace with Olive Branch — A45

**1932-39** **Typo.** ***Perf. 14x13½***

| No. | Design | Description | Unused | Used |
|---|---|---|---|---|
| 264 | A45 | 30c dp green | 1.00 | .55 |
| 265 | A45 | 40c brt violet | .30 | .30 |
| 266 | A45 | 45c yellow brown | 1.75 | 1.00 |
| 267 | A45 | 50c rose red | .25 | .25 |
| *a.* | | Imperf., pair | 140.00 | |
| *b.* | | Booklet pane of 10 | 5.50 | |
| 268 | A45 | 55c dull vio ('37) | .60 | .25 |
| 269 | A45 | 60c ocher ('37) | .30 | .25 |
| 270 | A45 | 65c violet brown | .50 | .50 |
| 271 | A45 | 65c brt ultra ('37) | .25 | .25 |
| *a.* | | Booklet pane of 10 | 7.00 | |
| 272 | A45 | 75c olive green | .25 | .30 |
| 273 | A45 | 80c orange ('38) | .25 | .25 |
| 274 | A45 | 90c dk red | 32.50 | 2.00 |
| 275 | A45 | 90c brt green ('38) | .25 | .25 |
| 276 | A45 | 90c ultra ('38) | .90 | .25 |
| *a.* | | Booklet pane of 10 | 8.50 | |
| 277 | A45 | 1fr orange | 3.25 | .25 |
| 278 | A45 | 1fr rose pink ('38) | 3.25 | .50 |
| 279 | A45 | 1.25fr brown ol | 75.00 | 4.75 |
| 280 | A45 | 1.25fr rose car ('39) | 1.90 | 2.25 |
| 281 | A45 | 1.40fr brt red vio ('39) | 5.75 | 5.25 |
| 282 | A45 | 1.50fr deep blue | .30 | .30 |
| 283 | A45 | 1.75fr magenta | 4.00 | .50 |
| | | *Nos. 264-283 (20)* | 132.55 | 20.20 |
| | | Set, never hinged | 275.00 | |

The 50c is found in 4 types, differing in the lines below belt and size of "c."

For surcharges and overprints see Nos. 298, 333, 401-403, 405-409, M7-M9, S1.

Le Puy-en-Velay — A46

**1933** **Engr.** ***Perf. 13***

| No. | Design | Description | Unused | Used |
|---|---|---|---|---|
| 290 | A46 | 90c rose | 3.00 | 1.10 |
| | | Never hinged | 5.75 | |

Aristide Briand A47

Paul Doumer A48

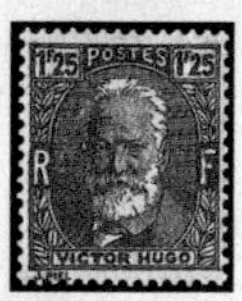

Victor Hugo — A49

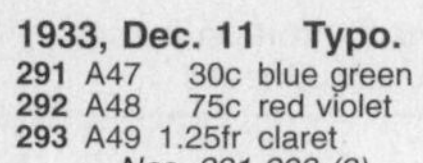

**1933, Dec. 11** **Typo.** ***Perf. 14x13½***

| No. | Design | Description | Unused | Used |
|---|---|---|---|---|
| 291 | A47 | 30c blue green | 17.00 | 8.00 |
| 292 | A48 | 75c red violet | 27.50 | 1.90 |
| 293 | A49 | 1.25fr claret | 6.00 | 2.25 |
| | | *Nos. 291-293 (3)* | 50.50 | 12.15 |
| | | Set, never hinged | 110.00 | |

Dove and Olive Branch — A50

**1934, Feb. 20**

| No. | Design | Description | Unused | Used |
|---|---|---|---|---|
| 294 | A50 | 1.50fr ultra | 50.00 | 15.00 |
| | | Never hinged | 95.00 | |

Joseph Marie Jacquard — A51

**1934, Mar. 14** **Engr.** ***Perf. 14x13***

| No. | Design | Description | Unused | Used |
|---|---|---|---|---|
| 295 | A51 | 40c blue | 3.00 | 1.10 |
| | | Never hinged | 4.50 | |

Jacquard (1752-1834), inventor of an improved loom for figured weaving.

Jacques Cartier A52

**1934, July 18** ***Perf. 13***

| No. | Design | Description | Unused | Used |
|---|---|---|---|---|
| 296 | A52 | 75c rose lilac | 30.00 | 2.25 |
| 297 | A52 | 1.50fr blue | 50.00 | 4.25 |
| | | Set, never hinged | 210.00 | |

Cartier's discovery of Canada, 400th anniv.

No. 279 Surcharged

**1934, Nov.** ***Perf. 14x13½***

| No. | Design | Description | Unused | Used |
|---|---|---|---|---|
| 298 | A45 | 50c on 1.25fr brn ol | 3.75 | .65 |
| | | Never hinged | 7.00 | |

**Catalogue values for unused stamps in this section, from this point to the end of the section, are for Never Hinged items.**

Breton River Scene A53

**1935, Feb.** **Engr.** ***Perf. 13***

| No. | Design | Description | Unused | Used |
|---|---|---|---|---|
| 299 | A53 | 2fr blue green | 70.00 | 1.00 |
| | | Hinged | 32.50 | |

S. S. Normandie A54

**1935, Apr.**

| No. | Design | Description | Unused | Used |
|---|---|---|---|---|
| 300 | A54 | 1.50fr dark blue | 29.00 | 2.00 |
| | | Hinged | 14.00 | |
| *a.* | | 1.50fr pale blue ('36) | 145.00 | 19.00 |
| | | Hinged | 55.00 | |
| *b.* | | 1.50fr blue green ('36) | *30,000.* | *12,500.* |
| | | Hinged | *19,000.* | |
| *c.* | | 1.50fr turquoise ('36) | 400.00 | 40.00 |
| | | Hinged | 275.00 | |

Maiden voyage of the transatlantic steamship, the "Normandie."

Benjamin Delessert A55

**1935, May 20**

| No. | Design | Description | Unused | Used |
|---|---|---|---|---|
| 301 | A55 | 75c blue green | 47.50 | 1.75 |
| | | Hinged | 17.50 | |

Opening of the International Savings Bank Congress, May 20, 1935.

View of St. Trophime at Arles — A56

**1935, May 3**

| No. | Design | Description | Unused | Used |
|---|---|---|---|---|
| 302 | A56 | 3.50fr dark brown | 70.00 | 4.25 |
| | | Hinged | 27.50 | |

Victor Hugo (1802-85) — A57

**1935, May 30** ***Perf. 14x13***

| No. | Design | Description | Unused | Used |
|---|---|---|---|---|
| 303 | A57 | 1.25fr magenta | 8.25 | 2.00 |
| | | Hinged | 4.00 | |

Cardinal Richelieu — A58

**1935, June 12** ***Perf. 13***

| No. | Design | Description | Unused | Used |
|---|---|---|---|---|
| 304 | A58 | 1.50fr deep rose | 70.00 | 1.75 |
| | | Hinged | 20.00 | |

Tercentenary of the founding of the French Academy by Cardinal Richelieu.

Jacques Callot — A59

**1935, Nov.** ***Perf. 14x13***

| No. | Design | Description | Unused | Used |
|---|---|---|---|---|
| 305 | A59 | 75c red | 19.00 | .75 |
| | | Hinged | 10.00 | |

300th anniv. of the death of Jacques Callot, engraver.

André Marie Ampère (1775-1836), Scientist, by Louis Boilly — A60

**1936, Feb. 27** ***Perf. 13***

| No. | Design | Description | Unused | Used |
|---|---|---|---|---|
| 306 | A60 | 75c brown | 37.50 | 2.00 |
| | | Hinged | 17.50 | |

Windmill at Fontvielle, Immortalized by Daudet — A61

**1936, Apr. 27**

**307** A61 2fr ultra 5.75 .40
Hinged 3.00

Publication, in 1866, of Alphonse Daudet's "Lettres de mon Moulin," 75th anniv.

Pilâtre de Rozier and his Balloon A62

**1936, June 4**

**308** A62 75c Prus blue 37.50 2.75
Hinged 19.00

150th anniversary of the death of Jean Francois Pilâtre de Rozier, balloonist.

Rouget de Lisle — A63

"La Marseillaise" — A64

**1936, June 27**

**309** A63 20c Prus green 5.75 2.00
Hinged 3.25
**310** A64 40c dark brown 11.50 3.25
Hinged 5.50

Cent. of the death of Claude Joseph Rouget de Lisle, composer of "La Marseillaise."

Canadian War Memorial at Vimy Ridge A65

**1936, July 26**

**311** A65 75c henna brown 25.00 2.00
Hinged 9.50
**312** A65 1.50fr dull blue 32.50 9.50
Hinged 16.00

Unveiling of the Canadian War Memorial at Vimy Ridge, July 26, 1936.

A66

Jean Léon Jaurès A67

**1936, July 30**

**313** A66 40c red brown 5.75 1.40
Hinged 4.00
**314** A67 1.50fr ultra 32.50 3.75
Hinged 13.00

Assassination of Jean Léon Jaurès (1859-1914), socialist and politician.

Herald — A68

Allegory of Exposition A69

**1936, Sept. 15 Typo. *Perf. 14x13½***

**315** A68 20c brt violet 1.00 .50
Hinged .30
**316** A68 30c Prus green 4.00 1.75
Hinged 2.40
**317** A68 40c ultra 2.50 .50
Hinged 1.00
**318** A68 50c red orange 2.25 .25
Hinged 1.00
**319** A69 90c carmine 25.00 7.50
Hinged 11.00
**320** A69 1.50fr ultra 67.50 4.00
Hinged 30.00
*Nos. 315-320 (6)* 102.25 14.50

Publicity for the 1937 Paris Exposition.

"Peace" A70

**1936, Oct. 1 Engr. *Perf. 13***

**321** A70 1.50fr blue 27.50 4.00
Hinged 12.50

Skiing A71

**1937, Jan. 18**

**322** A71 1.50fr dark blue 14.00 1.75
Hinged 7.00

Intl. Ski Meet at Chamonix-Mont Blanc.

Pierre Corneille, Portrait by Charles Le Brun — A72

**1937, Feb. 15**

**323** A72 75c brown carmine 3.75 1.40
Hinged 1.90

300th anniv. of the publication of "Le Cid."

**Paris Exposition Issue**

Exposition Allegory A73

**1937, Mar. 15**

**324** A73 1.50fr turq blue 4.00 1.25
Hinged 2.25

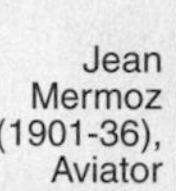

Jean Mermoz (1901-36), Aviator A74

Memorial to Mermoz — A75

**1937, Apr. 22**

**325** A74 30c dk slate green 1.00 .55
Hinged .50
**326** A75 3fr dark violet 13.50 3.75
Hinged 6.25
*a.* 3fr violet 15.00 4.50
Hinged 6.75

Electric Train A76

Streamlined Locomotive A77

**1937, May 31**

**327** A76 30c dk green 1.40 1.75
Hinged 1.00
**328** A77 1.50fr dk ultra 15.00 8.25
Hinged 7.25

13th International Railroad Congress.

**Intl. Philatelic Exhibition Issue**

Souvenir Sheet

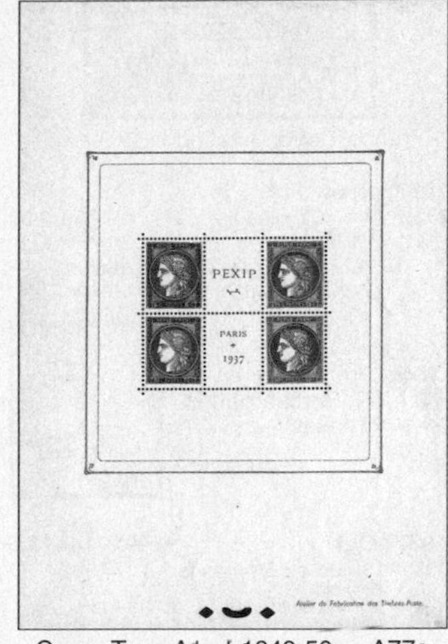

Ceres Type A1 of 1849-50 — A77a

**1937, June 18 Typo. *Perf. 14x13½***

**329** A77a Sheet of 4 700.00 300.00
Lightly hinged in margins 360.00
*a.* 5c ultra & dark brown 90.00 47.50
*b.* 15c red & rose red 90.00 47.50
*c.* 30c ultra & rose red 90.00 47.50
*d.* 50c red & dark brown 90.00 47.50
*e.* Sheet of 4, imperf 3,000.
Lightly hinged in margins 2,350.

Issued in sheets measuring 150x220mm.

The sheets were sold only at the exhibition in Paris, a ticket of admission being required for each sheet purchased.

René Descartes, by Frans Hals — A78

**1937, June Engr. *Perf. 13***

**Inscribed "Discours sur la Méthode"**

**330** A78 90c copper red 3.25 1.40
Hinged 1.90

**Inscribed "Discours de la Méthode"**

**331** A78 90c copper red 11.00 1.75
Hinged 5.50

3rd centenary of the publication of "Discours de la Méthode" by René Descartes.

France Congratulating USA — A79

**1937, Sept. 17**

**332** A79 1.75fr ultra 4.50 2.00
Hinged 2.50

150th anniv. of the US Constitution.

No. 277 Surcharged in Red

**1937, Oct.** ***Perf. 14x13½***

**333** A45 80c on 1fr orange 1.90 .85
Hinged .80
*a.* Inverted surcharge *1,225.*
Hinged *825.00*

Mountain Road at Iseran A80

**1937, Oct. 4** **Engr.** ***Perf. 13***

**334** A80 90c dark green 3.75 .30
Hinged 1.90

Issued in commemoration of the opening of the mountain road at Iseran, Savoy.

Ceres — A81

**1938-40** **Typo.** ***Perf. 14x13½***

**335** A81 1.75fr dk ultra 1.40 .55
Hinged .55
**336** A81 2fr car rose ('39) .30 .30
Hinged .25
**337** A81 2.25fr ultra ('39) 15.00 1.10
Hinged 8.00
**338** A81 2.50fr green ('39) 3.00 .50
Hinged 1.25
**339** A81 2.50fr vio blue ('40) 1.25 .75
Hinged .65
**340** A81 3fr rose lilac ('39) 1.25 .50
Hinged .55
*Nos. 335-340 (6)* 22.20 3.70

For surcharges see Nos. 397-399.

Léon Gambetta (1838-82), Lawyer and Statesman — A82

**1938, Apr. 2** **Engr.** ***Perf. 13***

**341** A82 55c dark violet .55 .40
Hinged .35

Arc de Triomphe of Orange A82a

Miners A83

Keep and Gate of Vincennes A86

Palace of the Popes, Avignon A84

Medieval Walls of Carcassonne — A85

Port of St. Malo — A87

**1938**

**342** A82a 2fr brown black 1.75 1.25
Hinged .55
**343** A83 2.15fr violet brn 9.50 1.00
Hinged 4.75
**344** A84 3fr car brown 26.50 5.00
Hinged 12.50
**345** A85 5fr deep ultra 1.50 .40
Hinged .75
**346** A86 10fr brown, *blue* 3.25 1.90
Hinged 1.50
**347** A87 20fr dk blue green 80.00 19.00
Hinged 37.50
*Nos. 342-347 (6)* 122.50 28.55

For surcharges see Nos. 410-413.

Clément Ader, Air Pioneer A88

**1938, June 16**

**348** A88 50fr ultra (thin paper) 150.00 65.00
Hinged 95.00
*a.* 50fr dark ultra (thick paper) 175.00 77.50
Hinged 100.00

For surcharge, see No. 414.

Soccer Players A89

**1938, June 1**

**349** A89 1.75fr dark ultra 29.00 13.50
Hinged 13.50

World Cup Soccer Championship.

Costume of Champagne Region — A90

**1938, June 13**

**350** A90 1.75fr dark ultra 7.50 4.50
Hinged 3.75

Tercentenary of the birth of Dom Pierre Pérignon, discoverer of the champagne process.

Jean de La Fontaine — A91

**1938, July 8**

**351** A91 55c dk blue green 1.00 .80
Hinged .65

Jean de La Fontaine (1621-1695) the fabulist.

Seal of Friendship and Peace, Victoria Tower and Arc de Triomphe A92

**1938, July 19**

**352** A92 1.75fr ultra 1.25 .80
Hinged .65

Visit of King George VI and Queen Elizabeth of Great Britain to France.

Mercury — A93

**1938-42** **Typo.** ***Perf. 14x13½***

**353** A93 1c dark brown ('39) .25 .25
Hinged .25
**354** A93 2c slate grn ('39) .25 .25
Hinged .25
**355** A93 5c rose .25 .25
Hinged .25
**356** A93 10c ultra .25 .25
Hinged .25
**357** A93 15c red orange .25 .25
Hinged .25
**358** A93 15c orange brn ('39) 1.00 .50
Hinged .55
**359** A93 20c red violet .25 .25
Hinged .25
**360** A93 25c blue green .25 .25
Hinged .25
**361** A93 30c rose red ('39) .25 .25
Hinged .25
**362** A93 40c dk violet ('39) .25 .25
Hinged .25
**363** A93 45c lt green ('39) .80 .50
Hinged .50
**364** A93 50c deep blue ('39) 4.00 .40
Hinged 2.25
**365** A93 50c dk green ('41) .55 .35
Hinged .30
**366** A93 50c grnsh blue ('42) .25 .25
Hinged .25
**367** A93 60c red orange ('39) .25 .25
Hinged .25
**368** A93 70c magenta ('39) .25 .25
Hinged .25
**369** A93 75c dk org brn ('39) 7.50 2.50
Hinged 3.75
*Nos. 353-369 (17)* 16.85 7.25

No. 366 exists imperforate. See Nos. 455-458. For overprints and surcharge see Nos. 404, 499-502.

Self-portrait — A95

**1939, Mar. 15** **Engr.** ***Perf. 13***

**370** A95 2.25fr Prussian blue 8.25 3.50
Hinged 3.50

Paul Cézanne (1839-1906), painter.

Georges Clemenceau and Battleship Clemenceau — A96

**1939, Apr. 18**

**371** A96 90c ultra 1.00 .75
Hinged .50

Laying of the keel of the warship "Clemenceau," Jan. 17, 1939.

Statue of Liberty, French Pavilion, Trylon and Perisphere A97

**1939-40**

**372** A97 2.25fr ultra 17.00 6.50
Hinged 8.00
**373** A97 2.50fr ultra ('40) 22.50 9.50
Hinged 8.50

New York World's Fair.

Joseph Nicéphore Niepce and Louis Jacques Mandé Daguerre A98

**1939, Apr. 24**

**374** A98 2.25fr dark blue 16.00 7.00
Hinged 7.00

Centenary of photography.

Iris — A99

**1939-44** **Typo.** ***Perf. 14x13½***

**375** A99 80c red brown ('40) .25 .25
Hinged .25
**376** A99 80c yellow grn ('44) .25 .25
Hinged .25
**377** A99 1fr green 1.00 .25
Hinged .55
**378** A99 1fr crimson ('40) .40 .35
Hinged .25
*a.* Booklet pane of 10 7.50
**379** A99 1fr grnsh blue ('44) .25 .25
Hinged .25
**380** A99 1.20fr violet ('44) .25 .25
Hinged .25
**381** A99 1.30fr ultra ('40) .25 .25
Hinged .25
**382** A99 1.50fr red org ('41) .25 .25
Hinged .25
**383** A99 1.50fr henna brn ('44) .25 .25
Hinged .25
**384** A99 2fr violet brn ('44) .25 .25
Hinged .25
**385** A99 2.40fr car rose ('44) .25 .25
Hinged .25
**386** A99 3fr orange ('44) .25 .25
Hinged .25
**387** A99 4fr ultra ('44) .25 .25
Hinged .25
*Nos. 375-387 (13)* 4.15 3.35

Pumping Station at Marly A100

**1939 Engr. *Perf. 13***

**388** A100 2.25fr brt ultra 25.00 5.00
Hinged 11.00

France's participation in the International Water Exposition at Liège.

St. Gregory of Tours — A101

**1939, June 10**

**389** A101 90c red .90 .55
Hinged .50

14th centenary of the birth of St. Gregory of Tours, historian and bishop.

"The Oath of the Tennis Court" by Jacques David A102

**1939, June 20**

**390** A102 90c deep slate green 3.50 1.90
Hinged 1.90

150th anniversary of French Revolution.

Cathedral of Strasbourg — A103

**1939, June 23**

**391** A103 70c brown carmine 1.50 1.00
Hinged .75

500th anniv. of the completion of Strasbourg Cathedral.

Porte Chaussée, Verdun A104

**1939, June 23**

**392** A104 90c black brown 1.00 .80
Hinged .80

23rd anniv. of the Battle of Verdun.

View of Pau A105

**1939, Aug. 25**

**393** A105 90c brt rose, *gray bl* 1.25 1.25
Hinged .80

Maid of Languedoc A106

Bridge at Lyons A107

**1939**

**394** A106 70c black, *blue* .50 .40
Hinged .40
**395** A107 90c dull brown vio 1.00 *1.25*
Hinged .90

Imperforates

Nearly all French stamps issued from 1940 onward exist imperforate. Officially 20 sheets, ranging from 25 to 100 subjects, were left imperforate.

Georges Guynemer (1894-1917), World War I Ace — A108

**1940, Nov. 7**

**396** A108 50fr ultra 16.00 9.00
Hinged 8.00

Stamps of 1938-39 Surcharged in Carmine

**1940-41 *Perf. 14x13½***

**397** A81 1fr on 1.75fr dk ultra .30 .30
Hinged .25
**398** A81 1fr on 2.25fr ultra ('41) .30 .30
Hinged .25
**399** A81 1fr on 2.50fr grn ('41) 1.40 1.40
Hinged .65
*Nos. 397-399 (3)* 2.00 2.00

Stamps of 1932-39 Surcharged in Carmine, Red (#408) or Black (#407)

**1940-41 *Perf. 13, 14x13½***

**400** A22 30c on 35c grn ('41) .30 .30
Hinged .25
**401** A45 50c on 55c dl vio ('41) .30 .30
Hinged .25
*a.* Inverted surcharge *1,000.*
**402** A45 50c on 65c brt ultra ('41) .30 .30
Hinged .25
**403** A45 50c on 75c ol grn ('41) .30 .30
Hinged .25
**404** A93 50c on 75c dk org brn ('41) .30 .30
Hinged .25
**405** A45 50c on 80c org ('41) .30 .30
Hinged .25
**406** A45 50c on 90c ultra ('41) .30 .30
Hinged .25
*a.* Inverted surcharge *550.00*
*b.* "05" instead of "50" *9,000.* 6,400.
**407** A45 1fr on 1.25fr rose car (Bk) ('41) .30 .30
Hinged .25
**408** A45 1fr on 1.40fr brt red vio (R) ('41) .40 .40
Hinged .25
*a.* Double surcharge *1,600.*
**409** A45 1fr on 1.50fr dk bl ('41) 1.40 1.40
Hinged .25
**410** A83 1fr on 2.15fr vio brn .40 .40
Hinged .25
**411** A85 2.50fr on 5fr dp ultra ('41) .40 .40
Hinged .25
*a.* Double surcharge *350.00* 190.00
**412** A86 5fr on 10fr brn, *bl* ('41) 1.90 1.90
Hinged 1.00
**413** A87 10fr on 20fr dk bl grn ('41) 1.60 1.60
Hinged 1.00
**414** A88 20fr on 50fr dk ultra (#348a) ('41) 70.00 37.50
Hinged 29.00
*a.* 20fr on 50fr ultra, thin paper (#348) 75.00 50.00
*Nos. 400-414 (15)* 78.50 46.00

Issued: No. 410, 1940; others, 1941

Marshal Pétain — A109

**1941 *Perf. 13***

**415** A109 40c red brown .40 .25
**416** A109 80c turq blue .45 .40
**417** A109 1fr red .25 .25
**418** A109 2.50fr deep ultra 1.40 1.10
*Nos. 415-418 (4)* 2.50 2.00

For No. 417 with surcharge, see No. B111.

Frédéric Mistral — A110

**1941, Feb. 20 *Perf. 14x13***

**419** A110 1fr brown lake .25 .25

Issued in honor of Frédéric Mistral, poet and Nobel prize winner for literature in 1904.

Beaune Hospital A111

View of Angers A112

Ramparts of St. Louis, Aiguesmortes — A113

**1941**

**420** A111 5fr brown black .35 .25
**421** A112 10fr dark violet .60 .45
**422** A113 20fr brown black 1.10 .80
*Nos. 420-422 (3)* 2.05 1.50

**Inscribed "Postes Francaises"**

**1942**

**Imprint: "FELTESSE" at right**

**423** A111 15fr brown lake .60 .40

A114

A115

Marshal Pétain — A116

**1941-42 Typo. *Perf. 14x13½***

**427** A114 20c lilac ('42) .25 .25
**428** A114 30c rose red .25 .25
**429** A114 40c ultra .25 .25
**431** A115 50c dp green .25 .25
**432** A115 60c violet ('42) .25 .25
**433** A115 70c saph ('42) .25 .25
**434** A115 70c orange ('42) .25 .25
**435** A115 80c brown .25 .25
**436** A115 80c emerald ('42) .25 .25
**437** A115 1fr rose red .25 .25
**438** A115 1.20fr red brn ('42) .25 .25
**439** A116 1.50fr rose .25 .25
**440** A116 1.50fr dl red brn ('42) .25 .25
*a.* Booklet pane of 10 2.75
**441** A116 2fr blue grn ('42) .25 .25
**443** A116 2.40fr rose red ('42) .25 .25
**444** A116 2.50fr ultra .25 .55
**445** A116 3fr orange .25 .25
**446** A115 4fr ultra ('42) .25 .25
**447** A115 4.50fr dk green ('42) .25 .25
*Nos. 427-447 (19)* 4.75 5.05

Nos. 431 to 438 measure 16½x20½mm.

No. 440 was forged by the French Underground ("Defense de la France") and used to frank clandestine journals, etc., from Feb. to June, 1944. The forgeries were ungummed, both perf. 11½ and imperf., with a back handstamp covering six stamps and including the words: "Atelier des Faux."

For surcharge see No. B134.

A117

A118

**1942** **Engr.** ***Perf. 14x13***

| | | | | |
|---|---|---|---|---|
| **448** | A115 | 4fr brt ultra | .25 | .25 |
| **449** | A115 | 4.50fr dark green | .25 | .25 |
| **450** | A117 | 5fr Prus green | .25 | .25 |

***Perf. 13***

| | | | | |
|---|---|---|---|---|
| **451** | A118 | 50fr black | 3.00 | 3.00 |
| | | *Nos. 448-451 (4)* | 3.75 | 3.75 |

Nos. 448 and 449 measure 18x21½mm.

Jules Massenet — A119

**1942, June 22** ***Perf. 14x13***
**452** A119 4fr Prus green .25 .25

Jules Massenet (1842-1912), composer.

Stendhal (Marie Henri Beyle) — A120

**1942, Sept. 14** ***Perf. 13***
**453** A120 4fr blk brn & org red .40 .40

Stendhal (1783-1842), writer.

André Blondel — A121

**1942, Sept. 14**
**454** A121 4fr dull blue .40 .40

André Eugène Blondel (1863-1938), physicist.

**Mercury Type of 1938-42**
**Inscribed "Postes Françaises"**

**1942** ***Perf. 14x13½***

| | | | | |
|---|---|---|---|---|
| **455** | A93 | 10c ultra | .25 | .25 |
| **456** | A93 | 30c rose red | .25 | .25 |
| **457** | A93 | 40c dark violet | .25 | .25 |
| **458** | A93 | 50c turq blue | .25 | .25 |
| | | *Nos. 455-458 (4)* | 1.00 | 1.00 |

Town-Hall Belfry, Arras — A122

**1942, Dec. 8** **Engr.** ***Perf. 13***
**459** A122 10fr green .25 .25

Lyon — A123

Coats of Arms.

**1943** **Typo.** ***Perf. 14x13½***

| | | | | |
|---|---|---|---|---|
| **460** | A123 | 5fr shown | .30 | .30 |
| **461** | A123 | 10fr Brittany | .40 | .40 |
| **462** | A123 | 15fr Provence | 1.75 | 1.10 |
| **463** | A123 | 20fr Ile de France | 1.40 | 1.20 |
| | | *Nos. 460-463 (4)* | 3.85 | 3.00 |

Antoine Lavoisier (1743-94), French Scientist — A127

**1943, July 5** **Engr.** ***Perf. 14x13***
**464** A127 4fr ultra .25 .25

Lake Lerie and Meije Dauphiné Alps A128

**1943, July 5** ***Perf. 13***
**465** A128 20fr dull gray grn .75 .75

Nicolas Rolin, Guigone de Salins and Hospital of Beaune A129

**1943, July 21**
**466** A129 4fr blue .25 .25

500th anniv. of the founding of the Hospital of Beaune.

Arms of Flanders — A130

**1944, Mar. 27** **Typo.** ***Perf. 14x13½***

| | | | | |
|---|---|---|---|---|
| **467** | A130 | 5fr shown | .25 | .25 |
| **468** | A130 | 10fr Languedoc | .25 | .25 |
| **469** | A130 | 15fr Orleans | .60 | .55 |
| **470** | A130 | 20fr Normandy | 1.00 | .85 |
| | | *Nos. 467-470 (4)* | 2.10 | 1.90 |

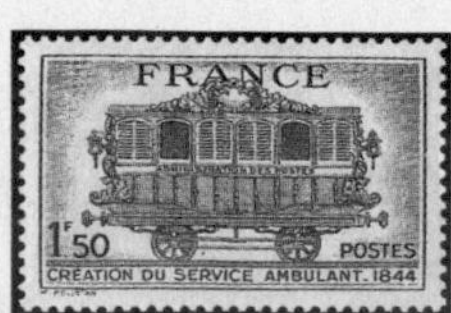

Edouard Branly — A134

**1944, Feb. 21** **Engr.** ***Perf. 14x13***
**471** A134 4fr ultra .25 .25

Cent. of the birth of Edouard Branly, electrical inventor.

Early Postal Car A135

**1944, June 10** ***Perf. 13***
**472** A135 1.50fr dark blue green .55 .45

Cent. of France's traveling postal service.

Chateau de Chenonceaux — A136

**1944, June 10**

| | | | | |
|---|---|---|---|---|
| **473** | A136 | 15fr lilac brown | .60 | .45 |
| *a.* | | 15fr black brown | 10.50 | 3.00 |
| *b.* | | 15fr black | 100.00 | 55.00 |

See No. 496.

Claude Chappe — A137

**1944, Aug. 14** ***Perf. 14x13***
**474** A137 4fr dark ultra .25 .25

150th anniv. of the invention of an optical telegraph by Claude Chappe (1763-1805).

Arc de Triomphe — OS2

**Unwmk.**

**1944, Oct. 9** **Litho.** ***Perf. 11***

| | | | | |
|---|---|---|---|---|
| **475** | OS2 | 5c brt red violet | .25 | .25 |
| **476** | OS2 | 10c lt gray | .25 | .25 |
| **476A** | OS2 | 25c brown | .25 | .25 |
| **476B** | OS2 | 50c olive bis | .25 | .25 |
| **476C** | OS2 | 1fr pck green | .25 | .25 |
| **476D** | OS2 | 1.50fr rose pink | .25 | .25 |
| **476E** | OS2 | 2.50fr purple | .25 | .25 |
| **476F** | OS2 | 4fr ultra | .25 | .25 |
| **476G** | OS2 | 5fr black | .25 | .25 |
| **476H** | OS2 | 10fr yellow org | 27.50 | 21.00 |
| | | *Nos. 475-476H (10)* | 29.75 | 23.25 |

Nos 475-476H were printed by the U.S. Bureau of Engaving and Printing and were intended to be used by an Allied Military government, which was expected to administer the liberated areas of France. Instead, the Allies recognized the authority of Gen. de Gaulle's Provisional Government over these territories, and these stamps were transferred to the Free French in July, 1944. They were put on sale in liberated areas as the Allied armies advanced, and on Oct. 9, they were officially issued in Paris.

See Nos. 523A-523J.

Gallic Cock A138

Marianne A139

**1944** **Litho.** ***Perf. 12***

| | | | | |
|---|---|---|---|---|
| **477** | A138 | 10c yellow grn | .25 | .25 |
| **478** | A138 | 30c dk rose vio | .30 | .35 |
| **479** | A138 | 40c blue | .25 | .25 |
| **480** | A138 | 50c dark red | .25 | .25 |
| **481** | A139 | 60c olive brown | .25 | .25 |
| **482** | A139 | 70c rose lilac | .25 | .25 |
| **483** | A139 | 80c yellow grn | .90 | .90 |
| **484** | A139 | 1fr violet | .25 | .25 |
| **485** | A139 | 1.20fr dp carmine | .25 | .25 |
| **486** | A139 | 1.50fr deep blue | .25 | .25 |
| **487** | A138 | 2fr indigo | .25 | .25 |
| **488** | A139 | 2.40fr red orange | 1.10 | 1.10 |
| **489** | A139 | 3fr dp blue grn | .25 | .25 |
| **490** | A139 | 4fr grnsh blue | .25 | .25 |
| **491** | A139 | 4.50fr black | .25 | .25 |
| **492** | A139 | 5fr violet blue | 3.75 | 3.75 |
| **493** | A138 | 10fr violet | 4.50 | 4.25 |
| **494** | A138 | 15fr olive brown | 4.25 | 4.25 |
| **495** | A138 | 20fr dk slate grn | 3.75 | 3.75 |
| | | *Nos. 477-495 (19)* | 21.55 | 21.35 |

Nos. 477-495 were issued first in Corsica after the Allied landing, and released in Paris Nov. 15, 1944.

**Chateau Type Inscribed "RF"**

**1944, Oct. 30** **Engr.** ***Perf. 13***
**496** A136 25fr black .75 .55

Thomas Robert Bugeaud — A141

**1944, Nov. 20**
**497** A141 4fr myrtle green .25 .25

Battle of Isly, Aug. 14th, 1844.

Church of St. Denis A142

**1944, Nov. 20**
**498** A142 2.40fr brown carmine .30 .30

800th anniv. of the Church of St. Denis.

Type of 1938-42, Overprinted in Black

**Inscribed "Postes Francaises"**

**1944** ***Perf. 14x13½***

| | | | | |
|---|---|---|---|---|
| **499** | A93 | 10c ultra | .25 | .25 |
| **500** | A93 | 30c rose red | .25 | .25 |
| **501** | A93 | 40c dark violet | .25 | .25 |
| **502** | A93 | 50c grnsh blue | .25 | .25 |
| | | *Nos. 499-502 (4)* | 1.00 | 1.00 |

The overprint "RF" in various forms, with or without Lorraine Cross, was also applied to stamps of the French State at Lyon and fourteen other cities.

French Forces of the Interior and Symbol of Liberation — A143

**1945, Jan.**
**503** A143 4fr dark ultra .30 .30

Issued to commemorate the Liberation.

Stamps of the above design, and of one incorporating "FRANCE" in the top panel, were printed by photo. in England during WW II upon order of the Free French Government. They were not issued. There are 3 values in each design; 25c green, 1fr red, 2.50fr blue. Value: set, above design, $100; set inscribed "FRANCE," $600.

Marianne — A144

*Perf. 11½x12½*

**1944-45 Engr. Unwmk.**

| No. | Type | Value | Color | Unused | Used |
|---|---|---|---|---|---|
| **504** | A144 | 10c | ultra | .25 | .25 |
| **505** | A144 | 30c | bister | .25 | .25 |
| **506** | A144 | 40c | indigo | .25 | .25 |
| **507** | A144 | 50c | red orange | .25 | .25 |
| **508** | A144 | 60c | chalky blue | .25 | .25 |
| **509** | A144 | 70c | sepia | .25 | .25 |
| **510** | A144 | 80c | deep green | .25 | .25 |
| **511** | A144 | 1fr | lilac | .25 | .25 |
| **512** | A144 | 1.20fr | dk ol grn | .25 | .25 |
| **513** | A144 | 1.50fr | rose ('44) | .25 | .25 |
| **514** | A144 | 2fr | dk brown | .25 | .25 |
| **515** | A144 | 2.40fr | red | .25 | .25 |
| **516** | A144 | 3fr | brt ol grn | .25 | .25 |
| **517** | A144 | 4fr | brt ultra | .25 | .25 |
| **518** | A144 | 4.50fr | slate gray | .25 | .25 |
| **519** | A144 | 5fr | brt orange | .25 | .25 |
| **520** | A144 | 10fr | yellow grn | .25 | .25 |
| **521** | A144 | 15fr | lake | .25 | .25 |
| **522** | A144 | 20fr | brown org | 1.10 | 1.10 |
| **523** | A144 | 50fr | deep purple | 2.90 | 2.40 |
| | | | *Nos. 504-523 (20)* | 8.50 | 8.00 |

The 2.40fr exists imperf. in a miniature sheet of 4 which was not issued. Value: never hinged $6,500; unused $4,500.

Compare with type A1759. See Nos. 4905, 4909.

### Arc de Triomphe Type of 1944

**1945, Feb. 12 Litho. *Perf. 11***

**Denominations in Black**

| No. | Type | Value | Color | Unused | Used |
|---|---|---|---|---|---|
| **523A** | OS2 | 30c | orange | .25 | .25 |
| **523B** | OS2 | 40c | pale gray | .25 | .25 |
| **523C** | OS2 | 50c | olive bis | .25 | .25 |
| **523D** | OS2 | 60c | violet | .25 | .25 |
| **523E** | OS2 | 80c | emerald | .25 | .25 |
| **523F** | OS2 | 1.20fr | brown | .25 | .25 |
| **523G** | OS2 | 1.50fr | vermilion | .25 | .25 |
| **523H** | OS2 | 2fr | yellow | .25 | .25 |
| **523I** | OS2 | 2.40fr | dark rose | .25 | .25 |
| **523J** | OS2 | 3fr | brt red violet | .25 | .25 |
| | | | *Nos. 523A-523J (10)* | 2.50 | 2.50 |

Coat of Arms A145

Ceres A146

Marianne — A147

**1945-47 Typo. *Perf. 14x13½***

| No. | Type | Value | Color | Unused | Used |
|---|---|---|---|---|---|
| **524** | A145 | 10c | brown black | .25 | .25 |
| **525** | A145 | 30c | dk blue green | .25 | .25 |
| **526** | A145 | 40c | lilac rose | .25 | .25 |
| **527** | A145 | 50c | violet blue | .25 | .25 |
| **528** | A146 | 60c | brt ultra | .25 | .25 |
| **530** | A146 | 80c | brt green | .25 | .25 |
| **531** | A146 | 90c | dull grn ('46) | .65 | .55 |
| **532** | A146 | 1fr | rose red | .25 | .25 |
| **533** | A146 | 1.20fr | brown black | .25 | .25 |
| **534** | A146 | 1.50fr | rose lilac | .25 | .25 |
| **535** | A147 | 1.50fr | rose pink | .25 | .25 |
| **536** | A147 | 2fr | myrtle green | .25 | .25 |
| **536A** | A146 | 2fr | lt bl grn ('46) | .25 | .25 |
| **537** | A147 | 2.40fr | scarlet | .30 | .30 |
| **538** | A146 | 2.50fr | brown ('46) | .25 | .25 |
| **539** | A147 | 3fr | sepia | .25 | .25 |
| **540** | A147 | 3fr | deep rose ('46) | .25 | .25 |
| **541** | A147 | 4fr | ultra | .25 | .25 |
| **541A** | A147 | 4fr | violet ('46) | .25 | .25 |
| **541B** | A147 | 4.50fr | ultra ('47) | .25 | .25 |
| **542** | A147 | 5fr | lt green | .25 | .25 |
| **542A** | A147 | 5fr | rose pink ('47) | .25 | .25 |
| **543** | A147 | 6fr | brt ultra | .35 | .25 |
| **544** | A147 | 6fr | crim rose ('46) | 1.60 | .90 |
| **545** | A147 | 10fr | red orange | .45 | .30 |
| **546** | A147 | 10fr | ultra ('46) | 1.20 | .75 |
| **547** | A147 | 15fr | brt red vio | 3.00 | 1.60 |
| | | | *Nos. 524-547 (27)* | 12.55 | 9.65 |

No. 531 is known only precanceled. See second note after No. 132.

Due to a reduction of the domestic postage rate, No. 542A was sold for 4.50fr.

Compare with type A1814. See Nos. 576-580, 594-602, 614, 615, 650-654, 4906, 4908. For surcharges see Nos. 589, 610, 706, Reunion 270-276, 278, 285, 290-291, 293, 295.

**1945-46 Engr. *Perf. 14x13***

| No. | Type | Value | Color | Unused | Used |
|---|---|---|---|---|---|
| **548** | A147 | 4fr | dark blue | .25 | .25 |
| **549** | A147 | 10fr | dp blue ('46) | 1.10 | .55 |
| **550** | A147 | 15fr | brt red vio ('46) | 6.75 | 1.75 |
| **551** | A147 | 20fr | blue grn ('46) | 1.00 | .55 |
| **552** | A147 | 25fr | red ('46) | 6.75 | 1.50 |
| | | | *Nos. 548-552 (5)* | 15.85 | 4.60 |

Nos. 548-552 have "GANDON" at lower right in design, and no inscription below design.

Marianne — A148

**1945 Engr. *Perf. 13***

| No. | Type | Value | Color | Unused | Used |
|---|---|---|---|---|---|
| **553** | A148 | 20fr | dark green | 1.00 | .90 |
| **554** | A148 | 25fr | violet | 1.10 | 1.10 |
| **555** | A148 | 50fr | red brown | 1.50 | 1.50 |
| **556** | A148 | 100fr | brt rose car | 10.00 | 5.50 |
| | | | *Nos. 553-556 (4)* | 13.60 | 9.00 |

CFA

French stamps inscribed or surcharged "CFA" and new value are listed under Réunion at the end of the French listings.

Arms of Metz A149

Arms of Strasbourg A150

**1945, Mar. 3 *Perf. 14x13***

| No. | Type | Value | Color | Unused | Used |
|---|---|---|---|---|---|
| **557** | A149 | 2.40fr | dull blue | .25 | .25 |
| **558** | A150 | 4fr | black brown | .25 | .25 |

Liberation of Metz and Strasbourg.

Costumes of Alsace and Lorraine and Cathedrals of Strasbourg and Metz A151

**1945, May 16 *Perf. 13***

| No. | Type | Value | Color | Unused | Used |
|---|---|---|---|---|---|
| **559** | A151 | 4fr | henna brown | .25 | .25 |

Liberation of Alsace and Lorraine. See No. 4907.

World Map Showing French Possessions — A152

**1945, Sept. 17**

| No. | Type | Value | Color | Unused | Used |
|---|---|---|---|---|---|
| **560** | A152 | 2fr | Prussian blue | .25 | .25 |

No. B193 Surcharged in Black

**1946 *Perf. 14x13½***

| No. | Type | Value | Color | Unused | Used |
|---|---|---|---|---|---|
| **561** | SP147 | 3fr on 2fr+1fr | red org | .25 | .25 |

Arms of Corsica — A153

**1946 Unwmk. Typo. *Perf. 14x13½***

| No. | Type | Value | Color | Unused | Used |
|---|---|---|---|---|---|
| **562** | A153 | 10c | shown | .25 | .25 |
| **563** | A153 | 30c | Alsace | .25 | .25 |
| **564** | A153 | 50c | Lorraine | .25 | .25 |
| **565** | A153 | 60c | County of Nice | .25 | .25 |
| | | | *Nos. 562-565 (4)* | 1.00 | 1.00 |

For surcharges see Reunion Nos. 268-269.

Reaching for "Peace" — A157

Holding the Dove of Peace — A158

**1946, July 29 Engr. *Perf. 13***

| No. | Type | Value | Color | Unused | Used |
|---|---|---|---|---|---|
| **566** | A157 | 3fr | Prussian green | .25 | .25 |
| **567** | A158 | 10fr | dark blue | .25 | .25 |

Peace Conference of Paris, 1946.

Vézelay A159

Luxembourg Palace — A160

Rocamadour A161

Pointe du Raz, Finistère A162

**1946 Unwmk. *Perf. 13***

| No. | Type | Value | Color | Unused | Used |
|---|---|---|---|---|---|
| **568** | A159 | 5fr | rose violet | .25 | .25 |
| **569** | A160 | 10fr | dark blue | .25 | .25 |
| **570** | A161 | 15fr | dk violet brn | 3.50 | .55 |
| **571** | A162 | 20fr | slate gray | 1.00 | .25 |
| | | | *Nos. 568-571 (4)* | 5.00 | 1.30 |

See Nos. 591-592. For surcharges see Reunion Nos. 277, 279.

Globe and Wreath — A163

**1946, Nov.**

| No. | Type | Value | Color | Unused | Used |
|---|---|---|---|---|---|
| **572** | A163 | 10fr | dark blue | .25 | .25 |

Gen. conf. of UNESCO, Paris, 1946.

Cannes A164

Stanislas Square, Nancy A165

**1946-48 Engr. *Perf. 13***

| No. | Type | Value | Color | Unused | Used |
|---|---|---|---|---|---|
| **573** | A164 | 6fr | rose red | 1.10 | .40 |
| **574** | A165 | 25fr | black brown | 3.00 | .25 |
| **575** | A165 | 25fr | dark blue ('48) | 10.00 | .90 |
| | | | *Nos. 573-575 (3)* | 14.10 | 1.55 |

For surcharges see Reunion Nos. 280-281.

### Ceres & Marianne Types of 1945

**1947 Unwmk. Typo. *Perf. 14x13½***

| No. | Type | Value | Color | Unused | Used |
|---|---|---|---|---|---|
| **576** | A146 | 1.30fr | dull blue | .25 | .25 |
| **577** | A147 | 3fr | green | 1.50 | .25 |
| **578** | A147 | 3.50fr | brown red | .60 | .30 |
| **579** | A147 | 5fr | blue | .25 | .25 |
| **580** | A147 | 6fr | carmine | .25 | .25 |
| | | | *Nos. 576-580 (5)* | 2.85 | 1.30 |

Colonnade of the Louvre A166

La Conciergerie, Paris Prison — A167

La Cité, Oldest Section of Paris A168

Place de la Concorde A169

**1947, May 7 Engr. *Perf. 13***

| No. | Type | Value | Color | Unused | Used |
|---|---|---|---|---|---|
| **581** | A166 | 3.50fr | chocolate | .30 | .30 |
| **582** | A167 | 4.50fr | dk slate gray | .30 | .30 |
| **583** | A168 | 6fr | red | .85 | .85 |
| **584** | A169 | 10fr | bright ultra | .85 | .85 |
| | | | *Nos. 581-584 (4)* | 2.30 | 2.30 |

12th UPU Cong., Paris, May 7-July 7. See No. 5035a.

Auguste Pavie — A170

**1947, May 30**

| | | | |
|---|---|---|---|
| **585** A170 4.50fr sepia | | .30 | .25 |

Cent. of the birth of Auguste Pavie, French pioneer in Laos.

Francois Fénelon — A171

**1947, July 12**

| | | | |
|---|---|---|---|
| **586** A171 4.50fr chocolate | | .30 | .25 |

Issued to honor Francois de Salignac de la Mothe-Fénelon, prelate and writer.

Fleur-de-Lis and Double Carrick Bend — A172

**1947, Aug. 2** **Unwmk.**

| | | | |
|---|---|---|---|
| **587** A172 5fr brown | | .30 | .25 |

6th World Boy Scout Jamboree held at Moisson, Aug. 9th-18th, 1947.

Captured Patriot — A173

**1947, Nov. 10** **Engr.** ***Perf. 13***

| | | | |
|---|---|---|---|
| **588** A173 5fr sepia | | .40 | .35 |

No. 576 Surcharged in Carmine

**1947, Nov.** **Typo.** ***Perf. 14x13½***

| | | | |
|---|---|---|---|
| **589** A146 1fr on 1.30fr dull blue | | .25 | .25 |

View of Conques — A174

**1947, Dec. 18** **Engr.** ***Perf. 13***

| | | | |
|---|---|---|---|
| **590** A174 15fr henna brown | | 3.50 | .70 |

For surcharge see Reunion No. 282.

**Types of 1946-47**

**1948** **Re-engraved**

| | | | |
|---|---|---|---|
| **591** A160 12fr rose carmine | | 2.50 | .45 |
| **592** A160 15fr bright red | | .60 | .40 |
| **593** A174 18fr dark blue | | 3.50 | .40 |
| *Nos. 591-593 (3)* | | 6.60 | 1.25 |

"FRANCE" substituted for inscriptions "RF" and "REPUBLIQUE FRANCAISE."

**Marianne Type of 1945**

**1948-49** **Typo.** ***Perf. 14x13½***

| | | | |
|---|---|---|---|
| **594** A147 2.50fr brown | | 2.75 | 1.25 |
| **595** A147 3fr lilac rose | | .25 | .25 |
| **596** A147 4fr lt blue grn | | .25 | .25 |
| **597** A147 4fr brown org | | 2.50 | .90 |
| **598** A147 5fr lt blue grn | | .60 | .25 |
| **599** A147 8fr blue | | .30 | .25 |
| **600** A147 10fr brt violet | | .25 | .25 |
| **601** A147 12fr ultra ('49) | | 2.50 | .25 |
| **602** A147 15fr crim rose ('49) | | .85 | .25 |
| *a.* Booklet pane of 10 | | 150.00 | |
| *Nos. 594-602 (9)* | | 10.25 | 3.90 |

No. 594 known only precanceled. See second note after No. 132.

François René de Chateaubriand — A175

**1948, July 3** **Engr.** ***Perf. 13***

| | | | |
|---|---|---|---|
| **603** A175 18fr dark blue | | .30 | .25 |

Vicomte de Chateaubriand (1768-1848).

Philippe François M. de Hautecloque (Gen. Jacques Leclerc) — A176

**1948, July 3**

| | | | |
|---|---|---|---|
| **604** A176 6fr gray black | | .30 | .25 |

See Nos. 692-692A.

Chaillot Palace A177

A178

**1948, Sept. 21**

| | | | |
|---|---|---|---|
| **605** A177 12fr carmine rose | | .35 | .30 |
| **606** A178 18fr indigo | | .35 | .30 |

Meeting of the UN General Assembly, Paris, 1948.

Genissiat Dam A179

**1948, Sept. 21**

| | | | |
|---|---|---|---|
| **607** A179 12fr carmine rose | | .85 | .75 |

Paul Langevin — A180

**1948, Nov. 17** ***Perf. 14x13***

| | | | |
|---|---|---|---|
| **608** A180 5fr shown | | .50 | .25 |
| **609** A180 8fr Jean Perrin | | .50 | .25 |

Placing of the ashes of physicists Langevin (1872-1946) and Perrin (1870-1942) in the Pantheon.

**No. 580 Surcharged with New Value and Bars in Black**

**1949, Jan.** ***Perf. 14x13½***

| | | | |
|---|---|---|---|
| **610** A147 5fr on 6fr carmine | | .25 | .25 |

Arctic Scene — A181

**1949, May 2** ***Perf. 13***

| | | | |
|---|---|---|---|
| **611** A181 15fr indigo | | .30 | .25 |

French polar explorations.

**Types of 1849 and 1945**

**1949, May 9** **Engr.** ***Imperf.***

| | | | |
|---|---|---|---|
| **612** A1 15fr red | | 3.00 | 3.00 |
| **613** A1 25fr deep blue | | 3.00 | 3.00 |

***Perf. 14x13***

| | | | |
|---|---|---|---|
| **614** A147 15fr red | | 3.00 | 3.00 |
| **615** A147 25fr deep blue | | 3.00 | 3.00 |
| *a.* Strip of 4, #612-615 + label | | 14.00 | 12.00 |
| *Nos. 612-615 (4)* | | 12.00 | 12.00 |

Cent. of the 1st French postage stamps.

Arms of Burgundy — A182

Arms: 50c, Guyenne (Aquitania). 1fr, Savoy. 2fr, Auvergne. 4fr, Anjou.

**1949, May 11** **Typo.** ***Perf. 14x13½***

| | | | |
|---|---|---|---|
| **616** A182 10c blue, red & yel | | .25 | .25 |
| **617** A182 50c blue, red & yel | | .25 | .25 |
| **618** A182 1fr brown & red | | .40 | .25 |
| **619** A182 2fr green, yel & red | | .40 | .25 |
| **620** A182 4fr blue, red & yel | | .30 | .25 |
| *Nos. 616-620 (5)* | | 1.60 | 1.25 |

See Nos. 659-663, 694-699, 733-739, 782-785. For surcharges see Reunion Nos. 283-284, 288-289, 297, 301, 305, 311.

Collegiate Church of St. Barnard and Dauphiné Arms A183

**1949, May 14** **Engr.** ***Perf. 13***

| | | | |
|---|---|---|---|
| **621** A183 12fr red brown | | .30 | .25 |

600th anniv. of France's acquisition of the Dauphiné region.

US and French Flags, Plane and Steamship A184

**1949, May 14**

| | | | |
|---|---|---|---|
| **622** A184 25fr blue & carmine | | .45 | .35 |

Franco-American friendship.

Cloister of St. Wandrille Abbey A185

**1949, May 18**

| | | | |
|---|---|---|---|
| **623** A185 25fr deep ultra | | .30 | .25 |

See No. 649. For surcharge see Reunion No. 287.

**Type of 1849 Inscribed "1849-1949" in Lower Margin**

**1949, June 1**

| | | | |
|---|---|---|---|
| **624** A1 10fr brown orange | | 55.00 | 40.00 |
| *a.* Sheet of 10 | | 700.00 | 450.00 |

Cent. of the 1st French postage stamp.

No. 624 has wide margins, 40x52mm from perforation to perforation. Sold for 110fr, which included cost of admission to the Centenary Intl. Exhib., Paris, June 1949.

Claude Chappe — A186

15fr, François Arago & André M. Ampère. 25fr, Emile Baudot. 50fr, Gen. Gustave A. Ferrié.

**Inscribed: "C.I.T.T. PARIS 1949"**

**1949, June 13** **Unwmk.** ***Perf. 13***

| | | | |
|---|---|---|---|
| **625** A186 10fr vermilion | | .75 | .70 |
| **626** A186 15fr sepia | | .75 | .70 |
| **627** A186 25fr deep claret | | 1.90 | 1.90 |
| **628** A186 50fr deep blue | | 3.75 | 2.75 |
| *Nos. 625-628 (4)* | | 7.15 | 6.05 |

International Telegraph and Telephone Conference, Paris, May-July 1949.

Jean Racine — A187

**1949**

| | | | |
|---|---|---|---|
| **629** A187 12fr sepia | | .30 | .25 |

Death of Jean Racine, dramatist, 250th anniv.

Abbey of St. Bertrand de Comminges A188

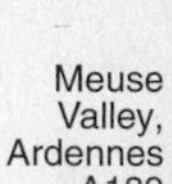

Meuse Valley, Ardennes A189

Mt. Gerbier de Jonc, Vivarais A190

**1949 Engr.**

| | | | |
|---|---|---|---|
| 630 A188 20fr dark red | .25 | .25 |
| 631 A189 40fr Prus green | 12.50 | .25 |
| 632 A190 50fr sepia | 2.10 | .25 |
| *Nos. 630-632 (3)* | 14.85 | .75 |

For surcharge see Reunion No. 286.

A191

**1949, Oct. 18**

633 A191 15fr deep carmine .25 .25

50th anniv. of the Assembly of Presidents of Chambers of Commerce of the French Union.

UPU Allegory A192

**1949, Nov. 7**

| | | |
|---|---|---|
| 634 A192 5fr dark green | .25 | .25 |
| 635 A192 15fr deep carmine | .30 | .25 |
| 636 A192 25fr deep blue | 1.00 | .90 |
| *Nos. 634-636 (3)* | 1.55 | 1.40 |

UPU, 75th anniversary.

Raymond Poincaré — A193

**1950, May 27 Unwmk. *Perf. 13***

637 A193 15fr indigo .30 .25

Charles Péguy and Cathedral at Chartres A194

François Rabelais — A195

**1950, June**

| | | |
|---|---|---|
| 638 A194 12fr dk brown | .30 | .25 |
| 639 A195 12fr red brown | .60 | .45 |

Chateau of Chateaudun — A196

**1950, Nov. 25**

640 A196 8fr choc & bis brn .55 .40

Madame Récamier A197

Marie de Sévigné A198

**1950**

| | | |
|---|---|---|
| 641 A197 12fr dark green | .45 | .40 |
| 642 A198 15fr ultra | .45 | .40 |

See footnote after No. 4642.

Palace of Fontainbleau — A199

**1951, Jan. 20**

643 A199 12fr dark brown .75 .60

Jules Ferry — A200

**1951, Mar. 17**

644 A200 15fr bright red .40 .40

Hands Holding Shuttle A201

**1951, Apr. 9**

645 A201 25fr deep ultra .75 .45

Intl. Textile Exposition, Lille, April-May, 1951.

Jean-Baptiste de la Salle — A202

**1951, Apr. 28**

646 A202 15fr chocolate .45 .35

300th anniv. of the birth of Jean-Baptiste de la Salle, educator and saint.

Map and Anchor A203

**1951, May 12**

647 A203 15fr deep ultra .60 .30

50th anniv. of the creation of the French colonial troops.

Vincent d'Indy A204

**1951, May 15**

648 A204 25fr deep green 1.50 1.50

Vincent d'Indy, composer, birth cent.

**Abbey Type of 1949**

**1951**

649 A185 30fr bright blue 4.00 3.25

**Marianne Type of 1945-47**

**1951 Typo. *Perf. 14x13½***

| | | |
|---|---|---|
| 650 A147 5fr dull violet | .30 | .25 |
| 651 A147 6fr green | 4.75 | .45 |
| 652 A147 12fr red orange | .70 | .25 |
| 653 A147 15fr ultra | .25 | .25 |
| *a.* Booklet pane of 10 | 60.00 | |
| 654 A147 18fr cerise | 15.00 | 1.20 |
| *Nos. 650-654 (5)* | 21.00 | 2.40 |

Professors Nocard, Bouley and Chauveau; Gate at Lyons School A205

**1951, June 8 Engr. *Perf. 13***

655 A205 12fr red violet .60 .40

Issued to honor Veterinary Medicine.

Gen. Picqué, Cols. Roussin and Villemin; Val de Grace Dome A206

**1951, June 17 Unwmk.**

656 A206 15fr red brown .75 .40

Issued to honor Military Medicine.

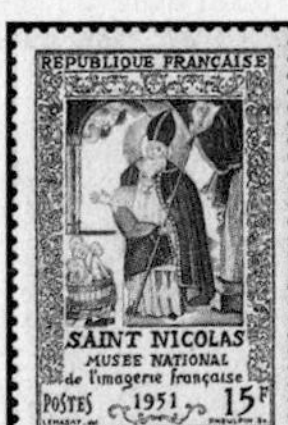

St. Nicholas, by Jean Didier — A207

**1951, June 23**

657 A207 15fr ind, dp claret & org 1.00 .75

Chateau Bontemps, Arbois A208

**1951, June 23**

658 A208 30fr indigo .75 .25

For surcharge see Reunion No. 296.

**Arms Type of 1949**

Arms of: 10c, Artois. 50c, Limousin. 1fr, Béarn. 2fr, Touraine. 3fr, Franche-Comté.

**1951, June Typo. *Perf. 14x13½***

| | | |
|---|---|---|
| 659 A182 10c red, vio bl & yel | .25 | .25 |
| 660 A182 50c green, red & blk | .25 | .25 |
| 661 A182 1fr blue, red & yel | .25 | .25 |
| 662 A182 2fr vio bl, red & yel | .60 | .25 |
| 663 A182 3fr red, vio bl & yel | .45 | .30 |
| *Nos. 659-663 (5)* | 1.80 | 1.30 |

Seal of Paris — A209

**Unwmk.**

**1951, July 7 Engr. *Perf. 13***

664 A209 15fr dp bl, dk brn & red .55 .30

2,000th anniv. of the founding of Paris.

Maurice Nogues and Globe — A210

**1951, Oct. 13**

665 A210 12fr indigo & blue .70 .60

Maurice Nogues, aviation pioneer.

Charles Baudelaire A211

Poets: 12fr, Paul Verlaine. 15fr, Arthur Rimbaud.

**1951, Oct. 27**

| | | |
|---|---|---|
| 666 A211 8fr purple | .70 | .45 |
| 667 A211 12fr gray | .70 | .45 |
| 668 A211 15fr dp green | .70 | .45 |
| *Nos. 666-668 (3)* | 2.10 | 1.35 |

Georges Clemenceau, Birth Cent. — A212

**1951, Nov. 11**

669 A212 15fr black brown .55 .35

Chateau du Clos, Vougeot A213

**1951, Nov. 17**

670 A213 30fr blk brn & brn 5.25 1.75

Chaillot Palace and Eiffel Tower A214

**1951, Nov. 6**

| | | |
|---|---|---|
| 671 A214 18fr red | .90 | .60 |
| 672 A214 30fr deep ultra | 1.50 | 1.50 |

Opening of the Geneva Assembly of the United Nations, Paris, Nov. 6, 1951.

Observatory, Pic du Midi — A215

Abbaye aux Hommes, Caen — A216

**1951, Dec. 22**
**673** A215 40fr violet 4.50 .25
**674** A216 50fr black brown 4.00 .25

For surcharge see Reunion No. 294.

Marshal Jean de Lattre de Tassigny, 1890-1952 A217

**1952, May 8 Unwmk. *Perf. 13***
**675** A217 15fr violet brown .75 .45

See No. 717.

Gate of France, Vaucouleurs — A218

**1952, May 11**
**676** A218 12fr brown black 1.00 .75

Flags and Monument at Narvik, Norway A219

**1952, May 28**
**677** A219 30fr violet blue 2.50 1.75

Battle of Narvik, May 27, 1940.

Chateau de Chambord A220

**1952, May 30**
**678** A220 20fr dark purple .45 .25

For surcharge see Reunion No. 292.

Assembly Hall, Strasbourg A221

**1952, May 31**
**679** A221 30fr dark green 6.50 4.50

Issued to honor the Council of Europe.

Monument, Bir-Hacheim Cemetery — A222

**1952, June 14**
**680** A222 30fr rose lake 3.00 1.75

10th anniv. of the defense of Bir-Hacheim.

Abbey of the Holy Cross, Poitiers — A223

**1952, June 21**
**681** A223 15fr bright red .40 .40

14th cent. of the foundation of the Abbey of the Holy Cross at Poitiers.

Leonardo da Vinci, Amboise Chateau and La Signoria, Florence A224

**1952, July 9**
**682** A224 30fr deep ultra 7.00 5.25

Leonardo da Vinci, 500th birth anniv.

Garabit Viaduct A225

**1952, July 5**
**683** A225 15fr dark blue .45 .45

Sword and Military Medals, 1852-1952 — A226

**1952, July 5**
**684** A226 15fr choc, grn & yel .45 .40

Cent. of the creation of the Military Medal.

Dr. René Laennec — A227

**1952, Nov. 7**
**685** A227 12fr dark green .60 .45

Versailles Gate, Painted by Utrillo A228

**1952, Dec. 20**
**686** A228 18fr violet brown 2.25 1.50

Publicity for the restoration of Versailles Palace. See No. 728.

Mannequin — A229

**1953, Apr. 24 Unwmk. *Perf. 13***
**687** A229 30fr blue blk & rose vio .75 .30

Dressmaking industry of France.

Gargantua of François Rabelais A230

Célimène from The Misanthrope A231

Figaro, from the Barber of Seville — A232

Hernani of Victor Hugo — A233

**1953**
**688** A230 6fr dp plum & car .25 .25
**689** A231 8fr indigo & ultra .25 .25
**690** A232 12fr vio brn & dk grn .25 .25
**691** A233 18fr vio brn & blk brn .50 .25
*Nos. 688-691 (4)* 1.25 1.00

For surcharge see Reunion No. 298.

**Type of 1948**

**Inscribed "Général Leclerc Maréchal de France"**

**1953-54**
**692** A176 8fr red brown .75 .60
**692A** A176 12fr dk grn & gray grn ('54) 2.25 1.50

Issued to honor the memory of General Jacques Leclerc.

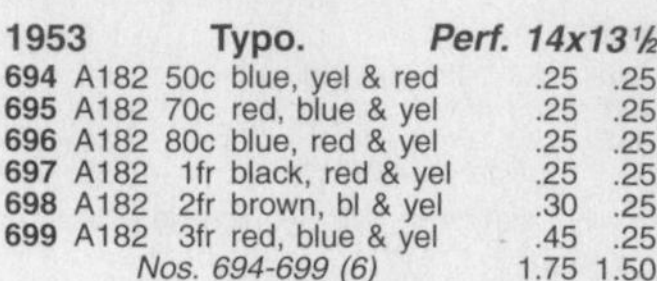

Map and Cyclists, 1903-1953 A234

**1953, July 26**
**693** A234 12fr red brn, ultra & blk 1.75 1.10

50th anniv. of the Bicycle Tour de France.

**Arms Type of 1949**

50c, Picardy. 70c, Gascony. 80c, Berri. 1fr, Poitou. 2fr, Champagne. 3fr, Dauphiné.

**1953 Typo. *Perf. 14x13½***
**694** A182 50c blue, yel & red .25 .25
**695** A182 70c red, blue & yel .25 .25
**696** A182 80c blue, red & yel .25 .25
**697** A182 1fr black, red & yel .25 .25
**698** A182 2fr brown, bl & yel .30 .25
**699** A182 3fr red, blue & yel .45 .25
*Nos. 694-699 (6)* 1.75 1.50

Swimming A235

**1953, Nov. 28 Engr. *Perf. 13***
**700** A235 20fr shown 1.90 .25
**701** A235 25fr Track 10.50 .25
**702** A235 30fr Fencing 1.90 .25
**703** A235 40fr Canoe racing 11.00 .25
**704** A235 50fr Rowing 6.00 .25
**705** A235 75fr Equestrian 30.00 11.00
*Nos. 700-705 (6)* 61.30 12.25

For surcharges see Reunion Nos. 299-300.

**No. 654 Surcharged with New Value and Bars in Black**

**1954 *Perf. 14x13½***
**706** A147 15fr on 18fr cerise .40 .25

Farm Woman A236

Gallic Cock A237

**1954 Typo.**
**707** A236 4fr blue .25 .25
**708** A236 8fr brown red 4.75 1.00
**709** A237 12fr cerise 3.00 .55
**710** A237 24fr blue green 16.00 3.25
*Nos. 707-710 (4)* 24.00 5.05

Nos. 707-710 are known only precanceled. See second note after No. 132.

See Nos. 833-834, 840-844, 910-913, 939, 952-955. For surcharges see Reunion Nos. 324, 326-327.

Tapestry and Gobelin Workshop — A238

Designs: 30fr, Book manufacture. 40fr, Porcelain and glassware. 50fr, Jewelry and metalsmith's work. 75fr, Flowers and perfumes.

**1954, May 6 Engr. *Perf. 13***
**711** A238 25fr red brn car & blk brn 9.50 .45
**712** A238 30fr dk grn & lil gray 1.10 .25
**713** A238 40fr dk brn, vio brn & org brn 3.50 .25
**714** A238 50fr brt ultra, dl grn & org brn 1.10 .25
**715** A238 75fr dp car & magenta 11.00 1.10
*Nos. 711-715 (5)* 26.20 2.30

For surcharges see Reunion Nos. 303-304.

Entrance to Exhibition Park — A239

**1954, May 22**
**716** A239 15fr blue & dk car .30 .25

Founding of the Fair of Paris, 50th anniv.

**De Lattre Type of 1952**

**1954, June 5**

**717** A217 12fr vio bl & indigo 1.50 .75

Allied Landings A240

**1954, June 5**

**718** A240 15fr scarlet & ultra 1.75 .90

The 10th anniversary of the liberation.

View of Lourdes A241

Street Corner, Quimper — A242

Views: 8fr, Seine valley, Les Andelys. 10fr, Beach at Royan. 18fr, Cheverny Chateau. 20fr, Beach, Gulf of Ajaccio.

**1954**

| | | | | |
|---|---|---|---|---|
| **719** | A241 | 6fr ultra, ind & dk grn | .30 | .25 |
| **720** | A241 | 8fr brt blue & dk grn | .30 | .25 |
| **721** | A241 | 10fr aqua & org brn | .25 | .25 |
| **722** | A242 | 12fr rose vio & dk vio | .30 | .25 |
| **723** | A241 | 18fr bl, dk grn & ind | 2.50 | .50 |
| **724** | A241 | 20fr blk brn, bl grn & red brn | 2.25 | .25 |
| | | *Nos. 719-724 (6)* | 5.90 | 1.75 |

See No. 873. For surcharges see Reunion Nos. 302, 306-310. See footnote after No. 4642.

Abbey Ruins, Jumièges — A243

**1954, June 13**

**725** A243 12fr vio bl, ind & dk grn 1.50 .75

13th centenary of Abbey of Jumièges.

St. Philibert Abbey, Tournus — A244

**1954, June 18**

**726** A244 30fr indigo & blue 4.00 3.00

1st conf. of the Intl. Center of Romance Studies.

View of Stenay A245

**1954, June 26**

**727** A245 15fr dk brn & org brn .70 .30

Acquisition of Stenay by France, 300th anniv.

**Versailles Type of 1952**

**1954, July 10**

**728** A228 18fr dp bl, ind & vio brn 7.50 4.50

Villandry Chateau A246

**1954, July 17**

**729** A246 18fr dk bl & dk bl grn 4.00 3.00

Napoleon Awarding Legion of Honor Decoration A247

**1954, Aug. 14**

**730** A247 12fr scarlet 1.20 .75

150th anniv. of the 1st Legion of Honor awards at Camp de Boulogne.

Cadets Marching Through Gateway A248

**1954, Aug. 1**

**731** A248 15fr vio gray, dk bl & car 1.00 1.00

150th anniversary of the founding of the Military School of Saint-Cyr.

Allegory — A249

**1954, Oct. 4**

**732** A249 30fr indigo & choc 4.00 3.00

Issued to publicize the fact that the metric system was first introduced in France.

**Arms Type of 1949**

Arms: 50c, Maine. 70c, Navarre. 80c, Nivernais. 1fr, Bourbonnais. 2fr, Angoumois. 3fr, Aunis. 5fr, Saintonge.

**1954** **Typo.** ***Perf. 14x13½***

| | | | | |
|---|---|---|---|---|
| **733** | A182 | 50c multicolored | .25 | .25 |
| **734** | A182 | 70c green, red & yel | .25 | .25 |
| **735** | A182 | 80c blue, red & yel | .25 | .25 |
| **736** | A182 | 1fr red, blue & yel | .25 | .25 |
| **737** | A182 | 2fr black, red & yel | .25 | .25 |
| **738** | A182 | 3fr brown, red & yel | .25 | .25 |
| **739** | A182 | 5fr blue & yellow | .25 | .25 |
| | | *Nos. 733-739 (7)* | 1.75 | 1.75 |

Duke de Saint-Simon — A250

**1955, Feb. 5** **Engr.** ***Perf. 13***

**740** A250 12fr dk brn & vio brn .45 .30

Louis de Rouvroy, Duke de Saint-Simon (1675-1755).

Allegory and Rotary Emblem A251

**1955, Feb. 23**

**741** A251 30fr vio bl, bl & org 2.00 .75

50th anniv. of Rotary International.

Marianne — A252

**1955-59** **Typo.** ***Perf. 14x13½***

| | | | | |
|---|---|---|---|---|
| **751** | A252 | 6fr fawn | 2.00 | 1.40 |
| **752** | A252 | 12fr green | 2.40 | 1.10 |
| *a.* | | Bklt. pane of 10 + 2 labels | 30.00 | |
| **753** | A252 | 15fr carmine | .25 | .25 |
| *a.* | | Booklet pane of 10 | 10.00 | |
| **754** | A252 | 18fr green ('58) | .25 | .25 |
| **755** | A252 | 20fr ultra ('57) | .30 | .25 |
| **756** | A252 | 25fr rose red ('59) | 1.00 | .25 |
| *a.* | | Booklet pane of 8 | 40.00 | |
| *b.* | | Booklet pane of 10 | 30.00 | |
| | | *Nos. 751-756 (6)* | 6.20 | 3.50 |

No. 751 was issued in coils of 1,000.

No. 752 was issued in panes of 10 stamps and two labels with marginal instructions for folding to form a booklet.

Nos. 754-755 are found in two types, distinguished by the numerals. On the 18fr there is no serif at left of base of the "1" on the 1st type. The 2nd type has a shorter "1" with no serifs at base. On the 20fr the 2nd type has a well formed "2" and the horiz. lines of the "F" of the denomination are longer and of equal length.

No. 756 also in two types, distinguished by border width. On the 1st type, the border is thicker than the width of the letters. On the 2nd type, the border is thinner than the width of the letters.

For surcharges see Reunion Nos. 330-331.

Philippe Lebon, Inventor of Illuminating Gas A253

Inventors: 10fr, Barthélemy Thimonnier, sewing machine. 12fr, Nicolas Appert, canned foods. 18fr, Dr. E. H. St. Claire Deville, aluminum. 25fr, Pierre Martin, steel making. 30fr, Bernigaud de Chardonnet, rayon.

**1955, Mar. 5** **Engr.** ***Perf. 13***

| | | | | |
|---|---|---|---|---|
| **757** | A253 | 5fr dk vio bl & bl | .70 | .60 |
| **758** | A253 | 10fr dk brn & org brn | .70 | .60 |
| **759** | A253 | 12fr dk green | .90 | .70 |
| **760** | A253 | 18fr dk vio bl & ind | 2.25 | 1.40 |
| **761** | A253 | 25fr dk brnsh pur & vio | 2.50 | 1.50 |
| **762** | A253 | 30fr rose car & scar | 2.50 | 1.50 |
| | | *Nos. 757-762 (6)* | 9.55 | 6.30 |

St. Stephen Bridge, Limoges A254

**1955, Mar. 26** **Unwmk.** ***Perf. 13***

**763** A254 12fr yel brn & dk vio brn 1.20 1.00

Gloved Model in Place de la Concorde — A255

**1955, Mar. 26**

**764** A255 25fr blk brn, vio bl & blk .75 .25

French glove manufacturing. See footnote after No. 4642.

Jean Pierre Claris de Florian A256

**1955, Apr. 2**

**765** A256 12fr blue green .60 .40

200th anniv. of the birth of Jean Pierre Claris de Florian, fabulist.

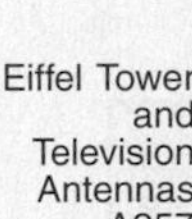

Eiffel Tower and Television Antennas A257

**1955, Apr. 16**

**766** A257 15fr indigo & ultra .75 .70

French advancement in television.

Wire Fence and Guard Tower A258

**1955, Apr. 23**

**767** A258 12fr dk gray bl & brn blk .75 .60

10th anniv. of the liberation of concentration camps.

Electric Train A259

**1955, May 11**

**768** A259 12fr blk brn & slate bl 1.60 1.10

Issued to publicize the electrification of the Valenciennes-Thionville railroad line.

Jacquemart of Moulins — A260

**1955, May 28**

**769** A260 12fr black brown 1.40 1.00

Jules Verne and Nautilus A261

**1955, June 3**
**770** A261 30fr indigo 6.00 3.75

50th anniv. of the death of Jules Verne.

Auguste and Louis Lumière and Motion Picture Projector A262

**1955, June 12**
**771** A262 30fr rose brown 5.25 3.25

Invention of motion pictures, 60th anniv.

Jacques Coeur and His Mansion at Bourges A263

**1955, June 18**
**772** A263 12fr violet 1.90 1.20

5th centenary of the death of Jacques Coeur (1395?-1456), French merchant.

Corvette "La Capricieuse" — A264

**1955, July 9**
**773** A264 30fr aqua & dk blue 3.75 3.25

Centenary of the voyage of La Capricieuse to Canada.

Bordeaux A265

Designs: 8fr, Marseille. 10fr, Nice. 12fr, Valentre bridge, Cahors. 18fr, Uzerche. 25fr, Fortifications, Brouage.

**1955, Oct. 15**
**774** A265 6fr carmine lake .25 .25
**775** A265 8fr indigo .45 .25
**776** A265 10fr dp ultra .25 .25
**777** A265 12fr violet & brn .25 .25
**778** A265 18fr bluish grn & ind .60 .25
**779** A265 25fr org brn & red brn .75 .25
*Nos. 774-779 (6)* 2.55 1.50

See Nos. 838-839. For surcharges see Reunion Nos. 312-317, 323.

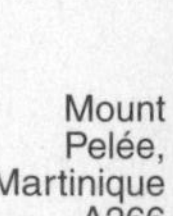

Mount Pelée, Martinique A266

**1955, Nov. 1**
**780** A266 20fr dk & lt purple 2.40 .25

Gérard de Nerval — A267

**1955, Nov. 11**
**781** A267 12fr lake & sepia .40 .25

Centenary of the death of Gérard de Nerval (Labrunie), author.

### Arms Type of 1949

Arms of: 50c, County of Foix. 70c, Marche. 80c, Roussillon. 1fr, Comtat Venaissin.

*Perf. 14x13½*
**1955, Nov. 19 Typo. Unwmk.**
**782** A182 50c multicolored .25 .25
**783** A182 70c red, blue & yel .25 .25
**784** A182 80c brown, yel & red .25 .25
**785** A182 1fr blue, red & yel .25 .25
*Nos. 782-785 (4)* 1.00 1.00

Concentration Camp Victim and Monument — A268

**1956, Jan. 14 Engr. *Perf. 13***
**786** A268 15fr brn blk & red brn .45 .40

Natl. memorial for Nazi deportation victims erected at the Natzwiller Struthof concentration camp in Alsace.

Belfry at Douai — A269

**1956, Feb. 11**
**787** A269 15fr ultra & indigo .40 .40

Col. Emil Driant A270

**1956, Feb. 21**
**788** A270 15fr dark blue .30 .25

40th anniv. of the death of Col. Emil Driant during the battle of Verdun.



Trench Fighting — A271

**1956, Mar. 3**
**789** A271 30fr indigo & dk olive 1.50 1.25

40th anniversary of Battle of Verdun.

A272

A272a

A272b



A272c

Scientists: 12fr, Jean Henri Fabre, Entomology. 15fr, Charles Tellier, Refrigeration. 18fr, Camille Flammarion, Popular Astronomy. 30fr, Paul Sabatier, Catalytic Chemistry.

**1956, Apr. 7**
**790** A272 12fr vio brn & org brn .75 .40
**791** A272a 15fr vio bl & int blk .75 .40
**792** A272b 18fr brt ultra 1.40 1.25
**793** A272c 30fr Prus grn & dk grn 3.50 2.00
*Nos. 790-793 (4)* 6.40 4.05

Grand Trianon, Versailles A273

**1956, Apr. 14**
**794** A273 12fr vio brn & gray grn 1.10 .75

Symbols of Latin American and French Culture A274

**1956, Apr. 21**
**795** A274 30fr brown & red brn 1.60 1.40

Issued in recognition of the friendship between France and Latin America.

"The Smile of Reims" and Botticelli's "Spring" A275

**1956, May 5**
**796** A275 12fr black & green .60 .40

Issued to emphasize the cultural and artistic kinship of Reims and Florence.

Leprosarium and Maltese Cross — A276

**1956, May 12**
**797** A276 12fr sepia, red brn & red .40 .35

Issued in honor of the Knights of Malta.

St. Yves de Treguier A277

**1956, May 19**
**798** A277 15fr bluish gray & blk .35 .25

St. Yves, patron saint of lawyers.

Marshal Franchet d'Esperey — A278

**1956, May 26**
**799** A278 30fr deep claret 2.25 1.40

Centenary of the birth of Marshal Louis Franchet d'Esperey.

Miners Monument — A279

**1956, June 2**
**800** A279 12fr violet brown .45 .40

Town Montceau-les-Mines, 100th anniv.

Basketball — A280

Sports: 40fr, Pelota (Jai alai). 50fr, Rugby. 75fr, Mountain climbing.

**1956, July 7**
**801** A280 30fr gray vio & blk 1.10 .25
**802** A280 40fr brown & vio brn 4.00 .25
**803** A280 50fr rose vio & vio 1.50 .25
**804** A280 75fr indigo, grn & bl 9.00 1.75
*Nos. 801-804 (4)* 15.60 2.50

For surcharges see Reunion Nos. 318-321.

### Europa Issue

"Rebuilding Europe" — A281

*Perf. 13½x14*
**1956, Sept. 15 Typo. Unwmk.**
**805** A281 15fr rose & rose lake .75 .25

*Perf. 13*

**Engr.**

**806** A281 30fr lt blue & vio bl 4.50 .75

Issued to symbolize the cooperation among the six countries comprising the Coal and Steel Community.

No. 805 measures 21x35½mm, No. 806 measures 22x35½mm.

Dam at Donzère-Mondragon — A282

Cable Railway to Pic du Midi — A283

Rhine Port of Strasbourg A284

**1956, Oct. 6** **Engr.** ***Perf. 13***

**807** A282 12fr gray vio & vio brn 1.10 .90
**808** A283 18fr indigo 2.25 1.50
**809** A284 30fr indigo & dk blue 9.50 4.50
*Nos. 807-809 (3)* 12.85 6.90

French technical achievements.

Antoine-Augustin Parmentier — A285

**1956, Oct. 27**

**810** A285 12fr brown red & brown .65 .45

Parmentier, nutrition chemist, who popularized the potato in France.

Petrarch — A286

Portraits: 12fr, J. D. Lully. 15fr, J. J. Rousseau. 18fr, Benjamin Franklin. 20fr, Frederic Chopin. 30fr, Vincent van Gogh.

**1956, Nov. 10**

**811** A286 8fr green .60 .45
**812** A286 12fr claret .60 .45
**813** A286 15fr dark red .90 .45
**814** A286 18fr ultra 1.90 1.50
**815** A286 20fr brt violet 2.40 1.50
**816** A286 30fr brt grnsh blue 4.75 2.25
*Nos. 811-816 (6)* 11.15 6.60

Famous men who lived in France.

Pierre de Coubertin and Olympic Stadium A287

**1956, Nov. 24**

**817** A287 30fr dk blue gray & pur 1.50 .90

Issued in honor of Baron Pierre de Coubertin, founder of the modern Olympic Games.

Homing Pigeon A288

**1957, Jan. 12**

**818** A288 15fr dp ultra, ind & red brn .40 .25

Victor Schoelcher — A289

**1957, Feb. 16** **Engr.**

**819** A289 18fr lilac rose .45 .40

Issued in honor of Victor Schoelcher, who freed the slaves in the French Colonies.

Sèvres Porcelain A290

**1957, Mar. 23** **Unwmk.** ***Perf. 13***

**820** A290 30fr ultra & vio blue .60 .40

Bicentenary of the porcelain works at Sèvres (in 1956).

Gaston Planté and Storage Battery A291

Designs: 12fr, Antoine Béclère and X-ray apparatus. 18fr, Octave Terrillon, autoclave, microscope and surgical instruments. 30fr, Etienne Oemichen and early helicopter.

**1957, Apr. 13**

**821** A291 8fr gray blk & dp cl .30 .25
**822** A291 12fr dk bl, blk & emer .35 .25
**823** A291 18fr rose red & mag 1.00 .90
**824** A291 30fr green & slate grn 2.10 1.60
*Nos. 821-824 (4)* 3.75 3.00

Uzès Chateau A292

**1957, Apr. 27**

**825** A292 12fr slate bl & bis brn .40 .40

Jean Moulin — A293

Portraits: 10fr, Honoré d'Estienne d'Orves. 12fr, Robert Keller. 18fr, Pierre Brossolette. 20fr, Jean-Baptiste Lebas.

**1957, May 18**

**826** A293 8fr violet brown .90 .30
**827** A293 10fr black & vio bl .90 .30
**828** A293 12fr brown & sl grn 1.00 .35
**829** A293 18fr purple & blk 1.40 1.10
**830** A293 20fr Prus bl & dk bl 1.40 .90
*Nos. 826-830 (5)* 5.60 2.95

Issued in honor of the heroes of the French Underground of World War II.

See Nos. 879-882, 915-919, 959-963, 990-993.

Le Quesnoy — A294

**1957, June 1**

**831** A294 8fr dk slate green .25 .25

See No. 837.

Symbols of Justice A295

**1957, June 1**

**832** A295 12fr sepia & ultra .25 .25

French Cour des Comptes, 150th anniv.

**Farm Woman Type of 1954**

**1957-59** ***Perf. 14x13½***

**833** A236 6fr orange .25 .25
**833A** A236 10fr brt green ('59) .40 .25
**834** A236 12fr red lilac .25 .25
*Nos. 833-834 (3)* .90 .75

Nos. 833-834 issued without precancellation.

Symbols of Public Works A296

**1957, June 20** **Engr.** ***Perf. 13***

**835** A296 30fr sl grn, brn & ocher 1.50 1.00

Brest A297

**1957, July 6**

**836** A297 12fr gray grn & brn ol .90 .75

**Scenic Types of 1955, 1957**

Designs: 15fr, Le Quesnoy. 35fr, Bordeaux. 70fr, Valentre bridge, Cahors.

**1957, July 19** **Unwmk.**

**837** A294 15fr dk bl grn & sep .25 .25
**838** A265 35fr dk bl grn & sl grn 2.90 .90
**839** A265 70fr black & dull grn 16.00 1.60
*Nos. 837-839 (3)* 19.15 2.75

For surcharge see Reunion No. 322.

**Gallic Cock Type of 1954**

**1957** **Typo.** ***Perf. 14x13½***

**840** A237 5fr olive bister .25 .25
**841** A237 10fr bright blue 1.50 .25
**842** A237 15fr plum 1.25 .50
**843** A237 30fr bright red 9.00 2.10
**844** A237 45fr green 19.00 9.00
*Nos. 840-844 (5)* 31.00 12.10

Nos. 840-844 are known only precanceled. See second note after No. 132.

Leo Lagrange and Stadium A298

**1957, Aug. 31** **Engr.** ***Perf. 13***

**845** A298 18fr lilac gray & blk .40 .40

Intl. University Games, Paris, 8/31-9/8.

"United Europe" — A299

**1957, Sept. 16**

**846** A299 20fr red brown & green *.40 .30*
**847** A299 35fr dk brown & blue *.90 .75*

A united Europe for peace and prosperity.

Auguste Comte — A300

**1957, Sept. 14**

**848** A300 35fr brown red & sepia .40 .25

Centenary of the death of Auguste Comte, mathematician and philosopher.

Roman Amphitheater, Lyon — A301

**1957, Oct. 5** ***Perf. 13***

**849** A301 20fr brn org & brn vio .40 .25

2,000th anniv. of the founding of Lyon.

Sens River, Guadeloupe A302

Beynac-Cazenac, Dordogne — A303

Designs: 10fr, Elysee Palace. 25fr, Chateau de Valencay, Indre. 35fr, Rouen Cathedral. 50fr, Roman Ruins, Saint-Remy. 65fr, Evian-les-Bains.

**1957, Oct. 19**

**850** A302 8fr green & lt brn .25 .25
**851** A302 10fr dk ol bis & vio brn .25 .25
**852** A303 18fr indigo & dk brn .25 .25
**853** A302 25fr bl gray & vio brn .55 .25
**854** A303 35fr car rose & lake .25 .25
**855** A302 50fr ol grn & ol bister .35 .25
**856** A302 65fr dk blue & indigo .60 .30
*Nos. 850-856 (7)* 2.50 1.80

See Nos. 907-909. See footnote after No. 4642. For overprint and surcharges see No. 1O1, Reunion Nos. 325, 328-329, 332-334.

Nicolaus Copernicus — A304

Portraits: 10fr, Michelangelo. 12fr, Miguel de Cervantes. 15fr, Rembrandt. 18fr, Isaac Newton. 25fr, Mozart. 35fr, Johann Wolfgang von Goethe.

**1957, Nov. 9** **Engr.** ***Perf. 13***

**857** A304 8fr dark brown .65 .30
**858** A304 10fr dark green .65 .45
**859** A304 12fr dark purple .65 .45
**860** A304 15fr brown & org brn .80 .60
**861** A304 18fr deep blue 1.10 .80
**862** A304 25fr lilac & claret 1.25 .90
**863** A304 35fr blue 1.50 1.00
*Nos. 857-863 (7)* 6.60 4.50

Louis Jacques Thénard A305

**1957, Nov. 30** **Unwmk.**

**864** A305 15fr ol bis & grnsh blk .40 .30

Centenary of the death of L. J. Thenard, chemist, and the founding of the Charitable Society of the Friends of Science.

Dr. Philippe Pinel — A306

French Physicians: 12fr, Fernand Widal. 15fr, Charles Nicolle. 35fr, René Leriche.

**1958, Jan. 25**

**865** A306 8fr brown olive .65 .45
**866** A306 12fr brt vio blue .65 .45
**867** A306 15fr deep blue 1.00 .50
**868** A306 35fr black 1.40 .80
*Nos. 865-868 (4)* 3.70 2.20

Joseph Louis Lagrange — A307

French Scientists: 12fr, Urbain Jean Joseph Leverrier. 15fr, Jean Bernard Leon Foucault. 35fr, Claude Louis Berthollet.

**1958, Feb. 15** ***Perf. 13***

**869** A307 8fr blue & vio blue .65 .35
**870** A307 12fr sepia & gray .75 .35
**871** A307 15fr slate grn & grn 1.40 .60
**872** A307 35fr maroon & cop red 1.75 .90
*Nos. 869-872 (4)* 4.55 2.20

**Lourdes Type of 1954**

**1958**

**873** A241 20fr grnsh bl & ol .30 .25

Le Havre A308

Maubeuge — A309

Designs: 18fr, Saint-Die. 25fr, Sete.

**1958, Mar. 29** **Engr.** ***Perf. 13***

**874** A308 12fr ol grn & car rose .55 .35
**875** A309 15fr brt purple & brn .60 .35
**876** A309 18fr ultra & indigo .90 .65
**877** A308 25fr dk bl, bl grn & brn 1.25 .65
*Nos. 874-877 (4)* 3.30 2.00

Reconstruction of war-damaged cities.

French Pavilion, Brussels A310

**1958, Apr. 12**

**878** A310 35fr brn, dk grn & bl .30 .25

Issued for the Universal and International Exposition at Brussels.

**Heroes Type of 1957**

8fr, Jean Cavaillès. 12fr, Fred Scamaroni. 15fr, Simone Michel-Levy. 20fr, Jacques Bingen.

**1958, Apr. 19**

**879** A293 8fr violet & black .60 .45
**880** A293 12fr ultra & green .60 .45
**881** A293 15fr brown & gray 1.50 .85
**882** A293 20fr olive & ultra 1.25 .85
*Nos. 879-882 (4)* 3.95 2.60

Issued in honor of the heroes of the French Underground in World War II.

Bowling A311

Sports: 15fr, Naval joust. 18fr, Archery, vert. 25fr, Breton wrestling, vert.

**1958, Apr. 26**

**883** A311 12fr rose & brown .75 .75
**884** A311 15fr bl, ol gray & grn 1.00 .75
**885** A311 18fr green & brown 1.75 1.00
**886** A311 25fr brown & indigo 2.50 1.75
*Nos. 883-886 (4)* 6.00 4.25

Senlis Cathedral — A312

**1958, May 17**

**887** A312 15fr ultra & indigo .40 .25

Bayeux Tapestry Horsemen A313

**1958, June 21**

**888** A313 15fr blue & carmine .35 .25

Common Design Types pictured following the introduction.

**Europa Issue, 1958**
Common Design Type

**1958, Sept. 13** **Engr.** ***Perf. 13***
**Size: 22x36mm**

**889** CD1 20fr rose red .40 .25
**890** CD1 35fr ultra 1.25 .30

Foix Chateau A314

**1958, Oct. 11**

**891** A314 15fr ultra, grn & ol brn .40 .25

City Halls, Paris and Rome A315

**1958, Oct. 11**

**892** A315 35fr gray, grnsh bl & rose red .40 .25

Issued to publicize the cultural ties between Rome and Paris and the need for European unity.

UNESCO Building, Paris A316

Design: 35fr, Different view of building.

**1958, Nov. 1** ***Perf. 13***

**893** A316 20fr grnsh blue & ol bis .25 .25
**894** A316 35fr dk sl grn & red org .25 .25

UNESCO Headquarters in Paris opening, Nov. 3.

Soldier's Grave in Wheat Field — A317

**1958, Nov. 11**

**895** A317 15fr dk green & ultra .30 .25

40th anniv. of the World War I armistice.

Arms of Marseille — A318

Cities: 70c, Lyon. 80c, Toulouse. 1fr, Bordeaux. 2fr, Nice. 3fr, Nantes. 5fr, Lille. 15fr, Algiers.

**1958-59** **Typo.** ***Perf. 14x13½***

**896** A318 50c dk blue & ultra .25 .25
**897** A318 70c multicolored .25 .25
**898** A318 80c red, blue & yel .25 .25
**899** A318 1fr dk bl, yel & red .25 .25
**900** A318 2fr dk bl, red & grn .25 .25
**901** A318 3fr multicolored .25 .25
**902** A318 5fr dk brown & red .25 .25
**903** A318 15fr multi ('59) .25 .25
*Nos. 896-903 (8)* 2.00 2.00

See Nos. 938, 940, 973, 1040-1042, 1091-1095, 1142-1144. For surcharges see Reunion Nos. 336, 345-346, 350-351, 353.

Arc de Triomphe and Flowers — A319

**1959, Jan. 17** **Engr.** ***Perf. 13***

**904** A319 15fr brn, bl, grn, cl & red .40 .30

Paris Flower Festival.

Symbols of Learning and Medal A320

**1959, Jan. 24** ***Perf. 13***

**905** A320 20fr lake, blk & vio .25 .25

Sesquicentennial of the Palm Leaf Medal of the French Academy.

Charles de Foucauld A321

**1959, Jan. 31**

**906** A321 50fr dp brn, bl & mar .40 .30

Issued to honor Father Charles de Foucauld, explorer and missionary of the Sahara.

**Type of 1957**

Designs: 30fr, Elysee Palace. 85fr, Evian-les Bains. 100fr, Sens River, Guadeloupe.

**1959, Feb. 10**

**907** A302 30fr dk slate green 2.00 .25
**908** A302 85fr deep claret 3.00 .30
**909** A302 100fr deep violet 25.00 .30
*Nos. 907-909 (3)* 30.00 .85

### Gallic Cock Type of 1954

**1959** **Typo.** ***Perf. 14x13½***

| No. | Type | Description | Unused | Used |
|---|---|---|---|---|
| **910** | A237 | 8fr violet | .40 | .25 |
| **911** | A237 | 20fr yellow grn | 1.50 | .50 |
| **912** | A237 | 40fr henna brn | 3.25 | 1.60 |
| **913** | A237 | 55fr emerald | 15.00 | 6.00 |
| | | *Nos. 910-913 (4)* | 20.15 | 8.35 |

Nos. 910-913 were issued with precancellation. See second note after No. 132. See Nos. 952-955.

Miners' Tools and School A322

**1959, Apr. 11** **Engr.** ***Perf. 13***

| No. | Type | Description | Unused | Used |
|---|---|---|---|---|
| **914** | A322 | 20fr red, blk & blue | .25 | .25 |

175th anniv. of the National Mining School.

### Heroes Type of 1957

Portraits: No. 915, The five martyrs of the Buffon school. No. 916, Yvonne Le Roux. No. 917, Médéric-Védy. No. 918, Louis Martin-Bret. 30fr, Gaston Moutardier.

**1959, Apr. 25** **Engr.** ***Perf. 13***

| No. | Type | Description | Unused | Used |
|---|---|---|---|---|
| **915** | A293 | 15fr black & vio | .30 | .25 |
| **916** | A293 | 15fr mag & rose vio | .30 | .30 |
| **917** | A293 | 20fr green & grnsh bl | .30 | .25 |
| **918** | A293 | 20fr org brn & brn | .45 | .30 |
| **919** | A293 | 30fr magenta & vio | .50 | .40 |
| | | *Nos. 915-919 (5)* | 1.85 | 1.50 |

Dam at Foum el Gherza A323

Marcoule Atomic Center — A324

Designs: 30fr, Oil field at Hassi Messaoud, Sahara. 50fr, C. N. I. T. Building (Centre National des Industries et des Techniques).

**1959, May 23**

| No. | Type | Description | Unused | Used |
|---|---|---|---|---|
| **920** | A323 | 15fr olive & grnsh bl | .30 | .25 |
| **921** | A324 | 20fr brt car & red brn | .40 | .40 |
| **922** | A324 | 30fr dk blue, brn & grn | .40 | .40 |
| **923** | A323 | 50fr ol grn & sl blue | .65 | .45 |
| | | *Nos. 920-923 (4)* | 1.75 | 1.50 |

French technical achievements.

Marceline Desbordes-Valmore — A325

**1959, June 20**

| No. | Type | Description | Unused | Used |
|---|---|---|---|---|
| **924** | A325 | 30fr blue, brn & grn | .25 | .25 |

Centenary of the death of Marceline Desbordes-Valmore, poet.

Pilots Goujon and Rozanoff A326

**1959, June 13**

| No. | Type | Description | Unused | Used |
|---|---|---|---|---|
| **925** | A326 | 20fr lt blue & org brn | .40 | .40 |

Issued in honor of Charles Goujon and Col. Constantin Rozanoff, test pilots.

Tancarville Bridge A327

**1959, Aug. 1** **Engr.** ***Perf. 13***

| No. | Type | Description | Unused | Used |
|---|---|---|---|---|
| **926** | A327 | 30fr dk blue, brn & ol | .40 | .25 |

Marianne and Ship of State — A328

**1959, July** **Typo.** ***Perf. 14x13½***

| No. | Type | Description | Unused | Used |
|---|---|---|---|---|
| **927** | A328 | 25fr black & red | .30 | .25 |

See Nos. 942, 3521, 4410a, 4513. For surcharge see No. B336.

Jean Jaures — A329

**1959, Sept. 12** **Engr.** ***Perf. 13***

| No. | Type | Description | Unused | Used |
|---|---|---|---|---|
| **928** | A329 | 50fr chocolate | .40 | .25 |

Jean Jaures, socialist leader, birth cent.

### Europa Issue, 1959

Common Design Type

**1959, Sept. 19**

**Size: 22x36mm**

| No. | Type | Description | Unused | Used |
|---|---|---|---|---|
| **929** | CD2 | 25fr bright green | .30 | .25 |
| **930** | CD2 | 50fr bright violet | 1.10 | .55 |

Blood Donors A330

**1959, Oct. 17** **Engr.**

| No. | Type | Description | Unused | Used |
|---|---|---|---|---|
| **931** | A330 | 20fr magenta & gray | .25 | .25 |

French-Spanish Handshake — A331

**1959, Oct. 24** ***Perf. 13***

| No. | Type | Description | Unused | Used |
|---|---|---|---|---|
| **932** | A331 | 50fr blue, rose car & org | .45 | .30 |

300th anniv. of the signing of the Treaty of the Pyrenees.

Polio Victim Holding Crutches — A332

**1959, Oct. 31**

| No. | Type | Description | Unused | Used |
|---|---|---|---|---|
| **933** | A332 | 20fr dark blue | .25 | .25 |

Vaccination against poliomyelitis.

Henri Bergson — A333

**1959, Nov. 7**

| No. | Type | Description | Unused | Used |
|---|---|---|---|---|
| **934** | A333 | 50fr lt red brown | .35 | .25 |

Henri Bergson, philosopher, birth cent.

Avesnes-sur-Helpe — A334

Design: 30fr, Perpignan.

**1959, Nov. 14**

| No. | Type | Description | Unused | Used |
|---|---|---|---|---|
| **935** | A334 | 20fr sepia & blue | .40 | .25 |
| **936** | A334 | 30fr brn, dp claret & bl | .40 | .25 |

New NATO Headquarters, Paris — A335

**1959, Dec. 12**

| No. | Type | Description | Unused | Used |
|---|---|---|---|---|
| **937** | A335 | 50fr green, brn & ultra | .45 | .30 |

10th anniv. of the NATO.

### Types of 1958-59 and

Farm Woman A336

Sower A337

Designs: 5c, Arms of Lille. 15c, Arms of Algiers. 25c, Marianne and Ship of State.

***Perf. 14x13½***

**1960-61** **Unwmk.** **Typo.**

| No. | Type | Description | Unused | Used |
|---|---|---|---|---|
| **938** | A318 | 5c dk brown & red | 2.60 | .25 |
| **939** | A336 | 10c brt green | .25 | .25 |
| **940** | A318 | 15c red, ultra, yel & grn | .50 | .25 |
| **941** | A337 | 20c grnsh bl & car rose | .25 | .25 |
| **942** | A328 | 25c ver & ultra | 1.60 | .25 |
| *b.* | | Booklet pane of 8 | 27.50 | |
| *c.* | | Booklet pane of 10 | 32.50 | |
| **942A** | A337 | 30c gray & ultra ('61) | 1.10 | .30 |
| | | *Nos. 938-942A (6)* | 6.30 | 1.55 |

See Nos. 707-708, 833-834 for the Farm Woman type (A336), but with no decimals in denominations.

For surcharges see Reunion Nos. 337-338, 341. For overprint see Algeria No. 286.

Laon Cathedral A338

Kerrata Gorge — A339

Designs: 30c, Fougères Chateau. 50c, Mosque, Tlemcen. 65c, Sioule Valley. 85c, Chaumont Viaduct. 1fr, Cilaos Church, Reunion.

**1960, Jan. 16** **Engr.** ***Perf. 13***

| No. | Type | Description | Unused | Used |
|---|---|---|---|---|
| **943** | A338 | 15c blue & indigo | .25 | .25 |
| **944** | A338 | 30c blue, sepia & grn | 1.75 | .25 |
| **945** | A339 | 45c brt vio & ol gray | .60 | .25 |
| **946** | A339 | 50c sl grn & lt cl | 1.20 | .25 |
| **947** | A338 | 65c sl grn, bl & blk brn | 1.10 | .25 |
| **948** | A338 | 85c blue, sep & grn | 1.75 | .25 |
| **949** | A339 | 1fr vio bl, bl & grn | 2.50 | .25 |
| | | *Nos. 943-949 (7)* | 9.15 | 1.75 |

For surcharges see Reunion Nos. 335, 340, 342. For overprint see Algeria Nos. 288-289.

Pierre de Nolhac A340

**1960, Feb. 13**

| No. | Type | Description | Unused | Used |
|---|---|---|---|---|
| **950** | A340 | 20c black & gray | .45 | .30 |

Centenary of the birth of Pierre de Nolhac, curator of Versailles and historian.

Museum of Art and Industry, Saint-Etienne — A341

**1960, Feb. 20**

| No. | Type | Description | Unused | Used |
|---|---|---|---|---|
| **951** | A341 | 30c brn, car & slate | .45 | .30 |

### Gallic Cock Type of 1954

**1960** **Typo.** ***Perf. 14x13½***

| No. | Type | Description | Unused | Used |
|---|---|---|---|---|
| **952** | A237 | 8c violet | .40 | .25 |
| **953** | A237 | 20c yellow grn | 1.90 | .30 |
| **954** | A237 | 40c henna brn | 7.50 | 1.75 |
| **955** | A237 | 55c emerald | 24.00 | 11.00 |
| | | *Nos. 952-955 (4)* | 33.80 | 13.30 |

Nos. 952-955 were issued only precanceled. See second note after No. 132. See Nos. 910-913.

View of Cannes A342

**1960, Mar. 5** **Engr.** ***Perf. 13***

| No. | Type | Description | Unused | Used |
|---|---|---|---|---|
| **956** | A342 | 50c red brn & lt grn | .45 | .40 |

Meeting of European municipal administrators, Cannes, Mar., 1960.

Woman of Savoy and Alps A343

Woman of Nice and Shore A344

**1960 Unwmk. *Perf. 13***

| | | | | |
|---|---|---|---|---|
| **957** | A343 30c slate green | .50 | .40 |
| **958** | A344 50c brn, yel & rose | .50 | .30 |

Cent. of the annexation of Nice and Savoy.

### Heroes Type of 1957

Portraits: No. 959, Edmund Debeaumarché. No. 960, Pierre Massé. No. 961, Maurice Ripoche. No. 962, Leonce Vieljeux. 50c, Abbé René Bonpain.

**1960, Mar. 26**

| | | | |
|---|---|---|---|
| **959** | A293 20c bister & blk | 1.10 | .90 |
| **960** | A293 20c pink & rose cl | 1.10 | .90 |
| **961** | A293 30c vio & brt vio | 1.50 | .90 |
| **962** | A293 30c sl bl & brt bl | 2.10 | 1.75 |
| **963** | A293 50c sl grn & red brn | 2.40 | 2.10 |
| | *Nos. 959-963 (5)* | 8.20 | 6.55 |

Issued in honor of the heroes of the French Underground of World War II.

"Education" and Children A345

**1960, May 21 Engr. *Perf. 13***

**964** A345 20c rose lilac, pur & blk .25 .25

1st secondary school in Strasbourg, 150th anniv.

Blois Chateau A346

View of La Bourboule A347

**1960, May**

| | | | |
|---|---|---|---|
| **965** | A346 30c dk bl, sep & grn | .60 | .45 |
| **966** | A347 50c ol brown, car & grn | .60 | .35 |

Lorraine Cross — A348

**1960, June 18**

**967** A348 20c red brn, dk brn & yel grn .45 .25

20th anniv. of the French Resistance Movement in World War II.

Marianne — A349

**1960, June 18 Typo. *Perf. 14x13½***

| | | | |
|---|---|---|---|
| **968** | A349 25c lake & gray | .25 | .25 |
| *a.* | Booklet pane of 8 | 4.50 | |
| *b.* | Booklet pane of 10 | 3.50 | |

See Nos. 3522, 4410b, 4514. For surcharge see Reunion No. 339. For overprint see Algeria No. 287.

Jean Bouin and Stadium A350

**1960, July 9 Engr. *Perf. 13***

**969** A350 20c blue, mag & ol gray .35 .25

17th Olympic Games, Rome, 8/25-9/11.

### Europa Issue, 1960
Common Design Type

**1960, Sept. 17 *Perf. 13***
**Size: 36x22mm**

| | | | |
|---|---|---|---|
| **970** | CD3 25c green & bluish grn | .25 | .25 |
| **971** | CD3 50c maroon & red lilac | .25 | .25 |

Lisieux Basilica A351

**1960, Sept. 24 *Perf. 13***

**972** A351 15c blue, gray & blk .25 .25

### Arms Type of 1958-59

Design: Arms of Oran.

**1960, Oct. 15 Typo. *Perf. 14x13½***

**973** A318 5c red, bl, yel & emer .25 .25

Madame de Stael by François Gerard — A352

**1960, Oct. 22 Engr. *Perf. 13***

**974** A352 30c dull claret & brn .35 .25

Madame de Stael (1766-1817), writer.

Gen. J. B. E. Estienne A353

**1960, Nov. 5**

**975** A353 15c lt lilac & black .35 .25

Centenary of the birth of Gen. Jean Baptiste Eugene Estienne.

Marc Sangnier and Youth Hostel at Bierville A354

**1960, Nov. 5**

**976** A354 20c blue, blk & lilac .25 .25

Issued to honor Marc Sangnier, founder of the French League for Youth Hostels.

Badge of Order of Liberation — A355

**1960, Nov. 14 Engr. *Perf. 13***

**977** A355 20c black & brt green .40 .25

Order of Liberation, 20th anniversary.

Lapwings A356

Birds: 30c, Puffin. 45c, European teal. 50c, European bee-eaters.

**1960, Nov. 12**

| | | | |
|---|---|---|---|
| **978** | A356 20c multicolored | .25 | .25 |
| **979** | A356 30c multicolored | .25 | .25 |
| **980** | A356 45c multicolored | .60 | .45 |
| **981** | A356 50c multicolored | .55 | .40 |
| | *Nos. 978-981 (4)* | 1.65 | 1.35 |

Issued to publicize wildlife protection.

André Honnorat A357

**1960, Nov. 19**

**982** A357 30c blue, blk & green .30 .25

Honnorat, statesman, fighter against tuberculosis and founder of the University City of Paris, an intl. students' community.

St. Barbara and Medieval View of School A358

**1960, Dec. 3 Engr.**

**983** A358 30c red, bl & ol brn .30 .25

St. Barbara School, Paris, 500th anniv.

"Mediterranean" by Aristide Maillol — A359

**1961, Feb. 18 Unwmk. *Perf. 13***

**984** A359 20c carmine & indigo .25 .25

Aristide Maillol, sculptor, birth cent.

Marianne by Cocteau — A360

**1961, Feb. 23**

**985** A360 20c blue & carmine .25 .25

A second type has an extra inverted V-shaped mark (a blue flag top) at right of hair tip. Value unused $2.25, used 35 cents.

See Nos. 3523, 4410c, 4515.

For surcharge see Reunion No. 357.

Paris Airport, Orly A361

**1961, Feb. 25**

**986** A361 50c blk, dk bl, & bluish grn .45 .25

Inauguration of new facilities at Orly airport.

George Méliès and Motion Picture Screen A362

**1961, Mar. 11**

**987** A362 50c pur, indigo & ol bis .50 .35

Cent. of the birth of George Méliès, motion picture pioneer.

Jean Baptiste Henri Lacordaire — A363

**1961, Mar. 25 *Perf. 13***

**988** A363 30c lt brown & black .30 .25

Cent. of the death of the Dominican monk Lacordaire, orator and liberal Catholic leader.

A364

**1961, Mar. 25**

**989** A364 30c grn, red brn & red .25 .25

Introduction of tobacco use into France, fourth centenary. By error stamp portrays Jan Nicquet instead of Jean Nicot.

### Heroes Type of 1957

Portraits: No. 990, Jacques Renouvin. No. 991, Lionel Dubray. No. 992, Paul Gateaud. No. 993, Mère Elisabeth.

**1961, Apr. 22**

| | | | |
|---|---|---|---|
| **990** | A293 20c blue & lilac | .75 | .35 |
| **991** | A293 20c gray grn & blue | .75 | .35 |
| **992** | A293 30c brown org & blk | 1.40 | .65 |
| **993** | A293 30c violet & blk | .90 | .80 |
| | *Nos. 990-993 (4)* | 3.80 | 2.15 |

Bagnoles-de-l'Orne — A365

**1961, May 6**

**994** A365 20c olive, ocher, bl & grn .25 .25

Dove, Olive Branch and Federation Emblem — A366

**1961, May 6**
**995** A366 50c brt bl, grn & mar .30 .25

World Federation of Ex-Service Men.

Deauville in 19th Century A367

**1961, May 13** **Engr.**
**996** A367 50c rose claret 1.25 .90

Centenary of Deauville.

La Champmeslé A368

French actors: No. 998, Talma. No. 999, Rachel. No. 1000, Gérard Philipe. No. 1001, Raimu.

**1961, June 10** **Unwmk.** ***Perf. 13***
**Dark Carmine Frame**

| | | | | |
|---|---|---|---|---|
| **997** | A368 | 20c choc & yel grn | .60 | .25 |
| **998** | A368 | 30c brown & crimson | .60 | .35 |
| **999** | A368 | 30c yel grn & sl grn | .65 | .35 |
| **1000** | A368 | 50c olive & choc | 1.10 | .45 |
| **1001** | A368 | 50c bl grn & red brn | 1.10 | .45 |
| | | *Nos. 997-1001 (5)* | 4.05 | 1.85 |

Issued to honor great French actors and in connection with the Fifth World Congress of the International Federation of Actors.

Mont-Dore, Snowflake and Cable Car — A369

**1961, July 1**
**1002** A369 20c orange & rose lilac .25 .25

Pierre Fauchard — A370

**1961, July 1**
**1003** A370 50c dk green & blk .40 .30

Bicentenary of the death of Pierre Fauchard, 1st surgeon dentist.

St. Theobald's Church, Thann — A371

**1961, July 1**
**1004** A371 20c sl grn, vio & brn .45 .25

800th anniversary of Thann.

**Europa Issue, 1961**
Common Design Type

**1961, Sept. 16** ***Perf. 13***
**Size: 35x22mm**

**1005** CD4 25c vermilion .25 .25
**1006** CD4 50c ultramarine .25 .25

Beach and Sailboats, Arcachon A372

Designs: 15c, Saint-Paul, Maritime Alps. 45c, Sully-sur-Loire Chateau. 50c, View of Cognac. 65c, Rance Valley and Dinan. 85c, City hall and Rodin's Burghers, Calais. 1fr, Roman gates of Lodi, Medea, Algeria.

**1961, Oct. 9** **Engr.** ***Perf. 13***

| | | | | |
|---|---|---|---|---|
| **1007** | A372 | 15c blue & purple | .25 | .25 |
| **1008** | A372 | 30c ultra, sl grn & lt brn | .25 | .25 |
| **1009** | A372 | 45c vio bl, red brn & grn | .25 | .25 |
| **1010** | A372 | 50c grn, Prus bl & sl | .75 | .25 |
| **1011** | A372 | 65c red brn, sl grn & bl | .25 | .25 |
| **1012** | A372 | 85c sl grn, sl & red brn | .35 | .25 |
| **1013** | A372 | 1fr dk bl, sl & bis | 3.50 | .25 |
| | | *Nos. 1007-1013 (7)* | 5.60 | 1.75 |

For surcharges see Reunion Nos. 347-348. For overprint see Algeria No. 290.

Blue Nudes, by Matisse — A373

Paintings: 50c, "The Messenger," by Braque. 85c, "The Cardplayers," by Cézanne. 1fr, "The 14th July," by Roger de La Fresnaye.

**1961, Nov. 10** ***Perf. 13x12***

| | | | | |
|---|---|---|---|---|
| **1014** | A373 | 50c dk brn, bl, blk & gray | 2.25 | 1.20 |
| **1015** | A373 | 65c grn, vio, & ultra | 3.75 | 1.90 |
| **1016** | A373 | 85c blk, brn, red & ol | 1.50 | 1.10 |
| **1017** | A373 | 1fr multicolored | 3.00 | 1.90 |
| | | *Nos. 1014-1017 (4)* | 10.50 | 6.10 |

Liner France A374

**1962, Jan. 11** **Engr.** ***Perf. 13***
**1018** A374 30c dk blue, blk & car .60 .35

New French liner France.

Skier Going Downhill — A375

**1962, Jan. 27** ***Perf. 13***
**1019** A375 30c shown .25 .25
**1020** A375 50c Slalom .35 .25

Issued to publicize the World Ski Championships, Chamonix, Feb. 1962.

Maurice Bourdet — A376

**1962, Feb. 17**
**1021** A376 30c slate .30 .25

60th anniv. of the birth of Maurice Bourdet, radio commentator and resistance hero.

Pierre-Fidele Bretonneau — A377

**1962, Feb. 17**
**1022** A377 50c brt lilac & blue .35 .25

Centenary of the death of Pierre-Fidele Bretonneau, physician.

Chateau and Bridge, Laval, Mayenne — A378

**1962, Feb. 24**
**1023** A378 20c bis brn & slate grn .25 .25

Gallic Cock — A379

**1962-65** ***Perf. 13***

| | | | | |
|---|---|---|---|---|
| **1024** | A379 | 25c ultra, car & brn | .25 | .25 |
| *a.* | | Bklt. pane of 4 (horiz. strip) | 2.50 | |
| **1024B** | A379 | 30c gray grn, red & brn ('65) | .85 | .25 |
| *c.* | | Booklet pane of 5 | 5.00 | |
| *d.* | | Booklet pane of 10 | 10.00 | |

No. 1024 was also issued on experimental luminescent paper in 1963. Value $750.

See Nos. 3524, 4410d, 4516.

Ramparts of Vannes A380

Dunkirk — A381

Paris Beach, Le Touquet A381a

**1962** **Engr.** ***Perf. 13***

| | | | | |
|---|---|---|---|---|
| **1025** | A380 | 30c dark blue | .60 | .50 |
| **1026** | A381 | 95c grn, bis & red lil | .75 | .40 |
| **1027** | A381a | 1fr grn, red brn & bl | .40 | .25 |
| | | *Nos. 1025-1027 (3)* | 1.75 | 1.15 |

No. 1026 for the 300th anniv. of Dunkirk.

Stage Setting and Globe A382

**1962, Mar. 24** **Unwmk.**
**1028** A382 50c sl grn, ocher & mag .40 .25

International Day of the Theater, Mar. 27.

Memorial to Fighting France, Mont Valerien A383

Resistance Heroes' Monument, Vercors — A384

Design: 50c, Ile de Sein monument.

**1962, Apr. 7**

| | | | | |
|---|---|---|---|---|
| **1029** | A383 | 20c olive & slate grn | .50 | .40 |
| **1030** | A384 | 30c bluish black | .60 | .45 |
| **1031** | A384 | 50c blue & indigo | .75 | .60 |
| | | *Nos. 1029-1031 (3)* | 1.85 | 1.45 |

Issued to publicize memorials for the French Underground in World War II.

Malaria Eradication Emblem and Swamp — A385

**1962, Apr. 14** **Engr.**
**1032** A385 50c dk blue & dk red .35 .25

WHO drive to eradicate malaria.

Nurses with Child and Hospital — A386

**1962, May 5 Unwmk. Perf. 13**
**1033** A386 30c bl grn, gray & red brn .25 .25

National Hospital Week, May 5-12.

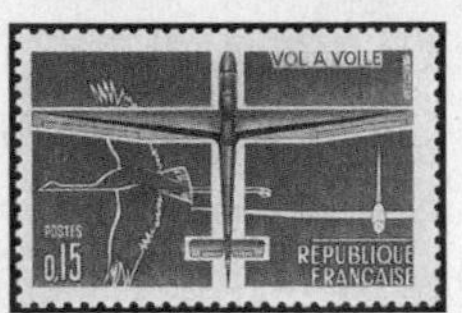

Glider A387

20c, Planes showing development of aviation.

**1962, May 12**
**1034** A387 15c orange red & brn .30 .25
**1035** A387 20c lil rose & rose cl .35 .25

Issued to publicize sports aviation.

School Emblem — A388

**1962, May 19 Engr.**
**1036** A388 50c mar, ocher & dk vio .40 .25

Watchmaker's School at Besançon, cent.

Louis XIV and Workers Showing Modern Gobelin A389

**1962, May 26 Unwmk. Perf. 13**
**1037** A389 50c ol, sl grn & car .40 .25

Gobelin tapestry works, Paris, 300th anniv.

Blaise Pascal A390

**1962, May 26**
**1038** A390 50c slate grn & dp org .40 .25

Blaise Pascal (1623-1662), mathematician, scientist and philosopher.

Palace of Justice, Rennes A391

**1962, June 12**
**1039** A391 30c blk, grysh bl & grn 1.00 .75

**Arms Type of 1958-59**

5c, Amiens. 10c, Troyes. 15c, Nevers.

**1962-63 Typo. Perf. 14x13½**
**1040** A318 5c ver, ultra & yel .25 .25
**1041** A318 10c red, ultra & yel ('63) .25 .25
**1042** A318 15c ver, ultra & yel .25 .25
*Nos. 1040-1042 (3)* .75 .75

Phosphor Tagging

In 1970 France began to experiment with luminescence. Phosphor bands have been added to Nos. 1041, 1143, 1231, 1231C, 1292A-1294B, 1494-1498, 1560-1579B, etc.

Rose — A392

Design: 30c, Old-fashioned rose.

**1962, Sept. 8 Engr. Perf. 13**
**1043** A392 20c ol, grn & brt car .45 .30
**1044** A392 30c dk sl grn, ol & car .55 .40

**Europa Issue, 1962**

Common Design Type

**1962, Sept. 15**

**Size: 36x22mm**

**1045** CD5 25c violet .25 .25
**1046** CD5 50c henna brown .35 .25

Space Communications Center, Pleumeur-Bodou, France — A394

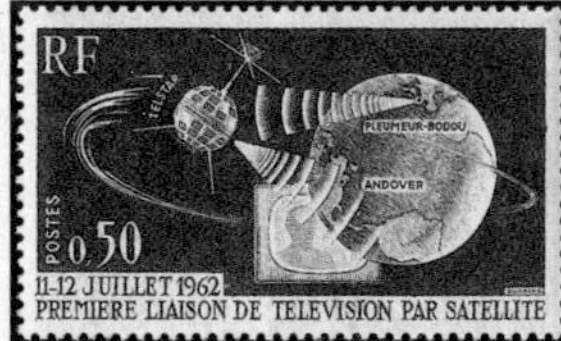

Telstar, Earth and Television Set — A395

**1962, Sept. 29 Engr. Perf. 13**
**1047** A394 25c gray, yel & grn .25 .25
**1048** A395 50c dk bl, grn & ultra .40 .30

1st television connection of the US and Europe through Telstar satellite, July 11-12.
For surcharges see Reunion Nos. 343-344.

"Bonjour Monsieur Courbet" by Gustave Courbet — A396

Paintings: 65c, "Madame Manet on Blue Sofa," by Edouard Manet. 1fr, "Guards officer on horseback," by Theodore Géricault, vert.

**1962, Nov. 9 Perf. 13x12, 12x13**
**1049** A396 50c multicolored 2.25 1.50
**1050** A396 65c multicolored 2.25 1.40
**1051** A396 1fr multicolored 4.50 2.00
*Nos. 1049-1051 (3)* 9.00 4.90

Bathyscaph "Archimede" — A397

**1963, Jan. 26 Unwmk. Perf. 13**
**1052** A397 30c dk blue & blk .25 .25

French deep-sea explorations.

Flowers and Nantes Chateau A398

**1963, Feb. 11**
**1053** A398 30c vio bl, car & sl grn .25 .25

Nantes flower festival.

St. Peter, Window at St. Foy de Conches A399

50c, Jacob Wrestling with the Angel, by Delacroix.

**1963, Mar. 2 Perf. 12x13**
**1054** A399 50c multicolored 2.40 1.50
**1055** A399 1fr multicolored 3.25 2.25

See Nos. 1076-1077.

Hungry Woman and Wheat Emblem A400

**1963, Mar. 21 Engr. Perf. 13**
**1056** A400 50c slate grn & brn .40 .25

FAO "Freedom from Hunger" campaign.

Cemetery and Memorial, Glières — A401

Design: 50c, Memorial, Ile de la Cité, Paris.

**1963, Mar. 23 Unwmk. Perf. 13**
**1057** A401 30c dk brown & olive .40 .30
**1058** A401 50c indigo .40 .30

Heroes of the resistance against the Nazis.

Beethoven, Birthplace at Bonn and Rhine A402

No. 1060, Emile Verhaeren, memorial at Roisin & residence. No. 1061, Giuseppe Mazzini, Marcus Aurelius statue & Via Appia, Rome. No. 1062, Emile Mayrisch, Colpach Chateau & blast furnace, Esch. No. 1063, Hugo de Groot, Palace of Peace, The Hague & St. Agatha Church, Delft.

**1963, Apr. 27 Unwmk. Perf. 13**
**1059** A402 20c ocher, sl & brt grn .30 .25
**1060** A402 20c purple, blk & mar .30 .25
**1061** A402 20c maroon, sl & ol .30 .25
**1062** A402 20c mar, dk brn & ocher .30 .25
**1063** A402 30c dk brn, vio & ocher .30 .25
*Nos. 1059-1063 (5)* 1.50 1.25

Issued to honor famous men of the European Common Market countries.

Hotel des Postes and Stagecoach, 1863 — A403

**1963, May 4**
**1064** A403 50c grayish black .35 .25

1st Intl. Postal Conference, Paris, 1863.

Lycée Louis-le-Grand, Belvédère, Panthéon and St. Etienne du Mont Church — A404

**1963, May 18**
**1065** A404 30c slate green .30 .25

400th anniversary of the Jesuit Clermont secondary school, named after Louis XIV.

St. Peter's Church and Ramparts, Caen A405

**1963, June 1 Unwmk. Perf. 13**
**1066** A405 30c gray blue & brn .25 .25

Radio Telescope, Nançay — A406

**1963, June 8 Engr.**
**1067** A406 50c dk bl & dk brn .45 .35

Amboise Chateau A407

Saint-Flour — A408

Designs: 50c, Côte d'Azur Varoise. 85c, Vittel. 95c, Moissac.

**1963, June 15**

1068 A407 30c slate, grn & bis .25 .25
1069 A407 50c dk grn, dk bl & hn brn .30 .25
1070 A408 60c ultra, dk grn & hn brn .40 .25
1071 A407 85c dk grn, yel grn & brn 1.00 .25
1072 A408 95c brnsh black .60 .25
*Nos. 1068-1072 (5)* 2.55 1.25

For surcharge see Reunion No. 355.

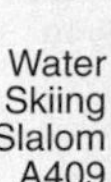

Water Skiing Slalom
A409

**1963, Aug. 31 Unwmk. *Perf. 13***

1073 A409 30c sl grn, blk & car .30 .25

World Water Skiing Championships, Vichy.

**Europa Issue, 1963**
Common Design Type

**1963, Sept. 14**
**Size: 36x22mm**

1074 CD6 25c red brown .25 .25
1075 CD6 50c green .35 .25

**Art Type of 1963**

Designs: 85c, "The Married Couple of the Eiffel Tower," by Marc Chagall. 95c, "The Fur Merchants," window, Chartres Cathedral.

**1963, Nov. 9 Engr. *Perf. 12x13***

1076 A399 85c multicolored 1.10 .90
1077 A399 95c multicolored .50 .40

**Philatec Issue**
Common Design Type

**1963, Dec. 14 Unwmk. *Perf. 13***

1078 CD118 25c dk gray, sl grn & dk car .25 .25

For surcharge see Reunion No. 349.

Radio and Television Center, Paris
A411

**1963, Dec. 15 Engr.**

1079 A411 20c org brn, slate & ol .25 .25

Fire Brigade Insignia, Symbols of Fire, Water and Civilian Defense
A412

**1964, Feb. 8 Engr. *Perf. 13***

1082 A412 30c blue, org & red .40 .25

Issued to honor the fire brigades and civilian defense corps.

Handicapped Laboratory Technician — A413

**1964, Feb. 22 Unwmk. *Perf. 13***

1083 A413 30c grn, red brn & brn .25 .25

Rehabilitation of the handicapped.

John II the Good (1319-64) by Girard d'Orleans
A414

**1964, Apr. 25 *Perf. 12x13***

1084 A414 1fr multicolored 1.10 .75

Stamp of 1900
A415

Mechanized Mail Handling
A416

Designs: No. 1086, Stamp of 1900, Type A17. No. 1088, Telecommunications.

**1964, May 9 *Perf. 13***

1085 A415 25c bister & dk car .25 .25
1086 A415 25c bister & blue .25 .25
1087 A416 30c blk, bl & org brn .25 .25
1088 A416 30c blk, car rose & bluish grn .25 .25
*a.* Strip of 4, #1085-1088 + label 1.10 1.00

Printed in sheets of 20 stamps, containing five No. 1088a. The label shows the Philatec emblem in green.

**Type of Semi-Postal Issue**
with "25e ANNIVERSAIRE" added

**1964, May 9**

1089 SP208 25c multicolored .25 .25

25th anniversary, night airmail service.

Madonna and Child from Rose Window of Notre Dame
A417

**1964, May 23 *Perf. 12x13***

1090 A417 60c multicolored .50 .40

Notre Dame Cathedral, Paris, 800th anniv.

**Arms Type of 1958-59**

Arms: 1c, Niort. 2c, Guéret. 12c, Agen. 18c, Saint-Denis, Réunion. 30c, Paris.

**1964-65 Typo. *Perf. 14x13½***

1091 A318 1c vio blue & yel .25 .25
1092 A318 2c emer, vio bl & yel .25 .25
1093 A318 12c black, red & yel .25 .25
1094 A318 18c multicolored .25 .25
1095 A318 30c vio bl & red ('65) .30 .25
*a.* Booklet pane of 10 15.00
*Nos. 1091-1095 (5)* 1.30 1.25

Gallic Coin — A418

***Perf. 13½x14***

**1964-66 Typo. Unwmk.**

1096 A418 10c emer & bister .75 .25
1097 A418 15c org & bister ('66) .30 .25
1098 A418 25c lilac & brn .45 .25
1099 A418 50c brt blue & brn .85 .75
*Nos. 1096-1099 (4)* 2.35 1.50

Nos. 1096-1099 are known only precanceled. See second note after No. 132. See Nos. 1240-1242, 1315-1318, 1421-1424.

Postrider, Rocket and Radar Equipment — A419

**1964, June 5 Engr. *Perf. 13***

1100 A419 1fr brn, dk red & dk bl 17.50 13.50

Sold for 4fr, including 3fr admission to PHILATEC. Issued in sheets of 8 stamps and 8 labels (2x8 subjects with labels in horizontal rows 1, 4, 5, 8; stamps in rows 2, 3, 6, 7). Commemorative inscriptions on side margins. Value $150.

Caesar's Tower, Provins — A420

Chapel of Notre Dame du Haut, Ronchamp
A421

**1964-65**

1101 A421 40c sl grn, dk brn & brn ('65) .25 .25
1102 A420 70c slate, grn & car .30 .25
1103 A421 1.25fr brt bl, sl grn & ol .70 .25
*Nos. 1101-1103 (3)* 1.25 .75

The 40c was issued in vertical coils in 1971. Every 10th coil stamp has a red control number printed twice on the back.

For surcharges see Reunion Nos. 352, 361.

Mandel — A422

**1964, July 4 Unwmk. *Perf. 13***

1104 A422 30c violet brown .25 .25

Georges Mandel (1885-1944), Cabinet minister, executed by the Nazis.

Judo — A423

**1964, July 4**

1105 A423 50c dk blue & vio brn .25 .25

18th Olympic Games, Tokyo, 10/10-25/64.

Champlevé Enamel from Limoges, 12th Century
A424

Design: No. 1107, The Lady (Claude Le Viste?) with the Unicorn, 15th cent. tapestry.

**1964 *Perf. 12x13***

1106 A424 1fr multicolored .75 .50
1107 A424 1fr multicolored .40 .30

No. 1106 shows part of an enamel sepulchral plate portraying Geoffrey IV, Count of Anjou and Le Maine (1113-1151), who was called Geoffrey Plantagenet.

Issue dates: No. 1106, July 4. No. 1107, Oct. 31.

Paris Taxis Carrying Soldiers to Front, 1914
A425

**1964, Sept. 5 Unwmk. *Perf. 13***

1108 A425 30c black, blue & red .25 .25

50th anniversary of Battle of the Marne.

**Europa Issue, 1964**
Common Design Type

**1964, Sept. 12 Engr.**
**Size: 22x36mm**

1109 CD7 25c dk car, dp ocher & grn .25 .25
1110 CD7 50c vio, yel grn & dk car .25 .25

**Cooperation Issue**
Common Design Type

**1964, Nov. 6 Unwmk. *Perf. 13***

1111 CD119 25c red brn, dk brn & dk bl .25 .25

Joux Chateau — A427

**1965, Feb. 6 Engr.**

1112 A427 1.30fr redsh brn, brn red & dk brn .90 .25

"The English Girl from the Star" by Toulouse-Lautrec — A428

St. Paul on the Damascus Road, Window, Cathedral of Sens — A429

Leaving for the Hunt — A430

Apocalypse Tapestry, 14th Century A431

"The Red Violin" by Raoul Dufy — A432

Designs: No. 1115, "August" miniature of Book of Hours of Jean de France, Duc de Berry ("Les Très Riches Heures du Duc de Berry"), painted by Flemish brothers, Pol, Hermant and Jannequin Limbourg, 1411-16. No. 1116, Scene from oldest existing set of French tapestries, showing the Winepress of the Wrath of God (Revelations 14: 19-20).

**1965** ***Perf. 12x13, 13x12***

| | | | | | |
|---|---|---|---|---|---|
| **1113** | A428 | 1fr multicolored | | .40 | .30 |
| **1114** | A429 | 1fr multicolored | | .40 | .30 |
| **1115** | A430 | 1fr multicolored | | .30 | .30 |
| **1116** | A431 | 1fr multicolored | | .30 | .30 |
| **1117** | A432 | 1fr blk, pink & car | | .30 | .30 |
| | | *Nos. 1113-1117 (5)* | | 1.70 | 1.50 |

No. 1114 issued to commemorate the 800th anniversary of the Cathedral of Sens.

Issued: No. 1113, 3/12; No. 1114, 6/5; No. 1115, 9/25; No. 1116, 10/30; No. 1117, 11/6.

Returning Deportees, 1945 — A433

**1965, Apr. 1** **Unwmk.** ***Perf. 13***

**1118** A433 40c Prussian green .45 .25

20th anniv. of the return of people deported during World War II.

House of Youth and Culture, Troyes A434

**1965, Apr. 10** **Engr.**

**1119** A434 25c ind, brn & dk grn .25 .25

20th anniv. of the establishment of recreational cultural centers for young people.

Woman Carrying Flowers — A435

**1965, Apr. 24** **Unwmk.** ***Perf. 13***

**1120** A435 60c dk grn, dp org & ver .30 .25

Tourist Campaign of Welcome & Amiability.

Flags of France, US, USSR and Great Britain Crushing Swastika — A436

**1965, May 8**

**1121** A436 40c black, car & blue .30 .25

20th anniv. of victory in World War II.

Telegraph Key, Syncom Satellite and Pleumeur-Bodou Station — A437

**1965, May 17**

**1122** A437 60c dk blue, brn & blk .30 .25

Centenary of the ITU.

Croix de Guerre — A438

**1965, May 22** **Engr.**

**1123** A438 40c red, brn & brt grn .35 .25

50th anniv. of the Croix de Guerre medal.

Cathedral of Bourges — A439

Moustiers-Sainte-Marie — A440

Views: 30c, Road and tunnel, Mont Blanc. 60c, Aix-les-Bains, sailboat. 75c, Tarn Gorge, Lozère mountains. 95c, Vendée River, man poling boat, and windmill. 1fr, Prehistoric stone monuments, Carnac.

**1965**

| | | | | | |
|---|---|---|---|---|---|
| **1124** | A439 | 30c bl, vio bl & brn vio | | .25 | .25 |
| **1125** | A439 | 40c gray bl & redsh brn | | .25 | .25 |
| **1126** | A440 | 50c grn, bl gray & bis | | .25 | .25 |
| **1127** | A439 | 60c blue & red brn | | .45 | .25 |
| **1128** | A439 | 75c brown, bl & grn | | .75 | .60 |
| **1129** | A440 | 95c brown, grn & bl | | 4.50 | .75 |
| **1130** | A440 | 1fr gray, grn & brn | | .75 | .25 |
| | | *Nos. 1124-1130 (7)* | | 7.20 | 2.60 |

No. 1124 for the opening of the Mont Blanc Tunnel. No. 1125 (Bourges Cathedral) was issued in connection with the French Philatelic Societies Federation Congress, held at Bourges.

Issued: 40c, June 5; 50c, June 19; 30c, 60c, July 17; others, July 10.

For surcharges see Reunion Nos. 354, 362, 365.

### Europa Issue, 1965
Common Design Type

**1965, Sept. 25** ***Perf. 13***
**Size: 36x22mm**

| | | | | | |
|---|---|---|---|---|---|
| **1131** | CD8 | 30c red | | .25 | .30 |
| **1132** | CD8 | 60c gray | | .45 | .25 |

Planting Seedling — A441

**1965, Oct. 2**

**1133** A441 25c slate grn, yel grn & red brn .25 .25

National reforestation campaign.

Etienne Régnault, "Le Taureau" and Coast of Reunion — A442

**1965, Oct. 2**

**1134** A442 30c indigo & dk car .25 .25

Tercentenary of settlement of Reunion.

Atomic Reactor and Diagram, Symbols of Industry, Agriculture and Medicine — A443

**1965, Oct. 9**

**1135** A443 60c brt blue & blk .50 .30

Atomic Energy Commission, 20th anniv.

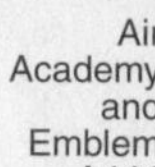

Air Academy and Emblem A444

**1965, Nov. 6** ***Perf. 13***

**1136** A444 25c dk blue & green .35 .30

Air Academy, Salon-de-Provence, 50th anniv.

### French Satellite A-1 Issue
Common Design Type

Design: 60c, A-1 satellite.

**1965, Nov. 30** **Engr.** ***Perf. 13***

| | | | | | |
|---|---|---|---|---|---|
| **1137** | CD121 | 30c Prus bl, brt bl & blk | | .25 | .25 |
| **1138** | CD121 | 60c blk, Prus bl & brt bl | | .40 | .25 |
| *a.* | | Strip of 2, #1137-1138 + label | | .65 | .65 |

Launching of France's 1st satellite, 11/26/65.

For surcharges see Reunion Nos. 358-359.

Arms of Auch — A446

Cities: 20c, Saint-Lô. 25c, Mont-de-Marsan.

**Typographed, Photogravure (20c)**
**1966** ***Perf. 14x13; 14 (20c)***

| | | | | | |
|---|---|---|---|---|---|
| **1142** | A446 | 5c blue & red | | .25 | .25 |
| **1143** | A446 | 20c vio bl, sil, gold & red | | .25 | .25 |
| **1144** | A446 | 25c red brown & ultra | | .30 | .25 |
| | | *Nos. 1142-1144 (3)* | | .80 | .75 |

The 5c and 20c were issued in sheets and in vertical coils. In the coils, every 10th stamp has a red control number on the back.

For surcharges see Reunion Nos. 360-360A.

### French Satellite D-1 Issue
Common Design Type

**1966, Feb. 18** **Engr.** ***Perf. 13***

**1148** CD122 60c blue blk, grn & cl .25 .25

Horses from Bronze Vessel of Vix — A448

"The Newborn" by Georges de La Tour — A449

The Baptism of Judas (4th Century Bishop of Jerusalem) — A450

"The Moon and the Bull" Tapestry by Jean Lurçat A451

"Crispin and Scapin" by Honoré Daumier — A452

**1966** *Perf. 13x12, 12x13*

**1149** A448 1fr multicolored .40 .35
**1150** A449 1fr multicolored .40 .35
**1151** A450 1fr multicolored .40 .35
**1152** A451 1fr multicolored .40 .30
**1153** A452 1fr multicolored .40 .30
*Nos. 1149-1153 (5)* 2.00 1.65

The design of No. 1149 is a detail from a 6th century B.C. vessel, found in 1953 in a grave near Vix, Cote d'Or.

The design of No. 1151 is from a stained glass window in the 13th century Sainte-Chapelle, Paris.

No. 1150 exists in an imperf, ungummed souv. sheet with 2 progressive die proofs, issued for benefit of the Postal Museum, and not postally valid. Value $2.

Issued: No. 1149, 3/26; No. 1150, 6/25; No. 1151, 10/22; No. 1152, 11/19; No. 1153, 12/10.

Chessboard, Knight, Emblems for King and Queen — A453

**1966, Apr. 2** **Engr.** *Perf. 13*

**1154** A453 60c sepia, gray & dk vio bl .45 .30

Issued to publicize the Chess Festival.

Rhone Bridge, Pont-Saint-Esprit — A454

**1966, Apr. 23** **Unwmk.** *Perf. 13*

**1155** A454 25c black & dull blue .25 .25

St. Michael Slaying the Dragon — A455

**1966, Apr. 30** **Litho. & Engr.**

**1156** A455 25c multicolored .25 .25

Millenium of Mont-Saint-Michel.

Stanislas Leszczynski, Lunéville Chateau — A456

**1966, May 6** **Engr.**

**1157** A456 25c slate, grn & brn .25 .25

200th anniv. of the reunion of Lorraine and Bar (Barrois) with France.

St. Andrew's and Sèvre River, Niort — A457

**1966, May 28** **Engr.** *Perf. 13*

**1158** A457 40c brt bl, indigo & grn .30 .25

Bernard Le Bovier de Fontenelle and 1666 Meeting Room A458

**1966, June 4**

**1159** A458 60c dk car rose & brn .30 .25

300th anniversary, Académie des Sciences.

William the Conqueror, Castle and Norman Ships — A459

**1966, June 4**

**1160** A459 60c brown red & dp bl .40 .30

900th anniversary of Battle of Hastings.

Tracks, Globe and Eiffel Tower A460

**1966, June 11**

**1161** A460 60c dk brn, car & dull bl .50 .25

19th International Railroad Congress.

Oléron Bridge A461

**1966, June 20**

**1162** A461 25c Prus bl, brn & bl .25 .25

Issued to commemorate the opening of Oléron Bridge, connecting Oléron Island in the Bay of Biscay with the French mainland.

**Europa Issue, 1966**
Common Design Type

**1966, Sept. 24** **Engr.** *Perf. 13*
**Size: 22x36mm**

**1163** CD9 30c Prussian blue .25 .25
**1164** CD9 60c red .30 .25

Vercingetorix at Gergovie, 52 B.C. — A462

Bishop Remi Baptizing King Clovis, 496 A.D. — A463

Design: 60c, Charlemagne attending school (page holding book for crowned king).

**1966, Nov. 5** *Perf. 13*

**1165** A462 40c choc, grn & gray bl .30 .25
**1166** A463 40c dk red brn & blk .30 .25
**1167** A463 60c pur, rose car & brn .30 .25
*Nos. 1165-1167 (3)* .90 .75

Map of Pneumatic Post and Tube A464

**1966, Nov. 11**

**1168** A464 1.60fr maroon & indigo .60 .30

Centenary of Paris pneumatic post system.

Val Chateau — A465

**1966, Nov. 19** **Engr.** *Perf. 13*

**1169** A465 2.30fr dk bl, sl grn & brn 1.50 .25

Rance Power Station A466

**1966, Dec. 3**

**1170** A466 60c dk bl, sl grn & brn .45 .25

Tidal power station in the estuary of the Rance River on the English Channel.

European Broadcasting Union Emblem — A467

**1967, Mar. 4** **Engr.** *Perf. 13*

**1171** A467 40c dk blue & rose brn .25 .25

3rd Intl. Congress of the European Broadcasting Union, Paris, Mar. 8-22.

Father Juniet's Gig by Henri Rousseau — A468

Francois I by Jean Clouet A469

The Bather by Jean-Dominique Ingres — A470

St. Eloi, the Goldsmith, at Work — A471

**1967** **Engr.** *Perf. 13x12, 12x13*

**1172** A468 1fr multicolored .30 .25
**1173** A469 1fr multicolored .30 .25
**1174** A470 1fr multicolored .30 .25
**1175** A471 1fr multicolored .30 .25
*Nos. 1172-1175 (4)* 1.20 1.00

The design of No. 1175 is from a 16th century stained glass window in the Church of Sainte Madeleine, Troyes.

Issued: No. 1172, 4/15; No. 1173, 7/1; No. 1174, 9/9; No. 1175, 10/7.

Snow Crystal and Olympic Rings — A472

**1967, Apr. 22 Photo. *Perf. 13***

**1176** A472 60c brt & lt blue & red .35 .25

Issued to publicize the 10th Winter Olympic Games, Grenoble, Feb. 6-18, 1968.

French Pavilion, EXPO '67 — A473

**1967, Apr. 22 Engr.**

**1177** A473 60c dull bl & bl grn .35 .30

Intl. Exhibition EXPO '67, Montreal, Apr. 28-Oct. 27, 1967.

For surcharge see Reunion No. 363.

**Europa Issue, 1967**

Common Design Type

**1967, Apr. 29 Size: 22x36mm**

**1178** CD10 30c blue & gray .25 .25
**1179** CD10 60c brown & lt blue .30 .25

Great Bridge, Bordeaux A474

**1967, May 8**

**1180** A474 25c olive, blk & brn .25 .25

Nungesser, Coli and "L'Oiseau Blanc" A475

**1967, May 8**

**1181** A475 40c slate, dk & lt brn .30 .25

40th anniv. of the attempted transatlantic flight of Charles Nungesser and François Coil, French aviators.

Gouin House, Tours — A476

**1967, May 13 Engr. *Perf. 13***

**1182** A476 40c vio bl, red brn & red .30 .25

Congress of the Federation of French Philatelic Societies in Tours.

Ramon and Alfort Veterinary School A477

**1967, May 27**

**1183** A477 25c brn, dp bl & yel grn .25 .25

200th anniv. of the Alfort Veterinary School and to honor Professor Gaston Ramon (1886-1963).

Robert Esnault-Pelterie, Diamant Rocket and A-1 Satellite — A478

**1967, May 27**

**1184** A478 60c slate & vio blue .30 .25

Issued to honor Robert Esnault-Pelterie (1881-1957), aviation and space expert.

City Hall, Saint-Quentin A479

Saint-Germain-en-Laye — A480

Views: 60c, Clock Tower, Vire. 75c, Beach, La Baule, Brittany. 95c, Harbor, Boulogne-sur-Mer. 1fr, Rodez Cathedral. 1.50fr, Morlaix; old houses, grotesque carving, viaduct.

**1967**

**1185** A479 50c bl, sl bl & brn .25 .25
**1186** A479 60c dp bl, sl bl & dk red brn .30 .25
**1187** A480 70c rose car, red brn & bl .30 .25
**1188** A480 75c multicolored 1.10 .60
**1189** A480 95c sky bl, lil & sl grn 1.10 .60
**1190** A479 1fr indigo & bl gray .45 .25
**1191** A479 1.50fr brt bl, brt grn & red brn .90 .35
*Nos. 1185-1191 (7)* 4.40 2.55

Issued: 1fr, 1.50fr, June 10; 70c, June 17; 50c, 60c, 95c, July 8; 75c, July 24.

Orchids — A481

**1967, July 29 Engr. *Perf. 13***

**1192** A481 40c dp car, brt pink & pur .50 .40

Orleans flower festival.

Scales of Justice, City and Harbor A482

**1967, Sept. 4**

**1193** A482 60c dk plum, dl bl & ocher .50 .30

9th Intl. Accountancy Cong., Paris, 9/6-12.

Cross of Lorraine, Soldiers and Sailors — A483

**1967, Oct. 7 Engr. *Perf. 13***

**1194** A483 25c brn, dp ultra & bl .25 .25

25th anniv. of the Battle of Bir Hacheim.

Marie Curie, Bowl Glowing with Radium A484

**1967, Oct. 23 Engr. *Perf. 13***

**1195** A484 60c dk blue & ultra .30 .25

Marie Curie (1867-1934), scientist who discovered radium and polonium, Nobel prize winner for physics and chemistry.

Lions Emblem A485

**1967, Oct. 28**

**1196** A485 40c dk car & vio bl .70 .40

50th anniversary of Lions International.

For surcharge see Reunion No. 364.

Marianne (by Cheffer) — A486

**1967, Nov. 4 Engr.**

**1197** A486 25c dark blue .25 .25
**1198** A486 30c bright lilac .25 .25
*a.* Booklet pane of 5 6.00
*b.* Booklet pane of 10 12.00

Coils (vertical) of Nos. 1197 and 1231 show a red number on the back of every 10th stamp.

See Nos. 1230-1231C, 3525, 4410e, 4517.

For surcharges see Reunion Nos. 367-368, 389.

Stamps of various colors and printing methods with denomination of €1 were limited printings sold in 2010. See footnote after No.3478.

King Philip II (Philip Augustus) at Battle of Bouvines A487

Designs: No. 1200, Election of Hugh Capet as King, horiz. 60c, King Louis IX (St. Louis) holding audience for the poor.

**1967, Nov. 13 Engr. *Perf. 13***

**1199** A487 40c gray & black .30 .25
**1200** A487 40c dp bluish grn & blue .30 .25
**1201** A487 60c grn & dk red brn .40 .25
*Nos. 1199-1201 (3)* 1.00 .75

Commemorative Medal — A488

**1968, Jan. 6 Engr. *Perf. 13***

**1202** A488 40c dk slate grn & bis .25 .25

50th anniversary of postal checking service.

Various Road Signs — A489

**1968, Feb. 24**

**1203** A489 25c lil, red & dk bl grn .25 .25

Issued to publicize road safety.

Prehistoric Paintings, Lascaux Cave — A490

Arearea (Merriment) by Paul Gauguin — A491



The Dance by Emile Antoine Bourdelle A492

Portrait of the Model by Auguste Renoir A493

**1968 Engr. *Perf. 13x12, 12x13***

**1204** A490 1fr multicolored .50 .30
**1205** A491 1fr multicolored .50 .30
**1206** A492 1fr car & gray olive .50 .30
**1207** A493 1fr multicolored .50 .30
*Nos. 1204-1207 (4)* 2.00 1.20

Issued: No. 1204, 4/13; No. 1205, 9/21; No. 1206, 10/26; No. 1207, 11/9.

Audio-visual Institute, Royan — A494

**1968, Apr. 13 *Perf. 13***

**1208** A494 40c slate grn, brn & Prus bl .25 .25

5th Conference for World Cooperation with the theme of teaching living languages by audio-visual means.

**Europa Issue, 1968**

Common Design Type

**1968, Apr. 27 Size: 36x22mm**

**1209** CD11 30c brt red lil & ocher .25 .25
**1210** CD11 60c brown & lake .60 .30

Alain René Le Sage — A495

**1968, May 4**

**1211** A495 40c blue & rose vio .25 .25

Alain René Le Sage (1668-1747), novelist and playwright.

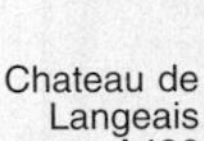

Chateau de Langeais A496

**1968, May 4**

**1212** A496 60c slate bl, grn & red brn .65 .30

Pierre Larousse A497

**1968, May 11 Engr. *Perf. 13***

**1213** A497 40c rose vio & brown .25 .25

Pierre Larousse (1817-75), grammarian, lexicographer and encyclopedist.

Gnarled Trunk and Fir Tree — A498

**1968, May 18 Engr. *Perf. 13***

**1214** A498 25c grnsh bl, brn & grn .25 .25

Twinning of Rambouillet Forest in France and the Black Forest in Germany.

Map of Papal Enclave, Valréas, and John XXII Receiving Homage A499

**1968, May 25**

**1215** A499 60c brn, bis brn & pur .40 .25

Papal enclave at Valréas, 650th anniv.

Louis XIV, Arms of France and Flanders A500

**1968, June 29**

**1216** A500 40c rose car, gray & lemon .25 .25

300th anniv. of the Treaty of Aachen which reunited Flanders with France.

Martrou Bridge, Rochefort A501

**1968, July 20**

**1217** A501 25c sky bl, blk & dk red brn .25 .25

Letord Lorraine Bimotor Plane over Map of France A502

**1968, Aug. 17 Engr. *Perf. 13***

**1218** A502 25c brt blue, indigo & red .40 .25

1st regularly scheduled air mail route in France from Paris to St. Nazaire, 50th anniv.

Tower de Constance, Aigues-Mortes A503

**1968, Aug. 31**

**1219** A503 25c red brn, sky bl & olive bister .25 .25

Bicentenary of the release of Huguenot prisoners from the Tower de Constance, Aigues-Mortes.

Cathedral and Pont Vieux, Beziers A504

**1968, Sept. 7 Engr. *Perf. 13***

**1220** A504 40c ind, bis & grn .95 .30

"Victory" over White Tower of Salonika — A505

**1968, Sept. 28**

**1221** A505 40c red lilac & plum .25 .25

50th anniv. of the armistice on the eastern front in World War I, Sept. 29, 1918.

Louis XV, Arms of France and Corsica A506

**1968, Oct. 5 *Perf. 13***

**1222** A506 25c ultra, grn & blk .25 .25

Return of Corsica to France, 200th anniv.

Relay Race A507

**1968, Oct. 12**

**1223** A507 40c ultra, brt grn & ol brn .40 .25

19th Olympic Games, Mexico City, 10/12-27.

Polar Camp with Helicoptor, Plane and Snocat Tractor — A508

**1968, Oct. 19**

**1224** A508 40c Prus bl, lt grnsh bl & brn red .30 .25

20 years of French Polar expeditions.

For surcharge see Reunion No. 366.

Leon Bailby, Paris Opera Staircase and Hospital Beds — A509

**1968, Oct. 26**

**1225** A509 40c ocher & maroon .25 .25

50th anniv. of the "Little White Beds" children's hospital fund.

"Victory" over Arc de Triomphe and Eternal Flame — A510

**1968, Nov. 9 Engr. *Perf. 13***

**1226** A510 25c dk car rose & dp blue .25 .25

50th anniv. of the armistice which ended World War I.

Death of Bertrand Du Guesclin at Chateauneuf-de-Randon, 1380 — A511

No. 1228, King Philip IV (the Fair) and first States-General assembly, 1302, horiz. 60c, Joan of Arc leaving Vaucouleurs, 1429.

**1968, Nov. 16**

**1227** A511 40c green, ultra & brn .30 .25
**1228** A511 40c cop red, grn & gray .30 .25
**1229** A511 60c vio bl, sl bl & bis .40 .30
*Nos. 1227-1229 (3)* 1.00 .80

See No. 1260.

**Marianne Type of 1967**

**1969-70 Engr. *Perf. 13***

**1230** A486 30c green .35 .25
*a.* Booklet pane of 10 8.50
**1231** A486 40c deep carmine .45 .25
*a.* Booklet pane of 5 (horiz. strip) 7.50
*b.* Booklet pane of 10 8.50
*d.* With label ('70) .50 .25

**Typo. *Perf. 14x13***

**1231C** A486 30c blue green .25 .25
*Nos. 1230-1231C (3)* 1.05 .75

No. 1231d was issued in sheets of 50 with alternating labels showing coat of arms of Perigueux, arranged checkerwise, to commemorate the inauguration of the Perigueux stamp printing plant.

The 40c coil is noted after No. 1198.

Church of Brou, Bourg-en-Bresse — A512

Views: 80c, Vouglans Dam, Jura. 85c, Chateau de Chantilly. 1.15fr, Sailboats in La Trinité-sur-Mer harbor.

**1969 Engr. *Perf. 13***

**1232** A512 45c olive, bl & red brn .25 .25
**1233** A512 80c ol bis, brn red & dk brn .40 .25
**1234** A512 85c sl grn, dl bl & gray .75 .50
**1235** A512 1.15fr brt bl, gray grn & brn .75 .50
*Nos. 1232-1235 (4)* 2.15 1.50

"February" Bas-relief from Amiens Cathedral
A513

Philip the Good, by Roger van der Weyden
A514

Sts. Savin and Cyprian before Ladicius, Mural, St. Savin, Vienne — A515

The Circus, by Georges Seurat
A515a

**1969** ***Perf. 12x13***

| | | | | |
|---|---|---|---|---|
| **1236** | A513 | 1fr dk green & brn | .40 | .25 |
| **1237** | A514 | 1fr multicolored | .40 | .25 |
| **1238** | A515 | 1fr multicolored | .40 | .25 |
| **1239** | A515a | 1fr multicolored | .40 | .25 |
| | | *Nos. 1236-1239 (4)* | 1.60 | 1.00 |

Issue dates: No. 1236, Feb. 22; No. 1237, May 3; No. 1238, June 28; No. 1239, Nov. 8.

**Gallic Coin Type of 1964-66**

**1969** **Typo.** ***Perf. 13½x14***

| | | | | |
|---|---|---|---|---|
| **1240** | A418 | 22c brt green & vio | .30 | .25 |
| **1241** | A418 | 35c red & ultra | .85 | .40 |
| **1242** | A418 | 70c ultra & red brn | 3.75 | 1.75 |
| | | *Nos. 1240-1242 (3)* | 4.90 | 2.40 |

Nos. 1240-1242 are known only precanceled. See note after No. 132.

Hautefort Chateau
A516

**1969, Apr. 5** **Engr.** ***Perf. 13***

**1243** A516 70c blue, slate & bister .40 .25

Irises
A517

**1969, Apr. 12** **Photo.**

**1244** A517 45c multicolored .35 .25

3rd Intl. Flower Show, Paris, 4/23-10/5.

**Europa Issue, 1969**

Common Design Type

**1969, Apr. 26** **Engr.** ***Perf. 13***

**Size: 36x22mm**

| | | | | |
|---|---|---|---|---|
| **1245** | CD12 | 40c carmine rose | .25 | .25 |
| **1246** | CD12 | 70c Prussian blue | .30 | .25 |

Albert Thomas and Thomas Memorial, Geneva
A518

**1969, May 10** **Engr.** ***Perf. 13***

**1247** A518 70c brn, ol bis & ind .40 .25

ILO, 50th anniv., and honoring Thomas (1878-1932), director of the ILO (1920-32).

Garigliano Battle Scene, 1944 — A519

**1969, May 10**

**1248** A519 45c black & violet .40 .30

25th anniv. of the Battle of the Garigliano against the Germans.

Chateau du Marché, Chalons-sur-Marne
A520

**1969, May 24**

**1249** A520 45c bis, dull bl & grn .40 .30

Federation of French Philatelic Societies, 42nd congress.

Parachutists over Normandy Beach — A521

**1969, May 31**

**1250** A521 45c dk blue & vio bl .85 .40

Landing of Special Air Service and Free French commandos in Normandy, June 6, 1944, 25th anniv.

Monument of the French Resistance, Mt. Mouchet — A522

**1969, June 7**

**1251** A522 45c dk grn, slate & ind .60 .45

25th anniv. of the battle of Mt. Mouchet between French resistance fighters and the Germans, June 2 and 10, 1944.

French Troops Landing in Provence — A523

**1969, Aug. 23** **Engr.** ***Perf. 13***

**1252** A523 45c slate & blk brn .75 .45

25th anniv. of the landing of French and American forces in Provence, Aug. 15, 1944.

Russian and French Aviators — A524

**1969, Oct. 18** **Engr.** ***Perf. 13***

**1253** A524 45c slate, dp bl & car .75 .45

Issued to honor the French aviators of the Normandy-Neman Squadron who fought on the Russian Front, 1942-45.

Kayak on Isère River
A525

**1969, Aug. 2** **Engr.** ***Perf. 13***

**1254** A525 70c org brn, ol & dk bl .40 .25

Intl. Canoe and Kayak Championships, Bourg-Saint-Maurice, Savoy, July 31-Aug. 6.

Napoleon as Young Officer and his Birthplace, Ajaccio — A526

**1969, Aug. 16**

**1255** A526 70c brt grnsh bl, ol & rose vio .40 .25

Napoleon Bonaparte (1769-1821).

For surcharge see Reunion No. 370.

Drops of Water and Diamond — A527

**1969, Sept. 27**

**1256** A527 70c blk, dp bl & brt grn .40 .25

European Water Charter.

Mediterranean Mouflon — A528

**1969, Oct. 11**

**1257** A528 45c ol, blk & org brn .60 .50

Issued to publicize wildlife protection.

Central School of Arts and Crafts
A529

**1969, Oct. 18**

**1258** A529 70c dk grn, yel grn & org .40 .25

Inauguration of the Central School of Arts and Crafts at Chatenay-Malabry.

Nuclear Submarine "Le Redoutable" — A530

**1969, Oct. 25**

**1259** A530 70c dp bl, grn & sl grn .40 .25

**Type of 1968 and**

Henri IV and Edict of Nantes — A531

Designs: No. 1260, Pierre Terrail de Bayard wounded at Battle of Brescia (after a painting in Versailles). No. 1262, Louis XI, Charles the Bold and map of France.

**1969, Nov. 8** **Engr.** ***Perf. 13***

| | | | | |
|---|---|---|---|---|
| **1260** | A511 | 80c brn, bister & blk | .45 | .25 |
| **1261** | A531 | 80c blk & vio bl | .45 | .25 |
| **1262** | A531 | 80c ol, dp grn & dk red brn | .45 | .25 |
| | | *Nos. 1260-1262 (3)* | 1.35 | .75 |

"Firecrest" and Alain Gerbault — A532

**1970, Jan. 10 Engr. *Perf. 13***

**1263** A532 70c ind, brt bl & gray .45 .30

Completion of Alain Gerbault's trip around the world aboard the "Firecrest," 1923-29, 40th anniv.

Gendarmery Emblem, Mountain Climber, Helicopter, Motorcyclists and Motorboat — A533

**1970, Jan. 31**

**1264** A533 45c sl grn, dk bl & brn .80 .40

National Gendarmery, founded 1791.

Field Ball Player — A534

**1970, Feb. 21 Engr. *Perf. 13***

**1265** A534 80c slate green .45 .40

7th Intl. Field Ball Games, Feb. 26-Mar. 8.

Alphonse Juin and Church of the Invalides — A535

**1970, Feb. 28**

**1266** A535 45c gray bl & dk brn .35 .25

Issued to honor Marshal Alphonse Pierre Juin (1888-1967), military leader.

Aerotrain A536

**1970, Mar. 7**

**1267** A536 80c purple & gray .45 .40

Introduction of the aerotrain, which reaches a speed of 320 miles per hour.

Pierre Joseph Pelletier, Joseph Bienaimé Caventou, Quinine Formula and Cell — A537

**1970, Mar. 21 Engr. *Perf. 13***

**1268** A537 50c slate grn, sky bl & dp car .35 .25

Discovery of quinine, 150th anniversary.

Pink Flamingos — A538

**1970, Mar. 21**

**1269** A538 45c olive, gray & pink .35 .25

European Nature Conservation Year, 1970.

Diamant B Rocket and Radar — A539

**1970, Mar. 28**

**1270** A539 45c bright green .50 .25

Space center in Guyana and the launching of the Diamant B rocket, Mar. 10, 1970.

**Europa Issue, 1970**

Common Design Type

**1970, May 2 Engr. *Perf. 13***

**Size: 36x22mm**

**1271** CD13 40c deep carmine .25 .25
**1272** CD13 80c sky blue .40 .25

Annunication, by Primitive Painter of Savoy, 1480 — A540

The Triumph of Flora, by Jean Baptiste Carpeaux — A541

Diana Returning from the Hunt, by François Boucher — A542

Dancer with Bouquet, by Edgar Degas A543

**1970 *Perf. 12x13, 13x12***

**1273** A540 1fr multicolored .50 .35
**1274** A541 1fr red brown .50 .35
**1275** A542 1fr multicolored .50 .35
**1276** A543 1fr multicolored .50 .35
*Nos. 1273-1276 (4)* 2.00 1.40

Issued: No. 1273, 5/9; No. 1274, 7/4; No. 1275, 10/10; No. 1276, 11/14.

Arms of Lens, Miner's Lamp and Pit Head A544

**1970, May 16 Engr. *Perf. 13***

**1277** A544 40c scarlet .25 .25

43rd Natl. Congress of the Federation of French Philatelic Societies, Lens, May 14-21.

Diamond Rock, Martinique A545

1,30

OBSERVATOIRE DE HAUTE-PROVENCE-CNRS

REPUBLIQUE FRANÇAISE

Haute Provence Observatory and Spiral Nebula — A546

Designs: 95c, Chancelade Abbey, Dordogne. 1fr, Gosier Islet, Guadeloupe.

**1970, June 20 Engr. *Perf. 13***

**1278** A545 50c sl grn, brt bl & plum .30 .25
**1279** A545 95c lt ol, car & brn .80 .80
**1280** A545 1fr sl grn, brt bl & dk car rose .90 .25
**1281** A546 1.30fr dk bl, vio bl & dk grn 1.10 .90
*Nos. 1278-1281 (4)* 3.10 2.20

Hand Reaching for Freedom — A547

**1970, June 27**

**1282** A547 45c vio bl, bl & bister .40 .25

Liberation of concentration camps, 25th anniv.

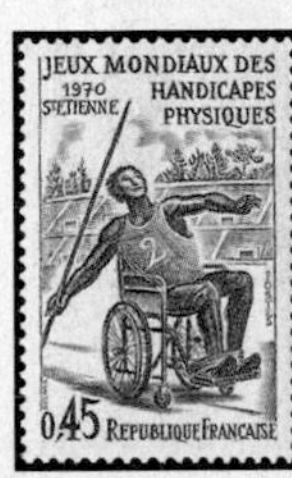


Handicapped Javelin Thrower — A548

**1970, June 27**

**1283** A548 45c rose car, ultra & emer .40 .25

Issued to publicize the International Games of the Handicapped, St. Etienne, June 1970.

Pole Vault — A549

**1970, Sept. 11 Engr. *Perf. 13***

**1284** A549 45c car, bl & indigo .45 .25

First European Junior Athletic Championships, Colombes, Sept. 11-13.

Royal Salt Works, Arc-et-Senans — A550

**1970, Sept. 26**

**1285** A550 80c bl, brn & dk grn .70 .65

Restoration of the 18th cent. Royal Salt Works buildings, by Claude Nicolas Ledoux (1736-1806) at Arc-et-Senans, for use as a center for studies of all aspects of future human life.

Armand Jean du Plessis, Duc de Richelieu — A551

Designs: No. 1287, Battle of Fontenoy, 1745. No. 1288, Louis XIV and Versailles.

**1970, Oct. 17 Engr. *Perf. 13***

**1286** A551 45c blk, sl & car rose .50 .30
**1287** A551 45c org, brn & indigo .50 .30
**1288** A551 45c sl grn, lem & org brn .50 .30
*Nos. 1286-1288 (3)* 1.50 .90

UN Headquarters in New York and Geneva — A552

**1970, Oct. 24 Engr. *Perf. 13***
**1289** A552 80c ol, dp ultra & dk pur .40 .25

25th anniversary of the United Nations.

View of Bordeaux and France No. 43 — A553

**1970, Nov. 7**
**1290** A553 80c vio bl & gray bl .40 .25

Centerary of the Bordeaux issue.

Col. Denfert-Rochereau and Lion of Belfort, by Frederic A. Bartholdi — A554

**1970, Nov. 14**
**1291** A554 45c dk bl, ol & red brn .40 .25

Centenary of the siege of Belfort during Franco-Prussian War.

Marianne (by Bequet) — A555

**1971-74 Typo. *Perf. 14x13***
**1292** A555 45c sky blue .30 .25
**1292A** A555 60c green ('74) .50 .25

For surcharges see Reunion Nos. 371, 397-398.

**Engr. *Perf. 13***
**1293** A555 50c rose carmine .30 .25
*a.* Bklt. pane of 5 (horiz. strip) 5.00
*b.* Booklet pane of 10 10.00
**1294** A555 60c green ('74) 4.00 .25
*a.* Booklet pane of 10 65.00
**1294B** A555 80c car rose ('74) .50 .25
*c.* Booklet pane of 5 9.00
*d.* Booklet pane of 10 12.00
*Nos. 1293-1294B (3)* 4.80 .75

Nos. 1294 and 1294B issued also in vertical coils with control number on back of every 10th stamp.

No. 1293 issued only in booklets and in vertical coils with red control number on back of every 10th stamp.

See Nos. 1494-1498, 3526, 4410f, 4518.

St. Matthew, Sculpture from Strasbourg Cathedral A556

Winnower, by François Millet A557

The Dreamer, by Georges Rouault A558

**1971 Engr. *Perf. 12x13***
**1295** A556 1fr dark red brown .50 .40
**1296** A557 1fr multicolored .50 .40
**1297** A558 1fr multicolored .50 .40
*Nos. 1295-1297 (3)* 1.50 1.20

Issued: No. 1295, 1/23; No. 1296, 4/3; No. 1297, 6/5.

Figure Skating Pair A560

**1971, Feb. 20 Engr. *Perf. 13***
**1299** A560 80c vio bl, sl & aqua .50 .30

World Figure Skating Championships, Lyons, Feb. 23-28.

Underwater Exploration — A561

**1971, Mar. 6**
**1300** A561 80c blue blk & bl grn .45 .25

International Exhibition of Ocean Exploration, Bordeaux, Mar. 9-14.

Cape Horn Clipper "Antoinette" and Solidor Castle, Saint-Malo — A562

**1971, Apr. 10 Engr. *Perf. 13***
**1301** A562 80c blue, pur & slate .80 .45

For surcharge see Reunion No. 372.

Pyrenean Chamois — A563

**1971, Apr. 24 Engr. *Perf. 13***
**1302** A563 65c bl, dk brn & brn ol .50 .30

National Park of Western Pyrenees.

**Europa Issue, 1971**
Common Design Type and

Santa Maria della Salute, Venice A564

**1971, May 8 Engr. *Perf. 13***
**1303** A564 50c blue gray & ol bis .30 .25

**Size: 36x22mm**
**1304** CD14 80c rose lilac .45 .40

Cardinal, Nobleman and Lawyer — A565

Storming of the Bastille — A566

Design: No. 1306, Battle of Valmy.

**1971**
**1305** A565 45c bl, rose red & pur .45 .30
**1306** A565 45c bl, ol bis & brn red .50 .30
**1307** A566 65c dk brn, gray bl & mag .65 .45
*Nos. 1305-1307 (3)* 1.60 1.05

No. 1305 commemorates the opening of the Estates General, May 5, 1789; No. 1306, Battle of Valmy (Sept. 20, 1792) between French and Prussian armies; 65c, Storming of the Bastille, Paris, July 14, 1789.

Issued: No. 1305, 5/8; No. 1306, 9/18; 65c, 7/10.

Grenoble A568

**1971, May 29 Engr. *Perf. 13***
**1308** A568 50c ocher, lil & rose red .35 .25

44th Natl. Cong. of the Federation of French Philatelic Societies, Grenoble, May 30-31.

"Rural Family Aid" Shedding Light on Village — A569

**1971, June 5**
**1309** A569 40c vio, bl & grn .25 .25

Aid for rural families.
For surcharge see Reunion No. 373.

Chateau and Fort de Sedan A570

Pont d'Arc, Ardèche Gorge — A571

Views: 60c, Sainte Chapelle, Riom. 65c, Fountain and tower, Dole. 90c, Tower and street, Riquewihr.

**1971 Engr. *Perf. 13***
**1310** A571 60c black, grn & bl .30 .25
**1311** A571 65c lil, ocher & blk .55 .25
**1312** A571 90c grn, vio brn & red brn .55 .25
**1313** A570 1.10fr sl grn, Prus bl & brn .65 .45
**1314** A571 1.40fr sl grn, bl & dk brn .75 .25
*Nos. 1310-1314 (5)* 2.80 1.45

Issued: 60c, 6/19; 65c, 90c, 7/3; 1.10fr, 1.40fr, 6/12.
For surcharges see Reunion Nos. 374, 381.

**Gallic Coin Type of 1964-66**

**1971, July 1 Typo. *Perf. 13½x14***
**1315** A418 26c lilac & brn .30 .25
**1316** A418 30c lt brown & brn .35 .25
**1317** A418 45c dull green & brn 1.20 .40
**1318** A418 90c red & brown 1.50 .75
*Nos. 1315-1318 (4)* 3.35 1.65

Nos. 1315-1318 are known only precanceled. See second paragraph after No. 132.

Bourbon Palace A572

**1971, Aug. 28 Engr. *Perf. 13***
**1319** A572 90c violet blue .50 .35

59th Conf. of the Interparliamentary Union.

Embroidery and Tool Making A573

**1971, Oct. 16**
**1320** A573 90c brn red, brt lil & cl .50 .30

40th anniv. of the first assembly of presidents of artisans' guilds.
For surcharge see Reunion No. 375.

Reunion Chameleon A574

**1971, Nov. 6 Photo. *Perf. 13***

**1321** A574 60c brn, yel, grn & blk .65 .45

Nature protection.

**De Gaulle Issue**

Common Design Type and

De Gaulle in Brazzaville, 1944 — A576

Designs: No. 1324, De Gaulle entering Paris, 1944. No. 1325, Pres. de Gaulle, 1970.

**1971, Nov. 9 Engr.**

**1322** CD134 50c black .65 .45
**1323** A576 50c ultra .65 .45
**1324** A576 50c rose red .65 .45
**1325** CD134 50c black .65 .45
*a.* Strip of 4, #1322-1325 + label 3.00 2.50
*Nos. 1325a (1)* 3.00 2.50

1st anniv. of the death of Charles de Gaulle. See Reunion Nos. 377, 380.

Antoine Portal and first Session of Academy — A577

**1971, Nov. 13**

**1326** A577 45c dk purple & mag .40 .25

Sesquicentennial of the founding of the National Academy of Medicine; Baron Antoine Portal was first president.

L'Etude, by Jean Honoré Fragonard A578

Women in Garden, by Claude Monet A579

St. Peter Presenting Pierre de Bourbon, by Maitre de Moulins A580

Boats, by André Derain — A581

**1972 Engr. *Perf. 12x13, 13x12***

**1327** A578 1fr black & multi .50 .40
**1328** A579 1fr slate grn & multi 1.00 .50
**1329** A580 2fr dk brown & multi 1.25 1.00
**1330** A581 2fr yellow & multi 1.25 1.00
*Nos. 1327-1330 (4)* 4.00 2.90

Issued: No. 1327, 1/22; No. 1328, 6/17; No. 1329, 10/14; No. 1330, 12/16.

Map of South Indian Ocean, Penguin and Ships — A582

**1972, Jan. 29 *Perf. 13***

**1331** A582 90c black, bl & ocher .50 .30

Bicentenary of discovery of the Crozet and Kerguelen Islands.

Slalom and Olympic Emblems A583

**1972, Feb. 7**

**1332** A583 90c dk olive & dp car .50 .30

11th Winter Olympic Games, Sapporo, Japan, Feb. 3-13.

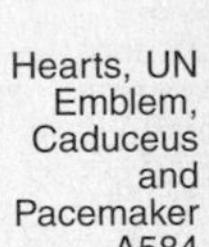

Hearts, UN Emblem, Caduceus and Pacemaker A584

**1972, Apr. 8 Engr. *Perf. 13***

**1333** A584 45c dk car, org & gray .35 .25

"Your heart is your health," world health month.

Red Deer, Sologne Plateau — A585

Charlieu Abbey A585a

Bazoches-du-Morvand Chateau — A586

Saint-Just Cathedral, Narbonne A587

**1972 *Perf. 13***

**1334** A585 1fr ocher & red brn .50 .25
**1335** A585a 1.20fr sl & dull brn .65 .25
**1336** A586 2fr sl grn, blk & red brn 1.00 .25
**1337** A587 3.50fr bl, gray ol & car rose 1.50 .45
*Nos. 1334-1337 (4)* 3.65 1.20

Issued: 1fr, 9/10; 1.20fr, 4/29; 2fr, 9/9; 3.50fr, 4/8.
For surcharge see Reunion No. 388.

Eagle Owl — A588

Nature protection: 60c, Salmon, horiz.

**1972**

**1338** A588 60c grn, ind & brt bl 1.50 .60
**1339** A588 65c sl, ol brn & sep .80 .50

Issue dates: 60c, May 27; 65c, Apr. 15.

**Europa Issue**

Common Design Type and

Aix-la-Chapelle Cathedral — A589

**1972, Apr. 22 Engr. *Perf. 13***

**1340** A589 50c yel, vio brn & dk ol .25 .25

**Photo.**

**Size: 22x36mm**

**1341** CD15 90c red org & multi .50 .35
*Nos. 1341 (1)* .50 .35

Bouquet Made of Hearts and Blood Donors' Emblem — A590

**1972, May 5 Engr.**

**1342** A590 40c red .30 .25

20th anniv. of the Blood Donors Association of Post and Telecommunications Employees.
For surcharge see Reunion No. 383.

Newfoundlander "Côte d'Emeraude" A591

**1972, May 6**

**1343** A591 90c org, vio bl & sl grn .75 .55

Cathedral, Saint-Brieuc A592

**1972, May 20**

**1344** A592 50c lilac rose .35 .25

45th Congress of the Federation of French Philatelic Societies, Saint-Brieuc, May 21-22.

Hand Holding Symbol of Postal Code A593

**1972, June 3 Typo. *Perf. 14x13***

**1345** A593 30c green, blk & car .25 .25
**1346** A593 50c car, blk & yel .30 .25

Introduction of postal code system.
For surcharges see Reunion Nos. 384-385.

Old and New Communications A594

**1972, July 1 Engr. *Perf. 13***

**1347** A594 45c slate & vio blue .40 .25

21st Intl. Congress of P.T.T. (Post, Telegraph & Telephone) Employees, Paris, 7/1-7.

Hurdler and Olympic Rings A595

**1972, July 8**

**1348** A595 1fr deep olive .50 .25

20th Olympic Games, Munich, 8/26-9/11.

Hikers and Mt. Aigoual — A596

**1972, July 15** **Photo.** ***Perf. 13***
**1349** A596 40c brt rose & multi .75 .30

Intl. Year of Tourism and 25th anniv. of the Natl. Hikers Association.

Bicyclist — A597

**1972, July 22** **Engr.**
**1350** A597 1fr gray, brn & lil 1.20 .60

World Bicycling Championships, Marseille, July 29-Aug. 2.

"Incroyables and Merveilleuses," 1794 — A598

French History: 60c, Bonaparte at the Arcole Bridge. 65c, Egyptian expedition (soldiers and scientists finding antiquities; pyramids in background).

**1972** **Engr.** ***Perf. 13***
**1351** A598 45c ol, dk grn & car rose .40 .30
**1352** A598 60c red, blk & ind .65 .35
**1353** A598 65c ocher, ultra & choc .65 .35
*Nos. 1351-1353 (3)* 1.70 1.00

. Issued: 45c, Oct. 7; 60c, 65c, Nov. 11.

Champollion, Rosetta Stone with Key Inscription — A599

**1972, Oct. 14**
**1354** A599 90c vio bl, brn red & blk .50 .30

Sesquicentennial of the deciphering of hieroglyphs by Jean-François Champollion.

St. Teresa, Portal of Notre Dame of Alençon A600

**1973, Jan. 6** **Engr.** ***Perf. 13***
**1355** A600 1fr Prus blue & indigo .50 .30

Centenary of the birth of St. Teresa of Lisieux, the Little Flower (Thérèse Martin, 1873-1897), Carmelite nun.

Anthurium (Martinique) — A601

**1973, Jan. 20** **Photo.**
**1356** A601 50c gray & multi .35 .25

Colors of France and Germany Interlaced — A602

**1973, Jan. 22**
**1357** A602 50c multicolored .40 .25

10th anniv. of the Franco-German Cooperation Treaty. See Germany No. 1101.

Polish Immigrants — A603

**1973, Feb. 3** **Engr.** ***Perf. 13***
**1358** A603 40c slate grn, dp car & brn .40 .25

50th anniversary of Polish immigration into France, 1921-1923.

Last Supper, St. Austremoine Church, Issoire — A604

Kneeling Woman, by Charles Le Brun A605

Angel, Wood, Moutier-D'Ahun — A606

Lady Playing Archlute, by Antoine Watteau A607

**1973** **Engr.** ***Perf. 12x13***
**1359** A604 2fr brown & multi 1.25 .75
**1360** A605 2fr dk red & yel 1.25 .75
**1361** A606 2fr ol brn & vio brn 1.25 .75
**1362** A607 2fr black & multi 1.25 .75
*Nos. 1359-1362 (4)* 5.00 3.00

Issued: No. 1359, 2/10; No. 1360, 4/28; No. 1361, 5/26; No. 1362, 9/22.

Tuileries Palace, Telephone Relays A608

Oil Tanker, Francis I Lock A609

Airbus A300-B A610

**1973**
**1363** A608 45c ultra, sl grn & bis .30 .25
**1364** A609 90c plum, blk & bl .55 .25
**1365** A610 3fr dk brn, bl & blk 1.25 .65
*Nos. 1363-1365 (3)* 2.10 1.15

French technical achievements.
Issued: 45c, 5/15; 90c, 10/27; 3fr, 4/7.

**Europa Issue 1973**
Common Design Type and

City Hall, Brussels, CEPT Emblem — A611

**1973, Apr. 14** **Engr.** ***Perf. 13***
**1366** A611 50c brt pink & choc .40 .25

**Photo.**
**Size: 36x22mm**
**1367** CD16 90c slate grn & multi 1.25 .75

Masonic Lodge Emblem A612

**1973, May 12** **Engr.** ***Perf. 13***
**1368** A612 90c magenta & vio bl .50 .30

Bicentenary of the Free Masons of France.

Guadeloupe Raccoon A613

White Storks A614

**1973**
**1369** A613 40c lilac, sepia & olive .35 .25
**1370** A614 60c blk, aqua & org red .50 .25

Nature protection.
Issue dates: 40c, June 23; 60c, May 12.

**Tourist Issue**

Doubs Waterfall A615

Clos-Lucé, Amboise A617

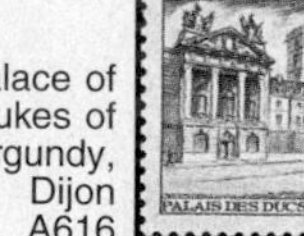

Palace of Dukes of Burgundy, Dijon A616

Design: 90c, Gien Chateau.

**1973** **Engr.** ***Perf. 13***
**1371** A615 60c multicolored .30 .25
**1372** A616 65c red & purple .30 .25
**1373** A616 90c Prus bl, ind & brn .40 .25
**1374** A617 1fr ocher, bl & sl grn .45 .25
*Nos. 1371-1374 (4)* 1.45 1.00

Issued: 60c, 9/8; 65c, 5/19; 90c, 8/18; 1fr, 6/23.
For surcharge see Reunion No. 387.

Academy Emblem — A618

**1973, May 26**
**1375** A618 1fr lil, slate grn & red .50 .30

Academy of Overseas Sciences, 50th anniv.

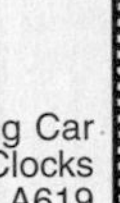

Racing Car and Clocks A619

**1973, June 2**

**1376** A619 60c dk brown & blue .50 .30

24-hour automobile race at Le Mans, 50th anniv.

Five-master France II — A620

**1973, June 9**

**1377** A620 90c ultra, Prus bl & ind .90 .45

For surcharge see Reunion No. 386.

Tower and Square, Toulouse — A621

**1973, June 9**

**1378** A621 50c purple & red brn .30 .25

46th Congress of the Federation of French Philatelic Societies, Toulouse, June 9-12.

Dr. Armauer G. Hansen — A622

**1973, Sept. 29 Engr. *Perf. 13***

**1379** A622 45c grn, dk ol & ocher .30 .25

Centenary of the discovery of the Hansen bacillus, the cause of leprosy.

Ducretet and his Transmission Diagram — A623

**1973, Oct. 6**

**1380** A623 1fr yel grn & magenta .40 .30

75th anniversary of the first transmission of radio signals from the Eiffel Tower to the Pantheon by Eugene Ducretet (1844-1915).

Molière as Sganarelle — A624

**1973, Oct. 20**

**1381** A624 1fr dk red & olive brn .45 .30

Moliere (Jean-Baptiste Poquelin; 1622-1673), playwright and actor.

Pierre Bourgoin and Philippe Kieffer A625

**1973, Oct. 27**

**1382** A625 1fr red, rose cl & vio bl .45 .30

Pierre Bourgoin (1907-70), and Philippe Kieffer (1899-1963), heroes of the Free French forces in World War II.

Napoleon, Jean Portalis and Palace of Justice, Paris — A626

Exhibition Halls — A627

The Coronation of Napoleon, by Jean Louis David — A628

**1973 Engr. *Perf. 13***

**1383** A626 45c blue, choc & gray .40 .30

**1384** A627 60c ol, sl grn & brn .40 .40

**1385** A628 1fr sl grn, ol & claret .55 .40

*Nos. 1383-1385 (3)* 1.35 1.10

History of France. 45c, for the preparation of the Code Napoleon; 60c, Napoleon's encouragement of industry; 1fr, his coronation.

Issued: 45c, 11/3; 60c, 11/24; 1fr, 11/12.

Eternal Flame, Arc de Triomphe — A629

**1973, Nov. 10**

**1386** A629 40c pur, vio bl & red .40 .30

50th anniv. of the Eternal Flame at the Arc de Triomphe, Paris.

Weather Vane — A630

**1973, Dec. 1**

**1387** A630 65c ultra, blk & grn .40 .30

50th anniv. of the Dept. of Agriculture.

Human Rights Flame and Man — A631

**1973, Dec. 8 Engr. *Perf. 13***

**1388** A631 45c car, org & blk .30 .25

25th anniversary of the Universal Declaration of Human Rights.

Postal Museum — A632

**1973, Dec. 19**

**1389** A632 50c maroon & bister .30 .25

Opening of new post and philately museum, Paris.

ARPHILA 75 Emblem A633

**1974, Jan. 19 Engr. *Perf. 13***

**1390** A633 50c brn, bl & brt lil .30 .25

ARPHILA 75 Philatelic Exhibition, Paris, June 1975.

For surcharge see Reunion No. 390.

Concorde over Charles de Gaulle Airport A634

Turbotrain T.G.V. 001 A635

Phenix Nuclear Power Station A636

**1974 Engr. *Perf. 13***

**1391** A634 60c pur & ol gray .40 .30

**1392** A635 60c multicolored .85 .40

**1393** A636 65c multicolored .40 .30

*Nos. 1391-1393 (3)* 1.65 1.00

French technical achievements.

Issued: No. 1391, 3/18; No. 1392, 8/31; 65c, 9/21.

Cardinal Richelieu, by Philippe de Champaigne — A637

Painting by Joan Miró A638

Canal du Loing, by Alfred Sisley — A639

"In Honor of Nicolas Fouquet," Tapestry by Georges Mathieu A640

**Engr., Photo. (#1395, 1397)**

**1974 *Perf. 12x13, 13x12***

**1394** A637 2fr multicolored 1.25 1.00

**1395** A638 2fr multicolored 1.25 1.00

**1396** A639 2fr multicolored 1.25 1.00

**1397** A640 2fr multicolored 1.25 1.00

*Nos. 1394-1397 (4)* 5.00 4.00

Nos. 1394-1397 are printed in sheets of 25 with alternating labels publicizing "ARPHILA 75," Paris, June 6-16, 1975.

Issued: No. 1394, 3/23; No. 1395, 9/14; No. 1396, 11/9; No. 1397, 11/16.

For surcharges see Reunion Nos. 391-394.

French Alps and Gentian A641

**1974, Mar. 30 Engr. *Perf. 13***

**1398** A641 65c vio blue & gray .40 .25

Centenary of the French Alpine Club.

**Europa Issue 1974**

"Age of Bronze," by Auguste Rodin — A642

"Air," by Aristide Maillol A643

**1974, Apr. 20** *Perf. 13*

**1399** A642 50c brt rose lil & blk .30 .25
**1400** A643 90c olive & brown .55 .40

Sea Rescue — A644

**1974, Apr. 27**

**1401** A644 90c multicolored .50 .30

Reorganized sea rescue organization.
For surcharge see Reunion No. 395.

Council Building, View of Strasbourg and Emblem — A645

**1974, May 4** **Engr.** *Perf. 13*

**1402** A645 45c indigo, bister & bl .30 .25

25th anniversary of the Council of Europe.

**Tourist Issue**

View of Salers A646

Basilica of St. Nicolas de Porte — A647

Seashell over Corsica — A648

Design: 1.10fr, View of Lot Valley.

**1974** **Engr.** *Perf. 13*

**1403** A646 65c yel grn & choc .25 .25
**1404** A646 1.10fr choc & sl grn .45 .30
**1405** A647 2fr gray & lilac .80 .30
**1406** A648 3fr multicolored 1.00 .40
*Nos. 1403-1406 (4)* 2.50 1.25

Issued: 65c, 6/22; 1.10fr, 9/7; 2fr, 10/12; 3fr, 5/11.

Bison A649

Giant Armadillo of Guyana A650

**1974**

**1407** A649 40c bis, choc & bl .35 .25
**1408** A650 65c slate, olive & grn .35 .25

Nature protection.
Issued: No. 1407, 5/25; No. 1408, 10/19.

Americans Landing in Normandy and Arms of Normandy — A651

General Marie-Pierre Koenig — A652

Order of the French Resistance — A653

**1974**

**1409** A651 45c grn, rose & ind .80 .50
**1410** A652 1fr multicolored .50 .35
**1411** A653 1fr multicolored .65 .50
*Nos. 1409-1411 (3)* 1.95 1.35

30th anniversary of the liberation of France from the Nazis. Design of No. 1410 includes diagram of battle of Bir-Hakeim and Free French and Bir-Hakeim memorials.

Issued: 45c, 6/8; No. 1410, 5/25; No. 1411, 11/23.

See No. B478.

Pfister House, 16th Century, Colmar — A654

**1974, June 1**

**1412** A654 50c multicolored .25 .25

47th Congress of the Federation of French Philatelic Societies, Colmar, May 30-June 4.

Chess A655

**1974, June 8**

**1413** A655 1fr dk brown & multi .50 .30

21st Chess Olympiad, Nice, June 6-30.

Facade with Statue of Louis XIV, and 1675 Medal — A656

**1974, June 15**

**1414** A656 40c indigo, bl & brn .30 .25

300th anniversary of the founding of the Hotel des Invalides (Home for poor and sick officers and soldiers).

Peacocks Holding Letter, and Globe — A657

**1974, Oct. 5** **Engr.** *Perf. 13*

**1415** A657 1.20fr ultra, dp grn & dk car .50 .30

Centenary of Universal Postal Union.
For surcharge see Reunion No. 396.

Copernicus and Heliocentric System — A658

**1974, Oct. 12**

**1416** A658 1.20fr multicolored .50 .25

500th anniversary of the birth of Nicolaus Copernicus (1473-1543), Polish astronomer.

**Tourist Issue**

Palace of Justice, Rouen A659

Saint-Pol-de-Leon A660

Chateau de Rochechouart — A661

**1975** **Engr.** *Perf. 13*

**1417** A659 85c multicolored .50 .30
**1418** A660 1.20fr bl, bis & choc .50 .30
**1419** A661 1.40fr brn, ind & grn .60 .30
*Nos. 1417-1419 (3)* 1.60 .90

Issued: 85c, 1/25; 1.20fr, 1/18; 1.40fr, 1/11.

Snowy Egret — A662

**1975, Feb. 15** **Engr.** *Perf. 13*

**1420** A662 70c brt blue & bister .40 .30

Nature protection.

Gallic Coin — A663

**1975, Feb. 16** **Typo.** *Perf. 13½x14*

**1421** A663 42c orange & mag .90 .45
**1422** A663 48c lt bl & red brn 1.00 .70
**1423** A663 70c brt pink & red 1.75 1.00
**1424** A663 1.35fr lt green & brn 2.40 1.25
*Nos. 1421-1424 (4)* 6.05 3.40

Nos. 1421-1424 are known only precanceled. See second note after No. 132. See Nos. 1460-1463, 1487-1490.

The Eye — A664

Ionic Capital — A665

Graphic Art — A666

Ceres — A667

**1975** **Engr.** ***Perf. 13***

**1425** A664 1fr red, pur & org .45 .30
**1426** A665 2fr grn, sl grn & mag .80 .55
**1427** A666 3fr dk car & ol grn 1.25 .90
**1428** A667 4fr red, sl grn & bis 1.60 1.25
*Nos. 1425-1428 (4)* 4.10 3.00

**Souvenir Sheet**

**1429** Sheet of 4 7.50 7.50
*a.* A664 2fr dp car & slate blue 1.00 1.00
*b.* A665 3fr brt bl, sl bl & dp car 1.40 1.40
*c.* A666 4fr slate blue, brt bl & plum 2.00 2.00
*d.* A667 6fr brt bl, sl bl & plum 2.50 2.50

ARPHILA 75, Intl. Philatelic Exhibition, Paris, 6/6-16. Issued: 1fr, 3/1; 2fr, 3/22; 3fr, 4/19; 4fr, 5/17; No. 1429, 4/2.

Pres. Georges Pompidou — A668

**1975, Apr. 3** **Engr.** ***Perf. 13***

**1430** A668 80c black & gray .40 .25

Georges Pompidou (1911-74), President of France, 1969-74.

Paul as Harlequin, by Picasso — A669

Europa; 1.20fr, Woman on Balcony, by Kees van Dongen

**1975, Apr. 26** **Photo.** ***Perf. 13***

**1431** A669 80c multi .45 .35
**1432** A669 1.20fr multi, horiz. .80 .70

Machines, Globe, Emblem A670

**1975, May 3** **Engr.**

**1433** A670 1.20fr blue, blk & red .50 .30

World Machine Tool Exhib., Paris, 6/7-26.

Senate Assembly Hall A071

**1975, May 24** **Engr.** ***Perf. 13***

**1434** A671 1.20fr olive & dk car .50 .30

Centenary of the Senate of the Republic.

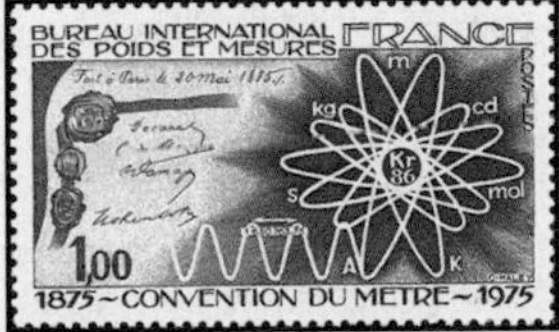

Meter Convention Document, Atom Diagram and Waves — A672

**1975, May 31**

**1435** A672 1fr multicolored .50 .30

Cent. of Intl. Meter Convention, Paris, 1875.

Metro Regional Train A673

"Gazelle" Helicopter A674

**1975**

**1436** A673 1fr indigo & brt bl .55 .30
**1437** A674 1.30fr vio bl & grn .60 .40

French technical achievements. Issue dates: 1fr, June 21; 1.30fr, May 31.

Youth and Flasks, Symbols of Study and Growth — A675

**1975, June 21**

**1438** A675 70c red pur & blk .30 .25

Student Health Foundation.

People's Theater, Bussang, and Maurice Pottecher A676

**1975, Aug. 9** **Engr.** ***Perf. 13***

**1439** A676 85c multicolored .35 .25

80th anniversary of the People's Theater at Bussang, founded by Maurice Pottecher.

**Regions of France**

Central France A677

Aquitaine A678

Limousin A679

Picardy A680

Burgundy A681

Loire A682

Guyana A683

Auvergne A684

Poitou-Charentes A685

Southern Pyrenees A686

Pas-de-Calais — A687

**1975-76** **Engr.** ***Perf. 13***

**1440** A677 25c blue & yel grn .25 .25
**1441** A678 60c multicolored .25 .25
**1442** A679 70c multicolored .50 .35
**1443** A680 85c bl, grn & org .70 .35
**1444** A681 1fr red, yel & mar .70 .35
**1445** A682 1.15fr bl, bis & grn .70 .35
**1446** A683 1.25fr multicolored .65 .50
**1447** A684 1.30fr dk bl & red .85 .50
**1448** A685 1.90fr sl, ol & Prus bl 1.00 .50
**1449** A686 2.20fr multicolored 1.10 1.00
**1450** A687 2.80fr car, bl & blk 1.40 1.00
*Nos. 1440-1450 (11)* 8.10 5.40

Issued: 85c, 11/15; 1fr, 10/25; 1.15fr, 9/6; 1.30fr, 10/4/75; 1.90fr, 12/6; 2.80fr, 12/13; 25c, 1/31/76; 2.20fr, 1/10/76; 60c, 5/22/76; 70c, 5/29/76; 1.25fr, 10/16/76.

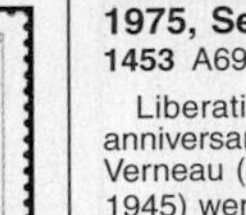

A690

French Flag, F.-H. Manhes, Jean Verneau, Pierre Kaan

**1975, Sept. 27**

**1453** A690 1fr multicolored .60 .30

Liberation of concentration camps, 30th anniversary. F.-H. Manhes (1889-1959), Jean Verneau (1890-1944) and Pierre Kaan (1903-1945) were French resistance leaders, imprisoned in concentration camps.

A691

Monument, by Joseph Riviere.

**1975, Oct. 11**

**1454** A691 70c multicolored .45 .30

Land Mine Demolition Service, 30th anniversary. Monument was erected in Alsace to honor land mine victims.

Symbols of Suburban Living A692

**1975, Oct. 18**

**1455** A692 1.70fr brown, bl & grn .75 .50

Creation of new towns.

Women and Rainbow — A693

**1975, Nov. 8** **Photo.**

**1456** A693 1.20fr silver & multi .50 .40

International Women's Year 1975.

Saint-Nazaire Bridge — A694

**1975, Nov. 8** **Engr.**

**1457** A694 1.40fr bl, ind & grn .60 .30

French and Russian Flags — A695

**1975, Nov. 22**

**1458** A695 1.20fr bl, red & ocher .50 .30

Franco-Soviet diplomatic relations, 50th anniv.

Frigate Melpomene A696

**1975, Dec. 6**
**1459** A696 90c multicolored 1.00 .50

### Gallic Coin Type of 1975

**1976, Jan. 1 Typo.** ***Perf. 13½x14***

| | | | | | |
|---|---|---|---|---|---|
| **1460** | A663 | 50c | lt green & brn | 1.00 | .65 |
| **1461** | A663 | 60c | lilac & brn | 1.60 | .95 |
| **1462** | A663 | 90c | orange & brn | 2.00 | 1.25 |
| **1463** | A663 | 1.60fr | violet & brn | 3.75 | 1.90 |
| | | | *Nos. 1460-1463 (4)* | 8.35 | 4.75 |

Nos. 1460-1463 are known only precanceled. See second note after No. 132.

Lintel, St. Genis des Fontaines Church A697

Venus of Brassempouy (Paleolithic) — A698

"The Joy of Life," by Robert Delaunay A699

Ramses II, from Abu Simbel Temple, Egypt — A700

Still Life, by Maurice de Vlaminck — A701

**1976 Engr.** ***Perf. 13***
**1464** A697 2fr blue & slate bl 1.10 .60
**1465** A698 2fr dk brn & yel 1.10 .60

**Photo.** ***Perf. 12½x13***
**1466** A699 2fr multicolored 1.10 .60

**Engr.** ***Perf. 13x12½***
**1467** A700 2fr multicolored .80 .50

***Perf. 13***
**1468** A701 2fr multicolored .80 .50
*Nos. 1464-1468 (5)* 4.90 2.80

Issued: No. 1464, 1/24; No. 1465, 3/6; No. 1466, 7/24; No. 1467, 9/4; No. 1468, 12/18.

### Tourist Issue

Chateau Fort de Bonaguil A702

Lodève Cathedral — A703

Biarritz A704

Thiers — A705

Ussel — A706

Chateau de Malmaison A707

**1976 Engr.** ***Perf. 13***

| | | | | | |
|---|---|---|---|---|---|
| **1469** | A702 | 1fr | multicolored | .35 | .25 |
| **1470** | A703 | 1.10fr | violet blue | .40 | .25 |
| **1471** | A704 | 1.40fr | multicolored | .60 | .25 |
| **1472** | A705 | 1.70fr | multicolored | .60 | .25 |
| **1473** | A706 | 2fr | multicolored | .90 | .25 |
| **1474** | A707 | 3fr | multicolored | 1.10 | .25 |
| | | | *Nos. 1469-1474 (6)* | 3.95 | 1.50 |

Issued: 1fr, 2fr, 7/10; 1.10fr, 11/13; 1.40fr, 9/25; 1.70fr, 10/9; 3fr, 4/10.

Destroyers, Association Emblem A708

**1976, Apr. 24**
**1475** A708 1fr vio bl, mag & lem .50 .30

Naval Reserve Officers Assoc., 50th anniv.

Gate, Rouen — A709

**1976, Apr. 24**
**1476** A709 80c olive gray & sal .35 .25

49th Congress of the Federation of French Philatelic Societies, Rouen, Apr. 23-May 2.

Young Person — A710

**1976, Apr. 27**
**1477** A710 60c bl grn, ind & car .35 .25

JUVAROUEN 76, International Youth Philatelic Exhibition, Rouen, Apr. 25-May 2.

### Europa Issue

Ceramic Pitcher, Strasbourg, 18th Century A711

1.20fr, Sevres porcelain plate & CEPT emblem.

**1976, May 8 Photo.** ***Perf. 13***
**1478** A711 80c multicolored .30 .30
**1479** A711 1.20fr multicolored .65 .55

Count de Vergennes and Benjamin Franklin — A712

**1976, May 15 Engr.** ***Perf. 13***
**1480** A712 1.20fr multicolored .50 .30

American Bicentennial.

Battle of Verdun Memorial — A713

**1976, June 12 Engr.**
**1481** A713 1fr multicolored .45 .25

Battle of Verdun, 60th anniversary.

Communication A714

**1976, June 12 Photo.**
**1482** A714 1.20fr multicolored .50 .40

Troncais Forest — A715

**1976, June 19 Engr.**
**1483** A715 70c green & multi .35 .25

Protection of the environment.

Cross of Lorraine — A716

**1976, June 19**
**1484** A716 1fr multicolored .50 .25

Association of Free French, 30th anniv.

Symphonie Communications Satellite — A717

**1976, June 26 Photo.**
**1485** A717 1.40fr multicolored .65 .50

French technical achievements.

### Gallic Coin Type of 1975

**1976, July 1 Typo.** ***Perf. 13½x14***

| | | | | | |
|---|---|---|---|---|---|
| **1487** | A663 | 52c | ver & dk brn | .40 | .30 |
| **1488** | A663 | 62c | vio & dk brn | 1.00 | .70 |
| **1489** | A663 | 95c | tan & dk brn | 1.00 | .90 |
| **1490** | A663 | 1.70fr | dk bl & dk brn | 2.75 | 1.40 |
| | | | *Nos. 1487-1490 (4)* | 5.15 | 3.30 |

Nos. 1487-1490 are known only precanceled. See second note after No. 132.

Paris Summer Festival — A719

**1976, July 10** **Engr.**
**1491** A719 1fr multicolored .50 .30

Summer festival in Tuileries Gardens, Paris.

Emblem and Soldiers A720

**1976, July 8**
**1492** A720 1fr blk, dp bl & mag .50 .25

Officers Reserve Corps, centenary.

Sailing A721

**1976, July 17**
**1493** A721 1.20fr blue, blk & vio .50 .25

21st Olympic Games, Montreal, Canada, July 17-Aug. 1.

**Marianne Type of 1971-74**

**1976** **Typo.** ***Perf. 14x13***
**1494** A555 80c green .40 .25

**Engr.** ***Perf. 13***
**1495** A555 80c green 1.25 .50
*a.* Booklet pane of 10 15.00
**1496** A555 1fr carmine rose .50 .25
*a.* Booklet pane of 5 4.00
*b.* Booklet pane of 10 8.00
*Nos. 1495-1496 (2)* 1.75 .75

No. 1495 issued in booklets only. "POSTES" 6mm long on Nos. 1292A and 1494; 4mm on others.

Nos. 1494, 1496 were issued untagged in 1977.

**Coil Stamps**

**1976, Aug. 1** **Engr.** ***Perf. 13 Horiz.***
**1497** A555 80c green .80 .55
**1498** A555 1fr carmine rose .80 .55

Red control number on back of every 10th stamp.

Woman's Head, by Jean Carzou — A722

**1976, Sept. 18** **Engr.** ***Perf. 13x12½***
**1499** A722 2fr multicolored .90 .65

Old and New Telephones A723

**1976, Sept. 25** **Engr.** ***Perf. 13***
**1500** A723 1fr multicolored .50 .25

Centenary of first telephone call by Alexander Graham Bell, Mar. 10, 1876.

Festival Emblem and Trophy, Pyrenees, Hercules and Pyrène — A724

**1976, Oct. 2**
**1501** A724 1.40fr multicolored .65 .40

10th Intl. Tourist Film Festival, Tarbes, 10/4-10.

Police Emblem — A725

**1976, Oct. 9** **Engr.** ***Perf. 13***
**1502** A725 1.10fr ultra, red & ol .50 .30

National Police, help and protection.

Atomic Particle Accelerator, Diagram A726

**1976, Oct. 22** **Photo.**
**1503** A726 1.40fr multicolored .75 .45

European Center for Nuclear Research (CERN).

"Exhibitions" — A727

**1976, Nov. 20** **Engr.** ***Perf. 13***
**1504** A727 1.50fr multicolored .75 .50

Trade Fairs and Exhibitions.

Abstract Design A728

**1976, Nov. 27** **Photo.**
**1505** A728 1.10fr multicolored .50 .40

Customs Service.

Atlantic Museum, Port Louis — A729

**1976, Dec. 4** **Engr.**
**1506** A729 1.45fr grnsh bl & olive .60 .50

**Regions of France**

Réunion A730

Martinique A731

Franche-Comté A732

Brittany A733

Languedoc-Roussillon — A734

Rhône-Alps A735

Champagne-Ardennes A736

Alsace A737

**Photo. (1.45fr, 1.50fr, 2.50fr); Engr.**
**1977** ***Perf. 13***
**1507** A730 1.45fr grn & lil rose .65 .40
**1508** A731 1.50fr multicolored .65 .60
**1509** A732 2.10fr multicolored .90 .65
**1510** A733 2.40fr multicolored 1.10 .35
**1511** A734 2.50fr multicolored 1.10 .85
**1512** A735 2.75fr Prus blue 1.40 .80
**1513** A736 3.20fr multicolored 1.40 .80
**1514** A737 3.90fr multicolored 2.50 1.50
*Nos. 1507-1514 (8)* 9.70 5.95

Issued: 1.45fr, 2/5; 1.50fr, 1/29; 2.10fr, 1/8; 2.40fr, 2/19; 2.50fr, 1/15; 2.75fr, 1/22; 3.20fr, 4/16; 3.90fr, 2/26.

Pompidou Cultural Center — A738

**1977, Feb. 5** **Engr.** ***Perf. 13***
**1515** A738 1fr multicolored .35 .25

Inauguration of the Georges Pompidou National Center for Art and Culture, Paris.

Dunkirk Harbor A739

**1977, Feb. 12**
**1516** A739 50c multicolored .25 .25

Expansion of Dunkirk harbor facilities.

Bridge at Mantes, by Corot — A740

Virgin and Child, by Rubens A741

Tridimensional Design, by Victor Vasarely — A742

Head and Eagle, by Pierre-Yves Tremois A743

**1977** **Engr.** ***Perf. 13x12½***
**1517** A740 2fr multicolored .95 .75

***Perf. 12x13***
**1518** A741 2fr multicolored 1.10 .75

***Perf. 12½x13***

**1519** A742 3fr sl grn & pale lil 1.25 .75

**Photo.**

**1520** A743 3fr dark red & blk 1.40 1.25
*Nos. 1517-1520 (4)* 4.70 3.50

Issue dates: No. 1517, Feb. 12; No. 1518, Nov. 5; No. 1519, Apr. 7; No. 1520, Sept. 17.

Hand Holding Torch and Sword — A744

**1977, Mar. 5** **Engr.** ***Perf. 13***

**1521** A744 80c ultra & multi .45 .30

"France remembers its dead."

Pisces — A745

Zodiac Signs: 58c, Cancer. 61c, Sagittarius. 68c, Taurus. 73c, Aries. 78c, Libra. 1.05fr, Scorpio. 1.15fr, Capricorn. 1.25fr, Leo. 1.85fr, Aquarius. 2fr, Virgo. 2.10fr, Gemini.

**1977-78** **Engr.** ***Perf. 13***

**1522** A745 54c violet blue .65 .30
**1523** A745 58c emerald 1.00 .40
**1524** A745 61c brt blue .55 .30
**1525** A745 68c deep brown .85 .35
**1526** A745 73c rose carmine 1.50 .80
**1527** A745 78c vermilion .65 .35
**1528** A745 1.05fr brt lilac 1.50 .75
**1529** A745 1.15fr orange 2.25 1.40
**1530** A745 1.25fr lt olive grn 1.25 .60
**1531** A745 1.85fr slate grn 2.75 1.25
**1532** A745 2fr blue green 3.00 1.75
**1533** A745 2.10fr lilac rose 1.65 1.00
*Nos. 1522-1533 (12)* 17.60 9.25

Issued: 54c, 68c, 1.05fr, 1.85fr, 4/1/77; others, 1978.

Nos. 1522-1533 are known only precanceled. See second note after No. 132.

Village in Provence A746

Europa: 1.40fr, Brittany port.

**1977, Apr. 23**

**1534** A746 1fr multicolored .45 .25
**1535** A746 1.40fr multicolored 1.00 .35

Flowers and Gardening A747

**1977, Apr. 23** **Engr.** ***Perf. 13***

**1536** A747 1.70fr multicolored .80 .50

National Horticulture Society, centenary.

Symbolic Flower A748

**1977, May 7**

**1537** A748 1.40fr multicolored .65 .40

Intl. Flower Show, Nantes, May 12-23.

Battle of Cambray A749

**1977, May 14**

**1538** A749 80c multicolored .40 .30

Capture of Cambray and the incorporation of Cambresis District into France, 300th anniv.

Carmes Church, School, Map of France — A750

**1977, May 14**

**1539** A750 1.10fr multicolored .50 .30

Catholic Institutes in France.

Modern Constructions A751

**1977, May 21**

**1540** A751 1.10fr multicolored .50 .30

European Federation of the Construction Industry.

Annecy Castle A752

**1977, May 28**

**1541** A752 1fr multicolored .50 .30

Congress of the Federation of French Philatelic Societies, Annecy, May 28-30.

**Tourist Issue**

Abbey, Pont-à-Mousson — A753

Abbey Tower, Saint-Amand-les-Eaux A754

Collegiate Church of Dorat A755

Fontenay Abbey A756

Bayeux Cathedral — A757

Chateau de Vitré A758

**1977** **Engr.** ***Perf. 13***

**1542** A753 1.25fr multicolored .50 .30
**1543** A754 1.40fr multicolored .50 .30
**1544** A755 1.45fr multicolored .55 .35
**1545** A756 1.50fr multicolored .55 .25
**1546** A757 1.90fr black & yel .75 .30
**1547** A758 2.40fr black & yel .80 .30
*Nos. 1542-1547 (6)* 3.65 1.80

Issued: 1.25fr, 10/1; 1.40fr, 9/17; 1.45fr, 7/16; 1.50fr, 6/4; 1.90fr, 7/9; 2.40fr, 9/24.

Polytechnic School and "X" — A759

**1977, June 4** **Engr.** ***Perf. 13***

**1548** A759 1.70fr multicolored .70 .30

Relocation at Palaiseau of Polytechnic School, founded 1794.

Soccer and Cup — A760

**1977, June 11**

**1549** A760 80c multicolored .60 .40

Soccer Cup of France, 60th anniversary.

De Gaulle Memorial A761

**Photo. & Embossed**

**1977, June 18**

**1550** A761 1fr gold & multi 1.00 .40

5th anniversary of dedication of De Gaulle memorial at Colombey-les-Deux-Eglises.

Stylized Map of France — A762

**1977, June 18** **Engr.** ***Perf. 13***

**1551** A762 1.10fr ultra & red .50 .30

French Junior Chamber of Commerce.

Battle of Nancy — A763

**1977, June 25**

**1552** A763 1.10fr blue & slate .60 .40

Battle of Nancy between the Dukes of Burgundy and Lorraine, 500th anniversary.

Arms of Burgundy — A764

**1977, July 2**

**1553** A764 1.25fr ol brn & slate grn .55 .25

Annexation of Burgundy by the French Crown, 500th anniversary.

Association Emblem A765

**1977, July 8**

**1554** A765 1.40fr ultra, olive & red .65 .25

French-speaking Parliamentary Association.

Red Cicada — A766

**1977, Sept. 10 Photo. *Perf. 13***
1555 A766 80c multicolored .40 .30

Nature protection.

French Handicrafts A767

**1977, Oct. 1 Engr. *Perf. 13***
1556 A767 1.40fr multicolored .40 .45

French craftsmen.

Industry and Agriculture — A768

**1977, Oct. 22**
1557 A768 80c brown & olive .30 .25

Economic & Social Council, 30th anniv.

Table Tennis A769

**1977, Dec. 17 Engr. *Perf. 13***
1558 A769 1.10fr multicolored 1.25 .75

French Table Tennis Federation, 50th anniv., and French team, gold medal winner, Birmingham.

Abstract, by Roger Excoffon — A770

**1977, Dec. 17 *Perf. 13x12½***
1559 A770 3fr multicolored 1.40 1.00

Sabine, after David — A771

**1977-78 Engr. *Perf. 13***

| | | | | |
|---|---|---|---|---|
| 1560 | A771 | 1c slate | .25 | .25 |
| 1561 | A771 | 2c brt violet | .25 | .25 |
| 1562 | A771 | 5c slate green | .25 | .25 |
| 1563 | A771 | 10c red brown | .25 | .25 |
| 1564 | A771 | 15c Prus blue | .25 | .25 |
| 1565 | A771 | 20c brt green | .25 | .25 |
| 1566 | A771 | 30c orange | .25 | .25 |
| 1567 | A771 | 50c red lilac | .25 | .25 |
| 1568 | A771 | 80c green | .50 | .25 |
| *a.* | | Booklet pane of 10 | 10.00 | |
| 1569 | A771 | 80c olive | .50 | .25 |
| 1570 | A771 | 1fr red | .60 | .25 |
| *a.* | | Booklet pane of 5 | 7.00 | |
| *b.* | | Booklet pane of 10 | 10.00 | |
| 1571 | A771 | 1fr green | .50 | .25 |
| *a.* | | Booklet pane of 10 | 7.00 | |
| 1572 | A771 | 1.20fr red | .55 | .25 |
| *a.* | | Booklet pane of 5 | 5.00 | |
| *b.* | | Booklet pane of 10 | 8.50 | |
| 1573 | A771 | 1.40fr brt blue | 1.00 | .25 |
| 1574 | A771 | 1.70fr grnsh blue | .75 | .25 |
| 1575 | A771 | 2fr emerald | .90 | .25 |
| 1576 | A771 | 2.10fr lilac rose | 1.00 | .25 |
| 1577 | A771 | 3fr dark brown | 1.25 | .25 |
| | | *Nos. 1560-1577 (18)* | 9.55 | 4.50 |

Issued: Nos. 1560-1567, 1573, 1575, 1577, 4/3/78; Nos. 1568, 1570, 12/19/77; Nos. 1569, 1571, 1572, 1574, 1576, 6/5/78.

### Coil Stamps

**1978 *Perf. 13 Horiz.***

| | | | | |
|---|---|---|---|---|
| 1578 | A771 | 80c bright green | 1.10 | .90 |
| 1579 | A771 | 1fr bright green | 1.50 | .90 |
| 1579A | A771 | 1fr bright red | 1.10 | .90 |
| 1579B | A771 | 1.20fr bright red | 1.10 | .90 |
| | | *Nos. 1578-1579B (4)* | 4.80 | 3.60 |

See Nos. 1658-1677, 3527, 4410g, 4520, 5336-5343.
For similar design inscribed "REPUBLIQUE FRANCAISE" see type A900.

Percheron, by Jacques Birr A772

Osprey — A773

**1978 Photo. *Perf. 13***
1580 A772 1.70fr multicolored 1.00 .80

**Engr.**
1581 A773 1.80fr multicolored .90 .50

Nature protection.
Issue dates: 1.70fr, Jan. 7; 1.80fr, Oct. 14.

Tournament, 1662, Etching — A774

Institut de France and Pont des Arts, Paris, by Bernard Buffet — A776

Horses, by Yves Brayer — A777

**1978 Engr. *Perf. 12x13***
1582 A774 2fr black 1.00 .80

***Perf. 13x12***
1584 A776 3fr multicolored 1.40 1.25
1585 A777 3fr multicolored 1.40 1.25
*Nos. 1582-1585 (3)* 3.80 3.30

Issued: 2fr, 1/14; No. 1584, 2/4; No. 1585, 12/9.

Communications School and Tower — A778

**1978, Jan. 19 Engr. *Perf. 13***
1586 A778 80c Prussian blue .40 .25

Natl. Telecommunications School, cent.

Swedish and French Flags, Map of Saint Barthelemy A779

**1978, Jan. 19**
1587 A779 1.10fr multicolored .55 .25

Centenary of the reunion with France of Saint Barthelemy Island, West Indies.

### Regions of France

Ile de France — A780

Tanker, Refinery, Flower, Upper Normandy A781

Lower Normandy A782

**1978 Photo. *Perf. 13***
1588 A780 1fr red, blue & blk .45 .25

**Engr.**
1589 A781 1.40fr multicolored .60 .30

**Photo.**
1590 A782 1.70fr multicolored .80 .30
*Nos. 1588-1590 (3)* 1.85 .85

Issued: 1fr, 3/4; 1.40fr, 1/21; 1.70fr, 3/31.

Stylized Map of France — A788

**1978, Feb. 11 Engr. *Perf. 13***
1596 A788 1.10fr violet & green .45 .25

Program of administrative changes, 15th anniv.

Young Stamp Collector — A789

**1978, Feb. 25**
1597 A789 80c multicolored .35 .25

JUVEXNIORT, Youth Philatelic Exhibition, Niort, Feb. 25-March 5.

### Tourist Issue

Verdon Gorge — A790

Saint-Saturnin Church — A792

Pont Neuf, Paris A791

Our Lady of Bec-Hellouin Abbey — A793

Chateau D'Esquelbecq — A794

Aubazine Abbey A795

Fontevraud Abbey A796

**1978 Engr. *Perf. 13***

**1598** A790 50c multicolored .25 .25
**1599** A791 80c multicolored .35 .25
**1600** A792 1fr black .45 .25
**1601** A793 1.10fr multicolored .50 .25
**1602** A794 1.10fr multicolored .50 .25
**1603** A795 1.25fr carmine & brn .60 .30
**1604** A796 1.70fr multicolored .80 .30
*Nos. 1598-1604 (7)* 3.45 1.85

Issued: 1.25fr, 2/18; 50c, 3/6; No. 1601, 3/26; 80c, 5/27; 1fr, 6/10; 1.70fr, 6/3; No. 1602, 6/17.

See No. 5035b.

Fish and Corals — A797

**1978, Apr. 15 Photo. *Perf. 13***

**1605** A797 1.25fr multicolored .80 .70

Port Cros National Park, 15th anniversary.

Flowers, Butterflies and Houses — A798

**1978, Apr. 22 Engr. *Perf. 13***

**1606** A798 1.70fr multicolored 1.25 .50

Beautification of France campaign, 50th anniv.

Hands Shielding Source of Heat and Light A799

**1978, Apr. 22**

**1607** A799 1fr multicolored .50 .25

Energy conservation.

World War I Memorial near Lens — A800

**1978, May 6**

**1608** A800 2fr lemon & magenta .50 .30

Colline Notre Dame de Lorette memorial of World War I.

Fountain of the Innocents, Paris — A801

Europa: 1.40fr, Flower Park Fountain, Paris.

**1978, May 6**

**1609** A801 1fr multicolored .40 .25
**1610** A801 1.40fr multicolored .75 .30

Maurois Palace, Troyes — A802

**1978, May 13**

**1611** A802 1fr multicolored .45 .25

51st Congress of the Federation of French Philatelic Societies, Troyes, May 13-15.

Roland Garros Tennis Court and Player — A803

**1978, May 27**

**1612** A803 1fr multicolored 1.00 .40

Roland Garros Tennis Court, 50th anniv.

Hand and Plant — A804

**1978, Sept. 9 Engr. *Perf. 13***

**1613** A804 1.30fr brown, red & grn .50 .25

Encouragement of handicrafts.

Printing Office Emblem — A805

**1978, Sept. 23**

**1614** A805 1fr multicolored .50 .25

National Printing Office, established 1538.

Fortress, Besançon, and Collegiate Church, Dole — A806

Valenciennes and Maubeuge — A807

**1978**

**1615** A806 1.20fr multicolored .55 .25
**1616** A807 1.20fr multicolored .55 .25

Reunion of Franche-Comté and Valenciennes and Maubeuge with France, 300th anniversary.

Issued: No. 1615, 9/23; No. 1616, 9/30.

Sower Type of 1906-1937 and Academy Emblem — A808

**1978, Oct. 7**

**1617** A808 1fr multicolored .45 .30

Academy of Philately, 50th anniversary.

Gymnasts, Strasbourg Cathedral, Storks — A809

**1978, Oct. 21**

**1618** A809 1fr multicolored .50 .30

19th World Gymnastics Championships, Strasbourg, Oct. 23-26.

Various Sports — A810

**1978, Oct. 21**

**1619** A810 1fr multicolored .50 .30

Sports for all.

Polish Veterans' Monument — A811

**1978, Nov. 11**

**1620** A811 1.70fr multicolored .75 .45

Polish veterans of World War II.

Railroad Car and Monument, Compiègne Forest, Rethondes A812

**1978, Nov. 11 Engr. *Perf. 13***

**1621** A812 1.20fr indigo .60 .30

60th anniversary of World War I armistice.

Handicapped People — A813

**1978, Nov. 18**

**1622** A813 1fr multicolored .45 .25

Rehabilitation of the handicapped.

Human Rights Emblem A814

**1978, Dec. 9 Engr. *Perf. 13***

**1623** A814 1.70fr dk brown & blue .80 .40

30th anniversary of Universal Declaration of Human Rights.

Child and IYC Emblem A815

**1979, Jan. 6 Engr. *Perf. 13***

**1624** A815 1.70fr multicolored 1.25 .80

International Year of the Child.

"Music," 15th Century Miniature — A816

**1979, Jan. 13 *Perf. 13x12½***

**1625** A816 2fr multicolored 1.00 .80

Diana Taking a Bath, d'Ecouen Castle A817

Church at Auvers-on-Oise, by Vincent Van Gogh — A818

Head of Marianne, by Salvador Dali
A819

Fire Dancer from The Magic Flute, by Chaplain Midy
A820

**1979** **Photo.** ***Perf. 12½x13***

| | | | | |
|---|---|---|---|---|
| **1626** | A817 | 2fr multicolored | 1.00 | .80 |
| **1627** | A818 | 2fr multicolored | 1.50 | .80 |
| **1628** | A819 | 3fr multicolored | 1.50 | 1.00 |
| **1629** | A820 | 3fr multicolored | 1.50 | 1.00 |
| | | *Nos. 1626-1629 (4)* | 5.50 | 3.60 |

Issued: No. 1626, 9/22; No. 1627, 10/27; No. 1628, 11/19; No. 1629, 11/26.

Orange Agaric — A821

Mushrooms: 83c, Death trumpet. 1.30fr, Olive wood pleurotus. 2.25fr, Cauliflower claveria.

**1979, Jan. 15** **Engr.** ***Perf. 13***

| | | | | |
|---|---|---|---|---|
| **1630** | A821 | 64c orange | .40 | .25 |
| **1631** | A821 | 83c brown | .40 | .25 |
| **1632** | A821 | 1.30fr yellow bister | .85 | .40 |
| **1633** | A821 | 2.25fr brown purple | 1.25 | .85 |
| | | *Nos. 1630-1633 (4)* | 2.90 | 1.75 |

Nos. 1630-1633 are known only precanceled. See second note after No. 132.

Victor Segalen
A822

**1979, Jan. 20**

| | | | | |
|---|---|---|---|---|
| **1634** | A822 | 1.50fr multicolored | .60 | .30 |

Physician, explorer and writer (1878-1919).

Hibiscus and Palms — A823

**1979, Feb. 3**

| | | | | |
|---|---|---|---|---|
| **1635** | A823 | 35c multicolored | .25 | .25 |

International Flower Festival, Martinique.

Buddha, Stupas, Temple of Borobudur
A824

**1979, Feb. 24**

| | | | | |
|---|---|---|---|---|
| **1636** | A824 | 1.80fr ol & slate grn | .85 | .40 |

Save the Temple of Borobudur, Java, campaign.

Boy, by Francisque Poulbot (1879-1946)
A825

**1979, Mar. 24** **Photo.**

| | | | | |
|---|---|---|---|---|
| **1637** | A825 | 1.30fr multicolored | .60 | .25 |

### Tourist Issue

Chateau de Maisons, Laffitte
A826

Bernay and St. Pierre sur Dives Abbeys — A827

View of Auray — A827a

Steenvorde Windmill — A828

Wall Painting, Niaux Cave
A829

Royal Palace, Perpignan
A830

**1979** **Engr.** ***Perf. 13***

| | | | | |
|---|---|---|---|---|
| **1638** | A826 | 45c multicolored | .45 | .25 |
| **1639** | A827 | 1fr multicolored | .45 | .25 |
| **1640** | A827a | 1fr multicolored | .55 | .25 |
| **1641** | A828 | 1.20fr multicolored | .65 | .25 |
| **1642** | A829 | 1.50fr multicolored | .70 | .40 |
| **1643** | A830 | 1.70fr multicolored | .75 | .60 |
| | | *Nos. 1638-1643 (6)* | 3.55 | 2.00 |

Issued: 45c, 10/6; No. 1639, 6/16; No. 1640, 6/30; 1.20fr, 6/12; 1.50fr, 7/9; 1.70fr, 4/21.

Honey Bee
A831

**1979, Mar. 31** **Engr.** ***Perf. 13***

| | | | | |
|---|---|---|---|---|
| **1644** | A831 | 1fr multicolored | .50 | .30 |

Nature protection.

St. Germain des Prés Abbey
A832

**1979, Apr. 21**

| | | | | |
|---|---|---|---|---|
| **1645** | A832 | 1.40fr multicolored | .60 | .30 |

Simoun Mail Monoplanes, 1935, and Map of Mail Routes — A833

Europa: 1.70fr, Floating spheres used on Seine during siege of Paris, 1870.

**1979, Apr. 28**

| | | | | |
|---|---|---|---|---|
| **1646** | A833 | 1.20fr multicolored | .75 | .35 |
| **1647** | A833 | 1.70fr multicolored | 1.00 | .50 |

Ship and View of Nantes
A834

**1979, May 5** **Engr.** ***Perf. 13***

| | | | | |
|---|---|---|---|---|
| **1648** | A834 | 1.20fr multicolored | .55 | .30 |

52nd National Congress of French Philatelic Societies, Nantes, May 5-7.

Royal Palace, 1789 — A835

**1979, May 19**

| | | | | |
|---|---|---|---|---|
| **1649** | A835 | 1fr car rose & pur | .45 | .25 |

European Elections
A836

**1979, May 19** **Photo.** ***Perf. 13***

| | | | | |
|---|---|---|---|---|
| **1650** | A836 | 1.20fr multicolored | .55 | .25 |

European Parliament, 1st direct elections, June 10.

Joan of Arc Monument
A837

**1979, May 24** **Engr.**

| | | | | |
|---|---|---|---|---|
| **1651** | A837 | 1.70fr brt lilac rose | .70 | .40 |

Joan of Arc, the Maid of Orleans (1412-1431).

Felix Guyon and Catheters
A840

**1979, June 23**

| | | | | |
|---|---|---|---|---|
| **1652** | A840 | 1.80fr sepia & blue | .80 | .35 |

Felix Guyon (1831-1920), urologist.

Lantern Tower, La Rochelle — A841

Towers: 88c, Chartres Cathedral. 1.40fr, Bourges Cathedral. 2.35fr, Amiens Cathedral.

**1979, Aug. 13** **Engr.** ***Perf. 13***

| | | | | |
|---|---|---|---|---|
| **1653** | A841 | 68c vio brn & blk | .35 | .25 |
| **1654** | A841 | 88c ultra & blk | .40 | .25 |
| **1655** | A841 | 1.40fr gray grn & blk | .65 | .50 |
| **1656** | A841 | 2.35fr dull brn & blk | 1.10 | .60 |
| | | *Nos. 1653-1656 (4)* | 2.50 | 1.60 |

Nos. 1653-1656 are known only precanceled. See second note after No. 132. See Nos. 1684-1687, 1719-1722, 1814-1817.

Telecom '79 — A842

**1979, Sept. 22**

| | | | | |
|---|---|---|---|---|
| **1657** | A842 | 1.10fr multicolored | .45 | .25 |

3rd World Telecommunications Exhibition.

### Sabine Type of 1977-78

**1979-81** **Engr.** ***Perf. 13***

| | | | | |
|---|---|---|---|---|
| **1658** | A771 | 40c brown ('81) | .25 | .25 |
| **1659** | A771 | 60c red brn ('81) | .25 | .25 |
| **1660** | A771 | 70c violet blue | .35 | .25 |
| **1661** | A771 | 90c brt lilac ('81) | .45 | .30 |
| **1662** | A771 | 1fr gray olive | .45 | .25 |
| **1663** | A771 | 1.10fr green | .50 | .25 |
| **1664** | A771 | 1.20fr green ('80) | .40 | .25 |
| **1665** | A771 | 1.30fr rose red | .55 | .25 |
| **1666** | A771 | 1.40fr rose red ('80) | .60 | .25 |
| **1667** | A771 | 1.60fr purple | .75 | .30 |
| **1668** | A771 | 1.80fr ocher | .80 | .50 |
| **1669** | A771 | 3.50fr lt ol grn ('81) | 1.40 | .60 |
| **1670** | A771 | 4fr brt car ('81) | 1.60 | .40 |
| **1671** | A771 | 5fr brt grnsh bl ('81) | 2.00 | .30 |
| | | *Nos. 1658-1671 (14)* | 10.35 | 4.40 |

### Coil Stamps

**1979-80** ***Perf. 13 Horiz.***

| | | | | |
|---|---|---|---|---|
| **1674** | A771 | 1.10fr green | 1.25 | .60 |
| **1675** | A771 | 1.20fr green ('80) | .70 | .50 |
| **1676** | A771 | 1.30fr rose red | 1.25 | .60 |
| **1677** | A771 | 1.40fr rose red ('80) | .45 | .40 |
| | | *Nos. 1674-1677 (4)* | 3.65 | 2.10 |

Lorraine Region — A845

**1979, Nov. 10**
**1678** A845 2.30fr multicolored 1.00 .30

Gears A847

**1979, Nov. 17** ***Perf. 13***
**1680** A847 1.80fr multicolored .80 .30

Central Technical School of Paris, 150th anniv.

Judo Throw A848

**1979, Nov. 24** **Engr.**
**1681** A848 1.60fr multicolored .75 .40

World Judo Championships, Paris, Dec.

Violins — A849

**1979, Dec. 10**
**1682** A849 1.30fr multicolored .60 .35

Eurovision A850

**1980, Jan. 12** **Engr.** ***Perf. 13x13½***
**1683** A850 1.80fr multicolored .90 .70

### Tower Type of 1979

Designs: 76c, Chateau d'Angers. 99c, Chateau de Kerjean. 1.60fr, Chateau de Pierrefonds. 2.65fr, Chateau de Tarascon.

**1980, Jan. 21** **Engr.**
**1684** A841 76c grnsh bl & blk .35 .30
**1685** A841 99c slate grn & blk .45 .30
**1686** A841 1.60fr red & blk .75 .55
**1687** A841 2.65fr brn org & blk 1.25 .65
*Nos. 1684-1687 (4)* 2.80 1.80

Nos. 1684-1687 are known only precanceled. See second note after No. 132.

Self-portrait, by Albrecht Dürer, Philexfrance '82 Emblem — A851

Woman Holding Fan, by Ossip Zadkine A852

Abstract, by Raoul Ubak — A853

Hommage to J.S. Bach, by Jean Picart Le Doux — A854

Peasant, by Louis Le Nain A855

Woman with Blue Eyes, by Modigliani A856

Abstract, by Hans Hartung A857

### Engraved, Photogravure (#1691, 1694)

**1980** ***Perf. 12½x13, 13x12½***
**1688** A851 2fr multicolored 1.00 .80
**1689** A852 3fr multicolored 1.40 1.00
**1690** A853 3fr multicolored 1.40 1.00
**1691** A854 3fr multicolored 1.40 1.00
**1692** A855 3fr multicolored 1.40 1.00
**1693** A856 4fr multicolored 1.75 1.25
**1694** A857 4fr ultra & black 1.75 1.25
*Nos. 1688-1694 (7)* 10.10 7.30

Issued: No. 1688, 6/7; No. 1689, 1/19; No. 1690, 2/2; No. 1691, 9/20; No. 1693, 10/26; No. 1692, 11/10; No. 1694, 12/20.

Giants of the North Festival — A858

**1980, Feb. 16** ***Perf. 13***
**1695** A858 1.60fr multicolored .75 .30

French Cuisine — A859

**1980, Feb. 23**
**1696** A859 90c red & lt brown .60 .40

Woman Embroidering A860

### Photogravure and Engraved

**1980, Mar. 29** ***Perf. 13***
**1697** A860 1.10fr multicolored .50 .30

Fight Against Cigarette Smoking — A861

**1980, Apr. 5** **Photo.** ***Perf. 13***
**1698** A861 1.30fr multicolored .50 .25

Aristide Briand — A862

Europa: 1.80fr, St. Benedict.

**1980, Apr. 26** **Engr.** ***Perf. 13***
**1699** A862 1.30fr multicolored .60 .30
**1700** A862 1.80fr red & red brown .85 .50

Aristide Briand (1862-1932), prime minister, 1909-1911, 1921-1922; St. Benedict, patron saint of Europe.

Liancourt, College, Map of Northwestern France — A863

**1980, May 19** **Engr.** ***Perf. 13***
**1701** A863 2fr dk green & pur .80 .30

National College of Arts and Handicrafts (founded by Larochefoucauld Liancourt) bicentenary.

Cranes, Town Hall Tower, Dunkirk — A864

**1980, May 24**
**1702** A864 1.30fr multicolored .60 .25

53rd Natl. Congress of French Federation of Philatelic Societies, Dunkirk, May 24-26.

### Tourist Issue

Chateau de Maintenon A866

Cordes A865

Montauban A867

St. Peter's Abbey, Solesmes A868

Puy Cathedral A869

**1980 Engr. *Perf. 13***

**1703** A865 1.50fr multicolored .55 .30
**1704** A866 2fr multicolored .80 .30
**1705** A867 2.30fr multicolored 1.00 .30
**1706** A868 2.50fr multicolored 1.25 .30
**1707** A869 3.20fr multicolored 1.40 .50
*Nos. 1703-1707 (5)* 5.00 1.70

Issued: No. 1703, 4/5; No. 1704, 6/7; No. 1705, 5/7; No. 1706, 9/20; No. 1707, 5/12.

Graellsia Isabellae A870

**1980, May 31 Photo.**
**1708** A870 1.10fr multicolored .70 .30

Association Emblem — A871

**1980, June 10 Photo.**
**1709** A871 1.30fr red & blue .55 .25

Intl. Public Relations Assoc., 25th anniv.

Marianne, French Architecture A872

**1980, June 21 Engr.**
**1710** A872 1.50fr bluish & gray blk .70 .30

Heritage Year.

Earth Sciences A873

**1980, July 5**
**1711** A873 1.60fr dk brown & red .70 .50

International Geological Congress.

Rochambeau's Landing — A874

**1980, July 15**
**1712** A874 2.50fr multicolored 1.10 .50

Rochambeau's landing at Newport, R.I. (American Revolution), bicentenary.

Message of Peace, by Yaacov Agam — A875

**1980, Oct. 4 Photo. *Perf. 11½x13***
**1713** A875 4fr multicolored 1.75 1.00

French Golf Federation A876

**1980, Oct. 18 Engr.**
**1714** A876 1.40fr multicolored .60 .30

Comedie Francaise, 300th Anniversary A877

**1980, Oct. 18**
**1715** A877 2fr multicolored .75 .40

Charles de Gaulle — A878

**1980, Nov. 10 Photo. *Perf. 13***
**1716** A878 1.40fr multicolored .90 .50

40th anniversary of De Gaulle's appeal of June 18, and 10th anniversary of his death.

Guardsman — A879

**1980, Nov. 24 Engr. *Perf. 13***
**1717** A879 1.70fr multicolored .80 .45

Rambouillet Chateau A880

**1980, Dec. 6 Engr. *Perf. 13***
**1718** A880 2.20fr multicolored 1.00 .35

**Tower Type of 1979**

Designs: 88c, Imperial Chapel, Ajaccio. 1.14fr, Astronomical Clock, Besancon. 1.84fr, Coucy Castle ruins. 3.05fr, Font-de-Gaume cave drawing, Les Eyzies de Tayac.

**1981, Jan. 11 Engr. *Perf. 13***
**1719** A841 88c dp mag & blk .40 .25
**1720** A841 1.14fr ultra & blk .55 .30
**1721** A841 1.84fr dk green & blk .85 .50
**1722** A841 3.05fr brn red & blk 1.40 .80
*Nos. 1719-1722 (4)* 3.20 1.85

Nos. 1719-1722 are known only precanceled. See second note after No. 132.

Microelectronics — A881

**1981 Photo.**
**1723** A881 1.20fr shown .55 .30
**1724** A881 1.20fr Biology .55 .30
**1725** A881 1.40fr Energy .65 .30
**1726** A881 1.80fr Marine exploration .85 .50
**1727** A881 2fr Telemetry .90 .65
*Nos. 1723-1727 (5)* 3.50 2.05

Issue dates: No. 1723, 2/5; others, 3/28.

Abstract, by Albert Gleizes A882

**1981, Feb. 28 *Perf. 12½x13***
**1728** A882 4fr multicolored 1.75 .90

The Footpath by Camille Pissaro — A883

**1981, Apr. 18 Engr. *Perf. 13x12½***
**1729** A883 2fr multicolored 1.00 .80

Child Watering Smiling Map of France — A884

**1981, Mar. 14 Engr. *Perf. 13***
**1730** A884 1.40fr multicolored .65 .25

Sully Chateau, Rosny-sur-Seine — A885

**1981, Mar. 21**
**1731** A885 2.50fr multicolored 1.10 .40

**Tourist Issue**

Roman Temple, Nimes — A886

**1981, Apr. 11 Engr. *Perf. 13***
**1732** A886 1.70fr multicolored .85 .30

Church of St. Jean, Lyon — A887

St. Anne d'Auray Basilica — A888

**1981**
**1733** A887 1.40fr dk red & dk brn .65 .30
**1734** A888 2.20fr blue & black 1.00 .40

Issue dates: 1.40fr, May 30; 2.20fr, July 4.

Vaucelles Abbey A889

Notre Dame of Louviers A890

**1981**
**1735** A889 2fr red & black .90 .40
**1736** A890 2.20fr red brn & dk brn 1.00 .50
*Nos. 1732-1736 (5)* 4.40 1.90

Issue dates: 2fr, Sept. 19; 2.20fr, Sept. 26.

**Europa Issue**

Folkdances A891

**1981, May 4 *Perf. 13***
**1737** A891 1.40fr Bouree .65 .25
**1738** A891 2fr Sardane 1.00 .40

Bookbinding — A892

**1981, Apr. 4 *Perf. 13***
**1739** A892 1.50fr olive & car rose .70 .40

Cadets — A893

**1981, May 16**
**1740** A893 2.50fr multicolored 1.00 .30

Military College at St. Maixent centenary.

Man Drawing Geometric Diagram — A894

**1981, May 23** **Photo.**
**1741** A894 2fr shown 1.00 .75
**1742** A894 2fr Faces 1.00 .75
*a.* Pair, #1741-1742 + label 2.50 2.00

PHILEXFRANCE '82 Stamp Exhibition, Paris, June 11-21, 1982.

Theophraste Renaudot and Emile de Girardin — A895

**1981, May 30** **Engr.**
**1743** A895 2.20fr black & red 1.00 .30

350th anniversary of La Gazette (founded by Renaudot), and death centenary of founder of Le Journal (de Girardin).

Public Gardens, Vichy — A896

**1981, June 6**
**1744** A896 1.40fr multicolored .65 .30

54th National Congress of French Federation of Philatelic Societies, Vichy.

Higher National College for Commercial Studies Centenary A897

**1981, June 20** ***Perf. 13***
**1745** A897 1.40fr multicolored .65 .30

Sea Shore Conservation — A898

**1981, June 20**
**1746** A898 1.60fr multicolored .75 .55

World Fencing Championship, Clermont-Ferrand, July 2-13 — A899

**1981, June 27**
**1747** A899 1.80fr multicolored .85 .45

Sabine, after David — A900

**1981, Sept. 1** **Engr.**
**1755** A900 1.40fr green .70 .25
**1756** A900 1.60fr red .80 .25
**1757** A900 2.30fr blue 1.40 .85
*Nos. 1755-1757 (3)* 2.90 1.35

**Coil Stamps**

**1981** **Engr.** ***Perf. 13 Horiz.***
**1758** A900 1.40fr green .75 .50
**1759** A900 1.60fr red .75 .50

Highway Safety ("Drink or Drive") A901

**1981, Sept. 5** ***Perf. 13***
**1768** A901 1.60fr multicolored .75 .30

45th Intl. PEN Club Congress — A902

**1981, Sept. 19** ***Perf. 13***
**1769** A902 2fr multicolored 1.00 .35

Jules Ferry, Statesman — A903

**1981, Sept. 26** ***Perf. 12½x13***
**1770** A903 1.60fr multicolored .75 .35

Free compulsory public school centenary.

Natl. Savings Bank Centenary A904

**1981, Sept. 21** **Photo.** ***Perf. 13***
**1771** A904 1.40fr multicolored .65 .25
**1772** A904 1.60fr multicolored .75 .25

The Divers, by Edouard Pignon — A905

**1981, Oct. 3** ***Perf. 13x12½***
**1773** A905 4fr multicolored 1.75 .90

Alleluia, by Alfred Manessier A906

**1981, Dec. 19** **Photo.** ***Perf. 12x13***
**1774** A906 4fr multicolored 1.75 .90

**Tourist Issue**

Saint-Emilion — A907

Crest — A908

**1981** **Engr.** ***Perf. 13x12½***
**1775** A907 2.60fr dk red & lt ol grn 1.10 .25
***Perf. 13***
**1776** A908 2.90fr dk green 1.20 .25

Issued: No. 1775, 10/10; No. 1776, 11/28.

150th Anniv. of Naval Academy A909

**1981, Oct. 17** ***Perf. 13***
**1777** A909 1.40fr multicolored .65 .30

A910

St. Hubert Kneeling before the Stag, 15th cent. sculpture.

**1981, Oct. 24**
**1778** A910 1.60fr multicolored .75 .30

Museum of hunting and nature.

A911

V. Schoelcher, J. Jaures, J. Moulin, the Pantheon.

**1981, Nov. 2**
**1779** A911 1.60fr blue & dull pur .75 .30

Intl. Year of the Disabled A912

**1981, Nov. 7**
**1780** A912 1.60fr multicolored .75 .25

Men Leading Cattle, 2nd Cent. Roman Mosaic — A913

**1981, Nov. 14** ***Perf. 13x12***
**1781** A913 2fr multicolored 1.00 .75

Virgil's birth bimillennium.

Martyrs of Chateaubriant A914

**1981, Dec. 12** **Engr.** ***Perf. 13***
**1782** A914 1.40fr multicolored .70 .25

Liberty, after Delacroix — A915

**1982** **Engr.** ***Perf. 13***
**1783** A915 5c dk green .25 .25
**1784** A915 10c dull red .25 .25
**1785** A915 15c brt rose lilac .35 .35
**1786** A915 20c brt green .25 .25
**1787** A915 30c orange .25 .25
**1788** A915 40c brown .25 .25
*a.* Bklt. pane of 5, 4 No. 1784, No. 1788 ('87) 1.00
**1789** A915 50c lilac .25 .25
**1790** A915 60c lt red brn .30 .25
**1791** A915 70c ultra .35 .25
**1792** A915 80c lt olive grn .35 .25
**1793** A915 90c brt lilac .40 .25
**1794** A915 1fr olive green .30 .25
**1795** A915 1.40fr green .65 .25
**1796** A915 1.60fr green .75 .25
**1797** A915 1.60fr red .75 .25
**1798** A915 1.80fr red .85 .25
**1799** A915 2fr brt yel grn .85 .25
**1800** A915 2.30fr blue 1.50 1.25

**1801** A915 2.60fr blue 1.25 1.00
**1802** A915 3fr chocolate 1.40 .30
**1803** A915 4fr brt carmine 1.75 .30
**1804** A915 5fr gray blue 2.25 .25
*Nos. 1783-1804 (22)* 15.55 7.45

### Coil Stamps

***Perf. 13 Horiz.***

**1805** A915 1.40fr green 1.25 .90
**1806** A915 1.60fr red 1.25 .90
**1807** A915 1.60fr green .85 .50
**1807A** A915 1.80fr red .90 .50
*Nos. 1805-1807A (4)* 4.25 2.80

Issued: 5c-50c, 1fr-1.40fr, 2fr, 2.30fr, 5fr, No. 1797, 1/2; 1.80fr, 2.60fr, No. 1796, 6/1; 60c-90c, 3fr, 4fr, 11/3.

See Nos. 1878-1897A, 2077-2080, 3528, 4410h, 4521. For surcharge see No. 2115.

### Tourist Issue

St. Pierre and Miquelon A916

Corsica A917

Renaissance Fountain, Aix-en Provence — A918

Collonges-la-Rouge — A919

Castle of Henry IV, Pau A920

Lille — A921

Chateau Ripaille, Haute-Savoie — A921a

**1982** **Engr.** ***Perf. 12½***

**1808** A916 1.60fr dk blue & blk 1.25 .30
**1809** A917 1.90fr blue & red .90 .25

***Perf. 13***

**1810** A918 2fr multicolored .90 .40
**1811** A919 3fr multicolored 1.25 .40
**1812** A920 3fr ultra & dk bl 1.25 .40

Issued: 1.60fr, 1.90fr, Jan. 9; 2fr, June 21, No. 1811, July 5, No. 1812, May 15.

***Perf. 13x12½***

**1813** A921 1.80fr dull red & ol .85 .25
**1813A** A921a 2.90fr multicolored 1.40 .80
*Nos. 1808-1813A (7)* 7.80 2.80

Issue dates: 1.80fr, Oct. 16; 2.90fr, Sept. 4.

### Tower Type of 1979

97c, Tanlay Castle, Yonne. 1.25fr, Salses Fort, Pyrenees-Orientales. 2.03fr, Montlhery Tower, Essonne. 3.36fr, Chateau d'If Bouches-du-Rhone.

**1982, Jan. 11** **Engr.** ***Perf. 13***

**1814** A841 97c olive grn & blk .45 .25
**1815** A841 1.25fr red & blk .55 .25
**1816** A841 2.03fr sepia & blk .95 .50
**1817** A841 3.36fr ultra & blk 1.50 .80
*Nos. 1814-1817 (4)* 3.45 1.80

Nos. 1814-1817 are known only precanceled. See second note after No. 132.

800th Birth Anniv. of St. Francis of Assisi A922

**1982, Feb. 6** **Photo. & Engr.**

**1818** A922 2fr black & blue .90 .40

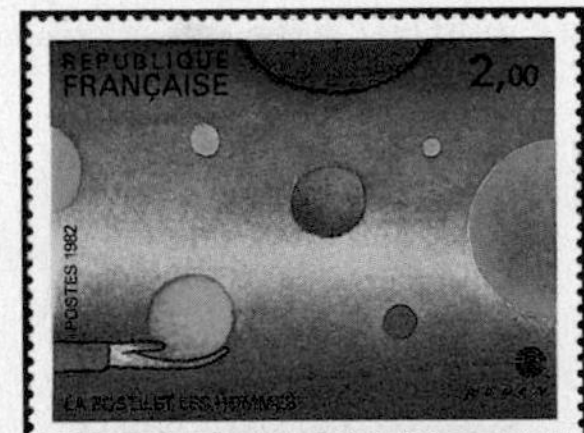


Posts and Mankind — A923

Posts and Technology — A924

**1982, Feb. 13** **Photo.**

**1819** A923 2fr multicolored 1.50 1.25
**1820** A924 2fr multicolored 1.50 1.25
*a.* Pair, #1819-1820 + label 3.50 3.00

PHILEXFRANCE '82 Stamp Exhibition, Paris, June 11-21.

Souvenir Sheet

Marianne, by Jean Cocteau — A925

**1982, June 11**

**1821** A925 Sheet of 2 10.00 9.00
*a.* 4fr red & blue *4.00 3.50*
*b.* 6fr blue & red *5.00 4.50*

Sold only with 20fr show admission ticket.

Scouting Year A926

**1982, Feb. 20** **Engr.**

**1822** A926 2.30fr yel grn & blk 1.00 .30

31st Natl. Census — A927

**1982, Feb. 27** **Photo.**

**1823** A927 1.60fr multicolored .75 .25

Bale-Mulhouse Airport Opening — A928

**1982, Mar. 15** **Engr.** ***Perf. 13***

**1824** A928 1.90fr multicolored .90 .50

Fight Against Racism A929

**1982, Mar. 20**

**1825** A929 2.30fr brn & red org 1.00 .50

Blacksmith — A930

**1982, Apr. 17**

**1826** A930 1.40fr multicolored .65 .40

Europa 1982 A931

**1982, Apr. 24**

**1827** A931 1.60fr Treaty of Rome, 1957 .90 .30
**1828** A931 2.30fr Treaty of Verdun, 843 1.20 .40

1982 World Cup A932

**1982, Apr. 28**

**1829** A932 1.80fr multicolored .90 .30

Young Greek Soldier, Hellenic Sculpture, Agde A933

**1982, May 15** ***Perf. 12½x13***

**1830** A933 4fr multicolored 1.90 1.00

Embarkation for Ostia, by Claude Gellee — A934

The Lacemaker, by Vermeer A935

Turkish Chamber, by Balthus — A936

**1982** **Photo.** ***Perf. 13x12½, 12½x13***

**1831** A934 4fr multicolored 1.90 1.00
**1832** A935 4fr multicolored 1.90 1.00
**1833** A936 4fr multicolored 1.90 1.00
*Nos. 1831-1833 (3)* 5.70 3.00

Issued: No. 1831, 6/19; No. 1832, 9/4; No. 1833, 11/6.

35th Intl. Film Festival, Cannes — A937

**1982, May 15** **Photo.** ***Perf. 13***

**1834** A937 2.30fr multicolored 1.00 .75

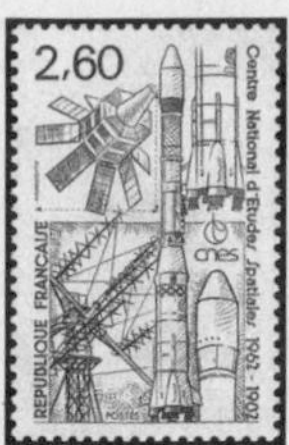


Natl. Space Studies Center, 20th Anniv. — A938

**1982, May 15** **Engr.**
**1835** A938 2.60fr multicolored 1.20 .50

A939

**1982, June 4** **Photo.**
**1836** A939 2.60fr multicolored 1.20 .50

Industrialized Countries' Summit Meeting, Versailles, June 4-6.

A940

**1982, June 4** **Engr.** ***Perf. 13***
**1837** A940 1.60fr ol grn & dk grn .75 .25

Jules Valles (1832-1885), writer.

Frederic and Irene Curie, Radiation Diagrams A941

**1982, June 26**
**1838** A941 1.80fr multicolored .85 .30

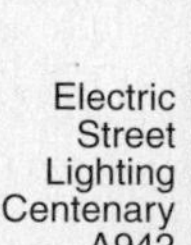

Electric Street Lighting Centenary A942

**1982, July 10**
**1839** A942 1.80fr dk blue & vio .90 .30

The Family, by Marc Boyan A943

**Photogravure and Engraved**
**1982, Sept. 18** ***Perf. 12½x13***
**1840** A943 4fr multicolored 1.75 1.00

Natl. Fed. of Firemen, Cent. — A944

**1982, Sept. 18** **Engr.** ***Perf. 13***
**1841** A944 3.30fr red & sepia 1.60 .40

Marionettes — A945

**1982, Sept. 25**
**1842** A945 1.80fr multicolored .90 .30

Rugby A946

**1982, Oct. 9**
**1843** A946 1.60fr multicolored 1.50 .30

Higher Education A947

**1982, Oct. 16**
**1844** A947 1.80fr red & black .90 .30

TB Bacillus Centenary A948

**1982, Nov. 13**
**1845** A948 2.60fr red & black 1.10 .40

St. Teresa of Avila (1515-82) — A949

**1982, Nov. 20**
**1846** A949 2.10fr multicolored 1.00 .45

Leon Blum (1872-1950), Politician — A950

**1982, Dec. 18** **Engr.** ***Perf. 13***
**1847** A950 1.80fr dk brn & brn .85 .25

Cavelier de la Salle (1643-1687), Explorer — A951

**1982, Dec. 18** ***Perf. 13x12½***
**1848** A951 3.25fr multicolored 1.25 .50

Spring — A952

**1983, Jan. 17** **Engr.** ***Perf. 13***
**1849** A952 1.05fr shown .45 .25
**1850** A952 1.35fr Summer .50 .30
**1851** A952 2.19fr Autumn 1.00 .75
**1852** A952 3.63fr Winter 1.40 1.10
*Nos. 1849-1852 (4)* 3.35 2.40

Nos. 1849-1852 known only precanceled. See second note after No. 132.

Provence-Alpes-Cote d'Azur — A953

Brantome (Perigord) A954

REPUBLIQUE FRANÇAISE
3,00
Concarneau

Concarneau — A955

Noirlac Abbey A956

**1983** **Photo.** ***Perf. 13***
**1853** A953 1fr multicolored .45 .25

**Engr.**
***Perf. 13x12½***
**1854** A954 1.80fr multicolored .85 .25

***Perf. 13***
**1855** A955 3fr multicolored 1.25 .60

***Perf. 13x12½***
**1856** A956 3.60fr multicolored 1.60 .30

Issued: 1fr, 1/8; 1.80fr, 2/5; 3fr, 6/11; 3.60fr, 7/2.

Jarnac A957

Charleville-Mezieres — A958

**1983** ***Perf. 13x12½***
**1857** A957 2fr multicolored .90 .35
**1858** A958 3.10fr multicolored 1.40 .85
*Nos. 1853-1858 (6)* 6.45 2.60

Issued: 2fr, Oct. 8; 3.10fr, Sept. 17.

Martin Luther (1483-1546) — A959

**1983, Feb. 12** **Engr.** ***Perf. 13***
**1859** A959 3.30fr dk brn & tan 1.40 .55

Alliance Francaise Centenary A960

**1983, Feb. 19**
**1860** A960 1.80fr multicolored .85 .30

Danielle Casanova (d. 1942), Resistance Leader A961

**1983, Mar. 8**
**1861** A961 3fr blk & red brn 1.25 .30

World Communications Year — A962

**1983, Mar. 12** **Photo.**
**1862** A962 2.60fr multicolored 1.10 .65

Manned Flight Bicentenary — A963

**1983, Mar. 19** **Photo.** ***Perf. 13***
**1863** 2fr Hot air balloon .80 .55
**1864** 3fr Hydrogen balloon 1.25 .70
*a.* A963 Pair, #1863-1864 + label 2.25 2.25

Female Nude, by Raphael A964

Aurora-Set, by Dewasne — A965

**1983** **Engr.** ***Perf. 13***

**1865** A964 4fr multicolored 1.75 1.00

**Photo.**

**1866** A965 4fr multicolored 1.75 1.00

Issued: No. 1866, 3/19; No. 1865, 4/9.

Illustration from Perrault's Folk Tales, by Gustave Dore A966

**1983, June 18** **Engr.** ***Perf. 13***

**1867** A966 4fr red & black 1.75 1.00

Homage to Jean Effel A967

**1983, Oct. 15**

**1868** A967 4fr multicolored 1.75 1.00

Le Lapin Agile, by Utrillo — A968

**1983, Dec. 3** ***Perf. 13x12½***

**1869** A968 4fr multicolored 1.75 1.00

Thistle — A969

**1983, Apr. 23** **Engr.** ***Perf. 12½x12***

| | | | | |
|---|---|---|---|---|
| **1870** | A969 1fr shown | | .35 | .30 |
| **1871** | A969 2fr Martagon lily | | .80 | .30 |
| **1872** | A969 3fr Aster | | 1.25 | .60 |
| **1873** | A969 4fr Aconite | | 1.75 | .60 |
| | *Nos. 1870-1873 (4)* | | 4.15 | 1.80 |

Europa 1983 — A970

1.80fr, Symbolic shutter. 2.60fr, Lens-to-screen diagram.

**1983, Apr. 29** ***Perf. 13***

**1874** A970 1.80fr multi 1.00 .40
**1875** A970 2.60fr multi 1.25 .75

Centenary of Paris Convention for the Protection of Industrial Property — A971

**1983, May 14** **Photo.** ***Perf. 13***

**1876** A971 2fr multicolored .85 .30

French Philatelic Societies Congress, Marseille A972

**1983, May 21** **Engr.** ***Perf. 13***

**1877** A972 1.80fr multicolored .85 .35

**Liberty Type of 1982**

**1983-87** **Engr.** ***Perf. 13***

| | | | | |
|---|---|---|---|---|
| **1878** | A915 | 1.70fr green | .75 | .25 |
| **1879** | A915 | 1.80fr green | .80 | .25 |
| **1880** | A915 | 1.90fr green | 1.25 | .25 |
| **1881** | A915 | 2fr red | .90 | .25 |
| **1882** | A915 | 2fr green | .90 | .25 |
| **1883** | A915 | 2.10fr red | .95 | .25 |
| **1884** | A915 | 2.20fr red | 2.00 | .25 |
| *a.* | | Booklet pane of 10 | 20.00 | |
| *b.* | | Bklt. pane, #1788, 4 #1884 | 8.50 | |
| *c.* | | With label ('87) | 1.00 | .25 |
| **1885** | A915 | 2.80fr blue | 1.25 | .90 |
| **1886** | A915 | 3fr blue | 1.25 | .50 |
| **1887** | A915 | 3.20fr blue | 1.50 | .90 |
| **1888** | A915 | 3.40fr blue | 1.60 | .75 |
| **1889** | A915 | 3.60fr blue | 1.60 | .65 |
| **1890** | A915 | 10fr purple | 4.50 | .25 |
| **1891** | A915 | (1.90fr) green | .90 | .25 |
| **1892** | A915 | (2fr) green | .90 | .25 |
| | | *Nos. 1878-1892 (15)* | 21.05 | 6.20 |

**Coil Stamps**

**Engr.** ***Perf. 13 Horiz.***

| | | | | |
|---|---|---|---|---|
| **1893** | A915 | 1.70fr green | .90 | .80 |
| **1894** | A915 | 1.80fr green | 1.00 | .50 |
| **1895** | A915 | 1.90fr green | 1.25 | .30 |
| **1896** | A915 | 2fr red | 1.00 | .30 |
| **1897** | A915 | 2.10fr red | 1.10 | .60 |
| **1897A** | A915 | 2.20fr red | 1.00 | .50 |
| | | *Nos. 1893-1897A (6)* | 6.25 | 3.00 |

No. 1891 is inscribed "A," No. 1892 "B."

No. 1884c was issued in sheets of 50 plus 50 alternating labels picturing the PHILEX-FRANCE '89 emblem to publicize the international philatelic exhibition.

Issued: 2.80fr, 10fr, No. 1881, 6/1; 1.70fr, 2.10fr, 3fr, 7/1/84; 1.80fr, 2.20fr, 3.20fr, 8/1/85; 3.40fr, No. 1891, 8/1/86; 1.90fr, 9/13/86; No. 1882, 10/15/87; 3.60fr, No. 1892, 8/1/87.

For surcharge see No. 2115.

50th Anniv. of Air France A973

**1983, June 18**

**1898** A973 3.45fr multicolored 1.50 .85

Treaties of Versailles and Paris Bicentenary — A974

**1983, Sept. 2** ***Perf. 13x12½***

**1899** A974 2.80fr multicolored 1.40 .60

Jewelry Making A975

**1983, Sept. 10** **Photo.** ***Perf. 13***

**1900** A975 2.20fr multicolored .90 .35

30th Anniv. of Customs Cooperation Council — A976

**1983, Sept. 22** **Engr.** ***Perf. 13x12½***

**1901** A976 2.30fr multicolored 1.00 .40

Michaux's Bicycle A977

**1983, Oct. 1** **Engr.** ***Perf. 13***

**1902** A977 1.60fr multicolored 1.10 .30

Natl. Weather Forecasting — A978

**1983, Oct. 22** **Engr.** ***Perf. 12½x13***

**1903** A978 1.50fr multicolored .70 .25

Berthie Albrecht (1893-1943) — A979

**1983, Nov. 5**

**1904** A979 1.60fr dk brown & olive .75 .30
**1905** A979 1.60fr Rene Levy (1906-1943) .75 .30

Resistance heroines.

A980

**1983, Dec. 16**

**1906** A980 2fr dk gray & red .80 .25

Pierre Mendes France (1907-1982), Premier.

Union Leader Waldeck-Rousseau A981

**1984, Mar. 22** ***Perf. 13***

**1907** A981 3.60fr multi 1.60 .30

Trade Union centenary.

Homage to the Cinema, by Cesar A982

**1984, Feb. 4** **Engr.** ***Perf. 12½x13***

**1908** A982 4fr multicolored 1.75 1.00

Four Corners of the Sky, by Jean Messagier — A983

**1984, Mar. 31** **Photo.** ***Perf. 13x12½***

**1909** A983 4fr multicolored 1.75 1.00

Dining Room Corner, at Cannet, by Pierre Bonnard — A984

**Photogravure and Engraved**

**1984, Apr. 14** ***Perf. 12½x12***

**1910** A984 4fr multicolored 1.75 1.00

Pythia, by Andre Masson A985

Painter at the Feet of His Model, by Helion A986

**1984 Photo. *Perf. 12x13***

**1911** A985 5fr multicolored 2.25 1.00
**1912** A986 5fr multicolored 2.25 1.00

Issue dates: No. 1911, 10/13; No. 1912, 12/1.

Guadeloupe — A987

**1984, Feb. 25 *Perf. 13***

**1913** A987 2.30fr Map, West Indian dancers 1.00 .30

Vauban Citadel, Belle Ile-en-Mer A988

Cordouan Lighthouse — A989

**1984 Engr. *Perf. 13***

**1914** A988 2.50fr multicolored 1.10 .35
**1915** A989 3.50fr multicolored 1.60 .40

Issued: No. 1914, 5/26; No. 1915, 6/23.

La Grande Chartreuse Monastery, 900th Anniv. A990

Palais Ideal, Hauterives-Drome — A991

Montsegur Chateau A992

**1984**

**1916** A990 1.70fr multicolored .80 .40
**1917** A991 2.10fr multicolored .95 .30
**1917A** A992 3.70fr multicolored 1.60 .40
*Nos. 1914-1917A (5)* 6.05 1.85

Issued: 1.70fr, 7/7; 2.10fr, 6/30; 3.70fr, 9/15.

Flora Tristan (1803-44), Feminist A992a

**1984, Mar. 8**

**1918** A992a 2.80fr multicolored 1.25 .50

Playing Card Suits — A993

**1984, Apr. 11 Engr.**

**1919** A993 1.14fr Hearts .50 .45
**1920** A993 1.47fr Spades .65 .55
**1921** A993 2.38fr Diamonds 1.00 .75
**1922** A993 3.95fr Clubs 1.60 1.25
*Nos. 1919-1922 (4)* 3.75 3.00

Nos. 1919-1922 known only precanceled. See second note after No. 132.

450th Anniv. of Cartier's Landing in Quebec A994

**1984, Apr. 20 Photo. & Engr.**

**1923** A994 2fr multicolored .90 .25

See Canada No. 1011.

Philex '84, Dunkirk A995

**1984, Apr. 21 *Perf. 13x12½***

**1924** A995 1.60fr multicolored .75 .35

Europa (1959-84) A996

**1984, Apr. 28 Engr. *Perf. 13***

**1925** A996 2fr red brown .80 .30
**1926** A996 2.80fr blue 1.25 .50

2nd European Parliament Election A997

**1984, Mar. 24 Photo. *Perf. 13***

**1927** A997 2fr multicolored .90 .25

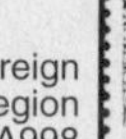

Foreign Legion A998

**1984, Apr. 30 Engr. *Perf. 13x12½***

**1928** A998 3.10fr multicolored 1.40 .50

40th Anniv. of Liberation A999

**Photogravure and Engraved**

**1984, May 8 *Perf. 12½x13***

**1929** A999 2fr Resistance .85 .50
**1930** A999 3fr Landing 1.25 .60
*a.* Pair, #1929-1930 + label 2.50 2.00

Olympic Events — A1000

**1984, June 1 *Perf. 13***

**1931** A1000 4fr multicolored 1.75 1.00

Intl. Olympic Committee, 90th anniv. and 1984 Summer Olympics.

Engraving — A1001

**1984, June 8 Engr.**

**1932** A1001 2fr multicolored .90 .25

Bordeaux A1002

**1984, June 9 *Perf. 13x12½***

**1933** A1002 2fr red .85 .25

French Philatelic Societies Congress, Bordeaux.

Natl. Telecommunications College, 40th Anniv. — A1003

**1984, June 16 Photo. *Perf. 13***

**1934** A1003 3fr Satellite, phone, keyboard 1.25 .30

25th Intl. Geography Congress, Paris — A1004

**1984, Aug. 25 Engr. *Perf. 13x12½***

**1935** A1004 3fr Alps 1.25 .45

Telecom I Satellite A1005

**1984, Sept. 1 Photo. *Perf. 13***

**1936** A1005 3.20fr multicolored 1.50 .50

High-speed Train Mail Transport A1006

**1984, Sept. 8**

**1937** A1006 2.10fr Electric train, Paris-Lyon 1.00 .25

Local Birds — A1007

**Photogravure and Engraved**

**1984, Sept. 22 *Perf. 12½x12***

**1938** A1007 1fr Gypaetus barbatus .45 .25
**1939** A1007 2fr Circaetus gallicus .90 .25
**1940** A1007 3fr Accipiter nisus 1.40 .75
**1941** A1007 5fr Peregrine falcon 2.25 .55
*Nos. 1938-1941 (4)* 5.00 1.80

Marx Dormoy (1888-1941) A1008

**1984, Sept. 22 Engr. *Perf. 13***

**1942** A1008 2.40fr multicolored 1.00 .30

A1009

**1984, Oct. 6 Engr. *Perf. 12½x13***

**1943** A1009 3fr Automobile plans 1.40 .30

100th anniv. of the automobile.

A1010

**1984, Nov. 3**

**1944** A1010 2.10fr multicolored .95 .30

Pres. Vincent Auriol (1884-1966).

9th 5-Year Plan A1011

**1984, Dec. 8 Photo. *Perf. 13***
**1945** A1011 2.10fr dk blue & scar .95 .25

French Language Promotion — A1012

**1985, Jan. 15 Engr. *Perf. 12½x13***
**1946** A1012 3fr multicolored 1.25 .30

**Tourism Issue**

View of Vienne A1013

Cathedral at Montpelier A1014

St. Michel de Cuxa (Codalet) Abbey — A1015

Talmont Church, Saintonge Romane A1016

Solutre A1017

**1985 *Perf. 13x12½***
**1947** A1013 1.70fr ol blk & dk grn .75 .25
**1948** A1014 2.10fr sepia & org .90 .25
**1949** A1015 2.20fr multicolored .90 .35
**1950** A1016 3fr multicolored 1.25 .55
**1951** A1017 3.90fr multicolored 1.50 .40
*Nos. 1947-1951 (5)* 5.30 1.80

Issue dates: 1.70fr, Jan. 19; 2.10fr, Mar. 30; 2.20fr, July 6; 3fr, June 15; 3.90fr, Sept. 28.

French TV, 50th Anniv. A1018

**1985, Jan. 26 Photo. *Perf. 13***
**1952** A1018 2.50fr multicolored 1.10 .50

Months of the Year — A1019

**1985, Feb. 11 Engr.**
**1953** A1019 1.22fr January .60 .35
**1954** A1019 1.57fr February .70 .40
**1955** A1019 2.55fr March 1.25 .90
**1956** A1019 4.23fr April 2.00 1.25

**1986, Feb. 10 Engr. *Perf. 13***
**1957** A1019 1.28fr May .65 .35
**1958** A1019 1.65fr June .75 .40
**1959** A1019 2.67fr July 1.25 1.00
**1960** A1019 4.44fr August 2.25 1.60

**1987, Feb. 16 Engr.**
**1961** A1019 1.31fr September .70 .35
**1962** A1019 1.69fr October .75 .40
**1963** A1019 2.74fr November 1.25 1.00
**1964** A1019 4.56fr December 2.25 1.75
*Nos. 1953-1964 (12)* 14.40 9.75

Nos. 1953-1964 are known only precanceled. See second note after No. 132.

St. Valentine, by Raymond Peynet A1020

**1985, Feb. 14 Photo. *Perf. 13x12½***
**1965** A1020 2.10fr multicolored .95 .25

Pauline Kergomard (1838-1925) A1021

**1985, Mar. 8 Engr. *Perf. 13x12½***
**1966** A1021 1.70fr int bl & cop red .75 .25

Stained Glass Window, Strasbourg Cathedral A1022

Still-life with Candle, Nicolas de Stael — A1023

**1985 Engraved *Perf. 12x13***
**1967** A1022 5fr multicolored 2.25 1.25

**Photo.**
***Perf. 13x12***

**1968** A1023 5fr multicolored 2.25 1.00

Issue dates: No. 1967, 4/13; No. 1968, 6/1.

Untitled Abstract by Jean Dubuffet — A1024

Octopus Overlaid on Manuscript, by Pierre Alechinsky — A1025

**Photogravure; Engraved (#1970)**
**1985 *Perf. 13x12½***
**1969** A1024 5fr multicolored 2.25 1.00
**1970** A1025 5fr multicolored 2.25 1.00

Issued: No. 1969, 10/14; No. 1970, 10/12.

The Dog, Abstract by Alberto Giacometti (1901-1966) — A1026

**1985, Dec. 7 Engr. *Perf. 13x12½***
**1971** A1026 5fr grnsh blk & lt lem 2.25 1.00

Housing in Givors A1027

Contemporary architecture by Jean Renaude.

**1985, Apr. 20 Engr. *Perf. 13***
**1972** A1027 2.40fr blk, yel org & ol grn 1.00 .50

Landevennec Abbey, 1500th Anniv. — A1028

**1985, Apr. 20 *Perf. 13x12½***
**1973** A1028 1.70fr green & brn vio .75 .25

A1029

Europa: 2.10fr, Adam de la Halle (1240-1285), composer. 3fr, Darius Milhaud (1892-1974), composer.

**1985, Apr. 27 *Perf. 12½x13***
**1974** A1029 2.10fr dr bl, blk, & brt bl .95 .30
**1975** A1029 3fr dk bl, brt bl & blk 1.40 .50

A1030

**1985, May 8 *Perf. 13x12½***
**1976** A1030 2fr Return of peace .75 .50
**1977** A1030 3fr Return of liberty 1.25 .50
*a.* Pair, #1976-1977 + label 2.25 2.00

Liberation of France from German occupation forces, 40th anniv.

Natl. Philatelic Congress, Tours — A1031

**1985, May 25 *Perf. 12½x13***
**1978** A1031 2.10fr Tours Cathedral .95 .30

Rabies Vaccine Cent. A1032

**1985, June 1 *Perf. 13x12½***
**1979** A1032 1.50fr Pasteur inoculating patient .70 .30

Mystere Falcon-900 A1033

**1985, June 1 *Perf. 13***
**1980** A1033 10fr blue 4.50 2.00

Lake Geneva Life-Saving Society Cent. A1034

**1985, June 15**
**1981** A1034 2.50fr blk, red & brt ultra 1.00 .40

UN, 40th Anniv. — A1035

**1985, June 26 *Perf. 13x12½***
**1982** A1035 3fr multicolored 1.10 .30

Huguenot Cross — A1036

**1985, Aug. 31 Engr. *Perf. 12½x13***
**1983** A1036 2.50fr dp vio, dk red brn & dk red 1.00 .30

King Louis XIV revoked the Edict of Nantes on Oct. 18, 1685, dispossessing French Protestants of religious and civil liberty.

A1037

Trees, leaves and fruit of the beech, elm, oak and spruce varieties.

**1985, Sept. 21 Engr. *Perf. 12½***
**1984** A1037 1fr shown .45 .25
**1985** A1037 2fr Ulmus montana .90 .25
**1986** A1037 3fr Quercus pedunculata 1.25 .60
**1987** A1037 5fr Picea abies 2.25 .30
*Nos. 1984-1987 (4)* 4.85 1.40

A1038

La France Mourning the Dead, Eternal Flame.

**1985, Nov. 2 Engr. *Perf. 12½x13***
**1988** A1038 1.80fr brn, org & lake .85 .25

Memorial Day.

A1039

**1985, Nov. 9 Engr.**
**1989** A1039 3.20fr black & blue 1.25 .40

Charles Dullin, 1885-1949, impresario, theater.

A1040

**1985, Nov. 16 Engr. *Perf. 13x12½***
**1990** A1040 2.20fr red & black .90 .25

National information system.

Thai Ambassadors at the Court of King Louis XIV, Painting A1041

**1986, Jan. 25 Engr. *Perf. 13***
**1991** A1041 3.20fr rose lake & blk 1.25 .65

Normalization of diplomatic relations with Thailand, 300th anniv.

Leisure, by Fernand Leger A1042

**1986, Feb. 1 Photo. *Perf. 13***
**1992** A1042 2.20fr multicolored .90 .25

1936 Popular Front, 50th anniv.

Venice Carnival, Paris — A1043

**1986, Feb. 12 *Perf. 12½x13***
**1993** A1043 2.20fr multicolored .90 .25

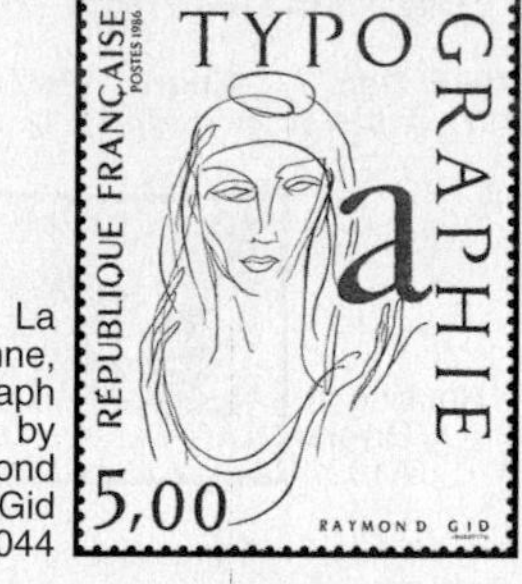
La Marianne, Typograph by Raymond Gid A1044

**Photogravure & Engraved**
**1986, Mar. 3 *Perf. 12½x13½***
**1994** A1044 5fr black & dk red 2.25 1.00

**Tourism Issue**

Filitosa, South Corsica A1045

Loches Chateau A1046

Norman Manor, St. Germain de Livet A1047

Notre-Dame-en-Vaux Monastery, Marne — A1048

Market Square, Bastide de Monpazier, Dordogne — A1049

**1986 Engr. *Perf. 13***
**1995** A1045 1.80fr multicolored .85 .25
**1996** A1046 2fr int blue & blk .90 .50
**1997** A1047 2.20fr grnsh bl, brn & grn 1.00 .35
**1998** A1048 2.50fr henna brn & sepia 1.10 .40

***Perf. 13x12½***
**1999** A1049 3.90fr blk & yel org 1.75 .90
*Nos. 1995-1999 (5)* 5.60 2.40

Issued: 2.20fr, 3/3; 2fr, 6/14; 2.50fr, 6/9; 1.80fr, 3.90fr, 7/5.

Louise Michel (1830-1905), Anarchist — A1050

**1986, Mar. 10 Engr.**
**2000** A1050 1.80fr dk red & gray blk .80 .25

City of Science and Industry, La Villette — A1051

**1986, Mar. 17**
**2001** A1051 3.90fr multicolored 1.60 .50

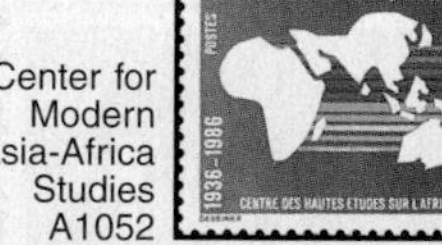
Center for Modern Asia-Africa Studies A1052

**1986, Apr. 12 Photo. *Perf. 13***
**2002** A1052 3.20fr Map 1.25 .25

Skibet, Abstract by Maurice Esteve — A1053

Virginia, Abstract by Alberto Magnelli — A1054

Abstract, by Pierre Soulages — A1055

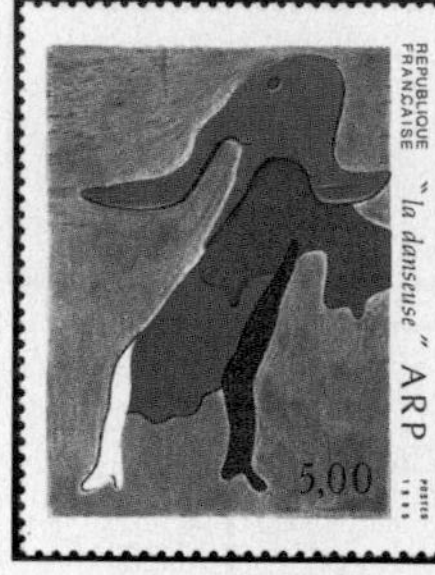
The Dancer, by Jean Arp A1056

Isabelle d'Este, by Leonardo da Vinci A1057

***Perf. 12½x13, 13x12½ (#2005, 2006)***
**1986 Photo., Engr. (#2005, 2007)**
**2003** A1053 5fr multicolored 2.25 1.00
**2004** A1054 5fr multicolored 2.25 1.00
**2005** A1055 5fr brt vio, blk & brn gray 2.25 1.00
**2006** A1056 5fr multicolored 2.25 1.00
**2007** A1057 5fr blk, red brn & grnsh yel 2.25 1.00
*Nos. 2003-2007 (5)* 11.25 5.00

Issued: No. 2003, 4/14; No. 2004, 6/25; No. 2005, 6/22; Nos. 2006, 2007, 11/10.

Victor Basch (1863-1944), IPY Emblem — A1058

**1986, Apr. 28 Engr. *Perf. 13***
**2008** A1058 2.50fr black & yel grn 1.10 .25

International Peace Year.

Europa 1986 A1059

**1986, Apr. 28** *Perf. 13x12½*
**2009** A1059 2.20fr Civet cat 1.00 .30
**2010** A1059 3.20fr Bat 1.40 .60

St. Jean-Marie Vianney, Curé of Ars A1060

**1986, May 3** **Engr.** *Perf. 13x12½*
**2011** A1060 1.80fr sepia, brn org & brn .80 .25

Philatelic Societies Federation Congress, Nancy — A1061

**1986, May 17** *Perf. 13*
**2012** A1061 2.20fr Exposition Center .90 .25

Mens World Volleyball Championship A1062

**1986, May 24** **Engr.** *Perf. 13*
**2013** A1062 2.20fr dk vio, brn vio & scar .90 .30

Statue of Liberty, Cent. — A1063

**1986, July 4** *Perf. 13*
**2014** A1063 2.20fr scar & dk blue 1.00 .30

See US No. 2224.

1st Ascent of Mt. Blanc, 1786 A1064

**1986, Aug. 8** **Engr.** *Perf. 13x12½*
**2015** A1064 2fr J. Balmat, M.G. Paccard .90 .50

Pierre-Louis Moreau de Maupertuis (1698-1759), La Condamine and Sextant — A1065

**1986, Sept. 5**
**2016** A1065 3fr multicolored 1.25 .55

Lapland Expedition, 250th anniv., proved Earth's poles are flattened.
See Finland No. 741.

Marcassite A1066

**1986, Sept. 13** *Perf. 12½*
**2017** A1066 2fr shown .90 .25
**2018** A1066 3fr Quartz 1.40 .25
**2019** A1066 4fr Calcite 1.75 .70
**2020** A1066 5fr Fluorite 2.25 .70
*Nos. 2017-2020 (4)* 6.30 1.90

Souvenir Sheet

Natl. Film Industry, 50th Anniv. — A1067

Personalities and film scenes: a, Louis Feuillade, The Vampires. b, Max Linder. c, Sacha Guitry, Romance of the Trickster. d, Jean Renoir, The Grand Illusion. e, Marcel Pagnol, The Baker's Woman. f, Jean Epstein, The Three-Sided Mirror. g, Rene Clair, Women of the Night. h, Jean Gremillon, Talk of Love. i, Jacques Becker, Helmet of Gold. j, Francois Truffaut, The Young Savage.

**1986, Sept. 20** **Photo.** *Perf. 13x12½*
**2021** A1067 Sheet of 10 10.00 10.00
***a.-j.*** 2.20fr any single 1.00 1.00

Scene from Le Grand Meaulnes, by Henry Alain-Fournier (b. 1886), Novelist — A1068

**1986, Oct. 4** **Engr.** *Perf. 12½x13*
**2022** A1068 2.20fr black & dk red .90 .25

Professional Education, Cent. — A1069

**1986, Oct. 4**
**2023** A1069 1.90fr brt vio & dp lil rose .85 .25

World Energy Conf., Cannes — A1070

**1986, Oct. 5** **Photo.** *Perf. 13*
**2024** A1070 3.40fr multicolored 1.50 .50

Mulhouse Technical Museum — A1071

**1986, Dec. 1** **Engr.**
**2025** A1071 2.20fr int blue, dk red & blk 1.00 .50

Museum at Orsay, Opening — A1072

**1986, Dec. 10** **Photo.**
**2026** A1072 3.70fr bluish blk & pck bl 1.60 .60

Fulgence Bienvenue (1852-1934), and the Metro — A1073

**1987, Jan. 17** **Engr.** *Perf. 13*
**2027** A1073 2.50fr vio brn, brn & dk grn 1.10 .30

A1074

**1987, Jan. 24**
**2028** A1074 1.90fr grn & grnsh blk .85 .25

Raoul Follereau (1903-1977), care for lepers.

A1075

**1987, Mar. 7** **Engr.** *Perf. 12½x13*
**2029** A1075 1.90fr black & red .85 .25

Cutlery industry, Thiers.

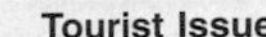
**Tourist Issue**

Redon, Ille et Vilaine A1076

Azay-le-Rideau Chateau — A1077

Meuse District — A1078

Etretat A1079

Les Baux-de-Provence — A1080

**1987** **Engr.** *Perf. 13*
**2030** A1076 2.20fr dp rose lil, blk & brn ol 1.00 .25
**2031** A1077 2.50fr Prus blue & olive grn 1.25 .55

*Perf. 12½*
**2032** A1078 3.70fr multicolored 1.75 1.40

**Photo.** *Perf. 13*
**2033** A1079 2.20fr multicolored 1.00 .25

**Engr.**
**2034** A1080 3fr dk ol bis & dp vio 1.25 .40
*Nos. 2030-2034 (5)* 6.25 2.85

Issued: No. 2030, 3/7; No. 2033, 6/12; 2.50fr, 5/9; 3fr, 6/27; 3.70fr, 5/30.

Charles Edouard Jenneret (Le Corbusier) (1887-1965), Architect — A1081

**1987, Apr. 11** **Photo.** *Perf. 13x12½*
**2035** A1081 3.70fr Abstract 1.60 .50

Europa 1987 A1082

Modern architecture: 2.20fr, Metal factory at Boulogne-Billancourt, by architect Claude Vasconi. 3.40fr, Rue Mallet-Stevens housing, by Robert Mallet-Stevens.

**1987, Apr. 25** **Engr.** *Perf. 13x12½*
**2036** A1082 2.20fr dk blue & grn 1.00 .50
**2037** A1082 3.40fr brn & dk grn 1.50 .65

Abstract Painting, by Bram van Velde — A1083

Woman under Parasol, by Eugene Boudin (1824-1898) — A1084

Precambrien, by Camille Bryen — A1085

World, Bronze Sculpture by Antoine Pevsner — A1086

***Perf. 12½x13, 13x12½ (Nos. 2039, 2041)***

**Photo., Engr. (Nos. 2039, 2041)**

**1987**

**2038** A1083 5fr multicolored 2.25 1.00
**2039** A1084 5fr multicolored 2.25 1.00
**2040** A1085 5fr multicolored 2.25 1.00
**2041** A1086 5fr bister & blk 2.25 1.00
*Nos. 2038-2041 (4)* 9.00 4.00

Issue dates: No. 2038, 4/25; No. 2039, 5/23; No. 2040, 9/12; No. 2041, 11/14.

Gaspard de Montagnes, from a Manuscript Illustration — A1087

**1987, May 9 Engr. *Perf. 13***
**2042** A1087 1.90fr dp grn & sepia .85 .25

Henri Pourrat (1887-1959), novelist.

Natl. Philatelic Societies Congress, Lens A1088

**1987, June 6 *Perf. 13x13½***
**2043** A1088 2.20fr choc & red .90 .30

Involvement of U.S. Forces in WW I, 70th Anniv. A1089

Design: Stars and Stripes, troops, Gen. John J. Pershing (1860-1948), American army commander.

**1987, June 13 *Perf. 13***
**2044** A1089 3.40fr olive grn, saph & ver 1.50 .70

A1090

**1987, June 17 Photo.**
**2045** A1090 2fr multicolored .90 .50

6th Intl. Cable Car Transport Congress, Grenoble.

A1091

**1987, June 20 Litho.**
**2046** A1091 1.90fr pale chalky blue & blk .90 .50

Accession of Hugh Capet (c.938-996), 1st king of France, millenary.

A1092

**1987, June 20 Engr. *Perf. 12½x13***
**2047** A1092 2.20fr multicolored .90 .30

La Fleche Natl. Military School.

A1093

**1987, June 27 Photo. *Perf. 13***
**2048** A1093 1.90fr multicolored .90 .55

World Assembly of Expatriate Algerians, Nice.

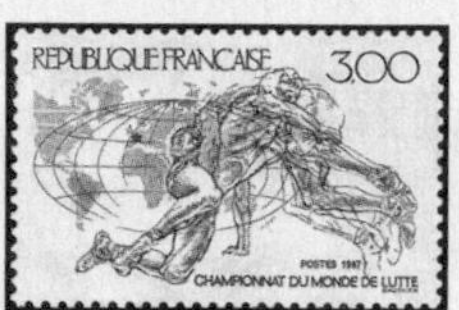

World Wrestling Championships — A1094

**1987, Aug. 21 Engr.**
**2049** A1094 3fr brt pur, vio gray & brt olive grn 1.25 .60

Mushrooms A1095

2fr, Gyroporus cyanescens. 3fr, Gomphus clavatus. 4fr, Morchella conica. 5fr, Russula virescens.

**1987, Sept. 5 *Perf. 12½***
**2050** A1095 2fr multicolored .90 .25
**2051** A1095 3fr multicolored 1.25 .30
**2052** A1095 4fr multicolored 1.75 .60
**2053** A1095 5fr multicolored 2.25 .60
*Nos. 2050-2053 (4)* 6.15 1.75

William the Conqueror (c. 1027-1087) A1096

**1987, Sept. 5 *Perf. 13***
**2054** A1096 2fr Bayeux Tapestry detail .90 .30

Montbenoit Le Saugeais A1097

Design: Abbey of Medieval Knights, cloisters, winter scene.

**1987, Sept. 19**
**2055** A1097 2.50fr saph, blk & scar 1.10 .55

Pasteur Institute, Cent. — A1098

**1987, Oct. 3**
**2056** A1098 2.20fr dp blue & dk red .85 .25

Blaise Cendrars (1887-1961), Poet and Novelist — A1099

Pen and ink portrait by Modigliani.

**1987, Nov. 6 *Perf. 12½***
**2057** A1099 2fr brt grn, buff & blk .90 .35

Treaty of Andelot, 1400th Anniv. — A1100

**1987, Nov. 28 *Perf. 12½x13***
**2058** A1100 3.70fr multicolored 1.60 .55

Gen. Leclerc (1902-1947), Marshal of France — A1101

**1987, Nov. 28 *Perf. 13x12½***
**2059** A1101 2.20fr multicolored .90 .25

**Liberty Type of 1982**

**1987-90 *Perf. 13***
**2077** A915 3.70fr brt lilac rose 1.75 .30
**2078** A915 (2.10fr) green ('90) .95 .25
**2079** A915 (2.30fr) red ('90) 1.00 .25
*Nos. 2077-2079 (3)* 3.70 .80

**Coil Stamp**

**Engr.**

***Perf. 13 Horiz.***

**2080** A915 2fr emerald green .90 .30

Issued: 2fr, 8/1; 3.70fr, 11/16; Nos. 2078-2079, 1/2.

Nos. 2078-2079 are inscribed "C."

Franco-German Cooperation Treaty, 25th Anniv. — A1102

**1988, Jan. 15 *Perf. 13***
**2086** A1102 2.20fr Adenauer, De Gaulle 1.00 .30

See Fed. Rep. of Germany No. 1546.

Marcel Dassault (1892-1986), Aircraft Designer — A1103

**1988, Jan. 23** **Photo.**

**2087** A1103 3.60fr brt ultra, gray blk & dk red 1.60 .70

Communications A1104

Angouleme Festival prize-winning cartoons.

**1988, Jan. 29** **Photo.** ***Perf. 13½x13***

**Booklet Stamps**

**2088** A1104 2.20fr Pellos 1.00 .40
**2089** A1104 2.20fr Reiser 1.00 .40
**2090** A1104 2.20fr Marijac 1.00 .40
**2091** A1104 2.20fr Fred 1.00 .40
**2092** A1104 2.20fr Moebius 1.00 .40
**2093** A1104 2.20fr Gillon 1.00 .40
**2094** A1104 2.20fr Bretecher 1.00 .40
**2095** A1104 2.20fr Forest 1.00 .40
**2096** A1104 2.20fr Mezieres 1.00 .40
**2097** A1104 2.20fr Tardi 1.00 .40
**2098** A1104 2.20fr Lob 1.00 .40
**2099** A1104 2.20fr Bilal 1.00 .40
*a.* Bklt. pane of 12, #2088-2099 12.00 8.50

Great Synagogue, Rue Victoire, Paris — A1105

**1988, Feb. 7** **Litho.** ***Perf. 13***

**2100** A1105 2fr black & gold .90 .25

The Four Elements — A1106

**1988, Feb. 1** **Engr.** ***Perf. 13***

**2101** A1106 1.36fr Air .65 .40
**2102** A1106 1.75fr Water .80 .40
**2103** A1106 2.83fr Fire 1.25 1.00
**2104** A1106 4.75fr Earth 2.25 1.75
*Nos. 2101-2104 (4)* 4.95 3.55

Nos. 2101-2104 known only precanceled. See second note after No. 132.

PHILEXFRANCE '89 — A1107

**1988, Mar. 4**

**2105** A1107 2.20fr #1885, emblem 1.00 .25

Postal Training College, Cent. A1108

**1988, Mar. 29**

**2106** A1108 3.60fr multicolored 1.60 .40

Philex-Jeunes '88, Youth Stamp Show — A1109

**1988, Apr. 8** ***Perf. 13x12½***

**2107** A1109 2fr multicolored .90 .25

Blood Donation — A1110

**1988, Apr. 9** **Photo.** ***Perf. 13½x13***

**2108** A1110 2.50fr multicolored 1.10 .40

Europa 1988 A1111

Communication and transportation.

**1988, Apr. 30** **Engr.** ***Perf. 13***

**2109** A1111 2.20fr Cables, satellites 1.00 .30
**2110** A1111 3.60fr Rail cars 1.75 .40

Jean Monnet (1888-1979), Economist — A1112

**1988, May 10** ***Perf. 12½x13***

**2111** A1112 2.20fr black & brn ol 1.00 .25

Philatelic Congress, Valence A1113

**1988, May 21** ***Perf. 13x12½***

**2112** A1113 2.20fr multicolored 1.00 .35

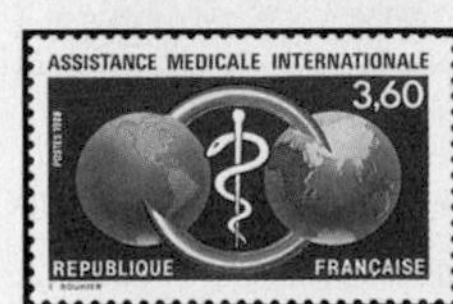


Intl. Medical Assistance A1114

**1988, May 28** **Photo.** ***Perf. 13***

**2113** A1114 3.60fr multicolored 1.60 .50

Aid to the Handicapped — A1115

**1988, May 28**

**2114** A1115 3.70fr multicolored 1.60 .50

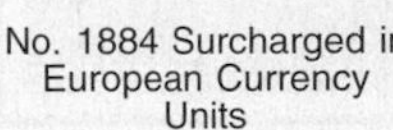

No. 1884 Surcharged in European Currency Units

**1988, Apr. 16** **Engr.**

**2115** A915 2.20fr red 1.00 .25

**Tourist Issue**

Hermes Dicephalus (Roman Empire), Frejus — A1116

**1988, June 12** **Engr.** ***Perf. 13x12½***

**2116** A1116 3.70fr multicolored 1.75 .80

Ship Museum, Douarnenez — A1117

Chateau Sedieres, Correze — A1118

Cirque de Gavarnie A1119

**1988** ***Perf. 13, 12½x13 (#2118)***

**2117** A1117 2fr multicolored .90 .25
**2118** A1118 2.20fr multicolored 1.00 .35
**2119** A1119 3fr multicolored 1.25 .40

Issued: 2.20fr, 7/2; 2fr, 7/4; 3fr, 7/23.

View of Perouges, Ain A1120

**1988, Sept. 10** ***Perf. 13x12½***

**2120** A1120 2.20fr multicolored 1.00 .25
*Nos. 2116-2120 (5)* 5.90 2.05

French Revolution, Bicent. — A1121

Designs: 3fr, Assembly of the Three Estates, Vizille. 4fr, Day of the Tiles (Barricades), Grenoble.

**1988, June 18** **Engr.**

**2121** A1121 3fr multicolored 1.25 1.00
**2122** A1121 4fr multicolored 1.75 1.00
*a.* Pair, #2121-2122 + label 3.50 3.00

PHILEXFRANCE '89.

Buffon's Natural History — A1122

**1988, June 18** ***Perf. 12½***

**2123** A1122 2fr Otters .90 .25
**2124** A1122 3fr Stag 1.25 .30
**2125** A1122 4fr Fox 1.75 .70
**2126** A1122 5fr Badger 2.25 .60
*Nos. 2123-2126 (4)* 6.15 1.85

Alpine Troops, Cent. — A1123

**1988, June 25** ***Perf. 13***

**2127** A1123 2.50fr multicolored 1.10 .60

Roland Garros (1888-1918), 1st Pilot to Fly Across the Mediterranean, Sept. 23, 1913 — A1124

**1988, July 2** **Engr.** ***Perf. 13x12½***

**2128** A1124 2fr brt grn bl & olive .90 .25

Nov. 11, 1918 Armistice Ending World War I, 70th Anniv. A1125

**1988, Sept. 10** **Engr.** ***Perf. 13***

**2129** A1125 2.20fr brt blue, gray & blk 1.00 .25

*Homage to Leon Degand,* Sculpture by Robert Jacobsen A1126

**1988, Sept. 22** ***Perf. 12½x13***
**2130** A1126 5fr blk & dp claret 2.25 1.00

French-Danish cultural exchange program, 10th anniv. See Denmark No. 860.

Strasbourg, 2000th Anniv. — A1127

**1988, Sept. 24** ***Perf. 13***
**2131** A1127 2.20fr Municipal arms 1.00 .25

St. Mihiel Sepulcher, by Ligier Richier (c. 1500-1567), Sculptor — A1128

*Composition,* 1954, by Serge Poliakoff (1906-1969) — A1129

*La Pieta de Villeneuve-les-Avignon,* by Enguerrand Quarton (1444-1466) — A1130

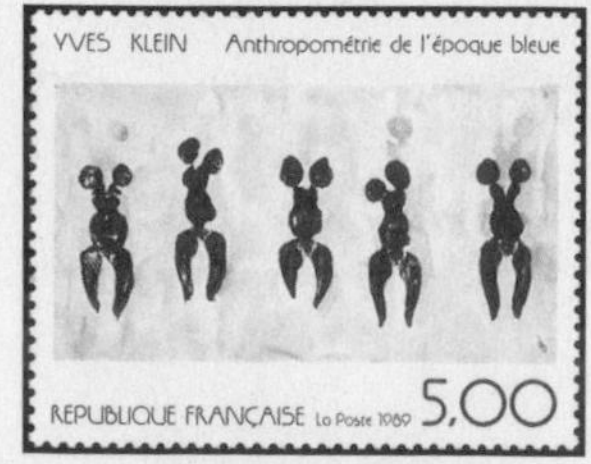

*Anthropometry of the Blue Period,* by Yves Klein — A1131

**1988-89** **Engr.** ***Perf. 13x12½***
**2132** A1128 5fr black brown 2.25 1.00

**Photo.**

**2133** A1129 5fr multicolored 2.25 1.00
**2134** A1130 5fr multicolored 2.25 1.00
**2135** A1131 5fr multi ('89) 2.25 1.00
*Nos. 2132-2135 (4)* 9.00 4.00

Issue dates: No. 2132, 10/15; No. 2133, 10/22; No. 2134, 12/10; No. 2135, 1/21.

Thermal Springs A1132

**1988, Nov. 21** **Engr.** ***Perf. 13x12½***
**2136** A1132 2.20fr multicolored 1.00 .25

*Metamecanique,* by Jean Tinguely — A1133

**1988, Nov. 25** **Photo.**
**2137** A1133 5fr multicolored 2.25 1.00

See Switzerland No. 828.

UN Declaration of Human Rights, 40th Anniv. A1134

**1988, Dec. 12** **Litho.** ***Perf. 13***
**2138** A1134 2.20fr dk bl & grnsh bl 1.00 .25

French Revolution, Bicent. — A1135

**1989, Jan. 1** **Photo.** ***Perf. 13x12½***
**2139** A1135 2.20fr red & vio blue 1.00 .25

Valentin Hauy (1745-1822), Founder of the School for the Blind, Paris, 1791 — A1136

**Photo. & Embossed**

**1989, Jan. 28**
**2140** A1136 2.20fr multicolored 1.00 .40

Estienne School, Cent. — A1137

**1989, Feb. 4** **Engr.** ***Perf. 12½***
**2141** A1137 2.20fr gray, black & red 1.00 .25

European Parliament Elections A1138

**1989, Mar. 4** **Litho.** ***Perf. 13***
**2142** A1138 2.20fr multicolored 1.00 .25

A1139

**1989** **Engr.** ***Perf. 12½x13***
**2143** A1139 2.20fr Liberty 1.00 .25
**2144** A1139 2.20fr Equality 1.00 .25
**2145** A1139 2.20fr Fraternity 1.00 .25
*a.* Strip of 3, #2143-2145 + label 3.00 2.50

Bicent. of the French revolution and the Declaration of Rights of Man and the Citizen. No. 2145a contains inscribed label picturing PHILEXFRANCE '89 emblem.

Issue dates: No. 2143, 3/18; No. 2144, 4/22; No. 2145, 5/27; No. 2145a, 7/14.

French-Soviet Joint Space Flight — A1140

**1989, Mar. 4** **Litho.** ***Perf. 13***
**2146** A1140 3.60fr multicolored 1.60 .50

Historic Sights, Paris — A1141

Designs: No. 2147, Arche de la Defense. No. 2148, Eiffel Tower. No. 2149, Grand Louvre. No. 2150, Notre Dame Cathedral. No. 2151, Bastille Monument and Opera de la Bastille. No. 2151a has a continuous design.

**1989, Apr. 21** **Engr.** ***Perf. 13x12½***
**2147** A1141 2.20fr multicolored 1.00 .75
**2148** A1141 2.20fr multicolored 1.00 .75
**2149** A1141 2.20fr multicolored 1.00 .75
**2150** A1141 2.20fr multicolored 1.00 .75
**2151** A1141 2.20fr multicolored 1.00 .75
*a.* Strip of 5, #2147-2151 5.00 5.00

Europa 1989 A1142

Children's games.

**1989, Apr. 29** ***Perf. 13***
**2152** A1142 2.20fr Hopscotch 1.00 .30
**2153** A1142 3.60fr Catch (ball) 1.60 .60

ITU Plenipotentiaries Conference, Nice — A1143

**1989, May 23** **Litho.**
**2154** A1143 3.70fr dk bl, dl org & red 1.60 .40

**Tourist Issue**

Fontainebleau Forest — A1144

Vaux le Vicomte — A1145

La Brenne — A1146

**1989, May 20** **Engr.** ***Perf. 13***
**2155** A1144 2.20fr multicolored .90 .30

***Perf. 13x12½***

**2156** A1145 3.70fr ol bis & blk 1.60 .75
**2157** A1146 4fr violet blue 1.60 .75
*Nos. 2155-2157 (3)* 4.10 1.80

Issued: 2.20fr, 5/20; 3.70fr, 7/14; 4fr, 8/25.

World Cycling Championships, Chambery — A1147

**1989, June 3** **Litho.** ***Perf. 13***
**2158** A1147 2.20fr multi 1.00 .25

Jehan de Malestroit, Dept. of Morbihan — A1148

**1989, June 10** **Engr.** ***Perf. 12½x13***
**2159** A1148 3.70fr multicolored 1.60 .55

Preliminary Sketch (Detail) for *Oath of the Tennis Court,* by David — A1149

*Regatta with Wind Astern,* by Charles Lapicque
A1150

**1989, June 19 Photo. *Perf. 13x12½***

**2160** A1149 5fr multicolored 2.25 1.00

***Perf. 12½***

**2161** A1150 5fr multicolored 2.25 1.00

No. 2160 for French revolution bicent. Issued: No. 2160, 6/19; No. 2161, 9/23.

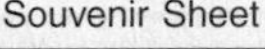

Souvenir Sheet

Revolution Bicentennial — A1151

Revolutionaries: a, Madame Roland (1754-1793). b, Camille Desmoulins (1760-1794). c, Condorcet (1743-1794). d, Kellermann (1735-1820).

**1989, June 26 Engr. *Perf. 13***

**2162** A1151 Sheet of 4 4.00 3.50
*a.-d.* 2.20fr any single 1.00 .60

A1152

2.20fr, 15th Summit of the Arch Meeting of Leaders from Industrial Nations, July 14-16.

**1989, July 14 Photo.**

**2163** A1152 2.20fr multicolored 1.00 .35

Declaration of the Rights of Man and the Citizen, Versailles, Aug. 26, 1789 — A1153

Details of an anonymous 18th-19th cent. painting in Carnavalet Museum: No. 2168a, Preamble, Article I. No. 2168b, Articles VII-XI. No. 2168c, Articles II-VI. No. 2168d, Articles XII-XVII.

**Litho. & Engr.**

**1989, Aug. 26 *Perf. 13x11½***

**2164** A1153 2.50fr Preamble, Article I 1.00 .80
**2165** A1153 2.50fr Art. II-VI 1.00 .80
**2166** A1153 2.50fr Art. VII-XI 1.00 .80
**2167** A1153 2.50fr Art. XII-XVII 1.00 .80
*a.* Strip, #2164-2167 + label 4.50 3.25

**Souvenir Sheet**

***Perf. 13x12½***

**2168** A1153 Sheet of 4 10.00 10.00
*a.-d.* 5fr any single 2.25 2.00

No. 2168 contains 4 52x41mm stamps. Sold for 50fr, including admission fee to PHILEX-FRANCE '89.

Value of No. 2168 is for examples on plain paper. Examples on fluorescent paper seem to have been distributed in North America, and may not have been distributed widely or made available in Europe. Value $400.

Musical Instruments — A1154

**1989 Litho. *Perf. 12x12½***

**2169** A1154 1.39fr Harp .65 .50
**2170** A1154 1.79fr Piano .80 .50
**2171** A1154 2.90fr Trumpet 1.25 1.00
**2172** A1154 4.84fr Violin 2.25 1.75
*Nos. 2169-2172 (4)* 4.95 3.75

Nos. 2169-2172 are known only precanceled. See second note after No. 132.

See Nos. 2233-2239, 2273-2283, 2303-2306, 2368-2371.

TGV Atlantic
A1155

**1989, Sept. 23 Photo. *Perf. 13***

**2173** A1155 2.50fr dk bl, sil & red 1.10 .50

Clermont-Ferrand Tramway, Cent. — A1156

**1989, Oct. 28 Engr.**

**2174** A1156 3.70fr blk & dk ol bis 1.75 .40

Villers-Cotterets Ordinance, 450th Anniv. — A1157

**1989, Oct. 28 Engr.**

**2175** A1157 2.20fr blk, dp cl & red 1.00 .25

Baron Augustin-Louis Cauchy (1789-1857), Mathematician — A1158

**1989, Nov. 10 *Perf. 13x12½***

**2176** A1158 3.60fr red, blk & bl grn 1.60 .50

Marshal Jean de Lattre de Tassigny (1889-1952) — A1159

**1989, Nov. 18 *Perf. 13***

**2177** A1159 2.20fr bl, blk & red 1.00 .25

Harki Soldiers of France
A1160

**1989, Dec. 9 Photo.**

**2178** A1160 2.20fr multicolored 1.00 .30

Marianne — A1161

**1990-92 Engr. *Perf. 13***

**2179** A1161 10c brn blk .25 .25
*a.* Bklt. pane, #2180, 4 #2179 1.00
**2180** A1161 20c lt green .25 .25
**2181** A1161 50c brt violet .25 .25
**2182** A1161 1fr orange .45 .25
**2183** A1161 2fr apple grn .90 .25
**2184** A1161 2.10fr dark grn .95 .25
**2185** A1161 2.20fr dark grn 1.00 .25
**2186** A1161 2.20fr emerald 1.00 .25
**2187** A1161 2.30fr red 1.00 .25
*a.* Bklt. pane, #2180, 4 #2187 5.00
**2188** A1161 2.50fr red 1.10 .25
**2189** A1161 3.20fr blue 1.50 .75
**2190** A1161 3.40fr blue 1.60 .40
**2191** A1161 3.80fr lilac rose 1.75 .30
**2192** A1161 4fr lilac rose 1.90 .25
**2193** A1161 4.20fr lilac rose 1.90 .25
**2194** A1161 5fr greenish blue 2.25 .25
**2195** A1161 10fr violet 4.50 .25
**2196** A1161 (2.20fr) dk grn 1.00 .25
**2197** A1161 (2.50fr) red 1.10 .25
*Nos. 2179-2197 (19)* 24.65 5.45

**Coil Stamps**

***Perf. 13 Horiz.***

**2198** A1161 2.10fr dk grn 1.00 .25
**2199** A1161 2.20fr dk grn 1.00 .60
**2200** A1161 2.30fr red 1.00 .25
**2201** A1161 2.50fr red 1.10 .25
*Nos. 2198-2201 (4)* 4.10 1.35

***Die Cut***

**Self-Adhesive**

**2202** A1161 2.30fr red 1.00 .25
*a.* Booklet pane of 10 10.00
**2203** A1161 2.50fr red 1.10 .25
*a.* Booklet pane of 10 11.00
*b.* Booklet pane of 5 5.50
**2204** A1161 (2.50fr) red 1.10 .25
*a.* Booklet pane of 10 11.00
*Nos. 2202-2204 (3)* 3.20 .75

Issued: No. 2187, 1/2; No. 2198, 1/1; 10c, 20c, 50c, 3.20fr, 3.80fr, 3/26; No. 2202, 1/29; Nos. 2182-2183, 2194-2195, 5/21; Nos. 2196-2197, 8/19/91; 2.20fr, 2.50fr, 3.40fr, 4fr, 9/30/91; Nos. 2179a, 2187a, 2199, 2201, 1991; 4.20fr, 9/24/92; Nos. 2203-2204, 1992; 2.10fr, 1993.

Peelable paper backing serves as booklet cover for Nos. 2202, 2203. No. 2203b has separate backing with no printing.

Nos. 2196-2197, 2204 inscribed "D."

See Nos. 2333-2348, 3529, 4410i, 4522.

Lace Work
A1162

**1990, Feb. 3 Engr. *Perf. 13x12½***

**2205** A1162 2.50fr red 1.00 .40

1992 Winter Olympics, Albertville — A1163

**1990, Feb. 9 Photo. *Perf. 13***

**2206** A1163 2.50fr multicolored 1.00 .25

Charles de Gaulle (1890-1970)
A1164

**1990, Feb. 24 Engr. *Perf. 12½x13***

**2207** A1164 2.30fr brt vio, vio bl & blk 1.00 .25

Max Hymans (1900-1961), Planes and ACC Emblem — A1165

**1990, Mar. 3 *Perf. 13***

**2208** A1165 2.30fr brt vio, brt bl & dk ol grn 1.00 .25

*Profile of a Woman,* by Odilon Redon
A1166

Head of Christ, Wissembourg — A1167

Cambodian Dancer by Auguste Rodin — A1168

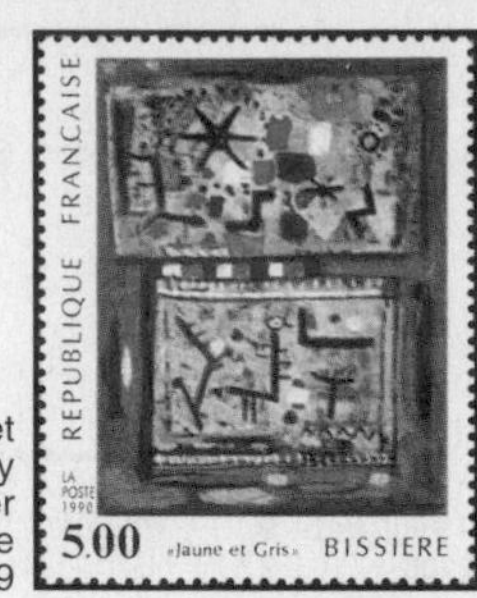

Jaune et Gris by Roger Bissiere
A1169

**1990** **Litho.** ***Perf. 13½x14***
**2209** A1166 5fr multicolored 2.25 1.00

***Perf. 12½x13***

**Engr.**

**2210** A1167 5fr multicolored 2.25 1.00
**2211** A1168 5fr multicolored 2.25 1.00

**Photo.**

**2212** A1169 5fr multicolored 2.25 1.00
*Nos. 2209-2212 (4)* 9.00 4.00

Issue dates: No. 2209, Mar. 3; No. 2210, June 16; No. 2211, June 9; No. 2212, Dec. 8.

Jean Guehenno (1890-1978)
A1170

**Litho. & Engr.**

**1990, Mar. 24** ***Perf. 13***
**2213** A1170 3.20fr buff & red brn 1.50 .40

**Tourism Series**

Flaran Abbey, Gers
A1171

**1990, Apr. 21** **Engr.** ***Perf. 13***
**2214** A1171 3.80fr sepia & blk 1.75 .50

Cluny
A1172

Pont Canal de Briare
A1173

Cap Canaille, Cassis
A1174

**1990**
**2215** A1172 2.30fr multicolored 1.00 .25
**2216** A1173 2.30fr multicolored 1.00 .25
**2217** A1174 3.80fr multicolored 1.75 .50
*Nos. 2215-2217 (3)* 3.75 1.00

Issued: No. 2215, 6/23; No. 2216, 7/7; 3.80fr, 7/14.

Europa 1990
A1175

Post offices.

**1990, Apr. 28** **Engr.** ***Perf. 13***
**2218** A1175 2.30fr Macon 1.00 .30
**2219** A1175 3.20fr Cerizay 1.50 .60

Arab World Institute — A1176

**1990, May 5** ***Perf. 12½x13***
**2220** A1176 3.80fr brt bl, dk red & dp bl 1.75 .40

Labor Day, Cent.
A1177

**1990, May 1** **Photo.** ***Perf. 13***
**2221** A1177 2.30fr multicolored 1.00 .25

Villefranche-sur-Saone — A1178

**1990, June 2** **Engr.** ***Perf. 13x12½***
**2222** A1178 2.30fr multicolored 1.00 .25

National philatelic congress.

A1179

**1990, June 6** ***Perf. 13x12½***
**2223** A1179 2.30fr La Poste 1.00 .25

Whitbread trans-global yacht race.

A1181

**1990, June 17** ***Perf. 12½x13***
**2225** A1181 2.30fr multicolored 1.00 .25

De Gaulle's Call for French Resistance, 50th anniv.

Franco-Brazilian House, Rio de Janeiro — A1182

**1990, July 14** ***Perf. 13***
**2226** A1182 3.20fr multicolored 1.50 .70

See Brazil No. 2255.

A1183

**1990, Oct. 6** **Engr.** ***Perf. 12½***
**2227** A1183 2fr Rutilus rutilus .90 .25
**2228** A1183 3fr Perca fluviatilis 1.25 .25
**2229** A1183 4fr Salmo salar 1.75 .40
**2230** A1183 5fr Esox lucius 2.25 .40
*Nos. 2227-2230 (4)* 6.15 1.30

A1184

**1990, Sept. 29** **Photo.** ***Perf. 12½x13***
**2231** A1184 2.30fr multicolored 1.00 .30

Natl. Institute of Geography, 50th anniv.

**Souvenir Sheet**

French Revolution, Bicentennial — A1185

Designs: a, Gaspard Monge. b, Abbe Gregoire. c, Creation of the Tricolor. d, Creation of the French departments.

**1990, Oct. 15** **Engr.** ***Perf. 13***
**2232** A1185 Sheet of 4 4.50 4.00
*a.-d.* 2.50fr any single 1.10 .90

**Musical Instrument Type of 1989**

**1990, Sept. 1** **Litho.** ***Perf. 13***
**2233** A1154 1.46fr Accordion .65 .40
**2234** A1154 1.89fr Breton bagpipe .75 .60
**2235** A1154 3.06fr Tambourin 1.50 1.50
**2236** A1154 5.10fr Hurdy-gurdy 2.50 2.40
*Nos. 2233-2236 (4)* 5.40 4.90

**1990, Nov.** **Litho.** ***Perf. 13***
**2237** A1154 1.93fr like #2169 1.00 .60
**2238** A1154 2.39fr like #2170 1.10 .80
**2239** A1154 2.74fr like #2172 1.25 1.25
*Nos. 2237-2239 (3)* 3.35 2.65

Nos. 2233-2239 are known only precanceled. See second note after No. 132.

Maurice Genevoix (1890-1980), Novelist — A1186

**1990, Nov. 12** **Engr.** ***Perf. 13***
**2240** A1186 2.30fr lt green & blk 1.00 .25

Organization for Economic Cooperation and Development, 30th Anniv. — A1187

**1990, Dec. 15** **Litho.**
**2241** A1187 3.20fr dk & lt blue 1.50 .70

"The Swing" by Auguste Renoir (1841-1919) — A1188

**1991, Feb. 23** **Engr.** ***Perf. 12½x13***
**2242** A1188 5fr multicolored 2.25 1.00

Youth Philatelic Exhibition, Cholet
A1189

**1991, Mar. 30** **Litho.** ***Perf. 13***
**2243** A1189 2.50fr multicolored 1.10 .40

**Art Series**


Le Noeud Noir by Georges Seurat (1859-1891) — A1190

Apres Nous La Maternite, by Max Ernst (1891-1976) — A1191

Volte Faccia by Francois Rouan A1192

O Tableau Noir by Roberto Matta (b. 1911) — A1193

**1991 Engr. *Perf. 12½x13***
**2244** A1190 5fr pale yellow & blk 2.25 1.00

**Photo. *Perf. 13***
**2245** A1191 2.50fr multicolored 1.00 .70

**Engr. *Perf. 12½x13***
**2246** A1192 5fr black 2.25 1.00

**Photo. *Perf. 13x12½***
**2247** A1193 5fr multicolored 2.25 1.00
*Nos. 2244-2247 (4)* 7.75 3.70

Issued: No. 2244, 4/13: No. 2245, 10/10; No. 2246, 11/9; No. 2247, 11/30.

Wolfgang Amadeus Mozart (1756-1791), Composer — A1194

**1991, Apr. 9 Photo. *Perf. 13***
**2248** A1194 2.50fr bl, blk & red 1.10 .60

National Printing Office, 350th Anniv. — A1195

**1991, Apr. 13**
**2249** A1195 4fr multicolored 1.75 .75

**Tourism Series**

Chevire Bridge, Nantes — A1196

Carennac Castle A1197

Pipe Organ, Wasquehal A1198

Valley of Munster A1199

**1991 Engr. *Perf. 13***
**2250** A1196 2.50fr multicolored 1.10 .25

***Perf. 12x13***
**2251** A1197 2.50fr multicolored 1.10 .30

***Perf. 12***
**2252** A1198 4fr black & buff 1.75 .55

***Perf. 13x12½***
**2253** A1199 4fr violet 1.75 .55
*Nos. 2250-2253 (4)* 5.70 1.65

Issue dates: No. 2250, Apr. 27; Nos. 2251, 2253, July 6; No. 2252, June 22.

Europa — A1200

2.50fr, Ariane launch site, French Guiana. 3.50fr, Television satellite.

**1991, Apr. 27 *Perf. 12½x13***
**2254** A1200 2.50fr multi 1.10 .25
**2255** A1200 3.50fr multi 1.60 .55

Compare with No. 2483.

Concours Lepine, 90th Anniv. — A1201

**1991, Apr. 27 *Perf. 13***
**2256** A1201 4fr multicolored 1.75 .75

French Assoc. of Small Manufacturers and Inventors.

Philatelic Society Congress, Perpignan A1202

**1991, May 18**
**2257** A1202 2.50fr multicolored 1.10 .25

French Open Tennis Championships, Cent. — A1203

**1991, May 24 Engr. *Perf. 13***
**2258** A1203 3.50fr multicolored 1.60 .50

Souvenir Sheet

French Revolution, Bicent. — A1204

Designs: a, Theophile Malo Corret, La Tour d'Auvergne (1743-1800). b, Liberty Tree. c, National police, bicent. d, Louis Antoine-Leon de St. Just (1767-1794).

**1991, June 1 Engr. *Perf. 13***
**2259** A1204 Sheet of 4 4.50 3.50
*a.-d.* 2.50fr any single 1.10 .80

A1205

**1991, June 13 Photo. *Perf. 13***
**2260** A1205 2.50fr multicolored 1.10 .40

Gaston III de Foix (Febus) (1331-1391), general.

Wildlife — A1206

Designs: 2fr, Ursus arctos. 3fr, Testudo hermanni. 4fr, Castor fiber. 5fr, Alcedo atthis.

**1991, Sept. 14 Engr. *Perf. 12½***
**2261** A1206 2fr multi .90 .30
**2262** A1206 3fr multi 1.25 .30
**2263** A1206 4fr multi 1.75 .70
**2264** A1206 5fr multi 2.25 .70
*Nos. 2261-2264 (4)* 6.15 2.00

10th World Forestry Congress A1207

**1991, Sept. 22 Engr. *Perf. 13x12½***
**2265** A1207 2.50fr multicolored 1.10 .25

School of Public Works, Cent. A1208

**1991, Oct. 5 Litho. & Engr. *Perf. 13***
**2266** A1208 2.50fr multicolored 1.10 .30

Marcel Cerdan (1916-1949), Middleweight Boxing Champion — A1209

**1991, Oct. 19 Photo. *Perf. 13***
**2267** A1209 2.50fr black & red 1.00 .30

Amnesty International, 30th Anniv. — A1210

**1991, Oct. 19**
**2268** A1210 3.40fr multicolored 1.50 .60

1992 Winter Olympics, Albertville — A1211

**1991, Nov. 14 Engr. *Perf. 13***
**2269** A1211 2.50fr Olympic flame 1.10 .25

Fifth Handicapped Olympics — A1212

**1991, Dec. 7 *Perf. 13***
**2270** A1212 2.50fr dk & lt blue 1.10 .25

Voluntary Attachment of Mayotte to France, Sesquicentennial — A1213

**1991, Dec. 21 Engr.**
**2271** A1213 2.50fr multicolored 1.10 .25

French Pavilion, Expo '92, Seville
A1214

**Litho. & Engr.**

**1992, Jan. 18** *Perf. 13*
**2272** A1214 2.50fr multicolored 1.10 .25

### Musical Instruments Type of 1989

**1992, Jan. 31** **Litho.** *Perf. 13*
**2273** A1154 1.60fr Guitar 60.00 25.00
**2274** A1154 1.98fr like #2233 3.00 2.25
**2275** A1154 2.08fr Saxophone 1.25 1.00
**2276** A1154 2.46fr like #2234 1.25 1.00
**2277** A1154 2.98fr Banjo 1.50 1.50
**2278** A1154 3.08fr like #2235 6.00 4.00
**2279** A1154 3.14fr like #2236 2.00 1.50
**2280** A1154 3.19fr like #2169 7.00 4.00
**2281** A1154 5.28fr Xylophone 3.00 1.50
**2282** A1154 5.30fr like #2170 3.00 1.50
**2283** A1154 5.32fr like #2172 3.00 1.50
*Nos. 2273-2283 (11)* 91.00 44.75

***Perf. 12***

*2273a* A1154 1.60fr Guitar *7.50* *4.50*
*2274a* A1154 1.98fr like #2233 *150.00* *140.00*
*2275a* A1154 2.08fr Saxophone *40.00* *30.00*
*2276a* A1154 2.46fr like #2234 *12.00* *7.50*
*2278a* A1154 3.08fr like #2235 *12.00* *7.50*
*2279a* A1154 3.14fr like #2236 60.00 *50.00*
*2280a* A1154 3.19fr like #2169 *8.00* *5.00*
*2281a* A1154 5.28fr Xylophone *30.00* *20.00*
*2282a* A1154 5.30fr like #2170 *75.00* *60.00*
*2283a* A1154 5.32fr like #2172 *25.00* *20.00*
*Nos. 2273a-2283a (10)* *419.50* *344.50*

Nos. 2273-2283 are known only precanceled. See 2nd note after No. 132. See Nos. 2303-2306.

1992 Summer Olympics, Barcelona
A1215

**1992, Apr. 3** **Photo.** *Perf. 13*
**2284** A1215 2.50fr multicolored 1.10 .25

See Greece No. 1730.

Marguerite d'Angouleme (1492-1549)
A1216

**1992, Apr. 11** **Litho.** *Perf. 13*
**2285** A1216 3.40fr multicolored 1.60 .75

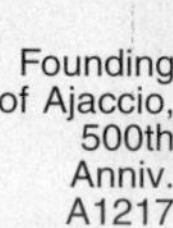

Founding of Ajaccio, 500th Anniv.
A1217

Virgin and Child Beneath a Garland by Botticelli.

**1992, Apr. 30** **Photo.** *Perf. 13*
**2286** A1217 4fr multicolored 1.75 .60

Europa — A1218

Discovery of America, 500th Anniv.: 2.50fr, Map, navigation instruments. 3.40fr, Sailing ship, map.

**1992, May 9** **Engr.** *Perf. 13x12½*
**2287** A1218 2.50fr multicolored 1.25 .30
**2288** A1218 3.40fr multicolored 1.75 .60

Intl. Bread and Cereal Congress — A1219

**1992, May 30** **Litho.** *Perf. 13*
**2289** A1219 3.40fr multicolored 1.60 .70

### Tourism Series

Ourcq Canal
A1220

**1992, May 30** **Engr.** *Perf. 13*
**2290** A1220 4fr black, blue & grn 1.75 .40

Mt. Aiguille — A1221

**1992, June 27** **Engr.** *Perf. 13*
**2291** A1221 3.40fr multicolored 1.60 .70

First ascension of Mt. Aiguille, 500th anniv.

Lorient
A1222

**1992, July 4** **Engr.** *Perf. 13*
**2292** A1222 4fr multicolored 1.25 .25

Biron Castle — A1223

**1992, July 4** *Perf. 12½x13*
**2293** A1223 2.50fr multicolored 1.75 .40

Natl. Philatelic Societies Congress, Niort
A1224

**1992, June 6** **Photo.** *Perf. 13*
**2294** A1224 2.50fr multicolored 1.10 .25

Natl. Art Festival.

1992 Olympic Games, Albertville and Barcelona
A1225

**1992, June 19** *Perf. 12½x13½*
**2295** A1225 2.50fr multicolored 1.10 .30

Tautavel Man
A1226

**1992, June 20** **Photo.** *Perf. 13*
**2296** A1226 3.40fr multicolored 1.60 .60

Portrait of Jacques Callot (1592-1635), by Claude Deruet — A1227

**1992, June 27** **Engr.** *Perf. 12x13*
**2297** A1227 5fr buff & brown 2.25 1.00

Flowers — A1228

2fr, Pancratium maritimum. 3fr, Drosera rotundifolia. 4fr, Orchis palustris. 5fr, Nuphar luteum.

**1992, Sept. 12** **Engr.** *Perf. 12½*
**2298** A1228 2fr multicolored .90 .30
**2299** A1228 3fr multicolored 1.25 .30
**2300** A1228 4fr multicolored 1.75 .60
**2301** A1228 5fr multicolored 2.25 .60
*Nos. 2298-2301 (4)* 6.15 1.80

First French Republic, Bicent.
A1229

**1992, Sept. 26** *Perf. 13*
**2302** A1229 2.50fr multicolored 1.10 .25

### Musical Instruments Type of 1989

**1992, Oct.** **Litho.** *Perf. 13*
**2303** A1154 1.73fr like #2273 .80 .25
**2304** A1154 2.25fr like #2275 1.00 .50
**2305** A1154 3.51fr like #2277 2.00 1.00
**2306** A1154 5.40fr like #2281 2.75 1.75
*Nos. 2303-2306 (4)* 6.55 3.50

Nos. 2303-2306 are known only precanceled. See second note after No. 132.

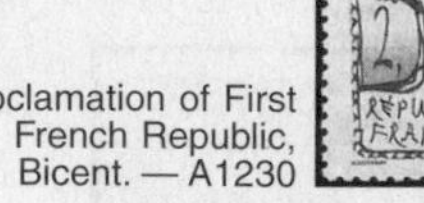

Proclamation of First French Republic, Bicent. — A1230

Paintings or drawings by contemporary artists: No. 2307, Tree of Freedom, by Pierre Alechinsky. No. 2308, Portrait of a Young Man, by Martial Raysse. No. 2309, Marianne with Body and Head of Rooster, by Gerard Garouste. No. 2310, "Republique Francaise," by Jean-Charles Blais.

**1992, Sept. 26** **Engr.** *Perf. 13*
**2307** A1230 2.50fr red 1.10 .25
**2308** A1230 2.50fr red 1.10 .25
**2309** A1230 2.50fr red 1.10 .25
**2310** A1230 2.50fr red 1.10 .25
*Nos. 2307-2310 (4)* 4.40 1.00

Single European Market
A1231

**1992, Nov. 6** **Photo.** *Perf. 12½x13½*
**2311** A1231 2.50fr multicolored 1.10 .30

First Mail Flight from Nancy to Luneville, 80th Anniv.
A1232

**1992, Nov. 12** *Perf. 13*
**2312** A1232 2.50fr multicolored 1.10 .40

Marcel Paul (1900-1982), Minister of Industrial Production — A1233

**1992, Nov. 13** **Engr.**
**2313** A1233 4.20fr claret & blue 1.90 .50

Contemporary Art — A1234

No. 2314, Le Rendezvous d'Ephese, by Paul Delvaux, Belgium. No. 2315, Abstract painting, by Alberto Burri, Italy. No. 2316, Abstract painting, by Antoni Tapies, Spain. No. 2317, Portrait of John Edwards, by Francis Bacon, Great Britain.

**1992 Photo. *Perf. 13x12½***
**2314** A1234 5fr multicolored 2.25 1.00
**2315** A1234 5fr multicolored 2.25 1.00
**2316** A1234 5fr multicolored 2.25 1.00
**2317** A1234 5fr multicolored 2.25 1.00
*Nos. 2314-2317 (4)* 9.00 4.00

Issued: No. 2314, 11/20; Nos. 2315-2317, 11/21.

See Nos. 2379-2390.

Gypsy Culture — A1235

**1992, Dec. 5 Photo. *Perf. 13***
**2318** A1235 2.50fr multicolored 1.10 .25

Yacht "La Poste," Entrant in Whitbread Trans-Global Race — A1236

**1993, Feb. 6 Engr. *Perf. 12***
**2319** A1236 2.50fr multicolored 1.10 .30

See No. 2375.

Water Birds — A1237

**1993, Feb. 6 *Perf. 12½x12***
**2320** A1237 2fr Harle piette .90 .30
**2321** A1237 3fr Fuligule nyroca 1.25 .30
**2322** A1237 4fr Tadorne de belon 1.75 .60
**2323** A1237 5fr Harle huppe 2.25 .70
*Nos. 2320-2323 (4)* 6.15 1.90

Memorial to Indochina War, Frejus A1238

**Litho. & Engr.**

**1993, Feb. 16 *Perf. 13x13½***
**2324** A1238 4fr multicolored 1.75 .60

Stamp Day — A1239

**1993, Mar. 6 Photo. *Perf. 13***
**2325** A1239 2.50fr red & multi 1.50 .80
**2326** A1239 2.50fr +60c red & multi 1.25 1.00
*a.* Bklt. pane of 4 #2325, 3 #2326 + label 10.00

Mediterranean Youth Games, Agde — A1240

**1993, Mar. 13 Photo. *Perf. 13***
**2327** A1240 2.50fr multicolored 1.10 .25

Human Rights, Intl. Mixed Masonic Order, Cent. — A1241

**1993, Apr. 3 Engr. *Perf. 13***
**2328** A1241 3.40fr blue & black 1.60 .50

Contemporary Art — A1242

Europa: 2.50fr, Painting, Rouge Rythme Bleu, by Olivier Debre. 3.40fr, Sculpture, Le Griffu, by Germaine Richier, vert.

***Perf. 13x12½, 12½x13***

**1993, Apr. 17 Litho.**
**2329** A1242 2.50fr multicolored 1.10 .30
**2330** A1242 3.40fr multicolored 1.60 .80

**Marianne Type of 1990**

**1993-96 Engr. *Perf. 13***
**2333** A1161 2fr blue 1.00 .25
**2334** A1161 2.40fr emerald 1.25 .25
**2335** A1161 2.70fr emerald 1.40 .25
**2336** A1161 3.50fr apple green 1.60 .30
**2337** A1161 3.80fr blue 1.75 .50
**2338** A1161 4.40fr blue 2.00 .40
**2339** A1161 4.50fr mag 2.00 .40
**2340** A1161 (2.50fr) red 1.75 .25
Complete booklet, 10 #2340 17.50
*Nos. 2333-2340 (8)* 12.75 2.60

***Perf. 13 Horiz.***

**Coil Stamps**

**2341** A1161 2.40fr emerald 1.10 .60
**2342** A1161 2.70fr emerald 1.60 .25
**2343** A1161 (2.80fr) red 1.75 .25

**Self-Adhesive**

***Die Cut***

**2344** A1161 70c brown 13.00 9.00

***Serpentine Die Cut Vert.***

**2345** A1161 70c brown 13.00 9.00
**2346** A1161 1fr orange 4.25 2.50
*a.* Booklet pane, 3 #2348, 1 #2346 9.00
Complete bklt., 2 #2346a 20.00

***Die Cut***

**2347** A1161 (2.50fr) red 1.75 .25
*a.* Booklet pane of 10 (see footnote) 17.50
*b.* Bklt. pane of 4 + label 7.00
*c.* Booklet pane, #2344, 3 #2347 + label 30.00
*d.* Booklet pane of 10 (see footnote) 15.00

***Serpentine Die Cut 6¾ Vert.***

**2348** A1161 (2.80fr) red 1.75 .25
*a.* Bklt. pane of 4 + label 7.00
*b.* Booklet pane of 10 (see footnote) 17.50
*c.* Booklet pane, #2345, 3 #2348 + label 19.00
*d.* Booklet pane of 10 (see footnote) 17.50
*e.* Booklet pane of 10 (see footnote) 17.50
*f.* Booklet pane of 10 (see footnote) —

Nos. 2340, 2347 pay postage for the first class letter rate and sold for 2.50fr when first released. They have no denomination or letter inscription. Nos. 2343 and 2348 had a face value of 2.80fr when released.

No. 2347a has all stamps adjoining and has selvage covering backing paper (booklet cover), No. 2347d is comprised of two strips of 5 stamps each with yellow backing paper showing.

No. 2348b has the same format as No. 2347a. No. 2348d has a format similar to No. 2347d except there is a narrow selvage strip between the left six stamps and the right four stamps. No. 2348e is like No. 2348f but lacks the selvage strip. No. 2348f has a format similar to No. 2347a except it has a wide selvage strip between the left four stamps and the right six stamps.

Backing paper of Nos. 2347b and 2347c may have cuts along fold and were sold in a booklet for 20fr.

Issued: #2340, 2347, 4/19/93; 70c, July; 2fr, 7/31/94; Nos. 2341-2343, 4/1/94; Nos. 2345, 2348, 2/14/94; 1fr, 2.70fr, 3.80fr, 4.50fr, 3/18/96.

**Tourism Series**

Chinon — A1243

**1993, Apr. 24 Engr. *Perf. 13x12½***
**2355** A1243 4.20fr dk grn, ol grn & brn 2.00 .80

Village of Minerve — A1244

**1993, July 17 *Perf. 13***
**2356** A1244 4.20fr red brown & yel grn 2.00 .50

Chaise-Dieu Abbey — A1245

Montbeliard — A1246

**1993**
**2357** A1245 2.80fr multicolored 1.25 .30
**2358** A1246 4.40fr multicolored 2.00 .60
*Nos. 2355-2358 (4)* 7.25 2.20

Issued: No. 2357, 9/4; No. 2358, 9/11.

Ninth European Conference on Protection of Human Rights — A1247

**1993, May 8 Engr. *Perf. 12½x13***
**2359** A1247 2.50fr multicolored 1.10 .30

Django Reinhardt (1910-1953), Musician — A1248

**1993, May 14 Litho. *Perf. 13***
**2360** A1248 4.20fr multicolored 1.90 .50

Louise Weiss (1893-1983), Suffragist — A1249

**1993, May 15 Engr. *Perf. 13x12½***
**2361** A1249 2.50fr blk, buff & red 1.10 .30

Philatelic Society Congress, Lille A1250

**1993, May 29 Engr. *Perf. 13x12½***
**2362** A1250 2.50fr bl, dk bl & lil 1.10 .40

Natural History Museum, Bicent. A1251

**Litho. & Engr.**

**1993, June 5 *Perf. 13***
**2363** A1251 2.50fr multicolored 1.10 .30

Martyrs and Heroes of the Resistance — A1252

**1993, June 18 Photo. *Perf. 13***
**2364** 2.50fr red, black & gray 1.10 .60
**2365** 4.20fr red, black & gray 1.90 1.00
*a.* A1252 Pair, #2364-2365 3.00 2.50

A1254

**1993, July 10 Engr. *Perf. 13x12½***
**2366** A1254 2.50fr multicolored 1.10 .30

Claude Chappe's Semaphore Telegraph, bicent.

A1255

**1993, July 10 Engr.** ***Perf. 12½x13***

**2367** A1255 3.40fr bl, grn & red 1.50 .70

Train to Lake Artouste, Laruns, highest train ride in Europe.

**Musical Instruments Type of 1989**

**1993, July 1 Litho.** ***Perf. 13***

**2368** A1154 1.82fr like #2171 .80 .25
**2369** A1154 2.34fr like #2235 1.10 .60
**2370** A1154 3.86fr like #2236 1.75 .90
**2371** A1154 5.93fr like #2281 2.75 1.75
*Nos. 2368-2371 (4)* 6.40 3.50

Nos. 2368-2371 are known only precanceled. See note after No. 132.

Liberation of Corsica, 50th Anniv. — A1256

**1993, Sept. 9 Engr.** ***Perf. 13***

**2372** A1256 2.80fr lake, bl & blk 1.25 .30

Saint Thomas, by Georges de la Tour (1593-1652) — A1257

**1993, Sept. 9 Photo.** ***Perf. 12½x13***

**2373** A1257 5fr multicolored 2.25 1.00

Service as Military Hospital of Val de Grace Monastery, Bicent. — A1258

**1993, Sept. 25 Engr.** ***Perf. 13***

**2374** A1258 3.70fr multicolored 1.60 .30

**Whitbread Trans-Global Race Type**

**1993, Sept. 27 Engr.** ***Perf. 12***

**2375** A1236 2.80fr multicolored 1.25 .40

The Muses, by Maurice Denis (1870-1943) — A1259

**1993, Oct. 2 Photo.** ***Perf. 12½x13***

**2376** A1259 5fr multicolored 2.25 1.00

The Clowns, by Albert Gleizes (1881-1953) A1260

**1993, Oct. 2 Photo.** ***Perf. 13½x12½***

**2377** A1260 2.80fr multicolored 1.25 .30

Natl. Circus Center, Chalons-sur-Marne.

Clock Tower Bellringer Statues of Lambesc — A1261

**1993, Oct. 9 Engr.** ***Perf. 13x12½***

**2378** A1261 4.40fr multicolored 2.00 .60

**European Contemporary Art Type**

Designs: No. 2379, Abstract, by Takis. No. 2380, Abstract, by Maria Helena Vieira da Silva. No. 2381, Abstract Squares, by Sean Scully. No. 2382, Abstract, by Georg Baselitz, Germany.

**1993-94 Photo.** ***Perf. 13x12½***

**2379** A1234 5fr blk & ver 2.25 1.00
**2380** A1234 5fr multicolored 2.25 1.00
**2381** A1234 6.70fr multicolored 3.00 1.00

***Perf. 13***

**2382** A1234 6.70fr multicolored 3.00 1.00
*Nos. 2379-2382 (4)* 10.50 4.00

Issued: No. 2379, 10/9/93; No. 2380, 12/11/93; No. 2381, 1/29/94; No. 2382, 11/19/94.

Greetings A1266

Greeting, artist: No. 2383, Happy Birthday, Claire Wendling. No. 2384, Happy Birthday, Bernard Olivie. No. 2385, Happy Anniversary, Stephane Colman. No. 2386, Happy Anniversary, Guillaune Sorel. No. 2387, With Love, Jean-Michel Thiriet. No. 2388, Please Write, Etienne Davodeau. No. 2389, Congratulations, Johan de Moor. No. 2390, Good luck, "Mezzo." No. 2391, Best Wishes, Nicolas de Crecy. No. 2392, Best Wishes, Florence Magnin. No. 2393, Merry Christmas, Thierry Robin. No. 2394, Merry Christmas, Patrick Prugne.

**1993, Oct. 21 Photo.** ***Perf. 13½x13***

**Booklet Stamps**

**2383** A1266 2.80fr multicolored 1.25 .30
**2384** A1266 2.80fr multicolored 1.25 .30
**2385** A1266 2.80fr multicolored 1.25 .30
**2386** A1266 2.80fr multicolored 1.25 .30
**2387** A1266 2.80fr multicolored 1.25 .30
**2388** A1266 2.80fr multicolored 1.25 .30
**2389** A1266 2.80fr multicolored 1.25 .30
**2390** A1266 2.80fr multicolored 1.25 .30
**2391** A1266 2.80fr multicolored 1.25 .30
**2392** A1266 2.80fr multicolored 1.25 .30
**2393** A1266 2.80fr multicolored 1.25 .30
**2394** A1266 2.80fr multicolored 1.25 .30
*a.* Bklt. pane, #2383-2394 15.00

***Perf. 12½***

*2383a* A1266 2.80fr 1.25 .30
*2384a* A1266 2.80fr 1.25 .30
*2385a* A1266 2.80fr 1.25 .30
*2386a* A1266 2.80fr 1.25 .30
*2387a* A1266 2.80fr 1.25 .30
*2388a* A1266 2.80fr 1.25 .30
*2389a* A1266 2.80fr 1.25 .30
*2390a* A1266 2.80fr 1.25 .30
*2391a* A1266 2.80fr 1.25 .30
*2392a* A1266 2.80fr 1.25 .30
*2393a* A1266 2.80fr 1.25 .30
*2394b* A1266 2.80fr 1.25 .30
*c.* Booklet pane of 12, #2383a-2393a, 2394b 16.50

**Souvenir Sheet**

European Stamp Exhibition, Salon du Timbre — A1267

a, Rhododendrons. b, Flowers in park, Paris.

**1993, Nov. 10** ***Perf. 13***

**2395** A1267 2.40fr #a.-b.+ 2 labels 12.00 10.00

Sold for 15fr.

Louvre Museum, Bicent. A1268

**1993, Nov. 20**

**2396** A1268 2.80fr Louvre, 1793 1.25 1.00
**2397** A1268 4.40fr Louvre, 1993 2.00 1.25
*a.* Pair, #2396-2397 3.50 2.50

Glassware, 1901 — A1269

Cast Iron, c. 1900 — A1270

Furniture, c. 1902 — A1271

Stoneware, c. 1898 — A1272

Decorative arts by: No. 2398, Emile Galle (1846-1904). No. 2399, Hector Guimard (1867-1942). No. 2400, Louis Majorelle (1859-1926). No. 2401, Pierre-Adrien Dalpayrat (1844-1910).

***Perf. 13½x12½***

**1994. Jan. 22 Photo.**

**2398** A1269 2.80fr multicolored 1.25 .35
**2399** A1270 2.80fr multicolored 1.25 .35
**2400** A1271 4.40fr multicolored 2.00 .65
**2401** A1272 4.40fr multicolored 2.00 .65
*Nos. 2398-2401 (4)* 6.50 2.00

Stained Glass Window, St. Julian's Cathedral, Le Mans A1273

**1994, Feb. 12 Engr.** ***Perf. 12½x13***

**2402** A1273 6.70fr multicolored 3.00 1.00

City of Bastia — A1274

**1994, Feb. 19** ***Perf. 13x12½***

**2403** A1274 4.40fr blue & brown 2.00 .60

**Tourism Series**

Argentat A1275

**1994, June 18 Engr.** ***Perf. 12x12½***

**2404** A1275 4.40fr red brown & rose carmine 2.00 .60

European Parliamentary Elections — A1276

**1994, Feb. 26** **Litho.** ***Perf. 13***
**2405** A1276 2.80fr multicolored 1.25 .25

Laurent Mourguet (1769-1844), Creator of Puppet, Guignol — A1277

**1994, Mar. 4** **Photo.** ***Perf. 13***
**2406** A1277 2.80fr multicolored 1.25 .30

French Polytechnic Institute, Bicent. A1277a

**1994, Mar. 11**
**2407** A1277a 2.80fr multicolored 1.25 .30

Stamp Day A1278

**1994, Mar. 12** **Engr.** ***Perf. 13***
**2408** A1278 2.80fr blue & red *2.00 1.60*
**2409** A1278 2.80fr +60c blue & red *1.40 1.25*
*a.* Booklet pane of 4 #2408, 3 #2400 + 1 label *25.00*

No. 2408 issued only in booklets.

Swedish Ballet Costume — A1279

Banquet for Gustavus III at the Trianon, 1784, by Lafrensen — A1280

French-Swedish cultural relations: No. 2411, Tuxedo costume for Swedish ballet. No. 2412, Viking ships. No. 2413, Viking ship. No. 2415, Swedish, French flags.

**1994, Mar. 18** **Engr.** ***Perf. 13***
**2410** A1279 2.80fr multicolored 1.25 1.00
**2411** A1279 2.80fr multicolored 1.25 1.00
**2412** A1279 2.80fr multicolored 1.25 1.00
**2413** A1279 2.80fr multicolored 1.25 1.00
**2414** A1280 3.70fr multicolored 3.00 2.00
**2415** A1280 3.70fr multicolored 3.00 2.00
*a.* Booklet pane of #2410-2415 16.00

See Sweden Nos. 2065-2070.

Pres. Georges Pompidou (1911-1974) A1281

**1994, Apr. 9** **Engr.** ***Perf. 13***
**2416** A1281 2.80fr olive brown 1.25 .30

Resistance of the Maquis, 50th Anniv. A1282

**1994, Apr. 9**
**2417** A1282 2.80fr multicolored 1.25 .30

Philexjeunes '94, Grenoble — A1283

**1994, Apr. 22** **Photo.**
**2418** A1283 2.80fr multicolored 1.25 .30

Europa A1284

Discoveries: 2.80fr, AIDS virus, by scientists of Pasteur Institute. 3.70fr, Formula for wave properties of matter, developed by Louis de Brogile.

**1994, Apr. 30** **Photo. & Engr.**
**2419** A1284 2.80fr multicolored 1.25 .30
*a.* With label 1.25 .75
**2420** A1284 3.70fr multicolored 1.75 85

No. 2419a issued Dec. 1, 1994.

Opening of Channel Tunnel — A1285

Designs: Nos. 2421, 2423, British lion, French rooster, meeting over Channel. Nos. 2422, 2424, Joined hands above speeding train.

**1994, May 3** **Photo.** ***Perf. 13***
**2421** A1285 2.80fr dk blue & multi 1.25 .30
**2422** A1285 2.80fr dk blue & multi 1.25 .30
*a.* Pair, #2421-2422 2.75 1.50
**2423** A1285 4.30fr lt blue & multi 2.00 .90
**2424** A1285 4.30fr multicolored 2.00 .90
*a.* Pair, #2423-2424 4.50 2.25
*Nos. 2421-2424 (4)* 6.50 2.40

See Great Britain Nos. 1558-1561.

Asian Development Bank, Board of Governors Meeting, Nice — A1286

**1994, May 3** **Photo.** ***Perf. 13***
**2425** A1286 2.80fr multicolored 1.25 .30

Federation of French Philatelic Societies, 67th Congress, Martigues A1287

**1994, May 20** **Engr.** ***Perf. 12x12½***
**2426** A1287 2.80fr multicolored 1.25 .30

Court of Cassation A1288

**Litho. & Engr.**

**1994, June 3** ***Perf. 13***
**2427** A1288 2.80fr multicolored 1.25 .30

D-Day, 50th Anniv. A1289

No. 2429, Tank, crowd waving Allied flags.

**1994, June 4** **Engr.**
**2428** A1289 4.30fr multicolored 2.00 .50
**2429** A1289 4.30fr multicolored 2.00 .50

Liberation of Paris, 50th anniv. (No. 2429).

Mount St. Victoire, by Paul Cezanne (1839-1906) — A1290

**1994, June 18** **Photo.** ***Perf. 13***
**2430** A1290 2.80fr multicolored 1.25 .30

Intl. Olympic Committee, Cent. A1291

**1994, June 23** **Litho.** ***Perf. 13***
**2431** A1291 2.80fr multicolored 1.25 .25

Saulx River Bridge, Rupt aux Nonains A1292

**1994, July 2** **Engr.**
**2432** A1292 2.80fr blackish blue 1.25 .25

Organ, Poitiers Cathedral — A1293

**1994, July 2** ***Perf. 13x12½***
**2433** A1293 4.40fr multicolored 2.00 .55

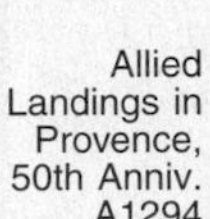

Allied Landings in Provence, 50th Anniv. A1294

**1994, Aug. 13** **Engr.** ***Perf. 13***
**2434** A1294 2.80fr multicolored 1.25 .30

Moses and the Daughters of Jethro, by Nicolas Poussin (1594-1665) — A1295

**1994, Sept. 10**
**2435** A1295 4.40fr yel brn & blk 1.90 .90

Natl. Conservatory of Arts and Crafts, Bicent. — A1296

**1994, Sept. 24** ***Perf. 13x12½***
**2436** A1296 2.80fr Foucault's pendulum 1.25 .25

The Great Cascade, St. Cloud Park — A1297

**1994, Sept. 24** ***Perf. 12½x13***
**2437** A1297 3.70fr multicolored 1.75 .60

Leaves — A1298

**1994** **Litho.** ***Perf. 13***
**2438** A1298 1.91fr Oak .85 .40
**2439** A1298 2.46fr Sycamore 1.10 .70
**2440** A1298 4.24fr Chestnut 2.00 1.00
**2441** A1298 6.51fr Holly 3.00 1.75
*Nos. 2438-2441 (4)* 6.95 3.85

Nos. 2438-2441 are known only precanceled. See second note after No. 132.

See Nos. 2517-2520.

Ecole Normale Superieure (Teachers' School), Bicent. — A1299

**1994, Oct. 8** **Engr.** ***Perf. 13***
**2442** A1299 2.80fr red & dk bl 1.25 .25

Georges Simenon (1903-89), Writer A1300

**Litho. & Engr.**
**1994, Oct. 15** ***Perf. 13***
**2443** A1300 2.80fr multicolored 1.25 .25

See Belgium No. 1567, Switzerland No. 948.

Souvenir Sheet

European Stamp Exhibition — A1301

a, Flowers in park, Paris. b, Dalhias, vert.

**1994, Oct. 15** **Photo.** ***Perf. 13***
**2444** A1301 2.80fr Sheet of 2, #a.-b. 10.00 9.00

No. 2444 sold for 16fr.

Natl. Drug Addiction Prevention Day — A1302

**1994, Oct. 15**
**2445** A1302 2.80fr multicolored 1.25 .25

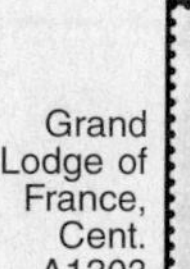

Grand Lodge of France, Cent. A1303

**1994, Nov. 5** **Engr.**
**2446** A1303 2.80fr multicolored 1.25 .25

Alain Colas (1943-78), Sailor A1304

**1994, Nov. 19**
**2447** A1304 3.70fr green & black 1.60 .60

French Natl. Press Federation, 50th Anniv. A1305

**1994, Dec. 9** **Photo.** ***Perf. 13***
**2448** A1305 2.80fr multicolored 1.25 .30

Champs Elysees — A1306

**1994, Dec. 31**
**2449** A1306 4.40fr multicolored 2.00 .75

No. 2449 printed with se-tenant label.

Souvenir Sheet

Motion Pictures, Cent. — A1307

Faces on screen and: a, Projector at right. b, Projector facing away from screen. c, Projector facing screen. d, Reels of film.

**1995, Jan. 14** **Photo.** ***Perf. 13***
**2450** A1307 Sheet of 4 5.00 5.00
*a.-d.* 2.80fr any single 1.00 1.00

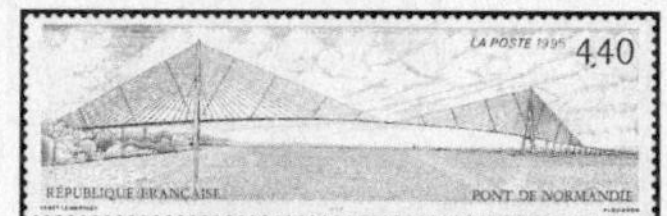


Normandy Bridge — A1308

**1995, Jan. 20** **Engr.** ***Perf. 13***
**2451** A1308 4.40fr multicolored 2.00 .75

European Notaries Public — A1309

**1995, Jan. 21** ***Perf. 13x12***
**2452** A1309 2.80fr multicolored 1.25 .30

Louis Pasteur (1822-95) — A1310

**1995, Feb. 18** **Photo.** ***Perf. 13***
**2453** A1310 3.70fr multicolored 1.60 1.00

**Art Series**

St. Taurin's Reliquary, Evreaux A1311

Study for the Dream of Happiness, by Pierre Prud'hon (1758-1823) — A1312

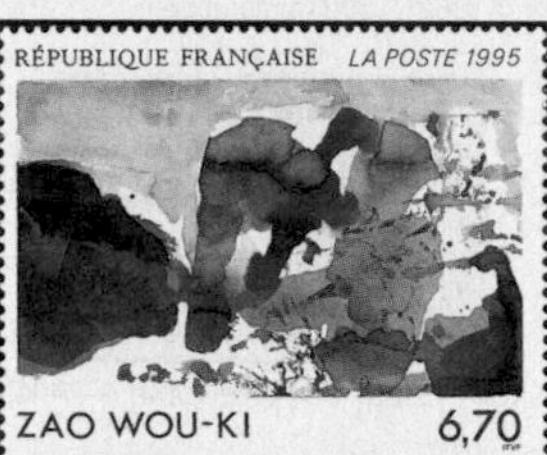


Abstract, by Zao Wou-ki — A1313

Abstract, by Per Kirkeby, Denmark — A1314

**1995** **Photo. & Engr.** ***Perf. 12x13***
**2454** A1311 6.70fr multicolored 3.00 1.10

**Engr.**
***Perf. 13x12***
**2455** A1312 6.70fr slate & blue 3.00 1.10

**Litho.**
***Perf. 14***
**2456** A1313 6.70fr multicolored 3.00 1.10

**Photo.**
***Perf. 13***
**2457** A1314 6.70fr multicolored 3.00 1.10
*Nos. 2454-2457 (4)* 12.00 4.40

Issued: No. 2454, 2/25; No. 2455, 5/12; No. 2456, 6/10; No. 2457, 9/23.

**Tourism Series**

Stenay Malt Works A1315

Remiremont, Vosges — A1316

Nyons Bridge, Drome A1317

Barbizon, Home of Landscape Artists A1318

**1995** **Engr.** ***Perf. 13x12½***
**2458** A1315 2.80fr ol & dk grn 1.25 .30
**2459** A1316 2.80fr brn, grn & bl 1.25 .30

***Perf. 12½x13***
**2460** A1317 4.40fr multicolored 2.00 .75

**Photo.**
***Perf. 13½***
**2461** A1318 4.40fr multicolored 2.00 .75
*Nos. 2458-2461 (4)* 6.50 2.10

Issued: No. 2458, 2/25; No. 2459, 5/13; No. 2460, 5/20; No. 2461, 9/30.

A1319

John J. Audubon (1785-1851) A1320

Designs: No. 2462, Snowy egret. No. 2463, Band-tailed pigeon. 4.30fr, Common tern. 4.40fr, Brown-colored rough-legged buzzard.

**1995, Feb. 25** **Photo.** ***Perf. 12½x12***
**2462** A1319 2.80fr multicolored 1.25 .40
**2463** A1320 2.80fr multicolored 1.25 .40
**2464** A1319 4.30fr multicolored 2.00 .75
**2465** A1320 4.40fr multicolored 2.00 .75
*a.* Souvenir sheet of 4, #2462-2465, perf. 13 7.00 7.00
*Nos. 2462-2465 (4)* 6.50 2.30

Stamp Day A1321

**1995, Mar. 4** **Engr.** ***Perf. 13***
**2466** A1321 2.80fr multicolored 2.00 1.00
**2467** A1321 2.80fr +60c multi 1.50 1.25
*a.* Booklet pane, 4 #2466, 3 #2467+label 15.00
Complete booklet, #2467 16.00

No. 2466 issued only in booklets.

Work Councils, 50th Anniv. — A1322

**1995, Mar. 7 Engr. *Perf. 13***
**2468** A1322 2.80fr dk bl, brn & sky bl 1.25 .30

Advanced Institute of Electricity, Cent. A1323

**1995, Mar. 11 Photo.**
**2469** A1323 3.70fr multicolored 1.75 .60

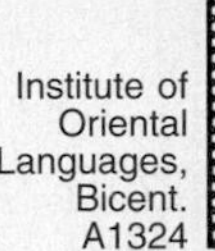

Institute of Oriental Languages, Bicent. A1324

**1995, Mar. 25 Photo. *Perf. 13***
**2470** A1324 2.80fr multicolored 1.25 .30

Jean Giono (1895-1970), Writer — A1325

**1995, Mar. 25 Engr.**
**2471** A1325 3.70fr multicolored 1.75 .60

Iron and Steel Industry in Lorraine — A1326

**1995, Apr. 1 *Perf. 13x12***
**2472** A1326 2.80fr multicolored 1.25 .30

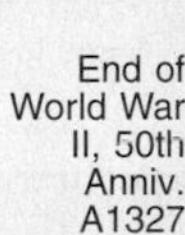

End of World War II, 50th Anniv. A1327

Europa: 2.80fr, Barbed wire, laurel wreath. 3.70fr, Broken sword, emblem of European Union.

**1995, Apr. 29 Photo. *Perf. 13***
**2473** A1327 2.80fr multicolored 1.25 .40
**2474** A1327 3.70fr multicolored 1.75 1.00

Forestry Profession, Ardennes — A1328

**1995, May 2 Engr. *Perf. 12½x13***
**2475** A1328 4.40fr multicolored 2.00 .60

End of World War II, 50th Anniv. A1329

**1995, May 8 Photo. *Perf. 13***
**2476** A1329 2.80fr multicolored 1.25 .30

Natl. Assembly — A1330

**1995, May 13 Photo. *Perf. 13x12½***
**2477** A1330 2.80fr multicolored 1.25 .60

French's People's Relief Assoc., 50th Anniv. A1331

**1995, May 20 Engr. *Perf. 12½x13***
**2478** A1331 2.80fr multicolored 1.25 .30

Scenes of France — A1332

No. 2479, Forest, Vosges. No. 2480, Massif, Brittany. No. 2481, Wetlands, cattle, Camargue. No. 2482, Volcanoes, Auvergne.

**1995, May 27 *Perf. 13***
**2479** A1332 2.40fr green 1.10 .25
**2480** A1332 2.40fr green 1.10 .25
**2481** A1332 2.80fr red 1.25 .30
**2482** A1332 2.80fr red 1.25 .30
*Nos. 2479-2482 (4)* 4.70 1.10

Ariane Rocket on Launch Pad, French Guiana — A1333

**1995, March 28 Engr. *Perf. 12½x13***
**2483** A1333 2.80fr bl, grn & red 1.25 .30

Compare with No. 2254.

A1334

**1995, June 2 Engr. *Perf. 13***
**2484** A1334 2.80fr multicolored 1.25 .30

68th Congress of French Federation of Philatelic Organizations, Orleans.

Town of Correze — A1335

**1995, June 3**
**2485** A1335 4.40fr multi 2.00 .60

A1336

Fables of Jean de la Fontaine (1621-95): No. 2486, The Grasshopper and The Ant. No. 2487, The Frog Who Could Make Himself Larger than an Ox. No. 2488, The Wolf and the Lamb. No. 2489, The Crow and the Fox. No. 2490, The Cat, the Weasel, and the Small Rabbit. No. 2491, The Tortoise and the Hare.

**1995, June 24 Photo. *Perf. 13***
**2486** A1336 2.80fr multicolored 1.40 .50
**2487** A1336 2.80fr multicolored 1.40 .50
**2488** A1336 2.80fr multicolored 1.40 .50
**2489** A1336 2.80fr multicolored 1.40 .50
**2490** A1336 2.80fr multicolored 1.40 .50
**2491** A1336 2.80fr multicolored 1.40 .50
*a.* Strip, #2486-2491 + 2 labels 9.00 8.00

Velodrome d'Hiver Raid — A1337

**1995, July 9 Photo. *Perf. 13***
**2492** A1337 2.80fr multicolored 1.25 .30

André Maginot (1877-1932), Creator of Maginot Line — A1338

**1995, Sept. 9 Engr. *Perf. 13***
**2493** A1338 2.80fr multicolored 1.25 .30

Women's Grand Masonic Lodge of France, 50th Anniv. — A1339

**1995, Sept. 16 *Perf. 13x12½***
**2494** A1339 2.80fr multicolored 1.25 .30

Hospital Pharmacies, 500th Anniv. — A1340

**1995, Sept. 23 *Perf. 12½x13***
**2495** A1340 2.80fr multicolored 1.25 .30

Natl. School of Administration, 50th Anniv. — A1341

**1995, Oct. 5 Photo. *Perf. 13***
**2496** A1341 2.80fr multicolored 1.25 .30

The Cradle, by Berthe Morisot (1841-95) A1342

**1995, Oct. 7 Litho. *Perf. 13½x14***
**2497** A1342 6.70fr multicolored 3.00 1.00

The French Institute, Bicent. — A1343

**1995, Oct. 14 Engr. *Perf. 12½x13***
**2498** A1343 2.80fr blk, grn & red 1.25 .30

Automobile Club of France, Cent. A1344

**1995, Nov. 4 Engr. *Perf. 13x12½***
**2499** A1344 4.40fr blk, bl & red 2.00 .60

UN, 50th Anniv. A1345

**1995, Nov. 16 Photo. *Perf. 13***
**2500** A1345 4.30fr multicolored 2.00 .60

Francis Jammes (1868-1938), Poet — A1346

**1995, Dec. 2** **Engr.** ***Perf. 13***
**2501** A1346 3.70fr black & blue 1.60 .60

A1347

**1995, Dec. 9** **Litho. & Engr.**
**2502** A1347 2.80fr Evry Cathedral 1.25 .30

A1348

**1995, Dec. 12** **Photo.** ***Perf. 13***
**2503** A1348 2.80fr multicolored 1.25 .30

1998 World Cup Soccer Championships, France.

**Art Series**

Abstract, by Lucien Wercollier — A1349

Design: No. 2505, The Netherlands (Horizon), abstract photograph, by Jan Dibbets.

**1996** ***Perf. 13x12½***
**2504** A1349 6.70fr multicolored 3.00 1.00
**2505** A1349 6.70fr multicolored 3.00 1.00

Issued: No. 2504, 1/20; No. 2505, 2/10.

Arawak Civilization, Saint Martin — A1350

Design: 2.80fr, Dog figurine, 550 B.C.

**1996, Feb. 10** **Engr.** ***Perf. 13***
**2506** A1350 2.80fr multicolored 1.25 .30

The Augustus Bridge over the Nera River, by Camille Corot (1796-1875) — A1351

**1996, Mar. 2** **Litho.** ***Perf. 13***
**2507** A1351 6.70fr multicolored 3.00 1.00

St. Patrick A1352

**1996, Mar. 16** **Photo.** ***Perf. 13***
**2508** A1352 2.80fr multicolored 1.25 .30

The Sower, 1903 — A1353

**1996, Mar. 16** **Litho. & Engr.**
**2509** A1353 2.80fr multicolored 2.00 1.50
**2510** A1353 2.80fr +60c multi 1.50 1.25
*a.* Booklet pane, 4 #2509, 3 #2510 + label 13.00
Complete booklet, #2510a 15.00

Stamp Day.

Jacques Rueff (1896-1978), Economist — A1354

**1996, Mar. 23** **Engr.** ***Perf. 13x12½***
**2511** A1354 2.80fr multicolored 1.25 .30

René Descartes (1596-1650) A1355

**1996, Mar. 30** **Engr.** ***Perf. 12½x13***
**2512** A1355 4.40fr red 2.00 .75

Gas & Electric Industries, 50th Anniv. A1356

**1996, Apr. 6** **Photo.** ***Perf. 13***
**2513** A1356 3fr multicolored 1.25 .30

Natl. Parks A1357

**1996, Apr. 20**
**2514** A1357 3fr Cévennes 1.25 .40
**2515** A1357 4.40fr Vanoise 2.00 .75
**2516** A1357 4.40fr Mercantour 2.00 .75
*Nos. 2514-2516 (3)* 5.25 1.90

See Nos. 2569-2572.

**Leaf Type of 1994**

**1996, Mar.** **Litho.** ***Perf. 13***
**2517** A1298 1.87fr Ash .85 .25
**2518** A1298 2.18fr Beech 1.00 .50
**2519** A1298 4.66fr Walnut 2.10 1.00
**2520** A1298 7.11fr Elm 3.00 1.75
*Nos. 2517-2520 (4)* 6.95 3.50

Nos. 2517-2520 are known only precanceled. Values for precanceled stamps in first column are for those which have not been through the post and have original gum. Values in second column are for postally used, gumless stamps.

Madame Marie de Sévigné (1626-96), Writer — A1358

**1996, Apr. 27** **Photo.** ***Perf. 13***
**2521** A1358 3fr multicolored 1.25 .40

Europa.

Natl. Institute of Agronomy Research, 50th Anniv. A1359

**1996, May 4** **Photo.** ***Perf. 13***
**2522** A1359 3.80fr multicolored 1.75 .60

Joan of Arc's House, Domremy-La-Pucelle — A1360

**1996, May 11**
**2523** A1360 4.50fr multicolored 2.10 .75

RAMOGE Agreement Between France, Italy, Monaco, 20th Anniv. A1361

**1996, May 14** **Photo. & Engr.**
**2524** A1361 3fr multicolored 1.25 .30

See Monaco No. 1998, Italy No. 2077.

69th Congress of Federation of Philatelic Assoc., Clermont-Ferrand — A1362

**1996, May 24** **Engr.** ***Perf. 13***
**2525** A1362 3fr brn, red & grn 1.25 .30

**Tourism Series**

Bitche, Moselle A1363

Iles Sanguinaires, Ajaccio, Southern Corsica — A1364

Thoronet Abbey, Var A1365

Chambéry Cathedral, Savoie A1366

**1996** **Engr.** ***Perf. 12½x13***
**2526** A1363 3fr multicolored 1.25 .30
**2527** A1364 3fr multicolored 1.25 .30

***Perf. 13x12½***
**2528** A1365 3.80fr brn & claret 1.75 .60

**Photo.**
***Perf. 13***
**2529** A1366 4.50fr multicolored 2.00 .75

Issued: No. 2526, 5/25; No. 2527, 6/1; 3.80fr, 7/6; 4.50fr, 6/8.

1998 World Cup Soccer Championships, France — A1367

Various stylized soccer plays, name of host city in France.

**1996, June 1** **Photo.** ***Perf. 13***
**2530** A1367 3fr Lens 1.25 .30
**2531** A1367 3fr Toulouse 1.25 .30
**2532** A1367 3fr Saint-Etienne 1.25 .30
**2533** A1367 3fr Montpellier 1.25 .30
*Nos. 2530-2533 (4)* 5.00 1.20

See Nos. 2584-2587, 2623-2624, sheet of 10, No. 2624a.

**Art Series**

Gallo-Roman Bronze Statue of Horse, Neuvy-en-Sullias, Loiret — A1368

Imprints of Cello Fragments, by Arman — A1369

**1996 Engr. *Perf. 13***
**2534** A1368 6.70fr multicolored 3.00 1.00

**Photo.**
**2535** A1369 6.70fr multicolored 3.00 1.00

Issued: No. 2534, 6/8; No. 2535, 9/21.

Modern Olympic Games, Cent. — A1371

**1996, June 15 Photo. *Perf. 13***
**2537** A1371 3fr multicolored 1.25 .30

A1372

**1996, June 15 Engr. *Perf. 12½x13***
**2538** A1372 4.40fr deep purple 2.00 .70

Jacques Marette (1922-84), Member of Parliament.

A1373

**1996, June 29 Photo. *Perf. 13***
**2539** A1373 3fr multicolored 1.25 .30

Train between Ajaccio and Vizzavona, cent.

A1374

**1996, Sept. 6 Engr. *Perf. 13x12½***
**2540** A1374 3fr dark blue & yel 1.25 .30

Notre Dame de Fourvière Basilica, Lyon, cent.

Baptism of Clovis, 1500th Anniv. A1375

**1996, Sept. 14 *Perf. 13***
**2541** A1375 3fr multicolored 1.25 .30

Henri IV High School, Bicent. — A1376

**1996, Oct. 12 Engr. *Perf. 12½x13***
**2542** A1376 4.50fr brown & blue 2.00 .80

UNICEF, 50th Anniv. A1377

**1996, Oct. 19 Photo. *Perf. 13***
**2543** A1377 4.50fr multicolored 2.00 .80

Economic and Social Council, 50th Anniv. — A1378

**1996, Oct. 26 Engr. *Perf. 13***
**2544** A1378 3fr red, black & blue 1.25 .30

UNESCO, 50th Anniv. A1379

**1996, Nov. 2 Litho. *Perf. 13***
**2545** A1379 3.80fr multicolored 1.75 .60

Autumn Stamp Show, 50th Anniv. — A1380

**1996, Nov. 7 Photo. *Perf. 13***
**2546** A1380 3fr multicolored 1.25 .30

A1381

**1996, Nov. 16**
**2547** A1381 3fr multicolored 1.25 .30

Creation of French Overseas Departments, 50th anniv.

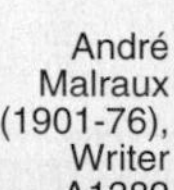

André Malraux (1901-76), Writer A1382

**1996, Nov. 23 Engr. *Perf. 13***
**2548** A1382 3fr deep green black 1.25 .30

French School in Athens, 150th Anniv. A1383

**1996, Nov. 23 Photo.**
**2549** A1383 3fr multicolored 1.25 .30

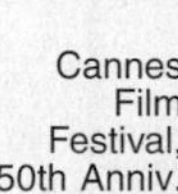

Cannes Film Festival, 50th Anniv. A1384

**1996, Nov. 30**
**2550** A1384 3fr multicolored 1.25 .30

New National Library of France A1385

**1996, Dec. 14**
**2551** A1385 3fr multicolored 1.25 .30

Francois Mitterrand (1916-96) — A1386

**1997, Jan. 4**
**2552** A1386 3fr multicolored 1.25 .30

Participatory Innovation A1387

**1997, Jan. 24 Photo. *Perf. 13***
**2553** A1387 3fr multicolored 1.25 .30

Georges Pompidou Natl. Center of Art and Culture, 20th Anniv. A1388

**1997, Jan. 31 Engr. *Perf. 12½x13***
**2554** A1388 3fr multicolored 1.25 .30

Happy Holiday A1389

**1997, Feb. 8 Photo. *Perf. 13***
**2555** A1389 3fr shown 1.25 .30
**2556** A1389 3fr Happy birthday 1.25 .30

Natl. School of Bridges and Highways, 250th Anniv. A1390

**Photo. & Engr.**

**1997, Feb. 14 *Perf. 12½x13***
**2557** A1390 3fr multicolored 1.25 .30

Saint-Laurent-du-Maroni, French Guiana — A1391

**Photo. & Engr.**

**1997, Feb. 22 *Perf. 12½x13***
**2558** A1391 3fr multicolored 1.25 .30

**Art Series**

Church Fresco, Tavant A1392

Painting by Bernard Moninot — A1393

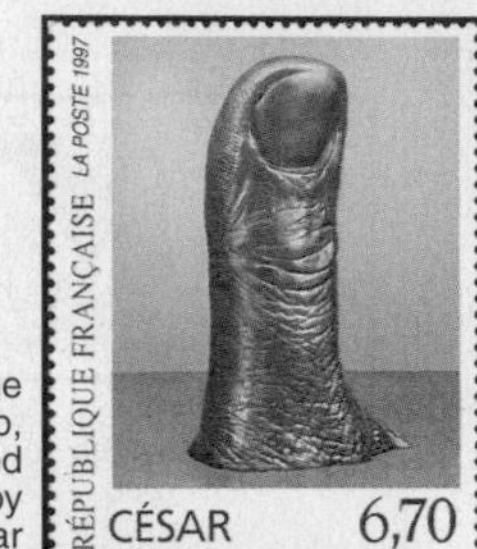


The Thumb, Polished Bronze, by César A1394

Grapes and Pomegranates, by Jean Baptiste Chardin — A1395

**1997 Engr. *Perf. 13***

| | | | | | |
|---|---|---|---|---|---|
| **2559** | A1392 | 6.70fr | multicolored | 3.00 | 1.00 |

**Photo.**

| | | | | | |
|---|---|---|---|---|---|
| **2560** | A1393 | 6.70fr | multicolored | 3.00 | 1.00 |
| **2561** | A1394 | 6.70fr | multicolored | 3.00 | 1.00 |
| **2562** | A1395 | 6.70fr | multicolored | 3.00 | 1.00 |
| | *Nos. 2559-2562 (4)* | | | 12.00 | 4.00 |

Issued: No. 2559, 3/1; No. 2560, 3/29; No. 2561, 9/13; No. 2562, 9/27.

**Tourism Series**

Millau — A1396

Guimiliau Church Close — A1398

Fresco, Saint Eutrope des Salles-Lavauguyon — A1397

Sablé-Sur-Sarthe — A1399

**1997 Engr. *Perf. 12½x13***

| | | | | | |
|---|---|---|---|---|---|
| **2563** | A1396 | 3fr | grn & dk bl grn | 1.25 | .30 |

***Perf. 13***

| | | | | | |
|---|---|---|---|---|---|
| **2564** | A1397 | 4.50fr | multicolored | 2.10 | .75 |
| **2565** | A1398 | 3fr | multicolored | 1.25 | .30 |

***Perf. 12½x13***

| | | | | | |
|---|---|---|---|---|---|
| **2566** | A1399 | 3fr | multicolored | 1.25 | .30 |
| | *Nos. 2563-2566 (4)* | | | 5.85 | 1.65 |

Issued: No. 2563, 3/15; No. 2564, 6/14; No. 2565, 7/12; No. 2566, 9/20.

Vignette of Type A17 — A1400

**Litho. & Engr.**

**1997, Mar. 15 *Perf. 13½x13***

| | | | | | |
|---|---|---|---|---|---|
| **2567** | A1400 | 3fr | multicolored | 2.50 | 1.50 |
| **2568** | A1400 | 3fr | +60c multi | 1.50 | 1.25 |
| *a.* | Booklet pane, 4 #2567, 3 #2568 + label | | | 15.00 | |
| | Complete booklet, #2568a | | | 16.00 | |

Stamp Day.

No. 2567 issued only in booklets.

**National Parks Type of 1996**

No. 2569, Parc des Ecrins. No. 2570, Guadeloupe Park. No. 2571, Parc des Pyrénées. No. 2572, Port-Cros Park.

**1997, Apr. 12 Photo. *Perf. 13***

| | | | | | |
|---|---|---|---|---|---|
| **2569** | A1357 | 3fr | multi | 1.25 | .40 |
| **2570** | A1357 | 3fr | multi | 1.25 | .40 |
| **2571** | A1357 | 4.50fr | multi | 2.00 | .70 |
| **2572** | A1357 | 4.50fr | multi | 2.00 | .70 |
| | *Nos. 2569-2572 (4)* | | | 6.50 | 2.20 |

Puss-in-Boots A1401

**1997, Apr. 26 Engr. *Perf. 13***

| | | | | | |
|---|---|---|---|---|---|
| **2573** | A1401 | 3fr | blue | 1.25 | .30 |

Europa.

Philexjeunes '97, Nantes — A1402

**1997, May 2 Litho. *Perf. 13***

| | | | | | |
|---|---|---|---|---|---|
| **2574** | A1402 | 3fr | multicolored | 1.25 | .30 |

Cartoon Journey of a Letter A1403

"Envelope": No. 2575, Writing letter. No. 2576, Climbing ladder to go into letter box. No. 2577, On wheels. No. 2578, Following postman carrying another "Envelope." No. 2579, Held by girl. No. 2580, At feet of girl reading long letter.

**1997, May 8 Photo. *Perf. 13***

| | | | | | |
|---|---|---|---|---|---|
| **2575** | A1403 | 3fr | multicolored | 1.25 | 1.00 |
| **2576** | A1403 | 3fr | multicolored | 1.25 | 1.00 |
| **2577** | A1403 | 3fr | multicolored | 1.25 | 1.00 |
| **2578** | A1403 | 3fr | multicolored | 1.25 | 1.00 |
| **2579** | A1403 | 3fr | multicolored | 1.25 | 1.00 |
| **2580** | A1403 | 3fr | multicolored | 1.25 | 1.00 |
| *a.* | Strip of 6, #2575-2580 + label | | | 8.00 | 8.00 |

**Self-Adhesive**

***Serpentine Die Cut 11***

| | | | | | |
|---|---|---|---|---|---|
| **2580B** | A1403 | 3fr | like #2575 | 1.25 | 1.00 |
| **2580C** | A1403 | 3fr | like #2576 | 1.25 | 1.00 |
| **2580D** | A1403 | 3fr | like #2577 | 1.25 | 1.00 |
| **2580E** | A1403 | 3fr | like #2578 | 1.25 | 1.00 |
| **2580F** | A1403 | 3fr | like #2579 | 1.25 | 1.00 |
| **2580G** | A1403 | 3fr | like #2580 | 1.25 | 1.00 |
| *h.* | Booklet pane, 2 each #2580B-2580G | | | 15.00 | 15.00 |

By its nature No. 2580h is a complete booklet. The peelable paper backing serves as a booklet cover.

See Nos. 2648-2659.

Honoring French Soldiers in North Africa (1952-62) A1404

**1997, May 10 Litho. *Perf. 13***

| | | | | | |
|---|---|---|---|---|---|
| **2581** | A1404 | 3fr | multicolored | 1.25 | .30 |

French Federation of Philatelic Associations, 70th Congress, Versailles — A1405

**1997, May 17 Photo. *Perf. 13***

| | | | | | |
|---|---|---|---|---|---|
| **2582** | A1405 | 3fr | multicolored | 1.25 | .40 |

Printed with se-tenant label.

Château de Plessis-Bourré, Maine and Loire Rivers — A1406

**1997, May 24 Litho. & Engr.**

| | | | | | |
|---|---|---|---|---|---|
| **2583** | A1406 | 4.40fr | multicolored | 2.00 | 1.25 |

**1998 World Cup Soccer Championships Type**

Stylized action scenes, name of host city in France.

**1997, May 31 Photo. *Perf. 13½***

| | | | | | |
|---|---|---|---|---|---|
| **2584** | A1367 | 3fr | Lyon | 1.25 | .30 |
| **2585** | A1367 | 3fr | Marseilles | 1.25 | .30 |
| **2586** | A1367 | 3fr | Nantes | 1.25 | .30 |
| **2587** | A1367 | 3fr | Paris | 1.25 | .30 |
| | *Nos. 2584-2587 (4)* | | | 5.00 | 1.20 |

Saint Martin of Tours (316-97) Apostle of the Gauls A1408

**1997, July 5 Engr. *Perf. 13***

| | | | | | |
|---|---|---|---|---|---|
| **2588** | A1408 | 4.50fr | multicolored | 2.00 | .75 |

Marianne — A1409

**1997, July 14 Engr. *Perf. 13***

| | | | | | |
|---|---|---|---|---|---|
| **2589** | A1409 | 10c | brown | .25 | .25 |
| **2590** | A1409 | 20c | brt blue grn | .25 | .25 |
| **2591** | A1409 | 50c | purple | .25 | .25 |
| **2592** | A1409 | 1fr | bright org | .45 | .25 |
| **2593** | A1409 | 2fr | bright blue | 1.00 | .30 |
| **2594** | A1409 | 2.70fr | bright grn | 1.25 | .25 |
| **2595** | A1409 | (3fr) | red | 1.90 | .25 |
| **2596** | A1409 | 3.50fr | apple grn | 1.60 | .25 |
| **2597** | A1409 | 3.80fr | blue | 1.75 | .25 |
| **2598** | A1409 | 4.20fr | dark org | 1.90 | .30 |
| **2599** | A1409 | 4.40fr | blue | 2.00 | .30 |
| **2600** | A1409 | 4.50fr | bright pink | 2.10 | .30 |
| **2601** | A1409 | 5fr | brt grn blue | 5.25 | .30 |

| | | | | | |
|---|---|---|---|---|---|
| **2602** | A1409 | 6.70fr | dark grn | 3.00 | .30 |
| *a.* | Souvenir sheet, #2594-2600, 2602 | | | 14.00 | 14.00 |
| **2603** | A1409 | 10fr | violet | 4.50 | .35 |
| *a.* | Souvenir sheet, #2589-2593, 2601, 2603 | | | 12.00 | 12.00 |
| | *Nos. 2589-2603 (15)* | | | 27.45 | 4.15 |

**Self-Adhesive**

**Booklet Stamps**

***Die Cut x Serpentine Die Cut 7***

| | | | | | |
|---|---|---|---|---|---|
| **2603B** | A1409 | 1fr | brt org | 2.25 | .50 |
| *c.* | Booklet pane, #2603B, 3 #2604 | | | 7.75 | |
| | Booklet, 2 #2603Bc | | | 16.00 | |
| **2604** | A1409 | (3fr) | red | 1.40 | .25 |
| *a.* | Booklet pane of 10 | | | 14.00 | |

**Coil Stamps**

***Perf. 13 Horiz.***

| | | | | | |
|---|---|---|---|---|---|
| **2604B** | A1409 | 2.70fr | bright grn | 1.25 | .50 |
| **2605** | A1409 | (3fr) | red | 1.75 | .25 |

Nos. 2595, 2604-2605 were valued at 3fr on day of issue.

Issued: Nos. 2602a, 2603a, 11/12/01. No. 2603B, 9/1/97.

See Nos. 2835-2835C, 2921-2922, 3530, 4410j, 4523.

1997 World Rowing Championships, Savoie — A1410

**1997, Aug. 30 Engr. *Perf. 13x12½***

| | | | | | |
|---|---|---|---|---|---|
| **2606** | A1410 | 3fr | blue & magenta | 1.25 | .30 |

Basque Corsairs A1411

**1997, Sept. 13 *Perf. 13***

| | | | | | |
|---|---|---|---|---|---|
| **2607** | A1411 | 3fr | multicolored | 1.25 | .30 |

Saint-Maurice Basilica, Epinal — A1412

**1997, Sept. 20 *Perf. 13x12½***

| | | | | | |
|---|---|---|---|---|---|
| **2608** | A1412 | 3fr | multicolored | 1.25 | .30 |

Fresh Fish Merchants, Port of Boulogne A1413

**1997, Sept. 26 *Perf. 13***

| | | | | | |
|---|---|---|---|---|---|
| **2609** | A1413 | 3fr | multicolored | 1.25 | .30 |

Japan Year — A1414

**1997, Oct. 4 Engr. *Perf. 13***

| | | | | | |
|---|---|---|---|---|---|
| **2610** | A1414 | 4.90fr | multicolored | 1.00 | 1.25 |

1997 World Judo Championships — A1415

**1997, Oct. 9 Photo. *Perf. 13***
**2611** A1415 3fr multicolored 1.25 .30

Sceaux Estate, Hauts-de-Seine — A1416

**1997, Oct. 11**
**2612** A1416 3fr multicolored 1.25 .30

Saar-Lorraine-Luxembourg Summit — A1417

**1997, Oct. 16 Photo. *Perf. 13***
**2613** A1417 3fr multicolored 1.25 .30

See Germany No. 1982, Luxembourg No. 972.

College of France A1418

**1997, Oct. 18 Engr.**
**2614** A1418 4.40fr multicolored 2.00 .70

Quality — A1419

**1997, Oct. 18 Photo.**
**2615** A1419 4.50fr multicolored 2.00 .80

A1420

Season's Greetings A1421

**1997 Photo. *Perf. 13***
**2616** A1420 3fr Cat & mouse 1.50 .30

**Photo. & Embossed**

**2617** A1421 3fr Mailman 1.25 .30

Issued: No. 2616, 11/8; No. 2617, 11/22.

Protection of Abused Children — A1422

**1997, Nov. 20 Photo.**
**2618** A1422 3fr multicolored 1.25 .30

Marshal Jacques Leclerc (Philippe de Haute Cloque) (1902-47) A1423

**1997, Nov. 28 Photo. *Perf. 13***
**2619** A1423 3fr multicolored 1.25 .30

Philexfrance '99, World Stamp Exposition — A1424

**1997, Dec. 6 Engr.**
**2620** A1424 3fr red & blue 1.25 .30

Abbey of Moutier D'Ahun, Creuse A1425

**1997, Dec. 13**
**2621** A1425 4.40fr multicolored 2.00 .70

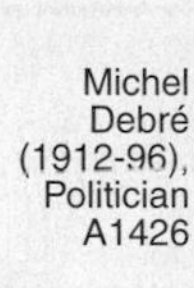

Michel Debré (1912-96), Politician A1426

**1998, Jan. 15 Photo.**
**2622** A1426 3fr multicolored 1.25 .30

**1998 World Cup Soccer Championships Type**

Stylized action scenes, name of host city in France.

**1998, Jan. 24 *Perf. 13½***
**2623** A1367 3fr Saint-Denis 1.25 .30
**2624** A1367 3fr Bordeaux 1.25 .30
*a.* Sheet of 10, #2530-2533, #2584-2587, #2623-2624 + label 14.00 14.00

National Assembly, Bicent. — A1427

**1998, Jan. 24 *Perf. 13***
**2625** A1427 3fr multicolored 1.25 .30

Valentine's Day A1428

**1998, Jan. 31**
**2626** A1428 3fr multicolored 1.25 .30

Office of Mediator of the Republic, 25th Anniv. A1429

**1998, Feb. 5**
**2627** A1429 3fr multicolored 1.25 .30

A1430

**1998, Feb. 28 Photo. *Perf. 12½***
**2628** A1430 3fr multicolored 1.25 .30

**Self-Adhesive**

***Serpentine Die Cut***

**2629** A1430 3fr like #2628 1.25 .30
*a.* Booklet pane of 10 14.00 14.00
*b.* Sheet of 1 + 7 labels 17.00 16.00

1998 World Cup Soccer Championships, France.

The peelable paper backing of No. 2629a serves as a booklet cover.

See No. 2665.

A1431

**1998, Feb. 21 Engr. *Perf. 13½x13***
**2630** A1431 3fr Detail of design A16 3.00 1.60
**2631** A1431 3fr +60c like #2630 1.50 1.40
*a.* Booklet pane, 4 #2630, 3 #2631 + label 14.00
Complete booklet, #2631a 15.00

Stamp Day. No. 2630 issued only in booklets.

A1432

**1998, Feb. 28 Engr. *Perf. 13***
**2632** A1432 4.50fr blue 2.00 .75

Father Franz Stock (1904-48), prison chaplain.

Happy Birthday A1433

**1998, Mar. 13 Photo. *Perf. 13x13½***
**2633** A1433 3fr multicolored 1.25 .30

Union of Mulhouse with France, Bicent. A1434

**1998, Mar. 14**
**2634** A1434 3fr multicolored 1.25 .30

Citeaux Abbey, 900th Anniv. A1435

**1998, Mar. 14 Engr. *Perf. 13***
**2635** A1435 3fr multicolored 1.25 .30

Sous-Préfecture Hotel, Saint-Pierre, Réunion — A1436

**1998, Apr. 4 Engr. *Perf. 13***
**2636** A1436 3fr multicolored 1.25 .30

Réunion's architectural heritage.

"The Return," by René Magritte — A1437

**1998, Apr. 18 Photo.**
**2637** A1437 3fr multicolored 1.40 .50

See Belgium No. 1691.

Edict of Nantes, 400th Anniv. A1438

**1998, Apr. 18 Litho.**
**2638** A1438 4.50fr Henry IV 2.00 .75

**Art Series**

Delacroix 1798-1863

6,70 La Poste 1998 RÉPUBLIQUE FRANÇAISE

Detail from "Entry of the Crusaders into Constantinople," by Delacroix (1798-1863) — A1439

Le Printemps, by Pablo Picasso (1881-1973) — A1440

Neuf Moules Malic, by Marcel Duchamp (1887-1968) — A1441

Vision After the Sermon, by Paul Gauguin (1848-1903) — A1442

**1998 Engr. *Perf. 12x13***

**2639** A1439 6.70fr multicolored 3.00 1.00

**Litho.**

***Perf. 13***

**2640** A1440 6.70fr multicolored 3.00 1.00

**Photo.**

**2641** A1441 6.70fr multicolored 3.00 1.00
**2642** A1442 6.70fr multicolored 3.00 1.00

Issued: No. 2639, 4/25; No. 2640, 5/15; No. 2641, 10/17; No. 2642, 12/5.

Abolition of Slavery, 150th Anniv. A1443

**1998, Apr. 25 Litho. *Perf. 13***

**2643** A1443 3fr multicolored 1.25 .30

**Tourism Series**

Le Gois Causeway, Island of Noirmoutier, Vendée — A1444

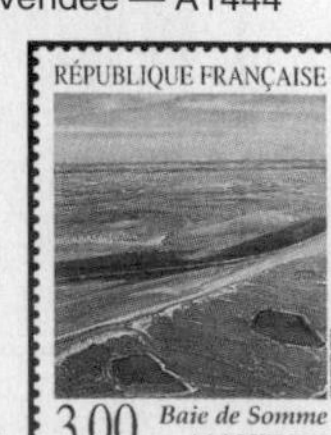

Bay of Somme, Picardy — A1445

Château de Crussol, Ardèche A1446

Collegiate Church of Mantes — A1447

**1998, May 2 Photo.**

**2644** A1444 3fr multicolored 1.25 .30
**2645** A1445 3fr multicolored 1.25 .30

**Engr.**

**2646** A1446 3fr multicolored 1.25 .30
**2647** A1447 4.40fr multicolored 2.00 .70
*Nos. 2644-2647 (4)* 5.75 1.60

Issued: No. 2644, 5/2; No. 2645, 6/27; No. 2646, 7/4; No. 2647, 9/19.

**Journey of a Letter Type**

Historic "letters:" No. 2648, Dove carrying letter, Noah's Ark. No. 2649, Egyptian writing letter on papyrus. No. 2650, Soldier running to Athens with letter to victory at Marathon. No. 2651, Knight carrying letter on horseback. No. 2652, Writing letters with quill and ink. No. 2653, Astronaut carrrying letter in space from earth to the moon.

**1998, May 9 Photo. *Perf. 13x13½***

**2648** A1403 3fr multicolored 1.25 1.00
**2649** A1403 3fr multicolored 1.25 1.00
**2650** A1403 3fr multicolored 1.25 1.00
**2651** A1403 3fr multicolored 1.25 1.00
**2652** A1403 3fr multicolored 1.25 1.00
**2653** A1403 3fr multicolored 1.25 1.00
*a.* Strip, #2648-2653 + label 8.00 6.50

**Booklet Stamps**

**Self-Adhesive**

***Serpentine Die Cut 11***

**2654** A1403 3fr like #2648 1.25 1.00
**2655** A1403 3fr like #2649 1.25 1.00
**2656** A1403 3fr like #2650 1.25 1.00
**2657** A1403 3fr like #2651 1.25 1.00
**2658** A1403 3fr like #2652 1.25 1.00
**2659** A1403 3fr like #2653 1.25 1.00
*a.* Bklt. pane, 2 ea #2654-2659 16.00 14.00

By its nature No. 2659a is a complete booklet. The peelable paper backing serves as a booklet cover.

League of Human Rights, Cent. — A1448

**1998, May 9 *Perf. 13***

**2660** A1448 4.40fr multicolored 2.00 .70

Henri Collet (1885-1951), Composer — A1449

**1998, May 15 Engr. *Perf. 12x13***

**2661** A1449 4.50fr black, gray & buff 2.00 .80

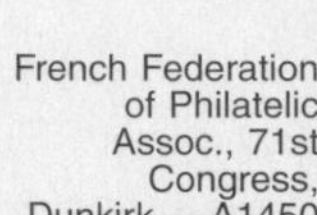

French Federation of Philatelic Assoc., 71st Congress, Dunkirk — A1450

**Photo. & Engr.**

**1998, May 29 *Perf. 13***

**2662** A1450 3fr multicolored 1.25 .30

Mont-Saint-Michel — A1451

**1998, June 6 Photo. *Perf. 13***

**2663** A1451 3fr multicolored 1.40 .30

Natl. Music Festival — A1452

**1998, June 13**

**2664** A1452 3fr multicolored 1.25 .50

Europa.

**1998 World Cup Soccer Championships Type with Added**

Inscription, "Champion du Monde"

**1998, July 12 Photo. *Perf. 12½***

**2665** A1430 3fr multicolored 1.25 .30

Stéphane Mallarmé (1842-98), Poet A1453

**Photo. & Engr.**

**1998, Sept. 5 *Perf. 13***

**2666** A1453 4.40fr multicolored 2.00 .70

Flowers — A1453a

1.87fr, Liseron. 2.18fr, Coquelicot. 4.66fr, Violette. 7.11fr, Bouton d'or.

**1998, Sept. 9 Litho. *Perf. 13***

**2666A** A1453a 1.87fr multi .85 .25
**2666B** A1453a 2.18fr multi 1.00 .50
**2666C** A1453a 4.66fr multi 2.10 1.00
**2666D** A1453a 7.11fr multi 3.00 1.75
*Nos. 2666A-2666D (4)* 6.95 3.50

Nos. 2666A-2666D are known only precanceled. See second note after No. 132.

Aéro Club of France, Cent. — A1454

**1998, Sept. 12 Photo.**

**2667** A1454 3fr multicolored 1.25 .30

A1455

"The Little Prince," by Antoine de Saint-Exupéry (1900-44): a, Standing in uniform with sword, horiz. b, Seated on wall. c, "The Little Prince on Asteroid B-612." d, Pouring water from sprinkling can. e, Walking along cliff, fox, horiz.

**1998, Oct. 23 Photo. *Perf. 13***

**2668** Strip of 5 + 2 labels 6.50 4.00
*a.-e.* A1455 3fr any single 1.25 .70
*f.* Souv. sheet, #2668a-2668e 8.00 8.00

Philexfrance '99. No. 2668f was released 9/12 and sold for 25fr.

Hall of Heavenly Peace, Imperial Palace, Beijing, China A1456

**1998, Sept. 12 Photo. *Perf. 13x13½***

**2669** A1456 3fr shown 1.25 .40
**2670** A1456 4.90fr The Louvre, France 2.40 1.25

See People's Republic of China Nos. 2895-2896.

Garnier Palace, Home of the Paris Opera — A1457

**1998, Sept. 19 Photo. *Perf. 13***

**2671** A1457 4.50fr multicolored 2.00 .70

Horses A1458

**1998, Sept. 27**

**2672** A1458 2.70fr Camargue 1.10 .30
**2673** A1458 3fr Pottok 1.25 .40
**2674** A1458 3fr French trotter 1.25 .40
**2675** A1458 4.50fr Ardennais 2.10 .80
*Nos. 2672-2675 (4)* 5.70 1.90

Paris Auto Show, Cent.
A1459

**1998, Oct. 1** ***Perf. 12***

**2676** A1459 3fr multicolored 1.25 .30

5th Republic, 40th Anniv.
A1460

**1998, Oct. 3** **Photo.** ***Perf. 13***

**2677** A1460 3fr blue, gray & red 1.25 .30

Saint-Dié, Capital of Vosges Mountain Region — A1461

**1998, Oct. 3** **Engr.** ***Perf. 13***

**2678** A1461 3fr Tower of Liberty 1.25 .30

End of World War I, 80th Anniv.
A1462

**1998, Oct. 17** **Photo.** ***Perf. 13x13½***

**2679** A1462 3fr multicolored 1.25 .30

Intl. Union for the Conservation of Nature and Natural Resources, 50th Anniv. — A1463

**1998, Nov. 3** **Litho.**

**2680** A1463 3fr multicolored 1.25 .40

New Year
A1464

Christmas
A1465

**1998, Nov. 7** **Photo.** ***Perf. 13***

**Background Colors**

**2681** A1464 3fr deep blue 1.60 .70
**2682** A1465 3fr green 1.60 .70
**2683** A1464 3fr yellow 1.60 .70
**2684** A1465 3fr red 1.60 .70
**2685** A1464 3fr green 1.60 .70
*a.* Strip of 5, #2681-2685 6.50 3.50

Issued in sheets of 10 stamps. Location of "Bonne Annee" and "Meilleurs Voeux" varies.

Doctors Without Borders
A1466

**1998, Nov. 21** ***Perf. 13x13½***

**2686** A1466 3fr multicolored 1.25 .30

European Parliament, Strasbourg
A1467

**1998, Dec. 5** **Photo.** ***Perf. 13***

**2687** A1467 3fr multicolored 1.25 .30

Universal Declaration of Human Rights, 50th Anniv.
A1468

No. 2688, Faces of people of various races, globe. No. 2689, René Cassin (1887-1976), principal author of Declaration, Eleanor Roosevelt (1884-1962), Chaillot Palace, Paris.

**1998, Dec. 10** **Litho.** ***Perf. 13***

**2688** A1468 3fr multicolored 1.25 .40
**2689** A1468 3fr multicolored 1.25 .40

Discovery of Radium, Cent., ZOE Reactor, 50th Anniv.
A1469

**1998, Dec. 15** **Photo.** ***Perf. 13***

**2690** A1469 3fr multicolored 1.25 .30

Introduction of the Euro — A1470

**1999** **Engr.** ***Perf. 13***

**2691** A1470 3fr red & blue 1.25 .25

**Booklet Stamps**

**Self-Adhesive**

***Die Cut x Serpentine Die Cut 7***

**2691A** A1470 3fr red & blue 1.25 .25
*b.* Booklet pane of 10 12.50

Issued: No. 2691, 1/1/99. No. 2691A, 2/15/99. Values are shown in both Francs and Euros on Nos. 2691-2691A. No. 2691Ab is a complete booklet.

Euro currency did not circulate until 2002.

French Postage Stamps, 150th Anniv.
A1471

**1999, Jan. 1** **Photo.** ***Perf. 13***

**Booklet Stamps**

**2692** A1471 3fr black & red 7.00 6.00
**2693** A1471 3fr red & black 1.25 1.00
*a.* Booklet pane, #2692, 4 #2693 + label 13.00
Complete booklet, #2693a 14.00

No. 2692 has black denomination; No. 2693 has red denomination.

Stamp Day.

Public Assistance Hospital, Paris, 150th Anniv.
A1472

**1999, Jan. 9**

**2694** A1472 3fr multicolored 1.25 .30

Diplomatic Relations with Israel, 50th Anniv. — A1473

**1999, Jan. 24**

**2695** A1473 4.40fr multicolored 2.00 .75

Festival Stamps
A1474

**1999, Feb. 6** **Photo.** ***Perf. 13***

**2696** A1474 3fr Stars, "Je t'aime" 1.25 .30
**2697** A1474 3fr Rose 1.25 .30

**Booklet Stamps**

**Self-Adhesive**

***Die Cut Perf. 10***

**2698** A1474 3fr like #2696 1.25 .30
**2699** A1474 3fr like #2697 1.25 .30
*a.* Bklt. pane, 5 ea #2698-2699 14.00

No. 2699a is a complete booklet.

**Art Series**

St. Luke the Evangelist, Sculpture by Jean Goujon (1510-66)
A1475

Painting, "Waterlillies in Moonlight," by Claude Monet (1840-1926) — A1476

Stained Glass, Cathedral of Auch, by Arnauld de Moles, 16th Cent.
A1477

Charles I, King of England, by Sir Anthony Van Dyck
A1478

**1999** **Engr.** ***Perf. 13***

**2700** A1475 6.70fr multicolored 3.00 1.00

**Litho.**

**2701** A1476 6.70fr multicolored 3.00 1.00

**Engr.**

**2702** A1477 6.70fr multicolored 3.00 1.00

**Photo.**

***Perf. 13¼x13***

**2703** A1478 6.70fr multicolored 3.00 1.00
*Nos. 2700-2703 (4)* 12.00 4.00

Issued: No. 2700, 2/13; No. 2701, 5/29; No. 2702, 6/19; No. 2703, 11/11.

National Census — A1479

**1999, Feb. 20** **Photo.** ***Perf. 13½***

**2704** A1479 3fr multicolored 1.25 .30

Cultural Heritage of Lebanon
A1480

Mosaic illustrating transformation of Zeus into bull, Natl. Museum of Beirut.

**1999, Feb. 27** ***Perf. 12½***

**2705** A1480 4.40fr multicolored 2.00 .70

Asterix, by Albert Uderzo and Rene Goscinny
A1481

**1999, Mar. 6** **Photo.** ***Perf. 13¼***

**2706** A1481 3fr multicolored 1.25 .30
*a.* Perf. 13¼x12¾ 1.40 1.20

**Booklet Stamp**

*Perf. 13¼x12¾*

2707 A1481 3fr +60c like #2706 3.00 1.50
b. Booklet pane, 4 #2706a, 3 #2707 + label 14.00
Complete booklet, #2707b 15.00

**Souvenir Sheet**

2707A A1481 3fr +60c like #2706 2.50 2.00

Stamp Day. Stamp design in No. 2707A continues into the margins.

Council of Europe, 50th Anniv. A1482

**1999, Mar. 19**

2708 A1482 3fr multicolored 1.25 .30

A1483

Announcements — A1483a

No. 2709, Marriage (Oui). No. 2710, It's a boy (C'est un garcon). No. 2711, It's a girl (C'est une fille). No. 2712, Thank you.

**1999, Mar. 20** *Perf. 13*

2709 A1483 3fr multi 1.25 .30
2710 A1483 3fr multi 1.25 .30
2711 A1483 3fr multi 1.25 .30
2712 A1483a 3fr multi 1.25 .30
*Nos. 2709-2712 (4)* 5.00 1.20

See Nos. 2721-2722.

Souvenir Sheet

PhilexFrance '99 — A1484

Works of art: a, Venus de Milo. b, Mona Lisa, by Da Vinci. c, Liberty Guiding the People, by Delacroix.

**Litho. & Engr.**

**1999, Mar. 26** *Perf. 13¼*

2713 A1484 Sheet of 3 80.00 60.00
a.-b. 5fr each 17.50 12.50
c. 10fr multicolored 37.50 30.00

No. 2713 sold for 50fr, with 30fr serving as a donation to the Assoc. for the Development of Philately.

Elections to the European Parliament A1485

**1999, Mar. 27 Photo.** *Perf. 13*

2714 A1485 3fr multicolored 1.25 .30

Richard I, the Lion-Hearted (1157-1199), King of England — A1486

**1999, Apr. 10 Engr.** *Perf. 13x12½*

2715 A1486 3fr multicolored 1.25 .35

**Tourism Series**

Dieppe A1487

Haut-Koenigsbourg Castle, Bas-Rhin — A1488

Birthpalce of Champollion, Figeac — A1489

Chateau, Arnac-Pompadour — A1490

**1999 Engr.** *Perf. 13½*

2716 A1487 3fr multicolored 1.25 .30

**Litho. & Engr.**

*Perf. 13*

2717 A1488 3fr multicolored 1.40 .50
2718 A1489 3fr multicolored 1.25 .30

**Engr.**

2719 A1490 3fr multicolored 1.25 .30
*Nos. 2716-2719 (4)* 5.15 1.40

Issued: No. 2716, 4/17; No. 2717, 5/15; No. 2718, 6/26; No. 2719, 7/10.

The Camargue Nature Preserve A1491

**1999, Apr. 24 Photo.** *Perf. 13x13½*

2720 A1491 3fr multicolored 1.25 .30

Europa.

**Announcements Type of 1999 and**

A1492

No. 2721, Nice Holiday (bonnes vacances). No. 2722, Happy Birthday (joyeux anniversaire). No. 2723, Long Live Vacations (Vive les vacances).

**1999, May 13 Photo.** *Perf. 13*

2721 A1483 3fr multi 1.25 .30
2722 A1483 3fr multi 1.25 .30
2723 A1492 3fr multi 1.25 .30
*Nos. 2721-2723 (3)* 3.75 .90

Saint Pierre, Martinique A1493

**1999, May 15**

2724 A1493 3fr multicolored 1.25 .30

Detail of "Noctuelles" Dish, by Émile Gallé, School of Nancy Museum A1494

**1999, May 22**

2725 A1494 3fr multicolored 1.25 .30

Souvenir Sheet

World Old Roses Competition, Lyon — A1495

a, 4.50fr, Mme. Caroline Testout. b, 3fr, Mme. Alfred Carrière. c, 4.50fr, La France.

**1999, May 28** *Perf. 13½x13*

2726 A1495 Sheet of 3, #a.-c. 5.50 4.50

Court of Saint-Emilion, 800th Anniv. — A1496

**1999, May 29 Engr.** *Perf. 13¼x13*

2727 A1496 3.80fr multicolored 1.75 .60

Hotel de la Monnaie, French Mint Headquarters — A1497

**1999, June 5 Engr.** *Perf. 13*

2728 A1497 4.50fr brn org & bl 2.00 .75

A1498

**1999, June 12 Photo.** *Perf. 13¼*

2729 A1498 3fr multicolored 1.25 .30

Countess of Segur (1799-1874), children's storyteller.

A1499

**1999, June 19** *Perf. 13*

2730 A1499 3fr Welcome 1.25 .30

René Caillié (1799-1838), Explorer of Africa — A1500

**1999, June 26 Engr.** *Perf. 13¼*

2731 A1500 4.50fr multicolored 2.00 .75

1st French Postage Stamps, 150th Anniv. A1501

**1999, July 2 Photo.** *Perf. 11¾x13*

2732 A1501 6.70fr multicolored 3.00 1.00

PhilexFrance '99, World Philatelic Exhibition.

No. 2732 was printed with a se-tenant label and contains a holographic image. Soaking in water may affect the hologram.

Celebrating the Year 2000 A1502

**1999, July 5 Photo.** *Perf. 13*

2733 A1502 3fr multicolored 1.25 .30

Year 2000 Stamp Design Contest Winner — A1503

**1999, July 6**

2734 A1503 3fr multicolored 1.25 .30

Total Solar Eclipse, Aug. 11, 1999 A1504

**1999, July 8** ***Perf. 12x12¼***

**2735** A1504 3fr multicolored 1.25 .30

Gathering of Tall Ships, Rouen, July 9-18 A1505

Sailing ships: a, Simón Bolivar. b, Iskra. c, Statsraad Lehmkuhl. d, Asgard II. e, Belle Poule. f, Belem. g, Amerigo Vespucci. h, Sagres. i, Europa. j, Cuauhtemoc.

**1999, July 10** **Photo.** ***Perf. 13***

**2736** 1fr Sheet of 10 6.50 6.50
*a.-j.* A1505 any single .60 .50

1999 Rugby World Cup, Cardiff, Wales A1506

**1999, Sept. 11** **Photo.** ***Perf. 13¼***

**2737** A1506 3fr multicolored 1.25 .40
*a.* Miniature sheet of 10 12.50

Value is for copy with surrounding selvage.

One stamp in No. 2737a has a missing "F" in the printer's mark.

Frédéric Ozanam (1813-53), Historian — A1507

**1999, Sept. 11** **Engr.** ***Perf. 13***

**2738** A1507 4.50fr multicolored 2.00 .75

Emmaus Movement, 50th Anniv. A1508

**1999, Sept. 26** **Photo.** ***Perf. 13***

**2739** A1508 3fr multicolored 1.25 .30

Cats and Dogs — A1509

**1999, Oct. 2** **Photo.** ***Perf. 13¼***

**2740** A1509 2.70fr Chartreux cat 1.25 .30
**2741** A1509 3fr European cat 1.25 .30
**2742** A1509 3fr Pyrenean Mountain dog 1.25 .30
**2743** A1509 4.50fr Brittany spaniel 2.00 .75
*Nos. 2740-2743 (4)* 5.75 1.65

Frédéric Chopin (1810-49), Composer A1510

**1999, Oct. 17** **Engr.** ***Perf. 13¼***

**2744** A1510 3.80fr multicolored 1.75 .75

See Poland No. 3484.

A1511

Best Wishes for Year 2000 A1512

**1999, Nov. 20** **Photo.** ***Perf. 13x13¼***

**2745** A1511 3fr multi 1.25 .30
**2746** A1512 3fr multi 1.25 .30

No. 2746 was printed with se-tenant label.

Paris Metro, Cent. A1513

**1999, Dec. 4** **Photo.** ***Perf. 13***

**2747** A1513 3fr multi 1.25 .30

Council of State, Bicent. — A1514

**1999, Dec. 11**

**2748** A1514 3fr multi 1.25 .30

Reconstruction of Lighthouses — A1515

**2000, Jan. 1** **Photo.** ***Perf. 13x12¾***

**2749** A1515 3fr multi 1.25 .30

Reconstruction of San Juan de Salvamento Lighthouse, Argentina and replication of its design at La Rochelle, France.

Hearts A1516

**2000, Jan. 8** **Photo.** ***Perf. 13***

**2750** A1516 3fr Snakes 1.25 .30
**2751** A1516 3fr Face 1.25 .30
*a.* Souvenir sheet, 3 #2750, 2 #2751 8.00 6.50

### Self-Adhesive Booklet Stamps
### *Serpentine Die-Cut*

**2752** A1516 3fr Like #2750 1.25 .30
**2753** A1516 3fr Like #2751 1.25 .30
*a.* Bklt. pane, 5 ea #2752-2753 12.50

Values for Nos. 2750-2751 are for copies with surrounding selvage. No. 2753a is a complete booklet.

Bank of France, Bicent. — A1517

**2000, Jan. 15** **Litho.** ***Perf. 13***

**2754** A1517 3fr multi 1.25 .30

Prefectorial Corps, Bicent. — A1518

**2000, Feb. 17** **Photo.** ***Perf. 13x12¼***

**2755** A1518 3fr multi 1.25 .30

### Art Series

Venus and the Graces Offering Gifts to a Young Girl, by Sandro Botticelli (1445-1510) — A1519

The Waltz, by Camille Claudel A1520

Visage Rouge, by Gaston Chaissac A1521

Carolingian Mosaic, Germigny-des-Prés — A1522

**2000** **Photo.** ***Perf. 13¼x13***

**2756** A1519 6.70fr multi 3.00 1.00
**2757** A1520 6.70fr multi 3.00 1.00
**2758** A1521 6.70fr multi 3.00 1.00
**2759** A1522 6.70fr multi 3.00 1.00

Issued: No. 2756, 2/25; No. 2757, 4/8; No. 2758, 9/23; 10/21.

### Tourism Series

Carcassonne — A1523

Saint-Guilhem-Le-Désert — A1524

Gérardmer A1525

Abbey Church of Ottmarsheim — A1526

**2000** **Photo.** ***Perf. 13***

**2760** A1523 3fr multi 1.25 .30

**Engr.**
***Perf. 13¼***

**2761** A1524 3fr multi 1.25 .30
**2762** A1525 3fr multi 1.25 .30

***Perf. 12¼x13***

**2763** A1526 3fr multi 1.25 .30
*Nos. 2760-2763 (4)* 5.00 1.20

Issued: No. 2760, 3/3; No. 2761, 4/8; No. 2762, 4/17; No. 2763, 6/17.

Tintin — A1527

**2000, Mar. 11 Photo. *Perf. 13¼***

2764 A1527 3fr multi 1.25 .30
*a.* Perf. 13½x13 1.40 1.20

***Perf. 13½x13***

2765 A1527 3fr + 60c multi 2.50 2.00
*a.* Booklet pane, 4 #2764a, 3 #2765 + label 14.00
Complete booklet, #2765a 15.00
*b.* Souvenir sheet of 1 2.50 2.00

Stamp Day.

Bretagne Parliament Building Restoration — A1528

**2000, Mar. 25 Photo. *Perf. 13¼***

2766 A1528 3fr multi 1.25 .30

Madagascar Periwinkles — A1529

**2000, Mar. 25 Litho. *Perf. 13x13¼***

2767 A1529 4.50fr multi 2.00 .80

Felicitations A1530

**2000, Apr. 7 Photo. *Perf. 13x13¼***

2768 A1530 3fr multi 1.25 .30

The 20th Century — A1531

No. 2769: a, France as World Cup soccer champions, 1998, vert. b, Marcel Cerdan wins middleweight boxing title, 1948. c, Charles Lindbergh flies solo across Atlantic, 1927. d, Jean-Claude Killy wins three Winter Olympics gold medals, 1968, vert. e, Carl Lewis wins four Olympic gold medals, 1984, vert.

***Perf. 13¼x13 (vert. stamps), 13x13¼***

**2000, Apr. 15**

2769 A1531 Sheet, 2 ea #a-e 14.00 14.00
*a.-e.* 3fr any single 1.40 .75

Top part of No. 2769 contains Nos. 2769a-2769e and is separated from bottom part of sheet by a row of rouletting.

See No. 2787, 2804, 2837, 2881, 2915.

Automobiles — A1532

No. 2770: a, Bugatti 35. b, Citroen Traction. c, Renault 4CV. d, Simca Chambord. e, Hispano-Suiza K6. f, Volkswagen Beetle. g, 1962 Cadillac. h, Peugeot 203. i, Citroen DS19. j, Ferrari 250 GTO.

**2000, May 5 *Perf. 13¼x13***

2770 A1532 Sheet of 10, #a.-j. 7.50 7.50
*a.-e.* 1fr any single .45 .35
*f.-j.* 2fr any single .90 .60

**Europa, 2000**

Common Design Type

**2000, May 9 Photo. *Perf. 13¼***

2771 CD17 3fr multi 1.25 .40

Henry-Louis Duhamel du Monceau (1700-82), Agronomist — A1533

**2000, May 13 Engr. *Perf. 13***

2772 A1533 4.50fr multi 2.00 .80

French Federation of Philatelic Associations, 73rd Congress, Nevers — A1534

**2000, May 19 Engr. *Perf. 13¼***

2773 A1534 3fr multi 1.25 .30

Happy Vacation — A1535

**2000, June 1 Photo. *Perf. 13¼x13***

2774 A1535 3fr multi 1.25 .30

A1536

**2000, June 3 Engr. *Perf. 13x12¼***

2775 A1536 3fr multi 1.25 .30

First Ascent of Annapurna, 50th anniv.

Nature A1537

2.70fr, Agrias sardanapalus butterfly. No. 2777, Giraffe. No. 2778, Allosaurus. 4.50fr, Tulipa lutea.

**2000, June 17 Photo. *Perf. 13¼***

2776 A1537 2.70fr multi 1.25 .30
2777 A1537 3fr multi, vert. 1.25 .30
2778 A1537 3fr multi 1.25 .30
2779 A1537 4.50fr multi, vert 2.00 .75
*a.* Souvenir sheet, #2776-2779 6.00 6.00
*Nos. 2776-2779 (4)* 5.75 1.65

Antoine de Saint-Exupéry (1900-44), Aviator, Writer — A1538

**2000, June 24 Photo. *Perf. 13¼x13***

2780 A1538 3fr multi 1.25 .30

Yellow Train of Cerdagne, Cent. A1539

**2000, July 14 *Perf. 13x13¼***

2781 A1539 3fr multi 1.25 .30

Folklore A1540

**2000, Aug. 12 Photo. *Perf. 13***

2782 A1540 4.50fr multi 2.00 .80

2000 Summer Olympics, Sydney A1541

Designs: No. 2783, Cycling, fencing, relay racer. No. 2784, Relay racer, judo, diving.

**2000, Sept. 9**

2783 A1541 3fr multi 1.40 .30
2784 A1541 3fr multi 1.40 .30
*a.* Pair, #2783-2784 3.00 2.00
*b.* Sheet, 5 #2784a + label 15.00 15.00

Olymphilex 2000, Sydney (No. 2784b).

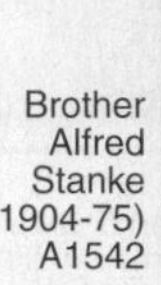

Brother Alfred Stanke (1904-75) A1542

**2000, Sept. 23 Engr.**

2785 A1542 4.40fr multi 2.00 .70

S.O.S. Amitié, 40th Anniv. A1543

**2000, Sept. 30 Litho. *Perf. 13***

2786 A1543 3fr multi 1.40 .30

**20th Century Type**

No. 2787: a, Man on the Moon, 1969, vert. b, Paid vacations, 1936. c, Invention of washing machine, 1901, vert. d, Woman suffrage, 1944, vert. e, Universal Declaration of Human Rights, 1948.

***Perf. 13¼x13 (vert. stamps), 13x13¼***

**2000, Sept. 30 Photo.**

2787 A1531 Sheet, 2 each #a-e 14.00 14.00
*a.-e.* 3fr Any single 1.40 .50

The top and bottom parts of No. 2787 contains Nos. 2787a-2787e and are separated by a row of rouletting.

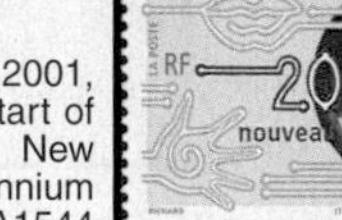
2001, Start of New Millennium A1544

**2000, Oct. 14 Litho. *Perf. 13***

2788 A1544 3fr multi 1.40 .30

The Lovers' Kiosk, by Peynet A1545

**2000, Nov. 4 Engr. *Perf. 13¼x13***

2789 A1545 3fr multi 1.40 .50

Endangered Birds — A1546

**2000, Nov. 4** **Photo.** ***Perf. 13¼***
**2790** A1546 3fr Kiwi 1.40 .40
**2791** A1546 5.20fr Falcon 2.50 1.50

See New Zealand Nos. 1688, 1694.

Start of the 3rd Millennium — A1547

**2000, Nov. 9** **Photo.** ***Perf. 13x13¼***
**2792** A1547 3fr multi + label 1.40 .30

Issued in sheets of 10 stamps + 10 labels, which could be personalized for an extra fee.

Holiday Greetings A1548

**2000, Nov. 11** ***Perf. 12¼x13***
**2793** A1548 3fr Meilleurs voeux 1.40 .30

***Perf. 13¼***

**2794** A1548 3fr Bonne année 1.40 .30

Union of Metallurgical & Mining Industries, Cent. — A1549

**Engr. with Foil Application**

**2000, Dec. 9** ***Perf. 13x13¼***
**2795** A1549 4.50fr multi 2.10 .90

World Handball Championships — A1550

**2001, Jan. 20** **Photo.** ***Perf. 13¼***
**2796** A1550 3fr multi 1.40 .30

Heart A1551

**2001, Jan. 27**
**2797** A1551 3fr multi 1.40 .30
*a.* Souvenir sheet of 5 10.00 10.00

Value of No. 2797 is for copy with surrounding selvage.

**Art Series**

The Peasant Dance, by Pieter Breughel, the Elder — A1552

Hotel des Chevaliers de Saint-Jean-de-Jérusalem — A1553

Yvette Guilbert Singing "Linger, Longer, Loo," by Henri de Toulouse-Lautrec (1864-1901) — A1554

Honfleur at Low Tide, by Johan Barthold Jongkind — A1555

**Engr., Photo (#2800), Litho (#2801)**

**2001** ***Perf. 13x13¼, 13¼x13 (#2800)***
**2798** A1552 6.70fr multi 3.00 1.00
**2799** A1553 6.70fr multi 3.00 1.00
**2800** A1554 6.70fr multi 3.00 1.00
**2801** A1555 6.70fr multi 3.00 1.00
*Nos. 2798-2801 (4)* 12.00 4.00

Issued: No. 2798, 2/3; No. 2799, 4/21; No. 2800, 9/8; No. 2801, 10/27.

Gaston Lagaffe, by André Franquin A1556

**2001, Feb. 24** **Photo.** ***Perf. 13¼***
**2802** A1556 3fr multi 1.40 .30
*a.* Perf. 13¼x13 1.40 1.20

***Perf. 13¼x13***

**2803** A1556 3fr +60c multi 3.00 1.50
*a.* Souvenir sheet of 1 6.00 3.50
*b.* Booklet pane, 5 #2802a, 3 #2803 18.00
Booklet, #2803b 19.00

Stamp Day.

**20th Century Type of 2000**

No. 2804 — Communications: a, Television. b, Compact disc. c, Advertisements, vert. d, Radio, vert. e, Portable telephone, vert.

***Perf. 13¼x13 (vert. stamps), 13x13¼***

**2001, Mar. 17** **Photo.**
**2804** A1531 Sheet, 2 each #a-e 14.00 14.00
*a.-e.* 3fr Any single 1.40 .75

Top part of No. 2804 contains Nos. 2804a-2804e and is separated from bottom part by a row of rouletting.

Announcements — A1557

Designs: No. 2805, It's a girl. No. 2806, It's a boy. No. 2807, Thank you. 4.50fr, Yes (marriage).

**2001** **Frame Color** ***Perf. 13***
**2805** A1557 3fr brt pink 1.40 .30
*a.* Litho., stamp + label 6.50 6.50
**2806** A1557 3fr brt blue 1.40 .30
*a.* Litho., stamp + label 6.50 6.50
**2807** A1557 3fr brt yel grn 1.40 .30
*a.* Litho., stamp + label 6.50 6.50
**2808** A1557 4.50fr orange 2.10 .75
*Nos. 2805-2808 (4)* 6.30 1.65

Issued: Nos. 2805-2808, 3/23; Nos. 2805a-2807a, 11/8.

Nos. 2805a-2807a were issued in sheets of 10 stamps and 10 labels that sold for 60fr on day of issue. The labels could be personalized. Frames on Nos. 2805 and 2806 look splotchy, while those on Nos. 2805a and 2806a have a distinct dot structure. The frame on No. 2807 has tightly spaced small dots, while on No. 2807a, the dots are more widely spaced.

Wildlife — A1558

**2001, Apr. 21** **Photo.** ***Perf. 13¼***
**2809** A1558 2.70fr Squirrel 1.25 .40
**2810** A1558 3fr Roe deer 1.40 .40
**2811** A1558 3fr Hedgehog, horiz. 1.40 .40
**2812** A1558 4.50fr Ermine 2.10 .75
*a.* Souvenir sheet, #2809-2812 7.00 6.50

**Tourism Issue**

Nogent-le-Rotrou A1559

Besançon A1560

Calais A1561

Château de Grignan A1562

**Engr., Litho & Engr. (#2813)**

**2001** ***Perf. 13¼x13 (#2813), 13***
**2813** A1559 3fr multi 1.40 .40
**2814** A1560 3fr multi 1.40 .30
**2815** A1561 3fr multi 1.40 .30
**2816** A1562 3fr multi 1.40 .30
*Nos. 2813-2816 (4)* 5.60 1.30

Issued: No. 2813, 4/28; No. 2814, 5/5; No. 2815, 6/16; No. 2816, 7/7.

Europa — A1563

**2001, May 8** **Photo.** ***Perf. 13***
**2817** A1563 3fr multi 1.40 .35

Gardens of Versailles — A1564

**2001, May 12**
**2818** A1564 4.40fr multi 2.00 .80

Singers — A1565

Designs: No. 2819, Claude François (1939-78). No. 2820, Léo Ferré (1916-93). No. 2821, Serge Gainsbourg (1928-91). No. 2822, Dalida (1933-87). No. 2823, Michel Berger (1947-92). No. 2824, Barbara (1930-97).

**2001, May 19** **Photo.** ***Perf. 13***
**2819** A1565 3fr multi 1.40 .75
**2820** A1565 3fr multi 1.40 .75
**2821** A1565 3fr multi 1.40 .75
**2822** A1565 3fr multi 1.40 .75
**2823** A1565 3fr multi 1.40 .75
**2824** A1565 3fr multi 1.40 .75
*a.* Souvenir sheet, #2819-2824 12.00 12.00
*Nos. 2819-2824 (6)* 8.40 4.50

No. 2824a sold for 28fr with the Red Cross receiving 10fr of that.

Old Lyon — A1566

**2001, May 19** **Engr.** ***Perf. 13¼***
**2825** A1566 3fr multi 1.40 .30

French Federation of Philatelic Associations 74th Congress, Tours — A1567

**2001, June 1**

2826 A1567 3fr multi 1.40 .30

Jean Vilar (1912-71), Actor A1568

**Litho. & Engr.**

**2001, June 7** *Perf. 13*

2827 A1568 3fr multi 1.40 .40

Vacation A1569

**2001, June 10 Litho.** *Perf. 13*

2828 A1569 3fr multi 1.40 .30

**Booklet Stamp**

**Self-Adhesive**

2829 A1569 3fr multi 1.40 .30
a. Booklet of 10 14.00

1 Euro Coin A1570

**2001, June 23 Photo.** *Perf. 12½*

2830 A1570 3fr multi 1.40 .30

Value is for copy with surrounding selvage.

Albert Caquot (1881-1976), Engineer — A1571

**2001, June 30 Engr.** *Perf. 13¼*

2831 A1571 4.50fr multi 2.00 .75

Law Guaranteeing Freedom of Association, Cent. — A1572

**2001, July 1 Photo.** *Perf. 13*

2832 A1572 3fr multi 1.40 .30

Trains — A1573

No. 2833: a, Eurostar. b, American 220. c, Crocodile. d, Crampton. e, Garratt 59. f, Pacific Chapelon. g, Mallard. h, Capitole. i, Autorail Panoramique. j, 230 Class P8.

**2001, July 6 Photo.** *Perf. 13¼*

2833 A1573 Sheet of 10 10.00 8.00
a.-j. 1.50fr Any single .90 .65

Geneva Convention on Refugees, UN High Commisioner for Refugees, 50th Anniv. — A1574

**2001, July 28** *Perf. 13*

2834 A1574 4.50fr multi 2.00 .75

**Marianne Type of 1997 Inscribed "RF" at Lower Left Instead of "La Poste"**

**2001 Engr.** *Perf. 13*

2835 A1409 (3fr) red 1.40 .25
d. Sheet of 15 + 15 labels 60.00 —

***Serpentine Die Cut 6¾ Vert.***

**Self-Adhesive**

2835A A1409 (3fr) red 1.40 .25
b. Booklet of 10 15.00
e. No. 2835 with attached label 6.00

No. 2835Ae is from a sheet having either small or large-sized labels that could be personalized.

**2001, Aug. 1 Engr.** *Perf. 13 Horiz.*

**Coil Stamp**

**Water-Activated Gum**

2835C A1409 (3fr) red 1.40 .25

Issued: Nos. 2835, 2835C, 8/1; No. 2835A, 9/24. No. 2835Ae, 2004.

No. 2835d sold for €10.03. Labels could be personalized for an additional price.

Pierre de Fermat (1601-65), Mathematician — A1575

**2001, Aug. 19 Engr.** *Perf. 13¼x13*

2836 A1575 4.50fr multi 2.00 .75

**20th Century Type of 2000**

No. 2837 — Science: a, First man in space. b, DNA. c, Chip cards. d, Laser. e, Penicillin.

***Perf. 13¼x13 (vert. stamps), 13***

**2001, Sept. 22 Photo.**

2837 A1531 Sheet, 2 each #a-e 14.00 14.00
a.-e. 3fr Any single 1.40 .70

Top part of No. 2837 contains Nos. 2837a-2837e and is separated from bottom part of sheet by a row of rouletting.

Astrolabe Sculpture, Val-de-Reuil A1576

**2001, Sept. 29** *Perf. 13*

2838 A1576 3fr multi 1.40 .30

Halloween A1577

**2001, Oct. 20**

2839 A1577 3fr multi 1.40 .30
a. Souvenir sheet of 5 + 4 labels 8.00 8.00

Jean Pierre-Bloch (1905-99), Human Rights Advocate — A1578

**2001, Nov. 8 Engr.** *Perf. 13*

2840 A1578 4.50fr multi 2.00 .75

Albert Decaris (1901-88), Artist A1579

**2001, Nov. 9 Engr.** *Perf. 13¼x13*

2841 A1579 3fr multi 1.40 .40

Jacques Chaban-Delmas (1915-2000), Politician — A1580

**2001, Nov. 10 Engr.** *Perf. 13x13¼*

2842 A1580 3fr multi 1.40 .40

Holiday Greetings A1581

Designs: Nos. 2843, 2845 Bonne Année (Happy New Year). Nos. 2844, 2846 Meilleurs Voeux (Best wishes).

**2001, Nov. 9 Litho.** *Perf. 13*

2843 A1581 3fr multi 1.40 .30
2844 A1581 3fr multi 1.40 .30

**Serpentine Die Cut 11**

**Self-Adhesive**

**Booklet Stamps**

2845 A1581 3fr multi 1.40 .30
2846 A1581 3fr multi 1.40 .30
a. Booklet, 5 each # 2845-2846 14.00

Fountains A1582

Designs: 3fr, Nejjarine Fountain, Fez, Morocco. 3.80fr, Wallace Fountain, Paris.

**2001, Dec. 14 Photo.** *Perf. 13¼*

2847 A1582 3fr multi 1.40 .40
2848 A1582 3.80fr multi 1.75 1.00

See Morocco Nos. 914-915.

**100 Cents = 1 Euro (€)**

Marianne (With Euro Denominations) A1583

**2002, Jan. 1 Engr.** *Perf. 13*

2849 A1583 1c yellow .25 .25
2850 A1583 2c brown .25 .25
2851 A1583 5c brt bl grn .25 .25
2852 A1583 10c purple .25 .25
2853 A1583 20c brt org .60 .30
2854 A1583 41c brt green 1.20 .25
2855 A1583 50c dk blue 1.50 .25
2856 A1583 53c apple grn 1.60 .40
2857 A1583 58c blue 1.75 .50
2858 A1583 64c dark org 1.90 .50
2859 A1583 67c brt blue 2.00 .50
a. 67c deep blue 2.00 .50
2860 A1583 69c brt pink 2.10 .60
2861 A1583 €1 Prus blue 3.00 .80
2862 A1583 €1.02 dk green 3.00 .90
a. Souvenir sheet, #2835, 2854, 2856-2858, 2859a, 2860, 2862 15.00 15.00
2863 A1583 €2 violet 6.00 1.50
a. Souvenir sheet, #2849-2853, 2855, 2861, 2863 12.00 12.00
*Nos. 2849-2863 (15)* 25.65 7.50

**Coil Stamp**

***Perf. 13 Horiz.***

2864 A1583 41c brt green 1.50 .30

See Nos. 2952-2957, 3043, 3043P-3043Q.

Orchids — A1584

Designs: 29c, Orchis insularis. 33c, Ophrys fuciflora.

**2002, Jan. 2 Litho.** *Perf. 13*

2865 A1584 29c multi 1.00 .30
2866 A1584 33c multi 1.50 .40

Nos. 2865-2866 are known only precanceled. See second note after No. 132.

See Nos. 2958-2959, 3046, 3168.

Heart of Voh, Photograph by Yann Arthurs-Bertrand — A1585

**2002, Jan. 18** **Photo.** ***Perf. 13¼***

| | | | | |
|---|---|---|---|---|
| **2867** | A1585 46c multi | | 1.40 | .40 |
| *a.* | Souvenir sheet of 5 | | 7.00 | 7.00 |

Value of No. 2867 is for stamp with surrounding selvage.

2002 Winter Olympics, Salt Lake City — A1586

**2002, Jan. 26** ***Perf. 13***

| | | | |
|---|---|---|---|
| **2868** | A1586 46c multi | 1.40 | .30 |

**Art Series**

Sphere Concorde, by Jesús Rafael Soto A1587

The Kiss, by Gustav Klimt A1588

The Dancers, by Fernando Botero A1589

Self-Portrait, by Elisabeth Vigée-Lebrun — A1590

**2002** **Photo.** ***Perf. 13¼x13***

| | | | |
|---|---|---|---|
| **2869** | A1587 75c multi | 2.25 | 1.00 |
| **2870** | A1588 €1.02 multi | 3.00 | 1.00 |
| **2871** | A1589 €1.02 multi | 3.00 | 1.00 |
| | **Engr.** | | |
| **2872** | A1590 €1.02 multi | 3.00 | 1.00 |
| | *Nos. 2869-2872 (4)* | 11.25 | 4.00 |

Issued: No. 2869, 11/11. No. 2870, 2/8; No. 2871, 4/27. No. 2872, 10/12.

Alain Bosquet (1919-98), Poet — A1591

**2002, Feb. 16** **Engr.** ***Perf. 13***

| | | | |
|---|---|---|---|
| **2873** | A1591 58c multi | 1.75 | .80 |

It's A Girl A1592

It's A Boy A1593

Yes A1594

**2002, Feb. 23** **Photo.**

| | | | |
|---|---|---|---|
| **2874** | A1592 46c multi | 1.40 | .30 |
| **2875** | A1593 46c multi | 1.40 | .30 |
| **2876** | A1594 69c multi | 2.00 | .80 |
| | *Nos. 2874-2876 (3)* | 4.80 | 1.40 |

Europa — A1595

**2002, Mar. 2** ***Perf. 13¼***

| | | | |
|---|---|---|---|
| **2877** | A1595 46c multi | 1.40 | .30 |

Boule and Bill, by Jean Roba — A1596

Designs: 46c, Boule, Bill, bird. 46c+9c, Boule, Bill, ball.

**2002, Mar. 16** ***Perf. 13¼***

| | | | |
|---|---|---|---|
| **2878** | A1596 46c multi | 1.40 | .50 |
| *a.* | Perf. 13¼x13 | 1.40 | 1.20 |
| | ***Perf. 13¼x13*** | | |
| **2879** | A1596 46c +9c multi | 3.00 | 1.50 |
| *a.* | Souvenir sheet of 1 | 3.00 | 2.50 |
| *b.* | Booklet pane, 5 #2878a, 3 #2879 | 18.00 | — |
| | Booklet, #2879b | 19.00 | |

Stamp Day. No. 2879 surtax for Red Cross. Stamp on No. 2879a has continuous design.

Nimes Amphitheater — A1597

**Litho. & Engr.**

**2002, Mar. 22** ***Perf. 13***

| | | | |
|---|---|---|---|
| **2880** | A1597 46c multi | 1.40 | .30 |

**20th Century Type of 2000**

No. 2881 — Transportation: a, Concorde supersonic airplane. b, TGV train. c, Ocean liner France, vert. d, Mobylette motor scooter, vert. e, Citroen 2 CV automobile, vert.

***Perf. 13, 13¼x13 (vert. stamps)***

**2002, Mar. 23** **Photo.**

| | | | |
|---|---|---|---|
| **2881** | A1531 Sheet, 2 each #a-e | 14.00 | 14.00 |
| *a.-e.* | 46c Any single | 1.40 | .75 |

Top part of No. 2881 contains Nos. 2881a-2881e and is separated from bottom part of sheet by a row of rouletting.

Encounter of Matthew Flinders and Nicolas Boudin, Bicent. A1598

Map of Australia, portrait and ship of: 46c, Flinders. 79c, Boudin.

**2002, Apr. 4** ***Perf. 13¼***

| | | | |
|---|---|---|---|
| **2882** | A1598 46c multi | 1.40 | .40 |
| **2883** | A1598 79c multi | 2.25 | 1.50 |

See Australia Nos. 2053-2054.

**Tourism Series**

La Charité-sur-Loire — A1599

Collioure A1600

Locronan A1601

Neufchateau — A1602

**Engraved (#2884, 2886), Photo. (#2885)**

**2002** ***Perf. 13¼***

| | | | |
|---|---|---|---|
| **2884** | A1599 46c multi | 1.40 | .30 |
| **2885** | A1600 46c multi | 1.40 | .30 |
| **2886** | A1601 46c multi | 1.40 | .30 |
| **2887** | A1602 46c multi | 1.40 | .30 |
| | *Nos. 2884-2887 (4)* | 5.60 | 1.20 |

Issue dates: No. 2884, 4/6; No. 2885, 6/22; No. 2886, 7/13; No. 2887, 10/12/02.

Numbers have been reserved for additional stamps in this set.

Birthday Greetings A1603

Invitation A1604

**2002, Apr. 6** **Photo.** ***Perf. 13***

| | | | |
|---|---|---|---|
| **2888** | A1603 46c multi | 1.40 | .30 |
| *a.* | Litho., stamp + label | 6.00 | 6.00 |
| **2889** | A1604 46c multi | 1.40 | .30 |
| *a.* | Litho., stamp + label | 6.00 | 6.00 |

Issued: Nos. 2888a, 2889a, 11/7. Nos. 2888a and 2889a were issued in sheets of 10 stamps and 10 labels that sold for €6.19 on day of issue. The labels could be personalized.

No. 2888a has a duller blue in "Anniversaire" than No. 2888, but is otherwise quite similar in appearance. The gold ink on No. 2889a has a more coppery look than that on No. 2889.

100th Paris-Roubaix Bicycle Race — A1605

**2002, Mar. 13**

| | | | |
|---|---|---|---|
| **2890** | A1605 46c multi | 1.40 | .30 |

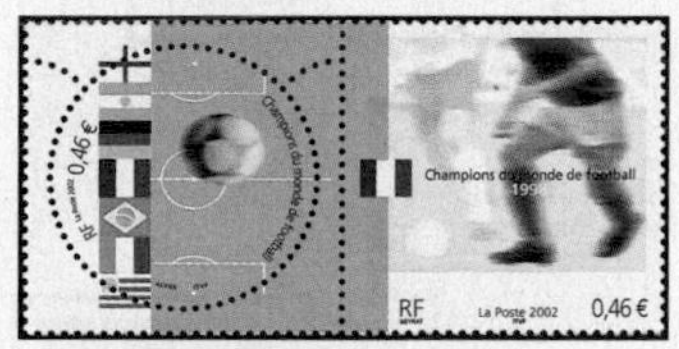


2002 World Cup Soccer Championships, Japan and Korea — A1606

No. 2891: a, Flags, soccer ball and field (32mm diameter). b, Soccer player, year of French championship.

**2002, Apr. 27** ***Perf. 12¾***

| | | | |
|---|---|---|---|
| **2891** | A1606 Horiz. pair | 2.75 | 2.50 |
| *a.-b.* | 46c Any single | 1.40 | .30 |
| *c.* | Sheet, 5 #2891 | 15.00 | 15.00 |

Issued: No. 2891c, 5/18.

See Argentina No. 2184, Brazil No. 2840, Germany No. 2163, Italy No. 2526 and Uruguay No. 1946.

Marine Life A1607

Designs: 41c, Sea turtle (tortue luth), vert. No. 2893, Killer whale (orque). No. 2894, Dolphin (grand dauphin). 69c, Seal (phoque veau marin).

**2002, May 4** ***Perf. 13¼***

| | | | |
|---|---|---|---|
| **2892** | A1607 41c multi | 1.25 | .30 |
| **2893** | A1607 46c multi | 1.25 | .30 |
| **2894** | A1607 46c multi | 1.25 | .30 |
| **2895** | A1607 69c multi | 2.00 | .75 |
| *a.* | Souvenir sheet, #2892-2895 | 6.50 | 6.50 |
| | *Nos. 2892-2895 (4)* | 5.75 | 1.65 |

Worldwide Fund for Nature (No. 2895a).

French Federation of Philatelic Associations 75th Congress, Marseilles — A1608

**2002, May 17** **Engr.** ***Perf. 13***

| | | | |
|---|---|---|---|
| **2896** | A1608 46c multi | 1.40 | .40 |

Legion of Honor, Bicent. — A1609

**2002, May 18** **Photo.**
**2897** A1609 46c multi 1.40 .30

Rocamadour
A1610

**2002, May 25** ***Perf. 13¼***
**2898** A1610 46c multi 1.40 .30

Louis Delgrés (1766-1802), Soldier — A1611

**2002, May 25**
**2899** A1611 46c multi 1.40 .30

Vacation
A1612

**2002, June 8** **Litho.** ***Perf. 13***
**2900** A1612 46c multi 1.40 .30

**Self-Adhesive**

***Serpentine Die Cut 11***

**2901** A1612 46c multi 1.40 .30
*a.* Booklet pane of 10 14.00

World Disabled Athletics Championships — A1613

**2002, June 15** **Photo.** ***Perf. 13¼***
**2902** A1613 46c multi 1.40 .30

Saint-Ser Chapel — A1614

**2002, June 22** **Engr.** ***Perf. 13x13¼***
**2903** A1614 46c multi 1.40 .30

Metz Cathedral Stained Glass A1615

**2002, July 6** **Engr.** ***Perf. 13¼x13***
**2904** A1615 46c multi 1.40 .40

Jazz Musicians — A1616

Designs: No. 2905, Louis Armstrong (1901-71). No. 2906, Ella Fitzgerald (1918-96). No. 2907, Duke Ellington (1899-1974). No. 2908, Stéphane Grappelli (1908-97). No. 2909, Michel Petrucciani (1962-99), horiz. No. 2910, Sidney Bechet (1897-1959), horiz.

**2002, July 13** **Photo.** ***Perf. 13***
**2905** A1616 46c multi 1.40 .75
**2906** A1616 46c multi 1.40 .75
**2907** A1616 46c multi 1.40 .75
**2908** A1616 46c multi 1.40 .75
**2909** A1616 46c multi 1.40 .75
**2910** A1616 46c multi 1.40 .75
*a.* Souvenir sheet, #2905-2910 12.00 12.00
*Nos. 2905-2910 (6)* 8.40 4.50

No. 2910a sold for €4.36, with the Red Cross receiving €1.60 of that.

Pilgrimages to Notre Dame de la Salette, 150th Anniv. A1617

**2002, Aug. 15** **Engr.** ***Perf. 13¼x13***
**2911** A1617 46c multi 1.40 .30

Choreography — A1618

**2002, Sept. 13** **Photo.** ***Perf. 13x13¼***
**2912** A1618 53c multi 1.60 .70

Motorcycles — A1619

No. 2913: a, Honda 750 four. b, Terrot 500 RGST. c, Majestic. d, Norton Commando 750. e, Voxan 1000 Café Racer. f, BMW R90S. g, Harley Davidson Hydra Glide. h, Triumph Bonneville 650. i, Ducati 916. j, Yamaha 500 XT.

**2002, Sept. 14** ***Perf. 13¼x13***
**2913** A1619 Sheet of 10 12.00 12.00
*a.-e.* 16c any single .75 .60
*f.-j.* 30c any single .90 .75

Georges Perec (1936-82), Writer — A1620

**2002, Sept. 21** **Engr.** ***Perf. 13¼***
**2914** A1620 46c multi 1.40 .30

**20th Century Type of 2000**

No. 2915 — Photographs of everyday life: a, Family on motor scooter, 1955, vert. b, Man, horse and wagon, 1947. c, Woman ironing, 1950. d, Boy at fountain, 1950, vert. e, Girl in classroom, 1965, vert.

***Perf. 13¼x13 (vert. stamps), 13***

**2002, Sept. 28** **Photo.**
**2915** A1531 Sheet, 2 each #a-e 14.00 14.00
*a.-e.* 46c Any single 1.40 .75

Top part of No. 2915 contains Nos. 2915a-2915e and is separated from bottom part of sheet by a row of rouletting.

Emile Zola (1840-1902), Novelist — A1621

**2002, Oct. 5** ***Perf. 13***
**2916** A1621 46c multi 1.40 .30

Souvenir Sheet

European Capitals — A1622

Attractions in Rome: a, Trevi Fountain. b, Coliseum, horiz. c, Trinità de Monti Church and Spanish Steps. d, St. Peter's Basilica, horiz.

**2002, Nov. 7** ***Perf. 13¼x13, 13x13¼***
**2917** A1622 Sheet of 4 6.00 6.00
*a.-d.* 46c Any single 1.40 .90

See Nos. 2985, 3052, 3138, 3223, 3340, 3535, 3728, 3908, 3986, 4183, 4365.

Globe and Microcircuits A1623

**2002, Nov. 8** **Photo.** ***Perf. 13***
**2918** A1623 46c multi 1.40 .30
*a.* Litho., stamp + label 6.00 6.00

Issued: No. 2918a, 11/7. No. 2918a was issued in sheets of 10 stamps and 10 labels that sold for €6.19 on day of issue. The labels could be personalized.

No. 2918a has a hairline at top, above "RF" that No. 2918 does not have, but is otherwise quite similar in appearance.

Holiday Greetings A1624

**2002, Nov. 8** **Photo.** ***Perf. 13***
**2919** A1624 46c multi 1.40 .30
*a.* Litho., stamp + label 6.00 6.00

**Booklet Stamp**

**Self-Adhesive**

***Serpentine Die Cut 11***

**2920** A1624 46c multi 1.40 .30
*a.* Booklet pane of 10 14.00

Issued: No. 2919a, 11/7. No. 2919a was issued in sheets of 10 stamps and 10 labels that sold for €6.19 on day of issue. The labels could be personalized.

No. 2919a has a finer dot structure, which is most noticeable in the chimney smoke, than No. 2919.

**Marianne Type of 1997 Inscribed "RF" at Lower Left**

**2002, Nov. 9** **Engr.** ***Perf. 13***
**2921** A1409 (41c) bright green 1.20 .25

**Coil Stamp**

***Perf. 13 Horiz.***

**2922** A1409 (41c) bright green 1.20 .25

Alexandre Dumas (Father) (1802-70), Writer A1625

**2002, Nov. 30** **Photo.** ***Perf. 13***
**2924** A1625 46c multi 1.40 .30

Léopold Sédar Senghor (1906-2001), President of Senegal, Poet — A1626

**2002, Dec. 20**
**2925** A1626 46c multi 1.40 .30

Hearts A1627

**2003, Jan. 11** *Perf. 13¼*
**2926** A1627 46c Four hearts 1.40 .30
*a.* Souvenir sheet of 5 7.00 7.00
**2927** A1627 69c Roses 2.00 .75

Values for Nos. 2926-2927 are for examples with surrounding selvage.

Thank You A1628

Birth A1629

**2003, Jan. 11** *Perf. 13*
**2928** A1628 46c multi 1.40 .30
**2929** A1629 46c brt org & brt bl 1.40 .30

Franco-German Cooperation Treaty, 40th Anniv. — A1630

**2003, Jan. 16** *Perf. 13¼*
**2930** A1630 46c multi 1.40 .40

Delegation for Land-use Planning and Regional Action, 40th Anniv. A1631

**2003, Feb. 8** **Photo.** *Perf. 13*
**2931** A1631 46c multi 1.40 .30

Geneviève de Gaulle Anthonioz (1920-2002), World War II Resistance Fighter — A1632

**2003, Feb. 11**
**2932** A1632 46c blk & ol brn 1.40 .30

Paris Chamber of Commerce and Industry, Bicent. — A1633

**2003, Feb. 22** *Perf. 13¼*
**2933** A1633 46c multi 1.40 .30

Lucky Luke, by Morris (Maurice De Bevere) — A1634

Lucky Luke and Jolly Jumper: 46c, Skipping rope on ball on high wire. 46c+9c, Following dog, Rantanplan.

**2003, Mar. 15** **Photo.** *Perf. 13¼*
**2934** A1634 46c multi 1.40 .65
*a.* Perf. 13¼x13 1.40 .65

*Perf. 13¼x13*

**2935** A1634 46c +9c multi 3.50 2.00
*a.* Souvenir sheet of 1 3.00 2.50
*b.* Booklet pane, 5 #2934a, 3 #2935 17.50 —
Complete booklet, #2935b 18.00

Stamp Day.

Birds A1635

Designs: 41c, Colibri à tete bleue (Cyanophaia bicolor). No. 2937, Toucan ariel (Ramphastos vitellinus). No. 2938, Colibri grenat (Eulampis jugularis), vert. 69c, Terpsiphone de Bourbon (Terpsiphone bourbonnensis).

**2003, Mar. 22** **Photo.** *Perf. 13¼*
**2936** A1635 41c multi 1.20 .30
**2937** A1635 46c multi 1.40 .30
**2938** A1635 46c multi 1.40 .30
**2939** A1635 69c multi 2.00 .75
*a.* Souvenir sheet, #2936-2939 7.00 7.00
*Nos. 2936-2939 (4)* 6.00 1.65

Nantes A1636

**2003, Apr. 4** **Engr.**
**2940** A1636 46c multi 1.40 .30

Pierre Bérégovoy (1925-93), Prime Minister — A1637

**2003, Apr. 30** **Engr.** *Perf. 13x13¼*
**2941** A1637 46c multi 1.40 .30

Milan Stefanik (1880-1919), Czechoslovakian General — A1638

**2003, May 3** *Perf. 13¼*
**2942** A1638 50c multi 1.50 .40

See Slovakia No. 428.

Europa — A1639

**2003, May 8** **Photo.**
**2943** A1639 50c multi 1.50 .40

Charter of Fundamental Rights of the European Union — A1640

**2003, May 8**
**2944** A1640 50c multi 1.50 .30

Aircraft Carrier "Charles de Gaulle" A1641

**2003, May 8** **Engr.**
**2945** A1641 50c multi 1.50 .30

Aspects of Life in the French Regions A1642

No. 2946: a, Beach cabins. b, Fishing net. c, Vineyards of Champagne. d, Camembert cheese, vert. e, Foie gras, vert. f, Petanque. g, Puppet show (Guignol), vert. h, Crepe, vert. i, Cassoulet. j, Limoges porcelain.

**2003, May 24** **Photo.** *Perf. 13*
**2946** Sheet of 10 16.00 16.00
*a.-j.* A1642 50c Any single 1.50 1.30

No. 2946 has three vertical rows of rouletting, separating sheet into quarters.

Nos. 2946a-2946j were also issued in large booklets containing panes of 1 of each stamp. The booklet sold for €19.

See Nos. 2978, 3007, 3047, 3106, 3139, 3192, 3234, 3299, 3300-3301, 3357, 3427, 3505.

**Art Series**

"The Dying Slave" and "The Rebel Slave," by Michelangelo — A1643

The Red Buoy, by Paul Signac A1644

Untitled Abstract by Vassily Kandinsky A1645

Marilyn, by Andy Warhol A1646

**2003** **Engr.** *Perf. 13¼x13*
**2947** A1643 75c multi 2.50 1.25

**Photo.**

**2948** A1644 75c multi 2.50 1.25

**Litho.**

**2949** A1645 €1.11 multi 3.50 1.25
**2950** A1646 €1.11 multi 3.50 1.40
*Nos. 2947-2950 (4)* 12.00 5.15

Issued: No. 2947, 5/24. Nos. 2948, 2949, 7/5. No. 2950, 11/8.

A sheet containing 3 No. 2949 and 12 imperforate color progressive proofs was bound in a book that sold for €60.

Happy Birthday A1647

**2003, May 31** **Photo.** *Perf. 13¼*
**2951** A1647 50c multi 1.50 .35
*a.* Souvenir sheet of 5 7.50 7.50
*b.* Litho., stamp + label 1.75 1.75

Issued: No. 2951b, 2004. No. 2951b was issued in sheets of 10 stamps + 10 labels that sold for €6.67 on day of issue. The labels could be personalized. The background on

No. 2951 looks splotchy while that of No. 2951b has a dot structure.

### Marianne With Euro Denominations Type of 2002

**2003, June 1 Engr. *Perf. 13***

| | | | | |
|---|---|---|---|---|
| **2952** | A1583 | 58c apple grn | 1.75 | .40 |
| **2953** | A1583 | 70c yellow grn | 2.00 | .50 |
| **2954** | A1583 | 75c bright blue | 2.25 | .25 |
| **2955** | A1583 | 90c dark blue | 2.60 | 1.00 |
| **2956** | A1583 | €1.11 red lilac | 3.25 | .25 |
| **2957** | A1583 | €1.90 violet brown | 5.75 | .40 |
| *a.* | | Souvenir sheet, #2835, 2921, 2952-2957 | 22.00 | 22.00 |
| | | *Nos. 2952-2957 (6)* | 17.60 | 2.80 |

No. 2957a issued 2/28/04.

### Orchids Type of 2002

Designs: 30c, Platanthera chlorantha. 35c, Dactylorhiza savogiensis.

**2003, June 1 Litho. *Perf. 13***

| | | | | |
|---|---|---|---|---|
| **2958** | A1584 | 30c multi | 1.00 | .30 |
| **2959** | A1584 | 35c multi | 1.50 | .40 |

Nos. 2958-2959 are known only precanceled, See second note after No. 132.

French Federation of Philatelic Associations 76th Congress, Mulhouse A1648

**2003, June 6 Engr. *Perf. 13¼***

| | | | | |
|---|---|---|---|---|
| **2960** | A1648 | 50c multi | 1.50 | .30 |

Vacation — A1649

***Perf. 12¾x13¼***

**2003, June 14 Litho.**

| | | | | |
|---|---|---|---|---|
| **2961** | A1649 | 50c multi | 1.50 | .30 |

**Self-Adhesive Booklet Stamp**

***Serpentine Die Cut 11***

| | | | | |
|---|---|---|---|---|
| **2962** | A1649 | 50c multi | 1.50 | .30 |
| *a.* | | Booklet pane of 10 | 15.00 | |

### Tourism Issue

Notre Dame de l'Epine Basilica — A1650

Tulle A1651

Arras — A1652

Pontarlier A1653

***Perf. 13x13¼, 13 (#2965)***

**2003, June 21 Engr.**

| | | | | |
|---|---|---|---|---|
| **2963** | A1650 | 50c multi | 1.50 | .30 |
| **2964** | A1651 | 50c multi | 1.50 | .30 |
| **2965** | A1652 | 50c multi | 1.50 | .30 |
| **2966** | A1653 | 50c multi | 1.50 | .30 |
| | | *Nos. 2963-2966 (4)* | 6.00 | 1.20 |

Issued: Nos. 2963, 2964, 6/21. No. 2965, 9/20. No. 2966, 10/11.

French Freemasonry, 275th Anniv. — A1654

**2003, June 28 Engr. *Perf. 13¼x13***

| | | | | |
|---|---|---|---|---|
| **2967** | A1654 | 50c multi | 1.50 | .30 |

Tour de France Bicycle Race, Cent. A1655

No. 2968: a, Maurice Garin, winner of 1903 race. b, Cyclist with arms raised.

**2003, June 28 Photo. *Perf. 13***

| | | | | |
|---|---|---|---|---|
| **2968** | A1655 | Vert. pair | 3.00 | 2.00 |
| *a.-b.* | | 50c Either single | 1.50 | .30 |

Values are for stamps with surrounding selvage.

Saint-Père Church, Yonne — A1656

**2003, July 12 Engr. *Perf. 13¼***

| | | | | |
|---|---|---|---|---|
| **2969** | A1656 | 50c multi | 1.50 | .30 |

World Track and Field Championships, Paris — A1657

**2003, July 19 Photo. *Perf. 13***

| | | | | |
|---|---|---|---|---|
| **2970** | A1657 | 50c multi | 1.50 | .30 |

Characters From French Literature — A1658

Designs: No. 2971, Eugène-François Vidocq (1775-1857), convict and police official. No. 2972, Esmerelda, from *Notre-Dame de Paris,* by Victor Hugo. No. 2973, Claudine, from *Claudine* novels, by Colette. No. 2974, Nana, from *Rougon-Macquart,* by Emile Zola. No. 2975, La Comte de Monte-Cristo, from *La Comte de Monte-Cristo,* by Alexandre Dumas (pere). No. 2976, Gavroche, from *Les Miserables,* by Hugo.

**2003, Aug. 30 Photo. *Perf. 13***

| | | | | |
|---|---|---|---|---|
| **2971** | A1658 | 50c multi | 1.50 | .75 |
| **2972** | A1658 | 50c multi | 1.50 | .75 |
| **2973** | A1658 | 50c multi | 1.50 | .75 |
| **2974** | A1658 | 50c multi | 1.50 | .75 |
| **2975** | A1658 | 50c multi | 1.50 | .75 |
| **2976** | A1658 | 50c multi | 1.50 | .75 |
| *a.* | | Souvenir sheet, #2971-2976 | 14.00 | 14.00 |
| | | *Nos. 2971-2976 (6)* | 9.00 | 4.50 |

No. 2976a sold for €4.60, with the Red Cross receiving €1.60 of that.

Ahmad Shah Massoud (1953-2001), Afghan Northern Alliance Leader — A1659

**2003, Sept. 9**

| | | | | |
|---|---|---|---|---|
| **2977** | A1659 | 50c multi | 1.50 | .30 |

### Aspects of Life in French Regions Type of 2003

No. 2978: a, Chateau de Chenonceau. b, House, Alsace. c, Roof, Bourgogne. d, Genoese Tower, Corsica, vert. e, Arc de Triomphe, vert. f, Farm house, Provence. g, Pointe du Raz, vert. h, Mont Blanc, vert. i, Basque house. j, Pont du Gard.

**2003, Sept. 20 Photo. *Perf. 13***

| | | | | |
|---|---|---|---|---|
| **2978** | | Sheet of 10 | 15.00 | 15.00 |
| *a.-j.* | | A1642 50c Any single | 1.50 | 1.25 |

No. 2978 has three vertical rows of rouletting, separating sheet into quarters.

Nos. 2978a-2978j were also issued in large booklets containing panes of 1 of each stamp. The booklet sold for €19.

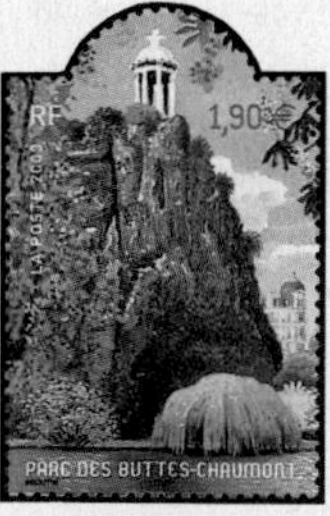

Gardens and Parks — A1660

No. 2979: a, Buttes-Chaumont Park. b, Jardin du Luxembourg.

**2003, Sept. 27 *Perf. 13¼x13***

| | | | | |
|---|---|---|---|---|
| **2979** | | Sheet of 2 | 12.00 | 12.00 |
| *a.-b.* | | A1660 €1.90 Either single | 6.00 | 6.00 |

Salon du Timbre 2004. No. 2979 has four vertical rows of rouletting, separating sheet into fifths, with the two stamps in the central fifth.

See Nos. 3029, 3118, 3201, 3316, 3429.

Motor Vehicles — A1661

No. 2980: a, 1954 Isobloc 648 DP 102 bus (Autocar). b, 1950 SFV 302 Tractor. c, 1938 Delahaye fire truck with mechanical aerial ladder. d, Renault Kangaroo Express postal van. e, 1932 Renault TN6 Paris city bus. f, 1910 Berliet 22hp Type M delivery truck. g, 1957 Berliet T100 heavy-duty truck. h, Citroen police van. i, Citroen DS ambulance. j, 1964 Hotchkiss fire truck.

**2003, Oct. 24 Photo. *Perf. 13¼***

| | | | | |
|---|---|---|---|---|
| **2980** | A1661 | Sheet of 10 | 9.00 | 9.00 |
| *a.-e.* | | 20c Any single | .55 | .45 |
| *f.-j.* | | 30c Any single | 1.00 | .75 |

Philexjeunes 2003 Philatelic Exhibition, Dunkerque.

A1662

Holiday Greetings A1663

**2003, Nov. 6 Photo. *Perf. 13***

| | | | | |
|---|---|---|---|---|
| **2981** | A1662 | 50c multi | 1.50 | .35 |
| *a.* | | Litho., stamp + label | 6.00 | 6.00 |

**Litho.**

| | | | | |
|---|---|---|---|---|
| **2982** | A1663 | 50c multi | 1.50 | .35 |
| *a.* | | Sheet of 10 + 10 labels | 60.00 | 60.00 |

**Booklet Stamp Self-Adhesive**

***Serpentine Die Cut 11¼***

| | | | | |
|---|---|---|---|---|
| **2983** | A1663 | 50c multi | 1.50 | .35 |
| *a.* | | Booklet pane of 10 | 16.00 | |

Nos. 2981a, 2982a, 2004. Nos. 2981a and 2982 were issued in sheets of 10 stamps + 10 labels that sold for €6.67 each on day of issue. The labels could be personalized. The background on No. 2981 looks splotchy while that of No. 2981a has a dot structure.

A souvenir sheet containing No. 2982 was sold for €6 by mail order only. It was not available through standing order subscriptions and was not offered in the philatelic bureau's sales catalog. 50,000 copies of this sheet were printed. Value $100.

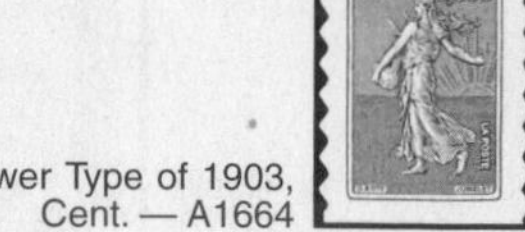

Sower Type of 1903, Cent. — A1664

*Serpentine Die Cut 6¾ Vert.*

**2003, Nov. 6** **Engr.**

**Booklet Stamp**

**2984** A1664 50c red 3.50 2.00
*a.* Booklet pane, 5 each # 2984, 2835A 25.00

See No. 4727b.

**European Capitals Type of 2002**

No. 2985 — Attractions in Luxembourg: a, Citadelle Saint-Esprit. b, Notre Dame Cathedral, horiz. c, Adolphe Bridge, horiz. d, Grand Duke's Palace.

*Perf. 13¼x13, 13x13¼*

**2003, Nov. 7** **Photo.**

**2985** A1622 Sheet of 4 7.50 7.50
*a.-d.* 50c Any single 1.50 1.00

Indian and French Artisan's Work A1665

Designs: 50c, Illumination depicting rooster, France, 15th cent. 90c, Jewelry design, India, 19th cent.

**2003, Nov. 29** **Engr.** *Perf. 13¼x13*

**2986** A1665 50c multi 1.50 .45
**2987** A1665 90c multi 2.60 1.50

See India No. 2040.

Launch of the Queen Mary 2 — A1666

**2003, Dec. 12** **Photo.** *Perf. 13¼*

**2988** A1666 50c multi 1.50 .30

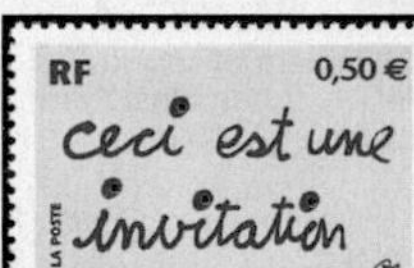


Greetings A1667

**Holes punched through dots in "i's."**

**2004, Jan. 9** **Photo.** *Perf. 13*

**2989** A1667 50c shown 1.50 .30
**2990** A1667 50c Un grand merci 1.50 .30

**No Holes Punched Through Dots of "i's"**

**Stamp + Label**

**2991** A1667 50c Like No. 2989 6.00 6.00
**2992** A1667 50c Like No. 2990 6.00 6.00

Nos. 2991-2992 were issued in sheets of 10 stamps + 10 labels that sold for €6.67 on day of issue. The labels could be personalized.

Compare with Type A2203. See Nos. 3096-3097D, 3569A-3569B.

It's a Boy A1668

It's a Girl A1669

**2004** **Litho.** *Perf. 13*

**Stamp + Label**

**2993** A1668 50c multi 6.00 6.00
**2994** A1669 50c multi 6.00 6.00

**Booklet Stamps**

**Self-Adhesive**

*Serpentine Die Cut 11*

**2995** A1668 50c multi 1.50 .35
*a.* Booklet pane of 10 15.00
**2996** A1669 50c multi 1.50 .35
*a.* Booklet pane of 10 15.00

Nos. 2993-2994 were issued in sheets of 10 stamps + 10 labels that sold for €6.67 on day of issue. The labels could be personalized.

Nos. 2995-2996 issued 1/9/04.

Hearts A1670

Designs: 50c, Chanel No. 5 perfume bottle. 75c, Woman, Eiffel Tower.

**2004, Jan. 9** **Photo.** *Perf. 13*

**2997** A1670 50c multi 1.50 .35
*a.* Souvenir sheet of 5 7.50 7.50
*b.* Litho., stamp + label, perf. 13¼ 6.00 6.00
**2998** A1670 75c multi 2.25 .75
*a.* Litho., stamp + label, perf. 13¼ 6.00 6.00

Nos. 2997b and 2998a were each printed in sheets of 10 stamps + 10 labels that could be personalized and sold for €6.69 and €10 respectively. On No. 2997b, there are large brown dots arranged in circles in the shading on the green rectangles, while on No. 2997 the brown dots are small and arranged in rows. On No. 2998a, the dots in the sky are larger and father apart than the tiny dots found on No. 2998.

Values are for stamps with surrounding selvage.

See Nos. 3133, 3135.

**Tourism Issue**

Lille, 2004 European Cultural Capital A1671

**2004, Jan. 10** **Photo.** *Perf. 13*

**2999** A1671 50c multi 1.50 .35

**Art Series**

Statue of Liberty, Sculpted by Frederic Auguste Bartholdi (1834-1904) — A1672

**2004, Feb. 21** **Engr.** *Perf. 13¼x13*

**3000** A1672 90c multi 2.60 1.50

Queen Eleanor of Aquitaine (c. 1122-1204) A1673

**2004, Feb. 28** *Perf. 13x13¼*

**3001** A1673 50c multi 1.50 .35

Stamp Day — A1674

Characters of Walt Disney: 45c, Donald Duck. 50c, Mickey Mouse. 75c, Minnie Mouse.

**2004, Mar. 6** **Photo.** *Perf. 13¼*

**3002** A1674 50c multi 1.50 .35
*a.* Perf. 13¼x13 (from booklet pane) 1.50 .35

**Booklet Stamps**

*Perf. 13¼x13*

**3003** A1674 45c multi 2.25 1.00
**3004** A1674 75c multi 2.25 .75
*a.* Booklet pane, 2 #3003, 4 each #3002a, 3004 23.00 —
Complete booklet, #3004a 24.00

Civil Code, Bicent. A1675

**2004, Mar. 12** **Engr.** *Perf. 13¼x13*

**3005** A1675 50c multi 1.50 .35

George Sand (1804-76), Writer A1676

**2004, Mar. 20** **Engr.** *Perf. 13¼x13*

**3006** A1676 50c multi 1.50 .35

**Aspects of Life in French Regions Type of 2003**

No. 3007: a, Cutlery. b, Produce of Provence, vert. c, Beaujolais grapes, vert. d, Bread. e, Woman wearing coif, vert. f, Oysters, vert. g, Quiche Lorraine. h, Bullfighting. i, Clafoutis. j, Bagpipers.

**2004, Mar. 26** **Photo.** *Perf. 13*

**3007** Sheet of 10 15.00 15.00
*a.-j.* A1642 50c Any single 1.50 1.25

No. 3007 has three vertical rows of rouletting, separating sheet into quarters.

Clermont-Ferrand — A1677

**2004, Mar. 26** **Engr.** *Perf. 13¼*

**3008** A1677 50c multi 1.50 .30

Entente Cordiale, Cent. — A1678

Designs: 50c, Coccinelle, by Sonia Delaunay. 75c, Lace 1 (trial proof) 1968, by Sir Terry Frost.

**2004, Apr. 6** **Photo.** *Perf. 13¼*

**3009** A1678 50c multi 1.50 .35
**3010** A1678 75c multi 2.25 .85

See Great Britain Nos. 2200-2201.

Road Safety — A1679

**2004, Apr. 7**

**3011** A1679 50c multi 1.50 .30

See United Nations Offices in Geneva No. 424.

**Art Series**

La Méridienne d'Après Millet, by Vincent van Gogh — A1680

**2004, July 2** **Photo.** *Perf. 13x13¼*

**3012** A1680 75c multi 2.50 .95

**Art Series**

Un Combat de Coqs, by Jean-Léon Gérôme — A1681

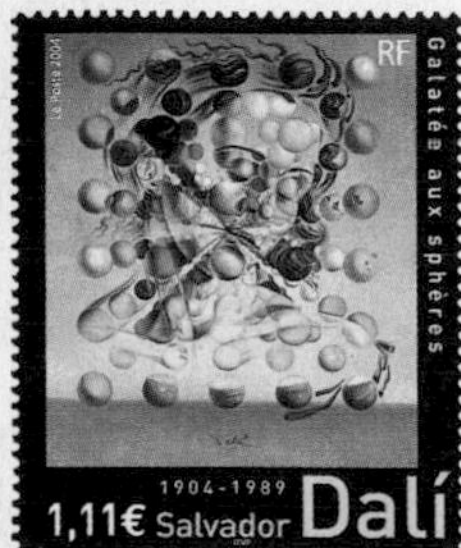


Galatée aux Sphères, by Salvador Dali A1682

**2004** **Photo.** *Perf. 13x13¼*

**3013** A1681 €1.11 multi 3.50 1.25
**3014** A1682 €1.11 multi 3.50 1.25

Issued: No. 3013, 4/17; No. 3014, 6/19.

### Tourism Issue

Bordeaux — A1683

Vaux-sur-Mer — A1684

Notre Dame de l'Assomption Cathedral, Luçon — A1685

**2004 Litho. & Engr.** *Perf. 13*
**3015** A1683 50c multi 1.50 .30

**Engr.**
*Perf. 13¼*
**3016** A1684 50c multi 1.50 .30
**3017** A1685 50c multi 1.50 .30

Issued: No. 3015, 4/26; No. 3016, 7/17; No. 3017, 10/2.

Farm Animals A1686

**2004, Apr. 26 Photo.** *Perf. 13¼*
**3018** A1686 45c Rabbit 1.25 .30
**3019** A1686 50c Cow, vert. 1.50 .30
**3020** A1686 50c Chicken 1.50 .30
**3021** A1686 75c Burro, vert. 2.25 .90
*a.* Souvenir sheet, #3018-3021 7.00 7.00

Expansion of the European Union A1687

**2004, May 1 Photo.** *Perf. 13¼*
**3022** A1687 50c multi 1.50 .30

Battle of Dien Bien Phu, 50th Anniv. — A1688

**2004, May 7** *Perf. 13¼x13*
**3023** A1688 50c multi 1.50 .30

Europa A1689

**2004 Photo.** *Perf. 13x13¼*
**3024** A1689 50c multi 1.50 .30

**Litho.**
**Booklet Stamp**
**Self-Adhesive**
***Serpentine Die Cut 11***
**3025** A1689 50c multi 1.50 .30
*a.* Booklet pane of 10 15.00

Issued: No. 3024, 5/9; No. 3025, 6/4.

Blake and Mortimer, Comic Book Characters by Edgar P. Jacobs A1690

Blake and Mortimer and: 50c, Brick wall, vert. €1, Blue background.

**2004, May 15 Photo.** *Perf. 13¼*
**3026** A1690 50c multi 1.50 .30
**3027** A1690 €1 multi 3.00 1.25

See Belgium No. 2020.

FIFA (Fédération Internationale de Football Association), Cent. — A1691

**2004, May 20** *Perf. 13¼x13*
**3028** A1691 50c multi 1.50 .30

### Gardens and Parks Type of 2003

No. 3029: a, Jardin des Tuileries. b, Parc Floral de Paris.

**2004, June 4** *Perf. 13¼x13*
**3029** Sheet of 2 12.00 12.00
*a.-b.* A1660 €1.90 Either single 5.75 5.00
*c.* Souvenir sheet, #2979a-2979b, 3029a-3029b 35.00 35.00

Salon du Timbre 2004. No. 3029 has four vertical rows of rouletting, separating sheet into fifths, with the two stamps in the central fifth.

D-Day Invasion of France, 60th Anniv. — A1692

**2004, June 5** *Perf. 13*
**3030** A1692 50c multi 1.50 .30

Organ Donation A1693

**2004, June 22** *Perf. 13¼*
**3031** A1693 50c multi 1.50 .30

Pierre Dugua de Mons, Leader of First French Settlement in Acadia, and Ship A1694

**Litho. & Engr.**
**2004, June 26** *Perf. 13*
**3032** A1694 90c multi 2.75 1.00

See Canada No. 2044.

Napoleon I and the Imperial Guard — A1695

Designs: No. 3033, Light cavalry (Chasseur à cheval). No. 3034, Artilleryman and cannon (Artilleur à pied), horiz. No. 3035, Dragoon. No. 3036, Mameluke. No. 3037, Napoleon I. No. 3038, Grenadier (Grenadier à pied).

**2004, June 26** **Photo.**
**3033** A1695 50c multi 1.50 .75
**3034** A1695 50c multi 1.50 .75
**3035** A1695 50c multi 1.50 .75
**3036** A1695 50c multi 1.50 .75
**3037** A1695 50c multi 1.50 .75
**3038** A1695 50c multi 1.50 .75
*a.* Souvenir sheet, #3033-3038 12.50 12.50
*Nos. 3033-3038 (6)* 9.00 4.50

No. 3038a sold for €4.60, with the Red Cross receiving €1.60 of that.

French Federation of Philatelic Associations 77th Congress, Paris — A1696

**Litho. & Engr.**
**2004, June 27** *Perf. 13¼x13*
**3039** A1696 50c multi 1.50 .30

2004 Summer Olympics, Athens — A1697

**2004, June 28 Photo.** *Perf. 13¼*
**3040** 50c Modern athletes 1.50 .75
**3041** 50c Ancient athletes 1.50 .75
*a.* A1697 Pair, #3040-3041 3.25 2.25

Printed in sheets containing five of each stamp.

A souvenir sheet containing No. 3041 was issued Aug. 2 and sold for €2.51. Value $20.

Happy Birthday A1698

**2004, June 30 Photo.** *Perf. 13¼*
**3042** A1698 50c multi 1.50 .30
*a.* Souvenir sheet of 5 7.50 7.50
*b.* Litho. stamp + label 6.00 6.00

No. 3042b printed in sheets of 10 stamps + 10 labels that could be personalized that sold for €8. No. 3042b has a dark green inscription at left with a distinct dot pattern. No. 3042 has a lighter green inscription.

### Marianne Type of 1997 Inscribed "RF" at Lower Left and Type of 2002 With Euro Denominations

**2004 Litho.** *Perf. 13*
**3043** Sheet of 15 + 15 labels 60.00 60.00
*a.* A1583 1c orange yellow .25 .25
*b.* A1583 2c brown .25 .25
*c.* A1583 5c brt bl green .25 .25
*d.* A1583 10c purple .30 .30
*e.* A1583 20c orange .60 .60
*f.* A1583 58c apple green 1.75 1.75
*g.* A1583 70c olive 2.10 2.10
*h.* A1583 75c sky blue 2.25 2.25
*i.* A1583 90c dark blue 2.75 2.75
*j.* A1583 €1 Prussian blue 3.00 3.00
*k.* A1583 €1.11 red lilac 3.25 3.25
*l.* A1583 €1.90 violet brown 5.75 5.75
*m.* A1583 €2 violet 6.00 6.00
*n.* A1409 (45c) green 1.40 1.40
*o.* A1409 (50c) red 1.50 1.50

**Engr.**
***Serpentine Die Cut 6¾ Vert***
**Self-Adhesive**
**3043P** A1583 75c brt blue + label 8.75 8.75
**3043Q** A1583 €1.11 red lilac + label 10.50 10.50

No. 3043 sold for €10.03. Stamps have a glossy varnish.

Labels on Nos. 3043P-3043Q could be personalized.

Marianne and Emblem of World Fund to Combat AIDS, Tuberculosis and Smoking — A1699

**2004, July 1 Engr.** *Perf. 13*
**3044** A1699 (50c) red 1.50 .35

Extreme Sports — A1700

No. 3045: a, Skateboarding. b, Parachuting. c, Sailboarding. d, Surfing. e, Luge. f, BMX bicycling. g, Paragliding. h, Jetskiing. i, Snowboarding. j, Rollerblading.

**2004, July 3 Photo. *Perf. 13¼x13***

**3045** A1700 Sheet of 10 7.50 7.50
*a.-e.* 20c Any single .60 .50
*f.-j.* 30c Any single .90 .75

### Orchid Type of 2002

Design: 39c, Orchis insularis.

**2004, Sept. 1 Litho. *Perf. 13***

**3046** A1584 39c multi 1.50 .75

No. 3046 known only precanceled. See second note after No. 132.

### Aspects of Life in the French Regions Type of 2003

No. 3047: a, House, Normandy. b, Chambord Chateau. c, Gorges, Tarn, vert. d, Notre Dame Cathedral, Paris, vert. e, Windmill, vert. f, Cave dwellings. g, Creek, Cassis, vert. h, Cap-Ferret Lighthouse, vert. i, Castle ruins. j, Alpine chalet.

**2004, Sept. 18 Photo. *Perf. 13***

**3047** Sheet of 10 15.00 15.00
*a.-j.* A1642 50c Any single 1.50 1.25

No. 3047 has three vertical rows of rouletting separating sheet into quarters.
Each stamp exists in booklet pane of 1 from booklet that sold for €19.

Halloween
A1701

**2004, Oct. 9 Litho. *Perf. 13***

**3048** A1701 50c multi 1.50 .30

Félix Eboué (1884-1944), Colonial Governor — A1702

**2004, Oct. 16 Photo.**

**3049** A1702 50c multi 1.50 .30

Ouistreham Lighthouse
A1703

**2004, Oct. 30 *Perf. 13¼***

**3050** A1703 50c multi 1.50 .30

Marianne — A1704

***Serpentine Die Cut 6¾ Vert.***

**2004, Nov. 10 Engr.**

### Booklet Stamp
### Self-Adhesive

**3051** A1704 50c multi 3.00 2.00
*a.* Booklet pane, 5 each #2835A, 3051 22.50

### European Capitals Type of 2002

No. 3052 — Attractions in Athens: a, Greek Academy. b, Parthenon. c, Odeon of Herodes Atticus. d, Church of the Holy Apostles, vert.

***Perf. 13x13¼, 13¼x13***

**2004, Nov. 11 Photo.**

**3052** A1622 Sheet of 4 7.50 7.50
*a.-d.* 50c Any single 1.50 .90

A1705

A1706

A1707

A1708

A1709

Holiday Greetings
A1710

**2004, Nov. 12 Photo. *Perf. 13***

**3053** A1705 50c multi 1.50 .30

### Litho.

**3054** A1706 50c multi + label 6.00 6.00
**3055** A1707 50c multi + label 6.00 6.00
**3056** A1708 50c multi + label 6.00 6.00
**3057** A1709 50c multi + label 6.00 6.00
**3058** A1710 50c multi + label 6.00 6.00
*a.* Vert. strip of 5, #3054-3059 + 5 labels 30.00 30.00
Miniature sheet, 2 #3058a + 10 labels 70.00 70.00

### Booklet Stamps
### Self-Adhesive

***Serpentine Die Cut 11¼x11***

**3059** A1706 50c multi 1.50 .30
**3060** A1707 50c multi 1.50 .30
**3061** A1708 50c multi 1.50 .30
**3062** A1709 50c multi 1.50 .30
**3063** A1710 50c multi 1.50 .30
*a.* Booklet pane, 2 each #3059-3063 15.00
*Nos. 3053-3063 (11)* 39.00 31.80

Miniature sheet containing Nos. 3054-3058 sold for €6.69. Labels could be personalized. No. 3055 exists in a souvenir sheet of 1 stamp without label that sold for €3. Value $35.

Henri Wallon (1812-1904), Historian and Politician — A1711

**2004, Nov. 13 Photo. *Perf. 13***

**3064** A1711 50c multi 1.50 .30

Opening of Millau Viaduct — A1712

**2004, Dec. 14 Photo. *Perf. 13***

**3065** A1712 50c multi 2.50 1.00

Marianne — A1713

### Inscribed "ITVF" at Bottom

**2005-07 Engr. *Perf. 13***

**3066** A1713 1c yellow .25 .25
*a.* Inscribed "Phil@poste" at bottom .25 .25
**3067** A1713 5c brown black .25 .25
*a.* Inscribed "Phil@poste" at bottom .25 .25
**3068** A1713 10c violet .25 .25
**3069** A1713 (45c) green 1.60 .25
*a.* Inscribed "Phil@poste" at bottom 1.60 .25
**3070** A1713 (50c) red 3.00 .25
*a.* Sheet of 15 + 15 labels 70.00 70.00
*b.* Inscribed "Phil@poste" at bottom 2.00 .25
**3071** A1713 55c dark blue 1.60 .50
**3072** A1713 58c olive green 1.75 .40
**3073** A1713 64c dark green 1.90 .40
**3074** A1713 70c dark green 2.10 .50
**3075** A1713 75c light blue 2.25 .25
**3076** A1713 82c fawn 4.00 .50
**3077** A1713 90c dark blue 2.75 .80
**3078** A1713 €1 orange 3.00 .25
*a.* Inscribed "Phil@poste" at bottom 3.25 .75
**3079** A1713 €1.11 red violet 3.25 .25
**3080** A1713 €1.22 red violet 3.00 .30
**3081** A1713 €1.90 chocolate 5.75 .30
**3082** A1713 €1.98 chocolate 6.00 1.25
*Nos. 3066-3082 (17)* 42.70 6.95

### Self-Adhesive (#3083-3085)

***Serpentine Die Cut 6¾ Vert.***

**3083** A1713 (50c) red 1.50 .25
*a.* Booklet pane of 10 (see footnote) 15.00
*b.* Booklet pane of 10 (see footnote) 15.00
*c.* Booklet pane of 20 30.00
*d.* As #3083, with "Phil@poste" inscription 1.50 .25
*e.* Booklet pane, 10 #3083d 15.00
*f.* Booklet pane of 12 #3083d 17.00
*g.* No. 3083 with attached label 7.50
**3084** A1713 82c fawn + label 12.00 12.00
**3085** A1713 €1.22 red violet 15.00 15.00

### Coil Stamps

***Perf. 13 Horiz.***

**3086** A1713 (45c) green 2.00 .30
*a.* Inscribed "Phil@poste" at bottom 1.40 .25
**3087** A1713 (50c) red 2.00 .25
*c.* Inscribed "Phil@poste" at bottom — —
**3087A** A1713 55c dark blue 2.50 1.25
*b.* Inscribed "Phil@poste" at bottom 1.60 .25
*Nos. 3083-3087A (6)* 35.00 29.05

Issued: Nos. 1c, 10c, (45c), (50c), 58c, 70c, 75c, 90c, €1, €1.11, €1.90, 1/8. 5c, No. 3071, 64c, 82c, €1.22, €1.98, 3/1. No. 3087A, 7/15. Nos. 3083d, 3083e, 10/1/06. Nos. 3066a, 3067a, 3069a, 3070b, 2006. No. 3083f, Jan. 2007. Nos. 3083g, 3084-3085, Apr. 2007. No. 3086a was issued in 2008 and sold for 50c. No. 3087b was issued in 2008 and sold for 55c.

Face values shown for Nos. 3069, 3070, 3083, 3086 and 3087 are those the stamps sold for on the day of issue. On day of issue, No. 3069a sold for 49c; No. 3070b for 54c.

No. 3070a sold for €10.03 and the labels could be personalized for an additional fee.

No. 3083a has a narrow strip of selvage separating the four stamps at left, from the six stamps, at right, and is on a white backing paper. No. 3083b is comprised of two horizontal strips of five stamps on a yellow backing paper. No. 3083d sold for 54c on day of issue.

No. 3083g was printed in sheets containing 15 stamps + 15 small or large-sized labels that could be personalized. Nos. 3084 and 3085 were each printed in sheets of 30 stamps + 30 large-sized labels that could be personalized.

A sheet of 10 litho. stamps similar to No. 3068 + 10 labels exists, but was not sold.

See Nos. 3211, 3211N, 3212, 3247-3255E, 3302, 3383-3388A, 3389, 3531, 4410k, 4524.

Rabbi Shlomo Yitshaqi (Rashi) (1040-1105) — A1714

**2005, Jan. 16 Engr. *Perf. 13¼***

**3088** A1714 50c multi 1.75 .30

Hearts
A1715

Designs: 53c, Polka dots. 82c, Bird and flowers.

**2005, Jan. 29 Photo. *Perf. 13¼***

**3089** A1715 53c multi 1.50 .30
*a.* Souvenir sheet of 5 7.50 7.50
*b.* Litho, stamp + label 6.00 6.00
**3090** A1715 82c multi 2.50 1.00
*a.* Litho, stamp + label 6.00 6.00

Values are for stamps with surrounding selvage.

Sheets of 10 of No. 3089b sold for €6.86, and sheets of 10 of No. 3090a sold for €8.78. Labels could be personalized for an additional fee.

See Nos. 3134, 3136.

New Year 2005 (Year of the Rooster)
A1716

### Photo. & Embossed

**2005, Jan. 29 *Perf. 13½x13***

**3091** A1716 (50c) multi 1.75 .30

Printed in sheets of 10. See No. 4969a.

Rotary International, Cent. — A1717

**2005, Feb. 19 Photo. *Perf. 13¼***

**3092** A1717 53c multi 1.50 .30

See No. 3227A.

Titeuf — A1718

Nadia — A1719

Manu — A1720

**2005, Feb. 28 Photo. *Perf. 13¼***

| | | | |
|---|---|---|---|
| **3093** | A1718 (50c) red & multi | 1.50 | .30 |
| *a.* | Perf. 13¼x13 (booklet stamp) | 1.50 | .30 |

**Booklet Stamps**

| | | | |
|---|---|---|---|
| **3094** | A1719 (45c) green & multi | 3.00 | .60 |
| **3095** | A1720 (90c) blue & multi | 2.50 | 1.00 |
| *a.* | Booklet pane, 2 #3094, 4 each #3093a, 3095 | 22.00 | — |
| | Complete booklet, #3095a | 23.00 | |

Characters from Titeuf, comic strip by Zep. Stamp Day.

**Greetings Type of 2004 Inscribed "Lettre 20g"**

Designs: Nos. 3096, 3097A, "Ceci est une invitation." Nos. 3097, 3097B, "Un grand merci."

No. 3097C, "Ceci est une invitation." No. 3097D, "Un grand merci."

**2005-06 Photo. *Perf. 13***

**Holes Punched Through Dots of "i's"**

| | | | |
|---|---|---|---|
| **3096** | A1667 (53c) brt lil rose & yel | 2.00 | .30 |
| **3097** | A1667 (53c) brt yel grn & red lil | 2.00 | .30 |

**Litho.**

**No Holes Punched Through Dots of "i's"**

**Stamp + Label**

| | | | |
|---|---|---|---|
| **3097A** | A1667 (53c) brt lil rose & yel | 5.00 | |
| **3097B** | A1667 (53c) brt yel grn & red lil | 5.00 | |

**Self-Adhesive**

**No Holes Punched Through Dots of "i's"**

***Serpentine Die Cut 11¼x11***

**Stamp + Label**

| | | | |
|---|---|---|---|
| **3097C** | A1667 (53c) brt lil rose & yel | 5.00 | 5.00 |
| **3097D** | A1667 (53c) brt yel grn & rrd lil | 5.00 | 5.00 |

Nos. 3097A-3097B were issued in sheets of 10 stamps + 10 labels that sold for €8 on day of issue. The labels could be personalized.

Nos. 3097C-3097D were each issued in sheets of 10 stamps + 10 labels that sold for €8.61. Labels could be personalized.

Issued: Nos. 2096-3097B, 3/1/05. Nos. 3097C-3097D, 2006.

**Art Series**

The Guitarist, by Jean-Baptiste Greuze (1725-1805) — A1721

White Bear, Sculpture by François Pompon — A1722

Sicile, by Nicolas de Stael — A1723

**2005 Photo. *Perf. 13x13¼***

| | | | | |
|---|---|---|---|---|
| **3098** | A1721 | 82c multi | 2.50 | .50 |
| **3099** | A1722 | 90c multi | 3.00 | 1.25 |
| **3100** | A1723 | €1.22 multi | 3.75 | 1.25 |

Issued: €1.22, 3/5. 90c, 7/2. 82c, 9/24.

Orchids — A1725

Designs: No. 3102, Cypripedium calceolus. No. 3103, Paphiopedilum Mabel Sanders. 55c, Oncidium papilio. 82c, Paphinia cristata, horiz.

**2005, Mar. 11 Photo. *Perf. 13¼***

| | | | |
|---|---|---|---|
| **3102** | A1725 53c multi | 1.60 | .30 |
| **3103** | A1725 53c multi | 1.60 | .30 |
| **3104** | A1725 55c multi | 1.60 | .30 |
| **3105** | A1725 82c multi | 2.50 | .60 |
| *a.* | Souvenir sheet, #3102-3105 | 7.50 | 7.50 |
| | *Nos. 3102-3105 (4)* | 7.30 | 1.50 |

**Aspects of Life in French Regions Type of 2003**

No. 3106: a, Nautical jousting. b, Clocks of Franche-Comte, vert. c, Cantal cheese and bread, vert. d, Dancers and accordion player. e, Bouillabaisse. f, P'tit Quinquin statue, vert. g, Rillettes (chopped pork). h, Sauerkraut and sausage, beer stein. i, Pelota, vert. j, Sugar cane, vert.

**2005, Mar. 19 Photo. *Perf. 13***

| | | | |
|---|---|---|---|
| **3106** | Sheet of 10 | 16.00 | 16.00 |
| *a.-j.* | A1642 53c Any single | 1.50 | 1.25 |

No. 3106 has three vertical rows of rouletting, separating sheet into quarters.

Each stamp exists in a booklet pane of 1 from a booklet that sold for €19. Value $50.

**Tourism Issue**

Aix-en-Provence — A1726

Gulf of Morbihan — A1727

Villefranche-sur-Mer — A1728

La Roque-Gageac — A1729

**2005 Engr. *Perf. 13¼, 13 (#3108)***

| | | | |
|---|---|---|---|
| **3107** | A1726 53c multi | 1.60 | .30 |

**Photo.**

| | | | |
|---|---|---|---|
| **3108** | A1727 53c multi | 1.60 | .30 |
| **3109** | A1728 53c multi | 1.60 | .30 |

**Engr.**

| | | | |
|---|---|---|---|
| **3110** | A1729 53c multi | 1.60 | .30 |

Issued: No. 3107, 4/1; No. 3108, 5/5; No. 3109, 6/4; No. 3110, 7/23.

Happy Birthday A1730

**2005, Apr. 2 Photo. *Perf. 13***

| | | | |
|---|---|---|---|
| **3111** | A1730 (53c) multi | 2.00 | .30 |
| *a.* | Souvenir sheet of 5 | 10.00 | 9.00 |
| *b.* | Litho., stamp + label | 8.00 | 8.00 |

Sheets of 10 and 10 labels of No. 3111b sold for €6.86. Labels could be personalized for an additional fee.

Albert Einstein (1879-1955), Physicist — A1731

**2005, Apr. 16 *Perf. 13¼***

| | | | |
|---|---|---|---|
| **3112** | A1731 53c multi | 1.60 | .30 |

Alexis de Tocqueville (1805-59), Writer — A1732

**2005, Apr. 23 Engr. *Perf. 13x13¼***

| | | | |
|---|---|---|---|
| **3113** | A1732 90c multi | 2.75 | 1.00 |

Liberation of Concentration Camp Internees, 60th Anniv. — A1733

**2005, Apr. 24 Photo. *Perf. 13¼***

| | | | |
|---|---|---|---|
| **3114** | A1733 53c multi | 1.60 | .30 |

Battle of Austerlitz, Bicent. A1734

**Litho. & Engr.**

**2005, May 4 *Perf. 13¼***

| | | | |
|---|---|---|---|
| **3115** | A1734 55c multi | 1.60 | .45 |

See Czech Republic No. 3273.

French Federation of Philatelic Associations, 78th Congress, Nancy — A1735

**2005, May 5 Engr. *Perf. 13***

| | | | |
|---|---|---|---|
| **3116** | A1735 53c multi + label | 1.60 | .30 |

A souvenir sheet of one stamp without label exists. Value $12.

Europa — A1736

**2005, May 8 Photo. *Perf. 13¼***

| | | | |
|---|---|---|---|
| **3117** | A1736 53c multi | 1.60 | .30 |

**Gardens and Parks Type of 2003**

Souvenir Sheet

No. 3118 — Sculptures in Jardin de la Fontaine, Nimes: a, Denomination in green. b, Denomination in white.

**2005, May 15 *Perf. 13¼x13***

| | | | |
|---|---|---|---|
| **3118** | Sheet of 2 | 12.00 | 12.00 |
| *a.-b.* | A1660 €1.98 Either single | 6.00 | 6.00 |

Salon du Timbre 2005. No. 3118 has four vertical rows of rouletting, separating sheet into fifths, with the two stamps in the central fifth.

Vacation
A1737

***Serpentine Die Cut 11***

**2005, May 23** **Litho.**

**Booklet Stamp**

**Self-Adhesive**

**3119** A1737 (53c) multi 2.00 .25
*a.* Booklet pane of 10 20.00

Stories by Jules Verne (1828-1905)
A1738

Designs: No. 3120, Five Weeks in a Balloon (Cinq Semaines en Ballon). No. 3121, From the Earth to the Moon (De la Terre à la Lune). No. 3122, Journey to the Center of the Earth (Voyage au Centre de la Terre), horiz. No. 3123, Michael Strogoff, horiz. No. 3124, Around the World in Eighty Days (Le Tour du Monde en Quatre-vingts Jours). No. 3125, 20,000 Leagues Under the Sea (Vingt Mille Lieues Sous les Mers).

**2005, May 28** **Photo.** ***Perf. 13***

**3120** A1738 53c multi 1.60 .75
**3121** A1738 53c multi 1.60 .75
**3122** A1738 53c multi 1.60 .75
**3123** A1738 53c multi 1.60 .75
**3124** A1738 53c multi 1.60 .75
**3125** A1738 53c multi 1.60 .75
*a.* Souvenir sheet, #3120-3125 12.00 12.00
*Nos. 3120-3125 (6)* 9.60 4.50

No. 3125a sold for €4.80 with the Red Cross receiving €1.62 of that.

Miniature Sheet

Gordon Bennett Cup, Cent. — A1739

No. 3126 — Inscriptions: a, La Coupe Gordon Bennett (Car No. 1 facing right). b, La Coupe Gordon Bennett (Car No. 1 facing left). c, La Formule 1, vert. d, Le Rallye-Raid, vert. e, Les Rallyes. f, La Course d'endurance.

**2005, June 2** **Photo.** ***Perf.***

**3126** A1739 Sheet of 10, #a-b, 2 each #c-f 19.00 19.00
*a.-f.* 53c Any single 1.75 .85

A souvenir sheet containing No. 3126a sold for €3. Value $100.

Environmental Charter — A1740

**2005, June 5** **Litho.** ***Perf. 13***

**3127** A1740 53c multi, *lt green* 1.60 .30

Enactment of Handicapped Persons Rights Law — A1741

**2005, June 18** **Photo.** ***Perf. 13¼***

**3128** A1741 53c multi 1.60 .30

It's a Boy
A1742

It's a Girl
A1743

**2005** **Litho.** ***Perf. 13x13¼***

**3129** A1742 (53c) multi + label 5.00 5.00
**3130** A1743 (53c) multi + label 5.00 5.00

**Booklet Stamps**

**Self-Adhesive**

***Serpentine Die Cut 11¼x11***

**3131** A1742 (53c) multi 2.00 .30
*a.* Booklet pane of 10 20.00
*b.* Sheet of 10 + 10 labels 50.00
**3132** A1743 (53c) multi 2.00 .30
*a.* Booklet pane of 10 20.00
*b.* Sheet of 10 + 10 labels 50.00

Sheets of 10 stamps and 10 labels of Nos. 3129 and 3130 each sold for €6.86. Nos. 3131b and 3132b each sold for €8.61. Labels could be personalized for an additional fee.

**Hearts Types of 2004-05**

***Serpentine Die Cut***

**2005, July 15** **Photo.**

**Self-Adhesive**

**3133** A1670 50c Like #2997 4.00 2.50
**3134** A1715 53c Like #3089 4.00 3.00
**3135** A1670 75c Like #2998 6.00 3.50
**3136** A1715 82c Like #3090 6.00 4.00
*Nos. 3133-3136 (4)* 20.00 13.00

Haras du Pin Natl. Stud Farm
A1744

**2005, July 16** ***Perf. 13***

**3137** A1744 53c multi 1.60 .30

**European Capitals Type of 2002**

No. 3138 — Attractions in Berlin: a, Brandenburg Gate. b, Kaiser Wilhelm Memorial Church, vert. c, Philharmonic Hall. d, Reichstag.

***Perf. 13x13¼, 13¼x13***

**2005, Aug. 27** **Photo.**

**3138** A1622 Sheet of 4 7.00 7.00
*a.-d.* 53c Any single 1.75 1.00

**Aspects of Life in the French Regions Type of 2003**

No. 3139: a, Lake Annecy. b, Etretat Cliffs, vert. c, Pigeon house, vert. d, Wash house (lavoir). e, Banks of the Seine. f, Carnac megaliths. g, House, Sologne. h, Pilat Sand Dune. i, Stiff Lighthouse, vert. j, Stone hut (borie), vert.

**2005, Sept. 17** ***Perf. 13***

**3139** Sheet of 10 17.00 17.00
*a.-j.* A1642 53c Any single 1.60 1.25

No. 3139 has three vertical rows of rouletting, separating sheet into quarters.

Nos. 3139a-3139j were also issued in large booklets containing panes of 1 of each stamp. The booklet sold for €19. Value $60.

**Art Series**

Les Halles Centrales, Designed by Victor Baltard (1805-74) — A1745

**2005, Sept. 17** **Engr.** ***Perf. 13x13¼***

**3140** A1745 €1.22 multi 3.75 1.10

Breast Cancer Awareness
A1746

**2005, Oct. 1** **Photo.** ***Perf. 13¼***

**3141** A1746 53c multi 1.60 .30

A1747

A1748

A1749

A1750

A1754

A1755

Cat, Comics by Philippe Geluck
A1756

Additional designs (continued in column 3): A1751, A1752, A1753.

A1751

A1752

A1753

***Serpentine Die Cut 11¼x11***

**2005, Oct. 1** **Litho.**

**Booklet Stamps**

**Self-Adhesive**

**3142** A1747 (53c) multi 2.00 .30
**3143** A1748 (53c) multi 2.00 .30
**3144** A1749 (53c) multi 2.00 .30
**3145** A1750 (53c) multi 2.00 .30
**3146** A1751 (53c) multi 2.00 .30
**3147** A1752 (53c) multi 2.00 .30
**3148** A1753 (53c) multi 2.00 .30
**3149** A1754 (53c) multi 2.00 .30
**3150** A1755 (53c) multi 2.00 .30
**3151** A1756 (53c) multi 2.00 .30
*a.* Booklet pane of 10, #3142-3151 20.00

Raymond Aron (1905-83), Philosopher
A1757

**2005, Oct. 7** **Engr.** ***Perf. 13¼x13***

**3152** A1757 53c multi 1.60 .30

Souvenir Sheet

The Annunciation, by Raphael — A1758

No. 3153: a, Drawing of Angel, painting of Virgin Mary. b, Painting of Angel, drawing of Virgin Mary.

**Litho. & Engr.**

**2005, Nov. 10** ***Perf. 13x13¼***

**3153** A1758 Sheet of 2 4.00 4.00
*a.* 53c multi 1.60 1.60
*b.* 55c multi 1.75 1.75

See Vatican City Nos. 1312-1314.

Marianne — A1759

*Serpentine Die Cut 6¾ Vert.*

**2005, Nov. 11 Engr.**

**Booklet Stamp**

**Self-Adhesive**

**3154** A1759 53c red 3.50 3.00
*a.* Booklet pane, 5 each #3083, 3154 25.00

See No. 4911.

Video Game Characters — A1760

No. 3155: a, Link. b, Pac-Man. c, Prince of Persia. d, Spyro. e, Donkey Kong. f, Mario. g, Adibou. h, Rayman. i, Lara Croft. j, The Sims.

**2005, Nov. 11 Photo.** *Perf. 13¼x13*

**3155** A1760 Sheet of 10 9.00 9.00
*a.-e.* 20c Any single .60 .50
*f.-j.* 33c Any single 1.00 .75

Avicenna (980-1037), Scientist — A1761

**2005, Nov. 12 Engr.** *Perf. 13x13¼*

**3156** A1761 53c multi 1.60 .30

Holiday Greetings A1762

Designs: Nos. 3157, 3162, Bear, three penguins and sled. Nos. 3158, 3163, Two penguins, reindeer and sled. Nos. 3159, 3164, Two penguins, bear and sled. Nos. 3160, 3165, Three penguins. Nos. 3161, 3166, Two penguins, reindeer and snowman.

**2005, Nov. 12 Litho.** *Perf. 13*

**3157** A1762 (53c) multi + label 6.00 4.00
**3158** A1762 (53c) multi + label 6.00 4.00
**3159** A1762 (53c) multi + label 6.00 4.00
**3160** A1762 (53c) multi + label 6.00 4.00
**3161** A1762 (53c) multi + label 6.00 4.00
*a.* Vert. strip of 5, #3157-3161, + 5 labels *30.00 30.00*
Miniature sheet, 2 #3161a *60.00 60.00*

**Booklet Stamps**

**Self-Adhesive**

*Serpentine Die Cut 11¼x11*

**3162** A1762 (53c) multi 2.00 .30
**3163** A1762 (53c) multi 2.00 .30
**3164** A1762 (53c) multi 2.00 .30
**3165** A1762 (53c) multi 2.00 .30
**3166** A1762 (53c) multi 2.00 .30
*a.* Booklet pane, 2 each #3162-3166 16.00
*Nos. 3157-3166 (10)* 40.00 21.50

Miniature sheet containing Nos. 3157-3161 sold for €6.86. Labels could be personalized.

No. 3161 exists in a souvenir sheet of one stamp without label, that sold for €3. Value $30.

Jacob Kaplan (1895-1994), Grand Rabbi of France — A1763

**2005, Nov. 14 Engr.** *Perf. 13*

**3167** A1763 53c multi 1.60 .30

**Orchid Type of 2002**

Design: Orchis insularis.

**2005 Litho.** *Perf. 13*

**3168** A1584 42c multi 2.50 .75

No. 3168 is known only precanceled. See second note after No. 132.

Law Separating Church and State, Cent. — A1764

**2005, Dec. 3 Photo.** *Perf. 13¼x13*

**3169** A1764 53c multi 1.60 .30

Hearts A1765

Designs: (53c), Hearts, octagons and diamonds. (82c), Heart and stripes.

**2006, Jan. 7 Photo.** *Perf. 13¼*

**3170** A1765 (53c) multi 1.60 .30
*a.* Souvenir sheet of 5 10.00 8.00
*b.* Litho., stamp + label 5.00 5.00
**3171** A1765 (82c) multi 3.00 1.00
*a.* Litho., stamp + label 12.00 12.00

**Self-Adhesive**

*Serpentine Die Cut*

**3172** A1765 (53c) Like #3170 4.00 3.00
*a.* Sheet of 10 + 10 labels 40.00
**3173** A1765 (82c) Like #3171 6.00 4.50
*a.* Sheet of 10 + 10 labels 60.00

Values are for stamps with surrounding selvage. Sheets of 10 of No. 3170b sold for €6.86, and sheets of No. 3172a sold for €8.61; No. 3173a for €11.54. Labels could be personalized for an additional fee.

New Year 2006 (Year of the Dog) — A1766

**2006, Jan. 21 Photo.** *Perf. 13¼x13*

**3174** A1766 (53c) multi 1.60 .30

A souvenir sheet containing No. 3174 sold for €3. Value $8.

See No. 4969b.

Impressionist Paintings — A1767

Designs: Nos. 3175a, 3176, Portraits from the Country, by Gustave Caillebotte. Nos. 3175b, 3183, Dancers, by Edgar Degas. Nos. 3175c, 3181, Marguerite Gachet in the Garden, by Vincent van Gogh. Nos. 3175d, 3179, Two Young Girls at the Piano, by Auguste Renoir. Nos. 3175e, 3177, The Butterfly Hunt, by Berthe Morisot. Nos. 3175f, 3184, Luncheon on the Grass, by Edouard Manet. Nos. 3175g, 3182, Evening Air, by Henri-Edmond Cross. Nos. 3175h, 3180, The Shepherdess (Young Peasant Girl with a Stick), by Camille Pissarro. Nos. 3175i, 3178, Mother and Child, by Mary Cassatt. Nos. 3175j, 3185, Women of Tahiti on the Beach, by Paul Gauguin.

**2006 Litho.** *Perf. 13¼*

**3175** Sheet of 10 +10 labels 60.00 60.00
*a.-j.* A1767 (53c) Any single + label 5.00 5.00

**Booklet Stamps**

**Self-Adhesive**

*Serpentine Die Cut 11¼x11*

**3176** A1767 (53c) multi 2.00 .30
**3177** A1767 (53c) multi 2.00 .30
**3178** A1767 (53c) multi 2.00 .30
**3179** A1767 (53c) multi 2.00 .30
**3180** A1767 (53c) multi 2.00 .30
**3181** A1767 (53c) multi 2.00 .30
**3182** A1767 (53c) multi 2.00 .30
**3183** A1767 (53c) multi 2.00 .30
**3184** A1767 (53c) multi 2.00 .30
**3185** A1767 (53c) multi 2.00 .30
*a.* Booklet pane of 10, #3176-3185 20.00
*b.* Sheet of 10, #3176-3185, + 10 labels *110.00*

Issued: No. 3175, 6/1; Nos. 3176-3185, 1/21. No. 3175 sold for €6.86. No. 3185b sold for €8.61. Labels could be personalized.

2006 Winter Olympics, Turin — A1768

**2006, Feb. 4 Photo.** *Perf. 13*

**3186** A1768 53c multi 1.60 .30

Spirou — A1769

Fantasio, Spip and Spirou — A1770

Fantasio A1771

**2006, Feb. 25** *Perf. 13¼*

**3187** A1769 (53c) multi 2.00 .30
*a.* Perf. 13¼x13 (booklet stamp) 1.25 .30

**Booklet Stamps**

*Perf. 13¼x13*

**3188** A1770 (48c) multi 2.50 1.00
**3189** A1771 (90c) multi 3.00 .75
*a.* Booklet pane, 4 each #3187a, 3188, 2 #3189 23.00 —
Complete booklet, #3189a 24.00

Characters from Spirou, by Robert Velter. Stamp Day.

Courrières Coal Mine Disaster, Cent. — A1772

**2006, Feb. 25** *Perf. 13¼*

**3190** A1772 53c multi 1.60 .30

Douaumont Ossuary — A1773

**2006, Mar. 4 Engr.**

**3191** A1773 53c multi 1.60 .30

**Aspects of Life in the French Regions Type of 2003**

No. 3192: a, Yellow plums (mirabelle). b, Salt marsh (marais salants). c, Butter (beurre). d, Roquefort cheese, vert. e, Olive oil, vert. f, Carnival, vert. g, Grape harvests (vendanges), vert. h, Waiter at café, vert. i, Transhumance of livestock. j, Marshland gardens (hortillonages).

**2006, Mar. 25 Photo.** *Perf. 13*

**3192** Sheet of 10 16.00 16.00
*a.-j.* A1642 53c Any single 1.60 1.25

No. 3192 has three vertical rows of rouletting, separating sheet into quarters.

Nos. 3192a-3192j were also issued in large booklets containing panes of 1 of each stamp. The booklet sold for €19. Value $35.

**Tourism Issue**

Yvoire A1774

Dijon A1775

Antibes Juan-les-Pins — A1776

Thionville A1777

**2006 Photo. *Perf. 13***

**3193** A1774 53c multi 1.60 .30

**Engr.**

***Perf. 13¼***

**3194** A1775 53c multi 1.60 .30

**Litho. & Engr.**

***Perf. 13x13¼***

**3195** A1776 53c multi 1.60 .30

**Engraved**

**3196** A1777 54c multi 1.60 .40
*Nos. 3193-3196 (4)* 6.40 1.30

Issued: No. 3193, 3/25; No. 3194, 4/7. No. 3195, 7/15. No. 3196, 9/16.

**Art Series**

Prehistoric Drawings in Rouffignac Cave — A1778

Bathers, by Paul Cézanne — A1779

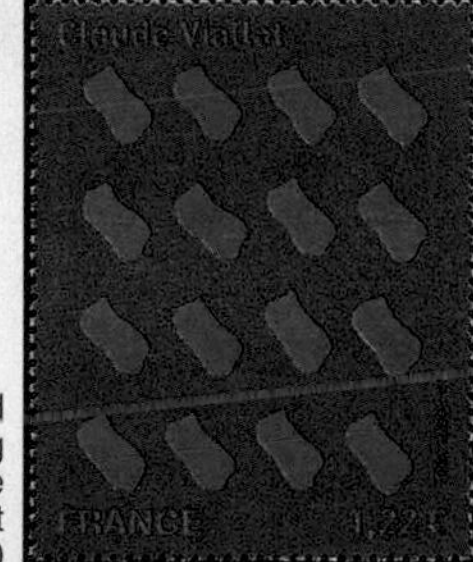


Untitled Painting by Claude Viallat A1780

Beggars Receiving Alms at the Door of a House, by Rembrandt A1781

**Engr., Photo (#3198, 3199)**

**2006 *Perf. 13x13¼***

**3197** A1778 55c multi 2.25 .75
**3198** A1779 82c multi 2.50 1.00

***Perf. 13¼x13***

**3199** A1780 €1.22 brt pink & bl grn 3.75 1.25
**3200** A1781 €1.30 multi 4.75 1.25
*Nos. 3197-3200 (4)* 13.25 4.25

Issued: 82c, 4/8; 55c, 5/27; No. 3199, 6/3. No. 3200, 11/10.

**Gardens and Parks Type of 2003**

Souvenir Sheet

No. 3201: a, Vallée-aux-Loups Park. b, Albert Kahn Gardens.

**2006, Apr. 22 Photo. *Perf. 13¼x13***

**3201** Sheet of 2 13.00 13.00
*a.-b.* A1660 €1.98 Either single 6.00 5.00
*c.* Souvenir sheet, #3118a, 3118b, 3201a, 3201b 50.00 50.00

Salon du Timbre 2006. No. 3201 has four vertical rows of rouletting, separating sheet into fifths, with the two stamps in the central fifth.

No. 3201c issued 6/16.

Young Animals A1782

Designs: No. 3202, Puppy. No. 3203, Kitten. 55c, Foal, horiz. 82c, Lamb, horiz..

**2006, Apr. 22 *Perf. 13¼***

**3202** A1782 53c multi 1.60 .30
**3203** A1782 53c multi 1.60 .30
**3204** A1782 55c multi 1.60 .30
**3205** A1782 82c multi 2.40 .75
*a.* Souvenir sheet, #3202-3205 7.50 7.50
*Nos. 3202-3205 (4)* 7.20 1.65

Europa A1783

**2006, Apr. 30**

**3206** A1783 53c multi 1.60 .30

Pierre Bayle (1647-1706), Philiosopher A1784

**2006, May 2 Engr. *Perf. 13x13¼***

**3207** A1784 53c blk & brn 1.60 .30

Remembrance of Slavery Day, 5th Anniv. — A1785

**2006, May 10 Photo. *Perf. 13¼***

**3208** A1785 53c multi 1.60 .30

Vacation A1786

***Serpentine Die Cut 11¼x11***

**2006, May 27 Litho.**

**Booklet Stamp**

**Self-Adhesive**

**3209** A1786 (53c) multi 2.00 .25
*a.* Booklet pane of 10 20.00

Miniature Sheet

2006 World Cup Soccer Championships, Germany — A1787

No. 3210: a, Replacement players (39x25mm). b, Fans (39x25mm). c, Player with ball near chest (32mm diameter). d, Player kicking ball (32mm diameter). e, Goalie throwing ball (32mm diameter). f, Player making scissor kick (32mm diameter). g, Two players (32mm diameter). h, Referee (25x39mm). i, Coach (39x25mm). j, Cameramen (39x25mm).

**2006, May 27 Photo. *Perf. 12¾***

**3210** A1787 Sheet of 10 16.00 16.00
*a.-j.* 53c Any single 1.60 1.25

**Marianne Type of 2005**

**2006 Litho. *Perf. 13***

**3211** Sheet of 15, #a-k, 2 each #l-m, + 15 labels 70.00 70.00
*a.* A1713 1c yellow orange .35 .35
*b.* A1713 5c dark brown .35 .35
*c.* A1713 10c violet .55 .55
*d.* A1713 55c blue 2.75 2.75
*e.* A1713 64c olive green 3.25 3.25
*f.* A1713 75c light blue 3.50 3.50
*g.* A1713 82c fawn 4.25 4.25
*h.* A1713 90c dark blue 4.50 4.50
*i.* A1713 €1 dull orange 5.00 5.00
*j.* A1713 €1.22 red violet 6.00 6.00
*k.* A1713 €1.98 brown 9.50 9.50
*l.* A1713 (48c) green 2.50 2.50
*m.* A1713 (53c) red 2.60 2.60

***Serpentine Die Cut 11¼***

**Self-Adhesive**

**3211N** Sheet of 15, #3211No-3211Ny, 2 each #3211Nz, 3211Naa, + 15 labels *250.00*
*o.* A1713 1c yellow orange .75 .75
*p.* A1713 5c dark brown .75 .75
*q.* A1713 10c violet 1.25 1.25
*r.* A1713 55c blue 6.75 6.75
*s.* A1713 64c olive green 7.50 7.50
*t.* A1713 75c light blue 8.75 8.75
*u.* A1713 82c fawn 9.50 9.50
*v.* A1713 90c dark blue 11.00 11.00
*w.* A1713 €1 dull orange 12.00 12.00
*x.* A1713 €1.22 red violet 15.00 15.00
*y.* A1713 €1.98 brown 20.00 20.00
*z.* A1713 (48c) green 5.50 5.50
*aa* A1713 (53c) red 6.25 6.25

**Etched on Foil**

***Die Cut Perf. 13***

**3212** A1713 €5 *silver* 17.50 12.50

Nos. 3211a-3211m, 3211No-3211Naa and 3212 have "Phil@poste" inscription at bottom. Nos. 3211 and 3211N have stamps with a glossy varnish. No. 3211 sold for €12.04 and labels could be personalized. No. 3211N sold for €15.05 and labels could be personalized. No. 3212 was sold in a protective package.

Costumes From Operas by Wolfgang Amadeus Mozart — A1788

Designs: No. 3213, The Magic Flute. No. 3214, Don Giovanni. No. 3215, The Marriage of Figaro. No. 3216, The Clemency of Titus. No. 3217, The Abduction from the Seraglio (L'enlèvement au Sérail). No. 3218, Cosi Fan Tutte.

**2006, June 17 Photo. *Perf. 13***

**3213** A1788 53c multi 1.60 .75
**3214** A1788 53c multi 1.60 .75
**3215** A1788 53c multi 1.60 .75
**3216** A1788 53c multi 1.60 .75
**3217** A1788 53c multi 1.60 .75
**3218** A1788 53c multi 1.60 .75
*a.* Souvenir sheet, #3213-3218 12.00 12.00
*Nos. 3213-3218 (6)* 9.60 4.50

Nos. 3213-3218 were each printed in souvenir sheets containing one stamp that sold as a set for €15, and in booklet panes containing one stamp in a large book that sold for €19. Value: set of 6 sheets $40; set of 6 panes in book $50. No. 3218a sold for €4.80, with the Red Cross receiving €1.62 of that.

UNESCO World Heritage Sites A1789

Designs: 53c, Provins. 90c, Mont Saint-Michel.

**2006, June 17 Photo. *Perf. 13¼***

**3219** A1789 53c multi 1.60 .30
**3220** A1789 90c multi 2.75 1.20

See United Nations Offices in Geneva Nos. 459-461.

Garnier Opera House, Paris — A1790

**2006, June 18 Engr. *Perf. 13x13¼***

**3221** A1790 53c multi + label 1.60 .40

French Federation of Philatelic Associations 79th Congress, Paris. No. 3221 exists in a souvenir sheet of 1 (without label), issued in 2007 that sold for €3. Value, $12.

Happy Birthday A1791

**2006, June 19 Photo. *Perf. 13***

**3222** A1791 (53c) multi 2.00 .30
*a.* Souvenir sheet of 5 10.00 10.00
*b.* Litho. stamp + label 6.00 6.00

***Serpentine Die Cut 11***

**Self-Adhesive**

**3222C** A1791 (53c) multi + label 15.00 15.00

Sheets of 10 of No. 3222b sold for €6.86. No. 3222C was printed in sheets of 10 stamps + 10 labels that sold for €8.61. Labels could be personalized for an additional fee.

**European Capitals Type of 2002**

Souvenir Sheet

No. 3223 — Attractions in Nicosia, Cyprus: a, Chrysaliniotissa Church. b, Archaeological Museum. c, Famagusta Gate. d, Archbishop's residence (Archeveché).

**2006, June 20 Photo. *Perf. 13x13¼***

**3223** A1622 Sheet of 4 7.00 7.00
*a.-d.* 53c Any single 1.60 1.00

Tango Dancing A1792

**2006, June 21** **Photo.** ***Perf. 12¼***
**3224** A1792 53c Dancers 1.60 .30
**3225** A1792 90c Musician 2.75 1.20

See Argentina Nos. 2395-2396.

La Poste's Business Foundation, 10th Anniv. — A1793

**2006, June 22** **Litho.** ***Perf. 13***
**3226** A1793 (53c) multi, *tan* 2.00 .30

French Open Golf Championship, Cent. — A1794

**Photo. & Embossed**
**2006, June 24** ***Perf. 13***
**3227** A1794 53c multi 1.60 .30

A souvenir sheet containing No. 3227 sold for €3. Value $8.

**Rotary International Type of 2005**
***Serpentine Die Cut 11***
**2006, July 1** **Photo.**
**Self-Adhesive**
**3227A** A1717 53c multi 5.00 4.00

French Soccer Team's Second-Place Showing in 2006 World Cup — A1795

**2006, July 5** **Photo.** ***Perf. 13¼***
**Size: 35x26mm**
**3228** A1795 53c multi 1.60 .40
**Litho.**
**Size: 35x22mm**
***Perf. 13***
**3229** A1795 53c multi + label 5.00 4.00
***Serpentine Die Cut 11¼x11***
**Self-Adhesive**
**3229A** A1795 53c multi + label 13.00 13.00

No. 3229 was printed in sheets of 10 stamps and 10 labels that sold for €6.94. Value $55. No. 3229A was printed in sheets of 10 stamps + 10 labels that sold for €8.61. Value $150. Labels could be personalized.

Quai Branly Museum — A1796

**2006, July 8** **Photo.** ***Perf. 13x13¼***
**3230** A1796 53c multi 1.60 .40

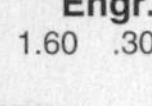

Reinstatement of Capt. Alfred Dreyfus, Cent. — A1797

**2006, July 12** **Engr.**
**3231** A1797 53c multi 1.60 .30

Claude-Joseph Rouget de Lisle (1760-1836), Composer of "La Marseillaise" — A1798

**2006, July 13** **Photo.** ***Perf. 13¼***
**3232** A1798 53c multi 1.60 .30

Pablo Casals (1876-1973), Cellist — A1799

**2006, July 29**
**3233** A1799 53c multi 1.60 .30

**Aspects of Life in French Regions Type of 2003**

No. 3234: a, Catalan Towers. b, La Croisette, Cannes. c, Brocéliande Forest. d, Volcanic craters, Auvergne, vert. e, Les Invalides, Paris, vert. f, Chateau de Chaumont, Chaumont-sur-Loire. g, Ardèche Gorges, vert. h, Flour mill, Valmy, vert. i, Grotto of Messabielle, Lourdes. j, Calanches de Piana, Corsica.

**2006, Sept. 2** **Photo.** ***Perf. 13***
**3234** Sheet of 10 16.00 16.00
*a.-j.* A1642 54c Any single 1.60 1.25

No. 3234 has three vertical rows of rouletting, separating sheet into quarters.

Nos. 3234a-3234j were also issued in large booklets containing panes of 1 of each stamp. The booklet sold for €19. Value $35.

A1800

A1801

A1802

A1803

A1804

A1805

A1806

A1807

A1808

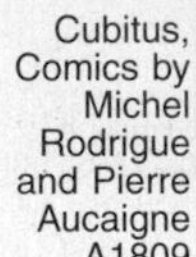

Cubitus, Comics by Michel Rodrigue and Pierre Aucaigne A1809

***Serpentine Die Cut 11¼x11***
**2006, Sept. 20** **Litho.**
**Self-Adhesive**
**Booklet Stamps**
**3235** A1800 (54c) multi 2.00 .30
**3236** A1801 (54c) multi 2.00 .30
**3237** A1802 (54c) multi 2.00 .30
**3238** A1803 (54c) multi 2.00 .30
**3239** A1804 (54c) multi 2.00 .30
**3240** A1805 (54c) multi 2.00 .30
**3241** A1806 (54c) multi 2.00 .30
**3242** A1807 (54c) multi 2.00 .30
**3243** A1808 (54c) multi 2.00 .30
**3244** A1809 (54c) multi 2.00 .30
*a.* Booklet pane of 10, #3235-3244 20.00

Sculptures by Constantin Brancusi (1876-1957) — A1810

Designs: 54c, Sleeping Muse. 85c, Sleep.

**2006, Sept. 25** **Photo.** ***Perf. 13¼***
**3245** A1810 54c multi 1.60 .30
**3246** A1810 85c multi 2.75 .90

See Romania Nos. 4878-4879.

**Marianne Type of 2005**
**2006** **Engr.** ***Perf. 13***
**Inscribed "Phil@poste" at Bottom**
**3247** A1713 10c gray .30 .25
**3248** A1713 60c dark blue 1.75 .40
**3249** A1713 70c yel green 2.10 .40
**3250** A1713 85c purple 2.75 .50
**3251** A1713 86c fawn 2.75 .50
**3252** A1713 €1.15 blue 3.50 .75
**3253** A1713 €1.30 rod violet 4.00 1.00
**3254** A1713 €2.11 chocolate 6.25 .50
*Nos. 3247-3254 (8)* 23.40 4.30

**Coil Stamp**
***Perf. 13 Horiz.***
**3255** A1713 60c dark blue 2.00 .75

***Serpentine Die Cut 11¼***
**Self-Adhesive**
**3255A** A1713 (54c) red + label 12.00 12.00
**3255C** A1713 60c dark blue + label 13.00 13.00
**3255D** A1713 82c fawn + label 15.00 15.00
**3255E** A1713 86c fawn + label 13.00 13.00
*Nos. 3255A-3255E (4)* 53.00 53.00

Issued: Nos. 3247-3255, 10/1, others, 2006.

A number has been reserved for an additional stamp. Nos. 3255A, 3255C and 3255E were printed in sheets of 15 stamps + 15 labels that could be personalized. No. 3255D was printed in sheets containing 10 stamps + 10 large labels or 15 stamps and 15 small labels. Labels could be personalized. Sheets of No. 3255A sold for €13.29; No. 3255C, €14.04; No. 3255E, €17.31. For Nos. 3255A, 3255C, 3255D and 3255E, adjacent labels came in large and small sizes.

Aviation Without Borders — A1811

**2006, Oct. 7** **Photo.** ***Perf. 13***
**3256** A1811 54c multi 1.60 .30

Henri Moissan (1852-1907), 1906 Nobel Chemistry Laureate — A1812

**2006, Oct. 14** **Engr.** ***Perf. 13¼x13***
**3257** A1812 54c multi 1.60 .30

"Shared Memories," Intl. Conference on Veterans, Paris — A1813

**2006, Oct. 26** **Photo.** ***Perf. 13¼***
**3258** A1813 54c multi 1.60 .30

Marianne — A1814

***Serpentine Die Cut 6¾ Vert.***
**2006, Nov. 8** **Engr.**
**Self-Adhesive**
**Booklet Stamp**
**3259** A1814 54c red 4.00 3.00
*a.* Booklet pane, 5 each #3083d, 3259 30.00

See No. 4910.

Miniature Sheet

Flying Machines — A1815

No. 3260: a, Gustave Ponton d'Amécourt's helicopter. b, Alberto Santos-Dumont's monoplane, "Demoiselle," horiz. c, Jean Marie Le Bris's bird-shaped glider, horiz. d, Clément Ader's "Avion III," horiz. e, Henri Fabré's seaplane, horiz. f, Jean-Pierre Blanchard's balloon.

**Litho. & Engr.**

**2006, Nov. 9** ***Perf. 13***

| | | | | |
|---|---|---|---|---|
| **3260** | A1815 | Sheet of 6 | 10.00 | 10.00 |
| *a.-f.* | | 54c Any single | 1.60 | 1.40 |

Inauguration of Aulnay-sous-Bois to Bondy Tram-Train Line — A1816

**2006, Nov. 18 Photo.** ***Perf. 13x13¼***

| | | | | |
|---|---|---|---|---|
| **3261** | A1816 | 54c multi | 1.60 | .30 |

Holiday Greetings A1817

Designs: No. 3262, Reindeer, sleigh, four penguins. No. 3263, Reindeer with fishing pole, three penguins. No. 3264, Reindeer, Christmas tree, two penguins. No. 3265, Reindeer skating, three penguins. No. 3266, Reindeer with gift boxes, three penguins.

**2006, Nov. 25 Litho.** ***Perf. 13¼***

| | | | | |
|---|---|---|---|---|
| **3261A** | A1817 | (54c) multi + label | 2.00 | .30 |
| **3261B** | A1817 | (54c) multi + label | 2.00 | .30 |
| **3261C** | A1817 | (54c) multi + label | 2.00 | .30 |
| **3261D** | A1817 | (54c) multi + label | 2.00 | .30 |
| **3261E** | A1817 | (54c) multi + label | 2.00 | .30 |
| *f.* | | Vert. strip of 5, #3261A-3261E, + 5 labels | 12.00 | 12.00 |
| | | Miniature sheet, 2 #3261Ef | 30.00 | 30.00 |

**Self-Adhesive**

**Booklet Stamps**

***Serpentine Die Cut 11¼x11***

| | | | | |
|---|---|---|---|---|
| **3262** | A1817 | (54c) multi | 2.00 | .30 |
| **3263** | A1817 | (54c) multi | 2.00 | .30 |
| **3264** | A1817 | (54c) multi | 2.00 | .30 |
| **3265** | A1817 | (54c) multi | 2.00 | .30 |
| **3266** | A1817 | (54c) multi | 2.00 | .30 |
| *a.* | | Booklet pane, 2 each #3262-3266 | 20.00 | |
| | | *Nos. 3262-3266 (5)* | 10.00 | 1.50 |

Miniature sheet containing Nos. 3261A-3261E sold for €6.94. Value $60. Labels could be personalized. Value $60.

A souvenir sheet containing a perf. 13 example of No. 3266 sold for €3. Value $17.50. A sheet containing 5 No. 3261A + 5 labels exists, but was not sold.

Grand Masonic Lodge of France A1818

**2006, Dec. 1 Photo.** ***Perf. 13x13¼***

| | | | | |
|---|---|---|---|---|
| **3267** | A1818 | 54c multi | 1.60 | .30 |

Alain Poher (1909-96), Politician, and Senate Building A1819

**2006, Dec. 2 Engr.** ***Perf. 13¼***

| | | | | |
|---|---|---|---|---|
| **3268** | A1819 | 54c multi | 1.60 | .30 |

Opening of New Paris Tramway A1820

**2006, Dec. 16 Photo.** ***Perf. 13¼***

| | | | | |
|---|---|---|---|---|
| **3269** | A1820 | 54c multi | 1.75 | .30 |

**Orchids Type of 2002**

Designs: 31c, Platanthera chlorantha. 36c, Dactylorhiza savogiensis. 43c, Orchis insularis.

**2007, Jan. 2 Litho.** ***Perf. 13***

| | | | | |
|---|---|---|---|---|
| **3270** | A1584 | 31c multi | 1.50 | .50 |
| **3271** | A1584 | 36c multi | 1.50 | .60 |
| **3272** | A1584 | 43c multi | 2.50 | .75 |
| | | *Nos. 3270-3272 (3)* | 5.50 | 1.85 |

Nos. 3270-3272 are known only precanceled. See second note after No. 132.

Hearts A1821

"Givenchy" in: (54c), Black and white. (86c), Red.

**2007, Jan. 6 Photo.** ***Perf. 13¼***

**Inscribed "Lettre 20 g"**

| | | | | |
|---|---|---|---|---|
| **3273** | A1821 | (54c) red & black | 2.00 | .30 |
| *a.* | | Souvenir sheet of 5 | 10.00 | 10.00 |

**Inscribed "Lettre 50 g"**

| | | | | |
|---|---|---|---|---|
| **3274** | A1821 | (86c) black & red | 3.00 | 1.00 |

Values are for stamps with surrounding selvage.

***Serpentine Die Cut***

**Self-Adhesive**

| | | | | |
|---|---|---|---|---|
| **3275** | A1821 | (54c) Like #3273 | 16.00 | 13.00 |

**Inscribed "Lettre 50 g"**

| | | | | |
|---|---|---|---|---|
| **3276** | A1821 | (86c) Like #3274 | 16.00 | 13.00 |

New Year 2007 (Year of the Pig) — A1822

**2007, Jan. 27 Photo.** ***Perf. 13¼x13***

| | | | | |
|---|---|---|---|---|
| **3277** | A1822 | (54c) multi | 2.00 | .30 |
| *a.* | | Litho., stamp + label | 8.00 | 8.00 |

***Serpentine Die Cut 11***

**Self-Adhesive**

| | | | | |
|---|---|---|---|---|
| **3277B** | A1822 | (54c) multi + label | 15.00 | 15.00 |

No. 3277 has a somewhat blurrier image than No. 3277a. Sheets of 5 #3277a + 5 labels sold for €3.51. Value $15. Labels could be personalized. No. 3277 exists in a souvenir sheet of 1 that sold for €3. Value $12.

No. 3277B was printed in sheets of 10 + 10 labels that sold for €8.86. Value $150. Labels could be personalized.

See No. 4969c.

Egyptian Hippopotamus Figurine — A1823

Head of Aphrodite A1824

Winged Victory of Samothrace A1825

Fresco, Pompeii A1826

King Amenemhet III of Egypt A1827

Statue of Juno A1828

Egyptian Harpist A1829

Etruscan Sarcophagus of Husband and Wife — A1830

Egyptian Statue of Seated Scribe A1831

Head of Pericles A1832

***Serpentine Die Cut 11¼x11***

**2007, Jan. 27 Litho.**

**Booklet Stamps**

**Self-Adhesive**

| | | | | |
|---|---|---|---|---|
| **3279** | A1823 | (54c) multi | 2.00 | .30 |
| **3280** | A1824 | (54c) multi | 2.00 | .30 |
| **3281** | A1825 | (54c) multi | 2.00 | .30 |
| **3282** | A1826 | (54c) multi | 2.00 | .30 |
| **3283** | A1827 | (54c) multi | 2.00 | .30 |
| **3284** | A1828 | (54c) multi | 2.00 | .30 |
| **3285** | A1829 | (54c) multi | 2.00 | .30 |
| **3286** | A1830 | (54c) multi | 2.00 | .30 |
| **3287** | A1831 | (54c) multi | 2.00 | .30 |
| **3288** | A1832 | (54c) multi | 2.00 | .30 |
| *a.* | | Booklet pane of 10, #3279-3288 | 20.00 | |

**Tourism Issue**

Valenciennes A1833

**2007 Engr.** ***Perf. 13¼***

| | | | | |
|---|---|---|---|---|
| **3289** | A1833 | 54c red & blue | 1.50 | .30 |

Issued: No. 3289, 2/3.

**Tourism Issue**

Limoges A1834

**2007 Engr.** ***Perf. 13¼***

| | | | | |
|---|---|---|---|---|
| **3290** | A1834 | 54c multi | 2.25 | .30 |

Issued: No. 3290, 3/23.

**Tourism Issue**

Arcachon A1835

**2007, May 19 Photo.** ***Perf. 13¼***

| | | | | |
|---|---|---|---|---|
| **3291** | A1835 | 54c multi | 2.25 | .30 |

**Tourism Issue**

Castres A1836

**2007, July 20 Engr.** ***Perf. 13¼***

| | | | | |
|---|---|---|---|---|
| **3292** | A1836 | 54c multi | 1.60 | .30 |

**Tourism Issue**

Firminy — A1837

**2007, Sept. 15 Engr.** ***Perf. 13¼***

| | | | | |
|---|---|---|---|---|
| **3293** | A1837 | 54c multi | 1.75 | .30 |

Rights of France A1838

**2007, Feb. 5 Photo.** ***Perf. 13¼***

| | | | | |
|---|---|---|---|---|
| **3294** | A1838 | 54c multi | 2.00 | .30 |

### Art Issue

Book Illumination from Sélestat Library — A1839

Galerie des Glaces, Versailles Palace — A1840

La Barrière Fleurie, by Paul Sérusier A1841

Gallic Boar Ensign — A1842

***Perf. 12¼x13, 13¼x13 (#3297), 13x13¼ (#3296, 3298)***

**Engraved, Photo. (#3296, 3297, 3298A)**

**2007-08**

**3295** A1839 60c multi 1.75 .60
**3296** A1840 85c multi 3.50 1.00
**3297** A1841 86c multi 3.00 1.00
**3298** A1842 €1.30 multi 4.50 1.25
*Nos. 3295-3298 (4)* 12.75 3.85

**Self-Adhesive**

***Serpentine Die Cut 11***

**3298A** A1840 85c multi 20.00 12.00

Issued: No. 3295, 2/10. No. 3297, 10/13. No. 3298, 6/2. No. 3296, 11/10. No. 3298A, 2008.

### Aspects of Life in the French Regions Type of 2003

No. 3299: a, Baux-de-Provence. b, Banks of the Loire. c, Grande-Chartreuse Massif. d, Saint-Tropez. e, Doubs Waterfall, vert. f, Fontainebleau Forest, vert. g, Chantilly Castle. h, Saint-Malo. i, Ballon d'Alsace, vert. j, Midi Canal, vert.

**2007, Feb. 24 Photo. *Perf. 13***
**3299** Sheet of 10 16.00 16.00
*a.-j.* A1642 54c Any single 1.50 1.25

No. 3299 has three vertical rows of rouletting, separating sheet into quarters.

Nos. 3299a-3299j were also issued in large booklets containing panes of 1 of each stamp. The booklet sold for €19.

### Aspects of Life in French Regions Type of 2003 Inscribed "Lettre Prioritaire 20g"

Designs: Nos. 3300-3301, Arc de Triomphe, vert.

**2007, Feb. Photo. *Perf. 13***
**3300** A1642 (54c) multi + label 8.00 8.00

***Serpentine Die Cut 11x11¼***

**3301** A1642 (54c) multi + label 45.00 45.00

Nos. 3300-3301 each were printed in sheets of 10 stamps + 10 different labels that sold for €6.85. Value of sheets: No. 3300, $80; No. 3301, $450.

### Marianne Type of 2005

**2007 Litho. *Perf. 13***

**Stamps Inscribed "Phil@poste"**

**Without Varnish**

**3302** Sheet of 15, #a-k, 2 each #l-m, + 15 labels 250.00 250.00
*a.* A1713 1c yellow orange 1.25 1.25
*b.* A1713 5c brown 1.65 1.65
*c.* A1713 10c gray 3.00 3.00
*d.* A1713 60c blue 11.50 11.50
*e.* A1713 70c lt yellow green 13.50 13.50
*f.* A1713 85c purple 16.00 16.00
*g.* A1713 86c pink 17.00 17.00
*h.* A1713 €1 orange 21.00 21.00
*i.* A1713 €1.15 light blue 23.00 23.00
*j.* A1713 €1.30 red violet 25.00 25.00
*k.* A1713 €2.11 maroon 37.50 37.50
*l.* A1713 (49c) blue green 10.00 10.00
*m.* A1713 (54c) red 11.50 11.50

No. 3302 sold for €14.40 and has personalizable labels.

Harry Potter — A1843

Designs: (49c), Ron Weasley. (85c), Hermione Granger.

**2007, Mar. 12 Photo. *Perf. 13¼***
**3303** A1843 (54c) red & multi 2.00 .30
*a.* Souvenir sheet of 1 2.50 2.00
*b.* Perf. 13¼x13 (booklet stamp) 2.00 .30

**Booklet Stamps**

***Perf. 13¼x13***

**3304** A1843 (49c) grn & multi 2.50 1.00
**3305** A1843 (85c) blue & multi 3.00 .60
*a.* Booklet pane of 10, 4 #3303b, 3 each #3304-3305 22.50 —
Complete booklet, #3305a 22.50

Stamp Day. Sheets of five serpentine die cut 11 self-adhesive stamps of each denomination and five labels that could not be personalized exist. Each sheet sold for €6.50. Value, set $150.

Albert Londres (1884-1932), Journalist — A1844

**2007, Mar. 16 Engr. *Perf. 13x13¼***
**3306** A1844 54c multi 1.60 .30

Six different souvenir sheets containing one No. 3306 exist. The set sold for €15. Value, set $45.

Audit Office, Bicent. A1845

**2007 *Perf. 13¼x13***
**3307** A1845 54c multi 2.00 .30

***Serpentine Die Cut 11***

**Self-Adhesive**

**3307A** A1845 54c multi 5.00 4.00

Issued: No. 3307, 3/17; No. 3307A, 7/20.

Treaty of Rome, 50th Anniv. A1846

**2007, Mar. 23 Photo. *Perf. 13¼***
**3308** A1846 54c multi 1.50 .30

Sébastaen Le Prestre de Vauban (1633-1707), Military Engineer — A1847

**2007, Mar. 30 Engr.**
**3309** A1847 54c multi 1.50 .30

2007 Rugby World Cup A1848

**2007, Apr. 14 Photo. *Perf. 13¼***
**3310** A1848 54c multi 1.50 .30
*a.* Perf. 13x13¼ + label 5.00 5.00

***Serpentine Die Cut 11¼***

**Self-Adhesive**

**3311** A1848 54c multi + label 12.50 12.50

No. 3310a was printed in sheets of 5 stamps and 5 labels that could be personalized that sold for €4.20. Value $60.

No. 3311 was printed in sheets of 10 + 10 labels that could be personalized. Sheets sold for €10.60. Value, sheet $125.

Endangered Animals in Overseas Departments A1849

Designs: No. 3312, Antillean iguana. No. 3313, Raccoon, horiz. 60c, Jaguar, horiz. 86c, Barau's petrel, horiz..

**2007, Apr. 28 Photo. *Perf. 13¼***
**3312** A1849 54c multi 1.50 .30
**3313** A1849 54c multi 1.50 .30
**3314** A1849 60c multi 1.75 .60
**3315** A1849 86c multi 2.40 .60
*a.* Souvenir sheet, #3312-3315 7.25 7.25
*Nos. 3312-3315 (4)* 7.15 1.80

### Gardens and Parks Type of 2003

Souvenir Sheet

No. 3316 — Parc de la Tete d'Or, Lyon: a, Red flowers. b, White flowers.

**2007, Apr. 28 *Perf. 13¼x13***
**3316** Sheet of 2 12.00 12.00
*a.-b.* A1660 €2.11 Either single 6.00 5.00

Salon du Timbre. No. 3316 has four vertical rows of rouletting, separating sheet into fifths, with the two stamps in the central fifth.

Vacations A1850

Designs: No. 3317, Wooden fence and red hollyhocks. No. 3318, Angelfish. No. 3319, Blue flowers. No. 3320, Blueberries. No. 3321, Canoes. No. 3322, Dyed wool hanging on rods. No. 3323, Glacier. No. 3324, Palm tree. No. 3325, Beach umbrellas and woman. No. 3326, Boxes of color pigments.

***Serpentine Die Cut 11¼x11***

**2007, Apr. 28 Litho.**

**Booklet Stamps**

**Self-Adhesive**

**3317** A1850 (54c) multi 1.75 .30
**3318** A1850 (54c) multi 1.75 .30
**3319** A1850 (54c) multi 1.75 .30
**3320** A1850 (54c) multi 1.75 .30
**3321** A1850 (54c) multi 1.75 .30
**3322** A1850 (54c) multi 1.75 .30
**3323** A1850 (54c) multi 1.75 .30
**3324** A1850 (54c) multi 1.75 .30
**3325** A1850 (54c) multi 1.75 .30
**3326** A1850 (54c) multi 1.75 .30
*a.* Booklet pane of 10, #3317-3326 17.50

Europa A1851

**2007, May 1 Photo. *Perf. 13¼***
**3327** A1851 60c multi 1.50 .40

Scouting, cent.

Intl. Sailing Federation, Cent. — A1852

**2007, May 4 *Perf. 13***
**3328** A1852 85c multi 2.25 .80

A souvenir sheet containing No. 3328 sold for €3. Value, $12.

Tintin and Snowy — A1853

Characters from Tintin comic strips and books, by Hergé: No. 3330, Professor Calculus (Tournesol). No. 3331, Captain Haddock. No. 3332, Thomson and Thompson (Dupondt). No. 3333, Bianca Castafiore. No. 3334, Chang (Tchang).

**2007, May 12**
**3329** A1853 54c multi 1.50 .50
**3330** A1853 54c multi 1.50 .50
**3331** A1853 54c multi 1.50 .50
**3332** A1853 54c multi 1.50 .50
**3333** A1853 54c multi 1.50 .50
**3334** A1853 54c multi 1.50 .50
*a.* Souvenir sheet, #3329-3334 13.50 13.50

No. 3334a sold for €5, with the Red Cross receiving €1.76 of that.

Religious Art — A1854

Designs: 54c, Nativity, 15th cent. miniature, from Armenia. 85c, The Smile of Reims.

**2007, May 22** ***Perf. 13¼***

**3335** A1854 54c multi 1.60 .30
**3336** A1854 85c multi 2.50 1.00

See Armenia Nos. 749-750.

Inauguration of Eastern France TGV Train Service — A1855

**2007, June 9** ***Perf. 13***

**3337** A1855 54c multi 1.50 .30

French Federation of Philatelic Associations 80th Congress, Poitiers — A1856

**2007, June 15** **Engr.** ***Perf. 13x13¼***

**3338** A1856 54c multi + label 1.75 .30

Miniature Sheet

2007 Rugby World Cup, France — A1857

No. 3339 — Inscriptions: a, Touche (Throw-in, 30x39mm elliptical). b, Melée (scrum). c, Attaque (player running with ball). d, Essai (try). e, Transformation (kick, 30x39mm elliptical). f, Passe (pass). g, Raffut (stiff-arm). h, Haka (dance). i, Plaquage (tackle). j, Supporteurs (fans).

**2007, June 23** ***Perf. 13x13¼***

**3339** A1857 Sheet of 10 17.00 17.00
*a.-j.* 54c Any single 1.50 1.25

**European Capitals Type of 2002**

Souvenir Sheet

No. 3340 — Attractions in Brussels: a, Maison du Roi (Royal Palace). b, Hotel du Ville (City Hall), vert. c, Mannekin Pis, vert. d, Atomium.

***Perf. 13x13¼, 13¼x13 (vert. stamps)***

**2007, June 30**

**3340** A1622 Sheet of 4 7.50 7.50
*a.-d.* 54c Any single 1.60 .00

Association of French Mayors, Cent. — A1858

**2007, July 5** **Photo.** ***Perf. 13¼***

**3341** A1858 54c multi 1.50 .30

Pierre Pfimlin (1907-2000), Mayor of Strasbourg A1859

**2007, July 7** **Photo.** ***Perf. 13¼***

**3342** A1859 60c multi 1.75 .60

2007 Rugby World Cup, France A1860

**Litho. With Three-Dimensional Plastic Affixed**

**2007, Sept. 5** ***Serpentine Die Cut 11***

**Self-Adhesive**

**3343** A1860 €3 multi 10.00 6.00

Happy Birthday A1861

**2007, Sept. 8** **Photo.** ***Perf. 13x13¼***

**3344** A1861 (54c) multi 5.00 .30
*a.* Litho., with attached label 2.40 2.40

No. 3344 was printed in a sheet of 5; No. 3344a was printed in a sheet of 5 + 5 labels that sold for €4.20.

Gift Boxes — A1862

Boxes and: Nos. 3345a, 3346, Butterflies. Nos. 3345b, 3348, Flowers. Nos. 3345c, 3347, Hearts. Nos. 3345d, 3350, Musical notes. Nos. 3345e, 3349, Bubbles.

**2007, Sept. 8** **Litho.** ***Perf. 13¼***

**3345** Sheet of 5 + 5 labels 12.00 12.00
*a.-e.* A1862 (54c) Any single + label 2.40 2.40

**Self-Adhesive**

**Booklet Stamps**

***Serpentine Die Cut 11***

**3346** A1862 (54c) multi 1.60 .55
**3347** A1862 (54c) multi 1.60 .55
**3348** A1862 (54c) multi 1.60 .55
**3349** A1862 (54c) multi 1.60 .55
**3350** A1862 (54c) multi 1.60 .55
*a.* Booklet pane of 5 #3346-3350 8.00

No. 3345 sold for €4.20.

Sully Prudhomme (1839-1907), Poet — A1863

**2007, Sept. 15** **Engr.** ***Perf. 13¼***

**3351** A1863 €1.30 multi 3.75 1.25

A1864



A1865

A1866

A1867

Cows A1868

***Serpentine Die Cut 11***

**2007, Sept. 20** **Litho.**

**Self-Adhesive**

**Booklet Stamps**

**3352** A1864 (54c) multi 1.60 .55
**3353** A1865 (54c) multi 1.60 .55
**3354** A1866 (54c) multi 1.60 .55
**3355** A1867 (54c) multi 1.60 .55
**3356** A1868 (54c) multi 1.60 .55
*a.* Booklet pane, 2 each #3352-3356 16.00
*Nos. 3352-3356 (5)* 8.00 2.75

**Aspects of Life in French Regions Type of 2003**

No. 3357: a, Sèvres porcelain. b, Grasse perfume. c, Christmas market. d, Marseille soap. e, Giants, vert. f, Basque beret, vert. g, Aubusson tapestries. h, Lyonnaise tavern. i, Slipper, vert. j, Canteloupe, vert.

**2007, Sept. 29** **Photo.** ***Perf. 13***

**3357** Sheet of 10 16.00 16.00
*a.-j.* A1642 54c Any single 1.60 .55

No. 3357 has three vertical rows of rouletting separating sheet into quarters.

Nos. 3357a-3357j were also issued in large booklets containing panes of 1 of each stamp. The booklet sold for €19. Value $55.

Space Age, 50th Anniv. — A1869

**2007, Oct. 4** ***Perf. 13x12½***

**3358** A1869 85c multi 2.40 1.00

Medical Research Foundation, 60th Anniv. — A1870

**2007, Oct. 20** ***Perf. 13¼***

**3359** A1870 54c multi 1.60 .30

Guy Moquet (1924-41), World War II Resistance Fighter — A1871

**2007, Oct. 22** **Engr.**

**3360** A1871 54c multi 1.60 .30

Dole A1872

**2007, Nov. 2**

**3361** A1872 54c multi 1.60 .30

Personalized Stamp With Country Name on Short Side — A1873

Personalized Stamp With Country Name on Long Side A1874

***Serpentine Die Cut 11¼ Syncopated***

**2007, Nov.** **Litho.**

**Self-Adhesive**

**Inscribed: "Lettre Prioritaire 20 g"**

**3362** A1873 (54c) multi 6.00 6.00
**3363** A1874 (54c) multi 6.00 6.00

**Inscribed: "Monde 20 g"**

**3364** A1873 (85c) multi 6.00 6.00
**3365** A1874 (85c) multi 6.00 6.00

**Inscribed: "Lettre Prioritaire 50 g"**

**3366** A1873 (86c) multi 6.00 6.00
**3367** A1874 (86c) multi 6.00 6.00
*Nos. 3362-3367 (6)* 36.00 36.00

Nos. 3362-3367 were each printed in sheets of ten, having vignettes that could be personalized or chosen from a library of stock designs, two of which are shown on the illustrated stamps. Sheets of Nos. 3362 and 3363 each sold for €10.03, and sheets of Nos. 3364-3367 each sold for €13.38. Sheets were made available with different frame colors. Starting in 2008, numerous sheets containing stamps with these frames having various preselected vignettes were produced and sold by La Poste for various prices per sheet, each well above the franking value of the stamps at the time of issue. Any stamp with a vignette and/or frame color differing from the items shown is an equivalent item to those shown.

Jean-Baptiste Charcot (1867-1936), Polar Explorer A1875

Ship Pourquoi-Pas? — A1876

**2007, Nov. 8 Engr. *Perf. 13x12¾***

| | | | |
|---|---|---|---|
| **3368** | A1875 54c multi | 1.60 | .55 |
| **3369** | A1876 60c multi | 1.75 | .60 |
| *a.* | Horiz. pair, #3368-3369 | 3.50 | 1.25 |

See Greenland No. 505. A sheet containing Nos. 3368-3369 sold for €4 in 2008.

Marianne — A1877

***Serpentine Die Cut 6¾ Vert.***

**2007, Nov. 8 Engr.**

**Self-Adhesive**

**Booklet Stamp**

| | | | |
|---|---|---|---|
| **3370** | A1877 54c red | 3.00 | 2.00 |
| *a.* | Booklet pane, 6 each #3083d, 3370 | 27.50 | |

Miniature Sheet

Lighthouses — A1878

No. 3371: a, Cap Fréhel Lighthouse. b, Espiguette Lighthouse. c, D'ar-Men Lighthouse. d, Grand-Léjon Lighthouse. e, Porquerolles Lighthouse, horiz. f, Chassiron Lighthouse, horiz.

**Litho. & Engr.**

**2007, Nov. 9 *Perf. 13***

| | | | |
|---|---|---|---|
| **3371** | A1878 Sheet of 6 | 9.75 | 9.75 |
| *a.-f.* | 54c Any single | 1.60 | .55 |

2007 Women's World Handball Championships, France — A1879

**2007, Nov. 10 Photo. *Perf. 13¼***

| | | | |
|---|---|---|---|
| **3372** | A1879 54c multi | 1.60 | .30 |

Holiday Greetings A1880

No. 3377: a, Squirrel with stocking cap. b, Bird with party hat. c, Hedgehog with party cap. d, Dog with stocking cap. e, Deer with stocking cap.

No. 3378, Squirrel with stocking cap. No. 3379, Bird with party hat. No. 3380, Deer with stocking cap. No. 3381, Hedgehog with party hat. No. 3382, Dog with stocking cap.

**2007, Nov. 24 Litho. *Perf. 13¼***

| | | | |
|---|---|---|---|
| **3377** | Sheet of 5 + 5 labels | 20.00 | 20.00 |
| *a.-e.* | A1880 (54c) Any single + label | 2.50 | 2.50 |

**Booklet Stamps**

**Self-Adhesive**

***Serpentine Die Cut 11***

| | | | |
|---|---|---|---|
| **3378** | A1880 (54c) multi | 2.00 | .30 |
| **3379** | A1880 (54c) multi | 2.00 | .30 |
| **3380** | A1880 (54c) multi | 2.00 | .30 |
| **3381** | A1880 (54c) multi | 2.00 | .30 |
| **3382** | A1880 (54c) multi | 2.00 | .30 |
| *a.* | Booklet pane, 2 each #3378-3382 | 20.00 | |

No. 3377 sold for €4.20 and had labels that could not be personalized.

A souvenir sheet of 1 of No. 3381 sold for €3. Value, $12.

**Marianne Type of 2005**

**2008 Engr. *Perf. 13***

| | | | |
|---|---|---|---|
| **3383** | A1713 (65c) dk blue | 2.50 | .40 |
| **3384** | A1713 72c yel green | 2.25 | .40 |
| **3385** | A1713 88c fawn | 2.75 | .50 |
| **3386** | A1713 €1.25 blue | 4.00 | .80 |
| **3387** | A1713 €1.33 red vio | 4.25 | .85 |
| **3388** | A1713 €2.18 choc | 6.50 | 1.40 |
| | *Nos. 3383-3388 (6)* | 22.25 | 4.35 |

**Coil Stamp**

***Perf. 13 Horiz.***

| | | | |
|---|---|---|---|
| **3388A** | A1713 (65c) dk blue | 3.00 | .40 |

Issued: Nos. 3383-3388A, 3/1.

**Marianne Type of 2005**

***Serpentine Die Cut 6¾ Vert.***

**2008 Engr.**

**Booklet Stamp**

**Self-Adhesive**

| | | | |
|---|---|---|---|
| **3389** | A1713 (60c) blue | 2.50 | .50 |
| *a.* | Booklet pane of 12 | 30.00 | |

Issued: No. 3389, 1/2.

Hearts A1881

Designs: (54c), Face. (86c), (88c), Plant with heart-shaped leaves.

**2008, Jan. 5 Photo. *Perf. 13¼***

| | | | |
|---|---|---|---|
| **3390** | A1881 (54c) multi | 1.60 | .30 |
| *a.* | Souvenir sheet of 5 | 8.00 | 8.00 |
| *b.* | Sheet of 10 + 10 labels | 20.00 | — |
| **3391** | A1881 (86c) multi | 2.60 | 1.00 |

**Self-Adhesive**

***Serpentine Die Cut***

| | | | |
|---|---|---|---|
| **3392** | A1881 (54c) multi | 16.00 | 12.00 |
| **3392A** | A1881 (88c) multi | 16.00 | 12.00 |

Values are for stamps with surrounding selvage.

Nos. 3390, 3390a, 3390b, 3391-3392 issued 1/5/08. No. 3390b was sold for €6.86. Labels could not be personalized.

New Year 2008 (Year of the Rat) — A1882

**2008, Jan. 26 Photo. *Perf. 13¼x13***

| | | | |
|---|---|---|---|
| **3393** | A1882 (54c) multi | 1.60 | .30 |

Printed in sheets of 5. A souvenir sheet of one No. 3393 sold for €3.

See No. 4969d.

Paintings A1883

Designs: No. 3394, Legend of St. Francis: Sermon to the Birds, by Giotto di Bondone. No. 3395, Seaport at Sunset, by Claude Lorrain. No. 3396, The Birth of Venus, by Sandro Botticelli. No. 3397, Napoleon Bonaparte Crossing the Alps, by Jacques-Louis David. No. 3398, La Belle Jardinière (Madonna and Child with St. John the Baptist), by Raphael, vert. No. 3399, Head of a Girl in a Turban, by Jan Vermeer, vert. No. 3400, Summer, by Giuseppe Arcimboldo, vert. No. 3401, Mona Lisa, by Leonardo da Vinci, vert. No. 3402, Infant Maria Marguerita, by Diego Velásquez, vert. No. 3403, Money Changer with Wife, by Quentin Massys (Metsys), vert.

***Serpentine Die Cut 11***

**2008, Jan. 26 Litho.**

**Booklet Stamps**

**Self-Adhesive**

| | | | |
|---|---|---|---|
| **3394** | A1883 (54c) multi | 1.60 | .55 |
| **3395** | A1883 (54c) multi | 1.60 | .55 |
| **3396** | A1883 (54c) multi | 1.60 | .55 |
| **3397** | A1883 (54c) multi | 1.60 | .55 |
| **3398** | A1883 (54c) multi | 1.60 | .55 |
| **3399** | A1883 (54c) multi | 1.60 | .55 |
| **3400** | A1883 (54c) multi | 1.60 | .55 |
| **3401** | A1883 (54c) multi | 1.60 | .55 |
| **3402** | A1883 (54c) multi | 1.60 | .55 |
| **3403** | A1883 (54c) multi | 1.60 | .55 |
| *a.* | Booklet pane of 10, #3394-3403 | 16.00 | |

France Stadium, 10th Anniv. A1884

**2008, Jan. 28 Photo. *Perf. 13¼***

| | | | |
|---|---|---|---|
| **3404** | A1884 54c multi | 1.60 | .30 |

**Tourism Issue**

Vendôme A1885

La Rochelle — A1886

Toulon A1887

Richelieu A1888

Le Havre — A1889

**2008 Engr. *Perf. 13¼***

| | | | |
|---|---|---|---|
| **3405** | A1885 54c multi | 1.60 | .30 |

***Perf. 13***

| | | | |
|---|---|---|---|
| **3406** | A1886 55c multi | 1.50 | .30 |
| **3407** | A1887 55c multi | 1.50 | .30 |
| **3408** | A1888 55c multi | 1.50 | .30 |
| **3409** | A1889 55c multi | 1.50 | .30 |
| | *Nos. 3405-3409 (5)* | 7.60 | 1.50 |

Issued: No. 3405, 2/2; No. 3406, 4/5; Nos. 3407-3408, 7/5; No. 3409, 9/13. A souvenir sheet of one of No. 3406 sold for €3.

**Art Issue**

Globes of Vincenzo Coronelli A1890

Young Girl Warming Her Hands at a Large Stove, by Jean-Jacues Henner — A1891

Untitled Work by Gérard Garouste A1892

A Theater Box Office, by Honoré Daumier
A1893

**Litho. & Engr., Photo (A1891-A1892), Engr. (A1893)**

**2008** *Perf. 13¼x13*

| | | | | |
|---|---|---|---|---|
| **3410** | A1890 | 85c multi | 3.00 | 1.25 |
| **3411** | A1891 | 88c multi | 3.00 | .60 |
| **3412** | A1892 | €1.33 multi | 4.00 | 1.25 |
| **3413** | A1893 | €1.33 choc & bl gray | 4.50 | 1.00 |
| | | *Nos. 3410-3413 (4)* | 14.50 | 4.10 |

**Self-Adhesive**

***Serpentine Die Cut 11***

| | | | | |
|---|---|---|---|---|
| **3413A** | A1891 | 88c multi | 6.00 | 4.00 |
| **3413B** | A1892 | €1.33 multi | 12.00 | 50.00 |
| **3413C** | A1893 | €1.33 choc & bl gray | 200.00 | 75.00 |
| | | *Nos. 3413A-3413C (3)* | 218.00 | 129.00 |

Issued: No. 3410, 2/11; No. 3412, 6/19; No. 3411, 10/18; No. 3413, 11/7.

A souvenir sheet containing No. 3410 sold for €3.

Emir Abdelkader (1808-83), Algerian Leader — A1894

**2008, Feb. 20** **Engr.** *Perf. 13¼*

**3414** A1894 54c multi 1.75 .30

Droopy Dog
A1895

Red-haired Woman
A1896

The Wolf
A1897

Design: €2.18, Droopy Dog, diff.

**2008, Mar. 1** **Photo.** *Perf. 13¼*

| | | | | |
|---|---|---|---|---|
| **3415** | A1895 | (55c) multi | 1.75 | .30 |
| **3416** | A1896 | (55c) multi | 1.75 | .30 |
| **3417** | A1897 | (55c) multi | 1.75 | .30 |
| *a.* | | Strip of 3, #3415-3417 | 5.25 | 1.90 |

**Souvenir Sheet**

***Perf. 13x13¼***

**3418** A1895 €2.18 multi 6.75 6.75

**Booklet Stamps**

**Self-Adhesive**

***Serpentine Die Cut 11***

| | | | | |
|---|---|---|---|---|
| **3419** | A1895 | (55c) multi | 1.75 | .30 |
| **3420** | A1896 | (55c) multi | 1.75 | .30 |
| **3421** | A1897 | (55c) multi | 1.75 | .30 |
| *a.* | | Booklet pane of 10, 4 #3419, 3 each #3420-3421 | 17.50 | |

Cartoon characters created by Tex Avery; Stamp Day. No. 3418 contains one 35x27mm stamp that has thermographic ink (on cartoon balloon) that when warmed, changes color allowing a message below the ink to appear.

Nos. 3419-3421 exist in three sheets, each containing 5 of each stamp + 5 non-personalizable labels. Each sheet sold for €6.50. Value, each $40.

Sound Recording Libraries
A1898

**2008, Mar. 15** **Photo.** *Perf. 13¼*

**3422** A1898 55c multi 1.75 .30

Flowers — A1899

Designs: 37c, Aquilegia. 38c, Tulipa sp. 44c, Bellis perennis. 45c, Primula veris.

**2008, Mar. 1** **Litho.** *Perf. 13*

| | | | | |
|---|---|---|---|---|
| **3423** | A1899 | 37c multi | 1.25 | .60 |
| **3424** | A1899 | 38c multi | 1.25 | .60 |
| **3425** | A1899 | 44c multi | 1.75 | .70 |
| **3426** | A1899 | 45c multi | 1.75 | .70 |
| | | *Nos. 3423-3426 (4)* | 6.00 | 2.60 |

Nos. 3423-3426 are known only precanceled. See second note after No. 132.

Compare with types A2174-A2177.

**Aspects of Life in French Regions Type of 2003**

No. 3427: a, Chateau d'Ussé, Rigny-Ussé. b, Vézelay. c, Place des Vosges, Le Marais district, Paris. d, Le Marais Poitevin (Poitevin Marsh). e, Cugarel Windmill, Castelnaudary, vert. f, Red granite coastal rocks, vert. g, Honfleur. h, La Petite France district, Strasbourg. i, La Boétie House, Sarlat-la-Canéda, vert. j, Marfate Cirque, Reunion, vert.

**2008, Mar. 29** **Photo.** *Perf. 13*

| | | | | |
|---|---|---|---|---|
| **3427** | | Sheet of 10 | 17.50 | 17.50 |
| *a.-j.* | | A1642 55c Any single | 1.75 | 1.25 |

No. 3427 has three vertical rows of rouletting, separating sheet into quarters. Nos. 3427a-3427j were also issued in a large booklet containing panes of 1 of each stamp. The booklet sold for €19.

Lyon — A1900

**Litho. & Engr.**

**2008, Apr. 4** *Perf. 13*

**3428** A1900 55c multi 1.75 .30

**Gardens and Parks Type of 2003**

No. 3429: a, Parc Longchamp, Marseille. b, Parc Borely, Marseille.

**2008** **Photo.** *Perf. 13¼x13*

| | | | | |
|---|---|---|---|---|
| **3429** | | Sheet of 2 | 13.50 | 13.50 |
| *a.-b.* | | A1660 €2.18 Either single | 6.75 | 3.50 |
| *c.* | | Miniature sheet of 4, #3316a, 3316b, 3429a, 3429b | 50.00 | 50.00 |

Salon du Timbre. No. 3429 has four vertical rows of rouletting, separating sheet into fifths, with the two stamps in the central fifth.

Issued: No. 3429, 4/12; No. 3429c, 6/14.

Prehistoric Animals
A1901

Designs: No. 3430, Phorusrhacos. No. 3431, Smilodon. 65c, Megaloceros, horiz. 88c, Mammoth, horiz.

**2008, Apr. 19** *Perf. 13¼*

| | | | | |
|---|---|---|---|---|
| **3430** | A1901 | 55c multi | 1.75 | .30 |
| **3431** | A1901 | 55c multi | 1.75 | .30 |
| **3432** | A1901 | 65c multi | 2.00 | .50 |
| **3433** | A1901 | 88c multi | 2.75 | 1.00 |
| *a.* | | Miniature sheet, #3430-3433 | 8.25 | 8.25 |
| | | *Nos. 3430-3433 (4)* | 8.25 | 2.10 |

First Heart Transplant in Europe, 40th Anniv. — A1902

**2008, Apr. 24** *Perf. 13¼x13*

**3434** A1902 55c red & black 1.60 .30

Valentré Bridge, Cahors
A1903

**2008, Apr. 26** **Engr.** *Perf. 13x13¼*

**3435** A1903 55c multi 1.60 .30

Europa
A1904

**2008, May 4** **Photo.** *Perf. 13x13¼*

**3436** A1904 55c multi 1.75 .30

**Self-Adhesive**

***Serpentine Die Cut 11***

**3436A** A1904 55c multi 3.00 3.00

Quebec City, Canada, 400th Anniv.
A1905

**2008, May 16** **Engr.** *Perf. 13*

**3437** A1905 85c multi 2.75 1.00

See Canada No. 2269.

A souvenir sheet containing No. 3437 and Canada No. 2269 sold for $4.99 in Canada and was sold in France for €15 as part of a set additionally containing six different souvenir sheets containing only No. 3437.

Happy Birthday
A1906

**2008, May 28** **Photo.**

**3438** A1906 (55c) multi 1.75 .30

Printed in sheets of 5.

It's a Boy
A1907

It's a Girl
A1908

**2008, May 28** ***Serpentine Die Cut 11***

**Booklet Stamps**

**Self-Adhesive**

| | | | | |
|---|---|---|---|---|
| **3439** | A1907 | (55c) multi, unscratched panel | 2.00 | 2.00 |
| *a.* | | Scratched panel | | .60 |
| *b.* | | Booklet pane of 10 #3439 | 20.00 | |
| **3440** | A1908 | (55c) multi, unscratched panel | 2.00 | 2.00 |
| *a.* | | Scratched panel | | .60 |
| *b.* | | Booklet pane of 10 #3440 | 20.00 | |

Scratch-off panels on Nos. 3439-3440 cover pictures and text for baby boy and girl, respectively.

Vacations
A1909

Designs: No. 3441, Ferns. No. 3442, Butterfly on leaf. No. 3443, Hands holding plant's leaves. No. 3444, Coconut palm tree. No. 3445, Path beside forest lake. No. 3446, Golf ball, putter and hole. No. 3447, Water lily and lily pads. No. 3448, Watering cans and foliage. No. 3449, Sliced kiwi fruit. No. 3450, Shelled and unshelled peas.

***Serpentine Die Cut 11***

**2008, May 28** **Litho.**

**Booklet Stamps**

**Self-Adhesive**

| | | | | |
|---|---|---|---|---|
| **3441** | A1909 | (55c) multi | 1.75 | .60 |
| **3442** | A1909 | (55c) multi | 1.75 | .60 |
| **3443** | A1909 | (55c) multi | 1.75 | .60 |
| **3444** | A1909 | (55c) multi | 1.75 | .60 |
| **3445** | A1909 | (55c) multi | 1.75 | .60 |
| **3446** | A1909 | (55c) multi | 1.75 | .60 |
| **3447** | A1909 | (55c) multi | 1.75 | .60 |
| **3448** | A1909 | (55c) multi | 1.75 | .60 |
| **3449** | A1909 | (55c) multi | 1.75 | .60 |
| **3450** | A1909 | (55c) multi | 1.75 | .60 |
| *a.* | | Booklet pane of 10, #3441-3450 | 17.50 | |

Evreux Belfry — A1910

**2008, May 31** **Engr.** *Perf. 13*

**3451** A1910 55c multi 1.60 .60

French Federation of Philatelic Associations 81st Congress, Paris — A1911

**2008, June 14** *Perf. 13x13¼*

| | | | | |
|---|---|---|---|---|
| **3452** | A1911 | 55c multi + label | 1.60 | .60 |

Marianne and Stars A1912

Hand Depositing Ballot A1913

Tree in Hand A1914

Dove A1915

**2008** **Engr.** *Perf. 13*

| | | | | |
|---|---|---|---|---|
| **3453** | A1912 | 1c yellow | .25 | .25 |
| **3454** | A1912 | 5c gray brown | .25 | .25 |
| **3455** | A1912 | 10c gray | .30 | .25 |
| **3456** | A1912 | (50c) green | 1.60 | .25 |
| **3457** | A1912 | (55c) red | 1.75 | .40 |
| **3458** | A1912 | (65c) dark blue | 2.10 | .50 |
| **3459** | A1912 | 72c olive green | 2.25 | .60 |
| **3460** | A1912 | 85c purple | 2.75 | .70 |
| **3461** | A1912 | 88c fawn | 2.75 | .70 |
| **3462** | A1912 | €1 orange | 3.25 | .80 |
| **3463** | A1912 | €1.25 blue | 4.00 | 1.00 |
| **3464** | A1912 | €1.33 red violet | 4.25 | 1.10 |
| **3465** | A1912 | €2.18 chocolate | 7.00 | 2.40 |

**Self-Adhesive (#3466)**

**Etched on Foil**

***Die Cut Perf. 13***

| | | | | |
|---|---|---|---|---|
| **3466** | A1912 | €5 *silver* | 16.00 | 16.00 |
| | | *Nos. 3453-3466 (14)* | 48.50 | 25.20 |

**Litho.**

***Perf. 13***

| | | | |
|---|---|---|---|
| **3467** | Sheet of 15, #3467a-3467k, 2 each #3467l-3467m, + 15 labels | 40.00 | 40.00 |
| *a.* | A1912 1c yellow | .25 | .25 |
| *b.* | A1912 5c brown | .25 | .25 |
| *c.* | A1912 10c gray | .35 | .35 |
| *d.* | A1912 (65c) dark blue | 2.40 | 2.40 |
| *e.* | A1912 72c olive green | 2.60 | 2.60 |
| *f.* | A1912 85c purple | 3.00 | 3.00 |
| *g.* | A1912 88c fawn | 3.25 | 3.25 |
| *h.* | A1912 €1 orange | 3.50 | 3.50 |
| *i.* | A1912 €1.25 blue | 4.50 | 4.50 |
| *j.* | A1912 €1.33 red violet | 4.75 | 4.75 |
| *k.* | A1912 €2.18 brn violet | 7.75 | 7.75 |
| *l.* | A1912 (50c) green | 1.75 | 1.75 |
| *m.* | A1912 (55c) red | 2.00 | 2.00 |

**Coil Stamps**

***Perf. 13 Horiz.***

**Engr.**

| | | | | |
|---|---|---|---|---|
| **3468** | A1912 | (50c) green | 3.50 | 2.00 |
| **3469** | A1912 | (55c) red | 4.00 | 2.00 |
| **3470** | A1912 | (65c) dark blue | 4.50 | 2.00 |

**Booklet Stamps (Types A1913-A1915)**

**Self-Adhesive**

***Serpentine Die Cut 6¾ Vert.***

| | | | | |
|---|---|---|---|---|
| **3471** | A1912 | (55c) red | 2.50 | 1.00 |
| *a.* | | Booklet pane of 20 | 50.00 | |
| *b.* | | Booklet pane of 10 | 25.00 | |
| *c.* | | Booklet pane of 12 | 30.00 | |
| **3472** | A1913 | 55c red | 2.50 | 1.00 |
| **3473** | A1914 | 55c red | 2.50 | 1.00 |
| **3474** | A1915 | 55c red | 2.50 | 1.00 |
| *a.* | | Booklet pane of 12, 6 #3471, 2 each #3472-3474 | 30.00 | |
| **3475** | A1912 | (65c) dark blue | 2.50 | 1.00 |
| *a.* | | Booklet pane of 12 | 30.00 | |
| **3476** | A1913 | 65c dark blue | 2.50 | 1.00 |
| **3477** | A1914 | 65c dark blue | 2.50 | 1.00 |
| **3478** | A1915 | 65c dark blue | 2.50 | 1.00 |
| *a.* | | Booklet pane of 12, 6 #3475, 2 each #3476-3478 | 30.00 | |
| | | *Nos. 3471-3478 (8)* | 20.00 | 8.00 |

Issued: No. 3457, 6/17; No. 3741c, 9/8; No. 3466, 7/1; No. 3475a, 2009; others, 6/14. On day of issue, No. 3467 sold for €12.54. Labels on No. 3467 could not be personalized.

No. 3471b is comprised of two horizontal strips of five stamps on a yellow backing paper. Nos. 3471 and 3475 were also printed in sheets of 100 later in 2008.

See Nos. 3532, 3551-3566, 3612-3616E, 3730, 3871-3882, 4410I, 4525.

Typographed, engraved and silk-screened perf. 13 stamps of types A486 and A1912 with denomination of €1 in red were produced in pairs with 2 labels and photogravure perf. 13 stamps of these types with denominations of €1 in blue, green and multicolored were printed in blocks of 8 + 8 labels. These items were created in very limited quantities in 2010.

Ecology A1916

Designs: No. 3479, Tree. No. 3480, Bicycle. No. 3481, World map. No. 3482, Computer. No. 3483, Water droplets. No. 3484, Sun. No. 3485, Two plastic bottles. No. 3486, Three plastic bottles. No. 3487, Apple core. No. 3488, Strawberry.

***Serpentine Die Cut 11***

**2008, June 14** **Photo.**

**Booklet Stamps**

**Self-Adhesive**

| | | | | |
|---|---|---|---|---|
| **3479** | A1916 | (55c) multi | 1.75 | .50 |
| **3480** | A1916 | (55c) multi | 1.75 | .50 |
| **3481** | A1916 | (55c) multi | 1.75 | .50 |
| **3482** | A1916 | (55c) multi | 1.75 | .50 |
| **3483** | A1916 | (55c) multi | 1.75 | .50 |
| **3484** | A1916 | (55c) multi | 1.75 | .50 |
| **3485** | A1916 | (55c) multi | 1.75 | .50 |
| **3486** | A1916 | (55c) multi | 1.75 | .50 |
| **3487** | A1916 | (55c) multi | 1.75 | .50 |
| **3488** | A1916 | (55c) multi | 1.75 | .50 |
| *a.* | | Booklet pane of 10, #3479-3488 | 17.50 | |

Trapeze Artist — A1917

Bareback Rider — A1918

Clown — A1919

Lion Tamer — A1920

Clown — A1921

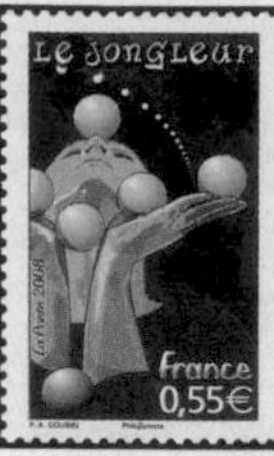


Juggler — A1922

**2008, June 15** **Photo.** *Perf. 13*

| | | | | |
|---|---|---|---|---|
| **3489** | A1917 | 55c multi | 1.75 | .60 |
| **3490** | A1918 | 55c multi | 1.75 | .60 |
| **3491** | A1919 | 55c multi | 1.75 | .60 |
| **3492** | A1920 | 55c multi | 1.75 | .60 |
| **3493** | A1921 | 55c multi | 1.75 | .60 |
| **3494** | A1922 | 55c multi | 1.75 | .60 |
| *a.* | | Souvenir sheet, #3489-3494 | 16.50 | 16.50 |
| | | *Nos. 3489-3494 (6)* | 10.50 | 3.60 |

No. 3494a sold for €5.10, with the Red Cross receiving €1.80 of that.

2008 Summer Olympics, Beijing — A1923

Designs: No. 3495, Equestrian, cycling. No. 3496, Swimming, rowing, horiz. No. 3497, Judo, fencing, horiz. No. 3498, Tennis, running.

***Perf. 13¼x13, 13x13¼***

**2008, June 16**

| | | | | |
|---|---|---|---|---|
| **3495** | A1923 | 55c multi | 1.75 | .60 |
| **3496** | A1923 | 55c multi | 1.75 | .60 |
| **3497** | A1923 | 55c multi | 1.75 | .60 |
| *a.* | | Pair, #3496-3497 | 3.50 | 1.75 |
| **3498** | A1923 | 55c multi | 1.75 | .60 |
| *a.* | | Vert. pair, #3495, 3498 | 3.50 | 1.75 |
| | | *Nos. 3495-3498 (4)* | 7.00 | 2.40 |

Nos. 3495-3498 were printed in a sheet of 10 containing 2 each #3495 and #3498 and 3 each #3496-3497.

Charles de Gaulle Memorial, Paris A1924

**2008, June 18** **Engr.** *Perf. 13¼*

| | | | | |
|---|---|---|---|---|
| **3499** | A1924 | 55c multi | 1.75 | .60 |

Miniature Sheet

European Projects — A1925

No. 3500: a, Map of Europe, 1-euro coin. b, Flags of France and European Union, horiz (French Presidency of European Union). c, Earth and Galileo satellite, horiz. d, Students and flags (Erasmus higher education program).

**2008, June 19** **Photo.** *Perf. 13*

| | | | | |
|---|---|---|---|---|
| **3500** | A1925 | Sheet of 4 | 7.00 | 7.00 |
| *a.-d.* | | 55c Any single | 1.75 | .60 |

Miniature Sheet

Famous Ships — A1926

No. 3501: a, Confiance. b, Grande Hermine, horiz. c, Boudeuse, horiz. d, Astrolabe, horiz. e, Hermione, horiz. f, Boussole.

**2008, June 20**

| | | | | |
|---|---|---|---|---|
| **3501** | A1926 | Sheet of 6 | 10.50 | 10.50 |
| *a.-f.* | | 55c Any single | 1.75 | .60 |

French and Brazilian Landscapes — A1927

Designs: 55c, Amazonian forest, Brazil. 85c, Glacier, France.

**2008, July 13**

| | | | | |
|---|---|---|---|---|
| **3502** | A1927 | 55c multi | 1.75 | .60 |
| **3503** | A1927 | 85c multi | 2.75 | .90 |
| *a.* | | Horiz. pair, #3502-3503 | 4.50 | 2.25 |

See Brazil No. 3052.

Mediterranean Summit, Paris — A1928

**2008, July 13** *Perf. 13¼*

| | | | | |
|---|---|---|---|---|
| **3504** | A1928 | 55c multi | 1.75 | .60 |

**Aspects of Life in French Regions Type of 2003**

No. 3505: a, Espadrilles. b, Stew (pot au feu). c, Chestnuts (chataigne). d, Fireworks (feu d'artifice). e, Epinal prints (l'image d'Epinal), vert. f, Lentils (lentille), vert. g, Reblochon cheese. h, Calissons (candy). i, Stilt walker (les échasses), vert. j, Mustard (moutarde), vert.

**2008, Sept. 6** **Photo.** *Perf. 13*

| | | | |
|---|---|---|---|
| **3505** | Sheet of 10 | 15.00 | 15.00 |
| *a.-j.* | A1642 55c Any single | 1.50 | .50 |

No. 3505 has three vertical rows of rouletting, separating sheet into quarters.

Nos. 3505a-3505j also were issued in large booklets containing panes of 1 of each stamp. The booklet sold for €19.

Josselin A1929

**2008, Sept. 20** **Engr.** *Perf. 13¼*

| | | | | |
|---|---|---|---|---|
| **3506** | A1929 | 55c multi | 1.75 | .50 |

A1930

A1931

A1932

A1933

A1934

A1935

A1936

A1937

A1938

Garfield, Comic Strip by Jim Davis A1939

*Serpentine Die Cut 11¼x11*

**2008, Sept. 18 Photo.**

**Booklet Stamps**

**Self-Adhesive**

| | | | | |
|---|---|---|---|---|
| **3507** | A1930 (55c) multi | 1.75 | .50 |
| **3508** | A1931 (55c) multi | 1.75 | .50 |
| **3509** | A1932 (55c) multi | 1.75 | .50 |
| **3510** | A1933 (55c) multi | 1.75 | .50 |
| **3511** | A1934 (55c) multi | 1.75 | .50 |
| **3512** | A1935 (55c) multi | 1.75 | .50 |
| **3513** | A1936 (55c) multi | 1.75 | .50 |
| **3514** | A1937 (55c) multi | 1.75 | .50 |
| **3515** | A1938 (55c) multi | 1.75 | .50 |
| **3516** | A1939 (55c) multi | 1.75 | .50 |
| *a.* | Booklet pane of 10, #3507-3516 | 17.50 | |
| | *Nos. 3507-3516 (10)* | 17.50 | 5.00 |

"I Am Sport" A1940

**2008, Oct. 2 Photo. *Perf. 12½***

| | | | |
|---|---|---|---|
| **3517** | A1940 55c multi | 1.50 | .50 |

Values are for stamps with surrounding selvage.

Fifth Republic, 50th Anniv. A1941

**2008. Oct. 4 *Perf. 13¼***

| | | | |
|---|---|---|---|
| **3518** | A1941 55c multi | 1.50 | .50 |

Seascapes of Viet Nam and France — A1942

Designs: 55c, Along Bay, Viet Nam. 85, Strait of Bonifacio, France.

**2008, Oct. 15 Photo. *Perf. 13x12¾***

| | | | |
|---|---|---|---|
| **3519** | A1942 55c multi | 1.40 | .45 |
| **3520** | A1942 85c multi | 2.25 | .75 |

See Viet Nam Nos. 3340-3341.

**Types of 1959-2008**

*Serpentine Die Cut 6¾ Vert.*

**2008, Nov. 6 Photo.**

**Booklet Stamps**

**Self-Adhesive**

| | | | |
|---|---|---|---|
| **3521** | A328 55c multi | 1.40 | .45 |
| **3522** | A349 55c multi | 1.40 | .45 |
| **3523** | A360 55c multi | 1.40 | .45 |
| **3524** | A379 55c multi | 1.40 | .45 |
| **3525** | A486 55c dark red | 1.40 | .45 |
| **3526** | A555 55c rose carmine | 1.40 | .45 |
| **3527** | A771 55c bright red | 1.40 | .45 |
| **3528** | A915 55c red | 1.40 | .45 |
| **3529** | A1161 55c red | 1.40 | .45 |
| **3530** | A1409 55c red | 1.40 | .45 |
| **3531** | A1713 55c red | 1.40 | .45 |
| **3532** | A1912 55c red | 1.40 | .45 |
| *a.* | Booklet pane of 12, #3521-3532 | 17.00 | |
| | *Nos. 3521-3532 (12)* | 16.80 | 5.40 |

Landmarks of France and Israel — A1943

Airplane, stamped first flight cover and: 55c, Haifa waterfront, Israel. 85c, Eiffel Tower, Paris.

**2008, Nov. 6 Photo. *Perf. 13***

| | | | |
|---|---|---|---|
| **3533** | A1943 55c multi | 1.40 | .45 |
| **3534** | A1943 85c multi | 2.25 | .75 |

First flight between France and Israel, 60th anniv. See Israel Nos. 1750-1751.

**European Capitals Type of 2002**

No. 3535 — Attractions in Prague: a, Tour du Petit Coté (Charles Bridge and Tower), vert. b, Hotel de ville horloge astronomique et calandrier (City Hall astronomical clock), vert. c, Eglise Notre-Dame-de-Tyn (Tyn Cathedral), vert. d, Le Chateau (Hradcany Castle).

*Perf. 13¼x13, 13x13¼ (#3535d)*

**2008, Nov. 7 Photo.**

| | | | |
|---|---|---|---|
| **3535** | A1622 Sheet of 4 | 5.75 | 5.75 |
| *a.-d.* | 55c Any single | 1.40 | .45 |

A1944 A1945

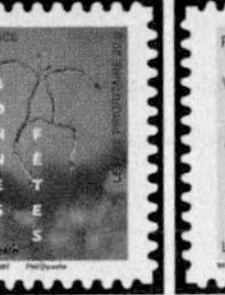

A1946 A1947

A1948 A1949

A1950

A1951

A1952

A1953

A1954

A1955

A1956

Happy Holidays A1957

*Serpentine Die Cut 11¼x11*

**2008, Nov. 8 Photo.**

**Booklet Stamps**

**Self-Adhesive**

| | | | |
|---|---|---|---|
| **3536** | A1944 (55c) multi | 1.40 | .45 |
| **3537** | A1945 (55c) multi | 1.40 | .45 |
| **3538** | A1946 (55c) multi | 1.40 | .45 |
| **3539** | A1947 (55c) multi | 1.40 | .45 |
| **3540** | A1948 (55c) multi | 1.40 | .45 |
| **3541** | A1949 (55c) multi | 1.40 | .45 |

*Serpentine Die Cut 11x11¼*

| | | | |
|---|---|---|---|
| **3542** | A1950 (55c) multi | 1.40 | .45 |
| **3543** | A1951 (55c) multi | 1.40 | .45 |
| **3544** | A1952 (55c) multi | 1.40 | .45 |
| **3545** | A1953 (55c) multi | 1.40 | .45 |
| **3546** | A1954 (55c) multi | 1.40 | .45 |
| **3547** | A1955 (55c) multi | 1.40 | .45 |
| **3548** | A1956 (55c) multi | 1.40 | .45 |
| **3549** | A1957 (55c) multi | 1.40 | .45 |
| *a.* | Booklet pane of 14, #3536-3549 | 20.00 | |
| | *Nos. 3536-3549 (14)* | 19.60 | 6.30 |

A souvenir sheet containing one perf. 13x13¼ stamp like No. 3543 with water-activated gum sold for €3.

End of World War I, 90th Anniv. A1958

**2008, Nov. 11 Engr. *Perf. 13¼***

| | | | |
|---|---|---|---|
| **3550** | A1958 55c multi | 1.40 | .45 |

**Marianne and Stars Type of 2008**

*Serpentine Die Cut 6¾ Vert.*

**2008 Engr. Self-Adhesive**

| | | | | |
|---|---|---|---|---|
| **3551** | A1912 | 1c yellow | .25 | .25 |
| **3552** | A1912 | 5c gray brown | .25 | .25 |
| **3553** | A1912 | 10c gray | .30 | .30 |
| **3554** | A1912 | (50c) green | 1.40 | 1.40 |
| **3555** | A1912 | 72c olive green | 2.00 | 2.00 |
| **3556** | A1912 | 85c purple | 2.40 | 2.40 |
| **3557** | A1912 | 88c fawn | 2.50 | 2.50 |
| **3558** | A1912 | €1 orange | 2.75 | 2.75 |
| **3559** | A1912 | €1.25 blue | 3.50 | 3.50 |
| **3560** | A1912 | €1.33 red violet | 3.75 | 3.75 |
| **3561** | A1912 | €2.18 chocolate | 6.00 | 6.00 |
| | *Nos. 3551-3561 (11)* | | 25.10 | 25.10 |

*Serpentine Die Cut 6¾ Horiz.*

**Coil Stamps**

| | | | | |
|---|---|---|---|---|
| **3564** | A1912 | (50c) green | 1.40 | 1.40 |
| **3565** | A1912 | (55c) red | 1.50 | 1.50 |
| **3566** | A1912 | (65c) dark blue | 1.90 | 1.90 |
| | *Nos. 3564-3566 (3)* | | 4.80 | 4.80 |

Nos. 3551-3561 each were printed in sheets of 100.

Flowers — A1959

Designs: 31c, Helianthus annuus. 33c, Magnolia.

**2008, Nov. 12 Litho. *Perf. 13***

| | | | |
|---|---|---|---|
| **3567** | A1959 31c multi | .80 | .25 |
| **3568** | A1959 33c multi | .85 | .25 |

Nos. 3567-3568 are known only precanceled. See note under No. 132.

Trees and Map of Mediterranean Area — A1960

**2008, Nov. 20 Photo. *Perf. 13x12¾***

| | | | |
|---|---|---|---|
| **3569** | A1960 85c multi | 2.50 | .75 |

See Lebanon No. 645.

**Greetings Type of 2004 Inscribed "Lettre Prioritaire 20g"**

Designs: No. 3569A, "Ceci est une invitation." No. 3569B, "Un grand merci."

**2008 Photo.** ***Serpentine Die Cut 11***

**Self-Adhesive**

**3569A** A1667 (55c) brt lil rose & yel 1.60 1.60
**3569B** A1667 (55c) brt yel grn & red lil 1.60 1.60

Louis Braille (1809-52), Educator of the Blind — A1961

**Engr. & Embossed**

**2009, Jan. 4** ***Perf. 13x12¾***

**3570** A1961 55c blk & violet 1.50 .50

New Year 2009 (Year of the Ox) — A1962

**2009, Jan. 10 Photo.** ***Perf. 13¼x13***

**3571** A1962 (55c) multi 1.50 .50

No. 3571 was printed in sheets of 5. A souvenir sheet of 1 sold for €3. Value, $8.
See No. 4970a.

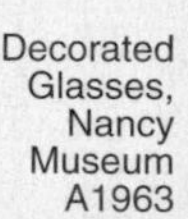

Decorated Glasses, Nancy Museum A1963

Decorated Clock, Louvre Museum A1964

Marquetry, Valençay Chateau A1965

Quimper Faience, Sèvres Museum A1966

Enamelwork, Apt Cathedral — A1967

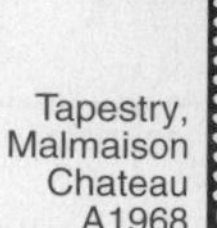

Tapestry, Malmaison Chateau A1968

Stained Glass, St. Joan of Arc Church, Rouen A1969

Cabinetwork, Louvre Museum — A1970

Wrought Iron, Army Museum, Paris A1971

Mosaic, Palace of Versailles A1972

Jewelry, Malmaison Chateau A1973

Crystal, Clichy Glassworks — A1974

**Booklet Stamps**

***Serpentine Die Cut 11***

**2009, Jan. 10** **Self-Adhesive**

**3572** A1963 (55c) multi 1.50 .50
**3573** A1964 (55c) multi 1.50 .50
**3574** A1965 (55c) multi 1.50 .50
**3575** A1966 (55c) multi 1.50 .50
**3576** A1967 (55c) multi 1.50 .50
**3577** A1968 (55c) multi 1.50 .50
**3578** A1969 (55c) multi 1.50 .50
**3579** A1970 (55c) multi 1.50 .50
**3580** A1971 (55c) multi 1.50 .50
**3581** A1972 (55c) multi 1.50 .50
**3582** A1973 (55c) multi 1.50 .50
**3583** A1974 (55c) multi 1.50 .50
*a.* Booklet pane of 12, #3572-3583 18.00
*Nos. 3572-3583 (12)* 18.00 6.00

René I, Duke of Anjou (1409-80) A1975

**2009, Jan. 16 Engr.** ***Perf. 13¼***

**3584** A1975 55c multi 1.50 .50

Hearts A1976

Flowers and: (55c), One parrot. (88c), Two parrots.

**2009, Jan. 17 Photo.** ***Perf. 13¼***

**3585** A1976 (55c) multi 1.50 .50
*a.* Souvenir sheet of 5 7.50 7.50
**3586** A1976 (88c) multi 2.40 1.25

**Self-Adhesive**

***Serpentine Die Cut***

**3587** A1976 (55c) multi 1.50 .50
**3588** A1976 (88c) multi 2.40 1.25
*a.* Booklet pane of 12 29.00
*Nos. 3585-3588 (4)* 7.80 3.50

**Tourism Issue**

Les Sables D'Olonne A1977

Menton — A1978

Chaumont A1979

Château de la Bâtie d'Urfé A1980

Bordeaux — A1981

Abbey of Royaumont A1982

**Photo., Engr. (#3590, 3592-3594)**

**2009** ***Perf. 13¼, 13 (#3593)***

**3589** A1977 55c multi 1.40 .45
**3590** A1978 56c multi 1.40 .45
**3591** A1979 56c multi 1.60 .55
**3592** A1980 56c multi 1.60 .55

***Perf. 13***

**3593** A1981 56c multi 1.60 .55
**3594** A1982 56c multi 1.75 .60
*Nos. 3589-3594 (6)* 9.35 3.15

**Self-Adhesive**

***Serpentine Die Cut 11***

**3594A** A1981 56c multi 1.60 1.60

Issued: No. 3589, 1/31; No. 3590, 2/21; No. 3591, 5/16. No. 3592, 6/6; Nos. 3593, 3594A, 6/20. No. 3594, 9/26.

Miniature Sheet

World Alpine Skiing Championships, Val d'Isère — A1983

No. 3595: a, Super combined skier. b, Slalom skier. c, Downhill (Descente) skier. d, Giant slalom skier. e, Skiers at Val d'Isère.

**2009, Jan. 31 Photo.** ***Perf. 13x13¼***

**3595** A1983 Sheet of 5 7.00 7.00
*a.-e.* 55c Any single 1.40 .45

France Foundation, 40th Anniv. — A1984

**2009, Feb. 5 Photo.** ***Perf. 13¼***

**3596** A1984 55c multi 1.40 .45

**Art Series**

Angel, St. Cecilia Cathedral, Albi A1985

La Promenade, by Hansi (Jean-Jacques Waltz) — A1986

Wrapping of Pont-Neuf, by Christo and Jeanne-Claude — A1987

Paintings by Pierre-Auguste Renoir — A1988

No. 3600: a, Monsieur et Madame Bernheim de Villers. b, Gabrielle à la Rose.

***Perf. 13, 13x13¼ (#3598), 13¼x13 (#3599)***

**2009** **Litho. (#3597), Photo.**

**3597** A1985 85c multi 2.25 1.10
**3598** A1986 90c multi 2.75 1.40
**3599** A1987 €1.35 multi 3.75 1.90
*Nos. 3597-3599 (3)* 8.75 4.40

**Souvenir Sheet**

***Perf. 13¼***

**3600** A1988 Sheet of 2 6.50 6.50
*a.* 85c multi 2.50 1.25
*b.* €1.35 multi 4.00 2.00

**Self-Adhesive**

*Serpentine Die Cut 11*

**3601** A1985 85c multi 2.50 2.50
**3602** A1986 90c multi 2.75 2.75
**3603** A1987 €1.35 multi 3.75 3.75

Issued: No. 3597, 2/7; No. 3598, 10/24; Nos. 3599, 3603, 6/13 No. 3600, 11/5. A souvenir sheet of 1 of No. 3597 sold for €3.

Road Runner and Wile E. Coyote A1989

Sylvester and Tweety Bird A1990

Daffy Duck and Bugs Bunny A1991

Design: €1, Yosemite Sam, Wile E. Coyote, Sylvester, Tasmanian Devil, Bugs Bunny, Daffy Duck, Road Runner, Marvin the Martian and Tweety Bird.

**2009, Feb. 28 Photo. *Perf. 13x13¼***

**3605** A1989 56c multi 1.40 .45
**3606** A1990 56c multi 1.40 .45
**3607** A1991 56c multi 1.40 .45
*a.* Strip of 3, #3605-3607 4.25 1.40
*Nos. 3605-3607 (3)* 4.20 1.35

**Souvenir Sheet**

**3608** A1989 €1 multi 2.60 1.25

**Booklet Stamps**

**Self-Adhesive**

**Litho.**

*Serpentine Die Cut 11*

**3609** A1989 (56c) multi 1.40 .45
**3610** A1991 (56c) multi 1.40 .45
**3611** A1990 (56c) multi 1.40 .45
*a.* Booklet pane of 12, 4 each #3609-3611 17.00
*Nos. 3609-3611 (3)* 4.20 1.35

Stamp Day. No. 3608 contains one 80x26mm stamp. Sheets of five serpentine die cut 11 self-adhesive stamps like Nos. 3605-3607 and 5 labels each sold for €6.50.

**Marianne and Stars Type of 2008**

**2009, Feb. 28 Engr. *Perf. 13***

**3612** A1912 73c ol grn 1.90 .50
**3613** A1912 90c fawn 2.25 .55
**3614** A1912 €1.30 blue 3.25 .85
**3615** A1912 €1.35 red vio 3.50 .90
**3616** A1912 €2.22 choc 5.75 1.40
*Nos. 3612-3616 (5)* 16.65 4.20

***Serpentine Die Cut 6¾ Vert.***

**Self-Adhesive**

**3616A** A1912 73c ol grn 1.90 1.90
**3616B** A1912 90c fawn 2.25 2.25
**3616C** A1912 €1.30 blue 3.25 3.25
**3616D** A1912 €1.35 red vio 3.50 3.50
**3616E** A1912 €2.22 choc 5.75 5.75
*Nos. 3616A-3616E (5)* 16.65 16.65

Constitutional Council — A1992

**2009, Mar. 5 Photo. *Perf. 13¼***

**3617** A1992 56c multi 1.40 .45

**Self-Adhesive**

*Serpentine Die Cut 11*

**3617A** A1992 56c multi 1.60 1.60

Papal Palace, Avignon — A1993

**2009, Mar. 7 Engr. *Perf. 13x12¾***

**3618** A1993 70c multi 1.90 .65

Portraits of Women by Titouan Lamazou A1994

Designs: No. 3619, Helena, United States. No. 3620, Dayu, Indonesia. No. 3621, Deborah, France. No. 3622, Kabari, Bangladesh. No. 3623, Mei Mei, China. No. 3624, Malika, Morocco. No. 3625, Dayan, Colombia. No. 3626, Francine, Rwanda. No. 3627, Blessing, Nigeria. No. 3628, Nandita, India. No. 3629, Elmas, Turkey. No. 3630, Nadia, Brazil.

*Serpentine Die Cut 11*

**2009, Mar. 9 Litho.**

**Booklet Stamps**

**Self-Adhesive**

**3619** A1994 (56c) multi 1.50 .50
**3620** A1994 (56c) multi 1.50 .50
**3621** A1994 (56c) multi 1.50 .50
**3622** A1994 (56c) multi 1.50 .50
**3623** A1994 (56c) multi 1.50 .50
**3624** A1994 (56c) multi 1.50 .50
**3625** A1994 (56c) multi 1.50 .50
**3626** A1994 (56c) multi 1.50 .50
**3627** A1994 (56c) multi 1.50 .50
**3628** A1994 (56c) multi 1.50 .50
**3629** A1994 (56c) multi 1.50 .50
**3630** A1994 (56c) multi 1.50 .50
*a.* Booklet pane of 12, #3619-3630 18.00
*Nos. 3619-3630 (12)* 18.00 6.00

Mâcon — A1995

**2009, Mar. 27 Engr. *Perf. 13x12¾***

**3631** A1995 56c multi 1.50 .50

**Souvenir Sheet**

Protection of Polar Regions — A1996

No. 3632: a, Iceberg and bird. b, Emperor penguins, vert.

***Perf. 13x13¼, 13¼x13 (85c)***

**2009, Mar. 28 Litho. & Engr.**

**3632** A1996 Sheet of 2 4.00 4.00
*a.* 56c multi 1.50 .50
*b.* 85c multi 2.50 .85

Aimé Césaire (1913-2008), Martinique Politician A1997

**2009, Apr. 17 Photo. *Perf. 13¼x13***

**3633** A1997 56c multi 1.50 .50

Flora of the French Regions A1998

Designs: No. 3634, Plum (quetsche), Alsace. No. 3635, Plum (mirabelle), Lorraine. No. 3636, Birch tree, Centre. No. 3637, Bee orchid, Champagne-Ardenne. No. 3638, Lily, Paris. No. 3639, Bluebells, Ile de France. No. 3640, Gorse, Bretagne. No. 3641, Lily-of-the-valley, Pays de la Loire. No. 3642, Apples, Basse-Normandie. No. 3643, Beech leaves, Haute-Normandie. No. 3644, Rose, Picardie. No. 3645, Potatoes, Nord-Pas de Calais. No. 3646, Olives, Provence-Alpes-Côte d'Azur. No. 3647, Chestnut, Corse. No. 3648, Wild thyme, Languedoc-Roussillon. No. 3649, Yellow gentian, Auvergne. No. 3650, Boletus mushroom, Limousin. No. 3651, Saltwort, Poitou-Charentes. No. 3652, Maritime pine, Aquitaine. No. 3653, Norway spruce, Franche-Comté. No. 3654, Awara palm, French Guiana. No. 3655, Toulouse violet, Midi-Pyrénées. No. 3656, Blueberries, Rhône-Alpes. No. 3657, Black currants, Bourgogne.

*Serpentine Die Cut 11*

**2009, Apr. 25 Photo.**

**Booklet Stamps**

**Self-Adhesive**

**3634** A1998 (56c) multi 1.50 .50
**3635** A1998 (56c) multi 1.50 .50
*a.* Booklet pane of 2, #3634-3635 3.00
**3636** A1998 (56c) multi 1.50 .50
**3637** A1998 (56c) multi 1.50 .50
*a.* Booklet pane of 2, #3636-3637 3.00
**3638** A1998 (56c) multi 1.50 .50
**3639** A1998 (56c) multi 1.50 .50
*a.* Booklet pane of 2, #3638-3639 3.00
**3640** A1998 (56c) multi 1.50 .50
**3641** A1998 (56c) multi 1.50 .50
*a.* Booklet pane of 2, #3640-3641 3.00
**3642** A1998 (56c) multi 1.50 .50
**3643** A1998 (56c) multi 1.50 .50
*a.* Booklet pane of 2, #3642-3643 3.00
**3644** A1998 (56c) multi 1.50 .50
**3645** A1998 (56c) multi 1.50 .50
*a.* Booklet pane of 2, #3644-3645 3.00
Complete booklet, #3635a, 3637a, 3639a, 3641a, 3643a, 3645a 18.00
**3646** A1998 (56c) multi 1.50 .50
**3647** A1998 (56c) multi 1.50 .50
*a.* Booklet pane of 2, #3646-3647 3.00
**3648** A1998 (56c) multi 1.50 .50
**3649** A1998 (56c) multi 1.50 .50
*a.* Booklet pane of 2, #3648-3649 3.00
**3650** A1998 (56c) multi 1.50 .50
**3651** A1998 (56c) multi 1.50 .50
*a.* Booklet pane of 2, #3650-3651 3.00
**3652** A1998 (56c) multi 1.50 .50
**3653** A1998 (56c) multi 1.50 .50
*a.* Booklet pane of 2, #3652-3653 3.00
**3654** A1998 (56c) multi 1.50 .50
**3655** A1998 (56c) multi 1.50 .50
*a.* Booklet pane of 2, #3654-3655 3.00
**3656** A1998 (56c) multi 1.50 .50
**3657** A1998 (56c) multi 1.50 .50
*a.* Booklet pane of 2, #3656-3657 3.00
Complete booklet, #3647a, 3649a, 3651a, 3653a, 3655a, 3657a 18.00
*Nos. 3634-3657 (24)* 36.00 12.00

**Souvenir Sheet**

Europa — A1999

No. 3658: a, Saturn. b, Exoplanet.

**2009, May 3 Litho. *Perf. 13¼x13***

**3658** A1999 Sheet of 2 4.00 4.00
*a.-b.* 70c Either single 2.00 .65

Intl. Year of Astronomy.

A2000

Vacations A2001

Designs: No. 3659, Tennis ball on red clay court. No. 3660, Red-striped director's chair. No. 3661, Red turban. No. 3662, Ladybug. No. 3663, Red air mattress. No. 3664, Cherry tomatoes. No. 3665, Rooster. No. 3666, Poppy. No. 3667, License plate of Bonaire, Netherlands Antilles. No. 3668, Monarch butterfly. No. 3669, Raspberries. No. 3670, Door-knocker on red door. No. 3671, Flowers near house number. No. 3672, Red boat, rope and cleat.

*Serpentine Die Cut 11*

**2009, May 13 Litho.**

**Booklet Stamps**

**Self-Adhesive**

**3659** A2000 (56c) multi 1.60 .55
**3660** A2000 (56c) multi 1.60 .55
**3661** A2000 (56c) multi 1.60 .55
**3662** A2000 (56c) multi 1.60 .55
**3663** A2000 (56c) multi 1.60 .55
**3664** A2000 (56c) multi 1.60 .55
**3665** A2001 (56c) multi 1.60 .55
**3666** A2001 (56c) multi 1.60 .55
**3667** A2001 (56c) multi 1.60 .55
**3668** A2001 (56c) multi 1.60 .55
**3669** A2001 (56c) multi 1.60 .55
**3670** A2001 (56c) multi 1.60 .55
**3671** A2001 (56c) multi 1.60 .55
**3672** A2001 (56c) multi 1.60 .55
*a.* Booklet pane of 14, #3659-3672 22.50
*Nos. 3659-3672 (14)* 22.40 7.70

Timber-frame Houses, Alsace — A2002

Azay-le-Rideau Chateau — A2003

Notre Dame Cathedral, Paris A2004

Vineyards, Bordeaux A2005

Nice A2006

Mont-Saint-Michel — A2007

Eiffel Tower
A2008

Provence
A2009

***Serpentine Die Cut 11***

**2009, May 13 Litho.**

**Booklet Stamps**

**Self-Adhesive**

| | | | | |
|---|---|---|---|---|
| **3673** | A2002 (85c) multi | | 2.40 | .80 |
| **3674** | A2003 (85c) multi | | 2.40 | .80 |
| **3675** | A2004 (85c) multi | | 2.40 | .80 |
| **3676** | A2005 (85c) multi | | 2.40 | .80 |
| **3677** | A2006 (85c) multi | | 2.40 | .80 |
| **3678** | A2007 (85c) multi | | 2.40 | .80 |
| **3679** | A2008 (85c) multi | | 2.40 | .80 |
| **3680** | A2009 (85c) multi | | 2.40 | .80 |
| *a.* | Booklet pane of 8, #3673-3680 | | 19.50 | |
| | *Nos. 3673-3680 (8)* | | 19.20 | 6.40 |

Nos. 3678 and 3679 each were printed in sheets of 50 in 2010.

John Calvin (1509-64), Theologian and Religious Reformer
A2010

**2009, May 22 Engr.** ***Perf. 13¼***

| | | | |
|---|---|---|---|
| **3681** | A2010 56c multi | 1.60 | .55 |

Miniature Sheet

Chocolate — A2011

No. 3682: a, Cacao leaves, pods and beans. b, Aztec Indian. c, Spanish soldier. d, Castle. e, Map of French Atlantic coast. f, European man and woman of 16th cent. g, Production of chocolate. h, Chocolate bar. i, Cocoa service. j, Person eating chocolate bar.

**2009, May 23 Photo.** ***Perf. 13***

| | | | |
|---|---|---|---|
| **3682** | A2011 Sheet of 10 | 16.00 | 16.00 |
| *a.-j.* | 56c Any single | 1.60 | .55 |

No. 3682 is impregnated with a chocolate scent.

French Federation Of Philatelic Associations 82nd Congress, Tarbes — A2012

**2009, June 12 Engr.** ***Perf. 13x13¼***

| | | | |
|---|---|---|---|
| **3683** | A2012 56c multi + label | 1.60 | .55 |

Jean Moulin Memorial, Rhône
A2013

**2009, June 20 Engr.** ***Perf. 13¼***

| | | | |
|---|---|---|---|
| **3684** | A2013 56c multi | 1.60 | .55 |

***Serpentine Die Cut 11***

**Self-Adhesive**

| | | | |
|---|---|---|---|
| **3685** | A2013 56c multi | 1.60 | 1.60 |

Endangered Animals
A2014

Designs: No. 3686, Giant panda. No. 3687, Rhinoceros. 70c, Aurochs, horiz. 90c, California condor, horiz.

**2009, June 20 Photo.** ***Perf. 13¼***

| | | | |
|---|---|---|---|
| **3686** | A2014 56c multi | 1.60 | .55 |
| **3687** | A2014 56c multi | 1.60 | .55 |
| **3688** | A2014 70c multi | 2.00 | .65 |
| **3689** | A2014 90c multi | 2.50 | .85 |
| *a.* | Souvenir sheet of 4, #3686-3689 | 7.75 | 7.75 |
| | *Nos. 3686-3689 (4)* | 7.70 | 2.60 |

Gordon Bennett Aviation Cup, Cent.
A2015

**2009, June 27 Engr.** ***Perf. 13¼***

| | | | |
|---|---|---|---|
| **3690** | A2015 56c blk & brn | 1.60 | .55 |

Etienne Dolet (1509-46), Printer and Translator — A2016

**2009, July 4 Engr.** ***Perf. 13x13¼***

| | | | |
|---|---|---|---|
| **3691** | A2016 56c multi | 1.60 | .55 |

Miniature Sheet

Fair Attractions — A2017

Designs: a, Parachute jump. b, Ferris wheel. c, Roller coaster. d, Carousel. e, Candy apple. f, Fishing arcade game.

**2009, Sept. 5 Photo.** ***Perf. 13***

| | | | |
|---|---|---|---|
| **3692** | A2017 Sheet of 6 | 10.50 | 10.50 |
| *a.-f.* | 56c Any single | 1.75 | .60 |

A2018

Invitation — A2019

Designs: No. 3693, Yellow background, man with red violet pants and shoes. No. 3694, Red background, woman wearing dress. No. 3695, Red violet background, woman scattering papers. No. 3696, Light blue background, cow with flowers. No. 3697, Blue background, man with red violet pants and blue shoes. No. 3698, Brown black background, birthday cake with slice on cake server. No. 3699. Yellow green background, man with brown pants and green shoes. No. 3700, Green background, man with blue pants and shoes. No. 3701, Brown background, cut birthday cake. No. 3702, Red violet background, woman with red violet pants and shoes. No. 3703, Pink background, woman with balloons. No. 3704, Red background, bird. No. 3705, Yellow green background, woman with green skirt and shoes. No. 3706, Orange background, woman scattering papers.

***Serpentine Die Cut 11***

**2009, Sept. 5 Litho.**

**Booklet Stamps**

**Self-Adhesive**

| | | | |
|---|---|---|---|
| **3693** | A2018 (56c) multi | 1.75 | .60 |
| **3694** | A2018 (56c) multi | 1.75 | .60 |
| **3695** | A2018 (56c) multi | 1.75 | .60 |
| **3696** | A2018 (56c) multi | 1.75 | .60 |
| **3697** | A2018 (56c) multi | 1.75 | .60 |
| **3698** | A2018 (56c) multi | 1.75 | .60 |
| **3699** | A2018 (56c) multi | 1.75 | .60 |
| **3700** | A2018 (56c) multi | 1.75 | .60 |
| **3701** | A2019 (56c) multi | 1.75 | .60 |
| **3702** | A2019 (56c) multi | 1.75 | .60 |
| **3703** | A2019 (56c) multi | 1.75 | .60 |
| **3704** | A2019 (56c) multi | 1.75 | .60 |
| **3705** | A2019 (56c) multi | 1.75 | .60 |
| **3706** | A2019 (56c) multi | 1.75 | .60 |
| *a.* | Booklet pane of 14, #3693-3706 | 24.50 | |
| | *Nos. 3693-3706 (14)* | 24.50 | 8.40 |

Eugène Vaillé (1875-1959), First Conservator of the Postal Museum — A2020

**2009, Sept. 19 Engr.** ***Perf. 13¼***

| | | | |
|---|---|---|---|
| **3707** | A2020 56c multi | 1.75 | .60 |

**Self-Adhesive**

***Serpentine Die Cut 11***

| | | | |
|---|---|---|---|
| **3708** | A2020 56c multi | 1.75 | 1.75 |

Souvenir Sheet

Jardin des Plantes, Paris — A2021

No. 3709: a, Gazebo. b, Mexican Hothouse.

**2009, Sept. 19 Photo.** ***Perf. 13¼x13***

| | | | |
|---|---|---|---|
| **3709** | A2021 Sheet of 2 | 13.00 | 13.00 |
| *a.-b.* | €2.22 Either single | 6.50 | 3.25 |

Salon du Timbre.

A2022

Le Petit Nicolas, by René Goscinny
A2023

Designs: No. 3710, Nicolas, wearing striped shirt, holding envelope and book bag. No. 3711, Geoffroy. No. 3712, Eudes. No. 3713, Nicolas, wearing scarf, holding envelope and book bag. No. 3714, Nicolas writing. No. 3715, Joachim. No. 3716, "Chouette, des nouvelles!" No. 3717, Character at typewriter. No. 3718, "Vous me ferez cent lignes!" No. 3719, "Chère Maman. . ." No. 3720, "C'est toi la plus jolie!", vert. No. 3721, "J'ai fait le bonheur de tout le monde.", vert. No. 3722, "Moi, je veux pas grand chose réellement. . .", vert. No. 3723, "C'est pout toi, Maman!", vert.

***Serpentine Die Cut 11***

**2009, Sept. 19 Litho.**

**Booklet Stamps**

**Self-Adhesive**

| | | | |
|---|---|---|---|
| **3710** | A2022 (56c) multi | 1.75 | .60 |
| **3711** | A2022 (56c) multi | 1.75 | .60 |
| **3712** | A2022 (56c) multi | 1.75 | .60 |
| **3713** | A2022 (56c) multi | 1.75 | .60 |
| **3714** | A2022 (56c) multi | 1.75 | .60 |
| **3715** | A2022 (56c) multi | 1.75 | .60 |
| **3716** | A2023 (56c) multi | 1.75 | .60 |
| **3717** | A2023 (56c) multi | 1.75 | .60 |
| **3718** | A2023 (56c) multi | 1.75 | .60 |
| **3719** | A2023 (56c) multi | 1.75 | .60 |
| **3720** | A2023 (56c) multi | 1.75 | .60 |
| **3721** | A2023 (56c) multi | 1.75 | .60 |
| **3722** | A2023 (56c) multi | 1.75 | .60 |
| **3723** | A2023 (56c) multi | 1.75 | .60 |
| *a.* | Booklet pane of 14, #3710-3723 | 24.50 | |
| | *Nos. 3710-3723 (14)* | 24.50 | 8.40 |

René de Saint-Marceaux (1845-1915), Sculptor of UPU Monument — A2024

**Litho. & Engr.**

**2009, Oct. 9** ***Perf. 13x13¼***

| | | | |
|---|---|---|---|
| **3724** | A2024 70c multi | 2.10 | .70 |

See Switzerland No. 9022.

Miniature Sheet

Dolls — A2025

No. 3725: a, Porcelain doll. b, GéGé doll, horiz. c, Rag doll, horiz. d, Bella doll, horiz. e, Baigneur Petitcollin, horiz. f, Unglazed porcelain doll (poupée en biscuit).

**2009, Oct. 17** ***Perf. 13***

| | | | |
|---|---|---|---|
| **3725** | A2025 Sheet of 6 | 10.50 | 10.50 |
| *a.-f.* | 56c Any single | 1.75 | .60 |

Juliette Dodu (1848-1909), Spy — A2026

**2009, Oct. 28 Engr. *Perf. 13¼***
**3726** A2026 56c multi 1.75 .60

**Self-Adhesive**
***Serpentine Die Cut 11***
**3727** A2026 56c multi 1.75 1.75

**European Capitals Type of 2002**
Miniature Sheet

No. 3728 — Attractions in Lisbon: a, Hieronymites Monastery. b, Bairro Alto Quarter, vert. c, Belém Tower. d, Monument to the Discoveries.

***Perf. 13x13¼, 13¼x13 (#3728b)***
**2009, Nov. 5 Photo.**
**3728** A1622 Sheet of 4 7.00 7.00
*a.-d.* 56c Any single 1.75 .60

Francisco de Miranda (1750-1816), Revolutionist in France and Venezuela — A2027

**2009, Nov. 6 Photo. *Perf. 13¼***
**3729** A2027 85c multi 2.60 .90

See Venezuela No. 1693.

**Marianne and Stars Type of 2008**
Miniature Sheet
**Photo., Engr. (#3456-3458)**
**2009, Nov. 6 *Perf. 13***
**3730** Sheet of 13, #3456-3458, 3730a-3730j + label 31.00 31.00
*a.* A1912 1c yellow .25 .25
*b.* A1912 5c gray brown .25 .25
*c.* A1912 10c gray .30 .30
*d.* A1912 73c olive green 2.25 2.25
*e* A1912 85c purple 2.60 2.60
*f.* A1912 90c fawn 2.75 2.75
*g.* A1912 €1 orange 3.00 3.00
*h.* A1912 €1.30 blue 4.00 4.00
*i.* A1912 €1.35 red violet 4.00 4.00
*j.* A1912 €2.22 chocolate 6.50 6.50

Euromed Postal Conference — A2028

**2009, Nov. 7 Engr. *Perf. 13¼***
**3731** A2028 56c multi 1.75 .60

A2029

A2030

A2031

A2032

A2033

A2034

A2035

A2036

A2037

A2038

A2039

A2040

A2041

A2042

***Serpentine Die Cut 11***
**2009, Nov. 7 Photo.**
**Booklet Stamps**
**Self-Adhesive**

**3732** A2029 (56c) multi 1.75 .60
**3733** A2030 (56c) multi 1.75 .60
**3734** A2031 (56c) multi 1.75 .60
**3735** A2032 (56c) multi 1.75 .60
**3736** A2033 (56c) multi 1.75 .60
**3737** A2034 (56c) multi 1.75 .60
**3738** A2035 (56c) multi 1.75 .60
**3739** A2036 (56c) multi 1.75 .60
**3740** A2037 (56c) multi 1.75 .60
**3741** A2038 (56c) multi 1.75 .60
**3742** A2039 (56c) multi 1.75 .60
**3743** A2040 (56c) multi 1.75 .60
**3744** A2041 (56c) multi 1.75 .60
**3745** A2042 (56c) multi 1.75 .60
*a.* Booklet pane of 14, #3732-3745 24.50
*Nos. 3732-3745 (14)* 24.50 8.40

A souvenir sheet containing one No. 3743 sold for €3.

Helicopter Carrier Jeanne d'Arc — A2043

Sailors of the Jeanne d'Arc — A2044

**2009, Nov. 21 Engr. *Perf. 13x12¾***
**3746** A2043 56c multi 1.75 .60
**3747** A2044 56c multi 1.75 .60
*a.* Horiz. pair, #3746-3747 3.50 1.20

A souvenir sheet containing Nos. 3746-3747 sold for €3.

Asterix, Comic Strip by René Goscinny and Albert Uderzo — A2045

No. 3749: a, Assurancetorix on rope (40x30mm). b, Eight characters, horiz. (80x26mm). c, Falbala with basket (30x40mm). d, Idefix and bone, horiz. (22x19mm). e, Obelix carrying rock (50x100mm).

**2009, Dec. 2 Photo. *Perf. 13***
**3748** A2045 56c multi 1.75 .60
**3749** Sheet of 6, #3748, 3749a-3749e 15.50 15.50
*a.* A2045 56c multi, perf. 13x13¼ 2.50 2.50
*b.* A2045 56c multi, perf. 13 2.50 2.50
*c.* A2045 56c multi, perf. 13¼x13 2.50 2.50
*d.* A2045 56c multi, perf. 13¼x12½ 2.50 2.50
*e.* A2045 56c multi, perf. 13x12¼ 2.50 2.50

No. 3749 sold for €5.20, with the Red Cross receiving €1.84 of that. No. 3749e has a gritty substance affixed to the rock.

A2046

Hearts A2047

Type I — Bow ties extend to perforations.
Type II — Bow ties do not touch perforations (red frame all around).

**2010, Jan. 8 Photo. *Perf. 13¼***
**3750** A2046 56c multi, type I 1.60 .55

***Perf.***
**3751** A2046 56c multi, type II 1.60 .55

***Perf. 13¼***
**3752** A2047 90c multi 2.50 1.25
*Nos. 3750-3752 (3)* 5.70 2.35

**Self-Adhesive**
***Serpentine Die Cut***
**3753** A2046 56c multi, type I 1.60 1.60
**3754** A2047 90c multi 2.50 2.50

Values for Nos. 3750, 3752 are for stamps with surrounding selvage. No. 3751 was printed in sheets of 5.

New Year 2010 (Year of the Tiger) — A2048

**2010, Jan. 15 Photo. *Perf. 13¼x13***
**3755** A2048 56c multi 1.60 .55

No. 3755 was printed in sheets of 5. A souvenir sheet of 1 sold for €3.

See No. 4970b.

Abbé Pierre (1912-2007), Founder of Emmaus Movement A2049

**2010, Jan. 22 Engr. *Perf. 13¼***
**3756** A2049 56c multi 1.60 .55

**Self-Adhesive**
***Serpentine Die Cut 11***
**3757** A2049 56c multi 1.60 1.60

A souvenir sheet containing No. 3756 was printed in 2011 and sold for €3.

Musical Instruments in Art — A2050

Designs: No. 3758, Lyre, by Gustave Moreau. No. 3759, Harp (Harpe), by François André Vincent. No. 3760, Violincello (Violincelle), by Karl Gustav Klingstedt. No. 3761, Guitar (Guitare), by Camille Roqueplan. No. 3762, Horn (Cor), by Daniel Rabel. No. 3763, Saxophone, by Marthe and Juliette Vesque. No. 3764, Organ (Orgue), by François Garas. No. 3765, Bugle (Clairon), by Auguste Mayer. No. 3766, Clavecin, by Louis Carrogis Carmontelle. No. 3767, Piano, by Pierre-Désiré Lamy. No. 3768, Tambourine (Tambourin), by Théodore Chassériau. No. 3769, Drums (Tambour), by Jacques-Antoine Delaistre.

***Serpentine Die Cut 11***
**2010, Jan. 30 Photo.**
**Booklet Stamps**
**Self-Adhesive**

**3758** A2050 (56c) multi 1.60 .55
**3759** A2050 (56c) multi 1.60 .55
**3760** A2050 (56c) multi 1.60 .55
**3761** A2050 (56c) multi 1.60 .55
**3762** A2050 (56c) multi 1.60 .55
**3763** A2050 (56c) multi 1.60 .55
**3764** A2050 (56c) multi 1.60 .55
**3765** A2050 (56c) multi 1.60 .55
**3766** A2050 (56c) multi 1.60 .55
**3767** A2050 (56c) multi 1.60 .55
**3768** A2050 (56c) multi 1.60 .55
**3769** A2050 (56c) multi 1.60 .55
*a.* Booklet pane of 12, #3758-3769 19.50
*Nos. 3758-3769 (12)* 19.20 6.60

See Nos. 3882A-3882B.

2010 Winter Olympics, Vancouver A2051

**2010, Feb. 6 *Perf. 13x13¼***
**3770** A2051 85c Figure skaters 2.40 1.25
**3771** A2051 85c Skier 2.40 1.25
*a.* Horiz. pair, #3770-3771 4.80 2.50
*b.* Tete-beche block of 4, 2 #3771a 9.60 5.00

**Art Issue**

Museum of Art and Industry (La Piscine), Roubaix — A2052

The Beach at Calais at Ebb Tide, by Joseph Mallord William Turner — A2053

Maman, by Louise Bourgeois — A2054

Allegory of Spring, by Sandro Botticelli — A2055

No. 3775: a, Flora, Zephyrus and Chloris. b, The Three Graces.

**2010 Photo. *Perf. 13x13¼***

| | | | | |
|---|---|---|---|---|
| **3772** | A2052 | 85c multi | 2.10 | 1.10 |
| **3773** | A2053 | €1.35 multi | 3.75 | 1.90 |
| **3774** | A2054 | €1.35 multi | 3.50 | 1.75 |
| | | *Nos. 3772-3774 (3)* | 9.35 | 4.75 |

***Perf. 13¼x13***

| | | | | |
|---|---|---|---|---|
| **3775** | A2055 | Sheet of 2 | 6.25 | 6.25 |
| *a.* | | 87c multi | 2.40 | 1.25 |
| *b.* | | €1.40 multi | 3.75 | 1.90 |

**Self-Adhesive**

***Serpentine Die Cut 11***

**Photo.**

| | | | | |
|---|---|---|---|---|
| **3776** | A2052 | 85c multi | 2.10 | 2.10 |
| **3776A** | A2055 | 87c Like #3775b | 2.40 | 2.40 |
| **3777** | A2053 | €1.35 multi | 3.75 | 3.75 |
| **3778** | A2054 | €1.35 multi | 3.50 | 3.50 |
| **3779** | A2055 | €1.40 Like #3775a | 3.75 | 3.75 |
| | | *Nos. 3776-3779 (5)* | 15.50 | 15.50 |

Issued: Nos. 3772, 3776, 5/15; Nos. 3773, 3777, 2/19; Nos. 3774, 3778, 6/17; No. 3775, 11/8/10; Nos. 3776A, 3779, 11/18/10.

A2056

Stamp Day — A2057

**2010, Feb. 27 Engr. *Perf. 13***

| | | | | |
|---|---|---|---|---|
| **3780** | A2056 | 56c blue & red | 1.60 | .55 |

**Souvenir Sheet**

**Litho. & Embossed**

***Perf. 13¼x13***

| | | | | |
|---|---|---|---|---|
| **3781** | A2057 | €2 multi | 5.50 | 2.75 |

Protection of Water A2058

Inscriptions: No. 3782, Grands mammifères marins (large marine mammals). No. 3783, Marée noire (black tide). No. 3784, Irrigation. No. 3785, Plaisir de l'eau (pleasure of water). No. 3786, Inondation (flood). No. 3787, Source. No. 3788, Aigues vertes (green water). No. 3789, Secheresse (drought). No. 3790, Hydro-électricité (hydroelectricity). No. 3791, Géothermie (geothermal energy). No. 3792, Pluies acides (acid rain). No. 3793, Fonte des glaciers (melting of glaciers).

***Serpentine Die Cut 11***

**2010, Feb. 27 Photo.**

**Booklet Stamps**

**Self-Adhesive**

| | | | | |
|---|---|---|---|---|
| **3782** | A2058 | (56c) multi | 1.60 | .55 |
| **3783** | A2058 | (56c) multi | 1.60 | .55 |
| **3784** | A2058 | (56c) multi | 1.60 | .55 |
| **3785** | A2058 | (56c) multi | 1.60 | .55 |
| **3786** | A2058 | (56c) multi | 1.60 | .55 |
| **3787** | A2058 | (56c) multi | 1.60 | .55 |
| **3788** | A2058 | (56c) multi | 1.60 | .55 |
| **3789** | A2058 | (56c) multi | 1.60 | .55 |
| **3790** | A2058 | (56c) multi | 1.60 | .55 |
| **3791** | A2058 | (56c) multi | 1.60 | .55 |
| **3792** | A2058 | (56c) multi | 1.60 | .55 |
| **3793** | A2058 | (56c) multi | 1.60 | .55 |
| *a.* | | Booklet pane of 12, #3782-3793 | 19.50 | |
| | | *Nos. 3782-3793 (12)* | 19.20 | 6.60 |

Savoy as Part of France, 150th Anniv. A2059

**2010, Mar. 27 Engr. *Perf. 13¼x13***

| | | | | |
|---|---|---|---|---|
| **3794** | A2059 | 56c multi | 1.60 | .55 |

**Self-Adhesive**

***Serpentine Die Cut 11***

| | | | | |
|---|---|---|---|---|
| **3795** | A2059 | 56c multi | 1.60 | 1.60 |

**Tourism Issue**

Villeneuve lez Avignon A2060

Orcival Basilica — A2061

Pornic — A2062

Arcueil-Cachan Aqueduct Bridge — A2063

**2010 Engr. *Perf. 13¼***

| | | | | |
|---|---|---|---|---|
| **3796** | A2060 | 56c multi | 1.50 | .50 |
| **3797** | A2061 | 56c multi | 1.40 | .45 |

***Perf. 13***

| | | | | |
|---|---|---|---|---|
| **3798** | A2062 | 56c multi | 1.40 | .45 |

***Perf. 13¼***

| | | | | |
|---|---|---|---|---|
| **3799** | A2063 | 58c multi | 1.60 | .55 |
| | | *Nos. 3796-3799 (4)* | 5.90 | 1.95 |

**Self-Adhesive**

**Engr.**

***Serpentine Die Cut 11***

| | | | | |
|---|---|---|---|---|
| **3800** | A2060 | 56c multi | 1.50 | 1.50 |

Issued: Nos. 3796, 3800, 4/17; No. 3797, 5/13; No. 3798, 5/25; No. 3799, 9/24.

A2064

A2065

A2066

A2067

A2068

A2069

A2070

A2071

A2072

A2073

A2074

Campaign Against Violence Toward Women — A2075

***Serpentine Die Cut 11***

**2010, Apr. 20 Litho.**

**Booklet Stamps**

**Self-Adhesive**

| | | | | |
|---|---|---|---|---|
| **3801** | A2064 | (56c) multi | 1.50 | .50 |
| **3802** | A2065 | (56c) multi | 1.50 | .50 |
| **3803** | A2066 | (56c) multi | 1.50 | .50 |
| **3804** | A2067 | (56c) multi | 1.50 | .50 |
| **3805** | A2068 | (56c) multi | 1.50 | .50 |
| **3806** | A2069 | (56c) multi | 1.50 | .50 |
| **3807** | A2070 | (56c) multi | 1.50 | .50 |
| **3808** | A2071 | (56c) multi | 1.50 | .50 |
| **3809** | A2072 | (56c) multi | 1.50 | .50 |
| **3810** | A2073 | (56c) multi | 1.50 | .50 |
| **3811** | A2074 | (56c) multi | 1.50 | .50 |
| **3812** | A2075 | (56c) multi | 1.50 | .50 |
| *a.* | | Booklet pane of 12, #3801-3812 | 18.00 | |
| | | *Nos. 3801-3812 (12)* | 18.00 | 6.00 |

Colmar A2076

**2010, Apr. 23 Engr. *Perf. 13¼***

| | | | | |
|---|---|---|---|---|
| **3813** | A2076 | 56c multi | 1.50 | .50 |

**Self-Adhesive**

***Serpentine Die Cut 11***

| | | | | |
|---|---|---|---|---|
| **3814** | A2076 | 56c multi | 1.50 | 1.50 |

National Sheepcote, Rambouillet — A2077

**2010, May 1 *Perf. 13¼***

| | | | | |
|---|---|---|---|---|
| **3815** | A2077 | 90c multi | 2.40 | 1.25 |

Europa
A2078

**2010, May 9** **Photo.**

| | | | | |
|---|---|---|---|---|
| **3816** | A2078 70c multi | | 1.75 | .60 |

Miniature Sheet

Stamp Bourse in Paris, 150th Anniv. — A2079

No. 3817 — Famous philatelists: a, Pres. Franklin Delano Roosevelt (1882-1945). b, Lucien Berthelot (1903-85), President of International Philatelic Federation. c, Louis Yvert (1866-1950), stamp catalogue publisher, horiz. d, Arthur Maury (1844-1907), stamp catalogue publisher, horiz. e, Alberto Bolaffi (1874-1944), stamp catalogue publisher.

**2010, May 13** **Engr.** ***Perf. 13***

| | | | |
|---|---|---|---|
| **3817** A2079 | Sheet of 5 | 7.00 | 7.00 |
| *a.-e.* | 56c Any single | 1.40 | .45 |

Deauville, 150th Anniv. A2080

**2010, May 14** **Photo.** ***Perf. 13¼***

| | | | |
|---|---|---|---|
| **3818** | A2080 85c multi | 2.10 | 1.10 |

Mother Teresa (1910-97), Humanitarian A2081

**2010, May 27** **Engr.** ***Perf. 13¼x13***

| | | | |
|---|---|---|---|
| **3819** | A2081 85c multi | 2.10 | 1.10 |

**Self-Adhesive**

***Serpentine Die Cut 11***

| | | | |
|---|---|---|---|
| **3820** | A2081 85c multi | 2.10 | 2.10 |

Institute of Human Paleontology, Paris, Cent. — A2082

**2010, June 1** ***Perf. 13x12¾***

| | | | |
|---|---|---|---|
| **3821** | A2082 56c multi | 1.40 | .45 |

See Monaco No. 2597.

Nice as Part of France, 150th Anniv. A2083

**2010, June 11** **Photo.** ***Perf. 13¼***

| | | | |
|---|---|---|---|
| **3822** | A2083 56c multi | 1.40 | .45 |

**Self-Adhesive**

***Serpentine Die Cut 11***

| | | | |
|---|---|---|---|
| **3823** | A2083 56c multi | 1.40 | 1.40 |

Front Side of No. 3824

Rear Side of No. 3824 — A2084

A2085

2010 World Cup Soccer Championships, South Africa — A2086

No. 3825: a, Soccer player and ball. b, Soccer players, vert. c, South African building, vert. d, Aerial view of Cape Town.

**2010** **Photo.** ***Perf. 13x12¾***

| | | | |
|---|---|---|---|
| **3824** | A2084 56c multi | 2.75 | .50 |

***Perf. 13x13¼, 13¼x13***

| | | | |
|---|---|---|---|
| **3825** A2085 | Sheet of 4 | 8.50 | 8.50 |
| *a.-d.* | 85c Any single | 2.10 | 1.10 |

**Embossed and Etched on Silver**

***Die Cut Perf. 12¾***

**Self-Adhesive**

| | | | |
|---|---|---|---|
| **3826** | A2086 €5 *silver* | 12.50 | 12.50 |

Issued: Nos. 3824, 3825, 6/13; No. 3826, 6/11. No. 3824 is gummed on both sides and sold for €1.12. Both sides of the stamp could be used. Values for used examples of No. 3824 are for stamps canceled on either or both sides.

Launch of Soyuz Space Flights From French Guiana A2087

**2010, June 12** **Photo.** ***Perf. 13¼***

| | | | |
|---|---|---|---|
| **3827** | A2087 85c multi | 2.25 | 1.10 |

**Self-Adhesive**

***Serpentine Die Cut 11***

| | | | |
|---|---|---|---|
| **3828** | A2087 85c multi | 2.25 | 2.25 |

Souvenir Sheet

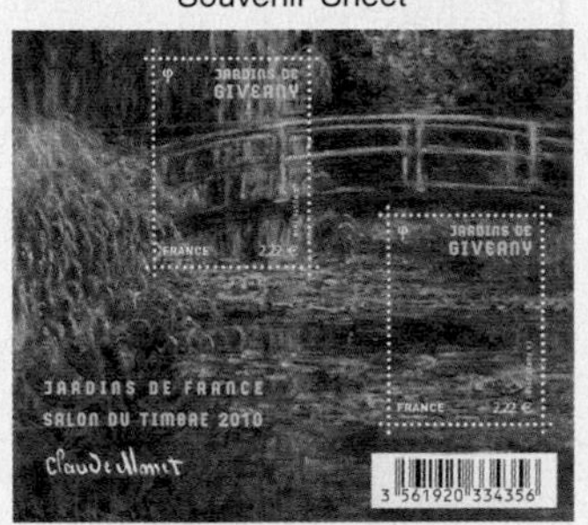


Jardins de Giverny, by Claude Monet — A2088

No. 3829: a, Bridge. b, Pond.

**2010, June 12** ***Perf. 13¼x13***

| | | | |
|---|---|---|---|
| **3829** A2088 | Sheet of 2 | 11.50 | 11.50 |
| *a.-b.* | €2.22 Either single | 5.75 | 3.00 |
| *c.* | Souvenir sheet, #3709a, 3709b, 3829a, 3829b | 22.50 | 22.50 |

2010 Salon du Timbre (No. 3829c).

Regional Cuisine A2089

Designs: No. 3830, Eclade (grilled mussels), Poitou-Charentes. No. 3831, Baeckaoffe (stew), Alsace. No. 3832, Tomme des Pyrénées cheese, Midi-Pyrénées. No. 3833, Tarte aux mirabelles (plum tart), Lorraine. No. 3834, Potage aux cresson (watercress soup), Ile-de-France. No. 3835, Flamiche (leek pie), Picardy. No. 3836, Pont l'Evêque cheese, Basse-Normandie. No. 3837, Blanc manger (blancmange), Antilles. No. 3838, Caviar, Aquitaine. No. 3839, Chapon (capon), Franche-Comté. No. 3840, Fourme d'Ambert cheese, Auvergne. No. 3841, Tarte tatin (upside-down apple tart), Centre.

No. 3842, Quenelles (dumplings), Rhône-Alpes. No. 3843, Escalope normande (veal cutlet), Haute-Normandie. No. 3844, Maroilles cheese, Nord-Pas-de-Calais. No. 3845, Clafoutis (baked fruit and batter), Limousin. No. 3846, Gougères (cheese pastry), Bourgogne. No. 3847, Tian (baked vegetables), Provence-Alpes-Côte d'Azur. No. 3848, Broccio cheese, Corsica. No. 3849, Abricots rouges au miel (apricots in honey), Languedoc-Roussillon. No. 3850, Homard breton (lobster), Bretagne. No. 3851, Brochet au beurre blanc (pike with white butter), Pays de la Loire. No. 3852, Chaource cheese, Champagne-Ardennes. No. 3853, Paris-Brest (butter cream-filled pastry), Paris.

***Serpentine Die Cut 11***

**2010, June 12** **Photo.**

**Booklet Stamps**

**Self-Adhesive**

| | | | |
|---|---|---|---|
| **3830** | A2089 (56c) multi | 1.40 | .45 |
| **3831** | A2089 (56c) multi | 1.40 | .45 |
| **3832** | A2089 (56c) multi | 1.40 | .45 |
| **3833** | A2089 (56c) multi | 1.40 | .45 |
| *a.* | Booklet pane of 4, #3830-3833 | 5.60 | |
| **3834** | A2089 (56c) multi | 1.40 | .45 |
| **3835** | A2089 (56c) multi | 1.40 | .45 |
| **3836** | A2089 (56c) multi | 1.40 | .45 |
| **3837** | A2089 (56c) multi | 1.40 | .45 |
| *a.* | Booklet pane of 4, #3834-3837 | 5.60 | |
| **3838** | A2089 (56c) multi | 1.40 | .45 |
| **3839** | A2089 (56c) multi | 1.40 | .45 |
| **3840** | A2089 (56c) multi | 1.40 | .45 |
| **3841** | A2089 (56c) multi | 1.40 | .45 |
| *a.* | Booklet pane of 4, #3838-3841 | 5.60 | |

| | | | |
|---|---|---|---|
| | Complete booklet, #3833a, 3837a, 3841a | 17.00 | |
| **3842** | A2089 (56c) multi | 1.40 | .45 |
| **3843** | A2089 (56c) multi | 1.40 | .45 |
| **3844** | A2089 (56c) multi | 1.40 | .45 |
| **3845** | A2089 (56c) multi | 1.40 | .45 |
| *a.* | Booklet pane of 4, #3842-3845 | 5.60 | |
| **3846** | A2089 (56c) multi | 1.40 | .45 |
| **3847** | A2089 (56c) multi | 1.40 | .45 |
| **3848** | A2089 (56c) multi | 1.40 | .45 |
| **3849** | A2089 (56c) multi | 1.40 | .45 |
| *a.* | Booklet pane of 4, #3846-3849 | 5.60 | |
| **3850** | A2089 (56c) multi | 1.40 | .45 |
| **3851** | A2089 (56c) multi | 1.40 | .45 |
| **3852** | A2089 (56c) multi | 1.40 | .45 |
| **3853** | A2089 (56c) multi | 1.40 | .45 |
| *a.* | Booklet pane of 4, #3850-3853 | 5.60 | |
| | Complete booklet, #3845a, 3849a, 3853a | 17.00 | |
| | *Nos. 3830-3853 (24)* | 33.60 | 10.80 |

Romanesque Art — A2090

Designs: No. 3854, Bas-relief, Tournus. No. 3855, Interior of Cistercian Abbey, Léoncel. No. 3856, Painting, St. Sever. No. 3857, Serrabone Priory, Boule d'Amont. No. 3858, Sculpture, L'Ile-Bouchard. No. 3859, Painting, Citeaux Abbey. No. 3860, Fresco from St. Martin's Church, Nohant-Vic. No. 3861, Bas-relief, Clermont-Ferrand. No. 3862, Fresco, St. Jacques-des-Guérets. No. 3863, Bas-relief, Angouleme. No. 3864, Painting of the Consecration of the third Abbey Church, Cluny. No. 3865, Bas-reliefs, tympanum of Saint-Foy Abbey Church, Conques.

***Serpentine Die Cut 11***

**2010, June 14** **Photo.**

**Booklet Stamps**

**Self-Adhesive**

| | | | |
|---|---|---|---|
| **3854** | A2090 (56c) multi | 1.40 | .45 |
| **3855** | A2090 (56c) multi | 1.40 | .45 |
| **3856** | A2090 (56c) multi | 1.40 | .45 |
| **3857** | A2090 (56c) multi | 1.40 | .45 |
| **3858** | A2090 (56c) multi | 1.40 | .45 |
| **3859** | A2090 (56c) multi | 1.40 | .45 |
| **3860** | A2090 (56c) multi | 1.40 | .45 |
| **3861** | A2090 (56c) multi | 1.40 | .45 |
| **3862** | A2090 (56c) multi | 1.40 | .45 |
| **3863** | A2090 (56c) multi | 1.40 | .45 |
| **3864** | A2090 (56c) multi | 1.40 | .45 |
| **3865** | A2090 (56c) multi | 1.40 | .45 |
| *a.* | Booklet pane of 12, #3854-3865 | 17.00 | |
| | *Nos. 3854-3865 (12)* | 16.80 | 5.40 |

See Nos. 3870A-3870B.

Miniature Sheet

Mills — A2091

No. 3866: a, Windmill, Montbrun-Lauragais. b, Windmill, Cassel. c, Aigremonts Windmill, Bléré, horiz. d, Daudet Windmill, Fontvieille, horiz. e, Flour mill, Villeneuve-d'Ascq. f, Birlot Watermill, Ile-de-Bréhat, horiz.

**Litho. & Engr.**

**2010, June 15** ***Perf. 13***

| | | | |
|---|---|---|---|
| **3866** A2091 | Sheet of 6 | 8.50 | 8.50 |
| *a.-f.* | 56c Any single | 1.40 | .45 |

2010 Youth Olympics, Singapore A2092

**2010, June 16 Photo. *Perf. 13¼***

| | | | |
|---|---|---|---|
| **3867** | A2092 85c multi | 2.25 | 1.10 |

Souvenir Sheet

Charles de Gaulle's Appeal of June 18 Speech, 70th Anniv. — A2093

**2010, June 18 Engr. *Perf. 13x13¼***

| | | | |
|---|---|---|---|
| **3868** | A2093 56c multi | 1.40 | .45 |

Conciergerie, Paris — A2094

**2010, June 19**

| | | | |
|---|---|---|---|
| **3869** | A2094 56c multi + label | 1.40 | .45 |

French Federation of Philatelic Associations, 83rd Congress, Paris.

French Pavilion, Expo 2010, Shanghai A2095

**2010, June 20 Photo. *Perf. 13¼***

| | | | |
|---|---|---|---|
| **3870** | A2095 85c multi | 2.25 | 1.10 |

**Romanesque Art Type of 2010**

Designs: No. 3870A, Like #3855. No. 3870B, Like #3858.

***Serpentine Die Cut 11***

**2010, June 21 Litho.**

**Self-Adhesive**

| | | | |
|---|---|---|---|
| **3870A** | A2090 (56c) multi | 1.40 | 1.40 |
| **3870B** | A2090 (56c) multi | 1.40 | 1.40 |

Nos. 3870A-3870B each were printed in sheets of 50. The red panels of Nos. 3855 and 3858 are splotchy, typical of photogravure printings. Under magnification black dots can be seen in the red panels on Nos. 3870A-3870B.

**Marianne and Stars Type of 2008**

**2010, July 1 Engr. *Perf. 13***

| | | | | |
|---|---|---|---|---|
| **3871** | A1912 | 75c olive green | 1.90 | .50 |
| **3872** | A1912 | 87c purple | 2.25 | .55 |
| **3873** | A1912 | 95c fawn | 2.40 | .60 |
| **3874** | A1912 | €1.35 blue | 3.50 | .90 |
| **3875** | A1912 | €1.40 red violet | 3.50 | .90 |
| **3876** | A1912 | €2.30 chocolate | 5.75 | 1.50 |
| | *Nos. 3871-3876 (6)* | | 19.30 | 4.95 |

**Self-Adhesive**

***Serpentine Die Cut 6¾ Vert.***

| | | | | |
|---|---|---|---|---|
| **3877** | A1912 | 75c olive green | 1.90 | 1.90 |
| **3878** | A1912 | 87c purple | 2.25 | 2.25 |
| **3879** | A1912 | 95c fawn | 2.40 | 2.40 |
| **3880** | A1912 | €1.35 blue | 3.50 | 3.50 |
| **3881** | A1912 | €1.40 red violet | 3.50 | 3.50 |
| **3882** | A1912 | €2.30 chocolate | 5.75 | 5.75 |
| | *Nos. 3877-3882 (6)* | | 19.30 | 19.30 |

**Musical Instruments Type of 2010**

Designs: No. 3882A, Like #3761. No. 3882B, Like #3767.

***Serpentine Die Cut 11***

**2010, July 1 Litho.**

**Self-Adhesive**

| | | | |
|---|---|---|---|
| **3882A** | A2050 (58c) multi | 1.50 | 1.50 |
| **3882B** | A2050 (58c) multi | 1.50 | 1.50 |

Nos. 3882A-3882B were each printed in sheets of 50. The gray blue portions of Nos. 3761 and 3767 are splotchy, typical of photogravure printings, and not splotchy on Nos. 3882A and 3882B.

Independence of French Colonies in Africa, 50th Anniv. — A2096

**2010, July 15 Photo. *Perf. 13¼***

| | | | |
|---|---|---|---|
| **3883** | A2096 87c multi | 2.25 | 1.10 |

**Self-Adhesive**

***Serpentine Die Cut 11***

| | | | |
|---|---|---|---|
| **3884** | A2096 87c multi | 2.25 | 2.25 |

Butterflies A2097

Designs: Nos. 3885, 3886b, Morpho menelaus. No. 3886a, Cerura vinula caterpillar. 75c, Thersamolycaena dispar, vert. 95c, Callophrys rubi.

**Litho. (#3885, 3886a), Litho. & Embossed**

**2010, Sept. 3 *Perf. 13¼***

| | | | |
|---|---|---|---|
| **3885** | A2097 58c multi | 1.50 | .50 |
| **3886** | Sheet of 4 | 7.50 | 7.50 |
| *a.* | A2097 58c multi | 1.50 | .50 |
| *b.* | A2097 58c multi | 1.50 | .50 |
| *c.* | A2097 75c multi | 2.00 | .65 |
| *d.* | A2097 95c multi | 2.50 | .85 |

Universal Israelite Alliance, 150th Anniv. A2098

**Litho. & Engr.**

**2010, Sept. 7 *Perf. 13¼***

| | | | |
|---|---|---|---|
| **3887** | A2098 58c multi | 1.50 | .50 |

A2099

A2100

A2101

A2102

A2103

A2104

A2105

A2106

A2107

A2108

A2109

Cartoons With Letters A2110

***Serpentine Die Cut 11***

**2010, Oct. 11 Photo.**

**Booklet Stamps**

**Self-Adhesive**

| | | | |
|---|---|---|---|
| **3888** | A2099 (58c) multi | 1.75 | .60 |
| **3889** | A2100 (58c) multi | 1.75 | .60 |
| **3890** | A2101 (58c) multi | 1.75 | .60 |
| **3891** | A2102 (58c) multi | 1.75 | .60 |
| **3892** | A2103 (58c) multi | 1.75 | .60 |
| **3893** | A2104 (58c) multi | 1.75 | .60 |
| **3894** | A2105 (58c) multi | 1.75 | .60 |
| **3895** | A2106 (58c) multi | 1.75 | .60 |
| **3896** | A2107 (58c) multi | 1.75 | .60 |
| **3897** | A2108 (58c) multi | 1.75 | .60 |
| **3898** | A2109 (58c) multi | 1.75 | .60 |
| **3899** | A2110 (58c) multi | 1.75 | .60 |
| *a.* | Booklet pane of 12, #3888-3899 | 21.00 | |
| | *Nos. 3888-3899 (12)* | 21.00 | 7.20 |

Aviation Pioneers — A2111

Designs: Nos. 3900, 3902, Elise Deroche (1882-1919).

No. 3901: a, Hubert Latham (1883-1912). b, Orville (1871-1948) and Wilbur Wright (1867-1912). c, Henry Farman (1874-1958). d, Jules Védrines (1881-1919). e, Léon Delagrange (1872-1910).

**2010, Oct. 15 Photo. *Perf. 13***

| | | | |
|---|---|---|---|
| **3900** | A2111 58c multi | 1.75 | .60 |
| **3901** | Sheet of 6, #3900, 3901a-3901e | 15.00 | 15.00 |
| *a.-e.* | A2111 58c Any single | 2.50 | 2.50 |

**Self-Adhesive**

***Serpentine Die Cut 11***

| | | | |
|---|---|---|---|
| **3902** | A2111 58c multi | 1.75 | 1.75 |

No. 3901 sold for € 5.40, with the Red Cross receiving €1.92 of that.

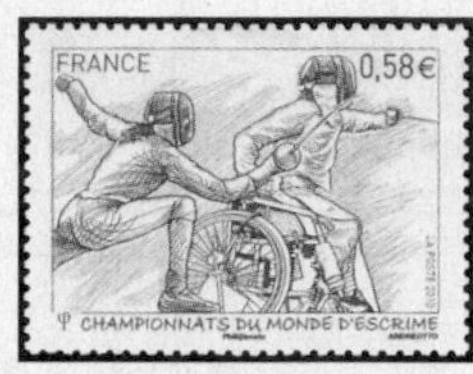

World Fencing Championships, Paris — A2112

Designs: 58c, Wheelchair fencing. 87c, Fencing.

**2010, Oct. 22 Engr. *Perf. 13x13¼***

| | | | |
|---|---|---|---|
| **3903** | A2112 58c multi | 1.75 | .60 |
| **3904** | A2112 87c multi | 2.50 | .85 |
| *a.* | Horiz. pair, #3903-3904 + central label | 4.25 | 1.50 |

Paris Bar Association, Bicent. — A2113

**2010, Oct. 28 Photo. *Perf. 13¼***

| | | | |
|---|---|---|---|
| **3905** | A2113 58c black & lt blue | 1.75 | .60 |

**Self-Adhesive**

***Serpentine Die Cut 11***

| | | | |
|---|---|---|---|
| **3906** | A2113 58c black & lt blue | 1.75 | 1.75 |

Villeneuve-sur-Lot — A2114

**2010, Oct. 30 Engr. *Perf. 13¼***

| | | | |
|---|---|---|---|
| **3907** | A2114 58c multi | 1.75 | .60 |

**European Capitals Type of 2002**

Miniature Sheet

No. 3908 — Attractions in Paris: a, Arc de Triomphe de l'Etoile. b, Notre Dame Cathedral. c, Garnier Opera House. d, Eiffel Tower, vert.

***Perf. 13x13¼, 13¼x13 (#3908d)***

**2010, Nov. 4 Photo.**

| | | | |
|---|---|---|---|
| **3908** | A1622 Sheet of 4 | 7.00 | 7.00 |
| *a.-d.* | 58c Any single | 1.75 | .60 |

A2115

A2116

A2117

A2118

A2119 A2120

A2121

A2122

A2123

A2124

A2125

A2126

A2127

"Best Wishes" — A2128

*Serpentine Die Cut 11*

**2010, Nov. 5 Photo.**

**Booklet Stamps**

**Self-Adhesive**

| | | | | |
|---|---|---|---|---|
| **3909** | A2115 (58c) multi | | 1.75 | .60 |
| **3910** | A2116 (58c) multi | | 1.75 | .60 |
| **3911** | A2117 (58c) multi | | 1.75 | .60 |
| **3912** | A2118 (58c) multi | | 1.75 | .60 |
| **3913** | A2119 (58c) multi | | 1.75 | .60 |
| **3914** | A2120 (58c) multi | | 1.75 | .60 |
| **3915** | A2121 (58c) multi | | 1.75 | .60 |
| **3916** | A2122 (58c) multi | | 1.75 | .60 |
| **3917** | A2123 (58c) multi | | 1.75 | .60 |
| **3918** | A2124 (58c) multi | | 1.75 | .60 |
| **3919** | A2125 (58c) multi | | 1.75 | .60 |
| **3920** | A2126 (58c) multi | | 1.75 | .60 |
| **3921** | A2127 (58c) multi | | 1.75 | .60 |
| **3922** | A2128 (58c) multi | | 1.75 | .60 |
| *a.* | Booklet pane of 14, #3909-3922, + 14 stickers | | 24.50 | |
| | *Nos. 3909-3922 (14)* | | 24.50 | 8.40 |

A souvenir sheet containing one perf. 13x13¼ example of No. 3915 with water-activated gum sold for €3.

First French Revenue Stamp, 150th Anniv. — A2129

*Serpentine Die Cut 6¾ Vert.*

**2010, Nov. 6 Engr.**

**Booklet Stamp**

**Self-Adhesive**

| | | | |
|---|---|---|---|
| **3923** | A2129 (58c) brown | 1.60 | .40 |
| *a.* | Booklet pane of 12, 6 each #3471, 3923 | 19.50 | |

**Souvenir Sheet**

Primitive Flemish Paintings — A2130

No. 3924: a, Madonna and Child, by Roger de la Pasture. b, Portrait of Laurent Froimont, by Rogier van der Weyden.

**2010, Nov. 6 Photo. *Perf. 13***

| | | | |
|---|---|---|---|
| **3924** | A2130 Sheet of 2 | 10.00 | 10.00 |
| *a.-b.* | €1.80 Either single | 5.00 | 2.50 |

See Belgium No. 2478.

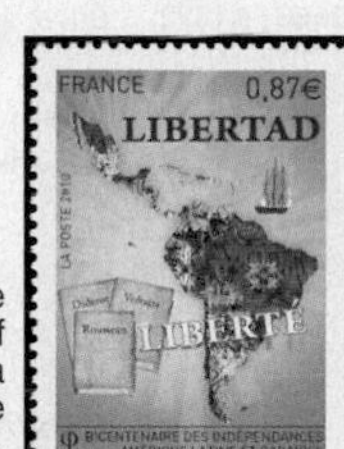

Independence Movements of Latin America and the Caribbean, Bicent. — A2131

**2010, Nov. 27 *Perf. 13¼***

| | | | |
|---|---|---|---|
| **3925** | A2131 87c multi | 2.40 | .80 |

Hearts A2132

Designs: 58c, Multicolored outlines of hearts. 95c, Red heart.

**Photo., Photo. With Foil Application (95c)**

**2011, Jan. 7 *Perf. 13***

| | | | |
|---|---|---|---|
| **3926** | A2132 58c multi | 1.60 | .55 |
| *a.* | Sheet of 5 | 8.00 | 8.00 |
| **3927** | A2132 95c black & red | 2.60 | .85 |

**Self-Adhesive**

***Serpentine Die Cut***

| | | | |
|---|---|---|---|
| **3928** | A2132 58c multi | 1.60 | 1.60 |
| **3929** | A2132 95c black & red | 2.60 | 2.60 |

New Year 2011 (Year of the Rabbit) — A2133

**2011, Jan. 14 Photo. *Perf. 13¼x13***

| | | | |
|---|---|---|---|
| **3930** | A2133 58c multi | 1.60 | .55 |

No. 3930 was printed in sheets of 5. A souvenir sheet of 1 sold for €3.

See No. 4970c.

Mulhouse Tram-Train A2134

**2011, Jan. 14 Engr. *Perf. 13¼***

| | | | |
|---|---|---|---|
| **3931** | A2134 58c multi | 1.60 | .55 |

Fabric Designs A2135

Fabric designs from: Nos. 3932, 3936, French Polynesia. Nos. 3933, 3942, Japan. No. 3934, France, from 1780. No. 3935, Ivory Coast. No. 3937, Italy. No. 3938, Iran. No. 3939, Egypt. No. 3940, India. No. 3941, China. No. 3943, Peru. No. 3944, Morocco. No. 3945, France, from First Empire period.

*Serpentine Die Cut 11*

**2011, Jan. 21 Photo.**

**Self-Adhesive**

**With Faint Blue Dots Behind Type in Area Below Vignette**

| | | | |
|---|---|---|---|
| **3932** | A2135 (58c) multi | 1.60 | 1.60 |
| **3933** | A2135 (58c) multi | 1.60 | 1.60 |

**Booklet Stamps**

**Without Dots Behind Type In Area Below Vignette**

| | | | |
|---|---|---|---|
| **3934** | A2135 (58c) multi | 1.60 | .55 |
| **3935** | A2135 (58c) multi | 1.60 | .55 |
| **3936** | A2135 (58c) multi | 1.60 | .55 |
| **3937** | A2135 (58c) multi | 1.60 | .55 |
| **3938** | A2135 (58c) multi | 1.60 | .55 |
| **3939** | A2135 (58c) multi | 1.60 | .55 |
| **3940** | A2135 (58c) multi | 1.60 | .55 |
| **3941** | A2135 (58c) multi | 1.60 | .55 |
| **3942** | A2135 (58c) multi | 1.60 | .55 |
| **3943** | A2135 (58c) multi | 1.60 | .55 |
| **3944** | A2135 (58c) multi | 1.60 | .55 |
| **3945** | A2135 (58c) multi | 1.60 | .55 |
| *a.* | Booklet pane of 12, #3934-3945 | 19.50 | |
| | *Nos. 3934-3945 (12)* | 19.20 | 6.60 |

Marie Curie (1867-1934), Chemist A2136

**2011, Jan. 27 Engr. *Perf. 13¼***

| | | | |
|---|---|---|---|
| **3946** | A2136 87c red & dk blue | 2.40 | .80 |

**Self-Adhesive**

***Serpentine Die Cut 11***

| | | | |
|---|---|---|---|
| **3947** | A2136 87c red & dk blue | 2.40 | 2.40 |

Intl. Year of Chemistry.

**Art Issue**

Plongée, by Jean Bazaine — A2137

Le Kiosque des Noctambules, Sculpture by Jean-Michel Othoniel — A2138

Buddha, by Odilon Redon A2139

Dying Centaur, Sculpture, by Antoine Bourdelle (1861-1929) — A2140

The Three Nymphs, Sculpture by Aristide Maillol (1861-1944) — A2140a

**2011 Photo. *Perf. 13x13¼***

| | | | | |
|---|---|---|---|---|
| **3948** | A2137 | 87c multi | 2.50 | 1.25 |

***Perf. 13¼x13***

| | | | | |
|---|---|---|---|---|
| **3949** | A2138 | €1.40 multi | 3.75 | 1.90 |
| **3950** | A2139 | €1.40 multi | 3.75 | 1.90 |
| | *Nos. 3948-3950 (3)* | | 10.00 | 5.05 |

**Souvenir Sheet**

**Engr.**

| | | | |
|---|---|---|---|
| **3951** | Sheet of 2 | 6.50 | 6.50 |
| *a.* | A2140 89c multi | 2.50 | 1.25 |
| *b.* | A2140a €1.45 multi | 4.00 | 2.00 |

**Self-Adhesive**

***Serpentine Die Cut 11***

| | | | | |
|---|---|---|---|---|
| **3952** | A2137 | 87c multi | 2.50 | 2.50 |
| **3953** | A2138 | €1.40 multi | 3.75 | 3.75 |
| **3954** | A2139 | €1.40 multi | 3.75 | 3.75 |
| **3955** | A2140 | 89c multi | 2.50 | 2.50 |
| **3955A** | A2140a | €1.45 multi | 4.00 | 4.00 |
| | *Nos. 3952-3955A (5)* | | 16.50 | 16.50 |

Issued: Nos. 3948, 3952, 3/18; Nos. 3949, 3953, 2/11; Nos. 3950, 3954, 4/1; Nos. 3951, 3955, 3955A, 11/4.

Marianne and Hand Planting Seedling A2141

Strawberry and Strawberry Plant — A2142

**2011, Feb. 26 Engr. *Perf. 13***

**3956** A2141 58c multi 1.75 .60

**Souvenir Sheet**

**Photo. & Engr.**

***Perf. 13¼x13***

**3957** A2142 €2 multi 5.75 3.00

Stamp Day. No. 3957 has printing and a strawberry-scented scratch-and-sniff panel on the reverse.

Hand Planting Seedling A2143

Leaf on Edge of Cliff A2144

Flora and Earth A2145

Hedgehog and Plants A2146

Field A2147

Tree With Various Fruits A2148

Man Carrying Earth in Wheelbarrow — A2149

Heart-shaped Plants in Flower Pots — A2150

Hands Holding Potatoes A2151

Man Watering Tree on Earth A2152

Earth on Plant A2153

Farmer's Field and House A2154

***Serpentine Die Cut 11***

**2011, Feb. 26 Photo.**

**Self-Adhesive**

**Smooth, Glossy Paper**

**3958** A2143 (58c) multi 1.75 1.75
**3959** A2144 (58c) multi 1.75 1.75
**3960** A2145 (58c) multi 1.75 1.75
*Nos. 3958-3960 (3)* 5.25 5.25

**Booklet Stamps**

**Rough, Textured Paper**

**3961** A2143 (58c) multi 1.75 .60
**3962** A2144 (58c) multi 1.75 .60
**3963** A2146 (58c) multi 1.75 .60
**3964** A2147 (58c) multi 1.75 .60
**3965** A2148 (58c) multi 1.75 .60
**3966** A2149 (58c) multi 1.75 .60
**3967** A2150 (58c) multi 1.75 .60
**3968** A2151 (58c) multi 1.75 .60
**3969** A2152 (58c) multi 1.75 .60
**3970** A2153 (58c) multi 1.75 .60
**3971** A2154 (58c) multi 1.75 .60
**3972** A2145 (58c) multi 1.75 .60
*a.* Booklet pane of 12, #3961-3972 21.00
*Nos. 3961-3972 (12)* 21.00 7.20

Stamp Day.

Tristan Corbière (1845-75), Poet A2155

**2011, Mar. 4 Engr. *Perf. 13***

**3973** A2155 75c multi 2.10 .70

Art of Miss.Tic (Radhia de Ruiter) A2156

Woman and text: No. 3974, Femme de lêtre. No. 3975, Je suis la votelle du mot voyou. No. 3976, Femme de tête mais l'esprit de corps. No. 3977, Tout achever sauf le désir. No. 3978, Soyons heureuses en attendant le bonheur. No. 3979, Je crois en l'éternel féminin. No. 3980, L'homme est le passé de la femme. No. 3981, Le masculin l'emporte mais où? No. 3982, Je ne me suis pas laissé défaire. No. 3983, Mieux que rien c'est pas assez. No. 3984, Il fait un temps de chienne. No. 3985, Cueillir l'éros de la vie.

***Serpentine Die Cut 11***

**2011, Mar. 8 Photo.**

**Booklet Stamps**

**Self-Adhesive**

**3974** A2156 (58c) black & red 1.75 .60
**3975** A2156 (58c) black & red 1.75 .60
**3976** A2156 (58c) black & red 1.75 .60
**3977** A2156 (58c) black & red 1.75 .60
**3978** A2156 (58c) black & red 1.75 .60
**3979** A2156 (58c) black & red 1.75 .60
**3980** A2156 (58c) black & red 1.75 .60
**3981** A2156 (58c) black & red 1.75 .60
**3982** A2156 (58c) black & red 1.75 .60
**3983** A2156 (58c) black & red 1.75 .60
**3984** A2156 (58c) black & red 1.75 .60
**3985** A2156 (58c) black & red 1.75 .60
*a.* Booklet pane of 12, #3974-3985 21.00
*Nos. 3974-3985 (12)* 21.00 7.20

Intl. Women's Day.

**European Capitals Type of 2002**

Miniature Sheet

No. 3986 — Attractions in Budapest: a, Parliament. b, Pont des Chaînes (Chain Bridge). c, Royal Palace. d, Bains Szécheny (Szechenyi Baths), vert.

***Perf. 13x13¼, 13¼x13 (#3986d)***

**2011, Mar. 25 Photo.**

**3986** A1622 Sheet of 4 7.00 7.00
*a.-d.* (58c) Any single 1.75 .60

**Tourism Issue**

Angers A2157

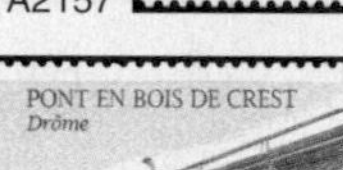

Wooden Bridge, Crest A2158

Autun — A2159

Varengeville-sur-Mer — A2160

Notre Dame Church, Royan — A2161

**2011 Engr. *Perf. 13¼***

**3987** A2157 58c multi 1.75 .60
**3988** A2158 58c multi 1.75 .60

***Perf. 13***

**3989** A2159 58c multi 1.75 .60

***Perf. 13¼***

**3990** A2160 58c multi 1.75 .60
**3991** A2161 60c multi 1.75 .60
*Nos. 3987-3991 (5)* 8.75 3.00

Issued: No. 3990, 6/24. No. 3991, 10/23.

Gothic Houses of Worship A2162

Designs: Nos. 3992, 4001, Notre Dame Cathedral, Strasbourg. Nos. 3993, 4002, Notre Dame Cathedral, Amiens. Nos. 3994, 4005, Sainte-Chapelle, Paris. No. 3995, St. Etienne Cathedral, Sens. No. 3996, Notre Dame Cathedral, Chartres. No. 3997, Notre Dame Cathedral, Laon. No. 3998, St. Etienne Cathedral, Metz. No. 3999, St. Pierre Cathedral, Beauvais. No. 4000, St. Etienne Cathedral, Bourges. No. 4003, Notre Dame Cathedral, Bayeux. No. 4004, Notre Dame Cathedral, Rouen. No. 4006, St. Denis Basilica, Saint-Denis.

***Serpentine Die Cut 11***

**2011, Apr. 15 Litho.**

**3992** A2162 (58c) multi 1.75 1.75
**3993** A2162 (58c) multi 1.75 1.75
**3994** A2162 (58c) multi 1.75 1.75
*Nos. 3992-3994 (3)* 5.25 5.25

**Photo.**

**Booklet Stamps**

**3995** A2162 (58c) multi 1.75 .60
**3996** A2162 (58c) multi 1.75 .60
**3997** A2162 (58c) multi 1.75 .60
**3998** A2162 (58c) multi 1.75 .60
**3999** A2162 (58c) multi 1.75 .60
**4000** A2162 (58c) multi 1.75 .60
**4001** A2162 (58c) multi 1.75 .60
**4002** A2162 (58c) multi 1.75 .60
**4003** A2162 (58c) multi 1.75 .60
**4004** A2162 (58c) multi 1.75 .60
**4005** A2162 (58c) multi 1.75 .60
**4006** A2162 (58c) multi 1.75 .60
*a.* Booklet pane of 12, #3995-4006 21.00
*Nos. 3995-4006 (12)* 21.00 7.20

On lithographed stamps, "Phil@poste" is sharp and crisp, while on photogravure stamps it is muddy and unclear.

Dogs A2163

Designs: No. 4007, Labrador retriever. No. 4008a, Berger allemand (German shepherd), vert. 75c, Caniche (poodle). 95c, Yorkshire terrier, vert.

***Perf. 13¼, 13¼x13¼x12¾x13¼ (#4008b)***

**2011, Apr. 28 Photo.**

**4007** A2163 58c multi 1.75 .60
**4008** Sheet of 4, #4008a-4008c, 4007 8.50 8.50
*a.* A2163 58c multi 1.75 .60
*b.* A2163 75c multi 2.25 .75
*c.* A2163 95c multi 2.75 .90

Souvenir Sheet

Reims Cathedral, 800th Anniv. — A2164

No. 4009 — Stained-glass window depicting: a, King. b, Saint and man.

**2011, May 6 Engr. *Perf.***

**4009** A2164 Sheet of 2 4.25 4.25
*a.* 58c multi 1.75 .60
*b.* 87c multi 2.50 .85

A souvenir sheet containing Nos. 4009a-4009b with a different sheet margin sold for €3.

Europa
A2165

**2011, May 8 Photo. *Perf. 13¼***

**4010** A2165 75c multi 2.10 .70

**Self-Adhesive**

***Serpentine Die Cut 11***

**4011** A2165 75c multi 2.10 2.10

Intl. Year of Forests.

Claude Bourgelat (1712-79), Founder of World's First Veterinary School
A2166

**2011, May 14 Engr. *Perf. 13¼***

**4012** A2166 58c dark blue 1.75 .60

**Self-Adhesive**

***Serpentine Die Cut 11***

**4013** A2166 58c dark blue 1.75 1.75

Regional Festivals and Traditions
A2167

Inscriptions and location: Nos. 4014, 4018, La Braderie, Lille. Nos. 4015, 4033, La Saint-Vincent Tournante, Bourgogne. No. 4016, Le Théâtre des Cabotans, Amiens. No. 4017, Le Feu d'Artifices du 14 Juillet, Paris. No. 4019, Les Médiévales, Provins. No. 4020, La Bénédiction de la Mer, Port-en-Bessin-Huppain. No. 4021, La Fête du Hareng, Haute-Normandie. No. 4022, La Fête des Brodeuses, Pont-l'Abbé. No. 4023, La Fête des Chalands Fleuris, Saint-André-des-Eaux. No. 4024, La Force Basque, Biarritz, Hendaye and Esplette. No. 4025, Les Nuits Romanes, Poitou-Charentes. No. 4026, La Sardane, Céret. No. 4027, La Fête de la Transhumance, Midi-Pyrénées. No. 4028, La Saint Nicolas, Lorraine. No. 4029, Le Mariage de l'Ami Fritz, Marlenheim. No. 4030, Les Fêtes Johanniques, Reims. No. 4031, Les Soufflacuis, Saint-Claude. No. 4032, La Fête de l'Estive, allanche. No. 4034, La Foire aux Potirons, Tranzault. No. 4035, La Frairie des Petits Ventres, Limoges. No. 4036, La Fête du Citron, Menton. No. 4037, La Fête des Lumières, Lyon. No. 4038, L'Abolition de l'Esclavage, Réunion. No. 4039, Les Chants Corses, Corsica.

**2011 Litho. *Serpentine Die Cut 11***

**Self-Adhesive**

**4014** A2167 (58c) multi 1.75 1.75
**4015** A2167 (58c) multi 1.75 1.75

**Photo.**

**Booklet Stamps**

**4016** A2167 (58c) multi 1.75 .60
**4017** A2167 (58c) multi 1.75 .60
**4018** A2167 (58c) multi 1.75 .60
**4019** A2167 (58c) multi 1.75 .60
*a.* Booklet pane of 4, #4016-4019 7.00
**4020** A2167 (58c) multi 1.75 .60
**4021** A2167 (58c) multi 1.75 .60
**4022** A2167 (58c) multi 1.75 .60
**4023** A2167 (58c) multi 1.75 .60
*a.* Booklet pane of 4, #4020-4023 7.00
**4024** A2167 (58c) multi 1.75 .60
**4025** A2167 (58c) multi 1.75 .60
**4026** A2167 (58c) multi 1.75 .60
**4027** A2167 (58c) multi 1.75 .60
*a.* Booklet pane of 4, #4024-4027 7.00
Complete booklet, #4019a, 4023a, 4027a 21.00
**4028** A2167 (58c) multi 1.75 .60
**4029** A2167 (58c) multi 1.75 .60
**4030** A2167 (58c) multi 1.75 .60
**4031** A2167 (58c) multi 1.75 .60
*a.* Booklet pane of 4, #4028-4031 7.00
**4032** A2167 (58c) multi 1.75 .60
**4033** A2167 (58c) multi 1.75 .60
**4034** A2167 (58c) multi 1.75 .60
**4035** A2167 (58c) multi 1.75 .60
*a.* Booklet pane of 4, #4032-4035 7.00
**4036** A2167 (58c) multi 1.75 .60
**4037** A2167 (58c) multi 1.75 .60
**4038** A2167 (58c) multi 1.75 .60
**4039** A2167 (58c) multi 1.75 .60
*a.* Booklet pane of 4, #4036-4039 7.00
Complete booklet, #4031a, 4035a, 4039a 21.00
*Nos. 4016-4039 (24)* 42.00 14.40

The black text on No. 4014 is sharper than that on No. 4018. The black text on No. 4015 is sharper than that on No. 4033.

Issued: No. 4014, 6/30, Nos. 4016-4039, 5/28.

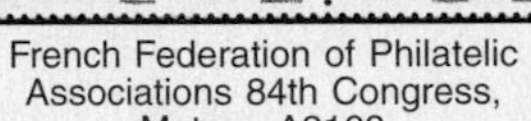


French Federation of Philatelic Associations 84th Congress, Metz — A2168

**2011, June 10 Engr. *Perf. 13x13¼***

**4040** A2168 58c multi + label 1.75 .60

A souvenir sheet containing No. 4040 was issued in 2012 and sold fro €3.

Miniature Sheet

Bicycles — A2169

No. 4041 — Inscriptions: a, Bicyclette à Pneumatiques. b, Draisenne, horiz. c, Vélocipède à Pédales, horiz. d, Vélo de Ville, horiz. e, Bicyclette à Chaine, horiz. f, Grand Bi.

**Litho. & Engr.**

**2011, June 17 *Perf. 13***

**4041** A2169 Sheet of 6 10.50 10.50
*a.-f.* 58c Any single 1.75 .60

Pres. Georges Pompidou (1911-74), and Pompidou Center, Paris
A2170

**2011, June 22 Engr. *Perf. 13¼***

**4042** A2170 58c gray grn & brt bl 1.75 .60

Train des Pignes, Provence, Cent.
A2171

**2011, June 24**

**4043** A2171 58c multi 1.75 .60

Organization for Economic Cooperation and Development, 50th Anniv. — A2172

**2011, June 24 Photo.**

**4044** A2172 87c multi 2.50 .85

World Judo Championships, Paris — A2173

**2011, July 1 *Perf. 13x12¾***

**4045** A2173 89c multi 2.50 .85

Aquilegia
A2174

Tulipa Sp.
A2175

Bellis Perennis
A2176

Primula Veris
A2177

**2011, July 1 Litho. *Perf. 13***

**4046** A2174 (38c) multi 1.10 .25
**4047** A2175 (39c) multi 1.10 .25
**4048** A2176 (46c) multi 1.40 .30
**4049** A2177 (47c) multi 1.40 .30
*Nos. 4046-4049 (4)* 5.00 1.10

Nos. 4046-4049 are known only precanceled. See note after No. 132.

Compare with Nos. 3423-3426.

"Ecopli 20g" — A2178

"Lettre Prioritaire 20g" — A2179

"Europe 20g" — A2180

"Monde 20g" — A2181

"Lettre Prioritaire 50g" A2182

"Lettre Prioritaire 100g" A2183

"Lettre Prioritaire 250g" — A2184

**Engr., Litho. (#4057a-4057d)**

**2011 *Perf. 13***

**4050** A2178 (55c) gray 1.60 .25
**4051** A2179 (60c) red 1.75 .40
**4052** A2180 (77c) dark blue 2.25 .60
**4053** A2181 (89c) purple 2.50 .65
**4054** A2182 (€1) fawn 3.00 .75
**4055** A2183 (€1.45) red violet 4.25 1.10
**4056** A2184 (€2.40) chocolate 6.75 2.40
*Nos. 4050-4056 (7)* 22.10 6.15

**Souvenir Sheet**

**4057** Sheet of 7, #4050-4052, 4057a-4057d, + label 21.50 21.50
*a.* A2181 (89c) purple, litho. 2.50 2.50
*b.* A2182 (€1) fawn, litho. 2.75 2.75
*c.* A2183 (€1.45) red violet, litho. 4.00 4.00
*d.* A2184 (€2.40) chocolate, litho. 6.75 6.75

**Coil Stamps**

***Perf. 13 Horiz.***

**4058** A2179 (60c) red 1.75 .40
**4059** A2180 (77c) blue 2.25 .60

**Self-Adhesive**

***Serpentine Die Cut 6¾ Vert.***

**4060** A2178 (55c) gray 1.60 1.60
**4061** A2179 (60c) red 1.75 1.75
*a.* Booklet pane of 12 21.00
*b.* Booklet pane of 20 35.00
*c.* Booklet pane of 10 17.50
**4062** A2180 (77c) blue 2.25 2.25
*a.* Booklet pane of 12 27.00
**4063** A2181 (89c) purple 2.50 2.50
**4064** A2182 (€1) fawn 3.00 3.00
**4065** A2183 (€1.45) red violet 4.25 4.25
**4066** A2184 (€2.40) chocolate 6.75 6.75
*Nos. 4060-4066 (7)* 22.10 22.10

Issued: Nos. 4050-4056, Nos. 4060-4066, 7/1; No. 4057, 11/3; Nos. 4058-4059, 7/6; No. 4061a, 7/1; Nos. 4061b-4061c, 4/16/12; No. 4062a, 8/16. See Nos. 4089-4090.

G20 and G8 Summits, Cannes and Deauville
A2185

**2011, July 8 Photo. *Perf. 12¼***

**4067** A2185 89c multi 2.50 .85

**Self-Adhesive**

***Serpentine Die Cut 11***

**4068** A2185 89c multi 2.50 2.50

A2186

2011 Rugby World Cup, New Zealand
A2187

No. 4069: a, Player with ball behind scrum. b, Player carrying ball, vert. c, Auckland skyline, vert. d, Lake and mountains, New Zealand.

€5, Two players.

*Perf. 13¼x13, 13x13¼*

**2011, July 8** **Photo.**

**4069** A2186 Sheet of 4 10.00 10.00
*a.-d.* 89c Any single 2.50 .85

**Embossed and Etched on Silver**
**Self-Adhesive**
***Die Cut Perf. 12¾***

**4070** A2187 €5 silver 14.00 14.00

**Protection of Water Type of 2010**
***Serpentine Die Cut 11***

**2011, Sept. 9** **Litho.**

**Self-Adhesive**

**4071** A2058 (60c) Like #3782 1.75 1.75
**4072** A2058 (60c) Like #3787 1.75 1.75

Nos. 4071-4072 have a dot structure not found on Nos. 3782 and 3787, which are printed by photogravure.

Souvenir Sheet

Gardens — A2188

No. 4073: a, Cheverny Gardens. b, Villandry Gardens.

**2011, Sept. 16 Photo.** ***Perf. 13¼x13***

**4073** A2188 Sheet of 2 13.00 13.00
*a.-b.* €2.40 Either single 6.50 3.25

Salon du Timbre 2012.

Firefighters of Paris, Bicent. — A2189

No. 4074: a, Horse-drawn fire wagon (38x38mm). b, Fireman holding hose (26x40mm). c, Firemen attending to victim on gurney, ambulance (26x40mm). d, Fireman with rescue dog (30x40mm). e, Firefighter's badge (26x40mm). f, Firemen in truck holding flag, Arc de Triomphe (26x40mm). g, Fireman wearing helmet without visor (30x40mm). h, Firemen in antique fire truck (40x26mm). i, Fireman and modern ladder truck (40x26mm). j, j, Fireman wearing helmet with visor (30x40mm).

***Perf. 13, 13¼ (#4074a), 13¼x13 (#4074d, 4074g, 4074j)***

**2011, Sept. 16**

**4074** A2189 Sheet of 10 17.50 17.50
*a.-j.* 60c Any single 1.75 .60

**Self-Adhesive**
***Serpentine Die Cut 11***

**4075** A2189 60c Like #4074b 1.75 1.75
**4076** A2189 60c Like #4074i 1.75 1.75

A set of six souvenir sheets, each containing one example of Nos. 4074a, 4074b, 4074f, 4074h, 4074i, and 4074j, sold for €15.

TGV Train Service, 30th Anniv. A2190

**2011, Sept. 27** ***Perf. 13¼***

**4077** A2190 60c multi 1.75 .60

**Self-Adhesive**
***Serpentine Die Cut 11***

**4078** A2190 60c multi 1.75 1.75

A2191 A2192

Marianne, Stars and Leaf
A2193 A2194

**2011, Sept. 30** **Engr.** ***Perf. 13***

**4079** A2191 (57c) green 1.60 .25
**4080** A2192 (95c) yellow green 2.60 .55
**4081** A2193 (€1.40) blue green 4.00 .80
**4082** A2194 (€2.30) dk bl green 6.25 1.25
*Nos. 4079-4082 (4)* 14.45 2.85

**Coil Stamp**
***Perf. 13 Horiz.***

**4083** A2191 (57c) green 1.60 .25

**Self-Adhesive**
***Serpentine Die Cut 6¾ Vert.***

**4084** A2191 (57c) green 1.60 1.60
*a.* Booklet pane of 10 16.00
*b.* Booklet pane of 12 19.50
*c.* Booklet pane of 20 32.00
**4085** A2192 (95c) yellow green 2.60 2.60
**4086** A2193 (€1.40) blue green 4.00 4.00
**4087** A2194 (€2.30) dk bl green 6.25 6.25

***Serpentine Die Cut 6¾ Horiz.***

**4088** A2191 (57c) green 1.60 .40
*Nos. 4084-4088 (5)* 16.05 14.85

**Marianne and Stars Types of 2011**
***Serpentine Die Cut 6¾ Horiz.***

**2011, Oct. 1** **Engr.**

**Coil Stamps**
**Self-Adhesive**

**4089** A2179 (60c) red 1.75 .40
**4090** A2180 (77c) dark blue 2.10 .60

Souvenir Sheet

World Weight Lifting Championships, Paris — A2195

No. 4091: a, Male weight lifter (43mm diameter). b, Female weight lifter (49mm diameter).

**2011, Oct. 7** **Photo.** ***Perf.***

**4091** A2195 Sheet of 2 4.25 4.25
*a.* 60c multi 1.75 .60
*b.* 89c multi 2.50 .85

Souvenir Sheets

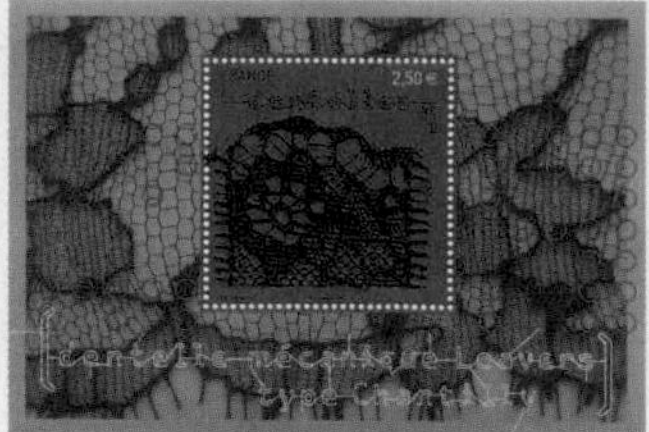

Chantilly Lace — A2196

Lace of Puy-en-Velay Region — A2197

Alençon Lace — A2198

Calais Lace — A2199

**Litho. with Lace Affixed**

**2011, Oct. 8**

**4092** A2196 €2.50 multi 7.00 7.00
**4093** A2197 €2.50 multi 7.00 7.00
**4094** A2198 €2.50 multi 7.00 7.00
**4095** A2199 €2.50 multi 7.00 7.00
*Nos. 4092-4095 (4)* 28.00 28.00

National Center for Space Studies, 50th Anniv. A2200

**2011, Oct. 12** **Engr.** ***Perf. 13¼***

**4096** A2200 60c multi 1.75 .60

Discovery of Clipperton Island, 200th Anniv. A2201

**2011, Oct. 21**

**4097** A2201 €1 multi 2.75 .90

Second-Place Finish of French Team in 2011 Rugby World Cup Championships — A2202

**2011, Oct. 23** **Photo.**

**4098** A2202 60c multi 1.75 .60

Values are for stamp with surrounding selvage.

Words of Ben A2203

"Ben" (artist Benjamin Vautier) and inscription: No. 4099, Je suis timbré. No. 4100, J'aime écrire. No. 4101, Les mots c'est la vie. No. 4102, Entre nous. . . No. 4103, Cette idée. . . voyage. No. 4104, Pour l'instant tout va bien. No. 4105, Enfin de l'art. No. 4106, J'ai quelque chose à dire. No. 4107, Mots d'amour. No. 4108, Ceci est un lettre. No. 4109, Garderem lo moral. No. 4110, Vous êtes formidables!

***Serpentine Die Cut 11***

**2011, Oct. 24** **Photo.**

**Booklet Stamps**
**Self-Adhesive**

**4099** A2203 (60c) multi 1.75 .60
**4100** A2203 (60c) multi 1.75 .60
**4101** A2203 (60c) multi 1.75 .60
**4102** A2203 (60c) multi 1.75 .60
**4103** A2203 (60c) multi 1.75 .60
**4104** A2203 (60c) multi 1.75 .60
**4105** A2203 (60c) multi 1.75 .60
**4106** A2203 (60c) multi 1.75 .60
**4107** A2203 (60c) multi 1.75 .60
**4108** A2203 (60c) multi 1.75 .60
**4109** A2203 (60c) multi 1.75 .60
**4110** A2203 (60c) multi 1.75 .60
*a.* Booklet pane of 12, #4099-4110 21.00
*Nos. 4099-4110 (12)* 21.00 7.20

Compare with type A1667.

Gaston Monnerville (1897-1991), Senate President A2204

**2011, Nov. 7** **Engr.** ***Perf. 13¼***

**4111** A2204 60c multi 1.75 .60

Henri Mouhot (1826-61), Explorer of Southeast Asia A2205

**2011, Nov. 7**

**4112** A2205 89c multi 2.50 .85

Christmas A2206

Paintings: No. 4113, Adoration of the Shepherds, by Robert Campin, Master of Flémalle.

No. 4114, Adoration of the Shepherds, by Mathias Stormer. No. 4115, The Newborn, by Georges de La Tour. No. 4116, Adoration of the Magi, by Italian School artist. No. 4117, Adoration of the Magi, by Francisco de Zurbaran. No. 4118, Nativity, by Jean Fouquet. No. 4119, Nativity, by the Master of the Nativity in the Louvre. No. 4120, Triptych of the Adoration of the Magi, by the Master of 1518. No. 4121, Adoration of the Magi, by Peter Paul Rubens. No. 4122, Adoration of the Infant Jesus, by the Master of Moulins. No. 4123, Adoration of the Child, by the Master of the St. Bartholomew Altarpiece. No. 4124, Scenes from the Life of Christ - Nativity, by Mariotto di Nardo.

***Serpentine Die Cut 11***

**2011, Nov. 7 — Photo.**

**Booklet Stamps**
**Self-Adhesive**

| | | | | |
|---|---|---|---|---|
| **4113** | A2206 | (60c) multi | 1.75 | .60 |
| **4114** | A2206 | (60c) multi | 1.75 | .60 |
| **4115** | A2206 | (60c) multi | 1.75 | .60 |
| **4116** | A2206 | (60c) multi | 1.75 | .60 |
| **4117** | A2206 | (60c) multi | 1.75 | .60 |
| **4118** | A2206 | (60c) multi | 1.75 | .60 |
| **4119** | A2206 | (60c) multi | 1.75 | .60 |
| **4120** | A2206 | (60c) multi | 1.75 | .60 |
| **4121** | A2206 | (60c) multi | 1.75 | .60 |
| **4122** | A2206 | (60c) multi | 1.75 | .60 |
| **4123** | A2206 | (60c) multi | 1.75 | .60 |
| **4124** | A2206 | (60c) multi | 1.75 | .60 |
| *a.* | | Booklet pane of 12, #4113-4124 | 21.00 | |
| | | *Nos. 4113-4124 (12)* | 21.00 | 7.20 |

A souvenir sheet containing one perf. 13x13¼ example of No. 4115 with water-activated gum sold for €3.

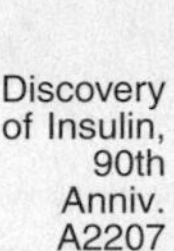

Discovery of Insulin, 90th Anniv. A2207

**2011, Nov. 17 — Photo. — *Perf. 13¼***

| | | | | |
|---|---|---|---|---|
| **4125** | A2207 | 60c multi | 1.75 | .60 |

***Serpentine Die Cut 11***
**Self-Adhesive**

| | | | | |
|---|---|---|---|---|
| **4126** | A2207 | 60c multi | 1.75 | .60 |

Year of Overseas Territories A2208

Drawings of: No. 4127, Carved rocks, Guadeloupe. No. 4128, Harbor, Cayenne, French Guiana. No. 4129, Beach scence, New Caledonia. No. 4130, Tattoo designs of tiki and compass rose, French Polynesia. No. 4131, Tree blossoms, St. Martin. No. 4132, Buildings, St. Pierre and Miquelon. No. 4133, House, Martinique. No. 4134, Man on path near Morne Langevin, Reunion. No. 4135, Pirogue, near Mt. Choungi, Mayotte. No. 4136, Building, Saint-Barthélemy. No. 4137, Kava bowl and building, Wallis and Futuna Islands. No. 4138, Penguins, French Southern and Antarctic Territories (T.A.A.F).

***Serpentine Die Cut 11***

**2011, Nov. 25 — Photo.**

**Booklet Stamps**
**Self-Adhesive**

| | | | | |
|---|---|---|---|---|
| **4127** | A2208 | (60c) multi | 1.75 | .60 |
| **4128** | A2208 | (60c) multi | 1.75 | .60 |
| **4129** | A2208 | (60c) multi | 1.75 | .60 |
| **4130** | A2208 | (60c) multi | 1.75 | .60 |
| **4131** | A2208 | (60c) multi | 1.75 | .60 |
| **4132** | A2208 | (60c) multi | 1.75 | .60 |
| **4133** | A2208 | (60c) multi | 1.75 | .60 |
| **4134** | A2208 | (60c) multi | 1.75 | .60 |
| **4135** | A2208 | (60c) multi | 1.75 | .60 |
| **4136** | A2208 | (60c) multi | 1.75 | .60 |
| **4137** | A2208 | (60c) multi | 1.75 | .60 |
| **4138** | A2208 | (60c) multi | 1.75 | .60 |
| *a.* | | Booklet pane of 12, #4127-4138 | 21.00 | |
| | | *Nos. 4127-4138 (12)* | 21.00 | 7.20 |

New Year 2012 (Year of the Dragon) A2209

**2012, Jan. 6 — *Perf. 13¼x13***

| | | | | |
|---|---|---|---|---|
| **4139** | A2209 | 60c multi | 1.60 | .55 |

No. 4139 was printed in sheets of 5. A souvenir sheet of one sold for €3.
See No. 4970d.

A2210

Hearts A2211

**2012, Jan. 13 — Photo. — *Perf. 13***

| | | | | |
|---|---|---|---|---|
| **4140** | A2210 | €1 red & black | 2.75 | .95 |

**Self-Adhesive**
***Serpentine Die Cut***

| | | | | |
|---|---|---|---|---|
| **4141** | A2210 | €1 red & black | 2.75 | 2.75 |

**On Plastic**

| | | | | |
|---|---|---|---|---|
| **4142** | A2211 | 60c red & black | 1.60 | 1.60 |
| *a.* | | Souvenir sheet of 5 | 8.00 | |

Brass Relief, France, 18th Cent. A2212

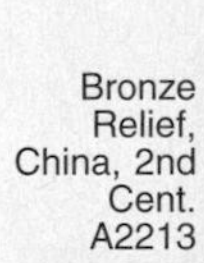

Bronze Relief, China, 2nd Cent. A2213

Copper and Silver Relief, Egypt, 14th Cent. A2214

Marble Relief, Andalusia, 11th Cent. A2215

Sardonyx Relief, Italy, 13th Cent. A2216

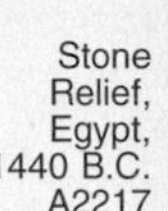

Stone Relief, Egypt, 1440 B.C. A2217

**Litho., Engr. (olive gray stamps)**
***Serpentine Die Cut 11***

**2012, Jan. 20 — Self-Adhesive**

**Booklet Stamps**

| | | | | |
|---|---|---|---|---|
| **4143** | A2212 | (60c) multi | 1.60 | .55 |
| **4144** | A2212 | (60c) olive gray | 1.60 | .55 |
| **4145** | A2213 | (60c) multi | 1.60 | .55 |
| **4146** | A2213 | (60c) olive gray | 1.60 | .55 |
| **4147** | A2214 | (60c) multi | 1.60 | .55 |
| **4148** | A2214 | (60c) olive gray | 1.60 | .55 |
| **4149** | A2215 | (60c) multi | 1.60 | .55 |
| **4150** | A2215 | (60c) olive gray | 1.60 | .55 |
| **4151** | A2216 | (60c) multi | 1.60 | .55 |
| **4152** | A2216 | (60c) olive gray | 1.60 | .55 |
| **4153** | A2217 | (60c) multi | 1.60 | .55 |
| **4154** | A2217 | (60c) olive gray | 1.60 | .55 |
| *a.* | | Booklet pane of 12, #4143-4154 | 19.50 | |
| | | *Nos. 4143-4154 (12)* | 19.20 | 6.60 |

**Art Issue**

Morning Sun, by Edward Hopper — A2218

**2012, Feb. 3 — Photo. — *Perf. 13x13¼***

| | | | | |
|---|---|---|---|---|
| **4155** | A2218 | €1.45 multi | 4.00 | 2.00 |

**Self-Adhesive**
***Serpentine Die Cut 11***

| | | | | |
|---|---|---|---|---|
| **4156** | A2218 | €1.45 multi | 4.00 | 4.00 |

Flowers — A2219

Designs: No. 4157, Arums. No. 4158, Tulips. No. 4159, Roses. No. 4160, Violets. No. 4161, Pansies (Pensée). No. 4162, Lily of the valley (Muguet). No. 4163, Irises. No. 4164, Dahlias. No. 4165, Poppies (Coquelicot). No. 4166, Peonies (Pivoine). No. 4167, Daisies (Marguerite). No. 4168, Pinks (Oeillet).

***Serpentine Die Cut 11***

**2012, Feb. 10 — Self-Adhesive**

**Booklet Stamps**

| | | | | |
|---|---|---|---|---|
| **4157** | A2219 | (60c) multi | 1.60 | .55 |
| **4158** | A2219 | (60c) multi | 1.60 | .55 |
| **4159** | A2219 | (60c) multi | 1.60 | .55 |
| **4160** | A2219 | (60c) multi | 1.60 | .55 |
| **4161** | A2219 | (60c) multi | 1.60 | .55 |
| **4162** | A2219 | (60c) multi | 1.60 | .55 |
| **4163** | A2219 | (60c) multi | 1.60 | .55 |
| **4164** | A2219 | (60c) multi | 1.60 | .55 |
| **4165** | A2219 | (60c) multi | 1.60 | .55 |
| **4166** | A2219 | (60c) multi | 1.60 | .55 |
| **4167** | A2219 | (60c) multi | 1.60 | .55 |
| **4168** | A2219 | (60c) multi | 1.60 | .55 |
| *a.* | | Booklet pane of 12, #4157-4168 | 19.50 | |
| | | *Nos. 4157-4168 (12)* | 19.20 | 6.60 |

Grand Mosque of Paris, 90th Anniv. — A2220

**2012, Feb. 11 — Engr. — *Perf. 13¼***

| | | | | |
|---|---|---|---|---|
| **4169** | A2220 | 60c multi | 1.60 | .55 |

Henri Queuille (1884-1970), Prime Minister — A2221

**2012, Feb. 17**

| | | | | |
|---|---|---|---|---|
| **4170** | A2221 | €1 black & brown | 2.75 | .95 |

Portraits of Women — A2222

Details of paintings: No. 4171, Young Woman in a Ball Gown, by Berthe Morisot. No. 4172, Portrait of Lydia Cassat, by Mary Cassatt. No. 4173, Biskra Woman, by Marie Caire. No. 4174, Woman with Turban, by Marie Laurencin. No. 4175, Madame Molé-Raymond, by Elisabeth Vigée-Lebrun. No. 4176, Portrait of a Young Woman, by Edgar Degas. No. 4177, Mandy, by Edouard Barnard Lintott. No. 4178, Orphan Girl at the Cemetery, by Eugène Delacroix. No. 4179, Woman with a Mirror, by Titian. No. 4180, Madeleine Bernard, by Paul Gauguin. No. 4181, Young Woman, by Hippolyte Flandrin. No. 4182, Portrait of Berthe Morisot with a Bouquet of Violets, by Edouard Manet.

***Serpentine Die Cut 11***

**2012, Mar. 8 — Photo.**

**Booklet Stamps**
**Self-Adhesive**

| | | | | |
|---|---|---|---|---|
| **4171** | A2222 | (60c) multi | 1.60 | .55 |
| **4172** | A2222 | (60c) multi | 1.60 | .55 |
| **4173** | A2222 | (60c) multi | 1.60 | .55 |
| **4174** | A2222 | (60c) multi | 1.60 | .55 |
| **4175** | A2222 | (60c) multi | 1.60 | .55 |
| **4176** | A2222 | (60c) multi | 1.60 | .55 |
| **4177** | A2222 | (60c) multi | 1.60 | .55 |
| **4178** | A2222 | (60c) multi | 1.60 | .55 |
| **4179** | A2222 | (60c) multi | 1.60 | .55 |
| **4180** | A2222 | (60c) multi | 1.60 | .55 |
| **4181** | A2222 | (60c) multi | 1.60 | .55 |
| **4182** | A2222 | (60c) multi | 1.60 | .55 |
| *a.* | | Booklet pane of 12, #4171-4182 | 19.50 | |
| | | *Nos. 4171-4182 (12)* | 19.20 | 6.60 |

**European Capitals Type of 2002**
Miniature Sheet

No. 4183 — Attractions in Copenhagen, Denmark: a, The Little Mermaid statue. b, Amalienborg Palace, horiz. c, Rosenborg Castle. d, Nyhavn, horiz.

***Perf. 13¼x13, 13x13¼ (horiz. stamps)***

**2012, Mar. 23 — Photo.**

| | | | | |
|---|---|---|---|---|
| **4183** | A1622 | Sheet of 4 | 6.50 | 6.50 |
| *a.-d.* | | 60c Any single | 1.60 | .55 |

**Tourism Issue**

Moulins — A2223

**2012, Mar. 23 Engr. *Perf. 13x12¾***

| | | | | |
|---|---|---|---|---|
| **4184** | A2223 60c multi | | 1.60 | .55 |

Miniature Sheet

Way of St. James — A2224

No. 4185: a, Via Turonensis in Paris. b, Via Lemovicensis in Vézelay, horiz. c, Via Podiensis in Puy-en Velay, horiz. d, Via Tolosana in Arles.

**Litho. & Engr.**

**2012, Mar. 30 *Perf. 13***

| | | | | |
|---|---|---|---|---|
| **4185** | A2224 | Sheet of 4 | 8.50 | 8.50 |
| ***a.-d.*** | | 77c Any single | 2.10 | .70 |

Fruits A2225

Designs: No. 4186, Pineapple (Ananas). No. 4187, Melon. No. 4188, White grapes (Raisins blancs). No. 4189, Hazel nuts (Noisettes). No. 4190, Kiwis. No. 4191, Gooseberries (Groseilles à maquereaux). No. 4192, Green papayas (Papayes vertes). No. 4193, Dates (Dattes). No. 4194, Bananas (Bananes vertes). No. 4195, Mangos (Mangues). No. 4196, Pippin apples (Pommes "Reinette grise"). No. 4197, Pear (Poire William).

***Serpentine Die Cut 11***

**2012, Mar. 30 Photo.**

**Booklet Stamps**
**Self-Adhesive**

| | | | |
|---|---|---|---|
| **4186** | A2225 (57c) multi | 1.50 | .50 |
| **4187** | A2225 (57c) multi | 1.50 | .50 |
| **4188** | A2225 (57c) multi | 1.50 | .50 |
| **4189** | A2225 (57c) multi | 1.50 | .50 |
| **4190** | A2225 (57c) multi | 1.50 | .50 |
| **4191** | A2225 (57c) multi | 1.50 | .50 |
| **4192** | A2225 (57c) multi | 1.50 | .50 |
| **4193** | A2225 (57c) multi | 1.50 | .50 |
| **4194** | A2225 (57c) multi | 1.50 | .50 |
| **4195** | A2225 (57c) multi | 1.50 | .50 |
| **4196** | A2225 (57c) multi | 1.50 | .50 |
| **4197** | A2225 (57c) multi | 1.50 | .50 |
| ***a.*** | Booklet pane of 12, #4186-4197 | 18.00 | |
| | *Nos. 4186-4197 (12)* | 18.00 | 6.00 |

**Tourism Issue**

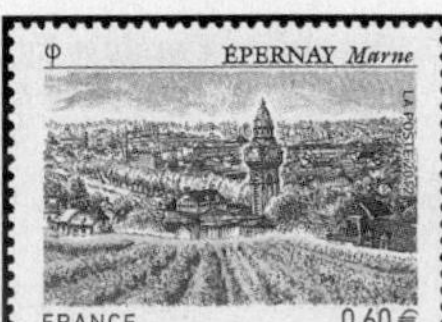


Epernay A2226

**2012, Apr. 13 Engr. *Perf. 13¼***

| | | | |
|---|---|---|---|
| **4198** | A2226 60c multi | 1.60 | .55 |

Tropical Fish — A2227

Designs: No. 4199, Amphiprion ocellaris. No. 4200a, Phycodurus eques, hoirz. No. 4200b, Heniochus acuminatus, horiz. No. 4200c, Pomacanthus imperator.

**2012, Apr. 20 Photo. *Perf. 13¼***

| | | | |
|---|---|---|---|
| **4199** | A2227 60c multi | 1.60 | .55 |
| **4200** | Sheet of 4, #4199, 4200a-4200c | 8.00 | 8.00 |
| ***a.*** | A2227 60c multi | 1.60 | .55 |
| ***b.*** | A2227 77c multi | 2.10 | .70 |
| ***c.*** | A2227 €1 multi | 2.60 | .90 |

Art A2228

Designs: No. 4201, Douglas Castle, painting by unknown Chinese artist. No. 4202, Crab, sculpture by Cheung Yee. Nos. 4203, 4205, The Racecourse — Amateur Jockeys Close to a Carriage, painting by Edgar Degas. No. 4204, The Horse, sculpture by Raymnond Duchamp-Villon.

**2012, May 3 Photo. *Perf. 13¼***

| | | | |
|---|---|---|---|
| **4201** | A2228 60c multi | 1.60 | .55 |
| **4202** | A2228 60c multi | 1.60 | .55 |
| **4203** | A2228 89c multi | 2.40 | .80 |
| **4204** | A2228 89c multi | 2.40 | .80 |
| | *Nos. 4201-4204 (4)* | 8.00 | 2.70 |

**Self-Adhesive**

***Serpentine Die Cut 11***

| | | | |
|---|---|---|---|
| **4205** | A2228 89c multi | 2.40 | 2.40 |

See Hong Kong Nos. 1490-1493.

Cubist Art A2229

Designs: No. 4206, La Table Louis-Philippe, by Roger de La Fresnaye. No. 4207, Three Figures Under a Tree, by Pablo Picasso. No. 4208, The Three Poets, by Louis Marcoussis, vert. No. 4209, Still Life with a Red Ball, by Auguste Herbin, vert. No. 4210, The Blue Bird, by Jean Metzinger, vert. No. 4211, The 14th of July, by Fernand Léger, vert. No. 4212, Music, by Frantisek Kupka. No. 4213, Rugby, by André Lhote. No. 4214, The War Song, Portrait of Florent Schmitt, by Albert Gleizes, vert. No. 4215, The Book, by Juan Gris, vert. No. 4216, Compotier et Cartes, by Georges Braque, vert. No. 4217, Marine, by Lyonel Feininger, vert.

**2012, May 10 *Serpentine Die Cut 11***

**Booklet Stamps**
**Self-Adhesive**

| | | | |
|---|---|---|---|
| **4206** | A2229 (60c) multi | 1.50 | .50 |
| **4207** | A2229 (60c) multi | 1.50 | .50 |
| **4208** | A2229 (60c) multi | 1.50 | .50 |
| **4209** | A2229 (60c) multi | 1.50 | .50 |
| **4210** | A2229 (60c) multi | 1.50 | .50 |
| **4211** | A2229 (60c) multi | 1.50 | .50 |
| **4212** | A2229 (60c) multi | 1.50 | .50 |
| **4213** | A2229 (60c) multi | 1.50 | .50 |
| **4214** | A2229 (60c) multi | 1.50 | .50 |
| **4215** | A2229 (60c) multi | 1.50 | .50 |
| **4216** | A2229 (60c) multi | 1.50 | .50 |
| **4217** | A2229 (60c) multi | 1.50 | .50 |
| ***a.*** | Booklet pane of 12, #4206-4217 | 18.00 | |
| | *Nos. 4206-4217 (12)* | 18.00 | 6.00 |

Pacific 231 K8 Locomotive, Cent. — A2230

**2012, May 11 Engr. *Perf. 13¼***

| | | | |
|---|---|---|---|
| **4218** | A2230 60c multi | 1.50 | .50 |

**Self-Adhesive**

***Serpentine Die Cut 11***

| | | | |
|---|---|---|---|
| **4219** | A2230 60c multi | 1.50 | 1.50 |

A souvenir sheet of one of No. 4218 sold for €3.

St. Joan of Arc (c. 1412-31) — A2231

**Photo. & Engr.**

**2012, May 11 *Perf. 13***

| | | | |
|---|---|---|---|
| **4220** | A2231 77c multi | 2.00 | .65 |

See Vatican City No. 1499.

Souvenir Sheet

Battle of Denain, 300th Anniv. — A2232

**2012, May 12 Photo. *Perf. 13¼***

| | | | |
|---|---|---|---|
| **4221** | A2232 77c multi | 2.00 | .65 |

Birds — A2233

Designs: No. 4222a, Little bustard (Outarde canepetière). No. 4222b, Bluethroat (Gorgebleue à miroir), horiz. No. 4222c, Osprey (Balbuzard pêcheur). Nos. 4222d, 4223, Atlantic puffin (Macareux moine).

***Perf. 13¼x13, 13x13¼ (#4222b)***

**2012, May 12**

| | | | | |
|---|---|---|---|---|
| **4222** | | Sheet of 4 | 6.00 | 6.00 |
| ***a.-d.*** | A2233 57c Any single | | 1.50 | .50 |

**Self-Adhesive**

***Serpentine Die Cut 11***

| | | | |
|---|---|---|---|
| **4223** | A2233 57c multi | 1.50 | 1.50 |

Bird Protection League, cent.

Europa — A2234

**2012, May 20 Engr. *Perf. 13***

| | | | |
|---|---|---|---|
| **4224** | A2234 77c multi | 2.00 | .65 |

**Self-Adhesive**

***Serpentine Die Cut 11***

| | | | |
|---|---|---|---|
| **4225** | A2234 77c multi | 2.00 | 2.00 |

**Tourism Issue**

Chateau de Suscinio A2235

**2012, May 26 *Perf. 13¼***

| | | | |
|---|---|---|---|
| **4226** | A2235 60c multi | 1.50 | .50 |

Souvenir Sheet

Saint-Cloud Park, Paris — A2236

No. 4227: a, Cascade. b, Reflecting ponds,

**2012, June 9 Photo. *Perf. 13x13¼***

| | | | | |
|---|---|---|---|---|
| **4227** | A2236 | Sheet of 2 | 12.00 | 12.00 |
| ***a.-b.*** | | €2.40 Either single | 6.00 | 3.00 |
| ***c.*** | | Souvenir sheet of 4, #4073a, 4073b, 4227a, 4227b | 24.00 | 24.00 |

2012 Salon du Timbre, Paris.

Historic Residences — A2237

Designs: Nos. 4228, 4245, Palais du Luxembourg, Paris. No. 4229, Château Guillaume-le-Conquérant, Falaise. No. 4230, Château des Comtes de Foix. No. 4231, Château de Boulogne sur Mer. No. 4232, Château de Saumur. No. 4233, Château d' Anjony, Tournemire. No. 4234, Château de Pompadour. No. 4235, Citadelle de Corte. No. 4236, Forteresse de Salses. No. 4237, Château d'If. No. 4238, Hôtel de Mauroy, Troyes. No. 4239, Maison Pfister, Colmar. No. 4240, Château du Taureau, Baie de Morlaix. No. 4241, Palais Ducal de Nevers. No. 4242, Château d'Azay-le-Rideau. No. 4243, Château de Puyguilhem. No. 4244, Château de Crazannes. No. 4246, Château de Vaux-le-Vicomte. No. 4247, Château de Brémontier-Merval. No. 4248, Château de Lesdiguières, Vixille. No. 4249, Château de Pierrefonds. No. 4250, Villa Palladienne de Syam. No. 4251, Maison Souques-Pagès, Pointe-à-Pitre. No. 4252, Villa Majorelle, Nancy.

***Serpentine Die Cut 11***

**2012, June 9 Litho.**

**Self-Adhesive**

| | | | |
|---|---|---|---|
| **4228** | A2237 (60c) multi | 1.50 | 1.50 |

**Photo.**

**Booklet Stamps**

| | | | |
|---|---|---|---|
| **4229** | A2237 (60c) multi | 1.50 | .50 |
| **4230** | A2237 (60c) multi | 1.50 | .50 |
| **4231** | A2237 (60c) multi | 1.50 | .50 |
| **4232** | A2237 (60c) multi | 1.50 | .50 |
| ***a.*** | Booklet pane of 4, #4229-4232 | 6.00 | |
| **4233** | A2237 (60c) multi | 1.50 | .50 |
| **4234** | A2237 (60c) multi | 1.50 | .50 |
| **4235** | A2237 (60c) multi | 1.50 | .50 |
| **4236** | A2237 (60c) multi | 1.50 | .50 |
| ***a.*** | Booklet pane of 4, #4233-4236 | 6.00 | |

**4237** A2237 (60c) multi 1.50 .50
**4238** A2237 (60c) multi 1.50 .50
**4239** A2237 (60c) multi 1.50 .50
**4240** A2237 (60c) multi 1.50 .50
*a.* Booklet pane of 4, #4237-4240 6.00
Complete booklet, #4232a, 4236a, 4240a 18.00
**4241** A2237 (60c) multi 1.50 .50
**4242** A2237 (60c) multi 1.50 .50
**4243** A2237 (60c) multi 1.50 .50
**4244** A2237 (60c) multi 1.50 .50
*a.* Booklet pane of 4, #4241-4244 6.00
**4245** A2237 (60c) multi 1.50 .50
**4246** A2237 (60c) multi 1.50 .50
**4247** A2237 (60c) multi 1.50 .50
**4248** A2237 (60c) multi 1.50 .50
*a.* Booklet pane of 4, #4245-4248 6.00
**4249** A2237 (60c) multi 1.50 .50
**4250** A2237 (60c) multi 1.50 .50
**4251** A2237 (60c) multi 1.50 .50
**4252** A2237 (60c) multi 1.50 .50
*a.* Booklet pane of 4, #4249-4252 6.00
Complete booklet, #4244a, 4248a, 4252a 18.00
*Nos. 4229-4252 (24)* 36.00 12.00

Lettering, most evident in the "Phil@poste" inscription at bottom, is sharp on No. 4228 and fuzzy on No. 4245.

Miniature Sheet

Soldiers — A2238

No. 4253: a, Croisé (crusader), 12th cent. b, Vercingetorix (c. 82-46 B.C.), Gallic chieftain, horiz. c, Fantassin (foot soldier), 16th cent. d, Tambour (drummer), 18th cent. e, Grognard (member of Napoleon's Old Guard). f, Fantassin (foot soldier), 1914.

**Litho. & Engr.**

**2012, June 10** *Perf. 13*
**4253** A2238 Sheet of 6 9.00 9.00
*a.-f.* 60c Any single 1.50 .50

A set of six souvenir sheets, each containing one example of Nos. 4253a-4253f, sold for €15.

Handball A2239

**Embossed and Etched on Silver**
**2012, June 11** *Die Cut Perf. 12¾*
**Self-Adhesive**
**4254** A2239 €5 silver 12.50 12.50

2012 Summer Olympics, London — A2240

**2012, June 12 Photo.** *Perf. 13*
**4255** A2240 89c multi 2.25 .75

Miles Davis (1926-91), Jazz Trumpet Player — A2241

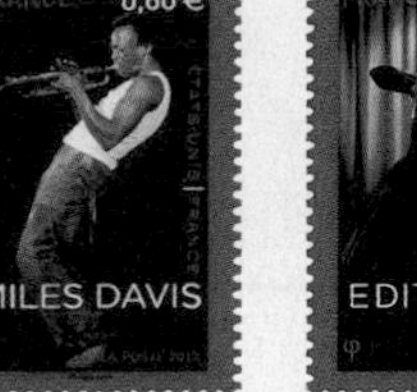


Edith Piaf (1915-63), Singer — A2242

**2012, June 12** *Perf. 13*
**4256** A2241 60c multi 1.50 .50
**4257** A2242 89c multi 2.25 .75
*a.* Horiz. pair, #4256-4257 3.75 1.25

See United States Nos. 4692-4693.

Vegetables A2243

Designs: No. 4258, Peas (petits pois). No. 4259, Salad greens (salades). Nos. 4260, Pimentos (piments). No. 4261, Green beans (haricots vers). No. 4262, Broccoli (chou brocoli). No. 4263, Zucchini (courgettes). No. 4264, Snap beans (haricots mange-tout). No. 4265, Leeks (poireaux). No. 4266, Green peppers (poivron "Lamuyo"). No. 4267, Artichoke (artichaut "Gros Camus"). No. 4268, Squashes (potirons vers). No. 4269, Cabbage (chou cabus).

***Serpentine Die Cut 11***
**2012, June 13 Self-Adhesive**
**Booklet Stamps**
**4258** A2243 (57c) multi 1.40 .45
**4259** A2243 (57c) multi 1.40 .45
**4260** A2243 (57c) multi 1.40 .45
**4261** A2243 (57c) multi 1.40 .45
**4262** A2243 (57c) multi 1.40 .45
**4263** A2243 (57c) multi 1.40 .45
**4264** A2243 (57c) multi 1.40 .45
**4265** A2243 (57c) multi 1.40 .45
**4266** A2243 (57c) multi 1.40 .45
**4267** A2243 (57c) multi 1.40 .45
**4268** A2243 (57c) multi 1.40 .45
**4269** A2243 (57c) multi 1.40 .45
*a.* Booklet pane of 12, #4258-4269 17.00
*Nos. 4258-4269 (12)* 16.80 5.40

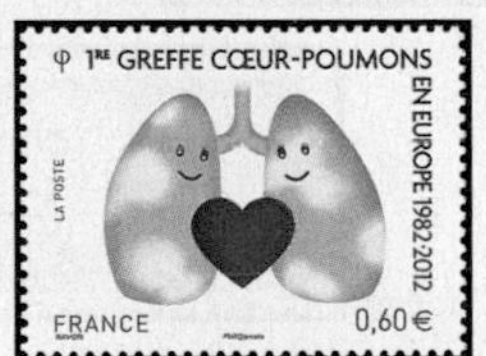


First Heart-Lung Transplant in Europe, 30th Anniv. — A2244

**2012, June 14** *Perf. 13¼*
**4270** A2244 60c multi 1.50 .50

Issenheim Altarpiece, 500th Anniv. — A2245

Sheet with Altarpiece Doors Closed (Covering Stamps)

No. 4271: a, St. Augustine, "Le Retable d'Issenheim" at right (19x56mm). b, St. Hieronymus, "Le Retable d'Issenheim" at left (19x56mm). c, St. Anthony (34x65mm).

***Perf. 13¼x13, 13 (#4271c)***
**2012, June 15 Litho.**
**4271** A2245 Sheet of 3 12.50 12.50
*a.-b.* €1.50 Either single 3.75 1.25
*c.* €2 multi 5.00 1.75

Card stock doors printed on both sides that depict artwork on the two alterpiece doors, are pasted on top of each other at the left and right of the stamps. Values for the sheet are for examples with all four doors affixed.

Musée d'Orsay, Paris — A2246

**2012, June 16 Engr.** *Perf. 13x13¼*
**4272** A2246 60c multi + label 1.50 .50

French Federation of Philatelic Associations, 85th Congress, Paris.

**Tourism Issue**

Pointe Saint-Mathieu — A2247

**2012, June 22** *Perf. 13¼*
**4273** A2247 57c multi 1.40 .45

Souvenir Sheet

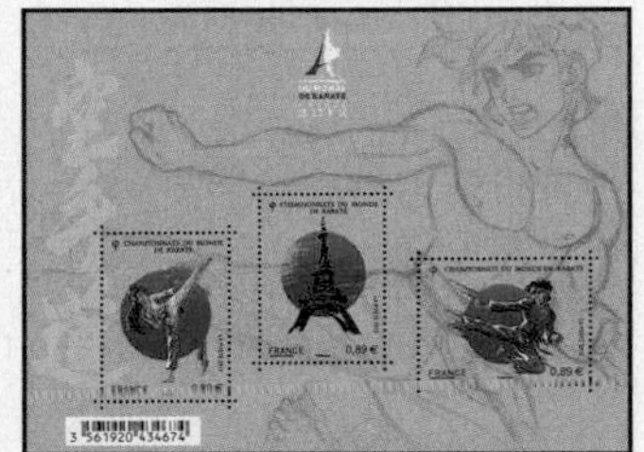

2012 World Karate Championships, Paris — A2248

No. 4274: a, Karateka kicking. b, Eiffel Tower. c, Karateka kicking, horiz.

***Perf. 13¼x13, 13x13¼ (#4274c)***
**2012, Sept. 7 Photo.**
**4274** A2248 Sheet of 3 7.25 7.25
*a.-c.* 89c Any single 2.40 .80

2012 World Pétanque Championships, Marseille — A2249

**Photo. & Embossed**
**2012, Sept. 14** *Perf. 13x13¼*
**4275** A2249 89c multi 2.40 .80

**Art Issue**

Figures Representing Seven Continents, by Jaume Plensa, Place Masséna, Nice — A2250

**2012, Sept. 14 Photo.**
**4276** A2250 €1.45 multi 3.75 1.90

Camp des Milles, World War II Internment Camp — A2251

**2012, Sept. 21 Engr.**
**4277** A2251 60c multi 1.60 .55

**Tourism Issue**

Verneuil-sur-Avre — A2252

**2012, Sept. 21** *Perf. 13¼*
**4278** A2252 60c multi 1.60 .55

Marianne and Stars A2253

**2012, Oct. 1** *Perf. 13*
**4279** Souvenir sheet of 3, #4051, 4079, 4279a 5.00 5.00
*a.* A2253 60c orange 1.60 .55

Torch, Marianne and Stars A2254

The Temptation of St. Anthony, by Hieronymus Bosch — A2255

Items on Fire A2256

Designs: No. 4282, Lava (La lave). No. 4283, Welder (la soudure). No. 4284, Glass-blowing (Le travail du verre). No. 4285, Flame of the Unknown Soldier, Paris (La flamme du soldat inconnu). No. 4286, Halloween jack o'lantern. No. 4287, People around Midsummer's Eve bonfire (Feu de la Saint-Jean). No. 4288, Fire fighters and fire (Les pompiers). No. 4289, Charcoal fire (Les braises). No. 4290, Candles (bougies). No. 4291, Light show (Spectacle). No. 4292, Sunset (Coucher de soleil). No. 4293, Birthday candles on cake (Bougies d'anniversaire).

**2012, Oct. 13 Engr. *Perf. 13***

**4280** A2254 60c orange & red 1.60 .55

**Souvenir Sheet**

**Litho. & Engr.**

***Perf. 13x13¼***

**4281** A2255 €2 multi 5.25 2.60

**Photo.**

**Booklet Stamps**

**Self-Adhesive**

**4282** A2256 (60c) multi 1.60 .55
**4283** A2256 (60c) multi 1.60 .55
**4284** A2256 (60c) multi 1.60 .55
**4285** A2256 (60c) multi 1.60 .55
**4286** A2256 (60c) multi 1.60 .55
**4287** A2256 (60c) multi 1.60 .55
**4288** A2256 (60c) multi 1.60 .55
**4289** A2256 (60c) multi 1.60 .55
**4290** A2256 (60c) multi 1.60 .55
**4291** A2256 (60c) multi 1.60 .55
**4292** A2256 (60c) multi 1.60 .55
**4293** A2256 (60c) multi 1.60 .55
*a.* Booklet pane of 12, #4282-4293 19.50
*Nos. 4282-4293 (12)* 19.20 6.60

Stamp Day. An illustration and a bar code is found on the reverse of the sheet margin of No. 4281.

**Historic Residences Type of 2012**

Design: (60c), Chaâteau d'If.

***Serpentine Die Cut 11***

**2012, Oct. 29 Litho.**

**Self-Adhesive**

**4294** A2237 (60c) multi 1.60 1.60

Lettering, most evident in the "Phil@poste" inscription at bottom, is sharp on No. 4294 and fuzzy on No. 4237.

Court House, Lyon — A2257

**2012, Oct. 26 Engr. *Perf. 13***

**4295** A2257 60c multi 1.60 .55

Lion of Belfort Statue, by Frédéric Auguste Bartholdi — A2258

**2012, Nov. 2 *Perf. 13x13¼***

**4296** A2258 60c multi + label 1.60 .55

Timbres Passion 2012 Stamp Exhibition, Belfort. A souvenir sheet containing No. 4296 was issued in 2013 and sold for €3.

King Henri IV of France (1553-1610), Co-Prince of Andorra — A2259

**2012, Nov. 8**

**4297** A2259 60c multi 1.60 .55
*a.* Sheet of 10, 5 each #4297, French Andorra #710 16.00 16.00

See French Andorra No. 710.

**Souvenir Sheet**

The Masked Ball, Opera by Daniel Auber — A2260

No. 4298: a, Auber (1782-1871). b, King Gustav III of Sweden (1746-92), main character in opera.

**Litho. & Engr.**

**2012, Nov. 9 *Perf. 13¼***

**4298** A2260 Sheet of 2 3.75 3.75
*a.* 60c multi 1.60 .55
*b.* 77c multi 2.00 .65

See Sweden No. 2697.

**Souvenir Sheet**

Organ from Church of St. Jacques, Lunéville — A2261

No. 4299 — Various details of organ's ornamentation: a, 89c. b, €1.45, vert.

***Perf. 13x13¼, 13¼x13***

**2012, Nov. 10 Engr.**

**4299** A2261 Sheet of 2 6.25 6.25
*a.* 89c multi 2.40 .80
*b.* €1.45 multi 3.75 1.25

Laurent Bonnevay (1870-1957), Politician, and Apartment Building — A2262

**2012, Nov. 12 Engr. *Perf. 13¼***

**4300** A2262 57c multi 1.50 .50

Bonnevay Law on rent-controlled housing, cent.

**Souvenir Sheet**

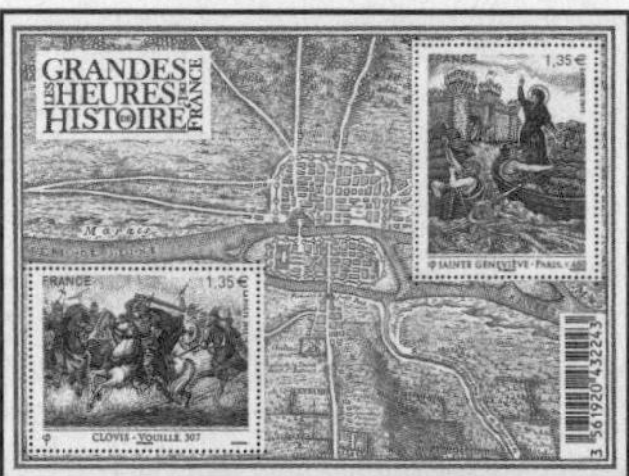


French History — A2263

No. 4301: a, Intercession by St. Geneviève on behalf of Paris, c. 480. b, Clovis at Battle of Vouillé, 507, horiz.

***Perf. 13¼x13, 13x13¼***

**2012, Nov. 12**

**4301** A2263 Sheet of 2 7.00 7.00
*a.-b.* €1.35 Either single 3.50 1.10

A2264



A2265

A2266

A2267

A2268

A2269

A2270

A2271

A2272

A2273

A2274

Greetings Stamps A2275

**Booklet Stamps**

***Serpentine Die Cut 11***

**2012, Nov. 12 Photo.**

**Self-Adhesive**

**4302** A2264 (57c) multi 1.50 .50
**4303** A2265 (57c) multi 1.50 .50
**4304** A2266 (57c) multi 1.50 .50
**4305** A2267 (57c) multi 1.50 .50
**4306** A2268 (57c) multi 1.50 .50
**4307** A2269 (57c) multi 1.50 .50
**4308** A2270 (57c) multi 1.50 .50
**4309** A2271 (57c) multi 1.50 .50
**4310** A2272 (57c) multi 1.50 .50
**4311** A2273 (57c) multi 1.50 .50
**4312** A2274 (57c) multi 1.50 .50
**4313** A2275 (57c) multi 1.50 .50
*a.* Booklet pane of 12, #4302-4313 18.00
*Nos. 4302-4313 (12)* 18.00 6.00

A souvenir sheet containing one perf. 13x13¼ example of No. 4309 with water-activated gum sold for €3.

See No. 4329.

Elysée Treaty, 50th Anniv. A2276

**2013, Jan. 2 Litho. *Perf. 13***

**4314** A2276 80c multi 2.25 .75

See Germany No. 2703.

New Year 2013 (Year of the Snake) — A2277

**2013, Jan. 4 Photo. *Perf. 13¼x13***

**4315** A2277 63c multi 1.75 .60

No. 4315 was printed in sheets of 5. A souvenir sheet of one sold for €3.

See No. 4971a.

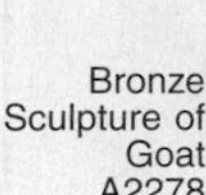

Bronze Sculpture of Goat
A2278

Terra Cotta Figurine of Rabbit, From Studio of Bernard Palissy
A2279

Bronze Sculpture of Buffalo
A2280

Brass Sculpture of Rooster
A2281

Bronze Sculpture of Tiger, by Antoine Louis Barye
A2282

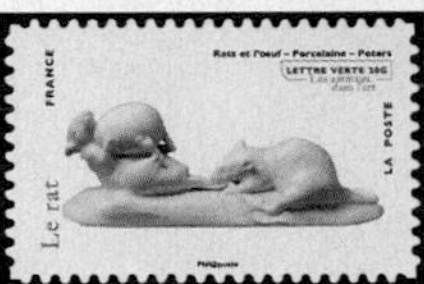

Porcelain Figurine of Rats and Egg
A2283

Glazed Clay Figurine of Pig
A2284

Bronze Sculpture of Monkey, by Jacques Lehmann
A2285

Enameled Stone Sculpture of Dog
A2286

Earthenware Figurine of Dragon
A2287

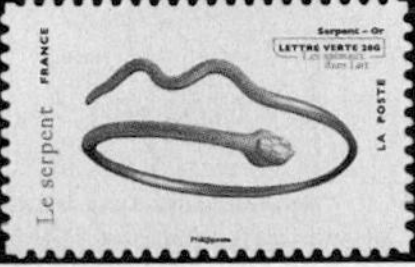

Gold Sculpture of Snake
A2288

Bronze Sculpture of Horse, by Edgar Degas
A2289

**2013, Jan. 4** ***Serpentine Die Cut 11***
**Booklet Stamps**
**Self-Adhesive**

| | | | | |
|---|---|---|---|---|
| **4316** | A2278 (58c) multi | 1.60 | .55 |
| **4317** | A2279 (58c) multi | 1.60 | .55 |
| **4318** | A2280 (58c) multi | 1.60 | .55 |
| **4319** | A2281 (58c) multi | 1.60 | .55 |
| **4320** | A2282 (58c) multi | 1.60 | .55 |
| **4321** | A2283 (58c) multi | 1.60 | .55 |
| **4322** | A2284 (58c) multi | 1.60 | .55 |
| **4323** | A2285 (58c) multi | 1.60 | .55 |
| **4324** | A2286 (58c) multi | 1.60 | .55 |
| **4325** | A2287 (58c) multi | 1.60 | .55 |
| **4326** | A2288 (58c) multi | 1.60 | .55 |
| **4327** | A2289 (58c) multi | 1.60 | .55 |
| *a.* | Booklet pane of 12, #4316-4327 | 19.50 | |
| | *Nos. 4316-4327 (12)* | 19.20 | 6.60 |

Marseille, 2013 European Capital of Culture
A2290

**2013, Jan. 12** **Photo.** ***Perf. 13¼***

| | | | |
|---|---|---|---|
| **4328** | A2290 80c multi | 2.25 | .75 |

**Greetings Type of 2012**
***Serpentine Die Cut 11***
**2013, Jan. 14** **Litho.**
**Self-Adhesive**

| | | | |
|---|---|---|---|
| **4329** | A2265 (58c) multi | 1.60 | 1.60 |

Lettering, most evident in the "Phil@poste" inscription at bottom, is sharp on No. 4329 and fuzzy on No. 4303.

Souvenir Sheet

Notre Dame Cathedral, Paris, 850th Anniv. — A2291

No. 4330 — Stained-glass window depicting: a, Peasant with scythe (44x44mm). b, Madonna and Child (42mm diameter).

**Litho., Sheet Margin Litho. & Engr.**
**2013, Jan. 19** ***Perf.***

| | | | |
|---|---|---|---|
| **4330** | A2291 Sheet of 2 | 7.25 | 7.25 |
| *a.* | €1.05 multi | 3.00 | 1.00 |
| *b.* | €1.55 multi | 4.25 | 1.40 |
| *c.* | Sheet of 2, #4330a, 4330b, lithographed sheet margin | 13.50 | 13.50 |

No. 4330c has a different margin design and sold for €5.

**Art Issue**

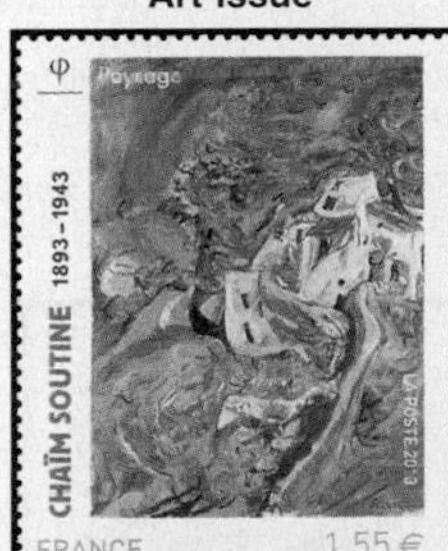

Landscape, by Chaim Soutine (1893-1943) — A2292

**2013, Jan. 25** **Photo.** ***Perf. 13¼x13***

| | | | |
|---|---|---|---|
| **4331** | A2292 €1.55 multi | 4.25 | 2.10 |

A2293

A2294

Hearts — A2295

No. 4334: a, Two white hearts embellished with flowers. b, Bird with long tail. c, Swan facing left. d, Swan facing right.

**2013, Jan. 25** ***Perf. 13¼***

| | | | |
|---|---|---|---|
| **4332** | A2293 58c multi | 1.60 | .55 |
| **4333** | A2294 97c multi | 2.75 | .90 |

**Souvenir Sheet**
***Perf.***

| | | | |
|---|---|---|---|
| **4334** | A2295 Sheet of 5, #4332, 4334a-4334d | 8.00 | 8.00 |
| *a.-d* | 58c Any single | 1.60 | .55 |

**Self-Adhesive**
***Serpentine Die Cut***

| | | | |
|---|---|---|---|
| **4335** | A2293 58c multi | 1.60 | 1.60 |
| **4336** | A2294 97c multi | 2.75 | 2.75 |

Values for Nos. 4332-4333 are for stamps with surrounding selvage.

**Art Issue**

85.8 Degree Arc x 16, Sculpture, by Bernar Venet — A2296

**2013, Feb. 1** ***Perf. 13x13¼***

| | | | |
|---|---|---|---|
| **4337** | A2296 €1.55 multi | 4.25 | 2.10 |

Animal Proverbs and Idioms
A2297

Designs: No. 4338, Qui vole un oeuf vole un boeuf ("Who steals an egg steals an ox"). No. 4339, Etre serrés come des sardines ("Be packed like sardines"). No. 4340, Etre heureux comme un poisson dans l'eau ("Be happy as a fish in water"). No. 4341, Pleurer des larmes de crocodile ("Cry crocodile tears"). No. 4342, Quand les poules auront des dents ("When chickens have teeth" or "When pigs fly"). No. 4343, Avaler des couleuvres ("To swallow snakes" or "To endure affronts"). No. 4344, Le chat parti, les souris dansent ("The cat's away, the mice will play"). No. 4345, Sauter du coq à l'âne ("Jump from the rooster to the donkey" or "Jump from one thing to another"). No. 4346, Se regarder en chiens de faience ("To stare like clay dogs" or "To stare menacingly at each other"). No. 4347, Ménager la chèvre et le chou ("To take care of the goat and the cabbage" or "To run with the hares and hunt with the hounds"). No. 4348, Cela ne se trouve pas sous les sabots d'un cheval ("That is not under the hooves of a horse"). No. 4349, Pratique la politique de l'autruche ("Practice the policy of an ostrich" or "Bury one's head in the sand like an ostrich").

**2013, Feb. 4** ***Serpentine Die Cut 11***
**Booklet Stamps**
**Self-Adhesive**

| | | | |
|---|---|---|---|
| **4338** | A2297 (58c) multi | 1.60 | .55 |
| **4339** | A2297 (58c) multi | 1.60 | .55 |
| **4340** | A2297 (58c) multi | 1.60 | .55 |
| **4341** | A2297 (58c) multi | 1.60 | .55 |
| **4342** | A2297 (58c) multi | 1.60 | .55 |
| **4343** | A2297 (58c) multi | 1.60 | .55 |
| **4344** | A2297 (58c) multi | 1.60 | .55 |
| **4345** | A2297 (58c) multi | 1.60 | .55 |
| **4346** | A2297 (58c) multi | 1.60 | .55 |
| **4347** | A2297 (58c) multi | 1.60 | .55 |
| **4348** | A2297 (58c) multi | 1.60 | .55 |
| **4349** | A2297 (58c) multi | 1.60 | .55 |
| *a.* | Booklet pane of 12, #4338-4349 | 19.50 | |
| | *Nos. 4338-4349 (12)* | 19.20 | 6.60 |

Compare types A2297 and A2498.

Raphael Elizé (1891-1945), First Black Mayor in France — A2298

**2013, Feb. 15** **Engr.** ***Perf. 13¼***

| | | | |
|---|---|---|---|
| **4350** | A2298 63c multi | 1.75 | .60 |

Miniature Sheet

Way of St. James — A2299

No. 4351: a, Via Lemovicensis in Neuvy-Saint-Sépulchre. b, Via Turonensis in Aulnay. c, Via Tolosana in Saint-Gilles, horiz. d, Via Podiensis in Conques, horiz.

**Litho. & Engr.**
**2013, Feb. 22** ***Perf. 13***

| | | | |
|---|---|---|---|
| **4351** | A2299 Sheet of 4 | 8.50 | 8.50 |
| *a.-d.* | 80c Any single | 2.10 | .70 |

50th International Agricultural Show, Paris — A2300

**2013, Feb. 25** **Photo.** ***Perf. 13¼***

| | | | |
|---|---|---|---|
| **4352** | A2300 95c multi | 2.50 | .85 |

Intl. Women's Day
A2301

Qualities of women in Aïcha des Gazelles Rally, Morocco: No. 4353, Courage. No. 4354,

Partage (sharing). No. 4355, Dépassement de soi (surpassing oneself). No. 4356, Entraide (mutual aid). No. 4357, Enthusiasme (enthusiasm). No. 4358, Solidarité (solidarity). No. 4359, Esprit d'équipe (team spirit). No. 4360, Engagement. No. 4361, Emotion. No. 4362, Performance. No. 4363, Confiance (confidence). No. 4364, Respect.

**2013, Mar. 8** ***Serpentine Die Cut 11***
**Booklet Stamps**
**Self-Adhesive**

**4353** A2301 (58c) multi 1.50 .50
**4354** A2301 (58c) multi 1.50 .50
**4355** A2301 (58c) multi 1.50 .50
**4356** A2301 (58c) multi 1.50 .50
**4357** A2301 (58c) multi 1.50 .50
**4358** A2301 (58c) multi 1.50 .50
**4359** A2301 (58c) multi 1.50 .50
**4360** A2301 (58c) multi 1.50 .50
**4361** A2301 (58c) multi 1.50 .50
**4362** A2301 (58c) multi 1.50 .50
**4363** A2301 (58c) multi 1.50 .50
**4364** A2301 (58c) multi 1.50 .50
*a.* Booklet pane of 12, #4353-4364 18.00
*Nos. 4353-4364 (12)* 18.00 6.00

See No. 4406.

**European Capitals Type of 2002**
Miniature Sheet

No. 4365 — Attractions in Madrid, Spain: a, Plaza Mayor. b, Almudena Cathedral, horiz. c, Palace of Communication (Cibeles Palace), horiz. d, Royal Palace, horiz.

***Perf. 13¼x13 (#4365a), 13x13¼***
**2013, Mar. 15**

**4365** A1622 Sheet of 4 6.50 6.50
*a.-d.* 63c Any single 1.60 .55

Opening of Jacques Chaban-Delmas Vertical Lift Bridge, Bordeaux — A2302

**2013, Mar. 16** ***Perf. 13¼***
**4366** A2302 58c multi 1.50 .50

Water Towers, Designed by Philolaos Tloupas, Valence — A2303

**2013, Mar. 22** **Engr.**
**4367** A2303 58c multi 1.50 .50

Spring Philatelic Show, Mâcon — A2304

**2013, Apr. 5** ***Perf. 13¼***
**4368** A2304 63c multi 1.75 .60

Horses A2305

Horse breeds and horses at work: No. 4369, Breton horse. No. 4370, Norman Cob horse. No. 4371, Boulonnais horse. No. 4372, Trait du Nord horse. No. 4373, Ardennais horse. No. 4374, Comtois horse. No. 4375, Poitevin Mulsassier horse. No. 4376, Horse pulling wagon (Attelage en roulotte). No. 4377, Percheron horse. No. 4378, Horse working in vineyard (Travail de la vigne). No. 4379, Auxois horse. No. 4380, Horse pulling logs in forest (Débardage en forêt).

***Serpentine Die Cut 11***
**2013, Apr. 5** **Photo.**
**Booklet Stamps**
**Self-Adhesive**

**4369** A2305 (58c) multi 1.50 .50
**4370** A2305 (58c) multi 1.50 .50
**4371** A2305 (58c) multi 1.50 .50
**4372** A2305 (58c) multi 1.50 .50
**4373** A2305 (58c) multi 1.50 .50
**4374** A2305 (58c) multi 1.50 .50
**4375** A2305 (58c) multi 1.50 .50
**4376** A2305 (58c) multi 1.50 .50
**4377** A2305 (58c) multi 1.50 .50
**4378** A2305 (58c) multi 1.50 .50
**4379** A2305 (58c) multi 1.50 .50
**4380** A2305 (58c) multi 1.50 .50
*a.* Booklet pane of 12, #4369-4380 18.00
*Nos. 4369-4380 (12)* 18.00 6.00

Champs-Elysées Theater, Paris, Cent. — A2306

**2013, Apr. 8** **Engr.** ***Perf. 13¼***
**4381** A2306 €1.05 multi 2.75 .90

Chateau des Vaux, Home of Apprentices of Auteuil — A2307

**2013, Apr. 12**
**4382** A2307 58c multi 1.50 .50

Bats A2308

Designs: No. 4383, Rhinolophus ferrumequinum.

No. 4384: a, Pteropus seychellensis comorensis, vert. b, Plecotus macrobullaris, vert. c, Myotis nattereri.

**2013, Apr. 19** **Photo.**
**4383** A2308 58c multi 1.50 .50

**Miniature Sheet**

**4384** Sheet of 4, #4383, 4384a-4384c 8.00 8.00
*a.* A2308 58c multi 1.50 .50
*b.* A2308 80c multi 2.10 .70
*c.* A2308 €1.05 multi 2.75 .90

Notre Dame de Melun Collegiate Church, 1000th Anniv. A2309

**2013, Apr. 20** **Engr.**
**4385** A2309 63c multi 1.75 .60

Impressionist Paintings Depicting Water — A2310

Designs: No. 4386, L'Ile de la Grande Jatte, Neuilly-sur-Seine, by Alfred Sisley. No. 4387, L'Estaque - Vue du Golfe de Marseille (Gulf of Marseille as Seen from L'Estaque), by Paul Cézanne. No. 4388, Sur la Plage (On the Beach), by Edouard Manet. No. 4389, L'Anse des Pilotes au Havre, Haute Mer Après Midi, Soleil, by Camille Pissarro. No. 4390, Régates à Argenteuil (Regatta at Argenteuil), by Claude Monet. No. 4391, Alphonsine Fournaise, by Pierre-Auguste Renoir. No. 4392, La Rivière Blanche (Breton Boy by the Aven River), by Paul Gauguin. No. 4393, L'Homme à la Barre (Man at the Helm), by Théo van Rysselberghe. No. 4394, Les Pecheurs à la Ligne, Etude pour la Grande Jatte (Fishermen), by Georges Seurat. No. 4395, Dans le Port de Rouen (In the Port of Rouen), by Albert Lebourg. No. 4396, La Nuit Etoilée, Arles (Starry Night Over the Rhone), by Vincent van Gogh. No. 4397, La Jetée de Deauville (The Jetty at Deauville), by Louis-Eugène Boudin.

***Serpentine Die Cut 11***
**2013, Apr. 29** **Photo.**
**Booklet Stamps**
**Self-Adhesive**

**4386** A2310 (58c) multi 1.50 .50
**4387** A2310 (58c) multi 1.50 .50
**4388** A2310 (58c) multi 1.50 .50
**4389** A2310 (58c) multi 1.50 .50
**4390** A2310 (58c) multi 1.50 .50
**4391** A2310 (58c) multi 1.50 .50
**4392** A2310 (58c) multi 1.50 .50
**4393** A2310 (58c) multi 1.50 .50
**4394** A2310 (58c) multi 1.50 .50
**4395** A2310 (58c) multi 1.50 .50
**4396** A2310 (58c) multi 1.50 .50
**4397** A2310 (58c) multi 1.50 .50
*a.* Booklet pane of 12, #4386-4397 18.00
*Nos. 4386-4397 (12)* 18.00 6.00

See Nos. 4449-4452.

Rixheim — A2311

**2013, May 3** **Litho. & Engr.** ***Perf. 13***
**4398** A2311 63c multi 1.75 .60

A souvenir sheet of one No. 4398 sold for €3.

Charles Gonzaga (1580-1637), Duke of Mantua and Monferrat, Founder of Charleville A2312

**2013, May 6** **Engr.** ***Perf. 13¼***
**4399** A2312 80c red & black 2.25 .75

World Table Tennis Championships, Paris — A2313

Designs: 63c, Female player (blue shirt). 95c, Male player (red shirt).

**2013, May 13** ***Perf. 13x13¼***
**4400** A2313 63c multi 1.75 .60
**4401** A2313 95c multi 2.50 .80
*a.* Horiz. pair, #4400-4401, + central label 4.25 1.40

Cathedral and Jules Verne Circus, Amiens — A2314

**2013, May 17**
**4402** A2314 63c multi + label 1.75 .60

French Federation of Philatelic Associations, 86th Congress, Amiens. A souvenir sheet containing No. 4402 was issued in 2014 and sold for €3.20.

Europa — A2315

Designs: No. 4403, Mail coach, 1840. No. 4404, Renault Kangoo ZE mail van.

**2013, May 19** **Photo.**
**4403** 80c multi 2.25 .75
**4404** 80c multi 2.25 .75
*a.* A2315 Horiz. pair, #4403-4404 4.50 1.50

**Souvenir Sheet**

Works of André Le Nôtre (1613-1700), Landscape Architect for King Louis XVI — A2316

No. 4405 — Fountains and gardens at: a, Versailles. b, Chantilly.

**2013, May 31** ***Perf. 13x13¼***
**4405** A2316 Sheet of 2 14.00 14.00
*a.-b.* €2.55 Either single 7.00 2.50
*c.* Sheet of 2, #4405a-4405b, different sheet margin 24.00 24.00

No. 4405c sold for €9.

**Intl. Women's Day Type of 2013**
***Serpentine Die Cut 11***
**2013, June 1** **Litho.**
**Self-Adhesive**

**4406** A2301 (58c) Like #4359 1.60 1.60

No. 4406 has a dot structure not found on No. 4359, which is printed by photogravure.

Abbaye-aux-Dames, Saintes — A2317

**2013, June 14** **Engr.** ***Perf. 13¼***
**4407** A2317 63c multi 1.75 .60

Jacques Baumel (1918-2006), Politician — A2318

**2013, June 15**

**4408** A2318 €1.05 multi 3.00 1.00

Miniature Sheet

100th Tour de France Bicycle Race — A2319

No. 4409: a, Rider wearing yellow jersey, Annecy in background (40x30mm). b, Rider wearing polka-dot jersey near Bagnères-de-Bigorre (26x40mm). c, Rider wearing light blue and dark blue jersey near Mont Ventoux (26x40mm). d, Peloton going along Alpe d'Huez mountain road (40x40mm). e, Rider wearing green jersey in foreground, Calvi in background (40x26mm). f, Rider wearing white jersey, Versailles Palace in background (40x30mm). g, Rider wearing yellow jersey winning race, Arc de Triomphe, Paris (30x40mm). h, Rider in red and black jersey, Mont-Saint-Michel (40x26mm).

***Perf. 13x13¼ (#4409a, 4409f), 13¼x13 (#4409g), 13***

**2013, June 29** **Photo.**

**4409** A2319 Sheet of 8 15.50 15.50
*a.-d.* 58c Any single 1.50 .50
*e.-f.* 80c Either single 2.10 .70
*g.-h.* 95c Either single 2.50 .85

A souvenir sheet containing Nos. 4409e and 4409g sold for €4.

**Types of 1959-2008**

Miniature Sheet

**2013** **Engr.** ***Perf. 13***

**4410** Sheet of 12 21.00 21.00
*a.* A328 63c black 1.75 .60
*b.* A349 63c black 1.75 .60
*c.* A360 63c black 1.75 .60
*d.* A379 63c black 1.75 .60
*e.* A486 63c black 1.75 .60
*f.* A555 63c black 1.75 .60
*g.* A771 63c black 1.75 .60
*h.* A915 63c black 1.75 .60
*i.* A1161 63c black 1.75 .60
*j.* A1409 63c black 1.75 .60
*k.* A1713 63c black 1.75 .60
*l.* A1912 63c black 1.75 .60
*m.* Booklet pane of 12, #4410a-4410l 21.00 —

No. 4410 was only sold together with No. 4437a.

Issued: No. 4410, 7/15; No. 4410m, 11/6

Marianne and Children A2320

Marianne and Children "Ecopli" A2321

Marianne and Children "Lettre Prioritaire" A2322

Marianne and Children "Europe" A2323

Marianne and Children "Monde" — A2324

Type A2322 gram limits (at LL): Nos. 4415, 4422, 4428, 4435, 20g. Nos. 4419, 4432, 50g. Nos. 4420, 4433, 100g. Nos. 4421, 4434, 250g.

**2013, July 15** **Engr.** ***Perf. 13***

**4411** A2320 1c yellow .25 .25
**4412** A2320 5c dk brown .25 .25
**4413** A2320 10c brown .25 .25
**4414** A2321 (56c) dk gray 1.50 .30
**4415** A2322 (63c) red 1.75 .35
*a.* As No. 4415, engraved, glossy paper (#4437g) 1.75 1.75
*b.* As No. 4415, photogravure, glossy paper (#4437g) 1.75 1.75
*c.* As No. 4415, litho., glossy paper (#4437g) 1.75 1.75
*d.* As No. 4415, typo., glossy paper (#4437g) 1.75 1.75
*e.* As No. 4415, silk-screened, glossy paper (#4437g) 1.75 1.75
*f.* No. 4415a with overprint "Marianne 1944-2014" (#4437o) 1.75 1.75
*g.* No. 4415b with overprint "Marianne 1944-2014" (#4437o) 1.75 1.75
*h.* No. 4415c with overprint "Marianne 1944-2014" (#4437o) 1.75 1.75
*i.* No. 4415d with overprint "Marianne 1944-2014" (#4437o) 1.75 1.75
*j.* No. 4415e with overprint "Marianne 1944-2014" (#4437o) 1.75 1.75
**4416** A2323 (80c) blue 2.10 .45
**4417** A2324 (95c) purple 2.50 .65
**4418** A2320 €1 orange 2.60 .65
**4419** A2322 (€1.05) fawn 2.75 .70
**4420** A2322 (€1.55) red violet 4.00 1.00
**4421** A2322 (€2.55) chocolate 6.75 2.40
*Nos. 4411-4421 (11)* 24.70 7.25

**Coil Stamps**

***Perf. 13 Horiz.***

**4422** A2322 (63c) red 1.75 .35
**4423** A2323 (80c) blue 2.10 .45

**Self-Adhesive**

***Serpentine Die Cut 6¾ Vert.***

**4424** A2320 1c yellow .25 .25
**4425** A2320 5c dk brown .25 .25
**4426** A2320 10c brown .25 .25
**4427** A2321 (56c) dk gray 1.50 1.50
**4428** A2322 (63c) red 1.75 .35
*a.* Booklet pane of 10 17.50
*b.* Booklet pane of 12 21.00
*c.* Booklet pane of 20 35.00
**4429** A2323 (80c) blue 2.10 .45
*a.* Booklet pane of 12 25.50
**4430** A2324 (95c) purple 2.50 2.50
**4431** A2320 €1 orange 2.60 2.60
**4432** A2322 (€1.05) fawn 2.75 2.75
**4433** A2322 (€1.55) red violet 4.00 4.00
**4434** A2322 (€2.55) chocolate 6.75 6.75
*Nos. 4424-4434 (11)* 24.70 21.65

**Coil Stamps**

***Serpentine Die Cut 6¾ Horiz.***

**4435** A2322 (63c) red 1.75 .35
**4436** A2323 (80c) blue 2.10 .45

Issued: Nos. 4415a-4415e, 11/6; Nos. 4415f-4415j, 11/6/14. No. 4415e uses an ink that is shinier than that used on No. 4415a that causes the small lettering at the base of the stamp to be indistinct. Nos. 4415f-4415j had a franking value of 66c on day of issue. Compare with types A2534, A2536. See No. 4519.

Marianne and Tree "Lettre Verte" — A2325

Type A2325 gram limits (at LL): Nos. 4437, 4441, 4442, 4446, 20g. Nos. 4438, 4443, 50g. Nos. 4439, 4444, 100g. Nos. 4440, 4445, 250g.

**2013, July 15** **Engr.** ***Perf. 13***

**4437** A2325 (58c) green 1.50 .25
*a.* Souvenir sheet of 2, #4415, 4437 3.25 3.25
*b.* As No. 4437, engraved, glossy paper (#4437g) 1.60 1.60
*c.* As No. 4437, photogravure, glossy paper (#4437g) 1.60 1.60
*d.* As No. 4437, litho., glossy paper (#4437g) 1.60 1.60
*e.* As No. 4437, typo., glossy paper (#4437g) 1.60 1.60
*f.* As No. 4437, silk-screened, glossy paper (#4437g) 1.60 1.60
*g.* Sheet of 40, 8 each #4415a, 4437b, 4 each #4415b, 4415e, 4437d, 4437e, 2 each #4415c, 4415d, 4437c, 4437f, + label 67.00 67.00
*h.* Booklet pane of 2, #4415, 4437 3.50 —
Complete booklet, #4410m, 4437h 24.50
*i.* Booklet pane of 2, #4079, 4437 3.00 —
*j.* No. 4437b with overprint "Marianne 1944-2014" (#4437o) 1.60 1.60
*k.* No. 4437c with overprint "Marianne 1944-2014" (#4437o) 1.60 1.60
*l.* No. 4437d with overprint "Marianne 1944-2014" (#4437o) 1.60 1.60
*m.* No. 4437e with overprint "Marianne 1944-2014" (#4437o) 1.60 1.60
*n.* No. 4437f with overprint "Marianne 1944-2014" (#4437o) 1.60 1.60
*o.* Sheet of 40, 8 each #4415f, 4437j, 4 each #4415g, 4415j, 4437l, 4437m, 2 each #4415h, 4415i, 4437k, 4437n, + label 67.00 67.00
**4438** A2325 (97c) yel grn 2.60 .55
**4439** A2325 (€1.45) dk bl grn 3.75 .80
**4440** A2325 (€2.35) dk bl grn 6.25 1.25
*Nos. 4437-4440 (4)* 14.10 2.85

**Coil Stamp**

***Perf. 13 Horiz.***

**4441** A2325 (58c) green 1.50 .25

**Self-Adhesive**

***Serpentine Die Cut 6¾ Vert.***

**4442** A2325 (58c) green 1.50 .25
*a.* Booklet pane of 10 15.00
*b.* Booklet pane of 12 18.00
**4443** A2325 (97c) yel grn 2.60 2.60
**4444** A2325 (€1.45) dk bl grn 3.75 3.75
**4445** A2325 (€2.35) dk bl grn 6.25 6.25
*Nos. 4442-4445 (4)* 14.10 12.85

**Coil Stamp**

***Serpentine Die Cut 6¾ Horiz.***

**4446** A2325 (58c) green 1.50 .25

Issued: Nos. 4437b-4437h, 11/6, No. 4437i-4437o, 11/6/14. No. 4437a was only sold together with No. 4410. No. 4437a is 144x106mm. A 209x103mm sheet similar to No. 4473a was sold with a folder for €4.

No. 4437f uses an ink that is shinier than that used on No. 4437b that causes the small lettering at the base of the stamp to be indistinct. Nos. 4437j-4437n each had a franking value of 61c on day of issue.

The 80x52mm label on No. 4437g depicting an enlarged example of Type A2325 is not valid for postage. The 80x52mm label on No. 4437o was also overprinted "Marianne 1944-2014" but is not valid for postage.

Compare with type A2535.

See No. 4512.

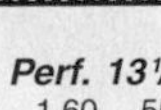

Gaston Doumergue (1863-1937), Politician A2326

**2013, Aug. 1** **Engr.** ***Perf. 13¼***

**4447** A2326 58c dark blue 1.60 .55

Pierre-Georges Latécoère (1883-1943), Aircraft Manufacturer — A2327

**2013, Aug. 15** **Photo.**

**4448** A2327 €1.05 multi 3.00 1.00

**Impressionist Paintings Type of 2013**

Designs: No. 4449, Like #4387. No. 4450, Like #4389. No. 4451, Like #4390. No. 4452, Like #4396.

***Serpentine Die Cut 11***

**2013, Aug. 26** **Litho.**

**Self-Adhesive**

**4449** A2310 (58c) multi 1.60 1.60
**4450** A2310 (58c) multi 1.60 1.60
**4451** A2310 (58c) multi 1.60 1.60
**4452** A2310 (58c) multi 1.60 1.60
*Nos. 4449-4452 (4)* 6.40 6.40

Nos. 4449-4452 each have a dot structure in the colored panels at right that is not found on the photogravure stamps. The appearance of "France" on Nos. 4449-4452 appears lighter and grayer than that found on the photogravure stamps.

Patronage Law, 10th Anniv. — A2328

**2013, Sept. 5** **Photo.** ***Perf. 13¼***

**4453** A2328 63c multi 1.75 .60

Sculpture of Virgin Mary and Infant Jesus A2329

Keystone, Sainte-Chapelle de Vincennes — A2330

Mirror With Ivory Carving of Chess Players A2331

Annunciation of the Virgin, Reims Cathedral A2332

Carving of Rooster, St. Pierre's Cathedral, Poitiers A2333

Decorated Mirror of Louis d'Anjou A2334

Marriage of the Virgin, Notre Dame Cathedral, Paris A2335

Angel From Canopy of King Charles VII — A2336

Illumination From Les Très Riches Heures du Duc de Berry A2337

Reliquary Medallion A2338

Illumination from Heures de François de Guise A2339

Bas-relief of Man Presenting Flower to Woman A2340

*Serpentine Die Cut 11*

**2013, Sept. 6 Photo.**

**Booklet Stamps Self-Adhesive**

| | | | | |
|---|---|---|---|---|
| **4454** | A2329 (63c) multi | | 1.75 | .60 |
| **4455** | A2330 (63c) multi | | 1.75 | .60 |
| **4456** | A2331 (63c) multi | | 1.75 | .60 |
| **4457** | A2332 (63c) multi | | 1.75 | .60 |
| **4458** | A2333 (63c) multi | | 1.75 | .60 |
| **4459** | A2334 (63c) multi | | 1.75 | .60 |
| **4460** | A2335 (63c) multi | | 1.75 | .60 |
| **4461** | A2336 (63c) multi | | 1.75 | .60 |
| **4462** | A2337 (63c) multi | | 1.75 | .60 |
| **4463** | A2338 (63c) multi | | 1.75 | .60 |
| **4464** | A2339 (63c) multi | | 1.75 | .60 |
| **4465** | A2340 (63c) multi | | 1.75 | .60 |
| *a.* | Booklet pane of 12, #4454-4465 | | 21.00 | |
| | *Nos. 4454-4465 (12)* | | 21.00 | 7.20 |

Gothic art.

French Heritage A2341

Designs: No. 4466, House of the Lumière Brothers, Lyon. No. 4467, Buffon Museum, Montbard. No. 4468, House of George Sand, Nohant. No. 4469, House of Georges Clemenceau, Saint-Vincent-sur-Jard. No. 4470, Château de La Motte-Tilly, La Motte-Tilly. No. 4471, Castle and ramparts, Carcassonne. No. 4472, Château de Carrouges, Carrouges. No. 4473, Château de Champs-sur-Marne, Champs-sur-Marne. No. 4474, Aligned stones of Carnac. No. 4475, Roman structures (Mausoleum of the Julii, Triumphal arch of Glanum), Saint-Rémy-de-Provence. No. 4476, Mosaics at Montcaret archaeological site. No. 4477, Gallo-Roman Villa, Montmaurin.

*Serpentine Die Cut 11*

**2013, Sept. 6 Photo.**

**Booklet Stamps Self-Adhesive**

| | | | |
|---|---|---|---|
| **4466** | A2341 (58c) multi | 1.60 | .55 |
| **4467** | A2341 (58c) multi | 1.60 | .55 |
| **4468** | A2341 (58c) multi | 1.60 | .55 |
| **4469** | A2341 (58c) multi | 1.60 | .55 |
| *a.* | Booklet pane of 4, #4466-4469 | 6.50 | |
| **4470** | A2341 (58c) multi | 1.60 | .55 |
| **4471** | A2341 (58c) multi | 1.60 | .55 |
| **4472** | A2341 (58c) multi | 1.60 | .55 |
| **4473** | A2341 (58c) multi | 1.60 | .55 |
| *a.* | Booklet pane of 4, #4470-4473 | 6.50 | |
| **4474** | A2341 (58c) multi | 1.60 | .55 |
| **4475** | A2341 (58c) multi | 1.60 | .55 |
| **4476** | A2341 (58c) multi | 1.60 | .55 |
| **4477** | A2341 (58c) multi | 1.60 | .55 |
| *a.* | Booklet pane of 4, #4474-4477 | 6.50 | |
| | Complete booklet, #4469a, 4473a, 4477a | 19.50 | |
| | *Nos. 4466-4477 (12)* | 19.20 | 6.60 |

Judicial Police of Paris, Cent. — A2342

**2013, Sept. 13 Photo. *Perf. 13¼***

| | | | |
|---|---|---|---|
| **4478** | A2342 63c multi | 1.75 | .60 |

**Art Issue**

Faience Vase, by Théodore Deck (1823-91) A2343

**2013, Sept. 20 Photo. *Perf. 13¼x13***

| | | | |
|---|---|---|---|
| **4479** | A2343 €1.55 multi | 4.25 | 2.10 |

Alexandre Yersin (1863-1943), Bacteriologist — A2344

Yersin as: 63c, Older man. 95c, Young man.

**2013, Sept. 20 Engr. *Perf. 13x13¼***

| | | | |
|---|---|---|---|
| **4480** | A2344 63c multi | 1.75 | .60 |
| **4481** | A2344 95c multi | 2.60 | .85 |

See Viet Nam Nos. 3488-3489.

**Art Issue**

Souvenir Sheet

Paintings by Georges Braque (1882-1963) — A2345

No. 4482: a, Le Guéridon. b, Le Salon.

**2013, Sept. 27 Photo. *Perf. 13x13¼***

| | | | |
|---|---|---|---|
| **4482** | A2345 Sheet of 2 | 8.50 | 8.50 |
| *a.-b.* | €1.55 Either single | 4.25 | 2.10 |

St. Bernard of Clairvaux (1090-1153), Abbot, and His Birthplace, Fontaine-lès-Dijon — A2346

**2013, Oct. 4 Engr. *Perf. 13¼***

| | | | |
|---|---|---|---|
| **4483** | A2346 58c multi | 1.60 | .55 |

Miniature Sheet

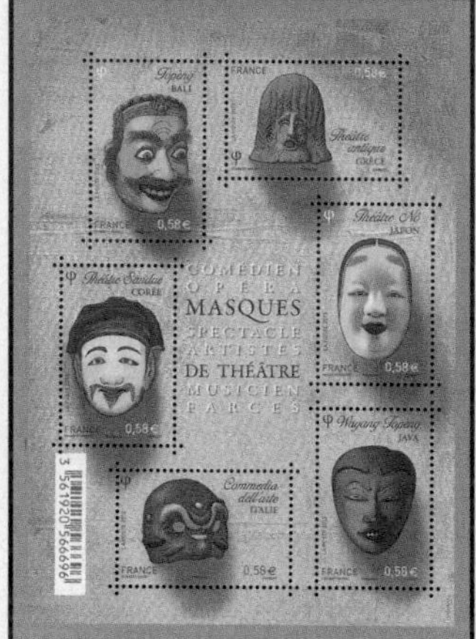

Theatrical Masks — A2347

No. 4484: a, Balinese Topeng. b, Greek theater mask, horiz. c, Korean Sandae mask. d, Japanese Noh theater mask. e, Italian Commedia dell'arte mask, horiz. f, Javanese shadow theater mask.

**2013, Oct. 4 Litho. & Engr. *Perf. 13***

| | | | |
|---|---|---|---|
| **4484** | A2347 Sheet of 6 | 9.75 | 9.75 |
| *a.-f.* | 58c Any single | 1.60 | .55 |

A set of six souvenir sheets, each containing one each of Nos. 4484a-4484f, sold for €15.

Marianne and Balloon A2348

Balloons and Paraglider — A2349

Man Blowing on Fire A2350

Bottle of Air in Water A2351

Man Pumping Air Into Tire A2352

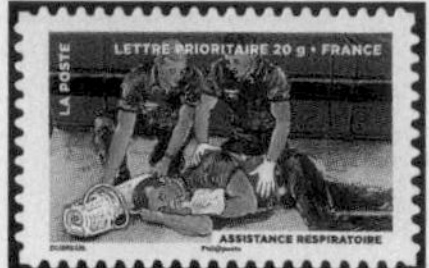

Paramedics Tending to Man Wearing Oxygen Mask A2353

Hang Glider A2354

Sailboat A2355

Birds A2356

Hummingbird and Flowers — A2357

Horn Player A2358

Runner A2359

Polynesian Canoe A2360

Wind Turbine A2361

**2013, Oct. 12 Engr. *Perf. 13***

| | | | |
|---|---|---|---|
| **4485** | A2348 58c multi | 1.60 | .55 |

**Photo. & Embossed**

**Souvenir Sheet**

***Perf. 13¼x13***

| | | | |
|---|---|---|---|
| **4486** | A2349 €2.35 multi | 6.50 | 3.25 |

**Photo.**

**Booklet Stamps Self-Adhesive**

***Serpentine Die Cut 11***

| | | | |
|---|---|---|---|
| **4487** | A2350 (63c) multi | 1.75 | .60 |
| **4488** | A2351 (63c) multi | 1.75 | .60 |
| **4489** | A2352 (63c) multi | 1.75 | .60 |
| **4490** | A2353 (63c) multi | 1.75 | .60 |
| **4491** | A2354 (63c) multi | 1.75 | .60 |
| **4492** | A2355 (63c) multi | 1.75 | .60 |
| **4493** | A2356 (63c) multi | 1.75 | .60 |

| | | | | | |
|---|---|---|---|---|---|
| **4494** | A2357 | (63c) multi | | 1.75 | .60 |
| **4495** | A2358 | (63c) multi | | 1.75 | .60 |
| **4496** | A2359 | (63c) multi | | 1.75 | .60 |
| **4497** | A2360 | (63c) multi | | 1.75 | .60 |
| **4498** | A2361 | (63c) multi | | 1.75 | .60 |
| *a.* | Booklet pane of 12, #4487-4498 | | | 21.00 | |
| | *Nos. 4487-4498 (12)* | | | 21.00 | 7.20 |

Stamp Day. See Nos. 4535-4536.

Miniature Sheet

Television Personalities — A2362

No. 4499: a, Pierre Sabbagh (1918-94), news reporter and producer. b, Léon Zitrone (1914-95), news and sports reporter. c, Catherine Langeais (1923-98), show host. d, Denise Glaser (1920 83), show host and producer. e, Jacqueline Joubert (1921-2005), show host and producer, horiz. f, Pierre Desgraupes (1918-93), news reporter, horiz.

**2013, Oct. 18 Photo. *Perf. 13***

| | | | | |
|---|---|---|---|---|
| **4499** | A2362 | Sheet of 6 | 9.75 | 9.75 |
| *a.-f.* | 58c Any single | | 1.60 | .55 |

Little Pleasures A2363

Designs: No. 4500, People and tea set (Thé partagé). No. 4501, Tree of life (Arbre de vie). No. 4502, Peacock holding letter (Paon messager). No. 4503, Carousel (Carrousel). No. 4504, Tree and falling coins (Pluie d'écus). No. 4505, Robin (Le rouge-gorge). No. 4506, Child and dove (Enfant de paix). No. 4507, Flying horse and rider (Cheval porte-bonheur). No. 4508, Cookies, pastries and snacks (Gourmandises). No. 4509, Citrus fruit and blossoms (Magie d'agrumes). No. 4510, Mother, child and flowers (Bienveillance). No. 4511, Shoe filled with gifts (L'escarpin).

***Serpentine Die Cut 11***

**2013, Oct. 25 Photo.**

**Booklet Stamps Self-Adhesive**

| | | | | |
|---|---|---|---|---|
| **4500** | A2363 | (58c) multi | 1.60 | .55 |
| **4501** | A2363 | (58c) multi | 1.60 | .55 |
| **4502** | A2363 | (58c) multi | 1.60 | .55 |
| **4503** | A2363 | (58c) multi | 1.60 | .55 |
| **4504** | A2363 | (58c) multi | 1.60 | .55 |
| **4505** | A2363 | (58c) multi | 1.60 | .55 |
| **4506** | A2363 | (58c) multi | 1.60 | .55 |
| **4507** | A2363 | (58c) multi | 1.60 | .55 |
| **4508** | A2363 | (58c) multi | 1.60 | .55 |
| **4509** | A2363 | (58c) multi | 1.60 | .55 |
| **4510** | A2363 | (58c) multi | 1.60 | .55 |
| **4511** | A2363 | (58c) multi | 1.60 | .55 |
| *a.* | Booklet pane of 12, #4500-4511 | | 19.50 | |
| | *Nos. 4500-4511 (12)* | | 19.20 | 6.60 |

A souvenir sheet containing a perf. 12¾ example of No. 4510 with water-activated gum sold for €3.

**Types of 1959-2013**

***Serpentine Die Cut 11***

**2013, Nov. 6 Engr.**

**Booklet Stamps Self-Adhesive**

| | | | | |
|---|---|---|---|---|
| **4512** | A2325 | (58c) green | 1.60 | .35 |
| **4513** | A328 | 63c black | 1.75 | .60 |
| **4514** | A349 | 63c black | 1.75 | .60 |
| **4515** | A360 | 63c black | 1.75 | .60 |
| **4516** | A379 | 63c black | 1.75 | .60 |
| **4517** | A486 | 63c black | 1.75 | .60 |
| **4518** | A555 | 63c black | 1.75 | .60 |
| **4519** | A2322 | (63c) red | 1.75 | .60 |
| **4520** | A771 | 63c black | 1.75 | .60 |
| **4521** | A915 | 63c black | 1.75 | .60 |
| **4522** | A1161 | 63c black | 1.75 | .60 |
| **4523** | A1409 | 63c black | 1.75 | .60 |
| **4524** | A1713 | 63c black | 1.75 | .60 |
| **4525** | A1912 | 63c black | 1.75 | .60 |
| *a.* | Booklet pane of 14, #4512-4525 | | 24.50 | |
| | *Nos. 4512-4525 (14)* | | 24.35 | 8.15 |

Trade Treaty Between France and Denmark, 350th Anniv. A2364

Map and compass rose with ship at: 63c, Right. 80c, Left.

**2013, Nov. 7 Engr. *Perf. 13***

| | | | | |
|---|---|---|---|---|
| **4526** | A2364 | 63c multi | 1.75 | .60 |
| **4527** | A2364 | 80c multi | 2.25 | .75 |

See Denmark Nos. 1663-1664.

Fashion A2365

Designs: No. 4528, Finished dresses on three dress forms. No. 4529, Flower, three women wearing white dresses. No. 4530, Three dress forms. No. 4531, Three women wearing white dresses.

**2013, Nov. 8 Photo. *Perf. 13¼***

| | | | | |
|---|---|---|---|---|
| **4528** | A2365 | 63c multi | 1.75 | .60 |
| **4529** | A2365 | 63c multi | 1.75 | .60 |
| **4530** | A2365 | 95c multi | 2.60 | .85 |
| **4531** | A2365 | 95c multi | 2.60 | .85 |
| | *Nos. 4528-4531 (4)* | | 8.70 | 2.90 |

See Singapore Nos. 1640-1643.

Souvenir Sheet

French History — A2366

No. 4532: a, Battle of Muret, 1213. b, Capture of Tournoel, 1212.

**2013, Nov. 8 Engr. *Perf. 13x13¼***

| | | | | |
|---|---|---|---|---|
| **4532** | A2366 | Sheet of 2 | 8.00 | 8.00 |
| *a.-b.* | €1.45 Either single | | 4.00 | 1.40 |

National Order of Merit, 50th Anniv. — A2367

**2013, Nov. 9 Engr. *Perf. 13¼***

| | | | | |
|---|---|---|---|---|
| **4533** | A2367 | 63c blue | 1.75 | .60 |

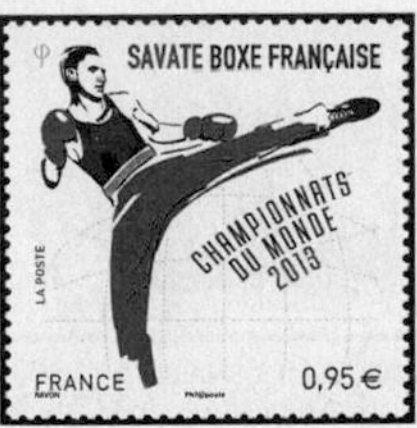

2013 French Kickboxing World Championships, Clermont-Ferrand — A2368

**2013, Nov. 16 Photo. *Perf. 13***

| | | | | |
|---|---|---|---|---|
| **4534** | A2368 | 95c multi | 2.60 | .85 |

**Sailboat and Horn Player Types of 2013**

***Serpentine Die Cut 11***

**2013, Nov. 18 Litho.**

**Self-Adhesive**

| | | | | |
|---|---|---|---|---|
| **4535** | A2355 | (63c) multi | 1.75 | 1.75 |
| **4536** | A2358 | (63c) multi | 1.75 | 1.75 |

"Phil@poste" is sharper on Nos. 4535-4536 than on Nos. 4492 and 4495.

Items with Spirals A2369

Spirals in: No. 4537, Solarium shell (Coquillage solarium). No. 4538, Pottery design from Iznik, Turkey (Céramique Iznik). No. 4539, Spirograph. No. 4540, Red rose (Rose rouge). No. 4541, Ammonite fossil (Fossile d'ammonite). No. 4542, Chinese highway interchange (Echangeur Shanghai Nanpu). No. 4543, Kite (Cerf-volant). No. 4544, Cyclone Ingrid. No. 4545, Tree rings (Sapincoupe transversale). No. 4546, Basket (Vannerie). No. 4547, Lighthouse staircase (Phare de la Coubre). No. 4548, School of barracudas (Banc des barracudas).

***Serpentine Die Cut 11***

**2014, Jan. 4 Photo.**

**Booklet Stamps Self-Adhesive**

| | | | | |
|---|---|---|---|---|
| **4537** | A2369 | (66c) multi | 1.75 | .60 |
| **4538** | A2369 | (66c) multi | 1.75 | .60 |
| **4539** | A2369 | (66c) multi | 1.75 | .60 |
| **4540** | A2369 | (66c) multi | 1.75 | .60 |
| **4541** | A2369 | (66c) multi | 1.75 | .60 |
| **4542** | A2369 | (66c) multi | 1.75 | .60 |
| **4543** | A2369 | (66c) multi | 1.75 | .60 |
| **4544** | A2369 | (66c) multi | 1.75 | .60 |
| **4545** | A2369 | (66c) multi | 1.75 | .60 |
| **4546** | A2369 | (66c) multi | 1.75 | .60 |
| **4547** | A2369 | (66c) multi | 1.75 | .60 |
| **4548** | A2369 | (66c) multi | 1.75 | .60 |
| *a.* | Booklet pane of 12, #4537-4548 | | 21.00 | |
| | *Nos. 4537-4548 (12)* | | 21.00 | 7.20 |

See Nos. 4566-4567, 4698.

Hearts A2370

"Baccarat" and: 61c, Chandelier. €1.02, Goblet.

**Silk-Screened, Engraved & Embossed**

**2014, Jan. 7 *Perf. 13***

| | | | | |
|---|---|---|---|---|
| **4549** | A2370 | 61c multi | 1.75 | .60 |
| *a.* | Souvenir sheet of 5 | | 8.75 | 8.75 |
| **4550** | A2370 | €1.02 multi | 2.75 | .90 |

**Silk-Screened & Engraved**

***Serpentine Die Cut***

**Self-Adhesive**

| | | | | |
|---|---|---|---|---|
| **4551** | A2370 | 61c multi | 1.75 | 1.75 |
| **4552** | A2370 | €1.02 multi | 2.75 | 2.75 |

See No. 4651.

Anne, Duchess of Brittany (1477-1514) A2371

**Litho. & Engr.**

**2014, Jan. 11 *Perf. 13***

| | | | | |
|---|---|---|---|---|
| **4553** | A2371 | 66c multi | 1.75 | .60 |

A souvenir sheet of one sold for €3.20.

Signs of the Zodiac A2372

Designs: No. 4554, Aries (Bélier). No. 4555, Taurus (Taureau). No. 4556, Gemini (Gémeaux). No. 4557, Cancer. No. 4558, Leo (Lion). No. 4559, Virgo (Vierge). No. 4560, Libra (Balance). No. 4561, Scorpio (Scorpion). No. 4562, Sagittarius (Sagittaire). No. 4563, Capricorn (Capricorne). No. 4564, Aquarius (Verseau). No. 4565, Pisces (Poissons).

***Serpentine Die Cut 11***

**2014, Jan. 20 Photo.**

**Booklet Stamps Self-Adhesive**

| | | | | |
|---|---|---|---|---|
| **4554** | A2372 | (61c) multi | 1.75 | .60 |
| **4555** | A2372 | (61c) multi | 1.75 | .60 |
| **4556** | A2372 | (61c) multi | 1.75 | .60 |
| **4557** | A2372 | (61c) multi | 1.75 | .60 |
| **4558** | A2372 | (61c) multi | 1.75 | .60 |
| **4559** | A2372 | (61c) multi | 1.75 | .60 |
| **4560** | A2372 | (61c) multi | 1.75 | .60 |
| **4561** | A2372 | (61c) multi | 1.75 | .60 |
| **4562** | A2372 | (61c) multi | 1.75 | .60 |
| **4563** | A2372 | (61c) multi | 1.75 | .60 |
| **4564** | A2372 | (61c) multi | 1.75 | .60 |
| **4565** | A2372 | (61c) multi | 1.75 | .60 |
| *a.* | Booklet pane of 12, #4554-4565 | | 21.00 | |
| | *Nos. 4554-4565 (12)* | | 21.00 | 7.20 |

**Items With Spirals Type of 2014**

Designs: No. 4566, Like #4542. No. 4567, Like #4543.

***Serpentine Die Cut 11***

**2014, Jan. 27 Litho.**

**Self-Adhesive**

| | | | | |
|---|---|---|---|---|
| **4566** | A2369 | (66c) multi | 1.75 | 1.75 |
| **4567** | A2369 | (66c) multi | 1.75 | 1.75 |

"Phil@poste" is sharper on Nos. 4566-4567 than on Nos. 4542-4543.

New Year 2014 (Year of the Horse) — A2373

**2014, Jan. 31 Photo. *Perf. 13¼x13***

| | | | | |
|---|---|---|---|---|
| **4568** | A2373 | 66c multi | 1.75 | .60 |

No. 4568 was printed in sheets of 5. A souvenir sheet of one sold for €3.20.

See No. 4971b.

### Art Issue

Bust of Julius Caesar A2374

**2014, Feb. 14 Engr.** ***Perf. 13¼x13***
**4569** A2374 €1.65 multi 4.50 2.25

Cattle Breeds A2375

Inscriptions: No. 4570, La Bretonne Pie Noir. No. 4571, L'Armoricaine. No. 4572, La Béarnaise. No. 4573, La Maraîchine. No. 4574, La Mirandaise. No. 4575, La Villard de Lans. No. 4576, La Saosnoise. No. 4577, La Nantaise. No. 4578, La Bordelaise. No. 4579, La Lourdaise. No. 4580, La Casta. No. 4581, La Ferrandaise.

***Serpentine Die Cut 11***
**2014, Feb. 22 Photo.**
**Booklet Stamps Self-Adhesive**

| | | | | |
|---|---|---|---|---|
| **4570** | A2375 (61c) multi | | 1.75 | .60 |
| **4571** | A2375 (61c) multi | | 1.75 | .60 |
| **4572** | A2375 (61c) multi | | 1.75 | .60 |
| **4573** | A2375 (61c) multi | | 1.75 | .60 |
| **4574** | A2375 (61c) multi | | 1.75 | .60 |
| **4575** | A2375 (61c) multi | | 1.75 | .60 |
| **4576** | A2375 (61c) multi | | 1.75 | .60 |
| **4577** | A2375 (61c) multi | | 1.75 | .60 |
| **4578** | A2375 (61c) multi | | 1.75 | .60 |
| **4579** | A2375 (61c) multi | | 1.75 | .60 |
| **4580** | A2375 (61c) multi | | 1.75 | .60 |
| **4581** | A2375 (61c) multi | | 1.75 | .60 |
| *a.* | Booklet pane of 12, #4570-4581 | | 21.00 | |
| | *Nos. 4570-4581 (12)* | | 21.00 | 7.20 |

### Art Issue

Tokyo 04, Photograph by Maxime Bruno — A2376

**2014, Feb. 28 Litho.** ***Perf. 13x13¼***
**4582** A2376 €1.65 multi 4.50 2.25

**Miniature Sheet**

Way of St. James — A2377

No. 4583: a, Via Lemovicensis in Bazas. b, Via Podiensis in Moissac. c, Via Tolosana in Auch. d, Via Turonensis in Pons.

**Litho. & Engr.**
**2014, Mar. 14** ***Perf. 13***
**4583** A2377 Sheet of 4 9.00 9.00
*a.-d.* 83c Any single 2.25 .75

Alexandre Glais-Bizoin (1800-77), Politician — A2378

**2014, Mar. 15 Engr.** ***Perf. 13x13¼***
**4584** A2378 66c multi 1.90 .65

Bears A2379

Designs: No. 4585, Giant panda (Panda géant).
No. 4586: a, Spectacled bear (Ours andin). b, Kermode bear (Ours Kermode). c, Polar bear (Ours polaire).

**2014, Mar. 21 Photo.** ***Perf. 13¼***
**4585** A2379 61c multi 1.75 .60

**Miniature Sheet**

**4586** Sheet of 4, #4585, 4586a-4586c 7.00 7.00
*a.-c.* A2379 61c Any single 1.75 .60

Diplomatic Relations Between France and People's Republic of China, 50th Anniv. — A2380

Designs: 66c, Qinhuai River, Nanjing. 98c, Seine River, Paris.

**2014, Mar. 27 Engr.** ***Perf. 13x13¼***
**4587** A2380 66c multi 1.90 .65
**4588** A2380 98c multi 2.75 .90

See People's Republic of China Nos. 4172-4173.

### Art Issue

Painting by Joan Mitchell (1925-92) A2381

**2014, Mar. 28 Litho.** ***Perf. 13¼x13***
**4589** A2381 €1.65 multi 4.50 2.25

Sell and Buy Used Items A2382

Turn Off Appliances A2383

Fruits and Vegetables A2384

Fix Leaks Quickly A2385

Sort and Recycle Paper A2386

Control Indoor Temperatures — A2387

Conserve Water A2388

People in Carpool A2389

Use Public Transportation — A2390

Save Energy A2391

Drive Ecologically Friendly Automobiles A2392

Recycle Waste Products A2393

***Serpentine Die Cut 11***
**2014, Apr. 3 Photo.**
**Booklet Stamps Self-Adhesive**

| | | | | |
|---|---|---|---|---|
| **4590** | A2382 (61c) multi | | 1.75 | .60 |
| **4591** | A2383 (61c) multi | | 1.75 | .60 |
| **4592** | A2384 (61c) multi | | 1.75 | .60 |
| **4593** | A2385 (61c) multi | | 1.75 | .60 |
| **4594** | A2386 (61c) multi | | 1.75 | .60 |
| **4595** | A2387 (61c) multi | | 1.75 | .60 |
| **4596** | A2388 (61c) multi | | 1.75 | .60 |
| **4597** | A2389 (61c) multi | | 1.75 | .60 |
| **4598** | A2390 (61c) multi | | 1.75 | .60 |
| **4599** | A2391 (61c) multi | | 1.75 | .60 |
| **4600** | A2392 (61c) multi | | 1.75 | .60 |
| **4601** | A2393 (61c) multi | | 1.75 | .60 |
| *a.* | Booklet pane of 12, #4590-4601 | | 21.00 | |
| | *Nos. 4590-4601 (12)* | | 21.00 | 7.20 |

Opera Theater, Clermont-Ferrand — A2394

**2014, Apr. 4 Engr.** ***Perf. 13¼***
**4602** A2394 61c multi 1.75 .60

Spring Philatelic Show, Clermont-Ferrand.

Marguerite Duras (1914-96), Writer and Film Director — A2395

**2014, Apr. 4 Engr.** ***Perf. 13¼***
**4603** A2395 €1.10 multi 3.00 1.00

Arrest and Deportation of Jews at Izieu Orphanage, 70th Anniv. A2396

**Litho. & Engr.**
**2014, Apr. 6** ***Perf. 13x13¼***
**4604** A2396 61c multi 1.75 .60

**Miniature Sheet**

European Capitals — A2397

No. 4605 — Attractions in Vienna: a, Secession Building. b, Belvedere Palace, horiz. c, Karlskirche (St. Charles' Church). d, Hofburg Palace, horiz.

***Perf. 13¼x13, 13x13¼***
**2014, Apr. 18 Photo.**
**4605** A2397 Sheet of 4 + 3 labels 7.75 7.75
*a.-d.* 66c Any single 1.90 .65

**Souvenir Sheet**

French History — A2398

No. 4606: a, St. Louis (1214-70) (35x66mm). b, Battle of Bouvines, 1214 (52x41mm)

**2014, Apr. 25 Engr. *Perf. 13x13¼***

| | | | | |
|---|---|---|---|---|
| **4606** | A2398 Sheet of 2 | | 9.50 | 9.50 |
| *a.-b.* | €1.65 Either single | | 4.75 | 2.25 |
| *c.* | Souvenir sheet of 4, #4532a, 4532b, 4606a, 4606b | | 17.00 | 17.00 |

Salon du Timbre 2014 (No. 4606c). Issued: No. 4606c, 6/23/14.

Palace of Poitiers — A2399

**2014, May 1 Engr. *Perf. 13x13¼***

| | | | |
|---|---|---|---|
| **4607** | A2399 61c multi + label | 1.75 | .60 |

Vacation A2400

Designs: No. 4608, Dog with sunglasses eating ice cream bar. No. 4609, Snail with trailer for shell. No. 4610, Crab building sand castle. No. 4611, Cats dancing. No. 4612, Turtle playing lute, turtle dancing. No. 4613, Lobster holding beach gear. No. 4614, Chicken and egg wearing headphones. No. 4615, Fish surfing. No. 4616, Ram with backpack and mountain climbing gear. No. 4617, Rabbits on tandem bicycle. No. 4618. Frogs with umbrellas in swan boat. No. 4619, Geese, tent, snails on picnic plate.

***Serpentine Die Cut 11***

**2014, May 3 Photo.**

**Booklet Stamps**
**Self-Adhesive**

| | | | |
|---|---|---|---|
| **4608** | A2400 (61c) multi | 1.75 | .60 |
| **4609** | A2400 (61c) multi | 1.75 | .60 |
| **4610** | A2400 (61c) multi | 1.75 | .60 |
| **4611** | A2400 (61c) multi | 1.75 | .60 |
| **4612** | A2400 (61c) multi | 1.75 | .60 |
| **4613** | A2400 (61c) multi | 1.75 | .60 |
| **4614** | A2400 (61c) multi | 1.75 | .60 |
| **4615** | A2400 (61c) multi | 1.75 | .60 |
| **4616** | A2400 (61c) multi | 1.75 | .60 |
| **4617** | A2400 (61c) multi | 1.75 | .60 |
| **4618** | A2400 (61c) multi | 1.75 | .60 |
| **4619** | A2400 (61c) multi | 1.75 | .60 |
| *a.* | Booklet pane of 12, #4608-4619 | 21.00 | |
| | *Nos. 4608-4619 (12)* | 21.00 | 7.20 |

Harp Created by Jean Henri Naderman, 1787 A2401

**2014, May 4 Photo. *Perf. 13¼x13***

| | | | |
|---|---|---|---|
| **4620** | A2401 83c multi | 2.25 | .75 |

Europa.

Opening of English Channel Tunnel, 20th Anniv. A2402

**2014, May 6 Engr. *Perf. 13¼***

| | | | |
|---|---|---|---|
| **4621** | A2402 66c multi | 1.90 | .65 |

**Tourism Series**

Boulogne-sur-Mer — A2403

**2014, May 9 Engr. *Perf. 13x12¾***

| | | | |
|---|---|---|---|
| **4622** | A2403 61c multi | 1.75 | .60 |

D-Day, 70th Anniv. — A2404

**2014, June 5 Photo. *Perf. 13x12¾***

| | | | |
|---|---|---|---|
| **4623** | A2404 66c multi | 1.90 | .65 |

Two souvenir sheets of one, issued in 2014 and in 2015, each sold for €3.20.

**Tourism Issue**

Pontigny Abbey, Yonne — A2405

**2014, June 7 Engr. *Perf. 13¼***

| | | | |
|---|---|---|---|
| **4624** | A2405 61c multi | 1.75 | .60 |

Massacre of Tulle, 70th Anniv. A2406

**2014, June 9 Photo. *Perf. 13¼***

| | | | |
|---|---|---|---|
| **4625** | A2406 66c multi | 1.90 | .65 |

Souvenir Sheet

Benjamin Rabier (1864-1939), Comic Book Illustrator — A2407

No. 4626: a, Duckling hatching, ring with rabbits, chick and chicken (41x41mm). b, Rabier, chicken, rabbit and duck (30x41mm).

**2014, June 14 Engr. *Perf. 13¼***

| | | | |
|---|---|---|---|
| **4626** | A2407 Sheet of 2 | 5.00 | 5.00 |
| *a.* | 66c multi | 1.90 | .65 |
| *b.* | €1.10 multi | 3.00 | 1.00 |

A 200x95mm sheet containing Nos. 4626a and 4626b, but having a different margin design sold for €6.

See Nos. 4676, 4680.

Trains A2408

Designs: No. 4627, Buddicom No. 33, Haute-Normandie. No. 4628, Z 209, Vallée de Chamonix. No. 4629, Pacific Chapelon Nord 3.1192, Paris, Gare du Nord. No. 4630, Micheline XM 5005, Haute-Marne. No. 4631, Mikado 141 R 1187, Côte Vermeille. No. 4632, BB 12125, Moselle. No. 4633, Z 6181, Ile-de-France. No. 4634, BB 66001, Les Cévennes. No. 4635, BB 9004, Les Landes. No. 4636, RTG T 2057, Gare de Boulogne-Aroglisseurs. No. 4637, CC 6572, Limoges, Gare des Bénédictins. No. 4638, TGV Duplex, Gare de Belfort-Montbéliard TGV.

***Serpentine Die Cut 11***

**2014, June 14 Photo.**

**Booklet Stamps**
**Self-Adhesive**

| | | | |
|---|---|---|---|
| **4627** | A2408 (66c) multi | 1.90 | .65 |
| **4628** | A2408 (66c) multi | 1.90 | .65 |
| **4629** | A2408 (66c) multi | 1.90 | .65 |
| **4630** | A2408 (66c) multi | 1.90 | .65 |
| *a.* | Booklet pane of 4, #4627-4630 | 7.60 | |
| **4631** | A2408 (66c) multi | 1.90 | .65 |
| **4632** | A2408 (66c) multi | 1.90 | .65 |
| **4633** | A2408 (66c) multi | 1.90 | .65 |
| **4634** | A2408 (66c) multi | 1.90 | .65 |
| *a.* | Booklet pane of 4, #4631-4634 | 7.60 | |
| **4635** | A2408 (66c) multi | 1.90 | .65 |
| **4636** | A2408 (66c) multi | 1.90 | .65 |
| **4637** | A2408 (66c) multi | 1.90 | .65 |
| **4638** | A2408 (66c) multi | 1.90 | .65 |
| *a.* | Booklet pane of 4, #4635-4638 | 7.60 | |
| | Complete booklet, #4630a, 4634a, 4638a | 23.00 | |
| | *Nos. 4627-4638 (12)* | 22.80 | 7.80 |

Paris Zoo, 80th Anniv. — A2409

**2014, June 15 Photo. *Perf. 13***

| | | | |
|---|---|---|---|
| **4639** | A2409 98c multi | 2.75 | .95 |

A souvenir sheet containing No. 4639 sold for €3.20.

Jean Jaurès (1859-1914), Assassinated Socialist Party Leader — A2410

Jaurès: 61c, Without hat. €1.02, With hat.

**2014, June 17 Engr. *Perf. 13¼***

| | | | |
|---|---|---|---|
| **4640** | A2410 61c blue | 1.75 | .60 |
| **4641** | A2410 €1.02 red | 2.75 | .95 |
| *a.* | Horiz. pair, #4640-4641 | 4.50 | 2.25 |

See Nos. 4675, 4679.

Miniature Sheet

The 1950s — A2411

No. 4642: a, Automobile. b, Electricity advertisement, vert. c, People packing for vacation, vert. d, Vendor in movie theater. e, Musicians. f, Two women modeling fashions, veret.

**2014, June 18 Photo. *Perf. 13***

| | | | |
|---|---|---|---|
| **4642** | A2411 Sheet of 6 | 11.50 | 11.50 |
| *a.-f.* | 66c Any single | 1.90 | .65 |

See Nos. 4677, 4678.

A set of 10 miniature sheets containing reproductions of old French stamps (Nos. 641, 722, 764, 850, B34, B92, B97, B172, B248 and C22) with denominations was produced in limited quantities and offered only as a complete set. Each sheet contained five reproductions of one of the ten stamps in different colors, one with a €2.20 denomination and four with €2.45 denominations.

Ceres — A2412

**2014, June 18 Engr. *Imperf.***

**With Printer's Inscription at Base of Stamp**

| | | | |
|---|---|---|---|
| **4643** | A2412 €1 rose carmine | 2.75 | 1.40 |
| **4644** | A2412 €1 red | 2.75 | 1.40 |

**Typo.**

| | | | |
|---|---|---|---|
| **4645** | A2412 €1 vermilion | 2.75 | 1.40 |
| *a.* | With printer information at top of stamp | 2.75 | 1.40 |
| **4646** | A2412 €1 rose | 2.75 | 1.40 |
| *a.* | With printer information at top of stamp | 2.75 | 1.40 |
| | *Nos. 4643-4646 (4)* | 11.00 | 5.60 |

Printed in sheets of 20 containing Nos. 4645a, 4646a, 5 each Nos. 4643-4644, 4 each Nos. 4645-4646. See No. 4727a.

**Tourism Issue**

Coareze A2413

Locmariaquer — A2414

**2014 Engr. *Perf. 13¼***

| | | | |
|---|---|---|---|
| **4647** | A2413 61c multi | 1.75 | .60 |
| **4648** | A2414 61c multi | 1.75 | .60 |

Issued: No. 4647, 6/19; No. 4648, 6/20. See Nos. 4673, 4674.

French Institute, Paris — A2415

**2014, June 21 Engr. *Perf. 13x13¼***

| | | | |
|---|---|---|---|
| **4649** | A2415 61c multi + label | 1.75 | .60 |

French Federation of Philatelic Associations, 87th Congress, Paris. See No. 4672.

### Art Issue

The Seine at Pont du Carrousel, by Jean Dufy (1888-1964) — A2416

**2014, June 22 Litho.** ***Perf. 13x13¼***
**4650** A2416 €1.65 multi 4.50 2.25

See No. 4681.

### Baccarat Hearts Type of 2014
### Silk-Screened & Engraved

**2014, June 23** ***Perf.***
**4651** A2370 €3 multi 8.25 4.25

No. 4651 was printed in sheets of 5.

National Institute of Health and Medical Research, 50th Anniv. A2417

**2014, July 3 Photo.** ***Perf. 13¼***
**4652** A2417 66c multi 1.75 .60

Jeanne Antoine Poisson, Marquise de Pompadour (1721-64), Patron of the Arts — A2418

**2014, July 4 Engr.** ***Perf. 13¼***
**4653** A2418 66c multi 1.75 .60

### Art Issue

Les Boîtes de Conserve, by Jean Fautrier (1898-1964) — A2419

**2014, July 11 Engr.** ***Perf. 13x13¼***
**4654** A2419 €1.65 multi 4.50 2.25

General Mobilization of World War I Troops, Cent. — A2420

**2014, Aug. 2 Engr.** ***Perf. 13x13¼***
**4655** A2420 66c blue & red 1.75 .60

Miniature Sheet

2014 World Equestrian Games, Normandy — A2421

No. 4656: a, Dressage (40x30mm). b, Endurance (40x30mm). c, Concours complet d'équitation (40x40mm). d, Para-dressage (30x40mm). e, Voltige (30x40mm). f, Attelage (40x40mm). g, Saut d'obstacles (40x30mm). h, Reining (40x30mm).

**2014, Aug. 23 Photo.** ***Perf. 13x13¼***
**4656** A2421 Sheet of 8 17.50 8.75
*a.-d.* 61c Any single 1.60 .55
*e.-h.* €1.02 Any single 2.75 .90

A souvenir sheet containing examples of Nos. 4656e and 4656f with different perforations, sold for €6.

Charles Péguy (1873-1914), Writer — A2422

**2014, Sept. 5 Engr.** ***Perf. 13¼***
**4657** A2422 €1.55 multi 4.00 1.40

Renaissance Objets d'Art — A2423

Designs: No. 4658, Gardens of Château de Villandry. No. 4659, Clock, Rouen. No. 4660, Stairway sculpture, by Jean Goujon. No. 4661, Sculpture of salamander, Château de Fontainbleau. No. 4662, Buckle of King Charles IX. No. 4663, Detail of tapestry depicting Jupiter and Latona. No. 4664, Portrait of King Francis I, by Jean Clouet. No. 4665, Stainedd-glass window depicting angel playing flute, Sainte-Etienne Cathedral, Sens. No. 4666, Enamel painting of Ulysses, by Léonard Limousin. No. 4667, Book cover by Étienne Roffet. No. 4668, Armor of King Henri II. No. 4669, Stained-glass emblem of Queen Anne of Brittany depicting ermine and crown.

***Serpentine Die Cut 11***

**2014, Sept. 6** **Photo.**

### Booklet Stamps
### Self-Adhesive

**4658** A2423 (61c) multi 1.60 .55
**4659** A2423 (61c) multi 1.60 .55
**4660** A2423 (61c) multi 1.60 .55
**4661** A2423 (61c) multi 1.60 .55
**4662** A2423 (61c) multi 1.60 .55
**4663** A2423 (61c) multi 1.60 .55
**4664** A2423 (61c) multi 1.60 .55
**4665** A2423 (61c) multi 1.60 .55
**4666** A2423 (61c) multi 1.60 .55
**4667** A2423 (61c) multi 1.60 .55
**4668** A2423 (61c) multi 1.60 .55
**4669** A2423 (61c) multi 1.60 .55
*a.* Booklet pane of 12, #4658-4669 19.50
*Nos. 4658-4669 (12)* 19.20 6.60

Souvenir Sheet

First Battle of the Marne, Cent. — A2424

No. 4670: a, Troops and automobile. b, Troops on horseback.

### Photo. & Litho.

**2014, Sept. 12** ***Perf. 13¼***
**4670** A2424 Sheet of 2 4.25 2.10
*a.* 66c multi 1.75 .60
*b.* 98c multi 2.50 .85

A souvenir sheet containing Nos. 4670a and 4670b but with as different margin sold for €5.

### Art Issue

Mural on Necker Hospital Staircase, by Keith Haring (1958-90) A2425

**2014, Sept. 19 Photo.** ***Perf. 12¼x13***
**4671** A2425 €2.65 multi 6.75 3.50

### Types of 2014
### *Serpentine Die Cut 11*

**2014, Sept. 25** **Photo.**

### Booklet Stamps
### Self-Adhesive

**4672** A2415 61c Like #4649 + label (22x16mm) 1.60 .55
**4673** A2413 61c Like #4647 (22x16mm) 1.60 .55
**4674** A2414 61c Like #4648 (21x16mm) 1.60 .55
**4675** A2410 61c Like #4640 (15x22mm) 1.60 .55
**4676** A2407 66c Like #4626a (21x22mm) 1.75 .60
**4677** A2411 66c Like #4642e (30x22mm) 1.75 .60
**4678** A2411 66c Like #4642a (30x22mm) 1.75 .60
**4679** A2410 €1.02 Like #4641 (15x22mm) 2.60 .85
**4680** A2407 €1.10 Like #4626b (15x22mm) 2.75 .90
**4681** A2416 €1.65 Like #4650 (46x38mm) 4.25 1.40
*a.* Booklet pane of 10, #4672-4681 + label 21.50
*Nos. 4672-4681 (10)* 21.25 7.15

Sense of Smell A2426

Designs: No. 4682, Man and woman in love. No. 4683, Dog with magnifying glass. No. 4684, Coffee pot and cup. No. 4685, Skunks. No. 4686, Perfume atomizer. No. 4687, Athletic shoe and flowers. No. 4688, Fish with clothespin on nose. No. 4689, Cheese and foxes. No. 4690, Roast chicken. No. 4691, Woman smelling rose. No. 4692, Mother and baby. No. 4693, Face, herbs and spices.

***Serpentine Die Cut 11***

**2014, Oct. 1** **Photo.**

### Booklet Stamps
### Self-Adhesive

**4682** A2426 (61c) multi 1.60 .55
**4683** A2426 (61c) multi 1.60 .55
**4684** A2426 (61c) multi 1.60 .55
**4685** A2426 (61c) multi 1.60 .55
**4686** A2426 (61c) multi 1.60 .55
**4687** A2426 (61c) multi 1.60 .55
**4688** A2426 (61c) multi 1.60 .55
**4689** A2426 (61c) multi 1.60 .55
**4690** A2426 (61c) multi 1.60 .55
**4691** A2426 (61c) multi 1.60 .55
**4692** A2426 (61c) multi 1.60 .55
**4693** A2426 (61c) multi 1.60 .55
*a.* Booklet pane of 12, #4682-4693 19.50
*Nos. 4682-4693 (12)* 19.20 6.60

Douai Court House 300th Anniv. A2427

**2014, Oct. 3 Engr.** ***Perf. 13¼***
**4694** A2427 83c multi 2.10 .70

Green Turtle A2428

**2014, Oct. 9 Litho.** ***Perf. 13x13¼***
**4695** A2428 98c multi 2.50 .85

See Comoro Islands No. , French Southern & Antarctic Territories No. 511, Malagasy Republic No. 1637, Mauritius No. 1144, Seychelles No. 904.

Salsa Dancers — A2429

Break Dancers — A2430

**2014, Oct. 11 Engr.** ***Perf. 13¼***
**4696** A2429 61c multi 1.50 .50

### Souvenir Sheet
### Litho.
### *Perf. 13¼x13*

**4697** A2430 €2.45 multi 6.25 2.10

Stamp Day.

### Items With Spirals Type of 2014
### *Serpentine Die Cut 11*

**2014, Oct. 15** **Litho.**

### Self-Adhesive

**4698** A2369 (66c) Like #4540 1.75 1.75

"Phil@poste" is sharper on No. 4698 than on No. 4540.

Maximilien Vox (1894-1974), Creator of Typographical Classification System — A2431

**2014, Oct. 17 Engr.** ***Perf. 13¼***
**4699** A2431 €1.10 multi 2.75 .90

Miniature Sheet

Cameras — A2432

No. 4700: a, 1865 Derogy four-lens camera. b, 1902 Girard Le Reve folding camera. c, 1930 Kodak Beau Brownie camera. d, 1898 Bazin & Leroy Stereocycle camera. e, 1910 folding camera, horiz. f, 1935 Gaumont Spido Reportage camera.

**Litho. & Engr.**

**2014, Oct. 24** *Perf. 13*

| | | | | |
|---|---|---|---|---|
| **4700** | A2432 | Sheet of 6 | 10.50 | 5.25 |
| *a.-f.* | | 66c Any single | 1.75 | .60 |

A set of six souvenir sheets containing one example of Nos. 4700a-4700f sold as a set for €16.

A2433

A2434

A2435

A2436

A2437

A2438

A2439

A2440

A2441

A2442

A2443

A2444

*Serpentine Die Cut 11*

**2014, Oct. 24** **Photo.**

**Booklet Stamps**
**Self-Adhesive**

| | | | | | |
|---|---|---|---|---|---|
| **4701** | A2433 | (61c) | multi | 1.50 | .50 |
| **4702** | A2434 | (61c) | multi | 1.50 | .50 |
| **4703** | A2435 | (61c) | multi | 1.50 | .50 |
| **4704** | A2436 | (61c) | multi | 1.50 | .50 |
| **4705** | A2437 | (61c) | multi | 1.50 | .50 |
| **4706** | A2438 | (61c) | multi | 1.50 | .50 |
| **4707** | A2439 | (61c) | multi | 1.50 | .50 |
| **4708** | A2440 | (61c) | multi | 1.50 | .50 |
| **4709** | A2441 | (61c) | multi | 1.50 | .50 |
| **4710** | A2442 | (61c) | multi | 1.50 | .50 |
| **4711** | A2443 | (61c) | multi | 1.50 | .50 |
| **4712** | A2444 | (61c) | multi | 1.50 | .50 |
| *a.* | Booklet pane of 12, #4701-4712 | | | 18.00 | |
| | *Nos. 4701-4712 (12)* | | | 18.00 | 6.00 |

A souvenir sheet containing one perf. 13¼ example of a stamp like No. 4706 sold for €3.20.

New French Industries A2446

Inscriptions: No. 4714, Usine du futur. No. 4715, Transition numérique. No. 4716, Développement durable. No. 4717, Patrimoine. No. 4718, Gastronomie. No. 4719, Transition energétique. No. 4720, Elégance. No. 4721, Economi sociale et solidaire. No. 4722, Electromobilité. No. 4723, Exportations. No. 4724, Métiers d'art. No. 4725, Innovation 2030.

*Serpentine Die Cut 11*

**2014, Oct. 27** **Photo.**

**Booklet Stamps**
**Self-Adhesive**

| | | | | | |
|---|---|---|---|---|---|
| **4714** | A2446 | (61c) | multi | 1.50 | .50 |
| **4715** | A2446 | (61c) | multi | 1.50 | .50 |
| **4716** | A2446 | (61c) | multi | 1.50 | .50 |
| **4717** | A2446 | (61c) | multi | 1.50 | .50 |
| **4718** | A2446 | (61c) | multi | 1.50 | .50 |
| **4719** | A2446 | (61c) | multi | 1.50 | .50 |
| **4720** | A2446 | (61c) | multi | 1.50 | .50 |
| **4721** | A2446 | (61c) | multi | 1.50 | .50 |
| **4722** | A2446 | (61c) | multi | 1.50 | .50 |
| **4723** | A2446 | (61c) | multi | 1.50 | .50 |
| **4724** | A2446 | (61c) | multi | 1.50 | .50 |
| **4725** | A2446 | (61c) | multi | 1.50 | .50 |
| *a.* | Booklet pane of 12, #4714-4725 | | | 18.00 | |
| | *Nos. 4714-4725 (12)* | | | 18.00 | 6.00 |

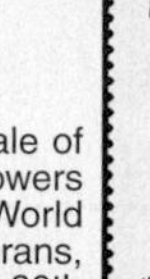


Public Sale of Blue Cornflowers Made by World War I Veterans, 80th Anniv. — A2447

**2014, Nov. 6** **Photo.** *Perf. 13¼*

| | | | | |
|---|---|---|---|---|
| **4726** | A2447 | €1.10 multi | 2.75 | .90 |

**Types of 2003-14**

**2014, Nov. 6** **Engr.** *Perf. 13*

| | | | |
|---|---|---|---|
| **4727** | Sheet of 4, #4079, 4437, 4727a, 4727b | 6.00 | 3.00 |
| *a.* | A2412 61c green (20x26mm) | 1.50 | .50 |
| *b.* | A1664 61c green | 1.50 | .50 |
| *c.* | Booklet pane of 12, 6 each #4727a-4727b | 18.00 | — |
| | Complete booklet, #4437b, 4727c | 21.00 | |

Evariste de Parny (1753-1814), Poet — A2448

**2014, Nov. 7** **Engr.** *Perf. 13¼*

| | | | |
|---|---|---|---|
| **4728** | A2448 83c multi | 2.10 | .70 |

Republican Security Companies (Riot Control Forces), 70th Anniv. — A2449

**2014, Dec. 8** **Photo.** *Perf. 13x12¾*

| | | | |
|---|---|---|---|
| **4729** | A2449 €1.10 multi | 2.75 | .90 |

Handicrafts A2450

Inscriptions: Nos. 4730, 4742, Pierres précieuses (jewelery making). No. 4731, Bois (sanding wood). No. 4732, Verre (glass making). No. 4733, Métal (blacksmithing). No. 4734, Tissu (embroidery). No. 4735, Terre (pottery making). No. 4736, Papier (paper making). No. 4737, Tissu (weaving). No. 4738, Cuir (leather work). No. 4739, Bois (barrel making). No. 4740, Pierre (sculpting). No. 4741, Végétal (flower arranging).

**2015** **Litho.** *Serpentine Die Cut 11*

**Self-Adhesive**

| | | | | | |
|---|---|---|---|---|---|
| **4730** | A2450 | (76c) | multi | 1.75 | 1.75 |

**Photo.**

**Booklet Stamps**

| | | | | | |
|---|---|---|---|---|---|
| **4731** | A2450 | (76c) | multi | 1.75 | .60 |
| **4732** | A2450 | (76c) | multi | 1.75 | .60 |
| **4733** | A2450 | (76c) | multi | 1.75 | .60 |
| **4734** | A2450 | (76c) | multi | 1.75 | .60 |
| **4735** | A2450 | (76c) | multi | 1.75 | .60 |
| **4736** | A2450 | (76c) | multi | 1.75 | .60 |
| **4737** | A2450 | (76c) | multi | 1.75 | .60 |
| **4738** | A2450 | (76c) | multi | 1.75 | .60 |
| **4739** | A2450 | (76c) | multi | 1.75 | .60 |
| **4740** | A2450 | (76c) | multi | 1.75 | .60 |
| **4741** | A2450 | (76c) | multi | 1.75 | .60 |
| **4742** | A2450 | (76c) | multi | 1.75 | .60 |
| *a.* | Booklet pane of 12, #4731-4742 | | | 21.00 | |
| | *Nos. 4731-4742 (12)* | | | 21.00 | 7.20 |

No. 4730 has a visible dot pattern in the upper right part of the vignette and a sharper "Phil@poste" than No. 4742. Issued: Nos. 4730, 1/5; others 1/3.

**Art Issue**

The Great Wave, by Katsushika Hokusai (1760-1849) — A2451

**2015, Jan. 16** **Photo.** *Perf. 13x13¼*

| | | | |
|---|---|---|---|
| **4743** | A2451 €1.90 multi | 4.50 | 2.25 |

Hearts — A2452

"JC de Castelbajac," people kissing and: 68c, Hearts. €1.15, Flowers.

**2015, Jan. 23** **Photo.** *Perf.*

**With White Frame Around Stamp**

| | | | |
|---|---|---|---|
| **4744** | A2452 68c multi | 1.60 | .55 |

**Without White Frame Around Stamp**

*Perf. 13*

| | | | |
|---|---|---|---|
| **4745** | A2452 68c multi | 1.60 | .55 |
| **4746** | A2452 €1.15 multi | 2.60 | .85 |

**Self-Adhesive**

*Serpentine Die Cut*

| | | | |
|---|---|---|---|
| **4747** | A2452 68c multi | 1.60 | 1.60 |
| **4748** | A2452 €1.15 multi | 2.60 | 2.60 |

No. 4744 was printed in sheets of 5. Values for Nos. 4745-4748 are for examples with surrounding selvage. Designs on Nos. 4745-4748 continue onto the surrounding selvage.

New Year 2015 (Year of the Goat) — A2453

**2015, Jan. 30** **Photo.** *Perf. 13¼x13*

| | | | |
|---|---|---|---|
| **4749** | A2453 76c multi | 1.75 | .60 |

No. 4749 was printed in sheets of 5. A souvenir sheet of one sold for €3.20. See No. 4971c.

Drawings of Hands A2454

Drawing by: No. 4750, Alphonse Legros. No. 4751, Unknown 18th century Italian School artist. No. 4752, Paul Delaroche. No. 4753, Gustave Moreau. No. 4754, Eugène Carrière. No. 4755, Pablo Picasso. No. 4756, Annibale Carrache. No. 4757, Unknown 17th century Italian School artist (four hands holding handles). No. 4758, Louis Tocque (one hand). No. 4759, Pierre Mignard. No. 4760, Tocque (two hands holding hoop with flowers). No. 4761, Unknown 17th Italian School artist (hand, water drop and goblet).

*Serpentine Die Cut 11*

**2015, Jan. 30** **Litho.**

**Booklet Stamps**
**Self-Adhesive**

| | | | | | |
|---|---|---|---|---|---|
| **4750** | A2454 | (68c) | multi | 1.60 | .55 |
| **4751** | A2454 | (68c) | multi | 1.60 | .55 |
| **4752** | A2454 | (68c) | multi | 1.60 | .55 |
| **4753** | A2454 | (68c) | multi | 1.60 | .55 |
| **4754** | A2454 | (68c) | multi | 1.60 | .55 |
| **4755** | A2454 | (68c) | multi | 1.60 | .55 |
| **4756** | A2454 | (68c) | multi | 1.60 | .55 |
| **4757** | A2454 | (68c) | multi | 1.60 | .55 |

**4758** A2454 (68c) multi 1.60 .55
**4759** A2454 (68c) multi 1.60 .55
**4760** A2454 (68c) multi 1.60 .55
**4761** A2454 (68c) multi 1.60 .55
*a.* Booklet pane of 12, #4750-4761 19.50
*Nos. 4750-4761 (12)* 19.20 6.60

Landmine Removal Service, 70th Anniv, A2455

**2015, Feb. 20 Photo.** ***Perf. 13¼***
**4762** A2455 €1.20 multi 2.75 .90

Goat Breeds A2456

Inscriptions: No. 4763, La Créole. No. 4764, La Poitevine. No. 4765, L'Alpine. No. 4766, La Chèvre du Massif Central. No. 4767, La Lorraine. No. 4768, La Rove. No. 4769, La Chèvre des Fossés. No. 4770, La Saanen. No. 4771, La Pyrénéenne. No. 4772, L'Angora. No. 4773, La Provençale. No. 4774, La Corse.

***Serpentine Die Cut 11***
**2015, Feb. 21 Photo.**

**Booklet Stamps Self-Adhesive**

**4763** A2456 (68c) multi 1.50 .50
**4764** A2456 (68c) multi 1.50 .50
**4765** A2456 (68c) multi 1.50 .50
**4766** A2456 (68c) multi 1.50 .50
**4767** A2456 (68c) multi 1.50 .50
**4768** A2456 (68c) multi 1.50 .50
**4769** A2456 (68c) multi 1.50 .50
**4770** A2456 (68c) multi 1.50 .50
**4771** A2456 (68c) multi 1.50 .50
**4772** A2456 (68c) multi 1.50 .50
**4773** A2456 (68c) multi 1.50 .50
**4774** A2456 (68c) multi 1.50 .50
*a.* Booklet pane of 12, #4763-4774 18.00
*Nos. 4763-4774 (12)* 18.00 6.00

Souvenir Sheet

Enamel Art of Léonard Limosin (c. 1505-77) — A2457

No. 4775: a, The Judgment of Paris. b, Eritrean Sibyl (Sybila Richea), vert.

***Perf. 13x13¼, 13¼x13***
**2015, Feb. 27 Photo.**
**4775** A2457 Sheet of 2 8.50 8.50
*a.-b.* €1.90 Either single 4.25 1.40
*c.* Souvenir sheet of 2, #4775a-4775b, #4775a at right 14.00 14.00

No. 4775c sold for €6.20.

Souvenir Sheet

Basilica of Saint-Denis — A2458

No. 4776: a, Tombs (41x30mm). b, Stained-glass window (41x41mm).

**2015, Mar. 14 Engr.** ***Perf. 13¼***
**4776** A2458 Sheet of 2 4.50 4.50
*a.* 76c multi 1.75 .60
*b.* €1.25 multi 2.75 .90

A souvenir sheet of 2, containing Nos. 4776a-4776b, with No. 4776a at left sold for €6.20.

Spring Philatelic Show, Paris — A2459

**2015, Mar. 19 Engr.** ***Perf. 13x12¾***
**4777** A2459 68c multi 1.50 .50

Belgian Government in Exile in Sainte-Adresse, Cent. — A2460

Mailboxes, Belgian government officials in exile and: 76c, French and Belgian flags, building. 95c, Ministerial residence.

**2015, Mar. 19 Photo.** ***Perf. 13¼***
**4778** A2460 76c multi 1.75 .60
**4779** A2460 95c multi 2.10 .70
*a.* Souvenir sheet of 2, #4778-4779 7.00 7.00

No. 4779a sold for €3.20. See Belgium No. 2748.

**Art Issue**

L'O, Light Sculpture by Yann Kersalé A2461

**2015, Mar. 20 Photo.** ***Perf. 13¼***
**4780** A2461 €1.90 multi 4.25 2.10

Nicole Mangin (1878-1919), World War I Physician — A2462

**2015, Mar. 21 Engr.** ***Perf. 13x13¼***
**4781** A2462 68c multi 1.50 .50

Renaissance Architecture A2463

Designs: No. 4782, Château d'Amboise. No. 4783, Château de Valençay. No. 4784, Palais Ducal de Nevers. No. 4785, Château de Villandry. No. 4786, Château d'Ancy-le-Franc. No. 4787, Palais du Louvre. No. 4788, Château de Chambord. No. 4789, Château d'Ecouen. No. 4790, Château d'Azay-le-Rideau. No. 4791, Château de Chenonceau. No. 4792, Château d'Anet. No. 4793, Château de Blois.

***Serpentine Die Cut 11***
**2015, Mar. 27 Litho.**

**Booklet Stamps Self-Adhesive**

**4782** A2463 (68c) multi 1.50 .50
**4783** A2463 (68c) multi 1.50 .50
**4784** A2463 (68c) multi 1.50 .50
**4785** A2463 (68c) multi 1.50 .50
**4786** A2463 (68c) multi 1.50 .50
**4787** A2463 (68c) multi 1.50 .50
**4788** A2463 (68c) multi 1.50 .50
**4789** A2463 (68c) multi 1.50 .50
**4790** A2463 (68c) multi 1.50 .50
**4791** A2463 (68c) multi 1.50 .50
**4792** A2463 (68c) multi 1.50 .50
**4793** A2463 (68c) multi 1.50 .50
*a.* Booklet pane of 12, #4782-4793 18.00
*Nos. 4782-4793 (12)* 18.00 6.00

Saintes-Maries-de-la-Mer Religious Procession, 700th Anniv. — A2464

**2015, Mar. 29 Engr.** ***Perf. 13¼***
**4794** A2464 68c multi 1.50 .50

Miniature Sheet

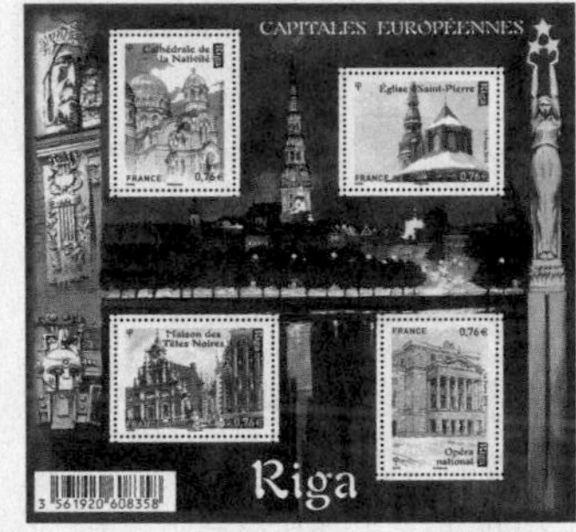

European Capitals — A2465

No. 4795 — Attractions in Riga, Latvia: a, Nativity Cathedral. b, St. Peter's Church, horiz. c, House of the Blackheads, horiz. d, National Opera.

***Perf. 13¼x13, 13x13¼***
**2015, Apr. 3 Photo.**
**4795** A2465 Sheet of 4 7.00 7.00
*a.-d.* 76c Any single 1.75 .60

Croix de Guerre, Cent. — A2466

**2015, Apr. 8 Engr.** ***Perf. 13¼***
**4796** A2466 76c multi 1.75 .60

Souvenir Sheet

French History — A2467

No. 4797: a, Coronation of Charlemagne, 768. b, Educational reforms of Charlemagne, 789, horiz.

***Perf. 13¼x13, 13x13¼***
**2015, Apr. 10 Engr.**
**4797** A2467 Sheet of 2 8.50 8.50
*a.-b.* €1.90 Either single 4.25 1.40

French and Indian Cooperation in Space, 50th Anniv. — A2468

Designs: 76c, Saral satellite. €1.20, Megha-Tropiques satellite.

**2014, Apr. 10 Photo.** ***Perf. 13¼***
**4798** A2468 76c multi 1.75 .60
**4799** A2468 €1.20 multi 2.75 .90

See India Nos. 2725-2726.

Chalon-sur-Saône A2469

**2015, Apr. 17 Engr.** ***Perf. 13¼***
**4800** A2469 68c multi 1.60 .55

Liberation of Concentration Camps, 70th Anniv. — A2470

**2015, Apr. 24 Photo.** ***Perf. 13¼***
**4801** A2470 76c multi 1.75 .60

Miniature Sheet

Way of St. James — A2471

No. 4802 — Sites in: a, Oloron-Sainte-Marie. b, Aire-sur l'Adour, vert. c, Saint-Jean-Pied-de Port. d, Blaye.

**Litho. & Engr.**
**2015, Apr. 24** ***Perf. 13***
**4802** A2471 Sheet of 4 9.00 9.00
*a.-d.* 95c Any single 2.25 .75

Europa — A2472

**2015, May 2 Photo.** ***Perf. 13¼***
**4803** A2472 95c multi 2.25 .75

Paintings of Flowers — A2473

Designs: No. 4804, Irises and Red Geraniums, by Paul Cézanne. No. 4805, Peonies, by Paul Gauguin. No. 4806, Carnations, by Jeanne Magnin. No. 4807, Wisteria, by Pierre Bracquemond. No. 4808, Daisies and Hydrangea, by Emile Boutin. No. 4809, Roses and Anémones, by Vincent van Gogh. No. 4810, Gladioluses, by Auguste Renoir. No. 4811, Wildflowers by Odilon Redon. No. 4812, Peonies, by Edouard Manet. No. 4813, Roses, by Gustave Caillebotte. No. 4814, Queens Daisies, by Marie Duhem. No. 4815, Roses, by Henri Fantin-Latour.

*Serpentine Die Cut 11*

**2015, May 2 Litho.**

**Booklet Stamps Self-Adhesive**

| | | | | |
|---|---|---|---|---|
| **4804** | A2473 (68c) multi | | 1.60 | .55 |
| **4805** | A2473 (68c) multi | | 1.60 | .55 |
| **4806** | A2473 (68c) multi | | 1.60 | .55 |
| **4807** | A2473 (68c) multi | | 1.60 | .55 |
| **4808** | A2473 (68c) multi | | 1.60 | .55 |
| **4809** | A2473 (68c) multi | | 1.60 | .55 |
| **4810** | A2473 (68c) multi | | 1.60 | .55 |
| **4811** | A2473 (68c) multi | | 1.60 | .55 |
| **4812** | A2473 (68c) multi | | 1.60 | .55 |
| **4813** | A2473 (68c) multi | | 1.60 | .55 |
| **4814** | A2473 (68c) multi | | 1.60 | .55 |
| **4815** | A2473 (68c) multi | | 1.60 | .55 |
| *a.* | Booklet pane of 12, #4804-4815 | | 19.50 | |
| | *Nos. 4804-4815 (12)* | | 19.20 | 6.60 |

Victory in World War II, 70th Anniv. — A2474

**2015, May 7 Photo. *Perf. 13¼***

| | | | |
|---|---|---|---|
| **4816** | A2474 68c multi | 1.50 | .50 |

Marshal Jacques II de Chabannes, Lord of La Palice (1470-1525) — A2475

**2015, May 15 Engr. *Perf. 13¼***

| | | | |
|---|---|---|---|
| **4817** | A2475 76c multi | 1.75 | .60 |

Mâcon — A2476

**2015, May 22 Engr. *Perf. 13x13¼***

| | | | |
|---|---|---|---|
| **4818** | A2476 68c multi + label | 1.50 | .50 |

French Federation of Philatelic Associations, 88th Congress, Mâcon.

17th World Convention of Rose Societies, Lyon A2477

Designs: 76c, Red and pink roses. €1.20, Pink and yellow roses.

**2015, May 29 Photo. *Perf. 13¼***

| | | | |
|---|---|---|---|
| **4819** | A2477 76c multi | 1.75 | .60 |
| **4820** | A2477 €1.20 multi | 2.75 | .90 |
| *a.* | Horiz. pair, #4819-4820 | 4.50 | 2.25 |

A souvenir sheet containing Nos. 4819-4820 sold for €6.20.

Service Central d'Etat Civil, 50th Anniv. — A2478

**2015, June 6 Engr. *Perf. 13¼***

| | | | |
|---|---|---|---|
| **4821** | A2478 €1.25 multi | 2.75 | .90 |

The 1960's — A2479

No. 4822: a, Radio France Headquarters. b, Men and women dancing, vert. c, Movie poster for *Les Demoiselles de Rochefort,* vert. d, 1961 Peugeot 404 convertible. e, Ocean liner SS France. f, Women wearing short dresses, vert.

**2015, June 12 Photo. *Perf. 13***

| | | | |
|---|---|---|---|
| **4822** | A2479 Sheet of 6 | 10.50 | 10.50 |
| *a.-f.* | 76c Any single | 1.75 | .60 |

Hartmannswillerkopf National Monument — A2480

**2015, June 19 Engr. *Perf. 13¼***

| | | | |
|---|---|---|---|
| **4823** | A2480 95c multi | 2.10 | .70 |

Saint-Martial Church, Lestards — A2481

**2015, June 24 Engr. *Perf. 13¼***

| | | | |
|---|---|---|---|
| **4824** | A2481 68c multi | 1.50 | .50 |

A2482

A2483

A2484

A2485

A2486

A2487

A2488

A2489

A2490

A2491

A2492

Vacations A2493

*Serpentine Die Cut 11*

**2015, June 29 Photo.**

**Booklet Stamps Self-Adhesive**

| | | | | |
|---|---|---|---|---|
| **4825** | A2482 (68c) multi | | 1.50 | .50 |
| **4826** | A2483 (68c) multi | | 1.50 | .50 |
| **4827** | A2484 (68c) multi | | 1.50 | .50 |
| **4828** | A2485 (68c) multi | | 1.50 | .50 |
| **4829** | A2486 (68c) multi | | 1.50 | .50 |
| **4830** | A2487 (68c) multi | | 1.50 | .50 |
| **4831** | A2488 (68c) multi | | 1.50 | .50 |
| **4832** | A2489 (68c) multi | | 1.50 | .50 |
| **4833** | A2490 (68c) multi | | 1.50 | .50 |
| **4834** | A2491 (68c) multi | | 1.50 | .50 |
| **4835** | A2492 (68c) multi | | 1.50 | .50 |
| **4836** | A2493 (68c) multi | | 1.50 | .50 |
| *a.* | Booklet pane of 12, #4825-4836 | | 18.00 | |
| | *Nos. 4825-4836 (12)* | | 18.00 | 6.00 |

Haguenau, 900th Anniv. A2494

**2015, July 3 Engr. *Perf. 13¼***

| | | | |
|---|---|---|---|
| **4837** | A2494 68c multi | 1.50 | .50 |

Martin Nadaud (1815-98), Mason and Politician A2495

**2015, July 3 Engr. *Perf. 13¼***

| | | | |
|---|---|---|---|
| **4838** | A2495 68c multi | 1.50 | .50 |

Gilberto Bosques (1892-1995), Mexican Diplomat Who Saved Jews In World War II — A2496

Bosques and: 76c, Notre Dame de la Garde Basilica, Marseilles, and signed travel visa. €1.20, Embassy, Mexican consular handstamp.

**2015, July 16 Litho. *Perf. 13***

| | | | |
|---|---|---|---|
| **4839** | A2496 76c multi | 1.75 | .60 |
| **4840** | A2496 €1.20 multi | 2.75 | .90 |
| *a.* | Horiz. pair, #4839-4840 | 4.50 | 2.25 |

See Mexico Nos. 2940-2941.

Animal Eyes A2497

Eye of: No. 4841, Requin à aileron blanc du lagon (whitetip reef shark). No. 4842, Petit-duc du Grant (southern white-faced owl). No. 4843, Rainette à yeux rouges (red-eyed tree frog). No. 4844, Toucan. No. 4845, Coq de race Brahma (Brahma chicken). No. 4846, Agame (agama lizard). No. 4847, Ara hyacinthe (hyacinth macaw). No. 4848, Iguane des Fidji (Fiji banded iguana). No. 4849, Tarente géante (giant wall gecko). No. 4850, Serpentaire (serpent eagle). No. 4851, Poisson-lime gribouillé (scrawled filefish). No. 4852, Gypaète barbu (bearded vulture).

*Serpentine Die Cut 11*

**2015, July 31 Photo.**

**Booklet Stamps**
**Self-Adhesive**

| | | | | |
|---|---|---|---|---|
| **4841** | A2497 | (76c) multi | 1.75 | .60 |
| **4842** | A2497 | (76c) multi | 1.75 | .60 |
| **4843** | A2497 | (76c) multi | 1.75 | .60 |
| **4844** | A2497 | (76c) multi | 1.75 | .60 |
| **4845** | A2497 | (76c) multi | 1.75 | .60 |
| **4846** | A2497 | (76c) multi | 1.75 | .60 |
| **4847** | A2497 | (76c) multi | 1.75 | .60 |
| **4848** | A2497 | (76c) multi | 1.75 | .60 |
| **4849** | A2497 | (76c) multi | 1.75 | .60 |
| **4850** | A2497 | (76c) multi | 1.75 | .60 |
| **4851** | A2497 | (76c) multi | 1.75 | .60 |
| **4852** | A2497 | (76c) multi | 1.75 | .60 |
| *a.* | Booklet pane of 12, #4841-4852 | | 21.00 | |
| | *Nos. 4841-4852 (12)* | | 21.00 | 7.20 |

Animal Proverbs and Idioms
A2498

Designs: No. 4853, Un froid de canard ("Freezing cold"). No. 4854, Rire comme une baleine ("Laughing like a whale"). No. 4855, Comme un chien dans un jeu de quilles ("Like a bull in a China shop"). No. 4856, Prendre le taureau par les cornes ("Take the bull by the horns"). No. 4857, Fier comme un paon ("Proud as a peacock"). No. 4858, Donner de la confiture aux cochons ("Cast pearls before swine"). No. 4859, Avoir un appétit d'oiseau ("Have the appetite of a bird"). No. 4860, Donner sa langue au chat ("Cat got your tongue?"). No. 4861, Etre le bouc émissaire ("Be the scapegoat"). No. 4862, Faire le pied de grue ("To cool one's heels"). No. 4863, Araignée du soir espoir ("A spider in the evening, hope"). No. 4864, Poser un lapin ("To stand someone up").

*Serpentine Die Cut 11*

**2015, Aug. 28 Photo.**

**Booklet Stamps**
**Self-Adhesive**

| | | | | |
|---|---|---|---|---|
| **4853** | A2498 | (68c) multi | 1.60 | .55 |
| **4854** | A2498 | (68c) multi | 1.60 | .55 |
| **4855** | A2498 | (68c) multi | 1.60 | .55 |
| **4856** | A2498 | (68c) multi | 1.60 | .55 |
| **4857** | A2498 | (68c) multi | 1.60 | .55 |
| **4858** | A2498 | (68c) multi | 1.60 | .55 |
| **4859** | A2498 | (68c) multi | 1.60 | .55 |
| **4860** | A2498 | (68c) multi | 1.60 | .55 |
| **4861** | A2498 | (68c) multi | 1.60 | .55 |
| **4862** | A2498 | (68c) multi | 1.60 | .55 |
| **4863** | A2498 | (68c) multi | 1.60 | .55 |
| **4864** | A2498 | (68c) multi | 1.60 | .55 |
| *a.* | Booklet pane of 12, #4853-4864 | | 19.50 | |
| | *Nos. 4853-4864 (12)* | | 19.20 | 6.60 |

Compare types A2498 and A2297.

Souvenir Sheet

Battle of Huningue, 200th Anniv. — A2499

**2015, Aug. 29 Photo. *Perf. 13¼***

| | | | | |
|---|---|---|---|---|
| **4865** | A2499 | €1.25 multi | 3.00 | 1.00 |

2015 World Rowing Championships, Aiguebelette
A2500

Boat with: 76c, Two female rowers. €1.20, Male rowers (35x26mm).

**2015, Aug. 30 Photo. *Perf. 13x13¼***

| | | | | |
|---|---|---|---|---|
| **4866** | A2500 | 76c multi | 1.75 | .60 |
| **4867** | A2500 | €1.20 multi | 2.75 | .90 |
| *a.* | Horiz. pair, #4866-4867 | | 4.50 | 2.25 |

Marianne and Children "Europe" With Data Matrix Code
A2501

Marianne and Children "Monde" With Data Matrix Code
A2502

**2015, Sept. 4 Engr. *Perf. 13***

| | | | | |
|---|---|---|---|---|
| **4868** | A2501 | (95c) blue | 2.25 | .75 |
| **4869** | A2502 | (€1.20) purple | 2.75 | .90 |

**Self-Adhesive**

*Serpentine Die Cut 6¾ Vert.*

| | | | | |
|---|---|---|---|---|
| **4870** | A2501 | (95c) blue | 2.25 | .75 |
| *a.* | Booklet pane of 6 | | 13.50 | |
| **4871** | A2502 | (€1.20) purple | 2.75 | .90 |

The Data Matrix codes on types A2501 and A2502 differ, but all examples of stamps of either type have identical codes. Compare with Types A2538-A2539.

**Art Issue**

Woman with White Stockings, by Suzanne Valadon (1865-1938) — A2503

**2015, Sept. 18 Photo. *Perf. 13¼x13***

| | | | | |
|---|---|---|---|---|
| **4872** | A2503 | €1.90 multi | 4.25 | 2.10 |

*Freedom, Equality, Fraternity,* Painting by Jonone in National Assembly
A2504

**2015, Sept. 19 Photo. *Perf. 13¼***

| | | | | |
|---|---|---|---|---|
| **4873** | A2504 | 76c multi | 1.75 | .60 |

Landing of French on Mauritius, 300th Anniv. — A2505

**2015, Sept. 25 Photo. *Perf. 13¼***

| | | | | |
|---|---|---|---|---|
| **4874** | A2505 | 76c multi | 1.75 | .60 |

See Mauritius No. 1147.

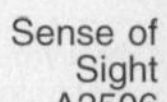

Sense of Sight
A2506

Designs: No. 4875, Room with a window (Chambre avec vue). No. 4876, Eye chart (A ma vue). No. 4877, Land in sight (Terre en vue). No. 4878, Eye (A vue d'oeil). No. 4879, Sun on horizon (Déjà vue). No. 4880, Women viewed through binoculars (Jumelles en vue). No. 4881, Planets (Vue imprenable). No. 4882, Nose and butterfly (A vue de nez). No. 4883, Diver and pool (Vue plongeante). No. 4884, Clouds (A perte de vue). No. 4885, Woman wearing mask (Ni vue, ni connue). No. 4886, Ghost and pink flying elephant (Vue de l'esprit).

*Serpentine Die Cut 11*

**2015, Sept. 25 Photo.**

**Booklet Stamps**
**Self-Adhesive**

| | | | | |
|---|---|---|---|---|
| **4875** | A2506 | (68c) multi | 1.60 | .55 |
| **4876** | A2506 | (68c) multi | 1.60 | .55 |
| **4877** | A2506 | (68c) multi | 1.60 | .55 |
| **4878** | A2506 | (68c) multi | 1.60 | .55 |
| **4879** | A2506 | (68c) multi | 1.60 | .55 |
| **4880** | A2506 | (68c) multi | 1.60 | .55 |
| **4881** | A2506 | (68c) multi | 1.60 | .55 |
| **4882** | A2506 | (68c) multi | 1.60 | .55 |
| **4883** | A2506 | (68c) multi | 1.60 | .55 |
| **4884** | A2506 | (68c) multi | 1.60 | .55 |
| **4885** | A2506 | (68c) multi | 1.60 | .55 |
| **4886** | A2506 | (68c) multi | 1.60 | .55 |
| *a.* | Booklet pane of 12, #4875-4886 | | 19.50 | |
| | *Nos. 4875-4886 (12)* | | 19.20 | 6.60 |

Jean-Henri Fabre (1823-1915), Entomologist — A2507

**2015, Oct. 2 Litho. *Perf. 13¼***

| | | | | |
|---|---|---|---|---|
| **4887** | A2507 | €2.60 multi | 6.00 | 2.00 |

A souvenir sheet of one of No. 4887 sold for €6.20.

Pierre Laroque (1907-97), Director of Social Security, and Ambroise Croizat (1901-51), Politician
A2508

**2015, Oct. 6 Photo. *Perf. 13x13¼***

| | | | | |
|---|---|---|---|---|
| **4888** | A2508 | 68c multi | 1.50 | .50 |

French Social Security System, 70th anniv.

Tango Dancers — A2509

Ballet Preljocaj — A2510

**Litho. & Engr.**

**2015, Oct. 10 *Perf. 13¼***

| | | | | |
|---|---|---|---|---|
| **4889** | A2509 | 68c multi | 1.50 | .50 |

**Photo.**

**Souvenir Sheet**

| | | | | |
|---|---|---|---|---|
| **4890** | A2510 | €1.15 multi | 2.60 | .85 |

Stamp Day. A souvenir sheet of one No. 4889 was produced in 2016 and sold for €3.20.

Saint-Gobain Corporation, 350th Anniv. — A2511

**Litho. & Engr.**

**2015, Oct. 14 *Perf. 13¼***

| | | | | |
|---|---|---|---|---|
| **4891** | A2511 | 68c multi | 1.50 | .50 |

Laure Diebold-Mutschler (1915-65), Resistance Leader in World War II — A2512

**2015, Oct. 16 Engr. *Perf. 13¼***

| | | | | |
|---|---|---|---|---|
| **4892** | A2512 | 68c multi | 1.50 | .50 |

A2513

A2514

A2515

A2516

A2517

A2518

A2519

A2520

A2521

A2522

A2523

Happy New Year — A2524

***Serpentine Die Cut 11***

**2015, Oct. 30** **Photo.**

**Booklet Stamps**
**Self-Adhesive**

**4893** A2513 (68c) multi 1.50 .50
**4894** A2514 (68c) multi 1.50 .50
**4895** A2515 (68c) multi 1.50 .50
**4896** A2516 (68c) multi 1.50 .50
**4897** A2517 (68c) multi 1.50 .50
**4898** A2518 (68c) multi 1.50 .50
**4899** A2519 (68c) multi 1.50 .50
**4900** A2520 (68c) multi 1.50 .50
**4901** A2521 (68c) multi 1.50 .50
**4902** A2522 (68c) multi 1.50 .50
**4903** A2523 (68c) multi 1.50 .50
**4904** A2524 (68c) multi 1.50 .50
*a.* Booklet pane of 12, #4893-4904 18.00
*Nos. 4893-4904 (12)* 18.00 6.00

A souvenir sheet containing one perf. 12¾ example of a stamp like No. 4902 sold for €3.20.

**Types of 1944-45 with Denominations in Euro Currency and Types of 2005-06**

**2015, Nov. 5** **Engr.** ***Perf. 13x12¾***
**4905** A144 €1 dark blue 2.10 .70

***Perf. 12¾x13***
**4906** A147 €1 dark blue 2.10 .70

***Perf. 13***
**4907** A151 €4 dark blue 8.50 2.60
*Nos. 4905-4907 (3)* 12.70 4.00

**Booklet Stamps**
**4908** A147 76c red, 15x19mm design 1.60 .55
**4909** A144 76c red, 15x19mm design 1.60 .55
*a.* Booklet pane of 2, #4908-4909 3.25 —
**4910** A1814 76c red 1.60 .55
**4911** A1759 76c red 1.60 .55
*a.* Booklet pane of 12, 6 each #4910-4911 19.50 —
Complete booklet, #4909a, 4911a 23.00
*Nos. 4908-4911 (4)* 6.40 2.20

Nos. 4905-4907 were printed in sheets of 14 containing 6 each Nos. 4905-4906 and 2 No. 4907.

Tapestry Depicting the Sacrifice of Abraham — A2525

Unicorn Hide, Tapetry by Nicolas Buffe — A2526

**2015, Nov. 6** **Litho.** ***Perf. 13***
**Flocked Paper**
**4912** A2525 76c multi 1.60 .55
**4913** A2526 €1.20 multi 2.60 .85
*a.* Horiz. pair, #4912-4913, + central label 4.25 1.40

Aubusson, International City of Tapestries.

Miniature Sheet

Music Boxes — A2527

No. 4914 — Inscriptions: a, La pendule à orgues. b, La leçon de chant. c, L'automate magicien. d, Boite à musique danseuse. e, L'oiseau chanteur, horiz. f, La joueuse de typanon.

**Litho. & Engr.**

**2015, Nov. 6** ***Perf. 13***
**4914** A2527 Sheet of 6 9.00 9.00
*a.-f.* 68c Any single 1.50 .50

Nos. 4914a-4914f were each printed in souvenir sheets containing one stamp that sold as a set for €16.

Souvenir Sheet

Roland Barthes (1915-80), Semiotician — A2528

**2015, Nov. 12** **Engr.** ***Perf. 13¼***
**4915** A2528 €1.15 multi 2.50 .85

Roosters A2529

Designs: No. 4916, Coq gaulois.
No. 4917: a, Coq de Houdan. b, Coq meusien. c, Coq de Marans.

**2015, Nov. 13** **Photo.** ***Perf. 13¼***
**4916** A2529 68c multi 1.50 .50
**4917** Sheet of 4, #4916, 4917a-4917c 6.00 6.00
*a.-c.* A2529 68c Any single 1.50 .50

Two souvenir sheets, one containing Nos. 4916 and 4917b, and the other containing Nos. 4917a and 4917c, sold as a set for €6.20.

National Forestry Office, 50th Anniv. A2530

**2015, Nov. 20** **Photo.** ***Perf. 13¼***
**4918** A2530 68c multi 1.50 .50

COP21 Climate Conference, Paris A2531

**2015, Nov. 24** **Photo.** ***Perf. 13¼***
**4919** A2531 (€1.20) multi 2.60 .85

Values are for stamps with surrounding selvage.

Launch of Astérix Satellite, 50th Anniv. — A2532

**2015, Nov. 26** **Photo.** ***Perf. 13¼***
**4920** A2532 68c multi 1.50 .50
*a.* Tete-beche pair 3.00 1.00

City Halls A2533

City Hall in: No. 4921, La Pernelle. No. 4922, Brunstatt. No. 4923, Chambourcy. No. 4924, Châteaugiron. No. 4925, Sennecey-le-Grand. No. 4926, Saint-Nicolas-de-la-Grave. No. 4927, Caudebec-en-Caux. No. 4928, Cercy-la-Tour. No. 4929, Clamart. No. 4930, Créteil. No. 4931, Toul. No. 4932, Le Pêchereau.

***Serpentine Die Cut 11***

**2015, Dec. 10** **Photo.**

**Booklet Stamps**
**Self-Adhesive**

**4921** A2533 (70c) multi 1.60 .55
**4922** A2533 (70c) multi 1.60 .55
**4923** A2533 (70c) multi 1.60 .55
**4924** A2533 (70c) multi 1.60 .55
**4925** A2533 (70c) multi 1.60 .55
**4926** A2533 (70c) multi 1.60 .55
**4927** A2533 (70c) multi 1.60 .55
**4928** A2533 (70c) multi 1.60 .55
**4929** A2533 (70c) multi 1.60 .55
**4930** A2533 (70c) multi 1.60 .55
**4931** A2533 (70c) multi 1.60 .55
**4932** A2533 (70c) multi 1.60 .55
*a.* Booklet pane of 12, #4921-4932 19.50
*Nos. 4921-4932 (12)* 19.20 6.60

Marianne and Children, "Ecopli" Without Gram Limit Inscription A2534

Marianne and Tree, "Lettre Verte" Without Gram Limit Inscription A2535

Marianne and Children, "Lettre Prioritaire" Without Gram Limit Inscription — A2536

**2016, Jan. 1** **Engr.** ***Perf. 13***
**4933** A2534 (68c) gray black 1.50 .30
**4934** A2535 (70c) emerald 1.60 .35
**4935** A2536 (80c) red 1.75 .45
*Nos. 4933-4935 (3)* 4.85 1.10

**Coil Stamps**

***Perf. 13 Horiz.***
**4936** A2535 (70c) green 1.60 .35
**4937** A2536 (80c) red 1.75 .45

**Self-Adhesive**

***Serpentine Die Cut 6¾ Vert.***
**4938** A2534 (68c) gray black 1.50 .30
**4939** A2535 (70c) emerald 1.60 .35
*a.* Booklet pane of 10 16.00
*b.* Booklet pane of 12 19.50
**4940** A2536 (80c) scarlet 1.75 .45
*a.* Booklet pane of 10 17.50
*b.* Booklet pane of 12 21.00
*c.* Booklet pane of 20 35.00
*Nos. 4938-4940 (3)* 4.85 1.10

Compare with types A2321, A2322 and A2325. See No. B775.

Marianne and Children "Europe" With Data Matrix Code Without Gram Limit Inscription
A2538

Marianne and Children "Monde" With Data Matrix Code Without Gram Limit Inscription
A2539

**2016, Jan. 1 Engr. *Perf. 13***

| | | | | | |
|---|---|---|---|---|---|
| **4942** | A2538 | (€1) | blue | 2.25 | .75 |
| **4943** | A2539 | (€1.25) | purple | 2.75 | .90 |

**Self-Adhesive**

***Serpentine Die Cut 6¾ Vert.***

| | | | | | |
|---|---|---|---|---|---|
| **4944** | A2538 | (€1) | blue | 2.25 | .75 |
| **4945** | A2539 | (€1.25) | dp reddish vio | 2.75 | .90 |

Compare with types A2501-A2502. Data Matrix codes differ on types A2501 and A2538, and on types A2502 and A2539.

Minerals — A2540

Designs: No. 4946, Gold (or), No. 4947, Labradorite. No. 4948, Topaz (topaze). No. 4949, Amethyst (amethyste). No. 4950, Olivine. No. 4951, Quartz. No. 4952, Turquoise. No. 4953, Fluorite. No. 4954, Sulfur (soufre). No. 4955, Ruby (rubis). No. 4956, Silver (argent). No. 4957, Copper (cuivre).

***Serpentine Die Cut 11***

**2016, Jan. 7 Photo.**

**Booklet Stamps**
**Self-Adhesive**

| | | | | | |
|---|---|---|---|---|---|
| **4946** | A2540 | (80c) | multi | 1.75 | .60 |
| **4947** | A2540 | (80c) | multi | 1.75 | .60 |
| **4948** | A2540 | (80c) | multi | 1.75 | .60 |
| **4949** | A2540 | (80c) | multi | 1.75 | .60 |
| **4950** | A2540 | (80c) | multi | 1.75 | .60 |
| **4951** | A2540 | (80c) | multi | 1.75 | .60 |
| **4952** | A2540 | (80c) | multi | 1.75 | .60 |
| **4953** | A2540 | (80c) | multi | 1.75 | .60 |
| **4954** | A2540 | (80c) | multi | 1.75 | .60 |
| **4955** | A2540 | (80c) | multi | 1.75 | .60 |
| **4956** | A2540 | (80c) | multi | 1.75 | .60 |
| **4957** | A2540 | (80c) | multi | 1.75 | .60 |
| *a.* | Booklet pane of 12, #4946-4957 | | | 21.00 | |
| | *Nos. 4946-4957 (12)* | | | 21.00 | 7.20 |

A2541

A2542

Winning Designs in Children's Stamp Design Contest — A2543

**2016, Jan. 11 Photo. *Perf. 13¼***

| | | | | | |
|---|---|---|---|---|---|
| **4958** | A2541 | 70c | multi | 1.60 | .55 |
| **4959** | A2542 | 70c | multi | 1.60 | .55 |
| **4960** | A2543 | 70c | multi | 1.60 | .55 |
| *a.* | Horiz. strip of 3, #4958-4960 | | | 5.00 | 1.75 |
| | *Nos. 4958-4960 (3)* | | | 4.80 | 1.65 |

Hearts
A2544

"Courrèges" and: Nos. 4961, 4965, Light blue heart, bright pink denomination. No. 4962, No. 4966, White heart, slate denomination.

No. 4963 — "Courrèges," light blue heart and denomination in: a, Pale yellow. b, Light blue. c, Dark blue. d, Bright orange.

No. 4964 — "Courrèges," and heart in: a, Bright pink. b, Bright green. c, Bright yellow. d, Dark blue. e, Bright orange.

**Photo., Litho. (#4964)**

**2016 *Perf. 13***

| | | | | | |
|---|---|---|---|---|---|
| **4961** | A2544 | 70c | multi | 1.60 | .55 |
| **4962** | A2544 | €1.40 | multi | 3.25 | 1.10 |

***Perf.***

| | | | |
|---|---|---|---|
| **4963** | Sheet of 5, #4961, 4963a-4963d | 8.00 | 8.00 |
| *a.-d.* | A2544 70c Any single | 1.60 | .55 |
| **4964** | Sheet of 5 | 34.00 | 34.00 |
| *a.-e.* | A2544 €3 Any single | 6.75 | 3.50 |

**Self-Adhesive**

***Serpentine Die Cut***

| | | | | | |
|---|---|---|---|---|---|
| **4965** | A2544 | 70c | multi | 1.60 | .55 |
| **4966** | A2544 | €1.40 | multi | 3.25 | 1.10 |

Issued: No. 4964, 5/19; others, 1/15. Values for Nos. 4961-4962 are for stamps with surrounding selvage.

**Art Issue**

Black, Red Over Black on Red, by Mark Rothko (1903-70)
A2545

**2016, Jan. 22 Photo. *Perf. 13¼x13***

| | | | | | |
|---|---|---|---|---|---|
| **4967** | A2545 | €1.60 | multi | 3.50 | 1.75 |

**New Year Types of 2005-15 and**

New Year 2016 (Year of the Monkey)
A2546

**2016, Jan. 29 Photo. *Perf. 13¼x13***

| | | | |
|---|---|---|---|
| **4968** | A2546 80c multi | 1.75 | .60 |
| **4969** | Sheet of 4 | 8.75 | 8.75 |
| *a.* | A1716 80c multi | 2.10 | 2.10 |
| *b.* | A1766 80c multi | 2.10 | 2.10 |
| *c.* | A1822 80c multi | 2.10 | 2.10 |
| *d.* | A1882 80c multi | 2.10 | 2.10 |
| **4970** | Sheet of 4 | 8.75 | 8.75 |
| *a.* | A1962 80c multi | 2.10 | 2.10 |
| *b.* | A2048 80c multi | 2.10 | 2.10 |
| *c.* | A2133 80c multi | 2.10 | 2.10 |
| *d.* | A2209 80c multi | 2.10 | 2.10 |
| **4971** | Sheet of 4, #4968, 4971a-4971c | 8.75 | 8.75 |
| *a.* | A2277 80c multi | 2.10 | 2.10 |
| *b.* | A2373 80c multi | 2.10 | 2.10 |
| *c.* | A2453 80c multi | 2.10 | 2.10 |
| | *Nos. 4969-4971 (3)* | 26.25 | 26.25 |

No. 4968 was printed in sheets of 5. A souvenir sheet of 1 #4968 sold for €3.20. Nos. 4969-4971 sold as a set for €12.

Sense of Hearing
A2549

Ear, playback buttons and: No. 4972, Cricket. No. 4973, Various insects. No. 4974, Man's head and singing angels. No. 4975, Marbles rolling down stairs. No. 4976, Pinball game. No. 4977, Water drip. No. 4978, Bird. No. 4979, Lion. No. 4980, Musicians. No. 4981, Sea shell. No. 4982, Harp, lyre, hands, butterflies and flowers. No. 4983, Children.

***Serpentine Die Cut 11***

**2016, Jan. 30 Litho.**

**Booklet Stamps**
**Self-Adhesive**

| | | | | | |
|---|---|---|---|---|---|
| **4972** | A2549 | (70c) | multi | 1.60 | .55 |
| **4973** | A2549 | (70c) | multi | 1.60 | .55 |
| **4974** | A2549 | (70c) | multi | 1.60 | .55 |
| **4975** | A2549 | (70c) | multi | 1.60 | .55 |
| **4976** | A2549 | (70c) | multi | 1.60 | .55 |
| **4977** | A2549 | (70c) | multi | 1.60 | .55 |
| **4978** | A2549 | (70c) | multi | 1.60 | .55 |
| **4979** | A2549 | (70c) | multi | 1.60 | .55 |
| **4980** | A2549 | (70c) | multi | 1.60 | .55 |
| **4981** | A2549 | (70c) | multi | 1.60 | .55 |
| **4982** | A2549 | (70c) | multi | 1.60 | .55 |
| **4983** | A2549 | (70c) | multi | 1.60 | .55 |
| *a.* | Booklet pane of 12, #4972-4983 | | | 19.50 | |
| | *Nos. 4972-4983 (12)* | | | 19.20 | 6.60 |

Marguerite Long (1874-1966), Pianist — A2550

**2016, Feb. 12 Engr. *Perf. 13¼***

| | | | | | |
|---|---|---|---|---|---|
| **4984** | A2550 | 70c | multi | 1.50 | .50 |

**Art Issue**

Annie Hall, by Jan Toorop (1858-1928) — A2551

**2016, Feb. 19 Litho. *Perf. 13***

| | | | | | |
|---|---|---|---|---|---|
| **4985** | A2551 | €2.80 | multi | 6.25 | 3.25 |

Georges Charpak (1924-2010), 1992 Nobel Laureate in Physics — A2552

**2016, Feb. 26 Engr. *Perf. 13¼***

| | | | | | |
|---|---|---|---|---|---|
| **4986** | A2552 | 70c | gold & multi | 1.50 | .50 |

Roosters — A2557

Inscriptions: No. 4987, Coq Barbezieux. No. 4988, Coq Bourbonnais. No. 4989, Coq Gaulois, No. 4990, Coq Gournay. No. 4991, Coc Coucou de Rennes. No. 4992, Coq Faverolles. No. 4993, Coq d'Alsace. No. 4994, Coq Bresse. No. 4995, Coq Meusien. No. 4996, Coq Marans. No. 4997, Coq Gâtinais. No. 4998, Coq La Flèche.

***Serpentine Die Cut 11***

**2016, Feb. 27 Photo.**

**Booklet Stamps**
**Self-Adhesive**

| | | | | | |
|---|---|---|---|---|---|
| **4987** | A2557 | (70c) | multi | 1.50 | .50 |
| **4988** | A2557 | (70c) | multi | 1.50 | .50 |
| **4989** | A2557 | (70c) | multi | 1.50 | .50 |
| **4990** | A2557 | (70c) | multi | 1.50 | .50 |
| **4991** | A2557 | (70c) | multi | 1.50 | .50 |
| **4992** | A2557 | (70c) | multi | 1.50 | .50 |
| **4993** | A2557 | (70c) | multi | 1.50 | .50 |
| **4994** | A2557 | (70c) | multi | 1.50 | .50 |
| **4995** | A2557 | (70c) | multi | 1.50 | .50 |
| **4996** | A2557 | (70c) | multi | 1.50 | .50 |
| **4997** | A2557 | (70c) | multi | 1.50 | .50 |
| **4998** | A2557 | (70c) | multi | 1.50 | .50 |
| *a.* | Booklet pane of 12, #4987-4998 | | | 18.00 | |
| | *Nos. 4987-4998 (12)* | | | 18.00 | 6.00 |

Pierre Messmer (1916-2007), Prime Minister — A2558

**2016, Mar. 11 Engr. *Perf. 13¼***

| | | | | | |
|---|---|---|---|---|---|
| **4999** | A2558 | 80c | multi | 1.90 | .65 |

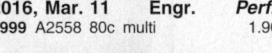

Sophie Germain (1776-1831), Mathematician — A2559

**2016, Mar. 18 Engr. *Perf. 13¼***

| | | | | | |
|---|---|---|---|---|---|
| **5000** | A2559 | 70c | multi | 1.60 | .55 |

Notre-Dame-des-Missions Church, Epinay-sur-Seine — A2560

**2016, Mar. 18 Engr. *Perf. 13¼***

| | | | | | |
|---|---|---|---|---|---|
| **5001** | A2560 | 70c | multi | 1.60 | .55 |

Auteuil Apprentices, 150th Anniv. — A2561

**2016, Mar. 18 Photo. *Perf. 13¼***
**5002** A2561 70c multi 1.60 .55

2016 European Soccer Championships, France — A2562

**2016 Photo. *Perf. 13***
**5003** A2562 €1 multi 2.25 .75
*a.* Souvenir sheet of 5 11.50 11.50
**5004** A2562 €2 multi 4.50 2.25

Issued: No. 5003, 3/26; No. 5004, 5/19. Values are for stamps with surrounding selvage. No. 5004 was printed in sheets of 5 and has varnish covering the trophy in the design.

Sculptor A2563

**2016, Mar. 31 Engr. *Perf. 12¼***
**5005** A2563 70c multi 1.60 .55

Spring Philatelic Show, Belfort — A2564

**2016, Apr. 1 Engr. *Perf. 13x12¾***
**5006** A2564 70c multi 1.60 .55

Portraits — A2565

Designs: No. 5007, Portrait of a Young Boy, by Paul Gauguin. No. 5008, Portrait of the Artist's Son, by Paul Cézanne. No. 5009, Young Woman Wearing a Black Hat, by Pierre-Auguste Renoir. No. 5010, Young Woman with a Low-cut Dress and Flower in Hair, by Berthe Morisot. No. 5011, Margot Lux with a Wide Hat, by Mary Cassatt. No. 5012, Portrait of Irma Brunner, La Viennoise, by Edouard Manet. No. 5013, Portrait of Léon Bonnat, by Edgar Degas. No. 5014, Self-portrait, by Gustave Caillebotte. No. 5015, Portrait of a Young Girl, by Armand Guillaumin. No. 5016, Self-portrait, by Vincent van Gogh. No. 5017, Portrait of Blanche Hoschedé, by Claude Monet. No. 5018, Woman with a Green Scarf, by Camille Pissarro.

***Serpentine Die Cut 11***
**2016, Apr. 2 Litho.**
**Booklet Stamps**
**Self-Adhesive**

**5007** A2565 (70c) multi 1.60 .55
**5008** A2565 (70c) multi 1.60 .55
**5009** A2565 (70c) multi 1.60 .55
**5010** A2565 (70c) multi 1.60 .55
**5011** A2565 (70c) multi 1.60 .55
**5012** A2565 (70c) multi 1.60 .55
**5013** A2565 (70c) multi 1.60 .55
**5014** A2565 (70c) multi 1.60 .55
**5015** A2565 (70c) multi 1.60 .55
**5016** A2565 (70c) multi 1.60 .55
**5017** A2565 (70c) multi 1.60 .55
**5018** A2565 (70c) multi 1.60 .55
*a.* Booklet pane of 12, #5007-5018 19.50
*Nos. 5007-5018 (12)* 19.20 6.60

Edmond Locard (1877-1966), Forensic Scientist A2567

**2016, Apr. 15 Engr. *Perf. 13¼***
**5020** A2567 70c multi 1.60 .55

Marquis de Jouffroy d'Abbans (1751-1832) and Steamboat — A2568

**2016, Apr. 22 Engr. *Perf. 13¼***
**5021** A2568 €1.25 red & blue 3.00 1.00

Steamboat navigation on the Seine, 200th anniv.

Deposits and Consignments Fund, 200th Anniv. — A2569

**Engr. & Embossed**
**2016, Apr. 28 *Perf. 13¼***
**5022** A2569 80c black & red 1.90 .60

A self-adhesive version of this stamp on a cream-colored paper was printed in sheets of 4 that were produced in limited quantities.

Europa A2570

**2016, May 8 Photo. *Perf. 13¼***
**5023** A2570 €1 multi 2.25 .75

Think Green Issue.

Saint-Brevin-les-Pins — A2571

**2016, May 13 Photo. *Perf. 13¼***
**5024** A2571 70c multi 1.60 .55

Soccer Plays — A2572

Inscriptions: No. 5025, Frappe (kick). No. 5026, Coup du sombrero (heading ball). No. 5027, Amorti poitrine (chest stop). No. 5028, Coup franc laucarne (corner kick). No. 5029, Reprise de volée (volley). No. 5030, Aile de pigeon (pigeon wing). No. 5031, Arrêt gardien (goalie's save). No. 5032, Coup du foulard (behind-the-planted-leg kick). No. 5033, Coup de pied retourné (bicycle kick). No. 5034, Joueuse qui gagne (winning player).

***Serpentine Die Cut 11***
**2016, May 19 Litho.**
**Booklet Stamps**
**Self-Adhesive**

**5025** A2572 (70c) multi 1.60 .55
**5026** A2572 (70c) multi 1.60 .55
**5027** A2572 (70c) multi 1.60 .55
**5028** A2572 (70c) multi 1.60 .55
**5029** A2572 (70c) multi 1.60 .55
**5030** A2572 (70c) multi 1.60 .55
**5031** A2572 (70c) multi 1.60 .55
**5032** A2572 (70c) multi 1.60 .55
**5033** A2572 (70c) multi 1.60 .55
**5034** A2572 (70c) multi 1.60 .55
*a.* Booklet pane of 10, #5025-5034 16.00
*Nos. 5025-5034 (10)* 16.00 5.50

**Types of 1947-78**
Souvenir Sheet
**Engr., Sheet Margin Photo. & Embossed With Foil Application**
**2016, May 19 *Perf. 13***
**5035** Sheet of 3 13.50 13.50
*a.* A169 €2 blue 4.50 2.25
*b.* A791 €2 gray & dull brown 4.50 2.25
*c.* SP171 €2 gray black 4.50 2.25

2016 Paris-Philex Stamp Show.

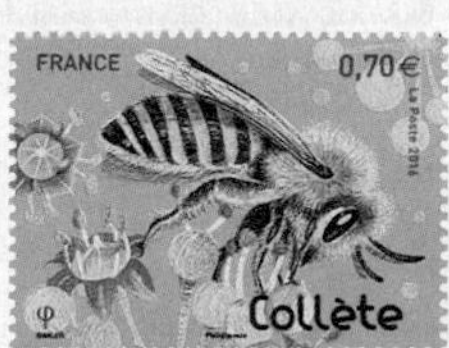


Bees A2573

Inscriptions: No. 5036, Collète.
No. 5037: a, Osmie, vert. b, Anthophore. c, Mégachile, vert.

**2016, May 20 Photo. *Perf. 13¼***
**5036** A2573 70c multi 1.60 .55
**5037** Sheet of 4, #5036, 5037a-5037c 6.50 6.50
*a.-c.* A2573 70c Any single 1.60 .55

Two souvenir sheets, one containing Nos. 5036 and 5037a, and the other containing Nos. 5037b and 5037c, sold as a set for €6.20.

Place des Vosges, Paris — A2574

**2016, May 21 Engr. *Perf. 13x13¼***
**5038** A2574 70c multi + label 1.60 .55

French Federation of Philatelic Associations, 89th Congress, Paris.

Miniature Sheet

The 1970's — A2575

No. 5039: a, Renault 5 automobile. b, Women's fashions, vert. c, Skiers, chair lift and resort, vert. d, L'île aux Enfants children's televison show. e, Parc des Princes Stadium, Paris. f, People dancing at discotheque, vert.

**2016, May 21 Photo. *Perf. 13***
**5039** A2575 Sheet of 6 11.50 11.50
*a.-f.* 80c Any single 1.90 .60

Louise Labé (c. 1524-1566), Poet — A2576

**2016, May 22 Engr. *Perf. 13x13¼***
**5040** A2576 €1.40 multi 3.25 1.10

Battle of Verdun, Cent. — A2577

**2016, May 29 Engr. *Perf. 13x12¾***
**5041** A2577 70c multi 1.60 .55

A souvenir sheet containing No. 5041 sold for €3.20.

Saint-Etienne School of Mines, 200th Anniv. — A2578

**2016, June 3 Engr. *Perf. 13¼***
**5042** A2578 70c multi 1.60 .55

Diplomatic Relations Between France and South Korea, 130th Anniv. — A2579

Designs: 80c, Korean Celadon incense burner, 12th. cent. €1.25, French reliquary.

**2016, June 3 Photo. *Perf. 13¼***

| | | | | |
|---|---|---|---|---|
| **5043** | A2579 | 80c multi | 1.90 | .60 |
| **5044** | A2579 | €1.25 multi | 2.75 | .90 |

See South Korea No. 2469.

French History — A2580

No. 5045: a, Catherine de Medici (1519-89), Queen of France. b, 1520 meeting of King Henry VIII of England and King François I of France at Field of the Cloth of Gold, horiz.

***Perf. 13¼x13, 13x13¼***

**2016, June 3 Engr.**

| | | | | |
|---|---|---|---|---|
| **5045** | A2580 | Sheet of 2 | 6.50 | 6.50 |
| *a.-b.* | | €1.40 Either single | 3.25 | 1.60 |

A 200x95mm sheet containing Nos. 5045a and 5045b, but with a different margin design sold for €6.20.

First Women in French Government, 80th Anniv. — A2581

**2016, June 4 Photo. *Perf. 13***

| | | | | |
|---|---|---|---|---|
| **5046** | A2581 | 70c red & black | 1.60 | .55 |

Cécile Brunschvicg (1877-1946), Undersecretary of State for National Education; Irène Joliot-Curie (1897-1956), Undersecretary of State for Scientific Research; Suzanne Lacore (1875-1975), Undersecretary of State for Public Health.

**Art Issue**

Lost Illusions, by Charles Gleyre (1806-74) — A2582

**2016, June 5 Engr. *Perf. 13x13¼***

| | | | | |
|---|---|---|---|---|
| **5047** | A2582 | €1.60 multi | 3.75 | 1.90 |

Holy Cross Abbey, Quimperlé A2583

**2016, June 17 Engr. *Perf. 13¼***

| | | | | |
|---|---|---|---|---|
| **5048** | A2583 | 70c multi | 1.60 | .55 |

League of Education, 150th Anniv. A2584

**2016, June 23 Photo. *Perf. 13¼***

| | | | | |
|---|---|---|---|---|
| **5049** | A2584 | €1 multi | 2.25 | .75 |

Pierre Mauroy (1928-2013), Prime Minister — A2585

**2016, June 24 Engr. *Perf. 13¼***

| | | | | |
|---|---|---|---|---|
| **5050** | A2585 | 80c multi | 1.90 | .60 |

Academy of Sciences, 350th Anniv. A2586

**2016, June 28 Photo. *Perf. 13¼***

| | | | | |
|---|---|---|---|---|
| **5051** | A2586 | €2.50 multi | 5.75 | 1.90 |

**Souvenir Sheet**

Battle of the Somme, Cent. — A2587

No. 5052: a, Soldiers shaking hands, castle and British tank. b, Damaged Albert Cathedral, Theipval Memorial, Visitor's Center.

**2016, July 1 Photo. *Perf. 13¼***

| | | | | |
|---|---|---|---|---|
| **5052** | A2587 | Sheet of 2 | 4.25 | 4.25 |
| *a.* | | 80c multi | 1.90 | .60 |
| *b.* | | €1 multi | 2.25 | .75 |

A 200x95mm sheet containing Nos. 5052a and 5052b, but with a different margin design sold for €6.20.

A2588

A2589

A2590

A2591

A2592

A2593

A2594

A2595

A2596

A2597

A2598

Summer Vacation A2599

***Serpentine Die Cut 11***

**2016, July 2 Photo.**

**Booklet Stamps Self-Adhesive**

| | | | | |
|---|---|---|---|---|
| **5053** | A2588 | (70c) multi | 1.60 | .55 |
| **5054** | A2589 | (70c) multi | 1.60 | .55 |
| **5055** | A2590 | (70c) multi | 1.60 | .55 |
| **5056** | A2591 | (70c) multi | 1.60 | .55 |
| **5057** | A2592 | (70c) multi | 1.60 | .55 |
| **5058** | A2593 | (70c) multi | 1.60 | .55 |
| **5059** | A2594 | (70c) multi | 1.60 | .55 |
| **5060** | A2595 | (70c) multi | 1.60 | .55 |
| **5061** | A2596 | (70c) multi | 1.60 | .55 |
| **5062** | A2597 | (70c) multi | 1.60 | .55 |
| **5063** | A2598 | (70c) multi | 1.60 | .55 |
| **5064** | A2599 | (70c) multi | 1.60 | .55 |
| *a.* | | Booklet pane of 12, #5053-5064 | 19.50 | |
| | | *Nos. 5053-5064 (12)* | 19.20 | 6.60 |

Mediterranean Sea Fish — A2600

**2016, July 9 Photo. *Perf. 13x12½***

| | | | | |
|---|---|---|---|---|
| **5065** | A2600 | €1 multi | 2.25 | .75 |

Flowers — A2601

Inscriptions: No. 5066, Oiseau de paradis (bird-of-paradise flower). No. 5067, Coquelicot (poppy). No. 5068, Muguet (lily-of-the-valley). No. 5069, Balisier (heliconia). No. 5070, Lys rouge (red lily). No. 5071, Iris. No. 5072, Rose. No. 5073, Tournesol (sunflower). No. 5074, Jonquille (jonquil). No. 5075, Marguerite (daisy). No. 5076, Belle-de-nuit (four o'clock flower). No. 5077, Passiflore (passionflower).

***Serpentine Die Cut 11***

**2016, July 30 Photo.**

**Booklet Stamp Self-Adhesive**

| | | | | |
|---|---|---|---|---|
| **5066** | A2601 | (80c) multi | 1.75 | .60 |
| **5067** | A2601 | (80c) multi | 1.75 | .60 |
| **5068** | A2601 | (80c) multi | 1.75 | .60 |
| **5069** | A2601 | (80c) multi | 1.75 | .60 |
| **5070** | A2601 | (80c) multi | 1.75 | .60 |
| **5071** | A2601 | (80c) multi | 1.75 | .60 |
| **5072** | A2601 | (80c) multi | 1.75 | .60 |
| **5073** | A2601 | (80c) multi | 1.75 | .60 |
| **5074** | A2601 | (80c) multi | 1.75 | .60 |
| **5075** | A2601 | (80c) multi | 1.75 | .60 |
| **5076** | A2601 | (80c) multi | 1.75 | .60 |
| **5077** | A2601 | (80c) multi | 1.75 | .60 |
| *a.* | | Booklet pane of 12, #5066-5077 | 21.00 | |
| | | *Nos. 5066-5077 (12)* | 21.00 | 7.20 |

Eagle Dam, Soursac, and World War II Resistance Fighters — A2602

**2016, Sept. 2 Engr. *Perf. 13x12¾***

| | | | | |
|---|---|---|---|---|
| **5078** | A2602 | €3.20 multi | 7.25 | 2.40 |

Animal Proverbs and Idioms A2603

Designs: No. 5079, Courir plusieurs lièvres à la fois ("to try to do more than one thing at once"). No. 5080, Quand on parle du loup on en voit la queue ("speak of the devil and he appears"). No. 5081, Avoir des oursins dans le porte-monnaie ("to be stingy"). No. 5082, Avoir une mémoire d'éléphant ("have the memory of an elephant"). No. 5083, Muet comme une carpe ("silent like a carp"). No. 5084, La part du lion ("the lion's share"). No. 5085, Dormir comme un loir ("to sleep like a log"). No. 5086, Etre le dindon de la farce ("being the butt of the joke"). No. 5087, Peigner la girafe ("to do nothing effective"). No. 5088, C'est le serpent qui se mord la queue ("to be in a vicious cycle"). No. 5089, Monter sur ses grands chevaux ("to get carried away"). No. 5090, Bayer aux corneilles ("to stand and gape").

***Serpentine Die Cut 11***

**2016, Sept. 3 Photo.**

**Booklet Stamps Self-Adhesive**

| | | | | |
|---|---|---|---|---|
| **5079** | A2603 | (70c) multi | 1.60 | .55 |
| **5080** | A2603 | (70c) multi | 1.60 | .55 |
| **5081** | A2603 | (70c) multi | 1.60 | .55 |
| **5082** | A2603 | (70c) multi | 1.60 | .55 |
| **5083** | A2603 | (70c) multi | 1.60 | .55 |
| **5084** | A2603 | (70c) multi | 1.60 | .55 |
| **5085** | A2603 | (70c) multi | 1.60 | .55 |
| **5086** | A2603 | (70c) multi | 1.60 | .55 |
| **5087** | A2603 | (70c) multi | 1.60 | .55 |
| **5088** | A2603 | (70c) multi | 1.60 | .55 |
| **5089** | A2603 | (70c) multi | 1.60 | .55 |
| **5090** | A2603 | (70c) multi | 1.60 | .55 |
| *a.* | | Booklet pane of 12, #5079-5090 | 19.50 | |
| | | *Nos. 5079-5090 (12)* | 19.20 | 6.60 |

Léo Ferré (1916-93), Musician A2604

**2016, Sept. 8 Photo. *Perf. 12¼***

**5091** A2604 €1.40 multi 3.25 1.10

Françoise Giroud (1916-2003), Minister of Culture — A2605

**2016, Sept. 9 Engr. *Perf. 13x13¼***

**5092** A2605 80c lt blue & maroon 1.75 .60

Characters From *Les Legendaires,* Cartoons by Patrick Sobral A2606

Designs: No. 5093, Danael. No. 5094, Jadina and Shimy.

**2016, Sept. 16 Photo. *Perf. 13¼***

**5093** A2606 70c multi 1.60 .55
**5094** A2606 70c multi 1.60 .55
*a.* Horiz. pair, #5093-5094, + 2 alternating labels 3.20 1.10

A2607

A2608

A2609

A2610

A2611

A2612

A2613

A2614

A2615

A2616

A2617

Stars and Heavenly Bodies A2618

***Serpentine Die Cut 11***

**2016, Oct. 1 Photo.**

**Booklet Stamps**

**Self-Adhesive**

**5095** A2607 (70c) multi 1.60 .55
**5096** A2608 (70c) multi 1.60 .55
**5097** A2609 (70c) multi 1.60 .55
**5098** A2610 (70c) multi 1.60 .55
**5099** A2611 (70c) multi 1.60 .55
**5100** A2612 (70c) multi 1.60 .55
**5101** A2613 (70c) multi 1.60 .55
**5102** A2614 (70c) multi 1.60 .55
**5103** A2615 (70c) multi 1.60 .55
**5104** A2616 (70c) multi 1.60 .55
**5105** A2617 (70c) multi 1.60 .55
**5106** A2618 (70c) multi 1.60 .55
*a.* Booklet pane of 12, #5095-5106 19.50
*Nos. 5095-5106 (12)* 19.20 6.60

Charleston Dancers A2619

Ballet Dancer in *Swan Lake* — A2620

**2016, Oct. 8 Engr. *Perf. 13¼***

**5107** A2619 70c multi 1.60 .55

**Souvenir Sheet**

**Photo. & Embossed**

***Perf. 13¼x13***

**5108** A2620 €1.40 multi 3.25 1.10

Stamp Day.

Eclair Airplane Propellers, Cent. A2621

**2016, Oct. 13 Photo. *Perf. 13¼***

**5109** A2621 70c multi 1.60 .55

St. Étienne Cathedral, Toul — A2622

**2016, Oct. 21 Engr. *Perf. 13x13¼***

**5110** A2622 70c multi + label 1.60 .55



Architecture of Paris and Lisbon — A2623

Designs: 80c, Rua Augusta Arch, Lisbon. €1, Buildings along Rue Royale, Paris.

**2016, Oct. 21 Engr. *Perf. 13x12½***

**5111** A2623 80c multi 1.75 .60
**5112** A2623 €1 multi 2.25 .75

See Portugal Nos. 3847-3848.

Pres. François Mitterrand (1916-96) A2624

**2016, Oct. 26 Engr. *Perf. 13¼***

**5113** A2624 80c multi 1.75 .60

**Miniature Sheet**

European Capitals — A2625

No. 5114 — Attractions in Amsterdam, Netherlands: a, Begijnhof (Le Béguinage). b, Rijksmuseum. c, Westerkerk, vert. d, Canals and buildings.

***Perf. 13¼x13½, 13½x13¼***

**2016, Nov. 3 Photo.**

**5114** A2625 Sheet of 4 7.00 7.00
*a.-d.* 80c Any single 1.75 .60

Peace and Commerce ("Type Sage" With Denominations in Euro Currency) — A2626a

A2626

Type I: The "N" of "INV" is under the "B" of "REPUBLIQUE."

Type II: The "N" of "INV" is under the "U" of "REPUBLIQUE."

**2016, Nov. 3 Engr. *Perf. 12¾x13¼***

**Type I**

**5115** A2626 €1 dark green 2.25 .75

**Type II**

**5116** A2626 €1 dark green 2.25 .75
*a.* Pair, #5115-5116 4.50 1.50

**Booklet Stamps**

**Type I**

**Design Size: 15x19mm**

***Perf. 12¾x13***

**5117** A2626 80c red 1.75 .45
**5118** A2626a 80c black 1.75 .45
*a.* Booklet pane of 2, #5117-5118 3.50 —
*b.* Booklet pane of 12, 6 each #5117-5118 21.00 —
Complete booklet, #5118a, 5118b 24.50

Nos. 5115-5116 were printed in sheets containing 10 of each stamp.

Brive-la-Gaillarde — A2627

**2016, Nov. 4 Engr. *Perf. 13x12¾***

**5119** A2627 70c multi 1.50 .50

Miniature Sheet

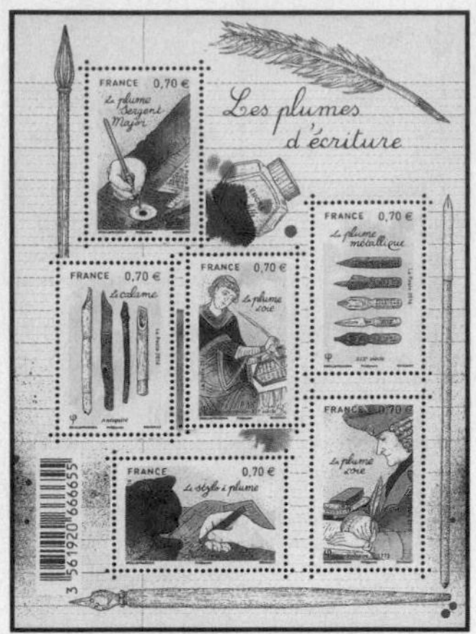

Pens — A2628

No. 5120: a, Person dipping Sergent-Major pen into ink, 19th cent. b, Calames (ancient reed pen). c, Monk with quill pen, 12th cent. d, Metallic pen nibs, 19th cent. e, Cat, writer with fountain pen, horiz. f, Voltaire writing with quill pen, 1775.

**Litho. & Engr.**

**2016, Nov. 4** ***Perf. 13***

| | | | | |
|---|---|---|---|---|
| **5120** | A2628 | Sheet of 6 | 9.00 | 9.00 |
| *a.-f.* | | 70c Any single | 1.50 | .50 |
| *g.* | | Souvenir sheet of 3, #5120a, 5120d, 5120e | 6.75 | 6.75 |
| *h.* | | Souvenir sheet of 3, #5120b, 5120c, 5120f | 6.75 | 6.75 |

Nos. 5120g and 5120h were sold as a set for €6.20.

Restoration and Reopening of Bièvre River — A2629

**2016, Nov. 5** **Photo.** ***Perf. 13¼***

**5121** A2629 70c multi 1.50 .50

**Art Issue**

Souvenir Sheet

Paintings by Marie Laurencin (1883-1956) — A2630

No. 5122: a, Portrait of Baroness Gourgaud in Black Mantilla, 1923. b, Young Girl with Guitar, 1940.

**2016, Nov. 6** **Photo.** ***Perf. 13¼x13***

| | | | | |
|---|---|---|---|---|
| **5122** | A2630 | Sheet of 2 | 7.00 | 7.00 |
| *a.-b.* | | €1.60 Either single | 3.50 | 1.75 |

National Office of Veterans and War Victims, Cent. — A2631

**2016, Nov. 9** **Photo.** ***Perf. 13¼***

**5123** A2631 70c multi 1.50 .50

Jewelery Making A2632

**2016, Nov. 10** **Engr.** ***Perf. 12¼***

**5124** A2632 €1 multi 2.25 .75

A2633

A2634

A2635

A2636

A2637

A2638

A2639

A2640

A2641

A2642

A2643

Contest Stamps With Scratch-off Panel — A2644

***Serpentine Die Cut 11***

**2016, Nov. 14** **Photo.**

**Booklet Stamps**
**Self-Adhesive**
**Unscrached Panels**

| | | | | |
|---|---|---|---|---|
| **5125** | A2633 (70c) multi | | 1.50 | .50 |
| *a.* | Scratched panel | | | .35 |
| **5126** | A2634 (70c) multi | | 1.50 | .50 |
| *a.* | Scratched panel | | | .35 |
| **5127** | A2635 (70c) multi | | 1.50 | .50 |
| *a.* | Scratched panel | | | .35 |
| **5128** | A2636 (70c) multi | | 1.50 | .50 |
| *a.* | Scratched panel | | | .35 |
| **5129** | A2637 (70c) multi | | 1.50 | .50 |
| *a.* | Scratched panel | | | .35 |
| **5130** | A2638 (70c) multi | | 1.50 | .50 |
| *a.* | Scratched panel | | | .35 |
| **5131** | A2639 (70c) multi | | 1.50 | .50 |
| *a.* | Scratched panel | | | .35 |
| **5132** | A2640 (70c) multi | | 1.50 | .50 |
| *a.* | Scratched panel | | | .35 |
| **5133** | A2641 (70c) multi | | 1.50 | .50 |
| *a.* | Scratched panel | | | .35 |
| **5134** | A2642 (70c) multi | | 1.50 | .50 |
| *a.* | Scratched panel | | | .35 |
| **5135** | A2643 (70c) multi | | 1.50 | .50 |
| *a.* | Scratched panel | | | .35 |
| **5136** | A2644 (70c) multi | | 1.50 | .50 |
| *a.* | Scratched panel | | | .35 |
| *b.* | Booklet pane of 12, #5125-5136 | | 18.00 | |
| | *Nos. 5125-5136 (12)* | | 18.00 | 6.00 |

Gold scratch-off panels on Nos. 5125-5136 hide codes that could be entered at the contest website for a chance to win various prizes.

Stained-Glass Windows — A2645

Window from: No. 5137, Notre Dame Cathedral, Coutances. No. 5138, Saint-Denis Chapel, Paris. No. 5139, Notre Dame Cathedral, Chartres. No. 5140, Saint-Nazaire Basilica, Carcassonne. No. 5141, Notre Dame Cathedral, Strasbourg. No. 5142, Saint-Savin-de-Gartempe Abbey, Saint-Savin. No. 5143, Saint-Etienne Cathedral, Bourges. No. 5144, Saint-Julien Cathedral, Le Mans. No. 5145, Saint-Denis Basilica, Saint-Denis. No. 5146, Notre Dame Cathedral, Bayeux. No. 5147, Saint-Pierre Cathedral, Beauvais. No. 5148, Notre Dame Cathedral, Paris.

***Serpentine Die Cut 11***

**2016, Nov. 26** **Photo.**

**Booklet Stamps**
**Self-Adhesive**

| | | | |
|---|---|---|---|
| **5137** | A2645 (70c) multi | 1.50 | .50 |
| **5138** | A2645 (70c) multi | 1.50 | .50 |
| **5139** | A2645 (70c) multi | 1.50 | .50 |
| **5140** | A2645 (70c) multi | 1.50 | .50 |
| **5141** | A2645 (70c) multi | 1.50 | .50 |
| **5142** | A2645 (70c) multi | 1.50 | .50 |
| **5143** | A2645 (70c) multi | 1.50 | .50 |
| **5144** | A2645 (70c) multi | 1.50 | .50 |
| **5145** | A2645 (70c) multi | 1.50 | .50 |
| **5146** | A2645 (70c) multi | 1.50 | .50 |
| **5147** | A2645 (70c) multi | 1.50 | .50 |
| **5148** | A2645 (70c) multi | 1.50 | .50 |
| *a.* | Booklet pane of 12, #5137-5148 | 18.00 | |
| | *Nos. 5137-5148 (12)* | 18.00 | 6.00 |

French Academy in Rome, 350th Anniv. A2646

**2016, Nov. 30** **Photo.** ***Perf. 13¼***

**5149** A2646 €1 chestnut & red 2.25 .75

A souvenir sheet of one sold for €3.50. See Italy No. 3433

Landscape Reflections A2647

Designs: No. 5150, Nusa Dua, Bali, Indonesia. No. 5151, Siwa Oasis, Egypt. No. 5152, Mont Blanc, France. No. 5153, Laguna Colorada, Bolivia. No. 5154, Mount Shompole, Tanzania. No. 5155, Moremi Game Reserve, Botswana. No. 5156, Mount Fuji, Japan. No. 5157, Dolomites, Italy. No. 5158, Avenue of Baobabs, Madagascar. No. 5159, Mountains, Sermersooq Municipality, Greenland. No. 5160, Everglades, United States. No. 5161, Mountains, Ultima Esperanza Province, Chile.

***Serpentine Die Cut 11***

**2017, Jan. 7** **Photo.**

**Booklet Stamps**
**Self-Adhesive**

| | | | |
|---|---|---|---|
| **5150** | A2647 (85c) multi | 1.90 | .65 |
| **5151** | A2647 (85c) multi | 1.90 | .65 |
| **5152** | A2647 (85c) multi | 1.90 | .65 |
| **5153** | A2647 (85c) multi | 1.90 | .65 |
| **5154** | A2647 (85c) multi | 1.90 | .65 |
| **5155** | A2647 (85c) multi | 1.90 | .65 |
| **5156** | A2647 (85c) multi | 1.90 | .65 |
| **5157** | A2647 (85c) multi | 1.90 | .65 |
| **5158** | A2647 (85c) multi | 1.90 | .65 |
| **5159** | A2647 (85c) multi | 1.90 | .65 |
| **5160** | A2647 (85c) multi | 1.90 | .65 |

5161 A2647 (85c) multi 1.90 .65
*a.* Booklet pane of 12, #5150-5161 23.00
*Nos. 5150-5161 (12)* 22.80 7.80

**Art Issue**
Souvenir Sheet

Art by Marc Chagall (1887-1985) — A2648

No. 5162: a, Peace (stained-glass window), 1976. b, Paradise (painting), 1961.

**2017, Jan. 13 Photo. *Perf. 13¼***
5162 A2648 Sheet of 2 7.50 4.00
*a.-b.* €1.70 Either single 3.75 1.90

A2649

Hearts A2650

**2017, Jan. 20 Photo. *Perf. 13¼***
5163 A2649 73c multi 1.60 .55
*a.* Souvenir sheet of 5 8.00 8.00
5164 A2650 €1.46 multi 3.25 1.10

**Self-Adhesive**
***Perf.***
5165 A2649 73c multi 1.60 .55
5166 A2650 €1.46 multi 3.25 1.10

Values for Nos. 5163-5164 are for stamps with surrounding selvage.

**Tourism Issue**

Chateau de Pailly A2651

**2017, Jan. 28 Engr. *Perf. 13¼***
5167 A2651 73c multi 1.60 .55

Rat — A2652

Ox — A2653

Tiger — A2654

Rabbit A2655

Dragon A2656

Snake — A2657

Horse — A2658

Goat — A2659

Monkey A2660

Rooster A2661

Dog — A2662

Pig — A2663

***Serpentine Die Cut 11***
**2017, Jan. 28 Photo.**
**Booklet Stamps**
**Self-Adhesive**

5168 A2652 (73c) multi 1.60 .55
5169 A2653 (73c) multi 1.60 .55
5170 A2654 (73c) multi 1.60 .55
5171 A2655 (73c) multi 1.60 .55
5172 A2656 (73c) multi 1.60 .55
5173 A2657 (73c) multi 1.60 .55
5174 A2658 (73c) multi 1.60 .55
5175 A2659 (73c) multi 1.60 .55
5176 A2660 (73c) multi 1.60 .55
5177 A2661 (73c) multi 1.60 .55
5178 A2662 (73c) multi 1.60 .55
5179 A2663 (73c) multi 1.60 .55
*a.* Booklet pane of 12, #5168-5179 19.50
*Nos. 5168-5179 (12)* 19.20 6.60

New Year 2017 (Year of the Rooster).

Women and Lucien Neuwirth (1924-2013), Politician — A2664

**2017, Feb. 9 Photo. *Perf. 13¼***
5180 A2664 85c multi 1.90 .65

Passage of Neuwirth Law legalizing birth control, 50th anniv.

**Art Issue**

La Vue de Village, by Frédéric Bazille (1841-70) A2665

**2017, Feb. 17 Photo. *Perf. 13¼x13***
5181 A2665 €1.70 multi 3.75 1.90

Farm Animals A2666

Designs: No. 5182, Bélier (ram). No. 5183, Laperau (rabbit). No. 5184, Anesse (female donkey). No. 5185, Dindon (turkey). No. 5186, Oie (goose). No. 5187, Veau (calf). No. 5188, Porcelet (piglet). No. 5189, Anon (male donkey). No. 5190, Canard (duck). No. 5191, Brebis (ewe). No. 5192, Vache (cow). No. 5193, Poule (hen).

***Serpentine Die Cut 11***
**2017, Feb. 24 Photo.**
**Booklet Stamps**
**Self-Adhesive**

5182 A2666 (73c) multi 1.60 .55
5183 A2666 (73c) multi 1.60 .55
5184 A2666 (73c) multi 1.60 .55
5185 A2666 (73c) multi 1.60 .55
5186 A2666 (73c) multi 1.60 .55
5187 A2666 (73c) multi 1.60 .55
5188 A2666 (73c) multi 1.60 .55
5189 A2666 (73c) multi 1.60 .55
5190 A2666 (73c) multi 1.60 .55
5191 A2666 (73c) multi 1.60 .55
5192 A2666 (73c) multi 1.60 .55
5193 A2666 (73c) multi 1.60 .55
*a.* Booklet pane of 12, #5182-5193 19.50
*Nos. 5182-5193 (12)* 19.20 6.60

Anne Morgan (1873-1952), Philanthropist and Provider of War Relief — A2667

**2017, Feb. 24 Engr. *Perf. 13¼***
5194 A2667 85c multi 1.90 .65

Montmartre — A2668

**2017, Mar. 9 Engr. *Perf. 13x12¾***
5195 A2668 73c multi 1.60 .55

Spring Philatelic Show, Paris.

Miniature Sheet

European Capitals — A2669

No. 5196 — Attractions in Valletta, Malta: a, Palais des Grand Maîtres (Grandmaster's Palace). b, Gallarija (building balconies). c, St. John's Co-cathedral, vert. d, Fort Saint Elmo (canals and buildings).

***Perf. 13x13¼, 13¼x13***
**2017, Mar. 10 Photo.**
5196 A2669 Sheet of 4 7.75 7.75
*a.-d.* 85c Any single 1.90 .65

Germaine Ribière (1917-99), Resistance Fighter Who Saved Jews in World War II — A2670

**2017, Mar. 10 Engr. *Perf. 13¼***
5197 A2670 €1.10 multi 2.40 .80

Waltzers A2671

The Star, by Edgar Degas (1834-1917) — A2672

**2017, Mar. 11 Engr. *Perf. 13¼***

**5198** A2671 73c multi 1.60 .55

**Souvenir Sheet**

**Photo.**

***Perf. 13¼x13***

**5199** A2672 €1.46 multi 3.25 1.10

Stamp Day.

Law on Commercial And Industrial Credit, Cent. — A2673

**2017, Mar. 13 Photo. *Perf. 13¼***

**5200** A2673 85c multi 1.90 .65

French-Algerian War Ceasefire, 55th Anniv. — A2674

**2017, Mar. 15 Photo. *Perf. 13¼***

**5201** A2674 €1.30 multi 2.75 .90

Maurice Faure (1922-2014), Politician A2675

**2017, Mar. 25 Engr. *Perf. 13¼***

**5202** A2675 85c multi 1.90 .65

Photographs of Items Looking Like Masks, by Michelangelo Durazzo — A2676

Mask number: No. 5203, 7. No. 5204, 13. No. 5205, 12. No. 5206, 9. No. 5207, 32. No. 5208, 29. No. 5209, 26. No. 5210, 35. No. 5211, 3. No. 5212, 17. No. 5213, 21. No. 5214, 44.

***Serpentine Die Cut 11***

**2017, Mar. 31 Photo.**

**Booklet Stamps**

**Self-Adhesive**

**5203** A2676 (73c) multi 1.60 .55
**5204** A2676 (73c) multi 1.60 .55
**5205** A2676 (73c) multi 1.60 .55
**5206** A2676 (73c) multi 1.60 .55
**5207** A2676 (73c) multi 1.60 .55
**5208** A2676 (73c) multi 1.60 .55
**5209** A2676 (73c) multi 1.60 .55
**5210** A2676 (73c) multi 1.60 .55
**5211** A2676 (73c) multi 1.60 .55
**5212** A2676 (73c) multi 1.60 .55
**5213** A2676 (73c) multi 1.60 .55
**5214** A2676 (73c) multi 1.60 .55
*a.* Booklet pane of 12, #5203-5214 19.50
*Nos. 5203-5214 (12)* 19.20 6.60

Ironwork A2677

**2017, Mar. 31 Engr. *Perf. 12¼***

**5215** A2677 73c multi 1.60 .55

Souvenir Sheet

Battle of Vimy Ridge, Cent. — A2678

No. 5216: a, Pillars and statue. b, Statue of weeping woman.

**2017, Apr. 7 Engr. *Perf. 13¼***

**5216** A2678 Sheet of 2 5.00 5.00
*a.* 85c multi 1.90 .65
*b.* €1.30 multi 3.00 1.00

See Canada Nos. 2981-2982.

Souvenir Sheet

Second Battle of Chemin des Dames, Cent. — A2679

No. 5217: a, Seven Senegalese soldiers. b, Eight soldiers in Dragon Cavern.

**2017, Apr. 14 Photo. *Perf. 13¼***

**5217** A2679 Sheet of 2 5.00 5.00
*a.-b.* €1.10 Either single 2.40 .80

A 200x95mm sheet containing Nos. 5217a and 5217b, but with a different margin design sold for €6.20.

Jean-Baptiste Charcot (1867-1936), Polar Explorer, and Ship Pourquoi-Pas? — A2680

**2017, Apr. 22 Engr. *Perf. 13x12¾***

**5218** A2680 €1.30 multi 3.00 1.00

A souvenir sheet containing No. 5218 sold for €3.20.

Concours Lépine Inventor's Show — A2681

**2017, Apr. 27 Photo. *Perf. 13¼***

**5219** A2681 €1.30 multi 3.00 1.00

Flowers in Objets d' Art — A2682

Inscription: No. 5220, Cristal pierres & or (crystal stones and gold). No. 5221, Bois peint & doré (painted and gilded wood). No. 5222, Argent travaillé (worked silver). No. 5223, Faïence & glaçure, peinte (glazed and painted faience). No. 5224, Bronze doré (gilded bronze). No. 5225, Mosaique, pierres dures (stone mosaic). No. 5226, Porcelaine tendre (soft porcelain). No. 5227, Bois sculpté (sculpted wood). No. 5228, Laine & soie (wool and silk). No. 5229, Bois gravé (engraved wood). No. 5230, Perles, diamants, or & argent (pearls, diamonds, gold and silver). No. 5231, Coton & fil de soie, broderie (cotton and silk thread embroidery).

***Serpentine Die Cut 11***

**2017, Apr. 28 Photo.**

**Booklet Stamps**

**Self-Adhesive**

**5220** A2682 (73c) multi 1.60 .55
**5221** A2682 (73c) multi 1.60 .55
**5222** A2682 (73c) multi 1.60 .55
**5223** A2682 (73c) multi 1.60 .55
**5224** A2682 (73c) multi 1.60 .55
**5225** A2682 (73c) multi 1.60 .55
**5226** A2682 (73c) multi 1.60 .55
**5227** A2682 (73c) multi 1.60 .55
**5228** A2682 (73c) multi 1.60 .55
**5229** A2682 (73c) multi 1.60 .55
**5230** A2682 (73c) multi 1.60 .55
**5231** A2682 (73c) multi 1.60 .55
*a.* Booklet pane of 12, #5220-5231 19.50
*Nos. 5220-5231 (12)* 19.20 6.60

Cholet — A2683

**2017, Apr. 28 Engr. *Perf. 13x13¼***

**5232** A2683 73c multi + label 1.60 .55

French Federation of Philatelic Associations, 90th Congress, Cholet.

Bid of Paris to Host 2024 Summer Olympics and Paralympics — A2684

**2017, May 13 Photo. *Perf. 13x13¼***

**5233** A2684 73c multi + label 1.75 .60

For overprint, see No. 5303.

Chambord, Azay-le-Rideau and Chenonceau Chateaus — A2685

**2017, May 14 Photo. *Perf. 13x12¾***

**5234** A2685 €1.10 multi 2.50 .85

Europa.

Coupe de France Soccer Tournament, Cent. — A2686

**2017, May 19 Photo. *Perf. 13¼***

**5235** A2686 73c multi 1.75 .60

Saint-Benoît-sur-Loire Abbey — A2687

**2017, May 19 Engr. *Perf. 13¼***

**5236** A2687 73c multi 1.75 .60

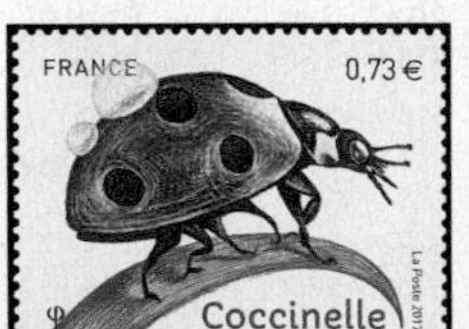

Insects A2688

Designs: No. 5237, Coccinelle (ladybug).

No. 5238: a, Demoiselle (banded damselfly). b, Hanneton (cockchafer), vert. c, Carabe (beetle), vert.

**2017, May 19 Photo. *Perf. 13¼***

**5237** A2688 73c multi 1.75 .60
**5238** Sheet of 4, #5237, 5238a-5238c 7.00 7.00
*a.-c.* A2688 73c Any single 1.75 .60

Two souvenir sheets, one containing Nos. 5237 and 5238c, and the other containing Nos. 5238a and 5238b, sold as a set for €6.20.

National Sea Rescue Society, 50th Anniv. A2689

**2017, May 23 Photo. *Perf. 13¼***

**5239** A2689 85c multi 1.90 .65

Lions Clubs International, Cent. — A2690

**2017, May 27 Photo. *Perf. 13¼***

**Booklet Stamps Self-Adhesive**

**5240** A2690 85c multi 1.90 .65

Haunted House Ride A2691

Bumper Cars A2692

Cotton Candy A2693

Carousel A2694

Candy Apples A2695

Duck Hooking Game A2696

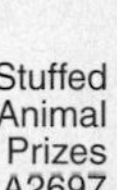

Stuffed Animal Prizes A2697

Ferris Wheel A2698

Roller Coaster A2699

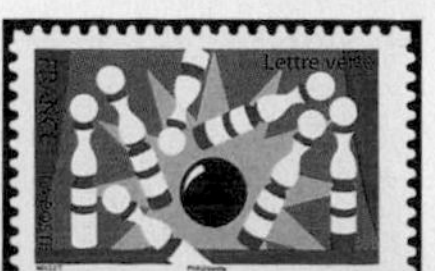

Bowling A2700

Swing Ride A2701

Slide A2702

***Serpentine Die Cut 11***

**2017, June 2 Photo.**

**Booklet Stamps Self-Adhesive**

| | | | | |
|---|---|---|---|---|
| **5241** | A2691 (73c) multi | | 1.75 | .60 |
| **5242** | A2692 (73c) multi | | 1.75 | .60 |
| **5243** | A2693 (73c) multi | | 1.75 | .60 |
| **5244** | A2694 (73c) multi | | 1.75 | .60 |
| **5245** | A2695 (73c) multi | | 1.75 | .60 |
| **5246** | A2696 (73c) multi | | 1.75 | .60 |
| **5247** | A2697 (73c) multi | | 1.75 | .60 |
| **5248** | A2698 (73c) multi | | 1.75 | .60 |
| **5249** | A2699 (73c) multi | | 1.75 | .60 |
| **5250** | A2700 (73c) multi | | 1.75 | .60 |
| **5251** | A2701 (73c) multi | | 1.75 | .60 |
| **5252** | A2702 (73c) multi | | 1.75 | .60 |
| *a.* | Booklet pane of 12, #5241-5252 | | 21.00 | |
| | *Nos. 5241-5252 (12)* | | 21.00 | 7.20 |

Louis Vicat (1786-1861), Buildings and Bridge — A2703

**2017, June 2 Photo. *Perf. 13¼***

**5253** A2703 €1.30 multi 3.00 1.00

Invention of artificial cement by Vicat, 200th anniv.

**Art Issue**

Woman, Sculpture by Jeanne Bardey (1872-1954) — A2704

**2017, June 2 Engr. *Perf. 13¼x13***

**5254** A2704 €1.70 multi 4.00 2.00

Rochefort-en-Terre — A2705

**2017, June 14 Engr. *Perf. 13¼***

**5255** A2705 73c multi 1.75 .60

Arrival of American Troops in World War I, Cent. A2706

**2017, June 23 Engr. *Perf. 13¼***

**5256** A2706 €1.30 multi 3.00 1.00

Joachim Murat (1767-1815), French Marshal and Admiral and King of Naples — A2707

**2017, June 23 Engr. *Perf. 13¼***

**5257** A2707 85c multi 2.00 .70

Harness Race at Rambouillet Hippodrome — A2708

**2017, June 24 Photo. *Perf. 13¼***

**5258** A2708 73c multi 1.75 .60

Diplomatic Relations Between France and the Philippines, 70th Anniv. A2709

Unnamed painting by: 85c, Philippine painter Macario Vitalis (1898-1989). €1.30, French painter Jacques Villon (1875-1963).

**2017, June 26 Photo. *Perf. 13¼***

| | | | |
|---|---|---|---|
| **5259** | A2709 85c multi | 2.00 | .70 |
| **5260** | A2709 €1.30 multi | 3.00 | 1.00 |
| *a.* | Souvenir sheet of 2, #5259-5260 | 7.50 | 7.50 |

No. 5260a sold for €3.20. See Philippines No.

**Souvenir Sheet**

French History — A2710

No. 5261: a, Anne of France (1461-1522), Duchess of Beaujeu (41x53mm oval stamp). b, Treaty of Picquigny, 1475 (53x42mm).

***Perf., Perf. 13x13¼ (#5261b)***

**2017, June 30 Engr.**

| | | | |
|---|---|---|---|
| **5261** | A2710 Sheet of 2 | 7.00 | 7.00 |
| *a.-b.* | €1.46 Either single | 3.50 | 1.25 |

A 200x95mm sheet containing Nos. 5261a and 5261b, but with a different margin design sold for €6.50.

Grains A2711

Designs: No. 5262, Avoine (oats). No. 5263, Blé dur (durum wheat). No. 5264, Mais (corn). No. 5265, Millet. No. 5266, Riz (rice). No. 5267, Seigle (rye). No. 5268, Blé tendre (soft wheat). No. 5269, Epeautre (spelt). No. 5270, Orge (barley). No. 5271, Petit épautre (einkorn wheat). No. 5272, Sorgho (sorghum). No. 5273, Triticale.

***Serpentine Die Cut 11***

**2017, June 30 Photo.**

**Booklet Stamps Self-Adhesive**

| | | | |
|---|---|---|---|
| **5262** | A2711 (85c) multi | 2.00 | .70 |
| **5263** | A2711 (85c) multi | 2.00 | .70 |
| **5264** | A2711 (85c) multi | 2.00 | .70 |
| **5265** | A2711 (85c) multi | 2.00 | .70 |
| **5266** | A2711 (85c) multi | 2.00 | .70 |
| **5267** | A2711 (85c) multi | 2.00 | .70 |
| **5268** | A2711 (85c) multi | 2.00 | .70 |
| **5269** | A2711 (85c) multi | 2.00 | .70 |
| **5270** | A2711 (85c) multi | 2.00 | .70 |
| **5271** | A2711 (85c) multi | 2.00 | .70 |
| **5272** | A2711 (85c) multi | 2.00 | .70 |
| **5273** | A2711 (85c) multi | 2.00 | .70 |
| *a.* | Booklet pane of 12, #5262-5273 | 24.00 | |
| | *Nos. 5262-5273 (12)* | 24.00 | 8.40 |

Cherbourg-en-Cotentin — A2712

**2017, July 7 Engr. *Perf. 13¼***

**5274** A2712 73c multi 1.75 .60

Trees of the Mediterranean Area — A2713

**2017, July 10 Photo. *Perf. 13¼***

**5275** A2713 €1.10 multi 2.60 .90

2017 World Wrestling Championships, Paris — A2714

**2017, July 22 Photo. *Perf. 13x12¾***

**5276** A2714 €1.30 multi 3.25 1.10

Espelette Pepper A2715

Woman Holding Strawberry A2716

Loaf of Bread, Croissant and Roll A2717

Chocolate Bar Elephant A2718

Beans A2719

Lobster A2720

Woman Drinking Citrus Juice A2721

Cows and Cheese A2722

Tomato and Olive Salad A2723

Toucan With Cup of Coffee A2724

Toast With Flavored Honey A2725

People Drinking Mint Tea A2726

*Serpentine Die Cut 11*

**2017, Aug. 5 Photo.**

**Booklet Stamps Self-Adhesive**

| | | | | |
|---|---|---|---|---|
| **5277** | A2715 (73c) multi | | 1.75 | .60 |
| **5278** | A2716 (73c) multi | | 1.75 | .60 |
| **5279** | A2717 (73c) multi | | 1.75 | .60 |
| **5280** | A2718 (73c) multi | | 1.75 | .60 |
| **5281** | A2719 (73c) multi | | 1.75 | .60 |
| **5282** | A2720 (73c) multi | | 1.75 | .60 |
| **5283** | A2721 (73c) multi | | 1.75 | .60 |
| **5284** | A2722 (73c) multi | | 1.75 | .60 |
| **5285** | A2723 (73c) multi | | 1.75 | .60 |
| **5286** | A2724 (73c) multi | | 1.75 | .60 |
| **5287** | A2725 (73c) multi | | 1.75 | .60 |
| **5288** | A2726 (73c) multi | | 1.75 | .60 |
| *a.* | Booklet pane of 12, #5277-5288 | | 21.00 | |
| | *Nos. 5277-5288 (12)* | | 21.00 | 7.20 |

Sense of taste.

Le Havre, 500th Anniv. A2727

**2017, Aug. 31 Engr. *Perf. 13¼***

**5289** A2727 85c multi 2.10 .70

Bridges A2728

Designs: No. 5290, Pont du Gard, Vers-Pont-du-Gard, France. No. 5291, Pont du Diable, Saint-Jean-de-Fos, France. No. 5292, Morlaix Viaduct, Morlaix, France. No. 5293, Digoin Canal Bridge, Digoin, France. No. 5294, Garabit Viaduct, Ruynes-en-Margeride, France. No. 5295, Tower Bridge, London. No. 5296, Pont Valentré, Cahors, France. No. 5297, Ponte Vecchio, Florence. No. 5298, U Bein Bridge, Amarapura, Myanmar. No. 5299, Manhattan and Brooklyn Bridges, New York City. No. 5300, Pont Alexandre III and Pont de la Concorde, Paris. No. 5301, Rochefort-Martrou Transporter Bridge, Rochefort, France.

*Serpentine Die Cut 11*

**2017, Sept. 1 Photo.**

**Booklet Stamps Self-Adhesive**

| | | | | |
|---|---|---|---|---|
| **5290** | A2728 (73c) multi | | 1.75 | .60 |
| **5291** | A2728 (73c) multi | | 1.75 | .60 |
| **5292** | A2728 (73c) multi | | 1.75 | .60 |
| **5293** | A2728 (73c) multi | | 1.75 | .60 |
| **5294** | A2728 (73c) multi | | 1.75 | .60 |
| **5295** | A2728 (73c) multi | | 1.75 | .60 |
| **5296** | A2728 (73c) multi | | 1.75 | .60 |
| **5297** | A2728 (73c) multi | | 1.75 | .60 |
| **5298** | A2728 (73c) multi | | 1.75 | .60 |
| **5299** | A2728 (73c) multi | | 1.75 | .60 |
| **5300** | A2728 (73c) multi | | 1.75 | .60 |
| **5301** | A2728 (73c) multi | | 1.75 | .60 |
| *a.* | Booklet pane of 12, #5290-5301 | | 21.00 | |
| | *Nos. 5290-5301 (12)* | | 21.00 | 7.20 |

Normandie-Niemen Air Regiment, 75th Anniv. — A2729

**2017, Sept. 1 Engr. *Perf. 13x12¾***

**5302** A2729 €1.30 multi 3.25 1.10

A souvenir sheet containing No. 5302, a denominated example of No. 5302 with black and red inks only, and a non-denominated example of No. 5302 without the black and red inks sold for €6.20. See Russia No. 7843.

**No. 5233 Overprinted in Dark Blue**

**Method and Perf. As Before**

**2017, Sept. 13**

**5303** A2684 73c multi + label 1.75 .60

Selection of Paris as host city of 2024 Summer Olympics.

**Art Issue**

The Kiss, Sculpture by Auguste Rodin (1840-1917) — A2730

**2017, Sept. 15 Engr. *Perf. 13¼x13***

**5304** A2730 €1.30 multi 3.25 1.60

A souvenir sheet containing No. 5304 sold for €3.20.

Nadia Boulanger (1887-1979), Conductor and Teacher — A2731

**2017, Sept. 16 Engr. *Perf. 13¼x13***

**5305** A2731 85c multi 2.00 .70

Jeanne Lanvin (1867-1946), Fashion Designer — A2732

**2017, Sept. 23 Photo. *Perf. 13¼x13***

**5306** A2732 €1.46 multi 3.50 1.25

A souvenir sheet containing No. 5306 sold for €3.20.

Characters Maestro, Nabot and Globus From *Hello Maestro!* Animated Television Series A2733

**2017, Sept. 23 Photo. *Perf. 13¼***

**5307** A2733 73c multi 1.75 .60

Woman in Hoop — A2734

Elephant Act — A2735

Rabbit in Magician's Hat — A2736

Mime — A2737

Lion Tamer A2738

Acrobat A2739

Human Tower — A2740

Clown Playing Guitar — A2741

Ringmaster A2742

Unicyclist A2743

Trick Rider on Horse A2744

Aerial Contortionist A2745

*Serpentine Die Cut 11*

**2017, Sept. 29 Photo.**

**Booklet Stamps Self-Adhesive**

| | | | | |
|---|---|---|---|---|
| **5308** | A2734 (73c) multi | | 1.75 | .60 |
| **5309** | A2735 (73c) multi | | 1.75 | .60 |
| **5310** | A2736 (73c) multi | | 1.75 | .60 |
| **5311** | A2737 (73c) multi | | 1.75 | .60 |
| **5312** | A2738 (73c) multi | | 1.75 | .60 |
| **5313** | A2739 (73c) multi | | 1.75 | .60 |
| **5314** | A2740 (73c) multi | | 1.75 | .60 |
| **5315** | A2741 (73c) multi | | 1.75 | .60 |
| **5316** | A2742 (73c) multi | | 1.75 | .60 |
| **5317** | A2743 (73c) multi | | 1.75 | .60 |
| **5318** | A2744 (73c) multi | | 1.75 | .60 |
| **5319** | A2745 (73c) multi | | 1.75 | .60 |
| *a.* | Booklet pane of 12, #5308-5319 | | 21.00 | |
| | *Nos. 5308-5319 (12)* | | 21.00 | 7.20 |

Circus acts.

Electronic Military Transmissions, 150th Anniv. — A2746

**2017, Sept. 29** **Photo.** ***Perf. 13¼***

**5320** A2746 €1.46 multi 3.50 1.25

Father Victor Dillard (1897-1945), Minister to Deported French Slaves of Germany in World War II — A2747

**2017, Oct. 6** **Engr.** ***Perf. 13¼***

**5321** A2747 73c multi 1.75 .60

Miniature Sheet

Actors and Actresses — A2748

No. 5322: a, Magali Noel (1931-2015). b, Bruno Crémer (1929-2010). c, Odile Versois (1930-80). d, Jean-Claude Brialy (1933-2007).

**2017, Oct. 13** **Photo.** ***Perf. 13¼***

**5322** A2748 Sheet of 4 8.00 8.00

*a.-d.* 85c Any single 2.00 .70

Joseph Peyré (1892-1968), Writer — A2749

**2017, Oct. 20** **Engr.** ***Perf. 13¼***

**5323** A2749 €1.10 multi 2.60 .90

# Subject Index of French Commemorative Issues

## FRANCE

### SEMI-POSTAL STAMPS

No. 162 Surcharged in Red

and

SP2

**1914 Unwmk. Typo. *Perf. 14x13½***

**B1** A22 10c + 5c red 5.00 4.25
Never hinged 7.00
**B2** SP2 10c + 5c red 32.50 3.25
Never hinged 90.00
*a.* Booklet pane of 10 600.00
Never hinged 800.00

Issue dates: No. B1, Aug. 11; No. B2, Sept. 10.

See Nos. B746a, B746b.
For overprint see Offices in Morocco No. B8.

Widow at Grave SP3

War Orphans SP4

Woman Plowing — SP5

"Trench of Bayonets" SP6

Lion of Belfort SP7

"La Marseillaise" — SP8

**1917-19**

**B3** SP3 2c + 3c vio brn 4.50 5.00
Never hinged 10.00
**B4** SP4 5c + 5c grn ('19) 21.00 9.50
Never hinged 60.00
**B5** SP5 15c + 10c gray green 30.00 27.50
Never hinged 85.00
**B6** SP5 25c + 15c dp bl 80.00 57.50
Never hinged 175.00
**B7** SP6 35c + 25c slate & vio 135.00 125.00
Never hinged 350.00
**B8** SP7 50c + 50c pale brn & dk brn 225.00 180.00
Never hinged 650.00
**B9** SP8 1fr + 1fr cl & mar 425.00 400.00
Never hinged 1,100.
**B10** SP8 5fr + 5fr dp bl & blk 1,600. 1,550.
Never hinged 4,000.
*Nos. B3-B10 (8)* 2,521. 2,355.

See No. B20-B23. For surcharges see No. B12-B19.

Hospital Ship and Field Hospital SP9

**1918, Aug.**

**B11** SP9 15c + 5c sl & red 125.00 60.00
Never hinged 250.00

See No. B746d.

Semi-Postal Stamps of 1917-19 Surcharged

**1922, Sept. 1**

**B12** SP3 2c + 1c violet brn .50 *.80*
Never hinged 1.00
**B13** SP4 5c + 2½c green .80 *1.25*
Never hinged 1.50
**B14** SP5 15c + 5c gray grn 1.25 *1.60*
Never hinged 2.60
**B15** SP5 25c + 5c deep bl 2.30 *2.50*
Never hinged 4.75
**B16** SP6 35c + 5c slate & vio 13.00 *15.00*
Never hinged 30.00
**B17** SP7 50c + 10c pale brn & dk brn 19.00 *24.00*
Never hinged 39.00
*a.* Pair, one without surcharge
**B18** SP8 1fr + 25c cl & mar 32.50 *37.50*
Never hinged 60.00
**B19** SP8 5fr + 1fr bl & blk 150.00 *155.00*
Never hinged 275.00
*Nos. B12-B19 (8)* 219.35 237.65
Set, never hinged 415.00

Style and arrangement of surcharge differs for each denomination.

**Types of 1917-19**

**1926-27**

**B20** SP3 2c + 1c violet brn 1.50 1.40
Never hinged 4.00
**B21** SP7 50c + 10c ol brn & dk brn 20.00 12.50
Never hinged 72.50
**B22** SP8 1fr + 25c dp rose & red brn 55.00 42.50
Never hinged 150.00
**B23** SP8 5fr + 1fr sl bl & blk 105.00 100.00
Never hinged 240.00
*Nos. B20-B23 (4)* 181.50 156.40

**Sinking Fund Issues**

Types of Regular Issues of 1903-07 Surcharged in Red or Blue

**1927, Sept. 26**

**B24** A22 40c + 10c lt blue (R) 5.75 5.75
Never hinged 10.50
**B25** A20 50c + 25c green (Bl) 8.25 *9.00*
Never hinged 14.00

Surcharge on No. B25 differs from illustration.

Type of Regular Issue of 1923 Surcharged in Black

**B26** A23 1.50fr + 50c orange 14.50 14.00
Never hinged 37.50
*a.* Pair, one without surcharge *2,000.*
*Nos. B24-B26 (3)* 28.50 28.75

See Nos. B28-B33, B35-B37, B39-B41.

Industry and Agriculture SP10

**1928, May Engr. *Perf. 13½***

**B27** SP10 1.50fr + 8.50fr dull blue 140.00 *150.00*
Never hinged 225.00
*a.* Blue green 500.00 *550.00*
Never hinged 725.00

**Types of 1903-23 Issues Surcharged like Nos. B24-B26**

**1928, Oct. 1 *Perf. 14x13½***

**B28** A22 40c + 10c gray lilac (R) 13.00 *14.00*
Never hinged 32.50
**B29** A20 50c + 25c orange brn (Bl) 32.50 29.00
Never hinged 60.00
**B30** A23 1.50fr + 50c rose lilac (Bk) 52.50 42.50
Never hinged 100.00
*Nos. B28-B30 (3)* 98.00 85.50

**Types of 1903-23 Issues Surcharged like Nos. B24-B26**

**1929, Oct. 1**

**B31** A22 40c + 10c green 18.00 *19.00*
Never hinged 37.50
**B32** A20 50c + 25c lilac rose 30.00 30.00
Never hinged 60.00
**B33** A23 1.50fr + 50c chestnut 60.00 *65.00*
Never hinged 130.00
*Nos. B31-B33 (3)* 108.00 114.00

"The Smile of Reims" SP11

**1930, Mar. 15 Engr. *Perf. 13***

**B34** SP11 1.50fr + 3.50fr red vio 80.00 *82.50*
Never hinged 130.00
*a.* Booklet pane of 4 300.00
Never hinged 525.00
*b.* Booklet pane of 8 600.00
Never hinged 1,050.
Complete booklet, #B34b 1,100.

Booklets containing No. B34 have two panes of 4 (No. B34a) connected by a gutter, the complete piece constituting #B34b, which is stapled into the booklet through the gutter. See footnote after No. 4642.

**Types of 1903-07 Issues Surcharged like Nos. B24-B25**

**1930 Oct. 1 *Perf. 14x13½***

**B35** A22 40c + 10c cerise 20.00 *21.00*
Never hinged 70.00
**B36** A20 50c + 25c gray brown 37.50 *42.50*
Never hinged 120.00
**B37** A22 1.50fr + 50c violet 65.00 *70.00*
Never hinged 190.00
*Nos. B35-B37 (3)* 122.50 133.50

Allegory, French Provinces SP12

**1931, Mar. 1 *Perf. 13***

**B38** SP12 1.50fr + 3.50fr green 125.00 *140.00*
Never hinged 300.00

**Types of 1903-07 Issues Surcharged like Nos. B24-B25**

**1931, Oct. 1 *Perf. 14x13½***

**B39** A22 40c + 10c ol grn 40.00 *45.00*
Never hinged 100.00
**B40** A20 50c + 25c gray vio 100.00 *110.00*
Never hinged 235.00
**B41** A22 1.50fr + 50c deep red 100.00 *110.00*
Never hinged 200.00
*Nos. B39-B41 (3)* 240.00 265.00

**Catalogue values for unused stamps in this section, from this point to the end of the section, are for Never Hinged items.**

"France" Giving Aid to an Intellectual SP13

Symbolic of Music SP14

**1935, Dec. 9 Engr. *Perf. 13***

**B42** SP13 50c + 10c ultra 4.00 2.50
Hinged 2.50
**B43** SP14 50c + 2fr dull red 125.00 45.00
Hinged 55.00

The surtax was for the aid of distressed and exiled intellectuals.
For surcharge see No. B47.

Statue of Liberty — SP15

**1936-37**

**B44** SP15 50c + 25c dk blue ('37) 7.50 5.00
Hinged 4.00
**B45** SP15 75c + 50c violet 20.00 10.00
Hinged 9.50

Surtax for the aid of political refugees.
For surcharge see No. B47.

Children of the Unemployed SP16

**1936, May**

**B46** SP16 50c + 10c copper red 7.50 5.00
Hinged 4.50

The surtax was for the aid of children of the unemployed.

No. B43 Surcharged in Black

**1936, Nov.**

**B47** SP14 20c on 50c + 2fr dull red 4.75 3.50
Hinged 3.25

Jacques Callot SP17

Anatole France (Jacques Anatole Thibault) — SP18

Hector Berlioz SP19

Victor Hugo SP20

Auguste Rodin SP21

Louis Pasteur SP22

**1936-37** **Engr.**

**B48** SP17 20c + 10c brown car 4.50 2.50
Hinged 2.25

**B49** SP18 30c + 10c emer ('37) 5.00 2.75
Hinged 2.25

**B50** SP19 40c + 10c emer 4.50 2.75
Hinged 2.25

**B51** SP20 50c + 10c copper red 8.75 3.75
Hinged 3.75

**B52** SP21 90c + 10c rose red ('37) 13.00 6.50
Hinged 6.00

**B53** SP22 1.50fr + 50c deep ultra 40.00 20.00
Hinged 20.00
*Nos. B48-B53 (6)* 75.75 38.25

The surtax was used for relief of unemployed intellectuals.

**1938**

**B54** SP18 30c + 10c brown car 3.00 1.75
Hinged 1.75

**B55** SP17 35c + 10c dull green 3.50 2.40
Hinged 2.40

**B56** SP19 55c + 10c dull vio 10.00 4.00
Hinged 6.00

**B57** SP20 65c + 10c ultra 11.50 4.00
Hinged 6.00

**B58** SP21 1fr + 10c car lake 8.50 4.50
Hinged 4.75

**B59** SP22 1.75fr + 25c dp blue 35.00 17.00
Hinged 17.00
*Nos. B54-B59 (6)* 71.50 33.65

Tug of War SP23

Foot Race SP24

Hiking — SP25

**1937, June 16**

**B60** SP23 20c + 10c brown 3.00 2.25
Hinged 1.60

**B61** SP24 40c + 10c red brown 3.00 2.25
Hinged 1.60

**B62** SP25 50c + 10c black brn 3.00 2.25
Hinged 1.60
*Nos. B60-B62 (3)* 9.00 6.75

The surtax was for the Recreation Fund of the employees of the Post, Telephone and Telegraph.

Pierre Loti (Louis Marie Julien Viaud) SP26

**1937, Aug.**

**B63** SP26 50c + 20c rose car 7.50 5.00
Hinged 3.75

The surtax was for the Pierre Loti Monument Fund.

"France" and Infant SP27

**1937-39**

**B64** SP27 65c + 25c brown vio 5.25 2.75
Hinged 3.25

**B65** SP27 90c + 30c pck bl ('39) 3.50 2.75
Hinged 2.10

The surtax was used for public health work.

Winged Victory of Samothrace — SP28

**1937, Aug.**

**B66** SP28 30c blue green 175.00 40.00
Hinged 65.00

**B67** SP28 55c red 175.00 40.00
Hinged 65.00

On sale at the Louvre for 2.50fr. The surtax of 1.65fr was for the benefit of the Louvre Museum.

Jean Baptiste Charcot — SP29

**1938-39**

**B68** SP29 65c + 35c dk bl grn 3.00 3.00
Hinged 1.60

**B69** SP29 90c + 35c brt red vio ('39) 30.00 13.50
Hinged 11.00

Surtax for the benefit of French seamen.

Palace of Versailles SP30

**1938, May 9**

**B70** SP30 1.75fr + 75c dp bl 37.50 19.00
Hinged 19.00

Natl. Exposition of Painting and Sculpture at Versailles.

The surtax was for the benefit of the Versailles Concert Society.

French Soldier — SP31

**1938, May 16**

**B71** SP31 55c + 70c brown vio 8.50 5.25
Hinged 4.75

**B72** SP31 65c + 1.10fr pck bl 8.50 5.25
Hinged 4.75

The surtax was for a fund to erect a monument to the glory of the French Infantrymen.

Monument — SP32

**1938, May 25**

**B73** SP32 55c + 45c vermilion 22.50 12.50
Hinged 10.00

The surtax was for a fund to erect a monument in honor of the Army Medical Corps.

Reims Cathedral — SP33

**1938, July 10**

**B74** SP33 65c + 35c ultra 17.50 10.50
Hinged 8.50

Completion of the reconstruction of Reims Cathedral, July 10, 1938.

"France" Welcoming Her Sons — SP34

**1938, Aug. 8**

**B75** SP34 65c + 60c rose car 8.50 5.75
Hinged 4.00

The surtax was for the benefit of French volunteers repatriated from Spain.

**Curie Issue**

Common Design Type

**1938, Sept. 1**

**B76** CD80 1.75fr + 50c dp ultra 21.00 12.50
Hinged 8.75

Victory Parade Passing Arc de Triomphe SP36

**1938, Oct. 8**

**B77** SP36 65c + 35c brown car 5.75 4.50
Hinged 3.25

20th anniversary of the Armistice.

Student and Nurse — SP37

**1938, Dec. 1**

**B78** SP37 65c + 60c pck blue 15.00 8.25
Hinged 8.00

The surtax was for Student Relief.

Blind Man and Radio SP38

**1938, Dec.**

**B79** SP38 90c + 25c brown vio 15.00 9.00
Hinged 8.00

The surtax was used to help provide radios for the blind.

Civilian Facing Firing Squad — SP39

**1939, Feb. 1**

**B80** SP39 90c + 35c black brn 17.00 10.50
Hinged 8.75

The surtax was used to erect a monument to civilian victims of World War I.

Red Cross Nurse — SP40

**1939, Mar. 24**

**B81** SP40 90c + 35c dk sl grn, turq bl & red 13.00 8.25
Hinged 6.75

75th anniv. of the Intl. Red Cross Society. See No. B746c.

Army Engineer SP41

**1939, Apr. 3**

**B82** SP41 70c + 50c vermilion 12.50 8.25
Hinged 6.00

Army Engineering Corps. The surtax was used to erect a monument to those members who died in World War I.

Ministry of Post, Telegraph and Telephone
SP42

**1939, Apr. 8**

**B83** SP42 90c + 35c turq blue 37.50 20.00
Hinged 19.00

The surtax was used to aid orphans of employees of the postal system. Opening of the new building for the Ministry of Post, Telegraph and Telephones.

Mother and Child — SP43

**1939, Apr. 24**

**B84** SP43 90c + 35c red 3.75 2.50
Hinged 2.40

The surtax was used to aid children of the unemployed.

50th Anniv. of the Eiffel Tower — SP44

**1939, May 5**

**B85** SP44 90c + 50c red violet 15.00 9.00
Hinged 8.75

The surtax was used for celebration festivities.

Puvis de Chavannes — SP45

Claude Debussy
SP46

Honoré de Balzac
SP47

Claude Bernard
SP48

**1939-40**

**B86** SP45 40c + 10c ver 1.75 1.00
Hinged .80

**B87** SP46 70c + 10c brn vio 8.25 2.50
Hinged 3.50

**B87A** SP46 80c + 10c brn vio ('40) 9.00 7.50
Hinged 4.25

**B88** SP47 90c + 10c brt red vio 7.25 2.50
Hinged 3.25

**B88A** SP47 1fr + 10c brt red vio ('40) 9.00 7.50
Hinged 4.25

**B89** SP48 2.25fr + 25c brt ultra 28.00 11.50
Hinged 14.50

**B89A** SP48 2.50fr + 25c brt ultra ('40) 9.00 7.50
Hinged 4.25

*Nos. B86-B89A (7)* 72.25 40.00

The surtax was used to aid unemployed intellectuals.

Mothers and Children
SP49 SP50

**1939, June 15**

**B90** SP49 70c + 80c bl, grn & vio 5.25 4.50
Hinged 3.25

**B91** SP50 90c + 60c dk brn, dl vio & brn 8.50 5.25
Hinged 4.75

The surtax was used to aid France's repopulation campaign.

"The Letter" by Jean Honoré Fragonard — SP51

**1939, July 6**

**B92** SP51 40c + 60c multi 4.25 2.75
Hinged 2.40

The surtax was used for the Postal Museum. See footnote after No. 4642.

Statue of Widow and Children — SP52

**1939, July 20**

**B93** SP52 70c + 30c brown vio 25.00 12.00
Hinged 12.00

Surtax for the benefit of French seamen.

French Soldier
SP53

Colonial Trooper
SP54

**1940, Feb. 15**

**B94** SP53 40c + 60c sepia 3.25 2.75
Hinged 1.50

**B95** SP54 1fr + 50c turq blue 3.25 2.75
Hinged 1.50

The surtax was used to assist the families of mobilized men.

World Map Showing French Possessions — SP55

**1940, Apr. 15**

**B96** SP55 1fr + 25c scarlet 2.50 1.50
Hinged 1.50

Marshal Joseph J. C. Joffre
SP56

Marshal Ferdinand Foch — SP57

Gen. Joseph S. Gallieni
SP58

Woman Plowing
SP59

**1940, May 1**

**B97** SP56 80c + 45c choc 6.00 3.75
Hinged 3.00

**B98** SP57 1fr + 50c dk vio 4.50 3.00
Hinged 2.50

**B99** SP58 1.50fr + 50c brown red 4.50 3.00
Hinged 2.50

**B100** SP59 2.50fr + 50c indigo & dl bl 12.00 7.50
Hinged 6.00

*Nos. B97-B100 (4)* 27.00 17.25

The surtax was used for war charities. See footnote after No. 4642.

Doctor, Nurse, Soldier and Family
SP60

Nurse and Wounded Soldier
SP61

**1940, May 12**

**B101** SP60 80c + 1fr dk grn & red 7.25 3.50
Hinged 3.50

**B102** SP61 1fr + 2fr sep & red 9.00 3.50
Hinged 3.50

The surtax was used for the Red Cross. See Nos. B747a, B747e.

Nurse with Injured Children — SP62

**1940, Nov. 12**

**B103** SP62 1fr + 2fr sepia 1.25 .80
Hinged .80

The surtax was used for victims of the war.

Wheat Harvest
SP63

Sowing
SP64

Picking Grapes
SP65

Grazing Cattle
SP66

**1940, Dec. 2**

**B104** SP63 80c + 2fr brn blk 3.00 1.50
Hinged 1.40

**B105** SP64 1fr + 2fr chestnut 3.00 1.50
Hinged 1.40

**B106** SP65 1.50fr + 2fr brt vio 3.00 1.50
Hinged 1.40

**B107** SP66 2.50fr + 2fr dp grn 3.25 1.75
Hinged 1.75

*Nos. B104-B107 (4)* 12.25 6.25

The surtax was for national relief.

Prisoners of War
SP67 SP68

**1941, Jan. 1**

**B108** SP67 80c + 5fr dark grn 1.50 1.50

**B109** SP68 1fr + 5fr rose brn 1.50 1.50

The surtax was for prisoners of war.

Science Fighting Cancer
SP69

**1941, Feb. 20**

**B110** SP69 2.50fr + 50c slate blk & brn 1.50 1.25

Surtax used for the control of cancer.

No. 417 Surcharged in Blue

**1941, Mar. 4**
**B111** A109 1fr + 10c crimson .25 .25

Men Hauling Coal SP70

"France" Aiding Needy Man SP71

**1941**

| | | | | |
|---|---|---|---|---|
| **B112** | SP70 | 1fr + 2fr sepia | 2.25 | 1.00 |
| **B113** | SP71 | 2.50fr + 7.50fr dk bl | 7.50 | 2.00 |

The surtax was for Marshal Pétain's National Relief Fund.

Liner Pasteur SP72

**1941, July 17** **Red Surcharge**
**B114** SP72 1fr + 1fr on 70c dk bl grn .30 .30

World Map, Mercator Projection SP73

**1941**
**B115** SP73 1fr + 1fr multi .65 .45

Fisherman — SP74

**1941, Oct. 23**
**B116** SP74 1fr + 9fr dk blue grn .80 .70

Surtax for benefit of French seamen.

**Arms of Various Cities**

Nancy SP75

Lille SP76

Rouen SP77

Bordeaux SP78

Toulouse SP79

Clermont-Ferrand SP80

Marseille SP81

Lyon SP82

Rennes SP83

Reims SP84

Montpellier SP85

Paris SP86

**1941** ***Perf. 14x13***

| | | | | |
|---|---|---|---|---|
| **B117** | SP75 | 20c + 30c brn blk | 2.75 | 2.00 |
| **B118** | SP76 | 40c + 60c org brn | 2.75 | 2.00 |
| **B119** | SP77 | 50c + 70c grnsh blue | 2.75 | 2.00 |
| **B120** | SP78 | 70c + 80c rose vio | 2.75 | 2.00 |
| **B121** | SP79 | 80c + 1fr dp rose | 2.75 | 2.00 |
| **B122** | SP80 | 1fr + 1fr black | 2.75 | 2.00 |
| **B123** | SP81 | 1.50fr + 2fr dk bl | 2.75 | 2.00 |
| **B124** | SP82 | 2fr + 2fr dk vio | 2.75 | 2.00 |
| **B125** | SP83 | 2.50fr + 3fr brt grn | 2.75 | 2.00 |
| **B126** | SP84 | 3fr + 5fr org brn | 2.75 | 2.00 |
| **B127** | SP85 | 5fr + 6fr brt ultra | 2.75 | 2.00 |
| **B128** | SP86 | 10fr + 10fr dk red | 2.75 | 2.00 |
| | | *Nos. B117-B128 (12)* | 33.00 | 24.00 |

Count de La Pérouse SP87

**1942, Mar. 23** ***Perf. 13***
**B129** SP87 2.50fr + 7.50fr ultra 1.25 1.40

Jean Francois de Galaup de La Pérouse, (1741-88), French navigator and explorer. The surtax was for National Relief.

Planes over Fields SP88

**1942, Apr. 4**
**B130** SP88 1.50fr + 3.50fr lt vio 2.40 2.40

The surtax was for the benefit of French airmen and their familes.

Alexis Chabrier SP89

**1942, May 18**
**B131** SP89 2fr + 3fr sepia 1.25 1.25

Emmanuel Chabrier (1841-1894), composer, birth centenary. The surtax was for works of charity among musicians.

Symbolical of French Colonial Empire SP90

**1942, May 18**
**B132** SP90 1.50fr + 8.50fr black 1.10 1.10

The surtax was for National Relief.

Jean de Vienne SP91

**1942, June 16**
**B133** SP91 1.50fr + 8.50fr sepia 1.10 1.10

600th anniv. of the birth of Jean de Vienne, 1st admiral of France. The surtax was for the benefit of French seamen.

Type of Regular Issue, 1941 Surcharged in Carmine

**1942, Sept. 10** ***Perf. 14x13½***
**B134** A116 1.50fr + 50c brt ultra .25 .25

The surtax was for national relief ("Secours National").

**Arms of Various Cities**

Chambéry SP92

La Rochelle SP93

Poitiers SP94

Orléans SP95

Grenoble SP96

Angers SP97

Dijon SP98

Limoges SP99

Le Havre SP100

Nantes SP101

Nice SP102

St. Etienne SP103

***Perf. 14x13***
**1942, Oct.** **Unwmk.** **Engr.**

| | | | | |
|---|---|---|---|---|
| **B135** | SP92 | 50c + 60c blk | 3.50 | 3.25 |
| **B136** | SP93 | 60c + 70c grnsh blue | 3.50 | 3.25 |
| **B137** | SP94 | 80c + 1fr rose | 3.50 | 3.25 |
| **B138** | SP95 | 1fr + 1.30fr dk green | 3.50 | 3.25 |
| **B139** | SP96 | 1.20fr + 1.50fr rose vio | 3.50 | 3.25 |
| **B140** | SP97 | 1.50fr + 1.80fr slate bl | 3.50 | 3.25 |
| **B141** | SP98 | 2fr + 2.30fr deep rose | 3.50 | 3.25 |
| **B142** | SP99 | 2.40fr + 2.80fr slate grn | 3.50 | 3.25 |
| **B143** | SP100 | 3fr + 3.50fr dp violet | 3.50 | 3.25 |
| **B144** | SP101 | 4fr + 5fr lt ultra | 3.50 | 3.25 |
| **B145** | SP102 | 4.50fr + 6fr red | 3.50 | 3.25 |
| **B146** | SP103 | 5fr + 7fr brt red vio | 3.50 | 3.25 |
| | | *Nos. B135-B146 (12)* | 42.00 | 39.00 |

The surtax was for national relief.

Tricolor Legion SP104

**1942, Oct. 12** ***Perf. 13***

| | | | | |
|---|---|---|---|---|
| **B147** | SP104 | 1.20 + 8.80fr dk blue | 10.00 | 10.00 |
| *a.* | | Vert. pair, #B147, B148 + albino impression | 22.50 | 25.00 |
| **B148** | SP104 | 1.20 + 8.80fr crim | 10.00 | 10.00 |

These stamps were printed in sheets of 20 stamps and 5 albino impressions arranged: 2 horizontal rows of 5 dark blue stamps, 1 row of 5 albino impressions, and 2 rows of 5 crimson stamps.

Marshal Henri Philippe Pétain SP105 SP106

**1943, Feb. 8**

**B149** SP105 1fr + 10fr rose red 2.75 2.75
**B150** SP105 1fr + 10fr blue 2.75 2.75
**B151** SP106 2fr + 12fr rose red 2.75 2.75
**B152** SP106 2fr + 12fr blue 2.75 2.75
*a.* Strip, #B149-B152 + label 12.50 12.50

The surtax was for national relief. Printed in sheets of 20, the 10 blue stamps at left, the 10 rose red at right, separated by a vert. row of 5 white labels bearing a tri-colored battle-ax.

Marshal Pétain — SP107

"Work" — SP108

"Family" SP109

"State" SP110

Marshal Pétain — SP111

**1943, June 7**

**B153** SP107 1.20fr + 1.40fr dull vio 12.00 11.00
**B154** SP108 1.50fr + 2.50fr red 12.00 11.00
**B155** SP109 2.40fr + 7fr brown 12.00 11.00
**B156** SP110 4fr + 10fr dk violet 12.00 11.00
**B157** SP111 5fr + 15fr red brown 12.00 11.00
*a.* Strip of 5, #B153-B157 100.00 100.00

Pétain's 87th birthday.
The surtax was for national relief.

Civilians Under Air Attack — SP112

**1943, Aug. 23**

**B158** SP112 1.50fr + 3.50fr black .40 .40

Surtax was for bomb victims at Billancourt, Dunkirk, Lorient, Saint-Nazaire.

Civilians Doing Farm Work — SP113

Prisoner's Family Doing Farm Work SP114

**1943, Sept. 27**

**B159** SP113 1.50fr + 8.50fr sepia .75 .75
**B160** SP114 2.40fr + 7.60fr dk grn .80 .80

The surtax was for families of war prisoners.

Michel de Montaigne — SP115

1.20fr+1.50fr, Francois Clouet. 1.50fr+3fr, Ambrose Paré. 2.40fr+4fr, Chevalier Pierre de Bayard. 4fr+6fr, Duke of Sully. 5fr+10fr, Henri IV.

**1943, Oct. 2**

**B161** SP115 60c + 80c Prus green 1.75 1.75
**B162** SP115 1.20fr + 1.50fr black 1.50 1.50
**B163** SP115 1.50fr + 3fr deep ultra 1.50 1.50
**B164** SP115 2.40fr + 4fr red 1.50 1.50
**B165** SP115 4fr + 6fr dull brn red 1.75 1.75
**B166** SP115 5fr + 10fr dull green 1.75 1.75
*Nos. B161-B166 (6)* 9.75 9.75

The surtax was for national relief. Issued to honor famous 16th century Frenchmen.

Picardy Costume — SP121

Designs: 18th Century Costumes: 1.20fr+2fr, Brittany. 1.50fr+4fr, Ile de France. 2.40+5fr, Burgundy. 4fr+6fr, Auvergne. 5fr+7fr, Provence.

**1943, Dec. 27**

**B167** SP121 60c + 1.30fr sepia 1.60 1.60
**B168** SP121 1.20fr + 2fr lt vio 1.60 1.60
**B169** SP121 1.50fr + 4fr turq blue 1.60 1.60
**B170** SP121 2.40fr + 5fr rose car 1.60 1.60
**B171** SP121 4fr + 6fr chlky blue 2.50 2.50
**B172** SP121 5fr + 7fr red 2.50 2.50
*Nos. B167-B172 (6)* 11.40 11.40

The surtax was for national relief. See footnote after No. 4642.

Admiral Tourville — SP127

**1944, Feb. 21**

**B173** SP127 4fr + 6fr dull red brn .60 .60

300th anniv. of the birth of Admiral Anne-Hilarion de Cotentin Tourville (1642-1701).

Charles Gounod — SP128

**1944, Mar. 27** *Perf. 14x13*

**B174** SP128 1.50fr + 3.50fr sepia .75 .60

50th anniv. of the death of Charles Gounod, composer (1818-1893).

Marshal Pétain SP129

Farming SP130

Industry SP131

**1944, Apr. 24** *Perf. 13*

**B175** SP129 1.50fr + 3.50fr sepia 3.00 3.00
**B176** SP130 2fr + 3fr dp ultra .50 .45
**B177** SP131 4fr + 6fr rose red .50 .45
*Nos. B175-B177 (3)* 4.00 3.90

Marshal Henri Pétain's 88th birthday.

Modern Streamliner, 19th Cent. Train — SP132

**1944, Aug. 14**

**B178** SP132 4fr + 6fr black 1.50 1.50

Centenary of the Paris-Rouen, Paris-Orléans railroad.

Molière (Jean-Baptiste Poquelin) — SP133

Designs: 80c+2.20fr, Jules Hardouin Mansart. 1.20fr+2.80fr, Blaise Pascal. 1.50fr+3.50fr, Louis II of Bourbon. 2fr+4fr, Jean-Baptiste Colbert. 4fr+6fr, Louis XIV.

**1944, July 31**

**B179** SP133 50c + 1.50fr rose car 1.50 1.00
**B180** SP133 80c + 2.20fr dk green 1.50 1.00
**B181** SP133 1.20fr + 2.80fr black 1.50 1.00
**B182** SP133 1.50fr + 3.50fr brt ultra 1.50 1.00
**B183** SP133 2fr + 4fr dull brn red 1.50 1.00
**B184** SP133 4fr + 6fr red 1.50 1.00
*Nos. B179-B184 (6)* 9.00 6.00

Noted 17th century Frenchmen.

Angoulême SP139

Chartres SP140

Amiens SP141

Beauvais SP142

Albi — SP143

**1944, Nov. 20**

**B185** SP139 50c + 1.50fr black .60 .40
**B186** SP140 80c + 2.20fr rose vio .60 .40
**B187** SP141 1.20fr + 2.80fr brn car .60 .40
**B188** SP142 1.50fr + 3.50fr dp blue .60 .40
**B189** SP143 4fr + 6fr orange red .60 .40
*Nos. B185-B189 (5)* 3.00 2.00

French Cathedrals.

Coat of Arms of Renouard de Villayer — SP144

**1944, Dec. 9** **Engr.**

**B190** SP144 1.50fr + 3.50fr dp brn .25 .25

Stamp Day.

Sarah Bernhardt — SP145

**1945, May 16** **Unwmk.** *Perf. 13*

**B191** SP145 4fr + 1fr dk violet brn .30 .25

100th anniv. of the birth of Sarah Bernhardt, actress.

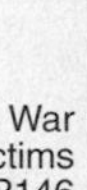

War Victims SP146

**1945, May 16**

**B192** SP146 4fr + 6fr dk violet brn .25 .25

The surtax was for war victims of the P.T.T.

Tuberculosis Patient — SP147

**1945, May 16 Typo. *Perf. 14x13½***

**B193** SP147 2fr + 1fr red orange .25 .25

Surtax for the aid of tuberculosis victims. For surcharge see No. 561.

Boy and Girl — SP148

**1945, July 9 Engr. *Perf. 13***

**B194** SP148 4fr + 2fr Prus green .25 .25

The surtax was used for child welfare.

Burning of Oradour Church — SP149

**1945, Oct. 13**

**B195** SP149 4fr + 2fr sepia .25 .25

Destruction of Oradour, June, 1944.

Louis XI and Post Rider SP150

**1945, Oct. 13**

**B196** SP150 2fr + 3fr deep ultra .35 .25

Stamp Day.

For overprint see French West Africa No. B2.

Ruins of Dunkirk SP151

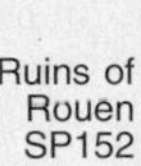

Ruins of Rouen SP152

Ruins of Caen SP153

Ruins of Saint-Malo SP154

**1945, Nov. 5**

| | | | | |
|---|---|---|---|---|
| **B197** | SP151 | 1.50fr + 1.50fr red brown | .40 | .30 |
| **B198** | SP152 | 2fr + 2fr violet | .40 | .30 |
| **B199** | SP153 | 2.40fr + 2.60fr blue | .40 | .30 |
| **B200** | SP154 | 4fr + 4fr black | .40 | .30 |
| | | *Nos. B197-B200 (4)* | 1.60 | 1.20 |

The surtax was to aid the suffering residents of Dunkirk, Rouen, Caen and Saint Malo.

Alfred Fournier SP155

Henri Becquerel SP156

**1946, Feb. 4 Engr. *Perf. 13***

**B201** SP155 2fr + 3fr red brown .30 .25

**B202** SP156 2fr + 3fr violet .30 .25

Issued to raise funds for the fight against venereal disease (No. B201) and for the struggle against cancer (No. B202).

No. B202 for the 50th anniv. of the discovery of radioactivity by Henri Becquerel.

See No. B221.

Church of the Invalides, Paris — SP157

**1946, Mar. 11**

**B203** SP157 4fr + 6fr red brown .30 .25

The surtax was to aid disabled war veterans.

French Warships SP158

**1946, Apr. 8**

**B204** SP158 2fr + 3fr gray black .75 .40

The surtax was for naval charities.

"The Letter" by Jean Siméon Chardin — SP159

**1946, May 25**

**B205** SP159 2fr + 3fr brown red .40 .30

The surtax was used for the Postal Museum.

Fouquet de la Varane — SP160

**1946, June 29**

**B206** SP160 3fr + 2fr sepia .50 .25

Stamp Day.

François Villon — SP161

Designs: 3fr+1fr, Jean Fouquet. 4fr+3fr, Philippe de Commynes. 5fr+4fr, Joan of Arc. 6fr+5fr, Jean de Gerson. 10fr+6fr, Charles VII.

**1946, Oct. 28**

| | | | | |
|---|---|---|---|---|
| **B207** | SP161 | 2fr + 1fr dk Prus grn | 1.25 | .90 |
| **B208** | SP161 | 3fr + 1fr dk blue vio | 1.25 | .90 |
| **B209** | SP161 | 4fr + 3fr henna brn | 1.25 | .90 |
| **B210** | SP161 | 5fr + 4fr ultra | 1.25 | .90 |
| **B211** | SP161 | 6fr + 5fr sepia | 1.25 | .90 |
| **B212** | SP161 | 10fr + 6fr red | 1.25 | .90 |
| | | *Nos. B207-B212 (6)* | 7.50 | 5.40 |

Church of St. Sernin, Toulouse SP167

Notre Dame du Port, Clermont-Ferrand SP168

Cathedral of St. Front, Perigueux SP169

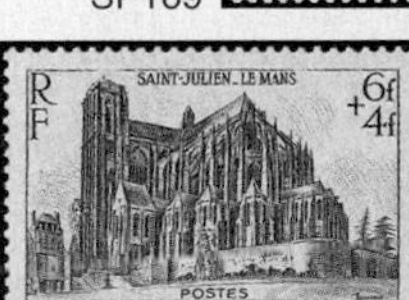

Cathedral of St. Julien, Le Mans SP170

Cathedral of Notre Dame, Paris — SP171

**1947 Engr.**

| | | | | |
|---|---|---|---|---|
| **B213** | SP167 | 1fr + 1fr car rose | .85 | .60 |
| **B214** | SP168 | 3fr + 2fr dk bl vio | 2.25 | 1.40 |
| **B215** | SP169 | 4fr + 3fr henna brn | 1.10 | .90 |
| **B216** | SP170 | 6fr + 4fr dp bl | 1.10 | .90 |
| **B217** | SP171 | 10fr + 6fr dk gray grn | 2.25 | 1.60 |
| | | *Nos. B213-B217 (5)* | 7.55 | 5.40 |

See No. 5035c.

François Michel le Tellier de Louvois — SP172

**1947, Mar. 15**

**B218** SP172 4.50fr + 5.50fr car rose 1.10 .55

Stamp Day, Mar. 15, 1947.

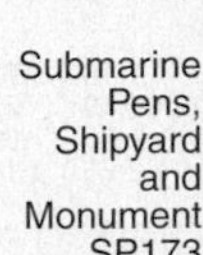

Submarine Pens, Shipyard and Monument SP173

**1947, Aug. 2**

**B219** SP173 6fr + 4fr bluish black .50 .30

British commando raid on the Nazi U-boat base at St. Nazaire, 1942.

Liberty Highway Marker — SP174

**1947, Sept. 5**

**B220** SP174 6fr + 4fr dk green .75 .55

The surtax was to help defray maintenance costs of the Liberty Highway.

**Fournier Type of 1946**

**1947, Oct. 20**

**B221** SP155 2fr + 3fr indigo .30 .25

Louis Braille — SP175

**1948, Jan. 19**

**B222** SP175 6fr + 4fr purple .30 .25

Etienne Arago — SP176

**1948, Mar. 6**

**B223** SP176 6fr + 4fr black brn .45 .25

Stamp Day, March 6-7, 1948.

Alphonse de Lamartine — SP177

Designs: 3fr+2fr, Alexandre A. Ledru-Rollin. 4fr+3fr, Louis Blanc. 5fr+4fr, Albert (Alexandre Martin). 6fr+5fr, Pierre J. Proudhon. 10fr+6fr, Louis Auguste Blanqui. 15fr+7fr, Armand Barbés. 20fr+8fr, Dennis A. Affre.

**1948, Apr. 5 Engr. *Perf. 13***

**B224** SP177 1fr + 1fr dk grn 1.10 .75
**B225** SP177 3fr + 2fr henna brn 1.10 .75
**B226** SP177 4fr + 3fr vio brn 1.10 .75
**B227** SP177 5fr + 4fr lt bl grn 2.50 1.50
**B228** SP177 6fr + 5fr indigo 2.25 1.10
**B229** SP177 10fr + 6fr car rose 2.25 1.10
**B230** SP177 15fr + 7fr sl blk 2.50 1.50
**B231** SP177 20fr + 8fr purple 2.50 1.50
*Nos. B224-B231 (8)* 15.30 8.95

Centenary of the Revolution of 1848.

Dr. Léon Charles Albert Calmette SP178

**1948, June 18**

**B232** SP178 6fr + 4fr dk grnsh bl .75 .35

1st Intl. Congress on the Calmette-Guerin bacillus vaccine.

Farmer — SP179

Designs: 5fr+3fr, Fisherman. 8fr+4fr, Miner. 10fr+6fr, Metal worker.

**1949, Feb. 14**

**B233** SP179 3fr + 1fr claret .65 .45
**B234** SP179 5fr + 3fr dk blue .75 .45
**B235** SP179 8fr + 4fr indigo .75 .45
**B236** SP179 10fr + 6fr dk red .80 .45
*Nos. B233-B236 (4)* 2.95 1.80

Étienne François de Choiseul and Post Cart — SP180

**1949, Mar. 26**

**B237** SP180 15fr + 5fr dk green .80 .45

Stamp Day, Mar. 26-27, 1949.

Baron de la Brède et de Montesquieu SP181

Designs: 8fr+2fr, Voltaire. 10fr+3fr, Antoine Watteau. 12fr+4fr, Georges de Buffon. 15fr+5fr, Joseph F. Dupleix. 25fr+10fr, A. R. J. Turgot.

**1949, Nov. 14**

**B238** SP181 5fr + 1fr dk grn 2.50 1.50
**B239** SP181 8fr + 2fr indigo 2.50 1.50
**B240** SP181 10fr + 3fr brn red 3.00 1.90
**B241** SP181 12fr + 4fr purple 3.50 1.90
**B242** SP181 15fr + 5fr rose car 3.75 2.25
**B243** SP181 25fr + 10fr ultra 4.50 3.00
*Nos. B238-B243 (6)* 19.75 12.05

"Spring" SP182

Designs: 8fr+2fr, Summer. 12fr+3fr, Autumn. 15fr+4fr, Winter.

**1949, Dec. 19**

**B244** SP182 5fr + 1fr green 1.50 .90
**B245** SP182 8fr + 2fr yel org 1.90 1.10
**B246** SP182 12fr + 3fr purple 1.90 1.50
**B247** SP182 15fr + 4fr dp blue 3.50 1.75
*Nos. B244-B247 (4)* 8.80 5.25

Postman — SP183

**1950, Mar. 11**

**B248** SP183 12fr + 3fr dp bl 3.00 1.75

Stamp Day, Mar. 11-12, 1950. See footnote after No. 4642.

André de Chénier — SP184

8fr+3fr, J. L. David. 10fr+4fr, Lazare Carnot. 12fr+5fr, G. J. Danton. 15fr+6fr, Maximilian Robespierre. 20fr+10fr, Louis Hoche.

**1950, July 10 Engr. *Perf. 13***

**Frames in Indigo**

**B249** SP184 5fr + 2fr brn vio 10.00 5.25
**B250** SP184 8fr + 3fr blk brn 10.00 5.50
**B251** SP184 10fr + 4fr lake 11.00 5.75
**B252** SP184 12fr + 5fr red brn 13.00 6.00
**B253** SP184 15fr + 6fr dk grn 14.00 6.00
**B254** SP184 20fr + 10fr dk vio bl 14.00 6.00
*Nos. B249-B254 (6)* 72.00 34.50

Alexandre Brongniart, Bust by Houdon — SP185

15fr+3fr, "L'Amour" by Etienne M. Falconet.

**1950, Dec. 22**

**B255** SP185 8fr + 2fr ind & car 2.00 1.25
**B256** SP185 15fr + 3fr red brn & car 2.25 1.25

The surtax was for the Red Cross.

Mail Car Interior — SP186

**1951, Mar. 10 Unwmk. *Perf. 13***

**B257** SP186 12fr + 3fr lilac gray 3.00 2.25

Stamp Day, Mar. 10-11, 1951.

Alfred de Musset — SP187

8fr+2fr, Eugène Delacroix. 10fr+3fr, J.-L. Gay-Lussac. 12fr+4fr, Robert Surcouf. 15fr+5fr, C. M. Talleyrand. 30fr+10fr, Napoleon I.

**Frames in Dark Brown**

**1951, June 2**

**B258** SP187 5fr + 1fr dk grn 5.25 3.00
**B259** SP187 8fr + 2fr vio brn 7.50 3.00
**B260** SP187 10fr + 3fr grnsh black 6.75 3.00
**B261** SP187 12fr + 4fr dk vio brn 6.75 3.75
**B262** SP187 15fr + 5fr brn car 6.75 3.75
**B263** SP187 30fr + 10fr indigo 12.00 6.00
*Nos. B258-B263 (6)* 45.00 22.50

Child at Prayer by Le Maître de Moulins SP188

18th Century Child by Quentin de la Tour SP189

**1951, Dec. 15 Cross in Red**

**B264** SP188 12fr + 3fr dk brown 3.00 1.75
**B265** SP189 15fr + 5fr dp ultra 3.50 2.00

The surtax was for the Red Cross.

Stagecoach of 1844 SP190

**1952, Mar. 8 *Perf. 13***

**B266** SP190 12fr + 3fr dp green 3.50 2.25

Stamp Day, Mar. 8, 1952.

Gustave Flaubert — SP191

Portraits: 12fr+3fr, Edouard Manet. 15fr+4fr, Camille Saint-Saens. 18fr+5fr, Henri Poincaré. 20fr+6fr, Georges-Eugene Haussmann. 30fr+7fr, Adolphe Thiers.

**1952, Oct. 18**

**Frames in Dark Brown**

**B267** SP191 8fr + 2fr indigo 6.75 3.00
**B268** SP191 12fr + 3fr vio blue 6.75 3.00
**B269** SP191 15fr + 4fr dk grn 6.75 3.00
**B270** SP191 18fr + 5fr dk brn 7.50 3.75
**B271** SP191 20fr + 6fr car 8.25 4.50
**B272** SP191 30fr + 7fr purple 9.00 4.50
*Nos. B267-B272 (6)* 45.00 21.75

Cupid from Diana Fountain Versailles SP192

15fr+5fr, Similar detail, cupid facing left.

**1952, Dec. 13 Cross in Red**

**B273** SP192 12fr + 3fr dk grn 4.25 2.50
**B274** SP192 15fr + 5fr indigo 4.25 2.50
*a.* Booklet pane of 10 225.00
Complete booklet 375.00

The surtax was for the Red Cross.

Count d'Argenson SP193

**1953, Mar. 14**

**B275** SP193 12fr + 3fr dp blue 2.50 1.50

Day of the Stamp. Surtax for the Red Cross.

St. Bernard — SP194

12fr+3fr, Olivier de Serres. 15fr+4fr, Jean Philippe Rameau. 18fr+5fr, Gaspard Monge. 20fr+6fr, Jules Michelet. 30fr+7fr, Marshal Hubert Lyautey.

**1953, July 9**

**B276** SP194 8fr + 2fr ultra 6.00 3.00
**B277** SP194 12fr + 3fr dk grn 6.00 3.00
**B278** SP194 15fr + 4fr brn car 9.00 4.50
**B279** SP194 18fr + 5fr dk blue 10.00 5.25
**B280** SP194 20fr + 6fr dk pur 10.00 5.25
**B281** SP194 30fr + 7fr brown 10.00 5.25
*Nos. B276-B281 (6)* 51.00 26.25

The surtax was for the Red Cross.

Madame Vigée-Lebrun and her Daughter — SP195

Design: 15fr+5fr, "The Return from Baptism," by Louis Le Nain.

**1953, Dec. 12 Cross in Red**

**B282** SP195 12fr + 3fr red brn 7.50 3.75
*a.* Bklt. pane, 4 each, gutter btwn. 85.00
**B283** SP195 15fr + 5fr indigo 10.00 5.25

The surtax was for the Red Cross.

Count Antoine de La Vallette — SP196

**1954, Mar. 20 Engr. *Perf. 13***

**B284** SP196 12fr + 3fr dp grn & choc 3.75 2.25

Stamp Day, Mar. 20, 1954.

Louis IX — SP197

Portraits: 15fr+5fr, Jacques Benigne Bossuet. 18fr+6fr, Sadi Carnot. 20fr+7fr, Antoine Bourdelle. 25fr+8fr, Dr. Emile Roux. 30fr+10fr, Paul Valéry.

**1954, July 10**

**B285** SP197 12fr + 4fr dp bl 17.50 10.00
**B286** SP197 15fr + 5fr pur 21.00 10.00
**B287** SP197 18fr + 6fr dk brn 21.00 10.00
**B288** SP197 20fr + 7fr crim 26.00 13.00
**B289** SP197 25fr + 8fr ind 26.00 13.00
**B290** SP197 30fr + 10fr dp claret 26.00 13.00
*Nos. B285-B290 (6)* 137.50 69.00

See Nos. B303-B308, B312-B317.

"The Sick Child," by Eugene Carrière — SP198

Design: 15fr+5fr, "Young Girl with Doves," by Jean Baptiste Greuze.

**1954, Dec. 18 Cross in Red**

**B291** SP198 12fr + 3fr vio gray & indigo 10.00 4.50
*a.* Bklt. pane, 4 each, gutter btwn. 110.00
**B292** SP198 15fr + 5fr dk brn & org brn 10.50 6.00

No. B291a for 90th anniv. of the Red Cross.
The surtax was for the Red Cross.

Balloon Post, 1870 SP199

**1955, Mar. 19 Unwmk. *Perf. 13***

**B293** SP199 12fr + 3fr multi 3.75 2.25

Stamp Day, Mar. 19-20, 1955.

King Philip II — SP200

Portraits: 15fr+6fr, Francois de Malherbé. 18fr+7fr, Sebastien de Vauban. 25fr+8fr, Charles G. de Vergennes. 30fr+9fr, Pierre S. de Laplace. 50fr+15fr, Pierre Auguste Renoir.

**1955, June 11**

**B294** SP200 12fr + 5fr brt pur 13.50 7.50
**B295** SP200 15fr + 6fr dp bl 13.50 7.50
**B296** SP200 18fr + 7fr dp green 13.50 7.50
**B297** SP200 25fr + 8fr gray 19.00 9.00
**B298** SP200 30fr + 9fr rose brn 26.00 10.00
**B299** SP200 50fr + 15fr blue grn 26.00 11.00
*Nos. B294-B299 (6)* 111.50 52.50

See Nos. B321-B326.

Child with Cage by Pigalle — SP201

Design: 15fr+5fr, Child with Goose, by Boethus of Chalcedon.

**1955, Dec. 17 Cross in Red**

**B300** SP201 12fr + 3fr claret 6.50 3.75
**B301** SP201 15fr + 5fr dk bl 5.25 3.00
*a.* Booklet pane of 10 150.00
Complete booklet 300.00

The surtax was for the Red Cross.

Francois of Taxis SP202

**1956, Mar. 17 Engr. *Perf. 13***

**B302** SP202 12fr + 3fr ultra, grn & dk brn 2.25 1.10

Stamp Day, Mar. 17-18, 1956.

**Portrait Type of 1954**

Portraits: No. 303, Guillaume Budé. No. B304, Jean Goujon. No. B305, Samuel de Champlain. No. B306, Jean Simeon Chardin. No. B307, Maurice Barrès. No. B308, Maurice Ravel.

**1956, June 9 *Perf. 13***

**B303** SP197 12fr + 3fr saph 4.00 3.00
**B304** SP197 12fr + 3fr lil gray 4.00 3.00
**B305** SP197 12fr + 3fr brt red 5.25 3.00
**B306** SP197 15fr + 5fr green 6.75 4.50
**B307** SP197 15fr + 5fr vio brn 6.75 4.50
**B308** SP197 15fr + 5fr dp vio 9.00 4.50
*Nos. B303-B308 (6)* 35.75 22.50

Peasant Boy by Le Nain — SP203

Design: 15fr+5fr, Gilles by Watteau.

**1956, Dec. 8 Unwmk.**
**Cross in Red**

**B309** SP203 12fr + 3fr ol gray 2.25 1.10
*a.* Bklt. pane, 4 ea, gutter btwn. 40.00
**B310** SP203 15fr + 5fr rose lake 2.50 1.25

The surtax was for the Red Cross.

Genoese Felucca, 1750 SP204

**1957, Mar. 16 *Perf. 13***

**B311** SP204 12fr +3fr bluish gray & brn blk 1.60 1.00

Day of the Stamp, Mar. 16, 1957, and honoring the Maritime Postal Service.

**Portrait Type of 1954**

**1957, June 15**

Portraits: No. B312, Jean de Joinville. No. B313, Bernard Palissy. No. B314, Quentin de la Tour. No. B315, Hugues Félicité Robert de Lamennais. No. B316, George Sand. No. B317, Jules Guesde.

**B312** SP197 12fr + 3fr ol gray & ol grn 1.90 1.10
**B313** SP197 12fr + 3fr grnsh blk & grnsh bl 1.90 1.10
**B314** SP197 15fr + 5fr cl & brt red 3.00 1.40
**B315** SP197 15fr + 5fr ultra & ind 2.75 1.40
**B316** SP197 18fr + 7fr grnsh blk & dk grn 3.25 1.60
**B317** SP197 18fr + 7fr dk vio brn & red brn 3.25 1.60
*Nos. B312-B317 (6)* 16.05 8.20

Blind Man and Beggar, Engraving by Jacques Callot — SP205

Design: 20fr+8fr, Women beggars.

**1957, Dec. 7 Engr. *Perf. 13***

**B318** SP205 15fr + 7fr ultra & red 3.50 1.75
*a.* Bklt. pane, 4 ea, gutter btwn. 45.00 45.00
**B319** SP205 20fr + 8fr dk vio brn & red 4.50 2.40

The surtax was for the Red Cross.

Motorized Mail Distribution SP206

**1958, Mar. 15**

**B320** SP206 15fr + 5fr multi 1.20 .75

Stamp Day, Mar. 15.

**Portrait Type of 1955**

Portraits: No. B321, Joachim du Bellay. No. B322, Jean Bart. No. B323, Denis Diderot. No. B324, Gustave Courbet. 20fr+8fr, J. B. Carpeaux. 35fr+15fr, Toulouse-Lautrec.

**1958, June 7 Engr. *Perf. 13***

**B321** SP200 12fr + 4fr yel grn 1.40 .90
**B322** SP200 12fr + 4fr dk blue 1.40 .90
**B323** SP200 15fr + 5fr dull cl 1.50 1.00
**B324** SP200 15fr + 5fr ultra 1.60 1.10
**B325** SP200 20fr + 8fr brt red 1.60 1.00
**B326** SP200 35fr + 15fr green 2.10 1.10
*Nos. B321-B326 (6)* 9.60 6.00

St. Vincent de Paul — SP207

Portrait: 20fr+8fr, J. H. Dunant.

**1958, Dec. 6 Unwmk.**
**Cross in Carmine**

**B327** SP207 15fr + 7fr grayish grn 1.00 .45
*a.* Bklt. pane, 4 each, gutter btwn. 20.00
**B328** SP207 20fr + 8fr violet 1.00 .45

The surtax was for the Red Cross. See No. B747d.

Plane Landing at Night SP208

**1959, Mar. 21**

**B329** SP208 20fr + 5fr sl grn, blk & rose .45 .30

Issued for Stamp Day, Mar. 21, and to publicize night air mail service.
The surtax was for the Red Cross.
See No. 1089.

Geoffroi de Villehardouin and Ships — SP209

Designs: No. B331, André Le Nôtre and formal garden. No. B332, Jean Le Rond d'Alembert, books and wheel. No. B333, David d'Angers, statue and building. No. B334, M. F. X. Bichat and torch. No. B335, Frédéric Auguste Bartholdi, Statue of Liberty and Lion of Belfort.

**1959, June 13 Engr. *Perf. 13***

**B330** SP209 15fr + 5fr vio blue 1.00 .60
**B331** SP209 15fr + 5fr dk sl grn 1.00 .60
**B332** SP209 20fr + 10fr olive bis .90 .60
**B333** SP209 20fr + 10fr dk gray 1.10 .65
**B334** SP209 30fr + 10fr dk car rose 1.00 .65
**B335** SP209 30fr + 10fr org brn 1.20 .65
*Nos. B330-B335 (6)* 6.20 3.75

The surtax was for the Red Cross.

No. 927 Surcharged

**1959, Dec. Typo. *Perf. 14x13½***

**B336** A328 25fr + 5fr black & red .25 .25

Surtax for the flood victims at Frejus.

Charles Michel de l'Épée — SP210

Design: 25fr+10fr, Valentin Hauy.

**1959, Dec. 5 Engr. *Perf. 13***
**Cross in Carmine**

**B337** SP210 20fr + 10fr blk & cl 1.60 1.00
*a.* Bklt. pane, 4 each, gutter btwn. 30.00
**B338** SP210 25fr + 10fr dk blue & blk 2.00 1.10

The surtax was for the Red Cross.

Ship Laying Underwater Cable SP211

**1960, Mar. 12**

**B339** SP211 20c + 5c grnsh bl & dk bl 1.10 .90

Issued for the Day of the Stamp. The surtax went to the Red Cross.

Refugee Girl Amid Ruins — SP212

**1960, Apr. 7**

**B340** SP212 25c + 10c grn, brn & ind .30 .25

World Refugee Year, July 1, 1959-June 30, 1960. The surtax was for aid to refugees.

Michel de L'Hospital SP213

No. B342, Henri de la Tour D'Auvergne, Viscount of Turenne. No. B343, Nicolas Boileau (Despreaux). No. B344, Jean-Martin Charcot, M.D. No. B345, Georges Bizet. 50c+15c, Edgar Degás.

**1960, June 11 Engr. *Perf. 13***

**B341** SP213 10c + 5c pur & rose car 1.10 .90
**B342** SP213 20c + 10c ol & vio brn 1.90 1.60
**B343** SP213 20c + 10c Prus grn & dp yel grn 1.50 1.25
**B344** SP213 30c + 10c rose car & rose red 2.60 2.25
**B345** SP213 30c + 10c dk bl & vio bl 3.00 2.50
**B346** SP213 50c + 15c sl bl & gray 3.50 2.75
*Nos. B341-B346 (6)* 13.60 11.25

The surtax was for the Red Cross.
See Nos. B350-B355.

Staff of the Brotherhood of St. Martin — SP214

25c+10c, St. Martin, 16th cent. wood sculpture.

**1960, Dec. 3 Unwmk. *Perf. 13***

**B347** SP214 20c + 10c rose cl & red 2.60 2.25
*a.* Bklt. pane, 4 each, gutter btwn. 32.50
**B348** SP214 25c + 10c lt ultra & red 2.60 2.25

The surtax was for the Red Cross.

Letter Carrier, Paris 1760 — SP215

**1961, Mar. 18 *Perf. 13***

**B349** SP215 20c + 5c sl grn, brn & red .60 .45

Stamp Day. Surtax for Red Cross.

**Famous Men Type of 1960**

Designs: 15c+5c, Bertrand Du Guesclin. No. B351, Pierre Puget. No. B352, Charles Coulomb. 30c+10c, Antoine Drouot. 45c+10c, Honoré Daumier. 50c+15c, Guillaume Apollinaire.

**1961, May 20 Engr.**

**B350** SP213 15c + 5c red brn & blk 1.60 1.50
**B351** SP213 20c + 10c dk grn & lt bl 1.50 1.50
**B352** SP213 20c + 10c ver & rose car 1.75 1.50
**B353** SP213 30c + 10c blk & brn org 1.75 1.50
**B354** SP213 45c + 10c choc & dk grn 2.60 2.25
**B355** SP213 50c + 15c dk car rose & vio 2.60 2.25
*Nos. B350-B355 (6)* 11.80 10.50

"Love" by Rouault — SP216

Designs from "Miserere" by Georges Rouault: 25c+10c, "The Blind Consoles the Seeing."

**1961, Dec. 2 *Perf. 13***

**B356** SP216 20c + 10c brn, blk & red 1.90 1.50
*a.* Bklt. pane, 4 each, gutter btwn. 30.00
**B357** SP216 25c + 10c brn, blk & red 2.25 1.90

The surtax was for the Red Cross.

Medieval Royal Messenger SP217

**1962, Mar. 17**

**B358** SP217 20c + 5c rose red, bl & sepia .60 .55

Stamp Day. Surtax for Red Cross.

Denis Papin, Scientist — SP218

Portraits: No. B360, Edme Bouchardon, sculptor. No. B361, Joseph Lakanal, educator. 30c+10c, Gustave Charpentier, composer. 45c+15c, Edouard Estaunié, writer. 50c+20c, Hyacinthe Vincent, physician and bacteriologist.

**1962, June 2 Engr.**

**B359** SP218 15c + 5c bluish grn & dk gray 1.50 1.25
**B360** SP218 20c + 10c cl brn 1.50 1.25
**B361** SP218 20c + 10c gray & sl 1.50 1.25
**B362** SP218 30c + 10c brt bl & ind 1.90 1.60
**B363** SP218 45c + 15c org brn & choc 2.10 1.75
**B364** SP218 50c + 20c grnsh bl & blk 2.00 1.75
*Nos. B359-B364 (6)* 10.50 8.85

The surtax was for the Red Cross.

Rosalie Fragonard by Fragonard — SP219

Design: 25c+10c, Child dressed as Pierrot.

**1962, Dec. 8 Cross in Red**

**B365** SP219 20c + 10c redsh brown .90 .75
*a.* Bklt. pane, 4 ea, gutter btwn. 32.00
**B366** SP219 25c + 10c dull grn 1.50 1.40

The surtax was for the Red Cross.
For surcharges see Reunion Nos. B16-B17.

Jacques Amyot, Classical Scholar SP220

30c+10c, Pierre de Marivaux, playwright. 50c+20c, Jacques Daviel, surgeon.

**1963, Feb. 23 Unwmk. *Perf. 13***

**B367** SP220 20c + 10c mar, gray & pur .75 .65
**B368** SP220 30c + 10c Prus grn & mar .75 .65
**B369** SP220 50c + 20c ultra, ocher & ol .90 .75
*Nos. B367-B369 (3)* 2.40 2.05

The surtax was for the Red Cross.

Roman Chariot SP221

**1963, Mar. 16 Engr.**

**B370** SP221 20c + 5c brn org & vio brn .25 .25

Stamp Day. Surtax for Red Cross.

Étienne Méhul, Composer SP222

Designs: 30c+10c, Nicolas-Louis Vauquelin, chemist. 50c+20c, Alfred de Vigny, poet.

**1963, May 25 Unwmk. *Perf. 13***

**B371** SP222 20c + 10c dp bl, dk brn & dp org .90 .75
**B372** SP222 30c + 10c mag, gray ol & blk .75 .65
**B373** SP222 50c + 20c sl, blk & brn 1.20 1.00
*Nos. B371-B373 (3)* 2.85 2.40

The surtax was for the Red Cross.

"Child with Grapes" by David d'Angers and Centenary Emblem — SP223

25c+10c, "The Fifer," by Edouard Manet.

**1963, Dec. 9 Unwmk. *Perf. 13***

**B374** SP223 20c + 10c black & red .65 .55
*a.* Bklt. pane, 4 each, gutter btwn. 9.00 9.00
**B375** SP223 25c + 10c sl grn & red .65 .55

Cent. of the Intl. and French Red Cross. Surtax for the Red Cross.
For surcharges see Reunion Nos. B18-B19.

Post Rider, 18th Century SP224

**1964, Mar. 14 Engr.**

**B376** SP224 20c + 5c Prus green .25 .25

Issued for Stamp Day.

Resistance Memorial by Watkin, Luxembourg Gardens — SP225

De Gaulle's 1940 Poster "A Tous les Francais" SP226

Street Fighting in Paris and Strasbourg. SP227

Designs: 20c+5c, "Deportation," concentration camp with watchtower and barbed wire. No. B379, Allied troops landing in Normandy and Provence.

**1964 Engr. *Perf. 13***

**B377** SP225 20c + 5c slate blk .45 .40

***Perf. 12x13***

**B378** SP226 25c + 5c dk red, bl, red & blk .75 .60

***Perf. 13***

**B379** SP227 30c + 5c blk, bl & org brn .60 .55
**B380** SP227 30c + 5c org brn, cl & blk .60 .55
**B381** SP225 50c + 5c dk grn .60 .55
*Nos. B377-B381 (5)* 3.00 2.65

20th anniv. of liberation from the Nazis.
Issue dates: Noz. B377, B381, 3/21; No. B378, 6/18; No. B379, 6/6; No. B380, 8/22.

President René Coty — SP229

Portraits: No. B383, John Calvin. No. B384, Pope Sylvester II (Gerbert).

**1964 Unwmk. *Perf. 13***

**B382** SP229 30c + 10c dp cl & blk .30 .25
**B383** SP229 30c + 10c dk grn, blk & brn .30 .25
**B384** SP229 30c + 10c slate & cl .30 .25
*Nos. B382-B384 (3)* .90 .75

The surtax was for the Red Cross.
Issued: No. B382, 4/25; No. B383, 5/25; No. B384, 6/1.

Jean Nicolas Corvisart — SP230

Portrait: 25c+10c, Dominique Larrey.

**Cross in Carmine**

**1964, Dec. 12 Engr.**

**B385** SP230 20c + 10c black .30 .25
*a.* Bklt. pane, 4 ea, gutter btwn. 3.50
**B386** SP230 25c + 10c black .30 .25

Jean Nicolas Corvisart (1755-1821), physician of Napoleon I, and Dominique Larrey (1766-1842), Chief Surgeon of the Imperial Armies. The surtax was for the Red Cross.
For surcharges see Reunion Nos. B20-B21.

Paul Dukas, Composer — SP231

No. B387, Duke François de La Rochefoucauld, writer. No. B388, Nicolas Poussin, painter. No. B389, Duke Charles of Orléans, poet.

**1965, Feb. Engr. *Perf. 13***

**B387** SP231 30c + 10c org brn & dk bl .30 .25
**B388** SP231 30c + 10c car & dk red brn .30 .25
**B389** SP231 40c + 10c dk red brn, dk red & Prus bl .45 .40
**B390** SP231 40c + 10c dk brn & sl bl .45 .40
*Nos. B387-B390 (4)* 1.50 1.30

The surtax was for the Red Cross.
Issued: Nos. B387, B390 2/13; Nos. B388-B389 2/20.

Packet "La Guienne" SP232

**1965, Mar. 29 Unwmk. *Perf. 13***

**B391** SP232 25c + 10c multi .40 .40

Issued for Stamp Day, 1965. "La Guienne" was used for transatlantic mail service. Surtax was for the Red Cross.

Infant with Spoon by Auguste Renoir — SP233

Design: 30c+10c, Coco Writing (Renoir's daughter Claude).

**1965, Dec. 11 Engr. *Perf. 13***

**Cross in Carmine**

**B392** SP233 25c + 10c slate .25 .25
*a.* Bklt. pane, 4 ea, gutter btwn. 2.75
**B393** SP233 30c + 10c dull red brn .25 .25

The surtax was for the Red Cross.
For surcharges see Reunion Nos. B22-B23.

Francois Mansart and Carnavalet Palace, Paris SP234

No. B395, St. Pierre Fourier and Basilica of St. Pierre Fourier, Mirecourt. No. B396, Marcel Proust and St. Hilaire Bridge, Illiers. No. B397, Gabriel Fauré, monument and score of "Penelope." No. B398, Elie Metchnikoff, microscope and Pasteur Institute. No. B399, Hippolyte Taine and birthplace.

**1966 Engr. *Perf. 13***

**B394** SP234 30c + 10c dk red brn & grn .25 .25
**B395** SP234 30c + 10c blk & gray grn .25 .25
**B396** SP234 30c + 10c ind, sep & grn .25 .25
**B397** SP234 30c + 10c bis brn & ind .25 .25
**B398** SP234 30c + 10c blk & dl brn .25 .25
**B399** SP234 30c + 10c grn & ol brn .25 .25
*Nos. B394-B399 (6)* 1.50 1.50

The surtax was for the Red Cross.
Issued: Nos. B394-B396, 2/12; others, 6/25.

Engraver Cutting Die and Tools SP235

**1966, Mar. 19 Engr. *Perf. 13***

**B400** SP235 25c + 10c slate, dk brn & dp org .25 .25

Stamp Day. Surtax for Red Cross.

Angel of Victory, Verdun Fortress, Marching Troops — SP236

**1966, May 28 *Perf. 13***

**B401** SP236 30c + 5c Prus bl, ultra & dk bl .25 .25

Victory of Verdun, 50th anniversary.

First Aid on Battlefield, 1859 — SP237

No. B403, Nurse giving first aid to child, 1966.

**Cross in Carmine**

**1966, Dec. 10 Engr. *Perf. 13***

**B402** SP237 25c + 10c green .25 .25
*a.* Bklt. pane, 4 ea, gutter btwn. 3.50
**B403** SP237 30c + 10c slate .30 .25

The surtax was for the Red Cross.
See No. B746e. For surcharges see Reunion Nos. B24-B25.

Emile Zola — SP238

No. B405, Beaumarchais (pen name of Pierre Augustin Caron). No. B406, St. Francois de Sales (1567-1622). No. B407, Albert Camus (1913-1960).

**1967 Engr. *Perf. 13***

**B404** SP238 30c + 10c sl bl & bl .30 .25
**B405** SP238 30c + 10c rose brn & lil .30 .25
**B406** SP238 30c + 10c dl vio & pur .30 .25
**B407** SP238 30c + 10c brn & dl cl .30 .25
*Nos. B404-B407 (4)* 1.20 1.00

The surtax was for the Red Cross.
Issued: Nos. B404-B405, 2/4; others, 6/24.

Letter Carrier, 1865 — SP239

**1967, Apr. 8**

**B408** SP239 25c + 10c indigo, grn & red .30 .25

Issued for Stamp Day.

Ivory Flute Player — SP240

30c+10c, Violin player, ivory carving.

**Cross in Carmine**

**1967, Dec. 16 Engr. *Perf. 13***

**B409** SP240 25c + 10c dl vio & lt brn .30 .25
*a.* Bklt. pane, 4 ea, gutter btwn. 3.50
**B410** SP240 30c + 10c grn & lt brn .35 .25

The surtax was for the Red Cross.
For surcharges see Reunion Nos. B26-B27.

Ski Jump and Long Distance Skiing — SP241

Designs: 40c+10c, Ice hockey. 60c+20c, Olympic flame and snowflakes. 75c+25c, Woman figure skater. 95c+35c, Slalom.

**1968, Jan. 27**

**B411** SP241 30c + 10c ver, gray & brn .30 .30
**B412** SP241 40c + 10c lil, lem & brt mag .30 .30
**B413** SP241 60c + 20c dk grn, org & brt vio .40 .40
**B414** SP241 75c + 25c brt pink, yel grn & blk .50 .50
**B415** SP241 95c + 35c bl, brt pink & red brn .60 .50
*Nos. B411-B415 (5)* 2.10 2.00

Issued for the 10th Winter Olympic Games, Grenoble, Feb. 6-18.

Rural Mailman, 1830 — SP242

**1968, Mar. 16 Engr. *Perf. 13***

**B416** SP242 25c + 10c multi .25 .25

Issued for Stamp Day.

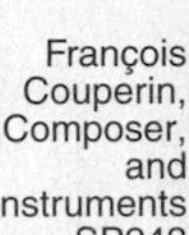

François Couperin, Composer, and Instruments SP243

Portraits: No. B418, Gen. Louis Desaix de Veygoux (1768-1800) and scene showing his death at the Battle of Marengo, Italy. No. B419, Saint-Pol Roux (pen name of Paul-Pierre Roux, 1861-1940), Christ on the Cross and ruins of Camaret-sur-Mer. No. B420, Paul Claudel (poet and diplomat, 1868-1955) and Joan of Arc at the stake.

**1968 Engr. *Perf. 13***

**B417** SP243 30c + 10c pur & rose lil .25 .25
**B418** SP243 30c + 10c dk grn & brn .25 .25
**B419** SP243 30c + 10c cop red & ol bis .25 .25
**B420** SP243 30c + 10c dk brn & lil .25 .25
*Nos. B417-B420 (4)* 1.00 1.00

Issue dates: Nos. B417-B418, Mar. 23; Nos. B419-B420, July 6.

Spring, by Nicolas Mignard — SP244

Paintings by Nicolas Mignard; 30c+10c, Fall. No. B423, Summer. No. B424, Winter.

**1968-69 Engr. *Perf. 13***

**Cross in Carmine**

**B421** SP244 25c + 10c pur & dk bl .30 .25
*a.* Bklt. pane, 4 ea #B421-B422 with gutter btwn.) 3.00
**B422** SP244 30c + 10c brn & car red .30 .30
**B423** SP244 40c + 15c dk brn & brn ('69) .45 .30
*a.* Bklt. pane, 4 ea #B423, B424 with gutter btwn.) 3.50
**B424** SP244 40c + 15c pur & Prus bl ('69) .45 .30
*Nos. B421-B424 (4)* 1.50 1.15

The surtax was for the Red Cross.
For surcharges see Reunion Nos. B28-B31.

Mailmen's Omnibus, 1881 SP245

**1969, Mar. 15 Engr. *Perf. 13***

**B425** SP245 30c + 10c brn, grn & blk .25 .25

Issued for Stamp Day.
For surcharge see Reunion No. B32.

Gen. Francois Marceau — SP246

Portraits: No. B427, Charles Augustin Sainte-Beuve (1804-1869), writer. No. B428, Albert Roussel (1869-1937), musician. No. B429, Marshal Jean Lannes (1769-1809). No. B430, Georges Cuvier (1769-1832), naturalist. No. B431, André Gide, (1869-1951), writer.

**1969**

**B426** SP246 50c + 10c brn red .40 .35
**B427** SP246 50c + 10c slate bl .40 .35
**B428** SP246 50c + 10c dp vio bl .40 .35
**B429** SP246 50c + 10c choc .40 .35
**B430** SP246 50c + 10c dp plum .40 .35
**B431** SP246 50c + 10c blue grn .40 .35
*Nos. B426-B431 (6)* 2.40 2.10

The surtax was for the Red Cross.
Issued: Nos. B426-B428, Mar. 24; No. B429, May 10; Nos. B430-B431, May 17.

Gen. Jacques Leclerc, La Madeleine and Battle — SP247

**1969, Aug. 23 Engr. *Perf. 13***
**B432** SP247 45c + 10c slate & ol .75 .60

Liberation of Paris, 8/25/44, 25th anniv.

**Inscribed Liberation de Strasbourg**

**1969, Nov. 22 Engr. *Perf. 13***
**B433** SP247 70c + 10c brn, choc & olive 2.75 2.00

25th anniv. of the liberation of Strasbourg.

Philibert Delorme, Architect, and Chateau d'Anet SP248

Designs: No. B435, Louis Le Vau (1612-1670), architect, and Vaux-le-Vicomte Chateau, Paris. No. B436, Prosper Merimée (1803-1870), writer, and Carmen. No. B437, Alexandre Dumas (1802-1870), writer, and Three Musketeers. No. B438, Edouard Branly (1844-1940), physicist, electric circuit and convent of the Carmes, Paris. No. B439, Maurice de Broglie (1875-1960), physicist, and X-ray spectrograph.

**1970 Engr. *Perf. 13***
**B434** SP248 40c + 10c slate grn .40 .35
**B435** SP248 40c + 10c dk car .40 .35
**B436** SP248 40c + 10c Prus blue .40 .35
**B437** SP248 40c + 10c violet bl .40 .35
**B438** SP248 40c + 10c dp brown .40 .35
**B439** SP248 40c + 10c dk gray .40 .35
*Nos. B434-B439 (6)* 2.40 2.10

The surtax was for the Red Cross.
Issued: No. B434-B436, 2/14; others, 4/11.

City Mailman, 1830 — SP249

**1970, Mar. 14**
**B440** SP249 40c + 10c blk, ultra & dk car rose .30 .25

Issued for Stamp Day.

For surcharge see Reunion No. B33.

"Life and Death" — SP250

**1970, Apr. 4**
**B441** SP250 40c + 10c brt bl, ol & car rose .25 .25

Issued to publicize the fight against cancer in connection with Health Day, Apr. 7.

Marshal de Lattre de Tassigny — SP251

**1970, May 8 Engr. *Perf. 13***
**B442** SP251 40c + 10c slate & vio bl .50 .30

25th anniv. of the entry into Berlin of French troops under Marshal Jean de Lattre de Tassigny, May 8, 1945.

Lord and Lady, Dissay Chapel Fresco — SP252

No. B444, Angel holding whips, from fresco in Dissay Castle Chapel, Vienne, c. 1500.

**1970, Dec. 12 Engr. *Perf. 13***
**Cross in Carmine**
**B443** SP252 40c + 15c green .30 .25
 *a.* Bklt. pane, 4 ea, gutter btwn. 12.50
**B444** SP252 40c + 15c cop red .30 .25

The surtax was for the Red Cross.
For surcharges see Reunion Nos. B34-B35.

Daniel-Francois Auber and "Fra Diavolo" Music — SP253

No. B446, Gen. Charles Diego Brosset (1898-1944), Basilica of Fourvière. No. B447, Victor Grignard (1871-1935), chemist, Nobel Prize medal. No. B448, Henri Farman (1874-1958), plane. No. B449, Gen. Charles Georges Delestraint (1879-1945), scroll. No. B450, Jean Eugène Robert-Houdin (1805-71), magician's act.

**1971 Engr. *Perf. 13***
**B445** SP253 50c + 10c brn vio & brn .50 .30
**B446** SP253 50c + 10c dk sl grn & ol gray .50 .30
**B447** SP253 50c + 10c brn red & olive .50 .30
**B448** SP253 50c + 10c vio bl & vio .50 .30
**B449** SP253 50c + 10c pur & cl .60 .45
**B450** SP253 50c + 10c sl grn & bl grn .60 .45
*Nos. B445-B450 (6)* 3.20 2.10

The surtax was for the Red Cross.
Issued: Nos. B445-B446, 3/6; No. B447, 5/8; No. B448, 5/29; Nos. B449-B450, 10/16.

Army Post Office, 1914-1918 SP254

**1971, Mar. 27 Engr. *Perf. 13***
**B451** SP254 50c + 10c ol, brn & bl .40 .30

Stamp Day, 1971.
For surcharge see Reunion No. B36.

Girl with Dog, by Greuze — SP255

Design: 50c+10c, "The Dead Bird," by Jean-Baptiste Greuze (1725-1805).

**1971, Dec. 11 Cross in Carmine**
**B452** SP255 30c + 10c violet bl .55 .45
 *a.* Bklt. pane, 4 each, gutter btwn. 6.00
**B453** SP255 50c + 10c dp car .55 .45

The surtax was for the Red Cross.
For surcharges see Reunion Nos. B37-B38.

Aristide Bergès (1833-1904) SP256

No. B455, Paul de Chomedey (1612-76), founder of Montreal, and arms of Neuville-sur-Vanne. No. B456, Edouard Belin (1876-1963), inventor. No. B457, Louis Blériot (1872-1936), aviation pioneer. No. B458, Adm. François Joseph, Count de Grasse (1722-88), hero of the American Revolution. No. B459, Théophile Gautier (1811-72), writer.

**1972 Engr. *Perf. 13***
**B454** SP256 50c + 10c blk & grn .50 .40
**B455** SP256 50c + 10c blk & bl .50 .40
**B456** SP256 50c + 10c blk & lil rose .50 .40
**B457** SP256 50c + 10c red & blk .50 .40
**B458** SP256 50c + 10c org & blk .50 .40
**B459** SP256 50c + 10c blk & brn .50 .40
*Nos. B454-B459 (6)* 3.00 2.40

The surtax was for the Red Cross.
Issued: Nos. B454-B455, 2/19; No. B456, 6/24; No. B457, 7/1; Nos. B458-B459, 9/9.

Rural Mailman, 1894 — SP257

**1972, Mar. 18 Engr. *Perf. 13***
**B460** SP257 50c + 10c bl, yel & ol gray .50 .40

Stamp Day 1972.
For surcharge see Reunion No. B39.

Nicolas Desgenettes SP258

Designs: 30c+10c, René Nicolas Dufriche, Baron Desgenettes, M.D. (1762-1837). 50c+10c, François Joseph Broussais, M.D. (1772-1838).

**1972, Dec. 16 Engr. *Perf. 13***
**B461** SP258 30c + 10c sl grn & red .40 .30
 *a.* Bklt. pane, 4 ea, gutter btwn. 7.00
**B462** SP258 50c + 10c red .45 .40

The surtax was for the Red Cross.
See No. B747b. For surcharges see Reunion Nos. B40-B41.

Tony Garnier (1869-1948), architect — SP259

No. B463, Gaspard de Coligny (1519-1572), admiral and Huguenot leader. No. B464, Ernest Renan (1823-1892), philologist and historian. No. B465, Alberto Santos Dumont (1873-1932), Brazilian aviator. No. B466, Gabrielle-Sidonie Colette (1873-1954), writer. No. B467, René Duguay-Trouin (1673-1736), naval commander. No. B468, Louis Pasteur (1822-1895), chemist, bacteriologist. No. B469, Tony Garnier (1869-1948), architect.

**1973 Engr. *Perf. 13***
**B463** SP259 50c + 10c multi .50 .40
**B464** SP259 50c + 10c multi .50 .40
**B465** SP259 50c + 10c multi .50 .40
**B466** SP259 50c + 10c multi .50 .40
**B467** SP259 50c + 10c multi .50 .40
**B468** SP259 50c + 10c multi .50 .40
**B469** SP259 50c + 10c multi .50 .40
*Nos. B463-B469 (7)* 3.50 2.80

Issued: No. B463, 2/17; No. B464, 4/28; No. B465, 5/26; No. B466, 6/2; No. B467, 6/9; No. B468, 10/6; No. B469, 11/17.

Mail Coach, 1835 SP260

**1973, Mar. 24 Engr. *Perf. 13***
**B470** SP260 50c + 10c grnsh blue .40 .25

Stamp Day, 1973.
For surcharge see Reunion No. B42.

Mary Magdalene SP261

50c+10c, Mourning woman. Designs are from 15th cent. Tomb of Tonnerre.

**1973, Dec. 1**
**B471** SP261 30c + 10c sl grn & red .40 .30
 *a.* Bklt. pane, 4 each, gutter btwn. 6.00
**B472** SP261 50c + 10c dk gray & red .45 .40

Surtax was for the Red Cross.
For surcharges see Reunion Nos. B43-B44.

St. Louis-Marie de Montfort — SP262

Portraits: No. B474, Francis Poulenc (1899-1963), composer. No. B475, Jules Barbey d'Aurevilly (1808-1889), writer. No. B476, Jean Giraudoux (1882-1944), writer.

**1974, Feb. 23** **Engr.** ***Perf. 13***
**B473** SP262 50c + 10c multi .50 .40
**B474** SP262 50c + 10c multi .50 .40
**B475** SP262 80c + 15c multi .60 .50
**B476** SP262 80c + 15c multi .60 .50
*Nos. B473-B476 (4)* 2.20 1.80

Issue dates: No. B473, Mar. 9; No. B474, July 20; Nos. B475-B476, Nov. 16.

Automatically Sorted Letters — SP263

**1974, Mar. 9** **Engr.** ***Perf. 13***
**B477** SP263 50c + 10c multi .30 .25

Stamp Day 1974. Automatic letter sorting center, Orleans-la-Source, opened 1/30/73.
For surcharge see Reunion No. B45.

Order of Liberation and 5 Honored Cities — SP264

**1974, June 15** **Engr.** ***Perf. 13***
**B478** SP264 1fr + 10c multi .55 .30

30th anniv. of liberation from the Nazis.

"Summer" — SP265

Designs: B481, "Spring" (girl on swing). B482, "Fall" (umbrella and rabbits).

**1974, Nov. 30** **Engr.** ***Perf. 13***
**B479** SP265 60c + 15c multi .45 .40
*a.* Bklt. pane, 4 ea, gutter btwn. 6.00
**B480** SP266 80c + 15c multi .45 .40

For surcharges see Reunion Nos. B46-B47.

"Winter" — SP266

**1975, Nov. 29**
**B481** SP265 60c + 15c multi .40 .30
*a.* Bklt. pane, 4 ea, gutter btwn. 4.75
**B482** SP266 80c + 20c multi .50 .40

Surtax was for the Red Cross.

Dr. Albert Schweitzer SP267

Edmond Michelet SP268

André Siegfried and Map SP269

No. B483, Albert Schweitzer (1875-1965), medical missionary. No. B484, Edmond Michelet (1899-1970), Resistance hero, statesman. No. B485, Robert Schuman (1886-1963), promoter of United Europe. No. B486, Eugene Thomas (1903-69), minister of PTT. No. B487, André Siegfried (1875-1959), political science professor, writer.

**1975** **Engr.** ***Perf. 13***
**B483** SP267 80c + 20c multi .50 .40
**B484** SP268 80c + 20c bl & ind .50 .40
**B485** SP268 80c + 20c blk & ind .50 .40
**B486** SP268 80c + 20c blk & sl .50 .40
**B487** SP269 80c + 20c blk & bl .50 .40
*Nos. B483-B487 (5)* 2.50 2.00

Issued: No. B483, 1/11; No. B484, 2/22; No. B485, 5/10; No. B486, 6/28; No. B487, 11/15.

Second Republic Mailman's Badge — SP270

**1975, Mar. 8** **Photo.**
**B488** SP270 80c + 20c multi .45 .35

Stamp Day.

"Sage" Type of 1876 — SP271

**1976, Mar. 13** **Engr.** ***Perf. 13***
**B489** SP271 80c + 20c blk & lil .40 .35

Stamp Day 1976.

Marshal A. J. de Moncey — SP272

No. B491, Max Jacob (1876-1944), Dadaist writer, by Picasso. No. B492, Jean Mounet-Sully (1841-1916), actor. No. B493, Gen. Pierre Daumesnil (1776-1832). No. B494, Eugène Fromentin (1820-1876), painter.

**1976** **Engr.** ***Perf. 13***
**B490** SP272 80c + 20c multi .40 .30
**B491** SP272 80c + 20c red brn & ol .40 .30
**B492** SP272 80c + 20c multi .40 .30
**B493** SP272 1fr + 20c multi .50 .30
**B494** SP272 1fr + 20c multi .50 .30
*Nos. B490-B494 (5)* 2.20 1.50

Issued: No. B490, 5/22; No. B491, 7/22; No. B492, 8/28; No. B493, 9/4; No. B494, 9/25.

Anna de Noailles — SP273

**1976, Nov. 6** **Engr.** ***Perf. 13***
**B495** SP273 1fr + 20c multi .50 .30

Anna de Noailles (1876-1933), writer & poet.

St. Barbara — SP274

Design: 1fr+25c, Cimmerian Sibyl. Sculptures from Brou Cathedral.

**1976, Nov. 20** **Cross in Carmine**
**B496** SP274 80c + 20c violet .45 .40
*a.* Bklt. pane, 4 ea, gutter btwn. 6.00
**B497** SP274 1fr + 25c dk brown .65 .45

Surtax was for the Red Cross.

Marckolsheim Relay Station Sign — SP275

**1977, Mar. 26** **Engr.** ***Perf. 13***
**B498** SP275 1fr + 20c multi .40 .25

Stamp Day.

Edouard Herriot, Statesman and Writer — SP276

Designs: No. B500, Abbé Breuil (1877-1961), archaeologist. No. B501, Guillaume de Machault (1305-1377), poet and composer. No. B502, Charles Cross (1842-1888).

**1977** **Engr.** ***Perf. 13***
**B499** SP276 1fr + 20c multi .40 .30
**B500** SP276 1fr + 20c multi .40 .30
**B501** SP276 1fr + 20c multi .40 .30
**B502** SP276 1fr + 20c multi .40 .30
*Nos. B499-B502 (4)* 1.60 1.20

Issued: No. B499, 10/8; No. B500, 10/15; No. B501, 11/12; No. B502, 12/3.

Christmas Figurine, Provence — SP277

1fr+25c, Christmas figurine (woman), Provence.

**1977, Nov. 26**
**B503** SP277 80c + 20c red & ind .40 .30
*a.* Bklt. pane, 4 ea, gutter btwn. 4.50
**B504** SP277 1fr + 25c red & sl grn .45 .30

Surtax was for the Red Cross.

Marie Noel, Writer — SP278

No. B506, Georges Bernanos (1888-1948), writer. No. B507, Leo Tolstoy (1828-1910), Russian writer. No. B508, Charles Marie Leconte de Lisle (1818-1894), poet. No. B509, Voltaire (1694-1778) and Jean Jacques Rousseau (1712-1778). No. B510, Claude Bernard (1813-1878), physiologist.

**1978** **Engr.** ***Perf. 13***
**B505** SP278 1fr + 20c multi .40 .30
**B506** SP278 1fr + 20c multi .40 .30
**B507** SP278 1fr + 20c multi .40 .30
**B508** SP278 1fr + 20c multi .40 .30
**B509** SP278 1fr + 20c multi .40 .30
**B510** SP278 1fr + 20c multi .40 .30
*Nos. B505-B510 (6)* 2.40 1.80

Issued: No. B505, 2/11; No. B506, 2/18; No. B507, 4/15; No. B508, 3/26; No. B509, 7/1; No. B510, 9/16.

Mail Collection, 1900 — SP279

**1978, Apr. 8** **Engr.** ***Perf. 13***
**B511** SP279 1fr + 20c multi .40 .30

Stamp Day 1978.

SP280

1fr+25c, The Hare & the Tortoise. 1.20fr+30c, The City Mouse & the Country Mouse.

**1978, Dec. 2** **Engr.** ***Perf. 13***
**B512** SP280 1fr + 25c multi .60 .50
*a.* Bklt. pane, 4 ea, gutter btwn. 6.00
**B513** SP280 1.20fr + 30c multi .65 .55

Surtax was for the Red Cross.

SP281

No. B514, Ladislas Marshal de Berchény (1689-1778). No. B515, Leon Jouhaux (1879-1954), labor leader. No. B516, Peter Abelard (1079-1142), theologian and writer. No. B517, Georges Courteline (1860-1929), humorist. No. B518, Simone Weil (1909-1943), social philosopher. No. B519, André Malraux (1901-1976), novelist.

**1979 Engr. *Perf. 13***

| | | | | |
|---|---|---|---|---|
| **B514** | SP281 | 1.20fr + 30c multi | .50 | .40 |
| **B515** | SP281 | 1.20fr + 30c multi | .50 | .40 |
| **B516** | SP281 | 1.20fr + 30c multi | .50 | .40 |
| **B517** | SP281 | 1.20fr + 30c multi | .50 | .40 |
| **B518** | SP281 | 1.30fr + 30c multi | .60 | .40 |
| **B519** | SP281 | 1.30fr + 30c multi | .60 | .40 |
| | | *Nos. B514-B519 (6)* | 3.20 | 2.40 |

Issued: No. B514, 1/13; No. B515, 5/12; No. B516, 6/9; No. B517, 6/25; No. B518, 11/12; No. B519, 11/26.

General Post Office, from 1908 Post Card SP282

**1979, Mar. 10 Engr. *Perf. 13***

| | | | | |
|---|---|---|---|---|
| **B520** | SP282 | 1.20fr + 30c multi | .50 | .30 |

Stamp Day 1979.

Woman, Stained-Glass Window — SP283

Stained-glass windows, Church of St. Joan of Arc, Rouen: 1.30fr+30c, Simon the Magician.

**1979, Dec. 1 *Perf. 13***

| | | | | |
|---|---|---|---|---|
| **B521** | SP283 | 1.10fr + 30c multi | .50 | .40 |
| **B522** | SP283 | 1.30fr + 30c multi | .60 | .45 |
| *a.* | | Bklt. pane, 4 each #521-522, with gutter btwn., perf. 12½x13 | 6.00 | |

Surtax was for the Red Cross.

Eugene Viollet le Duc (1814-1879), Architect — SP284

Jean-Marie de Le Mennais (1780-1860), Priest and Educator — SP285

No. B524, Jean Monnet (1888-1979), economist and diplomat. No. B525, Viollet le Duc (1814-1879), architect and writer. No. B526, Frederic Mistral (1830-1914), poet. No. B527, Saint-John Perse (Alexis Leger, 1887-1975), poet and diplomat. No. B528, Pierre Paul de Riquet (1604-1680), canal builder.

**1980 Engr. *Perf. 13***

| | | | | |
|---|---|---|---|---|
| **B523** | SP284 | 1.30fr + 30c multi | .60 | .55 |
| **B524** | SP285 | 1.30fr + 30c multi | .60 | .55 |
| **B525** | SP285 | 1.40fr + 30c blue | .60 | .55 |
| **B526** | SP285 | 1.40fr + 30c black | .60 | .55 |
| **B527** | SP285 | 1.40fr + 30c multi | .60 | .55 |
| **B528** | SP284 | 1.40fr + 30c multi | .60 | .55 |
| | | *Nos. B523-B528 (6)* | 3.60 | 3.30 |

Issued: No. B523, Feb. 16; Nos. B524-B526, Sept. 6; Nos. B527-B528, Oct. 11.

The Letter to Melie, by Avati, Stamp Day, 1980 — SP286

**1980, Mar. 8 Photo.**

| | | | | |
|---|---|---|---|---|
| **B529** | SP286 | 1.30fr + 30c multi | .50 | .40 |

Filling the Granaries, Choir Stall Detail, Amiens Cathedral — SP287

No. B531, Grapes from the Promised Land.

**1980, Dec. 6 Engr. *Perf. 13***

| | | | | |
|---|---|---|---|---|
| **B530** | SP287 | 1.20fr + 30c red & dk red brn | .50 | .40 |
| **B531** | SP287 | 1.40fr + 30c red & dk red brn | .60 | .40 |
| *a.* | | Bklt. pane, 4 #B530-B531, with gutter btwn., perf. 12½x13 | 6.50 | |

Sister Anne-Marie Javouhey (1779-1851), Founded Congregation of St. Joseph of Cluny — SP288

No. B532, Louis Armand (1905-71), railway engineer. No. B533, Louis Jouvet (1887-1951), theater director. No. B534, Marc Boegner (1881-1970), peace worker. No. B536, Jacques Offenbach (1819-80), composer. No. B537, Pierre Teilhard de Chardin (1881-1955), philosopher.

Nos. B532-B533, B537 vert.

**1981 Engr. *Perf. 13***

| | | | | |
|---|---|---|---|---|
| **B532** | SP288 | 1.20 + 30c multi | .55 | .45 |
| **B533** | SP288 | 1.20 + 30c multi | .55 | .45 |
| **B534** | SP288 | 1.40 + 30c multi | .55 | .45 |
| **B535** | SP288 | 1.40 + 30c multi | .55 | .45 |
| **B536** | SP288 | 1.40 + 30c multi | .55 | .45 |
| **B537** | SP288 | 1.40 + 30c multi | .55 | .45 |
| | | *Nos. B532-B537 (6)* | 3.30 | 2.70 |

Issued: No. B532, 5/23; No. B533, 6/13; No. B534, 11/14; No. B535, 2/7; No. B536, 2/14; No. B537, 5/23.

The Love Letter, by Goya — SP289

**1981, Mar. 7 *Perf. 13x12½***

| | | | | |
|---|---|---|---|---|
| **B538** | SP289 | 1.40 + 30c multi | .65 | .60 |

Stamp Day 1981.

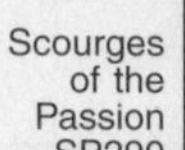

Scourges of the Passion SP290

Stained-glass Windows, Church of the Sacred Heart, Audincourt: 1.60fr+30c, "Peace."

**1981, Dec. 5 Photo. *Perf. 13***

| | | | | |
|---|---|---|---|---|
| **B539** | SP290 | 1.40 + 30c multi | .60 | .55 |
| **B540** | SP290 | 1.60 + 30c multi | .75 | .65 |
| *a.* | | Bklt. pane, 4 ea, gutter btwn. | 6.00 | |

Guillaume Postel (1510-1581), Theologian — SP291

No. B542, Henri Mondor (1885-1962), physician. No. B543, Andre Chantemesse (1851-1919), Scientist. No. B544, Louis Pergaud (1882-1915), writer. No. B545, Robert Debre (1882-1978), writer. No. B546, Gustave Eiffel (1832-1923), engineer.

**1982 Engr. *Perf. 13***

| | | | | |
|---|---|---|---|---|
| **B541** | SP291 | 1.40 + 30c multi | .60 | .50 |
| **B542** | SP291 | 1.40 + 30c dk brn & dk bl | .60 | .50 |
| **B543** | SP291 | 1.60 + 30c multi | .60 | .50 |
| **B544** | SP291 | 1.60 + 40c multi | .60 | .50 |
| **B545** | SP291 | 1.60 + 40c dk blue | .65 | .60 |
| **B546** | SP291 | 1.80 + 40c sepia | .65 | .60 |
| | | *Nos. B541-B546 (6)* | 3.70 | 3.20 |

Woman Reading, by Picasso — SP292

**1982, Mar. 27 *Perf. 13x12½***

| | | | | |
|---|---|---|---|---|
| **B547** | SP292 | 1.60 + 40c multi | .75 | .60 |

Stamp Day.

SP293

Jules Verne books: 1.60fr+30c, Five Weeks in a Balloon. 1.80fr+40c, 20,000 Leagues under the Sea.

**1982, Nov. 20 *Perf. 13***

| | | | | |
|---|---|---|---|---|
| **B548** | SP293 | 1.60 + 30c multi | .65 | .50 |
| **B549** | SP293 | 1.80 + 40c multi | .75 | .60 |
| *a.* | | Bklt. pane, 4 each #B548-B549, with gutter btwn., perf. 12½x13 | 8.00 | |

Surtax was for Red Cross.

SP294

No. B550, Andre Messager (1853-1929). No. B551, J.A. Gabriel (1698-1782), architect. No. B552, Hector Berlioz (1803-69), composer. No. B553, Max Fouchet (1913-80). No. B554, Rene Cassin (1887-1976). No. B555, Stendhal (Marie Henri Beyle, 1783-1842).

**1983 Engr. *Perf. 12½x13***

| | | | | |
|---|---|---|---|---|
| **B550** | SP294 | 1.60 + 30c multi | .65 | .60 |
| **B551** | SP294 | 1.60 + 30c multi | .65 | .60 |
| **B552** | SP294 | 1.80 + 40c dp lil & blk | .65 | .60 |
| **B553** | SP294 | 1.80 + 40c multi | .75 | .60 |
| **B554** | SP294 | 2fr + 40c multi | .80 | .65 |
| **B555** | SP294 | 2fr + 40c multi | .80 | .65 |
| | | *Nos. B550-B555 (6)* | 4.30 | 3.70 |

Issued: No. B550, 1/15; No. B551, 4/16; No. B552, 1/22; No. B553, 4/30; No. B554, 6/25; No. B555, 11/12.

Man Dictating a Letter, by Rembrandt — SP295

**Photo. & Engr.**

**1983, Feb. 26 *Perf. 13X12½***

| | | | | |
|---|---|---|---|---|
| **B556** | SP295 | 1.80 + 40c multi | .90 | .60 |

Stamp Day.

Virgin with Child, Baillon, 14th Cent. — SP296

Design: No. B558, Virgin with Child, Genainville, 16th Cent.

**1983, Nov. 26 Engr. *Perf. 13***

| | | | | |
|---|---|---|---|---|
| **B557** | SP296 | 1.60 + 40c shown | .65 | .45 |
| **B558** | SP296 | 2fr + 40c multi | .75 | .45 |
| *a.* | | Bklt. pane, 4 #B557-B558, with gutter btwn., perf. 12½x13 | 6.50 | |

Emile Littre (1801-1881), Physician — SP297

No. B560, Jean Zay (1904-44). No. B561, Pierre Corneille (1606-1684. No. B562, Gaston Bachelard (1884-1962). No. B563, Jean Paulhan (1884-1968). No. B564, Evariste Galois (1811-1832).

**1984 Engr. *Perf. 13***

| | | | | |
|---|---|---|---|---|
| **B559** | SP297 | 1.60fr + 40c plum & blk | .65 | .60 |
| **B560** | SP297 | 1.60fr + 40c dk grn & blk | .65 | .60 |
| **B561** | SP297 | 1.70fr + 40c dp vio & blk | .75 | .60 |
| **B562** | SP297 | 2fr + 40c gray & blk | .75 | .60 |
| **B563** | SP297 | 2.10fr + 40c dk brn & blk | .90 | .65 |
| **B564** | SP297 | 2.10fr + 40c ultra & blk | .90 | .65 |
| | | *Nos. B559-B564 (6)* | 4.60 | 3.70 |

SP298

Diderot Holding a Letter, by L.M. Van Loo.

**1984, Mar. 17 Engr. *Perf. 12½x13***
**B565** SP298 2fr + 40c multi .90 .60

SP299

The Rose Basket, by Caly.

**1984, Nov. 24 Photo. *Perf. 12½x13***
**B566** SP299 2.10fr + 50c pnksh (basket) & multi .80 .60
*a.* Salmon (basket) & multi, perf. 13½x13 .90 .60
*b.* As "a," bklt. pane of 10 + 2 labels 9.00

Surtax was for the Red Cross.

Jules Romains (1885-1972) — SP300

Authors: No. B568, Jean-Paul Sartre (1905-1980). No. B569, Romain Rolland (1866-1944). No. B570, Roland Dorgeles (1885-1973). No. B571, Victor Hugo (1802-1885). No. B572, Francois Mauriac (1885-1970).

**1985, Feb. 23 Engr. *Perf. 13***
**B567** SP300 1.70fr + 40c 1.10 .90
**B568** SP300 1.70fr + 40c 1.10 .90
**B569** SP300 1.70fr + 40c 1.10 .90
**B570** SP300 2.10fr + 50c 1.25 1.00
**B571** SP300 2.10fr + 50c 1.25 1.00
**B572** SP300 2.10fr + 50c 1.25 1.00
*a.* Bklt. pane, 1 each + 2 labels, perf. 15x14½ 15.00
*Nos. B567-B572 (6)* 7.05 5.70

SP301

Stamp Day: Canceling apparatus invented by Eugene Daguin (1849-1888).

**1985, Mar. 16 Engr. *Perf. 12½x13***
**B573** SP301 2.10fr + 50c brn blk & bluish gray .90 .60

SP302

Issenheim Altarpiece retable.

**1985, Nov. 23 Photo.**
**B574** SP302 2.20fr + 50c multi .80 .60
*a.* As "b," bklt. pane of 10 8.00
*b.* Perf. 13½x13 .90 .60

Surtax for the Red Cross.

SP303

Famous men: No. B575, Francois Arago (1786-1853), physician, politician. No. B576, Henri Moissan (1852-1907), chemist. No. B577, Henri Fabre (1882-1984), engineer. No. B578, Marc Seguin (1786-1875), engineer. No. B579, Paul Heroult (1863-1914), chemist.

**1986, Feb. 22 Engr. *Perf. 13***
**B575** SP303 1.80fr + 40c multi .75 .65
**B576** SP303 1.80fr + 40c multi .75 .65
**B577** SP303 1.80fr + 40c multi .75 .65
**B578** SP303 2.20fr + 50c multi .80 .65
**B579** SP303 2.20fr + 50c multi .80 .65
*a.* Bklt. pane of 5, #B575-B579, + 3 labels 6.00
*Nos. B575-B579 (5)* 3.85 3.25

SP304

**1986, Mar. 1 Engr. *Perf. 13x12½***
**B580** SP304 2.20fr + 50c brn blk *4.50 4.50*

Pierre Cot (1895-1977).

Mail Britzska SP305

**1986, Apr. 5 *Perf. 13***
**B581** SP305 2.20fr + 60c pale tan & dk vio brn .85 .60

**Booklet Stamp**

**B582** SP305 2.20fr + 60c buff & blk .85 .60
*a.* Bklt. pane of 6 + 2 labels 6.00

Stamp Day. See Nos. B590-B591, B599-B600, B608-B609.

Stained Glass Window (detail), by Vieira da Silva, St. Jacques of Reims Church, Marne — SP306

**1986, Nov. 24 Photo. *Perf. 12½x13***
**B583** SP306 2.20fr + 60c multi .85 .60
*a.* As "b," bklt. pane of 10 9.00
*b.* Perf. 13½x13 .90 .60

Surtaxed to benefit the natl. Red Cross.

Physicians and Biologists SP307

No. B584, Charles Richet (1850-1935). No. B585, Eugene Jamot (1879-1937). No. B586, Bernard Halpern (1904-1978). No. B587, Alexandre Yersin (1863-1943). No. B588, Jean Rostand (1894-1977). No. B589, Jacques Monod (1910-1976).

**1987, Feb. 21 Engr. *Perf. 13***
**B584** SP307 1.90fr + 50c deep ultra .75 .60
**B585** SP307 1.90fr + 50c dull lil .75 .60
**B586** SP307 1.90fr + 50c grnish gray .75 .60
**B587** SP307 2.20fr + 50c grnish gray .85 .65
**B588** SP307 2.20fr + 50c deep ultra .85 .65
**B589** SP307 2.20fr + 50c dull lil .85 .65
*a.* Bklt. pane of 6, #B584-B589 *5.00*
*Nos. B584-B589 (6)* 4.80 3.75

**Stamp Day Type of 1986**

Stamp Day 1987: Berline carriage.

**1987, Mar. 14 Engr.**
**B590** SP305 2.20fr + 60c buff & sepia .85 .60

**Booklet Stamp**

**B591** SP305 2.20fr + 60c pale & dk bl .85 .60
*a.* Bklt. pane of 6 + 2 labels 6.00

Flight Into Egypt, Retable by Melchior Broederlam SP308

**1987, Nov. 21 Photo. *Perf. 12½x13***
**B592** SP308 2.20fr +60c multi .85 .60
*a.* As "b," bklt. pane of 10 + 2 labels 8.00
*b.* Perf. 13½x13 .90 .60

Surtaxed to benefit the Red Cross.

Explorers SP309

Profiles & maps: No. B593, Marquis Abraham Duquesne (1610-1688), naval commander. No. B594, Pierre Andre de Suffren (1729-1788). No. B595, Jean-Francois de La Perouse (1741-1788). No. B596, Mahe de La Bourdonnais (1699-1753). No. B597, Louis-Antoine de Bougainville (1729-1811). No. B598, Jules Dumont d'Urville (1790-1842).

**1988, Feb. 20 Engr. *Perf. 13***
**B593** SP309 2fr + 50c multi .75 .50
**B594** SP309 2fr + 50c multi .75 .50
**B595** SP309 2fr + 50c multi .75 .50
**B596** SP309 2.20fr + 50c multi .85 .60
**B597** SP309 2.20fr + 50c multi .85 .60
**B598** SP309 2.20fr + 50c multi .85 .60
*a.* Bklt. pane of 6, #B593-B598 4.50

**Stamp Day Type of 1986**

Stamp Day 1988: Postal coach.

**1988, Mar. 29 Engr.**
**B599** SP305 2.20fr +60c dk lilac .85 .60

**Booklet Stamp**

**B600** SP305 2.20fr +60c sepia .85 .60
*a.* Bklt. pane of 6 + 2 labels 5.00

Intl. Red Cross, 125th Anniv. — SP310

**1988, Nov. 19 Engr. *Perf. 12½x13***
**B601** SP310 2.20fr +60c multi .85 .60
*a.* As"b," bklt. pane of 10+2 labels 8.00
*b.* Perf. 13½x13 .85 .75

See No. B747c.

Revolution Leaders and Heroes SP311

No. B602, Emmanuel Joseph Sieyes (1748-1836). No. B603, Honore Gabriel Riqueti, Comte de Mirabeau (1749-91). No. B604, Louis Marie de Noailles (1756-1804). No. B605, Lafayette. No. B606, Antoine Pierre Joseph Marie Barnave (1761-93). No. B607, Jean Baptiste Drouet (1763-1824).

**1989, Feb. 25 Engr. *Perf. 13***
**B602** SP311 2.20fr +50c multi .85 .60
**B603** SP311 2.20fr +50c multi .85 .60
**B604** SP311 2.20fr +50c multi .85 .60
**B605** SP311 2.20fr +50c multi .85 .60
**B606** SP311 2.20fr +50c multi .85 .60
**B607** SP311 2.20fr +50c multi .85 .60
*a.* Bklt. pane, 1 each + 2 labels 5.00

French Revolution, bicent.

**Stamp Day Type of 1986**

Design: Paris-Lyon stagecoach.

**1989, Apr. 15 Engr. *Perf. 13***
**B608** SP305 2.20fr +60c pale bl & dk bl .85 .60

**Booklet Stamp**

**B609** SP305 2.20fr +60c pale lil & pur .85 .60
*a.* Bklt. pane of 6 + 2 labels 6.00

Stamp Day 1989.

Bird From a Silk Tapestry, Lyon, 18th Cent. — SP312

**1989, Nov. 18 Photo. *Perf. 12½x13***
**B610** SP312 2.20fr +60c multi .85 .60
*a.* As "b," bklt. pane of 10 9.00
*b.* Perf. 13½x13 .90 .60

Surtax for the natl. Red Cross.

1992 Winter Olympics, Albertville SP313

**1990, Feb. 9 Engr. *Perf. 13***
**B611** SP313 2.30fr +20c red, bl & blk .90 .70

See Nos. B621-B627, B636-B637, B639.

Stamp Day SP314

**1990, Mar. 17 Photo.**
**B612** SP314 2.30fr +60c ultra, bl & brt yel .90 .70

**Booklet Stamp**

**B613** SP314 2.30fr +60c ultra, grn, yel & brt grn .90 .70
*a.* Bklt. pane of 6 + 2 labels 6.00

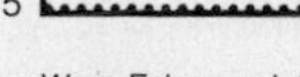

SP315

Quimper or Brittany Ware Faience plate.

**1990, May 5 Photo. *Perf. 12½x13***

**B614** SP315 2.30fr +60c multi .90 .70
*a.* As "b," bklt. pane of 10+2 labels 9.00
*b.* Perf. 13½x13 .95 .70

Surcharge benefited the Red Cross.

SP316

No. B615, Aristide Bruant. No. B616, Maurice Chevalier. No. B617, Tino Rossi. No. B618, Edith Piaf. No. B619, Jacques Brel. No. B620, Georges Brassens.

**1990, June 16 Photo. *Perf. 13***

**B615** SP316 2.30fr +50c multi .90 .70
**B616** SP316 2.30fr +50c multi .90 .70
**B617** SP316 2.30fr +50c multi .90 .70
**B618** SP316 2.30fr +50c multi .90 .70
**B619** SP316 2.30fr +50c multi .90 .70
**B620** SP316 2.30fr +50c multi .90 .70
*a.* Bklt. pane, 1 each +2 labels 5.00

### Albertville Olympic Type

Designs: No. B621, Ski jumping. No. B622, Speed skiing. No. B623, Slalom skiing. No. B624, Cross-country skiing. No. B625, Ice hockey. No. B626, Luge. No. B627, Curling.

**1990-91 Engr. *Perf. 13***

**B621** SP313 2.30fr +20c multi .90 .70
**B622** SP313 2.30fr +20c multi .90 .70
**B623** SP313 2.30fr +20c multi .90 .70
**B624** SP313 2.30fr +20c multi .90 .70
**B625** SP313 2.30fr +20c multi .90 .70
**B626** SP313 2.50fr +20c multi .90 .70
**B627** SP313 2.50fr +20c multi .90 .70
*Nos. B621-B627 (7)* 6.30 4.90

Issued: No. B621, 12/22/90; No. B622, 12/29/90; No. B623, 1/19/91; No. B624, 2/2/91; No. B625, 2/9/91; No. B626, 3/2/91; No. B627, 4/20/91.

No. B624 inscribed "La Poste 1992."

Paul Eluard (1895-1952) — SP317

Poets: No. B629, Andre Breton (1896-1966). No. B630, Louis Aragon (1897-1982). No. B631, Francis Ponge (1899-1988). No. B632, Jacques Prevert (1900-1977). No. B633, Rene Char (1907-1988).

**1991, Feb. 23 Engr. *Perf. 12½x13***

**B628** SP317 2.50fr +50c multi 1.00 .75
**B629** SP317 2.50fr +50c multi 1.00 .75
**B630** SP317 2.50fr +50c multi 1.00 .75
**B631** SP317 2.50fr +50c multi 1.00 .75
**B632** SP317 2.50fr +50c multi 1.00 .75
**B633** SP317 2.50fr +50c multi 1.00 .75
*a.* Bklt. pane, 1 each +2 labels, perf. 13 6.00

Stamp Day
SP318

**1991, Mar. 16 Photo. *Perf. 13***

**B634** SP318 2.50fr +60c blue machine 1.00 .75
**B635** SP318 2.50fr +60c purple machine 1.00 .75
*a.* Bklt. pane of 6 + 2 labels 6.00

### Winter Olympics Type of 1990

No. B636, Acrobatic skiing. No. B637, Alpine skiing.

**1991 Engr. *Perf. 13***

**B636** SP313 2.50fr +20c multi 1.00 .75
**B637** SP313 2.50fr +20c multi 1.00 .75

Issued: No. B636, Aug. 3; No. B637, Aug. 17.

Nos. B636-B637 inscribed "La Poste 1992."

The Harbor of Toulon by Francois Nardi
SP319

**1991, Dec. 2 Photo. *Perf. 13x12½***

**B638** SP319 2.50fr +60c multi 1.00 .75
*a.* Perf. 13x13½ 1.10 .75
*b.* As "a," bklt. pane of 10 + 2 labels 9.00

Surtax for the Red Cross.

### Winter Olympics Type of 1990
Miniature Sheet

No. B639: a, like #B611. b, like #B621. c, like #B622. d, like #B623. e, like #B624. f, like #B625.

**1992, Feb. 8 Engr. *Perf. 13***

**B639** Sheet of 10 + label 15.00 15.00
*a.-f.* SP313 2.50fr +20c multi 1.00 .75

No. B639 contains one each B626-B627, B636-B637, B639a-B639f. Central label is litho.

Stamp Day
SP320

**1992, Mar. 7 Litho. *Perf. 13***

**B640** SP320 2.50fr +60c gray people 1.00 .75

### Booklet Stamp
Photo.

**B641** SP320 2.50fr +60c red people 1.00 .75
*a.* Bklt. pane of 6 + 2 labels 6.00

SP321

Composers: No. B642, Cesar Franck (1822-1890). No. B643, Erik Satie (1866-1925). No. B644, Florent Schmitt (1870-1958). No. B645, Arthur Honegger (1892-1955). No. B646, Georges Auric (1899-1983). No. B647, Germaine Tailleferre (1892-1983).

**1992, Apr. 11 Photo. *Perf. 13***

**B642** SP321 2.50fr +50c multi 1.00 .75
**B643** SP321 2.50fr +50c multi 1.00 .75
**B644** SP321 2.50fr +50c multi 1.00 .75
**B645** SP321 2.50fr +50c multi 1.00 .75
**B646** SP321 2.50fr +50c multi 1.00 .75
**B647** SP321 2.50fr +50c multi 1.00 .75
*a.* Bklt. pane of 6, #B642-B647 6.00

SP322

**1992, Nov. 28 Photo. *Perf. 13½x13***

**B648** SP322 2.50fr +60c multi 1.00 .70
*a.* Bklt. pane of 10 + 2 labels 9.00

Mutual Aid, Strasbourg. Surtax for the Red Cross.

Writers
SP323

No. B649, Guy de Maupassant (1850-93). No. B650, Alain (Emile Chartier) (1868-1951). No. B651, Jean Cocteau (1889-1963). No. B652, Marcel Pagnol (1895-1974). No. B653, Andre Chamson (1900-83). No. B654, Marguerite Yourcenar (1903-87).

**1993, Apr. 24 Engr. *Perf. 13***

**B649** SP323 2.50fr +50c multi 1.00 .75
**B650** SP323 2.50fr +50c multi 1.00 .75
**B651** SP323 2.50fr +50c multi 1.00 .75
**B652** SP323 2.50fr +50c multi 1.00 .75
**B653** SP323 2.50fr +50c multi 1.00 .75
**B654** SP323 2.50fr +50c multi 1.00 .75
*a.* Bklt. pane of 6, #B649-B654 + 2 labels 6.00

When Nos. B650-B654 are normally centered, inscriptions at base of the lower panel are not parallel to the perforations at bottom. On all six stamps the lower panel is not centered between the side perforations.

SP324

St. Nicolas, Image of Metz.

**1993, Nov. 27 Engr. *Perf. 12½x13***

**B655** SP324 2.80fr +60c multi 1.10 .75
*a.* Perf. 13½x13 1.20 .75
*b.* As "a," Bklt. pane of 10 +2 labels 12.00

Surtax for Red Cross.

SP325

Stage and Screen Personalities: No. B656, Yvonne Printemps (1894-1977). No. B657, Fernandel (1903-71). No. B658, Josephine Baker (1906-75). No. B659, Bourvil (1917-70). No. B660, Yves Montand (1921-91). No. B661, Coluche (1944-86).

**1994, Sept. 17 Photo. *Perf. 13***

**B656** SP325 2.80fr +60c multi 1.10 .75
**B657** SP325 2.80fr +60c multi 1.10 .75
**B658** SP325 2.80fr +60c multi 1.10 .75
**B659** SP325 2.80fr +60c multi 1.10 .75
**B660** SP325 2.80fr +60c multi 1.10 .75
**B661** SP325 2.80fr +60c multi 1.10 .75
*a.* Bklt. pane, #B656-B661 + 2 labels 6.00

SP326

Designs: No. B662, St. Vaast, Arras Tapestry. No. B663, Brussels tapestry from Reydams workshop, Horse Museum, Saumur.

**1994-95 Photo. *Perf. 12½x13***

**B662** SP326 2.80fr +60c multi 1.10 .75
*a.* Perf. 13½x13 1.20 .75
*b.* Bklt. pane, 10 #B662a + 2 labels 12.00
Complete booklet, #B662b 13.00
**B663** SP326 2.80fr +60c multi 1.10 .75
*a.* Perf. 13½x13 1.20 .75
*b.* Bklt. pane, 10 #B663a + 2 labels 12.00
Complete booklet, #B663b 13.00

Surtax for Red Cross.

Issued: No. B662, 11/26/94; No. B663, 5/13/95.

SP327

Provencal Nativity Figures: No. B664, The Shepherd. No. B665, The Miller. No. B666, The Simpleton and the Tambour Player. No. B667, The Fishmonger. No. B668, The Scissor Grinder. No. B669, The Elders.

**1995, Nov. 25 Engr. *Perf. 13***

**B664** SP327 2.80fr +60c multi 1.10 .85
**B665** SP327 2.80fr +60c multi 1.10 .85
**B666** SP327 2.80fr +60c multi 1.10 .85
**B667** SP327 2.80fr +60c multi 1.10 .85
**B668** SP327 2.80fr +60c multi 1.10 .85
**B669** SP327 2.80fr +60c multi 1.10 .85
*a.* Booklet pane, Nos. B664-B669 + 2 labels 7.50
Complete booklet, No. B669a 11.00

SP328

Famous Fictional Detectives and Criminals: No. B670, Rocambole. No. B671, Arsène Lupin. No. B672, Joseph Rouletabille. No. B673, Fantômas. No. B674, Commissioner Maigret. No. B675, Nestor Burma.

**1996, Oct. 5 Photo. *Perf. 13***

**B670** SP328 3fr +60c multi 1.10 .85
**B671** SP328 3fr +60c multi 1.10 .85
**B672** SP328 3fr +60c multi 1.10 .85
**B673** SP328 3fr +60c multi 1.10 .85
**B674** SP328 3fr +60c multi 1.10 .85
**B675** SP328 3fr +60c multi 1.10 .85
*a.* Booklet pane, #B670-B675 + 2 labels 7.50
Complete booklet, #B675a 11.00

Christmas
SP329

**1996, Nov. 16 Photo. *Perf. 12¾x13***

**B676** SP329 3fr +60c multi 1.10 .85
*a.* Perf. 13¼x13 1.20 .85
*b.* Booklet pane, 10 #B676a + 2 labels 12.00 —
Complete booklet, #B676b 13.00

Surtax for Red Cross.

Adventure Heroes
SP330

No. B677, Sir Lancelot. No. B678, Pardaillan. No. B679, D'Artagnan. No. B680, Cyrano de Bergerac. No. B681, Captain Fracasse. No. B682, Le Bossu.

**1997, Oct. 25 Photo. *Perf. 13***

**B677** SP330 3fr +60c multi 1.10 .85
**B678** SP330 3fr +60c multi 1.10 .85
**B679** SP330 3fr +60c multi 1.10 .85
**B680** SP330 3fr +60c multi 1.10 .85
**B681** SP330 3fr +60c multi 1.10 .85
**B682** SP330 3fr +60c multi 1.10 .85
*a.* Booklet pane, #B677-B682 + 2 labels 7.50
Complete booklet, #682a 7.50

Christmas, New Year — SP331

**1997, Nov. 6 Photo. *Perf. 12¾x13***

**B683** SP331 3fr +60c multi 1.10 .90
*a.* Perf. 13¼x13 1.20 .95
*b.* Booklet pane, 10 #B683a + 2 labels 12.00 —
Complete booklet, #B683b 13.00

Surtax for the Red Cross.

SP332

Actors of the French Cinema: No. B684, Romy Schneider (1938-82). No. B685, Simone Signoret (1921-85). No. B686, Jean Gabin (1904-76). No. B687, Louis de Funés (1914-83). No. B688, Bernard Blier (1916-89). No. B689, Lino Ventura (1919-87).

**1998, Oct. 3 Photo. *Perf. 13***

**B684** SP332 3fr +60c multi 1.10 .85
**B685** SP332 3fr +60c multi 1.10 .85
**B686** SP332 3fr +60c multi 1.10 .85
**B687** SP332 3fr +60c multi 1.10 .85
**B688** SP332 3fr +60c multi 1.10 .85
**B689** SP332 3fr +60c multi 1.10 .85
*a.* Booklet pane, #B684-B689 + label 7.50
Complete booklet, #B689a 8.00

Christmas SP333

**1998, Nov. 5 Photo. *Perf. 12½x13***

**B690** SP333 3fr +60c multi 1.10 .85
*a.* Perf. 13½x13 1.20 .85
*b.* Booklet pane, 10 #B690a + 2 labels 12.00
Complete booklet, #B690b 13.00

Surtax for Red Cross.

Famous Photographers — SP334

Photographs by: No. B691, Robert Doisneau (1912-94). No. B692, Brassai (Gyula Halasz) (1899-1984). No. B693, Jacques Lartigue (1894-1986). No. B694, Henri Cartier-Bresson (1908-2004). No. B695, Eugene Atget (1857-1927). No. B696, Felix Nadar (1820-1910).

**1999, July 10 Photo. *Perf. 13***

**B691** SP334 3fr +60c multi 1.10 .85
**B692** SP334 3fr +60c multi 1.10 .85
**B693** SP334 3fr +60c multi 1.10 .85
**B694** SP334 3fr +60c multi 1.10 .85
**B695** SP334 3fr +60c multi 1.10 .85
**B696** SP334 3fr +60c multi 1.10 .85
*a.* Booklet pane, #B691-B696 7.50
Complete booklet, #B696a 8.00

New Year 2000 — SP335

**1999, Nov. 10 Photo. *Perf. 12¾x13***

**B697** SP335 3fr +60c multi 1.20 .85
*a.* Perf. 13½x13 1.25 .85
*b.* Booklet pane, 10 #B697a + 2 labels 9.00
Complete booklet, #B697b 10.00

Surtax for Red Cross.

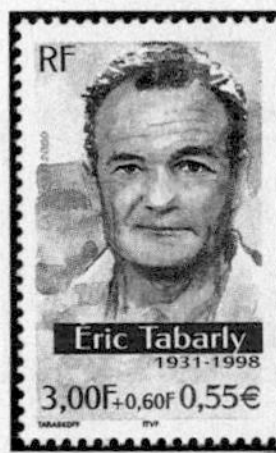

Adventurers SP336

No. B698, Eric Tabarly (1931-98), sailor. No. B699, Alexandra David-Néel (1868-1969), opera singer, Asian traveler. No. B700, Haroun Tazieff (1914-98), vulcanologist. No. B701, Paul-Emile Victor (1907-55), ethnologist, polar explorer. No. B702, Jacques-Yves Cousteau (1910-97), oceanographer. No. B703, Norbert Casteret (1897-1987), speleologist.

**2000, Sept. 16 Photo. *Perf. 13¼x13***

**B698** SP336 3fr +60c multi 1.20 .85
**B699** SP336 3fr +60c multi 1.20 .85
**B700** SP336 3fr +60c multi 1.20 .85
**B701** SP336 3fr +60c multi 1.20 .85
**B702** SP336 3fr +60c multi 1.20 .85
**B703** SP336 3fr +60c multi 1.20 .85
*a.* Booklet pane, #B698-B703 7.00
Booklet, #B703a 7.50

Toy Airplane — SP337

**2000, Nov. 9 Photo. *Perf. 13¼x13***

**B704** SP337 3fr +60c multi 1.10 .85
*a.* Booklet pane of 10 + 2 labels 12.00
Booklet, #B704a 13.00

Surtax for Red Cross.

Santa Claus and Tree Ornaments SP338

**2001, Nov. 8 Photo. *Perf. 12¾x13***

**B705** SP338 3fr +60c multi 1.10 .85
*a.* Perf 13½x13 1.20 .85
*b.* Booklet pane of 10 11.00 —
Booklet, #B705a 11.00

Surtax for Red Cross.

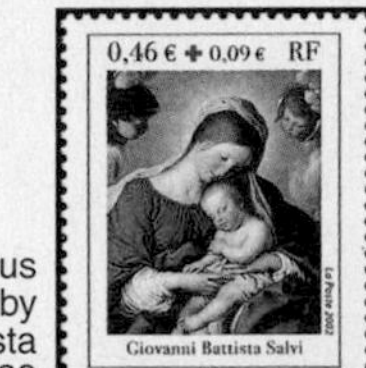

Infant Jesus Asleep, by Giovanni Battista Salvi — SP339

**2002, Nov. 7 Photo. *Perf. 12¾x13***

**B706** SP339 46c +9c multi 1.10 .85
*a.* Perf. 13½x13 1.20 .85
*b.* As "a," booklet pane of 10 11.00 —
Booklet, #B706b 11.00

Surtax for Red Cross.

Virgin with Grapes, by Pierre Mignard — SP340

**2003, Nov. 6 Photo. *Perf. 13¼x13***
**Booklet Stamp**

**B707** SP340 50c +(16c) multi 1.50 1.00
*a.* Booklet pane of 10 15.00 —
Complete booklet, #B707a 15.00

Surtax for Red Cross.

Virgin With Child, Attributed to Cretan School — SP341

**2004, Nov. 10 Photo. *Perf. 13¼x13***
**Booklet Stamp**

**B708** SP341 50c +(16c) multi 1.50 1.00
*a.* Booklet pane of 10 + 2 labels 15.00 —
Complete booklet, #B708a 15.00

Surtax for Red Cross.

Dec. 26, 2004 Tsunami Victim Relief SP342

**2005, Jan. 13 Engr. *Perf. 13***

**B709** SP342 (50c) +20c red 1.75 .50

Virgin and Child, by Hans Memling SP343

**2005, Nov. 10 Photo. *Perf. 13½x13***
**Booklet Stamp**

**B710** SP343 53c +(17c) multi 1.50 1.00
*a.* Booklet pane of 10 + 2 labels 15.00 —
Complete booklet, #B710a 15.00

Surtax for Red Cross.

SP344

Children's Art — SP345

**2006, Nov. 25 Photo. *Perf. 13½x13***
**Booklet Stamps**

**B711** SP344 (54c) +(17c) multi 1.90 .85
**B712** SP345 (54c) +(17c) multi 1.90 .85
*a.* Booklet pane, 5 each #B711-B712, + 2 labels 19.00 —
Complete booklet, #B712a 19.00

Surtax for Red Cross.

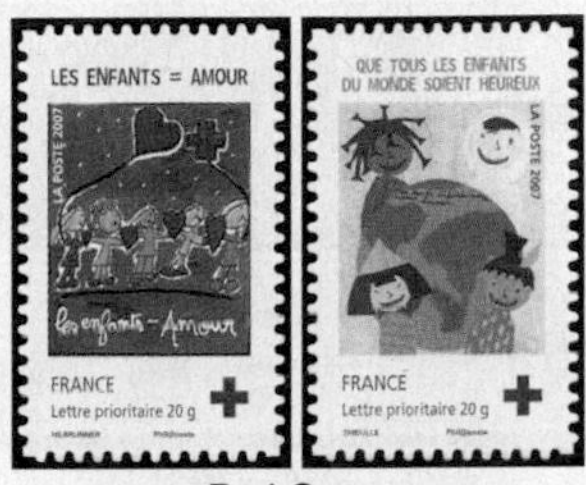

Red Cross
SP346 SP347

***Serpentine Die Cut 11***
**2007, Nov. 24 Photo.**
**Self-Adhesive**
**Booklet Stamps**

**B713** SP346 (54c) +(17c) multi 1.90 .85
**B714** SP347 (54c) +(17c) multi 1.90 .85
*a.* Booklet pane, 5 each #B713-B714 19.00

Surtax for Red Cross.

Red Cross
SP348 SP349

***Serpentine Die Cut 11x11¼***
**2008, Nov. 8 Photo.**
**Booklet Stamps**
**Self-Adhesive**

**B715** SP348 (55c) +(18c) multi 1.90 .85
**B716** SP349 (55c) +(18c) multi 1.90 .85
*a.* Booklet pane of 10, 2 each #B715-B716 19.00

Surtax for Red Cross.

Miniature Sheet

Red Cross — SP350

No. B717: a, Henri Dunant. b, Battle of Solferino. c, Pélias et Nélée, by Georges Braque, horiz. d, Geneva Conventions. e, Globe and symbols of the International Red Cross and Red Crescent Societies.

**2009, Sept. 19 Photo. *Perf. 13***

**B717** SP350 Sheet of 5 12.00 12.00
*a.-e.* 56c +(40c) Any single 2.50 2.50

Surtax for Red Cross.

Haiti Earthquake Relief — SP351

**2010, Jan. 19 Engr. *Perf. 13***
**B718** SP351 (56c) +44c red 2.25 1.50

**Self-Adhesive**
***Serpentine Die Cut 11***
**B719** SP351 (56c) +44c red 4.50 4.00

Surtax was for French Red Cross relief efforts in Haiti.

Miniature Sheet

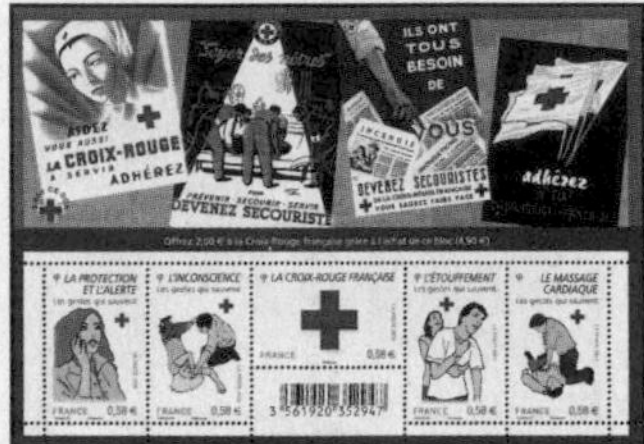
Red Cross — SP352

No. B720: a, Woman on telephone. b, Man assisting unconscious woman. c, Red Cross emblem, horiz. d, Woman performing Heimlich maneuver on choking man. e, Cardio-pulmonary resuscitation.

**Photo., Photo. & Embossed (#B720c)**
**2010, Nov. 5 *Perf. 13***
**B720** SP352 Sheet of 5 12.00 8.00
*a.-e.* 58c +(40c) Any single 2.00 1.25

Surtax for Red Cross.

Miniature Sheet

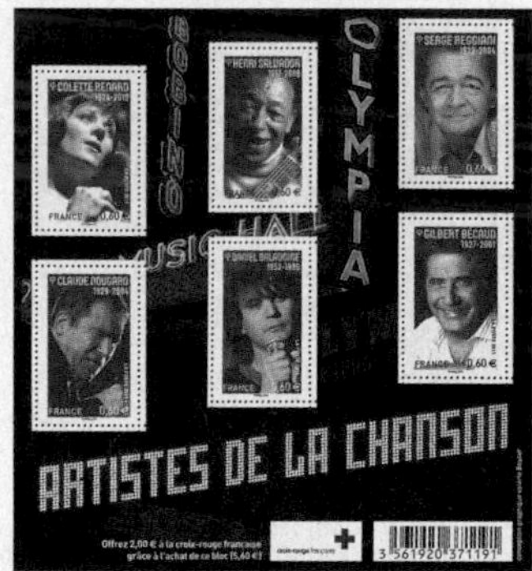
Singers — SP353

No. B721: a, Colette Renard (1924-2010). b, Henri Salvador (1917-2008). c, Serge Reggiani (1922-2004). d, Claude Nougaro (1929-2004). e, Daniel Balavoine (1952-86). f, Gilbert Bécaud (1927-2001).

**2011, Oct. 14 Photo. *Perf. 13***
**B721** SP353 Sheet of 6 12.00 9.00
*a.-f.* 60c + (33⅓c) Any single 2.00 1.50

Surtax for Red Cross.

Miniature Sheet

Red Cross — SP354

No. B722: a, People carrying person on litter. b, Three hands. c, Red Cross, horiz. d, Red Cross volunteer teaching illiterates. e, Red Cross volunteer giving bottle to infant.

**2011, Nov. 4**
**B722** SP354 Sheet of 5 10.00 7.50
*a.-e.* 60c + (40c) Any single 2.00 1.50

Surtax for Red Cross.

Miniature Sheet

Movie Stars — SP355

No. B723: a, Françoise Dorléac (1942-67). b, Jean Marais (1913-98). c, Jacqueline Maillan (1923-92). d, Michel Serrault (1928-2007). e, Philippe Noiret (1930-2006). f, Annie Girardot (1931-2011).

**2012, Oct. 19**
**B723** SP355 Sheet of 6 12.00 9.00
*a.-f.* 60c + (33⅓c) Any single 2.00 1.50

Surtax for Red Cross.

Miniature Sheet

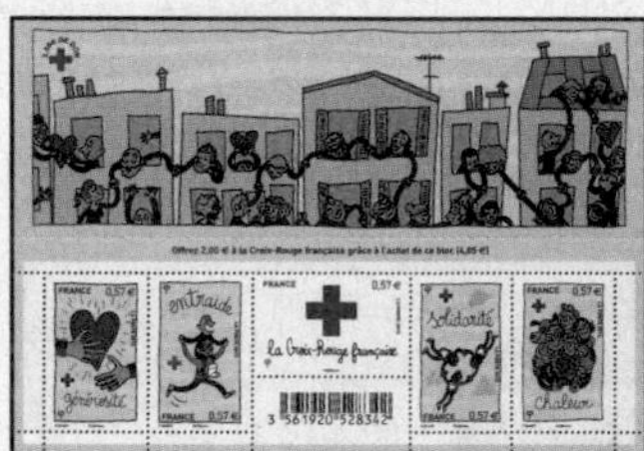
Red Cross — SP356

No. B724: a, Heart and hands. b, Man carrying man with injured foot. c, Red Cross, horiz. d, Three parachutists. e, People and dog hugging heart.

**2012, Nov. 8**
**B724** SP356 Sheet of 5 12.50 12.50
*a.-e.* 57c + (40c) Any single 2.50 2.50

Surtax for Red Cross.

Loire River SP357

The Loire River at: No. B725, Mont Gerbier de Jonc. No. B726, Lac de Grangent. No. B727, Bec d'Allier. No. B728, Gien. No. B729, Pointe de Coupain. No. B730, Blois. No. B731, Candes-Saint-Martin. No. B732, Ingrandes-sur-Loire. No. B733, Champtoceaux. No. B734, Marais de Brière.

**2013, June 1 *Serpentine Die Cut 11***
**Booklet Stamps**
**Self-Adhesive**

**B725** SP357 (58c+20c) multi 1.60 .50
**B726** SP357 (58c+20c) multi 1.60 .50
**B727** SP357 (58c+20c) multi 1.60 .50
**B728** SP357 (58c+20c) multi 1.60 .50
**B729** SP357 (58c+20c) multi 1.60 .50
**B730** SP357 (58c+20c) multi 1.60 .50
**B731** SP357 (58c+20c) multi 1.60 .50
**B732** SP357 (58c+20c) multi 1.60 .50
**B733** SP357 (58c+20c) multi 1.60 .50
**B734** SP357 (58c+20c) multi 1.60 .50
*a.* Booklet pane of 10, #B725-B734 18.00
*Nos. B725-B734 (10)* 16.00 5.00

Surtax for the Red Cross.

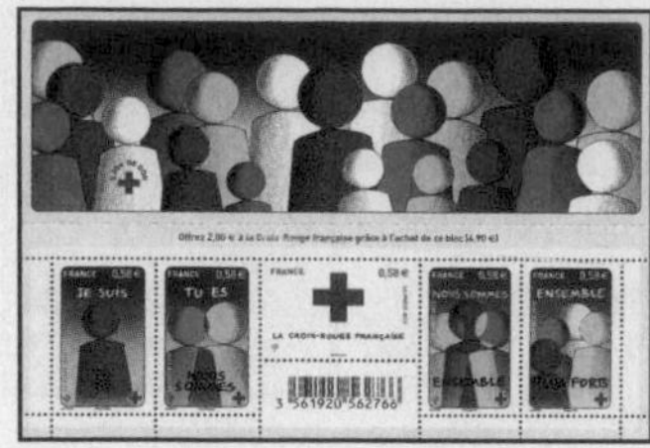
Red Cross — SP358

No. B735: a, One stylized person. b, Two stylized people. c, Red Cross, horiz. d, Three stylized people. e, Four stylized people.

**2013, Nov. 7 Photo. *Perf. 13***
**B735** SP358 Sheet of 5 10.00 7.50
*a.-e.* 58c + (40c) Any single 1.75 1.25

Surtax for Red Cross.

Flowers SP359

Designs: No. B736, Roses. No. B737, Daisies (Marguerite). No. B738, Tulips (Tulipe). No. B739, Sunflowers (Tournesol). No. B740, Irises. No. B741, Orchids (Orchidée). No. B742, Jonquils (Jonquille). No. B743, Lilies (Lys). No. B744, Carnations (Oeillet). No. B745, Gardenias (Gardénia).

***Serpentine Die Cut 11***
**2014, May 24 Photo.**
**Booklet Stamps**
**Self-Adhesive**

**B736** SP359 (61c) + (20c) multi 1.75 1.00
**B737** SP359 (61c) + (20c) multi 1.75 1.00
**B738** SP359 (61c) + (20c) multi 1.75 1.00
**B739** SP359 (61c) + (20c) multi 1.75 1.00
**B740** SP359 (61c) + (20c) multi 1.75 1.00
**B741** SP359 (61c) + (20c) multi 1.75 1.00
**B742** SP359 (61c) + (20c) multi 1.75 1.00
**B743** SP359 (61c) + (20c) multi 1.75 1.00
**B744** SP359 (61c) + (20c) multi 1.75 1.00
**B745** SP359 (61c) + (20c) multi 1.75 1.00
*a.* Booklet pane of 10, #B736-B745 20.00
*Nos. B736-B745 (10)* 17.50 10.00

Red Cross, 150th anniv. Surtax for Red Cross.

**Semi-Postal Stamps of 1914-88 Redrawn**

**2014, June 14 Litho.**
**B746** Sheet of 5 14.00 14.00
*a.* SP2 61c +30c like #B2, perf. 13¼ 2.50 2.50
*b.* A22 61c +30c like #B1, perf. 13¼ 2.50 2.50
*c.* SP40 61c +30c like #B81, perf. 13 2.50 2.50
*d.* SP9 61c +30c like #B11, perf. 13x13¼ 2.50 2.50
*e.* SP237 61c +30c like #B403, perf. 13 2.50 2.50
**B747** Sheet of 5 14.00 14.00
*a.* SP60 61c +30c like #B101, perf. 13x13¼ 2.50 2.50
*b.* SP258 61c +30c like #B462, perf. 13 2.50 2.50
*c.* SP310 61c +30c like #B601, perf. 13¼x13 2.50 2.50
*d.* SP207 61c +30c like #B328, perf. 13 2.50 2.50
*e.* SP61 61c +30c like #B102, perf. 13x13¼ 2.50 2.50

Nos. B746-B747 sold together as a set for €12.

Miniature Sheet

French Red Cross, 150th Anniv. — SP360

No. B748: a, Jean-Henri Dunant, 1864. b, White angel with Red Cross arm band treating soldier, 1914. c, Red cross and 150th anniv. emblem, horiz. d, Red Cross worker giving aid to refugee, 1945. e, Red Cross workers in Haiti, 2010.

**2014, Nov. 7 Photo. *Perf. 13***
**B748** SP360 Sheet of 5 10.00 8.00
*a.-e.* 61c+(30c) Any single 2.00 1.25

Surtax for the Red Cross.

SP361

SP362

SP363

SP364

SP365

SP366

SP367

Red Cross Workers in Action SP368

***Serpentine Die Cut 11***
**2015, May 16 Litho.**
**Booklet Stamps**
**Self-Adhesive**

**B749** SP361 (68c+25c) multi 2.10 2.10
**B750** SP362 (68c+25c) multi 2.10 2.10
**B751** SP363 (68c+25c) multi 2.10 2.10

| | | | | |
|---|---|---|---|---|
| B752 | SP364 | (68c+25c) multi | 2.10 | 2.10 |
| B753 | SP365 | (68c+25c) multi | 2.10 | 2.10 |
| B754 | SP366 | (68c+25c) multi | 2.10 | 2.10 |
| B755 | SP367 | (68c+25c) multi | 2.10 | 2.10 |
| B756 | SP368 | (68c+25c) multi | 2.10 | 2.10 |
| a. | | Booklet pane of 8, #B749-B756 | 17.00 | |
| | | *Nos. B749-B756 (8)* | 16.80 | 16.80 |

Surtax for the Red Cross.

Miniature Sheet

Red Cross — SP369

No. B757: a, Red cross, heart and arrows. b, Sun, red crosses, ambulance. c, Red cross and text, horiz. d, Red cross and heart. e, Red Cross and text, diff.

**2015, Nov. 7 Photo. *Perf. 13***

| | | | | |
|---|---|---|---|---|
| B757 | SP369 | Sheet of 5 | 11.50 | 11.50 |
| a.-e. | | 68c+(40c) Any single | 2.25 | 2.25 |

Surtax for the Red Cross.

SP370

SP371

SP372

SP373

SP374

SP375

SP376

Red Cross Workers SP377

***Serpentine Die Cut 11***

**2016, Apr. 30 Litho.**

**Booklet Stamps Self-Adhesive**

| | | | | |
|---|---|---|---|---|
| B758 | SP370 | (70c+25c) multi | 2.25 | 2.25 |
| B759 | SP371 | (70c+25c) multi | 2.25 | 2.25 |
| B760 | SP372 | (70c+25c) multi | 2.25 | 2.25 |
| B761 | SP373 | (70c+25c) multi | 2.25 | 2.25 |
| B762 | SP374 | (70c+25c) multi | 2.25 | 2.25 |
| B763 | SP375 | (70c+25c) multi | 2.25 | 2.25 |
| B764 | SP376 | (70c+25c) multi | 2.25 | 2.25 |
| B765 | SP377 | (70c+25c) multi | 2.25 | 2.25 |
| a. | | Booklet pane of 8, #B758-B765 | 18.00 | |
| | | *Nos. B758-B765 (8)* | 18.00 | 18.00 |

Surtax for the Red Cross.

Miniature Sheet

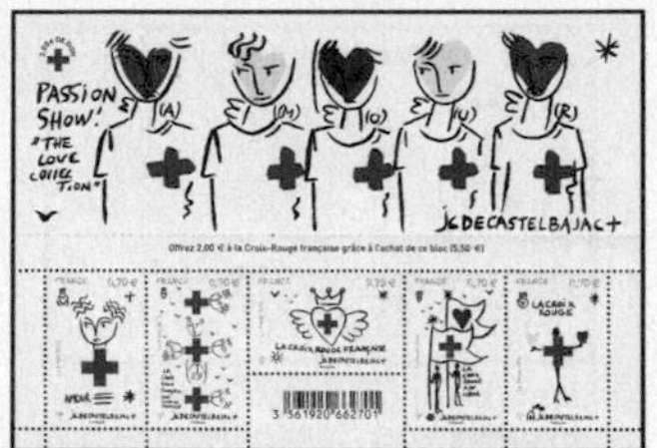


Red Cross — SP378

No. B766: a, Head on top of cross. b, Heads and three crosses. c, Cross in winged and crowned heart, horiz. d, Flags with cross and heart. e, Stylized person with cross as torso and arms.

**2016, Nov. 5 Photo. *Perf. 13***

| | | | | |
|---|---|---|---|---|
| B766 | SP378 | Sheet of 5 | 12.00 | 12.00 |
| a.-e. | | 70c+(40c) Any single | 2.40 | 2.40 |

Surtax for the Red Cross.

SP379

SP380

SP381

SP382

SP383

SP384

SP385

Work of the Red Cross SP386

***Serpentine Die Cut 11***

**2017, May 5 Photo.**

**Booklet Stamps Self-Adhesive**

| | | | | |
|---|---|---|---|---|
| B767 | SP379 | (73c+25c) multi | 2.25 | 2.25 |
| B768 | SP380 | (73c+25c) multi | 2.25 | 2.25 |
| B769 | SP381 | (73c+25c) multi | 2.25 | 2.25 |
| B770 | SP382 | (73c+25c) multi | 2.25 | 2.25 |
| B771 | SP383 | (73c+25c) multi | 2.25 | 2.25 |
| B772 | SP384 | (73c+25c) multi | 2.25 | 2.25 |
| B773 | SP385 | (73c+25c) multi | 2.25 | 2.25 |
| B774 | SP386 | (73c+25c) multi | 2.25 | 2.25 |
| a. | | Booklet pane of 8, #B767-B774 | 18.00 | |
| | | *Nos. B767-B774 (8)* | 18.00 | 18.00 |

Surtax for Red Cross.

**Marianne and Children "Lettre Prioritaire" Without Gram Limit Inscription Type of 2016**

**2017, Oct. 20 Photo. *Perf. 13***

| | | | | |
|---|---|---|---|---|
| B775 | A2536 | (85c+66c) red | 3.50 | 3.50 |

No. B775 was printed in sheets of 3 that sold for €4.55, €2 of which was for the Red Cross.

## AIR POST STAMPS

Nos. 127, 130 Overprinted in Dark Blue or Black

***Perf. 14x13½***

**1927, June 25 Unwmk.**

| | | | | |
|---|---|---|---|---|
| C1 | A18 | 2fr org & bl (DB) | 200.00 | 225.00 |
| | | Never hinged | 400.00 | |
| C2 | A18 | 5fr dk bl & buff | 200.00 | 225.00 |
| | | Never hinged | 400.00 | |

On sale only at the Intl. Aviation Exhib. at Marseilles, June, 1927. One set could be purchased by each holder of an admission ticket. Excellent counterfeits exist.

Nos. 242, 196 Surcharged

**1928, Aug. 23**

| | | | | |
|---|---|---|---|---|
| C3 | A33 | 10fr on 90c | 2,400. | 1,800. |
| | | Never hinged | 3,500. | |
| a. | | Inverted surcharge | 16,500. | 16,500. |
| | | Never hinged | 25,000. | |
| b. | | Space between "10" and bars 6½mm | 3,100. | 3,100. |
| | | Never hinged | 5,100. | |
| C4 | A23 | 10fr on 1.50fr | 10,000. | 8,250. |
| | | Never hinged | 14,000. | |
| a. | | Space between "10" and bars 6½mm | 13,000. | 13,000. |
| | | Never hinged | 20,000. | |

Nos. C3-C4 received their surcharge in New York by order of the French consul general. They were for use in paying the 10fr fee for letters leaving the liner Ile de France on a catapulted hydroplane when the ship was one day off the coast of France on its eastward voyage.

The normal space between "10" and bars is 4½mm, but on 10 stamps in each pane of 50 the space is 6½mm. Counterfeits exist.

View of Marseille, Church of Notre Dame at Left — AP1

**1930-31 Engr. *Perf. 13***

| | | | | |
|---|---|---|---|---|
| C5 | AP1 | 1.50fr dp carmine | 21.00 | 4.00 |
| | | Never hinged | 40.00 | |
| a. | | With perf. initials "E.I.P.A.30" | 2,750. | 3,750. |
| | | Never hinged | 3,600. | |
| C6 | AP1 | 1.50fr dk bl ('31) | 19.00 | 2.25 |
| | | Never hinged | 35.00 | |
| a. | | 1.50fr ultramarine | 50.00 | 21.00 |
| | | Never hinged | 90.00 | |
| b. | | As "a," with perf. initials "E.I.P.A.30" | 450.00 | 350.00 |
| | | Never hinged | 700.00 | |

Nos. C5a, C6a were sold at the Intl. Air Post Exhib., Paris, Nov. 6-20, 1930, at face value plus 5fr, the price of admission.

Forgeries abound of Nos. C5a and C6b. Certificates from recognized authorities are recommended.

Blériot's Monoplane AP2

**1934, Sept. 1 *Perf. 13***

| | | | | |
|---|---|---|---|---|
| C7 | AP2 | 2.25fr violet | 24.00 | 6.00 |
| | | Never hinged | 32.50 | |

1st flight across the English Channel, by Louis Blériot.

Plane over Paris AP3

**1936**

| | | | | |
|---|---|---|---|---|
| C8 | AP3 | 85c deep green | 2.25 | 2.25 |
| | | Never hinged | 6.50 | |
| C9 | AP3 | 1.50fr blue | 10.50 | 5.50 |
| | | Never hinged | 18.00 | |
| C10 | AP3 | 2.25fr violet | 18.00 | 7.00 |
| | | Never hinged | 35.00 | |
| C11 | AP3 | 2.50fr rose | 32.50 | 8.25 |
| | | Never hinged | 45.00 | |
| C12 | AP3 | 3fr ultra | 26.00 | 2.50 |
| | | Never hinged | 37.50 | |
| C13 | AP3 | 3.50fr orange brn | 62.50 | 24.00 |
| | | Never hinged | 105.00 | |
| C14 | AP3 | 50fr emerald | 825.00 | 325.00 |
| | | Never hinged | 1,450. | |
| b. | | 50fr green | 850.00 | 350.00 |
| | | Never hinged | 1,500. | |
| | | *Nos. C8-C14 (7)* | 976.75 | 374.50 |

Monoplane over Paris — AP4

Paper with Red Network Overprint

**1936, July 10 *Perf. 12½***

| | | | | |
|---|---|---|---|---|
| C15 | AP4 | 50fr ultra | 625.00 | 310.00 |
| | | Never hinged | 1,700. | |

Airplane and Galleon — AP5

Airplane and Globe AP6

**1936, Aug. 17** *Perf. 13*

**C16** AP5 1.50fr dk ultra 17.50 5.25
Never hinged 35.00
**C17** AP6 10fr Prus green 290.00 130.00
Never hinged 700.00

100th air mail flight across the South Atlantic.

**Catalogue values for unused stamps in this section, from this point to the end of the section, are for Never Hinged items.**

Centaur and Plane — AP7

Iris — AP8

Zeus Carrying Hebe AP9

Chariot of the Sun AP10

**1946-47** **Engr.** **Unwmk.**

**C18** AP7 40fr dk green .55 .25
**C19** AP8 50fr rose pink .60 .25
**C20** AP9 100fr dk blue ('47) 6.25 3.25
**C21** AP10 200fr red 5.25 1.50
*Nos. C18-C21 (4)* 12.65 5.25

Issued: 50fr, 200fr, 5/27; 40fr, 7/1; 100fr, Jan.

For surcharges see Reunion Nos. C35-C38.

Ile de la Cité, Paris, and Gull — AP11

**1947, May 7**

**C22** AP11 500fr dk Prus grn 45.00 27.50

UPU 12th Cong., Paris, May 7-July 7. See footnote after No. 4642.

View of Lille AP12

Air View of Paris — AP13

200fr, Bordeaux. 300fr, Lyon. 500fr, Marseille.

**1949-50** **Unwmk.** *Perf. 13*

**C23** AP12 100fr sepia 1.20 .40
**C24** AP12 200fr dk bl grn 11.50 .75
**C25** AP12 300fr purple 15.00 9.00
**C26** AP12 500fr brt red 55.00 4.75
**C27** AP13 1000fr blk, dull gray vio ('50) 130.00 24.00
*Nos. C23-C27 (5)* 212.70 38.90

For surcharges see Reunion Nos. C39-C41.

Alexander III Bridge and Petit Palais, Paris — AP14

**1949, June 13**

**C28** AP14 100fr brown car 5.25 5.25

International Telegraph and Telephone Conference, Paris, May-July 1949.

Jet Plane, Mystère IV — AP15

Planes: 200fr, Noratlas. 500fr, Miles Magister. 1000fr, Provence.

**1954, Jan. 16**

**C29** AP15 100fr red brn & bl 2.25 .25
**C30** AP15 200fr blk brn & vio bl 9.00 .25
**C31** AP15 500fr car & org 175.00 10.50
**C32** AP15 1000fr vio brn, bl grn & ind 95.00 14.00
*Nos. C29-C32 (4)* 281.25 25.00

See No. C37. For surcharges see Reunion Nos. C42-C45, C48.

Maryse Bastié and Plane AP16

**1955, June 4** **Unwmk.** *Perf. 13*

**C33** AP16 50fr dp plum & rose pink 5.25 3.75

Issued to honor Maryse Bastié, 1898-1952.

Morane Saulnier 760 Paris AP17

Designs: 500fr, Caravelle. 1000fr, Alouette helicopter.

**1957-59** **Engr.** *Perf. 13*

**C34** AP17 300fr sl grn, grnsh bl & sep ('59) 5.00 2.25
**C35** AP17 500fr dp ultra & blk 21.00 3.00
**C36** AP17 1000fr lil, ol blk & blk ('58) 45.00 19.00
*Nos. C34-C36 (3)* 71.00 24.25

See Nos. C38-C41. For surcharges see Reunion Nos. C46-C47, C49-C51.

**Types of 1954-59**

Planes: 2fr, Noratlas. 3fr, MS760, Paris. 5fr, Caravelle. 10fr, Alouette helicopter.

**1960, Jan. 11**

**C37** AP15 2fr vio bl & ultra 1.10 .25
*a.* 2fr ultramarine 3.00 .75
**C38** AP17 3fr sl grn, grnsh bl & sep 1.20 .25
**C39** AP17 5fr dp ultra & blk 2.25 .65
**C40** AP17 10fr lil, ol blk & blk 10.00 2.00
*Nos. C37-C40 (4)* 14.55 3.15

**Type of 1957-59**

Design: 2fr, Jet plane, Mystère 20.

**1965, June 12** **Engr.** *Perf. 13*

**C41** AP17 2fr slate bl & indigo .75 .25

**Concorde Issue**

Common Design Type

**1969, Mar. 2** **Engr.** *Perf. 13*

**C42** CD129 1fr indigo & brt bl .75 .35

The 0.95fr stamp in this design was prepared but not issued. Value $30,000.

Jean Mermoz, Antoine de Saint-Exupéry and Concorde — AP19

**1970, Sept. 19** **Engr.** *Perf. 13*

**C43** AP19 20fr blue & indigo 8.00 .55

Jean Mermoz (1901-36) and writer Antoine de Saint-Exupéry (1900-44), aviators and air mail pioneers.

Balloon, Gare d'Austerlitz, Paris — AP20

**1971, Jan. 16** **Engr.** *Perf. 13*

**C44** AP20 95c bl, vio bl, org & sl grn .75 .55

Centenary of the balloon post from besieged Paris, 1870-71.

Didier Daurat, Raymond Vanier and Plane Landing at Night — AP21

**1971, Apr. 17** **Engr.** *Perf. 13*

**C45** AP21 5fr Prus bl, blk & lt grn 1.75 .25

Didier Daurat (1891-1969) and Raymond Vanier (1895-1965), aviation pioneers.

For surcharge see Reunion No. C52.

Hélène Boucher, Maryse Hilsz and Caudron-Renault and Moth-Morane Planes — AP22

Design: 15fr, Henri Guillaumet, Paul Codos, Latécoère 521, Guillaumet's crashed plane in Andes, skyscrapers.

**1972-73** **Engr.** *Perf. 13*

**C46** AP22 10fr plum, red & sl 3.50 .40
**C47** AP22 15fr dp car, gray & brn ('73) 5.25 .75

Hélène Boucher (1908-34), Maryse Hilsz (1901-46), Henri Guillaumet (1902-40) and Paul Codos (1896-1960), aviation pioneers.

Issue dates: 10fr, June 10; 15fr, Feb. 24.

Concorde AP23

**1976, Jan. 10** **Engr.** *Perf. 13*

**C48** AP23 1.70fr brt bl, red & blk .75 .40

First flight of supersonic jet Concorde from Paris to Rio de Janeiro, Jan. 21.

Planes over the Atlantic, New York-Paris — AP24

**1977, June 4** **Engr.** *Perf. 13*

**C49** AP24 1.90fr multicolored .75 .40

1st transatlantic flight by Lindbergh from NY to Paris, 50th anniv., and 1st attempted westbound flight by French aviators Charles Nungesser and Francois Coli.

Plane over Flight Route AP25

**1978, Oct. 14** **Engr.** *Perf. 13*

**C50** AP25 1.50fr multicolored .60 .35

65th anniversary of first airmail route from Villacoublay to Pauillac, Gironde.

Rocket, Concorde, Exhibition Hall — AP26

**1979, June 9** **Engr.** *Perf. 13*

**C51** AP26 1.70fr ultra, org & brn .75 .60

33rd International Aerospace and Space Show, Le Bourget, June 11-15.

First Nonstop Transatlantic Flight, Paris-New York — AP27

**1980, Aug. 30** **Engr.** *Perf. 13*

**C52** AP27 2.50fr vio brn & ultra .90 .30

34th Intl. Space and Aeronautics Exhibition, June 5-14 AP28

**1981, June 6** **Engr.** *Perf. 13*

**C53** AP28 2fr multicolored 1.20 .40

Dieudonné Costes and Joseph Le Brix and their Breguet Bi-plane — AP29

**1981, Sept. 12** **Engr.**
**C54** AP29 10fr dk brown & red 3.50 .40

1st So. Atlantic crossing, Oct. 14-15, 1927.

Seaplane Late-300 — AP30

**1982, Dec. 4** **Engr.**
**C55** AP30 1.60fr multicolored .75 .40

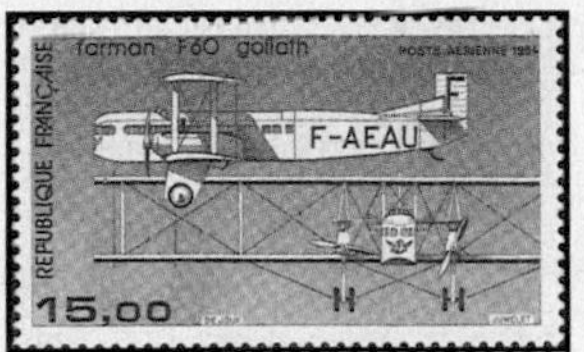


Farman F-60 Goliath — AP31

Planes: 20fr, CAMS-53 seaplane. 30fr, Wibault 283 Monoplane. 50fr, Dewoitine 338.

**1984-87** **Engr.**
**C56** AP31 15fr dark blue 5.00 .75
**C57** AP31 20fr dp org ('85) 6.50 .75
**C58** AP31 30fr brt vio ('86) 10.00 1.50
**C59** AP31 50fr green ('87) 15.00 4.50
*Nos. C55-C59 (5)* 37.25 7.90

Issued: 15fr, 3/3; 20fr, 3/2; 30fr, 10/11; 50fr, 4/11.

Breguet XIV — AP32

**1997, Nov. 15** **Photo.** ***Perf. 13x13¼***
**C60** AP32 20fr shown 9.00 3.00
*a.* Perf. 13x12½ 6.00 1.50
**C61** AP32 30fr Potez 25 12.50 3.50
*a.* Perf. 13x12½ 10.00 2.25

Issued: No. C60 11/15/97; No. C60a, 7/13/98; 30fr, 7/13/98.

Airbus A300-B4 — AP33

**1999, Apr. 10** **Photo.** ***Perf. 13x13¼***
**C62** AP33 15fr multicolored 15.00 3.00
*a.* Perf. 13x12½ 5.25 1.25

Couzinet 70 — AP34

**2000, Feb. 12** ***Perf. 13¼x13¼***
**C63** AP34 50fr multi 17.50 6.00
*a.* Perf. 13x12½ 22.50 7.50

First Flight of Airbus A300, 30th Anniv. — AP35

**2002, Oct. 26** **Photo.** ***Perf. 13x13¼***
**C64** AP35 €3 multi 7.00 1.50

No. C64 was issued both in panes of 40 and 10, same perforation.

Jacqueline Auriol (1917-2000), Pilot, and Jet — AP36

**Litho. & Engr.**

**2003, June 21** ***Perf. 13***
**C65** AP36 €4 multi 9.00 2.25
*a.* Miniature sheet of 10 90.00 —

Marie Marvingt (1875-1963), Pilot — AP37

**Litho. & Engr.**

**2004, June 29** ***Perf. 13¼x13***
**C66** AP37 €5 multi 11.00 3.00
*a.* Sheet of 10 110.00 —

Adrienne Bolland (1895-1975), Pilot — AP38

**Litho. & Engr.**

**2005, Oct. 22** ***Perf. 13***
**C67** AP38 €2 multi 4.50 1.50
*a.* Miniature sheet of 10 45.00

Airbus A380 — AP39

**2006, June 23** **Photo.** ***Perf. 13x13¼***
**C68** AP39 €3 multi 6.50 1.50
*a.* Miniature sheet of 10 65.00 —

Helicopters, Cent. — AP40

**2007, Feb. 19** **Photo.** ***Perf. 13x12½***
**C69** AP40 €3 multi 6.50 1.50
*a.* Perf. 13x13¼ 9.00 2.25

No. C69 was issued in panes of 40; No. C69a in panes of 10.

French Acrobatic Patrol — AP41

**Litho. & Engr.**

**2008, Sept. 13** ***Perf. 13***
**C70** AP41 €3 multi 6.50 1.50

Louis Blériot (1872-1936) and Blériot XI Airplane — AP42

**Litho. & Engr.**

**2009, July 25** ***Perf. 13x12¾***
**C71** AP42 €2 multi 4.50 1.25

First flight across English Channel, cent.

Henri Fabre (1882-1984) and Le Canard Seaplane — AP43

**Litho. & Engr.**

**2010, Mar. 27** ***Perf. 13***
**C72** AP43 €3 multi 6.50 1.50

First seaplane flight, cent.

Henri Pequet (1888-1974), Pilot for First Official Air Mail Flight in India — AP44

**2011, Feb. 18**
**C73** AP44 €2 multi 4.50 1.25

First French Airmail Flight Between Nancy and Luneville, Cent. — AP45

**2012, July 30**
**C74** AP45 €3 multi 6.50 1.50

First Parachute Jump by Adolphe Pégoud (1889-1915), Cent. — AP46

**2013, June 13**
**C75** AP46 €2.55 multi 5.50 1.50
*a.* Miniature sheet of 10 65.00 65.00

First Trans-Mediterranean Flight by Roland Garros, Cent. — AP47

**2013, Sept. 21** **Photo.** ***Perf. 13x12¾***
**C76** AP47 €3.40 multi 8.00 1.50

Caroline Aigle (1974-2007), First Female Fighter Pilot in French Air Force — AP48

**Litho. & Engr.**

**2014, Apr. 5** ***Perf. 13***
**C77** AP48 €3.55 multi 8.50 1.50

Gaston Caudron (1882-1915), Pilot and Aircraft Manufacturer — AP49

**Litho & Engr.**

**2015, June 15** ***Perf. 13***
**C78** AP49 €4.10 multi 9.00 2.00

Edouard Nieuport (1875-1911), Aviator and Airplane Manufacturer, and Nieuport 11 — AP50

**Litho. & Engr.**

**2016, June 10** ***Perf. 13***
**C79** AP50 €4.80 multi 11.00 5.50

Georges Guynemer (1894-1917), Ace Fighter Pilot in World War I, and Spad XIII — AP51

**Litho. & Engr.**

**2017, Sept. 8** ***Perf. 13***
**C80** AP51 €5.10 multi 12.00 6.00

## AIR POST SEMI-POSTAL STAMPS

**Catalogue values for unused stamps in this section are for Never Hinged items.**

Antoine de Saint-Exupéry — SPAP1

Col. Jean Dagnaux SPAP2

**1948** **Unwmk.** **Engr.** ***Perf. 13***
**CB1** SPAP1 50fr + 30fr vio brn 2.75 1.60
**CB2** SPAP2 100fr + 70fr dk blue 3.75 2.25

Modern Plane and Ader's "Eole" SPAP3

**1948, Feb.**
**CB3** SPAP3 40fr + 10fr dk blue 1.60 1.50

50th anniv. of the flight of Clément Ader's plane, the Eole, in 1897.

## POSTAGE DUE STAMPS

D1

**1859-70** **Unwmk.** **Litho.** ***Imperf.***
**J1** D1 10c black 30,500. 240.00
**J2** D1 15c black ('70) 140.00 *250.00*

In the lithographed stamps the central bar of the "E" of "CENTIMES" is very short, and the accent on "a" slants at an angle of 30 degree, for the 10c and 17 degree for the 15c, while on the typographed the central bar of the "E" is almost as wide as the top and bottom bars and the accent on the "a" slants at an angle of 47 degree.

No. J2 is known rouletted unofficially.

**1859-78** **Typo.**
**J3** D1 10c black 30.00 17.50
**J4** D1 15c black ('63) 35.00 15.00
**J5** D1 20c black ('77) 4,100.
**J6** D1 25c black ('71) 150.00 50.00
*a.* Double impression 6,000.
**J7** D1 30c black ('78) 225.00 125.00
**J8** D1 40c blue ('71) 325.00 *425.00*
*a.* 40c ultramarine 6,500. 5,700.
*b.* 40c Prussian blue 2,600.
**J9** D1 60c bister ('71) 475.00 *1,050.*
**J10** D1 60c blue ('78) 60.00 *110.00*
*a.* 60c dark blue 600.00 *725.00*
**J10B** D1 60c black 2,700.

The 20c & 60c black were not put into use.

Nos. J3, J4, J6, J8 and J9 are known rouletted unofficially and Nos. J4, J6, J7 and J10 pin-perf. unofficially.

D2

**1882-92** ***Perf. 14x13½***
**J11** D2 1c black 2.50 2.50
**J12** D2 2c black 30.00 26.00
**J13** D2 3c black 30.00 25.00
**J14** D2 4c black 60.00 40.00
**J15** D2 5c black 130.00 32.50
**J16** D2 10c black 110.00 2.50
**J17** D2 15c black 77.50 10.50
**J18** D2 20c black 350.00 140.00
**J19** D2 30c black 210.00 2.50
**J20** D2 40c black 140.00 60.00
**J21** D2 50c blk ('92) 600.00 175.00
**J22** D2 60c blk ('84) 600.00 57.50
**J23** D2 1fr black 750.00 350.00
**J24** D2 2fr blk ('84) 1,400. 825.00
**J25** D2 5fr blk ('84) 3,000. 1,600.

Excellent counterfeits exist of Nos. J23-J25.

See Nos. J26-J45A. For overprints and surcharges see Offices in China Nos. J1-J6, J33-J40, Offices in Egypt, Alexandria J1-J5, Port Said J1-J8, Offices in Zanzibar 60-62, J1-J5, Offices in Morocco 9-10, 24-25, J1-J5, J10-J12, J17-J22, J35-J41.

**1884**
**J26** D2 1fr brown 400.00 90.00
**J27** D2 2fr brown 190.00 130.00
**J28** D2 5fr brown 450.00 325.00

**1893-1941**
**J29** D2 5c blue ('94) .25 .30
**J30** D2 10c brown .25 .30
**J31** D2 15c lt grn ('94) 28.00 1.40
**J32** D2 20c ol grn ('06) 6.50 .65
**J33** D2 25c rose ('23) 6.50 3.75
**J34** D2 30c red ('94) .25 .25
**J35** D2 30c org red ('94) 475.00 85.00
**J36** D2 40c rose ('25) 11.50 4.50
**J37** D2 45c grn ('24) 9.00 5.25
**J38** D2 50c brn vio ('95) .50 .30
*a.* 50c lilac .50 .30
**J39** D2 60c bl grn ('25) 1.00 .55
**J40** D2 1fr rose, *straw* ('96) 475.00 375.00
**J41** D2 1fr red brn, *straw* ('20) 9.50 .30
**J42** D2 1fr red brn ('35) 1.25 .40
**J43** D2 2fr red org ('10) 225.00 65.00
**J44** D2 2fr brt vio ('26) .65 *.75*
**J45** D2 3fr magenta ('26) .65 *.75*
**J45A** D2 5fr red org ('41) 1.40 *2.25*

D3

**1908-25**
**J46** D3 1c olive grn 1.00 *1.25*
**J47** D3 10c violet 1.10 .30
*a.* Imperf., pair 175.00
**J48** D3 20c bister ('19) 40.00 1.25
**J49** D3 30c bister ('09) 14.00 .40
**J50** D3 50c red ('09) 275.00 60.00
**J51** D3 60c red ('25) 2.75 *3.75*
*Nos. J46-J51 (6)* 333.85 66.95

"Recouvrements" stamps were used to recover charges due on undelivered or refused mail which was returned to the sender.

For surcharges see Offices in Morocco Nos. J6-J9, J13-J16, J23-J26, J42-J45.

Nos. J49-J50 Surcharged

**1917**
**J52** D3 20c on 30c bister 20.00 4.00
**J53** D3 40c on 50c red 10.50 4.00
*a.* Double surcharge 475.00

In Jan. 1917 several values of the current issue of postage stamps were handstamped "T" in a triangle and used as postage due stamps.

Recouvrements Stamps of 1908-25 Surcharged

**1926**
**J54** D3 50c on 10c lilac 3.50 3.25
**J55** D3 60c on 1c ol grn 7.00 5.00
**J56** D3 1fr on 60c red 18.00 10.00
**J57** D3 2fr on 60c red 18.00 10.50
*Nos. J54-J57 (4)* 46.50 28.75

D4

**1927-31**
**J58** D4 1c olive grn ('28) 1.00 1.00
**J59** D4 10c rose ('31) 1.90 1.40
**J60** D4 30c bister 4.50 .50
**J61** D4 60c red 4.50 .50
**J62** D4 1fr violet 14.00 3.25
**J63** D4 1fr Prus grn ('31) 17.00 .55
**J64** D4 2fr blue 80.00 42.50
**J65** D4 2fr olive brn ('31) 150.00 26.00
*Nos. J58-J65 (8)* 272.90 75.70

Nos. J62 to J65 have the numerals of value double-lined.

Nos. J64, J62 Surcharged in Red or Black

**1929**
**J66** D4 1.20fr on 2fr blue 42.50 11.00
**J67** D4 5fr on 1fr vio (Bk) 65.00 15.00

No. J61 Surcharged

**1931**
**J68** D4 1fr on 60c red 30.00 2.75

**Catalogue values for unused stamps in this section, from this point to the end of the section, are for Never Hinged items.**

Sheaves of Wheat — D5

***Perf. 14x13½***

**1943-46** **Unwmk.** **Typo.**
**J69** D5 10c sepia .25 .25
**J70** D5 30c brt red vio .25 .25
**J71** D5 50c blue grn .25 .25
**J72** D5 1fr brt ultra .25 .25
**J73** D5 1.50fr rose red .25 .25
**J74** D5 2fr turq blue .25 .25
**J75** D5 3fr brn org .30 .25
**J76** D5 4fr dp vio ('45) 4.50 2.25
**J77** D5 5fr brt pink .40 .25
**J78** D5 10fr red org ('45) 2.50 .60
**J79** D5 20fr ol bis ('46) 8.00 2.25
*Nos. J69-J79 (11)* 17.20 7.10

**Type of 1943**
**Inscribed "Timbre Taxe"**

**1946-53**
**J80** D5 10c sepia ('47) .75 .40
**J81** D5 30c brt red vio ('47) .75 .40
**J82** D5 50c blue grn ('47) 19.00 6.50
**J83** D5 1fr brt ultra ('47) .25 .25
**J85** D5 2fr turq blue .25 .25
**J86** D5 3fr brown org .25 .25
**J87** D5 4fr deep violet .25 .25
**J88** D5 5fr brt pink ('47) .25 .25
**J89** D5 10fr red org ('47) .25 .25
**J90** D5 20fr olive bis ('47) 1.25 .30
**J91** D5 50fr dk green ('50) 19.00 .75
**J92** D5 100fr dp green ('53) 65.00 6.00
*Nos. J80-J92 (12)* 107.25 15.85

For surcharges see Reunion Nos. J36-J44.

Sheaves of Wheat — D6

**1960** **Typo.** ***Perf. 14x13½***
**J93** D6 5c bright pink 2.75 .40
**J94** D6 10c red orange 3.75 .25
**J95** D6 20c olive bister 3.50 .75
**J96** D6 50c dark green 9.75 .75
**J97** D6 1fr deep green 40.00 1.50
*Nos. J93-J97 (5)* 59.75 3.65

For surcharges see Reunion Nos. J46-J48. For overprints see Algeria Nos. J49-J53.

D7

Flowers: 5c, Centaury. 10c, Gentian. 15c, Corn poppy. 20c, Violets. 30c, Forget-me-not. 40c, Columbine. 50c, Clover. 1fr, Soldanel.

**1964-71** **Typo.** ***Perf. 14x13½***
**J98** D7 5c car rose, red & grn ('65) .25 .25
**J99** D7 10c car rose, brt bl & grn ('65) .25 .25
**J100** D7 15c brn, grn & red .25 .25
**J101** D7 20c dk grn, grn & vio ('71) .25 .25
**J102** D7 30c brn, ultra & grn .25 .25
**J103** D7 40c dk grn, scar & yel ('71) .25 .25
**J104** D7 50c vio bl, car & grn ('65) .25 .25
**J105** D7 1fr vio bl, lil & grn ('65) .40 .25
*Nos. J98-J105 (8)* 2.15 2.00

For surcharges see Reunion Nos. J49-J55.

D8

**1982-83** **Engr.** ***Perf. 13***
**J106** D8 10c Ampedus Cinnabarinus .25 .25
**J107** D8 20c Dorcadion fuliginator .25 .25
**J108** D8 30c Leptura cordigera .25 .25
**J109** D8 40c Paederus littoralis .25 .25
**J110** D8 50c Pyrochroa coccinea .25 .25
**J111** D8 1fr Scarites laevigatus .40 .25
**J112** D8 2fr Trichius gallicus .65 .25
**J113** D8 3fr Adalia alpina 1.00 .25
**J114** D8 4fr Apoderus coryli 1.40 .25
**J115** D8 5fr Trichodes alvearius 1.75 .25
*Nos. J106-J115 (10)* 6.45 2.50

Issued: 30c, 40c, 3fr, 5fr, 1/3/83; others, 1/4/82.

## MILITARY STAMPS

Regular Issue Overprinted in Black or Red

**1901-39** **Unwmk.** ***Perf. 14x13½***
**M1** A17 15c orange ('01) 65.00 6.00
*a.* Inverted overprint 300.00 150.00
*b.* Imperf., pair 425.00
**M2** A19 15c pale red ('03) 65.00 6.00
**M3** A20 15c slate grn ('04) 52.50 6.00
*a.* No period after "M" 110.00 57.50
*b.* Imperf., pair 290.00
**M4** A20 10c rose ('06) 30.00 8.25
*a.* No period after "M" 82.50 45.00
*b.* Imperf., pair 350.00

**M5** A22 10c red ('07) 1.75 1.00
*a.* Inverted overprint 105.00 65.00
*b.* Imperf., pair 190.00
**M6** A20 50c vermilion ('29) 4.75 1.00
*a.* No period after "M" 32.50 18.00
*b.* Period in front of F 32.50 18.00
**M7** A45 50c rose red ('34) 2.75 .55
*a.* No period after "M" 29.00 16.00
*b.* Inverted overprint 150.00 110.00
**M8** A45 65c brt ultra (R) ('38) .30 .30
*a.* No period after "M" 29.00 16.00
**M9** A45 90c ultra (R) ('39) .40 .35
*Nos. M1-M9 (9)* 222.45 29.45

"F. M." are initials of Franchise Militaire (Military Frank). See No. S1.

**Catalogue values for unused stamps in this section, from this point to the end of the section, are for Never Hinged items.**

M1

**1946-47 Typo.**
**M10** M1 dark green 1.75 .65
**M11** M1 rose red ('47) .30 .25

Nos. M10-M11 were valid also in the French colonies.

Flag — M2

**1964, July 20** ***Perf. 13x14***
**M12** M2 multicolored .30 .35

## OFFICIAL STAMPS

### FOR THE COUNCIL OF EUROPE

For use only on mail posted in the post office in the Council of Europe Building, Strasbourg.

**Catalogue values for unused stamps in this section are for Never Hinged items.**

**For French stamp inscribed "Conseil de l'Europe" see No. 679.**

**France No. 854 Overprinted: "CONSEIL DE L'EUROPE"**

**Unwmk.**

**1958, Jan. 14 Engr.** ***Perf. 13***
**1O1** A303 35fr car rose & lake .75 *2.00*

Council of Europe Flag — O1

**1958-59 Flag in Ultramarine**
**1O2** O1 8fr red org & brn vio .25 .25
**1O3** O1 20fr yel & lt brn .25 .25
**1O4** O1 25fr lil rose & sl grn ('59) .60 .30
**1O5** O1 35fr red .40 .25
**1O6** O1 50fr lilac rose ('59) .75 .75
*Nos. 1O2-1O6 (5)* 2.25 1.80

**1963, Jan. 3 Flag in Ultramarine**
**1O7** O1 20c yel & lt brn .90 .65
**1O8** O1 25c lil rose & sl grn 1.40 1.10
**1O9** O1 50c lilac rose 1.90 1.60
*Nos. 1O7-1O9 (3)* 4.20 3.35

Centime value stamps shown the denomination as "0,20," etc.

**1965-71**

**Flag in Ultramarine & Yellow**
**1O10** O1 25c ver, yel & sl grn .75 .55
**1O11** O1 30c ver & yel .35 .35
**1O12** O1 40c ver, yel & gray .75 .55
**1O13** O1 50c red, yel & grn 1.50 1.10
**1O14** O1 60c ver, yel & vio 1.10 1.00
**1O15** O1 70c ver, yel & dk brn 2.25 2.10
*Nos. 1O10-1O15 (6)* 6.70 5.65

Issue dates: 25c, 30c, 60c, 1/16/65; 50c, 2/20/71; others, 3/24/69.

**Type of 1958 Inscribed "FRANCE" Flag in Ultramarine & Yellow**

**1975-76 Engr.** ***Perf. 13***
**1O16** O1 60c org, yel & emer .60 .55
**1O17** O1 80c yel & mag .75 .60
**1O18** O1 1fr car, yel & gray ol ('76) 1.50 1.25
**1O19** O1 1.20fr org, yel & bl 4.00 2.25
*Nos. 1O16-1O19 (4)* 6.85 4.65

Issue dates: 1fr, 10/16; others, 11/22.

New Council Headquarters, Strasbourg — O2

**1977, Jan. 22 Engr.** ***Perf. 13***
**1O20** O2 80c car & multi .80 .50
**1O21** O2 1fr brown & multi .75 .30
**1O22** O2 1.40fr gray & multi 1.50 .75
*Nos. 1O20-1O22 (3)* 3.05 1.55

Human Rights Emblem in Upper Left Corner

**1978, Oct. 14**
**1O23** O2 1.20fr red lilac & multi .45 .40
**1O24** O2 1.70fr blue & multi .60 .55

30th anniversary of the Universal Declaration of Human Rights.

**Council Headquarters Type of 1977**

**1980, Nov. 24 Engr.** ***Perf. 13***
**1O25** O2 1.40fr olive .50 .50
**1O26** O2 2fr blue gray .75 .75

New Council Headquarters, Strasbourg — O3

**1981-84 Engr.**
**1O27** O3 1.40fr multicolored .50 .50
**1O28** O3 1.60fr multicolored .50 .40
**1O29** O3 1.70fr emerald .60 .40
**1O30** O3 1.80fr multicolored .70 .60
**1O31** O3 2fr multicolored .75 .40
**1O32** O3 2.10fr red .75 .60
**1O33** O3 2.30fr multicolored .85 .60
**1O34** O3 2.60fr multicolored .90 .75
**1O35** O3 2.80fr multicolored 1.00 .75
**1O36** O3 3fr brt blue 1.10 .90
*Nos. 1O27-1O36 (10)* 7.65 5.90

Issued: 1.40, 1.60, 2.30fr, 11/21; 1.80, 2.60fr, 11/13/82; 2, 2.80fr, 11/21/83; 1.70, 2.10, 3fr, 11/5/84.

Youth's Leg, Sneaker, Shattered Eggshell — O4

**1985, Aug. 31 Engr.** ***Perf. 13***
**1O37** O4 1.80fr brt green .70 .60
**1O38** O4 2.20fr vermilion .75 .60
**1O39** O4 3.20fr brt blue 1.10 1.00
*Nos. 1O37-1O39 (3)* 2.55 2.20

New Council Headquarters, Strasbourg — O5

**1986-87 Engr.** ***Perf. 13***
**1O40** O5 1.90fr green .70 .60
**1O41** O5 2fr brt yel grn .90 .60
**1O42** O5 2.20fr red .75 .60
**1O43** O5 3.40fr blue 1.20 1.00
**1O44** O5 3.60fr brt blue 1.40 1.10
*Nos. 1O40-1O44 (5)* 4.95 3.90

Issued: 1.90, 2.20, 3.40fr, 12/13; 2, 3.60fr, 10/10/87.

Council of Europe, 40th Anniv. — O6

**1989, Feb. 4 Litho. & Engr.**
**1O45** O6 2.20fr multicolored .90 .70
**1O46** O6 3.60fr multicolored 1.40 1.10

Denominations also inscribed in European Currency Units (ECUs).

Map of Europe — O7

**1990-91 Litho.** ***Perf. 13***
**1O47** O7 2.30fr multicolored .90 .75
**1O48** O7 2.50fr multicolored .90 .75
**1O49** O7 3.20fr multicolored 1.10 1.00
**1O50** O7 3.40fr multicolored 1.10 1.00
*Nos. 1O47-1O50 (4)* 4.00 3.50

Issued: 2.30fr, 3.20fr, 5/26/90; 2.50fr, 3.40fr, 11/23/91.

36 Heads, by Hundertwasser — O8

**1994, Jan. 15 Litho.** ***Perf. 13***
**1O51** O8 2.80fr multicolored 1.40 .75
**1O52** O8 3.70fr multicolored 2.25 1.00

Palace of Human Rights, Strasbourg — O9

**1996, June 1 Litho.** ***Perf. 13***
**1O53** O9 3fr multicolored 1.50 .75
**1O54** O9 3.80fr multicolored 1.75 1.00

Charioteer of Delphi — O10

**1999, Sept. 18 Photo.** ***Perf. 13***
**1O55** O10 3fr shown 1.40 .75
**1O56** O10 3.80fr Nike 1.75 1.00

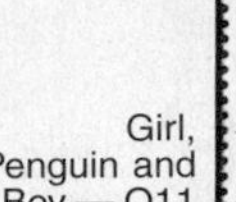

Girl, Penguin and Boy — O11

**2001, Dec. 1 Litho.** ***Perf. 13***
**1O57** O11 3fr red & multi 2.00 .70
**1O58** O11 3.80fr grn & multi 2.40 1.00

Hiker on Stars — O12

**2003, Oct. 18 Litho.** ***Perf. 13***
**1O59** O12 50c Hiker facing left 2.00 .70
**1O60** O12 75c Hiker facing right 2.50 1.20

O13

O14

**2005, Sept. 18 Litho.** ***Perf. 13***
**1O61** O13 55c multi 2.00 .75
**1O62** O14 75c multi 2.50 1.20

Map of Europe — O15

Sculpture by Mariano González Beltrán — O16

**2007, June 23 Litho.** ***Perf. 13***
**1O63** O15 60c multi 2.00 .75
**1O64** O16 85c multi 2.50 1.25

Council of Europe, 60th Anniv. — O17

European Court of Human Rights, 50th Anniv. — O18

**2009, May 16 Litho.** ***Perf. 13***
**1O65** O17 56c multi 2.00 .75
**1O66** O18 70c multi 2.50 1.25

Tree — O19 Chain — O20

**2010, Sept. 17 Litho. *Perf. 13***
**1O67** O19 75c multi 2.10 .75
**1O68** O20 87c multi 2.40 1.25

European Human Rights Convention, 60th anniv. (No. 1O68).

Map of Europe and Flags — O21

**2011, Sept. 9 Litho. *Perf. 13***
**1O69** O21 89c multi 2.50 1.25

European Social Charter, 50th anniv.

European Youth Center, Strasbourg, 40th Anniv. — O22

**2012, Sept. 28**
**1O70** O22 89c multi 2.40 1.25

Balance of Rights and Responsibilties of Citizens in a Democracy — O23

**2013, Sept. 27 Litho. *Perf. 13***
**1O71** O23 95c multi 2.60 1.25

European Directorate for the Quality of Medicines and Health Care, 50th Anniv. — O24

European Cultural Cooperation, 60th Anniv. — O25

**2014, Oct. 3 Photo. *Perf. 13***
**1O72** O24 83c multi 2.10 1.00
**1O73** O25 98c multi 2.50 1.25

European Union Flag, 60th Anniv. O26

**2015, Oct. 2 Litho. *Perf. 13***
**1O74** O26 95c multi 2.25 1.10

European Social Charter O27

**2016, Oct. 14 Litho. *Perf. 13***
**1O75** O27 €1 multi 2.25 2.25

Council of Europe Cultural Routes 30th Anniv. — O28

**2017, Oct. 13 Litho. *Perf. 13***
**1O76** O28 €1.10 multi 2.60 2.60

---

**FOR THE UNITED NATIONS EDUCATIONAL, SCIENTIFIC AND CULTURAL ORGANIZATION**

For use only on mail posted in the post office in the UNESCO Building, Paris.

**Catalogue values for unused stamps in this section are for Never Hinged items.**

---

**For French stamps inscribed "UNESCO" see Nos. 572, 893-894, 2545.**

---

Khmer Buddha and Hermes by Praxiteles O1

**1961-65 Unwmk. Engr. *Perf. 13***
**2O1** O1 20c dk gray, ol bis & bl .25 *.55*
**2O2** O1 25c blk, lake & grn .40 *.90*
**2O3** O1 30c choc & bis brn ('65) .90 *.60*
**2O4** O1 50c blk, red & vio bl .90 *1.75*
**2O5** O1 60c grnsh bl, red brn & rose lil ('65) 1.00 1.40
*Nos. 2O1-2O5 (5)* 3.45 5.20

Book and Globe — O2

**1966, Dec. 17**
**2O6** O2 25c gray .30 .25
**2O7** O2 30c dark red .45 .35
**2O8** O2 60c green .75 .65
*Nos. 2O6-2O8 (3)* 1.50 1.25

20th anniversary of UNESCO.

Human Rights Flame — O3

**1969-71 Engr. *Perf. 13***
**2O9** O3 30c sl grn, red & dp brn .30 .30
**2O10** O3 40c dk car rose, red & dp brn .45 .40
**2O11** O3 50c ultra, car & brn ('71) .75 .60
**2O12** O3 70c pur, red & sl 1.50 1.40
*Nos. 2O9-2O12 (4)* 3.00 2.70

Universal Declaration of Human Rights.

**Type of 1969 Inscribed "FRANCE"**

**1975, Nov. 15 Engr. *Perf. 13***
**2O13** O3 60c grn, red & dk brn .60 .55
**2O14** O3 80c ocher, red & red brn .90 .60
**2O15** O3 1.20fr ind, red & brn 3.00 2.25
*Nos. 2O13-2O15 (3)* 4.50 3.40

O4

**1976-78 Engr. *Perf. 13***
**2O16** O4 80c multi .65 .55
**2O17** O4 1fr multi .35 .30
**2O18** O4 1.20fr multi .50 .40
**2O19** O4 1.40fr multi 1.25 .90
**2O20** O4 1.70fr multi .75 .60
*Nos. 2O16-2O20 (5)* 3.50 2.75

Issued: 1.20, 1.70fr, 10/14/78; others, 10/23/76.

Slave Quarters, Senegal O5

Designs: 1.40fr, Mohenjo-Daro excavations, Pakistan. 2fr, Sans-Souci Palace, Haiti.

**1980, Nov. 17 Engr. *Perf. 13***
**2O21** O5 1.20fr multi .50 .50
**2O22** O5 1.40fr multi .55 .50
**2O23** O5 2fr multi .80 .65
*Nos. 2O21-2O23 (3)* 1.85 1.65



Hue, Vietnam — O7

Designs: 1.40fr, Building, Fez, Morocco. 1.60fr, Seated deity, Sukhotai, Thailand. 2.30fr, Fort St. Elmo, Malta, horiz. 2.60fr, St. Michael Church ruins, Brazil.

**1981-82**
**2O24** O7 1.40fr multi .50 .35
**2O25** O7 1.60fr multi .50 .35
**2O26** O7 1.80fr shown .70 .55
**2O27** O7 2.30fr multi .60 .50
**2O28** O7 2.60fr multi .75 .55
*Nos. 2O24-2O28 (5)* 3.05 2.30

Issued: 1.80fr, 2.60fr, 10/23/82; others, 12/12/81.

Mosque, Chinguetti, Mauritania O8

Roman Theater and Female Standing Sculpture, Carthage, Tunisia — O8a

Architecture: 1.70fr, Church, Lalibela, Ethiopia. 2.10fr, San'a, Yemen. 2.20fr, Old Town Square and wrought iron latticework, Havana. 2.80fr, Enclosure wall interior, Istanbul. 3fr, Church, Kotor, Yugoslavia. 3.20fr, Temple of Anuradhapura and bas-relief of two women, Sri Lanka.

**1983-85 Engr.**
**2O29** O8 1.70fr multi .55 .35
**2O30** O8a 1.80fr multi .65 .55
**2O31** O8 2fr multi .75 .40
**2O32** O8 2.10fr multi .75 .60
**2O33** O8a 2.20fr multi .75 .60
**2O34** O8 2.80fr multi 1.00 .60
**2O35** O8 3fr multi 1.10 .90
**2O36** O8a 3.20fr multi 1.10 1.00
*Nos. 2O29-2O36 (8)* 6.65 5.00

Issued: 2fr, 2.80fr, 10/10; 1.70fr, 2.10fr, 3fr, 10/22/84; 1.80fr, 2.20fr, 3.20fr, 10/26/85.

Tikal Temple, Guatemala — O9

3.40fr, Bagerhat Mosque, Bangladesh.

**1986, Dec. 6 Engr. *Perf. 13***
**2O37** O9 1.90fr shown .75 .65
**2O38** O9 3.40fr multicolored 1.25 1.20

The Parthenon, Athens O10

3.60fr, Temple of Philae, Egypt.

**1987, Dec. 5 Engr. *Perf. 13x12½***
**2O39** O10 2fr shown .90 .60
**2O40** O10 3.60fr multicolored 1.40 1.20

Shibam, Yemen People's Democratic Republic O11

2.30fr, San Francisco de Lima, Peru, vert.

***Perf. 13x12½, 12½x13***

**1990, Apr. 7 Engr.**
**2O41** O11 2.30fr multicolored .90 .75
**2O42** O11 3.20fr shown 1.20 1.00

Bagdaon Temple, Nepal — O12

3.40fr, Citadel of Harat, Afghanistan, horiz.

**1991, Nov. 23**

**2O43** O12 2.50fr choc & dk red .90 .75
**2O44** O12 3.40fr grn, brn & ol 1.20 1.00

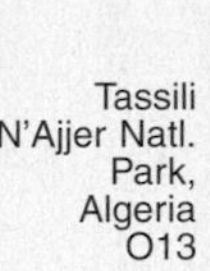

Tassili N'Ajjer Natl. Park, Algeria O13

Design: 2.80fr, Angkor Wat Archaeological Park, Cambodia, vert.

**1993, Oct. 23** Litho. *Perf. 13*

**2O45** O13 2.80fr multicolored 1.25 .75
**2O46** O13 3.70fr multicolored 1.50 1.00

UNESCO, 50th Anniv. O14

Designs: 3fr, Uluru Natl. Park, Australia. 3.80fr, Los Glaciares Natl. Park, Argentina.

**1996, June 1** Litho. *Perf. 13*

**2O47** O14 3fr multicolored 1.50 .75
**2O48** O14 3.80fr multicolored 2.00 1.00

Detail of Dionysus Fresco, Pompeii — O15

Moai Statues, Easter Island O16

**1998, Oct. 24** Litho. *Perf. 13*

**2O49** O15 3fr multicolored 1.50 .75
**2O50** O16 3.80fr multicolored 1.90 1.25

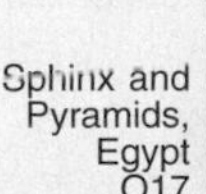

Sphinx and Pyramids, Egypt O17

Komodo Dragon, Komodo Natl. Park, Indonesia O18

**2001, Dec. 1** Litho. *Perf. 13*

**2O51** O17 3fr multi 2.00 .75
**2O52** O18 3.80fr multi 2.50 1.00

Reindeer, Lapland O19

Church of the Resurrection, St. Petersburg, Russia — O20

**2003, Dec. 6** Litho. *Perf. 13*

**2O53** O19 50c multi 2.00 .75
**2O54** O20 75c multi 2.50 1.40

Bison in Bialowieza Forest, Poland — O21

Petra, Jordan O22

**2005, Nov. 26** Litho. *Perf. 13*

**2O55** O21 55c multi 2.00 .75
**2O56** O22 90c multi 2.50 1.40

Siberian Tiger — O23

Luang Prabang, Laos O24

**2006, Dec. 7** Litho. *Perf. 13*

**2O57** O23 60c multi 2.00 .75
**2O58** O24 85c multi 2.50 1.25

Ksar d'Ait-Ben-Haddou, Morocco — O25

Koala, Australia — O26

**2007, Dec. 13** Litho. *Perf. 13*

**2O59** O25 60c multi 2.00 .75
**2O60** O26 85c multi 2.50 1.40

Gorilla — O27

Machu Picchu, Peru O28

**2008, Dec. 3** Litho. *Perf. 13*

**2O61** O27 65c multi 2.00 1.00
**2O62** O28 85c multi 2.50 1.25

Polar Bear O29

Suzhou, China O30

**2009, Dec. 9** Litho. *Perf. 13*

**2O63** O29 70c multi 2.10 1.00
**2O64** O30 85c multi 2.50 1.25

Alhambra, Spain O31

Alpaca O32

**2010, Dec. 1** Litho. *Perf. 13*

**2O65** O31 75c multi 2.00 1.00
**2O66** O32 87c multi 2.40 1.20

Bactrian Camel O33

Milford Sound, New Zealand O34

**2011, Oct. 19**

**2O67** O33 77c multi 2.10 1.00
**2O68** O34 89c multi 2.50 1.25

Stonehenge, Great Britain — O35

African Elephants O36

**2012, Nov. 22**

**2O69** O35 77c multi 2.00 1.00
**2O70** O36 89c multi 2.40 1.20

Japanese Cranes — O37

Sigiriya UNESCO World Heritage Site, Sri Lanka O38

**2013, Nov. 7** Litho. *Perf. 13*

**2O71** O37 58c multi 1.60 .80
**2O72** O38 95c multi 2.60 1.25

Trulli of Alberobello UNESCO World Heritage Site, Italy — O39

Hyacinth Macaw — O40

**2014, Nov. 8** Litho. *Perf. 13x13¼*

**2O73** O39 83c multi 2.10 1.00

*Perf. 13¼x13*

**2O74** O40 98c multi 2.50 1.25

African Gnu — O41

Sagrada Familia Basilica, Barcelona — O42

**2015, Nov. 6** Litho. *Perf. 13*

**2O75** O41 95c multi 2.00 2.00
**2O76** O42 €1.20 multi 2.60 2.60

UNESCO, 70th anniv.

Florida Panther — O43

Ruins, Ephesus, Turkey — O44

**2016, Sept. 9 Litho. *Perf. 13***

**2O77** O43 €1 multi 2.25 2.25
**2O78** O44 €1.25 multi 2.75 2.75

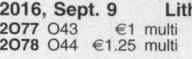

Samarkand, Uzbekistan — O45

Orangutan — O46

**2017, June 30 Litho. *Perf. 13***

**2O79** O45 €1.10 multi 2.50 2.50
**2O80** O46 €1.30 multi 3.00 3.00

## NEWSPAPER STAMPS

Coat of Arms — N1

**1868 Unwmk. Typo. *Imperf.***

**P1** N1 2c lilac 300.00 65.00
**P2** N1 2c (+ 2c) blue 600.00 275.00

***Perf. 12½***

**P3** N1 2c lilac 52.50 25.00
**P4** N1 2c (+ 4c) rose 250.00 100.00
**P5** N1 2c (+ 2c) blue 75.00 35.00
**P6** N1 5c lilac 1,250. 550.00

Nos. P2, P4, and P5 were sold for face plus an added fiscal charge indicated in parenthesis. Nos. P1, P3 and P6 were used simply as fiscals.

The 2c rose and 5c lilac imperforate and the 5c rose and 5c blue, both imperforate and perforated, were never put into use.

Nos. P1-P6 were reprinted for the 1913 Ghent Exhibition and the 1937 Paris Exhibition (PEXIP).

No. 109 Surcharged in Red

**1919 *Perf. 14x13½***

**P7** A16 ½c on 1c gray .30 .30
*a.* Inverted surcharge 1,200. 1,150.

### No. 156 Surcharged

**1933**

**P8** A22 ½c on 1c olive bister .30 .30

## PARCEL POST STAMPS

Inscribed "I APPORT A LA GARE" — PP1

***Perfs As Noted***

**1892 Unwmk. Typo.**

**Q1** PP1 25c brown, *yel*, perf 13½ 825.00 290.00
Never hinged 1,500.
**Q2** PP1 25c brown, *yel*, perf 11 30.00 24.00
Never hinged 45.00
*a.* Printed on both sides 400.00
Never hinged 650.00

Inscribed "II VALEUR DECLAREE" — PP2

**Q3** PP2 10c red, perf 13½ 1,000. 275.00
Never hinged 1,750.
**Q4** PP2 10c red, perf 10x13½ 875.00 325.00
Never hinged 1,600.
**Q5** PP2 10c org red, perf 11 30.00 14.00
Never hinged 42.50
**Q6** PP2 10c red, imperf 22.50 16.50
Never hinged 32.50

Inscribed "III LIVRAISON PAR EXPRESS" — PP3

**Q7** PP3 25c green, perf 13½ 57.50 32.50
Never hinged 115.00
**Q8** PP3 25c green, perf 11 45.00 24.00
Never hinged 70.00

See Nos. Q22-Q26.

Locomotive — PP4

A set of six stamps, in the design above, was prepared in 1901 as postal tax stamps for expedited parcels but were not issued. All are perf 14x13½. Values: 5c gray, $3, never hinged $4; 10c yellow green, $3, never hinged $5; 20c rose, $20, never hinged $29; 50c blue, $7, never hinged $11.50; 1fr brown, $8, never hinged $12; 2fr brown red, $37.50, never hinged $57.50.

PP5

**1918 *Perf. 11***

### Type I: Large Trefoil Under "N" of "MAJORATION"

**Q9** PP5 5c black 1.25 .85
Never hinged 2.00
**Q10** PP5 15c brn lilac 1.25 .85
Never hinged 2.00

***Imperforate***

**Q11** PP5 5c black 3.25 2.50
Never hinged 6.25
**Q12** PP5 15c brn lilac 9.00 4.25
Never hinged 14.00
*Nos. Q9-Q12 (4)* 14.75 8.45

40c values, perforated 11 and imperf, in orange, were prepared but not issued. Value, perf or imperf, $375.

### Type II: Small Trefoil Under "O" of "MAJORATION"

***Perf. 11***

**Q13** PP5 5c black 140.00 45.00
Never hinged 275.00
**Q14** PP5 35c red 3.75 2.50
Never hinged 5.00
**Q15** PP5 50c vio blue 4.50 1.60
Never hinged 7.00
**Q16** PP5 1fr yellow 4.25 1.60
Never hinged 7.00

***Imperforate***

**Q17** PP5 5c black 130.00 45.00
Never hinged 260.00
**Q18** PP5 15c brn lilac 30.00 16.50
Never hinged 50.00
**Q19** PP5 35c red 3.25 2.50
Never hinged 6.75
**Q20** PP5 50c vio blue 24.00 14.00
Never hinged 40.00
**Q21** PP5 1fr yellow 18.50 12.50
Never hinged 30.00
*Nos. Q13-Q21 (9)* 358.25 141.20

See Nos. Q41-Q44, Q143-Q145.
For surcharges, see Nos. Q28-Q40.

### Type of 1892

**1918-23 *Perf. 10½x11***

**Q22** PP1 30c brn, *yel* 37.50 16.50
Never hinged 55.00
*a.* Imperf 200.00
Never hinged 290.00
**Q23** PP1 60c brn, *straw* ('23) 47.50 30.00
Never hinged 70.00
*a.* Imperf 190.00
Never hinged 275.00
**Q24** PP2 15c vermilion ('22) 16.00 11.00
Never hinged 23.00
**Q25** PP3 30c green 40.00 21.00
Never hinged 57.50
*a.* Imperf 240.00
Never hinged 325.00
**Q26** PP3 60c green ('23) 75.00 50.00
Never hinged 110.00
*Nos. Q22-Q26 (5)* 216.00 128.50

PP6

**1924, Oct. *Perf. 14***

**Q27** PP6 15c rose & blue 4.00 3.75
Never hinged 5.00
*a.* Imperf 550.00
Never hinged 750.00

No. Q27 is a postal tax stamp, issued to show the collection of a new 15c excise fee on rail parcels. On July 3, 1925, its use was extended to all fiscal categories.

### Surcharged in Black or Red (R) on Nos. Q9//Q16 and Types of 1918

**1926 *Perf. 13***

**Q28** PP5 20c on 2fr rose 1.90 1.10
Never hinged 2.75
**Q29** PP5 30c on 2fr yellow 1.90 1.10
Never hinged 2.75
*a.* "0f30" omitted 190.00
Never hinged 250.00
**Q30** PP5 40c on 3fr gray 1.90 1.40
Never hinged 2.75
**Q31** PP5 45c on 3fr orange 1.90 1.40
Never hinged 2.75
*a.* Period after "f" omitted 19.00 19.00
Never hinged 30.00
**Q32** PP5 95c on 1fr yel 8.00 2.75
Never hinged 12.50
*a.* Imperf 90.00
Never hinged 150.00
**Q33** PP5 1.35fr on 3fr vio 10.50 4.50
Never hinged 14.00
On postal document 70.00
*a.* Imperf 150.00
Never hinged 225.00
**Q34** PP5 1.45fr on 5fr black (R) 1.90 1.00
Never hinged 2.75
**Q35** PP5 1.75fr on 2fr blue 10.50 4.50
Never hinged 14.00
**Q36** PP5 1.85fr on 10c orange 1.90 1.20
Never hinged 2.75
**Q37** PP5 1.95fr on 15c lilac ben 2.50 1.75
Never hinged 3.50
*a.* Imperf 110.00
Never hinged 175.00
**Q38** PP5 2.35fr on 25c green 1.90 1.00
Never hinged 2.75
*a.* Imperf 110.00
Never hinged 175.00
**Q39** PP5 2.90fr on 35c red 2.50 1.00
Never hinged 3.50
*a.* Dots before and after "f" 140.00
Never hinged 200.00
*b.* Imperf 125.00
Never hinged 190.00
**Q40** PP5 3.30fr on 50c blue violet (R) 2.50 1.25
Never hinged 3.50
*a.* Double surcharge 250.00
Never hinged 375.00
*b.* Imperf 90.00
Never hinged 140.00
*Nos. Q28-Q40 (13)* 49.80 23.95

### Type of 1918

**1926 *Perf. 11***

**Q41** PP5 10c orange 2.00 1.25
Never hinged 3.75
*a.* Imperf 4.00
Never hinged 6.50
**Q42** PP5 25c pale green 2.00 1.25
Never hinged 3.75
*a.* Imperf 4.00
Never hinged 6.50
**Q43** PP5 2fr pale blue 25.00 14.50
Never hinged 42.50
*a.* Imperf 50.00
Never hinged 80.00
**Q44** PP5 3fr violet 110.00 67.50
Never hinged 190.00
*a.* Imperf 225.00
Never hinged 360.00
*Nos. Q41-Q44 (4)* 139.00 84.50

Inscribed "APPORT A LA GARE" — PP7

**1926**

**Q45** PP7 1fr on 60c brn, *yel* 13.50 10.50
Never hinged 24.00
*a.* Imperf 190.00
Never hinged 300.00
**Q46** PP7 1fr brn, *yel* 17.50 13.00
Never hinged 30.00
**Q47** PP7 1.30fr on 1fr brn, *yel* 17.50 12.50
Never hinged 30.00
**Q48** PP7 1.50fr brn, *yel* 20.00 11.50
Never hinged 32.50
**Q49** PP7 1.65fr brn, *yel* 15.00 12.50
Never hinged 24.00
**Q50** PP7 1.90fr on 1fr brn, *yel* 17.50 12.50
Never hinged 30.00
**Q51** PP7 2.10fr on 1.65fr brn, *yel* 17.50 12.50
Never hinged 30.00
*Nos. Q45-Q51 (7)* 118.50 85.00

See Nos. Q91-Q95, footnote following No. Q102, Q143-Q145.

For overprints and surcharges, see Nos. Q76-Q78, Q83-Q86, Q91-Q92, boxed note following Q95, Q96-Q99, Q107-QQ109, boxed note following Q159.

PP8

Type I Type II Type III

**1926-38**

**Q52** PP8 15c brown, *yel*, type I 7.50 3.00
Never hinged 11.00
*a.* Imperf 180.00
Never hinged 275.00
**Q53** PP8 15c brown, *yel*, type II ('32) 8.00 4.25
Never hinged 11.50
*a.* Type III ('38) 210.00
Never hinged 275.00
*b.* As "a," imperf 240.00
Never hinged 300.00

Nos. Q52-Q53a were issued for use in Paris only. No. Q53a was prepared but not issued.

Inscribed "VALEUR DECLAREE" — PP9

The additional numerals overprinted on Nos. Q56-Q63 and on Nos. Q72-Q75 indicate the weight category of the parcels being sent.

**1926**

**Q54** PP9 50c on 15c red 3.00 1.60
Never hinged 5.00
*a.* Imperf 180.00
Never hinged 275.00
**Q55** PP9 50c red 750.00 750.00
Never hinged 1,200.
*a.* Imperf 1,200.
Never hinged 1,650.
**Q56** PP9 50c red, ovptd. "1" 4.50 2.00
Never hinged 7.00
*a.* Imperf 200.00
Never hinged 300.00
*b.* Double overprint "1" 300.00
Never hinged 400.00
**Q57** PP9 55c on 15c red, ovptd. "1" 6.75 5.00
Never hinged 11.50
*a.* Imperf 190.00
Never hinged —
**Q58** PP9 55c on 50c red, ovptd. "1" 6.75 5.00
Never hinged 11.50
**Q59** PP9 65c on 50c red 2.50 2.50
Never hinged 4.25
**Q60** PP9 65c on 50c red, ovptd. "1" 15.00 8.25
Never hinged 27.50
**Q61** PP9 1.50fr on 50c red, ovptd. "3" 7.00 5.00
Never hinged 12.00
*a.* Imperf 275.00
Never hinged 375.00
**Q62** PP9 2.00fr on 50c red, ovptd. "4" 8.25 3.75
Never hinged 14.00
**Q63** PP9 2.50fr on 50c red, ovptd. "5" 15.00 8.25
Never hinged 26.50
*Nos. Q54-Q63 (10)* 818.75 791.35

See Nos. Q79, Q93, Q150-Q152.

For overprints and surcharges, see No. Q87, boxed note following No. Q95, Q100, Q110, Q123-Q124, Q138.

Inscribed "LIVRAISON PAR EXPRESS" — PP10

**Q64** PP10 1.00fr on 60c grn 13.50 10.50
Never hinged 24.00
*a.* Imperf 225.00
Never hinged 325.00
**Q65** PP10 1.00fr green 125.00 75.00
Never hinged 250.00
**Q66** PP10 1.30fr on 1fr grn 16.50 12.50
Never hinged 29.00
**Q67** PP10 1.50fr green 16.50 15.00
Never hinged 32.50
**Q68** PP10 1.65fr green 16.50 15.00
Never hinged 32.50
**Q69** PP10 1.90fr on 1.50fr grn 16.50 12.50
Never hinged 30.00
**Q70** PP10 2.10fr on 1.65fr grn 30.00 14.00
Never hinged 50.00
*Nos. Q64-Q70 (7)* 234.50 154.50

For overprints and surcharges, see Nos. Q80-Q82, Q88-Q90, Q94, boxed note following Q95, Q101-Q105, Q111-Q113, Q125-Q132, Q139-Q141, Q146-Q149.

Inscribed "INTERETS A LA LIVRAISON" — PP11

**Q71** PP11 50c lilac 3.00 1.60
Never hinged 5.00
*a.* Imperf 225.00 190.00
Never hinged 325.00
**Q72** PP11 50c lil, ovptd. "1" 6.75 4.25
Never hinged 10.00
*a.* Imperf 200.00
Never hinged 300.00
**Q73** PP11 1.50fr on 50c lil, ovptd. "3" 7.50 5.00
Never hinged 11.50
*a.* Imperf 200.00
Never hinged 300.00
**Q74** PP11 2.00fr on 50c lil ovptd. "4" 10.00 7.00
Never hinged 16.00
**Q75** PP11 2.50fr on 50c lil ovptd. "5" 10.00 7.00
Never hinged 16.50
*a.* Imperf 210.00
Never hinged 310.00
*Nos. Q71-Q75 (5)* 37.25 24.85

1926 Issues Overprinted

**1928**

**Inscribed "APPORT A LA GARE"**

**Q76** PP7 1.00fr brn, *yel* 16.50 14.00
Never hinged 25.00
*a.* Imperf 190.00 190.00
Never hinged 300.00
**Q77** PP7 1.50fr brn, *yel* 16.50 13.00
Never hinged 25.00
**Q78** PP7 1.65fr brn, *yel* 16.50 13.00
Never hinged 25.00

**Inscribed "VALEUR DECLAREE"**

**Q79** PP9 50c red 5.75 4.25
Never hinged 8.25
*a.* Imperf 190.00 190.00
Never hinged 300.00
*b.* Inverted overprint 210.00
Never hinged 310.00

**Inscribed "LIVRAISON PAR EXPRESS"**

**Q80** PP10 1.00fr green 17.00 13.50
Never hinged 26.00
**Q81** PP10 1.50fr green 17.00 13.50
Never hinged 26.00
**Q82** PP10 1.65fr green 17.00 13.50
Never hinged 27.50
*Nos. Q76-Q82 (7)* 106.25 84.75

1926 Issues Surcharged

**1928**

**Inscribed "APPORT A LA GARE"**

**Q83** PP7 1.45fr on 60c brn, *yel* 7.00 6.75
Never hinged 10.00
**Q84** PP7 1.45fr on 1fr brn, *yel* 40.00 32.50
Never hinged 70.00
**Q85** PP7 2.15fr on 1.50fr brn, *yel* 62.50 42.50
Never hinged 105.00
**Q86** PP7 2.35fr on 1.65fr brn, *yel* 62.50 42.50
Never hinged 105.00

**Inscribed "VALEUR DECLAREE"**

**Q87** PP9 75c on 50c red 2.10 1.60
Never hinged 3.25
*a.* Imperf 210.00
Never hinged 400.00

**Inscribed "LIVRAISON PAR EXPRESS"**

**Q88** PP10 1.45fr on 1fr green 62.50 42.50
Never hinged 105.00
**Q89** PP10 2.15fr on 1.50fr green 62.50 42.50
Never hinged 105.00
**Q90** PP10 2.35fr on 1.65fr green 62.50 42.50
Never hinged 105.00
*Nos. Q83-Q90 (8)* 361.60 253.35

Types of 1926 and

PP12

**1933-34**

**Inscribed "APPORT A LA GARE"**

**Q91** PP7 1.45fr brn, *yel* 55.00 25.00
Never hinged 82.50
**Q92** PP7 2.35fr brn, *yel* 1,400.
Never hinged 1,900.

A 2.15fr value, brown on yellow paper, was prepared but not issued without overprint or surcharge.

For overprints and surcharges, see Nos. Q96, Q98, Q99, Q107-Q109, Q115, Q116, Q118, Q120-Q122, Q135-Q137.

**Inscribed "VALEUR DECLAREE"**

**Q93** PP9 75c red 18.00 3.25
Never hinged 22.50
*a.* Imperf 180.00

For overprints and surcharges on No. Q93, see Nos. Q110, Q123, Q124, Q138.

A 1.15fr black in this design, imperf, was prepared but not issued. Value, $400.

**Inscribed "LIVRAISON PAR EXPRESS"**

**Q94** PP10 1.45fr yel grn 450.00 300.00
Never hinged 675.00

Two other values, 2.15fr and 2.35fr were prepared but not issued without overprint or surcharge.

For overprints and surcharges, see Nos. Q101, Q103, Q105, Q111-Q113, Q125, Q126, Q128, Q130-Q132, Q139-Q141.

**Inscribed "COLIS ENCOMBRANT"**

**Q95** PP12 2fr blue ('34) 45.00 21.00
Never hinged 70.00

For overprints and surcharges, see Nos. Q106, Q114, Q133, Q134, Q142.

---

Nos. Q46, Q48, Q49, Q55, Q65, Q67 and Q68 overprinted "B" were not issued. Values: 1fr (No. Q46), $95; never hinged $130; 1.50fr (No. Q48), $95, never hinged $130; 1.65fr (No. Q49), $95, never hinged $130; 50c (No. Q55), $95, never hinged $130; 1fr (No. Q65), $92.50, never hinged $140; 1.50fr (No. Q67), $92.50, never hinged $140; 1.65fr (No. Q68), $92.50, never hinged $140.

---

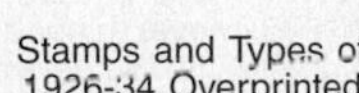
Stamps and Types of 1926-34 Overprinted

**1937**

**Inscribed "APPORT A LA GARE"**

**Q96** PP7 1.45fr brn, *yel* 6.75 6.75
Never hinged 10.00
**Q97** PP7 2.15fr on 1.50fr brn, *yel* 37.50 31.00
Never hinged 57.50
**Q98** PP7 2.15fr brn, *yel* 25.00 19.00
Never hinged 37.50
**Q99** PP7 2.35fr brn, *yel* 25.00 19.00
Never hinged 37.50

**Inscribed "VALEUR DECLAREE"**

**Q100** PP9 75c red 17.50 16.50
Never hinged 25.00
*a.* Imperf 225.00
Never hinged 325.00

**Inscribed "LIVRAISON PAR EXPRESS"**

**Q101** PP10 1.45fr green 17.50 16.50
Never hinged 25.00
**Q102** PP10 2.15fr on 1.50fr grn 17.50 16.50
Never hinged 25.00
**Q103** PP10 2.15fr green 42.50 30.00
Never hinged 67.50
*a.* Imperf 210.00
Never hinged 315.00
**Q104** PP10 2.35fr on 1.65fr grn 250.00 110.00
Never hinged 350.00
**Q105** PP10 2.35fr green 17.50 12.50
Never hinged 26.00

**Inscribed "COLIS ENCOMBRANT"**

**Q106** PP12 2fr blue 37.50 35.00
Never hinged 57.50
*Nos. Q96-Q106 (11)* 494.25 312.75

For overprints and surcharges, see Nos. Q146-Q149.

Types of 1933-34 Surcharged

**1937**

**Inscribed "APPORT A LA GARE"**

**Q107** PP7 1.85fr on 1.45fr brn, *yel* 15.00 12.50
Never hinged 26.00
**Q108** PP7 2.75fr on 2.15fr brn, *yel* 26.00 17.50
Never hinged 45.00
**Q109** PP7 3.05fr on 2.55fr brn, *yel* 50.00 26.00
Never hinged 90.00

**Inscribed "VALEUR DECLAREE"**

**Q110** PP9 .95fr on 75c red 42.50 25.00
Never hinged 67.50

**Inscribed "LIVRAISON PAR EXPRESS"**

**Q111** PP10 1.85fr on 1.45fr grn 70.00 45.00
Never hinged 120.00
**Q112** PP10 2.75fr on 2.15fr grn 70.00 45.00
Never hinged 120.00
**Q113** PP10 3.05fr on 2.35fr grn 70.00 45.00
Never hinged 120.00

**Inscribed "COLIS ENCOMBRANT"**

**Q114** PP12 2.60fr on 2fr bl 17.50 17.50
Never hinged 26.00
*Nos. Q107-Q114 (8)* 361.00 233.50

Stamps and Types of 1926-34 Overprinted

**1937**

**Inscribed "APPORT A LA GARE"**

**Q115** PP7 1.45fr brn, *yel* 3.00 2.50
Never hinged 4.50
**Q116** PP7 1.85fr on 1.45fr brn, *yel* 3.00 2.50
Never hinged 4.50
**Q117** PP7 2.15fr on 1.50fr brn, *yel* 2.50 2.50
Never hinged 4.25
**Q118** PP7 2.15fr brn, *yel* 42.50 35.00
Never hinged 62.50
**Q119** PP7 2.35fr on 1.65fr brn, *yel* 575.00 475.00
Never hinged 800.00
**Q120** PP7 2.35fr brn, *yel* 3.00 2.50
Never hinged 4.50
**Q121** PP7 2.75fr on 2.15fr brn, *yel* 3.25 2.50
Never hinged 5.75
**Q122** PP7 3.05fr on 2.35fr brn, *yel* 6.50 6.25
Never hinged 10.00

**Inscribed "VALEUR DECLAREE"**

**Q123** PP9 75c red 3.75 3.50
Never hinged 5.50
*a.* Pair, one without overprint 225.00
Never hinged 350.00
**Q124** PP9 95c on 75c red 3.00 3.00
Never hinged 3.75

**Inscribed "LIVRAISON PAR EXPRESS"**

**Q125** PP10 1.45fr green 4.25 3.25
Never hinged 6.25
**Q126** PP10 1.85fr on 1.45fr brn, *yel* 5.75 4.25
Never hinged 8.25
**Q127** PP10 2.15fr on 1.50fr grn 375.00 325.00
Never hinged 500.00
**Q128** PP10 2.15fr green 18.50 16.50
Never hinged 27.50

Q129 PP10 2.35fr on 1.65fr grn 675.00 725.00
Never hinged 775.00
Q130 PP10 2.35fr green 11.00 10.50
Never hinged 15.00
Q131 PP10 2.75fr on 2.15fr grn 35.00 45.00
Never hinged 55.00
Q132 PP10 3.05fr on 2.35fr grn 35.00 45.00
Never hinged 55.00

### Inscribed "COLIS ENCOMBRANT"

Q133 PP12 2fr blue 3.00 2.10
Never hinged 4.50
a. Pair, imperf between 130.00
Never hinged 210.00
Q134 PP12 2.60fr on 2fr bl 3.25 2.50
Never hinged 5.50
*Nos. Q115-Q134 (20)* 1,811. 1,714.

For additional surcharges, see Nos. Q146-Q149.

### Stamps and Types of 1933-34 Surcharged

**1938**

### Inscribed "APPORT A LA GARE"

Q135 PP7 2.30fr on 1.45fr brn, *yel* 3.75 3.00
Never hinged 5.50
Q136 PP7 3.45fr on 2.15fr brn, *yel* 3.75 3.00
Never hinged 5.50
Q137 PP7 3.85fr on 1.45fr brn, *yel* 3.75 3.00
Never hinged 5.50

### Inscribed "VALEUR DECLAREE"

Q138 PP9 1.15fr on 75c red 1.60 1.60
Never hinged 2.50

### Inscribed "LIVRAISON PAR EXPRESS"

Q139 PP10 2.30fr on 1.45fr grn 3.75 3.00
Never hinged 5.50
Q140 PP10 3.45fr on 2.15fr grn 3.75 3.00
Never hinged 5.50
Q141 PP10 3.85fr on 2.35fr grn 3.75 3.00
Never hinged 5.50

### Inscribed "COLIS ENCOMBRANT"

Q142 PP12 3.25fr on 2fr bl 1.60 1.60
Never hinged 2.50
*Nos. Q135-Q142 (8)* 25.70 21.20

For Nos. Q135-Q138, Q140-Q142 overprinted "E," see editor's note following No. Q159.

### Type of 1918

**1938** ***11, Imperf (#Q161)***

Q143 PP5 10c gray black 17.50 16.00
Never hinged 26.00
a. Imperf 26.00
Never hinged 42.50
Q144 PP5 20c brown lilac 17.50 16.00
Never hinged 26.00
a. Imperf 42.50
Never hinged 62.50
Q145 PP5 25c green, imperf *50.00* *20.00*
Never hinged *80.00*
*Nos. Q143-Q145 (3)* 85.00 52.00

Two additional values, a 10c rose lilac and a 15c ultramarine, were prepared with this set but not issued. Values, each stamp: $90, never hinged $150. Both stamps also exist imperf. Values, each: $82.50; never hinged $150.

Nos. Q103, Q105, Q112, Q113 Overprinted

**1938** ***Perf. 11***

Q146 PP10 2.30fr on 2.15fr green 62.50 62.50
Never hinged 80.00
Q147 PP10 2.30fr on 2.35fr green 62.50 62.50
Never hinged 80.00
Q148 PP10 2.30fr on 2.75fr on 2.15fr green 125.00 100.00
Never hinged 175.00
Q149 PP10 2.30fr on 3.05fr on 2.35fr green 125.00 100.00
Never hinged 175.00
*Nos. Q146-Q149 (4)* 375.00 325.00

### Types of 1926 and

PP13

PP14

PP15

PP16

**1938-39**

### Inscribed "VALEUR DECLAREE"

Q150 PP9 1fr red ('39) 2.50 2.50
Never hinged 4.00
Q151 PP9 1.15fr red 1.25 1.25
Never hinged 2.10
Imperf 140.00
Never hinged 225.00
Q152 PP9 5fr red ('39) 2.50 *2.75*
Never hinged 4.00

### Inscribed "AU DESSUS DE 10"

Q153 PP13 2.40fr brown, *yel* 2.50 *2.75*
Never hinged 4.00
Q154 PP13 3.50fr brown, *yel* 2.50 *2.75*
Never hinged 4.00
Q155 PP13 3.80fr brown, *yel* 2.50 *2.75*
Never hinged 4.00
Imperf 125.00
Never hinged 190.00

### Inscribed "REMBOURSEMENT"

Q156 PP14 2.50fr yel grn ('39) 2.50 2.25
Never hinged 4.00
Q157 PP14 7.50fr yel grn ('39) 2.75 2.50
Never hinged 4.25

### Inscribed "INTERET A LA LIVRAISON"

Q158 PP15 1fr lilac ('39) 9.50 6.75
Never hinged 14.00

### Inscribed "ENCOMBRANT"

Q159 PP16 3.20fr blue 11.00 7.50
Never hinged 16.00
*Nos. Q150-Q159 (10)* 39.50 33.75

Two additional values, 3.45fr and 3.85fr, type PP7, brown on yellow paper, imperforate, were prepared but not issued. Values, each: $140; never hinged, $225.

Nos. Nos. Q135-Q138, Q140-Q142 were overprinted "E" in 1939, in anticipation of new rates to take effect April 1, but were not issued. Values: 2.30fr on 1.45fr, $675, never hinged $1,000; 3.45fr on 2.15fr, $875, never hinged $1,300; 3.85fr on 2.35fr, $875, never hinged $1,300; 1.15fr on 75c, $300, never hinged $450; 3.45fr on 2.15fr, $2,800, never hinged $4,000; 3.85fr on 2.35fr, $2,800, never hinged $4,000; 3.25fr on 2fr, $675, never hinged $1,000.

In 1941, two sets were prepared in anticipation of new rate increases on April 1. They were not issued.

Six stamps in a new design, consisting of a 10c greenish gray, 30c blue, 50c brown, 1fr blue violet, 2fr orange and 5fr red. Values: 10c $185, never hinged $275; 30c $240, never hinged $350; 50c $240, never hinged $350; 1fr $185, never hinged $275; 2fr $185, never hinged $275; 5fr $185, never hinged $275.

Nos. Q93, Q153-Q155 and Q159 overprinted "E." Values: 75c; other values $575, never hinged.

PP17

PP18

### Without Denominations

**1941** ***Perf. 12½***

Q160 PP17 (2.70fr) brown 5.00 4.00
Never hinged 8.25
Q161 PP17 (3.90fr) blue 5.00 4.00
Never hinged 8.25
Q162 PP17 (4.20fr) green 5.00 4.00
Never hinged 8.25
Q163 PP18 (3.50fr) blue 9.50 8.50
Never hinged 12.50
*Nos. Q160-Q163 (4)* 24.50 20.50

Five stamps in the designs of PP20-PP22 below, but with blank value tablets, were prepared with Nos. Q160-Q163 but were not issued. Values: (1fr) brown, (5fr) red and (2.50fr) blue, each $60, never hinged $80; (7.50fr) green, $260, never hinged $360; (1fr) violet, $110, never hinged $160.

See Nos. Q178-Q181, Q200-Q206.

"Domicile" PP19

"Valeur Declaree" PP20

"Remboursement" PP21

"Interet A La Livraison" PP22

"Encombrant" — PP23

**1941** ***Perf. 12½, 13 (#Q167-171)***

Q164 PP19 2.70fr brown 6.00 5.00
Never hinged 10.00
Q165 PP19 3.90fr blue 6.00 5.00
Never hinged 10.00
Q166 PP19 4.20fr green 6.00 5.00
Never hinged 10.00
Q167 PP20 1fr brown 2.40 1.10
Never hinged 3.75
Q168 PP20 5fr red 1.20 *1.50*
Never hinged 1.90
Q169 PP21 2.50fr blue 1.20 *1.50*
Never hinged 1.90
Q170 PP21 7.50fr green 3.50 3.00
Never hinged 5.25
Q171 PP22 1fr violet .85 .75
Never hinged 1.50
Q172 PP23 3.50fr blue 32.50 16.00
Never hinged 47.50
*Nos. Q164-Q172 (9)* 59.65 38.85

See Nos. Q173-Q177, Q186-Q194, Q200-Q206.

For surcharges, see footnote following No. Q177, Nos. Q182-Q185, Q207-Q210.

### Types of 1941 with Bold Numerals

**1942, Feb.** ***Perf. 13***

Q173 PP20 1fr brown 1.25 1.10
Never hinged 1.90
Q174 PP20 5fr red 4.00 5.00
Never hinged 6.00
Q175 PP21 2.50fr blue 1.25 1.10
Never hinged 1.90
Q176 PP21 7.50fr green 6.00 *6.50*
Never hinged 9.75
Q177 PP22 1fr violet 60.00
Never hinged 95.00
*Nos. Q173-Q177 (5)* 72.50 13.70

See Nos. Q173-Q177, Q186-Q194, Q200-Q206. See No. Q194.

Nine stamps from the 1941-42 issues were surcharged "+3F / C.N.S. / Cheminots" to raise funds for a philatelic exhibition organized by railroad employees, which took place in Paris on Dec. 26 and 27, 1942. They were not valid for postage. Value, set: $110; never hinged $150.

Type of 1941 Inscribed in Value Tablets

**1943** ***Perf. 12½***

Q178 PP17 (3fr) brown 2.60 2.60
Never hinged 4.00
Q179 PP17 (4.30fr) blue 2.60 2.60
Never hinged 4.00
Q180 PP17 (4.70fr) green 2.60 2.60
Never hinged 4.00
Q181 PP18 (3.50fr) blue 6.00 6.00
Never hinged 12.00
*Nos. Q178-Q181 (4)* 13.80 13.80

### Stamps of 1941 Surcharged in Deep Blue or Red

**1943**

Q182 PP19 3fr on 2.70fr brn 12.50 12.50
Never hinged 19.00
Q183 PP19 4.3fr on 3.90fr blue (R) 2.25 *2.60*
Never hinged 4.00
Q184 PP19 4.7fr on 4.20fr green (R) 3.00 2.60
Never hinged 4.50
Q185 PP23 3.9fr on 3.50fr blue (R) 3.00 3.00
Never hinged 4.50
*Nos. Q182-Q185 (4)* 20.75 20.70

### Denominations in Black or Red

**1943** **Unwmk.**

Q186 PP19 3fr brn 3.50 *3.75*
Never hinged 5.00
Q187 PP19 4.3fr blue (R) 9.00 5.25
Never hinged 11.50

| | | |
|---|---|---|
| **Q188** PP19 4.7fr green (R) | 10.00 | 2.25 |
| Never hinged | 13.50 | |
| **Q189** PP23 3.9fr blue (R) | 65.00 | 52.50 |
| Never hinged | 97.50 | |
| *Nos. Q186-Q189 (4)* | 87.50 | 63.75 |

**1943 Wmk. 407**

| | | |
|---|---|---|
| **Q190** PP19 3fr brn | 11.00 | 9.75 |
| Never hinged | 19.00 | |
| **Q191** PP19 4.3fr blue | 19.00 | 12.00 |
| Never hinged | 30.00 | |
| **Q192** PP19 4.7fr green | 19.00 | 12.00 |
| Never hinged | 30.00 | |
| **Q193** PP23 3.9fr blue | 12.00 | 12.00 |
| Never hinged | 19.00 | |
| *Nos. Q190-Q193 (4)* | 61.00 | 45.75 |

**1944**

| | | |
|---|---|---|
| **Q194** PP21 20fr orange | 4.50 | *6.00* |
| Never hinged | 6.00 | |

Hydroelectric Dam — PP24

Electric Train — PP25

Power Line — PP26

**1944 *Perf. 12½***

| | | |
|---|---|---|
| **Q195** PP24 1fr violet | 6.00 | 6.00 |
| Never hinged | 8.25 | |
| **Q196** PP24 5fr red brn | 6.00 | 6.00 |
| Never hinged | 8.25 | |
| **Q197** PP25 2.5fr blue | 6.00 | 6.00 |
| Never hinged | 8.25 | |
| **Q198** PP25 7.5fr green | 6.00 | 6.00 |
| Never hinged | 8.25 | |
| **Q199** PP26 1fr vio blue | 6.00 | 6.00 |
| Never hinged | 8.25 | |
| *Nos. Q195-Q199 (5)* | 30.00 | 30.00 |

A 20fr orange, design PP25, was prepared but not issued. Values: $1,050; never hinged, $1,600.

Nos. Q195-Q199 exist unwatermarked, but were not issued in this form Values, each: $275; never hinged $375.

**Types of 1041 Inscribed "G" in Value Tablets**

**1945 Unwmk.**

| | | |
|---|---|---|
| **Q200** PP17 (5fr) brown | 5.00 | *5.25* |
| Never hinged | 6.50 | |
| **Q201** PP17 (7.20fr) blue | 5.00 | *5.25* |
| Never hinged | 6.50 | |
| **Q202** PP17 (7.60fr) green | 5.00 | *5.25* |
| Never hinged | 6.50 | |
| **Q203** PP18 (6.60fr) blue | 5.50 | *6.00* |
| Never hinged | 8.00 | |
| *Nos. Q200-Q203 (4)* | 20.50 | *21.75* |

**Wmk. 407**

| | | |
|---|---|---|
| **Q204** PP17 (5fr) brown | 15.00 | 15.00 |
| Never hinged | 21.00 | |
| **Q205** PP17 (7.20fr) blue | 11.00 | *11.00* |
| Never hinged | 16.50 | |
| **Q206** PP17 (7.60fr) green | 11.00 | *11.00* |
| Never hinged | 16.50 | |
| *Nos. Q204-Q206 (3)* | 37.00 | 37.00 |

**Nos. Q190-Q193 Surcharged**

**1945 Wmk. 407**

| | | |
|---|---|---|
| **Q207** PP19 5fr on 3fr brown | 5.50 | 5.50 |
| Never hinged | 8.00 | |
| **Q208** PP19 7.2fr on 4fr blue | 5.50 | 5.50 |
| Never hinged | 8.00 | |
| **Q209** PP19 7.8fr on 4.70fr green | 5.50 | 5.50 |
| Never hinged | 8.00 | |
| **Q210** PP23 6.6fr on 3.90fr blue | 6.75 | 6.75 |
| Never hinged | 10.00 | |
| *Nos. Q207-Q210 (4)* | 23.25 | 23.25 |

Nos. Q186-Q189 were also surcharged but were not issued. Values, each: $40; never hinged $67.50.

Electric Train — PP27

Transformer PP28

**1945 Denominations in Black**

| | | |
|---|---|---|
| **Q211** PP27 5fr brown | 14.00 | 14.00 |
| Never hinged | 20.00 | |
| **Q212** PP27 7.2fr blue | 13.50 | 13.50 |
| Never hinged | 20.00 | |
| **Q213** PP27 7.8fr green | 13.50 | 13.50 |
| Never hinged | 20.00 | |
| **Q214** PP28 6.6fr blue | 6.00 | 6.00 |
| Never hinged | 8.25 | |
| *Nos. Q211-Q214 (4)* | 47.00 | 47.00 |

Nos. Q211-Q213 without watermark were not issued. Value, set: $45; never hinged, $72.50.

A set of ten stamps in the design above were prepared in 1945 but were not issued. Value, each: $300; never hinged $475.

Four stamps of types PP27-PP28, inscribed "H" in the value tablet, were prepared but not issued. Value, set: $2,400; never hinged $4,000.

Locomotive — PP29

**Nos. Q215-216, Q222-Q223: 16x22mm; Nos. Q217-Q221, Q224-Q228: 18.5x22mm**

**1944 Wmk. 407 *Perf. 13***

| | | |
|---|---|---|
| **Q215** PP29 1fr deep green | 3.75 | 1.10 |
| Never hinged | 7.50 | |
| **Q216** PP29 2fr violet | 5.25 | 1.50 |
| Never hinged | 11.00 | |
| **Q217** PP29 5fr ultramarine | 24.00 | 1.50 |
| Never hinged | 32.50 | |
| **Q218** PP29 10fr red | 12.00 | 1.50 |
| Never hinged | 20.00 | |
| **Q219** PP29 20fr olive green | 10.00 | 1.50 |
| Never hinged | 16.00 | |
| **Q220** PP29 50fr red orange | 19.00 | 1.50 |
| Never hinged | 26.00 | |
| **Q221** PP29 100fr gray black | 35.00 | 1.50 |
| Never hinged | 52.50 | |
| *Nos. Q215-Q221 (7)* | 109.00 | 10.10 |

**Unwmk.**

| | | |
|---|---|---|
| **Q222** PP29 1fr deep green | 9.75 | 4.75 |
| Never hinged | 15.00 | |
| **Q223** PP29 2fr violet | 12.50 | 4.75 |
| Never hinged | 19.00 | |
| **Q224** PP29 5fr ultramarine | 40.00 | 4.75 |
| Never hinged | 65.00 | |
| **Q225** PP29 10fr red | 26.00 | 4.75 |
| Never hinged | 37.50 | |
| **Q226** PP29 20fr olive green | 19.00 | 4.75 |
| Never hinged | 30.00 | |
| **Q227** PP29 50fr red orange | 37.50 | 4.75 |
| Never hinged | 55.00 | |
| **Q228** PP29 100fr gray black | 67.50 | 5.25 |
| Never hinged | 97.50 | |
| *Nos. Q222-Q228 (7)* | 212.25 | 33.75 |

Nos. Q215-Q234 were issued for use on small packets. Effective January 1, 1946, the parcel and small packet services were unified, and all issued thereafter were valid for both services.

See Nos. Q229-Q254.

**Nos. Q229-Q230: 16x22mm; Nos. Q231-Q254: 18.5x22mm**

**1944-45 Wmk. 407**

| | | |
|---|---|---|
| **Q229** PP29 3fr gray | 6.00 | 1.50 |
| Never hinged | 11.00 | |
| **Q230** PP29 4fr black | 9.75 | 2.25 |
| Never hinged | 15.00 | |
| **Q231** PP29 7fr violet | 62.50 | 2.60 |
| Never hinged | 100.00 | |
| **Q232** PP29 8fr yel grn | 18.00 | 2.25 |
| Never hinged | 30.00 | |
| **Q233** PP29 9fr dk blue | 30.00 | 4.00 |
| Never hinged | 50.00 | |
| **Q234** PP29 30fr red brn | 82.50 | 1.50 |
| Never hinged | 125.00 | |
| *Nos. Q229-Q234 (6)* | 208.75 | 14.10 |

**1946**

| | | |
|---|---|---|
| **Q235** PP29 6fr claret | 16.00 | 1.50 |
| Never hinged | 23.00 | |
| **Q236** PP29 40fr yel brn | 24.00 | 1.50 |
| Never hinged | 35.00 | |
| **Q237** PP29 60fr lake red | 26.00 | 1.50 |
| Never hinged | 37.50 | |
| **Q238** PP29 70fr violet | 175.00 | 26.00 |
| Never hinged | 260.00 | |
| **Q239** PP29 80fr yel grn | 24.00 | 2.25 |
| Never hinged | 35.00 | |
| **Q240** PP29 90fr dk blue | 140.00 | 25.00 |
| Never hinged | 225.00 | |
| **Q241** PP29 200fr emer grn | 30.00 | 2.25 |
| Never hinged | 47.50 | |
| *Nos. Q235-Q241 (7)* | 435.00 | 60.00 |

**1947**

| | | |
|---|---|---|
| **Q242** PP29 5fr pale blue | 19.00 | 1.90 |
| Never hinged | 30.00 | |
| **Q243** PP29 7fr pale vio | 250.00 | 16.00 |
| Never hinged | 400.00 | |
| **Q244** PP29 9fr pale grn | 190.00 | 15.00 |
| Never hinged | 290.00 | |
| **Q245** PP29 30fr pale gray brn | 67.50 | 1.90 |
| Never hinged | 100.00 | |
| **Q246** PP29 70fr pale viol | 175.00 | 6.75 |
| Never hinged | 260.00 | |
| **Q247** PP29 90fr pale ultra | 130.00 | 2.25 |
| Never hinged | 200.00 | |
| **Q248** PP29 100fr yellow | 350.00 | 2.25 |
| Never hinged | 490.00 | |
| *Nos. Q242-Q248 (7)* | 1,182. | 46.05 |

**1948**

| | | |
|---|---|---|
| **Q249** PP29 500fr yel | 80.00 | 2.25 |
| Never hinged | 120.00 | |
| **Q250** PP29 1000fr yel | 290.00 | 10.00 |
| Never hinged | 425.00 | |

**1951-52**

| | | |
|---|---|---|
| **Q251** PP29 10fr grn | 52.50 | 7.50 |
| Never hinged | 82.50 | |
| **Q252** PP29 20fr vio | 52.50 | 13.50 |
| Never hinged | 82.50 | |
| **Q253** PP29 50fr blue | 65.00 | 9.00 |
| Never hinged | 100.00 | |
| **Q254** PP29 100fr rose ver | 19.00 | 1.50 |
| Never hinged | 26.00 | |
| *Nos. Q251-Q254 (4)* | 189.00 | 31.50 |

Electric Train — PP30

**1960**

| | | |
|---|---|---|
| **Q255** PP30 5c orange | 11.50 | 2.10 |
| Never hinged | 17.50 | |
| **Q256** PP30 10c red | 10.50 | 8.25 |
| Never hinged | 16.00 | |
| **Q257** PP30 20c dp red | 8.75 | 3.75 |
| Never hinged | 13.50 | |
| **Q258** PP30 30c dp red | 8.75 | 3.75 |
| Never hinged | 13.50 | |
| **Q259** PP30 40c dp red | 8.75 | 7.50 |
| Never hinged | 13.50 | |
| **Q260** PP30 50c dp red | 8.75 | 4.25 |
| Never hinged | 13.50 | |
| **Q261** PP30 60c dp red | 7.50 | 4.25 |
| Never hinged | 11.00 | |
| **Q262** PP30 70c dp red | 7.50 | 4.25 |
| Never hinged | 11.00 | |
| **Q263** PP30 80c dp red | 11.50 | 4.25 |
| Never hinged | 17.50 | |
| **Q264** PP30 90c dp red | 11.50 | 4.25 |
| Never hinged | 17.50 | |
| **Q265** PP30 1fr blue | 13.00 | 2.25 |
| Never hinged | 20.00 | |
| **Q266** PP30 2fr blue | 13.00 | 2.25 |
| Never hinged | 20.00 | |
| **Q267** PP30 3fr blue | 13.00 | 2.25 |
| Never hinged | 20.00 | |
| **Q268** PP30 4fr blue | 13.00 | 2.25 |
| Never hinged | 20.00 | |
| **Q269** PP30 5fr blue | 13.00 | 2.25 |
| Never hinged | 20.00 | |
| **Q270** PP30 10fr yellow | 15.00 | 2.50 |
| Never hinged | 22.50 | |
| **Q271** PP30 20fr dp grn | 20.00 | 16.00 |
| Never hinged | 30.00 | |
| *Nos. Q255-Q271 (17)* | 195.00 | 76.35 |

**1960 Unwmk.**

| | | |
|---|---|---|
| **Q272** PP30 5c orange | 14.00 | 6.25 |
| Never hinged | 32.50 | |
| **Q273** PP30 20c dp red | 210.00 | 55.00 |
| Never hinged | 325.00 | |
| **Q274** PP30 30c dp red | 150.00 | 55.00 |
| Never hinged | 325.00 | |
| **Q275** PP30 40c dp red | 110.00 | 30.00 |
| Never hinged | 160.00 | |
| **Q276** PP30 70c dp red | 22.50 | 7.50 |
| Never hinged | 32.50 | |
| **Q277** PP30 80c dp red | 22.50 | 6.50 |
| Never hinged | 32.50 | |
| **Q278** PP30 90c dp red | 22.50 | 6.50 |
| Never hinged | 32.50 | |
| **Q279** PP30 1fr blue | 20.00 | 3.75 |
| Never hinged | 30.00 | |
| **Q280** PP30 2fr blue | 20.00 | 3.75 |
| Never hinged | 30.00 | |
| **Q281** PP30 3fr blue | 20.00 | 3.75 |
| Never hinged | 30.00 | |
| **Q282** PP30 4fr blue | 20.00 | 3.75 |
| Never hinged | 30.00 | |
| **Q283** PP30 5fr blue | 20.00 | 3.75 |
| Never hinged | 30.00 | |
| **Q284** PP30 10fr yellow | 25.00 | 6.25 |
| Never hinged | 37.50 | |
| **Q285** PP30 20fr dp grn | 30.00 | 21.00 |
| Never hinged | 45.00 | |
| *Nos. Q272-Q285 (14)* | 706.50 | 212.75 |

## FRANCHISE STAMPS

**No. 276 Overprinted "F"**

**1939 Unwmk. *Perf. 14x13½***

| | | |
|---|---|---|
| **S1** A45 90c ultramarine | 1.90 | *2.50* |
| Never hinged | 2.75 | |
| *a.* Period following "F" | 30.00 | 30.00 |
| Never hinged | 50.00 | |

No. S1 was for the use of Spanish refugees in France. "F" stands for "Franchise."

## OCCUPATION STAMPS

**FRANCO-PRUSSIAN WAR Issued under German Occupation (Alsace and Lorraine)**

OS1

**1870 Typo. Unwmk. *Perf. 13½x14***

**Network with Points Up**

| | | |
|---|---|---|
| **N1** OS1 1c bronze green | 75.00 | *100.00* |
| *a.* 1c olive grn | 75.00 | *100.00* |
| **N2** OS1 2c dark brown | 125.00 | *175.00* |
| *a.* 2c red brown | 115.00 | *175.00* |
| **N3** OS1 4c gray | 135.00 | 100.00 |
| **N4** OS1 5c yel grn | 125.00 | 14.00 |
| **N5** OS1 10c bistre brn | 110.00 | 5.75 |
| *a.* 10c yellow brown | 110.00 | 6.50 |
| *b.* Network lemon yellow | 135.00 | 10.00 |
| **N6** OS1 20c ultra | 115.00 | 16.50 |
| **N7** OS1 25c brown | 150.00 | 100.00 |
| *a.* 25c black brown | 145.00 | 100.00 |

There are three varieties of the 4c and two of the 10c, differing in the position of the figures of value, and several other setting varieties.

**Network with Points Down**

| | | |
|---|---|---|
| **N8** OS1 1c olive grn | 350.00 | *625.00* |
| **N9** OS1 2c red brn | 150.00 | *650.00* |
| **N10** OS1 4c gray | 150.00 | 200.00 |
| **N11** OS1 5c yel grn | 6,500. | 650.00 |

**N12** OS1 10c bister 150.00 21.50
*a.* Network lemon yellow 225.00 50.00
**N13** OS1 20c ultra 225.00 90.00
**N14** OS1 25c brown 450.00 300.00

*Official imitations have the network with points downward. The "P" of "Postes" is 2½mm from the border in the imitations and 3mm in the originals.*

*The word "Postes" measures 12¾ to 13mm on the imitations, and from 11 to 12½mm on the originals.*

*The imitations are perf. 13½x14½; originals, perf. 13½x14¼.*

The stamps for Alsace and Lorraine were replaced by stamps of the German Empire on Jan. 1, 1872.

### WORLD WAR I
### German Stamps of 1905-16 Surcharged

**1916** Wmk. 125 *Perf. 14, 14½*

**N15** A16 3c on 3pf brown 1.25 1.25
**N16** A16 5c on 5pf green 1.25 1.25
**N17** A22 8c on 7½pf org 2.00 2.00
**N18** A16 10c on 10pf car 2.00 2.00
**N19** A22 15c on 15pf yel brn 1.25 1.25
**N20** A16 25c on 20pf blue 1.25 1.25
*a.* 25c on 20pf ultramarine 2.00 2.00
**N21** A16 40c on 30pf org & blk, *buff* 2.90 2.75
**N22** A16 50c on 40pf lake & blk 2.90 2.75
**N23** A16 75c on 60pf mag 12.50 12.50
**N24** A16 1fr on 80pf lake & blk, *rose* 12.50 12.50

**N25** A17 1fr25c on 1m car 47.50 47.50
*a.* Double surcharge —
**N26** A21 2fr50c on 2m gray bl 47.50 47.50
*a.* Double surcharge —
*Nos. N15-N26 (12)* 134.80 134.50

These stamps were also used in parts of Belgium occupied by the German forces.

**Catalogue values for unused stamps in this section, from this point to the end of the section, are for Never Hinged items.**

### WORLD WAR II
### Alsace
### Issued under German Occupation

Stamps of Germany 1933-36 Overprinted in Black

**1940** Wmk. 237 *Perf. 14*

**N27** A64 3pf olive bister .80 *.55*
**N28** A64 4pf dull blue .80 *.55*
**N29** A64 5pf brt green .80 *.55*
**N30** A64 6pf dark green .80 *.55*
*a.* Inverted overprint 1,500.
**N31** A64 8pf vermilion .80 *.55*
*a.* Inverted overprint 4,000.
**N32** A64 10pf chocolate .80 *.55*
**N33** A64 12pf dp carmine 1.00 *.55*
**N34** A64 15pf maroon 1.00 *.55*
**N35** A64 20pf brt blue 1.65 *.75*
**N36** A64 25pf ultra 1.65 *.75*
**N37** A64 30pf olive grn 1.65 *.75*
**N38** A64 40pf red violet 2.90 *1.00*
**N39** A64 50pf dk grn & blk 7.00 *3.25*
**N40** A64 60pf claret & blk 7.00 *3.25*
**N41** A64 80pf dk blue & blk 17.50 *7.00*
**N42** A64 100pf orange & blk 17.50 7.00
*Nos. N27-N42 (16)* 63.65 28.15

### Lorraine
### Issued under German Occupation

Stamps of Germany 1933-36 Overprinted in Black

**1940** Wmk. 237 *Perf. 14*

**N43** A64 3pf olive bister 1.00 .75
**N44** A64 4pf dull blue 1.00 .75
**N45** A64 5pf brt green 1.00 *4.00*
**N46** A64 6pf dark green 1.00 .75
**N47** A64 8pf vermilion 1.00 .75
**N48** A64 10pf chocolate 1.50 .85
**N49** A64 12pf deep carmine 1.50 .85
**N50** A64 15pf maroon 1.50 .75
*a.* Inverted surcharge —
**N51** A64 20pf brt blue 1.65 1.00
**N52** A64 25pf ultra 1.40 1.00
**N53** A64 30pf olive grn 2.10 1.00
**N54** A64 40pf red violet 2.50 1.25
**N55** A64 50pf dk grn & blk 6.00 3.00
**N56** A64 60pf claret & blk 6.00 3.00
**N57** A64 80pf dk blue & blk 18.00 7.50
**N58** A64 100pf orange & blk 18.00 7.50
*Nos. N43-N58 (16)* 65.15 *34.70*

Besetztes Gebiet Nordfrankreich

These three words, in a rectangular frame covering two stamps, were handstamped in black on Nos. 267, 367 and 369 and used in the Dunkerque region in July-August, 1940. The German political officer of Dunkerque authorized the overprint. The prevalence of forgeries and later favor overprints make expertization mandatory.

### ALLIED MILITARY GOVERNMENT

**Stamps formerly listed in this section as Nos. 2N1-2N20 are now listed with regular stamps of France as Nos. 475-476H and 523A-523J.**

## FRANCE OFFICES ABROAD

## OFFICES IN CHINA

Prior to 1923 several of the world powers maintained their own post offices in China for the purpose of sending and receiving overseas mail. French offices were maintained in Canton, Hoi Hao (Hoihow), Kwangchowan (Kouang-tchéou-wan), Mongtseu (Mong-tseu), Packhoi (Paknoi), Tong King (Tchongking), Yunnan Fou (Yunnanfu).

100 Centimes = 1 Franc
100 Cents = 1 Piaster
100 Cents = 1 Dollar

Peace and Commerce Stamps of France Ovptd. in Red, Carmine or Black

**1894-1900** Unwmk. *Perf. 14x13½*

**1** A15 5c green, *greenish* (R) 3.25 3.00
**2** A15 5c yel grn, I (R) ('00) 4.25 3.00
*a.* Type II 47.50 32.50
**3** A15 10c blk, *lav,* I (R) 9.25 3.00
*a.* Type II 27.50 *17.50*
**4** A15 15c bl (R) 12.50 4.25
**5** A15 20c red, *grn* 7.50 5.00
**6** A15 25c blk, *rose* (C) 9.25 2.50
*a.* Double overprint 225.00
*b.* Pair, one without overprint 550.00
*d.* Imperf 120.00 45.00
**7** A15 30c brn, *bis* 9.25 6.25
**8** A15 40c red, *straw* 9.25 7.50
**9** A15 50c car, *rose,* I 26.00 17.50
*a.* Carmine overprint 62.50
*b.* Type II (Bk) 25.00 16.00
**10** A15 75c dp vio, *org* (R) 80.00 60.00
**11** A15 1fr brnz grn, *straw* 17.00 8.50
*a.* Double overprint 425.00 *450.00*
**12** A15 2fr brn, *az* ('00) 30.00 29.00
**12A** A15 5fr red lil, *lav* 75.00 60.00
*b.* Red overprint 525.00
*Nos. 1-12A (13)* 292.50 209.50

For surcharges and overprints see Nos. 13-17, J7-J10, J20-J23.

No. 11 Surcharged in Black

**13** A15 25c on 1fr brnz grn, *straw* 125.00 75.00

No. 6 Surcharged in Red

**1901**

**14** A15 2c on 25c blk, *rose* 1,100. 340.00
**15** A15 4c on 25c blk, *rose* 1,350. 450.00
**16** A15 6c on 25c blk, *rose* 1,100. 375.00
**17** A15 16c on 25c blk, *rose* 325.00 200.00
*a.* Black surcharge *7,250.*
*Nos. 14-17 (4)* 3,875. 1,365.

Stamps of Indo-China Surcharged in Black

Two types of Nos. 18-33: type I, 13mmx3mm, "C" and "H" wide, "E" with fine serifs; type II, 12½mmx2¾mm, "C" and "H" narrower, "E" with heavy serifs.

**1902-04**

**18a** A3 1c blk, *lil bl* 2.50 2.50
**19** A3 2c brn, *buff* 4.25 4.25
**20a** A3 4c claret, *lav* 4.25 3.40
**21a** A3 5c yellow grn 5.00 3.40
**22** A3 10c red 6.75 6.00
**23** A3 15c gray 7.50 6.75
**24a** A3 20c red, *grn* 9.25 8.50
**25a** A3 25c blk, *rose* 12.50 12.50
**26** A3 25c blue 10.00 8.50
**27a** A3 30c brn, *bis* 9.25 8.50
**28a** A3 40c red, *straw* 25.00 21.00
**29** A3 50c car, *rose* 67.50 67.50
**30** A3 50c brn, *azure* 10.00 9.25
**31a** A3 75c vio, *org* 40.00 37.50
**32a** A3 1fr brnz grn, *straw* 45.00 42.50
**33a** A3 5fr red lil, *lavender* 97.50 90.00
*Nos. 18a-33a (16)* 356.25 332.05

The Chinese characters surcharged on Nos. 18-33 are the Chinese equivalents of the French values and therefore differ on each denomination. Two printings exist, differing slightly in the size of "CHINE." Values above are for the less expensive variety. See the *Scott Classic Specialized Cataloue of Stamps and Covers* for detailed listings. Many varieties of surcharge exist.

Liberty, Equality and Fraternity
A3

"Rights of Man"
A4

A5

**1902-03** **Typo.**

**34** A3 5c green 6.00 3.75
**35** A4 10c rose red ('03) 3.00 2.10
**36** A4 15c pale red 3.00 2.10
**37** A4 20c brn vio ('03) 8.50 7.25
**38** A4 25c blue ('03) 6.75 3.40
**39** A4 30c lilac ('03) 9.25 7.50
**40** A5 40c red & pale bl 19.00 16.00
**41** A5 50c bis brn & lav 23.00 19.00
**42** A5 1fr claret & ol grn 30.00 19.00
**43** A5 2fr gray vio & yel 62.50 45.00
**44** A5 5fr dk bl & buff 92.50 72.50
*Nos. 34-44 (11)* 263.50 197.60

For surcharges and overprints see Nos. 45, 57-85, J14-J16, J27-J30.

Surcharged in Black

**1903**

**45** A4 5c on 15c pale red 17.50 12.00
*a.* Inverted surcharge 135.00 75.00

### Stamps of Indo-China, 1904-06, Surcharged as Nos. 18-33 in Black

**1904-05**

**46** A4 1c olive grn 2.10 2.10
**47** A4 2c vio brn, *buff* 2.10 2.10
**47A** A4 4c cl, *bluish* 975.00 800.00
**48** A4 5c deep grn 2.10 2.10
**49** A4 10c carmine 3.00 3.00
**50** A4 15c org brn, *bl* (I) 3.00 3.00
**51** A4 20c red, *grn* 11.50 11.00
**52** A4 25c deep blue 10.00 6.00
**53** A4 40c blk, *bluish* 8.50 6.00
**54** A4 1fr pale grn 360.00 300.00
**55** A4 2fr brn, *org* 42.50 37.50
**56** A4 10fr org brn, *grn* 165.00 155.00
*Nos. 46-56 (12)* 1,585. 1,328.

Many varieties of the surcharge exist.

Stamps of 1902-03 Surcharged in Black

**1907**

**57** A3 2c on 5c green 2.50 1.60
**58** A4 4c on 10c rose red 2.50 1.75
*a.* Pair, one without surcharge —
**59** A4 6c on 15c pale red 3.40 2.50
**60** A4 8c on 20c brn vio 6.00 6.00
*a.* "8" inverted 75.00 75.00
**61** A4 10c on 25c blue 2.10 1.25
**62** A5 20c on 50c bis brn & lav 6.25 3.75
*a.* Double surcharge
*b.* Triple surcharge 440.00 440.00
**63** A5 40c on 1fr claret & ol grn 22.00 13.50
**64** A5 2pi on 5fr dk bl & buff 23.00 13.50
*a.* Double surcharge *2,300.* *1,900.*
*Nos. 57-64 (8)* 67.75 43.85

Stamps of 1902-03 Surcharged in Black

**1911-22**

**65** A3 2c on 5c green 2.10 1.50
**66** A4 4c on 10c rose red 2.50 1.75
**67** A4 6c on 15c org 5.00 2.10
**68** A4 8c on 20c brn vio 2.10 1.80
**69** A4 10c on 25c bl ('21) 4.25 2.10
**70** A4 20c on 50c bl ('22) 55.00 55.00
**71** A5 40c on 1fr cl & ol grn 7.50 6.00

No. 44 Surcharged

**73** A5 $2 on 5fr bl & buff ('22) 175.00 *200.00*
*Nos. 65-73 (8)* 253.45 270.25

### Types of 1902-03 Surcharged like Nos. 65-71

**1922**

75 A3 1c on 5c org 6.00 *6.75*
76 A4 2c on 10c grn 6.75 *7.50*
77 A4 3c on 15c org 9.25 *11.00*
78 A4 4c on 20c red brn 11.00 *13.50*
79 A4 5c on 25c dk vio 6.00 6.00
80 A4 6c on 30c red 12.00 11.00
82 A4 10c on 50c blue 14.50 12.00
83 A5 20c on 1fr claret & ol grn 35.00 *40.00*
84 A5 40c on 2fr org & pale bl 45.00 *55.00*
85 A5 $1 on 5fr dk bl & buff 150.00 *160.00*
*Nos. 75-85 (10)* 295.50 322.75

### POSTAGE DUE STAMPS

Postage Due Stamps of France Handstamped in Red or Black

**1901-07 Unwmk. *Perf. 14x13½***

J1 D2 5c lt bl (R) 7.50 4.25
a. Double overprint 160.00
J2 D2 10c choc (R) 11.00 6.00
a. Double overprint 160.00
J3 D2 15c lt grn (R) 11.00 7.50
a. Pair, one stamp without ovpt. 275.00
b. Imperf, single 160.00
J4 D2 20c ol grn (R) ('07) 12.50 11.00
J5 D2 30c carmine 17.00 12.00
a. Double overprint 160.00
J6 D2 50c lilac 17.00 12.50
a. Triple overprint 160.00
b. Pair, one stamp without overprint 275.00
*Nos. J1-J6 (6)* 76.00 53.25

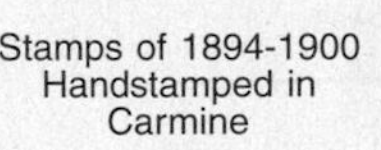

Stamps of 1894-1900 Handstamped in Carmine

**1903**

J7 A15 5c yel grn — 2,250.
a. Purple handstamp — —
b. 5c green, *greenish* — —
J8 A15 10c blk, *lavender* — —
a. Purple handstamp — —
J9 A15 15c blue *2,750.* 1,250.
a. Purple handstamp — —
J10 A15 30c brn, *bister* *1,500.* 350.00
a. Purple handstamp — —

### Same Handstamp on Stamps of 1902-03 in Carmine

**1903**

J14 A3 5c green — 2,000.
a. Purple handstamp — —
J15 A4 10c rose red 750. 425.00
a. Purple handstamp — —
J16 A4 15c pale red 750. 325.00
a. Purple handstamp — —

Stamps of 1894-1900 Handstamped in Carmine

**1903**

J20 A1 5c yellow green — 1,100.
a. Purple handstamp — —
b. 5c green, *greenish* — —
J21 A1 10c blk, *lavender* — —
a. Purple handstamp — —
J22 A1 15c blue 1,250. 350.
a. Purple handstamp — —
J23 A1 30c brn, *bister* 600. 325.
a. Purple handstamp — —

### Same Handstamp on Stamps of 1902-03 in Carmine or Purple

**1903**

J27 A3 5c green (C) — 1,750.
a. Purple handstamp — —
J28 A4 10c rose red (C) 340. 225.
a. Purple handstamp — —
J29 A4 15c pale red (C) 675. 225.
a. Purple handstamp — —
J30 A4 30c lilac (P) — —

The handstamps on Nos. J7-J30 are found inverted, double, etc.

The cancellations on these stamps should have dates between Sept. 1, and Nov. 30, 1903, to be genuine.

### Postage Due Stamps of France, 1893-1910 Surcharged like Nos. 65-71

**1911**

J33 D2 2c on 5c blue 3.00 2.50
a. Double surcharge 140.00 —
J34 D2 4c on 10c choc 3.00 2.50
a. Double surcharge 140.00 —
J35 D2 8c on 20c ol grn 3.40 3.00
a. Double surcharge 140.00 —
J36 D2 20c on 50c lilac 3.40 3.00
*Nos. J33-J36 (4)* 12.80 11.00

**1922**

J37 D2 1c on 5c blue 82.50 *95.00*
J38 D2 2c on 10c brn 145.00 *165.00*
J39 D2 4c on 20c ol grn 145.00 *165.00*
J40 D2 10c on 50c brn vio 125.00 *185.00*
*Nos. J37-J40 (4)* 497.50 610.00

### CANTON

Stamps of Indo-China, 1892-1900, Overprinted in Red

**1901 Unwmk. *Perf. 14x13½***

1 A3 1c blk, *lil bl* 2.10 2.10
1A A3 2c brn, *buff* 2.50 2.50
2 A3 4c claret, *lav* 4.25 4.25
2A A3 5c grn, *grnsh* 600.00 600.00
3 A3 5c yel grn 3.40 3.40
4 A3 10c blk, *lavender* 7.25 7.25
5 A3 15c blue, quadrille paper 6.75 6.75
6 A3 15c gray 7.50 7.50
a. Double overprint 19.00
7 A3 20c red, *grn* 22.50 22.50
8 A3 25c blk, *rose* 13.50 13.50
9 A3 30c brn, *bister* 32.50 32.50
10 A3 40c red, *straw* 32.50 32.50
11 A3 50c car, *rose* 35.00 35.00
12 A3 75c dp vio, *org* 35.00 35.00
13 A3 1fr brnz grn, *straw* 45.00 45.00
14 A3 5fr red lil, *lav* 250.00 250.00
*Nos. 1-14 (16)* 1,100. 1,100.

The Chinese characters in the overprint on Nos. 1-14 read "Canton." On Nos. 15-64, they restate the denomination of the basic stamp.

Surcharged in Black

**1903-04**

15 A3 1c blk, *lil bl* 4.25 4.25
16 A3 2c brn, *buff* 4.50 4.25
17 A3 4c claret, *lav* 4.50 4.25
18 A3 5c yellow green 4.25 4.25
19 A3 10c rose red 4.50 4.25
20 A3 15c gray 4.50 4.25
21 A3 20c red, *grn* 21.00 17.50
22 A3 25c blue 7.50 7.50
23 A3 25c blk, *rose* ('04) 10.00 8.50
24 A3 30c brn, *bister* 27.50 21.00
25 A3 40c red, *straw* 67.50 55.00
26 A3 50c car, *rose* 340.00 310.00
27 A3 50c brn, *az* ('04) 85.00 72.50
28 A3 75c dp vio, *org* 67.50 67.50
a. "INDO-CHINE" inverted *55,000.*
29 A3 1fr brnz grn, *straw* 67.50 67.50
30 A3 5fr red lil, *lav* 67.50 67.50
*Nos. 15-30 (16)* 787.50 720.00

Many varieties of the surcharge exist on Nos. 15-30.

Stamps of Indo-China, 1892-1906, Surcharged in Red or Black

A second printing of the 1906 surcharges of Canton, Hoi Hao, Kwangchowan, Mongtseu, Packhoi, Tong King and Yunnan Fou was made in 1908. The inks are grayish instead of full black and vermilion instead of carmine. Values are for the cheaper variety which usually is the second printing.

The 4c and 50c of the 1892 issue of Indo-China are known with this surcharge and similarly surcharged for other cities in China. The surcharges on these two stamps are always inverted. It is stated that they were irregularly produced and never issued.

**1906**

31 A4 1c ol grn (R) 2.50 2.50
32 A4 2c vio brn, *buff* 2.50 2.50
33 A4 4c cl, *bluish* (R) 2.50 2.50
34 A4 5c dp grn (R) 2.10 2.10
35 A4 10c carmine 3.00 3.00
36 A4 15c org brn, *bl* 22.50 22.50
37 A4 20c red, *grn* 12.50 12.50
38 A4 25c deep blue 5.00 5.00
39 A4 30c pale brn 17.00 17.00
40 A4 35c blk, *yel* (R) 12.50 12.50
41 A4 40c blk, *bluish* (R) 21.00 21.00
42 A4 50c bister brn 14.50 14.50
43 A3 75c dp vio, *org* (R) 67.50 67.50
44 A4 1fr pale grn 30.00 30.00
45 A4 2fr brn, *org* (R) 42.50 42.50
46 A3 5fr red lil, *lav* 92.50 92.50
47 A4 10fr org brn, *grn* 85.00 85.00
*Nos. 31-47 (17)* 435.10 435.10

Surcharge exists inverted on 1c, 25c & 1fr.

Stamps of Indo-China, 1907, Srchd. in Red or Blue

**Chinese Characters**

**1908**

48 A5 1c ol brn & blk 1.25 1.25
49 A5 2c brn & blk 1.25 1.25
50 A5 4c bl & blk 2.50 1.25
51 A5 5c grn & blk 2.50 2.10
52 A5 10c red & blk (Bl) 3.40 2.50
53 A5 15c vio & blk 4.25 3.40
54 A6 20c vio & blk 5.00 5.00
55 A6 25c bl & blk 5.00 4.25
56 A6 30c brn & blk 8.50 8.50
57 A6 35c ol grn & blk 8.50 8.50
58 A6 40c brn & blk 11.00 8.50
59 A6 50c car & blk (Bl) 11.00 8.50
60 A7 75c ver & blk (Bl) 11.00 10.00
61 A8 1fr car & blk (Bl) 18.00 15.00
62 A9 2fr grn & blk 45.00 37.50
63 A10 5fr bl & blk 62.50 55.00
64 A11 10fr pur & blk 92.50 92.50
*Nos. 48-64 (17)* 293.15 265.00

### Nos. 48-64 Surcharged with New Values in Cents or Piasters in Black, Red or Blue

**1919**

65 A5 ⅖c on 1c 1.25 1.25
66 A5 ⅘c on 2c 1.25 1.25
67 A5 1⅗c on 4c (R) 1.25 1.25
68 A5 2c on 5c 1.60 1.60
69 A5 4c on 10c (Bl) 2.10 1.60
a. Chinese "2" instead of "4" 42.50 42.50
70 A5 6c on 15c 2.50 2.10
71 A6 8c on 20c 4.25 2.10
72 A6 10c on 25c 5.00 1.60
73 A6 12c on 30c 2.10 2.10
a. Double surcharge 140.00 140.00
74 A6 14c on 35c 2.10 1.60
a. Closed "4" 10.00 10.00
75 A6 16c on 40c 2.50 1.60
76 A6 20c on 50c (Bl) 2.50 2.10
77 A7 30c on 75c (Bl) 2.50 2.10
78 A8 40c on 1fr (Bl) 12.50 7.50
79 A9 80c on 2fr (R) 19.00 12.00
80 A10 2pi on 5fr (R) 32.50 32.50
81 A11 4pi on 10fr (R) 32.50 32.50
*Nos. 65-81 (17)* 127.40 106.75

### HOI HAO

Stamps of Indo-China Overprinted in Red

**1901 Unwmk. *Perf. 14x13½***

1 A3 1c blk, *lil bl* 3.40 3.40
2 A3 2c brn, *buff* 4.25 4.25
3 A3 4c claret, *lav* 4.25 4.25
4 A3 5c yel grn 5.00 5.00
5 A3 10c blk, *lavender* 13.50 12.00
6 A3 15c blue 1,850. 800.00
7 A3 15c gray 7.50 5.00
8 A3 20c red, *grn* 32.50 25.00
9 A3 25c blk, *rose* 17.00 12.50
10 A3 30c brn, *bister* 67.50 67.50
11 A3 40c red, *straw* 67.50 67.50
12 A3 50c car, *rose* 67.50 67.50
13 A3 75c dp vio, *org* 250.00 225.00
14 A3 1fr brnz grn, *straw* 800.00 740.00
15 A3 5fr red lil, *lav* 800.00 675.00
*Nos. 1-15 (15)* 3,990. 2,714.

The Chinese characters in the overprint on Nos. 1-15 read "Hoi Hao." On Nos. 16-66, they restate the denomination of the basic stamp.

Surcharged in Black

**1903-04**

16 A3 1c blk, *lil bl* 2.50 2.50
17 A3 2c brn, *buff* 2.50 2.50
18 A3 4c claret, *lav* 4.25 4.25
19 A3 5c yel grn 4.25 4.25
20 A3 10c red 4.25 4.25
21 A3 15c gray 5.00 5.00
22 A3 20c red, *grn* 7.50 7.50
23 A3 25c blue 5.00 5.00
24 A3 25c blk, *rose* ('04) 8.50 8.50
25 A3 30c brn, *bister* 6.75 6.75
26 A3 40c red, *straw* 32.50 32.50
27 A3 50c car, *rose* 30.00 30.00
28 A3 50c brn, *az* ('04) 170.00 170.00
29 A3 75c dp vio, *org* 50.00 50.00
a. "INDO-CHINE" inverted *45,000.*
30 A3 1fr brnz grn, *straw* 67.50 67.50
31 A3 5fr red lil, *lav* 225.00 225.00
*Nos. 16-31 (16)* 625.50 625.50

Many varieties of the surcharge exist on Nos. 1-31.

Stamps of Indo-China, 1892-1906, Surcharged in Red or Black

**1906**

32 A4 1c ol grn (R) 8.50 8.50
33 A4 2c vio brn, *buff* 8.50 8.50
34 A4 4c cl, *bluish* (R) 8.50 8.50
35 A4 5c dp grn (R) 8.50 8.50
36 A4 10c carmine 8.50 8.50
37 A4 15c org brn, *bl* 32.50 32.50
38 A4 20c red, *grn* 13.50 13.50
39 A4 25c deep blue 11.00 11.00
40 A4 30c pale brn 13.50 13.50
41 A4 35c blk, *yel* (R) 21.00 21.00
42 A4 40c blk, *bluish* (R) 21.00 21.00
43 A4 50c gray brn 21.00 21.00
44 A3 75c dp vio, *org* (R) 62.50 62.50
45 A4 1fr pale grn 62.50 62.50
46 A4 2fr brn, *org* (R) 62.50 62.50
47 A3 5fr red lil, *lav* 135.00 135.00
48 A4 10fr org brn, *grn* 150.00 150.00
*Nos. 32-48 (17)* 648.50 648.50

Stamps of Indo-China, 1907, Srchd. in Red or Blue

**Chinese Characters**

**1908**

49 A5 1c ol brn & blk 1.70 1.70
50 A5 2c brn & blk 1.70 1.70
51 A5 4c bl & blk 1.70 1.70
52 A5 5c grn & blk 3.00 3.00
53 A5 10c red & blk (Bl) 3.00 3.00
54 A5 15c vio & blk 6.75 6.75
55 A6 20c vio & blk 7.50 7.50
56 A6 25c bl & blk 7.50 7.50
57 A6 30c brn & blk 7.50 7.50
58 A6 35c ol grn & blk 7.50 7.50
59 A6 40c brn & blk 8.50 8.50
61 A6 50c car & blk (Bl) 10.00 10.00
62 A7 75c ver & blk (Bl) 10.00 10.00
63 A8 1fr car & blk (Bl) 29.00 29.00
64 A9 2fr grn & blk 42.50 42.50
65 A10 5fr bl & blk 75.00 75.00
66 A11 10fr pur & blk 110.00 110.00
*Nos. 49-66 (17)* 332.85 332.85

### Nos. 49-66 Surcharged with New Values in Cents or Piasters in Black, Red or Blue

**1919**

67 A5 ⅖c on 1c 1.25 1.25
68 A5 ⅘c on 2c 1.25 1.25
69 A5 1⅗c on 4c (R) 2.10 2.10
70 A5 2c on 5c 2.50 2.50
71 A5 4c on 10c (Bl) 3.00 3.00
a. Chinese "2" instead of "4" 14.50 14.50

| No. | Type | Description | Unused | Used |
|---|---|---|---|---|
| 72 | A5 | 6c on 15c | 2.50 | 2.50 |
| 73 | A6 | 8c on 20c | 4.25 | 4.25 |
| a. | | "S" of "CENTS" omitted | 170.00 | 170.00 |
| 74 | A6 | 10c on 25c | 6.75 | 6.75 |
| 75 | A6 | 12c on 30c | 4.25 | 4.25 |
| 76 | A6 | 14c on 35c | 3.40 | 3.40 |
| a. | | Closed "4" | 42.50 | 42.50 |
| 77 | A6 | 16c on 40c | 4.25 | 4.25 |
| 79 | A6 | 20c on 50c (Bl) | 3.40 | 3.40 |
| 80 | A7 | 30c on 75c (Bl) | 11.00 | 11.00 |
| 81 | A8 | 40c on 1fr (Bl) | 22.00 | 22.00 |
| 82 | A9 | 80c on 2fr (R) | 62.50 | 62.50 |
| 83 | A10 | 2pi on 5fr (R) | 92.50 | 92.50 |
| a. | | Triple surch. of new value | 750.00 | *750.00* |
| 84 | A11 | 4pi on 10fr (R) | 225.00 | 225.00 |
| | | *Nos. 67-84 (17)* | 451.90 | 451.90 |

## KWANGCHOWAN

A Chinese Territory leased to France, 1898 to 1945.

Stamps of Indo-China, 1892-1906, Surcharged in Red or Black

**1906 Unwmk. *Perf. 14x13½***

| No. | Type | Description | Unused | Used |
|---|---|---|---|---|
| 1 | A4 | 1c ol grn (R) | 8.50 | 8.50 |
| 2 | A4 | 2c vio brn, *buff* | 8.50 | 8.50 |
| 3 | A4 | 4c cl, *bluish* (R) | 8.50 | 8.50 |
| 4 | A4 | 5c dp grn (R) | 8.50 | 8.50 |
| 5 | A4 | 10c carmine | 8.50 | 8.50 |
| 6 | A4 | 15c org brn, *bl* | 32.50 | 32.50 |
| 7 | A4 | 20c red, *grn* | 13.50 | 13.50 |
| 8 | A4 | 25c deep blue | 11.00 | 11.00 |
| 9 | A4 | 30c pale brn | 13.50 | 13.50 |
| 10 | A4 | 35c blk, *yel* (R) | 21.00 | 21.00 |
| 11 | A4 | 40c blk, *bluish* (R) | 21.00 | 21.00 |
| 12 | A4 | 50c bister brn | 25.00 | 25.00 |
| 13 | A3 | 75c dp vio, *org* (R) | 67.50 | 67.50 |
| 14 | A4 | 1fr pale grn | 42.50 | 42.50 |
| 15 | A4 | 2fr brn, *org* (R) | 55.00 | 55.00 |
| 16 | A3 | 5fr red lil, *lav* | 225.00 | 225.00 |
| 17 | A4 | 10fr org brn, *grn* | 275.00 | 275.00 |
| | | *Nos. 1-17 (17)* | 845.00 | 845.00 |

Various varieties of the surcharge exist on Nos. 2-10.

Stamps of Indo-China, 1907, Srchd. in Red or Blue

**Value in Chinese**

**1908**

| No. | Type | Description | Unused | Used |
|---|---|---|---|---|
| 18 | A5 | 1c ol brn & blk | 1.70 | 1.70 |
| 19 | A5 | 2c brn & blk | 1.70 | 1.70 |
| 20 | A5 | 4c bl & blk | 1.70 | 1.70 |
| 21 | A5 | 5c grn & blk | 1.70 | 1.70 |
| 22 | A5 | 10c red & blk (Bl) | 1.70 | 1.70 |
| 23 | A5 | 15c vio & blk | 4.25 | 4.25 |
| 24 | A6 | 20c vio & blk | 6.75 | 6.75 |
| 25 | A6 | 25c bl & blk | 6.75 | 6.75 |
| 26 | A6 | 30c brn & blk | 10.00 | 10.00 |
| 27 | A6 | 35c ol grn & blk | 14.50 | 14.50 |
| 28 | A6 | 40c brn & blk | 14.50 | 14.50 |
| 30 | A6 | 50c car & blk (Bl) | 17.00 | 17.00 |
| 31 | A7 | 75c ver & blk (Bl) | 17.00 | 17.00 |
| 32 | A8 | 1fr car & blk (Bl) | 24.00 | 24.00 |
| 33 | A9 | 2fr grn & blk | 32.50 | 32.50 |
| 34 | A10 | 5fr bl & blk | 75.00 | 75.00 |
| 35 | A11 | 10fr pur & blk | 105.00 | 105.00 |
| a. | | Double surcharge | 1,050. | |
| b. | | Triple surcharge | 1,050. | |
| | | *Nos. 18-35 (17)* | 335.75 | 335.75 |

The Chinese characters overprinted on Nos. 1 to 35 repeat the denomination of the basic stamp.

Nos. 18-35 Srchd. in Cents or Piasters in Black, Red or Blue

**1919**

| No. | Type | Description | Unused | Used |
|---|---|---|---|---|
| 36 | A5 | 2/5c on 1c | 1.25 | .85 |
| 37 | A5 | 4/5c on 2c | 1.25 | .85 |
| 38 | A5 | 1 3/5c on 4c (R) | 1.25 | .85 |
| 39 | A5 | 2c on 5c | 2.10 | 1.25 |
| a. | | "2 CENTS" inverted | 97.50 | |
| 40 | A5 | 4c on 10c (Bl) | 3.75 | 3.40 |
| 41 | A5 | 6c on 15c | 2.10 | 2.10 |
| 42 | A6 | 8c on 20c | 4.25 | 4.25 |
| 43 | A6 | 10c on 25c | 14.50 | 13.50 |
| 44 | A6 | 12c on 30c | 3.40 | 3.40 |
| 45 | A6 | 14c on 35c | 3.40 | 3.40 |
| a. | | Closed "4" | 45.00 | 37.50 |
| 46 | A6 | 16c on 40c | 2.10 | 2.10 |
| 48 | A6 | 20c on 50c (Bl) | 2.10 | 2.10 |
| 49 | A7 | 30c on 75c (Bl) | 11.00 | 11.00 |
| 50 | A8 | 40c on 1fr (Bl) | 12.00 | 12.00 |
| a. | | "40 CENTS" inverted | | |
| 51 | A9 | 80c on 2fr (R) | 20.00 | 20.00 |
| 52 | A10 | 2pi on 5fr (R) | 175.00 | 175.00 |
| 53 | A11 | 4pi on 10fr (R) | 32.50 | 32.50 |
| | | *Nos. 36-53 (17)* | 291.95 | 288.55 |

Stamps of Indo-China, 1922-23, Overprinted in Black, Red or Blue

**1923**

| No. | Type | Description | Unused | Used |
|---|---|---|---|---|
| 54 | A12 | 1/10c blk & sal (Bl) | .35 | .35 |
| 55 | A12 | 1/5c dp bl & blk (R) | .35 | .35 |
| a. | | Black overprint | 135.00 | |
| 56 | A12 | 2/5c ol brn & blk (R) | .40 | .40 |
| 57 | A12 | 4/5c brt rose & blk | .60 | .60 |
| 58 | A12 | 1c yel brn & blk (Bl) | .60 | .60 |
| 59 | A12 | 2c gray grn & blk (R) | .95 | .95 |
| 60 | A12 | 3c vio & blk (R) | 1.00 | 1.00 |
| 61 | A12 | 4c org & blk | 1.25 | 1.25 |
| 62 | A12 | 5c car & blk | 1.25 | 1.25 |
| 63 | A13 | 6c dl red & blk | 1.25 | 1.25 |
| 64 | A13 | 7c ol grn & blk | 1.70 | 1.70 |
| 65 | A13 | 8c black (R) | 2.50 | 2.50 |
| 66 | A13 | 9c yel & blk | 2.50 | 2.50 |
| 67 | A13 | 10c bl & blk | 2.10 | 2.10 |
| 68 | A13 | 11c vio & blk | 2.10 | 2.10 |
| 69 | A13 | 12c brn & blk | 2.10 | 2.10 |
| 70 | A13 | 15c org & blk | 3.00 | 3.00 |
| 71 | A13 | 20c bl & blk, *straw* (R) | 3.00 | 3.00 |
| 72 | A13 | 40c ver & blk, *bluish* (Bl) | 3.40 | 3.40 |
| 73 | A13 | 1pi bl grn & blk, *grnsh* | 7.50 | 7.50 |
| 74 | A13 | 2pi vio brn & blk, *pnksh* (Bl) | 17.00 | 17.00 |
| | | *Nos. 54-74 (21)* | 54.90 | 54.90 |

Accent omitted varieties exist for Nos. 54-74. For detailed listings, see "Scott Classic Specialized Catalogue of Stamps and Covers 1840-1940".

Indo-China Stamps of 1927 Overprinted in Black or Red

**1927**

| No. | Type | Description | Unused | Used |
|---|---|---|---|---|
| 75 | A14 | 1/10c lt ol grn (R) | .35 | .35 |
| 76 | A14 | 1/5c yellow | .35 | .35 |
| 77 | A14 | 2/5c lt blue (R) | .50 | .50 |
| 78 | A14 | 4/5c dp brown | .50 | .50 |
| 79 | A14 | 1c orange | .85 | .85 |
| 80 | A14 | 2c blue grn (R) | 1.25 | 1.25 |
| 81 | A14 | 3c indigo (R) | 1.25 | 1.25 |
| 82 | A14 | 4c lilac rose | 1.25 | 1.25 |
| 83 | A14 | 5c deep violet | 1.25 | 1.25 |
| 84 | A15 | 6c deep red | 1.25 | 1.25 |
| 85 | A15 | 7c lt brown | 1.25 | 1.25 |
| 86 | A15 | 8c gray grn (R) | 1.25 | 1.25 |
| 87 | A15 | 9c red violet | 1.70 | 1.70 |
| 88 | A15 | 10c lt bl (R) | 1.70 | 1.70 |
| 89 | A15 | 11c orange | 1.70 | 1.70 |
| 90 | A15 | 12c myr grn (R) | 1.70 | 1.70 |
| 91 | A16 | 15c dl rose & ol brn | 3.00 | 3.00 |
| 92 | A16 | 20c vio & sl (R) | 2.50 | 2.50 |
| 93 | A17 | 25c org brn & lil rose | 2.50 | 2.50 |
| 94 | A17 | 30c dp bl & ol gray (R) | 1.70 | 1.70 |
| 95 | A18 | 40c ver & lt bl | 1.70 | 1.70 |
| 96 | A18 | 50c lt grn & sl (R) | 2.50 | 2.50 |
| 97 | A19 | 1pi dk bl, blk & yel (R) | 4.25 | 4.25 |
| 98 | A19 | 2pi red, dp bl & org (R) | 6.00 | 6.00 |
| a. | | Double overprint | 160.00 | |
| | | *Nos. 75-98 (24)* | 42.25 | 42.25 |

Accent omitted varieties exist for Nos. 75-90. For detailed listings, see "Scott Classic Specialized Catalogue of Stamps and Covers 1840-1940".

Stamps of Indo-China, 1931-41, Overprinted in Black or Red

**1937-41 *Perf. 13, 13½***

| No. | Type | Description | Unused | Used |
|---|---|---|---|---|
| 99 | A20 | 1/10c Prus blue | .25 | .25 |
| 100 | A20 | 1/5c lake | .25 | .25 |
| 101 | A20 | 2/5c orange red | .40 | .40 |
| 102 | A20 | 1/2c red brown | .35 | .35 |
| 103 | A20 | 4/5c dk violet | .35 | .35 |
| 104 | A20 | 1c black brown | .35 | .35 |
| 105 | A20 | 2c dk green | .35 | .35 |
| a. | | Inverted overprint | 140.00 | |
| 106 | A21 | 3c dk green | .75 | .75 |
| 107 | A21 | 3c yel brn ('41) | .35 | .35 |
| 108 | A21 | 4c dk blue (R) | 1.00 | 1.00 |
| 109 | A21 | 4c dk green ('41) | .35 | .35 |
| 110 | A21 | 4c yel org ('41) | 2.75 | 2.75 |
| 111 | A21 | 5c dp violet | .95 | .95 |
| 112 | A21 | 5c dp green ('41) | .50 | .50 |
| 113 | A21 | 6c orange red | .65 | .65 |
| 114 | A21 | 7c black (R) ('41) | .65 | .65 |
| 115 | A21 | 8c rose lake ('41) | .75 | .75 |
| 116 | A21 | 9c blk, *yel* (R) ('41) | 1.00 | 1.00 |
| d. | | Black overprint | 9.25 | 9.25 |
| 117 | A22 | 10c dk blue (R) | 1.10 | 1.10 |
| 118 | A22 | 10c ultra, *pink* (R) ('41) | .85 | .85 |
| 119 | A22 | 15c dk bl (R) | .75 | .75 |
| 120 | A22 | 18c bl (R) ('41) | .65 | .65 |
| 121 | A22 | 20c rose | .75 | .75 |
| 122 | A22 | 21c olive grn | .75 | .75 |
| 123 | A22 | 22c green ('41) | .60 | .60 |
| 124 | A22 | 25c dp violet | 3.00 | 3.00 |
| 125 | A22 | 25c dk bl (R) ('41) | .85 | .85 |
| 126 | A22 | 30c orange brn | .85 | .85 |
| 127 | A23 | 50c dk brown | 1.10 | 1.10 |
| 128 | A23 | 60c dl violet | 1.10 | 1.10 |
| 129 | A23 | 70c lt bl (R) ('41) | .85 | .85 |
| 130 | A23 | 1pi yel green | 2.10 | 2.10 |
| 131 | A23 | 2pi red | 2.25 | 2.25 |
| | | *Nos. 99-131 (33)* | 29.55 | 29.55 |

Accent omitted varieties exist for Nos. 99-124 and No. 126. For detailed listings, see "Scott Classic Specialized Catalogue of Stamps and Covers 1840-1940".

Common Design Types pictured following the introduction.

### Colonial Arts Exhibition Issue

Common Design Type

**Souvenir Sheet**

**1937 Engr. *Imperf.***

| No. | Type | Description | Unused | Used |
|---|---|---|---|---|
| 132 | CD79 | 30c grn & sepia | 9.25 | *11.00* |

### New York World's Fair Issue

Common Design Type

**1939 Unwmk. *Perf. 12½x12***

| No. | Type | Description | Unused | Used |
|---|---|---|---|---|
| 133 | CD82 | 13c car lake | 1.25 | 1.25 |
| 134 | CD82 | 23c ultra | 1.25 | 1.25 |

### Petain Issue

Indo-China Nos. 209-209A Overprinted "KOUANG TCHEOU" in Blue or Red

**1941 Engr. *Perf. 12½x12***

| No. | Type | Description | Unused | Used |
|---|---|---|---|---|
| 135 | A27a | 10c car lake (B) | .85 | |
| 136 | A27a | 25c blue (R) | .85 | |

Nos. 135-136 were issued by the Vichy government in France, but were not placed on sale in Kwangchowan.

For surcharges, see Nos. B9-B10.

### Indo-China Types of 1937-41 without "RF" Overprinted "KOUANG TCHEOU" in Blue or Red

**1942-44**

| No. | Type | Description | Unused | Used |
|---|---|---|---|---|
| 137 | A20 | 2/5c orange red | .25 | |
| 138 | A20 | 1/2c red brown | .25 | |
| 139 | A20 | 1c black brown | .35 | |
| 140 | A20 | 2c dark green | .65 | |
| 141 | A21 | 3c yellow brown | .65 | |
| 142 | A21 | 4c yellow orange | .35 | |
| 143 | A21 | 5c deep green | .50 | |
| 144 | A21 | 9c black, *yellow* | .35 | |
| 145 | A22 | 10c ultramarine, *pink* (R) | .60 | |
| 146 | A22 | 18c blue (R) | 190.00 | |
| 147 | A22 | 22c green | .60 | |
| 148 | A22 | 30c orange brown | .65 | |
| 149 | A23 | 50c dark brown | .60 | |
| 150 | A23 | 60c dull violet | .65 | |
| 151 | A23 | 70c light blue (R) | .85 | |
| 152 | A23 | 1pi yellow green | 1.30 | |
| 153 | A23 | 2pi red | 1.40 | |
| | | *Nos. 137-153 (17)* | 200.00 | |

Nos. 137-153 were issued by the Vichy government in France, but were not placed on sale in Kwangchowan.

## SEMI-POSTAL STAMPS

### French Revolution Issue

Common Design Type

**1939 Unwmk. Photo. *Perf. 13***

**Name and Value typo. in Black**

| No. | Type | Description | Unused | Used |
|---|---|---|---|---|
| B1 | CD83 | 6c + 2c green | 9.25 | 9.25 |
| B2 | CD83 | 7c + 3c brown | 9.25 | 9.25 |
| B3 | CD83 | 9c + 4c red org | 9.25 | 9.25 |
| B4 | CD83 | 13c + 10c rose pink | 9.25 | 9.25 |
| B5 | CD83 | 23c + 20c blue | 9.25 | 9.25 |
| | | *Nos. B1-B5 (5)* | 46.25 | 46.25 |

### Indo-China Nos. B19A and B19C Overprinted "KOUANG-TCHEOU" in Blue or Red, and Common Design Type

**1941 Photo. *Perf. 13½***

| No. | Type | Description | Unused | Used |
|---|---|---|---|---|
| B6 | SP1 | 10c + 10c red (B) | .85 | |
| B7 | CD86 | 15c + 30c mar & car | .85 | |
| B8 | SP2 | 25c + 10c blue (R) | .85 | |
| | | *Nos. B6-B8 (3)* | 2.55 | |

Nos. B6-B8 were issued by the Vichy government in France, but were not placed on sale in Kwangchowan.

### Indo-China Nos. B21A-B21B Overprinted in Blue or Red

**1944 Engr. *Perf. 12½x12***

| No. | Type | Description | Unused | Used |
|---|---|---|---|---|
| B9 | A27a | 5c + 15c on 25c deep blue (R) | 1.00 | |
| B10 | A27a | +25c on 10c car lake | 1.10 | |

Colonial Development Fund.

Nos. B9-B10 were issued by the Vichy government in France, but were not placed on sale in Kwangchowan.

## AIR POST SEMI-POSTAL STAMPS

### Indo-China Nos. CB2-CB4 Overprinted "KOUANG-TCHEOU" in Blue or Red

***Methods and Perfs as Before***

**1942, June 22**

| No. | Type | Description | Unused | Used |
|---|---|---|---|---|
| CB1 | SPAP1 | 15c + 35c green (R) | .95 | |
| CB2 | SPAP2 | 20c + 60c brown | .95 | |
| CB3 | SPAP3 | 30c +90c car red | .95 | |
| | | *Nos. CB1-CB3 (3)* | 2.85 | |

Native children's welfare fund.

Nos. CB1-CB3 were issued by the Vichy government in France, but were not placed on sale in Kwangchowan.

### Colonial Education Fund

Indo-China No. CB5 Overprinted "KOUANG-TCHEOU" in Blue or Red

***Perf. 12½x13½***

**1942, June 22 Engr.**

| No. | Type | Description | Unused | Used |
|---|---|---|---|---|
| CB4 | CD86a | 12c + 18c blue & red | 1.00 | |

No. CB4 was issued by the Vichy government in France, but was not placed on sale in Kwangchowan.

## MONGTSEU (MENGTSZ)

Stamps of Indo-China Surcharged in Black

**1903-04 Unwmk. *Perf. 14x13½***

| No. | Type | Description | Unused | Used |
|---|---|---|---|---|
| 1 | A3 | 1c blk, *lil bl* | 7.50 | 7.50 |
| 2 | A3 | 2c brn, *buff* | 6.75 | 6.75 |
| 3 | A3 | 4c claret, *lav* | 8.50 | 8.50 |
| 4 | A3 | 5c yel grn | 6.00 | 6.00 |
| 5 | A3 | 10c red | 9.25 | 9.25 |
| 6 | A3 | 15c gray | 10.00 | 10.00 |
| 7 | A3 | 20c red, *grn* | 12.50 | 12.50 |
| 7C | A3 | 25c blk, *rose* | 725.00 | 725.00 |
| 8 | A3 | 25c blue | 12.50 | 12.50 |
| 9 | A3 | 30c brn, *bister* | 11.00 | 11.00 |

| No. | Type | Description | Unused | Used |
|---|---|---|---|---|
| 10 | A3 | 40c red, *straw* | 75.00 | 75.00 |
| 11 | A3 | 50c car, *rose* | 440.00 | 440.00 |
| 12 | A3 | 50c brn, *az* ('04) | 150.00 | 150.00 |
| 13 | A3 | 75c dp vio, *org* | 120.00 | 120.00 |
| *a.* | | "INDO-CHINE" inverted | 67,500. | |
| 14 | A3 | 1fr brnz grn, *straw* | 110.00 | 110.00 |
| 15 | A3 | 5fr red lil, *lav* | 110.00 | 110.00 |
| | | *Nos. 1-15 (16)* | 1,814. | 1,814. |

Many surcharge varieties exist on Nos. 1-15.

Stamps of Indo-China, 1892-1906, Surcharged in Red or Black

**1906**

| No. | Type | Description | Unused | Used |
|---|---|---|---|---|
| 16 | A4 | 1c ol grn (R) | 5.00 | 5.00 |
| 17 | A4 | 2c vio brn, *buff* | 5.00 | 5.00 |
| 18 | A4 | 4c cl, *bluish* (R) | 5.00 | 5.00 |
| 19 | A4 | 5c dp grn (R) | 6.00 | 6.00 |
| 20 | A4 | 10c carmine | 5.00 | 5.00 |
| 21 | A4 | 15c org brn, *bl* | 35.00 | 35.00 |
| 22 | A4 | 20c red, *grn* | 13.50 | 13.50 |
| 23 | A4 | 25c deep blue | 10.00 | 10.00 |
| 24 | A4 | 30c pale brn | 13.50 | 13.50 |
| 25 | A4 | 35c blk, *yel* (R) | 12.50 | 12.50 |
| 26 | A4 | 40c blk, *bluish* (R) | 20.00 | 20.00 |
| 27 | A4 | 50c bister brn | 21.00 | 21.00 |
| 28 | A3 | 75c dp vio, *org* (R) | 67.50 | 67.50 |
| *a.* | | "INDO-CHINE" inverted | 67,500. | |
| 29 | A4 | 1fr pale grn | 42.50 | 42.50 |
| 30 | A4 | 2fr brn, *org* (R) | 55.00 | 55.00 |
| 31 | A3 | 5fr red lil, *lav* | 140.00 | 140.00 |
| 32 | A4 | 10fr org brn, *grn* | 150.00 | 150.00 |
| *a.* | | Chinese characters inverted | 1,750. | *2,100.* |
| | | *Nos. 16-32 (17)* | 606.50 | 606.50 |

Inverted varieties of the surcharge exist on Nos. 19, 22 and 32.

Stamps of Indo-China, 1907, Srchd. in Red or Blue

**Value in Chinese**

**1908**

| No. | Type | Description | Unused | Used |
|---|---|---|---|---|
| 33 | A5 | 1c ol brn & blk | 1.25 | 1.25 |
| 34 | A5 | 2c brn & blk | 1.25 | 1.25 |
| 35 | A5 | 4c bl & blk | 1.25 | 1.25 |
| 36 | A5 | 5c grn & blk | 1.25 | 1.25 |
| 37 | A5 | 10c red & blk (Bl) | 3.00 | 3.00 |
| 38 | A5 | 15c vio & blk | 3.00 | 3.00 |
| 39 | A6 | 20c vio & blk | 6.00 | 6.00 |
| 40 | A6 | 25c bl & blk | 15.00 | 15.00 |
| 41 | A6 | 30c brn & blk | 6.75 | 6.75 |
| 42 | A6 | 35c ol grn & blk | 7.50 | 7.50 |
| 43 | A6 | 40c brn & blk | 5.00 | 5.00 |
| 45 | A6 | 50c car & blk (Bl) | 6.75 | 6.75 |
| 46 | A7 | 75c ver & blk (Bl) | 14.50 | 14.50 |
| 47 | A8 | 1fr car & blk (Bl) | 13.50 | 13.50 |
| 48 | A9 | 2fr grn & blk | 19.00 | 19.00 |
| 49 | A10 | 5fr bl & blk | 105.00 | 105.00 |
| 50 | A11 | 10fr pur & blk | 125.00 | 125.00 |
| | | *Nos. 33-50 (17)* | 335.00 | 335.00 |

The Chinese characters overprinted on Nos. 1 to 50 repeat the denomination of the basic stamp.

Nos. 33-50 Srchd. in Cents or Piasters in Black, Red or Blue

**1919**

| No. | Type | Description | Unused | Used |
|---|---|---|---|---|
| 51 | A5 | ⅖c on 1c | 1.70 | 1.70 |
| 52 | A5 | ⅘c on 2c | 1.70 | 1.70 |
| 53 | A5 | 1⅗c on 4c | 1.70 | 1.70 |
| 54 | A5 | 2c on 5c | 1.70 | 1.70 |
| 55 | A5 | 4c on 10c (Bl) | 3.00 | 3.00 |
| 56 | A5 | 6c on 15c | 3.00 | 3.00 |
| 57 | A6 | 8c on 20c | 6.75 | 6.75 |
| 58 | A6 | 10c on 25c | 5.00 | 5.00 |
| 59 | A6 | 12c on 30c | 5.00 | 5.00 |
| 60 | A6 | 14c on 35c | 3.40 | 3.40 |
| *a.* | | Closed "4" | 21.00 | 21.00 |
| 61 | A6 | 16c on 40c | 4.25 | 4.25 |
| 63 | A6 | 20c on 50c (Bl) | 5.00 | 5.00 |
| 64 | A7 | 30c on 75c (Bl) | 9.25 | 9.25 |
| 65 | A8 | 40c on 1fr (Bl) | 10.00 | 10.00 |
| 66 | A9 | 80c on 2fr (R) | 10.00 | 10.00 |
| *a.* | | Triple surch., one inverted | 550.00 | 550.00 |
| 67 | A10 | 2pi on 5fr (R) | 200.00 | 200.00 |
| *a.* | | Triple surch., one inverted | 625.00 | 625.00 |
| *b.* | | Double surcharge | 925.00 | 925.00 |
| 68 | A11 | 4pi on 10fr (R) | 30.00 | 30.00 |
| | | *Nos. 51-68 (17)* | 301.45 | 301.45 |

## PAKHOI

Stamps of Indo-China Surcharged in Black

**1903-04 Unwmk. *Perf. 14x13½***

| No. | Type | Description | Unused | Used |
|---|---|---|---|---|
| 1 | A3 | 1c blk, *lil bl* | 6.75 | 6.75 |
| 2 | A3 | 2c brn, *buff* | 6.75 | 6.75 |
| 3 | A3 | 4c claret, *lav* | 6.75 | 6.75 |
| 4 | A3 | 5c yel grn | 5.00 | 5.00 |
| 5 | A3 | 10c red | 5.00 | 5.00 |
| 6 | A3 | 15c gray | 5.00 | 5.00 |
| 7 | A3 | 20c red, *grn* | 11.00 | 11.00 |
| 8 | A3 | 25c blue | 9.25 | 9.25 |
| 9 | A3 | 25c blk, *rose*('04) | 6.75 | 6.75 |
| 10 | A3 | 30c brn, *bister* | 8.50 | 8.50 |
| 11 | A3 | 40c red, *straw* | 57.50 | 57.50 |
| 12 | A3 | 50c car, *rose* | 340.00 | 340.00 |
| 13 | A3 | 50c brn, *az* ('04) | 47.50 | 47.50 |
| 14 | A3 | 75c dp vio, *org* | 67.50 | 67.50 |
| *a.* | | "INDO-CHINE" inverted | 47,500. | |
| 15 | A3 | 1fr brnz grn, *straw* | 67.50 | 67.50 |
| 16 | A3 | 5fr red lil, *lav* | 135.00 | 135.00 |
| | | *Nos. 1-16 (16)* | 785.75 | 785.75 |

Many varieties of the surcharge exist.

Stamps of Indo-China 1892-1906, Surcharged in Red or Black

**1906**

| No. | Type | Description | Unused | Used |
|---|---|---|---|---|
| 17 | A4 | 1c ol grn (R) | 8.50 | 8.50 |
| 18 | A4 | 2c vio brn, *buff* | 8.50 | 8.50 |
| 19 | A4 | 4c cl, *bluish* (R) | 8.50 | 8.50 |
| 20 | A4 | 5c dp grn (R) | 8.50 | 8.50 |
| 21 | A4 | 10c carmine | 8.50 | 8.50 |
| 22 | A4 | 15c org brn,*bl* | 32.50 | 32.50 |
| 23 | A4 | 20c red, *grn* | 13.50 | 13.50 |
| 24 | A4 | 25c deep blue | 11.00 | 11.00 |
| 25 | A4 | 30c pale brn | 13.50 | 13.50 |
| 26 | A4 | 35c blk, *yel* (R) | 21.00 | 21.00 |
| 27 | A4 | 40c blk, *bluish*(R) | 21.00 | 21.00 |
| 28 | A4 | 50c bister brn | 21.00 | 21.00 |
| 29 | A3 | 75c dp vio, *org* (R) | 67.50 | 67.50 |
| 30 | A4 | 1fr pale grn | 42.50 | 42.50 |
| 31 | A4 | 2fr brn, *org*(R) | 55.00 | 55.00 |
| 32 | A3 | 5fr red lil, *lav* | 140.00 | 140.00 |
| 33 | A4 | 10fr org brn, *grn* | 150.00 | 150.00 |
| | | *Nos. 17-33 (17)* | 631.00 | 631.00 |

Various surcharge varieties exist on Nos. 17-24.

### Stamps of Indo-China, 1907, Surcharged "PAKHOI" and Value in Chinese in Red or Blue

**1908**

| No. | Type | Description | Unused | Used |
|---|---|---|---|---|
| 34 | A5 | 1c ol brn & blk | 1.25 | 1.25 |
| 35 | A5 | 2c brn & blk | 1.25 | 1.25 |
| 36 | A5 | 4c bl & blk | 1.25 | 1.25 |
| 37 | A5 | 5c grn & blk | 1.70 | 1.70 |
| 38 | A5 | 10c red & blk (Bl) | 1.70 | 1.70 |
| 39 | A5 | 15c vio & blk | 2.10 | 2.10 |
| 40 | A6 | 20c vio & blk | 2.50 | 2.50 |
| 41 | A6 | 25c bl & blk | 3.00 | 3.00 |
| 42 | A6 | 30c brn & blk | 3.40 | 3.40 |
| 43 | A6 | 35c ol grn & blk | 3.40 | 3.40 |
| 44 | A6 | 40c brn & blk | 3.40 | 3.40 |
| 46 | A6 | 50c car & blk (Bl) | 3.40 | 3.40 |
| 47 | A7 | 75c ver & blk (Bl) | 7.25 | 7.25 |
| 48 | A8 | 1fr car & blk (Bl) | 7.50 | 7.50 |
| 49 | A9 | 2fr grn & blk | 16.00 | 16.00 |
| 50 | A10 | 5fr bl & blk | 85.00 | 85.00 |
| 51 | A11 | 10fr pur & blk | 150.00 | 150.00 |
| | | *Nos. 34-51 (17)* | 294.10 | 294.10 |

The Chinese characters overprinted on Nos. 1 to 51 repeat the denomination of the basic stamps.

### Nos. 34-51 Surcharged with New Values in Cents or Piasters in Black, Red or Blue

**1919**

| No. | Type | Description | Unused | Used |
|---|---|---|---|---|
| 52 | A5 | ⅖c on 1c | 1.25 | 1.25 |
| *a.* | | "PAK-HOI" and Chinese double | 170.00 | |
| 53 | A5 | ⅘c on 2c | 1.25 | 1.25 |
| 54 | A5 | 1⅗c on 4c (R) | 1.25 | 1.25 |
| 55 | A5 | 2c on 5c | 2.50 | 2.50 |
| 56 | A5 | 4c on 10c (Bl) | 3.40 | 3.40 |
| 57 | A5 | 6c on 15c | 1.70 | 1.70 |
| 58 | A6 | 8c on 20c | 3.40 | 3.40 |
| 59 | A6 | 10c on 25c | 5.00 | 5.00 |
| 60 | A6 | 12c on 30c | 1.70 | 1.70 |
| *a.* | | "12 CENTS" double | 675.00 | |
| 61 | A6 | 14c on 35c | 1.25 | 1.25 |
| *a.* | | Closed "4" | 14.50 | 14.50 |
| 62 | A6 | 16c on 40c | 3.00 | 3.00 |
| 64 | A6 | 20c on 50c (Bl) | 2.10 | 2.10 |
| 65 | A7 | 30c on 75c (Bl) | 9.25 | 9.25 |
| 66 | A8 | 40c on 1fr (Bl) | 12.50 | 12.50 |
| 67 | A9 | 80c on 2fr (R) | 10.00 | 10.00 |
| 68 | A10 | 2pi on 5fr (R) | 16.00 | 16.00 |
| 69 | A11 | 4pi on 10fr (R) | 35.00 | 35.00 |
| | | *Nos. 52-69 (17)* | 110.55 | 110.55 |

## TCHONGKING (CHUNGKING)

Stamps of Indo-China Surcharged in Black

**1903-04 Unwmk. *Perf. 14x13½***

| No. | Type | Description | Unused | Used |
|---|---|---|---|---|
| 1 | A3 | 1c blk, *lil bl* | 5.00 | 5.00 |
| 2 | A3 | 2c brn, *buff* | 5.00 | 5.00 |
| 3 | A3 | 4c claret, *lav* | 6.00 | 6.00 |
| 4 | A3 | 5c yel grn | 6.00 | 6.00 |
| 5 | A3 | 10c red | 6.00 | 6.00 |
| 6 | A3 | 15c gray | 6.00 | 6.00 |
| 7 | A3 | 20c red, *grn* | 8.50 | 8.50 |
| 8 | A3 | 25c blue | 55.00 | 55.00 |
| 9 | A3 | 25c blk, *rose* ('04) | 10.00 | 10.00 |
| 10 | A3 | 30c brn, *bister* | 15.00 | 15.00 |
| 11 | A3 | 40c red, *straw* | 62.50 | 62.50 |
| 12 | A3 | 50c car, *rose* | 225.00 | 225.00 |
| 13 | A3 | 50c brn, *az* ('04) | 140.00 | 140.00 |
| 14 | A3 | 75c vio, *org* | 45.00 | 45.00 |
| 15 | A3 | 1fr brnz grn, *straw* | 60.00 | 60.00 |
| 16 | A3 | 5fr red lil, *lav* | 105.00 | 105.00 |
| | | *Nos. 1-16 (16)* | 760.00 | 760.00 |

Many surcharge varieties exist on Nos. 1-14.

Stamps of Indo-China and French China, issued in 1902 with similar overprint, but without Chinese characters, were not officially authorized.

Stamps of Indo-China, 1892-1906, Surcharged in Red or Black

**1906**

| No. | Type | Description | Unused | Used |
|---|---|---|---|---|
| 17 | A4 | 1c ol grn (R) | 8.50 | 8.50 |
| 18 | A4 | 2c vio brn, *buff* | 8.50 | 8.50 |
| 19 | A4 | 4c cl, *bluish* (R) | 8.50 | 8.50 |
| 20 | A4 | 5c dp grn (R) | 8.50 | 8.50 |
| 21 | A4 | 10c carmine | 8.50 | 8.50 |
| 22 | A4 | 15c org brn, *bl* | 32.50 | 32.50 |
| 23 | A4 | 20c red, *grn* | 13.50 | 13.50 |
| 24 | A4 | 25c deep blue | 11.00 | 11.00 |
| 25 | A4 | 30c pale brn | 13.50 | 13.50 |
| 26 | A4 | 35c blk, *yellow* (R) | 21.00 | 21.00 |
| 27 | A4 | 40c blk, *bluish* (R) | 21.00 | 21.00 |
| 28 | A4 | 50c bis brn | 25.00 | 25.00 |
| 29 | A3 | 75c dp vio, *org* (R) | 67.50 | 67.50 |
| 30 | A4 | 1fr pale grn | 42.50 | 42.50 |
| 31 | A4 | 2fr brn, *org* (R) | 55.00 | 55.00 |
| 32 | A3 | 5fr red lil, *lav* | 140.00 | 140.00 |
| 33 | A4 | 10fr org brn, *grn* | 150.00 | 150.00 |
| | | *Nos. 17-33 (17)* | 635.00 | 635.00 |

Variety "T" omitted in surcharge occurs once in each sheet of Nos. 17-33. For detailed listings, see "Scott Classic Specialized Catalogue of Stamps and Values". Other surcharge varieties exist. Inverted surcharge on 1c and 2c are of private origin.

### Stamps of Indo-China, 1907, Surcharged "TCHONGKING" and Value in Chinese in Red or Blue

**1908**

| No. | Type | Description | Unused | Used |
|---|---|---|---|---|
| 34 | A5 | 1c ol brn & blk | .85 | .85 |
| 35 | A5 | 2c brn & blk | .85 | .85 |
| 36 | A5 | 4c bl & blk | 1.25 | 1.25 |
| 37 | A5 | 5c grn & blk | 2.10 | 2.10 |
| 38 | A5 | 10c red & blk (Bl) | 2.10 | 2.10 |
| 39 | A5 | 15c vio & blk | 3.00 | 3.00 |
| 40 | A6 | 20c vio & blk | 3.00 | 3.00 |
| 41 | A6 | 25c bl & blk | 5.50 | 5.50 |
| 42 | A6 | 30c brn & blk | 3.40 | 3.40 |
| 43 | A6 | 35c ol grn & blk | 7.50 | 7.50 |
| 44 | A6 | 40c brn & blk | 15.00 | 15.00 |
| 45 | A6 | 50c car & blk (Bl) | 12.00 | 12.00 |
| 46 | A7 | 75c ver & blk (Bl) | 10.00 | 10.00 |
| 47 | A8 | 1fr car & blk (Bl) | 13.50 | 13.50 |
| 48 | A9 | 2fr grn & blk | 85.00 | 85.00 |
| 49 | A10 | 5fr bl & blk | 37.50 | 37.50 |
| 50 | A11 | 10fr pur & blk | 225.00 | 225.00 |
| | | *Nos. 34-50 (17)* | 427.55 | 427.55 |

The Chinese characters overprinted on Nos. 1 to 50 repeat the denomination of the basic stamp.

### Nos. 34-50 Surcharged with New Values in Cents or Piasters in Black, Red or Blue

**1919**

| No. | Type | Description | Unused | Used |
|---|---|---|---|---|
| 51 | A5 | ⅖c on 1c | 1.25 | 1.25 |
| 52 | A5 | ⅘c on 2c | 1.25 | 1.25 |
| 53 | A5 | 1⅗c on 4c (R) | 1.25 | 1.25 |
| 54 | A5 | 2c on 5c | 1.70 | 1.70 |
| 55 | A5 | 4c on 10c (Bl) | 1.25 | 1.25 |
| 56 | A5 | 6c on 15c | 1.70 | 1.70 |
| 57 | A6 | 8c on 20c | 3.00 | 3.00 |
| 58 | A6 | 10c on 25c | 8.50 | 8.50 |
| 59 | A6 | 12c on 30c | 3.00 | 1.25 |
| 60 | A6 | 14c on 35c | 2.10 | 1.70 |
| *a.* | | Closed "4" | 35.00 | 35.00 |
| 61 | A6 | 16c on 40c | 2.10 | 1.70 |
| *a.* | | "16 CENTS" double | 125.00 | 125.00 |
| 62 | A6 | 20c on 50c (Bl) | 11.00 | 10.00 |
| 63 | A7 | 30c on 75c (Bl) | 9.25 | 6.75 |
| 64 | A8 | 40c on 1fr (Bl) | 9.25 | 6.75 |
| 65 | A9 | 80c on 2fr (R) | 9.25 | 6.75 |
| 66 | A10 | 2pi on 5fr (R) | 9.25 | 9.25 |
| 67 | A11 | 4pi on 10fr (R) | 17.50 | 17.50 |
| | | *Nos. 51-67 (17)* | 92.60 | 79.80 |

## YUNNAN FOU

### (Formerly Yunnan Sen, later known as Kunming)

Stamps of Indo-China Surcharged in Black

**1903-04 Unwmk. *Perf. 14x13½***

| No. | Type | Description | Unused | Used |
|---|---|---|---|---|
| 1 | A3 | 1c blk, *lil bl* | 6.75 | 6.75 |
| 2 | A3 | 2c brn, *buff* | 6.75 | 6.75 |
| 3 | A3 | 4c claret, *lav* | 7.50 | 7.50 |
| 4 | A3 | 5c yel green | 6.75 | 6.75 |
| 5 | A3 | 10c red | 7.50 | 7.50 |
| 6 | A3 | 15c gray | 7.50 | 7.50 |
| 7 | A3 | 20c red, *grn* | 12.50 | 12.50 |
| 8 | A3 | 25c blue | 7.50 | 7.50 |
| 9 | A3 | 30c brn, *bister* | 12.50 | 12.50 |
| 10 | A3 | 40c red, *straw* | 75.00 | 60.00 |
| 11 | A3 | 50c car, *rose* | 350.00 | 350.00 |
| 12 | A3 | 50c brn, *az* ('04) | 180.00 | 180.00 |
| 13 | A3 | 75c dp vio, *org* | 67.50 | 62.50 |
| *a.* | | "INDO-CHINE" inverted | 47,500. | |
| 14 | A3 | 1fr brnz grn, *straw* | 67.50 | 62.50 |
| 15 | A3 | 5fr red lil, *lav* | 125.00 | 125.00 |
| | | *Nos. 1-15 (15)* | 940.25 | 915.25 |

The Chinese characters overprinted on Nos. 1 to 15 repeat the denomination of the basic stamp.

Many varieties of the surcharge exist.

Stamps of Indo-China, 1892-1906, Surcharged in Red or Black

**1906 Unwmk. *Perf. 14x13½***

| No. | Type | Description | Unused | Used |
|---|---|---|---|---|
| 17 | A4 | 1c ol grn (R) | 5.00 | 5.00 |
| 18 | A4 | 2c vio brn, *buff* | 5.00 | 5.00 |
| 19 | A4 | 4c cl, *bluish* (R) | 5.00 | 5.00 |
| 20 | A4 | 5c dp grn (R) | 5.00 | 5.00 |
| 21 | A4 | 10c carmine | 5.00 | 5.00 |
| 22 | A4 | 15c org brn, *bl* | 35.00 | 35.00 |
| 23 | A4 | 20c red, *grn* | 13.50 | 13.50 |
| 24 | A4 | 25c deep blue | 11.00 | 11.00 |
| 25 | A4 | 30c pale brn | 13.50 | 13.50 |
| 26 | A4 | 35c blk, *yel* (R) | 17.00 | 17.00 |
| 27 | A4 | 40c blk, *bluish* (R) | 17.00 | 17.00 |
| 28 | A4 | 50c bister brn | 21.00 | 21.00 |
| 29 | A3 | 75c dp vio, *org* (R) | 67.50 | 67.50 |
| 30 | A4 | 1fr pale grn | 42.50 | 42.50 |
| 31 | A4 | 2fr brn, *org* (R) | 55.00 | 55.00 |
| 32 | A3 | 5fr red lil, *lav* | 140.00 | 140.00 |
| 33 | A4 | 10fr org brn, *grn* | 150.00 | 150.00 |
| | | *Nos. 17-33 (17)* | 608.00 | 608.00 |

Various varieties of the surcharge exist on Nos. 18, 20, 21 and 27.

### Stamps of Indo-China, 1907, Surcharged "YUNNANFOU," and Value in Chinese in Red or Blue

**1908**

| No. | Type | Description | Unused | Used |
|---|---|---|---|---|
| 34 | A5 | 1c ol brn & blk | 1.25 | 1.25 |
| 35 | A5 | 2c brn & blk | 1.25 | 1.25 |
| 36 | A5 | 4c bl & blk | 2.10 | 2.10 |
| 37 | A5 | 5c grn & blk | 3.00 | 3.00 |
| 38 | A5 | 10c red & blk (Bl) | 3.00 | 3.00 |
| 39 | A5 | 15c vio & blk | 6.75 | 6.75 |
| 40 | A6 | 20c vio & blk | 6.25 | 6.25 |
| 41 | A6 | 25c bl & blk | 9.25 | 9.25 |
| 42 | A6 | 30c brn & blk | 7.50 | 7.50 |
| 43 | A6 | 35c ol grn & blk | 7.50 | 7.50 |
| 44 | A6 | 40c brn & blk | 8.50 | 8.50 |
| 45 | A6 | 50c car & blk (Bl) | 9.25 | 9.25 |

46 A7 75c ver & blk (Bl) 11.00 11.00
47 A8 1fr car & blk (Bl) 17.00 17.00
48 A9 2fr grn & blk 29.00 29.00
a. "YUNANNFOU" 2,500. 2,500.
49 A10 5fr bl & blk 60.00 60.00
a. "YUNANNFOU" 2,500. 2,500.
50 A11 10fr pur & blk 120.00 120.00
a. "YUNANNFOU" 2,500. 2,500.
*Nos. 34-50 (17)* 302.60 302.60

The Chinese characters overprinted on Nos. 17-50 repeat the denomination of the basic stamp.

**Nos. 34-50 Surcharged with New Values in Cents or Piasters in Black, Red or Blue**

**1919**

51 A5 2/5c on 1c 1.25 1.25
a. New value double 140.00
52 A5 4/5c on 2c 1.25 1.25
53 A5 1 3/5c on 4c (R) 1.25 1.25
54 A5 2c on 5c 2.10 2.10
a. Triple surcharge 210.00
55 A5 4c on 10c (Bl) 1.70 1.70
56 A5 6c on 15c 3.00 3.00
57 A6 8c on 20c 2.10 2.10
58 A6 10c on 25c 3.75 3.75
59 A6 12c on 30c 9.25 9.25
60 A6 14c on 35c 14.50 14.50
a. Closed "4" 140.00 140.00
61 A6 16c on 40c 9.25 9.25
62 A6 20c on 50c (Bl) 3.00 3.00
63 A7 30c on 75c (Bl) 9.25 9.25
64 A8 40c on 1fr (Bl) 35.00 35.00
65 A9 80c on 2fr (R) 14.50 14.50
a. Triple surch., one inverted 250.00
66 A10 2pi on 5fr (R) 67.50 67.50
67 A11 4pi on 10fr (R) 35.00 35.00
*Nos. 51-67 (17)* 213.65 213.65

## OFFICES IN CRETE

Austria, France, Italy and Great Britain maintained their own post offices in Crete during the period when that country was an autonomous state.

100 Centimes = 1 Franc

Liberty, Equality and Fraternity A1

"Rights of Man" A2

Liberty and Peace (Symbolized by Olive Branch) — A3

***Perf. 14x13½***

**1902-03 Unwmk. Typo.**

1 A1 1c dark gray 2.35 2.75
a. A1 1c light gray 2.35 2.75
2 A1 2c violet brown 2.35 2.75
3 A1 3c red orange 2.35 2.75
4 A1 4c yellow brown 2.35 2.75
5 A1 5c green 2.35 2.75
6 A2 10c rose red 2.75 2.75
7 A2 15c pale red ('03) 4.25 3.00
8 A2 20c brown vio ('03) 5.25 4.00
9 A2 25c blue ('03) 6.75 4.50
10 A2 30c lilac ('03) 6.75 4.50
11 A3 40c red & pale bl 13.00 13.00
12 A3 50c bis brn & lav 18.00 15.00
13 A3 1fr claret & ol grn 24.50 22.50
14 A3 2fr gray vio & yel 25.00 37.50
a. Imperf, pair 675.00
15 A3 5fr dk blue & buff 62.50 60.00
*Nos. 1-15 (15)* 180.50 180.50
Set, never hinged 375.00

A4

A5

**1903 Black Surcharge**

16 A4 1pi on 25c blue 55.00 47.50
17 A5 2pi on 50c bis brn & lav 75.00 57.50
18 A5 4pi on 1fr claret & ol grn 110.00 100.00
19 A5 8pi on 2fr gray vio & yel 140.00 *145.00*
20 A5 20pi on 5fr dk bl & buff 235.00 225.00
*Nos. 16-20 (5)* 615.00 575.00

## OFFICES IN EGYPT

French post offices formerly maintained in Alexandria and Port Said.

100 Centimes = 1 Franc

### ALEXANDRIA

Stamps of France Ovptd. in Red, Blue or Black

**1899-1900 Unwmk. *Perf. 14x13½***

1 A15 1c blk, *lil bl* (R) 2.10 2.10
a. Double overprint 150.00
b. Triple overprint 180.00
2 A15 2c brn, *buff* (Bl) 3.25 2.50
3 A15 3c gray, *grysh* (Bl) 3.25 2.50
4 A15 4c cl, *lav* (Bl) 4.25 3.25
5 A15 5c yel grn, (I) (R) 6.00 3.25
a. Type II (R) 160.00 97.50
6 A15 10c blk, *lav,* (I) (R) 9.25 7.50
a. Type II (R) 62.50 37.50
7 A15 15c blue (R) 9.25 4.25
8 A15 20c red, *grn* 14.50 7.50
9 A15 25c blk, *rose* (R) 7.50 4.25
a. Inverted overprint 97.50
b. Double ovpt., one invtd. 160.00
10 A15 30c brn, *bis* 15.00 12.00
11 A15 40c red, *straw* 13.50 13.50
12 A15 50c car, *rose* (II) 35.00 17.50
a. Type I 150.00 27.50
13 A15 1fr brnz grn, *straw* 32.50 22.50
14 A15 2fr brn, *az* ('00) 82.50 80.00
15 A15 5fr red lil, *lav* 120.00 110.00
*Nos. 1-15 (15)* 357.85 292.60

A2

A3

A4

**1902-13**

16 A2 1c pale gray .80 .65
17 A2 2c violet brn .75 .75
18 A2 3c red orange .75 .75
19 A2 4c yellow brn 1.00 .85
20 A2 5c green 5.00 4.25
21 A3 10c rose red 1.50 .75
22 A3 15c orange ('13) 1.75 1.25
a. 15c pale red ('03) 4.75 1.60
23 A3 20c brn vio ('03) 3.00 1.50
24 A3 25c blue ('03) 1.75 .75
25 A3 30c violet ('03) 7.50 4.25
26 A4 40c red & pale bl 5.00 2.50
27 A4 50c bis brn & lav 11.00 3.00
28 A4 1fr cl & ol grn 10.00 4.25
29 A4 2fr gray vio & yel 24.00 12.00
30 A4 5fr dk bl & buff 29.00 17.00
*Nos. 16-30 (15)* 102.80 54.50

The 2c, 5c, 10c, 20c and 25c exist imperf. Value, each $55.

See #77-86. For surcharges see #31-73, B1-B4.

Stamps of 1902-03 Surcharged Locally in Black

**1921**

31 A2 2m on 5c green 7.50 5.00
32 A2 3m on 3c red org 14.50 12.00
a. Larger numeral 140.00 125.00
33 A3 4m on 10c rose 6.75 6.00
34 A2 5m on 1c gray 14.50 12.00
35 A2 5m on 4c yel brn 19.00 13.50
36 A3 6m on 15c orange 6.75 6.00
a. Larger numeral 110.00 110.00
37 A3 8m on 20c brn vio 7.50 6.00
a. Larger numeral 80.00 60.00
38 A3 10m on 25c blue 4.25 4.25
a. Inverted surcharge 45.00 45.00
b. Double surcharge 45.00 45.00
39 A3 12m on 30c vio 17.50 17.50
40 A2 15m on 2c vio brn 14.50 14.50

Nos. 26-30 Surcharged

41 A4 15m on 40c 25.00 19.00
42 A4 15m on 50c (#27a) 12.00 12.00
43 A4 30m on 1fr 175.00 175.00
44 A4 60m on 2fr 250.00 250.00
a. Larger numeral 1,050. 1,050.
45 A4 150m on 5fr 350.00 350.00

**Port Said Nos. 20 and 19 Surcharged like Nos. 32 and 40**

45A A2 3m on 3c red org 150.00 150.00
46 A2 15m on 2c vio brn 150.00 150.00
*Nos. 31-46 (17)* 1,225. 1,203.

Alexandria No. 28 Srchd.

**1921**

46A A4 30m on 15m on 1fr 1,200. *1,350.*

The surcharge "15 Mill." was made in error and is canceled by a bar.

The surcharges were lithographed on Nos. 31, 33, 38, 39 and 42 and typographed on the other stamps of the 1921 issue. Nos. 34, 36 and 37 were surcharged by both methods.

Alexandria Stamps of 1902-03 Surcharged in Paris

**1921-23**

47 A2 1m on 1c slate 3.25 2.50
48 A2 2m on 5c green 2.25 1.90
49 A3 4m on 10c rose 2.75 2.50
50 A3 4m on 10c green ('23) 2.50 2.50
51 A2 5m on 3c red org ('23) 6.75 5.00
52 A3 6m on 15c orange 2.25 1.90
53 A3 8m on 20c brn vio 2.25 1.25
54 A3 10m on 25c blue 1.40 1.25
55 A3 10m on 30c vio 4.25 3.25
56 A3 15m on 50c bl ('23) 3.25 3.00

Nos. 27-30 and Type of 1902 Surcharged

57 A4 15m on 50c 5.00 3.25
58 A4 30m on 1fr 4.25 3.00
59 A4 60m on 2fr 2,250. *2,400.*
60 A4 60m on 2fr org & pale bl ('23) 13.50 13.00
61 A4 150m on 5fr 13.50 8.50
*Nos. 47-58,60-61 (14)* 67.15 52.80

**Stamps and Types of 1902-03 Surcharged with New Values and Bars in Black**

**1925**

62 A2 1m on 1c slate 1.25 1.25
63 A2 2m on 5c orange 1.25 1.25
64 A2 2m on 5c green 1.75 1.75
65 A3 4m on 10c green 1.10 .85
66 A2 5m on 3c red org 1.50 1.25
67 A3 6m on 15c orange 1.40 1.25
68 A3 8m on 20c brn vio 1.75 1.40
69 A3 10m on 25c blue 1.10 1.00
70 A3 15m on 50c blue 2.40 1.40
71 A4 30m on 1fr cl & ol grn 3.50 2.90
72 A4 60m on 2fr org & pale bl 4.25 3.50
73 A4 150m on 5fr dk bl & buff 6.00 5.00
*Nos. 62-73 (12)* 27.25 22.80

**Types of 1902-03 Issue**

**1927-28**

77 A2 3m orange ('28) 2.50 2.10
81 A3 15m slate blue 2.50 2.10
82 A3 20m rose lil ('28) 6.75 5.00
84 A4 50m org & blue 11.00 9.35
85 A4 100m sl bl & buff 15.00 12.00
86 A4 250m gray grn & red 25.00 16.00
*Nos. 77-86 (6)* 62.75 46.55

### SEMI-POSTAL STAMPS

Regular Issue of 1902-03 Surcharged in Carmine

**1915 Unwmk. *Perf. 14x13½***

B1 A3 10c + 5c rose 1.25 1.25

**Sinking Fund Issue**

Type of 1902-03 Issue Surcharged in Blue or Black

**1927-30**

B2 A3 15m + 5m deep org 6.00 6.00
B3 A3 15m + 5m red vio ('28) 9.25 9.25
a. 15m + 5m violet ('30) 15.00 15.00

**Type of 1902-03 Issue Surcharged as in 1927-28**

**1929**

B4 A3 15m + 5m fawn 12.00 12.00

### POSTAGE DUE STAMPS

Postage Due Stamps of France, 1893-1920, Surcharged in Paris in Black

**1922 Unwmk. *Perf. 14x13½***

J1 D2 2m on 5c blue 2.50 2.50
J2 D2 4m on 10c brown 2.50 2.50
J3 D2 10m on 30c rose red 3.00 3.00
J4 D2 15m on 50c brn vio 3.25 3.25
J5 D2 30m on 1fr red brn, *straw* 4.50 4.50
*Nos. J1-J5 (5)* 15.75 15.75

D3

**1928 Typo.**

J6 D3 1m slate 1.60 1.60
J7 D3 2m light blue 1.25 1.25
J8 D3 4m lilac rose 1.75 1.75
J9 D3 5m gray green 2.00 2.00
J10 D3 10m light red 2.50 2.50
J11 D3 20m violet brn 2.25 2.25
J12 D3 30m green 5.00 5.00
J13 D3 40m lt violet 6.25 6.25
*Nos. J6-J13 (8)* 22.60 22.60

Nos. J6-J13 were also available for use in Port Said.

### PORT SAID

Stamps of France Overprinted in Red, Blue or Black

**1899-1900 Unwmk. *Perf. 14x13½***

1 A15 1c blk, *lil bl* (R) 2.10 1.70
2 A15 2c brn, *buff* (bl) 2.10 1.70
3 A15 3c gray, *grysh* (Bl) 2.10 2.10
4 A15 4c claret, *lav* (Bl) 1.75 *2.10*
5 A15 5c yel grn (I) (R) 11.00 5.00
a. Type II (R) 55.00 25.00
6 A15 10c blk, *lav* (I) (R) 14.00 12.50
a. Type II (R) 72.50 55.00
7 A15 15c blue (R) 14.00 8.50
8 A15 20c red, *grn* 17.00 11.00
9 A15 25c blk, *rose* (R) 14.00 5.00
a. Double overprint 300.00
b. Inverted overprint 300.00
10 A15 30c brn, *bister* 17.00 14.00
a. Inverted overprint 325.00
11 A15 40c red, *straw* 14.00 14.00
12 A15 50c car, *rose* (II) 20.00 14.00
a. Type I 300.00 100.00
b. Double overprint (II) 425.00
13 A15 1fr brnz grn, *straw* 30.00 17.50
14 A15 2fr brn, *az* ('00) 75.00 65.00
15 A15 5fr red lil, *lav* 120.00 92.50
*Nos. 1-15 (15)* 354.05 266.60

Regular Issue Surcharged in Red

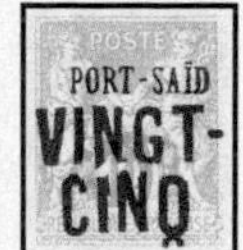

**1899**

16 A15 25c on 10c blk, *lav* 130.00 32.50
a. Inverted surcharge 250.00

**With Additional Surcharge "25" in Red**

17 A15 25c on 10c blk, *lav* 475.00 160.00
a. "25" inverted 1,500. 1,400.
b. "25" in black 2,600.
c. As "b," "VINGT CINQ" inverted 3,400.
d. As "b," "25" vertical 3,400.
e. As "c" and "d" 3,400.

A2

A3

A4

**1902-03 Typo.**

18 A2 1c pale gray ('16) .65 .65
19 A2 2c violet brn .75 .75
20 A2 3c red orange .85 .75
21 A2 4c yellow brown 1.10 .90
22 A2 5c blue green ('04) 1.20 .85
a. 5c yellow green 5.00 3.00
23 A3 10c rose red 1.60 1.10
24 A3 15c pale red ('03) 3.25 2.25
a. 15c orange 5.00 3.00
25 A3 20c brn vio ('03) 3.25 2.25
26 A3 25c blue ('03) 2.50 1.60
27 A3 30c gray violet ('03) 6.75 5.00
28 A4 40c red & pale bl 6.00 4.25
29 A4 50c bis brn & lav 9.25 6.75
30 A4 1fr claret & ol grn 12.00 9.25
31 A4 2fr gray vio & yel 15.00 15.00
32 A4 5fr dk bl & buff 35.00 32.50
*Nos. 18-32 (15)* 99.15 83.85

See Nos. 83-92. For surcharges see Nos. 33-80, B1-B4.

Stamps of 1902-03 Surcharged Locally

**1921**

33 A2 2m on 5c green 10.00 10.00
a. Inverted surcharge 50.00 50.00
34 A3 4m on 10c rose 9.25 9.25
a. Inverted surcharge 50.00 50.00
35 A2 5m on 1c slate 14.00 14.00
b. 5m on 1c light gray 26.00 26.00
c. Surcharged "2 Milliemes" on #35 67.50 67.50
36 A2 5m on 2c 24.00 24.00
a. Surcharged "2 Milliemes" 75.00 75.00
b. As "a," inverted 160.00 160.00
37 A2 5m on 3c 15.00 15.00
a. Inverted surcharge 62.50 62.50
b. On Alexandria #18 400.00 400.00
38 A2 5m on 4c 11.00 11.00
a. Inverted surcharge 80.00 80.00
39 A2 10m on 2c 25.00 25.00
40 A2 10m on 4c 35.00 35.00
a. Inverted surcharge 85.00 85.00
b. Double surcharge 100.00 105.00
41 A3 10m on 25c 9.25 9.25
a. Inverted surcharge 85.00 85.00
42 A3 12m on 30c 42.50 42.50
43 A2 15m on 4c 10.00 10.00
a. Inverted surcharge 85.00 85.00
b. Double surcharge 92.50 97.50
44 A3 15m on 15c pale red 67.50 67.50
a. Inverted surcharge 160.00 160.00
45 A3 15m on 20c 67.50 67.50
a. Inverted surcharge 160.00 160.00
46 A4 30m on 50c 300.00 300.00
47 A4 60m on 50c 350.00 350.00
48 A4 150m on 50c 400.00 400.00

Nos. 46, 47 and 48 have a bar between the numerals and "Millièmes," which is in capital letters.

**Same Surcharge on Stamps of French Offices in Turkey, 1902-03**

49 A2 2m on 2c vio brn 160.00 160.00
50 A2 5m on 1c gray 150.00 150.00
a. "5" inverted 7,250.
*Nos. 33-50 (18)* 1,700. 1,700.

Nos. 28-32 Surcharged

51 A4 15m on 40c 60.00 60.00
52 A4 15m on 50c 85.00 85.00
b. Bar below 15 50.00 50.00
53 A4 30m on 1fr 300.00 300.00
54 A4 60m on 2fr 85.00 *92.50*
55 A4 150m on 5fr 250.00 *275.00*
*Nos. 51-55 (5)* 780.00 812.50

**Overprinted "MILLtEMES"**

51a A4 15m on 40c 425.00 425.00
52a A4 15m on 50c 500.00 500.00
53a A4 30m on 1fr 1,400. 1,400.
54a A4 60m on 2fr 400.00 400.00
55a A4 150m on 5fr 1,050. 1,050.
*Nos. 51a-55a (5)* 3,775. 3,775.

Stamps of 1902-03 Surcharged in Paris

**1921-23**

56 A2 1m on 1c slate 1.60 1.60
57 A2 2m on 5c green 1.60 1.60
58 A3 4m on 10c rose 2.50 2.50
59 A2 5m on 3c red org 9.25 9.25
60 A3 6m on 15c orange 3.25 3.25
a. 6m on 15c pale red 14.00 14.00
61 A3 8m on 20c brn vio 5.00 5.00
62 A3 10m on 25c blue 2.50 2.50
63 A3 10m on 30c violet 7.50 7.50
64 A3 15m on 50c blue 6.75 6.75

Nos. 29-32 and Type of 1902 Surcharged

65 A4 15m on 50c 6.00 6.00
66 A4 30m on 1fr 9.25 9.25
67 A4 60m on 2fr 130.00 130.00
68 A4 60m on 2fr org & pale blue 12.50 12.50
69 A4 150m on 5fr 20.00 20.00
*Nos. 56-69 (14)* 217.70 217.70

Stamps and Types of 1902-03 Surcharged

**1925**

70 A2 1m on 1c light gray .75 .75
71 A2 2m on 5c green 1.10 1.10
72 A3 4m on 10c rose red .90 .90
73 A2 5m on 3c red org 1.10 1.10
74 A3 6m on 15c orange 1.10 1.10
75 A3 8m on 20c brn vio 1.00 1.00
76 A3 10m on 25c blue 1.40 1.40
77 A3 15m on 50c blue 1.60 1.60
78 A4 30m on 1fr cl & ol grn 2.75 2.75
79 A4 60m on 2fr org & pale blue 2.50 2.50
80 A4 150m on 5fr dk bl & buff 4.25 4.25
*Nos. 70-80 (11)* 18.45 18.45

**Type of 1902-03 Issue and**

A5

**1927-28**

83 A5 3m orange ('28) 2.10 2.10
87 A3 15m slate bl 2.50 2.50
88 A3 20m rose lil ('28) 2.50 2.50
90 A4 50m org & blue 4.50 4.50
91 A4 100m slate bl & buff 6.00 6.00
92 A4 250m gray grn & red 9.25 9.25
*Nos. 83-92 (6)* 26.85 26.85

## SEMI-POSTAL STAMPS

Regular Issue of 1902-03 Surcharged in Carmine

**1915 Unwmk. *Perf. 14x13½***

B1 A3 10c + 5c rose 1.60 1.60

**Sinking Fund Issue**

Type of 1902-03 Issue Surcharged like Alexandria Nos. B2-B3 in Blue or Black

**1927-30**

B2 A3 15m + 5m dp org (Bl) 5.00 5.00
B3 A3 15m + 5m red vio ('28) 8.50 8.50
b. 15m + 5m violet ('30) 14.00 14.00
B4 A3 15m + 5m fawn ('29) 10.00 10.00
*Nos. B2-B4 (3)* 23.50 23.50

## POSTAGE DUE STAMPS

Postage Due Stamps of France, 1893-1906, Srchd. Locally in Black

**1921 Unwmk. *Perf. 14x13½***

J1 D2 12m on 10c brown 62.50 *67.50*
J2 D2 15m on 5c blue 92.50 *105.00*
J3 D2 30m on 20c ol grn 92.50 *105.00*
a. Inverted surcharge 1,100. 1,100.
J4 D2 30m on 50c red vio 3,000. 3,400.

Same Surcharged in Red or Blue

**1921**

J5 D2 2m on 5c bl (R) 55.00 *60.00*
a. Blue surcharge 300.00 300.00
b. Accent omitted from "è" of "Millièmes" 190.00 200.00
c. Second "m" of "Millièmes" inverted 190.00 200.00
d. "S" of "Millièmes" omitted 190.00 225.00
J6 D2 4m on 10c brn (Bl) 55.00 *62.50*
a. Surcharged "15 Millièmes" 725.00 725.00
b. Accent omitted from "è" of "MILLIèMES" 190.00 200.00
c. Second "m" of "Millièmes" inverted 190.00 200.00
d. "S" of "Millièmes" omitted 190.00 225.00
J7 D2 10m on 30c red (Bl) 55.00 *60.00*
a. Inverted surcharge 160.00 160.00
b. Accent omitted from "è" of "Millièmes" 190.00 190.00
c. Second "M" of "Millièmes" inverted 190.00 190.00
d. "S" of "Millièmes" omitted 190.00 225.00
e. "Q" for "0" in surcharge (1Qm) 1,450. 1,500.
J8 D2 15m on 50c brn vio (Bl) 67.50 *72.50*
a. Inverted surcharge 160.00 160.00
b. Accent omitted from "è" of "Millièmes" 190.00 190.00
c. Second "m" of "Millièmes" inverted 190.00 190.00
d. "S" of "Millièmes" omitted 210.00 240.00
e. As "a," accent omitted from è of "Millièmes" 425.00
*Nos. J5-J8 (4)* 232.50 255.00

Alexandria Nos. J6-J13 were also available for use in Port Said.

# OFFICES IN TURKEY (LEVANT)

Various powers maintained post offices in the Turkish Empire before World War I by authority of treaties which ended with the signing of the Treaty of Lausanne in 1923. The foreign post offices were closed Oct. 27, 1923.

100 Centimes = 1 Franc
25 Centimes = 40 Paras = 1 Piaster

Stamps of France Surcharged in Black or Red

**1885-1901 Unwmk. *Perf. 14x13½***

1 A15 1pi on 25c yel, *straw* 550.00 16.00
a. Inverted surcharge 2,600. 2,400.
2 A15 1pi on 25c blk, *rose* (R) ('86) 4.25 1.25
Never hinged 8.00
a. Inverted surcharge 400.00 325.00
3 A15 2pi on 50c car, *rose* (II) ('90) 18.00 3.00
Never hinged 35.00
a. Type I ('01) 375.00 50.00
Never hinged 725.00
4 A15 3pi on 75c car, *rose* 30.00 15.00
Never hinged 60.00
5 A15 4pi on 1fr brnz grn, *straw* 30.00 15.00
Never hinged 60.00
6 A15 8pi on 2fr brn, *az* ('00) 37.50 25.00
Never hinged 67.50
7 A15 20pi on 5fr red lil, *lav* ('90) 110.00 60.00
Never hinged 225.00
*Nos. 1-7 (7)* 779.75 135.25

A2

A3

A4

**Nos. 29, 32, 36 and Types of A4 Surcharged**

No. 34

No. 35

**1902-07 Typo. *Perf. 14x13½***

21 A2 1c gray .65 .65
Never hinged 1.25
22 A2 2c vio brn .65 .65
23 A2 3c red org .65 .65
24 A2 4c yel brn 3.00 1.10
a. Imperf., pair 90.00
25 A2 5c grn ('06) 1.00 .65
26 A3 10c rose red 1.00 .65
27 A3 15c pale red ('03) 3.00 1.25
28 A3 20c brn vio ('03) 3.25 2.00
29 A3 25c blue ('07) 45.00 *60.00*
a. Imperf., pair 425.00

30 A3 30c lilac ('03) 6.00 3.00
31 A4 40c red & pale bl 6.00 3.25
32 A4 50c bis brn & lav ('07) 190.00 *225.00*
*a.* Imperf., pair 925.00
33 A4 1fr claret & ol grn ('07) 425.00 450.00
*a.* Imperf., pair 1,100.

**Black Surcharge**

34 A3 1pi on 25c bl ('03) 1.20 .65
*a.* Second "I" omitted 32.50 25.00
*b.* Double surcharge 72.50 60.00
35 A4 2pi on 50c bis brn & lavender 4.25 1.60
36 A4 4pi on 1fr cl & ol grn 5.00 2.10
*a.* Imperf., pair 750.00
37 A4 8pi on 2fr gray vio & yel 20.00 15.00
38 A4 20pi on 5fr dk bl & buff 10.00 6.00
*Nos. 21-38 (18)* 725.65 774.20

Nos. 29, 32-33 were used during the early part of 1907 in the French Offices at Harar and Diredawa, Ethiopia. Djibouti and Port Said stamps were also used.

No. 27 Surcharged in Green

**1905**

39 A3 1pi on 15c pale red 2,100. 325.
*a.* "Piastte" 6,500. 1,450.

**Stamps of France 1900-21 Surcharged**

On A22

On A20

On A18

**1921-22**

40 A22 30pa on 5c grn 1.00 1.00
41 A22 30pa on 5c org 1.00 .85
42 A22 1pi20pa on 10c red 1.10 1.10
43 A22 1pi20pa on 10c grn 1.10 .85
44 A22 3pi30pa on 25c bl 1.60 1.00
45 A22 4pi20pa on 30c org 1.60 1.10
*a.* "4" omitted 1,050.
46 A20 7pi20pa on 50c bl 1.60 1.25
47 A18 15pi on 1fr car & ol grn 3.00 2.10
48 A18 30pi on 2fr org & pale bl 12.50 10.00
49 A18 75pi on 5fr dk bl & buff 11.00 7.50
*Nos. 40-49 (10)* 35.50 26.75

Stamps of France, 1903-07, Handstamped

**1923**

52 A22 1pi20pa on 10c red 62.50 60.00
54 A20 3pi30pa on 15c gray grn (GC) 25.00 25.00
55 A22 7pi20pa on 35c vio 30.00 30.00
*b.* 1pi20pa on 35c violet 1,400. 1,400.
*Nos. 52-55 (3)* 117.50 115.00

## CAVALLE (CAVALLA)

Stamps of France Ovptd. or Srchd. in Carmine, Red, Blue or Black

**1893-1900 Unwmk. *Perf. 14x13½***

1 A15 5c grn, *grnsh* (R) 25.00 21.00
*a.* Type II (C) 25.00 21.00
2 A15 5c yel grn (I) ('00) (R) 21.00 21.00
3 A15 10c blk, *lav* (II) 26.00 26.00
*a.* 10c black, *lavender* (I) 180.00 150.00
4 A15 15c blue (R) 47.50 30.00
*a.* 15c blue (C) 47.50 30.00
5 A15 1pi on 25c blk, *rose* 28.00 20.00
6 A15 2pi on 50c car, *rose* 92.50 65.00
7 A15 4pi on 1fr brnz grn, *straw* (R) 97.50 87.50
*b.* 4pi on 1fr brnz grn, *straw* (C) 95.00 87.50
8 A15 8pi on 2fr brn, *az* ('00) (Bk) 120.00 120.00
*Nos. 1-8 (8)* 457.50 390.50
Set, never hinged 1,000.

A3

A4

A5

A6

**1902-03**

9 A3 5c green 2.25 1.75
*a.* 5c yel grn 2.50 2.00
10 A4 10c rose red ('03) 2.25 1.75
11 A4 15c orange 2.25 1.75
*a.* 15c pale red ('03) 12.50 12.50

**Surcharged in Black**

12 A5 1pi on 25c bl 4.75 3.00
13 A6 2pi on 50c bis brn & lav 13.00 7.00
14 A6 4pi on 1fr cl & ol grn 16.00 13.00
15 A6 8pi on 2fr gray vio & yel 21.00 19.00
*Nos. 9-15 (7)* 61.50 47.25

## DEDEAGH (DEDEAGATCH)

Stamps of France Ovptd. or Srchd. in Carmine, Red, Blue or Black

**1893-1900 Unwmk. *Perf. 14x13½***

1 A15 5c grn, *grnsh* (II) (R) 18.00 15.00
*a.* Type II (C) 18.00 15.00
2 A15 5c yel grn (I) ('00) (R) 14.50 14.00
3 A15 10c blk, *lav* (II) 27.50 20.00
*a.* Type I 47.50 32.50
*b.* As "a," double overprint 300.00
4 A15 15c blue (II) (R) 37.50 30.00
*a.* Type II (C) 37.50 30.00
5 A15 1pi on 25c blk, *rose* 42.50 37.50
6 A15 2pi on 50c car, *rose* 70.00 50.00
7 A15 4pi on 1fr brnz grn, *straw* (R) 82.50 70.00
8 A15 8pi on 2fr brn, *az* ('00) (Bk) 120.00 95.00
*Nos. 1-8 (8)* 412.50 331.50
Set, never hinged 1,000.

A3

A4

A5

A6

**1902-03**

9 A3 5c green ('03) 3.00 2.50
*a.* 5c yellow green 3.50 3.00
10 A4 10c rose red ('03) 3.50 2.75
11 A4 15c orange 5.00 3.75
*a.* 15c rose red ('03) 7.00 6.00
15 A5 1pi on 25c bl ('03) 3.50 2.75
16 A6 2pi on 50c bis brn & lav 11.50 10.00
*a.* Double surcharge 300.00
17 A6 4pi on 1fr cl & ol grn 22.50 18.50
18 A6 8pi on 2fr gray vio & yel 32.50 27.50
*Nos. 9-18 (7)* 81.50 67.75
Set, never hinged 175.00

## PORT LAGOS

Stamps of France Ovptd. or Srchd. in Carmine, Red or Blue

**1893 Unwmk. *Perf. 14x13½***

1 A15 5c grn, *grnsh* (R) 30.00 *32.50*
*a.* 5c grn, *grnsh* (C) 30.00 32.50
2 A15 10c blk, *lav* 62.50 47.50
3 A15 15c blue (R) 92.50 72.50
*a.* 15c blue (C) 97.50 77.50
4 A15 1pi on 25c blk, *rose* 77.50 62.50
5 A15 2pi on 50c car, *rose* 185.00 97.50
6 A15 4pi on 1fr brnz grn, *straw* (R) 112.50 97.50
*Nos. 1-6 (6)* 560.00 410.00
Set, never hinged 1,300.

## VATHY (SAMOS)

Stamps of France Ovptd. or Srchd. in Carmine, Red, Blue or Black

**1894-1900 Unwmk. *Perf. 14x13½***

1 A15 5c grn, *grnsh* (R) 8.75 8.00
*a.* 5c grn, *grnsh* (II) (C) 10.00 8.75
2 A15 5c yel grn (I) ('00) (R) 8.75 7.50
*a.* Type II 87.50 87.50
3 A15 10c blk, *lav* (I) 17.50 15.00
*a.* Type II 50.00 47.50
4 A15 15c blue (R) 17.50 15.00
5 A15 1pi on 25c blk, *rose* 17.50 11.50
6 A15 2pi on 50c car, *rose* 30.00 27.50
7 A15 4pi on 1fr brnz grn, *straw* (R) 42.50 35.00
8 A15 8pi on 2fr brn, *az* ('00) (Bk) 75.00 75.00
9 A15 20pi on 5fr lil, *lav* ('00) (Bk) 110.00 110.00
*Nos. 1-9 (9)* 327.50 304.50
Set, never hinged 600.00

# OFFICES IN ZANZIBAR

Until 1906 France maintained post offices in the Sultanate of Zanzibar, but in that year Great Britain assumed direct control over this protectorate and the French withdrew their postal system.

16 Annas = 1 Rupee

**Stamps of France Surcharged in Red, Carmine, Blue or Black**

**1894-96 Unwmk. *Perf. 14x13½***

1 A15 ½a on 5c grn, *grnsh* 10.00 7.50
2 A15 1a on 10c blk, *lav* (Bl) 15.00 12.50
3 A15 1½a on 15c bl ('96) 22.50 21.00
*a.* "ANNAS" 100.00 92.50
4 A15 2a on 20c red, *grn* ('96) (Bk) 19.00 15.00
*a.* "ANNA" 2,300. 2,300.
5 A15 2½a on 25c blk, *rose* (Bl) 12.50 9.25
*a.* Double surcharge 250.00 250.00
6 A15 3a on 30c brn, *bis* ('96) (Bk) 21.00 18.00
7 A15 4a on 40c red, *straw* ('96) (Bk) 29.00 25.00
8 A15 5a on 50c car, *rose* (Bl) 37.50 32.50
9 A15 7½a on 75c vio, *org* ('96) 500.00 400.00
10 A15 10a on 1fr brnz grn, *straw* 67.50 55.00
11 A15 50a on 5fr red lil, *lav* ('96) (Bk) 325.00 260.00
*Nos. 1-11 (11)* 1,059. 855.75

**1894**

12 A15 ½a & 5c on 1c blk, *lil bl* (R) 200.00 *220.00*
13 A15 1a & 10c on 3c gray, *grysh* (R) 180.00 *200.00*
14 A15 2½a & 25c on 4c cl, *lav* (Bk) 230.00 *275.00*
15 A15 5a & 50c on 20c red, *grn* (Bk) 250.00 *275.00*
16 A15 10a & 1fr on 40c red, *straw* (Bk) 475.00 *525.00*
*Nos. 12-16 (5)* 1,335. 1,495.

There are two distinct types of the figures 5c, four of the 25c and three of each of the others of this series.

Stamps of France Srchd. in Red, Carmine, Blue or Black

**1896-1900**

17 A15 ½a on 5c grn, *grnsh* (R) 11.00 8.50
18 A15 ½a on 5c yel grn (I) (R) 7.50 6.75
*a.* Type II 9.25 7.50
19 A15 1a on 10c blk, *lav* (II) (Bl) 9.25 7.50
*a.* Type I 22.50 19.00
20 A15 1½a on 15c bl (R) 11.00 9.25
21 A15 2a on 20c red, *grn* 9.25 9.25
*a.* "ZANZIBAR" double 210.00 210.00
*b.* "ZANZIBAR" triple 210.00 210.00
22 A15 2½a on 25c blk, *rose* (Bl) 11.00 9.25
*a.* Inverted surcharge 275.00 210.00
23 A15 3a on 30c brn, *bis* 11.00 9.25
24 A15 4a on 40c red, *straw* 13.50 10.00
25 A15 5a on 50c rose, *rose* (II) (Bl) 45.00 32.50
*a.* Type I 125.00 100.00
26 A15 10a on 1fr brnz grn, *straw* (R) 29.00 25.00
27 A15 20a on 2fr brn, *az* 35.00 29.00
*a.* "ZANZIBAS" 675.00 *750.00*
*b.* "ZANZIBAR" triple 1,600.
28 A15 50a on 5fr lil, *lav* 67.50 62.50
*a.* "ZANZIBAS" *9,250.*
*Nos. 17-28 (12)* 260.00 218.75

For surcharges see Nos. 50-54.

A4

A5

**1897**

29 A4 2½a & 25c on ½a on 5c grn, *grnsh* 1,300. 240.
30 A4 2½a & 25c on 1a on 10c *lav* *4,500.* 1,100.
31 A4 2½a & 25c on 1½a on 15c blue *4,400.* 950.
32 A5 5a & 50c on 3a on 30c brn, *bis* *4,400.* 950.
33 A5 5a & 50c on 4a on 40c red, *straw* *4,500.* 1,300.

**Printed on the Margins of Sheets of French Stamps**

A6

A7

***Perf. 14x13½ on one or more sides***

**1897**

34 A6 2½a & 25c grn, *grnsh* 1,300.
35 A6 2½a & 25c blk, *lav* *4,000.*
36 A6 2½a & 25c blue *3,000.*
37 A7 5a & 50c brn, *bis* *2,900.*
38 A7 5a & 50c red, *straw* *4,000.*

There are 5 varieties of figures in the above surcharges.

**Surcharged in Red or Black**

A8

A9

A10

**1902-03** ***Perf. 14x13½***

39 A8 ½a on 5c grn (R) 6.75 6.00
40 A9 1a on 10c rose red ('03) 7.50 7.50
41 A9 1½a on 15c pale red ('03) 15.00 14.00
42 A9 2a on 20c brn vio ('03) 18.00 15.00
43 A9 2½a on 25c bl ('03) 18.00 15.00
44 A9 3a on 30c lil ('03) 13.00 13.00
*a.* 5a on 30c (error) 325.00 *375.00*
45 A10 4a on 40c red & pale bl 30.00 25.00
46 A10 5a on 50c bis brn & lav 25.00 21.00
47 A10 10a on 1fr cl & ol grn 32.50 29.00
48 A10 20a on 2fr gray vio & yel 85.00 75.00
49 A10 50a on 5fr dk bl & buff 100.00 92.50
*Nos. 39-49 (11)* 350.75 313.00

For see Reunion Nos. 55-59.

**Nos. 23-24 Surcharged in Black**

a

b

c

**1904**

50 A15 (a) 25c & 2½a on 4a on 40c 1,000.
51 A15 (b) 50c & 5a on 3a on 30c 1,200.
52 A15 (b) 50c & 5a on 4a on 40c 6,500. 1,200.
53 A15 (c) 1fr & 10a on 3a on 30c 2,000.
54 A15 (c) 1fr & 10a on 4a on 40c 2,000.

**Nos. 39-40, 44 Surcharged in Red or Black**

d

e

f

g

55 A8 (d) 25c & 2a on ½a on 5c (R) 3,100. 140.00
56 A9 (e) 25c & 2½a on 1a on 10c 6,500. 150.00
*a.* Inverted surcharge 1,500.
57 A9 (e) 25c & 2½a on 3a on 30c 2,400.
*a.* Inverted surcharge 4,100.
*b.* Double surch., both invtd. 2,600.
58 A9 (f) 50c & 5a on 3a on 30c 1,250.
59 A9 (g) 1fr & 10a on 3a on 30c 2,000.

**No. J1-J3 With Various Surcharges Overprinted:**

**"Timbre" in Red**

60 D1 ½a on 5c blue 450.00

**Overprinted "Affrancht" in Black**

61 D1 1a on 10c brown 450.00

**With Red Bars Across "CHIFFRE" and "TAXE"**

62 D1 1½a on 15c green 1,000.

The illustrations are not exact reproductions of the new surcharges but are merely intended to show their relative positions and general styles.

**POSTAGE DUE STAMPS**

Postage Due Stamps of France Srchd. in Red, Blue or Black Like Nos. 17-28

**1897** **Unwmk.** ***Perf. 14x13½***

J1 D2 ½a on 5c blue (R) 21.00 12.50
J2 D2 1a on 10c brn (Bl) 21.00 12.50
*a.* Inverted surcharge 160.00 *190.00*
J3 D2 1½aon 15c grn (R) 32.50 12.50
J4 D2 3a on 30c car (Bk) 29.00 21.00
J5 D2 5a on 50c lil (Bl) 32.50 25.00
*a.* 2½a on 50c lilac (Bl) 1,400. 1,300.
*Nos. J1-J5 (5)* 136.00 83.50

For overprints see Nos. 60-62.

## REUNION

LOCATION — An island in the Indian Ocean about 400 miles east of Madagascar
GOVT. — Department of France
AREA — 970 sq. mi.
POP. — 490,000 (est. 1974)
CAPITAL — St. Denis

The colony of Réunion became an integral part of the Republic, acquiring the same status as the departments in metropolitan France, under a law effective Jan. 1, 1947.

On Jan. 1, 1975, stamps of France replaced those inscribed or overprinted "CFA."

100 Centimes = 1 Franc

**Catalogue values for unused stamps in this country are for Never Hinged items, beginning with Scott 224 in the regular postage section, Scott B15 in the semi-postal section, Scott C18 in the airpost section, and Scott J26 in the postage due section.**

**For French stamps inscribed "Reunion" see Nos. 949, 1507.**

A1

A2

**1852** **Unwmk.** **Typo.** ***Imperf.***

1 A1 15c black, *blue* *39,000.* *25,000.*
2 A2 30c black, *blue* *39,000.* *25,000.*

Four varieties of each value.

*The reprints are printed on a more bluish paper than the originals. They have a frame of a thick and a thin line, instead of one thick and two thin lines. Value, $62.50 each.*

**Stamps of French Colonies Surcharged or Overprinted in Black**

a

**Overprint Type "a"**

**1885**

3 A1(a) 5c on 40c org, *yelsh* 450.00 375.00
*a.* Inverted surcharge 2,250. 2,100.
*b.* Double surcharge 2,250. 2,100.
4 A1(a) 25c on 40c org, *yelsh* 70.00 55.00
*a.* Inverted surcharge 1,000. 900.00
*b.* Double surcharge 1,000. 900.00
5 A5(a) 5c on 30c brn, *yelsh* 70.00 57.50
*a.* "5" inverted 3,500. 3,000.
*b.* Double surcharge 1,100. 900.00
*c.* Inverted surcharge 1,000. 900.00
6 A4(a) 5c on 40c org, *yelsh* (I) 62.50 45.00
*a.* 5c on 40c org, *yelsh* (II) 2,500. 2,500.
*b.* Inverted surcharge (I) 1,100. 900.00
*c.* Double surcharge (I) 1,100. 900.00
7 A8(a) 5c on 30c brn, *yelsh* 22.50 10.00
8 A8(a) 5c on 40c ver, *straw* 135.00 115.00
*a.* Inverted surcharge 950.00 850.00
*b.* Double surcharge 925.00 850.00
9 A8(a) 10c on 40c ver, *straw* 27.50 22.50
*a.* Inverted surcharge 950.00 850.00
*b.* Double surcharge 950.00 850.00
10 A8(a) 20c on 30c brn, *yelsh* 90.00 75.00

b

**Overprint Type "b"**
**With or Without Accent on "E"**

**1891**

11 A4 40c org, *yelsh* (I) 575.00 550.00
*a.* 40c orange, *yelsh* (II) *6,750.* *6,750.*
*b.* Double overprint 750.00 750.00
12 A7 80c car, *pnksh* 80.00 62.50
13 A8 30c brn, *yelsh* 52.50 52.50
14 A8 40c ver, *straw* 42.50 42.50
15 A8 75c car, *rose* 475.00 475.00
16 A8 1fr brnz grn, *straw* 62.50 52.50

***Perf. 14x13½***

17 A9 1c blk, *lil bl* 4.75 4.00
*a.* Inverted overprint 60.00 60.00
*b.* Double overprint 52.50 52.50
18 A9 2c brn, *buff* 6.50 5.00
*a.* Inverted overprint 40.00 40.00
19 A9 4c claret, *lav* 10.00 8.00
*a.* Inverted overprint 72.50 72.50
20 A9 5c grn, *grnsh* 11.50 9.00
*a.* Inverted overprint 60.00 60.00
*b.* Double overprint 60.00 57.50
21 A9 10c blk, *lav* 40.00 8.00
*a.* Inverted overprint 90.00 80.00
*b.* Double overprint 100.00 80.00
22 A9 15c blue 57.50 9.00
*a.* Inverted overprint 120.00 110.00
23 A9 20c red, *grn* 45.00 30.00
*a.* Inverted overprint 175.00 150.00
*b.* Double overprint 175.00 150.00
24 A9 25c blk, *rose* 50.00 7.25
*a.* Inverted overprint 125.00 120.00
25 A9 35c dp vio, *yel* 45.00 35.00
*b.* Inverted overprint 180.00 175.00
26 A9 40c red, *straw* 72.50 62.50
*a.* Inverted overprint 240.00 225.00
27 A9 75c car, *rose* 675.00 575.00
*a.* Inverted overprint 1,600. 1,400.
28 A9 1fr brnz grn, *straw* 575.00 500.00
*a.* Inverted overprint 1,600. 1,500.
*b.* Double overprint 1,500. 1,400.

The varieties "RUNION," "RUENION," "REUNIONR," "ERUNION," "EUNION," "REUNIN," "REUNIOU" and "REUNOIN" are found on most stamps of this group. See *Scott Classic Specialized Catalogue of Stamps and Covers* for detailed listings. There are also many broken letters.

For surcharges see Nos. 29-33, 53-55.

**No. 23 with Additional Surcharge in Black**

c

d

e

f

**1891**

29 A9(c) 02c on 20c red, *grn* 14.50 14.50
*a.* Inverted surcharge 90.00 90.00
*b.* No "c" after "02" 57.50 57.50
30 A9(c) 15c on 20c red, *grn* 18.00 18.00
*a.* Inverted surcharge 70.00 70.00
31 A9(d) 2c on 20c red, *grn* 5.00 5.00
32 A9(e) 2c on 20c red, *grn* 6.00 5.75
33 A9(f) 2c on 20c red, *grn* 10.00 10.00
*Nos. 29-33 (5)* 53.50 53.25

The varieties "RUNION" and "RUENION" appear on several stamps from this set. See *Scott Classic Specialized Catalogue of Stamps and Covers* for listings.

Navigation and Commerce — A14

**1892-1905** **Typo.** ***Perf. 14x13½***

**Name of Colony in Blue or Carmine**

34 A14 1c blk, *lil bl* 2.00 1.25
35 A14 2c brn, *buff* 2.00 1.25
36 A14 4c claret, *lav* 3.25 2.25
37 A14 5c grn, *grnsh* 7.25 2.25
38 A14 5c yel grn ('00) 1.75 1.75
39 A14 10c blk, *lav* 9.50 3.50
40 A14 10c red ('00) 4.50 4.50
41 A14 15c bl, quadrille paper 30.00 3.50
42 A14 15c gray ('00) 10.00 3.50
43 A14 20c red, *grn* 20.00 9.00
44 A14 25c blk, *rose* 22.50 3.50
*a.* "Reunion" double 425.00 *450.00*
45 A14 25c blue ('00) 29.00 27.50
46 A14 30c brn, *bis* 23.00 12.00
47 A14 40c red, *straw* 32.50 19.00
48 A14 50c car, *rose* 80.00 42.50
*a.* "Reunion" in red and blue 500.00 500.00

**49** A14 50c brn, *az* ("Reunion" in car) ('00) 57.50 50.00
**50** A14 50c brn, *az* ("Reunion" in bl) ('05) 57.50 50.00
**51** A14 75c dp vio, *org* 62.50 45.00
*a.* "Reunion" double 375.00 375.00
**52** A14 1fr brnz grn, *straw* 50.00 35.00
*a.* "Reunion" double 360.00 *375.00*
*Nos. 34-52 (19)* 504.75 317.25

Perf. 13½x14 stamps are counterfeits.

For surcharges and overprint see Nos. 56-59, 99-106, Q1.

**French Colonies No. 52 Surcharged in Black**

g

h

j

**1893**

**53** A9(g) 2c on 20c red, *grn* 3.25 3.25
**54** A9(h) 2c on 20c red, *grn* 6.00 6.00
**55** A9(j) 2c on 20c red, *grn* 22.50 22.50
*Nos. 53-55 (3)* 31.75 31.75

Reunion Nos. 47-48, 51-52 Surcharged in Black

**1901**

**56** A14 5c on 40c red, *straw* 7.00 7.00
*a.* Inverted surcharge 47.50 47.50
*b.* No bar 240.00 240.00
*c.* Thin "5" — —
*d.* "5" inverted 1,400. 1,200.
**57** A14 5c on 50c car, *rose* 7.75 7.25
*a.* Inverted surcharge 47.50 47.50
*b.* No bar 240.00 240.00
*c.* Thin "5" —
**58** A14 15c on 75c vio, *org* 22.50 22.50
*a.* Inverted surcharge 57.50 57.50
*b.* No bar 240.00 240.00
*c.* Thin "5" and small "1" 47.50 47.50
*d.* As "c," inverted 800.00 800.00
**59** A14 15c on 1fr brnz grn, *straw* 19.00 19.00
*a.* Inverted surcharge 57.50 57.50
*b.* No bar 240.00 240.00
*c.* Thin "5" and small "1" 47.50 47.50
*d.* As "c," inverted —
*Nos. 56-59 (4)* 56.25 55.75

Map of Réunion A19

Coat of Arms and View of St. Denis A20

View of St. Pierre A21

**1907-30** **Typo.**

**60** A19 1c vio & lt rose .30 .30
**61** A19 2c brn & ultra .30 .30
**62** A19 4c ol grn & red .40 .40
*a.* Center double 225.00
**63** A19 5c grn & red 1.35 .40
**64** A19 5c org & vio ('22) .30 .30
**65** A19 10c car & grn 2.75 .40
**66** A19 10c grn ('22) .30 .30
**67** A19 10c brn red & org red, *bluish* ('26) .70 .70
**68** A19 15c blk & ultra ('17) .55 .40
*a.* Center double 250.00 250.00
**69** A19 15c gray grn & bl grn ('26) .40 .40
**70** A19 15c bl & lt red ('28) .55 .45
**71** A20 20c gray grn & bl grn .45 .45
*a.* Center omitted 1,100. 1,100.
**72** A20 25c dp bl & vio brn 7.00 4.00
**73** A20 25c lt brn & bl ('22) .55 .55
**74** A20 30c yel brn & grn 1.50 1.00
**75** A20 30c rose & pale rose ('22) 1.50 1.50
**76** A20 30c gray & car rose ('26) .55 .55
**77** A20 30c dp grn & yel grn ('28) 1.20 1.20
**78** A20 35c ol grn & bl 1.75 1.10
**79** A20 40c gray grn & brn ('25) .70 .70
**80** A20 45c vio & car rose 1.90 1.10
**81** A20 45c red brn & ver ('25) .90 .90
**82** A20 45c vio & red org ('28) 3.00 2.75
**83** A20 50c red brn & ultra 5.00 1.75
**84** A20 50c bl & ultra ('22) 1.40 1.40
**85** A20 50c yel & vio ('26) 1.10 1.10
**86** A20 60c dk bl & yel brn ('25) 1.10 1.10
**87** A20 65c vio & lt bl ('28) 1.60 1.40
**88** A20 75c red & car rose .80 .70
**89** A20 75c ol brn & red vio ('28) 2.50 2.25
**90** A20 90c brn red & brt red ('30) 9.00 8.25
**91** A21 1fr ol grn & bl 1.50 1.40
**92** A21 1fr blue ('25) .95 .95
**93** A21 1fr yel brn & lav ('28) 1.50 .70
**94** A21 1.10fr org brn & rose lil ('28) 1.50 1.40
**95** A21 1.50fr dk bl & ultra ('30) 16.00 16.00
**96** A21 2fr red & grn 6.75 4.25
**97** A21 3fr red vio ('30) 14.50 9.50
**98** A21 5fr car & vio brn 11.50 6.75
*Nos. 60-98 (39)* 105.60 79.05

For surcharges see Nos. 107-121, 178-180, B1-B3.

**Stamps of 1892-1900 Surcharged in Black or Carmine**

**1912**

**Spacing between figures of surcharge 1.5mm (5c), 2mm (10c)**

**99** A14 5c on 2c brn, *buff* 1.60 1.60
**100** A14 5c on 15c gray (C) 1.40 1.40
*a.* Inverted surcharge 210.00 210.00
**101** A14 5c on 20c red, *grn* 2.40 2.40
**102** A14 5c on 25c blk, *rose* (C) 1.60 1.60
**103** A14 5c on 30c brn, *bis* (C) 1.40 1.40
**104** A14 10c on 40c red, *straw* 1.40 1.40
**105** A14 10c on 50c brn, *az* (C) 5.75 5.75
**106** A14 10c on 75c dp vio, *org* 9.50 9.50
*Nos. 99-106 (8)* 25.05 25.05

Two spacings between the surcharged numerals are found on Nos. 99 to 106. For detailed listings, see the *Scott Classic Specialized Catalogue of Stamps and Covers.*

No. 62 Surcharged

**1917**

**107** A19 1c on 4c ol grn & red 2.00 2.00
*a.* Inverted surcharge 80.00 80.00
*b.* Double surcharge 70.00 70.00
*c.* In pair with unsurcharged #62 625.00 625.00

Stamps and Types of 1907-30 Surcharged in Black or Red

**1922-33**

**108** A20 40c on 20c grn & yel .80 .80
*a.* Double surcharge, one inverted 175.00 175.00
*b.* Center double 175.00 175.00
*c.* Surcharge omitted 1,200. 1,200.
**109** A20 50c on 45c red brn & ver ('33) 1.20 1.20
**109A** A20 50c on 45c vio & red org ('33) 325.00 275.00
*b.* Double surcharge 1,750.
**110** A20 50c on 65c vio & lt bl ('33) 1.20 1.20
**111** A20 60c on 75c red & rose .85 .85
*a.* Double surcharge 225.00 225.00
**112** A19 65c on 15c blk & ultra (R) ('25) 2.00 2.00
**113** A19 85c on 15c blk & ultra (R) ('25) 2.00 2.00
**114** A20 85c on 75c red & cer ('25) 2.25 2.25
**115** A20 90c on 75 brn red & rose red ('27) 2.25 2.25
*Nos. 108-109,110-115 (8)* 12.55 12.55

Stamps and Type of 1907-30 Srchd. in Black or Red

**1924-27**

**116** A21 25c on 5fr car & brn 1.10 1.10
*a.* Double surcharge 110.00
**117** A21 1.25fr on 1fr bl (R) ('26) 1.10 1.10
*a.* Double surcharge 125.00
**118** A21 1.50fr on 1fr ind & ultra, *bluish* ('27) 1.50 1.50
*a.* Double surcharge 140.00
*b.* Surcharge omitted 200.00
**119** A21 3fr on 5fr dl red & lt bl ('27) 4.25 3.00
**120** A21 10fr on 5fr bl grn & brn red ('27) 19.50 17.00
**121** A21 20fr on 5fr blk brn & rose ('27) 24.00 19.00
*Nos. 116-121 (6)* 51.45 42.70

Common Design Types pictured following the introduction.

**Colonial Exposition Issue**
Common Design Types

**1931** **Engr.** ***Perf. 12½***
**Name of Country Typo. in Black**

**122** CD70 40c dp green 5.50 5.50
**123** CD71 50c violet 5.50 5.50
**124** CD72 90c red orange 5.50 5.50
**125** CD73 1.50fr dull blue 5.50 5.50
*Nos. 122-125 (4)* 22.00 22.00

Cascade of Salazie — A22

Waterfowl Lake and Anchain Peak — A23

Léon Dierx Museum, St. Denis — A24

***Perf. 12, 12½ and Compound***

**1933-40** **Engr.**

**126** A22 1c violet .25 .25
**127** A22 2c dark brown .25 .25
**128** A22 3c rose vio ('40) .25 .25
**129** A22 4c olive green .25 .25
**130** A22 5c red orange .25 .25
**131** A22 10c ultramarine .25 .25
**132** A22 15c black .25 .25
**133** A22 20c indigo .30 .25
**134** A22 25c red brown .40 .30
**135** A22 30c dark green .40 .40
**136** A23 35c green ('38) .55 .55
**137** A23 40c ultramarine .55 .55
**138** A23 40c brn blk ('40) .40 .40
**139** A23 45c red violet 1.00 1.00
**140** A23 45c green ('40) .45 .45
**141** A23 50c red .30 .25
**142** A23 55c brn org ('38) 1.50 1.00
**143** A23 60c dull bl ('40) .45 .45
**144** A23 65c olive green 1.10 .80
**145** A23 70c ol grn ('40) .65 .65
**146** A23 75c dark brown 5.00 4.25
**147** A23 80c black ('38) 1.00 .80
**148** A23 90c carmine 2.50 2.10
**149** A23 90c dl rose vio ('39) 1.00 1.00
**150** A23 1fr green 2.00 .70
**151** A23 1fr dk car ('38) 2.50 .70
**152** A23 1fr black ('40) .70 .70
**153** A24 1.25fr orange brown .70 .55
**154** A24 1.25fr brt car rose ('39) 1.00 1.00
**155** A22 1.40fr pck bl ('40) 1.00 1.00
**156** A24 1.50fr ultramarine .40 .40
**157** A22 1.60fr dk car rose ('40) 1.40 1.40
**158** A24 1.75fr olive green 1.00 .65
**159** A22 1.75fr dk bl ('38) 1.40 .85
**160** A24 2fr vermilion .55 .55
**161** A22 2.25fr brt ultra ('39) 2.00 2.00
**162** A22 2.50fr chnt ('40) 1.40 1.40
**163** A24 3fr purple .55 .55
**164** A24 5fr magenta .55 .55
**165** A24 10fr dark blue 1.10 1.10
**166** A24 20fr red brown 1.50 1.50
*Nos. 126-166 (41)* 39.05 32.55

For overprints and surcharges see Nos. 177A, 181-220, 223, C1.

60c, 1fr without "RF," see Nos. 237A-238B.

**Paris International Exposition Issue**
Common Design Types

**1937** ***Perf. 13***

**167** CD74 20c dp vio 2.25 2.25
**168** CD75 30c dk grn 2.25 2.25
**169** CD76 40c car rose 2.25 2.25
**170** CD77 50c dk brn & blk 2.10 2.10
**171** CD78 90c red 2.10 2.10
**172** CD79 1.50fr ultra 2.25 2.25
*Nos. 167-172 (6)* 13.20 13.20
Set, never hinged 20.00

**Colonial Arts Exhibition Issue**
Souvenir Sheet
Common Design Type

**1937** ***Imperf.***

**173** CD74 3fr ultra 8.50 *10.00*
Never hinged 16.00

**New York World's Fair Issue**
Common Design Type

**1939** **Engr.** ***Perf. 12½x12***

**174** CD82 1.25fr car lake 1.40 1.40
**175** CD82 2.25fr ultra 1.40 1.40
Set, never hinged 4.50

For overprints, see Nos. 221-222.

St. Denis Roadstead and Marshal Pétain A25

**1941 Unwmk. *Perf. 11½x12***

**176** A25 1fr brown .80
**177** A25 2.50fr blue .80
Set, never hinged 2.00

Nos. 176-177 were issued by the Vichy government in France, but were not placed on sale in Réunion.

For surcharges, see Nos. B13-B14.

No. 144 Surcharged in Carmine

**1943**

**177A** 1fr on 65c olive grn 1.10 .65
Never hinged 1.60

De Pronis Landing on Reunion — A25a

**1943 *Perf. 12½x12***

**177B** A25a 60c blk brn & red .55
**177C** A25a 80c green & blue .40
**177D** A25a 1.50fr dk brn red .35
**177E** A25a 4fr ultra & red .35
**177F** A25a 5fr red brn & black .55
**177G** A25a 10fr violet & green .65
*Nos. 177B-177G,C13A-C13F (12)* 5.70
Set, never hinged 8.00

300th Ann. of French settlement on Réunion.

Nos. 177B-177G were issued by the Vichy government in France, but were not placed on sale in Réunion.

**Stamps of 1907 Overprinted in Blue Violet**

q

**1943 Unwmk. *Perf. 14x13½***

**178** A19(q) 4c ol gray & pale red 6.00 6.00
**179** A20(q) 75c red & lil rose 1.75 1.75
**180** A21(q) 5fr car & vio brn 60.00 60.00

Stamps of 1933-40 Overprinted in Carmine, Black or Blue Violet

**181** A22(r) 1c rose vio (C) 1.00 1.00
**182** A22(r) 2c blk brn (C) 1.00 1.00
**183** A22(r) 3c rose vio (C) 1.00 1.00
**184** A22(r) 4c ol yel (C) 1.00 1.00
**185** A22(r) 5c red org 1.00 1.00
**186** A22(r) 10c ultra (C) 1.00 1.00
**187** A22(r) 15c blk (C) 1.00 1.00
**188** A22(r) 20c ind (C) 1.00 1.00
**189** A22(r) 25c red brn (BlV) 1.25 1.25
**190** A22(r) 30c dk grn (C) 1.40 1.40
**191** A23(q) 35c green 1.00 1.00
**192** A23(q) 40c dl ultra (C) 1.00 1.00
**193** A23(q) 40c brn blk (C) 1.00 1.00
**194** A23(q) 45c red vio 1.00 1.00
**195** A23(q) 45c green 1.00 1.00
**196** A23(q) 50c org red 1.00 1.00
**197** A23(q) 55c brn org 1.00 1.00
**198** A23(q) 60c dl bl (C) 3.00 3.00
**199** A23(q) 65c ol grn 1.00 1.00
**200** A23(q) 70c ol grn (C) 2.25 2.25
**201** A23(q) 75c dk brn (C) 5.25 5.25
**202** A23(q) 80c blk (C) 1.00 1.00
**203** A23(q) 90c dl rose vio 1.00 1.00
**204** A23(q) 1fr green 1.00 1.00
**205** A23(q) 1fr dk car 1.00 1.00
**206** A23(q) 1fr blk (C) 3.00 3.00
**207** A24(q) 1.25fr org brn (BlV) 1.00 1.00
**208** A24(q) 1.25fr brt car rose 3.00 3.00
**209** A22(r) 1.40fr pck bl (C) 2.00 2.00
**210** A24(q) 1.50fr ultra (C) 1.00 1.00
**211** A22(r) 1.60fr dk car rose 2.10 2.10
**212** A24(q) 1.75fr ol grn (C) 2.75 2.75
**213** A22(r) 1.75fr dk bl (C) 4.50 4.50
**214** A24(q) 2fr vermilion 1.00 1.00
**215** A22(r) 2.25fr brt ultra (C) 4.50 4.50
**216** A22(r) 2.50fr chnt (BlV) 7.50 7.50
**217** A24(q) 3fr pur (C) 1.00 1.00
**218** A24(q) 5fr brn lake (BlV) 2.10 2.10
**219** A24(q) 10fr dk bl (C) 8.50 8.50
**220** A24(q) 20fr red brn (BlV) 13.00 13.00

**New York World's Fair Issue Overprinted in Black or Carmine**

**221** CD82(q) 1.25fr car lake 4.00 4.00
**222** CD82(q) 2.25fr ultra (C) 4.00 4.00
*Nos. 178-222 (45)* 165.85 165.85
Set, never hinged 235.00

**No. 177A Overprinted**

**1943 Unwmk. *Perf. 12½***

**223** A23 1fr on 65c ol grn .85 .85

**Catalogue values for unused stamps in this section, from this point to the end of the section, are for Never Hinged items.**

Produce of Réunion A26

**1943 Photo. *Perf. 14½x14***

**224** A26 5c dull brown .25 .25
**225** A26 10c blue & lt blue .25 .25
**226** A26 25c emerald .25 .25
**227** A26 30c dp orange .25 .25
**228** A26 40c dk slate grn .25 .25
**229** A26 80c rose violet .65 .50
**230** A26 1fr red brown .25 .25
**231** A26 1.50fr crimson .65 .50
**232** A26 2fr black .65 .50
**233** A26 2.50fr ultra 1.00 .70
**234** A26 4fr dk violet 1.25 .90
**235** A26 5fr bister 1.25 .90
**236** A26 10fr dark brown 1.75 1.40
**237** A26 20fr dark green 2.75 1.75
*Nos. 224-237 (14)* 11.45 8.65

For surcharges see Nos. 240-247.

Type of 1933-40 without "RF"

**1944 Engr. *Perf. 12½***

**237A** A23 60c dull blue 1.40 1.00
**237B** A23 1fr black & blue 1.40 1.00

Nos. 237A-237B were issued by the Vichy government in France, but were not placed on sale in Réunion.

**Eboue Issue**

Common Design Type

**1945 Engr. *Perf. 13***

**238** CD91 2fr black 1.00 1.00
**239** CD91 25fr Prussian green 1.40 1.00

**Nos. 224, 226 and 233 Surcharged in Carmine or Black**

**1945 *Perf. 14½x14***

**240** A26 50c on 5c dl brn (C) .30 .25
**241** A26 60c on 5c dl brn (C) .30 .25
**242** A26 70c on 5c dl brn (C) .30 .25
**243** A26 1.20fr on 5c dl brn (C) .70 .50
**244** A26 2.40fr on 25c emer .70 .50
**245** A26 3fr on 25c emer 1.25 .90
**246** A26 4.50fr on 25c emer 1.25 .90
**247** A26 15fr on 2.50fr ultra (C) 1.75 1.10
*Nos. 240-247 (8)* 6.55 4.65

Various double and inverted overprints exist for Nos. 240-247.

Cliff — A27

Cutting Sugar Cane — A28

Cascade A29

Banana Tree A30

Mountain Scene A31

Ship Approaching Réunion — A32

**1947 Unwmk. Photo. *Perf. 13½***

**249** A27 10c org & grnsh blk .25 .25
**250** A27 30c org & brt bl .25 .25
**251** A27 40c org & brn .25 .25
**252** A28 50c bl grn & brn .25 .25
**253** A28 60c dk bl & brn .25 .25
**254** A28 80c brn & ol brn .55 .45
**255** A29 1fr dl bl & vio brn .55 .45
**256** A29 1.20fr bl grn & gray .80 .65
**257** A29 1.50fr org & vio brn .80 .65
**258** A30 2fr gray bl & bl grn .80 .65
**259** A30 3fr vio brn & bl grn .80 .65
**260** A30 3.60fr dl red & rose red .90 .70
**261** A30 4fr gray bl & buff .80 .70
**262** A31 5fr rose lil & brn 1.25 .70
**263** A31 6fr bl & brn 1.50 .75
**264** A31 10fr org & ultra 3.25 1.50
**265** A32 15fr gray bl & vio brn 4.75 2.75
**266** A32 20fr bl & org 6.50 4.00
**267** A32 25fr rose lil & brn 8.00 4.25
*Nos. 249-267 (19)* 32.50 20.10

Nos. 249-267 exist imperf. Value, set $100.

**Stamps of France, 1945-49, Surcharged type "a" or "b" in Black or Carmine**

On A147

Others

**1949 Unwmk. *Perf. 14x13½, 13***

**268** A153 10c on 30c .30 .25
**269** A153 30c on 50c .60 .25
**270** A146 50c on 1fr 1.40 .90
**271** A146 60c on 2fr 8.00 1.40
**272** A147 1fr on 3fr 2.00 .70
**273** A147 2fr on 4fr 8.00 1.60
**274** A147 2.50fr on 5fr 20.00 11.00
**275** A147 3fr on 6fr 2.25 1.40
**276** A147 4fr on 10fr 2.00 1.60
**277** A162 5fr on 20fr (C) 10.00 1.40
**278** A147 6fr on 12fr 29.00 2.25
**279** A160 7fr on 12fr 9.00 3.00
**280** A165 8fr on 25fr (C) 37.50 3.25
**281** A165 10fr on 25fr (C) 2.75 1.40
**282** A174 11fr on 18fr (C) 16.00 2.25
*Nos. 268-282 (15)* 148.80 32.65

The letters "C. F. A." are the initials of "Colonies Francaises d'Afrique," referring to the currency which is expressed in French Africa francs.

The surcharge on Nos. 277, 279, 282 includes two bars.

**1950 *Perf. 14x13½***

**283** A182 10c on 50c bl, red & yel .55 .55
**284** A182 1fr on 2fr grn, yel & red (#619) 10.00 3.50
**285** A147 2fr on 5fr lt grn 18.00 4.25
*Nos. 283-285 (3)* 28.55 8.30

**France Nos. 630 & 623 Surcharged**

**1950-51 *Perf. 13***

**286** A188 5fr on 20fr dk red 10.00 1.75
**287** A185 8fr on 25fr dp ultra ('51) 10.00 1.75

**Stamps of France, 1951-52, Surcharged in Black or Red**

No. 288

No. 292

**1951-52 *Perf. 14x13½, 13***

**288** A182 50c on 1fr bl, red & yel .70 .70
**289** A182 1fr on 2fr vio bl, red & yel (#662) .70 .70
**290** A147 2fr on 5fr dl vio 4.25 2.00
**291** A147 3fr on 6fr grn 8.00 1.60
**292** A220 5fr on 20fr dk pur (R; '52) 3.00 1.75

**293** A147 6fr on 12fr red org ('52) 9.00 2.00
**294** A215 8fr on 40fr vio (R) ('52) 6.50 .70
**295** A147 9fr on 18fr cerise 21.00 4.25
**296** A208 15fr on 30fr ind (R) 11.00 2.25
*Nos. 288-296 (9)* 64.15 15.95

The surcharge on Nos. 292, 294 and 296 include two bars.

France No. 697 Surcharged in Black

**1953** *Perf. 14x13½*
**297** A182 50c on 1fr blk, red & yel .35 .25

France No. 688 Surcharged Type "c" in Black

*Perf. 13*
**298** A230 3fr on 6fr dp plum & car 1.20 .80

**France Nos. 703 and 705 Surcharged in Red or Blue**

No. 299

No. 300

**1954**
**299** A235 8fr on 40fr (R) 38.50 7.50
**300** A235 20fr on 75fr 80.00 32.50

**France Nos. 698, 721, 713, and 715 Surcharged in Black**

No. 301 No. 304

**301** A182 1fr on 2fr 4.75 2.10
**302** A241 4fr on 10fr 4.50 1.25
**303** A238 8fr on 40fr 11.00 1.60
**304** A238 20fr on 75fr 14.50 1.60

The surcharge on Nos. 303 and 304 includes two bars.

**France Nos. 737, 719 and 722-724 Surcharged in Black or Red**

a

b

**305** A182(b) 1fr on 2fr .50 .50
**306** A241(a) 2fr on 6fr (R) .80 .50
**307** A242(a) 6fr on 12fr 11.00 1.75
**308** A241(b) 9fr on 18fr 12.00 5.00
**309** A241(a) 10fr on 20fr 8.00 1.40
*Nos. 299-309 (11)* 185.55 55.70

The surcharge on Nos. 306-308 includes two bars; on No. 309 three bars.

**France No. 720 Surcharged in Red**

**1955** *Perf. 13*
**310** A241 3fr on 8fr brt bl & dk grn 1.40 1.10

**France Nos. 785, 774-779 Surcharged in Black or Red**

No. 311

No. 317

*Perf. 14x13½, 13*
**1955-56** **Typo., Engr.**
**311** A182 50c on 1fr .45 .30
**312** A265 2fr on 6fr ('56) 1.20 .70
**313** A265 3fr on 8fr 1.00 .50
**314** A265 4fr on 10fr 1.25 .50
**315** A265 5fr on 12fr (R) 1.30 .50
**316** A265 6fr on 18fr (R) 1.00 .50
**317** A265 10fr on 25fr 1.75 .50
*Nos. 311-317 (7)* 7.95 3.50

The surcharge on Nos. 312-317 includes two bars.

**France Nos. 801-804 Surcharged in Black or Red**

No. 318 No. 319

No. 320 No. 321

**1956** **Engr.** *Perf. 13*
**318** A280(a) 8fr on 30fr (R) 5.25 1.10
**319** A280(b) 9fr on 40fr 7.75 3.00
**320** A280(a) 15fr on 50fr 9.25 1.60
**321** A280(a) 20fr on 75fr (R) 8.50 2.25
*Nos. 318-321 (4)* 30.75 7.95

The surcharge on Nos. 318, 319 and 321 includes two bars.

France Nos. 837 and 839 Surcharged in Red

**1957** *Perf. 13*
**322** A294 7fr on 15fr 1.20 .55
**323** A265 17fr on 70fr 6.75 2.10

The surcharge on Nos. 322-323 includes two bars.

No. 322 has three types of "7" in the sheet of 50. There are 34 of the "normal" 7; 10 of a slightly thinner 7, and 6 of a slightly thicker 7.

**France Nos. 755-756, 833-834, 851-855, 908, 949 Surcharged in Black or Red Type "a", "b" or**

d

**Typographed, Engraved**
**1957-60** *Perf. 14x13½, 13*
**324** A236(b) 2fr on 6fr .30 .30
**325** A302(b) 3fr on 10fr ('58) .50 .50
**326** A236(b) 4fr on 12fr 3.50 .75
**327** A236(b) 5fr on 10fr 2.25 1.10
**328** A303(b) 6fr on 18fr 1.25 .50
**329** A302(a) 9fr on 25fr (R) ('58) 1.25 .65
**330** A252(a) 10fr on 20fr (R) 1.75 .30
**331** A252(a) 12fr on 25fr 6.75 .50
**332** A303(a) 17fr on 35fr 3.75 1.75
**333** A302(a) 20fr on 50fr 1.75 .80
**334** A302(a) 25fr on 85fr 4.00 1.60
**335** A339(d) 50fr on 1fr ('60) 3.00 .75
*Nos. 324-335 (12)* 30.05 9.50

The surcharge includes two bars on Nos. 324, 326-327, 329-331, 333 and 335.

**France Nos. 973, 939 and 968 Surcharged**

e f

**1961-63** **Typo.** *Perf. 14x13½*
**336** A318(e) 2fr on 5c multi .30 .25
*a.* Double surcharge 300.00 —
*b.* Inverted surcharge 1,000. —
**337** A336(e) 5fr on 10c brt grn 1.30 .50
**338** A336(b) 5fr on 10c brt grn ('63) 1.60 .75
**339** A349(f) 12fr on 25c lake & gray .30 .30
*Nos. 336-339 (4)* 3.50 1.80

The surcharge on No. 337 includes three bars. No. 338 has "b" surcharge and two bars.

**France Nos. 943, 941 and 946 Surcharged in Black or Red**

**Engraved, Typographed**
**1961** **Unwmk.** *Perf. 13, 14x13½*
**340** A338 7fr on 15c 1.00 .80
**341** A337 10fr on 20c .30 .30
**342** A339 20fr on 50c (R) 17.00 4.50
*Nos. 340-342 (3)* 18.30 5.60

Surcharge on No. 342 includes 3 bars.

**France Nos. 1047-1048 Surcharged**

No. 343

No. 344

**1963, Jan. 2** **Engr.** *Perf. 13*
**343** A394 12fr on 25c 1.00 .95
**344** A395 25fr on 50c 1.00 .95

1st television connection of the US and Europe through the Telstar satellite, July 11-12, 1962.

**France Nos. 1040-1041, 1007 and 1009 Surcharged**

No. 345 No. 346

No. 347

No. 348

**Typographed, Engraved**
**1963** *Perf. 14x13½, 13*
**345** A318 2fr on 5c .30 .30
**346** A318 5fr on 10c .25 .25
**347** A372 7fr on 15c .60 .50
**348** A372 20fr on 45c 1.25 .75
*Nos. 345-348 (4)* 2.40 1.80

Two-line surcharge on No. 345; No. 347 has currency expressed in capital "F" and two heavy bars through old value; two thin bars on No. 348.

France No. 1078 Surcharged

**1964, Feb. 8 Engr. *Perf. 13***

**349** CD118 12fr on 25c 1.25 1.25

"PHILATEC," Intl. Philatelic and Postal Techniques Exhib., Paris, June 5-21, 1964.

France Nos. 1092, 1094 and 1102 Surcharged

### Typographed, Engraved

**1964 *Perf. 14x13½, 13***

**350** A318 1fr on 2c .25 .25
**351** A318 6fr on 18c .30 .30
**352** A420 35fr on 70c 1.50 .95
*Nos. 350-352 (3)* 2.05 1.50

Surcharge on No. 352 includes two bars.

### France Nos. 1095, 1126, 1070 Surcharged

No. 353

No. 354

No. 355

**1965**

**353** A318 15fr on 30c .50 .30
**354** A440 25fr on 50c 1.00 .95
**355** A408 30fr on 60c 1.50 1.00
*Nos. 353-355 (3)* 3.00 2.25

Two bars obliterate old denomination on Nos. 354-355.

Etienne Regnault, "Le Taureau" and Coast of Reunion — A33

**1965, Oct. 3 Engr. *Perf. 13***

**356** A33 15fr bluish blk & dk car 1.00 .65

Tercentenary of settlement of Reunion.

France No. 985 Surcharged

**1966, Feb. 13 Engr. *Perf. 13***

**357** A360 10fr on 20c bl & car 1.60 .70

### French Satellite A-1 Issue
### France Nos. 1137-1138 Surcharged in Red

**1966, Mar. 27 Engr. *Perf. 13***

**358** CD121 15fr on 30c 1.10 1.00
**359** CD121 30fr on 60c 1.30 1.10
*a.* Strip of 2 + label 3.50 3.00

### France Nos. 1142, 1143, 1101 and 1127 Surcharged

No. 360

No. 361

**1967-69 Typo. *Perf. 14x13***

**360** A446 2fr on 5c bl & red .30 .30

**Photo. *Perf. 13***

**360A** A446 10fr on 20c multi ('69) .30 .30

**Engr.**

**361** A421 20fr on 40c multi 1.10 .95
**362** A439 30fr on 60c bl & red brn 1.30 .75

### EXPO '67 Issue
France No. 1177 Surcharged

**1967, June 12 Engr. *Perf. 13***

**363** A473 30fr on 60c dl bl & bl grn 2.40 1.75

EXPO '67, Montreal, Apr. 28-Oct. 27.

### Lions Issue
France No. 1196 Surcharged in Violet Blue

**1967, Oct. 29 Engr. *Perf. 13***

**364** A485 20fr on 40c 3.00 1.20

50th anniversary of Lions International.

### France No. 1130 Surcharged in Violet Blue

**1968, Feb. 26 Engr. *Perf. 13***

**365** A440 50fr on 1fr 2.75 1.60

### France No. 1224 Surcharged

**1968, Oct. 21 Engr. *Perf. 13***

**366** A508 20fr on 40c multi 1.50 1.00

20 years of French Polar expeditions.

France Nos. 1230-1231 Surcharged

**1969, Apr. 13 Engr. *Perf. 13***

**367** A486 15fr on 30c green .65 .50
**368** A486 20fr on 40c dp car .70 .30

### France No. 1255 Surcharged

**1969, Aug. 18 Engr. *Perf. 13***

**370** A526 35fr on 70c multi 1.60 1.35

Napoleon Bonaparte (1769-1821).

France No. 1293 Surcharged

**1971, Jan. 16 Engr. *Perf. 13***

**371** A555 25fr on 50c rose car .90 .30

### France No. 1301 Surcharged

**1971, Apr. 13 Engr. *Perf. 13***

**372** A562 40fr on 80c multi 2.00 1.40

France No. 1309 Surcharged

**1971, June 5 Engr. *Perf. 13***

**373** A569 15fr on 40c multi 1.00 .70

Aid for rural families.

France No. 1312 Surcharged

**1971, Aug. 30 Engr. *Perf. 13***

**374** A571 45fr on 90c multi 1.15 .95

### France No. 1320 Surcharged

**1971, Oct. 18 Engr. *Perf. 13***

**375** A573 45fr on 90c multi 1.40 1.00

40th anniversary of the first assembly of presidents of artisans' guilds.

Réunion Chameleon A34

**1971, Nov. 8 Photo. *Perf. 13***

**376** A34 25fr multi 1.40 1.10

Nature protection.

### Common Design Type and

De Gaulle in Brazzaville, 1944 — A35

Designs: No. 377, Gen. de Gaulle, 1940. No. 379, de Gaulle entering Paris, 1944. No. 380, Pres. de Gaulle, 1970.

**1971, Nov. 9 Engr.**

**377** CD134 25fr black 1.60 1.60
**378** A35 25fr ultra 1.60 1.60
**379** A35 25fr rose red 1.60 1.60
**380** CD134 25fr black 1.60 1.60
*a.* Strip of 4 + label 9.25 8.00

Charles de Gaulle (1890-1970), president of France.

Nos. 377-380 printed se-tenant in sheets of 20 containing 5 strips of 4 plus labels with Cross of Lorraine and inscription. Exists imperf. Value, strip $200.

### France No. 1313 Surcharged

50f CFA

**1972, Jan. 17 Engr. *Perf. 13***

**381** A570 50fr on 1.10fr multi 1.40 1.15

Map of South Indian Ocean, Penguin and Ships — A36

**1972, Jan. 31 Engr. *Perf. 13***
**382** A36 45fr blk, bl & ocher 2.25 2.25

Bicentenary of the discovery of the Crozet and Kerguelen Islands.

France No. 1342 Surcharged in Red

**1972, May. 8 Engr. *Perf. 13***
**383** A590 15fr on 40c red 1.00 .95

20th anniv. of Blood Donors' Assoc. of Post and Telecommunications Employees.

**France Nos. 1345-1346 Surcharged**

**1972, June 5 Typo. *Perf. 14x13***
**384** A593 15fr on 30c multi .45 .45
**385** A593 25fr on 50c multi .75 .65

Introduction of postal code system.

**France No. 1377 Surcharged in Ultramarine**

**1973, June 12 Engr. *Perf. 13***
**386** A620 45fr on 90c multi 2.00 1.35

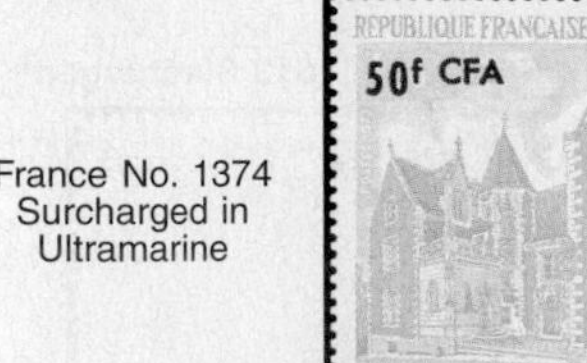


France No. 1374 Surcharged in Ultramarine

France No. 1336 Srchd. in Red

**1973 Engr. *Perf. 13***
**387** A617 50fr on 1fr multi (U) 1.15 .95
**388** A586 100fr on 2fr multi (R) 2.00 1.10

On No. 388, two bars cover "2.00".
Issue dates: 50fr, June 24; 100fr, Oct. 13.

France No. 1231C Surcharged in Black

**1973, Nov. Typo. *Perf. 14x13***
**389** A486 15fr on 30c bl grn 5.00 .80

**France No. 1390 Surcharged in Red**

**1974, Jan. 20 Engr. *Perf. 13***
**390** A633 25fr on 50c multi .70 .70

ARPHILA 75 Phil. Exhib., Paris, June 1975.

**France Nos. 1394-1397 Surcharged in Black, Ultramarine or Brown**

No. 391

No. 394

**Engr. (#391, 393), Photo. (#392, 394)**
**1974 *Perf. 12x13, 13x12***
**391** A637 100fr on 2fr (Blk) 2.50 2.40
**392** A638 100fr on 2fr (U) 3.25 2.40
**393** A639 100fr on 2fr (Br) 3.25 2.40
**394** A640 100fr on 2fr (U) 3.25 2.40
*Nos. 391-394 (4)* 12.25 9.60

Nos. 391-394 printed in sheets of 25 with alternating labels publicizing "ARPHILA 75," Paris June 6-16, 1975.

Two bars obliterate original denomination on Nos. 391-393.

**France No. 1401 Surcharged in Red**

**1974, Apr. 29 Engr. *Perf. 13***
**395** A644 45fr on 90c multi 1.90 1.40

Reorganized sea rescue organization.

**France No. 1415 Surcharged in Ultramarine**

**1974, Oct. 6 Engr. *Perf. 13***
**396** A657 60fr on 1.20fr multi 1.60 1.35

Centenary of Universal Postal Union.

France Nos. 1292A and 1294B Surcharged in Ultramarine

**1974, Oct. 19 Typo. *Perf. 14x13***
**397** A555 30fr on 60c grn 1.75 1.60

**Engr.**
***Perf. 13***
**398** A555 40fr on 80c car rose 2.10 1.75

---

## SEMI-POSTAL STAMPS

No. 65 Surcharged in Black or Red

**1915 Unwmk. *Perf. 14x13½***
**B1** A19 10c + 5c (Bk) 160.00 120.00
*a.* Inverted surcharge 450.00 350.00
**B2** A19 10c + 5c (R) 1.75 1.75
*a.* Inverted surcharge 77.50 77.50
*b.* Double surcharge, both inverted 675.00 675.00

No. 65 Surcharged in Red

**1916**
**B3** A19 10c + 5c 1.90 1.90

**Curie Issue**
Common Design Type

**1938 *Perf. 13***
**B4** CD80 1.75fr + 50c brt ultra 14.00 14.00
Never hinged 24.00

**French Revolution Issue**
Common Design Type

**1939 Photo. Unwmk.**
**Name and Value Typo. in Black**
**B5** CD83 45c + 25c grn 12.50 12.50
**B6** CD83 70c + 30c brn 12.50 12.50
**B7** CD83 90c + 35c red org 12.50 12.50
**B8** CD83 1.25fr + 1fr rose pink 12.50 12.50
**B9** CD83 2.25fr + 2fr blue 12.50 12.50
*Nos. B5-B9 (5)* 62.50 62.50
Set, never hinged 110.00

See CB1.

**Common Design Type and**

Artillery Colonel — SP1

Colonial Infantry SP2

**1941 Unwmk. *Perf. 13½***
**B10** SP1 1fr + 1fr red 1.60
**B11** CD86 1.50fr + 3fr claret 1.60
**B12** SP2 2.50fr + 1fr blue 1.60
*Nos. B10-B12 (3)* 4.80
Set, never hinged 6.50

Nos. B10-B12 were issued by the Vichy government in France, but were not placed on sale in Reunion. Nos. B10-B12 exist imperf. Value, set $200.

**Nos. 176-177 Surcharged in Black or Red**

**1944 Engr. *Perf. 12½x12***
**B13** 50c + 1.50fr on 2.50fr deep blue (R) .80
**B14** + 2.50fr on 1fr yel brn .80
Set, never hinged 2.00

Colonial Development Fund.

Nos. B13-B14 were issued by the Vichy government in France, but were not placed on sale in Réunion.

**Catalogue values for unused stamps in this section, from this point to the end of the section, are for Never Hinged items.**

**Red Cross Issue**
Common Design Type

**1944 *Perf. 14½x14***
**B15** CD90 5fr + 20fr black 1.60 1.10

The surtax was for the French Red Cross and national relief.

France Nos. B365-B366 Surcharged in Black

**1962, Dec. 10 Engr. *Perf. 13***
**B16** SP219 10 + 5fr on 20 + 10c 2.50 2.50
**B17** SP219 12 + 5fr on 25 + 10c 2.75 2.75

The surtax was for the Red Cross.

France Nos. B374-B375 Surcharged in Red

**1963, Dec. 9**
**B18** SP223 10 + 5fr on 20 + 10c 3.00 3.00
**B19** SP223 12 + 5fr on 25 + 10c 3.00 3.00

Centenary of the Intl. Red Cross. The surtax was for the Red Cross.

France Nos. B385-B386 Surcharged in Dark Blue

**1964, Dec. 13 Unwmk. *Perf. 13***

**B20** SP230 10 + 5fr on 20 + 10c 1.75 1.75
**B21** SP230 12 + 5fr on 25 + 10c 1.90 1.90

Jean Nicolas Corvisart (1755-1821) and Dominique Larrey (1766-1842), physicians. The surtax was for the Red Cross.

France Nos. B392-B393 Surcharged in Black

**1965, Dec. 12 Engr. *Perf. 13***

**B22** SP233 12 + 5fr on 25 + 10c 1.60 1.60
**B23** SP233 15 + 5fr on 30 + 10c 1.60 1.60

The surtax was for the Red Cross.

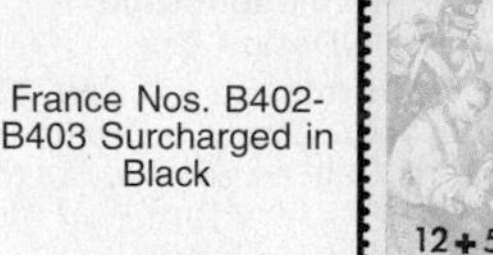

France Nos. B402-B403 Surcharged in Black

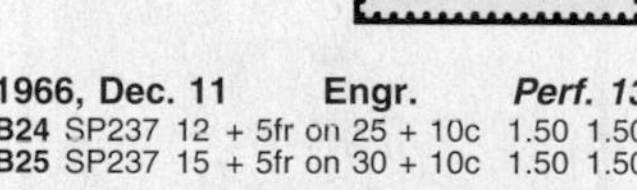

**1966, Dec. 11 Engr. *Perf. 13***

**B24** SP237 12 + 5fr on 25 + 10c 1.50 1.50
**B25** SP237 15 + 5fr on 30 + 10c 1.50 1.50

The surtax was for the Red Cross.

France Nos. B409-B410 Surcharged in Black

**1967, Dec. 17 Engr. *Perf. 13***

**B26** SP240 12 + 5fr on 25 + 10c 3.00 3.00
**B27** SP240 15 + 5fr on 30 + 10c 3.75 3.75

Surtax for the Red Cross.

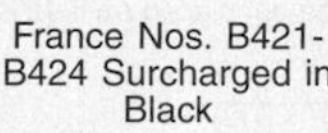

France Nos. B421-B424 Surcharged in Black

**1968-69 Engr. *Perf. 13***

**B28** SP244 12 + 5fr on 25 + 10c 1.70 1.50
**B29** SP244 15 + 5fr on 30 + 10c 1.90 1.50
**B30** SP244 20 + 7fr on 40 + 15c ('69) 1.60 1.50
**B31** SP244 20 + 7fr on 40 + 15c ('69) 1.60 1.50
*Nos. B28-B31 (4)* 6.80 6.00

The surtax was for the Red Cross.

**France No. B425 Surcharged in Black**

**1969, Mar. 17 Engr. *Perf. 13***

**B32** SP245 15fr + 5fr on 30c + 10c 1.40 1.40

Stamp Day.

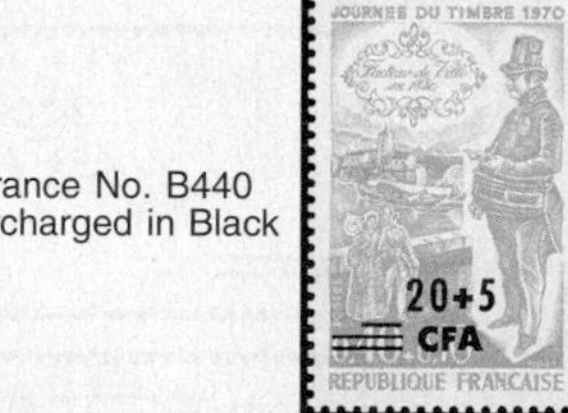

France No. B440 Surcharged in Black

**1970, Mar. 16 Engr. *Perf. 13***

**B33** SP249 20fr + 5fr on 40c + 10c 1.10 .95

Stamp day.

France Nos. B443-B444 Surcharged in Black

**1970, Dec. 14 Engr. *Perf. 13***

**B34** SP252 20 + 7fr on 40 + 15c 2.40 2.00
**B35** SP252 20 + 7fr on 40 + 15c 2.40 2.40

The surtax was for the Red Cross.

**France No. B451 Surcharged in Black**

**1971, Mar. 29 Engr. *Perf. 13***

**B36** SP254 25fr + 5fr on 50c + 10c 1.10 .90

Stamp Day.

France Nos. B452-B453 Surcharged in Black

**1971, Dec. 13**

**B37** SP255 15fr + 5fr on 30c + 10c 1.40 1.40
**B38** SP255 25fr + 5fr on 50c + 10c 1.40 1.40

The surtax was for the Red Cross.

France No. B460 Surcharged in Black

**1972, Mar. 20 Engr. *Perf. 13***

**B39** SP257 25fr + 5fr on 50c + 10c 1.20 1.20

Stamp Day.

France Nos. B461-B462 Surcharged in Red or Green

**1972, Dec. 16 Engr. *Perf. 13***

**B40** SP258 15 + 5fr on 30 + 10c 1.20 1.20
**B41** SP258 25 + 5fr on 50 + 10c (G) 1.40 1.40

Surtax was for the Red Cross.

**France No. B470 Surcharged in Red**

**1973, Mar. 26 Engr. *Perf. 13***

**B42** SP260 25fr +5fr on 50c +10c 1.40 1.40

Stamp Day.

France Nos. B471-B472 Surcharged in Red

**1973, Dec. 3 Engr. *Perf. 13***

**B43** SP261 15 +5fr on 30c +10c 1.40 1.40
**B44** SP261 25 +5fr on 50c +10c 1.40 1.40

Surtax was for the Red Cross.

France No. B477 Surcharged

**1974, Mar. 11 Engr. *Perf. 13***

**B45** SP263 25fr + 5fr on 50c + 10c 1.10 1.10

Stamp Day.

France Nos. B479-B480 Surcharged in Green or Red

**1974, Nov. 30 Engr. *Perf. 13***

**B46** SP265 30 + 7fr on 60 + 15c (G) 1.40 1.40
**B47** SP266 40 + 7fr on 80 + 15c (R) 1.40 1.40

Surtax was for the Red Cross.

## AIR POST STAMPS

No. 141 Ovptd. in Blue

**1937, Jan. 23 Unwmk. *Perf. 12½***

**C1** A23 50c red 290.00 250.00
*a.* Vert. pair, one without overprint 1,800. 1,800.
*b.* Inverted overprint 6,000.
*c.* As "b," in pair with unoverprinted stamp 26,000.

Flight of the "Roland Garros" from Reunion to France by aviators Laurent, Lenier and Touge in Jan.-Feb., 1937.

Airplane and Landscape — AP2

**1938, Mar. 1 Engr. *Perf. 12½***

**C2** AP2 3.65fr slate blue & car 1.00 .90
**C3** AP2 6.65fr brown & org red 1.00 .90
**C4** AP2 9.65fr car & ultra 1.00 .90
**C5** AP2 12.65fr brown & green 2.00 1.50
*Nos. C2-C5 (4)* 5.00 4.20
Set, never hinged 7.00

For overprints see Nos. C14-C17.

Plane and Bridge over East River AP3

Plane and Landscape AP4

**1942, Oct. 19 *Perf. 12x12½***

**C6** AP3 50c olive & pur .35
**C7** AP3 1fr dk bl & scar .35
**C8** AP3 2fr brn & blk .60
**C9** AP3 3fr rose lil & grn 1.10
**C10** AP3 5fr red org & red brn 1.10

**Frame Engr., Center Photo.**

**C11** AP4 10fr dk grn, red org & vio 1.10
**C12** AP4 20fr dk bl, brn vio & red 1.10
**C13** AP4 50fr brn car, Prus grn & bl 1.60
*Nos. C6-C13 (8)* 7.30
Set, never hinged 9.50

Nos. C6-C13 were issued by the Vichy government in France, but were not placed on sale in Réunion.

De Poivre
AP4a

**1943** *Perf. 12½x12*

| No. | Type | Description | Value |
|---|---|---|---|
| C13A | AP4a | 1fr sepia & red | .25 |
| C13B | AP4a | 2fr green & blue | .35 |
| C13C | AP4a | 3fr dk brown red | .40 |
| C13D | AP4a | 5fr ultra & red | .55 |
| C13E | AP4a | 10fr red brn & blk | .55 |
| C13F | AP4a | 20fr violet & green | .75 |
| | | *Nos. C13A-C13F (6)* | 2.85 |
| | | Set, never hinged | 4.00 |

300th Ann. of French settlement on Réunion.

Nos. C13A-C13F were issued by the Vichy government in France, but were not placed on sale in Réunion.

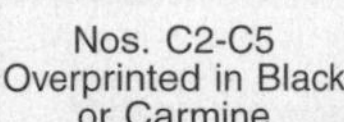
Nos. C2-C5 Overprinted in Black or Carmine

**1943** **Unwmk.** *Perf. 12½*

| No. | Type | Description | Unused | Used |
|---|---|---|---|---|
| C14 | AP2 | 3.65fr sl bl & car | 5.50 | 5.50 |
| C15 | AP2 | 6.65fr brn & org red | 5.50 | 5.50 |
| C16 | AP2 | 9.65fr car & ultra (C) | 5.50 | 5.50 |
| C17 | AP2 | 12.65fr brn & grn | 5.50 | 5.50 |
| | | *Nos. C14-C17 (4)* | 22.00 | 22.00 |
| | | Set, never hinged | 32.50 | |

**Catalogue values for unused stamps in this section, from this point to the end of the section, are for Never Hinged items.**

### Common Design Type

**1944** **Photo.** *Perf. 14½x14*

| No. | Type | Description | Unused | Used |
|---|---|---|---|---|
| C18 | CD87 | 1fr dk org | .50 | .30 |
| C19 | CD87 | 1.50fr brt red | .50 | .30 |
| C20 | CD87 | 5fr brn red | .70 | .45 |
| C21 | CD87 | 10fr black | 1.10 | .80 |
| C22 | CD87 | 25fr ultra | 1.25 | .95 |
| C23 | CD87 | 50fr dk grn | 1.25 | .95 |
| C24 | CD87 | 100fr plum | 1.75 | 1.25 |
| | | *Nos. C18-C24 (7)* | 7.05 | 5.00 |

### Victory Issue

Common Design Type

**1946, May 8** **Engr.** *Perf. 12½*

| No. | Type | Description | Unused | Used |
|---|---|---|---|---|
| C25 | CD92 | 8fr olive gray | 1.10 | .90 |

European victory of the Allied Nations in WWII.

### Chad to Rhine Issue

Common Design Types

**1946, June 6**

| No. | Type | Description | Unused | Used |
|---|---|---|---|---|
| C26 | CD93 | 5fr orange | 1.40 | .85 |
| C27 | CD94 | 10fr sepia | 1.40 | .85 |
| C28 | CD95 | 15fr grnsh blk | 1.40 | .85 |
| C29 | CD96 | 20fr lilac rose | 1.90 | 1.25 |
| C30 | CD97 | 25fr greenish blue | 1.90 | 1.25 |
| C31 | CD98 | 50fr green | 2.25 | 1.50 |
| | | *Nos. C26-C31 (6)* | 10.25 | 6.55 |

Shadow of Plane — AP5

Plane over Réunion — AP6

Air View of Réunion and Shadow of Plane — AP7

*Perf. 13x12½*

**1947, Mar. 24** **Photo.** **Unwmk.**

| No. | Type | Description | Unused | Used |
|---|---|---|---|---|
| C32 | AP5 | 50fr ol grn & bl gray | 11.00 | 8.00 |
| C33 | AP6 | 100fr dk brn & org | 17.00 | 12.50 |
| C34 | AP7 | 200fr dk bl & org | 21.00 | 14.00 |
| | | *Nos. C32-C34 (3)* | 49.00 | 34.50 |

France, Nos. C18-C21 Surcharged in Carmine or Black

**1949** **Unwmk.** *Perf. 13*

| No. | Type | Description | Unused | Used |
|---|---|---|---|---|
| C35 | AP7 | 20fr on 40fr (C) | 3.75 | 1.25 |
| C36 | AP8 | 25fr on 50fr | 4.75 | 1.40 |
| C37 | AP9 | 50fr on 100fr (C) | 11.00 | 4.25 |
| C38 | AP10 | 100fr on 200fr | 55.00 | 21.00 |
| | | *Nos. C35-C38 (4)* | 74.50 | 27.90 |

### France Nos. C24, C26 and C27 Surcharged in Black

No. C39

No. C40

No. C41

**1949-51**

| No. | Type | Description | Unused | Used |
|---|---|---|---|---|
| C39 | AP12 | 100fr on 200fr ('51) | 145.00 | 26.50 |
| C40 | AP12 | 200fr on 500fr | 55.00 | 21.00 |
| C41 | AP13 | 500fr on 1000fr ('51) | 325.00 | 210.00 |
| | | *Nos. C39-C41 (3)* | 525.00 | 257.50 |

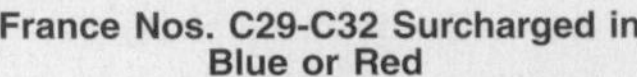

### France Nos. C29-C32 Surcharged in Blue or Red

No. C42

No. C43

No. C44

No. C45

**1954, Feb. 10**

| No. | Type | Description | Unused | Used |
|---|---|---|---|---|
| C42 | AP15 | 50fr on 100fr | 3.50 | 1.25 |
| C43 | AP15 | 100fr on 200fr (R) | 5.50 | 1.40 |
| C44 | AP15 | 200fr on 500fr | 45.00 | 12.50 |
| C45 | AP15 | 500fr on 1000fr | 37.50 | 12.50 |
| | | *Nos. C42-C45 (4)* | 91.50 | 27.65 |

### France Nos. C35-C36 Surcharged in Red or Black

No. C46

No. C47

**1957-58** **Engr.** *Perf. 13*

| No. | Type | Description | Unused | Used |
|---|---|---|---|---|
| C46 | AP17 | 200fr on 500fr (R) | 25.00 | 6.75 |
| C47 | AP17 | 500fr on 1000fr ('58) | 25.00 | 13.00 |

### France Nos. C37, C39-C40 Surcharged in Red or Black

No. C48

No. C49

No. C50

**1961-64**

| No. | Type | Description | Unused | Used |
|---|---|---|---|---|
| C48 | AP15 | 100fr on 2fr | 6.75 | 1.40 |
| C49 | AP17 | 200fr on 5fr | 7.00 | 3.25 |
| C50 | AP17 | 500fr on 10fr (B;'64) | 16.00 | 6.25 |
| | | *Nos. C48-C50 (3)* | 29.75 | 10.90 |

### France No. C41 Surcharged in Red

**1967, Jan. 27** **Engr.** *Perf. 13*

| No. | Type | Description | Unused | Used |
|---|---|---|---|---|
| C51 | AP17 | 100fr on 2fr sl bl & ind | 2.25 | .80 |

### France No. C45 Surcharged in Red

**1972, May 14** **Engr.** *Perf. 13*

| No. | Type | Description | Unused | Used |
|---|---|---|---|---|
| C52 | AP21 | 200fr on 5fr multi | 5.00 | 1.75 |

## AIR POST SEMI-POSTAL STAMP

### French Revolution Issue

Common Design Type

**1939** **Unwmk.** *Perf. 13*

**Name and Value Typo. in Orange**

| No. | Type | Description | Unused | Used |
|---|---|---|---|---|
| CB1 | CD83 | 3.65fr + 4fr brn blk | 25.00 | 25.00 |
| | | Never hinged | 37.50 | |

Felix Guyon Hospital, St. Denis — SPAP1

*Perf. 13½x12½*

**1942, June 22** **Engr.**

| No. | Type | Description | Value |
|---|---|---|---|
| CB2 | SPAP1 | 1.50fr + 3.50fr lt green | 1.00 |
| CB3 | SPAP1 | 2fr + 6fr yellow brown | 1.00 |
| | | Set, never hinged | 2.50 |

Native children's welfare fund.

Nos. CB2-CB3 were issued by the Vichy government in France, but were not placed on sale in Réunion.

### Colonial Education Fund

Common Design Type

**1942, June 22**

| No. | Type | Description | Value |
|---|---|---|---|
| CB4 | CD86a | 1.20fr + 1.80fr blue & red | .90 |
| | | Never hinged | 1.25 |

No. CB4 was issued by the Vichy government in France, but was not placed on sale in Réunion.

## POSTAGE DUE STAMPS

D1

**1889-92** **Unwmk.** **Type-set** *Imperf.*

**Without Gum**

| No. | Type | Description | Unused | Used |
|---|---|---|---|---|
| J1 | D1 | 5c black | 29.00 | 16.00 |
| J2 | D1 | 10c black | 35.00 | 16.00 |
| J3 | D1 | 15c black ('92) | 67.50 | 42.50 |

**J4** D1 20c black 50.00 27.50
**J5** D1 30c black 45.00 27.50
*Nos. J1-J5 (5)* 226.50 129.50

Ten varieties of each value.

Nos. J1-J2, J4-J5 issued on yellowish paper in 1889; Nos. J1-J3, J5 on bluish white paper in 1892.

Nos. J1-J5 exist with double impression. Values, each $125-$190.

D2

**1907 Typo. *Perf. 14x13½***

**J6** D2 5c carmine, *yel* .90 .90
**J7** D2 10c blue, *bl* .90 .90
**J8** D2 15c black, *bluish* 1.50 1.50
**J9** D2 20c carmine 1.50 1.50
**J10** D2 30c green, *grnsh* 2.25 2.25
**J11** D2 50c red, *green* 2.60 2.60
**J12** D2 60c carmine, *bl* 2.60 2.60
**J13** D2 1fr violet 3.00 3.00
*Nos. J6-J13 (8)* 15.25 15.25
Set, never hinged 27.50

Type of 1907 Issue Surcharged

**1927**

**J14** D2 2fr on 1fr org red 12.50 12.50
**J15** D2 3fr on 1fr org brn 12.50 12.50
Set, never hinged 40.00

Arms of Réunion — D3

**1933 Engr. *Perf. 13x13½***

**J16** D3 5c deep violet .25 .25
**J17** D3 10c dark green .25 .25
**J18** D3 15c orange brown .25 .25
**J19** D3 20c light red .35 .35
**J20** D3 30c olive green .35 .35
**J21** D3 50c ultramarine .80 .80
**J22** D3 60c black brown .80 .80
**J23** D3 1fr light violet .80 .80
**J24** D3 2fr deep blue .80 .80
**J25** D3 3fr carmine 1.00 1.00
*Nos. J16-J25 (10)* 5.65 5.65
Set, never hinged 8.75

**Catalogue values for unused stamps in this section, from this point to the end of the section, are for Never Hinged items.**

Numeral — D4

**1947 Unwmk. Photo. *Perf. 13***

**J26** D4 10c dark violet .25 .25
**J27** D4 30c brown .25 .25
**J28** D4 50c blue green .25 .25
**J29** D4 1fr orange .60 .45
**J30** D4 2fr red violet .60 .45
**J31** D4 3fr red brown .85 .65
**J32** D4 4fr blue 1.50 1.10
**J33** D4 5fr henna brown 2.00 1.40
**J34** D4 10fr slate green 2.00 1.40
**J35** D4 20fr violet blue 2.00 .90
*Nos. J26-J35 (10)* 10.30 7.10

France, Nos. J83-J92 Surcharged in Black

**1949-53**

**J36** D5 10c on 1fr brt ultra .25 .25
**J37** D5 50c on 2fr turq bl .45 .40
**J38** D5 1fr on 3fr brn org .60 .40
**J39** D5 2fr on 4fr dp vio .60 .40
**J40** D5 3fr on 5fr brt pink 6.50 2.75
**J41** D5 5fr on 10fr red org 1.10 .70
**J42** D5 10fr on 20fr ol bis 2.00 2.00
**J43** D5 20fr on 50fr dk grn ('50) 12.50 5.50
**J44** D5 50fr on 100fr dp grn ('53) 30.00 13.00
*Nos. J36-J44 (9)* 54.00 25.40

France Nos. J93, J95-J96 Surcharged

**1962-63 Typo. *Perf. 14x13½***

**J46** D6 1fr on 5c brt pink ('63) 3.00 1.10
**J47** D6 10fr on 20c ol bis ('63) 5.50 2.75
**J48** D6 20fr on 50c dk grn 22.00 12.50
*Nos. J46-J48 (3)* 30.50 16.35

France Nos. J98-J102, J104-J105 Surcharged

**1964-71 Unwmk. *Perf. 14x13½***

**J49** D7 1fr on 5c .25 .25
**J50** D7 5fr on 10c .30 .25
**J51** D7 7fr on 15c .50 .45
**J52** D7 10fr on 20c ('71) 1.40 .55
**J53** D7 15fr on 30c .65 .45
**J54** D7 20fr on 50c .80 .55
**J55** D7 50fr on 1fr 1.40 1.25
*Nos. J49-J55 (7)* 5.30 3.75

## PARCEL POST STAMP

Frame Typographed; Center Handstamped — PP1

**1890-1903 Unwmk. Typo. *Imperf.***

**Q1** PP1 10c black, *yellow*, black frame 400.00 200.00
**Q2** PP1 10c black, *yellow*, ultra frame 110.00 100.00
**Q3** PP1 10c black, *yellow*, bl grn frame 30.00 27.50

No. 40 Overprinted

**1906 Unwmk. *Perf. 14x13½***

**Q4** A14 10c red 22.50 22.50

Fiscal Stamps Surcharged — PP2

**1907-23 Unwmk. Typo. *Perf. 14***

**Q5** PP2 10c black on grayish brown ('07) 17.50 15.00
**Q6** PP2 10c red on gray ('23) 17.50 15.00

## FRENCH COLONIES

ˈfrench ˈkä-lə-nēz

From 1859 to 1906 and from 1943 to 1945 special stamps were issued for use in all French Colonies which did not have stamps of their own.

100 Centimes = 1 Franc

**Catalogue values for unused stamps in this country are for Never Hinged items, beginning with Scott B1 in the semi-postal section and Scott J23 in the postage due section.**

Perforations: Nos. 1-45 are known variously perforated privately.

Gum: Many of Nos. 1-45 were issued without gum. Some were gummed locally.

*Reprints: Nos. 1-7, 9-12, 24, 26-42, 44 and 45 were reprinted officially in 1887. These reprints are ungummed and the colors of both design and paper are deeper or brighter than the originals. Value for Nos. 1-6, $20 each.*

Eagle and Crown — A1

**1859-65 Unwmk. Typo. *Imperf.***

**1** A1 1c ol grn, *pale bl* ('62) 24.00 *27.50*
**2** A1 5c yel grn, *grnsh* ('62) 24.00 16.00
**3** A1 10c bister, *yel* 32.50 8.00
*a.* Pair, one sideways 1,000. 525.00
**4** A1 20c bl, *bluish* ('65) 35.00 13.50
**5** A1 40c org, *yelsh* 27.50 13.50
**6** A1 80c car rose, *pnksh* ('65) 110.00 60.00
*Nos. 1-6 (6)* 253.00 138.50

For surcharges, see Reunion Nos. 1-4.

Napoleon III
A2 A3

Ceres
A4

Napoleon III
A5

**1871-72 *Imperf.***

**7** A2 1c ol grn, *pale bl* ('72) 80.00 80.00
**8** A3 5c yel grn, *grnsh* ('72) 1,000. 400.00
**9** A4 10c bis, *yelsh* 375.00 130.00
*a.* Tête bêche pair *55,000.* *22,500.*
**10** A4 15c bis, *yelsh* ('72) 325.00 13.00
**11** A4 20c blue, *bluish* 750.00 125.00
*a.* Tête bêche pair — 18,000.
**12** A4 25c bl, *bluish* ('72) 175.00 13.00
**13** A5 30c brn, *yelsh* 175.00 60.00
**14** A4 40c org, *yelsh* (I) 250.00 13.00
*a.* Type II *3,500.* *650.00*
*b.* Pair, types I & II *7,250.* *1,750.*
**15** A5 80c rose, *pnksh* 1,100. 115.00
*Nos. 7-15 (9)* 4,230. 949.00

For 40c types I-II see illustrations over France #1.

For surcharges, see Reunion Nos. 5-6.

**See note after France No. 9 for additional information on Nos. 8-9, 11-12, 14.**

Ceres
A6 A7

**1872-77 *Imperf.***

**16** A6 1c ol grn, *pale bl* ('73) 13.00 *14.50*
**17** A6 2c red brn, *yelsh* ('76) 475.00 750.00
**18** A6 4c gray ('76) *11,000.* 475.00
**19** A6 5c grn, *pale bl* 17.50 9.50
**20** A7 10c bis, *rose* ('76) 240.00 13.00
**21** A7 15c bister ('77) 525.00 100.00
**22** A7 30c brn, *yelsh* 130.00 21.00
**23** A7 80c rose, *pnksh* ('73) 625.00 140.00

No. 17 was used only in Cochin China, 1876-77. Excellent forgeries of Nos. 17 and 18 exist.

With reference to the stamps of France and French Colonies in the same designs and colors see the note after France No. 9.

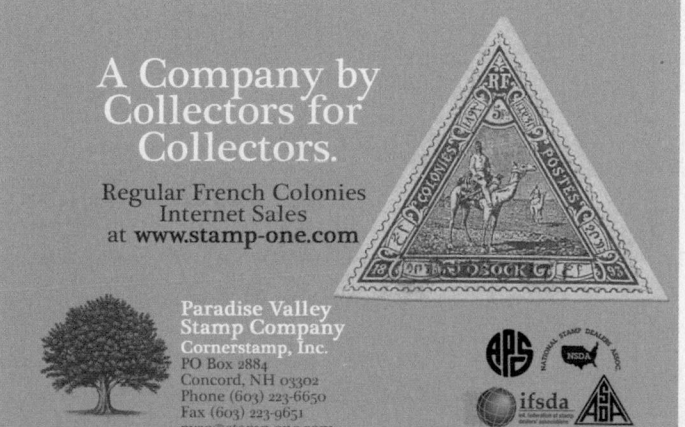

Peace and Commerce — A8

| 1877-78 | | Type I | | *Imperf.* |
|---|---|---|---|---|
| 24 | A8 | 1c grn, *grnsh* | 35.00 | *45.00* |
| 25 | A8 | 4c grn, *grnsh* | 24.00 | 14.50 |
| 26 | A8 | 30c brn, *yelsh* ('78) | 52.50 | 52.50 |
| 27 | A8 | 40c ver, *straw* | 35.00 | 21.00 |
| 28 | A8 | 75c rose, *rose* ('78) | 75.00 | *100.00* |
| 29 | A8 | 1fr brnz grn, *straw* | 60.00 | 67.50 |
| | | *Nos. 24-29 (6)* | 281.50 | 300.50 |
| | | **Type II** | | |
| 30 | A8 | 2c grn, *grnsh* | 17.50 | 11.00 |
| 31 | A8 | 5c grn, *grnsh* | 24.00 | 5.50 |
| 32 | A8 | 10c grn, *grnsh* | 125.00 | 24.00 |
| 33 | A8 | 15c gray, *grnsh* | 250.00 | 72.50 |
| 34 | A8 | 20c red brn, *straw* | 52.50 | 9.50 |
| 35 | A8 | 25c ultra *bluish* | 52.50 | 8.75 |
| *a.* | | 25c blue, *bluish* ('78) | *4,250.* | 175.00 |
| 36 | A8 | 35c vio blk, *org* ('78) | 67.50 | 32.50 |
| | | *Nos. 30-36 (7)* | 589.00 | 163.75 |
| | | *Nos. 24-36 (13)* | 870.50 | 464.25 |

**Type II**

| 1878-80 | | | | |
|---|---|---|---|---|
| 38 | A8 | 1c blk, *lil bl* | 21.00 | 21.00 |
| 39 | A8 | 2c brn, *buff* | 21.00 | *24.00* |
| 40 | A8 | 4c claret, *lav* | 32.50 | *45.00* |
| 41 | A8 | 10c blk, *lav* ('79) | 120.00 | 27.50 |
| 42 | A8 | 15c blue ('79) | 35.00 | 17.50 |
| 43 | A8 | 20c red, *grn* ('79) | 87.50 | 17.50 |
| 44 | A8 | 25c blk, *red* ('79) | 600.00 | 275.00 |
| 45 | A8 | 25c yel, *straw* ('80) | 725.00 | 32.50 |
| | | *Nos. 38-45 (8)* | 1,642. | 460.00 |

No. 44 was used only in Mayotte, Nossi-Be and New Caledonia. Forgeries exist.

The 3c yellow, 3c gray, 15c yellow, 20c blue, 25c rose and 5fr lilac were printed together with the reprints, and were never issued.

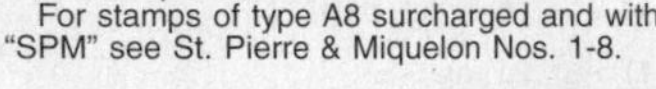

For stamps of type A8 surcharged and with "SPM" see St. Pierre & Miquelon Nos. 1-8.

Commerce — A9

| 1881-86 | | | | *Perf. 14x13½* |
|---|---|---|---|---|
| 46 | A9 | 1c blk, *lil bl* | 5.50 | 4.75 |
| 47 | A9 | 2c brn, *buff* | 5.50 | 4.75 |
| 48 | A9 | 4c claret, *lav* | 5.50 | 5.50 |
| 49 | A9 | 5c grn, *grnsh* | 6.50 | 3.25 |
| 50 | A9 | 10c blk, *lavender* | 11.00 | 4.75 |
| 51 | A9 | 15c blue | 16.00 | 3.25 |
| 52 | A9 | 20c red, *yel grn* | 52.50 | 18.00 |
| 53 | A9 | 25c yel, *straw* | 17.50 | 5.50 |
| 54 | A9 | 25c blk, *rose* ('86) | 24.00 | 3.25 |
| 55 | A9 | 30c brn, *bis* | 45.00 | 21.00 |
| 56 | A9 | 35c vio blk, *yel org* | 40.00 | 30.00 |
| *a.* | | 35c violet black, *yellow* | 100.00 | 52.50 |
| 57 | A9 | 40c ver, *straw* | 45.00 | 27.50 |
| 58 | A9 | 75c car, *rose* | 120.00 | 60.00 |
| 59 | A9 | 1fr brnz grn, *straw* | 80.00 | 45.00 |
| | | *Nos. 46-59 (14)* | 474.00 | 236.50 |

Nos. 46-59 exist imperforate. They are proofs and were not used for postage, except the 10c.

For stamps of type A9 surcharged with numerals see: Cochin China, Diego Suarez, Gabon, Malagasy (Madagascar), Nossi-Be, New Caledonia, Reunion, Senegal, Tahiti.

For stamps of type A9 surcharged and with "MQE" see Martinique Nos. 3-4. For stamps of type A9 surcharged and with "SPM" see St. Pierre & Miquelon Nos. 9-11, 15-18.

## SEMI-POSTAL STAMPS

**Catalogue values for unused stamps in this section are for Never Hinged items.**

Resistance Fighters — SP1

| 1943 | Unwmk. | Litho. | | *Rouletted* |
|---|---|---|---|---|
| B1 | SP1 | 1.50fr + 98.50fr ind & gray | 47.50 | *65.00* |
| | | Without label | 21.00 | *35.00* |

The surtax was for the benefit of patriots and the French Committee of Liberation.

No. B1 was printed in sheets of 10 (5x2) with adjoining labels showing the Lorraine cross.

Colonies Offering Aid to France SP2

| 1943 | | | | *Perf. 12* |
|---|---|---|---|---|
| B2 | SP2 | 9fr + 41fr red violet | 3.50 | 10.50 |

Surtax for the benefit of French patriots.

Patriots and Map of France SP3

| 1943 | | | | |
|---|---|---|---|---|
| B3 | SP3 | 50c + 4.50fr yel grn | 1.25 | *10.50* |
| B4 | SP3 | 1.50fr + 8.50fr cerise | 1.25 | *10.50* |
| B5 | SP3 | 3fr + 12fr grnsh bl | 1.25 | *10.50* |
| B6 | SP3 | 5fr + 15fr olive gray | 1.25 | *1.50* |
| | | *Nos. B3-B6 (4)* | 5.00 | 33.00 |

Surtax for the aid of combatants and patriots.

Refugee Family SP4

| 1943 | | | | |
|---|---|---|---|---|
| B7 | SP4 | 10fr + 40fr dull blue | 5.25 | *12.50* |

The surtax was for refugee relief work.

Woman and Child with Wing — SP5

| 1944 | | | | |
|---|---|---|---|---|
| B8 | SP5 | 10fr + 40fr grnsh blk | 6.75 | *21.00* |

Surtax for the benefit of aviation.

Nos. B1-B8 were prepared for use in the French Colonies, but after the landing of Free French troops in Corsica they were used there and later also in Southern France. They became valid throughout France in Nov. 1944.

## POSTAGE DUE STAMPS

D1

| 1884-85 | Unwmk. | Typo. | | *Imperf.* |
|---|---|---|---|---|
| J1 | D1 | 1c black | 4.00 | 4.00 |
| J2 | D1 | 2c black | 4.00 | 4.00 |
| J3 | D1 | 3c black | 4.00 | 4.00 |
| J4 | D1 | 4c black | 4.75 | 4.00 |
| J5 | D1 | 5c black | 6.50 | 3.25 |
| J6 | D1 | 10c black | 8.75 | 6.50 |
| J7 | D1 | 15c black | 13.00 | 10.50 |
| J8 | D1 | 20c black | 16.00 | 10.50 |
| J9 | D1 | 30c black | 17.50 | 8.75 |
| J10 | D1 | 40c black | 21.00 | 8.75 |
| J11 | D1 | 60c black | 27.50 | 16.00 |
| J12 | D1 | 1fr brown | 35.00 | 27.50 |
| *a.* | | 1fr black | 300.00 | |
| J13 | D1 | 2fr brown | 35.00 | 27.50 |
| *a.* | | 2fr black | 300.00 | *325.00* |
| J14 | D1 | 5fr brown | 110.00 | 67.50 |
| *a.* | | 5fr black | 425.00 | *450.00* |

Nos. J12a, J13a and J14a were not regularly issued.

| 1894-1906 | | | | |
|---|---|---|---|---|
| J15 | D1 | 5c pale blue | 1.60 | 1.60 |
| J16 | D1 | 10c gray brown | 1.60 | 1.60 |
| J17 | D1 | 15c pale green | 1.60 | 1.60 |
| J18 | D1 | 20c olive grn ('06) | 1.60 | 1.60 |
| J19 | D1 | 30c carmine | 2.75 | 1.60 |
| J20 | D1 | 50c lilac | 2.75 | 1.60 |
| J21 | D1 | 60c brown, *buff* | 4.50 | 2.75 |
| *a.* | | 60c dark violet, *buff* | 4.75 | 2.75 |
| J22 | D1 | 1fr red, *buff* | 7.50 | 4.50 |
| *a.* | | 1fr rose, *buff* | 27.50 | 19.00 |
| | | *Nos. J15-J22 (8)* | 23.90 | 16.85 |

For overprints see New Caledonia Nos. J1-J8.

**Catalogue values for unused stamps in this section, from this point to the end of the section, are for Never Hinged items.**

D2

| 1945 | | Litho. | | *Perf. 12* |
|---|---|---|---|---|
| J23 | D2 | 10c slate blue | .45 | *16.00* |
| J24 | D2 | 15c yel green | .45 | *16.00* |
| J25 | D2 | 25c deep orange | .45 | *16.00* |
| J26 | D2 | 50c greenish blk | 1.00 | *16.00* |
| J27 | D2 | 60c copper brn | 1.00 | *16.00* |
| J28 | D2 | 1fr deep red lil | 1.00 | *16.00* |
| J29 | D2 | 2fr red | 1.00 | *16.00* |
| J30 | D2 | 4fr slate gray | 4.50 | *20.00* |
| J31 | D2 | 5fr brt ultra | 4.50 | *20.00* |
| J32 | D2 | 10fr purple | 22.50 | *52.50* |
| J33 | D2 | 20fr dull brown | 4.00 | *20.00* |
| J34 | D2 | 50fr deep green | 7.25 | *27.50* |
| | | *Nos. J23-J34 (12)* | 48.10 | 252.00 |

# FRENCH CONGO

ˈfrench ˈkäŋ-ˌgō

LOCATION — Central Africa
GOVT. — French possession

French Congo was originally a separate colony, but was joined in 1888 to Gabon and placed under one commissioner-general with a lieutenant-governor presiding in Gabon and another in French Congo. In 1894 the military holdings in Ubangi were attached to French Congo, and in 1900 the Chad military protectorate was added. Postal service was not established in Ubangi or Chad, however, at that time. In 1906 Gabon and Middle Congo were separated and French Congo ceased to exist as such. Chad and Ubangi remained attached to Middle Congo as the joint dependency of "Ubangi-Chari-Chad," and Middle Congo stamps were used there.

Issues of the Republic of the Congo are listed under Congo People's Republic (ex-French).

100 Centimes = 1 Franc

**Watermarks**

Wmk. 122 Thistle Branch

Wmk. 123 — Rose Branch

Wmk. 124 Olive Branch

Stamps of French Colonies Surcharged Horizontally in Red or Black

| 1891 | | Unwmk. | | *Perf. 14x13½* |
|---|---|---|---|---|
| 1 | A9 | 5c on 1c blk, *lil bl* (R) | *6,500.* | *4,750.* |
| *a.* | | Double surcharge | 20,000. | |
| 2 | A9 | 5c on 1c blk, *lil bl* | 200.00 | 110.00 |
| *a.* | | Double surcharge | 650.00 | 425.00 |
| 3 | A9 | 5c on 15c blue | 350.00 | 180.00 |
| *a.* | | Double surcharge | 725.00 | 375.00 |
| 5 | A9 | 5c on 25c blk, *rose* | 130.00 | 52.50 |
| *a.* | | Inverted surcharge | | |
| *b.* | | Surcharge vertical | 275.00 | 115.00 |
| *c.* | | Double surcharge | 600.00 | 600.00 |

**First "O" of "Congo" is a Capital, "Francais" with Capital "F"**

| 1891-92 | | | | |
|---|---|---|---|---|
| 6 | A9 | 5c on 20c red, *grn* | 1,300. | 425.00 |
| 7 | A9 | 5c on 25c blk, *rose* | 200.00 | 100.00 |
| *a.* | | Surcharge vertical | 250.00 | 110.00 |
| 8 | A9 | 10c on 25c blk, *rose* | 240.00 | 67.50 |
| *a.* | | Inverted surcharge | 400.00 | 160.00 |
| *b.* | | Surcharge vertical | 300.00 | 100.00 |
| *d.* | | Double surcharge | 400.00 | 225.00 |
| 9 | A9 | 10c on 40c red, *straw* | 2,750. | 400.00 |
| 10 | A9 | 15c on 25c blk, *rose* | 225.00 | 52.50 |
| *a.* | | Surcharge vertical | 260.00 | 92.50 |
| *c.* | | Double surcharge | 400.00 | 200.00 |

**First "O" of Congo small Surcharge Vert., Down or Up No Period**

| | | | | |
|---|---|---|---|---|
| 11 | A9 | 5c on 25c blk, *rose* | 300.00 | 135.00 |
| 12 | A9 | 10c on 25c blk, *rose* | | — |
| 13 | A9 | 15c on 25c blk, *rose* | 425.00 | 190.00 |

**The listings Nos. 5a and 12 are being re-evaluated. The Catalogue Editors would appreciate any information on these stamps.**

Postage Due Stamps of French Colonies Surcharged in Red or Black Reading Down or Up

**1892** ***Imperf.***

| No. | Type | Description | Unused | Used |
|---|---|---|---|---|
| 14 | D1 | 5c on 5c blk (R) | 200.00 | 140.00 |
| a. | | Double surcharge | 1,450. | |
| 15 | D1 | 5c on 20c blk (R) | 200.00 | 140.00 |
| 16 | D1 | 5c on 30c blk (R) | 260.00 | 180.00 |
| 17 | D1 | 10c on 1fr brown | 200.00 | 140.00 |
| a. | | Double surcharge | 4,100. | |
| b. | | Surcharge horiz. | | *2,400.* |
| c. | | "Congo" omitted | | *475.00* |
| | | *Nos. 14-17 (4)* | 860.00 | 600.00 |

Excellent counterfeits of Nos. 1-17 exist.

Navigation and Commerce — A3

**1892-1900 Typo.** ***Perf. 14x13½***

**Colony Name in Blue or Carmine**

| No. | Type | Description | Unused | Used |
|---|---|---|---|---|
| 18 | A3 | 1c blk, *lil bl* | 1.60 | 1.60 |
| a. | | Name double | 225.00 | 175.00 |
| 19 | A3 | 2c brn, *buff* | 4.00 | 3.25 |
| a. | | Name double | 225.00 | 175.00 |
| 20 | A3 | 4c claret, *lav* | 4.00 | 3.25 |
| a. | | Name in blk and in blue | 225.00 | 175.00 |
| 21 | A3 | 5c grn, *grnsh* | 8.00 | 8.00 |
| 22 | A3 | 10c blk, *lavender* | 24.00 | 20.00 |
| a. | | Name double | 850.00 | 600.00 |
| 23 | A3 | 10c red ('00) | 4.00 | 4.00 |
| 24 | A3 | 15c blue, quadrille paper | 55.00 | 20.00 |
| 25 | A3 | 15c gray ('00) | 12.00 | 8.00 |
| 26 | A3 | 20c red, *grn* | 24.00 | 20.00 |
| 27 | A3 | 25c blk, *rose* | 24.00 | 16.00 |
| 28 | A3 | 25c blue ('00) | 12.00 | *12.00* |
| 29 | A3 | 30c brn, *bis* | 40.00 | 24.00 |
| 30 | A3 | 40c red, *straw* | 55.00 | 32.50 |
| 31 | A3 | 50c car, *rose* | 55.00 | 40.00 |
| 32 | A3 | 50c brn, *az* ('00) | 16.00 | 16.00 |
| a. | | Name double | 775.00 | 775.00 |
| 33 | A3 | 75c dp vio, *org* | 47.50 | 40.00 |
| 34 | A3 | 1fr brnz grn, *straw* | 55.00 | 40.00 |
| | | *Nos. 18-34 (17)* | 441.10 | 308.60 |

Perf. 13½x14 stamps are counterfeits.

For surcharges see Nos. 50-51.

No. 21 exists in yellow green on pale green. The stamp was prepared but not issued. Value, $4,000.

Leopard — A4

Type I

Type II

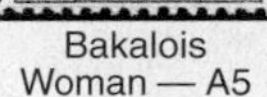

Bakalois Woman — A5

Coconut Grove — A6

Design A4 exists in two types. Type 1: end of left tusk extends behind and above right tusk. Type 2: end of left tusk does not appear behind right tusk. Type 2 of design A4 appears in position 91 of each pane of 100. For detailed listings, see the *Scott Catalogue Classic Specialized of Stamps & Covers.*

**1900-04 Wmk. 122** ***Perf. 11***

| No. | Type | Description | Unused | Used |
|---|---|---|---|---|
| 35 | A4 | 1c brn vio & gray lilac (1) | .80 | .80 |
| a. | | Background inverted | 75.00 | 75.00 |
| 36 | A4 | 2c brn & yel (1) | .80 | .80 |
| a. | | Imperf., pair | 80.00 | *80.00* |
| b. | | Pair, imperf between | 100.00 | *110.00* |
| 37 | A4 | 4c scar & gray bl | 1.60 | 1.20 |
| a. | | Background inverted | 95.00 | 87.50 |
| b. | | Type 2 | 55.00 | 55.00 |
| 38 | A4 | 5c grn & gray grn (1) | 2.75 | 1.60 |
| a. | | Imperf., pair | 140.00 | 140.00 |
| 39 | A4 | 10c red & rose pink (1) | 8.00 | 3.25 |
| a. | | Imperf., pair | 140.00 | 140.00 |
| 40 | A4 | 15c dl vio & ol grn (1) | 2.40 | 1.20 |
| a. | | Imperf. pair | 110.00 | |

**Wmk. 123**

| No. | Type | Description | Unused | Used |
|---|---|---|---|---|
| 41 | A5 | 20c yel grn & org (1) | 2.40 | 2.00 |
| 42 | A5 | 25c bl & pale bl | 3.50 | 2.40 |
| 43 | A5 | 30c car rose & org | 5.50 | 2.40 |
| 44 | A5 | 40c org brn & brt grn | 8.00 | 2.75 |
| a. | | Imperf., pair | 110.00 | 110.00 |
| b. | | Center and value inverted | 200.00 | 170.00 |
| 45 | A5 | 50c gray vio & lil | 8.00 | 6.50 |
| 46 | A5 | 75c red vio & org | 20.00 | 11.00 |
| a. | | Imperf., pair | 110.00 | 110.00 |

**Wmk. 124**

| No. | Type | Description | Unused | Used |
|---|---|---|---|---|
| 47 | A6 | 1fr gray lil & ol | 24.00 | 20.00 |
| a. | | Center and value inverted | 300.00 | 300.00 |
| b. | | Imperf., pair | 140.00 | 140.00 |
| 48 | A6 | 2fr car & brn | 47.50 | 32.50 |
| a. | | Imperf., pair | 300.00 | 300.00 |
| 49 | A6 | 5fr brn org & gray | 87.50 | 72.50 |
| a. | | 5fr ocher & gray | 750.00 | *950.00* |
| b. | | Center and value inverted | 450.00 | 450.00 |
| c. | | Wmk. 123 | 500.00 | 500.00 |
| d. | | Imperf., pair | 800.00 | 800.00 |
| | | *Nos. 35-49 (15)* | 222.75 | 160.90 |

For surcharges see Nos. 52-53.

Nos. 26 and 29 Surcharged in Black

**1900 Unwmk.** ***Perf. 14x13½***

| No. | Type | Description | Unused | Used |
|---|---|---|---|---|
| 50 | A3 | 5c on 20c red, *grn* | *26,000.* | *6,000.* |
| a. | | Double surcharge | | *18,000.* |
| 51 | A3 | 15c on 30c brn, *bis* | *20,000.* | *2,600.* |
| a. | | Double surcharge | | *6,000.* |

**Nos. 43 and 48 Surcharged in Black**

a

b

**1903 Wmk. 123** ***Perf. 11***

| No. | Type | Description | Unused | Used |
|---|---|---|---|---|
| 52 | A5 | 5c on 30c | 325.00 | 160.00 |
| a. | | Inverted surcharge | *2,750.* | |

**Wmk. 124**

| No. | Type | Description | Unused | Used |
|---|---|---|---|---|
| 53 | A6 | 10c on 2fr | 375.00 | 160.00 |
| a. | | Inverted surcharge | *2,750.* | |
| b. | | Double surcharge | *3,250.* | |

Counterfeits of the preceding surcharges are known.

## FRENCH EQUATORIAL AFRICA

'french ˌē-kwə-'tōr-ē-əl 'a-fri-kə

LOCATION — North of Belgian Congo and south of Libya

GOVT. — French Colony

AREA — 959,256 square miles

POP. — 4,491,785

CAPITAL — Brazzaville

In 1910 Gabon and Middle Congo, with its military dependencies, were politically united as French Equatorial Africa. The component colonies were granted administrative autonomy. In 1915 Ubangi-Chari-Chad was made an autonomous civilian colony and in 1920 Chad was made a civil colony. In 1934 the four colonies were administratively united as one colony, but this federation was not completed until 1936. Each colony had its own postal administration until 1936. The postal issues of the former colonial subdivisions are listed under the names of those colonies.

In 1958, French Equatorial Africa was divided into four republics: Chad, Congo, Gabon and Central African Republic (formerly Ubangi-Chari).

Stamps other than Nos. 189-192 are inscribed with "Afrique Equatoriale Francaise" or "AEF" and the name of one of the component colonies are listed under those colonies.

100 Centimes = 1 Franc

**Catalogue values for unused stamps in this country are for Never Hinged items, beginning with Scott 142 in the regular postage section, Scott B8A in the semi-postal section, Scott C17 in the airpost section, and Scott J12 in the postage due section.**

**Stamps of Gabon, 1932, Overprinted "Afrique Equatoriale Francaise" and Bars Similar to "a" and "b" in Black**

***Perf. 13x13½, 13½x13***

**1936 Unwmk.**

| No. | Type | Description | Unused | Used |
|---|---|---|---|---|
| 1 | A16 | 1c brown violet | .40 | *.80* |
| 2 | A16 | 2c black, *rose* | .80 | *.80* |
| 3 | A16 | 4c green | 1.20 | 1.60 |
| 4 | A16 | 5c grnsh blue | 1.20 | 1.60 |
| 5 | A16 | 10c red, *yel* | 1.20 | 1.60 |
| 6 | A17 | 40c brown violet | 4.00 | 3.25 |
| 7 | A17 | 50c red brown | 3.25 | 2.40 |
| 8 | A17 | 1fr yel grn, *bl* | 32.50 | 16.00 |
| 9 | A18 | 1.50fr dull blue | 8.00 | 4.00 |
| 10 | A18 | 2fr brown red | 20.00 | 16.00 |
| | | *Nos. 1-10 (10)* | 72.55 | 48.05 |

**Stamps of Middle Congo, 1933 Overprinted in Black**

a

b

c

**1936**

| No. | Type | Description | Unused | Used |
|---|---|---|---|---|
| 11 | A4 (b) | 1c lt brown | .40 | *.50* |
| 12 | A4 (b) | 2c dull blue | .40 | *.50* |
| 13 | A4 (b) | 4c olive green | 1.60 | 1.60 |
| 14 | A4 (b) | 5c red violet | .80 | 1.00 |
| 15 | A4 (b) | 10c slate | 1.60 | 1.25 |
| 16 | A4 (b) | 15c dk violet | 2.00 | 1.60 |
| 17 | A4 (b) | 20c red, *pink* | 2.00 | 1.60 |
| 18 | A4 (b) | 25c orange | 4.00 | 2.40 |
| 19 | A5 (a) | 40c orange brn | 5.50 | 2.75 |
| 20 | A5 (c) | 50c black violet | 5.50 | 2.40 |
| 21 | A5 (c) | 75c black, *pink* | 5.50 | 4.75 |
| 22 | A5 (a) | 90c carmine | 5.50 | 4.00 |
| 23 | A5 (c) | 1.50fr dark blue | 4.75 | 2.00 |
| 24 | A6 (a) | 5fr slate blue | 55.00 | 35.00 |
| 25 | A6 (a) | 10fr black | 35.00 | 30.00 |
| 26 | A6 (a) | 20fr dark brown | 35.00 | 32.50 |
| | | *Nos. 11-26 (16)* | 164.55 | 123.85 |

Other overprints inscribed "Afrique Equitoriale Française" in a different type font on earlier Middle Congo stamps are listed under Middle Congo.

Common Design Types pictured following the introduction.

**Paris International Exposition Issue**

Common Design Types

**1937, Apr. 15 Engr.** ***Perf. 13***

| No. | Type | Description | Unused | Used |
|---|---|---|---|---|
| 27 | CD74 | 20c dark violet | 2.40 | 2.40 |
| 28 | CD75 | 30c dark green | 2.40 | 2.40 |
| 29 | CD76 | 40c carmine rose | 2.40 | 2.40 |
| 30 | CD77 | 50c dk brn & bl | 2.40 | 2.40 |
| 31 | CD78 | 90c red | 3.25 | 3.25 |
| 32 | CD79 | 1.50fr ultra | 3.25 | 3.25 |
| | | *Nos. 27-32 (6)* | 16.10 | 16.10 |

Logging on Loéme River — A1

People of Chad — A2

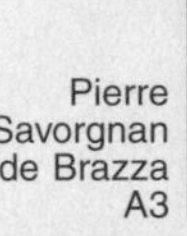
Pierre Savorgnan de Brazza A3

Emile Gentil — A4

Paul Crampel A5

Governor Victor Liotard A6

Two types of 25c:
Type I — Wide numerals (4mm).
Type II — Narrow numerals (3½mm).

**1937-40 Photo. *Perf. 13½x13***

| No. | Type | Description | Unused | Used |
|---|---|---|---|---|
| 33 | A1 | 1c brown & yel | .25 | .25 |
| 34 | A1 | 2c violet & grn | .25 | .25 |
| 35 | A1 | 3c blue & yel ('40) | .25 | .30 |
| 36 | A1 | 4c magenta & bl | .25 | .30 |
| 37 | A1 | 5c dk & lt green | .25 | .30 |
| 38 | A2 | 10c magenta & blue | .25 | .30 |
| 39 | A2 | 15c blue & buff | .25 | .30 |
| 40 | A2 | 20c brown & yellow | .25 | .30 |
| 41 | A2 | 25c cop red & bl (I) | .80 | .30 |
| *a.* | | Type II | 2.75 | 2.00 |
| 42 | A3 | 30c gray grn & grn | .80 | .55 |
| 43 | A3 | 30c chlky bl, ind & buff ('40) | .40 | .50 |
| 44 | A2 | 35c dp grn & yel ('38) | .80 | .80 |
| 45 | A3 | 40c cop red & bl | .40 | .30 |
| 46 | A3 | 45c dk bl & lt grn | 4.75 | 3.50 |
| 47 | A3 | 45c dp grn & yel grn ('40) | .40 | .80 |
| 48 | A3 | 50c brown & yellow | .50 | .25 |
| 49 | A3 | 55c pur & bl ('38) | .80 | .80 |
| 50 | A3 | 60c mar & gray bl ('40) | .80 | .85 |
| 51 | A4 | 65c dk bl & lt grn | .80 | .40 |
| 52 | A4 | 70c dp vio & buff ('40) | .80 | .95 |
| 53 | A4 | 75c ol blk & dl yel | 5.50 | 4.50 |
| 54 | A4 | 80c brn & yel ('38) | .40 | .80 |
| 55 | A4 | 90c copper red & buff | .55 | .40 |
| 56 | A4 | 1fr dk vio & lt grn | 2.40 | 1.20 |
| 57 | A3 | 1fr cer & dl org ('38) | 4.00 | 1.60 |
| 58 | A4 | 1fr bl grn & sl grn ('40) | .40 | .55 |
| 59 | A5 | 1.25fr cop red & buff | 2.40 | 1.20 |
| 60 | A5 | 1.40fr dk brn & pale grn ('40) | 1.20 | 1.25 |
| 61 | A5 | 1.50fr dk & lt blue | 1.60 | .80 |
| 62 | A5 | 1.60fr dp vio & buff ('40) | 1.60 | 1.25 |
| 63 | A5 | 1.75fr brn & yel | 2.00 | 1.20 |
| 64 | A4 | 1.75fr bl & lt bl ('38) | .80 | .80 |
| 65 | A5 | 2fr dk & lt green | 1.60 | .80 |
| 66 | A6 | 2.15fr brn, vio & yel ('38) | 1.20 | .80 |
| 67 | A6 | 2.25fr bl & lt bl ('39) | 1.60 | 1.60 |
| 68 | A6 | 2.50fr rose lake & buff ('40) | 2.00 | 1.40 |
| 69 | A6 | 3fr dk blue & buff | .80 | .50 |
| 70 | A6 | 5fr dk & lt green | 1.60 | 1.20 |
| 71 | A6 | 10fr dk violet & bl | 3.25 | 3.25 |
| 72 | A6 | 20fr ol blk & dl yel | 4.00 | 3.50 |
| | | *Nos. 33-72 (40)* | 52.95 | 40.90 |

For overprints and surcharges see Nos. 80-127, 129-141, B2-B3, B10-B13, B22-B23.

## Colonial Arts Exhibition Issue

Souvenir Sheet

Common Design Type

**1937 *Imperf.***

| No. | Type | Description | Unused | Used |
|---|---|---|---|---|
| 73 | CD79 | 3fr red brown | 12.00 | *16.00* |
| | | Never hinged | 16.00 | |

Count Louis Edouard Bouet-Willaumez and His Ship "La Malouine" — A7

**1938, Dec. 5 *Perf. 13½***

| No. | Type | Description | Unused | Used |
|---|---|---|---|---|
| 74 | A7 | 65c gray brown | 1.25 | 1.25 |
| 75 | A7 | 1fr deep rose | 1.25 | 1.25 |
| 76 | A7 | 1.75fr blue | 1.60 | 1.60 |
| 77 | A7 | 2fr dull violet | 2.40 | 2.40 |
| | | *Nos. 74-77 (4)* | 6.50 | 6.50 |
| | | Set, never hinged | 8.85 | |

Centenary of Gabon.

## New York World's Fair Issue

Common Design Type

**1939, May 10 Engr. *Perf. 12½x12***

| No. | Type | Description | Unused | Used |
|---|---|---|---|---|
| 78 | CD82 | 1.25fr carmine lake | .80 | 1.60 |
| 79 | CD82 | 2.25fr ultra | .80 | 1.60 |
| | | Set, never hinged | 2.40 | |

Libreville View and Marshal Petain A7a

**1941 Engr. *Perf. 12½x12***

| No. | Type | Description | Unused | Used |
|---|---|---|---|---|
| 79A | A7a | 1fr bluish green | .40 | |
| 79B | A7a | 2.50fr blue | .40 | |
| | | Set, never hinged | 1.60 | |

Nos. 79A-79B were issued by the Vichy government in France, but were not placed on sale in French Equatorial Africa.

For surcharges, see Nos. B36-B37.

## Stamps of 1936-40, Overprinted in Carmine or Black

Nos. 80-82, 84-88, 93

Nos. 83, 89-92, 94-125

**1940-41 *Perf. 13½x13***

| No. | Type | Description | Unused | Used |
|---|---|---|---|---|
| 80 | A1 | 1c brn & yel (C) | 4.00 | 4.00 |
| 81 | A1 | 2c vio & grn (C) | 4.00 | 4.00 |
| 82 | A1 | 3c blue & yel (C) | 4.00 | 4.00 |
| 83 | A4 | 4c ol grn (No. 13) | 24.00 | 16.00 |
| *b.* | | Inverted overprint | 120.00 | *150.00* |
| 84 | A1 | 5c dk grn & lt grn (C) | 4.00 | 4.00 |
| 85 | A2 | 10c magenta & bl | 4.00 | 4.00 |
| 86 | A2 | 15c blue & buff (C) | 4.00 | 4.00 |
| 87 | A2 | 20c brn & yel (C) | 4.00 | 4.00 |
| 88 | A2 | 25c cop red & bl | 4.00 | 4.00 |
| 89 | A3 | 30c gray grn & grn (C) | 16.00 | 16.00 |
| 90 | A3 | 30c gray grn & grn ('41) | 16.00 | 16.00 |
| 91 | A3 | 30c chlky bl, ind & buff (C) ('41) | 16.00 | 16.00 |
| 92 | A3 | 30c chlky bl, ind & buff ('41) | 16.00 | 16.00 |
| 93 | A2 | 35c dp grn & yel (C) | 4.00 | 4.00 |
| 94 | A3 | 40c cop red & bl | 4.00 | 4.00 |
| *b.* | | Inverted overprint | | *100.00* |
| 95 | A3 | 45c dp grn & yel grn (C) | 4.00 | 4.00 |
| 96 | A3 | 45c dp grn & yel grn ('41) | 16.00 | 16.00 |
| 97 | A3 | 50c brn & yel (C) | 4.00 | 4.00 |
| 98 | A3 | 50c brn & yel ('41) | 8.00 | 8.00 |
| 99 | A3 | 55c pur & bl (C) | 4.00 | 4.00 |
| 100 | A3 | 55c pur & bl ('41) | 16.00 | 16.00 |
| 101 | A3 | 60c mar & gray bl | 4.00 | 4.00 |
| 102 | A4 | 65c dk bl & lt grn | 4.00 | 4.00 |
| 103 | A4 | 70c dp vio & buff | 4.00 | 4.00 |
| 104 | A4 | 75c ol blk & dl yel | 80.00 | 80.00 |
| 105 | A4 | 80c brown & yellow | 4.00 | 4.00 |
| 106 | A4 | 90c cop red & buff | 4.00 | 4.00 |
| 107 | A4 | 1fr bl grn & sl grn | 8.00 | 8.00 |
| 108 | A4 | 1fr bl grn & sl grn (C) ('41) | 20.00 | 20.00 |
| 109 | A3 | 1fr cer & dl org | 4.00 | 4.00 |
| 110 | A5 | 1.40fr dk brn & pale grn | 4.00 | 4.00 |
| 111 | A5 | 1.50fr dk bl & lt bl | 4.00 | 4.00 |
| 112 | A5 | 1.60fr dp vio & buff | 4.00 | 4.00 |
| 113 | A5 | 1.75fr brown & yel | 4.00 | 4.00 |
| 114 | A6 | 2.15fr brn, vio & yel | 4.00 | 4.00 |
| 115 | A6 | 2.25fr bl & lt bl (C) | 4.00 | 4.00 |
| 116 | A6 | 2.25fr bl & lt bl ('41) | 16.00 | 16.00 |
| 117 | A6 | 2.50fr rose lake & buff | 4.00 | 4.00 |
| 118 | A6 | 3fr dk bl & buff (C) | 4.00 | 4.00 |
| 119 | A6 | 3fr dk bl & buff ('41) | 16.00 | 16.00 |
| 120 | A6 | 5fr dk grn & lt grn (C) | 4.00 | 4.00 |
| 121 | A6 | 5fr dk grn & lt grn ('41) | 140.00 | 140.00 |
| 122 | A6 | 10fr dk vio & bl (C) | 3.25 | 3.25 |
| 123 | A6 | 10fr dk vio & bl ('41) | 130.00 | 130.00 |
| 124 | A6 | 20fr ol blk & dl yel (C) | 4.00 | 4.00 |
| 125 | A6 | 20fr ol blk & dl yel ('41) | 16.00 | 16.00 |
| | | *Nos. 80-125 (46)* | 673.25 | 665.25 |

For overprints and surcharges see Nos. 129-132, B12-B13, B22-B23.

For types of Nos. 38//61 without "RF," see Nos. 155A-155B.

### Double Overprint

| No. | Type | Description | Unused | Used |
|---|---|---|---|---|
| *80a* | A1 | 1c | 325.00 | 225.00 |
| *81a* | A1 | 2c | 32.50 | |
| *82a* | A1 | 3c | 32.50 | |
| *83a* | A4 | 4c | 75.00 | |
| *84a* | A1 | 5c | 32.50 | |
| *85a* | A2 | 10c | 32.50 | 40.00 |
| *86a* | A2 | 15c | 32.50 | |
| *87a* | A2 | 20c | 32.50 | |
| *88a* | A2 | 25c | 55.00 | |
| *89a* | A3 | 30c | 110.00 | 120.00 |
| *90a* | A3 | 30c | 47.50 | 55.00 |
| *91a* | A3 | 30c | 47.50 | 47.50 |
| *93a* | A2 | 35c | 250.00 | |
| *94a* | A3 | 40c | 47.50 | |
| *96a* | A3 | 45c | 75.00 | |
| *98a* | A3 | 50c | 110.00 | 75.00 |
| *100a* | A3 | 55c | 75.00 | |
| *102a* | A4 | 65c | 45.00 | |
| *103a* | A4 | 70c | 47.50 | |
| *104a* | A4 | 75c | 175.00 | |
| *105a* | A4 | 80c | 47.50 | |
| *106a* | A4 | 90c | 45.00 | |
| ***b.*** | | one inverted | 120.00 | |
| *109a* | A4 | 1fr One inverted | 120.00 | |
| *110a* | A5 | 1.40fr | 47.50 | |
| *111a* | A5 | 1.50fr | 47.50 | |
| *114a* | A6 | 2.15fr | 40.00 | |
| *115a* | A6 | 2.25fr | 60.00 | |
| *116a* | A6 | 2.25fr | 47.50 | |
| *117a* | A6 | 2.50fr | 47.50 | |
| *119a* | A6 | 3fr | 60.00 | |
| *123a* | A6 | 10fr | 60.00 | *67.50* |
| *124a* | A6 | 20fr | 60.00 | |
| | | *Nos. 96a-124a (17)* | 1,035. | |

Nos. 48, 51 Surcharged in Black or Carmine

**1940**

| No. | Type | Description | Unused | Used |
|---|---|---|---|---|
| 126 | A3 | 75c on 50c | .80 | .80 |
| *a.* | | Double surcharge | 40.00 | |
| 127 | A4 | 1fr on 65c (C) | .80 | .80 |
| *a.* | | Double surcharge | 32.50 | |
| | | Set, never hinged | 3.20 | |

## Middle Congo No. 67 Overprinted in Carmine like No. 80

***Perf. 13½***

| No. | Type | Description | Unused | Used |
|---|---|---|---|---|
| 128 | A4 | 4c olive green | 65.00 | 65.00 |

Stamps of 1940 With Additional Overprint in Black

**1940 *Perf. 13½x13***

| No. | Type | Description | Unused | Used |
|---|---|---|---|---|
| 129 | A4 | 80c brown & yel | 24.00 | 16.00 |
| *a.* | | Overprint without "2" | 150.00 | |
| 130 | A4 | 1fr bl grn & sl grn | 24.00 | 20.00 |
| 131 | A3 | 1fr cer & dull org | 24.00 | 16.00 |
| 132 | A5 | 1.50fr dk bl & lt bl | 24.00 | 16.00 |
| | | *Nos. 129-132 (4)* | 96.00 | 68.00 |

Arrival of General de Gaulle in Brazzaville, capital of Free France, Oct. 24, 1940.

These stamps were sold affixed to post cards and at a slight increase over face value to cover the cost of the cards. Values for unused stamps are for examples without gum.

For surcharges see Nos. B12-B13, B22-B23.

Stamps of 1937-40 Overprinted in Black

1 mm between lines

2 mm between lines

**1941**

| No. | Type | Description | Unused | Used |
|---|---|---|---|---|
| 133 | A1 | 1c brown & yel | 4.00 | 4.00 |
| 134 | A1 | 2c violet & grn | 4.00 | 4.00 |
| 135 | A1 | 3c blue & yel | 4.00 | 4.00 |
| 136 | A1 | 5c dk & lt green | 4.00 | 4.00 |
| 137 | A2 | 10c magenta & bl | 4.00 | 4.00 |
| 138 | A2 | 15c blue & buff | 4.00 | 4.00 |
| 139 | A2 | 20c brown & yel | 4.00 | 4.00 |
| 140 | A2 | 25c copper red & bl | 4.00 | 4.00 |
| 141 | A2 | 35c dp grn & yel | 4.00 | 4.00 |
| *a.* | | Double overprint | 120.00 | |
| | | *Nos. 133-141 (9)* | 36.00 | 36.00 |
| | | Set, never hinged | 55.00 | |

There are 2 settings of the overprint on Nos. 133-141 & C10. The 1st has 1mm between lines of the overprint (Nos. 133-141), the 2nd has 2mm. Value, set with 2mm spacing $95.

**Catalogue values for unused stamps in this section, from this point to the end of the section, are for Never Hinged items.**

Phoenix — A8

**1941 Photo. *Perf. 14x14½***

| No. | Type | Description | Unused | Used |
|---|---|---|---|---|
| 142 | A8 | 5c brown | .30 | .25 |
| 143 | A8 | 10c dark blue | .30 | .25 |
| *a.* | | Denomination doubled | *125.00* | — |
| 144 | A8 | 25c emerald | .30 | .25 |
| 145 | A8 | 30c deep orange | .30 | .25 |
| 146 | A8 | 40c dk slate grn | .55 | .30 |
| 147 | A8 | 80c red brown | .55 | .30 |
| 148 | A8 | 1fr deep red lilac | .55 | .30 |
| 149 | A8 | 1.50fr brt red | .75 | .40 |
| 150 | A8 | 2fr gray | .75 | .40 |
| 151 | A8 | 2.50fr brt ultra | .95 | .70 |
| 152 | A8 | 4fr dull violet | .95 | .70 |
| 153 | A8 | 5fr yellow bister | .95 | .70 |
| 154 | A8 | 10fr deep brown | 1.40 | 1.00 |
| 155 | A8 | 20fr deep green | 1.75 | 1.25 |
| | | *Nos. 142-155 (14)* | 10.35 | 7.05 |

For surcharges see #158-165, B14-B21, B24-B35.

## Types of 1937-40 without "RF"

**1944 *Perf. 13½***

| No. | Type | Description | Unused | Used |
|---|---|---|---|---|
| 155A | A2 | 10c magenta & blue | 1.20 | |
| 155B | A2 | 15c blue & buff | 1.60 | |
| 155C | A3 | 60c maroon & gray blue | 1.60 | |
| 155D | A5 | 1.50fr dk & lt blue | 2.00 | |
| | | *Nos. 155A-155D (4)* | 6.40 | |

Nos. 155A-155D were issued by the Vichy government in France, but were not sold in French Equatorial Africa.

## Eboue Issue

Common Design Type

**1945 Unwmk. Engr. *Perf. 13***

| No. | Type | Description | Unused | Used |
|---|---|---|---|---|
| 156 | CD91 | 2fr black | .65 | .50 |
| 157 | CD91 | 25fr Prussian green | 1.90 | 1.50 |

Nos. 156-157 exist imperforate. Value, set $65.

**Nos. 142, 144 and 151 Surcharged with New Values and Bars in Red, Carmine or Black**

| 1946 | | | *Perf. 14x14½* | |
|---|---|---|---|---|
| **158** | A8 | 50c on 5c (R) | .80 | .65 |
| **159** | A8 | 60c on 5c (R) | .80 | .65 |
| **160** | A8 | 70c on 5c (R) | .80 | .65 |
| **161** | A8 | 1.20fr on 5c (C) | .80 | .65 |
| **162** | A8 | 2.40fr on 25c | 1.40 | 1.00 |
| **163** | A8 | 3fr on 25c | 1.40 | 1.00 |
| **164** | A8 | 4.50fr on 25c | 1.75 | 1.20 |
| **165** | A8 | 15fr on 2.50fr (C) | 1.90 | 1.40 |
| | | *Nos. 158-165 (8)* | 9.65 | 7.20 |

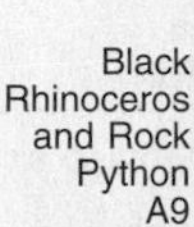

Black Rhinoceros and Rock Python A9

Jungle Scene — A10

Mountainous Shore Line — A11

Gabon Forest — A12

Niger Boatman — A13

Young Bacongo Woman — A14

| 1946 | Unwmk. | Engr. | *Perf. 12½* | |
|---|---|---|---|---|
| **166** | A9 | 10c deep blue | .40 | .25 |
| **167** | A9 | 30c violet blk | .40 | .25 |
| **168** | A9 | 40c dp orange | .40 | .25 |
| **169** | A10 | 50c violet bl | .80 | .50 |
| **170** | A10 | 60c dk carmine | .80 | .50 |
| **171** | A10 | 80c dk ol grn | .80 | .50 |
| **172** | A11 | 1fr dp orange | .80 | .30 |
| **173** | A11 | 1.20fr dp claret | .80 | .65 |
| **174** | A11 | 1.50fr dk green | 1.20 | .95 |
| **175** | A12 | 2fr dk vio brn | .40 | .25 |
| **176** | A12 | 3fr rose carmine | .80 | .50 |
| **177** | A12 | 3.60fr red brown | 3.25 | 2.50 |
| **178** | A12 | 4fr deep blue | .80 | .30 |
| **179** | A13 | 5fr dk brown | .80 | .25 |
| **180** | A13 | 6fr deep blue | 1.25 | .30 |
| **181** | A13 | 10fr black | 2.40 | .75 |
| **182** | A14 | 15fr brown | 2.40 | .80 |
| **183** | A14 | 20fr dp claret | 2.40 | .80 |
| **184** | A14 | 25fr black | 3.25 | .80 |
| | | *Nos. 166-184 (19)* | 24.15 | 11.40 |

Imperforates

Most French Equatorial Africa stamps from 1951 onward exist imperforate in issued and trial colors, and also in small presentation sheets in issued colors.

Pierre Savorgnan de Brazza — A15

| 1951, Nov. 5 | | | *Perf. 13* | |
|---|---|---|---|---|
| **185** | A15 | 10fr indigo & dk grn | 1.60 | .40 |

Cent. of the birth of Pierre Savorgnan de Brazza, explorer.

**Military Medal Issue**
Common Design Type
**Engraved and Typographed**

| 1952, Dec. 1 | | | *Perf. 13* | |
|---|---|---|---|---|
| **186** | CD101 | 15fr multicolored | 8.00 | 5.50 |

Lt. Gov. Adolphe L. Cureau A16

| 1954, Sept. 20 | | | **Engr.** | |
|---|---|---|---|---|
| **187** | A16 | 15fr ol grn & red brn | 2.00 | .80 |

Savannah Monitor A17

| 1955, May 2 | | | **Unwmk.** | |
|---|---|---|---|---|
| **188** | A17 | 8fr dk grn & claret | 2.40 | 1.25 |

International Exhibition for Wildlife Protection, Paris, May 1955.

**FIDES Issue**
Common Design Type

Designs: 5fr, Boali Waterfall and Power Plant, Ubangi-Chari. 10fr, Cotton, Chad. 15fr, Brazzaville Hospital, Middle Congo. 20fr, Libreville Harbor, Gabon.

| 1956, Apr. 25 | | | *Perf. 13x12½* | |
|---|---|---|---|---|
| **189** | CD103 | 5fr dk brn & claret | .65 | .30 |
| **190** | CD103 | 10fr blk & bluish grn | .65 | .30 |
| **191** | CD103 | 15fr ind & gray vio | .80 | .40 |
| **192** | CD103 | 20fr dk red & red org | 1.10 | .65 |
| | | *Nos. 189-192 (4)* | 3.20 | 1.65 |

**Coffee Issue**

Coffee A19

| 1956, Oct. | | Engr. | *Perf. 13* | |
|---|---|---|---|---|
| **193** | A19 | 10fr brn vio & vio bl | 1.60 | .40 |

Leprosarium at Mayumba and Maltese Cross — A20

| 1957, Mar. 11 | | | | |
|---|---|---|---|---|
| **194** | A20 | 15fr grn, bl grn & red | 2.00 | .80 |

Issued in honor of the Knights of Malta.

Giant Eland A21

| 1957, Nov. 4 | | | | |
|---|---|---|---|---|
| **195** | A21 | 1fr shown | .80 | .40 |
| **196** | A21 | 2fr Lions | .80 | .40 |
| **197** | A21 | 3fr Elephant, vert. | .80 | .40 |
| **198** | A21 | 4fr Greater kudu, vert. | .90 | .40 |
| | | *Nos. 195-198 (4)* | 3.30 | 1.60 |

WHO Building, Brazzaville A22

| 1958, May 19 | | Engr. | *Perf. 13* | |
|---|---|---|---|---|
| **199** | A22 | 20fr dk green & org brn | 1.60 | .80 |

10th anniv. of WHO.

**Flower Issue**
Common Design Type

| 1958, July 7 | | Photo. | *Perf. 12x12½* | |
|---|---|---|---|---|
| **200** | CD104 | 10fr Euadania | 1.60 | .65 |
| **201** | CD104 | 25fr Spathodea | 2.00 | .95 |

**Human Rights Issue**
Common Design Type

| 1958, Dec. 10 | | Engr. | *Perf. 13* | |
|---|---|---|---|---|
| **202** | CD105 | 20fr Prus grn & dk bl | 2.40 | 1.25 |

**SEMI-POSTAL STAMPS**

Common Design Type

| 1938, Oct. 24 | | | **Engr.** | |
|---|---|---|---|---|
| **B1** | CD80 | 1.75fr + 50c brt ultra | 24.00 | 24.00 |
| | | Never hinged | 32.50 | |

Nos. 51, 64 Surcharged in Black or Red

| 1938, Nov. 7 | | | *Perf. 13x13½* | |
|---|---|---|---|---|
| **B2** | A4 | 65c + 35c dk bl & lt grn (R) | 2.40 | 2.40 |
| **B3** | A4 | 1.75fr + 50c bl & lt bl | 4.00 | 4.00 |
| | | Set, never hinged | 12.00 | |

The surtax was for welfare.

**French Revolution Issue**
Common Design Type
Name and Value Typo. in Black

| 1939, July 5 | | | **Photo.** | |
|---|---|---|---|---|
| **B4** | CD83 | 45c + 25c green | 16.00 | 16.00 |
| **B5** | CD83 | 70c + 30c brown | 16.00 | 16.00 |
| **B6** | CD83 | 90c + 35c red org | 16.00 | 16.00 |
| **B7** | CD83 | 1.25fr + 1fr rose pink | 16.00 | 16.00 |
| **B8** | CD83 | 2.25fr + 2fr blue | 16.00 | 16.00 |
| | | *Nos. B4-B8 (5)* | 80.00 | 80.00 |
| | | Set, never hinged | 120.00 | |

Surtax used for the defense of the colonies.

**Catalogue values for unused stamps in this section, from this point to the end of the section, are for Never Hinged items.**

**Common Design Type and**

Native Artilleryman SP1

Gabon Infantryman SP2

| 1941 | | Photo. | *Perf. 13½* |
|---|---|---|---|
| **B8A** | SP1 | 1fr + 1fr red | 3.50 |
| **B8B** | CD86 | 1.50fr + 3fr maroon | 3.50 |
| **B8C** | SP2 | 2.50fr + 1fr blue | 3.50 |
| | | *Nos. B8A-B8C (3)* | 10.50 |

Nos. B8A-B8C were issued by the Vichy government in France, but were not placed on sale in French Equatorial Africa.

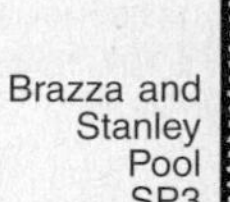

Brazza and Stanley Pool SP3

| 1941 | | Photo. | *Perf. 14½x14* | |
|---|---|---|---|---|
| **B9** | SP3 | 1fr + 2fr dk brn & red | 2.00 | 1.60 |

The surtax was for a monument to Pierre Savorgnan de Brazza.

Nos. 67, 71 Srchd. in Red

| 1943, June 28 | | | *Perf. 13½x13* | |
|---|---|---|---|---|
| **B10** | A6 | 2.25fr + 50fr | 47.50 | 32.50 |
| **B11** | A6 | 10fr + 100fr | 120.00 | 80.00 |

Nos. 129 and 132 with Add'l. Srch. in Carmine

| 1944 | | | | |
|---|---|---|---|---|
| **B12** | A4 | 80c + 10fr | 65.00 | 40.00 |
| **B13** | A5 | 1.50fr + 15fr | 65.00 | 40.00 |

Surcharged Vertically on Nos. 142-146, 148, 150-151

| | | *Perf. 14x14½* | | |
|---|---|---|---|---|
| **B14** | A8 | 5c + 10fr brown | 40.00 | 27.50 |
| **B15** | A8 | 10c + 10fr dk bl | 40.00 | 27.50 |
| **B16** | A8 | 25c + 10fr emer | 40.00 | 27.50 |
| **B17** | A8 | 30c + 10fr dp org | 40.00 | 27.50 |
| **B18** | A8 | 40c + 10fr dk sl grn | 40.00 | 27.50 |
| **B19** | A8 | 1fr + 10fr dp red lil | 40.00 | 27.50 |
| **B20** | A8 | 2fr + 20fr gray | 40.00 | 27.50 |
| **B21** | A8 | 2.50fr + 25fr brt ultra | 40.00 | 27.50 |
| | | *Nos. B12-B21 (10)* | 450.00 | 300.00 |

Nos. 129 and 132 with Add'l. Srch. in Carmine

**1944** ***Perf. 13½x13***

**B22** A4 80c + 10fr 65.00 40.00
**B23** A5 1.50fr + 15fr 65.00 40.00

Surcharged Vertically on Nos. 142-146, 148, 150-155

***Perf. 14x14½***

**B24** A8 5c + 10fr brn 40.00 27.50
**B25** A8 10c + 10fr dk bl 40.00 27.50
**B26** A8 25c + 10fr emer 40.00 27.50
**B27** A8 30c + 10fr dp org 40.00 27.50
**B28** A8 40c + 10fr dk sl grn 40.00 27.50
**B29** A8 1fr + 10fr dp red lil 40.00 27.50
**B30** A8 2fr + 20fr gray 40.00 27.50
**B31** A8 2.50fr + 25fr brt ultra 40.00 27.50
**B32** A8 4fr + 40fr dl vio 40.00 27.50
**B33** A8 5fr + 50fr yel bis 40.00 27.50
**B34** A8 10fr + 100fr dp brn 40.00 27.50
**B35** A8 20fr + 200fr dp grn 40.00 27.50
*Nos. B22-B35 (14)* 610.00 410.00

Nos. B12 to B35 were issued to raise funds for the Committee to Aid the Fighting Men and Patriots of France.

Nos. 79A-79B Srchd. in Black or Red

**1944** **Engr.** ***Perf. 12½x12***

**B36** 50c + 1.50fr on 2.50fr deep blue (R) .80
**B37** + 2.50fr on 1fr green .80

Colonial Development Fund.

Nos. B36-B37 were issued by the Vichy government in France, but were not placed on sale in French Equatorial Africa.

### Red Cross Issue
Common Design Type

**1944** **Photo.** ***Perf. 14½x14***

**B38** CD90 5fr + 20fr royal blue 1.60 1.20

The surtax was for the French Red Cross and national relief.

### Tropical Medicine Issue
Common Design Type

**1950, May 15** **Engr.** ***Perf. 13***

**B39** CD100 10fr + 2fr dk bl grn & vio brn 7.25 5.50

The surtax was for charitable work.

---

## AIR POST STAMPS

Hydroplane over Pointe-Noire — AP1

Trimotor over Stanley Pool — AP2

**1937** **Unwmk.** **Photo.** ***Perf. 13½***

**C1** AP1 1.50fr ol blk & yel .40 .40
**C2** AP1 2fr mag & blue .55 .55
**C3** AP1 2.50fr grn & buff .55 .55
**C4** AP1 3.75fr brn & lt grn .80 .80
**C5** AP2 4.50fr cop red & bl .90 .90
**C6** AP2 6.50fr bl & lt grn 1.60 1.60
**C7** AP2 8.50fr red brn & yel 1.60 1.60
**C8** AP2 10.75fr vio & lt grn 1.60 1.60
*Nos. C1-C8 (8)* 8.00 8.00

For overprints and surcharges see Nos. C9-C16, CB6.

### Nos. C1, C3-C7 Overprinted in Black like Nos. 133-141

No. C10

**1940-41**

**C9** AP1 1.50fr ('41) 240.00 240.00
**C10** AP1 2.50fr 4.00 4.00
*a.* Double overprint 275.00 275.00
*b.* Inverted overprint 275.00 275.00
**C11** AP1 3.75fr ('41) 240.00 240.00
**C12** AP2 4.50fr 4.50 4.50
*a.* Double overprint 275.00 275.00
**C13** AP2 6.50fr 4.00 4.00
*a.* Double overprint 130.00 130.00
**C14** AP2 8.50fr 4.00 4.00

No. C8 Surcharged in Carmine

**C15** AP2 50fr on 10.75fr 12.00 12.00

No. C3 Surcharged in Black

**C16** AP1 10fr on 2.50fr ('41) 95.00 95.00
*Nos. C9-C16 (8)* 603.50 603.50

Counterfeits of Nos. C9 and C11 exist. See note following No. 141.

**Catalogue values for unused stamps in this section, from this point to the end of the section, are for Never Hinged items.**

### Common Design Type

**1941** **Photo.** ***Perf. 14½x14***

**C17** CD87 1fr dark orange .65 .30
**C18** CD87 1.50fr brt red .95 .50
**C19** CD87 5fr brown red 1.60 .90
**C20** CD87 10fr black 1.75 1.00
**C21** CD87 25fr ultra 1.60 1.20
**C22** CD87 50fr dark green 1.60 1.20
**C23** CD87 100fr plum 2.25 1.25
*Nos. C17-C23 (7)* 10.40 6.35

### Types of 1937 without "RF" and

Sikorsky 5.43 Seaplane and Canoe — AP2a

***Perf. 13½, 13 (#C23M)***

**1943, Oct. 18-1944** **Unwmk.**

**C23A** AP1 1.50fr ol blk & yel .40
**C23B** AP1 2fr mag & blue .40
**C23C** AP1 2.50fr grn & buff .40
**C23D** AP1 3.75fr brn & lt grn .80
**C23E** AP2 4.50fr cop red & bl .80
**C23F** AP2 5fr green 1.20
**C23G** AP2 6.50fr bl & lt grn 1.20
**C23H** AP2 8.50fr red brn & yel 1.20
**C23I** AP2 10fr gray & brn ('44) 1.20
**C23J** AP2 10.75fr vio & lt grn 1.20
**C23K** AP2 20fr yel & brn red ('44) 1.60
**C23L** AP2 50fr gray grn & blk ('44) 2.40
**C23M** AP2a 100fr red brown ('44) 1.60
*Nos. C23A-C23M (13)* 14.40

Issue dates: Nos. C23I, C23K-L, 4/3/44; C23M, 6/26/44.

Nos. C23A-C23M were issued by the Vichy government in France, but were not sold in French Equatorial Africa.

### Victory Issue
Common Design Type

***Perf. 12½***

**1946, May 8** **Unwmk.** **Engr.**

**C24** CD92 8fr lilac rose 1.60 1.25

### Chad to Rhine Issue
Common Design Types

**1946, June 6**

**C25** CD93 5fr dk violet 1.60 1.20
**C26** CD94 10fr slate green 1.60 1.20
**C27** CD95 15fr deep blue 2.75 2.00
**C28** CD96 20fr red orange 2.75 2.00
**C29** CD97 25fr sepia 2.75 2.00
**C30** CD98 50fr brown carmine 3.25 2.40
*Nos. C25-C30 (6)* 14.70 10.80

Palms and Village — AP3

Village and Waterfront — AP4

Bearers in Jungle — AP5

**1946** **Engr.** ***Perf. 13***

**C31** AP3 50fr red brn 3.50 .80
**C32** AP4 100fr grnsh blk 5.25 1.25
**C33** AP5 200fr deep blue 12.00 2.00
*Nos. C31-C33 (3)* 20.75 4.05

### UPU Issue
Common Design Type

**1949, July 4**

**C34** CD99 25fr green 16.00 12.00

Brazza Holding Map — AP6

**1951, Nov. 5**

**C35** AP6 15fr brn, indigo & red 2.40 1.60

Cent. of the birth of Pierre Savorgnan de Brazza, explorer.

Archbishop Augouard and St. Anne Cathedral, Brazzaville — AP7

**1952, Dec. 1**

**C36** AP7 15fr ol grn, dk brn & vio brn 6.50 2.40

Cent. of the birth of Archbishop Philippe-Prosper Augouard.

Anhingas — AP8

**1953, Feb. 16**

**C37** AP8 500fr grnsh blk, blk & slate 47.50 8.00

### Liberation Issue
Common Design Type

**1954, June 6**

**C38** CD102 15fr vio & vio brn 12.00 8.00

Log Rafts — AP9

Designs: 100fr, Fishing boats and nets, Lake Chad. 200fr, Age of mechanization.

**1955, Jan. 24** **Engr.**

**C39** AP9 50fr ind, brn & dk grn 2.40 .80
**C40** AP9 100fr aqua, dk grn & blk brn 8.00 1.60
**C41** AP9 200fr red & deep plum 12.00 2.40
*Nos. C39-C41 (3)* 22.40 4.80

Gov. Gen. Félix Eboué, View of Brazzaville and the Pantheon — AP10

**1955, Apr. 30** **Unwmk.** ***Perf. 13***

**C42** AP10 15fr sep, brn & slate bl 6.50 2.40

Gen. Louis Faidherbé and African Sharpshooter AP11

**1957, July 20**

**C43** AP11 15fr sepia & org ver 3.50 2.00

Centenary of French African Troops.

---

## AIR POST SEMI-POSTAL STAMPS

### French Revolution Issue
Common Design Type

**1939** **Unwmk.** **Photo.** ***Perf. 13***

**Name and Value Typo. in Orange**

**CB1** CD83 4.50fr + 4fr brn blk 40.00 40.00

SPAP1

SPAP2

SPAP3

**Unwmk.**

**1942, June 22 Engr. *Perf. 13***

**CB2** SPAP1 1.50fr + 3.50fr green .80
**CB3** SPAP2 2fr + 6fr brown .80
**CB4** SPAP3 3fr + 9fr carmine .80
*Nos. CB2-CB4 (3)* 2.40

Native children's welfare fund.

Nos. CB2-CB4 were issued by the Vichy government in France, but were not placed on sale in French Equatorial Africa.

**Colonial Education Fund**
Common Design Type

**1942, June 22**

**CB5** CD86a 1.20fr + 1.80fr bl & red .80

No. CB5 was issued by the Vichy government in France, but was not placed on sale in French Equatorial Africa.

**No. C8 Surcharged in Red like Nos. B10-B11**

**1943, June 28 *Perf. 13½***

**CB6** AP2 10.75fr + 200fr 400.00 240.00

Counterfeits exist.

**POSTAGE DUE STAMPS**

Numeral of Value on Equatorial Butterfly — D1

**1937 Unwmk. Photo. *Perf. 13***

**J1** D1 5c redsh pur & lt bl .25 .40
**J2** D1 10c cop red & buff .25 .40
**J3** D1 20c dk grn & grn .30 .50
**J4** D1 25c red brn & buff .30 .50
**J5** D1 30c cop red & lt bl .50 .55
**J6** D1 45c mag & yel grn .75 .80
**J7** D1 50c dk ol grn & buff .80 .95
**J8** D1 60c redsh pur & yel .95 1.10
**J9** D1 1fr brown & yel 1.00 1.20
**J10** D1 2fr dk bl & buff 1.40 1.50
**J11** D1 3fr red brn & lt grn 1.50 1.75
*Nos. J1-J11 (11)* 8.00 9.65
Set, never hinged 12.00

**Catalogue values for unused stamps in this section, from this point to the end of the section, are for Never Hinged items.**

D2

**1947 Engr.**

**J12** D2 10c red .40 .25
**J13** D2 30c dp org .40 .25
**J14** D2 50c greenish bl .50 .30
**J15** D2 1fr carmine .55 .40
**J16** D2 2fr emerald .65 .50
**J17** D2 3fr dp red lil .65 .50
**J18** D2 4fr dp ultra 1.60 1.20
**J19** D2 5fr red brown 1.60 1.20
**J20** D2 10fr peacock blue 2.00 1.60
**J21** D2 20fr sepia 2.10 1.90
*Nos. J12-J21 (10)* 10.45 8.10

## FRENCH GUIANA

'french gē-'a-nə

LOCATION — On the northeast coast of South America bordering on the Atlantic Ocean.
GOVT. — French colony
AREA — 34,740 sq. mi.
POP. — 28,537 (1946)
CAPITAL — Cayenne

French Guiana became an overseas department of France in 1946.

100 Centimes = 1 Franc

**Catalogue values for unused stamps in this country are for Never Hinged items, beginning with Scott 171 in the regular postage section, Scott B12 in the semi-postal section, Scott C9 in the air-post section, and Scott J22 in the postage due section.**

See France No. 1446 for French stamp inscribed "Guyane."

Stamps of French Colonies Surcharged in Black

**1886, Dec. Unwmk. *Imperf.***

**1** A8 5c on 2c grn, *grnsh*, srchg 12mm high 750.00 675.00
*a.* Double surcharge 1,900. 1,900.
*b.* Surcharge 10½mm high 900.00 825.00
*c.* No "f" after "O" 950.00 850.00

***Perf. 14x13½***

**2** A9 5c on 2c brn, *buff*, srchg 12mm high 650.00 600.00
*a.* No "f" after "O" 525.00 450.00
*b.* As "a," double surcharge 1,700. 1,700.

Nos. 1-2 unused are valued without gum.

Stamps of French Colonies Overprinted in Black

**"Av" of Date Line Inverted-Reversed**

**1887, Apr. *Imperf.***

**4** A8 20c on 35c blk, *org* 70.00 57.50
*a.* Double surcharge 225.00 225.00
*b.* No "f" after "O" 150.00 150.00

**Date Line Heads "Avril 1887"**

**5** A8 5c on 2c grn, *grnsh* 175.00 125.00
*a.* Double surcharge 900.00 900.00
*b.* No "f" after "O" 375.00 375.00
*c.* Pair, one stamp without surcharge 1,500.
**6** A8 20c on 35c blk, *org* 375.00 375.00
*a.* Double surcharge 1,250. 1,250.
*b.* No "f" after "O" 850.00 850.00
*c.* Vertical pair, #6 + #4 2,200.
**7** A7 25c on 30c brn, *yelsh* 55.00 47.50
*a.* Double surcharge 900.00 900.00
*b.* No "f" after "O" 275.00 275.00

Nos. 4-7 unused are valued without gum.

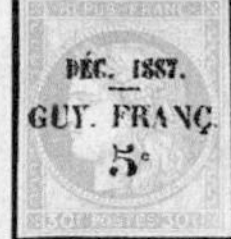

French Colonies Nos. 22 and 26 Surcharged

**8** A7 5c on 30c brn, *yelsh* 155.00 140.00
*a.* Double surcharge 800.00 800.00
*b.* Inverted surcharge 1,200. 1,200.
*c.* Pair, one without surcharge 1,600.
**9** A8 5c on 30c brn, *yelsh* 1,500. 1,500.

Nos. 8-9 unused are valued without gum.

**French Colonies Nos. 22 and 28 Surcharged**

**1888**

**10** A7 5c on 30c brn, *yelsh* 155.00 140.00
*b.* Double surcharge 500.00 500.00
*c.* Inverted surcharge 600.00 600.00
**11** A8 10c on 75c car, *rose* 400.00 290.00
No gum 290.00
*a.* Double surcharge 1,100. 1,100.
*b.* Pair, one stamp without surcharge 2,500.

No. 10 unused is valued without gum.

Stamps of French Colonies Overprinted in Black

**1892, Feb. 20 *Imperf.***

**12** A8 2c grn, *grnsh* 850.00 *975.00*
*a.* Inverted overprint 3,500.
**13** A7 30c brn, *yelsh* 155.00 155.00
*a.* Inverted overprint 575.00 575.00
**14** A8 35c blk, *orange* *2,850.* *3,000.*
**15** A8 40c red, *straw* 175.00 140.00
**16** A8 75c car, *rose* 180.00 140.00
*a.* Inverted overprint 625.00 550.00
**17** A8 1fr brnz grn, *straw* 210.00 160.00
*a.* Inverted overprint 800.00 800.00
*b.* Double overprint 800.00 800.00
*c.* Triple overprint 1,800. 1,800.

Nos. 12-14 unused are valued without gum.

**1892 *Perf. 14x13½***

**18** A9 1c blk, *lil bl* 47.50 35.00
**19** A9 2c brn, *buff* 45.00 37.50
**20** A9 4c claret, *lav* 42.50 37.50
**21** A9 5c grn, *grnsh* 47.50 35.00
*a.* Inverted overprint 150.00 150.00
*b.* Double overprint 150.00 150.00
**22** A9 10c blk, *lavender* 67.50 40.00
*a.* Inverted overprint 200.00 200.00
*b.* Double overprint 275.00 275.00
**23** A9 15c blue 67.50 45.00
*a.* Double overprint 275.00 200.00
**24** A9 20c red, *grn* 55.00 42.50
*a.* Inverted overprint 225.00 225.00
**25** A9 25c blk, *rose* 75.00 35.00
*a.* Double overprint 275.00 275.00
*b.* Triple overprint 300.00 300.00
**26** A9 30c brn, *bis* 47.50 40.00
**27** A9 35c blk, *orange* 225.00 225.00
*a.* Inverted overprint 575.00 575.00
**28** A9 40c red, *straw* 135.00 135.00
*a.* Inverted overprint 300.00 300.00
**29** A9 75c car, *rose* 145.00 125.00
**30** A9 1fr brnz grn, *straw* 250.00 220.00
*a.* Double overprint 375.00
*Nos. 18-30 (13)* 1,250. 1,053.

French Colonies No. 51 Surcharged

**1892, Dec.**

**31** A9 5c on 15c blue 70.00 47.50
*a.* Double surcharge 300.00 275.00
*b.* No "f" after "O" 160.00 135.00
*c.* Pair, one stamp without surcharge 1,700. 1,700.

Navigation and Commerce — A12

**1892-1904 Typo. *Perf. 14x13½***
**Name of Colony in Blue or Carmine**

**32** A12 1c blk, *lil bl* 2.00 1.75
**33** A12 2c brn, *buff* 1.45 1.45
**34** A12 4c claret, *lav* 2.00 1.90
*a.* "GUYANE" double 275.00
**35** A12 5c grn, *grnsh* 12.50 11.00
**36** A12 5c yel grn ('04) 2.40 1.60
**37** A12 10c blk, *lavender* 13.50 8.25
**38** A12 10c red ('00) 4.75 1.60
**39** A12 15c blue, quadrille paper 42.50 4.00
**40** A12 15c gray, *lt gray* ('00) 122.50 110.00
**41** A12 20c red, *grn* 25.00 18.00
**42** A12 25c blk, *rose* 20.00 5.50
**43** A12 25c blue ('00) 22.50 *22.50*
**44** A12 30c brn, *bis* 24.00 18.00
**45** A12 40c red, *straw* 24.00 16.00
**46** A12 50c car, *rose* 35.00 18.00
**47** A12 50c brn, *az* ('00) 26.00 26.00
**48** A12 75c dp vio, *org* 37.50 27.50
**49** A12 1fr brn grn, *straw* 18.00 14.00
**50** A12 2fr vio, *rose* ('02) 100.00 16.00
*Nos. 32-50 (19)* 615.60 323.05

Perf. 13½x14 stamps are counterfeits.

For surcharges see Nos. 87-93.

Great Anteater — A13

Washing Gold — A14

Palm Grove at Cayenne A15

**1905-28**

**51** A13 1c black .40 .40
**52** A13 2c blue .40 .40
*a.* Imperf 57.50
**53** A13 4c red brn .40 .40
**54** A13 5c green 1.25 1.10
**55** A13 5c org ('22) .40 *.45*
**56** A13 10c rose 1.50 1.10
**57** A13 10c grn ('22) .65 .40
**58** A13 10c red, *bluish* ('25) .45 .45
**59** A13 15c violet 1.75 1.25
**60** A14 20c red brn .65 .65
**61** A14 25c blue 3.00 1.60
**62** A14 25c vio ('22) .60 .50
**63** A14 30c black 2.50 1.00
**64** A14 30c rose ('22) .50 *.60*
**65** A14 30c red org ('25) .45 .45
**66** A14 30c dk grn, *grnsh* ('28) 1.35 1.35
**67** A14 35c blk, *yel* ('06) .65 .65
**68** A14 40c rose 1.50 .85
**69** A14 40c black ('22) .40 *.45*
**70** A14 45c olive ('07) 1.00 .95
**71** A14 50c violet 4.25 3.50
**72** A14 50c blue ('22) .55 *.65*
**73** A14 50c gray ('25) .80 .80
**74** A14 60c lil, *rose* ('25) .65 .65
**75** A14 65c myr grn ('26) .85 .80
**76** A14 75c green 1.60 1.40
**77** A14 85c magenta ('26) .85 .80
**78** A15 1fr rose .90 .85
*a.* Imperf 82.50
**79** A15 1fr bl, *bluish* ('25) .85 .80
**80** A15 1fr bl, *yel grn* ('28) 2.75 2.75
**81** A15 1.10fr lt red ('28) 1.50 1.50
**82** A15 2fr blue 1.35 1.35
**83** A15 2fr org red, *yel* ('26) 2.75 2.40
**84** A15 5fr black 8.50 6.50
*a.* Imperf 82.50
**85** A15 10fr grn, *yel* ('24) 14.00 *14.50*
*a.* Printed on both sides 140.00
**86** A15 20fr brn lake ('24) 17.50 17.50
*Nos. 51-86 (36)* 79.45 71.75

For surcharges see Nos. 94-108, B1-B2.

### Issue of 1892 Surcharged in Black or Carmine

**1912**

**Spacing between figures of surcharge 1.5mm (5c), 2mm (10c)**

**87** A12 5c on 2c brn, *buff* 1.60 *2.00*
**88** A12 5c on 4c cl, *lav* (C) 1.20 *1.60*
**89** A12 5c on 20c red, *grn* 1.75 *1.90*
**90** A12 5c on 25c blk, *rose* (C) 4.00 4.75
**91** A12 5c on 30c brn, *bis* (C) 1.75 *1.90*
**92** A12 10c on 40c red, *straw* 1.40 *1.90*
*a.* Pair, one stamp without surcharge 1,250.
**93** A12 10c on 50c car, *rose* 4.25 *5.25*
*a.* Double surcharge 550.00
*Nos. 87-93 (7)* 15.95 *19.30*

Two spacings between the surcharged numerals are found on Nos. 87 to 93. For detailed listings, see the *Scott Classic Specialized Catalogue of Stamps and Covers.*

No. 59 Surcharged in Various Colors

**1922**

**94** A13 1c on 15c vio (Bk) .65 *.75*
*a.* Double surcharge 90.00
**95** A13 2c on 15c vio (Bl) .65 *.75*
*a.* Inverted surcharge 97.50
*b.* In pair with unovptd. stamp 250.00
*c.* No. 95a, in pair with unovptd. stamp 850.00
**96** A13 4c on 15c vio (G) .65 *.75*
*a.* Double surcharge 90.00
*b.* In pair with unovptd. stamp 275.00
**97** A13 5c on 15c vio (R) .65 *.75*
*a.* In pair with unovptd. stamp 275.00
*Nos. 94-97 (4)* 2.60 3.00

Type of 1905-28 Srchd. in Blue

**1923**

**98** A15 10fr on 1fr grn, *yel* 22.50 *24.00*
**99** A15 20fr on 5fr lilac, *rose* 22.50 *24.00*

Stamps and Types of 1905-28 Srchd. in Black or Red

**1924-27**

**100** A13 25c on 15c vio ('25) .85 *.85*
*a.* Triple surcharge 130.00 130.00
*b.* In pair with unovptd. stamp 260.00
**101** A15 25c on 2fr bl ('24) .90 *.95*
*a.* Double surcharge 140.00
*b.* Triple surcharge 150.00
**102** A14 65c on 45c ol (R) ('25) 1.75 *1.90*
**103** A14 85c on 45c ol (R) ('25) 1.75 *1.90*
**104** A14 90c on 75c red ('27) 1.50 1.50
**105** A15 1.05fr on 2fr lt yel brn ('27) 1.50 1.50
**106** A15 1.25fr on 1fr ultra (R) ('26) 1.60 *1.75*
**107** A15 1.50fr on 1fr lt bl ('27) 1.60 *1.75*
**108** A15 3fr on 5fr vio ('27) 1.75 *2.00*
*a.* No period after "F" 12.00 12.00
*Nos. 100-108 (9)* 13.20 14.10

Carib Archer — A16

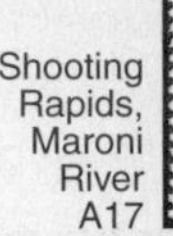

Shooting Rapids, Maroni River A17

Government Building, Cayenne — A18

**1929-40** *Perf. 13½x14*

**109** A16 1c gray lil & grnsh bl .25 .25
*a.* Imperf 35.00
**110** A16 2c dk red & bl grn .25 .25
*a.* Imperf 35.00
**111** A16 3c gray lil & grnsh bl ('40) .30 .30
**112** A16 4c ol brn & red vio .30 .30
**113** A16 5c Prus bl & red org .30 .30
**114** A16 10c mag & brn .30 .30
**115** A16 15c yel brn & red org .30 .30
*a.* Imperf 35.00
**116** A16 20c dk bl & ol grn .30 .30
**117** A16 25c dk red & dk brn .50 .50

*Perf. 14x13½*

**118** A17 30c dl & lt grn .70 .70
**119** A17 30c grn & brn ('40) .50 .50
**120** A17 35c Prus grn & ol grn ('38) 1.10 1.10
**121** A17 40c org brn & ol gray .30 .30
**122** A17 45c grn & dk brn 1.20 1.20
**123** A17 45c ol grn & lt grn ('40) .70 .70
**124** A17 50c dk bl & ol gray .40 .40
*a.* Imperf 35.00
**125** A17 55c vio bl & car ('38) 1.50 1.50
**126** A17 60c sal & grn ('40) .75 .75
*a.* Imperf 47.50
**127** A17 65c sal & grn 1.10 1.10
**128** A17 70c ind & sl bl ('40) 1.30 1.30
**129** A17 75c ind & sl bl 1.15 1.15
**130** A17 80c blk & vio bl ('38) .80 .80
**131** A17 90c dk red & ver 1.10 1.10
**132** A17 90c red vio & brn ('39) 1.30 1.30
**133** A17 1fr lt vio & brn .70 .70
**134** A17 1fr car & lt red ('38) 2.10 2.10
**135** A17 1fr blk & vio bl ('40) .80 .80
**136** A18 1.05fr ver & olivine 6.25 6.25
**137** A18 1.10fr ol brn & red vio 7.25 5.75
**138** A18 1.25fr blk brn & bl grn ('33) .80 .80
**139** A18 1.25fr rose & lt red ('39) 1.10 1.10
**140** A18 1.40fr ol brn & red vio ('40) 1.30 1.30
**141** A18 1.50fr dk bl & lt bl .40 .40
**142** A18 1.60fr ol brn & bl grn ('40) 1.30 1.30
**143** A18 1.75fr brn red & blk brn ('33) 2.25 2.25
**144** A18 1.75fr vio bl ('38) 1.75 1.75
**145** A18 2fr dk grn & rose red .65 .65
**146** A18 2.25fr vio bl ('39) 1.30 1.30
**147** A18 2.50fr cop red & brn ('40) 1.30 1.30
**148** A18 3fr brn red & red vio .75 .75
**149** A18 5fr dl vio & yel grn 1.25 1.25
**150** A18 10fr ol gray & dp ultra 1.50 1.50
**151** A18 20fr indigo & ver 2.50 2.50
*Nos. 109-151 (43)* 51.95 50.45

For types A16-A18 without "RF," see Nos. 170C-170E.

Common Design Types pictured following the introduction.

### Colonial Exposition Issue

Common Design Types

**1931** **Engr.** *Perf. 12½*

**Name of Country in Black**

**152** CD70 40c dp green 5.50 5.50
**153** CD71 50c violet 5.50 5.50
**154** CD72 90c red orange 5.50 5.50
**155** CD73 1.50fr dull blue 5.50 5.50
*Nos. 152-155 (4)* 22.00 22.00

Recapture of Cayenne by d'Estrées, 1676 — A19

Products of French Guiana A20

**1935, Oct. 21** *Perf. 13*

**156** A19 40c gray brn 5.75 5.75
**157** A19 50c dull red 10.00 8.00
**158** A19 1.50fr ultra 5.75 5.75
**159** A20 1.75fr lilac rose 12.50 11.50
**160** A20 5fr brown 10.00 9.00
**161** A20 10fr blue green 10.50 10.00
*Nos. 156-161 (6)* 54.50 50.00

Tercentenary of the founding of French possessions in the West Indies.

### Paris International Exposition Issue

Common Design Types

**1937, Apr. 15**

**162** CD74 20c deep violet 1.75 1.75
**163** CD75 30c dark green 1.75 1.75
**164** CD76 40c carmine rose 1.75 1.75
**165** CD77 50c dark brown 1.75 1.75
**166** CD78 90c red 1.75 1.75
**167** CD79 1.50fr ultra 2.25 2.25
*Nos. 162-167 (6)* 11.00 11.00

### Colonial Arts Exhibition Issue

Souvenir Sheet

Common Design Type

**1937** *Imperf.*

**168** CD75 3fr violet 11.50 *13.50*

### New York World's Fair Issue

Common Design Type

**1939, May 10** **Engr.** *Perf. 12½x12*

**169** CD82 1.25fr car lake 1.30 1.30
**170** CD82 2.25fr ultra 1.30 1.30

View of Cayenne and Marshal Petain A21a

**1941** **Engr.** *Perf. 12½x12*

**170A** A21a 1fr deep lilac .80 .80
**170B** A21a 2.50fr blue .80 .80

For surcharges, see Nos. B11A-B11B.

### Types of 1929-40 without "RF"

**1944** ***Methods and Perfs as Before***

**170C** A16 15c yel brn & red org 1.10
**170D** A17 1fr black & vio blue 1.10
**170E** A18 1.50fr dk blue & lt blue 1.40
*Nos. 170C-170E (3)* 3.60

Nos. 170C-170E were issued by the Vichy government in France, but were not issued in French Guiana.

**Catalogue values for unused stamps in this section, from this point to the end of the section, are for Never Hinged items.**

### Eboue Issue

Common Design Type

**1945** **Engr.** *Perf. 13*

**171** CD91 2fr black .95 .80
**172** CD91 25fr Prussian green 1.50 1.20

This issue exists imperforate.

Arms of Cayenne A22

**1945** **Litho.** *Perf. 12*

**173** A22 10c dp gray violet .30 .25
**174** A22 30c brown org .35 .25
**175** A22 40c lt blue .35 .25
**176** A22 50c violet brn .75 .60
**177** A22 60c orange yel .75 .60
**178** A22 70c pale brown .75 .60
**179** A22 80c lt green .75 .60
**180** A22 1fr blue .35 .25
**181** A22 1.20fr brt violet .75 .60
**182** A22 1.50fr dp orange 1.00 .75
**183** A22 2fr black 1.10 .85
**184** A22 2.40fr red 1.10 .85
**185** A22 3fr pink 1.10 .85
**186** A22 4fr dp ultra 1.30 1.00
**187** A22 4.50fr dp yel grn 1.30 1.00
**188** A22 5fr orange brn 1.30 1.00
**189** A22 10fr dk violet 1.30 1.00
**190** A22 15fr rose carmine 1.30 1..00
**191** A22 20fr olive green 1.50 1.25
*Nos. 173-191 (19)* 17.40 12.55

Hammock A23

Guiana Girl A26

Maroni River Bank A24

Inini Scene A25

Toucans A27

Parrots A28

*Perf. 13.*

**1947, June 2** **Unwmk.** **Engr.**

**192** A23 10c dk blue grn .30 .25
**193** A23 30c brt red .30 .25
**194** A23 50c dk vio brn .30 .25
**195** A24 60c grnsh blk .60 .45
**196** A24 1fr red brn .85 .60
**197** A24 1.50fr black brn .85 .60
**198** A25 2fr dp yel grn 1.10 .75
**199** A25 2.50fr dp ultra 1.10 .75
**200** A25 3fr red brn 1.00 .70
**201** A26 4fr black brn 2.50 1.25
**202** A26 5fr deep blue 1.75 1.10
**203** A26 6fr red brown 1.75 1.10
**204** A27 10fr deep ultra 7.25 4.75
**205** A27 15fr black brn 7.25 5.00
**206** A27 20fr red brn 9.25 5.00
**207** A28 25fr brt bl grn 13.00 8.50
**208** A28 40fr black brn 11.00 8.00
*Nos. 192-208 (17)* 60.15 39.30

## SEMI-POSTAL STAMPS

Regular Issue of 1905-28 Surcharged in Red

**1915 Unwmk. *Perf. 13½x14***

**B1** A13 10c + 5c rose 17.50 *18.00*
*a.* Inverted surcharge 250.00 250.00
*b.* Double surcharge 250.00 250.00

Regular Issue of 1905-28 Surcharged in Rose

**B2** A13 10c + 5c rose 1.60 1.60

**Curie Issue**
Common Design Type

**1938 *Perf. 13***
**B3** CD80 1.75fr + 50c brt ultra 13.50 13.50

**French Revolution Issue**
Common Design Type

**1939 Photo.**
**Name and Value in Black**

**B4** CD83 45c + 25c green 11.50 11.50
**B5** CD83 70c + 30c brown 11.50 11.50
**B6** CD83 90c + 35c red org 11.50 11.50
**B7** CD83 1.25fr + 1fr rose pink 11.50 11.50
**B8** CD83 2.25fr + 2fr blue 11.50 11.50
*Nos. B4-B8 (5)* 57.50 57.50

Common Design Type and

Colonial Infantryman — SP1

Colonial Policeman SP2

**1941 Photo. *Perf. 13½***
**B9** SP1 1fr + 1fr red 1.30
**B10** CD86 1.50fr + 3fr maroon 1.50
**B11** SP2 2.50fr + 1fr blue 1.30
*Nos. B9-B11 (3)* 4.10

Nos. B9-B11 were issued by the Vichy government in France, but were not placed on sale in French Guiana.

Nos. 170A-170B Srchd. in Black or Red

**1944 Engr. *Perf. 12½x12***
**B11A** 50c + 1.50fr on 2.50fr deep blue (R) .80
**B11B** + 2.50fr on 1fr dp lilac .80

Colonial Development Fund.
Nos. B11A-B11B were issued by the Vichy government in France, but were not placed on sale in French Guiana.

**Catalogue values for unused stamps in this section, from this point to the end of the section, are for Never Hinged items.**

**Red Cross Issue**
Common Design Type

**1944 *Perf. 14½x14***
**B12** CD90 5fr + 20fr dk copper brn 1.75 1.25

The surtax was for the French Red Cross and national relief.

## AIR POST STAMPS

Cayenne AP1

***Perf. 13½***
**1933, Nov. 20 Unwmk. Photo.**

**C1** AP1 50c orange brn .30 .30
**C2** AP1 1fr yellow grn .50 .50
**C3** AP1 1.50fr dk blue .70 .70
**C4** AP1 2fr orange .70 .70
**C5** AP1 3fr black .85 .85
**C6** AP1 5fr violet .85 .85
**C7** AP1 10fr olive grn .85 .85
**C8** AP1 20fr scarlet 1.25 1.25
*Nos. C1-C8 (8)* 6.00 6.00

For No. C1 without "RF," see No. C8A.
A 20fr violet exists, but was not regularly issued. Value, $175.

**Catalogue values for unused stamps in this section, from this point to the end of the section, are for Never Hinged items.**

**Type of 1933 without "RF" and**

AP1a

AP1b

***Perf. 13½, 13 (#C8C)***
**1941-44 Photo, Engr. (#C8C)**

**C8A** AP1 50c orange brn 1.00
**C8B** AP1a 50f bl grn & red brown ('42) 1.40
**C8C** AP1b 100f dk blue ('44) 1.60
*Nos. C8A-C8C (3)* 4.00

Nos. C8A-C8C were issued by the Vichy government in France, but were not placed on sale in French Guiana.

**Common Design Type**

**1945 Photo. *Perf. 14½x14***
**C9** CD87 50fr dark green 1.30 1.10
**C10** CD87 100fr plum 2.50 2.00

**Victory Issue**
Common Design Type

**1946, May 8 Engr. *Perf. 12½***
**C11** CD92 8fr black 1.75 1.25

**Chad to Rhine Issue**
Common Design Types

**1946, June 6**
**C12** CD93 5fr dk slate bl 1.75 1.50
**C13** CD94 10fr lilac rose 1.75 1.50
**C14** CD95 15fr dk vio brn 1.75 1.50
**C15** CD96 20fr dk slate grn 2.00 1.60
**C16** CD97 25fr vio brown 2.40 2.00
**C17** CD98 50fr bright lilac 3.00 2.25
*Nos. C12-C17 (6)* 12.65 10.35

Eagles — AP2

Tapir — AP3

Toucans — AP4

**1947, June 2 Engr. *Perf. 13***
**C18** AP2 50fr deep green 22.50 17.50
**C19** AP3 100fr red brown 15.00 13.00
**C20** AP4 200fr dk gray bl 30.00 24.00
*Nos. C18-C20 (3)* 67.50 54.50

## AIR POST SEMI-POSTAL STAMP

**French Revolution Issue**
Common Design Type
**Unwmk.**
**1939, July 5 Photo. *Perf. 13***
**Name & Value Typo. in Orange**

**CB1** CD83 5fr + 4fr brn blk 22.00 22.00

Nurse with Mother & Child — SPAP1

**Unwmk.**
**1942, June 22 Engr. *Perf. 13***
**CB2** SPAP1 1.50fr + 50c green 1.00
**CB3** SPAP1 2fr + 6fr brn & red 1.00

Native children's welfare fund.
Nos. CB2-CB3 were issued by the Vichy government in France, but were not placed on sale in French Guiana.

**Colonial Education Fund**
Common Design Type

**1942, June 22**
**CB4** CD86a 1.20fr + 1.80fr blue & red 1.10

No. CB4 was issued by the Vichy government in France, but was not placed on sale in French Guiana.

## POSTAGE DUE STAMPS

Postage Due Stamps of France, 1893-1926, Overprinted

**1925-27 Unwmk. *Perf. 14x13½***

**J1** D2 5c light blue .70 *.75*
*a.* In pair with unovptd. stamp 375.00
**J2** D2 10c brown 1.00 *1.10*
**J3** D2 20c olive green 1.10 *1.25*
**J4** D2 50c violet brown 1.50 *1.60*
**J5** D2 3fr magenta ('27) 11.00 *12.50*

Surcharged in Black

**J6** D2 15c on 20c ol grn 1.00 *1.10*
*a.* Blue surcharge 67.50
**J7** D2 25c on 5c lt bl 1.30 *1.40*
*a.* In pair with unovptd. stamp 375.00
**J8** D2 30c on 20c ol grn 1.50 *1.60*
**J9** D2 45c on 10c brn 1.50 *1.60*
**J10** D2 60c on 5c lt bl 1.50 *1.60*
**J11** D2 1fr on 20c ol grn 2.25 *2.40*
**J12** D2 2fr on 50c vio brn 2.25 *2.40*
*Nos. J1-J12 (12)* 26.60 *29.30*

Royal Palms — D3

Guiana Girl — D4

**1929, Oct. 14 Typo. *Perf. 13½x14***
**J13** D3 5c indigo & Prus bl .45 *.50*
**J14** D3 10c bis brn & Prus grn .45 *.50*
**J15** D3 20c grn & rose red .45 *.50*
**J16** D3 30c ol brn & rose red .45 *.50*
**J17** D3 50c vio & ol brn .95 *1.00*
**J18** D3 60c brn red & ol brn 1.30 *1.40*
**J19** D4 1fr dp bl & org brn 1.75 *1.90*
**J20** D4 2fr brn red & bluish grn 2.00 *2.10*
**J21** D4 3fr violet & blk 4.25 *4.50*
*Nos. J13-J21 (9)* 12.05 *12.90*

**Catalogue values for unused stamps in this section, from this point to the end of the section, are for Never Hinged items.**

D5

**1947, June 2 Engr. *Perf. 14x13***
**J22** D5 10c dk car rose .35 .35
**J23** D5 30c dull green .45 .45
**J24** D5 50c black .45 .45
**J25** D5 1fr brt ultra .55 .55
**J26** D5 2fr dk brown red .55 .55
**J27** D5 3fr deep violet 1.00 .80
**J28** D5 4fr red 1.30 1.10
**J29** D5 5fr brown violet 1.50 1.25
**J30** D5 10fr blue green 2.25 1.90
**J31** D5 20fr lilac rose 3.00 2.25
*Nos. J22-J31 (10)* 11.40 9.65

# FRENCH GUINEA

'french 'gi-nē

LOCATION — On the coast of West Africa, between Portuguese Guinea and Sierra Leone.
GOVT. — French colony
AREA — 89,436 sq. mi.
POP. — 2,058,442 (est. 1941)
CAPITAL — Conakry

French Guinea stamps were replaced by those of French West Africa around 1944-45. French Guinea became the Republic of Guinea Oct. 2, 1958. See "Guinea" for issues of the republic.

100 Centimes = 1 Franc

**See French West Africa No. 66 for additional stamp inscribed "Guinee" and "Afrique Occidentale Francaise."**

Navigation and Commerce — A1

***Perf. 14x13½***

**1892-1900 Typo. Unwmk.**

**Name of Colony in Blue or Carmine**

| No. | Type | Description | Unused | Used |
|---|---|---|---|---|
| 1 | A1 | 1c black, *lilac bl* | 2.40 | 1.60 |
| 2 | A1 | 2c brown, *buff* | 2.40 | 2.00 |
| 3 | A1 | 4c claret, *lav* | 3.25 | 2.00 |
| 4 | A1 | 5c green, *grnsh* | 8.00 | 8.00 |
| 5 | A1 | 10c blk, *lavender* | 8.00 | 4.75 |
| 6 | A1 | 10c red ('00) | 45.00 | 40.00 |
| 7 | A1 | 15c blue, quadrille paper | 16.00 | 8.00 |
| 8 | A1 | 15c gray, *lt gray* ('00) | 100.00 | 87.50 |
| 9 | A1 | 20c red, *grn* | 20.00 | 16.00 |
| 10 | A1 | 25c black, *rose* | 16.00 | 8.00 |
| 11 | A1 | 25c blue ('00) | 24.00 | 24.00 |
| 12 | A1 | 30c brown, *bis* | 40.00 | 32.50 |
| 13 | A1 | 40c red, *straw* | 40.00 | 32.50 |
| *a.* | | "GUINEE FRANCAISE" double | 475.00 | 475.00 |
| 14 | A1 | 50c car, *rose* | 47.50 | 35.00 |
| 15 | A1 | 50c brown, *az* ('00) | 40.00 | 40.00 |
| 16 | A1 | 75c dp vio, *org* | 65.00 | 47.50 |
| 17 | A1 | 1fr brnz grn, *straw* | 50.00 | 40.00 |
| | | *Nos. 1-17 (17)* | 527.55 | 429.35 |

Perf. 13½x14 stamps are counterfeits.
For surcharges see Nos. 48-54.

Fulah Shepherd — A2

**1904**

| No. | Type | Description | Unused | Used |
|---|---|---|---|---|
| 18 | A2 | 1c black, *yel grn* | 1.20 | 1.20 |
| 19 | A2 | 2c vio brn, *buff* | 1.20 | 1.20 |
| 20 | A2 | 4c carmine, *bl* | 1.60 | 1.60 |
| 21 | A2 | 5c green, *grnsh* | 1.60 | 1.60 |
| 22 | A2 | 10c carmine | 4.00 | 2.40 |
| 23 | A2 | 15c violet, *rose* | 12.00 | 5.50 |
| 24 | A2 | 20c carmine, *grn* | 16.00 | 16.00 |
| 25 | A2 | 25c blue | 16.00 | 10.00 |
| 26 | A2 | 30c brown | 24.00 | 24.00 |
| 27 | A2 | 40c red, *straw* | 35.00 | 24.00 |
| 28 | A2 | 50c brown, *az* | 32.50 | 24.00 |
| 29 | A2 | 75c green, *org* | 32.50 | 32.50 |
| 30 | A2 | 1fr brnz grn, *straw* | 47.50 | 47.50 |
| 31 | A2 | 2fr red, *org* | 87.50 | 87.50 |
| 32 | A2 | 5fr green, *yel grn* | 120.00 | 120.00 |
| | | *Nos. 18-32 (15)* | 432.60 | 399.00 |

For surcharges see Nos. 55-62.

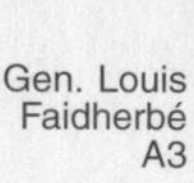

Gen. Louis Faidherbé A3

Oil Palm — A4

Dr. Noel Eugène Ballay A5

**1906-07**

**Name of Colony in Red or Blue**

| No. | Type | Description | Unused | Used |
|---|---|---|---|---|
| 33 | A3 | 1c gray | .80 | .80 |
| 34 | A3 | 2c brown | 1.20 | 1.20 |
| 35 | A3 | 4c brown, *bl* | 1.60 | 1.60 |
| 36 | A3 | 5c green | 4.00 | 2.00 |
| 37 | A3 | 10c carmine (B) | 24.00 | 1.60 |
| 38 | A4 | 20c black, *blue* | 8.00 | 4.00 |
| 39 | A4 | 25c blue, *pnksh* | 8.00 | 6.50 |
| 40 | A4 | 30c brown, *pnksh* | 8.00 | 4.00 |
| 41 | A4 | 35c black, *yellow* | 6.50 | 2.40 |
| 42 | A4 | 45c choc, *grnsh gray* | 8.00 | 4.00 |
| 43 | A4 | 50c dp violet | 16.00 | 12.00 |
| 44 | A4 | 75c blue, *org* | 12.00 | 4.00 |
| 45 | A5 | 1fr black, *az* | 20.00 | 24.00 |
| 46 | A5 | 2fr blue, *pink* | 40.00 | *45.00* |
| 47 | A5 | 5fr car, *straw* (B) | 60.00 | *65.00* |
| | | *Nos. 33-47 (15)* | 218.10 | *178.10* |

**Regular Issues Surcharged in Black or Carmine**

**1912**

**On Issue of 1892-1900**

| No. | Type | Description | Unused | Used |
|---|---|---|---|---|
| 48 | A1 | 5c on 2c brown, *buff* | 1.60 | *2.00* |
| 49 | A1 | 5c on 4c cl, *lav* (C) | 1.25 | *1.60* |
| 50 | A1 | 5c on 15c blue (C) | 1.25 | *1.60* |
| 51 | A1 | 5c on 20c red, *grn* | 4.00 | *5.25* |
| 52 | A1 | 5c on 30c brn, *bis* (C) | 5.50 | *6.50* |
| 53 | A1 | 10c on 40c red, *straw* | 2.40 | *3.25* |
| 54 | A1 | 10c on 75c dp vio, *org* | 8.00 | *9.50* |
| *a.* | | Double surcharge, inverted | 325.00 | |

**On Issue of 1904**

| No. | Type | Description | Unused | Used |
|---|---|---|---|---|
| 55 | A2 | 5c on 2c vio brn, *buff* | 1.20 | *1.20* |
| *a.* | | Pair, one without surcharge | 650.00 | |
| *b.* | | Inverted surcharge | 210.00 | |
| 56 | A2 | 5c on 4c car, *blue* | 1.20 | *1.20* |
| 57 | A2 | 5c on 15c violet, *rose* | 1.20 | *1.20* |
| 58 | A2 | 5c on 20c car, *grn* | 1.60 | 1.60 |
| 59 | A2 | 5c on 25c blue (C) | 1.60 | *2.00* |
| 60 | A2 | 5c on 30c brown (C) | 2.00 | *3.25* |
| 61 | A2 | 10c on 40c red, *straw* | 2.00 | *3.25* |
| 62 | A2 | 10c on 50c brn, *az* (C) | 5.50 | *6.50* |
| | | *Nos. 48-62 (15)* | 40.30 | 49.90 |

Two spacings between the surcharged numerals are found on Nos. 48 to 62. For detailed listings, see the *Scott Classic Specialized Catalogue of Stamps and Covers.*

Ford at Kitim — A6

**1913-33** ***Perf. 13½x14***

| No. | Type | Description | Unused | Used |
|---|---|---|---|---|
| 63 | A6 | 1c violet & bl | .25 | .25 |
| *a.* | | Imperf. | 72.50 | |
| 64 | A6 | 2c brn & vio brn | .25 | .25 |
| *a.* | | Double impression of vio brn | 160.00 | |
| 65 | A6 | 4c gray & black | .25 | .25 |
| 66 | A6 | 5c yel grn & bl grn | 1.20 | .40 |
| *a.* | | Booklet pane of 4 | — | |
| | | Complete booklet, 10 #66a | 275.00 | |
| 67 | A6 | 5c brn vio & grn ('22) | .40 | .25 |
| 68 | A6 | 10c red org & rose | 1.20 | .40 |
| *a.* | | Booklet pane of 4 | — | |
| | | Complete booklet, 10 #68a | 550.00 | |
| 69 | A6 | 10c yel grn & bl grn ('22) | .55 | .25 |
| 70 | A6 | 10c vio & ver ('25) | .80 | .40 |
| *a.* | | Imperf. | 45.00 | |
| 71 | A6 | 15c vio brn & rose, chalky paper ('16) | .80 | .40 |
| *a.* | | Booklet pane of 4 | — | |
| | | Complete booklet, 10 #71a | 1,200. | |
| 72 | A6 | 15c gray grn & yel grn ('25) | .40 | .40 |
| 73 | A6 | 15c red brn & rose lil ('27) | .40 | .30 |
| 74 | A6 | 20c brown & violet | .40 | .40 |
| 75 | A6 | 20c grn & bl grn ('26) | .80 | .80 |
| 76 | A6 | 20c brn red & brn ('27) | .80 | .50 |
| 77 | A6 | 25c ultra & blue | 2.75 | 1.60 |
| 78 | A6 | 25c black & vio ('22) | .80 | .80 |
| 79 | A6 | 30c vio brn & grn | 1.60 | 1.20 |
| 80 | A6 | 30c red org & rose ('22) | 1.20 | 1.10 |
| 81 | A6 | 30c rose red & grn ('25) | .30 | .30 |
| 82 | A6 | 30c dl grn & bl grn ('28) | 1.60 | 1.60 |
| 83 | A6 | 35c blue & rose | .55 | .55 |
| 84 | A6 | 40c green & gray | 1.20 | 1.20 |
| 85 | A6 | 45c brown & red | 1.20 | 1.20 |
| 86 | A6 | 50c ultra & black | 6.50 | 4.75 |
| 87 | A6 | 50c ultra & bl ('22) | 1.60 | .80 |
| 88 | A6 | 50c yel brn & ol ('25) | .80 | .80 |
| 89 | A6 | 60c vio, *pnksh* ('25) | .80 | .80 |
| 90 | A6 | 65c yel brn & sl bl ('26) | 2.00 | 1.20 |
| 91 | A6 | 75c red & ultra | 1.60 | 1.60 |
| 92 | A6 | 75c indigo & dl bl ('25) | .80 | 1.20 |
| 93 | A6 | 75c mag & yel grn ('27) | 1.60 | 1.20 |
| 94 | A6 | 85c ol grn & red brn ('26) | 1.20 | 1.20 |
| 95 | A6 | 90c brn red & rose ('30) | 5.50 | 4.75 |
| 96 | A6 | 1fr violet & black | 1.60 | 2.40 |
| 97 | A6 | 1.10fr vio & ol brn ('28) | 8.00 | 8.00 |
| 98 | A6 | 1.25fr vio & yel brn ('33) | 2.40 | 1.60 |
| 99 | A6 | 1.50fr dk bl & lt bl ('30) | 6.50 | 2.40 |
| 100 | A6 | 1.75fr ol brn & vio ('33) | 1.75 | 1.60 |
| 101 | A6 | 2fr orange & vio brn | 4.00 | 4.00 |
| 102 | A6 | 3fr red violet ('30) | 8.00 | 5.50 |
| 103 | A6 | 5fr black & vio | 16.00 | 16.00 |
| 104 | A6 | 5fr dl bl & blk ('22) | 4.00 | 2.40 |
| | | *Nos. 63-104 (42)* | 94.35 | 77.00 |

For surcharges see Nos. 105-115, B1.

Nos. 66, 68 and 77 pasted on colored cardboard and overprinted "VALEUR D'ECHANGE" were used as emergency currency in 1920.

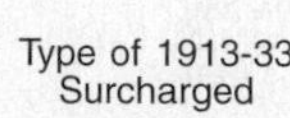

Type of 1913-33 Surcharged

**1922**

| No. | Type | Description | Unused | Used |
|---|---|---|---|---|
| 105 | A6 | 60c on 75c violet, *pnksh* | .40 | .40 |

Stamps and Type of 1913-33 Surcharged

**1924-27**

| No. | Type | Description | Unused | Used |
|---|---|---|---|---|
| 106 | A6 | 25c on 2fr org & brn (R) | .40 | .40 |
| 107 | A6 | 25c on 5fr dull bl & blk | .40 | .40 |
| 108 | A6 | 65c on 75c rose & ultra ('25) | 1.60 | 1.60 |
| 109 | A6 | 85c on 75c rose & ultra ('25) | 2.40 | 2.00 |
| 110 | A6 | 90c on 75c brn red & cer ('27) | 3.25 | 3.25 |
| 111 | A6 | 1.25fr on 1fr dk bl & ultra ('26) | 1.20 | 1.60 |
| 112 | A6 | 1.50fr on 1fr dp bl & lt bl ('27) | 2.40 | 2.40 |
| 113 | A6 | 3fr on 5fr mag & sl ('27) | 4.00 | 4.00 |
| 114 | A6 | 10fr on 5fr bl & bl grn, *bluish* ('27) | 8.00 | 8.00 |
| 115 | A6 | 20fr on 5fr rose lil & brn ol, *pnksh* ('27) | 20.00 | 20.00 |
| | | *Nos. 106-115 (10)* | 43.65 | 43.65 |

Common Design Types pictured following the introduction.

**Colonial Exposition Issue**

Common Design Types

**1931 Engr.** ***Perf. 12½***

**Name of Country in Black**

| No. | Type | Description | Unused | Used |
|---|---|---|---|---|
| 116 | CD70 | 40c deep green | 4.75 | 4.75 |
| *a.* | | "GUINÉE FRANCAISE" omitted | 55.00 | *67.50* |
| 117 | CD71 | 50c violet | 4.75 | 4.75 |
| 118 | CD72 | 90c red orange | 4.75 | 4.75 |
| *a.* | | "GUINÉE FRANCAISE" omitted | 55.00 | *70.00* |
| 119 | CD73 | 1.50fr dull blue | 5.50 | 5.50 |
| *a.* | | "GUINÉE FRANCAISE" omitted | 55.00 | *67.50* |
| | | *Nos. 116-119 (4)* | 19.75 | 19.75 |
| | | Set, never hinged | 32.00 | |

**Paris International Exposition Issue**

Common Design Types

**1937** ***Perf. 13***

| No. | Type | Description | Unused | Used |
|---|---|---|---|---|
| 120 | CD74 | 20c deep violet | 2.00 | 2.00 |
| 121 | CD75 | 30c dark green | 2.00 | 2.00 |
| 122 | CD76 | 40c carmine rose | 2.40 | 2.40 |
| 123 | CD77 | 50c dark brown | 1.60 | 1.60 |
| 124 | CD78 | 90c red | 1.60 | 1.60 |
| 125 | CD79 | 1.50fr ultra | 2.40 | 2.40 |
| | | *Nos. 120-125 (6)* | 12.00 | 12.00 |
| | | Set, never hinged | 20.25 | |

**Colonial Arts Exhibition Issue**

Souvenir Sheet

Common Design Type

**1937** ***Imperf.***

| No. | Type | Description | Unused | Used |
|---|---|---|---|---|
| 126 | CD76 | 3fr Prussian green | 12.00 | *16.00* |
| | | Never hinged | 16.00 | |

Guinea Village A7

Hausa Basket Workers A8

Forest Waterfall A9

Guinea Women — A10

**1938-40** ***Perf. 13***

| No. | Type | Description | Unused | Used |
|---|---|---|---|---|
| 128 | A7 | 2c vermilion | .25 | .25 |
| 129 | A7 | 3c ultra | .25 | .25 |
| 130 | A7 | 4c green | .25 | .25 |
| 131 | A7 | 5c rose car | .25 | .25 |
| 132 | A7 | 10c peacock blue | .25 | .25 |
| 133 | A7 | 15c violet brown | .25 | .25 |
| 134 | A8 | 20c dk carmine | .30 | .25 |
| 135 | A8 | 25c pck blue | .40 | .25 |
| 136 | A8 | 30c ultra | .40 | .25 |
| 137 | A8 | 35c green | .55 | .50 |
| 138 | A8 | 40c blk brn ('40) | .40 | .40 |

**139** A8 45c dk green ('40) .40 .40
**140** A8 50c red brown .55 .50
**141** A9 55c dk ultra 1.20 .80
**142** A9 60c dk ultra ('40) 1.20 1.20
**143** A9 65c green 1.20 .80
**144** A9 70c green ('40) 1.20 1.20
**145** A9 80c rose violet .80 .55
**146** A9 90c rose vio ('39) 1.25 1.25
**147** A9 1fr orange red 2.40 2.00
**148** A9 1fr brn blk ('40) .40 .40
**149** A9 1.25fr org red ('39) 1.40 1.40
**150** A9 1.40fr brown ('40) 1.20 1.20
**151** A9 1.50fr violet 2.40 2.00
**152** A10 1.60fr org red ('40) 1.60 1.60
**153** A10 1.75fr ultra .80 .80
**154** A10 2fr magenta 1.20 .80
**155** A10 2.25fr brt ultra ('39) 1.75 1.75
**156** A10 2.50fr brn blk ('40) 1.60 1.60
**157** A10 3fr peacock blue .95 .40
**158** A10 5fr rose violet .95 .80
**159** A10 10fr slate green 1.60 1.60
**160** A10 20fr chocolate 2.40 2.40
*Nos. 128-160 (33)* 32.00 28.60
Set, never hinged 45.00

For surcharges see Nos. B8-B11.

### Caillié Issue
Common Design Type

**1939** **Engr.** ***Perf. 12½x12***
**161** CD81 90c org brn & org .40 .80
**162** CD81 2fr brt violet .40 1.20
**163** CD81 2.25fr ultra & dk bl .40 1.20
*Nos. 161-163 (3)* 1.20 3.20
Set, never hinged 2.40

René Caillié, French explorer, death cent.

### New York World's Fair Issue
Common Design Type

**1939**
**164** CD82 1.25fr carmine lake .80 1.60
**165** CD82 2.25fr ultra .80 1.60
Set, never hinged 2.40

Ford at Kitim and Marshal Petain — A11

**1941** ***Perf. 12x12½***
**166** A11 1fr green .40 —
**167** A11 2.50fr deep blue .40 —
Set, never hinged 1.60

For surcharges, see Nos. B15-B16.

### Types of 1933-40 without "RF"

**1943-44** ***Perf. 13***
**168** A7 10c peacock blue .40
**169** A8 20c dk carmine .40
**170** A8 30c ultramarine .40
**171** A8 40c black brown 1.20
**172** A9 60c dk ultramarine 1.20
**173** A9 1.50fr violet 1.20
**174** A10 2fr magenta 1.60
*Nos. 168-174 (7)* 6.40
Set, never hinged 9.50

Nos. 168-174 were issued by the Vichy government in France, but were not placed on sale in French Guinea.

## SEMI-POSTAL STAMPS

Regular Issue of 1913 Surcharged in Red

**1915** **Unwmk.** ***Perf. 13½x14***
**B1** A6 10c + 5c org & rose 1.60 1.60

### Curie Issue
Common Design Type

**1938** **Engr.** ***Perf. 13***
**B2** CD80 1.75fr + 50c brt ultra 8.75 8.75
Never hinged 14.00

### French Revolution Issue
Common Design Type

**1939** **Photo.**
**Name and Value Typo. in Black**
**B3** CD83 45c + 25c green 9.50 9.50
**B4** CD83 70c + 30c brown 9.50 9.50
**B5** CD83 90c + 35c red org 9.50 9.50
**B6** CD83 1.25fr + 1fr rose pink 9.50 9.50
**B7** CD83 2.25fr + 2fr blue 9.50 9.50
*Nos. B3-B7 (5)* 47.50 47.50
Set, never hinged 80.00

Stamps of 1938, Surcharged in Black

**1941** **Unwmk.** ***Perf. 13***
**B8** A8 50c + 1fr red brn 4.00 4.00
**B9** A9 80c + 2fr rose vio 8.00 8.00
**B10** A9 1.50fr + 2fr brn 8.00 8.00
**B11** A10 2fr + 3fr magenta 8.00 8.00
*Nos. B8-B11 (4)* 28.00 28.00
Set, never hinged 55.00

### Common Design Type and

Senegalese Soldier SP1

Colonial Infantryman SP2

**1941** **Unwmk.** ***Perf. 13***
**B12** SP1 1fr + 1fr red 1.25
**B13** CD86 1.50fr + 3fr maroon 1.40
**B14** SP2 2.50fr + 1fr blue 1.40
*Nos. B12-B14 (3)* 4.05
Set, never hinged 6.50

Nos. B12-B14 were issued by the Vichy government in France, but were not placed on sale in the French Guinea.

Nos. 166-167 Surcharged in Black or Red

**1944** **Engr.** ***Perf. 12½x12***
**B15** 50c + 1.50fr on 2.50fr deep blue (R) .40
**B16** + 2.50fr on 1fr green .40
Set, never hinged 1.60

Colonial Development Fund.

Nos. B15-B16 were issued by the Vichy government in France, but were not placed on sale in French Guinea.

## AIR POST STAMPS

### Common Design Type

**1940** **Unwmk.** **Engr.** ***Perf. 12½x12***
**C1** CD85 1.90fr ultra .40 .40
**C2** CD85 2.90fr dark red .40 .40
**C3** CD85 4.50fr dk gray grn .80 .80
**C4** CD85 4.90fr yellow bis .80 .80
**C5** CD85 6.90fr dp orange 1.60 1.60
*Nos. C1-C5 (5)* 4.00 4.00
Set, never hinged 6.00

### Common Design Types

**1942** **Engr.**
**C6** CD88 50c car & blue .25
**C7** CD88 1fr brown & blk .30
**C8** CD88 2fr dk grn & red brn .30
**C9** CD88 3fr dk bl & scar .50
**C10** CD88 5fr vio & brn red .80

**Frame Engraved, Center Typographed**
**C11** CD89 10fr multicolored .80
**C12** CD89 20fr multicolored 1.20
**C13** CD89 50fr multicolored 1.60 —
*Nos. C6-C13 (8)* 5.75
Set, never hinged 12.00

There is doubt whether Nos. C6-C12 were officially placed in use.

## AIR POST SEMI-POSTAL STAMPS

**Dahomey types SPAP1-SPAP3 inscribed "Guinée Frcaise" or "Guinée"**
***Perf. 13½x12½, 13 (#CB3)***
**Photo, Engr. (#CB3)**

**1942, June 22**
**CB1** SPAP1 1.50fr + 3.50fr green .40 *5.50*
**CB2** SPAP2 2fr + 6fr brown .40 *5.50*
**CB3** SPAP3 3fr + 9fr car red .40 *5.50*
*Nos. CB1-CB3 (3)* 1.20 16.50
Set, never hinged 2.40

Native children's welfare fund.

### Colonial Education Fund
Common Design Type
***Perf. 12½x13½***

**1942, June 22** **Engr.**
**CB4** CD86a 1.20fr + 1.80fr blue & red .40 *5.50*
Never hinged .80

## POSTAGE DUE STAMPS

Fulah Woman — D1

**1905** **Unwmk.** **Typo.** ***Perf. 14x13½***
**J1** D1 5c blue 1.60 *3.25*
**J2** D1 10c brown 2.40 *3.25*
**J3** D1 15c green 8.00 6.50
**J4** D1 30c rose 8.00 6.50
**J5** D1 50c black 12.00 *13.00*
**J6** D1 60c dull orange 12.00 *16.00*
**J7** D1 1fr violet 40.00 *47.50*
*Nos. J1-J7 (7)* 84.00 96.00

Heads and Coast — D2

**1906-08**
**J8** D2 5c grn, *grnsh* ('08) 20.00 13.00
**J9** D2 10c violet brn ('08) 8.00 5.50
**J10** D2 15c dk blue ('08) 8.00 5.50
**J11** D2 20c blk, *yellow* 8.00 5.50
**J12** D2 30c red, *straw* ('08) 27.50 26.00
**J13** D2 50c violet ('08) 24.00 *26.00*
**J14** D2 60c blk, *buff* ('08) 24.00 21.00
**J15** D2 1fr blk, *pnksh* ('08) 16.00 13.50
*Nos. J8-J15 (8)* 135.50 116.00

D3

**1914**
**J16** D3 5c green .40 *.55*
**J17** D3 10c rose .40 *.65*
**J18** D3 15c gray .40 *.80*
**J19** D3 20c brown .80 .80
**J20** D3 30c blue .80 .80
**J21** D3 50c black 1.00 *1.25*
**J22** D3 60c orange 2.00 *2.40*
**J23** D3 1fr violet 2.00 *2.40*
*Nos. J16-J23 (8)* 7.80 9.65

Type of 1914 Issue Surcharged

**1927**
**J24** D3 2fr on 1fr lil rose 8.00 *8.00*
*a.* No period after "F" 27.50 *32.50*
**J25** D3 3fr on 1fr org brn 8.00 *8.00*

D4

**1938** **Engr.**
**J26** D4 5c dk violet .25 .30
**J27** D4 10c carmine .25 .30
**J28** D4 15c green .25 .30
**J29** D4 20c red brown .25 .40
**J30** D4 30c rose violet .25 .40
**J31** D4 50c chocolate .80 .70
**J32** D4 60c peacock blue .80 1.10
**J33** D4 1fr vermilion .80 1.10
**J34** D4 2fr ultra .80 1.10
**J35** D4 3fr black 1.60 1.60
*Nos. J26-J35 (10)* 6.05 7.30

For No. J27 without "RF," see No. J36.

### Type of 1938 without "RF"

**1944**
**J36** D4 10c carmine .80
Never hinged 1.20

No. J36 was issued by the Vichy government in France, but was not placed on sale in French Guinea.

# FRENCH INDIA

'french 'in-dē-ə

LOCATION — East coast of India bordering on Bay of Bengal.
GOVT. — French Territory
AREA — 196 sq. mi.
POP. — 323,295 (1941)
CAPITAL — Pondichéry

French India was an administrative unit comprising the five settlements of Chandernagor, Karikal, Mahé, Pondichéry and Yanaon. These united with India in 1949 and 1954.

100 Centimes = 1 Franc
24 Caches = 1 Fanon (1923)
8 Fanons = 1 Rupie

**Catalogue values for unused stamps in this country are for Never Hinged items, beginning with Scott 210 in the regular postage section, Scott B14 in the semi-postal section, and Scott C7 in the airpost section.**

Navigation and Commerce — A1

***Perf. 14x13½***

**1892-1907 Typo. Unwmk.**

**Colony Name in Blue or Carmine**

| No. | Type | Value | Description | Unused | Used |
|---|---|---|---|---|---|
| **1** | A1 | 1c | blk, *lil bl* | 1.40 | 1.00 |
| **2** | A1 | 2c | brn, *buff* | 2.40 | 1.50 |
| **3** | A1 | 4c | claret, *lav* | 3.00 | 2.50 |
| **4** | A1 | 5c | grn, *grnsh* | 6.00 | 3.75 |
| **5** | A1 | 10c | blk, *lavender* | 13.50 | 2.75 |
| **6** | A1 | 10c | red ('00) | 5.00 | 2.40 |
| **7** | A1 | 15c | blue, quadrille paper | 16.00 | 5.50 |
| **8** | A1 | 15c | gray, *lt gray* ('00) | 30.00 | 30.00 |
| **9** | A1 | 20c | red, *grn* | 8.00 | 5.50 |
| **10** | A1 | 25c | blk, *rose* | 5.25 | 2.75 |
| **11** | A1 | 25c | blue ('00) | 19.00 | 16.00 |
| **12** | A1 | 30c | brn, *bis* | 57.50 | 50.00 |
| **13** | A1 | 35c | blk, *yel* ('06) | 19.00 | 9.00 |
| **14** | A1 | 40c | red, *straw* | 7.50 | 7.25 |
| **15** | A1 | 45c | blk, *gray grn* ('07) | 5.25 | *6.00* |
| **16** | A1 | 50c | car, *rose* | 7.25 | 7.25 |
| **17** | A1 | 50c | brn, *az* ('00) | 16.00 | *17.50* |
| **18** | A1 | 75c | dp vio, *org* | 9.75 | *9.50* |
| **19** | A1 | 1fr | brnz grn, *straw* | 14.00 | *14.50* |
| | | | *Nos. 1-19 (19)* | 245.80 | *194.65* |

Perf. 13½x14 stamps are counterfeits.

Nos. 10 and 16 Surcharged in Carmine or Black

**1903**

| No. | Type | Value | Description | Unused | Used |
|---|---|---|---|---|---|
| **20** | A1 | 5c | on 25c blk, *rose* | 400.00 | 240.00 |
| **21** | A1 | 10c | on 25c blk, *rose* | 375.00 | 225.00 |
| **22** | A1 | 15c | on 25c blk, *rose* | 125.00 | 115.00 |
| **23** | A1 | 40c | on 50c car, *rose* (Bk) | 525.00 | 425.00 |
| | | | *Nos. 20-23 (4)* | 1,425. | 1,005. |

Counterfeits of Nos. 20-23 abound.

A2

**Revenue Stamp Surcharged in Black**

**1903**

| No. | Type | Value | Description | Unused | Used |
|---|---|---|---|---|---|
| **24** | A2 | 5c | gray blue | 30.00 | 30.00 |

The bottom of the revenue stamps were cut off.

Brahma — A5

Kali Temple near Pondichéry A6

**1914-22** ***Perf. 13½x14, 14x13½***

| No. | Type | Value | Description | Unused | Used |
|---|---|---|---|---|---|
| **25** | A5 | 1c | gray & blk | .30 | .30 |
| *a.* | | 1c | light gray & black | .55 | .55 |
| **26** | A5 | 2c | brn vio & blk | .30 | .30 |
| **27** | A5 | 2c | grn & brn vio ('22) | .45 | .45 |
| **28** | A5 | 3c | brown & blk | .40 | .40 |
| **29** | A5 | 4c | orange & blk | .40 | .40 |
| **30** | A5 | 5c | bl grn & blk | .70 | .70 |
| **31** | A5 | 5c | vio brn & blk ('22) | .60 | .60 |
| **32** | A5 | 10c | dp rose & blk | 1.25 | 1.25 |
| **33** | A5 | 10c | grn & blk ('22) | .90 | .90 |
| **34** | A5 | 15c | vio & blk | 1.10 | 1.10 |
| **35** | A5 | 20c | org red & blk | 2.00 | 2.00 |
| **36** | A5 | 25c | blue & blk | 2.00 | 2.00 |
| **37** | A5 | 25c | ultra & fawn ('22) | 1.60 | 1.60 |
| **38** | A5 | 30c | ultra & blk | 4.00 | 4.00 |
| **39** | A5 | 30c | rose & blk ('22) | 1.75 | 1.75 |
| **40** | A6 | 35c | choc & blk | 2.25 | 2.25 |
| **41** | A6 | 40c | org red & blk | 2.25 | 2.25 |
| **42** | A6 | 45c | bl grn & blk | 2.25 | 2.25 |
| **43** | A6 | 50c | dp rose & blk | 2.25 | 2.25 |
| **44** | A6 | 50c | ultra & bl ('22) | 3.00 | 3.00 |
| **45** | A6 | 75c | blue & blk | 4.50 | 4.50 |
| **46** | A6 | 1fr | yellow & blk | 4.50 | 4.50 |
| **47** | A6 | 2fr | violet & blk | 6.75 | 6.75 |
| **48** | A6 | 5fr | ultra & blk | 3.50 | 3.50 |
| **49** | A6 | 5fr | rose & blk ('22) | 5.50 | 5.50 |
| | | | *Nos. 25-49 (25)* | 54.50 | 54.50 |

For surcharges see Nos. 50-79, 113-116, 156A, B1-B5.

No. 34 Surcharged in Various Colors

**1922**

| No. | Type | Value | Description | Unused | Used |
|---|---|---|---|---|---|
| **50** | A5 | 1c | on 15c (Bk) | .80 | .80 |
| **51** | A5 | 2c | on 15c (Bl) | .80 | .80 |
| **53** | A5 | 5c | on 15c (R) | .80 | .80 |
| | | | *Nos. 50-53 (3)* | 2.40 | 2.40 |

**Stamps and Types of 1914-22 Surcharged with New Values in Caches, Fanons and Rupies in Black, Red or Blue**

No. 55

No. 69

No. 78

3 ROUPIES

**1923-28**

| No. | Type | Value | Description | Unused | Used |
|---|---|---|---|---|---|
| **54** | A5 | 1ca | on 1c gray & blk (R) | .30 | .30 |
| *a.* | | | Imperf. | 50.00 | 50.00 |
| **55** | A5 | 2ca | on 5c vio brn & blk | .50 | .50 |
| *a.* | | | Horizontal pair, imperf. between | — | |
| *b.* | | | Imperf. | 45.00 | 45.00 |
| **56** | A5 | 3ca | on 3c brn & blk | .55 | .55 |
| **57** | A5 | 4ca | on 4c org & blk | .80 | .80 |
| **58** | A5 | 6ca | on 10c grn & blk | .95 | .95 |
| *a.* | | | Double surcharge | 175.00 | |
| **59** | A6 | 6ca | on 45c bl grn & blk (R) | .95 | .95 |
| **60** | A5 | 10ca | on 20c dp red & bl grn ('28) | 2.50 | 2.50 |
| **61** | A5 | 12ca | on 15c vio & blk | .95 | .95 |
| **62** | A5 | 15ca | on 20c org & blk | 1.50 | 1.50 |
| **63** | A6 | 16ca | on 35c lt bl & yel brn ('28) | 2.60 | 2.60 |
| **64** | A5 | 18ca | on 30c rose & blk | 2.40 | 2.40 |
| **65** | A6 | 20ca | on 45c grn & dl red ('28) | 2.00 | 1.50 |
| **66** | A5 | 1fa | on 25c dp grn & rose red ('28) | 3.50 | 3.50 |
| **67** | A6 | 1fa3ca | on 35c choc & blk (Bl) | 1.10 | 1.10 |
| **68** | A6 | 1fa6ca | on 40c org & blk (R) | 1.50 | 1.25 |
| **69** | A6 | 1fa12ca | on 50c ultra & bl (Bl) | 1.75 | 1.50 |
| **70** | A6 | 1fa12ca | on 75c bl & blk (Bl) | 1.25 | 1.25 |
| *a.* | | | Double surcharge | 145.00 | |
| **71** | A6 | 1fa16ca | on 75c brn red & grn ('28) | 3.50 | 3.00 |
| **72** | A5 | 2fa9ca | on 25c ultra & fawn (Bl) | 1.50 | 1.20 |
| **73** | A6 | 2fa12ca | on 1fr vio & dk brn ('28) | 3.00 | 3.00 |
| **74** | A6 | 3fa3ca | on 1fr yel & blk (R) | 1.75 | 1.45 |
| *a.* | | | Double surcharge | 145.00 | |
| **75** | A6 | 6fa6ca | on 2fr vio & blk (Bl) | 5.25 | 4.50 |
| **76** | A6 | 1r | on 1fr grn & dp bl (R) ('26) | 9.50 | 7.75 |
| **77** | A6 | 2r | on 5fr rose & blk (R) | 7.50 | 7.00 |
| *a.* | | | Double surcharge | 145.00 | |
| **78** | A6 | 3r | on 2fr gray & bl vio (R) ('26) | 21.00 | 19.00 |
| **79** | A6 | 5r | on 5fr rose & blk, *grnsh* ('26) | 27.50 | 24.00 |
| | | | *Nos. 54-79 (26)* | 105.60 | 95.00 |

Nos. 60, 63, 66 and 73 have the original value obliterated by bars.

A7

A8

**1929**

| No. | Type | Value | Description | Unused | Used |
|---|---|---|---|---|---|
| **80** | A7 | 1ca | dk gray & blk | .25 | .25 |
| **81** | A7 | 2ca | vio brn & blk | .25 | .25 |
| **82** | A7 | 3ca | brn & blk | .25 | .25 |
| **83** | A7 | 4ca | org & blk | .30 | .30 |
| **84** | A7 | 6ca | gray grn & grn | .30 | .30 |
| **85** | A7 | 10ca | brn, red & grn | .30 | .30 |
| **86** | A8 | 12ca | grn & lt grn | .75 | .70 |
| **87** | A7 | 16ca | brt bl & blk | .95 | .95 |
| **88** | A7 | 18ca | brn red & ver | .95 | .95 |
| **89** | A7 | 20ca | dk bl & grn, *bluish* | .75 | .75 |
| **90** | A8 | 1fa | gray grn & rose red | .75 | .70 |
| **91** | A8 | 1fa6ca | red org & blk | .75 | .70 |
| **92** | A8 | 1fa12ca | dp bl & ultra | .75 | .70 |
| **93** | A8 | 1fa16ca | rose red & grn | .95 | .95 |
| **94** | A8 | 2fa12ca | brt vio & brn | 1.20 | 1.00 |
| **95** | A8 | 6fa6ca | dl vio & blk | 1.20 | 1.00 |
| *a.* | | | Imperf. | 50.00 | |
| **96** | A8 | 1r | gray grn & dp bl | 1.10 | 1.00 |
| **97** | A8 | 2r | rose & blk | 1.60 | 1.20 |
| *a.* | | | Imperf. | 50.00 | |
| **98** | A8 | 3r | lt gray & gray lil | 3.00 | 2.25 |
| **99** | A8 | 5r | rose & blk, *grnsh* | 3.00 | 2.40 |
| | | | *Nos. 80-99 (20)* | 19.35 | 16.90 |

For overprints and surcharges see Nos. 117-134, 157-176, 184-209G.

Common Design Types pictured following the introduction.

**Colonial Exposition Issue**

Common Design Types

**1931 Engr.** ***Perf. 12½***

| No. | Type | Value | Description | Unused | Used |
|---|---|---|---|---|---|
| **100** | CD70 | 10ca | deep green | 4.50 | *4.50* |
| **101** | CD71 | 12ca | violet | 4.50 | *4.50* |
| **102** | CD72 | 18ca | red orange | 4.50 | *4.50* |
| **103** | CD73 | 1fa12ca | dull blue | 4.50 | *4.50* |
| | | | *Nos. 100-103 (4)* | 18.00 | *18.00* |

**Paris International Exposition Issue**

Common Design Types

**1937** ***Perf. 13***

| No. | Type | Value | Description | Unused | Used |
|---|---|---|---|---|---|
| **104** | CD74 | 8ca | dp violet | 2.00 | *4.00* |
| **105** | CD75 | 12ca | dk green | 2.25 | *4.00* |
| **106** | CD76 | 16ca | car rose | 2.25 | *4.00* |
| **107** | CD77 | 20ca | dk brown | 1.40 | *4.00* |
| **108** | CD78 | 1fa12ca | red | 1.75 | *4.00* |
| **109** | CD79 | 2fa12ca | ultra | 2.25 | *4.00* |
| | | | *Nos. 104-109 (6)* | 11.90 | *24.00* |

For overprints see Nos. 135-139, 177-181.

**Colonial Arts Exhibition Issue**

Souvenir Sheet

Common Design Type

**1937** ***Imperf.***

| No. | Type | Value | Description | Unused | Used |
|---|---|---|---|---|---|
| **110** | CD79 | 5fa | red violet | 9.25 | *12.50* |

For overprint see No. 140.

**New York World's Fair Issue**

Common Design Type

**1939 Engr.** ***Perf. 12½x12***

| No. | Type | Value | Description | Unused | Used |
|---|---|---|---|---|---|
| **111** | CD82 | 1fa12ca | car lake | 1.25 | *4.00* |
| **112** | CD82 | 2fa12ca | ultra | 1.75 | *4.00* |

For overprints see Nos. 141-142, 182-183.

Temple near Pondichéry and Marshal Petain A9

**1941 Engr.** ***Perf. 12½x12***

| No. | Type | Value | Description | Unused | Used |
|---|---|---|---|---|---|
| **112A** | A9 | 1fa16ca | car & red | .80 | |
| *c.* | | | Denomination omitted | 55.00 | |
| **112B** | A9 | 4fa4ca | blue | .80 | |
| *d.* | | | Denomination omitted | 200.00 | |

Nos. 112A-112B were issued by the Vichy government in France, but were not placed on sale in French India.

For surcharges, see Nos. B13B-B13C.

**Nos. 62, 64, 67, 72 Overprinted in Carmine or Blue (#116)**

a

b

**1941 Unwmk.** ***Perf. 13½x14***

| No. | Type | Value | Description | Unused | Used |
|---|---|---|---|---|---|
| **113** | A5 (a) | 15ca | on 20c | 85.00 | 85.00 |
| **114** | A5 (a) | 18ca | on 30c | 16.00 | 16.00 |
| **115** | A6 (a) | 1fa3ca | on 35c | 130.00 | 130.00 |
| *a.* | | | Horiz. overprint | 125.00 | 125.00 |
| **116** | A5 (b) | 2fa9ca | on 25c | 1,600. | 1,150. |
| *a.* | | | Overprint "a" (Bl) | 1,400. | 1,150. |
| *b.* | | | Overprint "b" (C) | *2,100.* | *2,100.* |

**Nos. 81-99 Overprinted Type "a" in Carmine or Blue**

**1941**

| No. | Type | Value | Description | Unused | Used |
|---|---|---|---|---|---|
| **117** | A7 | 2ca | (C) | 12.50 | 12.50 |
| **118** | A7 | 3ca | (C) | 4.75 | 4.75 |
| **119** | A7 | 4ca | (C) | 13.50 | 13.50 |
| **120** | A7 | 6ca | (C) | 4.75 | 4.75 |

| No. | Type | Value | Unused | Used |
|---|---|---|---|---|
| **121** | A7 | 10ca (Bl) | 6.50 | 6.50 |
| **122** | A8 | 12ca (C) | 4.75 | 4.75 |
| **123** | A7 | 16ca (C) | 4.75 | 4.75 |
| **123A** | A7 | 18ca (Bl) | 675.00 | 675.00 |
| **124** | A7 | 20ca (C) | 4.75 | 4.75 |
| **125** | A8 | 1fa (Bl) | 4.75 | 4.75 |
| **126** | A8 | 1fa6ca (C) | 4.75 | 4.75 |
| **127** | A8 | 1fa12ca (C) | 6.50 | 6.50 |
| **128** | A8 | 1fa16ca (C) | 4.75 | 4.75 |
| **129** | A8 | 2fa12ca (C) | 4.75 | 4.75 |
| **130** | A8 | 6fa6ca (C) | 4.75 | 4.75 |
| **131** | A8 | 1r (C) | 4.75 | 4.75 |
| **132** | A8 | 2r (C) | 4.75 | 4.75 |
| **133** | A8 | 3r (C) | 6.50 | 6.50 |
| **134** | A8 | 5r (C) | 10.50 | 10.50 |
| | | *Nos. 117-123,124-134 (18)* | 113.00 | 113.00 |

### Same Overprints on Paris Exposition Issue of 1937

**1941** *Perf. 13*

| No. | Type | Value | Unused | Used |
|---|---|---|---|---|
| **135** | CD74 (b) | 8ca (C) | 10.00 | 10.00 |
| **135A** | CD74 (b) | 8ca (Bl) | 275.00 | 275.00 |
| *d.* | | Blk. overprint | 1,000. | 1,000. |
| **135B** | CD74 (a) | 8ca (C) | 180.00 | 180.00 |
| **135C** | CD74 (a) | 8ca (Bl) | 250.00 | 250.00 |
| **136** | CD75 (a) | 12ca (C) | 6.00 | 6.00 |
| **137** | CD76 (a) | 16ca (Bl) | 6.00 | 6.00 |
| *a.* | | Blk. overprint | 175.00 | 175.00 |
| **138** | CD78 (a) | 1fa12ca (Bl) | 6.00 | 6.00 |
| **139** | CD79 (a) | 2fa12ca (C) | 6.00 | 6.00 |
| | | *Nos. 135-139 (8)* | 739.00 | 739.00 |

Inverted overprints exist.

### Souvenir Sheet

### No. 110 Overprinted "FRANCE LIBRE" Diagonally in Blue Violet

Two types of overprint:
I — Overprint 37mm. With serifs.
II — Overprint 24mm, as type "a" shown above No. 113. No serifs.

**1941** **Unwmk.** ***Imperf.***

| No. | Type | Value | Unused | Used |
|---|---|---|---|---|
| **140** | CD79 | 5fa red vio (I) | 800.00 | 725.00 |
| *a.* | | Type II | 1,000. | 1,000. |
| *b.* | | As No. 140, inverted surcharge | 5,000. | 2,000. |

### Overprinted on New York World's Fair Issue, 1939

*Perf. 12½x12*

| No. | Type | Value | Unused | Used |
|---|---|---|---|---|
| **141** | CD82 (a) | 1fa12ca (Bl) | 4.75 | 4.75 |
| **142** | CD82 (a) | 2fa12ca (C) | 5.50 | 5.50 |

Lotus Flowers — A10

**1942** **Unwmk.** **Photo.** ***Perf. 14x14½***

| No. | Type | Value | Unused | Used |
|---|---|---|---|---|
| **143** | A10 | 2ca brown | .30 | .30 |
| **144** | A10 | 3ca dk blue | .30 | .30 |
| **145** | A10 | 4ca emerald | .30 | .30 |
| **146** | A10 | 6ca dk orange | .30 | .30 |
| **147** | A10 | 12ca grnsh blk | .30 | .30 |
| **148** | A10 | 16ca rose violet | .30 | .30 |
| **149** | A10 | 20ca dk red brn | .65 | .65 |
| **150** | A10 | 1fa brt red | .70 | .65 |
| **151** | A10 | 1fa18ca slate blk | .90 | .80 |
| **152** | A10 | 6fa6ca brt ultra | 1.60 | 1.50 |
| **153** | A10 | 1r dull violet | 1.40 | 1.40 |
| **154** | A10 | 2r bister | 1.75 | 1.60 |
| **155** | A10 | 3r chocolate | 1.75 | 1.60 |
| **156** | A10 | 5r dk green | 2.25 | 2.00 |
| | | *Nos. 143-156 (14)* | 12.80 | 12.00 |

### Stamps of 1923-39 Overprinted in Blue or Carmine

c

d

**1942-43** ***Perf. 13½x14, 14x13½***

### Overprinted on No. 64

| No. | Type | Value | Unused | Used |
|---|---|---|---|---|
| **156A** | A5 (c) | 18ca on 30c (B) | 300.00 | 230.00 |

### Overprinted on #81-82, 84, 86-99

| No. | Type | Value | Unused | Used |
|---|---|---|---|---|
| **157** | A7 (c) | 2ca (C) | 3.75 | 3.75 |
| *a.* | | "FRANCE LIBRE" in black | 250.00 | 175.00 |
| *b.* | | As No. 157, blk. overprint | 375.00 | 375.00 |
| *c.* | | As No. 157, bl. overprint | 500.00 | 500.00 |
| **158** | A7 (c) | 3ca (C) | 2.40 | 2.40 |
| **159** | A7 (c) | 6ca (Bl) | 3.25 | 3.25 |
| *a.* | | Car. overprint | 325.00 | |
| *b.* | | Blk. overprint | 725.00 | |
| *c.* | | Bl.-Blk. overprint | 50.00 | 35.00 |
| **160** | A8 (d) | 12ca (Bl) | 3.75 | 3.75 |
| **161** | A7 (c) | 16ca (C) | 3.25 | 3.25 |
| **162** | A7 (c) | 18ca (Bl) | 2.40 | 2.40 |
| **163** | A7 (c) | 20ca (Bl) ('43) | 7.25 | 5.50 |
| **164** | A7 (c) | 20ca (C) | 2.40 | 2.40 |
| *a.* | | Double overprint, one bl. one car. | 1,350. | 475.00 |
| **165** | A8 (d) | 1fa (Bl) | 2.40 | 2.40 |
| **166** | A8 (d) | 1fa6ca (C) | 3.25 | 3.25 |
| *a.* | | Bl. overprint | 300.00 | 225.00 |
| **167** | A8 (d) | 1fa12ca (C) | 3.25 | 3.25 |
| **168** | A8 (d) | 1fa16ca (Bl) | 3.25 | 3.25 |
| **169** | A8 (d) | 2fa12ca (Bl) | 100.00 | 80.00 |
| **170** | A8 (d) | 2fa12ca (C) | 3.25 | 3.25 |
| **171** | A8 (d) | 6fa6ca (C) | 4.00 | 4.00 |
| **172** | A8 (d) | 1r (C) | 7.25 | 7.25 |
| **173** | A8 (d) | 2r (C) | 7.25 | 7.25 |
| **174** | A8 (d) | 3r (C) | 7.25 | 7.25 |
| **175** | A8 (d) | 3r (Bl) ('43) | 200.00 | 175.00 |
| **176** | A8 (d) | 5r (C) | 7.25 | 7.25 |
| | | *Nos. 156A-176 (21)* | 676.85 | 560.10 |

### Same Overprints on Paris International Exposition Issue of 1937

*Perf. 13*

| No. | Type | Value | Unused | Used |
|---|---|---|---|---|
| **177** | CD74 (c) | 8ca (Bl) | 7.25 | 7.25 |
| **178** | CD75 (d) | 12ca (Bl) | 7.25 | 7.25 |
| **179** | CD76 (d) | 16ca (Bl) | 1,300. | 1,300. |
| **180** | CD78 (d) | 1fa12ca (Bl) | 7.25 | 7.25 |
| **181** | CD79 (d) | 2fa12ca (C) | 7.25 | 7.25 |

### Same Overprint on New York World's Fair Issue, 1939

*Perf. 12½x12*

| No. | Type | Value | Unused | Used |
|---|---|---|---|---|
| **182** | CD82 (d) | 1fa12ca (Bl) | 7.25 | 7.25 |
| **183** | CD82 (d) | 2fa12ca (C) | 7.25 | 7.25 |

No. 87 Surcharged in Carmine

**1942-43** ***Perf. 13½x14***

| No. | Type | Value | Unused | Used |
|---|---|---|---|---|
| **184** | A7 | 1ca on 16ca | 75.00 | 45.00 |
| **185** | A7 | 4ca on 16ca ('43) | 75.00 | 45.00 |
| **186** | A7 | 10ca on 16ca | 55.00 | 35.00 |
| **187** | A7 | 15ca on 16ca | 55.00 | 35.00 |
| **188** | A7 | 1fa3ca on 16ca ('43) | 72.50 | 45.00 |
| **189** | A7 | 2fa9ca on 16ca ('43) | 72.50 | 45.00 |
| **190** | A7 | 3fa3ca on 16ca ('43) | 55.00 | 35.00 |
| | | *Nos. 184-190 (7)* | 460.00 | 285.00 |

Nos. 95-99 Srchd. in Carmine

**1943** ***Perf. 14x13½***

| No. | Type | Value | Unused | Used |
|---|---|---|---|---|
| **191** | A8 | 1ca on 6fa6ca | 11.00 | 11.00 |
| **192** | A8 | 4ca on 6fa6ca | 12.50 | 12.50 |
| **193** | A8 | 10ca on 6fa6ca | 11.00 | 11.00 |
| **194** | A8 | 15ca on 6fa6ca | 11.00 | 11.00 |
| **195** | A8 | 1fa3ca on 6fa6ca | 11.00 | 11.00 |
| **196** | A8 | 2fa9ca on 6fa6ca | 12.50 | 12.50 |
| **197** | A8 | 3fa3ca on 6fa6ca | 12.50 | 12.50 |
| **198** | A8 | 1ca on 1r | 4.75 | 4.75 |
| **199** | A8 | 2ca on 1r | 1.60 | 1.60 |
| **200** | A8 | 4ca on 1r | 1.60 | 1.60 |
| **201** | A8 | 6ca on 2r | 1.60 | 1.60 |
| **202** | A8 | 10ca on 2r | 1.75 | 1.75 |
| **203** | A8 | 12ca on 2r | 1.60 | 1.60 |
| **204** | A8 | 15ca on 3r | 1.60 | 1.60 |
| **205** | A8 | 16ca on 3r | 1.60 | 1.60 |
| **206** | A8 | 1fa3ca on 3r | 1.60 | 1.60 |
| **207** | A8 | 1fa6ca on 5r | 2.00 | 2.00 |
| **208** | A8 | 1fa12ca on 5r | 2.40 | 2.40 |
| **209** | A8 | 1fa16ca on 5r | 2.40 | 2.40 |
| | | *Nos. 191-209 (19)* | 106.00 | 106.00 |

In 1943, 200 each of 27 stamps were overprinted in red or dark blue, "FRANCE TOUJOURS" and a Lorraine Cross within a circle measuring 17½mm in diameter. Overprinted were Nos. 81-99, 104-109, 111-112. Values, set: $25,000 unused; $6,000 used.

No. 95 Surcharged in Carmine

**1943** **Unwmk.** ***Perf. 14x13½***

| No. | Type | Value | Unused | Used |
|---|---|---|---|---|
| **209A** | A8 | 1ca on 6fa6ca | 35.00 | 27.50 |
| **209B** | A8 | 4ca on 6fa6ca | 35.00 | 27.50 |
| **209C** | A8 | 10ca on 6fa6ca | 24.00 | 16.00 |
| **209D** | A8 | 15ca on 6fa6ca | 24.00 | 16.00 |
| **209E** | A8 | 1fa3ca on 6fa6ca | 32.50 | 27.50 |
| **209F** | A8 | 2fa9ca on 6fa6ca | 32.50 | 27.50 |
| **209G** | A8 | 3fa3ca on 6fa6ca | 35.00 | 27.50 |
| | | *Nos. 209A-209G (7)* | 218.00 | 169.50 |

**Catalogue values for unused stamps in this section, from this point to the end of the section, are for Never Hinged items.**

### Eboue Issue

Common Design Type

**1945** **Engr.** ***Perf. 13***

| No. | Type | Value | Unused | Used |
|---|---|---|---|---|
| **210** | CD91 | 3fa8ca black | .80 | .70 |
| **211** | CD91 | 5r1fa16ca Prus grn | 1.40 | 1.25 |

Nos. 210 and 211 exist imperforate.

Apsaras — A11

Designs: 6ca, 8ca, 10ca, Dvarabalagar. 12ca, 15ca, 1fa, Vishnu. 1fa6ca, 2fa, 2fa2ca, Dvarabalagar (foot raised). 2fa12ca, 3fa, 5fa, Temple Guardian. 7fa12ca, 1r2fa, 1r4fa12ca, Tigoupalagar.

**1948** **Photo.** ***Perf. 13x13½***

| No. | Type | Value | Unused | Used |
|---|---|---|---|---|
| **212** | A11 | 1ca dk ol grn | .50 | .25 |
| **213** | A11 | 2ca orange brn | .50 | .25 |
| **214** | A11 | 4ca vio, *cr* | .55 | .30 |
| **215** | A11 | 6ca yellow org | 1.50 | .65 |
| **216** | A11 | 8ca gray blk | 1.50 | 1.10 |
| **217** | A11 | 10ca dl yel grn, *pale grn* | 1.50 | 1.10 |
| **218** | A11 | 12ca violet brn | 1.00 | .65 |
| **219** | A11 | 15ca Prus grn | 1.00 | .65 |
| **220** | A11 | 1fa vio, *pale rose* | 1.50 | .80 |
| **221** | A11 | 1fa6ca brown red | 1.50 | .85 |
| **222** | A11 | 2fa dk green | 1.50 | .85 |
| **223** | A11 | 2fa2ca blue, *cr* | 1.50 | 1.15 |
| **224** | A11 | 2fa12ca brown | 1.90 | 1.15 |
| **225** | A11 | 3fa dp orange | 3.25 | 1.25 |
| **226** | A11 | 5fa red vio, *rose* | 3.00 | 1.25 |
| **227** | A11 | 7fa12ca dk brown | 3.25 | 1.25 |
| **228** | A11 | 1r2fa brown blk | 6.00 | 4.50 |
| **229** | A11 | 1r4fa12ca olive grn | 6.50 | 5.00 |
| | | *Nos. 212-229 (18)* | 37.95 | 23.00 |

Brahman Ascetic — A12

**1952**

| No. | Type | Value | Unused | Used |
|---|---|---|---|---|
| **230** | A12 | 18ca rose red | 2.75 | 2.00 |
| **231** | A12 | 1fa15ca vio blue | 3.75 | 2.50 |
| **232** | A12 | 4fa olive grn | 4.25 | 3.50 |
| | | *Nos. 230-232 (3)* | 10.75 | 8.00 |

### Military Medal Issue

Common Design Type

**1952** **Engr. and Typo.** ***Perf. 13***

| No. | Type | Value | Unused | Used |
|---|---|---|---|---|
| **233** | CD101 | 1fa multi | 5.50 | *7.00* |

## SEMI-POSTAL STAMPS

Regular Issue of 1914 Surcharged in Red

Two printings: 1st, surcharge at bottom of stamp; 2nd, surcharge centered toward top.

**1915** **Unwmk.** ***Perf. 14x13½***

| No. | Type | Value | Unused | Used |
|---|---|---|---|---|
| **B1** | A5 | 10c + 5c rose & blk (1st) | 2.10 | 2.10 |
| *b.* | | Inverted surcharge | 210.00 | 210.00 |

There were two printings of this surcharge. In the first, it was placed at the bottom of the stamp; in the second, it was centered toward the top.

Regular Issue of 1914 Surcharged in Red

**1916**

| No. | Type | Value | Unused | Used |
|---|---|---|---|---|
| **B2** | A5 | 10c + 5c rose & blk | 21.00 | 21.00 |
| *a.* | | Inverted surcharge | 210.00 | 210.00 |
| *b.* | | Double surcharge | 210.00 | 210.00 |

No. 32 Surcharged

| No. | Type | Value | Unused | Used |
|---|---|---|---|---|
| **B3** | A5 | 10c + 5c rose & blk | 3.50 | 3.50 |

No. 32 Surcharged

| No. | Type | Value | Unused | Used |
|---|---|---|---|---|
| **B4** | A5 | 10c + 5c rose & blk | 1.60 | 1.60 |

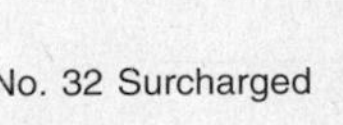

No. 32 Surcharged

| No. | Type | Value | Unused | Used |
|---|---|---|---|---|
| **B5** | A5 | 10c + 5c rose & blk | 2.25 | 2.25 |

### Curie Issue

Common Design Type

**1938** **Engr.** ***Perf. 13***

| No. | Type | Value | Unused | Used |
|---|---|---|---|---|
| **B6** | CD80 | 2fa12ca + 20ca brt ultra | 10.00 | 10.00 |

### French Revolution Issue

Common Design Type

**1939 Photo.**

**Name and Value Typo. in Black**

| | | | | |
|---|---|---|---|---|
| **B7** | CD83 | 18ca + 10ca grn | 5.75 | *6.50* |
| **B8** | CD83 | 1fa6ca + 12ca brn | 5.75 | *6.50* |
| **B9** | CD83 | 1fa12ca + 16ca red org | 5.75 | *6.50* |
| **B10** | CD83 | 1fa16ca + 1fa16ca rose pink | 5.75 | *6.50* |
| **B11** | CD83 | 2fa12ca + 3fa blue | 5.75 | *6.50* |
| | | *Nos. B7-B11 (5)* | 28.75 | *32.50* |

### Common Design Type and

Non-Commissioned Officer, Native Guard — SP1

Sepoy SP2

**1941 Photo. *Perf. 13½***

| | | | |
|---|---|---|---|
| **B12** | SP1 | 1fa16ca + 1fa16ca red | 1.25 |
| **B13** | CD86 | 2fa12ca + 5fa mar | 1.25 |
| **B13A** | SP2 | 4fa4ca + 1fa16ca bl | 1.25 |
| | | *Nos. B12-B13A (3)* | 3.75 |

Nos. B12-B13A were issued by the Vichy government in France, but were not placed on sale in French India.

Nos. 112A-112B Srchd. in Black or Red

**1944 Engr. *Perf. 12½x12***

| | | |
|---|---|---|
| **B13B** | 20ca + 2fa12ca on 4fa4ca deep blue (R) | 1.00 |
| **B13C** | + 4fa4ca on 1fa16ca car & red | 1.00 |

Colonial Development Fund.

Nos. B13B-B13C were issued by the Vichy government in France, but were not placed on sale in French India.

**Catalogue values for unused stamps in this section, from this point to the end of the section, are for Never Hinged items.**

### Red Cross Issue

Common Design Type

**1944 Photo. *Perf. 14½x14***

| | | | | |
|---|---|---|---|---|
| **B14** | CD90 | 3fa + 1r4fa dk ol brn | 1.50 | 1.25 |

The surtax was for the French Red Cross and national relief.

### Tropical Medicine Issue

Common Design Type

**1950 Engr. *Perf. 13***

| | | | | |
|---|---|---|---|---|
| **B15** | CD100 | 1fa + 10ca ind & dp bl | 6.00 | 4.00 |

The surtax was for charitable work.

## AIR POST STAMPS

Common Design Type

**1942 Unwmk. Photo. *Perf. 14½x14***

| | | | | |
|---|---|---|---|---|
| **C1** | CD87 | 4fa dark orange | .90 | *2.00* |
| **C2** | CD87 | 1r bright red | .90 | *2.00* |
| **C3** | CD87 | 2r brown red | 1.50 | *2.00* |
| **C4** | CD87 | 5r black | 1.50 | *3.00* |
| **C5** | CD87 | 8r ultra | 2.25 | *3.00* |
| **C6** | CD87 | 10r dark green | 2.25 | *3.00* |
| | | *Nos. C1-C6 (6)* | 9.30 | *15.00* |

**Catalogue values for unused stamps in this section, from this point to the end of the section, are for Never Hinged items.**

### Victory Issue

Common Design Type

**1946 Engr. *Perf. 12½***

| | | | | |
|---|---|---|---|---|
| **C7** | CD92 | 4fa dk blue green | 1.00 | *4.00* |

### Chad to Rhine Issue

Common Design Types

**1946, June 6**

| | | | | |
|---|---|---|---|---|
| **C8** | CD93 | 2fa12ca olive bis | 1.40 | *2.00* |
| **C9** | CD94 | 5fa dark blue | 1.40 | *2.00* |
| **C10** | CD95 | 7fa12ca dk purple | 2.25 | *2.00* |
| **C11** | CD96 | 1r2fa green | 2.25 | *3.00* |
| **C12** | CD97 | 1r4fa12ca dk car | 2.75 | *3.00* |
| **C13** | CD98 | 3r1fa violet brn | 2.75 | *3.00* |
| | | *Nos. C8-C13 (6)* | 12.80 | *15.00* |

A 3r ultramarine and red, picturing the Temple of Chindambaram, was sold at Paris June 7 to July 8, 1948, but not placed on sale in the colony. Values: $10 never hinged, $7 hinged.

Bas-relief Figure of Goddess — AP1

Wing and Temple — AP2

Bird over Palms — AP3

***Perf. 12x13, 13x12***

**1949 Photo. Unwmk.**

| | | | | |
|---|---|---|---|---|
| **C14** | AP1 | 1r yellow & plum | 6.00 | *10.00* |
| **C15** | AP2 | 2r green & dk grn | 6.00 | *10.00* |
| **C16** | AP3 | 5r lt bl & vio brn | 27.50 | *30.00* |
| | | *Nos. C14-C16 (3)* | 39.50 | *50.00* |

### UPU Issue

Common Design Type

**1949 Engr. *Perf. 13***

| | | | | |
|---|---|---|---|---|
| **C17** | CD99 | 6fa lilac rose | 11.50 | 8.75 |

Universal Postal Union, 75th anniv.

### Liberation Issue

Common Design Type

**1954, June 6**

| | | | | |
|---|---|---|---|---|
| **C18** | CD102 | 1fa sepia & vio brn | 11.00 | 8.00 |

## AIR POST SEMI-POSTAL STAMPS

Girl's School SPAP1

***Perf. 12½x13½***

**1942, June 22 Unwmk. Photo.**

| | | | |
|---|---|---|---|
| **CB1** | SPAP1 | 2fa12ca + 5fa20ca green | .95 |
| **CB2** | SPAP1 | 3fa8ca + 1r2fa yel brn | .95 |

Native children's welfare fund.

Nos. CB1-CB2 were issued by the Vichy government in France, but were not placed on sale in French India.

### Colonial Education Fund

Common Design Type

**1942, June 22**

| | | | |
|---|---|---|---|
| **CB3** | CD86a | 2fa + 3fa blue & red | .90 |

No. CB3 was issued by the Vichy government in France, but was not placed on sale in French India.

## POSTAGE DUE STAMPS

### Postage Due Stamps of France Surcharged like Nos. 54-75 in Black, Blue or Red

**1923 Unwmk. *Perf. 14x13½***

| | | | | |
|---|---|---|---|---|
| **J1** | D2 | 6ca on 10c brn | 1.25 | 1.25 |
| **J2** | D2 | 12ca on 25c rose (Bk) | 1.25 | 1.25 |
| **J3** | D2 | 15ca on 20c ol grn (R) | 1.60 | 1.60 |
| **J4** | D2 | 1fa6ca on 30c red | 1.60 | 1.60 |
| **J5** | D2 | 1fa12a on 50c brn vio | 2.75 | 2.75 |
| **J6** | D2 | 1fa15ca on 5c bl (Bk) | 3.00 | 3.00 |
| **J7** | D2 | 3fa3ca on 1fr red brn, *straw* | 3.25 | 3.25 |
| | | *Nos. J1-J7 (7)* | 14.70 | 14.70 |

### Types of Postage Due Stamps of French Colonies, 1884-85, Surcharged with New Values as in 1923 in Red or Black Bars over Original Values

**1928**

| | | | | |
|---|---|---|---|---|
| **J8** | D1 | 4ca on 20c gray lil | 1.60 | 1.60 |
| **J9** | D1 | 1fa on 30c orange | 3.25 | 3.25 |
| **J10** | D1 | 1fa16ca on 5c bl blk (R) | 3.25 | 3.25 |
| **J11** | D1 | 3fa on 1fr lt grn | 3.75 | 3.75 |
| | | *Nos. J8-J11 (4)* | 11.85 | 11.85 |

D3

**1929 Typo.**

| | | | | |
|---|---|---|---|---|
| **J12** | D3 | 4ca deep red | .50 | .50 |
| **J13** | D3 | 6ca blue | .65 | .65 |
| **J14** | D3 | 12ca green | .65 | .65 |
| **J15** | D3 | 1fa brown | 1.25 | 1.25 |
| **J16** | D3 | 1fa12ca lilac gray | 1.25 | 1.25 |
| **J17** | D3 | 1fa16ca buff | 1.75 | 1.75 |
| **J18** | D3 | 3fa lilac | 2.10 | 2.10 |
| | | *Nos. J12-J18 (7)* | 8.15 | 8.15 |

D4

**1948 Unwmk. Photo. *Perf. 13x13½***

| | | | | |
|---|---|---|---|---|
| **J19** | D4 | 1ca dk violet | .30 | .30 |
| **J20** | D4 | 2ca dk brown | .50 | .50 |
| **J21** | D4 | 6ca blue green | .50 | .50 |
| **J22** | D4 | 12ca dp orange | .70 | .70 |
| **J23** | D4 | 1fa dk car rose | .80 | .80 |
| **J24** | D4 | 1fa12ca brown | .80 | .80 |
| **J25** | D4 | 2fa dk slate bl | 1.25 | 1.25 |
| **J26** | D4 | 2fa12ca henna brn | 1.60 | 1.60 |
| **J27** | D4 | 5fa dk olive grn | 2.25 | 2.25 |
| **J28** | D4 | 1r dk blue vio | 3.00 | 3.00 |
| | | *Nos. J19-J28 (10)* | 11.70 | 11.70 |

# FRENCH MOROCCO

'french mə-'rä-ˌkō

LOCATION — Northwest coast of Africa
GOVT. — French Protectorate
AREA — 153,870 sq. mi.
POP. — 8,340,000 (estimated 1954)
CAPITAL — Rabat

French Morocco was a French Protectorate from 1912 until 1956 when it, along with the Spanish and Tangier zones of Morocco, became the independent country, Morocco.

Stamps inscribed "Tanger" were for use in the international zone of Tangier in northern Morocco.

100 Centimos = 1 Peseta
100 Centimes = 1 franc (1917)

**Catalogue values for unused stamps in this country are for Never Hinged items, beginning with Scott 177 in the regular postage section, Scott B26 in the semi-postal section, Scott C27 in the airpost section, Scott CB23A in the airpost semi-postal section, and Scott J46 in the postage due section.**

### French Offices in Morocco

Stamps of France Surcharged in Red or Black

Type I. The "N" of "INV" is under the "B" of "REPUBLIQUE."

Type II. The "N" of "INV" is under the "U" of "REPUBLIQUE."

**1891-1900 Unwmk. *Perf. 14x13½***

| | | | | |
|---|---|---|---|---|
| **1** | A15 | 5c on 5c grn, *grnsh* (R) | 16.00 | 4.00 |
| *a.* | | Imperf., pair | 175.00 | |
| **2** | A15 | 5c on 5c yel grn (II) (R) ('99) | 32.50 | 27.50 |
| *a.* | | Type I | 32.50 | 27.50 |
| **3** | A15 | 10c on 10c blk, *lav* (II) (R) | 32.50 | 4.00 |
| *a.* | | Type I | 45.00 | 20.00 |
| *b.* | | 10c on 25c black, *rose* | 1,100. | 1,200. |
| **4** | A15 | 20c on 20c red, *grn* | 40.00 | 32.50 |
| **5** | A15 | 25c on 25c blk, *rose* (R) | 32.50 | 4.00 |
| *a.* | | Double surcharge | 225.00 | |
| *b.* | | Imperf., pair | 175.00 | |
| **6** | A15 | 50c on 50c car, *rose* (II) | 105.00 | 47.50 |
| *a.* | | Type I | 375.00 | 260.00 |
| **7** | A15 | 1p on 1fr brnz grn, *straw* | 120.00 | 80.00 |
| **8** | A15 | 2p on 2fr brn, *az* (Bk) ('00) | 240.00 | 240.00 |
| | | *Nos. 1-8 (8)* | 618.50 | 439.50 |

No. 3b was never sent to Morocco.

France Nos. J15-J16 Overprinted in Carmine

**1893**

| | | | | |
|---|---|---|---|---|
| **9** | D2 | 5c black | 3,250. | 1,200. |
| **10** | D2 | 10c black | 2,900. | 800. |

Counterfeits exist.

**Surcharged in Red or Black**

A3

A4

A5

**1902-10**

11 A3 1c on 1c gray (R) ('08) 2.40 1.20
12 A3 2c on 2c vio brn ('08) 2.40 1.20
13 A3 3c on 3c red org ('08) 3.25 1.60
14 A3 4c on 4c yel brn ('08) 13.00 8.00
15 A3 5c on 5c grn (R) 12.00 4.00
*a.* Double surcharge 340.00
*b.* Triple surcharge 340.00
16 A4 10c on 10c rose red ('03) 8.00 4.00
*a.* Surcharge omitted 225.00
17 A4 20c on 20c brn vio ('03) 40.00 24.00
18 A4 25c on 25c bl ('03) 40.00 4.00
19 A4 35c on 35c vio ('10) 40.00 24.00
20 A5 50c on 50c bis brn & lav ('03) 67.50 16.00
21 A5 1p on 1fr cl & ol grn ('03) 120.00 80.00
22 A5 2p on 2fr gray vio & yel ('03) 160.00 120.00
*Nos. 11-22 (12)* 508.55 288.00

Nos. 11-14 exist spelled CFNTIMOS or GENTIMOS.

The 25c on 25c with surcharge omitted is listed as No. 81a.

For overprints and surcharges see Nos. 26-37, 72-79, B1, B3.

Postage Due Stamps Nos. J1-J2 Handstamped

**1903**

24 D2 5c on 5c light blue 1,500. 1,400.
25 D2 10c on 10c chocolate 2,800. 2,600.

Nos. 24 and 25 were used only on Oct. 10, 1903. Used stamps were not canceled, the overprint serving as a cancellation.

Numerous counterfeits exist.

Types of 1902-10 Issue Surcharged in Red or Blue

**1911-17**

26 A3 1c on 1c gray (R) 1.20 .90
27 A3 2c on 2c vio brn 1.20 1.20
28 A3 3c on 3c orange 1.20 1.20
29 A3 5c on 5c green (R) 1.20 .80
30 A4 10c on 10c rose 1.20 .80
*a.* Imperf., pair 275.00
31 A4 15c on 15c org ('17) 3.50 2.40
32 A4 20c on 20c brn vio 5.50 4.00
33 A4 25c on 25c blue (R) 2.40 1.60
34 A4 35c on 35c violet (R) 12.00 5.50
35 A5 40c on 40c red & pale bl ('17) 8.00 5.50
36 A5 50c on 50c bis brn & lav (R) 27.50 16.00
37 A5 1p on 1fr cl & ol grn 24.00 12.00
*Nos. 26-37 (12)* 88.90 51.90

For surcharges see Nos. B1, B3.

Stamps of this design were issued by the Cherifien posts in 1912-13. The Administration Cherifinne des Postes, Telegraphes et Telephones was formed in 1911 under French guidance. See Morocco in Vol. 4 for listings.

**French Protectorate Issue of 1911-17 Overprinted "Protectorat Francais"**

A6

A7

A8

**1914-21**

38 A6 1c on 1c lt gray .40 .50
*a.* 1c dk gray ('22) .55 .80
39 A6 2c on 2c vio brn .80 .50
40 A6 3c on 3c orange 1.20 .65
41 A6 5c on 5c green 1.20 .50
*a.* New value omitted 275.00 275.00
42 A7 10c on 10c rose .80 .30
*a.* New value omitted 550.00 550.00
43 A7 15c on 15c org ('17) .80 .80
*a.* New value omitted 120.00 120.00
44 A7 20c on 20c brn vio 4.75 3.50
*a.* "Protectorat Francais" double 300.00 300.00
45 A7 25c on 25c blue 3.25 .80
*a.* New value omitted 350.00 350.00
46 A7 25c on 25c violet ('21) 1.25 .40
*a.* "Protectorat Francais" omitted 80.00 80.00
*b.* "Protectorat Francais" double 175.00 175.00
*c.* "Protectorat Francais" dbl. (R + Bk) 175.00 175.00
47 A7 30c on 30c vio ('21) 20.00 9.00
48 A7 35c on 35c violet 4.75 1.60
49 A8 40c on 40c red & pale bl 20.00 8.75
*a.* New value omitted 375.00 375.00
50 A8 45c on 45c grn & bl ('21) 55.00 40.00
51 A8 50c on 50c bis brn & lav 2.40 .80
*a.* "Protectorat Francais" invtd. 200.00 200.00
*b.* "Protectorat Francais" double 450.00 450.00
52 A8 1p on 1fr cl & ol grn 5.50 .80
*a.* "Protectorat Francais" invtd. 350.00 350.00
*b.* New value double 200.00 200.00
*c.* New value dbl., one invtd. 210.00 210.00
53 A8 2p on 2fr gray vio & yel 8.00 4.00
*a.* New value omitted 175.00 175.00
*b.* "Protectorat Francais" omitted 110.00 110.00
*c.* New value double 225.00
*d.* New value dbl., one invtd.
54 A8 5p on 5fr dk bl & buff 15.00 8.00
*Nos. 38-54 (17)* 145.10 80.90

For surcharges see Nos. B2, B4-B5.

Tower of Hassan, Rabat — A9

Mosque of the Andalusians, Fez — A10

City Gate Chella A11

Koutoubiah, Marrakesh A12

Bab Mansour, Meknes A13

Roman Ruins, Volubilis A14

**1917 Engr. *Perf. 13½x14, 14x13½***

55 A9 1c grnsh gray .40 .40
56 A9 2c brown lilac .40 .40
57 A9 3c orange brn .40 .80
*a.* Imperf., pair 87.50
58 A10 5c yellow grn .40 .40
59 A10 10c rose red .80 .40
60 A10 15c dark gray .80 .40
*a.* Imperf., pair 65.00
61 A11 20c red brown 4.00 2.40
62 A11 25c dull blue 4.00 1.25
63 A11 30c gray violet 4.75 3.25
64 A12 35c orange 4.75 4.00
65 A12 40c ultra 1.60 1.60
66 A12 45c gray green 32.50 16.00
67 A13 50c dk brown 5.50 4.00
*a.* Imperf., pair 65.00
68 A13 1fr slate 16.00 4.00
*a.* Imperf., pair 65.00
69 A14 2fr black brown 160.00 95.00
70 A14 5fr dk gray grn 47.50 40.00
71 A14 10fr black 47.50 40.00
*Nos. 55-71 (17)* 331.30 214.30

See note following No. 115. See Nos. 93-105. For surcharges see Nos. 120-121.

Types of the 1902-10 Issue Overprinted

**1918-24 *Perf. 14x13½***

72 A3 1c dk gray .40 .80
73 A3 2c violet brn .40 .80
74 A3 3c red orange 1.20 1.20
75 A3 5c green 1.20 1.20
76 A3 5c orange ('23) 2.40 2.00
77 A4 10c rose 2.40 1.60
78 A4 10c green ('24) 2.40 1.60
79 A4 15c orange 1.60 1.20
80 A4 20c violet brn 2.40 2.40
81 A4 25c blue 2.40 2.40
*a.* "TANGER" omitted 450.00 450.00
82 A4 30c red org ('24) 4.00 2.75
83 A4 35c violet 4.00 2.40
84 A5 40c red & pale bl 4.00 2.40
85 A5 50c bis brn & lav 27.50 16.00
86 A4 50c blue ('24) 24.00 13.50
87 A5 1fr claret & ol grn 16.00 8.00
88 A5 2fr org & pale bl ('24) 80.00 72.50
89 A5 5fr dk bl & buff ('24) 67.50 65.00
*Nos. 72-89 (18)* 243.80 197.75

**Types of 1917 and**

Tower of Hassan, Rabat — A15

Bab Mansour, Meknes A16

Roman Ruins, Volubilis A17

**1923-27 Photo. *Perf. 13½***

90 A15 1c olive green .25 .25
91 A15 2c brown vio .25 .25
92 A15 3c yellow brn .25 .25
93 A10 5c orange .25 .25
94 A10 10c yellow grn .25 .25
95 A10 15c dk gray .25 .25
96 A11 20c red brown .25 .25
97 A11 20c red vio ('27) .40 .40
98 A11 25c ultra .40 .40
99 A11 30c deep red .40 .40
100 A11 30c turq bl ('27) 1.20 .80
101 A12 35c violet 1.20 .80
102 A12 40c orange red .25 .25
103 A12 45c deep green .40 .40
104 A16 50c dull turq .40 .40
105 A12 50c olive grn ('27) .80 .40
106 A16 60c lilac 1.20 .80
107 A16 75c red vio ('27) .80 .40
108 A16 1fr deep brown .80 .80
109 A16 1.05fr red brn ('27) 1.60 .80
110 A16 1.40fr dull rose ('27) .80 .80
111 A16 1.50fr turq bl ('27) 1.20 .40
112 A17 2fr olive brn 1.60 1.20
113 A17 3fr dp red ('27) 1.60 1.20
114 A17 5fr dk gray grn 4.00 2.75
115 A17 10fr black 12.00 4.75
*Nos. 90-115 (26)* 32.80 19.90

Nos. 90-110, 112-115 exist imperf. The stamps of 1917 were line engraved. Those of 1923-27 were printed by photogravure and have in the margin at lower right the imprint "Helio Vaugirard."

See No. B36. For surcharges see Nos. 122-123.

No. 102 Surcharged in Black

**1930**

120 A12 15c on 40c orange red 1.60 1.60
*a.* Surcharge bars omitted 72.50 72.50
*b.* Pair, one with surcharge omitted 350.00

**Nos. 100, 106 and 110 Surcharged in Blue Similarly to No. 176**

**1931**

121 A11 25c on 30c turq blue 2.50 2.10
*a.* Inverted surcharge 140.00 140.00
122 A16 50c on 60c lilac 1.20 .40
*a.* Inverted surcharge 150.00 150.00
*b.* Double surcharge 150.00 150.00
*c.* Surcharge bars omitted 90.00
123 A16 1fr on 1.40fr rose 3.25 1.60
*a.* Inverted surcharge 150.00 150.00
*b.* Surcharge bars omitted 90.00
*Nos. 121-123 (3)* 6.95 4.10

Old Treasure House and Tribunal, Tangier A18

Roadstead at Agadir A19

Post Office at Casablanca A20

Moulay Idriss of the Zehroun A21

Kasbah of the Oudayas, Rabat A22

Court of the Medersa el Attarine at Fez — A23

Kasbah of Si Madani el Glaoui at Ouarzazat A24

Saadiens' Tombs at Marrakesh — A25

**1933-34 Engr. *Perf. 13***

| No. | Type | Value | Color | Unused | Used |
|---|---|---|---|---|---|
| 124 | A18 | 1c | olive blk | .25 | .25 |
| 125 | A18 | 2c | red violet | .25 | .25 |
| 126 | A19 | 3c | dark brown | .25 | .25 |
| 127 | A19 | 5c | brown red | .25 | .25 |
| 128 | A20 | 10c | blue green | .30 | .30 |
| 129 | A20 | 15c | black | .40 | .30 |
| 130 | A20 | 20c | red brown | .40 | .30 |
| 131 | A21 | 25c | dark blue | .40 | .30 |
| 132 | A21 | 30c | emerald | .40 | .30 |
| 133 | A21 | 40c | black brn | .40 | .30 |
| 134 | A22 | 45c | brown vio | .80 | .65 |
| 135 | A22 | 50c | dk blue grn | .80 | .30 |
| *a.* | | | Booklet pane of 10 | — | |
| *b.* | | | Booklet pane of 20 | — | |
| | | | Complete booklet, #135b | 2,000. | |
| 136 | A22 | 65c | brown red | .40 | .30 |
| *a.* | | | Booklet pane of 10 | — | |
| *b.* | | | Booklet pane of 20 | — | |
| | | | Complete booklet, #136b | 65.00 | |
| 137 | A23 | 75c | red violet | .80 | .30 |
| 138 | A23 | 90c | orange red | .40 | .30 |
| 139 | A23 | 1fr | deep brown | 1.20 | .50 |
| 140 | A23 | 1.25fr | black ('34) | 1.60 | 1.50 |
| 141 | A24 | 1.50fr | ultra | .40 | .30 |
| 142 | A24 | 1.75fr | myr grn ('34) | .80 | .40 |
| 143 | A24 | 2fr | yellow brn | 4.75 | .80 |
| 144 | A24 | 3fr | car rose | 55.00 | 6.50 |
| 145 | A25 | 5fr | red brown | 12.00 | 2.50 |
| 146 | A25 | 10fr | black | 10.00 | 6.50 |
| 147 | A25 | 20fr | bluish gray | 9.50 | 7.25 |
| | | | *Nos. 124-147 (24)* | 101.75 | 30.90 |

Booklets containing Nos. 135 and 136 each have two panes of 10 (Nos. 135a, 136a) connected by a gutter, the complete piece constituting No. 135b or 136b, which is stapled into the booklet through the gutter.

For surcharges see Nos. 148, 176, B13-B20.

No. 135 Srchd. in Red

**1939**

| No. | Type | Description | Unused | Used |
|---|---|---|---|---|
| 148 | A22 | 40c on 50c dk bl grn | .95 | .50 |

Mosque of Salé — A26

Sefrou — A27

Cedars — A28

Goatherd A29

Ramparts of Salé — A30

Scimitar-horned Oryxes — A31

Valley of Draa A32

Fez — A33

**1939-42**

| No. | Type | Value | Color | Unused | Used |
|---|---|---|---|---|---|
| 149 | A26 | 1c | rose violet | .25 | .25 |
| 150 | A27 | 2c | emerald | .25 | .25 |
| 151 | A27 | 3c | ultra | .25 | .25 |
| 152 | A26 | 5c | dk bl grn | .25 | .25 |
| 153 | A27 | 10c | brt red vio | .25 | .25 |
| 154 | A28 | 15c | dk green | .25 | .25 |
| 155 | A28 | 20c | black grn | .25 | .25 |
| 156 | A29 | 30c | deep blue | .25 | .25 |
| 157 | A29 | 40c | chocolate | .25 | .25 |
| 158 | A29 | 45c | Prus green | .50 | .50 |
| 159 | A30 | 50c | rose red | 1.40 | .90 |
| 159A | A30 | 50c | Prus grn ('40) | .30 | .25 |
| 160 | A30 | 60c | turq blue | 1.25 | .75 |
| 160A | A30 | 60c | choc ('40) | .30 | .25 |
| 161 | A31 | 70c | dk violet | .25 | .25 |
| 162 | A32 | 75c | grnsh blk | .50 | .50 |
| 163 | A32 | 80c | pck bl ('40) | .30 | .25 |
| 163A | A32 | 80c | dk grn ('42) | .40 | .25 |
| 164 | A30 | 90c | ultra | .30 | .25 |
| 165 | A28 | 1fr | chocolate | .30 | .25 |
| 165A | A32 | 1.20fr | rose vio ('42) | .80 | .40 |
| 166 | A32 | 1.25fr | henna brn | 1.10 | .65 |
| 167 | A32 | 1.40fr | rose violet | .65 | .30 |
| 168 | A30 | 1.50fr | cop red ('40) | .30 | .25 |
| 168A | A30 | 1.50fr | rose ('42) | .25 | .25 |
| 169 | A33 | 2fr | Prus green | .25 | .25 |
| 170 | A33 | 2.25fr | dark blue | .65 | .50 |
| 170A | A26 | 2.40fr | red ('42) | .30 | .30 |
| 171 | A26 | 2.50fr | scarlet | .90 | .70 |
| 171A | A26 | 2.50fr | dp blue ('40) | 1.10 | .65 |
| 172 | A33 | 3fr | black brown | .50 | .30 |
| 172A | A26 | 4fr | dp ultra ('42) | .40 | .40 |
| 172B | A32 | 4.50fr | grnsh blk ('42) | .80 | .80 |
| 173 | A31 | 5fr | dark blue | .65 | .50 |
| 174 | A31 | 10fr | red | 1.25 | .90 |
| 174A | A31 | 15fr | Prus grn ('42) | 4.75 | 4.00 |
| 175 | A31 | 20fr | dk vio brn | 2.00 | 1.75 |
| | | | *Nos. 149-175 (37)* | 24.70 | 19.55 |
| | | | Set, never hinged | 32.50 | |

See Nos. 197-219. For surcharges see Nos. 244, 261-262, B21-B24, B26, B28, B32.

No. 136 Srchd. in Black

**1940**

| No. | Type | Description | Unused | Used |
|---|---|---|---|---|
| 176 | A22 | 35c on 65c brown red | 1.75 | .95 |
| *a.* | | Pair, one without surcharge | 3.25 | 2.40 |

The surcharge was applied on alternate rows in the sheet, making No. 176a. This was done to make a pair equal 1fr, the new rate.

**Catalogue values for unused stamps in this section, from this point to the end of the section, are for Never Hinged items.**

One Aim Alone-Victory — A34

**1943 Litho. *Perf. 12***

| No. | Type | Value | Color | Unused | Used |
|---|---|---|---|---|---|
| 177 | A34 | 1.50fr | deep blue | .40 | .25 |

Tower of Hassan, Rabat — A35

**1943**

| No. | Type | Value | Color | Unused | Used |
|---|---|---|---|---|---|
| 178 | A35 | 10c | rose lilac | .30 | .25 |
| 179 | A35 | 30c | blue | .30 | .25 |
| 180 | A35 | 40c | lake | .30 | .25 |
| 181 | A35 | 50c | blue green | .30 | .25 |
| 182 | A35 | 60c | dk vio brn | .30 | .25 |
| 183 | A35 | 70c | rose violet | .30 | .25 |
| 184 | A35 | 80c | gray green | .30 | .30 |
| 185 | A35 | 1fr | car lake | .30 | .25 |
| 186 | A35 | 1.20fr | violet | .30 | .25 |
| 187 | A35 | 1.50fr | red | .30 | .25 |
| 188 | A35 | 2fr | lt bl grn | .30 | .25 |
| 189 | A35 | 2.40fr | car rose | .30 | .35 |
| 190 | A35 | 3fr | olive brn | .30 | .30 |
| 191 | A35 | 4fr | dk ultra | .30 | .30 |
| 192 | A35 | 4.50fr | slate blk | .40 | .25 |
| 193 | A35 | 5fr | dull blue | .55 | .25 |
| 194 | A35 | 10fr | orange brn | .55 | .40 |
| 195 | A35 | 15fr | slate grn | 1.60 | .55 |
| 196 | A35 | 20fr | deep plum | 2.40 | .80 |
| | | | *Nos. 178-196 (19)* | 9.70 | 6.00 |

**Types of 1939-42**

***Perf. 13½x14, 14x13½***

**1945-47 Typo. Unwmk.**

| No. | Type | Value | Color | Unused | Used |
|---|---|---|---|---|---|
| 197 | A27 | 10c | red violet | .40 | .25 |
| 199 | A29 | 40c | chocolate | .40 | .25 |
| 200 | A30 | 50c | Prus grn | .40 | .25 |
| 203 | A28 | 1fr | choc ('46) | .40 | .35 |
| 204 | A32 | 1.20fr | vio brn ('46) | .40 | .30 |
| 205 | A27 | 1.30fr | blue ('47) | .80 | .40 |
| 206 | A30 | 1.50fr | deep red | .40 | .25 |
| 207 | A33 | 2fr | Prus grn | .40 | .25 |
| 209 | A33 | 3fr | black brn | .40 | .25 |
| 210 | A29 | 3.50fr | dk red ('47) | 1.20 | .80 |
| 212 | A31 | 4.50fr | magenta ('47) | .80 | .40 |
| 214 | A31 | 5fr | indigo | 1.20 | .55 |
| 215 | A32 | 6fr | chlky bl ('46) | .80 | .35 |
| 216 | A31 | 10fr | red | 2.00 | .80 |
| 217 | A31 | 15fr | Prus grn | 2.40 | .80 |
| 218 | A31 | 20fr | dk vio brn | 3.25 | 1.40 |
| 219 | A31 | 25fr | black brn | 3.25 | 2.10 |
| | | | *Nos. 197-219 (17)* | 18.90 | 9.75 |

For surcharges see Nos. 261-263, B26, B28, B32.

The Terraces — A37

Mountain District — A39

Fortress A38

Marrakesh A40

Gardens of Fez — A41

Ouarzazat District — A42

**1947 Engr. Unwmk. *Perf. 13***

| No. | Type | Value | Color | Unused | Used |
|---|---|---|---|---|---|
| 221 | A37 | 10c | black brn | .40 | .25 |
| 222 | A37 | 30c | brt red | .40 | .25 |
| 223 | A37 | 50c | brt grnsh bl | .40 | .25 |
| 224 | A37 | 60c | brt red vio | .40 | .25 |
| 225 | A38 | 1fr | black | .40 | .25 |
| 226 | A38 | 1.50fr | blue | .40 | .25 |
| 227 | A39 | 2fr | brt green | .80 | .40 |
| 228 | A39 | 3fr | brown red | .40 | .25 |
| 229 | A40 | 4fr | dk bl vio | .40 | .25 |
| 230 | A41 | 5fr | dk green | 1.20 | .55 |
| 231 | A40 | 6fr | crimson | .40 | .25 |
| 232 | A41 | 10fr | dp blue | 1.20 | .40 |
| 233 | A42 | 15fr | dk grn | 1.60 | 1.20 |
| 234 | A42 | 20fr | henna brn | 1.60 | .80 |
| 235 | A42 | 25fr | purple | 2.40 | 1.20 |
| | | | *Nos. 221-235 (15)* | 12.40 | 6.80 |

**1948-49**

| No. | Type | Value | Color | Unused | Used |
|---|---|---|---|---|---|
| 236 | A37 | 30c | purple | .40 | .25 |
| 237 | A38 | 2fr | vio brn ('49) | .80 | .40 |
| 238 | A40 | 4fr | green | .80 | .35 |
| 239 | A41 | 8fr | org ('49) | 1.60 | .80 |
| 240 | A41 | 10fr | blue | 1.20 | .40 |
| 241 | A42 | 10fr | car rose | .80 | .80 |
| 242 | A38 | 12fr | red | 1.20 | .80 |
| 243 | A42 | 18fr | deep blue | 2.40 | 1.20 |
| | | | *Nos. 236-243 (8)* | 9.20 | 5.00 |

For surcharges see Nos. 263, 293-294.

**No. 175 Surcharged with New Value and Wavy Lines in Carmine**

**1948**

| No. | Type | Description | Unused | Used |
|---|---|---|---|---|
| 244 | A31 | 8fr on 20fr dk vio brn | 1.20 | .80 |

Fortified Oasis A43

Walled City — A44

**1949**

| | | | | |
|---|---|---|---|---|
| **245** | A43 | 5fr blue green | 1.20 | .40 |
| **246** | A44 | 15fr red | 1.60 | .80 |
| **247** | A44 | 25fr ultra | 1.60 | .80 |
| | | *Nos. 245-247 (3)* | 4.40 | 2.00 |

See No. 300.

Detail, Gate of Oudayas, Rabat — A45

Nejjarine Fountain, Fez — A46

Garden, Meknes — A47

**1949** *Perf. 14x13*

| | | | | |
|---|---|---|---|---|
| **248** | A45 | 10c black | .40 | .25 |
| **249** | A45 | 50c rose brn | .40 | .25 |
| **250** | A45 | 1fr blue vio | .40 | .25 |
| **251** | A46 | 2fr dk car rose | .40 | .25 |
| **252** | A46 | 3fr dark blue | .80 | .25 |
| **253** | A46 | 5fr brt green | 1.20 | .25 |
| **254** | A47 | 8fr dk bl grn | 1.60 | .80 |
| **255** | A47 | 10fr brt red | 1.60 | .80 |
| | | *Nos. 248-255 (8)* | 6.80 | 3.10 |

Postal Administration Building, Meknes — A48

**1949, Oct.** *Perf. 13*

| | | | | |
|---|---|---|---|---|
| **256** | A48 | 5fr dark green | 2.40 | 2.00 |
| **257** | A48 | 15fr deep carmine | 2.40 | 2.00 |
| **258** | A48 | 25fr deep blue | 2.75 | 2.40 |
| | | *Nos. 256-258 (3)* | 7.55 | 6.40 |

75th anniv. of the UPU.

Todra Valley A49

**1950**

| | | | | |
|---|---|---|---|---|
| **259** | A49 | 35fr red brown | 1.60 | .40 |
| **260** | A49 | 50fr indigo | 1.60 | .40 |

See No. 270.

Nos. 204 and 205 Srchd. in Black or Blue

**1950** *Perf. 14x13½, 13½x14*

| | | | | |
|---|---|---|---|---|
| **261** | A32 | 1fr on 1.20fr vio brn (Bk) | .40 | .35 |
| **262** | A27 | 1fr on 1.30fr blue (Bl) | .40 | .25 |

The surcharge is transposed and spaced to fit the design on No. 262.

**No. 231 Surcharged with New Value and Wavy Lines in Black**

**1951** *Perf. 13*

| | | | | |
|---|---|---|---|---|
| **263** | A40 | 5fr on 6fr crimson | .80 | .25 |

Statue of Gen. Jacques Leclerc — A50

**1951, Apr. 28** **Engr.**

| | | | | |
|---|---|---|---|---|
| **264** | A50 | 10fr blue green | 2.40 | 2.00 |
| **265** | A50 | 15fr deep carmine | 2.75 | 2.00 |
| **266** | A50 | 25fr indigo | 2.75 | 2.00 |
| | | *Nos. 264-266 (3)* | 7.90 | 6.00 |

Unveiling of a monument to Gen. Leclerc at Casablanca, Apr. 28, 1951. See No. C39.

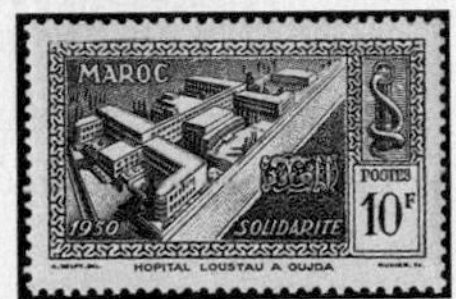

Loustau Hospital, Oujda A51

Designs: 15fr, New Hospital, Meknes. 25fr, New Hospital, Rabat.

**1951**

| | | | | |
|---|---|---|---|---|
| **267** | A51 | 10fr indigo & pur | 2.00 | 1.60 |
| **268** | A51 | 15fr Prus grn & red brn | 2.00 | 1.60 |
| **269** | A51 | 25fr dk brn & ind | 2.40 | 2.00 |

See No. C41.

| | | | | |
|---|---|---|---|---|
| | | *Nos. 267-269 (3)* | 6.40 | 5.20 |

**Todra Valley Type of 1950**

**1951**

| | | | | |
|---|---|---|---|---|
| **270** | A49 | 30fr ultramarine | 1.60 | .40 |

Pigeons at Fountain A52

Karaouine Mosque, Fez A53

Patio, Oudayas A54

Oudayas Point, Rabat A55

Patio of Old House — A56

Type I (No. 275)

MAROC

Type II (No. 276)

*Perf. 14x13, 13*

**1951-53** **Engr.** **Unwmk.**

| | | | | |
|---|---|---|---|---|
| **271** | A52 | 5fr magenta ('52) | .40 | .25 |
| **272** | A53 | 6fr bl grn ('52) | .40 | .40 |
| **273** | A52 | 8fr brown ('52) | .40 | .40 |
| **273A** | A53 | 10fr rose red ('53) | .40 | .35 |
| **274** | A53 | 12fr dp ultra ('52) | .80 | .40 |
| **275** | A54 | 15fr red brn (I) | 2.75 | .25 |
| **276** | A54 | 15fr red brn (II) | 1.20 | .25 |
| **277** | A55 | 15fr pur ('52) | 1.20 | .40 |
| **278** | A55 | 18fr red ('52) | 2.00 | 1.20 |
| **279** | A56 | 20fr dp grnsh bl ('52) | 2.40 | .80 |
| | | *Nos. 271-279 (10)* | 11.95 | 4.70 |

See Nos. 297-299.

8th-10th Cent. Capital — A57

Capitals: 20fr, 12th Cent. 25fr, 13th-14th Cent. 50fr, 17th Cent.

**1952, Apr. 5** *Perf. 13*

| | | | | |
|---|---|---|---|---|
| **280** | A57 | 15fr deep blue | 3.25 | 2.40 |
| **281** | A57 | 20fr red | 3.25 | 2.40 |
| **282** | A57 | 25fr purple | 3.25 | 2.40 |
| **283** | A57 | 50fr deep green | 3.25 | 2.40 |
| | | *Nos. 280-283 (4)* | 13.00 | 9.60 |

Casablanca Monument — A58

**1952 Sept. 22** **Engr. & Typo.**

| | | | | |
|---|---|---|---|---|
| **284** | A58 | 15fr multicolored | 3.50 | 2.40 |

Creation of the French Military Medal, cent.


Daggers of South Morocco — A59

Designs: 20fr and 25fr, Antique brooches.

**1953, Mar. 27** **Engr.**

| | | | | |
|---|---|---|---|---|
| **285** | A59 | 15fr dk car rose | 4.00 | 3.25 |
| **286** | A59 | 20fr violet brn | 4.00 | 3.25 |
| **287** | A59 | 25fr dark blue | 4.00 | 3.25 |
| | | *Nos. 285-287 (3)* | 12.00 | 9.75 |

See No. C46.

Post Rider and Public Letter-writer — A60

**1953, May 16**

| | | | | |
|---|---|---|---|---|
| **288** | A60 | 15fr violet brown | 2.00 | 1.60 |

Stamp Day, May 16, 1953.

Bine el Ouidane Dam — A61

**1953, Nov. 3** *Perf. 13*

| | | | | |
|---|---|---|---|---|
| **290** | A61 | 15fr indigo | 2.00 | 1.60 |

See No. 295.

Mogador Fortress — A62

Design: 30fr, Moorish knights.

**1953, Dec. 4**

| | | | | |
|---|---|---|---|---|
| **291** | A62 | 15fr green | 2.40 | 1.60 |
| **292** | A62 | 30fr red brown | 2.40 | 1.60 |

Issued to aid Army Welfare Work.

**Nos. 226 and 243 Surcharged with New Value and Wavy Lines in Black**

**1954**

| | | | | |
|---|---|---|---|---|
| **293** | A38 | 1fr on 1.50fr blue | .40 | .25 |
| **294** | A42 | 15fr on 18fr dp bl | 1.20 | .65 |

**Dam Type of 1953**

**1954, Mar. 8**

| | | | | |
|---|---|---|---|---|
| **295** | A61 | 15fr red brn & indigo | 1.60 | 1.20 |

Station of Rural Automobile Post — A63

**1954, Apr. 10**

| | | | | |
|---|---|---|---|---|
| **296** | A63 | 15fr dk blue grn | 1.40 | .80 |

Stamp Day, April 10, 1954.

**Types of 1951-53**

**1954** **Engr.** *Perf. 14x13*

| | | | | |
|---|---|---|---|---|
| **297** | A52 | 15fr dk blue green | 1.20 | .40 |

**Typo.**

| | | | | |
|---|---|---|---|---|
| **298** | A52 | 5fr magenta | 1.20 | .40 |
| **299** | A55 | 15fr rose violet | 1.60 | .40 |
| | | *Nos. 297-299 (3)* | 4.00 | 1.20 |

**Walled City Type of 1949**

**1954** **Engr.** *Perf. 13*

| | | | | |
|---|---|---|---|---|
| **300** | A44 | 25fr purple | 2.40 | .80 |

Marshal Lyautey at Rabat A64

Lyautey, Builder of Cities — A65

Designs: 15fr, Marshal Lyautey at Khenifra. 50fr, Hubert Lyautey, Marshal of France.

**1954, Nov. 17**

| | | | | |
|---|---|---|---|---|
| **301** | A64 | 5fr indigo | 2.40 | 2.00 |
| **302** | A64 | 15fr dark green | 3.25 | 2.75 |
| **303** | A65 | 30fr rose brown | 4.00 | 3.25 |
| **304** | A65 | 50fr dk red brn | 4.00 | 3.25 |
| | | *Nos. 301-304 (4)* | 13.65 | 11.25 |

Marshal Hubert Lyautey, birth cent.

Franco-Moslem Education — A66

Moslem Student at Blackboard — A67

Designs: 30fr, Moslem school at Camp Boulhaut. 50fr, Moulay Idriss College at Fez.

**1955, Apr. 16** **Unwmk.** ***Perf. 13***

**305** A66 5fr indigo 2.00 1.60
**306** A67 15fr rose lake 2.40 2.00
**307** A66 30fr chocolate 2.40 2.00
**308** A67 50fr dk blue grn 2.75 2.40
*Nos. 305-308 (4)* 9.55 8.00

Franco-Moslem solidarity.

Map and Rotary Emblem A68

**1955, June 11**

**309** A68 15fr bl & org brn 2.00 1.20

Rotary Intl., 50th anniv.

Post Office, Mazagan A69

**1955, May 24**

**310** A69 15fr red 1.20 .80

Stamp Day.

Bab el Chorfa, Fez A70

Mahakma (Courthouse), Casablanca A71

Fortress, Safi — A72

Designs: 50c, 1fr, 2fr, 3fr, Mrissa Gate, Salé. 10fr, 12fr, 15fr, Minaret at Rabat. 30fr, Menara Garden Marrakesh. 40fr, Tafraout Village. 50fr, Portuguese cistern, Mazagan. 75fr, Garden of Oudaya, Rabat.

**1955** ***Perf. 13½x13, 13x13½, 13***

**311** A70 50c brn vio .40 .25
**312** A70 1fr blue .40 .25
**313** A70 2fr red lilac .40 .25
**314** A70 3fr bluish blk .40 .25
**315** A70 5fr vermilion 1.60 .40
**316** A70 6fr green .75 .35
**317** A70 8fr orange brn 1.20 .40
**318** A70 10fr violet brn 1.60 .40
**319** A70 12fr greenish bl .80 .40
**320** A70 15fr magenta 1.10 .25
**321** A71 18fr dk green 2.00 .80
**322** A71 20fr brown lake 1.20 .40
**323** A72 25fr brt ultra 2.75 .40
**324** A72 30fr green 2.40 .80
**325** A72 40fr orange red 2.40 .40
**326** A72 50fr black brn 8.00 .80
**327** A71 75fr greenish bl 2.40 1.20
*Nos. 311-327 (17)* 29.80 8.00

Succeeding issues, released under the Kingdom, are listed under Morocco in Vol. 4.

---

## SEMI-POSTAL STAMPS

### French Protectorate

No. 30 Surcharged in Red

**1914** **Unwmk.** ***Perf. 14x13½***

**B1** A4 10c + 5c on 10c *24,000. 28,000.*

Known only with inverted red surcharge.

No. 42 Surcharged in Red

**B2** A7 10c + 5c on 10c rose 6.50 6.50
*a.* Double surcharge 175.00 175.00
*b.* Inverted surcharge 225.00 225.00
*c.* "c" omitted 110.00 110.00

On Nos. B1 and B2 the cross is set up from pieces of metal (quads), the horizontal bar being made from two long pieces, the vertical bar from two short pieces. Each cross in the setting of twenty-five differs from the others.

No. 30 Handstamp Surcharged in Red

**B3** A4 10c + 5c on 10c rose *1,650. 1,300.*

No. B3 was issued at Oujda. The surcharge ink is water-soluble.

No. 42 Surcharged in Vermilion or Carmine

**B4** A7 10c + 5c on 10c (V) 25.00 25.00
*a.* Double surcharge 240.00 240.00
*b.* Inverted surcharge 240.00 240.00
*c.* Double surch., one invtd. 200.00 200.00
**B5** A7 10c +5c on 10c (C) 475.00 525.00
*a.* Inverted surcharge 1,600. 1,600.

On Nos. B4-B5 the horizontal bar of the cross is single and not as thick as on Nos. B1-B2.

No. B5 was sold largely at Casablanca.

Carmine Surcharge SP1

Black Overprint SP2

**1915**

**B6** SP1 5c + 5c green 3.25 2.40
*a.* Inverted surcharge 300.00 300.00
**B7** SP2 10c + 5c rose 4.75 4.75

No. B6 was not issued without the Red Cross surcharge. No. B7 was used in Tangier.

France No. B2 Overprinted in Black

**B8** SP2 10c + 5c red 7.50 7.50

No. 30 Surcharged in Carmine — SP4

**1917**

**B9** SP4 10c + 5c on 10c rose 3.25 3.25

On No. B9 the horizontal bar of the cross is made from a single, thick piece of metal.

Marshal Hubert Lyautey — SP5

**1935, May 15** **Photo.** ***Perf. 13x13½***

**B10** SP5 50c + 50c red 9.50 9.50
**B11** SP5 1fr + 1fr dk grn 11.00 11.00
**B12** SP5 5fr + 5fr blk brn 45.00 45.00
*Nos. B10-B12 (3)* 65.50 65.50
Set, never hinged 98.00

Stamps of 1933-34 Surcharged in Blue or Red

**1938** ***Perf. 13***

**B13** A18 2c + 2c red vio 5.50 5.50
**B14** A19 3c + 3c dk brn 5.50 5.50
**B15** A20 20c + 20c red brn 5.50 5.50
**B16** A21 40c + 40c blk brn (R) 5.50 5.50
**B17** A22 65c + 65c brn red 5.50 5.50
**B18** A23 1.25fr + 1.25fr blk (R) 5.50 5.50
**B19** A24 2fr + 2fr yel brn 5.50 5.50
**B20** A25 5fr + 5fr red brn 5.50 5.50
*Nos. B13-B20 (8)* 44.00 44.00
Set, never hinged 64.00

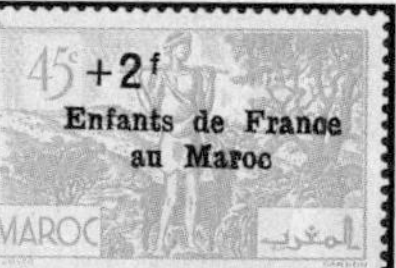

Stamps of 1939 Srchd. in Black

**1942**

**B21** A29 45c + 2fr Prus grn 6.75 4.75
**B22** A30 90c + 4fr ultra 6.75 4.75
**B23** A32 1.25fr + 6fr henna brn 8.00 6.50
**B24** A26 2.50fr + 8fr scarlet 8.00 6.50
*Nos. B21-B24 (4)* 29.50 22.50
Set, never hinged 40.00

The arrangement of the surcharge differs slightly on each denomination.

**Catalogue values for unused stamps in this section, from this point to the end of the section, are for Never Hinged items.**

No. 207 Surcharged in Black

**1945** **Unwmk.** ***Perf. 13½x14***

**B26** A33 2fr + 1fr Prus green .80 .50

For surcharge see No. B28.

Mausoleum of Marshal Lyautey — SP7

**1945** **Litho.** ***Perf. 11½***

**B27** SP7 2fr + 3fr dark blue .80 .40

The surtax was for French works of solidarity.

No. B26 Surcharged in Red

**1946** ***Perf. 13½x14***

**B28** A33 3fr (+ 1fr) on 2fr + 1fr .40 .25

Statue of Marshal Lyautey — SP8

***Perf. 13½x14, 13***

**1946, Dec. 16** **Engr.**

**B29** SP8 2fr + 10fr black 2.40 1.60
**B30** SP8 3fr + 15fr cop red 2.40 1.60
**B31** SP8 10fr + 20fr brt bl 3.25 2.40
*Nos. B29-B31 (3)* 8.05 5.60

The surtax was for works of solidarity.

No. 212 Surcharged in Rose Violet

**1947, Mar. 15** ***Perf. 13½x14***

**B32** A31 4.50fr + 5.50fr magenta 2.00 1.60

Stamp Day, 1947.

Map and Symbols of Prosperity from Phosphates SP9

**1947** *Perf. 13*

**B33** SP9 4.50fr + 5.50fr green 1.60 1.20

25th anniv. of the exploitations of the Cherifien Office of Phosphates.

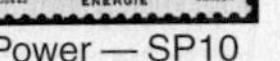

Power — SP10

Health — SP11

**1948, Feb. 9**

**B34** SP10 6fr + 9fr red brn 3.25 2.40
**B35** SP11 10fr + 20fr dp ultra 3.25 2.40

The surtax was for combined works of Franco-Moroccan solidarity.

**Type of Regular Issue of 1923, Inscribed: "Journee du Timbre 1948"**

**1948, Mar. 6**

**B36** A16 6fr + 4fr red brown 1.20 .80

Stamp Day, Mar. 6, 1948.

Battleship off Moroccan Coast SP12

**1948, Aug.**

**B37** SP12 6fr + 9fr purple 2.00 1.60

The surtax was for naval charities.

Wheat Field near Meknes SP13

Designs: 2fr+5fr, Olive grove, Taroudant. 3fr+7fr, Net and coastal view. 5fr+10fr, Aguedal Gardens, Marrakesh.

**1949, Apr. 12** **Engr.** **Unwmk.**

**Inscribed: "SOLIDARITÉ 1948"**

**B38** SP13 1fr + 2fr orange 2.00 1.60
**B39** SP13 2fr + 5fr car 2.00 1.60
**B40** SP13 3fr + 7fr pck bl 2.00 1.60
**B41** SP13 5fr + 10fr dk brn vio 2.00 1.60
*a.* Sheet of 4, #B38-B41 27.50 24.00
*Nos. B38-B41,CB31-CB34 (8)* 17.60 14.40

Gazelle Hunter, from 1899 Local Stamp SP14

**1949, May 1**

**B42** SP14 10fr + 5fr choc & car rose 2.00 1.60

Stamp Day and 50th anniversary of Mazagan-Marrakesh local postage stamp.

Moroccan Soldiers, Flag — SP15

**1949**

**B43** SP15 10fr + 10fr bright red 1.60 1.40

The surtax was for Army Welfare Work.

Rug Weaving — SP16

Designs: 2fr+5fr, Pottery making, 3fr+7fr, Bookbinding. 5fr+10fr, Copper work.

**Inscribed: "SOLIDARITE 1949"**

**1950, Apr. 11**

**B44** SP16 1fr + 2fr dp car 2.75 2.40
**B45** SP16 2fr + 5fr dk brnsh bl 2.75 2.40
**B46** SP16 3fr + 7fr dk pur 2.75 2.40
**B47** SP16 5fr + 10fr red brn 2.75 2.40
*a.* Sheet of 4, #B44-B47 32.50 24.00
*Nos. B44-B47,CB36-CB39 (8)* 20.60 17.60

Ruins of Sala Colonia at Chella SP17

**1950, Sept. 25** **Engr.** *Perf. 13*

**B48** SP17 10fr + 10fr dp magenta 2.00 *1.60*
**B49** SP17 15fr + 15fr indigo 2.00 1.60

The surtax was for Army Welfare Work.

---

## AIR POST STAMPS

### French Protectorate

Biplane over Casablanca AP1

**1922-27** **Photo.** **Unwmk.** *Perf. 13½*

**C1** AP1 5c dp orange ('27) .50 .50
**C2** AP1 25c dp ultra 1.20 1.20
**C3** AP1 50c grnsh blue .40 .40
**C4** AP1 75c dp blue 80.00 16.00
**C5** AP1 75c dp green .80 .40
**C6** AP1 80c vio brn ('27) 2.40 .80
**C7** AP1 1fr vermilion 1.20 .80
**C8** AP1 1.40fr brn lake ('27) 2.40 1.25
**C9** AP1 1.90fr dp blue ('27) 2.75 1.60
**C10** AP1 2fr black vio 2.40 1.20
*a.* 2fr deep violet 2.25 1.40
**C11** AP1 3fr gray blk 2.75 2.00
*Nos. C1-C11 (11)* 96.80 26.15

The 25c, 50c, 75c deep green and 1fr each were printed in two of three types, differing in frameline thickness, or hyphen in "Helio-Vaugirard" imprint.Values are for the more common types.

**Imperf., Pairs**

*C1a* AP1 5c 65.00 65.00
*C2a* AP1 25c 72.50 72.50
*C3a* AP1 50c 72.50 72.50
*C4a* AP1 75c 550.00 550.00
*C5a* AP1 75c 72.50 72.50
*C6a* AP1 80c 72.50 72.50
*C7a* AP1 1fr 90.00 90.00
*C10b* AP1 2fr 225.00 225.00

Nos. C8-C9 Srchd. in Blue or Black

**1931, Apr. 10**

**C12** AP1 1fr on 1.40fr (B) 2.40 2.40
*a.* Inverted surcharge 310.00 310.00
**C13** AP1 1.50fr on 1.90fr (Bk) 2.40 2.40

Rabat and Tower of Hassan AP2

Casablanca AP3

**1933, Jan.** **Engr.**

**C14** AP2 50c dark blue .80 .80
**C15** AP2 80c orange brn .80 .65
**C16** AP2 1.50fr brown red .80 .80
**C17** AP3 2.50fr carmine rose 6.50 1.20
**C18** AP3 5fr violet 3.25 1.75
**C19** AP3 10fr blue green 1.20 1.20
*Nos. C14-C19 (6)* 13.35 6.40

For surcharges see Nos. CB22-CB23.

Storks and Minaret, Chella — AP4

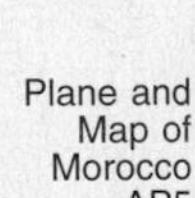

Plane and Map of Morocco AP5

**1939-40** *Perf. 13*

**C20** AP4 80c Prus green .25 .25
**C21** AP4 1fr dk red .25 .25
**C22** AP5 1.90fr ultra .40 .30
**C23** AP5 2fr red vio ('40) .40 .30
**C24** AP5 3fr chocolate .50 .25
**C25** AP4 5fr violet 1.40 .80
**C26** AP5 10fr turq blue 1.25 .55
*Nos. C20-C26 (7)* 4.45 2.70

**Catalogue values for unused stamps in this section, from this point to the end of the section, are for Never Hinged items.**

Plane over Oasis — AP6

**1944** **Litho.** *Perf. 11½*

**C27** AP6 50c Prus grn .50 .35
**C28** AP6 2fr ultra .50 .35
**C29** AP6 5fr scarlet .50 .35
**C30** AP6 10fr violet 1.40 1.10
**C31** AP6 50fr black 2.00 1.60
**C32** AP6 100fr dp bl & red 4.00 3.25
*Nos. C27-C32 (6)* 8.90 7.00

For surcharge see No. CB24.

Plane AP7

**1945** **Engr.** *Perf. 13*

**C33** AP7 50fr sepia 1.20 .95

Moulay Idriss — AP8

La Medina AP9

**1947-48**

**C34** AP8 9fr dk rose car .40 .30
**C35** AP8 40fr dark blue 1.20 .80
**C36** AP8 50fr dp claret ('47) 1.60 .40
**C37** AP9 100fr dp grnsh bl 3.25 1.20
**C38** AP9 200fr henna brn 8.00 1.60
*Nos. C34-C38 (5)* 14.45 4.30

**Leclerc Type of Regular Issue**

**1951, Apr. 28**

**C39** A50 50fr purple 3.25 2.75

Unveiling of a monument to Gen. Leclerc at Casablanca, Apr. 28, 1951.

Kasbah of the Oudayas, Rabat AP11

**1951, May 22**

**C40** AP11 300fr purple 24.00 12.00

Ben Smine Sanatorium AP12

**1951, June 4**

**C41** AP12 50fr pur & Prus grn 3.50 2.75

Fortifications, Chella — AP13

Plane Near Marrakesh AP14

Fort, Anti-Atlas Mountains AP15

View of Fez AP16

| 1952, Apr. 19 | Unwmk. | | Perf. 13 | |
|---|---|---|---|---|
| **C42** | AP13 | 10fr blue green | 1.60 | .80 |
| **C43** | AP14 | 40fr red | 2.40 | .80 |
| **C44** | AP15 | 100fr brown | 5.50 | 1.60 |
| **C45** | AP16 | 200fr purple | 10.50 | 4.00 |
| | | *Nos. C42-C45 (4)* | 20.00 | 7.20 |

Antique Brooches — AP17

| 1953, Mar. 27 | | | | |
|---|---|---|---|---|
| **C46** | AP17 | 50fr dark green | 4.00 | 3.25 |

"City" of the Agdal, Meknes AP18

20fr, Yakoub el Mansour, Rabat. 40fr, Ainchock, Casablanca. 50fr, El Aliya, Fedala.

| 1954, Mar. 8 | | | | |
|---|---|---|---|---|
| **C47** | AP18 | 10fr olive brown | 4.00 | 2.75 |
| **C48** | AP18 | 20fr purple | 4.00 | 2.75 |
| **C49** | AP18 | 40fr red brown | 4.00 | 2.75 |
| **C50** | AP18 | 50fr deep green | 4.00 | 2.75 |
| | | *Nos. C47-C50 (4)* | 16.00 | 11.00 |

Franco-Moroccan solidarity.

Naval Vessel and Sailboat — AP19

| 1954, Oct. 18 | | | | |
|---|---|---|---|---|
| **C51** | AP19 | 15fr dk blue green | 2.00 | 1.60 |
| **C52** | AP19 | 30fr violet blue | 2.40 | 2.00 |

Village in the Anti-Atlas — AP20

"Ksar es Souk," Rabat and Plane AP21

200fr, Estuary of Bou Regreg, Rabat and Plane.

| 1955, July 25 | Engr. | | Perf. 13 | |
|---|---|---|---|---|
| **C53** | AP20 | 100fr brt violet | 2.75 | .80 |
| **C54** | AP20 | 200fr brt carmine | 6.50 | 1.20 |
| **C55** | AP21 | 500fr grnsh blue | 16.00 | 4.00 |
| | | *Nos. C53-C55 (3)* | 25.25 | 6.00 |

## AIR POST SEMI-POSTAL STAMPS

### French Protectorate

Moorish Tribesmen SPAP1

Designs: 25c, Moor plowing with camel and burro. 50c, Caravan nearing Saffi. 75c, Walls, Marrakesh. 80c, Sheep grazing at Azrou. 1fr, Gate at Fez. 1.50fr, Aerial view of Tangier. 2fr, Aerial view of Casablanca. 3fr, Storks on old wall, Rabat. 5fr, Moorish fete.

*Perf. 13½*

| 1928, July 26 | Photo. | | Unwmk. | |
|---|---|---|---|---|
| **CB1** | SPAP1 | 5c dp blue | 5.25 | 5.25 |
| **CB2** | SPAP1 | 25c brn org | 5.25 | 5.25 |
| **CB3** | SPAP1 | 50c red | 5.25 | 5.25 |
| **CB4** | SPAP1 | 75c org brn | 5.25 | 5.25 |
| **CB5** | SPAP1 | 80c olive grn | 5.25 | 5.25 |
| **CB6** | SPAP1 | 1fr orange | 5.25 | 5.25 |
| **CB7** | SPAP1 | 1.50fr Prus bl | 5.25 | 5.25 |
| **CB8** | SPAP1 | 2fr dp brown | 5.25 | 5.25 |
| **CB9** | SPAP1 | 3fr dp violet | 5.25 | 5.25 |
| **CB10** | SPAP1 | 5fr brown blk | 5.25 | 5.25 |
| | | *Nos. CB1-CB10 (10)* | 52.50 | 52.50 |

These stamps were sold in sets only and at double their face value. The money received for the surtax was divided among charitable and social organizations. The stamps were not sold at post offices but solely by subscription to the Moroccan Postal Administration.

Overprinted in Red or Blue (25c, 50c, 75c, 1fr)

| 1929, Feb. 1 | | | | |
|---|---|---|---|---|
| **CB11** | SPAP1 | 5c dp blue | 5.25 | 5.25 |
| **CB12** | SPAP1 | 25c brown org | 5.25 | 5.25 |
| **CB13** | SPAP1 | 50c red | 5.25 | 5.25 |
| **CB14** | SPAP1 | 75c org brn | 5.25 | 5.25 |
| **CB15** | SPAP1 | 80c olive grn | 5.25 | 5.25 |
| **CB16** | SPAP1 | 1fr orange | 5.25 | 5.25 |
| **CB17** | SPAP1 | 1.50fr Prus bl | 5.25 | 5.25 |
| **CB18** | SPAP1 | 2fr dp brown | 5.25 | 5.25 |
| **CB19** | SPAP1 | 3fr dp violet | 5.25 | 5.25 |
| **CB20** | SPAP1 | 5fr brown blk | 5.25 | 5.25 |
| | | *Nos. CB11-CB20 (10)* | 52.50 | 52.50 |

These stamps were sold at double their face values and only in Tangier. The surtax benefited various charities.

Marshal Hubert Lyautey SPAP10

| 1935, May 15 | | | Perf. 13½ | |
|---|---|---|---|---|
| **CB21** | SPAP10 | 1.50fr + 1.50fr blue | 20.00 | 20.00 |

Nos. C14, C19 Surcharged in Red

| 1938 | | | Perf. 13 | |
|---|---|---|---|---|
| **CB22** | AP2 | 50c + 50c dk bl | 8.00 | 8.00 |
| **CB23** | AP3 | 10fr + 10fr bl grn | 5.50 | 5.50 |

**Catalogue values for unused stamps in this section, from this point to the end of the section, are for Never Hinged items.**

Plane over Oasis — SPAP11

| 1944 | Litho. | | Perf. 11½ | |
|---|---|---|---|---|
| **CB23A** | SPAP11 | 1.50fr + 98.50fr | 2.40 | 1.60 |

The surtax was for charity among the liberated French.

No. C29 Surcharged in Black

| 1946, June 18 | | | Perf. 11 | |
|---|---|---|---|---|
| **CB24** | AP6 | 5fr + 5fr scarlet | 1.60 | 1.20 |

6th anniv. of the appeal made by Gen. Charles de Gaulle, June 18, 1940. The surtax was for the Free French Association of Morocco.

Statue of Marshal Lyautey — SPAP12

| 1946, Dec. | Engr. | | Perf. 13 | |
|---|---|---|---|---|
| **CB25** | SPAP12 | 10fr +30fr dk grn | 6.50 | 2.75 |

The surtax was for works of solidarity.

Replenishing Stocks of Food — SPAP13

Agriculture SPAP14

| 1948, Feb. 9 | | | Unwmk. | |
|---|---|---|---|---|
| **CB26** | SPAP13 | 9fr +26fr dp grn | 2.00 | 1.60 |
| **CB27** | SPAP14 | 20fr +35fr brown | 2.00 | 1.60 |

The surtax was for combined works of Franco-Moroccan solidarity.

Tomb of Marshal Hubert Lyautey — SPAP15

| 1948, May 18 | | | Perf. 13 | |
|---|---|---|---|---|
| **CB28** | SPAP15 | 10fr +25fr dk grn | 1.60 | 1.25 |

Lyautey Exposition, Paris, June, 1948.

P.T.T. Clubhouse SPAP16

| 1948, June 7 | | | Engr. | |
|---|---|---|---|---|
| **CB29** | SPAP16 | 6fr + 34fr dk grn | 2.40 | 2.00 |
| **CB30** | SPAP16 | 9fr + 51fr red brn | 2.40 | 2.00 |

The surtax was used for the Moroccan P.T.T. employees vacation colony at Ifrane.

View of Agadir — SPAP17

Designs: 6fr+9fr, Fez. 9fr+16fr, Atlas Mountains. 15fr+25fr, Valley of Draa.

| 1949, Apr. 12 | | | Perf. 13 | |
|---|---|---|---|---|
| | **Inscribed: "SOLIDARITÉ 1948"** | | | |
| **CB31** | SPAP17 | 5fr +5fr dk grn | 2.40 | 2.00 |
| **CB32** | SPAP17 | 6fr +9fr org red | 2.40 | 2.00 |
| **CB33** | SPAP17 | 9fr +16fr blk brn | 2.40 | 2.00 |
| **CB34** | SPAP17 | 15fr +25fr ind | 2.40 | 2.00 |
| *a.* | | Sheet of 4, #CB31-CB34 | 32.50 | 24.00 |
| | | *Nos. CB31-CB34 (4)* | 9.60 | 8.00 |

Plane over Globe — SPAP18

| 1950, Mar. 11 | | | Engr. & Typo. | |
|---|---|---|---|---|
| **CB35** | SPAP18 | 15fr + 10fr bl grn & car | 1.60 | 1.25 |

Day of the Stamp, Mar. 11-12, 1950, and 25th anniv. of the 1st post link between Casablanca and Dakar.

Scenes and Map: Northwest Corner SPAP19

Designs (quarters of map): 6fr+9fr, NE, 9fr+16fr, SW. 15fr+25fr, SE.

| 1950, Apr. 11 | | | Engr. | |
|---|---|---|---|---|
| | **Inscribed: "SOLIDARITE 1949"** | | | |
| **CB36** | SPAP19 | 5fr +5fr dp ultra | 2.40 | 2.00 |
| **CB37** | SPAP19 | 6fr +9fr Prus grn | 2.40 | 2.00 |
| **CB38** | SPAP19 | 9fr +16fr dk brn | 2.40 | 2.00 |
| **CB39** | SPAP19 | 15fr +25fr brn red | 2.40 | 2.00 |
| *a.* | | Sheet of 4, #CB36-CB39 | 32.50 | 24.00 |
| | | *Nos. CB36-CB39 (4)* | 9.60 | 8.00 |

Arch of Triumph of Caracalla at Volubilis SPAP20

| 1950, Sept. 25 | | | Unwmk. | |
|---|---|---|---|---|
| **CB40** | SPAP20 | 10fr + 10fr sepia | 2.00 | 1.60 |
| **CB41** | SPAP20 | 15fr + 15fr bl grn | 2.00 | 1.60 |

The surtax was for Army Welfare Work.

Casablanca Post Office and First Air Post Stamp SPAP21

**1952, Mar. 8** *Perf. 13*

| | | | |
|---|---|---|---|
| CB42 SPAP21 | 15fr + 5fr red brn & dp grn | 4.75 | 4.00 |

Day of the Stamp, Mar. 8, 1952, and 30th anniv. of French Morocco's 1st air post stamp.

## POSTAGE DUE STAMPS

### French Offices in Morocco

France Postage Due Stamps and Types Surcharged in Red or Black

**1896** **Unwmk.** *Perf. 14x13½*

**On Stamps of 1891-93**

| | | | | |
|---|---|---|---|---|
| J1 | D2 | 5c on 5c lt bl (R) | 12.00 | 5.50 |
| J2 | D2 | 10c on 10c choc (R) | 16.00 | 6.50 |
| J3 | D2 | 30c on 30c car | 32.50 | 24.00 |
| *a.* | | Pair, one without surcharge | | |
| J4 | D2 | 50c on 50c lilac | 32.50 | 27.50 |
| *a.* | | "S" of "CENTIMOS" omitted | 340.00 | 250.00 |
| J5 | D2 | 1p on 1fr lil brn | 350.00 | 325.00 |

**1909-10** **On Stamps of 1908-10**

| | | | | |
|---|---|---|---|---|
| J6 | D3 | 1c on 1c ol grn (R) | 4.00 | 4.00 |
| J7 | D3 | 10c on 10c violet | 40.00 | 32.50 |
| J8 | D3 | 30c on 30c bister | 55.00 | 40.00 |
| J9 | D3 | 50c on 50c red | 80.00 | 72.50 |
| | | *Nos. J6-J9 (4)* | 179.00 | 149.00 |

Postage Due Stamps of France Surcharged in Red or Blue

**1911** **On Stamps of 1893-96**

| | | | | |
|---|---|---|---|---|
| J10 | D2 | 5c on 5c blue (R) | 4.75 | 4.75 |
| J11 | D2 | 10c on 10c choc (R) | 16.00 | 16.00 |
| *a.* | | Double surcharge | 225.00 | *260.00* |
| J12 | D2 | 50c on 50c lil (Bl) | 20.00 | 20.00 |

**On Stamps of 1908-10**

| | | | | |
|---|---|---|---|---|
| J13 | D3 | 1c on 1c ol grn (R) | 4.00 | 3.25 |
| J14 | D3 | 10c on 10c vio (R) | 8.00 | 8.00 |
| J15 | D3 | 30c on 30c bis (R) | 12.00 | 12.00 |
| J16 | D3 | 50c on 50c red (Bl) | 16.00 | 16.00 |
| | | *Nos. J10-J16 (7)* | 80.75 | 80.00 |

For surcharges see Nos. J23-J26.

### French Protectorate

France Postage Due Stamps of 1911 Issue Overprinted

**1915-17**

| | | | | |
|---|---|---|---|---|
| J17 | D4 | 1c on 1c black | .80 | .80 |
| *a.* | | New value double | 175.00 | |
| J18 | D4 | 5c on 5c blue | 3.25 | 2.00 |
| J19 | D4 | 10c on 10c choc | 4.00 | 2.00 |
| J20 | D4 | 20c on 20c ol grn | 4.00 | 2.00 |
| J21 | D4 | 30c on 30c rose red, *grayish* | 8.00 | 5.50 |
| J22 | D4 | 50c on 50c vio brn | 12.00 | 8.00 |
| | | *Nos. J17-J22 (6)* | 32.05 | 20.30 |

**Nos. J13 to J16 With Additional Overprint "Protectorat Francais"**

**1915**

| | | | | |
|---|---|---|---|---|
| J23 | D3 | 1c on 1c ol grn | 1.60 | 1.60 |
| J24 | D3 | 10c on 10c violet | 4.00 | 3.25 |
| J25 | D3 | 30c on 30c bister | 4.00 | 4.00 |
| J26 | D3 | 50c on 50c red | 4.00 | 4.00 |
| | | *Nos. J23-J26 (4)* | 13.60 | 12.85 |

D5

**1917-26** **Typo.**

| | | | | |
|---|---|---|---|---|
| J27 | D5 | 1c black | .25 | .25 |
| J28 | D5 | 5c deep blue | .40 | .25 |
| J29 | D5 | 10c brown | .40 | .40 |
| J30 | D5 | 20c olive green | 2.50 | 1.60 |
| J31 | D5 | 30c rose | .40 | .40 |
| J32 | D5 | 50c lilac brown | .80 | .40 |
| J33 | D5 | 1fr red brn, *straw* ('26) | .85 | .80 |
| J34 | D5 | 2fr violet ('26) | 2.40 | 1.60 |
| | | *Nos. J27-J34 (8)* | 8.00 | 5.70 |

See #J49-J56, Morocco #J1-J4. For surcharges see #J46-J48.

Postage Due Stamps of France, 1882-1906 Overprinted

**1918**

| | | | | |
|---|---|---|---|---|
| J35 | D2 | 1c black | 1.20 | 1.20 |
| J36 | D2 | 5c blue | 2.40 | 2.40 |
| J37 | D2 | 10c chocolate | 2.00 | 2.00 |
| J38 | D2 | 15c green, *grayish* | 4.75 | 4.75 |
| J39 | D2 | 20c olive green | 6.50 | 6.50 |
| J40 | D2 | 30c rose red, *grayish* | 16.00 | 16.00 |
| J41 | D2 | 50c violet brown | 24.00 | 24.00 |
| | | *Nos. J35-J41 (7)* | 56.85 | 56.85 |

Postage Due Stamps of France, 1908-19 Overprinted

**1918**

| | | | | |
|---|---|---|---|---|
| J42 | D3 | 1c olive green | 1.20 | 1.20 |
| J43 | D3 | 10c violet | 2.75 | 2.75 |
| J44 | D3 | 20c bister, *grayish* | 8.00 | 8.00 |
| J45 | D3 | 40c red | 20.00 | 20.00 |
| | | *Nos. J42-J45 (4)* | 31.95 | 31.95 |

**Catalogue values for unused stamps in this section, from this point to the end of the section, are for Never Hinged items.**

Nos. J31 and J29 Surcharged

**1944** **Unwmk.** *Perf. 14x13½*

| | | | | |
|---|---|---|---|---|
| J46 | D5 | 50c on 30c rose | 3.25 | 2.40 |
| J47 | D5 | 1fr on 10c brown | 5.50 | 4.00 |
| J48 | D5 | 3fr on 10c brown | 13.00 | 9.50 |
| | | *Nos. J46-J48 (3)* | 21.75 | 15.90 |

**Type of 1917-1926**

**1945-52** **Typo.**

| | | | | |
|---|---|---|---|---|
| J49 | D5 | 1fr brn lake ('47) | 1.20 | .80 |
| J50 | D5 | 2fr rose lake ('47) | 1.60 | .80 |
| J51 | D5 | 3fr ultra | .80 | .35 |
| J52 | D5 | 4fr red orange | .80 | .30 |
| J53 | D5 | 5fr green | 1.60 | .50 |
| J54 | D5 | 10fr yellow brn | 2.00 | .50 |
| J55 | D5 | 20fr carmine ('50) | 2.00 | .90 |
| J56 | D5 | 30fr dull brn ('52) | 2.75 | 1.60 |
| | | *Nos. J49-J56 (8)* | 12.75 | 5.75 |

## PARCEL POST STAMPS

### French Protectorate

PP1

**1917** **Unwmk.** *Perf. 13½x14*

| | | | | |
|---|---|---|---|---|
| Q1 | PP1 | 5c green | 1.20 | .80 |
| Q2 | PP1 | 10c carmine | 1.20 | .80 |
| Q3 | PP1 | 20c lilac brown | 1.20 | 1.00 |
| Q4 | PP1 | 25c blue | 1.60 | .80 |
| Q5 | PP1 | 40c dark brown | 2.40 | 1.60 |
| Q6 | PP1 | 50c red orange | 4.00 | .80 |
| Q7 | PP1 | 75c pale slate | 4.00 | 2.40 |
| Q8 | PP1 | 1fr ultra | 5.50 | .80 |
| Q9 | PP1 | 2fr gray | 12.00 | 1.60 |
| Q10 | PP1 | 5fr violet | 12.00 | 1.60 |
| Q11 | PP1 | 10fr black | 20.00 | 1.60 |
| | | *Nos. Q1-Q11 (11)* | 65.10 | 13.80 |

# FRENCH POLYNESIA

'french ˌpä-lə-'nē-zhə

## (French Oceania)

LOCATION — South Pacific Ocean
GOVT. — French Overseas Territory
AREA — 1,522 sq. mi.
POP. — 242,073 (1999 est.)
CAPITAL — Papeete

In 1903 various French Establishments in the South Pacific were united to form a single colony. Most important of the island groups are the Society Islands, Marquesas Islands, the Tuamotu group and the Gambier, Austral, and Rapa Islands. Tahiti, largest of the Society group, ranks first in importance.

100 Centimes = 1 Franc

**Catalogue values for unused stamps in this country are for Never Hinged items, beginning with Scott 136 in the regular postage section, Scott B11 in the semi-postal section, Scott C2 in the air-post section, Scott J18 in the postage due section, and Scott O1 in the officials section.**

Navigation and Commerce — A1

*Perf. 14x13½*

**1892-1907** **Typo.** **Unwmk.**

**Name of Colony in Blue or Carmine**

| | | | | |
|---|---|---|---|---|
| 1 | A1 | 1c black, *lil bl* | 1.60 | 1.60 |
| 2 | A1 | 2c brown, *buff* | 2.75 | 2.75 |
| 3 | A1 | 4c claret, *lav* | 4.50 | 4.00 |
| 4 | A1 | 5c green, *grnsh* | 13.50 | 9.50 |
| 5 | A1 | 5c yellow grn ('06) | 5.00 | 2.40 |
| 6 | A1 | 10c blk, *lavender* | 30.00 | 12.50 |
| 7 | A1 | 10c red ('00) | 5.00 | 2.40 |
| 8 | A1 | 15c blue, quadrille paper | 35.00 | 12.00 |
| 9 | A1 | 15c gray, *lt gray* ('00) | 10.00 | 7.25 |
| 10 | A1 | 20c red, *grn* | 17.50 | 16.00 |
| 11 | A1 | 25c black, *rose* | 60.00 | 30.00 |
| 12 | A1 | 25c blue ('00) | 32.50 | 16.00 |
| 13 | A1 | 30c brown, *bis* | 16.00 | 14.50 |
| 14 | A1 | 35c black, *yel* ('06) | 11.00 | 9.50 |
| 15 | A1 | 40c red, *straw* | 132.50 | 80.00 |
| 16 | A1 | 45c blk, *gray grn* ('07) | 6.75 | *6.75* |
| 17 | A1 | 50c car, *pale rose* | 10.00 | 10.00 |
| *a.* | | 50c rose, *pale rose* | 10.00 | 9.00 |
| 18 | A1 | 50c brown, *az* ('00) | 275.00 | 250.00 |
| 19 | A1 | 75c dp vio, *org* | 12.00 | 12.00 |
| 20 | A1 | 1fr brnz grn, *straw* | 13.50 | 13.50 |
| | | *Nos. 1-20 (20)* | 694.10 | 512.65 |

Perf. 13½x14 stamps are counterfeits.

For overprint and surcharge see Nos. 55, B1.

Tahitian Girl — A2

Kanakas — A3

Fautaua Valley — A4

**1913-30**

| | | | | |
|---|---|---|---|---|
| 21 | A2 | 1c violet & brn | .25 | .25 |
| 22 | A2 | 2c brown & blk | .25 | .25 |
| 23 | A2 | 4c orange & bl | .35 | .35 |
| 24 | A2 | 5c grn & yel grn | 1.60 | .90 |
| *a.* | | Double impression of yel grn | 500.00 | |
| 25 | A2 | 5c bl & blk ('22) | .50 | .50 |
| 26 | A2 | 10c rose & org | 2.25 | 2.25 |
| 27 | A2 | 10c bl grn & yel grn ('22) | 1.25 | 1.25 |
| 28 | A2 | 10c org red & brn red, *bluish* ('26) | 1.40 | 1.40 |
| 29 | A2 | 15c org & blk ('15) | .85 | .65 |
| *a.* | | Imperf., pair | 175.00 | |
| 30 | A2 | 20c black & vio | 1.10 | 1.00 |
| *a.* | | Imperf., pair | 175.00 | |
| 31 | A2 | 20c grn & bl grn ('26) | 1.00 | 1.00 |
| 32 | A2 | 20c brn red & dk brn ('27) | 1.60 | 1.60 |
| 33 | A3 | 25c ultra & blue | 1.50 | 1.25 |
| 34 | A3 | 25c vio & rose ('22) | .75 | .75 |
| 35 | A3 | 30c gray & brown | 5.00 | 4.00 |
| *a.* | | Imperf., pair | 325.00 | |
| 36 | A3 | 30c rose & red org ('22) | 3.25 | 3.25 |
| 37 | A3 | 30c blk & red org ('26) | .75 | .75 |
| 38 | A3 | 30c slate bl & bl grn ('27) | 1.75 | 1.75 |
| 39 | A3 | 35c green & rose | 1.25 | 1.25 |
| 40 | A3 | 40c black & green | 1.10 | 1.10 |
| 41 | A3 | 45c orange & red | 1.10 | 1.10 |
| 42 | A3 | 50c dk brown & blk | 17.50 | 13.50 |
| 43 | A3 | 50c ultra & bl ('22) | 1.25 | 1.25 |
| 44 | A3 | 50c gray & bl vio ('26) | 1.10 | 1.10 |
| 45 | A3 | 60c green & blk ('25) | 1.25 | 1.25 |
| 46 | A3 | 65c ol brn & red vio ('27) | 3.25 | 3.25 |
| 47 | A3 | 75c vio brn & vio | 2.50 | 2.50 |
| 48 | A3 | 90c brn red & rose ('30) | 16.50 | 16.50 |
| *a.* | | Imperf., pair | 225.00 | |
| 49 | A4 | 1fr rose & black | 6.25 | 4.25 |
| 50 | A4 | 1.10fr vio & dk brn ('28) | 1.60 | 1.60 |
| 51 | A4 | 1.40fr bis brn & vio ('29) | 4.00 | 4.00 |
| 52 | A4 | 1.50fr ind & bl ('30) | 16.50 | 16.50 |
| 53 | A4 | 2fr dk brown & grn | 6.25 | 4.25 |
| 54 | A4 | 5fr violet & bl | 11.00 | 11.00 |
| *a.* | | Imperf., pair | 500.00 | |
| | | *Nos. 21-54 (34)* | 117.80 | 107.55 |

For surcharges see Nos. 56-71, B2-B4.

No. 7 Overprinted

**1915**

| | | | | |
|---|---|---|---|---|
| 55 | A1 | 10c red | 6.75 | 6.75 |
| *a.* | | Inverted overprint | 225.00 | 225.00 |

For surcharge see No. B1.

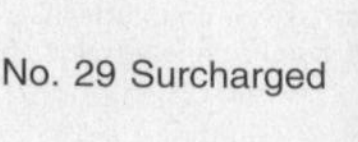

No. 29 Surcharged

**1916**

| | | | | |
|---|---|---|---|---|
| 56 | A2 | 10c on 15c org & blk | 3.50 | 3.50 |

No. 22 Surcharged

No. 41 Surcharged

No. 29 Surcharged

**1921**

| | | | | |
|---|---|---|---|---|
| 57 | A2 | 5c on 2c brn & blk | 36.00 | 36.00 |
| 58 | A3 | 10c on 45c org & red | 36.00 | 36.00 |
| 59 | A2 | 25c on 15c org & blk | 9.00 | 9.00 |
| | | *Nos. 57-59 (3)* | 81.00 | 81.00 |

On No. 58 the new value and date are set wide apart and without bar.

Types of 1913-30 Issue Surcharged in Black or Red

**1923-27**

| | | | | |
|---|---|---|---|---|
| 60 | A3 | 60c on 75c bl & brn | .75 | .75 |
| 61 | A4 | 65c on 1fr dk bl & ol (R) ('25) | 2.25 | 2.25 |
| 62 | A4 | 85c on 1fr dk bl & ol (R) ('25) | 2.25 | 2.25 |
| 63 | A3 | 90c on 75c brn red & cer ('27) | 3.00 | 3.00 |
| | | *Nos. 60-63 (4)* | 8.25 | 8.25 |

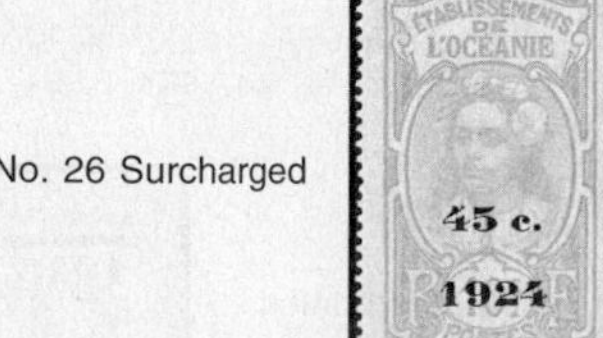

No. 26 Surcharged

**1924**

| | | | | |
|---|---|---|---|---|
| 64 | A2 | 45c on 10c rose & org | 3.00 | 3.00 |
| *a.* | | Inverted surcharge | *2,400.* | *2,400.* |

**Stamps and Type of 1913-30 Surcharged with New Value and Bars in Black or Red**

**1924-27**

| | | | | |
|---|---|---|---|---|
| 65 | A4 | 25c on 2fr dk brn & grn | 1.10 | 1.10 |
| 66 | A4 | 25c on 5fr vio & bl | 1.10 | 1.10 |
| 67 | A4 | 1.25fr on 1fr dk bl & ultra (R) ('26) | 1.20 | 1.20 |
| 68 | A4 | 1.50fr on 1fr dk bl & lt bl ('27) | 4.00 | 4.00 |
| 69 | A4 | 20fr on 5fr org & brt vio ('27) | 32.50 | 26.00 |
| | | *Nos. 65-69 (5)* | 39.90 | 33.40 |

Surcharged in Black or Red

**1926**

| | | | | |
|---|---|---|---|---|
| 70 | A4 | 3fr on 5fr gray & blue | 3.25 | 2.50 |
| 71 | A4 | 10fr on 5fr grn & blk (R) | 7.25 | 7.25 |

Papetoai Bay, Moorea A5

**1929, Mar. 25**

| | | | | |
|---|---|---|---|---|
| 72 | A5 | 3fr green & dk brn | 8.00 | 8.00 |
| 73 | A5 | 5fr lt blue & dk brn | 15.00 | 15.00 |
| 74 | A5 | 10fr lt red & dk brn | 45.00 | 45.00 |
| 75 | A5 | 20fr lilac & dk brn | 57.50 | 57.50 |
| | | *Nos. 72-75 (4)* | 125.50 | 125.50 |

For overprints see Nos. 128, 130, 132, 134.

Common Design Types pictured following the introduction.

**Colonial Exposition Issue**

Common Design Types

**1931, Apr. 13 Engr. *Perf. 12½***

**Name of Country Printed in Black**

| | | | | |
|---|---|---|---|---|
| 76 | CD70 | 40c deep green | 7.50 | 7.50 |
| 77 | CD71 | 50c violet | 7.50 | 7.50 |
| 78 | CD72 | 90c red orange | 7.50 | 7.50 |
| 79 | CD73 | 1.50fr dull blue | 7.50 | 7.50 |
| | | *Nos. 76-79 (4)* | 30.00 | 30.00 |

Spear Fishing A12

Tahitian Girl — A13

Idols A14

**1934-40 Photo. *Perf. 13½, 13½x13***

| | | | | |
|---|---|---|---|---|
| 80 | A12 | 1c gray black | .25 | .25 |
| 81 | A12 | 2c claret | .35 | .35 |
| 82 | A12 | 3c lt blue ('40) | .35 | .35 |
| 83 | A12 | 4c orange | .60 | .60 |
| 84 | A12 | 5c violet | .90 | .90 |
| 85 | A12 | 10c dark brown | .40 | .40 |
| 86 | A12 | 15c green | .60 | .60 |
| 87 | A12 | 20c red | .60 | .60 |
| 88 | A13 | 25c gray blue | .90 | .90 |
| 89 | A13 | 30c yellow green | 1.20 | 1.20 |
| 90 | A13 | 30c orange brn ('40) | .80 | .80 |
| 91 | A14 | 35c dp green ('38) | 4.00 | 4.00 |
| 92 | A13 | 40c red violet | .60 | .60 |
| 93 | A13 | 45c brown orange | 9.00 | 9.00 |
| 94 | A13 | 45c dk green ('39) | 1.60 | 1.60 |
| 95 | A13 | 50c violet | .60 | .60 |
| 96 | A13 | 55c blue ('38) | 6.75 | 6.75 |
| 97 | A13 | 60c black ('39) | .75 | .75 |
| 98 | A13 | 65c brown | 3.25 | 3.25 |
| 99 | A13 | 70c brt pink ('39) | 1.40 | 1.40 |
| 100 | A13 | 75c olive green | 9.00 | 9.00 |
| 101 | A13 | 80c violet brn ('38) | 2.00 | 2.00 |
| 102 | A13 | 90c rose red | .90 | .90 |
| 103 | A14 | 1fr red brown | .90 | .90 |
| 104 | A14 | 1.25fr brown violet | 8.25 | 8.25 |
| 105 | A14 | 1.25fr rose red ('39) | 1.25 | 1.25 |
| 106 | A14 | 1.40fr orange yel ('39) | 1.25 | 1.25 |
| 107 | A14 | 1.50fr blue | .90 | .90 |
| 108 | A14 | 1.60fr dull vio ('39) | 1.40 | 1.40 |
| 109 | A14 | 1.75fr olive | 6.75 | 6.75 |
| 110 | A14 | 2fr red | 1.10 | 1.10 |
| 111 | A14 | 2.25fr deep blue ('39) | 1.25 | 1.25 |
| 112 | A14 | 2.50fr black ('39) | 1.25 | 1.25 |
| 113 | A14 | 3fr brown org ('39) | 1.50 | 1.50 |
| 114 | A14 | 5fr red violet ('39) | 1.00 | 1.00 |
| 115 | A14 | 10fr dark green ('39) | 3.00 | 3.00 |
| 116 | A14 | 20fr dark brown ('39) | 3.50 | 3.50 |
| | | *Nos. 80-116 (37)* | 80.10 | 80.10 |

For overprints see Nos. 126-127, 129, 131, 133, 135.

**Paris International Exposition Issue**

Common Design Types

**1937 Engr. *Perf. 13***

| | | | | |
|---|---|---|---|---|
| 117 | CD74 | 20c deep violet | 3.50 | 3.50 |
| 118 | CD75 | 30c dark green | 3.50 | 3.50 |
| 119 | CD76 | 40c carmine rose | 3.50 | 3.50 |
| 120 | CD77 | 50c dk brown & blue | 4.25 | 4.25 |
| 121 | CD78 | 90c red | 4.25 | 4.25 |
| 122 | CD79 | 1.50fr ultra | 5.00 | 5.00 |
| | | *Nos. 117-122 (6)* | 24.00 | 24.00 |

**Colonial Arts Exhibition Issue**

Souvenir Sheet

Common Design Type

**1937 *Imperf.***

| | | | | |
|---|---|---|---|---|
| 123 | CD78 | 3fr emerald | 36.00 | *52.50* |
| | | Never hinged | 55.00 | |

**New York World's Fair Issue**

Common Design Type

**1939, May 10 Engr. *Perf. 12½x12***

| | | | | |
|---|---|---|---|---|
| 124 | CD82 | 1.25fr carmine lake | 2.40 | 2.40 |
| 125 | CD82 | 2.25fr ultra | 2.40 | 2.40 |
| | | Set, never hinged | 8.00 | |

Fautaua Valley and Marshal Petain A15

**1941 Engr. *Perf. 12½x12***

| | | | | |
|---|---|---|---|---|
| 125A | A15 | 1fr bluish green | 1.10 | |
| *c.* | | Denomination ("1F") omitted | 80.00 | |
| 125B | A15 | 2.50fr deep blue | 1.25 | |
| | | Set, never hinged | 3.25 | |

Nos. 125A-125B were issued by the Vichy government in France, but were not placed on sale in the French Polynesia.

For surcharges, see Nos. B12B-B12C.

Stamps of 1929-39 Ovptd. in Black or Red

**1941 *Perf. 14x13½, 13½x13***

| | | | | |
|---|---|---|---|---|
| 126 | A14 | 1fr red brown (BK) | 7.00 | *9.50* |
| *a.* | | Inverted overprint | 1,200. | |
| 127 | A14 | 2.50fr black | 8.00 | *11.00* |
| *a.* | | Inverted overprint | 1,200. | |
| 128 | A5 | 3fr grn & dk brn | 9.00 | 9.00 |
| 129 | A14 | 3fr brn org (Bk) | 10.00 | *12.00* |
| 130 | A5 | 5fr lt bl & dk brn | 9.00 | 9.00 |
| 131 | A14 | 5fr red vio (Bk) | 10.00 | 10.00 |
| 132 | A5 | 10fr lt red & dk brn | 25.00 | *30.00* |
| 133 | A14 | 10fr dark green | 90.00 | *110.00* |
| 134 | A5 | 20fr lil & dk brn | 135.00 | 135.00 |
| 135 | A14 | 20fr dark brown | 75.00 | *95.00* |
| | | *Nos. 126-135 (10)* | 378.00 | *430.50* |
| | | Set, never hinged | 480.00 | |

**Types of 1934-39 without "RF"**

**1942-44 Photo. *Perf. 13½***

| | | | |
|---|---|---|---|
| 135A | A12 | 10c dark brown | .65 |
| 135B | A13 | 30c orange brown | .85 |
| 135C | A14 | 1.50fr blue | 1.00 |
| 135D | A14 | 10fr dark green | 1.75 |
| 135E | A14 | 20fr dark brown | 2.50 |
| | | *Nos. 135A-135E (5)* | 6.75 |

Nos. 135A-135E were issued by the Vichy government in France, but were not placed on sale in French Polynesia.

**Catalogue values for unused stamps in this section, from this point to the end of the section, are for Never Hinged items.**

Ancient Double Canoe A16

**1942 Photo. *Perf. 14½x14***

| | | | | |
|---|---|---|---|---|
| 136 | A16 | 5c dark brown | .40 | .25 |
| 137 | A16 | 10c dk gray bl | .40 | .25 |
| 138 | A16 | 25c emerald | .40 | .25 |
| 139 | A16 | 30c red orange | .40 | .25 |
| 140 | A16 | 40c dk slate grn | .40 | .25 |
| 141 | A16 | 80c red brown | .40 | .25 |
| 142 | A16 | 1fr rose violet | .50 | .35 |
| 143 | A16 | 1.50fr brt red | .65 | .50 |
| 144 | A16 | 2fr gray black | 1.00 | .75 |
| 145 | A16 | 2.50fr brt ultra | 2.50 | 1.75 |
| 146 | A16 | 4fr dull violet | 1.75 | 1.25 |
| 147 | A16 | 5fr bister | 1.75 | 1.25 |
| 148 | A16 | 10fr deep brown | 2.50 | 1.90 |
| 149 | A16 | 20fr deep green | 3.00 | 2.10 |
| | | *Nos. 136-149 (14)* | 16.05 | 11.35 |

For surcharges see Nos. 152-159.

**Eboue Issue**

Common Design Type

**1945 Engr. *Perf. 13***

| | | | | |
|---|---|---|---|---|
| 150 | CD91 | 2fr black | 1.00 | .75 |
| 151 | CD91 | 25fr Prus green | 2.60 | 2.10 |

Nos. 150 and 151 exist imperforate.

**Nos. 136, 138 and 145 Surcharged with New Values and Bars in Carmine or Black**

**1946 *Perf. 14½x14***

| | | | | |
|---|---|---|---|---|
| 152 | A16 | 50c on 5c (C) | .65 | .50 |
| 153 | A16 | 60c on 5c (C) | .65 | .50 |
| 154 | A16 | 70c on 5c (C) | .65 | .50 |
| 155 | A16 | 1.20fr on 5c (C) | .80 | .65 |
| 156 | A16 | 2.40fr on 25c (Bk) | 1.60 | 1.25 |
| 157 | A16 | 3fr on 25c (Bk) | 1.00 | .75 |
| 158 | A16 | 4.50fr on 25c (Bk) | 2.00 | 1.50 |
| 159 | A16 | 15fr on 2.50fr (C) | 2.40 | 1.75 |
| | | *Nos. 152-159 (8)* | 9.75 | 7.40 |

Coast of Mooréa A17

Fisherman and Catch — A18

Tahitian Girl — A20

House at Faa — A19

Island of Borabora A21

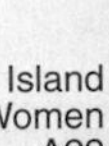

Island Women A22

**1948 Unwmk. Engr. *Perf. 13***

| No. | Type | Value / Color | Unused | Used |
|---|---|---|---|---|
| 160 | A17 | 10c brown | .50 | .35 |
| 161 | A17 | 30c blue green | .50 | .35 |
| 162 | A17 | 40c deep blue | .50 | .35 |
| 163 | A18 | 50c red brown | .50 | .35 |
| 164 | A18 | 60c dk brown ol | .65 | .50 |
| 165 | A18 | 80c brt blue | .65 | .50 |
| 166 | A19 | 1fr red brown | .65 | .35 |
| 167 | A19 | 1.20fr slate | .65 | .50 |
| 168 | A19 | 1.50fr deep ultra | .65 | .50 |
| 169 | A20 | 2fr sepia | 1.10 | .75 |
| 170 | A20 | 2.40fr red brown | 1.25 | 1.00 |
| 171 | A20 | 3fr purple | 11.50 | 2.50 |
| 172 | A20 | 4fr blue black | 2.40 | 1.40 |
| 173 | A21 | 5fr sepia | 3.75 | 1.60 |
| 174 | A21 | 6fr steel blue | 3.75 | 2.10 |
| 175 | A21 | 10fr dk brown ol | 4.75 | 1.75 |
| 176 | A22 | 15fr vermilion | 7.25 | 2.75 |
| 177 | A22 | 20fr slate | 7.25 | 3.25 |
| 178 | A22 | 25fr sepia | 9.00 | 5.00 |
| | | *Nos. 160-178 (19)* | 57.25 | 25.85 |

Imperforates

Most French Polynesia stamps from 1948 onward exist imperforate in issued and trial colors, and also in small presentation sheets in issued colors.

**Military Medal Issue**

Common Design Type

**1952, Dec. 1 Engr. & Typo.**

**179** CD101 3fr multicolored 13.50 10.00

Girl of Bora Bora — A23

**1955, Sept. 26 Engr.**

**180** A23 9fr dk brn, blk & red 11.00 7.25

**FIDES Issue**

Common Design Type

Design: 3fr, Dry dock at Papeete.

**1956, Oct. 22 Engr. *Perf. 13x12½***

**181** CD103 3fr grnsh blue 4.00 2.00

Girl Playing Guitar — A24

Designs: 4fr, 7fr, 9fr, Man with headdress. 10fr, 20fr, Girl with shells on beach.

**1958, Nov. 3 Unwmk. *Perf. 13***

| No. | Type | Value / Color | Unused | Used |
|---|---|---|---|---|
| 182 | A24 | 10c grn & redsh brn | .65 | .55 |
| 183 | A24 | 25c slate grn, cl & car | .80 | .60 |
| 184 | A24 | 1fr brt bl, brn & red org | 1.00 | .65 |
| 185 | A24 | 2fr brn, vio brn & vio | 1.10 | .65 |
| 186 | A24 | 4fr sl grn & org yel | 1.50 | 1.00 |
| 187 | A24 | 7fr red brn, grn & org | 3.00 | 1.60 |
| 188 | A24 | 9fr vio brn, grn & org | 5.50 | 2.25 |
| 189 | A24 | 10fr dk bl, brn & car | 5.00 | 2.25 |
| 190 | A24 | 20fr pur, rose red & brn | 9.00 | 5.00 |
| | | *Nos. 182-190 (9)* | 27.55 | 14.55 |

See Nos. 304-306.

**Human Rights Issue**

Common Design Type

**1958, Dec. 10**

**191** CD105 7fr dk gray & dk bl 13.00 8.75

**Flower Issue**

Common Design Type

**1959, Jan. 3 Photo. *Perf. 12½x12***

**192** CD104 4fr Breadfruit 6.50 4.00

Spear Fishing — A25

Tahitian Dancers A26

**1960, May 16 Engr. *Perf. 13***

**193** A25 5fr green, brn & lil 1.25 1.00
**194** A26 17fr ultra, brt grn & red brn 6.00 2.50

Post Office, Papeete A27

**1960, Nov. 19 Unwmk. *Perf. 13***

**195** A27 16fr green, bl & claret 5.50 3.25

Saraca Indica — A28

**1962, July 12 Photo. *Perf. 13***

**196** A28 15fr shown 15.00 14.00
**197** A28 25fr Hibiscus 24.00 16.00

Map of Australia and South Pacific — A29

**1962, July 18 *Perf. 13x12***

**198** A29 20fr multicolored 17.50 7.75

5th South Pacific Conf., Pago Pago, July 1962.

Spined Squirrelfish A30

Fish: 10fr, One-spot butterflyfish. 30fr, Radiate lionfish. 40fr, Horned boxfish.

**1962, Dec. 15 Engr. *Perf. 13***

| No. | Type | Value / Color | Unused | Used |
|---|---|---|---|---|
| 199 | A30 | 5fr black, mag & bis | 4.25 | 1.90 |
| 200 | A30 | 10fr multicolored | 6.25 | 2.75 |
| 201 | A30 | 30fr multicolored | 12.50 | 7.75 |
| 202 | A30 | 40fr multicolored | 15.50 | 11.50 |
| | | *Nos. 199-202 (4)* | 38.50 | 23.90 |

Soccer A30a

Design: 50fr, Throwing the javelin.

**1963, Aug. 29 Photo. *Perf. 12½***

**203** A30a 20fr brt ultra & brn 9.00 6.25
**204** A30a 50fr brt car rose & ultra 16.00 9.25

South Pacific Games, Suva, 8/29-9/7.

**Red Cross Centenary Issue**

Common Design Type

**1963, Sept. 2 Engr. *Perf. 13***

**205** CD113 15fr vio brn, gray & car 15.00 12.00

**Human Rights Issue**

Common Design Type

**1963, Dec. 10 Unwmk. *Perf. 13***

**206** CD117 7fr green & vio bl 15.00 10.00

**Philatec Issue**

Common Design Type

**1964, Apr. 9 Unwmk. *Perf. 13***

**207** CD118 25fr grn, dk sl grn & red 18.00 12.50

Tahitian Dancer A31

**1964, May 14 Engr. *Perf. 13***

**208** A31 1fr multicolored .40 .40
**209** A31 3fr dp claret, blk & org .90 .90

Soldiers, Truck and Battle Flag — A32

**1964, July 10 Photo. *Perf. 12½***

**210** A32 5fr multicolored 11.00 4.25

Issued to honor the Tahitian Volunteers of the Pacific Battalion. See No. C31.

Tuamotu Scene A33

Views: 4fr, Borabora. 7fr, Papeete Harbor. 8fr, Paul Gauguin's tomb, Marquesas. 20fr, Mangareva, Gambier Islands.

**1964, Dec. 1 Litho. *Perf. 12½x13***

| No. | Type | Value / Color | Unused | Used |
|---|---|---|---|---|
| 211 | A33 | 2fr multicolored | .90 | .50 |
| 212 | A33 | 4fr multicolored | 1.50 | .50 |
| 213 | A33 | 7fr multicolored | 3.00 | 1.25 |
| 214 | A33 | 8fr multicolored | 4.00 | 1.75 |
| 215 | A33 | 20fr multicolored | 9.50 | 2.50 |
| | | *Nos. 211-215,C32 (6)* | 28.40 | 10.50 |

Painting from a School Dining Room — A34

**1965, Nov. 29 Engr. *Perf. 13***

**216** A34 20fr dk brn, sl grn & dk car 20.00 12.00

Publicizing the School Canteen Program. See No. C38.

Outrigger Canoe on Lagoon A35

Ships: 11fr, Large cruising yacht, vert. 12fr, Motorboat for sport fishing. 14fr, Outrigger canoes with sails. 19fr, Schooner, vert. 22fr, Modern coaster "Oiseau des Iles II."

**1966, Aug. 30 Engr. *Perf. 13***

| No. | Type | Value / Color | Unused | Used |
|---|---|---|---|---|
| 217 | A35 | 10fr brt ultra, emer & mar | 2.75 | .90 |
| 218 | A35 | 11fr mar, dk bl & sl grn | 2.75 | 1.60 |
| 219 | A35 | 12fr emer, dk bl & red lil | 3.75 | 1.75 |
| 220 | A35 | 14fr brn, bl & slate grn | 5.50 | 2.00 |
| 221 | A35 | 19fr scar, sl grn & dp bl | 6.50 | 2.10 |
| 222 | A35 | 22fr multicolored | 9.50 | 4.00 |
| | | *Nos. 217-222 (6)* | 30.75 | 12.35 |

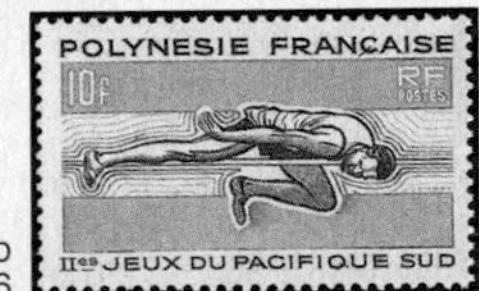
High Jump A36

Designs: 20fr, Pole vault, vert. 40fr, Women's basketball, vert. 60fr, Hurdling.

**1966, Dec. 15 Engr. *Perf. 13***

| No. | Type | Value / Color | Unused | Used |
|---|---|---|---|---|
| 223 | A36 | 10fr dk red, lem & blk | 2.25 | 1.50 |
| 224 | A36 | 20fr blue, emer & blk | 5.25 | 2.00 |
| 225 | A36 | 40fr emer, brt pink & blk | 10.00 | 5.00 |
| 226 | A36 | 60fr dull yel, bl & blk | 17.00 | 8.50 |
| | | *Nos. 223-226 (4)* | 34.50 | 17.00 |

2nd South Pacific Games, Nouméa, New Caledonia, Dec. 8-18.

Poi Pounder — A37

**1967, June 15 Engr. *Perf. 13***

**227** A37 50fr orange & blk 17.00 10.00

Society for Oceanic Studies, 50th anniv.

Javelin Throwing — A38

5fr, Spring dance. 15fr, Horse race. 16fr, Fruit carriers' race. 21fr, Canoe race.

**1967, July 11**

| No. | Type | Description | Unused | Used |
|---|---|---|---|---|
| 228 | A38 | 5fr multi, horiz. | 1.10 | .90 |
| 229 | A38 | 13fr multi | 4.50 | 1.50 |
| 230 | A38 | 15fr multi, horiz. | 4.50 | 1.60 |
| 231 | A38 | 16fr multi | 4.50 | 2.75 |
| 232 | A38 | 21fr multi, horiz. | 9.50 | 5.00 |
| | | *Nos. 228-232 (5)* | 24.10 | 11.75 |

Issued to publicize the July Festival.

Earring — A39

Art of the Marquesas Islands: 10fr, Carved mother-of-pearl. 15fr, Decorated canoe paddle. 23fr, Oil vessel. 25fr, Carved stilt stirrups. 30fr, Fan handles. 35fr, Tattooed man. 50fr, Tikis.

**1967-68 Engr. *Perf. 13***

| No. | Type | Description | Unused | Used |
|---|---|---|---|---|
| 233 | A39 | 10fr dp cl, dl red & ultra | 2.25 | .65 |
| 234 | A39 | 15fr black & emerald | 3.00 | 1.25 |
| 235 | A39 | 20fr ol gray, dk car & lt bl | 5.25 | 2.00 |
| 236 | A39 | 23fr dk brn, ocher & bl | 6.50 | 4.00 |
| 237 | A39 | 25fr dk brn, dk bl & lil | 6.50 | 3.75 |
| 238 | A39 | 30fr brown & red lilac | 8.25 | 4.00 |
| 239 | A39 | 35fr ultra & dk brn | 14.00 | 6.25 |
| 240 | A39 | 50fr brn, sl grn & lt bl | 15.00 | 7.25 |
| | | *Nos. 233-240 (8)* | 60.75 | 29.15 |

Issued: 20fr, 25fr, 30fr, 50fr, 12/19/67; others 2/28/68.

### WHO Anniversary Issue

Common Design Type

**1968, May 4 Engr. *Perf. 13***

| No. | Type | Description | Unused | Used |
|---|---|---|---|---|
| 241 | CD126 | 15fr bl grn, mar & dp vio | 11.00 | 4.75 |
| 242 | CD126 | 16fr org, lil & bl grn | 11.00 | 8.00 |

### Human Rights Year Issue

Common Design Type

**1968, Aug. 10 Engr. *Perf. 13***

| No. | Type | Description | Unused | Used |
|---|---|---|---|---|
| 243 | CD127 | 15fr blue, red & brn | 12.00 | 6.00 |
| 244 | CD127 | 16fr brn, brt pink & ultra | 12.00 | 8.00 |

Tiare Apetahi A40

Flower: 17fr, Tiare Tahiti.

**1969, Mar. 27 Photo. *Perf. 12½x13***

| No. | Type | Description | Unused | Used |
|---|---|---|---|---|
| 245 | A40 | 9fr multicolored | 2.10 | 1.10 |
| 246 | A40 | 17fr multicolored | 4.25 | 2.10 |

3rd South Pacific Games, Port Moresby, Papua and New Guinea, Aug. 13-23 — A41

**1969, Aug. 13 Engr. *Perf. 13***

| No. | Type | Description | Unused | Used |
|---|---|---|---|---|
| 247 | A41 | 9fr Boxer, horiz | 3.25 | 1.25 |
| 248 | A41 | 17fr High jump | 7.25 | 2.00 |
| 249 | A41 | 18fr Runner | 9.00 | 3.50 |
| 250 | A41 | 22fr Long jump | 12.00 | 7.25 |
| | | *Nos. 247-250 (4)* | 31.50 | 14.00 |

### ILO Issue

Common Design Type

**1969, Nov. 24 Engr. *Perf. 13***

| No. | Type | Description | Unused | Used |
|---|---|---|---|---|
| 251 | CD131 | 17fr org, emer & ol | 12.00 | 5.75 |
| 252 | CD131 | 18fr org, dk brn & vio bl | 12.00 | 6.75 |

Territorial Assembly A42

Buildings: 14fr, Governor's Residence. 17fr, House of Tourism. 18fr, Maeva Hotel. 24fr, Taharaa Hotel.

**1969, Dec. 22 Photo. *Perf. 12½x12***

| No. | Type | Description | Unused | Used |
|---|---|---|---|---|
| 253 | A42 | 13fr black & multi | 2.75 | 1.25 |
| 254 | A42 | 14fr black & multi | 4.25 | 1.50 |
| 255 | A42 | 17fr black & multi | 7.00 | 3.50 |
| 256 | A42 | 18fr black & multi | 7.75 | 4.00 |
| 257 | A42 | 24fr black & multi | 13.50 | 7.00 |
| | | *Nos. 253-257 (5)* | 35.25 | 17.25 |

Stone Figure with Globe — A43

Designs: 40fr, Globe, plane, map of Polynesia and men holding "PATA" sign, horiz. 60fr, Polynesian carrying globe.

**1970, Apr. 7 Engr. *Perf. 13***

| No. | Type | Description | Unused | Used |
|---|---|---|---|---|
| 258 | A43 | 20fr deep plum, gray & bl | 6.75 | 3.25 |
| 259 | A43 | 40fr emer, rose lil & ultra | 11.00 | 5.25 |
| 260 | A43 | 60fr red brn, bl & dk brn | 19.00 | 10.00 |
| | | *Nos. 258-260 (3)* | 36.75 | 18.50 |

Issued to publicize the 1970 Pacific Area Travel Association Congress (PATA).

### UPU Headquarters Issue

Common Design Type

**1970, May 20 Engr. *Perf. 13***

| No. | Type | Description | Unused | Used |
|---|---|---|---|---|
| 261 | CD133 | 18fr maroon, pur & brn | 10.00 | 4.75 |
| 262 | CD133 | 20fr lilac rose, ol & ind | 10.00 | 5.25 |

Night Fishing — A44

**1971, May 11 Photo. *Perf. 13***

| No. | Type | Description | Unused | Used |
|---|---|---|---|---|
| 263 | A44 | 10fr multicolored | 12.50 | 5.25 |
| | | *Nos. 263,C71-C73 (4)* | 37.50 | 19.75 |

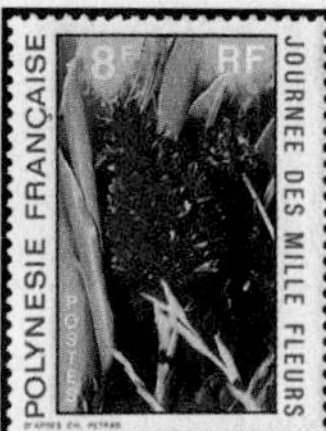


Flowers — A45

Designs: Various flowers. 12fr is horiz.

***Perf. 12½x13, 13x12½***

**1971, Aug. 27**

| No. | Type | Description | Unused | Used |
|---|---|---|---|---|
| 264 | A45 | 8fr multicolored | 2.25 | 1.00 |
| 265 | A45 | 12fr multicolored | 3.50 | 1.75 |
| 266 | A45 | 22fr multicolored | 5.75 | 3.00 |
| | | *Nos. 264-266 (3)* | 11.50 | 5.75 |

Day of a Thousand Flowers.

Water-skiing Slalom — A46

Designs: 20fr, Water-skiing, jump, vert. 40fr, Figure water-skiing.

**1971, Oct. 11 Engr. *Perf. 13***

| No. | Type | Description | Unused | Used |
|---|---|---|---|---|
| 267 | A46 | 10fr grnsh bl, dk red & brn | 6.25 | 2.00 |
| 268 | A46 | 20fr car, emer & brn | 9.00 | 4.00 |
| 269 | A46 | 40fr brn, grn & lil | 20.00 | 12.00 |
| | | *Nos. 267-269 (3)* | 35.25 | 18.00 |

World water-skiing championships, Oct. 1971.

### De Gaulle Issue

Common Design Type

30fr, As general, 1940. 50fr, As president, 1970.

**1971, Nov. 9 Engr. *Perf. 13***

| No. | Type | Description | Unused | Used |
|---|---|---|---|---|
| 270 | CD134 | 30fr red lilac & blk | 22.50 | 11.00 |
| 271 | CD134 | 50fr red lilac & blk | 29.00 | 18.50 |

Map of Tahiti and Jerusalem Cross A47

**1971, Dec. 18 Photo. *Perf. 13x12½***

| No. | Type | Description | Unused | Used |
|---|---|---|---|---|
| 272 | A47 | 28fr lt blue & multi | 14.00 | 8.50 |

2nd rally of French Boy Scouts and Guides, Taravao, French Polynesia.

"Alcoholism" — A48

**1972, Mar. 24 Photo. *Perf. 13***

| No. | Type | Description | Unused | Used |
|---|---|---|---|---|
| 273 | A48 | 20fr brown & multi | 11.50 | 5.75 |

Fight against alcoholism.

Mother and Child — A49

**1973, Sept. 26 Photo. *Perf. 12½x13***

| No. | Type | Description | Unused | Used |
|---|---|---|---|---|
| 274 | A49 | 28fr pale yellow & multi | 9.50 | 5.00 |

Day nursery.

Polynesian Golfer — A50

Design: 24fr, Atimaono Golf Course.

**1974, Feb. 27 Photo. *Perf. 13***

| No. | Type | Description | Unused | Used |
|---|---|---|---|---|
| 275 | A50 | 16fr multicolored | 8.50 | 3.25 |
| 276 | A50 | 24fr multicolored | 10.50 | 5.25 |

Atimaono Golf Course.

Hand Throwing Life Preserver to Puppy — A51

**1974, May 9 Photo. *Perf. 13***

| No. | Type | Description | Unused | Used |
|---|---|---|---|---|
| 277 | A51 | 21fr brt blue & multi | 12.00 | 5.00 |

Society for the Protection of Animals.

Around a Fire, on the Beach A52

Polynesian Views: 2fr, Lagoons and mountains. 6fr, Pebble divers. 10fr, Lonely Mountain and flowers, vert. 15fr, Sailing ship at sunset. 20fr, Lagoon and mountain.

**1974, May 22**

| No. | Type | Description | Unused | Used |
|---|---|---|---|---|
| 278 | A52 | 2fr multicolored | .90 | .60 |
| 279 | A52 | 5fr multicolored | 1.10 | .90 |
| 280 | A52 | 6fr multicolored | 1.90 | 1.10 |
| 281 | A52 | 10fr multicolored | 2.10 | 1.25 |
| 282 | A52 | 15fr multicolored | 4.25 | 1.75 |
| 283 | A52 | 20fr multicolored | 7.00 | 2.10 |
| | | *Nos. 278-283 (6)* | 17.25 | 7.70 |

Polynesian Woman and UPU Emblem — A53

**1974, Oct. 9 Engr. *Perf. 13***

| No. | Type | Description | Unused | Used |
|---|---|---|---|---|
| 284 | A53 | 65fr multicolored | 12.00 | 7.75 |

Centenary of Universal Postal Union.

Lion, Sun and Emblem — A54

**1975, June 17 Photo.**

| No. | Type | Description | Unused | Used |
|---|---|---|---|---|
| 285 | A54 | 26fr multicolored | 12.00 | 5.00 |

15th anniv. of Lions Intl. in Tahiti.

Fish and Leaf A55

**1975, July 9 Litho. *Perf. 12***

**286** A55 19fr dp ultra & green 10.00 4.25

Polynesian Association for the Protection of Nature.

Georges Pompidou, Pres. of France — A55a

**1976, Feb. 16 Engr. *Perf. 13***

**287** A55a 49fr dk violet & black 11.00 7.00

See France No. 1430.

Alain Gerbault and Sailboat A56

**1976, May 25 Photo. *Perf. 13***

**288** A56 90fr multicolored 13.50 9.00

Alain Gerbault's arrival in Bora Bora, 50th anniv.

Turtle — A57

Design: 42fr, Hand protecting bird.

**1976, June 24 Litho. *Perf. 12½***

**289** A57 18fr multicolored 14.00 4.25

**290** A57 42fr multicolored 20.00 11.00

World Ecology Day.

A. G. Bell, Telephone, Radar and Satellite — A58

**1976, Sept. 15 Engr. *Perf. 13***

**291** A58 37fr multicolored 10.00 5.00

Centenary of first telephone call by Alexander Graham Bell, Mar. 10, 1876.

Dugout Canoes — A59

**1976, Dec. 16 Litho. *Perf. 13x12½***

**292** A59 25fr Marquesas 3.75 2.75

**293** A59 30fr Raiatea 4.75 4.75

**294** A59 75fr Tahiti 9.50 5.75

**295** A59 100fr Tuamotu 12.00 7.00

*Nos. 292-295 (4)* 30.00 20.25

Sailing Ship — A60

Designs: Various sailing vessels.

**1977, Dec. 22 Litho. *Perf. 13***

**296** A60 20fr multicolored 6.25 2.00

**297** A60 50fr multicolored 7.25 2.25

**298** A60 85fr multicolored 9.00 3.75

**299** A60 120fr multicolored 15.00 5.75

*Nos. 296-299 (4)* 37.50 13.75

Hibiscus — A61

Designs: 10fr, Vanda orchids. 16fr, Pua (fagraea berteriana). 22fr, Gardenia.

**1978-79 Photo. *Perf. 12½x13***

**300** A61 10fr multicolored 1.10 .50

**301** A61 13fr multicolored 2.50 1.00

**302** A61 16fr multicolored 2.75 1.75

**303** A61 22fr multicolored 1.75 1.00

*Nos. 300-303 (4)* 8.10 4.25

Issued: 13fr, 16fr, 8/23; 10fr, 22fr, 1/25/79.

Girl with Shells on Beach — A62

Design A24 with "1958 1978" added: 28fr, Man with headdress. 36fr, Girl playing guitar.

**1978, Nov. 3 Engr. *Perf. 13***

**304** A62 20fr multicolored 3.00 .75

**305** A62 28fr multicolored 3.75 1.50

**306** A62 36fr multicolored 5.75 2.25

*a.* Souvenir sheet of 3 27.50 27.50

*Nos. 304-306 (3)* 12.50 4.50

20th anniv. of stamps inscribed: Polynesie Francaise. No. 306a contains Nos. 304-306 in changed colors.

Ships — A63

**1978, Dec. 29 Litho. *Perf. 13x12½***

**307** A63 15fr Tahiti 1.50 .80

**308** A63 30fr Monowai 2.75 1.25

**309** A63 75fr Tahitien 4.50 3.25

**310** A63 100fr Mariposa 8.50 3.25

*Nos. 307-310 (4)* 17.25 8.55

Porites Coral A64

Design: 37fr, Montipora coral.

**1979, Feb. 15 *Perf. 13x12½***

**311** A64 32fr multicolored 2.50 1.25

**312** A64 37fr multicolored 3.75 2.00

Raiatea A65

Landscapes: 1fr, Moon over Bora Bora. 2fr, Mountain peaks, Ua Pou. 3fr, Sunset over Motu Tapu. 5fr, Motu. 6fr, Palm and hut, Tuamotu.

**1979, Mar. 8 Photo. *Perf. 13x13½***

**313** A65 1fr multicolored .25 .25

**314** A65 2fr multicolored .25 .25

**315** A65 3fr multicolored .30 .25

**316** A65 4fr multicolored .45 .25

**317** A65 5fr multicolored .80 .35

**318** A65 6fr multicolored 1.00 .60

*Nos. 313-318 (6)* 3.05 1.95

See Nos. 438-443 for redrawn designs.

Dance Costumes A66

**1979, July 14 Litho. *Perf. 12½***

**319** A66 45fr Fetia 1.75 1.00

**320** A66 51fr Teanuanua 2.75 1.25

**321** A66 74fr Temaeva 3.75 2.25

*Nos. 319-321 (3)* 8.25 4.50

Hill, Great Britain No. 53, Tahiti No. 28 A67

**1979, Aug. 1 Engr. *Perf. 13***

**322** A67 100fr multicolored 5.00 3.00

Sir Rowland Hill (1795-1879), originator of penny postage.

Hastula Strigilata — A68

Shells: 28fr, Scabricola variegata. 35fr, Fusinus undatus.

**1979, Aug. 22 Litho. *Perf. 12½***

**323** A68 20fr multicolored 1.50 .50

**324** A68 28fr multicolored 2.00 1.00

**325** A68 35fr multicolored 2.75 2.00

*Nos. 323-325 (3)* 6.25 3.50

Statue Holding Rotary Emblem — A69

**1979, Nov. 30 Litho. *Perf. 13***

**326** A69 47fr multicolored 2.75 2.00

Rotary International, 75th anniversary; Papeete Rotary Club, 20th anniversary.

For overprint see No. 330.

Myripristis Murdjan A70

Fish: 8fr, Napoleon. 12fr, Emperor.

**1980, Jan. 21 Litho. *Perf. 12½***

**327** A70 7fr multicolored 1.00 .50

**328** A70 8fr multicolored 1.00 .65

**329** A70 12fr multicolored 1.65 .95

*Nos. 327-329 (3)* 3.65 2.10

No. 326 Overprinted and Surcharged in Gold

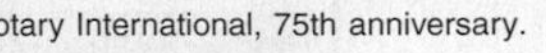

**1980, Feb. 23 Litho. *Perf. 13***

**330** A69 77fr on 47fr multi 5.75 3.25

Rotary International, 75th anniversary.

CNEXO Fish Hatchery A71

**1980, Mar. 17 Photo. *Perf. 13x13½***

**331** A71 15fr shown 1.75 .90

**332** A71 22fr Crayfish 1.75 .90

Papeete Post Office Building Opening A72

**1980, Apr. 30 Photo. *Perf. 13x12½***

**333** A72 50fr multicolored 2.50 1.50

Tiki and Festival Emblem — A73

**1980, June 30 Photo. *Perf. 13½***

**334** A73 34fr shown 1.25 .90
**335** A73 39fr Drum (pahu) 2.00 1.30
**336** A73 49fr Ax (to'i) 2.75 1.75
*a.* Souv. sheet of 3, #334-336 13.50 13.00
*Nos. 334-336 (3)* 6.00 3.95

South Pacific Arts Festival, Port Moresby, Papua New Guinea.

Titmouse Henparrot — A74

25fr, White sea-swallow, horiz. 45fr, Minor frigate bird, horiz.

***Perf. 13x12½, 12½x13***

**1980, Oct. 20 Photo.**

**337** A74 25fr multi 1.50 .70
**338** A74 35fr shown 1.75 .90
**339** A74 45fr multi 2.75 1.10
*Nos. 337-339 (3)* 6.00 2.70

Charles de Gaulle — A75

**1980, Nov. 9 Engr. *Perf. 12½x13***

**340** A75 100fr multicolored 5.00 3.25

Naso Vlamingi (Karaua) A76

16fr, Lutjanus vaigensis (toau). 24fr, Plectropomus leopardus (tonu).

**1981, Feb. 5 Litho. *Perf. 12½***

**341** A76 13fr shown 1.00 .50
**342** A76 16fr multi 1.10 .60
**343** A76 24fr multi 2.25 .75
*Nos. 341-343 (3)* 4.35 1.85

Indoor Fish Breeding Tanks, Cnexo Hatchery A77

**1981, May 14 Photo. *Perf. 13x13½***

**344** A77 23fr shown 1.10 .80
**345** A77 41fr Mussels 2.00 1.10

Folk Dancers A78

***Perf. 13x13½, 13½x13***

**1981, July 10 Litho.**

**346** A78 26fr shown 1.25 .65
**347** A78 28fr Dancer 1.25 1.10
**348** A78 44fr Dancers, vert. 2.10 1.50
*Nos. 346-348 (3)* 4.60 3.25

Sterna Bergii — A79

53fr, Ptilinopus purpuratus, vert. 65fr, Estrilda astrild, vert.

**1981, Sept. 24 Litho. *Perf. 13***

**349** A79 47fr shown 1.75 1.00
**350** A79 53fr multi 1.75 1.20
**351** A79 65fr multi 2.25 1.50
*Nos. 349-351 (3)* 5.75 3.70

See Nos. 370-372.

Huahine Island A80

**1981, Oct. 22 Litho. *Perf. 12½***

**352** A80 34fr shown 1.40 .75
**353** A80 134fr Maupiti 3.25 2.00
**354** A80 136fr Bora-Bora 3.25 2.00
*Nos. 352-354 (3)* 7.90 4.75

A81

**1982, Feb. 4 Photo. *Perf. 13x13½***

**355** A81 30fr Parrotfish 1.00 .75
**356** A81 31fr Regal angel 1.40 .75
**357** A81 45fr Spotted bass 1.50 1.25
*Nos. 355-357 (3)* 3.90 2.75

Pearl Industry A82

**1982, Apr. 22 Photo. *Perf. 13x13½***

**358** A82 7fr Pearl beds .85 .45
**359** A82 8fr Extracting pearls .85 .45
**360** A82 10fr Pearls 1.20 1.10
*Nos. 358-360 (3)* 2.90 2.00

Tahiti "No. 1A," Emblem — A83

**1982, May 12 Engr. *Perf. 13***

**361** A83 150fr multicolored 4.75 3.50
*a.* Souvenir sheet 16.00 16.00

PHILEXFRANCE Stamp Exhibition, Paris, June 11-21. No. 361a contains No. 361 in changed colors.

King Holding Carved Scepter — A84

Designs: Coronation ceremony.

**1982, July 12 Photo. *Perf. 13½x13***

**362** A84 12fr shown .50 .25
**363** A84 13fr King, priest .50 .25
**364** A84 17fr Procession 1.00 .50
*Nos. 362-364 (3)* 2.00 1.00

Championship Emblem — A85

**1982, Aug. 13 *Perf. 13***

**365** A85 90fr multicolored 2.75 2.00

4th Hobie-Cat 16 World Catamaran Sailing Championship, Tahiti, Aug. 15-21.

First Colloquium on New Energy Sources — A86

**1982, Sept. 29 Litho.**

**366** A86 46fr multicolored 1.75 1.00

Motu, Tuamotu Islet — A87

**1982, Oct. 12 Litho. *Perf. 13***

**367** A87 20fr shown .70 .35
**368** A87 33fr Tupai Atoll .90 .45
**369** A87 35fr Gambier Islds. 1.25 .55
*Nos. 367-369 (3)* 2.85 1.35

**Bird Type of 1981**

37fr, Sacred egret. 39fr, Pluvialis dominica, vert. 42fr, Lonchura castaneothorax.

**1982, Nov. 17 Litho. *Perf. 13***

**370** A79 37fr multi 1.40 .55
**371** A79 39fr multi 1.40 .65
**372** A79 42fr multi 1.75 .90
*Nos. 370-372 (3)* 4.55 2.10

Fish — A88

8fr, Acanthurus lineatus. 10fr, Caranx melampygus. 12fr, Carcharhinus melanopterus.

**1983, Feb. 9 Litho. *Perf. 13x13½***

**373** A88 8fr multi .70 .35
**374** A88 10fr multi .90 .35
**375** A88 12fr multi 1.40 .50
*Nos. 373-375 (3)* 3.00 1.20

The Way of the Cross, Sculpture by Damien Haturau — A89

**1983, Mar. 9 Litho. *Perf. 13***

**376** A89 7fr shown .25 .25
**377** A89 21fr Virgin and Child .70 .60
**378** A89 23fr Christ .90 .60
*Nos. 376-378 (3)* 1.85 1.45

Traditional Hats — A90

**1983, May 24 Litho. *Perf. 13x12½***

**379** A90 11fr Acacia .45 .30
**380** A90 13fr Niau .60 .30
**381** A90 25fr Ofe .80 .50
**382** A90 35fr Ofe, diff. 1.10 .60
*Nos. 379-382 (4)* 2.95 1.70

See Nos. 393-396.

Chieftain in Traditional Costume, Sainte-Christine Isld. — A91

Traditional Costumes, Marquesas Islds.

**1983, July 12 Photo. *Perf. 13***

**383** A91 15fr shown .70 .30
**384** A91 17fr Man .90 .40
**385** A91 28fr Woman 1.10 .50
*Nos. 383-385 (3)* 2.70 1.20

See Nos. 397-399, 419-421.

Polynesian Crowns — A92

Various flower garlands.

**1983, Oct. 19 Litho. *Perf. 13***

**386** A92 41fr multicolored 1.25 .90
**387** A92 44fr multicolored 1.40 .95
**388** A92 45fr multicolored 1.50 1.00
*Nos. 386-388 (3)* 4.15 2.85

See Nos. 400-402.

Martin Luther (1483-1546) A93

**1983, Nov. 10 Engr. *Perf. 13***

**389** A93 90fr black, brn & lil gray 2.25 1.10

Tiki Carvings — A94

Various carvings.

**1984, Feb. 8 Litho. *Perf. 12½x13***

**390** A94 14fr multicolored .50 .25
**391** A94 16fr multicolored .60 .45
**392** A94 19fr multicolored .75 .45
*Nos. 390-392 (3)* 1.85 1.15

**Hat Type of 1983**

**1984, June 20 Litho. *Perf. 13x12½***

**393** A90 20fr Aeho ope .50 .35
**394** A90 24fr Paeore .60 .35
**395** A90 26fr Ofe fei .75 .50
**396** A90 33fr Hua .80 .50
*Nos. 393-396 (4)* 2.65 1.70

**Costume Type of 1983**

34fr, Tahitian playing nose flute. 35fr, Priest, Oei-eitia. 39fr, Tahitian adult and child.

**1984, July 11 Litho. *Perf. 13***

**397** A91 34fr multi .75 .50
**398** A91 35fr multi .90 .50
**399** A91 39fr multi .90 .50
*Nos. 397-399 (3)* 2.55 1.50

**Garland Type of 1983**

**1984, Oct. 24 Litho. *Perf. 13x12½***

**400** A92 46fr Moto'i Lei .90 .50
**401** A92 47fr Pitate Lei 1.00 .60
**402** A92 53fr Bougainvillea Lei 1.25 .80
*Nos. 400-402 (3)* 3.15 1.90

4th Pacific Arts Festival, Noumea, New Caledonia, Dec. 8-22 — A95

**1984, Nov. 20 Litho. *Perf. 13***

**403** A95 150fr Statue, head-dress 3.50 2.25

See No. C213.

Paysage D'Anaa, by Jean Masson — A96

Paintings: 50fr, Sortie Du Culte, by Jacques Boulaire. 75fr, La Fete, by Robert Tatin. 85fr, Tahitiennes Sur La Plage, by Pierre Heyman.

***Perf. 12½x13, 13x12½***

**1984, Dec. 12 Litho.**

**404** A96 50fr multi, vert. 1.25 .70
**405** A96 65fr multicolored 1.40 .90
**406** A96 75fr multicolored 1.90 1.00
**407** A96 85fr multicolored 2.25 1.75
*Nos. 404-407 (4)* 6.80 4.35

Tiki Carvings — A97

**1985, Jan. 23 Litho. *Perf. 13½***

**408** A97 30fr multicolored .60 .35
**409** A97 36fr multicolored .80 .45
**410** A97 40fr multicolored .90 .75
*Nos. 408-410 (3)* 2.30 1.55

Polynesian Faces — A98

**1985, Feb. 20 Photo. *Perf. 12½x13***

**411** A98 22fr multicolored .40 .30
**412** A98 39fr multicolored .75 .40
**413** A98 44fr multicolored .95 .70
*Nos. 411-413 (3)* 2.10 1.40

Early Tahiti — A99

***Perf. 13x12½, 12½x13***

**1985, Apr. 24 Litho.**

**414** A99 42fr Entrance to Papeete .90 .55
**415** A99 45fr Girls, vert. 1.25 .75
**416** A99 48fr Papeete market 1.40 .85
*Nos. 414-416 (3)* 3.55 2.15

5th Intl. Congress on Coral Reefs, Tahiti A100

**1985, May 28 Litho. *Perf. 13½***

**417** A100 140fr Local reef formation 3.00 2.00

Printed se-tenant with label picturing congress emblem.

National Flag A101

**1985, June 28**

**418** A101 9fr Flag, natl. arms .65 .30

**Costume Type of 1983**

18th-19th Cent. Prints, Beslu Collection.

**1985, July 17 *Perf. 13***

**419** A91 38fr Tahitian dancer .95 .65
**420** A91 55fr Man and woman from Otahiti, 1806 1.25 .90
**421** A91 70fr Traditional chief 1.75 1.25
*Nos. 419-421 (3)* 3.95 2.80

Local Foods — A103

**1985-86 Litho. *Perf. 13***

**422** A103 25fr Roasted pig .85 .60
**423** A103 35fr Pit fire 1.10 .65
**423A** A103 80fr Fish in coconut milk 1.90 1.50
**423B** A103 110fr Fafaru 2.40 1.90
*Nos. 422-423B (4)* 6.25 4.65

Issued: 25fr, 35fr, 11/14; 80fr, 110fr, 5/20/86.

See Nos. 458-459, 474-475.

Catholic Churches — A104

90fr, St. Anne's, Otepipi. 100fr, St. Michael's Cathedral, Rikitea. 120fr, Cathedral, exterior.

**1985, Dec. 11 Litho. *Perf. 13***

**424** A104 90fr multi 1.75 1.00
**425** A104 100fr multi 1.90 1.00
**426** A104 120fr multi 2.25 1.50
*Nos. 424-426 (3)* 5.90 3.50

Nos. 424-426 printed se-tenant with labels picturing local religious art.

Crabs A105

**1986, Jan. 22 *Perf. 13½***

**427** A105 18fr Fiddler .90 .50
**428** A105 29fr Hermit 1.40 .65
**429** A105 31fr Coconut 2.40 .65
*Nos. 427-429 (3)* 4.70 1.80

Faces of Polynesia A106

**1986, Feb. 19 *Perf. 12½x13, 13x12½***

**430** A106 43fr Boy, fish 1.00 .50
**431** A106 49fr Boy, coral 1.25 .50
**432** A106 51fr Boy, turtle, vert. 1.40 .60
*Nos. 430-432 (3)* 3.65 1.60

Old Tahiti — A107

**1986, Mar. 18 *Perf. 13x12½***

**433** A107 52fr Papeete 1.00 .55
**434** A107 56fr Harpoon fishing 1.10 .55
**435** A107 57fr Royal Palace, Papeete 1.25 .70
*Nos. 433-435 (3)* 3.35 1.80

Tiki Rock Carvings — A108

**1986, Apr. 16**

**436** A108 58fr Atuona, Hiva Oa 1.40 .70
**437** A108 59fr Ua Huka Hill, Hane Valley 1.40 .70

**Landscapes Type Redrawn**

**1986-88 Litho. *Perf. 13½***

**438** A65 1fr multi, type 2 ('88) 2.50 .35
*a.* Type 1 ('86) 4.50 1.25
*b.* Type 3 ('91) 18.50 4.50
**439** A65 2fr multicolored .40 .25
**440** A65 3fr multicolored .45 .25
**441** A65 4fr multicolored ('87) 1.75 .40
**442** A65 5fr multicolored .75 .30
**443** A65 6fr multicolored .65 .30
*Nos. 438-443 (6)* 6.50 1.85

Nos. 438-443 printed in sharper detail, and box containing island name is taller. Nos. 439-443 margin is inscribed "CARTOR" instead of "DELRIEU."

No. 438 has three types of inscription below design: type 1, photographer's name at left, no inscription at right; type 2, photographer's name at left 9.5mm long, printer's name (Cartor) at right; type 3, photographer's name at left 12.5mm long, Cartor at right.

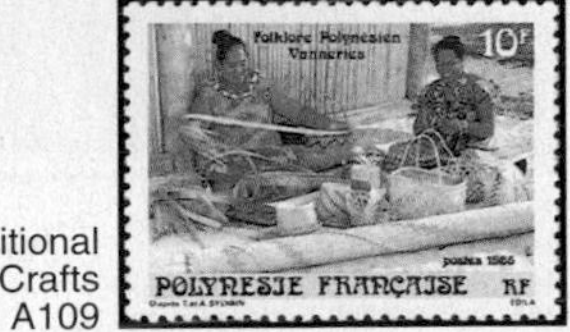

Traditional Crafts A109

***Perf. 13x12½, 12½x13***

**1986, July 17 Litho.**

**444** A109 8fr Quilting, vert. .25 .25
**445** A109 10fr Baskets, hats .25 .25
**446** A109 12fr Grass skirts .80 .30
*Nos. 444-446 (3)* 1.30 .80

Building a Pirogue (Canoe) A110

**1986, Oct. 21 Litho. *Perf. 13½***

**447** A110 46fr Boat-builders 1.00 .65
**448** A110 50fr Close-up 1.10 .85

Medicinal Plants — A111

**1986, Nov. 19** ***Perf. 13***

**449** A111 40fr Phymatosorus .90 .50
**450** A111 41fr Barringtonia asiatica 1.00 .50
**451** A111 60fr Ocimum bacilicum 1.60 .90
*Nos. 449-451 (3)* 3.50 1.90

See Nos. 495-497.

Polynesians A112

**1987, Jan. 21 Litho.** ***Perf. 13½***

**452** A112 28fr Old man .60 .35
**453** A112 30fr Mother and child .75 .50
**454** A112 37fr Old woman 1.00 .60
*Nos. 452-454 (3)* 2.35 1.45

Crustaceans — A113

34fr, Carpilius maculatus. 35fr, Parribacus antarticus. 39fr, Justitia longimana.

**1987, Feb. 18** ***Perf. 12½x13***

**455** A113 34fr multicolored 2.00 .65
**456** A113 35fr multicolored 2.00 .65
**457** A113 39fr multicolored 2.50 .65
*Nos. 455-457 (3)* 6.50 1.95

**Local Foods Type of 1985**

**1987, Mar. 19 Litho.** ***Perf. 13***

**458** A103 33fr Papaya poe 1.10 .70
**459** A103 65fr Chicken fafa 2.00 1.00

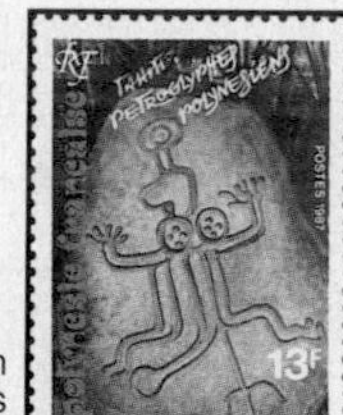


Polynesian Petroglyphs A114

**1987, May 13** ***Perf. 12½***

**460** A114 13fr Tipaerui, Tahiti .35 .25
**461** A114 21fr Turtle, Raiatea Is. .60 .35

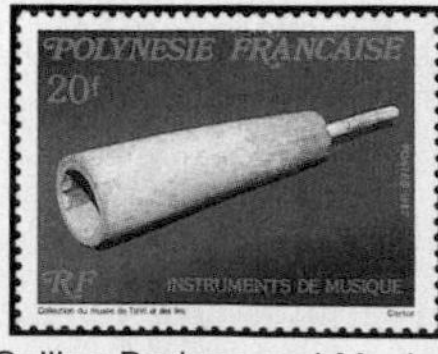


Calling Devices and Musical Instruments, Museum of Tahiti and the Isles — A115

**1987, July 1** ***Perf. 13½***

**462** A115 20fr Wood horn .65 .30
**463** A115 26fr Triton's conch .80 .65
**464** A115 33fr Nose flutes 1.00 .70
*Nos. 462-464 (3)* 2.45 1.65

Medicinal Plants — A116

46fr, Thespesia populnea. 53fr, Ophioglossum reticulatum. 54fr, Dicrocephala latifolia.

**1987, Sept. 16** ***Perf. 12½x13***

**465** A116 46fr olive green 1.00 .55
**466** A116 53fr reddish lilac 1.40 .55
**467** A116 54fr dp bluish grn 1.50 .55
*Nos. 465-467 (3)* 3.90 1.65

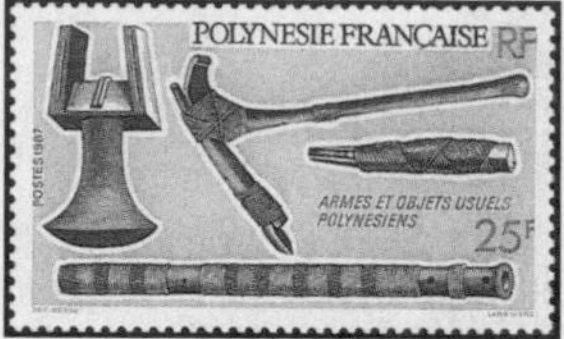


Ancient Weapons and Tools — A117

Designs: 25fr, Adze, war club, chisel, flute. 27fr, War clubs, tatooing comb, mallet. 32fr, Headdress, necklaces, nose flute.

**1987, Oct. 14 Engr.** ***Perf. 13***

**468** A117 25fr lt olive grn & blk .60 .40
**469** A117 27fr Prus grn & int blue .75 .45
**470** A117 32fr brt olive bis & brn blk .80 .55
*Nos. 468-470 (3)* 2.15 1.40

Catholic Missionaries — A118

Monsignors: 95fr, Rene Ildefonse Dordillon (1808-1888), bishop of the Marquesas Isls. 105fr, Tepano Jaussen (1815-1891), first bishop of Polynesia. 115fr, Paul Laurent Maze (1885-1976), archbishop of Papeete.

**1987, Dec. 9** **Litho.**

**471** A118 95fr multicolored 1.90 1.40
**472** A118 105fr multicolored 2.10 1.50
**473** A118 115fr multicolored 2.40 1.60
*Nos. 471-473 (3)* 6.40 4.50

**Local Foods Type of 1985**

**1988, Jan. 12 Litho.** ***Perf. 13***

**474** A103 40fr Crayfish (varo) 1.90 .55
**475** A103 75fr Bananas in coconut milk 2.75 1.10

Nos. 474-475 are vert.

Authors — A119

62fr, James Norman Hall (1887-1951). 85fr, Charles Bernard Nordhoff (1887-1947).

**1988, Feb. 10**

**476** A119 62fr multicolored 1.40 .75
**477** A119 85fr multicolored 1.90 .85

Traditional Housing — A120

11fr, Taranpoo Opoa Is., Raiatea. 15fr, Tahaa Village. 17fr, Community meeting house, Tahiti.

**1988, Mar. 16 Litho.** ***Perf. 13x12½***

**478** A120 11fr multicolored .50 .30
**479** A120 15fr multicolored .60 .30
**480** A120 17fr multicolored .60 .30
*Nos. 478-480 (3)* 1.70 .90

Point Venus Lighthouse, 120th Anniv. — A121

**1988, Apr. 21 Litho.** ***Perf. 13***

**481** A121 400fr multicolored 8.50 5.50

Tapa-cloth Paintings by Paul Engdahl A122

**1988, May 20**

**482** A122 52fr multicolored 1.25 .75
**483** A122 54fr multicolored 1.40 .85
**484** A122 64fr multicolored 1.50 1.10
*Nos. 482-484 (3)* 4.15 2.70

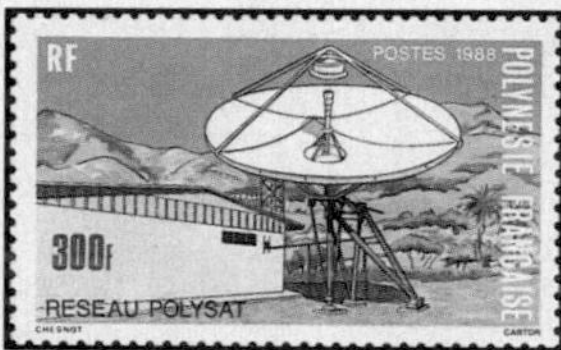


POLYSAT (Domestic Communications Network) — A123

**1988, June 15 Litho.** ***Perf. 12½x12***

**485** A123 300fr multicolored 6.00 4.75

Tahitian Dolls — A124

Designs: 42fr, Wearing grass skirt and headdress. 45fr, Wearing print dress and straw hat, holding guitar. 48fr, Wearing print dress and straw hat, holding straw bag.

**1988, June 27** ***Perf. 13x12½***

**486** A124 42fr multicolored 1.00 .60
**487** A124 45fr multicolored 1.25 .60
**488** A124 48fr multicolored 1.50 .75
*Nos. 486-488 (3)* 3.75 1.95

*Visiting a Marae at Nuku Hiva, Engraving by J. & E. Verreaux* A125

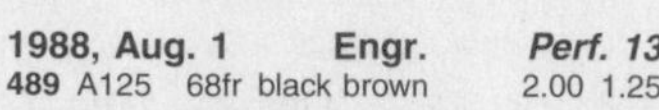

**1988, Aug. 1 Engr.** ***Perf. 13***

**489** A125 68fr black brown 2.00 1.25

**Size: 143x101mm**

**490** A125 145fr violet brn & grn 5.25 4.00

SYDPEX '88, July 30-Aug. 7, Australia. No. 490 pictures a Russian navy officer (probably Krusenstern) visiting the Marquesas Islanders; denomination LR.

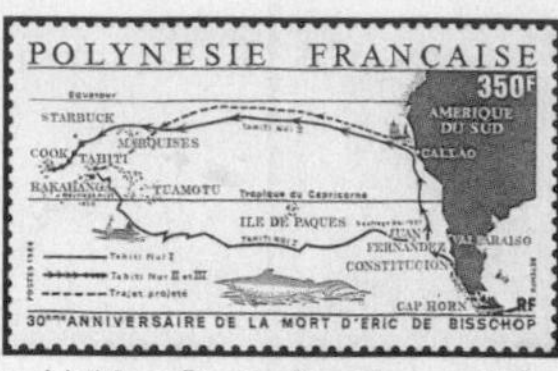


Map Linking South America and South Pacific Islands — A126

**1988, Aug. 30** **Engr.**

**491** A126 350fr multicolored 7.50 4.50

Eric de Bisschop (1890-1958), explorer who tried to prove that there was an exchange of peoples between the South Pacific islands and So. America, rather than that the island populations originated from So. America.

Seashells A127

**1988, Sept. 21 Litho.** ***Perf. 13½***

**492** A127 24fr Kermia barnardi .60 .35
**493** A127 35fr Vexillum suavis 1.00 .50
**494** A127 44fr Berthelinia 1.40 .75
*Nos. 492-494 (3)* 3.00 1.60

**Medicinal Plants Type of 1986**

23fr, Davallia solida. 36fr, Rorippa sarmentosa. 49fr, Lindernia crustacea.

**1988, Oct. 18 Engr.** ***Perf. 13***

**495** A111 23fr carmine lake .75 .30
**496** A111 36fr purple brown 1.10 .45
**497** A111 49fr deep blue 1.25 .70
*Nos. 495-497 (3)* 3.10 1.45

Protestant Missionaries — A128

80fr, Henry Nott (1774-1844). 90fr, Papeiha (1800-40). 100fr, Samuel Raapoto (1921-76).

**1988, Dec. 7** **Litho.**

**498** A128 80fr multi 1.50 .90
**499** A128 90fr multi 2.00 1.25
**500** A128 100fr multi 2.25 1.40
*Nos. 498-500 (3)* 5.75 3.55

Tahiti Post Office A129

**1989, Jan. 12** **Engr.**

**501** A129 30fr P.O., 1875 .75 .40
**502** A129 40fr P.O., 1915 1.00 .55

Center for Arts and Crafts A130

29fr, Marquesas Is. lidded bowl. 31fr, Mother-of-pearl pendant.

**1989, Feb. 15 Litho. *Perf. 12½***
503 A130 29fr multi .80 .40
504 A130 31fr multi .90 .45

**Copra Industry**

Extracting Coconut Meat From Shell — A131a

Drying Coconut Meat in Sun — A131

**1989, Mar. 16 Litho. *Perf. 13***
505 A131a 55fr multicolored *55.00 40.00*
506 A131 70fr multicolored *2.50 2.00*

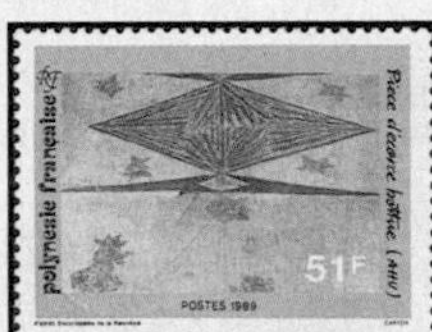


Tapa Art — A132

43fr, Wood statue (pole), Marquesas Islands, vert. 51fr, Hand-painted bark tapestry, Society Is. 56fr, Concentric circles, Tubuai, Austral Islands.

**1989, Apr. 18 Litho. *Perf. 13½***
507 A132 43fr multicolored .90 .60
508 A132 51fr shown 1.25 .75
509 A132 56fr multicolored 1.50 .90
*Nos. 507-509 (3)* 3.65 2.25

Polynesian Environment A133

**1989, May 17 Litho. *Perf. 13x12½***
510 A133 120fr shown 2.25 1.50
511 A133 140fr Diving for sea-shells 2.75 1.75

Polynesian Folklore A134

***Perf. 13x12½, 12½x13***

**1989, June 28 Litho.**
512 A134 47fr Stone-lifting contest, vert. 1.10 .55
513 A134 61fr Dancer, vert. 1.40 .70
514 A134 67fr Folk singers 1.75 .75
*Nos. 512-514 (3)* 4.25 2.00

*Bounty* Castaways, from an Etching by Robert Dodd — A135

**1989, July 7 Engr. *Perf. 13***
515 A135 100fr dp blue & bl grn 2.40 1.50

**Souvenir Sheet**

***Imperf***

516 A135 200fr dk ol grn & dk brn 12.00 12.00

PHILEXFRANCE '89 and 200th annivs. of the mutiny on the *Bounty* and the French revolution.

No. 515 printed se-tenant with label picturing exhibition emblem.

Reverend-Father Patrick O'Reilly (1900-1988) A136

**1989, Aug. 7 Engr. *Perf. 13x13½***
517 A136 52fr yel brn & myrtle grn 1.40 .75

**Miniature Sheet**

Messages A137

a, Get well soon. b, Good luck. c, Happy birthday. d, Keep in touch. e, Congratulations.

**1989, Sept. 27 Litho. *Perf. 12½***
518 A137 42fr Sheet of 5, #a.-e. 12.00 12.00

Sea Shells A138

**1989, Oct. 12 Litho. *Perf. 13½***
523 A138 60fr Triphoridae 1.60 .80
524 A138 69fr Muricidae favartia 1.75 .90
525 A138 73fr Muricidae morula 2.00 1.00
*Nos. 523-525 (3)* 5.35 2.70

*Te Faaturama*, c. 1892, by Gauguin A139

**1989, Nov. 19 Litho. *Perf. 12½x13***
526 A139 1000fr multicolored 22.00 12.50

Legends — A140

Designs: 66fr, Maui, birth of the islands, vert. 82fr, Mt. Rotui, the pierced mountain. 88fr, Princess Hina and the eel King of Lake Vaihiria.

**1989, Dec. 6 Litho. *Perf. 13***
527 A140 66fr olive brn & blk 1.40 .90
528 A140 82fr buff & blk 1.90 1.10
529 A140 88fr cream & blk 2.00 1.15
*Nos. 527-529 (3)* 5.30 3.15

Vanilla Orchid — A141

**1990, Jan. 11 Litho.**
530 A141 34fr Flower 1.35 .60
531 A141 35fr Bean pods 1.60 .60

Marine Life A142

**1990, Feb. 9 Litho. *Perf. 13½***
532 A142 40fr Kuhlia marginata 1.30 .55
533 A142 50fr Macrobrachium 1.50 .70

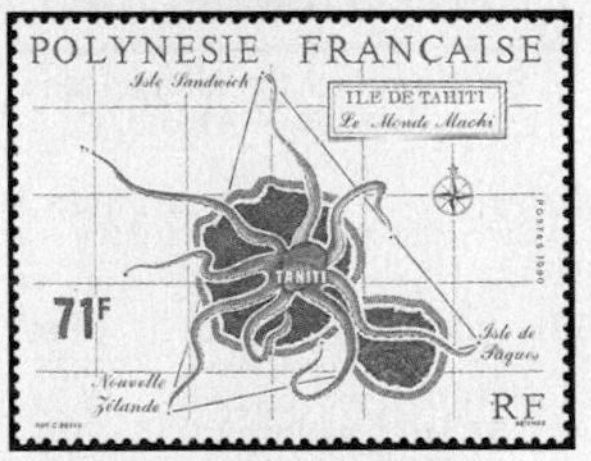


Tahiti, Center of Polynesian Triangle — A143

Maohi settlers and maps of island settlements: 58fr, Hawaiian Islands. 59fr, Easter Island. 63fr, New Zealand.

**1990, Mar. 14 Engr. *Perf. 13***
534 A143 58fr black 1.75 .85
535 A143 59fr bluish gray *45.00* 25.00
536 A143 63fr olive green 2.25 .95
537 A143 71fr Prussian blue 2.50 1.10
*Nos. 534-537 (4)* *51.50* 27.90

See Nos. 544-545.

Papeete Village, Cent. — A144

**1990, May 16 Litho.**
538 A144 150fr New City Hall 3.25 1.75
539 A144 250fr Old Town Hall 4.75 3.00

A145

Designs: Endangered birds.

**1990, June 5 *Perf. 13½***
540 A145 13fr Porzana tabuensis .75 .25
541 A145 20fr Vini ultramarina 1.75 .35

A146

**1990, July 10 *Perf. 13***
542 A146 39fr multicolored 1.10 .65

Lions Club in Papeete, 30th anniv.

Gen. Charles de Gaulle, Birth Cent. — A147

**1990, Sept. 2 Litho.**
543 A147 200fr multi 4.50 3.25

**No. 536 with Different Colors and Inscriptions**

**1990, Aug. 24 Engr. *Perf. 13***
544 A143 125fr Man, map 3.00 2.00

**Souvenir Sheet**

***Imperf***

545 A143 230fr like No. 544 6.00 6.00

New Zealand 1990.

Intl. Tourism Day — A148

**1990, Sept. 27 Litho. *Perf. 12½***
546 A148 8f red & yellow pareo 1.10 .35
547 A148 10fr yellow pareo 1.10 .35
548 A148 12fr blue pareo 1.10 .75
*Nos. 546-548 (3)* 3.30 1.45

Polynesian Legends — A149

170fr, Legend of the Uru. 290fr, Pipiri-ma, vert. 375fr, Hiro, God of Thieves, vert.

**1990, Nov. 7 Litho. *Perf. 13***

**549** A149 170fr multicolored 4.00 2.50
**550** A149 290fr multicolored 7.50 4.00
**551** A149 375fr multicolored 11.00 5.00
*Nos. 549-551 (3)* 22.50 11.50

Tiare Flower — A150

Designs: 28fr, Flower crown, lei. 30fr, Flowers in bloom. 37fr, Lei.

**1990, Dec. 5 *Perf. 12½***

**552** A150 28fr multicolored .70 .45
**553** A150 30fr multicolored .95 .45
**554** A150 37fr multicolored 1.20 .55
*Nos. 552-554 (3)* 2.85 1.45

Pineapple A151

**1991, Jan. 9 *Die Cut***

**Self-adhesive**

**555** A151 42fr shown 1.25 .90
**556** A151 44fr Pineapple field 1.75 1.10

Nos. 555-556 are on paper backing perf. 12½.

Marine Life A152

**1991, Feb. 7 *Perf. 12½***

**557** A152 7fr Nudibranch .45 .25
**558** A152 9fr Galaxaura tenera .70 .25
**559** A152 11fr Adusta cumingii .70 .25
*Nos. 557-559 (3)* 1.85 .75

Maohi Islands A153

18th Century scenes of: 68fr, Woman of Easter Island, vert. 84fr, Twin-hulled canoe, Hawaii. 94fr, Maori village, New Zealand.

**1991, Mar. 13 Engr. *Perf. 13***

**560** A153 68fr olive 47.50 32.50
**561** A153 84fr black 2.50 1.75
**562** A153 94fr brown 3.00 1.75
*Nos. 560-562 (3)* 53.00 36.00

Basketball, Cent. — A154

**1991, May 15 Litho. *Perf. 13***

**563** A154 80fr multicolored 1.75 1.25

Birds — A155

**1991, June 5 *Perf. 13½***

**564** A155 17fr Halcyon gambieri .60 .25
**565** A155 21fr Vini kuhlii .90 .35

Still Life with Oranges in Tahiti by Paul Gauguin — A156

**1991, June 9 Litho. *Perf. 13***

**566** A156 700fr multicolored 17.50 9.50

Sculptures of the Marquesas Islands — A157

56fr, White Tiki with Club, vert. 102fr, Warriors Carrying Tired Man, vert. 110fr, Native Canoe.

**1991, July 17 Litho. *Perf. 13***

**567** A157 56fr multicolored 1.25 .85
**568** A157 102fr multicolored 2.25 1.50
**569** A157 110fr multicolored 2.50 1.75
*Nos. 567-569 (3)* 6.00 4.10

Wolfgang Amadeus Mozart, Death Bicent. — A158

**1991, Aug. 28 Engr. *Perf. 13x12½***

**570** A158 100fr multicolored 3.00 1.75

Stone Fishing — A159

25fr, Fishing boats, vert. 57fr, Man hurling stone, vert. 62fr, Trapped fish.

**1991, Oct. 9 Litho. *Perf. 13***

**571** A159 25fr multi .60 .40
**572** A159 57fr multi 1.25 .90
**573** A159 62fr multi 1.50 1.25
*Nos. 571-573 (3)* 3.35 2.55

Phila Nippon '91 A160

Designs: 50fr, Drawings of marine life by Jules-Louis Lejeune, vert. 70fr, Sailing ship, La Coquille. 250fr, Contains designs from Nos. 574-575.

***Perf. 12½x13, 13x12½***

**1991, Nov. 16 Engr.**

**574** A160 50fr multicolored 1.30 .55
**575** A160 70fr multicolored 1.75 1.25

**Size: 100x75mm**

***Imperf***

**576** A160 250fr multicolored 6.00 6.00
*Nos. 574-576 (3)* 9.05 7.80

Central Bank for Economic Co-operation, 50th Anniv. — A161

**1991, Dec. 2 Litho. *Perf. 13x12½***

**577** A161 307fr multicolored 7.00 4.50

Christmas A162

***Perf. 12½x13, 13x12½***

**1991, Dec. 11 Litho.**

**578** A162 55fr Scuba divers 1.25 .75
**579** A162 83fr Underwater scene 1.75 1.35
**580** A162 86fr Nativity, vert. 1.75 1.35
*Nos. 578-580 (3)* 4.75 3.45

Tourism — A163

**1992, Feb. 12 *Perf. 13***

**581** A163 1fr shown .25 .25
**582** A163 2fr Horses, beach .35 .25
**583** A163 3fr Girl holding fish .50 .30
**584** A163 4fr Waterfalls, vert. .60 .35
**585** A163 5fr Sailing .75 .40
**586** A163 6fr Waterfalls, helicopter, vert. 1.00 .45
*Nos. 581-586 (6)* 3.45 2.00

Views from Space — A164

**1992, Mar. 18 Litho. *Perf. 13x12½***

**587** A164 46fr Tahiti 1.75 .90
**588** A164 72fr Mataiva 2.00 1.25
**589** A164 76fr Bora Bora 2.25 1.40

**Size: 130x100mm**

***Imperf***

**590** A164 230fr Satellite imaging system 6.00 5.75
*Nos. 587-590 (4)* 12.00 9.30

International Space Year.

World Health Day A165

**1992, Apr. 7 *Perf. 13½***

**591** A165 136fr multicolored 3.00 2.25

Discovery of America, 500th Anniv. — A166

**1992, May 22 *Perf. 13***

**592** A166 130fr multicolored 3.00 2.25

**Size: 140x100mm**

***Imperf***

**593** A166 250fr multicolored 6.00 6.00

World Columbian Stamp Expo '92, Chicago.

Traditional Dances — A167

Dance from: 95fr, Tahiti. 105fr, Hawaii. 115fr, Tonga.

**1992, June 17 Engr. *Perf. 13***

**594** A167 95fr brown black 1.90 1.60
**595** A167 105fr olive brown 2.10 1.75
**596** A167 115fr red brn & olive grn 2.50 1.75
*Nos. 594-596 (3)* 6.50 5.10

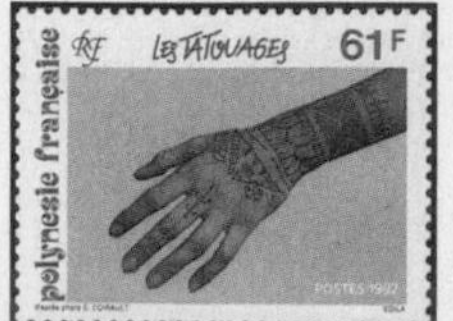


Tattoos A168

**1992, July 8 Litho. *Perf. 12½***

| | | | | |
|---|---|---|---|---|
| **597** | A168 | 61fr Hand | 1.90 | 1.25 |
| **598** | A168 | 64fr Man, vert. | 2.00 | 1.25 |

Children's Games A169

**1992, Aug. 5 *Perf. 13½***

| | | | | |
|---|---|---|---|---|
| **599** | A169 | 22fr Outrigger canoe models | .50 | .35 |
| **600** | A169 | 31fr String game | .75 | .45 |
| **601** | A169 | 45fr Stilt game, vert. | 1.25 | .70 |
| | | *Nos. 599-601 (3)* | 2.50 | 1.50 |

Herman Melville, 150th Anniv. of Arrival in French Polynesia — A170

**1992, Sept. 16 *Perf. 12½***

| | | | | |
|---|---|---|---|---|
| **602** | A170 | 78fr multicolored | 4.50 | 1.25 |

6th Festival of Pacific Arts, Rarotonga — A171

40fr, Men on raft. 65fr, Pirogues, Tahiti.

**1992, Oct. 16 Engr. *Perf. 13***

| | | | | |
|---|---|---|---|---|
| **603** | A171 | 40fr lake | 1.50 | .60 |
| **604** | A171 | 65fr blue | 2.00 | 1.00 |

First French Polynesian Postage Stamps, Cent. — A172

**1992, Nov. 18 Photo. *Perf. 13***

| | | | | |
|---|---|---|---|---|
| **605** | A172 | 200fr multicolored | 4.75 | 3.25 |

Paintings A173

55fr, Two Women Talking, by Erhard Lux. 60fr, Bouquet of Flowers, by Uschi. 75fr, Spearfisherman, by Pierre Kienlen. 85fr, Mother Nursing Child, by Octave Morillot.

**1992, Dec. 9 *Perf. 12½x13***

| | | | | |
|---|---|---|---|---|
| **606** | A173 | 55fr multicolored | 1.50 | .75 |
| **607** | A173 | 60fr multicolored | 1.75 | 1.40 |
| **608** | A173 | 75fr multicolored | 1.90 | 1.50 |
| **609** | A173 | 85fr multicolored | 2.50 | 1.60 |
| | | *Nos. 606-609 (4)* | 7.65 | 5.25 |

Net Thrower — A174

**1993, Feb. 10 Litho. *Die Cut***

**Self-Adhesive**

**Size: 26x36mm**

| | | | | |
|---|---|---|---|---|
| **610** | A174 | 46fr blue & multi | 1.50 | 1.00 |

**Size: 17x23mm**

| | | | | |
|---|---|---|---|---|
| **611** | A174 | 46fr green & multi | 1.50 | 1.00 |
| *a.* | | Booklet pane of 10 | 15.00 | |

Bonito Fishing — A175

**1993, Mar. 10 *Perf. 13½***

| | | | | |
|---|---|---|---|---|
| **612** | A175 | 68fr Line & hook | 1.60 | 1.25 |
| **613** | A175 | 84fr Boat, horiz. | 1.90 | 1.50 |
| **614** | A175 | 86fr Drying catch | 2.10 | 1.50 |
| | | *Nos. 612-614 (3)* | 5.60 | 4.25 |

Allied Airfield on Bora Bora, 50th Anniv. — A176

**1993, Apr. 5 *Perf. 13***

| | | | | |
|---|---|---|---|---|
| **615** | A176 | 120fr multicolored | 3.00 | 2.25 |

Jacques Boullaire, Artist, Birth Cent. — A177

Various scenes depicting life on: 32fr, Moorea. 36fr, Tuamotu. 39fr, Rurutu. 51fr, Nuku Hiva.

**1993, May 6 Engr.**

| | | | | |
|---|---|---|---|---|
| **616** | A177 | 32fr brown black | .90 | .50 |
| **617** | A177 | 36fr brick red | .90 | .65 |
| **618** | A177 | 39fr violet | 1.25 | .90 |
| **619** | A177 | 51fr light brown | 1.50 | 1.00 |
| | | *Nos. 616-619 (4)* | 4.55 | 3.05 |

Sports Festival — A178

**1993, May 15 Litho. *Perf. 12½***

| | | | | |
|---|---|---|---|---|
| **620** | A178 | 30fr multicolored | .85 | .50 |

Australian Mathematics Competition, 15th Anniv. — A179

**1993, July 1 Litho. *Perf. 13½***

| | | | | |
|---|---|---|---|---|
| **621** | A179 | 70fr multicolored | 1.75 | 1.10 |

Intl. Symposium on Inter-Plate Volcanism, French University of the Pacific, Punaauia A180

**1993, Aug. 2 Litho. *Perf. 13***

| | | | | |
|---|---|---|---|---|
| **622** | A180 | 140fr tan, blk & brn | 3.50 | 2.50 |

Taipei '93 — A181

**1993, Aug. 14 Litho. *Perf. 13½***

| | | | | |
|---|---|---|---|---|
| **623** | A181 | 46fr multicolored | 1.75 | .85 |

Exists without the Cartor imprint. Value, unused $17.50.

Tourism — A182

14fr, Boat tour. 20fr, Groom preparing for traditional wedding. 29fr, Beachside brunch.

**1993, Sept. 27**

| | | | | |
|---|---|---|---|---|
| **624** | A182 | 14fr multi, horiz. | .60 | .35 |
| **625** | A182 | 20fr multi | .65 | .35 |
| **626** | A182 | 29fr multi, horiz. | .75 | .45 |
| | | *Nos. 624-626 (3)* | 2.00 | 1.15 |

Exist without the Cartor imprint. Value, set unused $30.

Arrival of First French Gendarme in Tahiti, 150th Anniv. — A183

**1993, Oct. 14 *Perf. 13***

| | | | | |
|---|---|---|---|---|
| **627** | A183 | 100fr multicolored | 2.50 | 1.60 |

Exists without the Cartor imprint. Value, unused $17.50.

Alain Gerbault (1893-1941), Sailor — A184

**1993, Nov. 17 Engr. *Perf. 13***

| | | | | |
|---|---|---|---|---|
| **628** | A184 | 150fr red, green & blue | 4.00 | 2.75 |

Paintings — A185

Artists: 40fr, Vaea Sylvain. 70fr, A. Marere, vert. 80fr, J. Shelsher. 90fr, P.E. Victor, vert.

**1993, Dec. 3 Photo. *Perf. 13***

| | | | | |
|---|---|---|---|---|
| **629** | A185 | 40fr multicolored | 1.75 | .70 |
| **630** | A185 | 70fr multicolored | 2.50 | 1.25 |
| **631** | A185 | 80fr multicolored | 3.00 | 1.25 |
| **632** | A185 | 90fr multicolored | 3.50 | 1.50 |
| | | *Nos. 629-632 (4)* | 10.75 | 4.70 |

French School of the Pacific, 30th Anniv. A186

**1993, Dec. 7 Litho. *Perf. 12½***

| | | | | |
|---|---|---|---|---|
| **633** | A186 | 200fr multicolored | 5.00 | 3.50 |

Whales and Dolphins A187

**1994, Jan. 12 Litho. *Perf. 13½***

| | | | | |
|---|---|---|---|---|
| **634** | A187 | 25fr Whale breeching | .75 | .45 |
| **635** | A187 | 68fr Dolphins | 1.75 | 1.10 |
| **636** | A187 | 72fr Humpback whales, vert. | 2.00 | 1.25 |
| | | *Nos. 634-636 (3)* | 4.50 | 2.80 |

A188

**1994, Feb. 18 Litho. *Perf. 13½***

| | | | | |
|---|---|---|---|---|
| **637** | A188 | 51fr multicolored | 2.25 | .95 |

Hong Kong '94. New Year 1994 (Year of the Dog).

Sister Germaine Bruel — A189

**1994, Mar. 16**
**638** A189 180fr multicolored 4.00 3.00

Arrival of Nuns from St. Joseph of Cluny, 150th anniv.

Church of Jesus Christ of Latter-day Saints in French Polynesia, 150th Anniv. A190

**1994, Apr. 30 Litho. *Perf. 13½***
**639** A190 154fr Tahiti temple 3.50 2.75

Conservatory of Arts and Crafts, Bicent. — A191

**1994, May 25 Photo. *Perf. 13***
**640** A191 316fr multicolored 7.50 5.50

Regional Associated Center of Papeete, 15th anniv.

Internal Self-Government, 10th Anniv. — A192

**1994, June 29 Litho. *Perf. 13***
**641** A192 500fr multicolored 12.00 7.50

Tahitian Academy, 20th Anniv. — A193

**1994, July 2 Engr. *Perf. 13***
**642** A193 136fr multicolored 3.00 2.00

Scenes of Old Tahiti — A194

**1994, Aug. 10 Litho. *Perf. 13***
**643** A194 22fr Papara .90 .50
**644** A194 26fr Mataiea 1.10 .65
**645** A194 51fr Taravao, vert. 1.90 .95
*Nos. 643-645 (3)* 3.90 2.10

See Nos. 673-675.

Faaturuma, by Paul Gauguin (1848-1903) A195

**1994, Sept. 14 Litho. *Perf. 13***
**646** A195 1000fr multicolored 24.00 16.00

Epiphyllum Oxypetalum A196

**1994, Oct. 15 Litho. *Perf. 13½***
**647** A196 51fr multicolored 1.75 .95

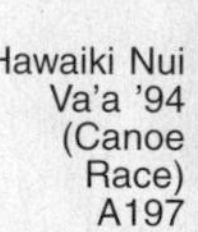

Hawaiki Nui Va'a '94 (Canoe Race) A197

Designs: a, 52fr, Yellow canoe, bow paddler. b, 76fr, Paddlers. c, 80fr, Paddlers, blue canoe. d, 94fr, Stern paddler, yellow canoe.

**1994, Nov. 10 Litho. *Perf. 13½x13***
**648** A197 Strip of 4, #a.-d. 8.00 4.75

No. 648 is a continuous design.

Paintings of French Polynesia — A198

62fr, Young girl, by Michelle Villemin. 78fr, Ocean tide, fish, by Michele Dallet. 102fr, Native carrying bundles of fruit, by Johel Blanchard. 110fr, View of coastline, by Pierre Lacouture.

**1994, Dec. 19 Litho. *Perf. 13***
**649** A198 62fr multi, vert. 1.75 .95
**650** A198 78fr multi, vert. 2.00 1.25
**651** A198 102fr multi, vert. 2.25 1.60
**652** A198 110fr multi 2.75 1.75
*Nos. 649-652 (4)* 8.75 5.55

Don Domingo de Boenechea's Tautira Expedition, 220th Anniv. — A199

**1995, Jan. 1**
**653** A199 92fr multicolored 2.25 1.25

South Pacific Tourism Year — A200

**1995, Jan. 11 Litho. *Perf. 13½***
**654** A200 92fr multicolored 2.25 1.40

New Year 1995 (Year of the Boar) A201

**1995, Feb. 1 Litho.**
**655** A201 51fr multicolored 1.75 .80

Portions of the design on No. 655 were applied by a thermographic process producing a shiny, raised effect.

Exists without the Cartor imprint. Value, unused $9.

University Teacher's Training Institute of the Pacific — A202

**1995, Mar. 8 Litho. *Perf. 13½***
**656** A202 59fr multicolored 1.50 .95

See New Caledonia No. 710 and Wallis & Futuna No. C182.

Nature Protection A203

**1995, May 4 Litho. *Perf. 13***
**657** Strip of 3 + 2 labels 4.25 4.25
*a.* A203 22fr Head of turtle .75 .35
*b.* A203 29fr Turtle swimming 1.00 .50
*c.* A203 91fr Black coral 2.50 1.50

Louis Pasteur (1822-95) — A204

**1995, May 8**
**658** A204 290fr dk blue & blue 6.75 4.00

Loti's Marriage, Novel by Julien Viaud (1850-1923) — A205

**1995, May 19 Photo. *Perf. 13***
**659** A205 66fr multicolored 2.00 1.10

A206

**1995, May 24 Litho. *Perf. 13½***
**660** A206 150fr multicolored 3.50 2.25

Tahitian Monoi beauty aid.

Birds — A207

**1995, June 7**
**661** A207 22fr Ptilinopus huttoni .65 .50
**662** A207 44fr Ducula galeata 1.40 .75

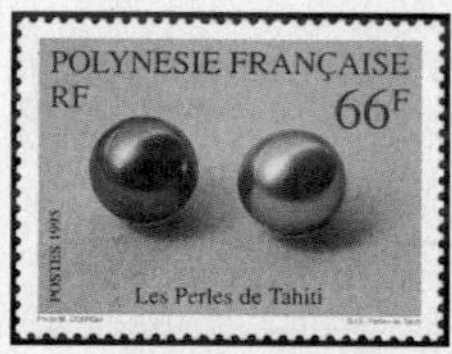
Tahitian Pearls A208

**1995, June 14**
**663** A208 66fr shown 1.60 1.10
**664** A208 84fr Eight pearls 2.10 1.40

On Nos. 663-664 portions of the design were applied by a thermographic process producing a shiny, raised effect.

Discovery of Marquesas Islands, 400th Anniv. — A209

a, Alvaro de Mendana de Neira, sailing ships. b, Pedro Fernandez de Quiros, map of islands.

**1995, July 21 Litho. *Perf. 13***
**665** Pair + label 8.00 6.00
*a.* A209 161fr multicolored 3.50 2.75
*b.* A209 195fr multicolored 4.50 3.25

A210

**1995, Aug. 12 Litho. *Perf. 13***
**666** A210 83fr multicolored 2.00 1.40

10th South Pacific Games, Tahiti.

Pandanus Plant — A211

No. 667a, Entire plant. b, Flower. c, Fruit. d, Using dry leaves for weaving.

**1995, Sept. 1 *Perf. 13½x13***
**667** Strip of 4 8.50 6.00
***a.-d.*** A211 91fr any single 2.00 1.50

Singapore '95.

UN, 50th Anniv. — A212

**1995, Oct. 24 Litho. *Perf. 13***
**668** A212 420fr multicolored 9.50 6.00

Paintings — A213

Designs: 57fr, The Paddler with the Yellow Dog, by Philippe Dubois, vert. 76fr, An Afternoon in Vaitape, by Maui Seaman, vert. 79fr, The Mama with the White Hat, by Simone Testeguide. 100fr, In Front of the Kellum House in Moorea, by Christian Deloffre.

**1995, Dec. 6 Photo. *Perf. 13***
**669** A213 57fr multicolored 1.50 .90
**670** A213 76fr multicolored 1.75 1.25
**671** A213 79fr multicolored 1.90 1.25
**672** A213 100fr multicolored 2.50 1.60
*Nos. 669-672 (4)* 7.65 5.00

**Scenes of Old Tahiti Type**

**1996, Jan. 17 Litho. *Perf. 13***
**673** A194 18fr Fautaua .65 .45
**674** A194 30fr District of Punaauia .80 .50
**675** A194 35fr Tautira .90 .60
*Nos. 673-675 (3)* 2.35 1.55

New Year 1996 (Year of the Rat) — A214

**1996, Feb. 19 Photo. *Perf. 13***
**676** A214 51fr multicolored 1.75 .80

Portions of the design on No. 676 were applied by a thermographic process producing a shiny, raised effect.

Paul-Emile Victor (1907-95), Explorer, Writer — A215

**1996, Mar. 7 Litho.**
**677** A215 500fr multicolored 12.00 8.00

Queen Pomare IV — A216

**1996, Mar. 1 Litho. *Perf. 13***
**678** A216 (51fr) multicolored 1.50 .80

***Serpentine Die Cut 7 Vert.***

**Self-Adhesive**

**Size: 17x24mm**

**678A** A216 (51fr) multicolored 2.00 1.15
***b.*** Booklet pane of 5 10.00
Complete booklet, 2 #678b 20.00

Sea Shells A217

10fr, Conus pertusus. 15fr, Cypraea alisonae. 25fr, Vexillum roseotinctum.

**1996, Apr. 10 Photo. *Perf. 13½x13***
**679** A217 10fr multicolored .45 .25
**680** A217 15fr multicolored .50 .25
**681** A217 25fr multicolored .95 .40
*Nos. 679-681 (3)* 1.90 .90

Portions of the designs on Nos. 679-681 were applied by a thermographic process producing a shiny, raised effect.

Return of the Pacific Battalion, 50th Anniv. — A218

**1996, May 5 Litho. *Perf. 13***
**682** A218 100fr multicolored 3.00 1.60

CHINA '96, 9th Asian Intl. Philatelic Exhibition A219

Design: 200fr, Chinese School, Tahiti, 1940.

**1996, May 18 *Perf. 13x13½***
**683** A219 50fr multicolored 1.25 .80

**Souvenir Sheet**

***Imperf***

**684** A219 200fr multicolored 4.50 3.40

Birds A220

**1996, June 12 Litho. *Perf. 13x13½***
**685** A220 66fr Sula sula 1.50 1.10
**686** A220 79fr Fregata minor 2.00 1.25
**687** A220 84fr Anous stolidus 2.00 1.40
*Nos. 685-687 (3)* 5.50 3.75

Musical Instruments A221

**1996, July 10 *Perf. 13x13½***
**688** A221 5fr Pahu, ukulele, toere .30 .25
**689** A221 9fr Toere .40 .25
**690** A221 14fr Pu, vivo .50 .25
*Nos. 688-690 (3)* 1.20 .75

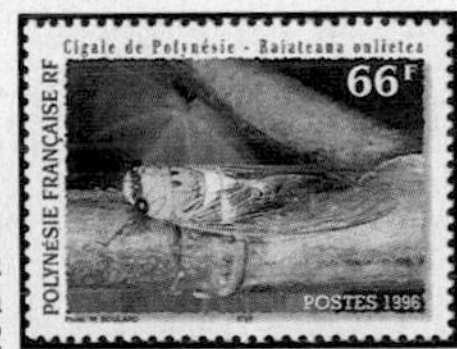
Raiateana Oulietea A222

**1996, Aug. 7 Litho. *Perf. 13x13½***
**691** A222 66fr multicolored 1.75 1.10

A223

**1996, Sept. 9 Litho. *Perf. 13***
**692** A223 70fr Ruahatu, God of the Ocean 1.75 1.10

7th Pacific Arts Festival.

A224

Stamp Day: Young Tahitian girl (Type A2), Noho Mercier, taken from photo by Henry Lemasson (1870-1956), postal administrator.

**1996, Oct. 16 Engr. *Perf. 13***
**693** A224 92fr black, red & blue 2.50 1.50

First Representative Assembly, 50th Anniv. — A225

**1996, Nov. 7 Litho. *Perf. 13***
**694** A225 85fr multicolored 2.00 1.10

Paintings of Tahitian Women — A226

Designs: 70fr, Woman lounging on Bora Bora Beach, by Titi Bécaud. 85fr, "Woman with Crown of Auti leaves," by Maryse Noguier, vert. 92fr, "Dreamy Woman," by Christine de Dinechin, vert. 96fr, Two working women, by Andrée Lang, vert.

**1996, Dec. 4 Litho. *Perf. 13***
**695** A226 70fr multicolored 2.00 .75
**696** A226 85fr multicolored 2.25 .90
**697** A226 92fr multicolored 2.50 1.00
**698** A226 96fr multicolored 3.00 1.00
*Nos. 695-698 (4)* 9.75 3.65

A227

**1997, Jan. 2 Litho. *Perf. 13***
**699** A227 55fr brown 1.25 .55

Society of South Sea Studies, 80th anniv.

A228

**1997, Feb. 7 Photo.** ***Perf. 13½x13***

| | | | | |
|---|---|---|---|---|
| **700** | A228 | 13fr multicolored | 1.00 | .30 |

New Year 1997 (Year of the Ox). Portions of the design were applied by a thermographic process producing a shiny, raised effect.

Arrival of Evangelists in Tahiti, Bicent. — A229

Designs: a, Sailing ship, "Duff." b, Painting, "Transfer of the Matavai District to the L.M.S. Missionaries," by Robert Smirke.

**1997, Mar. 5 Litho.** ***Perf. 13***

| | | | | |
|---|---|---|---|---|
| **701** | A229 | 43fr Pair, #a.-b. + label | 2.00 | 1.25 |

Tifaifai (Tahitian Bedspread) A230

Various leaf and floral patterns.

**1997, Apr. 16**

| | | | | |
|---|---|---|---|---|
| **702** | A230 | 1fr multicolored | .25 | .25 |
| **703** | A230 | 5fr multicolored | .25 | .25 |
| **704** | A230 | 70fr multicolored | 1.60 | .70 |
| | | *Nos. 702-704 (3)* | 2.10 | 1.20 |

PACIFIC 97 — A231

Sailing ships carrying mail, passengers between Tahiti and San Francisco: No. 705, Tropic Bird, 1897. No. 706, Papeete/Zélee, 1892.

**1997, May 29 Litho.** ***Perf. 13***

| | | | | |
|---|---|---|---|---|
| **705** | A231 | 92fr multicolored | 3.25 | 1.60 |
| **706** | A231 | 92fr multicolored | 3.25 | 1.60 |
| *a.* | | Pair, #705-706 | 6.50 | 6.50 |
| *b.* | | Souvenir sheet, #705-706 | 65.00 | 65.00 |

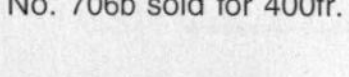
No. 706b sold for 400fr.

Island Scenes A232

No. 707, Flower. No. 708, Rowing canoe, sun behind mountain. No. 709, Throwing spears. No. 710. Aerial view of island. No. 711, Fish. No. 712, Women walking on beach. No. 713, Holding oyster shell with pearls. No. 714, Boat with sail down, sunset across water. No. 715, Snorkeling, sting ray. No. 716, Bananas, pineapples. No. 717, Palm tree, beach. No. 718, Women dancers in costume.

**1997, June 25 Litho.** ***Perf. 13***

**Booklet Stamps**

| | | | | |
|---|---|---|---|---|
| **707** | A232 | 85fr multicolored | 14.00 | 14.00 |
| **708** | A232 | 85fr multicolored | 14.00 | 14.00 |
| **709** | A232 | 85fr multicolored | 14.00 | 14.00 |
| **710** | A232 | 85fr multicolored | 14.00 | 14.00 |
| **711** | A232 | 85fr multicolored | 14.00 | 14.00 |
| **712** | A232 | 85fr multicolored | 14.00 | 14.00 |
| *a.* | | Bklt. pane of 6, #707-712 | 90.00 | |
| **713** | A232 | 85fr multicolored | 14.00 | 14.00 |
| **714** | A232 | 85fr multicolored | 14.00 | 14.00 |
| **715** | A232 | 85fr multicolored | 14.00 | 14.00 |
| **716** | A232 | 85fr multicolored | 14.00 | 14.00 |
| **717** | A232 | 85fr multicolored | 14.00 | 14.00 |
| **718** | A232 | 85fr multicolored | 14.00 | 14.00 |
| *a.* | | Bklt. pane of 6, #713-718 | 90.00 | |
| | | Complete booklet, 2 each #712a, #718a | 350.00 | |

Traditional Dance Costumes A233

Designs: 4fr, Warrior's costume. 9fr, Women's costume. 11fr, Couple.

**1997, July 10 Litho.** ***Perf. 13½x13***

| | | | | |
|---|---|---|---|---|
| **719** | A233 | 4fr multicolored | 1.00 | .30 |
| **720** | A233 | 9fr multicolored | 1.25 | .30 |
| **721** | A233 | 11fr multicolored | 2.00 | .30 |
| | | *Nos. 719-721 (3)* | 4.25 | .90 |

Kon-Tiki Expedition, 50th Anniv. — A234

**1997, Aug. 7 Litho.** ***Perf. 13***

| | | | | |
|---|---|---|---|---|
| **722** | A234 | 88fr multicolored | 2.25 | .80 |

Artists in Tahiti — A235

Designs: 85fr, Painting, "The Fruit Carrier," by Monique "Mono" Garnier-Bissol. 96fr, "Revival of Our Resources," mother of pearl painting, by Camélia Maraea. 110fr, "Tahitian Spirit," pottery, by Peter Owen, vert. 126fr, "Monoi," surrealist painting, by Elisabeth Stefanovitch.

**1997, Oct. 15 Litho.** ***Perf. 13***

| | | | | |
|---|---|---|---|---|
| **723** | A235 | 85fr multicolored | 1.90 | .80 |
| **724** | A235 | 96fr multicolored | 2.00 | .90 |
| **725** | A235 | 110fr multicolored | 2.50 | 1.00 |
| **726** | A235 | 126fr multicolored | 3.00 | 1.10 |
| | | *Nos. 723-726 (4)* | 9.40 | 3.80 |

Te Arii Vahine, by Paul Gauguin (1848-1903) — A236

**1997, Nov. 6 Litho.** ***Perf. 13***

| | | | | |
|---|---|---|---|---|
| **727** | A236 | 600fr multicolored | 13.00 | 8.00 |

Christmas A237

**1997, Dec. 3 Litho.** ***Perf. 13***

| | | | | |
|---|---|---|---|---|
| **728** | A237 | 118fr multicolored | 3.00 | 1.10 |

New Year 1998 (Year of the Tiger) A238

**1998, Jan. 28 Photo.** ***Perf. 13***

| | | | | |
|---|---|---|---|---|
| **729** | A238 | 96fr multicolored | 2.50 | .90 |

Portions of the design on No. 729 were applied by a thermographic process producing a shiny, raised effect.

Domestic Airline Network — A239

Designs: a, 70fr, Grumman Widgeon, 1950. b, 85fr, DHC 6 Twin-Otter, 1968. c, 70fr, Fairchild FH 227, 1980. d, 85fr, ATR 42-500, 1998.

**1998, Apr. 16 Photo.** ***Perf. 13***

| | | | | |
|---|---|---|---|---|
| **730** | A239 | Strip of 4, #a.-d. + label | 6.50 | 2.90 |

Orchids A240

5fr, Dendrobium "Royal King." 20fr, Oncidium "Ramsey." 50fr, Ascodenca "Laksi." 100fr, Cattleya "hybride."

**1998, May 14 Photo.** ***Perf. 13***

| | | | | |
|---|---|---|---|---|
| **731** | A240 | 5fr multi | .25 | .25 |
| **732** | A240 | 20fr multi, vert. | .50 | .25 |
| **733** | A240 | 50fr multi, vert. | 1.25 | .45 |
| **734** | A240 | 100fr multi | 2.25 | .95 |
| | | *Nos. 731-734 (4)* | 4.25 | 1.90 |

On Nos. 731-734 portions of the design were applied by a thermographic process producing a shiny, raised effect.

The Lovers, by Paul Gauguin (1848-1903) — A241

**1998, June 7 Photo.** ***Perf. 13x12½***

| | | | | |
|---|---|---|---|---|
| **735** | A241 | 1000fr multicolored | 22.50 | 9.00 |

Printed se-tenant with label.

1998 World Cup Soccer Championships, France — A242

**1998, June 10**

| | | | | |
|---|---|---|---|---|
| **736** | A242 | 85fr multicolored | 2.00 | .75 |

For overprint see No. 742.

Tahiti Festival of Flower and Shell Garlands — A243

Women wearing various garlands of flowers or shells.

**1998, July 16 Photo.** ***Perf. 13½***

| | | | | |
|---|---|---|---|---|
| **737** | A243 | 55fr multicolored | 1.50 | .50 |
| **738** | A243 | 65fr multicolored | 1.75 | .60 |
| **739** | A243 | 70fr multicolored | 2.00 | .65 |
| **740** | A243 | 80fr multicolored | 2.25 | .75 |
| | | *Nos. 737-740 (4)* | 7.50 | 2.50 |

Painting, "Underwater World of Polynesia," by Stanley Haumani A244

**1998, Sept. 10 Photo.** ***Perf. 12½x13***

| | | | | |
|---|---|---|---|---|
| **741** | A244 | 200fr multicolored | 4.00 | 2.00 |

No. 736 Overprinted in Blue & Black

**1998, Oct. 28 Photo.** ***Perf. 13½***

| | | | | |
|---|---|---|---|---|
| **742** | A242 | 85fr multicolored | 3.00 | 1.00 |

No. 742 has blue, white and red margins and No. 736 has white margins.

Autumn Philatelic Fair, Paris — A246

Watercolor paintings of Papeete Bay, by René Gillotin (1814-61), 250fr each: a, Beach at left, people. b, Beach at right, people.

**1998, Nov. 5** ***Perf. 13***

| | | | | |
|---|---|---|---|---|
| **743** | A246 | Pair, #a.-b. + label | 12.00 | 5.00 |
| *c.* | | Souvenir sheet, #a.-b., imperf. | 12.00 | 5.00 |

Life in Tahiti and the Islands A247

Paintings by André Deymonaz: 70fr, Return to the Market, vert. 100fr, Bonito Fish Stalls, vert. 102fr, Going Fishing. 110fr, Discussion after Church Services.

**1998, Dec. 10 Photo. *Perf. 13***

**744** A247 70fr multicolored 1.50 .80
**745** A247 100fr multicolored 2.00 1.00
**746** A247 102fr multicolored 2.25 1.00
**747** A247 110fr multicolored 2.50 1.10
*Nos. 744-747 (4)* 8.25 3.90

St. Valentine's Day — A248

**1999, Feb. 11 Litho. *Perf. 13***

**748** A248 96fr multicolored 2.50 .90

New Year 1999 (Year of the Rabbit) A249

**1999, Feb. 16**

**749** A249 118fr Rabbits, flowers 2.50 1.10

Portions of the design of No. 749 were applied by a thermographic process producing a shiny, raised effect.

Marine Life A250

Designs: 70fr, Ptérois volitans. 85fr, Hippocampus histrix. 90fr, Antennarius pictus. 120fr, Taenianotus triacanthus.

**1999, Mar. 18 Photo. *Perf. 13***

**750** A250 70fr multicolored 1.50 .65
**751** A250 85fr multicolored 1.90 .80
**752** A250 90fr multicolored 2.00 .80
**753** A250 120fr multicolored 2.75 1.10
*Nos. 750-753 (4)* 8.15 3.35

Portions of the designs on Nos. 750-753 were applied by a thermographic process producing a shiny, raised effect.

IBRA '99, World Philatelic Exhibition, Nuremberg A251

Tatooed men of Marquesas Islands, 1804: 90fr, Holding staff, fan. 120fr, Wearing blue cape.

**Photo. & Engr.**

**1999, Apr. 27 *Perf. 13¼***

**754** A251 90fr multicolored 2.00 .90
**755** A251 120fr multicolored 2.75 1.25

Mother's Day A252

**1999, May 27 Litho. *Perf. 13¼***

**756** A252 85fr Children, vert. 1.90 .75
**757** A252 120fr shown 2.75 1.00

A253

Island Fruits A254

No. 758, Breadfruit, vert. 120fr, Coconut.
No. 760: a, Papaya. b, Guava (goyave). c, Mombin. d, Rambutan. e, Star apple (pomme-etoile). f, Otaheite gooseberry (seurette). g, Rose apple. h, Star fruit (carambole). i, Spanish lime (quenette). j, Sweetsop (pomme-cannelle). k, Cashew (pomme de cajou). l, Passion fruit.

**1999 Litho. *Perf. 13½x13, 13x13½***

**758** A253 85fr multicolored 1.90 .75
**759** A253 120fr multicolored 2.75 1.10

**Souvenir Booklet**

**760** Complete bklt. 32.50
*a.-l.* A254 85fr Any single 2.00 1.40

Issued: No. 758, 120fr, 7/21; No. 760, 7/21.
No. 760 sold for 1200fr, and contains two booklet panes, containing Nos. 760a-760f, and Nos. 760g-760l. A second variety of No. 760 exists with selling price on cover as 1020fr. Value, complete booklet, $100.

No. 720, 1856 Letter, 1864 Postmark — A255

**1999, July 2 Litho. *Perf. 13***

**761** A255 180fr multicolored 4.00 2.25
*a.* Souvenir sheet of 1 12.00 12.00

150th anniv. of French postage stamps, PhilexFrance 99.
No. 761 issued se-tenant with label. No. 761a sold for 500fr.

Frédéric Chopin (1810-49), Composer — A256

**1999, July 2 Litho. *Perf. 13***

**762** A256 250fr multicolored 5.50 2.50

Malardé Medical Research Institute, 50th Anniv. — A257

**1999, Sept. 27**

**763** A257 400fr multicolored 8.75 3.75

Nudes A258

Paintings by: 85fr, J. Sorgniard. 120fr, J. Dubrusk. 180fr, C. Deloffre. 250fr, J. Gandouin.

**1999, Oct. 14 Litho. *Perf. 13***

**764** A258 85fr multi 2.10 .75
**765** A258 120fr multi 3.25 1.10
**766** A258 180fr multi 4.50 1.60
**767** A258 250fr multi 6.00 2.25
*Nos. 764-767 (4)* 15.85 5.70

Tahiti on the Eve of the Year 2000 A259

**1999, Nov. 10 Litho. *Perf. 13***

**768** A259 85fr multi 2.50 .75

5th Marquesas Islands Arts Festival A260

**1999, Dec. 10**

**769** A260 90fr multi 2.00 .80

Year 2000 — A261

85fr, Hands of adult and infant. 120fr, Eye.

**2000, Jan. 3 *Perf. 13¼x13, 13x13¼***

**770** A261 85fr multi, vert. 2.50 .75
**771** A261 120fr multi 3.25 1.10

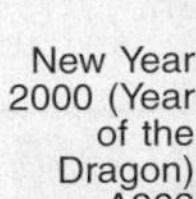

New Year 2000 (Year of the Dragon) A262

**2000, Feb. 5 Litho. *Perf. 13x13¼***

**772** A262 180fr multi 5.50 1.50

Portions of the design were applied by a thermographic process producing a shiny, raised effect.

Postal Service Emblem and Stamps A263

**2000, Mar. 15 Litho. *Perf. 13x13¼***

**773** A263 90fr multi 2.00 .75

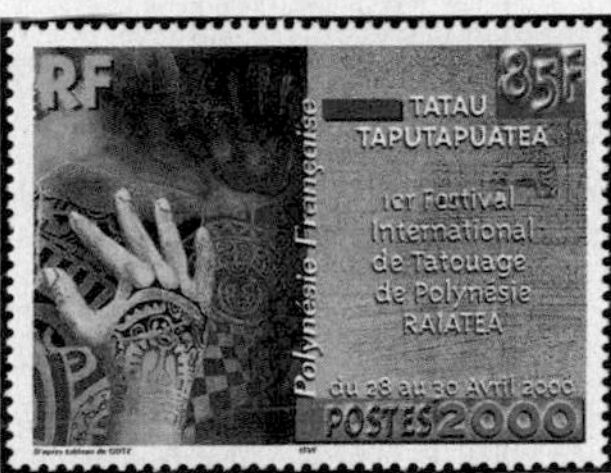


First Intl. Tattoo Festival, Raiatea — A264

Various tattoos.

**2000, Apr. 28 *Perf. 13***

**774** A264 85fr multi 1.90 .70
**775** A264 120fr multi 2.75 .95
**776** A264 130fr multi 2.90 1.00
**777** A264 160fr multi 3.50 1.25
*Nos. 774-777 (4)* 11.05 3.90

Beautiful Women of French Polynesia — A265

**2000, May 30**

**778** A265 300fr multi 7.50 3.00
*a.* Souvenir sheet of 1 12.00 12.00

No. 778a sold for 500fr.

Traditional Dresses — A266

Denominations: 85fr, 120fr, 160fr, 250fr.

**2000, June 21 Litho. *Perf. 13¼x13***

**779-782** A266 Set of 4 13.50 6.00

Mountains A267

Designs: 90fr, Mts. Aorai and Orohena. 180fr, Mts. Orohena and Aorai.

**2000, July 10** *Perf. 13x13¼*
**783-784** A267 Set of 2 6.00 2.60

Traditional Sports
A268

120fr, Fruit carrying. 250fr, Stone lifting, vert.

*Perf. 13x13¼, 13¼x13*
**2000, Sept. 15**
**785-786** A268 Set of 2 8.25 3.50

Native Woven Crafts
A269

No. 787, Fans. No. 788, Hat.

**2000, Oct. 3** **Litho.** *Perf. 13x13¼*
**787-788** A269 85fr Set of 2 3.75 1.75

Year of Ancient Tahitian Language Reo Ma'ohi
A270

**2000, Nov. 9** **Litho.** *Perf. 13x13¼*
**789** A270 120fr multi 2.75 1.20

Portions of the design were applied by a thermographic process producing a shiny, raised effect.

Advent of New Millennium — A271

**2000, Dec. 28**
**790** A271 85fr multi 2.50 .90

Central School, Cent. — A272

Designs: No. 791, 85fr, Central School. No. 792, 85fr, Paul Gauguin High School.

**2001, Jan. 16**
**791-792** A272 Set of 2 3.75 1.75

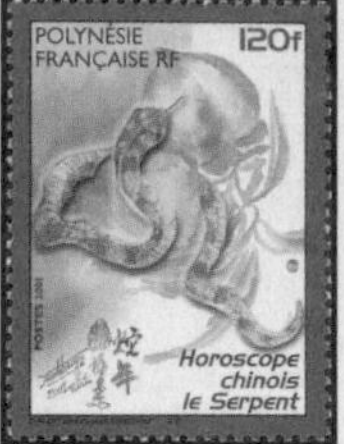


New Year 2001 (Year of the Snake) — A273

**2001, Jan. 24** *Perf. 13¼x13*
**793** A273 120fr multi 2.75 1.20

Portions of the design were applied by a thermographic process producing a shiny, raised effect.

Landscapes
A274

Designs: 35fr, Vaiharuru Waterfall. 50fr, Vahiria Lake, horiz. 90fr, Hakaui Valley.

*Perf. 13¼x13, 13x13¼*
**2001, Feb. 26** **Litho.**
**794-796** A274 Set of 3 6.00 1.75

Year of the Polynesian Child — A275

**2001, Mar. 28** **Litho.** *Perf. 13x13¼*
**797** A275 55fr multi 1.25 .55

Polynesian Singers — A276

Designs: 85fr, Eddie Lund. 120fr, Charley Mauu. 130fr, Bimbo. 180fr, Marie Mariteragi and Emma Terangi, horiz.

**2001, Apr. 12** *Perf. 13¼x13, 13x13¼*
**798-801** A276 Set of 4 11.50 5.00

Volunteers of the Pacific Batallion, 60th Anniv.
A277

**2001, Apr. 21** *Perf. 13x13¼*
**802** A277 85fr multi 2.25 .90

Surfing Waves of Teahupoo
A278

**2001, May 4**
**803** A278 120fr multi 2.75 1.20

Internal Autonomy, 17th Anniv.
A279

**2001, June 29** **Litho.** *Perf. 13*
**804** A279 250fr multi 5.50 2.50
*a.* Souvenir sheet of 1 12.00 12.00

No. 804a sold for 500fr.

Pirogue Racing — A280

Designs: 85fr, Male racers. 120fr, Female racers.

**2001, July 12** *Perf. 13¼x13*
**805-806** A280 Set of 2 4.50 2.00
*a.* Souvenir sheet, #805-806, imperf. 5.50 5.50

No. 806a sold for 250fr.

Hardwood Trees
A281

Designs: 90fr, Tou. 130fr, Ati. 180fr, Miro.

**2001, Oct. 23** **Litho.** *Perf. 13x13½*
**807-809** A281 Set of 3 11.00 8.00

AIDS Prevention
A282

**2001, Sept. 20** **Litho.** *Perf. 13x13¼*
**810** A282 55fr multi 2.75 1.10

Year of Dialogue Among Civilizations
A283

**2001, Oct. 9** *Perf. 13*
**811** A283 500fr multi 11.50 10.00

Perfume Flowers — A284

Designs: 35fr, Gardenia tahitensis. 50fr, Fagraea berteriana. 85fr, Gardenia jasminoides.

**2001, Nov. 8** *Perf. 13¼x13*
**812-814** A284 Set of 3 6.00 3.50

Portions of the designs were applied by a thermographic process producing a shiny, raised effect.

Christmas
A285

**2001, Dec. 6** *Perf. 13x13¼*
**815** A285 120fr multi 2.75 2.40

New Year 2002 (Year of the Horse)
A286

**2002, Feb. 12** **Litho.** *Perf. 13x13¼*
**816** A286 130fr multi 3.25 2.60

Portions of the design were applied by a thermographic process producing a shiny, raised effect.

Happy Holidays
A287

Greetings
A288

**2002, Feb. 28** **Background Colors**
**817** A287 55fr red 1.25 1.10
**818** A288 55fr blue 1.25 1.10
**819** A287 85fr blue 1.90 1.75
**820** A288 85fr green 1.90 1.75
*Nos. 817-820 (4)* 6.30 5.70

10th World Outrigger Canoe Championships — A289

Canoe rowers and emblems: 120fr, 180fr.

**2002, Mar. 9** **Photo.** *Perf. 13¼*
**821-822** A289 Set of 2 6.75 6.25

Sea Urchins
A290

Designs: 35fr, Echinometra sp. 50fr, Heterocentrotus trigonarius. 90fr, Echinothrix calamaris. 120fr, Toxopneustes sp.

**2002, Apr. 18** **Litho.** *Perf. 13x13¼*
**823-826** A290 Set of 4 6.50 6.25

Blood Donation — A291

**2002, May 3 Litho. *Perf. 13¼x13***
**827** A291 130fr multi 4.00 3.25

2002 World Cup Soccer Championships, Japan and Korea — A292

**2002, May 30**
**828** A292 85fr multi 2.10 1.75

Traditional Sports — A293

Designs: 85fr, Coconut husking. 120fr, Fruit carrying. 250fr, Javelin throwing.

**2002, June 27**
**829-831** A293 Set of 3 10.00 9.00

House of James Norman Hall — A294

**2002, July 4 *Perf. 13x13¼***
**832** A294 90fr multi 2.00 1.90

Papeete Market — A295

**2002, Aug. 30 Litho. *Perf. 13***
**833** A295 400fr multi 8.75 8.00
*a.* Souvenir sheet of 1 11.00 11.00

Amphilex 2002 Stamp Exhibition, Amsterdam (No. 833a). No. 833a sold for 500fr.

Pacific Oceanology Center, Vairoa A296

Designs: 55fr, Research pond, fish, shrimp, oyster, and flasks. 90fr, Aeriel view of center, fish, shrimp and oyster.

**2002, Sept. 26 Photo. *Perf. 13¼***
**834-835** A296 Set of 2 3.50 2.40

Taapuna Master 2002 Surfing Competition A297

**2002, Oct. 21 Litho. *Perf. 13x13¼***
**836** A297 120fr multi 2.75 2.00

Halophilic Flowers A298

Designs: 85fr, Hibiscus tiliaceus. 130fr, Scaveola sericea. 180fr, Guettarda speciosa.

**2002, Nov. 7**
**837-839** A298 Set of 3 8.75 6.75

Polynesians at Festivals A299

Designs: 55fr, Dancers and bus. 120fr, Musicians, vert.

**2002, Dec. 5 *Perf. 13x13¼, 13¼x13***
**840-841** A299 Set of 2 3.75 3.00

New Year 2003 (Year of the Ram) — A300

**2003, Feb. 1 Litho. *Perf. 13¼x13***
**842** A300 120fr multi 3.00 2.25

Portions of the design was applied by a thermographic process producing a shiny, raised effect.

Polynesian Women — A301

**2003, Mar. 8 Litho. *Perf. 13¼x13***
**843** A301 55fr multi 1.25 1.00

Waterfalls — A302

**2003, Apr. 10 *Perf. 13***
**844** A302 330fr multi 7.25 6.00

Old Papeete A303

Designs: 55fr, Automobiles and buildings, vert. 85fr, Ship in harbor. 90fr, People with bicycles in front of buildings (50x28mm). 120fr, Tree-lined street (50x28mm).

***Perf. 13¼x13, 13x13¼, 13***
**2003, May 15**
**845-848** A303 Set of 4 7.75 7.00
*848a* Souvenir sheet, #845-848 12.00 12.00

No. 848a sold for 550fr.

Fish — A304

**2003, June 12 Litho. *Perf. 13***
**849** A304 460fr multi 9.50 9.50

Portions of the design were applied by a thermographic process producing a shiny, raised effect.

Outrigger Canoes A305

Designs: No. 850, 85fr, shown. No. 851, 85fr, Three sailors on canoe at sea. No. 852, 85fr, Three sailors on canoe, vert. No. 853, 85fr, Sailor sitting on outrigger, vert.

***Perf. 13x13¼, 13¼x13***
**2003, July 11 Litho.**
**850-853** A305 Set of 4 7.50 6.50

Firewalkers A306

Orange-banded Cowrie — A307

**2003, Aug. 14 Photo. *Perf. 13¼***
**854** A306 130fr multi 2.50 2.50
***Perf. 13x13¼***
**855** A307 420fr multi 8.50 8.50

Are You Jealous? by Paul Gauguin (1848-1903) — A308

**2003, Sept. 11 *Perf. 13x12¼***
**856** A308 250fr multi 6.50 3.50

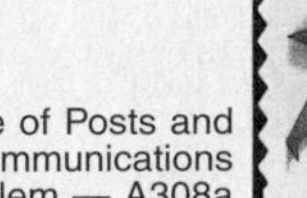
Office of Posts and Telecommunications Emblem — A308a

Type I: "Postes 2003" at right.
Type II: "Postes" only at right.

***Serpentine Die Cut 6½ Vert.***
**2003, Oct. 1 Engr.**
**Booklet Stamp**
**Self-Adhesive**
**856A** A308a (60fr) blue (type II), *2006* 10.00 1.00
*b.* Booklet pane of 10 100.00
*c.* Type I 40.00 24.00
*d.* As "c," booklet pane of 10 400.00
*e.* As #856A, inscribed "Phil@poste" 8.00 1.00
*f.* Booklet pane of 10 #856Ae 80.00

Issued: No. 856Ac, 10/1/03. No. 856A, 2006. No. 856Ae, 2007.
See Nos. 869, 1070-1070B.

French Polynesian Flag A309

**2003, Oct. 1 Litho. *Perf. 13x13¼***
**857** A309 (60fr) multi 1.50 1.25

Tiki — A310

**2003, Oct. 1 *Perf. 13¼x13***
**858** A310 100fr multi 3.00 2.00

Reissued in 2006 on shiny paper with much deeper colors. Values the same.

Flowers A311

Designs: 90fr, Orchid. 130fr, Rose de porcelain (torch ginger).

**2003, Oct. 4 Litho. *Perf. 13x13¼***
**859-860** A311 Set of 2 6.50 4.50

Portions of the designs were applied by a thermographic process producing a shiny, raised effect.

Bora Bora A312

Designs: No. 861, 60fr, Painting of Bora Bora by A. Van Der Heyde. No. 862, 60fr, Aerial photograph of Bora Bora.

**2003, Nov. 6 Litho. *Perf. 13x13¼***
**861-862** A312 Set of 2 5.00 2.75

Tiki — A313

**2003, Dec. 6** *Perf. 13*
**863** A313 190fr multi 4.00 4.00

Buildings and Palm Trees A314

**2003, Dec. 19** *Perf. 13x13¼*
**864** A314 90fr multi 3.00 1.90

New Year 2004 (Year of the Monkey) — A315

**2004, Jan. 22 Litho.** *Perf. 13¼x13*
**865** A315 130fr multi 3.50 3.50

A portion of the design was applied by a thermographic process producing a shiny, raised effect.

Scenes From Everyday Life A316

Designs: 60fr, Women working with cloth. 90fr, Street scene, vert.

***Perf. 13x13¼, 13¼x13***
**2004, Feb. 13** **Litho.**
**866-867** A316 Set of 2 3.25 3.25

Polynesian Woman — A317

**2004, Mar. 8** *Perf. 13¼x13*
**868** A317 90fr multi 4.00 1.90

**Post Emblem Type of 2003**
***Serpentine Die Cut 6¾ Vert.***
**2004, Apr. 22** **Engr.**
**Booklet Stamp**
**Self-Adhesive**

**869** A308a (90fr) red *6.00 2.00*
*a.* Booklet pane of 10 *60.00*
*b.* As #869, inscribed "Phil@poste" — —
*c.* Booklet pane of 10 #869b —

No. 869 lacks year date.

Polynesian Economic Development — A318

**2004, Apr. 23 Litho.** *Perf. 13x12¾*
**870** A318 500fr multi 11.00 10.00

Arahurahu Marae, Paea — A319

**2004, Apr. 23**
**871** A319 500fr multi 11.00 10.00

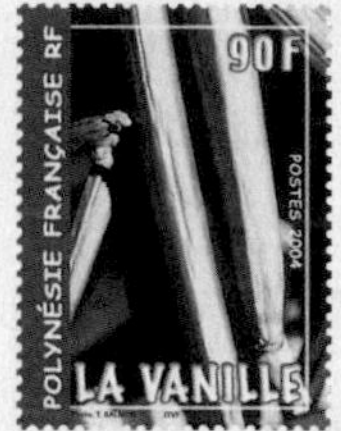

Vanilla — A320

**2004, May 14** *Perf. 13¼x13*
**872** A320 90fr multi 2.10 1.90

No. 872 is impregnated with a vanilla scent.

Mobile Snack Bars — A321

**2004, May 28** *Perf. 13x12¾*
**873** A321 300fr multi 6.50 6.25

Handicrafts A322

Designs: No. 874, 60fr, Artisan braiding fibers. No. 875, 60fr, Mother-of-pearl carving. No. 876, 90fr, Artisan carving statue. No. 877, 90fr, Hat.

**2004, June 26** *Perf. 13x13¼*
**874-877** A322 Set of 4 10.00 6.25

Portion of the designs were applied by a thermographic process producing a shiny, raised effect.

Involvement in South Pacific Area of Office of Posts and Telecommunications — A323

Designs: 100fr, Earth, Sun on horizon. 130fr, Satellite dish, building.

**2004, July 23 Photo.** *Perf. 13¼*
**878-879** A323 Set of 2 5.50 4.75

Information Technology and Communications A324

Designs: No. 880, 190fr, Computer keyboard, "@." No. 881, 190fr, Satellite, satellite dish.

**2004, Sept. 23 Litho.** *Perf. 13¼x13*
**880-881** A324 Set of 2 8.00 8.00

Omai, Polynesian Capt. James Cook Brought to England — A325

**2004, Oct. 14** *Perf. 13*
**882** A325 250fr multi 5.25 5.25

Shell Collectors A326

**2004, Nov. 10 Photo.** *Perf. 13¼*
**883** A326 60fr multi 1.60 1.40

A souvenir sheet of one sold for 250fr. Value $7.

Adenium Obesum A327

Alpinia Purpurata A328

Ixora Chinensis A329

Gardenia Taitensis A330

Heliconia Psittacorum — A331

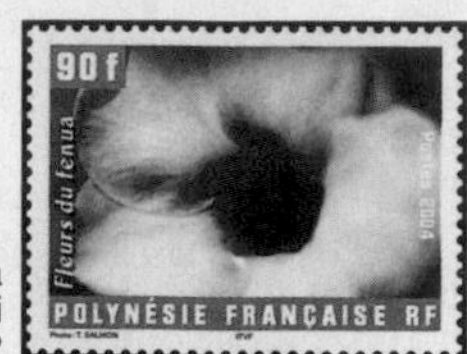

Allamanda Blanchetii A332

Otacanthus Caeruleus — A333

Hibiscus Rosa-sinensis — A334

Euphorba Milii A335

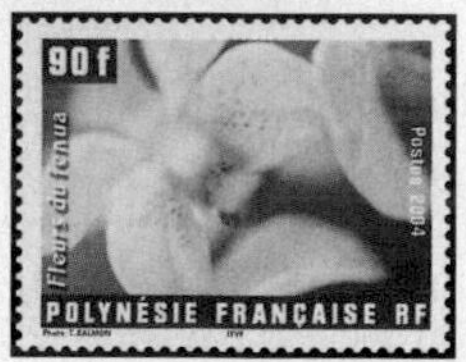

Asocenda Hybrid of Vanda x Ascocentrum — A336

Mussaenda Erythrophylia — A337

Bougainvillea Glabra — A338

**2004, Nov. 10 Litho.** *Perf. 13x13¼*

| | | | |
|---|---|---|---|
| **884** | Booklet pane of 6 | 17.50 | — |
| *a.* | A327 90fr multi | 2.50 | 2.50 |
| *b.* | A328 90fr multi | 2.50 | 2.50 |
| *c.* | A329 90fr multi | 2.50 | 2.50 |
| *d.* | A330 90fr multi | 2.50 | 2.50 |
| *e.* | A331 90fr multi | 2.50 | 2.50 |
| *f.* | A332 90fr multi | 2.50 | 2.50 |
| **885** | Booklet pane of 6 | 17.50 | — |
| *a.* | A333 90fr multi | 2.50 | 2.50 |
| *b.* | A334 90fr multi | 2.50 | 2.50 |
| *c.* | A335 90fr multi | 2.50 | 2.50 |
| *d.* | A336 90fr multi | 2.50 | 2.50 |
| *e.* | A337 90fr multi | 2.50 | 2.50 |
| *f.* | A338 90fr multi | 2.50 | 2.50 |
| | Complete booklet, #884-885 | 30.00 | |

Complete booklet sold for 1200fr.

Christmas A339

**2004, Dec. 17**
**886** A339 60fr multi 1.60 1.40

A portion of the design was applied by a thermographic process producing a shiny, raised effect.

Bamboo — A340

**2005, Feb. 9** ***Perf. 13¼x13***
**887** A340 130fr multi 3.00 3.00

New Year 2005. A portion of the design was applied by a thermographic process producing a shiny, raised effect.

People and Hut A341

**2005, Feb. 25** ***Perf. 13x13¼***
**888** A341 90fr multi 2.00 2.00

Polynesian Women — A342

Designs: 60fr, Woman wearing lei. 90fr, Woman wearing flower garland on head and robe.

**2005, Mar. 8** ***Perf. 13¼x13***
**889-890** A342 Set of 2 4.00 3.50

Woman Making Tapa Cloth — A343

**2005, Apr. 22** ***Perf. 13***
**891** A343 250fr multi 5.50 5.50

Tifaifai A344

**2005, Mar. 23 Litho.** ***Perf. 13x13¼***
**892** A344 5fr multi .25 .25

Angelfish A345

Designs: No. 893, 90fr, Centropyge bispinosa. No. 894, 90fr, Centropyge loricula. No. 895, 130fr, Centropyge heraldi. No. 896, 130fr, Centropyge flavissima.

**2005, May 27 Litho.** ***Perf. 13x13¼***
**893-896** A345 Set of 4 9.50 9.50
*896a* Souvenir sheet, #893-896 9.50 9.50

Portions of the designs were applied by a thermographic process producing a shiny, raised effect.

Historic Airplanes A346

Designs: No. 897, 60fr, TAI DC-8, first jet in Tahiti, 1961. No. 898, 60fr, Pan American Boeing 707, first foreign flight, 1963. No. 899, 100fr, Air France Boeing 707, first Air France flight to Tahiti, 1973. No. 900, 100fr, Air Tahiti Nui Airbus A340-300, first Tahitian airline, 2000.

**2005, June 24**
**897-900** A346 Set of 4 6.50 6.50

Musical Instruments A347

Designs: No. 901, 130fr, Drum. No. 902, 130fr, Nose flutes, horiz.

**2005, July 22** ***Perf. 13¼x13, 13x13¼***
**901-902** A347 Set of 2 5.50 5.50

Polynesian Landscapes — A348

**2005, Aug. 26** ***Perf. 13***
**903** A348 300fr multi 6.25 6.25

Pineapples A349

Designs: 90fr, Close-up of spines. 130fr, Entire fruit.

**2005, Sept. 23 Litho.** ***Perf. 13¼x13***
**904-905** A349 Set of 2 4.75 4.50

Nos. 904-905 are impregnated with pineapple scent.

Marae — A350

Marquesan Tohua — A351

**2005, Oct. 21** ***Perf. 13***
**906** A350 500fr multi 10.00 10.00
**907** A351 500fr multi 10.00 10.00

Autonomy, 20th Anniv. (in 2004) — A352

**2005, Nov. 10** ***Perf. 13¼x13***
**908** A352 60fr multi 4.00 1.75

No. 908 was printed in France and distributed there in June 2004 but was not sold in French Polynesia until 2005, where it was available from the philatelic bureau upon request, and not through standing orders.

O'Parrey Harbor, Tahiti A353

**2005, Nov. 10 Engr.** ***Perf. 13x12½***
**909** A353 100fr multi 2.00 2.00

Christmas A354

**2005, Dec. 16 Litho.** ***Perf. 13x13¼***
**910** A354 90fr multi 2.00 2.00

Lotus Flower A355

**Litho. & Silk-screened**
**2006, Jan. 30** ***Perf. 13x13¼***
**911** A355 130fr multi 2.60 2.60

A356

Hearts A357

**2006, Feb. 14 Photo.** ***Perf. 13***
**912** A356 60fr multi 1.25 1.25
**913** A357 90fr multi 1.90 1.90

Values are for stamps with surrounding selvage.

Polynesian Women — A358

Woman: 60fr, At water's edge. 90fr, With oil lamp.

**2006, Mar. 8 Litho.** ***Perf. 13¼x13***
**914-915** A358 Set of 2 3.75 3.25

Maupiti — A359

**2006, Apr. 26 Engr.** ***Perf. 13x13¼***
**916** A359 500fr multi 11.00 11.00

History of the Marquesas (Washington) Islands — A360

Designs: 60fr, Native man and woman. 130fr, Ships.

**2006, May 27 Litho.** ***Perf. 13¼x13***
**917-918** A360 Set of 2 4.00 4.00
*918a* Souvenir sheet, #917-918 4.00 4.00

Diners and Musicians — A361

**2006, June 6** *Perf. 13*
**919** A361 300fr multi 6.50 6.50

Polynesian Ground Dove A362

Tuamotu Sandpiper A363

**2006, June 21** *Perf. 13x13¼*
**920** A362 250fr multi 5.25 5.25
**921** A363 250fr multi 5.25 5.25

Heiva — A364

Designs: 90fr, Canoe race. 130fr, Stone lifting. 190fr, Dancer.

**2006, July 19** *Perf. 13¼x13*
**922-924** A364 Set of 3 8.75 8.75

Frangipani Flowers A365

**2006, Aug. 23 Litho.** *Perf. 13x13½*
**925** A365 90fr multi 2.25 1.90

No. 925 is impregnated with frangipani scent.

A366

World Tourism Day A367

Designs: 40fr, Ruins. No. 927, 90fr, Waterfall, woman and child. 130fr, Clothing at open-air market.

No. 929: a, Dancers with yellow skirts. b, Surfer. c, House and palm tree. d, Pearls. e, Fish and coral. f, Islanders in outrigger canoes.

No. 930: a, Woman in hammock. b, Stilt houses. c, Tower and boats. d, Horses and riders. e, Aerial view of island. f, Diver and sting ray.

**2006, Sept. 22** *Perf. 13¼x13*
**926-928** A366 Set of 3 6.00 6.00

**Booklet Stamps**
*Perf. 13x13¼*

**929** Booklet pane of 6 15.00 —
*a.-f.* A367 90fr Any single 2.00 2.00
**930** Booklet pane of 6 15.00 —
*a.-f.* A367 90fr Any single 2.00 2.00
Complete booklet, #929-930 30.00

Complete booklet sold for 1200fr.

Paintings A368

Designs: 60fr, Javelin Throwing, by Monique Garnier Bissol. 90fr, Market Life, by Albert Luzuy, horiz. 100fr, Island Quay, by Gilbert Chaussoy, horiz. 190fr, Vahine, by Olivier Louzé.

**2006, Oct. 25** *Perf. 13*
**931-934** A368 Set of 4 9.50 9.50

Engravings by Paul Gauguin (1848-1903) — A369

Engravings depicting: 60fr, Women. 130fr, Cow and man carrying items on stick.

**2006, Nov. 8 Engr.** *Perf. 13¼*
**935-936** A369 Set of 2 4.25 4.25

Children's Art A370

**2006, Dec. 13 Litho.** *Perf. 13x13¼*
**937** A370 90fr multi 2.00 2.00

Beach Gear — A371

Designs: 60fr, Flip-flops. 90fr, Surfboards.

***Serpentine Die Cut 11x11¼***
**2007 Photo. Self-Adhesive**
**938** A371 60fr multicolored 1.25 1.25
*a.* Blue tips of die cutting along left side 1.25 1.25
**939** A371 90fr multicolored 2.00 2.00
*a.* Light blue tips of die cutting along bottom 2.00 2.00

Issued: Nos. 938a, 939a, 1/24; Nos. 938-939, Feb. Nos. 938a and 939a are from the original printing, and are from sheets having adjacent stamps and die cutting that does not extend through the backing paper. Nos. 938-939, which were distributed to the philatelic trade, are from sheets with selvage around each stamp, and with rouletting that extends through the backing paper that allows the stamps to be removed from the sheet more easily.

New Year 2007 (Year of the Pig) A372

**2007, Feb. 19 Litho.** *Perf. 13x13¼*
**940** A372 130fr multi 3.50 3.50

Portions of the design were applied by a thermographic process producing a shiny, raised effect.

Painting of Polynesian Woman by Mathius — A373

Photograph of Polynesian Woman by John Stember — A374

**2007, Mar. 8 Litho.** *Perf. 13¼x13*
**941** A373 60fr multi 1.50 1.40
*Perf. 13x13¼*
**942** A374 90fr multi 2.25 2.00

Audit Office, Bicent. A375

**2007, Mar. 17 Engr.** *Perf. 13¼x13*
**943** A375 90fr multi 2.75 2.00

Shells — A376

Designs: 10fr, Lambis crocata pilsbryi. 60fr, Cypraea thomasi. 90fr, Cyrtulus serotinus. 130fr, Chicoreus laqueatus.

**2007, Apr. 25** **Litho.**
**944-947** A376 Set of 4 6.75 6.75
*947a* Souvenir sheet, #944-947 6.75 6.75

Coconut A377

**2007, May 23** *Perf. 13x13¼*
**948** A377 90fr multi 2.25 2.00

No. 948 is impregnated with a coconut scent.

Ships — A378

Designs: No. 949, 250fr, Gunboat Zélée. No. 950, 250fr, Passenger and cargo liner Sagittaire.

**2007, June 22** *Perf. 13*
**949-950** A378 Set of 2 12.00 11.50

Heiva Festival — A379

Various women dancers: 65fr, 100fr, 140fr.

**2007, July 4** *Perf. 13¼x13*
**951-953** A379 Set of 3 7.50 7.50

Arrival of Kon-Tiki Expedition in Polynesia, 60th Anniv. — A380

**Litho. & Silk-screened**
**2007, Aug. 7** *Perf. 13*
**954** A380 300fr multi 7.00 7.00

Arrival of Ship at Papeete Dock — A381

**2007, Aug. 29 Litho.** *Perf. 13*
**955** A381 190fr multi 4.50 4.50

Old and Modern Photos of Papeete — A382

Designs: 65fr, Rue Gauguin, 2007. 100fr, Rue de la Petite-Pologne (now Rue Gauguin), 1907.

**2007, Sept. 26**
**956-957** A382 Set of 2 4.75 4.00

Old Franc and Centime Notes — A383

Designs: 65fr, 1919 2-franc Chamber of Commerce note. 140fr, 1942 2-franc note. 500fr, 1943 50-centime note.

**2007, Oct. 26 Engr. *Perf. 13***
**958-960** A383 Set of 3 20.00 17.00

Flowers A384

Designs: 100fr, Hibiscus. 140fr, Bird-of-paradise (Oiseaux de paradis).

**Litho. & Silk-screened**
**2007, Nov. 8 *Perf. 13x13¼***
**961-962** A384 Set of 2 7.50 7.50

Christmas A385

**2007, Dec. 6 Litho. *Perf. 13x13¼***
**963** A385 100fr multi 2.50 2.50

Marine Life A386

Designs: 10fr, Himantura fai. 20fr, Tursiops truncatus. 40fr, Megaptera novaeangliae. 65fr, Negaprion acutidens.

**2008, Jan. 10**
**964-967** A386 Set of 4 4.00 4.00

New Year 2008 (Year of the Rat) — A387

**2008, Feb. 7 Photo. *Perf. 13¼x13***
**968** A387 140fr multi 3.75 3.75

Paintings of Women by Bénilde Menghini — A388

Designs: 65fr, Woman picking mangos. 100fr, Women scaling fish.

**2008, Mar. 7 Litho.**
**969-970** A388 Set of 2 4.25 4.25

Paintings by Polynesian Artists A389

Unnamed paintings depicting: No. 971, 100fr, Boat and reef, by Torea Chan. No. 972, 100fr, Polynesian man, by Raymond Vigor. No. 973, 100fr, Fruit bowl, by Teurarea Prokop, horiz.

**2008, Apr. 10 *Perf. 13x13¼, 13¼x13***
**971-973** A389 Set of 3 8.00 8.00

Pouvanaa a Oopa (1895-1977), Politician — A390

**2008, May 20 Litho. *Perf. 13***
**974** A390 500fr multi 13.00 13.00

Island Touring Vehicles — A391

Designs: 65fr, Motor scooter. 100fr, Bus, horiz.

***Serpentine Die Cut 11***
**2008, June 12 Photo.**
**Self-Adhesive**
**975-976** A391 Set of 2 4.50 4.50

Heiva Festival A392

Designs: 65fr, Woman with floral headdress. 140fr, Tattooed man. 190fr, Girl dancing.

**2008, July 16 Litho. *Perf. 13***
**977-979** A392 Set of 3 11.00 11.00

Sports — A393

Designs: No. 980, 140fr, Table tennis. No. 981, 140fr, Weight lifting.

**2008, Aug. 8 Litho. *Perf. 13¼x13***
**980-981** A393 Set of 2 7.00 7.00

End of Tahiti Nui Expedition, 50th Anniv. — A394

**2008, Aug. 29 Litho. *Perf. 13***
**982** A394 190fr multi 4.50 4.50

Eric de Bisschop (1890-1958), expedition leader.

Polynesian Scenes A395

No. 983: a, Woman crouching. b, Woman under shelter. c, Boat in bay near cliffs. d, Orange flowers. e, Red hibiscus flower. f, Island. g, Woman with headdress. h, White flower. i, Woman with headdress and flower garland. j, Pink flower. k, Islands. l, Bay near mountains.

***Serpentine Die Cut 11¼x11***
**2008, Sept. 8 Self-Adhesive**
**983** Booklet pane of 12 32.50
*a.-d.* A395 65fr Any single 1.50 1.50
*e.-h.* A395 100fr Any single 2.40 2.40
*i.-l.* A395 140fr Any single 3.25 3.25

Gardenia Taitensis in Bottle of Monoi Oil — A396

**2008, Sept. 17 *Perf. 13¼x13***
**984** A396 100fr multi 2.40 2.40

No. 984 is impregnated with a gardenia scent.

Aviation Anniversaries — A397

Designs: No. 985, 250fr, Air service between France and French Polynesia, 50th anniv. No. 986, 250fr, Air Tahiti Nui, 10th anniv.

**2008, Oct. 15 Litho. *Perf. 13***
**985-986** A397 Set of 2 11.00 11.00

French Polynesia Postage Stamps, 50th Anniv. — A398

Designs: 65fr, French Polynesia #185. 100fr, Vignette of French Polynesia #C24. 140fr, French Polynesia #J29.

**2008, Nov. 6 Engr. *Perf. 13***
**987-989** A398 Set of 3 6.75 6.75
*989a* Sheet of 3, #987-989 6.75 6.75

Boater and Dancer A399

**2008, Dec. 5 Litho. *Perf. 13x13¼***
**990** A399 100fr multi 2.25 2.25

Winning design in children's stamp design contest.

Hypolimnas Bolina A400

**Litho. & Silk-screened**
**2009, Jan. 16 *Perf. 13***
**991** A400 70fr multi 1.50 1.50

Fire Fighters — A401

Designs: 70fr, Fireman on aerial ladder. 140fr, Fireboat.

**2009, Feb. 13 Litho. *Perf. 13***
**992-993** A401 Set of 2 4.50 4.50

Paintings of Polynesian Women — A402

Designs: 70fr, Woman, by Myriam Stroken. 100fr, Woman with Guitar, by Stanley Haumani.

**2009, Mar. 30 Litho. *Perf. 13¼x13***
**994-995** A402 Set of 2 4.00 4.00

Jacques Brel (1929-78), Singer — A403

Colors: 70fr, Blue. 100fr, Brown.

**2009, Apr. 8 Engr.**
**996-997** A403 Set of 2 4.25 4.25

Pareo Fabric A404

Pareo in: (70fr), Blue. (100fr), Red. (140fr), Green.

***Serpentine Die Cut 11***
**2009, May 29 Litho.**
**Self-Adhesive**
**998-1000** A404 Set of 3 7.25 7.25

Heiva Celebrations of the Past — A405

Various Heiva dancers: 70fr, 100fr, 140fr. 100fr and 140fr are horiz.

***Perf. 13¼x13, 13x13¼***
**2009, June 19**
**1001-1003** A405 Set of 3 7.50 7.50

First Man on the Moon, 40th Anniv. A406

**2009, July 20 *Perf. 13¼***
**1004** A406 140fr multi 3.50 3.50

Water Activities A407

Designs: 70fr, Surfing. 100fr, Canoeing (pirogue).

***Serpentine Die Cut 11x11¼***
**2009, Aug. 7 Litho. Self-Adhesive**
**1005-1006** A407 Set of 2 4.00 4.00

Passion Fruit A408

**2009, Aug. 14 *Perf. 13x13¼***
**1007** A408 100fr multi 2.40 2.40

No. 1007 has a scratch-and-sniff coating on the fruit having a passion fruit scent.

Underwater Scenes — A409

Designs: 70fr, Scuba divers. 100fr, Turtles, horiz. 140fr, Whale, horiz.

**Litho. & Silk-screened**
***Perf. 13¼x13, 13x13¼***
**2009, Sept. 11**
**1008-1010** A409 Set of 3 7.75 7.75
*1010a* Sheet of 3, #1008-1010 7.75 7.75

Fish — A410

No. 1011: a, Chaetodon lunula. b, Chaetodon trichrous. c, Chaetodon ornatissimus. d, Chaetodon pelewensis. e, Pterois antennata. f, Myripristis berndti. g, Priacanthus hamrur. h, Epinephelus polyphekadion. i, Thalassoma lutescens. j, Thalassoma hardwicke. k, Pygoplites diacanthus. l, Coris gaimard.

***Serpentine Die Cut 11¼x11***
**2009, Sept. 11 Self-Adhesive**
**1011** Booklet pane of 12 31.00
*a.-d.* A410 70fr Any single 1.75 1.75
*e.-h.* A410 100fr Any single 2.50 2.50
*i.-l.* A410 140fr Any single 3.50 3.50

Paintings by Paul Gauguin (1848-1903) — A411

Designs: No. 1012, 250fr, Still Life with a Maori Statuette. No. 1013, 250fr, Still Life with Apples, horiz.

**2009, Oct. 16 Litho. *Perf. 13***
**1012-1013** A411 Set of 2 12.50 12.50

French Polynesia No. 180 — A412

**2009, Nov. 5 Engr.**
**1014** A412 500fr multi 12.50 12.50

Legend of the Coconut Tree — A413

**2009, Dec. 11 Litho. *Perf. 13¼x13***
**1015** A413 190fr multi 4.75 4.75

Papeete Post Office, 150th Anniv. — A414

**2010, Jan. 20**
**1016** A414 70fr multi 1.60 1.60

New Year 2010 (Year of the Tiger) A415

**Litho. & Silk-screened**
**2010, Feb. 15 *Perf. 13x13¼***
**1017** A415 140fr multi 3.25 3.25

Woman and Child — A416

Woman and child: 70fr, Facing forward. 100fr, Facing right.

**2010, Mar. 8 Litho. *Perf. 13¼x13***
**1018-1019** A416 Set of 2 4.00 4.00

Tattoos A417

Tattooed: No. 1020, 250fr, Woman (green background). No. 1021, 250fr, Man (dark red background).

**2010, Apr. 6**
**1020-1021** A417 Set of 2 11.50 11.50

Tiare Apetahi Flower A418

**Litho. & Silk-screened**
**2010, Apr. 20 *Perf. 13x13¼***
**1022** A418 70fr multi 1.50 1.50

Captain Frederick William Beechey (1796-1856), Explorer — A419

**2010, May 5 Litho.**
**1023** A419 140fr multi 3.00 3.00

Corals A420

Various corals: 70fr, 100fr, 140fr. 140fr is vert.

**Litho. & Silk-screened**
**2010, June 4 *Perf. 13x13¼, 13¼x13***
**1024-1026** A420 Set of 3 6.50 6.50
*1026a* Sheet of 3, #1024-1026 6.50 6.50

Heiva Festival — A421

Various festival participants: 100fr, 140fr, 190fr.

**2010, July 20 Litho. *Perf. 13¼x13***
**1027-1029** A421 Set of 3 9.50 9.50

Mango A422

**2010, Aug. 8 *Perf. 13x13¼***
**1030** A422 100fr multi 2.25 2.25

No. 1030 has a scratch-and-sniff coating on the fruit having a mango scent.

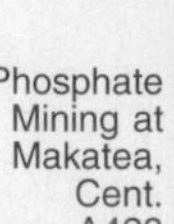

Phosphate Mining at Makatea, Cent. A423

Designs: 70fr, Office. 100fr, Train. 140fr, Mining operations.

**2010, Aug. 17 Litho. *Perf. 13x13¼***
**1031-1033** A423 Set of 3 6.75 6.75

Honotua Fiber Optic Submarine Cable Project — A424

***Serpentine Die Cut 11***
**2010, Sept. 15 Photo.**
**Self-Adhesive**
**1034** A424 70fr multi 1.75 1.75

Birds A425

No. 1035: a, Lori de Kuhl (Kuhl's lorikeet). b, Bécasseau Sanderling (Sanderling). c, Carpophade de la Société (Imperial pigeon). d, Tangara à dos rouge (Crimson-backed tanager). e, Ptilope de Hutton (Rapa fruit dove). f, Sterne huppée (Great crested tern). g, Gygis blanche (White tern). h, Lori Nonnette (Blue lorikeet). i, Chevalier errant (Wandering tattler). j, Martin chasseur des Gambier (Tuamotu kingfisher). k, Fou brun (Brown booby). l, Pluvier fauve (Pacific golden plover).

**Litho. & Silk-screened**
**2010, Sept. 15 Self-Adhesive**
**1035** Booklet pane of 12 28.00
*a.-l.* A425 100fr Any single 2.25 2.25

Tahiti Faa'a International Airport, 50th Anniv. — A426

**2010, Oct. 14 Litho. *Perf. 13***
**1036** A426 500fr multi 11.50 11.50

Sphinx Moth A427

**2010, Oct. 14 *Perf. 13x13½***
**1037** A427 5fr multi .25 .25

1948 Air Post Stamps of French Oceania — A428

Designs: 70fr, #C17. 100fr, #C18. 140fr, #C19.

**2010, Nov. 4 Engr. *Perf. 13***
**1038-1040** A428 Set of 3 7.25 7.25

Legend of Moua Puta A429

**2010, Dec. 9 Litho. *Perf. 13x13¼***
**1041** A429 70fr multi 1.60 1.60

Crabs A430

Designs: 20fr, Atergatopsis cf. germanini. 40fr, Zosimus aeneus. 70fr, Carpilius convexus. 100fr, Carpilius maculatus.

**2011, Jan. 18**
**1042-1045** A430 Set of 4 5.25 5.25
*1045a* Souvenir sheet of 4, #1042-1045 5.25 5.25

New Year 2011 (Year of the Rabbit) — A431

**Litho. & Silk-screened**
**2011, Feb. 3 *Perf. 13¼x13***
**1046** A431 140fr multi 3.25 3.25

Images of Polynesia — A432

No. 1047: a, Canoe race. b, Outrigger canoe. c, Aerial view of islands. d, Fish on reef. e, Pearls. f, Flowers.

***Serpentine Die Cut 11¼***
**2011, Mar. 8 Litho.**
**Self-Adhesive**
**1047** Booklet pane of 6 14.50
*a.-f.* A432 100fr Any single 2.40 2.40

Intl. Women's Year — A433

Designs: 70fr, Two women weaving. 100fr, Woman standing.

**2011, Mar. 8 *Perf. 13¼x13***
**1048-1049** A433 Set of 2 4.00 4.00

Pearl of Tahiti, 50th Anniv. — A434

**2011, Apr. 7 Litho.**
**1050** A434 140fr multi 3.50 3.50

Portions of the design were applied by a thermographic process producing a shiny, raised effect.

Transportation of the Past — A435

Designs: 70fr, Truck, 1939. 100fr, Horse-drawn carriages, 1900.

**2011, May 17 Litho. *Perf. 13***
**1051-1052** A435 Set of 2 4.25 4.25

Fishing — A436

Cartoons: 100fr, Fisherman in boat catching swordfish. 140fr, Spear fisherman and speared fish.

***Serpentine Die Cut 11***
**2011, June 22 Litho.**
**Self-Adhesive**
**1053-1054** A436 Set of 2 5.75 5.75

Carved Items — A437

Designs: 70fr, Coral pestle. 140fr, Basalt tiki. 190fr, Oceania rosewood container with lid, hoirz.

**2011, July 19 *Perf. 13¼x13, 13x13¼***
**1055-1057** A437 Set of 3 9.75 9.75

Orchid — A438

**2011, Aug. 17 Litho. *Perf. 13¼x13***
**1058** A438 140fr multi 3.25 3.25

No. 1058 is impregnated with an orchid scent.

Islands A439

Photographs of: 10fr, Rangiroa. 100fr, Ua Pou. 140fr, Bora Bora.

**2011, Sept. 27 *Perf. 13x13¼***
**1059-1061** A439 Set of 3 5.75 5.75

Marine Birds and Sea Life A440

No. 1062: a, Birds. b, Bird and whale. c, Dolphin and fish. d, Red striped fish, black and white striped angelfish. e, Blue and yellow striped fish. f, Lionfish, yellow fish. g, Ray. h, Shark. i, Sea turtle, fish, coral. j, Anemonefish, sea anemones. k, Crab. l, Moray eel, coral.

***Serpentine Die Cut 11¼x11***
**2011, Sept. 27 Self-Adhesive**
**1062** Booklet pane of 12 29.00
*a.-l.* A440 100fr Any single 2.40 2.40

Filming of *Mutiny on the Bounty* in Tahiti, 50th Anniv. — A441

**2011, Oct. 19 *Perf. 13***
**1063** A441 500fr multi 11.50 11.50

Fort Collet, Marquesas Islands — A442

No. 1064 — Engraving of Fort from 1854: a, Buildings without flags. b, Buildings with flags.

**2011, Nov. 3 Engr. *Perf. 13***
**1064** A442 250fr Horiz. pair, #a-b 11.50 11.50

Ta'aroa, Polynesian God of Creation — A443

**2011, Dec. 15 Litho. *Perf. 13¼x13***
**1065** A443 70fr multi 1.60 1.60

New Yeart 2012 (Year of the Dragon) A444

**Litho & Silk-screened**

**2012, Jan. 23** *Perf. 13*
**1066** A444 140fr multi 3.25 3.25

Papeete Maritime Station — A445

Ships in Papeete Harbor — A446

**2012, Jan. 27** **Litho.**
**1067** A445 70fr multi 1.60 1.60
**1068** A446 100fr multi 2.25 2.25

Port of Papeete Authority, 50th anniv.

Food Truck Vendors A447

*Serpentine Die Cut 11*
**2012, Feb. 22**
**Self-Adhesive**
**1069** A447 100fr multi 2.25 2.25

**Office of Posts and Telecommunications Emblem Type of 2003**
**Booklet Stamps**
*Serpentine Die Cut 6¾ Vert.*

**2012, Feb. 8** **Self-Adhesive**
**1070** A308a 5fr red violet .25 .25
*c.* Booklet pane of 10 #1070 1.25
**1070A** A308a (75fr) blue, type II 1.75 1.75
*d.* Booklet pane of 10 #1070A 17.50
**1070B** A308a (100fr) rose 2.25 2.25
*e.* Booklet pane of 10 #1070B 22.50
*Nos. 1070-1070B (3)* 4.25 4.25

Intl. Women's Day — A448

Designs: 70fr, Woman. 100fr, Woman and child.

**2012, Mar. 8** *Perf. 13¼x13*
**1071-1072** A448 Set of 2 3.75 3.75

Flowers — A449

No. 1073: a, Gingembre à abeilles. b, Reine de Malaisie. c, Opuhi alpinia rose. d, Zedoaire. e, Safran indien. f, Opuhi alpinia orchidée.

**2012, Mar. 8** *Serpentine Die Cut 11*
**Self-Adhesive**
**1073** Booklet pane of 6 13.50
*a.-f.* A449 100fr Any single 2.25 2.25

Nudibranchs — A450

Designs: 75fr, Glossodoris rufomarginata. 100fr, Elysia ornata. 190fr, Cyerce nigricans.

**Litho. & Silk-screened**

**2012, Apr. 26** *Perf. 13x13¼*
**1074-1076** A450 Set of 3 8.00 8.00
*1076b* Souvenir sheet of 3, #1074-1076 8.00 8.00

Tiurai (1842-1918), Healer — A451

**2012, June 18** **Litho.** *Perf. 13¼x13*
**1077** A451 75fr multi 1.60 1.60

Tamanu Orange Picking Contest — A452

**2012, June 27**
**1078** A452 75fr multi 1.60 1.60

Heiva Dancer A453

**2012, July 18** *Perf. 13x13¼*
**1079** A453 100fr multi 2.10 2.10

Grapefruits A454

**2012, Aug. 22**
**1080** A454 140fr multi 3.00 3.00

No. 1080 is impregnated with a grapefruit scent.

Airports A455

Airport at: 5fr, Bora Bora. 75fr, Tikehau. 100fr, Ua Pou.

**2012, Sept. 27**
**1081-1083** A455 Set of 3 4.00 4.00

Landscapes — A456

No. 1084: a, Moorea. b, Mangareva. c, Rurutu. d, Kauehi. e, Hiva Oa. f, Rapa.

*Serpentine Die Cut 11*
**2012, Sept. 27**
**Self-Adhesive**
**1084** Booklet pane of 6 13.50
*a.-f.* A456 100fr Any single 2.25 2.25

Turtles in Botanical Gardens, Papeari A457

Horses and Riders, Marquesas Islands A458

**2012, Oct. 17** *Perf. 13x13¼*
**1085** A457 75fr multi 1.60 1.60
**1086** A458 100fr multi 2.25 2.25

First Stamps of French Oceania, 120th Anniv. — A459

No. 1087: a, "Commerce," horse-drawn carriage, people near shore. b, People on rowboat, "Navigation."

**2012, Nov. 8** **Engr.** *Perf. 13xx13¼*
**1087** Horiz. pair, #a-b, + central label 11.00 11.00
*a.-b.* A459 250fr Either single 5.50 5.50

Season of Matari'i i Ni'a — A460

**2012, Nov. 20** **Litho.** *Perf. 13*
**1088** A460 75fr multi 1.75 1.75

Matavai Bay A461

**2012, Dec. 13** **Engr.**
**1089** A461 500fr blk & gray blue 11.00 11.00

Scenes of Everyday Life A462

Designs: 75fr, Street scene outside of Quinn's Bar, Papeete. 100fr, Street musicians.

**2013, Jan. 2** **Litho.** *Perf. 13x13¼*
**1090-1091** A462 Set of 2 4.00 4.00

New Year 2013 (Year of the Snake) A463

**Litho. & Silk-screened**

**2013, Feb. 11** *Perf. 13*
**1092** A463 140fr multi 3.00 3.00

Queen Pomare IV (1813-77) A464

*Serpentine Die Cut 11*
**2013, Feb. 28** **Photo.**
**Self-Adhesive**
**1093** A464 75fr multi 1.75 1.75

Legend of Tahiri Vahine — A465

Designs: 75fr, Tahiri Vahine (woman with fan). 100fr, Tahiri Vahine with other women.

**2013, Mar. 8** **Litho.** *Perf. 13¼x13*
**1094-1095** A465 Set of 2 4.00 4.00

Intl. Women's Day.

Flora and Fauna — A466

Designs: 20fr, Lemon (citron). 40fr, Lizard (lézard), horiz. 190fr, Chestnut-breasted mannikin (capuchin).

**Litho. & Silk-screened**

**2013, Apr. 26** ***Perf. 13¼x13, 13x13¼***

**1096-1098** A466 Set of 3 5.50 5.50
*1098a* Souvenir sheet of 3, #1096-1098 5.50 5.50

Jacques Brel (1929-78), Singer — A467

**2013, May 10** **Engr.** ***Perf. 13***

**1099** A467 500fr multi 11.50 11.50

Fruits A468

No. 110: a, Pineapples. b, Mangos. c, Bananas. d, Coconuts. e, Papayas. f, Watermelon.

**Litho. & Silk-screened**

**2013, May 10** ***Serpentine Die Cut 11***

**Self-Adhesive**

**1100** Booklet pane of 6 13.50
*a.-f.* A468 100fr Any single 2.25 2.25

Marine Life — A469

Designs: 5fr, Starfish. 10fr, Giant clam. 75fr, Sea anemone and clown fish. 100fr, Sea turtle.

**Litho. & Silk-screened**

**2013, June 7** ***Perf. 13x13¼***

**1101-1104** A469 Set of 4 4.25 4.25
*1104a* Souvenir sheet of 4, #1101-1104 4.25 4.25

Carousel at Heiva Fairground — A470

**2013, July 16** **Litho.** ***Perf. 13***

**1105** A470 100fr multi 2.25 2.25

Jasmine Flowers A471

**2013, Aug. 22** **Litho.** ***Perf. 13x13¼***

**1106** A471 100fr multi 2.25 2.25

No. 1106 is impregnated with a jasmine scent.

FIFA Beach Soccer World Cup Tournament, Tahiti — A472

**2013, Sept. 18** **Litho.** ***Perf. 13¼x13***

**1107** A472 140fr multi 3.25 3.25

A473

A474

A475

A476

A477

A478

Women

***Serpentine Die Cut 11***

**2013, Sept. 18** **Litho.**

**Self-Adhesive**

**1108** Booklet pane of 6, #1108a-1108f 13.50
*a.* A473 100fr multi 2.25 2.25
*b.* A474 100fr multi 2.25 2.25
*c.* A475 100fr multi 2.25 2.25
*d.* A476 100fr multi 2.25 2.25
*e.* A477 100fr multi 2.25 2.25
*f.* A478 100fr multi 2.25 2.25
*g.* A473 100fr Dated "2015" 1.75 1.75
*h.* A474 100fr Dated "2015" 1.75 1.75
*i.* A475 100fr Dated "2015" 1.75 1.75
*j.* A476 100fr Dated "2015" 1.75 1.75
*k.* A477 100fr Dated "2015" 1.75 1.75
*l.* A478 100fr Dated "2015" 1.75 1.75
*m.* Booklet pane of 6, #1180g-1108l 10.50

Issued: Nos. 1108g-1108m, 11/5/15.

Canoes — A479

Various canoes: 75fr, 100fr.

**2013, Oct. 17** **Litho.** ***Perf. 13***

**1109-1110** A479 Set of 2 4.00 4.00

Stock Certificates — A480

Stock certificate of: 250fr, Comptoirs Français d'Océanie. 300fr, Compagnie Française de Tahiti.

**2013, Nov. 6** **Engr.** ***Perf. 13***

**1111-1112** A480 Set of 2 12.50 12.50

Old Automobiles — A481

Designs: 75fr, 1915 Ford Model T. 100fr, 1950 Citroen Traction Avant.

**2013, Dec. 12** **Litho.** ***Perf. 13***

**1113-1114** A481 Set of 2 4.00 4.00

New Banknotes — A482

Designs: 10fr, 500-franc banknote. 20fr, 1000-franc banknote. 75fr, 5000-franc banknote. 100fr, 10,000-franc banknote.

**Litho. & Silk-Screened**

**2014, Jan. 20** ***Perf. 13***

**1115-1118** A482 Set of 4 4.75 4.75
*1118a* Souvenir sheet of 4, #1115-1118 4.75 4.75

Postal Check Center, 50th Anniv. A483

**2014, Jan. 27** **Litho.** ***Perf. 13x13¼***

**1119** A483 75fr multi 1.75 1.75

New Year 2014 (Year of the Horse) A484

**Litho. & Silk-Screened**

**2014, Jan. 31** ***Perf. 13***

**1120** A484 140fr multi 3.25 3.25

Intl. Year of Family Farming — A485

Designs: 75fr, Woman watering flower garden. 100fr, Farmers, fruits and vegetables.

**2014, Feb. 21** **Litho.** ***Perf. 13***

**1121-1122** A485 Set of 2 4.00 4.00

Intl. Women's Day A486

Design: 75fr, Head of woman with floral headdress. 100fr, Woman, vert.

***Perf. 13x13¼, 13¼x13***

**2014, Mar. 7** **Litho.**

**1123-1124** A486 Set of 2 4.00 4.00

Wild Boars A487

***Serpentine Die Cut 11***

**2014, Apr. 30** **Photo.**

**Self-Adhesive**

**1125** A487 100fr multi 2.40 2.40

A488

A489

A490

A491

A492

A493

***Serpentine Die Cut 11***

**2014, May 16** **Litho.**

**Self-Adhesive**

**1126** Booklet pane of 6 13.50
*a.* A488 100fr multi 2.25 2.25
*b.* A489 100fr multi 2.25 2.25
*c.* A490 100fr multi 2.25 2.25
*d.* A491 100fr multi 2.25 2.25
*e.* A492 100fr multi 2.25 2.25
*f.* A493 100fr multi 2.25 2.25

Graffiti art by Enos.

Sharks — A494

Designs: 10fr, Carcharhinus melanopterus. 40fr, Sphyrna mokarran. 75fr, Carcharhinus albimarginatus. 190fr, Galeocerdo cuvier.

**Litho. & Silk-Screened**

**2014, June 10** *Perf. 13*
**1127-1130** A494 Set of 4 7.25 7.25
*1130a* Souvenir sheet of 4, #1127-1130 7.25 7.25

Autonomy, 30th Anniv. — A495

**2014, June 27** **Litho.** *Perf. 13¼x13*
**1131** A495 75fr multi 1.75 1.75

Woman in Heiva Costume — A496

**2014, July 3** **Litho.** *Perf. 13¼x13*
**1132** A496 75fr multi 1.75 1.75

Jar of Honey, Honeybee and Honeycomb A497

**2014, Aug. 28** **Litho.** *Perf. 13x13¼*
**1133** A497 100fr multi 2.25 2.25

No. 1133 is impregnated with a honey scent.

Bombardment of Papeete, Cent. — A498

**Litho. & Engr.**

**2014, Sept. 30** *Perf. 13*
**1134** A498 300fr multi 6.50 6.50

World War I, cent.

Tiaré Flower A499

**2014, Nov. 6** **Litho.** *Perf. 13x13¼*
**1135** A499 2fr multi .25 .25

Sunset — A500

**2014, Nov. 6** **Litho.** *Perf. 13¼x13*
**1136** A500 77fr multi 1.60 1.60

Issuance of French Polynesia No. C30, 50th Anniv. A501

**2014, Nov. 6** **Litho.** *Perf. 13*
**1137** A501 500fr multi 10.50 10.50

Office of Posts and Telecommunications Emblem — A502

***Serpentine Die Cut 6¾ Vert.***

**2014, Nov. 6** **Litho.**

**Booklet Stamps Self-Adhesive**

**1138** A502 (75fr) deep blue 1.60 1.60
*a.* Booklet pane of 10 16.00
**1139** A502 (100fr) red 2.10 2.10
*a.* Booklet pane of 10 2.10

Legend of Pipiri Ma — A503

**2014, Dec. 12** **Litho.** *Perf. 13*
**1140** A503 75fr multi 1.50 1.50

Occupations A504

Designs: 10fr, Underwater spear fisherman. 20fr, Sculptor. 75fr, Masseuse, horiz. 100fr, Seamstress, horiz.

**2015, Jan. 29** **Litho.** *Perf. 13¼x13*
**1141** A504 10fr multi .25 .25
**1142** A504 20fr multi .40 .40

*Perf. 13x13¼*
**1143** A504 75fr multi 1.50 1.50
**1144** A504 100fr multi 1.90 1.90
*Nos. 1141-1144 (4)* 4.05 4.05

New Year 2015 (Year of the Goat) A505

**Litho. & Silk-Screened**

**2015, Feb. 19** *Perf. 13*
**1145** A505 140fr multi 2.60 2.60

Mama Dolphin at Sea Post Office A506

**2015, Mar. 26** **Litho.** *Perf. 13x13¼*
**1146** A506 75fr multi 1.40 1.40

Translation of Bible Into Tahitian by Henry Nott, 180th Anniv. — A507

Discovery of King George Islands by John Byron, 250th Anniv. — A508

**Litho. & Engr.**

**2015, May 13** *Perf. 13*
**1147** A507 140fr multi 2.60 2.60

**Litho.**

**1148** A508 190fr multi 3.50 3.50
*a.* Souvenir sheet of 2, #1147-1148 6.25 6.25

Coffee A509

**2015, July 1** **Litho.** *Perf. 13x13¼*
**1149** A509 100fr multi 1.90 1.90

No. 1149 is impregnated with a coffee scent.

Children's Art — A510

**2015, Aug. 1** **Litho.** *Perf. 13¼*
**1150** A510 1fr multi .25 .25

Orator A511

**2015, Aug. 5** **Litho.** *Perf. 13x13¼*
**1151** A511 80fr multi 1.50 1.50

Tropical Architecture A512

Designs: 80fr, Chez Vat Restaurant and Chez Alin Store. 100fr, Houses.

**2015, Aug. 14** **Litho.** *Perf. 13x13¼*
**1152-1153** A512 Set of 2 3.50 3.50

First Flight Between Tahiti and Santiago, Chile, 50th Anniv. A513

**2015, Aug. 31** **Litho.** *Perf. 13x13¼*
**1154** A513 80fr multi 1.50 1.50

1915 Postcard Depicting Papeete — A514

**2015, Sept. 29** **Litho.** *Perf. 13¼x13*
**1155** A514 300fr multi 5.75 5.75

Issuance of Tahiti No. B2, Cent. A515

**Litho. & Engr.**

**2015, Nov. 5** *Perf. 13¼x13*
**1156** A515 500fr multi 9.00 9.00
*a.* Souvenir sheet of 1 9.00 9.00

Sponges — A516

No. 1157: a, Clathrina n. sp. b, Dysidea n. sp. c, Haliclona n. sp. d, Ernstia n. sp. e, Stylissa flabelliformis. f, Darwinella n. sp.

*Serpentine Die Cut 11*

**2015, Nov. 5** **Litho.**

**Self-Adhesive**

**1157** Booklet pane of 6 10.50
*a.-f.* A516 100fr Any single 1.75 1.75

Papeete Market — A517

Designs: 80fr, Tower and awning. 100fr, Vendors and shoppers, horiz. 140fr, Fish vendors and shoppers, horiz.

**2015, Dec. 16** **Litho.** ***Perf. 13***

**1158-1160** A517 Set of 3 6.00 6.00

Ancient Adornments — A518

Designs: 10fr, Pa'e kea and pavahina. 20fr, Hei ku'a. 80fr, Peue kavi'i.

**2016, Jan. 29** **Litho.** ***Perf. 13x13¼***

**1161-1163** A518 Set of 3 2.00 2.00

New Year 2016 (Year of the Monkey) A519

**Litho. & Silk-screened**

**2016, Feb. 8** ***Perf. 13***

**1164** A519 140fr multi 2.60 2.60

Hikers — A520

*Serpentine Die Cut 11*

**2016, Mar. 18** **Litho.**

**Self-Adhesive**

**1165** A520 100fr multi 1.90 1.90

Ships — A521

Designs: 40fr, Queen Elizabeth 2. 80fr, France. 100fr, City of New York.

**Litho. & Silk-screened**

**2016, Apr. 22** ***Perf. 13***

**1166-1168** A521 Set of 3 4.25 4.25

Street Art in Papeete by Seth and HTJ — A522

**2016, May 27** **Litho.** ***Perf. 13***

**1169** A522 140fr multi 2.60 2.60

World Stamp Show 2016, New York.

Sandalwood — A523

**2016, June 17** **Litho.** ***Perf. 13x13¼***

**1170** A523 100fr multi 1.90 1.90

No. 1170 is impregnated with a sandalwood scent.

Miss Tahiti Pageant Winners — A524

No. 1171: a, Marie Moua, 1965. b, Moea Amiot, 1975. c, Ruth Manea, 1985. d, Timeri Baudry, 1995. e, Mihimana Sachet, 2005. f, Vaimiti Teiefitu, 2015.

*Serpentine Die Cut 11*

**2016, June 24** **Litho.**

**Self-Adhesive**

**1171** Booklet pane of 6 11.50
*a.-f.* A524 100fr Any single 1.90 1.90

See No. 1191.

Famous People Wearing Heiva Costumes A525

Designs: 80fr, Gilles Hollande. 100fr, Madeleine Moua (1899-1989).

**2016, July 11** **Litho.** ***Perf. 13¼x13***

**1172-1173** A525 Set of 2 3.50 3.50

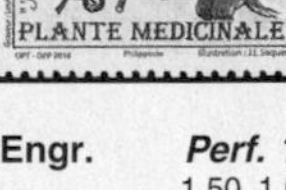

Premna Serratifolia A526

**2016, Aug. 12** **Engr.** ***Perf. 13***

**1174** A526 80fr multi 1.50 1.50

Woman and Plum Blossoms A527

**2016, Oct. 21** **Litho.** ***Perf. 13x13¼***

**1175** A527 300fr multi 5.75 5.75
*a.* Souvenir sheet of 1 5.75 5.75

PhilaTaipei 2016 International Philatelic Exhibition, Taipei.

Francis Ariioehau Sanford (1912-96), Politician A528

**2016, Nov. 3** **Engr.** ***Perf. 13***

**1176** A528 500fr multi 9.00 9.00

A529

A530

A531

A532

A533

Men — A534

*Serpentine Die Cut 11*

**2016, Nov. 3** **Litho.**

**Self-Adhesive**

**1177** Booklet pane of 6 10.50
*a.* A529 100fr multi 1.75 1.75
*b.* A530 100fr multi 1.75 1.75
*c.* A531 100fr multi 1.75 1.75
*d.* A532 100fr multi 1.75 1.75
*e.* A533 100fr multi 1.75 1.75
*f.* A534 100fr multi 1.75 1.75

Birds — A535

Designs: 80fr, Striated heron (héron strié). 100fr, Southern Marquesan reed warbler (rousserolle des Marquises).

**2016, Dec. 9** **Litho.** ***Perf. 13***

**1178-1179** A535 Set of 2 3.25 3.25
*1179a* Souvenir sheet of 2, #1178-1179 3.25 3.25

Society for Oceania Studics, Cent. — A536

**2017, Jan. 2** **Litho.** ***Perf. 13¼x13***

**1180** A536 100fr multi 1.75 1.75

Shells — A537

No. 1181: a, Lentigo lentiginosus. b, Mitra papalis. c, Monoplex aquatilis. d, Conus nussatella. e, Oxymeris maculata. f, Drupa clathrata.

*Serpentine Die Cut 11*

**2017, Jan. 3** **Litho.**

**Self-Adhesive**

**1181** Booklet pane of 6 10.50
*a.-f.* A537 100fr Any single 1.75 1.75

New Year 2017 (Year of the Rooster) A538

**Litho. & Silk-Screened**

**2017, Jan. 27** ***Perf. 13***

**1182** A538 140fr multi 2.60 2.60

Henri Cadousteau (1890-1946), Fighter Pilot, and Salmson 2A2 — A539

**Litho. & Silk-Screened**

**2017, Feb. 17** ***Perf. 13***

**1183** A539 80fr multi 1.40 1.40

International Women's Day — A540

Women wearing headdresses: 80fr, 100fr.

**2017, Mar. 8 Litho. *Perf. 13¼x13***
**1184-1185** A540 Set of 2 3.25 3.25

Polynesian Women of the Bounty — A541

**2017, Mar. 30 Litho. *Perf. 13***
**1186** A541 140fr multi 2.50 2.50

See Pitcairn Islands No. 827.

Underwater Scenes A542

Designs: 10fr, Woman laying on sea floor and ray. 20fr, Diver and school of fish. 80fr, Diver on sea floor and school of fish. 100fr, Woman sitting on sea floor and ray, diff.

**2017, May 5 Litho. *Perf. 13x13¼***
**1187-1190** A542 Set of 4 4.00 4.00
*1190a* Souvenir sheet of 4, #1187-1190 4.00 4.00

**Miss Tahiti Pageant Winners Type of 2016**

No. 1191: a, Sonia Agnieray, 1966. b, Patricia Servonnat, 1976. c, Loana Bohl, 1986. d, Hinerava Hiro, 1996. e, Tehere Pere, 2006. f, Vaea Ferrand, 2016.

***Serpentine Die Cut 11***
**2017, June 23 Litho.**
**Self-Adhesive**
**1191** Booklet pane of 6 11.50
*a.-f.* A524 100fr Any single 1.90 1.90

Oranges A543

**2017, June 23 Litho. *Perf. 13x13¼***
**1192** A543 100fr multi 1.90 1.90

No. 1192 is impregnated with an orange scent.

Heiva Celebration Dancers — A544

**2017, July 13 Litho. *Perf. 13¼x13***
**1193** A544 80fr multi 1.60 1.60

Lions Clubs International, Cent. — A545

**2017, Aug. 25 Litho. *Perf. 13¼x13***
**1194** A545 190fr multi 3.75 3.75

Cats and Dogs — A546

No. 1195: a, Cat named Kitty. b, Cat named Gribouille. c, Cat named Caramel. d, Dog named Peanuts. e, Dog named Lolly. f, Dog named Sydney.

***Serpentine Die Cut 11***
**2017, Aug. 25 Litho.**
**Self-Adhesive**
**1195** Booklet pane of 6 12.00
*a.-f.* A546 100fr Any single 2.00 2.00

Navigators and Boats — A547

Boat and: 40fr, Rodolphe Tuko Harry Williams (1920-86). 100fr, Francis Puara Cowan (1926-2009).

**2017, Sept. 27 Engr. *Perf. 13***
**1196-1197** A547 Set of 2 2.75 2.75

Hina Natua, 2017 Miss Heiva A548

**2017, Oct. 24 Litho. *Perf. 13***
**1198** A548 300fr multi 6.00 6.00

Brasilia 2017 International Philatelic Exhibition, Brasilia, Brazil.

Halloween A549

***Serpentine Die Cut 11***
**2017, Oct. 27 Litho.**
**Self-Adhesive**
**1199** A549 80fr multi 1.60 1.60

## SEMI-POSTAL STAMPS

Nos. 55 and 26 Surcharged in Red

**1915 Unwmk. *Perf. 14x13½***
**B1** A1 10c + 5c red 32.50 32.50
*a.* "e" instead of "c" 87.50 87.50
*b.* Inverted surcharge 225.00 225.00
*c.* Double surcharge 525.00 525.00
**B2** A2 10c + 5c rose & org 12.50 12.50
*a.* "e" instead of "c" 65.00 65.00
*b.* "c" inverted 65.00 65.00
*c.* Inverted surcharge 300.00 300.00
*d.* As "a," inverted surcharge 400.00
*e.* As "b," inverted surcharge 400.00

Surcharged in Carmine

**B3** A2 10c + 5c rose & org 5.50 5.50
*a.* "e" instead of "c" 45.00 45.00
*b.* Inverted surcharge 200.00 200.00
*c.* Double surcharge 200.00 200.00
*d.* As "a," inverted surcharge 325.00

Surcharged in Carmine

**1916**
**B4** A2 10c + 5c rose & org 5.50 5.50

**Curie Issue**
Common Design Type

**1938 Engr. *Perf. 13***
**B5** CD80 1.75fr + 50c brt ultra 20.00 20.00

**French Revolution Issue**
Common Design Type

**1939 Photo.**
**Name and Value Typo. in Black**
**B6** CD83 45c + 25c grn 17.50 17.50
**B7** CD83 70c + 30c brn 17.50 17.50
**B8** CD83 90c + 35c red org 17.50 17.50
**B9** CD83 1.25fr + 1fr rose pink 17.50 17.50
**B10** CD83 2.25fr + 2fr blue 17.50 17.50
*Nos. B6-B10 (5)* 87.50 87.50
Set, never hinged 145.00

**Catalogue values for unused stamps in this section, from this point to the end of the section, are for Never Hinged items.**

**Common Design Type and**

Marine Officer — SP1

"L'Astrolabe" — SP2

**1941 Photo. *Perf. 13½***
**B11** SP1 1fr + 1fr red 3.50
**B12** CD86 1.50fr + 3fr maroon 3.50
**B12A** SP2 2.50fr + 1fr blue 3.50
*Nos. B11-B12A (3)* 10.50

Nos. B11-B12A were issued by the Vichy government in France, and were not placed on sale in French Polynesia.

Nos. 125A-125B Srchd. in Black or Red

**1944 Engr. *Perf. 12½x12***
**B12B** 50c + 1.50fr on 2.50fr deep blue (R) 1.75
**B12C** + 2.50fr on 1fr green 1.75

Colonial Development Fund.

Nos. B12B-B12C were issued by the Vichy government in France, but were not placed on sale in French Polynesia.

**Red Cross Issue**
Common Design Type

**1944 Photo. *Perf. 14½x14***
**B13** CD90 5fr + 20fr peacock blue 2.00 1.60

The surtax was for the French Red Cross and national relief.

**Tropical Medicine Issue**
Common Design Type

**1950, July 17 Engr. *Perf. 13***
**B14** CD100 10fr + 2fr dk bl grn & dk grn 10.50 8.00

The surtax was for charitable work.

## AIR POST STAMPS

Seaplane in Flight AP1

***Perf. 13½***
**1934, Nov. 5 Unwmk. Photo.**
**C1** AP1 5fr green 1.25 1.25

For overprint see No. C2.
For Type AP1 without "RF," see Nos. C1A-C1D.

**Type of 1934 without "RF" and**

Beach Scene — AP1a

***Perf. 13½, 13 (#C1E)***
**1944 Photo, Engr. (#C1E)**
**C1A** AP1 5fr green .70
**C1B** AP1 10fr black 1.00
**C1C** AP1 20fr orange 1.10
**C1D** AP1 50fr gray blue 1.50
**C1E** AP1a 100fr turquoise blue 2.00
*Nos. C1A-C1E (5)* 6.30

Nos. C1A-C1E were issued by the Vichy government in France, but were not placed on sale in French Polynesia.

**Catalogue values for unused stamps in this section, from this point to the end of the section, are for Never Hinged items.**

No. C1 Overprinted in Red

**1941**

**C2** AP1 5fr green 7.25 4.75

### Common Design Type

**1942** ***Perf. 14½x14***

**C3** CD87 1fr dark orange .90 .65
**C4** CD87 1.50fr bright red .95 .70
**C5** CD87 5fr brown red 1.25 .95
**C6** CD87 10fr black 1.90 1.40
**C7** CD87 25fr ultra 2.75 2.10
**C8** CD87 50fr dark green 3.00 2.10
**C9** CD87 100fr plum 3.00 2.10
*Nos. C3-C9 (7)* 13.75 10.00

### Victory Issue

Common Design Type

**1946, May 8 Engr.** ***Perf. 12½***

**C10** CD92 8fr dark green 2.75 2.00

### Chad to Rhine Issue

Common Design Types

**1946, June 6**

**C11** CD93 5fr red orange 2.10 1.60
**C12** CD94 10fr dk olive bis 2.10 1.60
**C13** CD95 15fr dk yellow grn 2.10 1.60
**C14** CD96 20fr carmine 2.75 2.10
**C15** CD97 25fr dk rose violet 4.00 3.00
**C16** CD98 50fr black 4.50 3.50
*Nos. C11-C16 (6)* 17.55 13.40

Shearwater and Moorea Landscape — AP2

Fishermen — AP3

Shearwater over Maupiti Shoreline — AP4

**1948, Mar. 1 Unwmk.** ***Perf. 13***

**C17** AP2 50fr red brown 30.00 11.00
**C18** AP3 100fr purple 24.00 8.00
**C19** AP4 200fr blue green 52.50 17.50
*Nos. C17-C19 (3)* 106.50 36.50

### UPU Issue

Common Design Type

**1949**

**C20** CD99 10fr deep blue 20.00 15.00

Gauguin's "Nafea faaipoipo" — AP5

**1953, Sept. 24**

**C21** AP5 14fr dk brn, dk gray grn & red 80.00 65.00

50th anniv. of the death of Paul Gauguin.

### Liberation Issue

Common Design Type

**1954, June 6**

**C22** CD102 3fr dk grnsh bl & bl grn 10.00 8.00

Bahia Peak, Borabora — AP6

**1955, Sept. 26 Unwmk.** ***Perf. 13***

**C23** AP6 13fr indigo & blue 10.00 5.50

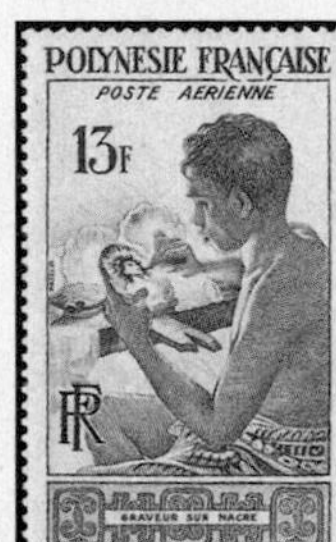


Mother-of-Pearl Artist — AP7

Designs: 50fr, "Women of Tahiti," Gauguin, horiz. 100fr, "The White Horse," Gauguin. 200fr, Night fishing at Moorea, horiz.

**1958, Nov. 3 Engr.** ***Perf. 13***

**C24** AP7 13fr multicolored 13.00 4.50
**C25** AP7 50fr multicolored 12.00 4.50
**C26** AP7 100fr multicolored 20.00 7.25
**C27** AP7 200fr lilac & slate 40.00 21.00
*Nos. C24-C27 (4)* 85.00 37.25

Airport, Papeete — AP8

**1960, Nov. 19**

**C28** AP8 13fr rose lil, vio, & yel grn 3.50 2.40

### Telstar Issue

Common Design Type

**1962, Dec. 5** ***Perf. 13***

**C29** CD111 50fr red lil, mar & vio bl 11.50 8.00

Tahitian Dancer — AP10

**1964, May 14 Photo.** ***Perf. 13***

**C30** AP10 15fr multicolored 4.75 2.00

Map of Tahiti and Free French Emblems — AP11

**1964, July 10 Unwmk.**

**C31** AP11 16fr multicolored 15.00 9.00

Issued to commemorate the rallying of French Polynesia to the Free French cause.

Moorea Scene — AP12

**1964, Dec. 1 Litho.** ***Perf. 13***

**C32** AP12 23fr multicolored 9.50 4.00

### ITU Issue

Common Design Type

**1965, May 17 Engr.** ***Perf. 13***

**C33** CD120 50fr vio, red brn & bl 80.00 52.50

Paul Gauguin — AP13

Design: 25fr, Gauguin Museum (stylized). 40fr, Primitive statues at Gauguin Museum.

**1965 Engr.** ***Perf. 13***

**C34** AP13 25fr olive green 7.50 4.50
**C35** AP13 40fr blue green 15.00 8.00
**C36** AP13 75fr brt red brown 20.00 15.00
*Nos. C34-C36 (3)* 42.50 27.50

Opening of Gauguin Museum, Papeete. Issued: 25fr, 75fr, 6/13. 40fr, 11/7.

Skin Diver with Spear Gun — AP14

**1965, Sept. 1 Engr.** ***Perf. 13***

**C37** AP14 50fr red brn, dl bl & dk grn 90.00 55.00

World Championships in Underwater Fishing, Tuamotu Archipelago, Sept. 1965.

Painting from a School Dining Room — AP15

**1965, Nov. 29**

**C38** AP15 80fr brn, bl, dl bl & red 22.50 17.50

School Canteen Program.

Radio Tower, Globe and Palm — AP16

**1965, Dec. 29 Engr.** ***Perf. 13***

**C39** AP16 60fr org, grn & dk brn 19.00 15.00

50th anniversary of the first radio link between Tahiti and France.

### French Satellite A-1 Issue

Common Design Type

Designs: 7fr, Diamant Rocket and launching installations. 10fr, A-1 satellite.

**1966, Feb. 7**

**C40** CD121 7fr choc, dp grn & lil 6.75 6.00
**C41** CD121 10fr lil, dp grn & dk brn 6.75 6.00
*a.* Pair, #C40-C41 + label 14.00 14.00

### French Satellite D-1 Issue

Common Design Type

**1966, May 10 Engr.** ***Perf. 13***

**C42** CD122 20fr multicolored 7.00 4.75

Papeete Harbor — AP17

**1966, June 30 Photo.** ***Perf. 13***

**C43** AP17 50fr multicolored 15.00 11.00

"Vive Tahiti" by A. Benichou — AP18

**1966, Nov. 28 Photo.** ***Perf. 13***

**C44** AP18 13fr multicolored 11.00 6.50

Explorer's Ship and Canoe — AP19

Designs: 60fr, Polynesian costume and ship. 80fr, Louis Antoine de Bougainville, vert.

**1968, Apr. 6 Engr.** ***Perf. 13***

**C45** AP19 40fr multicolored 8.75 3.25
**C46** AP19 60fr multicolored 11.50 6.50
**C47** AP19 80fr multicolored 14.50 8.75
*a.* Souv. sheet, #C45-C47 160.00 160.00
*Nos. C45-C47 (3)* 34.75 18.50

200th anniv. of the discovery of Tahiti by Louis Antoine de Bougainville. Issued: 40fr, 4/6/68.

The Meal, by Paul Gauguin — AP20

**1968, July 30 Photo.** ***Perf. 12x12½***
**C48** AP20 200fr multicolored 40.00 32.50

See Nos. C63-C67, C78-C82, C89-C93, C98.

Shot Put — AP21

**1968, Oct. 12 Engr.** ***Perf. 13***
**C49** AP21 35fr dk car rose & brt grn 16.00 9.00

19th Olympic Games, Mexico City, 10/12-27.

### Concorde Issue
Common Design Type

**1969, Apr. 17**
**C50** CD129 40fr red brn & car rose 55.00 35.00

PATA 1970 Poster — AP22

**1969, July 9 Photo.** ***Perf. 12½x13***
**C51** AP22 25fr blue & multi 17.50 7.25

Issued to publicize PATA 1970 (Pacific Area Travel Association Congress), Tahiti.

Underwater Fishing — AP23

52fr, Hand holding fish made up of flags, vert.

**1969, Aug. 5 Photo.** ***Perf. 13***
**C52** AP23 48fr blk, grnsh bl & red lil 35.00 13.50
**C53** AP23 52fr bl, blk & red 40.00 22.50

Issued to publicize the World Underwater Fishing Championships.

Gen. Bonaparte as Commander of the Army in Italy, by Jean Sebastien Rouillard — AP24

**1969, Oct. 15 Photo.** ***Perf. 12½x12***
**C54** AP24 100fr car & multi 80.00 67.50

Bicentenary of the birth of Napoleon Bonaparte (1769-1821).

Eiffel Tower, Torii and EXPO Emblem — AP25

Design: 30fr, Mount Fuji, Tower of the Sun and EXPO emblem, horiz.

**1970, Sept. 15 Photo.** ***Perf. 13***
**C55** AP25 30fr multicolored 20.00 8.00
**C56** AP25 50fr multicolored 27.50 12.00

EXPO '70 International Exposition, Osaka, Japan, Mar. 15-Sept. 13.

Pearl Diver Descending, and Basket — AP26

Designs: 5fr, Diver collecting oysters. 18fr, Implantation into oyster, horiz. 27fr, Open oyster with pearl. 50fr, Woman with mother of pearl jewelry.

**1970, Sept. 30 Engr.** ***Perf. 13***
**C57** AP26 2fr slate, grnsh bl & red brn 1.50 .90
**C58** AP26 5fr grnsh blue, ultra & org 2.75 1.50
**C59** AP26 18fr sl, mag & org 3.75 2.75
**C60** AP26 27fr brt pink, brn & dl lil 9.25 4.75
**C61** AP26 50fr gray, red brn & org 16.00 7.50
*Nos. C57-C61 (5)* 33.25 17.40

Pearl industry of French Polynesia.

The Thinker, by Auguste Rodin and Education Year Emblem — AP27

**1970, Oct. 15 Engr.** ***Perf. 13***
**C62** AP27 50fr bl, ind & fawn 17.00 10.50

International Education Year.

### Painting Type of 1968

Paintings by Artists Living in Polynesia: 20fr, Woman on the Beach, by Yves de Saint-Front. 40fr, Abstract, by Frank Fay. 60fr, Woman and Shells, by Jean Guillois. 80fr, Hut under Palms, by Jean Masson. 100fr, Polynesian Girl, by Jean-Charles Bouloc, vert.

***Perf. 12x12½, 12½x12***
**1970, Dec. 14 Photo.**
**C63** AP20 20fr brn & multi 8.00 4.00
**C64** AP20 40fr brn & multi 12.00 7.50
**C65** AP20 60fr brn & multi 16.00 11.00
**C66** AP20 80fr brn & multi 20.00 16.00
**C67** AP20 100fr brn & multi 26.00 22.50
*Nos. C63-C67 (5)* 82.00 61.00

South Pacific Games Emblem — AP28

**1971, Jan. 26** ***Perf. 12½***
**C68** AP28 20fr ultra & multi 8.00 5.00

Publicity for 4th South Pacific Games, held in Papeete, Sept. 8-19, 1971.

Memorial Flame — AP29

**1971, Mar. 19 Photo.** ***Perf. 12½***
**C69** AP29 5fr multicolored 8.00 5.00

In memory of Charles de Gaulle.

Soldier and Badge — AP30

**1971, Apr. 21**
**C70** AP30 25fr multicolored 11.00 6.75

30th anniversary of departure of Tahitian volunteers to serve in World War II.

### Water Sports Type

Designs: 15fr, Surfing, vert. 16fr, Skin diving, vert. 20fr, Water-skiing with kite.

**1971, May 11 Photo.** ***Perf. 13***
**C71** A44 15fr multicolored 6.50 3.50
**C72** A44 16fr multicolored 7.50 3.25
**C73** A44 20fr multicolored 11.00 7.75
*Nos. C71-C73 (3)* 25.00 14.50

Sailing AP31

**1971, Sept. 8** ***Perf. 12½***
**C74** AP31 15fr shown 6.50 3.50
**C75** AP31 18fr Golf 8.00 4.75
**C76** AP31 27fr Archery 12.00 7.25
**C77** AP31 53fr Tennis 20.00 13.50
*a.* Souv. sheet, #C74-C77 190.00 190.00
*Nos. C74-C77 (4)* 46.50 29.00

4th So. Pacific Games, Papeete, Sept. 8-19.

### Painting Type of 1968

Paintings by Artists Living in Polynesia: 20fr, Hut and Palms, by Isabelle Wolf. 40fr, Palms on Shore, by André Dobrowolski. 60fr, Polynesian Woman, by Françoise Séli, vert. 80fr, Holy Family, by Pierre Heymann, vert. 100fr, Crowd, by Nicolai Michoutouchkine.

**1971, Dec. 15 Photo.** ***Perf. 13***
**C78** AP20 20fr multicolored 7.50 4.50
**C79** AP20 40fr multicolored 11.00 7.50
**C80** AP20 60fr multicolored 13.00 10.00
**C81** AP20 80fr multicolored 18.00 12.50
**C82** AP20 100fr multicolored 30.00 22.50
*Nos. C78-C82 (5)* 79.50 57.00

Papeete Harbor — AP32

**1972, Jan. 13**
**C83** AP32 28fr violet & multi 11.00 8.00

Free port of Papeete, 10th anniversary.

Figure Skating and Dragon AP33

**1972, Jan. 25 Engr.** ***Perf. 13***
**C84** AP33 20fr ultra, lake & brt grn 9.00 7.00

11th Winter Olympic Games, Sapporo, Japan, Feb. 3-13.

South Pacific Commission Headquarters, Noumea — AP34

**1972, Feb. 5 Photo.** ***Perf. 13***
**C85** AP34 21fr blue & multi 11.00 5.25

South Pacific Commission, 25th anniv.

Festival Emblem — AP35

**1972, May 9 Engr.** ***Perf. 13***
**C86** AP35 36fr orange, bl & grn 8.00 5.25

So. Pacific Festival of Arts, Fiji, May 6-20.

Kon Tiki and Route, Callao to Tahiti — AP36

**1972, Aug. 18 Photo. *Perf. 13***

**C87** AP36 16fr dk & lt bl, blk & org 10.00 6.50

25th anniversary of the arrival of the raft Kon Tiki in Tahiti.

Charles de Gaulle and Memorial — AP37

**1972, Dec. 9 Engr. *Perf. 13***

**C88** AP37 100fr slate 62.50 42.50

### Painting Type of 1968

Paintings by Artists Living in Polynesia: 20fr, Horses, by Georges Bovy. 40fr, Sailboats, by Ruy Juventin, vert. 60fr, Harbor, by André Brooke. 80fr, Farmers, by Daniel Adam, vert. 100fr, Dancers, by Aloysius Pilioko, vert.

**1972, Dec. 14 Photo.**

**C89** AP20 20fr gold & multi 9.75 4.25
**C90** AP20 40fr gold & multi 12.00 6.75
**C91** AP20 60fr gold & multi 21.00 9.50
**C92** AP20 80fr dk grn, buff & dk brn 27.50 13.00
**C93** AP20 100fr gold & multi 32.50 25.00
*Nos. C89-C93 (5)* 102.75 58.50

St. Teresa and Lisieux Basilica AP38

**1973, Jan. 23 Engr. *Perf. 13***

**C94** AP38 85fr multicolored 25.00 17.50

Centenary of the birth of St. Teresa of Lisieux (1873-1897), Carmelite nun.

Nicolaus Copernicus — AP39

**1973, Mar. 7 Engr. *Perf. 13***

**C95** AP39 100fr brn, vio bl & red lil 30.00 17.50

Copernicus (1473-1543), Polish astronomer.

Plane over Tahiti — AP40

**1973, Apr. 3 Photo. *Perf. 13***

**C96** AP40 80fr ultra, gold & lt grn 22.50 16.00

Air France's World Tour via Tahiti.

DC-10 at Papeete Airport — AP41

**1973, May 18 Engr. *Perf. 13***

**C97** AP41 20fr bl, ultra & sl grn 16.00 9.00

Start of DC-10 service.

### Painting Type of 1968

Design: 200fr, "Ta Matete" (seated women), by Paul Gauguin.

**1973, June 7 Photo. *Perf. 13***

**C98** AP20 200fr multicolored 27.50 20.00

Paul Gauguin (1848-1903), painter.

Pierre Loti and Characters from his Books — AP42

**1973, July 4 Engr. *Perf. 13***

**C99** AP42 60fr multicolored 40.00 20.00

Pierre Loti (1850-1923), French naval officer and writer.

Woman with Flowers, by Eliane de Gennes AP43

Paintings by Artists Living in Polynesia: 20fr, Sun, by Jean Francois Favre. 60fr, Seascape, by Alain Sidet. 80fr, Crowded Bus, by Francois Ravello. 100fr, Stylized Boats, by Jackie Bourdin, horiz.

**1973, Dec. 13 Photo. *Perf. 13***

**C100** AP43 20fr gold & multi 8.00 2.75
**C101** AP43 40fr gold & multi 11.50 6.00
**C102** AP43 60fr gold & multi 17.00 10.50
**C103** AP43 80fr gold & multi 22.50 17.00
**C104** AP43 100fr gold & multi 27.50 20.00
*Nos. C100-C104 (5)* 86.50 56.25

Bird, Fish, Flower and Water — AP44

**1974, June 12 Photo. *Perf. 13***

**C105** AP44 12fr blue & multi 7.50 5.25

Nature protection.

Catamaran under Sail — AP45

**1974, July 22 Engr. *Perf. 13***

**C106** AP45 100fr multicolored 27.50 16.00

2nd Catamaran World Championships.

Still-life, by Rosine Temarui-Masson — AP46

Paintings by Artists Living in Polynesia: 40fr, Palms and House on Beach, by Marcel Chardon. 60fr, Man, by Marie-Françoise Avril. 80fr, Polynesian Woman, by Henriette Robin. 100fr, Lagoon by Moon-light, by David Farsi, horiz.

**1974, Dec. 12 Photo. *Perf. 13***

**C107** AP46 20fr gold & multi 18.00 8.50
**C108** AP46 40fr gold & multi 27.50 9.50
**C109** AP46 60fr gold & multi 32.50 12.00
**C110** AP46 80fr gold & multi 45.00 16.50
**C111** AP46 100fr gold & multi 65.00 27.50
*Nos. C107-C111 (5)* 188.00 74.00

See Nos. C122-C126.

Polynesian Gods of Travel — AP47

Designs: 75fr, Tourville hydroplane, 1929. 100fr, Passengers leaving plane.

**1975, Feb. 7 Engr. *Perf. 13***

**C112** AP47 50fr sep, pur & brn 11.00 6.00
**C113** AP47 75fr grn, bl & red 16.00 8.00
**C114** AP47 100fr grn, sep & car 25.00 15.00
*Nos. C112-C114 (3)* 52.00 29.00

Fifty years of Tahitian aviation.

French Ceres Stamp and Woman — AP48

**1975, May 29 Engr. *Perf. 13***

**C115** AP48 32fr ver, brn & blk 8.00 5.00

ARPHILA 75 International Philatelic Exhibition, Paris, June 6-16.

Shot Put and Games' Emblem AP50

**1975, Aug. 1 Photo. *Perf. 13***

**C117** AP50 25fr shown 4.75 3.00
**C118** AP50 30fr Volleyball 7.00 3.75
**C119** AP50 40fr Women's swimming 9.25 5.25
*Nos. C117-C119 (3)* 21.00 12.00

5th South Pacific Games, Guam, Aug. 1-10.

Flowers, Athlete, View of Montreal — AP51

**1975, Oct. 15 Engr. *Perf. 13***

**C120** AP51 44fr brt bl, ver & blk 11.00 6.50

Pre-Olympic Year 1975.

UPU Emblem, Jet and Letters — AP52

**1975, Nov. 5 Engr. *Perf. 13***

**C121** AP52 100fr brn, bl & ol 22.50 13.00

World Universal Postal Union Day.

### Paintings Type of 1974

Paintings by Artists Living in Polynesia: 20fr, Beach Scene, by R. Marcel Marius, horiz. 40fr, Roofs with TV antennas, by M. Anglade, horiz. 60fr, Street scene with bus, by J. Day, horiz. 80fr, Tropical waters (fish), by J. Steimetz. 100fr, Women, by A. van der Heyde.

**1975, Dec. 17 Litho. *Perf. 13***

**C122** AP46 20fr gold & multi 3.00 1.75
**C123** AP46 40fr gold & multi 6.00 3.00
**C124** AP46 60fr gold & multi 9.00 4.50
**C125** AP46 80fr gold & multi 12.00 7.50
**C126** AP46 100fr gold & multi 14.50 12.00
*Nos. C122-C126 (5)* 44.50 28.75

Concorde — AP53

**1976, Jan. 21 Engr. *Perf. 13***

**C127** AP53 100fr car, bl & ind 19.00 13.00

First commercial flight of supersonic jet Concorde from Paris to Rio, Jan. 21.

Adm. Rodney, Count de la Perouse, "Barfleur" and "Triomphant" in Battle — AP54

31fr, Count de Grasse and Lord Graves, "Ville de Paris" & "Le Terible" in Chesapeake Bay Battle.

**1976, Apr. 15 Engr. *Perf. 13***

**C128** AP54 24fr grnsh bl, lt brn & blk 5.00 2.50
**C129** AP54 31fr mag, red & lt brn 5.75 3.50

American Bicentennial.

King Pomaré I — AP55

Portraits: 21fr, King Pomaré II. 26fr, Queen Pomaré IV. 30fr, King Pomaré V.

**1976, Apr. 28 Litho. *Perf. 12½***

**C130** AP55 18fr olive & multi 1.75 .75
**C131** AP55 21fr multicolored 2.00 1.10
**C132** AP55 26fr gray & multi 2.75 1.25
**C133** AP55 30fr plum & multi 3.00 1.90
*Nos. C130-C133 (4)* 9.50 5.00

Pomaré Dynasty. See Nos. C141-C144.

Running and Maple Leaf — AP56

Designs: 34fr, Long jump, vert. 50fr, Olympic flame and flowers.

**1976, July 19 Engr. *Perf. 13***

**C134** AP56 26fr ultra & multi 4.25 2.10
**C135** AP56 34fr ultra & multi 6.00 2.75
**C136** AP56 50fr ultra & multi 11.50 5.00
*a.* Min. sheet, #C134-C136 90.00 90.00
*Nos. C134-C136 (3)* 21.75 9.85

21st Olympic Games, Montreal, Canada, July 17-Aug. 1.

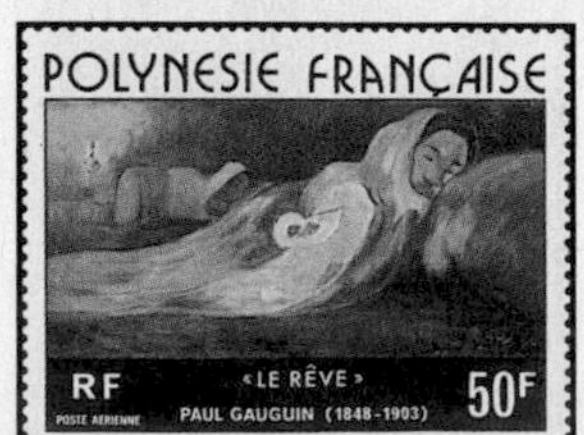


The Dream, by Paul Gauguin — AP57

**1976, Oct. 17 Photo. *Perf. 13***

**C137** AP57 50fr multicolored 11.00 7.25

Murex Steeriae — AP58

Sea Shells: 27fr, Conus Gauguini. 35fr, Conus marchionatus.

**1977, Mar. 14 Photo. *Perf. 12½x13***

**C138** AP58 25fr vio bl & multi 4.25 1.25
**C139** AP58 27fr ultra & multi 4.25 1.50
**C140** AP58 35fr blue & multi 5.00 2.00
*Nos. C138-C140 (3)* 13.50 4.75

See Nos. C156-C158.

**Royalty Type of 1976**

19fr, King Maputeoa, Mangareva. 33fr, King Camatoa V, Raiatea. 39fr, Queen Vaekehu, Marquesas. 43fr, King Teurarii III, Rurutu.

**1977, Apr. 19 Litho. *Perf. 12½***

**C141** AP55 19fr dull red & multi 1.25 .95
**C142** AP55 33fr dk blue & multi 1.90 1.25
**C143** AP55 39fr ultra & multi 1.90 1.25
**C144** AP55 43fr green & multi 2.75 1.90
*Nos. C141-C144 (4)* 7.80 5.35

Polynesian rulers.

Pocillopora AP59

Design: 25fr, Acropora, horiz.

***Perf. 13x12½, 12½x13***

**1977, May 23 Photo.**

**C145** AP59 25fr multicolored 1.90 1.10
**C146** AP59 33fr multicolored 2.75 1.90

3rd Symposium on Coral Reefs, Miami, Fla. See Nos. C162-C163.

De Gaulle Memorial — AP60

**Photogravure and Embossed**

**1977, June 18 *Perf. 13***

**C147** AP60 40fr gold & multi 7.00 5.00

5th anniversary of dedication of De Gaulle memorial at Colombey-les-Deux-Eglises.

Tahitian Dancer — AP61

**1977, July 14 Litho. *Perf. 12½***

**C148** AP61 27fr multicolored 4.00 2.50

Charles A. Lindbergh and Spirit of St. Louis — AP62

**1977, Aug. 18 Litho. *Perf. 12½***

**C149** AP62 28fr multicolored 7.00 3.50

Lindbergh's solo transatlantic flight from New York to Paris, 50th anniv.

Mahoe — AP63

**1977, Sept. 15 Photo. *Perf. 12½x13***

**C150** AP63 8fr shown 1.40 .80
**C151** AP63 12fr Frangipani 1.75 1.25

Palms on Shore — AP64

**1977, Nov. 8 Photo. *Perf. 12½x13***

**C152** AP64 32fr multicolored 10.00 4.50

Ecology, protection of trees.

Rubens' Son Albert AP65

**1977, Nov. 28 Engr. *Perf. 13***

**C153** AP65 100fr grnsh blk & rose cl 11.00 8.00

Peter Paul Rubens (1577-1640), painter, 400th birth anniversary.

Capt. Cook and "Discovery" — AP66

Design: 39fr, Capt. Cook and "Resolution."

**1978, Jan. 20 Engr. *Perf. 13***

**C154** AP66 33fr multicolored 2.50 3.00
**C155** AP66 39fr multicolored 3.00 3.50

Bicentenary of Capt. James Cook's arrival in Hawaii.

For overprints see Nos. C166-C167.

**Shell Type of 1977**

Sea Shells: 22fr, Erosaria obvelata. 24fr, Cypraea ventriculus. 31fr, Lambis robusta.

**1978, Apr. 13 Photo. *Perf. 13½x13***

**C156** AP58 22fr brt blue & multi 2.25 1.25
**C157** AP58 24fr brt blue & multi 2.25 1.50
**C158** AP58 31fr brt blue & multi 3.50 2.50
*Nos. C156-C158 (3)* 8.00 5.25

Tahitian Woman and Boy, by Gauguin AP67

**1978, May 7 *Perf. 13***

**C159** AP67 50fr multicolored 8.75 5.25

Paul Gauguin (1848-1903).

Antenna and ITU Emblem AP68

**1978, May 17 Litho. *Perf. 13***

**C160** AP68 80fr gray & multi 6.00 3.25

10th World Telecommunications Day.

Soccer and Argentina '78 Emblem — AP69

**1978, June 1**

**C161** AP69 28fr multicolored 3.25 2.10

11th World Cup Soccer Championship, Argentina, June 1-25.

**Coral Type of 1977**

Designs: 26fr, Fungia, horiz. 34fr, Millepora.

***Perf. 13x12½, 12½x13***

**1978, July 13 Photo.**

**C162** AP59 26fr multicolored 1.75 1.25
**C163** AP59 34fr multicolored 2.25 1.60

Radar Antenna, Polynesian Woman — AP70

**1978, Sept. 5 Engr. *Perf. 13***

**C164** AP70 50fr blue & black 3.00 1.75

Papenoo earth station.

Bird and Rainbow over Island — AP71

**1978, Oct. 5** **Photo.**
**C165** AP71 23fr multicolored 6.00 1.75

Nature protection.

**Nos. C154-C155 Overprinted**

No. C166

No. C167

**1979, Feb. 14** **Engr.** ***Perf. 13***
**C166** AP66 33fr multi 4.00 2.50
**C167** AP66 39fr multi (VBl) 5.00 3.50

Bicentenary of Capt. Cook's death. On No. C167 date is last line of overprint.

Children, Toys and IYC Emblem — AP72

**1979, May 3** **Engr.** ***Perf. 13***
**C168** AP72 150fr multicolored 12.00 7.00

International Year of the Child.

"Do you expect a letter?" by Paul Gauguin — AP73

**1979, May 20** **Photo.** ***Perf. 13***
**C169** AP73 200fr multicolored 16.00 8.00

Shell and Carved Head — AP74

**1979, June 30** **Engr.** ***Perf. 13***
**C170** AP74 44fr multicolored 3.50 2.00

Museum of Tahiti and the Islands.

Conference Emblem over Island AP75

**1979, Oct. 6** **Photo.** ***Perf. 13***
**C171** AP75 23fr multicolored 2.25 1.10

19th South Pacific Conf., Tahiti, Oct. 6-12.

Flying Boat "Bermuda" — AP76

Planes Used in Polynesia: 40fr, DC-4 over Papeete. 60fr, Britten-Norman "Islander." 80fr, Fairchild F-27A. 120fr, DC-8 over Tahiti.

**1979, Dec. 19** **Litho.** ***Perf. 13***
**C172** AP76 24fr multicolored 1.00 .50
**C173** AP76 40fr multicolored 1.75 1.00
**C174** AP76 60fr multicolored 2.75 1.50
**C175** AP76 80fr multicolored 3.50 2.25
**C176** AP76 120fr multicolored 6.00 3.00
*Nos. C172-C176 (5)* 15.00 8.25

See Nos. C180-C183.

Window on Tahiti, by Henri Matisse AP77

**1980, Feb. 18** **Photo.**
**C177** AP77 150fr multicolored 8.00 5.00

Marshi Metua No Tehamana, by Gauguin AP78

**1980, Aug. 24** **Photo.** ***Perf. 13***
**C178** AP78 500fr multicolored 18.00 13.00

Sydpex '80, Philatelic Exhibition, Sydney Town Hall — AP79

**1980, Sept. 29** **Photo.** ***Perf. 13***
**C179** AP79 70fr multicolored 8.00 5.25

**Aviation Type of 1979**

**1980, Dec. 15** **Litho.** ***Perf. 13***
**C180** AP76 15fr Catalina .75 .55
**C181** AP76 26fr Twin Otter 1.00 .70
**C182** AP76 30fr CAMS 55 1.25 .90
**C183** AP76 50fr DC-6 2.00 1.40
*Nos. C180-C183 (4)* 5.00 3.55

And The Gold of their Bodies, by Gauguin — AP80

**1981, Mar. 15** **Photo.** ***Perf. 13***
**C184** AP80 100fr multicolored 4.50 2.50

20th Anniv. of Manned Space Flight AP81

**1981, June 15** **Litho.** ***Perf. 12½***
**C185** AP81 300fr multicolored 9.00 7.00

First Intl. Pirogue (6-man Canoe) Championship — AP82

**1981, July 25** **Litho.** ***Perf. 13x12½***
**C186** AP82 200fr multicolored 5.50 4.50

Matavai Bay, by William Hodges — AP83

Paintings: 60fr, Poedea, by John Weber, vert. 80fr, Omai, by Joshua Reynolds, vert. 120fr, Point Venus, by George Tobin.

**1981, Dec. 10** **Photo.** ***Perf. 13***
**C187** AP83 40fr multicolored 1.10 .90
**C188** AP83 60fr multicolored 1.75 1.25
**C189** AP83 80fr multicolored 2.75 1.75
**C190** AP83 120fr multicolored 3.50 2.40
*Nos. C187-C190 (4)* 9.10 6.30

See Nos. C194-C197, C202-C205.

TB Bacillus Centenary — AP84

**1982, Mar. 24** **Engr.** ***Perf. 13***
**C191** AP84 200fr multicolored 5.00 3.00

1982 World Cup — AP85

**1982, May 18** **Litho.** ***Perf. 13***
**C192** AP85 250fr multicolored 6.50 4.50

French Overseas Possessions' Week, Sept. 18-25 — AP86

**1982, Sept. 17** **Engr.**
**C193** AP86 110fr multicolored 2.75 1.65

**Painting Type of 1981**

Designs: 50fr, The Tahitian, by M. Radiguet, vert. 70fr, Souvenir of Tahiti, by C. Giraud. 100fr, Beating Cloth Lengths, by Atlas JL the Younger. 160fr, Papeete Harbor, by C.F. Gordon Cumming.

**1982, Dec. 15** **Photo.** ***Perf. 13***
**C194** AP83 50fr multicolored 1.90 1.00
**C195** AP83 70fr multicolored 2.25 1.50
**C196** AP83 100fr multicolored 2.75 2.00
**C197** AP83 160fr multicolored 4.50 2.75
*Nos. C194-C197 (4)* 11.40 7.25

Wood Cutter, by Gauguin AP87

**Photo. & Engr.**

**1983, May 8** *Perf. 12½x13*
**C198** AP87 600fr multicolored 16.00 8.00

Voyage of Capt. Bligh — AP88

**1983, June 9 Litho.** *Perf. 13*
**C199** AP88 200fr Map, fruit 6.00 3.00

BRASILIANA '83 Intl. Stamp Exhibition, Rio de Janeiro, July 29-Aug. 7 — AP89

**1983, July 29 Litho.** *Perf. 13x12½*
**C200** AP89 100fr multicolored 2.50 1.75
*a.* Souvenir sheet 3.50 3.50

**1983, Aug. 4 Litho.** *Perf. 13x12½*
**C201** AP89 110fr Bangkok '83 3.00 2.00
*a.* Souvenir sheet 4.00 4.00

**Painting Type of 1981**

20th Cent. Paintings: 40fr, View of Moorea, by William Alister MacDonald (1861-1956). 60fr, The Fruit Carrier, by Adrian Herman Gouwe (1875-1965). 80fr, Arrival of the Destroyer Escort, by Nicolas Mordvinoff (1911-1977). 100fr, Women on a Veranda, by Charles Alfred Le Moine (1872-1918).

**1983, Dec. 22 Photo.** *Perf. 13*
**C202** AP83 40fr multi 1.00 .75
**C203** AP83 60fr multi, vert. 1.50 1.00
**C204** AP83 80fr multi, vert. 1.60 1.25
**C205** AP83 100fr multi 2.00 1.60
*Nos. C202-C205 (4)* 6.10 4.60

ESPANA '84 — AP90

Design: Maori canoers.

**1984, Apr. 27 Engr.** *Perf. 13*
**C206** AP90 80fr brn red & dk bl 2.25 1.50

**Souvenir Sheet**

**C207** AP90 200fr dk bl & dk red 7.25 7.25

Woman with Mango, by Gauguin AP91

**Photo. & Engr.**

**1984, May 27** *Perf. 12½x13*
**C208** AP91 400fr multicolored 11.00 6.00

Ausipex '84 — AP92

Details from Human Sacrifice of the Maori in Tahiti, 18th cent. engraving.

**1984, Sept. 5 Litho.** *Perf. 13x12½*
**C209** AP92 120fr Worshippers 3.00 2.25
**C210** AP92 120fr Preparation 3.00 2.25
*a.* Pair, #C209-C210 + label 7.50 7.50

**Souvenir Sheet**

**C211** AP92 200fr Entire 9.50 9.50

Painting by Gaugin (1848-1903) — AP93

Design: Where have we come from? What are we? Where are we going?

**1985, Mar. 17 Litho.** *Perf. 13½x13*
**C212** AP93 550fr multi 14.00 7.50

**4th Pacific Arts Festival Type**

**1985, July 3 Litho.** *Perf. 13*
**C213** A95 200fr Islander, tiki, artifacts 4.50 3.00

Intl. Youth Year — AP95

**1985, Sept. 18 Litho.**
**C214** AP95 250fr Island youths, frigate bird 5.50 3.25

ITALIA '85 — AP96

Designs: Ship sailing into Papeete Harbor, 19th century print.

**1985, Oct. 22 Engr.**
**C215** AP96 130fr multicolored 2.75 2.50

**Souvenir Sheet**

**C216** AP96 240fr multicolored 7.50 7.50

1st Intl. Marlin Fishing Contest, Feb. 27-Mar. 5 — AP97

**1986, Feb. 27 Litho.** *Perf. 12½*
**C217** AP97 300fr multicolored 6.50 4.00

Arrival of a Boat, c.1880 — AP98

**1986, June 24 Engr.** *Perf. 13*
**C218** AP98 400fr intense blue 8.75 5.25

STOCKHOLMIA '86 — AP99

Design: Dr. Karl Solander and Anders Sparrmann, Swedish scientists who accompanied Capt. Cook, and map of Tahiti.

**1986, Aug. 28 Engr.** *Perf. 13*
**C219** AP99 150fr multicolored 3.25 2.25

**Souvenir Sheet**

**C220** AP99 210fr multicolored 4.75 4.75

Protestant Churches — AP100

**1986, Dec. 17 Litho.** *Perf. 13*
**C221** AP100 80fr Tiva, 1955 1.75 .90
**C222** AP100 200fr Avera, 1880 4.50 2.10
**C223** AP100 300fr Papetoai, 1822 6.50 3.25
*Nos. C221-C223 (3)* 12.75 6.25

Broche Barracks, 120th Anniv. — AP101

**1987, Apr. 21 Litho.** *Perf. 12½x12*
**C224** AP101 350fr multicolored 7.75 5.00

CAPEX '87 — AP102

Design: George Vancouver (1757-1798), English navigator and cartographer, chart and excerpt from ship's log.

**1987, June 15 Engr.** *Perf. 13*
**C225** AP102 130fr multi 2.90 2.25

***Imperf***

**Size: 143x100mm**

**C226** AP102 260fr multicolored 5.75 5.75

Soyez Mysterieuses, from a 5-Panel Sculpture by Paul Gauguin, Gauguin Museum — AP103

**1987, Nov. 15** *Perf. 13*
**C227** AP103 600fr multicolored 14.00 9.50

---

## AIR POST SEMI-POSTAL STAMPS

**Catalogue values for unused stamps in this section are for Never Hinged items.**

**French Revolution Issue**

Common Design Type

**Unwmk.**

**1939, July 5 Photo.** *Perf. 13*

**Name and Value Typo. in Orange**

**CB1** CD83 5fr + 4fr brn blk 35.00 35.00

Mother & Children on Beach — SPAP1

***Perf. 12½x13½***

**1942, June 22 Engr.**
**CB2** SPAP1 1.50fr + 3.50fr green 2.00
**CB3** SPAP1 2fr + 6fr yellow brown 2.00

Native children's welfare fund.

Nos. CB2-CB3 were issued by the Vichy government in France, but were not placed on sale in French Polynesia.

**Colonial Education Fund**

Common Design Type

**1942, June 22**
**CB4** CD86a 1.20fr + 1.80fr blue & red 2.00

No. CB4 was issued by the Vichy government in France, but was not placed on sale in French Polynesia.

### POSTAGE DUE STAMPS

Postage Due Stamps of French Colonies, 1894-1906, Overprinted

**1926-27 Unwmk. *Perf. 14x13½***

| | | | | |
|---|---|---|---|---|
| **J1** D1 | 5c | light blue | .95 | .95 |
| **J2** D1 | 10c | brown | .95 | .95 |
| **J3** D1 | 20c | olive green | 1.40 | 1.40 |
| **J4** D1 | 30c | dull red | 1.60 | 1.60 |
| **J5** D1 | 40c | rose | 3.50 | 3.50 |
| **J6** D1 | 60c | blue green | 3.50 | 3.50 |
| **J7** D1 | 1fr | red brown, *straw* | 3.75 | 3.75 |
| **J8** D1 | 3fr | magenta ('27) | 15.00 | 15.00 |

**With Additional Surcharge of New Value**

| | | | |
|---|---|---|---|
| **J9** D1 | 2fr on 1fr orange red | 4.00 | 4.75 |
| | *Nos. J1-J9 (9)* | 34.65 | 35.40 |

Fautaua Falls, Tahiti — D2

Tahitian Youth — D3

**1929 Typo. *Perf. 13½x14***

| | | | | |
|---|---|---|---|---|
| **J10** D2 | 5c | lt blue & dk brn | .75 | .75 |
| **J11** D2 | 10c | vermilion & grn | .75 | .75 |
| **J12** D2 | 30c | dk brn & dk red | 1.75 | 1.75 |
| **J13** D2 | 50c | yel grn & dk brn | 1.40 | 1.40 |
| **J14** D2 | 60c | dl vio & yel grn | 4.00 | 4.00 |
| **J15** D3 | 1fr | Prus bl & red vio | 3.50 | 3.50 |
| **J16** D3 | 2fr | brn red & dk brn | 2.00 | 2.10 |
| **J17** D3 | 3fr | bl vio & bl grn | 2.10 | 2.40 |
| | | *Nos. J10-J17 (8)* | 16.25 | 16.65 |

**Catalogue values for unused stamps in this section, from this point to the end of the section, are for Never Hinged items.**

D4

**1948 Engr. *Perf. 14x13***

| | | | | |
|---|---|---|---|---|
| **J18** D4 | 10c | brt blue grn | .40 | .25 |
| **J19** D4 | 30c | black brown | .40 | .25 |
| **J20** D4 | 50c | dk car rose | .50 | .30 |
| **J21** D4 | 1fr | ultra | .65 | .50 |
| **J22** D4 | 2fr | dk blue green | .95 | .70 |
| **J23** D4 | 3fr | red | 1.90 | 1.40 |
| **J24** D4 | 4fr | violet | 2.00 | 1.60 |
| **J25** D4 | 5fr | lilac rose | 3.00 | 2.10 |
| **J26** D4 | 10fr | slate | 4.00 | 3.00 |
| **J27** D4 | 20fr | red brown | 5.50 | 4.25 |
| | | *Nos. J18-J27 (10)* | 19.30 | 14.35 |

Polynesian Club — D5

**1958 Unwmk. *Perf. 14x13***

| | | | | |
|---|---|---|---|---|
| **J28** D5 | 1fr | dk brn & grn | .65 | .65 |
| **J29** D5 | 3fr | bluish blk & hn brn | .90 | .90 |
| **J30** D5 | 5fr | brown & ultra | 1.10 | 1.10 |
| | | *Nos. J28-J30 (3)* | 2.65 | 2.65 |

Tahitian Bowl — D6

**1984-87 Litho. *Perf. 13***

| | | | | |
|---|---|---|---|---|
| **J31** D6 | 1fr | Mother-of-pearl fish hook, vert. | .25 | .25 |
| **J32** D6 | 3fr | shown | .25 | .25 |
| **J33** D6 | 5fr | Marquesan fan | .30 | .30 |
| **J34** D6 | 10fr | Lamp stand, vert. | .55 | .55 |
| **J35** D6 | 20fr | Wood headrest ('87) | .60 | .60 |
| **J36** D6 | 50fr | Wood scoop ('87) | 1.50 | 1.50 |
| | | *Nos. J31-J36 (6)* | 3.45 | 3.45 |

Issued: #J31-34, 3/15; #J35-J36, 8/18.

### OFFICIAL STAMPS

**Catalogue values for unused stamps in this section are for Never Hinged items.**

Breadfruit O1

Polynesian Fruits: 2fr, 3fr, 5fr, like 1fr. 7fr, 8fr, 10fr, 15fr, "Vi Tahiti." 19fr, 20fr, 25fr, 35fr, Avocados. 50fr, 100fr, 200fr, Mangos.

**1977, June 9 Litho. *Perf. 12½***

| | | | | |
|---|---|---|---|---|
| **O1** O1 | 1fr | ultra & multi | .40 | *.65* |
| **O2** O1 | 2fr | ultra & multi | .40 | *.65* |
| **O3** O1 | 3fr | ultra & multi | .40 | *.65* |
| **O4** O1 | 5fr | ultra & multi | .40 | *.65* |
| **O5** O1 | 7fr | red & multi | .65 | *.95* |
| **O6** O1 | 8fr | red & multi | .65 | *.95* |
| **O7** O1 | 10fr | red & multi | .95 | *1.25* |
| **O8** O1 | 15fr | red & multi | 1.40 | *1.60* |
| **O9** O1 | 19fr | black & multi | 1.60 | *2.00* |
| **O10** O1 | 20fr | black & multi | 1.75 | *2.40* |
| **O11** O1 | 25fr | black & multi | 2.50 | *2.75* |
| **O12** O1 | 35fr | black & multi | 3.25 | *3.50* |
| **O13** O1 | 50fr | black & multi | 3.25 | *3.50* |
| **O14** O1 | 100fr | red & multi | 7.25 | *8.00* |
| **O15** O1 | 200fr | ultra & multi | 14.00 | *16.00* |
| | | *Nos. O1-O15 (15)* | 38.85 | *45.50* |

**1982-86 *Perf. 13***

| | | | | |
|---|---|---|---|---|
| *O1a* O1 | 1fr | ultra & multi | .70 | *1.25* |
| *O2a* O1 | 2fr | ultra & multi | .70 | *1.25* |
| *O3a* O1 | 3fr | ultra & multi | .95 | *1.25* |
| *O4a* O1 | 5fr | ultra & multi | 2.25 | *2.40* |
| *O5a* O1 | 7fr | red & multi | 2.25 | *2.50* |
| *O6a* O1 | 8fr | red & multi | 3.25 | *3.50* |
| *O7a* O1 | 10fr | red & multi | 3.50 | *3.50* |
| *O8a* O1 | 15fr | red & multi ('84) | 3.50 | *3.50* |
| *O10a* O1 | 20fr | black & multi | 3.50 | *3.50* |
| *O11a* O1 | 25fr | black & multi ('84) | 3.50 | *3.50* |
| *O12a* O1 | 35fr | black & multi ('84) | 8.00 | *10.50* |
| *O13a* O1 | 50fr | black & multi ('84) | 20.00 | *22.50* |
| *O14a* O1 | 100fr | red & multi ('86) | 52.50 | *60.00* |
| *O15a* O1 | 200fr | ultra & multi ('86) | 67.50 | *80.00* |
| | | *Nos. O1a-O15a (14)* | 172.10 | *199.15* |

Nos. O1-O15 have dull finish (matte) gum. Nos. O1a-O15a have shiny gum.

Stamps and Postmarks — O2

1fr, French Colonies #5. 2fr, French Colonies #27, #12. 3fr, French Colonies #29, 1884 Papeete postmark. 5fr, Newspaper franked with surcharge of Tahiti #2, 1884 Papeete postmark. 9fr, #176. 10fr, #4, 1894 octagonal postmark. 20fr, #6, #8. 46fr, #48. 51fr, #147-148, Vaitepaua-Makatea Island postmark. 70fr, Visit Tahiti postmark on postal card piece. 85fr, #59 with 1921 manuscript cancel, vert. 100fr, #181. 200fr, #C21, 1st day cancel.

***Perf. 13¼, 13¼x13 (#O20), 13x13¼ (#O26)***

**1993-99 Litho.**

| | | | | |
|---|---|---|---|---|
| **O16** O2 | 1fr | multicolored | .25 | *.40* |
| *a.* | | Perf. 13¼x13 ('98) | 8.00 | *9.50* |
| **O17** O2 | 2fr | multicolored | .25 | *.40* |
| *a.* | | Perf. 13¼x13 ('97) | 1.00 | *1.25* |
| **O18** O2 | 3fr | multicolored | .25 | *.40* |
| *a.* | | Perf. 13¼x13 ('98) | 8.00 | *9.50* |
| **O19** O2 | 5fr | multicolored | .30 | *.55* |
| *a.* | | Perf. 13¼x13 ('97) | 1.00 | *1.25* |
| **O20** O2 | 9fr | multicolored | .80 | *1.25* |
| **O21** O2 | 10fr | multicolored | .30 | *.55* |
| *a.* | | Perf. 13¼x13 ('99) | 1.00 | .85 |
| **O22** O2 | 20fr | multicolored | .65 | *.95* |
| *a.* | | Perf. 13¼x13 ('99) | 8.00 | *9.50* |
| **O23** O2 | 46fr | multicolored | 1.40 | *1.60* |
| **O24** O2 | 51fr | multicolored | 2.50 | *3.25* |
| **O25** O2 | 70fr | multicolored | 2.40 | *2.75* |
| *a.* | | Perf. 13¼x13 ('97) | 4.00 | *6.50* |
| **O26** O2 | 85fr | multicolored | 2.50 | *3.25* |
| **O27** O2 | 100fr | multicolored | 2.75 | *3.50* |
| *a.* | | Perf. 13¼x13 ('99) | 2.40 | 1.90 |
| **O28** O2 | 200fr | multicolored | 5.25 | *6.50* |
| *a.* | | Perf. 13¼x13 ('97) | 5.00 | 4.50 |
| | | *Nos. O16-O28 (13)* | 19.60 | *25.35* |

Issued: 51fr, 4/6/94; 9fr, 85fr, 4/21/97; others, 1/13/93.

## FRENCH SOUTHERN & ANTARCTIC TERRITORY

'french 'sə-t͟hərn and ˌant-'ärk-tik 'ter-ə-ˌtōr-ēs

POP. — 130 staff

Formerly dependencies of Madagascar, these areas, comprising the Kerguelen Archipelago; St. Paul, Amsterdam and Crozet Islands and Adelle Land in Antarctica achieved territorial status on August 6, 1955.

100 Centimes = 1 Franc
100 Cents = 1 Euro (2002)

**Catalogue values for all unused stamps in this country are for Never Hinged items.**

**Madagascar No. 289 Ovptd. in Red**

**Unwmk.**

**1955, Oct. 28 Engr. *Perf. 13***

| | | | | |
|---|---|---|---|---|
| **1** A25 | 15f | dk grn & dp ultra | 10.00 | *27.50* |

Rockhopper Penguins, Crozet Archipelago — A1

New Amsterdam A2

Design: 10fr, 15fr, Elephant seal.

**1956, Apr. 25 Engr. *Perf. 13***

| | | | | |
|---|---|---|---|---|
| **2** A1 | 50c | dk blue, sepia & yel | .40 | *1.00* |
| **3** A1 | 1fr | ultra, org & gray | .40 | *1.00* |
| **4** A2 | 5fr | blue & dp ultra | 2.40 | *2.50* |
| **5** A2 | 8fr | gray vio & dk brn | 14.00 | *17.50* |
| **6** A2 | 10fr | indigo | 5.00 | 5.00 |
| **7** A2 | 15fr | indigo & brn vio | 6.50 | 6.50 |
| | | *Nos. 2-7 (6)* | 28.70 | 33.50 |

Polar Observation A3

**1957, Oct. 11**

| | | | | |
|---|---|---|---|---|
| **8** A3 | 5fr | black & violet | 2.50 | *4.25* |
| **9** A3 | 10fr | rose red | 3.50 | *5.00* |
| **10** A3 | 15fr | dark blue | 4.00 | *6.50* |
| | | *Nos. 8-10 (3)* | 10.00 | 15.75 |

International Geophysical Year, 1957-58.

Imperforates

Most stamps of this French possession exist imperforate in issued and trial colors, and also in small presentation sheets in issued colors.

**Flower Issue**
Common Design Type

Design: Pringlea, horiz.

**1959 Photo. *Perf. 12½x12***

| | | | | |
|---|---|---|---|---|
| **11** CD104 | 10fr | sal, grn & yel | 8.75 | 7.50 |

Common Design Types pictured following the introduction.

Light-mantled Sooty Albatross — A4

Designs: 40c, Skua, horiz. 12fr, King shag.

**1959, Sept. 14 Engr. *Perf. 13***

| | | | | |
|---|---|---|---|---|
| **12** A4 | 30c | blue, grn & red brn | .55 | *.85* |
| **13** A4 | 40c | blk, dl red brn & bl | .55 | *.85* |
| **14** A4 | 12fr | lt blue & blk | 10.00 | 8.00 |
| | | *Nos. 12-14 (3)* | 11.10 | 9.70 |

Coat of Arms — A5

**1959, Sept. 14 Typo. *Perf. 13x14***

**15** A5 20fr ultra, lt bl & yel 13.50 11.00

Sheathbills — A6

4fr, Sea leopard, horiz. 25fr, Weddell seal at Kerguélen, horiz. 85fr, King penguin.

**1960, Dec. 15 Engr. *Perf. 13***

**16** A6 2fr grnsh bl, gray & choc 2.00 *2.50*

**17** A6 4fr bl, dk brn & dk grn 8.00 7.75

**18** A6 25fr sl grn, bis brn & blk 77.50 45.00

**19** A6 85fr grnsh bl, org & blk 17.50 17.50

*Nos. 16-19 (4)* 105.00 72.75

Yves-Joseph de Kerguélen-Trémarec — A7

**1960, Nov. 22**

**20** A7 25fr red org, dk bl & brn 22.50 21.00

Yves-Joseph de Kerguélen-Trémarec, discoverer of the Kerguélen Archipelago.

Charcot, Compass Rose and "Pourquoi-pas?" — A8

**1961, Dec. 26 Unwmk. *Perf. 13***

**21** A8 25fr brn, grn & red 24.00 21.00

25th anniv. of the death of Commander Jean Charcot (1867-1936), Antarctic explorer.

Elephant Seals Fighting A9

**1963, Feb. 11 Engr. *Perf. 13***

**22** A9 8fr dk blue, blk & claret 10.00 8.00

See No. C4.

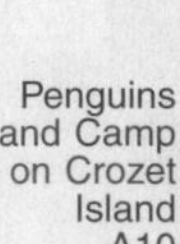

Penguins and Camp on Crozet Island A10

20fr, Research station & IQSY emblem.

**1963, Dec. 16 Unwmk. *Perf. 13***

**23** A10 5fr blk, red brn & Prus bl 55.00 45.00

**24** A10 20fr vio, sl & red brn 57.50 52.50

Intl. Quiet Sun Year, 1964-65. See No. C6.

Great Blue Whale A11

Black-browed Albatross — A12

10fr, Cape pigeons. 12fr, Phylica trees, Amsterdam Island. 15fr, Killer whale (orca).

**1966-69 Engr. *Perf. 13***

**25** A11 5fr brt bl & indigo 18.50 12.50

**26** A12 10fr sl, ind & ol brn 27.50 24.00

**27** A11 12fr brt bl, sl grn & lemon 17.50 16.00

**27A** A11 15fr ol, dk bl & ind 14.00 9.50

**28** A12 20fr slate, ol & org 280.00 225.00

*Nos. 25-28 (5)* 357.50 287.00

Issued: 5fr, 12/12; 20fr, 1/3/68; 10fr, 12fr, 1/6/69; 15fr, 12/21/69.

Aurora Australis, Map of Antarctica and Rocket — A13

**1967, Mar. 4 Engr. *Perf. 13***

**29** A13 20fr mag, blue & blk 22.00 20.00

Launching of the 1st space rocket from Adelie Land, Jan., 1967.

Dumont d'Urville A14

**1968, Jan. 20**

**30** A14 30fr lt ultra, dk bl & dk brn 110.00 75.00

Jules Sébastien César Dumont D'Urville (1790-1842), French naval commander and South Seas explorer.

**WHO Anniversary Issue**

Common Design Type

**1968, May 4 Engr. *Perf. 13***

**31** CD126 30fr red, yel & bl 62.50 47.50

**Human Rights Year Issue**

Common Design Type

**1968, Aug. 10 Engr. *Perf. 13***

**32** CD127 30fr grnsh bl, red & brn 55.00 47.50

Polar Camp with Helicopter, Plane and Snocat Tractor — A15

**1969, Mar. 17 Engr. *Perf. 13***

**33** A15 25fr Prus bl, lt grnsh bl & brn red 19.00 11.00

20 years of French Polar expeditions.

**ILO Issue**

Common Design Type

**1970, Jan. 1 Engr. *Perf. 13***

**35** CD131 20fr org, dk bl & brn 15.00 10.00

**UPU Headquarters Issue**

Common Design Type

**1970, May 20 Engr. *Perf. 13***

**36** CD133 50fr blue, plum & ol bis 40.00 27.50

Ice Fish A16

Fish: Nos. 38-43, Antarctic cods, various species. 135fr, Zanchlorhynchus spinifer.

**1971 Engr. *Perf. 13***

**37** A16 5fr brt grn, ind & org 2.50 1.25

**38** A16 10fr redsh brn & dp vio 3.50 1.50

**39** A16 20fr dp cl, brt grn & org 4.75 2.50

**40** A16 22fr pur, brn ol & mag 5.00 3.50

**41** A16 25fr grn, ind & org 5.75 3.75

**42** A16 30fr sep, gray & bl vio 6.00 4.50

**43** A16 35fr sl grn, dk brn & ocher 6.25 3.75

**44** A16 135fr Prus bl, dp org & ol grn 10.00 5.75

*Nos. 37-44 (8)* 43.75 26.50

Issued: Nos. 37-39, 41-42, 1/1; Nos. 40, 43-44, 12/22.

Map of Antarctica — A17

**1971, Dec. 22**

**45** A17 75fr red 19.00 19.00

Antarctic Treaty pledging peaceful uses of and scientific cooperation in Antarctica, 10th anniv.

Microzetia Mirabilis — A18

Insects: 15fr, Christiansenia dreuxi. 22f, Phtirocoris antarcticus. 30fr, Antarctophytosus atriceps. 40fr, Paractora drenxi. 140fr, Pringleophaga Kerguelenensis.

**1972**

**46** A18 15fr cl, org & brn 8.50 5.50

**47** A18 22fr vio bl, sl grn & yel 12.00 8.50

**48** A18 25fr grn, rose lil & pur 5.25 3.50

**49** A18 30fr blue & multi 15.00 9.00

**50** A18 40fr dk brn, ocher & blk 7.50 4.25

**51** A18 140fr bl, emer & brn 11.00 8.00

*Nos. 46-51 (6)* 59.25 38.75

Issued: Nos. 48, 50-51, 1/3; Nos. 46-47, 49, 12/16.

**De Gaulle Issue**

Common Design Type

Designs: 50fr, Gen. de Gaulle, 1940. 100fr, Pres. de Gaulle, 1970.

**1972, Feb. 1 Engr. *Perf. 13***

**52** CD134 50fr brt grn & blk 17.50 13.00

**53** CD134 100fr brt grn & blk 22.50 16.50

Kerguelen Cabbage — A19

Designs: 61fr, Azorella selago, horiz. 87fr, Acaena ascendens, horiz.

**1972-73**

**54** A19 45fr multicolored 8.00 4.75

**55** A19 61fr multicolored 3.00 2.50

**56** A19 87fr multicolored 5.00 3.50

*Nos. 54-56 (3)* 16.00 10.75

Issued: 45fr, 12/18; others, 12/13/73.

Mailship Sapmer and Map of Amsterdam Island — A20

**1974, Dec. 31 Engr. *Perf. 13***

**57** A20 75fr bl, blk & dk brn 6.00 5.00

25th anniversary of postal service.

Antarctic Tern — A21

Designs: 50c, Antarctic petrel. 90c, Sea lioness. 1fr, Weddell seal. 1.20fr, Kerguelen cormorant, vert. 1.40fr, Gentoo penguin, vert.

**1976, Jan. Engr. *Perf. 13***

**58** A21 40c multicolored 4.00 3.00

**59** A21 50c multicolored 4.25 3.00

**60** A21 90c multicolored 6.25 4.00

**61** A21 1fr multicolored 10.00 9.25

**62** A21 1.20fr multicolored 12.00 11.00

**63** A21 1.40fr multicolored 13.00 11.50

*Nos. 58-63 (6)* 49.50 41.75

James Clark Ross — A22

Design: 30c, Climbing Mount Ross.

**1976, Dec. 16 Engr. *Perf. 13***

**64** A22 30c multicolored 3.75 2.75

**65** A22 3fr multicolored 4.00 2.75

First climbing of Mount Ross, Kerguelen Island, Jan. 5, 1975.

James Cook — A23

**1976, Dec. 16**

**66** A23 70c multicolored 10.00 9.00

Bicentenary of Capt. Cook's voyage past Kerguelen Island. See No. C46.

Commerson's Dolphins — A24

**1977, Feb. 1 Engr. *Perf. 13***

**67** A24 1.10fr Blue whale 5.25 3.75
**68** A24 1.50fr shown 5.75 4.00

Macrocystis Algae — A25

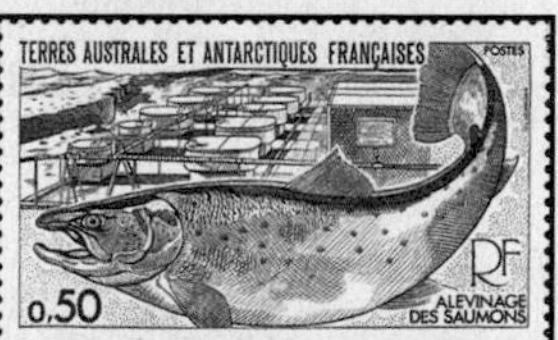

Salmon Hatchery — A26

Magga Dan — A27

Designs: 70c, Durvillea algae. 90c, Albatross. 1fr, Underwater sampling and scientists, vert. 1.40fr, Thala Dan and penguins.

**1977, Dec. 20 Engr. *Perf. 13***

**69** A25 40c ol brn & bis 1.20 .75
**70** A26 50c dk bl & pur 1.25 1.10
**71** A25 70c blk, grn & brn 1.40 1.00
**72** A26 90c grn, brt bl & brn 1.50 1.10
**73** A27 1fr slate 1.25 1.10
**74** A27 1.20fr multi 2.50 1.75
**75** A27 1.40fr multi 1.75 1.75
*Nos. 69-75 (7)* 10.85 8.55

See Nos. 77-79.

A28

Explorer with French and Expedition Flags.

**1977, Dec. 24**

**76** A28 1.90fr multicolored 6.25 5.25

French Polar expeditions, 1947-48.

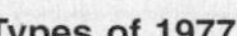

**Types of 1977**

40c, Forbin, destroyer. 50c Jeanne d'Arc, helicopter carrier. 1.40fr, Kerguelen cormorant.

**1979, Jan. 1 Engr. *Perf. 13***

**77** A27 40c black & blue 1.00 1.00
**78** A27 50c black & blue 1.25 1.15
**79** A26 1.40fr multicolored 1.25 1.25
*Nos. 77-79 (3)* 3.50 3.40

R. Rallier du Baty — A29

**1979, Jan. 1**

**80** A29 1.20fr citron & indigo 1.10 1.00

See Nos. 97, 100, 111, 117, 129, 135, 188.

French Navigators Monument, Hobart — A30

**1979, Jan. 1**

**81** A30 1fr multicolored .80 .75

French navigators and explorers.

Petrel — A31

**1979 Engr. *Perf. 13***

**82** A31 70c Rockhopper penguins, vert. .90 .90
**83** A31 1fr shown 1.10 1.10

Commandant Bourdais — A32

**1979**

**84** A32 1.10fr Doudart de Lagree, vert. .95 .90
**85** A32 1.50fr shown 1.10 1.10

Adm. Antoine d'Entrecasteaux A33

**1979**

**86** A33 1.20fr multicolored 1.00 1.00

Sebastian de el Cano — A34

Discovery of Amsterdam Island, 1522: 4fr, Victoria, horiz.

**1979**

**87** A34 1.40fr multicolored .85 .75
**88** A34 4fr multicolored 1.75 1.40

Adelie Penguins — A35

Adelie Penguin — A36

Sea Leopard A37

**1980, Dec. 15 Engr. *Perf. 13***

**89** A35 50c rose violet 1.10 1.00
**90** A36 60c multicolored 1.10 1.00
**91** A35 1.20fr multicolored 1.75 1.25
**92** A37 1.30fr multicolored 1.10 1.00
**93** A37 1.80fr multicolored 1.10 1.00
*Nos. 89-93 (5)* 6.15 5.25

20th Anniv. of Antarctic Treaty — A38

**1981, June 23 Engr. *Perf. 13***

**94** A38 1.80fr multicolored 3.75 3.75

Alouette II — A39

**1981-82 Engr. *Perf. 13***

**95** A39 55c brown & multi .50 .45
**96** A39 65c blue & multi .55 .45

**Explorer Type of 1979**

**1981**

**97** A29 1.40fr Jean Loranchet .70 .50

Landing Ship Le Gros Ventre, Kerguelen — A41

**1983, Jan. 3 Engr. *Perf. 13***

**98** A41 55c multicolored .80 .60

Our Lady of the Winds Statue and Church, Kerguelen — A42

**1983, Jan. 3**

**99** A42 1.40fr multicolored .80 .75

**Explorer Type of 1979**

Design: Martin de Vivies, Navigator.

**1983, Jan. 3**

**100** A29 1.60fr multicolored .80 .70

Eaton's Ducks A44

**1983, Jan. 3**

**101** A44 1.50fr multicolored .75 .55
**102** A44 1.80fr multicolored .80 .75

Trawler Austral — A45

**1983, Jan. 3**

**103** A45 2.30fr multicolored 1.25 1.00

Freighter Lady Franklin — A46

**1983, Aug. 4 Engr. *Perf. 13***

**104** A46 5fr multicolored 3.50 2.75

Glaciology — A47

Design: Scientists examining glacier, base.

**1984, Jan. 1 Engr. *Perf. 13***

105 A47 15c multicolored .30 .25
106 A47 1.70fr multicolored .70 .60

Crab-eating Seal — A48

Penguins — A49

**1984, Jan. 1**

107 A48 60c multicolored .50 .50
108 A49 70c multicolored .40 .40
109 A49 2fr multicolored 1.10 .90
110 A48 5.90fr multicolored 1.75 1.50
*Nos. 107-110 (4)* 3.75 3.30

**Explorer Type of 1979**

**1984, Jan. 1**

111 A29 1.80fr Alfred Faure .80 .65

Biomass — A51

**1985, Jan. 1 Engr. *Perf. 13***

112 A51 1.80fr multicolored .65 .50
113 A51 5.20fr multicolored 1.50 1.25

Emperor Penguins — A52

Snowy Petrel — A53

**1985, Jan. 1 Engr. *Perf. 13***

114 A52 1.70fr multicolored .90 .75
115 A53 2.80fr multicolored 1.10 1.00

Port Martin — A54

**1985, Jan. 1 Engr. *Perf. 13***

116 A54 2.20fr multicolored 1.10 .75

**Explorer Type of 1979**

**1985, Jan. 1 Engr. *Perf. 13***

117 A29 2fr Andre-Frank Liotard .80 .65

Antarctic Fulmar — A56

**1986, Jan. 1 Engr. *Perf. 13***

118 A56 1fr shown .50 .40
119 A56 1.70fr Giant petrels .75 .70
*Nos. 118-119,C91 (3)* 3.25 2.85

Echinoderms — A57

**1986, Jan. 1**

120 A57 1.90fr shown .85 .70

Cotula Plumosa — A58

**1986, Jan. 1**

121 A58 2.30fr shown .75 .70
122 A58 6.20fr Lycopodium. saururus 2.00 1.75

Shipping — A59

**1986, Jan. 1**

123 A59 2.10fr Var research ship .85 .75
124 A59 3fr Polarbjorn support ship 1.10 1.00

Marine Life — A60

**1987, Jan. 1 Engr. *Perf. 13½x13***

125 A60 50c dk blue & org .55 .45

Flora — A61

**1987, Jan. 1**

126 A61 1.80fr Poa cookii .65 .45
127 A61 6.50fr Lichen, Neuropogon taylori 1.90 1.40

Marret Base, Adelie Land — A62

**1987, Jan. 1**

128 A62 2fr yel brn, dk ultra & lake .80 .65

**Explorer Type of 1979**

**1987, Jan. 1**

129 A29 2.20fr Adm. Mouchez .85 .65

Reindeer — A64

**1987, Jan. 1**

130 A64 2.50fr black 1.25 1.00

Transport Ship Eure — A65

**1987, Jan. 1**

131 A65 3.20fr dk ultra, Prus grn & dk grn 1.25 1.00

Macaroni Penguins — A66

**1987, Jan. 1 *Perf. 13x12½***

132 A66 4.80fr multicolored 2.50 1.75

Elephant Grass — A67

**1988, Jan. 1 Engr. *Perf. 13***

133 A67 1.70fr Prus grn, emer & olive .75 .60

Rev.-Father Lejay, Explorer — A68

**1988, Jan. 1**

134 A68 2.20fr vio, ultra & blk .85 .70

**Explorer Type of 1979**

Design: Robert Gessain (1907-86).

**1988, Jan. 1**

135 A29 3.40fr gray, dk red & blk 1.25 1.00

Le Gros Ventre, 18th Cent. — A70

**1988, Jan. 1**

136 A70 3.50fr dp ultra, bl grn & brn 1.25 1.10

Mermaid and B.A.P. Jules Verne, Research Vessel — A71

**1988, Jan. 1**

137 A71 4.90fr gray & dk blue 2.25 1.60

La Fortune, Early 19th Cent. — A72

**1988, Jan. 1**

138 A72 5fr blk & dull bl grn 2.00 1.60

Wilson's Petrel — A73

**1988, Jan. 1**

139 A73 6.80fr blk, sepia & dl bl grn 2.75 2.00

See Nos. 143-144.

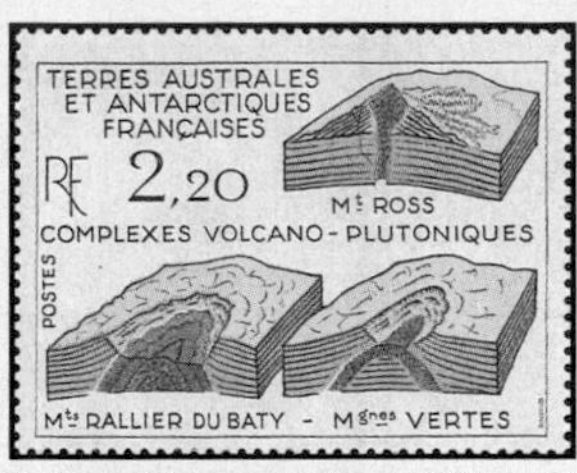


Mt. Ross Campaign (in 1987) — A74

**1988, Jan. 1** ***Perf. 13x12½***

**140** A74 2.20fr Volcanic rock cross-sections .75 .60
**141** A74 15.10fr Kerguelen Is. 4.25 3.50
*a.* Pair, #140-141 + label 6.50 6.50

Darrieus System Wind Vane Electric Generator — A75

**1988, Jan. 1** **Engr.** ***Perf. 13***

**142** A75 1fr dark blue & blue .50 .30

**Fauna Type of 1988**

**1989, Jan. 1** **Engr.**

**143** A73 1.10fr Lithodes .35 .35
**144** A73 3.60fr Blue petrel 1.40 1.10

Fern A76

**1989, Jan. 1**

**145** A76 2.80fr Blechnum penna Marina 1.00 .85

Minerals A77

**1989, Jan. 1**

**146** A77 5.10fr Mesotype 1.90 1.75
**147** A77 7.30fr Analcime 2.75 2.75

Henri and Rene Bossiere, Pioneers of the Kerguelen Isls. — A78

**1989, Jan. 1**

**148** A78 2.20fr multicolored 1.10 .65

Kerguelen Is. Sheep — A79

**1989, Jan. 1** ***Perf. 13½x13***

**149** A79 2fr multicolored .80 .60

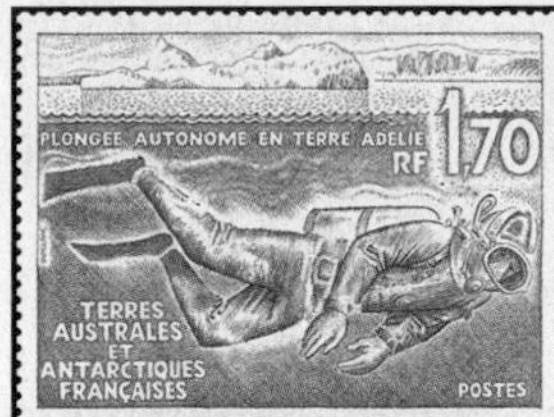


Scuba Diver, Adelie Coast — A80

**1989, Jan. 1**

**150** A80 1.70fr dk olive bis, blue & dk grn .75 .65

Map of Kerguelen Island, Protozoa and Copepod — A81

**1990, Jan. 1** **Engr.** ***Perf. 13***

**151** A81 1.10fr blk, brt blue & red brn .90 .50

Study of protista, Kerguelan Is.

Cattle on Farm, Sea Birds — A82

**1990, Jan. 1**

**152** A82 1.70fr Prus blue, grn & brn blk .80 .65

Rehabilitation of the environment, Amsterdam Is.

Quoy and *Copendium decollata* — A83

**1990, Jan. 1** ***Perf. 13½x13***

**153** A83 2.20fr brt blue, blk & red brn .90 .70

Jean Rene C. Quoy (1790-1869), naturalist, navigator.

Dumont d'Urville (1790-1842), Explorer — A84

**1990, Jan. 1**

**154** A84 3.60fr ultra & blk 1.50 1.00

Yellow-billed Albatross — A85

**1990, Jan. 1** ***Perf. 13x12½***

**155** A85 2.80fr multicolored 1.75 1.00

Aragonite A86

**1990, Jan. 1**

**156** A86 5.10fr deep ultra & dark yel grn 2.75 2.00

*Ranunculus pseudo trullifolius* — A87

**1990, Jan. 1** ***Perf. 13***

**157** A87 8.40fr dp bl, org & emer grn 3.00 2.50

**Penguin Type of Airpost 1974**

**1991, Jan. 1**

**158** AP18 50c blue grn, bl & blk .75 .45

Postal Service at Crozet Island, 30th anniv.

Moss — A88

**1991, Jan. 1** ***Perf. 13x12½***

**159** A88 1.70fr gray, brn & blk .80 .60

Adm. Max Douguet (1903-1989) A89

**1991, Jan. 1**

**160** A89 2.30fr org brn, blk & bl 1.25 .90

Lighter L'Aventure — A90

**1991, Jan. 1** **Engr.** ***Perf. 13***

**161** A90 3.20fr brn, grn & bl 1.50 1.10

Sea Lions — A91

**1991, Jan. 1** ***Perf. 13***

**162** A91 3.60fr blue & ol brn 2.25 1.50

Mordenite — A92

**1991, Jan. 1**

**163** A92 5.20fr blk, grn bl & grn 2.60 1.75

Champsocephalus Gunnari — A93

**1991, Jan. 1**

**164** A93 7.80fr blue & green 3.00 2.50

Antarctic Treaty, 30th Anniv. — A94

**1991, Jan. 1**

**165** A94 9.30fr ol grn & rose red 3.75 3.25

A95

Design: Colobanthus Kerguelensis.

**1992, Jan. 1** **Engr.** ***Perf. 13***

**166** A95 1fr bl grn, grn & brn .85 .40

Globe Challenge Yacht Race — A96

**1992, Jan. 1** **Litho.**
**167** A96 2.20fr multicolored 1.75 1.10

Dissostichus Eleginoides — A97

**1992, Jan. 1** **Engr.**
**168** A97 2.30fr blue, ol grn & red brn 1.60 1.10

Paul Tchernia A98

**1992, Jan. 1** **Engr.** ***Perf. 13***
**169** A98 2.50fr brown & green .95 .90

Capt. Marion Dufresne (1724-1772) — A99

**1992, Jan. 1** **Engr.** ***Perf. 13***
**170** A99 3.70fr red, blk & bl 1.60 1.30

Supply Ship Tottan, 1951 — A100

**1992, Jan. 1** **Engr.** ***Perf. 13***
**171** A100 14fr blue grn, brn & bl 5.50 4.50

WOCE Program — A101

**1992, Jan. 1**
**172** A101 25.40fr multi 11.00 9.50

Coat of Arms — A102

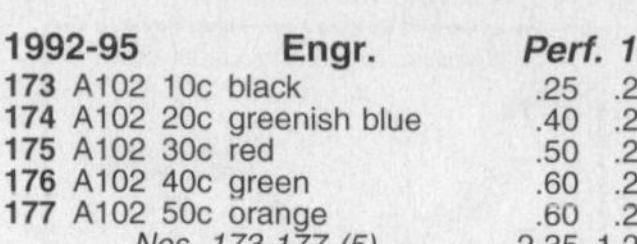

**1992-95** **Engr.** ***Perf. 13***
**173** A102 10c black .25 .25
**174** A102 20c greenish blue .40 .25
**175** A102 30c red .50 .25
**176** A102 40c green .60 .25
**177** A102 50c orange .60 .25
*Nos. 173-177 (5)* 2.35 1.25

Issued: 10c, 1/1/92; 20c, 30c, 1/1/93; 40c, 1/1/94; 50c, 1/2/95.

See Nos. 295-299.

Garnet A103

**1993, Jan. 1** **Engr.** ***Perf. 13***
**183** A103 1fr multicolored 1.40 .35

See Nos. 194, 203, 212, 222, 235, 244, 259, 279, 300, 330.

Research Ship Marion Dufresne, 20th Anniv. — A104

**1993, Jan. 1**
**184** A104 2.20fr multicolored 1.25 .70

Lyallia Kerguelensis A105

**1993, Jan. 1**
**185** A105 2.30fr blue & green 1.25 .70

A106

A107

**1993, Jan. 1**
**186** A106 2.50fr Killer whale 1.25 .80
**187** A107 2.50fr Skua 6.50 1.50

A108

Design: 2.50fr, Andre Prudhomme (1930-1959), Meteorologist. 22fr, Weather station, Adelie Land.

**1993, Jan. 1** ***Perf. 12½x13***
**188** 2.50fr blue, blk & org 1.00 .75
**189** 22fr org, blk & bl 7.50 5.25
*a.* A108 Pair, #188-189 + label 11.00 11.00

43rd Anniv. of Mètèo France in French Southern & Antarctic Territory.

Centriscops Obliquus — A109

**1993, Jan. 1** ***Perf. 13***
**190** A109 3.40fr multicolored 1.50 1.00

Freighter Italo Marsano — A110

**1993, Jan. 1**
**191** A110 3.70fr multicolored 1.75 .90

ECOPHY Program A111

**1993, Jan. 1**
**192** A111 14fr black, blue & brn 6.25 3.50

L'Astrolabe on Northeast Route, 1991 A112

**1993, Jan. 1**
**193** A112 22fr multicolored 9.00 6.25

**Mineral Type of 1993**

**1994, Jan. 1** **Engr.** ***Perf. 13***
**194** A103 1fr Cordierite 1.25 .70

Felis Catus — A113

**1994, Jan. 1**
**195** A113 2fr green & black 3.50 1.25

A114

**1994, Jan. 1** **Engr.** ***Perf. 13***
**196** A114 2.40fr dk brn, blk & bl 1.50 .65

A115

**1994, Jan. 1**
**197** A115 2.80fr slate blue 1.50 .80

Robert Pommier (1919-61) A116

**1994, Jan. 1**
**198** A116 2.80fr multicolored 1.50 .85

A117

Designs: 2.80fr, C.A. Vincendon Dumoulin (1811-58), hydrographer. 23fr, Measuring Earth's magnetic field.

**1994, Jan. 1** ***Perf. 12½x13***
**199** 2.80fr black & blue 1.50 1.00
**200** 23fr blue & black 7.25 5.00
*a.* A117 Pair, #199-200 + label 10.00 10.00

Rascasse — A119

**1994, Jan. 1** ***Perf. 13***
**201** A119 3.70fr bl grn & red brn 1.40 1.00

Kerguelen of Tremarec — A120

**1994, Jan. 1**
**202** A120 4.30fr multicolored 1.75 1.25

**Mineral Type of 1993**

**1995, Jan. 2** **Engr.** ***Perf. 13***
**203** A103 1fr Olivine 1.50 .40

Mancoglosse Antarctique — A121

**1995, Jan. 2**
**204** A121 2.40fr ol brn, vio & bl grn 1.25 1.00

Andree (1903-90) and Edgar de la Rue (1901-91) A122

**1995, Jan. 2**
**205** A122 2.80fr bl, red brn & mag 1.40 .90

SODAR Station — A123

**1995, Jan. 2**
**206** A123 2.80fr vio, mag & red brn 1.40 1.00

Mont D'Alsace — A124

**1995, Jan. 2**
**207** A124 3.70fr dk bl, vio, red brn 1.75 1.10

Balaenoptera Acutorostrata — A125

**1995, Jan. 2**
**208** A125 23fr blue, claret & ind 9.75 6.50

Sailing Ship Tamaris A126

**1995, Jan. 2**
**209** A126 25.80fr multicolored 10.00 6.75

L'Heroine, Crozet Islands Mission, 1837 — A127

**1995, Jan. 2**
**210** A127 27.30fr blue 11.00 7.25

Creation of the Territories, 40th Anniv. — A128

**1995, Aug. 7 Litho. *Imperf.***
**Size: 143x84mm**
**211** A128 30fr multicolored 15.00 15.00

**Mineral Type of 1993**

**1996, Jan. 1 Engr. *Perf. 13***
**212** A103 1fr Amazonite .90 .30

White-chinned Petrel — A129

**1996, Jan. 1**
**213** A129 2.40fr blue black 1.40 .70

Expedition Ship Yves de Kerguelen — A130

**1996, Jan. 1**
**214** A130 2.80fr multicolored 1.50 .75

Benedict Point Scientific Research Station, Amsterdam Island — A131

**1996, Jan. 1**
**215** A131 2.80fr multicolored 1.50 .75

Paul-Emile Victor (1907-1995), Polar Explorer — A132

Designs: 2.80fr, Victor crossing Greenland with sled dogs, 1936. 23fr, Victor, penguins, Dumont d'Urville Base, Adélie Land.

**1996, Jan. 1**
**216** A132 2.80fr multicolored 1.40 .85
**217** A132 23fr multicolored 11.50 7.50
*a.* Pair, #216-217 + label 14.00 14.00

Admiral Jacquinot (1796-1879), Antarctic Explorer — A133

**1996, Jan. 1**
**218** A133 3.70fr dark blue & blue 1.50 1.00

Trawler Austral — A134

**1996, Jan. 1 Photo. & Engr.**
**219** A134 4.30fr multicolored 2.25 1.25

Lycopodium Magellanicum — A135

**1996, Jan. 1 Engr.**
**220** A135 7.70fr multicolored 3.00 2.25

Search for Micrometeorites, Cape Prudhomme — A136

**1996, Jan. 1**
**221** A136 15fr vio, blk & grn bl 8.00 5.00

**Mineral Type of 1993**

**1997, Jan. 1 Engr. *Perf. 13x12½***
**222** A103 1fr Amethyst 1.25 .40

Storm Petrel — A137

**1997, Jan. 1 *Perf. 13***
**223** A137 2.70fr blue & indigo 1.50 .80

Rene Garcia (1915-95), Windmill A138

**1997, Jan. 1**
**224** A138 3fr multicolored 1.60 .90

Research Ship Marion Dufresne — A139

**Photo. & Engr.**

**1997, Jan. 1 *Perf. 13x12½***
**225** A139 3fr multicolored 1.60 .90

Jean Turquet (1867-1945) — A140

**1997, Jan. 1 Engr. *Perf. 13***
**226** A140 4fr black & brown 1.60 1.10

A141

**1997, Jan. 1**
**227** A141 5.20fr multicolored 2.40 1.50

Church of Our Lady of Birds, Crozet Island.

Army Health Service — A142

**1997, Jan. 1**
**228** A142 8fr multicolored 3.75 2.50

Poa Kerguelensis A143

**1997, Jan. 1**
**229** A143 29.20fr multi 12.50 8.50

French Polar Expeditions, 50th Anniv. — A144

Designs: No. 230, Greenland Expedition. No. 231, Port Martin, 1950-51, Marret Base, 1952, Adélie Land. No. 232, Dumont D'Urville, 1956, Charcot Station, Magnetic Pole, 1957.

**Photo. & Engr.**

**1997, Feb. 28** *Perf. 13x12½*

**230** 1fr multicolored 1.10 .70
**231** 1fr multicolored 1.10 .70
**232** 1fr multicolored 1.10 .70
*a.* A144 Strip of 3, #230-232 8.00 6.00

Yves-Joseph de Kerguelen Trémarec (1734-97) — A145

3fr, Portrait. 24fr, Cook's landing at Kerguelen Island, Dec. 1776.

**1997, Mar. 3** **Engr.** *Perf. 13*

**233** 3fr multicolored 1.25 .90
**234** 24fr multicolored 9.00 7.00
*a.* A145 Pair, #233-234 + label 14.00 11.00

No. 234 is 37x37mm.

**Mineral Type of 1993**

**1998, Jan. 2** **Engr.** *Perf. 13*

**235** A103 1fr Rock crystal 1.25 .40

Fisheries Management — A146

Designs: No. 236, Fishing boats. No. 237, Examining fish, performing research.

**1998, Jan. 2**

**236** A146 2.60fr multicolored 1.40 .70
**237** A146 2.60fr multicolored 1.40 .70
*a.* Pair, #236-237 + label 3.50 3.50

Gray-headed Albatross — A147

**1998, Jan. 2**

**238** A147 2.70fr multicolored 1.75 .75

Ecology of St. Paul Island — A148

**1998, Jan. 2**

**239** A148 3fr bl, brn & grn 2.25 1.00

Etienne Peau, Antarctic Explorer — A149

**1998, Jan. 2** *Perf. 13x13½*

**240** A149 3fr lilac, blue & black 1.75 .85

Georges Laclavere (1906-94), Geographer — A150

**1998, Jan. 2**

**241** A150 4fr lt org, blk & red brn 1.75 1.00

Mole Shark — A151

**1998, Jan. 2** *Perf. 13*

**242** A151 27fr multicolored 11.00 6.75

"Le Cancalais" — A152

**1998, Jan. 2**

**243** A152 29.20fr multicolored 11.50 7.00

**Mineral Type of 1993**

**1999, Jan. 1** **Engr.** *Perf. 13*

**244** A103 1fr Epidote, vert. 1.25 .40

Chinstrap Penguin — A153

**1999, Jan. 1**

**245** A153 2.70fr brn, blk & bl 1.60 .85

Pierre Sicaud (1911-98), Antarctic Explorer, Commander of Outpost at Kerguelen Islands — A154

**1999, Jan. 1**

**246** A154 3fr black & green 1.25 .80

Penguins of Crozet Islands — A155

**1999, Jan. 1**

**247** A155 3fr multicolored 3.00 .85

Jacques-André Martin (1911-49) — A156

**1999, Jan. 1**

**248** A156 4fr multicolored 1.75 1.00

Ray — A157

**1999, Jan. 1** *Perf. 12½*

**249** A157 5.20fr mag, bl & brn 2.25 2.25

Value is for stamp with surrounding rectangular selvage.

F.S. Floreal — A158

**1999, Jan. 1** **Photo.** *Perf. 13*

**250** A158 5.20fr multicolored 2.25 1.75

No. 250 was printed se-tenant with label. Value is for stamp with label attached.

"Pop Cat" Program, Kerguelen Islands — A159

**1999, Jan. 1** **Engr.**

**251** A159 8fr multicolored 4.75 3.00

Study of Albatrosses on Artificial Nests A160

**1999, Jan. 1**

**252** A160 16fr olive, grn & blk 6.50 4.25

Amsterdam Base, Kerguelen Base, 50th Anniv. — A161

**1999, Jan. 1**

**253** A161 3fr Amsterdam Base 4.50 1.00
**254** A161 24fr Kerguelen Base 8.50 5.00
*a.* Pair, #253-254 + label 15.00 12.00

Festuca Contracta A162

**1999, Jan. 1**

**255** A162 24fr dk grn, ol & bl grn 9.00 6.00

Geoleta Program — A163

**1999, Jan. 1** *Perf. 13x12½*

**256** A163 29.20fr blk, bl & red brn 11.00 7.00

Voyage of Marion Dufresne II — A164

a, Docked, Reunion. b, Passengers in dining salon. c, Penguins, Crozet Island. d, Postal manager of Alfred Faure, Crozet Island, vert. e, Port of France, Kerguelen Island. f, Port Couvreux, Kerguelen Island. g, Offloading stores, Port of France, Kerguelen Island. h, Port Jeanne d'arc, Kerguelen Island. i, St. Paul Island. j, Ruins of lobster cannery, St. Paul Island. k, Martin de Vivies Base, Amsterdam Island. l, Offloading cargo, Amsterdam Island.

**1999, May 1** **Litho.** *Perf. 13*

**257** A164 Souv. bklt., #a.-l. 90.00

Nos. 257a-257l are all non-denominated. Stamps are valid for 20 gram international letter rate. Each stamp appears on a separate booklet pane showing an enlarged design of the stamp. Booklet sold for 100fr.

See Nos. 294, 329, 359, 390, 420, 482.

Souvenir Sheet

PhilexFrance '99, World Philatelic Exhibition — A165

Antarctic postmarks on stamps: a, Malagasy Republic #280. b, Malagasy Republic #282. c, Malagasy Republic #C42. d, #21.

**1999, July 2 Litho. & Engr. *Perf. 13***
**258** A165 5.20fr Sheet of 4, #a.-d. 10.00 7.50

Nos. 258b-258c are each 40x52mm.

**Mineral Type of 1993**

**2000, Jan. Engr. *Perf. 12¾x13***
**259** A103 1fr Mica, *vert.* 1.25 .40

Puffin — A166

**2000, Jan. *Perf. 13x12¾***
**260** A166 2.70fr multi 2.00 .80

André Beaugé (1913-97) A167

**2000, Jan. *Perf. 12¾x13***
**261** A167 3fr multi 1.40 .60

Abby Jane Morrell — A168

**2000, Jan. *Perf. 13¼x13***
**262** A168 4fr multi 1.75 .95

Oceanographic Survey — A169

**2000, Jan. *Perf. 13x12½***
**263** A169 4.40fr multi 2.10 1.25

Sled Dog Hobbs — A170

**2000, Jan. *Perf. 12¾x13***
**264** A170 5.20fr multi 2.25 1.25

Sleep Study — A171

**2000, Jan. Photo. *Perf. 13x12½***
**265** A171 8fr multi + label 3.50 2.25

Ship "La Perouse" — A172

**2000, Jan. Engr. *Perf. 13x12½***
**266** A172 16fr multi 7.00 4.25

Lantern Fish — A173

**2000, Jan.**
**267** A173 24fr multi 10.50 6.00

Larose Bay — A174

**2000, Jan.**
**268** A174 27fr multi 11.00 7.00

Explorers A175

No. 269, Yves Joseph de Kerguelen-Trémarec (1734-97). No. 270, Jules Sébastien César Dumont D'Urville (1790-1842). No. 271, Raymond Rallier du Baty (1881-1978). No. 272, Edgar Aubert de La Rüe (1901-91). #273, Paul-Emile Victor (1907-95).

**2000, Jan. *Perf. 13***

**Booklet Stamps**

| | | | | |
|---|---|---|---|---|
| **269** | A175 3fr multi | 1.60 | .75 |
| **270** | A175 3fr multi | 1.60 | .75 |
| **271** | A175 3fr multi | 1.60 | .75 |
| **272** | A175 3fr multi | 1.60 | .75 |
| **273** | A175 3fr multi | 1.60 | .75 |
| *a.* | Bklt. pane, #269-273 + 2 labels | 9.00 | — |
| | Complete booklet, #273a | 10.00 | |

Souvenir Sheet

The Third Millennium — A176

No. 274: a, Penguins, Crozet Islands. b, Seals, Kerguelen Islands. c, Crustacean, Saint-Paul and Amsterdam Islands. d, Hovering vehicle, Adelie Land.

**2000, Jan. Photo. *Perf. 13***
**274** A176 3fr Sheet of 4, #a.-d. 8.50 5.50

Bird Demographic Studies — A177

Designs: 5.20fr, Bird banding. 8fr, Albatross, graph. 16fr, Emperor penguins, graph.

**2000, Jan. *Perf. 13x13¼***
**275** A177 5.20fr multi 2.00 1.00

**Size: 50x28mm**

| | | | |
|---|---|---|---|
| **276** | A177 8fr multi | 3.00 | 1.50 |
| **277** | A177 16fr multi | 6.50 | 4.00 |
| *a.* | Horiz. strip, #275-277 | 15.00 | *15.00* |

Relocation of Headquarters to Reunion — A178

**2000, Aug. 6 Litho. *Perf. 13***
**278** A178 27fr multi 12.00 9.00

**Mineral Type of 1993**

**2001, Jan. 1 Engr. *Perf. 13x12¾***
**279** A103 1fr Magnetite 1.25 .40

Diving Petrel — A179

**2001, Jan. 1 *Perf. 13x13¼***
**280** A179 2.70fr multi 1.50 .60

High Mountain Military Group A180

**2001, Jan. 1 *Perf. 13¼x13***
**281** A180 3fr multi 1.40 .65

Kerguelen Arch — A181

**2001, Jan. 1 *Perf. 13***
**282** A181 3fr blue gray 2.00 .70

Xavier-Charles Richert (1913-92) — A182

**2001, Jan. 1**
**283** A182 3fr multi 1.40 .65

Jean Coulomb — A183

**2001, Jan. 1**
**284** A183 4fr multi 1.75 .85

Memorial to 1874 Astronomical Observation, St. Paul Island A184

**2001, Jan. 1**
**285** A184 8fr brn & blk 3.50 1.75

Frigate La Fayette — A185

**2001, Jan. 1 *Perf. 13x13¼***
**286** A185 16fr multi 7.00 3.50

Squid — A186

**2001, Jan. 1**
**287** A186 24fr multi 10.50 5.00

Amateur Radio Link Between Space Station Mir and Crozet Island — A187

**2001, Jan. 1 Litho. *Perf. 13***
**288** A187 27fr multi 12.00 5.50

Bryum Laevigatum — A188

**2001, Jan. 1 Engr. *Perf. 13x12½***
**289** A188 29.20fr multi 13.00 6.00

Souvenir Sheet

Ships — A189

No. 290: a, Carmen. b, Austral. c, Ramuntcho. d, Samper 1.

**2001, Jan. 1 *Perf. 13x13½***
**290** A189 5.20fr Sheet of 4, #a-d 9.00 4.50

Souvenir Sheet

Wildlife — A190

No. 291: a, Albatrosses. b, Emperor penguins, horiz. c, Sea lions, horiz. d, Whales.

**2001, Jan. 1 Litho. *Perf. 13***
**291** A190 3fr Sheet of 4, #a-d 10.50 5.00

Antarctic Treaty, 40th Anniv. — A191

**2001, June 23 Engr. *Perf. 13x12¾***
**292** A191 5.20fr dark & sky blue 3.25 1.00

Commission for the Conservation of Antarctic Marine Living Resources, 20th Anniv. — A192

**2001, Oct. 22 Litho. *Perf. 13***
**293** A192 5.20fr multi 5.00 2.00

**Voyage Booklet Type of 1999**

Adélie Land: a, Boat in pack ice. b, Dumont d'Urville Base. c, Adélie penguin rookery. d, L'Astrolabe Glacier. e, Pointe Géologie Archipelago. f, Release of meteorological balloon. g, Equipment convoy. h, Helicopter transport of fresh supplies. i, Arrival of emperor penguins. j, Telecommunications center. k, Looking towards the Antarctic. l, Cape Prud'homme. m, Ship L'Astrolabe anchored. n, Dispatch of mail.

**2001, Oct. 29 *Perf. 13***
**294** A164 Souvenir booklet, 2 each #a-n 95.00

Nos. 294a-294n are all non-denominated. Stamps are valid for 20 gram international letter rate. Each stamp appears on a separate booklet pane showing an enlarged design of the stamp and on one pane with all of the stamps and four labels found at the center of the booklet. the booklet sold for 196.78fr.

100 Cents = 1 Euro (€)

**Arms Type of 1992-95 with Euro Denominations**

**2002, Jan. 2 Engr. *Perf. 13***
**295** A102 1c black .25 .25
**296** A102 2c greenish blue .25 .25
**297** A102 5c red .30 .25
**298** A102 10c green .40 .25
**299** A102 20c orange .70 .25
*Nos. 295-299 (5)* 1.90 1.25

**Mineral Type of 1993 with Euro Denomination**

**2002, Jan. 2 Engr. *Perf. 12¾x13***
**300** A103 15c Nepheline, vert. 1.00 .40

Albatross A193

**2002, Jan. 2 *Perf. 13¼x13***
**301** A193 41c multi 3.00 .80

Ship "Marion Dufresne" — A194

**2002, Jan. 2 *Perf. 13x13¼***
**302** A194 46c multi 1.40 .60

1963-83 Telegraph Station, Crozet Island A195

**2002, Jan. 2 Litho. *Perf. 13***
**303** A195 46c multi 1.50 .60

Jacques Dubois (1920-2000) A196

**2002, Jan. 2 Engr.**
**304** A196 61c multi 2.25 .90

Engraved Rock, Saint Paul Island — A197

**2002, Jan. 2 *Perf. 13x13¼***
**305** A197 79c multi 2.40 1.25

Kerguelen Cabbage A198

**2002, Jan. 2 *Perf. 12¼***
**306** A198 €1.22 multi 3.50 1.75

Passage of the Ship "Gauss," Cent. — A199

**2002, Jan. 2 *Perf. 13x12¼***
**307** A199 €2.44 multi 7.25 3.50

Crab — A200

**2002, Jan. 2 *Perf. 13x13¼***
**308** A200 €3.66 multi 11.00 5.25

Pack Ice Diatoms — A201

**2002, Jan. 2 Litho. *Perf. 13***
**309** A201 €4.12 multi 12.50 6.00

French Geographic Society Building, Paris — A202

**2002, Jan. 2 Engr. *Perf. 13¼x13***
**310** A202 €4.45 multi + label 13.50 8.00

Cartoker Program — A203

No. 311: a, 46c, Diagram of plate tectonics. b, €3.66, Geological map of Kerguelen Island.

**2002, Jan. 2 *Perf. 13x12¼***
**311** A203 Horiz. pair, #a-b, + central label 12.50 12.50

Souvenir Sheet

Olympic Games for Antarctic Animals — A204

No. 312: a, Albatrosses flying marathon. b, Langoustines diving, vert. c, Penguins riding bobsled course, vert. d, Killer whales performing synchronized swimming, vert.

**2002, Jan. 2 Litho. *Perf. 13***
**312** A204 46c Sheet of 4, #a-d 6.50 5.50

Souvenir Sheet

Animals and Their Young — A205

No. 313: a, Penguins. b, Sea lions. c, Albatrosses. d, Elephant seals.

**2002, Jan. 2**
**313** A205 79c Sheet of 4, #a-d 10.50 9.50

Introduction of the Euro A206

**2002, Feb. 17**
**314** A206 46c blue & black 3.50 .60

**Mineral Type of 1993**

**2003, Jan. Engr. *Perf. 13¼***
**315** A103 15c Apatite, vert. 1.25 .40

Lobster Processing Plant, Saint-Paul — A207

**2003, Jan. *Perf. 13x13¼***
**316** A207 41c multi 1.25 .65

Luc Marie Bayle (1914-2000), Painter — A208

**2003, Jan. Litho. *Perf. 13***
**317** A208 46c multi 1.50 .70

Emperor Penguins — A209

**2003, Jan.**
**318** A209 46c multi 2.75 .80

Otice Hydroacoustic Station — A210

**2003, Jan. Engr. *Perf. 13x13¼***
**319** A210 61c multi 1.90 1.00

Restoration of Port Jeanne d'Arc — A211

**2003, Jan. *Perf. 13x12¼***
**320** A211 79c multi 2.40 1.25

Phylica — A212

**2003, Jan. *Perf. 13x13¼***
**321** A212 €1.22 multi 4.50 2.25

Ship "Bougainville" A213

**2003, Jan. *Perf. 13¼x13***
**322** A213 €2.44 multi 7.25 4.25

Chub — A214

**2003, Jan. Engr. *Perf. 13x13¼***
**323** A214 €3.66 multi 11.00 6.50

Ile aux Pingouins — A215

**2003, Jan. *Perf. 13x12¼***
**324** A215 €3.66 black 11.00 6.50

Super Darn Antenna Array — A216

**2003, Jan. *Perf. 13***
**325** A216 €4.12 multi 12.50 7.00

Souvenir Sheet

Paintings Revised to Reflect a Less Southerly Antarctica — A217

No. 326: a, Triumph of Venus with fish and lobsters. b, King Louis XV and wife with penguins, vert. c, Jules Dumont d'Urville and wife in a grassy Adélie Land. d, Chevalier Yves de Kerguelin under umbrella, seal in pool, vert.

**2003, Jan. Litho.**
**326** A217 46c Sheet of 4, #a-d 6.50 6.50

Protective Clothing — A218

Cold-weather outerwear from: a, 1898. b, 1912. c, 2002. d, 1980, e, 1996.

**2003, Jan. Photo. *Perf. 13¼x13***
**327** Booklet pane of 5 12.00 —
*a.-e.* A218 79c Any single 2.40 1.25
Booklet, #327 12.00

Voyage of the Ship "Français," Cent. — A219

**2003, Aug. 31 Engr. *Perf. 13x13¼***
**328** Horiz. strip of 3 15.00 13.50
*a.* A219 79c Capt. J.-B. Charcot 2.50 1.25
*b.* A219 €1.22 Ship in ice, horiz. 4.00 2.00
*c.* A219 €2.44 Ship in harbor, horiz. 7.50 4.25

Stamp size: Nos. 328b-328c, 49x29mm.

**Voyage Booklet Type of 1999**

Recipes: a, Truite aus deux citrons (trout and waterfall). b, Veau d'Amsterdam à la savoyarde (cattle). c, Lapin "Volage" à la cannelle (rabbits, penguins). d, Rôti de légine de l'ile de l'est (fish). e, Civet de renne "Volcan du diable," (reindeer). f, Iles antarctiques flottantes. g, Langouste à la mode de Saint-Paul (lobster). h, Gigot de mouflon aux 5 épices et aux pommes (sheep). i, Cabot tropical (fish, ship). j, Tagine d'agneau aux épices de la Réunion (sheep). k, Moules au pastis (mussels). l, Glace à la menthe sauvage d'Amsterdam (mint plant).

**2003, Nov. 6 Litho. *Perf. 13***
**329** A164 Souvenir booklet, #a-l 60.00

Nos. 329a-329l are all non-denominated. Stamps are valid for 20 gram international letter rate. Each stamp appears on a separate booklet pane showing an enlarged design of the stamp. The booklet sold for €17.

**Mineral Type of 1993**

**2004, Jan. 1 Engr. *Perf. 13¼***
**330** A103 15c Chalcedony, vert. 1.25 .40

A220

**2004, Jan. 1 Engr. *Perf. 13x13¼***
**331** A220 45c multi 1.40 .85

Mario Marret, director of film "Terre Adélie."

Col. Robert Genty (1910-2001) A221

**2004, Jan. 1**
**332** A221 50c multi 1.75 .95

Albert Faure Base, Crozet Island, 40th Anniv. — A222

**2004, Jan. 1 Litho. & Engr.**
**333** A222 50c multi 1.50 .95

Péron's Dolphins — A223

**2004, Jan. 1 Litho. *Perf. 13***
**334** A223 75c multi 3.00 1.50

Twin Otter Flights A224

**2004, Jan. 1 Photo. *Perf. 12¾***
**335** A224 90c multi 2.75 1.75

Values are for stamps with surrounding selvage.

Iceberg — A225

**2004, Jan. 1 Engr. *Perf. 13x13¼***
**336** A225 €1.30 multi 4.00 2.40

Grave of Sailors from the Volage — A226

**2004, Jan. 1 *Perf. 13¼x13***
**337** A226 €2.50 multi 7.50 5.00

Krill — A227

**2004, Jan. 1 *Perf. 13x13¼***
**338** A227 €4 multi 12.00 8.00

Ship "Dives" — A228

**2004, Jan. 1**
**339** A228 €4.50 multi 13.50 9.25

Souvenir Sheet

Hydrological Surveys, Adélie Land — A229

**2004, Jan. 1 Litho. *Perf. 13***
**340** A229 €4.90 multi 15.00 10.50

Souvenir Sheet

Imaginary "TAAFland" Theme Park — A230

No. 341: a, Whale statue, pyramidal entrance structure. b, Showgirls, seals, vert. c, Boy and girl with ice cream cones, vert. d, Woman in swimsuit, penguins.

**2004, Jan. 1**
**341** A230 50c Sheet of 4, #a-d 8.00 8.00

Souvenir Sheet

Post Offices — A231

No. 342: a, Amsterdam Island. b, Crozet Island. c, Kerguelen Island. d, Adélie Land.

**2004, Jan. 1**
**342** A231 90c Sheet of 4, #a-d 12.00 12.00

Penguin and Liberty Cap — A232

**2004, June 26 Engr. *Perf. 13¼x13***
**343** A232 €4.50 multi 15.00 7.00

**Mineral Type of 1993**

**2005, Jan. 1 Engr. *Perf. 13¼***
**344** A103 15c Agate .80 .50

Albert Bauer (1916-2003), Glaciologist — A233

**2005, Jan. 1 *Perf. 13x13¼***
**345** A233 45c multi 2.00 1.75

Roger Barberot (1915-2002), Administrator A234

**2005, Jan. 1**
**346** A234 50c multi 2.00 2.00

Ship "Cap Horn" — A235

**2005, Jan. 1**
**347** A235 50c multi 2.00 2.00

Seal Pot A236

**2005, Jan. 1 Litho. *Perf. 13***
**348** A236 50c multi 2.25 2.25

Macgillivray's Prion — A237

**2005, Jan. 1 Engr. *Perf. 13x13¼***
**349** A237 75c multi 2.75 2.75

Studer Valley — A238

**2005, Jan. 1 *Perf. 13x12½***
**350** A238 90c multi 3.00 3.00

Peigne des Néréides A239

**2005, Jan. 1 *Perf. 12¼***
**351** A239 €2.50 multi 8.00 7.50

Harpovoluta Charcoti — A240

**2005, Jan. 1 *Perf. 13x12½***
**352** A240 €4 multi 14.00 14.00

Murray's Ray — A241

**2005, Jan. 1 Litho. *Perf. 13***
**353** A241 €4.50 multi 14.00 14.00

Elephant Seal and Oceanographic Chart — A242

**2005, Jan. 1 Engr.**
**354** A242 €4.90 multi 16.00 16.00

Concordia Station — A243

**2005, Jan. 3 Litho. *Perf. 13***
**355** A243 50c multi 1.75 1.75

Return of the Ship "Français," Cent. — A244

**2005, Mar. 4 Engr. *Perf. 13x13¼***
**356** A244 €4.50 multi + label 15.00 15.00

Disappearance of Paul-Emile Victor, 10th Anniv. — A245

**2005, Mar. 7 Litho. *Perf. 13***
**357** A245 50c multi 2.50 2.50

50th Anniversary Coat of Arms — A246

**2005, Aug. 6**
**358** A246 (90c) multi 3.00 3.00
*a.* Booklet pane of 1 4.00 —

No. 358a is found in No. 359.

**Voyage Booklet Type of 1999**

History: a, Discovery of Amsterdam Island, 1522. b, Discovery of Crozet Island, 1772. c, Discovery of Kerguelen Island, 1772, vert. d, Discovery of Adélie Land, 1840. e, Astronomers viewing 1874 transit of Venus on St. Paul Island. f, Wreck of the Strathmore, 1875. g, Port Jeanne d'Arc, 1908. h, Port-Couvreux, 1925. i, Building of Port-Martin, 1950. j, Antarctic Treaty, 1959. k, Building of fourth base, 1963-64.

**2005, Aug. 6 Litho. *Perf. 13***
**359** A164 Souvenir booklet, #a-k, 358a 70.00

Nos. 359a-359k are all non-denominated. Stamps are valid for 90c, the 20 gram international letter rate. Each stamp appears on a separate booklet pane showing an enlarged design of the stamp. The booklet sold for €18.

Penguins and No. 1 — A247

**2005, Nov. 2**
**360** A247 90c multi 3.25 3.25

French Southern & Antarctic Territories, 50th anniv.

Souvenir Sheet

Maps — A248

Maps of: a, Crozet Archipelago. b, Amsterdam and St. Paul Islands. c, Kerguelen Island. d, Adélie Land.

**Litho. & Engr.**

**2005, Nov. 10 *Perf. 13x13¼***
**361** A248 50c Sheet of 4, #a-d 6.50 6.50

French Southern & Antarctic Territories, 50th anniv.

Rutile A249

**2006, Jan. 1 Engr. *Perf. 13x12½***
**362** A249 15c multi .80 .80

Charles Vélain (1845-1925), Geologist — A250

**2006, Jan. 1 *Perf. 13x13¼***
**363** A250 48c pur & red 1.60 1.60

Albert Seyrolle (1887-1919), Mariner — A251

**2006, Jan. 1**
**364** A251 53c multi 1.60 1.60

Amsterdam Island Garden — A252

**2006, Jan. 1 Litho. *Perf. 13***
**365** A252 53c multi 1.60 1.60

Ship "Osiris" — A253

**2006, Jan. 1 Photo. *Perf. 13x13¼***
**366** A253 90c multi 3.00 3.00

Dumont d'Urville Base, 50th Anniv. — A254

**2006, Jan. 1 Engr. *Perf. 13x12½***
**367** A254 90c multi 2.75 2.75

Virgin of the Seal Hunters — A255

**2006, Jan. 1 *Perf. 12½x13***
**368** A255 €2.50 multi 7.50 7.50

Lagenorhynchus Cruciger — A256

**2006, Jan. 1 *Perf. 13x13¼***
**369** A256 €4 multi 12.00 12.00

Keguelen Hake — A257

**2006, Jan. 1**
**370** A257 €4.53 multi 13.50 13.50

Amsterdam Island Carbon Dioxide Measurements, 25th Anniv. — A258

**2006, Jan. 1**
**371** A258 €4.90 multi 15.00 15.00

Miniature Sheet

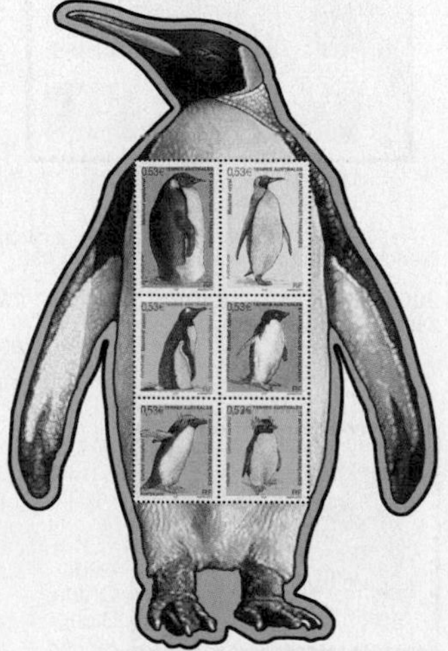
Penguins — A259

No. 372 — Penguin (background color): a, Emperor penguin (lilac, 22x36mm). b, King penguin (pale yellow green, 22x36mm). c, Gentoo penguin (green, 22x27mm). d, Adélie penguin (pink, 22x27mm). e, Macaroni penguin (orange, 22x27mm). f, Rockhopper penguin (blue, 22x27mm).

**Litho. & Engr.**

**2006, Jan. 1 *Perf. 13***
**372** A259 53c Sheet of 6, #a-f 12.00 12.00

Souvenir Sheet

Albatross — A260

**Litho. & Engr.**

**2006, June 1 *Perf. 13***
**373** A260 €4.53 multi 14.50 14.50

Souvenir Sheet

Albatross — A261

**Litho. & Engr.**

**2006, Nov. 8 *Perf. 13***
**374** A261 90c multi 3.50 3.50

Corundum A262

**2007, Jan. 1 Engr. *Perf. 13¼***
**375** A262 15c multi 1.25 1.25

A263

**2007, Jan. 1 *Perf. 13x13¼***
**376** A263 49c multi 1.50 1.50

Louis-Francois Aleno de Saint Aloüarn (1738-72), explorer who claimed Australia for France.

A264

**2007, Jan. 1**
**377** A264 54c multi 1.60 1.60

Marthe Emmanuel (1901-97), assistant to explorer Jean Charcot.

Cattle, Amsterdam Island — A265

**2007, Jan. 1** ***Perf. 13x12½***
**378** A265 54c multi 1.50 1.50

Ship Tonkinois — A266

**2007, Jan. 1** ***Perf. 13x13¼***
**379** A266 90c multi 2.50 2.50

Ile de la Baleine — A267

**2007, Jan. 1** ***Perf. 13x12½***
**380** A267 90c multi 2.50 2.50

Archaeology on Saint Paul Island — A268

**2007, Jan. 1** ***Perf. 12½x13***
**381** A268 €2.50 multi 7.00 7.00

Lampris Immaculatus — A269

**2007, Jan. 1** ***Perf. 13x12½***
**382** A269 €4 multi 11.00 11.00

Astonomy at Concordia — A270

**Litho. & Engr.**

**2007, Jan. 1** ***Perf. 13***
**383** A270 €4.90 multi 14.00 14.00

French Polar Expeditions, 60th Anniv. — A271

No. 384: a, Expedition headquarters, Paris, men shaking hands over globe. b, Expedition headquarters.

**2007, Jan. 1 Engr.** ***Perf. 13x13¼***
**384** Horiz. pair + central label 13.50 13.50
*a.* A271 54c multi 1.75 1.75
*b.* A271 €4 multi 11.00 11.00

**Miniature Sheet**

Albatrosses — A272

No. 385: a, Amsterdam albatross. b, Great albatross (Grand albatros). c, Black-browed albatross (Albatros à sourcils noir). d, Yellow-beaked albatross (Albatros à bec jaune). e, Sooty albatross (Albatros fuligineux).

**Litho. & Engr.**

**2007, Jan. 1** ***Perf. 13***
**385** A272 54c Sheet of 5, #a-e 8.00 8.00

Intl. Polar Year — A273

No. 386: a, Penguins. b, Map of Antarctica, French Southern & Antarctic Territories #9.

**2007, Mar. 1 Litho.** ***Perf. 13***
**386** Horiz. pair + central label 15.00 15.00
*a.* A273 90c multi 2.75 2.75
*b.* A273 €4 multi 12.00 12.00

Audit Office, Bicent. A274

**2007 Mar. 19 Engr.** ***Perf. 13¼***
**387** A274 90c multi 4.50 4.50

**Miniature Sheet**

Indian Ocean Islands — A275

No. 388: a, Ile Tromelin. b, Iles Glorieuses. c, Ile Juan de Nova. d, Ile Bassas da India. e, Ile Europa.

**2007, May 10 Photo.** ***Perf. 13x13¼***
**388** A275 54c Sheet of 5, #a-e 9.00 9.00

Path of Sun on June 21 Over Dumont d'Urville Base — A276

**2007, June 21**
**389** A276 90c multi 3.00 3.00

**Voyage Booklet Type of 1999**

No. 390 — Photographs of land features: a, Apostle Island, Crozet Archipelago. b, Chamonix Lake, Kerguelen Island. c, Phylicia forest, Amsterdam Island. d, Gulf of Morbihan, Kerguelen Islands. e, Mount Cook, Chamonix Lake and glacier, Kerguelen Islands. f, Tourbiéres Plateau, Amsterdam Island. g, Nuageuses Islands, Kerguelen Islands. h, Caldera, Amsterdam Island. i, Mount Cook, Kerguelen Island. j, Central Plateau, Kerguelen Island. k, Isle of Penguins, Crozet Archipelago. l, Antonelli Crater, Amsterdam Island. m, Lake on Possession Island, Crozet Archipelago. n, Rocks off Apostle Island, Crozet Archipelago. o, Geographic Society Peninsula, Kerguelen Island. p, Ronarch Peninsula, Kerguelen Island.

**2007, Nov. 8 Litho.** ***Perf. 13***
**390** A164 (90c) Souvenir booklet, #a-p 70.00

No. 390 sold for €20, and contains four panes, consisting of a block of four stamps of Nos. 390a-390d, 390e-390h, 390i-390l, and 390m-390p.

French Southern and Antarctic Territories Flag — A277

**2008, Jan. 1 Litho.** ***Perf. 13***

**Background Color**

| | | | | |
|---|---|---|---|---|
| **391** | A277 | 1c black | .25 | .25 |
| **392** | A277 | 2c blue | .35 | .35 |
| **393** | A277 | 5c red | .40 | .40 |
| **394** | A277 | 10c green | .40 | .40 |
| **395** | A277 | 20c brn orange | .80 | .80 |
| | | *Nos. 391-395 (5)* | 2.20 | 2.20 |

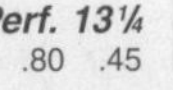
Spinel — A278

**2008, Jan. 1 Engr.** ***Perf. 13¼***
**396** A278 15c multi .80 .45

Samivel (1907-92), Writer — A279

**2008, Jan. 1** ***Perf. 13x13¼***
**397** A279 54c grn & brown 1.60 1.60

St. Paul Island — A280

**2008, Jan. 1**
**398** A280 54c blue & dk blue 1.60 1.60

Construction of Port Jeanne d'Arc, Cent. — A281

**2008, Jan. 1** ***Perf. 13x12¾***
**399** A281 90c multi 2.75 2.75

Rockhopper Penguins — A282

**2008, Jan. 1** ***Perf. 13x12½***
**400** A282 90c multi 2.75 2.75

Shipwreck of L'Esperance — A283

**2008, Jan. 1 Litho.** ***Perf. 13x12¾***
**401** A283 90c multi 2.75 2.75

Macrourus Carinatus — A284

**2008, Jan. 1 Engr.** ***Perf. 13x12½***
**402** A284 €4 multi 12.00 12.00

Galium Antarcticum
A285

**2008, Jan. 1** ***Perf. 12½x13***
**403** A285 €4.54 multi 13.50 13.50

Adélie Land Coastal Ichthyology Program
A286

**2008, Jan. 1** **Litho.** ***Perf. 13***
**404** A286 €4.90 multi 14.50 14.50

Souvenir Sheet

Kerguelen Fish Biomass Evaluation Project (POKER) — A287

**2008, Jan. 1** **Litho. & Engr.**
**405** A287 €2.50 multi 7.50 7.50

Souvenir Sheet

Elephant Seals — A288

No. 406: a, Head of adult female. b, Seals initiating combat. c, Juvenile seal. d, Head of adult male.

**2008, Jan. 1**
**406** A288 54c Sheet of 4, #a-d 6.50 6.50

Gérard Mégie (1946-2004), Ozone Researcher — A289

**2008, Feb. 15** **Engr.** ***Perf. 13x13¼***
**407** A289 54c multi 1.75 1.75

Miniature Sheet

Birds — A290

No. 408: a, Sooty tern (Sterne fulgineuse). b, Red-footed booby (Fou a pieds rouges), vert. c, Masked booby (Fou masque), vert. d, Great frigatebird (Fregate du Pacifique), vert. e, Tropicbird (Paille en queue).

***Perf. 13¼x13 (#408a, 408e), 13x13¼***
**2008, June 1** **Litho. & Engr.**
**408** A290 54c Sheet of 5, #a-e 8.50 8.50

Earth and Birds — A291

**2008, June 14** **Photo.** ***Perf. 13***
**409** A291 €4.54 multi 14.50 14.50

Ship Marion Dufresne — A292

**2008, Nov. 6** **Litho.** ***Perf. 13***
**410** A292 (55c) multi 1.75 1.75

Compare with type A194.

Pyrite
A293

**2009, Jan. 1** **Engr.** ***Perf. 13¼***
**411** A293 15c multi .60 .60

A294

**2009, Jan. 1** ***Perf. 13x13¼***
**412** A294 55c multi 1.60 1.60

Henri Paschal de Rochegude (1741-1834), naval officer.

A295

**2009, Jan. 1** ***Perf. 13***
**413** A295 55c multi 1.60 1.60

Charles Gaston Rouillon (1915-2007), director of French polar scientific expeditions.

Residence de France Seal of Kerguelen Islands, Cent. — A296

**2009, Jan. 1** **Litho.**
**414** A296 90c multi 2.50 2.50

Shark With Dorsal Spines — A297

**2009, Jan. 1** **Engr.** ***Perf. 13x12½***
**415** A297 €2.50 multi 7.00 7.00

Ship Jeanne d'Arc — A298

**2009, Jan. 1**
**416** A298 €4 multi 11.00 11.00

MACARBI Program Scallop Research
A299

**2009, Jan. 1** ***Perf. 12½x13***
**417** A299 €4.55 multi 13.00 13.00

Seaweed — A300

No. 418: a, Himantothallus grandifolius and iceberg. b, Laminaria pallida and seals.

**2009, Jan. 1** ***Perf. 13x13¼***
**418** Horiz. pair + central label 13.50 13.50
*a.* A300 90c multi 2.50 2.50
*b.* A300 €4 multi 11.00 11.00

Miniature Sheet

Petrels — A301

No. 419: a, Soft-plumaged petrel (Petrel soyeux). b, Wilson's petrel (Petrel de Wilson). c, Gray petrel (Petrel gris). d, Diving petrel (Petrel plongeur). e, Snow petrel (Petrel des neiges).

**Litho. & Engr.**
**2009, Jan. 1** ***Perf. 13¼x13***
**419** A301 55c Sheet of 5, #a-e 7.75 7.75

**Voyage Booklet Type of 1999**

No. 420 — Photographs: a, Frigatebirds, Europa Island. b, Beach on north coast of Europa Island. c, Mangroves, Europa Island. d, Flagpole, palm trees, Europa Island. e, Turtle on beach, Juan de Nova Island. f, Sandbanks off Juan de Nova Island. g, Tree, Juan de Nova Island. h, Grounded ship, Juan de Nova Island. i, Brown noddies, Glorioso Islands. j, Flower, Glorioso Islands. k, Pool of water, Glorioso Islands. l, Tree on islet, Glorioso Islands. m, Birds, Tromelin Island. n, Meteorological station, Tromelin Island. o, Coral fossil, Tromelin Island. p, Anchor, Tromelin Island.

**2009, Nov. 5** **Litho.** ***Perf. 13***
**420** A164 (90c) Souvenir booklet, #a-p 65.00

No. 420 sold for €21.50, and contains four panes, consisting of a block of four stamps of Nos. 420a-420d, 420e-420h, 420i-4290l, and 420m-420p.

Antarctic Treaty, 50th Anniv. — A302

**2009, Dec. 1** **Engr.** ***Perf. 13x13¼***
**421** A302 56c multi 1.75 1.75

Tourmaline
A303

**2010, Jan. 2** **Engr.** ***Perf. 13¼***
**422** A303 28c multi .80 .80

Dr. Jean Rivolier (1923-2007), Medical Researcher — A304

**2010, Jan. 2** **Litho.** ***Perf. 13***
**423** A304 56c multi 1.60 1.60

Birds on Ile du Lys — A305

**2010, Jan. 2 Engr. *Perf. 13x13¼***
424 A305 56c multi 1.60 1.60

Patureau House, Juan de Nova Island — A306

**2010, Jan. 2**
425 A306 56c multi 1.60 1.60

Program Crac-ice — A307

**2010, Jan. 2**
426 A307 90c multi 2.50 2.50

Supply Ship Ile St. Paul — A308

**2010, Jan. 2**
427 A308 €1.35 multi 3.75 3.75

Crozet Orca — A309

**2010, Jan. 2**
428 A309 €2.80 multi 7.75 7.75

Kerguelen Terns — A310

**2010, Jan. 2**
429 A310 €4.30 multi 12.00 12.00

Miniature Sheet

Sea Lions of Amsterdam Island — A311

No. 430: a, Sea lion and ship. b, Two sea lions on rocks, denomination at UR in black, hòriz. c, Sea lion, denomination at UL in black, horiz. d, Two sea lions near water, denomination in white at UR, horiz. e, Two sea lions, denomination at LL in black, horiz.

**Litho. & Engr.**

**2010, Jan. 2 *Perf. 13***
430 A311 56c Sheet of 5, #a-e 7.75 7.75

Miniature Sheet

Polar Transportation — A312

No. 431: a, Team of dogs pulling sled. b, Weasel M29C. c, Sno-cat 743. d, HB40-Castor. e, Challenger 65. f, PB 330.

**2010, Jan. 2**
431 A312 90c Sheet of 6, #a-f 15.00 15.00

Gabriel Pavilion, Paris — A313

**2010, May 28 Litho. *Perf. 13***
432 A313 56c multi 1.40 1.40

Second Elysée Philatelic Club Show, Paris.

Miniature Sheet

Albatross Protection — A314

No. 433: a, Albatross and chick on nest. b, Albatross facing left. c, Albatross facing right. d, Two juvenile albatrosses.

**Litho. & Engr.**

**2010, June 12 *Perf. 13***
433 A314 56c Sheet of 4, #a-d 5.75 5.75

French Southern & Antarctic Territories Booth at Espace Champerret Stamp Show — A315

**2010, Nov. 5 Litho. *Perf. 13***
434 A315 56c multi 3.00 3.00

**Self-Adhesive**

***Serpentine Die Cut 11***
435 A315 56c multi 3.00 3.00

Astronomical Observatory, Concordia Base, Antarctica and Southern Cross — A316

**Litho. & Engr.**

**2011, Jan. 2 *Perf. 13***
436 A316 56c multi 1.50 1.50

Martin de Viviès Base, Amsterdam Island — A317

**2011, Jan. 2 Engr. *Perf. 13x13¼***
437 A317 90c multi 2.40 2.40

Josef Enzensperger (1873-1903), Meteorologist A318

**2011, Jan. 2 *Perf. 13¼x13***
438 A318 90c multi 2.40 2.40

André Chastain (1906-62), Botanist A319

**2011, Jan. 2**
439 A319 €1.35 multi 3.75 3.75

Sheathbills — A320

**2011, Jan. 2 *Perf. 13x13¼***
440 A320 €1.35 black & purple 3.75 3.75

Artedidraco Orianae — A321

**2011, Jan. 2**
441 A321 €1.35 multi 3.75 3.75

Cruiser Lapérouse — A322

**2011, Jan. 2**
442 A322 €4.30 multi 11.50 11.50

Zircons — A323

No. 443: a, Zircons embedded in rock. b, Cut and polished zircon.

**Litho. & Engr.**

**2011, Jan. 2 *Perf. 13¼***
443 A323 Horiz. pair 1.75 1.75
*a.* 28c multi .75 .75
*b.* 34c multi .90 .90

December 8, 1929 Mail Plane Crash — A324

No. 444: a, Farman F190 airplane. b, Map of flight. c, Crew and crash covers.

**2011, Jan. 2 *Perf. 13***
444 Horiz. strip of 3 7.75 7.75
*a.* A324 56c multi 1.50 1.50
*b.* A324 90c multi 2.40 2.40
*c.* A324 €1.35 multi 3.75 3.75

Miniature Sheet

Whales — A325

No. 445: a, Baleine à bosse (humpback whale). b, Baleine franche australe (southern right whale). c, Cachalot (sperm whale). d, Rorqual de Rudolphi (sei whale).

**2011, Jan. 2**
445 A325 56c Sheet of 4, #a-d 6.00 6.00

Patrol Boat Osiris — A326

**2011, Apr. 1 Litho.**
446 A326 (60c) multi 1.75 1.75

Gentoo Penguins — A327

**2011, June 15 Litho. *Perf. 13***
**447** A327 €1 multi + label 3.00 3.00

Orré House (Prefect's Residence), St. Pierre, Reunion — A328

**2011, Sept. 19**
**448** A328 60c multi 1.75 1.75

Souvenir Sheet

Squadron Escort Forbin — A329

**2011, Nov. 3 Litho. & Engr.**
**449** A329 €1.10 multi 3.00 3.00

See St. Pierre & Miquelon No. 938.

Adélie Penguins — A330

**2011, Dec. 2 Litho. *Perf. 13***
**450** A330 60c multi 1.60 1.60

Penguin Breeding Grounds, Baie du Marin, Crozet Island — A331

Views of Baie du Marin in. No. 451, 60c, 1961. No. 452, 60c, 2011.

**2011, Dec. 23 *Perf. 13x13¼***
**451-452** A331 Set of 2 3.25 3.25

Ship Marion Dufresne in Mamoudzou Lagoon — A332

***Serpentine Die Cut 11***
**2011, Dec. 31**
**Self-Adhesive**
**453** A332 60c multi 1.60 1.60

See Mayotte No. 288.

Notodiscus Hookeri — A333

**2012, Jan. 2 Engr. *Perf. 13x13¼***
**454** A333 60c multi 1.60 1.60

Ship Marius Moutet — A334

**2012, Jan. 2**
**455** A334 60c multi 1.60 1.60

Weddell Seals — A335

**2012, Jan. 2 *Perf. 13¼x13***
**456** A335 €1 multi 2.60 2.60

Roald Amundsen (1872-1928), Polar Explorer A336

**2012, Jan. 2**
**457** A336 €1 multi 2.60 2.60

René-Emile Bossière (1857-1941), Kerguelen Island Business Entrepreneur A337

**2012, Jan. 2**
**458** A337 €1.45 multi 3.75 3.75

Lepidonotothen Larseni — A338

**Litho. & Silk-screened**
**2012, Jan. 2 *Perf. 13***
**459** A338 €2.40 multi 6.25 6.25

Diopside — A339

No. 460: a, Crystals. b, Crystal and cut stone.

**2012, Jan. 2 Engr. *Perf. 13¼***
**460** A339 Horiz. pair 1.75 1.75
*a.* 29c red & green .80 .80
*b.* 36c red & green .95 .95

Point Molloy, Kerguelen Island — A340

No. 461: a, Buildings at Point Molloy. b, Molloy seismological station, 1953-63.

**Litho. & Engr.**
**2012, Jan. 2 *Perf. 13x13¼***
**461** Horiz. pair 3.25 3.25
*a.-b.* A340 60c Either single 1.60 1.60

Military Presence in French Southern & Antarctic Territories — A341

No. 462: a, Second Regiment of Marine Infantry Parachutists on Europa Island. b, Detachment of the Mayotte Foreign Legion on the Glorioso Islands.

**Litho. & Silk-screened**
**2012, Jan. 2 *Perf. 13***
**462** Horiz. pair 3.25 3.25
*a.-b.* A341 60c Either single 1.60 1.60

Miniature Sheet

Derelict Whaling Station, Port-Jeanne d'Arc, Kerguelen Island — A342

No. 463: a, Eight storage tanks. b, Three boilers, vert. c, Two storage silos. d, House, vert.

**2012, Jan. 2 Photo.**
**463** A342 60c Sheet of 4, #a-d 6.25 6.25

Miniature Sheet

Nature Reserve Flora and Fauna — A343

No. 464: a, Gentoo penguin (manchot papou). b, White-chinned petrel (petrel a menton blanc). c, Lyallia kerguelensis. d, Anatalanta aptera.

**2012, Jan. 2 Litho. & Engr.**
**464** A343 Sheet of 4 8.50 8.50
*a.* 20c multi .55 .55
*b.* 60c multi 1.60 1.60
*c.* €1 multi 2.60 2.60
*d.* €1.45 multi 3.75 3.75

Miniature Sheet

Aircraft Used in Polar Regions — A344

No. 465: a, B-24 Liberator. b, DC-4 Skymaster. c, Nord 2501 Noratlas. d, C-130 Hercules. e, DC-3 Basler BT-67. f, DHC-6 Twin Otter.

**2012, Jan. 2**
**465** A344 €1 Sheet of 6, #a-f 16.00 16.00

Ile Longue, Kerguelen Islands A345

No. 466: a, 60c, Painting. b, €1, Painting, diff.

**2012, Apr. 13 Litho. *Perf. 13x13¼***
**466** A345 Pair, #a-b 4.25 4.25

No. 466 was printed in sheets containing two pairs.

Souvenir Sheet

Prince of Monaco Islands — A346

No. 467: a, Giant Antarctic petrel. b, Coastline of Prince of Monaco Islands.

**Litho. & Engr.**
**2012, June 9 *Perf. 13¼***
**467** A346 €1 Sheet of 2, #a-b 5.00 5.00

See Monaco No. 2680.

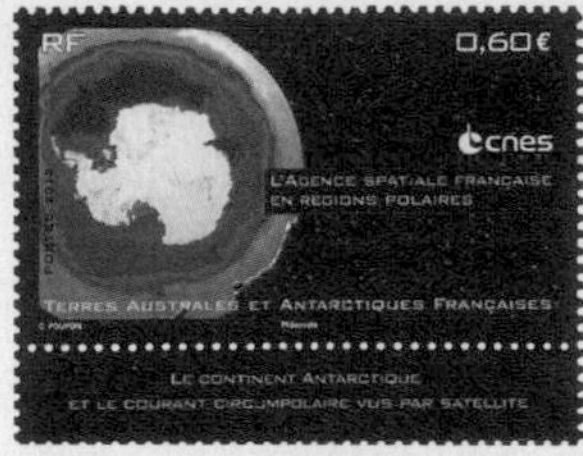

National Space Studies Center (CNES) Projects — A347

No. 468: a, Map of Antarctica. b, Penguin with tracking devices. c, Galileo satellite. d, Scientists deploying weather balloon. e, Pleaides satellite.

**2012, June 9 Photo. Perf. 13**

**468** Vert. strip of 5 + 5 labels 12.00 12.00
- *a.-b.* A347 60c Either single + label 1.50 1.50
- *c.-d.* A347 €1 Either single + label 2.50 2.50
- *e.* A347 €1.45 multi + label 3.75 3.75

French Polar Institute, 20th Anniv. — A348

**2012, July 12 Litho. Perf. 13¼x13**

**469** A348 60c multi 1.50 1.50

Souvenir Sheet

Bridge for Tracking Adélie Penguins — A349

**Litho. & Engr.**

**2012, Nov. 2 Perf. 13¼x13**

**470** A349 €2 multi 5.25 5.25

Flight of Maryse Hilsz to Juan de Nova Island, 80th Anniv. — A350

No. 471: a, Airplane, map of route. b, Hilsz (1901-46) in airplane.

**2012, Nov. 8 Litho. Perf. 13**

**471** A350 Horiz. pair 4.25 4.25
- *a.* 60c multi 1.60 1.60
- *b.* €1 multi 2.60 2.60

Prasiola Crispa and Penguins — A351

**2013, Jan. 1 Engr. Perf. 13x13¼**

**472** A351 65c multi 1.75 1.75

Charles Petitjean (1914-88), Pilot — A352

**2013, Jan. 1 Perf. 12½x13**

**473** A352 65c multi 1.75 1.75

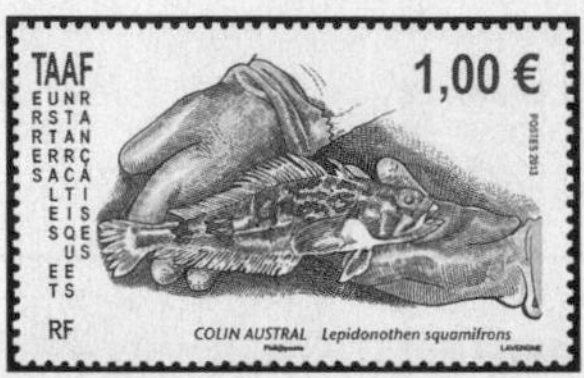

Lepidonothen Squamifrons — A353

**2013, Jan. 1 Perf. 13x13¼**

**474** A353 €1 multi 2.75 2.75

Sailboat "Le Mischief" A354

**2013, Jan. 1 Perf. 12¼**

**475** A354 €1 multi 2.75 2.75

Douglas Mawson (1882-1958), Antarctic Explorer, Huts and Penguins — A355

**Litho. & Engr.**

**2013, Jan. 1 Perf. 13**

**476** A355 €1.45 multi 4.00 4.00

Bernard-Marie Boudin, Chevalier de Tromelin (1735-1816), Explorer and Colonial Administrator — A356

**2013, Jan. 13 Litho.**

**477** A356 €2.40 multi 6.50 6.50

Hematite — A357

**2013, Jan. 1 Engr. Perf. 13¼**

**478** A357 Horiz. pair 2.75 2.75
- *a.* 40c Crystals 1.10 1.10
- *b.* 60c Crystal 1.60 1.60

Miniature Sheet

Eaton's Pintail — A358

No. 479: a, Duck in water. b, Heads of two ducks, vert. c, Duck and egss. d, Head of duck, ducks in flight.

**Litho. & Engr.**

**2013, Jan. 1 Perf. 13**

**479** A358 Sheet of 4 9.00 9.00
- *a.* 20c multi .55 .55
- *b.* 60c multi 1.60 1.60
- *c.* €1 multi 2.75 2.75
- *d.* €1.45 multi 4.00 4.00

Miniature Sheet

Helicopters — A359

No. 480: a, Sud-Ouest Djinn 1221. b, Bell 47 G2. c, Hiller 360. d, Sud-Est Alouette II 3130. e, Ecureuil AS 350. f, Panther AS 565

**2013, Jan. 1**

**480** A359 €1 Sheet of 6, #a-f 16.00 16.00

Souvenir Sheet

Engravings of Amsterdam and St. Paul Islands — A360

**2013, Jan. 1 Litho.**

**481** A360 €3.40 multi 9.00 9.00

**Voyage Booklet Type of 1999**

No. 482: a, Ship Astrolabe near Dumont d'Urville Station. b, The Astrolabe, helicopter and Adélie penguins. c, Astrolabe docked near Lion landing strip. d, Four Adélie penguins at Dumont d'Urville station. e, View of Dumon't d'Urville Station taken from the Astrolabe. f, Aerial view of Dumont d'Urville Station. g, Aurora Australis. h, Colony of Emperor penguins. i, Five men and plow at Cap Prudhomme Base. j, Aerial view of Cap Prudhomme Base, island at right. k, View of Cap Prudhomme Base, island at center. l, Two penguins. m, Italian, French and European Union flags at Concordia Base. n, Snow vehicle moving containers. o, Astronomical equipment near Concordia Base. p, Steps leading to containers.

**2013, Apr. 5 Litho. Perf. 13**

**482** A164 (€1) Souvenir booklet, #a-p 65.00

No. 482 sold for €25 and contains four panes, consisting of a block of four stamps of Nos. 482a-482d, 482e-482h, 482i-482l, and 482m-482p.

F.S. Floreal — A361

**2013, Apr. 5 Litho. Perf. 13**

**483** A361 (63c) multi 1.75 1.75

A362

Silhouettes of Emblems — A363

Designs: 1c, Green turtle. 2c, Helicopter. 3c, Penguin. 4c, Ship "Marion Dufresne." 63c, Green turtle, helicopter, penguin, ship, "TAAF."

**2013, Apr. 29 Engr. Perf. 13**

**484** A362 1c dk bl & bl .25 .25
**485** A362 2c purple .25 .25
**486** A362 3c dk grn & yel grn .25 .25
**487** A362 4c brn org & org .25 .25

**Litho. & Silk-screened**

***Perf. 13¼***

**488** A363 63c multi 1.75 1.75
*Nos. 484-488 (5)* 2.75 2.75

See Nos. 504-507, 568a.

Souvenir Sheet

Engraver, Map, Penguin — A364

**Engr. (Litho. Margin)**

**2013, May 17 Perf. 13**

**489** A364 €5 multi 13.50 13.50

Souvenir Sheets

Prélèvement d'une Fusov, by Laurent Tixador — A365

Jours Heureux à l'Ile de la Désolation, by Klavdij Sluban — A366

**2013, June 17 Litho. *Perf. 13***

| | | | |
|---|---|---|---|
| 490 | A365 | €1 multi | 2.75 2.75 |
| 491 | A366 | €1 black | 2.75 2.75 |

Ateliers des Ailleurs art project.

Souvenir Sheet

Whale and Stock Certificate for Kerguelen Fisheries Society — A367

**2013, Nov. 6 Litho. *Perf. 13¼x13***

| | | | |
|---|---|---|---|
| 492 | A367 | €1 multi | 2.75 2.75 |

Louis Jacquinot (1898-1993), Minister of Overseas France — A368

**2014, Jan. 2 Engr. *Perf. 13¼x13***

| | | | |
|---|---|---|---|
| 493 | A368 | 66c multi | 1.90 1.90 |

Bertrand Imbert (1924-2011), Leader of French Research for International Geophysical Year — A369

**2014, Jan. 2 Engr. *Perf. 12¾x13***

| | | | |
|---|---|---|---|
| 494 | A369 | 66c multi | 1.90 1.90 |

Tromelin Meteorological Station, 60th Anniv. — A370

**2014, Jan. 2 Engr. *Perf. 13x13¼***

| | | | |
|---|---|---|---|
| 495 | A370 | €1.55 multi | 4.25 4.25 |

Rock Carvings of Amsterdam Island — A371

**2014, Jan. 2 Engr. *Perf. 13x13¼***

| | | | |
|---|---|---|---|
| 496 | A371 | €1.55 multi | 4.25 4.25 |

Supply Ship "Le Malin" — A372

**2014, Jan. 2 Litho. *Perf. 13***

| | | | |
|---|---|---|---|
| 497 | A372 | €1.55 multi | 4.25 4.25 |

Bren Carrier on Kerguelen Island — A373

**2014, Jan. 2 Engr. *Perf. 13x13¼***

| | | | |
|---|---|---|---|
| 498 | A373 | €2 multi | 5.50 5.50 |

White Tower (Basalt Columns), Crozet Islands — A374

**2014, Jan. 2 Litho. *Perf. 13***

| | | | |
|---|---|---|---|
| 499 | A374 | €2 multi | 5.50 5.50 |

Lepidonotothen Mizops — A375

**2014, Jan. 2 Engr. *Perf. 13x13¼***

| | | | |
|---|---|---|---|
| 500 | A375 | €2.40 multi | 6.50 6.50 |

Fluorite — A376

No. 501: a, Polished stones. b, Crystal.

**2014, Jan. 2 Litho. *Perf. 13***

| | | | |
|---|---|---|---|
| 501 | A376 | Horiz. pair | 2.75 2.75 |
| *a.* | | 37c multi | 1.00 1.00 |
| *b.* | | 63c multi | 1.75 1.75 |

Miniature Sheet

Mollusks — A377

No. 502: a, Moule de Kerguelen (Kerguelen mussel). b, Volute de Challenger (Challenger volute). c, Moule de Magellan (Magellan mussel), vert. d, Buccin antarctique (Antarctic whelk). e, Laternule antarctique (Antarctic clam).

**Litho. & Engr.**

**2014, Jan. 2 *Perf. 13***

| | | | |
|---|---|---|---|
| 502 | A377 | 63c Sheet of 5, #a-e | 8.75 8.75 |

Miniature Sheet

Birds — A378

No. 503: a, Damier du Cap (Cape petrels). b, Manchot royal de Crozet (Crozet Island king penguins). c, Fulmar antarctique (Antarctic fulmars). d, Grand albatros de Crozet (Wandering albatrosses).

**2014, Jan. 2 Engr. *Perf. 13x12¾***

| | | | |
|---|---|---|---|
| 503 | A378 | Sheet of 4 | 11.00 11.00 |
| *a.-b.* | | 66c Either single | 1.90 1.90 |
| *c.* | | €1.05 multi | 2.75 2.75 |
| *d.* | | €1.55 multi | 4.25 4.25 |

**Silhouette of Emblems Type of 2013 and**

Silhouettes of Emblems — A379

A362 designs as before.
€7, Map of District of Crozet, dolphin, penguin, ship, "TAAF."

**2014, Mar. 7 Litho. *Perf. 13***
**Dated "2014"**

| | | | |
|---|---|---|---|
| 504 | A362 | 1c dk bl & bl | .25 .25 |
| *a.* | | Litho. & silk-screened (varnish on silhouette), dated "2015" | .25 .25 |
| *b.* | | As "a," dated "2016" | .25 .25 |
| 505 | A362 | 2c purple | .25 .25 |
| *a.* | | Litho. & silk-screened (varnish on silhouette), dated "2015" | .25 .25 |
| *b.* | | As "a," dated "2016" | .25 .25 |
| 506 | A362 | 3c dk grn & yel grn | .25 .25 |
| *a.* | | Litho. & silk-screened (varnish on silhouette), dated "2015" | .25 .25 |
| *b.* | | As "a," dated "2016" | .25 .25 |
| *c.* | | Pair, #505b-506b | .25 .25 |
| 507 | A362 | 4c brn org & org | .25 .25 |
| *a.* | | Litho. & silk-screened (varnish on silhouette), dated "2015" | .25 .25 |
| *b.* | | As "a," dated "2016" | .25 .25 |
| *c.* | | Pair, #504b, 507b | .25 .25 |

**Litho. & Silk-Screened**
***Perf. 13¼***

| | | | |
|---|---|---|---|
| 508 | A379 | €7 multi | 19.00 19.00 |
| | | *Nos. 504-508 (5)* | 20.00 20.00 |

Issued: Nos. 504a, 505a, 506a, 507a, 3/19; Nos. 504b, 505b, 506b, 507b, 3/30/16. See No. 568b.

Miniature Sheet

Commerson's Dolphins — A380

No. 509: a, 63c, Dolphin sticking head out of water. b, 66c, Three dolphins underwater. c, 66c, Dolphin breaching surface. d, €1.05, Dolphin above water.

**Litho. & Engr.**

**2014, June 26 *Perf. 13¼x13***

| | | | |
|---|---|---|---|
| 509 | A380 | Sheet of 4, #a-d | 8.25 8.25 |

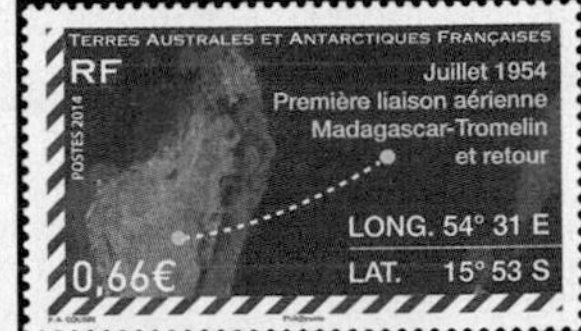


Map of Madagascar to Tromelin Flight — A381

AAC-1 Toucan — A382

AAC-1 Toucan and Stamped Cover from Tromelin — A383

**2014, Sept. 21 Litho. *Perf. 13***

| | | | |
|---|---|---|---|
| 510 | | Horiz. strip of 3 | 8.50 8.50 |
| *a.* | A381 | 66c multi | 1.75 1.75 |
| *b.* | A382 | €1.05 multi | 2.75 2.75 |
| *c.* | A383 | €1.55 multi | 4.00 4.00 |

First flight between Madagascar and Tromelin, 50th anniv.

Green Turtle A384

**2014, Oct. 9 Litho. *Perf. 13x13¼***

| | | | |
|---|---|---|---|
| 511 | A384 | €1.05 multi | 2.60 2.60 |

See Comoro Islands No. , France No. 4695, Malagasy Republic No. 1637, Mauritius No. 1144, Seychelles No. 904.

Gendarmes — A385

No. 512 — Gendarme on : a, Iles Eparses. b, Iles Kerguelen.

**Litho. & Silk-Screened**

**2014, Oct. 16 *Perf. 13***

| | | | |
|---|---|---|---|
| 512 | | Horiz. pair + central label | 3.50 3.50 |
| *a.-b* | A385 | 66c Either single | 1.75 1.75 |

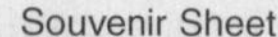

Souvenir Sheet

Amateur Radio — A386

No. 513: a, QSL card, radio key, amateur radio antenna on Tromelin Island. b, Radio operator, radio and antenna, vert.

***Perf. 13x13¼, 13¼x13***

**2014, Nov. 6** **Litho.**

**513** A386 Sheet of 2 2.75 2.75
*a.* 39c multi 1.00 1.00
*b.* 66c multi 1.75 1.75

Decauville Hopper Cars on Juan de Nova Island — A387

**2015, Jan. 1** **Engr.** ***Perf. 13x13¼***

**514** A387 66c multi 1.60 1.60

Euphausia Superba — A388

**Litho. & Engr.**

**2015, Jan. 1** ***Perf. 13¼***

**515** A388 66c multi 1.60 1.60

Emperor Penguin A389

**2015, Jan. 1** **Litho.** ***Perf. 13***

**516** A389 €1 multi 2.40 2.40

Leopard Seal in Adélie Land — A390

**2015, Jan. 1** **Engr.** ***Perf. 13¼x13***

**517** A390 €1.05 multi 2.60 2.60

Ship Radioleine — A391

**2015, Jan. 1** **Engr.** ***Perf. 13x13¼***

**518** A391 €2.40 multi 5.75 5.75

Antarctic Terns — A392

**Litho. & Engr.**

**2015, Jan. 1** ***Perf. 13***

**519** A392 €4.30 multi 10.50 10.50

Insects — A393

Designs: 66c, Amalopteryx maritima. €2, Ectemnorhinus vanhoeffenianus, horiz.

**2015, Jan.1** **Litho.** ***Perf. 13¼***

**520-521** A393 Set of 2 6.50 6.50

Beryl — A394

No. 522: a, Polihsed gemstones. b, Crystals in matrix.

**Litho. & Engr.**

**2015, Jan. 1** ***Perf. 13***

**522** A394 Horiz. pair 2.40 2.40
*a.* 34c multi .80 .80
*b.* 66c multi 1.60 1.60

Snowmobile Transport — A395

No. 523: a, Snowmobile pulling cargo. b, Snowmobile without cargo.

**2015, Jan. 1** **Litho.** ***Perf. 13¼***

**523** Horiz. pair 4.25 4.25
*a.* A395 66c multi 1.60 1.60
*b.* A395 €1.05 multi 2.60 2.60

Robert Guillard (1919-2013), Polar Explorations Chief of Operations — A396

No. 524 — Guillard and: a, Ship and penguins, Adélie Land. b, Expedition vehicles, Greenland.

**2015, Jan. 1** **Engr.** ***Perf. 13x13¼***

**524** Horiz. pair + central label 4.25 4.25
*a.* A396 66c multi 1.60 1.60
*b.* A396 €1.05 multi 2.60 2.60

Miniature Sheet

Fish — A397

No. 525: a, Chaenodraco wilsoni. b, Chaenodraco myersi. c, Pagetopsis macropterus. d, Pagetopsis maculatus.

**2015, Jan. 1** **Engr.** ***Perf. 13***

**525** A397 Sheet of 4 9.75 9.75
*a.-b.* 66c Either single 1.60 1.60
*c.* €1.05 multi 2.60 2.60
*d.* €1.55 multi 3.75 3.75

Paul-Emile Victor (1907-95), Polar Explorer — A398

**2015, Mar. 7** **Engr.** ***Perf. 13x12½***

**526** A398 €1 multi 2.25 2.25

Silhouettes of Saint-Paul & Amsterdam District Emblems — A399

**Litho. & Silk-Screened**

**2015, Mar. 19** ***Perf. 13¼***

**527** A399 50c multi 1.10 1.10

See No. 568d.

François Tabuteau (1921-2000), Polar Explorer — A400

**2015, Apr. 17** **Litho.** ***Perf. 13***

**528** A400 80c multi 1.90 1.90

French Southern and Antarctic Territories, 60th Anniv. — A401

No. 529 — Ship and: a, Airplane, seal, bird, turtle. b, Helicopter, birds, fish, killer whales. c, Penguins and birds in flight.

**2015, July 14** **Litho.** ***Perf. 13***

**529** Horiz. strip of 3 5.25 5.25
*a.-c.* A401 80c Any single 1.75 1.75

People Stranded Without Supplies on Saint Paul Island, 1930 — A402

**2015, Sept. 18** **Engr.** ***Perf. 13***

**530** A402 €1 multi 2.25 2.25

Ship *Marion Dufresne*, 20th Anniv. — A403

**2015** **Litho. & Engr.** ***Perf. 13***

**Denomination Color**

**531** A403 80c red 1.90 1.90
**532** A403 €1.35 blue 3.00 3.00

Issued: 80c, 10/4; €1.35, 11/5.

Souvenir Sheet

Penguin on Floating Ice — A404

**Litho. & Embossed**

**2015, Nov. 5** ***Perf. 13½x13***

**533** A404 €1.24 multi 2.75 2.75

Ships A405

No. 534: a, Croix du Sud I. b, Albius. c, Le Saint-Andre. d, Mascareignes III. e, Ile de la Reunion. f, Cap Horn I. g, Ile Bourbon.

**Litho. & Engr.**

**2015, Dec. 3** ***Perf. 13***

**534** Booklet pane of 7 19.50 —
*a.-g.* A405 €1.24 Any single 2.75 2.75
Complete booklet, #534 19.50

Lozère Waterfall A406

**2016, Jan. 2 Engr. *Perf. 13¼x13***
**535** A406 50c multi 1.10 1.10

Pringleophaga Crozetensis — A407

**2016, Jan. 2 Engr. *Perf. 12¼***
**536** A407 80c black 1.75 1.75

Serge Frolow, Director of Meteorological Service — A408

**2016, Jan. 2 Litho. *Perf. 13***
**537** A408 80c multi 1.75 1.75

Point d'Entrecasteaux — A409

**2016, Jan. 2 Engr. *Perf. 13x13¼***
**538** A409 €1.05 multi 2.40 2.40

Valdivia, Ship From 1898-99 German Deep Sea Expedition — A410

**2016, Jan. 2 Engr. *Perf. 13x12½***
**539** A410 €1.24 multi 2.75 2.75

Jean Volot (1921-2012), Polar Expedition Engineer and Priest — A411

**2016, Jan. 2 Engr. *Perf. 12½x13***
**540** A411 €1.35 multi 3.00 3.00

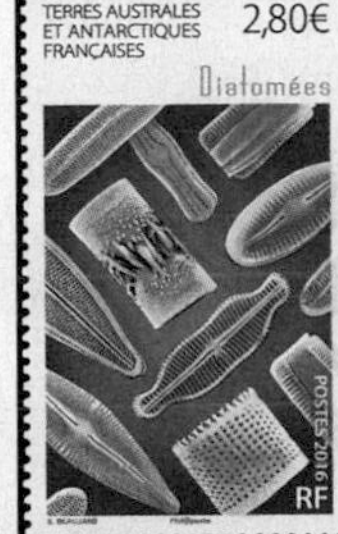


Diatoms — A412

**Litho. & Silk-Screened**

**2016, Jan. 2 *Perf. 13***
**541** A412 €2.80 multi 6.25 6.25

Schooner Rêve and Grave of Raoul Fleurié — A413

**2016, Jan. 2 Engr. *Perf. 13x13¼***
**542** A413 €2.80 multi 6.25 6.25

Sphene — A414

No. 543: a, Polished and cut gemstones. b, Crystal.

**Litho. & Silk-Screened**

**2016, Jan. 2 *Perf. 13***
**543** A414 Horiz. pair 2.25 2.25
*a.* 20c multi .50 .50
*b.* 80c multi 1.75 1.75

Kerguelen Island — A415

No. 544: a, Whaling. b, Ships from *The Ice Sphinx*, by Jules Verne. c, Cormoran-Vert Hostel, Christmas Harbor.

**2016, Jan. 2 Litho. *Perf. 13***
**544** Horiz. strip of 3 7.50 7.50
*a.* A415 80c cream & black 1.75 1.75
*b.* A415 €1.24 cream & black 2.75 2.75
*c.* A415 €1.35 cream & black 3.00 3.00

Souvenir Sheet

Flyovers of the Kerguelen Islands — A416

No. 545: a, RRS Discovery. b, De Havilland Gipsy Moth seaplane.

**2016, Jan. 2 Litho. *Perf. 13***
**545** A416 Sheet of 2 2.75 2.75
*a.* 44c multi 1.00 1.00
*b.* 80c multi 1.75 1.75

Miniature Sheet

Fish — A417

No. 546: a, Histiodraco velifer (52x41mm). b, Dolloidraco longedorsalis (60x27mm). c, Pogonophryne phyllopogon (60x27mm). d, Pogonophryne cf. barsukovi (52x31mm).

**2016, Jan. 2 Engr. *Perf. 13***
**546** A417 Sheet of 4 9.00 9.00
*a.-b.* 80c Either single 1.75 1.75
*c.* €1.05 multi 2.40 2.40
*d.* €1.35 multi 3.00 3.00

Miniature Sheet

Birds — A418

No. 547: a, Fulmar antarctique (Antarctic fulmar). b, Petrel geant (giant petrel), horiz. c, Damier du cap (cape petrel), horiz. d, Skua, horiz.

**Litho. & Engr.**

**2016, Jan. 2 *Perf. 13***
**547** A418 Sheet of 4 9.00 9.00
*a.* 70c multi 1.50 1.50
*b.* 80c multi 1.75 1.75
*c.* €1.05 multi 2.40 2.40
*d.* €1.45 multi 3.25 3.25

Silhouettes of Kerguelen District Emblems — A419

**Litho. & Silk-Screened**

**2016, Mar. 31 *Perf. 13¼***
**548** A419 80c multi 1.90 1.90

See No. 568c.

No. 2 and Rockhopper Penguin — A420

**2016, May 19 Litho. *Perf. 13***
**549** A420 €2 multi + label 4.50 4.50

Paris Philex 2016.

Souvenir Sheet

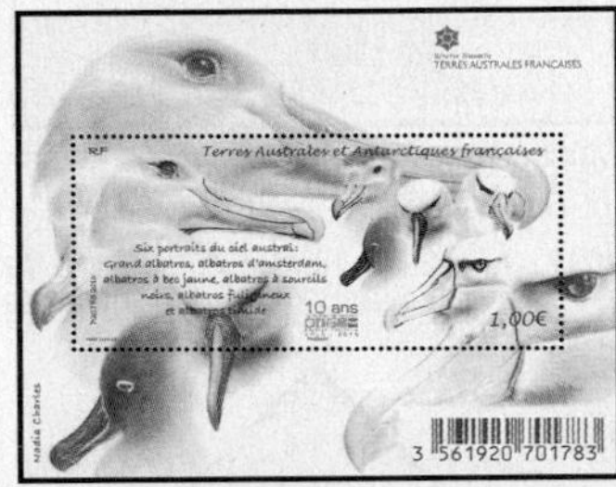


Albatrosses — A421

**2016, May 21 Litho. *Perf. 13¼x13***
**550** A421 €1 multi 2.25 2.25

Bernard Duboys de Lavigerie (1934-2008), Ionosphere Researcher A422

**2016, Oct. 1 Engr. *Perf. 13¼x13***
**551** A422 80c multi 1.90 1.90

Souvenir Sheet

Fillod Prefabricated Buildings In French Southern & Antarctic Territories, 60th Anniv. — A423

No. 552 — Prefabricated building and: a, Penguins. b, Ferdinand Fillod (1891-1956), building manufacturer.

**Litho. & Embossed**

**2016, Nov. 3 *Perf. 13***
**552** A423 Sheet of 2 9.25 9.25
*a.* €1.60 blue 3.50 3.50
*b.* €2.70 blue 5.75 5.75

Cirque du Château, Kerguelen Island — A424

**2016, Nov. 25 Litho. *Perf. 13***
**553** A424 50c multi 1.10 1.10

Cabins Near the Mortadella, Kerguelen Island — A425

**2017, Jan. 2 Litho. *Perf. 13***
**554** A425 80c multi 1.75 1.75

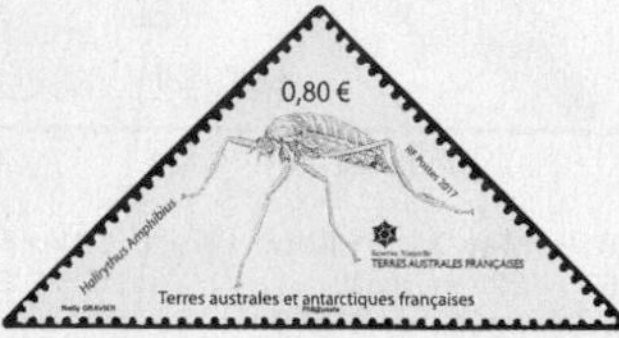
Halirythus Amphibius — A426

**2017, Jan. 2 Litho. *Perf. 13x13¼***
**555** A426 80c multi 1.75 1.75

1696 Landing of Willem de Vlamingh on Saint Paul and Amsterdam Islands — A427

**2017, Jan. 2 Litho. *Perf. 13***
**556** A427 €1 multi 2.10 2.10

Turborotalita Quinqueloba — A428

**Photo. & Embossed**
**2017, Jan. 2 *Perf. 13¼***
**557** A428 €1.24 multi 2.60 2.60

Values are for stamps with surrounding selvage.

Challenger 8 Tractor — A429

**2017, Jan. 2 Engr. *Perf. 13x13¼***
**558** A429 €1.24 multi 2.60 2.60

RV Ob, Flagship of 1956 Soviet Antarctic Expedition at Kerguelen Island — A430

**2017, Jan. 2 Engr. *Perf. 13x13¼***
**559** A430 €1.24 multi 2.60 2.60

Amalopteryx Maritima — A431

**2017, Jan. 2 Engr. *Perf. 13x13¼***
**560** A431 €1.55 multi 3.25 3.25

Slaves Abandoned on Tromelin Island After 1761 Shipwreck — A432

**Litho. & Engr.**
**2017, Jan. 2 *Perf. 13x13¼***
**561** A432 €1.55 multi 3.25 3.25

Pyroxene — A433

No. 562: a, Crystal. b, Polished and cut stones.

**Litho. & Silk-Screened**
**2017, Jan. 2 *Perf. 13***
**562** A433 Horiz. pair 2.25 2.25
*a.* 20c multi .45 .45
*b.* 80c multi 1.75 1.75

Founders of French Polar Expeditions — A434

Polar Expedition Port-Martin Station, Adélie Land — A435

**2017, Jan. 2 Engr. *Perf. 13x13¼***
**563** Horiz. pair + central label 4.50 4.50
*a.* A434 80c multi 1.75 1.75
*b.* A435 €1.24 multi 2.60 2.60

Souvenir Sheet

CASA CN-235 Over Island — A436

**2017, Jan. 2 Litho. *Perf. 13***
**564** A436 €3.90 multi 8.25 8.25

Souvenir Sheet

Tuna Fishing — A437

No. 565: a, Albacore tuna. b, Fishing trawler.

**Litho. & Engr.**
**2017, Jan. 2 *Perf. 13***
**565** A437 Sheet of 2 2.60 2.60
*a.* 44c multi .85 .85
*b.* 80c multi 1.75 1.75

Miniature Sheet

Gygis Alba — A438

No. 566: a, Two terns, blue background, vert. b, Chick, green background. c, Head of tern facing forward, blue background. d, Head of tern facing left, red background.

**Litho. & Engr.**
**2017, Jan. 2 *Perf. 13***
**566** A438 Sheet of 4 7.00 7.00
*a.-d.* 85c Any single 1.75 1.75

Miniature Sheet

Amphipods — A439

No. 567: a, Epimeria robusta. b, Epimeria inermis. c, Echiniphimedia scotti. d, Anchiphimedia dorsalis.

**2017, Jan. 2 Engr. *Perf. 13***
**567** A439 Sheet of 4 9.50 9.50
*a.-b.* 80c Either single 1.75 1.75
*c.* €1.24 multi 2.60 2.60
*d.* €1.55 multi 3.25 3.25

**Silhouettes of Emblems Types of 2013-16**
Miniature Sheet

**2017, Mar. 9 Litho. *Perf. 13***
**568** Sheet of 4 16.00 16.00
*a.* A363 (€1.24) multi 4.00 4.00
*b.* A379 (€1.24) multi 4.00 4.00
*c.* A419 (€1.24) multi 4.00 4.00
*d.* A399 (€1.24) multi 4.00 4.00

No. 568 sold for €7.50. Nos. 568a-568d are each inscribed "Lettre 20g tarif international."

Ship Marion Dufresne — A440

**Litho. & Engr.**
**2017, May 12 *Perf. 13***
**569** A440 (€1.24) multi 2.75 2.75

Ship L'Astrolabe — A441

**2017, Oct. 9 Engr. *Perf. 13x13¼***
**570** A441 €1.30 multi 3.00 3.00

Birds of the Arctic and Antarctic — A442

Designs: €1.41, Stercorarius maccormicki. €3.63, Aptenodytes forsteri.
No. 573: a, Like No. 571. b, Like No. 572.

**Litho. & Engr.**
**2017, Oct. 27 *Perf. 13x12¾***
**Stamps With Gray Frames**
**571-572** A442 Set of 2 12.00 12.00
**Souvenir Sheet**
**Stamps Without Gray Frames**
**573** Sheet of 2 + label 6.00 6.00
*a.* A442 €1 multi 2.40 2.40
*b.* A442 €1.50 multi 3.50 3.50

See Greenland Nos. 763-765.

## AIR POST STAMPS

Emperor Penguins and Map of Antarctica — AP1

**Unwmk.**
**1956, Apr. 25 Engr. *Perf. 13***
**C1** AP1 50fr lt ol grn & dk grn 42.50 29.00
**C2** AP1 100fr dl bl & indigo 35.00 25.00

Wandering Albatross — AP2

**1959, Sept. 14**
**C3** AP2 200fr brn red, bl & blk 40.00 27.50

Adélie Penguins — AP3

**1963, Feb. 11 Unwmk. *Perf. 13***
**C4** AP3 50fr blk, dk bl & dp cl 42.50 32.50

**Telstar Issue**
Common Design Type

**1962, Dec. 24**
**C5** CD111 50fr dp bl, ol & grn 29.00 21.00

Radio Towers, Adelie Penguins and IQSY Emblem — AP4

**1963, Dec. 16 Engr.**
**C6** AP4 100fr bl, ver & blk 110.00 87.50

International Quiet Sun Year, 1964-65.

Discovery of Adelie Land — AP5

**1965, Jan. 20 Engr. *Perf. 13***
**C7** AP5 50fr blue & indigo 125.00 87.50

125th anniversary of the discovery of Adelie Land by Dumont d'Urville.

**ITU Issue**
Common Design Type

**1965, May 17 Unwmk. *Perf. 13***
**C8** CD120 30fr multi 200.00 160.00

**French Satellite A-1 Issue**
Common Design Type

Designs: 25fr, Diamant rocket and launching installations. 30fr, A-1 satellite.

**1966, Mar. 2 Engr. *Perf. 13***
**C9** CD121 25fr dk grn, choc & sl 13.50 10.00
**C10** CD121 30fr choc, sl & dk grn 13.50 10.00
*a.* Pair, #C9-C10 + label 29.00 24.00

**French Satellite D-1 Issue**
Common Design Type

**1966, Mar. 27**
**C11** CD122 50fr dk pur, lil & org 57.50 40.00

Ionospheric Research Pylon, Adelie Land — AP6

**1966, Dec. 12**
**C12** AP6 25fr plum, bl & dk brn 32.50 17.50

Port aux Français, Emperor Penguin and Explorer — AP7

40fr, Aerial view of Saint Paul Island.

**1968-69 Engr. *Perf. 13***
**C13** AP7 40fr brt bl & dk gray 42.50 27.50
**C14** AP7 50fr lt ultra, dk grn & blk 175.00 110.00

Issue dates: 50fr, Jan. 21; 40fr, Jan. 5, 1969.

Kerguelen Island and Rocket — AP8

Design: 30fr, Adelie Land.

**1968, Apr. 22 Engr. *Perf. 13***
**C15** AP8 25fr sl grn, dk brn & Prus bl 19.00 14.00
**C16** AP8 30fr dk brn, sl grn & Prus bl 19.00 14.00
*a.* Pair, #C15-C16 + label 40.00 30.00

Space explorations with Dragon rockets, 1967-68.

Eiffel Tower, Antarctic Research Station, Ship from Paris Arms and Albatross AP9

**1969, Jan. 13**
**C17** AP9 50fr bright blue 45.00 35.00

5th Consultative Meeting of the Antarctic Treaty Powers, Paris, Nov. 18, 1968.

**Concorde Issue**
Common Design Type

**1969, Apr. 17**
**C18** CD129 85fr indigo & blue 55.00 37.50

Prepared but not issued with 87fr denomination. Value $3,000.

Map of Amsterdam Island AP10

Map of Kerguelen Island — AP11

Coat of Arms AP12

Designs: 50fr, Possession Island. 200fr, Point Geology Archipelago.

**1969-71 Engr. *Perf. 13***
**C19** AP10 30fr brown 19.00 12.50
**C20** AP11 50fr sl grn, bl & dk red 21.00 14.00
**C21** AP11 100fr blue & blk 85.00 40.00
**C22** AP10 200fr sl grn, brn & Prus bl 70.00 42.50
**C23** AP12 500fr peacock blue 20.00 15.00
*Nos. C19-C23 (5)* 215.00 124.00

30fr for the 20th anniv. of the Amsterdam Island Meteorological Station.
Issued: 100fr, 500fr, 12/21; 30fr, 3/27/70; 50fr, 12/22/70; 200fr, 1/1/71.

Port-aux-Français, 1970 — AP13

Design: 40fr, Port-aux-Français, 1950.

**1971, Mar. 9 Engr. *Perf. 13***
**C24** AP13 40fr bl, ocher & sl grn 19.00 12.00
**C25** AP13 50fr bl, grn ol & sl grn 19.00 12.00
*a.* Pair, #C24-C25 + label 40.00 27.50

20th anniversary of Port-aux-Français on Kerguelen Island.

Marquis de Castries Taking Possession of Crozet Island, 1772 — AP14

250fr, Fleur-de-lis flag raising on Kerguelen Is.

**1972 Engr. *Perf. 13***
**C26** AP14 100fr black 45.00 29.00
**C27** AP14 250fr black & dk brn 100.00 45.00

Bicentenary of the discovery of the Crozet and Kerguelen Islands.
Issue dates: 100fr, Jan. 24; 250fr, Feb. 23.

M. S. Galliéni — AP15

**1973, Jan. 25 Engr. *Perf. 13***
**C28** AP15 100fr black & blue 25.00 17.50

Exploration voyages of the Galliéni.

"Le Mascarin," 1772 — AP16

Sailing Ships: 145fr, "L'Astrolabe," 1840. 150fr, "Le Rolland," 1774. 185fr, "La Victoire," 1522.

**1973, Dec. 13 Engr. *Perf. 13***
**C29** AP16 120fr brown olive 6.75 4.75
**C30** AP16 145fr brt ultra 6.75 4.75
**C31** AP16 150fr slate 8.00 8.00
**C32** AP16 185fr ocher 10.50 8.00
*Nos. C29-C32 (4)* 32.00 25.50

Ships used in exploring Antarctica.
See Nos. C37-C38.

Alfred Faure Base — AP17

Design: Nos. C33-C35 show panoramic view of Alfred Faure Base.

**1974, Jan. 7 Engr. *Perf. 13***
**C33** AP17 75fr Prus bl, ultra & brn 8.00 5.25
**C34** AP17 110fr Prus bl, ultra & brn 11.00 8.00
**C35** AP17 150fr Prus bl, ultra & brn 14.00 8.00
*a.* Triptych, Nos. C33-C35 37.50 30.00

Alfred Faure Antarctic Base, 10th anniv.

Penguin, Map of Antarctica, Letters — AP18

**1974, Oct. 9 Engr. *Perf. 13***
**C36** AP18 150fr multicolored 7.00 5.50

Centenary of Universal Postal Union.

**Ship Type of 1973**

100fr, "Le Français." 200fr, "Pourquoi-pas?"

**1974, Dec. 16 Engr. *Perf. 13***
**C37** AP16 100fr brt blue 5.50 3.00
**C38** AP16 200fr dk car rose 9.00 4.50

Ships used in exploring Antarctica.

Rockets over Kerguelen Islands — AP19

Design: 90fr, Northern lights over map of northern coast of Russia.

**1975, Jan. 26** **Engr.** ***Perf. 13***

**C39** AP19 45fr purple & multi 7.00 4.00
**C40** AP19 90fr purple & multi 9.00 5.25
*a.* Pair, #C39-C40 + label 19.00 13.00

Franco-Soviet magnetosphere research.

"La Curieuse" — AP20

Ships: 2.70fr, Commandant Charcot. 4fr, Marion-Dufresne.

**1976, Jan.** **Engr.** ***Perf. 13***

**C41** AP20 1.90fr multicolored 3.25 2.00
**C42** AP20 2.70fr multicolored 5.00 3.25
**C43** AP20 4fr red & multi 9.00 4.25
*Nos. C41-C43 (3)* 17.25 9.50

Dumont d'Urville Base, 1956 — AP21

4fr, Dumont d'Urville Base, 1976, Adelie Land.

**1976, Jan.**

**C44** AP21 1.20fr multicolored 9.00 4.00
**C45** AP21 4fr multicolored 11.00 7.25
*a.* Pair, #C44-C45 + label 24.00 16.00

Dumont d'Urville Antarctic Base, 20th anniv.

Capt. Cook's Ships Passing Kerguelen Island — AP22

**1976, Dec. 31** **Engr.** ***Perf. 13***

**C46** AP22 3.50fr slate & blue 13.00 8.00

Bicentenary of Capt. Cook's voyage past Kerguelen Island.

Sea Lion and Cub AP23

**1977-79** **Engr.** ***Perf. 13***

**C47** AP23 4fr dk blue, grn ('79) 3.00 2.50
**C48** AP23 10fr multicolored 10.00 9.00

Satellite Survey, Kerguelen — AP24

Designs: 50c, 2.70fr, Satellites, Kerguelen. 70c, Geophysical laboratory. 1.90fr, Satellite and Kerguelen tracking station. 3fr, Satellites, Adelie Land.

**1977-79** **Engr.** ***Perf. 13***

**C49** AP24 50c multi ('79) .90 .70
**C50** AP24 70c multi ('79) .90 .70
**C51** AP24 1.90fr multi ('79) 1.60 1.40
**C52** AP24 2.70fr multi ('78) 2.75 2.00
**C53** AP24 3fr multicolored 4.25 3.25
*Nos. C49-C53 (5)* 10.40 8.05

Elephant Seals — AP25

**1979, Jan. 1**

**C54** AP25 10fr multicolored 5.50 4.50

Challenger — AP26

**1979, Jan. 1**

**C55** AP26 2.70fr black & blue 2.25 1.75

Antarctic expeditions to Crozet and Kerguelen Islands, 1872-1876.

La Recherche and L'Esperance — AP27

**1979**

**C56** AP27 1.90fr deep blue 1.50 1.10

Arrival of d'Entrecasteaux and Kermadec at Amsterdam Island, Mar. 28, 1792.

Lion Rock — AP28

**1979**

**C57** AP28 90c multicolored 1.10 .70

Natural Arch, Kerguelen Island, 1840 — AP29

**1979**

**C58** AP29 2.70fr multicolored 1.25 1.10

Phylica Nitida, Amsterdam Island — AP30

**1979**

**C59** AP30 10fr multicolored 4.00 3.25

Charles de Gaulle, 10th Anniversary of Death AP31

**1980, Nov. 9** **Engr.** ***Perf. 13***

**C60** AP31 5.40fr multicolored 11.00 8.00

HB-40 Castor Truck and Trailer — AP32

**1980, Dec. 15**

**C61** AP32 2.40fr multicolored 1.25 1.00

Supply Ship Saint Marcouf — AP33

**1980, Dec. 15**

**C62** AP33 3.50fr shown 1.60 1.10
**C63** AP33 7.30fr Icebreaker Norsel 2.50 2.00

Glacial Landscape, Dumont d'Urville Sea — AP34

Chionis — AP35

Adele Dumont d'Urville (1798-1842) — AP36

Arcad III — AP37

25th Anniv. of Charcot Station — AP38

Antares — AP39

**1981** **Engr.** ***Perf. 13, 12½x13 (2fr)***

**C64** AP34 1.30fr multicolored .70 .45
**C65** AP35 1.50fr black .70 .50
**C66** AP36 2fr black & lt brn .90 .85
**C67** AP37 3.85fr multicolored 1.60 1.25
**C68** AP38 5fr multicolored 1.75 1.50
**C69** AP39 8.40fr multicolored 2.75 2.25
*Nos. C64-C69 (6)* 8.40 6.80

PHILEXFRANCE '82 Stamp Exhibition, Paris, June 11-21 — AP40

**1982, June 11** **Engr.** ***Perf. 13***

**C70** AP40 8fr multicolored 5.50 5.25

French Overseas Possessions Week, Sept. 18-25 — AP41

**1982, Sept. 17 Engr. *Perf. 13***
**C71** AP41 5fr Commandant Charcot 1.75 1.75

Apostle Islands — AP42

**1983, Jan. 3 Engr. *Perf. 13***
**C72** AP42 65c multicolored .55 .35

Sputnik I, 25th Anniv. of Intl. Geophysical Year — AP43

Orange Bay Base, Cape Horn, 1883, Cent. — AP44

5.20fr, Scoresby Sound Base, Greenland, 50th anniv.

**1983, Jan. 3**
**C73** AP43 1.50fr multicolored .60 .60
**C74** AP44 3.30fr multicolored 1.75 1.75
**C75** AP44 5.20fr multicolored 2.00 2.00
*a.* Strip of 3, #C73-C75 4.50 4.50

AP45

**1983, Jan. 3**
**C76** AP45 4.55fr dark blue 4.00 3.00

Abstract, by G. Mathieu — AP46

**1983, Jan. 3 Photo. *Perf. 13x13½***
**C77** AP46 25fr multicolored 10.00 8.00

Erebus off Antarctic Ice Cap, 1842 — AP47

Port of Joan of Arc, 1930 — AP48

**1984, Jan. 1 Engr. *Perf. 13***
**C78** AP47 2.60fr ultra & dk blue 1.10 1.00
**C79** AP48 4.70fr multicolored 1.75 1.75

Aurora Polaris — AP49

**1984, Jan. 1 Photo.**
**C80** AP49 3.50fr multicolored 2.00 1.25

Manned Flight Bicentenary (1983) — AP50

Various balloons and airships.

**1984, Jan. 1 Engr.**
**C81** AP50 3.50fr multicolored 1.75 1.75
**C82** AP50 7.80fr multicolored 2.75 2.75
*a.* Pair, #C81-C82 + label 5.00 5.00

Patrol Boat Albatros — AP51

**1984, July 2 Engr. *Perf. 13***
**C83** AP51 11.30fr multi 4.25 4.25

NORDPOSTA Exhibition — AP52

**1984, Nov. 3 Engr. *Perf. 13***
**C84** AP52 9fr Scientific Vessel Gauss 4.50 3.50

Issued se-tenant with label.

Corsican Sheep — AP53

Amsterdam Albatross AP54

**1985, Jan. 1 Engr. *Perf. 13***
**C85** AP53 70c Mouflons .70 .40
**C86** AP54 3.90fr Diomedia amsterdamensis 1.60 1.25

La Novara, Frigate AP55

**1985, Jan. 1 Engr. *Perf. 13***
**C87** AP55 12.80fr La Novara at St. Paul 5.00 4.50

Explorer and Seal, by Tremois — AP56

Design: Explorer, seal, names of territories.

**1985, Jan. 1 Photo. *Perf. 13x12½***
**C88** AP56 30fr + label 11.00 8.50

Sailing Ships, Ropes, Flora & Fauna — AP57

**1985, Aug. 6 Engr. *Perf. 13***
**C89** AP57 2fr blk, brt bl & ol grn .70 .55
**C90** AP57 12.80fr blk, ol grn & brt bl 3.75 3.75
*a.* Pair, #C89-C90 + label 5.50 5.50

French Southern & Antarctic Territories, 30th anniv. No. C90a has continuous design with center label.

**Bird Type of 1986**

**1986, Jan. 1 Engr. *Perf. 13½x13***
**C91** A56 4.60fr Sea Gulls 2.00 1.75

Antarctic Atmospheric Research, 10th Anniv. — AP58

**1986, Jan. 1**
**C92** AP58 14fr blk, dk red & brt org 5.00 4.00

Jean Charcot (1867-1936), Explorer — AP59

**1986, Jan. 1**
**C93** AP59 2.10fr Ship Pourquoi Pas .90 .60
**C94** AP59 14fr Ship in storm 4.50 4.25
*a.* Pair, #C93-C94 + label 6.25 6.25

SPOT Satellite over the Antarctic — AP60

**1986, May 26 Engr. *Perf. 13***
**C95** AP60 8fr dp ultra, sep & dk ol grn 3.25 2.50

J.B. Charcot — AP61

**1987, Jan. 1 Engr. *Perf. 13x13½***
**C96** AP61 14.60fr multi 5.00 4.50

Ocean Drilling Program — AP62

**1987, Jan. 1 *Perf. 13½x13***
**C97** AP62 16.80fr lem, dk ultra & bluish blk 5.50 4.50

INMARSAT — AP63

**1987, Mar. 2 Engr. *Perf. 13***
**C98** AP63 16.80fr multi 8.00 7.50

French Polar Expeditions, 40th Anniv. — AP64

**1988, Jan. 1**
**C99** AP64 20fr lake, ol grn & plum 8.00 6.75

Views of Penguin Is. — AP65

**1988, Jan. 1**
**C100** AP65 3.90fr dk bl & sep 1.75 1.50
**C101** AP65 15.10fr dp grn, choc brn & dk bl 5.50 5.00

See Nos. C103, C109.

Founding of Permanent Settlements in the Territories, 40th Anniv. — AP66

**1989, Jan. 1 Engr. *Perf. 13½x13***
**C102** AP66 15.50fr black 5.00 4.75

**Island View Type**

**1989, Jan. 1**
**C103** AP65 8.40fr Apostle Islands 2.75 2.50

*La Curieuse* — AP68

**1989, Jan. 1 *Perf. 13x12½***
**C104** AP68 2.20fr multicolored .80 .70
**C105** AP68 15.50fr multi, diff. 5.00 5.00
*a.* Pair, #C104-C105 + label 6.00 6.00

No. C105a label continues the design.

French Revolution, Bicent. — AP69

**1989, July 14 Engr. *Perf. 13x12½***
**C106** AP69 5fr pink, dark olive grn & dark blue 5.50 3.50

**Souvenir Sheet**
***Perf. 13***

**C107** Sheet of 4 10.00 10.00
*a.* AP69 5fr Prus green, brt ultra & dark red 2.50 2.50

No. C107 for PHILEXFRANCE '89.

15th Antarctic Treaty Summit Conference — AP70

**1989, Oct. 9 Engr. *Perf. 13***
**C108** AP70 17.70fr multicolored 6.00 5.75

**Island View Type**

**1990, Jan. 1 Engr. *Perf. 13***
**C109** AP65 7.30fr Isle of Pigs, Crozet Isls. 3.00 2.40

*L'Astrolabe,* Expedition Team — AP72

**1990, Jan. 1**
**C110** AP72 15.50fr dk red vio & blk 5.00 5.00

Discovery of Adelie Land by Dumont D'Urville, 150th anniv.

*L'Astrolabe,* Commanded by Dumont D'Urville, 1840 — AP73

**1990, Jan. 1**
**C111** AP73 2.20fr *L'Astrolabe,* 1988 .80 .75
**C112** AP73 15.50fr shown 5.00 5.00
*a.* Pair, #C111-C112 + label 6.50 6.50

*Bird,* by Folon — AP74

**1990, Jan. 1 Litho. *Perf. 12½x13***
**C113** AP74 30fr multicolored 10.00 9.50

Albatross, Argos Satellite AP75

**1991, Jan. 1**
**C114** AP75 2.10fr red brn, bl & brn 1.50 .95

Climatological Research — AP76

3.60fr, Weather balloons, instruments. 20fr, Research ship.

**1991, Jan. 1 Engr. *Perf. 13***
**C115** AP76 3.60fr multi 1.40 1.40
**C116** AP76 20fr multi 7.75 7.75
*a.* Pair, #C115-C116 + label 10.00 10.00

Charles de Gaulle (1890-1970) — AP77

**1991, Jan. 1**
**C117** AP77 18.80fr blk, red & bl 7.75 7.75

Cape Petrel — AP78

**1992, Jan. 1 Engr. *Perf. 13***
**C118** AP78 3.40fr multicolored 2.25 1.40

French Institute of Polar Research and Technology — AP79

#C120, Polar bear with man offering flowers.

**1991, Dec. 16 Engr. *Perf. 13x12***
**C119** AP79 15fr multicolored 5.75 5.75
**C120** AP79 15fr multicolored 5.75 5.75
*a.* Strip, #C119-C120 + label 12.00 12.00

Christopher Columbus and Discovery of America — AP80

**1992, Jan. 1 *Perf. 13***
**C121** AP80 22fr multicolored 9.75 9.75

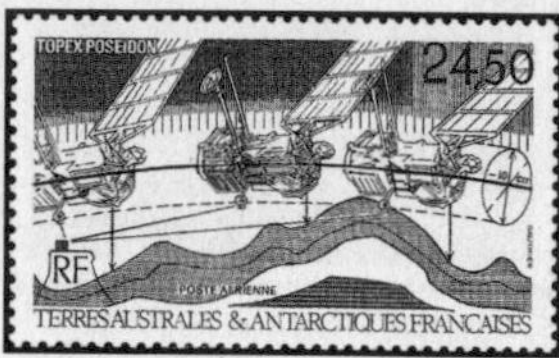

Mapping Satellite Poseidon — AP81

**1992, Jan. 1 Engr. *Perf. 13***
**C122** AP81 24.50fr multi 11.00 10.50

Dumont d'Urville Base, Adelie Land — AP82

**1992, Jan. 1 Litho. *Perf. 13x12½***
**C123** AP82 25.70fr multi 12.00 10.50

Amateur Radio — AP83

**1993, Jan. 1 Engr. *Perf. 13***
**C124** AP83 2fr multicolored 2.00 .75

New Animal Biology Laboratory, Adelie Land — AP84

**1993, Jan. 1**
**C125** AP84 25.40fr multicolored 11.00 6.75

Support Base D10 — AP85

**1993, Jan. 1**
**C126** AP85 25.70fr ol, red & bl 11.00 7.00

Opening of Adelie Land Airfield — AP86

**1993, Jan. 1**
**C127** AP86 30fr multicolored 13.00 8.75

Krill — AP87

**1994, Jan. 1** **Engr.** ***Perf. 13***
**C128** AP87 15fr black 6.50 4.00

Fishery Management — AP88

**1994, Jan. 1**
**C129** AP88 23fr multicolored 10.00 6.00

Satellite, Ground Station — AP89

Design: 27.30fr, Lidar Station.

**1994, Jan. 1**
**C130** AP89 26.70fr multicolored 12.00 7.00
**C131** AP89 27.30fr multicolored 12.00 7.25

Arrival of Emperor Penguins — AP90

**1994, Jan. 1** ***Perf. 13x12½***
**C132** AP90 28fr blue & black 13.00 8.00

Erebus Mission — AP91

**1995, Jan. 2** **Engr.** ***Perf. 13***
**C133** AP91 4.30fr bl, vio & slate 2.25 1.50

Moving of Winter Station, Charcot — AP92

**1995, Jan. 2** **Litho.**
**C134** AP92 15fr multicolored 6.50 4.25

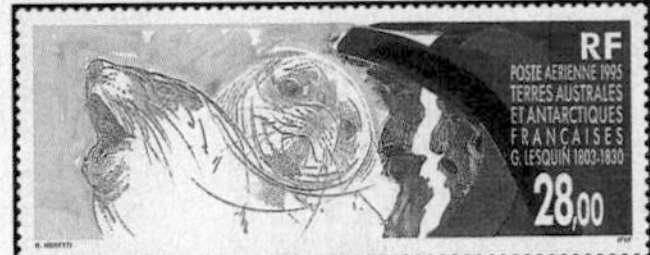

G. Lesquin (1803-30) — AP93

**1995, Jan. 2**
**C135** AP93 28fr multicolored 12.00 8.00

Map of East Island — AP94

**1996, Jan. 1** **Engr.** ***Perf. 13***
**C136** AP94 20fr multicolored 8.50 6.00

Expedition to Dome/C — AP95

**1996, Jan. 1**
**C137** AP95 23fr dark blue 10.00 7.00

Blue Whale, Southern Whale Sanctuary — AP96

**1996, Jan. 1**
**C138** AP96 26.70fr multicolored 12.00 8.00

Port-Couvreux — AP97

**1996, Jan. 1**
**C139** AP97 27.30fr multicolored 12.00 8.50

Jasus Paulensis AP98

**1997, Jan. 1** **Engr.** ***Perf. 12½x13***
**C140** AP98 5.20fr multicolored 3.00 1.75

Racing Yacht Charentes 2 — AP99

**1997, Jan. 1** **Litho.** ***Perf. 13***
**C141** AP99 16fr multicolored 8.00 5.50

John Nunn, Shipwrecked 1825-29, Hope Cottage — AP100

**1997, Jan. 1** **Engr.**
**C142** AP100 20fr multicolored 8.75 6.25

ICOTA Program — AP101

**1997, Jan. 1**
**C143** AP101 24fr multicolored 10.50 7.50

Harpagifer Spinosus — AP102

**1997, Jan. 1**
**C144** AP102 27fr multicolored 12.00 8.50

EPICA Program — AP103

**1998, Jan. 2** **Engr.** ***Perf. 13***
**C145** AP103 5.20fr dk brn & lil 2.50 1.40

First Radio Meteorological Station, Port Aux Francais — AP104

**1998, Jan. 2**
**C146** AP104 8fr black, blue & red 4.25 2.25

King Penguin, Argos Satellite AP105

**1998, Jan. 2** ***Perf. 12½x13***
**C147** AP105 16fr multicolored 7.00 4.75

Ranunculas Moseleyi AP106

**1998, Jan. 2**
**C148** AP106 24fr multicolored 10.50 6.50

Intl. Geophysical Year, 40th Anniv. — AP107

**1998, Oct.** **Engr.** ***Perf. 13x12½***
**C149** AP107 5.20fr dk bl, blk & brick red 3.00 1.50

# FRENCH SUDAN

'french sü-'dan

LOCATION — In northwest Africa, north of French Guinea and Ivory Coast
GOVT. — French Colony
AREA — 590,966 sq. mi.
POP. — 3,794,270 (1941)
CAPITAL — Bamako

In 1899 French Sudan was abolished as a separate colony and was divided among Dahomey, French Guinea, Ivory Coast, Senegal and Senegambia and Niger. Issues for French Sudan were resumed in 1921.

From 1906 to 1921 a part of this territory was known as Upper Senegal and Niger. A part of Upper Volta was added in 1933. See Mali.

100 Centimes = 1 Franc

See French West Africa No. 70 for stamp inscribed "Soudan Francais" and "Afrique Occidentale Francaise."

French Colonies Nos. 58-59 Srchd. in Black

*Perf. 14x13½*

**1894, Apr. 12** **Unwmk.**

1 A9 15c on 75c car, *rose* 4,600. 2,300.
2 A9 25c on 1fr brnz grn, *straw* 5,000. 1,700.

The imperforate stamp like No. 1 was made privately in Paris from a fragment of the lithographic stone which had been used in the Colony for surcharging No. 1.

Counterfeit surcharges exist.

Navigation and Commerce — A2

**1894-1900** **Typo.** ***Perf. 14x13½***
**Name of colony in Blue or Carmine**

3 A2 1c blk, *lil bl* 1.60 2.00
4 A2 2c brn, *buff* 2.40 2.75
5 A2 4c claret, *lav* 8.00 6.50
6 A2 5c grn, *grnsh* 12.00 12.00
7 A2 10c blk, *lav* 24.00 24.00
8 A2 10c red ('00) 8.00 8.00
9 A2 15c blue, quadrille paper 8.00 8.00
10 A2 15c gray, *lt gray* ('00) 8.00 8.00
11 A2 20c red, *grn* 40.00 35.00
12 A2 25c blk, *rose* 32.50 27.50
13 A2 25c blue ('00) 8.00 8.75
14 A2 30c brn, *bister* 40.00 40.00
15 A2 40c red, *straw* 40.00 35.00
16 A2 50c car, *rose* 55.00 65.00
17 A2 50c brn, *az* ('00) 16.00 16.00
18 A2 75c dp vio, *org* 55.00 55.00
19 A2 1fr brnz grn, *straw* 12.00 12.00
*Nos. 3-19 (17)* 370.50 365.50

Perf. 13½x14 stamps are counterfeits.

Nos. 8, 10, 13, 17 were issued in error. They were accepted for use in the other colonies.

Stamps and Types of Upper Senegal and Niger, 1914-17, Overprinted

**1921-30** ***Perf. 13½x14***

21 A4 1c brn vio & vio .25 .40
22 A4 2c dk gray & dl vio .30 .50
23 A4 4c blk & blue .30 .50
24 A4 5c ol brn & dk brn .30 .40
25 A4 10c yel grn & bl grn .90 .55
26 A4 10c red vio & bl ('25) .40 .50
27 A4 15c red brn & org .50 .55
28 A4 15c yel grn & dp grn ('25) .40 .40
29 A4 15c org brn & vio ('27) 1.60 1.60
30 A4 20c brn vio & blk .50 .55
31 A4 25c blk & bl grn 1.25 .80
a. Booklet pane of 4 —
Complete booklet, 5 #31a 650.00
Complete booklet, overprint omitted on one pane 16,000.
32 A4 30c red org & rose 1.60 1.60
33 A4 30c bl grn & blk ('26) .80 .70
34 A4 30c dl grn & bl grn ('28) 2.00 2.00
35 A4 35c rose & vio .40 .55
36 A4 40c gray & rose 1.25 1.25
37 A4 45c bl & ol brn 1.25 1.25
38 A4 50c ultra & bl 1.60 1.25
39 A4 50c red org & bl ('26) 1.25 1.25
40 A4 60c vio, *pnksh* ('26) 1.25 1.25
41 A4 65c bis & pale bl ('28) 1.60 1.60
42 A4 75c org & ol brn 1.60 2.00
43 A4 90c brn red & pink ('30) 5.50 5.50
44 A4 1fr dk brn & dl vio 1.60 2.00
45 A4 1.10fr gray lil & red vio ('28) 3.25 4.00
46 A4 1.50fr dp bl & bl ('30) 5.50 5.50
47 A4 2fr grn & bl 2.40 2.75
48 A4 3fr red vio ('30) 12.00 12.00
a. Double overprint 190.00
49 A4 5fr vio & blk 8.00 7.25
*Nos. 21-49 (29)* 59.55 60.45

Type of 1921 Surcharged

**1922, Sept. 28**

50 A4 60c on 75c vio, *pnksh* .80 .80

Stamps and Type of 1921-30 Surcharged

**1925-27**

51 A4 25c on 45c .80 .80
52 A4 65c on 75c 2.00 2.40
53 A4 85c on 2fr 2.00 2.40
54 A4 85c on 5fr 2.00 2.40
55 A4 90c on 75c brn red & sal pink ('27) 2.40 2.75
56 A4 1.25fr on 1fr dp bl & lt bl (R) ('26) 1.25 1.60
57 A4 1.50fr on 1fr dp bl & ultra ('27) 1.60 2.00
58 A4 3fr on 5fr dl red & brn org ('27) 6.50 5.50
59 A4 10fr on 5fr brn red & bl grn ('27) 24.00 21.00
60 A4 20fr on 5fr vio & ver ('27) 29.00 29.00
*Nos. 51-60 (10)* 71.55 69.85

Sudanese Woman — A4

Entrance to the Residency at Djenné — A5

Sudanese Boatman — A6

**1931-40** **Typo.** ***Perf. 13x14***

61 A4 1c dk red & blk .25 .25
62 A4 2c dp blue & org .25 .25
63 A4 3c dk red & blk ('40) .25 .25
64 A4 4c gray lil & rose .25 .25
65 A4 5c indigo & grn .25 .25
66 A4 10c ol grn & rose .25 .25
67 A4 15c blk & brt vio .40 .30
68 A4 20c hn brn & lt bl .40 .30
69 A4 25c red vio & lt red .40 .30
70 A5 30c grn & lt grn .80 .50
71 A5 30c dk bl & red org ('40) .30 .30
72 A5 35c ol grn & grn ('38) .40 .40
73 A5 40c ol grn & pink .40 .30
74 A5 45c dk bl & red org 1.20 .65
75 A5 45c ol grn & grn ('40) .50 .50
76 A5 50c red & black .40 .30
77 A5 55c ultra & car ('38) .40 .40
78 A5 60c brt bl & brn ('40) 1.20 1.20
79 A5 65c brt vio & blk .80 .55
80 A5 70c vio bl & car rose ('40) .80 .80
81 A5 75c brt bl & ol brn 2.40 2.00
82 A5 80c car & brn ('38) .80 .80
83 A5 90c dp red & red org 1.60 .80
84 A5 90c brt vio & sl blk ('39) .90 1.00
85 A5 1fr indigo & grn 8.00 2.40
86 A5 1fr rose red ('38) 5.50 1.60
87 A5 1fr car & brn ('40) .80 .80
88 A6 1.25fr vio & dl vio ('33) .80 .80
89 A6 1.25fr red ('39) .90 1.00
90 A6 1.40fr brt vio & blk ('40) .90 .90
91 A6 1.50fr dk bl & ultra .80 .55
92 A6 1.60fr brn & dp bl ('40) .90 .90
93 A6 1.75fr dk brn & dp bl ('33) .80 .80
94 A6 1.75fr vio bl ('38) .80 .80
95 A6 2fr org brn & grn .80 .55
96 A6 2.25fr vio bl & ultra ('39) 1.00 1.10
97 A6 2.50fr lt brown ('40) 1.60 1.60
98 A6 3fr Prus grn & brn .80 .40
99 A6 5fr red & blk 2.00 1.20
100 A6 10fr dull bl & grn 2.40 2.00
101 A6 20fr red vio & brn 3.25 2.40
*Nos. 61-101 (41)* 47.65 32.70

For surcharges see Nos. B7-B10.

For 10c and 30c, without "RF," see Nos. 120-121

Common Design Types pictured following the introduction.

### Colonial Exposition Issue
Common Design Types

**1931, Apr. 13** **Engr.** ***Perf. 12½***
**Name of Country Printed in Black**

102 CD70 40c deep green 4.75 4.75
103 CD71 50c violet 4.75 4.75
104 CD72 90c red orange 4.75 4.75
105 CD73 1.50fr dull blue 4.75 4.75
Set, never hinged 29.00

### Paris International Exposition Issue
Common Design Types

**1937, Apr. 15** ***Perf. 13***

106 CD74 20c deep violet 2.00 2.00
107 CD75 30c dark green 2.00 2.00
108 CD76 40c carmine rose 2.40 2.40
109 CD77 50c dark brown 1.60 1.60
110 CD78 90c red 1.60 1.60
111 CD79 1.50fr ultra 2.40 2.40
*Nos. 106-111 (6)* 12.00 12.00
Set, never hinged 20.25

### Colonial Arts Exhibition Issue
Souvenir Sheet
Common Design Type

**1937** **Engr.** ***Imperf.***

112 CD77 3fr magenta & blk 12.00 *16.00*
Never hinged 16.00

### Caillie Issue
Common Design Type

**1939, Apr. 5** ***Perf. 12½x12***

113 CD81 90c org brn & org .40 .80
114 CD81 2fr brt violet .40 1.20
115 CD81 2.25fr ultra & dk bl .40 1.20
*Nos. 113-115 (3)* 1.20 3.20
Set, never hinged 2.40

### New York World's Fair Issue
Common Design Type

**1939, May 10**

116 CD82 1.25fr car lake .80 1.60
117 CD82 2.25fr ultra .80 1.60
Set, never hinged 2.40

Entrance to the Residency at Djenné and Marshal Pétain — A7

**1941** **Engr.** ***Perf. 12x12½***

118 A7 1fr green .40 —
119 A7 2.50fr blue .40 —
Set, never hinged 1.60

For surcharges, see Nos. B14-B15.

### Types of 1931-40 without "RF"

**1943-44** **Typo.** ***Perf. 13½x14***

120 A4 10c ol green & rose .65
121 A5 30c dk bl & red org .95
Set, never hinged 2.00

Nos. 120-121 were issued by the Vichy government in France, but were not placed on sale in French Sudan.

Stamps of French Sudan were superseded by those of French West Africa.

## SEMI-POSTAL STAMPS

### Curie Issue
Common Design Type
**Unwmk.**

**1938, Oct. 24** **Engr.** ***Perf. 13***

B1 CD80 1.75fr + 50c brt ultra 12.50 12.50
Never hinged 21.00

### French Revolution Issue
Common Design Type

**1939, July 5** **Photo.**
**Name and Value Typo. in Black**

B2 CD83 45c + 25c green 10.00 10.00
B3 CD83 70c + 30c brown 10.00 10.00
B4 CD83 90c + 35c red org 10.00 10.00
B5 CD83 1.25fr + 1fr rose pink 10.00 10.00
B6 CD83 2.25fr + 2fr blue 10.00 10.00
*Nos. B2-B6 (5)* 50.00 50.00
Set, never hinged 87.50

Stamps of 1931-40, Surcharged in Black or Red

**1941** ***Perf. 13x14***

B7 A5 50c + 1fr red & blk (R) 4.00 4.00
B8 A5 80c + 2fr car & brn 8.00 8.00
B9 A6 1.50fr + 2fr dk bl & ultra 8.00 8.00
B10 A6 2fr + 3fr org brn & grn 8.00 8.00
*Nos. B7-B10 (4)* 28.00 28.00
Set, never hinged 55.00

**Common Design Type and**

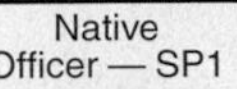

Native Officer — SP1

Aviation Officer — SP2

**1941 Photo. *Perf. 13½***

**B11** SP1 1fr + 1fr red 1.25
**B12** CD86 1.50fr + 3fr claret 1.40
**B13** SP2 2.50fr + 1fr blue 1.40
*Nos. B11-B13 (3)* 4.05
Set, never hinged 5.50

Surtax for the defense of the colonies.
Issued by the Vichy government in France, but not placed on sale in French Sudan.

Petain type of 1941 Surcharged in Black or Red

**1944 Engr. *Perf. 12x12½***

**B14** 50c + 1.50fr on 2.50fr deep blue (R) .40
**B15** + 2.50fr on 1fr green .40
Set, never hinged 1.60

Colonial Development Fund.
Nos. B14-B15 were issued by the Vichy government in France, but were not placed on sale in French Sudan.

## AIR POST STAMPS

**Common Design Type**
***Perf. 12½x12***

**1940, Feb. 8 Unwmk. Engr.**

**C1** CD85 1.90fr ultra .40 .40
**C2** CD85 2.90fr dark red .40 .40
**C3** CD85 4.50fr dk gray green .80 .80
**C4** CD85 4.90fr yellow bister .80 .80
**C5** CD85 6.90fr deep orange 1.60 1.60
*Nos. C1-C5 (5)* 4.00 4.00
Set, never hinged 5.20

**Common Design Types**

**1942, Oct. 19**

**C6** CD88 50c carmine & bl .40 —
**C7** CD88 1fr brown & blk .40
**C8** CD88 2fr dk grn & red brn .80
**C9** CD88 3fr dk blue & scar .80
**C10** CD88 5fr vio & brn red .80

**Frame Engr., Center Typo.**

**C11** CD89 10fr ultra, ind & gray blk 1.20
**C12** CD89 20fr rose car, mag & lt vio 1.60
**C13** CD89 50fr yel grn, dl grn & dl bl 2.00 —
*Nos. C6-C13 (8)* 8.00
Set, never hinged 12.00

There is doubt whether Nos. C7-C12 were officially placed in use.

## AIR POST SEMI-POSTAL STAMPS

**Types of Dahomey Air Post Semi-Postal Issue**
***Perf. 13½x12½, 13 (#CB3)***
**Photo, Engr. (#CB3)**

**1942, June 22**

**CB1** SPAP1 1.50fr + 3.50fr green .40 *5.50*
**CB2** SPAP2 2fr + 6fr brown .40 *5.50*
**CB3** SPAP2 3fr + 9fr car red .40 *5.50*
*Nos. CB1-CB3 (3)* 1.20 *16.50*
Set, never hinged 2.40

Native children's welfare fund.

**Colonial Education Fund**
Common Design Type
***Perf. 12½x13½***

**1942, June 22 Engr.**

**CB4** CD86a 1.20fr + 1.80fr blue & red .40 *5.50*
Never hinged .80

## POSTAGE DUE STAMPS

Postage Due Stamps of Upper Senegal and Niger Overprinted — D1

***Perf. 14x13½***

**1921, Dec. Unwmk. Typo.**

**J1** D1 5c green .40 .40
**J2** D1 10c rose .40 .40
**J3** D1 15c gray .40 .80
**J4** D1 20c brown 1.20 1.20
**J5** D1 30c blue 1.20 1.20
**J6** D1 50c black 2.00 2.40
**J7** D1 60c orange 2.40 2.40
**J8** D1 1fr violet 2.40 3.25
*Nos. J1-J8 (8)* 10.40 12.05

Type of 1921 Issue Surcharged

**1927, Oct. 10**

**J9** D1 2fr on 1fr lilac rose 8.00 8.00
**J10** D1 3fr on 1fr org brown 8.00 8.00

D2

**1931, Mar. 9**

**J11** D2 5c green .25 .30
**J12** D2 10c rose .25 .30
**J13** D2 15c gray .25 .50
**J14** D2 20c dark brown .25 .50
**J15** D2 30c dark blue .40 .55
**J16** D2 50c black .40 .55
**J17** D2 60c deep orange .80 .80
**J18** D2 1fr violet 1.20 1.20
**J19** D2 2fr lilac rose 1.60 1.60
**J20** D2 3fr red brown 1.60 1.60
*Nos. J11-J20 (10)* 7.00 7.90

# FRENCH WEST AFRICA

'french 'west 'a-fri-kə

LOCATION — Northwestern Africa
GOVT. — French colonial administrative unit
AREA — 1,821,768 sq. mi.
POP. — 18,777,163 (est.)
CAPITAL — Dakar

French West Africa comprised the former colonies of Senegal, French Guinea, Ivory Coast, Dahomey, French Sudan, Mauritania, Niger and Upper Volta.

In 1958, these former colonies became republics, eventually issuing their own stamps. Until the republic issues appeared, stamps of French West Africa continued in use. The Senegal and Sudanese Republics issued stamps jointly as the Federation of Mali, starting in 1959.

**Catalogue values for all unused stamps in this country are for Never Hinged items.**

Many stamps other than Nos. 65-72 and 77 are inscribed "Afrique Occidentale Francaise" and the name of one of the former colonies. See listings in these colonies for such stamps.

Senegal No. 156 Surcharged in Red

**1943 Unwmk. *Perf. 12½x12***

**1** A30 1.50fr on 65c dk vio 1.20 .90
**2** A30 5.50fr on 65c dk vio 1.60 .80
**3** A30 50fr on 65c dk vio 4.00 2.00

Mauritania No. 91 Surcharged in Red

**1943 *Perf. 13***

**4** A7 3.50fr on 65c dp grn .80 .40
**5** A7 4fr on 65c dp grn .80 .40
**6** A7 5fr on 65c dp grn 1.60 .80
**7** A7 10fr on 65c dp grn 1.60 .80
*Nos. 1-7 (7)* 11.60 6.10

**Senegal No. 143, 148 and 188 Surcharged with New Values in Black and Orange**

**1944 *Perf. 12½x12***

**8** A29 1.50fr on 15c blk (O) .80 .65
**9** A29 4.50fr on 15c blk (O) 1.20 .90
**10** A29 5.50fr on 2c brn 2.40 1.60
**11** A29 10fr on 15c blk (O) 4.00 1.75
**12** CD81 20fr on 90c org brn & org 2.40 1.75
**13** CD81 50fr on 90c org brn & org 6.50 3.25

**Mauritania No. 109 Surcharged in Black**

**14** CD81 15fr on 90c org brn & org 2.40 1.60
*Nos. 8-14 (7)* 19.70 11.50

Common Design Types pictured following the introduction.

**Eboue Issue**
Common Design Type

**1945 Engr. *Perf. 13***

**15** CD91 2fr black .80 .80
**16** CD91 25fr Prussian green 1.60 1.60

Nos. 15 and 16 exist imperforate.

Colonial Soldier — A1

**1945 Litho. *Perf. 12½x12, 12***

**17** A1 10c indigo & buff .40 .25
**18** A1 30c olive & yel .40 .25
**19** A1 40c blue & buff .40 .25
**20** A1 50c red org & gray .40 .25
**21** A1 60c ol brn & bl .80 .40
**22** A1 70c mag & cit .80 .40
**23** A1 80c bl grn & pale lem .80 .40
**24** A1 1fr brn vio & cit .80 .40
**25** A1 1.20fr gray brn & cit 4.00 2.40
**26** A1 1.50fr choc & pink .80 .40
**27** A1 2fr ocher and gray .80 .40
**28** A1 2.40fr red & gray 1.25 .80
**29** A1 3fr brn red & yelsh .80 .40
**30** A1 4fr ultra & pink .80 .40
**31** A1 4.50fr org brn & yelsh .80 .40
**32** A1 5fr dk pur & yelsh .80 .40
**33** A1 10fr ol grn & pink 1.60 .80
**34** A1 15fr orange & yel 2.40 1.20
**35** A1 20fr sl grn & grnsh 2.75 2.00
*Nos. 17-35 (19)* 21.60 12.20

Rifle Dance, Mauritania — A2

Bamako Dike, French Sudan — A3

Trading Canoe, Niger River — A4

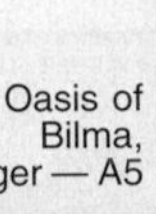

Oasis of Bilma, Niger — A5

Shelling Coconuts, Togo — A6

Kouandé Weaving, Dahomey A7

Donkey Caravan, Senegal A8

Crocodile and Hippopotamus, Ivory Coast — A9

Gathering Coconuts, French Guinea — A10

Bamako Fountain, French Sudan A11

Peul Woman of Dienné — A12

Bamako Market — A13

Dahomey Laborer A14

Woman of Mauritania A15

Fula Woman, French Guinea — A16

Djenné Mosque, French Sudan A17

Monorail Train, Senegal A18

Agni Woman, Ivory Coast — A19

Azwa Women at Niger River — A20

**1947 Engr. Unwmk.** ***Perf. 12½***

| No. | Type | Value | Color | Mint | Used |
|---|---|---|---|---|---|
| **36** | A2 | 10c | blue | .40 | .25 |
| **37** | A3 | 30c | red brn | .40 | .25 |
| **38** | A4 | 40c | gray grn | .40 | .25 |
| **39** | A5 | 50c | red brn | .40 | .25 |
| **40** | A6 | 60c | gray blk | .80 | .50 |
| **41** | A7 | 80c | brown vio | .80 | .50 |
| **42** | A8 | 1fr | maroon | .80 | .30 |
| **43** | A9 | 1.20fr | dk blue grn | 2.00 | 1.40 |
| **44** | A10 | 1.50fr | ultra | 2.00 | 1.10 |
| **45** | A11 | 2fr | red orange | .80 | .25 |
| **46** | A12 | 3fr | chocolate | .80 | .30 |
| **47** | A13 | 3.60fr | brown red | 1.60 | 1.40 |
| **48** | A14 | 4fr | deep blue | .80 | .30 |
| **49** | A15 | 5fr | gray green | .40 | .25 |
| **50** | A16 | 6fr | dark blue | .80 | .30 |
| **51** | A17 | 10fr | brn red | .80 | .25 |
| **52** | A18 | 15fr | sepia | 2.40 | .30 |
| **53** | A19 | 20fr | chocolate | 1.60 | .30 |
| **54** | A20 | 25fr | grnsh blk | 2.40 | .50 |
| | | | *Nos. 36-54 (19)* | 20.40 | 8.95 |

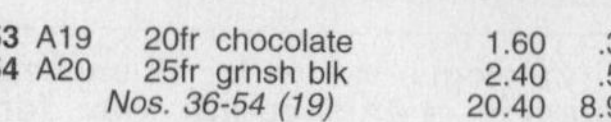

### Types of 1947

**1948** **Re-engraved**

| No. | Type | Value | Color | Mint | Used |
|---|---|---|---|---|---|
| **55** | A6 | 60c | brown olive | 1.20 | .80 |
| **56** | A12 | 3fr | chocolate | 1.20 | .55 |

Nos. 40 and 46 are inscribed "TOGO" in lower margin. Inscription omitted on Nos. 55 and 56.

---

Imperforates

Most stamps of French West Africa from 1949 onward exist imperforate in issued and trial colors, and also in small presentation sheets in issued colors.

---

### Military Medal Issue

Common Design Type

**Engraved and Typographed**

**1952, Dec. 1** ***Perf. 13***

**57** CD101 15fr multicolored 8.75 6.50

Treich Laplène and Map — A21

**1952, Dec. 1** **Engr.**

**58** A21 40fr brown lake 2.40 .40

Marcel Treich Laplène, a leading contributor to the development of Ivory Coast.

Medical Laboratory A22

**1953, Nov. 18**

**59** A22 15fr brn, dk bl grn & blk brn 1.60 .40

Couple Feeding Antelopes A23

**1954, Sept. 20**

**60** A23 25fr multicolored 2.00 .40

Gov. Noel Eugène Ballay A24

**1954, Nov. 29**

**61** A24 8fr indigo & brown 2.00 .80

Chimpanzee — A25

Giant Pangolin A26

**1955, May 2 Unwmk.** ***Perf. 13***

| No. | Type | Value | Color | Mint | Used |
|---|---|---|---|---|---|
| **62** | A25 | 5fr | dp vio & dk brn | 2.00 | .80 |
| **63** | A26 | 8fr | brn & bl grn | 2.00 | .80 |

International Exhibition for Wildlife Protection, Paris, May 1955.

Map, Symbols of Industry, Rotary Emblem A27

**1955, July 4**

**64** A27 15fr dark blue 2.40 .80

50th anniv. of the founding of Rotary Intl.

### FIDES Issue

Common Design Type

Designs: 1fr, Date grove, Mauritania. 2fr, Milo Bridge, French Guinea. 3fr, Mossi Railroad, Upper Volta. 4fr, Cattle raising, Niger. 15fr, Farm machinery and landscape, Senegal. 17fr, Woman and Niger River, French Sudan. 20fr, Palm oil production, Dahomey. 30fr, Road construction, Ivory Coast.

**1956 Engr.** ***Perf. 13x12½***

| No. | Type | Value | Color | Mint | Used |
|---|---|---|---|---|---|
| **65** | CD103 | 1fr | dk grn & dk bl grn | 1.60 | .65 |
| **66** | CD103 | 2fr | dk bl grn & bl | 1.60 | .65 |
| **67** | CD103 | 3fr | dk brn & red brn | 1.60 | 1.00 |
| **68** | CD103 | 4fr | dk car rose | 2.40 | 1.10 |
| **69** | CD103 | 15fr | ind & ultra | 1.60 | .55 |
| **70** | CD103 | 17fr | dk bl & ind | 2.40 | .75 |
| **71** | CD103 | 20fr | rose lake | 2.40 | .65 |
| **72** | CD103 | 30fr | dk pur & claret | 2.40 | 1.00 |
| | | | *Nos. 65-72 (8)* | 16.00 | 6.35 |

Coffee A28a

**1956, Oct. 22** ***Perf. 13***

**73** A28a 15fr dk blue green 1.60 .80

Mobile Leprosy Clinic and Maltese Cross A29

**1957, Mar. 11**

**74** A29 15fr dk red brn, pur & red 2.40 .80

Issued in honor of the Knights of Malta.

Map of Africa — A30

**1958, Feb. Unwmk.** ***Perf. 13***

**75** A30 20fr multicolored 1.60 .80

6h Intl.Cong. for African Tourism at Dakar.

"Africa" and Communications Symbols — A31

**1958, Mar. 15** **Engr.**

**76** A31 15fr org, ultra & choc 2.00 .80

Stamp Day. See No. 86.

Abidjan Bridge A32

**1958, Mar. 15**

**77** A32 20fr dk sl grn & grnsh bl 2.00 .80

Bananas A33

**1958, May 19** ***Perf. 13***

**78** A33 20fr rose lil, dk grn & olive 1.60 .40

### Flower Issue

Common Design Type

10fr, Gloriosa. 25fr, Adenopus. 30fr, Cyrtosperma. 40fr, Cistanche. 65fr, Crinum Moorei.

**1958-59 Photo.** ***Perf. 12x12½***

| No. | Type | Value | Color | Mint | Used |
|---|---|---|---|---|---|
| **79** | CD104 | 10fr | multicolored | 1.20 | .40 |
| **80** | CD104 | 25fr | red, yel & grn | 1.60 | .80 |
| **81** | CD104 | 30fr | multicolored | 2.00 | 1.20 |
| **82** | CD104 | 40fr | blk brn, grn & yel | 2.40 | 1.60 |
| **83** | CD104 | 65fr | multicolored | 3.25 | 1.60 |
| | | | *Nos. 79-83 (5)* | 10.45 | 5.60 |

Issued: 25fr, 40fr, 1/5/59; others, 7/7/58.

Moro Naba Sagha and Map — A34

**1958, Nov. 1 Engr.** ***Perf. 13***

**84** A34 20fr ol brn, car & vio 1.60 .80

10th anniv. of the reestablishment of the Upper Volta territory.

### Human Rights Issue

Common Design Type

**1958, Dec. 10**

**85** CD105 20fr maroon & dk bl 2.40 2.00

### Type of 1958 Redrawn

**1959, Mar. 21 Engr.** ***Perf. 13***

**86** A31 20fr red, grnsh bl & sl grn 2.75 2.40

Name of country omitted on No. 86; "RF" replaced by "CF," inscribed "Dakar-Abidjan." Stamp Day.

---

## SEMI-POSTAL STAMPS

### Red Cross Issue

Common Design Type

***Perf. 14½x14***

**1944, Dec. Photo. Unwmk.**

**B1** CD90 5fr + 20fr plum 6.50 4.75

The surtax was for the French Red Cross and national relief.

Type of France, 1945, Overprinted in Black

**1945, Oct. 13 Engr.** ***Perf. 13***

**B2** SP150 2fr + 3fr orange red 1.20 .80

### Tropical Medicine Issue

Common Design Type

**1950, May 15** ***Perf. 13***

**B3** CD100 10fr +2fr red brn & sep 9.50 7.25

The surtax was for charitable work.

---

## AIR POST STAMPS

### Common Design Type

**1945 Photo. Unwmk. *Perf. 14½x14***

| No. | Type | Description | Unused | Used |
|---|---|---|---|---|
| C1 | CD87 | 5.50fr ultra | 2.00 | 1.00 |
| C2 | CD87 | 50fr dark green | 3.50 | 1.40 |
| C3 | CD87 | 100fr plum | 4.00 | 1.50 |
| | | *Nos. C1-C3 (3)* | 9.50 | 3.90 |

### Victory Issue
Common Design Type

**1946, May 8 Engr. *Perf. 12½***

| No. | Type | Description | Unused | Used |
|---|---|---|---|---|
| C4 | CD92 | 8fr violet | 1.60 | 1.20 |

### Chad to Rhine Issue
Common Design Types

**1946, June 6**

| No. | Type | Description | Unused | Used |
|---|---|---|---|---|
| C5 | CD93 | 5fr brown car | 2.00 | 1.60 |
| C6 | CD94 | 10fr deep blue | 2.00 | 1.60 |
| C7 | CD95 | 15fr brt violet | 2.40 | 1.60 |
| C8 | CD96 | 20fr dk slate grn | 2.40 | 2.00 |
| C9 | CD97 | 25fr olive brn | 3.25 | 2.40 |
| C10 | CD98 | 50fr brown | 4.00 | 2.75 |
| | | *Nos. C5-C10 (6)* | 16.05 | 11.95 |

Antoine de Saint-Exupéry, Map and Natives — AP1

Plane over Dakar — AP2

Great White Egrets in Flight — AP3

Natives and Phantom Plane — AP4

**1947, Mar. 24 Engr.**

| No. | Type | Description | Unused | Used |
|---|---|---|---|---|
| C11 | AP1 | 8fr red brown | 1.60 | .80 |
| C12 | AP2 | 50fr rose violet | 4.00 | 1.20 |
| C13 | AP3 | 100fr ultra | 16.00 | 4.75 |
| C14 | AP4 | 200fr slate gray | 14.00 | 5.25 |
| | | *Nos. C11-C14 (4)* | 35.60 | 12.00 |

### UPU Issue
Common Design Type

**1949, July 4 *Perf. 13***

| No. | Type | Description | Unused | Used |
|---|---|---|---|---|
| C15 | CD99 | 25fr multicolored | 12.00 | 8.75 |

Vridi Canal, Abidjan — AP5

**1951, Nov. 5 Unwmk. *Perf. 13***

| No. | Type | Description | Unused | Used |
|---|---|---|---|---|
| C16 | AP5 | 500fr red org, bl grn & dp ultra | 32.50 | 4.75 |

### Liberation Issue
Common Design Type

**1954, June 6**

| No. | Type | Description | Unused | Used |
|---|---|---|---|---|
| C17 | CD102 | 15fr indigo & ultra | 12.00 | 5.50 |

Logging — AP6

Designs: 100fr, Radiotelephone exchange. 200fr, Baobab trees.

**1954, Sept. 20**

| No. | Type | Description | Unused | Used |
|---|---|---|---|---|
| C18 | AP6 | 50fr ol grn & org brn | 4.00 | .80 |
| C19 | AP6 | 100fr ind, dk brn & dk grn | 6.50 | 1.20 |
| C20 | AP6 | 200fr bl grn, grnsh blk & brn lake | 17.50 | 2.75 |
| | | *Nos. C18-C20 (3)* | 28.00 | 4.75 |

Gen. Louis Faidherbé and African Sharpshooter AP7

**1957, July 20 Unwmk. *Perf. 13***

| No. | Type | Description | Unused | Used |
|---|---|---|---|---|
| C21 | AP7 | 15fr indigo & blue | 2.00 | 1.60 |

Centenary of French African troops.

Gorée Island and Woman — AP8

Designs: 20fr, Map with planes and ships. 25fr, Village and modern city. 40fr, Seat of Council of French West Africa. 50fr, Worker, ship and peanut plant. 100fr, Bay of N'Gor.

**1958, Mar. 15 Engr.**

| No. | Type | Description | Unused | Used |
|---|---|---|---|---|
| C22 | AP8 | 15fr blk brn, grn & vio | 1.60 | .80 |
| C23 | AP8 | 20fr blk brn, dk bl & red brn | 1.60 | .80 |
| C24 | AP8 | 25fr blk vio, bis & grn | 1.60 | 1.20 |
| C25 | AP8 | 40fr dk bl, brn & grn | 1.60 | 1.20 |
| C26 | AP8 | 50fr violet, brn & grn | 3.25 | 1.60 |
| C27 | AP8 | 100fr brown, bl & grn | 6.50 | 2.40 |
| a. | | Souvenir sheet of 6, #C22-C27 | 20.00 | 16.00 |
| | | *Nos. C22-C27 (6)* | 16.15 | 8.00 |

Centenary of Dakar.

Woman Playing Native Harp — AP9

**1958, Dec. 1 Unwmk. *Perf. 13***

| No. | Type | Description | Unused | Used |
|---|---|---|---|---|
| C28 | AP9 | 20fr red brn, blk & gray | 1.60 | .80 |

Inauguration of Nouakchott as capital of Mauritania.

## POSTAGE DUE STAMPS

D1

**1947 Engr. Unwmk. *Perf. 13***

| No. | Type | Description | Unused | Used |
|---|---|---|---|---|
| J1 | D1 | 10c red | .40 | .25 |
| J2 | D1 | 30c deep orange | .40 | .25 |
| J3 | D1 | 50c greenish blk | .40 | .25 |
| J4 | D1 | 1fr carmine | .40 | .25 |
| J5 | D1 | 2fr emerald | .50 | .30 |
| J6 | D1 | 3fr red lilac | .90 | .65 |
| J7 | D1 | 4fr deep ultra | 1.10 | .80 |
| J8 | D1 | 5fr red brown | 2.25 | 1.60 |
| J9 | D1 | 10fr peacock blue | 2.90 | 2.25 |
| J10 | D1 | 20fr sepia | 5.25 | 3.75 |
| | | *Nos. J1-J10 (10)* | 14.50 | 10.35 |

## OFFICIAL STAMPS

Mask — O1

Designs: Various masks.

***Perf. 14x13***

**1958, June 2 Typo. Unwmk.**

| No. | Type | Description | Unused | Used |
|---|---|---|---|---|
| O1 | O1 | 1fr dk brn red | 1.10 | 1.00 |
| O2 | O1 | 3fr brt green | .65 | .55 |
| O3 | O1 | 5fr crim rose | .65 | .50 |
| O4 | O1 | 10fr light ultra | .80 | .65 |
| O5 | O1 | 20fr bright red | 1.60 | .80 |
| O6 | O1 | 25fr purple | 1.60 | .80 |
| O7 | O1 | 30fr green | 2.75 | 1.60 |
| O8 | O1 | 45fr gray black | 3.25 | 1.60 |
| O9 | O1 | 50fr dark red | 3.25 | 1.60 |
| O10 | O1 | 65fr brt ultra | 4.50 | 1.60 |
| O11 | O1 | 100fr olive bister | 10.50 | 2.75 |
| O12 | O1 | 200fr deep green | 21.00 | 5.50 |
| | | *Nos. O1-O12 (12)* | 51.65 | 18.95 |

# FUJEIRA

fü-ˈjī-rə

LOCATION — Oman Peninsula, Arabia, on Persian Gulf
GOVT. — Sheikdom under British protection

Fujeira is one of six Persian Gulf sheikdoms to join the United Arab Emirates which proclaimed independence Dec. 2, 1971. See United Arab Emirates.

100 Naye Paise = 1 Rupee

**Catalogue values for all unused stamps in this country are for Never Hinged items.**

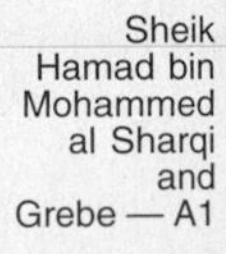

Sheik Hamad bin Mohammed al Sharqi and Grebe — A1

Sheik and: 2np, 50np, Arabian oryx. 3np, 70np, Hoopoe. 4np, 1r, Wild ass. 5np, 1.50r, Herons in flight. 10np, 2r, Arabian horses. 15np, 3r, Leopard. 20np, 5r, Camels. 30np, 10r, Hawks.

**Photo. & Litho.**

**1964 Unwmk. *Perf. 14***

**Size: 36x24mm**

| No. | Type | Description | Unused | Used |
|---|---|---|---|---|
| 1 | A1 | 1np gold & multi | .25 | .25 |
| 2 | A1 | 2np gold & multi | .25 | .25 |
| 3 | A1 | 3np gold & multi | .25 | .25 |
| 4 | A1 | 4np gold & multi | .25 | .25 |
| 5 | A1 | 5np gold & multi | .25 | .25 |
| 6 | A1 | 10np gold & multi | .25 | .25 |
| 7 | A1 | 15np gold & multi | .25 | .25 |
| 8 | A1 | 20np gold & multi | .25 | .25 |
| 9 | A1 | 30np gold & multi | .25 | .25 |

**Size: 43x28mm**

| No. | Type | Description | Unused | Used |
|---|---|---|---|---|
| 10 | A1 | 40np gold & multi | .35 | .25 |
| 11 | A1 | 50np gold & multi | .40 | .25 |
| 12 | A1 | 70np gold & multi | .45 | .25 |
| 13 | A1 | 1r gold & multi | .65 | .25 |
| 14 | A1 | 1.50r gold & multi | .95 | .25 |
| 15 | A1 | 2r gold & multi | 1.50 | .25 |

**Size: 53½x35mm**

| No. | Type | Description | Unused | Used |
|---|---|---|---|---|
| 16 | A1 | 3r gold & multi | 2.40 | .25 |
| 17 | A1 | 5r gold & multi | 2.25 | .35 |
| 18 | A1 | 10r gold & multi | 7.50 | .50 |
| | | *Nos. 1-18 (18)* | 18.70 | 4.85 |

Issued: 20np, 30np, 70np, 1.50r, 3r, 10r, Nov. 14; others, Sept. 22.
Exist imperf. Value, set $30.

Sheik Hamad and Shot Put A2

**1964, Dec. 6 *Perf. 14***

**Size: 43x28mm**

| No. | Type | Description | Unused | Used |
|---|---|---|---|---|
| 19 | A2 | 25np shown | .25 | .25 |
| 20 | A2 | 50np Discus | .25 | .25 |
| 21 | A2 | 75np Fencing | .25 | .25 |
| 22 | A2 | 1r Boxing | .35 | .30 |
| 23 | A2 | 1.50r Relay race | .50 | .35 |
| 24 | A2 | 2r Soccer | .60 | .40 |

**Size: 53½x35mm**

| No. | Type | Description | Unused | Used |
|---|---|---|---|---|
| 25 | A2 | 3r Pole vaulting | 1.15 | .50 |
| 26 | A2 | 5r Hurdling | 3.00 | .75 |
| 27 | A2 | 7.50r Equestrian | 4.25 | .90 |
| | | *Nos. 19-27 (9)* | 10.60 | 3.95 |

18th Olympic Games, Tokyo, 10/10-25/64.
Exist imperf. Value, set $12.

John F. Kennedy — A3

Kennedy: 10np, As sailor in the Pacific. 15np, As naval lieutenant. 20np, On speaker's rostrum. 25np, Sailing with family. 50np, With crowd of people. 1r, With Mrs. Kennedy, Lyndon B. Johnson. 2r, With Eisenhower on White House porch. 3r, With Mrs. Kennedy & Caroline. 5r, Portrait.

**1965, Feb. 23 Photo. *Perf. 13½***

**Size: 29x44mm**

**Black Design with Gold Inscriptions**

| No. | Type | Description | Unused | Used |
|---|---|---|---|---|
| 28 | A3 | 5np pale gray | .25 | .25 |
| 29 | A3 | 10np pale yellow | .25 | .25 |
| 30 | A3 | 15np pink | .25 | .25 |
| 31 | A3 | 20np pale greenish gray | .25 | .25 |
| 32 | A3 | 25np pale blue | .25 | .25 |
| 33 | A3 | 50np pale rose | .30 | .25 |

**Size: 33x51mm**

| No. | Type | Description | Unused | Used |
|---|---|---|---|---|
| 34 | A3 | 1r pale gray | .75 | .30 |
| 35 | A3 | 2r pale green | 1.25 | .40 |
| 36 | A3 | 3r pale gray | 2.50 | .50 |
| 37 | A3 | 5r pale yellow | 3.25 | .80 |
| | | *Nos. 28-37 (10)* | 9.30 | 3.50 |

Pres. John F. Kennedy (1917-1963). A souvenir sheet contains 2 29x44mm stamps similar to Nos. 36-37 with pale blue (3r) and pale rose (5r) backgrounds. Value (unused): perf $7; imperf $9.

Nos. 28-37 exist imperf. Value $14.

## AIR POST STAMPS

Wild Ass AP1

**Photo. & Litho.**

**1965, Aug. 16 Unwmk. *Perf. 13½***

**Size: 43x28mm**

| | | | | |
|---|---|---|---|---|
| **C1** | AP1 | 15np Grebe | .25 | .25 |
| **C2** | AP1 | 25np Arabian oryx | .25 | .25 |
| **C3** | AP1 | 35np Hoopoe | .35 | .25 |
| **C4** | AP1 | 50np Wild ass | .40 | .25 |
| **C5** | AP1 | 75np Herons in flight | .45 | .25 |
| **C6** | AP1 | 1r Arabian horses | .60 | .25 |

**Size: 53½x35mm**

| | | | | |
|---|---|---|---|---|
| **C7** | AP1 | 2r Leopard | 1.25 | .25 |
| **C8** | AP1 | 3r Camels | 2.50 | .25 |
| **C9** | AP1 | 5r Hawks | 4.50 | .50 |
| | | *Nos. C1-C9 (9)* | 10.55 | 2.50 |

Exist imperf. Value, set $11.

## AIR POST OFFICIAL STAMPS

**Type of Air Post Issue, 1965**

**Photo. & Litho.**

**1965, Nov. 10 Unwmk. *Perf. 13½***

**Size: 43x28mm**

| | | | | |
|---|---|---|---|---|
| **CO1** | AP1 | 75np Arabian horses | .60 | .25 |

***Perf. 13***

**Size: 53½x35mm**

| | | | | |
|---|---|---|---|---|
| **CO2** | AP1 | 2r Leopard | 1.50 | .40 |
| **CO3** | AP1 | 3r Camels | 2.50 | .60 |
| **CO4** | AP1 | 5r Hawks | 4.50 | 1.00 |
| | | *Nos. CO1-CO4 (4)* | 9.10 | 2.25 |

Exist imperf. Values same as perf.

## OFFICIAL STAMPS

**Type of Air Post Issue, 1965**

**Photo. & Litho.**

**1965, Oct. 14 Unwmk. *Perf. 13½***

**Size: 43x28mm**

| | | | | |
|---|---|---|---|---|
| **O1** | AP1 | 25np Grebe | .25 | .25 |
| **O2** | AP1 | 40np Arabian oryx | .25 | .25 |
| **O3** | AP1 | 50np Hoopoe | .35 | .25 |
| **O4** | AP1 | 75np Wild ass | .55 | .25 |
| **O5** | AP1 | 1r Herons in flight | 1.25 | .25 |
| | | *Nos. O1-O5 (5)* | 2.65 | 1.25 |

Exist imperf. Values same as perf.

# FUNCHAL

fün-ˈshäl

LOCATION — A city and administrative district in the Madeira island group in the Atlantic Ocean northwest of Africa

GOVT. — A part of the Republic of Portugal

POP. — 150,574 (1900)

Postage stamps of Funchal were superseded by those of Portugal.

1000 Reis = 1 Milreis

King Carlos — A1

**1892-93 Typo. Unwmk.**

***Perf. 11 ½, 12 ½, 13 ½***

| | | | | |
|---|---|---|---|---|
| **1** | A1 | 5r yellow | 4.00 | 2.00 |
| *a.* | | Half used as 2½r on entire newspaper | | 17.50 |
| **2** | A1 | 10r red violet | 3.00 | 2.00 |
| **3** | A1 | 15r chocolate | 4.00 | 2.50 |
| **4** | A1 | 20r lavender | 5.00 | 2.50 |
| *a.* | | Perf. 13½ | 10.00 | 7.50 |
| **5a** | A1 | 25r dark green | 8.00 | 1.00 |
| **6** | A1 | 50r ultramarine | 9.00 | 2.50 |
| **7** | A1 | 75r carmine | 10.00 | 6.00 |
| **8** | A1 | 80r yellow green | 15.00 | 11.00 |
| **9** | A1 | 100r brn, *yel* ('93) | 12.00 | 5.00 |
| *a.* | | Diagonal half used as 50r on cover | | 70.00 |
| **10** | A1 | 150r car, *rose* ('93) | 60.00 | 30.00 |
| **11** | A1 | 200r dk bl, *bl* ('93) | 75.00 | 45.00 |
| **12** | A1 | 300r dk bl, *sal* ('93) | 80.00 | 55.00 |
| | | *Nos. 1-12 (12)* | 285.00 | 164.50 |

Nos. 1-12 were printed on both enamel-surfaced and chalky papers. Values are for the most common varieties. For detailed listings, see the *Scott Classic Specialized Catalogue.*

*The reprints of this issue have shiny white gum and clean-cut perforation 13½. The shades differ from those of the originals and the uncolored paper is thin.*

King Carlos — A2

**Name and Value in Black except Nos. 25 and 34**

**1897-1905 *Perf. 11¾***

| | | | | |
|---|---|---|---|---|
| **13** | A2 | 2½r gray | .50 | .35 |
| *a.* | | Name and denomination inverted | 275.00 | |
| **14** | A2 | 5r orange | .50 | .35 |
| **15** | A2 | 10r light green | .50 | .35 |
| **16** | A2 | 15r brown | 5.50 | 5.00 |
| **17** | A2 | 15r gray grn ('99) | 3.75 | 2.75 |
| **18** | A2 | 20r gray vio | 1.40 | .75 |
| **19** | A2 | 25r sea green | 2.75 | .75 |
| **20** | A2 | 25r car rose ('99) | 1.40 | .55 |
| *a.* | | Booklet pane of 6 | — | |
| **21** | A2 | 50r dark blue | 10.00 | 5.00 |
| *a.* | | Perf. 12½ | 25.00 | 9.00 |
| **22** | A2 | 50r ultra ('05) | 1.50 | .90 |
| **23** | A2 | 65r slate blue ('98) | 1.25 | .90 |
| **24** | A2 | 75r rose | 2.00 | .95 |
| **25** | A2 | 75r brn & red, *yel* ('05) | 8.00 | 1.40 |
| **26** | A2 | 80r violet | 1.40 | 1.10 |
| **27** | A2 | 100r dark blue, *blue* | 1.40 | 1.10 |
| *a.* | | Diagonal half used as 50r on cover | | 75.00 |
| **28** | A2 | 115r org brn, *pink* ('98) | 5.00 | 1.40 |
| **29** | A2 | 130r gray brown, *buff* ('98) | 6.00 | 1.40 |
| **30** | A2 | 150r lt brn, *buff* | 6.00 | 1.25 |
| **31** | A2 | 180r sl, *pnksh* ('98) | 6.00 | 1.40 |
| **32** | A2 | 200r red vio, *pale lil* | 6.00 | 2.10 |
| **33** | A2 | 300r blue, *rose* | 6.00 | 2.10 |
| **34** | A2 | 500r blk & red, *bl* | 10.00 | 2.40 |
| *a.* | | Perf. 12½ | 20.00 | 7.75 |
| | | *Nos. 13-34 (22)* | 86.85 | 34.25 |

# Pronunciation Symbols

ə .... banana, collide, abut

ˈə, ˌə .... humdrum, abut

ə .... immediately preceding \l\, \n\, \m\, \ŋ\, as in battle, mitten, eaten, and sometimes open \ˈō-pᵊm\, lock and key \-ᵊŋ-\; immediately following \l\, \m\, \r\, as often in French table, prisme, titre

ər .... further, merger, bird

ˈər-, ˈə-r .... as in two different pronunciations of hurry \ˈhər-ē, ˈhə-rē\

a .... mat, map, mad, gag, snap, patch

ā .... day, fade, date, aorta, drape, cape

ä .... bother, cot, and, with most American speakers, father, cart

ȧ .... father as pronounced by speakers who do not rhyme it with *bother*; French patte

au̇ .... now, loud, out

b .... baby, rib

ch .... chin, nature \ˈnā-chər\

d .... did, adder

e .... bet, bed, peck

ˈē, ˌē .... beat, nosebleed, evenly, easy

ē .... easy, mealy

f .... fifty, cuff

g .... go, big, gift

h .... hat, ahead

hw .... whale as pronounced by those who do not have the same pronunciation for both *whale* and *wail*

i .... tip, banish, active

ī .... site, side, buy, tripe

j .... job, gem, edge, join, judge

k .... kin, cook, ache

k̲ .... German ich, Buch; one pronunciation of loch

l .... lily, pool

m .... murmur, dim, nymph

n .... no, own

ⁿ .... indicates that a preceding vowel or diphthong is pronounced with the nasal passages open, as in French *un bon vin blanc* \œⁿ -bōⁿ -vaⁿ -bläⁿ\

ŋ .... sing \ˈsiŋ\, singer \ˈsiŋ-ər\, finger \ˈfiŋ-gər\, ink \ˈiŋk \

ō .... bone, know, beau

ȯ .... saw, all, gnaw, caught

œ .... French boeuf, German Hölle

œ̄ .... French feu, German Höhle

ȯi .... coin, destroy

p .... pepper, lip

r .... red, car, rarity

s .... source, less

sh .... as in shy, mission, machine, special (actually, this is a single sound, not two); with a hyphen between, two sounds as in *grasshopper* \ˈgras-ˌhä-pər\

t .... tie, attack, late, later, latter

th .... as in thin, ether (actually, this is a single sound, not two); with a hyphen between, two sounds as in *knighthood* \ˈnīt-ˌhu̇d\

th̲ .... then, either, this (actually, this is a single sound, not two)

ü .... rule, youth, union \ˈyün-yən\, few \ˈfyü\

u̇ .... pull, wood, book, curable \ˈkyu̇r-ə-bəl\, fury \ˈfyu̇r-ē\

ue .... German füllen, hübsch

ue̅ .... French rue, German fühlen

v .... vivid, give

w .... we, away

y .... yard, young, cue \ˈkyü\, mute \ˈmyüt\, union \ˈyün-yən\

ʸ .... indicates that during the articulation of the sound represented by the preceding character the front of the tongue has substantially the position it has for the articulation of the first sound of *yard*, as in French *digne* \dēnʸ\

z .... zone, raise

zh .... as in vision, azure \ˈa-zhər\ (actually, this is a single sound, not two); with a hyphen between, two sounds as in *hogshead* \ˈhȯgz-ˌhed, ˈhägz-\

\ .... slant line used in pairs to mark the beginning and end of a transcription: \ˈpen\

ˈ .... mark preceding a syllable with primary (strongest) stress: \ˈpen-mən-ˌship\

ˌ .... mark preceding a syllable with secondary (medium) stress: \ˈpen-mən-ˌship\

\- .... mark of syllable division

( ) .... indicate that what is symbolized between is present in some utterances but not in others: *factory* \ˈfak-t(ə-)rē\

÷ .... indicates that many regard as unacceptable the pronunciation variant immediately following: *cupola* \ˈkyü-pə-lə, ÷-ˌlō\

# Illustrated Identifier

This section pictures stamps or parts of stamp designs that will help identify postage stamps that do not have English words on them.

Many of the symbols that identify stamps of countries are shown here as well as typical examples of their stamps.

See the Index and Identifier for stamps with inscriptions such as "sen," "posta," "Baja Porto," "Helvetia," "K.S.A.", etc.

*Linn's Stamp Identifier* is now available. The 144 pages include more than 2,000 inscriptions and more than 500 large stamp illustrations. Available from Linn's Stamp News, P.O. Box 4129, Sidney, OH 45365-4129, or amosadvantage.com

## 1. HEADS, PICTURES AND NUMERALS

### GREAT BRITAIN

Great Britain stamps never show the country name, but, except for postage dues, show a picture of the reigning monarch.

Victoria

Edward VII George V Edward VIII

George VI

Elizabeth II

Some George VI and Elizabeth II stamps are surcharged in annas, new paisa or rupees. These are listed under Oman.

Silhouette (sometimes facing right, generally at the top of stamp)

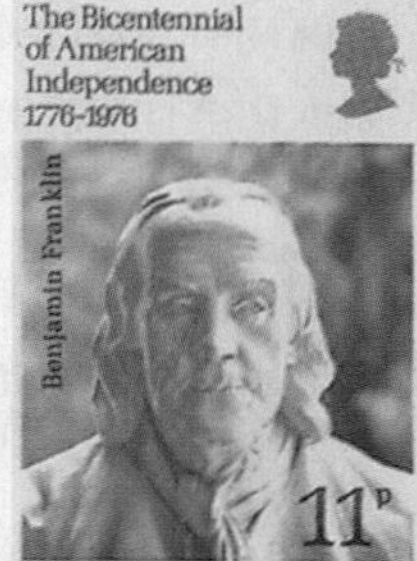


The silhouette indicates this is a British stamp. It is not a U.S. stamp.

### VICTORIA

Queen Victoria

### INDIA

Other stamps of India show this portrait of Queen Victoria and the words "Service" (or "Postage") and "Annas."

### AUSTRIA

### YUGOSLAVIA

(Also BOSNIA & HERZEGOVINA if imperf.)

### BOSNIA & HERZEGOVINA

Denominations also appear in top corners instead of bottom corners.

### HUNGARY

Another stamp has posthorn facing left

### BRAZIL

### AUSTRALIA

Kangaroo and Emu

### GERMANY

#### Mecklenburg-Vorpommern

## SWITZERLAND

## PALAU

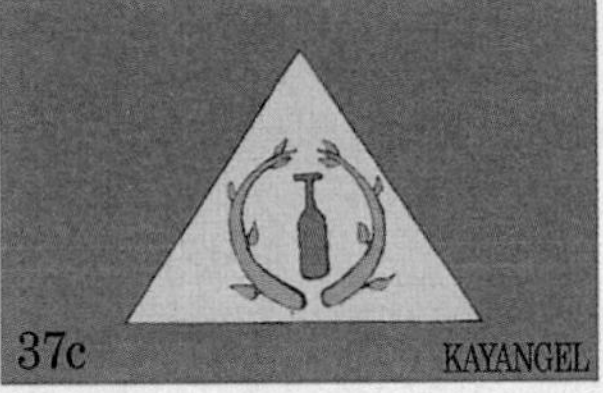


## 2. ORIENTAL INSCRIPTIONS

### CHINA

 中

Any stamp with this one character is from China (Imperial, Republic or People's Republic). This character appears in a four-character overprint on stamps of Manchukuo. These stamps are local provisionals, which are unlisted. Other overprinted Manchukuo stamps show this character, but have more than four characters in the overprints. These are listed in People's Republic of China.

Some Chinese stamps show the Sun.

Most stamps of Republic of China show this series of characters.

Stamps with the China character and this character are from People's Republic of China. 人

中国人民邮政
T.34.(5-1)

Calligraphic form of People's Republic of China

| (一) | (二) | (三) | (四) | (五) | (六) |
|---|---|---|---|---|---|
| 1 | 2 | 3 | 4 | 5 | 6 |
| (七) | (八) | (九) | (十) | (一十) | (二十) |
| 7 | 8 | 9 | 10 | 11 | 12 |

### Chinese stamps without China character

### REPUBLIC OF CHINA

## PEOPLE'S REPUBLIC OF CHINA

Mao Tse-tung

## MANCHUKUO

Temple

Emperor Pu-Yi

The first 3 characters are common to many Manchukuo stamps.

The last 3 characters are common to other Manchukuo stamps.

Orchid Crest

Manchukuo stamp without these elements

## JAPAN

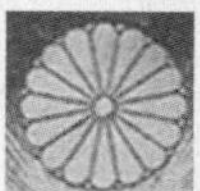

Chrysanthemum Crest

Country Name

Japanese stamps without these elements

The number of characters in the center and the design of dragons on the sides will vary.

## RYUKYU ISLANDS

Country Name

## PHILIPPINES (Japanese Occupation)

Country Name

## NETHERLANDS INDIES (Japanese Occupation)

Indicates Japanese Occupation

### Java

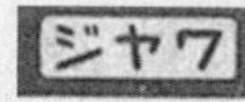


Country Name

### Sumatra

Country Name

## Moluccas, Celebes and South Borneo

Country Name

## NORTH BORNEO (Japanese Occupation)

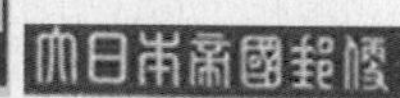

Indicates Japanese Occupation

Country Name

## MALAYA (Japanese Occupation)

Indicates Japanese Occupation

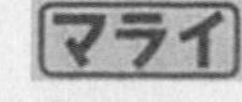


Country Name

## BURMA

### Union of Myanmar

ပြည်ထောင်စုမြန်မာနိုင်ငံတော်

Union of Myanmar

### (Japanese Occupation)

Indicates Japanese Occupation

シヤン

Country Name

Other Burma Japanese Occupation stamps without these elements

Burmese Script

## KOREA

These two characters, in any order, are common to stamps from the Republic of Korea (South Korea) or of the People's Democratic Republic of Korea (North Korea).

조선우표

This series of four characters can be found on the stamps of both Koreas. Most stamps of the Democratic People's Republic of Korea (North Korea) have just this inscription.

대한민국 우표

Indicates Republic of Korea (South Korea)

South Korean postage stamps issed after 1952 do not show currency expressed in Latin letters. Stamps wiith " HW," "HWAN," "WON," "WN," "W" or "W" with two lines through it, if not illustrated in listings of stamps before this date, are revenues. North Korean postage stamps do not have currency expressed in Latin letters.

Yin Yang appears on some stamps.

South Korean stamps show Yin Yang and starting in 1966, 'KOREA" in Latin letters

Example of South Korean stamps lacking Latin text, Yin Yang and standard Korean text of country name. North Korean stamps never show Yin Yang and starting in 1976 are inscribed "DPRK" or "DPR KOREA" in Latin letters.

## THAILAND

Country Name

King Chulalongkorn

King Prajadhipok and Chao P'ya Chakri

# 3. CENTRAL AND EASTERN ASIAN INSCRIPTIONS

## INDIA - FEUDATORY STATES

### Alwar

### Bhor

## Bundi

Similar stamps come with different designs in corners and differently drawn daggers (at center of circle).

## Dhar

## Duttia

## Faridkot

## Hyderabad

Similar stamps exist with different central design which is inscribed "Postage" or "Post & Receipt."

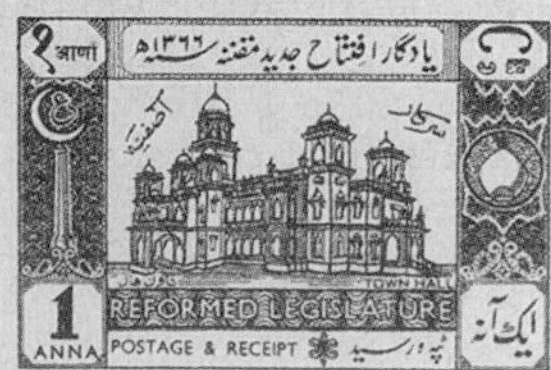


## Indore

## Jammu & Kashmir

Text varies.

## Jasdan

## Jhalawar

## Kotah

Size and text varies

## Nandgaon

## Nowanuggur

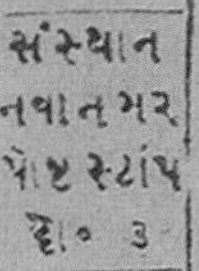

## Poonch

Similar stamps exist in various sizes with different text

## Rajasthan

## Rajpeepla

## Soruth

## Tonk

## BANGLADESH

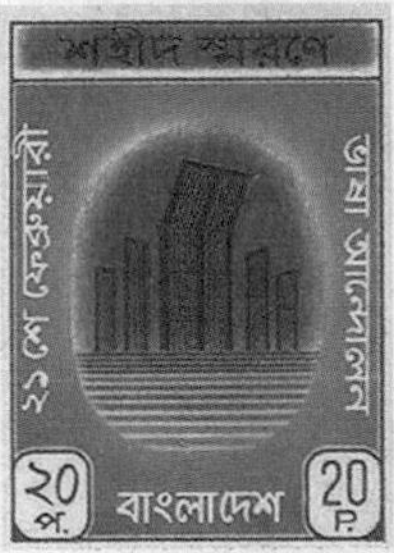


বাংলাদেশ

Country Name

## NEPAL

Similar stamps are smaller, have squares in upper corners and have five or nine characters in central bottom panel.

## TANNU TUVA

## ISRAEL

## GEORGIA

ს.ს.ს.რ. This inscription is found on other pictorial stamps.

Country Name

## ARMENIA

The four characters are found somewhere on pictorial stamps. On some stamps only the middle two are found.

## 4. AFRICAN INSCRIPTIONS

### ETHIOPIA

## 5. ARABIC INSCRIPTIONS

| ١ | ٢ | ٣ | ٤ | ٥ |
|---|---|---|---|---|
| 1 | 2 | 3 | 4 | 5 |
| ٦ | ٧ | ٨ | ٩ | ٠ |
| 6 | 7 | 8 | 9 | 0 |

### AFGHANISTAN

Many early Afghanistan stamps show Tiger's head, many of these have ornaments protruding from outer ring, others show inscriptions in black.

Arabic Script

Crest of King Amanullah

Mosque Gate & Crossed Cannons

The four characters are found somewhere on pictorial stamps. On some stamps only the middle two are found.

### BAHRAIN

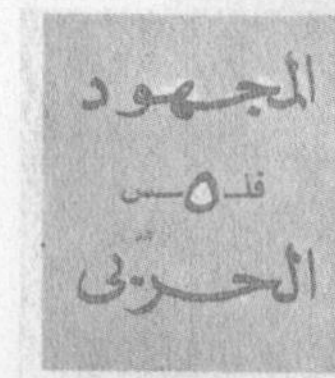

## EGYPT

Postage

## IRAN

Country Name

Royal Crown

Lion with Sword

Symbol

Emblem

## IRAQ

## JORDAN

## LEBANON

Similar types have denominations at top and slightly different design.

## LIBYA

Country Name in various styles

Other Libya stamps show Eagle and Shield (head facing either direction) or Red, White and Black Shield (with or without eagle in center).

Without Country Name

## SAUDI ARABIA

Tughra (Central design)

Palm Tree and Swords

## SYRIA

## Arab Government Issues

## THRACE

## YEMEN

## PAKISTAN

## PAKISTAN - BAHAWALPUR

Country Name in top panel, star and crescent

## TURKEY

Star & Crescent is a device found on many Turkish stamps, but is also found on stamps from other Arabic areas (see Pakistan-Bahawalpur)

Tughra (similar tughras can be found on stamps of Turkey in Asia, Afghanistan and Saudi Arabia)

Mohammed V

Mustafa Kemal

Plane, Star and Crescent

## TURKEY IN ASIA

Other Turkey in Asia pictorials show star & crescent. Other stamps show tughra shown under Turkey.

## 6. GREEK INSCRIPTIONS

### GREECE

Country Name in various styles (Some Crete stamps overprinted with the Greece country name are listed in Crete.)

Lepta

ΔΡΑΧΜΗ ΔΡΑΧΜΑΙ ΛΕΠΤΟΝ

Drachma Drachmas Lepton

Abbreviated Country Name 

Other forms of Country Name

No country name

### CRETE

Country Name

Crete stamps with a surcharge that have the year "1922" are listed under Greece.

## EPIRUS

Similar stamps have text above the eagle.

## IONIAN IS.

# 7. CYRILLIC INSCRIPTIONS

## RUSSIA

Postage Stamp

Imperial Eagle

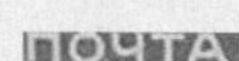

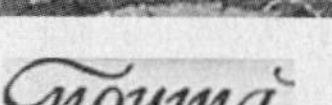

Postage in various styles

Abbreviation for Kopeck

Abbreviation for Ruble

Russia

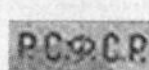

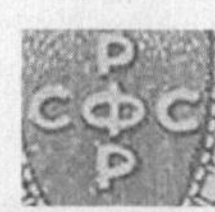

Abbreviation for Russian Soviet Federated Socialist Republic RSFSR stamps were overprinted (see below)

Abbreviation for Union of Soviet Socialist Republics

This item is footnoted in Latvia

## RUSSIA - Army of the North

"OKCA"

## RUSSIA - Wenden

## RUSSIAN OFFICES IN THE TURKISH EMPIRE

These letters appear on other stamps of the Russian offices.

The unoverprinted version of this stamp and a similar stamp were overprinted by various countries (see below).

## ARMENIA

## BELARUS

## FAR EASTERN REPUBLIC

Country Name

## FINLAND

Circles and Dots on stamps similar to Imperial Russia issues

## SOUTH RUSSIA

Country Name

## BATUM

Forms of Country Name

## TRANSCAUCASIAN FEDERATED REPUBLICS

Abbreviation for Country Name

## KAZAKHSTAN

ҚАЗАҚСТАН

Country Name

## KYRGYZSTAN

КЫРГЫЗСТАН

Country Name

## ROMANIA

## TAJIKISTAN

Country Name & Abbreviation

## UKRAINE

Пошта України

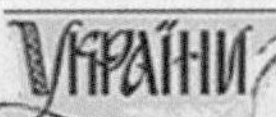

України

Україна

Country Name in various forms

УС РР

The trident appears on many stamps, usually as an overprint.

Abbreviation for Ukrainian Soviet Socialist Republic

## WESTERN UKRAINE

Abbreviation for Country Name

## AZERBAIJAN

AZƏRBAYCAN

Country Name

A.C.C.P.

Abbreviation for Azerbaijan Soviet Socialist Republic

## MONTENEGRO

ЦРНЕГОРЕ

ЦРНА ГОРА

Country Name in various forms

Abbreviation for country name

No country name (A similar Montenegro stamp without country name has same vignette.)

## SERBIA

СРПСКА СРБИЈА

Country Name in various forms

СРП. К.С.

Abbreviation for country name

No country name

## MACEDONIA

МАКЕДОНИЈА

МАКЕДОНИЈА

Country Name

МАКЕДОНСКИ ПОШТИ

11 Октомври 1997

МАКЕДОНСКИ

11 Октомври 1997

Different form of Country Name

## SERBIA & MONTENEGRO

## YUGOSLAVIA

ЈУГОСЛАВИЈА

Showing country name

No Country Name

## BOSNIA & HERZEGOVINA (Serb Administration)

РЕПУБЛИКА СРПСКА

Country Name

РЕПУБЛИКЕ СРПСКЕ

Different form of Country Name

No Country Name

## BULGARIA

Country Name Postage

Stotinka

Stotinki (plural) Abbreviation for Stotinki

Country Name in various forms and styles

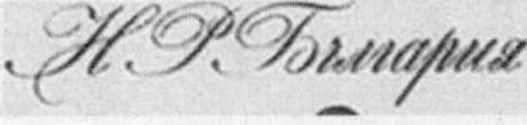

No country name

Abbreviation for Lev, leva

## MONGOLIA

Country name in one word Tugrik in Cyrillic

Country name in two words Mung in Cyrillic

Mung in Mongolian

Tugrik in Mongolian

Arms

No Country Name

# NEW WORLD OF TECHNOLOGY

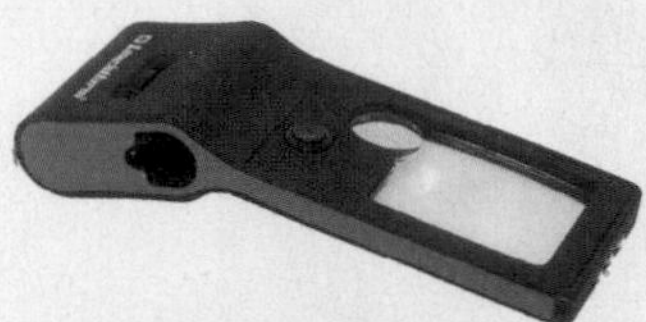

### 6-IN-1 LED POCKET MAGNIFIER/MICROSCOPE (55X)

A powerful LED microscope (up to 55X magnification) teams up with two aspheric Perspex lenses (3X magnification large and 10X magnification small) to examine objects at various levels of detail. Built-in focus wheel ensures clarity. View objects even in low-light conditions with three lighting functions: three LED flashlight, simple UV light, one white LED. Black composite housing.

| *Item* | *Retail* | *AA** |
|---|---|---|
| MG61LED | $21.95 | $19.95 |

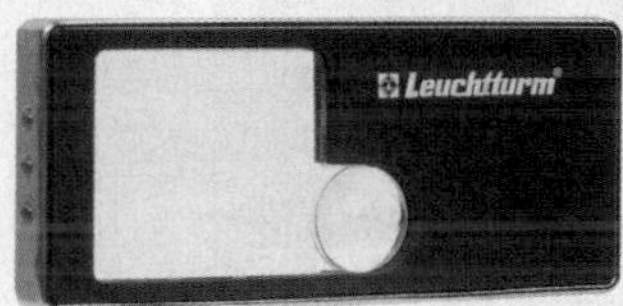


### 5-IN-1 MULTI-FUNCTION POCKET MAGNIFIER 2.5X-10X LED

A sturdy stainless steel frame houses two aspheric lenses: 2.5X rectangular and 10X round, plus three lighting functions: 3-LED side flashlight, 1-LED research light, simple 395nm long-wave UV light. A mini ballpoint pen, available to take notes, tucks inside the acrylic housing. Leatherette case & 3 #LR927 batteries included.

| *Item* | *Retail* | *AA** |
|---|---|---|
| MG51 | $15.95 | $13.95 |

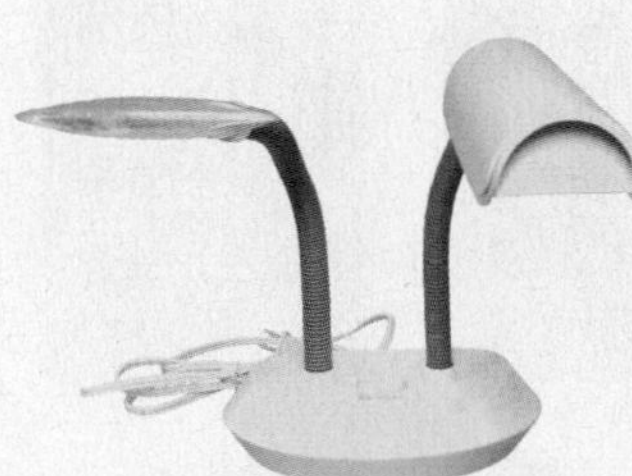

### 13W DUOFLEX MAGNIFIER DESK LAMP

The OttLite DuoFlex has a two-pronged approach to enhance your vision. First, the large 3X-5X magnifier enlarges your subject. Then the energy-efficient 13w "E" bulb spotlights the field. Flexible arms allow nearly infinite positioning. Long-term bulb is rated to last up to 10,000 hours.

| *Item* | *Retail* | *AA** |
|---|---|---|
| ACC213W | $109.99 | $59.99 |

### SCHAUBEK 10X LED & UV COMBO MAGNIFIER

This pocket-sized magnifier boasts 10X magnification with both LED and UV longwave light. Battery powered for maximum portability. Handy carrying case protects the 21mm magnifier while on the go.

| *Item* | *Retail* | *AA** |
|---|---|---|
| MG10XLUV | $39.99 | $34.99 |

### 3.2X LED ILLUMINATED MAGNIFIER

This 7" aluminum 3.2X magnifier is both beautiful and functional. Six LEDs surround the 1.375" lens to provide glare-free illumination. Zippered protective case and 2 AA batteries included.

| *Item* | *Retail* | *AA** |
|---|---|---|
| MG32XL | $35.95 | $31.95 |

### PHONESCOPE DIGITAL MICROSCOPE

Clip this compact Lighthouse Phonescope lens on your smartphone or tablet to transform it into a powerful digital microscope. See the smallest details and instantly capture high-quality images and videos. The precision macro glass lens offers up to 60X magnification and requires no batteries. Field of view: 1/2" (13mm). Phonescope works with all popular smartphones without scratching display. Image resolution and zoom function dependent upon your device.

| *Item* | *Retail* | *AA** |
|---|---|---|
| LHSCOPE | $25.99 | $21.99 |

### ZOOM 20X-40X MICROSCOPE WITH LED

This practical zoom microscope provides what collectors have been waiting for – outstanding clarity and resolution. Magnification is continuously adjustable between 20X and 40X. Powerful LED lighting illuminates the stage (3 #LR44 batteries included). Stand, examination slides, and slide covers also included.

| *Item* | *Retail* | *AA** |
|---|---|---|
| LHPM3 | $29.95 | $21.95 |

### BLACK TRUE COLOR LIGHT

A versatile, compact light that provides superior image and color rendering while reducing glare and eye strain. Technologically advanced light produces a precise blend of light for contrast and brightness that makes colors vibrant and details incredibly clear. The lamp comes with an "E"(electronic) tube for a quicker starting time. This does plug into an outlet for long uses.

| *Item* | *Retail* | *AA** |
|---|---|---|
| ACC191BB | $79.99 | $49.99 |

### ZOOM 10X-300X USB DIGITAL MICROSCOPE, 5.0 MEGAPIXEL

The industry-leading 5.0 megapixel resolution makes the smallest details on coins and stamps visible on your computer screen via the included USB cable. Up to 10x - 300x magnification available with this high-end digital microscope

| *Item* | *Retail* | *AA** |
|---|---|---|
| LHDM4 | $179.95 | $169.95 |

### LIGHTHOUSE DUAL WAVE ULTRAVIOLET LAMP

Examine your collectibles for both fluorescence (long wave) and phosphorescence (short wave) using one versatile ultraviolet lamp. Flip a switch to change quickly and easily between short and long UV rays (254 and 380nm). Short wave exposes tagging, while long wave reveals faults, tears, and repairs. Battery operated; requires 4x AA batteries (not included).

| *Item* | *Retail* | *AA** |
|---|---|---|
| LHL81 | $71.95 | $59.95 |

### 10X POCKET MAGNIFIER

This compact, portable and easy-to-use 10x pocket magnifier comes with its own illumination from a brilliant white LED. The glass lens is 18mm (3/4") in diameter.

| *Item* | *Retail* | *AA** |
|---|---|---|
| MG10XLED | $12.95 | $11.95 |

**Visit: AmosAdvantage.com**

**Call: 1-800-572-6885**

Outside U.S. & Canada Call: 1-800-572-6885

**SHIPPING & HANDLING:** United States: Order total $0-$10.00 charged $3.99 shipping. United States - Order total $10.01-$79.99 charged $7.99 shipping. United States - Order total $80.00 or more charged 10% of order total for shipping. Maximum Freight Charge $45.00. Canada: 20% of order total. Minimum charge $19.99 Maximum charge $200.00. Foreign orders are shipped via FedExl Intl. or USPS and billed actual freight.

**ORDERING INFORMATION:** *AA prices apply to paid subscribers of Amos Media titles, or orders placed online. Prices, terms and product availability subject to change. Taxes will apply in CA, OH, & IL. Shipping and handling rates will apply. See below.

## INDEX AND IDENTIFIER

All page numbers shown are those in this Volume 2B.

Postage stamps that do not have English words on them are shown in the Illustrated Identifier.

# ScottMounts



## PRE-CUT SINGLE MOUNTS

| ITEM | W x H (mm) | DESCRIPTION | MOUNTS | RETAIL | AA* |
|---|---|---|---|---|---|
| 901 | 40 x 25 | U.S. Standard Comm. Hor. Water Activated | 40 | $3.50 | **$2.39** |
| 902 | 25 x 40 | U.S. Standard Comm. Vert. Water Activated | 40 | $3.50 | **$2.39** |
| 903 | 25 x 22 | U.S. Regular Issue – Hor. Water Activated | 40 | $3.50 | **$2.39** |
| 904 | 22 x 25 | U.S. Regular Issue – Vert. Water Activated | 40 | $3.50 | **$2.39** |
| 905 | 41 x 31 | U.S. Semi-Jumbo – Horizontal | 40 | $3.50 | **$2.39** |
| 906 | 31 x 41 | U.S. Semi-Jumbo – Vertical | 40 | $3.50 | **$2.39** |
| 907 | 50 x 31 | U.S. Jumbo – Horizontal | 40 | $3.50 | **$2.39** |
| 908 | 31 x 50 | U.S. Jumbo – Vertical | 40 | $3.50 | **$2.39** |
| 909 | 25 x 27 | U.S. Famous Americans/Champions Of Liberty | 40 | $3.50 | **$2.39** |
| 910 | 33 x 27 | United Nations | 40 | $3.50 | **$2.39** |
| 911 | 40 x 27 | United Nations | 40 | $3.50 | **$2.39** |
| 976 | 67 x 25 | Plate Number Coils, Strips of Three | 40 | $6.25 | **$3.99** |
| 984 | 67 x 34 | Pacific '97 Triangle | 10 | $3.50 | **$2.39** |
| 985 | 111 x 25 | Plate Number Coils, Strips of Five | 25 | $6.25 | **$3.99** |
| 986 | 51 x 36 | U.S. Hunting Permit/Express Mail | 40 | $6.25 | **$3.99** |
| 1045 | 40 x 26 | U.S. Standard Comm. Hor. Self-Adhesive | 40 | $3.50 | **$2.39** |
| 1046 | 25 x 41 | U.S. Standard Comm. Vert. Self-Adhesive | 40 | $3.50 | **$2.39** |
| 1047 | 22 x 26 | U.S. Definitives Vert. Self Adhesive | 40 | $3.50 | **$2.39** |
| 966 | Value Pack | (Assortment pre-cut sizes) | 320 | $23.25 | **$15.25** |
| 975 | Best Pack | (Assortment pre-cut sizes - Black Only) | 160 | $14.75 | **$9.99** |

## PRE-CUT PLATE BLOCK, FDC, POSTAL CARD MOUNTS

| ITEM | W x H (mm) | DESCRIPTION | MOUNTS | RETAIL | AA* |
|---|---|---|---|---|---|
| 912 | 57 x 55 | Regular Issue Plate Block | 25 | $6.25 | **$3.99** |
| 913 | 73 x 63 | Champions of Liberty | 25 | $6.25 | **$3.99** |
| 914 | 106 x 55 | Rotary Press Standard Commemorative | 20 | $6.25 | **$3.99** |
| 915 | 105 x 57 | Giori Press Standard Commemorative | 20 | $6.25 | **$3.99** |
| 916 | 127 x 70 | Giori Press Jumbo Commemorative | 10 | $6.25 | **$3.99** |
| 917 | 165 x 94 | First Day Cover | 10 | $6.25 | **$3.99** |
| 918 | 140 x 90 | Postal Card Size/Submarine Booklet Pane | 10 | $6.25 | **$3.99** |
| 1048 | 152 x 107 | Large Postal Cards | 8 | $10.25 | **$6.99** |

## STRIPS 215MM LONG

| ITEM | W x H (mm) | DESCRIPTION | MOUNTS | RETAIL | AA* |
|---|---|---|---|---|---|
| 919 | 20 | U.S. 19th Century, Horizontal Coil | 22 | $7.99 | **$5.25** |
| 920 | 22 | U.S. Early Air Mail | 22 | $7.99 | **$5.25** |
| 921 | 24 | U.S., Vertical Coils, Christmas (#2400, #2428 etc.) | 22 | $7.99 | **$5.25** |
| 922 | 25 | U.S. Commemorative and Regular | 22 | $7.99 | **$5.25** |
| 1049 | 26 | U.S. Commemorative and Regular | 22 | $7.99 | **$5.25** |
| 923 | 27 | U.S. Famous Americans | 22 | $7.99 | **$5.25** |
| 924 | 28 | U.S. 19th Century, Liechtenstein | 22 | $7.99 | **$5.25** |
| 1050 | 29 | Virginia Dare, British Empire, etc. | 22 | $7.99 | **$5.25** |
| 925 | 30 | U.S. 19th Century; Jamestown, etc; Foreign | 22 | $7.99 | **$5.25** |
| 926 | 31 | U.S. Horizontal Jumbo and Semi-Jumbo | 22 | $7.99 | **$5.25** |
| 927 | 33 | U.S. Stampin' Future, UN | 22 | $7.99 | **$5.25** |
| 1054 | 34 | U.S. American Landmarks, Eclipse | 22 | $7.99 | **$5.25** |
| 928 | 36 | U.S. Hunting Permit, Canada | 15 | $7.99 | **$5.25** |
| 1051 | 37 | U.S., British Colonies | 22 | $7.99 | **$5.25** |
| 929 | 39 | U.S. Early 20th Century | 15 | $7.99 | **$5.25** |
| 930 | 41 | U.S. Vert. Semi-Jumbo ('77 Lafayette, Pottery, etc.) | 15 | $7.99 | **$5.25** |
| 931 | | Multiple Assortment: One strip of each size 22-41 above (SMKB) (2 x 25mm strips) | 12 | $7.99 | **$5.25** |
| 1052 | 42 | U.S., British Colonies | 22 | $7.99 | **$5.25** |
| 1053 | 43 | U.S., British Colonies | 22 | $7.99 | **$5.25** |
| 932 | 44 | U.S. Vertical Coil Pair Garden Flowers Booklet Pane | 15 | $7.99 | **$5.25** |
| 933 | 48 | U.S. Farley, Gutter Pair | 15 | $7.99 | **$5.25** |
| 934 | 50 | U.S. Jumbo (Lyndon Johnson, '74 U.P.U., etc.) | 15 | $7.99 | **$5.25** |
| 935 | 52 | U.S. Standard Commemorative Block (Butterflies) | 15 | $7.99 | **$5.25** |
| 936 | 55 | U.S. Standard Plate Block - normal margins | 15 | $7.99 | **$5.25** |
| 937 | 57 | U.S. Standard Plate Block - wider margins | 15 | $7.99 | **$5.25** |
| 938 | 61 | U.S. Blocks, Israel Tabs, '99 Christmas Madonna Pane | 15 | $7.99 | **$5.25** |

## STRIPS 240MM LONG

| ITEM | W x H (mm) | DESCRIPTION | MOUNTS | RETAIL | AA* |
|---|---|---|---|---|---|
| 939 | 63 | U.S. Jumbo Commemorative Horizontal Block | 10 | $9.25 | **$5.99** |
| 940 | 66 | U.S. CIPEX Souvenir Sheet, Self-Adhesive Booklet Pane (#2803a, 3012a) | 10 | $9.25 | **$5.99** |
| 941 | 68 | U.S. ATM Booklet Pane, Farley Gutter Pair & Souvenir Sheet | 10 | $9.25 | **$5.99** |
| 942 | 74 | U.S. TIPEX Souvenir Sheet | 10 | $9.25 | **$5.99** |
| 943 | 80 | U.S. Standard Commemorative Vertical Block | 10 | $9.25 | **$5.99** |
| 944 | 82 | U.S. Blocks of Four, U.N. Chagall | 10 | $9.25 | **$5.99** |
| 945 | 84 | Israel Tab Block, Mars Pathfinder Sheetlet | 10 | $9.25 | **$5.99** |
| 946 | 89 | Submarine Booklet, Souvenir Sheet World Cup, Rockwell | 10 | $9.25 | **$5.99** |
| 947 | 100 | U.S. '74 U.P.U. Block, U.N. Margin Inscribed Block | 7 | $9.25 | **$5.99** |
| 948 | 120 | Various Souvenir Sheets and Blocks | 7 | $9.25 | **$5.99** |

## STRIPS 265MM LONG

| ITEM | W x H (mm) | DESCRIPTION | MOUNTS | RETAIL | AA* |
|---|---|---|---|---|---|
| 1035 | 25 | U.S. Coils Strips of 11 | 12 | $9.25 | **$5.99** |
| 949 | 40 | U.S. Postal People Standard Standard & Semi-Jumbo Commemorative Strip | 10 | $9.25 | **$5.99** |
| 981 | 44 | U.S. Long self-adhesive booklet panes | 10 | $9.25 | **$5.99** |
| 1030 | 45 | Various (Canada Scott #1725-1734) | 10 | $9.25 | **$5.99** |
| 1036 | 46 | U.S. Long self adhesive booklet panes of 15 | 10 | $9.25 | **$5.99** |
| 950 | 55 | U.S. Regular Plate Block or Strip of 20 | 10 | $9.25 | **$5.99** |
| 951 | 59 | U.S. Double Issue Strip | 10 | $9.25 | **$5.99** |
| 952 | 70 | U.S. Jumbo Commemorative Plate Block | 10 | $12.50 | **$8.50** |
| 1031 | 72 | Various (Canada Scott #1305a-1804a) | 10 | $12.50 | **$8.50** |
| 1032 | 75 | Plate Blocks: Lance Armstrong, Prehistoric Animals, etc. | 10 | $12.50 | **$8.50** |
| 1060 | 76 | U.S. 1994 Stamp Printing Centennial Souvenir Sheet, etc. | 10 | $12.50 | **$8.50** |
| 953 | 91 | U.S. Self-Adhesive Booklet Pane '98 Wreath, '95 Santa | 10 | $12.50 | **$8.50** |
| 1033 | 95 | Mini-Sheet Plate Blocks w/top header | 10 | $12.50 | **$8.50** |
| 1061 | 96 | U.S., Foreign | 10 | $12.50 | **$8.50** |
| 954 | 105 | U.S. Standard Semi-Jumbo Commemorative Plate Number Strip | 10 | $12.50 | **$8.50** |
| 955 | 107 | Same as above–wide margin | 10 | $12.50 | **$8.50** |
| 956 | 111 | U.S. Gravure-Intaglio Plate Number Strip | 10 | $14.75 | **$9.99** |
| 1062 | 115 | Foreign Small Sheets | 10 | $17.50 | **$11.99** |
| 957 | 127 | U.S. 2000 Space S/S, World War II S/S | 10 | $17.50 | **$11.99** |
| 1063 | 131 | Looney Tunes sheets; World War II Souvenir Sheet Plate Block | 10 | $17.50 | **$11.99** |
| 1064 | 135 | U.S., Japan Gifts of Friendship sheet | 10 | $17.50 | **$11.99** |
| 958 | 137 | Great Britain Coronation | 10 | $17.50 | **$11.99** |
| 1065 | 139 | Sheets: Soda Fountain, Lady Bird Johnson, Earthscapes, etc. | 10 | $17.50 | **$11.99** |
| 1066 | 143 | Sheets: Merchant Marine Ships, 2013 Hanukkah, etc. | 10 | $17.50 | **$11.99** |
| 1067 | 147 | Sheets: Pickup Trucks, Animal Rescue, Washington D.C., etc. | 10 | $17.50 | **$11.99** |
| 1068 | 151 | Sheets: Go Green, Bicycling, Happy New Year, Ben Franklin, etc. | 10 | $17.50 | **$11.99** |

## STRIPS 265MM LONG, continued

| ITEM | W x H (mm) | DESCRIPTION | MOUNTS | RETAIL | AA* |
|---|---|---|---|---|---|
| 959 | 158 | American Glass, U.S. Football Coaches Sheets | 10 | $17.99 | **$12.50** |
| 1077 | 160 | Sheets: Pacific '97 Triangle Mini, Trans-Mississippi | 5 | $12.50 | **$8.50** |
| 1069 | 163 | Sheets: Modern Architecture, UN Human Rights, etc. | 5 | $12.50 | **$8.50** |
| 1070 | 167 | Sheets: John F. Kennedy, Classics Forever, Made in America, etc. | 5 | $12.50 | **$8.50** |
| 1071 | 171 | Film Directors, Foreign Souvenir Sheets | 5 | $12.50 | **$8.50** |
| 960 | 175 | Large Block, Souvenir Sheet | 5 | $12.50 | **$8.50** |
| 1072 | 181 | Sheets: Jimi Hendrix, Johnny Cash, American Photography, etc. | 5 | $17.50 | **$11.99** |
| 1073 | 185 | Frank Sinatra, Ronald Reagan, Arthur Ashe, Creast Cancer, etc. | 5 | $17.50 | **$11.99** |
| 1074 | 188 | Sheets: Yoda, 9/11 Heroes, Andy Warhol, Frida Kahlo, etc | 5 | $17.50 | **$11.99** |
| 1078 | 192 | Olympic, etc. | 5 | $17.50 | **$11.99** |
| 1075 | 198 | Sheets: Modern American Art, Super Heroes, Baseball Sluggers, etc. | 5 | $17.50 | **$11.99** |
| 1076 | 215 | Celebrity Chefs sheets; Foreign sheets | 5 | $17.50 | **$11.99** |
| 961 | 231 | U.S. Full Post Office Pane Regular and Commemorative | 5 | $17.99 | **$12.50** |

## SOUVENIR SHEETS/SMALL PANES

| ITEM | W x H (mm) | DESCRIPTION | MOUNTS | RETAIL | AA* |
|---|---|---|---|---|---|
| 962 | 204 x 153 | New Year 2000, U.S. Bicentennial S/S | 4 | $9.25 | **$5.99** |
| 963 | 187 x 144 | 55¢ Victorian Love Pane, U.N. Flag Sheet | 9 | $15.50 | **$10.25** |
| 964 | 160 x 200 | U.N., Israel Sheet | 10 | $15.50 | **$10.25** |
| 965 | 120 x 207 | U.S. AMERIPEX Presidential Sheet | 4 | $6.25 | **$3.99** |
| 968 | 229 x 131 | World War II S/S Plate Block Only | 5 | $9.25 | **$5.99** |
| 970 | 111 x 91 | Columbian Souvenir Sheet | 6 | $6.25 | **$4.75** |
| 972 | 148 x 196 | Apollo Moon Landing/Carnivorous Plants | 4 | $7.99 | **$5.25** |
| 989 | 129 x 122 | U.S. Definitive Sheet: Harte, Hopkins, etc. | 8 | $10.25 | **$6.99** |
| 990 | 189 x 151 | Chinese New Year | 5 | $10.25 | **$6.99** |
| 991 | 150 x 185 | Breast Cancer/Fermi/Soccer/'96 Folk Heroes | 5 | $10.25 | **$6.99** |
| 992 | 198 x 151 | Cherokee Strip Sheet | 5 | $10.25 | **$6.99** |
| 993 | 185 x 151 | Bernstein/NATO/Irish/Lunt/Gold Rush Sheets | 5 | $10.25 | **$6.99** |
| 994 | 198 x 187 | Postal Museum | 4 | $10.25 | **$6.99** |
| 995 | 156 x 187 | Sign Language/Statehood | 5 | $10.25 | **$6.99** |
| 996 | 188 x 197 | Illustrators, '98 Music: Folk, Gospel; Country/Western | 4 | $10.25 | **$6.99** |
| 997 | 151 x 192 | Olympic | 5 | $10.25 | **$6.99** |
| 998 | 174 x 185 | Buffalo Soldiers | 5 | $10.25 | **$6.99** |
| 999 | 130 x 198 | Silent Screen Stars | 5 | $10.25 | **$6.99** |
| 1000 | 190 x 199 | Stars Stripes/Baseball/Insects & Spiders/Legends West/ Aircraft, Comics, '96 Olympics, Civil War | 4 | $10.25 | **$6.99** |
| 1001 | 178 x 181 | Cranes | 4 | $10.25 | **$6.99** |
| 1002 | 183 x 212 | Wonders of the Sea, We the People | 3 | $10.25 | **$6.99** |
| 1003 | 156 x 264 | $14 Eagle | 4 | $10.25 | **$6.99** |
| 1004 | 159 x 270 | $9.95 Moon Landing | 4 | $10.25 | **$6.99** |
| 1005 | 159 x 259 | $2.90 Priority/$9.95 Express Mail | 4 | $10.25 | **$6.99** |
| 1006 | 223 x 187 | Hubble, Hollywood Legends, O'Keefe Sheets | 3 | $10.25 | **$6.99** |
| 1007 | 185 x 181 | Deep Sea Creatures, Olmsted Sheets | 4 | $10.25 | **$6.99** |
| 1008 | 152 x 228 | Indian Dances/Antique Autos | 5 | $10.25 | **$6.99** |
| 1009 | 165 x 150 | River Boat/Hanukkah | 6 | $10.25 | **$6.99** |
| 1010 | 275 x 200 | Dinosaurs/Large Gutter Blocks | 2 | $10.25 | **$6.99** |
| 1011 | 161 x 160 | Pacific '97 Triangle Mini Sheets | 6 | $10.25 | **$6.99** |
| 1012 | 174 x 130 | Road Runner, Daffy, Bugs, Sylvester & Tweety | 6 | $10.25 | **$6.99** |
| 1013 | 196 x 158 | Football Coaches | 4 | $10.25 | **$6.99** |
| 1014 | 184 x 184 | American Dolls, Flowering Trees Sheets | 4 | $10.25 | **$6.99** |
| 1015 | 186 x 230 | Classic Movie Monsters | 3 | $10.25 | **$6.99** |
| 1016 | 187 x 160 | Trans-Mississippi Sheet | 4 | $10.25 | **$6.99** |
| 1017 | 192 x 230 | Celebrate The Century | 3 | $10.25 | **$6.99** |
| 1018 | 156 x 204 | Space Discovery | 5 | $10.25 | **$6.99** |
| 1019 | 182 x 209 | American Ballet | 5 | $10.25 | **$6.99** |
| 1020 | 139 x 151 | Christmas Wreaths | 5 | $10.25 | **$6.99** |
| 1021 | 129 x 126 | Justin Morrill, Henry Luce | 8 | $10.25 | **$6.99** |
| 1022 | 184 x 165 | Baseball Fields, Bright Eyes | 4 | $10.25 | **$6.99** |
| 1023 | 185 x 172 | Shuttle Landing Pan Am Invert Sheets | 4 | $10.25 | **$6.99** |
| 1024 | 172 x 233 | Sonoran Desert | 3 | $10.25 | **$6.99** |
| 1025 | 150 x 166 | Prostate Cancer | 5 | $10.25 | **$6.99** |
| 1026 | 201 x 176 | Famous Trains | 4 | $10.25 | **$6.99** |
| 1027 | 176 x 124 | Canada - Historic Vehicles | 5 | $10.25 | **$6.99** |
| 1028 | 245 x 114 | Canada - Provincial Leaders | 5 | $10.25 | **$6.99** |
| 1029 | 177 x 133 | Canada - Year of the Family | 5 | $10.25 | **$6.99** |
| 1034 | 181 x 213 | Arctic Animals | 3 | $10.25 | **$6.99** |
| 1037 | 179 x 242 | Louise Nevelson | 3 | $10.25 | **$6.99** |
| 1038 | 179 x 217 | Library Of Congress | 3 | $10.25 | **$6.99** |
| 1039 | 182 x 232 | Youth Team Sports | 3 | $10.25 | **$6.99** |
| 1040 | 183 x 216 | Lucille Ball Scott #3523 | 3 | $10.25 | **$6.99** |
| 1041 | 182 x 244 | American Photographers | 3 | $10.25 | **$6.99** |
| 1042 | 185 x 255 | Andy Warhol | 3 | $10.25 | **$6.99** |
| 1043 | 165 x 190 | American Film Making | 4 | $10.25 | **$6.99** |
| 1044 | 28 x 290 | American Eagle PNC Strips of 11 | 12 | $9.25 | **$5.99** |

Available in clear or black backgrounds. Please specify color choice when ordering.

## 2017 NATIONAL, MINUTEMAN OR ALL-AMERICAN SUPPLEMENT MOUNT PACKS

| *ITEM* | *DESCRIPTION* | *RETAIL* | *AA** |
|---|---|---|---|
| 2017 B | 2017 National, Minuteman or All-American Supplement Mount Pack - BLACK | $49.99 | **$39.99** |
| 2017 C | 2017 National, Minuteman or All-American Supplement Mount Pack - CLEAR | $49.99 | **$39.99** |

**Visit AmosAdvantage.com**

**Call 1-800-572-6885**

Outside U.S. & Canada 937-498-0800

Mail to: P.O. Box 4129, Sidney OH 45365

**ORDERING INFORMATION:** *AA prices apply to paid subscribers of Amos Media titles, or orders placed online. Prices, terms and product availability subject to change. Taxes will apply in CA, OH, & IL. Shipping and handling rates will apply.
**SHIPPING & HANDLING: United States:** Order total $0-$10.00 charged $3.99 shipping; Order total $10.01-$79.99 charged $7.99 shipping; Order total $80.00 or more charged 10% of order total for shipping. Maximum Freight Charge $45.00. **Canada:** 20% of order total. Minimum charge $19.99; maximum charge $200.00. **Foreign:** Orders are shipped via FedEx Int'l. or USPS and billed actual freight.

# INDEX TO ADVERTISERS
# 2019 VOLUME 2B

# Vols. 2A-2B Number Additions, Deletions & Changes

| Number in 2018 Catalogue | Number in 2019 Catalogue |
|---|---|
| **Canadian Provinces** | |
| **Newfoundland** | |
| new | 234j |
| new | 248b |
| **Canada** | |
| new | 338b |
| new | 760b |
| new | 1181c |
| new | 1341b |
| new | 1357b |
| new | 1679c |
| new | 2070c |
| new | 2206c |
| new | 2710a |
| **Ceylon** | |
| new | 61a |
| **Chile** | |
| new | H1b |
| new | J1b |
| new | J2b |
| new | J3b |
| new | J4b |
| new | J5b |
| new | J6b |
| new | J7b |
| new | J8b |
| new | J9b |
| new | J1c |
| new | J2c |
| new | J3c |
| new | J4c |
| new | J5c |
| new | J6c |
| new | J7c |
| new | J8c |
| new | J9c |
| new | O1A |
| new | O1B |
| new | O1C |
| new | O22A |
| new | O28A |
| new | O29A |
| **Colombia** | |
| new | 527b |
| new | C14a |
| new | C16a |
| new | C86a |
| new | C371a |
| new | C19a |
| **Congo, Democratic Republic** | |
| new | 413b |
| **Cuba** | |
| new | 240b |
| new | 2581a |
| new | 3466a |
| new | 3696a |
| new | 3937a |
| new | 3964a |
| new | C22a |
| new | C23a |
| **Epirus** | |
| new | 4RR |
| new | 4CA |
| **Fiji** | |
| new | 1011A |
| new | 1152Ac |
| new | 1191Cd |
| new | 1192Ae |
| new | 1192Af |
| new | 1197Bc |
| new | 1197Ca |
| **Fiji** | |
| new | 1214B |
| new | 1216D |
| new | 1216e |
| new | 1220C |
| new | 1220D |
| new | 1220Da |
| new | 1249f |
| new | 1249g |
| new | 1253c |
| new | 1314e |
| new | 1315B |
| new | 1315Bc |
| **Fiume** | |
| new | 1A |
| 1a | 1b |
| **France** | |
| **Reunion** | |
| Q1 | Q4 |
| new | Q1-Q3 |
| new | Q5-Q6 |
| **French Equatorial Africa** | |
| new | 143a |
| **Funchal** | |
| new | 13a |

# 2019
# VOLUME 2B
# DEALER DIRECTORY
# YELLOW PAGE LISTINGS

**This section of your Scott Catalogue contains advertisements to help you conveniently find what you need, when you need it...!**

## Aerophilately

**HENRY GITNER PHILATELISTS, INC.**
PO Box 3077-S
Middletown, NY 10940
PH: 845-343-5151
PH: 800-947-8267
FAX: 845-343-0068
hgitner@hgitner.com
www.hgitner.com

## Appraisals

**DR. ROBERT FRIEDMAN & SONS STAMP & COIN BUYING CENTER**
2029 W. 75th St.
Woodridge, IL 60517
PH: 800-588-8100
FAX: 630-985-1588
stampcollections@drbobstamps.com
www.drbobfriedmanstamps.com

## Argentina

**GUILLERMO JALIL**
Maipu 466,local 4
1006 Buenos Aires
Argentina
guillermo@jalilstamps.com
philatino@philatino.com
www.philatino.com
www.jalilstamps.com

## Asia

**KELLEHER & ROGERS LTD.**
4 Finance Drive, Ste. 200
Danbury, CT 06810
PH: 203-297-6056
FAX: 203-297-6059
info@kelleherauctions.com
www.kelleherauctions.com

## Auctions

**DUTCH COUNTRY AUCTIONS**
The Stamp Center
4115 Concord Pike
Wilmington, DE 19803
PH: 302-478-8740
FAX: 302-478-8779
auctions@dutchcountryauctions.com
www.dutchcountryauctions.com

**KELLEHER & ROGERS LTD.**
4 Finance Drive, Ste. 200
Danbury, CT 06810
PH: 203-297-6056
FAX: 203-297-6059
info@kelleherauctions.com
www.kelleherauctions.com

## British Commonwealth

**COLLECTORS EXCHANGE ORLANDO STAMP SHOP**
1814A Edgewater Drive
Orlando, FL 32804
PH: 407-620-0908
PH: 407-947-8603
FAX: 407-730-2131
jlatter@cfl.rr.com
www.BritishStampsAmerica.com
www.OrlandoStampShop.com

**WORLDSTAMPS/ FRANK GEIGER PHILATELISTS**
PO Box 4743
Pinehurst, NC 28374
PH: 910-295-2048
info@WorldStamps.com
www.WorldStamps.com

**ARON R. HALBERSTAM PHILATELISTS, LTD.**
PO Box 150168
Van Brunt Station
Brooklyn, NY 11215-0168
PH: 718-788-3978
arh@arhstamps.com
www.arhstamps.com

**ROY'S STAMPS**
PO Box 28001
600 Ontario Street
St. Catharines, ON
CANADA L2N 7P8
Phone: 905-934-8377
Email: roystamp@cogeco.ca

**THE STAMP ACT**
PO Box 1136
Belmont, CA 94002
PH: 650-703-2342
thestampact@sbcglobal.net

## Buying

**DR. ROBERT FRIEDMAN & SONS STAMP & COIN BUYING CENTER**
2029 W. 75th St.
Woodridge, IL 60517
PH: 800-588-8100
FAX: 630-985-1588
stampcollections@drbobstamps.com
www.drbobfriedmanstamps.com

## Canada

**CANADA STAMP FINDER**
PO Box 92591
Brampton, ON L6W 4R1
PH: 514-238-5751
Toll Free in North America:
877-412-3106
FAX: 323-315-2635
canadastampfinder@gmail.com
www.canadastampfinder.com

## British Commonwealth



## Canada

**WORLDSTAMPS/ FRANK GEIGER PHILATELISTS**
PO Box 4743
Pinehurst, NC 28374
PH: 910-295-2048
info@WorldStamps.com
www.WorldStamps.com

**ROY'S STAMPS**
PO Box 28001
600 Ontario Street
St. Catharines, ON
CANADA L2N 7P8
Phone: 905-934-8377
Email: roystamp@cogeco.ca

## China

**KELLEHER & ROGERS LTD.**
4 Finance Drive, Ste. 200
Danbury, CT 06810
PH: 203-297-6056
FAX: 203-297-6059
info@kelleherauctions.com
www.kelleherauctions.com

**THE STAMP ACT**
PO Box 1136
Belmont, CA 94002
PH: 650-703-2342
thestampact@sbcglobal.net

## Collections

**DR. ROBERT FRIEDMAN & SONS STAMP & COIN BUYING CENTER**
2029 W. 75th St.
Woodridge, IL 60517
PH: 800-588-8100
FAX: 630-985-1588
stampcollections@drbobstamps.com
www.drbobfriedmanstamps.com

## Croatia

**WORLDSTAMPS/ FRANK GEIGER PHILATELISTS**
PO Box 4743
Pinehurst, NC 28374
PH: 910-295-2048
info@WorldStamps.com
www.WorldStamps.com

## Czechoslovakia

**WORLDSTAMPS/ FRANK GEIGER PHILATELISTS**
PO Box 4743
Pinehurst, NC 28374
PH: 910-295-2048
info@WorldStamps.com
www.WorldStamps.com

## Denmark

**WORLDSTAMPS/ FRANK GEIGER PHILATELISTS**
PO Box 4743
Pinehurst, NC 28374
PH: 910-295-2048
info@WorldStamps.com
www.WorldStamps.com

## Ducks

**MICHAEL JAFFE**
PO Box 61484
Vancouver, WA 98666
PH: 360-695-6161
PH: 800-782-6770
FAX: 360-695-1616
mjaffe@brookmanstamps.com
www.brookmanstamps.com

## British Commonwealth

## Estonia

**WORLDSTAMPS/
FRANK GEIGER PHILATELISTS**
PO Box 4743
Pinehurst, NC 28374
PH: 910-295-2048
info@WorldStamps.com
www.WorldStamps.com

## Ethiopia

**WORLDSTAMPS/
FRANK GEIGER PHILATELISTS**
PO Box 4743
Pinehurst, NC 28374
PH: 910-295-2048
info@WorldStamps.com
www.WorldStamps.com

## Europe-Western

**WORLDSTAMPS/
FRANK GEIGER PHILATELISTS**
PO Box 4743
Pinehurst, NC 28374
PH: 910-295-2048
info@WorldStamps.com
www.WorldStamps.com

## Falkland Islands

**WORLDSTAMPS/
FRANK GEIGER PHILATELISTS**
PO Box 4743
Pinehurst, NC 28374
PH: 910-295-2048
info@WorldStamps.com
www.WorldStamps.com

## France & Colonies

**WORLDSTAMPS/
FRANK GEIGER PHILATELISTS**
PO Box 4743
Pinehurst, NC 28374
PH: 910-295-2048
info@WorldStamps.com
www.WorldStamps.com

**E. JOSEPH McCONNELL, INC.**
PO Box 683
Monroe, NY 10949
PH: 845-783-9791
FAX: 845-782-0347
ejstamps@gmail.com
www.EJMcConnell.com

## French S. Antarctic

**WORLDSTAMPS/
FRANK GEIGER PHILATELISTS**
PO Box 4743
Pinehurst, NC 28374
PH: 910-295-2048
info@WorldStamps.com
www.WorldStamps.com

**E. JOSEPH McCONNELL, INC.**
PO Box 683
Monroe, NY 10949
PH: 845-783-9791
FAX: 845-782-0347
ejstamps@gmail.com
www.EJMcConnell.com

## Japan

**KELLEHER & ROGERS LTD.**
4 Finance Drive, Ste. 200
Danbury, CT 06810
PH: 203-297-6056
FAX: 203-297-6059
info@kelleherauctions.com
www.kelleherauctions.com

## Korea

**KELLEHER & ROGERS LTD.**
4 Finance Drive, Ste. 200
Danbury, CT 06810
PH: 203-297-6056
FAX: 203-297-6059
info@kelleherauctions.com
www.kelleherauctions.com

## Manchukuo

**KELLEHER & ROGERS LTD.**
4 Finance Drive, Ste. 200
Danbury, CT 06810
PH: 203-297-6056
FAX: 203-297-6059
info@kelleherauctions.com
www.kelleherauctions.com

## Middle East - Arab

**KELLEHER & ROGERS LTD.**
4 Finance Drive, Ste. 200
Danbury, CT 06810
PH: 203-297-6056
FAX: 203-297-6059
info@kelleherauctions.com
www.kelleherauctions.com

## Worldwide



## New Issues

**DAVIDSON'S STAMP SERVICE**
Personalized Service since 1970
PO Box 36355
Indianapolis, IN 46236-0355
PH: 317-826-2620
ed-davidson@earthlink.net
www.newstampissues.com

**WORLDSTAMPS/
FRANK GEIGER PHILATELISTS**
PO Box 4743
Pinehurst, NC 28374
PH: 910-295-2048
info@WorldStamps.com
www.WorldStamps.com

## Proofs & Essays

**HENRY GITNER
PHILATELISTS, INC.**
PO Box 3077-S
Middletown, NY 10940
PH: 845-343-5151
PH: 800-947-8267
FAX: 845-343-0068
hgitner@hgitner.com
www.hgitner.com

## Stamp Stores

### California

**BROSIUS STAMP, COIN &
SUPPLIES**
2105 Main St.
Santa Monica, CA 90405
PH: 310-396-7480
FAX: 310-396-7455
brosius.stamp.coin@hotmail.com

### Delaware

**DUTCH COUNTRY AUCTIONS**
The Stamp Center
4115 Concord Pike
Wilmington, DE 19803
PH: 302-478-8740
FAX: 302-478-8779
auctions@dutchcountryauctions.com
www.dutchcountryauctions.com

### Florida

**DR. ROBERT FRIEDMAN &
SONS STAMP & COIN
BUYING CENTER**
PH: 800-588-8100
FAX: 630-985-1588
stampcollections@drbobstamps.com
www.drbobfriedmanstamps.com

### Illinois

**DR. ROBERT FRIEDMAN &
SONS STAMP & COIN
BUYING CENTER**
2029 W. 75th St.
Woodridge, IL 60517
PH: 800-588-8100
FAX: 630-985-1588
stampcollections@drbobstamps.com
www.drbobfriedmanstamps.com

### Indiana

**KNIGHT STAMP & COIN CO.**
237 Main St.
Hobart, IN 46342
PH: 219-942-4341
PH: 800-634-2646
knight@knightcoin.com
www.knightcoin.com

## Stamp Stores

### New Jersey

**BERGEN STAMPS &
COLLECTIBLES**
306 Queen Anne Rd.
Teaneck, NJ 07666
PH: 201-836-8987
bergenstamps@gmail.com

**TRENTON STAMP & COIN CO**
Thomas DeLuca
Store: Forest Glen Plaza
1804 Highway 33
Hamilton Square, NJ 08690
Mail: PO Box 8574
Trenton, NJ 08650
PH: 609-584-8100
FAX: 609-587-8664
TOMD4TSC@aol.com

### New York

**CHAMPION STAMP CO., INC.**
432 West 54th St.
New York, NY 10019
PH: 212-489-8130
FAX: 212-581-8130
championstamp@aol.com
www.championstamp.com

**CK STAMPS**
42-14 Union St. # 2A
Flushing, NY 11355
PH: 917-667-6641
ckstampsllc@yahoo.com

### Ohio

**HILLTOP STAMP SERVICE**
Richard A. Peterson
PO Box 626
Wooster, OH 44691
PH: 330-262-8907 (0)
PH: 330-262-5378 (H)
hilltop@bright.net
www.hilltopstamps.com

## Supplies

**BROOKLYN GALLERY COIN &
STAMP, INC.**
8725 4th Ave.
Brooklyn, NY 11209
PH: 718-745-5701
FAX: 718-745-2775
info@brooklyngallery.com
www.brooklyngallery.com

## Topicals

**WORLDSTAMPS/
FRANK GEIGER PHILATELISTS**
PO Box 4743
Pinehurst, NC 28374
PH: 910-295-2048
info@WorldStamps.com
www.WorldStamps.com

**E. JOSEPH McCONNELL, INC.**
PO Box 683
Monroe, NY 10949
PH: 845-783-9791
FAX: 845-782-0347
ejstamps@gmail.com
www.EJMcConnell.com

## Topicals - Columbus

**MR. COLUMBUS**
PO Box 1492
Fennville, MI 49408
PH: 269-543-4755
David@MrColumbus1492.com
www.MrColumbus1492.com

## Topicals - Miscellaneous

**HENRY GITNER PHILATELISTS, INC.**
PO Box 3077-S
Middletown, NY 10940
PH: 845-343-5151
PH: 800-947-8267
FAX: 845-343-0068
hgitner@hgitner.com
www.hgitner.com

## United Nations

**BRUCE M. MOYER**
Box 99
East Texas, PA 18046
PH: 610-395-8410
FAX: 610-421-8020
moyer@unstamps.com
www.unstamps.com

## United States

**KEITH WAGNER**
ACS Stamp Company
2914 W 135th Ave
Broomfield, Colorado 80020
303-841-8666
www.ACSStamp.com

**BROOKMAN STAMP CO.**
PO Box 90
Vancouver, WA 98666
PH: 360-695-1391
PH: 800-545-4871
FAX: 360-695-1616
info@brookmanstamps.com
www.brookmanstamps.com

## U.S. Classics/Moderns

**BARDO STAMPS**
PO Box 7437
Buffalo Grove, IL 60089
PH: 847-634-2676
jfb7437@aol.com
www.bardostamps.com

## U.S.-Collections Wanted

**DUTCH COUNTRY AUCTIONS**
The Stamp Center
4115 Concord Pike
Wilmington, DE 19803
PH: 302-478-8740
FAX: 302-478-8779
auctions@dutchcountryauctions.com
www.dutchcountryauctions.com

**DR. ROBERT FRIEDMAN & SONS STAMP & COIN BUYING CENTER**
2029 W. 75th St.
Woodridge, IL 60517
PH: 800-588-8100
FAX: 630-985-1588
stampcollections@drbobstamps.com
www.drbobfriedmanstamps.com

## Wanted - Worldwide Collections

**DUTCH COUNTRY AUCTIONS**
The Stamp Center
4115 Concord Pike
Wilmington, DE 19803
PH: 302-478-8740
FAX: 302-478-8779
auctions@dutchcountryauctions.com
www.dutchcountryauctions.com

## Websites

**KEITH WAGNER**
ACS Stamp Company
2914 W 135th Ave
Broomfield, Colorado 80020
303-841-8666
www.ACSStamp.com

## Wholesale

**HENRY GITNER PHILATELISTS, INC.**
PO Box 3077-S
Middletown, NY 10940
PH: 845-343-5151
PH: 800-947-8267
FAX: 845-343-0068
hgitner@hgitner.com
www.hgitner.com

## Worldwide

**KELLEHER & ROGERS LTD.**
4 Finance Drive, Ste. 200
Danbury, CT 06810
PH: 203-297-6056
FAX: 203-297-6059
info@kelleherauctions.com
www.kelleherauctions.com

## Worldwide-Collections

**DR. ROBERT FRIEDMAN & SONS STAMP & COIN BUYING CENTER**
2029 W. 75th St.
Woodridge, IL 60517
PH: 800-588-8100
FAX: 630-985-1588
stampcollections@drbobstamps.com
www.drbobfriedmanstamps.com

# SCOTT® Specialty Series

Embark on a new collecting journey. There are Specialty pages available for more than 140 countries with some of them back in print after many years thanks to on-demand printing technology. Start a new collecting adventure with countries featured in Volume 2 of the new Scott Standard Postage Stamp Catalogue!

Specialty Series pages are sold as page units only. Binders, labels and slipcases are sold separately.

## *ALBUM SETS*

*These money-saving album sets include pages, binders and self-adhesive binder labels. Some set contents may vary, please call or visit or web site for specific information.*

### CANADA

| Item | | # of Pgs. | Retail | AA |
|---|---|---|---|---|
| 240CAN1 | 1851-1952 | 64 | $44.99 | $38.24 |
| 240CAN2 | 1953-1978 | 57 | $44.99 | $38.24 |
| 240CAN3 | 1979-1990 | 54 | $44.99 | $38.24 |
| 240CAN4 | 1991-1995 | 40 | $32.99 | $28.04 |
| 240CAN5 | 1996-2000 | 60 | $44.99 | $38.24 |
| 240CAN6 | 2001-2006 | 80 | $57.99 | $49.29 |
| 240S007 | 2007 #59 | 14 | $19.99 | $16.99 |
| 240S008 | 2008 #60 | 9 | $13.99 | $11.89 |
| 240S009 | 2009 #61 | 16 | $19.99 | $16.99 |
| 240S010 | 2010 #62 | 17 | $19.99 | $16.99 |
| 240S011 | 2011 #63 | 19 | $19.99 | $16.99 |
| 240S012 | 2012 #64 | 18 | $19.99 | $16.99 |
| 240S013 | 2013 #65 | 23 | $21.99 | $18.69 |
| 240S014 | 2014 #66 | 25 | $21.99 | $18.69 |
| 240S015 | 2015 #67 | 20 | $21.99 | $18.69 |
| 240S016 | 2016 #68 | | $25.99 | $21.99 |
| 240S017 | 2017 #69 | | $25.99 | $21.99 |
| 240BLANK | Blank Pages | 20 | $19.99 | $16.99 |
| LB012 | Label: Canada | | $3.99 | $2.99 |
| **240SET** | **Album Set 1851-2015** | | **$569.99** | **$469.99** |

*Supplemented in May*

### CAYMAN ISLANDS

| Item | | # of Pgs. | Retail | AA |
|---|---|---|---|---|
| 261CYI0 | 1900-1995 | 78 | $52.99 | $45.04 |
| 261CYI2 | 1996-2006 | 42 | $32.99 | $28.04 |
| 261CI07 | 2007 #11 | 4 | $9.99 | $8.49 |
| 261CI08 | 2008 #12 | 7 | $9.99 | $8.49 |
| 261CI09 | 2009 #13 | 4 | $9.99 | $8.49 |
| 261CI11 | 2011 #14 | 5 | $9.99 | $8.49 |
| 261CI12 | 2012 #15 | 4 | $9.99 | $8.49 |
| 261CI13 | 2013 #16 | 4 | $9.99 | $8.49 |
| 261CI14 | 2014 #17 | 3 | $6.99 | $5.94 |
| 261CI16 | 2016 #18 | | $11.99 | $9.99 |
| CAYBLANK | Blank Pages | 20 | $19.99 | $16.99 |
| LB150 | Label: Cayman Islands | | $3.99 | $2.99 |
| **261CISET** | **Album Set 1900-2015** | | **$199.99** | **$149.99** |

*Supplemented in June*

### CHILE

| Item | | # of Pgs. | Retail | AA |
|---|---|---|---|---|
| 645CHL1 | 1853-1977 | 73 | $49.99 | $42.49 |
| 645CHL2 | 1978-1993 | 74 | $49.99 | $42.49 |
| 645CHL3 | 1994-1997 | 25 | $21.99 | $18.69 |
| 645CHL4 | 1998-2006 | 49 | $49.99 | $42.49 |
| 645S007 | 2007 #13 | 5 | $9.99 | $8.49 |
| 645S008 | 2008 #14 | 10 | $13.99 | $11.89 |
| 645S009 | 2009 #15 | 10 | $13.99 | $11.89 |
| 645S010 | 2010 #16 | 8 | $13.99 | $11.89 |
| 645S011 | 2011 #17 | 5 | $9.99 | $8.49 |
| 645S012 | 2012 #18 | 3 | $6.99 | $5.94 |
| 645S013 | 2013 #19 | 4 | $9.99 | $8.49 |
| 645S014 | 2014 #20 | 5 | $9.99 | $8.49 |
| 645S015 | 2015 #21 | 5 | $9.99 | $8.49 |
| 645S016 | 2016 #22 | | $11.99 | $9.99 |
| **645SET** | **Album Set 1853-2015** | | **$369.99** | **$279.99** |

*Supplemented in September*

### CHINA

| Item | | # of Pgs. | Retail | AA |
|---|---|---|---|---|
| 480CHN1 | 1878-1949 | 91 | $57.99 | $49.29 |
| 480CHN2 | 1865-1950 | 101 | $69.99 | $59.49 |
| **480SET** | **Album Set 1878-1950** | | **$229.99** | **$169.99** |
| **CHINASET** | **China Complete 1878-2015** | | **$1,249.99** | **$989.99** |

### COLOMBIA

| Item | | # of Pgs. | Retail | AA |
|---|---|---|---|---|
| 646COL1 | 1856-1976 | 151 | $89.99 | $76.49 |
| 646COL2 | 1977-1994 | 58 | $44.99 | $38.24 |
| 646COL3 | 1995-1997 | 15 | $19.99 | $16.99 |
| 646COL4 | 1998-2006 | 58 | $44.99 | $38.24 |
| 646S007 | 2007 #13 | 7 | $9.99 | $8.49 |
| 646S009 | 2008-2009 #14 | 11 | $16.99 | $14.44 |
| 646S010 | 2010 #15 | 14 | $19.99 | $16.99 |
| 646S011 | 2011 #16 | 8 | $13.99 | $11.89 |
| 646S012 | 2012 #17 | 9 | $13.99 | $11.89 |
| 646S013 | 2013 #18 | 4 | $9.99 | $8.49 |
| 646S015 | 2015 #19 | 4 | $9.99 | $8.49 |
| 646S016 | 2016 #20 | | $11.99 | $9.99 |
| LB194 | Label: Colombia | | $3.99 | $2.99 |
| **646SET** | **Album Set 1856-2015** | | **$399.99** | **$299.99** |

*Supplemented in September*

### CYPRUS

| Item | | # of Pgs. | Retail | AA |
|---|---|---|---|---|
| 203CYP0 | 1880-1997 | 85 | $57.99 | $49.29 |
| 203CYP2 | 1998-2006 | 33 | $29.99 | $25.49 |
| 203CY07 | 2007 #9 | 3 | $6.99 | $5.94 |
| 203CY08 | 2008 #10 | 5 | $9.99 | $8.49 |
| 203CY09 | 2009 #11 | 4 | $9.99 | $8.49 |
| 203CY10 | 2010 #12 | 4 | $9.99 | $8.49 |
| 203CY11 | 2011 #13 | 6 | $9.99 | $8.49 |
| 203CY12 | 2012 #14 | 4 | $9.99 | $8.49 |
| 203CY13 | 2013 #15 | 6 | $9.99 | $8.49 |
| 203CY14 | 2014 #16 | 3 | $6.99 | $5.94 |
| 203CY15 | 2015 #17 | 8 | $13.99 | $11.89 |
| 203CY16 | 2016 #18 | | $11.99 | $9.99 |
| 203CY17 | 2017 #19 | | $11.99 | $9.99 |
| CYPBLANK | Blank Pages | 20 | $19.99 | $16.99 |
| LB188 | Label: Cyprus | | $3.99 | $2.99 |
| **203CYPSET** | **Album Set 1880-2015** | | **$219.99** | **$159.99** |

*Supplemented in May*

### CZECHOSLOVAKIA

| Item | | # of Pgs. | Retail | AA |
|---|---|---|---|---|
| 307CZH1 | 1918-1959 | 121 | $69.99 | $59.49 |
| 307CZH2 | 1960-1972 | 89 | $57.99 | $49.29 |
| 307CZH3 | 1973-1986 | 82 | $57.99 | $49.29 |
| 307CZH4 | 1987-1994 | 46 | $34.99 | $29.74 |
| 307CZH5 | 1995-1999 | 37 | $32.99 | $28.04 |
| 307CZH6 | 2000-2006 | 58 | $44.99 | $38.24 |
| 307S007 | 2007 #58 | 10 | $13.99 | $11.89 |
| 307S008 | 2008 #59 | 10 | $13.99 | $11.89 |
| 307S009 | 2009 #60 | 13 | $16.99 | $14.44 |
| 307S010 | 2010 #61 | 10 | $13.99 | $11.89 |
| 307S011 | 2011 #62 | 18 | $19.99 | $16.99 |
| 307S012 | 2012 #63 | 15 | $19.99 | $16.99 |
| 307S013 | 2013 #64 | 11 | $16.99 | $14.44 |
| 307S014 | 2014 #65 | 11 | $16.99 | $14.44 |
| 307S015 | 2015 #66 | 13 | $16.99 | $14.44 |
| 307S016 | 2016 #67 | | $22.99 | $19.99 |
| 307S017 | 2017 #68 | | $22.99 | $19.99 |
| CZEBLANK | Blank Pages | 20 | $19.99 | $16.99 |
| LB014 | Label: Czechoslovakia | | $3.99 | $2.99 |
| LB211 | Label: Czech Republic | | $3.99 | $2.99 |
| LB212 | Label: Slovakia | | $3.99 | $2.99 |
| **307SET** | **Album Set 1913-2015** | | **$599.99** | **$499.99** |

*Supplemented in August*

### DENMARK

| Item | | # of Pgs. | Retail | AA |
|---|---|---|---|---|
| 345DEN1 | 1851-1995 | 81 | $57.99 | $49.29 |
| 345DEN2 | 1996-2009 | 96 | $64.99 | $55.24 |
| 345DM10 | 2010 #15 | 19 | $19.99 | $16.99 |
| 345DM11 | 2011 #16 | 17 | $19.99 | $16.99 |
| 345DM12 | 2012 #17 | 15 | $19.99 | $16.99 |
| 345DM13 | 2013 #18 | 9 | $13.99 | $11.89 |
| 345DM14 | 2014 #19 | 7 | $9.99 | $8.49 |
| 345DM15 | 2015 #20 | 7 | $9.99 | $8.49 |
| 345DM16 | 2016 #21 | | $16.99 | $13.99 |
| 345DM17 | 2017 #22 | | $16.99 | $13.99 |
| DENBLANK | Blank Pages | 20 | $19.99 | $16.99 |
| LB157 | Label: Denmark | | $3.99 | $2.99 |
| **345DENSET** | **Album Set 1851-2015** | | **$249.99** | **$189.99** |

*Supplemented in June*

### FALKLAND ISLANDS

| Item | | # of Pgs. | Retail | AA |
|---|---|---|---|---|
| 261FAI0 | 1878-1995 | 100 | $69.99 | $59.49 |
| 261FAI2 | 1996-2006 | 66 | $44.99 | $38.24 |
| 261FI07 | 2007 #12 | 9 | $13.99 | $11.89 |
| 261FI08 | 2008 #13 | 7 | $9.99 | $8.49 |
| 261FI09 | 2009 #14 | 8 | $13.99 | $11.89 |
| 261FI10 | 2010 #15 | 14 | $19.99 | $16.99 |
| 261FI11 | 2011 #16 | 7 | $9.99 | $8.49 |
| 261FI12 | 2012 #17 | 13 | $16.99 | $14.44 |
| 261FI13 | 2013 #18 | 11 | $16.99 | $14.44 |
| 261FI14 | 2014 #19 | 5 | $9.99 | $8.49 |
| 261FI15 | 2015 #20 | 8 | $13.99 | $11.89 |
| 261FI16 | 2016 #21 | | $16.99 | $13.99 |
| LB170 | Label: Falkland Islands | | $3.99 | $2.99 |
| **261FISET** | **Album Set 1878-2015** | | **$249.99** | **$199.99** |

*Supplemented in July*

### FAROE ISLANDS

| Item | | # of Pgs. | Retail | AA |
|---|---|---|---|---|
| 345FIS0 | 1919-1995 | 30 | $29.99 | $25.49 |
| 345FIS2 | 1996-2009 | 46 | $34.99 | $29.74 |
| 345FI10 | 2010 #14 | 5 | $9.99 | $8.49 |
| 345FI11 | 2011 #15 | 4 | $9.99 | $8.49 |
| 345FI12 | 2012 #16 | 5 | $9.99 | $8.49 |
| 345FI13 | 2013 #17 | 4 | $9.99 | $8.49 |
| 345FI14 | 2014 #18 | 5 | $9.99 | $8.49 |
| 345FI15 | 2015 #19 | 5 | $9.99 | $8.49 |
| 345FI16 | 2016 #20 | | $11.99 | $9.99 |
| 345FI17 | 2017 #21 | | $11.99 | $9.99 |
| FAROBLANK | Blank Pages | | $19.99 | $16.99 |
| LB158 | Label: Faroe Islands | | $3.99 | $2.99 |
| **345FAISET** | **Album Set 1919-2015** | | **$189.99** | **$139.99** |

*Supplemented in June*

### FIJI

| Item | | # of Pgs. | Retail | AA |
|---|---|---|---|---|
| 624FJI1 | 1870-1993 | 64 | $44.99 | $38.24 |
| 624FJI2 | 1994-1997 | 16 | $19.99 | $16.99 |
| 624FJI3 | 1998-2006 | 49 | $39.99 | $33.99 |
| 624S007 | 2007 #14 | 7 | $9.99 | $8.49 |
| 624S008 | 2008 #15 | 5 | $9.99 | $8.49 |
| 624S009 | 2009 #16 | 3 | $6.99 | $5.94 |
| 624S010 | 2010 #17 | 5 | $9.99 | $8.49 |
| 624S011 | 2011 #18 | 4 | $9.99 | $8.49 |
| 624S012 | 2012 #19 | 3 | $6.99 | $5.94 |
| 624S013 | 2013 #20 | 5 | $9.99 | $8.49 |
| 624S014 | 2014 #21 | 3 | $6.99 | $5.94 |
| 624S016 | 2016 #22 | | $11.99 | $9.99 |
| LB130 | Label: Fiji | | $3.99 | $2.99 |
| **FIJISET** | **Album Set 1870-2014** | | **$219.99** | **$159.99** |

*Supplemented in August*

### FINLAND

| Item | | # of Pgs. | Retail | AA |
|---|---|---|---|---|
| 345FIN1 | 1856-1995 | 108 | $69.99 | $59.49 |
| 345FIN2 | 1996-2003 | 45 | $34.99 | $29.74 |
| 345FN04 | 2004 #9 | 10 | $13.99 | $11.89 |
| 345FN05 | 2005 #10 | 9 | $13.99 | $11.89 |
| 345FN06 | 2006 #11 | 8 | $13.99 | $11.89 |
| 345FN07 | 2007 #12 | 9 | $13.99 | $11.89 |
| 345FN08 | 2008 #13 | 14 | $19.99 | $16.99 |
| 345FN09 | 2009 #14 | 7 | $9.99 | $8.49 |
| 345FN10 | 2010 #15 | 11 | $16.99 | $14.44 |
| 345FN11 | 2011 #16 | 15 | $19.99 | $16.99 |
| 345FN12 | 2012 #17 | 13 | $16.99 | $14.44 |
| 345FN13 | 2013 #18 | 11 | $16.99 | $14.44 |
| 345FN14 | 2014 #19 | 13 | $16.99 | $14.44 |
| 345FN15 | 2015 #20 | 13 | $16.99 | $14.44 |
| 345FN16 | 2016 #21 | | $22.99 | $19.99 |
| 345FN17 | 2017 #22 | | $22.99 | $19.99 |
| FINBLANK | Blank Pages | 20 | $19.99 | $16.99 |
| LB017 | Label: Finland | | $3.99 | $2.99 |
| **345FINSET** | **Album Set 1856-2015** | | **$349.99** | **$269.99** |

*Supplemented in June*

### FRANCE

| Item | | # of Pgs. | Retail | AA |
|---|---|---|---|---|
| 310FRN1 | 1849-1958 | 70 | $49.99 | $42.49 |
| 310FRN2 | 1959-1976 | 66 | $44.99 | $38.24 |
| 310FRN3 | 1977-1987 | 59 | $44.99 | $38.24 |
| 310FRN4 | 1988-1994 | 54 | $44.99 | $38.24 |
| 310FRN5 | 1995-2000 | 55 | $44.99 | $38.24 |
| 310FRN6 | 2001-2005 | 98 | $64.99 | $55.24 |
| 310FRN7 | 2006-2009 | 107 | $69.99 | $59.49 |
| 310S010 | 2010 #45 | 20 | $19.99 | $16.99 |
| 310S011 | 2011 #46 | 24 | $21.99 | $18.69 |
| 310S012 | 2012 #47 | 39 | $32.99 | $28.04 |
| 310S013 | 2013 #48 | 29 | $24.99 | $21.24 |
| 310S014 | 2014 #49 | 28 | $24.99 | $21.24 |
| 310S015 | 2015 #50 | 34 | $29.99 | $25.49 |
| 310S016 | 2016 #51 | | $34.99 | $29.99 |
| 310S017 | 2017 #52 | | $34.99 | $29.99 |
| 310BLANK | Blank Pages | 20 | $19.99 | $16.99 |
| LB018 | Label: France | | $3.99 | $2.99 |
| **310SET** | **Album Set 1849-2015** | | **$669.99** | **$529.99** |

*Supplemented in May*

### FRENCH AFRICA

| Item | | # of Pgs. | Retail | AA |
|---|---|---|---|---|
| 310FRA1 | 1886-1977 | 252 | $129.99 | $110.49 |
| 310FRAS1 | 2010 Supplement (Addendum) | 8 | $13.99 | $11.89 |
| 310FRA2 | 1888-1974 | 235 | $129.99 | $110.49 |
| 310FRAS2 | 2010 Supplement (Addendum) | 22 | $19.99 | $16.99 |
| LB073 | Label: French Africa | | $3.99 | $2.99 |

### FRENCH COLONIES

| Item | | # of Pgs. | Retail | AA |
|---|---|---|---|---|
| 310FCP0 | 1859-1956 | 126 | $72.99 | $62.04 |
| LB020 | Label: French Colonies | | $3.99 | $2.99 |

### FRENCH OFFICES ABROAD

| Item | | # of Pgs. | Retail | AA |
|---|---|---|---|---|
| 310FOA0 | 1885-1941 | 40 | $32.99 | $28.04 |

### FRENCH POLYNESIA

| Item | | # of Pgs. | Retail | AA |
|---|---|---|---|---|
| 625FRP1 | 1892-1994 | 108 | $69.99 | $59.49 |
| 625FRP2 | 1995-2006 | 40 | $32.99 | $28.04 |
| 625S007 | 2007 #13 | 5 | $9.99 | $8.49 |
| 625S008 | 2008 #14 | 6 | $9.99 | $8.49 |
| 625S010 | 2010 #15 | 10 | $13.99 | $11.89 |
| 625S011 | 2011 #16 | 5 | $9.99 | $8.49 |
| 625S012 | 2012 #17 | 6 | $9.99 | $8.49 |
| 625S013 | 2013 #18 | 6 | $9.99 | $8.49 |
| 625S014 | 2014 #19 | 6 | $9.99 | $8.49 |
| 625S015 | 2015 #20 | 4 | $9.99 | $8.49 |
| 626S016 | 2016 #21 | | $11.99 | $9.99 |
| LB136 | Label: French Polynesia | | $3.99 | $2.99 |
| **FRPOSET** | **Album Set 1892-2015** | | **$229.99** | **$169.99** |

*Supplemented in August*

### FRENCH SOUTHERN & ANTARCTIC TERRITORIES

| Item | | # of Pgs. | Retail | AA |
|---|---|---|---|---|
| 626FSA1 | 1955-1994 | 38 | $32.99 | $28.04 |
| 626FSA2 | 1995-2006 | 37 | $32.99 | $28.04 |
| 626S007 | 2007 #10 | 6 | $9.99 | $8.49 |
| 626S008 | 2008 #11 | 6 | $9.99 | $8.49 |
| 626S010 | 2010 #12 | 6 | $9.99 | $8.49 |
| 626S011 | 2011 #13 | 4 | $9.99 | $8.49 |
| 626S012 | 2012 #14 | 7 | $9.99 | $8.49 |
| 626S013 | 2013 #15 | 7 | $9.99 | $8.49 |
| 626S014 | 2014 #16 | 9 | $13.99 | $11.89 |
| 626S015 | 2015 #17 | 3 | $6.99 | $5.94 |
| 626S016 | 2016 #18 | | $16.99 | $13.99 |
| LB141 | Label: French & Antarctic Territories | | $3.99 | $2.99 |
| **FSASET** | **Album Set 1955-2015** | | **$189.99** | **$139.99** |

**ORDERING INFORMATION:** *AA prices apply to paid subscribers of Amos Media titles, or for orders plwaced online. Prices, terms and product availability subject to change. Taxes will apply in CA, OH, & IL.

**SHIPPING & HANDLING: United States –** Order total $0-$10.00 charged $3.99 shipping; Order total $10.01-$79.99 charged $7.99 shipping; Order total $80.00 or more charged 10% of order total for shipping. Maximum Freight Charge $45.00. **Canada –** 20% of order total. Minimum charge $19.99 Maximum charge $200.00. **Foreign –** Orders are shipped via FedEx Int'l. or USPS and billed actual freight.

## Visit AmosAdvantage.com

## Call 800-572-6885

**Outside U.S. & Canada call: (937) 498-0800 • P.O. Box 4129, Sidney, OH 45365**